# 2024
# STANDARD POSTAGE
# STAMP CATALOGUE

**ONE HUNDRED AND EIGHTIETH EDITION IN SIX VOLUMES**

## Volume 3A

### G

| | |
|---:|:---|
| EDITOR-IN-CHIEF | Jay Bigalke |
| EDITOR-AT-LARGE | Donna Houseman |
| CONTRIBUTING EDITOR | Charles Snee |
| EDITOR EMERITUS | James E. Kloetzel |
| SENIOR EDITOR /NEW ISSUES AND VALUING | Martin J. Frankevicz |
| ADMINISTRATIVE ASSISTANT/CATALOGUE LAYOUT | Eric Wiessinger |
| PRINTING AND IMAGE COORDINATOR | Stacey Mahan |
| SENIOR GRAPHIC DESIGNER | Cinda McAlexander |
| SALES DIRECTOR | David Pistello |
| SALES DIRECTOR | Eric Roth |
| SALES DIRECTOR | Brenda Wyen |
| SALES REPRESENTATIVE | Julie Dahlstrom |

Released June 2023
Includes New Stamp Listings through the April 2023 *Scott Stamp Monthly* Catalogue Update

Copyright© 2023 by

# AMOS MEDIA

1660 Campbell Road, Suite A, Sidney, OH 45365
Publishers of *Linn's Stamp News, Scott Stamp Monthly, Coin World* and *Coin World Monthly.*

# Table of contents

See the following volumes for other country listings:
Volume 1A: United States, United Nations, Abu Dhabi-Australia; Volume 1B: Austria-B
Volume 2A: C-Cur; Volume 2B: Cyp-F
Volume 3B: H-I
Volume 4A: J-L; Volume 4B: M
Volume 5A: N-Phil; Volume 5B: Pit-Sam
Volume 6A: San-Tete; Volume 6B: Thai-Z

---

## Scott Catalogue Mission Statement

The Scott Catalogue Team exists to serve the recreational, educational and commercial hobby needs of stamp collectors and dealers.

We strive to set the industry standard for philatelic information and products by developing and providing goods that help collectors identify, value, organize and present their collections.

Quality customer service is, and will continue to be, our highest priority.
We aspire toward achieving total customer satisfaction.

---

# Copyright Notice

The contents of this book are owned exclusively by Amos Media Co. and all rights thereto are reserved under the Pan American and Universal Copyright Conventions.

Copyright ©2023 by Amos Media Co., Sidney, Ohio. Printed in U.S.A.

COPYRIGHT NOTE
Permission is hereby given for the use of material in this book and covered by copyright if:
(a) The material is used in advertising matter, circulars or price lists for the purpose of offering stamps for sale or purchase at the prices listed therein; and
(b) Such use is incidental to the business of buying and selling stamps and is limited in scope and length, i.e., it does not cover a substantial portion of the total number of stamps issued by any country or of any special category of stamps of any country; and
(c) Such material is not used as part of any catalogue, stamp album or computerized or other system based upon the Scott catalogue numbers, or in any updated valuations of stamps not offered for sale or purchase; and
(d) Such use is not competitive with the business of the copyright owner; and
(e) Such use is for editorial purposes in publications in the form of articles or commentary, except for computer software or the serialization of books in such publications, for which separate written permission is required.
Any use of the material in this book which does not satisfy all the foregoing conditions is forbidden in any form unless permission in each instance is given in writing by the copyright owner.

# Trademark Notice

The terms SCOTT, SCOTT'S, SCOTT CATALOGUE NUMBERING SYSTEM, SCOTT CATALOGUE NUMBER, SCOTT NUMBER and abbreviations thereof, are trademarks of Amos Media Co., used to identify its publications and its copyrighted system for identifying and classifying postage stamps for dealers and collectors. These trademarks are to be used only with the prior consent of Amos Media Co.

No part of this work may be reproduced in any form or by any means, electronic or mechanical, including photocopying, without permission in writing from Amos Media Co., P.O. Box 4129, Sidney, OH 45365-4129.

ISBN 978-0-89487-698-1

Library of Congress Card No. 2-3301

# What's new for 2024 Scott Standard Volume 3

Another catalog season is upon us as we continue the journey of the 155-year history of the Scott catalogs. The 2024 volumes are the 180th edition of the Scott *Standard Postage Stamp Catalogue*. Volume 3A includes listings for countries of the world beginning with the letter G. Listings for countries of the world H through I can be found in Vol. 3B.

This year's Vol. 3A cover features a 27-penny stamp from Great Britain's 2002 set of 10 Aerial Photographs of Coastline stamps (Scott 2029-2038). An Israel 2016 4.10-shekel Summer stamp (Scott 2106) with attached tab is shown on the Vol. 3B cover. The Israel stamp depicts a child holding a sailboat at the beach. A pair of flip-flops and a beach ball are shown on the attached tab.

Because Vol. 3B is a continuation of the first part of the Vol. 3 catalog, the introduction pages are not repeated in each volume.

The most significant changes in this year's catalog occurred in India Feudatory States, where we began a thorough review that is likely to span a few catalog seasons. The 2023 Scott *Classic Specialized Catalogue of Stamps and Covers 1840-1940* was the first to reflect a reorganization of listings of feudatory states from Alwar through Dungarpur.

That review resulted in more than 2,600 value changes and more than 700 number changes and additions. A number of those changes carried over and are now reflected for the first time in the 2024 Vol. 3 catalog. There are two pages of number changes included within this edition.

The country of Guatemala was reviewed extensively, and approximately 1,500 value changes were made, many of which were increases. One example was the 2015 Coral Reef Marine Life set of four stamps (Scott 712-715), which moved from $5.75 in unused and used condition to $8.25 and $6.50, respectively. The Reef Marine Life souvenir sheet (715a) increased from $19.50 to $20.50 in unused and used condition.

The market for Hong Kong stamps was reviewed, and only a handful of changes were made. The Scott catalog values showed great stability during the last year, and additional market resources reflected that steadiness.

The stamps of Horta also were reviewed. Just shy of 100 value changes were made, and almost all of them were increases.

Approximately 150 value changes, many of which were increases, were made for Inhambane. The set of 1903 King Carlos definitives (Scott 15-30) moved from $123.55 in unused condition to $148.90.

Great Britain Machin definitive stamps seem to be a fairly active collecting area at the moment. Approximately 125 value changes were made, most of which were increases. One such increase was for the set of six 2019 Machins (Scott MH479-MH484), which went from $35.50 in unused condition to $41.

Classic-era stamps of Ecuador were reviewed. Roughly 160 value changes were made, most of which were slight increases.

Classic Guatemala was also examined. Approximately 275 value changes, mostly increases, were recorded.

Approximately 125 value changes were made for the classic stamps of Honduras. A value replaced a dash for the 1877 Tegucigalpa stamp (Scott 16) in unused condition. The new value is $100.

Among the additional reviewed countries were Gabon, Gambia and Iraq.

Many other countries received less extensive reviews that are not noted in this letter. We encourage you to pay special attention to the Number Additions, Deletions and Changes listing in this volume. We also suggest reading the catalog introduction, which includes an abundance of useful information.

A digital subscription is also available for the Scott catalogs, and information about the subscription can be found online at www.amosadvantage.com.

Approximately 1,200 images of stamps not pictured in the Vol. 3 print edition were added to this year's Vol. 3 digital catalog.

Best wishes in your collecting pursuits!

Jay Bigalke, Scott catalog editor-in-chief

# Acknowledgments

Our appreciation and gratitude go to the following individuals who have assisted us in preparing information included in this year's Scott catalogues. Some helpers prefer anonymity. These individuals have generously shared their stamp knowledge with others through the medium of the Scott catalogue.

Those who follow provided information that is in addition to the hundreds of dealer price lists and advertisements and scores of auction catalogues and realizations that were used in producing the catalogue values. It is from those noted here that we have been able to obtain information on items not normally seen in published lists and advertisements. Support from these people goes beyond data leading to catalogue values, for they also are key to editorial changes.

A special acknowledgment to Liane and Sergio Sismondo of The Classic Collector for their assistance and knowledge sharing that have aided in the preparation of this year's Standard and Classic Specialized Catalogues.

Clifford J. Alexander
  (Carriers and Locals Society)
Roland Austin
Michael & Cecilia Ball (A To Z Stamps)
Jim Bardo (Bardo Stamps)
Brian M. Bleckwenn
  (The Philatelic Foundation)
Les Bootman
Roger S. Brody
Tom Brougham
  (Canal Zone Study Group)
Paul and Josh Buchsbayew
  (Cherrystone Auctions, Inc.)
Timothy Bryan Burgess
Tina and John Carlson (JET Stamps)
Jay T. Carrigan
Carlson Chambliss
Bob Coale
Tony L. Crumbley
  (Carolina Coin and Stamp, Inc.)
Christopher Dahle
Charles Deaton
Bob and Rita Dumaine
  (Sam Houston Duck Co.)
Charles Epting (H.R. Harmer)
Mike Farrell
David Feldman International Auctioneers
Robert A. Fisher
Jeffrey M. Forster
Robert S. Freeman

Henry L. Gitner
  (Henry Gitner Philatelists, Inc.)
Stan Goldfarb
Marc E. Gonzales
Daniel E. Grau
Bruce Hecht (Bruce L. Hecht Co.)
Eric Jackson
Michael Jaffe (Michael Jaffe Stamps, Inc.)
William A. (Bill) Jones
Allan Katz (Ventura Stamp Co.)
Patricia A. Kaufmann
  (Civil War Philatelic Society)
Jon Kawaguchi
  (Ryukyu Philatelic Specialist Society)
Han Ki Kim
Ingert Kuzych
Ulf Lindahl (Ethiopian Philatelic Society)
Ignacio Llach (Filatelia Llach, S.L.)
William K. McDaniel
Pat McElroy
Brian Metz
Mark S. Miller (India Study Circle)
Gary Morris (Pacific Midwest Co.)
Peter Mosiondz Jr.
Bruce M. Moyer
  (Moyer Stamps & Collectables)
Scott Murphy
  (Professional Stamp Experts)
Dr. Tiong Tak Ngo
Nik and Lisa Oquist

Don Peterson
  (International Philippine Philatelic
  Society)
Todor Drumev Popov
Dr. Charles Posner
Peter W. W. Powell
Ed Reiser (Century Stamp Co.)
Ghassan D. Riachi
Robert G. Rufe
Theodosios D. Sampson Ph.D.
Dennis W. Schmidt
Joyce and Chuck Schmidt
Guy Shaw
  (Mexico-Elmhurst Philatelic Society
  International)
J. Randall Shoemaker
  (Philatelic Stamp Authentication and
  Grading, Inc.)
Sergio and Liane Sismondo
  (The Classic Collector)
Jay Smith
Telah Smith
Mark Stelmacovich
Scott R. Trepel
  (Robert A. Siegel Auction Galleries)
Dan Undersander
Steven Unkrich
Herbert R. Volin
Val Zabijaka (Zabijaka Auctions)

# Addresses, telephone numbers, web sites, email addresses of general and specialized philatelic societies

Collectors can contact the following groups for information about the philately of the areas within the scope of these societies, or inquire about membership in these groups. Aside from the general societies, we limit this list to groups that specialize in particular fields of philately, particular areas covered by the Scott *Standard Postage Stamp Catalogue*, and topical groups. Many more specialized philatelic society exist than those listed below. These addresses are updated yearly, and they are, to the best of our knowledge, correct and current. Groups should inform the editors of address changes whenever they occur. The editors also want to hear from other such specialized groups not listed.

Unless otherwise noted all website addresses begin with http://

## General Societies

**American Philatelic Society,** 100 Match Factory Place, Bellefonte, PA 16823-1367; (814) 933-3803; https://stamps.org; apsinfo@stamps.org

**International Society of Worldwide Stamp Collectors,** Joanne Murphy, M.D., P.O. Box 19006, Sacramento, CA 95819; www.iswsc.org; executivedirector@iswsc.org

**Royal Philatelic Society of Canada,** P.O. Box 69080, St. Clair Post Office, Toronto, ON M4T 3A1 Canada; (888) 285-4143; www.rpsc.org; info@rpsc.org

**Royal Philatelic Society London,** 15 Abchurch Lane, London EX4N 7BW, United Kingdom; +44 (0) 20 7486 1044; www.rpsl.org.uk; secretary@rpsl.org.uk

## Libraries, Museums, and Research Groups

**American Philatelic Research Library,** 100 Match Factory Place, Bellefonte, PA 16823; (814) 933-3803; www.stamplibrary.org; library@stamps.org.

**V. G. Greene Philatelic Research Foundation,** P.O. Box 69100, St. Clair Post Office, Toronto, ON M4T 3A1, Canada; (416) 921-2073; info@greenefoundation.ca

### Aero/Astro Philately

**American Air Mail Society,** Stephen Reinhard, P.O. Box 110, Mineola, NY 11501; www.americanairmailsociety.org; sreinhard1@optonline.net

## Postal History

**Auxiliary Markings Club,** Jerry Johnson, 6621 W. Victoria Ave., Kennewick, WA 99336; www.postal-markings.org; membership-2010@postal-markings.org

**Postage Due Mail Study Group,** Bob Medland, Camway Cottage, Nanny Hurn's Lane, Cameley, Bristol BS39 5AJ, United Kingdom; 01761 45959; www.postageduemail.org.uk; secretary.pdmsg@gmail.com

**Postal History Society,** Yamil Kouri, 405 Waltham St. #347, Lexington, MA 02421; www.postalhistorysociety.org; yhkouri@massmed.org

**Post Mark Collectors Club,** Bob Milligan, 7014 Woodland Oaks Drive, Magnolia, TX 77354; (281) 259-2735; www.postmarks.org; bob.milligan0@gmail.com

**U.S. Cancellation Club,** Roger Curran, 18 Tressler Blvd., Lewisburg, PA 17837; rdcnrc@ptd.net

## Revenues and Cinderellas

**American Revenue Association,** Lyman Hensley, 473 E. Elm St., Sycamore, IL 60178-1934; www.revenuer.org; ilrno2@netzero.net

**Christmas Seal and Charity Stamp Society,** John Denune Jr., 234 E. Broadway, Granville, OH 43023; (740) 814-6031; www.seal-society.org

**National Duck Stamp Collectors Society,** Anthony J. Monico, P.O. Box 43, Harleysville, PA 19438-0043; www.ndscs.org; ndscs@ndscs.org

**State Revenue Society,** Kent Gray, P.O. Box 67842, Albuquerque, NM 87193; www.staterevenue.org; srssecretary@comcast.net

## Thematic Philately

**Americana Unit,** Dennis Dengel, 17 Peckham Road, Poughkeepsie, NY 12603-2018; www.americanaunit.org; ddengel@americanaunit.org

**American Topical Association,** Jennifer Miller, P.O. Box 2143, Greer, SC 29652-2143; (618) 985-5100; americantopical.org; ata@americantopical.org

**Astronomy Study Unit,** Leonard Zehr, 1411 Chateau Ave., Windsor, ON N8P 1M2, Canada; (416) 833-9317; www.astronomystudyunit.net; lenzehr@gmail.com

**Bicycle Stamps Club,** Corey Hjalseth, 1102 Broadway, Suite 200, Tacoma, WA 98402; (253) 318-6222; www.bicyclestampsclub.org; coreyh@evergreenhomeloans.com

**Biology Unit,** Chris Dahle, 1401 Linmar Drive NE, Cedar Rapids, IA 52402-3724; www.biophilately.org; chris-dahle@biophilately.org

**Bird Stamp Society,** Mr. S. A. H. (Tony) Statham, Ashlyns Lodge, Chesham Road, Berkhamsted, Herts HP4 2ST United Kingdom; www.bird-stamps.org/bss; tony.statham@sky.com

**Captain Cook Society,** Jerry Yucht, 8427 Leale Ave., Stockton, CA 95212, www.captaincooksociety.com; us@captaincooksociety.com

**The CartoPhilatelic Society,** Marybeth Sulkowski, 2885 Sanford Ave., SW, #32361, Grandville, MI 49418-1342; www.mapsonstamps.org; secretary@mapsonstamps.org

**Casey Jones Railroad Unit,** Jeff Lough, 2612 Redbud Land, Apt. C, Lawrence, KS 66046; www.uqp.de/cjr; jeffydplaugh@gmail.com

**Cats on Stamps Study Unit,** Robert D. Jarvis, 2731 Teton Lane, Fairfield, CA 94533; www.catstamps.info; catmews1@yahoo.com

**Chemistry and Physics on Stamps Study Unit,** Dr. Roland Hirsch, 13830 Metcalf Ave., Apt. 15218, Overland Park, KS 66223-8017; (301) 792-6296; www.cpossu.org; rfhirsch@cpossu.org

**Chess on Stamps Study Unit,** Barry Keith, 511 First St. N., Apt. 106; Charlottesville, VA 22902; www.chessonstamps.org; keithfam@embarqmail.com

**Cricket Philatelic Society,** A. Melville-Brown, 11 Weppons, Ravens Road, Shorham-by-Sea, West Sussex BN43 5AW, United Kingdom; www.cricketstamp.net; mel.cricket.100@googlemail.com

**Earth's Physical Features Study Group,** Fred Klein, 515 Magdalena Ave., Los Altos, CA 94024; http://epfsu.jeffhayward.com; epfsu@jeffhayward.com

**Ebony Society of Philatelic Events and Reflections (ESPER),** Don Neal, P.O. Box 5245, Somerset, NJ 08875-5245; www.esperstamps.org; esperdon@verizon.net

**Europa Study Unit,** Tonny E. Van Loij, 3002 S. Xanthia St.; Denver, CO 80231-4237; (303) 752-0189; www.europastudyunit.org; tvanloij@gmail.com

**Fire Service in Philately,** John Zaranek, 81 Hillpine Road, Cheektowaga, NY 14227-2259; (716) 668-3352; jczaranek@roadrunner.com

**Gastronomy on Stamps Study Unit,** David Wolfersburger, 5062 NW 35th Lane Road, Ocala, FL 34482; (314) 494-3795; www.gastronomystamps.org

**Gay and Lesbian History on Stamps Club,** Joe Petronie, P.O. Box 190842, Dallas, TX 75219-0842; www.glhsonline.org; glhsc@aol.com

**Gems, Minerals and Jewelry Study Unit,** Fred Haynes, 10 Country Club Drive, Rochester, NY 14618-3720; fredmhaynes55@gmail.com

**Graphics Philately Association,** Larry Rosenblum. 1030 E. El Camino Real, PMB 107, Sunnyvale, CA 94087-3759; www.graphics-stamps.org; larry@graphics-stamps.org

**Journalists, Authors and Poets on Stamps,** Christopher D. Cook, 7222 Hollywood Road, Berrien Springs, MI 49103; cdcook2@gmail.com

**Lighthouse Stamp Society,** www.lighthousestampsociety.org

**Lions International Stamp Club,** David McKirdy, s-Gravenwetering 248, 3062 SJ Rotterdam, Netherlands; 31(0) 10 212 0313; www.lisc.nl; davidmckirdy@aol.com

**Masonic Study Unit,** Gene Fricks, 25 Murray Way, Blackwood, NJ 08012-4400; genefricks@comcast.net

**Medical Subjects Unit,** Dr. Frederick C. Skvara, P.O. Box 6228, Bridgewater, NJ 08807; fcskvara@optonline.net

**Napoleonic Age Philatelists,** Ken Berry, 4117 NW 146th St., Oklahoma City, OK 73134-1746; (405) 748-8646; www.nap-stamps.org; krb4117@att.net

**Old World Archaeological Study Unit,** Caroline Scannell, 14 Dawn Drive, Smithtown, NY 11787-176; www.owasu.org; editor@owasu.org

**Petroleum Philatelic Society International,** Feitze Papa, 922 Meander Drive, Walnut Creek, CA 94598-4239; www.ppsi.org.uk; oildad@astound.net

**Rotary on Stamps Fellowship,** Gerald L. Fitzsimmons, 105 Calle Ricardo, Victoria, TX 77904; www.rotaryonstamps. org; glfitz@suddenlink.net

**Scouts on Stamps Society International,** Woodrow (Woody) Brooks, 498 Baldwin Road, Akron, OH 44312; (330) 612-1294; www.sossi.org; secretary@sossi.org

**Ships on Stamps Unit,** Erik Th. Matzinger, Voorste Havervelden 30, 4822 AL Breda, Netherlands; www. shipsonstamps.org; erikships@gmail.com

**Space Topic Study Unit,** David Blog, P.O. Box 174, Bergenfield, NJ 07621; www.space-unit.com; davidblognj@ gmail.com

**Stamps on Stamps Collectors Club,** Michael Merritt, 73 Mountainside Road, Mendham, NJ 07945; www. stampsonstamps.org; michael@mischu.me

**Windmill Study Unit,** Walter J. Hallien, 607 N. Porter St., Watkins Glenn, NY 14891-1345; (607) 229-3541; www. windmillworld.com

**Wine On Stamps Study Unit,** David Wolfersburger, 5062 NW 35th Lane Road, Ocala, FL 34482; (314) 494-3795; www.wine-on-stamps.org;

## United States

**American Air Mail Society,** Stephen Reinhard, P.O. Box 110, Mineola, NY 11501; www.americanairmailsociety. org; sreinhard1@optonline.net

**American First Day Cover Society,** P.O. Box 246, Colonial Beach VA 22443-0246; (520) 321-0880; www.afdcs.org; afdcs@afdcs.org

**Auxiliary Markings Club,** Jerry Johnson, 6621 W. Victoria Ave., Kennewick, WA 99336; www.postal-markings.org; membership-2010@ postal-markings.org

**American Plate Number Single Society,** Rick Burdsall, APNSS Secretary, P.O. BOX 1023, Palatine, IL 60078-1023; www.apnss.org; apnss.sec@gmail.com

**American Revenue Association,** Lyman Hensley, 473 E. Elm St., Sycamore, IL 60178-1934; www. revenuer.org; ilrno2@netzero.net

**American Society for Philatelic Pages and Panels,** Ron Walenciak, P.O. Box 1042, Washington Township, NJ 07676; www.asppp.org; ron.walenciak@asppp. org

**Canal Zone Study Group,** Mike Drabik, P.O. Box 281, Bolton, MA 01740, www.canalzonestudygroup.com; czsgsecretary@gmail.com

**Carriers and Locals Society,** John Bowman, 14409 Pentridge Drive, Corpus Christi, TX 78410; (361) 933-0757; www.pennypost.org; jbowman@stx. rr.com

**Christmas Seal & Charity Stamp Society,** John Denune Jr., 234 E. Broadway, Granville, OH 43023; (740) 814-6031; www.seal-society.org; john@ christmasseals.net

**Civil War Philatelic Society,** Patricia A. Kaufmann, 10194 N. Old State Road, Lincoln, DE 19960-3644; (302) 422-2656; www.civilwarphilatelicsociety.org; trishkauf@comcast.net

**Error, Freaks, and Oddities Collectors Club,** Scott Shaulis, P.O. Box 549, Murrysville, PA 15668-0549; (724) 733-4134; www.efocc.org; scott@ shaulisstamps.com

**National Duck Stamp Collectors Society,** Anthony J. Monico, P.O. Box 43, Harleysville, PA 19438-0043; www. ndscs.org; ndscs@ndscs.org

**Plate Number Coil Collectors Club (PNC3),** Gene Trinks, 16415 W. Desert Wren Court, Surprise, AZ 85374; (623) 322-4619; www.pnc3.org; gctrinks@ cox.net

**Post Mark Collectors Club,** Bob Milligan, 7014 Woodland Oaks Drive, Magnolia, TX 77354; (281) 259-2735; www.postmarks.org; bob.milligan0@ gmail.com

**Souvenir Card Collectors Society,** William V. Kriebel, www.souvenircards. org; kriebewv@drexel.edu

**United Postal Stationery Society,** Dave Kandziolka, 404 Sundown Drive, Knoxville, TN 37934; www.upss.org; membership@upss.org

**U.S. Cancellation Club,** Roger Curran, 18 Tressler Blvd., Lewisburg, PA 17837; rdcnrc@ptd.net

**U.S. Philatelic Classics Society,** Rob Lund, 2913 Fulton St., Everett, WA 98201-3733; www.uspcs.org; membershipchairman@uspcs.org

**US Possessions Philatelic Society,** Daniel F. Ring, P.O. Box 113, Woodstock, IL 60098; http://uspps.tripod.com; danielfring@hotmail.com

**United States Stamp Society,** Rod Juell, P.O. Box 3508, Joliet, IL 60434-3508; www.usstamps.org; execsecretary@usstamps.org

## Africa

**Bechuanalands and Botswana Society,** Otto Peetoom, Roos, East Yorkshire HU12 OLD, United Kingdom; 44(0)1964 670239; www. bechuanalandphilately.com; info@ bechuanalandphilately.com

**Egypt Study Circle,** Mike Murphy, 11 Waterbank Road, Bellingham, London SE6 3DJ United Kingdom; (44) 0203 6737051; www.egyptstudycircle.org.uk; secretary@egyptstudycircle.org.uk

**Ethiopian Philatelic Society,** Ulf Lindahl, 21 Westview Place, Riverside, CT 06878; (203) 722-0769; https:// ethiopianphilatelicsociety.weebly.com; ulindahl@optonline.net

**Liberian Philatelic Society,** P.O. Box 1570, Parker, CO 80134; www. liberiastamps.org; liberiastamps@ comcast.net

**Orange Free State Study Circle,** J. R. Stroud, RDPSA, 24 Hooper Close, Burnham-on-sea, Somerset TA8 1JQ United Kingdom; 44 1278 782235; www.orangefreestatephilately.org.uk; richard@richardstroud.plus.com

**Philatelic Society for Greater Southern Africa,** David McNamee, 15 Woodland Drive, Alamo, CA 94507; www.psgsa.org; alan.hanks@sympatico. ca

**Rhodesian Study Circle,** William R. Wallace, P.O. Box 16381, San Francisco, CA 94116; (415) 564-6069; www.rhodesianstudycircle.org.uk; bwall8rscr@earthlink.net

**Society for Moroccan and Tunisian Philately,** S.P.L.M., 206, Bld Pereire, 75017 Paris, France; http://splm-philatelie.org; splm206@aol.com

**South Sudan Philatelic Society,** William Barclay, 1370 Spring Hill Road, South Londonderry, VT 05155; barclayphilatelics@gmail.com

**Sudan Study Group,** Andy Neal, Bank House, Coedway, Shrewsbury SY5 9AR United Kingdom; www.sudanstamps.org; andywneal@gmail.com

**Transvaal Study Circle,** c/o 9 Meadow Road, Gravesend, Kent DA11 7LR United Kingdom; www.transvaalstamps.org.uk; transvaalstudycircle@aol.co.uk

**West Africa Study Circle,** Martin Bratzel, 1233 Virginia Ave., Windsor, ON N8S 2Z1 Canada; www.wasc.org.uk; marty_bratzel@yahoo.ca

## Asia

**Aden & Somaliland Study Group,** Malcom Lacey, 108 Dalestorth Road, Sutton-in-Ashfield, Nottinghamshire NG17 3AA, United Kingdom; www.stampdomain.com/aden; neil53williams@yahoo.co.uk

**Burma (Myanmar) Philatelic Study Circle,** Michael Whittaker, 1, Ecton Leys, Hillside, Rugby, Warwickshire CV22 5SL United Kingdom; https:// burmamyanmarphilately.wordpress.com/ burma-myanmar-philatelic-study-circle; manningham8@mypostoffice.co.uk

**Ceylon Study Circle,** Rodney W. P. Frost, 42 Lonsdale Road, Cannington, Bridgwater, Somerset TA5 2JS United Kingdom; 01278 652592; www. ceylonsc.org; rodney.frost@tiscali.co.uk

**China Stamp Society,** H. James Maxwell, 1050 W. Blue Ridge Blvd., Kansas City, MO 64145-1216; www. chinastampsociety.org; president@ chinastampsociety.org

**Hong Kong Philatelic Society,** John Tang, G.P.O. Box 446, Hong Kong; www. hkpsociety.com; hkpsociety@outlook.com

**Hong Kong Study Circle,** Robert Newton, www.hongkongstudycircle.com/ index.html; newtons100@gmail.com

**India Study Circle,** John Warren, P.O. Box 7326, Washington, DC 20044; (202) 488-7443; https://indiastudycircle.org; jw-kbw@earthlink.net

**International Philippine Philatelic Society,** James R. Larot, Jr., 4990 Bayleaf Court, Martinez, CA 94553; (925) 260-5425; www.theipps.info; jlarot@ccwater.com

**International Society for Japanese Philately,** P.O. Box 1283, Haddonfield NJ 08033; www.isjp.org; secretary@ isjp.org

**Iran Philatelic Study Circle,** Nigel Gooch, Marchwood, 56, Wickham Ave., Bexhill-on-Sea, East Sussex TN39 3ER United Kingdom; www.iranphilately.org; nigelmgooch@gmail.com

**Korea Stamp Society,** Peter Corson, 1109 Gunnison Place, Raleigh, NC 27609; (919) 787-7611; koreastampsociety.org; pbcorson@aol. com

**Nepal & Tibet Philatelic Study Circle,** Colin Hepper, 12 Charnwood Close, Peterborough, Cambs PE2 9BZ United Kingdom; http://fuchs-online.com/ntpsc; ntpsc@fuchs-online.com

**Pakistan Philatelic Study Circle,** Jeff Siddiqui, P.O. Box 7002, Lynnwood, WA 98046; jeffsiddiqui@msn.com

**Society of Indo-China Philatelists,** Ron Bentley, 2600 N. 24th St., Arlington, VA 22207; (703) 524-1652; www.sicp-online.org; ron.bentley@verizon.net

**Society of Israel Philatelists, Inc.,** Sarah Berezenko, 100 Match Factory Place, Bellefonte, PA 16823-1367; (814) 933-3803 ext. 212; www.israelstamps.com; israelstamps@gmail.com

## Australasia and Oceania

**Australian States Study Circle of the Royal Sydney Philatelic Club,** Ben Palmer, G.P.O. 1751, Sydney, NSW 2001 Australia; http://club.philas.org.au/states

**Fellowship of Samoa Specialists,** Trevor Shimell, 18 Aspen Drive, Newton Abbot, Devon TQ12 4TN United Kingdom; www.samoaexpress.org; trevor.shimell@gmail.com

**Malaya Study Group,** Michael Waugh, 151 Roker Lane, Pudsey, Leeds LS28 9ND United Kingdom; http://malayastudygroup.com; mawpud43@gmail.com

**New Zealand Society of Great Britain,** Michael Wilkinson, 121 London Road, Sevenoaks, Kent TN13 1BH United Kingdom; 01732 456997; www.nzsgb.org.uk; mwilkin799@aol.com

**Pacific Islands Study Circle,** John Ray, 24 Woodvale Ave., London SE25 4AE United Kingdom; www.pisc.org.uk; secretary@pisc.org.uk

**Papuan Philatelic Society,** Steven Zirinsky, P.O. Box 49, Ansonia Station, New York, NY 10023; (718) 706-0616; www.papuanphilatelicsociety.com; szirinsky@cs.com

**Pitcairn Islands Study Group,** Dr. Everett L. Parker, 207 Corinth Road, Hudson, ME 04449-3057; (207) 573-1686; www.pisg.net; eparker@hughes.net

**Ryukyu Philatelic Specialist Society,** Laura Edmonds, P.O. Box 240177, Charlotte, NC 28224-0177; (336) 509-3739; www.ryukyustamps.org; secretary@ryukyustamps.org

**Society of Australasian Specialists / Oceania,** Steve Zirinsky, P.O. Box 230049, New York, NY 10023-0049; www.sasoceania.org; president@sosoceania.org

**Sarawak Specialists' Society,** Stephen Schumann, 2417 Cabrallo Drive, Hayward, CA 94545; (510) 785-4794; www.britborneostamps.org.uk; vpnam@s-s-s.org.uk

**Western Australia Study Group,** Brian Pope, P.O. Box 423, Claremont, WA 6910 Australia; (61) 419 843 943; www.wastudygroup.com; wastudygroup@hotmail.com

## Europe

**American Helvetia Philatelic Society,** Richard T. Hall, P.O. Box 15053, Asheville, NC 28813-0053; www.swiss-stamps.org; secretary2@swiss-stamps.org

**American Society for Netherlands Philately,** Hans Kremer, 50 Rockport Court, Danville, CA 94526; (925) 820-5841; www.asnp1975.com; hkremer@usa.net

**Andorran Philatelic Study Circle,** David Hope, 17 Hawthorn Drive, Stalybridge, Cheshire SK15 1UE United Kingdom; www.andorranpsc.org.uk; andorranpsc@btinternet.com

**Austria Philatelic Society,** Ralph Schneider, P.O. Box 978, Iowa Park, TX 76376; (940) 213-5004; www.austriaphilatelicsociety.com; rschneiderstamps@gmail.com

**Channel Islands Specialists Society,** Richard Flemming, Burbage, 64 Falconers Green, Hinckley, Leicestershire, LE102SX, United Kingdom; www.ciss.uk; secretary@ciss.uk

**Cyprus Study Circle,** Rob Wheeler, 47 Drayton Ave., London W13 0LE United Kingdom; www.cyprusstudycircle.org; robwheeler47@aol.com

**Danish West Indies Study Unit of Scandinavian Collectors Club,** Arnold Sorensen, 7666 Edgedale Drive, Newburgh, IN 47630; (812) 480-6532; www.scc-online.org; valbydwi@hotmail.com

**Eire Philatelic Association,** John B. Sharkey, 1559 Grouse Lane, Mountainside, NJ 07092-1340; www.eirephilatelicassoc.org; jsharkeyepa@me.com

**Faroe Islands Study Circle,** Norman Hudson, 40 Queen's Road, Vicar's Cross, Chester CH3 5HB United Kingdom; www.faroeislandssc.org; jntropics@hotmail.com

**France & Colonies Philatelic Society,** Edward Grabowski, 111 Prospect St., 4C, Westfield, NJ 07090; (908) 233-9318; www.franceandcolsps.org; edjjg@alum.mit.edu

**Germany Philatelic Society,** P.O. Box 6547, Chesterfield, MO 63006-6547; www.germanyphilatelicusa.org; info@germanyphilatelicsocietyusa.org

**Gibraltar Study Circle,** Susan Dare, 22, Byways Park, Strode Road, Clevedon, North Somerset BS21 6UR United Kingdom; www.gibraltarstudycircle.wordpress.com; smldare@yahoo.co.uk

**International Society for Portuguese Philately,** Clyde Homen, 1491 Bonnie View Road, Hollister, CA 95023-5117; www.portugalstamps.com; ispp1962@sbcglobal.net

**Italy and Colonies Study Circle,** Richard Harlow, 7 Duncombe House, 8 Manor Road, Teddington, Middlesex TW118BE United Kingdom; 44 208 977 8737; www.icsc-uk.com; richardharlow@outlook.com

**Liechtenstudy USA,** Paul Tremaine, 410 SW Ninth St., Dundee, OR 97115-9731; (503) 538-4500; www.liechtenstudy.org; tremaine@liechtenstudy.org

**Lithuania Philatelic Society,** Audrius Brazdeikis, 9915 Murray Landing, Missouri City, TX 77459; (281) 450-6224; www.lithuanianphilately.com/lps; audrius@lithuanianphilately.com

**Luxembourg Collectors Club,** Gary B. Little, 7319 Beau Road, Sechelt, BC V0N 3A8 Canada; (604) 885-7241; http://lcc.luxcentral.com; gary@luxcentral.com

**Plebiscite-Memel-Saar Study Group of the German Philatelic Society,** Clayton Wallace, 100 Lark Court, Alamo, CA 94507; claytonwallace@comcast.net

**Polonus Polish Philatelic Society,** Daniel Lubelski, P.O. Box 2212, Benicia, CA 94510; (419) 410-9115; www.polonus.org; info@polonus.org

**Rossica Society of Russian Philately,** Alexander Kolchinsky, 1506 Country Lake Drive, Champaign, IL 61821-6428; www.rossica.org; alexander.kolchinsky@rossica.org

**Scandinavian Collectors Club,** Alan Warren, Scandinavian Collectors Club, P.O. Box 39, Exton PA 19341-0039; (612) 810-8640; www.scc-online.org; alanwar@att.net

**Society for Czechoslovak Philately,** Tom Cossaboom, P.O. Box 4124, Prescott, AZ 86302; (928) 771-9097; www.csphilately.org; klfck1@aol.com

**Society for Hungarian Philately,** Alan Bauer, P.O. Box 4028, Vineyard Haven, MA 02568; (617) 645-4045; www.hungarianphilately.org; alan@hungarianstamps.com

**Spanish Study Circle,** Edith Knight, www.spaincircle.wixsite.com/spainstudycircle; spaincircle@gmail.com

**Ukrainian Philatelic & Numismatic Society,** Martin B. Tatuch, 5117 8th Road N., Arlington, VA 22205-1201; www.upns.org; treasurer@upns.org

**Vatican Philatelic Society,** Dennis Brady, 4897 Ledyard Drive, Manlius NY 13104-1514; www.vaticanphilately.org; dbrady7534@gmail.com

**Yugoslavia Study Group,** Michael Chant, 1514 N. Third Ave., Wausau, WI 54401; 208-748-9919; www.yugosg.org; membership@yugosg.org

## Interregional Societies

**American Society of Polar Philatelists,** Alan Warren, P.O. Box 39, Exton, PA 19341-0039; (610) 321-0740; www.polarphilatelists.org; alanwar@att.net

**First Issues Collector's Club,** Kurt Streepy, 3128 E. Mattatha Drive, Bloomington, IN 47401; www.firstissues.org; secretary@firstissues.org

**Former French Colonies Specialist Society,** Col.fra, BP 628, 75367 Paris, France; www.colfra.org; postmaster@colfra.org

**France & Colonies Philatelic Society,** Edward Grabowski, 111 Prospect St., 4C, Westfield, NJ 07090; (908) 233-9318, www.franceandcolsps.org; edjjg@alum.mit.edu

**Joint Stamp Issues Society,** Richard Zimmermann, 29A, Rue Des Eviats, 67220 Lalaye, France; www.philarz.net; richard.zimmermann@club-internet.fr

**The King George VI Collectors Society,** Brian Livingstone, 21 York Mansions, Prince of Wales Drive, London SW11 4DL United Kingdom; www.kg6.info; livingstone484@btinternet.com

**International Society of Reply Coupon Collectors,** Peter Robin, P.O. Box 353, Bala Cynwyd, PA 19004; peterrobin@verizon.net

**Italy and Colonies Study Circle,** Richard Harlow, 7 Duncombe House, 8 Manor Road, Teddington, Middlesex TW118BE United Kingdom; 44 208 977 8737; www.icsc-uk.com; richardharlow@outlook.com

**St. Helena, Ascension & Tristan Da Cunha Philatelic Society,** Dr. Everett L. Parker, 207 Corinth Road, Hudson, ME 04449-3057; (207) 573-1686; www.shatps.org; eparker@hughes.net

**United Nations Philatelists,** Blanton Clement, Jr., P.O. Box 146, Morrisville, PA 19067-0146; www.unpi.com; bclemjunior@gmail.com

## Latin America

**Asociación Filatélica de Panamá,** Edward D. Vianna B. ASOFILPA, 0819-03400, El Dorado, Panama; http://asociacionfilatelicadepanama.blogspot.com; asofilpa@gmail.com

**Asociacion Mexicana de Filatelia (AMEXFIL),** Alejandro Grossmann, Jose Maria Rico, 129, Col. Del Valle, 3100 Mexico City, DF Mexico; www.amexfil.mx; amexfil@gmail.com

**Associated Collectors of El Salvador,** Pierre Cahen, Vipsal 1342, P.O. Box 02-5364, Miami FL 33102; www.elsalvadorphilately.org; sfes-aces@elsalvadorphilately.org

**Association Filatelic de Costa Rica,** Giana Wayman (McCarty), #SJO 4935, P.O. Box 025723, Miami, FL 33102-5723; 011-506-2-228-1947; scotland@racsa.co.cr

**Brazil Philatelic Association,** William V. Kriebel, www.brazilphilatelic.org, info@brazilphilatelic.org

**Canal Zone Study Group,** Mike Drabik, P.O. Box 281, Bolton, MA 01740; www.canalzonestudygroup.com; czsgsecretary@gmail.com

**Colombia-Panama Philatelic Study Group,** Allan Harris, 26997 Hemmingway Ct, Hayward CA 94542-2349; www.copaphil.org; copaphilusa@aol.com

**Falkland Islands Philatelic Study Groups,** Morva White, 42 Colton Road, Shrivenham, Swindon SN6 8AZ United Kingdom; 44(0) 1793 783245; www.fipsg.org.uk; morawhite@supanet.com

**Federacion Filatélica de la Republica de Honduras,** Mauricio Mejia, Apartado Postal 1465, Tegucigalpa, D.C. Honduras; 504 3399-7227; www.facebook.com/filateliadehonduras; ffrh@hotmail.com

**International Cuban Philatelic Society (ICPS),** Ernesto Cuesta, P.O. Box 34434, Bethesda, MD 20827; (301) 564-3099; www.cubafil.org; ecuesta@philat.com

**International Society of Guatemala Collectors,** Jaime Marckwordt, 449 St. Francis Blvd., Daly City, CA 94015-2136; (415) 997-0295; www.guatemalastamps.com; president@guatamalastamps.com

**Mexico-Elmhurst Philatelic Society International,** Eric Stovner, P.O. Box 10097, Santa Ana, CA 92711-0097; www.mepsi.org; treasurer@mepsi.org

**Nicaragua Study Group,** Erick Rodriguez, 11817 S. W. 11th St., Miami, FL 33184-2501; nsgsec@yahoo.com

## North America (excluding United States)

**British Caribbean Philatelic Study Group,** Bob Stewart, 7 West Dune Lane, Long Beach Township, NJ 08008; (941) 379-4108; www.bcpsg.com; bcpsg@comcast.net

**British North America Philatelic Society,** Andy Ellwood, 10 Doris Ave., Gloucester, ON K1T 3W8 Canada; www.bnaps.org; secretary@bnaps.org

**British West Indies Study Circle,** Steve Jarvis, 5 Redbridge Drive, Andover, Hants SP10 2LF United Kingdom; 01264 358065; www.bwisc.org; info@bwisc.org

**Bermuda Collectors Society,** John Pare, 405 Perimeter St., Mount Horeb, WI 53572; (608) 852-7358; www.bermudacollectorssociety.com; pare16@mhtc.net

**Haiti Philatelic Society,** Ubaldo Del Toro, 5709 Marble Archway, Alexandria, VA 22315; www.haitiphilately.org; u007ubi@aol.com

**Hawaiian Philatelic Society,** Gannon Sugimura, P.O. Box 10115, Honolulu, HI 96816-0115, www.hpshawaii.com; hiphilsoc@gmail.com

## Stamp Dealer Associations

**American Stamp Dealers Association, Inc.,** P.O. Box 513, Centre Hall PA 16828; (800) 369-8207; www.americanstampdealer.com; asda@americanstampdealer.com

**National Stamp Dealers Association,** Sheldon Ruckens, President, 3643 Private Road 18, Pinckneyville, IL 62274-3426; (618) 357-5497; www.nsdainc.org; nsda@nsdainc.org

## Youth Philately

**Young Stamp Collectors of America,** 100 Match Factory Place, Bellefonte, PA 16823; (814) 933-3803; https://stamps.org/learn/youth-in-philately; ysca@stamps.org

# Expertizing services

The following organizations will, for a fee, provide expert opinions about stamps submitted to them. Collectors should contact these organizations to find out about their fees and requirements before submitting philatelic material to them. The listing of these groups here is not intended as an endorsement by Amos Media Co.

## General Expertizing Services

**American Philatelic Expertizing Service (a service of the American Philatelic Society)**
100 Match Factory Place
Bellefonte PA 16823-1367
(814) 237-3803
www.stamps.org/stamp-authentication
apex@stamps.org
Areas of Expertise: Worldwide

**BPA Expertising, Ltd.**
P.O. Box 1141
Guildford, Surrey, GU5 0WR
United Kingdom
www.bpaexpertising.com
sec@bpaexpertising.org
Areas of Expertise: British Commonwealth, Great Britain, Classics of Europe, South America and the Far East

**Philatelic Foundation**
353 Lexington Avenue, Suite 804
New York NY 10016
(212) 221-6555
www.philatelicfoundation.org
philatelicfoundation@verizon.net
Areas of Expertise: U.S. & Worldwide

**Philatelic Stamp Authentication and Grading, Inc.**
P.O. Box 41-0880
Melbourne FL 32941-0880
(305) 345-9864
www.psaginc.com
info@psaginc.com
Areas of Expertise: U.S., Canal Zone, Hawaii, Philippines, Canada & Provinces

**Professional Stamp Experts**
P.O. Box 539309
Henderson NV 89053-9309
(702) 776-6522
www.gradingmatters.com
www.psestamp.com
info@gradingmatters.com
Areas of Expertise: Stamps and Covers of U.S., U.S. Possessions, British Commonwealth

**Royal Philatelic Society London Expert Committee**
15 Abchurch Lane
London, EX4N 7BW
United Kingdom
www.rpsl.limited/experts.aspx
experts@rpsl.limited
Areas of Expertise: Worldwide
Expertizing Services Covering Specific Fields or Countries

**China Stamp Society Expertizing Service**
1050 W. Blue Ridge Blvd.
Kansas City MO 64145
(816) 942-6300
hjmesq@aol.com
Areas of Expertise: China

**Civil War Philatelic Society Authentication Service**
C/O Stefan T. Jaronski
P.O. Box 232
Sidney, MT 59270-0232
www.civilwarphilatelicsociety.org/authentication/
authentication@civilwarphilatelicsociety.org
Areas of Expertise: Confederate stamps and postal history

**Errors, Freaks and Oddities Collectors Club Expertizing Service**
138 East Lakemont Drive
Kingsland GA 31548
(912) 729-1573
Areas of Expertise: U.S. errors, freaks and oddities

**Hawaiian Philatelic Society Expertizing Service**
P.O. Box 10115
Honolulu HI 96816-0115
www.stampshows.com/hps.html
hiphilsoc@gmail.com
Areas of Expertise: Hawaii

**Hong Kong Stamp Society Expertizing Service**
P.O. Box 206
Glenside PA 19038
Areas of Expertise: Hong Kong

**International Association of Philatelic Experts United States Associate members:**
Paul Buchsbayew
300 Frank W. Burr Blvd. - Second Floor
Box 35
Teaneck, NJ 07666.
(212) 977-7734
Areas of Expertise: Russia, Soviet Union

William T. Crowe
P.O. Box 2090
Danbury CT 06813-2090
wtcrowe@aol.com
Areas of Expertise: United States

**International Society for Japanese Philately Expertizing Committee**
132 North Pine Terrace
Staten Island NY 10312-4052
(718) 227-5229
Areas of Expertise: Japan and related areas, except WWII Japanese Occupation issues

**International Society for Portuguese Philately Expertizing Service**
P.O. Box 43146
Philadelphia PA 19129-3146
(215) 843-2106
s.s.washburne@worldnet.att.net
Areas of Expertise: Portugal and Colonies

**Mexico-Elmhurst Philatelic Society International Expert Committee**
Expert Committee Administrator
Marc E. Gonzales
P.O. Box 29040
Denver CO 80229-0040
www.mepsi.org/expert_committeee.htm
expertizations@mepsi.org
Areas of Expertise: Mexico

**Ukrainian Philatelic & Numismatic Society Expertizing Service**
30552 Dell Lane
Warren MI 48092-1862
Areas of Expertise: Ukraine, Western Ukraine

**V. G. Greene Philatelic Research Foundation**
P.O. Box 69100
St. Clair Post Office
Toronto, ON M4T 3A1
Canada
(416) 921-2073
www.greenefoundation.ca
info@greenefoundation.ca
Areas of Expertise: British North America

# Information on catalogue values, grade and condition

## Catalogue value

The Scott Catalogue value is a retail value; that is, an amount you could expect to pay for a stamp in the grade of Very Fine with no faults. Any exceptions to the grade valued will be noted in the text. The general introduction on the following pages and the individual section introductions further explain the type of material that is valued. The value listed for any given stamp is a reference that reflects recent actual dealer selling prices for that item.

Dealer retail price lists, public auction results, published prices in advertising and individual solicitation of retail prices from dealers, collectors and specialty organizations have been used in establishing the values found in this catalogue. Amos Media Co. values stamps, but Amos Media is not a company engaged in the business of buying and selling stamps as a dealer.

Use this catalogue as a guide for buying and selling. The actual price you pay for a stamp may be higher or lower than the catalogue value because of many different factors, including the amount of personal service a dealer offers, or increased or decreased interest in the country or topic represented by a stamp or set. An item may occasionally be offered at a lower price as a "loss leader," or as part of a special sale. You also may obtain an item inexpensively at public auction because of little interest at that time or as part of a large lot.

Stamps that are of a lesser grade than Very Fine, or those with condition problems, generally trade at lower prices than those given in this catalogue. Stamps of exceptional quality in both grade and condition often command higher prices than those listed.

Values for pre-1900 unused issues are for stamps with approximately half or more of their original gum. Stamps with most or all of their original gum may be expected to sell for more, and stamps with less than half of their original gum may be expected to sell for somewhat less than the values listed. On rarer stamps, it may be expected that the original gum will be somewhat more disturbed than it will be on more common issues. Post-1900 unused issues are assumed to have full original gum. From breakpoints in most countries' listings, stamps are valued as never hinged, due to the wide availability of stamps in that condition. These notations are prominently placed in the listings and in the country information preceding the listings. Some countries also feature listings with dual values for hinged and never-hinged stamps.

## Grade

A stamp's grade and condition are crucial to its value. The accompanying illustrations show examples of Very Fine stamps from different time periods, along with examples of stamps in Fine to Very Fine and Extremely Fine grades as points of reference. When a stamp seller offers a stamp in any grade from fine to superb without further qualifying statements, that stamp should not only have the centering grade as defined, but it also should be free of faults or other condition problems.

**FINE** stamps (illustrations not shown) have designs that are quite off center, with the perforations on one or two sides very close to the design but not quite touching it. There is white space between the perforations and the design that is minimal but evident to the unaided eye. Imperforate stamps may have small margins, and earlier issues may show the design just touching one edge of the stamp design. Very early perforated issues normally will have the perforations slightly cutting into the design. Used stamps may have heavier than usual cancellations.

**FINE-VERY FINE** stamps will be somewhat off center on one side, or slightly off center on two sides. Imperforate stamps will have two margins of at least normal size, and the design will not touch any edge. For perforated stamps, the perfs are well clear of the design, but are still noticeably off center. *However, early issues of a country may be printed in such a way that the design naturally is very close to the edges. In these cases, the perforations may cut into the design very slightly.* Used stamps will not have a cancellation that detracts from the design.

**VERY FINE** stamps will be just slightly off center on one or two sides, but the design will be well clear of the edge. The stamp will present a nice, balanced appearance. Imperforate stamps will be well centered within normal-sized margins. *However, early issues of* many countries may be printed in such a way that the perforations may touch the design on one or more sides. Where this is the case, a boxed note will be found defining the centering and margins of the stamps being valued. Used stamps will have light or otherwise neat cancellations. This is the grade used to establish Scott Catalogue values.

**EXTREMELY FINE** stamps are close to being perfectly centered. Imperforate stamps will have even margins that are slightly larger than normal. Even the earliest perforated issues will have perforations clear of the design on all sides.

**Amos Media Co. recognizes that there is no formally enforced grading scheme for postage stamps, and that the final price you pay or obtain for a stamp will be determined by individual agreement at the time of transaction.**

## Condition

*Grade addresses* only centering and (for used stamps) cancellation. *Condition* refers to factors other than grade that affect a stamp's desirability.

Factors that can increase the value of a stamp include exceptionally wide margins, particularly fresh color, the presence of selvage, and plate or die varieties. Unusual cancels on used stamps (particularly those of the 19th century) can greatly enhance their value as well.

Factors other than faults that decrease the value of a stamp include loss of original gum, regumming, a hinge remnant or foreign object adhering to the gum, natural inclusions, straight edges, and markings or notations applied by collectors or dealers.

Faults include missing pieces, tears, pin or other holes, surface scuffs, thin spots, creases, toning, short or pulled perforations, clipped perforations, oxidation or other forms of color changelings, soiling, stains, and such man-made changes as reperforations or the chemical removal or lightening of a cancellation.

## Grading illustrations

On the following two pages are illustrations of various stamps from countries appearing in this volume. These stamps are arranged by country, and they represent early or important issues that are often found in widely different grades in the marketplace. The editors believe the illustrations will prove useful in showing the margin size and centering that will be seen on the various issues.

In addition to the matters of margin size and centering, collectors are reminded that the very fine stamps valued in the Scott catalogues also will possess fresh color and intact perforations, and they will be free from defects.

Examples shown are computer-manipulated images made from single digitized master illustrations.

## Stamp illustrations used in the catalogue

It is important to note that the stamp images used for identification purposes in this catalogue may not be indicative of the grade of stamp being valued. Refer to the written discussion of grades on this page and to the grading illustrations on the following two pages for grading information.

**Fine-Very Fine** →

**SCOTT CATALOGUES VALUE STAMPS IN THIS GRADE**

**Very Fine** →

**Extremely Fine** →

**Fine-Very Fine** →

**SCOTT CATALOGUES VALUE STAMPS IN THIS GRADE**

**Very Fine** →

**Extremely Fine** →

**Fine-Very Fine** →

**SCOTT CATALOGUES VALUE STAMPS IN THIS GRADE**

**Very Fine** →

**Extremely Fine** →

**Fine-Very Fine** →

**SCOTT CATALOGUES VALUE STAMPS IN THIS GRADE**

**Very Fine** →

**Extremely Fine** →

# Gum Conditions

For purposes of helping to determine the gum condition and value of an unused stamp, Scott presents the following chart which details different gum conditions and indicates how the conditions correlate with the Scott values for unused stamps. Used together, the Illustrated Grading Chart on the previous pages and this Illustrated Gum Chart should allow catalogue users to better understand the grade and gum condition of stamps valued in the Scott catalogues.

**Never Hinged (NH; ★★):** A never-hinged stamp will have full original gum that will have no hinge mark or disturbance. The presence of an expertizer's mark does not disqualify a stamp from this designation.

**Original Gum (OG; ★):** Pre-1900 stamps should have approximately half or more of their original gum. On rarer stamps, it may be expected that the original gum will be somewhat more disturbed than it will be on more common issues. Post-1900 stamps should have full original gum. Original gum will show some disturbance caused by a previous hinge(s) which may be present or entirely removed. The actual value of a post-1900 stamp will be affected by the degree of hinging of the full original gum.

**Disturbed Original Gum:** Gum showing noticeable effects of humidity, climate or hinging over more than half of the gum. The significance of gum disturbance in valuing a stamp in any of the Original Gum categories depends on the degree of disturbance, the rarity and normal gum condition of the issue and other variables affecting quality.

**Regummed (RG; (★)):** A regummed stamp is a stamp without gum that has had some type of gum privately applied at a time after it was issued. This normally is done to deceive collectors and/or dealers into thinking that the stamp has original gum and therefore has a higher value. A regummed stamp is considered the same as a stamp with none of its original gum for purposes of grading.

| Gum Categories: | MINT N.H. | ORIGINAL GUM (O.G.) | | | | | NO GUM |
|---|---|---|---|---|---|---|---|
| | **Mint Never Hinged** *Free from any disturbance* | **Lightly Hinged** *Faint impression of a removed hinge over a small area* | **Hinge Mark or Remnant** *Prominent hinged spot with part or all of the hinge remaining* | **Large part o.g.** *Approximately half or more of the gum intact* | **Small part o.g.** *Approximately less than half of the gum intact* | **No gum** *Only if issued with gum* |
| Commonly Used Symbol: | ★★ | ★ | ★ | ★ | ★ | (★) |
| Pre-1900 Issues (Pre-1881 for U.S.) | *Very fine pre-1900 stamps in these categories trade at a premium over Scott value* | | | Scott Value for "Unused" | | Scott "No Gum" listings for selected unused classic stamps |
| From 1900 to breakpoints for listings of never-hinged stamps | Scott "Never Hinged" listings for selected unused stamps | Scott Value for "Unused" (Actual value will be affected by the degree of hinging of the full o.g.) | | | | |
| From breakpoints noted for many countries | Scott Value for "Unused" | | | | | |

# Understanding the listings

On the opposite page is an enlarged "typical" listing from this catalogue. Below are detailed explanations of each of the highlighted parts of the listing.

**1 Scott number** — Scott catalogue numbers are used to identify specific items when buying, selling or trading stamps. Each listed postage stamp from every country has a unique Scott catalogue number. Therefore, Germany Scott 99, for example, can only refer to a single stamp. Although the Scott catalogue usually lists stamps in chronological order by date of issue, there are exceptions. When a country has issued a set of stamps over a period of time, those stamps within the set are kept together without regard to date of issue. This follows the normal collecting approach of keeping stamps in their natural sets.

When a country issues a set of stamps over a period of time, a group of consecutive catalogue numbers is reserved for the stamps in that set, as issued. If that group of numbers proves to be too few, capital-letter suffixes, such as "A" or "B," may be added to existing numbers to create enough catalogue numbers to cover all items in the set. A capital-letter suffix indicates a major Scott catalogue number listing. Scott generally uses a suffix letter only once. Therefore, a catalogue number listing with a capital-letter suffix will seldom be found with the same letter (lower case) used as a minor-letter listing. If there is a Scott 16A in a set, for example, there will seldom be a Scott 16a. However, a minor-letter "a" listing may be added to a major number containing an "A" suffix (Scott 16Aa, for example).

Suffix letters are cumulative. A minor "b" variety of Scott 16A would be Scott 16Ab, not Scott 16b.

There are times when a reserved block of Scott catalogue numbers is too large for a set, leaving some numbers unused. Such gaps in the numbering sequence also occur when the catalogue editors move an item's listing elsewhere or have removed it entirely from the catalogue. Scott does not attempt to account for every possible number, but rather attempts to assure that each stamp is assigned its own number.

Scott numbers designating regular postage normally are only numerals. Scott numbers for other types of stamps, such as air post, semipostal, postal tax, postage due, occupation and others have a prefix consisting of one or more capital letters or a combination of numerals and capital letters.

**2 Illustration number** — Illustration or design-type numbers are used to identify each catalogue illustration. For most sets, the lowest face-value stamp is shown. It then serves as an example of the basic design approach for other stamps not illustrated. Where more than one stamp use the same illustration number, but have differences in design, the design paragraph or the description line clearly indicates the design on each stamp not illustrated. Where there are both vertical and horizontal designs in a set, a single illustration may be used, with the exceptions noted in the design paragraph or description line.

When an illustration is followed by a lower-case letter in parentheses, such as "A2(b)," the trailing letter indicates which overprint or surcharge illustration applies.

Illustrations normally are 70 percent of the original size of the stamp. Oversized stamps, blocks and souvenir sheets are reduced even more. Overprints and surcharges are shown at 100 percent of their original size if shown alone, but are 70 percent of original size if shown on stamps. In some cases, the illustration will be placed above the set, between listings or omitted completely. Overprint and surcharge illustrations are not placed in this catalogue for purposes of expertizing stamps.

**3 Paper color** — The color of a stamp's paper is noted in italic type when the paper used is not white.

**4 Listing styles** — There are two principal types of catalogue listings: major and minor.

Major listings are in a larger type style than minor listings. The catalogue number is a numeral that can be found with or without a capital-letter suffix, and with or without a prefix.

Minor listings are in a smaller type style and have a small-letter suffix or (if the listing immediately follows that of the major number) may show only the letter. These listings identify a variety of the major item. Examples include perforation and shade differences, multiples (some souvenir sheets, booklet panes and se-tenant combinations), and singles of multiples.

Examples of major number listings include 16, 28A, B97, C13A, 10N5, and 10N6A. Examples of minor numbers are 16a and C13Ab.

**5 Basic information about a stamp or set** — Introducing each stamp issue is a small section (usually a line listing) of basic information about a stamp or set. This section normally includes the date of issue, method of printing, perforation, watermark and, sometimes, some additional information of note. *Printing method, perforation and watermark apply to the following sets until a change is noted.* Stamps created by overprinting or surcharging previous issues are assumed to have the same perforation, watermark, printing method and other production characteristics as the original. Dates of issue are as precise as Scott is able to confirm and often reflect the dates on first-day covers, rather than the actual date of release.

**6 Denomination** — This normally refers to the face value of the stamp; that is, the cost of the unused stamp at the post office at the time of issue. When a denomination is shown in parentheses, it does not appear on the stamp. This includes the nondenominated stamps of the United States, Brazil and Great Britain, for example.

**7 Color or other description** — This area provides information to solidify identification of a stamp. In many recent cases, a description of the stamp design appears in this space, rather than a listing of colors.

**8 Year of issue** — In stamp sets that have been released in a period that spans more than a year, the number shown in parentheses is the year that stamp first appeared. Stamps without a date appeared during the first year of the issue.

Dates are not always given for minor varieties.

**9 Value unused and Value used** — The Scott catalogue values are based on stamps that are in a grade of Very Fine unless stated otherwise. Unused values refer to items that have not seen postal, revenue or any other duty for which they were intended. Pre-1900 unused stamps that were issued with gum must have at least most of their original gum. Later issues are assumed to have full original gum. From breakpoints specified in most countries' listings, stamps are valued as never hinged. Stamps issued without gum are noted. Modern issues with PVA or other synthetic adhesives may appear ungummed. Unused self-adhesive stamps are valued as appearing undisturbed on their original backing paper. Values for used self-adhesive stamps are for examples either on piece or off piece. For a more detailed explanation of these values, please see the "Catalogue Value," "Condition" and "Understanding Valuing Notations" sections elsewhere in this introduction.

In some cases, where used stamps are more valuable than unused stamps, the value is for an example with a contemporaneous cancel, rather than a modern cancel or a smudge or other unclear marking. For those stamps that were released for postal and fiscal purposes, the used value represents a postally used stamp. Stamps with revenue cancels generally sell for less.

Stamps separated from a complete se-tenant multiple usually will be worth less than a pro-rated portion of the se-tenant multiple, and stamps lacking the attached labels that are noted in the listings will be worth less than the values shown.

**10 Changes in basic set information** — Bold type is used to show any changes in the basic data given for a set of stamps. These basic data categories include perforation gauge measurement, paper type, printing method and watermark.

**11 Total value of a set** — The total value of sets of three or more stamps issued after 1900 are shown. The set line also notes the range of Scott numbers and total number of stamps included in the grouping. The actual value of a set consisting predominantly of stamps having the minimum value of 25 cents may be less than the total value shown. Similarly, the actual value or catalogue value of se-tenant pairs or of blocks consisting of stamps having the minimum value of 25 cents may be less than the catalogue values of the component parts.

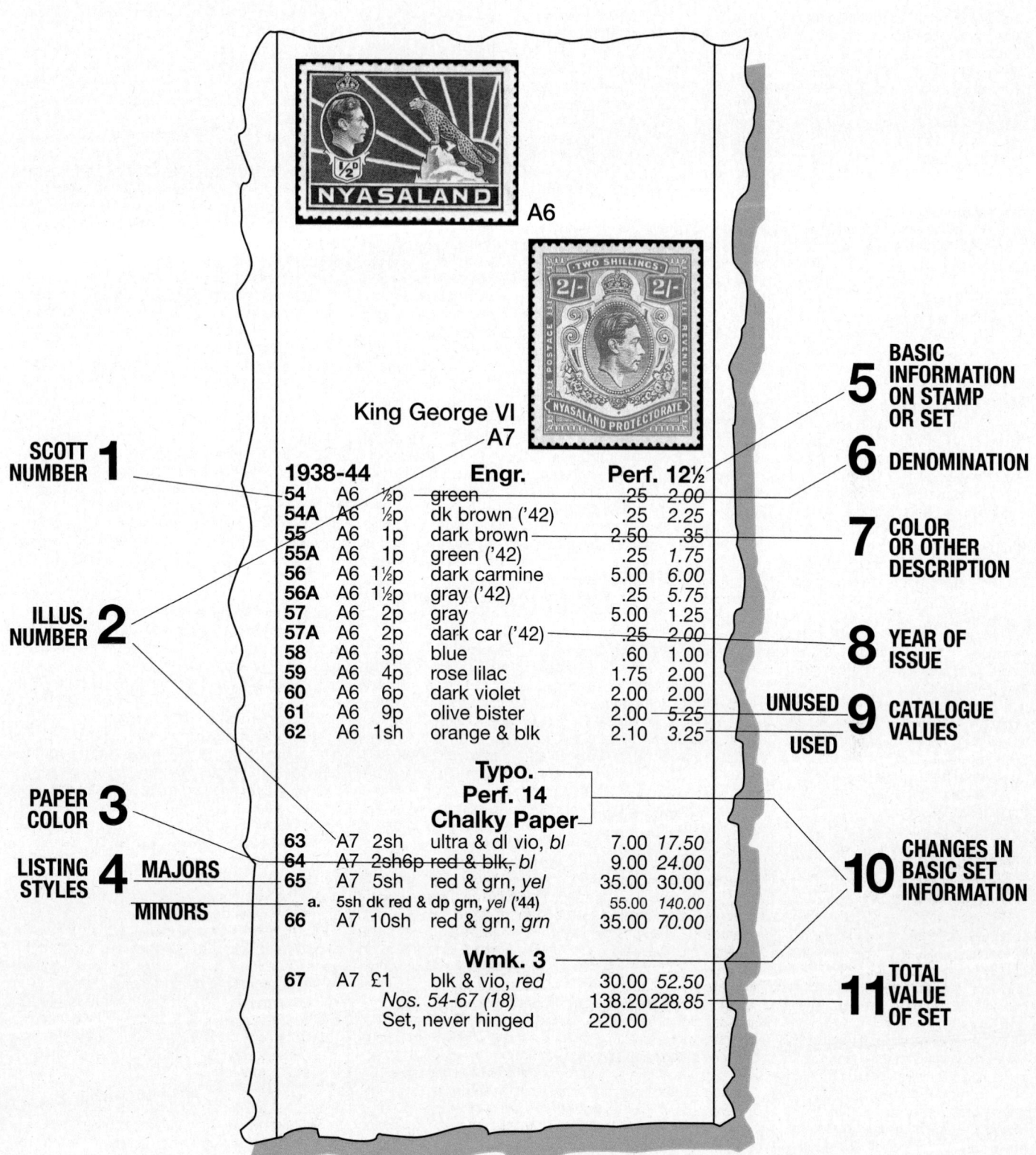

**BASIC INFORMATION ON STAMP OR SET** — **5**

**6** DENOMINATION

SCOTT NUMBER **1**

King George VI
A7

| | | | | Engr. | Perf. 12½ | |
|---|---|---|---|---|---|---|
| **1938-44** | | | | | | |
| **54** | A6 | ½p | green | | .25 | 2.00 |
| **54A** | A6 | ½p | dk brown ('42) | | .25 | 2.25 |
| **55** | A6 | 1p | dark brown | | 2.50 | .35 |
| **55A** | A6 | 1p | green ('42) | | .25 | 1.75 |
| **56** | A6 | 1½p | dark carmine | | 5.00 | 6.00 |
| **56A** | A6 | 1½p | gray ('42) | | .25 | 5.75 |
| **57** | A6 | 2p | gray | | 5.00 | 1.25 |
| **57A** | A6 | 2p | dark car ('42) | | .25 | 2.00 |
| **58** | A6 | 3p | blue | | .60 | 1.00 |
| **59** | A6 | 4p | rose lilac | | 1.75 | 2.00 |
| **60** | A6 | 6p | dark violet | | 2.00 | 2.00 |
| **61** | A6 | 9p | olive bister | | 2.00 | 5.25 |
| **62** | A6 | 1sh | orange & blk | | 2.10 | 3.25 |

**7** COLOR OR OTHER DESCRIPTION

**8** YEAR OF ISSUE

ILLUS. NUMBER **2**

UNUSED  **9** CATALOGUE VALUES
USED

**Typo.**
**Perf. 14**
**Chalky Paper**

| | | | | | | |
|---|---|---|---|---|---|---|
| **63** | A7 | 2sh | ultra & dl vio, *bl* | | 7.00 | 17.50 |
| **64** | A7 | 2sh6p | red & blk, *bl* | | 9.00 | 24.00 |
| **65** | A7 | 5sh | red & grn, *yel* | | 35.00 | 30.00 |
| a. | | 5sh dk red & dp grn, *yel* ('44) | | | 55.00 | 140.00 |
| **66** | A7 | 10sh | red & grn, *grn* | | 35.00 | 70.00 |

PAPER COLOR **3**

LISTING STYLES **4**  MAJORS

MINORS

**10** CHANGES IN BASIC SET INFORMATION

**Wmk. 3**

| | | | | | | |
|---|---|---|---|---|---|---|
| **67** | A7 | £1 | blk & vio, *red* | | 30.00 | 52.50 |
| | | Nos. 54-67 (18) | | | 138.20 | 228.85 |
| | | Set, never hinged | | | 220.00 | |

**11** TOTAL VALUE OF SET

# Catalogue listing policy

It is the intent of Amos Media Co. to list all postage stamps of the world in the Scott *Standard Postage Stamp Catalogue*. The only strict criteria for listing is that stamps be decreed legal for postage by the issuing country and that the issuing country actually have an operating postal system. Whether the primary intent of issuing a given stamp or set was for sale to postal patrons or to stamp collectors is not part of our listing criteria. Scott's role is to provide basic comprehensive postage stamp information. It is up to each stamp collector to choose which items to include in a collection.

It is Scott's objective to seek reasons why a stamp should be listed, rather than why it should not. Nevertheless, there are certain types of items that will not be listed. These include the following:

1. Unissued items that are not officially distributed or released by the issuing postal authority. If such items are officially issued at a later date by the country, they will be listed. Unissued items consist of those that have been printed and then held from sale for reasons such as change in government, errors found on stamps or something deemed objectionable about a stamp subject or design.

2. Stamps "issued" by non-existent postal entities or fantasy countries, such as Nagaland, Occusi-Ambeno, Staffa, Sedang, Torres Straits and others. Also, stamps "issued" in the names of legitimate, stamp-issuing countries that are not authorized by those countries.

3. Semi-official or unofficial items not required for postage. Examples include items issued by private agencies for their own express services. When such items are required for delivery, or are valid as prepayment of postage, they are listed.

4. Local stamps issued for local use only. Postage stamps issued by governments specifically for "domestic" use, such as Haiti Scott 219-228, or the United States nondenominated stamps, are not considered to be locals, since they are valid for postage throughout the country of origin.

5. Items not valid for postal use. For example, a few countries have issued souvenir sheets that are not valid for postage. This area also includes a number of worldwide charity labels (some denominated) that do not pay postage.

6. Egregiously exploitative issues such as stamps sold for far more than face value, stamps purposefully issued in artificially small quantities or only against advance orders, stamps awarded only to a selected audience such as a philatelic bureau's standing order customers, or stamps sold only in conjunction with other products. All of these kinds of items are usually controlled issues and/or are intended for speculation. These items normally will be included in a footnote.

7. Items distributed by the issuing government only to a limited group, club, philatelic exhibition or a single stamp dealer or other private company. These items normally will be included in a footnote.

8. Stamps not available to collectors. These generally are rare items, all of which are held by public institutions such as museums. The existence of such items often will be cited in footnotes.

The fact that a stamp has been used successfully as postage, even on international mail, is not in itself sufficient proof that it was legitimately issued. Numerous examples of so-called stamps from non-existent countries are known to have been used to post letters that have successfully passed through the international mail system.

There are certain items that are subject to interpretation. When a stamp falls outside our specifications, it may be listed along with a cautionary footnote.

A number of factors are considered in our approach to analyzing how a stamp is listed. The following list of factors is presented to share with you, the catalogue user, the complexity of the listing process.

**Additional printings** — "Additional printings" of a previously issued stamp may range from an item that is totally different to cases where it is impossible to differentiate from the original. At least a minor number (a small-letter suffix) is assigned if there is a distinct change in stamp shade, noticeably redrawn design, or a significantly different perforation measurement. A major number (numeral or numeral and capital-letter combination) is assigned if the editors feel the "additional printing" is sufficiently different from the original that it constitutes a different issue.

**Commemoratives** — Where practical, commemoratives with the same theme are placed in a set. For example, the U.S. Civil War Centennial set of 1961-65 and the Constitution Bicentennial series of 1989-90 appear as sets. Countries such as Japan and Korea issue such material on a regular basis, with an announced, or at least predictable, number of stamps known in advance. Occasionally, however, stamp sets that were released over a period of years have been separated. Appropriately placed footnotes will guide you to each set's continuation.

**Definitive sets** — Blocks of numbers generally have been reserved for definitive sets, based on previous experience with any given country. If a few more stamps were issued in a set than originally expected, they often have been inserted into the original set with a capital-letter suffix, such as U.S. Scott 1059A. If it appears that many more stamps than the originally allotted block will be released before the set is completed, a new block of numbers will be reserved, with the original one being closed off. In some cases, such as the U.S. Transportation and Great Americans series, several blocks of numbers exist. Appropriately placed footnotes will guide you to each set's continuation.

**New country** — Membership in the Universal Postal Union is not a consideration for listing status or order of placement within the catalogue. The index will tell you in what volume or page number the listings begin.

**"No release date" items** — The amount of information available for any given stamp issue varies greatly from country to country and even from time to time. Extremely comprehensive information about new stamps is available from some countries well before the stamps are released. By contrast some countries do not provide information about stamps or release dates. Most countries, however, fall between these extremes. A country may provide denominations or subjects of stamps from upcoming issues that are not issued as planned. Sometimes, philatelic agencies, those private firms hired to represent countries, add these later-issued items to sets well after the formal release date. This time period can range from weeks to years. If these items were officially released by the country, they will be added to the appropriate spot in the set. In many cases, the specific release date of a stamp or set of stamps may never be known.

**Overprints** — The color of an overprint is always noted if it is other than black. Where more than one color of ink has been used on overprints of a single set, the color used is noted. Early overprint and surcharge illustrations were altered to prevent their use by forgers.

**Personalized Stamps** — Since 1999, the special service of personalizing stamp vignettes, or labels attached to stamps, has been offered to customers by postal administrations of many countries. Sheets of these stamps are sold, singly or in quantity, only through special orders made by mail, in person, or through a sale on a computer website with the postal administrations or their agents for which an extra fee is charged, though some countries offer to collectors at face value personalized stamps having generic images in the vignettes or on the attached labels. It is impossible for any catalogue to know what images have been chosen by customers. Images can be 1) owned or created by the customer, 2) a generic image, or 3) an image pulled from a library of stock images on the stamp creation website. It is also impossible to know the quantity printed for any stamp having a particular image. So from a valuing standpoint, any image is equivalent to any other image for any personalized stamp having the same catalogue number. Illustrations of personalized stamps in the catalogue are not always those of stamps having generic images.

Personalized items are listed with some exceptions. These include:

1. Stamps or sheets that have attached labels that the customer cannot personalize, but which are nonetheless marketed as "personalized," and are sold for far more than the franking value.

2. Stamps or sheets that can be personalized by the customer, but where a portion of the print run must be ceded to the issuing country for sale to other customers.

3. Stamps or sheets that are created exclusively for a particular commercial client, or clients, including stamps that differ from any similar stamp that has been made available to the public.

4. Stamps or sheets that are deliberately conceived by the issuing authority that have been, or are likely to be, created with an excessive number of different face values, sizes, or other features that are changeable.

5. Stamps or sheets that are created by postal administrations using the same system of stamp personalization that has been put in place for use by the public that are printed in limited quantities and sold above face value.

6. Stamps or sheets that are created by licensees not directly affiliated or controlled by a postal administration.

Excluded items may or may not be footnoted.

**Se-tenants** — Connected stamps of differing features (se-tenants) will be listed in the format most commonly collected. This includes pairs, blocks or larger multiples. Se-tenant units are not always symmetrical. An example is Australia Scott 508, which is a block of seven stamps. If the stamps are primarily collected as a unit, the major number may be assigned to the multiple, with minors going to each component stamp. In cases where continuous-design or other unit se-tenants will receive significant postal use, each stamp is given a major Scott number listing. This includes issues from the United States, Canada, Germany and Great Britain, for example.

# Special notices

## Classification of stamps

The Scott Standard Postage Stamp Catalogue lists stamps by country of issue. The next level of organization is a listing by section on the basis of the function of the stamps. The principal sections cover regular postage, semi-postal, air post, special delivery, registration, postage due and other categories. Except for regular postage, catalogue numbers for all sections include a prefix letter (or number-letter combination) denoting the class to which a given stamp belongs. When some countries issue sets containing stamps from more than one category, the catalogue will at times list all of the stamps in one category (such as air post stamps listed as part of a postage set).

The following is a listing of the most commonly used catalogue prefixes.

Prefix.......Category
C..........Air Post
M.........Military
P..........Newspaper
N..........Occupation - Regular Issues
O..........Official
Q..........Parcel Post
J ..........Postage Due
RA .......Postal Tax
B..........Semi-Postal
E..........Special Delivery
MR.......War Tax

Other prefixes used by more than one country include the following:
H..........Acknowledgment of Receipt
I ...........Late Fee
CO.......Air Post Official
CQ.......Air Post Parcel Post
RAC.....Air Post Postal Tax
CF........Air Post Registration
CB .......Air Post Semi-Postal
CBO ....Air Post Semi-Postal Official
CE .......Air Post Special Delivery
EY........Authorized Delivery
S..........Franchise
G..........Insured Letter
GY .......Marine Insurance
MC.......Military Air Post
MQ ......Military Parcel Post
NC .......Occupation - Air Post
NO .......Occupation - Official
NJ........Occupation - Postage Due
NRA.....Occupation - Postal Tax
NB .......Occupation - Semi-Postal
NE .......Occupation - Special Delivery
QY .......Parcel Post Authorized Delivery
AR .......Postal-fiscal
RAJ......Postal Tax Due
RAB .....Postal Tax Semi-Postal
F .........Registration
EB........Semi-Postal Special Delivery
EO .......Special Delivery Official
QE .......Special Handling

## New issue listings

Updates to this catalogue appear each month in the *Linn's Stamp News* monthly magazine. Included in this update are additions to the listings of countries found in the Scott *Standard Postage Stamp Catalogue* and the *Specialized Catalogue of United States Stamps and Covers,* as well as corrections and updates to current editions of this catalogue.

From time to time there will be changes in the final listings of stamps from the *Linn's Stamp News* magazine to the next edition of the catalogue. This occurs as more information about certain stamps or sets becomes available.

The catalogue update section of the *Linn's Stamp News* magazine is the most timely presentation of this material available. Annual subscriptions to *Linn's Stamp News* are available from Linn's Stamp News, Box 4129, Sidney, OH 45365-4129.

## Number additions, deletions and changes

A listing of catalogue number additions, deletions and changes from the previous edition of the catalogue appears in each volume. See Catalogue Number Additions, Deletions & Changes in the table of contents for the location of this list.

## Understanding valuing notations

The *minimum catalogue value* of an individual stamp or set is 25 cents. This represents a portion of the cost incurred by a dealer when he prepares an individual stamp for resale. As a point of philatelic-economic fact, the lower the value shown for an item in this catalogue, the greater the percentage of that value is attributed to dealer mark up and profit margin. In many cases, such as the 25-cent minimum value, that price does not cover the labor or other costs involved with stocking it as an individual stamp. The sum of minimum values in a set does not properly represent the value of a complete set primarily composed of a number of minimum-value stamps, nor does the sum represent the actual value of a packet made up of minimum-value stamps. Thus a packet of 1,000 different common stamps — each of which has a catalogue value of 25 cents — normally sells for considerably less than $250!

The *absence of a retail value* for a stamp does not necessarily suggest that a stamp is scarce or rare. A dash in the value column means that the stamp is known in a stated form or variety, but information is either lacking or insufficient for purposes of establishing a usable catalogue value.

Stamp values in *italics* generally refer to items that are difficult to value accurately. For expensive items, such as those priced at $1,000 or higher, a value in italics indicates that the affected item trades very seldom. For inexpensive items, a value in italics represents a warning. One example is a "blocked" issue where the issuing postal administration may have controlled one stamp in a set in an attempt to make the whole set more valuable. Another example is an item that sold at an extreme multiple of face value in the marketplace at the time of its issue.

One type of warning to collectors that appears in the catalogue is illustrated by a stamp that is valued considerably higher in used condition than it is as unused. In this case, collectors are cautioned to be certain the used version has a genuine and contemporaneous cancellation. The type of cancellation on a stamp can be an important factor in determining its sale price. Catalogue values do not apply to fiscal, telegraph or non-contemporaneous postal cancels, unless otherwise noted.

Some countries have released back issues of stamps in canceled-to-order form, sometimes covering as much as a 10-year period. The Scott Catalogue values for used stamps reflect canceled-to-order material when such stamps are found to predominate in the marketplace for the issue involved. Notes frequently appear in the stamp listings to specify which items are valued as canceled-to-order, or if there is a premium for postally used examples.

Many countries sell canceled-to-order stamps at a marked reduction of face value. Countries that sell or have sold canceled-to-order stamps at *full* face value include United Nations, Australia, Netherlands, France and Switzerland. It may be almost impossible to identify such stamps if the gum has been removed, because official government canceling devices are used. Postally used examples of these items on cover, however, are usually worth more than the canceled-to-order stamps with original gum.

## Abbreviations

Scott uses a consistent set of abbreviations throughout this catalogue to conserve space, while still providing necessary information.

## Color Abbreviations

| | | | | | |
|---|---|---|---|---|---|
| amb | amber | crim | crimson | ol | olive |
| anil | aniline | cr | cream | olvn | olivine |
| ap | apple | dk | dark | org | orange |
| aqua | aquamarine | dl | dull | pck | peacock |
| az | azure | dp | deep | pnksh | pinkish |
| bis | bister | db | drab | Prus | Prussian |
| bl | blue | emer | emerald | pur | purple |
| bld | blood | gldn | golden | redsh | reddish |
| blk | black | grysh | grayish | res | reseda |
| bril | brilliant | grn | green | ros | rosine |
| brn | brown | grnsh | greenish | ryl | royal |
| brnsh | brownish | hel | heliotrope | sal | salmon |
| brnz | bronze | hn | henna | saph | sapphire |
| brt | bright | ind | indigo | scar | scarlet |
| brnt | burnt | int | intense | sep | sepia |
| car | carmine | lav | lavender | sien | sienna |
| cer | cerise | lem | lemon | sil | silver |
| chlky | chalky | lil | lilac | sl | slate |
| cham | chamois | lt | light | stl | steel |
| chnt | chestnut | mag | magenta | turq | turquoise |
| choc | chocolate | man | manila | ultra | ultramarine |
| chr | chrome | mar | maroon | Ven | Venetian |
| cit | citron | mv | mauve | ver | vermilion |
| cl | claret | multi | multicolored | vio | violet |
| cob | cobalt | mlky | milky | yel | yellow |
| cop | copper | myr | myrtle | yelsh | yellowish |

When no color is given for an overprint or surcharge, black is the color used. Abbreviations for colors used for overprints and surcharges include: "(B)" or "(Blk)," black; "(Bl)," blue; "(R)," red; and "(G)," green.

Additional abbreviations in this catalogue are shown below:

Adm. ... Administration
AFL ... American Federation of Labor
Anniv. ... Anniversary
APS ... American Philatelic Society
Assoc. ... Association
ASSR. ... Autonomous Soviet Socialist Republic
b. ... Born
BEP ... Bureau of Engraving and Printing
Bicent. ... Bicentennial
Bklt. ... Booklet
Brit. ... British
btwn ... Between
Bur. ... Bureau
c. or ca. ... Circa
Cat. ... Catalogue
Cent. ... Centennial, century, centenary
CIO ... Congress of Industrial Organizations
Conf. ... Conference
Cong. ... Congress
Cpl. ... Corporal
CTO ... Canceled to order
d. ... Died
Dbl. ... Double
EDU ... Earliest documented use
Engr ... Engraved
Exhib. ... Exhibition
Expo. ... Exposition
Fed. ... Federation
GB ... Great Britain
Gen. ... General
GPO ... General post office
Horiz. ... Horizontal
Imperf. ... Imperforate
Impt. ... Imprint
Intl. ... International
Invtd. ... Inverted
L. ... Left
Lieut., lt. ... Lieutenant
Litho. ... Lithographed

LL ... Lower left
LR ... Lower right
mm ... Millimeter
Ms. ... Manuscript
Natl. ... National
No. ... Number
NY ... New York
NYC ... New York City
Ovpt. ... Overprint
Ovptd. ... Overprinted
P ... Plate number
Perf. ... Perforated, perforation
Phil. ... Philatelic
Photo. ... Photogravure
PO ... Post office
Pr. ... Pair
P.R. ... Puerto Rico
Prec. ... Precancel, precanceled
Pres. ... President
PTT ... Post, Telephone and Telegraph
R ... Right
Rio ... Rio de Janeiro
Sgt. ... Sergeant
Soc. ... Society
Souv. ... Souvenir
SSR ... Soviet Socialist Republic, see ASSR
St. ... Saint, street
Surch. ... Surcharge
Typo. ... Typographed
UL ... Upper left
Unwmkd. ... Unwatermarked
UPU ... Universal Postal Union
UR ... Upper Right
US ... United States
USPOD ... United States Post Office Department
USSR ... Union of Soviet Socialist Republics
Vert. ... Vertical
VP ... Vice president
Wmk. ... Watermark
Wmkd. ... Watermarked
WWI ... World War I
WWII ... World War II

## Examination

Amos Media Co. will not comment upon the genuineness, grade or condition of stamps, because of the time and responsibility involved. Rather, there are several expertizing groups that undertake this work for both collectors and dealers. Neither will Amos Media Co. appraise or identify philatelic material. The company cannot take responsibility for unsolicited stamps or covers sent by individuals.

All letters, emails, etc. are read attentively, but they are not always answered because of time considerations.

## How to order from your dealer

When ordering stamps from a dealer, it is not necessary to write the full description of a stamp as listed in this catalogue. All you need is the name of the country, the Scott catalogue number and whether the desired item is unused or used. For example, "Japan Scott 422 unused" is sufficient to identify the unused stamp of Japan listed as "422 A206 5y brown."

# Basic stamp information

A stamp collector's knowledge of the combined elements that make a given stamp issue unique determines his or her ability to identify stamps. These elements include paper, watermark, method of separation, printing, design and gum. On the following pages each of these important areas is briefly described.

## Paper

Paper is an organic material composed of a compacted weave of cellulose fibers and generally formed into sheets. Paper used to print stamps may be manufactured in sheets, or it may have been part of a large roll (called a web) before being cut to size. The fibers most often used to create paper on which stamps are printed include bark, wood, straw and certain grasses. In many cases, linen or cotton rags have been added for greater strength and durability. Grinding, bleaching, cooking and rinsing these raw fibers reduces them to a slushy pulp, referred to by paper makers as "stuff." Sizing and, sometimes, coloring matter is added to the pulp to make different types of finished paper.

After the stuff is prepared, it is poured onto sieve-like frames that allow the water to run off, while retaining the matted pulp. As fibers fall onto the screen and are held by gravity, they form a natural weave that will later hold the paper together. If the screen has metal bits that are formed into letters or images attached, it leaves slightly thinned areas on the paper. These are called watermarks.

When the stuff is almost dry, it is passed under pressure through smooth or engraved rollers — dandy rolls — or placed between cloth in a press to be flattened and dried.

**Wove**     **Laid**     **Granite**

**Quadrille**     **Oblong Quadrille**     **Laid Batonne**

Stamp paper falls broadly into two types: wove and laid. The nature of the surface of the frame onto which the pulp is first deposited causes the differences in appearance between the two. If the surface is smooth and even, the paper will be of fairly uniform texture throughout. This is known as wove paper. Early papermaking machines poured the pulp onto a continuously circulating web of felt, but modern machines feed the pulp onto a cloth-like screen made of closely interwoven fine wires. This paper, when held to a light, will show little dots or points very close together. The proper name for this is "wire wove," but the type is still considered wove. Any U.S. or British stamp printed after 1880 will serve as an example of wire wove paper.

Closely spaced parallel wires, with cross wires at wider intervals, make up the frames used for what is known as laid paper. A greater thickness of the pulp will settle between the wires. The paper, when held to a light, will show alternate light and dark lines. The spacing and the thickness of the lines may vary, but on any one sheet of paper they are all alike. See Russia Scott 31-38 for examples of laid paper.

**Batonne,** from the French word meaning "a staff," is a term used if the lines in the paper are spaced quite far apart, like the printed ruling on a writing tablet. Batonne paper may be either wove or laid. If laid, fine laid lines can be seen between the batons.

**Quadrille** is the term used when the lines in the paper form little squares. Oblong quadrille is the term used when rectangles,

rather than squares, are formed. Grid patterns vary from distinct to extremely faint. See Mexico-Guadalajara Scott 35-37 for examples of oblong quadrille paper.

Paper also is classified as thick or thin, hard or soft, and by color. Such colors may include yellowish, greenish, bluish and reddish.

Brief explanations of other types of paper used for printing stamps, as well as examples, follow.

**Colored** — Colored paper is created by the addition of dye in the paper-making process. Such colors may include shades of yellow, green, blue and red. Surface-colored papers, most commonly used for British colonial issues in 1913-14, are created when coloring is added only to the surface during the finishing process. Stamps printed on surface-colored paper have white or uncolored backs, while true colored papers are colored through. See Jamaica Scott 71-73.

**Pelure** — Pelure paper is a very thin, hard and often brittle paper that is sometimes bluish or grayish in appearance. See Serbia Scott 169-170.

**Native** — This is a term applied to handmade papers used to produce some of the early stamps of the Indian states. Stamps printed on native paper may be expected to display various natural inclusions that are normal and do not negatively affect value. Japanese paper, originally made of mulberry fibers and rice flour, is part of this group. See Japan Scott 1-18.

**Manila** — This type of paper is often used to make stamped envelopes and wrappers. It is a coarse-textured stock, usually smooth on one side and rough on the other. A variety of colors of manila paper exist, but the most common range is yellowish-brown.

**Silk** — Introduced by the British in 1847 as a safeguard against counterfeiting, silk paper contains bits of colored silk thread scattered throughout. The density of these fibers varies greatly and can include as few as one fiber per stamp or hundreds. U.S. revenue Scott R152 is a good example of an easy-to-identify silk paper stamp.

Silk-thread paper has uninterrupted threads of colored silk arranged so that one or more threads run through the stamp or postal stationery. See Great Britain Scott 5-6 and Switzerland Scott 14-19.

**Granite** — Filled with minute cloth or colored paper fibers of various colors and lengths, granite paper should not be confused with either type of silk paper. Austria Scott 172-175 and a number of Swiss stamps are examples of granite paper.

**Chalky** — A chalk-like substance coats the surface of chalky paper to discourage the cleaning and reuse of canceled stamps, as well as to provide a smoother, more acceptable printing surface. Because the designs of stamps printed on chalky paper are imprinted on what is often a water-soluble coating, any attempt to remove a cancellation will destroy the stamp. Do not soak these stamps in any fluid. To remove a stamp printed on chalky paper from an envelope, wet the paper from underneath the stamp until the gum dissolves enough to release the stamp from the paper. See St. Kitts-Nevis Scott 89-90 for examples of stamps printed on this type of chalky paper.

**India** — Another name for this paper, originally introduced from China about 1750, is "China Paper." It is a thin, opaque paper often used for plate and die proofs by many countries.

**Double** — In philately, the term double paper has two distinct meanings. The first is a two-ply paper, usually a combination of a thick and a thin sheet, joined during manufacture. This type was used experimentally as a means to discourage the reuse of stamps.

The design is printed on the thin paper. Any attempt to remove a cancellation would destroy the design. U.S. Scott 158 and other Banknote-era stamps exist on this form of double paper.

The second type of double paper occurs on a rotary press, when the end of one paper roll, or web, is affixed to the next roll to save time feeding the paper through the press. Stamp designs are printed over the joined paper and, if overlooked by inspectors, may get into post office stocks.

**Goldbeater's Skin** — This type of paper was used for the 1866 issue of Prussia, and was a tough, translucent paper. The design was printed in reverse on the back of the stamp, and the gum applied over the printing. It is impossible to remove stamps printed on this type of paper from the paper to which they are affixed without destroying the design.

**Ribbed** — Ribbed paper has an uneven, corrugated surface made by passing the paper through ridged rollers. This type exists on some copies of U.S. Scott 156-165.

Various other substances, or substrates, have been used for stamp manufacture, including wood, aluminum, copper, silver and gold foil, plastic, and silk and cotton fabrics.

# Watermarks

Watermarks are an integral part of some papers. They are formed in the process of paper manufacture. Watermarks consist of small designs, formed of wire or cut from metal and soldered to the surface of the mold or, sometimes, on the dandy roll. The designs may be in the form of crowns, stars, anchors, letters or other characters or symbols. These pieces of metal — known in the paper-making industry as "bits" — impress a design into the paper. The design sometimes may be seen by holding the stamp to the light. Some are more easily seen with a watermark detector. This important tool is a small black tray into which a stamp is placed face down and dampened with a fast-evaporating watermark detection fluid that brings up the watermark image in the form of dark lines against a lighter background. These dark lines are the thinner areas of the paper known as the watermark. Some watermarks are extremely difficult to locate, due to either a faint impression, watermark location or the color of the stamp. There also are electric watermark detectors that come with plastic filter disks of various colors. The disks neutralize the color of the stamp, permitting the watermark to be seen more easily.

**Multiple watermarks of Crown Agents and Burma**

**Watermarks of Uruguay, Vatican City and Jamaica**

**WARNING: Some inks used in the photogravure process dissolve in watermark fluids (Please see the section on Soluble Printing Inks).** Also, see "chalky paper."

Watermarks may be found normal, reversed, inverted, reversed and inverted, sideways or diagonal, as seen from the back of the stamp. The relationship of watermark to stamp design depends on the position of the printing plates or how paper is fed through the press. On machine-made paper, watermarks normally are read from right to left. The design is repeated closely throughout the sheet in a "multiple-watermark design." In a "sheet watermark," the design appears only once on the sheet, but extends over many stamps. Individual stamps may carry only a small fraction or none of the watermark.

"Marginal watermarks" occur in the margins of sheets or panes of stamps. They occur on the outside border of paper (ostensibly outside the area where stamps are to be printed). A large row of letters may spell the name of the country or the manufacturer of the paper, or a border of lines may appear. Careless press feeding may cause parts of these letters and/or lines to show on stamps of the outer row of a pane.

# Soluble printing inks

**WARNING:** Most stamp colors are permanent; that is, they are not seriously affected by short-term exposure to light or water. Many colors, especially of modern inks, fade from excessive exposure to light. There are stamps printed with inks that dissolve easily in water or in fluids used to detect watermarks. Use of these inks was intentional to prevent the removal of cancellations. Water affects all aniline inks, those on so-called safety paper and some photogravure printings - all such inks are known as fugitive colors. Removal from paper of such stamps requires care and alternatives to traditional soaking.

# Separation

"Separation" is the general term used to describe methods used to separate stamps. The three standard forms currently in use are perforating, rouletting and die-cutting. These methods are done during the stamp production process, after printing. Sometimes these methods are done on-press or sometimes as a separate step. The earliest issues, such as the 1840 Penny Black of Great Britain (Scott 1), did not have any means provided for separation. It was expected the stamps would be cut apart with scissors or folded and torn. These are examples of imperforate stamps. Many stamps were first issued in imperforate formats and were later issued with perforations. Therefore, care must be observed in buying single imperforate stamps to be certain they were issued imperforate and are not perforated copies that have been altered by having the perforations trimmed away. Stamps issued imperforate usually are valued as singles. However, imperforate varieties of normally perforated stamps should be collected in pairs or larger pieces as indisputable evidence of their imperforate character.

## PERFORATION

The chief style of separation of stamps, and the one that is in almost universal use today, is perforating. By this process, paper between the stamps is cut away in a line of holes, usually round, leaving little bridges of paper between the stamps to hold them together. Some types of perforation, such as hyphen-hole perfs, can be confused with roulettes, but a close visual inspection reveals that paper has been removed. The little perforation bridges, which project from the stamp when it is torn from the pane, are called the teeth of the perforation.

As the size of the perforation is sometimes the only way to differentiate between two otherwise identical stamps, it is necessary to be able to accurately measure and describe them. This is done with a perforation gauge, usually a ruler-like device that has dots or graduated lines to show how many perforations may be counted in the space of two centimeters. Two centimeters is the space universally adopted in which to measure perforations.

**Perforation gauge**

To measure a stamp, run it along the gauge until the dots on it fit exactly into the perforations of the stamp. If you are using a graduated-line perforation gauge, simply slide the stamp along the surface until the lines on the gauge perfectly project from the center of the bridges or holes. The number to the side of the line of dots or lines that fit the stamp's perforation is the measurement. For example, an "11" means that 11 perforations fit between two centimeters. The description of the stamp therefore is "perf. 11." If the gauge of the perforations on the top and bottom of a stamp differs from that on the sides, the result is what is known as compound perforations. In measuring compound perforations, the gauge at top and bottom is always given first, then the sides. Thus, a stamp that measures 11 at top and bottom and 10½ at the sides is "perf. 11 x 10½." See U.S. Scott 632-642 for examples of compound perforations.

Stamps also are known with perforations different on three or all four sides. Descriptions of such items are clockwise, beginning with the top of the stamp.

A perforation with small holes and teeth close together is a "fine perforation." One with large holes and teeth far apart is a "coarse perforation." Holes that are jagged, rather than clean-cut, are "rough perforations." *Blind perforations* are the slight impressions left by the perforating pins if they fail to puncture the paper. Multiples of stamps showing blind perforations may command a slight premium over normally perforated stamps.

The term *syncopated perfs* describes intentional irregularities in the perforations. The earliest form was used by the Netherlands from 1925-33, where holes were omitted to create distinctive patterns. Beginning in 1992, Great Britain has used an oval perforation to help prevent counterfeiting. Several other countries have started using the oval perfs or other syncopated perf patterns.

A new type of perforation, still primarily used for postal stationery, is known as microperfs. Microperfs are tiny perforations (in some cases hundreds of holes per two centimeters) that allows items to be intentionally separated very easily, while not accidentally breaking apart as easily as standard perforations. These are not currently measured or differentiated by size, as are standard perforations.

perce en arc      perce en lignes

perce en points      oblique roulette

perce en scie      perce serpentin

## ROULETTING

In rouletting, the stamp paper is cut partly or wholly through, with no paper removed. In perforating, some paper is removed. Rouletting derives its name from the French roulette, a spur-like wheel. As the wheel is rolled over the paper, each point makes a small cut. The number of cuts made in a two-centimeter space determines the gauge of the roulette, just as the number of perforations in two centimeters determines the gauge of the perforation.

The shape and arrangement of the teeth on the wheels varies. Various roulette types generally carry French names:

*Perce en lignes* — rouletted in lines. The paper receives short, straight cuts in lines. This is the most common type of rouletting. See Mexico Scott 500.

*Perce en points* — pin-rouletted or pin-perfed. This differs from a small perforation because no paper is removed, although round, equidistant holes are pricked through the paper. See Mexico Scott 242-256.

*Perce en arc and perce en scie* — pierced in an arc or saw-toothed designs, forming half circles or small triangles. See Hanover (German States) Scott 25-29.

*Perce en serpentin* — serpentine roulettes. The cuts form a serpentine or wavy line. See Brunswick (German States) Scott 13-18.

Once again, no paper is removed by these processes, leaving the stamps easily separated, but closely attached.

## DIE-CUTTING

The third major form of stamp separation is die-cutting. This is a method where a die in the pattern of separation is created that later cuts the stamp paper in a stroke motion. Although some standard stamps bear die-cut perforations, this process is primarily used for self-adhesive postage stamps. Die-cutting can appear in straight lines, such as U.S. Scott 2522, shapes, such as U.S. Scott 1551, or imitating the appearance of perforations, such as New Zealand Scott 935A and 935B.

# Printing processes

## ENGRAVING (Intaglio, Line-engraving, Etching)

**Master die** — The initial operation in the process of line engraving is making the master die. The die is a small, flat block of softened steel upon which the stamp design is recess engraved in reverse.

Photographic reduction of the original art is made to the appropriate size. It then serves as a tracing guide for the initial outline of the design. The engraver lightly traces the design on the steel with his graver, then slowly works the design until it is completed. At various points during the engraving process, the engraver hand-inks the die and makes an impression to check his progress. These are known as progressive die proofs. After completion of the engraving, the die is hardened to withstand the stress and pressures of later transfer operations.

**Transfer roll**

**Transfer roll** — Next is production of the transfer roll that, as the name implies, is the medium used to transfer the subject from the master die to the printing plate. A blank roll of soft steel, mounted on a mandrel, is placed under the bearers of the transfer press to allow it to roll freely on its axis. The hardened die is placed on the bed of the press and the face of the transfer roll is applied to the die, under pressure. The bed or the roll is then rocked back and forth under increasing pressure, until the soft steel of the roll is forced into every engraved line of the die. The resulting impression on the roll is known as a "relief" or a "relief transfer." The engraved image is now positive in appearance and stands out from the steel. After the required number of reliefs are "rocked in," the soft steel transfer roll is hardened.

Different flaws may occur during the relief process. A defective relief may occur during the rocking in process because of a minute piece of foreign material lodging on the die, or some other cause. Imperfections in the steel of the transfer roll may result in a breaking away of parts of the design. This is known as a relief break, which will show up on finished stamps as small, unprinted areas. If a damaged relief remains in use, it will transfer a repeating defect to the plate. Deliberate alterations of reliefs sometimes occur. "Altered reliefs" designate these changed conditions.

**Plate** — The final step in pre-printing production is the making of the printing plate. A flat piece of soft steel replaces the die on the bed of the transfer press. One of the reliefs on the transfer roll is positioned over this soft steel. Position, or layout, dots determine the correct position on the plate. The dots have been lightly marked on the plate in advance. After the correct position of the relief is determined, the design is rocked in by following the same method used in making the transfer roll. The difference is that this time the image is being transferred from the transfer roll, rather than to it. Once the design is entered on the plate, it appears in reverse and is recessed. There are as many transfers entered on the plate as there are subjects printed on the sheet of stamps. It is during this process that double and shifted transfers occur, as well as re-entries. These are the result of improperly entered images that have not been properly burnished out prior to rocking in a new image.

Modern siderography processes, such as those used by the U.S. Bureau of Engraving and Printing, involve an automated form of rocking designs in on preformed cylindrical printing sleeves. The same process also allows for easier removal and re-entry of worn images right on the sleeve.

**Transferring the design to the plate**

Following the entering of the required transfers on the plate, the position dots, layout dots and lines, scratches and other markings generally are burnished out. Added at this time by the siderographer are any required guide lines, plate numbers or other marginal markings. The plate is then hand-inked and a proof impression is taken. This is known as a plate proof. If the impression is approved, the plate is machined for fitting onto the press, is hardened and sent to the plate vault ready for use.

On press, the plate is inked and the surface is automatically wiped clean, leaving ink only in the recessed lines. Paper is then forced under pressure into the engraved recessed lines, thereby receiving the ink. Thus, the ink lines on engraved stamps are slightly raised, and slight depressions (debossing) occur on the back of the stamp. Prior to the advent of modern high-speed presses and more advanced ink formulations, paper had to be dampened before receiving the ink. This sometimes led to uneven shrinkage by the time the stamps were perforated, resulting in improperly perforated stamps, or misperfs. Newer presses use drier paper, thus both *wet and dry printings* exist on some stamps.

**Rotary Press** — Until 1914, only flat plates were used to print engraved stamps. Rotary press printing was introduced in 1914, and slowly spread. Some countries still use flat-plate printing.

After approval of the plate proof, older rotary press plates require additional machining. They are curved to fit the press cylinder. "Gripper slots" are cut into the back of each plate to receive the "grippers," which hold the plate securely on the press. The plate is then hardened. Stamps printed from these bent rotary press plates are longer or wider than the same stamps printed from flat-plate presses. The stretching of the plate during the curving process is what causes this distortion.

**Re-entry** — To execute a re-entry on a flat plate, the transfer roll is re-applied to the plate, often at some time after its first use on the press. Worn-out designs can be resharpened by carefully burnishing out the original image and re-entering it from the transfer roll. If the original impression has not been sufficiently removed and the transfer roll is not precisely in line with the remaining impression, the resulting double transfer will make the re-entry obvious. If the registration is true, a re-entry may be difficult or impossible to distinguish. Sometimes a stamp printed from a successful re-entry is identified by having a much sharper and clearer impression than its neighbors. With the advent of rotary presses, post-press re-entries were not possible. After a plate was curved for the rotary press, it was impossible to make a re-entry. This is because the plate had already been bent once (with the design distorted).

However, with the introduction of the previously mentioned modern-style siderography machines, entries are made to the preformed cylindrical printing sleeve. Such sleeves are dechromed and softened. This allows individual images to be burnished out and re-entered on the curved sleeve. The sleeve is then rechromed, resulting in longer press life.

**Double Transfer** — This is a description of the condition of a transfer on a plate that shows evidence of a duplication of all, or a portion of the design. It usually is the result of the changing of the registration between the transfer roll and the plate during the rocking in of the original entry. Double transfers also occur when only a portion of the design has been rocked in and improper positioning is noted. If the worker elected not to burnish out the partial or completed design, a strong double transfer will occur for part or all of the design.

It sometimes is necessary to remove the original transfer from a plate and repeat the process a second time. If the finished re-worked image shows traces of the original impression, attributable to incomplete burnishing, the result is a partial double transfer.

With the modern automatic machines mentioned previously, double transfers are all but impossible to create. Those partially doubled images on stamps printed from such sleeves are more than likely re-entries, rather than true double transfers.

**Re-engraved** — Alterations to a stamp design are sometimes necessary after some stamps have been printed. In some cases, either the original die or the actual printing plate may have its "temper" drawn (softened), and the design will be re-cut. The resulting impressions from such a re-engraved die or plate may differ slightly from the original issue, and are known as "re-engraved." If the alteration was made to the master die, all future printings will be consistently different from the original. If alterations were made to the printing plate, each altered stamp on the plate will be slightly different from each other, allowing specialists to reconstruct a complete printing plate.

**Dropped Transfers** — If an impression from the transfer roll has not been properly placed, a dropped transfer may occur. The final stamp image will appear obviously out of line with its neighbors.

**Short Transfer** — Sometimes a transfer roll is not rocked its entire length when entering a transfer onto a plate. As a result, the finished transfer on the plate fails to show the complete design, and the finished stamp will have an incomplete design printed. This is known as a "short transfer." U.S. Scott No. 8 is a good example of a short transfer.

## TYPOGRAPHY (Letterpress, Surface Printing, Flexography, Dry Offset, High Etch)

Although the word "Typography" is obsolete as a term describing a printing method, it was the accepted term throughout the first century of postage stamps. Therefore, appropriate Scott listings in this catalogue refer to typographed stamps. The current term for this form of printing, however, is "letterpress."

As it relates to the production of postage stamps, letterpress printing is the reverse of engraving. Rather than having recessed areas trap the ink and deposit it on paper, only the raised areas of the design are inked. This is comparable to the type of printing seen by inking and using an ordinary rubber stamp. Letterpress includes all printing where the design is above the surface area, whether it is wood, metal or, in some instances, hardened rubber or polymer plastic.

For most letterpress-printed stamps, the engraved master is made in much the same manner as for engraved stamps. In this instance, however, an additional step is needed. The design is transferred to another surface before being transferred to the transfer roll. In this way, the transfer roll has a recessed stamp design, rather than one done in relief. This makes the printing areas on the final plate raised, or relief areas.

For less-detailed stamps of the 19th century, the area on the die not used as a printing surface was cut away, leaving the surface area raised. The original die was then reproduced by stereotyping or electrotyping. The resulting electrotypes were assembled in the required number and format of the desired sheet of stamps. The plate used in printing the stamps was an electroplate of these assembled electrotypes.

Once the final letterpress plates are created, ink is applied to the raised surface and the pressure of the press transfers the ink impression to the paper. In contrast to engraving, the fine lines of letterpress are impressed on the surface of the stamp, leaving a debossed surface. When viewed from the back (as on a typewritten page), the corresponding line work on the stamp will be raised slightly (embossed) above the surface.

## PHOTOGRAVURE (Gravure, Rotogravure, Heliogravure)

In this process, the basic principles of photography are applied to a chemically sensitized metal plate, rather than photographic paper. The design is transferred photographically to the plate through a halftone, or dot-matrix screen, breaking the reproduction into tiny dots. The plate is treated chemically and the dots form depressions, called cells, of varying depths and diameters, depending on the degrees of shade in the design. Then, like engraving, ink is applied to the plate and the surface is wiped clean. This leaves ink in the tiny cells that is lifted out and deposited on the paper when it is pressed against the plate.

Gravure is most often used for multicolored stamps, generally using the three primary colors (red, yellow and blue) and black. By varying the dot matrix pattern and density of these colors, virtually any color can be reproduced. A typical full-color gravure stamp will be created from four printing cylinders (one for each color). The original multicolored image will have been photographically separated into its component colors.

Modern gravure printing may use computer-generated dot-matrix screens, and modern plates may be of various types including metal-coated plastic. The catalogue designation of Photogravure (or "Photo") covers any of these older and more modern gravure methods of printing.

For examples of the first photogravure stamps printed (1914), see Bavaria Scott 94-114.

## LITHOGRAPHY (Offset Lithography, Stone Lithography, Dilitho, Planography, Collotype)

The principle that oil and water do not mix is the basis for lithography. The stamp design is drawn by hand or transferred from engraving to the surface of a lithographic stone or metal plate in a greasy (oily) substance. This oily substance holds the ink, which will later be transferred to the paper. The stone (or plate) is wet with an acid fluid, causing it to repel the printing ink in all areas not covered by the greasy substance.

Transfer paper is used to transfer the design from the original stone or plate. A series of duplicate transfers are grouped and, in turn, transferred to the final printing plate.

**Photolithography** — The application of photographic processes to lithography. This process allows greater flexibility of design, related to use of halftone screens combined with line work. Unlike photogravure or engraving, this process can allow large, solid areas to be printed.

**Offset** — A refinement of the lithographic process. A rubber-covered blanket cylinder takes the impression from the inked lithographic plate. From the "blanket" the impression is offset or transferred to the paper. Greater flexibility and speed are the principal reasons offset printing has largely displaced lithography. The term "lithography" covers both processes, and results are almost identical.

### EMBOSSED (Relief) Printing

Embossing, not considered one of the four main printing types, is a method in which the design first is sunk into the metal of the die. Printing is done against a yielding platen, such as leather or linoleum. The platen is forced into the depression of the die, thus forming the design on the paper in relief. This process is often used for metallic inks.

Embossing may be done without color (see Sardinia Scott 4-6); with color printed around the embossed area (see Great Britain Scott 5 and most U.S. envelopes); and with color in exact registration with the embossed subject (see Canada Scott 656-657).

## HOLOGRAMS

For objects to appear as holograms on stamps, a model exactly the same size as it is to appear on the hologram must be created. Rather than using photographic film to capture the image, holography records an image on a photoresist material. In processing, chemicals eat away at certain exposed areas, leaving a pattern of constructive and destructive interference. When the photoresist is developed, the result is a pattern of uneven ridges that acts as a mold. This mold is then coated with metal, and the resulting form is used to press copies in much the same way phonograph records are produced.

A typical reflective hologram used for stamps consists of a reproduction of the uneven patterns on a plastic film that is applied to a reflective background, usually a silver or gold foil. Light is reflected off the background through the film, making the pattern present on the film visible. Because of the uneven pattern of the film, the viewer will perceive the objects in their proper three-dimensional relationships with appropriate brightness. The first hologram on a stamp was produced by Austria in 1988 (Scott 1441).

## FOIL APPLICATION

A modern technique of applying color to stamps involves the application of metallic foil to the stamp paper. A pattern of foil is applied to the stamp paper by use of a stamping die. The foil usually is flat, but it may be textured. Canada Scott 1735 has three different foil applications in pearl, bronze and gold. The gold foil was textured using

a chemical-etch copper embossing die. The printing of this stamp also involved two-color offset lithography plus embossing.

## THERMOGRAPHY

In the 1990s stamps began to be enhanced with thermographic printing. In this process, a powdered polymer is applied over a sheet that has just been printed. The powder adheres to ink that lacks drying or hardening agents and does not adhere to areas where the ink has these agents. The excess powder is removed and the sheet is briefly heated to melt the powder. The melted powder solidifies after cooling, producing a raised, shiny effect on the stamps. See Scott New Caledonia C239-C240.

## COMBINATION PRINTINGS

Sometimes two or even three printing methods are combined in producing stamps. In these cases, such as Austria Scott 933 or Canada 1735 (described in the preceding paragraph), the multiple-printing technique can be determined by studying the individual characteristics of each printing type. A few stamps, such as Singapore Scott 684-684A, combine as many as three of the four major printing types (lithography, engraving and typography). When this is done it often indicates the incorporation of security devices against counterfeiting.

## INK COLORS

Inks or colored papers used in stamp printing often are of mineral origin, although there are numerous examples of organic-based pigments. As a general rule, organic-based pigments are far more subject to varieties and change than those of mineral-based origin.

The appearance of any given color on a stamp may be affected by many aspects, including printing variations, light, color of paper, aging and chemical alterations.

Numerous printing variations may be observed. Heavier pressure or inking will cause a more intense color, while slight interruptions in the ink feed or lighter impressions will cause a lighter appearance. Stamps printed in the same color by water-based and solvent-based inks can differ significantly in appearance. This affects several stamps in the U.S. Prominent Americans series. Hand-mixed ink formulas (primarily from the 19th century) produced under different conditions (humidity and temperature) account for notable color variations in early printings of the same stamp (see U.S. Scott 248-250, 279B, for example). Different sources of pigment can also result in significant differences in color.

Light exposure and aging are closely related in the way they affect stamp color. Both eventually break down the ink and fade colors, so that a carefully kept stamp may differ significantly in color from an identical copy that has been exposed to light. If stamps are exposed to light either intentionally or accidentally, their colors can be faded or completely changed in some cases.

Papers of different quality and consistency used for the same stamp printing may affect color appearance. Most pelure papers, for example, show a richer color when compared with wove or laid papers. See Russia Scott 181a, for an example of this effect.

The very nature of the printing processes can cause a variety of differences in shades or hues of the same stamp. Some of these shades are scarcer than others, and are of particular interest to the advanced collector.

# Luminescence

All forms of tagged stamps fall under the general category of luminescence. Within this broad category is fluorescence, dealing with forms of tagging visible under longwave ultraviolet light, and phosphorescence, which deals with tagging visible only under shortwave light. Phosphorescence leaves an afterglow and fluorescence does not. These treated stamps show up in a range of different colors when exposed to UV light. The differing wavelengths of the light activates the tagging material, making it glow in various colors that usually serve different mail processing purposes.

Intentional tagging is a post-World War II phenomenon, brought about by the increased literacy rate and rapidly growing mail volume. It was one of several answers to the problem of the need for more automated mail processes. Early tagged stamps served the purpose of triggering machines to separate different types of mail. A natural outgrowth was to also use the signal to trigger machines that faced all envelopes the same way and canceled them.

Tagged stamps come in many different forms. Some tagged stamps have luminescent shapes or images imprinted on them as a form of security device. Others have blocks (United States), stripes, frames (South Africa and Canada), overall coatings (United States), bars (Great Britain and Canada) and many other types. Some types of tagging are even mixed in with the pigmented printing ink (Australia Scott 366, Netherlands Scott 478 and U.S. Scott 1359 and 2443).

The means of applying taggant to stamps differs as much as the intended purposes for the stamps. The most common form of tagging is a coating applied to the surface of the printed stamp. Since the taggant ink is frequently invisible except under UV light, it does not interfere with the appearance of the stamp. Another common application is the use of phosphored papers. In this case the paper itself either has a coating of taggant applied before the stamp is printed, has taggant applied during the papermaking process (incorporating it into the fibers), or has the taggant mixed into the coating of the paper. The latter method, among others, is currently in use in the United States.

Many countries now use tagging in various forms to either expedite mail handling or to serve as a printing security device against counterfeiting. Following the introduction of tagged stamps for public use in 1959 by Great Britain, other countries have steadily joined the parade. Among those are Germany (1961); Canada and Denmark (1962); United States, Australia, France and Switzerland (1963); Belgium and Japan (1966); Sweden and Norway (1967); Italy (1968); and Russia (1969). Since then, many other countries have begun using forms of tagging, including Brazil, China, Czechoslovakia, Hong Kong, Guatemala, Indonesia, Israel, Lithuania, Luxembourg, Netherlands, Penrhyn Islands, Portugal, St. Vincent, Singapore, South Africa, Spain and Sweden to name a few.

In some cases, including United States, Canada, Great Britain and Switzerland, stamps were released both with and without tagging. Many of these were released during each country's experimental period. Tagged and untagged versions are listed for the aforementioned countries and are noted in some other countries' listings. For at least a few stamps, the experimentally tagged version is worth far more than its untagged counterpart, such as the 1963 experimental tagged version of France Scott 1024.

In some cases, luminescent varieties of stamps were inadvertently created. Several Russian stamps, for example, sport highly fluorescent ink that was not intended as a form of tagging. Older stamps, such as early U.S. postage dues, can be positively identified by the use of UV light, since the organic ink used has become slightly fluorescent over time. Other stamps, such as Austria Scott 70a-82a (varnish bars) and Obock Scott 46-64 (printed quadrille lines), have become fluorescent over time.

Various fluorescent substances have been added to paper to make it appear brighter. These optical brightners, as they are known, greatly affect the appearance of the stamp under UV light. The brightest of these is known as Hi-Brite paper. These paper varieties are beyond the scope of the Scott Catalogue.

Shortwave UV light also is used extensively in expertizing, since each form of paper has its own fluorescent characteristics that are impossible to perfectly match. It is therefore a simple matter to detect filled thins, added perforation teeth and other alterations that involve the addition of paper. UV light also is used to examine stamps that have had cancels chemically removed and for other purposes as well.

## Gum

The Illustrated Gum Chart in the first part of this introduction shows and defines various types of gum condition. Because gum condition has an important impact on the value of unused stamps, we recommend studying this chart and the accompanying text carefully.

The gum on the back of a stamp may be shiny, dull, smooth, rough, dark, white, colored or tinted. Most stamp gumming adhesives use gum arabic or dextrine as a base. Certain polymers such as polyvinyl alcohol (PVA) have been used extensively since World War II.

The *Scott Standard Postage Stamp Catalogue* does not list items by types of gum. The *Scott Specialized Catalogue of United States Stamps and Covers* does differentiate among some types of gum for certain issues.

Reprints of stamps may have gum differing from the original issues. In addition, some countries have used different gum formulas for different seasons. These adhesives have different properties that may become more apparent over time.

Many stamps have been issued without gum, and the catalogue will note this fact. See, for example, United States Scott 40-47. Sometimes, gum may have been removed to preserve the stamp. Germany Scott B68, for example, has a highly acidic gum that eventually destroys the stamps. This item is valued in the catalogue with gum removed.

## Reprints and reissues

These are impressions of stamps (usually obsolete) made from the original plates or stones. If they are valid for postage and reproduce obsolete issues (such as U.S. Scott 102-111), the stamps are reissues. If they are from current issues, they are designated as *second, third,*

etc., *printing*. If designated for a particular purpose, they are called *special printings*.

When special printings are not valid for postage, but are made from original dies and plates by authorized persons, they are *official reprints*. *Private reprints* are made from the original plates and dies by private hands. An example of a private reprint is that of the 1871-1932 reprints made from the original die of the 1845 New Haven, Conn., postmaster's provisional. *Official reproductions* or imitations are made from new dies and plates by government authorization. Scott will list those reissues that are valid for postage if they differ significantly from the original printing.

The U.S. government made special printings of its first postage stamps in 1875. Produced were official imitations of the first two stamps (listed as Scott 3-4), reprints of the demonetized pre-1861 issues (Scott 40-47) and reissues of the 1861 stamps, the 1869 stamps and the then-current 1875 denominations. Even though the official imitations and the reprints were not valid for postage, Scott lists all of these U.S. special printings.

Most reprints or reissues differ slightly from the original stamp in some characteristic, such as gum, paper, perforation, color or watermark. Sometimes the details are followed so meticulously that only a student of that specific stamp is able to distinguish the reprint or reissue from the original.

## Remainders and canceled to order

Some countries sell their stock of old stamps when a new issue replaces them. To avoid postal use, the remainders usually are canceled with a punch hole, a heavy line or bar, or a more-or-less regular-looking cancellation. The most famous merchant of remainders was Nicholas F. Seebeck. In the 1880s and 1890s, he arranged printing contracts between the Hamilton Bank Note Co., of which he was a director, and several Central and South American countries. The contracts provided that the plates and all remainders of the yearly issues became the property of Hamilton. Seebeck saw to it that ample stock remained. The "Seebecks," both remainders and reprints, were standard packet fillers for decades.

Some countries also issue stamps *canceled-to-order (CTO)*, either in sheets with original gum or stuck onto pieces of paper or envelopes and canceled. Such CTO items generally are worth less than postally used stamps. In cases where the CTO material is far more prevalent in the marketplace than postally used examples, the catalogue value relates to the CTO examples, with postally used examples noted as premium items. Most CTOs can be detected by the presence of gum. However, as the CTO practice goes back at least to 1885, the gum inevitably has been soaked off some stamps so they could pass as postally used. The normally applied postmarks usually differ slightly from standard postmarks, and specialists are able to tell the difference. When applied individually to envelopes by philatelically minded persons, CTO material is known as *favor canceled* and generally sells at large discounts.

## Cinderellas and facsimiles

*Cinderella* is a catch-all term used by stamp collectors to describe phantoms, fantasies, bogus items, municipal issues, exhibition seals, local revenues, transportation stamps, labels, poster stamps and many other types of items. Some cinderella collectors include in their collections local postage issues, telegraph stamps, essays and proofs, forgeries and counterfeits.

A *fantasy* is an adhesive created for a nonexistent stamp-issuing authority. Fantasy items range from imaginary countries (Occusi-Ambeno, Kingdom of Sedang, Principality of Trinidad or Torres Straits), to non-existent locals (Winans City Post), or nonexistent transportation lines (McRobish & Co.'s Acapulco-San Francisco Line).

On the other hand, if the entity exists and could have issued stamps (but did not) or was known to have issued other stamps, the items are considered bogus stamps. These would include the Mormon postage stamps of Utah, S. Allan Taylor's Guatemala and Paraguay inventions, the propaganda issues for the South Moluccas and the adhesives of the Page & Keyes local post of Boston.

*Phantoms* is another term for both fantasy and bogus issues.

*Facsimiles* are copies or imitations made to represent original stamps, but which do not pretend to be originals. A catalogue illustration is such a facsimile. Illustrations from the Moens catalogue of the last century were occasionally colored and passed off as stamps. Since the beginning of stamp collecting, facsimiles have been made for collectors as space fillers or for reference. They often carry the word "facsimile," "falsch" (German), "sanko" or "mozo" (Japanese), or "faux" (French) overprinted on the face or stamped on the back. Unfortunately, over the years a number of these items have had fake cancels applied over the facsimile notation and have been passed off as genuine.

# Forgeries and counterfeits

Forgeries and counterfeits have been with philately virtually from the beginning of stamp production. Over time, the terminology for the two has been used interchangeably. Although both forgeries and counterfeits are reproductions of stamps, the purposes behind their creation differ considerably.

Among specialists there is an increasing movement to more specifically define such items. Although there is no universally accepted terminology, we feel the following definitions most closely mirror the items and their purposes as they are currently defined.

Forgeries (also often referred to as Counterfeits) are reproductions of genuine stamps that have been created to defraud collectors. Such spurious items first appeared on the market around 1860, and most old-time collections contain one or more. Many are crude and easily spotted, but some can deceive experts.

An important supplier of these early philatelic forgeries was the Hamburg printer Gebruder Spiro. Many others with reputations in this craft included S. Allan Taylor, George Hussey, James Chute, George Forune, Benjamin & Sarpy, Julius Goldner, E. Oneglia and L.H. Mercier. Among the noted 20th-century forgers were Francois Fournier, Jean Sperati and the prolific Raoul DeThuin.

Forgeries may be complete replications, or they may be genuine stamps altered to resemble a scarcer (and more valuable) type. Most forgeries, particularly those of rare stamps, are worth only a small fraction of the value of a genuine example, but a few types, created by some of the most notable forgers, such as Sperati, can be worth as much or more than the genuine. Fraudulently produced copies are known of most classic rarities and many medium-priced stamps.

In addition to rare stamps, large numbers of common 19th- and early 20th-century stamps were forged to supply stamps to the early packet trade. Many can still be easily found. Few new philatelic forgeries have appeared in recent decades. Successful imitation of well-engraved work is virtually impossible. It has proven far easier to produce a fake by altering a genuine stamp than to duplicate a stamp completely.

Counterfeit (also often referred to as Postal Counterfeit or Postal Forgery) is the term generally applied to reproductions of stamps that have been created to defraud the government of revenue. Such items usually are created at the time a stamp is current and, in some cases, are hard to detect. Because most counterfeits are seized when the perpetrator is captured, postal counterfeits, particularly used on cover, are usually worth much more than a genuine example to specialists. The first postal counterfeit was of Spain's 4-cuarto carmine of 1854 (the real one is Scott 25). Apparently, the counterfeiters were not satisfied with their first version, which is now very scarce, and they soon created an engraved counterfeit, which is common. Postal counterfeits quickly followed in Austria, Naples, Sardinia and the Roman States. They have since been created in many other countries as well, including the United States.

An infamous counterfeit to defraud the government is the 1-shilling Great Britain "Stock Exchange" forgery of 1872, used on telegraph forms at the exchange that year. The stamp escaped detection until a stamp dealer noticed it in 1898.

# Fakes

*Fakes* are genuine stamps altered in some way to make them more desirable. One student of this part of stamp collecting has estimated that by the 1950s more than 30,000 varieties of fakes were known. That number has grown greatly since then. The widespread existence of fakes makes it important for stamp collectors to study their philatelic holdings and use relevant literature. Likewise, collectors should buy from reputable dealers who guarantee their stamps and make full and prompt refunds should a purchased item be declared faked or altered by some mutually agreed-upon authority. Because fakes always have some genuine characteristics, it is not always possible to obtain unanimous agreement among experts regarding specific items. These students may change their opinions as philatelic knowledge increases. More than 80 percent of all fakes on the philatelic market today are regummed, reperforated (or perforated for the first time), or bear forged overprints, surcharges or cancellations.

Stamps can be chemically treated to alter or eliminate colors. For example, a pale rose stamp can be re-colored to resemble a blue shade of high market value. In other cases, treated stamps can be made to resemble missing color varieties. Designs may be changed by painting, or a stroke or a dot added or bleached out to turn an ordinary variety into a seemingly scarcer stamp. Part of a stamp can be bleached and reprinted in a different version, achieving an inverted center or frame. Margins can be added or repairs done so deceptively that the stamps move from the "repaired" into the "fake" category.

Fakers have not left the backs of the stamps untouched either. They may create false watermarks, add fake grills or press out genuine grills.

A thin India paper proof may be glued onto a thicker backing to create the appearance an issued stamp, or a proof printed on cardboard may be shaved down and perforated to resemble a stamp. Silk threads are impressed into paper and stamps have been split so that a rare paper variety is added to an otherwise inexpensive stamp. The most common treatment to the back of a stamp, however, is regumming.

Some in the business of faking stamps have openly advertised fool-proof application of "original gum" to stamps that lack it, although most publications now ban such ads from their pages. It is believed that very few early stamps have survived without being hinged. The large number of never-hinged examples of such earlier material offered for sale thus suggests the widespread extent of regumming activity. Regumming also may be used to hide repairs or thin spots. Dipping the stamp into watermark fluid, or examining it under longwave ultraviolet light often will reveal these flaws.

Fakers also tamper with separations. Ingenious ways to add margins are known. Perforated wide-margin stamps may be falsely represented as imperforate when trimmed. Reperforating is commonly done to create scarce coil or perforation varieties, and to eliminate the naturally occurring straight-edge stamps found in sheet margin positions of many earlier issues. Custom has made straight-edged stamps less desirable. Fakers have obliged by perforating straight-edged stamps so that many are now uncommon, if not rare.

Another fertile field for the faker is that of overprints, surcharges and cancellations. The forging of rare surcharges or overprints began in the 1880s or 1890s. These forgeries are sometimes difficult to detect, but experts have identified almost all. Occasionally, overprints or cancellations are removed to create non-overprinted stamps or seemingly unused items. This is most commonly done by removing a manuscript cancel to make a stamp resemble an unused example. "SPECIMEN" overprints may be removed by scraping and repainting to create non-overprinted varieties. Fakers use inexpensive revenues or pen-canceled stamps to generate unused stamps for further faking by adding other markings. The quartz lamp or UV lamp and a high-powered magnifying glass help to easily detect removed cancellations.

The bigger problem, however, is the addition of overprints, surcharges or cancellations — many with such precision that they are very difficult to ascertain. Plating of the stamps or the overprint can be an important method of detection.

Fake postmarks may range from many spurious fancy cancellations to a host of markings applied to transatlantic covers, to adding normally appearing postmarks to definitives of some countries with stamps that are valued far higher used than unused. With the increased popularity of cover collecting, and the widespread interest in postal history, a fertile new field for fakers has come about. Some have tried to create entire covers. Others specialize in adding stamps, tied by fake cancellations, to genuine stampless covers, or replacing less expensive or damaged stamps with more valuable ones. Detailed study of postal rates in effect at the time a cover in question was mailed, including the analysis of each handstamp used during the period, ink analysis and similar techniques, usually will unmask the fraud.

# Restoration and repairs

Scott bases its catalogue values on stamps that are free of defects and otherwise meet the standards set forth earlier in this introduction. Most stamp collectors desire to have the finest copy of an item possible. Even within given grading categories there are variances. This leads to a controversial practice that is not defined in any universal manner: stamp *restoration*.

There are broad differences of opinion about what is permissible when it comes to restoration. Carefully applying a soft eraser to a stamp or cover to remove light soiling is one form of restoration, as is washing a stamp in mild soap and water to clean it. These are fairly accepted forms of restoration. More severe forms of restoration include pressing out creases or removing stains caused by tape. To what degree each of these is acceptable is dependent upon the individual situation. Further along the spectrum is the freshening of a stamp's color by removing oxide build-up or the effects of wax paper left next to stamps shipped to the tropics.

At some point in this spectrum the concept of *repair* replaces that of restoration. Repairs include filling thin spots, mending tears by reweaving or adding a missing perforation tooth. Regumming stamps may have been acceptable as a restoration or repair technique many decades ago, but today it is considered a form of fakery.

Restored stamps may or may not sell at a discount, and it is possible that the value of individual restored items may be enhanced over that of their pre-restoration state. Specific situations dictate the resultant value of such an item. Repaired stamps sell at substantial discounts from the value of sound stamps.

# Terminology

**Booklets** — Many countries have issued stamps in small booklets for the convenience of users. This idea continues to become increasingly popular in many countries. Booklets have been issued in many sizes and forms, often with advertising on the covers, the panes of stamps or on the interleaving.

The panes used in booklets may be printed from special plates or made from regular sheets. All panes from booklets issued by the United States and many from those of other countries contain stamps that are straight edged on the sides, but perforated between. Others are distinguished by orientation of watermark or other identifying features. Any stamp-like unit in the pane, either printed or blank, that is not a postage stamp, is considered to be a *label* in the catalogue listings.

Scott lists and values booklet panes. Modern complete booklets also are listed and valued. Individual booklet panes are listed only when they are not fashioned from existing sheet stamps and, therefore, are identifiable from their sheet stamp counterparts.

Panes usually do not have a used value assigned to them because there is little market activity for used booklet panes, even though many exist used and there is some demand for them.

**Cancellations** — The marks or obliterations put on stamps by postal authorities to show that they have performed service and to prevent their reuse are known as cancellations. If the marking is made with a pen, it is considered a "pen cancel." When the location of the post office appears in the marking, it is a "town cancellation." A "postmark" is technically any postal marking, but in practice the term generally is applied to a town cancellation with a date. When calling attention to a cause or celebration, the marking is known as a "slogan cancellation." Many other types and styles of cancellations exist, such as duplex, numerals, targets, fancy and others. See also "precancels," below.

**Coil Stamps** — These are stamps that are issued in rolls for use in dispensers, affixing and vending machines. Those coils of the United States, Canada, Sweden and some other countries are perforated horizontally or vertically only, with the outer edges imperforate. Coil stamps of some countries, such as Great Britain and Germany, are perforated on all four sides and may in some cases be distinguished from their sheet stamp counterparts by watermarks, counting numbers on the reverse or other means.

**Covers** — Entire envelopes, with or without adhesive postage stamps, that have passed through the mail and bear postal or other markings of philatelic interest are known as covers. Before the introduction of envelopes in about 1840, people folded letters and wrote the address on the outside. Some people covered their letters with an extra sheet of paper on the outside for the address, producing the term "cover." Used airletter sheets, stamped envelopes and other items of postal stationery also are considered covers.

**Errors** — Stamps that have some major, consistent, unintentional deviation from the normal are considered errors. Errors include, but are not limited to, missing or wrong colors, wrong paper, wrong watermarks, inverted centers or frames on multicolor printing, inverted or missing surcharges or overprints, double impressions, missing perforations, unintentionally omitted tagging and others. Factually wrong or misspelled information, if it appears on all examples of a stamp, are not considered errors in the true sense of the word. They are errors of design. Inconsistent or randomly appearing items, such as misperfs or color shifts, are classified as freaks.

**Color-Omitted Errors** — This term refers to stamps where a missing color is caused by the complete failure of the printing plate to deliver ink to the stamp paper or any other paper. Generally, this is caused by the printing plate not being engaged on the press or the ink station running dry of ink during printing.

**Color-Missing Errors** — This term refers to stamps where a color or colors were printed somewhere but do not appear on the finished stamp. There are four different classes of color-missing errors, and the catalog indicates with a two-letter code appended to each such listing what caused the color to be missing. These codes are used only for the United States' color-missing error listings.

**FO** = A *foldover* of the stamp sheet during printing may block ink from appearing on the face of a stamp. Instead, the color will appear on the back of the foldover (where it might fall on the back of the selvage or perhaps a bit on the back of the stamp or on the back of another stamp. FO also will be used in the case of foldunders, where the paper may fold underneath the other stamp paper and the color will print on the platen.

**EP** = When the extraneous paper is removed, an unprinted area of stamp paper remains and may show a color or colors to be totally missing on the finished stamp.

**CM** = A misregistration of the printing plates during printing will result in a *color misregistration*, and such a misregistraion may result in a color not appearing on the finished stamp.

**PS** = A *perforation shift* after printing may remove a color from the finished stamp. Normally, this will occur on a row of stamps at the edge of the stamp pane.

**Measurements** – When measurements are given in the Scott catalogues for stamp size, grill size or any other reason, the first measurement given is always for the top and bottom dimension, while the second measurement will be for the sides (just as perforation gauges are measured). Thus, a stamp size of 15mm x 21mm will indicate a vertically oriented stamp 15mm wide at top and bottom, and 21mm tall at the sides. The same principle holds for measuring or counting items such as U.S. grills. A grill count of 22x18 points (B grill) indicates that there are 22 grill points across by 18 grill points down.

**Overprints and Surcharges** — Overprinting involves applying wording or design elements over an already existing stamp. Overprints can be used to alter the place of use (such as "Canal Zone" on U.S. stamps), to adapt them for a special purpose ("Porto" on Denmark's 1913-20 regular issues for use as postage due stamps, Scott J1-J7) or to commemorate a special occasion (United States Scott 647-648).

A *surcharge* is a form of overprint that changes or restates the face value of a stamp or piece of postal stationery.

Surcharges and overprints may be handstamped, typeset or, occasionally, lithographed or engraved. A few hand-written overprints and surcharges are known.

**Personalized Stamps** — In 1999, Australia issued stamps with se-tenant labels that could be personalized with pictures of the customer's choice. Other countries quickly followed suit, with some offering to print the selected picture on the stamp itself within a frame that was used exclusively for personalized issues. As the picture used on these stamps or labels vary, listings for such stamps are for any picture within the common frame (or any picture on a se-tenant label), be it a "generic" image or one produced especially for a customer, almost invariably at a premium price.

**Precancels** — Stamps that are canceled before they are placed in the mail are known as precancels. Precanceling usually is done to expedite the handling of large mailings and generally allow the affected mail pieces to skip certain phases of mail handling.

In the United States, precancellations generally identified the point of origin; that is, the city and state. This information appeared across the face of the stamp, usually centered between parallel lines. More recently, bureau precancels retained the parallel lines, but the city and state designations were dropped. Recent coils have a service inscription that is present on the original printing plate. These show the mail service paid for by the stamp. Since these stamps are not intended to receive further cancellations when used as intended, they are considered precancels. Such items often do not have parallel lines as part of the precancellation.

In France, the abbreviation *Affranchts* in a semicircle together with the word *Postes* is the general form of precancel in use. Belgian precancellations usually appear in a box in which the name of the city appears. Netherlands precancels have the name of the city enclosed between concentric circles, sometimes called a "lifesaver." Precancellations of other countries usually follow these patterns, but may be any arrangement of bars, boxes and city names.

Precancels are listed in the Scott catalogues only if the precancel changes the denomination (Belgium Scott 477-478); if the precanceled stamp is different from the non-precanceled version (such as untagged U.S. precancels); or if the stamp exists only precanceled (France Scott 1096-1099, U.S. Scott 2265).

**Proofs and Essays** — Proofs are impressions taken from an approved die, plate or stone in which the design and color are the same as the stamp issued to the public. Trial color proofs are impressions taken from approved dies, plates or stones in colors that vary from the final version. An essay is the impression of a design that differs in some way from the issued stamp. "Progressive die proofs" generally are considered to be essays.

**Provisionals** — These are stamps that are issued on short notice and intended for temporary use pending the arrival of regular issues. They usually are issued to meet such contingencies as changes in government or currency, shortage of necessary postage values or military occupation.

During the 1840s, postmasters in certain American cities issued stamps that were valid only at specific post offices. In 1861, postmasters of the Confederate States also issued stamps with limited validity. Both of these examples are known as "postmaster's provisionals."

**Se-tenant** — This term refers to an unsevered pair, strip or block of stamps that differ in design, denomination or overprint.

Unless the se-tenant item has a continuous design (see U.S. Scott 1451a, 1694a) the stamps do not have to be in the same order as shown in the catalogue (see U.S. Scott 2158a).

**Specimens** — The Universal Postal Union required member nations to send samples of all stamps they released into service to the International Bureau in Switzerland. Member nations of the UPU received these specimens as samples of what stamps were valid for postage. Many are overprinted, handstamped or initial-perforated "Specimen," "Canceled" or "Muestra." Some are marked with bars across the denominations (China-Taiwan), punched holes (Czechoslovakia) or back inscriptions (Mongolia).

Stamps distributed to government officials or for publicity purposes, and stamps submitted by private security printers for official approval, also may receive such defacements.

The previously described defacement markings prevent postal use, and all such items generally are known as "specimens."

**Tete-Beche** — This term describes a pair of stamps in which one is upside down in relation to the other. Some of these are the result of intentional sheet arrangements, such as Morocco Scott B10-B11. Others occurred when one or more electrotypes accidentally were placed upside down on the plate, such as Colombia Scott 57a. Separation of the tete-beche stamps, of course, destroys the tete beche variety.

# Pronunciation Symbols

ə .... banana, collide, abut

'ə, ˌə .... humdrum, abut

ə .... immediately preceding \l\, \n\, \m\, \ŋ\, as in battle, mitten, eaten, and sometimes open \'ō-pᵊm\, lock and key \-ᵊŋ-\; immediately following \l\, \m\, \r\, as often in French table, prisme, titre

ər .... further, merger, bird

'ər-  
'ə-r  } .... as in two different pronunciations of hurry \'hər-ē, 'hə-rē\

a .... mat, map, mad, gag, snap, patch

ā .... day, fade, date, aorta, drape, cape

ä .... bother, cot, and, with most American speakers, father, cart

à .... father as pronunced by speakers who do not rhyme it with bother; French patte

aù .... now, loud, out

b .... baby, rib

ch .... chin, nature \'nā-chər\

d .... did, adder

e .... bet, bed, peck

'ē, ˌē .... beat, nosebleed, evenly, easy

ē .... easy, mealy

f .... fifty, cuff

g .... go, big, gift

h .... hat, ahead

hw .... whale as pronounced by those who do not have the same pronunciation for both whale and wail

i .... tip, banish, active

ī .... site, side, buy, tripe

j .... job, gem, edge, join, judge

k .... kin, cook, ache

k̲ .... German ich, Buch; one pronunciation of loch

l .... lily, pool

m .... murmur, dim, nymph

n .... no, own

ⁿ .... indicates that a preceding vowel or diphthong is pronounced with the nasal passages open, as in French un bon vin blanc \œⁿ-bōⁿ-vaⁿ-bläⁿ\

ŋ .... sing \'siŋ\, singer \'siŋ-ər\, finger \'fiŋ-gər\, ink \'iŋk\

ō .... bone, know, beau

ȯ .... saw, all, gnaw, caught

œ .... French boeuf, German Hölle

œ̄ .... French feu, German Höhle

ȯi .... coin, destroy

p .... pepper, lip

r .... red, car, rarity

s .... source, less

sh .... as in shy, mission, machine, special (actually, this is a single sound, not two); with a hyphen between, two sounds as in grasshopper \'gras-ˌhä-pər\

t .... tie, attack, late, later, latter

th .... as in thin, ether (actually, this is a single sound, not two); with a hyphen between, two sounds as in knighthood \'nīt-ˌhùd\

t̲h̲ .... then, either, this (actually, this is a single sound, not two)

ü .... rule, youth, union \'yün-yən\, few \'fyü\

ù .... pull, wood, book, curable \'kyùr-ə-bəl\, fury \'fyùr-ē\

ue .... German füllen, hübsch

ūe .... French rue, German fühlen

v .... vivid, give

w .... we, away

y .... yard, young, cue \'kyü\, mute \'myüt\, union \'yün-yən\

ʸ .... indicates that during the articulation of the sound represented by the preceding character the front of the tongue has substantially the position it has for the articulation of the first sound of yard, as in French digne \dēnʸ\

z .... zone, raise

zh .... as in vision, azure \'a-zhər\ (actually, this is a single sound, not two); with a hyphen between, two sounds as in hogshead \'hȯgz-ˌhed, 'hägz-\

\ .... slant line used in pairs to mark the beginning and end of a transcription: \'pen\

' .... mark preceding a syllable with primary (strongest) stress: \'pen-mən-ˌship\

ˌ .... mark preceding a syllable with secondary (medium) stress: \'pen-mən-ˌship\

- .... mark of syllable division

( ) .... indicate that what is symbolized between is present in some utterances but not in others: factory \'fak-t(ə-)rē\

÷ .... indicates that many regard as unacceptable the pronunciation variant immediately following: cupola \'kyü-pə-lə, ÷-ˌlō\

The system of pronunciation is used by permission from Merriam-Webster's Collegiate® Dictionary, Tenth Edition ©1993 by Merriam-Webster Inc., publisher of the Merriam-Webster® dictionaries.

# Currency conversion

| Country | Dollar | Pound | S Franc | Yen | HK $ | Euro | Cdn $ | Aus $ |
|---|---|---|---|---|---|---|---|---|
| Australia | 1.4113 | 1.7415 | 1.5417 | 0.0109 | 0.1799 | 1.5390 | 1.0606 | — |
| Canada | 1.3307 | 1.6421 | 1.4537 | 0.0103 | 0.1697 | 1.4511 | — | 0.9429 |
| European Union | 0.9170 | 1.1316 | 1.0017 | 0.0071 | 0.1169 | — | 0.6891 | 0.6498 |
| Hong Kong | 7.8428 | 9.6780 | 8.5676 | 0.0606 | — | 8.5527 | 5.8937 | 5.5571 |
| Japan | 129.35 | 159.62 | 141.30 | — | 16.493 | 141.06 | 97.204 | 91.653 |
| Switzerland | 0.9154 | 1.1296 | — | 0.0071 | 0.1167 | 0.9983 | 0.6879 | 0.6486 |
| United Kingdom | 0.8104 | — | 0.8853 | 0.0063 | 0.1033 | 0.8837 | 0.6090 | 0.5742 |
| United States | — | 1.2340 | 1.0924 | 0.0077 | 0.1275 | 1.0905 | 0.7515 | 0.7086 |

| Country | Currency | U.S. $ Equiv. |
|---|---|---|
| Gabon | Community of French Africa (CFA) franc | .0017 |
| Gambia | dalasy | .0162 |
| Georgia | lari | .3788 |
| Germany | euro | 1.0905 |
| Ghana | cedi | .0820 |
| Gibraltar | pound | 1.2340 |
| Great Britain | pound | 1.2340 |
| Alderney | pound | 1.2340 |
| Guernsey | pound | 1.2340 |
| Jersey | pound | 1.2340 |
| Isle of Man | pound | 1.2340 |
| Greece | euro | 1.0905 |
| Mount Athos | euro | 1.0905 |
| Greenland | Danish krone | .1466 |
| Grenada | East Caribbean dollar | .3704 |
| Grenada Grenadines | East Caribbean dollar | .3704 |
| Guatemala | quetzal | .1274 |
| Guinea | franc | .0001 |
| Guinea-Bissau | CFA franc | .0017 |
| Guyana | dollar | .0048 |
| Haiti | gourde | .0067 |
| Honduras | lempira | .0406 |
| Hong Kong | dollar | .1275 |
| Hungary | forint | .0028 |
| Iceland | krona | .0071 |
| India | rupee | .0122 |
| Indonesia | rupiah | .0001 |
| Iran | rial | .0001 |
| Iraq | dinar | .0007 |
| Ireland | euro | 1.0905 |
| Israel | shekel | .2895 |
| Italy | euro | 1.0905 |
| Ivory Coast | CFA franc | .0017 |

*Source: xe.com, Feb. 1, 2023. Figures reflect values as of Feb. 1, 2023.*

# British Commonwealth of Nations

## Dominions, Colonies, Territories, Offices and Independent Members

Comprising stamps of the British Commonwealth and associated nations.

A strict observance of technicalities would bar some or all of the stamps listed under Burma, Ireland, Kuwait, Nepal, New Republic, Orange Free State, Samoa, South Africa, South-West Africa, Stellaland, Sudan, Swaziland, the two Transvaal Republics and others but these are included for the convenience of collectors.

## 1. Great Britain

Great Britain: Including England, Scotland, Wales and Northern Ireland.

## 2. The Dominions, Present and Past

### AUSTRALIA

The Commonwealth of Australia was proclaimed on Jan. 1, 1901. It consists of six former colonies as follows:

| | |
|---|---|
| New South Wales | Victoria |
| Queensland | Tasmania |
| South Australia | Western Australia |

The following islands and territories are, or have been, administered by Australia: Australian Antarctic Territory, Christmas Island, Cocos (Keeling) Islands, Nauru, New Guinea, Norfolk Island, Papua.

### CANADA

The Dominion of Canada was created by the British North America Act in 1867. The following provinces were former separate colonies and issued postage stamps:

| | |
|---|---|
| British Columbia and Vancouver Island | Newfoundland |
| New Brunswick | Nova Scotia |
| | Prince Edward Island |

### FIJI

The colony of Fiji became an independent nation with dominion status on Oct. 10, 1970.

### GHANA

This state came into existence March 6, 1957, with dominion status. It consists of the former colony of the Gold Coast and the Trusteeship Territory of Togoland. Ghana became a republic July 1, 1960.

### INDIA

The Republic of India was inaugurated on Jan. 26, 1950. It succeeded the Dominion of India which was proclaimed Aug. 15, 1947, when the former Empire of India was divided into Pakistan and the Union of India. The Republic is composed of about 40 predominantly Hindu states of three classes: governor's provinces, chief commissioner's provinces and princely states. India also has various territories, such as the Andaman and Nicobar Islands.

The old Empire of India was a federation of British India and the native states. The more important princely states were autonomous. Of the more than 700 Indian states, these 43 are familiar names to philatelists because of their postage stamps.

#### CONVENTION STATES

| | |
|---|---|
| Chamba | Jhind |
| Faridkot | Nabha |
| Gwalior | Patiala |

### FEUDATORY STATES

| | |
|---|---|
| Alwar | Jammu and Kashmir |
| Bahawalpur | Jasdan |
| Bamra | Jhalawar |
| Barwani | Jhind (1875-76) |
| Bhopal | Kashmir |
| Bhor | Kishangarh |
| Bijawar | Kotah |
| Bundi | Las Bela |
| Bussahir | Morvi |
| Charkhari | Nandgaon |
| Cochin | Nowanuggur |
| Dhar | Orchha |
| Dungarpur | Poonch |
| Duttia | Rajasthan |
| Faridkot (1879-85) | Rajpeepla |
| Hyderabad | Sirmur |
| Idar | Soruth |
| Indore | Tonk |
| Jaipur | Travancore |
| Jammu | Wadhwan |

### NEW ZEALAND

Became a dominion on Sept. 26, 1907. The following islands and territories are, or have been, administered by New Zealand:

| | |
|---|---|
| Aitutaki | Ross Dependency |
| Cook Islands (Rarotonga) | Samoa (Western Samoa) |
| Niue | Tokelau Islands |
| Penrhyn | |

### PAKISTAN

The Republic of Pakistan was proclaimed March 23, 1956. It succeeded the Dominion which was proclaimed Aug. 15, 1947. It is made up of all or part of several Moslem provinces and various districts of the former Empire of India, including Bahawalpur and Las Bela. Pakistan withdrew from the Commonwealth in 1972.

### SOUTH AFRICA

Under the terms of the South African Act (1909) the self-governing colonies of Cape of Good Hope, Natal, Orange River Colony and Transvaal united on May 31, 1910, to form the Union of South Africa. It became an independent republic May 3, 1961.

Under the terms of the Treaty of Versailles, South-West Africa, formerly German South-West Africa, was mandated to the Union of South Africa.

### SRI LANKA (CEYLON)

The Dominion of Ceylon was proclaimed Feb. 4, 1948. The island had been a Crown Colony from 1802 until then. On May 22, 1972, Ceylon became the Republic of Sri Lanka.

## 3. Colonies, Past and Present; Controlled Territory and Independent Members of the Commonwealth

| | |
|---|---|
| Abu Dhabi | Barbuda |
| Aden | Basutoland |
| Aitutaki | Batum |
| Alderney | Bechuanaland |
| Anguilla | Bechuanaland Prot. |
| Antigua | Belize |
| Ascension | Bermuda |
| Australia | Botswana |
| Bahamas | British Antarctic Territory |
| Bahrain | British Central Africa |
| Bangladesh | British Columbia and |
| Barbados | Vancouver Island |

British East Africa
British Guiana
British Honduras
British Indian Ocean Territory
British New Guinea
British Solomon Islands
British Somaliland
Brunei
Burma
Bushire
Cameroons
Canada
Cape of Good Hope
Cayman Islands
Christmas Island
Cocos (Keeling) Islands
Cook Islands
Crete,
  British Administration
Cyprus
Dominica
East Africa & Uganda
  Protectorates
Egypt
Falkland Islands
Fiji
Gambia
German East Africa
Ghana
Gibraltar
Gilbert Islands
Gilbert & Ellice Islands
Gold Coast
Grenada
Griqualand West
Guernsey
Guyana
Heligoland
Hong Kong
Indian Native States
  (see India)
Ionian Islands
Jamaica
Jersey

Jordan
Kenya
Kenya, Uganda & Tanzania
Kiribati
Kuwait
Labuan
Lagos
Leeward Islands
Lesotho
Madagascar
Malawi
Malaya
  Federated Malay States
  Johore
  Kedah
  Kelantan
  Malacca
  Negri Sembilan
  Pahang
  Penang
  Perak
  Perlis
  Selangor
  Singapore
  Sungei Ujong
  Trengganu
Malaysia
Maldive Islands
Malta
Man, Isle of
Mauritius
Mesopotamia
Montserrat
Mozambique
Muscat
Namibia
Natal
Nauru
Nevis
New Britain
New Brunswick
Newfoundland
New Guinea
New Hebrides

New Republic
New South Wales
New Zealand
Niger Coast Protectorate
Nigeria
Niue
Norfolk Island
North Borneo
Northern Nigeria
Northern Rhodesia
North West Pacific Islands
Nova Scotia
Nyasaland Protectorate
Oman
Orange River Colony
Pakistan
Palestine
Papua New Guinea
Penrhyn Island
Pitcairn Islands
Prince Edward Island
Qatar
Queensland
Rhodesia
Rhodesia & Nyasaland
Ross Dependency
Rwanda
Sabah
St. Christopher
St. Helena
St. Kitts
St. Kitts-Nevis-Anguilla
St. Lucia
St. Vincent
Samoa
Sarawak
Seychelles
Sierra Leone
Singapore
Solomon Islands
Somaliland Protectorate
South Africa
South Arabia
South Australia

South Georgia
Southern Nigeria
Southern Rhodesia
South-West Africa
Sri Lanka
Stellaland
Straits Settlements
Sudan
Swaziland
Tanganyika
Tanzania
Tasmania
Tobago
Togo
Tokelau Islands
Tonga
Transvaal
Trinidad
Trinidad and Tobago
Tristan da Cunha
Trucial States
Turks and Caicos
Turks Islands
Tuvalu
Uganda
United Arab Emirates
Vanuatu
Victoria
Virgin Islands
Western Australia
Zambia
Zanzibar
Zimbabwe
Zululand

**POST OFFICES IN
FOREIGN COUNTRIES**
Africa
  East Africa Forces
  Middle East Forces
Bangkok
China
Morocco
Turkish Empire

# Make Collecting Easy with Scott Specialty Series Albums

## Scott Albums Feature:

• High quality chemically neutral paper printed on one side

• All spaces identified by Scott numbers with either illustrations or descriptions.

• All pages have matching borders

• Pages contain general postage issues, as well as complete back-of-the-book materials

• Albums supplemented annually

**For a complete list of Scott Specialty Series Pages available, visit us at
www.AmosAdvantage.com or call 800-572-6885. We would be glad to help!**

# Colonies, former colonies, offices, territories controlled by parent states

## Belgium
Belgian Congo
Ruanda-Urundi

## Denmark
Danish West Indies
Faroe Islands
Greenland
Iceland

## Finland
Aland Islands

## France

### COLONIES PAST AND PRESENT, CONTROLLED TERRITORIES
Afars & Issas, Territory of
Alaouites
Alexandretta
Algeria
Alsace & Lorraine
Anjouan
Annam & Tonkin
Benin
Cambodia (Khmer)
Cameroun
Castellorizo
Chad
Cilicia
Cochin China
Comoro Islands
Dahomey
Diego Suarez
Djibouti (Somali Coast)
Fezzan
French Congo
French Equatorial Africa
French Guiana
French Guinea
French India
French Morocco
French Polynesia (Oceania)
French Southern & Antarctic Territories
French Sudan
French West Africa
Gabon
Germany
Ghadames
Grand Comoro
Guadeloupe
Indo-China
Inini
Ivory Coast
Laos
Latakia
Lebanon
Madagascar
Martinique
Mauritania
Mayotte
Memel
Middle Congo
Moheli
New Caledonia
New Hebrides
Niger Territory

Nossi-Be
Obock
Reunion
Rouad, Ile
Ste.-Marie de Madagascar
St. Pierre & Miquelon
Senegal
Senegambia & Niger
Somali Coast
Syria
Tahiti
Togo
Tunisia
Ubangi-Shari
Upper Senegal & Niger
Upper Volta
Viet Nam
Wallis & Futuna Islands

### POST OFFICES IN FOREIGN COUNTRIES
China
Crete
Egypt
Turkish Empire
Zanzibar

## Germany

### EARLY STATES
Baden
Bavaria
Bergedorf
Bremen
Brunswick
Hamburg
Hanover
Lubeck
Mecklenburg-Schwerin
Mecklenburg-Strelitz
Oldenburg
Prussia
Saxony
Schleswig-Holstein
Wurttemberg

### FORMER COLONIES
Cameroun (Kamerun)
Caroline Islands
German East Africa
German New Guinea
German South-West Africa
Kiauchau
Mariana Islands
Marshall Islands
Samoa
Togo

## Italy

### EARLY STATES
Modena
Parma
Romagna
Roman States
Sardinia
Tuscany
Two Sicilies
  Naples
  Neapolitan Provinces
  Sicily

### FORMER COLONIES, CONTROLLED TERRITORIES, OCCUPATION AREAS
Aegean Islands
  Calimno (Calino)
  Caso
  Cos (Coo)
  Karki (Carchi)
  Leros (Lero)
  Lipso
  Nisiros (Nisiro)
  Patmos (Patmo)
  Piscopi
  Rodi (Rhodes)
  Scarpanto
  Simi
  Stampalia
Castellorizo
Corfu
Cyrenaica
Eritrea
Ethiopia (Abyssinia)
Fiume
Ionian Islands
  Cephalonia
  Ithaca
  Paxos
Italian East Africa
Libya
Oltre Giuba
Saseno
Somalia (Italian Somaliland)
Tripolitania

### POST OFFICES IN FOREIGN COUNTRIES
"ESTERO"*
Austria
China
  Peking
  Tientsin
Crete
Tripoli
Turkish Empire
  Constantinople
  Durazzo
  Janina
Jerusalem
Salonika
Scutari
Smyrna
Valona
*Stamps overprinted "ESTERO" were used in various parts of the world.

## Netherlands
Aruba
Caribbean Netherlands
Curacao
Netherlands Antilles (Curacao)
Netherlands Indies
Netherlands New Guinea
St. Martin
Surinam (Dutch Guiana)

## Portugal

### COLONIES PAST AND PRESENT, CONTROLLED TERRITORIES
Angola
Angra
Azores

Cape Verde
Funchal
Horta
Inhambane
Kionga
Lourenco Marques
Macao
Madeira
Mozambique
Mozambique Co.
Nyassa
Ponta Delgada
Portuguese Africa
Portuguese Congo
Portuguese Guinea
Portuguese India
Quelimane
St. Thomas & Prince Islands
Tete
Timor
Zambezia

## Russia

### ALLIED TERRITORIES AND REPUBLICS, OCCUPATION AREAS
Armenia
Aunus (Olonets)
Azerbaijan
Batum
Estonia
Far Eastern Republic
Georgia
Karelia
Latvia
Lithuania
North Ingermanland
Ostland
Russian Turkestan
Siberia
South Russia
Tannu Tuva
Transcaucasian Fed. Republics
Ukraine
Wenden (Livonia)
Western Ukraine

## Spain

### COLONIES PAST AND PRESENT, CONTROLLED TERRITORIES
Aguera, La
Cape Juby
Cuba
Elobey, Annobon & Corisco
Fernando Po
Ifni
Mariana Islands
Philippines
Puerto Rico
Rio de Oro
Rio Muni
Spanish Guinea
Spanish Morocco
Spanish Sahara
Spanish West Africa

### POST OFFICES IN FOREIGN COUNTRIES
Morocco
Tangier
Tetuan

# Dies of British colonial stamps

**DIE A:**

**1.** The lines in the groundwork vary in thickness and are not uniformly straight.

**2.** The seventh and eighth lines from the top, in the groundwork, converge where they meet the head.

**3.** There is a small dash in the upper part of the second jewel in the band of the crown.

**4.** The vertical color line in front of the throat stops at the sixth line of shading on the neck.

**DIE B:**

**1.** The lines in the groundwork are all thin and straight.

**2.** All the lines of the background are parallel.

**3.** There is no dash in the upper part of the second jewel in the band of the crown.

**4.** The vertical color line in front of the throat stops at the eighth line of shading on the neck.

**DIE I:**

**1.** The base of the crown is well below the level of the inner white line around the vignette.

**2.** The labels inscribed "POSTAGE" and "REVENUE" are cut square at the top.

**3.** There is a white "bud" on the outer side of the main stem of the curved ornaments in each lower corner.

**4.** The second (thick) line below the country name has the ends next to the crown cut diagonally.

|  |  |
|---|---|
| DIE Ia. | DIE Ib. |
| 1 as die II. | 1 and 3 as die II. |
| 2 and 3 as die I. | 2 as die I. |

**DIE II:**

**1.** The base of the crown is aligned with the underside of the white line around the vignette.

**2.** The labels curve inward at the top inner corners.

**3.** The "bud" has been removed from the outer curve of the ornaments in each corner.

**4.** The second line below the country name has the ends next to the crown cut vertically.

**Wmk. 1**
Crown and C C

**Wmk. 2**
Crown and C A

**Wmk. 3**
Multiple Crown
and C A

**Wmk. 4**
Multiple Crown
and Script C A

**Wmk. 4a**

**Wmk. 46**

**Wmk. 314**
St. Edward's Crown
and C A Multiple

**Wmk. 373**

**Wmk. 384**

**Wmk. 406**

# British Colonial and Crown Agents watermarks

Watermarks 1 to 4, 314, 373, 384 and 406, common to many British territories, are illustrated here to avoid duplication.

The letters "CC" of Wmk. 1 identify the paper as having been made for the use of the Crown Colonies, while the letters "CA" of the others stand for "Crown Agents." Both Wmks. 1 and 2 were used on stamps printed by De La Rue & Co.

Wmk. 3 was adopted in 1904; Wmk. 4 in 1921; Wmk. 46 in 1879; Wmk. 314 in 1957; Wmk. 373 in 1974; Wmk. 384 in 1985; Wmk 406 in 2008.

In Wmk. 4a, a non-matching crown of the general St. Edwards type (bulging on both sides at top) was substituted for one of the Wmk. 4 crowns which fell off the dandy roll. The non-matching crown occurs in 1950-52 printings in a horizontal row of crowns on certain regular stamps of Johore and Seychelles, and on various postage due stamps of Barbados, Basutoland, British Guiana, Gold Coast, Grenada, Northern Rhodesia, St. Lucia, Swaziland and Trinidad and Tobago. A variation of Wmk. 4a, with the non-matching crown in a horizontal row of crown-CA-crown, occurs on regular stamps of Bahamas, St. Kitts-Nevis and Singapore.

Wmk. 314 was intentionally used sideways, starting in 1966. When a stamp was issued with Wmk. 314 both upright and sideways, the sideways varieties usually are listed also — with minor numbers. In many of the later issues, Wmk. 314 is slightly visible.

Wmk. 373 is usually only faintly visible.

---

**VALUE THE WORLD**

## 2024 Scott Postage Stamp Catalogues

- Two-book volumes 1-6 improve user experience
- Thousands of value changes keep pace with market fluctuations
- Hundreds of new stamp listings
- Editorial enhancements throughout include added stamp images, expanded footnotes and much more

| Item# | Description | Retail | AA | Release Dates |
|---|---|---|---|---|
| C241 | 2024 Scott Volumes 1A & 1B (U.S., U.N. and Countries A-B) | $149.99 | **$114.99** | 4/1/23 |
| C242 | 2024 Scott Volumes 2A & 2B (Countries C-F) | $149.99 | **$114.99** | 5/1/23 |
| C243 | 2024 Scott Volumes 3A & 3B (Countries G-I) | $149.99 | **$114.99** | 6/1/23 |
| C244 | 2024 Scott Volumes 4A & 4B (Countries J-M) | $149.99 | **$114.99** | 7/1/23 |
| C245 | 2024 Scott Volumes 5A & 5B (Countries N-SAM) | $149.99 | **$114.99** | 8/1/23 |
| C246 | 2024 Scott Volumes 6A & 6B (Countries SAN-Z) | $149.99 | **$114.99** | 9/1/23 |
| C24SET | 2024 Scott Volume 1-6 Set | $846.64 | **$624.94** | |
| C24S | 2024 Scott U.S. Specialized | $139.99 | **$104.99** | 10/1/23 |
| C24C | 2024 Scott Classic Specialized | $179.99 | **$159.99** | 11/1/23 |

AmosAdvantage.com | 1-800-572-6885

*AA prices apply to paid subscribers of Amos Media titles, or orders placed online.
Prices, terms and product availability subect to change. Shipping and handling rates will apply.

# GABON

ga-'bō<sup>n</sup>

LOCATION — West coast of Africa, at the equator
GOVT. — Republic
AREA — 102,089 sq. mi.
POP. — 1,225,853 (1999 est.)
CAPITAL — Libreville

Gabon originally was under the control of French West Africa. In 1886, it was united with French Congo. In 1904, Gabon was granted a certain degree of colonial autonomy which prevailed until 1934, when it merged with French Equatorial Africa. Gabon Republic was proclaimed November 28, 1958.

100 Centimes = 1 Franc

Catalogue values for unused stamps in this country are for Never Hinged items, beginning with Scott 148 in the regular postage section, Scott B4 in the semi-postal section, Scott C1 in the air-post section, Scott CB1 in the air-post semi-postal section, Scott J34 in the postage due section, and Scott O1 in the officials section.

### Watermark

TOR C
CART
TOR C
CART

Wmk. 385

For detailed listings of overprint and surcharge varieties of Gabon Nos. 1-15, see the *Scott Classic Specialized Catalogue of Stamps and Covers.*

### Stamps of French Colonies of 1881-86 Handstamp Surcharged in Black

a       b

| 1886 | | Unwmk. | | Perf. 14x13½ |
|---|---|---|---|---|
| 1 | A9 (a) | 5c on 20c red, grn | 575.00 | 625.00 |
| 2 | A9 (b) | 10c on 20c red, grn | 550.00 | 575.00 |
| 3 | A9 (b) | 25c on 20c red, grn | 100.00 | 75.00 |
| e. | | 56-dot diamond grid around "GAB" | 6,750. | 2,100. |
| 4 | A9 (b) | 50c on 15c bl | 1,500. | 2,100. |
| 5 | A9 (b) | 75c on 15c bl | 1,900. | 2,300. |

Nos. 1-3 exist with double surcharge of numeral; No. 3 with "GAB" double or inverted, or with "25" double.
On Nos. 3 and 5 the surcharge slants down; on No. 4 it slants up. The number of dots varies.
Counterfeits of Nos. 1-15 exist.

### Handstamp Surcharged in Black — c

| 1888-89 | | | | |
|---|---|---|---|---|
| 6 | A9 | 15c on 10c blk, *lav* | 6,000. | 1,500. |
| 7 | A9 | 15c on 1fr brnz grn, *straw* | 2,400. | 1,200. |
| 8 | A9 | 25c on 5c grn, *grnsh* | 1,500. | 325.00 |
| a. | | Double surcharge | 4,000. | 4,000. |

| 9 | A9 | 25c on 10c blk, *lav* | 6,000. | 1,900. |
|---|---|---|---|---|
| 10 | A9 | 25c on 75c car, *rose* | 4,000. | 2,100. |

*Official reprints exist.*

### Postage Due Stamps of French Colonies Handstamp Surcharged in Black — d

| 1889 | | | Imperf. |
|---|---|---|---|---|
| 11 | D1 | 15c on 5c black | 325.00 | 275.00 |
| 12 | D1 | 15c on 30c black | 5,000. | 3,800. |
| 13 | D1 | 25c on 20c black | 150.00 | 120.00 |

Nos. 11 and 13 exist with "GABON," "TIMBRE" or "25" double; "TIMBRE" or "15" omitted, etc.

A8

| 1889 | | | Typeset |
|---|---|---|---|---|
| 14 | A8 | 15c blk, *rose* | 1,900. | 1,200. |
| 15 | A8 | 25c blk, *green* | 1,200. | 950. |

Ten varieties of each. Nos. 14-15 exist with "GAB" inverted, double or omitted, and with small "f" in "Francaise."

Navigation and Commerce — A9

### Name of Colony in Blue or Carmine

| 1904-07 | | Typo. | Perf. 14x13½ |
|---|---|---|---|---|
| 16 | A9 | 1c blk, *lil bl* | 1.40 | 1.40 |
| a. | | "GABON" double | 360.00 | 360.00 |
| 17 | A9 | 2c brn, *buff* | 2.10 | 1.40 |
| 18 | A9 | 4c claret, *lav* | 2.75 | 2.10 |
| 19 | A9 | 5c yellow green | 3.25 | 2.40 |
| 20 | A9 | 10c rose | 10.00 | 7.50 |
| 21 | A9 | 15c gray | 11.00 | 7.50 |
| 22 | A9 | 20c red, *grn* | 15.00 | 14.00 |
| 23 | A9 | 25c blue | 14.00 | 7.50 |
| 24 | A9 | 30c yel brn | 16.00 | 15.00 |
| 25 | A9 | 35c blk, *yel* ('06) | 24.00 | 24.00 |
| 26 | A9 | 40c red, *straw* | 25.00 | 20.00 |
| 27 | A9 | 45c blk, *gray grn* ('07) | 37.50 | 32.50 |
| 28 | A9 | 50c blue, *az* | 16.00 | 14.00 |
| 29 | A9 | 75c dp vio, *org* | 25.00 | 25.00 |
| 30 | A9 | 1fr brnz grn, *straw* | 40.00 | 40.00 |
| 31 | A9 | 2fr vio, *rose* | 80.00 | 80.00 |
| 32 | A9 | 5fr lil, *lav* | 127.50 | 127.50 |
| | | Nos. 16-32 (17) | 450.50 | 421.80 |

Perf. 13½x14 stamps are counterfeits.
For surcharges see Nos. 72-84.

Fang Warrior A10

Fang Woman A12

Libreville — A11

### Inscribed: "Congo Français"

| 1910 | | | Perf. 13½x14 |
|---|---|---|---|---|
| 33 | A10 | 1c choc & org | 2.00 | 2.00 |
| 34 | A10 | 2c black & choc | 2.75 | 2.75 |
| 35 | A10 | 4c vio & dp bl | 2.50 | 2.50 |
| 36 | A10 | 5c ol gray & grn | 4.00 | 4.00 |
| 37 | A10 | 10c red & car | 5.75 | 5.75 |
| 38 | A10 | 20c choc & dk vio | 8.00 | 8.00 |
| 39 | A11 | 25c dp bl & choc | 8.00 | 8.00 |
| 40 | A11 | 30c gray blk & red | 40.00 | 40.00 |
| 41 | A11 | 35c dk vio & grn | 24.00 | 24.00 |
| 42 | A11 | 40c choc & ultra | 32.50 | 32.50 |
| 43 | A11 | 45c car & vio | 52.50 | 52.50 |
| 44 | A11 | 50c bl grn & gray | 75.00 | 75.00 |
| 45 | A11 | 75c org & choc | 130.00 | 130.00 |
| 46 | A12 | 1fr dk brn & bis | 130.00 | 130.00 |

| 47 | A12 | 2fr car & brn | 325.00 | 325.00 |
|---|---|---|---|---|
| 48 | A12 | 5fr blue & choc | 325.00 | 325.00 |
| | | Nos. 33-48 (16) | 1,167. | 1,167. |

### Inscribed: "Afrique Equatoriale"

| 1910-22 | | | Dull Cream Paper | |
|---|---|---|---|---|
| 49 | A10 | 1c choc & org | .35 | .40 |
| 50 | A10 | 2c black & choc | .35 | .40 |
| b. | | 2c gray black & deep olive | .65 | .80 |
| 51 | A10 | 4c vio & dp bl | .35 | .50 |
| 52 | A10 | 5c ol gray & grn | .95 | .55 |
| 53 | A10 | 5c gray blk & ocher ('22) | 1.40 | 1.40 |
| 54 | A10 | 10c red & car | 1.40 | 1.00 |
| 55 | A10 | 10c yel grn & bl grn ('22) | 1.40 | 1.40 |
| 56 | A10 | 15c brn vio & rose ('18) | 1.25 | .80 |
| 57 | A10 | 20c ol brn & dk vio | 6.50 | 5.50 |
| 58 | A11 | 25c dp bl & choc | 1.40 | 1.00 |
| 59 | A11 | 25c Prus bl & blk ('22) | 1.60 | 1.60 |
| 60 | A11 | 30c gray blk & red | 1.60 | 1.60 |
| 61 | A11 | 30c rose & red ('22) | 2.00 | 2.40 |
| 62 | A11 | 35c dk vio & grn | 1.40 | 1.25 |
| 63 | A11 | 40c choc & ultra | 1.60 | 1.60 |
| 64 | A11 | 45c carmine & vio | 1.60 | 1.60 |
| 65 | A11 | 45c blk & red ('22) | 2.75 | 3.25 |
| 66 | A11 | 50c bl grn & gray | 2.00 | 2.00 |
| 67 | A11 | 50c dk bl & bl ('22) | 1.60 | 1.60 |
| 68 | A11 | 75c org & choc | 7.00 | 5.00 |
| 69 | A12 | 1fr dk brn & bis | 3.50 | 2.75 |
| 70 | A12 | 2fr car & brn | 7.00 | 6.50 |
| 71 | A12 | 5fr blue & choc | 7.00 | 8.50 |
| | | Nos. 49-71 (23) | 56.00 | 52.60 |

Nos. 49-51, 54, 62, 64 and 66 also exist on white paper. See the *Scott Classic Specialized Catalogue of Stamps and Covers* for listings.
For overprints and surcharges, see Nos 85-119, B1-B3.

### Stamps of 1904-07 Surcharged in Black or Carmine

### Spacing between figures of surcharge 1.5mm (5c), 2mm (10c)

| 1912 | | | | |
|---|---|---|---|---|
| 72 | A9 | 5c on 2c brn, *buff* | 1.60 | 2.00 |
| 73 | A9 | 5c on 4c cl, *lav* (C) | 1.60 | 2.00 |
| 74 | A9 | 5c on 15c gray (C) | 1.25 | 1.25 |
| 75 | A9 | 5c on 20c red, *grn* | 1.25 | 1.60 |
| 76 | A9 | 5c on 25c bl (C) | 1.25 | 1.60 |
| 77 | A9 | 5c on 30c pale brn (C) | 1.60 | 2.00 |
| 78 | A9 | 10c on 40c red, *straw* | 1.25 | 1.60 |
| a. | | Double surcharge | 2,400. | |
| 79 | A9 | 10c on 45c blk, *gray grn* (C) | 1.25 | 1.60 |
| 80 | A9 | 10c on 50c brn, *az* (C) | 1.60 | 2.00 |
| 81 | A9 | 10c on 75c dp vio, *org* | 1.60 | 2.00 |
| 82 | A9 | 10c on 1fr brnz grn, *straw* | 1.60 | 2.00 |
| 83 | A9 | 10c on 2fr vio, *rose* | 1.60 | 2.00 |
| a. | | Inverted surcharge | 340.00 | 340.00 |
| 84 | A9 | 10c on 5fr lil, *lav* | 4.00 | 4.25 |
| | | Nos. 72-84 (13) | 21.45 | 25.90 |

Two spacings between the surcharged numerals are found on Nos. 72 to 84. For detailed listings, see the *Scott Classic Specialized Catalogue of Stamps and Covers.*

### Stamps of 1910-22 Overprinted in Black, Blue or Carmine

On A10, A12

On A11

| 1924-31 | | | | |
|---|---|---|---|---|
| 85 | A10 | 1c brn & org | .35 | .35 |
| 86 | A10 | 2c blk & choc (Bl) | .35 | .70 |
| 87 | A10 | 4c violet & ind | .30 | .35 |
| 88 | A10 | 5c gray blk & ocher | .35 | .70 |
| 89 | A10 | 10c yel grn & bl grn | .70 | 1.10 |
| a. | | Double overprint (Bk & Bl) | 175.00 | |
| 90 | A10 | 10c dk bl & brn ('26) (C) | .40 | .40 |
| a. | | Overprint omitted | 350.00 | 350.00 |
| b. | | Double overprint | | 475.00 |

| 91 | A10 | 15c brn vio & rose (Bl) | 1.00 | 1.00 |
|---|---|---|---|---|
| 92 | A10 | 15c rose & brn vio ('31) | 1.25 | 1.25 |
| a. | | Overprint omitted | 250.00 | |
| 93 | A10 | 20c ol brn & dk vio (C) | .70 | 1.10 |
| a. | | Inverted overprint | 180.00 | 180.00 |
| b. | | Double overprint | | 400.00 |
| c. | | Double overprint, both inverted | 525.00 | |
| 94 | A11 | 25c Prus bl & blk (C) | .70 | 1.10 |
| 95 | A11 | 30c rose & red (Bl) | .70 | 1.10 |
| 96 | A11 | 30c blk & org ('26) | .70 | .85 |
| a. | | Overprint omitted | — | |
| 97 | A11 | 30c dk grn & bl grn ('28) | 1.25 | 1.25 |
| a. | | Overprint omitted | 1,800. | |
| 98 | A11 | 35c dk vio & grn (Bl) | .70 | 1.10 |
| 99 | A11 | 40c choc & ultra (C) | .75 | .75 |
| 100 | A11 | 45c blk & red (Bl) | 1.50 | 2.10 |
| 101 | A11 | 50c blk & bl (C) | 1.00 | 1.00 |
| 102 | A11 | 50c car & grn ('26) | .70 | .90 |
| 103 | A11 | 65c dp bl & red org ('27) | 3.50 | 3.50 |
| 104 | A11 | 75c org & brn | 2.25 | 2.25 |
| 105 | A11 | 90c brn red & rose ('30) | 2.75 | 2.75 |
| 106 | A12 | 1fr dk brn & bis | 1.40 | 1.75 |
| 107 | A12 | 1.10fr dl grn & rose red ('28) | 6.00 | 7.50 |
| 108 | A12 | 1.50fr pale bl & dk bl ('30) | 1.25 | 1.25 |
| a. | | Overprint omitted | 290.00 | |
| 109 | A12 | 2fr rose & brn | 2.25 | 2.75 |
| 110 | A12 | 3fr red vio ('30) | 7.00 | 7.00 |
| a. | | Overprint omitted | 275.00 | |
| 111 | A12 | 5fr dp bl & choc | 7.00 | 5.50 |
| | | Nos. 85-111 (27) | 46.80 | 51.35 |

### Types of 1924-31 Issues Surcharged with New Values in Black or Carmine

| 1925-28 | | | | |
|---|---|---|---|---|
| 112 | A12 | 65c on 1fr ol grn & brn | 1.25 | 1.25 |
| 113 | A12 | 85c on 1fr ol grn & brn | 1.25 | 1.25 |
| 114 | A11 | 90c on 75c brn red & cer ('27) | 1.75 | 1.75 |
| a. | | "90" omitted | 240.00 | |
| 115 | A12 | 1.25fr on 1fr dk bl & ultra (C) | 1.25 | 1.25 |
| 116 | A12 | 1.50fr on 1fr lt bl & dk bl ('27) | 2.00 | 2.00 |
| 117 | A12 | 3fr on 5fr mag & ol brn | 7.00 | 8.00 |
| 118 | A12 | 10fr on 5fr org brn & grn ('27) | 12.00 | 12.50 |
| 119 | A12 | 20fr on 5fr red vio & org red ('27) | 16.00 | 17.50 |
| | | Nos. 112-119 (8) | 42.50 | 45.50 |

Bars cover the old denominations on Nos. 114-119.

### Common Design Types pictured following the introduction.

### Colonial Exposition Issue
Common Design Types

| 1931 | | | Perf. 12½ |
|---|---|---|---|---|
| | | Name of Country in Black | | |
| 120 | CD70 | 40c dp green | 4.00 | 4.00 |
| 121 | CD71 | 50c violet | 4.00 | 4.00 |
| 122 | CD72 | 90c red orange | 4.00 | 4.00 |
| 123 | CD73 | 1.50fr dull blue | 5.50 | 5.50 |
| | | Nos. 120-123 (4) | 17.50 | 17.50 |

Timber Raft on Ogowe River A16

Count Savorgnan de Brazza A17

Village of Setta
Kemma — A18

## 1932-33    Photo.    Perf. 13x13½

| | | | | |
|---|---|---|---|---|
| 124 | A16 | 1c brown violet | .30 | .25 |
| 125 | A16 | 2c blk, *rose* | .30 | .25 |
| 126 | A16 | 4c green | .30 | .30 |
| 127 | A16 | 5c grnsh blue | .70 | .50 |
| 128 | A16 | 10c red, *yel* | .55 | .55 |
| 129 | A16 | 15c red, *grn* | .70 | .65 |
| 130 | A16 | 20c deep red | .70 | .65 |
| 131 | A16 | 25c brown red | .70 | .50 |
| 132 | A17 | 30c yellow grn | 2.00 | 1.60 |
| 133 | A17 | 40c brown vio | 2.25 | 1.10 |
| 134 | A17 | 45c blk, *dl grn* | 3.50 | 2.40 |
| 135 | A17 | 50c red brown | 1.60 | 1.25 |
| 136 | A17 | 65c Prus blue | 6.50 | 6.50 |
| 137 | A17 | 75c blk, *red org* | 4.00 | 3.25 |
| 138 | A17 | 90c rose red | 4.00 | 3.25 |
| 139 | A17 | 1fr yel grn, *bl* | 27.50 | 24.00 |
| 140 | A18 | 1.25fr dp vio ('33) | 2.25 | 2.00 |
| 141 | A18 | 1.50fr dull blue | 11.00 | 7.25 |
| 142 | A18 | 1.75fr grn ('33) | 2.50 | 2.00 |
| 143 | A18 | 2fr brn red | 52.50 | 45.00 |
| 144 | A18 | 3fr yel grn, *bl* | 6.00 | 4.50 |
| 145 | A18 | 5fr red brown | 15.00 | 13.50 |
| 146 | A18 | 10fr blk, *red org* | 32.50 | 27.50 |
| 147 | A18 | 20fr dk violet | 47.50 | 40.00 |
| | | Nos. 124-147 (24) | 224.85 | 188.75 |

For overprints see French Equatorial Africa
Nos. 1-10.

See French Equatorial Africa No. 192
for stamp inscribed "Gabon" and
"Afrique Equatoriale Francaise."

**Catalogue values for all unused
stamps in this section, from this
point to the end of the section, are
for Never Hinged items.**

## Republic

Prime Minister Leon
Mba — A19

### Unwmk.

| | | | | |
|---|---|---|---|---|
| **1959, Nov. 28** | | **Engr.** | **Perf. 13** | |
| 148 | A19 | 15fr shown | .40 | .25 |
| 149 | A19 | 25fr Mba, profile | .40 | .25 |

Proclamation of the Republic, 1st anniv.

### Imperforates

Most Gabon stamps from 1959
onward exist imperforate in issued
and trial colors, and also in small
presentation sheets in issued colors.

### C.C.T.A. Issue
Common Design Type

| | | | | |
|---|---|---|---|---|
| **1960, May 21** | | **Engr.** | **Perf. 13** | |
| 150 | CD106 | 50fr vio brn & Prus bl | 1.25 | 1.10 |

Flag & Map of Gabon &
UN Emblem — A20

### 1961, Feb. 9

| | | | | |
|---|---|---|---|---|
| 151 | A20 | 15fr multi | .30 | .25 |
| 152 | A20 | 25fr multi | .55 | .25 |
| 153 | A20 | 85fr multi | 1.65 | .90 |
| | | Nos. 151-153 (3) | 2.50 | 1.40 |

Gabon's admission to United Nations.

Combretum
A21

1fr, 5fr, Tulip tree, vert. 2fr, 3fr, Yellow
cassia.

## 1961, July 4    Unwmk.    Perf. 13

| | | | | |
|---|---|---|---|---|
| 154 | A21 | 50c rose red & grn | .30 | .25 |
| 155 | A21 | 1fr sl grn, red & bis | .30 | .25 |
| 156 | A21 | 2fr dk grn & yel | .30 | .25 |
| 157 | A21 | 3fr ol grn & yel | .55 | .55 |
| 158 | A21 | 5fr multi | .60 | .60 |
| 159 | A21 | 10fr grn & rose red | .60 | .60 |
| | | Nos. 154-159 (6) | 2.65 | 2.50 |

President Leon
Mba — A22

### 1962             Engr.

| | | | | |
|---|---|---|---|---|
| 160 | A22 | 15fr indigo, car & grn | .35 | .25 |
| 161 | A22 | 20fr brn blk, car & grn | .50 | .25 |
| 162 | A22 | 25fr brn, car & grn | .70 | .25 |
| | | Nos. 160-162 (3) | 1.55 | .75 |

Issued: 15fr, 2/9; 20fr, 11/15; 25fr, 8/17.

### Abidjan Games Issue
Common Design Type

| | | | | |
|---|---|---|---|---|
| **1962, July 21** | | **Photo.** | **Perf. 12½x12** | |
| 163 | CD109 | 20fr Foot race, start | .75 | .50 |
| 164 | CD109 | 50fr Soccer | 1.25 | 1.00 |
| | | Nos. 163-164,C6 (3) | 5.00 | 3.00 |

### African-Malgache Union Issue
Common Design Type

| | | | | |
|---|---|---|---|---|
| **1962, Sept. 8** | | | **Perf. 12½x12** | |
| 165 | CD110 | 30fr emer, bluish grn, red & gold | 1.60 | 1.25 |

Captain
Ntchorere and
Flags of France
and
Gabon — A23

### 1962, Nov. 23      Perf. 12

| | | | | |
|---|---|---|---|---|
| 166 | A23 | 80fr multi | 1.25 | .85 |

Capt. Ntchorere, who died for France, 6/7/40.

Waves Around
Globe — A23a

Design: 100fr, Orbit patterns around globe.

| | | | | |
|---|---|---|---|---|
| **1963, Sept. 19** | | **Photo.** | **Perf. 12½** | |
| 167 | A23a | 25fr ultra, grn & org | .55 | .55 |
| 168 | A23a | 100fr grn, ultra & red brn | 1.75 | 1.75 |

Issued to publicize space communications.

UNESCO
Emblem, Scales
and Tree — A23b

| | | | | |
|---|---|---|---|---|
| **1963, Dec. 10** | | **Engr.** | **Perf. 13** | |
| 169 | A23b | 25fr grn, dk gray & red brn | .70 | .25 |

15th anniv. of the Universal Declaration of
Human Rights.

Barograph and
WMO
Emblem — A23c

| | | | | |
|---|---|---|---|---|
| **1964, Mar. 23** | | **Unwmk.** | **Perf. 13** | |
| 170 | A23c | 25fr ol bis, sl grn & ultra | .90 | .60 |

UN's 4th World Meteorological Day, Mar. 23.

Arms of Gabon — A24

| | | | | |
|---|---|---|---|---|
| **1964, June 15** | **Photo.** | **Perf. 13x12½** | | |
| 171 | A24 | 25fr ocher & multi | .90 | .45 |

Tarpon — A25

Designs: 60fr, Gorilla, vert. 80fr, Buffalo.

| | | | | |
|---|---|---|---|---|
| **1964, July 15** | | **Engr.** | **Perf. 13** | |
| 172 | A25 | 30fr brn red, bl & blk | 1.25 | .70 |
| 173 | A25 | 60fr brn, grn & brn red | 2.25 | .90 |
| 174 | A25 | 80fr dk bl, grn & red brn | 2.40 | 1.25 |
| | | Nos. 172-174 (3) | 5.90 | 2.85 |

### Cooperation Issue
Common Design Type

| | | | | |
|---|---|---|---|---|
| **1964, Nov. 7** | | | | |
| 175 | CD119 | 25fr gray, dk brn & lt bl | .90 | .60 |

Dissotis
Rotundifolia — A26

5fr, Gloriosa superba. 15fr, Eulophia
horsfallii.

| | | | | |
|---|---|---|---|---|
| **1964, Nov. 16** | **Photo.** | **Perf. 12x12½** | | |
| **Flowers in Natural Colors** | | | | |
| 176 | A26 | 3fr deep grn | .30 | .25 |
| 177 | A26 | 5fr green | .55 | .30 |
| 178 | A26 | 15fr dark brn | .85 | .55 |
| | | Nos. 176-178 (3) | 1.70 | 1.10 |

Sun and IQSY
Emblem — A27

| | | | | |
|---|---|---|---|---|
| **1965, Feb. 25** | | | **Perf. 12½x12** | |
| 179 | A27 | 85fr multi | 1.40 | .80 |

International Quiet Sun Year, 1964-65.

Morse
Telegraph — A28

| | | | | |
|---|---|---|---|---|
| **1965, May 17** | | **Engr.** | **Perf. 13** | |
| 180 | A28 | 30fr multi | .90 | .60 |

Cent. of the ITU.

Manganese
Crusher,
Moanda — A29

Design: 60fr, Uranium mining, Mounana.

| | | | | |
|---|---|---|---|---|
| **1965, June 15** | | **Unwmk.** | **Perf. 13** | |
| 181 | A29 | 15fr brt bl, pur & red | .55 | .30 |
| 182 | A29 | 60fr brn, brt bl & red | 1.90 | .90 |

Issued to publicize Gabon's mineral wealth.

Field Ball — A30

| | | | | |
|---|---|---|---|---|
| **1965, July 15** | | **Engr.** | **Perf. 13** | |
| 183 | A30 | 25fr brt grn, blk & red | .75 | .35 |

1st African Games, Brazzaville, 7/18-25.
See No. C35.

Okoukoue Dance — A31

Design: 60fr, Mukudji dance.

| | | | | |
|---|---|---|---|---|
| **1965, Sept. 15** | | | **Perf. 13** | |
| 184 | A31 | 25fr brn, grn & yel | .40 | .25 |
| 185 | A31 | 60fr blk, dk red & brn | 1.50 | .60 |

Abraham
Lincoln — A32

| | | | | |
|---|---|---|---|---|
| **1965, Sept. 28** | **Photo.** | **Perf. 12½x13** | | |
| 186 | A32 | 50fr blue, blk, gold & buff | .90 | .40 |

Centenary of death of Abraham Lincoln.

Old & New Post
Offices and Mail
Transport — A33

| | | | | |
|---|---|---|---|---|
| **1965, Dec. 18** | | **Engr.** | **Perf. 13** | |
| 187 | A33 | 30fr bl, brt grn & choc | 1.75 | .75 |

Issued for Stamp Day, 1965.

Balumbu Mask — A34

Intl. Negro Arts Festival, Dakar, Senegal,
Apr. 1-24 — 10fr, Fang ancestral figure, Byeri.
25fr, Fang mask. 30fr, Okuyi mask, Myene.
85fr, Bakota leather mask.

| | | | | |
|---|---|---|---|---|
| **1966, Apr. 18** | **Photo.** | **Perf. 12x12½** | | |
| 188 | A34 | 5fr red, brn, blk & buff | .30 | .25 |
| 189 | A34 | 10fr brt grnsh bl, dk brn & yel | .30 | .25 |
| 190 | A34 | 25fr multicolored | .80 | .30 |
| 191 | A34 | 30fr mar, yel & blk | 1.10 | .50 |
| 192 | A34 | 85fr multicolored | 2.50 | 1.25 |
| | | Nos. 188-192 (5) | 5.00 | 2.55 |

WHO
Headquarters,
Geneva — A35

| | | | | |
|---|---|---|---|---|
| **1966, May 3** | **Photo.** | **Perf. 12½x13** | | |
| 193 | A35 | 50fr org yel, ultra & blk | 1.20 | .60 |

Inauguration of the WHO Headquarters,
Geneva.

Mother Learning to Write — A36

**1966, June 22   Photo.   Perf. 12x12½**
194  A36  30fr multi                     .90  .45
UNESCO literacy campaign.

Soccer Player — A37

Design: 90fr, Player facing left.

**1966, July 15   Engr.        Perf. 13**
195  A37  25fr brn, grn & ultra    1.00  .25
196  A37  90fr ultra & dk pur     1.75  .85
       Nos. 195-196,C45 (3)        5.25 2.10
8th World Cup Soccer Championship, Wembley, England, July 11-30.

Timber Industry — A38

Economic development: 85fr, Offshore oil rigs.

**1966, Aug. 17              Perf. 13**
197  A38  20fr red brn, lil & dk grn   .45  .35
198  A38  85fr dk brn, brt bl & brt
            grn                       3.25 1.25

Woman with Children at Bank Window — A39

**1966, Sept. 23   Engr.      Perf. 13**
199  A39  25fr brt bl, vio brn & sl
            grn                         .85  .45
Issued to publicize Savings Banks.

Scouts Around Campfire — A40

50fr, Boy Scout pledging ceremony, vert.

**1966, Oct. 17   Engr.       Perf. 13**
200  A40  30fr sl bl, car & dk brn   .85  .40
201  A40  50fr Prus bl, brn red &
            dk brn                    1.25  .50
Issued to honor Gabon's Boy Scouts.

Sikorsky S-43 Seaplane and Map of West Africa — A41

**1966, Dec. 17   Photo.   Perf. 12½x12**
202  A41  30fr multi                 1.90  .60
Stamp Day and for the 30th anniv. of the 1st air-mail service from Libreville to Port Gentil.

Hippopotami A42

Animals: 2fr, African crocodiles. 3fr, Water chevrotain. 5fr, Chimpanzees. 10fr, Elephants. 20fr, Leopards.

**1967, Jan. 5   Photo.     Perf. 13x14**
203  A42  1fr multi                  .30  .25
204  A42  2fr multi                  .45  .25
205  A42  3fr multi                  .45  .25
206  A42  5fr multi                  .50  .25
207  A42  10fr multi                1.50  .80
208  A42  20fr multi                3.50  .80
       Nos. 203-208 (6)             6.70 2.60

Lions International Emblem — A43

50fr, Lions emblem, map of Gabon and globe.

**1967, Jan. 14            Perf. 12½x13**
209  A43  30fr multicolored         .80  .25
210  A43  50fr blue & multi        1.00  .50
a.    Strip of 2, #209-210 + label 3.00 1.50
50th anniv. of Lions Intl.

Carnival Masks — A44

**1967, Feb. 4   Photo.   Perf. 12x12½**
211  A44  30fr brn, yel bis & bl   1.00  .45
Libreville Carnival, Feb. 4-7.

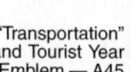

"Transportation" and Tourist Year Emblem — A45

**1967, Feb. 15            Perf. 12½x13**
212  A45  30fr multi               1.10  .45
International Tourist Year, 1967.

Olympic Diving Tower, Mexico City — A46

1968 Olympic Games: 30fr, Sun, snow crystals and Olympic rings. 50fr, Ice skating rink and view of Grenoble.

**1967, Mar. 18   Engr.       Perf. 13**
213  A46  25fr dk vio, grnsh bl &
            ultra                     .50  .25
214  A46  30fr grn, red lil & mar    .90  .45
215  A46  50fr ultra, grn & brn     1.25  .75
       Nos. 213-215 (3)             2.65 1.45

Symbolic of Atomic Energy Agency — A47

**1967, Apr. 15   Engr.       Perf. 13**
216  A47  30fr red brn, dk grn &
            ultra                     .90  .25
International Atomic Energy Agency.

Pope Paul VI, Papal Arms and Libreville Cathedral — A48

**1967, June 1   Engr.        Perf. 13**
217  A48  30fr ultra, grn & blk    1.10  .50
"Populorum progressio" encyclical by Pope Paul VI concerning underdeveloped countries.

Flags, Tree, Logger, Map of Gabon and Mask — A49

**1967, June 24   Engr.       Perf. 13**
218  A49  30fr multi                .85  .45
EXPO '67, International Exhibition, Montreal, Apr. 28-Oct. 27, 1967.

### Europafrica Issue

Map of Europe and Africa and Products — A50

**1967, July 18   Photo.   Perf. 12½x12**
219  A50  50fr multi               1.25  .60

UN Emblem, Women and Child — A51

**1967, Aug. 10   Engr.       Perf. 13**
220  A51  75fr brt blue, dk brn &
            emer                    1.60  .80
United Nations Commission for Women.

19th Century Mail Ships — A52

Design:  No. 222, Modern mail ships.

**1967, Nov. 17   Photo.     Perf. 12½**
221       30fr multi               1.40  .80
222       30fr multi               1.40  .80
a.    A52 Pair, #221-222           3.00 3.00
Stamp Day. No. 222a has continuous design.

Draconea Fragrans — A53

Trees: 10fr, Pycnanthus angolensis. 20fr, Disthemonanthus benthamianus.

**1967, Dec. 5   Engr.        Perf. 13**
                Size: 22x36mm
223  A53  5fr bl, emer & brn        .75  .35
224  A53  10fr grn, dk grn & bl     .90  .45
225  A53  20fr rose red, grn & ol  1.20  .70
       Nos. 223-225,C61-C62 (5)    7.20 4.50
For booklet pane see No. C62a.

WHO Regional Office — A54

**1968, Apr. 8   Engr.        Perf. 13**
226  A54  20fr multi                .85  .50
20th anniv. of the WHO.

Dam, Power Station and UNESCO Emblem — A55

**1968, June 18   Engr.       Perf. 13**
227  A55  15fr lake, org & Prus bl  .75  .40
Hydrological Decade (UNESCO), 1965-74.

Pres. Albert Bernard Bongo — A56

30fr, Pres. Bongo & arms of Gabon in background.

**1968, June 24   Photo.   Perf. 12x12½**
228  A56  25fr grn, buff & blk      .65  .25
229  A56  30fr rose lil, lt bl & blk .75  .25

Tanker, Refinery, and Map of Area Served A56a

**1968, July 30   Photo.     Perf. 12½**
230  A56a  30fr multi               .85  .50
Port Gentil (Gabon) Refinery opening, 6/12/68.

Open Book, Child and UNESCO Emblem — A57

**1968, Sept. 10   Engr.      Perf. 13**
231  A57  25fr vio bl, dl red & brn 1.25  .25
Issued for International Literacy Day.

A58

**1968, Oct. 15   Engr.       Perf. 13**
232  A58  20fr Coffee              2.00  .75
233  A58  40fr Cacao              1.25  .50

A59

**1968, Nov. 23   Engr.       Perf. 13**
234  A59  30fr "La Junon"         1.75  .70
Issued for Stamp Day.

A60

Lawyer, globe and human rights flame.

**1968, Dec. 10**
235  A60  20fr blk, bl grn & car   .75  .45
International Human Rights Year.

Okanda Gap — A61

Designs: 15fr, Barracuda. 25fr, Kinguele Waterfall, vert. 30fr, Sitatunga trophies, vert.

**1969, Mar. 28   Engr.       Perf. 13**
236  A61  10fr brn, bl & sl grn    .35  .25
237  A61  15fr brn red, emer & ind 2.25  .35
238  A61  25fr bl, pur & ol        .65  .30
239  A61  30fr multi              1.40  .50
       Nos. 236-239 (4)           4.65 1.40
Year of African Tourism, 1969.

Mvet (Musical Instrument) — A62

Musical Instruments: 30fr, Ngombi harp. 50fr, Ebele and Mbe drums. 100fr, Medzang xylophone.

**1969, June 6**    **Engr.**    *Perf. 13*
240 A62 25fr plum, ol & dp car   .50 .25
241 A62 30fr red brn, ol & dk brn   .50 .25
242 A62 50fr plum, ol & dp car   .95 .55
243 A62 100fr red brn, ol & dk brn   2.25 .85
    a.   Min. sheet of 4, #240-243   6.00 6.00
    Nos. 240-243 (4)   4.20 1.90

Aframomum Polyanthum (Zingiberaceae) — A63

African Plants: 2fr, Chlamydocola chlamydantha (Sterculiaceae). 5fr, Costus dinklagei (Zingiberaceae). 10fr, Cola rostrata (Sterculiaceae). 20fr, Dischistocalyx grandifolius (Acanthaceae).

**1969, July 15**   **Photo.**   *Perf. 12x12½*
244 A63 1fr multi   .30 .25
245 A63 2fr lt ol & multi   .30 .25
246 A63 5fr multi   .35 .25
247 A63 10fr slate & multi   .80 .35
248 A63 20fr yel & multi   1.20 .70
    Nos. 244-248 (5)   2.95 1.80

Tree of Life — A64

**1969, Aug. 17**     **Photo.**
249 A64 25fr multi   .60 .50

National renovation.

Drilling for Oil on Land — A65

Design: 50fr, Offshore drilling station.

**1969, Sept. 13**    *Perf. 12x12½*
250 A65 25fr multi   .75 .25
251 A65 50fr multi   1.25 .35
    a.   Strip of 2, #250-251 + label   2.50 1.50

20th anniv. of the ELF-SPAFE oil operations in Gabon.

Workers and ILO Emblem — A66

**1969, Oct. 29**    **Engr.**    *Perf. 13*
252 A66 30fr bl, sl grn & dp car   .90 .45

50th anniv. of the ILO.

Arms of Port Gentil — A67

Coats of Arms: 20fr, Lambarene. 30fr, Libreville.

---

**1969, Nov. 19**    **Photo.**    *Perf. 12*
253 A67 20fr red, gold, sil & blk   .85 1.25
254 A67 25fr bl, blk & gold   1.10 .25
255 A67 30fr bl & multi   1.40 .45
    Nos. 253-255 (3)   3.35 .95

See Nos. 267-269, 291-293, 321-326, 340-348, 409-417, 492-501.

Canoe Mail Transport — A68

**1969, Dec. 18**    **Engr.**    *Perf. 13*
256 A68 30fr brt grn, grnsh bl & red brn   1.10 .50

Issued for Stamp Day 1969.

Satellite, Globe, TV Screen and ITU Emblem — A69

**1970, May 17**    **Engr.**    *Perf. 13*
257 A69 25fr dk bl, dk red brn & blk   .80 .40

International Telecommunications Day.

**UPU Headquarters Issue**
Common Design Type

**1970, May 20**    **Engr.**    *Perf. 13*
258 CD133 30fr brt grn, brt rose lil & brn   .90 .55

Geisha and African Drummer — A70

**1970, May 27**   **Photo.**   *Perf. 12½x12*
259 A70 30fr ultra & multi   .90 .40

EXPO '70 Intl. Exhibition, Osaka, Japan, 3/15-9/13.

**ASECNA Issue**
Common Design Type

**1970, Aug. 26**    **Engr.**    *Perf. 13*
260 CD132 100fr brt grn & bl grn   1.75 .75

UN Emblem, Globe, Dove and Charts — A71

**1970, Oct. 24**   **Photo.**   *Perf. 12½x12*
261 A71 30fr Prus bl & multi   .90 .60

25th anniversary of the United Nations.

Bushbucks — A72

Designs: 15fr, Pels scaly-tailed flying squirrel. 25fr, Gray-cheeked monkey, vert. 40fr, African golden cat. 60fr, Sevaline genet.

**1970, Dec. 14**   **Photo.**   *Perf. 12½x13*
262 A72 5fr yel grn & multi   .45 .30
263 A72 15fr org & blk   .70 .40
264 A72 25fr vio & multi   1.40 .60
265 A72 40fr red & multi   2.75 1.10
266 A72 60fr bl & multi   4.00 2.10
    Nos. 262-266 (5)   9.30 4.50

**Arms Type of 1969**

20fr, Mouila. 25fr, Bitam. 30fr, Oyem.

**1971, Feb. 16**    **Photo.**    *Perf. 12*
267 A67 20fr ver, blk, sil & gold   .80 .25
268 A67 25fr emer, gold & blk   .80 .25
269 A67 30fr emer, gold, blk & red   1.10 .35
    Nos. 267-269 (3)   2.70 .85

---

Men of Four Races and Emblem — A73

**1971, Mar. 21**    **Engr.**    *Perf. 13*
270 A73 40fr multi   .90 .45

Intl. year against racial discrimination.

Map of Africa and Telecommunications System — A74

**1971, Apr. 30**    **Photo.**    *Perf. 13*
271 A74 30fr org & multi   .90 .45

Pan-African telecommunications system.

Charaxes Smaragdalis — A75

Butterflies: 10fr, Euxanthe crossleyi. 15fr, Epiphora rectifascia. 25fr, Imbrasia bouvieri.

**1971, May 26**    **Photo.**    *Perf. 13*
272 A75 5fr yel & multi   2.50 .45
273 A75 10fr bl & multi   4.00 .60
274 A75 15fr grn & multi   8.00 .70
275 A75 25fr ol & multi   9.50 1.10
    Nos. 272-275 (4)   24.00 2.85

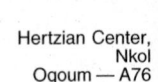

Hertzian Center, Nkol Ogoum — A76

**1971, June 17**    **Engr.**    *Perf. 13*
276 A76 40fr grn, blk & dk car   .90 .40

3rd World Telecommunications Day.

Mother Nursing Child — A77

**1971, Aug. 17**    **Engr.**    *Perf. 13*
277 A77 30fr lil rose, sep & ocher   .90 .45

Gabonese social security system, 15th anniv.

UN Headquarters and Emblem — A78

**1971, Sept. 30**    **Photo.**    *Perf. 13*
278 A78 30fr red & multi   .90 .45

10th anniv. of Gabon's admission to the UN.

Large Egret — A79

Birds: 40fr, African gray parrot. 50fr, Woodland Kingfisher. 75fr, Cameroon bareheaded rock-fowl. 100fr, Gold Coast touraco.

---

**1971, Oct. 12**    **Litho.**    *Perf. 13*
279 A79 30fr multi   1.25 .75
280 A79 40fr multi   2.10 1.00
281 A79 50fr multi   2.75 1.20
282 A79 75fr multi   3.75 1.25
283 A79 100fr multi   5.25 1.50
    Nos. 279-283 (5)   15.10 5.70

Asystasia Volgeliana — A80

Designs: Flowers of Acanthus Family after paintings by Noel Hallé.

**1972, Apr. 4**    **Photo.**    *Perf. 13*
284 A80 5fr pale cit & multi   .30 .25
285 A80 10fr multi   .40 .25
286 A80 20fr multi   .65 .40
287 A80 30fr lil rose & multi   1.00 .50
288 A80 40fr dk grn & multi   1.40 .75
289 A80 65fr red & multi   2.50 1.10
    Nos. 284-289 (6)   6.25 3.25

Louis Pasteur — A81

**1972, May 15**    **Engr.**    *Perf. 13*
290 A81 80fr dp org, pur & grn   1.25 .60

Sesquicentennial of the birth of Louis Pasteur (1822-1895), scientist and bacteriologist.

**Arms Type of 1969**

30fr, Franceville. 40fr, Makokou. 60fr, Tchibanga.

**1972, June 2**    **Photo.**    *Perf. 12*
291 A67 30fr sil & multi   .60 .25
292 A67 40fr grn & multi   .75 .25
293 A67 60fr blk, grn & sil   1.25 .55
    Nos. 291-293 (3)   2.60 1.05

Globe and Telecommunications Symbols — A81a

**1972, July 25**     *Perf. 13x12½*
294 A81a 40fr blk, yel & org   .90 .45

4th World Telecommunications Day.

Nat King Cole — A82

Black American Jazz Musicians: 60fr, Sidney Bechet. 100fr, Louis Armstrong.

**1972, Sept. 1**   **Photo.**   *Perf. 13x13½*
295 A82 40fr bl & multi   1.60 .35
296 A82 60fr org & multi   2.40 .70
297 A82 100fr multi   4.00 1.10
    Nos. 295-297 (3)   8.00 2.15

Blanding's Rear-fanged Snake — A83

Designs: 2fr, Beauty snake. 3fr, Egg-eating snake. 15fr, Striped ground snake. 25fr, Jameson's mamba. 75fr, Gabon viper.

**1972, Oct. 2**    **Litho.**    *Perf. 13*
298 A83 1fr lem & multi   .30 .25
299 A83 2fr red brn & multi   .40 .25
300 A83 3fr brn org & multi   .40 .25
301 A83 15fr multi   2.25 .40

**302** A83 25fr grn & multi 3.25 .45
**303** A83 50fr multi 5.00 .75
*Nos. 298-303 (6)* 11.60 2.35
See Nos. 330-332, 354-357.

Dr. Armauer G. Hansen, Lambarene Leprosarium A84

**1973, Jan. 28 Engr. *Perf. 13***
**304** A84 30fr Prus grn, sl grn & brn 1.10 .55
Centenary of the discovery of the Hansen bacillus, the cause of leprosy.

Charaxes Candiope — A85

Various butterflies: 15fr, Eunica pechueli. 20fr, Cyrestis camillus. 30fr, Charaxes castor. 40fr, Charaxes ameliae. 50fr, Pseudacrea boisduvali.

**1973, Feb. 23 Litho. *Perf. 13***
**305** A85 10fr shown 1.90 .40
**306** A85 15fr multicolored 2.25 .40
**307** A85 20fr multicolored 3.75 .85
**308** A85 30fr multicolored 5.00 1.25
**309** A85 40fr multicolored 6.00 1.75
**310** A85 50fr multicolored 6.50 2.10
*Nos. 305-310 (6)* 25.40 6.75

Balloon of Santos-Dumont, 1901 — A86

History of Aviation: 1fr, Montgolfier's balloon, 1783, vert. 3fr, Octave Chanute's biplane, 1896. 4fr, Clement Ader's Plane III, 1897. 5fr, Louis Bleriot crossing the Channel, 1909. 10fr, Fabre's hydravion, 1910.

**1973, May 3 Engr. *Perf. 13***
**311** A86 1fr grn, sl grn & dk brn .30 .25
**312** A86 2fr sl grn & brt bl .30 .25
**313** A86 3fr bl, sl & org .30 .25
**314** A86 4fr lil & dk pur .75 .25
**315** A86 5fr slate grn & org 1.10 .35
**316** A86 10fr rose lil & Prus bl 2.10 .50
*Nos. 311-316 (6)* 4.85 1.85

**1977 Coil Stamp**
**316A** A86 10fr aqua 3.50 .25
No. 316A has red control numbers on back of every 10th stamp.

INTERPOL Emblem — A87

**1973, June 26 Engr. *Perf. 13***
**317** A87 40fr magenta & ultra .90 .40
50th anniversary of the International Criminal Police Organization (INTERPOL).

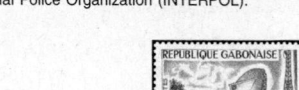
Earth Station "2 Decembre" — A88

**1973, July 2 Engr. *Perf. 13***
**318** A88 40fr slate grn, bl & brn .90 .40

Party Headquarters, Libreville — A89

**1973, Aug. 17 Photo.**
**319** A89 30fr multi .90 .25

**African Postal Union Issue**
Common Design Type
**1973, Sept. 12 Engr. *Perf. 13***
**320** CD137 100fr red lil, pur & bl 1.40 .75

**Arms Type of 1969**
5fr, Gamba. 10fr, Ogowe-Lolo. 15fr, Fougamou. 30fr, Kango. 40fr, Booue. 60fr, Koula-Moutou.

**1973-74 Photo. *Perf. 12***
**321** A67 5fr bl & multi ('74) .65 .25
**322** A67 10fr blk, red & gold ('74) .65 .25
**323** A67 15fr grn & multi ('74) .90 .25
**324** A67 30fr red & multi 1.60 .35
**325** A67 40fr red & multi 1.90 .55
**326** A67 60fr emer & multi 3.00 .70
*Nos. 321-326 (6)* 8.70 2.35
Issued Nos. 321-323, 2/13; Nos. 324-326, 10/4.

St. Teresa of Lisieux — A90

40fr, St. Teresa and Jesus carrying cross.

**1973, Dec. 4 Photo. *Perf. 13***
**327** A90 30fr blk & multi .90 .25
**328** A90 40fr blk & multi 1.10 .35
St. Teresa of the Infant Jesus (Thérèse Martin, 1873-97), Carmelite nun.

Human Rights Flame — A91

**1973, Dec. 10 Engr.**
**329** A91 20fr grn, red & ultra .60 .25
25th anniversary of the Universal Declaration of Human Rights.

**Wildlife Type of 1972**
Monkeys: 40fr, Mangabey. 60fr, Cercopithecus cephus. 80fr, Mona monkey.

**1974, Mar. 20 Litho. *Perf. 14***
**330** A83 40fr gray grn & multi 1.20 .45
**331** A83 60fr lt bl & multi 2.00 .50
**332** A83 80fr lil rose & multi 3.25 .80
*Nos. 330-332 (3)* 6.45 1.75

Ogowe River at Lambarene A93

50fr, Cape Estérias. 75fr, Poubara rope bridge.

**1974, July 30 Photo. *Perf. 13x13½***
**333** A93 30fr multi .60 .25
**334** A93 50fr multi .80 .25
**335** A93 75fr multi 1.75 .90
*Nos. 333-335 (3)* 3.15 1.40

Manioc — A94

Design: 50fr, Palms and dates.

**1974, Nov. 13 Photo. *Perf. 13x12½***
**336** A94 40fr org red & multi .90 .30
**337** A94 50fr bister & multi .90 .30

**UDEAC Issue**

Presidents and Flags of Cameroun, CAR, Congo, Gabon and Meeting Center A95

**1974, Dec. 8 Photo. *Perf. 13***
**338** A95 40fr multi .80 .30
See No. C156.

Hôtel du Dialogue A96

**1975, Jan. 20 Photo. *Perf. 13***
**339** A96 50fr multi .90 .45
Opening of Hôtel du Dialogue.

**Arms Type of 1969**
5fr, Ogowe-Ivindo. 10fr, Moabi. No. 342, Moanda. No. 343, Nyanga. 25fr, Mandji. No. 345, Mekambo. No. 346, Omboué. 60fr, Minvoul. 90fr, Mayumba.

**1975-77 Photo. *Perf. 12***
**340** A67 5fr red & multi .30 .25
**341** A67 10fr gold & multi .30 .25
**342** A67 15fr red, sil & blk .45 .25
**343** A67 15fr bl & multi .35 .25
**344** A67 25fr grn & multi .45 .25
**345** A67 50fr blk, gold & red 1.40 .45
**346** A67 50fr multi 1.50 .60
**347** A67 60fr multi 1.40 .60
**348** A67 90fr multi 1.90 .75
*Nos. 340-348 (9)* 8.05 3.55
Issued: Nos. 340-342, Jan. 21, 1975; Nos. 343-345, Aug. 17, 1976; Nos. 346-348, July 12, 1977.

Map of Africa with Lion's Head, and Lions Emblem A97

**1975, May 2 Typo. *Perf. 13***
**349** A97 50fr grn & multi 1.00 .50
Lions Club 17th congress, District 403, Libreville.

Hertzian Wave Transmitter Network, Map of Gabon — A98

**1975, July 8 Engr. *Perf. 13***
**350** A98 40fr multi .90 .60

City and Rural Women, Car, Train and Building A99

**1975, July 22 Engr. *Perf. 13***
**351** A99 50fr car, bl & brn 1.75 .50
International Women's Year 1975.

Scoutmaster Ange Mba, Emblems and Rope — A100

Design: 50fr, Hand holding rope, Scout, camp, Boy Scout and Nordjamb 75 emblems.

**1975, July 29**
**352** A100 40fr multi .60 .30
**353** A100 50fr grn, red & dk brn .90 .40
Nordjamb 75, 14th Boy Scout Jamboree, Lillehammer, Norway, July 29-Aug. 7.

**Wildlife Type of 1972**
Fish: 30fr, Lutjanus goreensis. 40fr, Galeoides decadactylus. 50fr, Sardinella aurita. 120fr, Scarus hoefleri.

**1975, Sept. 22 Litho. *Perf. 14***
**354** A83 30fr multi .55 .30
**355** A83 40fr multi 1.00 .50
**356** A83 50fr multi 1.60 .50
**357** A83 120fr multi 2.50 1.00
*Nos. 354-357 (4)* 5.65 2.30

Agro-Industrial Complex — A102

**1975, Dec. 15 Litho. *Perf. 12½***
**358** A102 60fr multi .90 .40
Inauguration of Agro-Industrial Complex, Franceville.

Tchibanga Bridge A103

Bridges of Gabon: 10fr, Mouila. 40fr, Kango. 50fr, Lambaréné, vert.

**1976, Jan. 30 Engr. *Perf. 13***
**359** A103 5fr multi .35 .25
**360** A103 10fr multi .45 .25
**361** A103 40fr multi 1.00 .30
**362** A103 50fr multi 1.25 .45
*Nos. 359-362 (4)* 3.05 1.25

Telephones 1876 and 1976, Satellite, A. G. Bell — A104

**1976, Mar. 10 Engr. *Perf. 13***
**363** A104 60fr dk bl, grn & sl grn .90 .40
Centenary of first telephone call by Alexander Graham Bell, Mar. 10, 1876.

Msgr. Jean Remy Bessieux A105

**1976, Apr. 30 Engr. *Perf. 13***
**364** A105 50fr grn, bl & sepia .90 .45
Death centenary of Msgr. Bessieux.

Athletes, Torch, Map of Africa, Games Emblem — A106

**1976, June 25 Photo. _Perf. 13x12½_**
365 A106 50fr multi .70 .25
366 A106 60fr org & multi .90 .30

First Central African Games (Zone 5), Libreville, June-July.

Motobécane, France — A107

Motorcycles: 5fr, Bultaco, Spain. 10fr, Suzuki, Japan. 20fr, Kawasaki, Japan. 100fr, Harley-Davidson, US.

**1976, July 20 Litho. _Perf. 12½_**
367 A107 3fr multi .40 .25
368 A107 5fr org & multi .40 .25
369 A107 10fr bl & multi .70 .30
370 A107 20fr multi 1.25 .30
371 A107 100fr car & multi 4.50 1.00
Nos. 367-371 (5) 7.25 2.10

Rice — A108

**1976, Oct. 15 Litho. _Perf. 13x13½_**
372 A108 50fr shown .70 .35
373 A108 60fr Pepper plants 1.00 .50

**1977, Apr. 22 Litho. _Perf. 13x13½_**
50fr, Banana plantation. 60fr, Peanut market.
374 A108 50fr multi .70 .35
375 A108 60fr multi 1.00 .50

Telecommunications Emblem and Telephone — A109

**1977, May 17 _Perf. 13_**
376 A109 60fr multi .90 .50

World Telecommunications Day.

View of Oyem — A110

50fr, Cape Lopez. 70fr, Lebamba Cave.

**1977, June 9 Litho. _Perf. 12½_**
377 A110 50fr multi .65 .30
378 A110 60fr multi .70 .40
379 A110 70fr multi .75 .45
Nos. 377-379 (3) 2.10 1.15

Conference Hall — A111

**1977, June 23 Photo. _Perf. 13x12½_**
380 A111 100fr multi 1.25 .75

Meeting of the OAU, Libreville.

Arms of Gabon — A112

**Size: 23x36mm**
**1977 Engr. _Perf. 13_**
381 A112 50fr blue 1.25 .50

**Size: 17x23mm**
382 A112 60fr orange 1.10 .50
a. Booklet pane of 5 6.00
383 A112 80fr red 1.60 .65
Nos. 381-383 (3) 3.95 1.65

No. 381 issued in coils, No. 382 in booklets only.
Issued: Nos. 381-382, June 23; No. 383, Sept.

Modern Buildings, Libreville A113

**1977, Aug. 17 Litho. _Perf. 12_**
387 A113 50fr multi .90 .25

National Festival 1977.

Paris to Vienna, 1902 A114

Renault Automobiles: 10fr, Coupé 1 2 CV, 1921. 30fr, Torpédo Scaphandrier, 1925. 40fr, Reinastella 40 CV, 1929. 100fr, Nerva Grand Sport, 1937. 150fr, Voiturette 1 CV, 1899. 200fr, Alpine Renault V6, 1977.

**1977, Aug 30 Engr. _Perf. 13_**
388 A114 5fr multi .50 .35
389 A114 10fr multi .75 .35
390 A114 30fr multi 1.40 .50
391 A114 40fr multi 2.10 .60
392 A114 100fr multi 6.00 2.25
Nos. 388-392 (5) 10.75 4.05

**Miniature Sheet**
393 Sheet of 2 + label 18.00 18.00
a. A114 150fr multi 5.25 5.25
b. A114 200fr multi 7.00 7.00

Louis Renault, French automobile pioneer, birth centenary. Nos. 383a-393b are perf. on 3 sides, without perforation between stamps and center label showing dark brown portrait of Renault.
See Nos. 395-400.

Globe — A115

**1978, Feb. 21 Engr. _Perf. 13x12½_**
394 A115 80fr multi .90 .60

World Leprosy Day.

**Automobile Type of 1977**
Citroen Cars: 10fr, Cabriolet, 1922. 50fr, Taxi, 1927. 60fr, Berline, 1932. 80fr, Berline, 1934. 150fr, Torpedo, 1919. 200fr, Berline, 1948. 250fr, Pallas, 1975.

**1978, May 9 Engr. _Perf. 13_**
395 A114 10fr multi .80 .35
396 A114 50fr multi 1.50 .45
397 A114 60fr multi 2.50 .95
398 A114 80fr multi 2.50 .95
399 A114 200fr multi 6.75 2.25
Nos. 395-399 (5) 14.05 4.95

**Miniature Sheet**
400 Sheet of 2 18.00 18.00
a. A114 150fr multi 5.25 5.25
b. A114 250fr multi 7.00 7.00

Andre Citroen (1878-1935), automobile designer and manufacturer.

Ndjole on Ogowe River A116

Views: 40fr, Lambarene lake district. 50fr, Owendo Harbor.

**1978, May 17 Litho. _Perf. 12½_**
401 A116 30fr multi .40 .25
402 A116 40fr multi .70 .25
403 A116 50fr multi .90 .35
Nos. 401-403 (3) 2.00 .85

Sternotomis Mirabilis — A117

Various Coleopteras.

**1978, June 21 Photo. _Perf. 12½x13_**
404 A117 20fr multi .80 .25
405 A117 60fr multi 2.40 .65
406 A117 75fr multi 3.50 .75
407 A117 80fr multi 3.75 .90
Nos. 404-407 (4) 10.45 2.55

Anti-Apartheid Emblem — A118

**1978, July 25 Engr. _Perf. 13_**
408 A118 80fr multi .75 .40

**Arms Type of 1969**
No. 409, Oyem. No. 410, Ogowe-Maritime ('79). No. 411, Lastoursville ('79). No. 412, Haut-Ogooue ('80). No. 413, M'Bigou ('79). No. 414, Estuaire ('80). No. 415, Bitam ('80). No. 416, Okondja. No. 417, Mimongo.

**1978-80 Photo. _Perf. 12_**
409 A67 5fr multicolored .30 .25
410 A67 5fr multicolored .30 .25
411 A67 10fr multicolored .30 .25
412 A67 10fr multicolored .30 .25
413 A67 15fr multicolored .45 .25
414 A67 20fr multicolored .30 .25
415 A67 30fr multicolored .30 .25
416 A67 40fr multicolored .80 .25
417 A67 60fr multicolored 1.25 .25
Nos. 409-417 (9) 4.30 2.25

Issued: Nos. 409, 416-417, 8/17; Nos. 410-411, 413, 3/21/79; Nos. 412, 414, 415, 8/13/80.

A119

**1978, Oct. 24 Engr. _Perf. 13_**
419 A119 80fr multi 1.00 .40

UNESCO campaign to save the Acropolis.

Penicillin Formula, A120

**1978, Nov. 21 Engr. _Perf. 13_**
420 A120 90fr multi 2.50 1.10

Alexander Fleming's discovery of antibiotics, 50th anniversary.

The Visitation — A121

80fr, Massacre of the Innocents. Woodcarvings from St. Michael's Church, Libreville.

**1978, Dec. 15 Photo.**
421 A121 60fr gold & multi .85 .40
422 A121 80fr gold & multi 1.00 .50

Christmas 1978. See Nos. 437-438.

Train and Map — A122

**1978, Dec. 27 Litho. _Perf. 12½_**
423 A122 60fr multi 1.50 .60

Inauguration of Trans-Gabon Railroad, Libreville to Njolé.

A123

Pre-Olympic Year (Kremlin Towers, Olympic Emblem, Ancestral Figure and): 80fr, Long jump, vert. 100fr, Yachts.

**1979, May 15 Engr. _Perf. 13_**
424 A123 60fr multi .60 .30
425 A123 80fr multi .75 .40
426 A123 100fr multi .95 .55
a. Miniature sheet of 3, #424-426 3.75 3.75
Nos. 424-426 (3) 2.30 1.25

Rowland Hill, Messenger and Gabon No. O9 — A124

Allamanda Schottii — A125

Designs: 80fr, Bakota mask and tulip tree flowers, vert. 150fr, Pigeon, UPU emblem, truck and canoe. No. 430b, Gloriosa superba. No. 430c, Phaeomeria magnifica, vert. No. 430d, Berlinia bracteosa, vert.

**1979, June 8 Photo. _Perf. 13_**
427 A124 50fr multi 1.10 1.10
428 A124 80fr multi 1.75 1.25

**Engr.**
429 A124 150fr multi 3.00 2.00
Nos. 427-429 (3) 5.85 4.35

**Souvenir Sheet**
**Photo. _Perf. 14_**
430 Sheet of 4 10.00 10.00
a. A125 100fr multicolored 2.00
b. A125 100fr multicolored 2.00
c. A125 100fr multicolored 2.00
d. A125 100fr multicolored 2.00

Philexafrique II, Libreville, June 8-17. Nos. 427-429 each printed in sheets of 10 with 5 labels showing exhibition emblem. No. 427 also commemorates Sir Rowland Hill (1795-1879), originator of penny postage. No. 430 has label with exhibition emblem.

IYC Emblem, Globe, Child with Bird — A126

**1979, June 15      Engr.      Perf. 13**
431 A126 100fr multi                  1.25  .70
International Year of the Child.

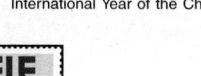

"TELECOM 79" — A127

**1979, Sept. 18    Litho.    Perf. 13x12½**
432 A127 80fr multi                  1.00  .40
3rd World Telecommunications Exhibition, Geneva, Sept. 20-26.

Sugar Cane Harvest — A128

**1979, Oct. 9     Photo.     Perf. 12½x13**
433 A128 25fr shown                  .45  .25
434 A128 30fr Yams                   .65  .25

Judo Throw — A129

**1979, Oct. 23      Engr.      Perf. 13**
435 A129 40fr multi                  1.90  .75
World Judo Championships, Paris, Dec.

Mother and Child, Map of Congo River Basin A130

**1979, Dec. 2      Litho.      Perf. 12**
436 A130 200fr multi                 2.50  .80
Medical Week, Dec. 2-9.

**Christmas Type of 1978**
Wood Carvings, St. Michael's Church, Libreville: 60fr, Flight into Egypt.  80fr, The Circumcision.

**1979, Dec. 12      Photo.      Perf. 13**
437 A121 60fr multi                  .90  .40
438 A121 80fr multi                  1.10  .40

Pres. Omar Bongo — A131

**1979-80      Litho.      Perf. 12½**
439 A131 60fr multi                  .90  .40
440 A131 80fr multi                  2.50  1.25
Bongo's 44th birthday (No. 439); re-election and inauguration (No. 440).

---

Issued: 60fr, 12/30/79; 80fr, 2/27/80.

OPEC, 20th Anniv. — A132

**1980, Mar. 27    Litho.    Perf. 13½x13**
441 A132 50fr multi                  .90  .35

Donguila Church A133

80fr, Bizengobibere Church.

**1980 Apr. 3      Litho.      Perf. 12½**
442 A133 60fr shown                  .65  .30
443 A133 80fr multicolored           .85  .35
Easter 1980.

De Brazza (1852-1905), Map of Gabon with Franceville — A134

**1980, June 30    Litho.    Perf. 12½**
444 A134 165fr multi                 2.50  1.10
Franceville Foundation centenary, founded by Savorgnan De Brazza.

20th Anniversary of Independence — A135

60cr, Leon Mba and Omar Bongo.

**1980, Aug. 17      Photo.      Perf. 13**
445 A135 60fr multicolored           .90  .25

World Tourism Conference, Manila, Sept. 27 A136

**1980, Sept. 10                    Engr.**
446 A136 80fr multi                  .90  .35

20th Anniversary of OPEC — A137

120fr, Men Holding OPEC emblem, vert.

**1980, Sept. 15    Litho.    Perf. 12½**
447 A137 90fr shown                  1.00  .40
448 A137 120fr multicolored          1.50  .60

Pseudochelidon Eurystomina — A138

---

**1980, Oct. 15    Photo.    Perf. 14x14½**
449 A138 50fr shown                  2.00  .50
450 A138 60fr multi                  2.50  .75
451 A138 80fr Pitta angolensis       4.00  1.00
452 A138 150fr Scotopelia peli       7.50  2.00
    Nos. 449-452 (4)                16.00  4.25

Statue of Bull, Bizangobibere Church — A139

**1980, Dec. 10    Photo.    Perf. 14x14½**
453 A139 60fr shown                  .90  .30
454 A139 80fr Male statue            1.10  .45
Christmas 1980.

Heinrich von Stephan — A140

**1981, Jan. 7      Engr.      Perf. 13**
455 A140 90fr brn & dk brn           .90  .35
Von Stephan (1831-97), UPU founder.

13th Anniversary of National Renovation Movement A141

**1981, Mar. 12    Litho.    Perf. 13x12½**
456 A141 60fr multi                  .80  .25

Lion Statue, Bizangobibere — A142

**1981, Apr. 12    Photo.    Perf. 14x14½**
457 A142 75fr multi                  .90  .40
458 A142 100fr multi                 1.10  .55
Easter 1981.

Port Gentil Lions Club Banner — A143

75fr, District 403. 80fr, Libreville Cocotiers. 100fr, Libreville Hibiscus. 165fr, Ekwata. 200fr, Haut-Ogooue.

**1981, May 1      Litho.      Perf. 12½**
459 A143 60fr shown                  .75  .25
460 A143 75fr multi                  .85  .30
461 A143 80fr multi                  .85  .35
462 A143 100fr multi                 1.10  .40
463 A143 165fr multi                 1.75  .70
464 A143 200fr multi                 2.25  .90
    Nos. 459-464 (6)                 7.55  2.90
Lions International, 23rd Congress of District 403, Libreville, May 1-3.

---

13th World Telecommunications Day — A144

**1981, May 17      Photo.      Perf. 13**
465 A144 125fr multi                 1.40  .55

Unity, Work and Justice — A145

**1981-96?      Photo.      Perf. 13**
466  A145  5fr beige & blk           .30  .25
467  A145  10fr pale lil & blk       .30  .25
468  A145  15fr brt yel grn & blk    .30  .25
469  A145  20fr pink & blk           .30  .25
470  A145  25fr vio & blk            .30  .25
471  A145  40fr red org & blk        .45  .25
472  A145  50fr bluish grn & blk     .55  .25
473  A145  75fr bis brn & blk        .65  .25
473A A145  90fr lt bl & blk ('83)    .80  .25
474  A145  100fr yel & blk           .90  .40
474A A145  125fr grn & blk ('83)     1.10  .35
474B A145  150fr brt pink & blk ('86) 1.25  .40
474C A145  175fr grnish bl & blk ('96) .55  .55
    Nos. 466-474B (12)               7.20  3.40
Issued: 5fr, 10fr, 15fr, 20fr, 25fr, 40fr, 50fr, 75fr, 100fr, 7/1. See Nos. 862-871, 959-960.

R.P. Klaine (Missionary), 70th Death Anniv. — A146

90fr, Archbishop Walker, 110th birth anniv.

**1981, July 2                    Litho.**
475 A146 70fr multi                  .80  .30
476 A146 90fr multi                  1.25  .35

Map of Gabon and Scout Sign — A147

**1981, July 16                    Perf. 12½**
477 A147 75fr multi                  1.00  .35
4th Pan-African Scouting Congress, Abidjan, Aug.

**No. 477 Overprinted: DAKAR / 28e CONFERENCE / MONDIALE DU / SCOUTISME**

**1981, July 23**
478 A147 75fr multi                  1.25  .45
28th World Scouting Conf., Dakar, Aug.

Intl. Year of the Disabled — A148

**1981, Aug. 6      Engr.      Perf. 13**
479 A148 100fr multi                 1.25  .65

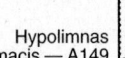

Hypolimnas
Salmacis — A149

100fr, Euphaedra themis. 150fr, Amauris
niavius. 250fr, Cymothoe lucasi.

**1981, Sept. 10　Litho.　Perf. 14½x14**
480 A149 75fr shown　　　　　　1.75　.60
481 A149 100fr multicolored　　　2.25　.75
482 A149 150fr multicolored　　　2.75　1.00
483 A149 250fr multicolored　　　4.25　1.75
　　Nos. 480-483 (4)　　　　　　11.00　4.10

Paul as Harlequin,
by Pablo Picasso
(1881-1973)
A150

**1981, Sept. 25　Perf. 14½x13½**
484 A150 500fr multi　　　　　　7.00　2.50

World Food
Day — A151

**1981, Oct. 16　Engr.　Perf. 13**
485 A151 350fr multi　　　　　　4.00　1.60

Traditional
Hairstyle — A152

Designs: Various hairstyles.

**1981, Nov. 12　Litho.　Perf. 14½x15**
486 A152 75fr multi　　　　　　　.90　.55
487 A152 100fr multi　　　　　　1.00　.50
488 A152 125fr multi　　　　　　1.60　.80
489 A152 200fr multi　　　　　　2.50　1.10
　a.　Souvenir sheet of 4, #486-489　6.50　6.50
　　Nos. 486-489 (4)　　　　　　6.00　2.95

See Nos. 609A-609B, 676.

Christmas
1981 — A153

Designs: Children's drawings.

**1981, Dec. 10　Perf. 14½x14**
490 A153 75fr Girls dancing　　　.90　.35
491 A153 100fr Dinner　　　　　1.25　.50

**Arms Type of 1969**

No. 492, Moyen-Ogooue. No. 493,
Cocobeach. No. 494, Woleu-N'tem. No. 495,
Lambarene. No. 496, Port Gentil District. No.
497, Medouneu. No. 498, Mouila. No. 499,
N'Djole. No. 500, N'Gounie. No. 501, Leconi.

**Perf. 12, 13 (#495-497)**

**1982-92　　　　　　　　Photo.**
492 A67 75fr multicolored　　　　.70　.25
493 A67 90fr multicolored　　　　.90　.25
494 A67 100fr multicolored　　　1.00　.25
495 A67 100fr multicolored　　　.90　.30
496 A67 100fr multicolored　　　.90　.35
497 A67 100fr multicolored　　　.90　.35
498 A67 100fr multicolored　　　1.00　.35
499 A67 135fr multicolored　　　1.10　.40
500 A67 150fr multicolored　　　1.25　.40
501 A67 160fr multicolored　　　1.10　.40
　　Nos. 492-501 (10)　　　　　9.75　3.50

Issued: Nos. 492, 494, 500, 1/13/82; Nos.
493, 498, 499, 8/7/84; Nos. 495, 501, 8/11/86;
No. 496, 4/17/91; No. 497, 8/12/92.

A154

**1982, Feb. 16　Litho.　Perf. 13**
502 A154 100fr multi　　　　　　2.00　1.10

Visit of Pope John Paul II, Feb. 17-19.

A155

**1982, Mar. 31　Engr.　Perf. 13**
503 A155 75fr black　　　　　　1.00　.75

Alfred de Musset (1810-1857), writer.

Merchant Navy
Ships — A156

**1982, Apr. 7　Litho.　Perf. 14½x14**
504 A156　75fr multicolored　　　.75　.30
505 A156 100fr Freighter　　　　1.00　.40
506 A156 200fr Oil tanker　　　　2.00　.85
　　Nos. 504-506 (3)　　　　　　3.75　1.55

See Nos. 588, 599.

TB Bacillus
Centenary
A157

**1982, Apr. 24　Litho.　Perf. 13**
507 A157 100fr multi　　　　　　1.50　.75

PHILEXFRANCE '82
Stamp Exhibition,
Paris, June 11-
21 — A158

**1982, Apr. 28　Perf. 12½**
508 A158 100fr Rope bridge　　　.85　.40
509 A158 200fr Sculptured head　1.90　.55
　a.　Pair, #508-509 + label　　　4.00　2.75

14th World Telecommunications
Day — A159

**1982, May 17　Perf. 13**
510 A159 75fr multi　　　　　　　.90　.40

1982 World
Cup — A160

Designs: Various soccer players.

**1982, May 19　　　　　Perf. 14x14½**
511 A160 100fr multi　　　　　　1.00　.40
512 A160 125fr multi　　　　　　1.10　.45
513 A160 200fr multi　　　　　　1.90　.75
　a.　Souvenir sheet of 3, #511-513,
　　　perf. 14½　　　　　　　　4.50　4.50
　　Nos. 511-513 (3)　　　　　　4.00　1.60

For overprints see Nos. 516-518.

2nd UN Conf. on Peaceful Uses of
Outer Space, Vienna, Aug. 9-21
A161

**1982, July 7　Engr.　Perf. 13**
514 A161 250fr Satellites　　　　2.75　1.25

White Carnations
A162

Designs: Various carnations.

**1982, June 9　Photo.　Perf. 14½x14**
515　　Strip of 3　　　　　　　4.00　1.75
　a.　A162 75fr multi　　　　　　.90　.45
　b.　A162 100fr multi　　　　　1.10　.50
　c.　A162 175fr multi　　　　　2.00　1.00

**Nos. 511-513a Overprinted in Red
with Semi-Finalists or Finalists**

**1982, Aug. 19　Litho.　Perf. 14x14½**
516 A160 100fr multi　　　　　　.90　.35
517 A160 125fr multi　　　　　　1.10　.45
518 A160 200fr multi　　　　　　1.90　.75
　a.　Souvenir sheet of 3　　　　4.50　4.50
　　Nos. 516-518 (3)　　　　　　3.90　1.55

Italy's victory in 1982 World Cup.

Phyllonotus
Duplex — A163

100fr, Chama crenulata. 125fr, Cardium
hians.

**1982, Sept. 22　　　　Perf. 14½x14**
519 A163　75fr shown　　　　　1.25　.50
520 A163 100fr multi　　　　　　1.50　.65
521 A163 125fr multi　　　　　　2.25　1.25
　　Nos. 519-521 (3)　　　　　　5.00　2.40

Okouyi Mask — A164

100fr, Ondoumbo reliquary. 150fr, Tsogho
statuette. 250fr, Fang bellows.

**1982, Oct. 13　Litho.　Perf. 14x14½**
522 A164　75fr shown　　　　　.65　.30
523 A164 100fr multi　　　　　　1.10　.40
524 A164 150fr multi　　　　　　1.90　.55
525 A164 250fr multi　　　　　　2.75　.95
　　Nos. 522-525 (4)　　　　　　6.40　2.20

St. Francis Xavier
Church — A165

**1982, Dec. 15　Litho.　Perf. 14x14½**
526 A165 100fr multicolored　　　.90　.35

Christmas 1982.

Trans-Gabon
Railroad
Inauguration
A166

**1983, Jan. 18　　　　　Perf. 12½**
527 A166 75fr multi　　　　　　　2.00　.50

5th African
Highway
Conference,
Libreville,
Feb. 6-11
A167

**1983, Feb. 2　　　　　　Perf. 13**
528 A167 100fr multi　　　　　　.90　.35

15th Anniv. of Natl.
Renewal — A168

Provincial Symbols: a. Bakota mask,
Ogowe Ivindo. b. Butterfly, Ogowe Lolo. c.
Buffalo, Nyanga. d. Isogho hairdo, Ngounie.
e. Tarpon, Ogowe Maritime. f. Manganese,
Haut Ogowe. g. Crocodiles, Moyen Ogowe.
h. Coffee plant. i. Epitorium trochiformis.

**1983, Mar. 12　Litho.　Perf. 13x13½**
529　　Strip of 9 + label　　　17.50　15.00
　a.　A168 75fr multi　　　　　1.00　.45
　b.　A168 90fr multi　　　　　1.25　.50
　c.　A168 90fr multi　　　　　1.25　.50
　d.　A168 100fr multi　　　　　1.40　.60
　e.　A168 125fr multi　　　　　1.60　.75
　f.　A168 125fr multi　　　　　1.60　.75
　g.　A168 125fr multi　　　　　1.60　.75
　h.　A168 135fr multi　　　　　1.90　.85
　i.　A168 135fr multi　　　　　1.90　.85

25th Anniv.
of Intl.
Maritime
Org.
A169

**1983, Mar. 17　　　　　Perf. 13**
530 A169 125fr multi　　　　　　1.40　.50

Pelican — A170

90fr, Water musk deer. 225fr, Elephant.
400fr, Iguana.

**1983, Apr. 20　Litho.　Perf. 15x14½**
531 A170　90fr multi　　　　　　.90　.35
532 A170 125fr shown　　　　　1.25　.45
533 A170 225fr multi　　　　　　3.25　.85
534 A170 400fr multi　　　　　　4.50　1.50
　a.　Souv. sheet of 4, #531-534　16.00　16.00
　　Nos. 531-534 (4)　　　　　　9.90　3.15

25th Anniv. of UN
Economic
Commission for
Africa — A171

**1983, Apr. 29　Litho.　Perf. 12½**
535 A171 125fr multi　　　　　　1.25　.50

15th World Telecommunications
Day — A172

**1983, May 17**    **Litho.**    *Perf. 13*
536 A172 90fr multi   1.25 .55
537 A172 90fr multi   1.25 .55
  *a.*   Pair, #536-537   3.50 3.50
Denomination of No. 536 in lower right, No. 537, upper left.

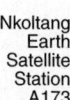

Nkoltang Earth Satellite Station A173

**1983, July 2**
538 A173 125fr multi   1.25 .60
10th anniv. of station; WCY.

Ivindo River Rapids A174

125fr, Ogooue River. 185fr, Wonga Wongue Preserve. 350fr, Coastal view.

**1983, Sept. 7**    **Engr.**    *Perf. 13*
539 A174 90fr shown   .85 .35
540 A174 125fr multicolored   1.40 .60
541 A174 185fr multicolored   2.00 .80
542 A174 350fr multicolored   3.75 1.50
  Nos. 539-542 (4)   8.00 3.25

Hand Drum, Mahongwe — A175

125fr, Okoukoue dancer. 135fr, Four-stringed fiddle. 260fr, Ndoumou dancer.

**1983, Oct. 12**    **Litho.**    *Perf. 14x14½*
543 A175 90fr shown   .90 .35
544 A175 125fr multicolored   1.40 .45
545 A175 135fr multicolored   1.50 .60
546 A175 260fr multicolored   3.00 1.10
  Nos. 543-546 (4)   6.80 2.50

Harmful Insects — A176

90fr, Glossinidae. 125fr, Belonogaster junceus. 300fr, Aedes aegypti. 350fr, Mylabris.

**1983, Nov. 9**
547 A176 90fr multicolored   1.60 .80
548 A176 125fr multicolored   2.00 1.10
549 A176 300fr multicolored   4.25 1.60
550 A176 350fr multicolored   5.25 2.10
  Nos. 547-550 (4)   13.10 5.60

Christmas 1983 — A177

Wood Carvings, St. Michael's Church, Libreville — 90fr, Adultress. 125fr, Good Samaritan.

*Perf. 14½x13½*
**1983, Dec. 14**    **Litho.**
551 A177 90fr multicolored   .80 .35
552 A177 125fr multicolored   1.40 .65

Boeing 737, No. 202 — A178

225fr, Lufthansa jet, Germany No. C2.

**1984, Jan. 12**    *Perf. 13x12½*
553 A178 125fr shown   1.25 .40
554 A178 225fr org & multi   2.50 .70
  *a.*   Pair, #553-554 + label   4.50 4.00
19th World UPU Congress, Hamburg, June 19-26.

3rd Anniv. of Africa 1 Radio Transmitter A179

**1984, Feb. 7**    **Litho.**    *Perf. 12½*
555 A179 125fr multi   1.25 .65

Local Flowers — A180

Various flowers.

**1984, Apr. 18**    **Litho.**    *Perf. 14x15*
556 A180 90fr multi   1.25 .45
557 A180 125fr multi   1.40 .55
558 A180 135fr multi   1.90 .65
559 A180 350fr multi   4.00 1.60
  Nos. 556-559 (4)   8.55 3.25

Fruit Trees — A181

**1984, Mar. 1**    **Litho.**    *Perf. 14½x14*
560 A181 90fr Coconut   1.15 .45
561 A181 100fr Papaya   1.40 .55
562 A181 125fr Mango   1.60 .65
563 A181 250fr Banana   3.75 1.25
  Nos. 560-563 (4)   7.90 2.90

World Telecommunications Day — A182

**1984, May 17**    *Perf. 13x13½*
564 A182 125fr multi   1.25 .65

Black Jazz Musicians — A183

**1984, July 5**    *Perf. 12½*
565 A183 90fr Lionel Hampton   1.75 .70
566 A183 125fr Charlie Parker   1.75 .70
567 A183 260fr Erroll Garner   3.50 1.75
  Nos. 565-567 (3)   7.00 3.15

View of Medouneu A184

125fr, Canoes, Ogooue River. 165fr, Railroad.

**1984, Sept. 1**    **Litho.**    *Perf. 13*
568 A184 90fr shown   .85 .40
569 A184 125fr multi   1.25 .55
570 A184 165fr multi   2.25 1.25
  Nos. 568-570 (3)   4.35 2.20

15th World UPU Day — A185

125fr, UPU emblem, globe, mail.

**1984, Oct. 9**    **Litho.**    *Perf. 13½*
571 A185 125fr multi   1.25 .50

40th Anniv., International Civil Aviation Organization A186

**1984, Dec. 1**    **Litho.**    *Perf. 13½*
572 A186 125fr Icarus   1.25 .65

Masks — A186a

90fr, Kouele. 125fr, Eventail Pounou. 150fr, Reliquaire Mahongoue. 250fr, Kota du Sud.

**1984, Oct. 30**    **Litho.**    *Perf. 14x15*
572A A186a 90fr multicolored   — —
572B A186a 125fr multicolored   — —
572C A186a 150fr multicolored   — —
572D A186a 250fr multicolored   — —

Christmas — A187

90fr, St. Michael's Church Libreville. 125fr, St. Michael's, diff.

**1984, Dec. 14**    **Litho.**    *Perf. 12½*
573   90fr multi   .90 .45
574   125fr multi   1.40 .65
  *a.*   A187 Pair, #573-574   2.50 2.00

World Leprosy Day — A188

**1985, Jan. 27**    **Litho.**    *Perf. 12½*
575 A188 125fr Hospital, Libreville   1.50 .55

International Youth Year — A189

**1985, Feb. 6**    **Litho.**    *Perf. 13x12½*
576 A189 125fr Silhouttes, wreath   1.25 .50

Birds — A190

**1984, Nov. 16**    **Litho.**    *Perf. 15x14*
577 A190 90fr Crowned crane   1.25 .75
578 A190 125fr Hummingbird   2.00 1.00
579 A190 150fr Toucan   2.50 1.25
  Nos. 577-579 (3)   5.75 3.00

Silhouettes, Emblem — A191

**1985, Mar. 20**    **Wmk. 385**    *Perf. 12½*
580 A191 125fr brt ultra, red & bl   1.25 .75
Cultural and Technical Cooperation Agency, 15th anniv.

Wildlife — A192

**1985, Apr. 17**    **Unwmk.**    *Perf. 15x14*
581 A192 90fr Aulacode   1.50 .50
582 A192 100fr Porcupine   1.50 .50
583 A192 125fr Giant pangolin   2.00 1.00
584 A192 350fr Antelope   5.00 2.25
  *a.*   Souvenir sheet of 4, #581-584   13.00 13.00
  Nos. 581-584 (4)   10.00 4.25

Georges Damas Aleka, Composer A193

90fr, Portrait, La Concorde score.

**1985, Apr. 30**    *Perf. 13*
585 A193 90fr multicolored   1.20 .35

ITU, 120th Anniv. — A194

**1985, May 17**    *Perf. 13½*
586 A194 125fr multi   1.25 .65
World Telecommunications Day.

A195

**1985, June 9**
587 A195 90fr Emblem   1.10 .60
Christian Youth Workers' Movement (J.O.C.) in Gabon, 30th anniv.

**Merchant Navy Ships Type of 1982**
**1985, July 1**    *Perf. 15x14*
588 A156 185fr Freighter Mpassa   2.00 .80

Posts and Telecommunications Administration, 20th Anniv. — A196

**1985, July 25**    *Perf. 13*
589 A196 90fr Headquarters   1.00 .50

President Bongo — A197

1000fr, View of Libreville.

**1985, Aug. 17**    *Perf. 14*
590 A197 250fr multi    3.50 1.60
591 A197 500fr multi    7.75 4.00
a.   Pair, #590-591 + 3 labels    14.00 14.00

*Imperf*
**Size: 120x90mm**
592 A197 1000fr multi    14.00 14.00
   *Nos. 590-592 (3)*    25.25 19.60

Natl. Independence, 25th anniv.
No. 592 has non-denominated vignettes of Nos. 590-591.

Org. of Petroleum Exporting Countries, 25th Anniv. — A198

**1985, Sept. 25**   **Wmk. 385**   *Perf. 13½*
593 A198 350fr multi    4.00 1.90

Intl. Center of the Bantu Civilizations A199

*Perf. 15x14*
**1985, Nov. 16**   **Litho.**   **Unwmk.**
594 A199 185fr multi    1.75 .95

St. Andrew's Church, Libreville — A199a

Design: 125fr, Church interior, horiz.

*Perf. 14x15, 15x14*
**1985, Dec. 16**    **Litho.**
594A A199a 90fr multicolored    — —
594B A199a 125fr multicolored    — —
Christmas.

UNESCO, 25th Anniv. A200

**1986, Jan. 5**   **Litho.**   *Perf. 12½*
595 A200 100fr multi    1.00 .45

A201

**1986, May 1**   **Litho.**   *Perf. 13½*
596 A201 150fr multi    1.75 .60
Rotary Intl. District 915, 4th conf.

---

A202

**1986, June 16**   **Litho.**   *Perf. 12½*
597 A202 150fr multi    1.50 .60
Natl. Week of Cartography, Libreville, June 16-20.

Coffee Flowers, Berries, Beans A203

**1986, Aug. 27**   **Litho.**   *Perf. 12½*
598 A203 125fr multi    1.50 .90
Organization of African and Madagascar Coffee Producers, 25th anniv.

**Merchant Navy Ships Type of 1982**

250fr, Merchantman L'Abanga.

**1986, June 24**   **Litho.**   *Perf. 15x14*
599 A156 250fr multicolored    3.00 1.25

Natl. Postage Stamp, Cent. A205

**1986, July 10**    *Perf. 13½x14½*
600 A205 500fr Boats, No. 4    7.00 3.50

Flowering Plants — A206

100fr, Allamanda neriifolia. 150fr, Musa cultivar. 160fr, Dissotis decumbens. 350fr, Campylospermum laeve.

**1986, July 23**    *Perf. 14½x15*
601 A206 100fr multicolored    1.10 .50
602 A206 150fr multicolored    1.60 .80
603 A206 160fr multicolored    1.60 .85
604 A206 350fr multicolored    4.50 2.10
   *Nos. 601-604 (4)*    8.80 4.25

Butterflies A207

**1986, Sept. 18**   **Litho.**   *Perf. 15x14*
605 A207 150fr Machaon    2.10 .60
606 A207 290fr Urania    4.75 1.40

St. Pierre Church, Libreville — A208

**1986, Dec. 23**   **Litho.**   *Perf. 15x14½*
607 A208 500fr multi    4.50 1.50
Christmas.

---

Trans-Gabon Railway from Owendo to Franceville, Inauguration A209

**1986, Dec. 30**    *Perf. 13*
608 A209 90fr multi    1.25 .50

**Souvenir Sheet**
609 A209 250fr multi    4.50 4.50

**Traditional Hairstyles Type of 1981**

**1986, Nov. 10**   **Litho.**   *Perf. 14x15*
609A A152 100fr blk, gray & yell    150.00 7.50
609B A152 150fr tan, blk & red brn    5.00 1.50

Fish — A210

90fr, Adioryx bastatus. 125fr, Scarus boefleri. 225fr, Cephalacanthus volitans. 350fr, Dasyatis marmorata.

**1987, Jan. 15**    *Perf. 15x14½*
610 A210 90fr multicolored    1.25 .60
611 A210 125fr multicolored    1.75 .85
612 A210 225fr multicolored    2.25 1.25
613 A210 350fr multicolored    3.25 1.90
a.   Souv. sheet of 4, Nos. 610-613    12.00 12.00
   *Nos. 610-613 (4)*    8.50 4.60
No. 613a issued Oct. 1987.

Raoul Follereau (1903-1977) — A211

**1987, Jan. 23**    *Perf. 12½*
614 A211 125fr multi    1.40 .85
World Leprosy Day.

Pres. Bongo Accepting the 1986 Dag Hammarskjold Peace Prize — A212

**1987, Mar. 31**   **Litho.**   *Perf. 13*
615 A212 125fr multi    1.10 .60

World Telecommunications Day — A213

**1987, May 17**   **Litho.**   *Perf. 13½*
616 A213 90fr multi    1.00 .40

---

Lions Club of Gabon, 30th Anniv. — A214

**1987, July 18**   **Litho.**   *Perf. 12x12½*
617 A214 90fr multi    1.00 .40

Pierre de Coubertin, Father of the Modern Olympics — A215

**1987, Aug. 29**
618 A215 200fr multi    1.90 .85

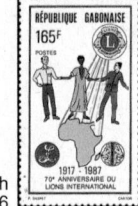

Lions Club Intl., 70th Anniv. — A216

**1987, Oct. 1**
619 A216 165fr multi    1.75 .65

World Post Day — A217

**1987, Oct. 9**   **Litho.**   *Perf. 13½*
620 A217 125fr multi    1.25 .75

Seashells — A218

**1987, Feb. 20**    *Perf. 15x14*
621 A218 90fr Natica fanel    1.20 .35
622 A218 125fr Natica fulminea cruentata    2.00 .45
a.   Souv. sheet of 2, Nos. 621-622    6.00 6.00

Intl. Year of Shelter for the Homeless A219

**1987, Oct. 5**    *Perf. 12½*
623 A219 90fr multi    1.10 .40

Solidarity with the South West African Peoples' Organization (SWAPO) — A220

225fr, Pres. Bongo, SWAPO leader.

**1987, Sept. 15**   **Litho.**   *Perf. 14½x15*
624 A220 225fr multicolored    1.75 .95

St. Anna of Odimba
Mission — A221

**1987, Nov. 2** *Perf. 13½*
625 A221 90fr multi 1.00 .30

Universal Child
Immunization
A222

**1987, Nov. 16** *Perf. 15x14½*
626 A222 100fr multi 1.00 .40

20th Anniv. of the
Presidency of Omar
Bongo — A223

**1987, Dec. 2** *Perf. 14½x13½*
627 A223 1000fr multi 10.00 5.50

Christmas
A224

90fr, St. Therese Church, Oyem.

**1987, Dec. 15** *Perf. 15x14½*
628 A224 90fr multicolored 1.00 .30

1988 Winter
Olympics,
Calgary
A225

**1987, Dec. 30** *Perf. 13½x14½*
629 A225 125fr multi 1.25 .50

Medicinal
Plants — A226

90fr, Cassia occidentalis. 125fr,
Tabernanthe iboga. 225fr, Cassia alata. 350fr,
Anthocleista schweinfurthii.

**1988, Jan. 26 Litho.** *Perf. 14x15*
630 A226 90fr multicolored 1.10 .55
631 A226 125fr multicolored 1.50 .55
632 A226 225fr multicolored 2.75 1.10
633 A226 350fr multicolored 5.00 2.75
a. Miniature sheet of 4, #630-
633 12.00 12.00
Nos. 630-633 (4) 10.35 4.95

World
Wildlife Fund
A227

African forest elephant, Loxodonta africana
cyclotis.

**1988, Feb. 29 Litho.** *Perf. 13½*
634 A227 25fr multi 2.25 .75
635 A227 40fr multi, diff. 3.00 1.50
636 A227 50fr multi, diff. 5.00 1.75
637 A227 100fr multi, diff. 8.25 3.25
Nos. 634-637 (4) 18.50 7.25

Traditional
Musical
Instruments
A228

90fr, Obamba hochet. 100fr, Fang sanza,
vert. 125fr, Mitsogho harp, vert. 165fr, Fang
xylophone.

**1988, Feb. 17** *Perf. 14*
638 A228 90fr multicolored 1.10 .70
639 A228 100fr multicolored 1.20 .70
640 A228 125fr multicolored 1.50 .90
641 A228 165fr multicolored 2.40 1.00
a. Souv. sheet of 4, Nos. 638-
641 7.00 7.00
Nos. 638-641 (4) 6.20 3.30

World Cup
Rugby
A229

*Perf. 13½x14½*
**1987, June 10 Litho.**
642 A229 350fr multi 4.25 1.90

Delta Post
Office
Inauguration
A230

**1988, Mar. 9**
643 A230 90fr multi 1.00 .30

World
Telecommunications
Day — A231

**1988, May 17** *Perf. 13½*
644 A231 125fr multi 1.25 .45

Storming of
the Bastille,
July 14,
1789
A232

**1988, May 30 Litho.** *Perf. 13*
645 A232 125fr multi 1.60 .50
PHILEXFRANCE '89.

Intl. Fund for
Agricultural
Development
(IFAD), 10th
Anniv. — A233

**1988, June 20** *Perf. 13½*
646 A233 350fr multi 4.25 1.60

Intl. Red Cross and Red Crescent
Organizations, 125th Annivs. — A234

**1988, July 15 Litho.** *Perf. 12½*
647 A234 125fr multi 1.25 .45

1988 Summer
Olympics,
Seoul — A235

**1988, Sept. 17 Litho.** *Perf. 15x14*
648 A235 90fr Tennis .80 .35
649 A235 100fr Swimming 1.10 .45
650 A235 350fr Running 3.25 1.60
651 A235 500fr Hurdles 5.50 2.00
a. Souv. sheet of 4, #648-651 13.00 13.00
Nos. 648-651 (4) 10.65 4.40

World Post
Day — A236

**1988, Oct. 9** *Perf. 13½*
652 A236 125fr blk, brt yel & brt
blue 1.25 .45

Christmas
A237

200fr, Medouneu Church.

**1988, Dec. 20 Litho.** *Perf. 15x14*
653 A237 200fr multi 2.00 .70

Natica Fanel —
A237a

**1988, July 1 Litho.** *Perf. 15x14*
653A A237a 90fr shown 25.00 5.00
653B A237a 125fr Natica sp. 25.00 7.50
c. Souv. sheet of 2, #653A-
653B — —

A238

**1989, Feb. 21** *Perf. 13½*
654 A238 175fr multi 1.25 .60
Chaine des Rotisseurs in Gabon, 10th anniv.

A239

**1989, Mar. 6 Litho.** *Perf. 13½*
655 A239 125fr multi 1.25 .55
Rabi Kounga oil field. See No. 707.

Traditional
Games
A240

*Perf. 13½x14½*
**1989, Mar. 20 Litho.**
656 A240 90fr multicolored 1.10 .55

Birds — A241

100fr, White-tufted bittern. 175fr, Gabon
gray parakeet. 200fr, Pygmy hornbill. 500fr,
Pope's martin.

**1989, Apr. 17 Litho.** *Perf. 14x15*
657 A241 100fr multicolored 1.00 .35
658 A241 175fr multicolored 1.50 .65
659 A241 200fr multicolored 1.90 .70
660 A241 500fr multicolored 4.75 2.10
a. Souv. sheet of 4, Nos. 657-
660 11.00 11.00
Nos. 657-660 (4) 9.15 3.80
See Nos. 750-753.

A242

**1989, Apr. 27** *Perf. 13*
661 A242 125fr multi 1.10 .45
8th Convention of Lions Intl. District 403,
Libreville, Apr. 27-29.

World
Telecommunications
Day — A243

**1989, May 17 Wmk. 385** *Perf. 13½*
662 A243 300fr multi 3.00 1.10

PHILEXFRANCE '89 — A244

Symbols of the French revolution, 1789.

**Wmk. 385**
**1989, July 7 Litho.** *Perf. 13*
663 A244 175fr multi 2.10 .80

French
Revolution,
Bicent.
A245

**1989, July 14 Wmk. 385**
664 A245 500fr multi 6.50 3.25

Fruit — A246

**Perf. 14½x15**

| 1989, May 30 | Litho. | Unwmk. |
|---|---|---|
| 665 A246 | 90fr Coconuts | 1.00 .45 |
| 666 A246 | 125fr Cabosse | 1.50 .50 |
| 667 A246 | 175fr Pineapple | 2.25 .80 |
| 668 A246 | 250fr Breadfruit | 2.75 1.25 |
| a. | Souv. sheet of 4, #665-668 | 8.50 8.50 |
|  | Nos. 665-668 (4) | 7.50 3.00 |

A247

| 1989, July 27 | Litho. | **Perf. 13** |
|---|---|---|
| 669 A247 | 100fr multi | 1.25 .50 |

International Association of Francophone Mayors (AIMF), 10th anniv.

African Development Bank, 25th Anniv. — A248

| 1989, Aug. 2 | Litho. | **Perf. 13** |
|---|---|---|
| 670 A248 | 100fr multi | 1.00 .40 |

*Apples and Oranges,* by Cezanne (1839-1906) A249

**Perf. 13½x14½**

| 1989, June 22 | Litho. |
|---|---|
| 671 A249 | 500fr multicolored | 6.00 3.25 |

1990 World Cup Soccer Championships, Italy — A250

Various athletes.

**Perf. 15x14½**

| 1989, Aug. 23 | Litho. | Unwmk. |
|---|---|---|
| 672 A250 | 100fr shown | .85 .35 |
| 673 A250 | 175fr multi, diff. | 1.60 .65 |
| 674 A250 | 300fr multi, diff. | 2.75 1.25 |
| 675 A250 | 500fr multi, diff. | 4.50 1.90 |
| a. | Souv. sheet of 4, #672-675 | 11.00 11.00 |
|  | Nos. 672-675 (4) | 9.70 4.15 |

**Traditional Hairstyles Type of 1981**

| 1989, Sept. 16 | | **Perf. 14½x15** |
|---|---|---|
| 676 A152 | 175fr gray, black & vio | 2.00 .85 |

Post Day — A252

**Granite Paper**

| 1989, Sept. 10 | Litho. | **Perf. 12** |
|---|---|---|
| 677 A252 | 175fr multicolored | 1.50 .80 |

Postal Service, 125th Anniv. (in 1987) A255

**Perf. 13½x14½**

| 1989 | Litho. | Unwmk. |
|---|---|---|
| 681 A255 | 90fr multicolored | 10.00 2.75 |

Dated 1988.

St. Louis Church, Port Gentil — A256

| 1989, Dec. 15 | Litho. | **Perf. 15x14** |
|---|---|---|
| 682 A256 | 100fr multicolored | 1.00 .40 |

Christmas. See Nos. 725-726, 757.

L'Ogooue', N'Gomo A256a

| 1989, Nov. 18 | Litho. | **Perf. 15x14** |
|---|---|---|
| 682A A256a | 100fr multicolored | — — |

Libreville Coat of Arms — A257

**Wmk. 385**

| 1990, Mar. 12 | Litho. | **Perf. 13½** |
|---|---|---|
| 683 A257 | 100fr multicolored | 1.00 .55 |

World Health Day — A258

**Unwmk.**

| 1990, Apr. 7 | Litho. | **Perf. 13** |
|---|---|---|
| 684 A258 | 400fr multicolored | 4.50 2.10 |

Prehistoric Tools — A259

Designs: 100fr, Hand axe. 175fr, Knife blade. 300fr, Arrowhead. 400fr, Double-bladed hand axe.

| 1990, Feb. 14 | Litho. | **Perf. 15x14** |
|---|---|---|
| 685 A259 | 100fr multi | 1.25 .60 |
| 685A A259 | 175fr multi | 2.10 1.40 |
| 685B A259 | 300fr multi | 3.75 1.50 |
| 685C A259 | 400fr multi | 6.25 4.50 |
| d. | Souvenir sheet of 4, #685-685C | 30.00 30.00 |
|  | Nos. 685-685C (4) | 13.35 8.00 |

See Nos. 727-730.

Fauna — A260

Designs: No. 686, 100fr, Cercopitheque. No. 686A, 175fr, Potamochoerus porcus, horiz. No. 686B, 200fr, Antilope du Gabon, horiz. No. 686C, 500fr, Papio mandrillus sphinx.

| 1990, Apr. 13 | | **Perf. 14** |
|---|---|---|
| 686-686C A260 | Set of 4 | 14.00 8.00 |
| 686Cd | Souvenir sheet of 4, #686-686C, + label | 15.00 15.00 |

First Postage Stamps, 150th Anniv. A261

| 1991, Jan. 9 | | **Perf. 13½x14½** |
|---|---|---|
| 687 A261 | 500fr multicolored | 7.00 3.50 |

Independence, 30th Anniv. — A263

| 1990, Aug. 17 | Litho. | **Perf. 13** |
|---|---|---|
| 693 A263 | 100fr multicolored | 1.00 .30 |

Mushrooms A263a

Various mushrooms.

| 1990, Sept. 12 | Litho. | **Perf. 15x14** |
|---|---|---|
| 693A A263a | 100fr multicolored | 6.00 1.10 |
| 693B A263a | 175fr multicolored | 12.00 2.25 |
| 693C A263a | 300fr multicolored | 17.50 4.25 |
| 693D A263a | 500fr multicolored | 24.50 6.50 |
|  | Nos. 693A-693D (4) | 60.00 14.10 |

Organization of Petroleum Exporting Countries (OPEC), 30th anniv. — A264

| 1990, Sept. 19 | Litho. | **Perf. 13** |
|---|---|---|
| 694 A264 | 200fr multicolored | 2.00 .85 |

1990 World Cup Soccer Championships, Italy — A264a

100fr, Goalie making save. 175fr, Four players, ball. 300fr, Goalie reaching for ball. 500fr, Player celebrating.

| 1990, June 8 | Litho. | **Perf. 15x14** |
|---|---|---|
| 694A A264a | 100fr multi | 10.00 5.00 |
| 694B A264a | 175fr multi | 10.00 5.00 |
| 694C A264a | 300fr multi | 10.00 5.00 |
| 694D A264a | 500fr multi | 10.00 5.00 |
| e. | Souvenir sheet, #694A-694D | |

World Post Day — A265

| 1990, Oct. 9 | | **Perf. 13½** |
|---|---|---|
| 695 A265 | 175fr blue, yel & blk | 1.75 .85 |

Traditional Bwiti Dancer — A265a

100fr, Ndjembe dancers.

| 1990, Apr. 25 | Litho. | **Perf. 15x14** |
|---|---|---|
| 695A A265a | 100fr multi | — |
| 695B A265a | 175fr shown | — |

Flowers — A266

100fr, Frangipanier. 175fr, Boule de feu. 200fr, Flamboyant. 300fr, Rose de porcelaine.

| 1991, Jan. 9 | Litho. | **Perf. 15x14** |
|---|---|---|
| 696 A266 | 100fr multi | 1.25 .60 |
| 697 A266 | 175fr multi | 2.10 1.00 |
| 698 A266 | 200fr multi | 2.40 1.10 |
| 699 A266 | 300fr multi | 3.75 1.75 |
| a. | Souvenir sheet of 4, #696-699 | 11.00 11.00 |
|  | Nos. 696-699 (4) | 9.50 4.45 |

Petroglyphs A267

100fr, Lizard figure. 175fr, Triangular figure. 300fr, Incused lines. 500fr, Concentric circles, circles in lines.

| 1991, Feb. 26 | Litho. | **Perf. 15x14** |
|---|---|---|
| 700 A267 | 100fr multi | 1.25 .60 |
| 701 A267 | 175fr multi | 2.00 1.25 |
| 702 A267 | 300fr multi | 3.50 1.50 |
| 703 A267 | 500fr multi | 5.75 3.00 |
| a. | Souvenir sheet of 4, #700-703 | 75.00 75.00 |
|  | Nos. 700-703 (4) | 12.50 6.35 |

Rubber Trees — A268

| 1991, Mar. 20 | Litho. | **Perf. 14x15** |
|---|---|---|
| 705 A268 | 100fr multicolored | 1.00 .45 |

World Telecommunications Day — A269

| 1991, May 17 | Litho. | **Perf. 13½** |
|---|---|---|
| 706 A269 | 175fr multicolored | 1.90 .95 |

**Rabi Kounga Oil Field Type of 1989**

| 1991 | Litho. | **Perf. 13½** |
|---|---|---|
| 707 A239 | 175fr multicolored | 150.00 |

Ngounie Women Washing Clothes — A271

| 1991, July 17 | Litho. | **Perf. 13½** |
|---|---|---|
| 708 A271 | 100fr multicolored | 1.00 .45 |

Craftsmen — A272

**1991, June 19** **Perf. 14x15**
709 A272 100fr Basket maker 1.10 .55
710 A272 175fr Wood carver 1.90 .95
711 A272 200fr Weaver 2.25 1.10
712 A272 500fr Thatch maker 5.75 2.75
*a.* Souvenir sheet of 4, #709-712 — —
Nos. 709-712 (4) 11.00 5.35

A273

Gabonese Medals: 100fr, Equatorial Knight's Star. 175fr, Equatorial Officer's Star. 200fr, Equatorial Commander's Star.

**1991, Aug. 18 Litho. Perf. 14x15**
**Gray Background**
713 A273 100fr multicolored .85 .50
714 A273 175fr multicolored .85 .90
715 A273 200fr multicolored 1.75 1.00
Nos. 713-715 (3) 3.45 2.40

See Nos. 735-737.

Fishing in
Gabon — A274

100fr, Bow-net fishing. 175fr, Trammel fishing. 200fr, Net fishing. 300fr, Seine fishing.

**1991, Sept. 18** **Perf. 15x14**
716 A274 100fr multi 1.00 .55
717 A274 175fr multi 1.60 .95
718 A274 200fr multi 2.00 1.00
719 A274 300fr multi 3.00 1.75
*a.* Souvenir sheet of 4, #716-719 9.50 9.50
Nos. 716-719 (4) 7.60 4.35

World Post
Day — A275

**1991, Oct. 9** **Perf. 13½**
720 A275 175fr blue & multi 1.75 .65
See Nos. 749, 786.

Termite
Mounds — A276

**1991, Nov. 6** **Perf. 14x15**
721 A276 100fr Phallic 1.25 .60
722 A276 175fr Cathedral 2.50 1.00
723 A276 200fr Mushroom 3.00 1.10
724 A276 300fr Arboreal 3.50 1.75
Nos. 721-724 (4) 10.25 4.45

**Church Type of 1989**
No. 725, Church of Makokou. No. 726, Church of Dibwangui.

**1991, Dec. 18 Litho. Perf. 15x14**
725 A256 100fr multicolored 1.00 .40
726 A256 100fr multicolored 1.00 .40

Christmas. No. 725 inscribed 1990.

**Prehistoric Tools Type of 1990**
Pottery: 100fr, Neolithic pot. 175fr, Bottle, 8th cent. 200fr, Vase, 8th cent. 300fr, Vase, 8th cent, diff.

**1992, Jan. 9 Litho. Perf. 14x15**
727 A259 100fr multi, vert. .85 .40
728 A259 175fr multi, vert. 1.60 .75
729 A259 200fr multi, vert. 1.60 .85
730 A259 300fr multi, vert. 3.25 1.25
*a.* Sheet of 4, #727-730 9.00 9.00
Nos. 727-730 (4) 7.30 3.25

Occupations — A277

**1992, Feb. 5**
731 A277 100fr Basket maker .85 .55
732 A277 175fr Blacksmith 1.60 .95
733 A277 200fr Boat builder 1.60 1.10
734 A277 300fr Hairdresser 3.25 1.75
*a.* Souvenir sheet of 4, #731-734 9.00 9.00
Nos. 731-734 (4) 7.30 4.35

No. 734a issued Feb. 9.

**Gabonese Medals Type of 1991**
Designs: 100fr, Equatorial Grand Officer's Star. 175fr, Grand Cross of Dignity and Equatorial Star. 200fr, Order of Merit.

**1992, Mar. 18 Litho. Perf. 14x15**
**Aquamarine Background**
735 A273 100fr multicolored .95 .50
736 A273 175fr multicolored 1.75 .90
737 A273 200fr multicolored 2.00 1.00
Nos. 735-737 (3) 4.70 2.40

A278

**1992, Apr. 19** **Perf. 13**
738 A278 500fr multicolored 6.00 3.00

Konrad Adenauer (1876-1967), German Statesman.

A279

**1992, May 17** **Perf. 13½**
739 A279 175fr multicolored 1.75 .65

World Telecommunications Day.

Butterflies
A280

100fr, Graphium policenes. 175fr, Acraea egina.

**1992, June 10 Litho. Perf. 15x14**
740 A280 100fr multi 1.25 .85
741 A280 175fr multi 2.50 1.25

A281

**1992, July 25** **Perf. 14x15**
742 A281 100fr Cycling 1.10 .55
743 A281 175fr Boxing 2.00 1.00
744 A281 200fr Pole vault 2.25 1.10
Nos. 742-744 (3) 5.35 2.65

1992 Summer Olympics, Barcelona.

Tribal Masks — A282

**1992, Sept. 16 Litho. Perf. 14x15**
745 A282 100fr Fang 1.00 .50
746 A282 175fr Mpongwe 1.75 .85
747 A282 200fr Kwele 1.75 1.10
748 A282 300fr Pounou 3.00 1.60
*a.* Souvenir sheet of 4, #745-748 9.00 9.00
Nos. 745-748 (4) 7.50 4.05

**World Post Day Type of 1991
Inscribed 1992**
**1992, Oct. 9 Litho. Perf. 13½**
749 A275 175fr bl grn & multi 1.75 .85

**Bird Type of 1989**
100fr, African owl. 175fr, Coliou strie. 200fr, Vulture. 300fr, Giant kingfisher.

**1992, Nov. 4 Litho. Perf. 14x15**
750 A241 100fr multi 2.10 .50
751 A241 175fr multi 3.50 1.00
752 A241 200fr multi 4.50 1.20
753 A241 300fr multi 6.75 1.50
*a.* Souvenir sheet of 4, #750-753 22.50 22.50
Nos. 750-753 (4) 16.85 4.20

Cattle — A283

Various scenes of cattle in pasture.

**1992, Dec. 10** **Perf. 15x14**
754 A283 100fr multicolored 1.00 .50
755 A283 175fr multicolored 1.75 .90
756 A283 200fr multicolored 2.00 1.00
Nos. 754-756 (3) 4.75 2.40

**Church Type of 1989**
100fr, Tchibanga Church.

**1992, Dec. 16**
757 A256 100fr multi 1.00 .40

Christmas.

Intl. Conference on
Nutrition,
Rome — A284

**1992, Dec. 20** **Perf. 13½**
758 A284 100fr multicolored 1.00 .40

Shells — A285

**1993, Jan. 6 Litho. Perf. 15x14**
759 A285 100fr Pugilina .90 .40
760 A285 175fr Conus pulcher 1.50 .70
761 A285 200fr Fusinus 2.00 .80
762 A285 300fr Cymatium 3.00 1.25
*a.* Souvenir sheet, #759-762 12.50 12.50
Nos. 759-762 (4) 7.40 3.15

World Leprosy
Day — A286

**1993, Jan. 28** **Perf. 13½**
763 A286 175fr multicolored 1.75 .85

Fernan-Vaz
Mission — A287

**1993, Feb. 3** **Perf. 15x14**
764 A287 175fr multicolored 2.50 1.25

Chappe's Semaphore
Telegraph,
Bicent. — A288

Designs: 100fr, Claude Chappe (1763-1805), engineer and inventor. 175fr, Chappe's signaling device and code. 200fr, Emile Baudot (1845-1903), devising telegraph code, early telegraph equipment. 300fr, Modern satellite, electronic chip and fiber optics.

**1993, Mar. 10 Litho. Perf. 13½**
765 A288 100fr multicolored 1.00 .50
766 A288 175fr multicolored 1.75 .90
767 A288 200fr multicolored 1.75 1.10
768 A288 300fr multicolored 3.00 1.60
*a.* Souvenir sheet of 4, #765-768 9.00 9.00
Nos. 765-768 (4) 7.50 4.10

Albert
Schweitzer's
Arrival in
Lambarene, 80th
Anniv. — A289

No. 770, Feeding chickens. No. 771, Holding babies.

**1993, Apr. 6 Litho. Perf. 13**
769 A289 500fr multicolored 6.00 2.75
*a.* Booklet pane of 1 6.50

**Booklet Stamps
Size: 26x37mm
Perf. 13½**
770 A289 250fr multi 3.50 1.40
*a.* Booklet pane of 4 20.00
771 A289 250fr multi 3.50 1.40
*a.* Booklet pane of 4 20.00
Nos. 769-771 (3) 13.00 5.55

Booklet containing one of each pane sold for 3000fr. Value $40.

Nicolaus
Copernicus,
Heliocentric Solar
System — A290

**1993, May 5 Litho. Perf. 15x14**
772 A290 175fr multicolored 1.40 .75

Polska '93.

A291

**1993, May 17**     *Perf. 13½*
773 A291 175fr multicolored    1.40   .75

World Telecommunications Day.

A292

Traditional Wine Making: 100fr, Still. 175fr, Extracting juice from palm roots. 200fr, Man in palm tree.

**1993, June 9**    **Litho.**    *Perf. 14*
774 A292 100fr multicolored    1.00   .45
775 A292 175fr multicolored    1.60   .80
776 A292 200fr multicolored    1.90   .95
   a.    Souvenir sheet of 3, #774-776   6.00   6.00
     Nos. 774-776 (3)    4.50   2.20

Crustaceans
A293

**1993, July 21**    **Litho.**    *Perf. 15x14*
777 A293 100fr Spiny lobster    .90   .60
778 A293 175fr Violin crab    1.45   .95
779 A293 200fr Crayfish    1.90   1.10
780 A293 300fr Spider crab    2.75   1.60
   a.    Souvenir sheet of 4, #777-780   7.00   4.25
     Nos. 777-780 (4)    7.00   4.25

Paris
'94 — A294

**1993, Aug. 10**    **Litho.**    *Perf. 13*
781 A294 100fr multicolored    1.00   .50

Animal
Traps — A295

**1993, Sept. 15**    **Litho.**    *Perf. 15x14*
782 A295 100fr Squirrel    1.10   .25
783 A295 175fr Small game    1.75   .55
784 A295 200fr Large game    1.90   .90
785 A295 300fr Palm rat    3.25   1.40
   a.    Souvenir sheet of 4, #782-785   8.00   3.10
     Nos. 782-785 (4)    8.00   3.10

**World Post Day Type of 1991
Inscribed 1993**

**1993, Oct. 9**     *Perf. 13½*
786 A275 175fr yellow & multi    1.75   .75

Making Bamboo
Toys — A296

**1993, Oct. 20**     *Perf. 11½*
787 A296 100fr multicolored    1.00   .55

Tourism — A297

**1993, Nov. 16**
788 A297 100fr Leconi Canyon    1.00   .25
789 A297 175fr La Lope Valley    1.60   .50

Christmas
A298

100fr, Catholic Mission, Mandji.

**1993, Dec. 20**     *Perf. 15x14*
790 A298 100fr multi    1.00   .55

Provincial Map — A299

**1993-94**    **Litho.**    *Perf. 14½*
791 A299   5fr yel & multi ('94)    —   —
792 A299   10fr gray & multi ('93)    —   —
   a.    Dated 1994    —   —
793 A299   25fr pink & multi ('93)    —   —
   a.    Dated 1994    —   —
794 A299   50fr grn & multi ('93)    —   —
795 A299   75fr lilac & multi ('94)    —   —
796 A299   100fr brnsh pink & multi ('94)    —   —
797 A299   175fr multi ('94)    —   —

   Issued: 10fr, 25fr, 50fr, 3/25; 5fr, 75fr, 100fr, 175fr, 1/28/94.
   Nos. 792 and 793 are dated 1993.

Vision of
Gabon's
Future
A300

**1994, Oct. 5**    **Litho.**    *Perf. 14½*
798 A300 500fr multicolored    3.00   1.50

1994 World Cup Soccer
Championships, US — A301

Designs: a, 100fr, Hands on soccer ball. b, 175fr, Two players, ball in air. c, 200fr, Legs of players. d, 300fr, Player, ball.

**1994, Apr. 5**     *Perf. 15x14*
799 A301   Sheet of 4, #a.-d.    35.00   35.00

UN, 50th Anniv. —
A301a

**1995, July 5**    **Litho.**    *Perf. 11¾x11½*
799E A301a 500fr multi

Prehistoric Wildlife — A302

No. 800: a, Sordes. b, Diplodocus (d-e, g-h). c, Eudimorphodon (b). d, Dimetrodon (a). e, Anuroenathus.   f,   Deinonychus, pachycephalosaurus (e). g, Triceratops (j). h, Hadrosaur (i, k-l). i, Genus Meganeura. j, Longisquama. k, Oviraptor. l, Monoclonius.

No. 801: a, Pistosaurus (d-e, h). b, Pteranodon (c). c, Coelophysis. d, Xenacanthus (g). e, Ischyodus (f, h-i). f, Placochelys. g, Dunkleosteus (j). h, Cymbospondylus (i). i, Enchodus. j, Paracybeloides (k). k, Nautiliod (h). l, Palaeospondylus.

No. 802: a, Tyrannosaurus rex (d). b, Apatosaurus (a, d-e). c, Dimorphodon. d, Stegasaurus (a, e). e, Archaeopteryx. f, Protoceratops. g, Ichthyosaur. h, Phobosuchus, deltoptychius. i, Parasaurolophus (f). j, Scapanorhynchus (g). k, Spathobathis, plesiosaurus (j, l). l, Cladoselacho.

**1995, Sept. 4**    **Litho.**    *Perf. 14*
800 A302 125fr Sheet of 12, #a.-l.    8.00   8.00
801 A302 225fr Sheet of 12, #a.-l.    13.50   13.50
802 A302 260fr Sheet of 12, #a.-l.    16.00   16.00
     Nos. 800-802 (3)    37.50   37.50
   Singapore '95 (No. 800).

Nobel Prize Fund Established,
Cent. — A303

No. 803 — Nobel Prize recipients: a, Walter H. Brattain, physics, 1956. b, Carl F. Cori, medicine, 1947. c, Gerty T. Cori, medicine, 1947. d, Owen Chamberlain, physics, 1959. e, Christian Anfinsen, chemistry, 1972. f, George de Hevesy, chemistry, 1943. g, Kenichi Fukui, chemistry, 1981. h, Élie Wiesel, peace, 1986. i, Carl F. Braun, physics, 1909.

No. 804: a, Georg Wittig, chemistry, 1979. b, Charles Dawes, peace, 1925. c, Frederic Mistral, literature, 1904. d, Juan Jimenez, literature, 1956. e, Michael S. Brown, medicine, 1985. f, Guglielmo Marconi, physics, 1909. g, Werner Forssmann, medicine, 1956. h, Francis W. Aston, chemistry, 1922. i, Martin Ryle, physics, 1974.

No. 805: a, Leon Jouhaux, peace, 1951. b, Rudolf L. Mossbauer, physics, 1961. c, George Seferis, literature, 1963. d, James Chadwick, physics, 1935. e, Aung San Suu Kyi, peace, 1991. f, John H. Nothrop, chemistry, 1946. g, Eduard Buchner, chemistry, 1907. h, Hans A. Bethe, physics, 1967. i, Nils Dalen, physics, 1912.

No. 806, 1500fr, Hermann Hesse, literature, 1946. No. 807, 1500fr, Albert Schweitzer, peace, 1952. No. 808, 1500fr, Nelson Mandela, peace, 1993.

**1995, Oct. 18**    **Litho.**    *Perf. 14*
803 A303 125fr Sheet of 9, #a.-i.    6.75   6.75
804 A303 225fr Sheet of 9, #a.-i.    9.00   9.00
805 A303 260fr Sheet of 9, #a.-i.    14.00   14.00
     Nos. 803-805 (3)    29.75   29.75

**Souvenir Sheets**
806-808 A303   Set of 3    27.00   27.00

Monseigneur Bessieux
(1803-76),
Evangelist — A306

**1995, Dec. 25**    **Litho.**    *Perf. 13*
811 A306 500fr multicolored    2.75   1.40

Louis Pasteur (1822-95), Microbiologist — A306a

Food and
Agriculture
Organization, 50th
Anniv. — A306b

**1995, Sept. 20**    **Litho.**    *Perf. 11¾*
811B A306b 500fr multi    10.00   10.00

Mbigou Rock Sculptor
— A306c

       *Perf. 14¼x14¾*
**1995, Nov. 15**     **Litho.**
811C A306c 500fr multi    30.00   —

Miniature Sheet of 8

World War II, 50th Anniv. — A307

No. 812: a, German generals planning attack. b, Afrika Korps troops ride tanks into El Agheila. c, German artillary fires on British positions in Tobruk. d, British soldiers surrender. e, British soldiers break siege of Tobruk. f, Allies advancing though barbed wire, El Alamein. g, German tanks retreat to Tunis. h, German tank surrenders.

**1996, Jan. 29**     *Perf. 14*
812 A307 125fr Sheet of 8, #a.-h. + label    6.50   2.75

World War II, 50th Anniv. — A308

No. 813: a, Pres. Franklin D. Roosevelt. b, Pres. Harry S Truman. c, Gen. George Marshall.
1000fr, Flags of US, Great Britain, USSR.

**1996, Jan. 26**    **Litho.**    *Perf. 14*
813 A308 225fr Strip of 3, #a.-c. 4.50 4.50
     **Souvenir Sheet**
814 A308 1000fr multicolored    6.50   6.50

No. 813 was issued in sheets of 9 stamps.

Dogs — A309

No. 815: a, Dalmatian. b, Basset hound. c, Harrier. d, German Shepherd. e, Bernese bouvier. f, Pug. g, West highland white terrier. h, Akita.

**1996, May 13**    **Litho.**    *Perf. 14*
815 A309 125fr Sheet of 8, #a.-h. 6.00 6.00

China '96 Philatelic Exhibition.

St. Pius X
Catholic Mission,
10th
Anniv. — A310

## (center column, Tourism additional)

## (additional center image detail)
Perf. 14¼x14¾
**1995, Dec. 12**     **Litho.**
811A A306a 500fr multi    45.00   10.00

Mgr. Marcel Lefebvre, interior of mission.

**1996, Mar. 4** — *Perf. 13½*
816 A310 100fr yellow & multi .90 .30
817 A310 125fr blue & multi 1.00 .50

Rotary, Intl. — A311

Rotary emblem and: 125fr, UN flag. 225fr, Natl. flag of Gabon. 260fr, Rotary, Intl. flag. 1500fr, Olympic flag.

**1996, July 3** **Litho.** *Perf. 14*
818-820 A311 Set of 3 4.00 3.00
**Souvenir Sheet**
821 A311 1500fr multicolored 9.00 9.00

Boy Scouts — A312

Designs: 125fr, Scout sign. 225fr, Constructing a lean-to. 260fr, Camping. 1500fr, Lord Baden-Powell.

**1996, July 15**
822-824 A312 Set of 3 3.00 2.25
**Souvenir Sheet**
825 A312 1500fr multicolored 9.00 9.00

Cercopithecus Solatus — A313

**1996, Mar. 6** *Perf. 13½x13*
826 A313 500fr multicolored 3.25 1.75

Fight Against AIDS — A314

**1996, Apr. 3** *Perf. 13½x13*
827 A314 500fr multicolored 3.25 1.75

Shells — A315

Designs: 100fr, Fusinus caparti. 260fr, Hexaplex rosarium. 500fr, Conus pulcher, horiz.

**1996** *Perf. 13½x13, 13x13½*
828-830 A315 Set of 3 5.25 3.50

1996 Summer Olympic Games, Atlanta — A316

**1996, May 8** *Perf. 11½*
831 A316 225fr Boxing 1.25 .75
832 A316 500fr Relay race 2.50 1.60

---

Campaign Against Use of Illegal Drugs — A317

**1996, Aug. 6** **Litho.** *Perf. 11½*
833 A317 500fr multicolored 2.75 1.25

Contemporary Paintings, by H. Moundounga — A318

**1996, Sept. 10**
834 A318 100fr Girl .65 .25
835 A318 125fr Three faces .85 .40
836 A318 225fr Eyes 1.50 .75
 a. Souvenir sheet, #834-836 3.25 3.25
 Nos. 834-836 (3) 3.00 1.40

Souvenir Sheet

Temple in Winter A319

**1996, May 13** **Litho.** *Perf. 14*
837 A319 500fr multicolored 4.50 2.25

China '96 Philatelic Exhibition, No. 837 was not available until March 1997.

Environmental Protection A320

Endangered species: 100fr, Galago alleni, vert. 125fr, Perodicticus potto. 225fr, Orycteropus afer. 260fr, Manis gigantea.

**1996, June 5** *Perf. 13½*
838-841 A320 Set of 4 5.00 3.25

Children's Paintings — A321

Designs: 100fr, Woman's arms encircling world, vert. 125fr, People forming circle around animals. 225fr, Slaughtering of elephants, vert.

**1996, Dec. 25** **Litho.** *Perf. 11½*
842-844 A321 Set of 3 1.75 1.25
 Dated 1996.

Traditional Houses — A322

Designs: 100fr, Mud & stick cabin. 125fr, Pygmy hut. 225fr, Bark-sided cabins. 260fr, Wood-sided cabins.

**1996, Nov. 6**
845-848 A322 Set of 4 4.50 2.75
 a. Souvenir sheet, #845-848 5.00 5.00

---

A323

**1996, Oct. 10**
849 A323 500fr multicolored 2.00 1.25
 Investiture of Pres. Nelson Mandela, 3rd anniv.

A324

UNICEF, 50th Anniv.: No. 850: a, Boy holding cup. b, Girl holding cup. c, Boy eating. 1500fr, Boy holding plate.

**1997, Apr. 9** **Litho.** *Perf. 14*
850 A324 260fr Sheet of 3, #a.-
 c. 4.00 4.00
**Souvenir Sheet**
851 A324 1500fr multicolored 8.50 8.50

UNESCO, 50th Anniv. — A325

No. 852, 225fr: a, Kyoto, Japan. b, Puma, Los Katios Natl. Park, Colombia. c, Abu Simbel Monument, Egypt. d, Old Rauma, Finland. e, Rotunda, City of Vicenza, Italy. f, Homes, China. g, Port of Salvador, Brazil. h, Delos Ruins, Greece.
No. 853, 225fr: a, Fasil Ghebbi Monument, Gondar Region, Ethiopia. b, Victoria Falls, Zambia. c, Zambezi Plains, Chewore Safari Areas, Zimbabwe. d, Nature Reserve, Niger. e, Banc D'Arguin Natl. Park, Mauritania. f, Gorée Island, Senegal. g, Djémila Ruins, Algeria. h, Mosque, Medina of Fez, Morocco.
1000fr, Terracotta warriors, Mausoleum of first Qin Emperor, China.

**1997, Apr. 16**
**Sheets of 8, #a-h, + Label**
852-853 A325 Set of 2 15.00 15.00
**Souvenir Sheet**
854 A325 1000fr multicolored 7.50 7.50

City Arms — A326

**1997, Mar. 12** **Litho.** *Perf. 11½x12*
855 A326 100fr N'Dendé .65 .25
856 A326 125fr Libreville .85 .35
857 A326 225fr Mitzic 1.50 .80
 Nos. 855-857 (3) 3.00 1.40

Return of Hong Kong to China — A327

---

Designs: 125fr, Skyline. 225fr, Skyline, diff. 260fr, Skyline at night, horiz. 500fr, Skyline at night, Deng Xiaoping (1904-97), horiz.

**1997, July 1** *Perf. 14*
858-861 A327 Set of 4 6.00 4.00

Nos. 858-859 were each issued in sheets of 4. Nos. 860-861 are 59x28mm and were issued in sheets of 3.

**Unity, Work and Justice Type of 1981**
**1994-95** **Litho.** *Perf. 11¾*
**Granite Paper**
862 A145 5fr grn blue & blk .30 .25
863 A145 10fr orange & black .30 .25
864 A145 25fr grey lilac & black .30 .25
865 A145 50fr salmon & black .45 .25
866 A145 75fr tan & blk .30 .25
867 A145 100fr pink & black .40 .25
868 A145 125fr yell grn & blk .70 .35
869 A145 175fr yellow & black — —
870 A145 225fr green & black — —
871 A145 260fr lt blue & black 1.60 .75
 Nos. 862-871 (10) 4.35 2.60

Issued: 50fr, 125fr, 9/30/95; others, 9/20/94.

Paintings — A328

**1995, Oct. 10** **Litho.** *Perf. 14*
872 A328 100fr Woman 1.00 .45
873 A328 125fr Stylized women 1.50 .65
873A A328 225fr Masked Face 2.00 1.10
 b. Souvenir sheet of 3, #872-
 873A 65.00 65.00

Raponda Walker, 25th Death Anniv. — A329

**1995, June 7** *Perf. 13½*
874 A329 500fr multicolored 10.00 5.00

Masks — A330

**1995, Feb. 15**
875 A330 100fr Bateke — —
876 A330 125fr Bavili — —
877 A330 225fr Fang — 10.00
878 A330 260fr Bandjabi 80.00 12.00
 a. Souvenir sheet of 4, #875-
 878 150.00 150.00

Shells — A331

100fr, Cymbium glans. 125fr, Muricidae murey. 225fr, Siliquaria. 260fr, Strombus latus.

**1995, Apr. 4**
879 A331 100fr multi 30.00 10.00
880 A331 125fr multi 30.00 10.00
880A A331 225fr multi 30.00 10.00
881 A331 260fr multi 30.00 10.00
 a. Souvenir sheet of 4,
 #879-880A, 881 175.00 175.00

Saint-Exupery French Cultural Center — A332

**1996, May 12**      **Perf. 13x13½**
883 A332 100fr black & multi    —   —
884 A332 125fr blue & multi    —   —
885 A332 225fr red & multi    —   12.00

Inter-Continental
Hotel, 50th
Anniv. — A333

**1996, Apr. 4**      **Perf. 13½**
886   A333 125fr creme & blue   —   10.00
886A A333 225fr lt yel & blue   —   10.00

Early Post Offices
— A333a

100fr, Port Gentil, 1917. 125fr, Cap-Lopez, 1888. 225fr, Libreville, 1862.

**1996, July 20   Litho.**   **Perf. 12x11½**
886B A333a 100fr multi    1.00   .50
886C A333a 125fr multi    1.00   .65
886D A333a 225fr multi    1.45   1.10

Flowers,
Butterflies,
Moths,
Insects — A334

Designs, vert: 125fr, Rubra tigridia pauonia, pieridae. 225fr, Acraeidae, strelitzia reginae. 260fr, Zautedeschia aethiopica, zonabris oculata. 500fr, Bee orchid, iron prominent moth caterpillar.
No. 891, 260fr: a, Liliaceae. b, Macrophylla, phoebis philea. c, Theaceae amugashita. d, Lilium american cultivars, vanessa atalanta. e, Hybrids, hippodamia convergens. f, Sibine stimulea, iridaceae.
No. 892, 260fr: a, Kalmialati. b, G. gandavensis, calopteryx maculata. c, Narcissus pseudonarcisus. d, Ipheton uniflorum, Tlemaris thysbe. e, Rudbackia hirta. f, Tritida grandiflora, danaus plexippus.
No. 893, 1500fr, Papilion zellicaon, geranium pelargonium, vert. No. 894, 1500fr, Anax jumus, gladstoniana, vert.

**1997, Aug. 11   Litho.**   **Perf. 14**
887-890 A334   Set of 4    6.00   4.50
     **Sheets of 6, #a-f**
891-892 A334   Set of 2   16.00 16.00
     **Souvenir Sheets**
893-894 A334   Set of 2   15.00 15.00

Protection of
Indigenous
Animals — A335

Designs: 100fr, Dendrohyrax arboreus. 125fr, Galago elegantulus. 225fr, Stephanoaetus coronatus.

**1997, June 5**      **Perf. 13½x13**
895-897 A335   Set of 3    3.00 2.00
897a   Souvenir sheet of 3, #895-897   6.50 6.50

Gabonese
Art — A336

Designs: 100fr, Droits de Creatures, vert. 125fr,   Ambassadeur,   vert.   225fr, Hallucinations.

**1997, May 8**   **Perf. 13½x13, 13x13½**
898-900 A336   Set of 3    3.00 3.00
900a   Souvenir sheet of 1, #900   1.50 1.50

---

Air Gabon, 20th
Anniv. — A337

**1997, June 1**      **Perf. 13x13½**
901 A337 125fr multicolored    .90   .50
902 A337 225fr multicolored    1.60   .80

First ACP Summit,
Libreville — A338

**1997, Nov. 6   Litho.**   **Perf. 13½x13**
903 A338 225fr multicolored    1.40   .70

Lions Club in Gabon,
40th Anniv. — A339

**1997, Oct. 8**      **Perf. 13½x13**
904 A339 225fr multicolored    1.40   .70

AIPLF, 30th
Anniv. — A340

**1997, Oct. 30**      **Perf. 12x11½**
905 A340 260fr multicolored    1.40   .65

Paul Gondjout, 1st
Pres. of the Natl.
Assembly — A341

**1997, Nov. 11**      **Perf. 14x14½**
906 A341 500fr multicolored    2.75 1.25

Heinrich von Stephan
(1831-97) — A342

**1997, Nov. 17**      **Perf. 11½x12**
907 A342 500fr multicolored    2.75 1.25

Princess Diana (1961-97) — A343

No. 908: a, 500fr. b, 300fr. c, 260fr. d, 225fr. e, f, 125fr.
3000fr, Diana in white dress.

**1998, Feb. 10   Litho.**   **Perf. 13½**
908 A343   Sheet of 6, #a.-f.    8.50 8.50
     **Souvenir Sheet**
909 A343 3000fr multicolored   15.00 15.00

---

District Arms — A344

Designs: 100fr, Akieni. 125fr, Pana. 225fr, Lebamba.

**1998, June 4   Litho.**   **Perf. 13½x13**
910-912 A344   Set of 3    3.00 1.50

Traditional
Tools — A345

Designs: 100fr, Yanghe. 125fr, Ikanga. 225fr, Ivedili.

**1997, Nov. 5   Litho.**   **Perf. 14**
913-915 A345   Set of 3    3.00 1.90

New Horizons
Foundation
A346

**1998, May 15   Litho.**   **Perf. 13x13½**
916   A346 225fr multicolored    1.40   .70

Protected
Animals — A347

Designs: 100fr, Hippopotamus amphibius. 125fr, Sylvicapra grimmia. 225fr, Pelecanus rufescens.

**1998, Apr. 17**      **Perf. 13½x13**
917 A347 100fr multicolored    .75   .40
918 A347 125fr multicolored    1.25   .70
919 A347 225fr multicolored    1.50   .85
a.   Souvenir sheet, #917-919   30.00 30.00

1998 World Cup
Soccer
Championships,
France — A348

Various soccer plays, country flags in background: 100fr, 125fr, 225fr, 260fr.

**1998, July 10   Litho.**   **Perf. 13½x13**
920-923 A348   Set of 4    4.75 2.75
923a   Sheet of 4, #920-923    5.00 5.00

ACCT, 26th
Anniv. — A349

**1998, Oct. 10**
924 A349 260fr multicolored    1.40   .65

Elimination of Land
Mines — A350

**1998, May 15   Litho.**   **Perf. 11½x12**
925 A350 260fr multicolored    1.60   .80

---

Gandhi — A351

**1998, Oct. 9**
926 A351 260fr multicolored    1.60   .80

Mother Teresa (1910-
97) — A352

**1998, June 30**
927 A352 500fr multicolored    2.75 1.40

Deng Xiaoping (1904-
97) — A353

**1998, Sept. 14**
928 A353 500fr multicolored    2.75 1.40

Intl. Year of the
Ocean — A354

**1999, Oct. 19   Litho.**   **Perf. 11½**
929 A354 125fr multicolored    2.50   .85
     Dated 1998.

Wooden Tools — A355

**1999**
930 A355 100fr Mortier    .70   .55
931 A355 125fr Pilon    1.00   .80
     Dated 1998.

Universal
Declaration of
Human
Rights — A356

**1999, Aug. 10**
932 A356 225fr multicolored    1.40   .80
     Dated 1998.

Space
Exploration
A357

Designs: No. 933, 225fr, Gemini 7. No. 934, 225fr, Skylab. No. 935, 225fr, Atlas Moon Explorer. No. 936, 225fr, Space Shuttle.
No. 937: a, Venera 4. b, TDRS. c, Sputnik II. d, Zond II. e, Untethered walk. f, Intelsat 6. g, Luna 16. h, Sputnik III. i, Vostok V. j, Lunar explorer. k, 2nd lunar landing. l, Conrad and Surveyor.
No. 938: a, Sputnik. b, Mariner 2. c, Apollo 11 Lunar Module. d, Gemini 7. e, Mir. f, Atlas Moon Explorer. g, Space Shuttle Orbit. h, Hubbell. i, Soyuz. j, Apollo 11 re-entry. k, Skylab. l, Venture Star.
No. 939: a, Lunar landing II. b, Gemini 7. c, Venture Star. d, Hubbell.

No. 940, 1500fr, Shuttle launch. No. 941, 1500fr, Untethered walk. No. 942, 1500fr, Apollo II. No. 943, 1500fr, Lunar landing module.

**1999, Apr. 30   Litho.   Perf. 14**
| | | | |
|---|---|---|---|
| 933-936 | A357 | Set of 4 | 3.75 | 2.00 |
| 937 | A357 | 100fr Sheet of 12, #a.-l. | 6.00 | 6.00 |
| 938 | A357 | 125fr Sheet of 12, #a.-l. | 8.50 | 8.50 |

**Sheet of 4**
| | | | |
|---|---|---|---|
| 939 | A357 | 225fr Sheet of 4, #a.-d. | 4.00 | 4.00 |

**Souvenir Sheets**
| | | | |
|---|---|---|---|
| 940-943 | A357 | Set of 4 | 35.00 | 35.00 |

Moon landing, 30th anniv.

Traditional Weapons — A358

Designs: 100fr, Sagaie. 125fr, Arbalète. 225fr, Couteau et jet.

**1999, Nov. 10   Perf. 13**
| | | | |
|---|---|---|---|
| 944-946 | A358 | Set of 3 | 3.00 | 1.60 |

Folklore — A358a

Designs: 125fr, Mitsogho reliquary. 225fr, Bwèri Fang sculpture.

**1999, July 2   Litho.   Perf. 13¼**
| | | | |
|---|---|---|---|
| 946A | A358a | 125fr multi | 125.00 | 10.00 |
| 946B | A358a | 225fr multi | 145.00 | — |

Democracy A359

**1999, Dec. 12   Litho.   Perf. 11¾**
| | | | |
|---|---|---|---|
| 947 | A359 | 100fr multicolored | .75 | .50 |

UPU, 125th Anniv. — A360

Designs: 100fr, People, map. 225fr, Emblem, letters, vert. 260fr, Great Wall of China, vert.

**1999, Aug. 21**
| | | | |
|---|---|---|---|
| 948 | A360 | 100fr multicolored | .60 | .40 |
| 949 | A360 | 225fr multicolored | 1.00 | .75 |
| 950 | A360 | 260fr multicolored | 1.50 | 1.00 |
| | | Nos. 948-950 (3) | 3.10 | 2.15 |

Manufacture of Aspirin, Cent. — A361

**1999, July 6**
| | | | |
|---|---|---|---|
| 951 | A361 | 225fr multicolored | 1.40 | .70 |

Mushrooms — A361a

Designs: 100fr, Amanite panthère. 125fr, Basidomycetes, horiz. 225fr, Basidomycetes, diff., horiz. 260fr, Amanite tue-mouches.

---

**Perf. 13¼x13, 13x13¼**
**1999, Apr. 30   Litho.**
| | | | |
|---|---|---|---|
| 951A-951D | A361a | Set of 4 | 8.00 | 8.00 |
| 951De | | Souvenir sheet of 4, #951A-951D | 120.00 | 120.00 |

PhilexFrance '99 — A362

**1999, July 2   Litho.   Perf. 13**
| | | | |
|---|---|---|---|
| 952 | A362 | 225fr multi | 3.00 | 1.40 |

No. 952 has a holographic image. Soaking in water may affect hologram.

Elephants A363

**1999   Perf. 13x13¼**
| | | | |
|---|---|---|---|
| 953 | A363 | 100fr multi | 3.00 | 1.25 |

PhilexFrance '99 World Philatelic Exhibition, Paris.

Central African Economic and Monetary Community Days — A364

Map of Africa at: 125fr, Circle of member's flags. 225fr, Rows of member's flags.

**1999, Nov. 23   Litho.   Perf. 14½**
| | | | |
|---|---|---|---|
| 954-955 | A364 | Set of 2 | 2.40 | 2.40 |

Pope John XXIII, St. Peter's Basilica — A365

**1999, Dec. 12   Litho.   Perf. 11¾**
| | | | |
|---|---|---|---|
| 956 | A365 | 100fr multi | 1.00 | .75 |

Announcement of 2nd Vatican Council, 40th anniv., Christmas.

**Unity, Work and Justice Type of 1981**
**1999, Dec. 12   Litho.   Perf. 11¾**
**Granite Paper**
| | | | |
|---|---|---|---|
| 959 | A145 | 40fr lil & blk | 1.00 | .25 |
| 960 | A145 | 90fr olive grn & blk | — | — |

Shells — A365a

Designs: 100fr, Harpa doris. 125fr, Thais haemastoma. 225fr, Cassis tessellata.

**1999, June 25   Litho.   Perf. 13x13½**
| | | | |
|---|---|---|---|
| 964-966 | A365a | Set of 3 | 5.00 | 5.00 |

Fish — A365b

Designs: 100fr, Epinephelus marginatus, mugil cephalus. 125fr, Brycinus macrolepidotus. 225fr, Oreochromis schwebischi. 260fr, Pomadasys peroteti, caranx hippos, ethmalosa fimbriata.

---

**1999, Apr. 26**
| | | | |
|---|---|---|---|
| 967-970 | A365b | Set of 4 | 5.50 | 5.50 |
| 970a | | Souvenir sheet of 4, #967-970 | 125.00 | — |

Expo 2000, Hanover — A366

**Perf. 11¾x11½**
**2000, Feb. 16   Litho.**
| | | | |
|---|---|---|---|
| 971 | A366 | 225fr multi | 2.00 | 1.00 |

Protected Animals — A367

Designs: 125fr, Haliaetus vocifer. 225fr, Panthera pardus. 260fr, Panthera leo.

**2000, June 5**
| | | | |
|---|---|---|---|
| 972-974 | A367 | Set of 3 | 8.00 | 2.50 |
| 974a | | Souvenir sheet of 3, #972-974 | 17.50 | 17.50 |

Events of the 20th Century — A368

Designs: 100fr, Universal Declaration of Human Rights, vert. 125fr, World War II. 225fr, First man on the moon.

**Perf. 11½x11¾, 11¾x11½**
**2000, July 20**
| | | | |
|---|---|---|---|
| 975-977 | A368 | Set of 3 | 3.00 | 3.00 |

Scientific Achievements of the 20th Century — A369

Designs: 100fr, Microprocessor, 1971. 125fr, Nuclear reactor, 1942. 225fr, Structure of DNA, 1953.

**2000, Nov. 28   Perf. 11¾x11½**
| | | | |
|---|---|---|---|
| 978-980 | A369 | Set of 3 | 3.00 | 3.00 |

See Nos. 1040-1042.

Tourism — A370

100fr, Pygmy village. 125fr, Lake region. 225fr, Poubara Waterfall. 260fr, Mt. Brazza.

**2000, Sept. 29   Perf. 13x13½**
| | | | |
|---|---|---|---|
| 981-984 | A370 | Set of 4 | 5.50 | 5.50 |
| 984a | | Miniature sheet of 4, #981-984 | 15.00 | 15.00 |

Y2K Bug — A371

**2000, Dec. 11   Perf. 11½x11¾**
| | | | |
|---|---|---|---|
| 985 | A371 | 225fr multi | 1.40 | 1.40 |

---

Dr. Albert Schweitzer (1875-1965) — A372

**2000, Jan. 14   Perf. 13¼x13**
| | | | |
|---|---|---|---|
| 986 | A372 | 260fr multi | 4.00 | 1.60 |

A373

Trains A374

Designs: No. 987, 100fr, Japanese Hikari trains. 125fr, Hungarian Bo-Bo electric locomotive. No. 989, 500fr, Pakistani electric locomotive. No. 990, 500fr, Belgian locomotive.
No. 991: a, 100fr, Korean Bo-Bo locomotive. b, 100fr, Moroccan electric locomotive. c, 100fr, Spanish electric locomotive. d, 500fr, Yugoslavian Type J2-441. e, 500fr, Chinese electric locomotive. f, 500fr, Norwegian Type E115.
No. 992: a, 100fr, Portuguese Diesel-electric locomotive. b, 100fr, Japanese mag-lev train. c, 100fr, Long Island Railroad diesel car. d, 500fr, German Type 103. e, 500fr, Romanian Co-Co locomotive. f, 500fr, English HST.
No. 993, 1500fr, English train "The Advanced." No. 994, 1500fr, French TGV 001. No. 995, 1500fr, Austrian Transalpine train. No. 996, 1500fr, Stourbridge Lion. No. 997, 1500fr, Puffing Billy, vert. No. 998, 1500fr, Union Pacific 4-8-8-4 Big Boy, vert. No. 999, French TGV, vert.

**Perf. 13¼x13¾, 13¾x13¼**
**2000, Dec. 10   Litho.**
| | | | |
|---|---|---|---|
| 987-990 | A373 | Set of 4 | 6.00 | 6.00 |

**Sheets of 6, #a-f**
| | | | |
|---|---|---|---|
| 991-992 | A373 | Set of 2 | 20.00 | 20.00 |

**Souvenir Sheets**
| | | | |
|---|---|---|---|
| 993-995 | A373 | Set of 3 | 24.00 | 24.00 |
| 996-999 | A374 | Set of 4 | 30.00 | 30.00 |

See Nos. 1024-1027, 1032-1033, 1036-1037. See Gambia Nos. 3917-3918.

A375

Prehistoric Animals A376

Designs: No. 1000, 100fr, Archaeopteryx. No. 1001, 100fr, Velociraptor, vert. No. 1002, 125fr, Torosaurus. No. 1003, 125fr, Corythosaurus, vert. No. 1004, 225fr, Pachycephalosaurus, vert. No. 1005, 500fr, Parasaurolophus.
No. 1006, 100fr, Pterodactylus. No. 1007, 125fr, Allosaurus. No. 1008, 125fr, Struthiomimus, vert. No. 1009, 225fr, Psittacosaurus, vert. No. 1010, 260fr, Parasauraolophus, vert. No. 1011, 500fr, Acanthostega.
No. 1012: a, 125fr, Camarasaurus. b, 125fr, Rhamphorhynchus. c, 125fr, Saltasaurus. d, 225fr, Camptosaurus. e, 225fr, Megalosaurus. f, 225fr, Allosaurus. g, 260fr, Anchisaurus. h, 260fr, Dilophosaurus. i, 260fr, Massospondylus.
No. 1013: a, 100fr, Stegosaurus. b, 100fr, Pteranodon. c, 100fr, Carnotaurus. d, 125fr, Iguanodon. e, 125fr, Pentaceratops. f, 125fr, Styracosaurus. g, 500fr, Deinonychus. h, 500fr, Stegoceras. i, 500fr, Struthiomimus.
No. 1014: a, 125fr, Volcano. b, 125fr, Pterodactylus. c, 125fr, Dimorphodon. d, 125fr, Alamosaurus. e, 225fr, Psittacosaurus. f,

225fr, Deinonychus. g, 225fr, Dromiceiomimus. h, 225fr, Yangchuanosaurus. i, 260fr, Protorosaurus. j, 260fr, Triceratops. k, 260fr, Daspletosaurus. l, 260fr, Pentaceratops.

No. 1015: a, 125fr, Brachiosaurus. b, 125fr, Scaphognathus. c, Mountain and sun. d, 125fr, Pteranodon. e, 225fr, Tyrannosaurus. f, 225fr, Ichthyosaurus. g, 225fr, Macroplata. h, 225fr, Dilophosaurus. i, 500fr, Stegosaurus. j, 500fr, Thecodontosaurus. k, 500fr, Saltasaurus. l, 500fr, Pachyrhinosaurus.

No. 1016, 225fr: a, Tyrannosaurus. b, Criorhynchus. c, Pterodactylus. d, Albertosaurus. e, Dromiceiomimus. f, Opisthocoelicaudia. g, Brachiosaurus. h, Pachycephalosaurus. i, Parasaurolophus. j, Edmontosaurus. k, Pentaceratops. l, Corythosaurus.

No. 1017, 260fr: a, Peteinosaurus. b, Volcanoes. c, Acanthostega. d, Ceresiosaurus. e, Pliosaur. f, Stethacanthus. g, Ichthyosaur. h, Pholidogaster. i, Gerrothorax. j, Diplocaulus. k, Mixosaurus. l, Echinoceras raricostatum.

No. 1018, 1500fr, Tyrannosaurus Rex. No. 1019, 1500fr, Arrhinoceratops. No. 1020, 1500fr, Argentinosaurus, vert. No. 1021, 1500fr, Cetiosaurus, vert. No. 1022, 1500fr, Archaeopteryx. No. 1023, Saltasaurus, vert.

**2000, Dec. 20**
| 1000-1005 | A375 | Set of 6 | 8.00 | 8.00 |
| 1006-1011 | A376 | Set of 6 | 8.00 | 8.00 |

**Sheets of 9, #a-i**
| 1012-1013 | A375 | Set of 2 | 20.00 | 20.00 |

**Sheets of 12, #a-l**
| 1014-1015 | A375 | Set of 2 | 30.00 | 30.00 |
| 1016-1017 | A375 | Set of 2 | 30.00 | 30.00 |

**Souvenir Sheets**
| 1018-1021 | A375 | Set of 4 | 30.00 | 30.00 |
| 1022-1023 | A376 | Set of 2 | 16.00 | 16.00 |

No. 1021 contains one 42x56mm stamp.

### Train Type of 2000 and

A377

Designs: 100fr, German Type 201. No. 1025, 225fr, German Type 112. No. 1026, 225fr, ICT. No. 1027, 260fr, ICE.

No. 1028, 260fr, French Electric BB9004. No. 1029, 260fr, French Type 232U 4-8-2. No. 1030, 500fr, French Type 241C 4-8-2 "Mountain." No. 1031, 500fr, German TEE.

No. 1032: a, 125fr, German Type 41. b, 125fr, German Type 39. c, 125fr, German Type 10. d, 500fr, German Type 99. e, 500fr, German Type 58. f, 500fr, German Type 44.

No. 1033: a, 225fr, German Type 229. b, 225fr, German Type 152. c, 225fr, German Type 101. d, 500fr, German Type 250. e, 500fr, German Type 232. f, 500fr, Type 216.

No. 1034: a, 125fr, Prussian Type P8 4-6-0. b, 125fr, Bavarian Type S3/6 4-6-2. c, 125fr, German Type 01 4-6-2. d, 500fr, German Electric "Crocodile." e, 500fr, Swiss Electric Type Be 4/6. f, 500fr, Swiss Electric Type Ae 6/6.

No. 1035: a, 125fr, Stirling 8ft Single 4-2-2 "No. 1," UK. b, 125fr, Greeley Pacific Type A3 4-6-2 "Flying Scotsman," UK. c, 125fr, Stanier Coronation Type 4-6-2 "Coronation Scot," UK. d, 500fr, Baldwin 4-4-0 "The General," US. e, Class J1 Hudson 4-8-4, US. f, "Super Chief" Diesel-electric, US.

No. 1036, 1500fr, Type 91. No. 1037, 1500fr, Type 57. No. 1038, Greeley Pacific Type A4 4-6-2 "Silver Link," UK. No. 1039, J Type 4-8-4, US.

**Perf. 13¼x13½, 13½x13¼**
**2000?**                                    **Litho.**
| 1024-1027 | A374 | Set of 4 | 4.00 | 4.00 |
| 1028-1031 | A377 | Set of 4 | 8.00 | 8.00 |

**Sheets of 6, #a-f**
| 1032-1033 | A374 | Set of 2 | 20.00 | 20.00 |
| 1034-1035 | A377 | Set of 2 | 19.00 | 19.00 |

**Souvenir Sheets**
| 1036-1037 | A374 | Set of 2 | 16.00 | 16.00 |
| 1038-1039 | A377 | Set of 2 | 16.00 | 16.00 |

Nos. 1038-1039 each contain one 56x42mm stamp.

Raponda Walker Foundation — A378

**2000, Dec. 25    Litho.    Perf. 11½**
| 1039A | A378 | 225fr multi | 1.10 | 1.10 |

---

End of the Millennium — A379

**2000, Dec. 11**
| 1039B | A379 | 225fr multi | 1.20 | 1.20 |

### Scientific Achievements of the 20th Century Type of 2000

Designs: 100fr, Isolation of insulin, 1921. 125fr, Invention of television, 1921. 225fr, Invention of the calculator, 1951.

**Perf. 11¾x11½**
**2000, Nov. 28                      Litho.**
| 1040-1042 | A369 | Set of 3 | 3.00 | 3.00 |

Dancers — A380

Designs: 100fr, Mengane dancers. 130fr, Maghouba dancers. 225fr, Ndjobi dancers.

**2001, Apr. 24    Litho.    Perf. 11¾**
| 1043 | A380 | 100fr multi | .50 | .30 |
| 1044 | A380 | 130fr multi | .50 | .30 |
| 1045 | A380 | 225fr multi | 1.00 | .50 |
| a. | | Souvenir sheet of 3, #1043-1045 | 3.00 | 2.50 |
| | | Nos. 1043-1045 (3) | 2.00 | 1.10 |

Flowers — A381

Design: 100fr, Pseudogardenia kallreyeri. 125fr, Ouratea turnerae. 225fr, Strophantus gratus. 260fr, Spathodea campanulata.

**2001                Litho.    Perf. 11¾**
| 1046-1049 | A381 | Set of 4 | 3.50 | 3.50 |
| 1049a | | Miniature sheet of 4, #1046-1049 | 3.50 | 3.50 |

Gabon Poste Emblem — A382

Color of denomination: 125fr, Green. 225fr, Blue.

**2003, Apr. 5    Litho.    Perf. 13x13¼**
| 1050-1051 | A382 | Set of 2 | 1.75 | 1.75 |

Orchids — A383

Designs: 100fr, Plectrelmintus caudatus. 125fr, Eulophia. 225fr, Jacinthe d'eau.

**2004, Feb. 20                      Perf. 13¼x13**
| 1052-1054 | A383 | Set of 3 | 3.00 | 2.25 |
| 1054a | | Souvenir sheet, #1052-1054 | 6.00 | 4.00 |

Cooperation Between Gabon and People's Republic of China, 30th Anniv. — A384

No. 1055: a, 125fr, Chinese Prime Minister Wen Jiabao, Gabon Pres. Omar Bongo and flags. b, 225fr, Coats of arms of People's Republic of China and Gabon. No. 1056, 2500fr, Like No. 1055a. No. 1057, 2500fr, Like No. 1055b.

---

**2004, Apr. 20              Perf. 12**
| 1055 | A384 | Horiz. pair, #a-b | 2.00 | 2.00 |

**Souvenir Sheets**
**Printed on Wood Veneer**
**Self-Adhesive**
| 1056-1057 | A384 | Set of 2 | 120.00 | |

Nos. 1056 and 1057 are airmail and each contains one 90x50mm stamp.

FIFA (Fédération Internationale de Football Association), Cent. — A385

Background color: 125fr, Blue. 225fr, Green.

**2004, Apr. 24    Litho.    Perf. 13x13¼**
| 1058-1059 | A385 | Set of 2 | 2.00 | 1.75 |

Biodiversity A386

Designs: 100fr, Hyperolius kuligae. 125fr, Chameleon, vert. 225fr, Merops malimbicus. 260fr, Owl.

**2004, June 5    Perf. 13x13¼, 13¼x13**
| 1060-1063 | A386 | Set of 4 | 5.50 | 5.50 |
| 1063a | | Souvenir sheet of 4, #1060-1063 | 4.00 | 3.00 |

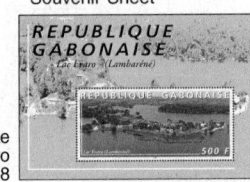

Rotary International, Cent. — A387

**2005, Feb. 23    Litho.    Perf. 13x13¼**
| 1064 | A387 | 125fr multi | 2.00 | 1.00 |

**Souvenir Sheet**
| 1065 | A387 | 2500fr multi | 12.00 | 12.00 |

**Souvenir Sheet**

Lake Evaro A388

**2005                Litho.    Perf. 13¾x13½**
| 1066 | A388 | 225fr multi | 3.00 | 2.00 |

**Souvenir Sheet**
| 1067 | A388 | 500fr multi | 12.00 | |

Christmas A389

No. 1068 — Carved wooden toys: a, 260fr, Antique car. b, 350fr, Logging truck.

**2005                        Perf. 13x13¼**
| 1068 | A389 | Pair, #a-b | 25.00 | |
| c. | | Souvenir sheet of 4, 2 each #1068a-1068b | 50.00 | |

---

Soccer Players and Flag — A390

**2005                        Perf. 13x13¼**
| 1069 | A390 | 225fr multi | 2.00 | 1.25 |

No. 1069 issued in sheets of 4.

Central African Network of Protected Areas — A391

**2007, May 28                    Perf. 13¼**
| 1070 | A391 | 500fr multi | 2.10 | 2.10 |

Petroleum Exploration in Gabon, 80th Anniv. — A392

Designs: No. 1071, 250fr, Ship and offshore drilling platform. No. 1072, 250fr, Oil drilling complex in jungle. No. 1073, 250fr, Oil workers. No. 1074, 500fr, Oil tanker at dock. No. 1075, 500fr, Elephants and oil drilling complex in jungle, vert. No. 1076, 500fr, Oil workers, vert.

**Perf. 13x13¼, 13¼x13**
**2008, May 5                      Litho.**
| 1071-1076 | A392 | Set of 6 | 11.00 | 11.00 |
| 1076a | | Sheet of 6, #1071-1076 | 11.00 | 11.00 |

**Souvenir Sheet**

Children's Drawings of Petroleum Industry — A393

No. 1077: a, Workers at Shell Gabon Terminal. b, Petroleum and Biodiversity.

**2008, Sept. 25    Litho.    Perf. 13x13¼**
| 1077 | A393 | 250fr Sheet of 2, #a-b | 2.25 | 2.25 |

Rule of Pres. Omar Bongo, 41st Anniv. — A394

**Litho. & Embossed**
**2008, Dec. 5              Perf. 13½x13**
| 1078 | A394 | 500fr multi | 2.25 | 2.25 |

**Litho. & Embossed With Foil Application**
| 1079 | A394 | 5000fr gold & multi | 22.50 | 22.50 |

Nos. 1078-1079 each were printed in sheets of 4.

Tenth World Conference of Regular Masonic Grand Lodges, Libreville — A395

**2009, Nov. 4    Litho.    Perf. 14x14½**
1080    A395    250fr multi    —

An additional stamp was issued in this set. The editors would like to examine any example of it.

Rotary International, 50th Anniv. in Gabon (in 2009) — A396

**2010    Litho.    Perf. 13x13¼**
1082    A396    250fr multi    1.00    .50

Gabon Numerique 2010 — A397

**2010, July**
1083    A397    500fr multi    2.00    1.25

A398        A399

Prize-winning Art in 50th Anniversary of Gabon Art Contest — A400

**2010, Aug.    Perf. 13¼x13, 13x13¼**
1084    A398    250fr multi    1.00    .50
1085    A399    250fr multi    1.00    .50
1086    A400    250fr multi    1.00    .50

Pres. Ali Bongo Ondimba — A401

**2010, Aug.    Perf. 13¼x13**
1087    A401    500fr multi    2.00    1.25

Gabon Presidents Léon Mba (1902-67), Omar Bongo (1935-2009) and Ali Bongo — A402

**2010, Aug.**
1088    A402    500fr multi    2.00    1.25
**Souvenir Sheet**
1089    A402    1500fr multi    20.00    15.00

A403

A404

Intl. Widows Day — A405

**2011, June 23    Litho.    Perf. 13x13¼**
1090    A403    250fr multi    2.50    2.50
1091    A404    250fr multi    2.50    2.50
    **Perf. 13¼x13**
1092    A405    250fr multi    2.50    2.50

2012 African Cup of Nations Soccer Championships, Gabon and Equatorial Guinea — A406

Flags of Gabon and Equatorial Guinea and mascot: 250fr, Holding ball on ground. 500fr, Dribbling ball.

**2012    Perf. 13x13¼**
1093-1094    A406    Set of 2    6.00    6.00

Souvenir Sheet

Dr. Albert Schweitzer (1875-1965), 1952 Nobel Peace Laureate — A407

**Litho. & Embossed With Foil Application**
**2013, July 6    Perf. 13**
1097    A407    3000fr sil & multi    —

Three additional stamps were issued in this set. The editors would like to examine any examples.

Map of Gabon and Pres. Omar Bongo Ondimba (1935-2009) — A408

**2014, June 5    Litho.    Die Cut**
**Self-Adhesive**
1100    A408    500fr multi    —

Three additional stamps were issued in this set. The editors would like to examine any examples.

A409

Pres. Ali Bongo Ondimba — A410

**2014, Dec. 1    Litho.    Perf. 12¾**
1103    A409    250fr multi    —
1104    A410    500fr multi    —

Cooperation Between Gabon and People's Republic of China, 40th Anniv. A411

Xi Jinping, President of People's Republic of China, and Gabon President Ali Bongo Ondimba A412

No. 1105: a, National Stadium, Angondjé, Gabon. b, Temple of Heaven, Beijing. c, Pandas. d, Elephants.

**2014, Dec. 1    Litho.    Perf. 12**
1105    Block of 4    —
    a.-d.    A411 500fr Any single    —
1106    A412    1000fr gold & multi    —
    a.    Souvenir sheet of 5, #1105a-1105d, 1106    —

First Oil From Remboué Oil Field A413

No. 1107 — Emblems of Gabon Oil Company and Remboué Oil Field and: a, Oil rig. b, Remboué River.

**2015, May 25    Litho.    Perf. 13**
1107    Horiz. pair    —
    a.    A413 250fr multi    —
    b.    A413 500fr multi    —

Constitutional Court — A414

Members of First College of Constitutional Court — A415

Members of Second College of Constitutional Court — A416

Marie Madeleine Mborantsuo, President of Constitutional Court — A417

No. 1108A: b, Marie Madeleine Mborantsuo. c, Augustin Boumah. d, Victor Afene. e, Paul

Malekou. f, Dominique Boungouere. g, Séraphin Ndaot-Rembogo. h, Marc-Aurelien Tondjokoue. i, Jean-Pierre Ndong. j, Louise Angue. k, Michel Antchouet. l, Dr. Hervé Moutsinga. Nos. 1108Ab-1108Al are each 30x40mm.

No. 1109: a, Mborantsuo. b, Boumah. c, Afene. d, Malekou. e, Tondjokoue. f, Boungouere. g, Ndaot-Rembogo. h, Ndong. i, Angue. j, Moutsinga. k, Antchouet.

**2019, Jan. 24    Litho.    Perf. 13**
1108    A414    350fr multi    —
1108A    Sheet of 11, #1108Ab-1108Al    —
    b.-j.    A415 700fr Any single    —
    k.-l.    A416 1000fr Either single    —
    **Souvenir Booklet**
1109    Souvenir booklet, #1109l, 1109m, 1109n, 1109o, 1110a    —
    a.-i.    A415 700fr Any single    —
    j.-k.    A416 1000fr Either single    —
    l.    Booklet pane of 3, #1109a-1109c    —
    m.    Booklet pane of 3, #1109d-1109f    —
    n.    Booklet pane of 3, #1109g-1109i    —
    o.    Booklet pane of 2, #1109j-1109k    —
    **Souvenir Sheet**
1110    A417    700fr multi    —
    a.    Booklet pane of 1    —

Dated 2018. No. 1110a is wider than No. 1110, being the same size as Nos. 1109l-1109o.

---

**SEMI-POSTAL STAMPS**

No. 37 Surcharged in Red

**1916    Unwmk.    Perf. 13½x14**
B1    A10    10c + 5c red & car    30.00    30.00
    a.    Double surcharge    200.00    225.00
    d.    In pair with unsurcharged stamp    550.00

**Same Surcharge on No. 54 in Red**
B2    A10    10c + 5c red & car    37.50    37.50
    a.    Double surcharge    200.00    225.00
    b.    Inverted surcharge    175.00
    c.    Double surcharge, one inverted    175.00    200.00
    d.    In pair with unsurcharged stamp    550.00

No. 54 Surcharged in Red

**1917**
B3    A10    10c + 5c red & car    2.40    2.40

**Catalogue values for unused stamps in this section, from this point to the end of the section, are for Never Hinged items.**

**Republic**
**Anti-Malaria Issue**
Common Design Type
**1962, Apr. 7    Engr.    Perf. 12½x12**
B4    CD108    25fr + 5fr yel grn    1.00    1.00

WHO drive to eradicate malaria.

**Freedom from Hunger Issue**
Common Design Type
**1963, Mar. 21    Unwmk.    Perf. 13**
B5    CD112    25fr + 5fr dk red, grn & brn    1.00    1.00

Red Cross — SP1

**1997, May 8    Litho.    Perf. 13½x13**
B6   SP1 150fr +75fr multi       1.40 1.10

## AIR POST STAMPS

Catalogue values for unused stamps in this section are for Never Hinged items.

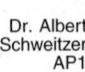

Dr. Albert Schweitzer AP1

**Unwmk.**
**1960, July 23    Engr.    Perf. 13**
C1   AP1 200fr org, dl red brn & ultra       7.00 3.50

For surcharge see No. C11.

Workmen Felling Tree — AP2

**1960, Oct. 8**
C2   AP2 100fr red brn, grn & blk   4.00 1.50

5th World Forestry Cong., Seattle, WA, Aug. 29-Sept. 10.

### Olympic Games Issue
French Equatorial Africa No. C37 Surcharged in Red Like Chad No. C1

**1960, Dec. 15**
C3   AP8 250fr on 500fr grnsh blk, blk & slate   8.00 8.00

17th Olympic Games, Rome, 8/25-9/11.

Lyre-tailed Honey Guide AP3

**1961, May 30         Perf. 13**
C4   AP3 50fr sl grn, red brn & ultra       4.50 1.00

See Nos. C14-C17.

### Air Afrique Issue
Common Design Type

**1962, Feb. 17    Engr.    Perf. 13**
C5   CD107 500fr sl grn, blk & bis       11.00 6.00

Long Jump — AP3a

---

**1962, July 21    Photo.    Perf. 12x12½**
C6   AP3a 100fr dk & lt bl, brn & blk       3.00 1.50

Issued to publicize the Abidjan Games.

Breguet 14, 1928 — AP4

Development of air transport: 20fr, Dragon biplane transport. 60fr, Caravelle jet. 85fr, Rocket-propelled aircraft.

**1962, Sept. 4    Engr.    Perf. 13**
C7   AP4 10fr dl red brn & sl     .65    .25
C8   AP4 20fr dk bl, sl & ocher     .90    .35
C9   AP4 60fr dk sl grn, blk & brn     2.25    .90
C10   AP4 85fr dk bl, blk & org   3.25   1.60
   a.   Souv. sheet of 4, #C7-C10    9.00 11.00
     Nos. C7-C10 (4)    7.05 3.10

Gabon's 1st phil. exhib., Libreville, Sept. 2-9.

### No. C1 Surcharged in Red: "100F/JUBILE GABONAIS/1913-1963"

**1963, Apr. 18**
C11   AP1 100fr on 200fr       3.50 1.75

50th anniv. of Dr. Albert Schweitzer's arrival in Gabon.

Post Office, Libreville AP5

**1963, Apr. 28    Photo.    Perf. 13x12**
C12   AP5 100fr multi       1.50   .90

### African Postal Union Issue
Common Design Type

**1963, Sept. 8    Unwmk.    Perf. 12½**
C13   CD114 85fr brt car, ocher & red       1.90   .80

### Bird Type of 1961

Birds: 100fr, Johanna's sunbird. 200fr, Blue-headed bee-eater, vert. 250fr, Crowned hawk-eagle, vert. 500fr, Narina trogon, vert.

**1963-64    Engr.    Perf. 13**
C14   AP3 100fr dk grn, vio bl & car       3.75   1.25
C15   AP3 200fr ol, vio bl & red   8.00   3.00
C16   AP3 250fr grn, blk & dk brn ('64)   15.00   4.00
C17   AP3 500fr multi   15.00   7.00
     Nos. C14-C17 (4)   41.75 15.25

Issued: Nos. C14-C15, C17, 10/7; No. C16, 9/23/64.

### 1963 Air Afrique Issue
Common Design Type

**1963, Nov. 19    Photo.    Perf. 13x12**
C18   CD115 50fr lt vio, gray, blk & grn       1.25 .65

### Europafrica Issue
Common Design Type

**1963, Nov. 30         Perf. 12x13**
C19   CD116 50fr vio, yel & dk brn   1.25 .75

### Chiefs of State Issue

Map and Presidents of Chad, Congo, Gabon and CAR — AP5a

**1964, June 23         Perf. 12½**
C20   AP5a 100fr multi       1.90   .90

See note after Central African Republic No. C19.

---

### Europafrica Issue

Globe and Emblems of Industry and Agriculture — AP6

**1964, July 20         Perf. 12x13**
C21   AP6 50fr red, olive & blue   1.40 .75

See note after Cameroun No. 402.

Start of Race — AP7

Athletes (Greek): 50fr, Massage at gymnasium, vert. 100fr, Anointing with oil before game, vert. 200fr, Four athletes.

**1964, July 30    Engr.    Perf. 13**
C22   AP7 25fr sl grn, dk brn & org       .75   .40
C23   AP7 50fr dk brn, sl grn & org brn       1.20   .45
C24   AP7 100fr vio bl, ol grn & dk brn       2.40   .90
C25   AP7 200fr dk brn, mag & org red       4.00 2.50
   a.   Min. sheet of 4, #C22-C25   12.00 12.00
     Nos. C22-C25 (4)   8.35 4.25

18th Olympic Games, Tokyo, Oct. 10-25.

Communications Symbols — AP7a

**1964, Nov. 2    Litho.    Perf. 12½x13**
C26   AP7a 25fr lt grn, dk brn & lt red brn       .90 .25

See note after Chad No. C19.

John F. Kennedy (1917-63) — AP8

**1964, Nov. 23    Photo.    Perf. 12½**
C27   AP8 100fr grn, org & blk   1.75 1.50
   a.   Souv. sheet of 4       9.00 9.00

Telephone Operator, Nurse and Police Woman AP9

**1964, Dec. 5    Engr.    Perf. 13**
C28   AP9 50fr car, bl & chocolate   1.40   .40

Social evolution of Gabonese women.

World Map and ICY Emblem AP10

---

**1965, Mar. 25    Unwmk.    Perf. 13**
C29   AP10 50fr org, Prus bl & grnsh bl       1.40 .70

International Cooperation Year.

Merchant Ship, 17th Century AP11

25fr, Galleon, 16th cent., vert. 85fr, Frigate, 18th cent., vert. 100fr, Brig, 19th cent.

**1965, Apr. 22    Photo.    Perf. 13**
C30   AP11 25fr lilac & multi   1.00   .55
C31   AP11 50fr yellow & multi   2.00   .80
C32   AP11 85fr multi   3.25 1.50
C33   AP11 100fr multi   4.50 2.00
     Nos. C30-C33 (4)   10.75 4.85

Red Cross Nurse Carrying Sick Child AP12

**1965, June 25    Engr.    Perf. 13**
C34   AP12 100fr brn, slate grn & red       2.25   .75

Issued for the Gabonese Red Cross.

Women's Basketball — AP13

**1965, July 15         Unwmk.**
C35   AP13 100fr sep, red org & brt lil       2.40   .90

African Games, Brazzaville, July 18-25.

Maps of Europe and Africa AP14

**1965, July 26    Photo.    Perf. 13x12**
C36   AP14 50fr multi       1.60 .50

See note after Cameroun No. 421.

Pres. Leon Mba — AP15

**1965, Aug. 17         Perf. 12½**
C37   AP15 25fr multi       .90 .50

Fifth anniversary of independence.

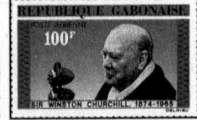

Sir Winston Churchill and Microphones AP16

**1965, Sept. 28    Photo.    Perf. 12½**
C38   AP16 100fr gold, blk & bl   2.00   .75

Sir Winston Spencer Churchill (1874-1965), statesman and World War II leader.

Dr. Albert Schweitzer AP17

## Embossed on Gold Foil
### Die-cut Perf. 14½, Approx.
**1965, Dec. 4**
**C39** AP17 1000fr gold          55.00 55.00
Dr. Albert Schweitzer (1875-1965), medical missionary, theologian and musician.

Pope John XXIII and St. Peter's AP18

**1965, Dec. 10    Photo.    Perf. 13x12½**
**C40** AP18 85fr multi          1.60  .75
Issued in memory of Pope John XXIII.

Anti-Malaria Treatment — AP19

**1966, Apr. 8    Photo.    Perf. 12½**
**C41** AP19 50fr shown          1.00  .60
  a.  Min. sheet of 4          7.00 7.00
**C42** AP19 100fr First aid          2.10 1.00
  a.  Min. sheet of 4          10.00 10.00
Issued for the Red Cross.

Diamant Rocket, A-1 Satellite and Map of Africa AP20

90fr, FR-1 satellite, Diamant rocket and earth.
**1966, May 18    Engr.    Perf. 13**
**C43** AP20 30fr dk pur, brt bl & red brn          .85  .50
**C44** AP20 90fr brt lil, red & pur          1.60  .80
French achievements in space.

Soccer and World Map — AP21

**1966, July 15    Engr.    Perf. 13**
**C45** AP21 100fr slate & brn red          2.50 1.00
8th World Soccer Cup Championship, Wembley, England, July 11-30.

Symbols of Industry and Transportation — AP22

**1966, July 26    Photo.    Perf. 12x13**
**C46** AP22 50fr multi          1.25  .65
3rd anniv. of the economic agreement between the European Economic Community and the African and Malgache Union.

### Air Afrique Issue, 1966
### Common Design Type
**1966, Aug. 31    Photo.    Perf. 13**
**C47** CD123 30fr org, blk & gray          .90  .35

---

Student and UNESCO Emblem — AP23

**1966, Nov. 4    Engr.    Perf. 13**
**C48** AP23 100fr dl bl, ocher & blk  1.90 .85
20th anniv. of UNESCO.

Libreville Airport AP24

**1966, Nov. 21    Engr.    Perf. 13**
**C49** AP24 200fr dp bl & red brn  4.50 1.50
Inauguration of Libreville Airport.

Farman 190 — AP25

Planes: 300fr, De Havilland Heron. 500fr, Potez 56.
**1967, Apr. 1    Engr.    Perf. 13**
**C50** AP25 200fr ultra, redsh pur & bl grn          4.00 1.75
**C51** AP25 300fr brn pur, dk red & brt bl          7.50 2.10
**C52** AP25 500fr brn car & dk grn          12.00 5.00
  Nos. C50-C52 (3)          23.50 8.85
For surcharge see No. C128.

Planes, Runways and ICAO Emblem AP26

**1967, May 19    Engr.    Perf. 13**
**C53** AP26 100fr plum, brt bl & yel grn          2.00 1.10
International Civil Aviation Organization.

Blood Donor and Bottles — AP27

100fr, Human heart and transfusion apparatus.
**1967, June 26    Photo.    Perf. 12½**
**C54** AP27 50fr ocher, red & sl          1.50  .55
  a.  Souvenir sheet of 4          7.50 7.50
**C55** AP27 100fr yel grn, red & gray          3.00 1.25
  a.  Souvenir sheet of 4          12.50 12.50
Issued for the Red Cross. Nos. C54a, C55a each contain 2 vertical tête bêche pairs.

Jamboree Emblem and Symbols of Orientation — AP28

---

Design: 100fr, Jamboree emblem, maps and Scouts of Africa and America.
**1967, Aug. 1    Engr.    Perf. 13**
**C56** AP28 50fr multi          1.50  .80
**C57** AP28 100fr brt grn, dp car & bl          2.25 1.60
12th Boy Scout World Jamboree, Farragut State Park, Idaho, Aug. 1-9.

### African Postal Union Issue, 1967
### Common Design Type
**1967, Sept. 9    Engr.    Perf. 13**
**C58** CD124 100fr dl bl, ol & red brn          2.00  .85

Mission Church AP29

**1967, Oct. 18    Engr.    Perf. 13**
**C59** AP29 100fr brt bl, dk grn & blk          2.75 1.25
125th anniv. of the arrival of American Protestant missionaries in Baraka-Libreville.

UN Emblem, Sword, Book and People — AP30

**1967, Nov. 7    Photo.    Perf. 13**
**C60** AP30 60fr dk red, vio bl & bis  1.10 .65
UN Commission on Human Rights.

### Tree Type of Regular Issue
Designs: 50fr, Baillonella toxisperma. 100fr, Aucoumea klaineana.
**1967, Dec. 5    Engr.    Perf. 13**
**Size: 26½x47½mm**
**C61** A53 50fr grn, brt bl & brn  1.60 1.10
**C62** A53 100fr multi          2.75 1.90
  a.  Bklt. pane of 5, #223-225, C61-C62 with gutter btwn.  8.00 8.00

Konrad Adenauer — AP31

**1968, Feb. 20    Photo.    Perf. 12½**
**C63** AP31 100fr blk, dl org & red          2.50 1.10
  a.  Souvenir sheet of 4          10.00 10.00
Issued in memory of Konrad Adenauer (1876-1967), chancellor of West Germany (1949-63). No. C63a includes 1967 CEPT (Europa) emblem.

Madonna of the Rosary by Murillo — AP32

90fr, Christ in Bonds, by Luis de Morales. 100fr, St. John on Patmos, by Juan Mates.
**1968, July 9    Photo.    Perf. 12½x12**
**C64** AP32 60fr multi          1.20  .55
**C65** AP32 90fr multi          1.40  .95
**C66** AP32 100fr multi, horiz.          1.90 1.10
  Nos. C64-C66 (3)          4.50 2.60
See Nos. C77, C102-C102B, C132-C133, C146-C148.

---

### Europafrica Issue

Stylized Knot AP32a

**1968, July 23    Photo.    Perf. 13**
**C67** AP32a 50fr yel brn, emer & lt ultra          1.10  .45
See note after Congo Republic No. C69.

Support for Red Cross AP33

50fr, Distribution of Red Cross gifts.
**1968, Aug. 13**
**C68** AP33 50fr multi          1.40  .65
**C69** AP33 100fr multi          2.75 1.40
  a.  Bklt. pane of 2, #C68, C69 with gutter btwn.          6.50 6.50
Issued for the Red Cross.

High Jump AP34

**1968, Sept. 3    Engr.**
**C70** AP34 25fr shown          .70  .50
**C71** AP34 30fr Bicycling, vert.   .85  .55
**C72** AP34 100fr Judo, vert.          2.25 1.25
**C73** AP34 200fr Boxing          4.25 2.10
  a.  Bklt. pane of 4, #C70-C71, C72-C73 with gutter btwn.  11.00 11.00
  Nos. C70-C73 (4)          8.05 4.40
Issued to publicize the 19th Summer Olympic Games, Mexico City, Oct. 12-27.

Pres. Mba, Flag and Arms of Gabon — AP35

### Embossed on Gold Foil
**1968, Nov. 28    Perf. 14½**
**C74** AP35 1000fr gold, grn, yel & dk bl          25.00 25.00
Death of Pres. Léon Mba (1902-67), 1st anniv.

Pres. Bongo, Maps of Gabon and Owendo Harbor AP36

**1968, Dec. 16    Photo.    Perf. 12½**
**C75** AP36 25fr shown          1.25  .25
**C76** AP36 30fr Owendo Harbor   1.25  .25
  a.  Strip of 2, #C75-C76 + label  3.00 3.00
Laying of the foundation stone for Owendo Harbor, June 24, 1968.

### PHILEXAFRIQUE Issue
### Painting Type of 1968
Design: 100fr, The Convent of St. Mary of the Angels, by Francois Marius Granet.
**1969, Jan. 8    Photo.    Perf. 12½x12**
**C77** AP32 100fr multi          3.50 3.50
Issued to publicize PHILEXAFRIQUE Philatelic Exhibition in Abidjan, Feb. 14-23. Printed with alternating brown label.

Mahatma
Gandhi — AP37

Portraits: 30fr, John F. Kennedy. 50fr, Robert F. Kennedy. 100fr, Martin Luther King, Jr.

**1969, Jan. 15**                    **Perf. 12½**
| | | | | |
|---|---|---|---|---|
| C78 | AP37 | 25fr peach & blk | .75 | .45 |
| C79 | AP37 | 30fr lt yel grn & blk | .75 | .45 |
| C80 | AP37 | 50fr lt bl & blk | 1.10 | .45 |
| C81 | AP37 | 100fr brt rose lil & blk | 2.25 | .90 |
| a. | | Souv. sheet of 4, #C78-C81 | 6.00 | 6.00 |
| | | Nos. C78-C81 (4) | 4.85 | 2.25 |

Issued to honor exponents of non-violence.

**2nd PHILEXAFRIQUE Issue**
Common Design Type
**1969, Feb. 14**                    **Perf. 13**
| | | | |
|---|---|---|---|
| C82 | CD128 50fr grn, ind & red brn | 2.00 | 2.00 |

Battle of Rivoli, by Henri
Philippoteaux — AP39

100fr, The Oath of the Army, by Jacques Louis David. 250fr, Napoleon with the Children on the Terrace in St. Cloud, by Louis Ducis.

**1969, Apr. 23**                    **Perf. 12½x12**
| | | | | |
|---|---|---|---|---|
| C83 | AP39 | 50fr brn & multi | 2.10 | 1.10 |
| C84 | AP39 | 100fr grn & multi | 2.50 | 2.00 |
| C85 | AP39 | 250fr lil & multi | 10.00 | 6.00 |
| | | Nos. C83-C85 (3) | 14.60 | 9.10 |

Birth bicentenary of Napoleon I.

Red Cross
Plane, Nurse
and Biafran
Children
AP40

20fr, Dispensary, ambulance & supplies. 25fr, Physician & nurse in children's ward. 30fr, Dispensary & playing children.

**1969, June 20  Photo.  Perf. 14x13½**
| | | | | |
|---|---|---|---|---|
| C86 | AP40 | 15fr lt ultra, dk brn & red | .55 | .25 |
| C87 | AP40 | 20fr emer, blk, brn & red | .75 | .45 |
| C88 | AP40 | 25fr grnsh bl, dk brn & red | .75 | .45 |
| C89 | AP40 | 30fr org yel, dk brn & red | .90 | .45 |
| | | Nos. C86-C89 (4) | 2.95 | 1.60 |

Red Cross help for Biafra.
A souvenir sheet contains four stamps similar to Nos. C86-C89, but lithographed and rouletted 13x13½. Gray margin with red inscription and Red Cross. Size: 118x75mm. Sold in cardboard folder. Value $4.

Astronauts
and Lunar
Landing
Module,
Apollo
11 — AP41

**Embossed on Gold Foil**

**1969, July 25   Die-cut Perf. 10½x10**
| | | | |
|---|---|---|---|
| C90 | AP41 1000fr gold | 25.00 | 25.00 |

See note after Algeria No. 427.

---

**Europafrica Issue**

African and European
Heads and
Symbols — AP42

**1970, June 5   Photo.   Perf. 12x13**
| | | | |
|---|---|---|---|
| C91 | AP42 50fr multi | 1.25 | .50 |

Icarus and
Sun — AP43

Designs: 100fr, Leonardo da Vinci's flying man, 1519. 200fr, Jules Verne's space shell approaching moon, 1865.

**1970, June 10   Engr.   Perf. 13**
| | | | | |
|---|---|---|---|---|
| C92 | AP43 | 25fr ultra, red & org | .70 | .45 |
| C93 | AP43 | 100fr ocher, plum & sl grn | 1.25 | .75 |
| C94 | AP43 | 200fr gray, ultra & dk car | 4.00 | 1.50 |
| a. | | Min. sheet of 3, #C92-C94 | 6.50 | 6.50 |
| | | Nos. C92-C94 (3) | 5.95 | 2.70 |

UAMPT
Emblem — AP44

**Embossed on Gold Foil**

**1970, June 18   Die-cut Perf. 12½**
| | | | |
|---|---|---|---|
| C95 | AP44 200fr gold, yel grn & bl | 3.00 | 1.50 |

Meeting of the Afro-Malagasy Union of Posts & Telecommuncations (UAMPT), Libreville, 6/17-23.

Throwing
Knives — AP45

Gabonese Weapons: 30fr, Assegai and crossbow, vert. 50fr, War knives, vert. 90fr, Dagger and sheath.

**1970, July 10   Engr.   Perf. 13**
| | | | | |
|---|---|---|---|---|
| C96 | AP45 | 25fr multi | .60 | .35 |
| C97 | AP45 | 30fr multi | .70 | .40 |
| C98 | AP45 | 50fr multi | 1.00 | .50 |
| C99 | AP45 | 90fr multi | 2.00 | .75 |
| a. | | Min. sheet of 4, #C96-C99 | 6.50 | 6.50 |
| | | Nos. C96-C99 (4) | 4.30 | 2.00 |

Japanese
Masks, Mt. Fuji
and Torii at
Miyajima
AP46

**Embossed on Gold Foil**

**1970, July 31   Die-cut Perf. 10**
| | | | |
|---|---|---|---|
| C100 | AP46 1000fr multi | 20.00 | 20.00 |

Issued to publicize EXPO '70 International Exhibition, Osaka, Japan, Mar. 15-Sept. 13.

---

Pres. Albert Bernard
Bongo — AP47

**Lithographed; Gold Embossed**
**1970, Aug. 17**                    **Perf. 12½**
| | | | |
|---|---|---|---|
| C101 | AP47 200fr multi | 5.00 | 2.25 |

10th anniversary of independence.

**Painting Type of 1968**
Paintings: 50fr, Portrait of a Young Man, School of Raphael. 100fr, Portrait of Jeanne d'Aragon, by Raphael. 200fr, Madonna with Blue Diadem, by Raphael.

**1970, Oct. 16   Photo.   Perf. 12½x12**
| | | | | |
|---|---|---|---|---|
| C102 | AP32 | 50fr multi | 1.10 | .50 |
| C102A | AP32 | 100fr blue & multi | 2.25 | .95 |
| C102B | AP32 | 200fr brn & multi | 4.50 | 2.50 |
| | | Nos. C102-C102B (3) | 7.85 | 3.95 |

Raphael (1483-1520).

**Miniature Sheets**

AP47a

Hugo
Junkers — AP47b

**1970, Dec. 5   Litho.   Perf. 12**
| | | | |
|---|---|---|---|
| C103 | AP47a   Sheet of 8 | 10.00 | 10.00 |
| a. | 15fr Sikorsky S-32 | | |
| b. | 25fr Fokker "Southern Cross" | | |
| c. | 40fr Dornier DO-18 | | |
| d. | 60fr Dornier DO-X | | |
| e. | 80fr Breguet "Bizerte" | | |
| f. | 125fr Douglas "Cloudster" | | |
| g. | 150fr De Havilland DH-2 | | |
| h. | 200fr Vickers "Vimi" | | |
| C104 | Sheet of 4 | 15.00 | 15.00 |
| a. | AP47b 200fr shown | | |
| b. | AP47b 300fr Claude Dornier | | |
| c. | AP47b 400fr Anthony Fokker | | |
| d. | AP47b 500fr Igor Sikorsky | | |

**Imperf**
| | | | |
|---|---|---|---|
| C105 | AP47a   Sheet of 8 | 10.00 | 10.00 |
| a. | 10fr Dornier "Spatz" | | |
| b. | 20fr Douglas DC-3 | | |
| c. | 30fr Dornier DO-7 "Wal" | | |
| d. | 50fr Sikorsky S-38 | | |
| e. | 75fr De Havilland "Moth" | | |
| f. | 100fr Supermarine "Spit-fire" | | |
| g. | 125fr Breguet XIX | | |
| h. | 150fr Fokker "Universal" | | |

**Size: 80x90mm**
| | | | |
|---|---|---|---|
| C106 | AP47b 1000fr Claude Dornier | 15.00 | 15.00 |

Claude Dornier (1884-1969), aviation pioneer. No. C104 exists imperf. Value $17.

Presidents
Bongo and
Pompidou
AP48

**1971, Feb. 11   Photo.   Perf. 13**
| | | | |
|---|---|---|---|
| C107 | AP48 50fr multi | 1.75 | .85 |

Visit of Georges Pompidou, Pres. of France.

---

Apollo 14 — AP48a

15fr, Lift off. 25fr, Achieving orbit. 40fr, Lunar module descent. 55fr, Lunar landing. 75fr, Lunar liftoff. 120fr, Earth re-entry.

**1971, Feb. 19**                    **Perf. 14**
**Yellow Inscriptions**
| | | | | |
|---|---|---|---|---|
| C108 | | 15fr multi | .25 | .25 |
| C108A | | 25fr multi | .45 | .30 |
| C108B | | 40fr multi | .80 | .60 |
| C108C | | 55fr multi | 1.00 | .65 |
| C108D | | 75fr multi | 1.50 | 1.00 |
| C108E | | 120fr multi | 2.50 | 1.50 |
| | | Nos. C108-C108E (6) | 6.50 | 4.30 |

**Souvenir Sheet**
| | | | |
|---|---|---|---|
| C108F | Sheet of 2 | 7.50 | 4.25 |
| g. | AP48a 100fr Modules attached | 3.00 | 1.75 |
| h. | AP48a 100fr like #C108E | 3.00 | 1.75 |

Nos. C108-C108F exist imperf. with white inscriptions. Same values.

Flowers and
Plane — AP49

25fr, Carnations. 40fr, Roses. 55fr, Daffodils. 75fr, Orchids. 120fr, Tulips.

**1971, May 7   Litho.   Perf. 13½x14**
| | | | | |
|---|---|---|---|---|
| C109 | AP49 | 15fr yellow & multi | .35 | .25 |
| C109A | AP49 | 25fr multi | .55 | .25 |
| C109B | AP49 | 40fr pink & multi | .90 | .30 |
| C109C | AP49 | 55fr blue & multi | 1.20 | .35 |
| C110 | AP49 | 75fr multi | 2.00 | .60 |
| C111 | AP49 | 120fr green & multi | 2.40 | .85 |
| a. | | Souv. sheet of 2, #C110-C111 | 6.00 | 6.00 |
| | | Nos. C109-C111 (6) | 7.40 | 2.60 |

"Flowers by air."

Napoleon's Death
Mask — AP50

Designs: 200fr, Longwood, St. Helena, by Jacques Marchand, horiz. 500fr, Sarcophagus in Les Invalides, Paris.

**1971, May 12   Photo.   Perf. 13**
| | | | | |
|---|---|---|---|---|
| C112 | AP50 | 100fr gold & multi | 2.75 | .70 |
| C113 | AP50 | 200fr gold & multi | 4.25 | 1.50 |
| C114 | AP50 | 500fr gold & multi | 10.00 | 3.50 |
| | | Nos. C112-C114 (3) | 17.00 | 5.70 |

Napoleon Bonaparte (1769-1821).

**Souvenir Sheet**

Charles
de
Gaulle
AP51

Designs: 40fr, President de Gaulle. 80fr, General de Gaulle. 100fr, Quotation.

**1971, June 18 Photo.** *Perf. 12½*
C115 AP51 Sheet of 5   9.00 9.00
  *a.* 40fr dark red & multi   .75 .75
  *b.* 80fr dark green & multi   .75 .75
  *c.* 100fr green, brown & yel   2.00 2.00

In memory of Gen. Charles de Gaulle (1890-1970), Pres. of France.
For surcharge see No. C126.

Red Crosses — AP52

**1971, June 29**
C116 AP52 50fr multicolored   1.25 .40

For the Red Cross of Gabon.
For surcharge see No. C143.

Uranium AP53

**1971, July 20 Photo.** *Perf. 13x12½*
C117 AP53 85fr shown   7.00 3.50
C118 AP53 90fr Manganese   8.00 4.00

Landing Module over Moon AP54

**Embossed on Gold Foil**

**1971, July 30** *Die-cut Perf. 10*
C119 AP54 1500fr multi   25.00 25.00

Apollo 11 and 15 US moon missions.

**African Postal Union Issue, 1971**
**Common Design Type**

Design: 100fr, Bakota copper mask and UAMPT building, Brazzaville, Congo.

**1971, Nov. 13 Photo.** *Perf. 13x13½*
C120 CD135 100fr bl & multi   1.75 .70

Ski Jump and Miyajima Torii — AP55

130fr, Speed skating and Japanese temple.

**1972, Jan. 31 Engr.** *Perf. 13*
C121 AP55 40fr hn brn, sl grn & vio bl   1.40 .50
C122 AP55 130fr hn brn, sl grn & vio bl   2.00 .75
  *a.* Souvenir sheet of 2, #C121-C122 + label   4.50 4.50

11th Winter Olympic Games, Sapporo, Japan, Feb. 3-13.

The Basin and Grand Canal, by Vanvitelli AP56

Paintings: 70fr, Rialto Bridge, by Canaletto (erroneously inscribed Caffi), vert. 140fr, Santa Maria della Salute, by Vanvitelli, vert.

**1972, Feb. 7 Photo.** *Perf. 13*
C123 AP56 60fr gold & multi   2.10 .70
C124 AP56 70fr gold & multi   3.25 1.00
C125 AP56 140fr gold & multi   5.75 1.50
  Nos. C123-C125 (3)   11.10 3.20

UNESCO campaign to save Venice.

**No. C115 Surcharged in Brown and Gold**
Souvenir Sheet

**1972, Feb. 11** *Perf. 12½*
C126 AP51 Sheet of 5   15.00 15.00
  *a.* 60fr on 40fr multi   2.00 2.00
  *b.* 120fr on 80fr multi   3.00 3.00
  *c.* 180fr on 100fr multi   6.25 6.25

Publicity for the erection of a memorial for Charles de Gaulle. Nos. C126a-C126b have surcharge and Cross of Lorraine in gold, 2 bars obliterating old denomination in brown; No. C126c has surcharge, cross and bars in brown. Two Lorraine Crosses and inscription (MEMORIAL DU GENERAL DE GAULLE) in brown added in margin.

Hotel Inter-Continental, Libreville — AP57

**1972, Feb. 26 Engr.** *Perf. 13*
C127 AP57 40fr bl, sl grn & org brn   .95 .35

**No. C51 Surcharged**

**1972, Mar. 3**
C128 AP25 50fr on 300fr multi   1.25 .35

Official visit of the Grand Master of the Knights of Malta, March 3.

Discobolus, by Alcamenes — AP58

Designs: 100fr, Doryphoros, by Polycletus. 140fr, Borghese gladiator, by Agasias.

**1972, May 10 Engr.** *Perf. 13*
C129 AP58 30fr rose cl & gray   .80 .40
C130 AP58 100fr rose cl & gray   1.75 .50
C131 AP58 140fr rose cl & gray   2.25 .70
  *a.* Min. of sheet of 3, #C129-C131   6.00 6.00
  Nos. C129-C131 (3)   4.80 1.60

20th Olympic Games, Munich, 8/26-9/10.
For surcharges see Nos. C134-C136.

**Painting Type of 1968**

Paintings: 30fr, Adoration of the Magi, by Peter Brueghel, the Elder, horiz. 40fr, Madonna and Child, by Marco Basaiti.

**1972, Oct. 30 Photo.** *Perf. 13*
C132 AP32 30fr gold & multi   1.10 .25
C133 AP32 40fr gold & multi   1.60 .25

Christmas 1972.

**Nos. C129-C131 Surcharged with New Value, Two Bars and Names of Athletes.**

**1972, Dec. 5 Engr.** *Perf. 13*
C134 AP58 40fr on 30fr   .90 .35
C135 AP58 120fr on 100fr   1.75 .65
C136 AP58 170fr on 140fr   2.75 1.00
  Nos. C134-C136 (3)   5.40 2.00

Gold medal winners in 20th Olympic Games: Daniel Morelon, France, Bicycling (C134); Kipchoge Keino, Kenya, steeplechase (C135); Mark Spitz, US, swimming (C136).

Globe with Space Orbits, Simulated Stamps AP59

**1973, Feb. 20 Photo.** *Perf. 13*
C137 AP59 100fr multi   2.25 .50
  *a.* Souv. sheet of 4, perf. 12x12½   25.00 25.00

PHILEXGABON 1973, Phil. Exhib., Libreville, Feb. 19-26. No. C137a exists imperf.

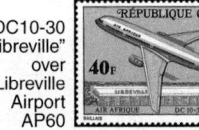

DC10-30 "Libreville" over Libreville Airport AP60

**1973, Mar. 19 Typo.** *Perf. 13*
C138 AP60 40fr blue & multi   2.50 1.25

Kinguélé Hydroelectric Station — AP61

Design: 40fr, Kinguélé Dam.

**1973, June 19 Engr.** *Perf. 13*
C139 AP61 30fr slate grn & dk ol   .80 .25
C140 AP61 40fr slate grn, dk ol & bl   1.10 .25
  *a.* Strip of 2, #C139-C140 + label   2.75 1.25

Hydroelectric installations at Kinguélé.

M'Bigou Stone Sculpture, Woman's Head — AP62

Design: 200fr, Sculpture, man's head.

**1973, July 5**
C141 AP62 100fr blk, bl & grn   1.60 .70
C142 AP62 200fr grn, sep & sl grn   3.00 1.25

**No. C116 Srchd. and Ovptd. in Ultramarine**

**1973, Aug. 16 Photo.** *Perf. 12½*
C143 AP52 100fr on 50fr multi   2.00 .65

African solidarity in drought emergency.

Astronauts and Lunar Rover on Moon AP63

**1973, Sept. 6 Engr.** *Perf. 13*
C144 AP63 500fr multi   8.50 4.00

Apollo 17 US moon mission, 12/7-19/73.

Presidents Houphouet Boigny (Ivory Coast) and De Gaulle AP64

**1974, Apr. 30 Engr.** *Perf. 13*
C145 AP64 40fr rose lilac & indigo   1.75 .75

30th anniv. of the Conf. of Brazzaville.

**Painting Type of 1968**

Impressionist Paintings: 40fr, Pleasure Boats, by Claude Monet, horiz. 50fr, Ballet Dancer, by Edgar Degas. 130fr, Young Girl with Flowers, by Auguste Renoir.

**1974, June 11 Photo.** *Perf. 13*
C146 AP32 40fr gold & multi   3.25 .50
C147 AP32 50fr gold & multi   5.00 .70
C148 AP32 130fr gold & multi   8.00 1.10
  Nos. C146-C148 (3)   16.25 2.30

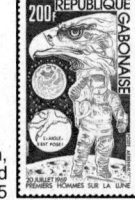

Astronaut on Moon, Eagle and Emblems — AP65

**1974, July 20 Engr.** *Perf. 13*
C149 AP65 200fr multi   2.50 .90

First men on the moon, 5th anniversary.

UPU Emblem, Letters, Pigeon — AP66

UPU cent.: 300fr, UPU emblem, letters, pigeons, diff.

**1974, Oct. 9 Engr.** *Perf. 13*
C150 AP66 150fr lt bl & Prus bl   2.25 .90
C151 AP66 300fr org & claret   4.50 1.75

Space Docking, US and USSR Crafts — AP67

**1974, Oct. 23 Engr.** *Perf. 13*
C152 AP67 1000fr grn, red & sl   9.00 5.25

Russo-American space cooperation.
For overprint see No. C169.

Soccer and Games Emblem AP68

Designs: Soccer actions.

**1974, Oct. 25**
C153 AP68 40fr grn, red & brn   .70 .25
C154 AP68 65fr red, brn & grn   .90 .35
C155 AP68 100fr grn, red & brn   1.25 .60
  *a.* Souv. sheet of 3, #C153-C155 + 3 labels   4.50 4.50
  Nos. C153-C155 (3)   2.85 1.20

World Cup Soccer Championship, Munich, June 13-July 7.

## UDEAC Issue

Presidents and Flags of Cameroun, CAR, Gabon and Congo AP68a

**1974, Dec. 8    Photo.    Perf. 13**
C156  AP68a  100fr gold & multi          1.10  .45

Annunciation, Tapestry, 15th Century — AP69

Christmas: 40fr, Visitation from 15th century tapestry, Notre Dame de Beaune, vert.

**1974, Dec. 11**
C157  AP69  40fr gold & multi          1.10  .30
C158  AP69  50fr gold & multi          1.25  .35

Dr. Schweitzer and Lambarene Hospital AP70

**1975, Jan. 14    Engr.    Perf. 13**
C159  AP70  500fr multi          9.00  3.00

Dr. Albert Schweitzer (1875-1965), medical missionary, birth centenary.

Crucifixion, by Bellini — AP71

Paintings: 150fr, Resurrection, Burgundian School, c. 1500.

**1975, Apr. 8    Photo.    Perf. 13½**
**Size: 26x45mm**
C160  AP71  140fr gold & multi          2.10  .60
**Size: 36x48mm**
**Perf. 13**
C161  AP71  150fr gold & multi          2.50  .70
Easter 1975.

Marc Seguin Locomotive, 1829 — AP72

Locomotives: 25fr, The Iron Duke, 1847. 40fr, Thomas Rogers, 1895. 50fr, The Soviet 272, 1934.

**1975, Apr. 8    Engr.    Perf. 13**
C162  AP72  20fr multi          1.75  .40
C163  AP72  25fr multi          2.25  .40
C164  AP72  40fr multi          3.00  .65
C165  AP72  50fr lil & multi          4.00  .75
      Nos. C162-C165 (4)          11.00  2.20

Swimming Pool, Montreal Olympic Games' Emblem AP73

Designs: 150fr, Boxing ring and emblem. 300fr, Stadium, aerial view, and emblem.

**1975, Sept. 30    Litho.    Perf. 13x12½**
C166  AP73  100fr multi          1.10  .30
C167  AP73  150fr multi          1.75  .60
C168  AP73  300fr multi          3.50  1.10
   a.    Min. sheet of 3, #C166-C168          7.00  7.00
      Nos. C166-C168 (3)          6.35  2.00
Pre-Olympic Year 1975.

### No. C152 Surcharged in Violet Blue: "JONCTION / 17 Juillet 1975"

**1975, Oct. 20    Engr.    Perf. 13**
C169  AP67  1000fr multi          9.50  4.50

Apollo-Soyuz link-up in space, July 17, 1975.

Annunciation, by Maurice Denis — AP74

Painting: 50fr, Virgin and Child with Two Saints, by Fra Filippo Lippi.

**1975, Dec. 9    Photo.    Perf. 13**
C170  AP74  40fr gold & multi          1.10  .40
C171  AP74  50fr gold & multi          1.40  .55
Christmas 1975.

Concorde and Globe — AP75

**1975, Dec. 29    Engr.    Perf. 13**
C172  AP75  500fr bl, vio bl & red  10.00  3.75
For overprint see No. C198.

No. C172 Surcharged

**1976, Jan. 21**
C173  AP75  1000fr on 500fr          16.00  8.00

Nos. C172-C173 for the 1st commercial flight of supersonic jet Concorde from Paris to Rio, Jan. 21.

Slalom and Olympic Games Emblem AP76

Design: 250fr, Speed skating and Winter Olympic Games emblem.

**1976, Apr. 22    Engr.    Perf. 13**
C174  AP76  100fr blk, bl & red          1.25  .40
C175  AP76  250fr blk, bl & red          3.00  1.40
   a.    Souvenir sheet          6.00  6.00
12th Winter Olympic Games, Innsbruck, Austria, Feb. 4-15. No. C175a contains 100fr and 250fr stamps in continuous design with additional inscription and skier between, but without perforations between the design elements.
   Size of perforated area: 125x27mm; size of sheet: 169x90mm.

Jesus Between the Thieves — AP77

Design: 130fr, St. Thomas putting finger into wounds of Jesus. Both designs after wood carvings in Church of St. Michael, Libreville.

**1976, Apr. 28    Litho.    Perf. 12½x13**
C176  AP77  120fr multi          1.25  .65
C177  AP77  130fr multi          2.00  .95
Easter 1976. See Nos. C188-C189, C220-C221.

Boston Tea Party AP78

Designs: 150fr, Battle of New York. 200fr, Demolition of statue of George III.

**1976, May 3    Engr.    Perf. 13**
C178  AP78  100fr multi          1.00  .50
C179  AP78  150fr multi          1.90  .70
C180  AP78  200fr multi          2.40  .80
   a.    Triptych, #C178-C180 + 2 labels          8.00  6.50
American Bicentennial.

### Nos. C178-C180 Overprinted: "4 JUILLET 1976"

**1976, July 4    Engr.    Perf. 13**
C181  AP78  100fr multi          1.00  .50
C182  AP78  150fr multi          1.90  .70
C183  AP78  200fr multi          2.40  .80
   a.    Triptych, #C181-C183 + 2 labels          8.00  6.50
Independence Day.

Running — AP79

200fr, Soccer. 260fr, High jump.

**1976, July 27    Litho.    Perf. 12½**
C184  AP79  100fr multi          1.10  .35
C185  AP79  200fr multi          2.50  .65
C186  AP79  260fr multi          3.25  .90
   a.    Souv. sheet of 3, #C184-C186, perf. 13          8.00  3.75
      Nos. C184-C186 (3)          6.85  1.90
21st Olympic Games, Montreal, Canada, July 17-Aug. 1.

Presidents Giscard d'Estaing and Bongo AP80

**1976, Aug. 5    Photo.    Perf. 13**
C187  AP80  60fr blue & multi          1.25  .30
Visit of Pres. Valèrie Giscard d'Estaing of France.

### Sculpture Type of 1976

Christmas: 50fr, Presentation at the Temple. 60fr, Nativity. Designs after wood Carvings in Church of St. Michael, Libreville.

**1976, Dec. 6    Litho.    Perf. 12½x13**
C188  AP77  50fr multi          1.00  .25
C189  AP77  60fr multi          1.10  .35

Oklo Fossil Reactor AP81

**1976, Dec. 15    Litho.    Perf. 13**
C190  AP81  60fr red & multi          1.10  .30

The Last Supper, by Juste de Gand AP82

100fr, The Deposition, by Nicolas Poussin.

**1977, Mar. 25    Litho.    Perf. 12½**
C191  AP82  50fr gold & multi          1.10  .25
C192  AP82  100fr gold & multi          2.25  .65
Easter 1977.

Air Gabon Plane and Insigne AP83

**1977, June 3    Litho.    Perf. 12½**
C193  AP83  60fr multi          1.10  .50
Air Gabon's first intercontinental route.

Beethoven, Piano and Score AP84

**1977, June 15    Engr.    Perf. 13**
C194  AP84  260fr slate          3.00  .95
Ludwig van Beethoven (1770-1827).

Lindbergh and Spirit of St. Louis AP85

**1977, Sept. 13    Engr.    Perf. 13**
C195  AP85  500fr multi          8.00  2.75
Charles A. Lindbergh's solo transatlantic flight from NY to Paris, 50th anniv.

Soccer AP86

**1977, Oct. 18    Photo.    Perf. 13x12½**
C196  AP86  250fr multi          2.75  1.10
Elimination games, World Soccer Cup, Buenos Aires, 1978.

Viking on Mars — AP87

**1977, Nov. 17    Engr.    Perf. 13**
C197  AP87  1000fr multi          10.00  8.00
Viking, US space probe.

No. C172 Overprinted: "PARIS NEW-YORK / PREMIER VOL / 22.11.77"

**1977, Nov. 22    Engr.    Perf. 13**
C198  AP75  500fr multi             9.00 5.00

Concorde, 1st commercial flight, Paris to NYC.

Lion Hunt, by Rubens AP88

Rubens Paintings: 80fr, Hippopotamus Hunt. 200fr, Head of Black Man, vert.

**1977, Nov. 24    Litho.    Perf. 13**
C199  AP88  60fr gold & multi       .95   .35
C200  AP88  80fr gold & multi      1.25   .50
C201  AP88  200fr gold & multi     3.00  1.10
   a.   Souv. sheet of 3, #C199-C201  7.50  7.50
   Nos. C199-C201 (3)              5.20  1.90

Peter Paul Rubens (1577-1640).

Adoration of the Kings, by Rubens AP89

Design: 80fr, Flight into Egypt, by Rubens.

**1977, Dec. 15    Litho.    Perf. 12½**
C202  AP89  60fr gold & multi      1.00   .30
C203  AP89  80fr gold & multi      1.10   .45

Christmas 1977; Peter Paul Rubens.

Paul Gauguin, Self-Portrait AP90

150fr, Flowers in vase and Maori statuette.

**1978, Feb. 8    Litho.    Perf. 12½x12**
C204  AP90  150fr multi            3.00   .60
C205  AP90  300fr multi            5.50  1.10

Paul Gauguin (1848-1903), French painter.

Pres. Bongo, Map of Gabon, Plane and Train — AP91

**Lithographed; Gold Embossed**
**1978, Mar. 12    Perf. 12½**
C206  AP91  500fr multi            7.00  1.75

10th anniversary of national renewal.

Soccer and Argentina '78 Emblem AP92

Argentina '78 Emblem and: 120fr, Three soccer players. 200fr, Jules Rimet Cup, vert.

**1978, July 18    Engr.    Perf. 13**
C207  AP92  100fr red, grn & brn    .85   .25
C208  AP92  120fr grn, red & brn   1.10   .40
C209  AP92  200fr brn & red        2.25   .55
   a.   Min. sheet of 3, #C207-C209  3.50  3.00
   Nos. C207-C209 (3)              4.20  1.20

11th World Cup Soccer Championship, Argentina, June 1-25.

### Nos. C207-C209a Overprinted in Ultramarine or Black

a

b

c

**1978, July 21    Engr.    Perf. 13**
C210  AP92(a)  100fr multi          .85   .30
C211  AP92(b)  120fr multi         1.10   .40
C212  AP92(c)  200fr multi         1.75   .65
   a.   Min. sheet of 3 (Bk)       5.50  5.50
   Nos. C210-C212 (3)              3.70  1.35

Argentina's World Cup victory.

Albrecht Dürer (age 13), Self-portrait AP93

Design: 250fr, Lucas de Leyde, by Dürer.

**1978, Sept. 15    Engr.    Perf. 13**
C213  AP93  100fr red brn & slate  1.25   .30
C214  AP93  250fr blk & red brn    3.50   .80

Dürer (1474-1528), German painter.

### Philexafrique II-Essen Issue
#### Common Design Types

Designs: No. C215, Gorilla and Gabon No. 280. No. C216, Stork and Saxony No. 1.

**1978, Nov. 1    Litho.    Perf. 13x12½**
C215  CD138  100fr multi           2.00  1.40
C216  CD139  100fr multi           2.00  1.40
   a.   Pair, #C215-C216 + label   6.50  4.00

No. C216a exists with two different labels: one for PHILEXAFRIQUE II and one for ESSEN '78.

Wright Brothers and Flyer — AP94

**1978, Dec. 19    Engr.    Perf. 13**
C217  AP94  380fr multi            4.50  1.10

75th anniversary of 1st powered flight.

Pope John Paul II — AP95

Design: 200fr, Popes Paul VI and John Paul I, St. Peter's Basilica and Square, horiz.

**1979, Jan. 24    Litho.    Perf. 12½**
C218  AP95  100fr multi            2.50   .35
C219  AP95  200fr multi            5.50   .80

#### Sculpture Type of 1976

Easter: 100fr, Disciples recognizing Jesus in the breaking of the bread. 150fr, Jesus appearing to Mary Magdalene. Designs after wood carvings in Church of St. Michael, Libreville.

**1979, Apr. 10    Litho.    Perf. 12½x13**
C220  AP77  100fr multi            1.25   .45
C221  AP77  150fr multi            1.75   .65

Capt. Cook and Ships — AP96

**1979, July 10    Engr.    Perf. 13**
C222  AP96  500fr multi            6.50  2.75

Capt. James Cook (1728-1779), explorer, death bicentenary.

Flags and Map of England and France, Bleriot, Bleriot XI — AP97

Aviation Retrospect: 1000fr, Astronauts walking on moon (gold embossed inset).

#### Perf. 12½x12, 12

**1979, Aug. 8    Litho.**
C223  AP97  250fr multi            3.00  1.00
C224  AP97  1000fr multi         11.00  3.75

1st flight over English Channel, 70th anniv.; Apollo 11 moon landing, 10th anniv.

Rotary Emblem, Map of Africa, Head — AP98

**1979, Sept. 25    Photo.    Perf. 13**
C225  AP98  80fr multi            1.25   .35

Rotary International, 75th anniversary.

Eugene Jamot, Tsetse Fly — AP99

**1979, Nov. 23    Engr.    Perf. 13**
C226  AP99  300fr multi           4.50  1.50

Eugene Jamot (1879-1937), discoverer of sleeping sickness cure.

Bobsledding, Lake Placid '80 Emblem — AP100

**1980, Feb. 25    Litho.    Perf. 12½**
C227  AP100  100fr shown          1.00   .40
C228  AP100  200fr Ski jump       2.10   .75
   a.   Souv. sheet of 2, #C227-C228  4.00  1.90

13th Winter Olympic Games, Lake Placid, NY, Feb. 12-24.

Jean Ingres — AP101

200fr, Jacques Offenbach. 360fr, Gustave Flaubert.

**1980, May 14    Engr.    Perf. 13**
C229  AP101  100fr shown          1.50   .50
C230  AP101  200fr multi          3.00   .95
C231  AP101  360fr multi          4.50  1.75
   Nos. C229-C231 (3)             9.00  3.20

12th World Telecommunications Day — AP102

**1980, May 17    Litho.    Perf. 12½**
C232  AP102  80fr multi           1.00   .35

Costes, Bellonte and Plane AP103

Design: 1000fr, Mermoz, sea plane.

**1980, July 16    Engr.    Perf. 13**
C233  AP103  165fr multi          1.40   .70
C234  AP103  1000fr multi         9.00  4.50

1st North Atlantic crossing, 50th anniv.; 1st South Atlantic air mail service, 50th anniv.

Running, Moscow '80 Emblem — AP104

**1980, July 25    Litho.**
C235  AP104  50fr shown           .75   .25
C236  AP104  100fr Pole vault     .90   .45
C237  AP104  250fr Boxing        2.50  1.00
   a.   Souv. sheet of 3, #C235-C237  6.00  4.00
   Nos. C235-C237 (3)            4.15  1.70

22nd Summer Olympic Games, Moscow, July 19-Aug. 3.

**Nos. C235-C237a Overprinted in Red, Brown, Ultramarine or Black**

No. C238

No. C239

No. C240

| | | |
|---|---|---|
| **1980, Sept. 25** | **Litho.** | **Perf. 13** |
| C238 AP104 50fr (R, vert. & horiz.) | .50 | .25 |
| C239 AP104 100fr (Br) | .95 | .40 |
| C240 AP104 250fr (U) | 2.50 | .85 |
| a. Souv. sheet of 3 (Blk) | 8.50 | 6.00 |
| Nos. C238-C240 (3) | 3.95 | 1.50 |

Pres. Charles de Gaulle — AP105

200fr, Pres. & Mrs. de Gaulle.

| | | |
|---|---|---|
| **1980, Nov. 9** | **Photo.** | **Perf. 13** |
| C241 AP105 100fr shown | 1.25 | .35 |
| C242 AP105 200fr multi | 2.40 | .70 |
| a. Souv. sheet of 2, #C241-C242 | 6.50 | 3.25 |

Pres. Charles de Gaulle (1890-1970).

AP106

60fr, Soccer Players. 190fr, Soccer player.

| | | |
|---|---|---|
| **1981, Feb. 19** | **Litho.** | **Perf. 13** |
| C243 AP106 60fr multi | .65 | .25 |
| C244 AP106 190fr multi | 2.10 | .75 |

ESPANA '82 World Cup Soccer Championship.

AP107

Spacecraft and Astronauts: 250fr, Yuri Gagarin. 500fr, Alan B. Shepard.

| | | |
|---|---|---|
| **1981, Mar. 26** | **Litho.** | **Perf. 13** |
| C245 AP107 150fr multi | 1.40 | .55 |
| C246 AP107 250fr multi | 2.40 | .85 |
| C247 AP107 500fr multi | 4.75 | 1.75 |
| a. Souv. sheet of 3, #C245-C247, perf. 12½ | 9.00 | 4.50 |
| Nos. C245-C247 (3) | 8.55 | 3.15 |

200th anniv. of discovery of Uranus by William Herschel (1738-1822).

Map of Africa and Emblems — AP108

| | | |
|---|---|---|
| **1981, June 1** | **Litho.** | **Perf. 12½** |
| C248 AP108 100fr multi | 1.00 | .40 |

Electric Power Distribution Union, 7th Congress, Libreville, June 1-5.

D-51 Steam Locomotive, Japan, and SNCF Turbotrain TGV-001, France AP109

200th Birth Anniv. of George Stephenson: 100fr, B&O Mallet 7100, US, Prussian T3 steam locomotive. 350fr, Stephenson and his Rocket, BB Alsthom electric locomotive, Central Africa.

| | | |
|---|---|---|
| **1981, June 4** | **Engr.** | **Perf. 13** |
| C249 AP109 75fr multi | 1.10 | .35 |
| C250 AP109 100fr multi | 1.60 | .45 |
| C251 AP109 350fr multi | 5.25 | 1.50 |
| a. Souvenir sheet of 3 | 7.50 | 3.25 |
| Nos. C249-C251 (3) | 7.95 | 2.30 |

No. C251a contains No. C249-C251 in changed colors.

**No. C251a Overprinted in 1 line across 3 stamps: "26 fevrier 1981-Record du monde de vitesse 380 km a l'heure"**
Souvenir Sheet

| | | |
|---|---|---|
| **1981, June 13** | **Engr.** | **Perf. 13** |
| C252 AP109 Sheet of 3 | 6.50 | 3.25 |

New world railroad speed record, set Feb. 26.

Intl. Letter Writing Week, Oct. 9-16 — AP110

| | | |
|---|---|---|
| **1981, Oct. 9** | **Photo.** | **Perf. 13** |
| C253 AP110 200fr multi | 2.00 | .90 |

Souvenir Sheet

22nd Anniv. of Independence — AP110a

| | | |
|---|---|---|
| **1982** | **Typo.** | **Perf. 13x12½** |
| | | **Self-Adhesive** |
| C253A AP110a 2000fr multi | 40.00 | 40.00 |

Printed on wood.

Still Life with a Mandolin, by George Braque (1882-1963) AP111

Design: 350fr, Boy Blowing Bubbles, by Edouard Manet (1832-1883), vert.

**Perf. 13x12½, 12½x13**

| | | |
|---|---|---|
| **1982, Oct. 5** | **Litho.** | |
| C254 AP111 300fr multi | 3.75 | 1.10 |
| C255 AP111 350fr multi | 6.00 | 1.25 |

Pre-olympic Year — AP112

| | | |
|---|---|---|
| **1983, Feb. 16** | **Litho.** | **Perf. 13** |
| C256 AP112 90fr Gymnast | .70 | .30 |
| C257 AP112 350fr Wind surfing | 4.00 | 1.10 |

Manned Flight Bicentenary — AP113

Balloons: 100fr, Transatlantic flight, 5th anniv. 125fr, Montgolfiere, 1783. 350fr, Rozier's balloon, 1783.

| | | |
|---|---|---|
| **1983, June 1** | **Engr.** | **Perf. 13** |
| C258 AP113 100fr multicolored | 1.00 | .40 |
| C259 AP113 125fr multicolored | 1.25 | .45 |
| C260 AP113 350fr multicolored | 3.75 | 1.50 |
| Nos. C258-C260 (3) | 6.00 | 2.35 |

Lady with Unicorn, by Raphael (1483-1520) AP114

| | | |
|---|---|---|
| **1983, June 19** | | **Perf. 12½x13** |
| C261 AP114 1000fr multi | 10.00 | 4.50 |

1984 Winter Olympics AP115

| | | |
|---|---|---|
| **1984, Feb. 8** | **Litho.** | **Perf. 12½** |
| C262 AP115 125fr Hockey | 1.40 | .25 |
| C263 AP115 350fr Figure skaters | 3.75 | .70 |

See No. C268.

Paris-Libreville-Paris Air Race, Mar. 15-28 — AP116

500fr, Planes, emblem.

| | | |
|---|---|---|
| **1984, Mar. 15** | **Litho.** | **Perf. 13x12½** |
| C264 AP116 500fr multi | 4.50 | 1.25 |

The Racetrack, by Edgar Degas AP117

| | | |
|---|---|---|
| **1984, Mar. 21** | | **Perf. 13** |
| C265 AP117 500fr multi | 8.00 | 3.00 |

1984 Summer Olympics — AP118

| | | |
|---|---|---|
| **1984, May 31** | **Litho.** | **Perf. 12½** |
| C266 AP118 90fr Basketball | .80 | .25 |
| C267 AP118 125fr Running | 1.25 | .25 |

**Nos. C262-C263, C266-C267 with Added Inscriptions**
Souvenir Sheet

| | | |
|---|---|---|
| **1984, Oct. 3** | **Litho.** | **Perf. 13** |
| C268 Sheet of 4 | 7.50 | 5.00 |
| a. AP118 90fr MEDAILLE D'OR: U.S.A. | .65 | .25 |
| b. AP118 125fr MEDAILLE D'OR: KORIR | .95 | .25 |
| c. AP115 125fr Hockey sur glace: U.R.S.S. | .95 | .25 |
| d. AP115 350fr Danse couple: J. Torvill-C. Dean | 2.75 | .55 |

**Souvenir Sheet**

Hamburg '84 Philatelic Exhibition — AP119

| | | |
|---|---|---|
| **1984** | **Typo.** | **Perf. 13x12½** |
| | | **Self-Adhesive** |
| C268A AP119 1000fr multi | 21.00 | 21.00 |

Printed on wood.

Dr. Albert Schweitzer (1875-1965) — AP119a

| | | |
|---|---|---|
| **1985, Sept. 5** | **Litho.** | **Perf. 12½** |
| C269 AP119a 350fr multi | 4.25 | .70 |

Flags of Gabon, UN — AP120

| | | |
|---|---|---|
| **1985, Sept. 20** | | |
| C270 AP120 225fr multi | 2.50 | .40 |

Admission of Gabon to UN, 25th anniv.

Central Post Office, Libreville, UPU
and Gabon Postal Emblems
AP121

**1985, Oct. 9**
C271 AP121 300fr multi     3.00 .60
World Post Day.

UN, 40th
Anniv. — AP122

**1985, Oct. 24**    **Litho.**    **Perf. 12½**
C272 AP122 350fr multi     3.50 .70

PHILEXAFRICA '85, Lome,
Togo — AP123

100fr, Scout campsite.150fr, Telecommunications, transportation.

**1985, Oct. 30**       **Perf. 13**
C273 AP123 100fr multicolored   2.00 .25
C274 AP123 150fr multicolored   3.50 .50
    a.   Pair, #C273-C274 + label   6.50 2.00

Gabon's Gift to the
UN — AP124

Design: Mother and Child, carved wood
statue, and UN emblem.

**1986, Mar. 15**    **Litho.**    **Perf. 13½**
C275 AP124 350fr multi     3.75 1.10

Lastour
Arriving in
Gabon
AP125

**1986, Mar. 25**    **Litho.**    **Perf. 12½**
C276 AP125 100fr multi     1.25 .45
Lastoursville, cent.

World Telecommunications
Day — AP126

**1986, May 17**       **Perf. 13½**
C277 AP126 300fr multi     2.50 .95

1986 World Cup Soccer
Championships, Mexico — AP127

100fr, Goal. 150fr, Dribbling, religious carving. 250fr, Players, map, soccer cup. 350fr,
Stadium, flags.

**1986, May 31**       **Perf. 12½**
C278 AP127 100fr multi     .90 .35
C279 AP127 150fr multi     1.25 .45
C280 AP127 250fr multi     2.25 .80
C281 AP127 350fr multi     3.00 1.10
    a.   Souv. sheet of 4, #C278-
        C281     10.00 4.75
    Nos. C278-C281 (4)     7.40 2.70
For overprints see Nos. C283-C286.

World Post
Day — AP128

**1986, Oct. 9**    **Litho.**    **Perf. 12½**
C282 AP128 500fr multi     4.50 1.50

**Nos. C278-C281 Ovptd.
"ARGENTINA 3 -R.F.A 2" in One or
Two Lines in Red**
**1986, Oct. 23**    **Litho.**    **Perf. 12½**
C283 AP127 100fr multi     .90 .35
C284 AP127 150fr multi     1.25 .45
C285 AP127 250fr multi     2.25 .80
C286 AP127 350fr multi     3.00 1.10
    Nos. C283-C286 (4)     7.40 2.70

The Renewal,
19th
Anniv. — AP129

**1987, Mar. 12**    **Litho.**    **Perf. 13**
C287 AP129 500fr multi     6.00 2.00

Konrad Adenauer
(1876-1967), West
German
Chancellor — AP130

**1987, Apr. 15**       **Perf. 12x12½**
C288 AP130 300fr mar, chlky bl
             & blk     4.00 1.25

Schweitzer
and Medical
Settlement
AP131

**1988, Apr. 17**    **Litho.**    **Perf. 12½x12**
C289 AP131 500fr multi     6.50 2.25
Dr. Albert Schweitzer (1875-1965), missionary physician and founder of the hospital
and medical settlement, Lambarene, Gabon.

Port Gentil
Refinery, 20th
Anniv.
AP132

**1988, Sept. 1**    **Litho.**    **Perf. 13½**
C290 AP132 350fr multi     4.00 1.75

De Gaulle's
Call for
French
Resistance,
50th Anniv.
AP133

**1990, June 18**    **Litho.**    **Perf. 13**
C291 AP133 500fr multicolored   7.50 2.50

Port of
Marseilles
by J. B.
Jongkind
(1819-1891)
AP134

**1991, Feb. 9**    **Litho.**    **Perf. 13**
C292 AP134 500fr multicolored   6.00 2.25

Discovery of
America,
500th Anniv.
AP135

**1992, Oct. 12**    **Litho.**    **Perf. 13**
C293 AP135 500fr multicolored   5.50 2.50

Antoine de Saint-Exupery (1900-
44) — AP136

**1994**       **Litho.**       **Perf. 13**
C294 AP136 500fr multicolored   3.25 1.60

Opening of
the Channel
Tunnel
AP137

**1994, Sept. 5**
C295 AP137 500fr multicolored   3.00 1.50

**AIR POST SEMI-POSTAL STAMPS**

**Catalogue values for unused
stamps in this section are for
Never Hinged items.**

Ramses II Paying Homage to Four
Gods, Wadi-es-Sabua — SPAP1

**Unwmk.**
**1964, Mar. 9**    **Engr.**    **Perf. 13**
CB1 SPAP1 10fr + 5fr dk bl & bis
            brn     1.00 1.00
CB2 SPAP1 25fr + 5fr dk car
           rose & vio bl   1.25 1.25

CB3 SPAP1 50fr + 5fr sl grn &
           claret     2.10 2.10
    Nos. CB1-CB3 (3)     4.35 4.35
UNESCO world campaign to save historic
monuments in Nubia.

**POSTAGE DUE STAMPS**

Postage Due Stamps of
France Overprinted

**1928**    **Unwmk.**    **Perf. 14x13½**
J1   D2   5c light blue    .40   .55
J2   D2   10c gray brown    .40   .65
J3   D2   20c olive green   1.05   1.60
J4   D2   25c bright rose   1.05   1.40
J5   D2   30c light red   1.60   2.00
J6   D2   45c blue green   2.00   2.40
J7   D2   50c brown violet   3.00   3.25
J8   D2   60c yellow brown   3.00   3.25
J9   D2   1fr red brown   3.00   3.25
J10   D2   2fr orange red   3.50   4.25
J11   D2   3fr bright violet   4.25   5.00
    Nos. J1-J11 (11)     23.25 27.60

Chief
Makoko, de
Brazza's
Aide
D3

Count
Savorgnan
de Brazza
D4

**1930**    **Typo.**    **Perf. 13½x14**
J12   D3   5c dk bl & olive   .70   1.10
J13   D3   10c dk red & brn   .70   1.10
J14   D3   20c green & brn   1.40   1.40
J15   D3   25c lt bl & brn   1.40   1.40
J16   D3   30c bis brn & Prus bl   2.25   2.00
J17   D3   45c Prus bl & ol   2.75   3.25
J18   D3   50c red vio & brn   3.50   4.00
J19   D3   60c gray lil & bl blk   7.00   6.50
J20   D4   1fr bis brn & bl blk   7.00   10.00
J21   D4   2fr violet & brn   10.50   14.00
J22   D4   3fr dp red & brn   17.50   15.00
    Nos. J12-J22 (11)     54.70 59.75

Fang Woman — D5

**1932**    **Photo.**    **Perf. 13x13½**
J23   D5   5c dk bl, *bl*   1.10   1.40
J24   D5   10c red brown   1.40   1.75
J25   D5   20c chocolate   1.75   2.00
J26   D5   25c yel grn, *bl*   1.75   2.00
J27   D5   30c car rose   1.75   2.10
J28   D5   45c red org, *yel*   7.00   7.00
J29   D5   50c dk violet   2.75   2.75
J30   D5   60c dull blue   3.75   3.75
J31   D5   1fr blk, *red org*   8.50   9.50
J32   D5   2fr dark green   11.00   12.00
J33   D5   3fr rose lake   9.00   11.50
    Nos. J23-J33 (11)     49.75 55.75

**Catalogue values for unused
stamps in this section, from this
point to the end of the section, are
for Never Hinged items.**

**Republic**

Pineapple
D6

**Unwmk.**
**1962, Dec. 10**    **Engr.**    **Perf. 11**
J34   D6   50c shown    .25 .25
J35   D6   50c Mangoes    .25 .25
    a.   Pair, #J34-J35     .35

| | | | | | |
|---|---|---|---|---|---|
| J36 | D6 | 1fr Avocados | | .25 | .25 |
| J37 | D6 | 1fr Tangerines | | .25 | .25 |
| a. | | Pair, #J36-J37 | | .50 | |
| J38 | D6 | 2fr Coconuts | | .25 | .25 |
| J39 | D6 | 2fr Grapefruit | | .25 | .25 |
| a. | | Pair, #J38-J39 | | .50 | |
| J40 | D6 | 5fr Oranges | | .35 | .35 |
| J41 | D6 | 5fr Papaya | | .35 | .35 |
| a. | | Pair, #J40-J41 | | 1.00 | |
| J42 | D6 | 10fr Breadfruit | | .75 | .75 |
| J43 | D6 | 10fr Guavas | | .75 | .75 |
| a. | | Pair, #J42-J43 | | 2.25 | |
| J44 | D6 | 25fr Lemons | | 1.00 | 1.00 |
| J45 | D6 | 25fr Bananas | | 1.00 | 1.00 |
| a. | | Pair, #J44-J45 | | 3.50 | |
| | | Nos. J34-J45 (12) | | 5.70 | 5.70 |

Pairs se-tenant at the base.

Charaxes Candiope — D7

Butterflies: 10fr, Charaxes ameliae. 25fr, Cyrestis camillus. 50fr, Charaxes castor. 100fr, Pseudacrea boisduvali.

| 1978, July 4 | | | Litho. | Perf. 13 | |
|---|---|---|---|---|---|
| J46 | D7 | 5fr multi | | .30 | .25 |
| J47 | D7 | 10fr multi | | .30 | .25 |
| J48 | D7 | 25fr multi | | .65 | .30 |
| J49 | D7 | 50fr multi | | 1.25 | .50 |
| J50 | D7 | 100fr multi | | 2.00 | .95 |
| | | Nos. J46-J50 (5) | | 4.50 | 2.25 |

## OFFICIAL STAMPS

Catalogue values for unused stamps in this section are for Never Hinged items.

Map of Gabon — O1

Designs: 25fr, 30fr, Flag of Gabon. 50fr, 85fr, 100fr, 200fr, Coat of Arms.

| 1968 | | Unwmk. | Photo. | Perf. 14 | |
|---|---|---|---|---|---|
| O1 | O1 | 1fr olive & multi | | .30 | .25 |
| O2 | O1 | 2fr multi | | .30 | .25 |
| O3 | O1 | 5fr lilac & multi | | .30 | .25 |
| O4 | O1 | 10fr emer & multi | | .30 | .25 |
| O5 | O1 | 25fr brn & multi | | .50 | .25 |
| O6 | O1 | 30fr org & multi | | .50 | .25 |
| O7 | O1 | 50fr multi | | .95 | .25 |
| O8 | O1 | 85fr multi | | 1.75 | .35 |
| O9 | O1 | 100fr yel & multi | | 2.10 | .45 |
| O10 | O1 | 200fr gray & multi | | 4.00 | 1.10 |
| | | Nos. O1-O10 (10) | | 11.00 | 3.65 |

Flag of Gabon — O2

| 1971-84 | | Typo. | | Perf. 13x14 | |
|---|---|---|---|---|---|
| O11 | O2 | 5fr multi ('81) | | .30 | .25 |
| O12 | O2 | 10fr multi | | .30 | .25 |
| O13 | O2 | 20fr multi ('81) | | .30 | .25 |
| O14 | O2 | 25fr multi ('84) | | .50 | .25 |
| O15 | O2 | 30fr multi ('78) | | .40 | .25 |
| O16 | O2 | 40fr multi ('72) | | .75 | .25 |
| O17 | O2 | 50fr multi ('76) | | .85 | .25 |
| O18 | O2 | 60fr multi ('77) | | 1.10 | .25 |
| O19 | O2 | 75fr multi ('81) | | .75 | .25 |
| O20 | O2 | 80fr multi ('77) | | 1.50 | .40 |
| O21 | O2 | 85fr multi ('78) | | 1.25 | .25 |
| O22 | O2 | 500fr multi ('78) | | 6.25 | 1.25 |
| | | Nos. O11-O22 (12) | | 14.25 | 4.15 |

## GAMBIA

ˈgam-bē-ə

LOCATION — Extending inland from the mouth of the Gambia River on the west coast of Africa
GOVT. — Republic in British Commonwealth
AREA — 4,068 sq. mi.
POP. — 1,087,000 (1995 est.)
CAPITAL — Banjul

The British Crown Colony and Protectorate of Gambia became independent in 1965 and a republic in 1970.

12 Pence = 1 Shilling
100 Bututs = 1 Dalasy (1971)

Catalogue values for unused stamps in this country are for Never Hinged items, beginning with Scott 144.

Queen Victoria — A1

### Typographed and Embossed

| 1869, Jan. | | Unwmk. | | Imperf. | |
|---|---|---|---|---|---|
| 1 | A1 | 4p pale brown | | 575.00 | 210.00 |
| | | No gum | | 400.00 | |
| a. | | 4p brown | | 650.00 | 210.00 |
| | | No gum | | 475.00 | |
| 2 | A1 | 6p blue | | 650.00 | 425.00 |
| | | No gum | | 450.00 | |
| a. | | 6p deep blue | | 625.00 | 240.00 |
| | | No gum | | 425.00 | |
| b. | | 6p pale blue | | 3,250. | 1,100. |
| | | No gum | | 2,400. | |

| 1874, Aug. | | | | Wmk. 1 | |
|---|---|---|---|---|---|
| 3 | A1 | 4p brown | | 400.00 | 200.00 |
| | | No gum | | 250.00 | |
| a. | | 4p pale brown | | 425.00 | 225.00 |
| | | No gum | | 250.00 | |
| 4 | A1 | 6p blue | | 350.00 | 200.00 |
| | | No gum | | 250.00 | |
| a. | | 6p deep blue | | 350.00 | |
| | | No gum | | 250.00 | |
| b. | | Panel sloping down from left to right | | 850.00 | 450.00 |
| | | No gum | | 600.00 | |

Nos. 1-4 are often seen with flat embossing. Unused values for are for fine-very fine examples with sharp, detailed embossing. Values for unused stamps without gum and used stamps are for examples with average embossing.
The name panel sloping down variety, No. 4b, is from a top right corner position. A top left corner position exists with a less noticeable sloping of the panel down from right to left; it is worth less.

| 1880, June | | | | Perf. 14 | |
|---|---|---|---|---|---|
| 5 | A1 | ½p orange | | 19.00 | 27.50 |
| a. | | ½p dull orange | | 20.00 | 27.50 |
| 6 | A1 | 1p maroon | | 12.00 | 6.00 |
| 7 | A1 | 3p rose | | 67.50 | 11.00 |
| 8 | A1 | 3p bright ultra | | 90.00 | 45.00 |
| a. | | 3p dull ultra | | 20.00 | 32.50 |
| 9 | A1 | 4p pale brown | | 325.00 | 25.00 |
| a. | | 4p brown | | 325.00 | 24.00 |
| 10 | A1 | 6p blue | | 130.00 | 45.00 |
| a. | | Panel sloping down from left to right | | 350.00 | 150.00 |
| b. | | 3p dull ultra | | 20.00 | 32.50 |
| 11 | A1 | 1sh green | | 275.00 | 150.00 |
| a. | | 6p deep blue | | 130.00 | 45.00 |
| | | Nos. 5-11 (7) | | 918.50 | 309.50 |

The watermark on Nos. 5-11 exists both upright and sideways. Values are for examples with watermark upright. Varieties with watermark sideways sell for higher prices.
See footnote following No. 4.

| 1886-93 | | | | Wmk. 2 Sideways | |
|---|---|---|---|---|---|
| 12 | A1 | ½p gray grn | | 5.00 | 3.25 |
| 13 | A1 | 1p rose car ('87) | | 10.50 | 12.50 |
| 14 | | 2p dp org | | 4.50 | 10.50 |
| b. | | 2p orange | | 15.00 | 5.00 |
| 15 | A1 | 2½p dp brt blue | | 12.50 | 2.25 |
| 16 | A1 | 3p gray | | 14.00 | 19.00 |
| 17 | A1 | 4p dp brown | | 13.00 | 2.50 |
| 18 | A1 | 6p sl grn ('93) | | 20.00 | 67.50 |
| a. | | 6p pale olive green ('86) | | 110.00 | 50.00 |
| b. | | 6p bronze green ('89) | | 47.50 | 72.50 |
| c. | | As "a," panel sloping down from left to right | | 325.00 | 125.00 |
| d. | | As "b," panel sloping down from left to right | | 95.00 | 180.00 |
| 19 | A1 | 1sh violet | | 5.00 | 24.00 |
| a. | | 1sh purple | | 10.00 | 22.50 |
| | | Nos. 12-19 (8) | | 84.50 | 141.50 |

See footnote following No. 4.

Queen Victoria — A2

| 1898, Jan. | | Typo. | | Wmk. 2 | |
|---|---|---|---|---|---|
| 20 | A2 | ½p gray green | | 3.00 | 1.75 |
| 21 | A2 | 1p carmine rose | | 3.50 | .75 |
| 22 | A2 | 2p brn org & pur | | 7.00 | 3.50 |
| 23 | A2 | 2½p ultramarine | | 6.00 | 2.50 |
| 24 | A2 | 3p red vio & ultra | | 50.00 | 12.50 |
| 25 | A2 | 4p brown & ultra | | 20.00 | 37.50 |
| 26 | A2 | 6p ol grn & car rose | | 19.00 | 60.00 |
| 27 | A2 | 1sh vio & green | | 45.00 | 85.00 |
| | | Nos. 20-27 (8) | | 153.50 | 193.50 |

King Edward VII — A3

| 1902-05 | | | | Perf. 14 | |
|---|---|---|---|---|---|
| 28 | A3 | ½p green | | 7.50 | 2.75 |
| 29 | A3 | 1p car rose | | 16.00 | 1.10 |
| 30 | A3 | 2p org & pur | | 3.50 | 2.50 |
| 31 | A3 | 2½p ultramarine | | 50.00 | 18.00 |
| 32 | A3 | 3p red vio & ultra | | 24.00 | 3.50 |
| 33 | A3 | 4p brn & ultra | | 10.00 | 42.50 |
| 34 | A3 | 6p ol grn & rose | | 19.50 | 14.50 |
| 35 | A3 | 1sh bluish vio & green | | 50.00 | 92.50 |
| 36 | A3 | 1sh6p grn & red, yel | | 13.00 | 26.00 |
| 37 | A3 | 2sh black & org | | 55.00 | 75.00 |
| 38 | A3 | 2sh6p pur & brn, yel | | 16.00 | 75.00 |
| 39 | A3 | 3sh red & grn, yel | | 22.50 | 72.50 |
| | | Nos. 28-39 (12) | | 287.00 | 425.35 |

Numerals of 5p, 7½p, 10p, 1sh6p, 2sh, 2sh6p and 3sh of type A3 are in color on plain tablet.
Issue dates: 1p, Mar. 13. ½p, 3p, Apr. 19. 2p, 2½p, 4p, 6p, 1sh, 2sh, June 14. 1sh6p, 2sh6p, 3sh, Apr. 6, 1905.
For surcharges, see Nos. 65-66.

| 1904-09 | | | | Wmk. 3 | |
|---|---|---|---|---|---|
| 41 | A3 | ½p green | | 4.50 | .30 |
| a. | | ½p blue green ('09) | | 15.00 | 7.00 |
| 42 | A3 | 1p car rose | | 4.50 | .25 |
| a. | | 1p carmine ('09) | | 17.50 | .25 |
| 43 | A3 | 2p org & pur ('06) | | 14.00 | 2.50 |
| 44 | A3 | 2p gray ('09) | | 2.50 | 11.00 |
| 45 | A3 | 2½p brt blue ('05) | | 17.50 | 5.00 |
| 46 | A3 | 3p red vio & ultra | | 21.00 | 2.00 |
| 47 | A3 | 3p vio, yel ('09) | | 8.00 | 1.10 |
| 48 | A3 | 4p brn & ultra ('06) | | 25.00 | 50.00 |
| 49 | A3 | 4p blk & red, yel ('09) | | 4.00 | .75 |
| 50 | A3 | 5p gray & black | | 20.00 | 30.00 |
| 51 | A3 | 5p org & vio ('09) | | 4.00 | 1.60 |
| 52 | A3 | 6p ol grn & rose ('06) | | 26.00 | 75.00 |
| 53 | A3 | 6p dull vio ('09) | | 3.50 | 1.50 |
| 54 | A3 | 7½p blue grn & red | | 22.50 | 65.00 |
| 55 | A3 | 7½p brn & ultra ('09) | | 5.50 | 2.50 |
| 56 | A3 | 10p ol bis & red | | 35.00 | 52.50 |
| 57 | A3 | 10p ol grn & car rose ('09) | | 7.50 | 7.00 |
| 58 | A3 | 1sh violet & grn | | 45.00 | 65.00 |
| 59 | A3 | 1sh blk, grn ('09) | | 8.00 | 17.50 |
| 60 | A3 | 1sh 6p vio & grn ('09) | | 30.00 | 75.00 |
| 61 | A3 | 2sh black & org | | 100.00 | 125.00 |
| 62 | A3 | 2sh vio & bl, bl ('09) | | 16.00 | 20.00 |
| 63 | A3 | 2sh 6p blk & red, bl ('09) | | 25.00 | 20.00 |
| 64 | A3 | 3sh vio & grn ('09) | | 50.00 | 50.00 |
| | | Nos. 41-64 (24) | | 499.00 | 680.50 |

### Nos. 38-39 Surcharged in Black

Type I                                         Type II

Type I — The word "PENNY" is 5mm from the horizontal bars.
Type II — "PENNY" is 4mm from the bars.

| 1906, Apr. | | | | Wmk. 2 | |
|---|---|---|---|---|---|
| 65 | A3 | ½p on 2sh6p, type I | | 57.50 | 65.00 |
| a. | | Type II | | 62.50 | 75.00 |
| 66 | A3 | 1p on 3sh | | 60.00 | 30.00 |
| a. | | Double surcharge | | 1,800. | 5,100. |

King George V — A4

| 1912-22 | | | | Wmk. 3 | |
|---|---|---|---|---|---|
| 70 | A4 | ½p dp green | | 3.75 | 1.50 |
| 71 | A4 | 1p carmine | | 3.00 | .75 |
| a. | | 1p scarlet ('16) | | 10.00 | .90 |
| 72 | A4 | 1½p ol brn & grn | | .75 | .30 |
| 73 | A4 | 2p gray | | .75 | 2.75 |
| 74 | A4 | 2½p dp brt blue | | 6.50 | 3.50 |
| 75 | A4 | 3p violet, yel | | 2.25 | .30 |
| 76 | A4 | 4p blk & red, yel | | 1.00 | 10.00 |
| 77 | A4 | 5p orange & vio | | 1.75 | 2.00 |
| 78 | A4 | 6p dl vio & red violet | | 3.00 | 2.50 |
| 79 | A4 | 7½p brn & ultra | | 6.50 | 17.50 |
| 80 | A4 | 10p ol grn & car rose | | 6.00 | 17.50 |
| 81 | A4 | 1sh blk, green | | 4.50 | 1.00 |
| a. | | 1sh black, emerald | | 3.75 | 28.00 |
| 82 | A4 | 1sh6p vio & green | | 24.00 | 10.00 |
| 83 | A4 | 2sh vio & bl, bl | | 11.00 | 6.00 |
| 84 | A4 | 2sh6p blk & red, bl | | 11.00 | 14.00 |
| 85 | A4 | 3sh yel & green | | 18.00 | 50.00 |
| 86 | A4 | 5sh org & red, yel ('22) | | 130.00 | 200.00 |
| | | Nos. 70-86 (17) | | 233.75 | 339.60 |

Numerals of 1½p, 5p, 7½p, 10p, 1sh6p, 2sh, 2sh6p, 3sh, 4sh and 5sh of type A3 are in color on colorless tablet. No. 86 is on chalky paper.

| 1921-22 | | | | Wmk. 4 | |
|---|---|---|---|---|---|
| 87 | A4 | ½p green | | .30 | 21.00 |
| 88 | A4 | 1p carmine | | 2.75 | 11.00 |
| 89 | A4 | 1½p ol grn & bl grn | | 3.00 | 25.00 |
| 90 | A4 | 2p gray | | 1.50 | 3.25 |
| 91 | A4 | 2½p ultramarine | | .75 | 13.00 |
| 92 | A4 | 5p org & violet | | 2.00 | 26.00 |
| 93 | A4 | 6p dl vio & red vio | | 3.50 | 22.50 |
| 94 | A4 | 7½p brn & ultra | | 3.25 | 57.50 |
| 95 | A4 | 10p yel grn & car rose | | 12.00 | 27.50 |
| 96 | A4 | 4sh gray & red ('22) | | 110.00 | 225.00 |
| | | Nos. 87-96 (10) | | 139.05 | 431.75 |

No. 96 is on chalky paper.

George V and Elephant A5          George V A6

| 1922-27 | | Engr. | | Wmk. 4 | |
|---|---|---|---|---|---|
| | | **Head and Shield in Black** | | | |
| 102 | A5 | ½p green | | .55 | .55 |
| 103 | A5 | 1p brown | | 1.25 | .30 |
| 104 | A5 | 1½p carmine | | 1.25 | .30 |
| 105 | A5 | 2p gray | | 2.25 | 5.00 |
| 106 | A5 | 2½p orange | | 3.50 | 15.00 |
| 107 | A5 | 3p ultramarine | | 1.10 | .25 |
| 108 | A5 | 4p car, org ('27) | | 29.00 | 40.00 |
| 109 | A5 | 5p yellow green | | 4.75 | 19.00 |
| 110 | A5 | 6p claret | | 1.25 | 1.00 |
| 111 | A5 | 7½p vio, yel ('27) | | 26.00 | 95.00 |
| 112 | A5 | 10p blue | | 8.00 | 24.00 |
| 113 | A6 | 1sh vio, org ('24) | | 5.75 | 2.50 |
| 114 | A6 | 1sh6p blue | | 26.00 | 24.00 |
| 115 | A6 | 2sh vio, blue | | 16.00 | 8.50 |
| 116 | A6 | 2sh6p dark green | | 17.00 | 14.00 |
| 117 | A6 | 3sh aniline vio | | 32.50 | 95.00 |
| a. | | 3sh black purple | | 300.00 | 475.00 |
| 118 | A6 | 4sh brown | | 19.00 | 26.00 |
| 119 | A6 | 5sh dk grn, yel ('26) | | 55.00 | 85.00 |
| 120 | A6 | 10sh yellow green | | 85.00 | 150.00 |
| | | Nos. 102-120 (19) | | 335.15 | 605.40 |

| 1922, Sept. 1 | | | | Wmk. 3 | |
|---|---|---|---|---|---|
| | | **Head & Shield in Black** | | | |
| 121 | A5 | 4p carmine, yel | | 8.00 | 7.25 |
| 122 | A5 | 7½p violet, yel | | 10.00 | 11.50 |
| 123 | A6 | 1sh violet, orange | | 42.50 | 52.50 |
| 124 | A6 | 5sh dk green, yel | | 75.00 | 250.00 |
| | | Nos. 121-124 (4) | | 135.50 | 321.25 |

Common Design Types pictured following the introduction.

### Silver Jubilee Issue
Common Design Type

| 1935, May 6 | | Wmk. 4 | | Perf. 11x12 | |
|---|---|---|---|---|---|
| 125 | CD301 | 1½p carmine & bl | | .55 | 2.75 |
| 126 | CD301 | 3p ultra & brn | | 1.25 | 2.50 |
| 127 | CD301 | 2¼p org & lt bl | | 2.25 | 7.00 |
| 128 | CD301 | 1sh brn vio & ind | | 9.00 | 13.00 |
| | | Nos. 125-128 (4) | | 13.05 | 25.25 |
| | | Set, never hinged | | 22.50 | |

### Coronation Issue
Common Design Type

| 1937, May 12 | | | | Perf. 11x11½ | |
|---|---|---|---|---|---|
| 129 | CD302 | 1p org brn | | .30 | 1.10 |
| 130 | CD302 | 1½p dark carmine | | .30 | 1.10 |
| 131 | CD302 | 3p deep ultra | | .35 | 1.75 |
| | | Nos. 129-131 (3) | | .95 | 3.95 |
| | | Set, never hinged | | 1.25 | |

King George VI and Elephant Badge of Gambia — A7

**1938-46**     *Perf. 12*

| | | | | |
|---|---|---|---|---|
| 132 | A7 | ½p bl grn & blk | .30 | .70 |
| 133 | A7 | 1p brn & red vio | .30 | .50 |
| 134 | A7 | 1½p rose red & brn lake | .30 | 2.00 |
| 134A | A7 | 1½p gray blk & ultra ('44) | .30 | 1.50 |
| 135 | A7 | 2p gray blk & ultra | 8.50 | 3.25 |
| 135A | A7 | 2p rose red & brn lake ('43) | .95 | 2.25 |
| 136 | A7 | 3p blue & brt bl | .30 | .25 |
| 136A | A7 | 5p dk vio brn & olive ('41) | .45 | .50 |
| 137 | A7 | 6p plum & ol grn | 1.75 | .35 |
| 138 | A7 | 1sh vio & sl blk | 2.75 | .25 |
| 138A | A7 | 1sh3p bl & choc ('46) | 2.25 | 2.00 |
| 139 | A7 | 2sh bl & dp rose | 7.50 | 3.25 |
| 140 | A7 | 2sh6p sl grn & sep | 9.50 | 2.50 |
| 141 | A7 | 4sh dk vio & red orange | 21.00 | 2.50 |
| 142 | A7 | 5sh org red & dk blue | 21.00 | 4.00 |
| 143 | A7 | 10sh blk & yel org | 22.50 | 8.50 |
| | | Nos. 132-143 (16) | 99.65 | 34.30 |
| | | Set, never hinged | 170.00 | |

Issued: 5p, 3/13; No. 135A, 10/1; No. 134A, 1/22; 1sh3p, 11/28; others, 4/1.

> Catalogue values for unused stamps in this section, from this point to the end of the section, are for Never Hinged items.

### Peace Issue
Common Design Type

**1946, Aug. 6**    **Engr.**    *Perf. 13½*

| | | | | |
|---|---|---|---|---|
| 144 | CD303 | 1½p black | .30 | .50 |
| 145 | CD303 | 3p deep blue | .30 | .45 |

### Silver Wedding Issue
Common Design Types

**1948, Dec. 24**   **Photo.**   *Perf. 14x14½*

| | | | | |
|---|---|---|---|---|
| 146 | CD304 | 1½p black | .30 | .25 |

*Perf. 11½x11*
Engr.; Name Typo.

| | | | | |
|---|---|---|---|---|
| 147 | CD305 | £1 purple | 21.00 | 21.00 |

### UPU Issue
Common Design Types
Engr.; Name Typo. on 3p, 6p
*Perf. 13½, 11x11½*

**1949, Oct. 10**      **Wmk. 4**

| | | | | |
|---|---|---|---|---|
| 148 | CD306 | 1½p slate | .30 | 1.50 |
| 149 | CD307 | 3p indigo | 1.25 | 2.00 |
| 150 | CD308 | 6p red lilac | .75 | 3.00 |
| 151 | CD309 | 1sh violet | .45 | .60 |
| | | Nos. 148-151 (4) | 2.75 | 7.10 |

### Coronation Issue
Common Design Type

**1953, June 2**    **Engr.**    *Perf. 13½x13*

| | | | | |
|---|---|---|---|---|
| 152 | CD312 | 1½p dk blue & black | .50 | .50 |

Palm Wine Tapping — A8

Designs: 1p, 1sh3p, Cutter. 1½p, 5sh, Wollof woman. 2½p, 2sh, Barra canoe. 3p, 10sh, "Lady Wright." 4p, 4sh, James Island. 1sh, 2sh6p, Woman farming. £1, Elephant badge of Gambia.

**1953, Nov. 2**      *Perf. 13½*

| | | | | |
|---|---|---|---|---|
| 153 | A8 | ½p dk green & car | .70 | .30 |
| 154 | A8 | 1p dk brn & ultra | 1.40 | .45 |
| 155 | A8 | 1½p gray & dk brn | .30 | .80 |
| 156 | A8 | 2½p car & black | .45 | .75 |
| 157 | A8 | 3p pur & indigo | .40 | .25 |
| 158 | A8 | 4p dp blue & blk | 1.50 | 2.50 |
| 159 | A8 | 6p dp plum & brn | 1.25 | .25 |
| 160 | A8 | 1sh green & yel brn | 1.25 | .55 |
| 161 | A8 | 1sh3p blue & vio bl | 12.50 | .55 |
| 162 | A8 | 2sh car & indigo | 7.50 | 4.00 |
| 163 | A8 | 2sh6p brn & bl grn | 9.00 | 2.25 |
| 164 | A8 | 4sh brn org & dp bl | 15.00 | 3.50 |
| 165 | A8 | 5sh ultra & brown | 4.00 | 3.00 |
| 166 | A8 | 10sh dk yel green & ultra | 21.00 | 11.00 |
| 167 | A8 | £1 black & bl grn | 22.50 | 12.00 |
| | | Nos. 153-167 (15) | 98.75 | 42.15 |

Palm Leaf and Elizabeth II, by Annigoni — A9

Design: 3p, 6p, Map of West Africa.

**Wmk. 314**

**1961, Dec. 2**    **Engr.**    *Perf. 11½*

| | | | | |
|---|---|---|---|---|
| 168 | A9 | 2p lilac & green | .30 | .40 |
| 169 | A9 | 3p brown & Prus grn | .80 | .25 |
| 170 | A9 | 6p car rose & dk blue | .80 | .65 |
| 171 | A9 | 1sh3p green & violet | .80 | 2.00 |
| | | Nos. 168-171 (4) | 2.70 | 3.30 |

Visit of Elizabeth II to Gambia, Dec., 1961.

### Freedom from Hunger Issue
Common Design Type

**1963, June 4**   **Photo.**   *Perf. 14x14½*

| | | | | |
|---|---|---|---|---|
| 172 | CD314 | 1sh3p car rose | .50 | .25 |

### Red Cross Centenary Issue
Common Design Type

**1963, Sept. 2**   **Litho.**   *Perf. 13*

| | | | | |
|---|---|---|---|---|
| 173 | CD315 | 2p black & red | .30 | .25 |
| 174 | CD315 | 1sh3p ultra & red | .50 | .75 |

Beautiful Long-tailed Sunbird — A10

Birds: 1p, Yellow-mantled whydah. 1½p, Cattle egret. 2p, Yellow-bellied parrot. 3p, Ring-necked parakeet. 4p, Amethyst starling. 6p, Village weaver. 1sh, Rufous-crowned roller. 1sh3p, Red-eyed turtle dove. 2sh6p, Double-spurred francolin. 5sh, Palm-nut vulture. 10sh, Orange-cheeked waxbill. £1, Emerald cuckoo.

*Perf. 12½x13*

**1963, Nov. 4**   **Photo.**   **Wmk. 314**
Multicolored Design & Inscription

| | | | | |
|---|---|---|---|---|
| 175 | A10 | ½p rose buff | .60 | .90 |
| 176 | A10 | 1p gray green | .60 | .25 |
| 177 | A10 | 1½p pale violet | 1.75 | .70 |
| 178 | A10 | 2p buff | 1.75 | .70 |
| 179 | A10 | 3p light gray | 1.75 | .95 |
| 180 | A10 | 4p lt yel green | 1.75 | .80 |
| 181 | A10 | 6p light blue | 1.75 | .25 |
| 182 | A10 | 1sh pale grysh grn | 1.75 | .25 |
| 183 | A10 | 1sh3p light blue | 9.00 | 2.25 |
| 184 | A10 | 2sh6p pale green | 6.50 | 2.00 |
| 185 | A10 | 5sh blue | 6.50 | 3.00 |
| 186 | A10 | 10sh tan | 9.00 | 9.00 |
| 187 | A10 | £1 pale rose | 22.50 | 13.00 |
| | | Nos. 175-187 (13) | 65.20 | 34.05 |

For overprints see Nos. 188-191, 193-205.

Nos. 176, 179, 182 and 183 Overprinted

**1963, Nov. 7**

| | | | | |
|---|---|---|---|---|
| 188 | A10 | 1p multicolored | .30 | .35 |
| 189 | A10 | 3p multicolored | .35 | .25 |
| 190 | A10 | 1sh multicolored | .35 | .35 |
| a. | | Double overprint | | 5,000. |
| 191 | A10 | 1sh3p multicolored | .45 | .45 |
| | | Nos. 188-191 (4) | 1.45 | 1.40 |

### Shakespeare Issue
Common Design Type

**1964, Apr. 23**   **Photo.**   *Perf. 14x14½*

| | | | | |
|---|---|---|---|---|
| 192 | CD316 | 6p ultramarine | .35 | .25 |

Nos. 175-187 Overprinted:
"INDEPENDENCE / 1965"
*Perf. 12½x13*

**1965, Feb. 18**   **Photo.**   **Wmk. 314**
Multicolored Design & Inscription

| | | | | |
|---|---|---|---|---|
| 193 | A10 | ½p rose buff | .30 | .85 |
| 194 | A10 | 1p gray green | .35 | .25 |
| 195 | A10 | 1½ pale violet | .50 | .85 |
| 196 | A10 | 2p buff | .65 | .30 |
| 197 | A10 | 3p light gray | .65 | .25 |
| 198 | A10 | 4p lt yel green | .65 | 1.50 |
| 199 | A10 | 6p light blue | .65 | .25 |
| 200 | A10 | 1sh pale grysh grn | .65 | .25 |
| 201 | A10 | 1sh3p light blue | .65 | .25 |
| 202 | A10 | 2sh6p pale green | .65 | .60 |
| 203 | A10 | 5sh blue | .65 | .65 |

| | | | | |
|---|---|---|---|---|
| 204 | A10 | 10sh tan | 1.50 | 3.50 |
| 205 | A10 | £1 pale rose | 7.75 | 8.50 |
| | | Nos. 193-205 (13) | 15.60 | 18.00 |

In the overprint, "1965" is flush at left side under "Independence" on the ½p, 1½p, 6p, 1sh3p and 2sh6p; it is centered on the others.

Flag of Gambia over Gambia River — A11

Design: 2p, 1sh6p, Coat of arms.

**1965, Feb. 18**   **Unwmk.**   *Perf. 14*

| | | | | |
|---|---|---|---|---|
| 206 | A11 | ½p slate & multi | .30 | .25 |
| 207 | A11 | 2p lt brown & multi | .30 | .25 |
| 208 | A11 | 7½p dk brown & multi | .35 | .30 |
| 209 | A11 | 1sh6p lt green & multi | .40 | .25 |
| | | Nos. 206-209 (4) | 1.35 | 1.05 |

Gambia's Independence.

ITU Emblem, Old and New Communication Equipment A12

**1965, May 17**   **Photo.**   *Perf. 14½x14*

| | | | | |
|---|---|---|---|---|
| 210 | A12 | 1p dull blue & silver | .40 | .25 |
| 211 | A12 | 1sh6p violet & gold | 1.25 | .30 |
| | | Cent. of the ITU. | | |

Winston Churchill and Parliament A13

**1966, Jan. 24**     *Perf. 14x14½*

| | | | | |
|---|---|---|---|---|
| 212 | A13 | 1p multicolored | .30 | .25 |
| 213 | A13 | 6p multicolored | .40 | .25 |
| 214 | A13 | 1sh6p multicolored | .60 | .60 |
| | | Nos. 212-214 (3) | 1.30 | 1.10 |

Sir Winston Leonard Spencer Churchill, statesman and WWII leader.

Red-cheeked Cordon Bleu and Emblem — A14

Birds: 1p, White-faced tree duck. 1½p, Red-throated bee eater. 2p, Pied kingfisher. 3p, Yellow-crowned bishop. 4p, Fish eagle. 6p, Bruce's green pigeon. 1sh, Blue-bellied roller. 1sh6p, African pigmy kingfisher. 2sh6p, Spur-winged goose. 5sh, Little woodpecker. 10sh, Violet plantain eater. £1, Pintailed whydah, vert.

*Perf. 12½x13*

**1966, Feb. 18**   **Photo.**   **Unwmk.**
Size: 29x25mm
Multicolored Design & Inscription

| | | | | |
|---|---|---|---|---|
| 215 | A14 | ½p gray | .75 | .30 |
| 216 | A14 | 1p bluish green | .30 | .45 |
| 217 | A14 | 1½p yel green | .30 | .35 |
| 218 | A14 | 2p rose lilac | 4.00 | .70 |
| 219 | A14 | 3p lilac | .30 | .25 |
| 220 | A14 | 4p blue | .40 | .30 |
| 221 | A14 | 6p gray | .30 | .25 |
| 222 | A14 | 1sh light green | .30 | .25 |
| 223 | A14 | 1sh6p bright blue | .60 | .25 |
| 224 | A14 | 2sh6p tan | .60 | .60 |
| 225 | A14 | 5sh gray green | .60 | .75 |
| 226 | A14 | 10sh ocher | .75 | 2.50 |

*Perf. 14x14½*
Size: 25x39mm

| | | | | |
|---|---|---|---|---|
| 227 | A14 | £1 pink | 1.00 | 6.00 |
| | | Nos. 215-227 (13) | 10.20 | 12.95 |

Coat of Arms, Old and New Views of Bathurst
A15

**Photo.; Silver Impressed (Arms)**
**1966, June 24**     *Perf. 14½x14*

| | | | | |
|---|---|---|---|---|
| 228 | A15 | 1p orange & dk brn | .30 | .25 |
| 229 | A15 | 2p lt ultra & dk brn | .30 | .25 |
| 230 | A15 | 6p emer & dk brown | .30 | .25 |
| 231 | A15 | 1sh6p brt pink & dk brn | .30 | .25 |
| | | Nos. 228-231 (4) | 1.20 | 1.00 |

150th anniv. of the founding of Bathurst.

Adonis and Atlantic Hotels and ITY Emblem
A16

**Photo.; Silver Impressed (Emblem)**
**1967, Dec. 20**     *Perf. 14½x14*

| | | | | |
|---|---|---|---|---|
| 232 | A16 | 2p lt yel green & brn | .30 | .25 |
| 233 | A16 | 1sh orange & brown | .30 | .25 |
| 234 | A16 | 1sh6p lilac rose & brn | .30 | .25 |
| | | Nos. 232-234 (3) | .90 | .75 |

International Tourist Year.

Handcuffs and Human Rights Flame — A17

Intl. Human Rights Year: 1sh, Fort Bullen. 5sh, Methodist Church.

**1968, July 15**   **Photo.**   *Perf. 14x13*

| | | | | |
|---|---|---|---|---|
| 235 | A17 | 1p gold & multi | .30 | .25 |
| 236 | A17 | 1sh gold & multi | .30 | .25 |
| 237 | A17 | 5sh gold & multi | .30 | 1.00 |
| | | Nos. 235-237 (3) | .90 | 1.50 |

Gambia #1, Victoria and Elizabeth II
A18

Designs: 6p, Gambia #2, Victoria & Elizabeth II. 2sh6p, Gambia #1-2, Elizabeth II.

**Photo. and Embossed**
*Perf. 14x13½*

**1969, Jan. 20**     **Wmk. 314**

| | | | | |
|---|---|---|---|---|
| 238 | A18 | 4p dull yel & dk brn | .30 | .25 |
| 239 | A18 | 6p dp yel grn & bl | .30 | .25 |
| 240 | A18 | 2sh6p dk bl gray, brn & bl | .75 | 1.40 |
| | | Nos. 238-240 (3) | 1.35 | 1.90 |

Centenary of Gambian postage stamps.

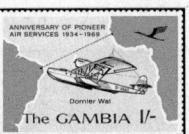

Dornier Wal, Route Gambia to Brazil and Lufthansa Emblem A19

2p, Plane & ship Westfalen, route Gambia to Brazil & Lufthansa emblem. 1sh6p, Zeppelin, route Gambia to Brazil & Lufthansa emblem.

*Perf. 13½x14*

**1969, Dec. 15**   **Litho.**   **Unwmk.**

| | | | | |
|---|---|---|---|---|
| 241 | A19 | 2p pink, org red & blk | .75 | .25 |
| 242 | A19 | 1sh buff, dl yel & blk | .75 | .25 |
| 243 | A19 | 1sh6p lt bl, ultra & blk | .85 | 1.40 |
| | | Nos. 241-243 (3) | 2.35 | 1.90 |

35th anniversary of pioneer air services.

Runner, Flag and Arms of Gambia — A20

**1970, July 16**     *Perf. 14½x14*
Flag in Red, Blue & Green

| | | | | |
|---|---|---|---|---|
| 244 | A20 | 1p pink & brown | .30 | .25 |
| 245 | A20 | 1sh ultra & brown | .30 | .25 |
| 246 | A20 | 5sh green & brown | .30 | .80 |
| | | Nos. 244-246 (3) | .90 | 1.30 |

9th Commonwealth Games, Edinburgh, Scotland, July 16-25.

Pres. Jawara and State House — A21

Republic Day, Apr. 24, 1970: 1sh, Pres. Sir Dauda Kairaba Jawara, vert. 1sh6p, Pres. Jawara and Gambia flag, vert.

**1970, Nov. 2          Litho.          Perf. 14**

| | | | | |
|---|---|---|---|---|
| 247 | A21 | 2p gray & multi | .30 | .25 |
| 248 | A21 | 1sh multicolored | .30 | .25 |
| 249 | A21 | 1sh6p pink & multi | .50 | .70 |
| | | Nos. 247-249 (3) | 1.10 | 1.20 |

Methodist Church, Georgetown A22

Designs: 1sh, Map of Africa and cross, vert. 1sh6p, John Wesley.

**1971, Apr. 16          Unwmk.          Perf. 14**

| | | | | |
|---|---|---|---|---|
| 250 | A22 | 2p multicolored | .30 | .25 |
| 251 | A22 | 1sh vio blue & multi | .30 | .25 |
| 252 | A22 | 1sh6p green & multi | .60 | .80 |
| | | Nos. 250-252 (3) | 1.20 | 1.30 |

Establishment of Methodist Mission, 150th anniv.

Yellowfin Tuna — A23

Fish from Gambian Waters: 4b, Peters' mormyrid. 6b, Tropical two-wing flying fish. 8b, African sleeper goby. 10b, Yellowtail snapper. 13b, Rock hind. 25b, West African eel cat. 38b, Tiger shark. 50b, Electric catfish. 63b, Swamp eel. 1.25d, Smalltooth sawfish. 2.50d, Barracuda. 5d, Brown bullhead.

**1971, July 1          Litho.          Perf. 14**
**Fish in Natural Colors**

| | | | | |
|---|---|---|---|---|
| 253 | A23 | 2b blue | .30 | .70 |
| 254 | A23 | 4b lemon | .30 | .70 |
| 255 | A23 | 6b lt blue green | .30 | .70 |
| 256 | A23 | 8b orange brown | .30 | .25 |
| 257 | A23 | 10b lt Prus blue | .30 | .70 |
| 258 | A23 | 13b orange yel | .30 | .25 |
| 259 | A23 | 25b green | .40 | .50 |
| 260 | A23 | 38b brick red | .70 | .40 |
| 261 | A23 | 50b Prus blue | .80 | .55 |
| 262 | A23 | 63b bister | .90 | 1.75 |
| 263 | A23 | 1.25d yel green | 1.50 | 3.00 |
| 264 | A23 | 2.50d deep rose | 2.50 | 4.50 |
| 265 | A23 | 5d ultramarine | 4.00 | 7.50 |
| | | Nos. 253-265 (13) | 12.60 | 21.05 |

Mungo Park, Scottish Landscape, Map of Gambia Basin — A24

Map of Gambia River Basin and: 25b, Park traveling in dugout canoe. 37b, Park's death under attack at Busa Rapids.

**Perf. 13½x14**
**1971, Sept. 10          Litho.          Unwmk.**

| | | | | |
|---|---|---|---|---|
| 270 | A24 | 4b ultra & multi | .30 | .25 |
| 271 | A24 | 25b yel green & multi | .75 | .45 |
| 272 | A24 | 37b brick red & multi | 1.50 | 2.00 |
| | | Nos. 270-272 (3) | 2.55 | 2.70 |

Mungo Park (1771-1806), Scottish explorer of the Gambia and Niger Rivers.

Radio Gambia and Pres. Jawara — A25

Designs: 25b, Map showing area reached by Radio Gambia. 37b, Like 4b.

**1972, July 1          Perf. 14**

| | | | | |
|---|---|---|---|---|
| 273 | A25 | 4b black & dull yel | .30 | .25 |
| 274 | A25 | 25b black, blue & red | .30 | .25 |
| 275 | A25 | 37b black & yel green | .30 | .75 |
| | | Nos. 273-275 (3) | .90 | 1.25 |

Radio Gambia, 10th anniv., May 1.

High Jump — A26

**1972, Aug. 31          Perf. 13½**

| | | | | |
|---|---|---|---|---|
| 276 | A26 | 4b emerald & multi | .30 | .25 |
| 277 | A26 | 25b lt ultra & multi | .30 | .25 |
| 278 | A26 | 37b red & multi | .40 | .40 |
| | | Nos. 276-278 (3) | 1.00 | .90 |

20th Olympic Games, Munich, 8/26-9/11.

Mandingo Woman — A27

Designs: 25b, Musician playing Mandingo 21-stringed lute (kora). 37b, Map of Mali empire and area of Mandingo language.

**1972, Oct. 18          Litho.          Perf. 14x14½**

| | | | | |
|---|---|---|---|---|
| 279 | A27 | 2b rose red & multi | .30 | .25 |
| 280 | A27 | 25b lt ultra & multi | .30 | .30 |
| 281 | A27 | 37b emerald & multi | .40 | .40 |
| | | Nos. 279-281 (3) | 1.00 | .95 |

International Conference on Mandingo Studies, London, June 30-July 3.

Ship Model with Lanterns — A28

Christmas: 2b, Lighted ship (lantern) carried by boys.

**1972, Dec. 1          Litho.          Perf. 13x13½**

| | | | | |
|---|---|---|---|---|
| 282 | A28 | 2b violet & multi | .30 | .25 |
| 283 | A28 | 1.25d blue & multi | .65 | .65 |

Peanuts, FAO Emblem — A29

**1973, Mar. 31          Litho.          Perf. 14½x14**

| | | | | |
|---|---|---|---|---|
| 284 | A29 | 2b red & multi | .30 | .25 |
| 285 | A29 | 25b lt blue & multi | .30 | .25 |
| 286 | A29 | 37b emerald & multi | .30 | .30 |
| | | Nos. 284-286 (3) | .90 | .80 |

Freedom from Hunger, 2nd UN development campaign.

Planting and Drying Rice — A30

25b, Sorghum (Guinea corn). 37b, Rice crop.

**1973, Apr. 30          Perf. 14½x14**

| | | | | |
|---|---|---|---|---|
| 287 | A30 | 2b shown | .30 | .25 |
| 288 | A30 | 25b multicolored | .30 | .25 |
| 289 | A30 | 37b multicolored | .30 | .25 |

Oil Palms — A31

**1973, July 16**

| | | | | |
|---|---|---|---|---|
| 290 | A31 | 2b shown | .30 | .25 |
| 291 | A31 | 25b Limes | .30 | .25 |
| 292 | A31 | 37b Oil palm fruits | .40 | .25 |

Cassava — A32

**1973, Oct. 15**

| | | | | |
|---|---|---|---|---|
| 293 | A32 | 2b shown | .30 | .25 |
| 294 | A32 | 50b Cotton | .40 | .45 |
| | | Nos. 287-294 (8) | 2.60 | 2.20 |

Gambian agriculture.

OAU Emblem A33

**1973, Nov. 1          Unwmk.          Perf. 13½x13**

| | | | | |
|---|---|---|---|---|
| 295 | A33 | 4b green, yel & black | .30 | .25 |
| 296 | A33 | 25b dp mag, yel & black | .30 | .25 |
| 297 | A33 | 37b blue, yel & black | .30 | .25 |
| | | Nos. 295-297 (3) | .90 | .75 |

10th anniv. of the OAU.

Red Cross — A34

**Perf. 14½x14**
**1973, Nov. 30          Wmk. 314**

| | | | | |
|---|---|---|---|---|
| 298 | A34 | 4b red & black | .30 | .25 |
| 299 | A34 | 25b ultra, red & black | .30 | .25 |
| 300 | A34 | 37b emer, red & black | .30 | .25 |
| | | Nos. 298-300 (3) | .90 | .75 |

25th anniv. of Gambia Red Cross Soc.

Flag of Gambia and Arms of Banjul — A35

**Perf. 13½x13**
**1973, Dec. 17          Unwmk.**

| | | | | |
|---|---|---|---|---|
| 301 | A35 | 4b yel green & multi | .30 | .25 |
| 302 | A35 | 25b ver & multi | .30 | .25 |
| 303 | A35 | 37b lt ultra & multi | .30 | .25 |
| | | Nos. 301-303 (3) | .90 | .75 |

Change of name of Bathurst to Banjul and of St. Mary's Island to Banjul Island.

UPU Emblem A36

**1974, Aug. 24          Litho.          Perf. 13½x13**

| | | | | |
|---|---|---|---|---|
| 304 | A36 | 4b lilac & multi | .30 | .25 |
| 305 | A36 | 37b blue & multi | .30 | .25 |

Centenary of Universal Postal Union.

Churchill at Harrow A37      Churchill in Uniform of 4th Hussars A38

Designs: 50b, Churchill as Prime Minister.

**1974, Nov. 30          Litho.          Perf. 13½**

| | | | | |
|---|---|---|---|---|
| 306 | A37 | 4b multicolored | .30 | .25 |
| 307 | A38 | 37b multicolored | .30 | .25 |
| 308 | A38 | 50b multicolored | .30 | .60 |
| | | Nos. 306-308 (3) | .90 | 1.10 |

Sir Winston Churchill (1874-1965).

WPY Emblem, Races of Man — A39

Symbolic Designs and WPY Emblem: 37b, Races multiplying and dividing like atom. 50b, World population.

**1974, Dec. 16          Litho.          Perf. 14**

| | | | | |
|---|---|---|---|---|
| 309 | A39 | 4b multicolored | .30 | .25 |
| 310 | A39 | 37b multicolored | .30 | .25 |
| 311 | A39 | 50b multicolored | .30 | .25 |
| | | Nos. 309-311 (3) | .90 | .75 |

World Population Year.

Dr. Schweitzer and Hospital, Lambarene A40

50b, Dr. Schweitzer examining patient. 1.25d, Dr. Schweitzer in boat on Ogowe River.

**1975, Jan. 14          Litho.          Perf. 14**

| | | | | |
|---|---|---|---|---|
| 312 | A40 | 10b multicolored | .30 | .25 |
| 313 | A40 | 50b multicolored | .45 | .25 |
| 314 | A40 | 1.25d multicolored | .85 | .75 |
| | | Nos. 312-314 (3) | 1.60 | 1.25 |

Dr. Albert Schweitzer (1875-1965), medical missionary, birth centenary.

Peace Dove — A41

10b, Gambia flag. 50b, Gambia coat of arms. 1.25d, Map of Gambia & Gambia River.

**1975, Feb. 18          Perf. 13**

| | | | | |
|---|---|---|---|---|
| 315 | A41 | 4b multicolored | .30 | .25 |
| 316 | A41 | 10b multicolored | .30 | .25 |
| 317 | A41 | 50b multicolored | .30 | .25 |
| 318 | A41 | 1.25d multicolored | .30 | .40 |
| | | Nos. 315-318 (4) | 1.20 | 1.15 |

10th anniversary of independence.

Public Services Graph, A.D.B. Emblem — A42

African Development Bank Emblem and: 50b, Plant symbolizing growth of Africa, fed by Development Bank. 1.25d, A.D.B. emblem surrounded by symbols of water, education, roads and hospitals.

**1975, Mar. 31          Litho.          Perf. 14**

| | | | | |
|---|---|---|---|---|
| 319 | A42 | 10b multicolored | .30 | .25 |
| 320 | A42 | 50b multicolored | .30 | .25 |
| 321 | A42 | 1.25d multicolored | .40 | .40 |
| | | Nos. 319-321 (3) | 1.00 | .90 |

African Development Bank, 10th anniv.

David, by
Michelangelo — A43

Bas-reliefs by Michelangelo: 50b, Madonna of the Steps. 1.25d, Battle of the Centaurs, horiz.

**1975, Nov. 14**     **Perf. 14½**
| 322 | A43 | 10b dull blue & multi | .30 | .25 |
| 323 | A43 | 50b sepia & multi | .30 | .25 |
| 324 | A43 | 1.25d green & multi | .60 | .60 |
| | | Nos. 322-324 (3) | 1.20 | 1.10 |

Michelangelo Buonarroti (1475-1564), Italian painter, sculptor and architect.

Gambia High School — A44

Designs: 50b, Pupil in laboratory and school emblem. 1.50d, School emblem.

**1975, Nov. 17**
| 325 | A44 | 10b multicolored | .30 | .25 |
| 326 | A44 | 50b multicolored | .30 | .25 |
| 327 | A44 | 1.50d multicolored | .35 | .35 |
| | | Nos. 325-327 (3) | .95 | .85 |

Gambia High School, centenary.

Teacher and IWY Emblem — A45

IWY: 10b, Women planting rice. 50b, Nurse holding baby. 1.50d, Woman traffic officer.

**1975, Dec. 15**    **Litho.**    **Perf. 14½**
| 328 | A45 | 4b yellow & multi | .30 | .25 |
| 329 | A45 | 10b multicolored | .30 | .25 |
| 330 | A45 | 50b multicolored | .35 | .25 |
| 331 | A45 | 1.50d blue & multi | .60 | .30 |
| | | Nos. 328-331 (4) | 1.55 | 1.05 |

Woman Golfer — A46

Designs: 50b, Golfer addressing ball. 1.50d, Golfer finishing iron shot.

**1976, Feb. 18**    **Litho.**    **Perf. 14½**
| 332 | A46 | 10b multicolored | .80 | .25 |
| 333 | A46 | 50b multicolored | 1.60 | .35 |
| 334 | A46 | 1.50d multicolored | 2.75 | 1.00 |
| | | Nos. 332-334 (3) | 5.15 | 1.60 |

11th anniversary of independence.

American Militiaman — A47

American Bicent.: 50b, Continental Army soldier. 1.25d, Declaration of Independence.

**1976, May 15**    **Litho.**    **Perf. 14x13½**
| 335 | A47 | 25b multicolored | .30 | .25 |
| 336 | A47 | 50b multicolored | .30 | .30 |
| 337 | A47 | 1.25d multicolored | .65 | .65 |
| a. | | Souvenir sheet of 3, #335-337 | 1.50 | 3.00 |
| | | Nos. 335-337 (3) | 1.25 | 1.20 |

Mother and Child, Christmas Decoration — A48

**1976, Oct. 28**    **Litho.**    **Perf. 14**
| 338 | A48 | 10b lt ultra & multi | .30 | .25 |
| 339 | A48 | 50b rose & multi | .30 | .25 |
| 340 | A48 | 1.25d yel grn & multi | .30 | .40 |
| | | Nos. 338-340 (3) | .90 | .90 |

Christmas.

Serval Cat and Wildlife Fund Emblem A49

Designs: 25b, Harnessed antelope. 50b, Sitatunga. 1.25d, Leopard.

**1976, Nov. 29**     **Perf. 13½x14**
| 341 | A49 | 10b multicolored | 4.50 | .50 |
| 342 | A49 | 25b multicolored | 6.00 | .50 |
| 343 | A49 | 50b multicolored | 11.00 | 1.00 |
| 344 | A49 | 1.25d multicolored | 17.50 | 6.00 |
| a. | | Souvenir sheet of 4, #341-344 | 65.00 | 20.00 |
| | | Nos. 341-344 (4) | 39.00 | 8.00 |

Abuko Nature Reserve.

Queen's Visit, 1961 — A50

Designs: 50b, The spurs and jeweled sword. 1.25d, The oblation of the sword.

**1977, Feb. 7**    **Litho.**    **Perf. 13½x14**
| 345 | A50 | 25b multicolored | .30 | .25 |
| 346 | A50 | 50b multicolored | .30 | .25 |
| 347 | A50 | 1.25d multicolored | .30 | .40 |
| | | Nos. 345-347 (3) | .90 | .90 |

25th anniv. of the reign of Elizabeth II.

Festival Emblem and Weaver — A51

**1977, Jan. 12**    **Litho.**    **Perf. 14**
| 348 | A51 | 25b multicolored | .30 | .25 |
| 349 | A51 | 50b multicolored | .30 | .25 |
| 350 | A51 | 1.25d multicolored | .60 | .60 |
| a. | | Souvenir sheet of 3, #348-350 | 2.40 | 3.50 |
| | | Nos. 348-350 (3) | 1.20 | 1.10 |

2nd World Black and African Festival, Lagos, Nigeria, Jan. 15-Feb. 12.

Stone Circles, near Kuntaur — A52

Tourism: 50b, Ruins of Fort on James Island. 1.25d, Mungo Park Monument.

**1977, Feb. 18**    **Litho.**    **Perf. 14½**
| 351 | A52 | 25b multicolored | .30 | .25 |
| 352 | A52 | 50b multicolored | .30 | .25 |
| 353 | A52 | 1.25d multicolored | .50 | .50 |
| | | Nos. 351-353 (3) | 1.10 | 1.00 |

Clerodendrum Splendens — A53

Flowers and Shrubs: 4b, White water lily. 6b, Fireball lily. 8b, Mussaenda elegans. 10b, Broad-leaved ground orchid. 13b, Fiber plant. 25b, False kapok. 38b, Baobab. 50b, Coral tree. 63b, Gloriosa lily. 1.25d, Bell-flowered mimosa. 2.50d, Kindin dolo. 5d, African tulip tree. 6b, 8b, 10b, 13b, 25b, 38b, 1.25d, 2.50d, vertical.

**1977, July 1**    **Litho.**    **Perf. 14½**
| 354 | A53 | 2b multicolored | .30 | .25 |
| 355 | A53 | 4b multicolored | .30 | .30 |
| 356 | A53 | 6b multicolored | .30 | .30 |
| 357 | A53 | 8b multicolored | .30 | .25 |
| 358 | A53 | 10b multicolored | 2.25 | .40 |
| 359 | A53 | 13b yellow & multi | .75 | .75 |
| a. | | Pale olive background | 2.75 | 4.25 |
| 360 | A53 | 25b multicolored | .30 | .25 |
| 361 | A53 | 38b multicolored | .30 | .70 |
| 362 | A53 | 50b multicolored | .40 | .55 |
| 363 | A53 | 63b multicolored | .45 | .75 |
| 364 | A53 | 1.25d multicolored | .65 | 1.50 |
| 365 | A53 | 2.50d multicolored | .75 | 1.50 |
| 366 | A53 | 5d multicolored | .90 | 2.50 |
| | | Nos. 354-366 (13) | 7.95 | 10.00 |

For surcharges see Nos. 390A-390C.

Crowned Crane, Nile Crocodile, Bush Buck — A54

Designs: 25b, Banjul Declaration, excerpt, flag colors. 50b, Banjul Declaration. 1.25d, Climbing lily, butterfly and moth.

**1977, Oct. 15**    **Litho.**    **Perf. 14**
| 367 | A54 | 10b lt blue & black | .30 | .25 |
| 368 | A54 | 25b multicolored | .35 | .25 |
| 369 | A54 | 50b multicolored | .60 | .25 |
| 370 | A54 | 1.25d red & black | 2.00 | .75 |
| | | Nos. 367-370 (4) | 3.25 | 1.50 |

Banjul Declaration, for the conservation of flora and fauna, Feb. 18, 1977.

Madonna, Flight into Egypt, by Rubens — A55

Rubens Paintings: 25b, Education of Mary by St. Ann. 50b, Child's head. 1d, Madonna surrounded by saints.

**1977, Dec. 15**    **Litho.**    **Perf. 14x13½**
| 371 | A55 | 10b multicolored | .30 | .25 |
| 372 | A55 | 25b multicolored | .30 | .25 |
| 373 | A55 | 50b multicolored | .45 | .35 |
| 374 | A55 | 1d multicolored | .65 | .85 |
| | | Nos. 371-374 (4) | 1.70 | 1.70 |

Peter Paul Rubens (1577-1640). Nos. 371-374 printed in sheets of 5 stamps and decorative label.

Dome of the Rock, Jerusalem A56

**1978, Jan. 3**    **Litho.**    **Perf. 14½**
| 375 | A56 | 8b olive green & multi | .75 | .25 |
| 376 | A56 | 25b red & multi | 2.75 | 1.00 |

Palestinian fighters and their families.

Walking on Greased Pole — A57

Designs: 50b, Pillow fight on greased pole. 1.25d, Rowers in long boat.

**1978, Feb. 18**     **Perf. 14**
| 377 | A57 | 10b multicolored | .30 | .25 |
| 378 | A57 | 50b multicolored | .30 | .25 |
| 379 | A57 | 1.25d multicolored | .30 | .30 |
| | | Nos. 377-379 (3) | .90 | .80 |

Independence Regatta celebrating 13th anniversary of independence.

### Elizabeth II Coronation Anniversary Issue
#### Souvenir Sheet
#### Common Design Types

**1978, Apr. 15**    **Litho.**    **Perf. 15**
| 380 | | Sheet of 6 | 1.50 | 1.50 |
| a. | | CD326 1d White grayhound of Richmond | .30 | .30 |
| b. | | CD327 1d Elizabeth II | .30 | .30 |
| c. | | CD328 1d Lion | .30 | .30 |

No. 380 contains 2 se-tenant strips of Nos. 380a-380c, separated by horizontal gutter with commemorative and descriptive inscriptions.

Verreaux's Eagle Owl — A58

Birds of Prey and Wildlife Fund Emblem: 25b, Lizard buzzard. 50b, West African harrier hawk. 1.25d, Long-crested hawk eagle.

**1978, Oct. 28**    **Litho.**    **Perf. 14x13½**
| 381 | A58 | 20b multicolored | 15.00 | .75 |
| 382 | A58 | 25b multicolored | 15.00 | .75 |
| 383 | A58 | 50b multicolored | 20.00 | 2.50 |
| 384 | A58 | 1.25d multicolored | 25.00 | 10.00 |
| | | Nos. 381-384 (4) | 75.00 | 14.00 |

Abuko Nature Reserve.

MV Lady Wright — A59

New river vessels: 25b, River vessel Lady Chilel Jawara. 1d, Cross section of Lady Chilel Jawara.

**1978, Dec. 1**    **Litho.**    **Perf. 14½**
| 385 | A59 | 8b multicolored | .30 | .25 |
| 386 | A59 | 25b multicolored | .40 | .40 |
| 387 | A59 | 1d multicolored | 1.25 | 1.25 |
| | | Nos. 385-387 (3) | 1.95 | 1.90 |

Motorized Police — A60

**1979, Feb. 18**    **Litho.**    **Perf. 14**
| 388 | A60 | 10b shown | .80 | .25 |
| 389 | A60 | 50b Fire engine | 1.50 | .30 |
| 390 | A60 | 1.25d Ambulance | 2.40 | 1.10 |
| | | Nos. 388-390 (3) | 4.70 | 1.65 |

14th anniversary of independence.

### Nos. 359, 363-364 Surcharged

**1979**     **Litho.**    **Perf. 14½**
| 390A | A53 | 25b on 13b multi | .30 | .35 |
| 390B | A53 | 25b on 63b multi | .30 | .25 |
| 390C | A53 | 25b on 1.25d multi | .30 | .25 |
| | | Nos. 390A-390C (3) | .90 | .85 |

Issued: No. 390A, 3/5; others, 3/26.

Ramsgate Sands, by William P. Frith — A61

Designs: 10b, 25b, IYC emblem and details from painting shown on 1d. 25b, vert.

**1979, May 25**    **Litho.**    **Perf. 14**
#### Size: 38x21mm, 21x38mm
| 391 | A61 | 10b multicolored | .30 | .25 |
| 392 | A61 | 25b multicolored | .30 | .25 |
#### Size: 56x21mm
| 393 | A61 | 1d multicolored | .75 | .75 |
| | | Nos. 391-393 (3) | 1.35 | 1.25 |

International Year of the Child.

Gambia No. 15, Maltese Cross Postmark A62

Gambian Stamps and Maltese Cross Postmark: 25b, #1. 50b, #208. 1.25d, #125.

**1979, Aug. 16   Litho.   Perf. 14½**

| | | | |
|---|---|---|---|
| 394 | A62 | 10b multicolored | .30 .25 |
| 395 | A62 | 25b multicolored | .30 .25 |
| 396 | A62 | 50b multicolored | .30 .25 |
| 397 | A62 | 1.25d multicolored | .30 .45 |
| a. | | Souvenir sheet of 1 | .75 1.25 |
| | | Nos. 394-397 (4) | 1.20 1.20 |

Sir Rowland Hill (1795-1879), originator of penny postage.

Abuko Earth Station, Construction A63

Telecommunications: 50b, Newly opened station. 1d, Intelsat satellites orbiting earth.

**1979, Sept. 20   Litho.   Perf. 14**

| | | | |
|---|---|---|---|
| 398 | A63 | 25b multicolored | .30 .25 |
| 399 | A63 | 50b multicolored | .30 .30 |
| 400 | A63 | 1d multicolored | .50 .50 |
| | | Nos. 398-400 (3) | 1.10 1.05 |

Apollo 11 Lift-off — A64

**1979, Oct. 17   Litho.   Perf. 14**

| | | | |
|---|---|---|---|
| 401 | A64 | 25b shown | .30 .25 |
| 402 | A64 | 38b Orbiting moon | .30 .25 |
| 403 | A64 | 50b Splashdown | .50 .50 |
| a. | | Souvenir booklet | 4.75 |
| b. | | Pane, 2 each 25b, 38b, 50b | 1.75 |
| c. | | Pane of 1 (2d Lunar module) | 1.50 |
| | | Nos. 401-403 (3) | 1.10 1.00 |

Apollo 11 moon landing, 10th anniversary. No. 403a contains Nos. 403b-403c printed on peelable, self-adhesive paper backing with Apollo 11 emblems on back. Stamps and panes are die-cut and have 1 to 3 sides rouletted 9½.

Large Spotted Acraea, Wildlife Fund Emblem A65

Wildlife Fund Emblem and Butterflies: 50b, Yellow pansy. 1d, Veined swallowtail. 1.25d, Foxy charaxes.

**1980, Jan. 3   Litho.   Perf. 13½x14**

| | | | |
|---|---|---|---|
| 404 | A65 | 25b multicolored | 10.00 .25 |
| 405 | A65 | 50b multicolored | 12.50 .50 |
| 406 | A65 | 1d multicolored | 17.50 1.00 |
| 407 | A65 | 1.25d multicolored | 20.00 3.00 |
| a. | | Souvenir sheet of 4, #404-407 | 90.00 15.00 |
| | | Nos. 404-407 (4) | 60.00 4.75 |

Abuko Nature Reserve.

Steam Launch "Vampire" A66

**1980, May 6   Litho.   Perf. 14½**

| | | | |
|---|---|---|---|
| 408 | A66 | 10b shown | .30 .25 |
| 409 | A66 | 25b "Lady Denham" | .35 .25 |

**Perf. 13½x14½**
**Size: 49x21mm**

| | | | |
|---|---|---|---|
| 410 | A66 | 50b "Mansa Kila Ba" | .50 .50 |
| 411 | A66 | 1.25d "Prince of Wales" | .65 .85 |
| | | Nos. 408-411 (4) | 1.80 1.85 |

London 80 Intl. Stamp Exhib., May 6-14. For surcharge see No. 497A.

---

**Queen Mother Elizabeth Birthday Issue**
**Common Design Type**

**1980, Aug. 4   Litho.   Perf. 14**

| | | | |
|---|---|---|---|
| 412 | CD330 | 67b multicolored | .40 .50 |

Phoenician Trading Vessel — A67

67b, Egyptian seagoing ship. 75b, Portuguese caravel. 1d, Spanish galleon.

**1980, Oct. 2   Litho.   Perf. 14½**

| | | | |
|---|---|---|---|
| 413 | A67 | 8b shown | .30 .25 |
| 414 | A67 | 67b multicolored | .70 .60 |
| 415 | A67 | 75b multicolored | .80 .70 |
| 416 | A67 | 1d multicolored | 1.00 .90 |
| | | Nos. 413-416 (4) | 2.80 2.45 |

Virgin and Child, by Francesco de Mura — A68

Christmas: 67b, Praying Virgin with Crown of Stars, by Correggio. 75b, Rest on the Flight, after Correggio.

**1980, Dec. 18   Litho.   Perf. 14**

| | | | |
|---|---|---|---|
| 417 | A68 | 8b multicolored | .30 .25 |
| 418 | A68 | 67b multicolored | .30 .25 |
| 419 | A68 | 75b multicolored | .30 .25 |
| | | Nos. 417-419 (3) | .90 .75 |

New Atlantic Hotel, Conference Emblem — A69

**1981, Feb. 18   Litho.   Perf. 14**

| | | | |
|---|---|---|---|
| 420 | A69 | 25b shown | .30 .25 |
| 421 | A69 | 75b Ancient stone circle | .40 .40 |
| 422 | A69 | 85b Conference emblem | .55 .55 |
| | | Nos. 420-422 (3) | 1.25 1.20 |

World Tourism Conference, Manila, Sept. 27 and 16th anniversary of independence.

13th World Telecomunications Day — A70

**1981, May 17   Litho.   Perf. 14**

| | | | |
|---|---|---|---|
| 423 | A70 | 50b No. 399 | .50 .35 |
| 424 | A70 | 50b No. 313 | .50 .35 |
| 425 | A70 | 85b ITU, WHO emblems | .75 .60 |
| | | Nos. 423-425 (3) | 1.75 1.30 |

**Royal Wedding Issue**
**Common Design Type**

**1981, July 22   Litho.   Perf. 13½x13**

| | | | |
|---|---|---|---|
| 426 | CD331 | 75b Bouquet | .30 .25 |
| 427 | CD331 | 1d Charles | .30 .25 |
| 428 | CD331 | 1.25d Couple | .30 .30 |
| | | Nos. 426-428 (3) | .90 .80 |

For surcharges see Nos. 439, 497C.

Planting Rice Seedlings — A71

50b, Spraying. 85b, Winnowing and drying.

**1981, Sept. 4   Litho.   Perf. 14**

| | | | |
|---|---|---|---|
| 429 | A71 | 10b shown | .30 .25 |
| 430 | A71 | 50b multicolored | .30 .30 |
| 431 | A71 | 85b multicolored | .30 .35 |
| | | Nos. 429-431 (3) | .90 .90 |

West African Rice Development Assoc., 10th anniv.

---

Abuko Nature Reserve — A72

Designs: Wildlife Fund emblem and reptiles.

**1981, Nov. 17   Litho.   Perf. 14**

| | | | |
|---|---|---|---|
| 432 | A72 | 40b Bosc's monitor | 15.00 .75 |
| 433 | A72 | 60b Dwarf crocodile | 17.50 1.50 |
| 434 | A72 | 80b Royal python | 20.00 2.50 |
| 435 | A72 | 85b Chameleon | 22.50 3.00 |
| | | Nos. 432-435 (4) | 75.00 7.75 |

30th Anniv. of West African Examinations Council — A73

**1982, Mar. 16   Litho.   Perf. 14**

| | | | |
|---|---|---|---|
| 436 | A73 | 60b Test room | .55 .40 |
| 437 | A73 | 85b 1st high school | .65 .55 |
| 438 | A73 | 1.10d Council office | .85 .75 |
| | | Nos. 436-438 (3) | 2.05 1.70 |

**No. 426 Surcharged**

**1982, Apr. 19   Litho.   Perf. 13½x13**

| | | | |
|---|---|---|---|
| 439 | CD331 | 60b on 75b multi | 3.00 1.50 |

Scouting Year — A74

**1982, May   Perf. 14**

| | | | |
|---|---|---|---|
| 440 | A74 | 85b Tree planting | 2.25 1.25 |
| 441 | A74 | 1.25d Woodworking | 2.50 2.25 |
| 442 | A74 | 1.27d Baden-Powell | 2.75 3.00 |
| | | Nos. 440-442 (3) | 7.50 6.50 |

1982 World Cup — A75

**1982, June 13   Litho.   Perf. 14**

| | | | |
|---|---|---|---|
| 443 | A75 | 10b Team | .30 .25 |
| 444 | A75 | 1.10d Players | 1.50 .75 |
| 445 | A75 | 1.25d Stadium | 1.50 .80 |
| 446 | A75 | 1.55d Cup | 1.75 1.00 |
| a. | | Souvenir sheet of 4, #443-446 | 6.00 6.00 |
| | | Nos. 443-446 (4) | 5.05 2.80 |

For surcharge see No. 497B.

**Princess Diana Issue**
**Common Design Type**

**1982, July 1   Litho.   Perf. 14½x14**

| | | | |
|---|---|---|---|
| 447 | CD333 | 10b Arms | .30 .25 |
| 448 | CD333 | 85b Diana | .60 .60 |
| 449 | CD333 | 1.10d Wedding | .75 .75 |
| 450 | CD333 | 2.50d Portrait | 1.25 1.25 |
| | | Nos. 447-450 (4) | 2.90 2.85 |

For surcharge see No. 479D.

Economic Community of West African States Development A76

Designs: 10b, Yundum Experimental Farm. 60b, Banjul/Kaolack Microwave Tower. 90b, Soap Factory, Denton Bridge Banjul. 1.25d, Control Tower, Yundum.

**1982, Nov. 5   Litho.   Perf. 14x14½**

| | | | |
|---|---|---|---|
| 451 | A76 | 10b multicolored | .30 .25 |
| 452 | A76 | 60b multicolored | 2.10 2.40 |
| 453 | A76 | 90b multicolored | 2.10 3.25 |
| 454 | A76 | 1.25d multicolored | 3.00 3.75 |
| | | Nos. 451-454 (4) | 7.50 9.65 |

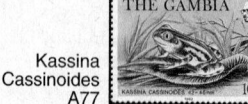

Kassina Cassinoides A77

---

20b, Hylarana galamensis. 85b, Euphlyctis occipitalis. 2d, Kassina senegalensis.

**1982, Dec.   Litho.   Perf. 14**

| | | | |
|---|---|---|---|
| 455 | A77 | 10b shown | 2.25 .25 |
| 456 | A77 | 20b multicolored | 4.00 .45 |
| 457 | A77 | 85b multicolored | 6.00 2.50 |
| 458 | A77 | 2d multicolored | 8.50 12.00 |
| | | Nos. 455-458 (4) | 20.75 15.20 |

A78

10b, Globe showing Gambia. 60b, Batik cloth. 1.10d, Bagging peanuts. 2.10d, Flag.

**1983, Mar. 14   Wmk. 373   Perf. 12**

| | | | |
|---|---|---|---|
| 459 | A78 | 10b multicolored | .30 .25 |
| 460 | A78 | 60b multicolored | .30 .35 |
| 461 | A78 | 1.10d multicolored | .35 .60 |
| 462 | A78 | 2.10d multicolored | .60 1.10 |
| | | Nos. 459-462 (4) | 1.55 2.30 |

Commonwealth Day.

Sisters of St. Joseph of Cluny Centenary A79

10b, Founder Anne Marie Javouhey, vert. 85b, Javouhey with children, house.

**1983, Apr. 8   Litho.   Perf. 14**

| | | | |
|---|---|---|---|
| 463 | A79 | 10b multicolored | .30 .25 |
| 464 | A79 | 85b multicolored | .45 .45 |

River Boats — A80

1b, Canoes. 2b, Upstream ferry. 3b, Dredging vessel. 4b, Harbor launch. 5b, Freighter. 10b, 60-foot launch. 20b, Multi-purpose vessel. 30b, Large sailing canoe. 40b, Passenger-cargo ferry. 50b, Cargo liner, diff. 75b, Fishing boats. 1d, Peanut river train. 1.25d, Groundnutter. 2.50d, Banjul-Barra ferry. 5d, Binlang Bolong. 10d, Passenger-cargo ferry, diff.

**1983, July 11   Litho.   Perf. 14**

| | | | |
|---|---|---|---|
| 465 | A80 | 1b multicolored | .30 .25 |
| 466 | A80 | 2b multicolored | .30 .25 |
| 467 | A80 | 3b multicolored | .30 .25 |
| 468 | A80 | 4b multicolored | .30 .30 |
| 469 | A80 | 5b multicolored | .30 .30 |
| 470 | A80 | 10b multicolored | .30 .30 |
| 471 | A80 | 20b multicolored | .40 .40 |
| 472 | A80 | 30b multicolored | .40 .40 |
| 473 | A80 | 40b multicolored | .40 .40 |
| 474 | A80 | 50b multicolored | .45 .45 |
| 475 | A80 | 75b multicolored | .55 .50 |
| 476 | A80 | 1d multicolored | .80 .60 |
| 477 | A80 | 1.25d multicolored | .85 1.25 |
| 478 | A80 | 2.50d multicolored | 1.50 2.25 |
| 479 | A80 | 5d multicolored | 2.75 4.50 |
| 480 | A80 | 10d multicolored | 5.75 7.25 |
| | | Nos. 465-480 (16) | 15.65 19.65 |

For overprints see Nos. 523-524.

World Communications Year — A81

10b, Local ferry. 85b, GPO telex, Banjul. 90b, Radio Gambia. 1.10d, Loading mail, Yundum Airport.

**1983, Oct. 10**

| | | | |
|---|---|---|---|
| 481 | A81 | 10b multi | .30 .25 |
| 482 | A81 | 85b multi | .55 .55 |
| 483 | A81 | 90b multi | .75 .75 |
| 484 | A81 | 1.10d multi | 1.25 1.00 |
| | | Nos. 481-484 (4) | 2.85 2.55 |

Osprey, Breeding Range — A82

Designs: Birds, Maps of Europe and Africa.

**1983, Sept. 12    Litho.    Perf. 14**
| | | | | |
|---|---|---|---|---|
| 485 | A82 | 10b multicolored | 2.75 | .65 |
| 486 | A82 | 60b multicolored | 4.50 | 4.25 |
| 487 | A82 | 85b multicolored | 5.25 | 4.75 |
| 488 | A82 | 1.10d multicolored | 6.00 | 7.25 |
| | | *Nos. 485-488 (4)* | 18.50 | 16.90 |

Raphael, 500th Birth Anniv. — A83

Details from St. Paul Preaching at Athens.

**1983, Nov. 1    Litho.    Perf. 14**
| | | | | |
|---|---|---|---|---|
| 489 | A83 | 60b multicolored | .55 | .55 |
| 490 | A83 | 85b multicolored | .65 | .65 |
| 491 | A83 | 1d multicolored | .70 | .70 |
| | | *Nos. 489-491 (3)* | 1.90 | 1.90 |

**Souvenir Sheet**
| | | | | |
|---|---|---|---|---|
| 492 | A83 | 2d multi, vert. | 1.75 | 1.75 |

Manned Flight, 200th Anniv. — A84

Flown covers and: 60b, Montgolfier Balloon. 85b, British Caledonian Aircraft. 96b, Junkers Airplane. 1.25d, Lunar module. 4d, Zeppelin.

**1983, Dec. 12    Litho.    Perf. 14**
| | | | | |
|---|---|---|---|---|
| 493 | A84 | 60b multicolored | .35 | .35 |
| 494 | A84 | 85b multicolored | .45 | .45 |
| a. | | Bklt. pane, 2 each #493, 494 | 3.75 | |
| 495 | A84 | 90b multicolored | .45 | .45 |
| 496 | A84 | 1.25d multicolored | .50 | .50 |
| a. | | Bklt. pane, 2 each #495, 496 | 4.50 | |
| | | *Nos. 493-496 (4)* | 1.75 | 1.75 |

**Souvenir Sheet**
| | | | | |
|---|---|---|---|---|
| 497 | A84 | 4d multicolored | 7.50 | 7.50 |

No. 497 issued in booklet containing Nos. 497, 494a, 496a.

**Nos. 411, 445, 428 and 449 Surcharged with Black Bars and New Value**
**Perfs. as before**

**1983, Dec. 14    Litho.**
| | | | |
|---|---|---|---|
| 497A | A66 | 1.50d on 1.25d, #411 | 40.00 |
| 497B | A75 | 1.50d on 1.25d, #445 | 40.00 |
| 497C | CD331 | 2d on 1.25d, #428 | 40.00 |
| 497D | CD333 | 2d on 1.10d, #449 | 40.00 |

The status of Nos. 497A-497D is questioned.

Easter — A85

Various Disney characters painting Easter eggs.

**1984, Apr. 15    Litho.    Perf. 11**
| | | | | |
|---|---|---|---|---|
| 498 | A85 | 1b multicolored | .30 | .25 |
| 499 | A85 | 2b multicolored | .30 | .25 |
| 500 | A85 | 3b multicolored | .30 | .25 |
| 501 | A85 | 4b multicolored | .30 | .25 |
| 502 | A85 | 5b multicolored | .30 | .25 |
| 503 | A85 | 10b multicolored | .30 | .25 |
| 504 | A85 | 60b multicolored | .35 | .35 |
| 505 | A85 | 90b multicolored | .80 | .80 |
| 506 | A85 | 5d multicolored | 3.00 | 3.00 |
| | | *Nos. 498-506 (9)* | 5.95 | 5.65 |

**Souvenir Sheet**
**Perf. 14**
| | | | | |
|---|---|---|---|---|
| 507 | A85 | 5d multicolored | 5.50 | 5.50 |

1984 Summer Olympics — A86

60b, Shot put, vert. 85b, High jump. 90b, Wrestling, vert. 1d, Gymnastics, vert. 1.25d, Swimming. 2d, Diving.

5d, Yachting, vert.

**1984, Mar. 30    Litho.    Perf. 14**
| | | | | |
|---|---|---|---|---|
| 508 | A86 | 60b multi | .30 | .30 |
| 509 | A86 | 85b multi | .45 | .45 |
| 510 | A86 | 90b multi | .45 | .45 |
| 511 | A86 | 1d multi | .50 | .50 |
| 512 | A86 | 1.25d multi | .60 | .60 |
| 513 | A86 | 2d multi | 1.00 | 1.00 |
| | | *Nos. 508-513 (6)* | 3.30 | 3.30 |

**Souvenir Sheet**
| | | | | |
|---|---|---|---|---|
| 514 | A86 | 5d multi | 3.00 | 3.00 |

For overprints see Nos. 570-576.

Nile Crododile — A87

4b, Young hatching. 6b, Adult carrying young. 90b, Adult. 1.50d, Adult, diff.
No. 518A as Nos. 515-518, without WWF emblem.

**1984, May 23**
| | | | | |
|---|---|---|---|---|
| 515 | A87 | 4b multi | 3.25 | .75 |
| 516 | A87 | 6b multi | 3.25 | .75 |
| 517 | A87 | 90b multi | 18.00 | 3.75 |
| 518 | A87 | 1.50d multi | 22.50 | 7.50 |
| | | *Nos. 515-518 (4)* | 47.00 | 12.75 |

**Souvenir Sheet**
| | | | | |
|---|---|---|---|---|
| 518A | A87 | Sheet of 4 | 8.50 | 6.00 |
| b.-e. | | each single | 2.00 | 1.50 |

**Lloyd's List Issue**
**Common Design Type**

60b, Banjul Port. 85b, Bulk cargo carrier. 90b, Sinking of the Dagomba. 1.25d, 19th-cent. frigate.

**1984, June 1    Litho.    Perf. 14**
| | | | | |
|---|---|---|---|---|
| 519 | CD335 | 60b multicolored | .75 | .60 |
| 520 | CD335 | 85b multicolored | .95 | .95 |
| 521 | CD335 | 90b multicolored | 1.00 | 1.00 |
| 522 | CD335 | 1.25d multicolored | 1.50 | 1.75 |
| | | *Nos. 519-522 (4)* | 4.20 | 4.30 |

**Nos. 478-479 Overprinted: "19th UPU / CONGRESS HAMBURG"**

**1984, June 19    Litho.    Perf. 14**
| | | | | |
|---|---|---|---|---|
| 523 | A80 | 2.50d multicolored | 1.50 | 1.75 |
| 524 | A80 | 5d multicolored | 2.75 | 3.50 |

1984 Summer Olympics — A88

**1984, July 28    Litho.    Perf. 14**
| | | | | |
|---|---|---|---|---|
| 525 | A88 | 60b Running | .50 | .40 |
| 526 | A88 | 85b Long jump | .60 | .55 |
| 527 | A88 | 90b Running, diff. | .60 | .55 |
| 528 | A88 | 1.25d Long jump, diff. | .80 | .70 |
| | | *Nos. 525-528 (4)* | 2.50 | 2.20 |

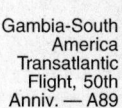

Gambia-South America Transatlantic Flight, 50th Anniv. — A89

60b, Graf Zeppelin D-LZ127. 85b, Dornier Wal on S.S. Westfalen. 90b, Dornier DO-18 D-ABYM. 1.25d, Dornier Wal D-2069.

**1984, Nov. 1    Litho.    Perf. 14**
| | | | | |
|---|---|---|---|---|
| 529 | A89 | 60b multicolored | 1.40 | 1.10 |
| 530 | A89 | 85b multicolored | 2.10 | 1.90 |
| 531 | A89 | 90b multicolored | 2.50 | 2.75 |
| 532 | A89 | 1.25d multicolored | 2.50 | 3.00 |
| | | *Nos. 529-532 (4)* | 8.50 | 8.75 |

Butterflies — A90

10b, Antanartia hippomene. 85b, Pseudacraea eurytus. 90b, Charaxes lactitinctus. 3d, Graphium pylades. 5d, Eurema hapale.

**1984, Nov. 27**
| | | | | |
|---|---|---|---|---|
| 533 | A90 | 10b multicolored | .35 | .25 |
| 534 | A90 | 85b multicolored | 1.25 | 1.00 |
| 535 | A90 | 90b multicolored | 1.50 | 1.00 |
| 536 | A90 | 3d multicolored | 3.50 | 4.25 |
| | | *Nos. 533-536 (4)* | 6.60 | 6.50 |

**Souvenir Sheet**
| | | | | |
|---|---|---|---|---|
| 537 | A90 | 5d multicolored | 12.50 | 12.50 |

Marine Life — A90a

55b, Penaeus duorarum. 75b, Caretta caretta. 1.50d, Physalia. 2.35d, Uca pugilator. 5d, Cowrie snail.

**1984, Nov. 27**
| | | | | |
|---|---|---|---|---|
| 538 | A90a | 55b multicolored | .40 | .35 |
| 539 | A90a | 75b multicolored | .60 | .50 |
| 540 | A90a | 1.50d multicolored | .95 | .95 |
| 541 | A90a | 2.35d multicolored | 1.60 | 1.60 |
| | | *Nos. 538-541 (4)* | 3.55 | 3.40 |

**Souvenir Sheets**
| | | | | |
|---|---|---|---|---|
| 542 | A90a | 5d multicolored | 4.75 | 4.75 |

UN Child Survival Campaign — A91

10b, Oral rehydration therapy. 85b, Growth monitoring. 1.10d, Breast-feeding. 1.50d, Universal immunization.

**1985, Feb. 27**
| | | | | |
|---|---|---|---|---|
| 543 | A91 | 10b multicolored | .30 | .25 |
| 544 | A91 | 85b multicolored | .45 | .45 |
| 545 | A91 | 1.10d multicolored | .60 | .60 |
| 546 | A91 | 1.50d multicolored | .70 | .70 |
| | | *Nos. 543-546 (4)* | 2.05 | 2.00 |

UN Decade for Women — A92

Design: 1d, 1.25d, Woman working in office.

**1985, Mar. 11**
| | | | | |
|---|---|---|---|---|
| 547 | A92 | 60b multicolored | .30 | .30 |
| 548 | A92 | 85b multicolored | .45 | .45 |
| 549 | A92 | 1d multicolored | .60 | .60 |
| 550 | A92 | 1.25d multicolored | .65 | .65 |
| | | *Nos. 547-550 (4)* | 2.00 | 2.00 |

Audubon Birth Bicent. — A93

Illustrations of North American bird species by John J. Audubon (1785-1851): 60b, Cathartes aura. 85b, Anhinga anhinga. 1.50d, Butoroides striatus. 5d, Aix sponsa. 10d, Gavia immer.

**1985, July 15**
| | | | | |
|---|---|---|---|---|
| 551 | A93 | 60b multicolored | 1.60 | .75 |
| 552 | A93 | 85b multicolored | 2.00 | 1.50 |
| 553 | A93 | 1.50d multicolored | 2.25 | 2.60 |
| 554 | A93 | 5d multicolored | 3.50 | 4.50 |
| | | *Nos. 551-554 (4)* | 9.35 | 9.35 |

**Souvenir Sheet**
| | | | | |
|---|---|---|---|---|
| 555 | A93 | 10d multicolored | 8.50 | 8.50 |

Queen Mother, 85th Birthday — A94

85b, Inspecting troops. 3d, Portrait. 5d, Portrait, diff.
10d, On parade with Prince Charles.

**1985, July 24**
| | | | | |
|---|---|---|---|---|
| 556 | A94 | 85b multicolored | .45 | .45 |
| 557 | A94 | 3d multicolored | 1.40 | 1.40 |
| 558 | A94 | 5d multicolored | 2.40 | 2.40 |
| | | *Nos. 556-558 (3)* | 4.25 | 4.25 |

**Souvenir Sheet**
| | | | | |
|---|---|---|---|---|
| 559 | A94 | 10d multicolored | 5.00 | 5.00 |

Life on the Mississippi, by Mark Twain (1835-1910) A95

Walt Disney characters: 60b, Portrait. 85b, Treasure. 1.50d, Helm of Calamity Jane. 2d, Antebellum Mansion, Missouri Shore. 2.35d, Music. 2.50d, Measuring Channel Depth, Natchez. 3d, Card Game aboard the Gold Dust. 5d, Statue. No. 568, Landing, St. Louis. No. 569, Goofy.

The 60b, 85b, 2.35d, 5d and No. 569 show scenes from "Faithful John" by the brothers Grimm.

**1985, Oct. 30**
| | | | | |
|---|---|---|---|---|
| 560 | A95 | 60b multicolored | .80 | .80 |
| 561 | A95 | 85b multicolored | 1.00 | 1.00 |
| 562 | A95 | 1.50d multicolored | 2.10 | 2.10 |
| 563 | A95 | 2d multicolored | 2.25 | 2.25 |
| 564 | A95 | 2.35d multicolored | 2.25 | 2.25 |
| 565 | A95 | 2.50d multicolored | 2.75 | 2.75 |
| 566 | A95 | 3d multicolored | 3.00 | 3.00 |
| 567 | A95 | 5d multicolored | 4.00 | 4.00 |
| | | *Nos. 560-567 (8)* | 18.15 | 18.15 |

**Souvenir Sheet**
| | | | | |
|---|---|---|---|---|
| 568 | A95 | 10d multicolored | 10.00 | 10.00 |
| 569 | A95 | 10d multicolored | 10.00 | 10.00 |

**Nos. 508-514 Ovptd. "GOLD MEDALIST" or "GOLD MEDAL," Name of Winner and Country**

60b, Claudia Losch, West Germany, women's shot put. 85b, Ulrike Meyfarth, West Germany, women's high jump. 90b, Pasquale Passarelli, West Germany, 126-pound Greco-Roman wrestling. 1d, Li Ning, China, men's gymnastic floor exercises. 1.25d, Michael Gross, West Germany, men's 100-meter butterfly and 200-meter freestyle swimming. 2d, Sylvie Bernier, Canada, women's springboard diving. 5d, US, Star Class yachting.

**1985, Nov. 11    Perf. 14**
| | | | | |
|---|---|---|---|---|
| 570 | A86 | 60b multicolored | .60 | .30 |
| 571 | A86 | 85b multicolored | .70 | .40 |
| 572 | A86 | 90b multicolored | .75 | .45 |
| 573 | A86 | 1d multicolored | .80 | .50 |
| 574 | A86 | 1.25d multicolored | 1.00 | .65 |
| 575 | A86 | 2d multicolored | 1.25 | 1.00 |
| | | *Nos. 570-575 (6)* | 5.10 | 3.30 |

**Souvenir Sheet**
| | | | | |
|---|---|---|---|---|
| 576 | A86 | 5d multicolored | 2.60 | 2.60 |

UN 40th Anniv. — A97

Views of Banjul: 85b, Independence Stadium. 2d, Central Bank. 4d, Port. 6d, Oyster Creek Bridge.

**1985, Nov. 15**
| | | | | |
|---|---|---|---|---|
| 577 | A97 | 85b multicolored | .65 | .65 |
| 578 | A97 | 2d multicolored | 1.50 | 1.50 |
| 579 | A97 | 4d multicolored | 3.75 | 3.75 |
| 580 | A97 | 6d multicolored | 5.00 | 5.00 |
| | | *Nos. 577-580 (4)* | 10.90 | 10.90 |

Natl. independence, 20th anniv.

UN FAO, 40th Anniv. — A98

**1985, Nov. 15**
| | | | | |
|---|---|---|---|---|
| 581 | A98 | 60b Corn | .80 | .80 |
| 582 | A98 | 1.10d Paddy | 1.25 | 1.25 |
| 583 | A98 | 3d Cow, calf | 3.50 | 3.50 |
| 584 | A98 | 5d Fruit | 4.50 | 4.50 |
| | | *Nos. 581-584 (4)* | 10.05 | 10.05 |

Diocese of Gambia and Guinea, 50th Anniv. — A99

Designs: 60b, Fishermen, Fotoba, Guinea. 85b, St. Mary's Primary School, Banjul. 1.10d, St. Mary's Cathedral, Banjul. 1.50d, Mobile Dispensary at Christy, Kunda, 1935-45.

**1985, Dec. 24**

| | | | | |
|---|---|---|---|---|
| 585 | A99 | 60b multicolored | .35 | .30 |
| 586 | A99 | 85b multicolored | .60 | .45 |
| 587 | A99 | 1.10d multicolored | .65 | .60 |
| 588 | A99 | 1.50d multicolored | 1.00 | .90 |
| | | Nos. 585-588 (4) | 2.60 | 2.25 |

Girl Guides, 75th Anniv. — A100

60b, Application, horiz. 85b, 2nd Bathurst, horiz. 1.50d, Lady Baden-Powell. 5d, Rosamond Fowlis, leader. 10d, Guides.

**1985, Dec. 27**

| | | | | |
|---|---|---|---|---|
| 589 | A100 | 60b multicolored | .35 | .35 |
| 590 | A100 | 85b multicolored | .55 | .55 |
| 591 | A100 | 1.50d multicolored | 1.10 | 1.10 |
| 592 | A100 | 5d multicolored | 3.50 | 3.50 |
| | | Nos. 589-592 (4) | 5.50 | 5.50 |

**Souvenir Sheet**

| | | | | |
|---|---|---|---|---|
| 593 | A100 | 10d multicolored | 6.50 | 6.50 |

Christmas — A101

Painting details: 60b, Virgin and Child, by Dirck Bouts (c. 1400-1475). 85b, The Annunciation, by Robert Campin (c. 1378-1444). 1.50d, Adoration of the Shepherds, by Gerard David (c. 1460-1523). 5d, The Nativity, by Gerard David. 10d, Adoration of the Magi, by Hieronymus Bosch (1450-1516).

**1985, Dec. 27**                                         *Perf. 15*

| | | | | |
|---|---|---|---|---|
| 594 | A101 | 60b multicolored | .30 | .25 |
| 595 | A101 | 85b multicolored | .40 | .40 |
| 596 | A101 | 1.50d multicolored | .80 | .80 |
| 597 | A101 | 5d multicolored | 1.50 | 1.50 |
| | | Nos. 594-597 (4) | 3.00 | 2.95 |

**Souvenir Sheet**

| | | | | |
|---|---|---|---|---|
| 598 | A101 | 10d multicolored | 5.25 | 5.25 |

Intl. Youth Year — A102

**1985, Dec. 31**                                         *Perf. 14*

| | | | | |
|---|---|---|---|---|
| 599 | A102 | 60b Mother's helper | .30 | .30 |
| 600 | A102 | 85b Wrestling | .45 | .45 |
| 601 | A102 | 1.10d Griot storyteller | .55 | 1.00 |
| 602 | A102 | 1.50d Crocodile pool | .90 | 1.25 |
| | | Nos. 599-602 (4) | 2.20 | 3.00 |

**Souvenir Sheet**

| | | | | |
|---|---|---|---|---|
| 603 | A102 | 5d Cow herder | 3.00 | 3.00 |

A103

Halley's Comet A104

---

Designs: 10b, Maria Mitchell (1818-1889), American astronomer, Kitt Peak Natl. Observatory, Papago Indian Reservation, Arizona. 20b, Apollo 11, Neil Armstrong steps on moon, 1969. 75b, Skylab 4, Kohoutek Comet, 1973. 1d, NASA Infrared Astronomical Satellite, 1983. 2d, Comet sighting, 1577, Turkish art. No. 609, NASA Intl. Cometary Explorer satellite. No. 610, Comet.

**1986, Mar.**

| | | | | |
|---|---|---|---|---|
| 604 | A103 | 10b multicolored | .35 | .25 |
| 605 | A103 | 20b multicolored | .65 | .25 |
| 606 | A103 | 75b multicolored | .90 | .55 |
| 607 | A103 | 1d multicolored | 1.25 | .80 |
| 608 | A103 | 2d multicolored | 1.75 | 1.40 |
| 609 | A103 | 10d multicolored | 4.75 | 5.00 |
| | | Nos. 604-609 (6) | 9.65 | 8.25 |

**Souvenir Sheet**

| | | | | |
|---|---|---|---|---|
| 610 | A104 | 10d multicolored | 7.50 | 7.50 |

For overprints see Nos. 650-656.

**Queen Elizabeth II, 60th Birthday**
Common Design Type

Designs: 1d, Royal family at Royal Tournament, 1936. 2.50d, Christening, 1983. No. 613, State visit to West Germany, 1978. No. 614, At Balmoral, 1935.

**1986, Apr. 21**

| | | | | |
|---|---|---|---|---|
| 611 | CD339 | 1d lt yel bis & blk | .50 | .40 |
| 612 | CD339 | 2.50d pale grn & multi | 1.00 | .75 |
| 613 | CD339 | 10d dl lil & multi | 3.00 | 3.00 |
| | | Nos. 611-613 (3) | 4.50 | 4.15 |

**Souvenir Sheet**

| | | | | |
|---|---|---|---|---|
| 614 | CD339 | 10d tan & black | 3.75 | 3.75 |

1986 World Cup Soccer Championships, Mexico — A105

75b, Block. 1d, Kneeing the ball. 2.50d, Kick. No. 618, Heading the ball. No. 619, Goalie catching ball.

**1986, May 2**

| | | | | |
|---|---|---|---|---|
| 615 | A105 | 75b multicolored | .60 | .60 |
| 616 | A105 | 1d multicolored | .85 | .85 |
| 617 | A105 | 2.50d multicolored | 2.50 | 2.50 |
| 618 | A105 | 5d multicolored | 6.00 | 6.00 |
| | | Nos. 615-618 (4) | 9.95 | 9.95 |

**Souvenir Sheet**

| | | | | |
|---|---|---|---|---|
| 619 | A105 | 10d multicolored | 10.00 | 10.00 |

For overprints see Nos. 639-643.

AMERIPEX '86 — A106

Exhibition emblem, automobiles and flags: 25b, 1986 Mercedes 500, Germany. 75b, 1935 Cord 810, US. 1d, 1957 Borgward Isabella Coupe, Germany. 1.25d, 1985-6 Lamborghini Countach, Italy. 2d, 1955 Ford Thunderbird, US. 2.25d, 1956 Citroen DS19, France. 5d, 1936 Bugatti Atlante, France. 10d, 1936 Horch 853, Germany. No. 628, 1913 Benz 8/20, Germany. No. 629, 1924 Steiger 10/50, Germany.

**1986, May 22**                                          *Perf. 15*

| | | | | |
|---|---|---|---|---|
| 620 | A106 | 25b multi | .30 | .25 |
| 621 | A106 | 75b multi | .40 | .35 |
| 622 | A106 | 1d multi | .45 | .55 |
| 623 | A106 | 1.25d multi | .50 | .65 |
| 624 | A106 | 2d multi | .60 | 1.00 |
| 625 | A106 | 2.25d multi | .70 | 1.10 |
| 626 | A106 | 5d multi | 1.00 | 2.25 |
| 627 | A106 | 10d multi | 2.50 | 4.00 |
| | | Nos. 620-627 (8) | 6.45 | 10.15 |

**Souvenir Sheets**

| | | | | |
|---|---|---|---|---|
| 628 | A106 | 12d multi | 4.75 | 4.75 |
| 629 | A106 | 12d multi | 4.75 | 4.75 |

Karl Benz automobile cent.

Statue of Liberty, Cent. — A107

---

Statue and famous emigrants: 20b, John Jacob Astor (1763-1848), financier. 1d, Jacob Riis (1849-1914), journalist. 1.25d, Igor Sikorsky (1889-1972), aeronautics engineer. 5d, Charles Boyer (1899-1978), actor. 10d, Statue, vert.

**1986, June 10**                                         *Perf. 14*

| | | | | |
|---|---|---|---|---|
| 630 | A107 | 20b multicolored | .30 | .25 |
| 631 | A107 | 1d multicolored | .60 | .60 |
| 632 | A107 | 1.25d multicolored | .65 | .65 |
| 633 | A107 | 5d multicolored | 2.75 | 2.75 |
| | | Nos. 630-633 (4) | 4.30 | 4.25 |

**Souvenir Sheet**

| | | | | |
|---|---|---|---|---|
| 634 | A107 | 10d multicolored | 5.50 | 5.50 |

**Royal Wedding Issue, 1986**
Common Design Type

1d, Engagement of Prince Andrew and Sarah Ferguson. 2.50d, Andrew. 4d, Andrew in flight uniform, other helicopter pilot. 7d, Couple, diff.

**1986, July 23**

| | | | | |
|---|---|---|---|---|
| 635 | CD340 | 1d multi | .45 | .45 |
| 636 | CD340 | 2.50d multi | 1.10 | 1.10 |
| 637 | CD340 | 4d multi | 2.25 | 2.25 |
| | | Nos. 635-637 (3) | 3.80 | 3.80 |

**Souvenir Sheet**

| | | | | |
|---|---|---|---|---|
| 638 | CD340 | 7d multi | 4.00 | 4.00 |

**Nos. 615-619 Overprinted "WINNERS / Argentina 3 / W. Germany 2" in Gold**

**1986, Sept. 16**           *Litho.*           *Perf. 14*

| | | | | |
|---|---|---|---|---|
| 639 | A105 | 75b multicolored | .40 | .40 |
| 640 | A105 | 1d multicolored | .60 | .60 |
| 641 | A105 | 2.50d multicolored | 1.25 | 1.25 |
| 642 | A105 | 10d multicolored | 5.00 | 5.00 |
| | | Nos. 639-642 (4) | 7.25 | 7.25 |

**Souvenir Sheet**

| | | | | |
|---|---|---|---|---|
| 643 | A105 | 10d multicolored | 6.50 | 6.50 |

Christmas, STOCKHOLMIA '86 — A108

Disney characters mailing letters in various countries.

**1986, Nov. 4**                                         *Perf. 11*

| | | | | |
|---|---|---|---|---|
| 644 | A108 | 1d Great Britain | 1.00 | .50 |
| 645 | A108 | 1.25d United States | 1.10 | .70 |
| 646 | A108 | 2d France | 1.75 | 1.25 |
| 647 | A108 | 2.35d Australia | 2.00 | 1.40 |
| 648 | A108 | 5d Germany | 2.25 | 2.25 |
| | | Nos. 644-648 (5) | 8.10 | 6.10 |

**Souvenir Sheet**

| | | | | |
|---|---|---|---|---|
| 649 | A108 | 10d Sweden | 8.25 | 8.25 |

**Nos. 604-610 Ovptd. in Silver**

**1986, Oct. 21**           *Litho.*           *Perf. 14*

| | | | | |
|---|---|---|---|---|
| 650 | A103 | 10b multicolored | .30 | .25 |
| 651 | A103 | 20b multicolored | .65 | .25 |
| 652 | A103 | 75b multicolored | 1.00 | .50 |
| 653 | A103 | 1d multicolored | 1.10 | .60 |
| 654 | A103 | 2d multicolored | 1.40 | 1.50 |
| 655 | A103 | 10d multicolored | 4.25 | 4.50 |
| | | Nos. 650-655 (6) | 8.70 | 7.60 |

**Souvenir Sheet**

| | | | | |
|---|---|---|---|---|
| 656 | A104 | 10d multicolored | 5.00 | 5.00 |

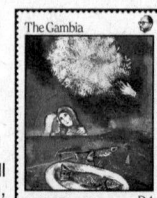

Marc Chagall (1887-1985), Artist — A109

Paintings, ceramicware, sculpture: 75b, Snowing. 85b, The Boat, 1957. 1d, Maternity,

---

1913. 1.25d, The Flute Player. 2.35d, Lovers and the Beast, 1957. 4d, Fishes at Saint Jean. 5d, Entering the Ring, 1968. 10d, Three Acrobats, 1956. No. 665, The Sabbath. No. 666, The Cattle Driver.

**1987, Feb. 6**                                          *Litho.*

| | | | | |
|---|---|---|---|---|
| 657 | A109 | 75b multi | .45 | .45 |
| 658 | A109 | 85b multi | .55 | .30 |
| 659 | A109 | 1d multi | .65 | .40 |
| 660 | A109 | 1.25d multi | .85 | .50 |
| 661 | A109 | 2.35d multi | 1.10 | 1.10 |
| 662 | A109 | 4d multi | 1.75 | 1.75 |
| 663 | A109 | 5d multi | 2.25 | 2.25 |
| 664 | A109 | 10d multi | 4.00 | 2.50 |

**Sizes: 110x95mm, 110x68mm**
*Imperf*

| | | | | |
|---|---|---|---|---|
| 665 | A109 | 12d multi | 5.75 | 5.75 |
| 666 | A109 | 12d multi | 5.75 | 5.75 |
| | | Nos. 657-666 (10) | 23.10 | 20.55 |

Musical Instruments A110

Various instruments from the Mandingo Empire: 75b, Bugarab, tabala. 1d, Balaphong, fiddle. 1.25d, Bolongbato, konting. 10d, Koras. 12d, Sabarrs.

**1987, Jan. 21**           *Litho.*           *Perf. 15*

| | | | | |
|---|---|---|---|---|
| 667 | A110 | 75b multicolored | .30 | .25 |
| 668 | A110 | 1d multicolored | .30 | .30 |
| 669 | A110 | 1.25d multicolored | .35 | .35 |
| 670 | A110 | 10d multicolored | 2.00 | 2.00 |
| | | Nos. 667-670 (4) | 2.95 | 2.90 |

**Souvenir Sheet**

| | | | | |
|---|---|---|---|---|
| 671 | A110 | 12d multicolored | 3.00 | 3.00 |

Nos. 669-670 vert.
For overprints see Nos. 750, 856-860.

America's Cup — A111

20b, America, 1851. 1d, Courageous, 1974. 2.50d, Volunteer, 1887. 10d, Intrepid, 1967. 12d, Australia II, 1983.

**1987, Apr. 3**                                          *Perf. 14*

| | | | | |
|---|---|---|---|---|
| 672 | A111 | 20b multi | .30 | .25 |
| 673 | A111 | 1d multi | .35 | .35 |
| 674 | A111 | 2.50d multi | .90 | .90 |
| 675 | A111 | 10d multi | 4.00 | 4.00 |
| | | Nos. 672-675 (4) | 5.55 | 5.50 |

**Souvenir Sheet**

| | | | | |
|---|---|---|---|---|
| 676 | A111 | 12d multi | 5.75 | 5.75 |

For overprint see No. 751.

Statue of Liberty, Cent. — A112

Photographs of restoration and unveiling in 1986: 1b, Shoulder, torch. 2b, Operation Sail flotilla. 3b, Tall ship, ships. 5b, Luxury liner, aircraft carrier. 50b, Statue's coiffure. 75b, Coiffure, diff. 1d, Workmen scaling statue. 1.25d, Back of statue. 10d, Front of Statue. 12d, Side of statue.

**1987, Apr. 9**                                          *Litho.*

| | | | | |
|---|---|---|---|---|
| 677 | A112 | 1b multicolored | .30 | .25 |
| 678 | A112 | 2b multicolored | .30 | .25 |
| 679 | A112 | 3b multicolored | .30 | .25 |
| 680 | A112 | 5b multicolored | .30 | .25 |
| 681 | A112 | 50b multicolored | .50 | .50 |
| 682 | A112 | 75b multicolored | .70 | .70 |
| 683 | A112 | 1d multicolored | .85 | .85 |
| 684 | A112 | 1.25d multicolored | 1.00 | 1.00 |
| 685 | A112 | 10d multicolored | 5.00 | 5.00 |
| 686 | A112 | 12d multicolored | 5.25 | 5.25 |
| | | Nos. 677-686 (10) | 14.50 | 14.30 |

Nos. 677, 681-686 vert.

Flowers from Abuko
Nature
Reserve — A113

75b, Lantana camara. 1d, Clerodendrum thomsoniae. 1.50d, Haemanthus multiflorus. 1.70d, Gloriosa simplex. 1.75d, Combretum microphyllum. 2.25d, Eulophia guineensis. 5d, Erythrina senegalensis. 15d, Dichrostachys glomerata.

No. 691, Costus spectabilis. No. 691A, Strophanthus preussii.

**1987, May 25**

| | | | | |
|---|---|---|---|---|
| 687 | A113 | 75b multi | .30 | .25 |
| 687A | A113 | 1d multi | .30 | .25 |
| 688 | A113 | 1.50d multi | .45 | .40 |
| 688A | A113 | 1.70d multi | .50 | .45 |
| 689 | A113 | 1.75d multi | .50 | .45 |
| 689A | A113 | 2.25d multi | .65 | .60 |
| 689B | A113 | 5d multi | 1.40 | 1.40 |
| 690 | A113 | 15d multi | 3.25 | 3.25 |
| | | *Nos. 687-690 (8)* | 7.35 | 7.05 |

**Souvenir Sheets**

| | | | | |
|---|---|---|---|---|
| 691 | A113 | 15d shown | 3.75 | 3.75 |
| 691A | A113 | 15d multi | 3.75 | 3.75 |

Nos. 691-691A are continuous designs. For overprint see No. 752.

CAPEX '87 — A115

Various buses.

**1987, June 15**

| | | | | |
|---|---|---|---|---|
| 692 | A115 | 20b multi, vert. | .55 | .25 |
| 693 | A115 | 75b multi | .75 | .25 |
| 694 | A115 | 1d multi | 1.60 | .75 |
| 695 | A115 | 10d multi, vert. | 4.00 | 4.00 |
| | | *Nos. 692-695 (4)* | 6.90 | 5.25 |

**Souvenir Sheet**

| | | | | |
|---|---|---|---|---|
| 696 | A115 | 12d multi | 7.00 | 7.00 |

For overprint see No. 749.

1988 Summer
Olympics,
Seoul — A116

50b, Women's basketball. 1d, Volleyball. 3d, Field hockey. 10d, Handball. 15d, Soccer.

**1987, July 3**

| | | | | |
|---|---|---|---|---|
| 697 | A116 | 50b multicolored | .30 | .25 |
| 698 | A116 | 1d multicolored | .60 | .30 |
| 699 | A116 | 3d multicolored | 1.10 | .90 |
| 700 | A116 | 10d multicolored | 3.50 | 3.00 |
| | | *Nos. 697-700 (4)* | 5.50 | 4.45 |

**Souvenir Sheet**

| | | | | |
|---|---|---|---|---|
| 701 | A116 | 15d multi | 5.00 | 5.00 |

Nos. 697-698 vert.

A117

The Twelve Days of Christmas,
Medieval Counting Song — A118

Designs: 20b, Partridge in a pear tree. 40b, 2 turtle doves. 60b, 3 French hens. 75b, 4 calling birds. 1d, 5 golden rings. 1.25d, 6 geese a-laying. 1.50d, 7 swans a-swimming.

---

2d, 8 maids a-milking. 3d, 9 ladies dancing. 5d, 10 lords a-leaping. 10d, 11 pipers piping. 12d, 12 drummers drumming.

**Miniature Sheet**

**1987, Nov. 2    Litho.    Perf. 14**

| | | | | |
|---|---|---|---|---|
| 702 | | Sheet of 12 | 14.50 | 14.50 |
| a. | A117 | 20b multicolored | .30 | .25 |
| b. | A117 | 40b multicolored | .30 | .25 |
| c. | A117 | 60b multicolored | .30 | .25 |
| d. | A117 | 75b multicolored | .30 | .25 |
| e. | A117 | 1d multicolored | .40 | .40 |
| f. | A117 | 1.25d multicolored | .45 | .45 |
| g. | A117 | 1.50d multicolored | .60 | .60 |
| h. | A117 | 2d multicolored | .75 | .75 |
| i. | A117 | 3d multicolored | 1.25 | 1.25 |
| j. | A117 | 5d multicolored | 1.90 | 1.90 |
| k. | A117 | 10d multicolored | 3.50 | 3.50 |
| l. | A117 | 12d multicolored | 4.25 | 4.25 |

**Souvenir Sheet**

| | | | | |
|---|---|---|---|---|
| 703 | A118 | 15d multi | 4.50 | 4.50 |

16th Boy Scout
Jamboree,
Australia, 1987-
88 — A119

75b, Singing around campfire. 1d, Nature study, African katydid. 1.25d, Bird watching, red-tailed tropicbird. 12d, Boarding bus. 15d, Nature study.

**1987, Nov. 9**

| | | | | |
|---|---|---|---|---|
| 704 | A119 | 75b multicolored | .55 | .30 |
| 705 | A119 | 1d multicolored | .85 | .40 |
| 706 | A119 | 1.25d multicolored | 1.60 | 1.00 |
| 707 | A119 | 12d multicolored | 4.75 | 4.75 |
| | | *Nos. 704-707 (4)* | 7.75 | 6.45 |

**Souvenir Sheet**

| | | | | |
|---|---|---|---|---|
| 708 | A119 | 15d multicolored | 7.75 | 7.75 |

Mickey Mouse, 60th Anniv.
A120

Disney animated characters and historic locomotives: 60b, Richard Trevithick's locomotive, 1804. 75b, Empire State Express 999, 1893. 1d, George Stephenson's Rocket, 1829. 1.25d, Santa Fe Mountain 2-10-2, 1920. 2d, Class GG-1 Pennsylvania, 1933. 5d, Stourbridge Lion, 1829. 10d, Best Friend of Charleston, 1830. 12d, M10001 Union Pacific, 1934. No. 717, Tres Grande Vitesse-SNCF, 1981, France. No. 718, The General, Western & Atlantic, 1855.

**1987, Dec. 9    Litho.    Perf. 14x13½**

| | | | | |
|---|---|---|---|---|
| 709 | A120 | 60b multicolored | .35 | .35 |
| 710 | A120 | 75b multicolored | .40 | .40 |
| 711 | A120 | 1d multicolored | .50 | .50 |
| 712 | A120 | 1.25d multicolored | .60 | .60 |
| 713 | A120 | 2d multicolored | .90 | .90 |
| 714 | A120 | 5d multicolored | 2.00 | 2.00 |
| 715 | A120 | 10d multicolored | 3.75 | 3.75 |
| 716 | A120 | 12d multicolored | 4.25 | 4.25 |
| | | *Nos. 709-716 (8)* | 12.75 | 12.75 |

**Souvenir Sheets**

| | | | | |
|---|---|---|---|---|
| 717 | A120 | 15d multicolored | 6.25 | 6.25 |
| 718 | A120 | 15d multicolored | 6.25 | 6.25 |

Fauna and
Flora — A121

50b, Duiker, acacia. 75b, Red-billed hornbill, casuarina. 90b, West African dwarf crocodile, rice. 1d, Leopard, papyrus. 1.25d, Crested cranes, millet. 2d, Waterbuck, baobab tree. 3d, Oribi, Senegal palm. 5d, Hippopotamus, papaya.
No. 727, Great white pelican. No. 728, Red-throated bee-eater.

**1988, Feb. 9    Litho.    Perf. 15**

| | | | | |
|---|---|---|---|---|
| 719 | A121 | 50b multicolored | .30 | .25 |
| 720 | A121 | 75b multicolored | .90 | .90 |
| 721 | A121 | 90b multicolored | .45 | .45 |
| 722 | A121 | 1d multicolored | .45 | .45 |
| 723 | A121 | 1.25d multicolored | .90 | .90 |
| 724 | A121 | 2d multicolored | .50 | .50 |
| 725 | A121 | 3d multicolored | .75 | .75 |
| 726 | A121 | 5d multicolored | 1.25 | 1.25 |
| | | *Nos. 719-726 (8)* | 5.50 | 5.45 |

**Souvenir Sheets**

| | | | | |
|---|---|---|---|---|
| 727 | A121 | 12d multicolored | 2.25 | 2.25 |
| 728 | A121 | 12d multicolored | 2.25 | 2.25 |

Nos. 720, 722, 724, 726 and 728 vert.

---

40th Wedding Anniv. of
Queen Elizabeth II and
Prince Philip — A122

75b, Wedding portrait, 1947. 1d, Couple at leisure. 3d, Wedding portrait, diff. 10d, Couple, c. 1987.
15d, Wedding party.

**1988, Mar. 15    Perf. 14**

| | | | | |
|---|---|---|---|---|
| 729 | A122 | 75b multicolored | .30 | .25 |
| 730 | A122 | 1d multicolored | .30 | .25 |
| 731 | A122 | 3d multicolored | .75 | .75 |
| 732 | A122 | 10d multicolored | 3.00 | 3.00 |
| | | *Nos. 729-732 (4)* | 4.35 | 4.25 |

**Souvenir Sheet**

| | | | | |
|---|---|---|---|---|
| 733 | A122 | 15d multicolored | 3.25 | 3.25 |

1988 Summer
Olympics,
Seoul — A123

1d, Archery, vert. 1.25d, Boxing, vert. 5d, Gymnastics, vert. 10d, 100-Meter sprint. 15d, Award ceremony, Olympic stadium.

**1988, May 3    Litho.    Perf. 14**

| | | | | |
|---|---|---|---|---|
| 734 | A123 | 1d multi | .30 | .25 |
| 735 | A123 | 1.25d multi | .30 | .25 |
| 736 | A123 | 5d multi | 1.50 | 1.25 |
| 737 | A123 | 10d multi | 3.00 | 2.50 |
| | | *Nos. 734-737 (4)* | 5.10 | 4.25 |

**Souvenir Sheet**

| | | | | |
|---|---|---|---|---|
| 738 | A123 | 15d multi | 3.75 | 3.75 |

Anniversaries & Events — A124

Designs: 50b, Red Cross flag. 75b, Friendship 7, piloted by John Glenn, 1963. 1d, British Airways Concorde jet. 1.25d, Spirit of St. Louis, piloted by Charles Lindbergh, 1927. 2d, X-15, piloted by Major William Knight, 1967. 3d, Bell X-1, piloted by Capt. Charles Yeager, 1947. 10d, Spanish galleon, British warship, 1588. 12d, The Titanic. No. 747, Kangaroo and joey. No. 748, Cathedral, modern church, vert.

**1988, May 15**

| | | | | |
|---|---|---|---|---|
| 739 | A124 | 50b multicolored | 1.10 | .55 |
| 740 | A124 | 75b multicolored | .70 | .60 |
| 741 | A124 | 1d multicolored | 2.25 | 1.00 |
| 742 | A124 | 1.25d multicolored | 1.10 | 1.10 |
| 743 | A124 | 2d multicolored | 1.60 | 1.60 |
| 744 | A124 | 3d multicolored | 1.90 | 1.90 |
| 745 | A124 | 10d multicolored | 3.75 | 3.75 |
| 746 | A124 | 12d multicolored | 6.00 | 6.00 |
| | | *Nos. 739-746 (8)* | 18.40 | 16.50 |

**Souvenir Sheets**

| | | | | |
|---|---|---|---|---|
| 747 | A124 | 15d multicolored | 3.75 | 3.75 |
| 748 | A124 | 15d multicolored | 3.75 | 3.75 |

Intl. Red Cross, 125th anniv. (50b); first American in space, 25th anniv. in 1987 (75b); 1st London-New York scheduled Concorde flight, 10th anniv. in 1987 (1d); first solo transatlantic flight, 60th anniv. in 1987 (1.25d); fastest speed flown, 6.72 Mach, 20th anniv. in 1987 (2d); 1st supersonic flight, 40th anniv. in 1987 (3d); defeat of the Spanish Armada, 400th anniv. (10d); maiden voyage of the Titanic, 75th anniv. in 1987 (12d); founding of Australia, bicentennial (No. 747); and founding of Berlin, 750th anniv. in 1987 (No. 748).

**Nos. 694, 670, 675 and 690 Ovptd. for Philatelic Exhibitions**

a    b

---

c    d

**1988, Apr. 19    Litho.    Perf. 14, 15**

| | | | | |
|---|---|---|---|---|
| 749 | A115(a) | 1d multi | .50 | .50 |
| 750 | A110(b) | 10d multi | 3.00 | 3.00 |
| 751 | A111(c) | 10d multi | 3.00 | 3.00 |
| 752 | A113(d) | 15d multi | 3.50 | 3.50 |
| | | *Nos. 749-752 (4)* | 10.00 | 10.00 |

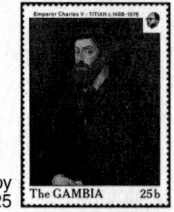

Paintings by
Titian — A125

Designs: 25b, Emperor Charles V, 1549. 50b, St. Margaret and the Dragon, 1565. 60b, Ranuccio Farnese, 1542. 75b, Tarquin and Lucretia, 1570. 1d, The Knight of Malta, c. 1550. 5d, Spain Succouring Faith, 1571. 10d, Doge Francesco Venier, 1555. 12d, Doge Grimani Before the Faith, c. 1555-1576. No. 761, Jealous Husband, 1511. No. 762, Venus Blindfolding Cupid, 1560.

**1988, July 7    Litho.    Perf. 13½x14**

| | | | | |
|---|---|---|---|---|
| 753 | A125 | 25b multicolored | .30 | .25 |
| 754 | A125 | 50b multicolored | .50 | .50 |
| 755 | A125 | 60b multicolored | .50 | .50 |
| 756 | A125 | 75b multicolored | .70 | .70 |
| 757 | A125 | 1d multicolored | .80 | .80 |
| 758 | A125 | 5d multicolored | 2.75 | 2.75 |
| 759 | A125 | 10d multicolored | 4.50 | 4.50 |
| 760 | A125 | 12d multicolored | 5.00 | 5.00 |
| | | *Nos. 753-760 (8)* | 15.05 | 15.00 |

**Souvenir Sheets**

| | | | | |
|---|---|---|---|---|
| 761 | A125 | 15d multicolored | 3.75 | 3.75 |
| 762 | A125 | 15d multicolored | 3.75 | 3.75 |

Tribute to John F.
Kennedy — A126

75b, Sailing. 1d, Peace Corps enactment. 1.25d, Public address, vert. 12d, Grave, Arlington Natl. Cemetery. 15d, Kennedy, vert.

**1988, Sept. 1    Litho.    Perf. 14**

| | | | | |
|---|---|---|---|---|
| 763 | A126 | 75b multicolored | .30 | .25 |
| 764 | A126 | 1d multicolored | .30 | .25 |
| 765 | A126 | 1.25d multicolored | .30 | .25 |
| 766 | A126 | 12d multicolored | 2.50 | 2.50 |
| | | *Nos. 763-766 (4)* | 3.40 | 3.25 |

**Souvenir Sheet**

| | | | | |
|---|---|---|---|---|
| 767 | A126 | 15d multicolored | 4.00 | 4.00 |

Entertainers — A127

20b, Emmett Lee Kelly (1898-1979), clown. 1d, Gambia Natl. Ensemble. 1.25d, Jackie Gleason (1916-87), comedian, & The Honeymooners cast. 1.50d, Stan Laurel (1890-1965) & Oliver Hardy (1892-1957), film comedy team. 2.50d, Yul Brynner (c. 1920-85), actor. 3d, Cary Grant (1904-86), actor. 10d, Danny Kaye (1913-87), comedian, actor. 20d, Charlie Chaplin (1889-1977), comedian, actor. No. 776, Harpo (1893-1964), Chico (1891-1961), Zeppo (1901-79) & Groucho (1890-1977) Marx, comedy team. No. 777, Fred Astaire (1899-1987) & Rita Hayworth (1918-87), dancers & film stars. Nos. 768-775 vert.

**1988, Nov. 9    Litho.**

| | | | | |
|---|---|---|---|---|
| 768 | A127 | 20b multi | .30 | .25 |
| 769 | A127 | 1d multi | .50 | .50 |
| 770 | A127 | 1.25d multi | .60 | .60 |

| | | | | |
|---|---|---|---|---|
| 771 | A127 | 1.50d multi | .65 | .65 |
| 772 | A127 | 2.50d multi | 1.00 | 1.00 |
| 773 | A127 | 3d multi | 1.25 | 1.25 |
| 774 | A127 | 10d multi | 3.75 | 3.75 |
| 775 | A127 | 20d multi | 6.50 | 6.50 |
| | *Nos. 768-775 (8)* | | 14.55 | 14.50 |

**Souvenir Sheets**

| | | | | |
|---|---|---|---|---|
| 776 | A127 | 15d multi | 7.00 | 7.00 |
| 777 | A127 | 15d multi | 7.00 | 7.00 |

Kelly's name is spelled incorrectly; Brynner's and Grant's dates are incorrect.

Zeppelin LZ7 Deutschland, 1910 — A128

Transportation innovations: 50b, Stephenson's Locomotion, 1825. 75b, General Motors Sun Racer, 1987. 1d, Sprague's Premiere, 1888. 1.25d, Gold Rush bicycle, 1986. 2.50d, 1st Liquid-fuel rocket, invented by Robert Goddard, 1925. 10d, Orukter Amphibolos, 1805. 12d, Sovereign of the Seas, 1988. No. 786, USS Nautilus, 1954, vert. No. 787, Fulton's Nautilus, early 19th cent.

**1988, Nov. 21     Litho.     Perf. 14**

| | | | | |
|---|---|---|---|---|
| 778 | A128 | 25b multi | .55 | .25 |
| 779 | A128 | 50b multi | .95 | .40 |
| 780 | A128 | 75b multi | 1.00 | .55 |
| 781 | A128 | 1d multi | 1.40 | .70 |
| 782 | A128 | 1.25d multi | 1.40 | .75 |
| 783 | A128 | 2.50d multi | 2.10 | 1.25 |
| 784 | A128 | 10d multi | 5.50 | 3.50 |
| 785 | A128 | 12d multi | 6.25 | 4.00 |
| | *Nos. 778-785 (8)* | | 19.15 | 11.40 |

**Souvenir Sheets**

| | | | | |
|---|---|---|---|---|
| 786 | A128 | 15d multi | 5.00 | 5.00 |
| 787 | A128 | 15d multi | 5.00 | 5.00 |

Discovery of America, 500th Anniv. (in 1992) — A129

Designs: 50b, Caravel, Henry the Navigator (1394-1460), Prince of Portugal, and coat of arms, vert. 75b, Jesse Ramsden's sextant, map of Africa, arms, vert. 1d, Hour glass, 15th cent., and map, vert. 1.25d, Henry and Vasco da Gama, vert. 2.50d, Da Gama and 15th cent. caravel, vert. 5d, Mungo Park (1771-1806), Scottish explorer, arms and map of Gambia River. 10d, Map of west African coast, 1563. 12d, Portuguese caravel, arms. No. 796, Caravel off the Gambian coast, 15th cent., vert. No. 797, European ship off Gambian coast, 15th cent., vert.

**1988, Dec. 1     Litho.     Perf. 14**

| | | | | |
|---|---|---|---|---|
| 788 | A129 | 50b multi | .85 | .60 |
| 789 | A129 | 75b multi | 1.00 | .70 |
| 790 | A129 | 1d multi | 1.25 | .80 |
| 791 | A129 | 1.25d multi | 1.40 | .90 |
| 792 | A129 | 2.50d multi | 1.75 | 1.50 |
| 793 | A129 | 5d shown | 3.00 | 2.50 |
| 794 | A129 | 10d multi | 5.00 | 4.00 |
| 795 | A129 | 12d multi | 5.25 | 4.50 |
| | *Nos. 788-795 (8)* | | 19.50 | 15.50 |

**Souvenir Sheets**

| | | | | |
|---|---|---|---|---|
| 796 | A129 | 15d multi | 5.00 | 5.00 |
| 797 | A129 | 15d multi | 5.00 | 5.00 |

Space Achievements A130

Galileo and: 50b, Futuristic aerospace plane and Ernst Mach (1838-1916), Austrian physicist, vert. 75b, OAO III astronomical satellite and Niels Bohr (1885-1962), Danish physicist and Nobel lauerate in 1922, vert. 1d, NASA space shuttle, future space station and Robert Goddard (1882-1945), American rocket scientist. 1.25d, Flyby of probe past Jupiter, 1979, and Edward Barnard (1857-1923), American astronomer who discovered Jupiter's 5th satellite in 1892. 2d, Hubble Space Telescope and George Hale (1868-1938), American astronomer, vert. 3d, Precision measurement of the distance between the Earth and the Moon by laser and Albert A. Michelson (1852-1931), Nobel lauerate in 1907 for research on the speed of light. 10d, HEAO-2 Einstein orbital satellite and Albert Einstein, vert. 20d, Voyager, 1st circumnavigation of the world without refueling, and the Wright Brothers. No. 806, Moon Ganymede passing the Great Red

Spot on Jupiter. No. 807, Apollo and Neil Armstrong, 1st man on the Moon, July 20, 1969, vert.

**1988, Dec. 12            Perf. 14**

| | | | | |
|---|---|---|---|---|
| 798 | A130 | 50b multi | .50 | .30 |
| 799 | A130 | 75b multi | .60 | .40 |
| 800 | A130 | 1d multi | .75 | .55 |
| 801 | A130 | 1.25d multi | .90 | .75 |
| 802 | A130 | 2d multi | 1.25 | 1.10 |
| 803 | A130 | 3d multi | 1.50 | 1.50 |
| 804 | A130 | 10d multi | 3.50 | 3.50 |
| 805 | A130 | 20d multi | 6.00 | 6.00 |
| | *Nos. 798-805 (8)* | | 15.00 | 14.10 |

**Souvenir Sheets**

| | | | | |
|---|---|---|---|---|
| 806 | A130 | 15d multi | 4.75 | 4.75 |
| 807 | A130 | 15d multi | 4.75 | 4.75 |

350th anniv. of the publication of Discourses, by Galileo.

Army Day — A131

75b, Troops on parade. 1d, Regimental flags. 1.25d, Drummer, vert. 10d, Atlantic Shooting Cup winner, vert. 15d, Assault course, vert. 20d, 105-mm gun.

**1989, Feb. 10     Litho.     Perf. 14**

| | | | | |
|---|---|---|---|---|
| 808 | A131 | 75b multicolored | .30 | .30 |
| 809 | A131 | 1d multicolored | .35 | .35 |
| 810 | A131 | 1.25d multicolored | .45 | .45 |
| 811 | A131 | 10d multicolored | 2.25 | 2.25 |
| 812 | A131 | 15d multicolored | 3.25 | 3.25 |
| 813 | A131 | 20d multicolored | 4.00 | 4.00 |
| | *Nos. 808-813 (6)* | | 10.60 | 10.60 |

**Miniature Sheet**

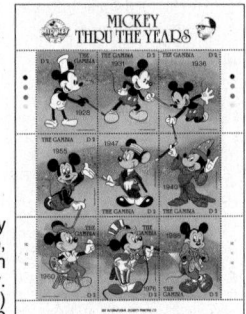

Mickey Mouse, 60th Anniv. (in 1988) A132

Mickey Mouse through the years: a, 1928. b, 1931. c, 1936. d, 1955. e, 1947. f, 1940. g, 1960. h, 1976. i, 1988. 15d, Birthday party.

**1989, Apr. 6     Litho.     Perf. 13x13½**

| | | | | |
|---|---|---|---|---|
| 814 | A132 | Sheet of 9 | 10.00 | 10.00 |
| *a.-i.* | | 2d any single | 1.00 | .90 |

**Size: 139x110mm**

*Imperf*

| | | | | |
|---|---|---|---|---|
| 815 | A132 | 15d multi | 6.00 | 6.00 |

Easter — A133

Paintings by Rubens: 50b, Le Coup de Lance, 1620. 75b, The Flagellation of Christ, 1617. 1d, The Lamentation for Christ, c. 1617. 1.25d, Descent from the Cross, c. 1611. 2d, The Holy Trinity, c. 1617. 5d, The Doubting Thomas. 10d, Lamentation over Christ, 1614. 12d, Lamentation over Christ with the Virgin and St. John, c. 1613. No. 824, The Last Supper, c. 1631. No. 825, The Raising of the Cross, c. 1610.

**1989, Apr. 14        Perf. 13½x14**

| | | | | |
|---|---|---|---|---|
| 816 | A133 | 50b multi | .40 | .25 |
| 817 | A133 | 75b multi | .50 | .35 |
| 818 | A133 | 1d multi | .50 | .35 |
| 819 | A133 | 1.25d multi | .55 | .40 |
| 820 | A133 | 2d multi | .90 | .70 |
| 821 | A133 | 5d multi | 1.60 | 1.50 |
| 822 | A133 | 10d multi | 2.50 | 2.50 |
| 823 | A133 | 12d multi | 2.75 | 2.75 |
| | *Nos. 816-823 (8)* | | 9.70 | 8.80 |

**Souvenir Sheets**

| | | | | |
|---|---|---|---|---|
| 824 | A133 | 15d multi | 4.25 | 4.25 |
| 825 | A133 | 15d multi | 4.25 | 4.25 |

Indigenous Birds — A134

20b, African emerald cuckoo. 60b, Gray-headed bush shrike. 75b, Crowned crane. 1d, Secretary bird. 2d, Red-billed hornbill. 5d, Superb sunbird. 10d, Little owl. 12d, Bateleur eagle.
No. 834, Red-billed fire finch. No. 835, Ostriches.

**1989, Apr. 24          Perf. 14**

| | | | | |
|---|---|---|---|---|
| 826 | A134 | 20b multicolored | .90 | .30 |
| 827 | A134 | 60b multicolored | 1.25 | .55 |
| 828 | A134 | 75b multicolored | 1.40 | .60 |
| 829 | A134 | 1d multicolored | 1.60 | .70 |
| 830 | A134 | 2d multicolored | 1.75 | 1.00 |
| 831 | A134 | 5d multicolored | 3.00 | 3.00 |
| 832 | A134 | 10d multicolored | 5.00 | 4.00 |
| 833 | A134 | 12d multicolored | 5.75 | 4.50 |
| | *Nos. 826-833 (8)* | | 20.65 | 14.65 |

**Souvenir Sheets**

| | | | | |
|---|---|---|---|---|
| 834 | A134 | 15d multicolored | 5.75 | 5.75 |
| 835 | A134 | 15d multicolored | 5.75 | 5.75 |

Indigenous Butterflies — A135

50b, Papilio antimachus. 75b, Euphaedra neophron. 1d, Aterica rabena. 1.25d, Salamis parhassus. 5d, Precis rhadama. 10d, Papilio demodocus. 12d, Charaxes etesippe. No. 843, 15d, Danaus formosa.
No. 844, Euphaedra ceres. No. 845, Cymothoe pluto.

**1989, May 15**

| | | | | |
|---|---|---|---|---|
| 836 | A135 | 50b multicolored | .60 | .25 |
| 837 | A135 | 75b multicolored | .75 | .45 |
| 838 | A135 | 1d multicolored | .75 | .45 |
| 839 | A135 | 1.25d multicolored | .90 | .90 |
| 840 | A135 | 5d multicolored | 2.25 | 2.25 |
| 841 | A135 | 10d multicolored | 3.75 | 3.75 |
| 842 | A135 | 12d multicolored | 4.25 | 4.25 |
| 843 | A135 | 15d multicolored | 4.75 | 4.75 |
| | *Nos. 836-843 (8)* | | 18.00 | 17.05 |

**Souvenir Sheets**

| | | | | |
|---|---|---|---|---|
| 844 | A135 | 15d multicolored | 8.00 | 8.00 |
| 845 | A135 | 15d multicolored | 8.00 | 8.00 |

Trains of Africa — A136

Designs: 50b, Nigerian coal train, 1959. 75b, 14A Class 2-6-6-2 Garratt, in Sudan. 1d, British (Pacific) in Sudan. 1.25d, American 0-8-0, 1925. 5d, Scottish 4-8-2, 1955. 7d, Scottish 4-8-2, 1926. 10d, British 4-6-0. 12d, American-made 2-6-0 in Ghana. No. 854, British 2-8-2 Class 25 facing forward, vert. No. 855, Class 25 facing left, vert.

**1989, June 15     Litho.     Perf. 14**

| | | | | |
|---|---|---|---|---|
| 846 | A136 | 50b multi | .55 | .30 |
| 847 | A136 | 75b multi | .65 | .40 |
| 848 | A136 | 1d multi | .70 | .50 |
| 849 | A136 | 1.25d multi | .85 | .80 |
| 850 | A136 | 5d multi | 2.25 | 2.25 |
| 851 | A136 | 7d multi | 2.50 | 2.50 |
| 852 | A136 | 10d multi | 4.00 | 4.00 |
| 853 | A136 | 12d multi | 4.50 | 4.75 |
| | *Nos. 846-853 (8)* | | 16.00 | 15.25 |

**Souvenir Sheets**

| | | | | |
|---|---|---|---|---|
| 854 | A136 | 15d multi | 6.00 | 6.00 |
| 855 | A136 | 15d multi | 6.00 | 6.00 |

**Nos. 667-671 Ovptd. "PHILEXFRANCE / '89"**

**1989, June 23     Litho.     Perf. 15**

| | | | | |
|---|---|---|---|---|
| 856 | A110 | 75b multi | .30 | .25 |
| 857 | A110 | 1d multi | .30 | .30 |
| 858 | A110 | 1.25d multi | .40 | .40 |
| 859 | A110 | 10d multi | 1.75 | 1.75 |
| | *Nos. 856-859 (4)* | | 2.75 | 2.70 |

**Souvenir Sheet**

| | | | | |
|---|---|---|---|---|
| 860 | A110 | 12d multi | 3.00 | 3.00 |

Paintings by Japanese Artists — A137

Paintings by Hiroshige unless noted otherwise: 50b, Sparrow and Bamboo. 75b, Peonies and a Canary, by Hokusai. 1d, Crane and Marsh Grasses. 1.25d, Crossbill and Thistle, by Hokusai. 2d, Cuckoo and Azalea, by Hokusai. 5d, Parrot on a Pine Branch. 10d, Mandarin Ducks in a Stream. 12d, Bullfinch and Drooping Cherry, by Hokusai. No. 869, Tit and Peony, horiz. No. 870, Peony and Butterfly, by Shigenobu, horiz.

**1989, July 7    Perf. 13½x14, 14x13½**

| | | | | |
|---|---|---|---|---|
| 861 | A137 | 50b multi | .60 | .30 |
| 862 | A137 | 75b multi | .80 | .40 |
| 863 | A137 | 1d multi | 1.00 | .50 |
| 864 | A137 | 1.25d multi | 1.10 | .60 |
| 865 | A137 | 2d multi | 1.50 | .90 |
| 866 | A137 | 5d multi | 2.00 | 2.00 |
| 867 | A137 | 10d multi | 3.25 | 3.25 |
| 868 | A137 | 12d multi | 3.50 | 3.50 |
| | *Nos. 861-868 (8)* | | 13.75 | 11.45 |

**Souvenir Sheets**

| | | | | |
|---|---|---|---|---|
| 869 | A137 | 15d multi | 5.50 | 5.50 |
| 870 | A137 | 15d multi | 5.50 | 5.50 |

1990 World Cup Soccer Championships, Italy — A138

Various athletes and Italian landmarks: 75b, Rialto Bridge, Venice. 1.25d, The Baptistery, Pisa. 7d, Casino San Remo. 12d, The Colosseum, Rome. No. 875, St. Mark's Cathedral, Venice. No. 876, Piazza Colonna, Rome.

**1989, Aug 25          Perf. 14**

| | | | | |
|---|---|---|---|---|
| 871 | A138 | 75b multi | .55 | .55 |
| 872 | A138 | 1.25d multi | .70 | .70 |
| 873 | A138 | 7d multi | 2.75 | 2.75 |
| 874 | A138 | 12d multi | 4.25 | 4.25 |
| | *Nos. 871-874 (4)* | | 8.25 | 8.25 |

**Souvenir Sheets**

| | | | | |
|---|---|---|---|---|
| 875 | A138 | 15d multi | 5.75 | 5.75 |
| 876 | A138 | 15d multi | 5.75 | 5.75 |

Medicinal Plants — A139

20b, Vitex doniana. 50b, Ricinus communis. 75b, Palisota hirsuta. 1d, Smilax kraussiana. 1.25d, Aspilia africana. 5d, Newbouldia laevis. 8d, Monodora tenuifolia. 10d, Gossypium arboreum.
No. 885, Kigelia africana. No. 886, Spathodea campanulata.

**1989, Sept. 18     Litho.     Perf. 14**

| | | | | |
|---|---|---|---|---|
| 877 | A139 | 20b multicolored | .30 | .25 |
| 878 | A139 | 50b multicolored | .30 | .25 |
| 879 | A139 | 75b multicolored | .35 | .35 |
| 880 | A139 | 1d multicolored | .45 | .45 |
| 881 | A139 | 1.25d multicolored | .55 | .55 |
| 882 | A139 | 5d multicolored | 1.90 | 1.90 |
| 883 | A139 | 8d multicolored | 3.00 | 3.00 |
| 884 | A139 | 10d multicolored | 3.50 | 3.50 |
| | *Nos. 877-884 (8)* | | 10.35 | 10.25 |

**Souvenir Sheets**

| | | | | |
|---|---|---|---|---|
| 885 | A139 | 15d multicolored | 6.00 | 6.00 |
| 886 | A139 | 15d multicolored | 6.00 | 6.00 |

Fish — A140

20b, Lookdown. 75b, Boarfish. 1d, Gray trigerfish. 1.25d, Skipjack tuna. 2d, Bermuda chub. 4d, Atlantic manta. 5d, Striped mullet. 10d, Ladyfish.
No. 895, Porcupinefish. No. 896, Shortfin makos.

## 1989, Oct. 19 — Litho. — Perf.

| | | | | |
|---|---|---|---|---|
| 887 | A140 | 20b multicolored | .30 | .25 |
| 888 | A140 | 75b multicolored | .65 | .65 |
| 889 | A140 | 1d multicolored | .70 | .70 |
| 890 | A140 | 1.25d multicolored | .80 | .80 |
| 891 | A140 | 2d multicolored | 1.00 | 1.00 |
| 892 | A140 | 4d multicolored | 2.00 | 2.00 |
| 893 | A140 | 5d multicolored | 2.50 | 2.50 |
| 894 | A140 | 10d multicolored | 3.50 | 3.50 |
| | | Nos. 887-894 (8) | 11.45 | 11.40 |

### Souvenir Sheet

| | | | | |
|---|---|---|---|---|
| 895 | A140 | 15d multicolored | 7.25 | 7.25 |
| 896 | A140 | 15d multicolored | 7.25 | 7.25 |

### Souvenir Sheet

The White House, Washington, D.C. — A141

## 1989, Nov. 17 — Litho. — Perf. 14

| | | | | |
|---|---|---|---|---|
| 897 | A141 | 10d multicolored | 2.50 | 2.50 |

World Stamp Expo '89.

World Stamp Expo '89, Washington, D.C. — A142

Disney characters riding carousel horses: 20b, Daniel Muller Indian pony. 50b, Herschell-Spillman steed. 75b, Gustav Dentzel stander. 1d, Muller armored stander. 1.25d, Jumper from the Smithsonian Collection. 2d, Illion "American Beauty." 8d, Zalar jumper. 10d, Parker buckling. No. 906, Philadelphia Tobaggan Co. Carousel, Elitch Gardens, Denver, CO. No. 907, PTC Roman chariot.

## 1989, Nov. 29 — Litho. — Perf. 14x13½

| | | | | |
|---|---|---|---|---|
| 898 | A142 | 20b multicolored | .70 | .30 |
| 899 | A142 | 50b multicolored | .90 | .50 |
| 900 | A142 | 75b multicolored | .95 | .60 |
| 901 | A142 | 1d multicolored | 1.00 | .70 |
| 902 | A142 | 1.25d multicolored | 1.10 | .80 |
| 903 | A142 | 2d multicolored | 1.60 | 1.10 |
| 904 | A142 | 8d multicolored | 4.50 | 4.50 |
| 905 | A142 | 10d multicolored | 4.75 | 4.75 |
| | | Nos. 898-905 (8) | 15.50 | 13.25 |

### Souvenir Sheets

| | | | | |
|---|---|---|---|---|
| 906 | A142 | 12d multicolored | 7.25 | 7.25 |
| 907 | A142 | 12d multicolored | 7.25 | 7.25 |

Nobel Prize Winners for Physiology and Great Medical Pioneers — A143

20b, Charles Nicolle (1866-1936), France, 1928 Prize, discovered transmission of typhus by body lice. 50b, Paul Ehrlich (1854-1915), Germany, 1908 Prize, immunology research. 75b, Selman Waksman (1888-1973), Russian-American, 1952 Prize, discovered antibiotic streptomycin, used to treat tuberculosis. 1d, Edward Jenner (1749-1823), Great Britain, discovered smallpox vaccine. 1.25d, Robert Koch (1843-1910), 1905 Prize, isolated the tubercle bacillus. 5d, Sir Alexander Fleming (1881-1955), Scotland, 1945 Prize, developed penicillin. 8d, Max Theiler (1899-1972), US, 1951 Prize, developed yellow fever vaccine. 10d, Louis Pasteur (1822-95), France, proved the germ theory of infection.

#916, C-9 Nightingale Aeromedical Airlift. #917, Hughes Vicking helicopter used in airlift.

## 1989, Dec. 12 — Perf. 14

| | | | | |
|---|---|---|---|---|
| 908 | A143 | 20b multicolored | 1.00 | .30 |
| 909 | A143 | 50b multicolored | 1.10 | .35 |
| 910 | A143 | 75b multicolored | 1.25 | .45 |
| 911 | A143 | 1d multicolored | 1.40 | .55 |
| 912 | A143 | 1.25d multicolored | 1.50 | .70 |
| 913 | A143 | 5d multicolored | 2.25 | 2.25 |
| 914 | A143 | 8d multicolored | 3.25 | 3.25 |
| 915 | A143 | 10d multicolored | 3.50 | 3.50 |
| | | Nos. 908-915 (8) | 15.25 | 11.40 |

### Souvenir Sheets

| | | | | |
|---|---|---|---|---|
| 916 | A143 | 15d multicolored | 5.50 | 5.50 |
| 917 | A143 | 15d multicolored | 5.50 | 5.50 |

Orchids — A144

20b, Bulbophyllum lepidum. 75b, Tridactyle tridactylites. 1d, Vanilla imperialis. 1.25d, Oeceoclades maculata. 2d, Polystachya affinis. 4d, Ancistrochilus rothschildianus. 5d, Angraecum distichum. 10d, Liparis guineensis.

No. 926, Eulophia guineensis. No. 927, Plectrelminthus caudatus.

## 1989, Dec. 18 — Perf. 14

| | | | | |
|---|---|---|---|---|
| 918 | A144 | 20b multicolored | .35 | .30 |
| 919 | A144 | 75b multicolored | .60 | .60 |
| 920 | A144 | 1d multicolored | .90 | .90 |
| 921 | A144 | 1.25d multicolored | 1.00 | 1.00 |
| 922 | A144 | 2d multicolored | 1.50 | 1.50 |
| 923 | A144 | 4d multicolored | 2.50 | 2.50 |
| 924 | A144 | 5d multicolored | 3.00 | 3.00 |
| 925 | A144 | 10d multicolored | 4.75 | 4.75 |
| | | Nos. 918-925 (8) | 14.60 | 14.55 |

### Souvenir Sheets

| | | | | |
|---|---|---|---|---|
| 926 | A144 | 15d multicolored | 6.50 | 6.50 |
| 927 | A144 | 15d multicolored | 6.50 | 6.50 |

Christmas — A145

Disney characters and classic automobiles: 20b, 1922 Pierce Arrow. 50b, 1919 Spyker. 75b, 1929 Packard. 1d, 1920 Daimler. 1.25d, 1924 Hispano Suiza. 2d, Opel Laubfrosch, 1924-27. 10d, 1927 Vauxhall 30/98. 12d, 1923 Peerless. No. 936, 1930 Bentley Supercharged, Santa Claus. No. 937, 1928 Stutz Blackhawk Speedster, picnic.

## 1989, Dec. 19 — Litho. — Perf. 14

| | | | | |
|---|---|---|---|---|
| 928 | A145 | 20b multicolored | .75 | .25 |
| 929 | A145 | 50b multicolored | 1.00 | .40 |
| 930 | A145 | 75b multicolored | 1.10 | .55 |
| 931 | A145 | 1d multicolored | 1.25 | .65 |
| 932 | A145 | 1.25d multicolored | 1.40 | .90 |
| 933 | A145 | 2d multicolored | 1.75 | 1.25 |
| 934 | A145 | 10d multicolored | 4.00 | 4.00 |
| 935 | A145 | 12d multicolored | 4.25 | 4.25 |
| | | Nos. 928-935 (8) | 15.50 | 12.25 |

### Souvenir Sheets

| | | | | |
|---|---|---|---|---|
| 936 | A145 | 15d multicolored | 7.75 | 7.75 |
| 937 | A145 | 15d multicolored | 7.75 | 7.75 |

Wimbledon Tennis Champions — A146

No. 938, John Newcombe. No. 939, G.W. Hillyard. No. 940, Roy Emerson. No. 941, Dorothy Chambers. No. 942, Donald Budge. No. 943, Suzanne Lenglen. No. 944, Laurence Doherty. No. 945, Helen Wills Moody. No. 946, Bjorn Borg. No. 947, Maureen Connolly. No. 948, Jean Borotra. No. 949, Maria Bueno. No. 950, Anthony Wilding. No. 951, Louise Brough. No. 952, Fred Perry. No. 953, Margaret Court. No. 954, Bill Tilden. No. 955, Billie Jean King. No. 956, Rod Laver. No. 957, Martina Navratilova.

No. 958, Rod Laver, diff. No. 959, Martina Navratilova, diff.

## 1990, Jan. 2 — Litho. — Perf. 15x14½

| | | | | |
|---|---|---|---|---|
| 938 | A146 | 20b multicolored | .30 | .25 |
| 939 | A146 | 20b multicolored | .30 | .25 |
| a. | | Pair, #938-939 | .40 | .40 |
| 940 | A146 | 50b multicolored | .30 | .30 |
| 941 | A146 | 50b multicolored | .30 | .30 |
| a. | | Pair, #940-941 | .65 | .65 |
| 942 | A146 | 75b multicolored | .40 | .40 |
| 943 | A146 | 75b multicolored | .40 | .40 |
| a. | | Pair, #942-943 | .85 | .85 |
| 944 | A146 | 1d multicolored | .45 | .45 |
| 945 | A146 | 1d multicolored | .45 | .45 |
| a. | | Pair, #944-945 | .95 | .95 |
| 946 | A146 | 1.25d multicolored | .50 | .50 |
| 947 | A146 | 1.25d multicolored | .50 | .50 |
| a. | | Pair, #946-947 | 1.10 | 1.10 |
| 948 | A146 | 4d multicolored | 1.10 | 1.10 |
| 949 | A146 | 4d multicolored | 1.10 | 1.10 |
| a. | | Pair, #948-949 | 2.50 | 2.50 |

| | | | | |
|---|---|---|---|---|
| 950 | A146 | 5d multicolored | 1.40 | 1.40 |
| 951 | A146 | 5d multicolored | 1.40 | 1.40 |
| a. | | Pair, #950-951 | 3.00 | 3.00 |
| 952 | A146 | 7d multicolored | 1.60 | 1.60 |
| 953 | A146 | 7d multicolored | 1.60 | 1.60 |
| a. | | Pair, #952-953 | 4.00 | 4.00 |
| 954 | A146 | 10d multicolored | 2.25 | 2.25 |
| 955 | A146 | 10d multicolored | 2.25 | 2.25 |
| a. | | Pair, #954-955 | 5.75 | 5.75 |
| 956 | A146 | 12d multicolored | 2.50 | 2.50 |
| 957 | A146 | 12d multicolored | 2.50 | 2.50 |
| a. | | Pair, #956-957 | 6.25 | 6.25 |
| | | Nos. 938-957 (20) | 21.60 | 21.50 |

### Souvenir Sheets

| | | | | |
|---|---|---|---|---|
| 958 | A146 | 15d multicolored | 6.75 | 6.75 |
| 959 | A146 | 15d multicolored | 6.75 | 6.75 |

1st Moon Landing, 20th Anniv. (in 1989) — A147

Designs: 20b, Eagle lunar module descending, horiz. 50b, Apollo 11 liftoff. 75b, Astronaut descending ladder, horiz. 1d, Astronaut, US flag over Sea of Tranquillity, horiz. 1.25d, Mission emblem. 1.75d, Crew, horiz. 8d, Lunar module, Sea of Tranquillity, horiz. 12d, Recovery of command module Columbia after splashdown. No. 968, Neil Armstrong returning to Eagle. No. 969, View of Earth.

## 1990, Feb. 16 — Perf. 14

| | | | | |
|---|---|---|---|---|
| 960 | A147 | 20b multicolored | .70 | .25 |
| 961 | A147 | 50b multicolored | .90 | .30 |
| 962 | A147 | 75b multicolored | 1.00 | .45 |
| 963 | A147 | 1d multicolored | 1.10 | .55 |
| 964 | A147 | 1.25d multicolored | 1.25 | .60 |
| 965 | A147 | 1.75d multicolored | 1.40 | 1.25 |
| 966 | A147 | 8d multicolored | 3.75 | 3.75 |
| 967 | A147 | 12d multicolored | 5.00 | 5.00 |
| | | Nos. 960-967 (8) | 15.10 | 12.15 |

### Souvenir Sheets

| | | | | |
|---|---|---|---|---|
| 968 | A147 | 15d multicolored | 5.00 | 5.00 |
| 969 | A147 | 15d multicolored | 5.00 | 5.00 |

### Miniature Sheet

Birds of Africa — A148

No. 970: a, White-faced owl. b, Village weaver. c, Red-throated bee eater. d, Brown harrier eagle. e, Red bishop. f, Scarlet-chested sunbird. g, Red-billed hornbill. h, Mosque swallow. i, White-faced tree duck. j, African fish eagle. k, Great white pelican. l, Carmine bee eater. m, Hadada ibis. n, Crocodile plover. o, Yellow-bellied sunbird. p, African skimmer. q, Woodland kingfisher. r, Jacana. s, Pygmy goose. t, Hamerkop.

## 1990, Apr. 12 — Litho. — Perf. 14

| | | | | |
|---|---|---|---|---|
| 970 | A148 | Sheet of 20 | 17.50 | 17.50 |
| a.-t. | | 1.25d any single | .80 | .80 |

RAF World War II Planes — A149

Designs: 10b, Bristol Blenheim Mk-1. 20b, Battle. 50b, Blenheim 4. 60b, Wellington 1C. 75b, Whitley 5. 1d, Hampden Mk-1. 1.25d, Spitfire 1A and Hurricane 1. 2d, Avro Manchester. 3d, Stirling. 5d, Handley Page Halifax B-2. 10d, Lancaster B-3. 12d, Mosquito B-4. No. 983, Lancaster B-3 over Hamburg. No. 984, Spitfire 1, Battle of Britain.

## 1990, Apr. 18 — Perf. 14

| | | | | |
|---|---|---|---|---|
| 971 | A149 | 10b multicolored | 1.00 | .50 |
| 972 | A149 | 20b multicolored | 1.10 | .50 |
| 973 | A149 | 50b multicolored | 1.15 | .50 |
| 974 | A149 | 60b multicolored | 1.20 | .50 |
| 975 | A149 | 75b multicolored | 1.30 | .50 |
| 976 | A149 | 1d multicolored | 1.35 | .50 |
| 977 | A149 | 1.25d multicolored | 1.40 | .55 |
| 978 | A149 | 2d multicolored | 1.50 | .80 |
| 979 | A149 | 3d multicolored | 1.75 | 1.25 |

| | | | | |
|---|---|---|---|---|
| 980 | A149 | 5d multicolored | 2.50 | 2.50 |
| 981 | A149 | 10d multicolored | 3.50 | 3.50 |
| 982 | A149 | 12d multicolored | 4.00 | 4.00 |
| | | Nos. 971-982 (12) | 21.75 | 15.60 |

### Souvenir Sheets

| | | | | |
|---|---|---|---|---|
| 983 | A149 | 15d multicolored | 5.75 | 5.75 |
| 984 | A149 | 15d multicolored | 5.75 | 5.75 |

Independence, 25th Anniv. — A150

Designs: 3d, Sir Dawda Jawara, President. 12d, Jet and map showing airport. 18d, National arms.

## 1990, June 5 — Litho. — Perf. 14

| | | | | |
|---|---|---|---|---|
| 985 | A150 | 1d multicolored | .30 | .25 |
| 986 | A150 | 3d multicolored | 1.10 | 1.10 |
| 987 | A150 | 12d multicolored | 5.00 | 5.00 |
| | | Nos. 985-987 (3) | 6.40 | 6.35 |

### Souvenir Sheet

| | | | | |
|---|---|---|---|---|
| 988 | A150 | 18d multicolored | 5.50 | 5.50 |

Baobab Tree — A151

10b, Woodcarving. 20b, Pres. Jawara. 50b, Map. 75b, Batik fabric. 1d, Bakau Beach Resort. 1.25d, Tendaba Camp. 2d, Shrimp industry. 5d, Peanut oil mill. 10d, Pottery, kora. 15d, Ansellia Africana orchid. 30d, Ancient stone rings, Euryphene gambiae.

## 1990, June 14 — Litho. — Perf. 14

| | | | | |
|---|---|---|---|---|
| 989 | A151 | 5b shown | .75 | .85 |
| 990 | A151 | 10b multicolored | .30 | .30 |
| 991 | A151 | 20b multicolored | .30 | .25 |
| 992 | A151 | 50b multicolored | 1.75 | .25 |
| 993 | A151 | 75b multicolored | .30 | .25 |
| 994 | A151 | 1d multicolored | .30 | .25 |
| 995 | A151 | 1.25d multicolored | .30 | .25 |
| 996 | A151 | 2d multicolored | .30 | .25 |
| 997 | A151 | 5d multicolored | 1.00 | .80 |
| 998 | A151 | 10d multicolored | 1.40 | 1.40 |
| 999 | A151 | 15d multicolored | 5.50 | 5.50 |
| 1000 | A151 | 30d multicolored | 6.50 | 6.50 |
| | | Nos. 989-1000 (12) | 18.70 | 16.85 |

Nos. 990, 999 vert.

Penny Black, 150th Anniv. — A152

## 1990, June 18

| | | | | |
|---|---|---|---|---|
| 1001 | A152 | 1.25d brt bl & blk | 1.50 | .50 |
| 1002 | A152 | 12d dark red & blk | 4.50 | 4.50 |

### Souvenir Sheet

| | | | | |
|---|---|---|---|---|
| 1003 | A152 | 15d sil, bis & blk | 6.50 | 6.50 |

Mickey Visits England A153

Walt Disney characters at: 20b, 10 Downing Street. 50b, Trafalgar Square. 75b, Cliffs of Dover. 1d, Tower of London. 5d, Hampton Court Palace. 8d, Magdalen Tower, Oxford University. 10d, Old London Bridge. 12d, Rosetta Stone, British Museum. No. 1012, Picadilly Circus. No. 1013, Houses of Parliament and Big Ben on the River Thames.

## 1990, June 19 — Perf. 14x13½

| | | | | |
|---|---|---|---|---|
| 1004 | A153 | 20b multicolored | .45 | .30 |
| 1005 | A153 | 50b multicolored | .65 | .35 |
| 1006 | A153 | 75b multicolored | .85 | .40 |
| 1007 | A153 | 1d multicolored | 1.10 | .50 |
| 1008 | A153 | 5d multicolored | 2.50 | 2.50 |
| 1009 | A153 | 8d multicolored | 3.00 | 3.00 |
| 1010 | A153 | 10d multicolored | 3.75 | 3.75 |
| 1011 | A153 | 12d multicolored | 4.75 | 4.75 |
| | | Nos. 1004-1011 (8) | 17.05 | 15.50 |

## Souvenir Sheets

| | | | | |
|---|---|---|---|---|
| 1012 | A153 | 18d multicolored | 8.50 | 8.50 |
| 1013 | A153 | 18d multicolored | 8.50 | 8.50 |

Stamp World London '90. Nos. 1004-1005, 1007, 1009 vert.

A154

**1990, July 19**     **Perf. 14**

| | | | | |
|---|---|---|---|---|
| 1014 | 6d | Girl facing left | 1.50 | 1.50 |
| 1015 | 6d | Young girl, diff. | 1.50 | 1.50 |
| 1016 | 6d | Seated in chair | 1.50 | 1.50 |
| a. | A154 | Strip of 3, #1014-1016 | 5.50 | 5.50 |

### Souvenir Sheet

| | | | | |
|---|---|---|---|---|
| 1017 | A154 | 18d like No. 1014 | 5.00 | 5.00 |

A156

Players from participating countries.

**1990, Sept. 24**     **Litho.**     **Perf. 14**

| | | | | |
|---|---|---|---|---|
| 1018 | A156 | 1d Italy | .45 | .45 |
| 1019 | A156 | 1.25d Argentina | .55 | .55 |
| 1020 | A156 | 3d Costa Rica | 1.10 | 1.10 |
| 1021 | A156 | 5d UAE | 1.60 | 1.60 |
| | | Nos. 1018-1021 (4) | 3.70 | 3.70 |

### Souvenir Sheets

| | | | | |
|---|---|---|---|---|
| 1022 | A156 | 18d Holland | 7.50 | 7.50 |
| 1023 | A156 | 18d Romania | 7.50 | 7.50 |

World Cup Soccer Championships, Italy.

A157

20b, Men's discus. 50b, Men's 100-meter race. 75b, Women's 400-meter race. 1d, Men's 200-meter race. 1.25d, Rhythmic gymnastics. 3d, Soccer. 10d, Men's marathon. 12d, Tornado class sailing.
No. 1032, Parade of flags. No. 1033, Stadium, card section.

**1990, Nov. 1**     **Litho.**     **Perf. 14**

| | | | | |
|---|---|---|---|---|
| 1024 | A157 | 20b multicolored | .40 | .25 |
| 1025 | A157 | 50b multicolored | .45 | .25 |
| 1026 | A157 | 75b multicolored | .50 | .30 |
| 1027 | A157 | 1d multicolored | .55 | .55 |
| 1028 | A157 | 1.25d multicolored | .45 | .45 |
| 1029 | A157 | 3d multicolored | 1.60 | 1.60 |
| 1030 | A157 | 10d multicolored | 4.25 | 4.25 |
| 1031 | A157 | 12d multicolored | 5.25 | 5.25 |
| | | Nos. 1024-1031 (8) | 13.45 | 12.90 |

### Souvenir Sheets

| | | | | |
|---|---|---|---|---|
| 1032 | A157 | 15d multicolored | 6.50 | 6.50 |
| 1033 | A157 | 15d multicolored | 6.50 | 6.50 |

1992 Summer Olympics, Barcelona.

Christmas — A158

Entire paintings or different details from: 20b, 7d, The Annunciation with St. Emidius by Crivelli. 50b, The Annunciation by Campin. 75b, The Solly Madonna by Raphael. 1.25d, The Tempi Madonna by Raphael. 2d, Madonna of the Linen Window by Raphael. 10d, The Orleans Madonna by Raphael. 15d, Madonna and Child by Crivelli. No. 1042, The Niccolini-Cowper Madonna by Raphael.

---

**1990, Dec. 24**     **Litho.**     **Perf. 13½x14**

| | | | | |
|---|---|---|---|---|
| 1034 | A158 | 20b multicolored | .45 | .25 |
| 1035 | A158 | 50b multicolored | .55 | .25 |
| 1036 | A158 | 75b multicolored | .70 | .25 |
| 1037 | A158 | 1.25d multicolored | .80 | .65 |
| 1038 | A158 | 2d multicolored | .90 | .90 |
| 1039 | A158 | 7d multicolored | 2.50 | 2.50 |
| 1040 | A158 | 10d multicolored | 3.00 | 3.00 |
| 1041 | A158 | 15d multicolored | 4.00 | 4.00 |
| | | Nos. 1034-1041 (8) | 12.90 | 11.80 |

### Souvenir Sheet

| | | | | |
|---|---|---|---|---|
| 1042 | A158 | 15d multicolored | 7.50 | 7.50 |

Peter Paul Rubens (1577-1640), Painter
A159

Entire paintings or different details from: 20b, 10d, No. 1054, The Lion Hunt. 1d, 1.25d, 3d, 15d, The Tiger Hunt. 5d, No. 1055, The Boar Hunt. No. 1056, The Crocodile and Hippopotamus Hunt. No. 1057, Saint George Slays the Dragon, vert.

**1990, Dec. 24**     **Litho.**     **Perf. 14x13½**

| | | | | |
|---|---|---|---|---|
| 1046 | A159 | 20b multicolored | .30 | .25 |
| 1047 | A159 | 75b multicolored | .30 | .25 |
| 1048 | A159 | 1d multicolored | .35 | .35 |
| 1049 | A159 | 1.25d multicolored | .45 | .45 |
| 1050 | A159 | 3d multicolored | 1.00 | 1.00 |
| 1051 | A159 | 5d multicolored | 1.40 | 1.40 |
| 1052 | A159 | 10d multicolored | 2.25 | 2.25 |
| 1053 | A159 | 15d multicolored | 3.00 | 3.00 |
| | | Nos. 1046-1053 (8) | 9.05 | 8.95 |

### Souvenir Sheets

| | | | | |
|---|---|---|---|---|
| 1054 | A159 | 15d multicolored | 4.00 | 4.00 |
| 1055 | A159 | 15d multicolored | 4.00 | 4.00 |
| 1056 | A159 | 15d multicolored | 4.00 | 4.00 |
| 1057 | A159 | 15d multicolored | 4.00 | 4.00 |

World Summit for Children — A160

**1991, Jan. 7**     **Litho.**     **Perf. 14**

| | | | | |
|---|---|---|---|---|
| 1058 | A160 | 1d multicolored | .80 | .80 |

Intl. Literacy Year A161

Walt Disney characters in "The Sword in the Stone": No. 1059a, Wart and Sir Kay. b. Merlin reading book. c. Wart learning geography. d. Wart writing on blackboard. e. Wart as bird, Madam Mim. f. Merlin and Madam Mim. g. Mim as dragon. h. Wart pulling sword from stone. i. Wart as King of England. No. 1060, Merlin, Wart in forest, vert. No. 1061, Knight trying to remove sword from stone, vert.

**1991, Feb. 14**     **Litho.**     **Perf. 14x13½**

| | | | | |
|---|---|---|---|---|
| 1059 | A161 | 3d Sheet of 9, #a- | | |
| | | | 15.00 | 15.00 |

### Souvenir Sheets

| | | | | |
|---|---|---|---|---|
| 1060 | A161 | 20d multicolored | 9.00 | 9.00 |
| 1061 | A161 | 20d multicolored | 9.00 | 9.00 |

### Miniature Sheets

Wildlife A162

No. 1062: a, Bebearia senegalensis. b, Graphium ridleyanus. c, Precis antilope. d, Charaxes ameliae. e, Addax. f, Sassaby. g, Civet. h, Green monkey. i, Spurwing goose. j, Red-billed hornbill. k, Osprey. l, Glossy ibis. m, Egyptian plover. n, Golden-tailed woodpecker. o, Green woodhoopoe. p, Gaboon viper.
No. 1063: a, Red-billed firefinch. b, Leaflove. c, Piacpiac. d, Emerald cuckoo. e,

---

Red colobus monkey. f, African elephant. g, Duiker. h, Giant eland. i, Oribi. j, West African dwarf crocodile. k, Crowned crane. l, Jackal. m, Yellow-throated longclaw. n, Abyssinian ground hornbill. o, Papilio hesperus. p, Papilio antimachus.
No. 1064: a, Martial eagle. b, Red-cheeked cordon-bleu. c, Red bishop. d, Great white pelican. e, Patas monkey. f, Vervet monkey. g, Roan antelope. h, Western hartebeest. i, Waterbuck. j, Warthog. k, Spotted hyena. l, Olive baboon. m, Palla decius. n, Acraea pharsalus. o, Neptidopsis ophione. p, Acraea caecilia.
No. 1065, African spoonbill, vert. No. 1066, Lion, vert. No. 1067, Buffalo weaver, vert.

**1991, May 31**     **Litho.**     **Perf. 14**

| | | | | |
|---|---|---|---|---|
| 1062 | A162 | 1d Sheet of 16, | | |
| | | #a.-p. | 6.50 | 6.50 |
| 1063 | A162 | 1.50d Sheet of 16, | | |
| | | #a.-p. | 9.00 | 9.00 |
| 1064 | A162 | 5d Sheet of 16, | | |
| | | #a.-p. | 25.00 | 25.00 |
| | | Nos. 1062-1064 (3) | 40.50 | 40.50 |

### Souvenir Sheets

| | | | | |
|---|---|---|---|---|
| 1065 | A162 | 18d multicolored | 6.00 | 6.00 |
| 1066 | A162 | 18d multicolored | 6.00 | 6.00 |
| 1067 | A162 | 18d multicolored | 6.00 | 6.00 |

Butterflies — A163

Designs: 20b, Papilio dardanus. 50b, Bematistes poggei. 1d, Vanessa cardiu. 1.50d, Amphicallia tigris. 3d, Hypolimnes dexithea. 8d, Acraea egina. 10d, Salmis temora. 15d, Precis octavia. No. 1076, Danaus chrysippus. No. 1077, Charaxes jasius. No. 1078, Papilio demodocus. No. 1079, Papilio nireus.

**1991, June 1**     **Litho.**     **Perf. 14**

| | | | | |
|---|---|---|---|---|
| 1068 | A163 | 20b multicolored | .60 | .35 |
| 1069 | A163 | 50b multicolored | .85 | .40 |
| 1070 | A163 | 1d multicolored | .95 | .55 |
| 1071 | A163 | 1.50d multicolored | 1.00 | .85 |
| 1072 | A163 | 3d multicolored | 1.50 | 1.25 |
| 1073 | A163 | 8d multicolored | 2.50 | 2.50 |
| 1074 | A163 | 10d multicolored | 3.25 | 3.25 |
| 1075 | A163 | 15d multicolored | 5.00 | 5.00 |
| | | Nos. 1068-1075 (8) | 15.65 | 14.15 |

### Souvenir Sheets

| | | | | |
|---|---|---|---|---|
| 1076 | A163 | 18d multicolored | 5.00 | 5.00 |
| 1077 | A163 | 18d multicolored | 5.00 | 5.00 |
| 1078 | A163 | 18d multicolored | 5.00 | 5.00 |
| 1079 | A163 | 18d multicolored | 5.00 | 5.00 |

While Nos. 1078-1079 have same release date as Nos. 1068-1077, the dollar value of Nos. 1078-1079 were lower when they were released.

### Royal Family Birthday, Anniversary

No. 1088, Elizabeth, Philip. No. 1089, Diana, sons, Charles.

### Common Design Type

**1991, Aug. 12**     **Litho.**     **Perf. 14**

| | | | | |
|---|---|---|---|---|
| 1080 | CD347 | 20b multi | .35 | .25 |
| 1081 | CD347 | 50b multi | .40 | .30 |
| 1082 | CD347 | 75b multi | .45 | .40 |
| 1083 | CD347 | 1d multi | .50 | .50 |
| 1084 | CD347 | 1.25d multi | .65 | .65 |
| 1085 | CD347 | 1.50d multi | .80 | .80 |
| 1086 | CD347 | 12d multi | 4.50 | 4.50 |
| 1087 | CD347 | 15d multi | 6.00 | 6.00 |
| | | Nos. 1080-1087 (8) | 13.65 | 13.40 |

### Souvenir Sheets

| | | | | |
|---|---|---|---|---|
| 1088 | CD347 | 18d multi | 4.50 | 4.50 |
| 1089 | CD347 | 18d multi | 6.50 | 6.50 |

20b, 75b, 1.50d, 15d, No. 1089, Charles and Diana, 10th wedding anniversary. Others, Queen Elizabeth II, 65th birthday.

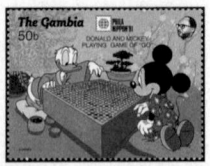

Phila Nippon '91 — A164

Walt Disney characters playing Japanese games and sports: 50b, Donald Duck and Mickey Mouse playing Go. 75b, Morty, Ferdie and Pete sumo wrestling. 1d, Minnie Mouse, Clarabelle, Daisy Duck playing battledore and shuttlecock. 1.25d, Goofy, Mickey at Okinawa bullfight, vert. 5d, Mickey as a Hawk Hunter Tagari, vert. 7d, Mickey, Minnie, and Donald

---

play Jan-Ken-Pon, vert. 10d, Goofy as archer. 15d, Morty, Ferdie fly Japanese kites, vert. No. 1098, Goofy batting in Japanese baseball game, vert. No. 1099, Mickey, Scrooge McDuck playing Japanese football, vert. No. 1100, Mickey fly fishing, vert. No. 1101, Mickey climbing Mt. Fuji, vert.

**Perf. 14x13½, 13½x14**

**1991, Aug. 22**     **Litho.**

| | | | | |
|---|---|---|---|---|
| 1090 | A164 | 50b multicolored | .50 | .30 |
| 1091 | A164 | 75b multicolored | .60 | .40 |
| 1092 | A164 | 1d multicolored | .70 | .45 |
| 1093 | A164 | 1.25d multicolored | .80 | .55 |
| 1094 | A164 | 5d multicolored | 2.25 | 2.25 |
| 1095 | A164 | 7d multicolored | 3.00 | 3.00 |
| 1096 | A164 | 10d multicolored | 4.00 | 4.00 |
| 1097 | A164 | 15d multicolored | 5.75 | 5.75 |
| | | Nos. 1090-1097 (8) | 17.60 | 16.70 |

### Souvenir Sheets

| | | | | |
|---|---|---|---|---|
| 1098 | A164 | 20d multicolored | 5.50 | 5.50 |
| 1099 | A164 | 20d multicolored | 5.50 | 5.50 |
| 1100 | A164 | 20d multicolored | 5.50 | 5.50 |
| 1101 | A164 | 20d multicolored | 5.50 | 5.50 |

Intl. Literacy Year — A165

Walt Disney characters in scenes from Rudyard Kipling's "Just So Stories": 50b, How the Whale Got His Throat. 75b, How the Camel Got His Hump. 1d, How the Leopard Got His Spots. 1.25d, The Elephant's Child. 1.50d, Singsong of Old Man Kangaroo. 7d, The Crab that Played with the Sea. 10d, The Cat that Walked by Himself. 15d, The Butterfly that Stamped. No. 1110, How the Alphabet was Made, vert. No. 1111, The Beginning of the Armadillos, vert. No. 1112, How the First Letter was Written, vert. No. 1113, How the Rhinoceros Got His Skin.

**1991, Aug. 28**     **Litho.**     **Perf. 14x13½**

| | | | | |
|---|---|---|---|---|
| 1102 | A165 | 50b multicolored | .80 | .30 |
| 1103 | A165 | 75b multicolored | .90 | .40 |
| 1104 | A165 | 1d multicolored | 1.00 | .45 |
| 1105 | A165 | 1.25d multicolored | 1.25 | .55 |
| 1106 | A165 | 1.50d multicolored | 1.40 | 1.40 |
| 1107 | A165 | 7d multicolored | 3.25 | 3.25 |
| 1108 | A165 | 10d multicolored | 4.50 | 4.50 |
| 1109 | A165 | 15d multicolored | 6.50 | 6.50 |
| | | Nos. 1102-1109 (8) | 19.60 | 17.35 |

### Souvenir Sheets

**Perf. 13½x14, 14x13½**

| | | | | |
|---|---|---|---|---|
| 1110 | A165 | 20d multicolored | 6.75 | 6.75 |
| 1111 | A165 | 20d multicolored | 6.75 | 6.75 |
| 1112 | A165 | 20d multicolored | 6.75 | 6.75 |
| 1113 | A165 | 20d multicolored | 6.75 | 6.75 |

Train Cabooses — A166

No. 1114: a, Steel cupola, Canadian Pacific. b, Four-wheel, Cumberland and Pennsylvania. c, Mexican slim gauge. d, All steel cupola, Northern Pacific. e, Four-wheel, Morristown & Erie. f, Streamlined cupola, Burlington Northern. g, Caboose coach, McCloud River. h, Wide vision, Santa Fe. i, Wide vision, Frisco.
No. 1115: a, Narrow gauge, Oahu Railway. b, Standard brake-van, British Railways. c, Wide view steel, Union Pacific. d, Four-wheel, Belt Railway of Chicago. e, Four-wheel, McCloud River. f, Logging, Angelina County Lumber Co. g, Narrow gauge, Coahuila & Zacatecas. h, Three-foot gauge, United Railways of Yucatan. i, Steel cupola, Rio Grande.
No. 1116: a, Four-wheel, Colorado & Southern. b, Transfer, Santa Fe. c, Wooden cupola, Canadian National. d, Transfer steel, Union Pacific. e, Caboose coach, Virginia & Truckee. f, Standard brake-van, British. g, Narrow gauge, Intl. Railways of Central America. h, Steel cupola, Northern Pacific. i, Wood, Burlington Northern.
No. 1117, Pennsylvania electric, vert. No. 1118, Unidentified caboose, trainman with flag, vert. No. 1119, Unidentified green wooden caboose behind yellow freight car.

### Sheets of 9

**1991, Sept. 12 Litho. Perf. 14x13½**

| | | | | |
|---|---|---|---|---|
| 1114 | A166 | 1d #a.-i. | 5.50 | 5.50 |
| 1115 | A166 | 2d #a.-i. | 5.50 | 5.50 |
| 1116 | A166 | 1.50d #a.-i. | 5.50 | 5.50 |
| | | Nos. 1114-1116 (3) | 16.50 | 16.50 |

**Souvenir Sheets**
*Perf. 12x13, 13x12*

| | | | | |
|---|---|---|---|---|
| 1117 | A166 | 20d multicolored | 5.50 | 5.50 |
| 1118 | A166 | 20d multicolored | 5.50 | 5.50 |
| 1119 | A166 | 20d multicolored | 5.50 | 5.50 |

While Nos. 1115-1116 and 1118-1119 have the same issue date as Nos. 1114 and 1117, the dollar value of Nos. 1115-1116 and 1118-1119 was lower when they were released.

Fish — A167

20b, Tiger shark. 25b, Common jewel fish. 50b, Five spot fish. 75b, Smalltooth sawfish. 1d, Five spot tilapia. 1.25d, Dwarf jewel fish. 1.50d, Five spot jewel fish. 3d, Bumphead. 10d, Egyptian mouthbrooder. 15d, Burton's mouthbrooder.

No. 1130, Great barracuda. No. 1131, Yellowtail snapper.

**1991, Oct. 28 Litho. Perf. 14x14½**

| | | | | |
|---|---|---|---|---|
| 1120 | A167 | 20b multicolored | .30 | .25 |
| 1121 | A167 | 25b multicolored | .30 | .25 |
| 1122 | A167 | 50b multicolored | .45 | .45 |
| 1123 | A167 | 75b multicolored | .45 | .45 |
| 1124 | A167 | 1d multicolored | .45 | .45 |
| 1125 | A167 | 1.25d multicolored | .45 | .45 |
| 1126 | A167 | 1.50d multicolored | .50 | .50 |
| 1127 | A167 | 3d multicolored | .80 | .80 |
| 1128 | A167 | 10d multicolored | 2.50 | 2.50 |
| 1129 | A167 | 15d multicolored | 3.50 | 3.50 |
| | | Nos. 1120-1129 (10) | 9.70 | 9.60 |

**Souvenir Sheets**

| | | | | |
|---|---|---|---|---|
| 1130 | A167 | 18d multicolored | 8.00 | 8.00 |
| 1131 | A167 | 18d multicolored | 8.00 | 8.00 |

While Nos. 1120-1122, 1125, 1129-1131 have the same issue date as Nos. 1123-1124, 1126-1128 the dollar value of Nos. 1120-1122, 1125, 1129-1130 was lower when they were released.

Hummel Figurines — A168

20b, No. 1141a, Girl and boy waving handkerchiefs. 75b, No. 1140a, Boy and girl under umbrella. 1d, No. 1140b, Two girls wearing scarfs. 1.50d, No. 1140c, Girl and boy in window with flower box. 2.50d, No. 1141b, Two girls with basket. 5d, No. 1141c, Boy wearing long pants, boy wearing shorts. 10d, No. 1141d, Two girls on fence. 15d, No. 1140d, Boy with stick, girl with bag.

**1991, Nov. 4 Litho. Perf. 14**

| | | | | |
|---|---|---|---|---|
| 1132 | A168 | 20b multicolored | .30 | .25 |
| 1133 | A168 | 75b multicolored | .30 | .25 |
| 1134 | A168 | 1d multicolored | .30 | .25 |
| 1135 | A168 | 1.50d multicolored | .45 | .45 |
| 1136 | A168 | 2.50d multicolored | .60 | .60 |
| 1137 | A168 | 5d multicolored | 1.00 | 1.00 |
| 1138 | A168 | 10d multicolored | 2.25 | 2.25 |
| 1139 | A168 | 15d multicolored | 3.00 | 3.00 |
| | | Nos. 1132-1139 (8) | 8.20 | 8.05 |

**Souvenir Sheets**

| | | | | |
|---|---|---|---|---|
| 1140 | A168 | 4d Sheet of 4, #a.-d. | 4.00 | 4.00 |
| 1141 | A168 | 5d Sheet of 4, #a.-d. | 5.00 | 5.00 |

Paintings by Vincent Van Gogh — A169

Designs: 20b, The Old Cemetery Tower at Nuenen in the Snow, horiz. 25b, Head of a Peasant Woman with White Cap. 50b, The Green Parrot. 75b, Vase with Carnations. 1d,

Vase with Red Gladioli. 1.25b, Beach at Scheveningen in Calm Weather, horiz. 1.50d, Boy Cutting Grass with a Sickle, horiz. 2d, Coleus Plant in a Flowerpot. 3d, Self-portrait, spring-summer 1887. 4d, Self-portrait. 5d, Self-portrait, diff. 6d, Self-portrait, spring 1887. 8d, Still Life with a Bottle, Two Glasses, Cheese and Bread. 10d, Still Life with Cabbage, Clogs and Potatoes, horiz. 12d, Montmartre: The Street Lamps. 15d, Head of a Peasant Woman with Brownish Cap. No. 1158, Arles: View From the Wheat Fields. No. 1159, Autumn Landscape. No. 1160, Montmartre: Quarry, The Mills, horiz. No. 1161, The Potato Eaters, horiz.

*Perf. 13½x14, 14x13½*

**1991, Dec. 5 Litho.**

| | | | | |
|---|---|---|---|---|
| 1142 | A169 | 20b multicolored | .40 | .25 |
| 1143 | A169 | 25b multicolored | .45 | .25 |
| 1144 | A169 | 50b multicolored | .50 | .25 |
| 1145 | A169 | 75b multicolored | .55 | .30 |
| 1146 | A169 | 1d multicolored | .60 | .35 |
| 1147 | A169 | 1.25d multicolored | .65 | .45 |
| 1148 | A169 | 1.50d multicolored | .70 | .55 |
| 1149 | A169 | 2d multicolored | .75 | .65 |
| 1150 | A169 | 3d multicolored | .90 | .90 |
| 1151 | A169 | 4d multicolored | 1.25 | 1.25 |
| 1152 | A169 | 5d multicolored | 1.50 | 1.50 |
| 1153 | A169 | 6d multicolored | 2.00 | 2.00 |
| 1154 | A169 | 8d multicolored | 2.75 | 2.75 |
| 1155 | A169 | 10d multicolored | 3.25 | 3.25 |
| 1156 | A169 | 12d multicolored | 4.25 | 4.25 |
| 1157 | A169 | 15d multicolored | 4.50 | 4.50 |

**Size: 127x102mm**
*Imperf*

| | | | | |
|---|---|---|---|---|
| 1158 | A169 | 20d multicolored | 7.00 | 7.00 |
| 1159 | A169 | 20d multicolored | 7.00 | 7.00 |
| 1160 | A169 | 20d multicolored | 7.00 | 7.00 |
| 1161 | A169 | 20d multicolored | 7.00 | 7.00 |
| | | Nos. 1142-1161 (20) | 53.00 | 51.45 |

While Nos. 1142-1143, 1146, 1148, 1150, 1153, 1155-1156, 1160-1161 have the same issue date as Nos. 1144-1145, 1147, 1149, 1151-1152, 1154, 1157-1159, the dollar value of Nos. 1142-1143, 1146, 1148, 1150, 1153, 1155-1156, 1160-1161 was lower when they were released.

Christmas — A170

Paintings by Fra Angelico: 20b, The Madonna of Humility. 50b, Madonna and Child with Angels. 75b, The Virgin and Child with Angels. 1d, Annunciation. 1.25d, Presentation in the Temple. 5d, Annunciation, diff. 10d, Madonna della Stella. 15d, Naming of St. John the Baptist. No. 1170, Annunciation and Adoration of the Magi. No. 1171, Coronation of the Virgin.

**1991, Dec. 23 Perf. 12**

| | | | | |
|---|---|---|---|---|
| 1162 | A170 | 20b multicolored | .30 | .25 |
| 1163 | A170 | 50b multicolored | .30 | .25 |
| 1164 | A170 | 75b multicolored | .30 | .25 |
| 1165 | A170 | 1d multicolored | .35 | .30 |
| 1166 | A170 | 1.25d multicolored | .40 | .35 |
| 1167 | A170 | 5d multicolored | 1.40 | 1.40 |
| 1168 | A170 | 10d multicolored | 2.25 | 2.25 |
| 1169 | A170 | 15d multicolored | 3.00 | 3.00 |
| | | Nos. 1162-1169 (8) | 8.30 | 8.05 |

**Souvenir Sheets**
*Perf. 14½*

| | | | | |
|---|---|---|---|---|
| 1170 | A170 | 20d multicolored | 5.00 | 5.00 |
| 1171 | A170 | 20d multicolored | 5.00 | 5.00 |

**Queen Elizabeth II's Accession to the Throne, 40th Anniv.**

No. 1176, Queen at left, yacht. No. 1177, Queen at right, boat.

**Common Design Type**

**1992, Feb. 6 Litho. Perf. 14**

| | | | | |
|---|---|---|---|---|
| 1172 | CD348 | 20b multicolored | .30 | .25 |
| 1173 | CD348 | 50b multicolored | .30 | .25 |
| 1174 | CD348 | 1d multicolored | .40 | .35 |
| 1175 | CD348 | 15d multicolored | 4.00 | 4.00 |
| | | Nos. 1172-1175 (4) | 5.00 | 4.85 |

**Souvenir Sheets**

| | | | | |
|---|---|---|---|---|
| 1176 | CD348 | 20d multicolored | 5.00 | 5.00 |
| 1177 | CD348 | 20d multicolored | 5.00 | 5.00 |

Famous Blues Musicians — A171

20b, Son House. 25b, W. C. Handy. 50b, Muddy Waters. 75b, Lightnin Hopkins. 1d, Ma Rainey. 1.25d, Mance Lipscomb. 1.50d, Mahalia Jackson. 2d, Ella Fitzgerald. 3d, Howlin Wolf. 5d, Bessie Smith. 7d, Leadbelly. 10d, Joe Willie Wilkins.

No. 1190, Gambian string drummer. No. 1191, Elvis Presley. No. 1192, Billie Holiday.

**1992, Feb. 12 Perf. 14**

| | | | | |
|---|---|---|---|---|
| 1178 | A171 | 20b multicolored | .30 | .25 |
| 1179 | A171 | 25b multicolored | .30 | .25 |
| 1180 | A171 | 50b multicolored | .35 | .35 |
| 1181 | A171 | 75b multicolored | .45 | .45 |
| 1182 | A171 | 1d multicolored | .50 | .50 |
| 1183 | A171 | 1.25d multicolored | .55 | .55 |
| 1184 | A171 | 1.50d multicolored | .65 | .65 |
| 1185 | A171 | 2d multicolored | .80 | .80 |
| 1186 | A171 | 3d multicolored | .95 | .95 |
| 1187 | A171 | 5d multicolored | 1.40 | 1.40 |
| 1188 | A171 | 7d multicolored | 1.75 | 1.75 |
| 1189 | A171 | 10d multicolored | 2.25 | 2.25 |
| | | Nos. 1178-1189 (12) | 10.25 | 10.15 |

**Souvenir Sheets**

| | | | | |
|---|---|---|---|---|
| 1190 | A171 | 20d multicolored | 5.00 | 5.00 |
| 1191 | A171 | 20d multicolored | 5.00 | 5.00 |
| 1192 | A171 | 20d multicolored | 5.00 | 5.00 |

While all stamps have the same issue date the dollar value of some was lower when they actually were released.

A172

Papal Visit, 1992 A172a

Designs: 1d, Pope John Paul II. 1.25d, Pope, Pres. Dwada Jawara. 20d, Flags, Papal arms. 25d, Pope at Mass.

**1992, Feb. 23 Litho. Perf. 14**

| | | | | |
|---|---|---|---|---|
| 1193 | A172 | 1d multicolored | .60 | .60 |
| 1194 | A172 | 1.25d multicolored | .70 | .70 |
| 1195 | A172 | 5.00d multicolored | 5.00 | 5.00 |
| | | Nos. 1193-1195 (3) | 6.30 | 6.30 |

**Souvenir Sheet**

| | | | | |
|---|---|---|---|---|
| 1196 | A172 | 25d multicolored | 7.00 | 7.00 |

**Embossed**
**Perf. 12**
**Without Gum**
**Size: 65x43mm**

| | | | | |
|---|---|---|---|---|
| 1196A | A172a | 50d gold | 25.00 | |

No. 1196A was not available until late 1993, exists imperf on large card.

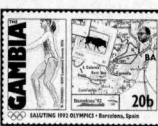

1992 Summer Olympics, Barcelona A173

20b, Map & Nadia Comaneci, gymnastics, Romania, 1976. 50b, D. Moorcraft, 5000 meters, Great Britain, 1984. 75b, M. Nemeth, javelin, Hungary, 1976. 1d, J. Pedraza, 20k walking, Mexico, 1968. 1.25d, Map, Spanish Arms & flag, Yachting soling class, Brazil, 1984. 1.50d, Spanish building, Field hockey, East Germany, 1984. 12d, Map & Michael Jordan, basketball, US, 1984. 15d, V. Borzov, 100 meters, USSR, 1972. No. 1205, Flamenco dancer, vert. No. 1206, Map & Bull.

**1992, Mar. 6 Litho. Perf. 14**

| | | | | |
|---|---|---|---|---|
| 1197 | A173 | 20b multicolored | .30 | .25 |
| 1198 | A173 | 50b multicolored | .40 | .30 |
| 1199 | A173 | 75b multicolored | .45 | .40 |
| 1200 | A173 | 1d multicolored | .50 | .50 |
| 1201 | A173 | 1.25d multicolored | .70 | .70 |
| 1202 | A173 | 1.50d multicolored | .75 | .75 |
| 1203 | A173 | 12d multicolored | 3.00 | 3.00 |
| 1204 | A173 | 15d multicolored | 5.00 | 5.00 |
| | | Nos. 1197-1204 (8) | 11.10 | 10.90 |

**Souvenir Sheet**

| | | | | |
|---|---|---|---|---|
| 1205 | A173 | 20d multicolored | 6.25 | 6.25 |
| 1206 | A173 | 20d multicolored | 6.25 | 6.25 |

While Nos. 1197, 1201-1203, 1206 have the same issue date as Nos. 1198-1200, 1204-1205, the value of Nos. 1197, 1201-1203, 1206 was lower when they were released.

Easter — A174

Paintings: 20b, Christ Presented to the People, by Rembrandt. 50b, Christ Carrying the Cross, by Mathias Grunewald. 75b, The Crucifixion, by Mathias Grunewald. 1d, The Crucifixion, by Rubens. 1.25d, The Road to Calvary (detail), by Tintoretto. 1.50d, The Road to Calvary (entire), by Tintoretto. 15d, The Crucifixion, by Masaccio. 20d, Descent from the Cross (detail), by Rembrandt. No. 1215, Crowning with Thorns (detail), by Titian. No. 1216, Crowning with Thorns, by Anthony Van Dyck.

**1992, Apr. 16 Litho. Perf. 13½**

| | | | | |
|---|---|---|---|---|
| 1207 | A174 | 20b multicolored | .30 | .25 |
| 1208 | A174 | 50b multicolored | .30 | .25 |
| 1209 | A174 | 75b multicolored | .30 | .25 |
| 1210 | A174 | 1d multicolored | .30 | .25 |
| 1211 | A174 | 1.25d multicolored | .45 | .35 |
| 1212 | A174 | 1.50d multicolored | .55 | .40 |
| 1213 | A174 | 15d multicolored | 3.75 | 3.75 |
| 1214 | A174 | 20d multicolored | 4.75 | 4.75 |
| | | Nos. 1207-1214 (8) | 10.70 | 10.25 |

**Souvenir Sheets**

| | | | | |
|---|---|---|---|---|
| 1215 | A174 | 25d multicolored | 6.25 | 6.25 |
| 1216 | A174 | 25d multicolored | 6.25 | 6.25 |

World Columbian Stamp Expo, Chicago — A175

Walt Disney characters in Chicago: 50b, Mickey at Navy pier. 1d, Mickey floats by Wrigley Building. 1.25d, Donald graduates from University of Chicago. 12d, Goofy at Chicago's Adler Planetarium. No. 1221, Goofy above Chicago at the Hancock Center, horiz.

**1992, Apr. 8 Litho. Perf. 13½x14**

| | | | | |
|---|---|---|---|---|
| 1217 | A175 | 50b multicolored | .50 | .25 |
| 1218 | A175 | 1d multicolored | .65 | .50 |
| 1219 | A175 | 1.25d multicolored | .80 | .75 |
| 1220 | A175 | 12d multicolored | 5.00 | 5.00 |
| | | Nos. 1217-1220 (4) | 6.95 | 6.50 |

**Souvenir Sheet**
*Perf. 14x13½*

| | | | | |
|---|---|---|---|---|
| 1221 | A175 | 18d multicolored | 7.50 | 7.50 |

No. 1220 has name spelled "Alder."

Granada '92 — A176

Mickey Mouse as Columbus: 20b, With map. 75b, Ideas rejected. 1.50d, Explores America. 15d, Returns to Spain. No. 1231, Embarks for America.

**1992, Apr. 8**    **Perf. 13½x14**
| | | | | |
|---|---|---|---|---|
| 1227 | A176 | 20b multicolored | .60 | .60 |
| 1228 | A176 | 75b multicolored | .80 | .80 |
| 1229 | A176 | 1.50d multicolored | 1.00 | 1.00 |
| 1230 | A176 | 15d multicolored | 4.75 | 4.75 |
| | | Nos. 1227-1230 (4) | 7.15 | 7.15 |

**Souvenir Sheet**
| | | | | |
|---|---|---|---|---|
| 1231 | A176 | 18d multicolored | 7.00 | 7.00 |

Flowers — A177

20b, Hibiscus. 50b, Calabash nutmeg. 75b, Silk cotton tree. 1d, Oncoba. 1.25d, Paintbrush plant. 1.50d, Tree gardenia. 5d, Glory bower. 5d, Ashanti blood. 10d, African peach. 12d, Butterfly bush. 15d, Crepe ginger. 18d, Spider tresses.

No. 1249, Water lily. No. 1250, Bougainvillea. No. 1251, Baobab tree. No. 1252, Climbing pea.

**1992, July 21**    **Litho.**    **Perf. 14**
| | | | | |
|---|---|---|---|---|
| 1237 | A177 | 20b multicolored | .30 | .25 |
| 1238 | A177 | 50b multicolored | .30 | .25 |
| 1239 | A177 | 75b multicolored | .30 | .30 |
| 1240 | A177 | 1d multicolored | .40 | .40 |
| 1241 | A177 | 1.25d multicolored | .50 | .50 |
| 1242 | A177 | 1.50d multicolored | .55 | .55 |
| 1243 | A177 | 2d multicolored | .70 | .70 |
| 1244 | A177 | 5d multicolored | 1.30 | 1.30 |
| 1245 | A177 | 10d multicolored | 2.25 | 2.25 |
| 1246 | A177 | 12d multicolored | 2.50 | 2.50 |
| 1247 | A177 | 15d multicolored | 3.00 | 3.00 |
| 1248 | A177 | 18d multicolored | 3.25 | 3.25 |
| | | Nos. 1237-1248 (12) | 15.35 | 15.25 |

**Souvenir Sheets**
| | | | | |
|---|---|---|---|---|
| 1249 | A177 | 20d multicolored | 4.25 | 4.25 |
| 1250 | A177 | 20d multicolored | 4.25 | 4.25 |
| 1251 | A177 | 20d multicolored | 4.25 | 4.25 |
| 1252 | A177 | 20d multicolored | 4.25 | 4.25 |

While Nos. 1240, 1242, 1244, 1247, 1250 have the same release date as Nos. 1237, 1241, 1243, 1248-1249, their values in relation to the dollar were higher when they were released.

Riverboats
A178

Riverboat and waterway: 20b, Joven Antonia, Gambia River. 50b, Dresden, Elbe River. 75b, Medway Queen, Medway River. 1d, Lady Wright, Gambia River. 1.25d, Devin, Vltava River. 1.50d, Lady Chilel, Gambia River. 5d, Robert Fulton, Hudson River. 10d, Coonawarra, Murray River. 12d, Nakusp, Columbia River. 15d, Lucy Ashton, Firth of Clyde. No. 1263, Rudesheim, Rhine River. No. 1264, City of Cairo, Mississippi River.

**1992, Aug. 3**    **Litho.**    **Perf. 14**
| | | | | |
|---|---|---|---|---|
| 1253 | A178 | 20b multicolored | .30 | .25 |
| 1254 | A178 | 50b multicolored | .30 | .25 |
| 1255 | A178 | 75b multicolored | .30 | .30 |
| 1256 | A178 | 1d multicolored | .40 | .40 |
| 1257 | A178 | 1.25d multicolored | .50 | .50 |
| 1258 | A178 | 1.50d multicolored | .60 | .60 |
| 1259 | A178 | 5d multicolored | 1.50 | 1.50 |
| 1260 | A178 | 10d multicolored | 2.25 | 2.25 |
| 1261 | A178 | 12d multicolored | 2.40 | 2.40 |
| 1262 | A178 | 15d multicolored | 3.00 | 3.00 |
| | | Nos. 1253-1262 (10) | 11.55 | 11.45 |

**Souvenir Sheets**
| | | | | |
|---|---|---|---|---|
| 1263 | A178 | 20d multicolored | 6.00 | 6.00 |
| 1264 | A178 | 20d multicolored | 6.00 | 6.00 |

**Miniature Sheet**

World War II in the Pacific
A179

Designs: a, USS Pennsylvania. b, Japanese attack begins. c, USS Ward sinking Japanese submarine. d, Ford Naval Air Station under attack. e, News bulletin announcing attack. f, Front page of Honolulu Star-Bulletin. g, Japanese invade Guam. h, US recovers Wake Island. i, Doolittle raids Japan from USS Hornet. j, Battle of Midway.

**1992**    **Litho.**    **Perf. 14½x15**
| | | | | |
|---|---|---|---|---|
| 1265 | A179 | 2d Sheet of 10, #a.-j. | 13.00 | 13.00 |

1992 Summer Olympics, Barcelona
A180

Designs: 20b, Women's double sculls. 50b, Kayak, vert. 75b, Women's precision rapid-fire shooting. 1d, Judo, vert. 1.25d, Javelin, vert. 1.50d, Gymnastics, vault, vert. 3d, Windsurfing, vert. 5d, High jump. No. 1274, Women's 200-meter backstroke. No. 1275, Table tennis.

**1992, Aug. 10**    **Litho.**    **Perf. 14**
| | | | | |
|---|---|---|---|---|
| 1266 | A180 | 20b multicolored | .30 | .30 |
| 1267 | A180 | 50b multicolored | .50 | .50 |
| 1268 | A180 | 75b multicolored | .70 | .70 |
| 1269 | A180 | 1d multicolored | .80 | .80 |
| 1270 | A180 | 1.25d multicolored | 1.00 | 1.00 |
| 1271 | A180 | 1.50d multicolored | 1.25 | 1.25 |
| 1272 | A180 | 3d multicolored | 2.00 | 2.00 |
| 1273 | A180 | 5d multicolored | 3.00 | 3.00 |
| | | Nos. 1266-1273 (8) | 9.55 | 9.55 |

**Souvenir Sheets**
| | | | | |
|---|---|---|---|---|
| 1274 | A180 | 18d multicolored | 6.25 | 6.25 |
| 1275 | A180 | 18d multicolored | 6.25 | 6.25 |

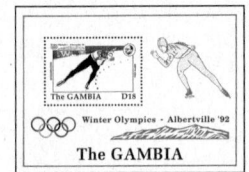

1992 Winter Olympics, Albertville — A181

Designs: 2d, Downhill skiing, vert. 10d, Four-man bobsled, vert. 12d, Ski jumping, vert. 15d, Slalom skiing.

No. 1280, 18d, Men's 500-meter speedskating. No. 1281, 18d, Pairs figure skating, vert.

**1992, Aug. 10**    **Litho.**    **Perf. 14**
| | | | |
|---|---|---|---|
| 1276-1279 | A181 | Set of 4 | 16.00 16.00 |

**Souvenir Sheets**
| | | | |
|---|---|---|---|
| 1280-1281 | A181 | Set of 2 | 14.00 14.00 |

Dinosaurs — A182

20b, Dryosaurus. 25b, Saurolophus. 50b, No. 1291, Allosaurus. 75b, Fabrosaurus. 1d, Deinonychus. 1.25d, No. 1292A, Cetiosaurus. 1.50d, Camptosaurus. 2d, No. 1292, Ornithosuchus. 3d, Spinosaurus. 5d, Ornithomimus. 10d, Kentrosaurus. 12d, Schlermochus.

**1992, Sept. 21**    **Litho.**    **Perf. 14**
| | | | | |
|---|---|---|---|---|
| 1283 | A182 | 20b multi | .45 | .45 |
| 1284 | A182 | 25b multi | .45 | .45 |
| 1284A | A182 | 50b multi | .55 | .55 |
| 1284B | A182 | 75b multi | .65 | .65 |
| 1284C | A182 | 1d multi | .65 | .65 |
| 1285 | A182 | 1.25d multi | .75 | .75 |
| 1286 | A182 | 1.50d multi | .75 | .75 |
| 1286A | A182 | 2d multi | .75 | .75 |
| 1287 | A182 | 3d multi | .80 | .80 |
| 1288 | A182 | 5d multi | 1.25 | 1.25 |
| 1289 | A182 | 10d multi | 2.25 | 2.25 |
| 1290 | A182 | 12d multi | 2.75 | 2.75 |
| | | Nos. 1283-1290 (12) | 12.05 | 12.05 |

**Souvenir Sheets**
| | | | | |
|---|---|---|---|---|
| 1291 | A182 | 25d multi | 6.50 | 6.50 |
| 1292 | A182 | 25d multi | 6.50 | 6.50 |
| 1292A | A182 | 25d multi | 6.50 | 6.50 |

Genoa '92.

Walt Disney's Goofy, 60th Anniv.
A183

Scenes from Disney cartoon films: 50b, Orphan's Benefit, 1934, 1941. 75b, Moose Hunters, 1937. 1d, Mickey's Amateurs, 1937. 1.25d, Lonesome Ghosts, 1937. 5d, Boat Builders, 1938. 7d, The Whalers, 1938. 10d, Goofy and Wilbur, 1939. 15d, Saludos Amigos, 1941. No. 1301, The Band Concert, 1935, vert. No. 1302, Goofy today, vert.

**1992**    **Litho.**    **Perf. 14x13½**
| | | | | |
|---|---|---|---|---|
| 1293 | A183 | 50b multicolored | .45 | .45 |
| 1294 | A183 | 75b multicolored | .65 | .65 |
| 1295 | A183 | 1d multicolored | .80 | .80 |
| 1296 | A183 | 1.25d multicolored | .80 | .80 |
| 1297 | A183 | 5d multicolored | 2.00 | 2.00 |
| 1298 | A183 | 7d multicolored | 2.50 | 2.50 |
| 1299 | A183 | 10d multicolored | 2.50 | 2.50 |
| 1300 | A183 | 15d multicolored | 3.00 | 3.00 |
| | | Nos. 1293-1300 (8) | 12.70 | 12.70 |

**Souvenir Sheets**
**Perf. 13½x14**
| | | | | |
|---|---|---|---|---|
| 1301 | A183 | 20d multicolored | 8.00 | 8.00 |
| 1302 | A183 | 20d multicolored | 8.00 | 8.00 |

Discovery of America, 500th Anniv. — A184

5d, Santa Maria. 12d, Pinta, Santa Maria, and Nina. 18d, Tree branch, green-winged macaw.

**1992, Oct.**    **Litho.**    **Perf. 14**
| | | | | |
|---|---|---|---|---|
| 1303 | A184 | 5d multi | 1.25 | 1.25 |
| 1304 | A184 | 12d multi | 2.25 | 2.25 |

**Souvenir Sheet**
| | | | | |
|---|---|---|---|---|
| 1305 | A184 | 18d multi, vert. | 8.00 | 8.00 |

Golf — A186

Pres. Jarwara playing golf and: 20b, Map, flag of Australia. 1d, Trophy, Gambian flag. 1.50d, Gambian flag. 2d, Map, flag of Japan. 3d, Map, flag of US. 5d, Trophy, 1985, Gambian flag (small portrait only). No. 1312, Map, flag of Scotland. 12d, Map, flag of Italy. No. 1312B, Pres. Jawara about to tee off. No. 1312C, Gambian flag (small portrait).

**1992**    **Litho.**    **Perf. 14**
| | | | | |
|---|---|---|---|---|
| 1306 | A186 | 20b multi | .70 | .70 |
| 1307 | A186 | 1d multi | .90 | .90 |
| 1308 | A186 | 1.50d multi | 1.10 | 1.10 |
| 1309 | A186 | 2d multi | 1.40 | 1.40 |
| 1310 | A186 | 3d multi | 1.75 | 1.75 |
| 1311 | A186 | 5d multi | 2.40 | 2.40 |
| 1312 | A186 | 10d multi | 3.50 | 3.50 |
| 1312A | A186 | 12d multi | 4.25 | 4.25 |
| | | Nos. 1306-1312A (8) | 16.00 | 16.00 |

**Souvenir Sheets**
| | | | | |
|---|---|---|---|---|
| 1312B | A186 | 10d multi | 8.00 | 8.00 |
| 1312C | A186 | 18d multi, horiz. | 8.00 | 8.00 |

No. 1306, Royal Melbourne Golf Course, Australia. No. 1309, Shinonoseki Golf Course, Japan. No. 1310, US Open, Pebble Beach. No. 1312, St. Andrew's Golf Course, Scotland. No. 1312A, Italian Open, Monticello, Milan.

Issued: 20b, 2d, 5d, Nos. 1312, 1312B, Dec. 8; others, Oct.

**Souvenir Sheet**

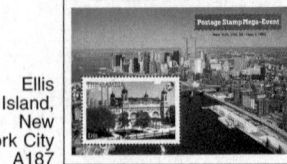

Ellis Island, New York City
A187

**1992, Oct. 28**    **Litho.**    **Perf. 14**
| | | | | |
|---|---|---|---|---|
| 1313 | A187 | 18d multicolored | 5.75 | 5.75 |

Postage Stamp Mega Event '92, New York City.

Christmas — A188

Details or entire paintings: 50b, The Holy Family, by Raphael. 75b, Madonna and Child with St. Elizabeth and the Infant St. John (Small Holy Family), by Raphael. 1d, The Holy Family as the Little Holy Family, by Raphael. 1.25d, Escape to Egypt, by Broederlam. 1.50d, Flight Into Egypt, by Isenbrant. No. 1319, The Flight into Egypt, by Cosimo Tura. No. 1320, Flight into Egypt, by Master of Hoogstraelen. No. 1321, The Holy Family, by El Greco. 4d, The Holy Family, by Bernard Van Orley. 5d, Holy Family with Infant Jesus Sleeping, by Charles Le Brun. 10d, Rest on the Flight to Egypt, by Gentileschi. 12d, Rest on the Flight to Egypt, by Orazio Gentileschi. No. 1326, The Holy Family, by Giorgione. No. 1327, Rest on the Flight to Egypt, by Simone Cantarino. No. 1328, The Flight to Egypt, by Vittore Carpaccio.

**1992, Nov. 3**    **Litho.**    **Perf. 13½x14**
| | | | | |
|---|---|---|---|---|
| 1314 | A188 | 50b multicolored | .30 | .25 |
| 1315 | A188 | 75b multicolored | .35 | .30 |
| 1316 | A188 | 1d multicolored | .40 | .35 |
| 1317 | A188 | 1.25d multicolored | .45 | .45 |
| 1318 | A188 | 1.50d multicolored | .45 | .45 |
| 1319 | A188 | 2d multicolored | .65 | .65 |
| 1320 | A188 | 2d multicolored | .65 | .65 |
| 1321 | A188 | 2d multicolored | .65 | .65 |
| 1322 | A188 | 4d multicolored | 1.00 | 1.00 |
| 1323 | A188 | 5d multicolored | 1.25 | 1.25 |
| 1324 | A188 | 10d multicolored | 2.00 | 2.00 |
| 1325 | A188 | 12d multicolored | 2.75 | 2.75 |
| | | Nos. 1314-1325 (12) | 10.90 | 10.65 |

**Souvenir Sheets**
| | | | | |
|---|---|---|---|---|
| 1326 | A188 | 25d multicolored | 4.00 | 4.00 |
| 1327 | A188 | 25d multicolored | 4.00 | 4.00 |
| 1328 | A188 | 25d multicolored | 4.00 | 4.00 |

A189

A190

A191

A192

A193

Anniversaries and Events — A195

Designs: No. 1329, Ariane 4 rocket. No. 1330, Berlin airlift. No. 1331, LZ127 Graf Zeppelin. 6d, Jentink's duiker. 7d, World map. 9d, Wolfgang Amadeus Mozart. No. 1335, America's Cup yacht Enterprise, 1930. No. 1336, Imperial parrot. No. 1337, Lions Intl. emblem. No. 1338, American Space shuttle. 15d, Prisoners of war returning home, Adenauer. 18d, First rigid airship, LZ1. No. 1341, European Space Agency's Hermes space shuttle. No. 1342, Scene from "The Marriage of Figaro." No. 1343, Face of Adenauer. No. 1344, Count Ferdinand von Zeppelin. No. 1345, Earth as seen from space.

| 1992-93 | | Litho. | Perf. | 14 |
|---|---|---|---|---|
| 1329 | A189 | 2d multicolored | .95 | .95 |
| 1330 | A191 | 1.25d multicolored | 1.25 | 1.25 |
| 1331 | A191 | 2d multicolored | .95 | .95 |
| 1332 | A192 | 6d multicolored | 2.10 | 2.10 |
| 1333 | A193 | 7d multicolored | 2.40 | 2.40 |
| 1334 | A190 | 9d multicolored | 4.00 | 4.00 |
| 1335 | A194 | 10d multicolored | 3.25 | 3.25 |
| 1336 | A192 | 10d multicolored | 2.75 | 2.75 |
| 1337 | A195 | 10d multicolored | 2.40 | 2.40 |
| 1338 | A189 | 12d multicolored | 2.40 | 2.40 |
| 1339 | A191 | 15d multicolored | 4.50 | 4.50 |
| 1340 | A191 | 18d multicolored | 2.90 | 2.90 |
| | | Nos. 1329-1340 (12) | 29.85 | 29.85 |

**Souvenir Sheets**

| 1341 | A189 | 18d multicolored | 5.75 | 5.75 |
|---|---|---|---|---|
| 1342 | A190 | 18d multicolored | 7.50 | 7.50 |
| 1343 | A191 | 18d multicolored | 7.50 | 7.50 |
| 1344 | A191 | 18d multicolored | 5.75 | 5.75 |
| 1345 | A192 | 18d multicolored | 5.75 | 5.75 |

Intl. Space Year (Nos. 1329, 1338, 1341). Wolfgang Amadeus Mozart, bicent. of death (Nos. 1334, 1342). Konrad Adenauer, 25th anniv. of death (Nos. 1330, 1339, 1343). Count Zeppelin, 75th anniv. of death (Nos. 1331, 1340, 1344). Earth Summit, Rio de Janeiro (Nos. 1332, 1336, 1345). Intl. Conf. on Nutrition, Rome (No. 1333). America's Cup yacht race (No. 1335). Lions Intl., 75th anniv. (No. 1337).

Issued: Nos. 1333, 1335, 1339, 1343, 1/93; others, 12/92.

Peace Corps, 25th Anniv. — A196

**1993, Feb.**

| 1346 | A196 | 2d multicolored | 1.40 | 1.40 |
|---|---|---|---|---|

Elvis Presley, 15th Anniv. of Death (in 1992) — A197

No. 1347: a, Portrait. b, With guitar. c, Holding microphone.

**1993**

| 1347 | A197 | 3d Strip of 3, #a.-c. | 2.75 | 2.75 |
|---|---|---|---|---|

**Miniature Sheets**

Baseball Films A198

No. 1348 — Movie and stars: a, Casey at the Bat, Wallace Beery, 1927, Elliott Gould, 1986. b, Babe Comes Home, Anna Q. Nilsson, Babe Ruth, 1927. c, Elmer the Great, Joe E. Brown, 1933. d, The Naughty Nineties, Bud Abbott and Lou Costello, 1945. e, Take Me Out to the Ball Game, Frank Sinatra, Gene Kelly, Esther Williams, 1949. f, Damn Yankees, Tab Hunter, Gwen Verdon, 1958. g, The Pride of St. Louis, Dan Dailey, 1952. h, Brewster's Millions, John Candy, Richard Pryor, 1985.

No. 1349: a, The Jackie Robinson Story, Jackie Robinson, Ruby Dee, 1950. b, Bang the Drum Slowly, Robert DeNiro, 1973. c, The Bingo Long Traveling All-Stars & Motor Kings, James Earl Jones, Billy Dee Williams, 1976. d, Bull Durham, Kevin Costner, Susan Sarandon, 1988. e, Eight Men Out, eight actors, 1988. f, Field of Dreams, Ray Liotta, 1989. g, Major League, Charlie Sheen, 1989. h, Mr. Baseball, Tom Selleck, 1992.

No. 1350, The Babe, John Goodman, 1992. No. 1351, The Natural, Robert Redford. No. 1351A, The Winning Team, Ronald Reagan. 351B, A League of Their Own, Tom Hanks, Madonna.

| 1993, Mar. 25 | | Litho. | Perf. | 13 |
|---|---|---|---|---|
| 1348 | A198 | 3d Sheet of 8, #a.- | | |
| | | h. | 7.50 | 7.50 |
| 1349 | A198 | 3d Sheet of 8, #a.- | | |
| | | h. | 7.50 | 7.50 |

**Souvenir Sheet**

| 1350 | A198 | 20d multi | 5.00 | 5.00 |
|---|---|---|---|---|
| 1351 | A198 | 20d multi, vert. | 5.00 | 5.00 |
| 1351A | A198 | 20d multi | 5.00 | 5.00 |
| 1351B | A198 | 20d multi, vert. | 5.00 | 5.00 |

**Miniature Sheets**

Louvre Museum, Bicent. A199

Details from paintings, by Jacques-Louis David (1748-1825): Nos. 1352a-b, Oath of the Horatii (diff. details). c, The Love of Paris & Helen. d, Rape of the Sabine Women. e, Leonidas of Thermopylae. f-h, Napoleon Crowning Josephine (left, center, right).

Details from paintings, by Antoine (c. 1588-1648) and Louis (1593-1648) Le Nain: No. 1353a, Inside Home of Peasants. b-c, The Tobacco Smokers (diff. details). d, The Cart. e, Peasants' Meal. f-g, Interior Portraits (diff. details). h, The Forge.

Details or entire paintings, by Leonardo Da Vinci: No. 1354a, St. John the Baptist. b, Virgin of the Rocks. c, Bacchus. d, Woman from the Court of Milan. e, The Virgin of the Rocks (detail). f, Mona Lisa. g, Mona Lisa (detail of hands). h, Two Horsemen, Study of the Horse.

No. 1355, Allegory of Victory, by Mathieu Le Nain (1607-1677). No. 1356, The Artist and Her Daughter, by Elisabeth Vigee-Lebrun (1755-1842).

| 1993, Jan. 7 | | Litho. | Perf. | 12 |
|---|---|---|---|---|
| 1352 | A199 | 3d Sheet of 8, #a.-h. | 7.50 | 7.50 |
| 1353 | A199 | 3d Sheet of 8, #a.-h. | 7.50 | 7.50 |
| 1354 | A199 | 3d Sheet of 8, #a.-h. | 7.50 | 7.50 |

**Souvenir Sheets**

*Perf. 14½*

| 1355 | A199 | 20d multicolored | 8.25 | 8.25 |
|---|---|---|---|---|
| 1356 | A199 | 20d multicolored | 8.25 | 8.25 |

Nos. 1355-1356 each contain one 55x88mm stamp.

**Miniature Sheet**

Animals of West Africa — A200

No. 1358: a, Giraffe. b, Baboon. c, Caracal. d, Large-spotted genet. e, Bushbuck. f, Red-fronted gazelle. g, Red-flanked duiker. h, Cape buffalo. i, African civet. j, Side-striped jackal. k, Ratel. l, Striped polecat.

No. 1359: a, Vervet. b, Blackish-green guenon. c, Long-tailed pangolin. d, Leopard. e,

Elephant. f, Hunting dog. g, Spotted hyena. h, Lion. i, Hippopotamus. j, Nile crocodile. k, Aardvark. l, Warthog.

| 1993, Apr. 5 | | Litho. | Perf. | 14 |
|---|---|---|---|---|
| 1358 | A200 | 2d Sheet of 12, #a.-l. | 10.00 | 10.00 |
| 1359 | A200 | 5d Sheet of 12, #a.-l. | 14.00 | 14.00 |

**Souvenir Sheet**

| 1360 | A200 | 20d like #1359b | 8.25 | 8.25 |
|---|---|---|---|---|

No. 1360 printed in continuous design with black frameline around stamp. A number has been reserved for an additional value in this set.

Long-Tailed Pangolin — A201

Pangolin in various positions on tree limb.

| 1993, Apr. 5 | | | | |
|---|---|---|---|---|
| 1362 | A201 | 1.25d multicolored | .70 | .70 |
| 1363 | A201 | 1.50d multicolored | .80 | .80 |
| 1364 | A201 | 2d multicolored | 1.00 | 1.00 |
| 1365 | A201 | 5d multicolored | 2.50 | 2.50 |
| | | Nos. 1362-1365 (4) | 5.00 | 5.00 |

**Souvenir Sheet**

| 1366 | A201 | 20d like #1363 | 7.50 | 7.50 |
|---|---|---|---|---|

World Wildlife Federation.
Nos. 1362-1365 exist imperf. Value, set of 4 $40. No. 1366 exists imperf. Value, $35.

Birds
A202  A203

Designs: 1.25d, Osprey. 1.50d, Egyptian vulture, horiz. 2d, Martial eagle. 3d, Ruppell's griffon vulture, horiz. 5d, Auger buzzard. 8d, Greater kestrel. 10d, Secretary bird. 15d, Bateleur eagle, horiz.

No. 1375a, Rose-ringed parakeet. b, Variable sunbird, c, Red-billed hornbill. d, Red-billed fire-finch. e, Common go-away bird. f, Crimson-breasted shrike. g, Gray-headed bush-shrike. h, Nicator. i, Egyptian plover. j, Congo peacock. k, Greater painted snipe. l, Crowned crane.

#1376, Verreaux's eagle. #1377, Tawny owl.

| 1993, Apr. 15 | | Litho. | Perf. | 14 |
|---|---|---|---|---|
| 1367 | A202 | 1.25d multicolored | 1.00 | .80 |
| 1368 | A202 | 1.50d multicolored | 1.25 | 1.00 |
| 1369 | A202 | 2d multicolored | 1.60 | 1.20 |
| 1370 | A202 | 3d multicolored | 2.00 | 1.60 |
| 1371 | A202 | 5d multicolored | 2.00 | 2.00 |
| 1372 | A202 | 8d multicolored | 2.75 | 2.75 |
| 1373 | A202 | 10d multicolored | 2.75 | 2.75 |
| 1374 | A202 | 15d multicolored | 3.50 | 3.50 |
| | | Nos. 1367-1374 (8) | 16.85 | 15.60 |

**Miniature Sheet**

| 1375 | A203 | 2d Sheet of 12, #a.-l. | 18.50 | 18.50 |
|---|---|---|---|---|

**Souvenir Sheets**

| 1376 | A202 | 20d multicolored | 8.50 | 8.50 |
|---|---|---|---|---|
| 1377 | A202 | 20d multicolored | 8.50 | 8.50 |

Nos. 1376-1377 each contain 1 56x42mm stamp.

Aviation Anniversaries A204

Designs: No. 1379, Guyot balloon, 1785, vert. No. 1380, Dr. Hugo Eckener, zeppelin LZ3 in flight. No. 1381, Sopwith Snipe. No. 1382, Eckener, LZ3 moored to ground. 8d, Eckener, Graf Zeppelin. 10d, Balloon, Comte D'Artois, 1785, vert. 15d, Royal Aircraft Factory S.E.5. No. 1386, Avro 504K. No. 1387, Eckener, LZ3 in flight, diff. No. 1388, Blanchard's flying ship, 1785, vert.

| 1993, May | | Litho. | Perf. | 14 |
|---|---|---|---|---|
| 1379 | A204 | 2d multicolored | .70 | .70 |
| 1380 | A204 | 2d multicolored | .70 | .70 |
| 1381 | A204 | 5d multicolored | 1.25 | 1.25 |
| 1382 | A204 | 5d multicolored | 1.25 | 1.25 |
| 1383 | A204 | 8d multicolored | 2.00 | 2.00 |
| 1384 | A204 | 10d multicolored | 2.25 | 2.25 |
| 1385 | A204 | 15d multicolored | 3.00 | 3.00 |
| | | Nos. 1379-1385 (7) | 11.15 | 11.15 |

**Souvenir Sheets**

| 1386 | A204 | 20d multicolored | 7.00 | 7.00 |
|---|---|---|---|---|
| 1387 | A204 | 20d multicolored | 7.00 | 7.00 |
| 1388 | A204 | 20d multicolored | 7.00 | 7.00 |

Dr. Hugo Eckener, 125th birth anniv. (Nos. 1380, 1382, 1383, 1387). Royal Air Force, 75th anniv. (Nos. 1381, 1385, 1386).
Nos. 1379, 1384, 1388 are airmail.

**Miniature Sheet**

Coronation of Queen Elizabeth II, 40th Anniv. — A205

Designs: a, 2d, Official coronation photograph. b, 5d, Orb and Scepter. c, 8d, Winston Churchill. d, 10d, Queen during Trooping of the Color.
20d, Portrait, by Joe King, 1972.

| 1993, June 2 | | | Perf. | 13½x14 |
|---|---|---|---|---|
| 1389 | A205 | Sheet of 8, 2 each #a.-d. | 13.00 | 13.00 |

**Souvenir Sheet**

*Perf. 14*

| 1390 | A205 | 20d multicolored | 8.00 | 8.00 |
|---|---|---|---|---|

No. 1390 contains one 28x42mm stamp.

**Miniature Sheet**

A206

No. 1391 — Benz Automobiles: a, 1894 Benz Velo. b, 1894 Benz. c, 1885 Benz. d, 1905 Benz Mannheim. e, 1892 Benz. f, 1900 Benz, blue. g, 1911 Benz. h, 1893 Benz Velo. i, 1900 Benz, black. j, 1900 Benz, red. k, 1911 Benz, front view. l, 1885 Benz, rear view.

No. 1393, 20d, 1900 Benz, diff.

No. 1392 — Ford automobiles: a, Henry Ford, age 30, 1910 Model T. b, 1896, green seat. c, Henry Ford with Barney Oldfield and 1902 racing car, 999. d, 1896, Henry Ford with bicycle. e, 1903 Model A. f, 1908 Model T, top down. g, 1908 Model T, top up. h, 1906 Model K. i, 1931 Model A. j, 1906 Model A. k, 1906 Model N. l, 1905 Model F.

No. 1394, 1896 Ford with red seat.

| 1993, June 7 | | | Perf. | 14 |
|---|---|---|---|---|
| 1391 | A206 | 2d Sheet of 12, #a.-l. | 7.50 | 7.50 |
| 1392 | A206 | 2d Sheet of 12, #a.-l. | 7.50 | 7.50 |

**Souvenir Sheets**

| 1393 | A206 | 20d multicolored | 6.00 | 6.00 |
|---|---|---|---|---|
| 1394 | A206 | 20d multicolored | 6.00 | 6.00 |

1st Benz 4-wheel automobile, cent. (Nos. 1391, 1393).
1st engine by Henry Ford, cent. (Nos. 1392, 1394).

**Miniature Sheets**

Entertainers — A207

No. 1395: a, Buddy Holly. b, Otis Redding. c, Bill Haley. d, Dinah Washington. e, Musical instruments. f, Ritchie Valens. g, Clyde McPhatter. h, Elvis Presley.

No. 1396: a-i, Various pictures of Madonna.
No. 1397: a-i, Various pictures of Elvis Presley.
No. 1398: a-i, Various pictures of Marilyn Monroe.

**1993, July 26  Litho.      Perf. 14**
| | | | | |
|---|---|---|---|---|
|**1395**|A207|3d Sheet of 8, #a.-|||
||||h.|10.00|10.00|
|**1396**|A207|3d Sheet of 9, #a.-|||
||||i.|10.00|10.00|
|**1397**|A207|3d Sheet of 9, #a.-|||
||||i.|10.00|10.00|
|**1398**|A207|3d Sheet of 9, #a.-|||
||||i.|10.00|10.00|
||*Nos. 1395-1398 (4)*||40.00|40.00|

Cats and Dogs — A208

No. 1399 — Cats, Siamese. b, Colorpoint longhair. c, Burmese. d, Birman. e, Snowshoe. f, Tonkinese. g, Foreign shorthair. h, Balinese. i, Oriental shorthair. j, Foreign shorthair, diff. k, Colorpoint longhair, diff. l, Colorpoint longhair, diff.
Dogs: No. 1400a, Shih tzu. b, Skye terrier. c, Berner laufhund. d, Boxer. e, Welsh corgi (Queen Elizabeth II). f, Dumfrieshire. g, Lurcher. h, Welsh corgi (Princess Anne). i, Pekinese. j, Papillon. k, Otterhound. l, Pug.
No. 1401, Colorpoint shorthair, vert. No. 1402, Burmese, vert. No. 1403, Long-haired dachshund. No. 1404, Cairn terrier.

**1993, Sept. 13  Litho.      Perf. 14**
| | | | | |
|---|---|---|---|---|
|**1399**|A208|2d Sheet of 12, #a.-l.|15.00|15.00|
|**1400**|A208|2d Sheet of 12, #a.-i.|14.00|14.00|
|**Souvenir Sheets**|||||
|**1401**|A208|20d multicolored|6.50|6.50|
|**1402**|A208|20d multicolored|6.50|6.50|
|**1403**|A208|20d multicolored|6.50|6.50|
|**1404**|A208|20d multicolored|6.50|6.50|

Taipei '93 — A209

Designs: No. 1405, Fawang Si Pagoda, Song Shan Mt., Henan. No. 1406, Wanshoubao Pagoda, Shashi. No. 1407, Red Pavilion, Shibaozhai. No. 1408, Songyue Si Pagoda, Song Shan Mt., Henan. No. 1409, Bond Center, Hong Kong. No. 1410, Tianning Si Pagoda, Beijing. No. 1411, Xuanzhuang Pagoda, Xian, Shenxi. No. 1412, Forbidden City, Beijing.
No. 1413 — Tang Dynasty funerary objects: a, Camel. b, Horse and female rider. c, Camel, diff. d, Yellow-glazed horse. e, Camel, diff. f, Horse with saddle.
No. 1414 — Pottery: a, Vase. b, Small wine cup. c, Fahua type Mei-ping vase. d, Urn vase, export ware. e, Tureen. f, Lidded Potiche.
No. 1415, Standing Buddhas,Hallway of Upper Huayan Si Temple, Datong, horiz. No. 1416, Seated Buddha, Main Hall, Shanhua Si Temple, Datong.

**1993, Sept. 27  Litho.      Perf. 14**
| | | | | |
|---|---|---|---|---|
|**1405**|A209|20b multicolored|.30|.25|
|**1406**|A209|20b multicolored|.30|.25|
|**1407**|A209|2d multicolored|.80|.80|
|**1408**|A209|2d multicolored|.80|.80|
|**1409**|A209|5d multicolored|1.75|1.75|
|**1410**|A209|5d multicolored|1.75|1.75|
|**1411**|A209|15d multicolored|3.25|3.25|
|**1412**|A209|15d multicolored|3.25|3.25|
||*Nos. 1405-1412 (8)*||12.20|12.10|
|**Miniature Sheets**|||||
|**1413**|A209|5d Sheet of 6, #a.-f.|13.00|13.00|
|**1414**|A209|5d Sheet of 6, #a.-f.|13.00|13.00|
|**Souvenir Sheets**|||||
|**1415**|A209|18d multicolored|5.50|5.50|
|**1416**|A209|18d multicolored|5.50|5.50|

**With Bangkok '93 Emblem**

No. 1417, Sanctuary of Prasat Phanom Wan. No. 1418, Lai Kham Vihan, Chiang Mai. No. 1419, Spirit Shrine, Bangkok. No. 1420, Walking Buddha, Wat Phra Si Ratana

Mahathat. No. 1421, Buddha, Sukhothai's Wat Mahathat. No. 1422, Gopura of Prasat Phanom Rung. No. 1423, Prang of Prasat Hin Phimai. No. 1424, Slender Chedis, Wat Yai Chai, Mongkon.
No. 1425 — Thai painting: a, Early Fruit Stand. b, Scene in Chinese Style, Wat Bovornivet. c, Buddha Descends from Tauatimsa. d, Sang Thong Tales, Lai Kham Vihan. e, The Damned in Hell, Wah Suthat. f, King Sanjaya Travels on Elephant, Wat Suwannaram.
No. 1426 — Thai Buddha sculpture: a, U Thong C, 14th-15th cent. b, Adorned Seated, 17th cent. c, Phra Chai, 19th cent. d, Bronze, 14th cent. e, U Thong A, bronze. f, Crowned, 14th-15th cent.
No. 1427, Ceramics, horiz. No. 1428, Character in Khon, dance drama.

**1993**
| | | | | |
|---|---|---|---|---|
|**1417**|A209|20b multicolored|.30|.25|
|**1418**|A209|20b multicolored|.30|.25|
|**1419**|A209|2d multicolored|.80|.80|
|**1420**|A209|2d multicolored|.80|.80|
|**1421**|A209|5d multicolored|1.75|1.75|
|**1422**|A209|5d multicolored|1.75|1.75|
|**1423**|A209|15d multicolored|3.25|3.25|
|**1424**|A209|15d multicolored|3.25|3.25|
||*Nos. 1417-1424 (8)*||12.20|12.10|
|**Miniature Sheets**|||||
|**1425**|A209|5d Sheet of 6, #a.-f.|13.00|13.00|
|**1426**|A209|5d Sheet of 6, #a.-f.|13.00|13.00|
|**Souvenir Sheets**|||||
|**1427**|A209|18d multicolored|5.50|5.50|
|**1428**|A209|18d multicolored|5.50|5.50|

**With Indopex '93 Emblem**

Designs: No. 1429, Pura Taman Ayun (garden temple), Mengwi, Bali. No. 1430, Natl. monument with statue of Prince Diponegoro, Jakarta. No. 1431, Candi Jawi, East Java. No. 1432, Guardian at Singosari Palace, East Java. No. 1433, Monument of Irian Jaya, (liberation), Jakarta. No. 1434, Central Temple, Prambanan complex, Lara Djonggrang. No. 1435, "Date of the Year Temple," Panataran complex, East Java. No. 1436, Brahma & Siva Temples, Loro Jonggrang, Java.
No. 1437 — Masks: a, Telek Luh. b, Jero Gde. c, Barong Macan. d, Monkey. e, Mata Gde. f, Jauk Kras.
No. 1438 — Paintings: a, Tree Mask, Soedibio, 1978. b, Dry Lizard, Hendra Gunawan, 1977. c, The Corn Eater, Sudjana Kerton, 1988. d, Night Watchman, Djoko Pekik, 1988. e, Hunger, Kerton, 1984. f, Arje Player, Soedjojono, 1971.
No. 1439, Stone carving, Brahma & Gods, Borobudur, Java, horiz. No. 1440, Effigies of the Dead, Torajaland, horiz.

**1993, Sept. 27  Litho.      Perf. 14**
| | | | | |
|---|---|---|---|---|
|**1429**|A209|20b multicolored|.30|.25|
|**1430**|A209|20b multicolored|.30|.25|
|**1431**|A209|2d multicolored|.80|.80|
|**1432**|A209|2d multicolored|.80|.80|
|**1433**|A209|5d multicolored|1.75|1.75|
|**1434**|A209|5d multicolored|1.75|1.75|
|**1435**|A209|15d multicolored|3.25|3.25|
|**1436**|A209|15d multicolored|3.25|3.25|
||*Nos. 1429-1436 (8)*||12.20|12.10|
|**Miniature Sheets**|||||
|**1437**|A209|5d Sheet of 6, #a.-f.|13.00|13.00|
|**1438**|A209|5d Sheet of 6, #a.-f.|13.00|13.00|
|**Souvenir Sheets**|||||
|**1439**|A209|18d multicolored|5.50|5.50|
|**1440**|A209|18d multicolored|5.50|5.50|

**Miniature Sheet**

Casey at the Bat A210

Nos. 1441-1443: Characters and scenes from Disney's animated film Casey at the Bat.

**1993, Oct. 25  Litho.   Perf. 14x13½**
| | | | | |
|---|---|---|---|---|
|**1441**|A210|2d Sheet of 9, #a.-i.|9.00|9.00|
|**Souvenir Sheets**|||||
|**1442**|A210|20d multicolored|7.00|7.00|
|**Perf. 13½x14**|||||
|**1443**|A210|20d multi, vert.|7.00|7.00|

Picasso — A211

Paintings: 2d, Woman with a Comb, 1906. 5d, The Mirror, 1932. 7d, Woman on a Pillow, 1969. 18d, The Three Dancers, 1925.

**1993, Oct. 7  Litho.      Perf. 14**
| | | | | |
|---|---|---|---|---|
|**1444-1446**|A211|Set of 3|5.00|5.00|
|**Souvenir Sheet**|||||
|**1447**|A211|18d multicolored|5.00|5.00|

Copernicus — A212

5d, Early astronomical instrument. 10d, Telescope.
18d, Copernicus.

**1993, Oct. 7  Perf. 14**
| | | | | |
|---|---|---|---|---|
|**1448-1449**|A212|Set of 2|4.00|4.00|
|**Souvenir Sheet**|||||
|**Perf. 12x13**|||||
|**1450**|A212|18d multi|5.00|5.00|

Polska '93 — A213

Paintings: 2d, Pont-Neuf, Paris, by Rudzka-Cybisowa, 1932. No. 1452, 10d, Honegger's Liturgical Symphony, by Bogusz, 1973. No. 1453, 10d, Niedzica castle. 18d, When You Enter Here, Whisper My Name Soundlessly, by Waniek, 1973.

**1993, Oct. 7  Perf. 14**
| | | | | |
|---|---|---|---|---|
|**1451-1453**|A213|Set of 3|6.75|6.75|
|**Souvenir Sheet**|||||
|**1454**|A213|18d multicolored|6.00|6.00|

1994 World Cup Soccer Championships, US — A214

Players, country: 1.25d, Hannich, Hungary; Stopyra, France. 1.50d, Labd, Morocco; Lineker, England. 2d, Segota, Canada; Morozov, Russia. 3d, Roger Milla, Cameroun. 5d, Rodax, Australia; Weiss, Czech Republic. 10d, Claesen, Belgium; Bossis & Amoros, France. 12d, Candida, Brazil; Ramirez, Costa Rica. 15d, Silva, Brazil; Platini, France. No. 1463, Muller, Brazil; McDonald, Ireland, horiz. No. 1463A, Buchwald and Matthaeus, Germany; Maradona, Argentina, horiz.

**1993, Nov. 22  Perf. 13½x14**
| | | | | |
|---|---|---|---|---|
|**1455**|A214|1.25d multi|.60|.60|
|**1456**|A214|1.50d multi|.65|.65|
|**1457**|A214|2d multi|.90|.90|
|**1458**|A214|3d multi|1.60|1.60|
|**1459**|A214|5d multi|2.25|2.25|
|**1460**|A214|10d multi|3.25|3.25|
|**1461**|A214|12d multi|3.50|3.50|
|**1462**|A214|15d multi|4.50|4.50|
||*Nos. 1455-1462 (8)*||17.25|17.25|
|**Souvenir Sheets**|||||
|**Perf. 13**|||||
|**1463**|A214|25d multi|8.50|8.50|
|**1463A**|A214|25d multi|8.50|8.50|

Christmas — A215

Designs: No. 1464, 25b, No. 1467, 2d, No. 1471, 15d, Details or entire painting, Adoration of the Magi, by Rubens.
Details or entire woodcut by Durer: No. 1465, 1d, Holy Family with Joachim & Anna. No. 1466, 1.50d, The Annunciation, Life of the Virgin. No. 1468, 2d, The Virgin Mary Worshipped by Albrecht Bonstetten. No. 1469, 7d, Virgin on a Throne, Crowned by an Angel. No. 1470, 10d, The Holy Family with Two Angels in a Portico (detail).
No. 1472, 20d, Adoration of the Magi, by Rubens. No. 1473, 20d, The Holy Family with Two Angels in a Portico, (entire), by Durer, horiz.

**1993, Dec. 1  Perf. 13½x14, 14x13½**
| | | | | |
|---|---|---|---|---|
|**1464-1471**|A215|Set of 8|14.00|14.00|
|**Souvenir Sheets**|||||
|**1472-1473**|A215|Set of 2|12.00|12.00|

Fine Art — A216

Paintings by Rembrandt: 50b, A Man in a Cap. No. 1476, Man with a Gold Helmet. 7d, A Franciscan Monk. 15d, The Apostle Paul. 20d, Dr. Tulp Demonstrating the Anatomy of the Arm, horiz.
Paintings by Matisse: 1.50d, Portrait of Pierre Matisse. No. 1477, Portrait of Auguste Pellerin (II). 5d, Andre Derain. 12d, The Young Sailor (II). No. 1483, Pianist and Checker Players, horiz.

**1993, Dec. 15  Perf. 13½x14**
| | | | | |
|---|---|---|---|---|
|**1474**|A216|50b multicolored|.75|.75|
|**1475**|A216|1.50d multicolored|1.25|1.25|
|**1476**|A216|2d multicolored|1.40|1.40|
|**1477**|A216|2d multicolored|1.50|1.50|
|**1478**|A216|5d multicolored|2.25|2.25|
|**1479**|A216|7d multicolored|3.00|3.00|
|**1480**|A216|12d multicolored|3.00|3.00|
|**1481**|A216|15d multicolored|3.50|3.50|
||*Nos. 1474-1481 (8)*||16.65|16.65|
|**Souvenir Sheets**|||||
|**Perf. 14x13½**|||||
|**1482**|A216|20d multicolored|7.50|7.50|
|**1483**|A216|20d multicolored|7.50|7.50|

Winter Sports — A217

Disney characters portraying sports: 50b, Ski ballet. 75b, Pairs figure skating. 1d, Speed skating. 1.25d, Biathlon. 4d, 4-Man bobsled. 5d, Luge. 7d, Figure skating. 10d, Downhill skiing. 15d, Ice hockey.
No. 1493, 20d, Cross country skiing. No. 1494, 20d, Mogul skiing.

**1993, Dec. 20  Perf. 13½x14**
| | | | | |
|---|---|---|---|---|
|**1484-1492**|A217|Set of 9|16.00|16.00|
|**Souvenir Sheets**|||||
|**1493-1494**|A217|20d Set of 2|13.00|13.00|

A218

Hong
Kong '94
A219

Stamps, painting, Spring Garden-1846, by M. Bruce: No. 1495, Hong Kong #357, left detail. No. 1496, Right detail, #1000.
No. 1497 — Museum of Qin Figures, Shaanxi Province, Tomb of First Emperor: a, Qin warriors, horses. b, Warrior in battle dress. c, Armor clad warrior. d, Chariot driver. e, Dog. f, Qin warriors.
No. 1498, Show emblem, Hong Kong #253, vert.

**1994, Feb. 18     Litho.     Perf. 14**
| | | | | |
|---|---|---|---|---|
| 1495 | | 1.50d multicolored | .70 | .40 |
| 1496 | | 1.50d multicolored | .70 | .40 |
| a. | A218 | Pair, #1495-1496 | 1.75 | 1.75 |
| 1497 | A219 | 1.50d Sheet of 6, #a.-f. | 5.00 | 5.00 |

**Souvenir Sheet**
| | | | | |
|---|---|---|---|---|
| 1498 | A218 | 20d multicolored | 5.75 | 5.75 |

Nos. 1495-1496 issued in sheets of 5 pairs. No. 1496a is a continuous design.
New Year 1994 (Year of the Dog) (Nos. 1497e, 1498).

New Year 1994
(Year of the Dog) — A220

Disney characters: 25b, Pluto the Racer. 50b, Fifi. 75b, Pluto, Jr. 1.25d, Goofy and Bowser. 1.50d, Butch. 2d, Toliver. 3d, Ronnie. 5d, Primo. 8d, Pluto's kid brother. 10d, Army mascot. 12d, Pluto and Dinah's pups. 18d, Bent Tail, Junior.
No. 1511, Pluto, Dinah. No. 1512, Eega Beeva, Dog Pflip, Goofy, horiz. No. 1513, Dinah's pups, Pluto.

**1994, Apr. 11     Litho.     Perf. 13½x14**
| | | | | |
|---|---|---|---|---|
| 1499-1510 | A220 | Set of 12 | 20.00 | 20.00 |

**Souvenir Sheets**
| | | | | |
|---|---|---|---|---|
| 1511 | A220 | 20d multicolored | 5.50 | 5.50 |

**Perf. 14x13½, 13½x14**
| | | | | |
|---|---|---|---|---|
| 1512 | A220 | 20d multicolored | 5.50 | 5.50 |
| 1513 | A220 | 20d multicolored | 5.50 | 5.50 |

Orchids — A221

Designs: 1d, Oeceoclades maculata. 1.25d, Angraecum distichum. 2d, Plectrelminthus caudatus. 5d, Tridactyle tridactylites. 8d, Bulbophyllum lepidum. 10d, Angraecum eburneum. 12d, Eulophia guineensis. 15d, Angraecum eichleranum.
No. 1522, Ancistrochilus rothschildianus. No. 1523, Vanilla imperialis.

**1994, May 1     Perf. 14**
| | | | | |
|---|---|---|---|---|
| 1514 | A221 | 1d multicolored | .50 | .30 |
| 1515 | A221 | 1.25d multicolored | .60 | .30 |
| 1516 | A221 | 2d multicolored | .70 | .40 |
| 1517 | A221 | 5d multicolored | 1.25 | 1.25 |
| 1518 | A221 | 8d multicolored | 2.00 | 2.00 |
| 1519 | A221 | 10d multicolored | 2.25 | 2.25 |
| 1520 | A221 | 12d multicolored | 2.50 | 2.50 |
| 1521 | A221 | 15d multicolored | 3.00 | 3.00 |
| | | Nos. 1514-1521 (8) | 12.80 | 12.10 |

**Souvenir Sheets**
| | | | | |
|---|---|---|---|---|
| 1522 | A221 | 25d multicolored | 6.50 | 6.50 |
| 1523 | A221 | 25d multicolored | 6.50 | 6.50 |

Easter — A222

Disney characters celebrate Easter: No. 1524, 25b, No. 1527, 4d, No. 1529, 8d, No. 1531, 12d, Ludwig von Drake. No. 1525, 50b, Minnie Mouse, Daisy Duck. No. 1526, 3d, Mickey Mouse. No. 1528, 5d, Donald Duck. No. 1530, 10d, Goofy.
No. 1532, 20d, Von Drake. No. 1533, 20d, Mickey, Minnie.

**1994, Apr. 11     Litho.     Perf. 13½x14**
| | | | | |
|---|---|---|---|---|
| 1524-1531 | A222 | Set of 8 | 14.00 | 14.00 |

**Souvenir Sheets**
| | | | | |
|---|---|---|---|---|
| 1532-1533 | A222 | Set of 2 | 12.00 | 12.00 |

Sierra Club,
Cent. — A223

No. 1534, 5d — Various views of: a-b, Prince William Sound. c-d, The Serengeti. e-f, Ross Island.
No. 1535, 5d: a-c, Briksdal Fjord, vert. d-f, Yosemite, vert.
No. 1536, 5d: a-b, Tibetan Plateau, vert. c-d, Yellowstone, vert. e, Ross Island, vert. f, The Serengeti, vert. g, Mount Erebus, vert. h, Ansel Adams Wilderness, vert.
No. 1537, 5d: a-b, Ansel Adams Wilderness. c-d, Mount Erebus. e, Prince William Sound. f, Yellowstone. g, Tibetan Plateau. h, Sierra Club emblem.

**1994, Apr. 25     Perf. 14**
**Miniature Sheets of 6, #a-f**
| | | | | |
|---|---|---|---|---|
| 1534-1535 | A223 | Set of 2 | 15.00 | 15.00 |

**Miniature Sheets of 8, #a-h**
| | | | | |
|---|---|---|---|---|
| 1536-1537 | A223 | Set of 2 | 22.50 | 22.50 |

Paintings of
Cats — A224

No. 1538, 5d: a, The Arena, by Harold Weston. b, Cat Killing a Bird, by Picasso. c, Cat and Butterfly, by Hokusai. d, Winter: Cat on a Cushion, by Steinlen. e, Rattown Tigers, by Prang. f, Cat on the Floor, by Steinlen. g, Cat and Kittens. h, Cats Looking Over a Fence, by Prang. i, Little White Kittens into Mischief, by Ives. j, Cat Bathing, by Hiroshige. k, Playtime, by Tuck. l, Summer: Cat on a Balustrade, by Steinlen.
No. 1539, 5d, vert.: a, Girl with a Kitten, by Perronneau. b, Still Life with Cat and Fish, by Chardin. c, Tinkle a Cat. d, Naughty Puss! e, Cats, by Steinlen. f, Girl in Red with Cat and Dog, by Phillips. g, Cat, Butterfly and Begonia, by Haronobu. h, Cat and Kitten, by Higgins. i, Woman with a Cat, by Renoir. j, Minnie from Outskirts of Village, by Thrall. k, The Fisher, by Tuck. l, Artist and His Family, by Vaenius.
No. 1540, 20d, The Morning Rising, by Lepicie. No. 1541, 20d, The Graham Children, by Hogarth, vert.

**1994, July 11     Litho.     Perf. 14**
**Sheets of 12, #a-l**
| | | | | |
|---|---|---|---|---|
| 1538-1539 | A224 | Set of 2 | 37.50 | 37.50 |

**Souvenir Sheets**
| | | | | |
|---|---|---|---|---|
| 1540-1541 | A224 | Set of 2 | 10.00 | 10.00 |

Monkeys — A225

Designs: 1d, Patas. 1.50d, Collared mangabey. 2d, Black and white colobus. 5d, Mona. 8d, Kirk's colobus. 10d, Vervet. 12d, Red colobus. 15d, Guinea baboon.
Heads of: No. 1550, 25d, Collared mangabey. No. 1551, 25d, Guinea baboon.

**1994, Aug. 1     Litho.     Perf. 14**
| | | | | |
|---|---|---|---|---|
| 1542-1549 | A225 | Set of 8 | 15.00 | 15.00 |

**Souvenir Sheets**
| | | | | |
|---|---|---|---|---|
| 1550-1551 | A225 | 25d Set of 2 | 16.00 | 16.00 |

D-Day, 50th
Anniv. — A226

Designs: 50b, Free Dutch sloop Soema joins attack. 75b, HMS Belfast fires on beach defenses. 1d, USS Texas hits Point Du Hoc. 2d, Free French cruiser George Leygues. 20d, HMS Ramillies.

**1994, Aug. 16**
| | | | | |
|---|---|---|---|---|
| 1552-1555 | A226 | Set of 4 | 3.50 | 3.50 |

**Souvenir Sheet**
| | | | | |
|---|---|---|---|---|
| 1556 | A226 | 20d multicolored | 6.00 | 6.00 |

First Manned Moon Landing, 25th
Anniv. — A227

No. 1557: a, Yuri Gagarin. b, Valentina Tereshkova. c, Ham (chimpanzee). d, Alexei Leonov. e, Neil Armstrong. f, Svetlana Y. Savitskaya. g, Marc Garneau. h, Vladimir Komarov. i, Ulf Merbold.
30d, Neil Armstrong, Edwin "Buzz" Aldrin, Michael Collins at press conference.

**1994, Aug. 16**
| | | | | |
|---|---|---|---|---|
| 1557 | A227 | 2d Sheet of 9, #a.-i. | 7.00 | 7.00 |

**Souvenir Sheet**
| | | | | |
|---|---|---|---|---|
| 1558 | A227 | 30d multicolored | 8.50 | 8.50 |

A228

PHILAKOREA '94 — A229

Designs: 50b, Kungnakchon Hall, Naejangsa. 2d, Kettle of Popchusa. 3d, Pomun Tourist Resort.
Paper screen panels, episode from Sanguozhi, 18th cent. Choson Dynasty: a, Warriors on horseback. b, Soldiers atop fort. c, Shooting with bows and arrows. d, Bowing before horse & rider. e, Fight on horseback. f, h, Charging on horses. g, Trudging through valley. i, j, Living peacefully.
20d, Traditional tombstone guardian, Taenung, vert.

**1994, Aug. 16     Perf. 14, 13½ (#1562)**
| | | | | |
|---|---|---|---|---|
| 1559-1561 | A228 | Set of 3 | 2.00 | 2.00 |
| 1562 | A229 | 1d Sheet of 10, #a.-j. | 10.00 | 10.00 |

**Souvenir Sheet**
| | | | | |
|---|---|---|---|---|
| 1563 | A228 | 20d multicolored | 6.50 | 6.50 |

A230

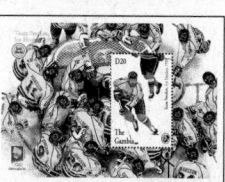

Intl. Olympic Committee,
Cent. — A231

Designs: 1.50d, Daley Thompson, Great Britain, decathlon, 1980, 1984. 5d, Heide Marie Rosendohl, Germany, long jump, 1972. 20d, Team Sweden, ice hockey, 1994.

**1994, Aug. 16     Perf. 14**
| | | | | |
|---|---|---|---|---|
| 1564 | A230 | 1.50d multicolored | .60 | .60 |
| 1565 | A230 | 5d multicolored | 1.50 | 1.50 |

**Souvenir Sheet**
| | | | | |
|---|---|---|---|---|
| 1566 | A231 | 20d multicolored | 7.00 | 7.00 |

Butterflies
A232

Designs: 1d, Mylothris rhodope. 1.25d, Iolaphilus menas. 2d, Neptis nemetes. 5d, Antanartia delius. 8d, Acraea caecilia. 10d, Papilio nireus. 12d, Pipilio menestheus. 15d, Iolaphilus julus.
No. 1575, 25d, Colotis evippe. No. 1576, 25d, Bematistes epaea.

**1994, Aug. 18     Perf. 14**
| | | | | |
|---|---|---|---|---|
| 1567-1574 | A232 | Set of 8 | 14.00 | 14.00 |

**Souvenir Sheets**
| | | | | |
|---|---|---|---|---|
| 1575-1576 | A232 | Set of 2 | 15.00 | 15.00 |

1994 World Cup
Soccer Championships,
US — A233

Designs: 50b, Bobby Charlton, England. 75b, Ferenc Puskas, Hungary. 1d, Paolo Rossi, Italy. 2d, Biri Biri, Gambian playing for Spain. 3d, Diego Maradona, Argentina. 8d, Johan Cruyff, Netherlands. 10d, Franz Beckenbauer, Germany. 15d, Thomas Dooley, US.
No. 1585, 25d, Pele, Brazil. No. 1586, 25d, Gordon Banks, England.

**1994, Sept. 1**
| | | | | |
|---|---|---|---|---|
| 1577-1584 | A233 | Set of 8 | 12.50 | 12.50 |

**Souvenir Sheets**
| | | | | |
|---|---|---|---|---|
| 1585-1586 | A233 | Set of 2 | 15.00 | 15.00 |

Mushrooms — A234

No. 1587, 5d: a, Agaricus campestris. b, Lepista nuda. c, Podaxis pistillaris. d, Oudemansiella radicata. e, Schizophyllum commune. f, Chlorophyllum molybdites. g, Hypholoma fasciculare. h, Mycena pura. i, Ganoderma lucidum.
No. 1588, 5d: a, Suillus luteus. b, Bolbitius vitellinus. c, Clitocybe nebularis. d, Omphalotus olearius. e, Auricularia auricula. f, Macrolepiota rhacodes. g, Volvariella volvacea. h, Psilocybe coprophila. i, Suillus granulatus.
No. 1589, 20d, Cyathus striatus. No. 1590, 20d, Leucoagaricus naucina.

**1994, Sept. 30**     **Sheets of 9, #a-i.**
1587-1588 A234   Set of 2    22.50 22.50

**Souvenir Sheets**
1589-1590 A234   Set of 2    14.00 14.00

Christmas — A235

French paintings: 50b, Expectant Madonna with St. Joseph, by unknown artist. 75b, Rest of the Holy Family, by Louis Le Nain. 1d, Rest on the Flight into Egypt, by Antoine Watteau. No. 1594, 2d, Noon, by Claude Lorrain. No. 1595, 2d, Rest on the Flight into Egypt, by Francois Boucher. No. 1596, 2d, Rest on the Flight into Egypt, by Jean-Honore Fragonard. 10d, The Holy Family, by Nicolas Poussin. 12d, Mystical Marriage of St. Catherine, by Pierre-Francois Mignard.
No. 1599, 25d, The Nativity by Torchlight, by Louis Le Nain. No. 1600, 25d, Adoration of the Shepherds, by Mathieu Le Nain.

**1994, Dec. 5**   **Litho.**   **Perf. 13½x14**
1591-1598 A235   Set of 8    10.00 10.00

**Souvenir Sheets**
1599-1600 A235   Set of 2    14.00 14.00

Marilyn Monroe (1926-62), Actress — A236

No. 1601: a-i, Various portraits.
No. 1602, 25d, Wearing red dress. No. 1603, 25d, Wearing long, dangling earrings.

**1995, Jan. 8**   **Litho.**   **Perf. 14**
1601 A236 4d Sheet of 9, #a-i.    10.00 10.00

**Souvenir Sheets**
1602-1603 A236   Set of 2    11.00 11.00

Elvis Presley (1935-77), Entertainer — A237

No. 1604: a, As child. b, Singing, later years. c, With mother. d, With wife, Priscilla. e, With gold medallion. f, Wearing army uniform. g, Singing, younger years. h, Wearing hat. i, With daughter, Lisa Marie.

**1995, Jan. 8**
1604 A237 4d Sheet of 9, #a-i.    10.00 10.00

Dinosaurs — A238

No. 1605: a, Pteranodon. b, Archaeopteryx. c, Rhamphorhynchus. d, Ornithomimus. e, Stegosaurus. f, Heterodontosaurus. g, Lystrosaurus. h, Euoplocephalus. i, Coelophysis. j, Staurilosaurus. k, Giantoperis. l, Diarthrognathus.
No. 1606: a, Archaeopteryx, diff. b, Vangehuanosaurus. c, Ceolophysis, diff. d, Plateosaurus. e, Baryonyx. f, Ornitholestes. g, Dryosaurus. h, Estemmenosuchus. i,

Macroplata. j, Shonisaurus. k, Muraeonosaurus. l, Archelon.
20d, Bactrosaurus. 22d, Tyrannosaurus, vert. No. 1609, 25d, Triceratops, vert. No. 1610, 25d, Spinosaurus.

**1995**   **Litho.**   **Perf. 14**
1605 A238 2d Sheet of 12, #a.-l.    9.00 9.00
1606 A238 3d Sheet of 12, #a.-l.    9.00 9.00

**Souvenir Sheets**
1607 A238 20d multi    7.00 7.00
1608 A238 22d multi    7.00 7.00
1609-1610 A238   Set of 2    14.00 14.00

New Year 1995 (Year of the Boar) — A239

No. 1611: Stylized boars with Chinese inscriptions in: a, Green. b, Blue violet. c, White. d, Black.
10d, Three boars.

**1995, May 4**     **Perf. 14½**
1611 A239 3d Sheet of 4, #a.-d. 3.00 3.00

**Souvenir Sheet**
1612 A239 10d multicolored    3.00 3.00

Water Birds — A240

Designs: 2d, Great white egret. 8d, Hammerkop. 10d, Shoveler. 12d, Crowned crane.
No. 1617: a, Pintail. b, Fulvous tree duck (a). c, Garganey. d, White-faced tree duck. e, White-backed duck. f, Egyptian goose. g, Pigmy goose. h, Little bittern (k). i, Redshank. j, Ringed plover. k, Black-winged stilt. l, Squacco heron (k).
No. 1618, 25d, Ferruginous duck. No. 1619, 25d, Moorhen.

**1995, May 8**     **Perf. 14**
1613-1616 A240   Set of 4    9.00 9.00
1617 A240 3d Sheet of 12, #a.-l.    10.00 10.00

**Souvenir Sheets**
1618-1619 A240   Set of 2    15.00 15.00

ECOWAS — A241

Designs: 2d, Free movement of people in Gambia. 5d, Captain Yaya AJJ Jammeh, Chairman of Arm Force Provisional Ruling Council, Head of State.

**1995, May 30**   **Litho.**   **Perf. 14**
1620 A241 2d multicolored    .55 .55
1621 A241 5d multicolored    1.40 1.40

Marine Life — A242

No. 1622, vert: a, Multicolored parrot fish. b, Sparisoma viride. c, Queen parrot fish. d, Bicolor parrot fish.
No. 1623: a, Leatherback turtle. b, Tiger shark. c, Surgeon fish. d, Emperor angelfish. e, Blue parro fish. f, Triggerfish. g, Sea horse. h, Lionfish. i, Moray eel. j, Red fin butterflyfish. k, Octopus. l, Ray.
No. 1624, 25d, Holacanthus ciliaris. No. 1625, 25d, Angelichthys isabelita.

**1995, June 20**
1622 A242 8d Strip of 4, #a.-d. 9.00 9.00
1623 A242 3d Sheet of 12, #a.-l.    10.00 10.00

**Souvenir Sheets**
1624-1625 A242   Set of 2    17.00 17.00

UN, 50th Anniv. — A243

No. 1626: a, 3d, Girls. b, 5d, Woman helping girl at blackboard. c, 8d, Girl writing on blackboard.
25d, Nurse holding baby on scales.

**1995, July 6**
1626 A243   Strip of 3, #a.-c. 3.50 3.50

**Souvenir Sheet**
1627 A243 25d multicolored    6.50 6.50

World War II Motion Pictures — A244

No. 1628 — Movie stars: a, Peter Lawford. b, Gene Tierney, Dana Andrews. c, Groucho, Gummo Marx. d, James Stewart. e, Chico, Harpo Marx. f, Tyrone Power. g, Cary Grant, Ingrid Bergman. h, Veronica Lake.
Motion pictures: No. 1629, 25d, A Lady Fights Back. No. 1630, 25d, Desert Victory.

**1995, July 6**
1628 A244 3d Sheet of 8, #a.-h. + label    10.00 10.00

**Souvenir Sheets**
1629-1630 A244   Set of 2    10.00 10.00

VJ Day, 50th Anniv. — A245

No. 1631: a, Fairey Firefly. b, Fairey Barracuda II. c, Vickers Supermarine Seafire II. d, HMS Repulse. e, HMS Illustrious. f, HMS Exeter.
25d, Bomber being shot down by 3-stack cruiser.

**1995, Aug. 1**
1631 A245 5d Sheet of 6, #a.-f. + label 9.25 9.25

**Souvenir Sheet**
1632 A245 25d multicolored    7.50 7.50

A246

Carrying sacks of grain: No. 1633a, 3d, Woman in pink. b, 5d, Two people. c, 8d, Man. 25d, Fisherman with net.

**1995, Aug. 1**   **Litho.**   **Perf. 14**
1633 A246   Strip of 3, #a.-c. 3.50 3.50

**Souvenir Sheet**
1634 A246 25d multicolored    6.00 6.00

FAO, 50th Anniv. No. 1633 is a continuous design.

A247

Nobel Prize Winners: 2d, Kenichi Fukui, chemistry, 1981. 3d, Gustav Stresemann, peace, 1929. 5d, Thomas Mann, literature, 1929. 8d, Albert Schweitzer, peace, 1952. 12d, Leo Esaki, physics, 1973. 15d, Lech Walsea, peace, 1983.
No. 1635: a, Marie Curie, chemistry, 1911. b, Adolf Butenandt, chemistry, 1939. c, Tonegawa Susumu, medicine, 1987. d, Nelly

Sachs, literature, 1966. e, Kawabata Yasunari, literature, 1968. f, Yukawa Hideki, physics, 1949. g, Paul Ehrlich, medicine, 1908. h, Sato Eisaku, peace, 1974. i, Carl von Ossietzky, peace, 1935.
25d, Willy Brandt, peace, 1971.

**1995, Aug. 1**
1634A-1634F A247   Set of 6    9.00 9.00
1635 A247 5d Sheet of 9, #a.-i.    10.00 10.00

**Souvenir Sheet**
1636 A247 25d multicolored    6.50 6.50

Rotary Intl., 90th Anniv. — A248

Designs: 15d, Paul Haris, Rotary emblem. 20d, Natl. flag, Rotary emblem.

**1995, Aug. 1**
1637 A248 15d multicolored    3.00 3.00

**Souvenir Sheet**
1638 A248 20d multicolored    5.25 5.25

Miniature Sheets of 3

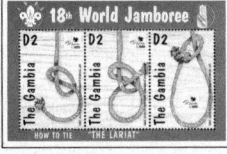

1995 Boy Scout Jamboree, Holland — A249

No. 1639 — How to tie the lariat: a, First step. b, Second step. c, Completed.
No. 1640 — How to tie bowline: a, 12d, First step. b, 10d, Second step. c, 5d, Completed.
No. 1641, 25d, Bowline used to lift injured scout. No. 1642, 25d, Hitch used in lifesaving lift.

**1995, Aug. 1**
1639 A249 2d Sheet of 3, #a.-c.    1.50 1.50
1640 A249   Sheet of 3, #a.-c.    7.00 7.00

**Souvenir Sheets**
1641-1642 A249   Set of 2    11.00 11.00

Queen Mother, 95th Birthday — A250

No. 1643: a, Drawing. b, Bright blue hat, dress. c, Formal portrait. d, Green hat, dress. 25d, Pale blue & white dress, blue hat.

**1995, Aug. 1**     **Perf. 13½14**
1643 A250 5d Strip or block of 4, #a.-d.    4.50 4.50

**Souvenir Sheet**
1644 A250 25d multicolored    5.50 5.50

No. 1643 was issued in sheets of 8 stamps.
Nos. 1643-1644 exist with black frame and overprint in sheet margin "In Memoriam 1900-2002" in one or two lines.

1996 Summer Olympics, Atlanta — A251

Designs: 1d, Bruce Jenner, US, decathlon. 1.25d, Greg Louganis, US, diving. 1.50d, Michael Gross, Germany 50-meter butterfly. 2d, Vasily Alexeev, USSR, weight lifting. 3d, Patrick Ewing, US, Juan Antonio Corbalan, Spain, basketball. 5d, Men's volleyball, US v. Brazil. 10d, John Svenden, West Germany, Armando Fernandez, US, water polo. 15d, Pertti Karppinen, Finland, single sculls.
No. 1653, vert: a, Stefano Cerioni, Italy, fencing. b, Alberto Covo, Italy, 10,000-meter

run. c, Mary Lou Retton, US, women's gymnastics. d, Vladimir Artemov, USSR, men's gymnastics. e, Florence Griffith-Joyner, US, 400-meter relay. f, Brazil, soccer. g, Nelson Valis, US, 1000-meter sprint cycling. h, Cheryl Miller, US, women's basketball.

No. 1654, 25d, Karen Stives, US, equestrian. No. 1655, 25d, Edwin Moses, US, 400-meter hurdles, vert.

**1995, Aug. 17**
1645-1652 A251   Set of 8   11.00 11.00
1653 A251 3d Sheet of 8, #a.-
  h.   7.50 7.50
**Souvenir Sheets**
1654-1655 A251   Set of 2   15.00 15.00

Volleyball, cent. (No. 1650).

Rotary, Intl., 90th Anniv., 1995 Boy Scout Jamboree, Holland — A252

Designs: 2d, Gambia Rotary contributing to education. No. 1657, 5d, Wood Badge course, Yundum, 1980. No. 1658, 5d, M.J.E. Sambou, organizing scout commissioner, vert.

**1995, Sept. 5**
1656-1658 A252   Set of 3   3.50 3.50

Flowers — A253

Designs: 2d, Zantedeschia rehmannii. 5d, Euadenia eminens. 10d, Passiflora vitifolia. 15d, Dietes grandiflora.

No. 1663, 3d: a, Canarina abyssinica. b, Nerine bowdenii. c, Zantedeschia aethiopica. d, Aframomum sceptrum. e, Schotia brachypetala. f, Catharanthus roseus. g, Protea grandiceps. h, Plumbago capensis. i, Uncarina grandidieri.

No. 1664, 3d: a, Kigelia africana. b, Hibiscus schizopetalus. c, Dombeya mastersii. d, Agapanthus orientalis. e, Strelitzia reginae. f, Spathodea campanulata. g, Rhodolaena bakeriana. h, Gazania rigens. i, Ixianthes retzioides.

No. 1665, 25d, Eulophia quartiniana. No. 1666, 25d, Gloriosa simplex.

**1995, Oct. 2   Litho.   Perf. 14**
1659-1662 A253   Set of 4   7.50 7.50
**Sheets of 9, #a-i**
1663-1664   Set of 2   14.50 14.50
**Souvenir Sheets**
1665-1666 A253   Set of 2   13.00 13.00

SOS Children's Villages — A254

Designs: No. 1667, 2d, Children playing near houses. No. 1668, 2d, Aid worker with child, vert. 5d, Children.

**1995, Oct. 9   Litho.   Perf. 14**
1667-1669 A254   Set of 3   2.25 2.25

Entertainers A255

No. 1670: a, Roy Orbison. b, Mick Jagger. c, Bruce Springsteen. d, Jimi Hendrix. e, Bill Haley. f, Gene Vincent. g, Buddy Holly. h, Jerry Lee Lewis. i, Chuck Berry.

No. 1671: a-i, Various pictures of James Dean.

No. 1672, 25d, James Dean. No. 1673, 25d, Elvis Presley.

---

**1995, Dec. 1   Litho.   Perf. 13½x14**
1670 A255 3d Sheet of 9, #a.-
  i.   8.00 8.00
1671 A255 3d Sheet of 9, #a.-
  i.   7.50 7.50
**Souvenir Sheets**
1672-1673 A255   Set of 2   16.00 16.00

Motion pictures, cent. (Nos. 1671-1672).

Christmas — A256

Details or entire paintings: 75b, Madonna of the Valley. 1d, Madonna, by Giotto. 2d, The Flight into Egypt, by Luca Giordano. 5d, The Epiphany, by Bondone. 8d, Virgin & Child, by Burgkmair. 12d, Madonna, by Bellini.

No. 1680, 25d, Mother and Child, by Rubens. No. 1681, 25d, The Christ, by Carpaccio.

**1995, Dec. 18**
1674-1679 A256   Set of 6   10.00 10.00
**Souvenir Sheets**
1680-1681 A256   Set of 2   16.00 16.00

Banjul Intl. Airport — A257

Denominations: 1d, 2d, 3d, 5d.

**1995, Dec. 21   Litho.   Perf. 14**
1682-1685 A257   Set of 4   3.50 3.50

UPU, 121st Anniv. — A258

Denominations: 1d, 2d, 3d, 7d.

**1995, Dec. 21**
1686-1689 A258   Set of 4   4.25 4.25

Marine Life — A259

Designs: 2d, Commerson's dolphin. 5d, Narwhal. 8d, True's beaked whale. 10d, Rough-toothed dolphin.

No. 1694, 3d — Dolphins: a, Northern rightwhale. b, Spotted. c, Common. d, Pacific white-sided. e, Atlantic humpbacked. f, Atlantic white-sided. g, White-beaked. h, Striped. i, Risso's.

No. 1695, 3d — Whales: a, Bryde's. b, Sperm. c, Humpback. d, Sei. e, Blue. f, Gray. g, Fin. h, Killer. i, Right.

No. 1696, 25d, Beluga, clymene dolphin. No. 1697, 25d, Bowhead whale, dall's porpoise, blue shark.

**1995, Dec. 22**
1690-1693 A259   Set of 4   6.25 6.25
**Sheets of 9, #a-i**
1694-1695 A259   Set of 2   16.00 16.00
**Souvenir Sheets**
1696-1697 A259   Set of 2   13.50 13.50

Cowboys and American Indians A260

---

Disney characters portraying Amerian Indians or in western scenes: 15b, Pete, Seminole. 20b, Donald, Chinook. 25b, Huey, Dewey, Louie, Blackfoot. 30b, Sharp shooter Minnie. 40b, Bull-riding Donald. 50b, Cattle-branding Mickey. 2d, Donald, Tlingit. 3d, Bronco-busting Mickey. 12d, Trick-roping Grandma Duck. No. 1707, 15d, Goofy the ranch hand. No. 1708, 15d, Mickey, Pomo. 20d, Minnie, Goofy, Navaho.

No. 1710, 25d, Minnie, Massachusetts Tribe. No. 1711, 25d, Pluto singing, vert. No. 1712, 25d, Donald with rope around neck, vert. No. 1713, 25d, Minnie, Shoshoni, vert.

**1995, Dec. 22   Perf. 14x13½**
1698-1709 A260   Set of 12   18.50 18.50
**Souvenir Sheets**
1710-1713 A260   Set of 4   28.00 28.00

New Year 1996 (Year of the Rat) — A261

No. 1714 — Various stylized rats: a, 63b. b, 75b. c, 1.50d. d, 4d.
No. 1715: a, Like #1714a. b, Like #1714d. c, Like #1714c. d, Like #1714b.
No. 1716, Two rats.

**1996, Jan. 2   Perf. 14½**
1714 A261   Strip of 4, #a.-d.   3.00 3.00
1715 A261 3d Sheet of 4, #a.-d.   3.25 3.25
**Souvenir Sheet**
1716 A261 10d multicolored   4.50 4.50

No. 1714 issued in sheets of 16 stamps.

Paintings from Metropolitan Museum of Art — A262

No. 1717, 4d: a, Don Tiburcio Pérez y Cuervo, by Goya. b, Jean Antoine Moltedo, by J.A.D. Ingres. c, The Letter, by Corot. d, General Etienne Maurice Gerard, by J.L. David. e, Portrait of the Artist, by Van Gogh. f, Joseph Henri Altés, by Degas. g, Princess de Broglie, by Ingres. h, Lady at the Table, by Cassatt.

No. 1718, 4d: a, Broken Eggs, by Greuze. b, Johann Joachim Winckelmann, by Mengs. c, Col. George K.H. Coussmaker, by Reynolds. d, Self Portrait with Pupils, by Labille-Guiard. e, Courtesan Holding a Fan, by Utamaro. f, The Woodgatherers, by Gainsborough. g, Mr. Grace D. Elliott, by Gainsborough. h, The Drummond Children, by Raeburn.

No. 1719, 4d: a, Sunflowers, by Monet. b, Still Life with Pansies, by Fantin-Latour. c, Parisians Enjoying the Park, by Monet. d, La Mére Larchevéque, by Pissarro. e, Rue de L'Epicerie, Rouen, by Pissarro. f, The Abduction of Rebecca, by Delacroix. g, Daughter, Abraham-Ben-Chimol, by Delacroix. h, Christ on Lake of Gennesaret, by Delacroix.

No. 1720, 4d: a, Henry Frederick, Prince of Wales, by Peake. b, Saints Peter, Martha, Mary & Leonard, by Correggio. c, Marriage Feast at Cana, by Juan de Flandes. d, Portrait of one of Wedigh Family, by Holbein. e, Guilluame Budé, by Clouet. f, Portrait of a Cardinal, by El Greco. g, St. Jerome as a Cardinal, by El Greco. h, Portrait of a Man, by Titian.

No. 1721, 25d, The Harvesters, by Bruegel. No. 1722, 25d, The Creation of the World and the Expulsion from Paradise, by Giovanni de Paolo. No. 1723, 25d, Henry IV at the Battle of Ivry, by Rubens. No. 1724, 25d, The Israelites Gathering Manna in the Desert, by Rubens.

**1996, Jan. 29   Litho.   Perf. 13½x14**
**Sheets of 8, #a-h**
1717-1720 A262   Set of 4   32.50 32.50
**Souvenir Sheets**
**Perf. 14**
1721-1724 A262   Set of 4   25.00 25.00

Nos. 1721-1724 each contain one 85x57mm stamp.

No. 1723 is actually in the Uffizi Gallery in Florence; No. 1724 in the Los Angeles County Museum of Art.

Nos. 1717-1724 exist imperf. Value, set of 8 sheets $100.

---

Traditional Fire Dance — A263

Designs: 1d, Blowing fire from mouth, vert. 2d, Like 1d, diff. 3d, Holding sticks of fire at leg, vert. 7d, Holding out two sticks of fire.

**1996, Jan. 29   Litho.   Perf. 14**
1725-1728 A263   Set of 4   4.50 4.50

Disney Characters Performing Good Deeds A264

Designs: 1d, Community blood drive. 4d, Adopt-a-pet. 5d, Christmas giving for the needy. 10d, Teaching outdoor skills. 15d, Teaching reading. 20d, Volunteer fire fighters. No. 1735, 25d, Highway volunteers. No. 1736, 25d, Counting whales.

**1996, Apr. 12   Litho.   Perf. 13½x14**
1729-1734 A264   Set of 6   12.00 12.00
**Souvenir Sheets**
1735-1736 A264   Set of 2   12.00 12.00

Bruce Lee (1940-73), Martial Arts Expert — A265

No. 1737: Various portraits. 25d, In fighting stance.

**1996, Apr. 1   Litho.   Perf. 14**
1737 A265 3d Sheet of 9, #a.-i.   7.50 7.50
**Souvenir Sheet**
1738 A265 25d multicolored   9.00 9.00

China '96, 9th Asian Intl. Philatelic Exhibition (No. 1737).

African Wildlife — A266

15d, African civet.
No. 1740: a, Roan antelope. b, Lesser bush baby. c, Leopard. d, Guinea forest red colobus. e, Kob. f, Common eland.
No. 1741: a, African buffalo. b, Topi. c, Vervet. d, Hippopotamus. e, Waterbuck. f, Senegal chameleon. g, Western green mamba. h, Slender snouted crocodile (i). i, Adanson's mud turtle.
No. 1742, 25d, Lion. No. 1743, 25d, Chimpanzee.

**1996, Apr. 15   Litho.   Perf. 14**
1739 A266 15d multicolored   3.25 3.25
1740 A266 3d Block of 6, #a.-f.   5.00 5.00
1741 A266 4d Sheet of 9, #a.-i.   7.50 7.50
**Souvenir Sheets**
1742-1743 A266   Set of 2   11.50 11.50

No. 1740 issued in sheets of 12 stamps.

Queen Elizabeth II, 70th Birthday — A267

No. 1744: a, Portrait wearing blue dress. b, Wearing white dress, crown. c, Younger picture, crown.
25d, Buckingham Palace, horiz.

**1996, May 9  Litho.  Perf. 13½x14**
1744  A267  8d Strip of 3, #a.-c.  4.75  4.75

**Souvenir Sheet**
**Perf. 14x13½**
1745  A267  25d multicolored  5.50  5.50

No. 1744 was issued in sheets of 9 stamps with each strip in a different order.

Classic Cars and Fire Engines — A268

No. 1746, 4d — Classic cars: a, 1912 Fiat Tipo 510, Italy. b, 1936 Toyota Model 4B Phaeton, Japan. c, 1924 NAG C4B, Germany. d, 1903 Cadillac, US. e, 1925 Bentley, Great Britain. f, 1909 Renault Model AX, France.

No. 1747, 4d — Fire engines: a, 1850 Pumper Hose Cart, US. b, 1891 Steam Fire Engine, US. c, 1864 Lausitzer, Germany. d, 1902 Chemical Engine, Great Britain. e, 1904 Motor Fire Engine, Great Britain. f, 1860 Colonia No. 5, Germany.

No. 1748, 25d, 1917 Mitsubishi Model A, Japan. No. 1749, 25d, 1865 Amoskeag steamer, US.

**1996, May 27  Perf. 14**
**Sheets of 6, #a-f**
1746-1747  A268  Set of 2  11.50  11.50

**Souvenir Sheets**
1748-1749  A268  Set of 2  12.00  12.00

Euro '96, 1996 European Soccer Championships, England — A269

Team pictures: No. 1750, 2d, Bulgaria. No. 1751, 2d, Croatia. No. 1752, 2d, Czech Republic. No. 1753, 2d, Denmark. No. 1754, 2d, England. No. 1755, 2d, France. No. 1756, 2d, Germany. No. 1757, 2d, Holland. No. 1758, 2d, Italy. No. 1759, 2d, Portugal. No. 1760, 2d, Romania. No. 1761, 2d, Russia. No. 1762, 2d, Scotland. No. 1763, 2d, Spain. No. 1764, 2d, Switzerland. No. 1765, 2d, Turkey.

No. 1766, 25d,Hristo Stoitchkov, Bulgaria, vert. No. 1767, 25d, Davor Suker, Croatia, vert. No. 1768, 25d, Pavel Hapal, Czech Republic. No. 1769, 25d, 1992 Denmark team, European championship winners. No. 1770, 25d, Bryan Robson, England, vert. No. 1771, 25d, 1984 Championship cup won by French team, vert. No. 1772, 25d, Jüegen Klinsmann, Germany. No. 1773, 25d, Ruud Gullit, Holland, vert. No. 1774, 25d, Roberto Baggio, Italy, vert. No. 1775, 25d, Eusebio, Portugal, vert. No. 1776, 25d, Gheorge Hagi, Romania, vert. No. 1777, 25d, Oleg Salenko, Russia, vert.No. 1778, 25d, Gary McAllister, Scotland, vert. No. 1779, 25d, Juan Goikoetxea, Spain, vert. No. 1780, 25d, Christophe Ohrel, Switzerland, vert. No. 1781, 25d, Hami Mandirali, Turkey, vert.

**1996, June 8  Litho.  Perf. 14**
1750-1765  A269  Set of 16  8.50  8.50

**Souvenir Sheets**
1766-1781  A269  Set of 16  90.00  90.00

Nos. 1750-1765 each exist in miniature sheets of 8 + 1 label.
See Nos. 1808-1819.

1996 Summer Olympic Games, Atlanta — A270

1912 Olympics, Stockholm: 1d, Ray Ewry, standing high jump. 2d, Fanny Durack, freestyle swimming. 5d, Stadium, scenes in Stocholm. 10d, Jim Thorpe, decathlon, pentathlon.
No. 1786, 3d — Winners in past Olympics: a, Japanese volleyball team, 1964. b, Li Neng, floor exercises, 1984. c, Sergei Bubka, pole vault, 1988. d, Nadia Comaneci, all around gymnastics, 1976. e, Edwin Moses, 400-meter hurdles, 1984. f, Vitaly Shcherbo, all around

gymnastics, 1992. g, Evelyn Ashford, 100-meters, 1984. h, Muhammad Ali, light heavyweight boxing, 1960. i, Carl Lewis, C. Smith, 400-meters relay, 1984.
No. 1787, 3d — 1992 Olympians: a, Fu Mingxia, platform diving. b, Heike Henkel, high jump. c, Spanish soccer team. d, Jackie Joyner-Kersee, heptathlon. e, Tatiana Gutsu, all around gymnastics. f, Michael Johnson, 400-meters. g, Lin Li, 200-meter individual medley. h, Gail Devers, 100-meters. i, Mike Powell, long jump.
No. 1788, 25d, Michael Gross, swimming, 1984, 1988, horiz. No. 1789, 25d, Ulrike Meyfarth, high jump, 1972, 1984.

**1996, July 18  Litho.  Perf. 14**
1782-1785  A270  Set of 4  3.25  3.25

**Sheets of 9, #a-i**
1786-1787  A270  Set of 2  8.00  8.00

**Souvenir Sheets**
1788-1789  A270  Set of 2  10.00  10.00

Jerusalem, 3000th Anniv. — A271

Designs: 1.50d, Roman costume, Pillar of Absalem. 2d, Turkish costume, Gate of Mercy. 3d, Greek costume, Church of the Holy Sepulcher. 10d, Western Wall of the Temple Mount, Hasidic costume.
25d, Emblem, King David Tower, vert.

**1996, July 25**
1790-1793  A271  Set of 4  5.00  5.00

**Souvenir Sheet**
1794  A271  25d multicolored  5.50  5.50

Radio, Cent. — A272

Designs: 1d, Glenn Miller. 4d, Louis Armstrong. 5d, Nat King Cole. 10d, Andrews Sisters.
25d, Harry S Truman.

**1996, July 25  Perf. 13½x14**
1795-1798  A272  Set of 4  5.00  5.00

**Souvenir Sheet**
1799  A272  25d multicolored  5.50  5.50

UNICEF, 50th Anniv. — A273

Designs: 63b, Boy holding shoes. 3d, Girl receiving vaccination. 8d, Boy with soup ladle. 10d, Girl with blanket.
25d, Boy receiving vaccination, horiz.

**1996, July 25  Perf. 14**
1800-1803  A273  Set of 4  4.25  4.25

**Souvenir Sheet**
1804  A273  25d multicolored  5.00  5.00

A274  A275

No. 1805: a, John F. Kennedy. b, Jacqueline Kennedy Onassis. c, Willy Brandt. d, Marilyn Monroe. e, Mao Tse Tung. f, Sung Ching Ling. g, Charles de Gaulle. h, Marlene Dietrich.
Nos. 1806-1807: Various portraits of Jacqueline Kennedy Onassis (1929-94).

**1996, Aug. 22**
1805  A274  5d Sheet of 8, #a.-h.  9.50  9.50
1806  A275  5d Sheet of 9, #a.-i.  11.00  11.00

**Souvenir Sheet**
1807  A274  25d multicolored  5.75  5.75

**Nos. 1751-1752, 1754, 1756, 1758, 1761, 1767-1768, 1770, 1772, 1774, 1777 With Added Inscriptions**
**1996, Aug. 26**
1808-1813  A269  Set of 6  3.50  3.50

**Souvenir Sheets**
1814-1819  A269  Set of 6  34.00  34.00

Nos. 1808-1813, each of which are 2d stamps, were issued in sheets of 8 + 1 label. Inscriptions on Nos. 1808-1813 and in sheet margins of Nos. 1814-1819, each of which are 25d stamps, show date of game, teams competing, and final score. Margin of the miniature sheets show additional information about individual games, and name of Germany as winner.
Team or team player shown as follows: Croatia (Nos. 1808, 1814), Czech Republic (Nos. 1809, 1815), England (Nos. 1810, 1816), Germany (Nos. 1811, 1817), Italy (Nos. 1812, 1818), Russia (Nos. 1813, 1819).

Richard Petty, NASCAR Driving Champion A276

No. 1820: a, 1969 Ford. b, Richard Petty. c, 1978 Dodge Magnum. d, 1987 Pontiac. e, 1989 Pontiac. f, 1975 Dodge Daytona.
25d, 1972 Plymouth.

**1996, Aug. 27**
1820  A276  5d Sheet of 6, #a.-f.  6.75  6.75

**Souvenir Sheet**
1821  A276  25d multicolored  5.00  5.00
No. 1821 contains one 85x28mm stamp.

Elvis Presley's 1st "Hit" Year, 40th Anniv. — A277

Designs: Various portraits.

**1996, Sept. 8  Litho.  Perf. 13½x14**
1822  A277  5d Sheet of 6, #a.-f.  6.50  6.50

Supermarine S6B's Schneider Trophy Victory, 65th Anniv. A278

No. 1823 — Spitfire aircraft: a, PR XIX, Royal Swedish Air Force. b, MK VB, US Army Air. c, MK VC, French Air Force. d, MK VB, Soviet Air Force. e, MK IXE, Netherlands East Indies Air Force. f, MK IXE, Israeli Defense Force. g, MK VIII, Royal Australian Air Force. h, MK VB, Turkish Air Force. i, PR XI, Royal Danish Air Force.
No. 1823J: k, K5054, first prototype aircraft. l, K9787, first production aircraft. m, MK 1A, "Battle of Britain." n, LF MK IXE, D-Day invasion markings. o, MK XII, first "Griffon" engined model. p, MK XIVC, SEAC markings. q, PR XIX, Royal Swedish Air Force. r, PR MK XIX. s, FMK 22/24 final variant.
No. 1824, The Supermarine S.6B S1595. No. 1824A, Supermarine S.6B S1595 seaplane.

**1996, Sept. 13  Litho.  Perf. 14**
1823  A278  4d Sheet of 9, #a.-i.  8.50  8.50
1823J  A278  4d Sheet of 9, #k.-s.  8.50  8.50

**Souvenir Sheets**
1824  A278  25d multicolored  7.00  7.00
1824A  A278  25d multicolored  7.00  7.00

Bob Dylan, Singer — A279

**1996, Sept. 8  Litho.  Perf. 14**
1825  A279  5d multicolored  1.60  1.60
Issued in sheets of 16.

Birds — A280

Designs: 50b, Egyptian plover. 63b, Painted snipe. 75b, Golden-breasted bunting. 1d, Bateleur. 1.50d, Didric cuckoo. 2d, European turtle dove. 3d, Village weaver. 4d, European roller. 5d, Cut-throat. 10d, Hoopoe. 15d, White-faced scops-owl. 20d, Narina trogan. 25d, Pied kingfisher. 30d, Common kestrel.

**1996, Oct. 22  Litho.  Perf. 14**
1826  A280  50b multicolored  .40  .40
1827  A280  63b multicolored  .45  .40
1828  A280  75b multicolored  .50  .40
1829  A280  1d multicolored  .75  .50
1830  A280  1.50d multicolored  .90  .60
1831  A280  2d multicolored  1.00  .60
1832  A280  3d multicolored  1.10  .60
1833  A280  4d multicolored  1.25  .60
1834  A280  5d multicolored  1.40  .75
1835  A280  10d multicolored  1.50  1.00
1836  A280  15d multicolored  3.25  3.25
1837  A280  20d multicolored  4.50  4.50
1838  A280  25d multicolored  5.50  5.50
1839  A280  30d multicolored  8.00  8.00
Nos. 1826-1839 (14)  30.50  27.10
See Nos. 1898-1900.

Christmas — A281

Details of painting, Assumption of the Madonna, by Titian: 1d, Watching assumption, cherub, clouds. 1.50d, Cherubs. 2d, Cherub. 3d, Cherub holding up cloud, outstretched arms below. 10d, People watching assumption. 15d, Cherubs pointing.
No. 1846, 25d, Madonna and Child with Two Angels, by Filippo Lippi, horiz. No. 1847, 25d, Virgin and Child with Infant St. John, by Raphael.

**1996, Nov. 18  Perf. 13½x14**
1840-1845  A281  Set of 6  6.75  6.75

**Souvenir Sheets**
1846-1847  A281  Set of 2  10.00  10.00

Sylvester Stallone in Movie, "Rocky" — A282

**1996, Nov. 21  Litho.  Perf. 14**
1848  A282  10d multicolored  2.00  2.00
Issued in sheets of 3.

Development Projects — A283

Designs: No. 1849, 63b, No. 1852, 2d, Arch 22, vert. 1d, Tractor, rice development project. 1.50d, Worker in rice paddy, vert. 3d, Banjul

Intl. Airport Terminal Building. 5d, Chamoi Bridge.
20d, Workers in rice paddy. 25d, Statue in front of Arch 22, vert.

| 1996 | | Litho. | Perf. 14 | |
|---|---|---|---|---|
| 1849-1854 | A283 | Set of 6 | 3.25 | 3.25 |

**Souvenir Sheets**

| 1855 | A283 | 20d multicolored | 4.00 | 4.00 |
|---|---|---|---|---|
| 1856 | A283 | 25d multicolored | 5.00 | 5.00 |

New Year 1997 (Year of the Ox) — A284

Nos. 1857-1858 — Various stylized oxen, background color: a, 63b, orange. b, 75b, purple. c, 1.50d, blue green. d, 4d, yellow orange. All stamps in No. 1858 are 3d.
10d, Ox with baby lying on its back.

| 1997, Jan. 16 | | | Perf. 15 | |
|---|---|---|---|---|
| 1857 | A284 | Strip of 4, #a.-d. | 2.00 | 2.00 |
| 1858 | A284 | 3d Sheet of 4, #a.-d. | 2.75 | 2.75 |

**Souvenir Sheet**
**Perf. 14**

| 1859 | A284 | 10d multicolored | 3.00 | 3.00 |
|---|---|---|---|---|

No. 1859 contains one 43x29mm stamp.

Mickey's Journey to the West A285

Nos. 1860-1861: a-f, Scenes from Disney's "Monkey King."
No. 1862, Donald, Mickey, vert. No. 1863, Wu-Kong Sun (The Monkey King), monkeys, Mickey. No. 1864, Mickey, Intelligent Tortoise, Master San Tang. No. 1865, Mickey, Minnie obtaining Buddhist scriptures.

| 1997, Jan. 28 | | | Perf. 14x13½ | |
|---|---|---|---|---|
| 1860 | A285 | 2d Sheet of 6, #a.-f. | 5.50 | 5.50 |
| g. | | No. 1860 overprinted | 5.50 | 5.50 |
| 1861 | A285 | 3d Sheet of 6, #a.-f. | 6.25 | 6.25 |
| g. | | No. 1861 overprinted | 7.00 | 7.00 |

**Souvenir Sheets**

| 1862 | A285 | 5d multi | 4.75 | 4.75 |
|---|---|---|---|---|
| a. | | With marginal overprint | 5.00 | 5.00 |
| 1863 | A285 | 10d multi | 4.75 | 4.75 |
| a. | | With marginal overprint | 5.00 | 5.00 |
| 1864 | A285 | 10d multi | 4.75 | 4.75 |
| a. | | With marginal overprint | 5.00 | 5.00 |
| 1865 | A285 | 15d multi | 4.75 | 4.75 |
| a. | | With marginal overprint | 5.00 | 5.00 |

Nos. 1860g, 1861g are overprinted in red in sheet margin: "70TH ANNIVERSARY OF MICKEY & MINNIE," and in black with "Happy Birthday," Mickey Mouse, and "1998" in emblem. Nos. 1862a, 1863a, 1864a, 1865a are overprinted in black in sheet margin with just "Happy Birthday" emblem.

**Souvenir Sheet**

Deng Xiaoping A286

No. 1867, Like No. 1866.

| 1996, May 13 | | Litho. | Perf. 13 | |
|---|---|---|---|---|
| 1866 | A286 | 5d shown | 5.25 | 5.25 |

**Litho. & Embossed**
**Die Cut Perf. 9**
**Size: 95x56mm**

| 1867 | A286 | 300d gold | | |
|---|---|---|---|---|

China '96. Nos. 1866-1867 were not available until March 1997.

Jackie Chan, Action Film Actor — A287

A287a

Various portraits.

| 1997, Feb. 12 | | | Perf. 14 | |
|---|---|---|---|---|
| 1868 | A287 | 4d Sheet of 8, #a.-h. | 7.00 | 7.00 |

**Souvenir Sheet**

| 1869 | A287 | 25d multi, horiz. | 6.00 | 6.00 |
|---|---|---|---|---|

**Litho. & Embossed**
**Die Cut Perf. 9**
**Without Gum**

| 1869A | A287a | 300d gold & multi | | |
|---|---|---|---|---|

Endangered Species — A288

No. 1870, 1.50d: a, Clouded leopard. b, Audouin's gull. c, Leatherback turtle. d, White-eared pheasant. e, Kakapo. f, Right whale. g, Black-footed ferret. h, Dwarf lemur. i, Peacock pheasant. j, Brown hyena. k, Cougar. l, Gharial. m, Monk seal. n, Mountain gorilla. o, Blyth's tragopan. p, Malayan tapir. q, Black rhinoceros. r, Polar bear. s, Red colobus. t, Tiger.
No. 1871, 1.50d: a, Arabian oryx. b, Baiji. c, Ruffed lemur. d, California condor. e, Blue-headed quail-dove. f, Numbat. g, Congo peacock. h, White uakari. i, Eskimo curlew. j, Gouldian finch. k, Coelacanth. l, Toucan barbet. m, Snow leopard. n, Queen Alexandra's birdwing. o, Dalmatian pelican. p, Chaco tortoise. q, Medong catfish. r, Helmeted hornbill. s, White-eyed river martin. t, Fluminense swallowtail.
No. 1872, 25d, Giant panda. No. 1873, 25d, Humpback whale. No. 1874, 25d, Japanese crane.

| 1997, Feb. 24 | | Sheets of 20, #a-t | | |
|---|---|---|---|---|
| 1870-1871 | A288 | Set of 2 | 18.50 | 18.50 |

**Souvenir Sheets**

| 1872-1874 | A288 | Set of 3 | 18.00 | 18.00 |
|---|---|---|---|---|

Hong Kong '97 (Nos. 1870-1871).

Jungle Book — A289

No. 1875: a, Monkey facing right. b, Bear. c, Elephant. d, Monkey facing left. e, Panther, butterfly. f, Buffalo. g, Mandrill. h, Tiger. i, Wolf. j, Cobra. k, Mongoose. l, Child's face, flower.

**1997**

| 1875 | A289 | 3d Sheet of 12, #a.-l. | 8.25 | 8.25 |
|---|---|---|---|---|

Mushrooms A290

Designs: 1d, Polyporus squamosus. 3d, Armillaria tabescens. 5d, Collybia velutipes. 10d, Sarcoscypha coccinea.
No. 1880, vert: a, Amanita caesarea. b, Lepiota procera. c, Hygophorus psittacinus. d, Russula xerampelina. e, Laccaria amethystina. f, Coprinus micaceus. g, Boletus edulis. h, Morchella esculenta. i, Otidea auricula.
25d, Volvariella bombycina.

| 1997, Mar. 10 | | Litho. | Perf. 14 | |
|---|---|---|---|---|
| 1876-1879 | A290 | Set of 4 | 4.50 | 4.50 |
| 1880 | A290 | 4d Sheet of 9, #a.-i. | 7.75 | 7.75 |

**Souvenir Sheet**

| 1881 | A290 | 25d multicolored | 7.00 | 7.00 |
|---|---|---|---|---|

UNESCO, 50th Anniv. A291

World Heritage sites: 1d, Horyu-Ji, Japan. 2d, Great Wall, China. 3d, City of Ayutthaya, Thailand. 4d, Ascension Convent, Santa Maria, Philippines. 10d, Dragons, Komodo Natl. Park, Indonesia. 15d, Timbuktu, Mali.
No. 1888, 4d, vert. — Various sites in Japan: a, g, h. Kyoto. b, Himeji-Jo. c, d, Horyu-Ji. e, f, Yakushima.
No. 1889, 4d, vert. — Various sites in China: a, b, c, Mogao Caves. d, e, Great Wall. f, g, h, Imperial Palace.
No. 1890, 4d, vert. — Various sites: a, Mt. Nimba Strict Nature Reserve, Guinea. b, Banc D'Argun Natl. Park, Mauritania. c, Marrakesh, Morocco. d, Ichkeul Natl. Park, Tunisia. e, Mali. f, Salonga Natl. Park, Zaire. g, Timgad, Algeria. h, Benin.
No. 1891, 5d — Various sites in Germany: a, b, c, Bamberg. d, e, Maulbronn.
No. 1892, 5d — Various sites in Greece: a, d, e, Ruins in Delphi. b, c, City of Rhodes.
No. 1893, 5d — Various sites in Japan: a, b, Shirakami-Sanchi. c, d, e, Himeji-Jo.
No. 1894, 25d, Cloisters, Santa Maria de Alcobaca, Portugal. No. 1895, 25d, Kyoto, Japan. No. 1896, 25d, Ruins of Kilwa Kisiwani, Tanzania. No. 1897, 25d, Plitvice Lakes Natl. Park, Croatia.

**1997, Mar. 24**

| 1882-1887 | A291 | Set of 6 | 7.25 | 7.25 |
|---|---|---|---|---|

**Sheets of 8, #a-h, + Label**

| 1888-1890 | A291 | Set of 3 | 20.00 | 20.00 |
|---|---|---|---|---|

**Sheets of 5, #a-e, + Label**

| 1891-1893 | A291 | Set of 3 | 15.50 | 15.50 |
|---|---|---|---|---|

**Souvenir Sheets**

| 1894-1897 | A291 | Set of 4 | 18.50 | 18.50 |
|---|---|---|---|---|

**Bird Type of 1996**

Designs: 40d, Temminck's courser. 50d, European bee-eater. 100d, Green-winged teal.

| 1997, Mar. 25 | | Litho. | Perf. 14 | |
|---|---|---|---|---|
| 1898 | A280 | 40d multicolored | 7.50 | 7.50 |
| 1899 | A280 | 50d multicolored | 9.50 | 9.50 |
| 1900 | A280 | 100d multicolored | 18.50 | 18.50 |
| | | Nos. 1898-1900 (3) | 35.50 | 35.50 |

Disney's 101 Dalmatians A293

No. 1901, vert.1: a, Dipstick. b, Fidget. c, Jewel. d, Lucky. e, Two-Tone. f, Wizzer.
No. 1902: a-i, Various "Playful Puppies."
No. 1903: a-i, Various "Mischievous puppies."
No. 1904, 25d, Hiding under sheep. No. 1905, 25d, Cruella. No. 1906, 25d, Looking at picture. No. 1907, 25d, Distributing mail, vert. No. 1908, 25d, Into paint. No. 1909, 25d, Playing video game.

| 1997, May 1 | | Perf. 13½x14, 14x13½ | | |
|---|---|---|---|---|
| 1901 | A293 | 50b Sheet of 6, #a.-f. | 3.00 | 3.00 |
| 1902 | A293 | 2d Sheet of 9, #a.-i. | 6.00 | 6.00 |
| 1903 | A293 | 2d Sheet of 9, #a.-i. | 8.00 | 8.00 |

**Souvenir Sheets**

| 1904-1909 | A293 | Set of 6 | 42.50 | 42.50 |
|---|---|---|---|---|

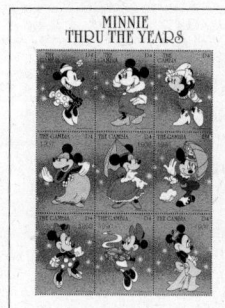

Minnie Thru the Years A294

No. 1910 — Minnie in various scenes dated: a, 1928. b, 1933. c, 1934. d, 1937. e, 1938. f, 1941. g, 1950. h, 1990. i, 1997. 25d, 1987.

| 1997, May 1 | | | Perf. 13½x14 | |
|---|---|---|---|---|
| 1910 | A294 | 4d Sheet of 9, #a.-i. | 12.00 | 12.00 |

**Souvenir Sheet**

| 1911 | A294 | 25d multicolored | 9.00 | 9.00 |
|---|---|---|---|---|

Juventus (World Club Soccer Champions), Cent. A295

No. 1912: a, Juventus, 1897. b, Player from early years, emblems. c, Giampiero Boniperti. d, Roberto Bettega. e, European/ South American Cup, 1996. f, Drawing in celebration of cent.

| 1997, May 9 | | Litho. | Perf. 14x13½ | |
|---|---|---|---|---|
| 1912 | A295 | 5d Sheet of 6, #a.-f. | 6.50 | 6.50 |

Queen Elizabeth II, Prince Philip, 50th Wedding Anniv. — A296

No. 1913: a, Queen. b, Royal Arms. c, Queen, Prince Philip. d, Queen holding flowers, Prince saluting. e, Royal Yacht Britannia. f, Prince Philip.
20d, Queen in red hat.

| 1997, May 20 | | | Perf. 14 | |
|---|---|---|---|---|
| 1913 | A296 | 4d Sheet of 6, #a.-f. | 6.00 | 6.00 |

**Souvenir Sheet**

| 1914 | A296 | 20d multicolored | 5.50 | 5.50 |
|---|---|---|---|---|

Paul P. Harris (1868-1947), Founder of Rotary Intl. — A297

Rotary emblem, portrait of Harris and: 10d, Tree of friendship planted by Sydney W. Pascall, Rotary Pres. 1931-32.
25d, Emblem, preserve planet earth.

| 1997, May 20 | | Litho. | Perf. 14 | |
|---|---|---|---|---|
| 1915 | A297 | 10d multicolored | 1.75 | 1.75 |

**Souvenir Sheet**

| 1916 | A297 | 25d multicolored | 5.00 | 5.00 |
|---|---|---|---|---|

Heinrich von Stephan (1831-97), Founder of UPU — A298

No. 1917 — Portrait of von Stephan and: a, Otto von Bismarck. b, UPU emblem. c, Two-horse team and wagon, Boston, 1900.
25d, Hamburg-Lübeck postilion, 1828.

**1997, May 20**

| 1917 | A298 | 5d Sheet of 3, #a.-c. | 3.25 | 3.25 |
|---|---|---|---|---|

**Souvenir Sheet**

| 1918 | A298 | 25d multicolored | 5.50 | 5.50 |
|---|---|---|---|---|

PACIFIC 97.

Chernobyl Disaster, 10th Anniv. — A299

Designs: No. 1919, Chabad's Children of Chernobyl. No. 1920, UNESCO.

| 1997, May 20 | | Litho. | Perf. 13½x14 | |
|---|---|---|---|---|
| 1919 | A299 | 15d multicolored | 2.75 | 2.75 |
| 1920 | A299 | 15d multicolored | 2.75 | 2.75 |

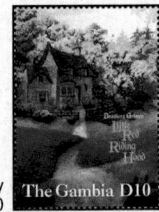

Grimm's Fairy Tales — A300

Mother Goose A301

No. 1921 — Scenes from "Little Red Riding Hood": a, Grandmother's house. b, Little Red Riding Hood. c, Wolf.
No. 1922, Little Red Riding Hood, wolf, horiz. No. 1923, Girl seated on chair from "I'll Tell You a Story."

**1997, May 20**    **Perf. 13½x14**
1921 A300 10d Sheet of 3, #a.-c. 6.25 6.25

**Souvenir Sheets**
**Perf. 14x13½**
1922 A300 10d multicolored   4.00 4.00
**Perf. 14**
1923 A301 25d multicolored   4.75 4.75

Paintings, by Hiroshige (1797-1858) — A302

No. 1924, 4d: a, Morning Glory and Cricket. b, Dragonfly and Begonia. c, Two Ducks Swimming among Reeds. d, A Black-Naped Oriole Perched on a Stem of Rose Mallow. e, A Pheasant on a Snow-covered Pine. f, A Cuckoo Flying through the Rain.
No. 1925, 4d: a, An Egret among Rushes. b, Peacock and Peonies. c, Three Wild Geese Flying across the Moon. d, A Cock in the Snow. e, A Pheasant and Bracken. f, Peonies.
No. 1926, 4d: a, Sparrow and Bamboo. b, Mandarin Ducks on an Icy Pond with Brown Leaves Falling. c, Blossoming Plum Tree. d, Java Sparrow and Magnolia. e, Chinese Bell-flowers and Miscanthus. f, A Small Black Bird Clinging to a Tendril of Ivy.
No. 1927, 5d: a, Sparrows and Camellia in Snow. b, Parrot on a Branch of Pine. c, A Long-tailed Blue Bird on a Branch of Flowering Plum. d, Sparrow and Bamboo. e, Bird in a Tree. f, A Wild Duck Swimming beneath Snow-laden Reeds.
No. 1928, 5d: a, Kingfisher above a Yellow-flowered Water Plant. b, Wagtail and Roses. c, A Mandarin Duck on a Snowy Bank. d, A Japanese White-eye on a Persimmon Branch. e, Sparrows and Camellia in Snow. f, Kingfisher and Moon above a Yellow-flowered Water Plant.
No. 1929, 5d: a, Sparrow and Bamboo. b, Birds Flying over Waves. c, Blossoming Plum Tree with Full Moon. d, Kingfisher and Iris. e, A Blue-and-white Flycatcher on a Hibiscus Flower. f, Mandarin Ducks in Snowfall.
Unidentified paintings of: No. 1930, 25d, Falcon on perch. No. 1931, 25d, Two birds seated on branch. No. 1932, 25d, Kingfisher above Iris. No. 1933, 25d, Like #1925c. No. 1934, 25d, Bird on grapevine. No. 1935, 25d, Small bird in flowering tree.

**1997, May 20**    **Perf. 14**
**Sheets of 6, #a-f**
1924-1926 A302   Set of 3   15.00 15.00
1927-1929 A302   Set of 3   19.00 19.00
**Souvenir Sheets**
1930-1935 A302   Set of 6   35.00 35.00

Return of Hong Kong & Macao to China A303

No. 1936: a, Signing of joint declaration on question of Macao, 1987. b, Deng Xiaoping sharing toast with Portugal's Prime Minister Anibal Cavaco Silva after signing declaration. c, Deng Xiaoping, Britain's Prime Minister Margaret Thatcher sharing toast after signing Sino-British Declaration, 1984. d, Signing of the Sino-British Joint Declaration on question of Hong Kong, 1984.
No. 1937: a, Sir Henry Pottinger, 1st governor of Hong Kong, 1841-44, Hong Kong Island ceded to Britain, 1843. b, Sir Hercules Robinson, governor 1859-65, Kowloon ceded to Britain, 1860. c, Sir Henry Blake, governor 1898-1903, New Territories leased to Britain, 1899.
No. 1938: a, Ships in harbor, Sir Henry Pottinger. b, Suspension bridge, Chris Patten, governor of Hong Kong, 1992-1997. c, Skyline at night, C.H. Tung, first Chinese chief executive, 1997.
No. 1939: a, Signing of Treaty of Nanking, 1842. b, Signing of Japanese surrender document, 1945. c, Signing of Sino-British Joint Declaration on question of Hong Kong, 1984, diff.

**1997, July 1**
1936 A303 3d Sheet of 4, #a.-d. 2.75 2.75
1937 A303 4d Sheet of 3, #a.-c. 2.75 2.75
1938 A303 5d Sheet of 3, #a.-c. 3.00 3.00
1939 A303 6d Sheet of 3, #a.-c. 3.50 3.50

Wonders of the World — A304

Designs: 63b, Great Mosque at Samarra, Iraq, vert. (24x38mm). 75b, Moai stone faces, Easter Island. 1d, Golden Gate Bridge, San Francisco. 1.50d, Statue of Liberty, New York, vert. (24x38mm). 2d, Parthenon, Greece. 3d, Pyramid of the Sun, Teotihuacán, Mexico.
No. 1946, 5d: a, Rock of Gibraltar. b, St. Peter's Basilica, Vatican City. c, Santa Sophia, Istanbul. d, Gateway Arch, St. Louis. e, Great Wall of China. f, Carcassonne, France.
No. 1947, 5d: a, Stonehenge, England. b, Hughes HK-1 Hercules "Spruce Goose" airplane. c, Hoverspeed catamaran, Great Britain. d, Jet powered "Thrust 2." e, Djoser Step Pyramid, Egypt. f, Mallard steam locomotive.
No. 1948, 25d, Grand Canyon of the Colorado River, Arizona. No. 1949, 25d, Mt. Everest, Nepal. No. 1950, 25d, Washington Monument, Washington, DC.

**1997, July 15**
1940-1945 A304   Set of 6   4.00 4.00
**Sheets of 6, #a-f**
1946-1947 A304   Set of 2   16.00 16.00
**Souvenir Sheets**
1948-1950 A304   Set of 3   16.00 16.00

1998 Winter Olympics, Nagano — A305

Designs: 5d, Downhill skiing. 10d, Luge. 15d, Speed skating. 20d, Ice hockey.
No. 1955, 5d: a, Luge, diff. b, Ice hockey (goalie). c, 4-man bobsled. d, Ski jumping. e, Curling. f, Women's figure skating. g, Speed skating, diff. h, Biathlon. i, Downhill skiing, diff.
No. 1956, 5d, vert: a, 2-man bobsled. b, Free-style skiing. c, Speed skating, diff. d, Downhill skiing, diff. e, Women's figure skating, diff. f, Slalom skiing. g, Pairs figure skating. h, Cross-country skiing. i, Ski jumping, diff.
No. 1957, 25d, Female figure skater, vert. No. 1958, 25d, 2-man bobsled, diff.

**1997, July 21**    **Litho.**    **Perf. 14**
1951-1954 A305   Set of 4   10.00 10.00
**Sheets of 9, #a-i**
1955-1956 A305   Set of 2   20.00 20.00
**Souvenir Sheets**
1957-1958 A305   Set of 2   13.00 13.00

Cats — A306

Designs: 63b, Scottish fold. 1.50d, American curl. 2d, British bi-color. 3d, Devon rex. 6d, Silver tabby 20d, Abyssinian.
No. 1965: a, Burmilla. b, Blue Burmese. c, Korat. d, British tabby. e, Foreign white. f, Somali.
No. 1966, 25d, Cornish rex. No. 1967, 25d, Siamese.

**1997, Aug. 12**
1959-1964 A306   Set of 6   8.25 8.25
1965 A306 5d Sheet of 6, #a.-f.   7.50 7.50
**Souvenir Sheets**
1966-1967 A306   Set of 2   11.50 11.50

Dinosaurs A307

Designs: 50b, Coelophysis, ornitholestes. 63b, Spinosaurus. 75b, Kentrosaurus. 1d, Ceratosaurus. 1.50d, Stygimoloch. 2d, Troodon. 3d, Velociraptor. 4d, Triceratops. 5d, Protoceratops. 10d, Ornithomimus. 15d, Stegosaurus. 20d, Ankylosaurus saichania.
No. 1980, 4d: a, Anurognathus. b, Pteranodon. c, Pterosaurus. d, Saltasaurus. e, Agathaumus. f, Stegosaurus. g, Albertosaurus libratus. h, 4 Lesothosaurus. i, 7 Lesothosaurus.
No. 1981, 4d: a, Tarbosaurus bataar. b, Brachiosaurus. c, Styracosaurus. d, Baryonyx. e, Coelophysis. f, Carnotaurus. g, Compsognathus longipes. h, Compsognathuselegant jaw. i, Stenonychosaurus.
No. 1982, 25d, Deinonychus. No. 1983, 25d, Seismosaurus.

**1997, June 23**    **Litho.**    **Perf. 14**
1968-1979 A307   Set of 12   16.00 16.00
**Sheets of 9, #a-i**
1980-1981 A307   Set of 2   13.50 13.50
**Souvenir Sheets**
1982-1983 A307   Set of 2   12.00 12.00
No. 1982 contains one 50x38mm stamp. No. 1983 contains one 89x28mm stamp.

Dogs — A308

Designs: 75b, Dalmatian. 1d, Rottweiler. 3d, Newfoundland. 4d, Great Dane. 10d, Old English sheepdog. 15d, Queensland heeler.
No. 1990: a, Akita. b, Welsh corgi. c, German shepherd. d, St. Bernard. e, Bullmastiff. f, Malamute.
No. 1991, 25d, Doberman pinscher. No. 1992, 25d, Boxer.

**1997, Aug. 12**
1984-1989 A308   Set of 6   8.25 8.25
1990 A308 5d Sheet of 6, #a.-f.   7.50 7.50
**Souvenir Sheets**
1991-1992 A308   Set of 2   11.50 11.50

1998 World Cup Soccer Championships, France — A309

Winning teams: 1d, Uruguay, 1950. 1.50d, W. Germany, 1954. 2d, Brazil, 1970. 3d, Brazil, 1962. 5d, Italy, 1938. 10d, Uruguay, 1930.
No. 1999, 4d: a, Brazil, 1994. b, Argentina, 1986. c, Brazil, 1970. d, Italy, 1934. e, Uruguay, 1958. f, England, 1966. g, Brazil, 1962. h, W. Germany, 1990.
No. 2000, 4d: a, Mario Kempes, Argentina, 1978. b, Ademir, Brazil, 1950. c, Muller, W. Germany, 1970. d, Lineker, England, 1986. e, Eusebio, Portugal, 1966. f, Schillaci, Italy,

1990. g, Lata, Poland, 1974. h, Rossi, Italy, 1982.
No. 2001, 4d, vert: a, Kinkladze, Georgia. b, Shearer, England. c, Dani, Portugal. d, Weah, Liberia. e, Ravanelli, Italy. f, Raducioiu, Romania. g, Peter Schmeichel, Denmark. h, Bergkamp, Holland.
No. 2002, 4d, vert: a, Moore, England, 1966. b, Fritzwalter, W. Germany, 1954. c, Beckenbauer, W. Germany, 1974. d, Zoff, Italy, 1982. e, Maradona, Argentina, 1986. f, Passarella, Argentina, 1978. g, Matthäus, W. Germany, 1990. h, Dunga, Brazil, 1994.
No. 2003, 25d, Pele, Brazil. No. 2004, 25d, Eusebio, Portugal. No. 2005, 25d, Juninho, Brazil. No. 2006, 25d, Philippe Albert, Belgium.

**1997, Sept. 4**   **Perf. 14x13½, 13½x14**
1993-1998 A309   Set of 6   4.00 4.00
**Sheets of 8, #a-h, + Label**
1999-2002 A309   Set of 4   27.50 27.50
**Souvenir Sheets**
2003-2006 A309   Set of 4   22.50 22.50

Sea Birds — A310

Designs: 5d, Red-legged cormorant. 10d, Roseate tern. 15d, Blue-footed booby. 20d, Sanderling.
No. 2011: a, Brown pelican. b, Galapagos penguin. c, Red billed tropic bird. d, Little tern. e, Dunlin. f, Kittiwake. g, Atlantic puffin. h, Wandering albatross. i, Masked booby. j, Glaucous winged gull. k, Artic tern. l, Piping plover.
No. 2012, 23d, Osprey. No. 2013, 23d, Long-tailed skua.

**1997, Aug. 4**   **Litho.**   **Perf. 14**
2007-2010 A310   Set of 4   11.00 11.00
2011 A310 3d Sheet of 12, #a.-l.   9.50 9.50
**Souvenir Sheets**
2012-2013 A310   Set of 2   10.00 10.00

A311

Diana, Princess of Wales (1961-97) — A312

Various portraits.

**1997, Nov. 26**   **Litho.**   **Perf. 14**
2014 A311 10d Sheet of 4, #a.-d. 7.50 7.50
**Souvenir Sheet**
2015 A312 25d multicolored   5.00 5.00

Christmas — A313

Entire paintings or details: 1d, Angel, by Rembrandt. 1.50d, Initiation into the Rites of Dionysus, in Villa dei Misteri, Pompeii. 2d, Pair of Erotes with Purple Cloaks. 3d, The Ecstasy of Saint Teresa, by Gianlorenzo Bernini (carving). 5d, Annunciation, by Mathias Grunewald. 10d, Angel Playing the Organ, by Stefan Lochner.

No. 2022, 25d, The Rest on the Flight into Egypt, by Caravaggio. No. 2023, 25d, Education of Cupid, by Titian.

**1997, Dec. 8**
2016-2021 A313 Set of 6      7.75  7.75
**Souvenir Sheets**
2022-2023 A313 Set of 2      9.50  9.50

New Year 1998 (Year of the Tiger) — A314

No. 2024 — Various stylized tigers with: a, Yellow brown background. b, Purple background. c, Brown background. d, Orange background.
10d, Tiger, landscape.

**1998, Jan. 5   Litho.   Perf. 14½**
2024 A314 3d Sheet of 4, #a.-d. 2.75 2.75
**Souvenir Sheet**
**Perf. 14**
2025 A314 10d multicolored      2.75 2.75
No. 2025 contains one 38x24mm stamp.

Trains — A315

No. 2026, 5d: a, Electric Train, Scotland. b, Beaconsfield, China. c, TGV, France. d, People Mover, England. e, ICE train, Germany. f, Montmartre Funicular, France.
No. 2027, 5d: a, SD70 Burlington Northern, US. b, Mallard, England. c, Baldwin 4-8-0, Peru. d, Sweden Rail. e, Rack Train, Amberawa-Java. f, Beyer-Peacock, Pakistan.
No. 2028, 25d, Monorail, England. No. 2029, 25d, Southern Pacific, US.

**1998, May 19   Litho.   Perf. 14**
**Sheets of 6, #a-f**
2026-2027 A315 Set of 2    13.00 13.00
**Souvenir Sheets**
2028-2029 A315 Set of 2     9.50  9.50

Flowers — A316

Designs, vert: 75b, Daffodil. 1.50d, Transvaal daisy. 3d, Torchlily. 4d, Ancistrochilus rothschildianus. 10d, Polystachya vulcanica. 15d, Gladiolus.
No. 2036: a, Adenium multiflorum. b, Huernia namaquensis. c, Gloriosa superba. d, Strelitzia reginae. e, Passiflora mollissima. f, Bauhinia variegata.
No. 2037, 25d, Aerangis rhodosticta, vert. No. 2038, 25d, Ansella gigantea, vert.

**1998, June 2   Litho.   Perf. 14**
2030-2035 A316 Set of 6     8.00  8.00
2036 A316 5d Sheet of 6, #a.-
        f.                   7.00  7.00
**Souvenir Sheets**
2037-2038 A316 Set of 2    11.00 11.00

Historical Aircraft — A317

No. 2039, 5d: a, Short Type 38, 1913. b, Fokker F.VII B 3m, 1925. c, Junkers F-13, 1919. d, Pitcairn "Mailwing," 1927. e, Douglas, 1920. f, Curtiss "Condor," 1934.
No. 2040, 5d: a, Wright Brothers, 1903. b, Curtiss, 1910. c, Farman, 1907. d, Bristol, 1911. e, Antoinette, 1908. f, Sopwith "Bat Boat," 1912.
No. 2041, 25d, Albatross, 1913. No. 2042, 25d, Boeing 247, 1932.

**1998, June 10   Sheets of 6, #a-f**
2039-2040 A317 Set of 2    14.00 14.00
**Souvenir Sheets**
2041-2042 A317 Set of 2    11.00 11.00
Nos. 2041-2042 each contain one 85x28mm stamp.

Disney's "Mulan" — A318

Characters from the animated movie — No. 2043: a, Mulan. b, Mushu. c, Little Brother. d, Cri-Kee. e, Grandmother Fa. f, Fa Li. g, Fa Zhou. h, Mulan and Khan.
No. 2044: a, Mulan riding Khan. b, Shang. c, Chi Fu. d, Chien-Po. e, Yao. f, Ling. g, Shan-Yu. h, Mulan, Shang & Mushu.
No. 2045, 25d, Mulan. No. 2046, 25d, Mulan riding Khan, diff. No. 2047, 25d, Mulan jumping in air. No. 2048, 25d, Mulan looking at Shang (in margin).

**1998, July 1   Litho.   Perf. 13½x14**
2043 A318 4d Sheet of 8, #a.-
        h.                  10.00 10.00
2044 A318 5d Sheet of 8, #a.-
        h.                  10.50 10.50
**Souvenir Sheets**
2045-2048 A318 Set of 4    27.50 27.50

Ferrari Automobiles — A318a

No. 2048A: c, 365 GTB/4. d, Daytona. e, 1966 275 GTB.
25d, 365 GTB/4, diff.

**1998, Oct. 29   Litho.   Perf. 14**
2048A A318a 10d Sheet of 3,
        #c-e                 5.25  5.25
**Souvenir Sheet**
**Perf. 13¾x14¼**
2048B A318a 25d multi        4.50  4.50
No. 2048A contains three 39x25mm stamps.

Famous People — A319

No. 2049, 4d — Jazz musicians: a, Sidney Bechet (1897-1959). b, Bechet playing clarinet. c, "Duke" Ellington conducting band. d, Ellington (1899-1974). e, Louis Armstrong (1900-71). f, Armstrong playing trumpet. g, Charlie "Bird" Parker playing saxophone. h, Parker (1920-55).
No. 2050, 4d — Composers: a, Cole Porter (1893-1964). b, "Born to Dance," by Porter. c, "Porgy and Bess," by George Gershwin. d, Gershwin (1898-1937). e, Richard Rodgers (1902-79) & Oscar Hammerstein II (1895-

1960). f, "The King and I," by Rodgers & Hammerstein. g, "West Side Story," by Leonard Bernstein. h, Bernstein (1918-90).
No. 2051, 25d, Ella Fitzgerald (1917-96). No. 2052, 25d, Irving Berlin (1888-1989), "Oh How I Hate to Get Up in the Morning."

**1998, Oct. 12   Litho.   Perf. 14**
**Sheets of 8, #a-h**
2049-2050 A319 Set of 2    14.00 14.00
**Souvenir Sheets**
2051-2052 A319 Set of 2    13.00 13.00
Nos. 2049b-2049c, 2049f-2049g, 2050b-2050c, 2050f-2050g are 53x38mm.

Sinking of the Titanic — A320

No. 2053: a, Capt. Edward J. Smith. b, Molly Brown. c, News of the disaster breaks. d, Benjamin Guggenheim. e, Isidor Strauss. f, Ida Strauss.
No. 2054, 25d, Picture of ship on postcard. No. 2055, 25d, Ship sinking. No. 2056, 25d, Remains of ship lying on bottom of ocean years later.

**1998, Oct. 25**
2053 A320 5d Sheet of 6, #a.-
        f.                   7.75  7.75
**Souvenir Sheets**
2054-2056 A320 Set of 3    18.00 18.00

Diana, Princess of Wales (1961-97) — A321

No. 2057: a, Inscription panel at left. b, Panel at right.

**1998, Oct. 29   Perf. 14½x14**
2057 A321 10d Horiz. pair, a-b 3.50 3.50
No. 2057 was printed in sheets containing 3 pairs.

Pablo Picasso (1881-1973) A322

Paintings: 3d, Death of Casagemas, 1901. 5d, Seated Woman, 1920, vert. 10d, Mother and Child, 1907, vert.
25d, Child Playing with a Toy Truck, 1953, vert.

**1998, Oct. 29   Perf. 14½**
2058-2060 A322 Set of 3     3.25  3.25
**Souvenir Sheet**
2061 A322 25d multicolored   4.50  4.50

A323

No. 2062 — Mahatma Gandhi (1869-1948): a, Age 62, 1932. b, Age 60, 1930, with Sarojini Naidu. c, Age 61, 1931, spinning yarn. d, Age 47, 1916.
25d, Age 61, 1931.

**1998, Oct. 29   Perf. 14**
2062 A323 10d Sheet of 4, #a.-d. 7.50 7.50
**Souvenir Sheet**
2063 A323 25d multicolored   5.00  5.00
Nos. 2062b-2062c are 53x39mm.

A324

Ships: 2d, Chinese Junk. 3d, HMS Victory. 10d, County Class Destroyer. 15d, Viking Longboat.
No. 2068, 5d, horiz: a, HMS Dreadnought. b, Truxton Class Cruiser. c, Queen Mary. d, Canberra. e, Queen Elizabeth. f, Queen Elizabeth 2.
No. 2069, 5d: a, Santa Maria. b, Mary Rose. c, Mayflower. d, Ark Royal. e, HMS Beagle. f, HMS Bounty.
No. 2070, 25d, Cutty Sark. No. 2071, 25d, Sovereign of the Seas.

**1998**
2064-2067 A324 Set of 4     5.50  5.50
**Sheets of 6, #a-f**
2068-2069 A324 Set of 2    11.00 11.00
**Souvenir Sheets**
2070-2071 A324 Set of 2     9.00  9.00
No. 2070 contains one 42x56mm stamp; No. 2071, one 56x42mm stamp.

1998 World Scouting Jamboree, Chile — A325

No. 2072: a, Scout handclasp. b, Small boat sailing. c, Scout salute.
No. 2073, Lord Robert Baden-Powell.

**1998, Oct. 29   Litho.   Perf. 14**
2072 A325 10d Sheet of 3, #a.-c. 5.50 5.50
**Souvenir Sheet**
2073 A325 25d multicolored   4.50  4.50

Royal Air Force, 80th Anniv. — A326

No. 2074, 5d: a, Sepecat Jaguar GR1. b, BAe Harrier GR7. c, Panavia Tornado GR1 firing Sidewinder AIM 9-L missle. d, Panavia Tornado GR1 on afterburner.
No. 2075, 5d: a, Sepecat Jaguar GR1A in low visibility gray finish. b, Panavia Tornado GR1A. c, Sepecat Jaguar GR1A in Bosnia theater camouflage finish. d, BAe Hawk 200.
No. 2076, 7d: a, Panavia Tornado GR1 flying left. b, BAe Hawk TIA. c, Sepecat Jaguar GR1A. d, Panavia Tornado GR1 flying right.
No. 2077, 20d, Eurofighters. No. 2078, 25d, Biplane, hawk's head. No. 2079, 25d, Lightning, Eurofighter. No. 2080, 25d, Biplane, hawk in flight. No. 2081, 25d, Lancaster, Eurofighter. No. 2082, 25d, Biplane, hawk perched.

**1998, Oct. 29   Sheets of 4, #a-d**
2074-2076 A326 Set of 3    12.50 12.50
**Souvenir Sheets**
2077-2082 A326 Set of 6    27.50 27.50

Paintings by Eugène Delacroix (1798-1863) A327

No. 2083, 4d: a, Mule Drivers from Tetuan. b, Encampment of Arab Mule Drivers. c, An Orange Seller. d, The Banks of the River. e, View of Tangier from the Seashore. f, Arab Horses Fighting in a Stable. g, Horses at the Trough. h, The Combat of the Giaour and Hassan.
No. 2084, 4d, vert: a, Moroccan from Tangier Standing. b, A Man of Tangier. c, Young Arab Standing with a Rifle. d, Moroccan Chieftan. e, Jewish Bride of Tangiers. f, Seated Jewess from Morocco. g, A seated Arab. h, Young Arab Seated by a Wall.
No. 2085, 4d: a, Turk Seated on a Sofa Smoking. b, View of Tangier from North African and Spanish Album. c, The Spanish Coast

at Salobrena from North African and Spanish Album. d, The Aissaouas. e, Sea View from the Heights of Dieppe. f, An Arab Fantasy. g, Arab Comic Fantasy. h, An Arab Camp at Night.

Details: No. 2086, 25d, Self-portrait, vert. No. 2087, 25d, Two Women of Algiers in Their Apartment. No. 2088, 25d, Massacre of Chios.

**1998, Oct. 29**     **Sheets of 8, #a-h**
2083-2085 A327   Set of 3   19.50 19.50

**Souvenir Sheets**
2086-2088 A327   Set of 3   14.00 14.00

Christmas — A328

Designs: 1d, Beagle in sock. 2d, Giraffe, wreath. 3d, Rainbow bee eater, ribbon, ornament. 4d, Adult deer. 5d, Fawn. 10d, Irish red and white setter in package.

No. 2095, 25d, Brown classic tabby kitten. No. 2096, 25d, Basset hound, rough collie.

**1998, Nov. 23**
2089-2094 A328   Set of 6   5.00 5.00

**Souvenir Sheets**
2095-2096 A328   Set of 2   9.00 9.00

New Year 1999 (Year of the Rabbit) — A329

No. 2097 — Stylized rabbits, background color: a, Olive brown. b, Green blue. c, Red brown. d, Pale orange.

**1999, Jan. 4**   **Litho.**   **Perf. 14½**
2097 A329  3d Sheet of 4, #a.-d.  2.40 2.40

**Souvenir Sheet**
2098 A329  10d multicolored   2.25 2.25

No. 2098 contains one 39x24mm stamp.

Disney's Jungle Book — A330

No. 2099: a, Mowgli, King Louie (bear). b, Mowgli, snake. c, Flunky Monkey. d, Monkey singing. e, Girl. f, Mowgli, Flunky Monkey. g, Mowgli, buzzards. h, Shere Khan (tiger).

No. 2100, 25d, Baby elephant, horiz. No. 2101, 25d, King Louie, horiz.

**1999, Mar. 11**  **Litho.**  **Perf. 13½x14**
2099 A330  5d Sheet of 8, #a.-h.  10.00 10.00

**Souvenir Sheets**
2100-2101 A330   Set of 2   10.00 10.00

Australia '99, World Stamp Expo — A331

No. 2102, 6d — African butterflies: a, Golden piper. b, Citrus swallowtail. c, Azure hairstreak. d, Two-tailed pasha. e, Blue pansy. f, African leaf butterfly.

No. 2103, 6d: a, Plain tiger. b, Blue swallowtail. c, Papilio mnesheus. d, Common opal. e, Forest green. f, Boisduval's false acraea.

No. 2104, 25d, Pirate butterfly, vert. No. 2105, 25d, Two-tailed pasha, vert.

**1999, Apr. 12**   **Litho.**   **Perf. 14**
**Sheets of 6, #a-f**
2102-2103 A331   Set of 2   13.00 13.00

**Souvenir Sheets**
2104-2105 A331   Set of 2   9.00 9.00

Wedding of Prince Edward and Sophie Rhys-Jones — A332

No. 2106 — Various portraits of couple showing Sophie with: a, Blue collar. b, Long hair. c, Red collar.
25d, Couple, horiz.

**1999, June 19**   **Litho.**   **Perf. 13½**
2106 A332  10d Sheet of 3, #a.-c.  5.00 5.00

**Souvenir Sheet**
2107 A332  25d multicolored   4.50 4.50

IBRA '99, World Philatelic Exhibition, Nuremberg — A333

Exhibition emblem, Adler 2-3-2 steam engine and: 4d, Samoa #104d. 5d, Samoa #55.

Emblem, sailing ship Friedrech August and: 10d, Samoa #64, #65. 15d, Samoa #67.
25d, Cover with Samoa #67 (part), 68.

**1999, July 6**     **Perf. 14x14¼**
2108-2111 A333   Set of 4   6.50 6.50

**Souvenir Sheet**
2112 A333  25d multicolored   4.50 4.50
No. 2112 contains one 60x40mm stamp.

Apollo 11 Moon Landing, 30th Anniv. — A334

No. 2113: a, Bell X-14A VTOL aircraft. b, Lunar landing practice rig. c, Early prototype lander. d, Zero gravity training. e, Jet pack training. f, Lunar lander pilot training.

No. 2114, 25d, Apollo 11 Eagle, horiz. No. 2115, 25d, Apollo 11 splash down, horiz.

**1999, July 6**     **Perf. 14**
2113 A334  6d Sheet of 6, #a.-f.  6.50 6.50

**Souvenir Sheets**
2114-2115 A334   Set of 2   10.00 10.00

**Souvenir Sheets**

PhilexFrance '99, World Philatelic Exhibition — A335

Early railroads: No. 2116, 25d, Road-railer carriage. No. 2117, 25d, 2-2-2 Passenger locomotive, 1846.

**1999, July 6**     **Perf. 13¾**
2116-2117 A335   Set of 2   10.00 10.00

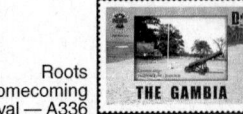

Roots Homecoming Festival — A336

Designs: 1d, Cannon, Freedom Post, Juffureh. 2d, Fort Bullen, Barra. 3d, James Fort Island.

**1999, June 21**   **Litho.**   **Perf. 14**
2118-2120 A336   Set of 3   1.25 1.25

UN Rights of the Child, 10th Anniv. A337

No. 2121 — Children: a, With head down on table. b, Drinking from cup. c, Drawing on paper.
25d, Child smiling under umbrella.

**1999, July 6**
2121 A337  10d Sheet of 3, #a.-c.  5.50 5.50

**Souvenir Sheet**
2122 A337  25d multicolored   4.50 4.50

Johann Wolfgang von Goethe (1749-1832), Poet — A338

No. 2123: a, Faust quaffs the spirit's nectar. b, Portraits of Goethe and Friedrich von Schiller (1759-1805). c, Faust contemplates mortality.
25d, Portrait of Goethe, vert.

**1999, July 6**
2123 A338  15d Sheet of 3, #a.-c.  8.00 8.00

**Souvenir Sheet**
2124 A338  25d multicolored   4.50 4.50

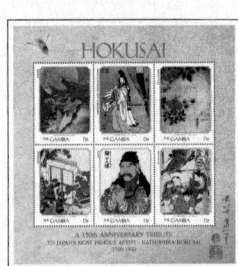

Paintings by Hokusai (1760-1849) — A339

No. 2125, 5d — Details or entire paintings: a, Bunshosei. b, Overthrower of Castles, Overthrower of Nations. c, Bee on Wild Rose. d, Sei Shonagon. e, Kuan-Yu. f, The Fifth Month.

No. 2126, 5d: a, Exotic Beauty. b, Wind (2 people). c, Dancing Monkey. d, Lady and Maiden on an Outing. e, Wind (3 people). f, Courtesan with Fan.

No. 2127, 25d, People on the Balcony of Sazaido. No. 2128, 25d, Caocao before the Battle of Chibi.

**1999, July 6**     **Perf. 13¾**
**Sheets of 6, #a-f**
2125-2126 A339   Set of 2   12.00 12.00

**Souvenir Sheets**
2127-2128 A339   Set of 2   10.00 10.00

Sea Birds — A340

Designs: 2d, American oystercatcher. 3d, Blue-footed booby. 10d, Western gull. 15d, Brown pelican.

No. 2133, 4d: a, Atlantic puffin. b, Red-tailed tropicbird. c, Reddish egret. d, Laughing gull. e, Great white egret. f, Northern gannet. g, Forster's tern. h, Great cormorant. i, Razor bill.

No. 2134, 4d: a, Adélie penguin. b, Black skimmer. c, Erect-crested penguin. d, Heerman's gull. e, Glaucous-winged gull. f, Layson albatross. g, White pelican. h, Tufted puffin. i, Black guillemot.

No. 2135: a, Razor bill. b, Shelduck. c, Sandwich tern. d, Arctic skua. e, Gannet. f, Common gull.

No. 2136, 25d, Pelicans. No. 2137, 25d, California gull. No. 2138, 25d, Gentoo penguin.

**1999, Aug. 1**     **Perf. 14**
2129-2132 A340   Set of 4   5.50 5.50

**Sheets of 9, #a-i**
2133-2134 A340   Set of 2   14.50 14.50
2135 A340  5d Sheet of 6, #a.-f.  10.00 10.00

**Souvenir Sheets**
2136-2138 A340   Set of 3   15.00 15.00

Nos. 2135-2138 have continuous designs.

Prehistoric Animals — A341

No. 2139, 3d: a, Diatryma. b, Pteranodon. c, Stegodon. d, Icaronycteris. e, Archaeopteryx. f, Chasmatosaurus. g, Tytthostonyx. h, Hyaenodon. i, Uintatherium. j, Hesperocyon. k, Ambelodon. l, Indricotherium.

No. 2140, 3d: a, Carnotaurus. b, Quetzalcoatlus. c, Peteinosaurus. d, Prenocephale. e, Hesperornis. f, Coelophysis. g, Camptosaurus. h, Panderichthys. i, Garudimimus. j, Cacops. k, Ichthyostega. l, Scutellosaurus.

No. 2141, 25d, Lepisosteus. No. 2142, 25d, Sabertooth cat. No. 2143, 25d, Deinonychus. No. 2144, 25d, Microceratops.

**1999, Aug. 1**   **Sheets of 12, #a-l**
2139-2140 A341   Set of 2   12.00 12.00

**Souvenir Sheets**
2141-2144 A341   Set of 4   19.00 19.00

Queen Mother, 100th Birthday (in 2000) — A342

No. 2145: a, Duchess of York, Princess Elizabeth, 1928. b, Lady Elizabeth Bowles-Lyon, 1923. c, Queen Elizabeth, 1946. d, Queen Mother, Prince Harry.
25d, Queen Mother celebrating 89th birthday, 1989.

**1999, Aug. 4**
2145 A342  10d Sheet of 4, #a.-d.
    + label   6.50 6.50

**Souvenir Sheet**
**Perf. 13¾**
2146 A342  25d multicolored   4.50 4.50

No. 2146 contains one 38x51mm stamp. Margins of sheets are embossed.
See Nos. 2555-2556.

Orchids — A343

Designs: 2d, Sophrocattleya. 3d, Cattleya. 4d, Brassolaeliocattleya. 5d, Brassoepidendrum. 10d, Sophrolaeliocattleya. 15d, Iwanagaara.

No. 2153, 6d: a, Brassolaeliocattleya (yellow). b, Cattleytonia. c, Laeliocattleya (yellow). d, Miltonia. e, Cattleya forbesii. f, Odontoglossum cervantesii.

No. 2154, 6d: a, Lycaste macrobulbon. b, Laeliocattleya (red). c, Brassocattleya (pink). d, Cattleya, diff. e, Brassocattleya (speckled). f, Brassolaeliocattleya (yellow & red).

No. 2155, 25d, Unnamed. No. 2156, 25d, Brassolaeliocattleya (white & red).

**1999, Aug. 1**   **Litho.**   **Perf. 14**
2147-2152 A343   Set of 6   7.25 7.25

**Sheets of 6, #a-f**
2153-2154 A343 Set of 2   14.00 14.00
**Souvenir Sheets**
2155-2156 A343 Set of 2   11.00 11.00

Marine
Fauna — A344

Designs: 1d, Sea gull. 1.50d, Portuguese man-of-war. 5d, Walrus. 10d, Manatee.
No. 2161, 3d: a, Anglefish. b, Leafy sea dragon. c, Hawksbill turtle. d, Mandarin fish. e, Candy cane sea star. f, Plate coral. g, Butter-lyfish. h, Coral polyp. i, Hermit crab. j, Strawberry shrimp. k, Giant blue clam. l, Sea cucumber.
No. 2162, 3d: a, Whale shark. b, Gray reef shark. c, New ZEngland octopus. d, Puffer fish. e, Lionfish. f, Squid. g, Chambered nautilus. h, Clown fish. i, Moray eel. j, Spiny lobster. k, Sotted ray. l, Clown anemone.
25d, Common dolphin.

**1999, Aug. 1**
2157-2160 A344 Set of 4   3.50 3.50
**Sheets of 12, #a-l**
2161-2162 A344 Set of 2   13.00 13.00
2163 A344 25d multicolored   5.00 5.00

Galapagos
Islands Marine
Fauna — A345

No. 2164: a, Swallow-tailed gull. b, Frigate bird. c, Red-footed booby. d, Galapagos hawk. e, Great blue heron. f, Masked booby. g, Bottlenose dolphins. h, Black grunts. i, Surgeonfish. j, Stingray. k, Pilot whales. l, Pacific green sea turtle. m, Shark. n, Sea lion. o, Marine iguana. p, Pacific manta ray. q, Moorish idol. r, Galapagos penguin. s, Silver grunts. t, Sea urchin. u, Wrasse. v, Almaco amberjack. w, Blue-chin parrotfish. x, Yellow sea urchin. y, Lobster. z, Grouper. aa, Scorpionfish. ab, Squirrelfish. ac, Octopus. ad, King angelfish. ae, Horned shark. af, Galapagos hogfish. ag, Puffer fish. ah, Moray eel. ai, Orange tube corals. aj, Whitestripe chromis. ak, Longnose hawkfish. al, Sea cucumber. am, Spotted hawkfish. an, Zebra moray eel.
25d, Emperor penguins.

**1999, Aug. 1**
2164 A345 1.50d Sheet of 40,
    #a.-an.   15.00 15.00
**Souvenir Sheet**
2165 A345   25d multicolored 5.25 5.25

**Souvenir Sheet**

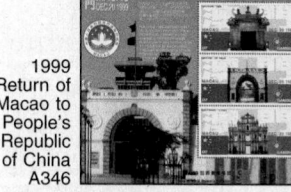

1999
Return of
Macao to
People's
Republic
of China
A346

No. 2166: a, Temple of A-ma. b, Border gate. c, Ruins of St. Paul's Cathedral.

**1999, Aug. 20**   **Litho.**   **Perf. 14**
2166 A346 7d Sheet of 3, #a-c   4.00 4.00

Space
Exploration — A347

Designs: 1d, Telstar I, horiz. 1.50d, Skylab. 2d, Mars 3 orbiter and lander. 3d, COBE. 10d, Astronaut Bruce McCandless. 15d, Apollo 13.
No. 2173, 6d: a, German V-2 rocket. b, Delta Straight 8. c, Ariane 4. d, Mercury on Atlas rocket. e, Saturn 1B. f, Cassini.
No. 2174, 6d, horiz.: a, Mariner 4. b, Viking Mars orbiter and lander. c, Giotto. d, Luna 9. e, Voyager. f, Galileo.

No. 2175, 6d, horiz.: a, Soviet Vostok 1. b, Apollo command and service modules. c, Mecury capsule. d, Apollo 16 lunar module. e, Gemini 8. f, Soviet Soyuz.
No. 2176, 25d, Apollo-Soyuz, horiz. No. 2177, 25d, Mars Pathfinder, horiz.

**1999**
2167-2172 A347 Set of 6   6.00 6.00
**Sheets of 6, #a-f**
2173-2175 A347 Set of 3   20.00 20.00
2176-2177 A347 Set of 2   12.00 12.00
Nos. 2176-2177 each contain one 57x43mm stamp.

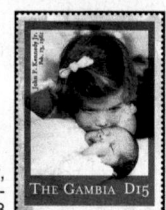

John F. Kennedy,
Jr. (1960-
99) — A348

No. 2178: a, In 1961. b, In 1970s. c, In 1997.

**1999, Dec. 7**
2178 A348 15d Sheet of 3, #a.-c. 7.25 7.25

Flowers — A349

Various flower photographs making up a photomosaic of Princess Diana.

**1999, Dec. 31**   **Litho.**   **Perf. 13¾**
2179 A349 3d Sheet of 8, #a.-h. 5.00 5.00
See No. 2290.

Millennium — A350

No. 2180, 3d — Highlights of 1450-1500: a, Da Vinci designs 1st flying machine. b, Gutenberg prints the Bible. c, 1st book in color printed. d, Ivan III becomes Grand Prince of Moscow. e, Ottomans capture Constantinople. f, Ming emperors rebuild Great Wall of China. g, Lorenzo de Medici begins rule in Florence. h, Henry VII becomes first Tudor king of England. i, Vasco da Gama sails to India. j, Aragon and Castile unite. k, Birth of Desiderius Erasmus. l, Cabot explores No. America. m, Henry VI wages War of the Roses. n, Bartholomeu Dias discovers Cape of Good Hope. o, Matthias Corvinus (Hunyadi) becomes king of Hungary. p, Columbus sails to America (60x40mm). q, Girolamo Savonarola burned at stake.
No. 2181, 3d — Highlights of 1900-1910: a, Max Planck develops quantum theory. b, Graf Ferdinand von Zeppelin constructs first airship. c, Marconi sends 1st transatlantic message. d, Queen Victoria dies. e, 1st Nobel Prize. f, Boer War ends. g, Wright Brothers' 1st flight. h, 1st teddy bears made in Germany. i, Work begins on Panama Canal. j, Einstein develops theory of relativity. k, 1905 revolution in Russia. l, San Francisco earthquake. m, Color photography developed by Louis Lumière. n, Picasso paints "Les Demoiselles d'Avignon." o, Peary reaches North Pole. p, Model T appears (60x40mm). q, 1st kibbutz founded in Holy Land.

**2000, Feb. 1**   **Perf. 12¾x12½**
**Sheets of 17, #a-q**
2180-2181 A350 Set of 2   20.00 20.00
Inscriptions are misspelled on several stamps on No. 2181.

New Year 2000 (Year
of the
Dragon) — A351

No. 2182 — Various dragons and Chinese characters with background colors: a, Blue green. b, Brownish gray. c, Red orange (purple dragon). d, Orange.
15d, Dull orange.

**2000, Feb. 5**   **Perf. 14x14½**
2182 A351 5d Sheet of 4, #a.-d. 4.25 4.25
**Souvenir Sheet**
**Perf. 14**
2183 A351 15d multi   3.00 3.00
No. 2183 contains one 42x28mm stamp.

African
Wildlife — A352

Designs: 50b, Indri. 75b, Nubian ibex. 1d, Grevy's zebra, vert. 2d, Bongo, vert. 3d, White rhinoceros. 4d, Lesser galago. 5d, Okapi, vert. 10d, Mhorr gazelle, vert.
No. 2192, 5d: a, Giant sable antelope. b, Greater kudu. c, Somali wild ass. d, Dorcas gazelle. e, Addax. f, Pelzeln's gazelle.
No. 2193, 6d: a, Cheetah. b, Chimpanzee. c, Angwantibo. d, Black rhinoceros. e, Bontebok. f, Giant eland.
No. 2194, 7d: a, Mountain gorilla. b, Blackfaced impala. c, Crowned lemur. d, Long-tailed ground roller. e, Brown hyena. f, Mountain zebra.
No. 2195, 7d: a, Sacred ibis. b, Mauritius kestrel. c, Barbary leopard. d, Radiated tortoise. e, Pygmy hippopotamus. f, Bald ibis.
No. 2196, 25d, Aye-aye. No. 2197, 25d, Black lechwe, vert. No. 2198, 25d, Nile crocodile. No. 2199, 25d, African elephant.

**2000, Feb. 18**   **Perf. 14**
2184-2191 A352 Set of 8   4.50 4.50
**Sheets of 6, #a.-f.**
2192-2195 A352 Set of 4   27.50 27.50
**Souvenir Sheets**
2196-2199 A352 Set of 4   22.50 22.50
AmeriStamp Expo, Portland, Ore. (No. 2194).

The Three
Stooges
A353

No. 2200: a, Curly pulling Moe's hair. b, Curly caught in wringer. c, Curly, Moe with drill. d, Moe pulling Larry's hair. e, Moe. f, Moe sticking finger in Curly's nose. g, Stooges pointing. h, Skull biting Curly's nose. i, Shemp.
No. 2201, 25d, Larry with crown. No. 2202, 25d, Curly on telephone, vert.

**2000, Jan. 14**   **Litho.**   **Perf. 13¼**
2200 A353 5d Sheet of 9, #a.-
    i.   8.50 8.50
**Souvenir Sheets**
2201-2202 A353 Set of 2   9.00 9.00
See Nos. 2446-2448.

I Love Lucy
A354

No. 2203: a, Lucy on sofa. b, Lucy, Ricky. c, Fred, Lucy, and Ethel. d, Lucy standing. e, Lucy, Ricky embracing. f, Lucy looking in mirror. g, Lucy with fists clenched. h, Lucy, Ricky on sofa. i, Lucy and Ethel.
No. 2204, 25d, Lucy, Ricky embracing, vert. No. 2205, 25d, Lucy looking in mirror, vert.

**2000, Jan. 14**   **Litho.**   **Perf. 13¼**
2203 A354 5d Sheet of 9, #a.-
    i.   9.00 9.00
**Souvenir Sheets**
2204-2205 A354 Set of 2   9.00 9.00
See Nos. 2440-2442, 2449-2451.

Betty
Boop — A355

No. 2206: a, In green and yellow outfit. b, In red dress. c, In red shirt and blue jeans. d, In green and brown outfit. e, Seated in chair. f, In orange shirt and blue jeans. g, In fur coat. h, In pink dress. i, With dumbbell and water bottle.
No. 2207, 25d, In yellow flowered dress. No. 2208, 25d, In bathtub.

**2000, Jan. 14**   **Litho.**   **Perf. 13¼**
2206 A355 5d Sheet of 9, #a.-
    i.   9.50 9.50
**Souvenir Sheets**
2207-2208 A355 Set of 2   9.50 9.50

Paintings of
Anthony Van
Dyck — A356

No. 2209: a, Samson and Delilah, c. 1619-20. b, Samson and Delilah sketch, 1618-20. c, Samson and Delilah, c. 1628-30.
No. 2210, 5d: a, The Adoration of the Shepherds. b, The Rest on the Flight to Egypt, The Virgin of the Partridges. c, Suffer the Little Children to Come Unto Me. d, Christ and the Moneychangers. e, Feast at the House of Simon the Pharisee. f, The Lamentation Over the Dead Christ.
No. 2211, 5d, vert.: a, Anton Giulo Brignole-Sale. b, Paolina Adorno Brignole-Sale. c, Battina Balbi Durazzo. d, Portrait of a Man of the Cattaneo Family. e, Portrait of a Woman. f, Elena Grimaldi Cattaneo.
No. 2212, 5d, vert.: a, A Genoese Senator. b, A Seated Gentlewoman. c, The Senator's Wife. d, A Genoese Lady, The Marchesa Balbi. e, Polyxena Spinola, Marchesa de Legones. f, Agostino Pallavicini.
No. 2213, 5d, vert.: a, Prince Rupert of the Palatinate. b, William II of Nassau and Orange. c, Prince Charles Louis of the Palatinate. d, Prince Rupert, Count Palatine. e, The Princess Mary. f, Prince Charles Louis, Count Palatine.
No. 2214, 5d, vert.: a, Sir George Villiers and Lady Katherine Manners as Adonis and Venus. b, Lady Mary Villiers with Lord Arran. c, Rachel de Ruvigny, Countess Southampton as Fortune. d, Venus at Forge of Vulcan. e, Daedalus and Icarus. f, The Clipping of Cupid's Wing.
No. 2215, 25d, A Man with His Son. No. 2216, 25d, Prince Charles Louis, Elector Palatine and His Brother, Prince Rupert of the Palatinate, vert. No. 2217, 25d, Venetia, Lady Digby, as Prudence, vert. No. 2218, 25d, Drunken Silenus, vert. No. 2219, 25d, Portrait of a Genoese Lady, vert. No. 2220, 25d, Charles II as Prince of Wales, vert. No. 2221, 25d, William II, Prince of Orange, and His Bride, Mary, Princess Royal of England, vert. No. 2222, 25d, The Three Eldest Children of Charles I, vert.

**2000, May 1**   **Perf. 13¾**
2209 A356 5d Sheet of 3, #a.-
    c.   2.75 2.75
**Sheets of 6, #a.-f.**
2210-2214 A356 Set of 5   27.50 27.50
**Souvenir Sheets**
2215-2222 A356 Set of 8   42.50 42.50

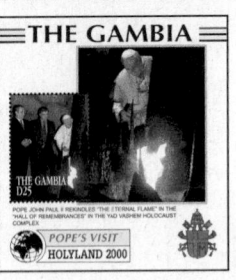

**THE GAMBIA**

Papal Visits
A357

No. 2223, 6d — 1991-92 Visits: a, Portugal. b, Poland. c, Hungary. d, Brazil. e, Senegal. f, Gambia. g, Guinea. h, Angola. i, Sao Tomé. j, Dominican Republic.
No. 2224, 6d — 1993 Visits: a, Benin. b, Uganda. c, Sudan. d, Albania. e, Spain. f, Jamaica. g, Mexico. h, United States. i, Lithuania. j, Latvia.
No. 2225, 6d — 1993-95 Visits: a, Estonia. b, Croatia. c, Philippines. d, Papua New Guinea. e, Australia. f, Sri Lanka. g, Czech Republic. h, Belgium. i, Slovakia. j, Cameroon.
No. 2226, 6d — 1995-96 Visits: a, South Africa. b, Kenya. c, United States. d, United Nations. e, Guatemala. f, Nicaragua. g, El Salvador. h, Venezuela. i, Tunisia. j, Slovenia.
No. 2227, 6d — 1996-98 Visits: a, Germany. b, Hungary. c, France, 1996. d, Bosnia. e, Czech Republic. f, Lebanon. g, Poland. h, France, 1997. i, Brazil. j, Cuba.
No. 2228, 6d — 1998-99 Visits: a, Nigeria. b, Austria. c, Croatia. d, Mexico. e, United States. f, Romania. g, Poland. h, Slovenia. i, India. j, Georgia.
No. 2229, 25d, Pope rekindles Eternal Flame. No. 2230, 25d, Pope blesses Holy Land. No. 2231, 25d, Pope places prayer on Western Wall. No. 2232, 25d, Pope assisted by Israeli president and prime minister. No. 2233, 25d, Pope prays at Western Wall. No. 2234, 25d, Pope receives Bible from chief rabbis. No. 2235, 25d, Pope touches bowl of soil. No. 2236, 25d, Pope at Yad Vashem, horiz.

**2000, May 15    Litho.    Perf. 13¾**
**Sheets of 10, #a.-j., + 2 labels**
2223-2228 A357    Set of 6    57.50 57.50
**Souvenir Sheets**
*Perf. 14½x14¾, 14¾x14½ (#2236)*
2229-2236 A357    Set of 8    33.00 33.00
Stamps from Nos. 2223-2228 are 28x47mm.

Mushrooms — A358

Designs: 4d, Morel. 5d, Chanterelle. 15d, Knight cap. 20d, Spindle.
No. 2241, 7d: a, Yellow parasol. b, Mottlegill. c, Poplar field cap. d, Caesar's e. Flame shield-cap. f, Lilac bonnet.
No. 2242, 7d: a, Common puffball. b, Earth star. c, Silky volvar. d, Stump puffball. e, Spindle-stemmed bolete. f, Fox-orange cort.
No. 2243, 25d, Red-stemmed tough shank. No. 2244, 25d, St. George's.

**2000, May 15    Perf. 14**
2237-2240 A358    Set of 4    7.50 7.50
**Sheets of 6, #a.-f.**
2241-2242 A358    Set of 2    15.00 15.00
**Souvenir Sheets**
2243-2244 A358    Set of 2    10.00 10.00

First Zeppelin Flight, Cent. A359

No. 2245: a, LZ-10. b, LZ-127. c, LZ-129. 25d, LZ-130.

**2000, May 1    Litho.    Perf. 14**
2245 A359    15d Sheet of 3, #a-c    8.25 8.25
**Souvenir Sheet**
2246 A359    25d multi    5.25 8.25
No. 2246 contains one 50x38mm stamp.

Prince William, 18th Birthday A360

No. 2247: a, As child. b, In sweater. c, In suit, with flowers. d, In suit. 25d, With Prince Harry.

**2000, May 1    Perf. 14**
2247 A360    7d Sheet of 4, #a-d    5.00 5.00
**Souvenir Sheet**
*Perf. 13¾*
2248 A360    25d multi    4.50 4.50
No. 2248 contains one 38x50mm stamp.

Berlin Film Festival, 50th Anniv. A361

No. 2249: a, Pane. Amore e Fantasia. b, Richard III. c, Smultronstället (Wild Strawberries). d, The Defiant Ones. e, The Living Desert. f, A Bout de Souffle. 25d, Twelve Angry Men.

**2000, May 1    Perf. 14**
2249 A361    7d Sheet of 6, #a-f    7.25 7.25
**Souvenir Sheet**
2250 A361    25d multi    4.50 4.50

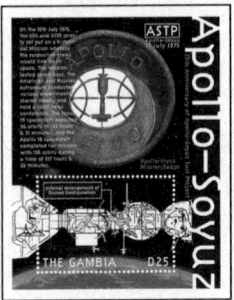

Apollo-Soyuz Mission, 25th Anniv. — A362

No. 2251: a, Donald K. Slayton. b, Thomas P. Stafford. c, Vance D. Brand. 25d, Diagram of docked spacecraft.

**2000, May 1**
2251 A362    15d Sheet of 3, #a-c    8.50 8.50
**Souvenir Sheet**
2252 A362    25d multi    4.50 4.50

**Souvenir Sheet**

2000 Summer Olympics, Sydney — A363

No. 2253: a, Paavo Nurmi. b, Basketball. c, Panathenian Stadium, Athens and Greek flag. d, Ancient Greek chariot racing.

**2000, May 1**
2253 A363    6d Sheet of 4, #a-d    5.00 5.00

Public Railways, 175th Anniv. — A364

No. 2254: a, Locomotion No. 1, George Stephenson. b, Chesapeake.

**2000, May 1**
2254 A364    15d Sheet of 2, #a-b    5.50 5.50

**Souvenir Sheet**

Johann Sebastian Bach (1685-1750) — A365

**2000, May 1**
2255 A365    25d multi    4.25 4.25

Popes A366

No. 2256, 7d: a, Pope Felix IV, 526-30. b, Gelasius I, 492-96. c, Gregory I, 590-604. d, Gregory IX, 1227-41. e, Gregory XII, 1406-15. f, Honorius III, 1216-27.
No. 2257, 7d: a, Gregory XIII, 1572-85. b, Urban I, 1088-99. c, Sixtus I, 115-125. d, Pius IX, 1846-78. e, Pius IV, 1559-65. f, Paschal I, 817-24.
No. 2258, 7d: a, Alexander VII, 1655-67. b, Benedict XI, 1303-04. c, Calixtus III, 1455-58. d, Celestine V, 1294. e, Clement IX, 1667-69. f, Fabian, 236-50.
No. 2259, 25d, Peter, 33-64. No. 2260, 25d, Damasus I, 366-384. No. 2261, 25d, John I, 523-526.

**2000, July 26    Litho.    Perf. 13¾**
**Sheets of 6, #a-f**
2256-2258 A366    Set of 3    24.00 24.00
**Souvenir Sheets**
2259-2261 A366    Set of 3    14.50 14.50

Butterflies — A367

Designs: 1.50d, Amphicalia tigris. 2d, Myrina silenus. 3d, Chrysiridia madagascarensis. 5d, Papilionidae. 10d, Dasiothia medea.

No. 2253: a, Paavo Nurmi...

**2000, Aug. 7    Perf. 14¾x14**
2262 A367    1.50d multi    .40 .25
2263 A367    2d multi    .50 .35
2264 A367    3d multi    1.25 .50
2265 A367    5d multi    1.50 .80
2266 A367    10d multi    2.10 1.60
*Nos. 2262-2266 (5)*    5.75 3.50
Nos. 2264-2266 exist dated 2003.
See Nos. 2436-2439, 2452-2452B, 2699.

**Souvenir Sheet**

Albert Einstein (1879-1955) — A368

**2000, May 1    Litho.    Perf. 14¼**
2267 A368    25d multi    5.00 5.00

Space A369

No. 2268, 7d: a, Uhuru. b, Rosat. c, I.U.E. d, Astro E. e, Exosat. f, Chandra.
No. 2269, 7d, vert.: a, Helios. b, Solar Max. c, SOHO. d, O.S.O. e, Special rocket launch. f, I.M.P.
No. 2270, 25d, XMM. No. 2271, 25d, Cassini Huygens.

**2000, May 1    Perf. 14**
**Sheets of 6, #a-f**
2268-2269 A369    Set of 2    14.00 14.00
**Souvenir Sheets**
2270-2271 A369    Set of 2    8.25 8.25
The Stamp Show 2000, London; World Stamp Expo 2000, Anaheim.

Monarchs — A370

No. 2272: a, Charles I of Great Britain, 1625-49. b, Clovis III, king of the Franks (691-95).
No. 2273, 7d: a, Charles II of France, 885-887. b, Catherine de Medici of France, 1547-59. c, Boris Godunov of Russia, 1598-1605. d, Basil III of Russia, 1505-33. e, Anne of Great Britain, 1702-14. f, Charles IX of France, 1560-74.
No. 2274, 7d: a, James IV of Scotland, 1488-1513. b, James V of Scotland, 1513-42. c, James VI of Scotland, 1567-1625. d, Mary of Scotland, 1542-67. e, Mary of Great Britain, 1689-94. f, Elizabeth II of Great Britain, 1952-present.
No. 2275, 25d, James Francis Edward Stuart. No. 2276, 25d, Robert I, the Bruce of Scotland, 1307-57. No. 2277, 25d, Bahadur Shah of India, 1837-57.

**2000, July 26    Perf. 13¾**
2272 A370    7d Sheet of 2, #a-b    2.50 2.50
**Sheets of 6, #a-f**
2273-2274 A370    Set of 2    14.00 14.00
**Souvenir Sheets**
2275-2277 A370    Set of 3    11.00 11.00

Puppies — A371

Designs: 1d, West Highland terrier. 1.50d, Bernese mountain dog. 3d, Yorkshire terrier. 4d, West Highland terrrier, diff. 10d, Chow chow. 15d, Poodle.
No. 2284: a, Border collie (brown and white). b, Border collie (black, brown and white). c, Yorkshire terrier. d, German shepherd. e, Beagle. f, Spaniel.

| 2000, Aug. 7 | | | Perf. 14¼ | |
|---|---|---|---|---|
| 2278-2283 | A371 | Set of 6 | 7.50 | 7.50 |
| 2284 | A371 | 7d Sheet of 6, #a-f | 8.50 | 8.50 |

**Souvenir Sheet**

| 2285 | A371 | 25d Boxer | 5.00 | 5.00 |
|---|---|---|---|---|

The Stamp Show 2000, London (Nos. 2284-2285).

Cats A372

No. 2286, 4d: a, Egyptian mau. b, Singapura. c, American shorthair. d, Cornish rex. e, Birman. f, Scottish fold. g, Turkish angora. h, Turkish van.
No. 2287, 5d: a, Ragdoll. b, Bombay. c, Korat. d, Somali. e, British shorthair. f, American curl. g, Maine coon cat. h, Like No. 2286h.
No. 2288, 25d, Cat and kitten. No. 2289, 25d, Cat.

| 2000, Aug. 7 | | Sheets of 8, #a-h | | |
|---|---|---|---|---|
| 2286-2287 | A372 | Set of 2 | 11.50 | 11.50 |

**Souvenir Sheets**

| 2288-2289 | A372 | Set of 2 | 9.50 | 9.50 |
|---|---|---|---|---|

The Stamp Show 2000, London.

**Flower Photomosaic Type of 1999 and**

Queen Mother, 100th Birthday A373

Designs: No. 2090, Various flower photographs making up a photomosaic of the Queen Mother.
No. 2290I: Various photos of religious scenes making up a photomosaic of Pope John Paul II.

| 2000, Aug. 7 | | Litho. | Perf. 13¾ | |
|---|---|---|---|---|
| 2290 | A349 | 5d Sheet of 8, #a-h | 7.50 | 7.50 |
| 2290I | A349 | 6d Sheet of 8, #j-q | 10.00 | 10.00 |

**Litho. & Embossed**
**Without Gum**
*Die Cut 9x8¾*

| 2291 | A373 | 85d multi | 22.50 | 22.50 |
|---|---|---|---|---|

Issued: Nos. 2290, 2291 8/7. No. 2290I, 8/8.

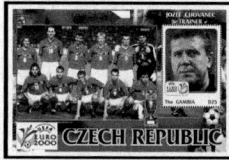

European Soccer Championships — A374

No. 2292, horiz. — Czech Republic: a, Nedved. b, Team photo. c, Maier. d, Antonin Panenka. e, Selessin Stadium, Liege. f, Patrik Berger.
No. 2293, horiz. — England: a, Alan Shearer. b, Team photo. c, David Seaman. d, Sol Campbell. e, Philips Stadium, Eindhoven. f, Southgate.

No. 2294, horiz. — Norway: a, Leonardsen. b, Team photo. c, Mykland. d, Solbakken. e, Rekdal.
No. 2295, horiz. — Slovenia: a, Aleksander Knavs. b, Team photo. c, Zlatko Zahovic. d, Ales Ceh. e, Stade Communal, Charleroi. f, Miran Pavlin.
No. 2296, horiz. — Sweden: a, Ljungberg. b, Team photo. c, Andersson. d, Nilsson. e, Schwarz.
No. 2297, horiz. — Turkey: a, Yalcin. b, Team photo. c, Buruk. d, Erdem. e, King Baudouin Stadium. f, Korkut.
No. 2298, 25d, Czech Republic coach, Jozef Chovanec. No. 2299, 25d, England coach Kevin Keegan. No. 2300, 25d, Norway coach Nils-Johan Semb. No. 2301, 25d, Slovenia coach Srecko Katanec. No. 2302, 25d, Sweden coaches, Söderberg and Lagerbäck. No. 2303, 25d, Turkey coach Mustafa Denizli.

| 2000, Aug. 7 | | Litho. | Perf. 13¾ | |
|---|---|---|---|---|
| 2292 | A374 | 7d Sheet of 6, #a-f | 7.50 | 7.50 |
| 2293 | A374 | 7d Sheet of 6, #a-f | 7.50 | 7.50 |
| 2294 | A374 | 7d Sheet of 6, #a-e, 2292e | 7.50 | 7.50 |
| 2295 | A374 | 7d Sheet of 6, #a-f | 7.50 | 7.50 |
| 2296 | A374 | 7d Sheet of 6, #a-e, 2293e | 7.50 | 7.50 |
| 2297 | A374 | 7d Sheet of 6, #a-f | 7.50 | 7.50 |
| | | *Nos. 2292-2297 (6)* | 45.00 | 45.00 |

**Souvenir Sheets**

| 2298-2303 | A374 | Set of 6 | 28.50 | 28.50 |
|---|---|---|---|---|

Paintings of Birds — A375

Designs: 1.50d, A White Pheasant and Other Fowl in a Classical Landscape, by Abraham Bisschop. 3d, Salmon-crested Cockatoo, by Bartolomeo Bimbi. 4d, A Great Bustard Cock and Other Birds, by Ludger Tom Ring. 15d, A Great Black-backed Gull and Other Birds, by Jokob Bogdani.
No. 2308, 5d: a, Peacocks, Hens and Mouse, by Tobias Stranover. b, Lady in a Red Jacket Feeding a Parrot, by Frans van Mieris. c, Birds by a Pool, by Melchior de Hondecoeter. d, Ganymede and the Eagle, by Peter Paul Rubens. e, Leda and the Swan, by Cesare de Sesto. f, Ducks and Ducklings at the Foot of a Tree in a Mediterranean Landscape, by Adriaen van Oolen. g, Portrait of the Falconer Robert Cheseman Carrying a Hooded Falcon, by Hans Holbein. h, A Golden Pheasant on a Stone Plinth, with Other Birds, by Jacobus Vonck.
No. 2309, 5d, horiz.: a, Still Life of Birds, by Caravaggio (hanging dead birds, basket). b, Turkeys with Young and Rock Doves, by Johan Wenzel Peter. c, The Threatened Swan, by Jan Asselyn. d, Still Life of Fruit and Birds in a Landscape, by Jakab Bogdany. e, Mobbing the Owl, by Tobias Stranover (owl at right, other birds). f, A Concert of Birds, by Hondecoeter (owl, cockatoo at center). g, Owls and Young Ones, by William Tomkins. h, Birds by a Stream, by Jean Baptiste Oudry.
No. 2310, 25d, The King Eagle Pursued to the Sun, by Philip Reinagle. No. 2311, 25d, Still Life of Birds, by Georg Flegl, horiz.

| 2000, Oct. 2 | | | Perf. 13½ | |
|---|---|---|---|---|
| 2304-2307 | A375 | Set of 4 | 4.75 | 4.75 |

**Sheets of 8, #a-h**

| 2308-2309 | A375 | Set of 2 | 14.00 | 14.00 |
|---|---|---|---|---|

**Souvenir Sheets**

| 2310-2311 | A375 | Set of 2 | 10.00 | 10.00 |
|---|---|---|---|---|

Descriptions of paintings are in margins on Nos. 2308-2311.

Paintings from the Prado A376

No. 2312, 6d: a, The Madonna of the Fish, by Raphael. b, The Holy Family with a Lamb, by Raphael. c, The Madonna of the Stair, by Andrea del Sarto. d, Moneychanger from The Moneychanger and his Wife, by Marinus van Reymerswaele. e, Madonna and Child by Jan Gossaert. f, Wife from The Moneychanger and his Wife.
No. 2313, 6d: a, Bearded man from St. Benedict's Supper, by Juan Andres Ricci. b, Our

Lady of the Immaculate Conception, by Francisco de Zurbarán. c, Monk with candle from St. Benedict's Supper. d, The Penitent Magdalen, by José de Ribera. e, Christ as Man of Sorrows, by Antonion de Pereda. f, St. Jerome, by Pereda.
No. 2314, 6d: a, Children with a Shell, by Bartolomé Esteban Murillo. b, Our Lady of the Immaculate Conception, by Murillo. c, The Good Shepherd, by Murillo. d, Woman with red headdress from The Parasol, by Francisco de Goya. e, A Rural Gift, by Ramon Bayeu. f, Woman with blue headdress from The Parasol.
No. 2315, 6d: a, Queen Isabella Farnese, by Jean Ranc. b, Young Woman Seen from the Back, by Jean-Baptiste Greuze. c, Charles III as a Child, by Ranc. d, James Bourdieu, by Sir Joshua Reynolds. e, Dr. Isaac Henrique Sequeira, by Thomas Gainsbourough. f, Portrait of a Clergyman, by Reynolds.
No. 2316, 6d: a, Portrait of a Young Woman, by Zacarias González Velázquez. b, The Painter Francisco de Goya, by Vicente Lopez Portaña. c, Portrait of a Girl, by Rafael Tejeo Diaz. d, Mary, from The Nativity, by Federico Barocci. e, Madonna and Child with St. John, by Correggio. f, Jesus, from The Nativity.
No. 2317, 6d: a, St. Andrew, by Francisco Rizi. b, Christ Crucified, by Diego Velázquez. c, St. Onuphrius, by Francisco Collantes. d, Charles II, by Juan Carreño de Miranda. e, St. Sebastian, by Carreño de Miranda. f, Peter Ivanovich Potemkin, by Carreño de Miranda.
No. 2318, 25d, The Defense of Cádiz Against the English, by Zurbarán. No. 2319, 25d, The Surrender of Juliers, by Jusepe Leonardo. No. 2320, 25d, The Holy Family with a Bird, by Murillo. No. 2321, 25d, Danäe, by Titian, horiz. No. 2322, 25d, Venus and Adonis, by Paolo Veronese, horiz. No. 2323, 25d, Jacob's Dream, by Ribera.

| 2000, Oct. 6 | Perf. 12x12¼, 12¼x12 | | | |
|---|---|---|---|---|
| | Sheets of 6, #a-f | | | |
| 2312-2317 | A376 | Set of 6 | 40.00 | 40.00 |

**Souvenir Sheets**

| 2318-2323 | A376 | Set of 6 | 28.50 | 28.50 |
|---|---|---|---|---|

Espana 2000, Intl. Philatelic Exhibition.

Battle of Britain, 60th Anniv. A377

No. 2324, 5d, horiz.: a, Hurricane downing German BF109. b, Spitfire over River Thames. c, Flight Lt. Denys E. Gilliam attacking German Dornier 217 planes. d, Hurricanes heading to intercept Luftwaffe bombers. e, Hurricanes returning to Croydon. f, G.A. Langley in combat with BF109. g, Bristol Blenheim IV over English Channel. h, Spitfires taking off from Hornchurch.
No. 2325, 5d, horiz.: a, Plane from 29th Blenheim Squadron heading to Norwegian coast. b, Luftwaffe pilot Helmut Wick downs RAF pilot John Cock. c, Spitfire downs Dornier 217 off Dover. d, Bristol Beaufighter IIF on patrol. e, Bolton-Paul Defiants intercept Luftwaffe bombers. f, Spitfire in dogfite with German Stuka JU-87 divebomber. g, Spitfire and Hurricane fly over London and River Thames. h, Gloster Gladiator.
No. 2326, 25d, Group Captain Frank Carey. No. 2327, 25d, German Commander Adolf Joseph Ferdinand Galland.

| 2000, Oct. 16 | | | Perf. 14 | |
|---|---|---|---|---|
| | Sheets of 8, #a-h | | | |
| 2324-2325 | A377 | Set of 2 | 14.00 | 14.00 |

**Souvenir Sheets**

| 2326-2327 | A377 | Set of 2 | 9.00 | 9.00 |
|---|---|---|---|---|

Composers — A378

No. 2328, 7d: a, Antonio Vivaldi. b, Giacomo Puccini. c, Franz Joseph Haydn. d, Leopold Stokowski. e, Felix Mendelssohn. f, Gaetano Donizetti.
No. 2329, 7d: a, Witold Lutoslawski. b, William Sterndale Bennett. c, Wolfgang Amadeus Mozart. d, Ludwig van Beethoven. e, Sergei Rachmaninoff. f, Peter Ilich Tchaikovsky.
No. 2330, 25d, Manuel de Falla. No. 2331, 25d, Fréderic Chopin.

| 2000, Oct. 2 | | Litho. | Perf. 13¾x13¼ | |
|---|---|---|---|---|
| | Sheets of 6, #a-f | | | |
| 2328-2329 | A378 | Set of 2 | 16.00 | 16.00 |

**Souvenir Sheets**

| 2330-2331 | A378 | Set of 2 | 10.00 | 10.00 |
|---|---|---|---|---|

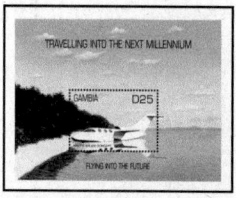

Transportation of the Future — A379

No. 2332 — Automobiles: b, Mazda RX-Evolv. c, Isuzu Kai. d, Ford 021C. e, Pontiac GTO. f, Chevrolet CERV III. g, Toyota Will VI.
No. 2333 — Aircraft: a, Blended wing body, BWB-1. b, Boeing 767-400 ERX. c, Lockheed concept. d, Boeing X. e, American National Aerospace plane X-30 concept. f, Hotol taking off from Russian AN-225.
No. 2334 — Trains: a, Maglev train MLU-002. b, Magnetic rail car. c, Monorail above ground concept. d, Seattle Monorail. e, Monorail above cabin concept. f, Monorail concept.
No. 2335 — Watercraft: h, Pendolare concept boat. i, Planesail boat. j, Airfoil concept. k, Ferry Sea Coaster concept. l, Shinaitoku Matu new sail technology. m, Supersport luxury yacht concept.
No. 2335G, 25d, Nautic Air 400 concept. No. 2335H, 25d, Maglev train. No. 2335I, 25d, Honda Sprocket concept. No. 2335J, 25d, Triton, US Coast Guard concept.

| 2000, Oct. 2 | | | Perf. 14 | |
|---|---|---|---|---|
| | Sheets of 6, #a-f | | | |
| 2332 | A379 | 7d Sheet of 6, #b-g | 8.00 | 8.00 |
| 2333 | A379 | 7d Sheet of 6, #a-f | 8.00 | 8.00 |
| 2334 | A379 | 8d Sheet of 6, #a-f | 9.00 | 9.00 |
| 2335 | A379 | 8d Sheet of 6, #h-m | 9.00 | 9.00 |

**Souvenir Sheets**

| 2335G-2335J | A379 | Set of 4 | 16.00 | 16.00 |
|---|---|---|---|---|

Nos. 2335 and 2335A contain one 56x41mm stamp.

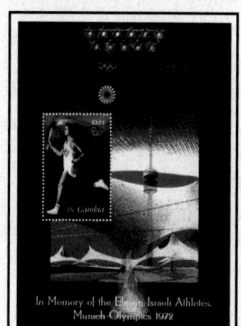

Massacre of Israeli Olympic Athletes, 1972 — A380

No. 2336, horiz.: a, Moshe Weinberg. b, Eliezer Halffin. c, Mark Slavin. d, Ze'ev Friedman. e, Joseph Romano. f, Kahat Shor. g, David Berger. h, Joseph Gottfreund. i, Andrei Schpitzer. j, Amitsur Shapira. k, Yaakov Springer. l, Olympic poster.

**2000, Nov. 9**
2336 A380 4d Sheet of 12, #a-l 9.00 9.00
**Souvenir Sheet**
2337 A380 25d Torchbearer 5.00 5.00

Ships — A381

Designs: 5d, Spanish Armada. 10d, Brazilian river gunboat Colombo. 15d, Russian Navy mine carrier Jenissel. 20d, Japanese battleship Yamato.
No. 2342, 7d: a, British first-rate battleship, 18th cent. b, Spanish galleon, 16th cent. c, Russian four-masted barque, 20th cent. d, Henri Grace à Dieu with flag on stern, 16th cent. e, Frontispiece of John Dee's Arte of Navigation, 16th cent. f, British ironclad, 19th cent.
No. 2343, 7d: a, Chinese junk, 18th cent. b, Two-masted cog, 15th cent. c, Henri Grace à Dieu, no flag on stern, 16th cent. d, St. Brendan and monks at sea, 6th cent. e, Figurehead. f, British carrack, 16th cent.
No. 2344, 25d, Challenger, 19th cent. No. 2345, 25d, Golden Hind, 16th cent.

**2000, Oct. 2    Litho.    Perf. 14**
2338-2341 A381 Set of 4 9.00 9.00
**Sheets of 6, #a-f**
2342-2343 A381 Set of 2 16.00 16.00
**Souvenir Sheets**
2344-2345 A381 Set of 2 9.50 9.50

Birds
A382

No. 2346, 7d, vert.: a, Pied flycatcher. b, Blackcap. c, Stonechat. d, Nightingale. e, Black-headed tchagra. f, Yellow wagtail.
No. 2347, 7d, vert.: a, Gray parrot. b, Great spotted cuckoo. c, Bar-tailed trogon. d, African hobby. e, Green turaco. f, Trumpeter hornbill.
No. 2348, 7d, vert.: a, Yellow-rumped tinkerbird. b, Greater honeyguide. c, Hoopoe. d, European roller. e, Carmine bee-eater. f, White-throated bee-eater.
No. 2349, 25d, European bee-eater. No. 2350, 25d, Bateleur. No. 2351, 25d, Secretary bird.

**2000, Oct. 2    Perf. 13¾x13¼**
**Sheets of 6, #a-f**
2346-2348 A382 Set of 3 24.00 24.00
**Souvenir Sheets**
2349-2351 A382 Set of 3 13.50 13.50

Ferrari Automobiles A383

Designs: 4d, 3335P. 5d, 5125. 10d, 312P. 25d, 330P4.

**2000, Nov. 15    Perf. 14**
2352-2355 A383 Set of 4 8.00 8.00

12th Classic Automobile Marathon — A384

No. 2356, 5d: a, Morgan. b, Rover. c, Marmon. d, Rolls Royce Silver Cloud. e, Rolls Royce Phantom. f, Mercedes 680S. g, Mercedes 74. h, Invicta.
No. 2357, 5d: a, Allard. b, Ford coupe. c, Citroen Pilot. d, Packard (white). e, Austin A90. f, Bentley. g, Packard (red). h, Aston Martin.
No. 2358, 25d, Cadillac. No. 2359, 25d, Morris Minor.

**2000, Nov. 15    Sheets of 8, #a-h**
2356-2357 A384 Set of 2 10.50 10.50
**Souvenir Sheets**
2358-2359 A384 Set of 2 10.00 10.00

Queen Mother, 100th Birthday — A385

**2000, Aug. 7    Litho.    Perf. 14**
2360 A385 7d multi 1.50 1.50
Printed in sheets of 6.

The Horse in Art — A386

Designs: 4d, At Full Stretch, by John Skeaping. 5d, The Burton, by Lionel Edwards. 10d, A Game of Polo, by Li Lin. 15d, St. George and the Dragon, by Raphael, vert.
No. 2365, 7d: a, Horses Emerging From the Sea, by Eugène Delacroix. b, The Ninth Duke of Marlborough on a Grey Horse, by Sir Alfred Munnings. c, Ovid in Exile Amongst the Scythians, by Delacroix. d, Early Morning Gallop, by Skeaping. e, Mare and Foal, by Munnings. f, Detail from Three-a-side Polo at Simla, by Edwards.
No. 2366, 7d, vert.: a, A Lady Hawking, by E. J. H. Vernet. b, Captain Robert Orme, by Sir Joshua Reynolds. c, Napoleon Crossing the Alps, by Jacques-Louis David. d, Nobby Gray, by Munnings. e, Amateur Jockeys Near a Carriage, by Edgar Degas. f, Detail from Three-a-side Polo at Simla, diff.
No. 2367, 25d, The Reckoning, by George Morland. No. 2368, 25d, One of the Family, by Frederic G. Cotman.

**2000, Oct. 2**
2361-2364 A386 Set of 4 5.75 5.75
**Sheets of 6, #a-f**
2365-2366 A386 Set of 2 15.00 15.00
**Souvenir Sheets**
2367-2368 A386 Set of 2 9.00 9.00

New Year 2001 (Year of the Snake) A387

No. 2369: a, Vermilion background. b, Purple background. c, Dark blue background. d, Light green background.

**2001, Jan. 2**
2369 A387 4d Sheet of 4, #a-d 2.75 2.75
**Souvenir Sheet**
2370 A387 15d Snake 3.00 3.00

Rijksmuseum, Amsterdam, Bicent. (in 2000) — A388

No. 2371, 7d, vert.: a, Vessels in a Strong wind, by Jan Porcellis. b, Seascape in the Morning, by Simon de Vlieger. c, Travelers at a Country Inn, by Isaack van Ostade. d, Orpheus with Animals in a Landscape, by Aelbert Cuyp. e, Italian With a Mountain Plateau, by Cornelis van Poelenburch. f, Boatmen and hill from Boatman Moored on a Lake Shore, by Adam Pynacker.
No. 2372, 7d, vert.: a, Cow, boatmen and sailboat from Boatmen Moored on a Lake Shore. b, The Ford in the River, by Jan Baptist Weenix. c, Two Horses Near a Gate in a Meadow, by Paulus Potter. d, Cows and Sheep at a Stream, by Karel Dujardin. e, Violin player from The Duet, by Cornelis Saftleven. f, Lute player from The Duet.
No. 2373, 7d, vert.: a, Teapot from Still Life With Turkey Pie, by Pieter Claesz. b, Bouquet of Flowers in a Vase, by Ambrosius Bosschaert. c, Vase from Still Life With Flowers, Fruit and Shells, by Balthasar van der Ast. d, Flowers and fruit from Still Life With Flowers, Fruit and Shells. e, Tulips in a Vase, by Hans Boulenger. f, Laid Table With Cheese and Fruit, by Floris van Dijck.
No. 2374, 7d, vert.: a, Turkey, from Still Life With Turkey Pie. b, Still Life With Gilt Goblet, by Willem Claesz Heda. c, Still Life With Lobster and Nautilus Cup, by Jan Davidsz de Heem. d, Bacchanal, by Moses van Uyttenbroeck. e, The Anatomy Lesson of Dr. Nicolaes Tulp, by Rembrandt. f, Johannes Lutma, by Jacob Backer.
No. 2375, 7d, vert.: a, The Meagre Company, by Frans Hals and Pieter Codde. b, The Twins Clara and Aelbert de Bray, by Salomon de Bray. c, Self-portrait, by Ferdinand Bol. d, Ambulatory of the New Church in Delft, with the Tomb of Willem the Silent, by Gerard Houckgeest. e, View of the Tomb of Willem in the New Church in Delft, by Emanuel de Witte. f, Mountainous Landscape, by Hercules Segers.
No. 2376, 7d, vert.: a, Lute player from Gallant Company by Codde. b, Men and archway from Gallant Company. c, Man on bended knee from The Marriage of Willem van Loon and Margaretha Bas, by Jan Miense Molenaer. d, Crowd from The Marriage of Willen van Loon and Margaretha Bas. e, Woman in black robe from The Marriage of Willem van Loon and Margaretha Bas. f, Johanna Le Maire, by Nicolaes Eliasz Pickenoy.
No. 2377, 25d, The Fall of Man, by Cornelis van Haarlem. No. 2378, 25d, The Art Gallery of Jan Gildemeester Jansz, by Jan Ekels II. No. 2379, 25d, View of the Nieuwe Kerk and the Rear of the Town Hall in Amsterdam, by Isaak Outwater. No. 2380, 25d, The Spendthrift, by Cornelis Troost. No. 2381, 25d, Morning Ride on the Beach, by Anton Mauve. No. 2382, 25d, Meadow Landscape With Cattle, by Willen Roelofs.

**2001, Jan. 15    Perf. 13¾**
**Sheets of 6, #a-f**
2371-2376 A388 Set of 6 42.50 42.50
**Souvenir Sheets**
2377-2382 A388 Set of 6 28.00 28.00

The Wizard of Oz, Cent. (in 2000) A389

No. 2383, 7d: a, Witch of the North. b, Poppies. c, Dorothy's house. d, Witch of the East. e, Dorothy. f, The Wizard.
No. 2384, 7d: a, Witch's wolf. b, Witch's forest. c, Witch's monkeys. d, Dorothy in poppies. e, Queen Mouse. f, Witch and evil bees.
No. 2385, 7d: a, Cowardly Lion. b, Land of Oz. c, Tin Man. d, Scarecrow. e, Toto. f, Munchkins.
No. 2386, 27d, Green Maiden. No. 2387, 27d, Gate keeper. No. 2388, 27d, Dorothy at crossroads, horiz.

**2001, Jan. 30    Sheets of 6, #a-f**
2383-2385 A389 Set of 3 24.00 24.00
**Souvenir Sheets**
2386-2388 A389 Set of 3 15.00 15.00

History of the Theater A390

No. 2389, 6d: a, Terra cotta statue. b, Tragic masks of King Priam. c, Euripides. d, Terra cotta statues of actors portraying drunks. e, Scene from Chinese play. f, Indian actors. g, Scene from Noh play, Japan. h, Scene from Clytemnestra.
No. 2390, 6d: a, William Shakespeare. b, Johann Wolfgang von Goethe. c, Moliere. d, Henrik Ibsen. e, George Bernard Shaw. f, Anton Chekhov. g, Sholom Aleichem. h, Tennessee Williams.
No. 2391, 25d, Sarah Bernhardt, vert. No. 2392, 25d, John Barrymore, vert.

**2001, Jan. 30    Perf. 14**
**Sheets of 8, #a-h**
2389-2390 A390 Set of 2 20.00 20.00
**Souvenir Sheet**
2391-2392 A390 Set of 2 10.00 10.00

Pokémon A391

No. 2393: a, Beedrill. b, Arbok. c, Machop. d, Vileplume. e, Clefairy. f, Poliwhirl.

**2001, Feb. 1**      **Perf. 13¾**
2393 A391 7d Sheet of 6, #a-f    6.00 6.00
**Souvenir Sheet**
2394 A391 25d Articuno      4.75 4.75

Orchids — A392

Designs: 1.50d, Encyclia alata. 2d, Dendrobium lasiantherum. 3d, Cymbidiella pardalina. No. 2398, 4d, Cymbidium lowianum. 5d, Cypripedium irapeanum. 15d, Doritas pulcherrima.
No. 2401: a, Epidendrum pseudepidendrum. b, Eriopsis biloba. c, Masdevallia coccinea. d, Odontoglossum lindleyanum. e, Oerstedella wallisii. f, Paphiopedilum acmodontum. g, Laelia rubescens. h, Huntleya wallisii. i, Lycaste longiscapa. j, Maxillaria variabilis. k, Mexicoa ghiesbrechtiana. l, Miltoniopsis phalaenopsis.
No. 2402: a, Sobralia candida. b, Phragmipedium basseae. c, Vanda rothchildiana. e, Telipogon pulchera. f, Rossioglossum insleayi.
No. 2403, 25d, Chaubardia heteroclita. No. 2404, 25d, Cychnoches loddigesii. No. 2405, 25d, Cattleya dowiana.

**2001, Feb. 1**   **Litho.**    **Perf. 14**
2395-2400 A392 Set of 6    6.00 6.00
2401 A392 4d Sheet of 12, #a-l    11.00 11.00
2402 A392 7d Sheet of 6, #a-f    9.00 9.00
**Souvenir Sheets**
2403-2405 A392 Set of 3    16.50 16.50
Hong Kong 2001 Stamp Exhibition (Nos. 2401-2405).

Medicinal Plants — A393

Designs: 3d, Pokeweed. 5d, Bay laurel. 10d, Coltsfoot. 15d, Marshmallow.
No. 2410, 8d, vert.: a, Restharrow. b, White willow. c, Sweet serge. d, Passion flower. e, Rosemary. f, Pepper.
No. 2411, 8d, vert.: a, Succory. b, Dandelion. c, Garlic. d, Hemp agrimony. e, Star thistle. f, Cypress.
No. 2412, 25d, Arbutus, vert. No. 2413, 25d, Olive, vert.

**2001, Mar. 1**
2406-2409 A393 Set of 4    5.75 5.75
**Sheets of 6, #a-f**
2410-2411 A393 Set of 2    18.00 18.00
**Souvenir Sheets**
2412-2413 A393 Set of 2    11.00 11.00

Japanese Art — A394

Designs: 1d, Mount Fuji and Tea Fields, by Matsuoka Eikyu. 2d, One heron from Herons and Flowers, by Okamoto Shuki. 3d, Two herons from Herons and Flowers. No. 2417, 3d, The Realm of Gods in Yingzhou, by Tomioka Tessai. No. 2418, 4d, Peach Blossom Spring in Wuling, by Tessai. No. 2419, 4d, Egret, by Takeuchi Seiho. No. 2420, 5d, Spring Colors of the Lake and Mountains, by Shoda Gyokan. No. 2421, 5d, Sparrows, by Seiho. No. 2422, 10d, Red Lotus and White Goose, by Goun Saku. No. 2423, 10d, Portrait of Ushiwakamaru, by Kano Osanobu. 15d, Woman Selling Flowers, by Ito Shoha. 20d, The Sound of the Ocean, by Matsumoto Ichiyo.
No. 2426, 5d — Birds and Flowers of the Twelve Months, by Sakai Hoitsu: a, Red and white flowers, bird on branch. b, Yellow flowers, bird on branch. c, White flowers, bird on branch. d, Blue flowers. e, Sun, white and blue flowers. f, Red and white flowers.
No. 2427, 5d — Birds and Flowers of the Twelve Months, by Hoitsu: a, Insect in sky, red pink and white flowers. b, Blue irises. c, Red, white light blue flowers. d, Fruit on tree. e, Bird standing in water. f, Snow-covered tree.
No. 2428, 7d — Birds and Flowers, by Soga Chokuan: a, White flowers. b, Rooster at R. c, Roosters at L, red flower at R. d, Rooster at R, white flowers. e, Birds in sky. f, Roosters at L and R, white and red flowers. g, Roosters at L and R. h, Rooster at L, tree and red flowers.
No. 2429, 7d — The Four Accomplishments, by Kaiho Yusho: a, Table. b, Two people near tree. c, Rock and hill. d, Two people. e, Rock and tree. f, One person. g, Three people. h, Three people, table.
No. 2430 — Book of Lacquer Paintings, by Shibata Zeshin: a, Flower. b, Birds. c, Butterfly on flower. d, Lobster.
No. 2431, 30d, Untitled painting (Yanagibashi at Ryogoku), by Utagawa Kuniyoshi, horiz. No. 2432, 30d, Poppies, by Tsuchida Bakusen, horiz. No. 2433, 30d, Puppies and Morning Glories, by Yamaguchi Soken, horiz. No. 2434, 30d, Deep Pool, by Nishimura Goun, horiz. No. 2435, 30d, Spring Farming Near a Riverside Village, by Mori Getsujo, horiz.

**2001, Apr. 17**
2414-2425 A394 Set of 12    15.00 15.00
**Sheets of 6, #a-f**
2426-2427 A394 Set of 2    12.00 12.00
**Sheets of 8, #a-h**
2428-2429 A394 Set of 2    21.00 21.00
2430 A394 10d Sheet of 4, #a-d    7.50 7.50
**Imperf.**
**Size: 118x88mm**
2431-2435 A394 Set of 5    27.50 27.50
Nos. 2428-2430 contain 28x42mm stamps. Phila Nippon '01, Japan.

**Butterflies Type of 2000**

Designs: 7d, Salamis temora. 8d, Cyrestus camillus. 20d, Papilio demodocus. 25d, Danaus chrysippus.

**2001**      **Perf. 14¾x14**
2436-2439 A367 Set of 4    11.50 11.50
No. 2439 exists dated 2003.

**I Love Lucy Type of 2000**

No. 2440: a, Lucy singing. b, Lucy with tambourine. c, Lucy with Ricky and Ethel. d, Lucy. e, Ethel and Ricky at piano. f, Ethel and Ricky on bench. g, Lucy at typewriter. h, Ethel singing. i, Lucy on bench.
No. 2441, 25d, Like No. 2440a, vert. No. 2442, 25d, Like No. 2440d, vert.

**2001**      **Perf. 13¾**
2440 A354 5d Sheet of 9, #a-i    8.75 8.75
**Souvenir Sheets**
2441-2442 A354 Set of 2    9.50 9.50

Horses A395

No. 2443, 7d, Head of: a, Akhal-Teke. b, Palomino. c, Kladruber. d, Paint Horse. e, Pinto. f, Kabardin.
No. 2444, 7d, horiz: a, Akhal-Teke. b, Kladruber. c, Palomino. d, Pinto. e, Paint Horse. f, Kabardin.
No. 2445, Palomino.

**2001**   **Litho.**    **Perf. 14**
**Sheets of 6, #a-f**
2443-2444 A395 Set of 2    14.50 14.50
**Souvenir Sheet**
2445 A395 25d multi    4.00 4.00

**Three Stooges Type of 2000**

No. 2446: a, Shemp as angel. b, Larry, Moe, Shemp, wearing feathered hats. c, Moe, Shemp and Larry wearing hospital uniforms. d, Larry with hammer, Shemp with gun, Moe, e, Moe, Larry, Shemp with woman. f, Moe and Shemp wearing tams. g, Moe, Larry, wagon wheel. h, Shemp, Moe, Larry in bus driver uniforms. i, Shemp hitting Larry and Moe.
No. 2447, 25d, Curly with telephone, skull, vert. No. 2448, 25d, Shemp on Moe's back, vert.

**2001**      **Perf. 13¾**
2446 A353 5d Sheet of 9, #a-i    6.00 6.00
**Souvenir Sheets**
2447-2448 A353 Set of 2    7.00 7.00

**I Love Lucy Type of 2000**

No. 2449 : a, Lucy crawling on building ledge. b, Lucy standing against wall, arms outstretched. c, Lucy in apartment. d, Lucy reclining on ledge. e, Lucy with hand on forehead. f, Lucy reclining against wall. g, Ricky, bound and gagged Lucy. h, Lucy on sofa. i, Lucy, robber.
No. 2450, 25d, Lucy, robber, vert. No. 2451, 25d, Bound and gagged Lucy, seated Ethel, vert.

**2001**
2449 A354 5d Sheet of 9, #a-i    6.00 6.00
**Souvenir Sheets**
2450-2451 A354 Set of 2    7.00 7.00

**Butterfly Type of 2000**

50d, Coeliades forestan. 75d, Ornithoptera alexandrae. 100d, Morpho cypris.

**2001**      **Perf. 14¾x14**
2452 A367 50d multicolored    6.00 6.00
2452A A367 75d multicolored    11.00 11.00
2452B A367 100d multicolored    13.00 13.00

Queen Victoria (1819-1901) — A396

No. 2453, horiz.: a, Reading speech from throne. b, Benjamin Disraeli. c, Riding in procession from Parliament.

**2001, Apr. 26**      **Perf. 14**
2453 A396 15d Sheet of 3, #a-c    9.00 9.00
**Souvenir Sheet**
2454 A396 25d Portrait    5.00 5.00

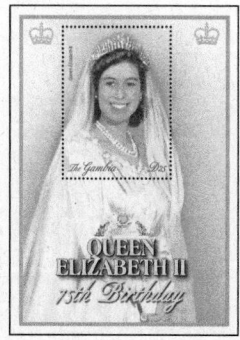

Queen Elizabeth II, 75th Birthday A397

No. 2456: a, In uniform. b, In pink hat. c, Wearing crown, facing R. d, Wearing crown, facing L.

**2001, Apr. 26**      **Perf. 14**
2455 A397 15d Sheet of 4, #a-d    9.00 9.00
**Souvenir Sheet**
2456 A397 25d In wedding dress    6.00 6.00

Flowers — A398

Designs: 1d, Disa uniflora. 4d, Monodora myristica. 6d, Clappertonia ficifolia. 20d, Calanthe rosea.
No. 2461, 7d: a, Vanilla planifolia. b, Strelitzia reginae. c, Gladiolus cardinalis. d, Arctotis venusta. e, Protea obtusifolia. f, Geissorhiza rochensis.
No. 2462, 7d: a, Canarina abyssinica. b, Amorphophallus abyssinicus. c, Calanthe rosea, diff. d, Gloriosa simplex. e, Clappertonia ficifolia, diff. f, Ansellia gigantea.
No. 2463, 25d, Arctoris venusta, diff. No. 2464, 25d, Geissorhiza rochensis, horiz.

**2001, Mar. 1**   **Litho.**    **Perf. 14**
2457-2460 A398 Set of 4    5.00 5.00
**Sheets of 6, #a-f**
2461-2462 A398 Set of 2    15.00 15.00
**Souvenir Sheets**
2463-2464 A398 Set of 2    8.50 8.50

Photomosaic of Queen Elizabeth II — A399

**2001, Apr. 26**
2465 A399 8d multi    1.50 1.50
Printed in sheets of 8, with and without marginal inscription "In Celebration of the 50th Anniversary of H. M. Queen Elizabeth II's Accession to the Throne.'

Marlene Dietrich A400

No. 2466: a, With head on forearm. b, With bare shoulder. c, With arms crossed. d, Wearing hat.

**2001, Apr. 26**      **Perf. 13¾**
2466 A400 10d Sheet of 4, #a-d    7.50 7.50

Mao Zedong (1893-1976) — A401

No. 2467: a, In 1935. b, In 1949. c, In 1951. 25d, In 1928.

**2001, Apr. 26**      **Perf. 14**
2467 A401 15d Sheet of 3, #a-c    7.50 7.50
**Souvenir Sheet**
2468 A401 25d multi    4.50 4.50

Giuseppe Verdi (1813-1901), Opera Composer — A402

No. 2469: a, Verdi with gray hair. b, Score and performers from La Traviata. c, Score and performer from Aida. d, Verdi with brown hair.

25d, Verdi and scores of Don Carlos and Rigoletto.

**2001, Apr. 26**
2469 A402 10d Sheet of 4, #a-d   8.00 8.00
**Souvenir Sheet**
2470 A402 25d multi       5.50 5.50

Monet Paintings A403

No. 2471, horiz.: a, Madame Monet on the Sofa. b, The Picnic. c, The Luncheon. d, Jean Monet on His Mechanical Horse.
25d, La Japonaise.

**2001, Apr. 26**          *Perf. 13¾*
2471 A403 10d Sheet of 4, #a-d   8.00 8.00
**Souvenir Sheet**
2472 A403 25d multi       5.00 5.00

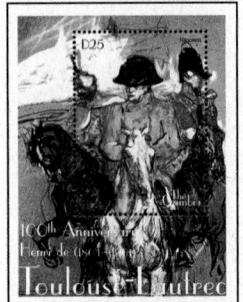

Toulouse-Lautrec Paintings — A404

No. 2473: a, At Le Rat Mort. b, The Milliner. c, Messaline.
25d, Napoleon.

**2001, Apr. 26**
2473 A404 7d Sheet of 3, #a-c   4.50 4.50
**Souvenir Sheet**
2474 A404 25d multi       5.50 5.50

Orchids — A405

Designs: 3d, Orchis morio. 4d, Fulophia speciosa. 5d, Angraecum leonis. 15d, Oeceoclades maculata.
No. 2479, 8d: a, Ceratostylis retisquama. b, Rangaeris rhipsalisocia. c, Phaius hybrid. d, Disa hybrid. e, Disa uniflora. f, Angraecum leonis.
No. 2480, 8d: horiz.: a, Satyrium erectum. b, Aeranthes grandiose. c, Aerangis somasticta. d, Polystachya bella. e, Eulophia guineensis. f, Disa blackii.
No. 2482, 25d, Disa kirstenbosch pride. No. 2482A, 25d, Aerangis eurnowiana

**2001, June 15**          *Perf. 14*
2475-2478 A405   Set of 4    5.00 5.00
**Sheets of 6, #a-f**
2479-2480 A405   Set of 2   16.00 16.00
**Souvenir Sheets**
2482    A405   multi         5.50 5.50
2482A   A405   multi         5.50 5.50

Belgica 2001 Intl. Stamp Exhibition, Brussels (Nos. 2479-2480).

SOS Children's Village — A406

**2001, July 2**
2483 A406 10d multi       2.00 2.00

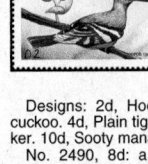

Flora & Fauna — A407

Designs: 2d, Hoopoe. 3d, Great spotted cuckoo. 4d, Plain tiger butterfly. 5d, Zebra duiker. 10d, Sooty managbey. 20d, Greater kudu.
No. 2490, 8d: a, Hippopotamus. b, Elephant. c, Parusta simplex. d, Gray heron. e, Charaxes imperialis. f, Gloriosa simplex.
No. 2491, 8d: a, Alpine swift. b, Blotched genet. c, Thomas' galago. d, Carmine bee-eater. e, Tree pangolin. f, Campbell's monkey.
No. 2492, 8d: a, Gray parrot. b, Rachel's weaver. c, European bee-eater. d, River kingfisher. e, Red river hog. f, Bushbuck.
No. 2493, 8d: a, Blue diadem butterfly. b, Fire-footed rope squirrel. c, Clappertonia ficifolia. d, Costus spectabilis. e, African migrant butterfly. f, Giant African snail.
No. 2494, 25d, Long-tailed pangolin, vert. No. 2495, 25d, Eurasian kestrel, vert.

**2001, July 16**
2484-2489 A407   Set of 6    8.50 8.50
**Sheets of 6, #a-f**
2490-2493 A407   Set of 4   36.00 36.00
**Souvenir Sheets**
2494-2495 A407   Set of 2    9.00 9.00

A408

Ducks and Geese — A409

Designs: 2d, Blue-winged teal. No. 2497, 3d, Red-crested pochard. No. 2498, 4d, Falcated teal. No. 2499, 5d, Mandarin duck. No. 2500, 10d, King eider. 15d, Hooded merganser.
No. 2502, 3d, Wood duck. No. 2503, 4d, Mallard. No. 2504, 5d, Barrow's goldeneye. No. 2505, 10d, Bufflehead.
No. 2506, 7d, horiz.: a, Barrow's goldeneye. b, Harlequin duck. c, Pintail. d, Black-bellied whistling duck. e, Cinnamon teal. f, Surf scoter.
No. 2507, 7d, horiz.: a, Black scoter. b, Black duck. c, Green-winged teal. d, Bufflehead. e, Red-breasted merganser. f, Fulvous whistling duck.
No. 2508, 8d: a, European wigeon. b, Mallard. c, Garganey. d, Pintail, diff. e, Shoveler. f, Green-winged teal.
No. 2509, 8d: a, Black duck. b, Bufflehead. c, Cinnamon teal, diff. d, Goldeneye. e, Ruddy shelduck. f, Ferruginous duck.
No. 2510, 8d: a, Masked duck. b, Old squaw. c, Ring-necked duck. d, Harlequin duck, diff. e, Redhead. f, Canvasback.
No. 2511, 25d, American wigeon. No. 2512, 25d, Wood duck. No. 2513, 25d, Baikal teal. No. 2514, 25d, Green-winged teal, horiz. No. 2515, 25d, Canada geese, horiz.

**2001, July 16**
2496-2501 A408   Set of 6    8.00 8.00
2502-2505 A409   Set of 4    5.00 5.00
**Sheets of 6, #a-f**
2506-2507 A409   Set of 2   16.00 16.00
2508-2510 A408   Set of 3   26.00 26.00
**Souvenir Sheets**
2511-2513 A408   Set of 3   15.00 15.00
2514-2515 A409   Set of 2   10.00 10.00

Cetaceans — A410

No. 2516, 7d: a, Killer whale (denomination at UR). b, Sperm whale (denomination at UR). c, Strap-toothed whale. d, Humpback whale. e, Southern right whale. f, Beluga.

No. 2517, 7d: a, Killer whale (denomination at LR). b, Sperm whale (denomination at LR). c, Narwhal. d, Gray whale. e, Blue whale. f, Northern right whale.
No. 2518, 25d, Killer whale. No. 2519, 25d, Humpback whale.

**2001, July 16**       **Sheets of 6, #a-f**
2516-2517 A410   Set of 2   18.00 18.00
**Souvenir Sheets**
2518-2519 A410   Set of 2   12.00 12.00

A411

Trains — A412

Designs: 2d, Rheingold Express. No. 2521, 10d, Amtrak train. No. 2522, 15d, The Blue Train. 20d, Cisalpino.
4d, Eurostar. No. 2525, 7d, Mallard. No. 2526, 10d, Rocket. No. 2527, 15d, TGV.
No. 2528, 7d: a, Eurostar, diff. b, Flying Hamburger. c, Coast Starlight. d, Tres Grande Vitesse. e, Golden Arrow. f, Shinkanzen "Max."
No. 2529, 7d: a, Siliguri to Darjeeling, India train. b, California Zephyr. c, Flying Scotsman. d, Trans-Siberian Express. e, Indian-Pacific. f, Thunersee.
No. 2530, 8d: a, Le Shuttle. b, Nord Express. c, 2-6-0, Switzerland. d, Duchess. e, Balkan Express. f, Class 44 2-10-0, Germany.
No. 2531, 8d: a, 7029 Clun Castle. b, Puffing Billy. c, ICE Electric. d, 4-4-2 S, Belgium. e, 2-8-2, Germany. f, PLM Coupe-Vents.
No. 2532, 25d, Cape Town to Victoria Falls train. No. 2533, 25d, The Southerner. No. 2534, 25d, Stanier Class 5 4-6-0. No. 2535, 25d, Flying Scotsman, diff.

**2001, July 31**          *Perf. 14*
2520-2523 A411   Set of 4    7.50 7.50
2524-2527 A412   Set of 4    6.00 6.00
**Sheets of 6, #a-f**
2528-2529 A411   Set of 2   17.00 17.00
2530-2531 A412   Set of 2   19.00 19.00
**Souvenir Sheets**
2532-2533 A411   Set of 2   10.00 10.00
2534-2535 A412   Set of 2   10.00 10.00

British Royal Navy — A413

Designs: 3d, St. Andrew, 1600s. 4d, Fleet maneuvers, 1914. 10d, HMS Illustrious, 1899. 15d, Battle of North Foreland, 1666.
No. 2540, 7d, horiz.: a, Mary Rose, 1512. b, Attack off Quebec, 1759. c, Armada campaign, 1588. d, Battle of Scheveningen, 1653. e, Blanche captures La Pique, 1795. f, Embarkation at Dover, 1520.
No. 2541, 7d, horiz. — Battles: a, Quiberon Bay, 1759. b, Barfleur, 1692. c, Nile, 1798. d, Trafalgar, 1805. e, Jutland, 1916. f, Camperdown, 1797.
No. 2542, 7d, horiz.: a, Battle of Navarino, 1827. b, Sinking of Eurydice, 1878. c, HMS Pantaloon captures Borboleta, 1845. d, Dardanelles, 1915. e, HMS Pickle captures Bolodora, 1829. f, HMS Invincible and Inflexible, Battle of the Falklands, 1914.
No. 2543, 25d, Ark Royal, 1582, horiz. No. 2544, 25d, Sovereign of the Seas, 1637, horiz.

**2001, Sept. 6**          *Litho.*
2536-2539 A413   Set of 4    7.00 7.00
**Sheets of 6, #a-f**
2540-2542 A413   Set of 3   27.00 27.00
**Souvenir Sheets**
2543-2544 A413   Set of 2   10.00 10.00

2002 World Cup Soccer Championships, Japan and Korea — A414

Jules Rimet Trophy and: 2d, Netherlands flag and player. 3d, Argentina flag and player. 4d, Ibaraki Kashima Stadium, Japan, horiz. 5d, George Best and Northern Ireland flag. 10d, Dino Zoff and Italian flag. 15d, Poster for 1938 tournament, France.
25d, Pat Bonner making save for Ireland.

**2001, Sept. 6**
2545-2550 A414   Set of 6    7.50 7.50
**Souvenir Sheet**
2551 A414 25d multi     5.00 5.00

No. 2551 contains one 56x42mm stamp.

European Royalty A415

No. 2552: a, King Harald V, Queen Sonja, Norway. b, Queen Margrethe II, Denmark. c, King Carl XVI Gustaf and Queen Silvia, Sweden. d, King Juan Carlos, Queen Sofia, Spain. e, Queen Beatrix, Netherlands. f, King Albert II, Queen Paola, Belgium.
No. 2553, 25d, Crown Prince Haakon, Princess Mette-Marit, Norway. No. 2554, 25d, King Juan Carlos, Spain, vert.

       *Perf. 14¼x14½, 14½x14¼*
**2001, Nov. 15**
2552 A415 7d Sheet of 6, #a-f   9.00 9.00
**Souvenir Sheets**
2553-2554 A415   Set of 2   11.00 11.00

**Queen Mother Type of 1999**

No. 2555: a, Duchess of York, Princess Elizabeth, 1928. b, Lady Elizabeth Bowes-Lyon, 1923. c, Queen Elizabeth, 1946. d, Queen Mother, Prince Harry.
40d, Queen Mother celebrating 89th birthday, 1989.

**2001, Dec. 13**          *Perf. 14*
2555 A342 15d Sheet of 4, #a-
             d + label   13.00 13.00
**Souvenir Sheet**
         *Perf. 13¾*
2556 A342 40d multi     8.00 8.00

No. 2556 contains one 38x50mm stamp.

Oriental Actors and Actresses — A416

No. 2557, 15d: a, Alex Fong. b, William So. c, Flora Chan. d, Rain Li.
No. 2558, 15d — Kelly Chen: a, Close-up. b, As child, with cherry. c, On swing. d, As child, with hand above eyes.
No. 2559, 15d — Jacky Cheung: a, At L, laughing, looking to R. b, Looking forward, mouth open. c, At R, laughing, looking L. d, Looking forward, mouth closed.
No. 2560, 15d — Andy Hui, and Chinese characters at: a, L (pink suit). b, R (yellow suit). c, L (yellow suit). d, R (pink suit).
No. 2561, 15d — Miriam Yeung, with roses and petals at: a, LR. b, LL. c, UR. d, UL.

**2001, Nov. 5 Litho. *Perf. 13¾x13¼***
**Sheets of 4, #a-d**
2557-2561 A416 Set of 5    40.00 40.00

New Year 2002 (Year of the Horse) A417

No. 2562 — Denomination at: a, UR. b, UL. c, LR. d, LL.
20d, African zebra.

**2001, Dec. 26**    *Perf. 13*
2562 A417 6d Miniature sheet of 4, #a-d    5.00 5.00
**Souvenir Sheet**
*Perf. 12½x13*
2563 A417 20d multi    5.00 5.00
No. 2563 contains one 68x31mm triangular stamp.

Jacqueline Kennedy Onassis (1929-94) — A418

No. 2564: a, As baby. b, At age 6. c, Engagement to J.F.K. d, In wedding gown, 1955. e, In 1960. f, In 1980.
30d, At wedding to Aristotle Onassis.

**2002, Jan. 24**    *Perf. 14*
2564 A418 7d Sheet of 6, #a-f    5.50 5.50
**Souvenir Sheet**
2565 A418 30d multi    4.50 4.50

Princess Diana (1961-97) — A419

No. 2566 — Diana and: a, Coral rose. b, White rose. c, Yellow rose. d, Purple rose.
40d, Portrait.

**2002, Jan. 24**
2566 A419 15d Sheet of 4, #a-d    12.00 12.00
**Souvenir Sheet**
2567 A419 40d multi    6.50 6.50

Moths — A420

Designs: 2d, Tiger moth. 3d, Hawk moth. No. 2570, 10d, Pericopid moth. 15d, Spurge hawk.
No. 2572, 10d (50x38mm): a, Sloane's urania. b, Saturniid moth. c, Black witch moth. d, Burnet moth on plant. e, Day-flying moth. f, Lime hawk moth.
No. 2573, 10d (50x38mm): a, Emperor moth. b, Millar's tiger. c, Hawk moth, diff. d,

Phrygionis privignara. e, Burnet moth, waterfall. f, Urania leilus.
No. 2574, 40d, Emerald moth. No. 2575, 40d, Red under-wing moth, vert.

***Perf. 14, 13¾ (#2572-2573)***
**2002, Jan. 24**
2568-2571 A420 Set of 4    6.75 6.75
**Sheets of 6, #a-f**
2572-2573 A420 Set of 2    25.00 25.00
**Souvenir Sheets**
2574-2575 A420 Set of 2    17.50 17.50

United We Stand — A421

**2002, Feb. 6**    *Perf. 13¾x13¼*
2576 A421 20d multi    2.75 2.75
Issued in sheets of 4.

Reign of Queen Elizabeth II, 50th Anniv. A422

No. 2577: a, With beige hat. b, With red hat. c, With blue hat. d, Near vehicle.
40d, Wearing uniform.

**2002, Feb. 6**    *Perf. 14½*
2577 A422 15d Sheet of 4, #a-d    12.00 12.00
**Souvenir Sheet**
2578 A422 40d multi    8.50 8.50
See No. 2704.

A423

Orchids A424

No. 2579, vert.: a, Machu piechu. b, Masdevallia copper angel. c, Masdevallia hirtzi. d, Tuakau canoy.
No. 2580: a, Eriopsis sceptrum. b, Sarcanthopsis muellem. c, Bougainville white. d, Telipogon klotzchianus.
No. 2581, 7d: a, Richard Mueller. b, Colmanara wildcat. c, Cycnoches chlorochilon. d, Vanda coerylea. e, Disa blackii. f, Unnamed.
No. 2582, 7d: a, Seagulls beaulu queen. b, Hazel Boyd. c, Costa Rica. d, Dendrobium infudibulum. e, Disa hybrid. f, Chysis.
No. 2583, 6d, horiz.: a, Spathoglottis portusfinschii. b, Dendrobium macrophyllum. c, Grammaneis ellisii. d, Stanhopea wardii. e, Dendrobium nindi. f, Dendrobium williamsianum.
No. 2584, 7d: a, Seutieama steeli. b, Dendrobium inaequale. c, Dendrobium lasiathera.

d, Calypso bulbosa. e, Vanda hindsii. f, Dendrobium violaceoflavens.
No. 2585, 8d, horiz.: a, Phaleonopsis rosenstomii. b, Cypripedium guttatum. c, Cypripedium reginae. d, Dendrobium engae. e, Diplocaulobium hydrophilum. f, Dendrobium cuthbertsonii.
No. 2586, 25d, Dendrobium nobile. No. 2587, 25d, Ancidium alliance, vert.
No. 2588, 25d, Menadenium labiosum. No. 2589, 25d, Dendrobium spectabile. No. 2590, 25d, Dendrobium canaliculatum, horiz.

**2001, June 15 Litho. *Perf. 14***
2579 A423 7d Sheet of 4, #a-d    9.00 9.00
2580 A424 10d Sheet of 4, #a-d    8.00 8.00
**Sheets of 6, #a-f**
2581-2582 A423 Set of 2    17.00 17.00
2583-2585 A424 Set of 3    27.00 27.00
**Souvenir Sheets**
2586-2587 A423 Set of 2    14.00 14.00
2588-2590 A424 Set of 3    27.00 27.00
Nos. 2579-2590 were not available until 2002. Belgica 2001 Intl. Stamp Exhibition (No. 2579).

Wildlife — A425

Designs: 2d, Martial eagle. 4d, Lion. 5d, Aardvark. 10d, Lion cub, vert.
No. 2595, 7d: a, Lion cub. b, Water buffalo. c, Topi. d, Hyena. e, Secretary bird. f, Genet.
No. 2596, 7d: a, Reedbuck. b, Hippopotamus. c, Waterbuck and malachite kingfisher. d, Hoopoe. e, White pelican. f, Waterbuck.
No. 2597, 25d, Hippopotamus. No. 2598, 25d, Crocodile.

**2001, July 16**
2591-2594 A425 Set of 4    5.50 5.50
**Sheets of 6, #a-f**
2595-2596 A425 Set of 2    18.00 18.00
**Souvenir Sheets**
2597-2598 A425 Set of 2    13.00 13.00
Nos. 2591-2598 were not available until 2002.

Pres. Theodore Roosevelt (1858-1919) — A426

No. 2599: a, Wearing hat and uniform. b, Close-up. c, With hand on chair. d, Wearing hat and neckerchief.
40d, Close-up, diff.

**2002, Jan. 24**
2599 A426 15d Sheet of 4, #a-d    9.00 9.00
**Souvenir Sheet**
2600 A426 40d multi    6.50 6.50

Betty Boop — A427

No. 2602, 40d, With gray ribbon in hair, horiz. No. 2603, 40d, With ice cream sundae.

**2002, Feb. 13**    *Perf. 13¾*
2601 A427 7d shown    1.10 1.10
**Souvenir Sheets**
2602-2603 A427 Set of 2    9.50 9.50
No. 2601 was issued in sheets of 9.

Shirley Temple in "Little Miss Broadway" — A428

No. 2604, horiz.: a, With man and old woman. b, Close-up. c, Waving. d, Holding man's tie. e, At hotel desk with men. f, Woman watching Temple point to tooth.
No. 2605: a, Dancing with young man. b, Dancing with old man with hat. c, Sitting with boy. d, Holding hands with old man.
30d, Wearing tiara and dancing with young man.

**2002, Feb. 13**
2604 A428 8d Sheet of 6, #a-f    6.00 6.00
2605 A428 10d Sheet of 4, #a-d    5.50 5.50
**Souvenir Sheet**
2606 A428 30d multi    4.25 4.25

2002 Winter Olympics, Salt Lake City — A429

Designs: No. 2607, 20d, Curling. No. 2608, 20d, Ski jumping.

**2002, Mar. 18**    *Perf. 14*
2607-2608 A429 Set of 2    7.00 7.00
   a. Souvenir sheet, #2607-2608    7.50 7.50

Chiune Sugihara, Japanese Diplomat Who Saved Jews in World War II — A430

**2002, Apr. 29**    *Perf. 13½x13¼*
2609 A430 10d multi    1.75 1.75
Printed in sheets of 4.

Intl. Year of Mountains — A431

No. 2610: a, Winkler Tower, Italy. b, Mt. Huanstan Chico, Peru. c, Hodaka Mountains, Japan. d, Mustagh Ata, Kashmir.
40d, Mt. Myoko, Japan.

**2002, July 1**    *Perf. 13¼x13½*
2610 A431 15d Sheet of 4, #a-d    9.50 9.50
**Souvenir Sheet**
2611 A431 40d multi    6.50 6.50

2002 World Cup Soccer Championships, Japan and Korea — A432

Players, dates and locations of matches — No. 2612, 9d: a, France v. Senegal. b, Uruguay v. Denmark. c, France v. Uruguay. d, Denmark v. Senegal. e, Denmark v. France. f, Senegal v. Uruguay.

No. 2613, 9d: a, Paraguay v. South Africa. b, Spain v. Slovenia. c, Spain v. Paraguay. d, South Africa v. Slovenia. e, South Africa v. Spain. f, Slovenia v. Paraguay.

No. 2614, 9d: a, Brazil v. Turkey. b, China v. Costa Rica. c, Brazil v. China. d, Costa Rica v. Turkey. e, Costa Rica v. Brazil. f, Turkey v. China.

No. 2615, 9d: a, South Korea v. Poland. b, US v. Portugal. c, South Korea v. US. d, Portugal v. Poland. e, Portugal v. South Korea. f, Poland v. US.

No. 2616, 9d: a, Germany v. Saudi Arabia. b, Ireland v. Cameroun. c, Germany v. Ireland. d, Cameroun v. Saudi Arabia. e, Cameroun v. Germany. f, Saudi Arabia v. Ireland.

No. 2617, 9d: a, England v. Sweden. b, Argentina v. Nigeria. c, Sweden v. Nigeria. d, Argentina v. England. e, Sweden v. Argentina. f, Nigeria v. England.

No. 2618, 9d: a, Croatia v. Mexico. b, Italy v. Ecuador. c, Italy v. Croatia. d, Mexico v. Ecuador. e, Mexico v. Italy. f, Ecuador v. Croatia.

No. 2619, 9d: a, Japan v. Belgium. b, Russia v. Tunisia. c, Japan v. Russia. d, Tunisia v. Belgium. e, Tunisia v. Japan. f, Belgium v. Russia.

Stadia and dates of matches between — No. 2620, 20d: a, France v. Senegal. b, Uruguay v. Denmark.

No. 2621, 20d: a, France v. Uruguay. b, Denmark v. Senegal.

No. 2622, 20d: a, Denmark v. France. b, Senegal v. Uruguay.

No. 2623, 20d: a, Paraguay v. South Africa. b, Spain v. Slovenia.

No. 2624, 20d: a, Spain v. Paraguay. b, South Africa v. Slovenia.

No. 2625, 20d: a, South Africa v. Spain. b, Slovenia v. Paraguay.

No. 2626, 20d: a, Brazil v. Turkey. b, China v. Costa Rica.

No. 2627, 20d: a, Brazil v. China. b, Costa Rica v. Turkey.

No. 2628, 20d: a, Costa Rica v. Brazil. b, Turkey v. China.

No. 2629, 20d: a, South Korea v. Poland. b, US v. Portugal.

No. 2630, 20d: a, South Korea v. US. b, Portugal v. Poland.

No. 2631, 20d: a, Portugal v. South Korea. b, Poland v. US.

No. 2632, 20d: a, Germany v. Saudi Arabia. b, Ireland v. Cameroun.

No. 2633, 20d: a, Germany v. Ireland. b, Cameroun v. Saudi Arabia.

No. 2634, 20d: a, Cameroun v. Germany. b, Saudi Arabia v. Ireland.

No. 2635, 20d: a, England v. Sweden. b, Argentina v. Nigeria.

No. 2636, 20d: a, Sweden v. Nigeria. b, Argentina v. England.

No. 2637, 20d: a, Sweden v. Argentina. b, Nigeria v. England.

No. 2638, 20d: a, Croatia v. Mexico. b, Italy v. Ecuador.

No. 2639, 20d: a, Italy v. Croatia. b, Mexico v. Ecuador.

No. 2640, 20d: a, Mexico v. Italy. b, Ecuador v. Croatia.

No. 2641, 20d: a, Japan v. Belgium. b, Russia v. Tunisia.

No. 2642, 20d: a, Japan v. Russia. b, Tunisia v. Belgium.

No. 2643, 20d: a, Tunisia v. Japan. b, Belgium v. Russia.

**2002, July 1**     *Perf. 13¼*

**Sheets of 6, #a-f**

2612-2619 A432   Set of 8   55.00 55.00

**Souvenir Sheets**

2620-2643 A432   Set of 24   110.00 110.00

See Nos. 2654-2656 for sheets with match results.

---

Popeye A433

No. 2644, 10d: a, Popeye on cross-country skis. b, Popeye ski jumping. c, Popeye slaloming. d, Popeye snowboarding.

No. 2645, 10d: a, Swee'Pea on sled. b, Olive Oyl on skis. c, Brutus. d, Wimpy on ice skates.

No. 2646, 25d: a, Popeye and Olive in bobsled. No. 2647, 25d, Brutus playing hockey. No. 2648, 25d, Olive on ice skates. No. 2649, 25d, Popeye speed skating, horiz.

**2002, June 17**   *Litho.*   *Perf. 14*

**Sheets of 4, #a-d**

2644-2645 A433   Set of 2   10.00 10.00

**Souvenir Sheets**

2646-2649 A433   Set of 4   14.00 14.00

20th World Scout Jamboree, Thailand — A434

No. 2650: a, Scout with bugle. b, Scout making fire. c, Scout fishing.
40d, Scout tying knot.

**2002, July 1**     *Perf. 13½x13¼*

2650 A434 15d Sheet of 3, #a-c   8.00 8.00

**Souvenir Sheet**

2651 A434 40d multi   6.50 6.50

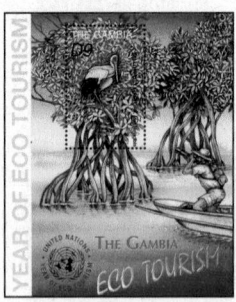

Intl. Year of Ecotourism — A435

No. 2652: a, Bird-of-Paradise flower. b, Goliath heron. c, Baobab tree. d, Roan antelope. e, Red tip butterfly. f, Egyptian cobra.
No. 2653, Yellow-billed stork.

**2002, July 1**

2652 A435 9d Sheet of 6, #a-d   10.00 10.00

**Souvenir Sheet**

2653 A435 9d multi   2.00 2.00

**Nos. 2616, 2617 and 2619 Redrawn With Match Scores**

No. 2654, 9d: a, Germany 8, Saudi Arabia 0. b, Ireland 1, Cameroun 1. c, Germany 1, Ireland 1. d, Cameroun 1, Saudi Arabia 0. e, Cameroun 0, Germany 2. f, Saudi Arabia 0, Ireland 3

No. 2655, 9d: a, England 1, Sweden 1. b, Argentina 1, Nigeria 0. c, Sweden 2, Nigeria 1. d, Argentina 0, England 1. e, Sweden 1, Argentina 1. f, Nigeria 0, England 0.

---

No. 2656, 9d: a, Japan 2, Belgium 2. b, Russia 2, Tunisia 0. c, Japan 1, Russia 0. d, Tunisia 1, Belgium 1. e, Japan 2, Tunisia 0. f, Belgium 3, Russia 2.

**2002, July 15**     *Perf. 13¼*

**Sheets of 6, #a-f**

2654-2656 A432   Set of 3   24.00 24.00

Elvis Presley (1935-77) — A436

**2002, Aug. 19**     *Perf. 13½x13¾*

2657 A436 5d multi   1.00 1.00

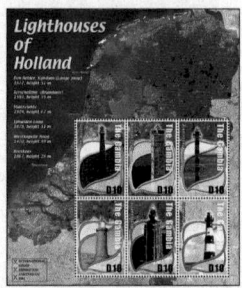

Things from the Netherlands — A437

Netherlands Lighthouses — A438

Netherlands Postage Stamps, 150th Anniv. — A439

Women's Traditional Costumes of the Netherlands — A440

No. 2658: a, Farm. b, Porcelain. c, Building. d, Ice skaters. e, Cheese, flowers and wooden shoes. f, Prince Willem-Alexander and his bride.

No. 2659: a, Den Helder. b, Terschelling. c, Maasvlakte. d, Ijmuiden. e, Westkapelle. f, Breskens.

No. 2660: a, Netherlands #1. b, Netherlands #B72. c, Netherlands #279. d, Netherlands #586. e, Netherlands #620. f, Netherlands #1108a.

No. 2661: a, Woman from Friesland (plaid headdress). b, Back of woman from Utrecht. c, Woman and child from Noord-Holland.

**2002, Aug. 30**     *Perf. 13½x13¼*

2658 A437 10d Sheet of 6, #a-f   10.00 10.00
2659 A438 10d Sheet of 6, #a-f   12.00 12.00

---

    *Perf. 13¼x13½*

2660 A439 10d Sheet of 6, #a-f   10.00 10.00

    *Perf. 13¼*

2661 A440 20d Sheet of 3, #a-c   11.00 11.00

Amphilex 2002 Intl. Stamp Exhibition, Amsterdam.

Marine Mammals and Flowers — A441

No. 2662, 10d: a, Blue whale. b, Pan-tropical spotted dolphin. c, Killer whale. d, Minke whale. e, Sperm whale. f, Pilot whale.

No. 2663, 10d: a, Juba-jamba. b, Devil's tongue. c, Rattle box. d, Vernonia purpurea. e, Seaside purslane. f, Fireball lily.

No. 2664, 50d, Humpback whale. No. 2665, 50d, Cape weed, swamp arum, vert.

**2002, Sept. 23**     *Perf. 14*

**Sheets of 6, #a-f**

2662-2663 A441   Set of 2   24.00 24.00

**Souvenir Sheets**

2664-2665 A441   Set of 2   20.00 20.00

See Nos. 2763-2764.

A442

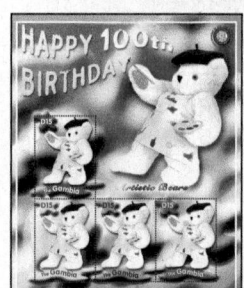

Teddy Bears, Cent. A443

No. 2666: a, Bear with green feathered cap. b, Bear with beer stein. c, Bear with flower bouquet. d, Bear with mountain hat.

No. 2667 — Color of denomination and country name: a, White. b, Red violet. c, Blue violet. d, Green.

**2002, Oct. 21**     *Perf. 14*

2666 A442 15d Sheet of 4, #a-d   7.00 7.00

    *Perf. 14¼*

2667 A443 15d Sheet of 4, #a-d   7.00 7.00

Christmas — A444

Designs: 3d, Madonna of Loreto, by Perugino. 5d, Madonna della Consolazione, by Perugino. 7d, Adoration of the Shepherds, by Perugino. 15d, Transfiguration of Christ, by Giovanni Bellini. 35d, Adoration of the Magi, by Perugino.

45d, Christ Blessing, by Bellini.

**2002, Nov. 4**      **Perf. 14**
2668-2672 A444   Set of 5    11.00 11.00
**Souvenir Sheet**
2673 A444 45d multi     7.50 7.50

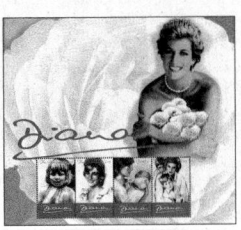

Princess Diana (1961-97) — A445

No. 2674, 15d — With red panel at bottom: a, As child. b, Wearing tiara. c, Holding baby. d, With children.

No. 2675, 15d: a, Wearing red hat. b, Wearing red and white hat. c, Wearing white gown. d, Wearing black gown and choker.

**2002, Nov. 18**    **Sheets of 4, #a-d**
2674-2675 A445   Set of 2    20.00 20.00

**Souvenir Sheet**

Gold-banded Forester Butterfly — A446

**2002**     **Litho.**     **Perf. 14**
2676 A446 60d multi     11.00 11.00

Birds A447

No. 2677: a, Black-crowned crane. b, Barn owl. c, African pygmy kingfisher. d, Audouin's gull. e, Royal tern. f, Blue-bellied roller.

**2002**
2677 A447 7d Sheet of 6, #a-f 10.00 10.00

Pres. John F. Kennedy (1917-63) — A448

No. 2678, 15d: a, With daughter Caroline. b, At typewriter. c, At wedding to Jacqueline. d, With Jacqueline.

No. 2679, 15d, vert: a, In naval uniform. b, As child. c, Wearing shirt with open collar. d, At microphone.

**2002, Nov. 8**    **Sheets of 4, #a-d**
2678-2679 A448   Set of 2    17.50 17.50

A449

Trains — A450

---

Designs: 2d, Paris, Lyon & Mediterranean Railway. 3d, Zugspitz rack train, Germany. No. 2682, 10d, Austrian State Railway Class 210. 15d, State Railway of Saxony.

4d, 1922 Great Britain Class A1 4-6-2. 5d, 1957 Tee four car train. No. 2686, 7d, 1928 German Rheingold Mitropa car. 8d, 1900 German Gerda 4-4-0.

No. 2688, 7d: a, French Natl. Railway Series 68. b, French Natl. Railway Mistral. c, Prussian State Railway. d, Austrian Southern Railway. e, Paris-Orleans Railway. f, German Federal Railway E10.

No. 2689, 7d: a, Royal Prussian Union Railway. b, Austrian Federal Railway. c, German Rugen steam locomotive. d, Rh B Ge 2/4 electric locomotive. e, Panoramic Express, Switzerland. f, Brunig steam engine, Swiss Natl. Railway.

No. 2690, 10d: a, 1813 Puffing Billy, Great Britain. b, Adler, Germany, 1836. c, 1906 German 4-6-0. d, Class 132 Co-Co, Germany.

No. 2691, 10d: a, 1832 Brother Jonathan 4-2-0, US. b, Medoc Class 2-4-0, Germany and Switzerland, 1857. c, 1908 German Class S 3/6 4-6-2. d, 1959 German Class VT 11.5.

No. 2692, 10d: a, 1843 Beuth 2-2-2, Germany. b, 1852 Crampton 4-2-0, France. c, 1932 Sut 877 Flying Hamburger, Germany. d, 1970 Class 103.1 Co-Co, Germany.

No. 2693, 25d, German Federal Railway V200. No. 2694, 25d, German Federal Railway Trans-Europe Express.

No. 2695, 25d, 1953 VT10.5, Germany. No. 2696, 25d,1973 Class ET 403 four-car electric, Germany.

**2002**
2680-2683 A449   Set of 4    9.50 9.50
2684-2687 A450   Set of 4    8.50 8.50
     **Sheets of 6, #a-f**
2688-2689 A450   Set of 2    18.00 18.00
     **Sheets of 4, #a-d**
2690-2692 A450   Set of 3    25.00 25.00
     **Souvenir Sheets**
2693-2694 A449   Set of 2    10.00 10.00
2695-2696 A450   Set of 2    10.00 10.00

Charles A. Lindbergh (1902-74), Aviator — A451

No. 2697, 15d: a, As child, with dog. b, As young man, brown violet background. c, With aviator goggles. d, Anne Morrow Lindbergh.

No. 2698, 15d: a, As child. b, As young man, blue background. c, Wearing uniform. d, Wearing suit and tie.

**2002, Nov. 18**    **Litho.**    **Perf. 14**
     **Sheets of 4, #a-d**
2697-2698 A451   Set of 2    22.00 22.00

     **Butterfly Type of 2000**
Designs: 4d, Amphicalia tigris.

**2003, Jan. 14**    **Perf. 14¾x14**
2699 A367 4d multi     .40 .40

New Year 2003 (Year of the Ram) A452

No. 2697: a, Tan background, brown ram. b, Purple background. c, Brown background, orange ram. d, Orange background, purple and red ram.

**2003, Jan. 27**     **Perf. 13¾**
2701 A452 10d Sheet of 4, #a-d   6.00 6.00

---

A453

Coronation of Queen Elizabeth II, 50th Anniv. — A454

No. 2702: a, Wearing tiara. b, Wearing blue hat. c, Wearing cape and hat.

**2003**     **Litho.**     **Perf. 14**
2702 A453   20d Sheet of 3, #a-c    10.00 10.00
     **Souvenir Sheet**
2703 A453 45d shown    7.50 7.50
     **Miniature Sheet**
     **Litho. & Embossed**
     **Perf. 13¼x13**
2704 A454 130d shown    25.00 25.00
Issued: Nos. 2702-2703, 5/13; 130d, 2/2.

Art by Yoshitoshi Taiso (1839-92) — A455

Designs: 5d, Concubine Washing Her Hands Under an Ornate Faucet. 10d, Housewife in an Inner Chamber Fanning a Fire. 15d, Geisha Catching a Firefly. 25d, A Young Geisha Dressed as an Elegant Young Man While Taking Part in the Niwaka Celebration.

No. 2709: a, Music Teacher Playing on a Samisen. b, An "Okamisan," or Proprietress of a Tea House, at Work. c, A City Merchant's Widow Absorbed in a Novelette. d, Busy Young Waitress Preoccupied With Her Responsibilities.

45d, A "Saikun," or Wife of a Government Official, Lighting an Oil Lamp.

**2003, Mar. 10**    **Litho.**    **Perf. 14¼**
2705-2708 A455   Set of 4    6.75 6.75
2709 A455 20d Sheet of 4, #a-d   10.00 10.00
     **Souvenir Sheet**
2710 A455 45d multi    4.75 4.75

Paintings by the Cranachs — A456

Paintings by Lucas Cranach the Elder (1472-1553) or Lucas Cranach the Younger (1515-86) (Y): 5d, Portrait of Johannes Scheyring. 7d, Rudolph Agricola. 10d, Portrait

---

Head of a Gentleman (Y). 20d, Hans von Lindau (Y).

No. 2715: a, Margravine Elizabeth von Ansbach (Y). b, Elector Joachim II of Brandenburg (Y). c, Portrait of a Nobleman (Y). d, Portrait of a Noblewoman (Y).

40d, The Ill-matched Couple.

**2003, Mar. 10**
2711-2714 A456   Set of 4    6.00 6.00
2715 A456 15d Sheet of 4, #a-d   9.50 9.50
     **Souvenir Sheet**
2716 A456 40d multi    5.00 5.00

Paintings by Wassily Kandinsky (1866-1944) — A457

Designs: 2d, Composition X. 4d, Arrow Towards the Circle. 5d, Yellow-Red-Blue. 7d, Accompanied Middle. 10d, In Blue. 20d, Round and Pointed.

No. 2723, vert.: a, Picture with Archer. b, Light. c, Picture in the Picture. d, White Stroke.

No. 2724, 45d, Improvisation XIX. No. 2725, 45d, On the Points.

**2003, Mar. 10**     **Perf. 14¼**
2717-2722 A457   Set of 6    7.25 7.25
2723 A457 15d Sheet of 4, #a-d    10.00 10.00
     **Size: 97x78mm**
     **Imperf**
2724-2725 A457   Set of 2    11.50 11.50

A458

Astronauts Killed In Space Shuttle Columbia Accident — A459

No. 2726, 15d — Michael P. Anderson: a, Columbia crew, brown background, country name at UL. b, Anderson and jet. c, Shuttle lifting off. d, Shuttle in orbit, Space Station.

No. 2727, 15d — Kalpana Chawla: a, Like No. 2726a, country name at LL. b, Shuttle being transported by jet. c, Shuttle glowing in re-entry. d, Chawla, astronaut spacewalking.

No. 2728, 15d — Laurel Blair Salton Clark: a, Like No. 2727a, green and red background. b, Shuttle in orbit, moon in background. c, Shuttle on launch pad. d, Clark and jet.

No. 2729, 15d — Ilan Ramon: a, Columbia crew, purple and yellow background. b, Ramon in jet. c, Shuttle with engines firing at launch pad. d, Shuttle in orbit.

No. 2730: a, Mission Specialist David M. Brown. b, Commander Rick D. Husband. c, Mission Specialist 4 Laurel Blair Salton Clark. d, Mission Specialist 4 Kalpana Chawla. e, Payload Commander, Michael P. Anderson. f, Pilot William C. McCool. g, Payload Specialist 4 Ilan Ramon.

**2003, Apr. 7**     **Perf. 14¼**
     **Sheets of 4, #a-d**
2726-2729 A458   Set of 4    35.00 35.00
     **Souvenir Sheet**
2730 A459 10d Sheet of 7, #a-g    10.00 10.00

A460

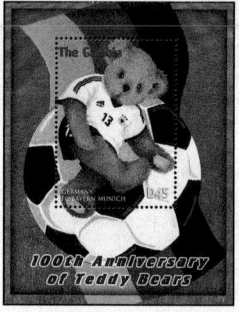

Teddy Bears A461

No. 2732, 15d — Bears with flags and soccer uniforms of: a, England. b, Brazil. c, Germany. d, Spain.

No. 2733, 15d — Bears with soocer uniforms of German teams: a, Schalke 04. b, FC Bayern Munich. c, Bayer Leaerkusen. d, Hertha Berlin.

No. 2734, 45d, FC Bayern Munich, white uniform. No. 2735, 45d, FC Bayern Munich red uniform, horiz.

**2003 Embroidered Imperf.**
**Self-Adhesive (#2731)**
2731 A460 150d shown          20.00 20.00
**Sheets of 4, #a-d**
**Litho.**
**Perf. 13¼**
2732-2733 A461 Set of 2       16.00 16.00
**Souvenir Sheets**
2734-2735 A461 Set of 2        9.50 9.50
Issued: No. 2731, Apr.; Nos. 2732-2735, 7/1.
No. 2731 was issued in sheets of 4.

Prince William, 21st Birthday A462

No. 2736: a, Wearing suit, no tie. b, Wearing suit and tie. c, Wearing blue shirt, no suit. 45d, Wearing polo uniform.

**2003, May 13 Litho. Perf. 14**
2736 A462 20d Sheet of 3, #a-c   9.00 9.00
**Souvenir Sheet**
2737 A462 45d multi              6.50 6.50

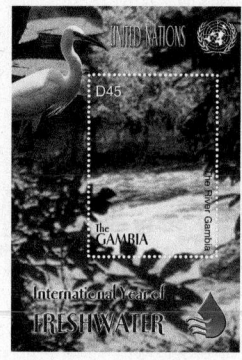

Intl. Year of Fresh Water A463

No. 2738 — Gambia River: a, Foliage at top. b, Foliage at top, silhouette of far shore at center. c, Trees at right. 45d, Gambia River rapids.

**2003, July 1 Perf. 13¼**
2738 A463 20d Sheet of 3, #a-c   8.50 8.50
**Souvenir Sheet**
2739 A463 45d multi              6.75 6.75

Tour de France Bicycle Race, Cent. A464

No. 2740, 15d: a, Henri Pelissier, 1923. b, Ottavio Bottecchia, 1924. c, Bottecchia, 1925. d, Lucien Buysse, 1926.

No. 2741, 15d: a, Nicholas Frantz, 1927. b, Frantz, 1928. c, Maurice de Waele, 1929. d, André Leducq, 1930.

No. 2742, 15d: a, Antonin Magne, 1931. b, Leducq, 1932. c, Georges Speicher, 1933. d, Magne, 1934.

**2003, July 1 Perf. 13¼**
**Sheets of 4, #a-d**
2740-2742 A464 Set of 3         30.00 30.00

General Motors Automobiles — A465

No. 2743, 15d — Cadillacs: a, 1937 Series 60. b, 1927 La Salle. c, 1930 V-16. d, 1931 V-16 Convertible.

No. 2744, 15d — Corvettes: a, 1960 Shark. b, 1964 Sting Ray Convertible. c, 1956 Convertible. d, 1967.

No. 2745, 45d, 1954 Cadillac Eldorado. No. 2746, 45d, 1964 Corvette Sting Ray.

**2003, July 1 Perf. 13¼x13½**
**Sheets of 4, #a-d**
2743-2744 A465 Set of 2         18.00 18.00
**Souvenir Sheets**
2745-2746 A465 Set of 2         13.00 13.00

History of Aviation A466

No. 2747, 15d: a, First powered flight by Wright Brothers, 1903. b, Goupy I, first full-size triplane, 1908. c, Deutschland LZ-7, first commercial airship, 1909. d, Lt. Col. Richard Byrd's flight over North Pole, 1926.

No. 2748, 15d: a, Granville Gee Bee, world speed record, 1932. b, Boeing 247D with all-metal construction retractable landing gear, 1933. c, Douglas DC-3, 1935. d, Amelia Earhart's solo flight from Hawaii to California, 1935.

No. 2749, 15d: a, First solar powered flight, by MacCready Solar Challenger, 1981. b, Voyager 2 space probe explores Saturn, 1981. c,

Space Shuttle Columbia, 1981. d, First non-stop non-refueled around the world flight, by Voyager, 1986.

No. 2750, 40d, Vought V-173 Short Takeoff and Landing research airplane, 1942. No. 2751, 40d, Pioneer 10 space probe, 1972. No. 2752, 40d, AD-1 scissors-wing SST, 1979.

**2003, July 14 Perf. 14**
**Sheets of 4, #a-d**
2747-2749 A466 Set of 3         24.00 24.00
**Souvenir Sheets**
2750-2752 A466 Set of 3         17.50 17.50

Ferrari Race Cars — A467

Designs: 2d, 126 C2. 3d, 312 T2. 5d, 312 T4. 7d, 126 C3. 10d, F399. 15d, F1-2000. 20d, F2001. 25d, F2002.

**2003, July 28 Perf. 14¼**
2753-2760 A467 Set of 8         11.00 11.00

Circus Performers — A468

No. 2761, 15d: a, Francesco Caroli. b, Lou Jacobs. c, Frankie Saluto. d, Gingernut.

No. 2762, 15d: a, Evgeny Maranogli. b, Saby. c, Colonel Joe. d, Puma.

**2003, Sept. 1 Perf. 14**
**Sheets of 4, #a-d**
2761-2762 A468 Set of 2         13.00 13.00

**Marine Mammals and Flowers Type of 2002**

No. 2763 — Insects and flowers: a, Colored shield-backed bug, Waltheria indica. b, Dragonfly, Red mangrove. c, Cotton stainer bug, Baissea multiflora. d, Harpagomantis. Mimosa pigra. e, Katydid, Coia cordifolia. f, African grasshopper, Urena labata.

50d, Giant swallowtail butterfly, Ipomoea cairica.

**2003 Perf. 14**
2763 A441 10d Sheet of 6, #a-f  12.00 12.00
**Souvenir Sheet**
2764 A441 50d multi             10.00 10.00

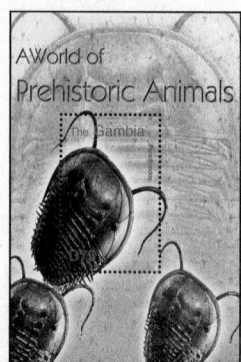

Prehistoric Animals — A469

No. 2765, 30d: a, Peteinosaurus. b, Pachycephalosaurus. c, Ichthyosaur. d, Anomalocaris.

No. 2766, 30d, horiz.: a, Criorhynchus. b, Seismosaurus. c, Triceratops. d, Stegosaurus.

No. 2767, 75d, Paradoxides. No. 2768, 75d, Edmontosaurus, horiz.

**2003, Nov. 4 Litho. Perf. 14**
**Sheets of 4, #a-d**
2765-2766 A469 Set of 2         25.00 25.00
**Souvenir Sheets**
2767-2768 A469 Set of 2         18.00 18.00

Christmas — A470

Paintings: 3d, Madonna of the Grand Duke, by Raphael. 5d, Madonna della Impannata, by Raphael. 7d, Adoration of the Magi, by Filippo Lippi. 60d, Adoration in the Woods, by Lippi.

75d, Madonna del Carmelo, by Giambattista Tiepolo.

**2003, Nov. 17 Perf. 14¼**
2769-2772 A470 Set of 4         10.00 10.00
**Souvenir Sheet**
2773 A470 75d multi             10.00 10.00

Leo Diamond — A471

**2003, Nov. 18 Perf. 13¼x13½**
2774 A471 15d multi              1.75 1.75
**Souvenir Sheet**
2775 A471 60d multi              9.00 9.00
No. 2774 issued in sheets of six.

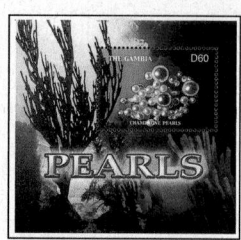

Pearls A472

No. 2776: a, South Sea pearls. b, Mabe pearls. c, Pinctada maxima. d, Australian pearls. e, Pearls on ocean floor. f, South Sea white pearls.

60d, Champagne pearls.

**2003, Nov. 18**
2776 A472 15d Sheet of 6, #a-f  14.00 14.00
**Souvenir Sheet**
2777 A472 60d multi              8.50 8.50

James Cagney (1899-1986) — A473

No. 2778: a, With solid tie. b, With hat. c, With gun. d, With lapel handkerchief. e, With plaid tie. f, With woman.

**2003 Perf. 14**
2778 A473 10d Sheet of 6, #a-f   8.00 8.00

Gambian pos⋯
declared the follow⋯
  Sheet of nine 2⋯
  Sheets of six⋯
Prey with Rotary⋯
Rotary emblem,⋯
van Gogh Pain⋯
Egypt, Fire Engin⋯
  Sheets of fou⋯
John Paul II, Nuc⋯
ers, Lighthouses⋯
Aircraft with Rota⋯
Pin-up Art;⋯
  Sheet of thre⋯
Birds with Rotary⋯
  Sheets of two⋯
ric World, Chine⋯
Tunes, Games a⋯

Clark Gable (1901-60) — A474

No. 2779: a, Wearing tuxedo and bow tie, hand showing. b, Wearing suit and tie, no mustache, no hand showing. c, Wearing tuxedo and bow tie, no hand showing. d, Wearing suit and tie, hand showing. e, Wearing suit and solid tie, with mustache. f, Wearing suit and striped tie, with mustache.

**2003**
2779 A474 10d Sheet of 6, #a-f     8.00 8.00

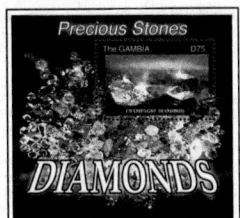

Diamonds — A475

No. 2780: a, Rough diamonds. b, Yellow diamonds. c, Pink diamonds. d, Blue diamonds. e, White diamonds. f, Green diamonds.
  75d, Champagne diamonds.

**Perf. 13¼x13½**
**2003, Nov. 18**                    **Litho.**
2780 A475 20d Sheet of 6, #a-
       f                      13.00 13.00
       **Souvenir Sheet**
2781 A475 75d multi            8.00 8.00

Designs: 20d,⋯
paper. 25d, Wom⋯
on emery paper.⋯
75d, Man with Pip⋯
  No. 2866: a, Po⋯
c, Painting on Ing⋯
  No. 2867, 75d⋯
ages in the Burn⋯
75d, Bird, horiz.

**2004, Feb. 17**
2862-2865 A502⋯
2866 A502 30⋯

       **Siz⋯

2867-2868 A502⋯

          S⋯

Deng Xiaop⋯
          L⋯

**2004, May 3⋯**
2869 A503 75⋯

          M⋯

Intl. Year
of Peace
A504

No. 2870:⋯
nuclear disarm⋯
music festival.

**2004, May 3⋯**
2870 A504 3⋯

Rare
and
Famous
Postage
Stamps

No. 2871:⋯
Britain #1.⋯
States #C3a⋯

Minerals
A476

No. 2782: a, Stilbite. b, Smoky quartz. c, Lapis lazuli. d, Amethyst. e, Black opals. f, Rubies.
  60d, Quartz.

**2003, Nov. 18**
2782 A476 15d Sheet of 6, #a-
       f                     12.00 12.00
       **Souvenir Sheet**
2783 A476 60d multi           6.50 6.50

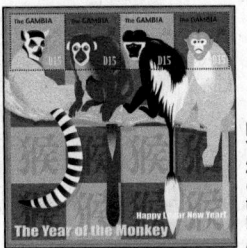

New Year 2004 (Year of the Monkey) A477

No. 2784: a, Monkey with white and brown face, white ears. b, Monkey with white and blue gray face. c, Monkey with white and brown face. d, Monkey with orange and white face.

**2004, Jan. 5**                     **Perf. 13¼**
2784 A477 15d Sheet of 4, #a-d   7.50 7.50

Paintings by Xu Beihong (1895-1953) — A478

No. 2785, vert.: a, Four Magpies. b, Cormorants. c, Under the Banyan Tree. d, Citrus Tree. e, Double Happiness. f, Rooster in Bamboo Garden.
  No. 2786: a, Bird on the Kapok Tree. b, Twin Pines.

**2004, Jan. 21  Litho.  Perf. 13½x13¼**
2785 A478 10d Sheet of 6, #a-f   7.75 7.75
                  **Perf. 13¼**
2786 A478 25d Sheet of 2, #a-b   6.50 6.50
  2004 Hong Kong Stamp Expo. No. 2785 contains six 28x42mm stamps.

FIFA (Fédération Internationale de Football Association), Cent. — A479

FIFA cups: No. 2787, 10d, World Cup. No. 2788, 10d, Jules Rimet Cup. No. 2789, 10d, Women's World Cup. No. 2790, 10d, Under 17 World Championship Cup. No. 2791, 10d, Under 19 Women's World Championship Cup. No. 2792, 10d, Club World Championship Cup. No. 2793, 10d, Confederations Cup. No. 2794, 10d, World Youth Championship Cup. No. 2795, 10d, Fustal (Indoor Soccer) World Championship Cup.

**2004, Feb. 16**                    **Perf. 13¼**
2787-2795 A479     Set of 9       9.50 9.50

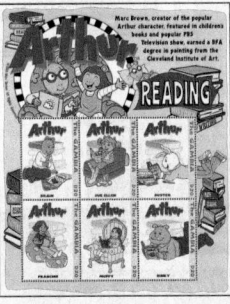

Arthur and Friends A480

No. 2796 — Characters reading: a, Brain. b, Sue Ellen. c, Buster. d, Francine. e, Muffy. f, Binky.
  No. 2797, 30d: a, Brain playing clarinet. b, Francine playing banjo. c, Buster playing flute. d, Sue Ellen playing violin.
  No. 2798, 30d: a, Brain playing bass. b, Francine playing drum. c, Buster playing tuba. d, Sue Ellen playing saxophone.

**2004, Feb. 16**
2796 A480 20d Sheet of 6,
                 #a-f          12.00 12.00
       **Sheets of 4, #a-d**
2797-2798 A480     Set of 2      21.00 21.00

Concorde and Queen Elizabeth 2 — A481

Concorde — A482

No. 2800, 25d — Concorde 216 G-BOAF and: a, British flag, with dots of blue at UR. b, British flag, no dots at UR, c, Clouds.
  No. 2801, 25d — Concorde 216 G-BOAF and: a, Statue of Liberty. b, Field of US flag. c, Stripes of US flag.
  No. 2802, 25d — Concorde 213 F-BTSD and: a, Top of Eiffel Tower. b, French flag, middle part of Eiffel Tower. c, French flag, first and second landings of Eiffel Tower.

**2004, Feb. 17**                    **Perf. 14**
2799 A481 60d multi           8.50 8.50
       **Sheets of 3, #a-c**
          **Perf. 13¼x13½**
2800-2802 A482    Set of 3    24.00 24.00

Paintings in the Hermitage, St. Petersburg, Russia — A483

No. 2803, vert.: a, Portrait of a Gentleman, by Domenico Capriolo. b, Sybil, by Dosso Dossi. c, A Woman in a Turban, by Anne-Louis Girodet-Trioson. d, Portrait of a Gentleman, by Ambrosius Holbein.
  75d, Husband and Wife, by Lorenzo Lotto.

**2004, Feb. 17**                    **Perf. 13¼**
2803 A483 30d Sheet of 4, #a-
       d                     12.50 12.50
              **Imperf**
2804 A483 75d multi           8.50 8.50
  St. Petersburg, 300th anniv. No. 2803 contains four 37x50mm stamps.

Paintings by Pablo Picasso A484

No. 2805, vert.: a, Girl in Chemise. b, Portrait of Jacinto Salvadó as Harlequin. c, Tumblers. d, Woman with a Crow.
  75d, The Siesta.

**2004, Feb. 17**                    **Perf. 13¼**
2805 A484 30d Sheet of 4, #a-d   13.50 13.50
              **Imperf**
2806 A484 75d multi           9.00 9.00
  No. 2805 contains four 37x50mm stamps.

Paintings by Norman Rockwell A485

No. 2807: a, Detail of 1957 Saturday Evening Post Illustration. b, Girl at Mirror. c, After the Prom. d, The Prom Dress.
  75d, Losing the Game.

**2004, Feb. 17**                    **Perf. 13¼**
2807 A485 30d Sheet of 4, #a-
       d                     12.50 12.50
       **Souvenir Sheet**
2808 A485 75d multi           7.50 7.50

Paintings by Kunichika Toyohara (1835-1900) A486

Designs: 10d, The Actor Kikugoro Onoe V as Moronao with the Late Sojuro Nakamura I as Hangan Enya. 15d, The Actor Kikugoro Onoe V as Kunimoto Shinohara with Danjuro Ichikawa IX as Takamori. 20d, The Actor Kikugoro Onoe V as Kansuke Yamamoto with Sadanji Ichikawa I as Daizo Ushikubo. 35d, The Actor Kikugoro Onoe V as the Ghost Seigen with Fukusuke Nakamura IV as Sakurahime.
  No. 2813: a, The Actor Sadanji Ichikawa I as the Fishmonger Fukashichi. b, The Actor Sadanji Ichikawa I as Umeomaru. c, The Actor Kuzo Ichikawa III as Shihei Fujiwara. d, The Actor Shikan Nakamura IV as Motome.
  75d, The Actor Udanji Ichikawa as Saihei Koya (Ozawa Keifu Tomofusa), horiz.

**2004, Feb. 17**
2809-2812 A486     Set of 4       8.00 8.00
2813 A486 30d Sheet of 4, #a-
       d                     12.50 12.50
       **Souvenir Sheet**
2814 A486 75d multi           5.25 5.25

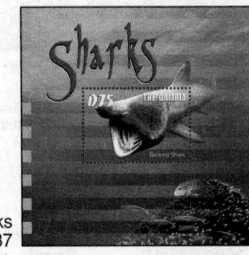

Sharks A487

No. 2815: a, Lemon shark. b, Nurse shark. c, Leopard shark. d, Starry smoothhound sharks.
  75d, Basking shark.

**2004, Mar. 8**                    **Perf. 13¼x13½**
2815 A487 30d Sheet of 4, #a-
       d                     14.00 14.00
       **Souvenir Sheet**
2816 A487 75d multi           8.50 8.50

No. 2817, vert...
American short...
Sphinx. c, Coppe...
mackerel tabby ...
75d, Copper-e...

**2004, Mar. 8**
2817 A488 30d ...

**So**
**Pe**
2818 A488 75d ...

Dogs
A489

No. 2819, ve...
Boston terrier. ...
75d, Borzoi.

**2004, Mar. 8**
2819 A489 30c ...

**S**
**P**
2820 A489 75...

Mu...

No. 2821, 3...
caria fraterna. ...
cybe psittacina...
No. 2822, ...
entoloma. b, ...
depiota. d, Sir...
75d, Russul...

**Perf. ...**
**2004, Mar. ...**
2821-2822 A4...

**S**
2823 A490 7...

No. 2824, ...
c, Stapelia. d...
No. 2825, ...
Isopogon lat...
Echinopsis. ...
75d, Epiph...

**2004, Mar. ...**

2824-2825 A...

2826 A491 ...

---

Elvis Presley (1935-77) — A517

No. 2912, 15d: a, Standing, with guitar, 1956. b, Wearing army hat, 1957. c, Holding guitar, 1968. d, Holding guitar, 1970. e, Playing guitar, 1972. f, Singing, 1973.
No. 2913, 15d: a, Seated, with guitar, 1956. b, With guitar, 1958. c, Playing guitar, 1964. d, Playing drums, 1966. e, On horse, 1968. f, Playing guitar, 1969.

**2005, Jan. 8**      **Sheets of 6, #a-f**
2912-2913 A517    Set of 2    20.00 20.00

New Year 2005 (Year of the Rooster) — A518

Paintings by Xu Beihong: 10d, Rooster. 40d, Black Rooster, horiz.

**2005, Jan.**      **Perf. 11½**
2914 A518 10d multi    1.25 1.25
**Souvenir Sheet**
2915 A518 40d multi    4.00 4.00
No. 2914 printed in sheets of 4. No. 2915 contains one 46x36mm stamp.

**Basketball Players Type of 2004**

Designs: No. 2916, 25d, Steve Nash, Dallas Mavericks. No. 2917, 25d, Shaquille O'Neal, Los Angeles Lakers.

**2005, Feb. 10**      **Perf. 14**
2916-2917 A512    Set of 2    4.00 4.00
Both players were on different teams when stamps were released.

Intl. Year of Rice (in 2004) A519

No. 2918, vert.: a, Rice terraces. b, Woman holding rice plants. c, Two people holding rice plants.
60d, Rice farmers.

**2005, Feb. 10**
2918 A519 30d Sheet of 3, #a-c    7.25 7.25
**Souvenir Sheet**
2919 A519 60d multi    6.50 6.50

Butterflies — A520

Designs: 1d, Belenois solilucis. 2d, Colotis evippe. 3d, Acraea cepheus. 5d, Bebearia senegalensis. 6d, Danaus chrysippus. 7d, Papilio dardanus. 10d, Graphium agamedes. 15d, Papilio hesperus. 25d, Charaxes boueti. 30d, Cymothoe egesta. 50d, Amauris albimaculata. 75d, Charaxes lucretius. 100d, Papilio zalmoxis. 200d, Papilio antimachus.

**Perf. 13¼x13½, 14¾x14¼ (7d, 30d)**
**2005, Apr. 4**
2920 A520 1d multi    .30 .25
2921 A520 2d multi    .35 .35
2922 A520 3d multi    .40 .40
2923 A520 5d multi    .50 .50
2924 A520 6d multi    .55 .55
2924A A520 7d multi    .75 .75
2925 A520 10d multi    1.00 1.00

---

| 2926 | A520 | 15d multi | 1.50 | 1.50 |
| 2927 | A520 | 25d multi | 2.00 | 2.00 |
| 2927A | A520 | 30d multi | 2.50 | 2.50 |
| 2928 | A520 | 50d multi | 3.75 | 3.75 |
| 2929 | A520 | 75d multi | 6.00 | 6.00 |
| 2929A | A520 | 100d multi | 8.50 | 8.50 |
| 2929B | A520 | 200d multi | 15.00 | 15.00 |

*Nos. 2920-2929B (14)*    43.10 43.05

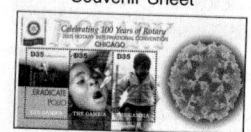

Battle of Trafalgar, Bicent. — A521

Designs: 5d, Santisima Trinidad. 10d, Victory firing at French flagship Bucentaure, horiz. 15d, Lord Horatio Nelson. 30d, French sailors from the Redoubtable boarding Victory. 60d, Vice-admiral Horatio Nelson.

**2005, Apr. 4**      **Perf. 14**
2930-2933 A521    Set of 4    7.00 7.00
**Souvenir Sheet**
2934 A521 60d multi    7.50 7.50

**Souvenir Sheet**

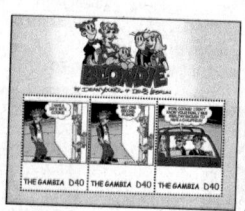

Rotary International, Cent. — A522

No. 2935: a, "Eradicate Polio," child receiving polio vaccine. b, Child receiving polio vaccine, diff. c, Child seated.

**2005, Apr. 4**
2935 A522 35d Sheet of 3, #a-c    9.50 9.50

Blondie, by Dean Young and Denis LeBrun A523

No. 2936, 40d: a, "I have a date with Cookie." b, "Wait one second, please." c, "Wow, Cookie! I didn't know your family was wealth enough to have a chauffeur!"
No. 2937, 40d: a, "Listen up, everybody. . ." b, "Then after he leaves you can get back to normal." c, "I want to see this place humming with activity and enthusiasm!"

**2005, Apr. 4**      **Perf. 13¼**
**Sheets of 3, #a-c**
2936-2937 A523    Set of 2    22.00 22.00

World Cup Soccer Championships, 75th Anniv. — A524

No. 2938 — Brazilian flag and scenes from 1950 World Cup: a, 1950 Uruguay team. b, Goal from Uruguay-Brazil championship game. c, Maracaná Municipal Stadium, Brazil. d, Alcide Edgardo Ghiggia.
60d, 1950 Uruguay team, diff.

**2005, Apr. 4**      **Perf. 14¼**
2938 A524 25d Sheet of 4, #a-d    10.00 10.00
**Souvenir Sheet**
2939 A524 60d multi    5.50 5.50

---

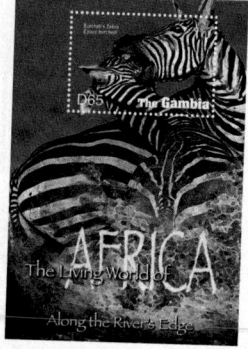

African Fauna A525

No. 2940, 25d: a, African fish eagle. b, Hummingbird hawkmoth. c, Nile crocodile. d, Blue wildebeest.
No. 2941, 25d: a, Bateleur eagle. b, Green mamba. c, Chimpanzee. d, Yellow pansy butterfly.
No. 2942, 25d: a, Jackass penguins. b, Leatherback turtle. c, Scaevola thunbergii. d, Cancrid crab.
No. 2943, 25d: a, Mediterranean monk seal. b, Horned boxfish. c, Scorpion fish. d, Cnidarians.
No. 2944, Burchell's zebra. No. 2945, 65d, Greater galago. No. 2946, 65d, Bottlenose dolphin, vert. No. 2947, 65d, Gerbera daisies, vert.

**2005, Apr. 4**      **Perf. 13¼x13½**
**Sheets of 4, #a-d**
2940-2943 A525    Set of 4    32.50 32.50
**Souvenir Sheets**
2944-2947 A525    Set of 4    22.50 22.50

Hans Christian Andersen (1805-75), Author — A526

No. 2942, horiz.: a, The Ugly Duckling. b, The Little Match Girl. c, The Rose Tree Regiment.
60d, The Emperor's New Clothes.

**2005, Apr. 4**      **Perf. 14**
2948 A526 35d Sheet of 3, #a-c    11.50 11.50
**Souvenir Sheet**
2949 A526 60d multi    7.00 7.00

Wedding of Prince Charles and Camilla Parker Bowles — A527

Various photos of couple with oval color of: No. 2950, 2d, Brown. No. 2951, 2d, Purple. No. 2952, 2d, Red brown.

**2005, Apr. 9**      **Perf. 13½**
2950-2952 A527    Set of 3    2.00 2.00
Each stamp printed in sheets of 4.

---

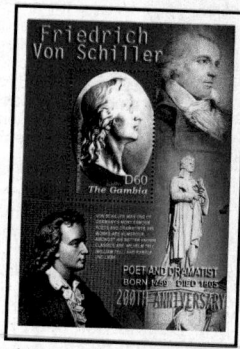

Friedrich von Schiller (1759-1805), Writer — A528

No. 2953: a, Statue of Schiller. b, Painting of Schiller. c, Bust of Schiller.
60d, Cameo of Schiller.

**2005, Apr. 4**    **Litho.**    **Perf. 14**
2953 A528 35d Sheet of 3, #a-c    10.00 10.00
**Souvenir Sheet**
2954 A528 60d multi    6.00 6.00

**Miniature Sheet**

End of World War II, 60th Anniv. A529

No. 2955 — Prince Bernhard of the Netherlands: a, And Prime Minister Pieter Gerbrandy. b, And Queen Wilhelmina. c, And Generals Bernard Montgomery and Hendrik Kruls. d, And people of Nimwegen. e, At German surrender. f, Returning home with family.

**2005, Apr. 14**    **Litho.**    **Perf. 12¾**
2955 A529 12d Sheet of 6, #a-f    5.00 5.00

End of World War II, 60th Anniv. A530

No. 2956, 20d — Dunkirk: a, Germans advance across France. b, Anthony C. Bartley. c, Ships and boats. d, Rescued soldiers.
No. 2957, 20d — D-Day: a, Allied troops hit the beaches of Normandy. b, Germans blast Sword Beach. c, Allied troops advance inland. d, Germans begin to surrender.
No. 2958, 80d, Operation Dynamo. No. 2959, 80d, Royal Navy lands on Gold Beach.

**2005, May 9**      **Perf. 13¼x13½**
**Sheets of 4, #a-d**
2956-2957 A530    Set of 2    20.00 20.00
**Souvenir Sheets**
2958-2959 A530    Set of 2    16.00 16.00

**Souvenir Sheet**

Expo 2005, Aichi, Japan A531

No. 2960: a, Mt. Kilimanjaro. b, Lion. c, Splitting of the Red Sea. d, Astronaut on Moon.

**2005, May 16**      **Perf. 12**
2960 A531 15d Sheet of 4, #a-d    8.00 8.00

Pope John Paul II (1920-2005) and Mother Teresa (1910-97) — A532

**2005, June 1**      *Perf. 14*
2961 A532 30d multi     3.50 3.50
Printed in sheets of 6.

Maimonides (1135-1204) — A533

No. 2962: a, Denomination in white. b, Denomination in red.

**2005, July 12**      *Perf. 12*
2962 A533 25d Pair, #a-b    5.50 5.50
Printed in sheets of 2 pairs.

VJ Day, 60th Anniv. A534

No. 2963, horiz. — Paintings by Jean Masterly: a, B-29 Flies Over the Missouri. b, Enola Gay Over Hiroshima. c, Dogfight Over the Pacific. d, Hellcat Fury Engages the Enemy.
80d, USS Enterprise Aircraft Carrier in the Battle of Midway.

**2005, July 12**      *Perf. 12¾*
2963 A534 25d Sheet of 4, #a-d    11.00 11.00
**Souvenir Sheet**
2964 A534 80d multi     8.00 8.00
No. 2963 contains four 40x31mm stamps.

Jules Verne (1828-1905), Writer — A535

No. 2965, horiz.: a, Hungary #C287. b, Monaco #1100. c, France #770.
80d, Scene from "From the Earth to the Moon."

**2005, July 12**
2965 A535 35d Sheet of 3, #a-c    10.00 10.00
**Souvenir Sheet**
2966 A535 80d multi     8.00 8.00

Souvenir Sheet

Albert Einstein (1879-1955), Physicist — A536

No. 2967: a, Einstein, country name in red. b, Einstein, country name in white. c, Israel #117.

**2005, July 28**
2967 A536 35d Sheet of 3, #a-c    11.00 11.00

American First Day Cover Society, 50th Anniv. — A537

**2005, July 29**
2968 A537 25d multi     2.75 2.75

Souvenir Sheet

Taipei 2005 Stamp Exhibition — A538

No. 2969: a, Presidential Palace, Taipei. b, Chiang Kai-Shek Memorial, Taipei. c, Queen's Head, Yehliu. d, National Palace Museum, Taipei.

**2005, Aug. 19**      *Perf. 14*
2969 A538 35d Sheet of 4, #a-d    13.00 13.00

First Europa Stamps, 50th Anniv. (in 2006) — A539

Designs: 35d, Mailman, Luxembourg #318. 40d, Stars, "50," France #806. 50d, Map of Europe, France #805.

**2005, Oct. 20**
2970-2972 A539 Set of 3    10.00 10.00
*2972a*   Souvenir sheet, #2970-2972 + label    10.00 10.00

Election of Pope Benedict XVI — A540

**2005, Nov. 15**      *Perf. 13½*
2973 A540 35d multi     3.50 3.50
Printed in sheets of 4.

Pope John Paul II (1920-2005) — A541

Pope John Paul II: No. 2974, 40d, Looking right. No. 2975, 40d, With arm raised. No. 2976, 40d, With hand to face. No. 2977, 40d, Praying with four men at side. No. 2978, 40d, Surrounded by praying clergymen. No. 2979, With praying hands of other people. No. 2980, 40d, Wearing miter, with crowd. No. 2981, 40d, Praying at church. No. 2982, 40d, With arms outstretched at church. No. 2983, 40d, Praying with rosary. No. 2984, 40d, Holding crucifix, round globe. No. 2985, 40d, Holding crucifix, oval world map. No. 2986, 40d, Holding crucifix, and at doorway. No. 2987, 40d, With crucifix at side of face. No. 2988, 40d, Holding crucifix in front of his face. No. 2989, 40d, Holding crucifix, with other arm raised. No. 2990, 40d, With crucifix, Papal arms. No. 2991, 40d, With Good Shepherd. No. 2992, 40d, Holding child. No. 2993, 40d, With UN emblem. No. 2994, 40d, Being assisted.
No. 2995, 80d, Bowing with crucifix. No. 2996, 80d, Wearing miter in front of church. No. 2997, 80d, With kneeling bishop. No. 2998, 80d, Holding microphone. No. 2999, 80d, With raised hands, Papal arms. No. 3000, 80d, With Virgin Mary.

**Embossed on Metal**
**2005**      *Die Cut Perf. 12½*
**Self-Adhesive**
**Silver-Colored Metal**
2974-2994 A541 Set of 21   120.00 120.00
**Gold-Colored Metal**
2995-3000 A541 Set of 6    55.00 55.00

Miniature Sheet

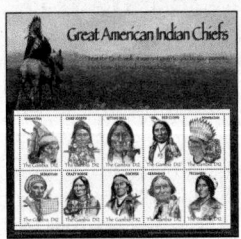

American Indian Chiefs — A542

No. 3001: a, Hiawatha. b, Chief Joseph. c, Sitting Bull. d, Red Cloud. e, Powhatan. f, Sequoyah. g, Crazy Horse. h, Cochise. i, Geronimo. j, Tecumseh.

**2005, Nov. 15**    *Litho.*    *Perf. 13½*
3001 A542 12d Sheet of 10, #a-j    11.00 11.00

Christmas — A543

Designs: 7d, The Annunciation, by Lorenzo di Credi. 10d, The Holy Family, by di Credi. 25d, The Adoration of the Magi, by Filippo Lippi. 30d, Marriage of St. Catherine, by Lippi. 65d, The Annunciation, by Fra Angelico.

**2005, Dec. 19**      *Perf. 13½x13¼*
3002-3005 A543 Set of 4    6.50 6.50
**Souvenir Sheet**
3006 A543 65d multi     6.00 6.00

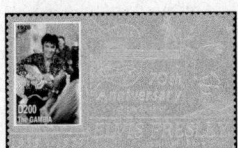

New Year 2006 (Year of the Dog) — A544

**2006, Jan. 3**      *Perf. 13¼*
3007 A544 15d multi     1.75 1.75
Printed in sheets of 4.

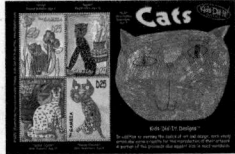

Elvis Presley (1935-77) — A545

*Serpentine Die Cut 7¾*
**2006, Jan. 24**    *Litho. & Embossed*
3008 A545 200d multi    16.00 16.00

Children's Drawings — A546

No. 3009, 25d — Cats: a, Kitty, by Raquel Bobolia. b, Jaguar, by Megan Albe. c, Quazy Jaguar, by Nick Abrams. d, Chelsy Cheetah, by Carly Bowerman.
No. 3010, 25d — Reptiles: a, Stripey, by Christopher Bowerman. b, Sea Turtle, by Tyler Overton. c, Hungry Lizard, by Jessica Shutt. d, Frogs, by Elyse Bobczynski.
No. 3011, 25d — Flowers: a, Three Flowers, by Lauren Van Way. b, Blossoms, by Michelle

Malachowsky. c, Flower Pot, by Van Way. d, Red Flower Pot, by Anne Wilks.

**2006, Jan. 24**    *Litho.*    *Perf. 13¼*
**Sheets of 4, #a-d**
3009-3011 A546 Set of 3    25.00 25.00

Queen Elizabeth II, 80th Birthday A547

No. 3012: a, Wearing military uniform. b, At coronation. c, On Time Magazine cover. d, Wearing wedding gown.
65d, Wearing robe and crown.

**2006, Feb. 27**      *Perf. 13¼*
3012 A547 30d Sheet of 4, #a-d    11.00 11.00
**Souvenir Sheet**
*Perf. 12*
3013 A547 65d multi     7.50 7.50

Worldwide Fund for Nature (WWF) — A548

No. 3014 — Black-crowned crane: a, Head. b, Standing on one leg. c, Birds in wild. d, Chick.

**2006, Feb. 27**      *Perf. 12¾*
3014 A548 30d Block or strip of 4, #a-d    9.50 9.50
*e.*   Souvenir sheet, 2 each #3014a-3014d    19.00 19.00

2006 Winter Olympics, Turin — A549

Designs: No. 3015, Norway #1048. No. 3015A, Poster for 1992 Albertville Winter Olympics. 15d, Norway #1047. No. 3017, Poster for 2002 Salt Lake City Winter Olympics. No. 3017A, France #B611, horiz. 25d, Poster for 1994 Lillehammer Winter Olympics.

**2006, Mar. 23**      *Perf. 13¼*
3015   A549 10d multicolored   1.00 1.00
3015A   A549 10d multicolored   1.00 1.00
3016   A549 15d multicolored   1.50 1.50
3017   A549 20d multicolored   2.00 2.00
3017A   A549 20d multicolored   2.25 2.25
3018   A549 25d multicolored   2.50 2.50
   *Nos. 3015-3018 (6)*    10.25 10.25

Marilyn Monroe (1926-62), Actress — A550

**2006, Apr. 6**
3019 A550 30d multi 2.50 2.50
Printed in sheets of 4.

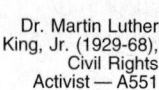

Dr. Martin Luther King, Jr. (1929-68), Civil Rights Activist — A551

**2006, May 27** *Perf. 11½x12*
3020 A551 40d multi 3.25 3.25
Printed in sheets of 3.

**Miniature Sheet**

American Philatelic Society, 120th Anniv. — A552

No. 3021 — United States stamps: a, #1120. b, #E14. c, #114. d, #C3. e, #894. f, #E2. g, #294. h, #Q2.

**2006, May 27** *Perf. 13¼*
3021 A552 17d Sheet of 8, #a-h 12.00 12.00
Washington 2006 World Philatelic Exhibition.

**Souvenir Sheet**

Ludwig Durr (1878-1956), Engineer, and Zeppelins — A553

No. 3022 — Durr and: a, Zeppelin NT. b, Zeppelin ZR-3 (U.S.S. Los Angeles). c, Zeppelin ZRS (U.S.S. Macon).

**2006, June 22** *Perf. 12¾*
3022 A553 40d Sheet of 3, #a-c 11.00 11.00

**Souvenir Sheet**

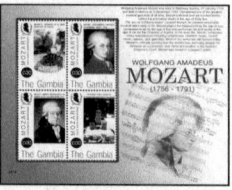

Wolfgang Amadeus Mozart (1756-91), Composer — A554

No. 3023: a, Mozart's Memorial, Vienna. b, Portrait of Mozart, by Barbara Kraft. c, Portrait of Mozart by unknown artist. d, Mozart family graves, Salzburg.

**2006, June 22**
3023 A554 30d Sheet of 4, #a-d 12.75 12.75

Rembrandt (1606-69), Painter — A555

Details from paintings: 10d, Jacob Blessing the Sons of Joseph. 12d, Jacob Blessing the Sons of Joseph, diff. 15d, Jacob Blessing the Sons of Joseph, diff. No. 3027, 25d, Jacob Wrestling with the Angel.
No. 3028, 25d — The Staalmeesters: a, Man wearing hat, leaning to right, "Rembrandt" in white. b, Man wearing hat, "Rembrandt" in white. c, Man without hat. d, Man wearing hat, "Rembrandt" in black.
No. 3029, 25d: a, Young Girl at Open Half-Door. b, Self-portrait, 1632-39. c, Self-portrait, 1640. d, Portrait of a Young Woman.
No. 3030, 25d — A Married Couple with Their Children: a, Man. b, Child, "Rembrandt" in white. c, Child, "Rembrandt" in black. d, Woman.
No. 3031, 65d — A Polish Nobleman. No. 3032, 65d, The Knight with the Falcon. No. 3033, 65d, A Young Woman in Fancy Dress. No. 3034, 65d, Portrait of a Lady with a Lap Dog.

**2006, Aug. 23** *Litho.* *Perf. 14¼*
3024-3027 A555 Set of 4 6.00 6.00
**Sheets of 4, #a-d**
3028-3030 A555 Set of 3 25.00 25.00
**Imperf**
**Size: 76x106mm**
3031-3034 A555 Set of 4 22.50 22.50

Queen Juliana of the Netherlands — A556

**2006, July 24** *Litho.* *Perf. 13¼*
3035 A556 15d multi 1.25 1.25
Printed in sheets of 6.

Princess Maxima of the Netherlands — A557

No. 3036: a, Head. b, Head and torso.

**2006, Dec. 6**
3036 A557 30d Pair, #a-b 4.75 4.75
Printed in sheets containing 3 of each stamp.

Christmas — A558

Designs: No. 3037, 25d, Gingerbread man. 30d, Christmas tree. 45d, Bell. 50d, Mittens.
No. 3041: a, 15d, Gingerbread man. b, 18d, Christmas tree. c, 25d, Bell.

**2006, Dec. 8** *Perf. 14*
3037-3040 A558 Set of 4 11.00 11.00
**Souvenir Sheet**
3041 A558 Sheet of 4, #3041a-3041c, 3040 7.75 7.75

**Miniature Sheet**

2006 World Cup Soccer Championships, Germany — A559

No. 3042 — World Cup and soccer ball with flag of: a, 10d, Australia. b, 20d, Germany. c, 25d, Sweden. d, 30d, Brazil.

**2006, Dec. 20** *Perf. 13¼*
3042 A559 Sheet of 4, #a-d 6.75 6.75

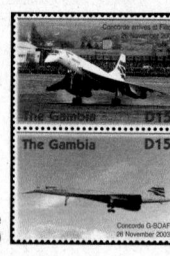

Concorde A560

No. 3043, 15d: a, Concorde arriving at Filton. b, Concorde G-BOAF in flight.
No. 3044, 15d: a, Concorde taking off from Toulouse. b, Concorde test pilot Andre Turcat.

**2006, Dec. 20** *Perf. 13¼x13½*
**Pairs, #a-b**
3043-3044 A560 Set of 2 8.00 8.00
Nos. 3043-3044 were each printed in sheets containing three pairs.

Space Achievements — A561

No. 3045, 20d — Various views of Mars Reconnaissance Orbiter.
No. 3046, 20d — Space Shuttle Columbia: a, Columbia attached to rocket boosters in flight. b, Lift-off of Columbia. c, Shuttle mission simulator. d, Mission control. e, Capt. John W. Young. f, Capt. Robert L. Crippen.
No. 3047, 25d — Giotto Comet Probe: a, Halley's Comet. b, Giotto Comet Probe, green and orange lines. c, Giotto Comet Probe. d, Comet and Giotto Comet Probe.
No. 3048, 25d — Viking 1: a, Viking 1 in flight. b, Viking 1 on Mars, text in black, denomination at UL. c, Viking 1 on Mars, text in black, denomination at UR. d, Viking 1 on Mars, "Viking 1" in white.
No. 3049, 65d, Venus Express. No. 3050, 65d, Hayabusa spacecraft. No. 3051, 65d, Luna 9, vert. No. 3052, 65d, Space Shuttle Discovery returns to space, vert.

**2006, Dec. 20** *Perf. 14*
**Sheets of 6, #a-f**
3045-3046 A561 Set of 2 27.50 27.50
**Sheets of 4, #a-d**
3047-3048 A561 Set of 2 16.00 16.00
**Souvenir Sheets**
3049-3052 A561 Set of 4 24.00 24.00

New Year 2007 (Year of the Pig) — A562

**2007, Feb. 15** *Perf. 13x13½*
3053 A562 20d multi 2.00 2.00
Printed in sheets of 4.

Scouting, Cent. — A563

Knot in: 30d, Green. 65d, Orange.

**2007, Feb. 15** *Perf. 13¼*
3054 A563 30d multi 2.75 2.75
**Souvenir Sheet**
3055 A563 65d multi 5.50 5.50
No. 3054 printed in sheets of 4.

**Miniature Sheets**

Programs of Pres. John F. Kennedy — A564

No. 3056, 25d — Peace Corps: a, Kennedy greeting Peace Corps volunteers at White House. b, R. Sargent Shriver, first director of Peace Corps. c, Kennedy signing executive order creating Peace Corps. d, Kennedy greeting Peace Corps volunteers.
No. 3057, 25d — Alliance for Progress: a, Kennedy in rocking chair. b, Kennedy and Cabinet. c, Volunteer Ida Shoatz in Peru. d, Kennedy speaking at University of Michigan.

**2007, Feb. 15** *Perf. 12¾*
**Sheets of 4, #a-d**
3056-3057 A564 Set of 2 17.50 17.50

Betty Boop A565

No. 3058 — Betty Boop: a, With hands at side. b, Holding flowers. c, With dog biting swimsuit. d, Wearing long red dress. e, With hands clasped. f, Holding top hat and cane.
No. 3059 — Betty Boop in: a, Red. b, Purple.

**2007, Feb. 15** *Litho.*
3058 A565 15d Sheet of 6, #a-f 9.00 9.00
**Souvenir Sheet**
3059 A565 40d Sheet of 2, #a-b 6.00 6.00

Pope Benedict XVI — A566

**2007, May 1** *Perf. 13¼*
3060 A566 12d multi 1.40 1.40
Printed in sheets of 8.

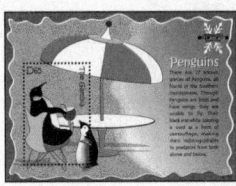

Intl. Polar Year A567

No. 3061 — Penguin: a, At bongo drums. b, With lei and grass skirt. c, At drum set. d, With purple guitar. e, At microphone. f, With yellow and orange guitar.
65d, Penguin in chair at table.

**2007, May 1**    **Litho.**
3061 A567 15d Sheet of 6, #a-
f    10.00 10.00
**Souvenir Sheet**
3062 A567 65d multi    8.50 8.50

Wedding of Queen Elizabeth II and Prince Philip, 60th Anniv. A568

No. 3063, vert. — Photos of Queen and Prince: a, On wedding day, gray brown frame. b, As older couple, gray brown frame. c, As older couple, pink frame. d, On wedding day, pink frame. e, On wedding day, blue gray frame. f, As older couple, blue gray frame.
65d, Queen and Prince, diff.

**2007, May 1**
3063 A568 15d Sheet of 6, #a-
f    10.00 10.00
**Souvenir Sheet**
3064 A568 65d multi    7.00 7.00

Princess Diana (1961-97) — A569

No. 3065, vert. — Diana wearing: a, Tiara, close-up. b, Light blue dress, close-up. c, Maroon dress, close-up. d, Tiara, from distance. e, Light blue dress, from distance. f, Maroon dress, from distance.
No. 3066, vert. — Diana wearing: a, Blue and white hat. b, Lilac and purple hat. c, Black dress. d, Red and white hat.
65d, Painting of Diana.

**2007, May 1**
3065 A569 15d Sheet of 6, #a-
f    9.50 9.50
3066 A569 25d Sheet of 4, #a-
d    10.00 10.00
**Souvenir Sheet**
3067 A569 65d multi    7.50 7.50

1986 Halley's Comet Merchandising Emblem — A570

No. 3068: a, Light olive green frame. b, Light blue frame. c, Violet black frame. d, Brown frame.
65d, Black background.

**2007, June 20**    **Perf. 13¼**
3068 A570 20d Sheet of 4, #a-d    7.50 7.50
**Souvenir Sheet**
3069 A570 65d black    6.50 6.50

Ferrari Automobiles, 60th Anniv. — A571

No. 3070: a, 1970 512 S. b, 1996 F 310. c, 1950 195 S. d, 1965 275 P2. e, 1980 Mondial 8. f, 1975 312 T. g, 1952 500 F2. h, 1986 GTB Turbo.

**2007, June 20**    **Perf. 13½x13¼**
3070 A571 12d Sheet of 8, #a-h    9.50 9.50

Paintings by Qi Baishi (1864-1957) — A572

No. 3071: a, Autumn Leaves and Magpie. b, Camellias. c, Pomegranates. d, Mynahs and Amaranthus.
65d, Magpie and Plum Blossoms.

**2007, July 16**    **Perf. 12½**
3071 A572 25d Sheet of 4, #a-d    9.50 9.50
**Souvenir Sheet**
**Perf. 11¼x11½**
3072 A572 65d multi    6.75 6.75

First Helicopter Flight, Cent. — A573

No. 3073: a, UH-1B/C. b, S-65/RH-53B. c, UH-1. d, BK 117. e, Autogyro. f, AS-61.
65d, AH-1 Huey Cobra.

**2007, July 16**    **Perf. 13¼**
3073 A573 15d Sheet of 6, #a-f    9.50 9.50
**Souvenir Sheet**
3074 A573 65d multi    8.00 8.00

The First Ladies of the United States of America — The Gambia D65 — Martha Washington

Wives of United States Presidents and First Ladies — A574

No. 3075: a, Martha Washington. b, Abigail Adams. c, Dolley Madison. d, Elizabeth Monroe. e, Louisa Adams. f, Emily Donelson. g, Angelica Van Buren. h, Anna Harrison. i, Letitia Tyler. j, Julia Tyler. k, Sarah Polk. l, Margaret Taylor. m, Abigail Fillmore. n, Jane Pierce. o, Eagle, flags, White House.
No. 3076: a, Harriet Johnston. b, Mary Lincoln. c, Eliza Johnson. d, Julia Grant. e, Lucy Hayes. f, Lucretia Garfield. g, Mary Arthur McElroy. h, Frances Cleveland. i, Caroline Harrison. j, Ida McKinley. k, Edith Roosevelt. l, Helen Taft. m, Ellen Wilson. n, Edith Wilson.
No. 3077: a, Florence Harding. b, Grace Coolidge. c, Lou Hoover. d, Eleanor Roosevelt. e, Bess Truman. f, Mamie Eisenhower. g, Jacqueline Kennedy. h, Lady Bird Johnson. i, Pat Nixon. j, Betty Ford. k, Rosalynn Carter. l, Nancy Reagan. m, Barbara Bush. n, Hillary Clinton. o, Laura Bush.
No. 3078, 65d, Martha Washington. No. 3079, 65d, Abigail Adams. No. 3080, 65d, Martha Jefferson. No. 3081, 65d, Martha Washington Jefferson Randolph. No. 3082, 65d, Dolley Madison. No. 3083, 65d, Elizabeth Monroe. No. 3084, 65d, Louisa Adams. No. 3085, 65d, Rachael Jackson. No. 3086, 65d, Emily Donelson. No. 3087, 65d, Hannah Van Buren. No. 3088, 65d, Angelica Van Buren. No. 3089, 65d, Anna Harrison. No. 3090, 65d, Letitia Tyler. No. 3091, 65d, Priscilla Tyler. No. 3092, 65d, Julia Tyler. No. 3093, 65d, Sarah Polk. No. 3094, 65d, Margaret Taylor. No. 3095, 65d, Mary Taylor. No. 3096, 65d, Abigail Fillmore. No. 3097, 65d, Jane Pierce. No. 3098, 65d, Harriet Johnston. No. 3099, 65d, Mary Lincoln. No. 3100, 65d, Eliza Johnson. No. 3101, 65d, Julia Grant. No. 3102, 65d, Lucy Hayes. No. 3103, 65d, Lucretia Garfield. No. 3104, 65d, Ellen Arthur. No. 3105, 65d, Mary Arthur McElroy. No. 3106, 65d, Frances Cleveland. No. 3107, 65d, Caroline Harrison. No. 3108, 65d, Mary Lord Harrison. No. 3109, 65d, Ida McKinley. No. 3110, 65d, Edith Roosevelt. No. 3111, 65d, Helen Taft. No. 3112, 65d, Ellen Wilson. No. 3113, 65d, Edith Wilson. No. 3114, 65d, Florence Harding. No. 3115, 65d, Grace Coolidge. No. 3116, 65d, Lou Hoover. No. 3117, 65d, Eleanor Roosevelt. No. 3118, 65d, Bess Truman. No. 3119, 65d, Mamie Eisenhower. No. 3120, 65d, Jacqueline Kennedy. No. 3121, 65d, Lady Bird Johnson. No. 3122, 65d, Pat Nixon. No. 3123, 65d, Betty Ford. No. 3124, 65d, Rosalynn Carter. No. 3125, 65d, Nancy Reagan. No. 3126, 65d, Barbara Bush. No. 3127, 65d, Hillary Clinton. No. 3128, 65d, Laura Bush.

**2007**    **Perf. 13¼**
3075 A574 10d Sheet of 15, #a-o    14.00 14.00
3076 A574 10d Sheet of 15, #a-n, 3075o    14.00 14.00
3077 A574 10d Sheet of 15, #a-o    14.00 14.00
Nos. 3075-3077 (3)    42.00 42.00
**Souvenir Sheets**
3078-3128 A574 Set of 51    250.00 250.00
3078a    Perf. 14¼    6.25 6.25
Issued: Nos. 3075-3077, 7/31. Nos. 3078-3128, 10/24. Nos. 3075-3077 each contain fifteen 25x37mm stamps.
No. 3078a was not issued in a souvenir sheet.
See No. 3293.

**Miniature Sheet**

Pres. Gerald R. Ford (1913-2006) — A575

No. 3129 — Ford: a, With wife, Betty. b, At Presidential inauguration ceremony. c, With Betty, Pres. Richard Nixon and Pat Nixon. d, At 90th birthday celebration.

**2007, Aug. 9**    **Litho.**    **Perf. 13¼**
3129 A575 25d Sheet of 4, #a-d    8.75 8.75

**Miniature Sheet**

Elvis Presley (1935-77) — A576

No. 3130 — Presley, guitar and background color of: a, Green. b, Tan. c, Orange. d, Black (white suit). e, Brown. f, Black (black jacket).

**2007, Sept. 6**
3130 A576 15d Sheet of 6, #a-f    8.25 8.25

**Miniature Sheets**

Intl. Holocaust Remembrance Day — A577

No. 3131, 14d — United Nations diplomats and delegates: a, Ronaldo Mota Sardenberg, Brazil. b, Alisher Vohidov, Uzbekistan. c, Martin Belinga-Eboutou, Cameroun. d, Fernand Poukre-Kono, Central African Republic. e, Heraldo Muñoz, Chile. f, Wang Guangya, China. g, Elbio O. Rosselli, Uruguay. h, Shashi Tharoor, Undersecretary General.
No. 3132, 14d: a, Basile Ikouebe, Republic of the Congo. b, Saul Weisleder, Costa Rica. c, Alcicle Djedje, Ivory Coast. d, Andreas D. Mavroiannis, Cyprus. e, Martin Palous, Czech Republic. f, Atoki Ileka, Democratic Republic of the Congo. g, Crispin S. Gregoire, Dominica. h, Parfait Onanga-Anyanga, Ambassador and Special Advisor of the 61st UN General Assembly.
No. 3133, 14d: a, Hoya Rashed Al-Khalifa, President of 61st UN General Assembly. b, Denis Dangue Rewaka, Gabon. c, Crispin Grey-Johnson, Gambia. d, Irakli Alasania, Georgia. e, Nana Effah-Apenteng, Ghana. f, Adamantios Vassilakis, Greece. g, Jorge Skinner-Klee Arenales, Guatemala. h, Jean-Maurice Ripert, France.
No. 3134, 14d: a, Hilari G. Davide, Jr., Philippines. b, Andrzej Towpik, Poland. c, Joao Manuel Guerra Salgueiro, Portugal. d, Alexei Tulbure, Moldova. e, Mihnea I. Motoc, Romania. f, Vitaly I. Churkin, Russia. g, Joseph Nsengimana, Rwanda. h, Augustine P. Mahiga, Tanzania.

**2007, Nov. 28**    **Litho.**    **Perf. 13½**
**Sheets of 8, #a-h**
3131-3134 A577 Set of 4    42.50 42.50

2008 Summer Olympics, Beijing — A578

**Die Cut Perf. 8½x8¼**
**2007, Nov. 29**    **Litho. & Embossed**
**Without Gum**
3135 A578 40d multi    20.00 20.00

Christmas A579

Designs: 25d, Girl at manger scene. 30d, Children eating holiday dishes. 45d, Boy with

Madonna and Child sculptures. 50d, Christmas celebrations with music.

**2007, Dec. 3**     **Litho.**     **Perf. 12**
3136-3139 A579   Set of 4      14.00 14.00

Souvenir Sheet

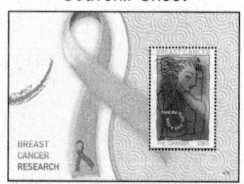

Breast Cancer Prevention — A580

**2007, Dec. 10**                  **Perf. 14**
3140 A580 65d multi              6.00 6.00

America's Cup Yacht Races — A581

No. 3141 — Various yachts with wide panels in: a, Blue. b, Yellow orange. c, Red. d, Orange.

**2007, Dec. 28**                  **Perf. 13¼**
3141        Strip of 4           7.75 7.75
  a.  A581 10d multi             .90   .90
  b.  A581 15d multi            1.50  1.50
  c.  A581 20d multi            1.90  1.90
  d.  A581 30d multi            3.00  3.00

Miniature Sheet

National Basketball Association Players — A582

No. 3142: a, Carmelo Anthony, Denver Nuggets. b, Kobe Bryant, Los Angeles Lakers. c, Vince Carter, New Jersey Nets. d, Allen Iverson, Denver Nuggets. e, LeBron James, Cleveland Cavaliers. f, Yao Ming, Houston Rockets. g, Steve Nash, Phoenix Suns. h, Shaquille O'Neal, Miami Heat. i, Dwayne Wade, Miami Heat.

**2007, Dec. 28**                  **Perf. 13¼**
3142 A582 10d Sheet of 9, #a-i   9.50 9.50

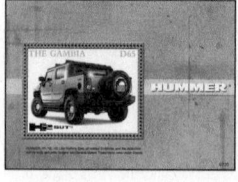

Hummer Vehicles A583

No. 3143: a, H2 on road, denomination in white. b, H2 on road, denomination in black. c, H2, white background. d, H2 on rocks.
65d, H2 SUT.

**2007, Dec. 28**                  **Perf. 13½**
3143 A583 25d Sheet of 4, #a-d   9.00 9.00

Souvenir Sheet

3144 A583 65d multi              6.00 6.00

New Year 2008 (Year of the Rat) — A584

**2008, Jan. 28**     **Litho.**     **Perf. 12**
3145 A584 30d multi              3.00 3.00
Printed in sheets of 4.

2008 Taipei Intl. Stamp Exhibition — A585

No. 3146, horiz. — Taipei landmarks: a, Temple and garden. b, Dr. Sun Yat-sen Memorial Hall. c, Natl. Opera House. d, Temple. 45d, Lover's Bridge, Tamsui.

**2008, Apr. 11**                  **Perf. 13¼**
3146 A585 12d Sheet of 4, #a-d   5.00 5.00

Souvenir Sheet
**Perf. 13¼x13½**

3147 A585 45d multi              4.50 4.50
No. 3146 contains four 42x28mm stamps.

Pioneer Satellites A586

No. 3148: a, Pioneer 1 in orbit, Moon in background. b, Pioneer 1 in nose cone. c, Pioneer 1.
No. 3149, horiz.: a, Technicians and Pioneer 3. b, Pioneer 3 in orbit. c, Pioneer 3 on launch pad.
No. 3150: a, Pioneer 1 on launch pad. b, Pioneer 1 in orbit, diff.
No. 3151: a, Pioneer 3. b, Pioneer 3 in orbit, Moon in background.
No. 3152, Pioneer 1, horiz. No. 3153, Pioneer 3, horiz.

**2008, Apr. 11**                  **Perf. 13¼**
3148 A586 15d Horiz. strip of 3,
            #a-c                 6.75 6.75
3149 A586 15d Vert. strip of 3,
            #a-c                 6.75 6.75
3150 A586 20d Pair, #a-b         5.00 5.00
3151 A586 20d Pair, #a-b         5.00 5.00

Souvenir Sheets
3152 A586 65d multi              7.50 7.50
**Perf. 13¼x13½**
3153 A586 65d multi              7.50 7.50
No. 3153 contains one 51x38mm stamp. Nos. 3148-3151 were issued in sheets containing two strips or pairs.

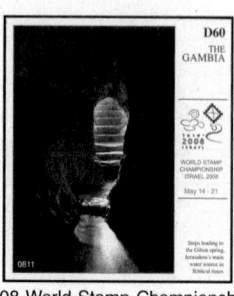

2008 World Stamp Championship, Israel — A587

**2008, May 14**                  **Imperf.**
3154 A587 60d multi              6.25 6.25

Miniature Sheet

Seven Wonders of the Ancient World A588

No. 3155: a, Mausoleum of Maussollos, Halicarnassus. b, Colossus of Rhodes. c, Tip of Giant Pyramid, Giza. d, Hanging Gardens of Babylon. e, Sphinx and Giant Pyramid. f, Lighthouse of Alexandria. g, Statue of Zeus, Olympia. h, Temple of Artemis, Ephesus.

**2008, May 16**                  **Perf. 13¼**
3155 A588 12d Sheet of 8, #a-
            h                   10.00 10.00

Miniature Sheet

Elvis Presley (1935-77) — A589

No. 3156 — Presley: a, Wearing striped jacket. b, With acoustic guitar. c, With arms on knee. d, With electric guitar.

**2008, May 16**
3156 A589 25d Sheet of 4, #a-d   9.50 9.50

Miniature Sheet

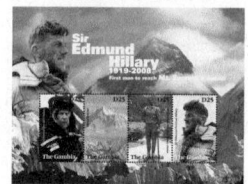

Sir Edmund Hillary (1919-2008), Mountaineer — A590

No. 3157: a, Hillary and flag. b, Mt. Everest. c, Statue of Hillary. d, Hillary as young man.

**2008, May 16**
3157 A590 25d Sheet of 4, #a-d   9.50 9.50

Miniature Sheet

2008 Summer Olympics, Beijing — A591

No. 3158: a, Suzanne Lenglen, 1920 Tennis gold medalist. b, Duke Kahanamoku, 1920 Swimming gold medalist. c, Nedo Nadi, 1920 Fencing gold medalist. d, Olympic rings and text "Olympex 2008."

**2008, May 28**                  **Perf. 12**
3158 A591 10d Sheet of 4, #a-d   4.00 4.00

Visit of Pope Benedict XVI to United States A592

**2008, June 12**                  **Perf. 13¼**
3159 A592 25d multi              2.50 2.50
Printed in sheets of 4.

United States Landmarks — A593

No. 3160, vert.: a, Grant's Tomb, New York. b, Jefferson Memorial, Washington, DC. c, Kennedy Eternal Flame, Arlington, Virginia. d, Capitol, Washington, DC. e, Lincoln Memorial, Washington, DC. f, Washington Monument, Washington, DC.
65d, Mount Rushmore, South Dakota.

**2008, June 12**
3160 A593 15d Sheet of 6, #a-f   8.50 8.50

Souvenir Sheet

3161 A593 65d multi              6.50 6.50

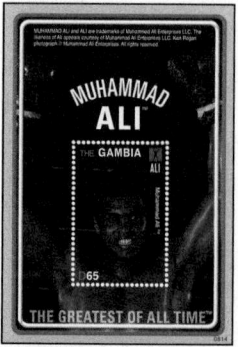

Muhammad Ali, Boxer — A594

No. 3162, 25d — Ali: a, With white trunks, fists in front of chest. b, Seated. c, With white trunks, arm extended. d, Wearing drawstring shorts.
No. 3163, 25d, horiz. — Ali: a, Behind microphone. b, With hand on chin. c, With fist raised. d, Running.
No. 3164, 65d, Head of Ali in color. No. 3165, 65d, Head of Ali in black and white.

**2008, July 21**                  **Perf. 11½**
            Sheets of 4, #a-d
3162-3163 A594   Set of 2       20.00 20.00
Souvenir Sheets
**Perf. 13¼**
3164-3165 A594   Set of 2       13.00 13.00
No. 3162 contains four 30x40mm stamps. No. 3163 contains four 40x30mm stamps.

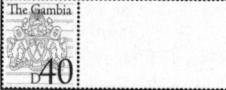

Gambia Coat of Arms A595

**2008, Sept. 15**   **Litho.**   **Perf. 14x15**
3166 A595 40d blk & mar + label  3.50 3.50
Printed in sheets of 8 stamps + 8 labels.

## Miniature Sheet

Marilyn Monroe (1926-62),
Actress — A596

No. 3167 — Monroe: a, Facing forward,
eyes open. b, Facing left. c, Facing right. d,
Facing forward, eyes shut.

**2008, Sept. 22** **Perf. 13¼**
3167 A596 25d Sheet of 4, #a-d 9.00 9.00

## Miniature Sheets

A597

End of
World
War I,
90th
Anniv.
A598

No. 3168: a, Generals talking. b, Soldier and
trench. c, Pilot. d, Pilot and propeller. e, Soldier wearing helmet. f, Officers standing in
row.
No. 3169: a, Soldiers at air field. b, Tanks. c,
Two soldiers. d, Soldiers at cannon.

**2008, Nov. 11** **Litho.** **Perf. 11½x12**
3168 A597 15d Sheet of 6, #a-
f 11.00 11.00
3169 A598 25d Sheet of 4, #a-
d 11.50 11.50

## Miniature Sheet

Prince
Charles,
60th
Birthday
A599

No. 3170: a, Wearing black suit. b, Wearing
top hat. c, Wearing gray suit. d, Wearing military uniform.

**2008, Nov. 14** **Perf. 11¼x11½**
3170 A599 25d Sheet of 4, #a-
d 10.00 10.00

Christmas
A600

Designs: 25d, Map of West Africa, ribbon
and bow. 30d, Red, blue and green bows. 45d,
Woman carrying gift on head, flag, vert. 50d,
Gifts, flag.

**2008, Dec. 1** **Perf. 14¾x14, 14x14¾**
3171-3174 A600 Set of 4 12.50 12.50

## Miniature Sheet

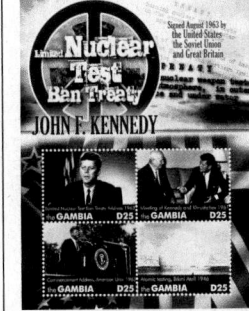

Signing
of
Limited
Nuclear
Test Ban
Treaty
A601

No. 3175: a, Pres. John F. Kennedy. b, Kennedy and Soviet Premier Nikita Khrushchev. c,
Kennedy at American University commence-
ment. d, Atomic bomb test, Bikini Atoll, 1946.

**2008, Dec. 4** **Perf. 11½x12**
3175 A601 25d Sheet of 4, #a-d 9.00 9.00

## Miniature Sheet

Pres. Abraham Lincoln (1809-
65) — A602

No. 3176: a, Lincoln with son, Tad. b, Lincoln wih beard in profile. c, Lincoln without
beard. d, Lincoln with beard.

**2008, Dec. 4** **Perf. 13¼**
3176 A602 25d Sheet of 4, #a-d 9.00 9.00

A603

A604

## Miniature Sheet

A605

Flowers
A606

No. 3177: a, Calotropis procera. b, Callian-
dra surinamensis. c, Plumeria alba. d, Quis-
qualis indica.
No. 3178: a, Adansonia digitata. b, Commelina benghalensis. c, Heliconia psittacorum. d,
Tabebuia rosea.

**2008, Dec. 31** **Perf. 12½**
3177 A603 25d Sheet of 4, #a-d 8.75 8.75
**Perf. 12**
3178 A604 25d Sheet of 4, #a-d 8.75 8.75
**Souvenir Sheets**
3179 A605 65d multi 6.50 6.50
3180 A606 65d multi 6.50 6.50

New Year 2009
(Year of the
Ox) — A607

**2009, Jan. 5** **Perf. 12**
3181 A607 25d multi 2.50 2.50
Printed in sheets of 4.

Inauguration of US
Pres. Barack
Obama — A608

No. 3183: a, Pres. Obama. b, Vice-president Joseph Biden.

**2009, Jan. 20** **Perf. 14x14¾**
3182 A608 16d shown 1.50 1.50
**Souvenir Sheet**
3183 A608 60d Sheet of 2, #a-
b 10.00 10.00
No. 3182 was printed in sheets of 9.

## Miniature Sheet

Pope John Paul II (1920-
2005) — A609

No. 3184 — Pope John Paul II at: a, Inaugural Mass, 1978. b, United Nations, 1979. c,
Warsaw, 1983. d, Denver, Colorado, 1993.

**2009, Feb. 4** **Perf. 13¼**
3184 A609 25d Sheet of 4, #a-
d 11.00 11.00

A610

A611

A612

A613

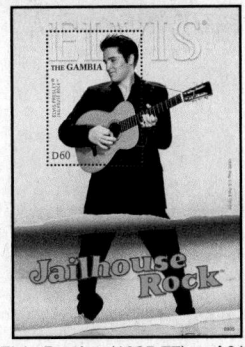

Elvis Presley (1935-77) — A614

No. 3185 — Presley wearing a, Black suit
and tie, white shirt. b, Black suit and shirt, no
tie. c, Red sweater. d, Brown shirt and gray tie.
e, Blue shirt. f, Gray sweater and white shirt.

**2009** **Perf. 13¼**
3185 A610 20d Sheet of 6, #a-
f 11.00 11.00
**Souvenir Sheets**
3186 A611 60d multi 6.00 6.00
3187 A612 60d multi 6.00 6.00
3188 A613 60d multi 6.00 6.00
3189 A614 60d multi 6.00 6.00
Issued: No. 3185, 4/30; others, 2/25.

## Miniature Sheet

Jet Li One Foundation — A615

No. 3190: a, Education. b, Jet Li. c, Poverty. d, Health. e, Environment. f, Disaster relief.

**2009, Apr. 1**            *Perf. 12¾*
3190 A615 40d Sheet of 6, #a-
f                                    22.50 22.50

### Souvenir Sheet

Great Wall of China A616

**2009, Apr. 10**            *Perf. 12*
3191 A616 80d multi                   7.50 7.50

China 2009 Intl. Philatelic Exhibition.

Visit to Cameroun of Pope Benedict XVI — A617

**2009, Apr. 30**            *Perf. 11½x11¼*
3192 A617 25d multi                   2.25 2.25

Printed in sheets of 4.

### Miniature Sheet

Whistle-stop Inaugural Journeys of US Presidents Abraham Lincoln and Barack Obama — A618

No. 3193: a, Inaugural speech of Pres. Obama. b, Inaugural speech of Pres. Lincoln. c, Lincoln, map of train route. d, Pres. Obama and Vice-president Joseph Biden on train in Wilmington, Delaware.

**2009, Apr. 30**            *Perf. 14¾x14*
3193 A618 25d Sheet of 4, #a-d       7.50 7.50

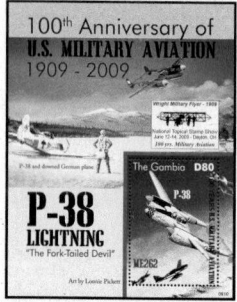

American Military Aviation, Cent. — A619

No. 3194, horiz.: a, B-17 and P-51 Escort. b, Doolittle's B-25. c, B-24. d, P-47D. e, F-86F. f, AT-6. g, F-80. h, F-15. i, T-38 and F-117. 80d, P-38 and ME-262.

**2009, June 12**            *Perf. 11½x11¼*
3194 A619 15d Sheet of 9, #a-
i                                    13.00 13.00

### Souvenir Sheet
**Perf. 13¼**
3195 A619 80d multi                   8.50 8.50

No. 3194 contains nine 40x30mm stamps. National Topical Stamp Show, Dayton, Ohio.

### Miniature Sheets

Michael Jackson (1958-2009), Singer — A620

No. 3196: a, 20d, Holding microphone. b, 20d, Wearing white jacket and hat. c, 30d, As "b." d, 30d, As "a."
No. 3197, horiz.: a, 20d, Wearing black jacket and hat. b, 20d, Wearing white jacket. c, 30d, As "a." d, 30d, As "b."

**Perf. 12x11½, 11½ (#3197)**
**2009, July 7**            Litho.
**Sheets of 4, #a-d**
3196-3197 A620 Set of 2             20.00 20.00

### Miniature Sheet

First Man on the Moon, 40th Anniv. A621

No. 3198: a, Obverse and reverse of US Susan B. Anthony dollar coin. b, Apollo 11 Lunar Module. c, Neil Armstrong. d, Apollo 11. e, Statue of Armstrong. f, Apollo 11 Command Module.

**2009, July 20**            *Perf. 13¼*
3198 A621 20d Sheet of 6, #a-
f                                    11.50 11.50

### Miniature Sheets

Dogs A622

No. 3199, 25d — Pembroke Welsh corgi: a, Jumping. b, Sitting in leaves. c, Sitting in front of flower basket. d, Sitting on lawn.
No. 3200, 25d — West Highland white terrier and: a, Upright basket. b, Beach ball. c, Gift boxes. d, Yellow flowers and basket on side.

**2009, Aug. 29**            *Perf. 12*
**Sheets of 4, #a-d**
3199-3200 A622 Set of 2             20.00 20.00

Birds — A623

Designs: 15d, Hamerkop. 20d, Pied kingfisher. No. 3203, 25d, Black-capped babbler. No. 3204, 40d, African darter.

No. 3205, 25d, vert.: a, Malachite kingfisher. b, Common bulbul. c, Black-crowned night heron. d, Wire-tailed swallow.
No. 3206, 40d: a, Sacred ibis. b, Little grebe.

**2009, Aug. 29**            *Perf. 11½*
3201-3204 A623 Set of 4              9.00 9.00
3205 A623 25d Sheet of 4, #a-d       9.00 9.00
### Souvenir Sheet
3206 A623 40d Sheet of 2, #a-b       8.00 8.00

### Miniature Sheet

Teenage Mutant Ninja Turtles, 25th Anniv. A624

No. 3207: a, Raphael. b, Leonardo. c, Michelangelo. d, Donatello.

**2009, Aug. 29**            *Perf. 13¼*
3207 A624 25d Sheet of 4, #a-d       9.00 9.00

Pres. Barack Obama and Queen Elizabeth II A625

No. 3208, horiz.: a, Pres. Obama. b, Queen Elizabeth II. c, Michelle Obama.
80d, Pres. Obama and Queen Elizabeth II at G20 World Leader Reception.

**2009, Aug. 29**            *Perf. 11½x12*
3208 A625 25d Sheet of 3, #a-c       7.00 7.00
### Souvenir Sheet
**Perf. 11½**
3209 A625 80d multi                   7.50 7.50

Pres. Barack Obama in Germany A626

No. 3210: a, Obama, Bishop Jochen Bohl, German Chancellor Angela Merkel. b, Obama. c, Merkel. d, Obama and Merkel.
65d, Obama, Merkel, Elie Wiesel and Bertrand Herz at Buchenwald Concentration Camp.

**2009, Oct. 22**            *Perf. 11½*
3210 A626 25d Sheet of 4, #a-d       9.00 9.00
### Souvenir Sheet
**Perf. 13¼**
3211 A626 65d multi                   6.50 6.50

No. 3210 contains four 30x40mm stamps.

Methodist Church Conference A627

Cross and map of: 25d, The Gambia. 35d, Africa, vert.

**2009**                    *Perf. 11½*
3212-3213 A627 Set of 2              5.50 5.50

## Miniature Sheet

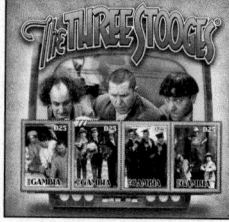

The Three Stooges A628

No. 3214 — Scenes from: a, Rockin' Thru the Rockies. b, The Sitter Downers. c, Violent is the Word for Curly. d, We Want Our Mummy.

**2009**                    *Perf. 13¼*
3214 A628 25d Sheet of 4, #a-d       8.50 8.50

### Miniature Sheet

Pres. Barack Obama, 2009 Nobel Peace Laureate A629

No. 3215 — Pres. Obama with: a, Microphones at LR. b, Microphones at LL. c, Foliage at right. d, Flag at right.

**2009, Dec. 30**  Litho.   *Perf. 13x13¼*
3215 A629 25d Sheet of 4, #a-d       8.50 8.50

Mushrooms — A630

Designs: 10d, Panaeolus bispora. No. 3217, 15d, Panaeolus tropicalis. 25d, Psilocybe mairei. 30d, Gymnopilus aeruginosus.
No. 3220, 15d, horiz.: a, Panaeolus retirugis. b, Gymnopilus junionius. c, Psilocybe natalensis. d, Panaeolus africanus. e, Panaeolus cinctulus. f, Panaeolus subbalteatus.

**2009, Dec. 30**            *Perf. 14x14¾*
3216-3219 A630 Set of 4              7.50 7.50
**Perf. 14¾x14**
3220 A630 15d Sheet of 6, #a-f       8.00 8.00

Butterflies — A631

Designs: 10d, Elegant acraea. No. 3222, 15d, Bamboo charaxes. 25d, Green-veined charaxes. 30d, Pink acraea.
No. 3225, 15d, horiz.: a, Abadima acraea. b, African common white. c, Cream-bordered charaxes. d, African caper white. e, Large spotted acraea. f, Tiny orange tip.

**2009, Dec. 30**            *Perf. 14x14¾*
3221-3224 A631 Set of 4              7.50 7.50
**Perf. 14¾x14**
3225 A631 15d Sheet of 6, #a-f       8.50 8.50

Christmas — A632

Designs: 10d, Map of Africa with stocking cap. 15d, Cane-shaped cookies. 25d, Christmas light display. 30d, Candle and poinsettia.

**2009, Dec. 30**            *Perf. 14x14¾*
3226-3229 A632 Set of 4              7.00 7.00

**Ferraris and Their Parts — A633**

No. 3230, 12d: a, Chassis of 1999 360 Modena. b, 1999 360 Modena.
No. 3231, 12d: a, Engine and drive train of 2003 F2003-GA. b, 2003 F2003-GA.
No.3232, 12d: a, Convertible roof of 2005 Superamerica. b, 2005 Superamerica.
No. 3233, 12d: a, Engine of 2008 California. b, 2008 California.

**2010, Feb. 24**     **Perf. 12**
**Vert. Pairs, #a-b**
3230-3233   A633    Set of 4     8.50 8.50

**Whales and Dolphins — A634**

Designs: 10d, Common dolphin. 15d, Pygmy killer whale. No. 3236, 25d, Short-finned pilot whale. 30d, Clymene dolphin.
No. 3228, 25d: a, Southern bottlenose whale. b, Fraser's dolphin. c, Atlantic humpbacked dolphin. d, Ginkgo-toothed beaked whale.
No. 3239, 35d: a, Blainville's beaked whalen. b, Atlantic spotted dolphin.

**2010, Feb. 24**    **Perf. 11½x11¼**
3234-3237   A634    Set of 4     7.50 7.50
            **Perf. 11½x12**
3238   A634   25d Sheet of 4, #a-d   8.50 8.50
          **Souvenir Sheet**
          **Perf. 11½x11¼**
3239   A634   35d Sheet of 2, #a-b   6.75 6.75

**Miniature Sheet**

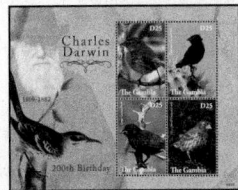

**Charles Darwin (1809-82), Naturalist — A635**

No. 3240 — Birds: a, Warbler finch. b, Common cactus finch. c, Large cactus finch. d, Small ground finch.

**2010, Feb. 24**     **Perf. 13¼**
3240   A635   25d Sheet of 4, #a-d   9.00 9.00

**Miniature Sheet**

**Pres. John F. Kennedy (1917-63) — A636**

No. 3241 — Kennedy: a, Curtainin background at left. b, At inauguration ceremony. c, With flag in background at right. d, With family.

**2010, Apr. 15**     **Perf. 12x11½**
3241   A636   30d Sheet of 4, #a-d   11.00 11.00

**Miniature Sheets**

**Pres. Abraham Lincoln (1809-65) — A637**

No. 3242, 25d — Lincoln and: a, Peter Cooper, Cooper Union. b, Mathew Brady, Brady Gallery. c, William Cullen Bryant, Great Hall, Cooper Union. d, Horace Greeley, Astor House.
No. 3243, 25d — Lincoln and: a, Brady, photograph of Lincoln by Brady. b, Alexander Gardner, photographs of Lincoln by Gardner. c, Victor David Brenner, Lincoln cent, Pres. Theodore Roosevelt. d, Daniel Chester French, statue of Lincoln in Lincoln Memorial.

**2010, Apr. 15**     **Perf. 11½x12**
       **Sheets of 4, #a-d**
3242-3243   A637    Set of 2    18.00 18.00

**Miniature Sheets**

A638

**Elvis Presley (1935-77) — A639**

No. 3244 — Presley: a, Holding microphone, facing right, cape and microphone cord visible. b, Holding microphone, leaning. c, Holding microphone, no cord visible. d, Standing with arms akimbo.
No. 3245 — Presley: a, With guitar. b, With microphone near mouth. c, With guitar, pointing, and holding microphone on stand. d, Holding microphone on stand, with guitar strap on shoulder.

**2010, Apr. 15**     **Perf. 11¼x11½**
3244   A638   25d Sheet of 4, #a-d   8.50 8.50
       **Perf. 13¼**
3245   A639   30d Sheet of 4, #a-d   11.00 11.00

**2010 World Cup Soccer Championships, South Africa — A640**

Soccer ball with flag of participating nations: No. 3246, 20d, Algeria. No. 3247, 20d, Argentina. No. 3248, 20d, Australia. No. 3249, 20d, Brazil. No. 3250, 20d, Cameroon. No. 3251, 20d, Chile. No. 3252, 20d, Denmark. No. 3253, 20d, England. No. 3254, 20d, France. No. 3255, 20d, Germany. No. 3256, 20d, Ghana. No. 3257, 20d, Greece. No. 3258, 20d, Honduras. No. 3259, 20d, Italy. No. 3260, 20d, Ivory Coast (Côte d'Ivoire). No. 3261, 20d, Japan. No. 3262, 20d, Korea DPR (North Korea). No. 3263, 20d, Korea Republic (South Korea). No. 3264, 20d, Mexico. No. 3265, 20d, Netherlands. No. 3266, 20d, New Zealand. No. 3267, 20d, Nigeria. No. 3268, 20d, Paraguay. No. 3269, 20d, Portugal. No. 3270, 20d,

Serbia. No. 3271, 20d, Slovakia. No. 3272, 20d, Slovenia. No. 3273, 20d, South Africa. No. 3274, 20d, Spain. No. 3275, 20d, Switzerland. No. 3276, 20d, United States. No. 3277, 20d, Uruguay.

**2010, May 24**     **Perf. 14x14¾**
3246-3277   A640    Set of 32   50.00 50.00
   Nos. 3246-3277 each were printed in sheets of 6.

**Traditional Musical Instruments — A641**

Designs: 2d, 25d, Wollof tabala. 3d, 30d, Jola bugarab. 5d, 35d, Fula rilty. 6d, 50d, Mandinka kontingo. 7d, 65d, Mandinka bolongbato. 10d, 100d, Mandinka kora. 15d, 200d, Mandinka kora, diff. 18d, Mandinka balafongo, horiz.

   **Perf. 11¼x11½, 11½x11¼**
**2010, June 8**
3278   A641    2d multi        .30   .25
3279   A641    3d multi        .30   .30
3280   A641    5d multi        .35   .35
3281   A641    6d multi        .40   .40
3282   A641    7d multi        .50   .50
3283   A641   10d multi        .70   .70
3284   A641   15d multi     1.00   1.00
3285   A641   18d multi     1.25   1.25
3286   A641   25d multi     1.75   1.75
3287   A641   30d multi     2.00   2.00
3288   A641   35d multi     2.40   2.40
3289   A641   50d multi     3.25   3.25
3290   A641   65d multi     4.00   4.00
3291   A641   100d multi    6.00   6.00
3292   A641   200d multi   10.00   10.00
   Nos. 3278-3292 (15)   34.20 34.10

**US First Ladies Type of 2007**
     Souvenir Sheet
   No. 3293, Michelle Obama.

**2010, June 8**     **Perf. 13¼**
3293   A574   65d multi    5.00 5.00

     **Miniature Sheet**

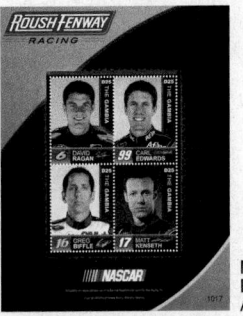

**NASCAR Drivers A642**

No. 3294: a, David Ragan. b, Carl Edwards. c, Greg Biffle. d, Matt Kenseth.

**2010, June 8**     **Perf. 13¼x13**
3294   A642   25d Sheet of 4, #a-d   8.50 8.50

     **Souvenir Sheet**

**Elvis Presley (1935-77) — A643**

No. 3295 — Presley wearing: a, Black jacket. b, White jacket.

**2010, June 11**     **Imperf.**
3295   A643   140d Sheet of 2, #a-b    27.50 27.50

     **Miniature Sheet**

**Elvis Presley (1935-77) — A644**

No. 3296 — Presley wearing: a, Checked shirt. b, Jacket and tie. c, Sweater. d, White shirt with open collar.

**2010, Apr. 15**   **Litho.**   **Perf. 13¼**
3296   A644   30d Sheet of 4, #a-d    11.00 11.00

**Lech Kaczynski (1949-2010), President of Poland — A645**

**2010, July 14**     **Perf. 12x11½**
3297   A645   30d multi    2.50 2.50
   Printed in sheets of 4.

     **Miniature Sheet**

**Accession to the Throne by King George V, Cent. — A646**

No. 3298: a, 1917 cartoon of King George V. b, King George V. c, King Edward VIII. d, Badge of the House of Windsor. e, King George VI. f, Queen Elizabeth II.

**2010, July 14**   **Litho.**   **Perf. 11¼x11½**
3298   A646   20d Sheet of 6, #a-f    11.00 11.00

**Visit of Pope Benedict XVI to Malta — A647**

Pope Benedict XVI wearing: No. 3299, 30d, Miter. No. 3300, 30d, Zucchetto.

**2010, Aug. 26**     **Perf. 13¼**
3299-3300   A647    Set of 2    5.50 5.50
   Nos. 3299-3300 each were printed in sheets of 5.

     **Miniature Sheet**

**Paintings by Sandro Botticelli (1445-1510) — A648**

No. 3301: a, Lamentation. b, Madonna del Magnificat. c, The Return of Judith to Bethulia. d, Venus from Venus and Mars. e, Mars from Venus and Mars. f, The Punishment of Korah.

**2010, Aug. 26**     **Perf. 11¼x11½**
3301   A648   20d Sheet of 6, #a-f    11.00 11.00

## Miniature Sheets

Mother Teresa (1910-97),
Humanitarian — A649

No. 3302, 30d — Mother Teresa at left, Princess Diana at right, with: a, Princess Diana bending to talk to Mother Teresa. b, Princess Diana with hands clasped at waist and Mother Teresa with hands clasped below chin. c, Mother Teresa and Princess Diana holding hands, Mother Teresa's arm at side. d, Mother Teresa and Princess Diana holding hands, Mother Teresa's arm extended.

No. 3303, 30d — Mother Teresa with: a, Pres. Ronald Reagan. b, Archbishop Desmond Tutu. c, Pope John Paul II. d, Queen Elizabeth II.

**2010, Aug. 26**          **Perf. 11½x12**
**Sheets of 4, #a-d**
3302-3303 A649   Set of 2      22.50 22.50

Robert Schumann (1810-56),
Composer — A650

No. 3304, horiz. — Schumann and: a, Birthplace. b, His wife, Clara. c, Schumann Monument, Zwickau, Germany. d, Grave marker, Bonn, Germany.
65d, Robert and Clara Schumann.

**2010, Aug. 26**          **Perf. 11½x12**
3304 A650   30d Sheet of 4, #a-
        d                    12.00 12.00
**Souvenir Sheet**
**Perf. 11¼x11½**
3305 A650   65d multi        6.50  6.50

Posters for Films Directed by Akira
Kurosawa (1910-98) — A651

No. 3306, 30d, vert.: a, Nora Inu (Stray Dog). b, Zoku Sugata Sanshiro (Sanshiro Sugata Part II). c, Shichinin no Samurai (Seven Samurai). d, Shizukanaru Ketto (The Quiet Duel).

No. 3307, 30d, vert.: a, Donzoko (The Lower Depths). b, Hakuchi (The Idiot). c, Ikimono no Kiroku (I Live in Fear). d, Ikiru.
80d, Ichiban Utsukushiku (The Most Beautiful).

**2010, Aug. 26**          **Perf. 13¼**
**Sheets of 4, #a-d**
3306-3307 A651   Set of 2     21.00 21.00
**Souvenir Sheet**
3308 A651   80d multi        8.00  8.00

Girl
Guides,
Cent.
A652

No. 3309 — Girl Guides emblem, centenary emblem and: a, Four Girl Guides in green uniforms. b, Four Girl Guides not wearing uniforms. c, Two Girl Guides. d, Three Girl Guides.
80d, Two Girl Guides with backpacks, vert.

**2010, Oct. 15**          **Perf. 11½x12**
3309 A652   30d Sheet of 4, #a-d   8.50 8.50
**Souvenir Sheet**
**Perf. 11¼x11½**
3310 A652   80d multi        5.75  5.75

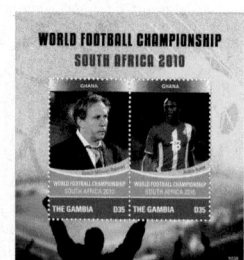

Players and Coaches in Second
Round Matches of 2010 World Cup
Soccer Championships — A653

No. 3311, 15d — United States vs. Ghana: a, Jay Demerit. b, Asamoah Gyan. c, Robbie Findley. d, Samuel Inkoom. e, Ricardo Clark. f, Stephen Appiah.

No. 3312, 15d — Uruguay vs. South Korea: a, Fernando Musiera. b, Lee Chung-Yong. c, Jorge Fucile. d, Cha Du-Ri. e, Maximiliano Pereira. f, Park Chu-Young.

No. 3313, 15d — Argentina vs. Mexico: a, Gabriel Heinze. b, Efrain Juarez. c, Carlos Tevez. d, Carlos Salcido. e, Lionel Messi. f, Andres Guardado.

No. 3314, 15d — Germany vs. England: a, Sami Khedira. b, Steven Gerrard. c, Philipp Lahm. d, Joe Cole. e, Lukas Podolski. f, Ashley Cole.

No. 3315, 35d — Ghana: a, Coach Milovan Rajevac. b, Andre Ayew.

No. 3316, 35d — Uruguay: a, Coach Oscar Tabarez. b, Diego Forlan.

No. 3317, 35d — Argentina: a, Coach Diego Maradona. b, Nicolas Otramendi.

No. 3318, 35d — Germany: a, Coach Joachim Loew. b, Thomas Mueller.

**2010, Oct. 15**          **Perf. 12**
**Sheets of 6, #a-f**
3311-3314 A653   Set of 4     30.00 30.00
**Souvenir Sheets of 2, #a-b**
3315-3318 A653   Set of 4     20.00 20.00

## Miniature Sheets

Characters From Star Trek
Movies — A654

No. 3319, 25d — Characters from Star Trek: Nemesis: a, Lt. Commander Data. b, Capt. Jean-Luc Picard. c, Commander William T. Riker. d, Lt. Commander Worf. e, Praetor Shinzon. f, Reman Viceroy Vkruk.

No. 3320, 25d, horiz. — Characters from Star Trek: First Contact: a, Worf. b, Riker and Picard. c, Data and Borg Queen. d, Dr. Zefram Cochrane. e, Lt. Commander Geordi La Forge. f, Picard and Dr. Beverly Crusher.

**2010, Nov. 5**   **Litho.**   **Perf. 12**
**Sheets of 6, #a-f**
3319-3320 A654   Set of 2     18.00 18.00

Christmas — A655

Paintings: 15d, Madonna with Child, by Carlo Crivelli. 25d, Nativity, Birth of Jesus, by Giotto di Bondone. 30d, The Journey of the Magi, by Stefano di Giovanni. 40d, Nativity, by Bernardo Daddi.

**2010, Dec. 25**
3321-3324 A655   Set of 4     7.75  7.75

## Souvenir Sheets

A656

Designs: No. 3325: a, Pope Leo XIII (1810-1903). b, Coat of arms of Pope Leo XIII. No. 3325C: d, St. Pius X (1835-1914). e, Arms of St. Pius X.

**2010, Dec. 25**   **Litho.**   **Imperf.**
**Without Gum**
3325 A656   100d Sheet of 2,
        #a-b             22.50 22.50
3325C A656  100d Sheet of 2,
        #a-b             22.50 22.50

Henri Dunant (1828-1910), Founder of
Red Cross — A657

No. 3326 — Red Cross, depictions of First Geneval Convention negotiations and portrait of Dunant in: a, Green blue. b, Brown. c, Purple. d, Blue.
65d, Portrait of Dunant, portraits of 1863 members of International Committee of the Red Cross.

**2010, Dec. 30**          **Perf. 12**
3326 A657   30d Sheet of 4, #a-d   8.50 8.50
**Souvenir Sheet**
3327 A657   65d multi        4.75  4.75

Paintings by Michelangelo Merisi da
Caravaggio (1573-1610) — A658

No. 3328, vert.: a, The Seven Works of Mercy. b, The Conversion on the Way to Damascus. c, Alof de Wignacourt. d, David and Goliath. e, The Death of the Virgin. f, The Raising of Lazarus.
60d, The Betrayal of Christ.

**2010, Dec. 30**
3328 A658   20d Sheet of 6, #a-f   8.50 8.50
**Souvenir Sheet**
3329 A658   60d multi        4.25  4.25

Pres. John F.
Kennedy (1917-
63) — A659

No. 3330, 30d — Pres. Kennedy and wife, Jacqueline: a, Standing. b, Sitting in limousine.
No. 3331, 30d — Pres. Kennedy and: a, Jacqueline, watching America's Cup race. b, Daughter Caroline.
No. 3332, 60d, Pres. Kennedy standing in limousine. No. 3333, 60d, With Jacqueline, leaving Air Force One, horiz.

**2010, Dec. 30**          **Perf. 12**
**Vert. Pairs, #a-b**
3330-3331 A659   Set of 2     8.50  8.50
**Souvenir Sheets**
3332-3333 A659   Set of 2     11.50 11.50

Nos. 3330-3331 each were printed in sheets containing two pairs.

A660

No. 3334, 30d — Denomination in black, Princess Diana wearing: a, Red hat. b, Black hat. c, White dress. d, Hooded raincoat.
No. 3335, 30d — Denomination in white, Princess Diana wearing: a, Tiara. b, Black hat with veil. c, Red hat. d, Black hat with bow.
80d, Princess Diana wearing white dress.

**2010, Dec. 30**          **Litho.**
**Sheets of 4, #a-d**
3334-3335 A660   Set of 2     15.00 15.00
**Souvenir Sheet**
3336 A660   80d multi        5.75  5.75

Bengal
Tiger
A661

No. 3337, vert. — Tiger with: a, Paws visible. b, Paws not shown.

**Perf. 13 Syncopated**
**2011, Feb. 8**          **Litho.**
3337 A661   30d Sheet of 4, 2
        each #a-b          9.00  9.00
**Souvenir Sheet**
**Perf. 12**
3338 A661   120d shown     9.00  9.00

Indipex 2011 World Philatelic Exhibition, New Delhi.

## Miniature Sheets

A662

Princess Diana (1961-97) — A663

No. 3339 — Princess Diana wearing: a, Black dress. b, Red and white polka dot dress. c, Red and black plaid blouse. d, Black dress and hat.
No. 3340 — Princess Diana wearing: a, Black dress and necklace. b, Red dress and tiara. c, Tiara and necklace. d, Black dress and headband.

**2011, Feb. 8**     **Perf. 12**
3339 A662 30d Sheet of 4, #a-d    9.00 9.00
3340 A663 30d Sheet of 4, #a-d    9.00 9.00

Engagement of Prince William and Catherine Middleton — A664

Designs: No. 3341, Couple. No. 3343, Couple, horiz.
No. 3342: a, Middleton. b, Prince William.
No. 3344, horiz.: a, Prince William. b, Middleton.

**2011, Feb. 8**     **Perf. 13 Syncopated**
3341 A664 30d multi    2.25 2.25
3342 A664 30d Horiz. pair, #a-b    4.50 4.50
                   **Perf. 12**
3343 A664 40d multi    3.00 3.00
             **Souvenir Sheet**
3344 A664 40d Sheet of 2, #a-d    6.00 6.00

No. 3341 was printed in sheets of 4. No. 3342 was printed in sheets containing two pairs. No. 3343 was printed in sheets of 2.

## Miniature Sheets

U.S. Civil War Battles, 150th Anniv. A665

No. 3345, 30d — Eagle, shield, Union and Confederate flags, Brigadier General Daniel Ruggles and Commander James Harmon Ward from Battle of Aquia Creek, May 29, 1861, and: a, Union vessels Pawnee and Thomas Freeborn. b, USS Thomas Freeborn at Mathias Point. c, Sighting a gun aboard the USS Thomas Freeborn. d, Attack on the Confederate batteries.
No. 3346, 30d — Eagle, shield, Union and Confederate flags, Colonel John B. Magruder and Brigadier General Ebenezer W. Peirce from Battle of Big Bethel, June 10, 1861, and: a, Fort Monroe wounded. b, Rodman gun battery at Fort Monroe. c, New York 5th Regiment (Duryee's Zouaves). d, New York 5th Regiment's charge on Big Bethel.
No. 3347, 30d — Eagle, shield, Union and Confederate flags, Colonel John S. Marmaduke and Brigadier General Nathaniel Lyon from Battle of Boonville, June 17, 1861, and: a, St. Louis riot. b, General Lyon departing Boonville. c, Battle scene. d, Confederates retreat from Union forces.
No. 3348, 30d — Eagle, shield, Union and Confederate flags, Colonel Stonewall Jackson

and Major General Robert Patterson from Battle of Hoke's Run, July 2, 1861, and: a, General Patterson's division crossing the Potomac. b, Union soldiers skirmish at Hoke's Run. c, Union scout at Shenandoah Valley. d, Union forces advance near Martinsburg.
No. 3349, 30d — Eagle, shield, Union and Confederate flags, Governor Claiborne Fox Jackson and Colonel Franz Sigel from Battle of Carthage, July 5, 1861, and: a, The Wide Wakes Demonstration. b, Colonel Sigel at the Missouri River. c, Battle scene. d, Union forces retreat to Sarcoxie.

**2011, Feb. 8**    **Perf. 13 Syncopated**
          **Sheets of 4, #a-d**
3345-3349 A665  Set of 5    45.00 45.00

Pres. Ronald Reagan (1911-2004) — A666

No. 3350, horiz. — Pres. Reagan and: a, Flags. b, Wife, Nancy. c, Helicopter. d, Horse.

**2011, Feb. 8**     **Perf. 12**
3350 A666 30d Sheet of 4, #a-d    9.00 9.00
             **Souvenir Sheet**
3351 A666 65d shown    5.00 5.00

## Miniature Sheet

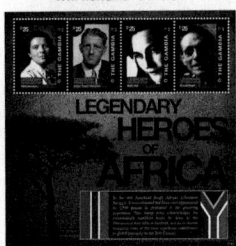

Jewish South African Anti-Apartheid Leaders — A667

No. 3352: a, Hilda Bernstein (1915-2006). b, Lionel "Rusty" Bernstein (1920-2002). c, Ruth First (1925-82). d, Ronald Segal (1932-2008).

**2011, Mar. 1**     **Litho.**
3352 A667 25d Sheet of 4, #a-d    7.25 7.25

First Man in Space, 50th Anniv. A668

No. 3353, 30d: a, Raising to vertical of Vostok rocket. b, Tracking ship Yuri Gagarin. c, U.S. astronaut John Glenn. d, Monument to Conquerors of Space, Moscow.
No. 3354, 30d, vert.: a, Yuri Gagarin, first man in space. b, U.S. astronaut Scott Carpenter. c, Vostok spaceship. d, Titanium statue.
No. 3355, 65d, Gagarin and Moon. No. 3356, 65d, Gagarin.

**2011, Mar. 29**     **Perf. 12**
          **Sheets of 4, #a-d**
3353-3354 A668  Set of 2    17.50 17.50
          **Souvenir Sheets**
     **Perf. 13 Syncopated**
3355-3356 A668  Set of 2    9.50 9.50

## Souvenir Sheets

A669

A670

A671

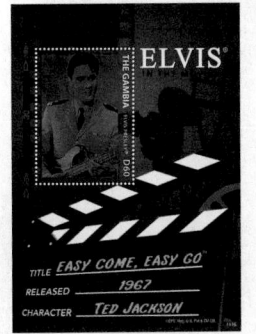

Elvis Presley (1935-77) — A672

**2011, Mar. 29**     **Perf. 12¾**
3357 A669 60d multi    4.50 4.50
3358 A670 60d multi    4.50 4.50
3359 A671 60d multi    4.50 4.50
3360 A672 60d multi    4.50 4.50
  Nos. 3357-3360 (4)    18.00 18.00

Wedding of Prince William and Catherine Middleton — A673

Designs: No. 3361, Couple.
No. 3362: a, Prince William. b, Middleton. 65d, Couple, diff.

**2011, Apr. 29**     **Perf. 12**
3361 A673 30d multi    2.25 2.25
3362 A673 30d Sheet of 4, 2 each #a-b    8.75 8.75
            **Souvenir Sheet**
3363 A673 65d multi    4.75 4.75

No. 3361 was printed in sheets of 4.

## Miniature Sheet

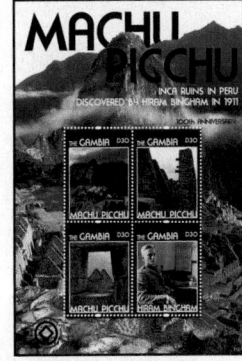

Discovery of Machu Picchu by Hiram Bingham, Cent. — A674

No. 3364: a, Aerial view of Machu Picchu. b, Stonework. c, Stone buildings as seen through hole in wall. d, Bingham.

**2011, May 16**    **Perf. 13 Syncopated**
3364 A674 30d Sheet of 4, #a-d    8.75 8.75

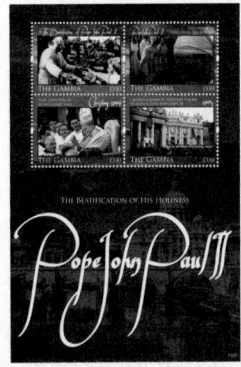

Beatification of Pope John Paul II — A675

No. 3365: a, Pope John Paul II greeting crowd. b, Pope John Paul II in procession, Sister Marie Simon Pierre. c, Pope John Paul II at Midnight mass. d, Crowd in St. Peter's Square honoring Pope John Paul II.
60d, Pope John Paul II and Mother Teresa.

**2011, May 16**    **Perf. 13 Syncopated**
3365 A675 30d Sheet of 4, #a-d    8.75 8.75
         **Souvenir Sheet**
          **Perf. 12¾**
3366 A675 60d multi    4.25 4.25

No. 3366 contains one 50x38mm stamp.

Cats A676

No. 3367: a, Munchkin. b, Ragamuffin. c, Chinchilla. d, Burman.
70d, Turkish Van.

**2011, May 16**    **Perf. 13 Syncopated**
3367 A676 30d Sheet of 4, #a-d    8.75 8.75
         **Souvenir Sheet**
          **Perf. 12**
3368 A676 70d multi    5.00 5.00

A677

A678

Parrots
A679

No. 3369: a, Masked lovebird. b, Madagascar lovebird. c, Red-fronted macaw. d, Senegal parrot.
No. 3370: a, Meyer's parrot. b, Peach-faced lovebirds. c, Rose-ringed parakeet.
No. 3371, 70d, Fischer's lovebird. No. 3372, 70d, African gray parrot.

**2011, May 16    Perf. 13 Syncopated**
3369  A677  30d Sheet of 4,
         #a-d                    8.75   8.75
3370  A678  40d Sheet of 3,
         #a-c                    8.75   8.75
**Souvenir Sheets**
**Perf.**
3371-3372  A679  Set of 2     10.00  10.00

A680

PhilaNippon '11, Yokohama — A681

No. 3373 — Origami: a, Brown elephant. b, Green frog. c, Red crab. d, Bright pink and blue cranes. e, Yellow and orange pinwheel. f, Light green praying mantis. g, Orange flower. h, Purple flowers.
No. 3374: a, Two cherry blossoms. b, Cherry blossom petals. c, Three cherry blossoms.
No. 3375, Crane. No. 3376, Cherry blossom and bud.

**Perf. 12. Perf. (A681)**
**2011, May 16                      Litho.**
3373  A680  15d Sheet of 8, #a-h  8.75  8.75
3374  A681  40d Sheet of 3, #a-c  8.75  8.75
**Souvenir Sheets**
3375  A680  65d multi            4.75  4.75
3376  A681  65d multi            4.75  4.75

Jane Goodall Institute, Gombe,
Tanzania, 50th Anniv. — A682

No. 3377: a, Jane Goodall. b, Baby chimpanzee hanging from tree. c, Head of chimpanzee. d, Goodall and chimpanzee.
No. 3378, horiz.: a, Goodall looking at hills through binoculars. b, Chimpanzee. c, Goodall, diff.
No. 3379, horiz.: a, Baby chimpanzee pointing. b, Goodall holding binoculars. c, Chimpanzee in tree.
80d, Adult and juvenile chimpanzee.

**Perf. 13¼x13, 12 (#3378-3379)**
**2011, May 26**
3377  A682  30d Sheet of 4, #a-
         d                        8.75   8.75
3378  A682  35d Sheet of 3, #a-
         c                        7.50   7.50
3379  A682  35d Sheet of 3. #a-
         c                        7.50   7.50
      Nos. 3377-3379 (3)        23.75  23.75
**Souvenir Sheet**
3380  A682  80d multi            5.75   5.75

Worldwide Fund
for Nature
(WWF) — A683

No. 3381 — Yellow-billed storks: a, Two birds in flight. b, Two birds in water. c, One bird landing, heads of two birds. d, Three birds in water.

**2011, June 30                    Perf. 12¾**
3381       Horiz. strip of 4     5.75   5.75
  a.-d.  A683 20d Any single     1.40   1.40
  e.   Souvenir sheet of 8, 2 each
         #3381a-3381d           11.50  11.50

A684

Pres. John F. Kennedy (1917-
63) — A685

No. 3382 — Kennedy: a, At microphone, pointing. b, At microphone. c, At microphone, with arms extended. d, In front of White House.

**2011, July 6                      Perf. 12**
3382  A684  30d Sheet of 4, #a-d  8.25  8.25
**Souvenir Sheet**
**Perf. 12¾x12½**
3383  A685  60d multi            4.25   4.25

Visit of U.S. Pres. Barack Obama to
the United Kingdom
A686

No. 3384, 30d: a, Pres. Barack Obama. b, First Lady Michelle Obama. c, Prince William. d, Catherine, Duchess of Cambridge.
No. 3385, 30d, horiz. — Obamas with: a, Queen Elizabeth II and Prince Philip. b, John Hall, Dean of Westminster Abbey. c, Prince

William and Catherine, Duchess of Cambridge. d, Prime Minister David Cameron and his wife, Samantha.
No. 3386: a, Cameron. b, Pres. Obama. 65d, horiz., Queen Elizabeth II and Pres. Obama, horiz.

**2011, July 25    Perf. 12, 12½ (#3387)**
**Sheets of 4, #a-d**
3384-3385  A686  Set of 2       18.50  18.50
3386  A686  35d Sheet of 2, #a-
         b                       5.50   5.50
**Souvenir Sheet**
3387  A686  65d multi            5.00   5.00
      No. 3387 contains one 51x38mm stamp.

British
Royalty — A687

Designs: No. 3388, 30d, King George V (1865-1936). No. 3389, 30d, King George VI (1895-1952). No. 3390, 30d, Queen Elizabeth II. No. 3391, 30d, Prince Philip.

**2011, Oct. 11                  Perf. 13¼x13**
3388-3391  A687  Set of 4        8.00   8.00
      Nos. 3388-3391 each were printed in sheets of 4.

**Miniature Sheet**

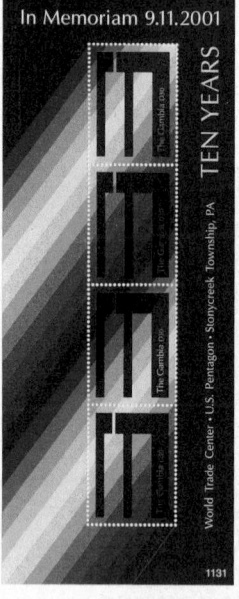

Sept. 11,
2001
Terrorist
Attacks,
10th
Anniv.
A688

No. 3392 — Color of stripe at upper left corner: a, Dark blue. b, Orange. c, Red violet. d, Green.

**2011, Oct. 11**
3392  A688  30d Sheet of 4, #a-d  8.00  8.00

**Miniature Sheet**

Inter
Milan
Soccer
Team
A689

No. 3393 — Team emblem and photos: a, Italian League, 1963. b, UEFA Champions League, 1963-64. c, Italian League, 1965. d, UEFA Champions League, 1964-65. e, Italian Super Cup, 2010. f, Intercontinental Cup, 1964. g, Intercontinental Cup, 1965. h, UEFA Cup, 1998. i, FIFA Club World Cup, 2010.

**2011, Oct. 11                    Perf. 12½**
3393  A689  12d Sheet of 9, #a-i  7.25  7.25

**Miniature Sheets**

A690

Pres. Abraham Lincoln (1809-
65) — A691

No. 3394 — Lincoln: a, Facing right. b, Standing, with hand on book. c, Facing left. d, Standing, with both arms bent.
No. 3395 — Lincoln: a, Seated, name in brown. b, Standing, name in brown. c, Seated, name in tan. d, Standing, name in tan.

**2011, Oct. 11                  Perf. 13¼x13**
3394  A690  25d Sheet of 4, #a-d  6.75  6.75
3395  A691  25d Sheet of 4, #a-d  6.75  6.75

Birds
A692

No. 3396, 16d: a, Bald eagle. b, European bee-eater. c, Keel-billed toucan. d, Red-crowned crane. e, Emperor penguin. f, Australian pelican.
No. 3397, 16d: a, African gray parrot. b, African darter. c, African fish eagle. d, African penguin. e, Reed cormorant. f, Spotted eagle-owl.
No. 3398, 80d, Lesser flamingo. No. 3399, 80d, African gray hornbill.

**2011, Oct. 11                  Perf. 13x12¾**
**Sheets of 6, #a-f, + label**
3396-3397  A692  Set of 2       13.00  13.00
**Souvenir Sheets**
**Perf. 13x13¼**
3398-3399  A692  Set of 2       10.50  10.50

Orchids
A693

No. 3400: a, Cephalanthera rubra. b, Aerangis biloba. c, Angreacum angustum. d, Ancistrochilus thomsonianus. e, Aerangis luteoalba. f, Polystacha carnosa.
No. 3401, vert.: a, Ansellia africana. b, Bulbophyllum falcatum. c, Angraecopsis ischnopus. d, Angraecum moandense.
No. 3402, 80d, Ancistrochilus rothschildianus. No. 3403, 80d, Bulbophyllum cochleatum, vert.

**2011, Oct. 11      Perf. 13 Syncopated**
3400  A693  20d Sheet of 6, #a-
         f                       8.00   8.00
3401  A693  30d Sheet of 4, #a-
         d                       8.00   8.00
**Souvenir Sheets**
3402-3403  A693  Set of 2       10.50  10.50

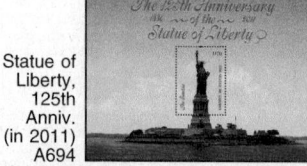

Statue of
Liberty,
125th
Anniv.
(in 2011)
A694

No. 3404: a, Frederic Auguste Bartholdi, sculptor of Statue of Liberty. b, Statue's torch

under construction. c, Statue's head under construction. d, Statue.
70d, Statue, diff.

**2012, Feb. 24** *Perf. 13 Syncopated*
3404 A694 30d Sheet of 4, #a-d 8.00 8.00
**Souvenir Sheet**
3405 A694 70d multi 4.75 4.75

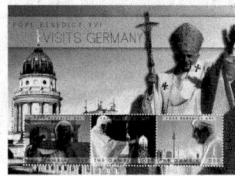

Visit of Pope Benedict XVI to Germany A695

No. 3406 — Pope Benedict XVI: a, Waving at Brandenburg Gate. b, Holding censer. c, Facing left, with Berlin skyline in background.
90d, Pope Benedict XVI wearing miter.

**2012, Feb. 24** *Perf. 12*
3406 A695 30d Sheet of 3, #a-c 6.00 6.00
**Souvenir Sheet**
3407 A695 90d multi 6.00 6.00

Puppies A696

No. 3408: a, Toy poodle. b, Yorkshire terrier. c, Beagle.
No. 3409: a, Rottweiler. b, Chihuahua. c, Golden retriever. d, German shepherd.
No. 3410, 100d, Maltese. No. 3411, 100d, Pomeranian.

**2012, Feb. 29**
3408 A696 40d Sheet of 3, #a-c 8.00 8.00
3409 A696 40d Sheet of 4, #a-d 11.00 11.00
**Souvenir Sheets**
3410-3411 A696 Set of 2 13.50 13.50

Christmas 2011 — A697

Paintings: 15d, Adoration of the Shepherds, by Gerard van Honthorst. 25d, Adoraton of the Shepherds, by Agnolo Bronzino. 30d, The Adoration of the Magi, by Peter Paul Rubens. 40d, The Journey of the Magi, by James Jacques Joseph Tissot.

**2012, Mar. 3** *Perf. 14*
3412-3415 A697 Set of 4 7.50 7.50

Sinking of the Titanic, Cent. A698

No. 3416: a, Staircase. b, Lifeboat. c, Parlor. 100d, Titanic.

**2012, Mar. 2** *Perf. 12*
3416 A698 45d Sheet of 3, #a-c 9.00 9.00
**Souvenir Sheet**
3417 A698 100d multi 6.75 6.75

Miniature Sheet

Ferrari Race Cars A699

No. 3418: a, 150 Italia. b, F10. c, F60. d, F2008.

**2012, Mar. 13** *Perf. 12*
3418 A699 30d Sheet of 4, #a-d 8.25 8.25

Souvenir Sheets

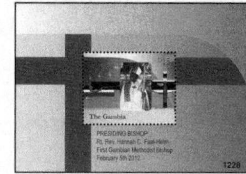

Bishop Hannah C. Faal-Heim, Gambian Methodist Presiding Bishop — A700

Bishop Faal-Heim, cross and: 15d, Map of Gambia. 25d, Church. 35d, Emblem of Gambian Methodist Church. 50d, Bishop Emeritus Peter Stephens.

**2012, Feb. 2** *Perf. 13x13¼*
3419-3422 A700 Set of 4 8.25 8.25

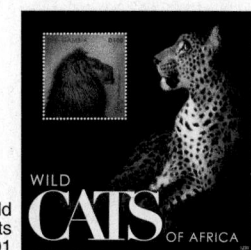

Wild Cats A701

No. 3423: a, Caracal. b, Cheetah. c, Jungle cat.
100d, Lion.

**2012, May 16** *Perf. 13¾*
3423 A701 40d Sheet of 3, #a-c 7.75 7.75
**Souvenir Sheet**
3424 A701 100d multi 6.50 6.50

British Monarchs — A702

Designs: No. 3425, 20d, King William I. No. 3426, 20d, King Henry II. No. 3427, 20d, King Henry IV. No. 3428, 20d, King Henry VI. No. 3429, 20d, King Richard III. No. 3430, 20d, Queen Elizabeth I. No. 3431, 20d, King James I. No. 3432, 20d, King Edward VII.

**2012, June 27** *Perf. 13¼x13*
3425-3432 A702 Set of 8 10.50 10.50
Nos. 3425-3432 each were printed in sheets of 8 + central label.

Miniature Sheet

2012 Summer Olympics, London — A703

No. 3433: a, High jump. b, Gymnastics. c, Uneven bars. d, Long jump.

**2012, June 27** *Perf. 14*
3433 A703 25d Sheet of 4, #a-d 6.50 6.50

Pres. Yahya A. J. J. Jammeh — A704

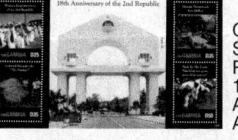

Gambian Second Republic, 18th Anniv. A705

No. 3435: a, 25d, Women empowerment of the Second Republic. b, 35d, Fort Bullen Historic Monument. c, 35d, Cultural masquerade, The Kumpo. d, 50d, Back to the land.
75d, Pres. Jammeh, diff.

**2012, July 22** *Perf. 14*
3434 A704 150d shown 9.75 9.75
*Perf. 12*
3435 A705 Sheet of 4, #a-d 9.50 9.50
**Souvenir Sheet**
3436 A704 75d multi 5.00 5.00

Miniature Sheet

Reign Of Queen Elizabeth II, 60th Anniv. A706

No. 3437 — Photographs of Queen Elizabeth II from: a, 1937. b, 1946. c, 1953. d, 1952. e, 1962. f, 2004.

**2012, July 31** *Perf. 13 Syncopated*
3437 A706 30d Sheet of 6, #a-f 11.50 11.50

Whales A707

No. 3438: a, Humpback whale. b, Bryde's whale. c, Southern right whale. d, Blue whale. e, Killer whale. f, Sperm whale.
100d, Minke whale.

**2012, Aug. 2** *Perf. 14*
3438 A707 30d Sheet of 6, #a-f 11.50 11.50
**Souvenir Sheet**
*Perf. 12*
3439 A707 100d multi 6.50 6.50

Drafting of the Emancipation Proclamation by Pres. Abraham Lincoln, 150th Anniv. — A708

No. 3440: a, Drawing of Lincoln seated at desk. b, Text of preliminary draft of the Emancipation Proclamation. c, Drawing of Lincoln writing the Emancipation Proclamation. d, First reading of the Emancipation Proclamation.
100d, Lincoln writing, vert.

**2012, Aug. 2** *Perf. 13 Syncopated*
3440 A708 40d Sheet of 4, #a-d 10.50 10.50
**Souvenir Sheet**
3441 A708 100d multi 6.50 6.50

Premiere of *The Three Stooges The Movie* A709

No. 3442: a, Moe grabbing heads of Larry and Curly, denomination in purple. b, Stooges on bicycle. c, Moe grabbing heads of Larry and Curly, denomination in orange. d, Stooges standing.
100d, Silhouette of Stooges, vert.

**2012, Aug. 2** *Perf. 12¾*
3442 A709 40d Sheet of 4, #a-d 10.50 10.50
**Souvenir Sheet**
3443 A709 100d multi 6.50 6.50

Souvenir Sheets

Record Covers of Elvis Presley A710

Record: No. 3444, 100d, Elvis Presley. No. 3445, 100d, All Shook Up and That's When Your Heartaches Begin. No. 3446, 100d, 50,000,000 Elvis Fans Can't Be Wrong. No. 3447, 100d, A Big Hunk O'Love and My Wish Came True. No. 3448, 100d, (You're the) Devil in Disguise and Please Don't Drag That String Around.

**2012, Aug. 2** *Perf. 12¾*
3444-3448 A710 Set of 5 32.50 32.50

Greek Olympic Stamps of 1896 A711

Designs: No. 3449, 100d, Greece #125 (1d stamp). No. 3450, 300d, Greece #117 (1 l stamp). No. 3451, 300d, Greece #118 (2 l stamp). No. 3452, 300d, Greece #119 (5 l stamp). No. 3453, 300d, Greece #120 (10 l stamp). No. 3454, 300d, Greece #121 (20 l stamp). No. 3455, 300d, Greece #122 (25 l stamp). No. 3456, 300d, Greece #123 (40 l stamp). No. 3457, 300d, Greece #124 (60 l stamp). No. 3458, 300d, Greece #126 (2d stamp). No. 3459, 300d, Greece #127 (5d stamp). No. 3460, 300d, Greece #128 (10d stamp).

**Litho. & Embossed With Foil Application**
**2012, Aug. 2** *Die Cut Perf. 7¾*
**Without Gum**
3449-3460 A711 Set of 12 220.00 220.00

Christmas — A712

Paintings: 5d, The Virgin of the Green Cushion, by Andrea Solario. 15d, The Adoration of the Magi, by Peter Paul Rubens. 25d, Bridgewater Madonna, by Raphael. 50d, The Nativity, by Domenico Ghirlandaio. 75d, Nativity and Adoration of Shepherds, by Bartolo di Fredi.

100d, Holy Family, by Rembrandt.

**Perf. 12¾x12½**
**2012, Sept. 25** Litho.
3461-3465 A712 Set of 5 11.00 11.00
**Souvenir Sheet**
3466 A712 100d multi 6.50 6.50

Miniature Sheets

A713

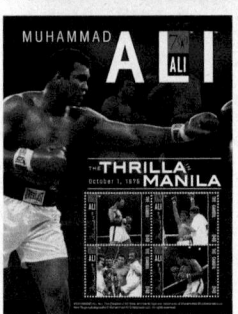

Oct. 1, 1975 Boxing Match Between Muhammad Ali and Joe Frazier, Manila, Philippines — A714

No. 3467: a, Ali at left, no lights at top. b, Frazier at left, ropes straight. c, Ali at left, lights at top, corner of ring in background. d, Frazier at left, corner of ring in background.
No. 3468: a, Ali in ring, facing right. b, Ali with arms raised. c, Ali and handlers with trophy. d, Ali, facing left, against ropes.

**2012, July 27** Litho. **Perf. 12½x13¼**
3467 A713 40d Sheet of 4, #a-d 10.50 10.50
**Perf. 12½x12**
3468 A714 40d Sheet of 4, #a-d 10.50 10.50

Miniature Sheet

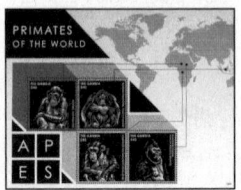

Primates A715

No. 3469: a, Bonobo. b, Bornean orangutan. c, Chimpanzee. d, Mountain gorilla.

**2012, Nov. 28** Litho. **Perf. 14x13¾**
3469 A715 40d Sheet of 4, #a-d 11.00 11.00

---

Miniature Sheets

NASA Achievements — A716

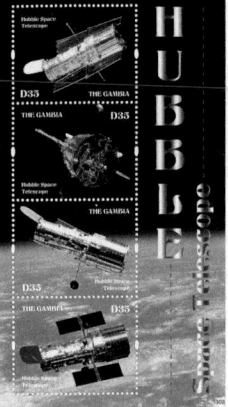

Hubble Space Telescope — A717

No. 3470: a, John Glenn, Jr., first U.S. astronaut to orbit Earth, 1962. b, Edwin A. "Buzz" Aldrin on Moon, 1969. c, Space Shuttle Discovery, 1984. d, Hubble Space Telescope, 1990.
No. 3471 — Hubble Space Telescope: a, Black background, denomination at LL. b, Black background, denomination at UR. c, Earth in background, denomination at LL. d, Earth in background, denomination at UR.

**Perf. 13 Syncopated**
**2012, Nov. 28** Litho.
3470 A716 35d Sheet of 4, #a-d 9.50 9.50
3471 A717 35d Sheet of 4, #a-d 9.50 9.50

Nos. 3470-3471 exist imperf. Value, set of 2 sheets $25.

Castles A718

No. 3472: a, Alnwick Castle, Scotland. b, Dover Castle, England. c, Edinburgh Castle, Scotland. d, Eilean Donan Castle, Scotland. e, Neuschwanstein Castle, Germany.
100d, Alcázar of Segovia, Spain.

**2012, Nov. 28** Litho. **Perf. 12**
3472 A718 30d Sheet of 5, #a-e 10.00 10.00
**Souvenir Sheet**
**Perf. 12½**
3473 A718 100d multi 6.75 6.75

No. 3473 contains one 38x51mm. Inscription on No. 3472c incorrectly states that Edinburgh Castle is in England.

Insects A719

No. 3474: a, Fiery searcher beetle. b, Blue milkweed beetle. c, Locust borer beetle. d, Grapevine beetle.
100d, Banded alder borer.

**2012, Dec. 31** Litho. **Perf. 12**
3474 A719 40d Sheet of 4, #a-d 9.50 9.50
**Souvenir Sheet**
3475 A719 100d multi 6.00 6.00

---

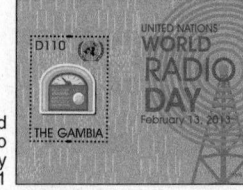

World Radio Day A721

No. 3477: a, Red orange radio with handle. b, Pink radio. c, Black radio. d, Tan and gray radio.
110d, Tan radio with dial.

**Perf. 13 Syncopated**
**2013, Feb. 4** Litho.
3477 A721 35d Sheet of 4, #a-d 8.25 8.25
**Souvenir Sheet**
3478 A721 110d multi 6.50 6.50

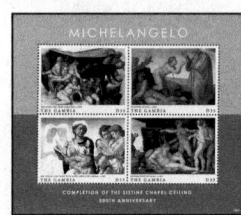

Completion of Painting of Sistine Chapel Ceiling by Michelangelo, 500th Anniv. (in 2012) — A722

No. 3479: a, The Expulsion from Paradise. b, Creation of Eve. c, The Virgin and Child with Saint John and Angels. d, Drunkenness of Noah.
110d, The Torment of Saint Anthony, vert.

**2013, Feb. 4** Litho. **Perf. 12½**
3479 A722 35d Sheet of 4, #a-d 8.25 8.25
**Souvenir Sheet**
3480 A722 110d multi 6.50 6.50

Shells A723

No. 3481: a, Chicoreus clausii. b, Tympanotonus. c, Distorsio smithi. d, Nerita senegalensis.
110d, Xenophora crispa senegalensis.

**2013, Feb. 20** Litho. **Perf. 12**
3481 A723 35d Sheet of 4, #a-d 8.25 8.25
**Souvenir Sheet**
3482 A723 110d multi 6.50 6.50

Turtles A724

No. 3483: a, Aldabra giant tortoise. b, African spurred tortoise. c, Leopard tortoise. d, Radiated tortoise.
110d, African helmeted turtle.

**Perf. 13 Syncopated**
**2013, Feb. 20** Litho.
3483 A724 35d Sheet of 4, #a-d 8.25 8.25
**Souvenir Sheet**
3484 A724 110d multi 6.50 6.50

---

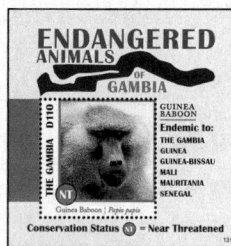

Endangered Animals — A725

No. 3485, 35d: a, Crowned lemur. b, Giant eland. c, African elephant. d, Lion. e, Black rhinoceros.
No. 3486, 35d: a, Nubian ibex. b, Gerenuk. c, Fossa. d, Striped hyena. e, Coquerel's sifaka.
No. 3487, 110d, Guinea baboon. No. 3488, 110d, Western red colobus.

**2013, Mar. 20** Litho. **Perf. 13¾**
**Sheets of 5, #a-e**
3485-3486 A725 Set of 2 21.00 21.00
**Souvenir Sheets**
3487-3488 A725 Set of 2 13.50 13.50

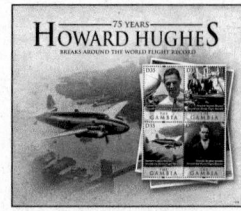

Setting of Around-the-World Flight Record by Howard Hughes, 75th Anniv. — A726

No. 3489: a, Hughes without suit in front of airplane. b, Hughes in car in ticker-tape parade. c, Airplane over Brooklyn Bridge. d, Hughes in suit in front of airplane.
110d, Crowd of people around airplane, horiz.

**Perf. 13 Syncopated**
**2013, Apr. 3** Litho.
3489 A726 35d Sheet of 4, #a-d 8.50 8.50
**Souvenir Sheet**
3490 A726 110d multi 6.75 6.75

First Flight of Boeing 314 Clipper Flying Boats, 75th Anniv. A727

No. 3491: a, View of front of airplane in water. b, Side view of airplane just above water. c, Eddie Allen, first pilot. d, Overhead view of airplane just above water.
110d, Airplane moving through water.

**Perf. 13 Syncopated**
**2013, Apr. 3** Litho.
3491 A727 35d Sheet of 4, #a-d 8.50 8.50
**Souvenir Sheet**
3492 A727 110d multi 6.75 6.75

A728

Coronation of Queen Elizabeth II, 60th Anniv. — A729

No. 3493 — Yellow bister panel and black-and-white photograph of Queen Elizabeth II: a, Wearing flowered hat, facing right. b, With Prince Philip. c, Wearing hat, facing left. d, Wearing crown in coach.

No. 3494 — Blue panel and photograph of Queen Elizabeth: a, With dark hair, facing forward. b, With dark hair, facing right. c, With gray hair. d, With dark hair, facing left.

No. 3495, 110d, Portrait of Queen Elizabeth II wearing crown. No. 3496, 110d, Flags and Queen Elizabeth II, horiz.

**2013, Apr. 3     Litho.     Perf. 14**
3493  A728  35d Sheet of 4, #a-
      d                          8.50  8.50
3494  A729  35d Sheet of 4, #a-
      d                          8.50  8.50
**Souvenir Sheets**
**Perf. 12**
3495-3496  A729  Set of 2      13.50  13.50

No. 3495 contains one 30x50mm stamp. No. 3496 contains one 50x30mm stamp.

Pres. John F. Kennedy (1917-63) — A730

No. 3497 — Pres. Kennedy: a, On telephone. b, Facing right. b, Facing left. c, In crowd.

110d, Pres. Kennedy and flag.

**2013, Apr. 4     Litho.     Perf. 12**
3497  A730  35d Sheet of 4, #a-d  8.50  8.50
**Souvenir Sheet**
3498  A730  110d multi            6.75  6.75

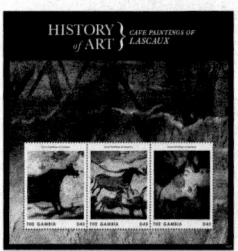

History of Art A731

No. 3499, 45d — Lascaux Cave Paintings: a, Horned animal. b, Animals without horns. c, Three horned animals, animal without horns.

No. 3500, 45d — Art of Ancient Greece: a, Hercules and Athena, c. 470 B.C. b, Venus de Milo statue, c. 130-100 B.C. c, Panathenaic amphora featuring runners, c. 520 B.C.

No. 3501, 110d, Bust of Nefertiti, c. 1345 B.C. No. 3502, 110d, Stonehenge, horiz.

**2013, Apr. 4     Litho.     Perf. 12½**
**Sheets of 3, #a-c**
3499-3500  A731  Set of 2      16.50  16.50
**Souvenir Sheets**
3501-3502  A731  Set of 2      13.50  13.50

Bees A732

No. 3503: a, Apis mellifera. b, Apis mellifera intermissa. c, Apis mellifera scutellata. d, Apis mellifera sahariensis.

110d, Apis mellifera sahariensis, diff.

**2013, Apr. 29     Litho.     Perf. 12**
3503  A732  35d Sheet of 4, #a-d  8.50  8.50
**Souvenir Sheet**
3504  A732  110d multi            6.75  6.75

Aircraft Carriers A733

No. 3505: a, Hosho, Japan. b, ARA Veinticinco de Mayo, Argentina. c, Graf Zeppelin, Germany. d, USS Saipan, U.S. 110d, USS Hornet, U.S.

**2013, Apr. 29     Litho.     Perf. 12**
3505  A733  35d Sheet of 4, #a-d  8.50  8.50
**Souvenir Sheet**
**Perf. 12½**
3506  A733  110d multi            6.75  6.75

No. 3506 contains one 51x38mm stamp.

A734

Pope Benedict XVI A735

No. 3507 — Photographs of Pope Benedict XVI at 2005 inauguration: a, On balcony with crowd in background. b, Facing forward with arms raised, both hands visible. c, Facing left with arms raised, one hand visible. d, Facing forward with arms raised, one hand visible.

No. 3508 — Photographs of Pope Benedict XVI at World Youth Day, Cologne, Germany, 2005: a, With German Pres. Horst Köhler. b, Behind microphone, holding paper. c, Behind microphone, holding paper, with other clergy. d, Praying near candles.

No. 3509, Pope Benedict XVI waving. No. 3510, 110d, Pope Benedict XVI with youths.

**Perf. 13 Syncopated**
**2013, Apr. 29                      Litho.**
3507  A734  35d Sheet of 4, #a-d  8.50  8.50
3508  A735  35d Sheet of 4, #a-d  8.50  8.50
**Souvenir Sheets**
3509  A734  110d multi            6.75  6.75
3510  A735  110d multi            6.75  6.75

Flowers A736

No. 3511, 35d: a, Broadleaf beechwood. b, Red daisy. c, Wagon tree. d, River beechwood.

No. 3512, 35d: a, Thistle protea. b, African violet. c, Common protea. d, King protea.

No. 3513, 110d, Welwitschia. No. 3514, 110d, Cape African queen.

**2013, May 7     Litho.     Perf. 13¾**
**Sheets of 4, #a-d**
3511-3512  A736  Set of 2      15.50  15.50
**Souvenir Sheets**
3513-3514  A736  Set of 2      12.00  12.00

Lady Margaret Thatcher (1925-2013), British Prime Minister — A737

No. 3515 — Thatcher: a, With hand on chin. b, With hand raised. c, With roses. d, Facing left.

110d, Thatcher facing right.

**Perf. 13 Syncopated**
**2013, June 3                      Litho.**
3515  A737  35d Sheet of 4, #a-d  7.75  7.75
**Souvenir Sheet**
3516  A737  110d multi            6.00  6.00

A738

No. 3517 — Pope Francis: a, Waving to crowd. b, Delivering first "Urbi et Orbi" blessing during Easter Mass. c, Greeting crowd in St. Peter's Square. d, Celebrating Mass during Lent.

**2013, June 3     Litho.     Perf. 12**
3517  A738  35d Sheet of 4,
      #a-d                        7.75  7.75

**Litho., Margin Embossed With Foil Application**
**Souvenir Sheet**
**Without Gum**
**Imperf**
3518  A739  275d multi          15.00  15.00

Election of Pope Francis A739

**Souvenir Sheet**

Elvis Presley (1935-77) — A740

**Litho., Margin Embossed With Foil Application**
**2013, July 22                      Imperf.**
**Without Gum**
3519  A740  300d multi          16.50  16.50

Fruits A741

No. 3520: a, Mangos. b, Baobab. c, Marulas. d, Kiwanos. 110d, Tamarinds.

**2013, Aug. 7     Litho.     Perf. 12**
3520  A741  35d Sheet of 4, #a-d  7.75  7.75
**Souvenir Sheet**
3521  A741  110d multi            6.00  6.00

Record New York to London Flight of Concorde, 25th Anniv. — A742

No. 3522 — Concorde: a, And New York City skyline. b, And Prince Charles, Princess Diana and dignitaries. c, Taking off. d, And Big Ben.

110d, Concorde and military jets.

**Perf. 12¾x12½**
**2013, Aug. 26                      Litho.**
3522  A742  35d Sheet of 4, #a-d  8.00  8.00
**Souvenir Sheet**
**Perf. 12½x12¾**
3523  A742  110d multi            6.25  6.25

Animals of Thailand A743

No. 3524, vert.: a, Asian elephant. b, Agile gibbon. c, Water buffalo.

No. 3525: a, Indochinese tiger. b, Dhole.

**2013, Aug. 26     Litho.     Perf. 12**
3524  A743  45d Sheet of 3, #a-c  7.75  7.75
**Souvenir Sheet**
3525  A743  55d Sheet of 2, #a-b  6.25  6.25

2013 World Stamp Exhibition, Bangkok, Thailand.

Birth of Prince George of Cambridge — A744

No. 3526: a, Duchess of Cambridge holding Prince George. b, Duke and Duchess of Cambridge. c, Duke of Cambridge holding Prince George. d, Prince George.

110d, Duke and Duchess of Cambridge, Prince George, horiz.

**2013, Sept. 10　Litho.　Perf. 12½**
3526　A744　35d Sheet of 4, #a-d　8.00　8.00
**Souvenir Sheet**
**Perf. 13¼**
3527　A744　110d multi　　6.25　6.25
No. 3527 contains one 51x38mm stamp.

Mushrooms — A745

No. 3528: a, Golden-edge bonnets. b, Common bonnets.
110d, Sickeners.

**2013, Sept. 30　Litho.　Perf. 14**
3528　A745　35d Pair, #a-b　　4.00　4.00
**Souvenir Sheet**
**Perf. 12¾x12½**
3529　A745　110d multi　　6.25　6.25
No. 3528 was printed in sheets containing two pairs. No. 3529 contains one 38x51mm stamp.

Miniature Sheet

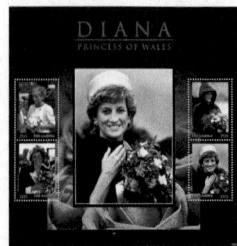

Princess Diana (1961-97) — A746

No. 3530 — Princess Diana holding flowers and wearing: a, White dress. b, Hooded raincoat. c, Jacket with striped lapels. d, Pink hat.

**2013, Oct. 7　Litho.　Perf. 12**
3530　A746　35d Sheet of 4, #a-d　8.00　8.00

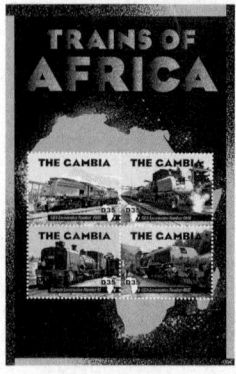

Trains
A747

No. 3531: a, GEA Locomotive Number 4009. b, GEA Locomotive Number 4048. c, Garratt Locomotive Number 81. d, GEA Locomotive Number 4047.
110d, 15F Class Locomotive Number 3150.

**2013, Oct. 7　Litho.　Perf. 12**
3531　A747　35d Sheet of 4, #a-d　8.00　8.00
**Souvenir Sheet**
**Perf. 14**
3532　A747　110d multi　　6.25　6.25

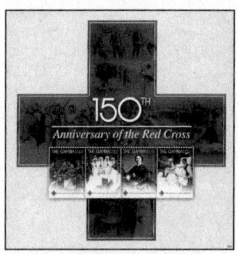

International Red Cross, 150th Anniv. — A748

No. 3533: a, Members of American Red Cross in Great Britain. b, Participants in Birmingham, Alabama American Red Cross Parade. c, Clara Barton, founder of American Red Cross. d, Red Cross workers doing laundry during World War I.
110d, Jean-Henri Dunant, co-founder of Intl. Red Cross.

**2013, Nov. 18　Litho.　Perf. 14**
3533　A748　35d Sheet of 4, #a-d　7.50　7.50
**Souvenir Sheet**
3534　A748　110d multi　　5.75　5.75

Miniature Sheet

Birds of
Brazil
A749

No. 3535: a, Blue-fronted amazon. b, Toco toucan. c, Hyacinth macaw. d, Scarlet ibis.

**2013, Nov. 18　Litho.　Perf. 12½**
3535　A749　35d Sheet of 4, #a-d　7.50　7.50
2013 Brasiliana Intl. Philatelic Exhibition, Rio de Janeiro.

Coronation
of Queen
Elizabeth II,
60th Anniv.
A750

**2013, Nov. 18　Embroidered　Imperf.**
**Self-Adhesive**
3536　A750　270d multi　　14.00　14.00

Christmas — A751

Paintings: 5d, Adoration of the Shepherds, by Ghirlandaio. 25d, Annunciation, by Masolino da Panicale. 75d, Madonna and Child with Angels, by Bernardo Daddi. 100d, Nativity Scene from Vyssí Brod Altarpiece, by Master of Vyssí Brod.

**2013, Dec. 2　Litho.　Perf. 12¾**
3537-3540　A751　Set of 4　11.00　11.00

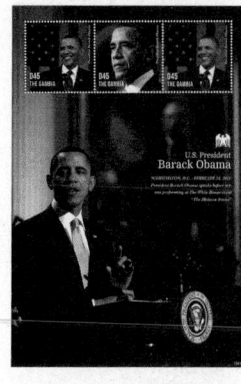

Pres.
Barack
Obama
A752

No. 3541: a, Head of Pres. Obama. b, Pres. Obama and U.S. flag.
No. 3542, 110d, Pres. Obama on telephone. No. 3543, 110d, Pres. Obama on airplane steps.

**2013, Dec. 9　Litho.　Perf. 13¾**
3541　A752　45d Sheet of 3,
　　　#3541a, 2
　　　#3541b　　7.00　7.00
**Souvenir Sheets**
**Perf. 12½**
3542-3543　A752　Set of 2　11.50　11.50
Nos. 3542-3543 each contain one 38x51mm stamp.

A753

Nelson Mandela (1918-2013),
President of South Africa — A754

No. 3545 — Mandela: a, Wearing black, red and gray patterned shirt. b, In black-and-white photograph with arms raised. c, In color photograph with arms raised. d, Wearing white shirt. e, Wearing blue and white shirt. f, With fist raised.
No. 3546, 110d, Wearing gray shirt with floral design, vert. No. 3547, 110d, Wearing suit and tie with arm raised, vert.

**2013, Dec. 15　Litho.　Perf. 13¾**
3544　A753　30d multi　　1.60　1.60
3545　A754　30d Sheet of 6, #a-
　　　f　　9.50　9.50
**Souvenir Sheets**
**Perf. 12¾**
3546-3547　A754　Set of 2　11.50　11.50
No. 3544 was printed in sheets of 6. Nos. 3546-3547 each contain one 38x51mm stamp.

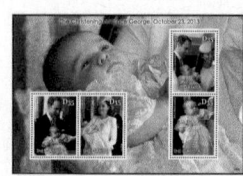

Christening of Prince George of
Cambridge — A755

No. 3548: a, Duke and Duchess of Cambridge holding Prince George. b, Duke of Cambridge holding Prince George. c, Duchess of Cambridge holding Prince George. d, Close-up of Prince George.
110d, Prince George, diff.

**2013, Dec. 31　Litho.　Perf. 14**
3548　A755　35d Sheet of 4, #a-d　7.25　7.25
**Souvenir Sheet**
3549　A755　110d multi　　5.75　5.75
No. 3549 contains one 38x51mm stamp.

Butterflies — A756

No. 3550: a, Tailed orange butterfly. b, Queen butterfly. c, Caribbean sailor butterfly. d, Tiger mimic queen butterfly. e, Caribbean sailor butterfly, green at bottom of stamp. f, Caribbean hairstreak butterfly. g, Lophanus pyrrhias. h, Caribbean banner butterfly. i, Caribbean skipper butterfly.
No. 3551, 135d: a, Thick-rimmed sailor butterfly. b, Caribbean sailor butterfly, diff.
No. 3552, 135d: a, American painted lady butterfly with light brown thorax. b, American painted lady butterfly with black thorax.

**2014, Feb. 26　Litho.　Perf. 13¾**
3550　A756　30d Sheet of 9, #a-
　　　i　　14.00　14.00
**Souvenir Sheets of 2, #a-b**
3551-3552　A756　Set of 2　27.00　27.00

World
War I,
Cent.
A757

No. 3553, 65d: a, Russian officer leading his troops. b, Russian soldiers taking aim. c, Russian troops marching off to war. d, Russian soldier charging the enemy.
No. 3554, 65d — Zeppelins: a, LZ-10 Schwaben. b, L3. c, LZ-127 Graf Zeppelin. d, LZ-13 Hansa.
No. 3555, 270d, Cannon and Czar Nicholas II of Russia (1868-1918). No. 3556, 270d, L3 Zeppelin, diff.

**2014, Feb. 26　Litho.　Perf. 14**
**Sheets of 4, #a-d**
3553-3554　A757　Set of 2　27.00　27.00
**Souvenir Sheets**
**Perf. 12½**
3555-3556　A757　Set of 2　28.00　28.00
Nos. 3555-3556 each contain one 51x38mm stamp.

A758

A759

A760

Pope Francis A761

Pope FRANCIS

No. 3557 — Pope Francis wearing: a, Miter and green vestments. b, Zucchetto, steeple in background. c, Zucchetto, greeting crowd. d, Miter and white vestments.

No. 3558 — Pope Francis wearing: a, Red vestments. b, Purple vestments. c, White vestments. d, Green vestments.

No. 3559 — Pope Francis: a, Holding crucifix. b, Blessing person wearing crown.

No. 3560 — Pope Francis: a, Arms not visible. b, With arm extended.

**2014, Mar. 24    Litho.    Perf. 14**
3557 A758 50d Sheet of 4, #a-d         10.50 10.50
3558 A759 50d Sheet of 4, #a-d         10.50 10.50
**Souvenir Sheets**
3559 A760 75d Sheet of 2, #a-b          8.00  8.00
3560 A761 75d Sheet of 2, #a-b          8.00  8.00

A762

A763

A764

African Penguins A765

Various photographs.

**2014, Apr. 2    Litho.    Perf. 13¾**
3561 A762 50d Sheet of 3, #a-c          8.00  8.00
3562 A763 50d Sheet of 4, #a-d         10.50 10.50
**Souvenir Sheets**
3563 A764 150d multi                    8.00  8.00
3564 A765 150d multi                    8.00  8.00

Worldwide Fund for Nature (WWF) — A766

Nos. 3565 and 3566: a, Two African darters on branch. b, African darter in water. c, One African darter on branch. d, African darter with wings extended.

**2014, Apr. 2    Litho.    Perf. 14**
3565 A766 32d Block or vert. strip of 4, #a-d    6.75  6.75
3566 A766 35d Block or vert. strip of 4, #a-d    7.50  7.50

Paintings A767

No. 3567, 50d — Paintings by Henri Rousseau: a, Tiger in a Tropical Storm. b, The Sleeping Gypsy. c, Carnival Evening.

No. 3568, 50d: a, Le Rifain Assis, by Henri Matisse. b, The Dance II, by Matisse. c, Judith and the Head of Holofernes, by Gustav Klimt.

No. 3569, 150d, Water Lilies, by Claude Monet. No. 3570, 150d, The Bed, by Henri de Toulouse-Lautrec.

**2014, Mar. 10    Litho.    Perf. 12¾**
**Sheets of 3, #a-c**
3567-3568 A767 Set of 2                16.00 16.00
**Imperf**
**Size: 99x99mm**
3569-3570 A767 Set of 2                16.00 16.00

A768

A769

A770

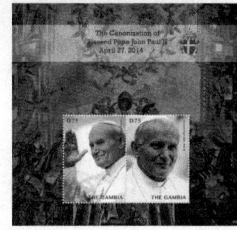
Canonization of Pope John Paul II — A771

No. 3571 — Pope John Paul II wearing miter: a, Waving, entire hand visible. b, Miter 24mm wide. c, Miter 21mm wide. d, Waving, hand partially visible.

No. 3572 — Pope John Paul II wearing zucchetto: a, Praying. b, Smiling, top of zucchetto not visible. c, Smiling, top of zucchetto visible. d, Seated, surrounded by Swiss Guards.

No. 3573 — Pope John Paul II wearing miter, blessing crowd: a, Back of hand visible. b, Palm of hand visible.

No. 3574 — Pope John Paul II wearing zucchetto: a, Waving, b, Not waving.

**2014, May 8    Litho.    Perf. 14**
3571 A768 50d Sheet of 4, #a-d         10.00 10.00
3572 A769 50d Sheet of 4, #a-d         10.00 10.00
**Souvenir Sheets**
**Perf. 12¾**
3573 A770 75d Sheet of 2, #a-b          7.50  7.50
3574 A771 75d Sheet of 2, #a-b          7.50  7.50

Hibiscus, National Flower of South Korea — A772

**2014, May 12    Litho.    Die Cut**
**Self-Adhesive**
3575 A772 30d multi                     1.50  1.50
No. 3575 was printed in sheets of 9.

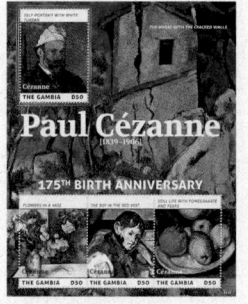
Paintings by Paul Cézanne (1839-1906) — A773

No. 3576, 50d: a, Self-portrait with White Turban. b, Flowers in a Vase. c, The Boy in the Red Vest. d, Still Life with Pomegranate and Pears.

No. 3577, 50d: a, Self-portrait with Palette. b, The Bathers. c, Madame Cézanne in a Red Dress. d, The Card Players.

No. 3578, 75d, horiz. — Details from Paul Alexis Reading at Zola's House: a. Zola holding quill pen. b, Alexis reading.

No. 3579, 75d, horiz. — Details from The Card Players: a, Player facing right, smoking pipe. b, Player facing left.

**2014, May 12    Litho.    Perf. 12¾**
**Sheets of 4, #a-d**
3576-3577 A773 Set of 2                20.00 20.00
**Souvenir Sheets of 2, #a-b**
3578-3579 A773 Set of 2                15.00 15.00

Dogs — A774

No. 3580: a, Weimaraner. b, Schnauzer. c, Chow chow. d, Boxer.
150d, Doberman pinscher.

**2014, June 23    Litho.    Perf. 12¾**
3580 A774 50d Sheet of 4, #a-d         10.00 10.00
**Souvenir Sheet**
3581 A774 150d multi                    7.50  7.50

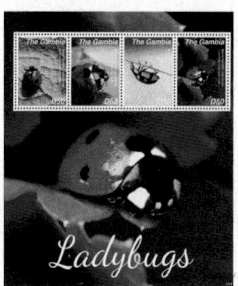
Ladybugs — A775

No. 3582: a, Seven-spotted ladybug on veined leaf. b, Seven-spotted ladybug on leaf, yellow area at UR. c, Multicolored Asian ladybug. d, Seven-spotted ladybug on leaf.

No. 3583: a, Ten-spotted lady bug. b, Spotless ladybug.

**2014, July 1    Litho.    Perf. 12**
3582 A775 50d Sheet of 4, #a-d         10.00 10.00
**Souvenir Sheet**
**Perf. 14**
3583 A775 75d Sheet of 2, #a-b          7.50  7.50
See Nos. 3594-3595.

A776

A777

A778

Berlin Wall Graffiti A779

No. 3584: a, People reading newspaper. b, Person jumping wall. c, Archway between legs. d, Zipper and Gernan text.

No. 3585: a, Automobile smashing through wall. b, Stylized faces with connected eyes. c, Stylized faces with large lips. d, Doves and Brandenburg Gate.

No. 3586: a, Crowd, wall at left. b, Crowd, wall at right.

No. 3587: a, Shackled hand in prison window. b, Dove carrying ball and chain.

**2014, July 1        Litho.        Perf. 14**
3584  A776  50d Sheet of 4, #a-d        10.00 10.00
3585  A777  50d Sheet of 4, #a-d        10.00 10.00

**Souvenir Sheets**
**Perf. 12**
3586  A778  75d Sheet of 2, #a-b        7.50  7.50
3587  A779  75d Sheet of 2, #a-b        7.50  7.50

Birds of Prey — A780

No. 3588: a, Crowned eagle. b, Pearl-spotted owlet. c, Steppe eagle. d, Peregrine falcon.
No. 3589: a, Pale chanting goshawk. b, Common kestrel.

**2014, Sept. 4        Litho.        Perf. 14**
3588  A780  50d Sheet of 4, #a-d        10.00 10.00

**Souvenir Sheet**
3589  A780  75d Sheet of 2, #a-b        7.50  7.50
See Nos. 3614-3615.

Meerkats — A781

No. 3590 — Meerkat facing: a, Right, brown background. b, Right, black background. c, Left, black background. d, Left, brown background.
110d, Six meerkats, horiz.

**2014, Sept. 4        Litho.        Perf. 14**
3590  A781  50d Sheet of 4, #a-d        10.00 10.00

**Souvenir Sheet**
**Perf. 12**
3591  A781  110d multi        5.50  5.50
See Nos. 3596-3597.

Space Exploration — A782

No. 3592: a, Cosmonaut Yuri Gagarin and Vostok 1. b, Vostok 1, large crescent moon at UL. c, Vostok 1, small crescent moon at top. b, Rocket designer Sergei Korolev, schematic drawings.
150d, Sputnik 1.

**2014, Sept. 4        Litho.        Perf. 14**
3592  A782  50d Sheet of 4, #a-d        10.00 10.00

**Souvenir Sheet**
**Perf. 12**
3593  A782  150d multi        7.50  7.50

**Ladybugs Type of 2014**
No. 3594: a, Two-spotted ladybug. b, Multicolored Asian ladybug (black with red spots), amidst plant matter. c, Multicolored Asian ladybug (brown with black spots) on bare ground. d, Spotless ladybug, diff.
No. 3595: a, Ten-spotted ladybug on branch. b, Multicolored Asian ladybug (brown with black spots) on leaf.

**2014        Litho.        Perf. 12**
3594  A775  50d Sheet of 4, #a-d        10.00 10.00

**Souvenir Sheet**
3595  A775  75d Sheet of 2, #a-b        7.50  7.50

**Meerkats Type of 2014**
Designs: 45d, Meerkat standing on rear legs.
110d, Meerkat on four legs, horiz.

**2014        Litho.        Perf. 12**
**Size of No. 3596: 30x50mm**
3596  A781  45d multi        2.25  2.25

**Souvenir Sheet**
3597  A781  110d multi        5.50  5.50
No. 3596 was printed in sheets of 6. No. 3597 contains one 40x30mm stamp.

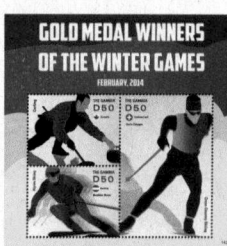

Gold Medalists at 2014 Winter Olympics — A783

No. 3598: a, Canadian men's curling team (40x30mm). b, Matthias Mayer, Alpine skiing (40x30mm). c, Dario Cologna, cross-country skiing, vert. (40x60mm).
No. 3600, vert.: a, Adelina Sotnikova, figure skating. b, Martin Fourcade, biathlon.

**2014, Sept. 15        Litho.        Perf. 14**
3598  A783  50d Sheet of 3, #a-c        7.50  7.50

**Souvenir Sheet**
3599  A783  75d Sheet of 2, #a-b        7.50  7.50

Dinosaurs — A784

No. 3600, 50d: a, Pteranodon longiceps. b, Archaeoceratops. c, Ampelosaurus. d, Apatosaurus.
No. 3601, 50d: a, Stegosaurus. b, Albertaceratops. c, Spinosaurus. d, Nedoceratops.
No. 3602, 150d, Kentrosaurus. No. 3603, 150d, Compsognathus.

**2014, Sept. 15        Litho.        Perf. 14**
**Sheets of 4, #a-d**
3600-3601  A784  Set of 2        20.00 20.00

**Souvenir Sheet**
3602-3603  A784  Set of 2        15.00 15.00

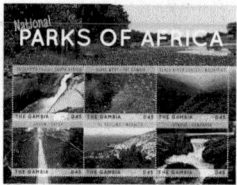

National Parks in Africa — A785

No. 3604: a, Augrabies Falls, South Africa. b, Kiang West, Gambia. c, Black River Gorges, Mauritius. d, Kakum, Ghana. e, Al Hoceim, Morocco. f, Bénoué, Cameroun.
No. 3605: a, Chobe, Botswana. b, Day Forest, Djibouti. c, Murchison Falls, Uganda. d, Arusha, Tanzania.
No. 3606, 75d: a, Amboseli, Kenya. b, Serengeti, Tanzania.
No. 3607, 75d: a, Andringitra, Madagascar. b, Nyika, Malawi.

**2014, Sept. 15        Litho.        Perf. 12½**
3604  A785  45d Sheet of 6, #a-f        13.50 13.50
3605  A785  50d Sheet of 4, #a-d        10.00 10.00

**Souvenir Sheets of 2, #a-b**
3606-3607  A785  Set of 2        15.00 15.00

**Miniature Sheets**

Downton Abbey Television Series — A786

No. 3608, 45d: a, Downton Abbey, buff background at top. b, Earl of Grantham. c, Mr. Carson. d, Anna Bates. e, Lady Mary Crawley.
No. 3609, 45d: a, Downton Abbey, white background at top. b, Mrs. Hughes. c, Countess of Grantham. d, Tom Branson. e, Thomas Barrow.

**2014, Oct. 14        Litho.        Perf. 14**
**Sheets of 5, #a-e**
3608-3609  A786  Set of 2        21.00 21.00

Christmas — A787

Cross and paintings: 5d, Adoration of the Shepherds, by Domenico Ghirlandaio. 25d, The Archangel Gabriel, by Masolino da Panicale. 75d, Madonna and Child with Angels, by Bernardo Daddi. 100d, Nativity Scene, by Meister von Hohenfurth.

**2014, Nov. 24        Litho.        Perf. 12¾**
3610-3613  A787  Set of 4        9.50  9.50

**Birds of Prey Type of 2014**
No. 3614: a, Bateleur. b, Red kite. c, African scops owl. d, Osprey.
No. 3615: a, Montagu's harrier. b, Secretary bird.

**2014        Litho.        Perf. 14**
3614  A780  50d Sheet of 4, #a-d        10.00 10.00

**Souvenir Sheet**
**Perf. 12**
3615  A780  75d Sheet of 2, #a-b        7.50  7.50

Endangered Animals — A788

No. 3616, 50d: a, African wild dog. b, Bornean orangutan. c, Black spider monkey. d, Amur tiger, denomination in white.
No. 3617, 50d: a, Two African wild dogs. b, Eastern lowland gorilla. c, Amur tiger, denomination in black. d, Chimpanzee.
No. 3618, 75d: a, Chimpanzee, diff. b, Cross River gorilla.
No. 3619, 75d: a, Sumatran rhinoceroses. b, Amur leopard.

**2014, Oct. 14        Litho.        Perf. 14**
**Sheets of 4, #a-d**
3616-3617  A788  Set of 2        18.50 18.50

**Souvenir Sheets of 2, #a-b**
**Perf. 12½**
3618-3619  A788  Set of 2        14.00 14.00
Nos. 3618-3619 both contain two 51x38mm stamps.

Butterflies — A789

No. 3620, 50d: a, African map butterfly. b, Green-banded swallowtail. c, Gold-banded forester. d, African caper white.
No. 3621, 50d: a, Citrus swallowtail. b, Angola white lady. c, African monarch. d, African swallowtail.
No. 3622, 150d, Blood red glider. No. 3623, 150d, Giant blue swallowtail.

**2014, Oct. 20        Litho.        Perf. 14**
**Sheets of 4, #a-d**
3620-3621  A789  Set of 2        18.50 18.50

**Souvenir Sheets**
**Perf. 12**
3622-3623  A789  Set of 2        14.00 14.00

**Souvenir Sheets**

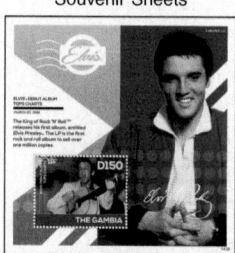

Elvis Presley (1935-77) — A790

Photographs of Presley with inscriptions: No. 3624, 150d, Elvis' debut album tops charts. No. 3625, 150d, Elvis donates yacht to St. Jude's Children's Research Hospital. No. 3626, 150d, Elvis receives first guitar. No. 3627, 150d, Elvis wins first Grammy award.

**2014, Oct. 14        Litho.        Perf. 14**
3624-3627  A790  Set of 4        28.00 28.00

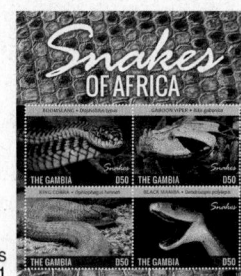

Snakes
A791

No. 3628, 50d: a, Boomslang. b, Gaboon viper. c, King cobra. d, Black mamba.
No. 3629, 50d: a, Leaf viper. b, Egg eating snake. c, Puff adder. d, Green mamba.
No. 3630, 150d, Red spitting cobra. No. 3631, 150d, Cape cobra, vert.

**2014, Dec. 31    Litho.    Perf. 12½**
**Sheets of 4, #a-d**
3628-3629  A791    Set of 2    18.50 18.50
**Souvenir Sheets**
3630-3631  A791    Set of 2    14.00 14.00

Taiwan Lantern Festival
A792

No. 3632: a, Dragon lantern. b, Archer lantern. c, Boar lantern. d, Flower lantern. e, Horse lantern.
150d, Flying lantern.

**2015, Jan. 15    Litho.    Perf. 14**
3632  A792    45d Sheet of 5,
            #a-e            10.50 10.50
**Souvenir Sheet**
**Perf. 12**
3633  A792    150d multi            7.00 7.00
Taipei 2015 International Stamp Exhibition.

World War I Posters From Australia
A793

World War I Posters From Italy
A794

No. 3634: a, Woman, damaged Australian flag. b, Bandaged soldier with rifle with bayonet. c, Soldier holding gun with arm extended towards battle. d, Monster with German helmet and bloody hands reaching for globe. e, Soldiers, bugler calling recruits. f, Bandaged soldier saluting.
No. 3635: a, Two women near woman with crown and sword. b, Woman and soldier with medals on suit lapel. c, Man wearing top hat, man wearing German helmet and bloody apron. d, Soldier with dagger, woman and child. e, Soldier and young girl. f, Soldier pointing.
No. 3636, Red Cross nurse. No. 3637, Cannon.

**2015, Mar. 2    Litho.    Perf. 12½**
3634  A793    45d Sheet of 6,
            #a-f            12.50 12.50
3635  A794    45d Sheet of 6,
            #a-f            12.50 12.50
**Souvenir Sheets**
3636  A793    150d multi            7.00 7.00
3637  A794    150d multi            7.00 7.00

Pres. Abraham Lincoln (1809-65) — A795

No. 3638: a, Lincoln with his family. b, Lincoln reading Emancipation Proclamation. c, Inauguration. d, Funeral of Lincoln.
150d, Lincoln family log cabin.

**2015, Apr. 1    Litho.    Perf. 14**
3638  A795    50d Sheet of 4, #a-d  9.50 9.50
**Souvenir Sheet**
**Perf. 12**
3639  A795    150d multi            7.00 7.00

Sir Winston Churchill (1874-1965), British Prime Minister — A796

No. 3640 — Churchill: a, Holding cane. b, As young man, wearing top hat. c, At lectern. d, Waving. e, On horse. f, Wearing military cap.
150d, Churchill wearing glasses.

**2015, Apr. 1    Litho.    Perf. 14**
3640  A796    45d Sheet of 6,
            #a-f            12.50 12.50
**Souvenir Sheet**
**Perf. 12½**
3641  A796    150d black            7.00 7.00
No. 3641 contains one 38x51mm stamp.

Paintings by Vincent van Gogh (1853-90) — A797

No. 3642: a, Vase with Irises. b, La Berceuse. c, Field with Poppies. d, Sunflowers.
150d, The Bedroom, horiz.

**2015, Apr. 1    Litho.    Perf. 12**
3642  A797    50d Sheet of 4, #a-d  9.50 9.50
**Souvenir Sheet**
**Perf. 12½**
3643  A797    150d multi            7.00 7.00
No. 3643 contains one 51x38mm stamp.

Roses
A798

No. 3644 — Color of roses: a, Dark pink. b, Red. c, Pale pink. d, Red violet.
150d, Grayish pink roses

**2015, Apr. 13    Litho.    Perf. 12**
3644  A798    50d Sheet of 4, #a-d  9.50 9.50
**Souvenir Sheet**
**Perf. 12**
3645  A798    150d multi            7.00 7.00
2015 Europhilex Stamp Exhibition, London.

Akatsuki (Venus Climate Orbiter)
A799

No. 3646 — Akatsuki and inscription: a, Venus orbiter mission. b, Closed approach, December 6, 2010. c, Solar magnetic field. d, Planetary meteorology.
150d, Launch of probe, May 20, 2010, vert.

**2015, July 1    Litho.    Perf. 12½x12**
3646  A799    50d Sheet of 4,
            #a-d            10.50 10.50
**Souvenir Sheet**
**Perf. 12x12½**
3647  A799    150d multi            7.75 7.75

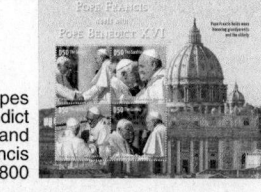

Popes Benedict XVI and Francis
A800

No. 3648: a, Popes clasping hands. b, Popes with hands on each other's shoulders. c, Popes clasping hands, face of Pope Benedict XVI not visible. d, Popes clasping hands, Pope Francis with hand near chin.
No. 3649, Pope Benedict XVI and Pope Francis getting ready to clasp hands, not touching.

**2015, July 13    Litho.    Perf. 13¾**
3648  A800    50d Sheet of 4,
            #a-d            10.00 10.00
**Souvenir Sheet**
**Perf. 12**
3649  A800    150d multi            7.50 7.50
No. 3649 contains one 40x30mm stamp.

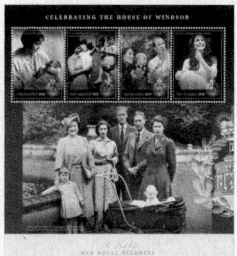

House of Windsor
A801

No. 3650: a, Queen Mother holding Princess Elizabeth. b, Queen Elizabeth II, Prince Philip, Prince Charles and Princess Anne. c, Duke and Duchess of Cambridge, Prince George. d, Duchess of Cambridge holding Princess Charlotte.
150d, Duke and Duchess of Cambridge, Princess Charlotte.

**2015, July 13    Litho.    Perf. 14**
3650  A801    50d Sheet of 4,
            #a-d            10.00 10.00
**Souvenir Sheet**
**Perf. 12**
3651  A801    150d multi            7.50 7.50
Birth of Princess Charlotte.

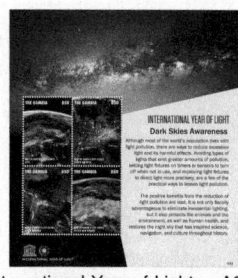

International Year of Light — A802

No. 3652 — Photograph of city lights in a, Asia. b, North America. c, South America. d, Africa and Europe.
150d, City lights of Europe, Africa and Asia.

**2015, July 13    Litho.    Perf. 14**
3652  A802    50d Sheet of 4,
            #a-d            10.00 10.00
**Souvenir Sheet**
**Perf. 12½**
3653  A802    150d multi            7.50 7.50
No. 3653 contains one 38x51mm stamp.

Fruits of Singapore — A803

No. 3654: a, Guavas. b, Custard apples. c, Chikus. d, Rose apples. e, Pomegranates. f, Soursops.
150d, Durians.

**2015, Aug. 3    Litho.    Perf. 14**
3654  A803    45d Sheet of 6,
            #a-f            14.00 14.00
**Souvenir Sheet**
**Perf. 12**
3655  A803    150d multi            7.75 7.75
Singapore 2015 World Stamp Exhibition.

International Telecommunication Union, 150th Anniv. — A804

No. 3656 — 150th anniv. emblem, sine wave and: a, Satellite above earth. b, Tower and satellite dish, orange sky. c, Satellite dish. d, Radio tower and clouds at bottom, blue sky. e, Communications tower at twilight.
150d, 150th anniv. emblem, sine wave, globe showing telecommunication connections.

**2015, Aug. 3    Litho.    Perf. 12**
3656  A804  45d Sheet of 5,
　　　　#a-e                      11.50 11.50
**Souvenir Sheet**
3657  A804  150d multi            7.75  7.75

Magna Carta, 800th Anniv. A805

No. 3658: a, King John. b, Magna Carta issued by Henry III, 1225. c, Original Magna Carta manuscript, 1215. d, King John signing Magna Carta, 1215.
150d, Original seal of Magna Carta, 1215, horiz.

**2015, Aug. 3    Litho.    Perf. 13¼x12½**
3658  A805  50d Sheet of 4,
　　　　#a-d                      10.00 10.00
**Souvenir Sheet**
**Perf. 12½x12**
3659  A805  150d multi            7.75  7.75

**Miniature Sheet**

Orchids A806

No. 3660: a, Ansellia africana. b, Paniculate polystachya. c, Polystachya galeata. d, Ancistrochilus rothschildianus.

**2015, Sept. 8    Litho.    Perf. 13¼x12½**
3660  A806  45d Sheet of 4, #a-d  9.25  9.25

Animals A807

No. 3661: a, African savanna hare. b, Bohor reedbuck. c, Striped polecat. d, Lesser spot-nosed monkey. e, Leopard. f, African wild dog.
150d, Four-toed hedgehog.

**2015, Sept. 30    Litho.    Perf. 13¾**
3661  A807  45d Sheet of 6,
　　　　#a-f                      14.00 14.00
**Souvenir Sheet**
3662  A807  150d multi            7.75  7.75

Visit of Pope Francis To New York City A808

No. 3663 — World Trade Center Memorial and: a, Pope not waving, rose at LR. b, Pope waving, hand at left, 2 roses behind head. c, Pope waving, hand at right, rose at LR. d, Pope not waving, rose at LL and at right. e, Pope waving, hand at left, rose at left and LR. f, Pope not waving, rose stem at right.
150d, Pope Francis waving, buildings.

**2015, Nov. 1    Litho.    Perf. 14**
3663  A808  45d Sheet of 6,
　　　　#a-f                      14.00 14.00
**Souvenir Sheet**
**Perf. 12**
3664  A808  150d multi            7.75  7.75

Christmas — A809

Paintings by Sandro Botticelli: 5d, Adoration of the Magi, 1475. 25d, Adoration of the Kings, 1470. 75d, Adoration of the Kings, 1470-75. 100d, Cestello Annunciation, 1489.

**2015, Nov. 2    Litho.    Perf. 12½**
3665-3668  A809  Set of 4         10.50 10.50

Queen Elizabeth II, Longest-Reigning British Monarch — A810

No. 3669 — Hat color: a, Carmine red. b, Peach. c, Beige. d, Blue.
150d, Queen Elizabeth II wearing pale yellow and black hat.

**2015, Nov. 25    Litho.    Perf. 14**
3669  A810  50d Sheet of 4,
　　　　#a-d                      10.00 10.00
**Souvenir Sheet**
**Perf. 12**
3670  A810  150d multi            7.75  7.75

Snakes A811

No. 3671: 50d: a, Milk snake. b, Bush viper. c, Female Bush viper. d, Mandarin rat snake.
No. 3672: 50d: a, Mangrove snake. b, Corn snake. c, Green tree python. d, Garter snake.
No. 3673: a, Grass snake. b, Boa constrictor.
150d, Green pit viper.

**2015, Dec. 7    Litho.    Perf. 14**
**Sheets of 4, #a-d**
3671-3672  A811  Set of 2        20.00 20.00
**Souvenir Sheets**
**Perf. 12**
3673  A811  75d Sheet of 2,
　　　　#a-b                       7.75  7.75
**Perf. 12½**
3674  A811  150d multi            7.75  7.75
No. 3674 contains one 51x38mm stamp.

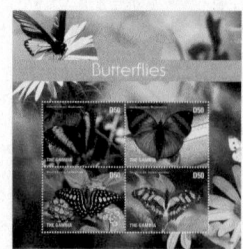

Butterflies — A812

No. 3675: 50d: a, Banded blue morpho. b, Blue shiny butterfly. c, Malachite butterfly. d, Tailed green jay.
No. 3676: 50d: a, Red postman. b, Postman butterfly. c, Protographium marcellus. d, Common cruiser butterfly.
No. 3677, 75d: a, Emerald swallowtail. b, Thoas swallowtail.
No. 3678, 75d: a, Paper kite butterfly. b, Piano key butterfly.

**2015, Dec. 7    Litho.    Perf. 12½**
**Sheets of 4, #a-d**
3675-3676  A812  Set of 2        20.00 20.00
**Sheets of 2, #a-b**
3677-3678  A812  Set of 2        15.50 15.50

Orchids A813

No. 3679, 50d: a, Orchipedum plantaginifolium. b, Satyrium coriifolium. c, Cattleya guttata. d, Cattleya granulosa.
No. 3680, 50d: a, Aganisia cyanea. b, Disa cernua. c, Coilostylis ciliaris. d, Masdevallia coccinea.
No. 3681, 75d: a, Disa uniflora. b, Ancistrochilus rothschildianus.
No. 3682, 75d: a, Satyrium erectum. b, Liparis nervosa.

**2015, Dec. 7    Litho.    Perf. 14**
**Sheets of 4, #a-d**
3679-3680  A813  Set of 2        20.00 20.00
**Sheets of 2, #a-b**
3681-3682  A813  Set of 2        15.50 15.50

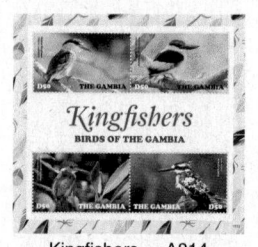

Kingfishers — A814

No. 3683: a, Striped kingfisher. b, Blue-breasted kingfisher. c, Malachite kingfisher. d, Pied kingfisher.
150d, Woodland kingfisher, vert.

**2015, Dec. 31    Litho.    Perf. 12**
3683  A814  50d Sheet of 4,
　　　　#a-d                      10.00 10.00
**Souvenir Sheet**
**Perf. 12½**
3684  A814  150d multi            7.75  7.75
No. 3684 contains one 38x51mm stamp.

Pres. Dwight D. Eisenhower (1890-1969) — A815

No. 3685 — Eisenhower as General in World War II: a, Seated with other officers. b, Getting into vehicle. c, Seated, holding pencil. d, Talking with combat soldiers. e, Seated, flag in background. f, Standing with other officers.
150d, Eisenhower in uniform, flag in background, vert.

**2015, Dec. 31    Litho.    Perf. 14**
3685  A815  45d Sheet of 6,
　　　　#a-f                      14.00 14.00
**Souvenir Sheet**
**Perf. 12½**
3686  A815  150d multi            7.75  7.75
No. 3686 contains one 38x51mm stamp.

Muhammad Ali (1942-2016), Boxer — A816

No. 3687 — Ali with: a, Trophy (30x80mm). b, Punching bag at UL (30x40mm). c, Part of punching bag at right (30x40mm). d, Part of punching bag at upper right (30x40mm). e, Entire punching bag at right (30x40mm).
150d, Ali with boxing gloves.

**2015, Dec. 31    Litho.    Perf. 14**
3687  A816  50d Sheet of 5,
　　　　#a-e                      13.00 13.00
**Souvenir Sheet**
**Perf. 12**
3688  A816  150d multi            7.75  7.75
No. 3688 contains one 30x50mm stamp.

Helmut Schmidt (1918-2013), German Chancellor — A817

No. 3689 — German flag, Schmidt and: a, U.S. Pres. Jimmy Carter, 1977. b, French Pres. Valéry Giscard d'Estaing, 1977. c, British Prime Minister Margaret Thatcher, 1979. d, Soviet General Secretary Leonid Brezhnev, 1981. e, German Chancellor Angela Merkel, 2008. f, Chinese Premier Li Keqiang, 2013.
150d, Schmidt and German flag.

**2015, Dec. 31    Litho.    Perf. 14**
3689  A817  45d Sheet of 6,
　　　　#a-f                      14.00 14.00
**Souvenir Sheet**
**Perf. 12**
3690  A817  150d multi            7.75  7.75
No. 3690 contains one 30x50mm stamp.

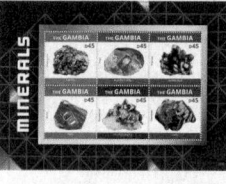

Minerals A818

No. 3691: a, Chalcopyrite. b, Topaz. c, Dioptase. d, Pyrite. e, Tetrahedrite. f, Cassiterite.
No. 3692: a, Amethyst. b, Vivianite. c, Stibnite. d, Garnet.
150d, Rhodochrosite.

**2015, Dec. 31    Litho.    Perf. 13¾**
3691  A818  45d Sheet of 6,
　　　　#a-f                      14.00 14.00
3692  A818  50d Sheet of 4,
　　　　#a-d                      10.00 10.00
**Souvenir Sheet**
3693  A818  150d multi            7.75  7.75

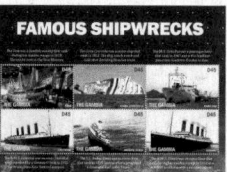

Famous Shipwrecks — A819

No. 3694: a, Vasa. b, Costa Concordia. c, Doña Paz. d, Lusitania. e, Andrea Doria. f, Titanic.

150d, U.S.S. Arizona Memorial.

**2016, Feb. 20   Litho.   Perf. 13½**
3694 A819  45d Sheet of 6,
#a-f                        13.50 13.50
**Souvenir Sheet**
**Perf. 12½x12**
3695 A819 150d multi           7.50  7.50
No. 3695 contains one 80x30mm stamp.

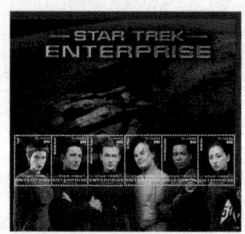

Characters from *Star Trek: Enterprise*
Television Series — A820

No. 3696: a, T'pol. b, Malcolm Reed. c,
Charles "Trip" Tucker. d, Dr. Phlox. e, Travis
Mayweather. f, Hoshi Sato.
150d, Jonathan Archer.

**2016, Feb. 20   Litho.   Perf. 14**
3696 A820  45d Sheet of 6,
#a-f                        14.00 14.00
**Souvenir Sheet**
**Perf. 13¾**
3697 A820 150d multi           7.50  7.50
No. 3697 contains one 35x35mm stamp.

Bougainvillea Flowers — A821

Oleander
Flowers
A822

No. 3698 — Various bougainvillea flowers,
as shown.
No. 3699 — Various oleander flowers, as
shown.
150d, Yellow cassia flowers.

**2016, Feb. 20   Litho.   Perf. 13¾**
3698 A821  45d Sheet of 6,
#a-f                        14.00 14.00
3699 A822  50d Sheet of 4,
#a-d                        10.00 10.00
**Souvenir Sheet**
3700 A822 150d multi           7.50  7.50

Queen
Elizabeth
II, 90th
Birthday
A823

No. 3701 — Queen Elizabeth II wearing: a,
Blue green and black coat and hat. b, Patterned coat, no hat. c, Dark blue coat and light
blue hat. d, Pale blue coat and hat.
195d, Queen Elizabeth II wearing sash and
tiara.

**2016, Apr. 1   Litho.   Perf. 12**
3701 A823  50d Sheet of 4, #a-d 9.25 9.25
**Souvenir Sheet**
**Perf. 12½**
3702 A823 195d multi           9.00  9.00
No. 3702 contains one 38x51mm stamp.

New York City Landmarks — A824

No. 3703: a, Flatiron Building (30x80mm). b,
Grand Central Terminal (30x40mm). c, New
York Stock Exchange (30x40mm). d, United
Nations Headquarters (30x40mm). e, Statue
of Liberty (30x40mm).
195d, New York City skyline, horiz.

**2016, Apr. 1   Litho.   Perf. 14**
3703 A824  40d Sheet of 5, #a-e 9.25 9.25
**Souvenir Sheet**
**Perf. 12**
3704 A824 195d multi           9.00  9.00
2016 World Stamp Show, New York. No.
3704 contains one 80x60mm stamp.

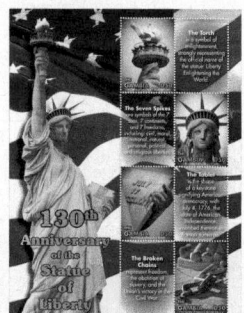

Statue of
Liberty,
130th
Anniv.
A825

No. 3705: a, Torch. b, Head and crown. c,
Tablet. d, Broken chains.
195d, Head, diff.

**2016, May 30   Litho.   Perf. 14**
3705 A825  50d Sheet of 4, #a-
d, + 4 labels              9.50  9.50
**Souvenir Sheet**
**Perf. 12¾**
3706 A825 195d multi           9.25  9.25
No. 3706 contains one 38x51mm stamp.

Terrorist
Attack
on World
Trade
Center,
15th
Anniv.
A826

No. 3707 — World Trade Center: a, At left,
clear blue skies. b, With Brooklyn Bridge in
foreground. c, At twilight, cloudy skies. d, At
right, partly cloudy blue skies. e, At center,
with gray skies, sun in background. f, At left,
with gray brown skies.
No. 3707, vert. — World Trade Center: a,
Daytime view. b, Twilight view.
195d, World Trade Center, Statue of Liberty.

**2016, May 30   Litho.   Perf. 14**
3707 A826  45d Sheet of 6,
#a-f                        13.00 13.00

**Souvenir Sheets**
**Perf. 12**
3708 A826 100d Sheet of 2,
#a-b                        9.50  9.50
**Perf. 12½**
3709 A826 195d multi           9.25  9.25
No. 3709 contains one 38x51mm stamp.

Souvenir Sheets

A827

A828

A829

Elvis Presley (1935-77) — A830

**2016, June 30  Litho.   Perf. 13x13½**
3710 A827 150d multi           7.00  7.00
**Perf. 13½x13**
3711 A828 150d multi           7.00  7.00
3712 A829 150d multi           7.00  7.00
3713 A830 150d multi           7.00  7.00
Nos. 3710-3713 (4)         28.00 28.00

William Shakespeare (1564-1616),
Writer — A831

No. 3714 — Scenes from *Romeo and Juliet*:
a, Sword fight. b, Romeo and Juliet embracing. c, Romeo embracing comatose Juliet. d,
Dead bodies of Romeo and Juliet.
150d, Shakespeare, vert.

**2016, July 14   Litho.   Perf. 13¾**
3714 A831  50d Sheet of 4, #a-d 9.50 9.50

**Souvenir Sheet**
**Perf. 12½**
3715 A831 150d multi           7.00  7.00
No. 3715 contains one 38x51mm stamp.

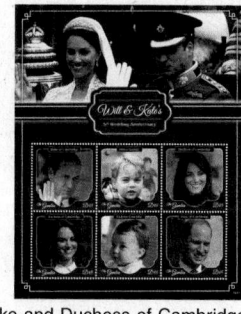

Duke and Duchess of Cambridge, 5th
Wedding Anniversary — A832

No. 3716: a, Duke waving. b, Prince
George. c, Duchess. d, Duchess wearing
white blouse. e, Princess Charlotte. f, Duke,
hands not visible.
No. 3717, horiz.: a, Duke and Duchess at
wedding. b, Duke, Duchess, Prince George
and Princess Charlotte.

**2016, Aug. 15   Litho.   Perf. 13¾**
3716 A832  45d Sheet of 6, #a-
f                           13.00 13.00
**Souvenir Sheet**
**Perf. 14**
3717 A832  75d Sheet of 2, #a-
b                           7.00  7.00
No. 3717 contains two 60x40mm stamps.

Luna 9,
50th
Anniv.
A833

No. 3718: a, Luna 10, Moon at LR. b, Luna
2, Moon at LL. c, Luna 9, Moon at UR. d, Luna
3, Moon at UL.
200d, Luna 9 Molniya Rocket launch, vert.

**2016, Sept. 9   Litho.   Perf. 14**
3718 A833  75d Sheet of 4,
#a-d                        14.50 14.50
**Souvenir Sheet**
**Perf. 12**
3719 A833 200d multi           9.50  9.50
No. 3718b is erroneously inscribed "Luna
10." The lauch date of Luna 2 is Sept. 12,
1959, not 1966.

Volcanoes — A834

No. 3720: a, Eyjafjallajökull, Iceland. b, Mt.
St. Helens, U.S. c, Krakatoa, Indonesia. d, Mt.
Fuji, Japan. e, Cotopaxi, Ecuador. f, Kilauea,
U.S.
170d, Mt. Vesuvius, Italy, vert.

**2016, Nov. 14   Litho.   Perf. 14**
3720 A834  55d Sheet of 6,
#a-f                        15.00 15.00
**Souvenir Sheet**
**Perf. 12½**
3721 A834 170d multi           7.75  7.75
No. 3721 contains one 38x51mm stamp.

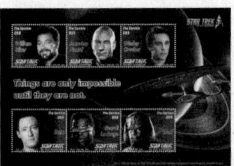

Characters From *Star Trek: The Next Generation* Television Series — A835

No. 3722: a, William Riker. b, Jean-Luc Picard. c, Wesley Crusher. d, Data. e, Geordi La Forge. f, Worf.
No. 3723: a, Beverly Crusher. b, Deanna Troi. c, Guinan.
No. 3724: a, La Forge, Data, Worf, Riker, Troi, Beverly Crusher, and Picard. b, U.S.S. Enterprise NCC-1701-D.

**2016, Nov. 3    Litho.    Perf. 14**
3722    A835    55d Sheet of 6, #a-f    15.00    5.00
**Perf.**
3723    A835    85d Sheet of 3, #a-c    12.00    12.00
**Souvenir Sheet**
**Perf. 12¾**
3724    A835    125d Sheet of 2, #a-b    11.50    11.50

No. 3723 contains three 38mm diameter stamps. No. 3724 contains two 51x38mm stamps.
On No. 3723b the last name "TROI" is spelled incorrectly.

Worldwide Fund for Nature (WWF) — A836

No. 3725 — Temminck's red colobus: a, With tree branch at left. b, Sitting. c, With tree branch at right. d, Head.

**2016, Nov. 14    Litho.    Perf. 12**
3725    A836    85d Block or horiz. strip of 4, #a-d    16.00    16.00
e.    Miniature sheet of 8, 2 each #3725a-3725d    32.00    32.00

Paintings by Hieronymus Bosch (c. 1450-1516) — A837

No. 3726 — Details from The Garden of Earthly Delights: a, Flock of birds from left panel. b, Water from center panel. c, Owl from center panel. d, Ear from right panel.
No. 3727 — Adoration of the Magi from circa: a, 1475 (Jesus on lap). b, 1499 (Jesus lifted).

**2016, Nov. 14    Litho.    Perf. 12**
3726    A837    85d Sheet of 4, #a-d    16.00    16.00
**Souvenir Sheet**
3727    A837    125d Sheet of 2, #a-b    11.50    11.50

Christmas — A838

Christmas tree ornaments: No. 3728, 85d, Rocking horse. No. 3729, 85d, Angel. No. 3730, 170d, Reindeer. No. 3731, 170d, Snowman.

**2016, Dec. 1    Litho.    Perf. 12¾**
3728-3731    A838    Set of 4    23.50    23.50

King Bhumibol Adulyadej of Thailand (1927-2016) — A839

No. 3732 — King Bhumibol Adulyadej: a, As young man, without hat, denomination at UR. b, As older man, wearing suit, denomination at UL. c, With Queen Sirikit, denomination at UR. d, With Queen Sirikit, denomination at UL. d, As young man wearing military hat, denomination at UR. e, As older man, wearing military uniform, denomination at UL.
No. 3733: a, Wearing ceremonial crown. b, Wearing military hat. c, Wearing suit aand tie, with Queen Sirikit. d, Wearing military uniform, with Queen Sirikit.

**2016, Dec. 28    Litho.    Perf. 14**
3732    A839    55d Sheet of 6, #a-f    16.00    16.00
3733    A839    85d Sheet of 4, #a-d    16.00    16.00

**Miniature Sheets**

Pres. John F. Kennedy (1917-63) — A841

No. 3734 — Pres. Kennedy in Navy in World War II: a, 60d, Wearing cap, in front of flat brick wall (40x30mm). b, 60d, Wearing cap, foliage in background (40x30mm). c, 60d, Without cap (40x30mm). d, 60d, Wearing cap, near corner of brick wall (40x30mm). e, 100d, With fellow crew members (80x30mm).
No. 3735 — Pres. Kennedy in Navy in World War II: a, Wearing dress cap. b, Without cap. c, In boat, wearing cap, facing right. d, In boat, wearing cap, facing left.

**2017, Feb. 7    Litho.    Perf. 14**
3734    A840    Sheet of 5, #a-e    15.50    15.50
3735    A841    75d Sheet of 4, #a-d    13.50    13.50

Mammals — A842

Designs: 2000d, Guinea baboon. 3000d, Spotted hyena. 5000d, Lion.

**2017, Mar. 8    Litho.    Perf. 12½x13¼**
3736    A842    2000d multi    90.00    90.00
3737    A842    3000d multi    130.00    130.00
3738    A842    5000d multi    220.00    220.00
Nos. 3736-3738 (3)    440.00    440.00

A843

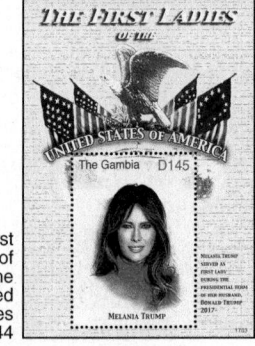

First Ladies of the United States A844

No. 3739, 20d: a, Martha Washington. b, Abigail Adams. c, Martha Jefferson. d, Dolley Madison. e, Elizabeth Monroe. f, Louisa Adams. g, Emily Donelson. h, Angelica Van Buren. i, Anna Harrison. j, Letitia Tyler. k, Julia Tyler. l, Sarah Polk. m, Margaret Taylor. n, Abigail Fillmore. o, Jane Pierce. p, Harriet Johnson.
No. 3740, 20d: a, Mary Lincoln. b, Eliza Johnson. c, Julia Grant. d, Lucy Hayes. e, Lucretia Garfield. f, Mary McElroy. g, Frances Cleveland (gray green portrait). h, Caroline Harrison. i, Frances Cleveland (gray portrait). j, Ida McKinley. k, Edith Roosevelt. l, Helen Taft. m, Ellen Wilson. n, Edith Wilson. o, Florence Harding. p, Grace Coolidge.
No. 3741, 20d: a, Lou Hoover. b, Eleanor Roosevelt. c, Bess Truman. d, Mamie Eisenhower. e, Jacqueline Kennedy. f, Claudia Johnson. g, Thelma Nixon. h, Elizabeth Ford. i, Eleanor Carter. j, Nancy Reagan. k, Barbara Bush. l, Hillary Clinton. m, Laura Bush. n, Michelle Obama. o, Melania Trump. p, White House and Seal of the Executive Office.
145d, Melania Trump.

**2017    Perf. 14**
**Sheets of 16, #a-p**
3739-3741    A843    Set of 3    42.00    42.00
**Souvenir Sheet**
**Perf. 13¼**
3742    A844    145d multi    6.50    6.50
Issued: Nos. 3739-3741, 7/10; No. 3742, 3/8. See Nos. 3920-3921.

**Miniature Sheet**

Princess Diana (1961-97) — A845

Various depictions of Princess Diana, as shown.

**2017, Apr. 14    Litho.    Perf. 13¾**
3743    A845    85d Sheet of 4, #a-d    15.00    15.00

Animals A846

No. 3744: a, North Sulawesi babirusa. b, Bog turtle. c, Owston's palm civet. d, Two-spined angelfish.
200d, Red panda, vert.

**2017, June 7    Litho.    Perf. 12½**
3744    A846    85d Sheet of 4, #a-d    15.00    15.00
**Souvenir Sheet**
3745    A846    200d multi    8.75    8.75

A847

Sunflowers — A848

Various photographs of sunflowers, as shown.

**2017, June 26    Litho.    Perf. 13¾**
3746    A847    85d Sheet of 4, #a-d    15.00    15.00
**Souvenir Sheet**
3747    A848    125d Sheet of 2, #a-b    11.00    11.00

**Miniature Sheet**

Proclamation of the House of Windsor, Cent. — A849

No. 3748, 55d: a, King Edward VII. b, King George V. c, King Edward VIII. d, King George VI. e, Queen Elizabeth II. f, Royal badge.

**2017, July 10    Litho.    Perf. 13¼**
3748    A849    Sheet of 6, #a-f    14.50    14.50

Meerkats A850

No. 3749: a, Meerkat on rock, front paws at left. b, Meerkat facing forward, rocks in background. c, Meerkat facing forward, foliage in background. d, Two meerkats.
No. 3750: a, Meerkat behind rock. b, Meerkat, rocks in background.

**2017, Aug. 2    Litho.    Perf. 14**
3749    A850    90d Sheet of 4, #a-d    16.00    16.00

## Souvenir Sheet

3750 A850 150d Sheet of 2, #a-b    13.50 13.50

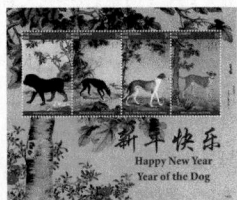

Paintings of Dogs by Lang Shining (Giuseppe Castiglione) (1688-1766) — A851

No. 3751, 85d: a, Heavenly Lion. b, Young Black Dragon. c, Dog in the Bamboo Shade. d, Yellow Leopard.
No. 3752, 85d: a, Young Gray Dragon. b, Golden-Winged Face. c, Star-Glancing Wolf. d, Flying Magpie.

**2017, Aug. 2    Litho.    *Perf. 12***
**Sheets of 4, #a-d**

3751-3752 A851  Set of 2    30.00 30.00

New Year 2018 (Year of the Dog).

A852

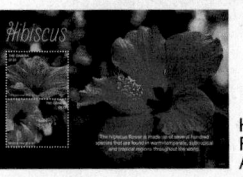

Hibiscus Flowers A853

Various photographs of hibiscus flowers, as shown.

**2017, Aug. 9    Litho.    *Perf. 13¾***

3753 A852  85d Sheet of 4, #a-d    15.00 15.00

**Souvenir Sheet**
***Perf. 12***

3754 A853 125d Sheet of 2, #a-b    11.00 11.00

Zeppelins — A854

No. 3755: a, LZ-127 Graf Zeppelin in hangar. b, People and automobiles near LZ-127 Graf Zeppelin. c, Count Ferdinand von Zeppelin in 1914. d, LZ-130 Graf Zeppelin II in flight.
170d, Count Ferdinand von Zeppelein (1838-1917), vert.

**2017, Oct. 12    Litho.    *Perf. 12***

3755 A854  85d Sheet of 4, #a-d    14.50 14.50

**Souvenir Sheet**
***Perf. 12½***

3756 A854 170d multi    7.25 7.25

No. 3756 contains one 38x51mm stamp.

## Souvenir Sheets

Elvis Presley (1935-77) — A855

Inscriptions: No. 3757, 170d, Breaks concert attendance record. No. 3758, 170d, Jamming with the Fab Four. No. 3759, 170d, Buys first Stutz Blackhawk. No. 3760, 170d, Introuduces his jumpsuits. vert.

**2017, Nov. 17    Litho.    *Perf. 12½***

3757-3760 A855  Set of 4    29.00 29.00

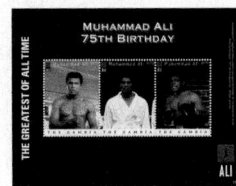

Muhammad Ali (1942-2016), Boxer — A856

No. 3761 — Ali: a, With bare fists. b, Wearing white robe. c, Wearing boxing gloves.
250d, Ali wearing suit and tie.

**2017, Dec. 17    Litho.    *Perf. 14***

3761 A856 175d Sheet of 3, #a-c    22.00 22.00

**Souvenir Sheet**
***Perf. 12½***

3762 A856 250d multi    10.50 10.50

No. 3762 contains one 38x51mm stamp.

Lions Clubs International, Cent. — A857

No. 3763 — Lions Clubs International emblem and: a, Hands of adult and child. b, Leaf and raindrop. c, Stalk of wheat. d, Eye.
No. 3764, vert. — Centennial Service Challenge emblem, hands, eye, stalk of wheat, and leaf, with frame color of: a, Yellow. b, Bluish violet.

**2017, Dec. 17    Litho.    *Perf. 13¾***

3763 A857  85d Sheet of 4, 3a-d    14.50 14.50

**Souvenir Sheet**
***Perf. 12½***

3764 A857  85d Sheet of 2, #a-b    7.25 7.25

No. 3764 contains two 38x51mm stamps.

## Miniature Sheet

World War II, 75th Anniv. A858

No. 3765 — American posters: a, Uncle Sam Army recruitment poster. b, 7th War Loan poster. c, Buy War Bonds poster. d, Loose Talk Can Cost Lives poster. e, Victory Liberty Loan poster. f, SPARS recruiting poster.

**2017, Dec. 17    Litho.    *Perf. 14***

3765 A858  55d Sheet of 6, #a-f    14.00 14.00

Lions A859

No. 3766 — Various pictures of lions: a, 70d. b, 80d. c, 90d. d, 100d.
No. 3767 — Various pictures of lions: a, 75d. b, 85d. c, 95d.

**2018, Jan. 4    Litho.    *Perf. 14***

3766 A859  Sheet of 4, #a-d    14.50 14.50

**Souvenir Sheet**
***Perf. 12***

3767 A859  Sheet of 3, #a-c    11.00 11.00

Fishing A860

No. 3768: a, 70d, Starry triggerfish. b, 80d, Harpoon fishing. c, 90d, Wahoos. d, 100d, Fishing boats.
170d, Dugout fishing boat.

**2018, Jan. 4    Litho.    *Perf. 14***

3768 A860  Sheet of 4, #a-d    14.50 14.50

**Souvenir Sheet**
***Perf. 12***

3769 A860 170d multi    7.25 7.25

No. 3769 contains one 50x30mm stamp.

Hamerkops — A861

No. 3770 — Various photographs of hamerkops: a, 65d. b, 75d. c, 85d. d, 95d.
No. 3771, horiz.: a, Head of hamerkop. b, Hamerkop.

**2018, Jan. 4    Litho.    *Perf. 14***

3770 A861  Sheet of 4, #a-d    13.50 13.50

**Souvenir Sheet**
***Perf. 12***

3771 A861 125d Sheet of 2, #a-b    10.50 10.50

## Miniature Sheet

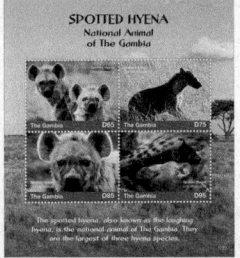

Spotted Hyenas A862

No. 3772 — Various photographs of spotted hyenas: a, 65d. b, 75d. c, 85d. d, 95d.

**2018, Jan. 4    Litho.    *Perf. 14***

3772 A862  Sheet of 4, #a-d    13.50 13.50

## Miniature Sheet

Visit of Pres. Donald Trump to the Philippines — A863

No. 3773: a, Philippines First Lady Honeylet Avanceña. b, Philippines President Rodrigo Duterte. c, U.S. President Donald Trump. d, Emblem of Association of South East Nations.

**2018, Jan. 4    Litho.    *Perf. 12***

3773 A863 85d Sheet of 4, #a-d    14.50 14.50

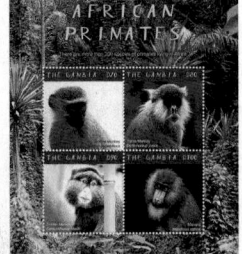

African Primates A864

No. 3774: a, 70d, Vervet monkey. b, 80d, Patas monkey. c, 90d, Golden monkey. d, 100d, Mandrill.
No. 3775, horiz.: a, Common chimpanzee. b, Eastern gorilla.

**2018, Mar. 27    Litho.    *Perf. 13¾***

3774 A864  Sheet of 4, #a-d    14.50 14.50

**Souvenir Sheet**
***Perf. 12½***

3775 A864 125d Sheet of 2, #a-b    10.50 10.50

No. 3775 contains two 51x38mm stamps.

Birds A865

No. 3776: a, Goliath heron. b, Greater flamingos. c, Glossy ibis. d, Little grebe.
No. 3777, horiz.: a, Yellow-billed stork. b, Egyptian goose. c, Pied kingfisher.

**2018, Mar. 27    Litho.    *Perf. 13¾***

3776 A865 85d Sheet of 4, #a-d    14.50 14.50

**Souvenir Sheet**
***Perf. 14***

3777 A865 85d Sheet of 3, #a-c    11.00 11.00

No. 3777 contains three 40x30mm stamps.

Gray Crowned Cranes A866

No. 3778 — Various photographs of gray crowned cranes: a, 120d. b, 125d. c, 130d.
215d, Gray crowned cranes, horiz.

**2018, Mar. 27    Litho.    *Perf. 13¾***

3778 A866  Sheet of 3, #a-c    16.00 16.00

**Souvenir Sheet**
***Perf. 14***

3779 A866 215d multi    9.00 9.00

No. 3779 contains one 80x30mm stamp.

U. S. Airmail Flights, Cent. A867

No. 3780: a, Amelia Earhart (1897-1937), wearing goggles, and Merrill CIT-9 Safety Plane. b, Cover with cachet of Earhart's solo transatlantic flight. c, Signed cacheted envelope for Earhart's flight around the world. d, Earhart, without goggles, and Merrill CIT-9 Safety Plane.

200d, Earhart and U.S. #C68.

**2018, Mar. 27**    **Litho.**    **Perf. 14**
3780 A867 95d Sheet of 4,
   #a-d     16.00 16.00
**Souvenir Sheet**
**Perf. 12**
3781 A867 200d multi     8.50 8.50
No. 3781 contains one 51x38mm stamp.

Planets A868

No. 3782: a, Jupiter. b, Uranus. c, Neptune and Pluto. d, Saturn.
No. 3783: a, Mercury and Venus. b, Earth. c, Mars.

**2018, Apr. 23**    **Litho.**    **Perf. 13¾**
3782 A868 95d Sheet of 4, #a-d     16.00 16.00
**Souvenir Sheet**
3783 A868 95d Sheet of 3, #a-c     12.00 12.00

Birds of Prey A869

No. 3784: a, 80d, Palm nut vulture. b, 90d, Tawny eagle. c, 100d, Yellow-billed kite. d, 110d, Long-crested eagle.
No. 3785: a, 100d, African harrier-hawk. b, 125d, Bateleur. c, 150d, Common buzzard.

**2018, Apr. 23**    **Litho.**    **Perf. 14**
3784 A869 Sheet of 4, #a-d     16.00 16.00
**Souvenir Sheet**
3785 A869 Sheet of 3, #a-c     16.00 16.00

African Mammals — A870

No. 3786: a, Caracal. b, Steenbok. c, Red river hogs. d, Meerkats.
No. 3783: a, Greater kudu. b, Aardwolf.

**2018, Apr. 23**    **Litho.**    **Perf. 14**
3786 A870 150d Sheet of 4,
   #a-d     25.50 25.50
**Souvenir Sheet**
**Perf. 12½**
3787 A870 150d Sheet of 3,
   #a-c     13.00 13.00
No. 3787 contains two 51x38mm stamps.

Miniature Sheet

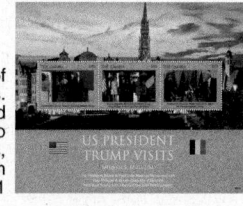

Visit of Pres. Donald Trump to Brussels, Belgium A871

No. 3788: a, Pres. Trump and wife, Melania. b, Belgian Queen Mathilde, King Philippe, Pres. Trump and wife, Melania. c, European Parliament President Antonio Tajani and Pres. Trump.

**2018, May 4**    **Litho.**    **Perf. 14**
3788 A871 95d Sheet of 3, #a-c     12.00 12.00

**Souvenir Sheet**

Tianmu Lake, People's Republic of China A872

**2018, May 14**    **Litho.**    **Perf. 12½**
3789 A872 500d multi     21.50 21.50
China National Stamp Exhibition, Changzhou.

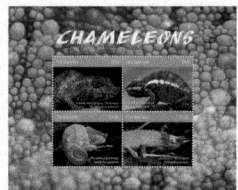

Chameleons — A873

No. 3790: a, 90d, Rosette-nosed pygmy chameleon. b, 95d, Panther chameleon. c, 100d, Parson's chameleon. d, 105d, Jackson's chameleon.
200d, Veiled chameleon.

**2018, May 22**    **Litho.**    **Perf. 14**
3790 A873 Sheet of 4, #a-d 16.50 16.50
**Souvenir Sheet**
**Perf. 12½**
3791 A873 200d multi     8.50 8.50
No. 3791 contains one 51x38mm stamp.

Miniature Sheet

Birth of Prince Louis of Cambridge — A874

No. 3792: a, Duke, at left, and Duchess of Cambridge, holding Prince Louis. b, Duke at right, and Duchess of Cambridge, holding Prince Louis. c, Duke, holding Prince Louis, and Duchess of Cambridge. d, Coat of arms of the Duke and Duchess of Cambridge.

**2018, June 18**    **Litho.**    **Perf. 13¾**
3792 A874 100d Sheet of 4,
   #a-d     17.00 17.00

Engagement of Prince Harry and Meghan Markle — A875

No. 3793 — Couple with Markle at: a, Left, without hat. b, Right. c, Left, wearing hat.
No. 3794: a, Prince Harry. c, Markle.

**2018, June 18**    **Litho.**    **Perf. 12**
3793 A875 95d Sheet of 3,
   #a-c     12.00 12.00
**Souvenir Sheet**
3794 A875 150d Sheet of 2,
   #a-b     13.00 13.00

Elvis Presley (1935-77) — A876

No. 3795 — Presley facing a: 50d, Right. b, 70d, Left.

**2018, June 30**    **Litho.**    **Perf. 12**
3795 A876 Vert. pair, #a-b     5.25 5.25

Souvenir Sheets

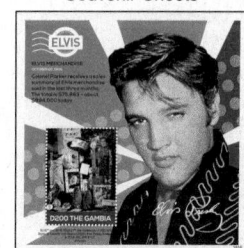

Elvis Presley (1935-77) — A877

Inscriptions: No. 3796, 200d, Elvis merchandise. No. 3797, 200d, King Creole. No. 3798, 200d, Most eligible bachelor. No. 3799, 200d, Elvis steps behind camera, horiz.

**2018, July 6**    **Litho.**    **Perf. 14**
3796-3799 A877 Set of 4     33.00 33.00

Souvenir Sheet

Nelson Mandela (1918-2013), President of South Africa — A878

**2018, July 18**    **Litho.**    **Perf. 13¾**
3800 A878 200d multi     8.50 8.50

Souvenir Sheet

2018 World Cup Soccer Championships, Russia — A879

No. 3801: a, French team. b, Victorious French team celebrationg. c, Croatian team.

**2018, Oct. 3**    **Litho.**    **Perf. 12½**
3801 A879 100d Sheet of 3,
   #a-c     12.50 12.50

Flight of Apollo 11, 50th Anniv. A880

No. 3802: a, Astronaut and U.S. flag on Moon (60x40mm). b, Astronaut's foot and footprint on Moon (30x40mm). c, Gold olive branch (30x40mm).
200d, Astronaut and Lunar Module on Moon, Apollo 11 mission emblem, horiz.

**2018, Oct. 3**    **Litho.**    **Perf. 14**
3802 A880 110d Sheet of 3,
   #a-c     13.50 13.50
**Souvenir Sheet**
**Perf. 12½**
3803 A880 200d multi     8.25 8.25
No. 3803 contains one 51x38mm stamp.

A881

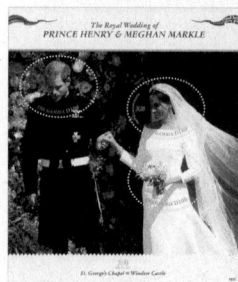

Wedding of Prince Harry and Meghan Markle A882

No. 3804: a, 70d, Coat of arms of the Duke of Sussex (30x40mm). b, 70d, Coat of arms of the Duchess of Sussex (30x40mm). c, 100d, Bride and groom (30x80mm).
No. 3805: a, Prince Harry. b, Meghan Markle. c, Bouquet of flowers.

**2018, Oct. 3**    **Litho.**    **Perf. 14**
3804 A881 Sheet of 5,
   #3804c, 2 each
   #3804a-3804b     15.50 15.50
**Souvenir Sheet**
**Perf.**
3805 A882 100d Sheet of 3,
   #a-c     12.50 12.50

A883

New Year 2019 (Year of the Pig) A884

**2018, Oct. 3**    **Litho.**    **Perf. 14**
3806 A883 100d multi    4.00 4.00
**Souvenir Sheet**
**Perf. 13¾**
3807 A884 100d multi    4.00 4.00

Miniature Sheet

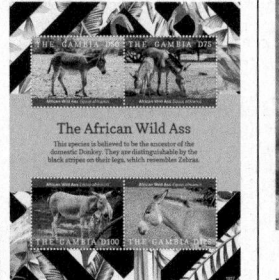

African Wild Asses A885

No. 3808 — Various photographs of African wild asses: a, 50d. b, 75d. c, 100d. d, 125d.

**2018, Oct. 10**    **Litho.**    **Perf. 14**
3808 A885   Sheet of 4, #a-d   14.50 14.50

Green Monkeys A886

No. 3809: a, 80d, Green monkey facing left. b, 100d, Two green monkeys. c, 120d, Head of green monkey.
200d, Green monkey, vert.

**2018, Oct. 10**    **Litho.**    **Perf. 14**
3809 A886   Sheet of 3, #a-c   12.50 12.50
**Souvenir Sheet**
3810 A886 200d multi    8.25 8.25

Dolphins A887

No. 3811: a, Fraser's dolphin. b, Short-beaked common dolphin. c, Striped dolphin. d, Rough-toothed dolphin.
200d, Atlantic humpback dolphin.

**2018, Oct. 10**    **Litho.**    **Perf. 12**
3811 A887   77d Sheet of 4, #a-d   12.50 12.50
**Souvenir Sheet**
3812 A887 200d multi    8.25 8.25

Large African Mammals — A888

No. 3813: a, Hippopotamus (50x30mm). b, Common warthog (51x38mm). c, Red river hog (51x38mm).
No. 3814: a, 100d, Leopard (30x40mm). b, 200d, Lion (60x40mm).

**Perf. 12 (#3813a), 12½ (#3813b-3813c)**

**2018, Oct. 10**    **Litho.**
3813 A888 100d Sheet of 3, #a-c   12.50 12.50
**Souvenir Sheet**
**Perf. 14**
3814 A888   Sheet of 2, #a-b   12.50 12.50

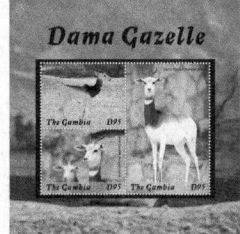

Dama Gazelles A889

No. 3815: a, Dama gazelle with head at right (40x30mm). b, Heads of two Dama gazelles (40x30mm). c, Dama gazelle with head at left (40x60mm).
No. 3816 — Head of Dama gazelle facing: a, Forward. b, Left.

**2018, Nov. 9**    **Litho.**    **Perf. 14**
3815 A889   95d Sheet of 3, #a-c   11.50 11.50
**Souvenir Sheet**
3816 A889 150d Sheet of 2, #a-b   12.00 12.00
No. 3816 contains two 30x40mm stamps.

Burchell's Zebras — A890

No. 3817 — Various photographs of Burchell's zebras: a, 60d. b, 80d. c, 100d. d, 120d. 200d, Burchell's zebra, vert.

**2018, Nov.9**    **Litho.**    **Perf. 12½**
3817 A890   Sheet of 4, #a-d   14.50 14.50
**Souvenir Sheet**
3818 A890 200d multi    8.00 8.00

Red River Hogs A891

No. 3819 — Various photographs of red river hogs: a, 90d. b, 95d. c, 100d. d, 105d. 200d, Two red river hogs, diff.

**2018, Dec. 19**    **Litho.**    **Perf. 14**
3819 A891   Sheet of 4, #a-d   16.00 16.00
**Souvenir Sheet**
3820 A891 200d multi    8.25 8.25

Miniature Sheets

Butterflies and Moths — A892

No. 3821: a, 50d, Figtree blue butterfly. b, 75d, Blue temora butterfly. c, 100d, Citrus swallowtail butterfly. d, 125d, Beartiful tiger butterfly.
No. 3822: a, 50d, Striped policeman butterfly. b, 100d, Club-tailed emperor butterfly. c, 150d, Madagascar diadem butterfly. d, 200d, Dorippus tiger butterfly.
No. 3823: a, 80d, Green sphinx moth. b, 80d, Madagascan sunset moth. c, 120d, Blue-banded swallowtail butterfly. d, 120d, Dotted border butterfly.
No. 3824: a, 100d: a, Yellow patch white butterfly. b, Wandering donkey butterfly, c, Pearl emperor butterfly. d, African map butterfly.

**2018, Dec. 19**    **Litho.**    **Perf.**
**Sheets of 4, #a-d**
3821-3824 A892   Set of 4   67.00 67.00

Miniature Sheet

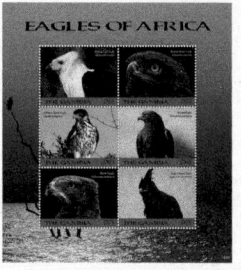

Eagles A893

No. 3825: a, 55d, African fish eagle. b, 55d, Brown snake eagle. c, 65d, African hawk-eagle. d, 65d, Booted eagle. e, 75d, Martial eagle. f, 75d, Long-crested eagle.

**2018, Dec. 31**    **Litho.**    **Perf. 14**
3825 A893   Sheet of 6, #a-f   16.00 16.00

Miniature Sheet

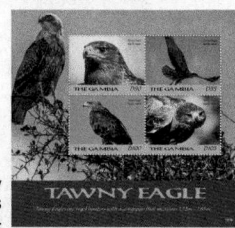

Tawny Eagles A894

No. 3826 — Various photographs of tawny eagles: a, 90d. b, 95d. c, 100d. d, 105d.

**2018, Dec. 31**    **Litho.**    **Perf. 14**
3826 A894   Sheet of 4, #a-d   16.00 16.00

Miniature Sheet

Small African Mammals — A895

No. 3827: a, 90d, Aardvark (30x40mm). b, 90d, Gambian mongoose (30x40mm). c, 120d, Red-flanked duiker (60x40mm). d, 120d, Senegal bushbaby (60x40mm).

**2018, Dec. 31**    **Litho.**    **Perf. 14**
3827 A895   Sheet of 4, #a-d   17.00 17.00

Black Rhinoceroses — A896

No. 3828 — Various photographs of Black rhinoceros: a, 50d. b, 100d. c, 150d. 250d, Black rhinoceros, diff.

**2019, Feb. 12**    **Litho.**    **Perf. 12**
3828 A896   Sheet of 3, #a-c   12.00 12.00
**Souvenir Sheet**
**Perf.**
3829 A896 250d multi    10.00 10.00
No. 3829 contains one 43x34mm oval stamp.

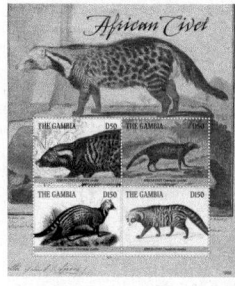

African Civets A897

No. 3830 — Various drawings of civets facing: a, 50d, Left. b, 50d, Right. c, 150d, Right. d, 150d, Left. 250d, African civet, diff.

**2019, Feb. 12**    **Litho.**    **Perf. 14**
3830 A897   Sheet of 4, #a-d   16.00 16.00
**Souvenir Sheet**
**Perf. 12½**
3831 A897 250d multi    10.00 10.00
No. 3831 contains one 51x38mm stamp.

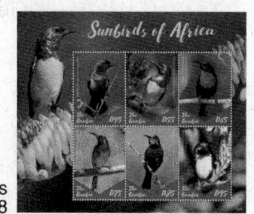

Sunbirds A898

No. 3832: a, 45d, Beautiful sunbird. b, 55d, Collared sunbird. c, 65d, Scarlet-chested sunbird. d, 75d, Orange-breasted sunbird. e, 85d, Marico sunbird. f, 95d, White-bellied sunbird. 250d, Orange-breasted sunbird, diff.

**2019, Feb. 27**    **Litho.**    **Perf. 14**
3832 A898   Sheet of 6, #a-f   17.00 17.00
**Souvenir Sheet**
**Perf. 12½**
3833 A898 250d multi    10.00 10.00
No. 3833 contains one 38x51mm stamp.

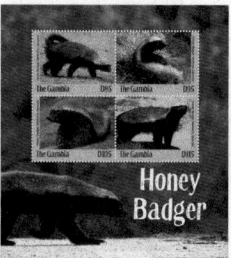

Honey Badgers A899

No. 3834 — Various photographs of Honey badgers: a, 85d. b, 95d. c, 105d. d, 115d.
No. 3835, 150d — Honey badger facing: a, Right. b, Left.

**2019, Apr. 4      Litho.      Perf. 14**
3834  A899   Sheet of 4, #a-d      16.00  16.00
**Souvenir Sheet**
3835  A899  150d Sheet of 2,
                #a-b                         12.00  12.00

Black
Storks
A900

White Storks
A901

Yellow-billed Storks — A902

Abdim's
Storks
A903

Saddle-billed Storks — A904

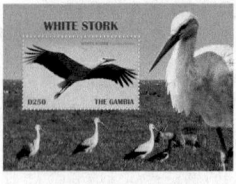

White
Stork
A905

No. 3836 — Various photographs of Black
storks: a, 50d. b, 60d, c, 70d. d, 80d. e, 90d. f,
100d.
No. 3837 — Various photographs of White
storks, as shown.
No. 3838 — Various photographs of Yellow-
billed storks: a, 50d. b, 100d. c, 150d. d, 200d.
No. 3839 — Various photographs of
Abdim's storks: a, Facing right. b, In tree. c, In
flight. d, Head.
No. 3840 — Various photographs of Saddle-
billed storks: a, 100d, Facing right (30x50mm).
b, 100d, Facing left (30x50mm). c, 150d, In
flight (60x50mm).

**2019, Apr. 4      Litho.      Perf. 14**
3836  A900   Sheet of 6, #a-f      18.00  18.00
3837  A901   70d Sheet of 6,
                #a-f                         17.00  17.00
**Perf. 12**
3838  A902   Sheet of 4, #a-d     20.00  20.00
3839  A903   100d Sheet of 4,
                #a-d                         20.00  20.00
3840  A904   Sheet of 3, #a-c     14.00  14.00
    Nos. 3836-3840 (5)                89.00  89.00
**Souvenir Sheet**
3840D  A905  250d multi                  10.00  10.00

---

Miniature Sheet

Gold Key
Star Trek
Comic
Book
Covers
A906

No. 3841 — Gold Key Star Trek comic book
edition: a, 45d, #60. b, 55d, #55. c, 65d, #37.
d, 75d, #35. e, 85d, #33. f, 95d, #30.

**2019, Apr. 17      Litho.      Perf. 12½**
3841  A906   Sheet of 6, #a-f      17.00  17.00

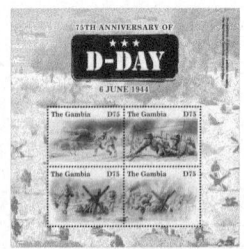

D-Day,
75th
Anniv.
A907

No. 3842: a, Soldiers and tank. b, Soldiers
crawling under barbed wire. c, Soldiers coming ashore. d, Soldiers coming ashore, burning ship at left.
250d, Soldier holding hand grenade.

**2019, May 31      Litho.      Perf. 14**
3842  A907   75d Sheet of 4,
                #a-d                         12.50  12.50
**Souvenir Sheet**
3843  A907   250d multi                  10.50  10.50

Caracals
A908

No. 3844 — Various photographs of caracals: a, 95d. b, 100d. c, 105d. d, 110d.
No. 3845, horiz.: a, Caracal. b, Head of
caracal.

**2019, May 31      Litho.      Perf. 12**
3844  A908   Sheet of 4, #a-d      17.00  17.00
**Souvenir Sheet**
**Perf. 14**
3845  A908   150d Sheet of 2,
                #a-b                         12.50  12.50

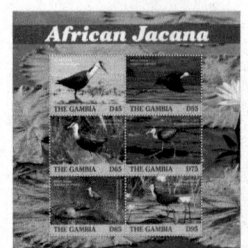

African
Jacanas
A909

No. 3846 — Various photographs of African
jacanas: a, 45d. b, 55d. c, 65d. d, 75d. e, 85d.
f, 95d.
250d, African jacana, vert.

**2019, June 8      Litho.      Perf. 14**
3846  A909   Sheet of 6, #a-f      17.00  17.00
**Souvenir Sheet**
**Perf. 12½**
3847  A909   250d multi                  10.00  10.00
No. 3847 contains one 38x51mm stamp.

---

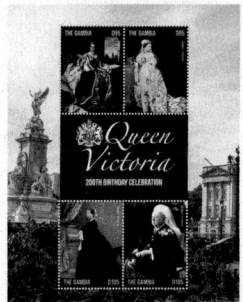

Queen Victoria (1819-1901) — A910

No. 3848: a, 95d, Portrait of Queen Victoria
by Franz Xaver Winterhalter. b, 95d, Photograph of Queen Victoria in wedding gown. c,
105d, 1861 Photograph of Queen Victoria by
John Mayall. d, 105d, Photograph of elderly
Queen Victoria by Hughes and Mullins.
250d, Queen Victoria in carriage.

**2019, June 8      Litho.      Perf. 14**
3848  A910   Sheet of 4, #a-d      16.00  16.00
**Souvenir Sheet**
**Perf. 12½**
3849  A910   250d multi                  10.00  10.00
No. 3849 contains one 38x51mm stamp.

Souvenir Sheet

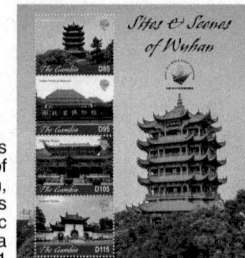

Buildings
of
Wuhan,
People's
Republic
of China
A911

No. 3850: a, 85d, Yellow Crane Tower. b,
95d, Hubei Provincial Museum. c, 105d,
Baotong Temple. d, 115d, Guiyuan Temple.

**2019, June 10      Litho.      Perf. 12**
3850  A911   Sheet of 4, #a-d      16.00  16.00
China 2019 World Stamp Exhibition, Wuhan.

Miniature Sheet

Birth of Archie Mountbatten-
Windsor — A912

No. 3851: a, 85d, Duke and Duchess of
Sussex. b, 95d, Duchess of Sussex. c, 105d,
Duke of Sussex. d, 115d, Duke and Duchess
of Sussex with son, Archie.

**2019, June 19      Litho.      Perf. 14**
3851  A912   Sheet of 4, #a-d      16.00  16.00

Lions
A913

No. 3852: a, 50d, Lion facing right. b, 50d,
Lion cubs. c, 150d, Lion (olive brown panel). d,
150d, Head of lion (red brown panel).
250d, Lion, diff.

---

**2019, July 31      Litho.      Perf. 14**
3852  A913   Sheet of 4, #a-d      16.00  16.00
**Souvenir Sheet**
**Perf. 12½**
3853  A913   250d multi                  10.00  10.00
    Singpex 2019 International Stamp Exhibi-
tion, Singapore. No. 3853 contains one
38x51mm stamp.

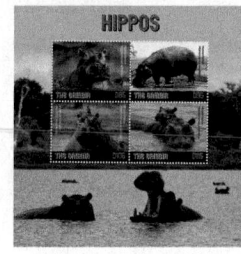

Hippopotami — A914

No. 3854 — Various photographs of hippopotami: a, 85d. b, 95d. c, 105d. d, 115d.
250d, Hippopotamus, vert.

**2019, Aug. 7      Litho.      Perf. 14**
3854  A914   Sheet of 4, #a-d      16.00  16.00
**Souvenir Sheet**
**Perf. 12½**
3855  A914   250d multi                  10.00  10.00
No. 3855 contains one 38x51mm stamp.

Gambian
Beaches
A915

No. 3856 — Beach in: a, 85d, Banjul. b,
95d, Kotu. c, 105d, Bakau. d, 115d,
Serrekunda.
250d, Cape Point Beach.

**2019, Aug. 7      Litho.      Perf. 14**
3856  A915   Sheet of 4, #a-d      16.00  16.00
**Souvenir Sheet**
3857  A915   250d multi                  10.00  10.00

Dorje Chang Buddha III, Religious
Leader
A916

No. 3858: a, Wearing yellow robe. b, Wearing hat.

**2019, Sept. 27      Litho.      Perf. 12½**
3858  A916   50d Pair, #a-b           4.00   4.00

Long-tailed Pangolins — A917

No. 3859: a, Pangolin curled up. b, Pangolin
on branch facing left. c, Pangolin facing right.
d, Pangolin on stump.
250d, Pangolin facing left.

**2019, Nov. 1      Litho.      Perf. 13¾**
3859  A917   100d Sheet of 4,
                #a-d                         16.00  16.00
**Souvenir Sheet**
3860  A917   250d multi                   9.75   9.75

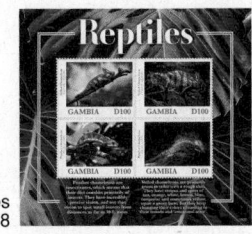

Reptiles
A918

No. 3861: a, Veiled chameleon with tail hanging below branch. b, Veiled chameleon with curled tail. c, Panther chameleon on cut branch. d, Panther chameleon on log.

**2019, Dec. 17          Perf. 14**
3861 A918 100d Sheet of 4,
#a-d
                              15.50 15.50

Miniature Sheet

Workers Combatting COVID-19
Pandemic — A919

No. 3862: a, Medical worker wearing protective face mask and eye protection. b, Rescue medic wearing helmet and protective face mask. c, Medical worker wearing protective face shield and patient wearing mask. d, Medical technician placing blood drop on microscope slide.

**2020, Aug. 7          Litho.          Perf. 14**
3862 A919 85d Sheet of 4, #a-
d
                              13.00 13.00

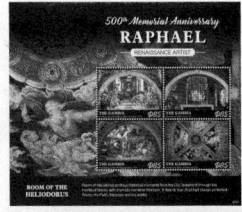

Frescoes of the Vatican's Room of
Heliodorus Painted by Raphael (1483-
1520) — A920

No. 3863: a, The Expulsion of Heliodorus from the Temple. b, Deliverance of St. Peter. c, The Meeting of Leo the Great and Attila. d, Ceiling of the Room of Heliodorus.
170d, The Mass at Bolsena.

**2020, Aug. 7          Litho.          Perf. 14**
3863 A920 85d Sheet of 4,
#a-d
                              13.00 13.00
**Souvenir Sheet**
**Perf. 12**
3864 A920 170d multi            6.75 6.75
No. 3864 contains one 50x30mm stamp.
No. 3863d inscription is missing the "H" in Heliodorus.

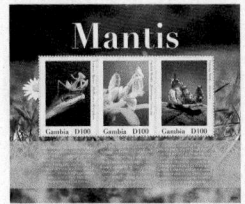

Mantises
A921

No. 3865: a, Unicorn mantis. b, Orchid mantis. c, Praying mantis.
250d, Legs of Praying mantis, horiz.

**2020, Aug. 7          Litho.          Perf. 14**
3865 A921 100d Sheet of 3,
#a-c
                              11.50 11.50
**Souvenir Sheet**
3866 A921 250d multi            9.75 9.75

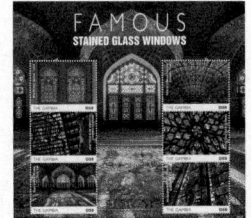

Visit to
France
of Pres.
Donald
Trump
A922

No. 3867: a, Canadian Prime Minister Justin Trudeau. b, President of France Emmanuel Macron. c, Pres. Trump. d, Queen Elizabeth II. e, German Chancellor Angela Merkel.
175d, Presidents Macron and Trump, horiz.

**2020, Aug. 7          Litho.          Perf. 14**
3867 A922 75d Sheet of 5,
#a-e
                              14.50 14.50
**Souvenir Sheet**
3868 A922 175d multi            6.75 6.75

Stained
Glass
Windows
A923

No. 3869 — Stained glass window from: a, Blue Mosque, Istanbul, Turkey. b, Palau de la Musica Catalana, Barcelona, Spain. c, Metropolitan Cathedral of St. Sebastian, Rio de Janeiro, Brazil. d, Sainte-Chapelle, Paris, France. e, Nasir al-Mulk Mosque, Shiraz, Iran. f, Washington National Cathedral, Washington, D.C.
200d, Chartres Cathedral, Chartres, France, vert.

**2020, Aug. 11          Litho.          Perf. 14**
3869 A923 50d Sheet of 6,
#a-f
                              11.50 11.50
**Souvenir Sheet**
3870 A923 200d multi            7.75 7.75

Miniature Sheet

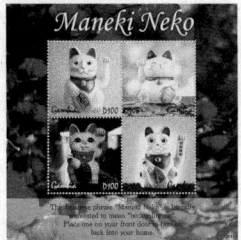

New
Year
2020
(Year of
the Rat)
A924

No. 3871 — Rats with background color of: a, Roset red. b, Magenta. c, Yellow. d, Cerise. e, Violet.

**2020, Aug. 31          Litho.          Perf. 13¾**
3871 A924 65d Sheet of 5, #a-
e
                              12.50 12.50

Maneki Neko (Japanese Waving Cat
Figurines) — A925

No. 3872: a, Figurine with pink background. b, Figurine on coins. c, Figurine on wooden table. d, Figurine with yellow background.
250d, Figurine, vert.

**2020, Sept. 30          Litho.          Perf. 13¾**
3872 A925 100d Sheet of 4,
#a-d
                              15.50 15.50
**Souvenir Sheet**
**Perf. 12½**
3873 A925 250d multi            9.75 9.75
No. 3873 contains one 38x51mm stamp.

Chinese
Paintings
by Dr.
Yuhua
Shouzhi
Wang
A926

No. 3874: a, 50d, Basket of flowers. b, 100d, Flowers. c, 150d, Basket of flowers, diff. 200d, Flowers, diff.

**2020, Sept. 30          Litho.          Perf. 14**
3874 A926     Sheet of 3, #a-c   11.50 11.50
**Souvenir Sheet**
**Perf. 12**
3875 A926 200d multi            7.75 7.75
No. 3875 contains one 30x80mm stamp.

Snakes
A927

No. 3876: a, Green tree viper. b, Amazon tree boa. c, Green pit viper. d, White-lipped island pit viper.
No. 3877: a, Western bush viper. b, Boomslang.

**2020, Sept. 30          Litho.          Perf. 13¾**
3876 A927 100d Sheet of 4,
#a-d
                              15.50 15.50
**Souvenir Sheet**
**Perf. 14**
3877 A927 150d Sheet of 2,
#a-b
                              11.50 11.50
No. 3877 contains two 40x30mm stamps.

Miniature Sheet

Victory in
Europe
Day,
75th
Anniv.
A928

No. 3878: a, Neville Chamberlain (1869-1940), British Prime Minister. b, Winston Churchill (1874-1965), British Prime Minister. c, Pres. Franklin D. Roosevelt (1882-1945). d, Pres. Dwight D. Eisenhower (1890-1969).

**2020, Sept. 30          Litho.          Perf. 14**
3878 A928 100d Sheet of 4,
#a-d
                              15.50 15.50

Miniature Sheet

Three-toed Sloths — A929

No. 3879 — Sloth with: a, Country name at LL, denomination at LR, inscription at UL reading up. b, Country name at UL, denomination at UR, inscription at LR. c, Country name at LL, denomination at LR, inscription at UL reading horizontally. d, Country name at UL, denomination at LL, inscription at LR.

**2020, Sept. 30          Litho.          Perf. 13¾**
3879 A929 100d Sheet of 4,
                              15.50 15.50

Miniature Sheet

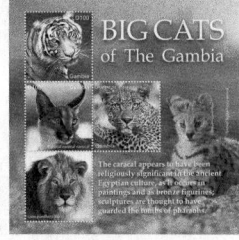

Large
Cats
A930

No. 3880: a, Tiger. b, Caracal. c, Leopard. d, Lion.

**2020, Sept. 30          Litho.          Perf. 13¾**
3880 A930 100d Sheet of 4,
#a-d
                              15.50 15.50

Miniature Sheet

Woodpeckers — A931

No. 3881: a, Fine-spotted woodpecker, denomination at UR. b, African gray woodpecker, denomination at LR. c, African gray woodpecker, denomination at UR. d, Fine-spotted woodpecker, denomination at LR.

**2020, Sept. 30          Litho.          Perf. 13¾**
3881 A931 100d Sheet of 4,
#a-d
                              15.50 15.50

Souvenir Sheet

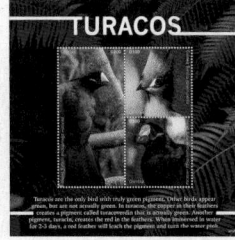

Turacos
A932

No. 3882: a, 100d, Guinea turaco (35x35mm). b, 100d, Violet turaco (35x35mm). c, 200d, Violet turaco (35x70mm).

**2020, Sept. 30          Litho.          Perf. 13¾**
3882 A932     Sheet of 3, #a-c   15.50 15.50

Souvenir Sheet

Japanese Raccoon Dog — A933

**2020, Sept. 30          Litho.          Perf. 12½**
3883 A933 250d multi            9.75 9.75

## Souvenir Sheet

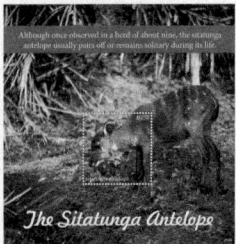

Sitatunga Antelope — A934

**2020, Sept. 30**    **Litho.**    **Perf. 13¾**
3884 A934 250d multi    9.75 9.75

## Miniature Sheet

Somali Ostriches — A935

No. 3885 — Various photographs of ostriches with denomination color of: a, Orange brown. b, Green. c, Blue violet. d, Red.

**2020, Oct. 30**    **Litho.**    **Perf. 12**
3885 A935 100d Sheet of 4,
   #a-d    15.50 15.50

## Miniature Sheet

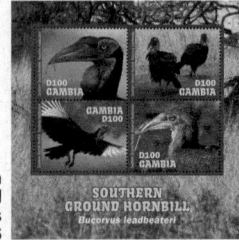

Southern
Ground
Hornbills
A936

No. 3886: a, Head of adult with red wattle. b, Two birds. c, Bird in flight. d, Head of juvenile.

**2020, Oct. 30**    **Litho.**    **Perf. 14**
3886 A936 100d Sheet of 4,
   #a-d    15.50 15.50

Yellow-Collared Lovebirds — A937

No. 3887: a, Bird flying to left. b, Bird standing. c, Bird flying to right.
250d, Head of bird.

**2020, Oct. 30**    **Litho.**    **Perf. 14**
3887 A937 100d Sheet of 3,
   #a-c    12.00 12.00
**Souvenir Sheet**
**Perf.**
3888 A937 250d multi    9.75 9.75
No. 3888 contains one 38mm diameter stamp.

A938

## Signing of the Abraham Accords A939

No. 3889: a, Israeli Prime Minister Benjamin Netanyahu. b, U.S. President Donald J. Trump. c, Netanyahu with U.S. Presidential Senior Advisor Jared Kushner. d, Signing ceremony. e, Dr. Abdullatif bin Rashid Al-Zayani, Bahrain's Minister of Foreign Affairs. f, Abdullah bin Zayed Al Nahyan, United Arab Emirate's Minister of Foreign Affairs.
250d, Netanyahu, Trump, Al-Zayani and Al Nahyan.

**2020, Oct. 30**    **Litho.**    **Perf. 14**
3889 A938 70d Sheet of 6,
   #a-f    16.50 16.50
**Souvenir Sheet**
3890 A939 250d multi    9.75 9.75

A940

Charles Dickens (1812-70),
Writer — A941

No. 3891: Various unattributed photographs and paintings, as shown.
No. 3892: a, Eyeglasses atop page from *A Christmas Carol.* b, Actor portraying Dickens reading a book.

**2020, Oct. 30**    **Litho.**    **Perf. 14**
3891 A940 80d Sheet of 5,
   #a-e    15.50 15.50
**Souvenir Sheet**
3892 A941 150d Sheet of 2,
   #a-b    12.00 12.00

A942

Ludwig van Beethoven (1770-1827),
Composer — A943

No. 3893: a, Violin and musical score. b, Statue of Beethoven, white background. c, Sign for Beethovenplatz 1, Vienna. d, Bust of Beethoven, black background. e, Monument to Beethoven, Vienna.

No. 3894: a, Gravesite monument. b, Bust of Beethoven, diff.

**2020, Oct. 30**    **Litho.**    **Perf. 14**
3893 A942 80d Sheet of 5,
   #a-e    15.50 15.50
**Souvenir Sheet**
3894 A943 150d Sheet of 2,
   #a-b    12.00 12.00

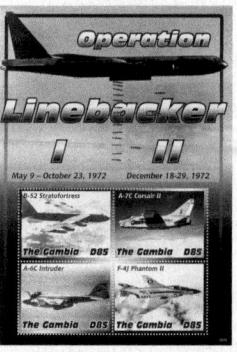

Airplanes Used In Operations
Linebacker I and II — A944

No. 3895: a, B-52 Stratofortress. b, A-7C Corsair II. c, A-6C Intruder. d, F-4J Phantom II.
170d, Aerial refueling of plane during operation.

**2020, Nov. 23**    **Litho.**    **Perf. 12½**
3895 A944 85d Sheet of 4,
   #a-d    13.50 13.50
**Souvenir Sheet**
3896 A944 170d multi    6.75 6.75

## Miniature Sheet

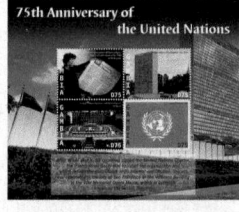

United
Nations,
75th
Anniv.
(in 2020)
A945

No. 3897: a, Eleanor Roosevelt holding Universal Declaration of Human Rights. b, United Nations Headquarters, New York City. c, United Nations Economic and Social Council Chamber. d, United Nations flag.

**2021, Jan. 15**    **Litho.**    **Perf. 13½x13¼**
3897 A945 75d Sheet of 4, #a-d    12.00 12.00

## Miniature Sheet

Arrival of the Mayflower in North
America, 400th Anniv. (in 2020) — A946

No. 3898: a, The Mayflower in Plymouth Harbor, by William Halsall. b, William Bradford reading the Mayflower Compact. c, Mayflower at Sea, by A.S. Burbank. d, The Embarkment of the Pilgrims, by Robert Walter Weir.

**2021, Jan. 15**    **Litho.**    **Perf. 13½x13¼**
3898 A946 100d Sheet of 4,
   #a-d    15.50 15.50

## Miniature Sheet

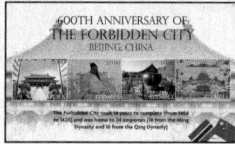

Forbidden City, Beijing, 600th Anniv.
(in 2020) — A947

No. 3899: a, Palace of Heavenly Purity. b, Yongli Emperor Zhu Di (1360-1424). c, Symbolic cistern. d, Ming Dynasty painting of the Forbidden City.

**2021, Jan. 15**    **Litho.**    **Perf. 13½x13¼**
3899 A947 100d Sheet of 4,
   #a-d    15.50 15.50

## Miniature Sheet

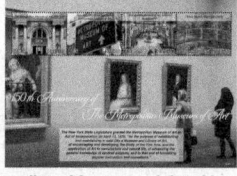

Metropolitan Museum of Art, New York
City, 150th Anniv. (in 2020) — A948

No. 3900: a, Main entrance. b, Street sign for museum. c, Museum lobby. d, Bridge over a Pond of Water Lilies, by Claude Monet.

**2021, Jan. 15**    **Litho.**    **Perf. 13½x13¼**
3900 A948 100d Sheet of 4,
   #a-d    15.50 15.50

A949

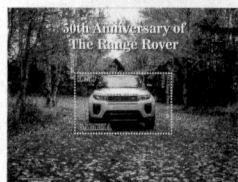

Range
Rovers,
50th
Anniv.
(in 2020)
A950

No. 3901: a, 2014 Land Range Rover Hybrid. b, 2011 Land Range Rover. c, 2016 Land Rover Evoque convertible. d, 2014 Land Rover Evoque convertible.
250d, 2014 Range Rover Evoque.

**2021, Jan. 15**    **Litho.**    **Perf. 13½x13¼**
3901 A949 100d Sheet of 4,
   #a-d    15.50 15.50
**Souvenir Sheet**
**Perf. 14½x14**
3902 A950 250d multi    9.75 9.75
No. 3902 contains one 50x30mm stamp.

A951

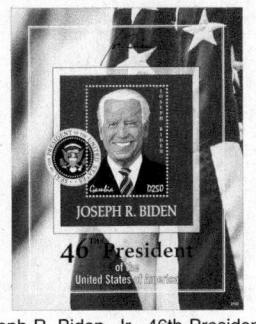

Joseph R. Biden, Jr., 46th President of the United States — A952

No. 3903 — Pres. Biden: a, Taking oath of office. b, Holding mug. c, Standing behind microphones. d, With Vice President Kamala Harris.
250d, Drawing of Pres. Biden.

**2021, Jan. 28    Litho.    Perf. 14**
3903  A951  100d Sheet of 4,
#a-d              15.50 15.50
**Souvenir Sheet**
**Perf. 12¾**
3904  A952  250d multi       9.75  9.75

Insects A953

No. 3905: a, Hawkmoth. b, Plain tiger butterfly. c, Dragonfly. d, Variegated grasshopper. e, African weaver ant. f, Bee.
250d, Ladybugs.

**2021, Mar. 15    Litho.    Perf. 14**
3905  A953  70d Sheet of 6,
#a-f             16.50 16.50
**Souvenir Sheet**
**Perf. 12¾**
3906  A953  250d multi       9.75  9.75
No. 3906 contains one 51x38mm stamp.

Hippopotamus Amphibius — A954

No. 3907: a, Two hippopotami, one with open mouth. b, One hippopotamus in water, with water droplets and denomination in black at LR. c, One hippopotamus in water, denomination in white at LR. d, Three hippopotami, animal at left with open mouth. e, Three hippopotami, animal in center with open mouth. f, One hippopotamus in water, denomination at UR.
250d, Two hippopotami with closed mouths.

**2021, Mar. 15    Litho.    Perf. 14**
3907  A954  70d Sheet of 6,
#a-f             16.50 16.50
**Souvenir Sheet**
**Perf. 12**
3908  A954  250d multi       9.75  9.75
No. 3908 contains one 80x30mm stamp.

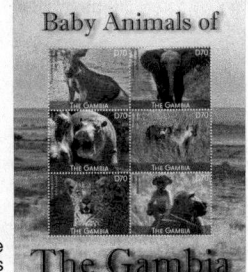

Juvenile Animals A955

No. 3909: a, Warthog. b, Elephant. c, Hippopotamus. d, Hyenas. e, Leopard. f, Baboons.
250d, Adult and juvenile bottlenose dolphins.

**2021, Mar. 15    Litho.    Perf. 14**
3909  A955  70d Sheet of 6,
#a-f             16.50 16.50
**Souvenir Sheet**
**Perf. 12**
3910  A955  250d multi       9.75  9.75
No. 3910 contains one 80x30mm stamp.

Loxodonta Africana — A956

No. 3911: a, Two adult elephants, denomination in black. b, Elephant facing left. c, Adult and juvenile elephants. d, Head of elephant. e, Two adult elephants, denomination in white.
250d, Adult and juvenile elephants, vert.

**2021, Mar. 15    Litho.    Perf. 14**
3911  A956  80d Sheet of 5,
#a-e             15.50 15.50
**Souvenir Sheet**
**Perf. 12½**
3912  A956  250d multi       9.75  9.75
No. 3912 contains one 38x51mm stamp.

95th Birthday of Queen Elizabeth II (1926-2022) — A957

No. 3913 — Queen Elizabeth II: a, As young woman. b, Wearing tiara. c, Wearing purple hat with white flower. d, Wearing red hat with red rose.
250d, Queen Elizabeth II wearing white hat.

**2021, Apr. 30    Litho.    Perf. 14**
3913  A957  95d Sheet of 4,
#a-d             15.00 15.00
**Souvenir Sheet**
**Perf. 12½**
3914  A957  250d multi       9.75  9.75
No. 3914 contains one 51x38mm stamp.

Duke and Duchess of Sussex, 3rd Wedding Anniversary — A958

No. 3915: a, Duke and Duchess, hands not visible (40x30mm). b, Duke and Duchess, hands visible (40x30mm). c, Duke and Duchess kissing on wedding day (40x30mm). d, Duke and Duchess waving on wedding day (40x30mm). e, Duke and Duchess with other family members (80x30mm).
250d, Duke and Duchess on steps on wedding day.

**2021, Apr. 30    Litho.    Perf. 14**
3915  A958  80d Sheet of 5,
#a-e             15.50 15.50
**Souvenir Sheet**
**Perf. 12½**
3916  A958  250d multi       9.75  9.75
No. 3916 contains one 51x38mm stamp.

Trains A959

No. 3917: a, Korean Bo-Bo locomotive. b, Moroccan electric locomotive. c, Spanish elecrtric locomotive. d, Yugoslavian Type J2-441. e, Chinese electric locomotive. f, Norwegian Type E115 electric locomotive.
250d, French TGV 001.

**2021, May 7    Litho.    Perf. 14**
3917  A959  70d Sheet of 6,
#a-f             16.50 16.50
**Souvenir Sheet**
3918  A959  250d multi       9.75  9.75
Compare with Gabon Nos. 991, 994.

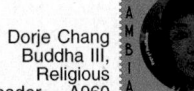

Dorje Chang Buddha III, Religious Leader — A960

**2021, May 26    Litho.    Perf. 13¼**
3919  A960  50d multi        2.00  2.00
No. 3919 was printed in sheets of 8.

**First Ladies of the United States Types of 2017**

Designs: Nos. 3920a, 3921, Dr. Jill Biden.

**2021, June 21    Litho.    Perf. 14**
3920  A843  Sheet of 16,
#3741a-3741o,
3920a            12.50 12.50
a.    20d multi    .75   .75
**Souvenir Sheet**
**Perf. 12½**
3921  A844  143d multi       5.75  5.75

New Year 2021 (Year of the Ox) A961

No. 3922 — Background color: a, Red. b, Brown. c, Blue. d, Green.

**2021, June 21    Litho.    Perf. 13¾**
3922  A961  85d Sheet of 4, #a-d    13.50 13.50

Elvis Presley (1935-77) — A962

No. 3923 — Presley: a, Wearing sunglasses. b, Wearing sequined jacket. c, Wearing white jacket with upturned collar. d, With orange background.

**2021, July 5    Litho.    Perf. 12**
3923  A962  100d Sheet of 4,
#a-d             16.00 16.00

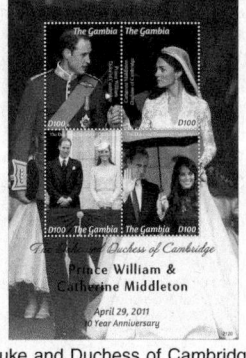

Duke and Duchess of Cambridge, 10th Wedding Anniversary — A963

No. 3924: a, Duke on wedding day. b, Duchess on wedding day. c, Duke and Duchess in front of building. d, Duke and Duchess under umbrella.
250d, Duke and Duchess, horiz.

**2021, July 5    Litho.    Perf. 14**
3924  A963  100d Sheet of 4,
#a-d             16.00 16.00
**Souvenir Sheet**
3925  A963  250d multi       9.75  9.75

**Souvenir Sheet**

Bitcoin A964

**2021, July 19    Litho.    Perf. 13¾**
3926  A964  260d multi      10.50 10.50

Erinaceinae — A965

No. 3927 — Photographs of various hedgehogs with denominations of: a, 60d. b, 70d. c, 80d. d, 90d. e, 100d.
250d, Hedgehog, horiz.

**2021, Sept. 1    Litho.    Perf. 13¾**
3927  A965  Sheet of 5, #a-e   16.00 16.00
**Souvenir Sheet**
**Perf. 12**
3928  A965  250d multi       9.75  9.75
No. 3928 contains one 50x30mm stamp.

Tursiops Truncatus — A966

No. 3929 — Photographs of various dolphins with denominations of: a, 50d. b, 60d. c, 70d. d, 80d (country name in white). e, 80d (country name in black). f, 90d.
250d, Dolphin, vert.

**2021, Sept. 1    Litho.    Perf. 14**
3929  A966    Sheet of 6, #a-f    17.00  17.00
**Souvenir Sheet**
3930  A966  250d multi    9.75  9.75

Crocodylinae — A967

No. 3931: a, 60d, Crocodile with open mouth. b, 60d, Crocodile with mouth closed. c, 70d, Eye of crocodile. d, 70d, Two crocodiles. e, 80d, Crocodile with open mouth, diff. f, 80d, Crocodile with mouth closed, diff.
250d, Captive crocodile feeding.

**2021, Sept. 1    Litho.    Perf. 14**
3931  A967    Sheet of 6, #a-f    16.50  16.50
**Souvenir Sheet**
**Perf. 13¾**
3932  A967  250d multi    9.75  9.75
No. 3932 contains one 35x35mm stamp.

September 11, 2001 Terrorist Attacks, 20th Anniv. — A968

No. 3933: a, Queen Elizabeth II laying wreath at Ground Zero. b, One World Trade Center, Brooklyn Bridge and Lower Manhattan skyline at night. c, One World Trade Center. d, Pigeon on September 11 Memorial reflecting pool.
250d, Twin towers of the World Trade Center, vert.

**2021, Sept. 11    Litho.    Perf. 14**
3933  A968  120d Sheet of 4,
              #a-d    19.00  19.00
**Souvenir Sheet**
**Perf. 12**
3934  A968  250d multi    9.75  9.75
No. 3934 contains one 30x50mm stamp.

A969

A970

A971

Gemini Space Program A972

No. 3935: a, Astronaut walking in space, spacecraft at right. b, Astronaut walking in space, camera visible.
No. 3936: a, Gemini capsule with open hatch, top of capsule visible. b, Gemini capsule in space. c, Gemini 5 Rendezvous Evaluation Pod. d, Gemini capsule with open hatch, bottom of capsule visible.
No. 3937, Rocket launch. No. 3938, Astronaut in capsule's hatch.

**2021, Oct. 1    Litho.    Perf. 13**
3935  A969  160d Pair, #a-b    12.50  12.50
3936  A970  120d Sheet of 4,
              #a-d    19.00  19.00
**Souvenir Sheets**
**Perf. 13x13¼**
3937  A971  250d multi    9.75  9.75
3938  A972  250d multi    9.75  9.75
No. 3935 was printed in sheets containing two pairs.

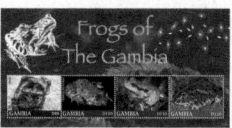

Amphibians — A973

No. 3939: a, 90d, Toad. b, 100d, Crowned bullfrog. c, 110d, Tree frog. d, 120d, Edible bullfrog.
250d, Reed frog.

**2021, Oct. 29    Litho.    Perf. 14**
3939  A973    Sheet of 4, #a-d    16.00  16.00
**Souvenir Sheet**
**Perf. 12½**
3940  A973  250d multi    9.75  9.75
No. 3940 contains one 51x38mm stamp.

Prince Philip (1921-2021) — A974

No. 3941: a, Color photograph of Prince Philip and Queen Elizabeth II. b, Black-and-white photograph of Prince Philip and Queen Elizabeth II. c, Prince Philip, Queen Elizabeth II and their children. d, Prince Philip, wall in background. e, Prince Philip, man and computer screen in background.
250d, Casket of Prince Philip.

**2021    Litho.    Perf. 14**
3941  A974  80d Sheet of 5,
              #a-e    15.50  15.50
**Souvenir Sheet**
**Perf. 12**
3942  A974  250d multi    9.25  9.25
No. 3942 contains one 50x30mm stamp. The date of issue for Nos. 3941-3942 is unknown, though it was alleged to be April 9, which is the day on which Prince Philip died.

Tourist Attractions of Dubai, United Arab Emirates — A975

No. 3943: a, Dubai Frame, Zabeel Park. b, Burj Khalifa. c, Al-Fahidi Historical District. d, Burj Al Arab. e, Jumeirah Mosque.

**2022, Jan. 19    Litho.    Perf. 14**
3943  A975  50d Sheet of 5, #a-e    9.50  9.50
**Miniature Sheet**

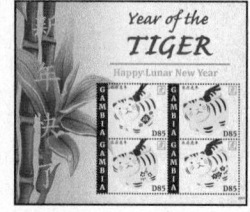

New Year 2022 (Year of the Tiger) A976

No. 3944: a, Pale yellow tiger with two flowers and diamond and Chinese character on side. leaf tip at UL. b, Yellow tiger without side markings. c, Yellow tiger with red circles on side, leaf tip at UL. d, Pale yellow tiger with three flowers on side.

**2022, Feb. 1    Litho.    Perf. 14**
3944  A976  85d Sheet of 4, #a-d    13.00  13.00

Reign of Queen Elizabeth II (1926-2022), 70th Anniv. — A977

No. 3945 — Queen Elizabeth II: a, At Bellevue Palace, Berlin. b, At Windsor Castle, wearing dark blouse. c, In Natal, South Africa as young woman. d, At Royal Albert Hall, London. e, In Hong Kong. f, At Windsor Castle, wearing checked dress.
250d, Queen Elizabeth II at Diamond Jubilee Thames River Pageant.

**2022, Feb. 6    Litho.    Perf. 14**
3945  A977  60d Sheet of 6,
              #a-f    13.50  13.50
**Souvenir Sheet**
**Perf. 12½**
3946  A977  250d multi    9.50  9.50
No. 3946 contains one 51x38mm stamp.

Princess Diana (1961-97) — A978

No. 3947 — Princess Diana: a, Wearing boas. b, With Princess Anne and Queen Mother Elizabeth. c, Waving and holding flowers. d, With Queen Elizabeth II. e, Wearing plaid jacket. f, Wearing hat.
250d, Princess Diana wearing blue and white dress, vert.

**2022, Mar. 14    Litho.    Perf. 14**
3947  A978  80d Sheet of 6,
              #a-f    18.00  18.00
**Souvenir Sheet**
**Perf. 12½**
3948  A978  250d multi    9.25  9.25
No. 3948 contains one 38x51mm stamp.

World War II Aircraft A979

No. 3949: a, North American P-51 Mustang. b, Avro Lancaster. c, Curtiss P-40 Warhawk. d, De Havilland Mosquito KA 114.
250d, Vought F4U Corsair.

**2022, Mar. 14    Litho.    Perf. 14**
3949  A979  100d Sheet of 4,
              #a-d    15.00  15.00
**Souvenir Sheet**
**Perf. 12½**
3950  A979  250d multi    9.25  9.25
No. 3950 contains one 51x38mm stamp.

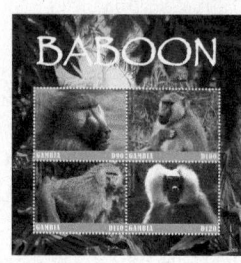

Baboons A980

No. 3951: a, 90d, Chacma baboon. b, 100d, Yellow baboon. c, 110d, Olive baboon. d, 120d, Hamadryas baboon.
250d, Guinea baboons.

**2022, Apr. 18    Litho.    Perf. 14**
3951  A980    Sheet of 4, #a-d    15.50  15.50
**Souvenir Sheet**
**Perf. 12**
3952  A980  250d multi    9.25  9.25
No. 3952 contains one 50x30mm stamp.

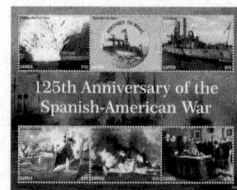

Spanish-American War, 125th Anniv. (in 2023) — A981

No. 3953: a, Sinking of the USS Maine. b, "Remember the Maine" button. c, USS Iowa. d, Battle of Manila Bay. e, Battle of Santiago de Cuba. f, Signing of Treaty of Paris, 1898.
250d, Theodore Roosevelt (1858-1919) and the Rough Riders, vert.

**2022, Apr. 18    Litho.    Perf. 14**
3953  A981  70d Sheet of 6,
              #a-f    15.50  15.50
**Souvenir Sheet**
**Perf. 12½**
3954  A981  250d multi    9.25  9.25
No. 3954 contains one 38x51mm stamp.

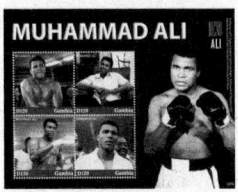

Muhammad Ali (1942-2016),
Boxer — A982

No. 3955 — Ali: a, Shirtless, hands not visible. b, Wearing shirt. c, Shirtless, with wrapped hands. d, Wearing robe.
250d, Ali throwing punch.

**2022, Apr. 18    Litho.    Perf. 13¾**
3955  A982  120d  Sheet of 4,
          #a-d              18.00  18.00
**Souvenir Sheet**
**Perf. 12**
3956  A982  250d multi           9.25   9.25
No. 3956 contains one 80x30mm stamp.

**Souvenir Sheet**

Peace
Dove,
Map of
Ukraine
and
Russia,
Ukrainian
and
Russian
Buildings
A983

**2022, May 30    Litho.    Perf. 12½**
3957  A983  250d multi           9.25   9.25

Monitor
Lizard
Varanus
A984

No. 3958 — Monitor lizard: a, Facing right, foliage in background above lizard. b, Facing right, black background above lizard. c, Facing left, with tongue out. d, Facing left, on tree. e, Facing left, "Varanus" in black.
250d, Two Monitor lizards, vert.

**2022, May 31    Litho.    Perf. 14**
3958  A984  80d  Sheet of 5,
          #a-e              15.00  15.00
**Souvenir Sheet**
**Perf. 12½**
3959  A984  250d multi           9.25   9.25
No. 3959 contains one 38x51mm stamp.

Orchids
A985

No. 3960: a, 60d, Blue orchid. b, 60d, Boat orchid. c, 70d, Crimson cattleya. d, 70d, Miltonia orchid. e, 80d, Venus slipper. f, 80d, Yellow moth orchid.
250d, Brassolaeliocattleya, vert.

**2022, May 31    Litho.    Perf. 13¾**
3960  A985  Sheet of 6, #a-f    15.50  15.50
**Souvenir Sheet**
**Perf. 12½**
3961  A985  250d multi           9.25   9.25
No. 3961 contains one 38x51mm stamp.

Prince
William,
40th
Birthday
A986

No. 3962: a, 60d, Prince William, wearing bow tie, with wife, Catherine. b, 60d, Prince William wearing blue jacket. c, 70d, Prince William and wife on wedding day. d, 70d, Prince William wearing sunglasses. e, 80d, Prince William and his grandmother, Queen Elizabeth II. f, 80d, Prince William and his mother, Princess Diana.
250d, Prince William with his wife and children, Queen Elizabeth II, Prince Charles and his wife, Camilla.

**2022, July 1    Litho.    Perf. 14**
3962  A986  Sheet of 6, #a-f    15.50  15.50
**Souvenir Sheet**
**Perf. 12**
3963  A986  250d multi           9.25   9.25
No. 3963 contains one 80x30mm stamp.

# GEORGIA

ˈjor-jə

LOCATION — South of Russia, bordering on the Black Sea and occupying the entire western part of Trans-Caucasia
GOVT. — Republic
AREA — 26,900 sq. mi.
POP. — 5,066,499 (1999 est.)
CAPITAL — Tbilisi (Tiflis)

Georgia was formerly a province of the Russian Empire and later a part of the Transcaucasian Federation of Soviet Republics. Stamps of Georgia were replaced in 1923 by those of Transcaucasian Federated Republics.
On Mar. 1, 1994, Georgia joined the Commonwealth of Independent States.

100 Kopecks = 1 Ruble
100 Kopecks = 1 Coupon (1993)
100 Tetri = 1 Lari (Sept. 25, 1995)

> Catalogue values for unused stamps in this country are for Never Hinged items, beginning with Scott 75 in the regular postage section, and Scott B10 in the semi-postal section.

## Tiflis
A 6k local stamp, imperforate and embossed without color on white paper, was issued in November, 1857, at Tiflis by authority of the viceroy. The square design shows a coat of arms.

**National Republic**

St. George
A1      A2

**1919    Litho.    Unwmk.    Perf. 11½**
1   A1  10k blue               .85    .85
2   A1  40k red orange         .85    .85
  a.  Tête bêche pair         30.00  30.00
3   A1  50k emerald            .85    .85
4   A1  60k red                .85    .85
5   A1  70k claret             .85    .85
6   A2  1r orange brown        .85    .85
      Nos. 1-6 (6)            5.10   5.10
**Imperf**
7   A1  10k blue               .85    .85
8   A1  40k red orange         .85    .85
  a.  Tête bêche pair         50.00  50.00
9   A1  50k emerald            .85    .85
10  A1  60k red                .85    .85
11  A1  70k claret             .85    .85
12  A2  1r orange brown        .85    .85
      Nos. 7-12 (6)           5.10   5.10

Queen Thamar — A3

**1920    Perf. 11½**
13  A3  2r red brown          1.00   1.40
14  A3  3r gray blue          1.00   1.40
15  A3  5r orange             1.00   1.40
      Nos. 13-15 (3)          3.00   4.20
**Imperf**
16  A3  2r red brown          1.00   1.40
17  A3  3r gray blue          1.00   1.40
18  A3  5r orange             1.00   1.40
      Nos. 16-18 (3)          3.00   4.20

Nos. 1-18 with parts of design inverted, sideways or omitted are fraudulent varieties.
Overprints meaning "Day of the National Guard, 12, 12, 1920" (5 lines) and "Recognition of Independence, 27, 1, 1921" (4 lines) were applied, probably in Italy, to remainders taken by government officials who fled when Russian forces occupied Georgia. Value, set $30.
"Constantinople" and new values were unofficially surcharged on stamps of 1919-20 by a consul in Turkey.

**Soviet Socialist Republic**

Soldier with       Peasant
Flag — A5          Sowing
                   Grain — A6

Industry and
Agriculture — A7

**1922    Unwmk.    Perf. 11½**
26  A5  500r rose             8.00   5.25
27  A6  1000r bister brown    8.00   5.25
28  A7  2000r slate          11.50   8.25
29  A7  3000r brown          11.50   8.25
30  A7  5000r green          11.50   8.25
      Nos. 26-30 (5)         50.50  35.25

Forgeries exist of Nos. 26-30.
Nos. 26 to 30 exist imperforate but were not so issued. Value for set, $200.

**Nos. 26-30 Handstamped with New Values in Violet**

**1923**
36  A6  10,000r on 1000r      8.75   6.50
  a.  Black surcharge        35.00  35.00
  b.  20,000r on 1000r      200.00
37  A7  15,000r on 2000r, blk
          surch.             9.25   8.50
  a.  Violet surcharge       40.00  40.00
38  A5  20,000r on 500r       9.25   8.50
  a.  Black surcharge        20.00  15.00
39  A7  40,000r on 5000r      8.75   5.50
  a.  Black surcharge        20.00  20.00
40  A7  80,000r on 3000r      9.25   8.50
  a.  Black surcharge        20.00  25.00
      Nos. 36-40 (5)         45.25  37.50

There were two types of the handstamped surcharges, with the numerals 5½mm and 6½mm high. The impressions are often too indistinct to measure or even to distinguish the numerals.
Double and inverted surcharges exist, as is usual with handstamps.

**Surcharged in Black**

43  A6  10,000r on 1000r      7.00   7.00
44  A7  15,000r on 2000r      4.50   4.50
  a.  Double surcharge      100.00
45  A5  20,000r on 500r       2.25   2.25
  a.  Inverted surcharge     50.00

46  A7  40,000r on 5000r      4.50   4.50
47  A7  80,000r on 3000r      4.50   4.50
      Nos. 43-47 (5)         22.75  22.75

Nos. 43, 45, 46 and 47 exist imperforate but were not so issued. Value $25 each.

**Russian Stamps of 1909-18 Handstamp Surcharged**

Type I — Surcharge 20x5½mm.
Type II — Surcharge 22x7¼mm.

**1923    Perf. 14½x15**
48  A14  10,000r on 7k bl   150.00 150.00
49  A11  15,000r on 15k red
          brn & bl
          (I)                15.00  15.00
  a.  Type II               10.00  10.00
  b.  As "a," surcharge inverted  25.00
**Type I Surcharge Handstamped on Armenia No. 141**
50  A11  15,000r on 5r on
          15k red
          brn & bl         500.00 500.00
  a.  Type II                      500.00
      Nos. 48-50 (3)        665.00 665.00

**Russian Stamps and Types of 1909-18 Surcharged in Dark Blue or Black**

**1923    Perf. 11½, 14½x15**
51  A14  75,000r on 1k org    3.50   4.25
  a.  Imperf.               150.00 150.00
52  A14  200,000r on 5k cl    4.00   5.00
53  A8   300,000r on 20k bl
          & car
          (Bk)               4.00   5.00
  a.  Dark blue surcharge    70.00  70.00
54  A14  350,000r on 3k red   7.00   8.00
  a.  Imperf.                7.00   7.25
  b.  Horiz. pair, imperf. btwn.  100.00
**Imperf**
55  A14  700,000r on 2k grn   7.00  10.00
  a.  Perf. 14½x15          27.50  32.50
      Nos. 51-55 (5)        25.50  32.25

> Catalogue values for unused stamps in this section, from this point to the end of the section, are for Never Hinged items.

**Republic**

Admission to UN,
1st Anniv. — A20

Map, flag, UN emblem.

**1993, July 31    Litho.    Perf. 13¼**
73  A20  25r green & multi     .75    .75
74  A20  50r brown & multi    1.10   1.10
75  A20  100r violet & multi  1.75   1.75
  a.  Souvenir sheet of 3, #73-75 + label  4.00   4.00
      Nos. 73-75 (3)         3.60   3.60

For overprint, see Nos. 327-328.

Natl.          Fresco, 18th
Arms,          Cent.
Flag           A22
A21

Apostle Simon,
11th Cent.
A23

Three Women, by
Lado Gudiashvili
A24

**1993, Oct. 11  Photo.  Perf. 12x11½**
76  A21  50k multicolored  .50  .50

**Litho.**
**Perf. 12x12½**
77  A22  50k multicolored  1.10  1.10
78  A23  1c  multicolored  .90  .90
79  A24  1c  multicolored  1.40  1.40
    Nos. 76-79 (4)  3.90  3.90

Nos. 76, 78-79 dated 1992.
For surcharges see Nos. 80-83, 93-95, 404, 458.

Surcharged in Claret, Black,
or Blue

**1994, May 31  Photo.  Perf. 12x11½**
80  A21  5000c on 50k #76 (C)  .65  .65

**Litho.**
**Perf. 12x12½**
81  A22  5000c on 50k #77
        (Blk)  .65  .65
82  A23  10,000c on 1c #78 (Bl)  .90  .90
83  A24  10,000c on 1c #79 (C)  .90  .90
    Nos. 80-83 (4)  3.10  3.10

Size and location of surcharge varies.

Places of Worship — A25

30c, Mtskheta Church. 40c, Gelati Church. 50c, Nikortsminda Church. 60c, Ikorta Church. 70c, Samtavisi Church. 80c, Bolnisi Sioni Cathedral. 90c, Gremi Citadel Church.

**1993, Oct. 11  Litho.  Perf. 13½**
84  A25  30c blue  .35  .35
85  A25  40c red brown  .45  .45
86  A25  50c olive brown  .55  .55
87  A25  60c rose carmine  .65  .65
88  A25  70c rose lake  .85  .85
89  A25  80c green  1.00  1.00
90  A25  90c slate  1.10  1.10
    Nos. 84-90 (7)  4.95  4.95

See Nos. 111-120.

Niko Nikoladze
(1843-1928)
A26

**1994, May 31  Litho.  Perf. 13½**
91  A26  150c black & gold  1.00  1.00

UPU, 120th
Anniv. — A27

**1994, May 30**
92  A27  200c multicolored  1.00  1.00

---

Nos. 77-79 Surcharged
in Green or Red

**1994  Litho.  Perf. 12x12½**
93  A22  200c on 50k #77  .50  .50
94  A23  300c on 1c #78 (R)  .55  .55
95  A24  500c on 1c #79  1.25  1.25
    Nos. 93-95 (3)  2.30  2.30

Set exists with inverted surcharges. Value $10.

A27a

**1994, Oct. 9  Litho.  Perf. 14**
95A  A27a  100c shown  2.75  2.75
95B  A27a  200c Monument  5.00  5.00

All Georgian Congress.

A28

Georgia Natl. Olympic Committee: 10c, Intl. year of sport & Olympic ideal. 15c, Olympic congress, cent. 20c, Intl. Olympic Committee, cent. 25c, Olympic truce.

**1995, Mar. 28  Litho.  Perf. 14½**
96-99  A28  Set of 4  7.50  7.50

Dated 1994.

Paintings by Niko Piromanashvili
(1862-1918) — A29

No. 100, Three Princes Carousing on the Grass. No. 101, Still life. No. 102, Georgian Woman with a Tambourine, vert. No. 103, Bear on a Moonlit Night, vert. No. 104, Woman with a Tankard of Beer, vert. No. 105, Deer, vert. No. 106, Fisherman, vert. No. 107, Giraffe, vert. No. 108, Boy on a Donkey, vert. No. 109, Brooder with Chicks.
No. 110, Family Picnicking.

**1995, Mar. 29  Litho.  Perf. 14**
100-109  A29  20c Set of 10  10.00  10.00

**Souvenir Sheet**
110  A29  100c multicolored  5.00  5.00

**Churches Type of 1993**

10c

20c

400c

---

1c, No. 120, Metechi, 1278-1289. 2c, No. 117, Alaverdi, 11th cent. 3c, No. 116, Dranda, 8th cent. No. 114, Sveti-Zchoveli, 1010-1019. No. 115, Kumurdo, 964. No. 118, Anauri, 17th cent. No. 119, Bitschvinta, 10th cent.

**Size: 25½x39mm**

**1995  Litho.  Perf. 14**
111  A25  1c  black & violet  1.50  1.50
112  A25  2c  black & sepia  1.50  1.50
113  A25  3c  black & red brn  1.50  1.50
114  A25  10c  black & violet  1.50  1.50
115  A25  10c  black & sepia  1.50  1.50
116  A25  10c  black & grn blue  1.50  1.50
117  A25  20c  black & slate  1.50  1.50
118  A25  20c  black & olive grn  1.50  1.50
119  A25  400c  black & org brn  1.50  1.50
120  A25  400c  black & red brn  1.50  1.50
    Nos. 111-120 (10)  15.00  15.00

Paolo Iashvili
(1894-1937)
A30

**1995, Apr. 1**
125  A30  300c multicolored  1.25  1.25

Prehistoric
Animals — A31

No. 126, Brontosaurus. No. 127, Saurolophus. No. 128, Scolosaurus. No. 129, Triceratops. No. 130, Parasaurolophus. No. 131, Ceratosaurus. No. 132, Deinonichus. No. 133, Tyrannosaurus. No. 134, Stegosaurus.
No. 135: a, Pterodactylus (d). b, Rhamphophynghus (c, e). c, Pteranodon. d, Spinosaurus. e, Tyrannosaurus (f, h, i). f, Velociraptor. g, Monoklonius. h, Ornithomimus. i, Mastodon.
100c, Deinonychus.

**1995  Litho.  Perf. 14**
126-134  A31  15c Set of 9  6.25  6.25

**Miniature Sheet of 9**
135  A31  15c #a.-i.  7.25  7.25

**Souvenir Sheet**
136  A31  100c multicolored  5.25  5.25

Issued: Nos. 126-134, 5/12.

UNESCO World
Heritage
Sites — A32

100c, Bagrati Cathedral. 500c, Jvari of Mtskhetha.

**1995, Aug. 30  Litho.  Perf. 14**
137  A32  100c multi  1.00  1.00

**Souvenir Sheet**
138  A32  500c multi, vert.  6.00  6.00

**Miniature Sheet**

Wildlife
Painting — A33

Design: Nos. a.-p., Various animals and birds.

**1995, Aug. 4**
139  A33  15c Sheet of 16, #a.-p.  9.75  9.75

**Miniature Sheets**

Birds — A34

---

Designs: Each 15t: Nos. 140a-140p, Various songbirds. Nos. 141a-141p, Various raptors.
Each 100t: No. 142, Songbird. No. 143, Owl.

**1996, Feb. 26  Litho.  Perf. 14**
140-141  A34  Set of 2  22.50  22.50
**Souvenir Sheets**
142-143  A34  Set of 2  12.50  12.50

**Miniature Sheet**

Fauna and Flora — A35

a, Stork's head. b, Stork's body (a, f), berries. c, Snake (d, g, h). d, Moth. e, Lizard. f, Songbirds. g, Insect, flowers. h, Bee on flower. i, Butterfly, flower. j, Frog, lily (f). k, Snail. l, Turtle (p). m. Lobster. n, Sea plant, eel (o). o, Fish. p, Salamander.

**1996, Mar. 14  Litho.  Perf. 14**
144  A35  10t Sheet of 16, #a.-
        p.  12.00  12.00

Dinosaurs — A36

**1996, Apr. 24  Litho.  Perf. 14**
145  A36  10t Sheet of 9, #a.-i.  7.50  7.50

Intl. Olympic
Committee,
Cent. — A37

Georgian Olympians, landmarks from earlier Summer Olympic Games: 1t, Helsinki, 1952. 2t, Melbourne, 1956. 3t, Rome, 1960. 4t, Tokyo, 1964. 5t, Mexico City, 1968. 6t, Munich, 1972. 7t, Montreal, 1976. 8t, Moscow, 1980. 9t, Seoul, 1988. 10t, Barcelona, 1992.
Early Greek: 50t, Wrestlers. 70t, Runner.

**1996, Aug. 16  Litho.  Perf. 14**
146-155  A37  Set of 10  7.50  7.50

**Souvenir Sheets**
156  A37  50t multicolored  7.00  7.00
157  A37  70t multicolored  8.50  8.50

Olymphilex '96 (No. 157).

Paintings
A38

Designs: 10t, Citizens of Paris, by Lado Gudiashvili. 20t, Abstract, by Wassily Kandinsky. 30t, Still Life, by David Kakabadze. 50t, Three Painters, by Shalva Kikodze.
80t, Portrait of Niko Pirosmani, by Pablo Picasso.

**1996, Aug. 2  Litho.  Perf. 14**
158  A38  10t multicolored  .40  .40
159  A38  20t multicolored  .70  .70
160  A38  30t multicolored  1.00  1.00
161  A38  50t multicolored  1.40  1.40

**Size: 72x90mm**
**Imperf**

162  A38  80t multicolored  3.00  3.00
    Nos. 158-162 (5)  6.50  6.50

A39

**1996, Dec. 25    Litho.    Perf. 13x14**
163  A39  30t Anton I (1720-88)    1.25  1.25

Ivan Javakhishvili
(1876-1940),
Writer — A40

**1997, Mar. 6          Perf. 14**
164  A40  50t multicolored    1.50  1.50

UN, 50th
Anniv. — A41

**1997, Mar. 5    Litho.    Perf. 14**
165  A41  30t purple & blue    1.25  1.25
166  A41  125t red & blue    3.50  3.50

Dogs — A42

Designs: 10t, Rottweiler. 30t, Gordon setter. 50t, St. Bernard. 60t, English bulldog. 70t, Caucasian sheep dog.
125t, Caucasian sheep dog, diff.

**1997, June 2    Litho.    Perf. 14**
167  A42  10t multicolored    .35  .35
168  A42  30t multicolored    .85  .85
169  A42  50t multicolored    1.40  1.40
170  A42  60t multicolored    1.60  1.60
171  A42  70t multicolored    2.00  2.00
 a.    Sheet of 6, #167-172    8.00
    Nos. 167-171 (5)    6.20  6.20
**Souvenir Sheet**
172  A42  125t multicolored    3.75  3.75

No. 171a contains stamp from No. 172 without the continuous design. Issued: 2/27/98.

Animated Film
Characters
A43

Designs: a, 20t, Two mice talking. b, 30t, Man in bed. c, 40t, Balloons, bear, girl on cloud. d, 50t, Animals dancing, tree. e, 60t, Duck dressed as woman, tree.

**1997, July 15    Litho.    Perf. 14**
173  A43  Strip of 5, #a.-e.    9.00  9.00

Georgian Women's Team, Winners of
1996 World Chess Olympiad — A44

No. 174: a, Maia Chiburdanidze, Nona Gaprindashvili, Nana Ioseliani, Nino Gurieli, 1992 winners. b, Chiburdanidze, Ioseliani, Ketevan Arakhamia, Gurieli, 1994 winners. c,

Chiburdanidze, Ioseliani, Arakhamia, Gurieli, 1996 winners.
No. 175: a, 20t, Vice-Champion Nana Alexandria, 1975, 1981. b, 40t, Chiburdanidze, 1978, 1981 (Vice-Champion), 1984, 1986, 1991. c, 20t, Ioseliani, 1988, 1993. d, 50t, Gaprindashvili, 1962, 1965, 1969, 1972, 1975 (Vice-Champion).

**1997, July 21    Litho.    Imperf.**
174  A44  30t Sheet of 3, #a.-c.+ label    3.25  3.25
175  A44  Sheet of 4, #a.-d.    4.25  4.25

Nos. 174-175 have simulated perforations.

A45

1998 Winter Olympic Games,
Nagano — A46

Stylized skier — No. 176: a, 20t. b, 30t. c, 40t. d, 50t.
Early hand-made winter apparel, equipment — No. 177: a, 20t, Snow shoe, hat, gloves. b, 30t, Scarf, snow shoe. c, 40t, Sled, gloves. d, 50t, Scarf, snow shoe.
No. 178, Stylized skier, diff. No. 179, Man's feet with snow shoes.

**1998, Feb. 8    Litho.    Perf. 14**
176  A45  Sheet of 4, #a.-d.    4.00  4.00
177  A46  Sheet of 4, #a.-d.    4.00  4.00
**Souvenir Sheets**
178  A45  70t multicolored    2.75  2.75
179  A46  70t multicolored    2.75  2.75

Moscow '97 — A47

Tiflis local postage stamp of 1857.

**1997, Oct. 17    Litho.    Perf. 13x14**
180  A47  80t multicolored    2.00  2.00
**Souvenir Sheet**
181  A47  1 l multicolored    3.00  3.00

Prince
Vakhushti
Bagrationi
(1696-1758)
A48

40t, Map of Georgia, 1745, portrait. 80t, Portrait.

**1997, Oct. 9**
182  A48  40t multi    1.00  1.00
183  A48  80t multi, vert.    2.00  2.00

World Delphic
Congress — A49

40t, Symbols of education, art & music, 1st World Junior Delphics. 80t, Building on mountaintop, 2nd World Delphic Cong.

**1997, Nov. 24    Litho.    Perf. 14**
184  A49  40t multicolored    1.50  1.50
185  A49  80t multicolored    3.00  3.00

Voyage of Jason
and the
Argonauts — A50

Plate and Vase Paintings: a, 30t, Greek galley from Rhodes, terracotta plate, 700-650BC. b, 40t, Preparation for Battle, vase painting, 460BC. c, 50t, Boreades, Phineus & Harpy, vase painting, 6th cent. d, 60t, Punishment of King Amicus, vase painting, 420-400BC. e, 70t, Argonauts in Colchis, vase painting, 4th cent. BC. f, 80t, The Dragon Vomiting Jason, vase painting, 490-485BC.

**1998, June 23  Litho.  Perf. 13x13½**
186  A50  Sheet of 6, #a.-f.    7.50  7.50

Independence, 80th
Anniv. — A51

**1998, Dec. 25    Litho.    Perf. 14**
187  A51  80t multicolored    3.00  3.00

Horses — A52

Various breeds.

**1998, Dec. 22**
188  A52  10t multicolored    .65  .65
189  A52  40t multicolored    1.75  1.75
190  A52  70t multicolored    3.00  3.00
191  A52  80t multicolored    3.50  3.50
    Nos. 188-191 (4)    8.90  8.90
**Souvenir Sheet**
**Imperf**
192  A52  100t multicolored    5.00  5.00

No. 192 has simulated perfs.

Locomotives
A53

Various locomotives built at Tbilisi Locomotives Works.

**1998, Dec. 24**
193  A53  10t multicolored    .40  .40
194  A53  30t multicolored    1.10  1.10
195  A53  40t multicolored    1.40  1.40
196  A53  50t multicolored    1.60  1.60
197  A53  80t multicolored    2.75  2.75
    Nos. 193-197 (5)    7.25  7.25
**Souvenir Sheet**
198  A53  100t multicolored    4.00  4.00

Europa — A54

(80t), Berikaoba. (100t), Chiakokonoba.

**1998, Dec. 31  Litho.  Perf. 13x12¾**
199  A54  (80t) multi    1.60  1.60
200  A54  (100t) multi    2.10  2.10

Wildlife — A55

10t, Vormela peregusna guld. 40t, Hyaena hyaena. 80t, Ursus arctos syriacus. 100t, Capra aegagrus erxleber.

**1999, Feb.    Litho.    Perf. 14x13½**
201  A55  10t multicolored    .40  .40
202  A55  40t multicolored    1.25  1.25
203  A55  80t multicolored    2.50  2.50
    Nos. 201-203 (3)    4.15  4.15
**Souvenir Sheet**
**Imperf**
204  A55  100t multicolored    3.25  3.25

Dated 1998. No. 204 has simulated perfs.

Ancient
and
Modern
Bridges
of Tbilisi
A56

Bridges: a, 10t, Michael. b, 40t, Saarbruken. c, 50t, N. Baratashvili. d, 60t, Mukhrani. e, 70t, Avlabari. f, 80t, Metekhi.

**1999, Feb.          Perf. 13½x14**
205  A56  Sheet of 6, #a.-f.    11.00  11.00

Mustela Lutreola,
Worldwide Fund
for
Wildlife — A57

(10t), Standing in water. (20t), Feeding. (30t), Two standing. (60t), In burrow.

**1999, Apr. 27    Litho.    Perf. 13x12¾**
206  A57  (10t) multi    1.25  1.25
207  A57  (20t) multi    1.25  1.25
208  A57  (30t) multi    1.25  1.25
209  A57  (60t) multi    1.25  1.25
 b.    Strip of 4, #206-209    14.00  14.00

Nos. 206-209 were issued in sheets of 10 of each denomination and as se-tenant blocks of 4 in sheets of 20. The stamps from the se-tenant sheets have thicker lettering in the country and Latin names. Singles from the se-tenant sheets of 20 and from the individual sheetlets of 10 are of equal value.

Europa — A58

(80t), Batsara-Babaneury Reserve. (100t), Lagodekhy Reserve.

**1999, Apr. 28    Litho.    Perf. 12¾x13**
210  A58  (80t) multi    2.50  2.50
211  A58  (100t) multi    3.00  3.00

Council of
Europe, 50th
Anniv. — A59

**1999, Nov.    Litho.    Perf. 12¾**
212  A59  50t shown    1.45  1.45
213  A59  80t Latin letters    2.00  2.00

Georgian Olympic
Committee, 10th
Anniv. — A60

**1999, Nov.          Perf. 13¾**
214  A60  20t multi    .90  .90
215  A60  50t multi    2.00  2.00

Butterflies — A61

Designs: 10t, Iphiclides podalirius. 20t, Parnassius apollo. 50t, Colias aurorina herrich-schaffer. 80t, Tomares romanovi.

**1999, Nov.**
216 A61 10t multi .50 .50
217 A61 20t multi .85 .85
218 A61 50t multi 1.60 1.60
219 A61 80t multi 3.50 3.50
Nos. 216-219 (4) 6.45 6.45

UPU, 125th Anniv. — A62

**1999, Nov.** Perf. 13¼x13½
220 A62 20t shown .75 .75
221 A62 80t Letter writer 2.75 2.75

Trucks — A63

**1999, Dec.** Perf. 13¾
Color of Truck
222 A63 20t green .75 .75
223 A63 40t red & yellow 1.40 1.40
224 A63 50t blue & white 1.75 1.75
225 A63 80t red & white 3.00 3.00
Nos. 222-225 (4) 6.90 6.90
Souvenir Sheet
226 A63 100t red 4.25 4.25

Souvenir Sheet

Svaneti, World Heritage Site A64

**1999, Dec.** Perf. 12¾
227 A64 100t multi 3.00 3.00

**Europa, 2000**
Common Design Type
Denominations: 80t, 100t.

**2000, Mar. 31** Litho. Perf. 12¾x13
228 CD17 multi 4.50 4.50
229 CD17 multi 4.50 4.50

Scenes from "The Knight in a Tiger's Skin," by Shota Rustaveli — A65

Denominations: 10t, 20t, 30t, 50t, 60t.

**2000, May 8** Perf. 14¼x13¾
230-234 A65 Set of 5 5.50 5.50
Souvenir Sheet
235 A65 80t multi + label 4.00 4.00
Nos. 230-235 also issued imperf. Value, set $10.

Christianity, 2000th Anniv. — A66

Icons: 20t, St. Nino the Preacher. 50t, The Savior. 80t, The Virgin Hodigitria.

**2000, May 10** Perf. 13¾
236-238 A66 Set of 3 5.00 5.00

Souvenir Sheet

Georgian State System, 3000th Anniv. A67

**2000, May 11** Perf. 13
239 A67 100t multi 5.00 5.00

Fish — A68

Various fish: 10t, 20t, 30t, 50t, 80t.

**2000, May 12** Perf. 13¾x13¼
240-244 A68 Set of 5 7.25 7.25

David Saradjishvili (1848-1911), Brandy Maker — A69

**2000, Sept. 20** Litho. Perf. 14¼x14
245 A69 80t multi 2.00 2.00

2000 Summer Olympics, Sydney — A70

No. 246: a, 20t, Runner at left. b, 50t, Runner at center. c, 80t, Runner at right.

**2000 Sept. 20** Perf. 13¾
246 A70 Strip of 3, #a-c 5.00 5.00

Millennium — A71

No. 247: a, 20t, "1999." b, 50t, "2000." c, 80t, "2001."

**2000, Sept. 20**
247 A71 Strip of 3, #a-c 6.00 6.00

Joint Georgia-Russia Space Reflector Project — A72

Designs: 20t, Astronauts at work. 80t, Reflector.

**2000, Dec. 11** Litho. Perf. 13¾
248-249 A72 Set of 2 4.00 4.00

Human Rights in Europe, 50th Anniv. — A73

Denomination colors: 50t, Orange brown. 80t, Blue.

**2000, Dec. 12** Perf. 14¼x14
250-251 A73 Set of 2 3.75 3.75

Mushrooms — A74

Designs: 10t, Cantharellus cibarius. 20t, Agaricus campestris. 30t, Armillariella mellea. 50t, Russula adusta. 80t, Cortinarus violaceus.

**2000, Dec. 14** Perf. 13¼x13½
252-256 A74 Set of 5 7.50 7.50

UN High Commissioner for Refugees, 50th Anniv. — A75

**2000, Dec. 14** Perf. 13½x14
257 A75 50t multi 1.50 1.50

**Houses of Worship Type of 1993**
Unidentified buildings. Colors: 10t, Brown. 50t, Blue.

**Size: 24x32mm**

**2000, Dec. 18** Perf. 13¼x13
258-259 A25 Set of 2 2.25 2.25

Writers — A76

Designs: 30t, Alexander Kazbegi (1848-93). 40t, Jakob Gogebashvili (1840-1912). 50t, Vadja Pshavela (1861-1915). 70t, Akaki Tsereteli (1840-1915). 80t, Ilia Chavchavadze (1837-1907).

**2000, Dec. 19** Perf. 13¼x13¾
260-264 A76 Set of 5 6.50 6.50

Alexander Kartveli (1896-1977), Aircraft Designer A77

Designs: 10t, P-47D Thunderbolt. 20t, F-84. 80t, F-105D Thunderchief.

**2000, Dec. 20** Perf. 13¾x14
265-267 A77 Set of 3 4.00 4.00
Souvenir Sheet
Perf. 13
268 A77 100t Portrait, vert. 3.50 3.50

Fire Fighting Service, 175th Anniv. — A78

**2000, Dec. 24** Perf. 13¾x14
269 A78 50t multi 2.25 2.25

Europa — A79

Designs: 40t, Ritsa Lake. 80t, Borjomi Park.

**2001, Sept. 10** Litho. Perf. 12½x13
270-271 A79 Set of 2 5.75 5.75
a. Booklet pane, 2 each #270-271, perf. 12½x13 on 3 sides 11.00
Booklet, #271a 12.00

Great Silk Route — A80

**2001, Sept. 20** Perf. 13x12½
272 A80 20t shown .75 .75
Souvenir Sheet
273 A80 80t Like 20t, no emblem 3.00 3.00

Kutaisi Synagogue — A81

**2001, Sept. 13** Litho. Perf. 13x14
274 A81 140t multi 4.50 4.50

First Europe-Asia Chess Match — A82

**2001, Sept. 18** Litho. Perf. 13¾
275 A82 1 l multi 4.00 4.00

Poets A83

No. 276: a, Taras Shevchenko (1814-61), Ukrainian poet. b, Akaki Tsereteli (1840-1915), Georgian poet.

**2001, Dec. 19** Perf. 13
276 A83 50t Horiz. pair, #a-b 3.25 3.25
See Ukraine No. 445.

Georgian National Ballet — A84

Designs: 30t, Dancers Iliko Sukhishvili (1907-85) and Nino Ramishvili (1910-2000), sketch for dance "Mtiuluri." 50t, Dancers, sketch for dance "Samaya." 80t, Sukhishvili, Ramishvili, and sketch for dance "Jeirani."

**2002, Feb. 11** Perf. 13½x13¼
277-279 A84 Set of 3 5.25 5.25

Port of Poti, 140th Anniv. A85

No. 280: a, Map, ship (black and white photograph). b, Mobile container crane, containers. c, Ship and tugboat, cargo hauler. d, Cargo hauler, small boat, container crane lifting container (black and white photograph). e, Ship, cargo hauler (black and white photograph). f, Cargo hauler, large ship.

**2002, Feb. 11**    *Perf. 13¼x13½*
280 A85 30t Sheet of 6, #a-f    6.00 6.00

A86

Ashot Kurapalatl Opiza — A87

**2002, Feb. 11**    *Perf. 13¼x13½*
281 A86 100t blue    2.50 2.50
     *Perf. 13¼*
282 A87   5 l brown    9.50 9.50

Europa — A88

Designs: 40t, Georgian Circus. 80t, Tbilisi Circus.

**2002, Mar. 22**    *Perf. 13½x13¼*
283-284 A88 Set of 2    3.75 3.75
   a. Booklet pane, 2 each #283-284, perf. 13½x13¼ on 3 sides    8.75
     Booklet, #284a    9.75

Convention on Status of Refugees, 50th Anniv. A89

**2002, May 15**   Litho.   *Perf. 13¼*
285 A89 50t multi    1.25 1.25

Dinamo Tbilisi, Winner of 1981 European Soccer Cup — A90

**2002, Sept. 23**    *Perf. 13¾*
286 A90 20t multi    2.50 2.50

Year of Dialogue Among Civilizations — A91

**2002, Sept. 23**    *Perf. 13x13¾*
287 A91 40t multi    1.75 1.75

Intl. Federation of Stamp Dealers Associations, 50th Anniv. — A92

**2002, Sept. 23**    *Perf. 13¼x13*
288 A92 100t No. 12    3.00 3.00

Fighter Aircraft — A93

Designs: 30t, SU-25 Scorpio. 80t, MiG 21U.

**2002, Sept. 23**    *Perf. 13¾x13*
289-290 A93 Set of 2    3.25 3.25

Traditional Costumes — A94

Men and women in various costumes: 20t, 30t, 50t.

**2002, Sept. 23**    *Perf. 13¾*
291-293 A94 Set of 3    4.00 4.00

Church Murals — A95

Murals from: 10t, 14th cent., vert. 30t, 16th-17th cent. 80t, 18th cent., vert.

     *Perf. 13½x13, 13x13½*
**2002, Sept. 23**
294-296 A95 Set of 3    5.25 5.25

Pectoral Crosses — A96

Designs: 10t, Crucifixion, 10th cent. 20t, Cross from Martvili, 7th-9th cent. 50t, Cross from Martvili, 10th cent. 80t, Cross of King Tamari, 12th cent.

**2002, Sept. 23**    *Perf. 14¼x14*
297-300 A96 Set of 4    6.00 6.00

Flowers — A97

Designs: 20t, Bellflower. 30t, Caucasia rhododendron. 50t, Anemone. 80t, Marsh marigold.

**2002, Sept. 23**    *Perf. 13x13¾*
301-304 A97 Set of 4    6.00 6.00

Souvenir Sheet

Alexandre Dumas (Père) (1802-70), French Novelist — A98

**2002, Sept. 23**    *Perf. 14x13¾*
305 A98 120t multi    4.25 4.25

Europa — A99

Poster art: 40t, Three men and donkey. 80t, Four people.

**2003, Mar. 10**    *Perf. 13½x13¼*
306-307 A99 Set of 2    4.00 4.00
   307a   Booklet pane, 2 each #306-307, perf. 13½x13¼ on 3 sides    8.75   —
     Complete booklet, #307a    9.75

Souvenir Sheet

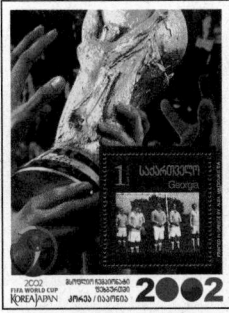

2002 World Cup Soccer Championships, Japan and Korea — A100

**2003, Apr. 25**    *Perf. 13¾*
308 A100 1 l multi    3.25 3.25

Souvenir Sheet

Paleontology — A101

No. 309: a, Stylized drawing of ancient European man. b, Skull.

**2003, Apr. 25**    *Perf. 12¾*
309 A101 60t Sheet of 2, #a-b    5.00 5.00

Margin of No. 309 has "1700000 YEARS OLD" overprinted in red brown on silver oval that is an overprint over an inscription that reads "17000000 YEARS OLD". Examples exist without the red brown overprint.

Youth — A102

**2003, June 20**   Litho.   *Perf. 14x14¼*
310 A102 50t multi    1.50 1.50

Women for Peace — A103

**2003, June 20**    *Perf. 13¾x13*
311 A103 50t multi    1.50 1.50

Zoo Animals — A104

Animals at Tbilisi Zoo: 20t, Elephant. 30t, Wolf. 40t, Ostrich. 50t, Bear.

**2003, Aug. 25**    *Perf. 14x13¾*
312-315 A104 Set of 4    4.75 4.75
   315a   Miniature sheet, 2 each #312-315    12.00 12.00

No. 315a was sold in a booklet cover but unattached, and is comprised of two tete-beche blocks of Nos. 312-315.

Minerals — A105

Minerals: 10t, Rock crystal. 20t, Agate with amethyst. 30t, Orpiment rose. 50t, Realgar with orpiment.

**2003, Aug. 25**    *Perf. 13¼x13*
316-319 A105 Set of 4    3.75 3.75
   319a   Miniature sheet, 2 each #316-319    9.00 9.00

No. 319a was sold in a booklet cover but unattached, and is composed of two tete-beche blocks of Nos. 316-319.

Fruit — A106

Designs: 10t, Prunus spinosa. 20t, Laurocerasus officinalis. 30t, Cydonia oblonga. 50t, Punica granatum. 80t, Pyrus caucasica.

**2003, Aug. 25**    *Perf. 14x13¾*
320-324 A106 Set of 5    6.00 6.00

Souvenir Sheet

Old Tbilisi, by Elene Akhvlediani (1901-75) — A107

**2003, Aug. 25**
325 A107 80t multi    3.00 3.00

## Souvenir Sheet

Self-portrait, by Vincent van Gogh (1853-90) — A108

**2003, Aug. 25**     *Perf. 13x12¾*
326 A108 100t multi     4.00 4.00

### Nos. 73, 75a Overprinted

**2003, Oct. 6**    *Litho.*    *Perf. 13¼*
327 A20 25t green & multi     .85 .85

**Souvenir Sheet**
328   Sheet, #327, 328a, 328b   6.00 6.00
a.   A20 50t brown & multi    1.60 1.60
b.   A20 100t violet & multi    3.50 3.50

First postage stamps, 10th anniv.

Intl. Association of Academies of Science, 10th Anniv. — A109

**2003, Nov. 28**     *Perf. 13¾x13¼*
329 A109 30t multi     1.10 1.10

East-West Energy Corridor A110

**2003, Nov. 28**     *Perf. 13¼x13¾*
330 A110 80t multi     2.50 2.50

Tourism — A111

Designs: 10t, Skiers, Bakuriani. 20t, Caves, Vardzia. 30t, Harbor, Batum. 50t, Lake Ritsa.

**2003, Nov. 28**     *Perf. 13¾x13¼*
331-334 A111   Set of 4    3.50 3.50
334a   Booklet pane, 2 each #331-334    7.00 —
  Complete booket, #334a    7.50

No. 334a is composed of two tete-beche blocks of Nos. 331-334.

Grapes — A112

Designs: 10t, Aladasturi. 20t, Rkhatsiteli. 30t, Ojaleshi. 50t, Goruli Mtsvane. 80t, Aleksandrouli (Khvanchkhara).

**2003, Nov. 28**
335-339 A112   Set of 5    7.00 7.00

Europa — A113

Designs: 40t, Merry Christmas. 80t, Happy Easter.

**2004, Jan. 28 Litho.**   *Perf. 13¼x13½*
340-341 A113   Set of 2    5.00 5.00
341a   Booklet pane, 4 each #340-341, perf. 13¼x13½ on 2 or 3 sides    17.50
  Complete booklet, #341a    20.00

A114

Design: Georgi Tsereteli (1904-73), Director of Institute of Oriental Studies.

**2004, Nov. 5 Litho.**   *Perf. 13¼x13¾*
342 A114 30t multi     1.10 1.10

**Souvenir Sheet**

Rose Revolution, 1st Anniv. — A115

No. 343: a, Crowd with flags. b, Protestors with flag sprayed with water.

**2004, Nov. 5**     *Perf. 13¼x13*
343 A115 50t Sheet of 2, #a-b   3.75 3.75

FIFA (Fédération Internationale de Football Association), Cent. — A116

Caricatures of soccer players: 20t, Boris Paichadze. 30t, Avtandil Gogoberidze. 50t, Mikheil Meskhi. 80t, David Kipiani.

**2004, Nov. 5**     *Perf. 13¾x13¼*
344-347 A116   Set of 4    5.00 5.00

2004 Summer Olympics, Athens A117

Sculptures of athletes by: 20t, B. Skhulukhia. 30t, V. Cherkezishvili. 50t, N. Jikia. 80t, L. Vardosanidze.

**2004, Nov. 5**     *Perf. 13¼x13¾*
348-351 A117   Set of 4    5.50 5.50

Ancient Jewelry — A118

Designs: 20t, Belt and buckle, 3rd-4th cent. 30t, Necklace and belt buckle, 3rd-4th cent. 40t, Necklace and pins, 2000-1500 B.C. 80t,

Necklace, 5th cent. B.C., double-voluted pins, 3rd millennium B.C.

**2004, Nov. 5**
352-355 A118   Set of 4    5.00 5.00

UNESCO World Heritage Sites — A119

Designs: 20t, Ushguli. 30t, Bagrati. 50t, Gelati. 60t, Samtavro. 70t, Svetitskhoveli. 80t, Jvari.

**2004, Nov. 5 Litho.**   *Perf. 14x13¼*
356-361 A119   Set of 6    9.50 9.50

Flag of Georgia — A120

**2005, Feb. 11 Litho.**   *Perf. 14x13¼*
362 A120 50t multi     1.75 1.75

Europa — A121

Loaves of bread and: 20t, Girl. 80t, Bakers.

**2005, May 27**     *Perf. 14x13¾*
363 A121 20t multi     .80 .80
364 A121 80t multi     4.25 4.25

**Booklet Stamps**
**Size: 29x41mm**
*Perf. 13¾ on 2, 3 or 4 Sides*
365 A121 20t multi     1.00 1.00
366 A121 80t multi     4.25 4.25
a.   Booklet pane, 2 each #365-366    10.50 —
b.   Booklet pane, 3 each #365-366    16.00 —
  Complete booklet, #366a, 366b    27.50

For overprints see Nos. 402-403.

Rabbi Abraam Khvoles — A122

**2005, June 1**     *Perf. 12*
367 A122 1 l multi     3.00 3.00

2008 Summer Olympics, Beijing — A123

**2005, Dec. 28 Litho.**   *Perf. 12*
368 A123 80t multi     2.40 2.40

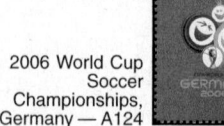

2006 World Cup Soccer Championships, Germany — A124

**2005, Dec. 28**
369 A124 100t multi     3.00 3.00

Georgian Ballet — A125

Designs: 40t, V. Tsiguadze. 50t, V. Chabukiani.

**2005, Dec. 28**
370-371 A125   Set of 2    3.00 3.00

Orchids — A126

Designs: 20t, Dactylorhiza euxina. 40t, Dactylorhiza iberica. 50t, Oprys caucasica. 80t, Orchis caucasica.

**2005, Dec. 28**
372-375 A126   Set of 4    6.00 6.00

Theaters — A127

Designs: No. 376, 30t, Georgian Drama Theater, Batumi. No. 377, 30t, Georgian Drama Theater, Kutaisi. No. 378, 30t, Abkhazian Drama Theater, Sukhumi. No. 379, 30t, Georgian Academic Theater, Tbilisi. No. 380, 30t, Georgian Drama Theater, Tbilisi. No. 381, 30t, Georgian Opera and Ballet Theater, Tbilisi. No. 382, 30t, Armenian Drama Theater, Tbilisi. No. 383, 30t, Ossetian Drama Theater, Tskhinvali.

**2005, Dec. 28**
376-383 A127   Set of 8    7.50 7.50

2006 Winter Olympics, Turin — A128

Designs: 10t, Speed skating. 20t, Biathlon. 30t, Ski jumping. 40t, Figure skating. 80t, Downhill skiing.

**2005, Dec. 29**
384-388 A128   Set of 5    5.00 5.00

**Souvenir Sheet**

Tbilisi Funicular, Cent. — A129

**2005, Dec. 30**
389 A129 100t multi     3.00 3.00

Europa Stamps, 50th Anniv. — A130

Designs: 10t, Various Georgian Europa stamps. 20t, Person inserting postcard in mail slot. 30t, France #805, Germany #748, magnifying glass, newspaper. 40t, Earth in ripped newspaper wrapper.

No. 394, 80t, Like 10t. No. 395, 80t, Like 20t. No. 396, 80t, Like 30t. No. 397, 80t, Like 40t.

**2006, Jan. 30**     *Perf. 12¾x13*
390-393 A130   Set of 4     3.75   3.75
**Souvenir Sheets**
394-397 A130   Set of 4     12.50   12.50

Europa — A131

Stars and: 20t, People holding flags. 80t, Earth, Georgian flag.

    *Perf. 13½x13¼*
**2006, June 30**       *Litho.*
398-399 A131   Set of 2     4.50   4.50
*399a*   Booklet pane, 4 each #398-
     399, perf. 13½x13¼ on 3
     sides          22.00    —
     Complete booklet, #399a   23.00

No. 399a contains two tete-beche pairs of Nos. 398-399.

Nos. 365-366
Overprinted

   *Perf. 13¾ on 2, 3 or 4 Sides*
**2006, Oct. 23**         *Litho.*
402 A121   20t multi     .90   .90
403 A121   80t multi     3.75   3.75
  *a.*   Sheet of 4, 2 each #402-403   9.50   9.50
  *b.*   Sheet of 6, 3 each #402-403   14.50   14.50

Europa stamps, 50th anniv. Nos. 403a and 403b are Nos. 366a and 366b removed from the booklet and overprinted on the stamps and margin.

No. 79 Surcharged
in Gray and Silver

**Method and Perf. As Before**
**2006, Nov. 2**
404 A24   10t on 1c #79     .40   .40

A132

Design: Nikola Tesla (1856-1943), Electrical Engineer, and Wireless Transmission Tower.

**2006, Nov. 15**   *Litho.*   *Perf. 12x12¼*
405 A132   50t multi     1.50   1.50

---

Souvenir Sheet

Georgian Wild West Show
Horsemen — A133

**2007, Jan. 25**   *Litho.*   *Perf. 12¼*
406 A133   100t multi     3.50   3.50

Tbilisi State
University,
Cent. — A134

**2007, Jan. 25**   *Litho.*   *Perf. 12¼x12*
407 A134   40t multi     1.10   1.10

Prince David
Guramishvili
(1705-92),
Poet — A135

**2007, July 11**      *Perf. 13¾x13¼*
408 A135   50t multi     1.40   1.40

2006 Chess
Olympics,
Turin — A136

**2007, July 11**
409 A136   200t multi     5.50   5.50

Famous
Men — A137

Designs: No. 410, Rembrandt (1606-69), painter. No. 411, Wolfgang Amadeus Mozart (1756-91), composer.

**2007, July 11**      *Perf. 13¾x13¼*
410 A137   100t multi     2.75   2.75
         *Perf. 13¾x14*
         **Size: 39x27mm**
411 A137   100t multi     2.75   2.75

Worldwide Fund for
Nature
(WWF) — A138

Aquila clanga: 30t, In flight. 40t, On branch. 50t, With prey. 60t, Head.

**2007, July 11**      *Perf. 13¼x13¾*
412-415 A138   Set of 4     5.50   5.50

Eagles — A139

---

Designs: 10t, Aquila rapax. 30t, Haliaeetus albicilla. 50t, Circaetus gallicus. 70t, Aquila chryaetus.

**2007, July 11**
416-419 A139   Set of 4     4.50   4.50

Georgian
Military — A140

Designs: 20t, Tanks. 30t, Soldiers. 40t, Ship. 50t, Helicopters.

**2007, July 11**      *Perf. 14¼x14*
420-423 A140   Set of 4     3.75   3.75

Ancient
Ships — A141

Various ships: 20t, 30t, 50t, 70t.

**2007, July 11**
424-427 A141   Set of 4     4.75   4.75

Souvenir Sheets

Guns
from
National
Museum
A142

Sculpture from National
Museum — A143

No. 428 — Various guns with background color of: a, Yellow. b, Buff. c, Light blue. d, Light green.

**2007, July 11**      *Perf. 13x13¼*
428 A142   50t Sheet of 4, #a-d   5.00   5.00
429 A143   100t multi     2.75   2.75

Souvenir Sheet

Magician, Cards and Dove — A144

     *Perf. 13¼x13¾*
**2008, Mar. 14**        *Litho.*
430 A144   1 l multi     3.50   3.50

Europa — A145

Designs: 90t, Scouts in boat and near tent. 1 l, Scouts around campfire.

**2008, Mar. 14**      *Perf. 14x13¾*
431-432 A145   Set of 2     6.00   6.00
*432a*   Booklet pane, 4 each
     #431-432         24.00   —
     Complete booklet, #432a   24.00

Scouting, cent. (in 2007). No. 432a contains two tete-beche pairs of Nos. 431-432.

---

Diplomatic Relations
Between Georgia
and Japan, 15th
Anniv. (in
2007) — A146

**2008, Mar. 14**   *Litho.*   *Perf. 13¾*
433 A146   1 l multi     3.50   3.50
         Dated 2007.

Mountains — A147

Designs: 20t, Mt. Ushba. 30t, Mt. Ushba, diff. 50t, Mt. Kazbeg. 70t, Mt. Shkhara.

**2008**    *Litho.*    *Perf. 13¼x13¾*
434-437 A147   Set of 4     6.25   6.25

Issued: 30t, 6/1; others, 3/14. Bottom panel with mountain name on No. 435 was overprinted in silver and black to correct inscription. No. 435 was not issued without overprint.

King David IV (1073-
1125) — A148

**2008, Dec. 5**   *Litho.*   *Perf. 13¾x14¼*
438 A148   50t multi     1.75   1.75

Europa — A149

Dove and: 90t, Georgia #398, cover with Georgia #213. 1 l, Letter, pencil, eyeglasses, Georgia #399.

**2008, Dec. 5**      *Perf. 13¾x14*
439-440 A149   Set of 2     7.00   7.00
*440a*   Booklet pane of 8, 4 each
     #439-440, perf. 13¾x13¼
     on 3 sides         28.00

No. 440a was sold with, but not attached to, a booklet cover.

2008 Summer
Olympics,
Beijing — A150

Designs: 10t, Shooting. 30t, Wrestling. 60t, Weight lifting. 80t, Judo.

**2008, Dec. 5**      *Perf. 14¼x14*
441-444 A150   Set of 4     6.75   6.75

Prince Sulkhan-
Saba Orbeliani
(1658-1725),
Monk — A151

**2009, Mar. 20**      *Perf. 13¼*
445 A151   60t multi     1.75   1.75

Kakutsa Cholokhashvili (1888-1930), Military Leader — A152

**2009, Mar. 20**
446 A152 80t multi 2.10 2.10

Port of Poti, 150th Anniv. — A153

**2009, Mar. 20**
447 A153 1 l multi 2.75 2.75

Grape Varieties — A154

Designs: 10t, Chkhaveri. 20t, Aleksandrouli. 30t, Rkatsiteli. 40t, Ojaleshi. 50t, Tsolikouri. 70t, Tavkveri. 90t, Saperavi.

**2009, Mar. 20**
448-454 A154 Set of 7 7.25 7.25

**Souvenir Sheet**

Anti-war Movement in Georgia — A155

No. 455: a, 30t, Flowers. b, 50t, Hands, Georgian flags. c, 70t, Demonstrators.

**2009, Mar. 20**
455 A155 Sheet of 3, #a-c 4.50 4.50

European Court of Human Rights, 50th Anniv. — A156

Council of Europe, 60th Anniv. — A157

**2009, Aug. 10** **Litho.** **Perf. 13¼**
456 A156 1 l multi 2.50 2.50
457 A157 2 l multi 5.00 5.00

**No. 79 Surcharged in Gold and Black**

**Method and Perf. As Before**
**2010, Sept. 9**
458 A24 1 l on 1c #79 2.50 2.50

Georgian National Rugby Team, 2009 European Champions A158

**2010, Oct. 15** **Litho.** **Perf. 13¼**
459 A158 5 l multi 9.00 9.00

Nodar Kumaritashvili (1988-2010), Luger Killed in Winter Olympics Practice Accident A159

**2010, Oct. 15** **Perf. 13¼x13½**
460 A159 5 l multi 9.00 9.00

Georgian Women's Chess Team, Four-time Chess Olympics Champion — A160

**2010, Oct. 15** **Perf. 13¼**
461 A160 7 l multi 12.00 12.00

Flowers — A161

**2010, Oct. 15** **Perf. 14x14¼**
462 A161 1 l Iris 1.50 1.50
463 A161 1.20 l Lilium 1.75 1.75
464 A161 2 l Viola 3.00 3.00
465 A161 3 l Colchicum 4.50 4.50
Nos. 462-465 (4) 10.75 10.75

Birds — A162

Designs: 20t, Grus grus. 40t, Perdix perdix. 50t, Tetraogallus caspius. 60t, Lyrurus mlokosiewiczi. 1 l, Tetrax tetrax.

**2010, Oct. 15** **Perf. 13¼**
466-470 A162 Set of 5 6.00 6.00
Latin names on 40t, 60t and 1 l are misspelled.

**Souvenir Sheet**

David Gareji Monastery Complex — A163

No. 471: a, Monastery complex. b, Frescoes on walls.

**2010, Oct. 15** **Litho.**
471 A163 60t Sheet of 2, #a-b 2.75 2.75

**Souvenir Sheet**

Georgian Alphabet A164

No. 472 — Columns of letters and: a, Numerals 1-40. b, Numerals 50-700. c, Numerals 800-10,000.

**2010, Oct. 15** **Perf. 13¼**
472 A164 40t Sheet of 3, #a-c 2.75 2.75

Europa — A165

Planets and: 2 l, Orbital diagram. 3 l, Pectoral of priestess depicting Sun.

**2010, Oct. 15** **Perf. 13½x13¼**
473-474 A165 Set of 2 10.00 10.00
474a Souvenir sheet of 2, #473-474 10.00 10.00
474b Booklet pane of 8, 4 each #473-474 40.00 —
Intl. Year of Astronomy. No. 474b was sold with, but unattached to, a booklet cover.

Flowers — A166

**2012, Apr. 11** **Perf. 13¼**
475 A166 10t Daisy .30 .25
476 A166 25t Carnation .60 .60
477 A166 50t Rose 1.25 1.25
478 A166 1 l Lilac 2.40 2.40
Nos. 475-478 (4) 4.55 4.50
Dated 2011.

**Souvenir Sheet**

Georgian Illuminated Manuscripts — A167

No. 479 — Various manuscripts: a, 1 l. b, 1.50 l. c, 2.50 l.

**2012, Apr. 11**
479 A167 Sheet of 3, #a-c 12.50 12.50
Dated 2011.

Past Olympic Champions of Georgia A168

Georgian flag, Olympic rings, list of winners and: 1.50 l, Parthenon, Athens. 2.50 l, Temple of Heaven, Beijing.

**2012, Apr. 11** **Perf. 12¾x13¼**
480-481 A168 Set of 2 10.00 10.00

A169

**2012, Apr. 11** **Perf. 13¼**
482 A169 4 l multi 10.00 10.00
United Nations High Commissioner for Refugees, 60th anniv. (in 2011).

Europa — A170

Designs: 3 l, Gergeti Glacier.
No. 484: a, 10t, Kolkheti Reserve. b, 10t, Tetnulkdi. c, 20t, Bakuriani Ski Resort. d, 20t, Alazani Valley. e, 30t, Imereti Caves. f, 30t, Gudauri Ski Resort. g, 40t, Borjomi-Kharagauli Reserve. h, 40t, Tusheti. i, 50t, Black Sea Coast. j, 50t, Keli Lake. k, 70t, Mountains in Adjara.

**2013, Apr. 15**
483 A170 3 l multi 6.50 6.50
**Miniature Sheet**
484 A170 Sheet of 12, #483, 484a-484k, + central label 14.50 14.50

Niko Pirosmani (1862-1918), Painter — A171

**2013, Apr. 15** **Perf. 13¼x13**
485 A171 1.80 l multi 4.00 4.00

**Miniature Sheet**

Cultural Heritage A172

No. 486: a, 1 l, Gold bracelets, 5th-4th cent. B.C. b, 2 l, Gold bowl, 2nd-1st cent, B.C. c, 3 l, Gold lion figurine, 4th-3rd cent. B.C. d, 4 l, Gold earrings, 5th-4th cent. B.C.

**2013, Apr. 15** **Perf. 14½**
486 A172 Sheet of 4, #a-d 21.50 21.50

**Souvenir Sheet**

Baku-Tbilisi-Kars Railway — A173

**2013, Apr. 15** **Perf. 12½**
487 A173 3 l multi 6.50 6.50

First Rules of Soccer, 150th Anniv. — A174

**2014, Dec. 22** **Litho.** **Perf. 13x13¼**
488 A174 1 l multi 2.25 2.25
Dated 2013.

Smiling Children — A175

**2014, Dec. 22** **Litho.** **Perf. 13x13¼**
489 A175 1 l multi 2.25 2.25
Dated 2013.

Smiling Man — A176

**2014, Dec. 22    Litho.    Perf. 14¼**
490 A176 1 l multi                    2.25 2.25
Dated 2013.

Diplomatic Relations With Latvia, 20th Anniv. — A177

**2014, Dec. 22    Litho.    Perf. 13¾**
491 A177 2 l multi                    4.25 4.25
See Latvia No. 871.

Swallows and Flowers A178

**2014, Dec. 22    Litho.    Perf. 13¼**
492 A178 3 l multi                    6.25 6.25
Dated 2013.

Europa — A179

Designs: No. 493, 1.50 l, No. 495a, 2 l, Horse-drawn postal wagon. No. 494, 1.50 l, No. 495b, 2 l, Postal automobile.

**2014, Dec. 22    Litho.    Perf. 13¼x13**
493-494 A179    Set of 2             6.50 6.50
**Souvenir Sheet**
495 A179 2 l Sheet of 2, #a-b        8.75 8.75
Dated 2013.

**Miniature Sheet**

Love A180

No. 496 — Wall with graffiti, flowers, butterfly and/or bird and country name in: a, Green. b, Purple. c, Red. d, Blue.

**2014, Dec. 22    Litho.    Perf. 13¾x14**
496 A180 2 l Sheet of 4, #a-d        16.50 16.50
Dated 2013.

**Miniature Sheet**

Cultural Heritage A181

No. 497: a, Golden temple pendants, 4th cent., B. C. b, Golden necklace, 5th cent., B. C. c, Golden necklace, 2nd-3rd cent. B. C. d, Golden headdress decoration, 4th cent. B. C.

**2014, Dec. 22    Litho.    Perf. 13¾**
497 A181 2 l Sheet of 4, #a-d        16.50 16.50
Dated 2013.

**Miniature Sheet**

Four Seasons A182

No. 498 — Tree in: a, Winter. b, Spring. c, Summer. d, Autumn.

**2014, Dec. 22    Litho.    Perf. 14¼**
498 A182 2 l Sheet of 4, #a-d        16.50 16.50
Dated 2013.

**Miniature Sheet**

Views of Old Tbilisi A183

No. 499: a, Statue and church on hilltop. b, Tower. c, Aerial view of buildings. d, Street scene.

**2014, Dec. 22    Litho.    Perf. 13¾**
499 A183 5 l Sheet of 4, #a-d        41.00 41.00
Dated 2013.

**Miniature Sheet**

Georgian Kings A184

No. 500: a, Pharnavaz (ruled 304-239 B. C.). b, Mirian (ruled 332-306 B. C.). c, Tamar (ruled 1184-1213). d, Vakhtang I Gorgasali (ruled 449-94). e, Aghmashenebeli (ruled 1089-1125). f, Giorgi (ruled 1314-46). g, Bagrat (ruled 975-1014).

**2014, Dec. 22    Litho.    Perf. 13x13¼**
500 A184 1 l Sheet of 7, #a-g        14.50 14.50
Dated 2013.

**Souvenir Sheet**

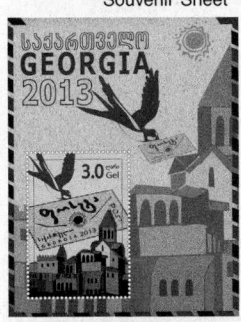

Carrier Pigeon A185

**Perf. 13¼x13½**
**2014, Dec. 22              Litho.**
501 A185 3 l multi                   6.25 6.25
Dated 2013.

Tbilisi Tram A186

**Perf. 13½x13¼**
**2014, Dec. 22              Litho.**
502 A186 3 l multi                   6.25 6.25
Dated 2013.

**Souvenir Sheet**

Tbilisi Doorway A187

**2014, Dec. 22    Litho.    Perf. 13¾**
503 A187 3 l multi                   6.25 6.25
Dated 2013.

**Souvenir Sheet**

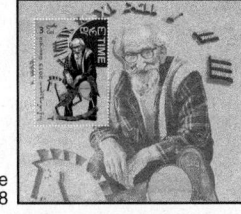

Time A188

**Perf. 13¼x13½**
**2014, Dec. 22              Litho.**
504 A188 3 l multi                   6.25 6.25
Dated 2013.

**Souvenir Sheet**

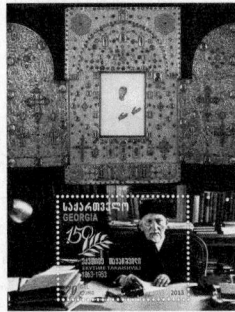

Ekvtime Takaishvili (1863-1953), Historian — A189

**2014, Dec. 22    Litho.    Perf. 13x13¼**
505 A189 7 l multi                   14.50 14.50
Dated 2013.

**Souvenir Sheet**

Giorgi Eristavi (1813-64), Playwright — A190

**2014, Dec. 22    Litho.    Perf. 13¾**
506 A190 7 l multi                   14.50 14.50
Dated 2013.

National Musical Instruments A191

**2015, Feb. 10    Litho.    Perf. 13x13¼**
**Stamp With White Frame**
507 A191 1.50 l multi                3.50 3.50
**Souvenir Sheet**
**Stamp With Tan Frame**
508 A191 1.50 l multi                3.50 3.50
Europa. Dated 2014.

International Telecommunication Union, 150th Anniv. — A192

**2015, July 22    Litho.    Perf. 13x13¼**
509 A192 1.50 l bright blue          2.50 2.50

European Youth Olympics Festival, Tbilisi — A193

Designs: No. 510, 2 l, Mascot. No. 511, 2 l, Emblem.

**2015, July 22    Litho.    Perf. 13¼x13**
510-511 A193    Set of 2             6.75 6.75
511a    Souvenir sheet of 2, #510-511    6.75 6.75

Europa — A194

Old toys: No. 512, 2 l, Wooden horse on wheels. No. 513, 2 l, Doll.

**2015, July 22    Litho.    Perf. 13¼x13**
512-513 A194    Set of 2             6.75 6.75
513a    Souvenir sheet of 2, #512-513    6.75 6.75

**Souvenir Sheet**

Boris Paichadze (1915-90), Soccer Player — A195

**2015, July 22    Litho.    Perf. 13x13¼**
514 A195 1.50 l multi                2.50 2.50

**Souvenir Sheet**

Poets A196

No. 515: a, Vazha-Pshavela (1861-1915). b, Akaki Tsereteli (1840-1915).

**2015, July 22    Litho.    Perf. 13x13¼**
515 A196 2 l Sheet of 2, #a-b        6.75 6.75

Independence, 25th Anniv. — A197

**Litho. With Foil Application**
**2016, Oct. 24**    *Perf. 13x13¼*
516 A197 2.90 l multi    3.25 3.25

Europa — A198

**2016, Oct. 24**   Litho.   *Perf. 13x13¼*
517 A198 2.90 l multi    3.25 3.25

Think Green Issue.

A199

Fairy Tale Characters — A200

*Serpentine Die Cut 13x12¼*
**2016, Oct. 24**    Litho.
**Self-Adhesive**
518 A199 30t multi    .55 .55
*Serpentine Die Cut 12¼x13*
519 A200 40t multi    .70 .70

Souvenir Sheet

Georgian Connections With the European Union — A201

**2016, Oct. 24**   Litho.   *Perf. 13¼x13*
520 A201 2 l multi    2.25 2.25

2016 Summer Olympics, Rio de Janeiro — A202

**2016, Oct. 24**   Litho.   *Perf. 13¼x13*
521 A202 2 l multi    3.25 3.25

Fauna — A203

Designs: 10t, Panurus biarmicus. 15t, Phoenicurus erythrogastrus. 20t, Panthera pardus.

*Serpentine Die Cut 12½*
**2016, Oct. 24**    Litho.
**Self-Adhesive**
522-524 A203   Set of 3    .85 .85

Staphylea Colchica A204

**2016, Dec. 15**   Litho.   *Perf. 13¼x13*
525 A204 35t multi    .85 .85

Souvenir Sheet

Ivane Javakhishvili (1876-1940), Historian — A205

**2016, Dec. 15**   Litho.   *Perf. 13x13¼*
526 A205 2.50 l multi    3.75 3.75

Souvenir Sheet

Georgian Architecture and Art — A206

No. 527: a, 2 l, Alaverdi Cathedral. b, 3 l, Religious painting from Alaverdi Cathedral.

**2016, Dec. 15**   Litho.   *Perf. 13¼*
527 A206   Sheet of 2, #a-b   7.00 7.00

Souvenir Sheet

Mountain Resorts A207

No. 528: a, Mestia. b, Bakuriani. c, Gudauri.

*Perf. 13¼x13¾*
**2016, Dec. 15**    Litho.
528 A207 1.25 l Sheet of 3, #a-c   5.50 5.50

Europa A208

Designs: No. 529, 2.50 l, Narikala Fortress. No. 530, 2.50 l, Rabati Castle.

**2017, Oct. 5**   Litho.   *Perf. 13¼x13*
529-530 A208   Set of 2    8.50 8.50
530a    Souvenir sheet of 2, #529-530    8.50 8.50

Democratic Republic of Georgia, Cent. — A209

No. 531: a, Georgian people on Independence Day, 1918. b, Coat of arms of Democratic Republic of Georgia.
No. 532, 3.50 l, Flag of Democratic Republic of Georgia. No. 533, 3.50 l. Democratic Republic of Georgia soldiers.

**2018, May 31**   Litho.   *Perf. 14*
531 A209 2.50 l Sheet of 2, #a-b   8.75 8.75
**Souvenir Sheets**
532-533 A209   Set of 2    12.50 12.50

Prince Vakhushti Batonishvili (1696-1757), Geographer and Historian — A210

**2018, June 14**   Litho.   *Perf. 13x13¼*
534 A210 80t multi    1.50 1.50

43rd World Chess Olympiad, Batumi — A211

**2018, June 14**   Litho.   *Perf. 13*
535 A211 80t multi    1.60 1.60

Prince Ilia Chavchavadze (1837-1907), Writer — A212

**2018, June 14**   Litho.   *Perf. 14*
536 A212 1 l multi    1.75 1.75

Nato Vachnadze (1904-53), Actress — A213

**2018, June 14**   Litho.   *Perf. 13x13¼*
537 A213 1 l multi    1.75 1.75

Nodar Dumbadze (1928-84), Writer — A214

**2018, June 14**   Litho.   *Perf. 13x13¼*
538 A214 1 l multi    1.75 1.75

Zakaria Paliashvili (1871-1933), Composer A215

**2018, June 14**   Litho.   *Perf. 13x13¼*
539 A215 1 l multi    1.75 1.75

Noe Zhordania (1868-1953), Journalist and Politician — A216

**2018, June 14**   Litho.   *Perf. 13¼x13*
540 A216 1 l multi    1.75 1.75

Diplomatic Relations Between Georgia and Brazil, 25th Anniv. — A217

**2018, June 14**   Litho.   *Perf. 13¼*
541 A217 1.50 l multi    2.75 2.75

2018 Winter Olympics, Pyeongchang, South Korea — A218

**2018, June 14**   Litho.   *Perf. 13¼x13*
542 A218 2 l multi    3.50 3.50

2018 Summer Youth Olympics, Buenos Aires — A219

**2018, June 14**   Litho.   *Perf. 14½*
543 A219 2 l multi    3.50 3.50

Europa — A220

Designs: No. 544, 2.90 l, Besleti Bridge. No. 545, 2.90 l, Freedom Bridge.

**2018, June 14**   Litho.   *Perf. 13x13¼*
544-545 A220   Set of 2    10.50 10.50

Souvenir Sheets

National Heroes A221

Designs: No. 546, 2.50 l, Gen. Giorgi Mazniashvili (1870-1937). No. 547, 2.50 l, Merab Kostava (1939-89), musician and poet.

**2018, June 14**   Litho.   *Perf. 13¼x13*
546-547 A221   Set of 2    9.00 9.00

## Souvenir Sheet

Prince Nikoloz Baratashvili (1817-45), Poet — A222

**2018, June 14**    **Litho.**    **Perf. 14¼**
548 A222 1.50 l multi      2.75 2.75

### Souvenir Sheet

Diplomatic Relations Between Georgia and Various Countries, 25th Anniv. — A223

**2018, June 14**    **Litho.**    **Perf. 13¾**
549 A223 3 l multi      5.50 5.50

### Souvenir Sheet

Self-Portrait, by David Kakabadze (1889-1952) A224

**2018, June 14**    **Litho.**    **Perf. 13¼x13**
550 A224 3 l multi      5.50 5.50

### Miniature Sheet

Endangered Animals in Red Book of Georgia — A225

No. 551: a, Lynx lynx. b, Sciurus anomalus. c, Cervus elaphus. d, Ursus arctos linnaeus.

**2018, July 6**    **Litho.**    **Perf. 13½**
551 A225 50t Sheet of 4, #a-d    3.50 3.50

Petre Otskheli (1907-37), Theater Set and Costume Designer — A226

---

No. 552 — Costumes from: a, 10t, Beatrice Cenci. b, 20t, Othello. c, 30t, Flying Decorator (man with brush). d, 40t, Flying Decorator (aviator). e, 50t, Surami Fortress. 1.50 l, Otskheli portrait.

**2018, July 6**    **Litho.**    **Perf. 14x13¾**
552 A226   Sheet of 5, #a-e, + label    2.75 2.75
     **Souvenir Sheet**
553 A226 1.50 l multi      2.75 2.75

Interparliamentary Assembly on Orthodoxy, 25th Anniv. — A227

**2018, Oct. 14**    **Litho.**    **Perf. 13¼**
554 A227 1 l multi      1.75 1.75

### Souvenir Sheet

Ivane Javakhishvili Tbilisi State University, Cent. — A228

**2018, Oct. 14**    **Litho.**    **Perf. 14**
555 A228 3 l multi      5.50 5.50

### Souvenir Sheet

Diplomatic Relations Between Georgia and Various Countries, 25th Anniv. — A229

**2018, Oct. 14**    **Litho.**    **Perf. 13¾**
556 A229 3 l multi      5.50 5.50

### Souvenir Sheet

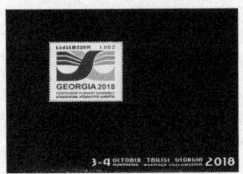

Posteurop Plenary Assembly, Tbilisi — A230

**2018, Oct. 14**   **Litho.**   **Perf. 13½x13¾**
557 A230 3 l multi      5.50 5.50

Zviad Gamsakhurdia (1939-93), First President of Georgia — A231

**2019, May 2**    **Litho.**    **Perf. 13x13¼**
558 A231 2 l multi      3.25 3.25

### Souvenir Sheet

First Georgian Postage Stamps, Cent. A232

---

No. 559: a, Georgia #2-3. b, Georgia #5. c, Georgia #1, 3, 4.

**2019, May 26**    **Litho.**    **Perf. 13¾**
559 A232 2.40 l Sheet of 3, #a-c    11.00 11.00

Europa — A233

Birds: No. 560, 2.40 l, Accipiter nisus. No. 561, 2.40 l, Phasianus colchicus, horiz.

**Perf. 14x13¾, 13¾x14**
**2019, Aug. 25**          **Litho.**
560-561 A233   Set of 2    7.50 7.50
561a    Souvenir sheet of 2, #560-561    7.50 7.50

### Souvenir Sheet

Council of Europe Anniversaries — A234

No. 562: a, Admission of Georgia to Council of Europe, 20th anniv. b, Council of Europe, 70th anniv.

**2019, Aug. 25**   **Litho.**   **Perf. 13x13¼**
562 A234 1.50 l Sheet of 2, #a-b   4.50 4.50

North Atlantic Treaty Organization, 70th Anniv. — A235

**2020, Jan. 27**    **Litho.**    **Perf. 14x13¾**
563 A235 2 l multi      3.00 3.00

Dated 2019.

Eastern Partnership, 10th Anniv. — A236

**2020, Jan. 27**    **Litho.**    **Perf. 13¾x14**
564 A236 2 l multi      3.00 3.00

### Souvenir Sheet

Zhiuli Shartava (1944-93), Abkhazian Politician — A237

**2020, Jan. 27**    **Litho.**    **Perf. 13¼x13**
565 A237 2.40 l multi      3.50 3.50

Dated 2019.

---

## Souvenir Sheet

Ambrosi Khelaia (1861-1927), Saint of Georgian Orthodox Church — A238

**2020, Jan. 27**   **Litho.**   **Perf. 13¼x13**
566 A238 2.40 l multi      3.50 3.50

Dated 2019.

### Souvenir Sheet

Lado Gudiashvili (1896-1980), Painter and Poet — A239

**2020, Jan. 27**    **Litho.**    **Perf. 13¼x13**
567 A239 3 l multi      4.50 4.50

Dated 2019.

Mohandas K. Gandhi (1869-1948), Indian Nationalist Leader — A240

**2020, Apr. 22**    **Litho.**    **Perf. 14**
568 A240 2.40 l multi      3.75 3.75

### Souvenir Sheet

Bertha von Suttner (1843-1914), 1905 Nobel Peace Laureate — A241

**2020, Apr. 22**    **Litho.**    **Perf. 14**
569 A241 2.40 l multi      3.75 3.75

### Souvenir Sheet

Mitrofan Lagidze (1869-1960), Creator of Flavored Mineral Waters — A242

**2020, Apr. 22**    **Litho.**    **Perf. 14**
570 A242 3 l multi      4.50 4.50

Lech Kaczinski (1949-2010), President of Poland — A243

**2020, June 7**    **Litho.**    **Perf. 14**
571 A243 2.40 l multi      3.75 3.75

Joint issue between Georgia and Poland. See Poland No. 4476.

1857 Tiflis Stamp, Map of Kojori-Tbilisi
Postal Route and Postrider — A244

**2020, Oct. 30    Litho.    Perf. 14½x14¼**
572    A244    2.70 l multi    3.75    3.75
    Europa. Ancient Postal Routes.

### Souvenir Sheet

Galaktion Tabidze (1892-1959),
Poet — A245

**2021, Feb. 5    Litho.    Perf. 14x13¾**
573    A245    3 l multi    4.00    4.00

2020
International
Festival of
Science and
Innovation
A246

**2021, Apr. 1    Litho.    Perf. 13¼**
574    A246    3 l multi    4.00    4.00

Endangered
Animals — A247

Pistacia mutica and: No. 575, 2.10 l, Gazella
subgutturosa. No. 576, 2.10 l, Aquila heliaca.

**2021, Sept. 22    Litho.    Perf. 14**
575-576    A247    Set of 2    7.00    7.00
576a    Souvenir sheet of 2, #575-
    576    7.00    7.00
    Europa.

Portrait of Dante
Alighieri, by Sergo
Kobuladze (1909-
78) — A248

**2021, Oct. 5    Litho.    Perf. 13¼x13½**
577    A248    3.70 l multi    4.00    4.00
    Alighieri (c. 1265-1321), writer.

### Souvenir Sheet

Lighthouses — A249

No. 578: a, Poti Lighthouse. b, Sokhumi
Lighthouse. c, Batumi Lighthouse.

**2022, Jan.    Litho.    Perf. 14x13¾**
578    A249    1.80 l    Sheet of 3, #a-c    7.00    7.00
    Dated 2021.

---

### Souvenir Sheet

Battle of
Didgori,
900th
Anniv.
(in 2021)
A250

**2022, Jan.    Litho.    Perf. 14**
579    A250    3.60 l multi    4.00    4.00
    Dated 2021.

### Souvenir Sheets

Tbilisi,
2021
World
Book
Capital
A251

Designs: No. 580, 2.15 l, Anthim the Iberian
(1650-1716), printer of first book in Georgia,
1709. No. 581, 2.15 l, King Vakhtang VI (1675-
1737), publisher of first scientific book in Georgia, 1721. No. 582, 2.15 l, Cover of 1924 literary journal H2SO4.

**2022, Jan.    Litho.    Perf. 14x13¾**
580-582    A251    Set of 3    7.25    7.25

---

### SEMI-POSTAL STAMPS

### Surcharge in Red or Black

SP1    SP2

SP3    SP4

**1922    Unwmk.    Perf. 11½**
B1    SP1    1000r on 50r vio (R)    .75    3.00
B2    SP2    3000r on 100r brn
    red    .75    3.00
B3    SP3    5000r on 250r gray
    grn    .75    3.00
B4    SP4    10,000r on 25r blue
    (R)    .75    3.00
    Nos. B1-B4 (4)    3.00    12.00

Nos. B1-B4 exist imperf but were not so
issued. Value slightly more than perforated
examples.

Georgian Natl. Olympic
Committee — SP10

**1994, May 27    Litho.    Perf. 13½**
B10    SP10    100c +50c multi    1.10    1.10

UNICEF, 50th
Anniv. — SP11

Children's paintings: 20t+5t, People on ladder above rainbow, vert. 30t+10t, Animal
character.

---

**Perf. 13x14, 14x13**
**1996, Dec. 20    Litho.**
B11    SP11    20t +5t multi    1.40    1.40
B12    SP11    30t +10t multi    1.90    1.90

In Remembrance
of Sept. 11, 2001
Terrorist
Attacks — SP12

**2001, Dec. 31    Litho.    Perf. 13x13¼**
B13    SP12    30t +10t multi    1.60    1.60

### Souvenir Sheet
B14    SP12    120t +10t multi    5.50    5.50

Campaign
Against
COVID-19
Pandemic
SP13

**2021, Feb. 18    Litho.    Perf. 13¼x13**
B15    SP13    1 l +1 l multi    2.75    2.75

### Souvenir Sheet

Maro Makashvili (1901-21), Nurse and
National Hero — SP14

**2021, Mar. 23    Litho.    Perf. 14x13¾**
B16    SP14    3 l + 1 l multi    5.25    5.25
    Dated 2020.

---

# GERMAN EAST AFRICA

ˈjər-mən ˈest ˈa-fri-kə

LOCATION — In East Africa, bordering
on the Indian Ocean
GOVT. — German Colony
AREA — 384,180 sq. mi.
POP. — 7,680,132 (1913)
CAPITAL — Dar-es Salaam

Following World War I, the greater
part of this German Colonial possession was mandated to Great Britain.
The British ceded to the Belgians the
provinces of Ruanda and Urundi (Belgian East Africa). The Kionga triangle
was awarded to the Portuguese and
became part of the Mozambique Colony. The remaining area became the
British    Mandated    Territory    of
Tanganyika.

64 Pesa = 1 Rupee
100 Heller = 1 Rupee (1905)
100 Centimes = 1 Franc (1916)
12 Pence = 1 Shilling (1916)
100 Cents = 1 Rupee (1917)
12 Pence = 1 Shilling 100 Cents = 1
Rupee (1917)

Stamps of Germany
Surcharged in Black

**1893    Unwmk.    Perf. 13½x14½**
**Surcharge 15¼mm long**
1    A9    2pes on 3pf brown    45.00    45.00
2    A9    3pes on 5pf green    55.00    45.00
3    A10    5pes on 10pf car    35.00    25.00
**Surcharge 16¼mm long**
4    A10    10pes on 20pf ultra    30.00    14.00

---

**Surcharge 16¾mm long**
5    A10    25pes on 50pf red
    brn    45.00    25.00
    Nos. 1-5 (5)    210.00    154.00

The surcharge also comes 16¾mm on No.
1; 14¼ or 16⅞mm on Nos. 2-3; 17½mm on
No. 5. See the *Scott Classic Catalogue* for
listings of these spacings.

Stamps of Germany
Surcharged in Black

**1896**
6    A9    2pes on 3pf dk brn    2.25    35.00
a.    2pes on 3pf light brown    25.00    40.00
b.    2pes on 3pf grayish brown    11.00    11.00
c.    2pes on 3pf reddish brown    100.00    200.00
7    A9    3pes on 5pf green    3.00    4.25
8    A10    5pes on 10pf car    6.00    4.00
9    A10    10pes on 20pf ultra    6.00    5.00
10    A10    25pes on 50pf red
    brn    30.00    25.00
    Nos. 6-10 (5)    47.25    73.25

A5

Kaiser's Yacht
"Hohenzollern"
A6

**1900    Typo.    Perf. 14**
11    A5    2p brown    2.75    1.50
12    A5    3p green    2.75    1.75
13    A5    5p carmine    3.00    2.25
14    A5    10p ultra    5.00    4.50
15    A5    15p org & blk, sal    5.00    6.00
16    A5    20p lake & blk    6.75    13.50
17    A5    25p pur & blk, sal    6.75    13.50
18    A5    40p lake & blk, rose    9.00    21.00
**Engr.**
**Perf. 14½x14**
19    A6    1r claret    19.00    45.00
20    A6    2r yel green    9.00    75.00
21a    A6    3r red & slate    120.00    175.00
    Nos. 11-21a (11)    189.00    359.00

**Value in Heller**
**1905    Typo.    Perf. 14**
22    A5    2½h brown    5.25    1.60
23    A5    4h dk olive green    24.00    11.00
a.    4h green    15.00    5.00
b.    4h dark yellowish green    30.00    19.00
24    A5    7½h carmine    15.00    1.50
25    A5    15h ultra    26.00    5.75
a.    15h violet blue    50.00    15.00
26    A5    20h org & blk, yel    15.00    15.00
27    A5    30h lake & blk    15.00    5.50
28    A5    45h pur & blk    30.00    35.00
29    A5    60h lake & blk, rose    45.00    90.00
    Nos. 22-29 (8)    175.25    165.35

**1905-16    Wmk. Lozenges (125)**
31    A5    2½h brn ('06)    .90    .90
32    A5    4h grn ('06)    .90    .60
b.    Booklet pane of 4 + 2 labels    45.00
c.    Booklet pane of 5 + label    400.00
33    A5    7½h car ('06)    1.10    1.60
b.    Booklet pane of 4 + 2 labels    45.00
c.    Booklet pane of 5 + label    400.00
34    A5    15h dk blue ('08)    2.10    1.40
35    A5    20h org & blk, yel
    ('11)    2.25    19.00
36    A5    30h lake & blk ('09)    2.40    7.50
37    A5    45h pur & blk ('06)    5.25    52.50
38    A5    60h lake & blk, rose    29.00    180.00
**Engr.**
**Perf. 14½x14**
39    A6    1r red ('16)    13.00    25,000.
40    A6    2r yel grn    45.00
41    A6    3r car & sl ('08)    45.00    225.00
a.    3r red & blackish green ('08)    150.00    375.00
    Nos. 31-41 (11)    146.90    25,489.

No. 40 was never placed in use.
The frame of No. 41a fluoresces bright
orange under ultra-violet light.
Forged cancellations are found on #35-39,
41.

In early 1916, German East African authorities ordered supplies of provisional stamps, printed by the press of the Evangelical Mission in Wuga. Three values in denominations most urgently needed were produced in March, but before they could be issued, new stocks of regular stamps were received from Germany. To prevent their capture by the British, the provisionals were buried until 1922, when they were retrieved by the German government and sold at auction. Because of their long storage in the tropical climate, 90-95% of the stamps were destroyed and those surviving are usually brittle and somewhat faded.

Values: 2½h violet brown, $55; 7½h, carmine, $25; 1r pink, $1,400.

---

## OCCUPATION STAMPS

### Issued Under Belgian Occupation
**Stamps of Belgian Congo, 1915, Handstamped "RUANDA" in Black, Blue or Red Violet**

| | | | |
|---|---|---|---|
| **1916** | | **Unwmk.** | **Perf. 13½ to 15** |
| N1 | A29 | 5c green & blk | 65.00 |
| N2 | A30 | 10c carmine & blk | 65.00 |
| N3 | A21 | 15c blue grn & blk | 125.00 |
| N4 | A31 | 25c blue & blk | 65.00 |
| N5 | A23 | 40c brown red & blk | 65.00 |
| N6 | A24 | 50c brown lake & blk | 75.00 |
| N7 | A25 | 1fr olive bis & blk | 400.00 |
| N8 | A27 | 5fr ocher & blk | 4,000. |
| | | *Nos. N1-N7 (7)* | 860.00 |

**Stamps of Belgian Congo, 1915, Handstamped "URUNDI" in Black, Blue or Red Violet**

| | | | |
|---|---|---|---|
| N9 | A29 | 5c green & blk | 65.00 |
| N10 | A30 | 10c carmine & blk | 65.00 |
| N11 | A21 | 15c bl grn & blk | 125.00 |
| N12 | A31 | 25c blue & blk | 65.00 |
| N13 | A23 | 40c brn red & blk | 65.00 |
| N14 | A24 | 50c brn lake & blk | 75.00 |
| N15 | A25 | 1fr ol bis & blk | 400.00 |
| N16 | A27 | 5fr ocher & blk | 4,000. |
| | | *Nos. N9-N15 (7)* | 860.00 |

Stamps of Belgian Congo overprinted "Karema," "Kigoma" and "Tabora" were not officially authorized.
Nos. N1-N16 exist with forged overprint.

**Stamps of Belgian Congo, 1915, Ovptd. in Dark Blue**

| | | | |
|---|---|---|---|
| **1916** | | | **Perf. 12½ to 15** |
| N17 | A29 | 5c green & blk | 1.00 | .30 |
| b. | | Inverted overprint | 225.00 | |
| N18 | A30 | 10c carmine & blk | 1.25 | .50 |
| a. | | Inverted overprint | 225.00 | |
| N19 | A21 | 15c bl grn & blk | 1.00 | .30 |
| N20 | A31 | 25c blue & blk | 7.25 | 1.75 |
| N21 | A23 | 40c brn red & blk | 20.00 | 6.00 |
| N22 | A24 | 50c brn lake & blk | 27.50 | 6.00 |
| N23 | A25 | 1fr olive bis & blk | 3.00 | .75 |
| a. | | Double overprint | 3.50 | 1.75 |
| N24 | A27 | 5fr ocher & blk | 3.50 | 1.75 |
| | | *Nos. N17-N24 (8)* | 64.50 | 17.35 |
| | | Set, never hinged | 90.00 | |

Nos. N17-N18, N20-N22 Surcharged in Black or Red

| | | | | |
|---|---|---|---|---|
| **1922** | | | | |
| N25 | A24 | 5c on 50c brn lake & blk | .60 | .45 |
| N26 | A29 | 10c on 5c grn & blk (R) | .60 | .40 |
| N27 | A23 | 25c on 40c brn red & blk (R) | 3.75 | 2.75 |
| N28 | A30 | 30c on 10c car & blk | .60 | .30 |

---

| | | | | |
|---|---|---|---|---|
| N29 | A31 | 50c on 25c bl & blk (R) | .60 | .30 |
| | | *Nos. N25-N29 (5)* | 6.15 | 4.20 |
| | | Set, never hinged | 21.50 | |

No. N25 has the surcharge at each side.

---

## ISSUED UNDER BRITISH OCCUPATION

**Stamps of Nyasaland Protectorate, 1913-15 Overprinted**

N.F.

| | | | | |
|---|---|---|---|---|
| **1916** | | **Wmk. 3** | | **Perf. 14** |
| N101 | A3 | ½p green | 1.75 | 9.50 |
| a. | | Double overprint (R & Bk) | | |
| N102 | A3 | 1p carmine | 1.75 | 3.75 |
| N103 | A3 | 3p violet, *yel* | 27.50 | 18.00 |
| a. | | Double overprint | | 26,000. |
| N104 | A3 | 4p scar & blk, *yel* | 52.50 | 42.00 |
| N105 | A3 | 1sh black, *green* | 72.50 | 72.50 |
| | | *Nos. N101-N105 (5)* | 156.00 | 145.75 |

"N.F." stands for "Nyasaland Force."

**Stamps of East Africa and Uganda, 1912-14, Overprinted in Black or Red**

G.E.A.

| | | | | |
|---|---|---|---|---|
| **1917** | | | | |
| N106 | A3 | 1c black (R) | .25 | .95 |
| N107 | A3 | 3c blue green | .25 | .25 |
| N108 | A3 | 6c carmine | .25 | .25 |
| N109 | A3 | 10c brown orange | .60 | .70 |
| N110 | A3 | 12c gray | .60 | 3.50 |
| N111 | A3 | 15c ultramarine | 2.25 | 6.50 |
| N112 | A3 | 25c scar & blk, *yel* | .90 | 7.00 |
| N113 | A3 | 50c violet & blk | 2.75 | 6.50 |
| N114 | A3 | 75c blk, *bl grn*, olive back (R) | 1.25 | 5.00 |
| a. | | 75c black, *emerald* (R) | 3.75 | 52.50 |

**Overprinted**

G.E.A.

| | | | | |
|---|---|---|---|---|
| N115 | A4 | 1r blk, *green* (R) | 6.50 | 8.00 |
| a. | | 1r black, *emerald* (R) | 14.00 | 65.00 |
| N116 | A4 | 2r blk & red, *bl* | 15.00 | 62.50 |
| N117 | A4 | 3r gray grn & vio | 17.50 | 95.00 |
| N118 | A4 | 4r grn & red, *yel* | 27.50 | 120.00 |
| N119 | A4 | 5r dl vio & ultra | 52.50 | 140.00 |
| N120 | A4 | 10r grn & red, *grn* | 160.00 | 450.00 |
| a. | | 10r grn & red, *emerald* | 210.00 | 700.00 |
| N121 | A3 | 20r vio & blk, *red* | 325.00 | 700.00 |
| N122 | A3 | 50r gray grn & red | 750.00 | 1,300. |
| | | *Nos. N106-N120 (15)* | 288.10 | 906.15 |

See Tanganyika for "G.E.A." overprints on stamps inscribed "East Africa and Uganda Protectorates" with watermark 4.

---

## SEMI-POSTAL STAMPS

### Issued under Belgian Occupation

**Semi-Postal Stamps of Belgian Congo, 1915, Overprinted**

A.O.

| | | | | |
|---|---|---|---|---|
| **1918** | | **Unwmk.** | **Perf. 14, 15** |
| NB1 | A29 | 5c + 10c grn & bl | .50 | .50 |
| NB2 | A30 | 10c + 15c car & bl | .80 | .50 |
| NB3 | A21 | 15c + 20c bl grn & bl | 1.00 | .50 |
| NB4 | A31 | 25c + 25c dp & pale bl | 1.50 | .50 |
| NB5 | A23 | 40c + 40c brn red & bl | 1.00 | .75 |
| NB6 | A24 | 50c + 50c brn lake & bl | 1.50 | 1.00 |
| NB7 | A25 | 1fr + 1fr ol bis & bl | 3.00 | 3.00 |
| NB8 | A27 | 5fr + 5fr ocher & bl | 10.00 | 10.00 |

---

| | | | | |
|---|---|---|---|---|
| NB9 | A28 | 10fr + 10fr grn & bl | 95.00 | 95.00 |
| | | *Nos. NB1-NB9 (9)* | 114.30 | 111.75 |

The letters "A.O." are the initials of "Afrique Orientale" (East Africa).

---

# GERMAN NEW GUINEA

ˈjər-mən ˈnü ˈgi-nē

LOCATION — A group of islands in the west Pacific Ocean, including a part of New Guinea and adjacent islands of the Bismarck Archipelago.
GOVT. — German Protectorate
AREA — 93,000 sq. mi.
POP. — 601,427 (1913)
CAPITAL — Herbertshohe (later Kokopo)

The islands were occupied by Australian troops during World War I and renamed "New Britain." By covenant of the League of Nations they were made a mandated territory of Australia in 1920. The old name of "New Guinea" has since been restored. Postage stamps were issued under all regimes. For other listings see New Britain (1914-15), North West Pacific Islands (1915-22) and New Guinea in Vol. 4.

100 Pfennig = 1 Mark

**Stamps of Germany Overprinted in Black**

| | | | | |
|---|---|---|---|---|
| **1897-99** | | **Unwmk.** | **Perf. 13½x14½** |
| 1 | A9 | 3pf brown | 7.50 | 7.50 |
| a. | | 3pf reddish brown ('99) | 130.00 | 225.00 |
| b. | | 3pf yellow brown ('98) | 30.00 | 52.50 |
| 2 | A9 | 5pf green | 5.25 | 4.50 |
| 3 | A10 | 10pf carmine | 6.00 | 7.50 |
| 4 | A10 | 20pf ultra | 9.00 | 11.00 |
| 5 | A10 | 25pf orange ('98) | 22.50 | 50.00 |
| a. | | Inverted overprint | 2,100. | |
| 6 | A10 | 50pf red brown | 30.00 | 45.00 |
| | | *Nos. 1-6 (6)* | 80.25 | 125.50 |

A3

Kaiser's Yacht "Hohenzollern"
A4

| | | | | |
|---|---|---|---|---|
| **1901** | | **Typo.** | **Perf. 14** |
| 7 | A3 | 3pf brown | 1.25 | 1.25 |
| 8 | A3 | 5pf green | 6.00 | 1.25 |
| 9 | A3 | 10pf carmine | 19.00 | 3.00 |
| 10 | A3 | 20pf ultra | 1.50 | 3.00 |
| 11 | A3 | 25pf org & blk, *yel* | 1.50 | 15.00 |
| 12 | A3 | 30pf org & blk, *sal* | 1.50 | 19.00 |
| 13 | A3 | 40pf lake & blk | 1.50 | 21.00 |
| 14 | A3 | 50pf pur & blk, *sal* | 2.00 | 18.00 |
| 15 | A3 | 80pf lake & blk, *rose* | 3.50 | 25.00 |
| | | **Engr.** | | |
| | | **Perf. 14½x14** | | |
| 16 | A4 | 1m carmine | 9.00 | 50.00 |
| 17 | A4 | 2m blue | 9.00 | 72.50 |
| 18 | A4 | 3m blk vio | 11.00 | 140.00 |
| 19 | A4 | 5m slate & car | 160.00 | 450.00 |
| | | *Nos. 7-19 (13)* | 226.75 | 819.00 |

Fake cancellations exist on Nos. 10-19.
The stamps of German New Guinea overprinted "G.R.I." and new values in British currency were all used in New Britain and are listed under that country as Nos. 1-29C, O1-2.

---

**German Colonies & Offices (British Occupation)**

North America's ultimate specialist. We have a **MILLION** dollar inventory of mint, used and special cancels.

**Send us your want list today!**

Looking to sell!
Well look no more!
Dial: 1 (877) 272-6693

**Colonial Stamp Company**
5757 Wilshire Blvd., Penthouse 8
Los Angeles, CA 90036 USA
Tel: 1 (323) 933-9435 Fax: 1 (323) 939-9930
**Toll Free in North America**
Tel: 1 (877) 272-6693 Fax: 1 (877) 272-6694
E-Mail: *info@colonialstampcompany.com*
URL: *www.colonialstampcompany.com*

A5     A6

Nos. 21-23 have "NEUGUINEA" as one word without a hyphen.

| | | | |
|---|---|---|---|
| | | **Wmk. Lozenges (125)** | |
| **1914-19** | | **Typo.** | **Perf. 14** |
| 20 | A3 | 3pf brown ('19) | 1.50 |
| 21 | A5 | 5pf green | 1.50 |
| 22 | A5 | 10pf carmine | 1.50 |
| | | **Engr.** | |
| | | **Perf. 14½x14** | |
| 23 | A6 | 5m slate & carmine | 30.00 |
| | | *Nos. 20-23 (4)* | 34.50 |

Nos. 20-23 were never placed in use.

# GERMAN SOUTH WEST AFRICA

'jər-mən 'sauth 'west 'a-fri-kə

LOCATION — In southwest Africa, bordering on the South Atlantic
GOVT. — German Colony
AREA — 322,450 sq. mi. (1913)
POP. — 94,372 (1913)
CAPITAL — Windhoek

The Colony was occupied by South African troops during World War I and in 1920 was mandated to the Union of South Africa by the League of Nations. See South West Africa in Vol. 6.

100 Pfennig = 1 Mark

### Stamps of Germany Overprinted

**1897    Unwmk.    Perf. 13½x14½**

| | | | | |
|---|---|---|---|---|
| 1 | A9 | 3pf dark brown | 7.50 | 11.00 |
| a. | | 3pf yellow brown | 45.00 | 2,600. |
| 2 | A9 | 5pf green | 4.00 | 4.50 |
| 3 | A10 | 10pf carmine | 21.00 | 17.50 |
| 4 | A10 | 20pf ultra | 7.50 | 5.25 |
| 5 | A10 | 25pf orange | 210.00 | 27,000. |
| 6 | A10 | 50pf red brown | 210.00 | 27,000. |
| | | Nos. 1-4 (4) | 40.00 | 38.25 |

Nos. 5 and 6 were prepared for issue but were not sent to the Colony. However, a small number were postally used from the Colony. Used values for Nos. 5 and 6 are for expertized stamps bearing genuine, contemporaneous Colony postmarks.

### Overprinted in Black on 2 lines

**1898-99**

| | | | | |
|---|---|---|---|---|
| 7 | A9 | 3pf dark brown | 3.75 | 19.00 |
| a. | | 3pf reddish brown | 50.00 | 190.00 |
| b. | | 3pf yellow brown | 7.50 | 11.00 |
| 8 | A9 | 5pf green | 3.75 | 3.00 |
| 9 | A10 | 10pf carmine | 3.75 | 3.75 |
| 10 | A10 | 20pf ultra | 15.00 | 13.50 |
| 11 | A10 | 25pf orange | 315.00 | 375.00 |
| 12 | A10 | 50pf red brown | 19.00 | 11.00 |

### Kaiser's Yacht "Hohenzollern"
A3          A4

**1901    Typo.    Perf. 14**

| | | | | |
|---|---|---|---|---|
| 13 | A3 | 3pf brown | 3.75 | 1.50 |
| 14 | A3 | 5pf green | 18.00 | 1.50 |
| 15 | A3 | 10pf carmine | 13.00 | .75 |
| 16 | A3 | 20pf ultra | 27.50 | 1.40 |
| 17 | A3 | 25pf org & blk, yel | 1.50 | 5.25 |
| 18 | A3 | 30pf org & blk, sal | 75.00 | 2.50 |
| 19 | A3 | 40pf lake & blk | 1.75 | 3.00 |
| 20 | A3 | 50pf pur & blk, sal | 2.00 | 2.00 |
| 21 | A3 | 80pf lake & blk, rose | 2.10 | 8.25 |

**Engr.**
**Perf. 14½x14**

| | | | | |
|---|---|---|---|---|
| 22 | A4 | 1m carmine | 120.00 | 29.00 |
| 23 | A4 | 2m blue | 29.00 | 35.00 |
| 24 | A4 | 3m blk vio | 30.00 | 45.00 |
| 25 | A4 | 5m slate & car | 180.00 | 150.00 |
| | | Nos. 13-25 (13) | 503.60 | 285.15 |

**Wmk. Lozenges (125)**

**1906-19    Typo.    Perf. 14**

| | | | | |
|---|---|---|---|---|
| 26 | A3 | 3pf dk brn ('07) | .75 | 3.50 |
| 27 | A3 | 5pf green | .75 | 1.35 |
| b. | | Bklt. pane of 6 (2 #27, 4 #28) | 65.00 | |
| c. | | Booklet pane of 5 + label | 600.00 | |
| 28 | A3 | 10pf lt rose | .90 | 1.40 |
| b. | | Booklet pane of 5 + label | 600.00 | |
| 29 | A3 | 20pf ultra ('11) | .90 | 3.50 |
| 30 | A3 | 30pf org & blk, pale yel ('11) | 15.00 | 50.00 |

**Engr.**
**Perf. 14½x14**

| | | | | |
|---|---|---|---|---|
| 31 | A4 | 1m carmine ('12) | 11.00 | 72.50 |
| 32 | A4 | 2m blue ('11) | 11.00 | 72.50 |
| 33 | A4 | 3m blk vio ('19) | 13.00 | |
| a. | | 3m gray violet | 67.50 | |
| 34 | A4 | 5m slate & car | 35.00 | 325.00 |
| a. | | 5m slate & rose red | 100.00 | 275.00 |
| | | Nos. 26-34 (9) | 88.30 | 529.75 |

Nos. 33, 33a, 34a were never placed in use. Forged cancellations are found on #30-32, 34.

# Mint Sheet Binders

| | Item | Retail | AA |
|---|---|---|---|
| Black Mint Sheet Binder | MBBK | $25.99 | **$20.79** |
| Black Mint Sheet Binder & 25 Black Mint Sheet Pages | MBBK3PB | $41.69 | **$35.44** |
| Black Mint Sheet Binder & 24 Clear Mint Sheet Pages | MBBK3PC | $40.99 | **$34.84** |
| Blue Mint Sheet Binder | MBBL | $25.99 | **$20.79** |
| Blue Mint Sheet Binder & 25 Black Mint Sheet Pages | MBBL3PB | $41.69 | **$35.44** |
| Blue Mint Sheet Binder & 24 Clear Mint Sheet Pages | MBBL3PC | $40.99 | **$34.84** |
| Red Mint Sheet Binder | MBRD | $24.99 | **$19.99** |
| Red Mint Sheet Binder& 25 Black Mint Sheet Pages | MBRD3PB | $41.69 | **$35.44** |
| Red Mint Sheet Binder& 24 Clear Mint Sheet Pages | MBRD3PC | $40.99 | **$34.84** |
| Gray Mint Sheet Binder | MBGY | $25.99 | **$20.79** |
| Gray Mint Sheet Binder & 25 Black Mint Sheet Pages | MBGY3PB | $41.69 | **$35.44** |
| Gray Mint Sheet Binder & 24 Clear Mint Sheet Pages | MBGY3PC | $40.99 | **$34.84** |
| Black Mint Sheet Pages Only (Pack of 25) | MS1 | $17.99 | **$15.29** |

# AmosAdvantage.com
## 1-800-572-6885

ORDERING INFORMATION: *AA prices apply to paid subscribers of Amos Media titles, or for orders placed online. Prices, terms and product availability subject to change.

# GERMAN STATES

ˈjər-mən ˈstāts

## Watermarks

Wmk. 92 — 17mm wide

Wmk. 93 — 14mm wide

Wmk. 94 — Horiz. Wavy Lines Wide Apart

Wmk. 95v — Vert. Wavy Lines Close Together

Wmk. 95h — Horiz. Wavy Lines Close Together

Wmk. 102 — Post Horn

Wmk. 116 — Crosses and Circles

Wmk. 128 — Wavy Lines

Wmk. 130 — Wreath of Oak Leaves

Wmk. 148 — Small Flowers

Wmk. 162 — Laurel Wreath

Wmk. 192 — Circles

## BADEN

LOCATION — In southwestern Germany
GOVT. — Former Grand Duchy
AREA — 5,817 sq. mi.
POP. — 1,432,000 (1864)
CAPITAL — Karlsruhe (Principal city)

---

Baden was a member of the German Confederation. In 1870 it became part of the German Empire.

60 Kreuzer = 1 Gulden

Values for unused stamps are for examples with original gum as defined in the catalogue introduction except for Nos. 1-9 which are valued without gum. Very fine examples of Nos. 1-9 will have one or two margins touching the frame-lines due to the very narrow spacing of the stamps on the plates. Stamps with margins clear of the framelines on all four sides are scarce and sell for considerably more.

A1

| | | | Typo. | Imperf. |
|---|---|---|---|---|
| **1851-52** | | **Unwmk.** | | |
| 1 | A1 | 1kr blk, *dk buff* | 275.00 | 250.00 |
| 2 | A1 | 3kr blk, *yellow* | 140.00 | 16.00 |
| 3 | A1 | 6kr blk, *yel grn* | 440.00 | 45.00 |
| 4 | A1 | 9kr blk, *lil rose* | 90.00 | 26.00 |
| | | *Nos. 1-4 (4)* | 945.00 | 337.00 |

**Thin Paper (First Printing, 1851)**

| | | | | |
|---|---|---|---|---|
| 1a | A1 | 1kr black, *buff* | 2,000. | 800.00 |
| 2a | A1 | 3kr blk, *org* | 675.00 | 35.00 |
| 3a | A1 | 6kr blk, *blue grn* | 2,250. | 90.00 |
| 4a | A1 | 9kr blk, *dp rose* | 2,800. | 160.00 |

No. 4b

| | | | | |
|---|---|---|---|---|
| 4b | A1 | 9kr blk, *bl grn* (error) | | 1,300,000. |

**1853-58**

| | | | | |
|---|---|---|---|---|
| 6 | A1 | 1kr black | 160.00 | 27.50 |
| a. | | Tête bêche gutter pair | | 35,000. |
| 7 | A1 | 3kr black, *green* | 160.00 | 14.00 |
| 8 | A1 | 3kr black, *bl* ('58) | 675.00 | 30.00 |
| a. | | Printed on both sides | | |
| 9 | A1 | 6kr black, *yellow* | 250.00 | 27.50 |
| | | *Nos. 6-9 (4)* | 1,245. | 99.00 |

The paper of No. 6 is 0.06-0.095mm thick.
*Reissues (1865) of Nos. 1, 2, 3, 6, 7 and 8 exist on thick paper and No. 9 on thin paper; the color of the last is brighter than that of the original.*

Coat of Arms — A2

**1860-62** — **Perf. 13½**

| | | | | |
|---|---|---|---|---|
| 10 | A2 | 1kr black | 87.50 | 30.00 |
| 12 | A2 | 3kr ultra ('61) | 87.50 | 22.00 |
| a. | | 3kr Prussian blue | 275.00 | 72.50 |
| 13 | A2 | 6kr red org ('61) | 95.00 | 72.50 |
| a. | | 6kr yellow orange ('62) | 180.00 | 87.50 |
| 14 | A2 | 9kr ultra ('61) | 250.00 | 175.00 |
| | | *Nos. 10-14 (4)* | 520.00 | 299.50 |

Examples of Nos. 10-14 and 18 with all perforations intact sell for considerably more.

Coat of Arms — A3

**1862** — **Perf. 10**

| | | | | |
|---|---|---|---|---|
| 15 | A2 | 1kr black | 65.00 | 87.50 |
| a. | | 1kr silver gray | 6,500. | 6,500. |
| 16 | A2 | 6kr Prus bl ('62) | 125.00 | 235.00 |
| 17 | A2 | 9kr brown | 80.00 | 72.50 |
| a. | | 9kr dark brown | 325.00 | 250.00 |

**Perf. 13½**

| | | | | |
|---|---|---|---|---|
| 18 | A3 | 3kr rose | 2,250. | 290.00 |

**1862-65** — **Perf. 10**

| | | | | |
|---|---|---|---|---|
| 19 | A3 | 1kr black ('64) | 47.50 | 15.00 |
| a. | | 1kr silver gray | | 2,250. |
| 20 | A3 | 3kr rose | 62.50 | 4.00 |
| a. | | Imperf. | 40,000. | 40,000. |
| 22 | A3 | 6kr ultra ('65) | 11.00 | 27.50 |
| a. | | 6kr Prussian blue ('64) | 575.00 | 70.00 |

---

| | | | | |
|---|---|---|---|---|
| 23 | A3 | 9kr brn ('64) | 16.00 | 30.00 |
| a. | | 9kr bister | 375.00 | 90.00 |
| b. | | Printed on both sides | | 6,500. |
| 24 | A3 | 18kr green | 400.00 | 575.00 |
| 25 | A3 | 30kr dp org | 32.50 | 2,250. |
| a. | | 30kr yellow orange | 140.00 | 2,400. |

Forged cancellations are known on No. 25.

A4

**1868**

| | | | | |
|---|---|---|---|---|
| 26 | A4 | 1kr green | 4.00 | 9.00 |
| 27 | A4 | 3kr rose | 2.75 | 4.50 |
| 28 | A4 | 7kr dull blue | 20.00 | 35.00 |
| a. | | 7kr sky blue | 42.50 | 100.00 |
| | | *Nos. 26-28 (3)* | 26.75 | 48.50 |

Forged cancellations are known on No. 28a.
The postage stamps of Baden were superseded by those of the German Empire on Jan. 1, 1872, but Official stamps were used during the year 1905.

---

Stamps of the Baden sector of the French Occupation Zone of Germany, issued in 1947-49, are listed under Germany, Occupation Issues.

---

## RURAL POSTAGE DUE STAMPS

RU1

**1862** — **Unwmk.** — **Perf. 10**
**Thin Paper**

| | | | | |
|---|---|---|---|---|
| LJ1 | RU1 | 1kr blk, *yellow* | 5.00 | 325.00 |
| a. | | Thick paper | 140.00 | 600.00 |
| LJ2 | RU1 | 3kr blk, *yellow* | 2.75 | 125.00 |
| a. | | Thick paper | 120.00 | 400.00 |
| LJ3 | RU1 | 12kr blk, *yellow* | 35.00 | 13,500. |
| a. | | Half used as 6kr on cover | | 25,000. |
| b. | | Quarter used as 3kr on cover | | |
| | | *Nos. LJ1-LJ3 (3)* | 42.75 | 13,950. |

On No. LJ3, "LAND-POST" is a straight line. Paper of #LJ1a, LJ2a is darker yellow. Forged cancellations abound on Nos. LJ1-LJ3.

---

## OFFICIAL STAMPS
### See Germany Nos. OL16-OL21.

## BAVARIA

LOCATION — In southern Germany
GOVT. — Kingdom
AREA — 30,562 sq. mi. (1920)
POP. — 7,150,146 (1919)
CAPITAL — Munich

Bavaria was a member of the German Confederation and became part of the German Empire in 1870. After World War I, it declared itself a republic. It lost its postal autonomy on Mar. 31, 1920.

60 Kreuzer = 1 Gulden
100 Pfennig = 1 Mark (1874)

Values for unused stamps are for examples with original gum as defined in the catalogue introduction. Unused examples of the 1849-78 issues without gum sell for about 50-60% of the figures quoted.

A1

---

Broken Circle — A1a

**1849** — **Unwmk.** — **Typo.** — **Imperf.**

| | | | | |
|---|---|---|---|---|
| 1 | A1 | 1kr black | 1,000. | 2,250. |
| a. | | 1kr deep black | 2,800. | 3,000. |
| b. | | Tête bêche pair | 125,000. | |

**With Silk Thread**

| | | | | |
|---|---|---|---|---|
| 2 | A1a | 3kr blue | 60.00 | 3.50 |
| a. | | 3kr greenish blue | 60.00 | 3.50 |
| b. | | 3kr deep blue | 60.00 | 3.50 |
| 3 | A1a | 6kr brown | 7,000. | 240.00 |

No. 1 exists with silk thread, from a single proof sheet, value about $4,000.

Complete circle — A2

**1850-58** — **With Silk Thread**

| | | | | |
|---|---|---|---|---|
| 4 | A2 | 1kr pink | 95.00 | 22.50 |
| 5 | A2 | 6kr brown | 50.00 | 6.50 |
| a. | | Half used as 3kr on cover | | 16,000. |
| 6 | A2 | 9kr yellow green | 70.00 | 16.00 |
| a. | | 9kr blue green ('53) | 11,000. | 150.00 |
| 7 | A2 | 12kr red ('58) | 150.00 | 140.00 |
| 8 | A2 | 18kr yel ('54) | 140.00 | 190.00 |
| | | *Nos. 4-8 (5)* | 505.00 | 375.00 |

**1862**

| | | | | |
|---|---|---|---|---|
| 9 | A2 | 1kr yellow | 80.00 | 20.00 |
| 10 | A1a | 3kr rose | 140.00 | 4.00 |
| a. | | 3kr carmine | 52.50 | 6.00 |
| 11 | A2 | 6kr blue | 70.00 | 40.00 |
| a. | | 6kr ultra | 160.00 | 12.00 |
| b. | | Half used as 3kr on cover | | 10,000. |
| 12 | A2 | 9kr bister | 110.00 | 16.00 |
| 13 | A2 | 12kr yel grn | 95.00 | 70.00 |
| a. | | Half used as 6kr on cover | | 32,000. |
| 14 | A2 | 18kr ver red | 900.00 | 140.00 |
| a. | | 18kr pale red | 190.00 | 450.00 |
| | | *Nos. 9-14 (6)* | 1,395. | 290.00 |

No. 11a was not put in use.

Coat of Arms — A3

**1867-68** — **Embossed**

| | | | | |
|---|---|---|---|---|
| 15 | A3 | 1kr yel grn | 65.00 | 12.00 |
| a. | | 1kr dark blue green | 300.00 | 52.50 |
| 16 | A3 | 3kr rose | 70.00 | 2.40 |
| a. | | Printed on both sides | | 5,000. |
| 17 | A3 | 6kr ultra | 45.00 | 19.00 |
| a. | | Half used as 3kr on cover | | 75,000. |
| 18 | A3 | 6kr bis ('68) | 80.00 | 50.00 |
| a. | | Half used as 3kr on cover | | 32,000. |
| 19 | A3 | 7kr ultra ('68) | 400.00 | 16.00 |
| 20 | A3 | 9kr bister | 45.00 | 35.00 |
| 21 | A3 | 12kr lilac | 350.00 | 95.00 |
| 22 | A3 | 18kr red | 140.00 | 175.00 |
| | | *Nos. 15-22 (8)* | 1,195. | 404.40 |

The paper of the 1867-68 issues often shows ribbed or laid lines.

**1870-72** — **Wmk. 92** — **Perf. 11½**
**Without Silk Thread**

| | | | | |
|---|---|---|---|---|
| 23 | A3 | 1kr green | 12.00 | 1.60 |
| 24 | A3 | 3kr rose | 24.00 | 1.60 |
| 25 | A3 | 6kr bister | 30.00 | 30.00 |
| 26 | A3 | 7kr ultra | 3.50 | 4.50 |
| a. | | 7kr Prussian blue | 20.00 | 14.00 |
| 27 | A3 | 9kr pale brn ('72) | 5.50 | 4.00 |
| 28 | A3 | 10kr yellow | 6.50 | 15.00 |
| 29 | A3 | 12kr lilac | 1,200. | 4,800. |
| 30 | A3 | 18kr dull brick red | 16.00 | 16.00 |
| b. | | 18kr dark brick red | 120.00 | 70.00 |

The paper of the 1870-75 issues frequently appears to be laid with the lines either close or wide apart.
See Nos. 33-37.
*Reprints exist.*

**Wmk. 93**

| | | | | |
|---|---|---|---|---|
| 23a | A3 | 1kr green | 100.00 | 9.50 |
| 24a | A3 | 3kr rose | 95.00 | 2.40 |
| 25a | A3 | 6kr bister | 175.00 | 70.00 |
| 26b | A3 | 7kr ultra | 140.00 | 35.00 |
| 27a | A3 | 9kr pale brown | 290.00 | 475.00 |
| 28a | A3 | 10kr yellow | 240.00 | 360.00 |
| 29a | A3 | 12kr lilac | 360.00 | 1,125. |
| 30a | A3 | 18kr dull brick red | 300.00 | 190.00 |
| c. | | 18kr dark brick red | 400.00 | 225.00 |

A4

## 1874-75　　Wmk. 92　　Imperf.

| 31 | A4 1m violet | 675.00 | 85.00 |
|---|---|---|---|

**Perf. 11½**

| 32 | A4 1m violet ('75) | 200.00 | 55.00 |
|---|---|---|---|

See Nos. 46-47, 54-57, 73-76.

## 1875　　　　　　　Wmk. 94

| 33 | A3 1kr green | .80 | 24.00 |
|---|---|---|---|
| 34 | A3 3kr rose | .80 | 8.00 |
| 35 | A3 7kr ultra | 5.25 | 275.00 |
| 36 | A3 10kr yellow | 30.00 | 250.00 |
| 37 | A3 18kr red | 24.00 | 200.00 |
|  | Nos. 33-37 (5) | 60.85 | 617.00 |

A5

## 1876-78　Embossed　Perf. 11½

| 38 | A5 3pf lt grn | 35.00 | 1.60 |
|---|---|---|---|
| 39 | A5 5pf dk grn | 90.00 | 16.00 |
| 40 | A5 5pf lilac ('78) | 160.00 | 20.00 |
| 41 | A5 10pf rose | 190.00 | 1.25 |
| 42 | A5 20pf ultra | 190.00 | 3.25 |
| 43 | A5 25pf yel brn | 175.00 | 6.50 |
| 44 | A5 50pf scarlet | 55.00 | 7.25 |
| 45 | A5 50pf brn ('78) | 800.00 | 27.50 |
| 46 | A4 1m violet | 1,900. | 90.00 |
| 47 | A4 2m orange | 24.00 | 12.00 |

The paper of the 1876-78 issue often shows ribbed lines.

See Nos. 48-53, 58-72. For overprints and surcharge see Nos. 237, O1-O5.

## 1881-1906　Wmk. 95v　Perf. 11½

| 48 | A5 3pf green | 12.00 | .80 |
|---|---|---|---|
| a. | Imperf. | 400.00 | 2,000. |
| 49 | A5 5pf lilac | 17.50 | 1.25 |
| 50 | A5 10pf carmine | 12.50 | .65 |
| a. | Imperf. | 400.00 | 2,000. |
| 51 | A5 20pf ultramarine | 14.00 | .80 |
| 52 | A5 25pf yellow brown | 125.00 | 3.50 |
| 53 | A5 50pf deep brown | 145.00 | 3.25 |
| 54 | A4 1m rose lil, white ('00) | 4.50 | 3.50 |
| a. | 1m brownish lilac, toned paper | 52.50 | 4.00 |
| 55 | A4 2m orange ('01) | 5.50 | 8.00 |
| a. | Toned paper ('90) | 90.00 | 14.00 |
| 56 | A4 3m olive gray ('00) | 24.00 | 30.00 |
| a. | White paper ('06) | 175.00 | 400.00 |
| 57 | A4 5m yel grn ('00) | 24.00 | 30.00 |
| a. | White paper ('06) | 150.00 | 350.00 |
|  | Nos. 48-57 (10) | 384.00 | 81.75 |

Nos. 54-55 are on white paper. Nos. 56-57 are on toned paper. A 2m lilac was not regularly issued.

## 1888-1900　Wmk. 95h　Perf. 14x14½

| 58 | A5 2pf gray ('00) | 2.40 | .55 |
|---|---|---|---|
| 59 | A5 3pf green | 9.25 | 2.10 |
| 60 | A5 3pf brown ('00) | .30 | .65 |
| 61 | A5 5pf lilac | 24.00 | 5.50 |
| 62 | A5 5pf dk grn ('00) | .30 | .65 |
| 63 | A5 10pf carmine | .40 | .80 |
| 64 | A5 20pf ultra | .40 | .80 |
| 65 | A5 25pf yel brn | 32.50 | 6.75 |
| 66 | A5 25pf orange ('00) | .60 | 1.10 |
| 67 | A5 30pf ol grn ('00) | .80 | 1.40 |
| 68 | A5 40pf yellow ('00) | .80 | 1.10 |
| 69 | A5 50pf dp brn | 60.00 | 6.75 |
| 70 | A5 50pf maroon ('00) | .50 | 1.60 |
| 71 | A5 80pf lilac ('00) | 3.25 | 4.00 |
|  | Nos. 58-71 (14) | 193.00 | 33.75 |

Nos. 59, 61, 65, 69 and 70 are on toned paper; Nos. 67-68 on white.

## 1888-99　　　　Toned Paper

| 58a | A5 2pf gray ('99) | 12.00 | 5.25 |
|---|---|---|---|
| 60a | A5 3pf dk ocher brn ('90) | 9.25 | .40 |
| 62a | A5 5pf dk green ('90) | 10.00 | .65 |
| 63a | A5 10pf car red | 6.75 | .80 |
| b. | Imperf. | 72.50 | 175.00 |
| 64a | A5 20pf ultra | 10.00 | 1.25 |
| 66a | A5 25pf org ('90) | 16.50 | 1.60 |
| 70a | A5 50pf mar ('90) | 47.50 | 2.40 |
| 71a | A5 80pf lilac ('99) | 32.50 | 12.00 |

## 1911, Jan. 23　　Wmk. 95v

| 72 | A5 5pf dark green | .65 | 13.50 |
|---|---|---|---|

## 1911, Jan.　Wmk. 95h　Perf. 11½

| 73 | A4 1m rose lilac | 4.00 | 27.50 |
|---|---|---|---|
| 74 | A4 2m orange | 17.00 | 37.50 |
| 75 | A4 3m olive gray | 17.00 | 57.50 |
| 76 | A4 5m pale yel grn | 17.00 | 57.50 |
|  | Nos. 73-76 (4) | 55.00 | 180.00 |

See note after No. 91 concerning used values.

A6

A7

A8

### Prince Regent Luitpold
**Perf. 14x14½**

## 1911　　Wmk. 95h　　Litho.

| 77 | A6 3pf brn, gray brn | .30 | .30 |
|---|---|---|---|
| a. | "911" for "1911" | 325.00 | 325.00 |
| 78 | A6 5pf dk grn, grn | .30 | .30 |
| a. | Tête bêche pair | 4.50 | 10.50 |
| b. | Booklet pane of 4 + 2 labels | 100.00 | 150.00 |
| c. | Bkt. pane of 5 + label | 225.00 | 375.00 |
| d. | Bklt. pane of 6 | 35.00 | |
| 79 | A6 10pf scar, buff | .30 | .30 |
| a. | Tête bêche pair | 5.75 | 62.50 |
| b. | "911" for "1911" | 15.00 | 15.00 |
| d. | Booklet pane of 5 + label | 65.00 | 30.00 |
| 80 | A6 20pf dp bl, bl | 2.00 | .75 |
| 81 | A6 25pf vio brn, buff | 3.25 | 1.25 |

**Perf. 11½**
**Wmk. 95v**

| 82 | A7 30pf org buff, buff | 2.25 | 1.25 |
|---|---|---|---|
| 83 | A7 40pf ol grn, buff | 4.00 | 1.25 |
| 84 | A7 50pf cl, gray brn | 3.25 | 3.25 |
| 84A | A7 60pf dk grn, buff | 3.25 | 3.25 |
| 85 | A7 80pf vio, gray brn | 9.00 | 11.00 |
| 86 | A8 1m brn, gray brn | 3.25 | 4.00 |
| 87 | A8 2m dk grn, grn | 4.75 | 12.00 |
| 88 | A8 3m lake, buff | 13.00 | 65.00 |
| 89 | A8 5m dk bl, buff | 13.00 | 45.00 |
| 90 | A8 10m org, yel | 22.50 | 65.00 |
| 91 | A8 20m blk brn, yel | 25.00 | 32.50 |
|  | Nos. 77-91 (16) | 109.40 | 246.40 |

90th birthday of Prince Regent Luitpold. All values exist in 2 types except No. 84A. Nos. 77-84, 85-91 exist imperf.

**Used values:** Nos. 73-76 and 77-91 often were canceled en masse for accounting purposes. These cancels are perfectly clear, and used values are for stamps canceled thus. Postally used examples are worth about twice as much.

Prince Regent
Luitpold — A9

## 1911, June 10　　　Unwmk.

| 92 | A9 5pf grn, yel & blk | .80 | 1.40 |
|---|---|---|---|
| b. | Horiz. pair, imperf. btwn. | 140.00 | 225.00 |
| 93 | A9 10pf rose, yel & blk | 1.25 | 2.40 |
| b. | Pair, imperf. between | 140.00 | 225.00 |

Silver Jubilee of Prince Regent Luitpold.

Used values of Nos. 94-275, B1-B3 are for postally used stamps. Canceled-to-order stamps, which abound, sell for same prices as unused.

A10

A11

King Ludwig
III — A12

**Perf. 14x14½**

## 1914-20　　Wmk. 95h　　Photo.

| 94 | A10 2pf gray ('18) | .25 | 2.00 |
|---|---|---|---|
| 95 | A10 3pf brown | .25 | 2.00 |
| 96 | A10 5pf yellow grn | 1.10 | 2.00 |
| a. | 5pf dark green | 1.10 | |
| b. | Tête bêche pair | 3.50 | 16.50 |
| c. | Booklet pane of 5 + 1 label | 16.00 | 60.00 |

| 97 | A10 7½pf dp grn ('16) | .25 | 2.00 |
|---|---|---|---|
| a. | Tête bêche pair | 2.40 | 11.00 |
| b. | Booklet pane of 6 | 16.00 | |
| 98 | A10 10pf vermilion | 1.40 | 2.00 |
| a. | Tête bêche pair | 3.50 | 16.50 |
| b. | Booklet pane of 5 + 1 label | 16.00 | 60.00 |
| 99 | A10 10pf car rose ('16) | .25 | 2.00 |
| 100 | A10 15pf ver ('16) | .25 | 2.00 |
| a. | Tête bêche pair | 2.40 | 11.00 |
| b. | Booklet pane of 5 + 1 label | 6.75 | 24.00 |
| 101 | A10 15pf car ('20) | 1.50 | 27.50 |
| 102 | A10 20pf blue | .25 | 2.00 |
| 103 | A10 25pf gray | .25 | 2.00 |
| 104 | A10 30pf orange | 1.25 | 2.00 |
| 105 | A10 40pf olive grn | .25 | 2.00 |
| 106 | A10 50pf red brn | .25 | 2.00 |
| 107 | A10 60pf blue grn | .80 | 2.00 |
| 108 | A10 80pf violet | .25 | 2.00 |

**Perf. 11½**
**Wmk. 95v**

| 109 | A11 1m brown | .25 | 2.00 |
|---|---|---|---|
| 110 | A11 2m violet | .30 | 2.75 |
| 111 | A11 3m scarlet | .40 | 5.50 |

**Wmk. 95h**

| 112 | A12 5m deep blue | .55 | 20.00 |
|---|---|---|---|
| 113 | A12 10m yellow grn | 1.75 | 55.00 |
| 114 | A12 20m brown | 3.25 | 80.00 |
|  | Nos. 94-114 (21) | 15.05 | 220.75 |

### No. 94 Surcharged

## 1916　Wmk. 95h　Perf. 14x14½

| 115 | A10 2½pf on 2pf gray | .25 | 2.00 |
|---|---|---|---|
| a. | Double surcharge | | |

### Ludwig III Types of 1914-20

## 1916-20　　　　　Imperf.

| 117 | A10 2pf gray | .25 | 14.50 |
|---|---|---|---|
| 118 | A10 3pf brown | .25 | 14.50 |
| 119 | A10 5pf pale yel grn | .25 | 14.50 |
| 120 | A10 7½pf dp green | .25 | 14.50 |
| a. | Tête bêche pair | 3.25 | 25.00 |
| 121 | A10 10pf car rose | .25 | 14.50 |
| 122 | A10 15pf vermilion | .25 | 14.50 |
| a. | Tête bêche pair | 3.25 | 25.00 |
| 123 | A10 20pf blue | .25 | 14.50 |
| 124 | A10 25pf gray | .25 | 14.50 |
| 125 | A10 30pf orange | .25 | 14.50 |
| 126 | A10 40pf olive grn | .25 | 14.50 |
| 127 | A10 50pf red brown | .25 | 14.50 |
| 128 | A10 60pf dark green | .25 | 16.00 |
| 129 | A10 80pf violet | .25 | 16.00 |
| 130 | A11 1m brown | .35 | 16.00 |
| 131 | A11 2m violet | .35 | 20.00 |
| 132 | A11 3m scarlet | .50 | 27.50 |
| 133 | A12 5m deep blue | .95 | 45.00 |
| 134 | A12 10m yellow green | 1.60 | 65.00 |
| 135 | A12 20m brown | 2.25 | 110.00 |
|  | Nos. 117-135 (19) | 9.25 | 475.00 |

### Stamps and Type of 1914-20 Overprinted

a

b

### Wmk. 95h or 95v

## 1919　　　　Perf. 14x14½
### Overprint "a"

| 136 | A10 3pf brown | .25 | 2.00 |
|---|---|---|---|
| 137 | A10 5pf yellow grn | .25 | 2.00 |
| 138 | A10 7½pf deep green | .25 | 2.00 |
| 139 | A10 10pf car rose | .25 | 2.00 |
| 140 | A10 15pf vermilion | .25 | 2.00 |
| 141 | A10 20pf blue | .25 | 2.00 |
| 142 | A10 25pf gray | .25 | 2.00 |
| 143 | A10 30pf orange | .25 | 2.00 |
| 144 | A10 35pf orange | .25 | 2.50 |
| a. | Without overprint | 100.00 | |
| 145 | A10 40pf olive grn | .25 | 2.00 |
| 146 | A10 50pf red brown | .25 | 2.00 |
| 147 | A10 60pf dark green | .25 | 2.00 |
| 148 | A10 75pf red brown | .25 | 2.00 |
| a. | Without overprint | 22.50 | 225.00 |
| 149 | A10 80pf violet | .25 | 2.00 |

**Perf. 11½**
### Overprint "a"

| 150 | A11 1m brown | .25 | 2.00 |
|---|---|---|---|
| 151 | A11 2m violet | .25 | 2.00 |
| 152 | A11 3m scarlet | .45 | 4.75 |

### Overprint "b"

| 153 | A12 5m deep blue | .90 | 12.00 |
|---|---|---|---|
| 154 | A12 10m yellow green | 1.40 | 50.00 |
| 155 | A12 20m dk brown | 2.50 | 50.00 |
|  | Nos. 136-155 (20) | 9.25 | 149.25 |

Inverted overprints exist on Nos. 137-143, 145-147, 149. Value, each $15.

Double overprints exist on Nos. 137, 139, 143, 145, 150. Values, $30-$75.

**Imperf**
### Overprint "a"

| 156 | A10 3pf brown | .25 | 20.00 |
|---|---|---|---|
| 157 | A10 5pf pale yel grn | .25 | 20.00 |
| 158 | A10 7½pf dp green | .25 | 20.00 |
| 159 | A10 10pf car rose | .25 | 20.00 |
| 160 | A10 15pf vermilion | .25 | 20.00 |
| 161 | A10 20pf blue | .25 | 20.00 |
| 162 | A10 25pf gray | .25 | 20.00 |
| 163 | A10 30pf orange | .25 | 20.00 |
| 164 | A10 35pf orange | .25 | 20.00 |
| a. | Without overprint | 13.00 | |
| 165 | A10 40pf olive grn | .25 | 20.00 |
| 166 | A10 50pf red brown | .25 | 20.00 |
| 167 | A10 60pf dk green | .25 | 20.00 |
| 168 | A10 75pf red brown | .25 | 20.00 |
| a. | Without overprint | 190.00 | |
| 169 | A10 80pf violet | .25 | 20.00 |
| 170 | A11 1m brown | .25 | 24.00 |
| 171 | A11 2m violet | .50 | 27.50 |
| 172 | A11 3m scarlet | .70 | 45.00 |

### Overprint "b"

| 173 | A12 5m deep blue | .95 | 55.00 |
|---|---|---|---|
| 174 | A12 10m yellow grn | 1.40 | 80.00 |
| 175 | A12 20m brown | 2.75 | 80.00 |
|  | Nos. 156-175 (20) | 10.05 | 591.50 |

### Stamps of Germany 1906-19 Overprinted

## 1919　Wmk. 125　Perf. 14, 14½

| 176 | A22 2½pf gray | .25 | 2.00 |
|---|---|---|---|
| 177 | A16 3pf brown | .25 | 2.00 |
| 178 | A16 5pf green | .25 | 2.00 |
| 179 | A22 7½pf orange | .25 | 2.00 |
| 180 | A16 10pf carmine | .25 | 2.00 |
| 181 | A22 15pf dk violet | .25 | 2.00 |
| a. | Double overprint | 375.00 | 1,050. |
| 182 | A16 20pf ultra | .25 | 2.00 |
| 183 | A16 25pf org & blk, yel | .25 | 2.00 |
| 184 | A22 35pf red brown | .25 | 2.00 |
| 185 | A16 40pf lake & blk | .40 | 2.00 |
| 186 | A16 75pf green & blk | .55 | 2.40 |
| 187 | A16 80pf lake & blk, rose | .55 | 3.25 |
| 188 | A17 1m car rose | 1.25 | 4.75 |
| 189 | A21 2m dull blue | 1.60 | 11.00 |
| 190 | A19 3m gray violet | 1.60 | 13.00 |
| 191 | A20 5m slate & car | 1.60 | 13.00 |
| a. | Inverted overprint | 3,575. | |
|  | Nos. 176-191 (16) | 9.80 | 67.40 |

### Bavarian Stamps of 1914-16 Overprinted

c

　d

### Wmk. 95h or 95v

## 1919-20　　　Perf. 14x14½
### Overprint "c"

| 193 | A10 3pf brown | .25 | 2.00 |
|---|---|---|---|
| 194 | A10 5pf yellow grn | .25 | 2.00 |
| 195 | A10 7½pf dp green | .25 | 16.00 |
| 196 | A10 10pf car rose | .25 | 2.00 |
| 197 | A10 15pf vermilion | .25 | 2.00 |
| 198 | A10 20pf blue | .25 | 2.00 |
| 199 | A10 25pf gray | .25 | 2.00 |
| 200 | A10 30pf orange | .25 | 2.00 |
| 201 | A10 40pf olive grn | .25 | 14.50 |
| 202 | A10 50pf red brown | .25 | 2.00 |
| 203 | A10 60pf dk green | .25 | 14.50 |
| 204 | A10 75pf olive bister | .40 | 14.50 |
| 205 | A10 80pf violet | .25 | 3.50 |

**Perf. 11½**
### Overprint "c"

| 206 | A11 1m brown | .25 | 3.50 |
|---|---|---|---|
| 207 | A11 2m violet | .25 | 2.00 |
| 208 | A11 3m scarlet | .35 | 6.00 |

### Overprint "d"

| 209 | A12 5m deep blue | 1.10 | 17.50 |
|---|---|---|---|
| 210 | A12 10m yellow grn | 2.00 | 35.00 |
| 211 | A12 20m dk brown | 2.40 | 60.00 |
|  | Nos. 193-211 (19) | 9.75 | 205.25 |

## PRUSSIA

LOCATION — The greater par[t of]
northern Germany.
GOVT. — Independent Kingdom
AREA — 134,650 sq. mi.
POP. — 40,165,219 (1910)
CAPITAL — Berlin

Prussia was a member of the [Ger]man Confederation and became p[art of]
the German Empire in 1870.

12 Pfennigs = 1 Silbergrosch[en]

60 Kreuzer = 1 Gulden (186[ ]

Values for unused stamps a[re for]
examples with original gum as d[escribed]
in the catalogue introduction. Exa[mples]
without gum sell for about 50% [of the]
figures quoted.

King Frederick
William IV
A1    A2

**1850-56 Engr. Wmk. 162**
**Background of Crossed L[ines]**

| | | | |
|---|---|---|---|
| 1 | A1 | 4pf yel grn ('56) | 110. |
| a. | | 4pf dark green | 160 |
| 2 | A1 | 6pf (½sg) red org | 90. |
| 3 | A2 | 1sg black, *rose* | 80. |
| 4 | A2 | 2sg black, *blue* | 110 |
| 5 | A2 | 3sg black, *yellow* | 110 |
| a. | | 3sg black, *orange buff* | 325 |
| | | Nos. 1-5 (5) | 500 |

See Nos. 10-13.

Reprints exist on waterma[rked and]
unwatermarked paper.

A3

**Solid Backgroun[d]**

**1857 Typo.**

| | | | |
|---|---|---|---|
| 6 | A3 | 1sg rose | 3 |
| a. | | 1sg carmine rose | |
| 7 | A3 | 2sg blue | |
| a. | | 2sg dark blue | |
| b. | | Half used as 1sg on cover | |
| 8 | A3 | 3sg orange | 1 |
| a. | | 3sg yellow | |
| b. | | 3sg deep orange | |
| | | Nos. 6-8 (3) | |

The reprints of Nos. 6-8 h[ave]
instead of a colon after "SILBE[R"]

A4

**Background of Cross[ed]**

**1858-60**

| | | | |
|---|---|---|---|
| 9 | A4 | 4pf green | |

**Engr.**

| | | | |
|---|---|---|---|
| 10 | A1 | 6pf (½sg) org ('59) | 1 |
| a. | | 6pf (½sg) brick red | |

**Typo.**

| | | | |
|---|---|---|---|
| 11 | A2 | 1sg rose | |
| 12 | A2 | 2sg blue | |
| a. | | 2sg dark blue | |
| b. | | Half used as 1sg on cover | |
| 13 | A2 | 3sg orange | |
| a. | | 3sg yellow | |
| | | Nos. 9-13 (5) | |

Coat of Ar[ms]
A6

**1861-67 Embossed**

| | | | |
|---|---|---|---|
| 14 | A6 | 3pf red lilac ('67) | |
| a. | | 3pf red violet ('65) | |

---

## [BRUNSWICK]

**Imperf., Pairs**

| | | | |
|---|---|---|---|
| 23a | A4 | ½gr | |
| 24a | A4 | 1gr | |
| 25b | A4 | 2gr | |
| 26a | A4 | 3gr | |

Stamps of Brunswick were su[perseded by]
those of the North German Conf[ederation]
Jan. 1, 1868.

## HAMBURG

LOCATION — Northern Ger[many]
GOVT. — A former Free City
AREA — 160 sq. mi.
POP. — 453,869 (1880)
CAPITAL — Hamburg

Hamburg was a member [of the Ger]man Confederation and bec[ame part of]
the German Empire in 1870[.]

16 Schillings = 1 M[ark]

Values for unused stam[ps are for]
examples with original gum [as described]
in the catalogue introducti[on. Examples]
without gum sell for about [50% of]
the figures quoted.

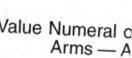

Value Numeral o[r]
Arms — A[ ]

**1859 Typo. Wmk. 12[ ]**

| | | | |
|---|---|---|---|
| 1 | A1 | ½s black | 1[ ] |
| 2 | A1 | 1s brown | 1[ ] |
| 3 | A1 | 2s red | 1[ ] |
| 4 | A1 | 3s blue | 1[ ] |
| 5 | A1 | 4s yellow green | 1[ ] |
| 6 | A1 | 7s orange | |
| 7 | A1 | 9s yellow | 2 |

See Nos. 13-21.

A2

**1864**

| | | | |
|---|---|---|---|
| 9 | A2 | 1¼s gray | |
| a. | | 1¼s lilac | |
| b. | | 1¼s red lilac | |
| c. | | 1¼s blue | |
| d. | | 1¼s greenish gray | |
| 12 | A3 | 2½s green | |

See Nos. 22-23[ ]
The 1¼s and 2½s have be[en]
watermarked and unwatermar[ked]

**1864-65 Typo.**

| | | | |
|---|---|---|---|
| 13 | A1 | ½s black | |
| a. | | Horiz. pair, imperf between | |
| 14 | A1 | 1s brown | |
| a. | | Half used as 1s on cover | |
| b. | | Horiz. pair, imperf between | |
| 15 | A1 | 2s red | |
| 17 | A1 | 3s ultra | |
| a. | | Imperf., pair | |
| b. | | Horiz. pair, imperf. vert. | |
| c. | | 3s blue | |
| 18 | A1 | 4s green | |
| 19 | A1 | 7s orange | |
| 20 | A1 | 7s vio ('65) | |
| a. | | Imperf., pair | |
| 21 | A1 | 9s yellow | |
| a. | | Vert. pair, imperf btwn. | |
| 22 | A2 | 1¼s lilac | |
| a. | | 1¼s red lilac | |
| b. | | 1¼s violet | |
| 23 | A3 | 2½s yel grn, blurred printing | |
| a. | | 2½s blue green | |

**Litho.**

The 1¼s has been
watermarked and unwatern[ ]
2½s on unwatermarked pap[er]

A4

---

## BAVARIA (continued)

**Imperf**
**Overprint "c"**

| | | | | |
|---|---|---|---|---|
| 212 | A10 | 3pf brown | .25 | 12.00 |
| 213 | A10 | 5pf pale yel grn | .25 | 12.00 |
| 214 | A10 | 7½pf deep green | .25 | 22.50 |
| 215 | A10 | 10pf car rose | .25 | 12.00 |
| 216 | A10 | 15pf vermilion | .25 | 12.00 |
| 217 | A10 | 20pf blue | .25 | 12.00 |
| a. | | Double overprint | 50.00 | |
| 218 | A10 | 25pf gray | .25 | 12.00 |
| 219 | A10 | 30pf orange | .25 | 12.00 |
| 220 | A10 | 40pf olive grn | .25 | 13.50 |
| 221 | A10 | 50pf red brn | .25 | 14.50 |
| 222 | A10 | 60pf dk green | .25 | 14.50 |
| 223 | A10 | 75pf olive bis | .25 | 14.50 |
| a. | | Without overprint | .25 | 35.00 |
| 224 | A10 | 80pf violet | 5.00 | |
| 225 | A11 | 1m brown | .25 | 14.50 |
| 226 | A11 | 2m violet | .25 | 22.50 |
| 227 | A11 | 3m scarlet | .25 | 22.50 |
| | | | .65 | 27.50 |

**Overprint "d"**

| | | | | |
|---|---|---|---|---|
| 228 | A12 | 5m deep blue | 1.10 | 40.00 |
| 229 | A12 | 10m yellow grn | 2.00 | 70.00 |
| 230 | A12 | 20m brown | 2.40 | 110.00 |
| | | Nos. 212-230 (19) | 9.90 | 493.50 |

Ludwig Type of 1914,
Printed in Various Colors
and Surcharged

1,25 M
Freistaat
Bayern

**1919 Perf. 11½**

| | | | | |
|---|---|---|---|---|
| 231 | A11 | 1.25m on 1m yel grn | .25 | 2.40 |
| 232 | A11 | 1.50m on 1m orange | .25 | 3.25 |
| 233 | A11 | 2.50m on 1m gray | .45 | 6.50 |
| | | Nos. 231-233 (3) | .95 | 12.15 |

**1920 Imperf.**

| | | | | |
|---|---|---|---|---|
| 234 | A11 | 1.25m on 1m yel grn | .30 | 35.00 |
| a. | | Without surcharge | 400.00 | |
| 235 | A11 | 1.50m on 1m org | .30 | 35.00 |
| a. | | Without surcharge | 8.00 | |
| 236 | A11 | 2.50m on 1m gray | .65 | 35.00 |
| a. | | Without surcharge | 8.00 | |
| | | Nos. 234-236 (3) | 1.25 | 105.00 |

No. 60 Surcharged in Dark
Blue

20   20

20   20

**1920 Perf. 14½**

| | | | | |
|---|---|---|---|---|
| 237 | A5 | 20pf on 3pf brown | .25 | 2.00 |
| a. | | Inverted surcharge | 9.00 | 30.00 |
| b. | | Double surcharge | 95.00 | 225.00 |

Plowman
A14

"Electricity"
Harnessing
Light to a
Water
Wheel
A15

Sower
A16

Madonna
and Child
A17

von Kaulbach's
"Genius" — A18

**TWENTY PFENNIG**
Type I — Foot of "2" turns downward.
Type II — Foot of "2" turns upward.

**1920 Perf. 14x14½**
**Wmk. 95h Typo.**

| | | | | |
|---|---|---|---|---|
| 238 | A14 | 5pf yellow grn | .25 | 2.40 |
| 239 | A14 | 10pf yellow grn | .25 | 2.40 |
| 240 | A14 | 15pf carmine | .25 | 2.40 |
| 241 | A15 | 20pf violet (I) | .25 | 2.40 |
| a. | | 20pf violet (II) | 10.00 | 1,400. |
| 242 | A15 | 30pf dp blue | .25 | 3.25 |
| 243 | A15 | 40pf brown | .25 | 2.40 |

| | | | | |
|---|---|---|---|---|
| 244 | A16 | 50pf vermilion | .25 | 2.40 |
| 245 | A16 | 60pf blue green | .25 | 2.40 |
| 246 | A16 | 75pf lilac rose | .25 | 2.40 |

**Perf. 12x11½**
**Wmk. 95v**

| | | | | |
|---|---|---|---|---|
| 247 | A17 | 1m car & gray | .35 | 2.40 |
| 248 | A17 | 1¼m ultra & ol bis | | |
| 249 | A17 | 1½m dk grn & gray | .25 | 2.40 |
| 250 | A17 | 2½m blk & gray | .25 | 3.25 |
| | | | .25 | 32.50 |

**Perf. 11½x12**
**Wmk. 95h**

| | | | | |
|---|---|---|---|---|
| 251 | A18 | 3m pale blue | .55 | 14.50 |
| 252 | A18 | 5m orange | .55 | 14.50 |
| 253 | A18 | 10m deep green | | |
| 254 | A18 | 20m black | .95 | 25.00 |
| | | | 1.40 | 32.50 |
| | | Nos. 238-254 (17) | 6.80 | 149.50 |

**Imperf. Pairs**

| | | | | |
|---|---|---|---|---|
| 238a | A14 | 5pf yellow grn | 65.00 | 450.00 |
| 239a | A14 | 10pf orange | 160.00 | |
| 241b | A15 | 20pf violet (I) | 65.00 | |
| 243a | A15 | 40pf brown | 140.00 | |
| 244a | A16 | 50pf vermilion | 80.00 | |
| 245a | A16 | 60pf blue green | 47.50 | |
| 246a | A16 | 75pf lilac rose | 47.50 | |
| 247a | A17 | 1m car & gray | 8.00 | 32.50 |
| 248a | A17 | 1¼m ultra & ol bis | 8.00 | 32.50 |
| 249a | A17 | 1½m dk grn & gray | | |
| 250a | A17 | 2½m blk & gray | 8.00 | 32.50 |
| 251a | A18 | 3m pale blue | 14.00 | 160.00 |
| 252a | A18 | 5m orange | 14.00 | 80.00 |
| 253a | A18 | 10m deep green | 14.00 | 80.00 |
| 254a | A18 | 20m black | 14.00 | 95.00 |
| | | | | 125.00 |

**1920 Perf. 12x11½**
**Litho. Wmk. 95v**

| | | | | |
|---|---|---|---|---|
| 255 | A17 | 2½m black & gray | .50 | 65.00 |

On No. 255 the background dots are small,
hazy and irregularly spaced. On No. 250 they
are large, clear, round, white and regularly
spaced in rows. The backs of the typo. stamps
usually show a raised impression of parts of
the design.

Deutsches
Reich

Stamps and Types of
Preceding Issue
Overprinted

**1920**

| | | | | |
|---|---|---|---|---|
| 256 | A14 | 5pf yellow green | .25 | 1.60 |
| a. | | Inverted overprint | 30.00 | |
| b. | | Imperf., pair | 37.50 | 375.00 |
| 257 | A14 | 10pf orange | .25 | 1.60 |
| a. | | Inverted overprint | 37.50 | 375.00 |
| b. | | Imperf., pair | 30.00 | 600.00 |
| 258 | A14 | 15pf carmine | .25 | 1.60 |
| a. | | Inverted overprint | 30.00 | |
| 259 | A15 | 20pf violet | .25 | 1.60 |
| a. | | Inverted overprint | 30.00 | 750.00 |
| b. | | Double overprint | 13.00 | |
| c. | | Imperf., pair | 50.00 | |
| 260 | A15 | 30pf deep blue | .25 | 1.60 |
| a. | | Inverted overprint | 30.00 | 375.00 |
| b. | | Imperf., pair | 50.00 | |
| 261 | A15 | 40pf brown | .25 | 1.60 |
| a. | | Inverted overprint | 30.00 | 750.00 |
| b. | | Imperf., pair | 50.00 | |
| 262 | A16 | 50pf vermilion | .25 | 2.40 |
| a. | | Inverted overprint | 30.00 | 900.00 |
| 263 | A16 | 60pf blue green | .50 | 1.40 |
| 264 | A16 | 75pf lilac rose | .40 | 5.25 |
| a. | | Inverted overprint | 30.00 | |
| 265 | A16 | 80pf dark blue | .40 | 2.75 |
| a. | | Without overprint | 100.00 | |
| b. | | Imperf., pair | 50.00 | |

Deutsches
Reich

Overprinted in Black or
Red

| | | | | |
|---|---|---|---|---|
| 266 | A17 | 1m car & gray | .50 | 2.75 |
| a. | | Imperf., pair | 50.00 | 375.00 |
| b. | | Inverted overprint | 52.50 | |
| 267 | A17 | 1¼m ultra & ol bis | .50 | 2.75 |
| a. | | Imperf., pair | 47.50 | |
| 268 | A17 | 1½m dk grn & gray | .50 | 3.50 |
| a. | | Imperf., pair | 47.50 | |
| 269 | A17 | 2m vio & ol bis | .80 | 4.00 |
| a. | | Without overprint | 32.50 | |
| b. | | Imperf., pair | 50.00 | |
| 270 | A17 | 2½m (#250) (R) | .25 | 2.75 |
| c. | | Imperf., pair | 50.00 | |

| | | | | |
|---|---|---|---|---|
| 270A | A17 | 2½m (#255) (R) | .95 | 95.00 |
| b. | | Imperf., pair | 50.00 | |

Nos. 251-254
Overprinted

Deutsches Reich

| | | | | |
|---|---|---|---|---|
| 271 | A18 | 3m pale blue | 3.25 | 9.50 |
| 272 | A18 | 4m dull red | 3.25 | 9.50 |
| a. | | Without overprint | 47.50 | 10.00 |
| 273 | A18 | 5m orange | 3.25 | 9.50 |
| 274 | A18 | 10m dp green | 5.25 | 16.00 |
| 275 | A18 | 20m black | 6.00 | 13.00 |
| | | Nos. 256-275 (21) | 27.55 | 190.15 |

Nos. 256-275 were available for postage
through all Germany, but were used almost
exclusively in Bavaria.

### SEMI-POSTAL STAMPS

5 Pf.
für Kriegs-
beschädigte
Freistaat
Bayern

Regular Issue of 1914-20
Surcharged in Black

**1919 Wmk. 95h Perf. 14x14½**

| | | | | |
|---|---|---|---|---|
| B1 | A10 | 10pf + 5pf car rose | .40 | 2.00 |
| a. | | Inverted surcharge | 26.00 | 65.00 |
| b. | | Surcharge on back | 50.00 | |
| c. | | Imperf., pair | 325.00 | |
| B2 | A10 | 15pf + 5pf ver | .40 | 2.00 |
| a. | | Inverted surcharge | 26.00 | 65.00 |
| b. | | Imperf., pair | 190.00 | |
| B3 | A10 | 20pf + 5pf blue | .40 | 2.40 |
| a. | | Inverted surcharge | 26.00 | 65.00 |
| b. | | Imperf., pair | 375.00 | |
| | | Nos. B1-B3 (3) | 1.20 | 6.40 |

Surtax was for wounded war veterans.

### POSTAGE DUE STAMPS

Bayer. Postsax.
3
1 Kreuzer
zum Empfänger
zahlend
D1

**With Silk Thread**

| | | | | |
|---|---|---|---|---|
| 1862 | | **Typeset Unwmk. Imperf.** | | |
| J1 | D1 | 3kr black | 125.00 | 325.00 |
| a. | | "Empfange" | 375.00 | 1,000. |

**Without Silk Thread**

| | | | | |
|---|---|---|---|---|
| 1870 | | **Typo. Wmk. 93 Perf. 11½** | | |
| J2 | D1 | 1kr black | 12.00 | 800.00 |
| a. | | Wmk. 92 | 55.00 | 1,750. |
| J3 | D1 | 3kr black | 12.00 | 475.00 |
| | | | 55.00 | 960.00 |

Deutsches
Reich

Type of 1876 Regular Issue
Overprinted in Red "Vom
Empfänger zahlbar"

D2

**1876 Wmk. 94**

| | | | | |
|---|---|---|---|---|
| J4 | D2 | 3pf gray | 16.00 | 40.00 |
| J5 | D2 | 5pf gray | 10.00 | 17.00 |
| J6 | D2 | 10pf gray | 3.25 | 1.25 |
| a. | | Vert. half used as 5pf on cover | | |
| | | Nos. J4-J6 (3) | 29.25 | 58.25 |

**1883 Wmk. 95v**

| | | | | |
|---|---|---|---|---|
| J7 | D2 | 3pf gray | 90.00 | 100.00 |
| J8 | D2 | 5pf gray | 55.00 | 70.00 |
| J9 | D2 | 10pf gray | 2.40 | .80 |
| a. | | "Empfänper" | 140.00 | 140.00 |
| b. | | "zahlbar" | 140.00 | 140.00 |
| c. | | Imperf. | 80.00 | 80.00 |
| | | Nos. J7-J9 (3) | 95.00 | |
| | | | 147.40 | 170.80 |

**1895-1903 Wmk. 95h Perf. 14½**

| | | | | |
|---|---|---|---|---|
| J10 | D2 | 2pf gray | .80 | 2.40 |
| J11 | D2 | 3pf gray ('03) | .80 | 2.50 |
| J12 | D2 | 5pf gray ('03) | 1.00 | 1.75 |
| J13 | D2 | 10pf gray ('03) | .60 | .90 |
| | | Nos. J10-J13 (4) | 3.20 | 7.55 |

O2

---

**1888 Rose-toned Paper**

| | | | | |
|---|---|---|---|---|
| J10a | D2 | 2pf gray | 2.00 | 4.75 |
| J11a | D2 | 3pf gray | 2.60 | 2.40 |
| b. | | Inverted overprint | 2,200. | |
| J12a | D2 | 5pf gray | 2.60 | 2.60 |
| J13a | D2 | 10pf gray | 2.60 | 1.25 |
| b. | | As "a," double overprint | | 2,200. |
| | | Nos. J10a-J13a (4) | 9.80 | 11.00 |

No. J13b was used at Pirmasens.

### Surcharged in Red in Each Corner

**1895**

| | | | |
|---|---|---|---|
| J14 | D2 | 2pf on 3pf gray | 150,000. |

Six used examples of No. J14 exist, all used
in Aichach. There are two covers (each bearing two examples) and two loose stamps.

---

### OFFICIAL STAMPS

Nos. 77-81, 84, 95-96, 98-99, 102
perforated with a large E were issued
for official use in 1912-16.

E

Regular Issue of 1888-
1900 Overprinted

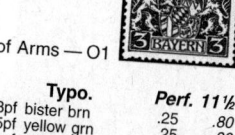

Coat of Arms — O1

**1908 Wmk. 95h Perf. 14½**

| | | | | |
|---|---|---|---|---|
| O1 | A5 | 3pf dk brown (R) | .75 | 4.50 |
| O2 | A5 | 5pf dk green (R) | .25 | .40 |
| O3 | A5 | 10pf carmine (G) | .25 | .40 |
| O4 | A5 | 25pf ultra (R) | .50 | .80 |
| O5 | A5 | 50pf maroon | 4.50 | 8.00 |
| | | Nos. O1-O5 (5) | 6.25 | 14.10 |

Nos. O1-O5 were issued for the use of railway officials. "E" stands for "Eisenbahn."

**1916-20 Typo. Perf. 11½**

| | | | | |
|---|---|---|---|---|
| O6 | O1 | 3pf bister brn | .25 | .80 |
| O7 | O1 | 5pf yellow grn | .25 | .80 |
| O8 | O1 | 7½pf grn, *grn* | .25 | .50 |
| O9 | O1 | 7½pf grn | .25 | |
| O10 | O1 | 10pf deep rose | .25 | 1.20 |
| O11 | O1 | 15pf red, *buff* | .25 | 1.20 |
| O12 | O1 | 15pf red | .30 | 1.20 |
| O13 | O1 | 20pf dp bl, *bl* | .25 | 1.20 |
| O14 | O1 | 20pf dp blue | 2.00 | 2.25 |
| O15 | O1 | 25pf gray | .25 | 1.20 |
| O16 | O1 | 30pf orange | .25 | .65 |
| O17 | O1 | 60pf dark green | .25 | .65 |
| O18 | O1 | 1m dl vio, *gray* | .25 | 1.25 |
| O19 | O1 | 1m maroon ('20) | .95 | 3.25 |
| | | Nos. O6-O19 (14) | 2.75 | 475.00 |
| | | | 8.50 | 491.15 |

Used values of Nos. O6-O69 are for
postally used stamps. Canceled-to-
order stamps, which abound, sell for
same prices as unused.

Official Stamps and
Type of 1916-17
Overprinted

Volksstaat
Bayern

**1918**

| | | | | |
|---|---|---|---|---|
| O20 | O1 | 3pf bister brn | .25 | 13.50 |
| O21 | O1 | 5pf yellow grn | .25 | 2.00 |
| O22 | O1 | 7½pf gray green | .25 | 13.00 |
| O23 | O1 | 10pf deep rose | .25 | 2.25 |
| O24 | O1 | 15pf red | .25 | 2.25 |
| O25 | O1 | 20pf blue | .25 | 2.25 |
| O26 | O1 | 25pf gray | .25 | 2.25 |
| O27 | O1 | 30pf orange | .25 | 2.25 |
| O28 | O1 | 35pf orange | .25 | 2.25 |
| O29 | O1 | 50pf olive gray | .25 | 2.50 |
| O30 | O1 | 60pf dark green | .25 | 2.50 |
| O31 | O1 | 75pf red brown | .30 | 13.50 |
| O32 | O1 | 1m dl vio, *gray* | .35 | 3.50 |
| O33 | O1 | 1m maroon | 1.10 | 14.50 |
| | | Nos. O20-O33 (14) | 4.00 | 375.00 |
| | | | 8.25 | 451.00 |

O3

O4

**1920** **Typo.** *Pe*
O34 O2 5pf yellow grn
O35 O2 10pf orange
O36 O2 15pf carmine
O37 O2 20pf violet
O38 O2 30pf dark blue
O39 O2 40pf bister

**Perf. 14½x14**
**Wmk. 95v**
O40 O3 50pf vermilion
O41 O3 60pf blue green
O42 O3 70pf dk violet
*a.* Imperf., pair
O43 O3 75pf deep rose
O44 O3 80pf dull blue
O45 O3 90pf olive green
O46 O4 1m dark brown
*a.* Imperf., pair
O47 O4 1¼m green
O48 O4 1½m vermilion
*a.* Imperf., pair
O49 O4 2½m deep blue
*a.* Imperf., pair
O50 O4 3m dark red
*a.* Imperf., pair
O51 O4 5m black
*a.* Imperf., pair
Nos. O34-O51 (18)

Stamps of Preceding Issue
Overprinted

**1920, Apr. 1**
O52 O2 5pf yellow green
*a.* Imperf., pair
O53 O2 10pf orange
O54 O2 15pf carmine
O55 O2 20pf violet
O56 O2 30pf dark blue
O57 O2 40pf bister
O58 O3 50pf vermilion
*a.* Imperf., pair
O59 O3 60pf blue green
O60 O3 70pf dark violet
O61 O3 75pf deep rose
O62 O3 80pf dull blue
O63 O3 90pf olive green

**Similar Ovpt., Words 8**
O64 O4 1m dark brown
*a.* Imperf., pair
O65 O4 1¼m green
O66 O4 1½m vermilion
O67 O4 2½m deep blue
*a.* Imperf., pair
O68 O4 3m dark red
O69 O4 5m black
Nos. O52-O69 (18)

Nos. O52-O69 could be use
Germany, but were almost excl
Bavaria.

## BERGEDOR

LOCATION — A town
Germany.
POP. — 2,989 (1861)

Originally Bergedorf bel
to the Free City of Hamb
Free City of Lübeck. In
purchased by Hamburg.

16 Schillings = 1

Values for unused sta
examples with original gu
in the catalogue introduc
without gum sell for abou
figures quoted. Values for
are for examples cancele
bars. Copies bearing date
marks sell for more.

Combined Arms of
and Hamburg
A1      A2

---

A4

**1865** *Roulette*
**Eagle embossed**
14 A4 1½s red lilac     30.00

*The 1872 reprints are imperforate a*
*out embossing. Values: unused, $120*
*hinged, $225.*
Counterfeit cancellations are found
1-14.
The stamps of Lübeck were supers
those of the North German Confeder
Jan. 1, 1868.

## MECKLENBURG-SCHW

LOCATION — In northern Ge
bordering on the Baltic Sea.
GOVT. — Grand Duchy
AREA — 5,065 sq. mi. (approx.
POP. — 674,000 (approx.)
CAPITAL — Schwerin

Mecklenburg-Schwerin was
ber of the German Confedera
became part of the German E
1870.

48 Schillings = 1 Thale

Values for unused stamps
examples with original gum a
in the catalogue introduction. E
without gum sell for about 70
figures quoted.

Coat of Arms
A1       A2

A1 has dots in background.

**1856** **Unwmk.** **Typo.**
1 A1 Four ¼s red     1
*a.* ¼s red
2 A2 3s yellow
3 A2 5s blue       2
Nos. 1-3 (3)

See Nos. 4, 6-8.

A3 has no dots in backgroun

**1864-67** **R**
4 A1 Four ¼s red     2
*a.* ¼s red
5 A3 Four ¼s red     :
6 A2 2s gray lil ('67)   1
*a.* 2s red violet ('66)
7 A2 3s org yel, wide
margin ('67)
*a.* Narrow margin ('65)
8 A2 5s bister brn     1
*b.* Thick paper

The overall size of No. 7, in
is 24½x24½mm. That o
23½x23mm.
The bister on white paper
Value $12.

Counterfeit cancellations
stamps valued higher used th
These stamps were supers
the North German Confeder
1868.

## MECKLENBURG-

LOCATION — In north
divided by Mecklenbu
GOVT. — Grand Duchy
AREA — 1,131 sq. mi.
POP. — 106,347
CAPITAL — Neustrelitz

---

**1865-66** *Rouletted 7 and 8*
22 A9 1⅛s red lilac
('66)      72.50 25.00
*a.* Half used as ⅛s on cover                    24,000.
23 A10 1⅛s carmine    60.00 45.00
24 A9 2s blue ('66)   145.00 160.00
25 A10 4s bister      65.00 80.00
Nos. 22-25 (4)       342.50 310.00

These stamps were superseded by those of
North German Confederation on Jan. 1, 1868.

## THURN AND TAXIS

A princely house which, prior to the
formation of the German Empire,
enjoyed the privilege of a postal monopo-
ly. These stamps were superseded on
July 1, 1867, by those of Prussia, followed by those of the North German
Postal District on Jan. 1, 1868, and later
by stamps of the German Empire on
Jan. 1, 1872.

Values are for stamps with four complete margins just clear of the frame-
lines. Stamps with margins just touching the framelines on one or two sides
are worth approximately 60% of the values quoted. Stamps with four large
margins are rare and command premiums of up to 500% over the values
quoted.
Values for unused stamps are for
examples with original gum as defined
in the catalogue introduction. Stamps
without gum sell for about 50% of the
figures quoted.

### NORTHERN DISTRICT
30 Silbergroschen or Groschen = 1
Thaler

A1

**1852-58** **Unwmk.** **Typo.** *Imperf.*
1 A1 ¼sgr, red brn
('54)      265.00 60.00
2 A1 ½sgr blk, buff ('58) 125.00 250.00
3 A1 ½sgr blk, green   725.00 40.00
4 A1 1sgr blk, dk bl   1,325. 140.00
5 A1 1sgr blk, lt bl ('53) 800.00 22.50
6 A1 3sgr blk, rose    850.00 32.50
*a.* Half used as 1sgr on cover    10,000.
7 A1 3sgr blk, brownish
yellow      1,000. 30.00
*a.* 3sgr blk, pale orange yellow 1,000. 80.00

*Reprints of Nos. 1-12, 15-20, 23-24, were*
*made in 1910. They have "ND" in script on the*
*back. Value, $6.50 each.*

A2

**1859-60**
8 A1 ¼sgr red ('60)    67.50 67.50
9 A1 ½gr green        300.00 95.00
10 A1 1sgr blue        300.00 45.00
11 A1 2sgr rose ('60)  145.00 80.00
12 A1 3sgr red brn
('60)      145.00 110.00
13 A2 5sgr rose        2.75 400.00
14 A2 10sgr orange     2.75 875.00

*Excellent forged cancellations exist on Nos.*
*13 and 14. For reprints, see note after No. 7.*

**1862-63**
15 A1 ¼sgr black ('63) 35.00 75.00
16 A1 ½sgr green ('63) 50.00 250.00
17 A1 ½sgr org yel     100.00 47.50
18 A1 1sgr rose ('63)  67.50 27.50
19 A1 2sgr blue ('63)  60.00 100.00
20 A1 3sgr bister ('63) 27.50 55.00
Nos. 15-20 (6)        340.00 555.00

For reprints, see note after No. 7.

**1865** *Rouletted*
21 A1 ¼sgr black       7.50 400.00
22 A1 ½sgr green       11.00 240.00
23 A1 ½sgr yellow      22.50 37.50
24 A1 1sgr brown       25.00 25.00

---

25 A1 2sgr blue        1.50 67.50
26 A1 3sgr bister      2.75 27.50
Nos. 21-26 (6)        70.25 797.50

For reprints, see note after No. 7.

**1866** *Rouletted in Colored Lines*
27 A1 ¼sgr black       2.00 1,250.
28 A1 ½sgr green       2.00 600.00
29 A1 ½sgr yellow      2.00 120.00
30 A1 1sgr rose        1.50 60.00
*a.* Horizontal pair without
rouletting between 150.00 1,500.
*b.* Half used as ½sgr on cover               52,500.
31 A1 2sgr blue        1.50 600.00
32 A1 3sgr bister      1.50 150.00
Nos. 27-32 (6)        10.50 2,780.

Forged cancellations on Nos. 2, 13-14, 15-
16, 21-22, 25-32 are plentiful.

### SOUTHERN DISTRICT
60 Kreuzer = 1 Gulden

A1

**1852-53** **Unwmk.** *Imperf.*
42 A1 1kr blk, lt grn  240.00 15.00
43 A1 3kr blk, dk bl   925.00 50.00
44 A1 3kr blk, bl ('53) 800.00 20.00
45 A1 6kr blk, rose    800.00 11.00
46 A1 9kr blk, brnish
yell      875.00 17.50
*a.* 9kr blk, pale orange yellow 750.00 45.00

*Reprints of Nos. 42-50, 53-56 were made in*
*1910. Each has "ND" in script on the back.*
*Value, each $6.50.*

A2

**1859**
47 A1 1kr green        25.00 10.00
48 A1 3kr blue         560.00 25.00
49 A1 6kr rose         560.00 67.50
50 A1 9kr yellow       560.00 67.50
51 A2 15kr lilac       2.75 175.00
52 A2 30kr orange      2.75 475.00

Forged cancellations exist on Nos. 51 and
52. For reprints, see note after No. 46.

**1862**
53 A1 3kr rose         13.50 30.00
54 A1 6kr blue         13.50 30.00
55 A1 9kr bister       13.50 35.00
Nos. 53-55 (3)        40.50 95.00

For reprints, see note after No. 46.

**1865** *Rouletted*
56 A1 1kr green        12.50 13.50
57 A1 3kr rose         18.50 7.50
58 A1 6kr blue         1.50 20.00
59 A1 9kr bister       2.25 22.50
Nos. 56-59 (4)        34.75 63.50

For reprint of No. 56, see note after No. 46.

**1866** *Rouletted in Colored Lines*
60 A1 1kr green        1.50 22.50
61 A1 3kr rose         1.50 20.00
62 A1 6kr blue         1.50 37.50
63 A1 9kr bister       1.50 32.50
Nos. 60-63 (4)        6.00 112.50

Forged cancellations exist on Nos. 51-52,
58-63.
The Thurn & Taxis Stamps, Northern and
Southern Districts, were replaced on July 1,
1867, by those of Prussia.

## WURTTEMBERG

LOCATION — In southern Germany
GOVT. — Kingdom
AREA — 7,530 sq. mi.
POP. — 2,580,000 (approx.)
CAPITAL — Stuttgart

Württemberg was a member of the
German Confederation and became a
part of the German Empire in 1870. It
gave up its postal autonomy on March

---

31, 1902, but official stamps were
issued until 1923.

16 Kreuzer = 1 Gulden
100 Pfennigs = 1 Mark (1875)

Values for unused stamps are for
examples with original gum as defined
in the catalogue introduction. Unused
stamps without gum of Nos. 1-46 sell
for about 60-70% of the figures quoted.
Unused stamps without gum of Nos.
47-54 sell for about 50% of the figures
quoted.

A1     A1a

**1851-52** **Unwmk.** **Typo.** *Imperf.*
1 A1 1kr blk, buff     1,125. 95.00
*a.* 1kr black, straw    3,500. 500.00
2 A1 3kr blk, yellow   275.00 7.25
*a.* 3kr black, orange   3,000. 300.00
4 A1 6kr blk, yel grn  1,450. 32.50
*a.* 6kr black, blue green 2,600. 50.00
5 A1 9kr blue          4,800. 37.50
6 A1a 18kr blk, dl vio
('52)      1,750. 725.00

*On the "reprints" the letters of "Württem-*
*berg" are smaller, especially the first "e"; the*
*right branch of the "r's" of Württemberg runs*
*upward in the reprints and downward in the*
*originals.*

Coat of Arms — A2

**With Orange Silk Threads**
**Typographed and Embossed**
**1857**
7 A2 1kr yel brn       800.00 80.00
*a.* 1kr dark brown      1,100. 225.00
9 A2 3kr yel org       400.00 14.00
10 A2 6kr green        800.00 65.00
11 A2 9kr car rose     1,925. 70.00
12 A2 18kr blue        3,350. 1,350.

Very fine examples of Nos. 7-12 with have
one or two margins touching, but not cutting,
the frameline.
See Nos. 13-46, 53.
The reprints have red or yellow silk threads
and are printed 2mm apart, while the originals
are ¾mm apart.

**1859** **Without Silk Threads**
13 A2 1kr brown        650.00 100.00
*a.* 1kr dark brown      2,000. 725.00
15 A2 3kr yel org      275.00 14.00
16 A2 6kr green        9,600. 125.00
17 A2 9kr car rose     1,275. 80.00
18 A2 18kr dark blue   3,000. 1,450.

*The colors of the reprints are brighter; they*
*are also printed 2mm apart instead of 1¼mm.*

**1860** *Perf. 13½*
19 A2 1kr brown        1,125. 125.00
20 A2 3kr yel org      325.00 9.50
21 A2 6kr green        3,000. 100.00
22 A2 9kr carmine      1,200. 120.00

**1861** **Thin Paper**
23 A2 1kr brown        950.00 275.00
*a.* 1kr black brown     1,000. 250.00
25 A2 3kr yel org      200.00 65.00
26 A2 6kr green        400.00 110.00
27 A2 9kr rose         1,275. 275.00
*a.* 9kr claret         1,500. 350.00
29 A2 18kr dark blue   3,000. 2,250.

Examples of Nos. 23-29 with all perforations
intact sell for considerably more.

**1862** *Perf. 10*
30 A2 1kr blk brn      650.00 440.00
31 A2 3kr yel org      800.00 47.50
32 A2 6kr green        525.00 160.00
33 A2 9kr claret       4,000. 800.00

**1863**
34 A2 1kr yel grn      45.00 13.50
*a.* 1kr green          400.00 95.00
36 A2 3kr rose         325.00 5.50
*a.* 3kr dark claret     1,600. 275.00

---

37 A2 6kr blue         160.00 55.00
39 A2 9kr yel brn      750.00 175.00
*b.* 9kr red brown       260.00 52.50
*b.* 9kr black brown     1,200. 190.00
40 A2 18kr orange      1,200. 400.00

**1865-68** *Rouletted 10*
41 A2 1kr yel grn      45.00 12.00
*a.* 1kr dark green      575.00 275.00
42 A2 3kr rose         45.00 3.25
*a.* 3kr claret         1,900. 250.00
43 A2 6kr blue         275.00 52.50
44 A2 7kr slate bl ('68) 960.00 125.00
45 A2 9kr bis brn      1,500. 120.00
*a.* 9kr red brown       1,150. 80.00
46 A2 18kr orange ('67) 1,800. 950.00

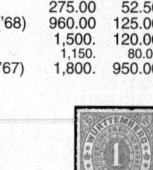
A3

**1869-73** **Typo. & Embossed**
47 A3 1kr yel grn      32.50 2.40
48 A3 2kr orange       175.00 140.00
49 A3 3kr rose         16.00 1.60
50 A3 7kr blue         67.50 17.50
51 A3 9kr lt brn ('73) 80.00 40.00
52 A3 14kr orange      88.00 45.00
*a.* 14kr lemon yellow   1,500. 1,500.
Nos. 47-52 (6)        459.00 246.50

See No. 54.

**1873** *Imperf.*
53 A3 70kr red violet  1,750. 4,000.
*a.* 70kr violet         2,900. 5,250.

Nos. 53 and 53a have single or double lines
of fine black dots printed in the gutters
between the stamps.

**1874** *Perf. 11½x11*
54 A3 1kr yellow green 110.00 40.00

A4     A5

**1875-1900** **Typo.**
55 A4 2pf sl gray ('93) 2.00 .95
56 A4 3pf green        20.00 1.60
57 A4 3pf brn ('90)    .80 .55
*a.* Imperf., pair       160.00
58 A4 5pf violet       9.50 .80
59 A4 5pf grn ('90)    1.60 .55
*a.* 5pf blue green      300.00 24.00
*b.* Imperf., pair       175.00
60 A4 10pf carmine     1.60 .80
*a.* 10pf rose          85.00 1.25
*b.* Imperf., pair       80.00
61 A4 20pf ultra       1.60 1.60
*a.* 20pf dull blue      1.60 1.60
*b.* Imperf., pair       175.00
62 A4 25pf red brn     125.00 12.00
63 A4 25pf org ('90)   2.75 1.60
*a.* Imperf., pair       175.00
64 A5 30pf org & blk
('00)      4.00 5.50
65 A5 40pf dp rose & blk
('00)      4.00 6.50
66 A4 50pf gray        725.00 40.00
67 A4 50pf gray grn    65.00 6.50
68 A4 50pf pur brn ('90) 3.25 .95
*a.* 50pf red brown      640.00 65.00
*b.* As #68, imperf., pair 175.00
69 A4 2m yellow        800.00 260.00
70 A4 2m ver, buff ('79) 2,800. 125.00
71 A5 2m org & blk
('86)      8.00 12.00
Telegraph cancel         4.50
*a.* 2m yellow & black   450.00 72.50
72 A5 5m bl & blk ('81) 45.00 160.00
Telegraph cancel         72.50
*a.* Double impression of figure of value      200.00

No. 70 has "Unverkäuflich" (not for sale)
printed on its back to remind postal clerks that
it, like No. 69, was for their use and not to be
sold to the public.
The regular postage stamps of Württemberg were superseded by those of the German
Empire in 1902. Official stamps were in use
until 1923.

## WURTTEMBERG OFFICIAL STAMPS

**For the Communal Authorities**

O1

**Perf. 11½x11**

| 1875-1900 | | Typo. | Unwmk. | |
|---|---|---|---|---|
| O1 | O1 | 2pf sl gray ('00) | 3.00 | 2.00 |
| O2 | O1 | 3pf brn ('96) | 3.00 | 2.00 |
| O3 | O1 | 5pf violet | 37.50 | 2.40 |
| a. | | Imperf., pair | | 3,000. |
| O4 | O1 | 5pf bl grn ('90) | 1.60 | 2.00 |
| a. | | Imperf., pair | 55.00 | |
| O5 | O1 | 10pf rose | 7.50 | 2.25 |
| a. | | Imperf., pair | 90.00 | |
| O6 | O1 | 25pf org ('00) | 22.50 | 8.00 |
| | | Nos. O1-O6 (6) | 75.10 | 18.65 |

See Nos. O12-O32. For overprints and surcharges see Nos. O7-O11, O40-O52, O59-O93.

**Used Values**

When italicized, used values for Nos. O7-O183 are for favor-canceled stamps. Postally used stamps command a premium.

**Stamps of Previous Issues Overprinted in Black**

| 1906, Jan. 30 | | | | |
|---|---|---|---|---|
| O7 | O1 | 2pf slate gray | 45.00 | |
| O8 | O1 | 3pf dk brown | 14.00 | 9.25 |
| O9 | O1 | 5pf green | 6.50 | 4.75 |
| O10 | O1 | 10pf deep rose | 6.50 | 4.75 |
| O11 | O1 | 25pf orange | 47.50 | 72.50 |
| | | Nos. O7-O11 (5) | 119.50 | 91.25 |

Centenary of Kingdom of Württemberg. Nos. O7-O11 also exist imperf but it is doubtful if they were ever issued in that condition.

| 1906-21 | | | Wmk. 116 | |
|---|---|---|---|---|
| O12 | O1 | 2pf slate gray | 4.00 | .40 |
| O13 | O1 | 2½pf gray blk ('16) | .80 | .25 |
| O14 | O1 | 3pf dk brown | .95 | .40 |
| O15 | O1 | 5pf green | .80 | .40 |
| O16 | O1 | 7½pf orange ('16) | .80 | .25 |
| O17 | O1 | 10pf dp rose | .80 | .40 |
| O18 | O1 | 10pf orange ('21) | .30 | .30 |
| O19 | O1 | 15pf yellow brn ('16) | 2.40 | .25 |
| O20 | O1 | 15pf purple ('17) | 1.25 | .25 |
| O21 | O1 | 20pf dp ultra ('11) | 1.60 | .40 |
| O22 | O1 | 20pf dp green ('21) | .30 | .30 |
| O23 | O1 | 25pf green | .95 | .30 |
| O24 | O1 | 25pf brn & blk ('17) | 1.25 | .25 |
| O25 | O1 | 35pf brown ('19) | 1.60 | .95 |
| O26 | O1 | 40pf rose red ('21) | .30 | .30 |
| O27 | O1 | 50pf rose lake ('11) | 14.50 | .40 |
| O28 | O1 | 50pf vio brn ('21) | .30 | .30 |
| O29 | O1 | 60pf olive grn ('21) | .50 | .30 |
| O30 | O1 | 1.25m emerald ('21) | .30 | .30 |
| O31 | O1 | 2m gray ('21) | .30 | .30 |
| O32 | O1 | 3m brown ('21) | .50 | .30 |
| | | Nos. O12-O32 (21) | 34.50 | 7.40 |

No. O24 contains solid black numerals.
Nos. O12-O32 exist imperf. Value, each pair, $6-$16.

O3

**Perf. 14½x14**

| 1916, Oct. 6 | | Typo. | Unwmk. | |
|---|---|---|---|---|
| O33 | O3 | 2½pf slate | 1.60 | 1.60 |
| O34 | O3 | 7½pf orange | 1.60 | 1.60 |
| O35 | O3 | 10pf car rose | 1.60 | 1.60 |
| O36 | O3 | 15pf yellow brn | 1.60 | 1.60 |
| O37 | O3 | 20pf blue | 1.60 | 1.60 |
| O38 | O3 | 25pf gray blk | 4.00 | 1.60 |
| O39 | O3 | 50pf red brown | 8.00 | 1.60 |
| | | Nos. O33-O39 (7) | 20.00 | 11.20 |

25th year of the reign of King Wilhelm II.

**Stamps of 1900-06 Surcharged**

**Perf. 11½x11**

| 1916, Sept. 10 | | | Wmk. 116 | |
|---|---|---|---|---|
| O40 | O1 | 25pf on 25pf orange | 4.00 | .95 |

**No. O13 Surcharged in Blue**

| 1919 | | | Wmk. 116 | |
|---|---|---|---|---|
| O42 | O1 | 2pf on 2½pf gray blk | .80 | .50 |

**Official Stamps of 1906-19 Overprinted**

| 1919 | | | | |
|---|---|---|---|---|
| O43 | O1 | 2½pf gray blk | .40 | .60 |
| O44 | O1 | 3pf dk brown | 12.00 | .60 |
| O45 | O1 | 5pf green | .30 | .60 |
| O46 | O1 | 7½pf orange | 1.00 | .60 |
| O47 | O1 | 10pf rose | .30 | .60 |
| O48 | O1 | 15pf purple | .30 | .60 |
| O49 | O1 | 20pf ultra | .40 | .60 |
| O50 | O1 | 25pf brown & blk | .40 | .60 |
| O51 | O1 | 35pf brown | 4.00 | .60 |
| O52 | O1 | 50pf red brown | 5.50 | .60 |
| | | Nos. O43-O52 (10) | 24.60 | 6.00 |

Stag — O4

**Wmk. 192**

| 1920, Mar. 19 | | Litho. | Perf. 14½ | |
|---|---|---|---|---|
| O53 | O4 | 10pf maroon | 1.45 | 1.60 |
| O54 | O4 | 15pf brown | 1.45 | 1.60 |
| O55 | O4 | 20pf indigo | 1.45 | 1.60 |
| O56 | O4 | 30pf deep green | 1.45 | 1.60 |
| O57 | O4 | 50pf yellow | 3.25 | 1.60 |
| O58 | O4 | 75pf bister | 3.25 | 1.60 |
| | | Nos. O53-O58 (6) | 12.30 | 9.60 |

**Official Stamps of 1906-19 Overprinted**

**Perf. 11½x11**

| 1920, Apr. 1 | | | Wmk. 116 | |
|---|---|---|---|---|
| O59 | O1 | 5pf green | 4.00 | 10.00 |
| O60 | O1 | 10pf deep rose | 2.40 | 4.75 |
| O61 | O1 | 15pf dp violet | 2.40 | 5.25 |
| O62 | O1 | 20pf ultra | 4.00 | 8.75 |
| a. | | Wmk. 192 | 4.75 | 8.75 |
| O63 | O1 | 50pf red brown | 6.50 | 20.00 |
| | | Nos. O59-O63 (5) | 19.30 | 48.75 |

Nos. O59 to O63 were available for official postage throughout all Germany but were used almost exclusively in Württemberg.

**Stamps of 1917-21 Surcharged in Black, Red or Blue**

| 1923 | | | | |
|---|---|---|---|---|
| O64 | O1 | 5m on 10pf orange | .25 | .50 |
| O65 | O1 | 10m on 15pf dp violet | .25 | .50 |
| O66 | O1 | 12m on 40pf rose red | .25 | .50 |
| O67 | O1 | 20m on 10pf orange | .80 | .50 |
| O68 | O1 | 25m on 20pf green | .25 | .50 |
| O69 | O1 | 40m on 20pf green | .25 | .50 |
| O70 | O1 | 50m on 60pf olive grn | .25 | .50 |

**Surcharged**

| | | | | |
|---|---|---|---|---|
| O71 | O1 | 60m on 1.25m emer | .25 | .50 |
| O72 | O1 | 100m on 40pf rose red | .25 | .50 |
| O73 | O1 | 200m on 2m gray (R) | .25 | .50 |
| O74 | O1 | 300m on 50pf red brn (Bl) | .25 | .50 |
| O75 | O1 | 400m on 3m brn (Bl) | .25 | .50 |
| O76 | O1 | 1000m on 60pf ol grn | .25 | .50 |
| O77 | O1 | 2000m on 1.25m emer | .25 | .50 |
| | | Nos. O64-O77 (14) | 4.05 | 7.00 |

**Abbreviations:**
Th = (Tausend) Thousand
Mil = (Million) Million
Mlrd = (Milliarde) Billion

**Surcharged**

| 1923 | | | | |
|---|---|---|---|---|
| O78 | O1 | 5th m on 10pf orange | .25 | .50 |
| O79 | O1 | 20th m on 40pf rose red | .25 | .50 |
| O80 | O1 | 50th m on 15pf violet | 1.00 | .50 |
| O81 | O1 | 75th m on 2m gray | 1.60 | .50 |
| O82 | O1 | 100th m on 20pf green | .25 | .50 |
| O83 | O1 | 250th m on 3m brown | .25 | .50 |

**Surcharged**

| | | | | |
|---|---|---|---|---|
| O84 | O1 | 1mil m on 60pf ol grn | 1.25 | .50 |
| O85 | O1 | 2mil m on 50pf red brn | .25 | .50 |
| O86 | O1 | 5mil m on 1.25m emer | .35 | .50 |

**Surcharged**

| | | | | |
|---|---|---|---|---|
| O87 | O1 | 4 mlrd m on 50pf red brn | 4.50 | .50 |
| O88 | O1 | 10 mlrd m on 3m brn | 3.25 | .50 |
| | | Nos. O78-O88 (11) | 13.20 | 5.50 |

**No. O23 Surcharged in Rentenpfennig as**

| 1923, Dec. | | | | |
|---|---|---|---|---|
| O89 | O1 | 3pf on 25pf orange | .50 | .40 |
| O90 | O1 | 5pf on 25pf orange | .40 | .40 |
| O91 | O1 | 10pf on 25pf orange | .40 | .40 |
| O92 | O1 | 20pf on 25pf orange | .50 | .40 |
| O93 | O1 | 25pf on 25pf orange | .40 | .40 |
| | | Nos. O89-O93 (5) | 2.20 | 2.00 |

**For the State Authorities**

O6

**Perf. 11½x11**

| 1881-1902 | | Typo. | Unwmk. | |
|---|---|---|---|---|
| O94 | O6 | 2pf sl gray ('96) | 1.60 | 1.60 |
| O95 | O6 | 3pf green | 25.00 | 4.50 |
| O96 | O6 | 3pf dk brn ('90) | 1.60 | 2.00 |
| | | Never hinged | 2.50 | |
| O97 | O6 | 5pf violet | 8.00 | 2.00 |
| O98 | O6 | 5pf green ('90) | 2.40 | 2.00 |
| O99 | O6 | 10pf rose | 8.00 | 1.90 |
| O100 | O6 | 20pf ultra | 1.00 | 2.40 |
| O101 | O6 | 25pf brown | 35.00 | 6.50 |
| O102 | O6 | 25pf orange ('90) | 5.25 | 1.40 |
| O103 | O6 | 30pf org & blk ('02) | 2.00 | 3.25 |
| O104 | O6 | 40pf dp rose & blk ('02) | 2.25 | 3.25 |
| O105 | O6 | 50pf gray grn | 6.50 | 8.75 |
| O106 | O6 | 50pf maroon ('91) | 1.60 | 4.00 |
| a. | | 50pf red brown ('90) | 240.00 | 1,750. |
| O107 | O6 | 1m yellow | 72.50 | 175.00 |
| O108 | O6 | 1m violet ('90) | 5.50 | 16.00 |
| | | Nos. O94-O108 (15) | 178.20 | 234.55 |

See #O119-O135. For overprints & surcharges see #O109-O118, O146-O164, O176-O183.

**Overprinted in Black**

| 1906 | | | | |
|---|---|---|---|---|
| O109 | O6 | 2pf slate gray | 27.00 | 5.00 |
| O110 | O6 | 3pf dk brown | 5.50 | 5.00 |
| O111 | O6 | 5pf green | 4.75 | 5.00 |
| O112 | O6 | 10pf dp rose | 4.50 | 5.00 |
| O113 | O6 | 20pf ultra | 4.75 | 5.00 |
| O114 | O6 | 25pf orange | 11.00 | 6.00 |
| O115 | O6 | 30pf org & blk | 9.50 | 7.50 |
| O116 | O6 | 40pf dp rose & blk | 32.50 | 7.50 |
| O117 | O6 | 50pf red brown | 32.50 | 7.50 |
| O118 | O6 | 1m purple | 65.00 | 7.50 |
| | | Nos. O109-O118 (10) | 197.00 | 61.00 |

Cent. of the kingdom of Württemberg. Nos. O109 to O118 are also found imperforate, but it is doubtful if they were ever issued

in that condition. Value, each: unused $45; never hinged $90.

| 1906-19 | | | Wmk. 116 | |
|---|---|---|---|---|
| O119 | O6 | 2pf slate gray | .50 | .40 |
| O120 | O6 | 2½pf gray blk ('16) | .55 | .40 |
| O121 | O6 | 3pf dk brown | .50 | .40 |
| O122 | O6 | 5pf green | .50 | .40 |
| O123 | O6 | 7½pf orange ('16) | .55 | .40 |
| O124 | O6 | 10pf deep rose | .50 | .40 |
| O125 | O6 | 15pf yel brn ('16) | .65 | .40 |
| O126 | O6 | 15pf purple ('17) | 1.25 | .40 |
| O127 | O6 | 20pf ultra | .65 | .40 |
| O128 | O6 | 25pf orange | .60 | .40 |
| O129 | O6 | 25pf brn & blk ('17) | .50 | .40 |
| O130 | O6 | 30pf org & blk | .50 | .40 |
| O131 | O6 | 35pf brown ('19) | 1.60 | 2.40 |
| O132 | O6 | 40pf dp rose & blk | .65 | .40 |
| O133 | O6 | 50pf red brown | .65 | .40 |
| O134 | O6 | 1m purple | 5.50 | .40 |
| O135 | O6 | 1m sl & blk ('17) | 11.00 | 1.55 |
| | | Nos. O119-O135 (17) | 26.50 | 9.95 |

**King Wilhelm II — O8**

| 1916 | | Unwmk. | Typo. | Perf. 14 | |
|---|---|---|---|---|---|
| O136 | O8 | 2½pf slate | .80 | .65 |
| O137 | O8 | 7½pf orange | .80 | .45 |
| O138 | O8 | 10pf carmine | .80 | .45 |
| O139 | O8 | 15pf yellow brn | .80 | .45 |
| O140 | O8 | 20pf blue | .80 | .45 |
| O141 | O8 | 25pf gray blk | 1.60 | .65 |
| O142 | O8 | 30pf green | 1.60 | 1.25 |
| O143 | O8 | 40pf claret | 2.40 | 1.25 |
| O144 | O8 | 50pf red brn | 3.25 | 1.85 |
| O145 | O8 | 1m violet | 3.25 | 2.50 |
| | | Nos. O136-O145 (10) | 16.10 | 9.95 |

25th year of the reign of King Wilhelm II.

**Stamps of 1890-1906 Surcharged**

| 1916-19 | | Wmk. 116 | Perf. 11½x11 | |
|---|---|---|---|---|
| O146 | O6 | 25pf on 25pf org | 2.75 | .80 |
| a. | | Without watermark | 35.00 | 13,400. |
| O147 | O6 | 50pf on 50pf red brn | 1.60 | 1.10 |
| a. | | Inverted surcharge | 32.50 | |

Beware of fake cancels on No. O146a.
No. O147a is considered a proof.

**No. O120 Surcharged in Blue**

| 1919 | | | Wmk. 116 | |
|---|---|---|---|---|
| O149 | O6 | 2pf on 2½pf gray blk | 1.60 | 1.60 |

**Official Stamps of 1890-1919 Overprinted**

| 1919 | | | | |
|---|---|---|---|---|
| O150 | O6 | 2½pf gray blk | .55 | .40 |
| O151 | O6 | 3pf dk brown | 7.25 | .80 |
| a. | | Without watermark | 52.50 | |
| O152 | O6 | 5pf green | .40 | .40 |
| O153 | O6 | 7½pf orange | .40 | .40 |
| O154 | O6 | 10pf rose | .40 | .40 |
| O155 | O6 | 15pf purple | .40 | .40 |
| O156 | O6 | 20pf ultra | .40 | .40 |
| O157 | O6 | 25pf brn & blk | .40 | .40 |
| a. | | Inverted overprint | 95.00 | 240.00 |
| O158 | O6 | 30pf org & blk | .80 | .40 |
| a. | | Inverted overprint | 475.00 | |
| O159 | O6 | 35pf brown | .55 | .40 |
| O160 | O6 | 40pf rose & blk | .55 | .40 |
| O161 | O6 | 50pf claret | .80 | .65 |
| | | Never hinged | 1.25 | |
| | | Postally used | | 5.00 |
| O162 | O6 | 1m slate & blk | .80 | .80 |
| | | Nos. O150-O162 (13) | 13.70 | 6.25 |

**Nos. O151, O151a Surcharged in Carmine**

| 1920 | | | Wmk. 116 | |
|---|---|---|---|---|
| O164 | O6 | 75pf on 3pf dk brn | 1.25 | 1.25 |
| a. | | Without watermark | 80.00 | 20.00 |

View of
Stuttgart — O9

10pf, 50pf, 2.50m, 3m, View of Stuttgart.
15pf, 75pf, View of Ulm. 20pf, 1m, View of
Tubingen. 30pf, 1.25m, View of Ellwangen.

**Wmk. 192**

| | | | Perf. 14½ | |
|---|---|---|---|---|
| **1920, Mar. 25** | | **Typo.** | | |
| O166 | O9 | 10pf maroon | .55 | 1.20 |
| O167 | O9 | 15pf brown | .55 | 1.20 |
| O168 | O9 | 20pf indigo | .55 | 1.20 |
| O169 | O9 | 30pf blue grn | .55 | 1.20 |
| O170 | O9 | 50pf yellow | .55 | 1.20 |
| O171 | O9 | 75pf bister | .55 | 1.20 |
| O172 | O9 | 1m orange red | .80 | 1.20 |
| O173 | O9 | 1.25m dp violet | .80 | 1.20 |
| O174 | O9 | 2.50m dark ultra | 2.00 | 1.20 |
| O175 | O9 | 3m yellow grn | 2.40 | 1.20 |
| | | Nos. O166-O175 (10) | 9.30 | 12.00 |

Official Stamps of 1906-19
Overprinted

| | | | | |
|---|---|---|---|---|
| **1920** | | **Wmk. 116** | **Perf. 11½x11** | |
| O176 | O6 | 5pf green | 2.40 | 4.00 |
| O177 | O6 | 10pf deep rose | 1.60 | 3.25 |
| O178 | O6 | 15pf purple | 1.60 | 3.25 |
| O179 | O6 | 20pf ultra | 1.60 | 1.60 |
| a. | | Wmk. 192 | 125.00 | 325.00 |
| O180 | O6 | 30pf orange & blk | 1.60 | 4.00 |
| O181 | O6 | 40pf dp rose & blk | 1.60 | 3.25 |
| O182 | O6 | 50pf red brown | 1.60 | 4.00 |
| O183 | O6 | 1m slate & blk | 2.40 | 8.00 |
| | | Nos. O176-O183 (8) | 14.40 | 31.35 |

The note after No. O63 will also apply to
Nos. O176-O183.

---

# NORTH GERMAN CONFEDERATION

Northern District
30 Groschen = 1 Thaler
Southern District
60 Kreuzer = 1 Gulden
Hamburg
16 Schillings = 1 Mark

---

Values for unused stamps are for
examples with original gum as defined
in the catalogue introduction. Stamps
without gum sell for about 50% of the
figures quoted.

A1          A2

*Rouletted 8½ to 10, 11 to 12½ and
Compound*

| | | | | |
|---|---|---|---|---|
| **1868** | | **Typo.** | | **Unwmk.** |
| 1 | A1 | ¼gr violet | 15.00 | 15.00 |
| 2 | A1 | ⅓gr green | 30.00 | 4.00 |
| 3 | A1 | ½gr orange | 30.00 | 2.50 |
| 4 | A1 | 1gr rose | 20.00 | 1.60 |
| b. | | Half used as ½gr on cover | | 3.25 |
| 5 | A1 | 2gr ultra | 80.00 | 3.25 |
| 6 | A1 | 5gr bister | 80.00 | 9.50 |
| 7 | A2 | 1kr green | 35.00 | 8.00 |
| 8 | A2 | 2kr orange | 55.00 | 55.00 |
| 9 | A2 | 3kr rose | 35.00 | 3.25 |
| 10 | A2 | 7kr ultra | 160.00 | 11.00 |
| 11 | A2 | 18kr bister | 35.00 | 65.00 |
| | | Nos. 1-11 (11) | 575.00 | 178.10 |

See Nos. 13-23.

**Imperf**

| | | | | |
|---|---|---|---|---|
| 1a | A1 | ¼gr red lilac | 200.00 | — |
| 2a | A1 | ⅓gr green | 95.00 | — |
| 3a | A1 | ½gr orange | 140.00 | — |
| 4a | A1 | 1gr rose | 80.00 | — |
| 5a | A1 | 2gr ultra | 275.00 | — |
| 6a | A1 | 5gr bister | 275.00 | — |
| 7a | A2 | 1kr green | 72.50 | 125.00 |
| 8a | A2 | 2kr orange | 200.00 | 95.00 |
| 9a | A2 | 3kr rose | 80.00 | 100.00 |
| 10a | A2 | 7kr ultra | 350.00 | 675.00 |
| 11a | A2 | 18kr bister | 350.00 | 675.00 |

---

A3

| | | | | |
|---|---|---|---|---|
| **1868** | | | | |
| 12 | A3 | (⅓s) lilac brown | 110.00 | 55.00 |
| d. | | Imperf | 200.00 | |

See No. 24.

| | | | | |
|---|---|---|---|---|
| **1869** | | | **Perf. 13½x14** | |
| 13 | A1 | ¼gr lilac | 14.50 | 16.00 |
| a. | | ¼gr red violet | 25.00 | 20.00 |
| 14 | A1 | ⅓gr green | 5.25 | 2.75 |
| 15 | A1 | ½gr orange | 5.25 | 3.50 |
| 16 | A1 | 1gr rose | 4.00 | 1.60 |
| 17 | A1 | 2gr ultra | 7.25 | 2.00 |
| 18 | A1 | 5gr bister | 8.75 | 10.00 |
| 19 | A2 | 1kr green | 12.75 | 10.00 |
| 20 | A2 | 2kr orange | 40.00 | 110.00 |
| 21 | A2 | 3kr rose | 7.25 | 3.25 |
| 22 | A2 | 7kr ultra | 11.00 | 12.00 |
| 23 | A2 | 18kr bister | 150.00 | 1,750. |
| | | Nos. 13-23 (11) | 266.00 | 1,921. |

Counterfeit cancels exist on No. 23.

| | | | | |
|---|---|---|---|---|
| **1869** | | | | |
| 24 | A3 | (⅓s) dull violet brown | 4.75 | 8.75 |

A4          A5

| | | | | |
|---|---|---|---|---|
| | | *Perf.* | *14x13½* | |
| 25 | A4 | 10gr gray | 325.00 | 400.00 |
| | | Pen cancellation | | 65.00 |
| 26 | A5 | 30gr blue | 240.00 | 960.00 |
| | | Pen cancellation | | 140.00 |

Counterfeit cancels exist on No. 26.
See Germany designs A2, A3 and A8 for
similar stamps.

---

## OFFICIAL STAMPS

O1

| | | | | |
|---|---|---|---|---|
| **1870** | | **Unwmk. Typo.** | **Perf. 14½x14** | |
| O1 | O1 | ¼gr black & buff | 27.50 | 45.00 |
| O2 | O1 | ⅓gr black & buff | 9.50 | 20.00 |
| O3 | O1 | ½gr black & buff | 2.75 | 4.00 |
| O4 | O1 | 1gr black & buff | 2.75 | 2.00 |
| O5 | O1 | 2gr black & buff | 7.25 | 4.75 |
| O6 | O1 | 1kr black & gray | 32.50 | 250.00 |
| O7 | O1 | 2kr black & gray | 80.00 | 875.00 |
| O8 | O1 | 3kr black & gray | 25.00 | 47.50 |
| O9 | O1 | 7kr black & gray | 45.00 | 275.00 |
| | | Nos. O1-O9 (9) | 232.25 | 1,523. |

Counterfeit cancels exist on Nos. O6-O9.
The stamps of the North German Confeder-
ation were replaced by those of the German
Empire on Jan. 1, 1872.

---

# GERMANY

ˈjər-mə-nē

LOCATION — In northern Europe bor-
dering on the Baltic and North Seas
AREA — 182,104 sq. mi. (until 1945)
POP. — 67,032,242 (1946)
CAPITAL — Berlin

---

In 1949 the Russian occupied areas
became a separate country, the German Democratic Republic. The country
was reunified Oct. 3, 1990.

30 Silbergroschen or Groschen = 1
Thaler
60 Kreuzer = 1 Gulden
100 Pfennigs = 1 Mark (1875)
100 Pfennigs = 1 Deutsche Mark
(1948)
100 Cents = 1 Euro (2002)

> Catalogue values for unused
> stamps in this country are for
> Never Hinged items, beginning
> with Scott 722 in the regular post-
> age section, Scott B338 in the
> semi-postal section, Scott C61 in
> the airpost section, Scott 9N103 in
> the Berlin regular postage section
> and Scott 9NB12 in the Berlin
> semi-postal section.

## Watermarks

Wmk. 48 —
Diagonal Zigzag
Lines

Wmk. 116 —
Crosses and
Circles

Wmk. 125 —
Lozenges

Wmk. 126 —
Network

Wmk. 127 —
Quatrefoils

Wmk. 192 —
Circles

Wmk. 223 —
Eagle

Wmk. 237 —
Swastikas

Wmk. 241 —
Cross

Wmk. 284 —
"DEUTSCHE
POST"
Multiple

Wmk. 285 —
Marbleized
Pattern

Wmk. 286 — D P Multiple

---

Wmk. 292 —
Flowers, Multiple

Wmk. 295 — B P
and Zigzag Lines

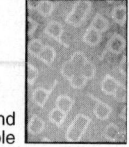

Wmk. 304 — DBP and
Rosettes Multiple

---

## Empire

Values for unused stamps are for
examples with original gum as defined
in the catalogue introduction. Any
exceptions are specifically mentioned.

Imperial Eagle — A1

| | | | | |
|---|---|---|---|---|
| | **Typographed, Center Embossed** | | | |
| **1872** | | **Unwmk.** | **Perf. 13½x14½** | |
| | | **Eagle with small shield** | | |
| 1 | A1 | ¼gr violet | 200.00 | 85.00 |
| 2 | A1 | ⅓gr green | 475.00 | 36.00 |
| a. | | Imperf. | | — |
| 3 | A1 | ½gr red orange | 950.00 | 40.00 |
| a. | | ½gr orange yellow | 1,100. | 47.50 |
| 4 | A1 | 1gr rose | 290.00 | 7.25 |
| a. | | Imperf. | | — |
| b. | | Half used as ½gr on cover | | 50,000. |
| 5 | A1 | 2gr ultra | 1,500. | 13.50 |
| a. | | Imperf. | | 8,500. |
| 6 | A1 | 5gr bister | 825.00 | 85.00 |
| a. | | Imperf. | | 10,000. |
| 7 | A1 | 1kr green | 650.00 | 50.00 |
| 8 | A1 | 2kr orange | 35.00 | 165.00 |
| a. | | 2kr red orange | 590.00 | 285.00 |
| 9 | A1 | 3kr rose | 1,700. | 14.50 |
| 10 | A1 | 7kr ultra | 2,350. | 85.00 |
| 11 | A1 | 18kr bister | 475.00 | 360.00 |

Values for imperforates are for stamps postmarked at Leipzig (⅓gr), Coblenz (1gr),
Hoengen (2gr) and Leutersdorf (5gr).

A2          A3

| | | | | |
|---|---|---|---|---|
| **1872** | | **Typo.** | **Perf. 14½x13½** | |
| 12 | A2 | 10gr gray | 50.00 | 1,300. |
| | | Pen cancellation | | 165.00 |
| 13 | A3 | 30gr blue | 95.00 | 2,500. |
| | | Pen cancellation | | 540.00 |

For similar designs see A8, North German
Confederation A4, A5.

A4

| | | | | |
|---|---|---|---|---|
| | **Center Embossed** | | | |
| **1872** | | | **Perf. 13½x14½** | |
| | | **Eagle with large shield** | | |
| 14 | A4 | ¼gr violet | 72.50 | 110.00 |
| 15 | A4 | ⅓gr yellow green | 32.50 | 13.50 |
| a. | | ⅓gr blue green | 120.00 | 110.00 |
| 16 | A4 | ½gr orange | 35.00 | 9.00 |
| 17 | A4 | 1gr rose | 67.50 | 5.50 |
| b. | | Half used as ½gr on cov-er | | 60,000. |
| 18 | A4 | 2gr ultra | 20.00 | 6.25 |
| 19 | A4 | 2½gr orange brn | 1,800. | 67.50 |
| a. | | 2½gr lilac brown | 4,750. | 500.00 |
| 20 | A4 | 5gr bister | 27.50 | 27.50 |
| a. | | Imperf. | | 7,500. |
| 21 | A4 | 1kr yel grn | 34.00 | 32.50 |
| a. | | 1kr blue green | 325.00 | 475.00 |
| 22 | A4 | 2kr orange | 450.00 | 2,250. |
| 23 | A4 | 3kr rose | 20.00 | 6.25 |
| 24 | A4 | 7kr ultra | 30.00 | 60.00 |

| | | | | |
|---|---|---|---|---|
| 25 | A4 | 9kr red brown | 400.00 | 375.00 |
| a. | | 9kr lilac brown | 1,350. | 400.00 |
| 26 | A4 | 18kr bister | 32.50 | 1,900. |

Values for Nos. 17a and 20a are for stamps postmarked at Potsdam (1gr), Damgarten or Anklam (5gr).

Nos. 14-26 with embossing inverted are fraudulent.

A5

**1874** **Brown Surcharge**

| | | | | |
|---|---|---|---|---|
| 27 | A5 | 2½gr on 2½gr brn | 40.00 | 42.50 |
| 28 | A5 | 9kr on 9kr brown | 82.50 | 425.00 |

A6    A7

### "Pfennige"

**1875-77** **Typo.**

| | | | | |
|---|---|---|---|---|
| 29 | A6 | 3pf blue green | 57.50 | 5.25 |
| 30 | A6 | 5pf violet | 97.50 | 3.75 |

### Center Embossed

| | | | | |
|---|---|---|---|---|
| 31 | A7 | 10pf rose | 42.50 | 1.50 |
| 32 | A7 | 20pf ultra | 450.00 | 1.90 |
| 33 | A7 | 25pf red brown | 500.00 | 18.00 |
| 34 | A7 | 50pf gray | 1,650. | 11.00 |
| 35 | A7 | 50pf ol gray ('77) | 1,900. | 14.00 |
| | | Nos. 29-35 (7) | 4,698. | 55.40 |

See Nos. 37-42. For surcharges see Offices in Turkey Nos. 1-6.

A8

**1875-90** **Typo.** **Perf. 14½x13½**

| | | | | |
|---|---|---|---|---|
| 36 | A8 | 2m brnsh pur ('90) | 75.00 | 6.00 |
| a. | | 2m purple ('75) | 1,900. | 340.00 |
| b. | | 2m dull vio pur ('89) | 1,500. | 60.00 |

No. 36a used is valued as a stamp with cds cancel dated between Jan. 1875 and November 17, 1884.

### Types of 1875-77, "Pfennig" without final "e"

**1880-83** **Perf. 13½x14½**

| | | | | |
|---|---|---|---|---|
| 37 | A6 | 3pf yel green | 3.00 | 1.50 |
| a. | | Imperf. | — | |
| 38 | A6 | 5pf violet | 2.25 | 2.00 |

### Center Embossed

| | | | | |
|---|---|---|---|---|
| 39 | A7 | 10pf red | 21.00 | 1.50 |
| a. | | Imperf. | 300.00 | |
| 40 | A7 | 20pf brt ultra | 6.00 | 1.50 |
| 41 | A7 | 25pf dull rose brn | 17.50 | 5.25 |
| a. | | 25pf red brown, thick paper | 175.00 | 6.00 |
| 42 | A7 | 50pf dp grayish ol grn | 15.00 | 1.50 |
| a. | | 50pf olive green | 200.00 | 1.50 |
| | | Nos. 37-42 (6) | 64.75 | 13.25 |

Values for Nos. 37-42 are for stamps on thin paper. Those on thick paper sell for considerably more.

A9    A10

**1889-1900** **Perf. 13½x14½**

| | | | | |
|---|---|---|---|---|
| 45 | A9 | 2pf gray ('00) | .90 | .90 |
| a. | | "REIGHSPOST" | 60.00 | 140.00 |
| 46 | A9 | 3pf brown | 3.00 | 1.40 |
| a. | | 3pf yellow brown | 9.00 | 1.40 |
| b. | | Imperf. | 600.00 | |
| c. | | 3pf reddish brown | 52.50 | 8.25 |
| 47 | A9 | 5pf green | 3.00 | 1.40 |
| 48 | A10 | 10pf carmine | 4.50 | 1.50 |
| a. | | Imperf. | 225.00 | |
| 49 | A10 | 20pf ultra | 7.50 | 1.40 |
| a. | | 20pf Prus blue | 2,250. | 115.00 |
| 50 | A10 | 25pf org ('90) | 30.00 | 2.00 |
| a. | | Imperf. | 260.00 | |
| 51 | A10 | 50pf chocolate | 30.00 | 1.40 |
| a. | | 50pf copper brown | 375.00 | 9.75 |
| b. | | Imperf. | 450.00 | |
| | | Nos. 45-51 (7) | 78.90 | 10.00 |
| | | Set, never hinged | 341.25 | |

For surcharges and overprints see Offices in China Nos. 1-6, 16, Offices in Morocco 1-6, Offices in Turkey 8-12.

Germania — A11

**1900, Jan. 1** **Perf. 14**

| | | | | |
|---|---|---|---|---|
| 52 | A11 | 2pf gray | .85 | .60 |
| a. | | Imperf. | 400.00 | |
| 53 | A11 | 3pf lt brown | .85 | 1.00 |
| a. | | Imperf. | 400.00 | |
| 54 | A11 | 5pf bl green | 1.60 | .90 |
| 55 | A11 | 10pf magenta | 2.40 | .75 |
| a. | | Imperf. | 60.00 | |
| 56 | A11 | 20pf ultra | 11.00 | .90 |
| 57 | A11 | 25pf org & blk, yel | 15.00 | 4.50 |
| 58 | A11 | 30pf org & blk, sal | 22.50 | .90 |
| 59 | A11 | 40pf car & black | 26.00 | 1.50 |
| 60 | A11 | 50pf reddsh pur & blk, sal | 27.50 | 1.20 |
| 61 | A11 | 80pf lake & blk, rose | 37.50 | 2.25 |
| | | Nos. 52-61 (10) | 145.20 | 14.50 |
| | | Set, never hinged | 650.00 | |

Early printings of Nos. 57-61 had "REICHSPOST" in taller and thicker letters than on the ordinary stamps.

For surcharges see Nos. 65B, Offices in China 17-32, Offices in Morocco 7-15, 32A, Offices in Turkey 13-20, 25-27.

### "REICHSPOST" Larger

| | | | | |
|---|---|---|---|---|
| 57a | A11 | 25pf | 1,900. | 6,500. |
| 58a | A11 | 30pf | 1,900. | 4,250. |
| 59a | A11 | 40pf | 1,900. | 4,250. |
| 60a | A11 | 50pf | 1,900. | 4,250. |
| 61a | A11 | 80pf | 1,900. | 4,250. |

General Post Office in Berlin — A12    "Union of North and South Germany" — A13

Unveiling Kaiser Wilhelm I Memorial, Berlin A14    Wilhelm II Speaking at Empire's 25th Anniversary Celebration A15

Type I

Type II

Two types of 3m:

I — The rein is loose, curved. The horse is looking to left. The emperor's face is defined by a curved line. The bottoms of the foot and stirrup are mostly flat.

II — The rein is tight, straight. The horse is looking straight ahead. The emperor's face is defined by an angular line like an inverted "V." The bottoms of the foot and stirrup have two protrusions.

Type I    Type II

Two types of 5m:

I — "5" is thick; "M" has slight serifs.
II — "5" thinner; "M" has distinct serifs.

**Engr.** **Perf. 14½x14**

| | | | | |
|---|---|---|---|---|
| 62 | A12 | 1m carmine rose | 100.00 | 3.25 |
| | | Never hinged | 400.00 | |
| 63 | A13 | 2m gray blue | 100.00 | 7.25 |
| | | Never hinged | 425.00 | |
| 64 | A14 | 3m black violet (I) | 110.00 | 45.00 |
| | | Never hinged | 600.00 | |
| 65 | A15 | 5m slate & car, I | 1,200. | 2,100. |
| | | Never hinged | 5,000. | |
| d. | | Red and white retouched | 350.00 | 360.00 |
| e. | | White only retouched | 575.00 | 575.00 |
| 65A | A15 | 5m slate & car, II | 350.00 | 360.00 |
| | | Never hinged | 1,325. | |

Nos. 62-65 exist perf. 11½.

The vignette and frame of No. 65 usually did not align perfectly during printing. Red paint was used to retouch the vignette and/or white paint was used to retouch the inner frame.

No. 62a is without gum.

For surcharges see Offices in China Nos. 33-36A, Offices in Morocco 16-19A, Offices in Turkey 21-24B, 28-30.

**Half of No. 54 Handstamp Surcharged in Violet**

**3PF**

**1901** **Perf. 14**

| | | | | |
|---|---|---|---|---|
| 65B | A11 | 3pf on half of 5pf | 9,000. | 7,000. |
| | | Never hinged | 25,000. | |

This provisional was produced aboard the German cruiser Vineta. The purser, with the ship commander's approval, surcharged and bisected 300 5pf stamps so the ship's post office could meet the need for a 3pf (printed matter rate). The crew wanted to send home U.S. newspapers reporting celebrations of the Kaiser's birthday.

Forgeries exist and improper usages as well.

A16

**1902** **Typo.**

| | | | | |
|---|---|---|---|---|
| 65C | A16 | 2pf gray | 1.50 | .60 |
| 66 | A16 | 3pf lt brown | .75 | 1.00 |
| a. | | "DFUTSCHES" | 9.75 | 42.50 |
| 67 | A16 | 5pf blue green | 4.00 | 1.00 |
| 68 | A16 | 10pf magenta | 9.00 | 1.00 |
| 69 | A16 | 20pf ultra | 30.00 | 1.00 |
| 70 | A16 | 25pf org & blk, yel | 45.00 | 2.10 |
| 71 | A16 | 30pf org & blk, sal | 60.00 | .60 |
| 72 | A16 | 40pf lake & blk | 90.00 | 1.00 |
| 73 | A16 | 50pf pur & blk, buff | 70.00 | 1.10 |

| | | | | |
|---|---|---|---|---|
| 74 | A16 | 80pf lake & blk, rose | 200.00 | 3.00 |
| | | Nos. 65C-74 (10) | 510.25 | 12.40 |
| | | Set, never hinged | 1,890. | |

Nos. 65C-74 exist imperf. Value, set: unused $1,600; never hinged $3,750.

See Nos. 80-91, 118-119, 121-123, 169, 174, 210. For surcharges see Nos. 133-136, B1, Offices in China 37-42, 47-52, Offices in Morocco 20-28, 33-41, 45-53, Offices in Turkey 31-38, 43-50, 55-59. For overprints, see Bavaria Nos. 177-178, 180, 182-183, 185-187. Poland Nos. 15, 17-19, 21, 24-26.

A17    A18

A19    A20

**Perf. 14¼-14½ (26x17 holes)**
**Engr.**

| | | | | |
|---|---|---|---|---|
| 75 | A17 | 1m car rose | 240.00 | 2.75 |
| a. | | Imperf. | 900.00 | 10,000. |
| 76 | A18 | 2m gray blue | 87.50 | 97.50 |
| 77 | A19 | 3m black violet | 225.00 | 19.00 |
| a. | | Imperf. | 900.00 | 10,000. |
| 78 | A20 | 5m slate & car | 200.00 | 19.00 |
| a. | | Imperf. | 900.00 | 2,500. |

See Nos. 92, 94-95, 102, 111-113. For surcharges see Nos. 115-116, Offices in China 43, 45-46, 53, 55-56, Offices in Morocco 29, 31-32, 42, 44, 54, 56-57, Offices in Turkey 39, 41-42, 51, 53-54. For overprints, see Bavaria Nos. 188, 190-191, Russia Nos. N2-N3, N5,N8-N12.

A21

| | | | | |
|---|---|---|---|---|
| 79 | A21 | 2m gray blue | 120.00 | 5.00 |
| a. | | Imperf. | 900.00 | 10,000. |
| | | Nos. 75-79 (5) | 872.50 | 143.25 |
| | | Set, never hinged | 4,060. | |

See Nos. 93, 114. For surcharges see Nos. 117, Offices in China 44, 54, Offices in Morocco 30, 43, 55, Offices in Turkey 40, 52. For overprint, see Bavaria No. 189.

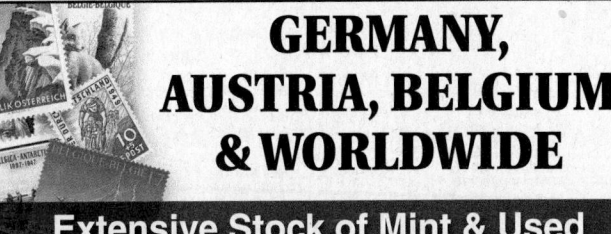

# GERMANY, AUSTRIA, BELGIUM & WORLDWIDE

## Extensive Stock of Mint & Used

*WRITE FOR A FREE 57-PAGE PRICE LIST:*

**ALMAZ CO.** Dept. VG

P.O. Box 100-812 • Vanderveer Station
Brooklyn, NY 11210
Phone/Fax (718) 241-6360
AlmazStamps@aol.com

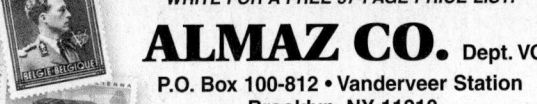

**1905-19　Typo.　Wmk. 125　Perf. 14**

| | | | | |
|---|---|---|---|---|
| 80 | A16 | 2pf gray ('05) | 1.60 | 2.60 |
| 81 | A16 | 3pf brown ('15) | .60 | 1.50 |
| 82 | A16 | 5pf grn (shades) | .60 | 1.50 |
| b. | | Bklt. pane of 5 + label ('11) | 250.00 | 500.00 |
| c. | | Bklt. pane of 4 + 2 labels ('10) | 400.00 | 800.00 |
| d. | | Bklt. pane of 2 + 4 labels ('12) | 250.00 | 500.00 |
| e. | | Bklt. pane, #82 + 5 #83 ('17) | 75.00 | 190.00 |
| f. | | Bklt. pane, 2 #82 + 4 #83 ('20) | 21.00 | 50.00 |
| g. | | Bklt. pane, 4 #82 + 2 #83 ('19) | 21.00 | 50.00 |
| 83 | A16 | 10pf red | .75 | 1.50 |
| b. | | Bklt. pane of 5 + label ('10) | 325.00 | 650.00 |
| c. | | Bklt. pane of 4 + 2 labels ('12) | 300.00 | 625.00 |
| d. | | 10pf carmine red | 2.00 | 1.75 |
| 84 | A16 | 20pf bl vio ('18) | 1.50 | 1.50 |
| a. | | 20pf light blue | 12.00 | 3.75 |
| b. | | 20pf ultramarine | 8.00 | 1.50 |
| c. | | Imperf. | 5,250. | 2,750. |
| d. | | Half used as 10pf on cover | | 750.00 |
| 85 | A16 | 25pf org & blk, yel | .60 | 1.50 |
| 86 | A16 | 30pf org & blk, buff | 2.00 | 1.50 |
| a. | | 30pf org & blk, cr | 26.00 | 90.00 |
| 87 | A16 | 40pf lake & black | 1.50 | 1.50 |
| 88 | A16 | 50pf pur & blk, buff | .75 | 1.50 |
| 89 | A16 | 60pf magenta | 2.00 | 1.50 |
| a. | | 60pf red violet | 22.50 | 13.50 |
| 90 | A16 | 75pf grn & blk ('19) | .25 | 2.25 |
| a. | | 75pf dk bluish grn & greenish blk | 1.10 | 3.00 |
| 91 | A16 | 80pf lake & blk, rose | 1.10 | 1.90 |

**Perf. 14½ (25x17 holes)**

**Engr.**

| | | | | |
|---|---|---|---|---|
| 92 | A17 | 1m car rose | 2.60 | 2.25 |
| 93 | A21 | 2m brt blue | 5.25 | 4.75 |
| a. | | 2m gray blue ('16) | 47.50 | 42.50 |
| 94 | A19 | 3m violet gray | 3.00 | 4.25 |
| b. | | 3m blk violet | 50.00 | 26.00 |
| 95 | A20 | 5m slate & car | 3.00 | 4.75 |
| a. | | Center inverted | 45,000. | 65,000. |
| | | Nos. 80-95 (16) | 27.10 | 36.25 |
| | | Set, Never Hinged | 73.00 | |

Pre-war printings of Nos. 80-91 have brighter colors and white instead of yellow gum. They sell for considerably more than the wartime printings which are valued here. No. 80 exists only from a pre-war printing.

Nos. 92-95 exist only from a wartime printing. The 1m-5m also exist perf 14¼-14¾ (26x17 holes) in both pre-war and wartime printings. Both of these printings are much more expensive than Nos. 92-95. See the *Scott Classic Specialized Catalogue* for detailed listings.

Labels in No. 82c contain an "X." The version with advertising is worth 3 times as much. No. 82f has three 10pf stamps in the top row. The version with 3 on the bottom row is worth 4 times as much.

No. 84d was used at Field Post Office No. 107 in 1915, and at Field Post Office No. 766 during 1917.

Surcharged and overprinted stamps of designs A16-A22 are listed under Allenstein, Belgium, Danzig, France, Latvia, Lithuania, Marienwerder, Memel, Poland, Romania, Russia, Saar, Upper Silesia and German States-Bavaria.

A22

**1916-19**

| | | | | Typo. |
|---|---|---|---|---|
| 96 | A22 | 2pf lt gray ('18) | .30 | 3.75 |
| 97 | A22 | 2½pf lt gray | .25 | 1.90 |
| 98 | A22 | 7½pf red orange | .50 | 2.25 |
| b. | | Bklt. pane, 4 #98 + 2 #100 | 110.00 | 275.00 |
| c. | | Bklt. pane, 2 #98 + 4 #99 | 125.00 | 300.00 |
| d. | | Bklt. pane, 2 #98 + 4 #100 | 110.00 | 275.00 |
| e. | | Bklt. pane, 2 #82 + 4 #98 | 37.50 | 90.00 |
| f. | | 7½pf yellow orange | 3.50 | 2.25 |
| 99 | A22 | 15pf yellow brown | 3.00 | 2.25 |
| 100 | A22 | 15pf dk violet ('17) | .35 | 2.00 |
| b. | | Bklt. pane, 4 #82 + 2 #100 | 110.00 | 275.00 |
| c. | | Bklt. pane, 4 #83 + 4 #100 | 82.50 | 210.00 |
| 101 | A22 | 15pf red brn ('19) | .30 | 2.25 |
| | | Nos. 96-101 (6) | 4.70 | 14.40 |
| | | Set, never hinged | 18.40 | |

See No. 120. For surcharge see No. B2. For overprints, see Bavaria Nos. 176, 179, 184, Poland Nos. 16, 20, 23, Russia Nos. N1, N4, N6-N7.

Nos. 98e and 100c have the 2 stamps first in the bottom row.

**Type of 1902**

**1920　Engr.　Wmk. 192　Perf. 14½**

| | | | | |
|---|---|---|---|---|
| 102 | A19 | 3m black violet | 1,875. | 3,750. |
| | | Never hinged | 4,500. | |

**Republic**
**National Assembly Issue**

A23　　　　　　A24

Rebuilding
Germany — A25

Designs: A23, Live Stump of Tree Symbolizing that Germany will Survive her Difficulties. A24, New Shoots from Oak Stump Symbolical of New Government.

**Perf. 13x13½**

**1919-20　Unwmk.**

| | | | | Typo. |
|---|---|---|---|---|
| 105 | A23 | 10pf carmine rose | .25 | 1.50 |
| 106 | A24 | 15pf brown & lt blue | .25 | 1.50 |
| 107 | A25 | 25pf bl grn & red | .25 | 1.50 |
| 108 | A25 | 30pf red vio & red ('20) | .25 | 2.25 |
| | | Nos. 105-108 (4) | 1.00 | 6.75 |
| | | Set, never hinged | 3.50 | |

**Types of 1902**

**Perf. 15x14½**

**1920　Wmk. 125　Offset**

| | | | | |
|---|---|---|---|---|
| 111 | A17 | 1m red | 3.75 | 2.40 |
| a. | | Double impression | 120.00 | 600.00 |
| 112 | A17 | 1.25m green | 3.75 | 1.90 |
| a. | | Double impression | 900.00 | |
| 113 | A17 | 1.50m yellow brown | .50 | 1.90 |
| c. | | As "a," double impression | 100.00 | 725.00 |
| 114 | A21 | 2.50m lilac rose | .50 | 2.50 |
| a. | | 2.50m magenta | 1.50 | 2.25 |
| b. | | 2.50m brown lilac | .75 | 2.25 |
| c. | | Double impression | 100.00 | 650.00 |
| d. | | As "a," double impression | 140.00 | 550.00 |
| e. | | As "b," double impression | 140.00 | 675.00 |
| | | Nos. 111-114 (4) | 8.50 | 8.70 |
| | | Set, never hinged | 27.00 | |

Nos. 111, 112 and 113 differ from the illustration in many minor respects. The numerals of Nos. 75 and 92 are outlined, with shaded background. Those of No. 111 are plain, with solid background and flags have been added to the top of the building, at right and left.

Types of 1902
Surcharged

**1920　Engr.　Perf. 14½**

| | | | | |
|---|---|---|---|---|
| 115 | A17 | 1.25m on 1m green | .40 | 6.00 |
| 116 | A17 | 1.50m on 1m org brn | .40 | 7.25 |
| 117 | A21 | 2.50m on 2m lilac rose | 8.75 | 180.00 |
| | | Nos. 115-117 (3) | 9.55 | 193.25 |
| | | Set, never hinged | 31.00 | |

**Germania Types of 1902-16**

**1920　Typo.　Perf. 14, 14½**

| | | | | |
|---|---|---|---|---|
| 118 | A16 | 5pf brown | .25 | 2.00 |
| 119 | A16 | 10pf orange | .25 | 1.50 |
| a. | | Tête bêche pair | 1.75 | 7.00 |
| d. | | Bklt. pane, 4 #119 + 2 #123 | 8.25 | 13.50 |
| 120 | A22 | 15pf violet brn | .25 | 1.90 |
| a. | | Imperf. | 67.50 | |
| c. | | Bklt. pane, 4 #84 + 2 #120 | 22.50 | 30.00 |
| 121 | A16 | 20pf green | .25 | 2.25 |
| a. | | Imperf. | | 1,200. |
| 123 | A16 | 30pf dull blue | 2.40 | 2.75 |
| a. | | Tête bêche pair | 3.50 | 13.50 |
| b. | | Bklt. pane, 2 #123 + 4 #124 | 8.25 | 15.00 |
| 124 | A16 | 40pf carmine rose | .25 | 1.90 |
| a. | | Tête bêche pair | 1.90 | 7.00 |
| b. | | Imperf. | 150.00 | 900.00 |
| d. | | Bklt. pane, 2 #124 + 4 #126 | 12.00 | 75.00 |
| 125 | A16 | 50pf red lilac | .60 | 2.25 |
| 126 | A16 | 60pf olive green | .25 | 1.60 |
| c. | | Imperf. | 2.75 | 20.00 |
| 127 | A16 | 75pf red violet | 160.00 | |
| 128 | A16 | 80pf blue violet | .60 | 1.90 |
| a. | | Imperf. | .25 | 2.25 |
| 129 | A16 | 1m violet & grn | 175.00 | |
| a. | | Imperf. | .25 | 2.25 |
| | | | 77.50 | |

| | | | | |
|---|---|---|---|---|
| 130 | A16 | 1¼m ver & mag | .25 | 1.90 |
| 131 | A16 | 2m carmine & bl | .60 | 1.50 |
| 132 | A16 | 4m black & rose | .25 | 2.25 |
| | | Nos. 118-132 (14) | 6.70 | 28.20 |
| | | Set, never hinged | 20.00 | |

**Stamps of 1920 Surcharged**

No. 133　　　　No. 135

Nos. 134, 136

**1921, Aug.**

| | | | | |
|---|---|---|---|---|
| 133 | A16 | 1.60m on 5pf | .25 | 2.25 |
| 134 | A16 | 3m on 1¼m | .25 | 2.60 |
| 135 | A16 | 5m on 75pf (G) | .25 | 2.25 |
| 136 | A16 | 10m on 75pf | .40 | 2.25 |
| | | Nos. 133-136 (4) | 1.15 | 9.35 |
| | | Set, never hinged | 4.50 | |

In 1920 the current stamps of Bavaria were overprinted "Deutsches Reich". These stamps were available for postage throughout Germany, but because they were used almost exclusively in Bavaria, they are listed among the issues of that state.

A26

Iron　　　　　Miners
Workers　　　　A28
A27

Farmers　　　　Post Horn
A29　　　　　　A30

Numeral of　　　Plowing — A32
Value — A31

**Wmk. Lozenges (125)**

**1921　Typo.　Perf. 14**

| | | | | |
|---|---|---|---|---|
| 137 | A26 | 5pf claret | .25 | 2.00 |
| 138 | A26 | 10pf olive green | .25 | 2.00 |
| a. | | Tête bêche pair | 5.50 | 37.50 |
| b. | | Bklt. pane, 5 #138 + 1 #141 | 12.00 | — |
| 139 | A26 | 15pf grnsh blue | .25 | 1.60 |
| 140 | A26 | 25pf dark brown | .25 | 1.60 |
| 141 | A26 | 30pf blue green | .25 | 1.60 |
| a. | | Tête bêche pair | 5.50 | 37.50 |
| b. | | Bklt. pane, 2 #124 + 4 #141 | 12.00 | 75.00 |
| 142 | A26 | 40pf red orange | .25 | 1.60 |
| 143 | A26 | 50pf violet | .30 | 1.60 |
| 144 | A27 | 60pf red violet | .25 | 1.60 |
| 145 | A27 | 80pf carmine rose | .25 | 5.25 |
| 146 | A28 | 100pf yellow grn | .30 | 2.00 |
| 147 | A28 | 120pf ultra | .25 | 1.60 |
| 148 | A29 | 150pf orange | .25 | 2.00 |
| 149 | A29 | 160pf slate grn | .25 | 8.50 |
| 150 | A30 | 2m dp vio & rose | .40 | 3.50 |
| 151 | A30 | 3m red & blk | .40 | 15.00 |
| 152 | A30 | 4m dp grn & yel grn | .25 | 3.50 |

**Engr.**

| | | | | |
|---|---|---|---|---|
| 153 | A31 | 5m orange | .35 | 2.25 |
| 154 | A31 | 10m carmine rose | .50 | 3.00 |
| 155 | A32 | 20m indigo & grn | 3.00 | 3.00 |
| a. | | Green background inverted | 190.00 | 1,050. |
| | | Nos. 137-155 (19) | 8.25 | 62.95 |
| | | Set, never hinged | 24.00 | |

See Nos. 156-209, 211, 222-223, 225, 227. For surcharges and overprints see Nos. 241-245, 247-248, 261-262, 273-276, B6-B7, O24.

**1922　Litho.　Perf. 14½x14**

| | | | | |
|---|---|---|---|---|
| 156 | A31 | 100m brown vio, buff | .25 | 1.40 |
| 157 | A31 | 200m rose, buff | .25 | 1.40 |
| 158 | A31 | 300m green, buff | .25 | 1.40 |
| 159 | A31 | 400m bis brn, buff | .55 | 2.25 |
| 160 | A31 | 500m orange, buff | .25 | 1.40 |
| | | Nos. 156-160 (5) | 1.55 | 7.85 |
| | | Set, never hinged | 3.70 | |

**Postally Used vs. CTO**

Values quoted for canceled stamps of the 1921-1923 issues are for postally used stamps. These bring higher prices than the plentiful canceled-to-order stamps made by applying genuine handstamps to remainders. C.T.O. examples sell for about the same price as unused stamps. Certification of postal usage by competent authorities is necessary.

**Perf. 14, 14½**

**1921-22　Typo.　Wmk. 126**

| | | | | |
|---|---|---|---|---|
| 161 | A26 | 5pf claret | .75 | 200.00 |
| 162 | A26 | 10pf olive grn | 7.00 | 190.00 |
| 163 | A26 | 15pf grnsh blue | .55 | 225.00 |
| 164 | A26 | 25pf dark brown | .25 | 3.75 |
| 165 | A26 | 30pf blue green | .85 | 325.00 |
| 166 | A26 | 40pf red orange | .25 | 3.75 |
| 167 | A26 | 50pf violet ('21) | .25 | 1.50 |
| 168 | A27 | 60pf red violet | .25 | 20.00 |
| 169 | A16 | 75pf carmine | .40 | 2.75 |
| 170 | A26 | 75pf deep ultra | .25 | 3.00 |
| 171 | A27 | 80pf car rose | .40 | 57.50 |
| 172 | A28 | 100pf olive green | .25 | 1.50 |
| a. | | Imperf. | 60.00 | 1,500. |
| 173 | A28 | 120pf ultra | .70 | 110.00 |
| 174 | A16 | 1¼m ver & mag | .25 | 1.50 |
| 175 | A29 | 150pf orange | .25 | 1.50 |
| a. | | Imperf. Never hinged | 37.50 / 110.00 | |
| 176 | A29 | 160pf slate green | .70 | 175.00 |
| 177 | A30 | 2m violet & rose | .25 | 1.50 |
| 178 | A30 | 3m red & yel ('21) | .25 | 1.50 |
| a. | | Imperf. Never hinged | 37.50 / 110.00 | 375.00 |
| 179 | A30 | 4m dp grn & yel grn | .25 | 1.50 |
| 180 | A30 | 5m org & yel | .30 | 2.00 |
| a. | | Imperf. | 135.00 | |
| 181 | A30 | 10m car & pale rose | .30 | 2.25 |
| a. | | Pale rose (background) omitted | 45.00 | 975.00 |
| 182 | A30 | 20m violet & org | .35 | 3.00 |
| 183 | A30 | 30m brown & yel | .25 | 1.50 |
| 184 | A30 | 50m dk grn & vio | .25 | 1.50 |
| | | Nos. 161-184 (24) | 15.55 | 1,337. |
| | | Set, never hinged | 49.00 | |

**1922-23**

SIX MARKS:
Type I — Numerals upright.
Type II — Numerals leaning toward the right and slightly thinner.

EIGHT MARKS:
Type I — Numerals 2½mm wide with thick strokes.
Type II — Numerals 2mm wide with thinner strokes.

| | | | | |
|---|---|---|---|---|
| 185 | A30 | 2m blue violet | .25 | 1.50 |
| a. | | Imperf. | 100.00 | |
| 186 | A30 | 3m red | .25 | 1.50 |
| 187 | A30 | 4m dark green | .25 | 1.50 |
| a. | | Imperf. | 30.00 | |
| b. | | 4m deep blue green | 1.50 | 5.25 |
| 188 | A30 | 5m orange | .25 | 1.50 |
| a. | | Imperf. | 80.00 | |
| 189 | A30 | 6m dark blue (II) | .25 | 1.50 |
| a. | | Type I | .25 | 1.90 |
| b. | | Imperf. | 70.00 | |
| 190 | A30 | 8m olive green (I) | .25 | 1.50 |
| a. | | Type II | .40 | 37.50 |
| 191 | A30 | 20m dk violet ('23) | .25 | 1.50 |
| 192 | A30 | 30m pur brn ('23) | .25 | 7.50 |
| 193 | A30 | 40m lt green | .25 | 2.25 |

**Engr.**

| | | | | |
|---|---|---|---|---|
| 194 | A31 | 5m orange | .25 | 1.75 |
| a. | | Imperf. | 125.00 | 2,750. |
| 195 | A31 | 10m carmine rose | .55 | 2.25 |
| 196 | A32 | 20m indigo & grn | .25 | 3.50 |
| a. | | Imperf. | 160.00 | 2,100. |
| b. | | Green background inverted | 32.50 | 675.00 |
| | | Nos. 185-196 (12) | 3.30 | 27.75 |
| | | Set, never hinged | 10.00 | |

**1922-23      Litho.      Perf. 14½x14**

| 198 | A31 | 50m indigo | .25 | 1.50 |
|---|---|---|---|---|
| 199 | A31 | 100m brn vio, *buff* ('23) | .25 | 1.40 |
| 200 | A31 | 200m rose, *buff* ('23) | .25 | 1.90 |
| 201 | A31 | 300m grn, *buff* ('23) | .25 | 1.35 |
| 202 | A31 | 400m bis brn, *buff* ('23) | .25 | 1.35 |
| 203 | A31 | 500m org, *buff* ('23) | .25 | 1.35 |
| 204 | A31 | 1000m gray ('23) | .25 | 1.35 |
| 205 | A31 | 2000m bl ('23) | .30 | 1.90 |
| 206 | A31 | 3000m brn ('23) | .25 | 1.50 |
| 207 | A31 | 4000m vio ('23) | .25 | 1.50 |
| a. | | Imperf. | 37.50 | 190.00 |
| 208 | A31 | 5000m gray grn ('23) | .30 | 1.50 |
| a. | | Imperf. | 52.50 | 225.00 |
| 209 | A31 | 100,000m ver ('23) | .25 | 1.40 |
| a. | | Imperf. | 52.50 | 225.00 |
| | | Nos. 198-209 (12) | 3.10 | 18.00 |
| | | Set, never hinged | 6.00 | |

**1920-22      Wmk. 127      Typo.**

| 210 | A16 | 1¼m ver & mag | 450.00 | 975.00 |
| | | Never hinged | 1,350. | |
| 211 | A30 | 50m grn & vio ('22) | 2.25 | 825.00 |
| | | Never hinged | 5.25 | |

Wmk. 127 was intended for use only in printing revenue stamps.

Arms of Munich — A33

**Wmk. Network (126)**
**1922, Apr. 22      Typo.      Perf. 13x13½**

| 212 | A33 | 1¼m claret | .25 | 1.90 |
| 213 | A33 | 2m dark violet | .25 | 1.90 |
| 214 | A33 | 3m vermilion | .25 | 1.90 |
| 215 | A33 | 4m deep blue | .25 | 1.90 |
| a. | | Imperf. | 75.00 | 225.00 |

**Wmk. Lozenges (125)**

| 216 | A33 | 10m brown, *buff* | .60 | 2.60 |
| 217 | A33 | 20m lilac rose, *pink* | 3.75 | 13.00 |
| | | Nos. 212-217 (6) | 5.35 | 23.20 |
| | | Set, never hinged | 18.00 | |

Munich Industrial Fair.

**Type of 1921 and**

Miners — A34

A35

**1922-23      Wmk. 126      Perf. 14**

| 221 | A34 | 5m orange | .25 | 12.00 |
| 222 | A29 | 10m dull blue ('22) | .25 | 1.50 |
| 223 | A29 | 12m vermilion ('22) | .25 | 1.50 |
| 224 | A34 | 20m red lilac | .25 | 1.50 |
| 225 | A34 | 25m ochre | .25 | 1.50 |
| 226 | A34 | 30m olive green | .25 | 2.25 |
| 227 | A34 | 40m green | .25 | 1.50 |
| 228 | A34 | 50m lt blue | .40 | 115.00 |
| 229 | A35 | 100m redsh pur | .25 | 1.50 |
| 230 | A35 | 200m carmine rose | .25 | 1.50 |
| 231 | A35 | 300m green | .25 | 1.50 |
| 232 | A35 | 400m brown | .25 | 5.75 |
| 233 | A35 | 500m red orange | .25 | 6.00 |
| 234 | A35 | 1000m slate | .25 | 1.50 |
| | | Nos. 221-234 (14) | 3.65 | 154.50 |
| | | Set, never hinged | | |

The 50m was issued only in vertical coils.
Nos. 222-223 exist imperf.
For surcharges and overprints see Nos. 246, 249-260, 263-271, 277, 310, B5, O22-O23, O25-O28.

Wartburg Castle
A36

Cathedral of Cologne
A37

**1923      Engr.**

| 237 | A36 | 5000m deep blue | .30 | 3.00 |
| a. | | Imperf. | 300.00 | 1,200. |
| 238 | A37 | 10,000m brn ol | .30 | 3.75 |
| | | Set, never hinged | 1.90 | |

**Abbreviations:**
Th = (Tausend) Thousand
Mil = (Million) Million
Mlrd = (Milliarde) Billion

A38

**1923      Typo.**

| 238A | A38 | 5th m grnsh blue | .25 | 16.50 |
| b. | | Imperf. | 90.00 | |
| 239 | A38 | 50th m bister | .25 | 1.50 |
| a. | | Imperf. | 22.50 | 3,750. |
| 240 | A38 | 75th m dark violet | .25 | 10.50 |
| | | Nos. 238A-240 (3) | .75 | 28.50 |
| | | Set, never hinged | 1.15 | |

For surcharges see Nos. 272, 278.

**Stamps and Types of 1922-23**
**Surcharged in Black, Blue, Green or Brown**

No. 241

8 Taufend

No. 243

15 Taufend

No. 246

20 Taufend

No. 253

100 Taufend

No. 269

2 Millionen

**Wmk. Lozenges (125)**
**1923      Perf. 14**

| 241 | A26 | 8th m on 30pf | .25 | 1.50 |
| a. | | "8" inverted | 21.00 | 340.00 |
| | | Never hinged | 57.50 | |

**Wmk. Network (126)**

| 242 | A26 | 5th m on 40pf | .25 | 1.60 |
| b. | | Double surcharge | 150.00 | |
| 242A | A26 | 8th m on 30pf | 22.50 | 6,000. |
| 243 | A29 | 15th m on 40m | .25 | 1.90 |
| a. | | Inverted surcharge | 600.00 | |
| b. | | Pair, one with surcharge omitted | 375.00 | |
| 244 | A29 | 20th m on 12m | .25 | 1.50 |
| a. | | Inverted surcharge | 115.00 | |
| b. | | Pair, one with surcharge omitted | 300.00 | |
| 245 | A29 | 20th m on 25m | .25 | 2.25 |
| 246 | A35 | 20th m on 200m | .25 | 2.25 |
| a. | | Inverted surcharge | 57.50 | 750.00 |
| 247 | A29 | 25th m on 25m | .25 | 13.50 |
| 248 | A29 | 30th m on 10m dp bl | .25 | 1.50 |
| a. | | Inverted surcharge | 67.50 | |
| 249 | A35 | 30th m on 200m pale bl (Bl) | .25 | 1.50 |
| a. | | Without surcharge | 115.00 | |
| 250 | A35 | 75th m on 300m yel grn | .25 | 13.50 |
| a. | | Imperf. | 45.00 | |
| b. | | Double surcharge | 150.00 | |
| 251 | A35 | 75th m on 400m yel grn | .25 | 1.50 |
| 252 | A35 | 75th m on 1000m yel grn | .25 | 1.90 |
| a. | | Without surcharge | 115.00 | |
| b. | | Double surcharge | 67.50 | |

| 253 | A35 | 100th m on 100m | .25 | 2.25 |
|---|---|---|---|---|
| a. | | Double surcharge | 37.50 | 450.00 |
| b. | | Inverted surcharge | 13.50 | 600.00 |
| 254 | A35 | 100th m on 400m bluish grn (G) | .25 | 1.50 |
| a. | | Imperf. | 42.50 | 750.00 |
| b. | | Without surcharge | 115.00 | |
| | | Never hinged | 225.00 | |
| 255 | A35 | 125th m on 1000m sal | .25 | 1.90 |
| 256 | A35 | 250th m on 200m | .25 | 5.25 |
| a. | | Inverted surcharge | 34.00 | |
| b. | | Double surcharge | 52.50 | |
| 257 | A35 | 250th m on 300m dp grn | .25 | 16.50 |
| a. | | Inverted surcharge | 34.00 | |
| 258 | A35 | 250th m on 400m | .25 | 19.00 |
| a. | | Inverted surcharge | 26.00 | |
| 259 | A35 | 250th m on 500m pink | .25 | 1.50 |
| a. | | Imperf. | 52.50 | 900.00 |
| 260 | A35 | 250th m on 500m red org | .25 | 19.00 |
| a. | | Double surcharge | 30.00 | 975.00 |
| b. | | Inverted surcharge | 37.50 | |
| 261 | A26 | 800th m on 5pf lt grn (G) | .25 | 4.25 |
| a. | | Imperf. | 34.00 | 150.00 |
| | | Never hinged | 90.00 | |
| 262 | A26 | 800th m on 10pf lt grn (G) | .25 | 5.00 |
| a. | | Imperf. | 30.00 | |
| 263 | A35 | 800th m on 200m | .25 | 75.00 |
| a. | | Double surcharge | 75.00 | 975.00 |
| b. | | Inverted surcharge | 37.50 | |
| 264 | A35 | 800th m on 300m lt grn (G) | .25 | 5.00 |
| a. | | Black surcharge | 30.00 | |
| 265 | A35 | 800th m on 400m dk brn | .25 | 12.00 |
| a. | | Inverted surcharge | 42.50 | — |
| b. | | Double surcharge | 75.00 | |
| 266 | A35 | 800th m on 400m lt grn (G) | .25 | 3.75 |
| 267 | A35 | 800th m on 500m lt grn (G) | .25 | 1,500. |
| a. | | 800th m on 500m red org (Bk) | 30.00 | |
| 268 | A35 | 800th m on 1000m lt grn (G) | .25 | 1.50 |
| 269 | A35 | 2mil m on 200m rose red | .25 | 2.10 |
| b. | | 2mil m on 200m car rose (#230) | 1,500. | |
| 270 | A35 | 2mil m on 300m dp grn | .25 | 2.10 |
| a. | | Inverted surcharge | 42.50 | |
| b. | | Double surcharge | 75.00 | — |
| 271 | A35 | 2mil m on 500m dl rose | .25 | 6.00 |
| 272 | A38 | 2mil m on 5th m dl rose | .25 | 1.50 |
| b. | | Imperf. | 37.50 | 150.00 |

Nos. 264a, 267a were not put in use.

**Serrate Roulette 13½**

| 273 | A26 | 400th m on 15pf bis (Br) | .25 | 4.50 |
| a. | | Imperf. | 52.50 | 260.00 |

| 274 | A26 | 400th m on 25pf bis (Br) | .25 | 4.50 |
|---|---|---|---|---|
| a. | | Imperf. | 90.00 | 260.00 |
| 275 | A26 | 400th m on 30pf bis (Br) | .25 | 4.50 |
| a. | | Imperf. | 45.00 | |
| b. | | Double surcharge | 90.00 | |
| 276 | A26 | 400th m on 40pf bis (Br) | .25 | 4.50 |
| a. | | Imperf. | 45.00 | |
| b. | | Double surcharge | 90.00 | |
| 277 | A35 | 2mil m on 200m rose red | .25 | 150.00 |
| 278 | A38 | 2mil m on 5th m dull rose | .25 | 9.00 |
| | | Nos. 241-278 (39) | 32.00 | 7,907. |
| | | Set, never hinged | 51.00 | |

Nos. 272-276 exist without surcharge. Value each, $150 unused, $375 never hinged.

A39

A39a

The stamps of types A39 and A39a usually have the value darker than the rest of the design.

**1923      Wmk. 126      Perf. 14**

| 280 | A39 | 500th m brown | .25 | 2.60 |
| 281 | A39 | 1mil m grnsh bl | .25 | 1.60 |
| a. | | Imperf. | 52.50 | 1,500. |
| | | Never hinged | 115.00 | |
| 282 | A39 | 2mil m dull vio | .25 | 19.50 |
| 284 | A39 | 4mil m yel grn | .25 | 1.50 |
| a. | | Value double | 45.00 | |
| b. | | Imperf. | 42.50 | |
| 285 | A39 | 5mil m rose | .25 | 1.50 |
| 286 | A39 | 10mil m red | .25 | 1.50 |
| a. | | Value double | 45.00 | 3,750. |
| 287 | A39 | 20mil m ultra | .25 | 1.90 |
| 288 | A39 | 30mil m red brn | .25 | 9.00 |
| 289 | A39 | 50mil m dull ol grn | .25 | 1.90 |
| a. | | Imperf. | 52.50 | 340.00 |
| b. | | Value inverted | 45.00 | |
| 290 | A39 | 100mil m gray | .25 | 1.50 |
| a. | | Imperf. | 67.50 | 375.00 |
| b. | | Value double | 45.00 | |
| 291 | A39 | 200mil m bis brn | .25 | 1.50 |
| a. | | Imperf. | 42.50 | |
| | | Never hinged | 97.50 | |
| 293 | A39 | 500mil m ol grn | .25 | 1.50 |
| 294 | A39a | 1mlrd m choc | .30 | 1.90 |
| 295 | A39a | 2mlrd m pale brn & grn | .25 | 1.90 |
| 296 | A39a | 5mlrd m yellow & brn | .25 | 1.90 |
| 297 | A39a | 10mlrd m ap grn & grn | .25 | 1.50 |
| a. | | Imperf. | 45.00 | 260.00 |
| 298 | A39a | 20mlrd m bluish grn & brn | .25 | 1.90 |
| 299 | A39a | 50mlrd m bl & dp bl | .25 | 34.00 |
| | | Nos. 280-299 (18) | 4.55 | 88.20 |

**FREE PRICE LISTS**
FOR GERMANY AND AUSTRIA, AND RELATED STATES, OCCUPATIONS, ETC.

Extensive price lists include something for everyone from beginners to specialists. Over 100,000 sets & singles listed on our website.

**R. SCHNEIDER**
P.O. BOX 978
IOWA PARK, TX 76367
Phone 618-975-2099, FAX 940-213-3596
Email: RSchneiderStamps@gmail.com
http://www.RSchneiderStamps.com

Set, never hinged 11.50

The variety "value omitted" exists on Nos. 280-281, 284-287, 290-291, 293-294, 296 and 298-299. Values $37.50 to $100 hinged, $75 to $190 never hinged.

See Nos. 301-309. For surcharges and overprints see Nos. 311-321, O40-O46.

### Serrate Roulette 13½

| | | | | |
|---|---|---|---|---|
| 301 | A39 | 10mil m red | .55 | 45.00 |
| 302 | A39 | 20mil m ultra | .55 | 300.00 |
| 303 | A39 | 50mil m dull grn | .55 | 6.00 |
| 304 | A39 | 200mil m bis brn | .55 | 11.50 |
| 305 | A39a | 1mlrd m choc | .55 | 7.50 |
| 306 | A39a | 2mlrd m pale brn & grn | .55 | 3.50 |
| 307 | A39a | 5mlrd m yel & brn | .75 | 2.25 |
| 308 | A39a | 20mlrd m bluish grn & brn | .75 | 11.50 |
| 309 | A39a | 50mlrd m bl & dp bl | 1.90 | 675.00 |
| | | Nos. 301-309 (9) | 6.70 | 1,062. |
| | | Set, never hinged | 18.50 | |

### Stamps and Types of 1923 Surcharged with New Values

**1923**      **Perf. 14**

**Design Type A35**

| | | | | |
|---|---|---|---|---|
| 310 | | 1mlrd m on 100m vio | .25 | 29.00 |
| a. | | Inverted surcharge | 115.00 | |

**Design Type A39**

| | | | | |
|---|---|---|---|---|
| 311 | | 5mlrd m on 2mil m | .25 | 130.00 |
| a. | | Inverted surcharge | 19.00 | |
| b. | | Double surcharge | 45.00 | |
| | | Never hinged | 110.00 | |
| 312 | | 5mlrd m on 4mil m | .25 | 22.50 |
| a. | | Inverted surcharge | 37.50 | 1,200. |
| b. | | Double surcharge | 37.50 | |
| 313 | | 5mlrd m on 10mil m | .25 | 2.60 |
| a. | | Inverted surcharge | 19.00 | 1,100. |
| b. | | Double surcharge | 37.50 | |
| 314 | | 10mlrd m on 20mil m | .25 | 4.50 |
| a. | | Double surcharge | 45.00 | |
| b. | | Inverted surcharge | 26.00 | |
| 315 | | 10mlrd m on 50mil m | .25 | 4.50 |
| a. | | Inverted surcharge | 19.00 | 900.00 |
| b. | | Double surcharge | 45.00 | |
| 316 | | 10mlrd m on 100mil m | .25 | 7.50 |
| a. | | Inverted surcharge | 26.00 | 1,500. |
| b. | | Double surcharge | 45.00 | |
| | | Nos. 310-316 (7) | 1.75 | 200.60 |
| | | Set, never hinged | 5.25 | |

No. 310b was issued in Bavaria only and is known as the Hitler provisional. Excellent forgeries exist.

### Serrate Roulette 13½
**Design Type A39**

| | | | | |
|---|---|---|---|---|
| 319 | | 5mlrd m on 10mil m | 1.90 | 180.00 |
| a. | | Inverted surcharge | 26.00 | 1,100. |
| b. | | Double surcharge | 45.00 | |
| 320 | | 5mlrd m on 20mil m | 3.75 | 105.00 |
| a. | | Inverted surcharge | 26.00 | 1,100. |
| 321 | | 10mlrd m on 50mil m | 1.90 | 37.50 |
| a. | | Inverted surcharge | 26.00 | 1,100. |
| | | Nos. 319-321 (3) | 7.55 | 322.50 |
| | | Set, never hinged | 22.50 | |

A40

**1923**      **Perf. 14**

| | | | | |
|---|---|---|---|---|
| 323 | A40 | 3pf brown | .40 | .25 |
| 324 | A40 | 5pf dark green | .40 | .25 |
| 325 | A40 | 10pf carmine | .40 | .25 |
| 326 | A40 | 20pf deep ultra | 1.15 | .40 |
| 327 | A40 | 50pf orange | 2.60 | 1.00 |
| 328 | A40 | 100pf brn vio | 8.25 | 1.10 |
| | | Nos. 323-328 (6) | 13.20 | 3.25 |
| | | Set, never hinged | 85.00 | |

For overprints see Nos. O47-O52.

### Imperf

| | | | | |
|---|---|---|---|---|
| 323a | A40 | 3pf | 105.00 | 260.00 |
| 324a | A40 | 5pf | 97.50 | — |
| 325a | A40 | 10pf | 135.00 | 260.00 |
| 326a | A40 | 20pf | 135.00 | 260.00 |
| 327a | A40 | 50pf | 975.00 | — |
| 328a | A40 | 100pf | 170.00 | 260.00 |
| | | Nos. 323a-328a (6) | 1,618. | 1,040. |
| | | Set, never hinged | 3,650. | |

### Value Omitted

| | | | | |
|---|---|---|---|---|
| 323b | A40 | 3pf | 180.00 | 300.00 |
| 324b | A40 | 5pf | 150.00 | 300.00 |
| 325b | A40 | 10pf | 150.00 | 300.00 |
| 326b | A40 | 20pf | 165.00 | 300.00 |
| 327b | A40 | 50pf | 150.00 | |
| 328b | A40 | 100pf | 150.00 | |
| | | Nos. 323b-328b (6) | 945.00 | |
| | | Set, never hinged | 2,475. | |

German Eagle — A41

**1924**      **Wmk. 126**

| | | | | |
|---|---|---|---|---|
| 330 | A41 | 3pf lt brown | .30 | .40 |
| 331 | A41 | 5pf lt green | .30 | .40 |
| 332 | A41 | 10pf vermilion | .40 | .40 |
| 333 | A41 | 20pf dull blue | 1.90 | .40 |
| 334 | A41 | 30pf rose lilac | 1.90 | .45 |
| 335 | A41 | 40pf olive green | 13.00 | .70 |
| 336 | A41 | 50pf orange | 15.00 | 1.15 |
| | | Nos. 330-336 (7) | 32.80 | 3.90 |
| | | Set, never hinged | 277.50 | |

The values above 5pf have "Pf" in the upper right corner.

For overprints see Nos. O53-O61.

### Imperf.

| | | | | |
|---|---|---|---|---|
| 330a | A41 | 3pf | 115.00 | 375.00 |
| 331a | A41 | 5pf | 150.00 | 375.00 |
| 332a | A41 | 10pf | 190.00 | |
| 333a | A41 | 20pf | 130.00 | |
| 334a | A41 | 30pf | 130.00 | |
| 335a | A41 | 40pf | 170.00 | |
| | | Nos. 330a-335a (6) | 885.00 | |
| | | Set, never hinged | 2,500. | |

Rheinstein Castle — A43     View of Cologne — A44

Marienburg Castle — A45

**1924**    **Engr.**    **Wmk. 126**

| | | | | |
|---|---|---|---|---|
| 337 | A43 | 1m green | 10.00 | 3.50 |
| a. | | Watermark sideways ('27) | 26.00 | 12.00 |
| 338 | A44 | 2m blue | 13.50 | 3.50 |
| 339 | A45 | 3m claret | 18.50 | 6.00 |
| | | Nos. 337-339 (3) | 42.00 | 13.00 |
| | | Set, never hinged | 155.00 | |

See No. 387.

Dr. Heinrich von Stephan

A46      A47

**1924-28**      **Typo.**

| | | | | |
|---|---|---|---|---|
| 340 | A46 | 10pf dark green | .75 | .30 |
| a. | | Imperf | | |
| 341 | A46 | 20pf dark blue | 1.50 | .75 |
| 342 | A47 | 60pf red brown | 3.75 | .75 |
| a. | | Chalky paper ('28) | 22.50 | 13.50 |
| 343 | A47 | 80pf slate | 9.75 | 1.50 |
| | | Nos. 340-343 (4) | 15.75 | 3.30 |
| | | Set, never hinged | 79.00 | |

Universal Postal Union, 50th anniversary.

Traffic Wheel — A48

**1925, May 30**      **Perf. 13½x13**

| | | | | |
|---|---|---|---|---|
| 345 | A48 | 5pf deep green | 3.75 | 5.25 |
| 346 | A48 | 10pf vermilion | 3.75 | 9.75 |
| | | Set, never hinged | 42.50 | |

German Traffic Exhibition, Munich, May 30-Oct. 11, 1925.

German Eagle Watching Rhine Valley — A49

**1925**      **Perf. 14**

| | | | | |
|---|---|---|---|---|
| 347 | A49 | 5pf green | 1.00 | .40 |
| 348 | A49 | 10pf vermilion | 1.00 | .40 |
| 349 | A49 | 20pf deep blue | 5.75 | 1.05 |
| | | Nos. 347-349 (3) | 7.75 | 1.85 |
| | | Set, never hinged | 45.00 | |

1000 years' union of the Rhineland with Germany.

Speyer Cathedral — A50

**1925, Sept. 11**      **Engr.**

| | | | | |
|---|---|---|---|---|
| 350 | A50 | 5m dull green | 35.00 | 15.00 |
| | | Never hinged | 130.00 | |

Johann Wolfgang von Goethe — A51

Designs: 3pf, 25pf, Goethe. 5pf, Friedrich von Schiller. 8pf, 20pf, Ludwig van Beethoven. 10pf, Frederick the Great. 15pf, Immanuel Kant. 30pf, Gotthold Ephraim Lessing. 40pf, Gottfried Wilhelm Leibnitz. 50pf, Johann Sebastian Bach. 80pf, Albrecht Durer.

**1926-27**    **Typo.**    **Perf. 14**

| | | | | |
|---|---|---|---|---|
| 351 | A51 | 3pf olive brown | 1.15 | .40 |
| 352 | A51 | 3pf bister ('27) | 1.15 | .40 |
| 353 | A51 | 5pf dark green | 1.15 | .40 |
| 354 | A51 | 8pf blue grn ('27) | 1.50 | .40 |
| 355 | A51 | 10pf carmine | 1.50 | .40 |
| 356 | A51 | 15pf vermilion | 2.25 | .40 |
| a. | | Booklet pane of 8 + 2 labels | 1,100. | 3,250. |
| 357 | A51 | 20pf myrtle grn | 10.50 | 1.15 |
| 358 | A51 | 25pf lt blue | 3.50 | .90 |
| 359 | A51 | 30pf olive grn | 6.50 | .60 |
| 360 | A51 | 40pf reddsh pur | 11.50 | .60 |
| 361 | A51 | 50pf brown | 14.50 | 7.50 |
| 362 | A51 | 80pf chocolate | 30.00 | 5.00 |
| | | Nos. 351-362 (12) | 85.20 | 18.15 |
| | | Set, never hinged | 875.00 | |

Nos. 351-354, 356 and 357 exist imperf. See *Scott Classic Specialized Catalogue of Stamps & Covers* for detailed listing.

Nos. 354, 356 and 358 Overprinted

**1927, Oct. 10**

| | | | | |
|---|---|---|---|---|
| 363 | A51 | 8pf blue green | 16.50 | 65.00 |
| 364 | A51 | 15pf vermilion | 16.50 | 65.00 |
| 365 | A51 | 25pf blue | 16.50 | 65.00 |
| | | Nos. 363-365 (3) | 49.50 | 195.00 |
| | | Set, never hinged | 180.00 | |

"I.A.A." stands for "Internationales Arbeitsamt," (Intl. Labor Bureau), an agency of the League of Nations. Issued in connection with a meeting of the I.A.A. in Berlin, Oct. 10-15, 1927, they were on sale to the public.

Pres. Friedrich Ebert A60      Pres. Paul von Hindenburg A61

**1928-32**    **Typo.**    **Perf. 14**

| | | | | |
|---|---|---|---|---|
| 366 | A60 | 3pf bister | .25 | .60 |
| 367 | A61 | 4pf lt blue ('31) | 1.10 | 1.20 |
| a. | | Tête bêche pair | 22.50 | 37.50 |
| b. | | Bklt. pane of 9 + label | 97.50 | 180.00 |
| 368 | A61 | 5pf lt green | .40 | .60 |
| a. | | Tête bêche pair | 18.00 | 30.00 |
| b. | | Imperf. | 105.00 | |
| c. | | Bklt. pane of 6 + 4 labels | 82.50 | 120.00 |
| d. | | Bklt. pane, 4 #368 + 6 #369 | 97.50 | 180.00 |
| 369 | A60 | 6pf lt olive grn ('32) | .75 | .70 |
| a. | | Bklt. pane, 2 #369 + 8 #373 | 97.50 | 180.00 |
| | | Never hinged | 165.00 | |
| 370 | A60 | 8pf dark green | .25 | .60 |
| a. | | Tête bêche pair | 18.00 | 30.00 |
| 371 | A60 | 10pf vermilion | 1.90 | 2.25 |
| 372 | A60 | 10pf red violet ('30) | 1.75 | .75 |
| 373 | A61 | 12pf orange ('32) | 1.50 | .70 |
| a. | | Tête bêche pair | 22.50 | 37.50 |
| 374 | A61 | 15pf car rose | .60 | .60 |
| a. | | Tête bêche pair | 18.00 | 30.00 |
| | | Never hinged | 30.00 | |
| b. | | Bklt. pane 6 + 4 labels | 82.50 | 120.00 |
| 375 | A60 | 20pf Prus green | 6.25 | 3.75 |
| a. | | Imperf. | 260.00 | |
| 376 | A60 | 20pf gray ('30) | 6.00 | .75 |
| 377 | A61 | 25pf blue | 7.50 | .90 |
| 378 | A60 | 30pf olive green | 5.25 | .90 |
| 379 | A61 | 40pf reddsh pur | 15.00 | .90 |
| 380 | A61 | 45pf orange | 9.00 | 3.00 |
| 381 | A61 | 50pf brown | 9.75 | 2.60 |
| 382 | A60 | 60pf brn red | 11.50 | 3.00 |

| | | | | |
|---|---|---|---|---|
| 383 | A61 | 80pf chocolate | 22.50 | 6.75 |
| 384 | A61 | 80pf yel bis ('30) | 7.50 | 2.25 |
| | | Nos. 366-384 (19) | 108.75 | 32.80 |
| | | Set, never hinged | 1,025. | |

Stamps of 1928 Overprinted

**1930, June 30**

| | | | | |
|---|---|---|---|---|
| 385 | A60 | 8pf dark green | 2.25 | .90 |
| 386 | A61 | 15pf carmine rose | 2.25 | .90 |
| | | Set, never hinged | 16.00 | |

Issued in commemoration of the final evacuation of the Rhineland by the Allied forces.

View of Cologne — A63

**1930**    **Engr.**    **Wmk. 126**
Inscribed: "Reichsmark"

| | | | | |
|---|---|---|---|---|
| 387 | A63 | 2m dark blue | 26.00 | 14.50 |
| | | Never hinged | 105.00 | |

A type of design A43 in green exists with "Reichsmark" instead of "Mark." It was not issued, though some examples are known in private hands. Value $15,000.

Pres. von Hindenburg — A64

**1932, Oct. 1**    **Typo.**    **Wmk. 126**

| | | | | |
|---|---|---|---|---|
| 391 | A64 | 4pf blue | .55 | .60 |
| 392 | A64 | 5pf brt green | .85 | .60 |
| 393 | A64 | 12pf dp orange | 5.00 | .60 |
| 394 | A64 | 15pf dk red | 3.00 | 9.75 |
| 395 | A64 | 25pf ultra | 2.40 | .75 |
| 396 | A64 | 40pf violet | 20.50 | 1.50 |
| 397 | A64 | 50pf dk brown | 3.75 | 10.50 |
| | | Nos. 391-397 (7) | 36.05 | 24.30 |
| | | Set, never hinged | 130.00 | |

85th birthday of von Hindenburg. See Nos. 401-431, 436-441. For surcharges and overprints see France N27-N58, Luxembourg N1-N16 and Poland N17-N29.

Frederick the Great — A65

**1933, Apr. 12**      **Photo.**

| | | | | |
|---|---|---|---|---|
| 398 | A65 | 6pf dk green | .80 | .90 |
| a. | | Tête bêche pair | 18.00 | 30.00 |
| 399 | A65 | 12pf carmine | 1.20 | .90 |
| a. | | Tête bêche pair | 18.00 | 30.00 |
| b. | | Bklt. pane of 5 + label | 37.50 | 65.00 |
| 400 | A65 | 25pf ultra | 42.50 | 21.00 |
| | | Nos. 398-400 (3) | 44.50 | 22.80 |
| | | Set, never hinged | 246.25 | |

Celebration of Potsdam Day.

### Hindenburg Type of 1932

**1933**      **Typo.**

| | | | | |
|---|---|---|---|---|
| 401 | A64 | 3pf olive bister | 16.50 | .75 |
| 402 | A64 | 4pf dull blue | 3.75 | .75 |
| 403 | A64 | 6pf dk green | 1.90 | .75 |
| 404 | A64 | 8pf dp orange | 6.00 | .75 |
| a. | | Bklt. pane, 3 #404 + 5 #406 | 110.00 | 150.00 |
| b. | | Open "D" | 19.00 | 3.75 |
| 405 | A64 | 10pf chocolate | 3.75 | .75 |
| 406 | A64 | 12pf dp carmine | 2.25 | .75 |
| a. | | Bklt. pane, 4 #392 + 4 #406 | 82.50 | 150.00 |
| 407 | A64 | 15pf dp claret | 5.25 | 26.00 |
| 408 | A64 | 20pf brt blue | 6.75 | 1.50 |
| 409 | A64 | 30pf olive grn | 6.75 | 1.35 |
| 410 | A64 | 40pf red violet | 30.00 | 2.60 |
| 411 | A64 | 50pf dk grn & blk | 15.00 | 2.25 |
| 412 | A64 | 60pf dp clar & blk | 30.00 | 1.00 |
| 413 | A64 | 80pf dk blue & blk | 9.00 | 1.15 |
| 414 | A64 | 100pf orange & blk | 26.00 | 13.00 |
| | | Nos. 401-414 (14) | 162.90 | 53.35 |
| | | Set, never hinged | 950.00 | |

### Hindenburg Type of 1932

**1933-36**    **Wmk. 237**    **Perf. 14**

| | | | | |
|---|---|---|---|---|
| 415 | A64 | 1pf black | .25 | .40 |
| a. | | Bklt. pane, 4 #415, 3 #417, label | 15.00 | 16.50 |
| b. | | Bklt. pane, 3 #415, 3 #416 + 2 #418 | 42.50 | 75.00 |
| c. | | Bklt. pane, 2 #415, 5 #420, label | 22.50 | 42.50 |
| d. | | Bklt. pane, 4 #415 + 4 #422 | 21.00 | 37.50 |

| | | | |
|---|---|---|---|
| 416 | A64 | 3pf org brn ('34) | .25 .40 |
| a. | | Bkt. pane, 4 #416 + 4 #418 | 22.50 42.50 |
| b. | | Bkt. pane, 4 #416 + 4 #419 | 21.00 37.50 |
| c. | | Bkt. pane, 6 #416, 1 #422, label | 11.50 16.50 |
| 417 | A64 | 4pf dull blue ('34) | .25 .40 |
| a. | | Bkt. pane, 3 #417, 4 #422, label | 21.00 37.50 |
| 418 | A64 | 5pf brt green ('34) | .25 .40 |
| a. | | Bkt. pane, 2 #418, 5 #419, label | 15.00 16.50 |
| b. | | Bkt. pane, 2 #418, 3 #419 + 3 #420 | 21.00 37.50 |
| c. | | Bkt. pane, 4 #418 + 4 #420 | 42.50 75.00 |
| 419 | A64 | 6pf dk green ('34) | .25 .40 |
| b. | | Bkt. pane of 7 + label | 9.00 16.50 |
| c. | | Bkt. pane, 1 #419, 6 #422, label | 67.50 105.00 |
| 420 | A64 | 8pf dp orange ('34) | .25 .40 |
| a. | | Bkt. pane, 3 #420, 4 #422, label | 15.00 16.50 |
| b. | | Open "D" | 4.25 4.50 |
| 421 | A64 | 10pf choc ('34) | .25 .40 |
| 422 | A64 | 12pf dp car ('34) | .25 .40 |
| a. | | Bkt. pane of 7 + label | 22.50 42.50 |
| 423 | A64 | 15pf maroon ('34) | .30 .40 |
| 424 | A64 | 20pf brt blue ('34) | .45 .40 |
| 425 | A64 | 25pf ultra ('34) | .45 .40 |
| 426 | A64 | 30pf olive grn ('34) | .75 .40 |
| 427 | A64 | 40pf red violet ('34) | 1.50 .40 |
| 428 | A64 | 50pf dk grn & blk ('34) | 3.00 .40 |
| 429 | A64 | 60pf claret & blk ('34) | .75 .40 |
| 430 | A64 | 80pf dk bl & blk ('36) | 2.25 1.20 |
| 431 | A64 | 100pf org & blk ('34) | 3.00 1.15 |
| | | Nos. 415-431 (17) | 14.45 8.35 |
| | | Set, never hinged | 65.00 |

Karl Peters — A66

Designs: 3pf, Franz Adolf E. Lüderitz. 6pf, Dr. Gustav Nachtigal. 12pf, Karl Peters. 25pf, Hermann von Wissmann.

**1934, June 30**  *Perf. 13x13½*

| | | | |
|---|---|---|---|
| 432 | A66 | 3pf brown & choc | 2.60 6.00 |
| 433 | A66 | 6pf dk grn & choc | .95 1.50 |
| 434 | A66 | 12pf dk car & choc | 3.00 1.50 |
| 435 | A66 | 25pf brt blue & choc | 9.50 19.50 |
| | | Nos. 432-435 (4) | 16.05 28.50 |
| | | Set, never hinged | 145.00 |

Issued in remembrance of the lost colonies of Germany.

### Hindenburg Memorial Issue
### Type of 1932
### With Black Border

**1934, Sept. 4**  *Perf. 14*

| | | | |
|---|---|---|---|
| 436 | A64 | 3pf olive bister | .45 .45 |
| 437 | A64 | 5pf brt green | .45 .55 |
| 438 | A64 | 6pf dk green | .90 .45 |
| 439 | A64 | 8pf vermilion | 2.25 .45 |
| 440 | A64 | 12pf deep carmine | 2.75 .45 |
| 441 | A64 | 25pf ultra | 6.75 8.25 |
| | | Nos. 436-441 (6) | 13.55 10.60 |
| | | Set, never hinged | 115.00 |

Swastika, Sun and Nuremberg Castle — A70

**1934, Sept. 1**  *Photo.*

| | | | |
|---|---|---|---|
| 442 | A70 | 6pf dark green | 3.00 .60 |
| 443 | A70 | 12pf dark carmine | 4.00 .60 |
| | | Set, never hinged | 65.00 |

Nazi Congress at Nuremberg.
Imperfs exist. Value never hinged, each $750.

Allegory "Saar Belongs to Germany" A71

German Eagle A72

**1934, Aug. 26**  **Typo.**  **Wmk. 237**

| | | | |
|---|---|---|---|
| 444 | A71 | 6pf dark green | 3.00 .60 |
| 445 | A72 | 12pf dark carmine | 3.75 .60 |
| | | Set, never hinged | 67.50 |

Issued to mark the Saar Plebiscite.

Friedrich von Schiller — A73

**1934, Nov. 5**

| | | | |
|---|---|---|---|
| 446 | A73 | 6pf green | 2.00 .60 |
| 447 | A73 | 12pf carmine | 4.75 .60 |
| | | Set, never hinged | 75.00 |

175th anniv. of the birth of von Schiller.

Germania Welcoming Home the Saar — A74

**1935, Jan. 16**  *Photo.*

| | | | |
|---|---|---|---|
| 448 | A74 | 3pf brown | .35 1.15 |
| 449 | A74 | 6pf dark green | .35 .75 |
| 450 | A74 | 12pf lake | 2.00 .75 |
| 451 | A74 | 25pf dark blue | 7.50 8.25 |
| | | Nos. 448-451 (4) | 10.20 10.90 |
| | | Set, never hinged | 90.00 |

Return of the Saar to Germany.

German Soldier — A75

**1935, Mar. 15**

| | | | |
|---|---|---|---|
| 452 | A75 | 6pf dark green | 1.50 1.50 |
| 453 | A75 | 12pf copper red | 1.60 1.50 |
| | | Set, never hinged | 16.00 |

Issued to commemorate War Heroes' Day.

Wreath and Swastika — A76

**1935, Apr. 26**  **Unwmk.**

| | | | |
|---|---|---|---|
| 454 | A76 | 6pf dark green | 1.05 1.35 |
| 455 | A76 | 12pf crimson | 1.60 1.35 |
| | | Set, never hinged | 19.00 |

Young Workers' Professional Competitions.

Heinrich Schütz — A77

### Wmk. Swastikas (237)

**1935, June 21**  **Engr.**  *Perf. 14*

| | | | |
|---|---|---|---|
| 456 | A77 | 6pf shown | 1.10 .75 |
| 457 | A77 | 12pf Bach | 1.10 .75 |
| 458 | A77 | 25pf Handel | 1.60 .90 |
| | | Nos. 456-458 (3) | 3.80 2.40 |
| | | Set, never hinged | 26.00 |

Schutz-Bach-Handel celebration.

"The Eagle" — A80

Designs: 12pf, Modern express train. 25pf, "The Hamburg Flyer." 40pf, Streamlined locomotive.

**1935, July 10**  *Perf. 14*

| | | | |
|---|---|---|---|
| 459 | A80 | 6pf dark green | .95 .75 |
| 460 | A80 | 12pf scarlet | .95 .75 |
| 461 | A80 | 25pf dk blue | 5.25 1.75 |
| 462 | A80 | 40pf red violet | 8.75 1.75 |
| | | Nos. 459-462 (4) | 15.90 5.00 |
| | | Set, never hinged | 97.50 |

Centenary of railroad in Germany.
Exist imperf. Values: Nos. 459-462, $475 each.

Bugler of Hitler Youth Movement — A84

**1935, July 25**  *Photo.*

| | | | |
|---|---|---|---|
| 463 | A84 | 6pf deep green | 1.15 2.25 |
| 464 | A84 | 15pf brown lake | 2.25 3.00 |
| | | Set, never hinged | 22.50 |

Hitler Youth Meeting.

Eagle and Swastika over Nuremberg — A85

**1935, Aug. 30**  **Engr.**

| | | | |
|---|---|---|---|
| 465 | A85 | 6pf gray green | 1.35 .55 |
| 466 | A85 | 12pf dark carmine | 2.00 .55 |
| | | Set, never hinged | 19.00 |

1935 Nazi Congress at Nuremberg.

Nazi Flag Bearer and Feldherrnhalle at Munich — A86

**1935, Nov. 5**  **Photo.**  *Perf. 13½*

| | | | |
|---|---|---|---|
| 467 | A86 | 3pf brown | .25 .70 |
| 468 | A86 | 12pf dark carmine | .60 .70 |
| | | Set, never hinged | 12.00 |

12th anniv. of the 1st Hitler "Putsch" at Munich, Nov. 9, 1923.

Airplane — A87

**1936, Jan. 6**

| | | | |
|---|---|---|---|
| 469 | A87 | 40pf sapphire | 6.00 3.00 |
| | | Never hinged | 50.00 |

10th anniv. of the Lufthansa air service.

Gottlieb Daimler A88

Carl Benz A89

Otto von Guericke — A90

**1936, Feb. 15**  *Perf. 14*

| | | | |
|---|---|---|---|
| 470 | A88 | 6pf dark green | .70 1.00 |
| 471 | A89 | 12pf copper red | .90 1.00 |
| | | Set, never hinged | 13.50 |

The 50th anniv. of the automobile; Intl. Automobile and Motorcycle Show, Berlin.

**1936, May 4**

| | | | |
|---|---|---|---|
| 472 | A90 | 6pf dark green | .30 .55 |
| | | Never hinged | 1.20 |

250th anniv. of the death of the German inventor, Otto von Guericke, May 11, 1686.

Symbolical of Municipalities — A91

**1936, June 3**

| | | | |
|---|---|---|---|
| 473 | A91 | 3pf dark brown | .50 .30 |
| 474 | A91 | 5pf deep green | .70 .30 |
| 475 | A91 | 12pf lake | .85 .60 |
| 476 | A91 | 25pf dark ultra | 1.75 1.05 |
| | | Nos. 473-476 (4) | 3.80 2.25 |
| | | Set, never hinged | 15.00 |

6th Intl. Cong. of Municipalities, June 7-13.

Allegory of Recreation Congress — A92

**1936, June 30**

| | | | |
|---|---|---|---|
| 477 | A92 | 6pf dark green | .65 .55 |
| 478 | A92 | 15pf deep claret | 1.25 1.00 |
| | | Set, never hinged | 13.50 |

World Congress for Vacation and Recreation held at Hamburg.

Salute to Swastika — A93

**1936, Sept. 3**  *Perf. 14*

| | | | |
|---|---|---|---|
| 479 | A93 | 6pf deep green | .55 .60 |
| 480 | A93 | 12pf copper red | .95 .60 |
| | | Set, never hinged | 10.50 |

The 1936 Nazi Congress.

Search

PhilaSearch

www.PhilaSearch.com

Shield Bearer — A94

**1937, Mar. 3      Engr.      Unwmk.**
481 A94  3pf brown            .45    .40
482 A94  6pf green            .60    .40
483 A94  12pf carmine        1.20    .75
    *Nos. 481-483 (3)*        2.25   1.55
    Set, never hinged        11.50

The Reich's Air Protection League.

German and Austrian
Carrying Nazi
Flag — A95

**Wmk. Swastikas (237)**
**1938, Apr. 8   Photo.   Perf. 14x13½**
**Size: 23x28mm**
484 A95  6pf dark green       .75    .60
    Never hinged             1.50

**Unwmk.        Perf. 12½**
**Size: 21½x26mm**
485 A95  6pf deep green       .75   1.30
    Never hinged             1.50

Union of Austria and Germany.

Cathedral
Island
A96

Hermann
Goering
Stadium
A97

Town Hall,
Breslau
A98

Centennial
Hall,
Breslau
A99

**1938, June 21    Engr.    Perf. 14**
486 A96  3pf dark brown       .30    .55
487 A97  6pf deep green       .30    .55
488 A98  12pf carmine         .75    .55
489 A99  15pf violet brown   1.75    .75
    *Nos. 486-489 (4)*        3.10   2.40
    Set, never hinged        12.00

16th German Gymnastic and Sports Festival held at Breslau, July 23-31, 1938.

Nazi Emblem — A100

**1939, Apr. 4    Photo.    Wmk. 237**
490 A100  6pf dark green     1.75   3.75
491 A100  12pf deep carmine  2.25   3.75
    Set, never hinged        19.00

Young Workers' Professional Competitions.

St. Mary's
Church
A101

The Krantor,
Danzig
A102

**1939, Sept. 18**
492 A101  6pf dark green      .45    .75
493 A102  12pf orange red     .65    .75
    Set, never hinged         3.75

Unification of Danzig with the Reich.

Johannes Gutenberg
and Library at
Leipzig — A103

Designs: 6pf, "High House," Leipzig. 12pf,
Old Town Hall, Leipzig. 25pf, View of Leipzig
Fair.

**Inscribed "Leipziger Messe"**
**Perf. 10½**
**1940, Mar. 3    Photo.    Unwmk.**
494 A103  3pf brown          .45    .45
495 A103  6pf dk gray green  .45    .45
496 A103  12pf henna brown   .45    .45
497 A103  25pf ultra         .90   1.15
    *Nos. 494-497 (4)*       2.25   2.50
    Set, never hinged        7.50

Leipzig Fair.

House of Nations,
Leipzig — A107

6pf, Concert Hall, Leipzig. 12pf, Leipzig Fair
Office. 25pf, Railroad Terminal, Leipzig.

**Inscribed: "Reichsmesse Leipzig,**
**1941"**
**1941, Mar. 1          Perf. 14x13½**
498 A107  3pf brown          .30   1.00
499 A107  6pf green          .30   1.00
500 A107  12pf dark red      .30   1.00
501 A107  25pf bright blue   .70   1.00
    *Nos. 498-501 (4)*       1.60   4.00
    Set, never hinged        9.75

Leipzig Fair.

Fashion
Allegory
A111

Vienna Fair
Hall
A112

"Burgtheater"
A113

Monument to
Prince
Eugene
A114

**1941, Mar. 8          Perf. 13½x14**
502 A111  3pf dark red brown  .45    .55
503 A112  6pf brt blue grn    .45    .55
504 A113  12pf scarlet        .45    .60
505 A114  25pf bright blue   1.25   1.50
    *Nos. 502-505 (4)*       2.60   3.20
    Set, never hinged        10.50

Vienna Fair.

A115

Adolf
Hitler — A116

**1941-44      Typo.      Perf. 14**
**Size: 18½x22½mm**
506 A115  1pf gray black      .25    .30
  a.  Bklt. pane, 4 #506 + 4
      #509                    6.75   15.00
      Never hinged           11.50
507 A115  3pf lt brown        .25    .30
  a.  Bklt. pane, 6 #507 + 2
      #510                    6.75   15.00
      Never hinged           11.50
508 A115  4pf Prus blue       .25    .30
  a.  Bklt. pane, 4 #508, 2
      #511 + 2 labels         6.75   15.00
      Never hinged           11.50
509 A115  5pf dp yel grn      .25    .30
510 A115  6pf violet          .25    .30
  a.  Bklt. pane of 7 + label 13.50  30.00
      Never hinged           22.50

511 A115  8pf red             .25    .30
511A A115 10pf dk brn ('42)   .25    .45
511B A115 12pf car ('42)      .25    .45

**Engr.**
512 A115  10pf dark brown     .40    .30
513 A115  12pf brt carmine    .40    .30
  a.  Bklt. pane of 6 + 2 labels  4.50  15.00
      Never hinged            7.50
514 A115  15pf brown lake     .30   1.50
515 A115  16pf peack grn      .25   1.50
516 A115  20pf lt blue        .25    .40
517 A115  24pf org brn        .25   1.50

**Size: 21½x26mm**
518 A115  25pf dark blue      .25    .45
519 A115  30pf olive green    .25    .45
520 A115  40pf magenta        .25    .45
521 A115  50pf myrtle green   .25    .45
522 A115  60pf brn pur        .25    .45
523 A115  80pf indigo         .25    .45
524 A116  1m dk slate grn     .45   5.25
              ('44)
  a.  Perf. 12½ ('42)        1.50   6.00
525 A116  2m violet ('44)    1.50  67.50
  a.  Perf. 12½ ('42)        1.20   6.00

**Perf. 12½**
526 A116  3m cop red         1.50  15.00
              ('42)
  a.  Perf. 14 ('44)         9.00  450.00
527 A116  5m dk bl ('42)     3.00  50.00
  a.  Perf. 14 ('44)         4.50  1,050.
    *Nos. 506-527 (24)*     11.80  148.65
    Set, #506-527, never
      hinged                30.00
    Set, #524a-527a, never
      hinged                42.50

Nos. 507, 510, 511, 511A, 511B, 520, 524-
526 exist imperf.
  For surcharge see No. MQ3. For overprints
see Austria Nos. 390-393, 398-403, 405-431,
Russia Nos. N9-N48.

Storm Trooper
Emblem — A117

**1942, Aug. 8    Photo.    Perf. 14**
528 A117  6pf purple          .25    .75
    Never hinged              .75

War Effort Day of the Storm Troopers.

Adolf Hitler — A118

**1944                        Engr.**
529 A118  42pf bright green   .25   1.90
    Never hinged              .30

Exists imperf. Value $750 hinged.
For overprint see Austria No. 404.

A119

**1946    Typo.    Wmk. 284    Perf. 14**
**Size: 18x22mm**
530 A119  1pf black           .25   3.00
531 A119  2pf black           .25    .25
532 A119  3pf yellow brn      .25   3.75
533 A119  4pf dk blue         .25   4.50
534 A119  5pf yellow grn      .25    .60
535 A119  6pf purple          .25    .25
536 A119  8pf dp ver          .25    .25
537 A119  10pf chocolate      .25    .60
538 A119  12pf bright red     .25    .25
539 A119  12pf slate gray     .25    .25
  a.  Bklt. pane, 5 #539 + 3 #542  9.00  115.00
      Never hinged           20.50
540 A119  15pf violet brn     .25   7.50
541 A119  15pf lt yel grn     .25    .40
542 A119  16pf slate green    .25    .40
543 A119  20pf lt blue        .25    .40
544 A119  24pf orange brn     .25    .40
  a.  Bklt. pane, 8 #544      9.00  115.00
      Never hinged           20.50
545 A119  25pf brt ultra      .25   7.50
546 A119  25pf orange yel     .25   1.15
547 A119  30pf olive          .25    .25
548 A119  40pf red violet     .25    .40
549 A119  42pf emerald        .75  30.00
550 A119  45pf brt red        .25    .40
551 A119  50pf dk ol grn      .25    .25
552 A119  60pf scarlet        .25    .25
553 A119  75pf deep ultra     .25    .25
554 A119  80pf dark blue      .25    .40
555 A119  84pf emerald        .25    .25

**Size: 24½x29½mm**
556 A119  1m olive green      .25    .40
    *Nos. 530-556 (27)*             64.30
    Set, never hinged         5.75

Imperf. examples of Nos. 543, 544 and 548
are usually from the souvenir sheet No. B295.
Most other denominations exist imperf.
  For overprints see Nos. 585A-599, 9N64,
10N17-10N21.

Planting
Olive
A120

Sower
A121

Laborer
A122

Reaping
Wheat
A123

Germany Reaching for
Peace — A124

**1947-48                    Perf. 14**
557 A120  2pf brown blk       .25    .40
558 A120  6pf purple          .25    .25
559 A121  8pf red             .25    .40
560 A121  10pf yel grn ('48)  .25    .60
561 A122  12pf gray           .25    .25
562 A120  15pf choc ('48)     .25   3.75
563 A123  16pf dk bl grn      .25    .40
564 A121  20pf blue           .25   1.50
565 A123  24pf brown org      .25    .40
566 A120  25pf orange yel     .25   1.50
567 A122  30pf red ('48)      .25   3.00
568 A121  40pf red vio        .25    .60
569 A123  50pf ultra ('48)    .25   1.90
571 A122  60pf red brn ('48)  .25    .75
  a.  60pf brown red          .25    .40
572 A122  80pf blue           .25   1.50
573 A123  84pf emerald        .25   2.25

**Engr.**
574 A124  1m bister           .25    .40
575 A124  2m dk brown vio     .25   1.50
576 A124  3m copper red       .25  19.00
577 A124  5m dk blue ('48)    .75  45.00
    *Nos. 557-577 (20)*             85.35
    Set, never hinged         7.50

Used examples of Nos. 576-577 with
expertized postal cancellations sell for much
more.
  For overprints see Nos. 600-633, 9N1-
9N34, 9N65-9N67, 10N1-10N16.

Heinrich von
Stephan — A125

**1947, May 15              Litho.**
578 A125  24pf orange brown   .25   1.50
579 A125  75pf dark blue      .25   1.50
    Set, never hinged          .75

50th anniv. of the death of Heinrich von Stephan, 1st postmaster general of the German
Empire.

**Leipzig Fair Issues**
Type of Semi-Postal Stamp of 1947

12pf, Maximilian I granting charter, 1497.
75pf, Estimating and collecting taxes, 1365.

**Perf. 13½x13**
**1947, Sept. 2    Litho.    Wmk. 284**
580 SP252  12pf carmine       .25   1.90
581 SP252  75pf dk vio blue   .25   1.90
    Set, never hinged          .90

**Type of Semi-Postal Stamp of 1947,**
**Dated 1948**

50pf, Merchants at customs barrier, 1388.
84pf, Arranging stocks of merchandise, 1433.

**1948, Mar. 2** — **Engr.**
582 SP252 50pf deep blue .25 1.50
583 SP252 84pf green .25 2.25
Set, never hinged .90

Exist imperf. Value, each, $450.

## Hanover Fair Issue

Weighing Goods for
Export — A126

**1948, May 22** **Typo.** **Perf. 14**
584 A126 24pf deep carmine .25 1.50
585 A126 50pf ultra .25 2.25
c. Pair, #584-585 2.25 19.00
Pair, never hinged 7.50
Set, never hinged .75

### For Use in the United States and British Zones
### Stamps of Germany 1946-47 Overprinted in Black

a                      b

### Overprint Type "a" on 1946 Numeral Issue

**1948** **Wmk. 284** **Perf. 14**
585A A119 2pf black 2.25 32.00
585B A119 8pf dp ver 4.50 65.00
586 A119 10pf chocolate .30 5.00
586A A119 12pf bright red 3.75 52.50
586B A119 12pf slate gray 65.00 575.00
586C A119 15pf violet brn 3.75 52.50
587 A119 15pf lt yel grn 1.20 16.50
587A A119 16pf slate green 10.00 200.00
587B A119 24pf orange brn 35.00 210.00
587C A119 25pf brt ultra 6.00 65.00
588 A119 25pf orange yel .60 11.50
589 A119 30pf olive .90 11.50
589A A119 40pf red violet 29.00 210.00
590 A119 45pf brt red 1.20 11.50
591 A119 50pf dk olive grn .75 7.50
592 A119 75pf dp ultra 2.25 24.00
593 A119 84pf emerald 2.25 24.00
Nos. 585A-593 (17) 185.05
Set, never hinged 375.00

### Same, Overprinted Type "b"

593A A119 2pf black 10.50 67.50
593B A119 8pf dp ver 18.00 190.00
593C A119 10pf dk brown 16.50 190.00
593D A119 12pf bright red 5.25 67.50
593E A119 12pf slate gray 130.00 1,050.
593F A119 15pf brn lil 5.25 52.50
594 A119 15pf lt yel grn .55 8.25
594A A119 16pf slate grn 19.00 170.00
594B A119 24pf org brn 21.00 210.00
594C A119 25pf brt ultra 5.25 65.00
594D A119 25pf orange yel 19.00 200.00
595 A119 30pf olive .75 6.75
595A A119 40pf red violet 26.00 250.00
596 A119 45pf brt red 1.50 12.00
597 A119 50pf dk ol grn 1.50 12.00
598 A119 75pf dp ultra 1.15 12.00
599 A119 84pf emerald 1.15 13.00
Nos. 593A-599 (17) 295.25
Set, never hinged 600.00

Nine other denominations of type A119 (1, 3, 4, 5, 6, 20, 42, 60 and 80pf) were also overprinted with types "a" and "b." These overprints were not authorized, but the stamps were sold at post offices and tolerated for postal use. Forgeries exist.

The overprints on Nos. 585A-599 have been extensively counterfeited.

### Overprint Type "a" on Stamps and Types of 1947 Pictorial Issue

600 A120 2pf brown black .25 .55
601 A120 6pf purple .25 .40
602 A121 8pf dp vermilion .25 .40
603 A121 10pf yellow green .25 .40
604 A122 12pf slate gray .25 .40
605 A120 15pf chocolate 2.60 15.00
606 A121 16pf dk blue green .55 2.60
607 A121 20pf blue .25 1.00
608 A123 24pf brown orange .25 .40
609 A120 25pf orange yellow .25 .40
610 A122 30pf red 1.00 4.50
611 A122 40pf red violet .30 2.00
612 A123 50pf ultra .35 1.60
614 A123 60pf red brown .35 .80
a. 60pf brown red 22.50 225.00
Never hinged 60.00
615 A122 80pf dark blue .55 2.00
616 A123 84pf emerald 1.60 6.00
Nos. 600-616 (16) 9.30 38.45
Set, never hinged 24.00

### Same, Overprinted Type "b"

617 A120 2pf brown black .35 2.60
618 A120 6pf purple .35 1.30
619 A121 8pf red .35 1.60
620 A121 10pf yellow green .25 .65
621 A122 12pf gray .35 1.60
622 A120 15pf chocolate .25 1.00
623 A121 16pf dk blue green .60 2.25
624 A121 20pf blue .25 .65
625 A120 24pf brown orange .25 1.30
626 A120 25pf orange yel 3.00 15.00
627 A122 30pf red .25 1.30
628 A123 40pf red violet .25 .65
629 A123 50pf ultra .25 .65
631 A123 60pf red brown .25 1.00
a. 60pf brown red .95 3.75
Never hinged 2.50
632 A122 80pf dark blue .25 1.00
633 A123 84pf emerald .40 1.30
Nos. 617-633 (16) 7.65 33.85
Set, never hinged 22.50

Most of Nos. 585A-633 exist with inverted and double overprints.

Frankfurt        Our
Town Hall        Lady's
A127             Church,
                 Munich
                 A128

Cologne          Brandenburg
Cathedral        Gate,
A129             Berlin
                 A130

Holsten Gate,
Lübeck — A131

Type I

Type II

Two types of mark values:
Type I — Four horiz. lines in stairs inside arch.
Type II — Seven horizontal lines in stairs inside arch.

### Perf. 11½x11, 11

**1948-51** **Litho.** **Wmk. 286**
634 A127 2pf black .25 .40
a. Perf. 14 1.00 5.00
635 A128 4pf orange brown .25 .40
a. Perf. 14 .55 .40
636 A129 5pf blue .25 .40
a. Perf. 14 .65 .40
637 A128 6pf orange brown .25 .40
638 A128 6pf orange .25 .40
a. Perf. 14 6.00 4.50
639 A127 8pf orange yel .25 .40
640 A128 8pf dk slate blue .25 .40
641 A129 10pf green .25 .40
a. Perf. 14 .65 .40
642 A128 15pf orange .80 4.50
643 A127 15pf lilac .50 .40
a. Perf. 14 4.50 .40
644 A127 16pf bluish green .40 2.60
645 A127 20pf blue .40 .40
646 A130 20pf carmine .25 .40
a. Perf. 14 1.60 .40
647 A130 24pf carmine .25 .40
648 A129 25pf vermilion .40 .40
a. Perf. 14 7.50 30.00
649 A130 30pf blue .55 .40
a. Perf. 14 11.00 .40

650 A128 30pf scarlet 1.00 5.25
651 A129 40pf dp rose lil .65 .40
a. Perf. 14 7.50 .40
652 A130 50pf ultra .55 1.60
653 A128 50pf bluish green .65 .40
a. Perf. 14 67.50 .40
654 A129 60pf violet brn 30.00 .40
a. Perf. 14 1.00 .40
655 A130 80pf red violet 1.05 .40
a. Perf. 14 45.00 .40
656 A128 84pf rose violet .65 6.00
657 A129 90pf rose lilac 1.05 .40
a. Perf. 14 60.00 .40

### Perf. 11, 11x11½

658 A131 1m yellow grn (I) 15.00 .55
a. Perf. 14 (II) ('51) 60.00 .40
b. Perf. 11 (II) 19.00 .40
659 A131 2m lilac (I) 13.50 .55
a. Type II 22.50 .40
660 A131 3m car rose (I) 15.00 2.25
a. Type II 75.00 .95
661 A131 5m blue (I) 22.50 21.00
a. Type II 90.00 3.00
Nos. 634-661 (28) 107.10 52.05
Set, never hinged 225.00
Set, 634a-658a, never hinged 550.00
Set, 658b-661a, never hinged 375.00

Imperforates of many values exist.
Specialists collect Nos. 634-661 with watermark in four positions: upright, D's facing left; upright, D's facing right; sideways, D's facing up; sideways, D's facing down.
Two types of perforation: line and comb. Nos. 634-657 are found both perf. 11 and 11½x11.

Herman Hildebrant
Wedigh — A132

### Wmk. 116

**1949, Apr. 22** **Engr.** **Perf. 14**
662 A132 10pf blue grn 1.00 2.25
663 A132 20pf rose carmine 1.00 1.60
664 A132 30pf blue 1.30 3.00
a. Sheet of 3, #662-664 34.00 260.00
Sheet, never hinged 105.00
Nos. 662-664 (3) 3.30 7.25
Set, never hinged 10.50

Hanover Export Fair, 1949.
No. 664a sold for 1 mark.

### Federal Republic
AREA — 95,520 sq. mi.
POP. — 62,040,000 (1974 est.)
CAPITAL — Bonn

"Reconstruction"
A133

**1949, Sept. 7** **Litho.** **Wmk. 286**
665 A133 10pf blue green 14.50 15.00
666 A133 20pf rose carmine 16.00 19.00
Set, never hinged 75.00

Opening of the first Federal Assembly.
Exist imperf. Value, each $875.

Bavaria Stamp — A134

Design: 30pf, Bavaria 6kr.

### Wmk. 285
**1949, Sept. 30** **Litho.** **Perf. 14**
667 A134 20pf red & dull blue 13.00 34.00
668 A134 30pf dull blue & choc 16.00 52.50
Set, never hinged 67.50

Cent. of German postage stamps. See No. B309.

Heinrich von Stephan, General Post Office and Guild House, Bern — A135

**1949, Oct. 9** **Wmk. 286**
669 A135 30pf dark blue 19.50 35.00
Never hinged 52.50

75th anniv. of the UPU.

Numeral and Post
Horn — A136

**1951-52** **Typo.** **Wmk. 295**
670 A136 2pf yellow grn .35 .85
671 A136 4pf yellow brn .55 .30
a. Booklet pane, 3 #671 + 3 #673 + 4 #677 110.00 900.00
Never hinged 280.00
672 A136 5pf dp rose vio 1.60 .30
673 A136 6pf orange 4.50 2.60
674 A136 8pf gray 4.50 6.00
675 A136 10pf dk green 1.30 .30
a. Booklet pane, 4 #675 + 5 #677 + label 110.00 900.00
Never hinged 280.00
676 A136 15pf purple 9.00 .85
677 A136 20pf carmine 1.00 .30
678 A136 25pf dk rose lake 19.00 5.25

### Engr.
### Size: 20x24½mm
679 A136 30pf blue 11.50 .55
680 A136 40pf rose lilac ('52) 26.00 .55
681 A136 50pf blue gray ('52) 37.50 .55
682 A136 60pf brown ('52) 26.00 .55
683 A136 70pf dp yel ('52) 135.00 14.50
684 A136 80pf carmine ('52) 135.00 2.00
685 A136 90pf yel grn ('52) 150.00 2.25
Nos. 670-685 (16) 562.80 37.70
Set, never hinged 1,700.

Imperfs. exist of Nos. 671, 673, 675, 681 & 684.

Wilhelm
Roentgen — A137

**1951, Dec. 10**
686 A137 30pf blue 24.00 15.00
Never hinged 60.00

50th anniv. of the awarding of the Nobel prize in physics to Wilhelm Roentgen.

Mona Lisa — A138

### Wmk. 285
**1952, Apr. 15** **Litho.** **Perf. 13½**
687 A138 5pf multicolored .40 2.00
Never hinged 1.05

500th anniv. of the birth of Leonardo da Vinci.

N. A. Otto — A139

### Wmk. 295
**1952, July 25** **Engr.** **Perf. 14**
688 A139 30pf deep blue 10.50 12.00
Never hinged 24.00

75th anniv. of the four-cycle gas engine.

Martin Luther — A140

**1952, July 25**
689 A140 10pf green 3.75 4.50
Never hinged 11.50

Issued to publicize the Lutheran World Federation Assembly, Hanover, 1952.

Freighter Off
Heligoland — A141

**1952, Sept. 6**
690 A141 20pf carmine    4.50 5.25
    Never hinged      11.50

    Return of Heligoland, Mar. 1, 1952.

Carl Schurz — A142

**Wmk. 285**
**1952, Sept. 17   Litho.    Perf. 13½**
691 A142 20pf blue, blk & brn
            org    6.50   7.50
    Never hinged      15.00

    Centenary of Carl Schurz's arrival in
America.

Thurn and Taxis
Postilion — A143

**1952, Oct. 25**
692 A143 10pf multicolored    1.50 2.25
    Never hinged      4.50

    1st Thurn and Taxis stamp, cent.

Philipp Reis — A144

**1952, Oct. 27   Photo.    Perf. 14**
693 A144 30pf blue    16.50 13.50
    Never hinged      42.50

    75 years of telephone service in Germany.

"Prevent Traffic
Accidents" — A145

**1953, Mar. 30   Litho.    Wmk. 285**
694 A145 20pf blk, red & bl grn    5.25 4.50
    Never hinged      13.50

Justus von Liebig — A146

**1953, May 12   Engr.    Wmk. 295**
695 A146 30pf dark blue    9.00 19.00
    Never hinged      26.00

    150th anniv. of the birth of Justus von
Liebig, chemist.

Red Cross and
Compass — A147

**Perf. 14x13½**
**1953, May 8   Litho.    Wmk. 285**
696 A147 10pf dp ol grn & red    4.50 5.75
    Never hinged      16.50

    125th anniv. of the birth of Henri Dunant,
founder of the Red Cross.

---

War Prisoner and
Barbed Wire — A148

**Typographed and Embossed**
**1953, May 9   Unwmk.    Perf. 14**
697 A148 10pf gray & black    1.60 .35
    Never hinged      5.25

    Issued in memory of the prisoners of war.

Train and Hand
Signal — A149

    Designs: 10pf, Pigeon and planes. 20pf,
Automobiles and traffic signal. 30pf, Ship,
barges and buoy.

**Wmk. 295**
**1953, June 20   Engr.    Perf. 14**
698 A149   4pf brown    1.60   3.75
699 A149 10pf deep green    4.00   6.00
700 A149 20pf red    4.50   7.50
701 A149 30pf dark blue    13.00 15.00
    Nos. 698-701 (4)    23.10 32.25
    Set, never hinged    65.00

    Exhibition of Transport and Communica-
tions, Munich, 1953.

Pres. Theodore
Heuss — A150

**1954-60     Typo.     Perf. 14**
       **Size: 18½x22mm**
702 A150   2pf citron    .25   .25
  a.    Booklet pane, 5 #702, 4
         #704 + label ('55)    22.50 130.00
         Never hinged    45.00
  b.    Booklet pane, 3 #702, 6
         #704 + label ('56)    3.75   60.00
         Never hinged    11.50
  c.    Booklet pane, 3 #702, 1
         #707, 5 #708 + label ('56)    7.50   75.00
         Never hinged    16.50
703 A150   4pf orange brn    .25   .25
704 A150   5pf rose lilac    .25   .25
  a.    Booklet pane, 2 #704, 7
         #708 + label ('55)    22.50 130.00
         Never hinged    45.00
705 A150   6pf lt brown    .25   .65
706 A150   7pf bluish green    .25   .30
707 A150   8pf gray    .25   .55
708 A150 10pf green    .25   .25
  a.    Booklet pane, 4 #708, 5
         #710 + label ('55)    22.50 130.00
         Never hinged    45.00
709 A150 15pf ultra    .25   .40
710 A150 20pf dk car rose    .25   .25
711 A150 25pf red brown    .25   .55
         **Engr.**
       **Size: 19½x24mm**
712 A150 30pf blue    3.75   4.50
713 A150 40pf red violet    1.30   .30
714 A150 50pf gray    57.50   .40
715 A150 60pf red brown    11.50   .55
716 A150 70pf olive    4.50   1.60
717 A150 80pf deep rose    .65   .65
718 A150 90pf deep green    3.75   2.00
       **Size: 24½x29½mm**
719 A150   1m olive green    .50   .30
720 A150   2m lt vio blue    .65   1.00
721 A150   3m deep plum    1.60   2.00
    Nos. 702-721 (20)    88.20 17.00
    Set, never hinged    225.00

    Coils and sheets of 100 were issued of the
5, 7, 10, 15, 20, 25, 40 and 70pf. Every fifth
coil stamp has a control number on the back.
    Printings of Nos. 704, 706, 708-711 and
708b were made on fluorescent paper beginning in 1960.
    Nos. 702, 709, 714 exist imperf. Value about
$425 each.
    See Nos. 737Ab, 755-761.

> **Catalogue values for unused
> stamps in this section, from this
> point to the end of the section, are
> for Never Hinged items.**

---

Paul Ehrlich and Emil
von Behring — A151

**Wmk. 285**
**1954, Mar. 13   Litho.    Perf. 13½**
722 A151 10pf dark green    9.00 3.00
    Centenary of the births of Paul Ehrlich and
Emil von Behring, medical researchers.
Exists imperf. Value $800.

15th Century
Printer — A152

**1954, May 5   Typo.    Wmk. 295**
723 A152 4pf chocolate    1.20 .55

    500th anniversary of the publication of
Gutenberg's 42-line Bible. Design from woodcut by Jost Amman.

Bishop's Miter and
Sword — A153

**Engraved; Center Embossed**
**1954, June 5   Unwmk.   Perf. 13½x14**
724 A153 20pf gray & red    6.75 3.75

    Martyrdom of Saint Boniface, 1200th anniv.

Carl F. Gauss — A154

**Wmk. 295**
**1955, Feb. 23   Engr.    Perf. 14**
725 A154 10pf deep green    4.50 .55

    Cent. of the death of Carl Friedrich Gauss,
mathematician.

A155

**Wmk. 304**
**1955, May 7   Litho.    Perf. 13½**
726 A155 10pf green    4.50 1.20

    Cent. of the birth of Oskar von Miller, electri-
cal engineer.

A156

**Engraved and Embossed**
**1955, May 9   Unwmk.    Perf. 13½x14**
727 A156 40pf blue    13.50 5.00

    Friedrich von Schiller, poet, 150th death
anniv.

1906
Automobile — A157

---

**Wmk. 304**
**1955, June 1   Typo.    Perf. 13½**
728 A157 20pf red & black    9.00 4.25

    German postal motor-bus service, 50th
anniv.

Arms of Baden-
Württemberg
A158

**Perf. 13x13½**
**1955, June 15   Litho.    Wmk. 295**
729 A158   7pf lemon, blk &
            brn red    4.25 2.60
730 A158 10pf lemon, blk &
            grn    5.00 2.00

    Baden-Württemberg Exhibition, Stuttgart,
1955.

Globe and Atomic
Symbol — A159

**1955, June 24   Photo.   Perf. 13½x14**
731 A159 20pf rose brown    9.00 .85

    Issued to encourage scientific research.

Orb and Symbols of
Battle — A160

**Photogravure and Embossed**
       **Perf. 14x13½**
**1955, Aug. 10        Unwmk.**
732 A160 20pf red lilac    7.50 2.60

    Issued in honor of Augsburg and the mil-
lenium of the Battle on the Lechfeld.

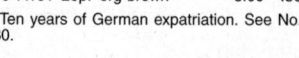

Family in
Flight — A161

**1955, Aug. 2   Engr.    Wmk. 304**
733 A161 20pf org brown    3.00 .50

    Ten years of German expatriation. See No.
930.

Railroad Signal,
Tracks — A162

**Perf. 13½x14**
**1955, Oct. 5   Litho.    Wmk. 304**
734 A162 20pf red & black    7.50 2.00

    European Timetable conf. at Wiesbaden,
Oct. 5-15, 1955.

A163

    Stifter monument and stylized Trees.

**1955, Oct. 22         Engr.**
735 A163 10pf dark green    3.00 2.00

    150th anniv. of the birth of Adalbert Stifter,
poet.

A164

**Lithographed and Embossed**
*Perf. 14x13½*
**1955, Oct. 24** Unwmk.
736 A164 10pf UN emblem 3.00 3.75
United Nations Day, Oct. 24, 1955.

Numeral — A165

**1955-58 Wmk. 304 Typo. Perf. 14**
737 A165 1pf gray .25 .35
**Wmk. 295**
737A A165 1pf gray ('58) 7.50 15.00
b. Bklt. pane of 10 (#707, 2
each #737A, #704, #708,
3 #710) 22.50 52.50
No. 737A was issued only in the booklet
pane, No. 737b. No. 737 was issued on fluorescent paper in 1963.

Numeral and
Signature — A166

**1956, Jan. 7 Engr. Wmk. 304**
738 A166 20pf dark red 6.00 2.00
125th anniv. of the birth of Heinrich von Stephan, co-founder of the UPU.

Clavichord — A167

**1956, Jan. 27** Litho.
739 A167 10pf dull lilac .80 .35
200th anniv. of the birth of Wolfgang
Amadeus Mozart, composer.

Heinrich Heine, Poet,
Death Cent. — A168

*Perf. 13x13½*
**1956, Feb. 17 Wmk. 295**
740 A168 10pf ol grn & blk 2.25 2.60

Old Buildings,
Lüneburg — A169

**Wmk. 304**
**1956, May 2 Engr. Perf. 14**
741 A169 20pf dull red 6.50 7.50
Millenary of Lüneburg.

Olympic Rings — A170

**1956, June 9 Perf. 13½x14**
742 A170 10pf slate green .65 .55
Issued to publicize the Olympic year, 1956.

Robert
Schumann — A171

**1956, July 28 Litho. Unwmk.**
743 A171 10pf citron, blk & red .65 .40
Schumann, composer, death cent.

Synod Emblem — A172

*Perf. 13½x13*
**1956, Aug. 8 Wmk. 304**
744 A172 10pf green 2.60 3.00
745 A172 20pf brown carmine 3.75 4.50
Meeting of German Protestants (Evangelical Synod), Frankfurt-on-Main, Aug. 8-12.

Thomas Mann — A173

**1956, Aug. 11 Engr. Perf. 13½x14**
746 A173 20pf pale rose vio 2.25 1.75
1st anniv. of the death of Thomas Mann,
novelist.

Maria Laach
Abbey — A174

**1956, Aug. 24 Photo. Perf. 13x13½**
747 A174 20pf brn lake & gray 1.75 1.75
800th anniv. of the dedication of the Maria
Laach Abbey.

**Europa Issue**

"Rebuilding
Europe" — A175

**1956, Sept. 15 Engr. Perf. 14**
748 A175 10pf green .65 .25
749 A175 40pf blue 6.75 .85
Issued to symbolize the cooperation among
the six countries comprising the Coal and
Steel Community.

Plan of Cologne
Cathedral and
Hand — A176

**1956, Aug. 29 Litho. Perf. 13x13½**
750 A176 10pf gray grn & red
brn 2.25 2.25
77th meeting of German Catholics,
Cologne, Aug. 29.

Map of the World
and Policeman's
Hand — A177

**1956, Sept. 1 Perf. 13½x13**
751 A177 20pf red org, grn & blk 2.25 2.25
Issued on the occasion of the International
Police Show, Essen, Sept. 1-23.

Pigeon Holding
Letter — A178

**1956, Oct. 27 Engr. Perf. 14**
752 A178 10pf green 1.30 .60
Issued to publicize the Day of the Stamp.

Cemetery
Crosses — A179

**1956, Nov. 17 Perf. 14x13½**
753 A179 10pf slate 1.30 .60
Issued to commemorate the people of Germany who died during WWII and to promote
the Society for the Care of Military
Cemeteries.

Saar Coat of
Arms — A180

**1957, Jan. 2 Litho. Perf. 13x13½**
754 A180 10pf bluish grn & brn .50 .40
Return of the Saar to Germany. See Saar
No. 262.

**Heuss Type of 1954**
**1956-57 Wmk. 304 Engr. Perf. 14**
**Size: 18½x22mm**
755 A150 30pf slate green .35 .55
756 A150 40pf lt ultra 1.30 .30
757 A150 50pf olive .85 .30
758 A150 60pf lt brown 2.50 .40
759 A150 70pf violet 8.25 .40
760 A150 80pf red orange 5.25 1.60
761 A150 90pf bluish green 13.50 .85
Nos. 755-761 (7) 32.00 4.40
Nos. 755-756 were printed on both ordinary
and fluorescent paper; Nos. 757-761 only on
ordinary paper. Issue dates: 40pf, 1956.
Others, 1957.
The 40pf and 70pf were also issued in coils.
Every fifth coil stamp has control number on
back.

Heinrich Hertz — A181

**1957, Feb. 22 Litho. Perf. 14**
762 A181 10pf lt green & blk 1.15 .55
Heinrich Hertz, physicist, birth cent.

Paul Gerhardt — A182

**1957, May 18 Engr.**
763 A182 20pf carmine lake .55 .50
350th anniv. of the birth of Paul Gerhardt,
Lutheran clergyman and hymn writer.

Tulip and Post
Horn — A183

**1957, June 8**
764 A183 20pf red orange .55 .50
Flora & Philately Exhib., Cologne, June 8-10.

Arms of Aschaffenburg,
1332 — A184

*Perf. 13x13½*
**1957, June 15 Wmk. 304**
765 A184 20pf dp salmon & blk .55 .50
1000th anniv. of the founding of the Abbey
and town of Aschaffenburg.

Scholars (Sapiens
Manuscript) — A185

**1957, June 24 Perf. 13½x13**
766 A185 10pf blk, bl grn & red
org .40 .35
Founding of Freiburg University, 500th anniv.

Modern
Passenger
Freighter
A186

**1957, June 25 Perf. 13½x14**
767 A186 15pf brt blue, blk & red .95 .95
Merchant Marine Day, June 25.

Liebig
Laboratory — A187

**1957, July 3 Engr. Perf. 14x13½**
768 A187 10pf dark green .40 .40
350th anniv. of the Justus Liebig School at
Ludwig University, Giessen.

Albert Ballin — A188

*Perf. 13½x14*
**1957, Aug. 15 Litho. Wmk. 304**
769 A188 20pf dk car rose & blk 1.15 .40
Cent. of the birth of Albert Ballin, founder of
the Hamburg-America Steamship Line.

Television
Screen — A189

**1957, Aug. 23 Engr. Perf. 14x13½**
770 A189 10pf blue vio & grn .40 .40
Issued to publicize the television industry.

**Europa Issue**

"United
Europe" — A190

**Lithographed; Tree Embossed**
**1957-58**    **Unwmk.**    *Perf. 14x13½*
771   A190   10pf yel grn & lt
     bl                  .35    .25
   **a.**    Imperf.      *300.00   300.00*
772   A190   40pf dk bl & lt bl    4.50   3.75

            **Wmk. 304**
772A A190   10pf yel grn & lt
     bl                  6.50   10.50
   *Nos. 771-772A (3)*    11.35   14.50
   A united Europe for peace and prosperity.
   Issued: Nos. 771-772, 9/16; No. 772A, 8/1958.

Water Lily
A191

European Robin
A192

            **Wmk. 304**
**1957, Oct. 4**    **Litho.**    *Perf. 14*
773   A191   10pf yel grn & org yel   .50   .40
774   A192   20pf multicolored       .50   .40
   Protection of wild animals and plants.

Carrier Pigeons — A193

**1957, Oct. 5**
775   A193   20pf dp car & blk      .75   .50
   Intl. Letter Writing Week, Oct. 6-12.

Baron vom Stein — A194

**1957, Oct. 26**    **Engr.**    *Perf. 13½x14*
776   A194   20pf red          1.20   .55
   200th anniv. of the birth of Baron Heinrich Friedrich vom und zum Stein, Prussian statesman.

Leo Baeck — A195

**1957, Nov. 2**
777   A195   20pf dark red      1.20   .55
   1st anniv. of the death of Rabbi Leo Baeck of Berlin.

Landschaft Building, Stuttgart — A196

       *Perf. 13x13½*
**1957, Nov. 16**    **Litho.**    **Wmk. 304**
778   A196   10pf ol blk, yel ol & cream                .75   .50
   500th anniversary of the Württemberg Landtag (Assembly).

Coach — A197

**1957, Nov. 26**    **Engr.**    *Perf. 14*
779   A197   10pf olive green     .65   .50
   Centenary of the death of Joseph V. Eichendorff, poet.

"Max and Moritz" — A198

   Design: 20pf, Wilhelm Busch.

**1958, Jan. 9**    **Litho.**    *Perf. 13½x13*
780   A198   10pf lt ol grn & blk   .25   .25
781   A198   20pf red & black     .65   .55
   50th anniv. of the death of Wilhelm Busch, humorist.

"Prevent Forest Fires" — A199

**1958, Mar. 5**               *Perf. 14*
782   A199   20pf brt red & blk    .60   .50

Rudolf Diesel — A200

**1958, Mar. 18**    **Engr.**    *Perf. 14*
783   A200   10pf dk blue grn    .35   .35
   Centenary of the birth of Rudolf Diesel, inventor.

Giraffe and Lion — A201

       *Perf. 13x13½*
**1958, May 7**    **Litho.**    **Wmk. 304**
784   A201   10pf brt yel grn & blk   .50   .35
   Zoo at Frankfort on the Main, cent. Exists imperf. Value $225.

View of Old Munich — A202

**1958, May 22**    **Engr.**    *Perf. 14x13½*
785   A202   20pf dark red       .50   .35
   800th anniversary of Munich.

Market Cross, Trier — A203

**1958, June 3**
786   A203   20pf dark red & black   .50   .35
   Millennium of the market of Trier (Treves).

Heraldic Eagle 5m Coin — A204

**1958, June 20**    **Litho.**    *Perf. 13x13½*
787   A204   20pf red & black     .60   .60
   10th anniv. of the German currency reform. Exists imperf. Value $300.

Turner Emblem and Oak Leaf — A205

       *Perf. 13½x14*
**1958, July 21**           **Wmk. 304**
788   A205   10pf gray, blk & dl grn   .35   .40
   150 years of German Turners and on the occasion of the 1958 Turner festival.

Schulze-Delitzsch
A206

**1958, Aug. 29**    **Engr.**    *Perf. 13½x14*
789   A206   10pf yellow green    .40   .35
   150th anniv. of the birth of Hermann Schulze-Delitzsch, founder of German trade organizations.

    Common Design Types
    pictured following the introduction.

      **Europa Issue, 1958**
       Common Design Type
**1958, Sept. 13**           **Litho.**
      **Size: 24½x30mm**
790   CD1   10pf yel grn & blue   .35   .25
791   CD1   40pf lt blue & red    *2.60*   .35

Nicolaus Cusanus (Nikolaus Krebs) — A207

**1958, Dec. 3**    **Litho.**    *Perf. 14x13½*
792   A207   20pf dk car rose & blk   .40   .35
   500th anniv. of the Cusanus Hospice at Kues, founded by Cardinal Nicolaus (1401-64).
   Exists imperf. Value $300, mint or used.

Pres. Theodor Heuss — A208

**1959**        **Wmk. 304**        *Perf. 14*
793   A208   7pf blue green      .25   .25
794   A208   10pf green           .35   .25
795   A208   20pf dk car rose     .35   .25
               **Engr.**
796   A208   40pf blue         10.50   .80
797   A208   70pf deep purple    3.75   .65
   *Nos. 793-797 (5)*       15.20   2.20
   Nos. 793-795 were issued in sheets of 100 and in coils. Every fifth coil stamp has a control number on the back.
   An experimental booklet containing one pane of 10 of No. 794 was sold at Darmstadt in 1960. Value $750.

Jakob Fugger — A209

**1959, Mar. 6**            *Perf. 13x13½*
798   A209   20pf dk red & black    .35   .40
   500th anniversary of the birth of Jakob Fugger the Rich, businessman and banker.

Adam Riese — A210

**1959, Mar. 28**         *Perf. 13½x13*
799   A210   10pf ol grn & blk     .35   .40
   Adam Riese (c. 1492-1559), arithmetic teacher, 400th death anniversary.

Alexander von Humboldt — A211

**1959, May 6**    **Engr.**    *Perf. 13½x14*
800   A211   40pf blue          1.45   1.15
   Alexander von Humboldt (1769-1859), naturalist and geographer, death centenary.

Buildings, Buxtehude — A212

**1959, June 20**    **Litho.**    *Perf. 14*
801   A212   20pf lt blue, ver & blk   .40   .40
   Millennium of town of Buxtehude.

Holy Coat of Trier — A213

    **Lithographed; Coat Embossed**
**1959, July 18**    **Wmk. 304**    *Perf. 14*
802   A213   20pf dull cl, buff & blk   .35   .35
   Showing of the seamless robe of Christ at the Cathedral of Trier, July 19-Sept. 20.

Synod Emblem — A214

**1959, Aug. 12**            **Litho.**
803   A214   10pf grn, brt vio & blk   .35   .35
   Meeting of German Protestants (Evangelical Synod), Munich, Aug. 12-16.

        **Souvenir Sheet**

A215

   Portraits: 10pf, George Friedrich Handel. 15pf, Louis Spohr. 20pf, Ludwig van Beethoven. 25pf, Joseph Haydn. 40pf, Felix Mendelssohn-Bartholdy.

## Perf. 14x13½
**1959, Sept. 8    Engr.    Wmk. 304**
804 A215 Sheet of 5                    19.00  37.50
  a.  10pf deep green         2.60   5.75
  b.  15pf blue               2.60   5.75
  c.  20pf dark carmine       2.60   3.75
  d.  25pf brown              2.60   7.50
  e.  40pf dark blue          2.60   5.75

Opening of Beethoven Hall in Bonn and to honor various anniversaries of German composers.

### Europa Issue, 1959
Common Design Type
**1959, Sept. 19    Litho.    Perf. 13½x14**
**Size: 24x29½mm**
805 CD2 10pf olive green               .30   .25
806 CD2 40pf gray blue                1.05   .35

Uprooted Oak Emblem — A216

**1960, Apr. 7    Perf. 13½x13**
807 A216 10pf grn, blk & lil           .25   .25
808 A216 40pf lt bl, blk & org        1.75  1.75

World Refugee Year, 7/1/59-6/30/60.

Philipp Melanchthon — A217

**1960, Apr. 19    Perf. 13½x14**
809 A217 20pf dk car rose & blk  1.00  1.00

400th anniversary of the death of Philipp Melanchthon, co-worker of Martin Luther in the German Reformation.

Symbols of Christ's Sufferings — A218

**1960, May 17    Perf. 14x13½**
810 A218 10pf Prus grn, gray & ocher                                 .30   .30

1960 Passion Play, Oberammergau, Bavaria.

Dove, Chalice and Crucifix — A219

**1960, July 30    Engr.    Perf. 14x13½**
811 A219 10pf dull green               .50   .35
812 A219 20pf maroon                   .65   .65

37th Eucharistic World Congress, Munich.

Wrestlers and Olympic Rings — A220

Sport scenes from Greek urns: 10pf, Sprinters. 20pf, Discus and Javelin throwers. 40pf, Chariot race.

**1960, Aug. 8    Wmk. 304**
813 A220  7pf red brown                .25   .25
814 A220 10pf olive green              .30   .25
815 A220 20pf vermilion                .30   .25
816 A220 40pf dark blue               1.00  1.00
  Nos. 813-816 (4)           1.85  1.75

17th Olympic Games, Rome, 8/25-9/11.

---

Hildesheim Cathedral, Miters, Cross and Crosier — A221

**1960, Sept. 6    Engr.    Perf. 13½x14**
817 A221 20pf claret                   .65   .40

St. Bernward (960-1022) and St. Godehard (960-1038), bishops.

### Europa Issue, 1960
Common Design Type
**1960, Sept. 19    Wmk. 304**
**Size: 30x25mm**
818 CD3 10pf ol grn & yel grn          .25   .25
819 CD3 20pf brt red & lt red          .65   .25
820 CD3 40pf bl & lt bl               1.00   .85
  Nos. 818-820 (3)           1.90  1.35

George C. Marshall — A222

**1960, Oct. 15    Litho.    Perf. 13x13½**
821 A222 40pf dp blue & blk           2.25  1.75

Issued to honor George C. Marshall, US general and statesman.

Steam Locomotive — A223

**1960, Dec. 7    Perf. 13½x14**
822 A223 10pf ol bis & blk             .30   .35

125th anniversary of German railroads.

St. George — A224

**Wmk. 304**
**1961, Apr. 23    Engr.    Perf. 14**
823 A224 10pf green                    .25   .30

Honoring Boy Scouts of the world on St. George's Day (patron saint of Boy Scouts).

Albrecht Dürer — A225

Portraits: 5pf, Albertus Magnus. 7pf, St. Elizabeth of Thuringia. 8pf, Johann Gutenberg. 15pf, Martin Luther. 20pf, Johann Sebastian Bach. 25pf, Balthasar Neumann. 30pf, Immanuel Kant. 40pf, Gotthold Ephraim Lessing. 50pf, Johann Wolfgang von Goethe. 60pf, Friedrich von Schiller. 70pf, Ludwig van Beethoven. 80pf, Heinrich von Kleist. 90pf, Prof. Franz Oppenheimer. 1m, Annette von Droste-Hülshoff. 2m, Gerhart Hauptmann.

**1961-64    Typo.    Perf. 14**
**Fluorescent or Ordinary Paper**
824 A225  5pf brn olive                .25   .25
  b.  Tête bêche pair ('63)  .60   .90
825 A225  7pf red brown                .25   .25
826 A225  8pf purple                   .25   .25
827 A225 10pf olive green              .25   .25
  b.  Tête bêche pair        .55  1.30
828 A225 15pf blue                     .25   .25
  b.  Tête bêche pair ('63)  .80  1.75
829 A225 20pf dk red                   .25   .25
  b.  Tête bêche pair ('63)  .55  1.60
830 A225 25pf brn red                  .25   .25

**Engr.**
831 A225 30pf black                    .25   .25
832 A225 40pf dk blue                  .25   .25
833 A225 50pf red brown                .25   .25
834 A225 60pf magenta ('62)            .30   .25
835 A225 70pf gray grn                 .25   .25
  a.  70pf deep green        .55   .25
836 A225 80pf brown                    .35   .35
837 A225 90pf bister ('64)             .30   .25

---

838 A225 1m violet blue                .50   .25
839 A225 2m brn ol ('62)              2.25   .25
  Nos. 824-839 (16)         6.45  4.35

Nos. 824-825, 827-830, 832, 834-835, 835a were issued in coils as well as in sheets. Every fifth coil stamp has a black control number on the back.

Nos. 824-839, including booklet panes and tête bêche pairs, were printed on fluorescent paper. Nos. 824-829 and 832 were also printed on ordinary paper.

Gottlieb Daimler's Car of 1886 and Signature — A226

Design: 20pf, Carl Benz's 3-wheel car of 1886 and signature.

**1961, July 3    Litho.**
840 A226 10pf green & blk              .25   .25
841 A226 20pf brick red & blk          .30   .30

75 years of motorized traffic.

Messenger, Nuremberg, 18th Century — A227

**Photogravure and Engraved**
**1961, Aug. 31    Wmk. 304    Perf. 14**
842 A227  7pf brown red & blk          .30   .30

Issued to publicize the exhibition "The Letter in Five Centuries," Nuremberg.

Cathedral, Speyer — A228

**1961, Sept. 2    Engr.**
843 A228 20pf vermilion                .30   .40

900th anniversary of Speyer Cathedral.

### Europa Issue, 1961
Common Design Type
**1961, Sept. 18    Litho.**
**Size: 28½x18½mm**
844 CD4 10pf olive green               .25   .25
845 CD4 40pf violet blue               .35   .50

No. 844 was printed on both ordinary and fluorescent paper.

Reis Telephone — A229

**Wmk. 304**
**1961, Oct. 26    Engr.    Perf. 14**
846 A229 10pf green                    .30   .35

Cent. of the demonstration of the 1st telephone by Philipp Reis.

Wilhelm Emanuel von Ketteler — A230

**1961, Dec. 22    Litho.**
847 A230 10pf olive grn & blk          .30   .35

Sesquicentennial of the birth of von Ketteler, Bishop of Mainz and pioneer in social development.

---

### Fluorescent Paper
was introduced for all stamps, starting with No. 848. Of the stamps before No. 848, those issued on both ordinary and fluorescent paper include Nos. 704, 706, 708-711, 737, 755-756, 824-829, 832, 844. Those issued only on fluorescent paper (up to No. 848) include Nos. 708b, 830-831, 833-839 and 842.

Drusus Stone and Old View of Mainz — A231

**1962, May 10    Engr.    Wmk. 304**
848 A231 20pf deep claret              .30   .35

The 2000th anniversary of Mainz.

Notes and Tuning Fork — A232

**1962, July 12    Litho.    Perf. 14**
849 A232 20pf red & black              .30   .40

Issued to show appreciation of choral singing. The music is from the choral movement for three voices "In dulci jubilo" from "Musae Sioniae" by Michael Praetorius.

"Faith, Thanksgiving, Service" — A233

**1962, Aug. 22    Engr.    Unwmk.**
850 A233 20pf magenta                  .30   .40

79th meeting of German Catholics, Hanover, Aug. 22-29.

Open Bible, Chrismon and Chalice — A234

**1962, Sept. 11    Litho.    Wmk. 304**
851 A234 20pf vermilion & blk          .30   .40

Württemberg Bible Society, 150th anniv.

### Europa Issue, 1962
Common Design Type
**1962, Sept. 17    Engr.**
**Size: 28x23mm**
852 CD5 10pf green                     .25   .25
853 CD5 40pf blue                      .40   .50

"Bread for the World" — A235

**Lithographed and Embossed**
**1962, Nov. 23    Perf. 14**
854 A235 20pf brown red & blk          .30   .40

Issued in connection with the Advent Collection of the Protestant Church in Germany.

Mother and Child Receiving Gift Parcel — A236

**1963, Feb. 9    Engr.**
855 A236 20pf dark carmine             .30   .35

Issued to express gratitude to the American organizations, CRALOG (Council of Relief Agencies Licensed to Operate in Germany) and CARE (Cooperative for American Remittances to Everywhere), for help during 1946-1962.

Globe, Cross, Seeds and Stalks of Wheat — A237

### Lithographed and Engraved
**1963, Feb. 27    Wmk. 304    Perf. 14**
856  A237  20pf gray, blk & red    .30   .35

German Catholic "Misereor" (I have compassion) campaign against hunger and illness.

Checkered Lily — A238

Flowers: 15pf, Lady's slipper. 20pf, Columbine. 40pf, Beach thistle.

**1963, Apr. 28    Litho.    Unwmk.**
857  A238  10pf multicolored    .25   .25
858  A238  15pf multicolored    .25   .25
859  A238  20pf multicolored    .25   .25
860  A238  40pf multicolored    .25   .25
    Nos. 857-860 (4)    1.00  1.00

Flora and Philately Exhibition, Hamburg.

Heidelberg Catechism — A239

**1963, May 2    Litho. & Engr.**
861  A239  20pf dp org, brn org & blk    .30   .35

400th anniv. of the Heidelberg Catechism, containing the doctrine of the reformed church.

Cross of Golgotha, Darkened Sun and Moon — A240

**1963, May 4    Litho.    Wmk. 304**
862  A240  10pf grn, dp car, blk & vio    .25   .30

Consecration of the Regina Martyrum Church, Berlin-Plötzensee, in memory of the victims of Nazism.

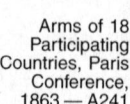

Arms of 18 Participating Countries, Paris Conference, 1863 — A241

**1963, May 7    Engr.**
863  A241  40pf violet blue    .35   .50

1st Intl. Postal Conf., Paris, 1863, cent.

Map Showing New Railroad Link, German and Danish Flags — A242

**1963, May 14    Litho.    Unwmk.**
864  A242  20pf multi    .30   .30

Inauguration of the "Bird Flight Line" railroad link between Germany and Denmark.

---

Cross — A243

### Lithographed and Embossed
**1963, May 24    Unwmk.    Perf. 14**
865  A243  20pf magenta, red & yel    .30   .30

Cent. of the founding of the Intl. Red Cross in connection with the German Red Cross cent. celebrations, Munster, May 24-26.

Synod Emblem and Crown of Barbed Wire — A244

**Perf. 13½x13**
**1963, July 24    Litho.    Wmk. 304**
866  A244  20pf dp orange & blk    .30   .35

Meeting of German Protestants (Evangelical Synod), Dortmund, July 24-28.

### Europa Issue, 1963
Common Design Type
**1963, Sept. 14    Engr.    Perf. 14**
Size: 28x23½mm
867  CD6  15pf green    .25   .30
868  CD6  20pf red    .25   .25

Old Town Hall, Hanover — A245

State Capitals: No. 870, Hamburg harbor, 775th anniv. No. 871, North Ferry pier, Kiel. No. 872, National Theater, Munich. No. 873, Fountain & building, Wiesbaden. No. 874, Reichstag Building, Berlin. No. 875, Gutenberg Museum, Mainz. No. 876, Jan Wellem (Johann Wilhelm II, 1658-1716) statue, Dusseldorf. No. 877, City Hall, Bonn. No. 878, City Hall, Bremen. No. 879, View of Stuttgart. No. 879A, Ludwig's Church, Saarbrucken.

**Perf. 14, 13½x13 (#873, 876, 877)**
**1964-65    Litho.    Unwmk.**
869   A245  20pf gray, blk & red    .25   .30
870   A245  20pf multicolored    .25   .30
871   A245  20pf multicolored    .25   .30
872   A245  20pf multicolored    .25   .30
873   A245  20pf multicolored    .25   .30
874   A245  20pf blue, blk, & grn    .25   .30
875   A245  20pf multicolored    .25   .30
876   A245  20pf multicolored    .25   .30
877   A245  20pf multi ('65)    .25   .30
878   A245  20pf multi ('65)    .25   .30
879   A245  20pf multi ('65)    .25   .30
879A  A245  20pf multi ('65)    .25   .30
    Nos. 869-879A (12)    3.00  3.60

View of Ottobeuren Abbey — A246

### Lithographed and Engraved
**1964, May 29    Perf. 14**
880  A246  20pf pink, red & blk    .25   .30

Ottobeuren Benedictine Abbey, 1200th anniv.

Pres. Heinrich Lübke — A247

**1964, July 1    Litho.    Perf. 14**
881  A247  20pf carmine    .25   .25
882  A247  40pf ultra    .25   .30

Lübke's re-election. See Nos. 974-975.

---

Sophie Scholl — A248

Designs: No. 884, Ludwig Beck. No. 885, Dietrich Bonhoeffer. No. 886, Alfred Delp. No. 887, Karl Friedrich Goerdeler. No. 888, Wilhelm Leuschner. No. 889, Count James von Moltke. No. 890, Count Claus Schenk von Stauffenberg.

**1964, July 20    Litho. & Engr.**
883  A248  20pf blue gray & blk    .55  1.00
884  A248  20pf blue gray & blk    .55  1.00
885  A248  20pf blue gray & blk    .55  1.00
886  A248  20pf blue gray & blk    .55  1.00
887  A248  20pf blue gray & blk    .55  1.00
888  A248  20pf blue gray & blk    .55  1.00
889  A248  20pf blue gray & blk    .55  1.00
890  A248  20pf blue gray & blk    .55  1.00
    Nos. 883-890 (8)    4.40  8.00

Issued to honor the German resistance to the Nazis, 1943-45. Printed in sheet of eight, containing one each of Nos. 883-890, se-tenant. Size: 148x105mm. The stamps were valid; the sheet was not, though widely used. Values: mint $6; used $11.

John Calvin — A249

**1964, Aug. 3    Litho.    Perf. 14**
891  A249  20pf red & black    .25   .30

Issued to honor the meeting of the International Union of the Reformed Churches in Germany, Frankfort on the Main, Aug. 3-13.

Benzene Ring, Kekulé's Formula — A250

Designs: 15pf, Cerenkov radiation, reactor in operation. 20pf, German gas engine.

**1964, Aug. 14    Unwmk.    Perf. 14**
892  A250  10pf dk brn, brt grn & blk  .25  .25
893  A250  15pf bl grn, ultra & blk    .25  .25
894  A250  20pf red, bl grn & blk    .25  .25
    Nos. 892-894 (3)    .75   .75

Progress in science and technology: 10pf, centenary of benzene formula by August Friedrich Kekulé; 15pf, 25 years of nuclear fission, Hahn and Strassmann; 20pf, centenary of German internal combustion engine, Nikolaus August Otto and Eugen Langen.

Ferdinand Lasalle — A251

**1964, Aug. 31    Litho.**
895  A251  20pf slate bl & blk    .25   .30

Cent. of the death of Ferdinand Lasalle, a founder of the German Labor Movement.

Radiating Sun — A252

**1964, Sept. 2    Engr.    Wmk. 304**
896  A252  20pf gray & red    .25   .30

80th meeting of German Catholics, Stuttgart, Sept. 2-6. The inscription from Romans 12:2: ". . . be ye transformed through the renewing of your mind."

---

### Europa Issue, 1964
Common Design Type
**1964, Sept. 14    Litho.    Unwmk.**
Size: 23x29mm
897  CD7  15pf yellow grn & lil    .25   .25
898  CD7  20pf rose & lilac    .25   .25

Judo — A253

**1964, Oct. 10**
899  A253  20pf multicolored    .25   .30

18th Olympic Games, Tokyo, Oct. 10-25.

Prussian Eagle — A254

### Lithographed and Embossed
**1964, Oct. 30    Unwmk.    Perf. 14**
900  A254  20pf brown org & blk    .25   .30

250 years of the Court of Accounts in Germany, founded as the Royal Prussian Upper Chamber of Accounts.

John F. Kennedy (1917-63) — A255

**1964, Nov. 21    Engr.    Wmk. 304**
901  A255  40pf dark blue    .30   .30

Castle Gate, Ellwangen — A256

Designs: (German buildings through 12 centuries): 10pf, Wall pavilion, Zwinger, Dresden. 15pf, Tegel Castle, Berlin. 20pf, Portico, Lorsch. 40pf, Trifels Fortress, Palatinate. 60pf, Treptow Gate, Neubrandenburg. 70pf, Osthofen Gate, Soest. 80pf, Elling Gate, Weissenburg.

**1964-66    Typo.    Unwmk.**
903  A256  10pf brown ('65)    .35   .25
904  A256  15pf dp gray grn ('65)    .35   .25
  b.    Tête bêche pair ('65)    1.00  2.00
905  A256  20pf dp rose red ('65)    .35   .25
  b.    Tête bêche pair ('66)    1.00  1.30

**Engr.**
908  A256  40pf dp violet ('65)    .35   .25
909  A256  50pf olive bister    .65   .25
910  A256  60pf rose red    1.00  .35
911  A256  70pf dark green ('65)    1.00  .35
912  A256  80pf chocolate    1.00  .35
    Nos. 903-912 (8)    5.05  2.30

Nos. 903-905, 908, 910-912 were issued in sheets of 100 and in coils. Every fifth coil stamp has a black control number on the back.

Illustrations from the Works of Matthias Claudius — A257

**1965, Jan. 21    Engr.    Perf. 14**
917  A257  20pf black & red    .25   .30

150th anniv. of the death of Matthias Claudius, poet and editor of the "Wandsbecker Bothe." Exists imperf. Value $225.

Otto von Bismarck by Franz von Lenbach — A258

**1965, Apr. 1    Litho.    Perf. 14**
918 A258 20pf black & dull red    .25   .30

Prince Otto von Bismarck (1815-1898), Prussian statesman and 1st chancellor of the German Empire.
Exists imperf. Value $750.

A259

Designs: 5pf, Traffic lights and signs. 10pf, Communications satellite and ground station. 15pf, Old and new post buses. 20pf, Semaphore telegraph and telecommunication tower. 40pf, Old and new railroad engines. 60pf, Jet Plane and Space Capsule. 70pf, Sailing ship and ocean liner.

**1965**
919 A259  5pf gray & multi        .25   .30
920 A259 10pf multicolored        .25   .30
921 A259 15pf multicolored        .25   .30
922 A259 20pf maroon & multi      .25   .30
923 A259 40pf dk blue & multi     .25   .30
924 A259 60pf dull vio, yel & lt bl  .25   .30
925 A259 70pf multicolored        .30  1.00
    Nos. 919-925 (7)             1.80  2.10

Intl. Transport and Communications Exhib., Munich, June 25-Oct. 30. No. 924 also for the 10th anniv. of the reopening of air service by Lufthansa. Issued: 60pf, 4/1; others, 6/25.
No. 919 exists imperf. Value $225.

Bouquet of Flowers — A260

**1965, May 1    Litho.**
926 A260 15pf multicolored        .25   .25

75th anniv. of May Day celebration in Germany.

ITU Emblem — A261

**1965, May 17    Unwmk.    Perf. 14**
927 A261 40pf dp blue & blk       .30   .35
    Cent. of the ITU.

Adolph Kolping — A262

**1965, May 26    Typo.**
928 A262 20pf black, gray & red   .25   .30

Kolping (1813-65). founder of the Catholic Unions of Journeymen, the Kolpingwork.

Rescue Ship — A263

**1965, May 29    Litho. & Engr.**
929 A263 20pf red & black         .25   .30

Cent. of the German Sea Rescue Service.

---

**Type of 1955 Dated "1945-1965"**
**Perf. 14x13½**
**1965, July 28    Engr.    Wmk. 304**
930 A161 20pf gray                .25   .30

20 years of German expatriation.

Synod Emblem and Labyrinth — A264

**Lithographed and Engraved**
**Perf. 13½x14**
**1965, July 28    Unwmk.**
931 A264 20pf dp bl, grnsh bl & blk   .25   .30

12th meeting of German Protestants (Evangelical Synod), Cologne, July 28-Aug. 1.

Waves and Stuttgart Television Tower — A265

**1965, July 28    Litho.    Perf. 13½x13**
932 A265 20pf dp bl, blk & brt pink   .25   .30

Issued to publicize the German Radio Exhibition, Stuttgart, Aug. 27-Sept. 5.

Stamps of Thurn and Taxis, 1852-59 — A266

**1965, Aug. 28    Perf. 14**
933 A266 20pf multicolored        .25   .30

125th anniv. of the introduction of postage stamps in Great Britain.

**Europa Issue, 1965**
**Common Design Type**
**Perf. 14x13½**
**1965, Sept. 27    Engr.    Wmk. 304**
**Size: 28x23mm**
934 CD8 15pf green                .25   .25
935 CD8 20pf dull red             .25   .25

Nordertor, Flensburg — A267

Designs: 5pf, Berlin Gate, Stettin. 10pf, Wall Pavilion, Zwinger, Dresden. 20pf, Portico, Lorsch. 40pf, Trifels Fortress, Palatinate. 50pf, Castle Gate, Ellwangen. 60pf, Treptow Gate, Neubrandenburg. 70pf, Osthofen Gate, Soest. 80pf, Elling Gate, Weissenburg. 90pf, Zschocke Ladies' Home, Königsberg. 1m, Melanchthon House, Wittenberg. 1.10m, Trinity Hospital, Hildesheim. 1.30m, Tegel Castle, Berlin. 2m, Löwenberg, Town Hall, interior view.

**1966-69    Unwmk.    Engr.    Perf. 14**
936 A267    5pf olive             .25   .25
937 A267   10pf dk brn ('67)      .25   .25
939 A267   20pf dk grn ('67)      .25   .25
940 A267   30pf yellow green      .25   .25
941 A267   50pf red ('67)         .25   .25
942 A267   40pf olive bis ('67)   .30   .25
943 A267   50pf dk bl ('67)       .35   .25
944 A267   60pf dp org ('67)     2.50  1.30
945 A267   70pf slate grn ('67)  1.05   .25
946 A267   80pf red brn ('67)    2.00  1.30
947 A267   90pf black             .75   .30
948 A267    1m dull blue          .75   .25
949 A267 1.10m red brown          .75   .30
950 A267 1.30m green ('69)       2.00  1.20
951 A267    2m purple            2.00   .55
    Nos. 936-951 (15)           13.70  7.20

Brandenburg Gate — A268

---

**1966-68    Typo.    Perf. 14**
952 A268 10pf chocolate           .30   .25
  a.  Bklt. pane, 4 #952, 2 #953, 4 #954 ('67)   4.50  15.00
  b.  Tête bêche pair             .65   .65
  c.  Bklt. pane, 2 #952, 4 #953   2.25  7.50
953 A268 20pf deep green          .30   .25
  a.  Tête bêche pair ('68)       .80   .85
  b.  Bklt. pane, 2 #952, 4 #954  1.60  6.00
954 A268 30pf red                 .30   .25
  a.  Tête bêche pair ('68)       .85  1.20
955 A268 50pf dark blue          1.05   .35
956 A268 100pf dp dull bl ('67)  9.75   .55
    Nos. 952-956 (5)            11.70  1.65

Nos. 952-956 were issued in sheets of 100 and in coils. Every fifth coil stamp has a black control number on the back.

Nathan Söderblom — A269

**1966, Jan. 15    Litho.    Perf. 13x13½**
959 A269 20pf dull lilac & blk    .25   .30

Soderblom (1866-1931),Swedish Protestant theologian, who worked for the union of Christian churches and received 1930 Nobel Peace Prize.

Cardinal von Galen — A270

**1966, Mar. 22    Litho.    Perf. 14**
960 A270 20pf dp lil rose, sal pink & blk   .25   .30

Clemens August Cardinal Count von Galen (1878-1946), anti-Nazi Bishop of Munster.

"The Miraculous Draught" — A271

**1966, July 13    Litho.    Perf. 14**
961 A271 30pf dp orange & blk     .25   .30

81st meeting of German Catholics, Bamberg, July 13-17.

G. W. Leibniz — A272

**1966, Aug. 24    Unwmk.    Perf. 14**
962 A272 30pf rose car, pink & blk   .25   .30

Gottfried Wilhelm Leibniz (1646-1716), philosopher and mathematician.

**Europa Issue, 1966**
**Common Design Type**
**1966, Sept. 24    Perf. 14**
**Size: 23x28½mm**
963 CD9 20pf multicolored         .25   .30
964 CD9 30pf multicolored         .25   .25

Diagram of Three-Phase Transmission — A273

**1966, Sept. 28    Litho.**
965 A273 20pf shown               .25   .25
966 A273 30pf Dynamo              .25   .25

Progress in science and technology: 20pf, 75th anniv. of three-phase power transmission; 30pf, cent.y of discovery by Werner von Siemens of the dynamoelectric principle.

---

UNICEF Emblem — A274

**1966, Oct. 24    Litho.    Perf. 14**
967 A274 30pf red, blk & gray     .25   .30

Awarding of the 1965 Nobel Peace Prize to UNICEF.

Werner von Siemens (1816-92), Electrical Engineer and Inventor — A275

**1966, Dec. 13    Engr.    Perf. 14**
968 A275 30pf maroon              .25   .30

**Europa Issue, 1967**
**Common Design type**
**1967, May 2    Photo.    Perf. 14**
**Size: 23x28mm**
969 CD10 20pf multi               .30   .30
970 CD10 30pf multi               .25   .25

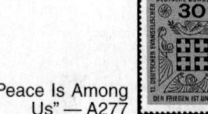

Franz von Taxis — A276

**Lithographed and Engraved**
**1967, June 3    Perf. 14**
971 A276 30pf dp orange & blk     .25   .30

450th anniv. of the death of Franz von Taxis, founder of the Taxis (Thurn and Taxis) postal system.

"Peace Is Among Us" — A277

**1967, June 21**
972 A277 30pf brt pink & blk      .25   .30

13th meeting of German Protestants (Evangelical Synod), Hanover, June 21-25.

Friedrich von Bodelschwingh A278

**Perf. 13½x13**
**1967, July 1    Litho.    Unwmk.**
973 A278 30pf redsh brown & blk   .25   .30

Cent. of Bethel Institution (for the incurable). Friedrich von Bodelschwingh (1877-1946), manager of Bethel (1910-46) & son of the founder.

**Lübke Type of 1964**
**1967, Oct. 14    Litho.    Perf. 14**
974 A247 30pf carmine             .25   .30
975 A247 50pf ultra               .35   .35

Re-election of President Heinrich Lübke.

The Wartburg, Eisenach — A279

**1967, Oct. 31    Engr.    Perf. 14**
976 A279 30pf red                 .30   .35

450th anniversary of the Reformation.

Cross and Map of South America — A280

**1967, Nov. 17    Photo.    Perf. 14**
977 A280 30pf multicolored    .25    .30

"Adveniat," aid movement of German Catholics for the Latin American church.

Koenig Printing Press — A281

Designs: 20pf, Zinc sulfide and lead sulfide crystals. 30pf, Schematic diagram of a microscope.

**1968, Jan. 12    Litho.    Perf. 14**
978 A281 10pf multicolored    .25    .25
979 A281 20pf multicolored    .25    .25
980 A281 30pf multicolored    .25    .25
Nos. 978-980 (3)    .75    .75

Progress in science and technology: 10pf, 150th anniv. of the Koenig printing press; 20pf, 1000th anniv. of mining in the Harz Mountains; 30pf, cent. of scientific microscope construction.

Symbols of Various Crafts — A282

**1968, Mar. 8    Litho.    Perf. 14**
981 A282 30pf multicolored    .30    .35
Traditions and progress of the crafts. Exists imperf. Value $250.

Souvenir Sheet

Adenauer, Churchill, de Gasperi and Schuman — A283

Portraits: 10pf, Winston S. Churchill. 20pf, Alcide de Gasperi. 30pf, Robert Schuman. 50pf, Konrad Adenauer.

**1968, Apr. 19    Litho.    Perf. 14**
**Black Inscriptions**
982 A283    Sheet of 4    2.00    2.00
  a.    10pf dark red brown    .50    .35
  b.    20pf green    .50    .40
  c.    30pf dark red    .50    .50
  d.    50pf bright blue    .50    .65

1st anniv. of the death of Konrad Adenauer (1876-1967), chancellor of West Germany (1949-63), and honoring leaders in building a united Europe.

**Europa Issue, 1968**
Common Design Type
**1968, Apr. 29    Photo.**
Size: 29x24½mm
983 CD11 20pf green, yel & brn    .25    .30
984 CD11 30pf car, yel & brn    .25    .25

Karl Marx (1818-83) — A284

**Lithgraphed and Engraved**
**1968, Apr. 29    Perf. 14**
985 A284 30pf red, black & gray    .25    .30

Pierre de Coubertin — A285

**1968, June 6    Unwmk.    Perf. 14**
986 A285 30pf lilac & dk pur    .55    .35
Nos. 986,B434-B437 (5)    3.65 2.70
19th Olympic Games, Mexico City, 10/12-27.

Opening Bars, "Die Meistersinger von Nurnberg," by Wagner — A286

**Lithographed and Photogravure**
**1968, June 21**
987 A286 30pf gray, blk & fawn    .25    .30
Cent. of the 1st performance of Richard Wagner's "Die Meistersinger von Nurnberg."

Konrad Adenauer (1876-1967) — A287

**1968, July 19    Litho.    Perf. 14**
988 A287 30pf dp orange & blk    .30    .30

Cross and Dove in Center of Universe A288

**1968, July 19    Litho. & Engr.**
989 A288 20pf brt grn, bl blk & yel    .30    .30
Issued to publicize the 82nd meeting of German Catholics, Essen, Sept. 4-8.

North German Confederation Nos. 4 and 10 — A289

**1968, Sept. 5    Engr.    Perf. 14**
990 A289 30pf cop red, gray vio & blk    .25    .30
Cent. of the stamps of the North German Confederation.

Arrows Symbolizing Determination — A290

**1968, Sept. 26    Photo.    Perf. 14**
991 A290 30pf multicolored    .25    .30
Centenary of the German trade unions.

Human Rights Flame — A291

**1968, Dec. 10    Photo.    Perf. 14**
992 A291 30pf multicolored    .25    .30
International Human Rights Year.

Junkers 52 — A292

Design: 30pf, Boeing 707.

**1969, Feb. 6    Litho.    Perf. 14**
993 A292 20pf green & multi    .35    .25
994 A292 30pf red & multi    .55    .25
50th anniv. of German airmail service.

Five-pointed Star — A293

**1969, Apr. 28    Litho.    Perf. 13½x13**
995 A293 30pf red & multi    .40    .30
50th anniv. of the ILO.

**Europa Issue, 1969**
Common Design Type
**1969, Apr. 28    Photo.    Perf. 14**
Size: 29x23mm
996 CD12 20pf green, blue & yel    .35    .25
997 CD12 30pf red brn, yel & blk    .35    .25

Heraldic Eagles of Federal and Weimar Republics — A294

**1969, May 23    Photo.    Perf. 14**
998 A294 30pf red, black & gold    1.00    .40
German Basic Law, 20th anniv., and the proclamation of the Weimar Constitution, 50th anniv.

Crosses — A295

**1969, June 4    Litho. & Engr.**
999 A295 30pf dk violet bl & cream    .40    .30
German War Graves Commission, 50th anniv.

Seashore — A296

**1969, June 4    Perf. 14**
1000 A296 10pf shown    .25    .25
1001 A296 20pf Foothills    .55    .25
1002 A296 30pf Mountains    .25    .25
1003 A296 50pf Riverbed    .65    .50
Nos. 1000-1003 (4)    1.70 1.35
Issued to publicize Nature Protection.

"Hungry for Justice" — A297

**1969, July 7    Litho.    Perf. 14**
1004 A297 30pf multicolored    .40    .30
14th meeting of German Protestants (Evangelical Synod), Stuttgart, July 16-20.

Electromagnetic Field — A298

**1969, Aug. 11    Litho.    Perf. 14**
1005 A298 30pf red & multi    .40    .30
Issued to publicize the German Radio Exhibition, Stuttgart, Aug. 29-Sept. 7.

Maltese Cross — A299

**1969, Aug. 11    Perf. 13x13½**
1006 A299 30pf red & black    .40    .30
Maltese Relief Service, founded 1955, world-wide activities in social services, first aid and disaster assistance.

Souvenir Sheet

Marie Juchacz, Marie-Elisabeth Lüders and Helene Weber — A300

**1969, Aug. 11    Engr.    Perf. 14**
1007 A300    Sheet of 3    1.20    .80
  a.    10pf olive    .30    .25
  b.    20pf dark green    .30    .25
  c.    30pf lake    .30    .25

50th anniv. of universal women's suffrage, Marie Juchacz (1879-1956), Marie-Elisabeth Lüders (1878-1966) and Helene Weber (1881-1962) were members of the German Reichstag.

Bavaria No. 16 — A301

**1969, Sept. 4    Litho. & Embossed**
1008 A301 30pf gray & rose    .40    .30
23rd meeting of the Federation of German Philatelists, Sept. 6, the 70th Philatelists' Day, Sept. 7, and the phil. exhib. "120 Years of Bavarian Stamps" in Garmish-Partenkirchen, Sept. 4-7.

Brine Pipe Line — A302

**1969, Sept. 4    Litho.    Perf. 13½x13**
1009 A302 20pf multicolored    .40    .30
350th anniversary of the Brine Pipe Line from Traunstein to Bad Reichenhall.

Rothenburg ob der Tauber — A303

**Lithographed and Engraved**
**1969, Sept. 4    Perf. 14**
1010 A303 30pf dark red & blk    .40    .30
See Nos. 1047-1049, 1067-1069A, 1106-1110.

Pope John XXIII (1881-1963) — A304

**1969, Oct. 2    Engr.    Perf. 13½x14**
1011  A304  30pf dark red    .35  .30

Mahatma Gandhi (1869-1948) — A305

**1969, Oct. 2    Litho.**
1012  A305  20pf yellow grn & blk    .30  .30

Ernst Moritz Arndt — A306

**1969, Nov. 13    Litho. & Engr.**
1013  A306  30pf gray & maroon    .35  .30
Arndt (1769-1860), historian, poet and member of German National Assembly.

Ludwig van Beethoven — A307

Portraits: 20pf, Georg Wilhelm Hegel (1770-1831), philosopher. 30pf, Friedrich Hölderlin (1770-1843), poet.

**1970, Mar. 20    Perf. 13½x14**
1014  A307  10pf pale vio & blk    .65  .25
1015  A307  20pf olive & blk    .40  .25
1016  A307  30pf rose & blk    .40  .25
    Nos. 1014-1016 (3)    1.45  .75

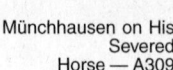

Saar No. 171 — A308

**1970, Apr. 29    Photo.    Perf. 14x13½**
1017  A308  30pf blk, red & gray grn    .35  .30
Issued to publicize the SABRIA National Stamp Exhibition, Saarbrucken, Apr. 29-May 4. No. 1017 was issued Apr. 29 at the SABRIA post office in Saarbrucken, on May 4 throughout Germany.

**Europa Issue, 1970**
Common Design Type
**1970, May 4    Engr.    Perf. 14x13½**
Size: 28x23mm
1018  CD13  20pf green    .30  .25
1019  CD13  30pf red    .30  .25

Münchhausen on His Severed Horse — A309

**1970, May 11    Litho.    Perf. 13½x13**
1020  A309  20pf multicolored    .35  .30
Soldier and storyteller Count Hieronymus C. F. von Münchhausen (1720-97).

Seagoing Vessel and Underpass — A310

**1970, June 18    Litho.    Perf. 14**
1021  A310  20pf multicolored    .35  .30
North Sea-Baltic Sea Canal, 75th anniv.

A311

5pf, Welder (industrial protection). 10pf, Mountain climbers (rescuer bringing down casualty). 20pf, Nurse Assisting Elderly Woman. 30pf, Fireman. 50pf, Stretcher bearer, casualty & ambulance. 70pf, Rescuer & drowning boy.

**1970    Photo.**
1022  A311  5pf dull blue & multi    .25  .25
1023  A311  10pf brown & multi    .25  .25
1024  A311  20pf green & multi    .30  .25
1025  A311  30pf red & multi    .65  .25
1026  A311  50pf brt blue & multi    .65  .35
1027  A311  70pf blue grn & multi    .80  .65
    Nos. 1022-1027 (6)    2.90  2.00
Honoring various voluntary services.
Issued: 20pf, 30pf, 6/18; others, 9/21.

Pres. Gustav Heinemann — A312

**1970-73    Engr.    Perf. 14**
1028  A312  5pf dark gray    .30  .25
1029  A312  10pf brown    .30  .25
1030  A312  20pf green    .30  .25
1030A A312  25pf dp yel grn    .40  .25
1031  A312  30pf red brown    .35  .25
1032  A312  40pf brown org    .35  .25
1033  A312  50pf dark blue    1.30  .25
1034  A312  60pf blue    .75  .25
1035  A312  70pf dark brown    .65  .30
1036  A312  80pf slate grn    .65  .30
1037  A312  90pf magenta    1.30  1.00
1038  A312  1m olive    1.00  .30
1038A A312  110pf olive gray    1.20  .65
1039  A312  120pf ocher    1.45  .65
1040  A312  130pf ocher    1.50  .65
1040A A312  140pf dk blue grn    1.50  .80
1041  A312  150pf purple    1.50  .65
1042  A312  160pf orange    2.10  .95
1042A A312  170pf orange    1.75  .65
1043  A312  190pf deep claret    2.25  .65
1044  A312  2m deep violet    2.25  .30
    Nos. 1028-1044 (21)    23.15  9.85
Issued: 5pf, 1m, 7/23/70; 10, 20pf, 10/23/70; 30, 90pf, 2m, 1/7/71; 40, 50, 70, 80pf, 4/8/71; 60pf, 6/25/71; 25pf, 8/27/71; 120, 160pf, 3/8/72; 130pf, 6/20/72; 150pf, 7/5/72; 170pf, 9/11/72; 110, 140, 190pf, 1/16/73.

Cross Seen through Glass — A313

**1970, Aug. 25    Litho.**
1045  A313  20pf emerald & yellow    .30  .25
Issued to publicize the world mission of Catholic missionaries who bring the Gospel to all peoples.

Cross — A314

**1970, Sept. 4    Perf. 13x13½**
1046  A314  20pf multicolored    .30  .25
Issued to publicize the 83rd meeting of German Catholics, Trier, Sept. 9-13.

**Town Type of 1969**
Designs: No. 1047, View of Cochem and Moselle River. No. 1048, Cathedral and view of Freiburg im Breisgau. No. 1049, View of Oberammergau.
**1970    Litho.    Perf. 14**
1047  A303  20pf apple grn & blk    .40  .30
1048  A303  20pf green & dk brn    .40  .30
1049  A303  30pf dp orange & blk    .35  .30
    Nos. 1047-1049 (3)    1.15  .90
Issued: No. 1047, 9/21; No. 1048, 11/4; No. 1049, 5/11.

Comenius — A315

**1970, Nov. 12    Perf. 13½x14**
1050  A315  30pf dark red & blk    .40  .30
John Amos Comenius (1592-1670), theologian and educator.

Friedrich Engels — A316

**1970, Nov. 27    Litho.    Perf. 14**
1051  A316  50pf red & vio blue    1.20  .65
Engels (1820-95), socialist, collaborator with Marx.

Imperial Eagle, 1872 — A317

**1971, Jan. 18    Litho.    Perf. 13½x14**
1052  A317  30pf multicolored    1.20  .30
Centenary of the German Empire.

Friedrich Ebert (Germany No. 378) — A318

**1971, Jan. 18    Perf. 13**
1053  A318  30pf red brn, ol & blk    1.20  .30
Ebert (1871-1925), 1st Pres. of the German Republic.

Molecule Diagram Textile Pattern — A319

**1971, Feb. 18    Litho.    Perf. 13½x13**
1054  A319  20pf brt grn, red & blk    .30  .25
Synthetic textile fiber research, 125th anniversary.

School Crossing — A320

Traffic Signs: 20pf, Proceed with caution. 30pf, Stop. 50pf, Pedestrian crossing.

**1971, Feb. 18    Perf. 14**
1055  A320  10pf black, ultra & red    .25  .25
1056  A320  20pf black, red & grn    .30  .25
1057  A320  30pf black, gray & red    .40  .25
1058  A320  50pf black, ultra & red    .65  .40
    Nos. 1055-1058 (4)    1.60  1.15
New traffic rules, effective Mar. 1, 1971.

Signal to Pass — A321

Traffic Signs: 10pf, Warning signal. 20pf, Drive at right. 30pf, "Observe pedestrian crossings."

**1971, Apr. 16    Photo.    Perf. 14**
1059  A321  5pf blue, blk & car    .30  .25
1060  A321  10pf multicolored    .30  .25
1061  A321  20pf brt grn, blk & car    .35  .25
1062  A321  30pf car & multi    .60  .25
    Nos. 1059-1062 (4)    1.55  1.00
New traffic rules, effective Mar. 1, 1971.

Luther Facing Charles V, Woodcut by Rabus — A322

**1971, Mar. 18    Perf. 14**
1063  A322  30pf red & black    .55  .30
450th anniversary of the Diet of Worms.

**Europa Issue, 1971**
Common Design Type
**1971, May 3    Photo.    Perf. 14**
Size: 28½x23mm
1064  CD14  20pf green, gold & blk    .30  .25
1065  CD14  30pf dp car, gold & blk    .30  .25

Thomas à Kempis — A323

**1971, May 3    Engr.**
1066  A323  30pf red & black    .50  .30
500th anniversary of the death of Thomas à Kempis (1379-1471), Augustinian monk, author of "The Imitation of Christ."

**Town Type of 1969**
20pf, View of Goslar. No. 1068, View of Nuremberg. No. 1069, Heligoland. 40pf, Heidelberg.

**1971-72    Litho. & Engr.    Perf. 14**
1067  A303  20pf brt green & blk    .40  .35
1068  A303  30pf vermilion & blk    .40  .30
1069  A303  30pf lt grn & blk ('72)    .40  .25
1069A A303  40pf org & blk ('72)    .50  .25
    Nos. 1067-1069A (4)    1.70  1.15
Issued: 20pf, 9/15; No. 1068, 5/21; Nos. 1069, 1069A, 10/20.

Dürer's Signature — A324

**1971, May 21    Engr.**
1070  A324  30pf copper red & blk    1.05  .30
500th anniversary of the birth of Albrecht Dürer (1471-1528), painter and engraver.

Congress Emblem — A325

**1971, May 28    Litho.    Perf. 13½x13**
1071  A325  30pf red, orange & blk    .40  .30
Ecumenical Meeting at Pentecost of the German Evangelical and Catholic Churches, Augsburg, June 2-5.

Illustration from New Astronomy, by Kepler — A326

**1971, June 25    Photo.    Perf. 14**
1072 A326 30pf brt car, gold & blk    .50 .30

Johannes Kepler (1571-1630), astronomer.

Dante Alighieri — A327

**1971, Sept. 3    Engr.    Perf. 14**
1073 A327 10pf black    .25 .25

650th anniversary of the death of Dante Alighieri (1265-1321), poet.

Accident Prevention — A328

Designs: 5pf, "Matches Cause Fires". 10pf, Broken ladder. 20pf, Hand and circular saw. 25pf, "Alcohol and automobile." 30pf, Safety helmets prevent injury. 40pf, Defective plug. 50pf, Nail sticking from board. 60pf, 70pf, Traffic safety (ball rolling before car). 1m, Hoisted cargo. 1.50m, Fenced-in open manhole.

**1971-74    Typo.    Perf. 14**
| | | | |
|---|---|---|---|
| 1074 | A328 | 5pf orange | .30 .25 |
| a. | Bklt. pane, 2 each #1074, 1077-1079 ('74) | | 5.25 11.00 |
| 1075 | A328 | 10pf dark brown | .30 .25 |
| a. | Bklt. pane, 4 #1075, 2 #1078 | | 2.60 2.60 |
| b. | Bklt. pane, 2 each #1075-1076, 1078-1079 ('75) | | 6.75 11.00 |
| c. | Bklt. pane, 2 each #1079, 1075, 1078, 1076 | | 13.50 16.50 |
| 1076 | A328 | 20pf purple | .35 .25 |
| 1077 | A328 | 25pf dp bl grn | .40 .25 |
| 1078 | A328 | 30pf dark red | .40 .25 |
| 1079 | A328 | 40pf magenta | .40 .25 |
| 1080 | A328 | 50pf Prus blue | 1.60 .25 |
| 1081 | A328 | 60pf violet blue | 1.00 .40 |
| 1082 | A328 | 70pf grn & vio bl | 1.00 .30 |
| 1083 | A328 | 100pf olive | 1.60 .25 |
| 1085 | A328 | 150pf red brown | 5.00 1.00 |
| | Nos. 1074-1085 (11) | | 12.35 3.70 |

Accident prevention.
Issued in sheets of 100 and in coils. Every fifth coil stamp has a control number on the back.
Issued: 25pf, 60pf, 9/10; 5pf, 10/29; 10pf, 30pf, 3/8/72; 40pf, 6/20/72; 20pf, 100pf, 7/5/72; 150pf, 9/11/72; 50pf, 1/16/73; 70pf, 6/5/73.

Deaconesses — A329

**1972, Jan. 20    Litho.    Perf. 13x13½**
1087 A329 25pf green, blk & gray    .40 .30

Wilhelm Löhe (1808-1872), founder of the Deaconesses Training Institute at Neuendettelsau.

Senefelder's Lithography Press — A330

**1972, Apr. 14    Litho.    Perf. 13½x13**
1088 A330 25pf multicolored    .40 .30

175th anniv. of the invention of the lithographic printing process by Alois Senefelder in 1796.

---

**Europa Issue 1972**
**Common Design Type**
**1972, May 2    Photo.    Perf. 13½x14**
**Size: 23x29mm**
1089 CD15 25pf yel grn, bl grn & yel    .55 .25
1090 CD15 30pf pink, lt blue & gray    .55 .25

Lucas Cranach, by Dürer — A331

**Lithographed and Engraved**
**1972, May 18    Perf. 14**
1091 A331 25pf green, buff & blk    .50 .30
Cranach (1472-1553), painter and engraver.

Archer in Wheelchair — A332

**1972, July 18    Litho.    Perf. 14**
1092 A332 40pf yel, blk & red brn    .55 .30
21st Stoke-Mandeville Games for the Paralyzed, Heidelberg, Aug. 1-10.

Kurt Schumacher — A333

**1972, Aug. 18    Litho. & Engr.**
1093 A333 40pf red & black    .95 .30
Schumacher (1895-1952), 1st chairman of the German Social Democratic Party.

Post Horn and Decree — A334

**1972, Aug. 18    Photo.**
1094 A334 40pf gold, car & blk    .65 .30
Centenary of the German Postal Museum, Berlin. Design shows page from Heinrich von Stephan's decree establishing the museum.

Open Book — A335

**1972, Sept. 11    Photo.    Perf. 13x13½**
1095 A335 40pf red & multi    .55 .30
International Book Year 1972.

Music by Heinrich Schütz — A336

**Lithographed and Engraved**
**1972, Sept. 29    Perf. 14**
1096 A336 40pf multicolored    .55 .30
300th anniversary of the death of Heinrich Schütz (1585-1672), composer.

---

Carnival Dancers — A337

**1972, Nov. 10    Litho.    Perf. 14**
1097 A337 40pf red & multi    .80 .30
Cologne Carnival sesquicentennial.

Heinrich Heine (1797-1856), Poet — A338

**1972, Dec. 13    Litho.    Perf. 14**
1098 A338 40pf rose, blk & red    .80 .30

"Bread for the World" — A339

**1972, Dec. 13    Photo.    Perf. 14**
1099 A339 30pf green & red    .40 .40
14th "Bread for the World-Developing Peace" campaign of the Protestant Church in Germany.

Würzburg Cathedral, 13th Century Seal — A340

**1972, Dec. 13    Litho.**
1100 A340 40pf dp car, lil rose & blk    .50 .30
Synod 72, meeting of Catholic bishoprics, Würzburg.

Colors of France and Germany Interlaced — A340a

**1973, Jan. 22    Litho.    Perf. 14**
**Size: 51x28mm**
1101 A340a 40pf multicolored    .95 .35
10th anniversary of the Franco-German Cooperation Treaty.

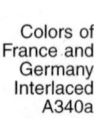

Meteorological Map — A341

**1973, Feb. 19    Litho.    Perf. 14**
1102 A341 30pf multicolored    .40 .30
Cent. of intl. meteorological cooperation.

Radio Tower and "Interpol" — A342

**1973, Feb. 19    Perf. 13½x13**
1103 A342 40pf blk & red    .40 .30
50th anniversary of International Criminal Police Organization (INTERPOL).

Nicolaus Copernicus and Solar System — A343

**1973, Feb. 19    Perf. 14**
1104 A343 40pf blk & red    .95 .30

---

Festival Poster — A344

**1973, Mar. 15    Photo.    Perf. 14**
1105 A344 40pf multicolored    .40 .30
German Turner Festival, Stuttgart, 6/12-17.

**Town Type of 1969**
Designs: 30pf, Saarbrücken. No. 1107, Ship in Hamburg Harbor. No. 1108, Rüdesheim. No. 1109, Aachen. No. 1110, Ships, Bremen Harbor.

**1973    Lithographed and Engraved**
| | | | |
|---|---|---|---|
| 1106 | A303 | 30pf yel grn & blk | .50 .25 |
| 1107 | A303 | 40pf red & blk | .65 .25 |
| 1108 | A303 | 40pf org red & blk | .65 .25 |
| 1109 | A303 | 40pf brn red & blk | .50 .25 |
| 1110 | A303 | 40pf red & blk | .50 .25 |
| | Nos. 1106-1110 (5) | | 2.80 1.25 |

Issued: Nos. 1107-1108, 3/15; others 10/19.

**Europa Issue 1973**
**Common Design Type**
**Size: 38½x21mm**
**1973, Apr. 30    Photo.    Perf. 13½x14**
1114 CD16 30pf grn, lt grn & yel    .35 .25
1115 CD16 40pf dp mag, lil & yel    .50 .25

Maximilian Kolbe — A345

**1973, May 25    Litho.    Perf. 14**
1116 A345 40pf red, blk & brn    .50 .30
Maximilian Kolbe (1894-1941), Polish priest who died in Auschwitz and was beatified in 1971.

"R" for Roswitha — A346

**1973, May 25**
1117 A346 40pf red, blk & yel    .50 .30
Millenary of the death of Roswitha of Gandersheim, Germany's first poetess.

"Not by Bread Alone" — A347

**1973, May 25    Photo.**
1118 A347 30pf multicolored    .35 .30
15th meeting of German Protestants (Evangelical Synod), Dusseldorf, June 27-July 1.

Environment Emblem and "Waste" — A348

30pf, "Water." 40pf, "Noise." 70pf, "Air."

**1973, June 5    Litho.**
| | | | |
|---|---|---|---|
| 1119 | A348 | 25pf multicolored | .35 .25 |
| 1120 | A348 | 30pf multicolored | .35 .25 |
| 1121 | A348 | 40pf org & multi | .80 .25 |
| 1122 | A348 | 70pf ultra & multi | 1.20 .60 |
| | Nos. 1119-1122 (4) | | 2.70 1.35 |

International environment protection and Environment Day, June 5.

Reconstructed Model of Schickard's Calculator — A349

**1973, June 12**
1123 A349 40pf org & multi    .55 .35

350th anniv. of the calculator built by Prof. Wilhelm Shickard, University of Tubingen.

Otto Wels (1873-1939), Leader of German Social Democratic Party — A350

**1973, Sept. 14    Litho.    Perf. 14**
1124 A350 40pf magenta & lilac    .60 .30

Lubeck Cathedral A351

**1973, Sept. 14    Litho. & Engr.**
1125 A351 40pf blk & multi    .80 .30

800th anniversary of Lubeck Cathedral.

Emblems from UN and German Flags — A352

**1973, Sept. 21    Litho.**
1126 A352 40pf multicolored    1.00 .30

Germany's admission to the UN.

Radio and Speaker, 1923 — A353

**1973, Oct. 19    Photo.    Perf. 14**
1127 A353 30pf brt grn & multi    .35 .25

50 years of German broadcasting.

Luise Otto-Peters — A354

**1974, Jan. 15    Litho. & Engr.**
1128 A354 40pf shown    .55 .40
1129 A354 40pf Helene Lange    .55 .40
1130 A354 40pf Gertrud Bäumer    .55 .40
1131 A354 40pf Rosa Luxemburg    .55 .40
  Nos. 1128-1131 (4)    2.20 1.60

Honoring German women writers and leaders in political and women's movements.

Drop of Blood and Police Car Light — A355

**1974, Feb. 15    Photo.    Perf. 14**
1132 A355 40pf carmine & ultra    .65 .30

Blood donor service in conjunction with accident emergency service.

Handicapped People — A356

**1974, Feb. 15    Litho.    Perf. 14**
1133 A356 40pf red & blk    .65 .30

Rehabilitation of the handicapped.

Thomas Aquinas Teaching — A357

**1974, Feb. 15**
1134 A357 40pf blk & red    .50 .30

St. Thomas Aquinas (1225-1274), scholastic philosopher.

Girls under Trees, by August Macke A358

Paintings: No. 1135, Deer in Red, by Franz Marc. 40pf, Portrait in Blue, by Alexej von Jawlensky, vert. 50pf, Pechstein (man) Asleep, by Erich Heckel, vert. 70pf, "Big Still-life," by Max Beckmann, 120pf, Old Farmer, by Ernst Ludwig Kirchner, vert.

**1974    Photo.**
1135 A358 30pf multicolored    .40 .25
1136 A358 30pf multicolored    .65 .25
1137 A358 40pf multicolored    .50 .25
1138 A358 50pf multicolored    .65 .30
1139 A358 70pf multicolored    .80 .65
1140 A358 120pf multicolored    1.60 1.30
  Nos. 1135-1140 (6)    4.60 3.00

German expressionist painters.
Issued: Nos. 1135, 1137, Feb. 15; Nos. 1136, 1138, Aug. 16; Nos. 1139-1140, Oct. 29.

Young Man, by Lehmbruck — A359

Europa: 40pf, Kneeling Woman, by Wilhelm Lehmbruck.

**1974, Apr. 17    Litho.    Perf. 14**
1141 A359 30pf multicolored    .50 .25
1142 A359 40pf multicolored    .50 .25

Immanuel Kant — A360

**1974    Litho. and Engr.    Perf. 14**
1143 A360 40pf Klopstock    .50 .30
**Engr.**
1144 A360 90pf shown    1.60 .40

Friedrich Gottlieb Klopstock (1724-1803), poet, and Immanuel Kant (1724-1804), philosopher.
Issue dates: 40pf, May 15; 90pf, Apr. 17.

**Souvenir Sheet**

Federal Eagle and Flag A361

**1974, May 15    Litho. & Embossed**
1145 A361 40pf gray brn & multi    1.15 1.60

Federal Republic of Germany, 25th anniv.

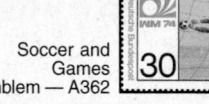

Soccer and Games Emblem — A362

Design: 40pf, Three soccer players.

**1974, May 15    Litho.**
1146 A362 30pf grn & multi    .80 .25
1147 A362 40pf org & multi    1.60 .25

World Cup Soccer Championship, Munich, June 13-July 7.

Crowned Cross Emblem of Diaconate — A363

**1974, May 15**
1148 A363 40pf multicolored    .50 .30

125th anniversary of the Diaconal Association of the German Protestant Church.

Landscape — A364

**1974, May 15**
1149 A364 30pf multicolored    .35 .30

To promote hiking and youth hostels.

Broken Bars of Prison Window — A365

**1974, July 16    Litho.    Perf. 14x13½**
1150 A365 70pf violet bl & blk    .85 .40

"Amnesty International," an organization for the protection of the rights of political, nonviolent, prisoners.

Hans Holbein, Self-portrait — A366

**Lithographed and Engraved**
**1974, July 16    Perf. 13½x14**
1151 A366 50pf multicolored    .65 .30

Hans Holbein the Elder (c. 1470-1524), painter.

Man and Woman Looking at Moon, by Friedrich A367

**1974, Aug. 16    Photo.    Perf. 14**
1152 A367 50pf multicolored    .85 .30

Caspar David Friedrich (1774-1840), German Romantic painter.

Swiss and German 19th Century Mail Boxes — A368

**1974, Oct. 29    Litho.    Perf. 14**
1153 A368 50pf red & multi    .95 .35

Centenary of Universal Postal Union.

Mothers and Foundation Emblem — A369

**1975, Jan. 15    Litho.    Perf. 13**
1154 A369 50pf multicolored    .65 .30

Convalescent Mothers' Foundation, 25th anniversary.

Annette Kolb (1875-1967), Writer — A370

German women writers: 40pf, Ricarda Huch (1864-1947), writer. 50pf, Else Lasker-Schüler (1869-1945), poetess. 70pf, Gertrud von Le Fort (1876-1971), writer.

**Lithographed and Engraved**
**1975, Jan. 15    Perf. 14**
1155 A370 30pf brown & multi    .55 .30
1156 A370 40pf multicolored    .50 .30
1157 A370 50pf claret & multi    .50 .30
1158 A370 70pf blue & multi    .80 .80
  Nos. 1155-1158 (4)    2.35 1.70

Dr. Albert Schweitzer A371

Design: 40pf, Hans Böckler.

**1975    Engr.**
1159 A371 40pf grn & blk    .65 .30
1160 A371 70pf bl & blk    1.50 .65

Böckler (1875-1951), German Workers' Union leader, and of Dr. Albert Schweitzer (1875-1965), medical missionary. Issued: 40pf, Feb. 14; 70pf, Jan. 15.

Head, by Michelangelo — A372

**1975, Feb. 14    Photo.    Perf. 14**
1161 A372 70pf vio bl & blk    1.30 1.20

Michelangelo Buonarroti (1475-1564), Italian sculptor, painter and architect.

Plan of St. Peter's, Rome — A373

**1975, Feb. 14**
1162 A373 50pf red & multi    .65 .30

Holy Year 1975, the "Year of Reconciliation."

Ice Hockey — A374

**1975, Feb. 14    Litho.    Perf. 14**
1163 A374 50pf bl & multi    .85 .30

Ice Hockey World Championship, Munich and Düsseldorf, Apr. 3-19.

Concentric Group, by Oskar Schlemmer — A375

Europa: 50pf, Bauhaus Staircase, painting by Oskar Schlemmer (1888-1943) and CEPT emblem.

**1975, Apr. 15**     **Litho. & Engr.**
1164 A375 40pf gray & multi    .40 .25
1165 A375 50pf gray & multi    .60 .25

Eduard Mörike, Weather Vane, Quill and Signature A376

**1975, May 15**
1166 A376 40pf multicolored     .35 .30
Eduard Mörike (1804-75), pastor and poet.

Joust, from Jousting Book of William IV — A377

**1975, May 15**    **Photo.**    **Perf. 14**
1167 A377 50pf multicolored     .80 .30
500th anniv. of the Wedding of Landshut, (last Duke of Landshut married the daughter of King of Poland, now a yearly local festival).

Cathedral of Mainz — A378

**1975, May 15**     **Litho. & Engr.**
1168 A378 40pf multicolored     .80 .30
Millennium of the Cathedral of Mainz.

View of Neuss, Woodcut — A379

**1975, May 15**
1169 A379 50pf multicolored     .55 .30
500th anniv. of the unsuccessful siege of Neuss by Duke Charles the Bold of Burgundy.

Satellite — A380

10pf, Electric train. 20pf, Old Weser lighthouse. 30pf, Rescue helicopter. 40pf, Space shuttle. 50pf, Radar station. 60pf, X-ray machine. 70pf, Shipbuilding. 80pf, Tractor. 100pf, Bituminous coal excavator. 110pf, Color TV camera. 120pf, Chemical plant. 130pf, Brewery. 140pf, Heating plant, Licterfelde. 150pf, 190pf, Power shovel. 160pf, Blast furnace. 180pf, Payloader. 200pf, Oil drilling. 230pf, Frankfurt Airport. 250pf, Airport. 300pf, Electro. RR. 500pf, Effelsberg radio telescope.

**1975-82**     **Engr.**    **Perf. 14**
1170 A380 5pf olive grn    .25 .25
1171 A380 10pf dp mag    .25 .25
1172 A380 20pf red org    .25 .25
1173 A380 30pf dp vio    .25 .25
1174 A380 40pf blue grn    .30 .25
1175 A380 50pf magenta    .35 .25
1176 A380 60pf red    .65 .25
1177 A380 70pf blue    .55 .25
1178 A380 80pf blue grn    .55 .25
1179 A380 100pf brown    .55 .25
1180 A380 110pf plum    1.30 .55
1181 A380 120pf dp ultra    .65 .30

1182 A380 130pf carmine    1.60 .55
1183 A380 140pf red    .80 .35
1184 A380 150pf red brown    2.00 .65
1185 A380 160pf dp green    1.05 .65
1186 A380 180pf dk brown    2.00 .65
1187 A380 190pf org brn    2.00 .55
1188 A380 200pf plum    1.30 .30
1189 A380 230pf dp pur    2.60 .80
1190 A380 250pf green    3.00 1.25
1191 A380 300pf olive brown    3.75 1.25
1192 A380 500pf dark blue    3.75 1.00
   *Nos. 1170-1192 (23)*    29.75 11.25

Issued: 40, 50, 100pf, 5/15; 10, 30, 70pf, 8/14; 80, 120, 160pf, 10/15; 5, 140, 200pf, 11/14; 20, 500pf, 2/17/76; 60pf, 11/16/78; 230pf, 5/17/79; 150, 180pf, 7/12/79; 110, 130, 300pf, 6/16/82; 190, 250pf, 7/15/82.

Market and Town Hall, Alsfeld — A381

No. 1197, Plönlein Corner, Siebers Tower and Kobolzeller Gate, Rothenburg. No. 1198, Town Hall (Steipe), Trier. No. 1199, View of Xanten.

**1975, July 15**     **Litho. & Engr.**
1196 A381 50pf multicolored    .65 .50
1197 A381 50pf multicolored    .65 .50
1198 A381 50pf multicolored    .65 .50
1199 A381 50pf multicolored    .65 .50
   *Nos. 1196-1199 (4)*    2.60 2.00

European Architectural Heritage Year.

Three Stages of Drug Addiction A382

**1975, Aug. 14**    **Photo.**    **Perf. 14**
1200 A382 40pf multicolored     .35 .30
Fight against drug abuse.

Matthias Erzberger A383

**1975, Aug. 14**     **Engr.**
1201 A383 50pf red & black     .55 .30
Erzberger (1875-1921), statesman, signer of Compiègne Armistice (1918) at end of World War I.

Sign of Royal Prussian Post, 1776 — A384

**1975, Aug. 14**     **Litho.**
1202 A384 10pf blue & multi     .35 .25
Stamp Day, 1975, and 76th German Philatelists' Day, Sept. 21.

**Souvenir Sheet**

Gustav Stresemann, Ludwig Quidde, Carl von Ossietzky — A385

**1975, Nov. 14**    **Engr.**    **Perf. 14**
1203 A385 Sheet of 3    2.00 1.60
 *a.-c.*    50pf, single stamp    .60 .50
German winners of Nobel Peace Prize. No. 1203 has litho. marginal inscription.

Olympic Rings, Symbolic Mountains — A386

**1976, Jan. 5**     **Litho. & Engr.**
1204 A386 50pf red & multi    1.30 .65
12th Winter Olympic Games, Innsbruck, Austria, Feb. 4-15.

Konrad Adenauer — A387

**1976, Jan. 5**     **Engr.**
1205 A387 50pf dark slate green   1.75 .30
Konrad Adenauer (1876-1967), Chancellor (1949-63).

Books by Hans Sachs — A388

**1976, Jan. 5**     **Litho.**
1206 A388 40pf multicolored     .55 .30
Hans Sachs (1494-1576), poet (meistersinger), 400th death anniversary.

Junkers F 13, 1926 — A389

**1976, Jan. 5**
1207 A389 50pf multicolored     .80 .30
Lufthansa, 50th anniversary.

German Eagle — A390

**1976, Feb. 17**    **Photo.**    **Perf. 14**
1208 A390 50pf red, blk & gold    .65 .30
Federal Constitutional Court, 25th anniv.

"EG" — A391

**1976, Apr. 6**    **Photo.**    **Perf. 14**
1209 A391 40pf red & multi    .65 .30
European Coal and Steel Community, 25th anniversary.

Wuppertal Suspension Train — A392

**1976, Apr. 6**     **Litho.**
1210 A392 50pf multicolored    .65 2.60
Wuppertal suspension railroad, 75th anniv.

Girl Selling Trinkets and Prints — A393

Europa: 50pf, Boy selling copperplate prints, and CEPT emblem. Ludwigsburg china figurines, c. 1765.

**1976, May 13**     **Photo.**
1211 A393 40pf olive & multi    .50 .25
1212 A393 50pf scarlet & multi    .50 .25

Dr. Carl Sonnenschein A394

**1976, May 13**     **Litho.**
1213 A394 50pf carmine & multi    .55 .30
Sonnenschein (1876-1929), Roman Catholic clergyman and social reformer.

Weber Conducting "Freischutz" in Covent Garden — A395

**1976, May 13**
1214 A395 50pf red brown & blk    .65 .30
Carl Maria von Weber (1786-1826), composer, 150th death anniversary.

Hymn, by Paul Gerhardt — A396

**1976, May 13**     **Engr. & Litho.**
1215 A396 40pf multicolored     .40 .30
Gerhardt (1607-76), Lutheran hymn writer.

Carl Schurz, American Flag, Capitol — A397

**1976, May 13**     **Litho.**
1216 A397 70pf multicolored    .85 .35
American Bicentennial.

Modern Stage — A398

**1976, July 14**    **Litho.**    **Perf. 14**
1217 A398 50pf multicolored    1.05 .30
Bayreuth Festival, centenary.

Bronze Ritual Chariot c. 1000 B.C. — A399

Archaeological Treasures: 40pf, Celtic gold vessel, 5th-4th centuries B.C. 50pf, Celtic silver torque, 2nd-1st centuries B.C. 120pf, Roman cup with masks, 1st century A.D.

**1976, July 14**
1218 A399 30pf multicolored    .35 .30
1219 A399 40pf multicolored    .50 .30
1220 A399 50pf multicolored    .65 .40
1221 A399 120pf multicolored    1.45 1.45
   *Nos. 1218-1221 (4)*    2.95 2.45

Golden Plover — A400

**1976, Aug. 17**
1222 A400 50pf multicolored .95 .30
Protection of birds.

"Simplicissimus
Teutsch" — A401

**1976, Aug. 17**
1223 A401 40pf multicolored .95 .30
Johann Jacob Christoph von Grimmelshausen, 300th birth anniversary; author of the "Adventures of Simplicissimus Teutsch."

Imperial Post Emblem, Höchst am Main, 18th Cent. — A402

**1976, Oct. 14 Litho. Perf. 14**
1224 A402 10pf brown & multi .30 .25
Stamp Day.

Caroline Neuber as Medea — A403

German Actresses: 40pf, Sophie Schröder (1781-1868) as Sappho. 50pf, Louise Dumont (1862-1932) as Hedda Gabler. 70pf, Hermine Körner (1878-1960) as Lady Macbeth.

**1976, Nov. 16 Photo.**
1225 A403 30pf multicolored .55 .25
1226 A403 40pf multicolored .55 .25
1227 A403 50pf multicolored .55 .30
1228 A403 70pf multicolored 1.05 .80
Nos. 1225-1228 (4) 2.70 1.60

Palais de l'Europe, Strasbourg A404

**1977, Jan. 13 Engr. Perf. 14**
1229 A404 140pf green & blk 1.45 .50
Inauguration of the new Council of Europe Headquarters, Jan. 28.

Scenes from Till Eulenspiegel — A405

**1977, Jan. 13 Litho.**
1230 A405 50pf multicolored .50 .30
Till Eulenspiegel (d. 1350), roguish fool and hero, his adventures reported in book of same name.

Pfaueninsel Castle — A406

10pf, Glucksburg. 25pf, Gemen. 30pf, Ludwigstein. 40pf, Eltz. 50pf, Neuschwanstein. 60pf, Marksburg. 70pf, Mespelbrunn. 90pf, Vischeringurg. 190pf, Pfaueninsel. 200pf, Burresheim. 210pf, Schwanenburg. 230pf, Lichtenberg.

**1977-79 Typo. Perf. 14**
1231 A406 10pf chalky blue .25 .25
  a. Bklt. pane, 4 #1231, 2 each
     #1234, 1236 4.25 6.75
  b. Bklt. pane, 4 #1231, 2
     #1234, 2 #1310 2.60 3.75
  c. Bklt. pane, 4 #1231, 2
     #1310, 2 #1312 6.00 6.50
  d. Bklt. pane, 2 each #1231,
     1234, 1310-1311 9.50 13.50
1232 A406 20pf red .25 .25
1233 A406 25pf red .35 .25
1234 A406 30pf olive brown .30 .25
1235 A406 40pf blue green .40 .25
1236 A406 50pf carmine .50 .25
1237 A406 60pf brown .65 .25
1238 A406 70pf Prus blue .65 .25
1239 A406 90pf violet blue 1.00 .55
1240 A406 190pf org brown 1.60 .65
1240A A406 200pf dp green 2.00 .65
1241 A406 210pf red brown 2.60 1.00
1242 A406 230pf green 2.60 1.00
Nos. 1231-1242 (13) 13.15 5.65
See Nos. 1308-1315.
Issued in sheets of 100 and in coils. Every fifth coil stamp has control number on the back.
Issued: 60, 200pf, 1/13; 40, 190pf, 2/16; 10, 30pf, 4/14; 50, 70pf, 5/17; 230pf, 11/16/78; 25, 90pf, 1/11/79; 20, 210pf, 2/14/79.

Souvenir Sheet

German Art Nouveau A407

Designs: 30pf, Floral ornament. 70pf, Athena, poster by Franz von Stuck. 90pf, Chair, c. 1902.

**1977, Feb. 16 Litho. Perf. 14**
1243 A407 Sheet of 3 2.10 1.30
  a. 30pf multicolored .65 .25
  b. 70pf multicolored .65 .40
  c. 90pf multicolored .75 .65
1st German Art Nouveau Exhib., 75th anniv.

Jean Monnet — A408

**1977, Feb. 16**
1244 A408 50pf black & yellow .55 .30
Jean Monnet (1888-1979), French proponent of unification of Europe, became first Honorary Citizen of Europe in Apr. 1976.

Flower Show Emblem — A409

**1977, Apr. 14**
1245 A409 50pf green & multi .65 .30
25th Federal Horticultural Show, Stuttgart, Apr. 29-Oct. 23.

Gauss Plane of Complex Numbers — A410

**1977, Apr. 14**
1246 A410 40pf silver & multi 1.05 .30
Carl Friedrich Gauss (1777-1855), mathematician, 200th birth anniversary.

Barbarossa Head, Cappenberg Reliquary — A411

**1977, Apr. 14**
1247 A411 40pf multicolored 1.00 .30
Staufer Year 1977. "Time of the Hohenstaufen" Exhibition, Stuttgart, Mar. 25-June 5, in connection with the 25th anniversary of Baden-Wurttemberg.

Rhön Highway — A412

Europa: 50pf, Rhine, Siebengebirge and train.

**1977, May 7 Litho. & Engr.**
1248 A412 40pf brt green & blk .55 .25
1249 A412 50pf brt red & blk .55 .25

Rubens, Self-portrait — A413

**1977, May 17 Engr.**
1250 A413 30pf brown black .65 .30
Peter Paul Rubens (1577-1640), Flemish painter, 400th birth anniversary.

Ulm Cathedral — A414

**1977, May 17 Litho. & Engr.**
1251 A414 40pf blue & sepia .55 .30
600th anniversary of Ulm Cathedral.

Madonna, Oldest Rector's Seal A415

Landgrave Philipp, Great Seal of University A416

**1977, May 17 Photo.**
1252 A415 50pf indigo & org red .65 .30
1253 A416 50pf indigo & org red .65 .30
Mainz University, 500th anniv. (No. 1252); Marburg University, 450th anniv. (No. 1253).

Morning, by Runge A417

**1977, July 13 Litho. Perf. 14**
1254 A417 60pf blue & multi 1.00 .35
Philipp Otto Runge (1777-1810), painter.

Bishop Ketteler's Coat of Arms — A418

**1977, July 13**
1255 A418 50pf multicolored .55 .30
Wilhelm Emmanuel von Ketteler (1811-1877), Bishop of Mainz, Reichstag member and social reformer, death centenary.

Fritz von Bodelschwingh A419

**1977, July 13 Litho. & Engr.**
1256 A419 50pf multicolored .65 .30
Pastor Fritz von Bodelschwingh (1877-1946), manager of Bethel Institute (for the incurable sick), birth centenary.

Jesus as Teacher, Great Seal of University — A420

**1977, Aug. 16 Photo.**
1257 A420 50pf multicolored .80 .30
Tübingen University, 500th anniversary.

Golden Hat, Schifferstadt, Bronze Age — A421

Archaeological Heritage: 120pf, Gilt helmet, from Prince's Tomb, Krefeld-Gellep. 200pf, Bronze Centaur's head, Schwarzenacker.

**1977, Aug. 16 Litho.**
1258 A421 30pf multicolored .35 .30
1259 A421 120pf multicolored 1.30 1.00
1260 A421 200pf multicolored 1.75 1.45
Nos. 1258-1260 (3) 3.40 2.75

Telephone Operator and Switchboard, 1881 — A422

**1977, Oct. 13 Litho. Perf. 14**
1261 A422 50pf multicolored .95 .30
German telephone centenary.

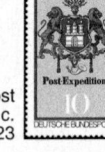

Arms of Hamburg, Post Emblem, c. 1861 — A423

**1977, Oct. 13**
1262 A423 10pf multicolored .35 .30
Stamp Day.

Wilhelm Hauff — A424

**1977, Nov. 10 Photo. Perf. 14**
1263 A424 40pf multicolored .40 .30
Wilhelm Hauff (1802-1827), writer and fabulist, 150th death anniversary.

Traveling Surgeon — A425

**1977, Nov. 10 Litho.**
1264 A425 50pf multicolored .65 .30
Dr. Johann Andreas Eisenbarth (1663-1727), traveling surgeon and adventurer.

Book Cover, by Alexander Schröder — A426

**1978, Jan. 12 Litho. Perf. 14**
1265 A426 50pf multicolored .55 .30
Rudolf Alexander Schröder (1878-1962), writer, designer, Lutheran minister.

"Refugees" A427

**1978, Jan. 12 Photo.**
1266 A427 50pf multicolored .55 .30
Friedland Aid Society for displaced Germans, 20th anniversary.

Souvenir Sheet

Gerhart Hauptmann, Hermann Hesse, Thomas Mann — A428

**1978, Feb. 16 Litho. Perf. 14**
1267 A428 Sheet of 3 2.10 1.20
a. 30pf multicolored .60 .30
b. 50pf multicolored .60 .30
c. 70pf multicolored .65 .50
German winners of Nobel Literature Prize.

Martin Buber (1878-1965), Writer and Philosopher — A429

**1978, Feb. 16**
1268 A429 50pf multicolored .60 .30

Museum Tower and Observatory — A430

**1978, Apr. 13 Litho. Perf. 14**
1269 A430 50pf multicolored .60 .30
German Museum for Natural Sciences and Technology, Munich, 75th anniversary.

Old City Halls — A431

Europa: 40pf, Bamberg. 50pf, Regensburg. 70pf, Esslingen on Neckar.

**Lithographed and Engraved**
**1978, May 22 Perf. 14**
1270 A431 40pf multicolored .55 .30
1271 A431 50pf multicolored .80 .30
1272 A431 70pf multicolored 1.00 .55
Nos. 1270-1272 (3) 2.35 1.15

Pied Piper of Hamelin — A432

**1978, May 22 Litho.**
1273 A432 50pf multicolored .65 .30
The Pied Piper led 130 children of Hamelin away never to be seen again.

Janusz Korczak — A433

**1978, July 13 Litho. Perf. 14**
1274 A433 90pf multicolored .95 .50
Dr. Janusz Korczak (1878-1942), physician, educator, proponent of children's rights.

Fossil Bat — A434

200pf, Eohippus (primitive horse), horiz.

**1978, July 13**
1275 A434 80pf multicolored 1.45 1.20
1276 A434 200pf multicolored 1.45 1.30
Archaeological heritage from Messel open-cast mine, c. 50 million years old.

Parliament, Bonn — A435

**1978, Aug. 17 Litho. Perf. 14**
1277 A435 70pf multicolored .95 .35
65th Interparliamentary Conf., Bonn, Sept. 3-14.

A436

Rose Window, Freiburg Cathedral.

**1978, Aug. 17**
1278 A436 40pf multicolored .40 .30
85th Congress of German Catholics, Freiburg, Sept. 13-17.

A437

Brentano as Butterfly, by Luise Duttenhofer.

**1978, Aug. 17**
1279 A437 30pf multicolored .40 .30
Clemens Brentano (1778-1842), poet.

A438

**1978, Aug. 17**
1280 A438 50pf multicolored .65 .30
European Human Rights Convention, 25th anniversary.

Baden Posthouse Sign, c. 1825 A439

Saxony No. 1 with "World Philatelic Movement" Cancel A440

**1978, Oct. 12 Litho. Perf. 14**
1281 A439 40pf multicolored .40 .25
1282 A440 50pf multicolored .40 .25
a. Pair, #1281-1282 1.00 1.05
Stamp Day and German Philatelists' Meeting, Frankfurt am Main, Oct. 12-15.

Easter at Walchensee, by Lovis Corinth — A441

Impressionist Paintings: 70pf, Horseman on Shore, by Max Liebermann, vert. 120pf, Lady with Cat, by Max Slevogt, vert.

**1978, Nov. 16 Photo. Perf. 14**
1283 A441 50pf multicolored .65 .40
1284 A441 70pf multicolored 1.00 .55
1285 A441 120pf multicolored 1.30 1.20
Nos. 1283-1285 (3) 2.95 2.15

Child and Building — A442

**1979, Jan. 11 Photo.**
1286 A442 60pf black & rose .80 .30
International Year of the Child and 20th anniv. of Declaration of Children's Rights.

Agnes Miegel — A443

**1979, Feb. 14 Photo. Perf. 14**
1287 A443 60pf multicolored .55 .30
Agnes Miegel (1879-1964), poet.

Film — A444

**1979, Feb. 14 Litho.**
1288 A444 50pf black & green .65 .30
25th German Short-Film Festival, Oberhausen, Apr. 23-28.

Parliament Benches in Flag Colors of Members A445

**1979, Feb. 14**
1289 A445 50pf multicolored .80 .30
European Parliament, first direct elections, June 7-10, 1979.

Emblems of Road Rescue Services A446

**1979, Feb. 14**
1290 A446 50pf multicolored .65 .30

A447

Europa: 50pf, Telegraph office, 1863. 60pf, Post Office window, 1854.

**1979, May 17 Litho. Perf. 14**
1291 A447 50pf multicolored .55 .25
1292 A447 60pf multicolored .65 .25

A448

**1979, May 17 Photo.**
1293 A448 60pf red & black .80 .30
Anne Frank (1929-45), author, Nazi victim.

First Electric Train, 1879 Berlin Exhibition A449

**1979, May 17**     **Litho.**
1294 A449 60pf multicolored    .80 .30
Intl. Transportation Exhib., Hamburg.

Hand Setting Radio Dial — A450

**1979, July 12**   **Litho.**   *Perf. 14*
1295 A450 60pf multicolored    .80 .30
World Administrative Radio Conference, Geneva, Sept. 24-Dec. 1.

Moses Receiving Tablets of the Law, by Lucas Cranach — A451

**1979, July 12**    **Litho. & Engr.**
1296 A451 50pf black & blue grn   .80 .30
450th anniv. of Martin Luther's Catechism.

Cross and Charlemagne's Emblem — A452

**1979, July 12**   **Litho. & Embossed**
1297 A452 50pf multicolored    .55 .30
1979 pilgrimage to Aachen.

Hildegard von Bingen with Manuscript — A453

**1979, Aug. 9**     **Litho.**
1298 A453 110pf multicolored    .95 .50
Hildegard von Bingen, Benedictine nun, mystic and writer, 800th death anniversary.

Diagram of Einstein's Photoelectric Effect — A454

Designs: No. 1300, Otto Hahn's diagram of the splitting of the uranium nucleus. No. 1301, Max von Laue's atom arrangement in crystals.

**1979, Aug. 9**     **Photo.**
1299 A454 60pf multicolored    .65 .35
1300 A454 60pf multicolored    1.30 .35
1301 A454 60pf multicolored    .65 .35
    Nos. 1299-1301 (3)    2.60 1.05
Birth centenaries of German Nobel Prize winners: Albert Einstein, physics, 1921; Otto Hahn, chemistry, 1944; Max von Laue, physics, 1914.

Pilot on Board — A455

**Lithographed and Engraved**
**1979, Oct. 11**     *Perf. 14*
1302 A455 60pf multicolored    .55 .30
Three centuries of pilots' regulations.

Birds in Garden, by Paul Klee A456

**1979, Nov. 14**     **Photo.**
1303 A456 90pf multicolored    .85 .50
Paul Klee (1879-1940), Swiss artist.

Mephistopheles and Faust — A457

**1979, Nov. 14**     **Litho.**
1304 A457 60pf multicolored    1.00 .30
Doctor Johannes Faust.

Energy Conservation — A458

**1979, Nov. 14**     *Perf. 13x13½*
1305 A458 40pf multicolored    .55 .30

### Castle Type A406 of 1977-79

Designs: 35pf, Lichtenstein. 40pf, Wolfsburg. 50pf, Inzlingen. 60pf, Rheydt. 80pf, Wilhelmsthal. 120pf, Charlottenburg. 280pf, Ahrensburg. 300pf, Herrenhausen.

| **1979-82** | **Typo.** | | *Perf. 14* | |
|---|---|---|---|---|
| 1308 | 35pf | org brown | .50 | .35 |
| 1309 | 40pf | brown | .55 | .25 |
| 1310 | 50pf | brt green | .60 | .25 |
| 1311 | 60pf | dp claret | .60 | .30 |
| 1312 | 80pf | olive brn | .85 | .30 |
| 1313 | 120pf | violet | 1.30 | .50 |
| 1314 | 280pf | blue | 2.75 | .80 |
| 1315 | 300pf | red | 3.25 | .65 |
| | *Nos. 1308-1315 (8)* | | 10.40 | 3.40 |

Issued: 60pf, 11/14; 40pf, 50pf, 2/14/80; 35pf, 80pf, 300pf, 6/16/82; 120pf, 280pf, 7/15/82.

Iphigenia, by Anselm Feuerbach A459

**1980, Jan. 10**     **Litho.**
1321 A459 50pf multicolored    .95 .30
Anselm Feuerbach (1829-1880), historical and portrait painter.

Flags of NATO and Members A460

**1980, Jan. 10**
1322 A460 100pf multicolored    1.30 .65
Germany's membership in NATO, 25th anniv.

Osnabruck, 1,200th Anniversary A461

**1980, Jan. 10**     **Litho. & Engr.**
1323 A461 60pf multicolored    .65 .30

Götz von Berlichingen, Painting on Glass — A462

**1980, Jan. 10**     **Litho.**
1324 A462 60pf multicolored    .65 .30
Götz von Berlichingen (1480-1562), knight.

Duden Dictionary, Old and New Editions — A463

**1980, Jan. 14**
1325 A463 60pf multicolored    .65 .30
Konrad Duden's German Language Dictionary, centenary of publication.

German Association for Public and Private Social Welfare Centenary A464

**1980, Apr. 10**
1326 A464 60pf multicolored    .65 .30

A465

Emperor Frederick I (Barbarossa) and Sons, Welf Chronicles, 12th century.

**1980, Apr. 10**
1327 A465 60pf multicolored    .85 .30
Imperial Diet of Geinhausen, 800th anniv.

A466

Europa: 50pf, Albertus Magnus (1193-1280), saint and doctor of the Church. 60pf, Gottfried Wilhelm Leibniz (1646-1716), philosopher.

**1980, May 8**    **Litho.**   *Perf. 14*
1328 A466 50pf multicolored    .75 .25
1329 A466 60pf multicolored    .75 .25

Confession of Augsburg, Engraving, 1630 — A467

**1980, May 8**
1330 A467 50pf multicolored    .60 .30
Reading of Confession of Augsburg to Charles V (first official creed of Lutheran Church), 450th anniversary.

Nature Preserves A468

**1980, May 8**     **Photo.**
1331 A468 40pf multicolored    .85 .30

Oscillogram Pulses and Ear — A469

**Lithographed and Embossed**
**1980, July 10**     *Perf. 14*
1332 A469 90pf multicolored    1.00 .35
16th Intl. Cong. for the Training and Education of the Hard of Hearing, Hamburg, 8/4-8.

A470

Design: Book of Daily Bible Readings, Title Page, 1731.

**1980, July 10**     **Litho.**
1333 A470 50pf multicolored    .60 .30
Moravian Brethren's Book of Daily Bible Readings, 250th edition.

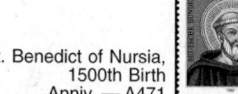

St. Benedict of Nursia, 1500th Birth Anniv. — A471

**1980, July 10**     *Perf. 13x13½*
1334 A471 50pf multicolored    .55 .30

Helping Hand — A472

**1980, Aug. 14**    **Litho. & Engr.**
1335 A472 60pf multicolored    .65 .30
Dr. Friedrich Joseph Haass (1780-1853), physician and philanthropist.

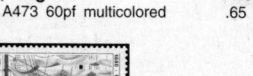

Marie von Ebner-Eschenbach (1830-1916), Writer — A473

**1980, Aug. 14**     **Photo.**
1336 A473 60pf multicolored    .65 .30

Ship's Rigging — A474

**1980, Aug. 14**     **Litho.**
1337 A474 60pf multicolored    .65 .30
Gorch Fock (pen name of Johan Kinau) (1880-1916), poet and dramatist.

A475

Design: Hoeing, Pressing Grapes, Wine Cellar, 14th Century Woodcuts.

**1980, Oct. 9**    **Litho.**   *Perf. 14*
1338 A475 50pf multicolored    .65 .30
Wine production in Central Europe, 2000th anniversary.

Setting Final Stone in South Tower, Cologne Cathedral — A476

**1980, Oct. 9**
1339 A476 60pf multicolored 1.30 .30
Completion of Cologne Cathedral, cent.

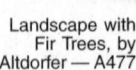

Landscape with Fir Trees, by Altdorfer — A477

**Lithographed and Engraved**
**1980, Nov. 13** *Perf. 14*
1340 A477 40pf multicolored .55 .30
Albrecht Altdorfer (1480-1538), painter and engraver.

Elly Heuss-Knapp — A478

**1981, Jan. 15** **Photo.**
1341 A478 60pf multicolored .65 .30
Elly Heuss-Knapp (1881-1951), founded Elly Heuss-Knapp Foundation (Rest and Recuperation for Mothers).

International Year of the Disabled A479

**1981, Jan. 15** **Litho.**
1342 A479 60pf multicolored .65 .30

European Urban Renaissance A480

**1981, Jan. 15** **Litho. & Engr.**
1343 A480 60pf multicolored .75 .30

Georg Philipp Telemann, Title Page of "Singet dem Herrn" Cantata — A481

**1981, Feb. 12** **Photo.**
1344 A481 60pf multicolored .65 .30
Georg Telemann (1681-1767), composer.

Foreign Guest Worker Integration A482

**1981, Feb. 12** **Litho.**
1345 A482 50pf multicolored .65 .30

Preservation of the Environment A483

**1981, Feb. 12**
1346 A483 60pf multicolored 1.05 .30

European Patent Office Centenary A484

**1981, Feb. 12**
1347 A484 60pf multicolored .65 .30

Chest Scintigram — A485

**1981, Feb. 12** *Perf. 13x13½*
1348 A485 40pf multi .55 .30
Early examination for the prevention of cancer.

A486

50pf, South German couple dancing in regional costumes. 60pf, Northern couple.

**1981, May 7** **Litho.** *Perf. 14*
1349 A486 50pf multicolored .55 .25
1350 A486 60pf multicolored .65 .25

Europa.

19th German Protestant Convention, Hamburg, June 17-21 — A487

**1981, May 7** **Photo.**
1351 A487 50pf multicolored .65 .30

A488

**1981, May 7** **Litho.**
1352 A488 60pf Altar figures .65 .30
Tilman Riemenschneider (1460-1531), sculptor, 450th death anniversary.

A489

**1981, July 16** **Litho.** *Perf. 14*
1353 A489 110pf multicolored 1.45 .40
Georg von Neumayer polar research station.

Energy Conservation Research A490

**1981, July 16**
1354 A490 50pf Solar generator .85 .30

Wildlife Protection — A491

**1981, July 16**
1355 A491 60pf Baby coot .95 .30

Cooperation in Third World Development A492

**1981, July 16**
1356 A492 90pf multicolored 1.05 .40

Wilhelm Raabe (1831-1910), Poet — A493

**1981, Aug. 13** **Litho. & Engr.**
1357 A493 50pf dk green & green .65 .30

Statement of Constitutional Freedom (Fundamental Concept of Democracy) A494

50pf, Separation of powers. 60pf, Sovereignty of the people.

**1981, Aug. 13** **Litho.** *Perf. 14*
1358 A494 40pf shown .75 .25
1359 A494 50pf multicolored .75 .25
1360 A494 60pf multicolored .95 .25
Nos. 1358-1360 (3) 2.45 .75

A495

People by Mailcoach, lithograph, 1855.

**1981, Oct. 8** **Litho.**
1361 A495 60pf multicolored .95 .30
Stamp Day, Oct. 25.

Antarctic Treaty, 20th Anniv. — A496

**1981, Nov. 12** **Litho.** *Perf. 14*
1362 A496 100pf multicolored 1.20 .40

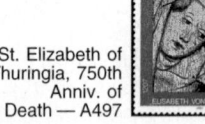

St. Elizabeth of Thuringia, 750th Anniv. of Death — A497

**1981, Nov. 12**
1363 A497 50pf multicolored .85 .30

Karl von Clausewitz, by W. Wach — A498

**1981, Nov. 12** **Photo.**
1364 A498 60pf multicolored .85 .30
Prussian general and writer, (1780-1831).

Social Insurance Centenary A499

**1981, Nov. 12**
1365 A499 60pf multicolored .65 .30

Pear-shaped Pot with Lid, 1715 — A500

**1982, Jan. 13** **Litho.**
1366 A500 60pf multicolored .65 .30
Johann Friedrich Bottger (1682-1719), originator of Dresden china, 300th birth anniv.

Energy Conservation A501

**1982, Jan. 13**
1367 A501 60pf multicolored .65 .30

A502

Illustration from The Town Band of Bremen (folktale).

**1982, Jan. 13**
1368 A502 40pf red & black .55 .30

A503

**1982, Feb. 18** **Photo.**
1369 A503 60pf multicolored 1.75 .30
Johann Wolfgang von Goethe (1749-1832), by Georg Melchior Kraus, 1776.

Robert Koch (1843-1910), Discoverer of Tubercle Bacillus, (1882) — A504

**1982, Feb. 18**
1370 A504 50pf multicolored 2.10 .30

Die Fromme Helene, by Wilhelm Busch (1832-1908) — A505

**1982, Apr. 15** **Litho.** *Perf. 13½x14*
1371 A505 50pf multicolored .85 .30

Europa 1982 — A506

50pf, Hambach Meeting sesquicentennial. 60pf, Treaties of Rome, 1957-1982.

**1982, May 5** **Litho.** *Perf. 14*
1372 A506 50pf multicolored .85 .25
1373 A506 60pf multicolored 1.15 .25

Kiel Regatta Week Centenary A507

**1982, May 5**
1374 A507 60pf multicolored .85 .30

Young Men's Christian Assoc. (YMCA) Centenary A508

**1982, May 5**
1375 A508 50pf multicolored .65 .30

"Don't Drink and Drive" — A509

**1982, July 15** Photo.
1376 A509 80pf red & black .85 .30

25th Anniv. of German Lepers' Org. — A510

**1982, July 15** Photo.
1377 A510 80pf multicolored .85 .30

Prevent Water Pollution — A511

**1982, July 15**
1378 A511 120pf multicolored 2.25 .40

Urea Model and Synthesis Formula — A512

**1982, Aug. 12** Photo.
1379 A512 50pf multicolored .80 .30
Friedrich Wohler (1800-1882), chemist, discoverer of organic chemistry.

St. Francis Preaching to the Birds, by Giotto — A513

**1982, Aug. 12** Litho.
1380 A513 60pf multicolored .80 .30
800th birth anniv. of St. Francis of Assisi and 87th German Catholics Cong., Dusseldorf, 9/1-5.

James Franck, Max Born — A514

**1982, Aug. 12** Litho. & Engr.
1381 A514 80pf multicolored 1.05 .40
James Franck (1882-1964) and Max Born (1882-1970), Nobel Prize physicists, developed quantum theory.

Stamp Day, Oct. 24 — A515

**1982, Oct. 14** Photo. Perf. 14
1382 A515 80pf Poster 1.20 .30

400th Anniv. of the Gregorian Calendar — A516

Design: Calendar illumination, by Johannes Rasch, 1586.

**1982, Oct. 14** Litho.
1383 A516 60pf multicolored .80 .30

A517

Presidents: a, Theodor Heuss, 1949-59. b, Heinrich Lubke, 1959-69. c, Gustav Heinemann, 1969-74. d, Walter Scheel, 1974-79. e, Karl Carstens, 1979-84.

**1982, Nov. 10**
1384 A517 Sheet of 5 5.00 4.50
a.-e. 80pf, single stamp .65 .65

A518

**1983, Jan. 13** Litho. Perf. 14
1385 A518 80pf gray & black 1.30 .40
Edith Stein (d. 1942), philosher and Carmelite Nun.

Persecution and Resistance, 1933-1945 A519

**1983, Jan. 13**
1386 A519 80pf multicolored 1.30 .40

Light Space Modulator, 1930 A520

Walter Gropius (1883-1969), Founder of Bauhaus Architecture: 60pf, Sanctuary, zinc lithograph, 1942. 80pf, Bauhaus Archives, Berlin, 1979.

**1983, Feb. 8**
1387 A520 50pf multicolored .65 .30
1388 A520 60pf multicolored .80 .30
1389 A520 95pf multicolored .95 .30
Nos. 1387-1389 (3) 2.40 .90

Federahannes, Swabian-Alemannic Carnival — A521

**1983, Feb. 8**
1390 A521 60pf multicolored .85 .30

4th Intl. Horticultural Show, Munich, Apr. 28-Oct. 9 — A522

**1983, Apr. 12** Litho. Perf. 14
1391 A522 60pf multicolored .85 .30

Europa 1983 — A523

Discoveries: 60pf, Movable type, printing press by Johannes Guttenburg. 80pf, Resonant circuit, electric flux lines, electromagnetic waves by Heinrich Hertz.

**1983, May 5** Litho. Perf. 14
1392 A523 60pf multicolored 1.60 .35
1393 A523 80pf multicolored 1.00 .35

Johannes Brahms (1833-1897), Composer — A524

**1983, May 5** Photo.
1394 A524 80pf multicolored 1.30 .40

Franz Kafka (1883-1924), Writer — A525

80pf, Signature, Tyn Church, Prague.

**1983, May 5**
1395 A525 80pf multicolored 1.30 .40

Beer Pureness Law, 450th Anniv. — A526

80pf, Brewers, engraving, 1677.

**1983, May 5** Litho.
1396 A526 80pf multicolored 1.30 .40

300th Anniv. of Immigration to US — A527

**1983, May 5** Litho. & Engr.
1397 A527 80pf Concord 1.30 .40
See US No. 2040.

Children and Road Safety — A528

**1983, July 14** Litho. Perf. 14
1398 A528 80pf multicolored 1.30 .40

50th Intl. Auto Show, Frankfurt, Sept. 15-25 — A529

**1983, July 14**
1399 A529 60pf multicolored .65 .30

Otto Warburg — A530

**1983, Aug. 11** Photo. Perf. 14
1400 A530 50pf multicolored .80 .40
Warburg (1883-1970), pioneer of modern biochemistry, 1931 Nobel prize winner in medicine.

Christoph Martin Wieland (1733-1813), Poet — A531

**1983, Aug. 11** Litho.
1401 A531 80pf multicolored 1.05 .40

10th Anniv. of UN Membership A532

**1983, Aug. 11** Photo.
1402 A532 80pf multicolored 1.45 .40

Rauhe Haus Orphanage Sesquicentennial A533

**1983, Aug. 11** Litho.
1403 A533 80pf multicolored 1.15 .40

Survey and Measuring Maps — A534

**1983, Aug. 11**
1404 A534 120pf multicolored 1.30 .50
Intl. Union of Geodesy and Geophysics Gen. Assembly, Hamburg, Aug. 15-26.

Stamp Day — A535

**1983, Oct. 13** Litho. Perf. 13½
1405 A535 80pf Postrider 1.20 .40

Martin Luther (1483-1546) — A536

80pf, Engraving by G. Konig.

**1983, Oct. 13** Perf. 14
1406 A536 80pf multi 2.00 .40

Customs Union Sesquicentennial A537

**1983, Nov. 10**
1407 A537 60pf multicolored 1.30 .30

Territorial Authorities (Federation, Land, Communities) A538

**1983, Nov. 10** Litho.
1408 A538 80pf multicolored 1.30 .40

Trier, 2000th Anniv. — A539

80pf, Black Gate, 175 A.D.

**1984, Jan. 12** Litho. & Engr.
1409 A539 80pf multi 1.45 .40

Philipp Reis (1834-1874) Physicist and Inventor — A540

**1984, Jan. 12**     **Litho.**
1410 A540 80pf multicolored   1.45 .40

Gregor Mendel (1822-1884), Basic Laws of Heredity — A541

**1984, Jan. 12**     **Litho.**
1411 A541 50pf multicolored   .85 .30

500th Anniv. of Michelstadt Town Hall — A542

**1984, Feb. 16**     **Litho.**
1412 A542 60pf multicolored   .85 .30

350th Anniv. of Oberammergau Passion Play — A543

**1984, Feb. 16**     **Photo.**
1413 A543 60pf multicolored   .85 .30

Second Election of Parliament, June 17 — A544

**1984, Apr. 12**   **Litho.**   **Perf. 13½**
1414 A544 80pf multicolored   1.75 .50

Europa (1959-1984) — A545

**1984, May 8**   **Photo.**   **Perf. 14**
1415 A545 60pf brt blue & blk   *1.05 .35*
1416 A545 80pf dull rose & blk   *1.05 .35*

A546

**1984, May 8**     **Engr.**
1417 A546 60pf multicolored   .65 .30
Nursery Rhyme Illustration, by Ludwig Richter (1803-84).

Statue, 1693 — A547

**1984, May 8**
1418 A547 80pf grn & dk grn   1.05 .40
St. Norbert von Xanten (1080-1134).

Barmer Theological Declaration, 50th Anniv. — A548

**1984, May 8**     **Litho.**
1419 A548 80pf Cross, text   1.05 .40

Souvenir Sheet

1984 UPU Congress — A549

a, Letter sorting, 19th cent. b, Scanner. c, H. von Stephan, founder.

**1984, June 19**   **Litho.**   **Perf. 14**
1420 A549   Sheet of 3   3.00 2.50
   *a.*   60pf multicolored   .80 .65
   *b.*   80pf multicolored   .80 .65
   *c.*   120pf multicolored   1.30 1.20

City of Neuss Bimillenium — A550

**1984, June 19**   **Litho. & Engr.**
1421 A550 80pf Tomb of Oclatius 1.05 .40

Friedrich Wilhelm Bessel (1784-1846), Astronomer — A551

80pf, Bessel function diagram.

**1984, June 19**
1422 A551 80pf multicolored   1.05 .40

88th German Catholic Convention, Munich, July 4-8 — A552

**1984, June 19**     **Photo.**
1423 A552 60pf Pope Pius XII   .85 .30

Town Hall, Duderstadt — A553

**1984, Aug. 21**   **Litho.**   **Perf. 14**
1424 A553 60pf multicolored   .80 .30

Medieval Document, Computer — A554

**1984, Aug. 21**
1425 A554 70pf multicolored   1.00 .40
10th Intl. Archives Congress, Bonn.

German Electron Synchrotron (DESY) Research Center, Hamburg A555

**1984, Aug. 21**     **Photo.**
1426 A555 80pf multicolored   1.30 .40

Schleswig-Holstein Canal Bicentenary — A556

**1984, Aug. 21**     **Litho.**
1427 A556 80pf Knoop lock   1.20 .40

Stamp Day — A557

80pf, Imperial Taxis Posthouse, Augsburg.

**1984, Oct. 18**   **Litho.**   **Perf. 14**
1428 A557 80pf multicolored   1.30 .55

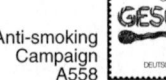

Anti-smoking Campaign A558

**1984, Nov. 8**     **Litho.**
1429 A558 60pf Match, text   .95 .30

Equal Rights for Men and Women — A559

80pf, Male & female symbols.

**1984, Nov. 8**
1430 A559 80pf multicolored   1.20 .40

Peace and Understanding A560

**1984, Nov. 8**
1431 A560 80pf Text   .95 .40

Augsburg, 2000th Anniv. — A561

80pf, Roman Emperor Augustus, Augsburg buildings.

**1985, Jan. 10**     **Litho.**
1432 A561 80pf multicolored   1.20 .35

Philipp Jakob Spener, Religious Leader (1635-1705) — A562

**1985, Jan. 10**     **Litho.**
1433 A562 80pf multicolored   1.05 .40

Deutches Wortebuch A563

**1985, Jan. 10**     **Litho.**
1434 A563 80pf Bros. Grimm, text   1.30 1.00

Romano Guardini, Theologist (1885-1968) — A564

**1985, Jan. 10**     **Litho.**
1435 A564 80pf multicolored   1.05 .40

Market and Coinage Rights in Verden, 1000th Anniv. — A565

**1985, Feb. 21**     **Litho.**
1436 A565 60pf multicolored   1.45 .30

German-Danish Border Areas and Flags — A566

**1985, Feb. 21**
1437 A566 80pf multicolored   1.60 .55
Bonn-Copenhagen declarations on mutual minorities, 30th anniv.

Johann Peter Hebel (1760-1826), Poet — A567

**1985, Apr. 16**     **Litho.**
1438 A567 80pf multicolored   .95 .40

Egon Erwin Kisch (1885-1948), Journalist — A568

60pf, Kisch using telephone.

**1985, Apr. 16**     **Litho.**
1439 A568 60pf multicolored   .85 .30

Europa 1985 — A569

European Music Year: 60pf, Georg Friedrich Handel, portrait of Handel. 80pf, Johann Sebastian Bach, portrait of Bach.

**1985, May 7**     **Photo.**
1440 A569 60pf multicolored   *1.50 .35*
1441 A569 80pf multicolored   *1.50 .35*

Dominikus Zimmermann (1685-1766), Architect — A570

**1985, May 7**     **Photo.**
1442 A570 70pf Stucco column   .95 .40

St. George's Cathedral, 750th Anniv. — A571

60pf, Cathedral, Limburg.

**1985, May 7**   **Litho.**   **Perf. 14**
1443 A571 60pf multicolored   .80 .40

Father Josef
Kentenich (1885-
1968)
A572

**1985, May 7** **Litho.**
1444 A572 80pf Portrait .95 .40

Forest
Conservation — A573

**1985, July 16** **Litho.** **Perf. 14**
1445 A573 80pf Clock, forest 1.50 .40

Intl. Youth
Year — A574

60pf, Scouts, scouting and IYY emblems.

**1985, July 16** **Perf. 14**
1446 A574 60pf multicolored .95 .40
30th World Scouting Conf., Munich, 7/15-19.

Frankfurt Stock
Exchange, 400th
Anniv. — A575

Design: Bourse, est. 1879, and Frankfurt
Eagle, the exchange emblem.

**1985, Aug. 13** **Perf. 14x14½**
1447 A575 80pf multicolored 1.20 .40

The Sunday
Walk, by Carl
Spitzweg (1808-
85)
A576

**1985, Aug. 13**
1448 A576 60pf multicolored 1.30 .40

Fritz Reuter (1810-
1874), Dialect
Author — A577

**1985, Oct. 15** **Litho.** **Perf. 14**
1449 A577 80pf Portrait, manuscript 1.60 .40

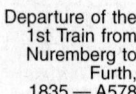

Departure of the
1st Train from
Nuremberg to
Furth,
1835 — A578

**1985, Nov. 12 Litho.** **Perf. 14x14½**
1450 A578 80pf Adler locomotive 1.60 .40
Founder Johannes Scharrer (1785-1844),
German Railways 150th anniv.

Reintegration of
German World War II
Refugees, 40th
Anniv. — A579

**1985, Nov. 12** **Perf. 14**
1451 A579 80pf multicolored 1.50 .40

Natl. Armed
Forces, 30th
Anniv. — A580

80pf, Iron Cross, natl. colors.

**1985, Nov. 12** **Perf. 14x14½**
1452 A580 80pf multicolored 2.25 .40

Benz Tricycle, Saloon Car, 1912, and
Modern Automobile
A581

**1986, Jan. 16** **Litho.** **Perf. 14**
1453 A581 80pf multicolored 1.60 .40
Automobile cent.

Bad Hersfeld,
1250th
Anniv. — A582

**1986, Feb. 13** **Litho.** **Perf. 14**
1454 A582 60pf multicolored .95 .40

Bach Contata, Detail,
by Oskar Kokoschka
(1886-1980) — A583

**1986, Feb. 13**
1455 A583 80pf Self portrait .95 .40

Halley's
Comet — A584

**1986, Feb. 13**
1456 A584 80pf multicolored 1.60 .50

Europa
1986 — A585

Details from Michelangelo's David: 60pf,
Mouth (pure water). 80pf, Nose, (pure air).

**1986, May 5** **Photo.** **Perf. 14**
1457 A585 60pf multicolored 1.00 .35
1458 A585 80pf multicolored 1.00 .35

St. Johannis
Monastery,
Walsrode
A586

**1986, May 5** **Litho. & Engr.**
1459 A586 60pf multicolored 1.05 .40
Monastery millennium and town of Walsrode, 603rd anniv.

King Ludwig II of
Bavaria (1845-
1886),
Neuschwanstein
Castle — A587

**1986, May 5** **Litho.**
1460 A587 60pf multicolored 1.75 .40

Karl Barth (1886-
1968), Protestant
Theologian — A588

**1986, May 5** **Engr.**
1461 A588 80pf blk, dk red & red
lil 1.20 .40

Religion,
Science,
Friendship and
Fatherland
A589

**1986, May 5** **Litho.**
1462 A589 80pf multicolored 1.20 .40
Union of German Catholic Students, 100th
assembly, Frankfurt, June 12-15.

Carl Maria von
Weber (1786-1826),
Mass in E-flat
Major — A590

**1986, June 20** **Litho.** **Perf. 14**
1463 A590 80pf multicolored 1.60 .40

Franz Liszt and
Signature
A591

**1986, June 20**
1464 A591 80pf dk blue & dk org 1.50 .40

Intl. Peace
Year — A592

**1986, June 20**
1465 A592 80pf multicolored 1.45 .40

Souvenir Sheet

Reichstag, Berlin — A593

Historic buildings: b, Koening Museum,
Bonn. c, Parliament, Bonn.

**1986, June 20**
1466 A593 Sheet of 3 3.75 3.25
a.-c. 80pf, any single .95 .95

European
Satellite
Technology
A594

Design: TV-SAT/TDF-1 over Europe.

**1986, June 20**
1467 A594 80pf multicolored 1.60 .50

Augsburg
Cathedral
Stained Glass
Window — A595

**1986, Aug. 14** **Perf. 14**
1468 A595 80pf multicolored 1.60 .40
Monuments protection.

King Frederick the
Great (1712-
1786) — A596

**1986, Aug. 14**
1469 A596 80pf multicolored 2.25 .40

German Skat Congress,
Cent. — A597

**1986, Aug. 14**
1470 A597 80pf Tournament card 1.60 .40

Organization for Economic
Cooperation and Development, 25th
Anniv. — A598

**1986, Aug. 14**
1471 A598 80pf multicolored 1.20 .40

Heidelberg
University, 600th
Anniv. — A599

**1986, Oct. 16** **Litho.**
1472 A599 80pf multicolored 1.30 .40

Stagecoach, Stamps from 1975-
1984 — A600

**1986, Oct. 16**
1473 A600 80pf multicolored 1.30 .40
Stamp Day, 50th Anniv.

A601

**1986, Nov. 13** **Litho.** **Perf. 14**
1474 A601 70pf multicolored .85 .40
Mary Wigman (1886-1973), dancer.

Famous Women — A602

Designs: 5pf, Emma Ihrer (1857-1911), politician, labor leader. 10pf, Paula Modersohn-
Becker (1876-1907), painter. 20pf, Cilly Aussem (1909-63), tennis champion. 30pf, Kathe
Kollwitz (1867-1945), painter, graphic artist.
40pf, Maria Sibylla Merian (1647-1717), naturalist, painter. 50pf, Christine Teusch (1888-
1968), minister of education and cultural
affairs. 60pf, Dorothea Erxleben (1715-62),
physician. 70pf, Elisabet Boehm (1859-1943),
social organizer. 80pf, Clara Schumann
(1819-96), pianist, composer. 100pf, Therese
Giehse (1898-1975), actress. 120pf, Elisabeth
Selbert (1896-1986), politician. 130pf, Lise
Meitner (1878-1968), physicist. 140pf, Cecile
Vogt (1875-1962), neurologist. 150pf, Sophie
Scholl (1921-43), member of anti-Nazi resistance. 170pf, Hannah Arendt (1906-75),
American political scientist. 180pf, Lotte Leh-
mann (1888-1976), soprano. 200pf, Bertha
von Suttner (1843-1914), 1905 Nobel Peace
Prize winner. 240pf, Mathilde Franziska
Anneke, (1817-84), American author. 250pf,

Queen Louise of Prussia (1776-1810). 300pf, Fanny Hensel (1805-47), composer-conductor. 350pf, Hedwig Dransfeld (1871-1925), women's rights activist. 500pf, Alice Salomon (1872-1948), feminist and social activist.

| 1986-91 | | Engr. | | Perf. 14 | |
|---|---|---|---|---|---|
| 1475 | A602 | 5pf | multi | .30 | .30 |
| 1476 | A602 | 10pf | multi | .40 | .35 |
| 1477 | A602 | 20pf | multi | .65 | .35 |
| 1478 | A602 | 30pf | multi | .35 | .30 |
| 1479 | A602 | 40pf | multi | .65 | .25 |
| 1480 | A602 | 50pf | multi | .65 | .25 |
| 1481 | A602 | 60pf | multi | .80 | .25 |
| 1482 | A602 | 70pf | multi | 1.00 | .55 |
| 1483 | A602 | 80pf | multi | .80 | .25 |
| 1484 | A602 | 100pf | multi | 1.00 | .35 |
| 1485 | A602 | 120pf | multi | 1.30 | .80 |
| 1486 | A602 | 130pf | multi | 2.00 | .65 |
| 1487 | A602 | 140pf | multi | 2.25 | 1.20 |
| 1488 | A602 | 150pf | multi | 2.25 | 1.20 |
| 1489 | A602 | 170pf | multi | 1.60 | 1.00 |
| 1490 | A602 | 180pf | multi | 2.00 | 1.00 |
| 1491 | A602 | 200pf | multi | 1.60 | .65 |
| 1492 | A602 | 240pf | multi | 2.25 | 1.60 |
| 1493 | A602 | 250pf | multi | 3.75 | 1.60 |
| 1493A | A602 | 300pf | multi | 2.00 | 1.00 |
| 1494 | A602 | 350pf | multi | 4.25 | 2.00 |
| 1494A | A602 | 500pf | multi | 5.25 | 2.60 |
| | | Nos. 1475-1494A (22) | | 37.10 | 18.50 |

Issued: 50pf, 80pf, 11/18; 40pf, 60pf, 9/17/87; 120pf, 11/7/87; 10pf, 4/14/88; 20pf, 130pf, 5/5/88; 100pf, 170pf, 240pf, 350pf, 11/10/88; 500pf, 1/12/89; 5pf, 2/9/89; 180pf, 250pf, 7/13/89; 140pf, 300pf, 8/10/89; 30pf, 70pf, 1/8/91; 150pf, 200pf, 2/14/91.
See Nos. 1723/1735, 2185-2188, Berlin Nos. 9N516-9N532.

A603

**1986, Nov. 13　　Litho.　　Perf. 14**
1495　A603　80pf multicolored　　.85　.40

Advent Collection for Church Projects in Latin America, 25th Anniv.

Berlin, 750th Anniv. A604

**1987, Jan. 15　　　　　　Litho.**
1496　A604　80pf multicolored　　1.60　.55

See Berlin No. 9N536.

Archbishop's Residence at Wurzburg, 1719-44 — A605

**1987, Jan. 15　　　　　　Photo.**
1497　A605　80pf multicolored　　1.30　.40

Balthasar Neumann (1687-1753), Baroque architect.

Ludwig Erhard (1897-1977), Economist, Chancellor 1963-66 — A606

**1987, Jan. 15**
1498　A606　80pf multicolored　　1.60　.35

1987 Census — A607

**1987, Jan. 15　　　　　　Litho.**
1499　A607　80pf Federal Eagle　　1.45　.40

Clemensworth Hunting Castle, 250th Anniv. — A608

**1987, Feb. 12　　　　　　Litho.**
1500　A608　60pf multicolored　　1.15　.40

Joseph von Fraunhofer (1787-1826), Optician, Physicist A609

80pf, Light spectrum diagram.

**1987, Feb. 12　　Litho. & Engr.**
1501　A609　80pf multicolored　　1.15　.40

Karl May (1842-1912), Novelist — A610

80pf, Apache Chief Winnetou.

**1987, Feb. 12　　　　　　Photo.**
1502　A610　80pf multicolored　　1.25　.40

Papal Arms, Madonna and Child, Buildings in Kevelaer A611

**1987, Apr. 9　　　　　　Litho.**
1503　A611　80pf multicolored　　1.45　.40

State visit of Pope John Paul II, Apr. 30-May 4; 17th Marian and 10th Mariological World Congress, Kevelaer, Sept. 11-20.

German Choral Soc., 125th Anniv. — A612

**1987, Apr. 9**
1504　A612　80pf multicolored　　1.15　.40

Europa 1987 — A613

Modern architecture: 60pf, German Pavilion, designed by Ludwig Mies van der Rohe, 1928 World's Fair, Barcelona. 80pf, Kohlbrand Bridge, 1974, Hamburg, designed by Thyssen Engineering.

**1987, May 5　　　　　　Litho.**
1505　A613　60pf multicolored　　1.05　.35
1506　A613　80pf multicolored　　1.30　.35

Organ Pipes, Signature — A614

**1987, May 5**
1507　A614　80pf multicolored　　.85　.40

Dietrich Buxtehude (c. 1637-1707), composer.

Wilhelm Kaisen (1887-1979), Bremen City Senate President A615

**1987, May 5**
1508　A615　80pf multicolored　　1.05　.40

Johann Albrecht Bengel (1687-1752), Lutheran Theologian — A616

**1987, May 5　　Photo.　　Perf. 14**
1509　A616　80pf multicolored　　1.00　.40

Kurt Schwitters (1887-1948), Artist — A617

**1987, May 5　　　　　　Litho.**
1510　A617　80pf multicolored　　1.05　.40

Rotary Intl. Convention, Munich, June 7-10 — A618

**1987, May 5　　　　　　Photo.**
1511　A618　70pf multicolored　　1.05　.40

A619

Design: Dulmen's Wild Horses, Merfelder Bruch Nature Reserve.

**1987, May 5**
1512　A619　60pf multicolored　　1.45　.40

European Environmental Conservation Year.

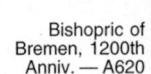

Bishopric of Bremen, 1200th Anniv. — A620

Design: Charlemagne, Bremen Cathedral, city arms, Bishop Willehad.

**1987, July 16　　Litho.　　Perf. 14**
1513　A620　80pf multicolored　　1.00　.40

7th European Rifleman's Festival, Lippstadt, Sept. 12-13 — A621

**1987, Aug. 20　　Litho.　　Perf. 14**
1514　A621　80pf multicolored　　1.00　.40

Stamp Day — A622

**1987, Oct. 15　　　　　　Litho.**
1515　A622　80pf Postmen, 1897　　.95　.75

Historic Sites and Objects — A623

Designs: 5pf, Brunswick Lion. 10pf, Frankfurt Airport. 20pf, No. 1526, Queen Nefertiti of Egypt, bust, Egyptian Museum, Berlin. 30pf, Corner tower, Celle Castle, 14th cent. 33pf, 120pf, Schleswig Cathedral. 38pf, 280pf, Statue of Roland, Bremen. 40pf, Chile House, Hamburg. 41pf, 170pf, Russian church, Wiesbaden. 45pf, Rastatt Castle. 50pf, Filigree tracery on spires, Freiburg Cathedral. 60pf, Bavaria Munich, bronze statue above the Theresienwiese, Hall of Fame. No. 1527, Heligoland. 80pf, Entrance to Zollern II coal mine, Dortmund. 90pf, 140pf, Bronze flagon from Reinheim. 100pf, Altotting Chapel, Bavaria. 200pf, Magdeburg Cathedral. 300pf, Hambach Castle. 350pf, Externsteine Bridge near Horn-Bad Meinberg. 400pf, Opera House, Dresden. 450pf, New Gate, Neubrandenburg. 500pf, State Theatre, Cottbus. 700pf, German Theater, Berlin.

| 1987-96 | | Typo. | | Perf. 14 | |
|---|---|---|---|---|---|
| 1515A | A623 | 5pf | multi | .35 | .30 |
| 1516 | A623 | 10pf | multi | .40 | .25 |
| 1517 | A623 | 20pf | multi | .40 | .30 |
| 1518 | A623 | 30pf | multi | .65 | .25 |
| 1519 | A623 | 33pf | multi | .40 | .30 |
| 1520 | A623 | 38pf | multi | .65 | .40 |
| 1521 | A623 | 40pf | multi | .40 | .40 |
| 1522 | A623 | 41pf | multi | .65 | .35 |
| 1523 | A623 | 45pf | multi | .40 | .35 |
| 1524 | A623 | 50pf | multi | .65 | .25 |
| 1525 | A623 | 60pf | multi | .65 | .25 |
| 1526 | A623 | 70pf | multi | .75 | .25 |
| 1527 | A623 | 70pf | multi | .40 | .30 |
| 1528 | A623 | 80pf | multi | .65 | .25 |
| a. | | Bklt. pane, 4 10pf, 2 50pf, 2 80pf ('89) | | 5.00 | 4.25 |
| b. | | Bklt. pane, 2 each 20pf, 80pf | | 4.25 | 5.75 |
| 1529 | A623 | 90pf | multi | 1.20 | 1.60 |
| 1530 | A623 | 100pf | multi | 2.25 | .30 |
| a. | | Bklt. pane, 2 each 10, 60, 80, 100pf | | 8.25 | 9.00 |
| b. | | Bklt. pane, 2 each 20, 50, 80, 100pf | | 9.50 | 10.50 |
| c. | | Booklet pane, 10 #1530 | | 19.00 | 16.50 |
| | | Complete booklet, #1530c | | 19.00 | |
| d. | | Booklet pane, 4 #1516, 2 each #1524, 1528, 1530 | | 9.00 | 9.00 |
| | | Complete booklet, #1530d | | 9.00 | |
| 1531 | A623 | 120pf | multi | 1.30 | .60 |
| 1532 | A623 | 140pf | multi | 1.60 | .55 |
| 1533 | A623 | 170pf | multi | 1.60 | .65 |
| 1534 | A623 | 200pf | multi | 1.75 | .60 |
| 1535 | A623 | 280pf | multi | 3.75 | 3.75 |
| 1536 | A623 | 300pf | multi | 2.25 | .40 |
| 1537 | A623 | 350pf | multi | 2.60 | .55 |
| 1538 | A623 | 400pf | multi | 3.00 | .55 |
| 1539 | A623 | 450pf | multi | 3.75 | 1.00 |
| 1540 | A623 | 500pf | multi | 4.25 | 1.20 |
| 1540A | A623 | 700pf | multi | 6.00 | 2.00 |
| | | Nos. 1515A-1540A (27) | | 42.70 | 17.95 |

Issued: 30, 50, 60, 80pf, 11/6/87; 10, 300pf, 1/14/88; 120pf, No. 1526, 7/14/88; 40, 90, 280pf, 8/11/88; 20, 33, 38, 140pf, 1/12/89; 100, 350pf, 2/9/89; 5pf, 2/15/90; 45p, No. 1527, 6/21/90; 170pf, 6/4/91; 400pf, 10/10/91; 450pf, 8/13/92; 200pf, 4/15/93; 500pf, 6/17/93; 41pf, 8/12/93; 700pf, 9/16/93; No. 1530b, 11/9/94; No. 1530d, 8/14/96.
See Nos. 1655-1663, 1838-60, 2199-2216, Berlin Nos. 9N543-9N557.

Christoph Willibald Gluck (1714-1787), Composer, and Score from the Opera Armide — A624

**1987, Nov. 6　　　　　　Perf. 14**
1541　A624　60pf car lake & dk gray　　.80　.35

Gerhart Hauptmann (1862-1946), Playwright A625

**1987, Nov. 6　　　　　　Litho.**
1542　A625　80pf blk & brk red　　1.20　.40

German Agro Action Organization, 125th Anniv. — A626

**1987, Nov. 6**      **Photo.**
1543 A626 80pf Rice field    1.20   .40

Mainz Carnival, 150th Anniv. — A627

**1988, Jan. 14**   **Litho.**   **Perf. 14**
1544 A627 60pf Jester      .95   .40

Jacob Kaiser (1888-1961), Labor Leader — A628

**1988, Jan. 14**     **Litho. & Engr.**
1545 A628 80pf black     .85   .40

Franco-German Cooperation Treaty, 25th Anniv. — A629

80pf, Adenauer, De Gaulle.

**1988, Jan. 14**
1546 A629 80pf multicolored   1.30   .55
See France No. 2086.

Beatification of Edith Stein and Rupert Mayer by Pope John Paul II in 1987 — A630

**1988, Jan. 14**      **Photo.**
1547 A630 80pf brown, blk & ver   .95   .40

A631

Woodcut (detail) by Ludwig Richter.

**1988, Feb. 18**      **Litho.**
1548 A631 60pf multicolored    .95   .40
Woodcut inspired by poem Solitude of the Green Woods, by Baron Joseph von Eichendorff (1788-1857).

A632

**1988, Feb. 18**      **Photo.**
1549 A632 80pf dk red & brn blk   1.20   .40
Arthur Schopenhauer (1788-1860), philosopher.

Friedrich Wilhelm Raiffeisen (1818-1888), Economist — A633

**1988, Feb. 18**      **Litho.**
1550 A633 80pf black & brt yel grn   1.30   .40
The German Raiffeisen Assoc., an agricultural cooperative credit soc., was founded by Raiffeisen.

Ulrich Reichsritter von Hutten (1488-1523), Humanist — A634

Design: Detail from an engraving published with Hutten's Conquestiones.

**1988, Apr. 14**     **Litho. & Engr.**
1551 A634 80pf multicolored   .95   .50

Europa 1988 — A635

Transport and communication: 60pf, Airbus A320. 80pf, Integrated Services Digital Network (ISDN) system.

**1988, May 5**      **Litho.**
1552 A635 60pf multicolored   .95   .40
1553 A635 80pf multicolored   .95   .40

City of Dusseldorf, 700th Anniv. — A636

**1988, May 5**
1554 A636 60pf multicolored   1.05   .40

Cologne University, 600th Anniv. — A637

**1988, May 5**
1555 A637 80pf multicolored    .95   .40

Jean Monnet (1888-1979), French Statesman — A638

**1988, May 5**
1556 A638 80pf multicolored    .95   .40

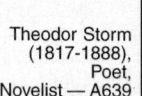

Theodor Storm (1817-1888), Poet, Novelist — A639

**1988, May 5**
1557 A639 80pf multicolored    .95   .40

German Volunteer Service, 25th Anniv. — A640

**1988, May 5**
1558 A640 80pf multicolored    .95   .40

Town of Meersburg, Millennium A641

**1988, July 14**    **Litho.**   **Perf. 14**
1559 A641 60pf multicolored   .80   .40

Leopold Gmelin (1788-1853), Chemist — A642

**1988, July 14**     **Litho. & Engr.**
1560 A642 80pf multicolored   .85   .40

Vernier Scale as a Symbol of Precision and Quality — A643

**1988, July 14**      **Litho.**
1561 A643 140pf multicolored   1.60   .80
Made in Germany.

August Bebel (1840-1913), Founder of the Social Democratic Party — A644

**1988, Aug. 11**      **Photo.**
1562 A644 80pf multicolored   1.20   .40

Intl. Red Cross, 125th Anniv. — A645

**1988, Oct. 13**     **Litho. & Engr.**
1563 A645 80pf scarlet & black   1.20   .40

Stamp Day — A646

**1988, Oct. 13**      **Litho.**
1564 A646 20pf Carrier pigeon   .55   .35

1st Nazi Pogrom, Nov. 9, 1938 — A647

Star, "Remembering is the secret of redemption," & burning synagogue in Baden-Baden.

**1988, Oct. 13**      **Photo.**
1565 A647 80pf dull pale pur & blk   .85   .40

Postage Stamps for Bethel, Cent. — A648

**1988, Nov. 10**      **Litho.**
1566 A648 60pf multicolored   .95   .40
The Postage Stamps for Bethel program was founded by Pastor Friedrich V. Bodelschwingh to employ disabled residents of Bethel.

Samaritan Association of Workers (ASB) Rescue Service, Cent. — A649

**1988, Nov. 10**
1567 A649 80pf multicolored   .95   .40

Bonn Bimillennium — A650

**1989, Jan. 12**      **Litho.**
1568 A650 80pf multicolored   1.30   .60
Bonn as capital of the federal republic, 40th anniv.

Bluxao I, 1955, by Willi Baumeister (1889-1955) — A651

**1989, Jan. 12**
1569 A651 60pf multicolored    .85   .40

Misereor and Brot fur die Welt, 30th Annivs. — A652

**1989, Jan. 12**      **Photo.**
1570 A652 80pf Barren and verdant soil   1.00   .40
Church organizations helping Third World nations to become self-sufficient in food production.

Cats in the Attic, Woodcut by Gerhard Marcks (1889-1981) A653

**1989, Feb. 9**    **Litho.**   **Perf. 14**
1571 A653 60pf multicolored   .85   .40

European Parliament 3rd Elections, June 18 — A654

Flags of member nations.

**1989, Apr. 20**      **Litho.**
1572 A654 100pf multicolored   1.75   .80

Europa 1989 — A655

**1989, May 5**
1573 A655 60pf Kites     1.00   .30
1574 A655 100pf Puppets   1.30   .35

Hamburg Harbor, 800th Anniv. — A656

**1989, May 5**
1575 A656 60pf multicolored   1.20   .40

Cosmas Damian Asam (1686-1739), Painter, Architect — A657

**1989, May 5**     **Litho. & Engr.**
1576 A657 60pf Fresco    .65 .40

Federal Republic of Germany, 40th Anniv. A658

100pf, Natl. crest, flag, presidents' signatures.

**1989, May 5**     **Photo.**
1577 A658 100pf multicolored    1.60 .60

Council of Europe, 40th Anniv. A659

100pf, Parliamentary Assembly, stars.

**1989, May 5**     **Perf. 14**
1578 A659 100pf multicolored    1.45 .65

Franz Xaver Gabelsberger (1789-1849), Inventor of a German Shorthand — A660

**1989, May 5**     **Litho.**
1579 A660 100pf multicolored    1.45 .50

Sts. Kilian, Colman and Totnan (d. 689), Martyred Missionaries, and Clover — A661

**1989, June 15**     **Litho.**
1580 A661 100pf multicolored    1.30 .55
See Ireland No. 748.

Friedrich Silcher (1789-1860), Composer, and *Lorelai* Score — A662

**1989, June 15**
1581 A662 80pf multicolored    .85 .40

Social Security Pension Insurance, Cent. A663

**1989, June 15**
1582 A663 100pf dull ultra, bl & ver    1.20 .50

Friedrich List (1789-1846), Economist A664

**1989, July 13**     **Engr.**     **Perf. 14**
1583 A664 170pf black & dark red    2.00 .80

*Summer Evening,* 1905, by Heinrich Vogler A665

**1989, July 13**     **Litho.**
1584 A665 60pf multicolored    .75 .40
Worpswede Artists' Village, cent.

A666

**1989, July 13**     **Photo.**
1585 A666 100pf slate grn, blk & gray    1.00 .50
Reverend Paul Schneider (d. 1939), martyr of Buchenwald concentration camp.

A667

**1989, Aug. 10**     **Litho.**
1586 A667 60pf multicolored    .95 .40
Frankfurt Cathedral, 750th anniv.

Child Welfare — A668

**1989, Aug. 10**     **Perf. 14**
1587 A668 100pf multicolored    1.15 .50

Trade Union of the Mining and Power Industries, Cent. — A669

**1989, Aug. 10**     **Perf. 14**
1588 A669 100pf multicolored    .95 .50

Reinhold Maier (1889-1971), Politician — A670

**1989, Oct. 12**     **Litho.**
1589 A670 100pf multicolored    1.15 .50

Restoration of St. James Church Organ, Constructed by Arp Schnitger, 1689 — A671

**1989, Nov. 16**
1590 A671 60pf multicolored    .95 .40

Speyer, 2000th Anniv. — A672

**1990, Jan. 12**    **Litho.**    **Perf. 14x14½**
1591 A672 60pf multicolored    .95 .40

A673

Design: *The Young Post Rider,* an Engraving by Albrecht Durer.

**Litho. & Engr.**
**1990, Jan. 12**     **Perf. 14**
1592 A673 100pf blksh pur, gray brn, beige    1.75 .55
Postal communications in Europe, 500th anniv. See Austria No. 1486, Belgium No. 1332, Berlin 9N584, and DDR No. 2791.

A674

**1990, Jan. 12**     **Litho.**
1593 A674 100pf multicolored    .95 .55
Riesling Vineyards, 500th anniv.

A675

**1990, Jan. 12**     **Litho. & Engr.**
1594 A675 100pf multicolored    1.20 .55
Addition of Lubeck to the UNESCO World Heritage List, 1987.

Seal of Col. Spittler, 1400, and Teutonic Order Heraldic Emblem — A676

**1990, Feb. 15**     **Litho.**
1595 A676 100pf multicolored    1.30 .55
Teutonic Order, 800th anniv.

A677

Design: Seal of Frederick II and Galleria Reception Hall at the Frankfurt Fair.

**1990, Feb. 15**
1596 A677 100pf multicolored    1.30 .55
Granting of fair privileges to Frankfurt by Frederick II, 750th anniv.

Youth Science and Technology Competition, 25th Anniv. — A678

**1990, Feb. 15**
1597 A678 100pf multicolored    1.30 .55

Nature and Environmental Protection — A679

**1990, Feb. 15**
1598 A679 100pf North Sea    1.60 .55

Labor Day, Cent. — A680

**1990, Apr. 19**    **Photo.**    **Perf. 14**
1599 A680 100pf dark red & blk    1.05 .55

German Assoc. of Housewives, 75th Anniv. — A681

**1990, Apr. 19**     **Litho.**
1600 A681 100pf multicolored    1.05 .55

Europa — A682

Post offices in Frankfurt am Main: 60pf, Thurn and Taxis Palace. 100pf, Modern Giro office.

**1990, May 3**     **Litho.**
1601 A682 60pf multicolored    1.20 .40
1602 A682 100pf multicolored    1.20 .40

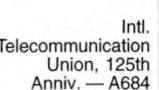

German Students' Fraternity, 175th Anniv. — A683

**1990, May 3**     **Litho. & Engr.**
1603 A683 100pf multicolored    1.30 .55

Intl. Telecommunication Union, 125th Anniv. — A684

**1990, May 3**     **Litho.**
1604 A684 100pf multicolored    1.05 .55

German Life Boat Institution, 125th Anniv. — A685

**1990, May 3**
1605 A685 60pf multicolored    .95 .50

Wilhelm Leuschner (1890-1944), Politician — A686

**1990, May 3**     **Litho. & Engr.**
1606 A686 100pf lt gray violet    1.30 .55

Rummelsberg Diaconal Institution, Cent. — A687

**1990, May 3**     **Litho.**
1607 A687 100pf multicolored    .95 .55

Charter of German Expellees, 40th Anniv. A688

**1990, June 21**     **Photo.**
1608 A688 100pf multicolored    1.20 .55

Intl. Chamber of Commerce, 30th Universal Congress A689

**1990, June 21**       **Litho.**
1609 A689 80pf multicolored    .95   .65

Matthias Claudius (1740-1815), Writer — A691

**1990, Aug. 9**       **Litho.**
1611 A691 100pf multicolored    1.20   .40

**Reunified Germany**
AREA — 137,179 sq. mi.
POP. — 82,087,361 (1999 est.)
CAPITAL — Berlin

German Reunification — A692

**1990, Oct. 3**    **Litho.**    **Perf. 14**
1612 A692 50pf black, red & yel   1.30   .50
1613 A692 100pf black, red & yel   2.25   .80

First Postage Stamps, 150th Anniv. — A693

**1990, Oct. 11**       **Litho.**
1614 A693 100pf multicolored    1.20   .40

Heinrich Schliemann (1822-1890), Archaeologist — A694

**1990, Oct. 11**
1615 A694 60pf multicolored    1.05   .40
See Greece No. 1705.

Kathe Dorsch (1912-1957), Actress — A695

**1990, Nov. 6**       **Photo.**
1616 A695 100pf red & violet    1.20   .55

Opening of Berlin Wall, 1st Anniv. — A696

**1990, Nov. 6**    **Photo.**    **Perf. 14**
1617 A696 50pf shown    1.00   .60
1618 A696 100pf Brandenburg Gate    1.60   .60
     **Souvenir Sheet**
1619    Sheet of 2    3.00   2.75
  *a.*   A696 50pf like No. 1617   1.00   1.00
  *b.*   A696 100pf like No. 1618   1.60   1.60
Rainbow continuous on stamps from No. 1619.

Pharmacy Profession, 750th Anniv. — A697

**1991, Jan. 8**       **Litho.**
1620 A697 100pf multicolored    1.30   .55

Hanover, 750th Anniv. — A698

**1991, Jan. 8**
1621 A698 60pf multicolored    .95   .40

Brandenburg Gate, Bicentennial A699

**1991, Jan. 8**       **Litho. & Engr.**
1622 A699 100pf gray, dk bl & red    1.45   .40

A700

**1991, Jan. 8**       **Photo.**
1623 A700 60pf multicolored    .80   .40
   Erich Buchholz (1891-1972), painter and architect.

A701

**1991, Jan. 8**       **Litho.**
1624 A701 100pf multicolored    1.15   .55
   Walter Eucken (1891-1950), economist.

25th Intl. Tourism Exchange, Berlin — A702

**1991, Jan. 8**
1625 A702 100pf multicolored    1.20   .40

     Souvenir Sheet

World Bobsled Championships, Altenberg — A703

**1991, Jan. 8**       **Perf. 12½x13**
1626 A703 100pf multicolored    1.60   2.00

Friedrich Spee von Langenfeld (1591-1635), Poet — A704

**1991, Feb. 14**    **Litho.**    **Perf. 14**
1627 A704 100pf multicolored    1.20   .40

A705

**1991, Mar. 12**
1628 A705 100pf multicolored    1.20   .40
   Ludwig Windthorst (1812-1891), politician.

A706

**1991, Mar. 12**
1629 A706 60pf multicolored    .80   .40
   Jan von Werth (1591-1652), general.

Flowers — A707

   30pf, Schweizer mannschild. 50pf, Wulfens primel (primula). 80pf, Sommerenzian (gentian). 100pf, Preiselbeere (cranberry). 350pf, Alpenedelweiss.

**1991, Mar. 12**       **Perf. 13**
1630 A707 30pf multicolored    .35   .35
1631 A707 50pf multicolored    .50   .50
1632 A707 80pf multicolored    .80   .35
1633 A707 100pf multicolored    1.15   .35
1634 A707 350pf multicolored    3.75   2.60
   Nos. 1630-1634 (5)    6.55   4.15

Battle of Legnica, 750th Anniv. — A708

     **Litho. & Engr.**
**1991, Apr. 9**       **Perf. 14**
1635 A708 100pf multicolored    1.30   .80
   See Poland No. 3019.

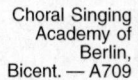

Choral Singing Academy of Berlin, Bicent. — A709

**1991, Apr. 9**
1636 A709 100pf multicolored    1.20   .55

Lette Foundation, 125th Anniv. — A710

**1991, Apr. 9**       **Photo.**
1637 A710 100pf multicolored    1.20   .40

Historic Aircraft — A711

   30pf, Junkers F13, 1930. 50pf, Grade Eindecker, 1909. 100pf, Fokker FIII, 1922. 165pf, Graf Zeppelin LZ 127, 1928.

**1991, Apr. 9**
1638 A711 30pf multicolored    .35   .35
1639 A711 50pf multicolored    .50   .35
1640 A711 130pf multicolored    1.30   .35
1641 A711 165pf multicolored    2.00   1.75
   Nos. 1638-1641 (4)    4.15   2.75

Europa — A712

   Satellites: 60pf, ERS-1. 100pf, Copernicus.

**1991, May 2**    **Litho.**    **Perf. 14**
1642 A712 60pf multicolored    1.00   .35
1643 A712 100pf multicolored    1.60   .35

Town Charters, 700th Anniv. — A713

   Design: Arms of Bernkastel, Mayen, Montabaur, Saarburg, Welschbillig, and Wittlich.

**1991, May 2**
1644 A713 60pf multicolored    .80   .40

Max Reger (1873-1916), Composer A714

**1991, May 2**
1645 A714 100pf multicolored    1.30   .40

Inter-City Express Railway — A715

**1991, May 2**
1646 A715 60pf multicolored    .80   .40

18th World Gas Congress, Berlin — A716

   Designs: 60pf, Wilhelm August Lampadius (1772-1842), chemist. 100pf, Gas street lamp.

**1991, June 4**    **Litho.**    **Perf. 13x12½**
1647    60pf lt blue & black    .85   .40
1648    100pf lt blue & black    1.00   .40
  *a.*   A716 Pair, #1647-1648 + label   2.10   2.25

Sea Birds — A717

   Designs: 60pf, Kampflaufer, Philomachus pugnax. 80pf, Zwergseeschwalbe, Sterna albifrons. 100pf, Ringelgans, Branta bernicla. 140pf, Seeadler, Haliaeetus albicilla.

**1991, June 4**       **Perf. 14**
1649 A717 60pf multicolored    .65   .40
1650 A717 80pf multicolored    1.00   .65
1651 A717 100of multicolored    1.00   .65
1652 A717 140pf multicolored    1.75   1.60
   Nos. 1649-1652 (4)    4.40   3.30

Paul Wallot (1841-1912), Architect A718

     **Litho. & Engr.**
**1991, June 4**       **Perf. 14**
1653 A718 100pf multicolored    1.30   .40

## Historic Sites Type of 1987

Designs: No. 1655, Frankfurt Airport. No. 1656, Wernigerode Town Hall. 60pf, Munich, Bavaria. 80pf, Zech Zollern II Dortmund. No. 1663, Wallfahrtskapelle Alloting. No. 1664, Schwerin Castle. 110pf, Regensburg Stone Bridge.

### Die Cut Perf 10¼x10¾ on 3 sides (#1656, 1664, 1666), Die Cut Imperf

| 1991-2001 | | | | Litho. |
|---|---|---|---|---|
| | **Self-Adhesive** | | | |
| 1655 | A623 | 10pf multi | 2.00 | 2.00 |
| 1656 | A623 | 10pf multi | 2.60 | 2.25 |
| 1659 | A623 | 60pf multi | 2.00 | 2.00 |
| 1661 | A623 | 80pf multi | 2.00 | 2.00 |
| 1663 | A623 | 100pf multi | 2.00 | 2.00 |
| a. | | Bklt. pane, 2 each #1655, 1659, 1661, 1663 | 16.00 | |
| 1664 | A623 | 100pf multi | 2.60 | 2.60 |
| 1666 | A623 | 100pf multi | 1.30 | 1.30 |
| a. | | Booklet, 2 each #1656, 1664, 8 #1666 | 27.00 | |
| | *Nos. 1655-1666 (7)* | | 14.50 | 14.15 |

Issued: Nos. 1655, 1659, 1661, 1663, 6/4. Nos. 1656, 1664, 110pf, 5/25/01.
Nos. 1655, 1659, 1661, 1663 issued on peelable paper backing serving as booklet cover.

Dragonflies — A719

50pf, No. 1671, Libellula depressa. No. 1672, 70pf, Sympetrum sanguineum. No. 1673, 80pf, Cordulegaster boltonii. No. 1674, 100pf, Aeshna viridis.

| 1991, July 9 | | Photo. | | Perf. 14 |
|---|---|---|---|---|
| 1670 | A719 | 50pf multicolored | .55 | .30 |
| 1671 | A719 | 60pf multicolored | 1.00 | .55 |
| 1672 | A719 | 60pf multicolored | 1.00 | .55 |
| 1673 | A719 | 60pf multicolored | 1.00 | .55 |
| 1674 | A719 | 60pf multicolored | 1.00 | .55 |
| a. | | Block of 4, #1671-1674 | 5.00 | 4.25 |
| 1675 | A719 | 70pf multicolored | .80 | .65 |
| 1676 | A719 | 80pf multicolored | .85 | .65 |
| 1677 | A719 | 100pf multicolored | .95 | .65 |
| | *Nos. 1670-1677 (8)* | | 7.15 | 4.45 |

Traffic Safety — A720

| 1991, July 9 | | | | Litho. |
|---|---|---|---|---|
| 1678 | A720 | 100pf multicolored | 1.30 | .55 |

Geneva Convention on Refugees, 40th Anniv. — A721

| 1991, July 9 | | | | |
|---|---|---|---|---|
| 1679 | A721 | 100pf blk, gray & pink | 1.20 | .40 |

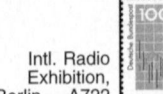
Intl. Radio Exhibition, Berlin — A722

| 1991, July 9 | | | | |
|---|---|---|---|---|
| 1680 | A722 | 100pf multicolored | 1.30 | .40 |

Reinold von Thadden-Trieglaff (1891-1976), Founder of German Protestant Convention — A723

| 1991, Aug. 8 | | Litho. | | Perf. 14 |
|---|---|---|---|---|
| 1681 | A723 | 100pf multicolored | 1.20 | .40 |

August Heinrich Hoffman von Fallersleben (1798-1874), Poet and Philologist A724

| 1991, Aug. 8 | | | | |
|---|---|---|---|---|
| 1682 | A724 | 100pf multicolored | 1.20 | .40 |

German national anthem, 150th anniv.

3-Phase Energy Transmission, Cent. — A725

| 1991, Aug. 8 | | | | |
|---|---|---|---|---|
| 1683 | A725 | 170pf multicolored | 2.00 | 1.00 |

Rhine-Ruhr Harbor, Duisburg, 275th Anniv. — A726

| 1991, Sept. 12 | | Litho. | | Perf. 14 |
|---|---|---|---|---|
| 1684 | A726 | 100pf multicolored | 1.20 | .40 |

### Souvenir Sheet

Theodor Korner (1791-1813), Poet — A727

| 1991, Sept. 12 | | | | Perf. 13x12½ |
|---|---|---|---|---|
| 1685 | A727 | Sheet of 2 | 2.00 | 2.60 |
| a. | | 60pf Sword and pen | 1.00 | 1.05 |
| b. | | 100pf Portrait | 1.00 | 1.05 |

Hans Albers (1891-1960), Actor — A728

| 1991, Sept. 12 | | Photo. | | Perf. 14 |
|---|---|---|---|---|
| 1686 | A728 | 100pf multicolored | 1.60 | .40 |

Postman, Spreewald Region — A729

| 1991, Oct. 10 | | Litho. | | Perf. 14 |
|---|---|---|---|---|
| 1687 | A729 | 100pf multicolored | 1.20 | .40 |

Stamp Day.

Bird Monument by Max Ernst — A730

| 1991, Oct. 10 | | | | |
|---|---|---|---|---|
| 1688 | A730 | 100pf multicolored | 1.20 | .40 |

Sorbian Legends — A731

60pf, Fiddler, water sprite. 100pf, Midday woman, woman from Nochten.

| 1991, Nov. 5 | | | | Perf. 13 |
|---|---|---|---|---|
| 1689 | A731 | 60pf multicolored | .80 | .40 |
| 1690 | A731 | 100pf multicolored | 1.20 | .40 |

### Souvenir Sheet

Wolfgang Amadeus Mozart, Death Bicent. — A732

| 1991, Nov. 5 | | Litho. | | Perf. 14 |
|---|---|---|---|---|
| 1691 | A732 | 100pf multicolored | 2.00 | 2.25 |

Otto Dix (1891-1969), Painter — A733

Designs: 60pf, Portrait of the Dancer Anita Berber. 100pf, Self-portrait.

| 1991, Nov. 5 | | Photo. | | Perf. 14 |
|---|---|---|---|---|
| 1692 | A733 | 60pf multicolored | .65 | .40 |
| 1693 | A733 | 100pf multicolored | 1.30 | .40 |

Julius Leber (1891-1945), Politician — A734

| 1991, Nov. 5 | | | | Litho. |
|---|---|---|---|---|
| 1694 | A734 | 100pf black & red | 1.20 | .40 |

Nelly Sachs (1891-1970), Writer — A735

| 1991, Nov. 5 | | | | |
|---|---|---|---|---|
| 1695 | A735 | 100pf violet | 1.20 | .50 |

City of Koblenz, 2000th Anniv. — A736

| 1992, Jan. 9 | | | | Perf. 13x12½ |
|---|---|---|---|---|
| 1696 | A736 | 60pf multicolored | 1.45 | .50 |

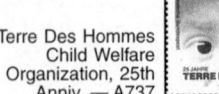
Terre Des Hommes Child Welfare Organization, 25th Anniv. — A737

| 1992, Jan. 9 | | Litho. | | Perf. 14 |
|---|---|---|---|---|
| 1697 | A737 | 100pf multicolored | 1.30 | .55 |

Martin Niemoller (1892-1984), Theologian — A738

| 1992, Jan. 9 | | | | |
|---|---|---|---|---|
| 1698 | A738 | 100pf multicolored | .95 | .40 |

Coats of Arms of States of the Federal Republic of Germany — A739

No. 1699, Baden-Wurttemberg. No. 1700, Bavaria. No. 1701, Berlin. No. 1702, Brandenburg. No. 1703, Bremen. No. 1704, Hamburg. No. 1705, Hesse. No. 1706, Mecklenburg-Western Pomerania. No. 1707, Lower Saxony. No. 1708, North Rhine - Westphalia. No. 1709, Rhineland-Palatinate. No. 1710, Saar. No. 1711, Saxony. No. 1712, Saxony-Anhalt. No. 1713, Schleswig-Holstein. No. 1714, Thuringia.

| 1992-94 | | | | Perf. 13½ |
|---|---|---|---|---|
| 1699 | 100pf multicolored | | 1.30 | .60 |
| 1700 | 100pf multicolored | | 1.30 | .60 |
| 1701 | 100pf multicolored | | 1.30 | .60 |
| 1702 | 100pf multicolored | | 1.30 | .60 |
| 1703 | 100pf multicolored | | 1.30 | .60 |
| 1704 | 100pf multicolored | | 1.30 | .60 |
| 1705 | 100pf multicolored | | 1.05 | .60 |
| 1706 | 100pf multicolored | | 1.05 | .60 |
| 1707 | 100pf multicolored | | 1.05 | .60 |
| 1708 | 100pf multicolored | | 1.05 | .60 |
| 1709 | 100pf multicolored | | 1.05 | .60 |
| 1710 | 100pf multicolored | | 1.15 | .60 |
| 1711 | 100pf multicolored | | 1.15 | .60 |
| 1712 | 100pf multicolored | | 1.15 | .60 |
| 1713 | 100pf multicolored | | 1.15 | .60 |
| 1714 | 100pf multicolored | | 1.15 | .60 |
| | *Nos. 1699-1714 (16)* | | 18.80 | 9.60 |

See No. B818.
Issued: No. 1699, 1/9/92; No. 1700, 3/12/92; No. 1701, 6/11/92; No. 1702, 7/16/92; No. 1703, 8/13/92; No. 1704, 9/10/92; No. 1705, 3/11/93; No. 1706, 6/17/93; No. 1707, 7/15/93; No. 1708, 8/12/93; No. 1709, 9/16/93; No. 1710, 1/13/94; No. 1711, 3/10/94; No. 1712, 6/16/94; No. 1713, 7/14/94; No. 1714, 9/8/94.

### Famous Women Type of 1986

80pf, Rahel Varnhagen von Ense (1771-1833), pioneer in women's movement. No. 1724, Elisabeth Schwarzhaupt (1901-86), politician. No. 1725, Louise Henriette of Orange (1627-67), mother of Frederick, King of Prussia. No. 1726, Grethe Weiser (1903-70), actress. No. 1727, Marlene Dietrich (1901-92), actress. No. 1728, Käte Strobel (1907-96), government minister. No. 1729, Marie-Elisabeth Lüders (1878-1966), politician. No. 1730, Marieluise Fleisser (1901-74), writer. No. 1731, Maria Probst (1902-67), politician. No. 1732, Nelly Sachs (1891-1970), writer. 400pf, Charlotte von Stein (1742-1827), confidant of Goethe. 440pf, Gret Palucca (1902-93), dancer. 450pf, Hedwig Courths-Mahler (1867-1950), novelist.

| 1992-2001 | | Engr. | | Perf. 14 |
|---|---|---|---|---|
| 1723 | A602 | 80pf blue & brn | .75 | .40 |
| 1724 | A602 | 100pf grn & org brn | .85 | .65 |
| 1725 | A602 | 100pf vio & bis | .75 | .40 |
| 1726 | A602 | 100pf ol bis & bl grn | .75 | .65 |
| 1727 | A602 | 110pf vio & dk | .85 | .55 |
| 1728 | A602 | 110pf ol & red brn | .80 | .65 |
| 1729 | A602 | 220pf grn bl & vio bl | 1.60 | 1.60 |
| 1730 | A602 | 220pf grn & brn | 1.30 | 1.30 |
| 1731 | A602 | 300pf dp blue & brn | 2.00 | 1.60 |
| 1732 | A602 | 300pf brn & vio | 2.00 | 2.00 |
| 1733 | A602 | 400pf lake & blk | 4.50 | 3.00 |
| 1734 | A602 | 440pf dp vio & dk car | 5.00 | 5.00 |
| 1735 | A602 | 450pf brt blue & blue | 5.00 | 3.75 |
| | *Nos. 1723-1735 (13)* | | 26.15 | 21.55 |

Issued: 400pf, 1/9/92; 450pf, 6/11/92; 80pf, No. 1725, 10/13/94; No. 1727, 8/14/97; No. 1729, 8/28/97; Nos. 1724, 1731, 10/16/97; 440pf, 10/8/98; Nos. 1726, 1728, 11/9/00; Nos. 1730, 1732, 1/11/01.
Nos. 1726, 1728, 1730 and 1732 are denominated in pfennigs and euros.

Arthur Honegger (1892-1955), Composer — A740

| 1992, Feb. 6 | | Photo. | | Perf. 14 |
|---|---|---|---|---|
| 1736 | A740 | 100pf sepia & black | 1.30 | .60 |

Ferdinand von Zeppelin (1838-1917), Airship Builder — A741

**1992, Feb. 6** Litho.
1737 A741 165pf multicolored 2.00 1.05

City of Kiel, 750th Anniv. — A742

**1992, Mar. 12**
1738 A742 60pf multicolored .95 .50

Konrad Adenauer — A743

**1992, Mar. 12** Photo.
1739 A743 100pf black & dull org 1.60 .50

Ernst Jakob Renz (1815-1892), Circus Director — A744

**1992, Mar. 12** Litho.
1740 A744 100pf multicolored 1.50 .50

Berlin Sugar Institute, 125th Anniv. — A745

**1992, Mar. 12** Perf. 13x12½
1741 A745 100pf multicolored 1.50 .70

Johann Adam Schall von Bell (1592-1666), Astronomer and Missionary A746

**1992, Apr. 9** Litho. Perf. 13x12½
1742 A746 140pf multicolored 2.00 1.00

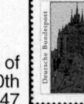

Erfurt, Capital of Thuringia, 1250th Anniv. — A747

**1992, May 7** Litho. Perf. 14
1743 A747 60pf multicolored 1.05 .50

Discovery of America, 500th Anniv. — A748

Europa: 60pf, Woodcut illustrating letters from Columbus, 1493. 100pf, Rene de Laudonniere and Chief Athore by Jacques le Moyne de Morgues, 1564.

**1992, May 7** Perf. 13½
1744 A748 60pf multicolored .75 .40
1745 A748 100pf multicolored 1.50 .40

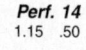

Order of Merit, 150th Anniv. — A749

**1992, May 7** Perf. 13
1746 A749 100pf multicolored 1.35 .50

St. Ludgerus, 1250th Birth Anniv. — A750

**1992, May 7** Litho. Perf. 14
1747 A750 100pf multicolored 1.35 .60

Adam Riese (1492-1559), Mathematician A751

**1992, May 7**
1748 A751 100pf multicolored 1.50 .55

Georg Christoph Lichtenberg (1742-1799), Physicist — A752

**1992, June 11** Litho. Perf. 14
1749 A752 100pf multicolored 1.35 .60

20th Century Paintings A753

Designs: 60pf, Landscape with a Horse, by Franz Marc (1880-1916). 100pf, Fashion Shop, by August Macke (1887-1914). 170pf, Murnau with a Rainbow, by Wassily Kandinsky (1866-1944).

**1992, June 11** Litho. Perf. 14
1750 A753 60pf multicolored .75 .60
1751 A753 100pf multicolored 1.15 .60
1752 A753 170pf multicolored 1.90 1.60
Nos. 1750-1752 (3) 3.80 2.80
See Nos. 1878-1880.

Leipzig Botanical Garden — A754

**1992, July 16** Litho. Perf. 13x12½
1753 A754 60pf multicolored .90 .50

Family Living — A755

**1992, July 16** Perf. 13½
1754 A755 100pf multicolored 1.50 .50

17th World Congress on Home Economics, Hanover A756

**1992, July 16** Photo. Perf. 14
1755 A756 100pf multicolored 1.35 .60

Egid Quirin Asam (1692-1750), Architect and Sculptor — A757

**1992, Aug. 13** Litho. Perf. 14
1756 A757 60pf multicolored 1.15 .50

German State Opera, Berlin, 250th Anniv. — A758

**1992, Aug. 13**
1757 A758 80pf multicolored 1.30 .50

Federation of German Amateur Theaters, Cent. — A759

**1992, Aug. 13**
1758 A759 100pf multicolored 1.35 .50

Construction of First Globe by Martin Behaim, 500th Anniv. — A760

**1992, Sept. 10** Perf. 13½
1759 A760 60pf multicolored 1.05 .50

Opening of Main-Danube Canal — A761

**1992, Sept. 10** Perf. 14
1760 A761 100pf multicolored 1.20 .50

Werner Bergengruen (1892-1964), Writer — A762

**1992, Sept. 10**
1761 A762 100pf blk, bl & gray 1.20 .50

Jewelry & Watch Industries in Pforzheim, 225th Anniv. — A763

**1992, Sept. 10**
1762 A763 100pf multicolored 1.20 .50

Balloon Post — A764

**1992, Oct. 15** Litho. Perf. 14
1763 A764 100pf multicolored 1.35 .60
Stamp Day.

Hugo Distler (1908-1942), Composer — A765

**1992, Oct. 15**
1764 A765 100pf violet & black 1.35 .50

Association of German Plant and Machine Builders, Cent. — A766

**1992, Oct. 15** Litho. & Engr.
1765 A766 170pf multicolored 1.75 1.05

Single European Market — A767

**1992, Nov. 5** Litho. Perf. 14
1766 A767 100pf multicolored 1.75 .60

Jochen Klepper (1903-1942), Writer — A768

Litho. & Engr.
**1992, Nov. 5** Perf. 14
1767 A768 100pf multicolored 1.35 .50

A769

**1992, Nov. 5** Photo.
1768 A769 100pf sepia & black 1.35 .50
Werner von Siemens (1816-1892), electrical engineer.

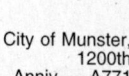

A770

**1992, Nov. 5** Litho.
1769 A770 100pf multicolored 1.35 .50
Gebhard Leberecht von Blucher (1742-1819), Commander of Prussian Army.

City of Munster, 1200th Anniv. — A771

**1993, Jan. 14** Litho. Perf. 14
1770 A771 60pf multicolored .90 .50

Sir Isaac Newton, Scientist — A772

**1993, Jan. 14** Litho. & Engr.
1771 A772 100pf multicolored 1.30 .50

North German Naval Observatory, Hamburg, 125th Anniv. — A773

**1993, Jan. 14** Litho. Perf. 13x12½
1772 A773 100pf multicolored 1.05 .50

Health and Safety in Workplace — A774

**1993, Jan. 14**    **Photo.**    *Perf. 14*
1773 A774 100pf blk, yel & bl    1.15 .50

Association of German Electrical Engineers, Cent. — A775

**1993, Jan. 14**
1774 A775 170pf multicolored    1.75 1.00

Leipzig Gewandhaus Orchestra, 250th Anniv. — A776

**1993, Feb. 11**    **Litho.**    *Perf. 13x12½*
1775 A776 100pf black & gold    1.05 .50

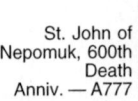

St. John of Nepomuk, 600th Death Anniv. — A777

**1993, Mar. 11**
1776 A777 100pf multicolored    1.20 .50

New Postal Codes — A778

**1993, Mar. 11**    *Perf. 14*
1777 A778 100pf multicolored    1.50 .50

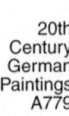

20th Century German Paintings A779

Designs: No. 1778, Cafe, by George Grosz (1893-1959). No. 1779, Sea and Sun, by Otto Pankok (1893-1966). No. 1780, Audience, by A. Paul Weber (1893-1980).

**1993, Mar. 11**
1778 A779 100pf multicolored    1.30 .75
1779 A779 100pf multicolored    1.30 .75
1780 A779 100pf multicolored    1.30 .75
   Nos. 1778-1780 (3)    3.90 2.25
See Nos. 1863-1865, 1922-1924.

Benedictine Abbeys of Maria Laach and Bursfelde, 900th Anniv. — A780

    **Litho. & Engr.**
**1993, Apr. 15**    *Perf. 14*
1781 A780 80pf multicolored    1.30 .55

5th Intl. Horticultural Show, Stuttgart A781

**1993, Apr. 15**    **Litho.**    *Perf. 13x12½*
1782 A781 100pf multicolored    1.05 .55

---

Contemporary Art — A782

Europa: 80pf, Storage Place, by Joseph Beuys (1921-1986). 100pf, Homage to the Square, by Joseph Albers (1888-1976).

**1993, May 5**    **Litho.**    *Perf. 13½x14*
1783 A782 80pf multicolored    1.15 .70
1784 A782 100pf multicolored    1.15 .70

Dahlwitz Hoppegarten (Hippodrome), Berlin, 125th Anniv. — A783

**1993, May 5**    **Litho.**    *Perf. 14*
1785 A783 80pf multicolored    1.05 .60

Lake Constance Steamer Hohentwiel A784

**1993, May 5**    **Photo.**
1786 A784 100pf multicolored    1.30 .55
See Austria No. 1618, Switzerland No. 931.

Schulpforta School for Boys, 450th Anniv. — A785

**1993, May 5**    **Litho.**
1787 A785 100pf multicolored    1.05 .55

Coburger Convent, 125th Anniv. — A786

**1993, May 5**    **Litho. & Engr.**
1788 A786 100pf black, green & red    1.05 .55

City of Potsdam, 1000th Anniv. — A787

**1993, June 17**    **Litho.**    *Perf. 13x12½*
1789 A787 80pf multicolored    1.30 .55

German UNICEF Committee, 40th Anniv. — A788

**1993, June 17**    **Litho.**    *Perf. 14*
1790 A788 100pf multicolored    1.05 .50

Friedrich Holderlin (1770-1843), Writer — A789

**1993, June 17**    **Photo.**    *Perf. 14*
1791 A789 100pf multicolored    1.30 .50

---

Hans Fallada (1893-1947), Novelist — A790

**1993, July 15**
1792 A790 100pf multicolored    1.35 .50

Scenic Regions in Germany A791

No. 1793, Rugen Island. No. 1794, Harz Mountains. No. 1795, Rhon Mountains. No. 1796, Bavarian Alps. No. 1797, Ore Mountains. No. 1798, Main River Valley. No. 1799, Mecklenburg lake district. No. 1800, Franconian Switzerland. No. 1801, Upper Lusatia. No. 1802, Sauerland. No. 1803, Havel River, Berlin. No. 1804, Holstein Switzerland. No. 1805, Saale. No. 1806, Spreewald. No. 1807, Eifel.

**1993-96**    **Litho.**    *Perf. 14*
    **Denominations 100pf**
1793 A791 multicolored    1.40 .75
1794 A791 multicolored    1.40 .75
1795 A791 multicolored    1.40 .75
1796 A791 multicolored    1.10 .80
1797 A791 multicolored    1.10 .80
1798 A791 multicolored    1.10 .80
1799 A791 multicolored    1.10 .80
1800 A791 multicolored    .80 .80
1801 A791 multicolored    .80 .80
1802 A791 multicolored    .80 .80
1803 A791 multicolored    .80 .80
1804 A791 multicolored    1.00 .80
1805 A791 multicolored    1.00 .80
1806 A791 multicolored    1.00 .80
1807 A791 multicolored    1.00 .80
   Nos. 1793-1807 (15)    15.80 11.85
Issued: Nos. 1793-1795, 7/15/93; Nos. 1796-1799, 7/14/94; Nos. 1800-1803, 7/6/95; Nos. 1804-1807, 4/11/96.
See Nos. 1938, 1974-1976, 2072-2073.

Mathias Klotz (1653-1743), Violin Maker — A792

**1993, Aug. 12**    **Litho.**    *Perf. 13x12½*
1808 A792 80pf multicolored    1.10 .50

Heinrich George (1893-1946), Actor — A793

**1993, Aug. 12**    *Perf. 14*
1809 A793 100pf multicolored    1.10 .60

Intl. Radio Exhibition, Berlin — A794

**1993, Aug. 12**
1810 A794 100pf multicolored    1.30 .60

Hans Leip (1893-1983), Poet and Painter — A795

**1993, Sept. 16**    **Litho.**    *Perf. 13*
1811 A795 100pf red, black & blue    1.60 .60

---

Birger Forell (1893-1958), Swedish Priest — A796

**1993, Sept. 16**    *Perf. 14*
1812 A796 100pf multicolored    1.60 .60

    Souvenir Sheet

For the Children A797

**1993, Sept. 16**
1813 A797 100pf multicolored    2.00 1.75

Peter I. Tchaikovsky (1840-93), Composer A798

**1993, Oct. 14**
1814 A798 80pf multicolored    1.40 .60

Max Reinhardt (1873-1943), Theatrical Director — A799

**1993, Oct. 14**
1815 A799 100pf buff, blk & red    1.50 .55

St. Hedwig of Silesia, 750th Death Anniv. — A800

**1993, Oct. 14**
1816 A800 100pf multicolored    1.60 .50
See Poland No. 3176.

Paracelsus (1493-1541), Physician, Teacher — A801

    **Litho. & Engr.**
**1993, Nov. 10**    *Perf. 14*
1817 A801 100pf multicolored    1.50 .55

Claudio Monteverdi (1567-1643), Composer A802

**1993, Nov. 10**    **Litho.**    *Perf. 13x12½*
1818 A802 100pf multicolored    1.50 .55

Willy Brandt (1913-92), Statesman — A803

**1993, Nov. 10**     *Perf. 14*
1819 A803 100pf multicolored    2.10 .90

Staade, 1000th Anniv. — A804

**Litho. & Engr.**     *Perf. 14*
**1994, Jan. 13.**
1820 A804 80pf multicolored    1.10 .50

Intl. Year of the Family — A805

**1994, Jan. 13**     **Litho.**
1821 A805 100pf multicolored    1.45 .70

Heinrich Hertz (1857-94), Physicist A806

**1994, Jan. 13**     *Perf. 13x12½*
1822 A806 200pf multicolored    2.60 1.05

Frankfurt Am Main, 1200th Anniv. — A807

**1994, Feb. 10**
1823 A807 80pf multicolored    1.10 .55

Fulda, 1250th Anniv. — A808

**1994, Mar. 10**     *Perf. 14*
1824 A808 80pf multicolored    1.25 .55

German Women's Associations, German Women's Council, Cent. — A809

**1994, Mar. 10**     *Perf. 13x12½*
1825 A809 100pf blk, red & yel    1.45 .60

Fourth European Parliamentary Elections A810

**1994, Mar. 10**     *Perf. 14*
1826 A810 100pf multicolored    1.60 .70

Foreigners in Germany: Living Together A811

**1994, Mar. 10**
1827 A811 100pf multicolored    1.15 .70

Church of Our Lady, Munich, 500th Anniv. — A812

**1994, Apr. 14**     **Litho.**     *Perf. 14*
1828 A812 100pf multicolored    1.90 .75

Europa — A813

Designs: 80pf, Ohm's Law, by Georg Simon Ohm. 100pf, Quantum theory, by Max Planck.

**1994, May 5**     **Photo.**
1829 A813 80pf multicolored    1.05 .45
1830 A813 100pf multicolored    1.05 .45
   Bklt. of 10, #1830    14.00 13.00

Souvenir Sheet

Carl Hagenbeck (1844-1913), Circus Director, Animal Trainer, and Berlin Zoo, 150th Anniv. — A814

Designs: a, Hagenbeck, circus animals, zoo entrance. b, Zoo entrance, animals.

**1994, May 5**     **Litho.**
1831 A814 Sheet of 2    3.75 4.25
  a.   100pf multicolored    1.60 1.50
  b.   200pf multicolored    2.00 1.90

Hans Pfitzner (1869-1949), Composer, Conductor — A815

**1994, May 5**
1832 A815 100pf multicolored    1.45 .60

Spandau Fortress, 400th Anniv. — A816

**1994, June 16**     **Litho.**     *Perf. 14*
1833 A816 80pf multicolored    1.20 .55

Herzogsagmuhle, Social Welfare Organization, Cent. — A817

**1994, June 16**     *Perf. 13*
1834 A817 100pf blue, yel & blk    1.20 .60

Emperor Frederick II (1194-1250) — A818

**1994, June 16**     *Perf. 13½x14*
1835 A818 400pf multicolored    4.50 3.75

Souvenir Sheet

Attempt to Assassinate Hitler, 50th Anniv. — A819

**1994, July 20**     **Litho.**     *Perf. 14*
1836 A819 100pf multicolored    2.00 2.60

### Historic Sites Type of 1987

No. 1838, Wernigerode Town Hall. No. 1839, Böttcherstrasse, Bremen. No. 1840, Berus Monument, Uberherrn. No. 1841, Wilhelmshöhe Hillside Park, Kassel. No. 1842, Kirchheim Castle. No. 1843, St. Reinoldi Church, Dortmund. No. 1844, Goethe-Schiller Monument. No. 1845, Schwerin Castle, Weimar. No. 1846, Bellevue Castle, Berlin. No. 1847, EXPO 2000, Hanover. No. 1848, Regensburg Stone Bridge. No. 1849, Brühl's Terrace, Dresden. No. 1850, St. Nikolai Cathedral, Greifswald. No. 1851, Grimma Town Hall. No. 1852, Wartburg Castle, Eisenach. No. 1853, Town hall, Bremen. No. 1854, Cologne Cathedral. No. 1855, Holsten Gate, Lübeck. No. 1856, Heidelberg Castle. No. 1857, Town Hall, Suhl-Heinrichs. No. 1858, Speyer Cathedral. No. 1859, St. Michael's Church, Hamburg. No. 1860, Hildesheim Town Hall.

| 1994-2001 | | Typo. | Perf. 14 | |
|---|---|---|---|---|
| 1838 | A623 | 10pf multi | .50 | .40 |
| 1839 | A623 | 20pf dk bl & brn org | .80 | .75 |
| 1840 | A623 | 47pf grn & gray | .50 | .45 |
| 1841 | A623 | 47pf dk grn & gray | .50 | .45 |
| 1842 | A623 | 50pf vio brn & beige | .80 | .75 |
| 1843 | A623 | 80pf dull grn & sepia | .75 | .60 |
| 1844 | A623 | 100pf bl & blk | .80 | .75 |
| a. | | Booklet pane of 10 | 9.00 | 8.25 |
| | | Complete booklet, #1844a | 9.75 | |
| 1845 | A623 | 100pf multi | 1.20 | 1.10 |
| 1846 | A623 | 110pf dk gray & buff | .90 | .40 |
| a. | | Booklet pane of 10 | 9.00 | 8.25 |
| | | Complete booklet, #1846a | 9.75 | |
| 1847 | A623 | 110pf org & bl | 1.05 | .60 |
| a. | | Booklet pane of 10 | 11.50 | 10.50 |
| | | Complete booklet, #1847a | 11.50 | |
| 1848 | A623 | 110pf multi | 1.10 | 1.10 |
| a. | | Booklet pane of 10 | 12.00 | 11.50 |
| | | Booklet, #1848a | 13.00 | |
| 1849 | A623 | 220pf grn & blk | 1.60 | .75 |
| 1850 | A623 | 220pf multi | 2.00 | 1.90 |
| 1851 | A623 | 300pf brn & ind | 2.40 | 2.25 |
| 1852 | A623 | 400pf vio brn & beige | 3.25 | 3.00 |
| 1853 | A623 | 440pf multi | 4.00 | 3.50 |
| 1854 | A623 | 440pf blk & gray | 4.00 | 3.75 |
| 1855 | A623 | 510pf red brn & ind | 4.00 | 3.75 |
| 1856 | A623 | 510pf brn & bis brn | 4.50 | 4.25 |
| 1857 | A623 | 550pf multi | 5.25 | 2.25 |
| 1858 | A623 | 640pf rose brn & gray bl | 7.00 | 3.75 |
| 1859 | A623 | 690pf blk & grn | 5.75 | 3.00 |
| 1860 | A623 | 720pf dk gray & lil | 6.50 | 6.00 |
| *Nos. 1838-1860 (23)* | | | 59.15 | 45.50 |

Issued: 550pf, 8/11/94; 640pf, 8/10/95; 690pf, 6/13/96; No. 1840, 7/17/97; Nos. 1846, 1849, 1853, 8/14/97; Nos. 1844, 1855, 8/28/97; No. 1847, 9/10/98; 10pf, No. 1848, 300pf, 9/28/00; Nos. 1845, 1850, 1/11/01. No. 1841, 80pf, 4/5/01. 720pf, 7/2/01. No. 1854, 8/9/01. 50pf, 400pf, 9/5/01. 20pf, No. 1856, 11/8/01.

Nos. 1838, 1839, 1841, 1842, 1843, 1845, 1848, 1850, 1851, 1852, 1854, 1856 and 1860 are denominated in pfennigs and euros.

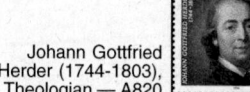

Johann Gottfried Herder (1744-1803), Theologian — A820

**1994, Aug. 11**     **Photo.**     *Perf. 14*
1862 A820 80pf multicolored    1.00 .50

### Paintings Type of 1993

Designs: 100pf, Maika, by Christian Schad. 200pf, Landscape, by Erich Heckel. 300pf, Couple Lying on Grass, by Gabriele Munter.

**1994, Aug. 11**     **Litho.**     *Perf. 14*
1863 A779 100pf multicolored    1.00 .60
1864 A779 200pf multicolored    1.75 1.50
1865 A779 300pf multicolored    2.60 2.40
  *Nos. 1863-1865 (3)*    5.35 4.50

Ethnological Museum, Leipzig, 125th Anniv. — A821

**1994, Sept. 8**     **Litho.**     *Perf. 13x12½*
1866 A821 80pf multicolored    1.20 .55

Hermann von Helmholtz (1821-94), Scientist — A822

**Litho. & Engr.**
**1994, Sept. 8**     *Perf. 13½x14*
1867 A822 100pf multicolored    1.45 .55

Willi Richter (1894-1972), Politician, Labor Leader — A823

**1994, Sept. 8**     **Litho.**
1868 A823 100pf multicolored    1.20 .50

Souvenir Sheet

For the Children A824

**1994, Sept. 8**     *Perf. 14*
1869 A824 100pf multicolored    2.00 1.90

Hans Sachs (1494-1576), Singer & Poet — A825

**1994, Oct. 13**     **Engr.**     *Perf. 13½x14*
1870 A825 100pf olive & maroon    1.20 .60

St. Wolfgang (924-94), Bishop of Regensburg — A826

**1994, Oct. 13**     **Litho.**     *Perf. 14*
1871 A826 100pf multicolored    1.20 .60

Mail Delivery, Spreewald Region, c. 1900 — A827

**1994, Oct. 13**
1872 A827 100pf multicolored    1.45 .60
   Stamp Day.

Quedlinburg, 1000th Anniv. — A828

**Litho. & Engr.**
**1994, Nov. 9**     *Perf. 14*
1873 A828 80pf multicolored    1.00 .55

Opening of the Berlin Wall, 5th Anniv. — A829

**1994, Nov. 9　Litho.　Perf. 13x12½**
1874　A829　100pf black, org & yel　1.20　.60

Natl. Assoc. for Preservation of German Graves Abroad, 75th Anniv. — A830

**1994, Nov. 9　　　Perf. 14**
1875　A830　100pf black & red　1.20　.60

Theodore Fontane (1819-98), Poet — A831

**1994, Nov. 9　　　Perf. 13½x14**
1876　A831　100pf multicolored　1.20　.60

Baron Friedrich von Steuben (1730-94) A832

**1994, Nov. 9　　　Perf. 14**
1877　A832　100pf multicolored　1.20　.60

**Paintings Type of 1992**

Designs: 100pf, The Water Tower in Bremen, by Franz Radziwill. 200pf, Still Life with a Cat, by Georg Schrimpf. 300pf, An Estate in Dangast, by Karl Schmidt-Rottluff.

**1995, Jan. 12　Litho.　Perf. 14**
1878　A753　100pf multicolored　1.20　.55
1879　A753　200pf multicolored　1.90　1.50
1880　A753　300pf multicolored　3.00　2.25
　　　Nos. 1878-1880 (3)　6.10　4.30

Province of Gera, 1000th Anniv. — A833

**1995, Jan. 12　　　Perf. 13½x13**
1881　A833　80pf multicolored　1.20　.55

Diet of Worms, 500th Anniv. — A834

**1995, Jan. 12　　　Perf. 13x12½**
1882　A834　100pf multicolored　1.20　.60

Frederick William of Brandenburg, the Great Elector (1620-88) — A835

**1995, Feb. 9　Litho.　Perf. 14**
1883　A835　300pf multicolored　3.25　2.40

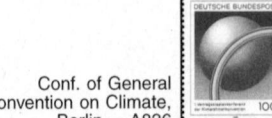

Conf. of General Convention on Climate, Berlin — A836

**1995, Mar. 9　Litho.　Perf. 14**
1884　A836　100pf multicolored　1.00　.60

Wilhelm Roentgen (1845-1923) A837

**1995, Mar. 9**
1885　A837　100pf multicolored　1.00　.60

Carolo-Wilhelmina Technical University, Braunschweig, 250th Anniv. — A838

**1995, Mar. 9**
1886　A838　100pf multicolored　1.15　.60

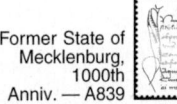

Former State of Mecklenburg, 1000th Anniv. — A839

**1995, Mar. 9**
1887　A839　100pf multicolored　1.00　.60

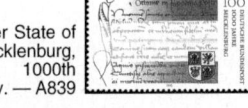

City of Regensburg, 750th Anniv. — A840

**1995, Apr. 6　Litho.　Perf. 14**
1888　A840　80pf multicolored　.90　.55

Freedom of Expression — A841

**1995, Apr. 6　　　Photo.**
1889　A841　100pf multicolored　1.00　.60

Dietrich Bonhoeffer (1906-45), Protestant Theologian A842

**1995, Apr. 6**
1890　A842　100pf multicolored　1.00　.60

Johann Conrad Schlaun (1695-1773), Architect — A843

**1995, Apr. 6　Litho.　Perf. 13**
1891　A843　200pf multicolored　2.00　1.60

Vincent Conferences in Germany, 150th Anniv. — A844

**1995, May 5　Litho.　Perf. 14**
1892　A844　100pf multicolored　1.00　.70

Schiller Society, Cent. — A845

**1995, May 5　　　Photo.**
1893　A845　100pf multicolored　1.00　.60

End of World War II, 50th Anniv. — A846

Designs: No. 1894, End of the war. 200pf, Moving towards United Europe.
No. 1896, Liberation of concentration camps. No. 1897: a, Destruction of buildings. b, Refugees.

**1995, May 5　Litho.　Perf. 14**
1894　A846　100pf red & black　1.20　.75
1895　A846　200pf bl, gray, yel & blk　1.75　1.50

**Souvenir Sheets**
1896　A846　100pf multicolored　1.60　1.90
1897　　　Sheet of 2　3.00　3.00
a.-b.　A846 100pf any single　1.40　1.30
　　　Europa (Nos. 1894-1895).

Kiel Canal, Cent. — A847

**1995, June 8　Litho.　Perf. 14**
1898　A847　80pf multicolored　1.20　.50

UN, 50th Anniv. — A848

**1995, June 8**
1899　A848　100pf gold, lil & gray　1.00　.60

Radio, Cent. — A849

100pf, Marconi, wireless apparatus.

**1995, June 8**
1900　A849　100pf multicolored　.90　.85

See Ireland Nos. 973-974, Italy 2038-2039, San Marino Nos. 1336-1337, Vatican City Nos. 978-979.

Carl Orff (1895-1982), Composer — A850

**1995, July 6　Litho.　Perf. 13x13½**
1901　A850　100pf multicolored　1.10　.60

Henry the Lion, Duke of Bavaria (1129-95) — A851

**1995, July 6　　　Perf. 14**
1902　A851　400pf multicolored　3.75　3.00

Kaiser Wilhelm Memorial Church, Berlin, Cent. — A852

**1995, Aug. 10　Photo.　Perf. 14**
1903　A852　100pf multicolored　1.25　.60

Franz Werfel (1890-1945), Author — A853

**1995, Aug. 10　　　Litho.**
1904　A853　100pf multicolored　1.10　.60

Franz Josef Strauss (1915-88), Politician — A854

**1995, Sept. 6　Photo.　Perf. 14x13½**
1905　A854　100pf multicolored　1.35　.75

Souvenir Sheet

German Film, Cent. A855

**1995, Sept. 6　　　Perf. 14**
1906　A855　Sheet of 3　5.50　7.50
a.　80pf Metropolis　1.35　1.50
b.　100pf Little Superman　1.35　1.50
c.　200pf The Sky Over Berlin　2.50　3.00

Kurt Schumacher (1895-1952), Politician — A856

**1995, Oct. 12　Litho.　Perf. 13**
1907　A856　100pf multicolored　1.10　.60

Souvenir Sheet

For the Children A857

**1995, Oct. 12　　　Perf. 14**
1908　A857　100pf multicolored　2.25　3.00

Leopold von Ranke (1795-1886), Historian — A858

**1995, Nov. 9　Litho.　Perf. 14**
1909　A858　80pf multicolored　.90　.55

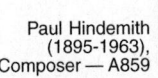

Paul Hindemith (1895-1963), Composer — A859

**1995, Nov. 9**
1910 A859 100pf multicolored   1.10 .60

Nobel Prize Fund Established, Cent. — A860

**1995, Nov. 9**     **Litho. & Engr.**
1911 A860 100pf Nobel, last will  1.45 .90
See Sweden Nos. 2155-2158.

CARE, 50th Anniv. — A861

**1995, Nov. 9**   **Litho.**   **Perf. 13x12½**
1912 A861 100pf multicolored   1.10 .60

Victims of a Divided Germany, 1945-89 — A862

**1995, Nov. 9**     **Perf. 14**
1913 A862 100pf Berlin Wall   1.20 .60

Borussia Dortmund, Soccer Champions A863

**1995, Dec. 6**   **Photo.**   **Perf. 14**
1914 A863 100pf multicolored   1.50 .75

Children's Missionary Work in Germany, 150th Anniv. — A864

**1996, Jan. 11**   **Litho.**   **Perf. 14**
1915 A864 100pf multicolored   1.10 .70

Friedrich von Bodelschwingh (1877-1946), Protestant Theologian — A865

**1996, Jan. 11**     **Perf. 13½**
1916 A865 100pf black & red   1.10 .70

Martin Luther (1483-1546), Theologian — A866

**1996, Feb. 8**   **Litho.**   **Perf. 14**
1917 A866 100pf multicolored   1.20 .85

Philipp Franz von Siebold (1796-1866), Physician and Diplomat A867

**1996, Feb. 17**     **Perf. 13x12½**
1918 A867 100pf multicolored   1.20 .85

Cathedral Square, Halberstadt, 1000th Anniv. — A868

**1996, Mar. 7**   **Litho.**   **Perf. 13**
1919 A868 80pf multicolored   .90 .45

August Cardinal Graf von Galen (1878-1946) — A869

**1996, Mar. 7**     **Perf. 13½**
1920 A869 100pf bl, gray & bis   1.10 .60

Giovanni Battista Tiepolo (1696-1770), Painter — A870

**1996, Mar. 7**     **Perf. 13**
1921 A870 200pf multicolored   2.00 1.45

**20th Century German Paintings Type of 1993**

Designs: 100pf, Sitting Female Nude, by Max Pechstein (1881-1955). 200pf, Abstract For Wilhelm Runge, by Georg Muche (1895-1987). 300pf, Still Life with Guitar, Book and Vase, by Helmut Kolle (1899-1931).

**1996, Mar. 7**     **Perf. 14**
1922 A779 100pf multicolored   1.10 .75
1923 A779 200pf multicolored   2.10 1.50
1924 A779 300pf multicolored   2.75 2.25
    *Nos. 1922-1924 (3)*   5.95 4.50

**Souvenir Sheet**

For the Children A871

100pf, Racing messenger.

**1996, Apr. 11**   **Litho.**   **Perf. 14**
1925 A871 100pf multi   2.00 1.75

Famous Women — A872

Europa: 80pf, Self-portrait, by Paula Modersohn-Becker (1876-1907). 100pf, Self-portrait, by Käthe Kollwitz (1867-1945).

**1996, May 3**
1926 A872 80pf multicolored   *1.20 .40*
1927 A872 100pf red & black   *1.20 .75*

Freising's Right to Hold Markets, 1000th Anniv. — A873

**1996, May 3**
1928 A873 100pf multicolored   .90 .70

Wolfgang Borchert (1921-47), Writer — A874

**1996, May 3**     **Perf. 13**
1929 A874 100pf multicolored   .90 .70

Ruhr Festival, Recklinghausen, 50th Anniv. — A875

**1996, May 3**
1930 A875 100pf multicolored   .90 .70

German Theater Assoc., 150th Anniv. — A876

**1996, May 3**   **Photo.**   **Perf. 14**
1931 A876 200pf multicolored   1.75 1.10

Academy of Arts in Berlin, 300th Anniv. — A877

**1996, June 13**   **Litho.**   **Perf. 13**
1932 A877 100pf multicolored   .90 .70

Gottfried Wilhelm Leibniz (1646-1716), Mathematician, Philosopher A878

**1996, June 13**     **Perf. 14**
1933 A878 100pf multicolored   .90 .70

City of Heidelberg, 800th Anniv. — A879

**1996, July 18**   **Litho.**   **Perf. 14**
1934 A879 100pf multicolored   .90 .70
  Complete booklet, 10 #1934   13.00

UNICEF, 50th Anniv. — A880

**1996, July 18**
1935 A880 100pf multicolored   .90 .70

Ludwig Thoma (1867-1921), Satirist — A881

**1996, July 18**     **Perf. 13x13½**
1936 A881 100pf multicolored   .90 .70

**Souvenir Sheet**

German Natl. Parks — A882

**1996, July 18**     **Perf. 14**
1937 A882  Sheet of 3   7.25 6.00
  *a.*  100pf Coastal   1.75 1.50
  *b.*  200pf Mudflat   1.75 1.50
  *c.*  300pf Sea-inlet   3.25 2.60

**Scenic Regions Type of 1993**

"Gendarmenmarkt," central district of Berlin.

**1996, Aug. 14**   **Litho.**   **Perf. 14**
1938 A791 100pf multicolored   .90 .70

Assoc. of German Philatelists, 50th Anniv. — A883

**1996, Aug. 14**   **Photo.**   **Perf. 14**
1939 A883 100pf multicolored   .90 .70

Paul Lincke (1866-1946), Musician, Composer — A884

**1996, Aug. 14**   **Litho.**   **Perf. 13**
1940 A884 100pf multicolored   .90 .70

UNESCO World Cultural Heritage — A885

Design: Closed blast furnace, Völklingen.

**1996, Aug. 14**     **Perf. 13½**
1941 A885 100pf multicolored   .90 .70

German Civil Code, Cent. — A886

**1996, Aug. 14**
1942 A886 300pf multicolored   3.00 2.25

Borussia Dortmund, Champion Soccer Club — A887

**1996, Aug. 27**
1943 A887 100pf multicolored   1.20 .70

Life Without Drugs — A888

**1996, Sept. 12**   **Photo.**   **Perf. 14**
1944 A888 100pf multicolored   1.00 .70

UNESCO World Cultural Heritage — A889

Design: Old Town, Bamberg

**1996, Sept. 12**   **Litho.**   **Perf. 14**
1945 A889 100pf multicolored   1.00 .70

Homeopathic Medicine, Bicent. — A890

Samuel Hahnemann (1755-1843), physician.

**1996, Sept. 12　Litho.　Perf. 14**
1946 A890 400pf multicolored　3.75 3.25

Anton Bruckner (1824-96), Composer — A891

**1996, Oct. 9　Litho.　Perf. 13**
1947 A891 100pf multicolored　1.00 .70

Donaueschingen Music Festival, 75th Anniv. — A892

**1996, Oct. 18　Litho.　Perf. 13½**
1948 A892 100pf multicolored　1.00 .70

Baron Ferdinand von Mueller (1825-96), Botanist — A893

**Litho. & Engr.**
**1996, Oct. 18　　　　　　Perf. 14**
1949 A893 100pf multicolored　1.00 .70
See Australia No. 1566.

Carl Zuckmayer (1896-1977), Playwright — A894

**1996, Nov. 14　Litho.　Perf. 13**
1950 A894 100pf red, gray & blue 1.00 .70

Carlo Schmid (1896-1979), Politician, Scholar & Writer — A895

**1996, Dec. 3　Photo.　Perf. 14**
1951 A895 100pf multicolored　.90 .70

Franz Schubert (1797-1828), Composer — A896

**1997, Jan. 16　Litho.　Perf. 14**
1952 A896 100pf multicolored　1.00 .70

Sepp Herberger (1897-1977), Soccer Coach — A897

**1997, Jan. 16**
1953 A897 100pf multicolored　1.10 .70

Traffic Safety for Children — A898

**1997, Jan. 16**
1954 A898 100pf multicolored　1.00 .70
See No. 1979.

Philipp Melanchthon (1497-1560), Protestant Reformer — A899

**1997, Feb. 4　Litho.　Perf. 14**
1955 A899 100pf multicolored　1.00 .70

Cologne Carnival, 175th Anniv. — A900

**1997, Feb. 4**
1956 A900 100pf multicolored　1.00 .70

Chancellor Ludwig Erhard (1897-1977) — A901

**1997, Feb. 4　　　　　Photo.**
1957 A901 100pf multicolored　1.10 .70

Leipzig Fair, 500th Anniv. — A902

**1997, Mar. 6　　　Perf. 13x12½**
1958 A902 100pf red, sil & blue 1.00 .70

German Architecture after 1945 — A903

Building, architect: a, Berlin Philharmonic, by Hans Scharoun. b, New National Gallery, Berlin, by Ludwig Mies van der Rohe. c, St. Mary, Queen of Peace Church, Neviges, by Gottfried Böhm. d, German Pavilion, 1967 World's Fair, Montreal, by Frei Otto.

**1997, Mar. 6　Litho.　Perf. 14**
1959　A903 Sheet of 4　　　5.50 6.00
a.-d.　　100pf any single　　1.25 1.20

City of Straubing, 1100th Anniv. — A904

**1997, Mar. 10　　　Perf. 13x12½**
1960 A904 100pf multicolored　1.10 .70

Heinrich von Stephan (1831-97) A905

**1997, Apr. 8　Litho.　Perf. 14**
1961 A905 100pf multicolored　1.20 .70

Augustusburg and Falkenlust Castles, UNESCO World Heritage Sites — A906

**1997, Apr. 8**
1962 A906 100pf multicolored　1.00 .70

Idar-Oberstein Gem & Jewelry Industry, 500th Anniv. — A907

**1997, Apr. 8　　　　Perf. 13½**
1963 A907 300pf multicolored　3.25 2.60

St. Adalbert (956-997) — A908

**1997, Apr. 23　Engr.　Perf. 14**
1964 A908 100pf deep violet　1.00 .70
See Poland No. 3337, Czech Republic No. 3012, Hungary No. 3569, Vatican City No. 1040.

Stories and Legends — A909

Europa: 80pf, Fisherman and his Wife. 100pf, Rübezahl of Riesengebirge (Giant Mountains).

**1997, May 5　Litho.　Perf. 14**
1965 A909 80pf multicolored　*1.25 .60*
1966 A909 100pf multicolored　*1.25 .75*

Sister Cities Movement, 50th Anniv. — A910

**1997, May 5**
1967 A910 100pf multicolored　1.10 .70

Souvenir Sheet

Society for Protection of German Forests, 50th Anniv. — A911

**1997, May 5**
1968　A911 Sheet of 2　　　4.00 3.75
a.　　100pf multicolored　　1.75 1.50
b.　　200pf multicolored　　1.75 1.50

Fr. Sebastian Kneipp (1821-97), Hydrotherapist A912

**1997, June 9　　　　　Perf. 13**
1969 A912 100pf multicolored　1.20 .70

Marshall Plan, 50th Anniv. — A913

**1997, June 9　　　　　Perf. 13**
1970 A913 100pf multicolored　1.10 .70

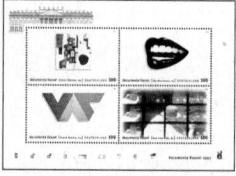

"Documenta" Intl. Exhibition of Modern Art, Kassel — A914

Designs: a, Composition, by Fritz Winter, 1956. b, Mouth No. 15, by Tom Wesselmann, 1968. c, Quathlamba, by Frank Stella, 1964. d, Video sculpture, Beuys/Bois, by Nam June Paik.

**1997, June 20　Litho.　Perf. 14**
1971 A914 100pf Sheet of 4, #a.-
　　　　　　　　　d.　　5.50 5.75
**a.-d.**　any single　　1.25 1.20

Müngsten Bridge, Cent. — A915

**1997, June 20　Litho.　Perf. 13½**
1972 A915 100pf multicolored　1.00 .70

Souvenir Sheet

For the Children A916

**1997, July 17　Photo.　Perf. 13½**
1973 A916 100pf multicolored　2.00 1.90

**Scenic Regions Type of 1993**

No. 1974, Bavarian Forest. No. 1975, Lüneburg Heath. No. 1976, North German Moorland.

**1997, Aug. 28　Litho.　Perf. 14**
1974 A791 110pf multicolored　1.20 .75
1975 A791 110pf multicolored　1.20 .75
1976 A791 110pf multicolored　1.20 .75
*Nos. 1974-1976 (3)*　　3.60 2.25

Centenary of Rudolf Diesel's Engine — A917

**1997, Aug. 28**     *Perf. 13*
1977 A917 300pf blue & gray    3.25 2.25

Cultivation of Potatoes in Germany, 350th Anniv. — A918

**1997, Sept. 17**   **Litho.**   *Perf. 13*
1978 A918 300pf multicolored    2.75 2.25

**Traffic Safety for Children Type**
**1997, Oct. 9**   **Litho.**   *Perf. 14*
1979 A898 10pf like #1954     .40 .25

Felix Mendelssohn-Bartholdy (1809-47), Composer — A919

**1997, Oct. 9**     *Perf. 13x13½*
1980 A919 110pf multicolored    1.10 .75

FC Bayern Munchen, 1997 German Soccer Champions A920

**1997, Oct. 16**   **Photo.**   *Perf. 14*
1981 A920 110pf multicolored    1.20 .75

Third Saar-Lorraine-Luxembourg Summit — A921

**1997, Oct. 16**     **Litho.**
1982 A921 110pf multicolored    1.20 .75
See Luxembourg No. 972, France No. 2613.

Charitable Assoc. of the German Catholic Church, Cent. — A922

**1997, Nov. 6**   **Photo.**   *Perf. 14*
1983 A922 110pf multicolored    1.10 .75

Heinrich Heine (1797-1856), Poet — A923

**1997, Nov. 6**   **Litho.**   *Perf. 13*
1984 A923 110pf multicolored    1.10 .75

No. 1984 was sold in sheets of 10. It was withdrawn from sale 11/18/97, because runes associated with Nazi Germany were printed on the decorative selvage of the sheet. Value of withdrawn sheet of 10, $35. It was again placed on sale in sheets with runes removed.

Gerhard Tersteegen (1697-1769), Author of Religious Hymns, Booklets — A924

**1997, Nov. 6**     *Perf. 14*
1985 A924 110pf multicolored    1.10 .75

Thomas Dehler (1897-1967), Politician A925

**1997, Nov. 6**
1986 A925 110pf multicolored    1.10 .75

Cistercian Monastery Maulbronn, UNESCO World Heritage Site — A926

**1998, Jan. 22**   **Litho.**   *Perf. 14*
1987 A926 100pf multicolored    1.10 .75

Glienicke Bridge, Berlin — A927

**1998, Jan. 22**
1988 A927 110pf multicolored    1.10 .75

City of Nördlingen, 1100th Anniv. — A928

**1998, Jan. 22**
1989 A928 110pf multicolored    1.10 .75
   a.   Booklet pane of 10    12.00 9.75
    Complete booklet, #1989a +
    20 self-adhesive labels   13.00

Bertolt Brecht (1898-1956), Playwright — A929

**1998, Feb. 5**
1990 A929 110pf multicolored    1.10 .75

Max Planck Society for Advancement of Science, 50th Anniv. — A930

**1998, Feb. 5**
1991 A930 110pf multicolored    1.10 .75

Town of Bad Frankenhausen, 1000th Anniv. — A931

**1998, Mar. 12**   **Litho.**   *Perf. 13*
1992 A931 110pf multicolored    1.10 .75

Peace of Westphalia, End of Thirty Years' War, 350th Anniv. — A932

**1998, Mar. 12**     *Perf. 14*
1993 A932 110pf black & red    1.10 .75

German State Parliament Buildings A933

Designs: No. 1994, Baden-Württemberg. No. 1995, Bavaria. No. 1996, Chamber of Deputies, Berlin. No. 1997, Brandenburg.

**1998, Mar. 12**
1994 A933 110pf multicolored    1.20 .75
1995 A933 110pf multicolored    1.20 .75
1996 A933 110pf multicolored    1.20 .75
1997 A933 110pf multicolored    1.20 .75
   Nos. 1994-1997 (4)    4.80 3.00
   See Nos. 2027, 2029-2031, 2074-2077, 2113-2116.

Hildegard von Bingen (1098-1179), Christian Mystic — A934

**1998, Apr. 16**
1998 A934 100pf multicolored    1.10 .75

Cistercian Abbey of St. Marienstern, Panschwitz-Kuckau, 750th Anniv. — A935

**1998, Apr. 16**     *Perf. 13x12½*
1999 A935 110pf multicolored    1.10 .75

Souvenir Sheet

For the Children A936

**1998, Apr. 16**     *Perf. 14*
2000 A936 110pf multicolored    2.25 1.90

Bayreuth Opera, 250th Anniv. A937

**1998, Apr. 16**     *Perf. 13½*
2001 A937 300pf multicolored    3.25 2.40

Ernst Jünger (1895-1998), Writer — A938

**1998, Apr. 22**     *Perf. 14*
2002 A938 110pf multicolored    1.20 .75

German Rural Women's Assoc. — A939

**1998, May 7**   **Litho.**   *Perf. 13*
2003 A939 110pf multicolored    1.20 .75

Europa and German Reunification Day — A940

**1998, May 7**     *Perf. 14½x14*
2004 A940 110pf multicolored    1.50 .75

Souvenir Sheet

German Constitution — A941

Designs: a, Parliamentary Council, Bonn, 1948, convening to draw up constitution. b, Natl. Assembly, St. Paul's Church, Frankfurt, 1848, electing pan-German constitutional Parliament.

**1998, May 7**     *Perf. 14*
2005 A941 Sheet of 2    4.50 5.25
   a.   110pf multicolored   2.25 2.25
   b.   220pf multicolored   2.25 2.25

Congress of German Catholics, 150th Anniv. — A942

**1998, June 10**   **Litho.**   *Perf. 13x13½*
2006 A942 110pf multicolored    1.20 .70

Deutsche Mark, 50th Anniv. — A943

**1998, June 19**     *Perf. 13*
2007 A943 110pf multicolored    2.00 .90

German Cultivation of Hops — A944

**1998, July 16**   **Litho.**   *Perf. 13*
2008 A944 110pf multicolored    1.20 .75

Founding of the European Central Bank, Frankfurt am Main A945

**1998, July 16**   **Photo.**   *Perf. 14*
2009 A945 110pf multicolored    2.00 1.05

## Souvenir Sheet

Saxon Switzerland Natl. Park — A945a

**1998, July 16**    **Litho.**    **Perf. 14**
2009A A945a   Sheet of 2    4.50 4.25
   *b.*    110pf multicolored    2.00 1.50
   *c.*    220pf multicolored    2.40 1.90

1998 Intl. Congress of Mathematicians, Berlin — A946

**1998, Aug. 20**   **Photo.**   **Perf. 14x13½**
2010 A946 110pf multicolored    1.20 .75

Grube Messel Fossil Beds A947     Würzburg Palace, Germany A948

UNESCO World Heritage Sites: No. 2013, Puning Temple, Chengde, People's Republic of China.

**1998, Aug. 20**   **Litho.**   **Perf. 13x12½**
2011 A947 100pf multicolored    1.20 .70

      **Perf. 13½x14**
2012 A948 110pf multicolored    1.50 .70
2013 A948 110pf multicolored    1.50 .70

See China People's Republic Nos. 2887-2888.

## Souvenir Sheet

20th Cent. German Design — A949

Designs: a, Glassware, by Peter Behrens, 1910. b, Teapot, by Marianne Brandt, 1924. c, Desk lamp, by Wilhelm Wagenfeld, 1924. d, "Wassily" chair, by Marcel Breuer, 1926.

**1998, Aug. 20**       **Perf. 14**
2014 A949   Sheet of 4    7.00 6.75
   *a.-d.*    110pf any single    1.60 1.50

See No. 2051.

Manfred Hausmann (1898-1986), Author — A950

**1998, Sept. 10**    **Litho.**    **Perf. 14**
2015 A950 110pf multicolored    1.20 .75

A951

**1998, Sept. 10**
2016 A951 110pf multicolored    1.40 .75
   Team 1 FC Kaiserslautern, 1998 German soccer champions.

Prevent Child Abuse — A952

**1998, Sept. 10**
2017 A952 110pf black & red    1.20 .75

Francke Charitable Institutions, Halle, 300th Anniv. — A953

**1998, Sept. 10**      **Perf. 13**
2018 A953 110pf Building    1.20 .75

Mail Boat, "Hiorten" — A954

**1998, Oct. 8**    **Litho.**    **Perf. 14**
2019 A954 110pf multicolored    1.20 .75
   Stamp Day.

Telephone Help Lines for People in Distress — A955

**1998, Oct. 8**      **Perf. 13x12½**
2020 A955 110pf multicolored    1.20 .75

Günther Ramin (1898-1956), Organist, Choir Leader — A956

**1998, Oct. 8**   **Photo.**   **Perf. 14x14½**
2021 A956 300pf multicolored    3.25 2.25

Saxony State Orchestra, Dresden, 450th Anniv. — A957

**1998, Nov. 12**    **Litho.**    **Perf. 14**
2022 A957 300pf multicolored    3.50 2.25

Universal Delcaration of Human Rights, 50th Anniv. — A958

**1998, Nov. 12**      **Perf. 13x12½**
2023 A958 110pf multicolored    1.20 .75
   See No. B848.

Weimar, 1999 European City of Culture, 1100th Anniv. — A959

**1999, Jan. 14**    **Litho.**    **Perf. 14**
2024 A959 100pf multicolored    1.20 .85
   *a.*    Booklet pane of 10    13.00 9.75
     Complete booklet, #2024a + 20 labels    13.00

The self-adhesive labels are part of the booklet cover.

International Year of the Elderly — A960

**1999, Jan. 14**      **Perf. 13**
2025 A960 110pf multicolored    1.30 .85

Katharina von Bora (1499-1552), Wife of Martin Luther, from Painting by Lucas Cranach — A961

**1999, Jan. 14**      **Perf. 14**
2026 A961 110pf multicolored    1.30 .85

**State Parliaments Type of 1998**

The Hessian Parliament.

**1999, Jan. 14**
2027 A933 110pf multicolored    1.30 .85

Erich Kästner (1899-1974), Writer — A963

**1999, Feb. 18**    **Litho.**    **Perf. 13**
2028 A963 300pf multicolored    3.25 2.40

**State Parliaments Type of 1998**

Buildings: No. 2029, Hamburg. No. 2030, Mecklenburg-Western Pomerania. No. 2031, Bremen City Parliament.

**1999**      **Litho.**      **Perf. 14**
2029 A933 110pf multicolored    1.30 .85
2030 A933 110pf multicolored    1.30 .85
2031 A933 110pf multicolored    1.30 .85
   Nos. 2029-2031 (3)    3.90 2.55

Issued: Nos. 2029-2030, 3/11; No. 2031, 4/27.

NATO, 50th Anniv. — A963a

**1999, Mar. 11**      **Photo.**
2032 A963a 110pf multicolored    1.30 .85

Fraunhofer Society, 50th Anniv. — A964

**1999, Mar. 11**    **Litho.**    **Perf. 13**
2033 A964 110pf multicolored    1.30 .85

Expo 2000, Hanover — A965

**1999, Apr. 27**
2034 A965 110pf multicolored    1.30 .85
   See No. 2083.

German Automobile Club, Cent. — A966

**1999, Apr. 27**      **Photo.**
2035 A966 110pf multicolored    1.30 .85

German Cancer Relief Organization, 25th Anniv. — A967

**1999, Apr. 27**    **Litho.**    **Perf. 13**
2036 A967 110pf multicolored    1.30 .85

Knights of St. John of Jerusalem and Knights of Malta, 900th Anniv. — A968

**1999, May 4**
2037 A968 110pf multicolored    1.30 .85

Berlin Airlift, 1948-49 — A969

**1999, May 4**    **Photo.**    **Perf. 14**
2038 A969 110pf multicolored    1.30 .85

Council of Europe, 50th Anniv. — A970

**1999, May 4**    **Litho.**    **Perf. 13**
2039 A970 110pf multicolored    1.50 .85

## Souvenir Sheet

Berchtesgaden Natl. Park — A971

**1999, May 4**      **Perf. 14**
2040 A971 110pf multicolored    3.00 3.00
   Europa.

## Souvenir Sheet

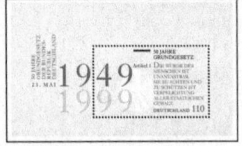

Basic Law, 50th Anniv. A972

**1999, May 21**    **Litho.**    *Perf. 14*
2041 A972 110pf multicolored    2.00 3.00

## Souvenir Sheet

Federal Republic of Germany, 50th Anniv. — A973

Scenes from 1949, 1999: a, Leaders gathering, session of Parliament. b, Child carrying wood, child picking flower. c, Building "The Wall," people walking where "The Wall" has been removed. d, Soldiers, government assembly.

**1999, May 21**
2042 A973 Sheet of 4    6.50 6.75
a.-d.   110pf any single    1.50 1.50

SOS Children's Village, 50th Anniv. — A974

**1999, June 10**    **Litho.**    *Perf. 13¾x14*
2043 A974 110pf multicolored    1.30 .75

Paderborn Bishopric, 1200th Anniv. — A975

**1999, June 10**    *Perf. 14*
2044 A975 110pf multicolored    1.30 .75

Johann Strauss, the Younger (1825-99) — A976

**1999, June 10**    **Photo.**    *Perf. 13¾*
2045 A976 300pf multicolored    3.50 2.25

Dominikus-Ringeisen Institution, Ursberg, 115th Anniv. — A977

**1999, July 15**    **Litho.**
2046 A977 110pf multicolored    1.30 .75

Pres. Gustav Heinemann (1899-1976) — A978

**1999, July 15**
2047 A978 110pf multicolored    1.30 .75

---

Cultural Foundation of the Federal States — A979

Sculpture: 110pf, Old Woman Smiling, by Ernst Barlach (1870-1938). 220pf, Bust of a Thinker, by Wilhelm Lehmbruck (1881-1919).

**1999, July 15**    **Photo.**    *Perf. 14*
2048 A979 110pf multicolored    1.30 .75
2049 A979 220pf multicolored    2.25 1.50

First Peace Conference in The Hague, Cent. — A980

**1999, July 15**    **Litho.**    *Perf. 13¼x13*
2050 A980 300pf multicolored    3.50 2.10

### 20th Cent. German Design Type of 1998

#### Souvenir Sheet

Designs: a, HF1 Television set, by Herbert Hirche, 1958. b, Knife, fork, spoon and teaspoon, by Peter Raacke, 1959. c, Pearl bottle, by Günter Kupetz, 1969. d, "Transrapid," Maglev train, by Alexander Neumeister, 1982.

**1999, Aug. 12**    **Litho.**    *Perf. 14*
#### Souvenir Sheet
2051   Sheet of 4    6.50 6.00
a.-d.   A949 110pf any single    1.60 1.35

Johann Wolfgang von Goethe (1749-1832), Poet — A981

**1999, Aug. 12**    *Perf. 13¾*
2052 A981 110pf multicolored    1.30 .85
See Korea Nos. 1964-1965.

#### Souvenir Sheet

For the Children A982

**1999, Aug. 12**    *Perf. 13¼*
2053 A982 110pf multicolored    2.00 2.00

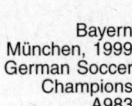

Bayern München, 1999 German Soccer Champions A983

**1999, Sept. 16**    **Litho.**    *Perf. 14*
2054 A983 110pf multicolored    1.30 .85

Federal Association of German Book Traders Peace Prize, 50th Anniv. — A984

**1999, Sept. 16**    **Photo.**    *Perf. 13¾*
2055 A984 110pf multicolored    1.20 .85

Richard Strauss (1864-1949), Composer — A985

**1999, Sept. 16**    **Litho.**    *Perf. 13¼*
2056 A985 300pf multicolored    3.50 2.40

---

Göltzsch Valley Bridge — A986

**1999, Oct. 14**    **Litho.**    *Perf. 14*
2057 A986 110pf multicolored    1.20 .85

German Federation of Trade Unions, 50th Anniv. — A987

**1999, Oct. 14**
2058 A987 110pf red & black    1.20 .85

Endangered Species — A988

**1999, Nov. 4**    **Litho.**    *Perf. 13¾*
2059 A988 100pf Large horseshoe bat    1.20 .85

EXPO 2000, Hanover — A989

**2000, Jan. 13**    **Litho.**    *Perf. 14x14¼*
2060 A989 100pf multi    1.20 .85
See No. 2094.

Holy Year 2000 — A990

**2000, Jan. 13**    *Perf. 13¾*
2061 A990 110pf multi    1.30 .85

Completion of Aachen Cathedral, 1200th Anniv. — A991

**2000, Jan. 13**
2062 A991 110pf Charlemagne    1.30 .85

German Soccer Assoc., Cent. — A992

**2000, Jan. 13**    **Photo.**
2063 A992 110pf multi    1.60 .85
Value is for stamp with surrounding selvage.

Herbert Wehner (1906-90), Politician — A993

**2000, Jan. 13**
2064 A993 110pf multi    1.30 .85

---

Albert Schweitzer (1875-1965), Humanitarian A994

**2000, Jan. 13**    **Litho.**    *Perf. 14x13¾*
2065 A994 110pf multi    1.30 .85

Prevention of Violence Against Women A995

**2000, Jan. 13**    *Perf. 14*
2066 A995 110pf multi    1.30 .85

Berlin Intl. Film Festival, 50th Anniv. — A996

**2000, Feb. 17**    **Litho.**    *Perf. 14*
2067 A996 100pf multi    1.20 .85

Johannes Gutenberg (c. 1400-1468) — A997

**2000, Feb. 17**    *Perf. 13¾*
2068 A997 110pf red & black    1.30 .85

Friedrich Ebert (1871-1925), President of German Reich — A998

**2000, Feb. 17**    **Photo.**
2069 A998 110pf multi    1.30 .85

Düsseldorf Carnival, 175th Anniv. — A999

**2000, Feb. 17**    **Litho.**    *Perf. 13x13½*
2070 A999 110pf multi    1.40 .85

Kurt Weill (1900-50), Composer A1000

**2000, Feb. 17**    *Perf. 14*
2071 A1000 300pf multi    3.50 2.40

### Scenic Regions Type of 1993

Designs: No. 2072, Passau. No. 2073, Saar River bend, Mettlach.

**2000**    **Litho.**    *Perf. 13¾x14*
2072 A791 110pf multi    1.30 .85
2073 A791 110pf multi    1.30 .85
Issued: No. 2072, 3/16.

### State Parliament Building Type

No. 2074, Lower Saxony. No. 2075, North Rhine-Westphalia. No. 2076, Rhineland-Palatinate. No. 2077, Saarland.

**2000**    **Litho.**    *Perf. 13¾x14*
2074 A933 110pf multi    1.30 .85
2075 A933 110pf multi    1.40 .85
2076 A933 110pf multi    1.40 .90

*Perf. 14*
2077 A933 110pf multi    1.20 .90
*Nos. 2074-2077 (4)*    5.30 3.50

Issued: No. 2074, 3/16; No. 2075, 4/13; No. 2076, 8/14; No. 2077, 11/9.

Pinwheel — A1001

**2000, Mar. 16    Litho.    Perf. 13¾**
2078  A1001  110pf multi                    1.60 1.20

Souvenir Sheet

Hainich National Park A1002

**2000, Mar. 16                 Perf. 13¼**
2079  A1002  110pf multi                    2.00 2.00

Blue Wonder Bridge, Dresden — A1003

**2000, Apr. 13    Litho.    Perf. 13¼**
2080  A1003  100pf multi                    1.20  .75

**Cultural Foundation Type of 1999**

Designs: 110pf, The Expulsion from Paradise, sculpture by Leonhard Kern. 220pf, Silver table fountain, 1652-53, by Melchior Gelb.

**2000, Apr. 13                 Perf. 14x14¼**
2081  A979  110pf multi                     1.50 1.05
2082  A979  220pf multi                     2.25 1.60

**Expo 2000 Type of 1999**
**2000, Apr. 13          Die Cut Perf. 11**
**Booklet Stamp**
**Self-Adhesive**
2083  A965  110pf multi                     6.50 3.75
   a.    Booklet pane of 10                    65.00

No. 2083a is a complete booklet.

Griefswald, 750th Anniv. — A1004

**Litho. & Engr.**
**2000, Apr. 13                 Perf. 14x14¼**
2084  A1004  110pf multi                    1.30  .85

Nikolaus Ludwig von Zinzendorf (1700-60), Religious Leader — A1005

**2000, May 12    Photo.    Perf. 13¾**
2085  A1005  110pf multi                    1.30  .75

**Europa, 2000**
**Common Design Type**
**2000, May 12    Litho.    Perf. 13¾**
2086  CD17  110pf multi                     1.75  .90
**Booklet Stamp**
**Self-Adhesive**
**Die Cut Perf. 10¾**
2087  CD17  110pf multi                     2.60 1.20
   a.    Complete booklet of 10               27.00

Einkommende Zeitungen, First Daily Newspaper, 350th Anniv. — A1006

**2000, June 8    Litho.    Perf. 13¾x14**
2088  A1006  110pf multi                    1.40  .85

Chambers of Handicrafts in Germany, Cent. — A1007

**2000, June 8                 Perf. 14**
2089  A1007  300pf gray & org              3.50 2.40

Zugspitze Weather Station, Cent. A1008

**2000, July 13    Litho.    Perf. 13¾x14**
2090  A1008  100pf multi                    1.50  .85

Federal Disaster Relief Organization, 50th Anniv. — A1009

**2000, July 13                 Perf. 14**
2091  A1009  110pf multi                    1.50  .85

Johann Sebastian Bach (1685-1750) A1010

**2000, July 13                 Perf. 13¼**
2092  A1010  110pf multi                    1.50  .85

First Zeppelin Flight, Cent. — A1011

**2000, July 13**
2093  A1011  110pf multi                    1.50  .85

**Expo 2000 Type of 2000**
110pf, Expo emblem, Earth, fingerprint.

**2000, Aug. 14    Litho.    Perf. 14x14¼**
2094  A989  110pf multi                     1.50  .85

Friedrich Nietzsche (1844-1900), Philosopher A1012

**2000, Aug. 14                 Perf. 13¼**
2095  A1012  110pf multi                    1.50  .85

Ernst Wiechert (1887-1950), Writer — A1013

**2000, Aug. 14                 Perf. 13¾**
2096  A1013  110pf multi                    1.60  .85

"For You" A1014

**2000, Sept. 14    Litho.    Perf. 13x13¼**
2097  A1014  100pf multi                    1.20  .85

Souvenir Sheet

For the Children A1015

**2000, Sept. 14                 Perf. 13¾x14**
2098  A1015  110pf multi                    2.00 2.00

Adolph Kolping (1813-65) — A1016

**2000, Sept. 14                 Perf. 13¼**
2099  A1016  110pf multi                    1.30  .85

Kolping Society, 150th anniv.

Federal Court of Justice, 50th Anniv. — A1017

**Litho. & Engr.**
**2000, Sept. 14                 Perf. 14x14¼**
2100  A1017  110pf multi                    1.40  .85

Bernhard Nocht Institute for Tropical Medicine, Cent. A1018

**2000, Sept. 14    Litho.    Perf. 13¾x14**
2101  A1018  300pf multi                    4.25 2.60

Reunification of Germany, 10th Anniv. — A1019

**2000, Sept. 28                 Perf. 13¼**
2102  A1019  110pf multi                    1.50  .85

Stamp Day — A1020

**2000, Oct. 12    Litho.    Perf. 13x13¼**
2103  A1020  110pf multi                    1.40  .85

Rainer Maria Rilke (1875-1926), Poet — A1021

**2000, Nov. 9    Litho.    Perf. 13¼x13½**
2104  A1021  110pf multi                    1.40  .90

Arnold Bode (1900-77), Artist — A1022

**2000, Nov. 9                 Perf. 13¼**
2105  A1022  110pf red & black             1.40 1.15

Leonhart Fuchs (1501-66), Botanist — A1023

**2001, Jan. 11    Litho.    Perf. 13¾**
2106  A1023  100pf multi                    1.30  .75

Kingdom of Prussia, 300th Anniv. — A1024

**2001, Jan. 11                 Perf. 14**
2107  A1024  110pf multi                    1.30  .75

Association of Disabled War Veterans, 50th Anniv. — A1025

**2001, Jan. 11    Photo.    Perf. 14**
2108  A1025  110pf multi                    1.30  .75

Youth Helpline Federation A1026

**2001, Jan. 11    Litho.    Perf. 13¾x14**
2109  A1026  110pf multi                    1.30  .75

Albert Lortzing (1801-51), Opera Composer — A1027

**2001, Jan. 11                 Perf. 13¾**
2110  A1027  110pf multi                    1.30  .75

Martin Bucer (1491-1551), Theologian — A1028

**2001, Feb. 8    Litho.    Perf. 13¾**
2111  A1028  110pf multi                    1.40  .90

Johann Heinrich Voss (1751-1826), Translator of Greek Classics — A1029

**2001, Feb. 8** *Perf. 13¼*
2112 A1029 300pf multi 4.00 2.60
See No. 2157.

**State Parliament Type of 1998**
Design: No. 2113, Saxony. No. 2114, Saxony-Anhalt. No. 2115, Schleswig-Holstein. No. 2116, Thuringia.

**2001** *Litho.* *Perf. 13¾x14*
2113 A933 110pf multi 1.30 .75
2114 A933 110pf multi 1.30 .75
2115 A933 110pf multi 1.30 .75
2116 A933 110pf multi 1.30 .75
Nos. 2113-2116 (4) 5.20 3.00

Issued: No. 2113, 3/8/01. No. 2114, 5/10. No. 2115, 7/12. No. 2116, 9/5.

Erich Ollenhauer (1901-63), Politician A1030

**2001, Mar. 8** *Litho.* *Perf. 14*
2117 A1030 110pf multi 1.60 .75

Karl Arnold (1901-58), Politician — A1031

**2001, Mar. 8** *Perf. 13¼*
2118 A1031 110pf multi 1.30 .75

Federal Border Police, 50th Anniv. — A1032

**2001, Mar. 8** *Litho.* *Perf. 13¾*
2119 A1032 110pf multi 1.30 .75

Rendsburg Railway Bridge — A1033

**2001, Apr. 5** *Litho.* *Perf. 14*
2120 A1033 100pf multi 1.50 .75

Folk Music A1034

**2001, Apr. 5** *Perf. 13x13½*
2121 A1034 110pf multi 1.30 .75

"Post!" A1035

**2001, Apr. 5** *Photo.* *Perf. 14*
2122 A1035 110pf multi 1.30 .75

Goethe Institute, 50th Anniv. A1036

**2001, Apr. 5** *Litho.*
2123 A1036 300pf multi 3.50 2.25

Endangered Species A1037

Designs: No. 2124, Mountain gorilla. No. 2125, Indian rhinoceros.

**2001, May 10** *Litho.* *Perf. 14*
2124 A1037 110pf multi 1.40 .90
2125 A1037 110pf multi 1.40 .90
See Nos. 2132-2133.

Europa — A1038

**2001, May 10** *Perf. 13¾*
2126 A1038 110pf multi 1.75 .85

Werner Egk (1901-83), Composer A1039

**2001, May 10** *Perf. 14*
2127 A1039 110pf multi 1.50 .75

St. Catherine's Monastery, 750th Anniv., Oceanographic Museum, 50th Anniv. — A1040

**2001, June 13** *Litho.* *Perf. 13x13¼*
2128 A1040 110pf multi 1.30 .75

Catholic Court Church, Dresden, 250th Anniv. — A1041

**2001, June 13** *Perf. 13¼*
2129 A1041 110pf multi 1.30 .75

Canzow Village Church A1042

**2001, July 12** *Photo.* *Perf. 14x14¼*
2130 A1042 110pf multi 1.30 .75
Conservation of sacred monuments.

**Souvenir Sheet**

Health A1043

No. 2131: a, Hand (circulatory diseases). b, Chest (cancer). c, Abdomen (infectious diseases). d, Head (depression).

**2001, July 12** *Litho.* *Perf. 13x13½*
2131 A1043 Sheet of 4 7.50 5.00
a.-d. 110pf Any single 1.75 1.15

**Endangered Species Type of 2001**
*Die Cut Perf. 11¼x11*
**2001, July 12** *Litho.*
**Booklet Stamps**
**Self-Adhesive**
2132 A1037 110pf Like #2124 2.10 1.30
2133 A1037 110pf Like #2125 2.10 1.30
a. Booklet, 5 each #2132-2133 29.00

Furth Dragon Lancing Festival — A1044

**2001, Aug. 9** *Litho.* *Perf. 13¼*
2134 A1044 100pf multi 1.15 .70

Himmelsberg Lime Tree Natural Monument — A1045

**2001** *Perf. 13¾x14*
2135 A1045 110pf multi 1.30 .75
**Booklet Stamp**
**Self-Adhesive**
*Die Cut Perf. 9¾x10½*
2135A A1045 110pf multi 3.50 1.50
b. Booklet of 20 70.00
Issued: No. 2135, 8/9; No. 2135A, 9/13.

Lifelong Learning A1046

**2001, Aug. 9** *Perf. 14*
2136 A1046 110pf multi 1.30 .75

Federal Constitutional Court, 50th Anniv. — A1047

**2001, Sept. 5**
2137 A1047 110pf multi 1.30 .75

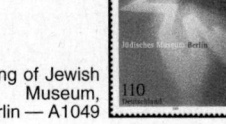

First World Congress of Union Network International — A1048

**2001, Sept. 5** *Perf. 13x13½*
2138 A1048 110pf multi 1.30 .75

Opening of Jewish Museum, Berlin — A1049

**2001, Sept. 5** *Photo.* *Perf. 13¾*
2139 A1049 110pf multi 1.30 .75

**Souvenir Sheet**

For Children A1050

**2001, Sept. 5** *Litho.* *Perf. 13¾x14*
2140 A1050 110pf multi 1.75 1.35

"For You" A1051

**2001, Oct. 11** *Perf. 13x13¼*
2141 A1051 110pf multi 1.30 .75

Werner Heisenberg (1901-76), Physicist — A1052

**2001, Nov. 8** *Litho.* *Perf. 13¾*
2142 A1052 300pf multi 4.25 2.40

**Souvenir Sheet**

German Antarctic Expeditions, Cent. — A1053

Expedition vessels: a, Gauss. b, Polarstern.

**2001, Nov. 8** *Perf. 13¾x14*
2143 A1053 Sheet of 2, #a-b 5.00 3.50
a. 110pf multi 1.75 1.15
b. 220pf multi 3.00 1.90

Introduction of the Euro, Jan. 1 — A1054

**2002, Jan. 10** *Litho.* *Perf. 13¾*
2144 A1054 56c multi 2.00 1.30
**Coil Stamp**
*Perf. 10½*
**Self-Adhesive**
2144A A1054 56c multi 4.75 2.25

Hans von Dohnanyi (1902-45), Documenter of Nazi Atrocities — A1055

**2002, Jan. 10** *Photo.*
2145 A1055 56c multi 1.30 .75
2145A A1055 56c multi 350.00 225.00

No. 2145A has "2002" in upper right corner and colored face and name. Approximately 320 small panes of 10 of No. 2145A were accidentally mixed in with approved stock of No. 2145 and sold over post office counters.

Bautzen, 1000th Anniv. — A1056

**2002, Jan. 10**   **Litho.**   **Perf. 13¾**
2146   A1056 56c multi    1.30   .75

*Die Cut Perf. 11*
**Litho.**
**Booklet Stamp**
**Self-Adhesive**
2146A A1056 56c multi    5.75   3.00
   b.   Booklet of 10    35.00

More
Tolerance
A1057

**2002, Jan. 10**     **Perf. 13¾x14**
2147   A1057 56c multi    1.30   .75

Adolph Freiherr
Knigge (1762-96),
Writer — A1058

**2002, Feb. 7**   **Litho.**   **Perf. 13¾**
2148   A1058 56c multi    1.40   .85

Berlin Subway
System,
Cent. — A1059

**2002, Feb. 7**     **Perf. 13¼**
2149   A1059 56c multi    1.75   .85

Johann Christoph
Schuster's
Mechanical
Calculator
A1060

**2002, Mar. 7**   **Litho.**   **Perf. 14**
2150   A1060 56c multi    1.40   .85
Cultural Foundation of the Federal States.

Deggendorf,
1000th
Anniv. — A1061

**2002, Mar. 7**
2151   A1061 56c multi    1.30   .75

Ecksberg Foundation
for the Mentally
Handicapped, 150th
Anniv. — A1062

**Litho. & Engr.**
**2002, Apr. 4**     **Perf. 14x13¾**
2152   A1062 56c multi    1.30   .75

Freemason's
Museum,
Cent. — A1063

**2002, Apr. 4**   **Litho.**   **Perf. 14**
2153   A1063 56c multi    1.40   .85

Baden-Württemberg,
50th Anniv. — A1064

**2002, Apr. 4**     **Perf. 13¼**
2154   A1064 56c multi    1.40   .85

"Post"
A1065

**2002, Apr. 4**     **Perf. 13x13½**
2155   A1065 56c multi    1.30   .75

Federal
Employment
Services, 50th
Anniv. — A1066

**2002, Apr. 4**     **Perf. 14**
2156   A1066 153c black & red   3.75   2.25

**Voss Type of 2001**
*Die Cut Perf. 10¼*
**2002, Apr. 4**     **Litho.**
**Coil Stamp**
**Self-Adhesive**
2157   A1029 €1.53 multi   5.75   3.50
   Dated 2001. No. 2157 was sold only for euro currency.

Europa — A1067

**2002**   **Litho.**   **Perf. 13¼**
2158   A1067 56c multi    1.30   .75

**Self-Adhesive**
**Coil Stamp**
*Die Cut Perf. 10¼*
2158A A1067 56c multi    3.50   2.25
   Issued: No. 2158, 5/2; No. 2158A, 7/4.

Garden Kingdom of Dessau-Wörlitz,
UNESCO World Heritage
Site — A1068

**2002**     **Perf. 13¾x14**
2159   A1068 56c multi    1.40   .85

**Booklet Stamp**
**Self-Adhesive**
*Die Cut Perf. 10¾*
2159A A1068 56c multi    2.25   1.05
   b.   Booklet of 20    52.50
   Issued: No. 2159, 5/2; No. 2159A, 8/8.

Halle-Wittenberg
University, 500th
Anniv. — A1069

**2002, May 2**     **Perf. 14**
2160   A1069 56c multi    1.30   .75

Children's Church,
150th
Anniv. — A1070

**2002, May 2**     **Perf. 13¼**
2161   A1070 56c multi    1.40   .85

**Souvenir Sheet**

Documenta 11 Art Exhibition — A1071

**2002, May 2**     **Perf. 13¾x14**
2162   A1071 56c multi    2.25   1.50

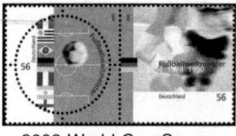
2002 World Cup Soccer
Championships, Japan and
Korea — A1072

No. 2163: a, Flags, soccer ball and field (28mm diameter). b, Soccer players, years of German championships.

**2002, May 2**     **Perf. 13¾**
2163   A1072   Horiz. pair    3.00   1.75
   a.-b.   56c Any single    1.40   .90
   See Argentina No. 2184, Brazil No. 2840, France No. 2891, Italy No. 2526 and Uruguay No. 1946.

Albrecht Daniel Thaer (1752-1828),
Agronomist — A1073

**2002, May 2**     **Perf. 13x13½**
2164   A1073 225c multi    5.75   3.75

Yellow Feather in Red, by Ernst
Wilhelm Nay (1902-68)
A1074

**2002, June 6**   **Litho.**   **Perf. 13¾x14**
2165   A1074 56c multi    1.30   .75

Endangered
Species
A1075

Designs: 51c, Desmoulins whorl snail. 56c, Freshwater pearl mussel.

**2002, June 6**     **Perf. 14x14¼**
2166   A1075 51c multi    1.40   .75
2167   A1075 56c multi    1.40   .75
   See Czech Republic No. 3173.

World
Hunger
Help
A1076

**2002, July 4**   **Litho.**   **Perf. 13¾x14**
2168   A1076 51c multi    1.15   .75

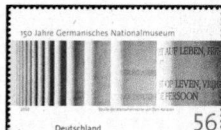
Natl.
Germanic
Museum,
150th
Anniv.
A1077

**2002, July 4**
2169   A1077 56c multi    1.30   .75

Hermann
Hesse (1877-
1962),
Writer — A1078

**2002, July 4**     **Perf. 14**
2170   A1078 56c multi    1.30   .75

**Souvenir Sheet**

Hochharz Natl. Park — A1079

**2002, July 4**     **Perf. 13¾x14**
2171   A1079 56c multi    1.75   1.15

Josef Felder (1900-
2000), Politician,
Journalist — A1080

**2002, Aug. 8**   **Litho.**   **Perf. 13**
2172   A1080 56c multi    1.40   .85

Volunteer Fire
Brigades
A1081

**2002, Aug. 8**     **Perf. 14**
2173   A1081 56c multi    1.40   .85

A1082

**Litho. & Engr.**
**2002, Aug. 8**     **Perf. 13¾x14**
2174   A1082 56c blk & Prus blue   1.40   .85
   Museum Island, Berlin, UNESCO World Heritage Site.

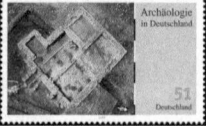
Communications Museum,
Berlin — A1083

**2002, Aug. 8**   **Litho.**   **Perf. 14**
2175   A1083 153c multi    3.50   2.25

Foundation
Walls of
Roman Villa
Bathhouse,
Wurmlingen
A1084

**2002, Sept. 5**   **Litho.**   **Perf. 13¾x14**
2176   A1084 51c multi    1.15   .75

Rotes Elisabeth-Ufer, by Ernst Ludwig Kirchner (1880-1938) — A1085

**2002, Sept. 5**
2177 A1085 112c multi 2.50 1.50

Souvenir Sheet

For Children A1086

**2002, Sept. 5** Perf. 13x13½
2178 A1086 56c multi 1.75 1.75

Heinrich von Kleist (1777-1811), Writer — A1087

**2002, Oct. 10** Litho. Perf. 13
2179 A1087 56c multi 1.30 .75

Eugen Jochum (1902-87), Conductor A1088

**2002, Oct. 10** Perf. 14x14¼
2180 A1088 56c multi 1.30 .75

Otto von Guericke (1602-86), Physicist A1089

**2002, Oct. 10** Perf. 14
2181 A1089 153c multi 4.25 2.40

Federal Agency for Civic Education, 50th Anniv. — A1090

**2002, Nov. 7** Litho. Perf. 13¼
2182 A1090 56c blk, red & org 1.30 .75

German Television, 50th Anniv. — A1091

**2002, Nov. 7** Perf. 14
2183 A1091 56c multi 1.50 .75

Halle Market Church, by Lyonel Feininger (1871-1956) — A1092

**2002, Dec. 5** Litho. Perf. 13¾x14
2184 A1092 55c multi 1.30 .75

**Famous Women Type of 1986 With Euro Denominations Only**

Designs: 45c, Annette von Droste-Hülshoff (1797-1848), poet. 55c, Hildegard Knef (1925-2002), actress. €1, Marie Juchacz (1879-

1956), politician. €1.44, Esther von Kirchbach (1894-1946), writer.

**2002-03** Engr. Perf. 14
2185 A602 45c ol grn & Prus bl 1.15 .75
2186 A602 55c car & blk 1.15 .75
2187 A602 €1 dk bl & claret 2.25 1.35
2188 A602 €1.44 dk bl & ocher 3.00 2.00
Nos. 2185-2188 (4) 7.55 4.85
Issued: 45c, 55c, €1.44, 12/27/02; €1, 1/16/03.

**Historic Sites Type of 1987 With Euro Denominations Only**

Designs: 25c, Prince's Residence, Arolsen. 40c, Bach Statue, Leipzig.44c, Berlin Philharmonic Hall. 45c, Tönninger Packhaus (Warehouse, Tönning). 55c, Old Opera House, Frankfurt. €1, Porta Nigra, Trier. €1.44, Birthplace of Ludwig van Beethoven, Bonn. €1.60, Bauhaus, Dessau. €1.80, Stuttgart Staatsgalerie. €2, Equestrian statue, Bamberg. €2.20, Monument to Theodor Fontane, Neuruppin. €2.60, Barque "Seute Deern," Bremerhaven. €4.10, Gabled houses, Wismar.

**2002-04** Litho. Perf. 14
2199 A623 5c olive & turq .35 .25
2200 A623 25c multi .60 .40
2201 A623 40c pur & grn .95 .60
2202 A623 44c blk & yel 1.15 .60
2203 A623 45c gray blk & brick red 1.15 .75
2204 A623 55c blk & yel 1.15 .75
2205 A623 €1 blk & greenish gray 2.25 1.35
2206 A623 €1.44 gray grn & pink 4.25 2.60
2207 A623 €1.60 slate & org 3.50 2.25
2208 A623 €1.80 dull grn & brn 4.75 2.60
2209 A623 €2 brn blk & lake 4.75 3.00
2210 A623 €2.20 blue blk & gray bl 5.75 3.75
2211 A623 €2.60 blue & red 7.00 3.75
2212 A623 €4.10 lt grn & red vio 10.50 6.00

**Coil Stamps**
**Self-Adhesive**
**Die Cut Perf. 10¼x11**
**Photo.**
2213 A623 €1.44 gray grn & pink 4.75 2.60
**Litho.**
2214 A623 55c blk & yel 1.15 .75

**Booklet Stamps**
**Die Cut Perf. 10¼x11 on 3 Sides**
2215 A623 45c gray blk & brick red 3.00 1.90
2216 A623 55c blk & yel 1.40 .90
a. Booklet 4 #2215, 8 #2216 25.00
Nos. 2199-2216 (18) 58.40 34.80

Issued: 44c, 45c, 55c, €1, €1.60, 12/27/02; €1.44, €2.20, 1/16/03; €1.80, €2, 2/13/03; €2.60, €4.10, 3/6/03; No. 2213, June 2003. 25c, 40c, 1/8/04; 5c, 2/5/04.

Kronach, 1000th Anniv. — A1093

**2003, Jan. 16** Litho. Perf. 14
2222 A1093 45c multi 1.15 .70

Georg Elser (1903-45), Failed Assassin of Hitler — A1094

**2003, Jan. 16** Perf. 13¼
2223 A1094 55c multi 1.40 .85

Treaty for German-French Cooperation, 40th Anniv. — A1095

**2003, Jan. 16** Perf. 13¾
2224 A1095 55c multi 1.40 .85

Bible Year — A1096

**2003, Jan. 16** Perf. 14x14¼
2225 A1096 55c multi 1.40 .85

Proun 30t, by El Lissitzky (1890-1941) A1097

**2003, Jan. 16**
2226 A1097 144c multi 3.50 2.00
Cultural Foundation of the Federal States.

Rose — A1098

**2003, Feb. 13** Litho. Perf. 14
2227 A1098 55c multi 1.30 .75

**Booklet Stamp**
**Self-Adhesive**
**Die Cut Perf. 10x10¼**
2228 A1098 55c multi 1.60 .85
a. Booklet pane of 10 16.50

Junger Argentinier, by Max Beckmann A1099

Composition, by Adolf Hölzel — A1100

**2003, Feb. 13** Perf. 13¾x14
2229 A1099 55c multi 1.40 .75
2230 A1100 100c multi 2.10 1.35

Souvenir Sheet

Boys' Choirs A1101

No. 2231: a, Thomanerchor Leipzig. b, Dredner Kreuzchor. c, Regensburger Domspatzen.

**2003, Feb. 13** Perf. 14x14¼
2231 A1101 Sheet of 3 5.25 3.75
a. 45c multi 1.50 1.00
b. 55c multi 1.50 1.00
c. 100c multi 2.10 1.35

Cologne Cathedral, UNESCO World Heritage Site — A1102

**2003, Mar. 6** Perf. 13¼
2232 A1102 55c multi 1.40 .85

**Self-Adhesive**
**Coil Stamp**
**Die Cut Perf. 10¼**
2233 A1102 55c multi 1.60 .85

Intl. Horticultural Exhibition 2003, Rostock — A1103

**2003, Apr. 10** Litho. Perf. 13¼
2234 A1103 45c multi 1.30 .75

German Museum, Munich, Cent. — A1104

**2003, Apr. 10** Photo. Perf. 14x14¼
2235 A1104 55c multi 1.40 .85

Deutsche Welle Radio, 50th Anniv. A1105

**2003, Apr. 10** Litho. Perf. 14
2236 A1105 55c multi 1.40 .85

German Society for the Protection of Children, 50th Anniv. — A1106

**2003, Apr. 10** Perf. 13¼
2237 A1106 55c multi 1.40 .85

Reinhold Schneider (1903-58), Writer — A1107

**2003, May 8** Litho. Perf. 13¼
2238 A1107 55c multi 1.30 .85

Ecumenical Church Conference, Berlin — A1108

**2003, May 8** Perf. 14
2239 A1108 55c multi 1.40 .85

Justus von Liebig (1803-73), Chemist A1109

**2003, May 8**
2240 A1109 55c multi 1.40 .85

German General Automobile Club, Cent. A1110

**2003, May 8** Perf. 13¼x13½
2241 A1110 55c multi 1.40 .85

Europa A1111

**2003, May 8**
2242 A1111 55c multi 1.40 .85

Hans Jonas (1903-93), Philosopher — A1112

**2003, May 8**     *Perf. 13¾x14*
2243 A1112 220c multi     5.25 3.25

Five Digit Postal Codes, 10th Anniv. A1113

**2003, June 12**   Litho.   *Perf. 14*
2244 A1113 55c multi     1.40 .85

Salzach River Bridge, Laufen, Germany - Oberndorf, Austria, Cent. — A1114

**2003, June 12**
2245   A1114 55c multi     1.40 .85
   **Die Cut Perf 14**
   **Booklet Stamp**
   **Self-Adhesive**
2245A A1114 55c multi     2.25 1.00
*b.*    Booklet pane of 20     47.50
    See Austria No. 1922.

**Souvenir Sheet**

Unteres Odertal National Park A1115

**2003, June 12**     *Perf. 13x13½*
2246 A1115 55c multi     1.50 1.15

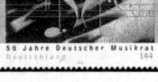

German Music Council, 50th Anniv. — A1116

**2003, June 12**     *Perf. 14*
2247 A1116 144c multi     3.50 2.10
   **Self-Adhesive**
   **Booklet Stamp**
   *Die Cut Perf. 11¼x11*
2247A A1116 144c multi     3.50 2.10
*b.*    Booklet pane of 10     42.50
    Issued: No. 2247, 6/12/03; No. 2247A, 1/8/04.

Scenic Regions in Germany A1117

**2003, July 10**   Litho.   *Perf. 13x13½*
2248 A1117 55c Ruhr Region     1.40 .85

Andreas Hermes (1878-1964), Politician A1118

**2003, July 10**   Photo.   *Perf. 14x14¼*
2258 A1118 55c multi     1.30 .75

Petrified Forest, Chemnitz — A1119

**2003, Aug. 7**   Litho.   *Perf. 13¼*
2259 A1119 144c multi     3.50 2.25

**City Views**

Market, Munich — A1120

Buildings in Old City, Görlitz A1121

**2003, Aug. 7**   Litho.   *Perf. 13¼*
2260   A1120 45c multi     1.30 .75
      *Perf. 13x13½*
2261   A1121 55c multi     1.30 .75
   **Self-Adhesive**
   **Booklet Stamp**
   *Die Cut Perf. 11x 10¾*
2261A A1120 45c multi     1.50 .70
*b.*    Booklet pane of 10     16.50
    Issued: Nos. 2260, 2261, 8/7/03; No. 2261A, 1/8/04.

Theodor W. Adorno (1903-69), Philosopher A1122

**2003, Sept. 11**     *Perf. 14*
2262 A1122 55c multi     1.30 .75

Bietigheim Enzviadukt, 150th Anniv. — A1123

**2003, Sept. 11**     *Perf. 13x13½*
2263 A1123 55c multi     1.40 .85

**Souvenir Sheet**

For Children A1124

**2003, Sept. 11**     *Perf. 13¾x14*
2264 A1124 55c multi     1.60 1.15

Mailbox — A1125

**2003, Oct. 9**   Litho.   *Perf. 13¼*
2265 A1125 55c multi     1.40 .85

German Lifesaving Association A1126

**2003, Oct. 9**     *Perf. 13¾*
2266 A1126 144c multi     3.50 2.10

Opera House, Dresden, by Gottfried Semper (1803-79), Architect A1127

**2003, Nov. 13**   Litho.   *Perf. 13x13½*
2267 A1127 55c multi     1.30 .75

German Catholic Women's Organization, Cent. — A1128

**2003, Nov. 13**     *Perf. 14*
2268 A1128 55c multi     1.30 .75

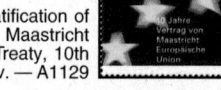

Ratification of Maastricht Treaty, 10th Anniv. — A1129

**2003, Nov. 13**
2269 A1129 55c multi     1.40 .85

Landshut, 800th Anniv. A1130

**2004, Jan. 8**   Litho.   *Perf. 14*
2270 A1130 45c multi     1.05 .70

Schleswig, 1200th Anniv. — A1131

**2004, Jan. 8**     *Perf. 13¼*
2271 A1131 55c multi     1.30 .75

Arnstadt, 1300th Anniv. — A1132

**2004, Feb. 5**   Litho.   *Perf. 13¼*
2272 A1132 55c multi     1.40 .85

Greetings A1133

**2004, Feb. 5**     *Perf. 14*
2273 A1133 55c multi     1.40 .85

Joseph Schmidt (1904-42), Singer A1134

**2004, Mar. 11**   Litho.   *Perf. 14*
2274 A1134 55c multi     1.40 .85

Paul Ehrlich (1854-1915) and Emil von Behring (1854-1917), Physicians — A1135

**2004, Mar. 11**
2275 A1135 144c multi     3.50 2.10

**Souvenir Sheet**

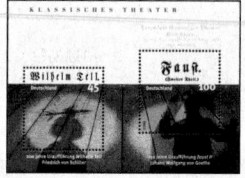

Classical Theater A1136

No. 2276: a, Premiere of *William Tell*, by Friedrich von Schiller, bicent. b, Premiere of *Faust*, by Johann Wolfgang von Goethe, 150th anniv.

**2004, Mar. 11**     *Perf. 13¾*
2276 A1136   Sheet of 2     3.75 2.60
*a.*    45c multi     1.40 .90
*b.*    100c multi     2.25 1.35

Bauhaus World Heritage Sites, Weimar and Dessau A1137

**2004, Apr. 7**   Litho.   *Perf. 14*
2277 A1137 55c multi     1.40 .85

White Stork — A1138

**2004, Apr. 7**
2278 A1138 55c multi     1.40 .85

Kurt Georg Kiesinger (1904-88), Chancellor A1139

**2004, Apr. 7**     *Perf. 13¾*
2279 A1139 55c multi     1.30 .75

Electric Light Bulb of Heinrich Göbel, 150th Anniv. — A1140

**2004, Apr. 7**
2280 A1140 220c red & blue     5.25 3.50

Europa — A1141

**2004, May 6**   Litho.   *Perf. 13¼*
2281 A1141 45c multi     1.15 .70

Expansion of the European Union — A1142

**2004, May 6**
2282 A1142 55c multi 1.15 .70

St. Boniface of Mainz (c. 675-754) — A1143

**2004, May 6** *Perf. 13¾*
2283 A1143 55c multi 1.30 .75

Reinhard Schwarz-Schilling (1904-85), Composer — A1144

**2004, May 6** *Perf. 14*
2284 A1144 55c multi 1.30 .75

Ludwigsburg Castle, 300th Anniv. — A1145

**2004, May 6**
2285 A1145 144c multi 3.50 2.10

Wattenmeer National Park — A1146

**2004, June 3** *Litho. Perf. 13*
2286 A1146 55c multi 1.30 .75

German - Russian Youth Meeting — A1147

**2004, June 3** *Perf. 13¾*
2287 A1147 55c multi 1.30 .75
See Russia No. 6845.

Transatlantic Speed Record-Breaking Voyage of the Steamship "Bremen," 75th Anniv. — A1148

**2004, July 8** *Litho. Perf. 14*
2288 A1148 55c multi 1.30 .75
**Booklet Stamp**
**Self-Adhesive**
*Die Cut Perf. 14*
2288A A1148 55c multi 1.30 .75
*b.* Booklet pane of 20 35.00

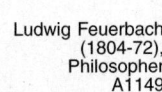

Ludwig Feuerbach (1804-72), Philosopher A1149

**2004, July 8** *Perf. 13¾*
2289 A1149 144c multi 3.50 2.10

Lighthouses A1150

**2004, July 8** *Perf. 13¾*
2290 A1150 45c Griefswalder Oie 1.30 .75
2291 A1150 55c Roter Sand 1.30 .75
*Die Cut Perf. 10¼*
**Coil Stamp**
**Self-Adhesive**
2291A A1150 55c Roter Sand 1.30 .75
See Nos. 2344-2345B, 2390-2391, 2447-2448, 2491-2494, 2537-2538, 2574-2575, 2629-2632, 2673, 2680-2681, 2737-2738, 2793-2794, 2847-2848, 2928-2929, 2978-2979, 3040-3042.

Memorial Church, Speyer, Cent. — A1151

**2004, Aug. 12** *Litho. Perf. 13¾*
2292 A1151 55c multi 1.40 .85

Camellia A1152

**2004, Aug. 12** *Perf. 14*
2293 A1152 55c multi 1.30 .75
**Booklet Stamp**
**Self-Adhesive**
*Die Cut Perf. 10x10¼*
2294 A1152 55c multi 1.60 .90
*a.* Booklet pane, 5 each #2228, 2294 16.50

Engelbert Humperdinck (1854-1921), Composer A1153

**2004, Sept. 9** *Litho. Perf. 14*
2295 A1153 45c multi 1.15 .70

Eduard Mörike (1804-75), Poet — A1154

**2004, Sept. 9**
2296 A1154 55c multi 1.30 .75

For Children — A1155

**2004, Sept. 9** *Perf. 13¾*
2297 A1155 55c multi 1.30 .75

Egon Eiermann (1904-70), Architect A1156

**2004, Sept. 9** *Perf. 14*
2298 A1156 100c multi 2.25 1.35

Federal Social Court, 50th Anniv. — A1157

**Litho. & Embossed**
**2004, Sept. 9** *Perf. 13¾*
2299 A1157 144c multi 3.50 2.10

Dornier Do X — A1158

**2004, Oct. 7** *Litho. Perf. 14*
2300 A1158 55c multi 1.30 .75
Stamp Day.

Winter Scene A1159

**2004, Nov. 4**
2301 A1159 55c multi 1.30 .75

International Space Station A1160

**2004, Nov. 4**
2302 A1160 55c multi 1.30 .75

The Secret, by Felix Nussbaum (1904-44) A1161

**2004, Nov. 4**
2303 A1161 55c multi 1.30 .75

Forchheim, 1200th Anniv. — A1162

**2005, Jan. 3** *Litho. Perf. 13¼*
2304 A1162 45c multi 1.05 .60

Adoration of the Magi, St. Clara's Church, Cologne — A1163

**2005, Jan. 3**
2305 A1163 55c multi 1.30 .75
See No. 2509.

Sculpture of Celtic Prince Found in Glauberg — A1164

**2005, Jan. 3** *Perf. 13¾*
2306 A1164 144c multi 3.50 2.10

Flowers — A1165

Designs: 5c, Krokus (crocus). 10c, Tulpe (tulip). 20c, Tagetes (marigold). 25c, Malve (mallow). 35c, Dahlie (dahlia). 40c, Leberblümchen (hepatica). 45c, Margerite (daisy). 50c, Aster. 55c, Klatschmohn (red poppy). 65c, Sonnenhut (rudbeckia). 70c, Kartaüsernelke (clusterhead pink). 90c, Narzisse (narcissus). 95c, Sonnenblume (sunflower). 100c, Tränendes herz (Bleeding heart). 145c, Schwertlilie (iris). 220c, Edelweiss. 390c, Feuerlilie (tiger lily). 430c, Rittersporn (larkspur).

**2005-06** *Litho. Perf. 14*
2307 A1165 5c multi .35 .25
2308 A1165 10c multi .35 .25
2309 A1165 20c multi .50 .30
*a.* Miniature sheet, 4 each #2307-2308, 2 each #2309 2.75 2.75
2310 A1165 25c multi .70 .40
2311 A1165 35c multi .85 .55
2312 A1165 40c multi .95 .60
2313 A1165 45c multi 1.05 .60
2314 A1165 50c multi 1.15 .70
2315 A1165 55c multi 1.40 .75
2316 A1165 65c multi 1.60 1.00
2317 A1165 70c multi 1.75 1.00
2318 A1165 90c multi 2.00 1.30
2319 A1165 95c multi 3.50 1.50
2320 A1165 100c multi 2.25 1.35
2321 A1165 145c multi 3.00 2.00
2322 A1165 220c multi 5.25 3.25
2323 A1165 390c multi 10.50 6.75
2324 A1165 430c multi 13.00 8.25
Nos. 2307-2324 (18) 50.15 30.80

**Coil Stamp**
**Self-Adhesive**
*Die Cut Perf. 10¼x10*
2325 A1165 25c multi .60 .40
2326 A1165 35c multi .85 .55
2326A A1165 55c multi 1.50 .75
2326B A1165 90c multi 2.00 1.30
*a.* Booklet pane of 10 25.00

Issued: 95c, 430c, 1/3. 45c, 4/7. No. 2310, 50c, 6/2. 20c, No. 2315, 7/7. 5c, 8/11.10c, 40c, 9/8. No. 2326A, 7/7. No. 2325, 35c, 90c, 145c, 1/2/06. 65c, 3/2/06. 70c, 220c, 4/13/06. 390c, 5/4/06. 100c, 7/13/06. No. 2309a, 3/1/07.
See Nos. 2405-2423, 2814-2819, 2880-2886, 2968-2971, 2986, 3009-3012, 3058-3062, 3085-3086, 3103-3116, 3130-3132, 3160, 3178, 3260-3263.

Advertising Pillars, 150th Anniv. — A1166

**2005, Feb. 10** *Litho. Perf. 13¾*
2327 A1166 55c multi 1.35 .75

Berlin Cathedral, Cent. — A1167

**2005, Feb. 10** *Perf. 13*
2328 A1167 95c multi 2.25 1.30
**Booklet Stamp**
**Self-Adhesive**
*Die Cut Perf. 11*
2329 A1167 95c multi 2.60 1.30
*a.* Booklet pane of 10 30.00

Bonn-Copenhagen Declaration, 50th Anniv. — A1168

**2005, Mar. 3**     *Perf. 14*
2330 A1168 55c multi    1.35 .75
See Denmark No. 1322.

Resumption of Regulated Civil Aviation, 50th Anniv. A1169

**2005, Mar. 3**
2331 A1169 155c multi    3.75 2.10

Postal Workers — A1170

Designs: No. 2332, Postman on bicycle. No. 2333, Postman on snowy hillside.

**2005, Mar. 3**     *Perf. 13¾*
2332 A1170 55c multi    1.50 .75
2333 A1170 55c multi    1.50 .75
See Nos. 2348-2349.

Mittelland Canal, Cent. — A1171

**2005, Apr. 7**   *Litho.*   *Perf. 14*
2334 A1171 45c multi    1.20 .75

Bavarian Forest National Park — A1172

**2005, Apr. 7**     *Perf. 13¾*
2335 A1172 55c multi    1.35 .75

Hans Christian Andersen (1805-75), Author — A1173

**2005, Apr. 7**     *Perf. 14*
2336 A1173 144c multi    3.75 2.25

**Coil Stamp**
**Self-Adhesive**
*Die Cut Perf. 10¼*

2336A A1173 144c multi    4.25 2.60

Founding of Die Brücke Expressionist Group, Cent. — A1174

**2005, May 12**   *Litho.*   *Perf. 13¾*
2337 A1174 55c buff, blk & red   1.35 .75

Paris Treaty, 50th Anniv. — A1175

**2005, May 12**
2338 A1175 55c black & red   1.35 .75

Friedrich von Schiller Year — A1176

**2005, May 12**     *Perf. 14*
2339 A1176 55c multi    1.35 .75

Pope John Paul II (1920-2005) A1177

**2005, May 12**
2340 A1177 55c multi    1.35 .75

Europa A1178

**2005, May 12**
2341 A1178 55c multi    *1.35 .75*

Sixth Congress of European Organization of Supreme Audit Institutions, Bonn — A1179

**2005, June 2**   *Litho.*   *Perf. 13¾*
2342 A1179 55c multi    1.35 .75

20th World Youth Day — A1180

**2005, June 2**     *Perf. 14*
2343 A1180 55c multi    1.35 .75
See Vatican City No. 1298.

**Lighthouse Type of 2004**

Designs: Nos. 2344, 2345B, Brunsbüttel, Jetty 1. No. 2345A, Griefswalde Oie. 55c, Westerheversand.

**2005, July 7**   *Litho.*   *Perf. 13¾*
2344 A1150 45c multi    1.10 .60
2345 A1150 55c multi    1.35 .75

**Booklet Stamps**
**Self-Adhesive**
*Die Cut Perf. 10¾*

2345A A1150 45c multi    1.20 .60
2345B A1150 45c multi    1.20 .60
    *c.*   Booklet pane, 5 each
      #2345A-2345B   12.00

Albert Einstein's Theory of Relativity, Cent. — A1181

**2005, July 7**     *Perf. 14*
2346 A1181 55c multi    1.35 .75

**Souvenir Sheet**

Prussian Castles and Gardens A1182

**2005, July 7**     *Perf. 13x13½*
2347 A1182 220c multi    5.50 3.50

**Self-Adhesive**
**Booklet Stamp**
*Die Cut Perf. 11*

2347A A1182 220c multi    5.50 3.50
   *b.*   Booklet pane of 10   60.00
Issued: No. 2347, 7/7. No. 2347A, 11/3.

**Postal Workers Type of 2005**

Designs: No. 2348, Postman on punt. No. 2349, Postman with handcart.

**2005, Aug. 11**   *Litho.*   *Perf. 13¾*
2348 A1170 55c multi    1.35 .75
2349 A1170 55c multi    1.35 .75

German Friends of Nature, Cent. — A1183

**2005, Aug. 11**     *Perf. 13¼*
2350 A1183 144c multi    3.75 2.10

Magdeburg, 1200th Anniv. A1184

**2005, Sept. 8**   *Litho.*   *Perf. 14*
2351 A1184 55c multi    1.35 .75

For Children A1185

**2005, Sept. 8**
2352 A1185 55c multi    1.35 .75

Peace of Augsburg, 450th Anniv. — A1186

**2005, Sept. 8**     *Perf. 13¾*
2353 A1186 55c multi    1.35 .75
See No. 2508.

Max Schmeling (1905-2005), Boxer — A1187

**2005, Sept. 8**     *Perf. 14*
2354 A1187 55c multi    1.35 .75

Dedication of Rebuilt Church of Our Lady, Dresden A1188

**2005, Oct. 13**   *Litho.*   *Perf. 14*
2355 A1188 55c multi    1.35 .75

Adalbert Stifter (1805-68), Writer — A1189

**2005, Oct. 13**     *Perf. 13¾*
2356 A1189 95c multi    2.40 1.50

St. Leonhard's Day Procession, Bad Tölz — A1190

**2005, Nov. 3**   *Litho.*   *Perf. 13¼*
2357 A1190 45c multi    1.10 .60

Federal Armed Forces, 50th Anniv. — A1191

**2005, Nov. 3**     *Perf. 13¾*
2358 A1191 55c multi    1.35 .75

Diplomatic Relations With Israel, 40th Anniv. — A1192

**2005, Nov. 3**
2359 A1192 55c multi    1.35 .75
See Israel No. 1619.

Awarding of Nobel Peace Prize to Bertha von Suttner, Cent. — A1193

**2005, Nov. 3**     *Perf. 14*
2360 A1193 55c multi    1.35 .75

Awarding of Nobel Physiology or Medicine Prize to Robert Koch, Cent. — A1194

**2005, Nov. 3**     *Perf. 13¼*
2361 A1194 144c multi    3.75 2.10

Halle, 1200th Anniv. A1195

**2006, Jan. 2**   *Litho.*   *Perf. 14*
2362 A1195 45c multi    1.10 .60

Winter A1196

**2006, Jan. 2**   *Litho.*   *Perf. 14*
2363 A1196 55c multi    1.35 .75
See No. 2400.

Spring
A1197

**2006, Apr. 13**    **Litho.**    *Perf. 14*
2364 A1197 55c multi    1.35   .75
See No. 2397.

Summer
A1198

**2006, July 13**    **Litho.**    *Perf. 14*
2365 A1198 55c multi    1.35   .75
See No. 2398.

Autumn
A1199

**2006, Oct. 5**    **Litho.**    *Perf. 14*
2366 A1199 55c multi    1.35   .75
See No. 2399.

Wolfgang Amadeus
Mozart (1756-91),
Composer — A1200

**2006, Jan. 2**    **Litho.**    *Perf. 13¼*
2367 A1200 55c multi    1.35   .75

Golden Bull of
Emperor
Charles
IV — A1201

**2006, Jan. 2**    *Perf. 14*
2368 A1201 145c multi    3.75 2.25

**Self-Adhesive**
**Booklet Stamp**
*Die Cut Perf. 10*

2369 A1201 145c multi    4.25 2.25
   *a.*   Booklet pane of 10    42.50

St. Michael's
Church,
Schwäbisch
Hall, 850th
Anniv.
A1202

**2006, Feb. 9**    **Litho.**    *Perf. 14*
2370 A1202 55c multi    1.35   .75

Frisian Council,
50th Anniv.
A1203

**2006, Feb. 9**
2371 A1203 90c multi    2.10 1.30

Ingolstadt, 1200th
Anniv. — A1204

**2006, Mar. 2**    **Litho.**    *Perf. 13¼*
2372 A1204 55c multi    1.35   .75

---

Karl Friedrich
Schinkel (1781-
1841), Architect
A1205

**2006**    *Perf. 14*
2373 A1205 55c multi    1.35   .75

**Coil Stamp**
**Self-Adhesive**
*Die Cut Perf. 10x10¼*

2373A A1205 55c multi    1.75 1.00
   Issued: No. 2373, 3/2. No. 2373A, 7/13.

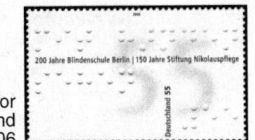

Care for
the Blind
A1206

**Litho. & Embossed**
**2006, Mar. 2**    *Perf. 13x13½*
2374 A1206 55c black & gray    1.35   .75
   Berlin School for the Blind, 200th Anniv.,
Nikolaus Care Foundation, 150th Anniv.

Pres.
Johannes Rau
(1931-2006)
A1207

**2006, Mar. 2**    **Litho.**    *Perf. 14*
2375 A1207 55c multi    1.35   .75

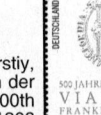

Viadrina University,
Frankfurt an der
Oder, 500th
Anniv. — A1208

**Litho. & Embossed**
**2006, Apr. 13**    *Perf. 13¾*
2376 A1208 55c multi    1.35   .75

Self-Portrait in Fur
Coat, by Albrecht
Dürer — A1209

**2006, Apr. 13**    **Litho.**
2377 A1209 145c multi    3.50 2.00

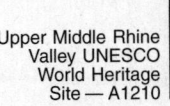

Upper Middle Rhine
Valley UNESCO
World Heritage
Site — A1210

**2006, May 4**    **Litho.**    *Perf. 13¾*
2378 A1210 55c multi    1.35   .75

**Self-Adhesive**
**Booklet Stamp**
*Die Cut Perf. 11*

2379 A1210 55c multi    1.45   .90
   *a.*   Booklet pane of 10    14.50

Europa
A1211

**2006, May 4**    *Perf. 14*
2380 A1211 55c multi    1.35   .75

---

Gerd Bucerius
(1906-95),
Publisher and
Politician
A1212

**2006, May 4**
2381 A1212 85c multi    2.10 1.20

Stefan Andres
(1906-70),
Writer — A1213

**2006, June 8**
2382 A1213 55c multi    1.35   .75

John
Augustus
Roebling
(1806-69),
Bridge
Designer
A1214

**2006, June 8**    *Perf. 14*
2383 A1214 145c multi    3.75 2.10

**Self-Adhesive**
**Coil Stamp**
*Die Cut Perf. 11*

2384 A1214 145c multi    4.25 2.60

Standardized
Motor Vehicle
Identification,
Cent. — A1215

**2006, July 13**    **Litho.**    *Perf. 14*
2385 A1215 45c multi    1.20   .60

Burghausen
Castle,
Burghausen
A1216

**2006, July 13**
2386 A1216 55c multi    1.35   .75

Saskia van
Uylenburgh, by
Rembrandt (1606-
69) — A1217

**2006, July 13**    *Perf. 13¾*
2387 A1217 70c multi    1.75 1.00
   See Netherlands No. 1253. The design of
No. 2387 was reproduced without the permission of the German authorities in a Netherlands booklet pane that also contains a similar
Netherlands stamp.

Discovery of
Neanderthal
Man Bones,
150th Anniv.
A1218

**2006, Aug. 10**    **Litho.**    *Perf. 14*
2388 A1218 220c multi    5.50 3.50

**Souvenir Sheet**

Black
Forest
A1219

**2006, Aug. 10**    *Perf. 13¾*
2389 A1219 55c multi    1.60 1.00

---

**Lighthouses Type of 2004**
Designs: 45c, Neuland. 55c, Hohe Weg.

**2006, Aug. 10**    *Perf. 13¾*
2390 A1150 45c multi    1.10   .60
2391 A1150 55c multi    1.35   .75

"Captain of
Köpenick" — A1220

**2006, Sept. 7**    **Litho.**    *Perf. 13¼*
2392 A1220 55c multi    1.45   .85
   Theft of town funds and arrest of mayor in
Köpenick by petty thief Friedrich Wilhelm
Voigt, who masqueraded as an army officer,
cent.

For
Children — A1221

**2006, Sept. 7**
2393 A1221 55c multi    1.35   .75

Hanseatic
League, 650th
Anniv.
A1222

**Litho. & Engr.**
**2006, Sept. 7**    *Perf. 14*
2394 A1222 70c multi    1.75 1.15
   See Sweden No. 2541

Stamp
Day — A1223

**2006, Oct. 5**    **Litho.**    *Perf. 14*
2395 A1223 55c multi    1.35   .75

Hannah
Arendt
(1906-75),
Political
Scientist
A1224

**2006, Oct. 5**    *Perf. 13¾x14*
2396 A1224 145c multi    4.50 2.25

**Seasons Types of 2006**
*Die Cut Perf. 14*
**2006, Nov. 9**    **Litho.**
**Booklet Stamps**
**Self-Adhesive**

2397 A1197 55c Spring    1.50   .75
2398 A1198 55c Summer    1.50   .75
2399 A1199 55c Autumn    1.50   .75
2400 A1196 55c Winter    1.50   .75
   *a.*   Booklet pane, 5 each #2397-
     2400    30.00

Eugen Bolz (1881-
1945),
Politician — A1225

**2006, Nov. 9**    *Perf. 13¾*
2401 A1225 45c multi    1.20   .60

Joseph Cardinal Höffner (1906-87) — A1226

**2006, Nov. 9**     *Perf. 13¼*
2402 A1226 55c multi    1.35   .75

Werner Forssmann (1904-79), 1956 Physiology or Medicine Nobel Laureate A1227

**2006, Nov. 9**     *Perf. 14*
2403 A1227 90c multi    2.40 1.50

### Flowers Type of 2005

Designs: 25c, Gartennelke (carnation). 28c, Tausendgüldenkraut (centaury). 45c, Maiglöckchen (lily of the valley). 55c, Gartenrose (rose). 58c, Kuhschelle (pasque flower). 60c, Kaiserkrone (kaiser's crown). 65c, Sonnenhut (rudbeckia). 70c, Kartäusernelke (clusterhead pink). 75c, Ballonblume (balloon flower). 100c, Tränendes herz (bleeding heart). 180c, Akelei (columbine). 200c, Goldmohn (California poppy). 240c, Prachtkerze (white gaura). 410c, Frauenschuh (lady's slipper). 500c, Enzian (gentian).

**2006-14**    *Litho.*    *Perf. 14*
2404 A1165 25c multi    .75   .40
2405 A1165 28c multi    .75   .45
2406 A1165 45c multi    1.20   .70
2407 A1165 55c multi    1.35   .75
2408 A1165 58c multi    1.50   .90
2409 A1165 60c multi    1.45   .90
2410 A1165 75c multi    1.75 1.05
2411 A1165 180c multi    4.50 2.75
2412 A1165 200c multi    5.00 2.75
2413 A1165 240c multi    6.00 3.75
2414 A1165 410c multi    10.25 6.50
2415 A1165 500c multi    11.00 6.75
   *Nos. 2404-2415 (12)*    45.50 27.65

### Coil Stamps
#### Self-Adhesive
*Die Cut Perf. 10¼x10*
2416 A1165 25c multi    .75   .40
2417 A1165 28c multi    .75   .45
2418 A1165 58c multi    1.50   .90

### Booklet Stamps
2419 A1165 45c multi    1.10   .70
  a.   Booklet pane of 10    12.50
2420 A1165 55c multi    1.35   .75
  a.   Booklet pane of 10    17.50
2421 A1165 60c multi    1.45   .90
  f.   Booklet pane of 10    17.50
2422 A1165 65c multi    1.45   .90
  a.   Booklet pane of 5 + 5 etiquettes    8.75
2423 A1165 70c multi    1.60 1.00
  b.   Booklet pane of 5 + 5 etiquettes    9.50
  c.   Booklet pane of 10    19.00
2423A A1165 100c multi    2.40 1.50
  d.   Booklet pane of 10    27.50
   *Nos. 2416-2423A (9)*    12.35 7.50

Issued: 200c, 11/9/06; 55c, 6/12/08. 25c, 10/9/08. No. 2416, 6/12/08; No. 2420, 6/12/08, No. 2420a, 3/11/10; Nos. 2422-2423, 1/2/09. No. 2414, 1/2/10. No. 2406, 5/6/10; No. 2423c, 6/10/2010; 75c, 1/3/11; No. 2419, 3/1/11, 500c, 7/7/11. 58c, 240c, 12/6/12; No. 2418, 12/6/12; 60c, 12/5/13; 100c, 10/10/13; 180c, 6/5/14. 28c, 7/3/14.

No. 2420 was also issued in coils.

Fürth, 1000th Anniv. — A1228

**2007, Jan. 2**    *Litho.*    *Perf. 13¼*
2424 A1228 45c multi    1.20   .70

#### Booklet Stamp
#### Self-Adhesive
*Die Cut Perf. 11*
2425 A1228 45c multi    1.20   .70
  a.   Booklet pane of 10    12.00

---

Germany, 2007 President of the European Union — A1229

#### Litho. & Embossed
**2007, Jan. 2**     *Perf. 13¾*
2426 A1229 55c multi    1.35   .75

Bamberg Bishopric, 1000th Anniv. — A1230

**2007, Jan. 2**    *Litho.*    *Perf. 13¼*
2427 A1230 55c multi    1.35   .75

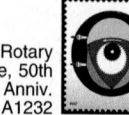

Admission of Saarland into Federal Republic, 50th Anniv. A1231

**2007, Jan. 2**     *Perf. 14*
2428 A1231 55c multi    2.10 1.35

#### Booklet Stamp
#### Self-Adhesive
*Die Cut Perf. 10x10¼*
2428A A1231 55c multi    1.35   .75
  b.   Booklet pane of 10    14.50

Wankel Rotary Engine, 50th Anniv. A1232

**2007, Jan. 2**
2429 A1232 145c multi    3.50 2.10

Johann Christian Senckenberg (1707-72), Founder of Hospital, Frankfurt am Main — A1233

**2007, Feb. 8**    *Litho.*    *Perf. 14*
2430 A1233 90c multi    2.10 1.35

Munich Jewish Center A1234

**2007, Mar. 1**    *Litho.*    *Perf. 14*
2431 A1234 55c multi    1.35   .75

Paul Gerhardt (1607-76), Hymn Writer — A1235

**2007, Mar. 1**
2432 A1235 55c multi    1.35   .75

The Unearthing of the Cross, by Adam Elsheimer — A1236

**2007, Mar. 1**     *Perf. 13¼*
2433 A1236 55c multi    1.45   .75

---

Rome Treaty, 50th Anniv. — A1237

**2007, Mar. 1**     *Perf. 13¾*
2434 A1237 55c multi    1.35   .75

Leaders of Anti-Nazi Resistance Movement A1238

**2007, Mar. 1**     *Perf. 13¾x14*
2435 A1238 55c multi    1.35   .75

Claus Schenk Graf von Stauffenberg (1907-44), Hitler assassination plotter, and Helmuth James Graf von Moltke (1907-45), founding member of Kreisau Circle resistance group.

Pope Benedict XVI, 80th Birthday A1239

**2007, Apr. 12**    *Litho.*    *Perf. 14*
2436 A1239 55c multi    1.35   .75

Letter Writing — A1240

No. 2437, Boy writing letter. No. 2438, Boy mailing letter.

**2007, Apr. 12**     *Perf. 13¾*
2437 A1240 55c multi    1.20   .75
2438 A1240 55c multi    1.20   .75
   See Nos. 2454-2455.

Publication of World Map of Martin Waldseemuller, 500th Anniv. — A1241

#### Litho. & Engr.
**2007, Apr. 12**     *Perf. 14*
2439 A1241 220c multi    6.75 4.25

Europa A1242

**2007, May 3**    *Litho.*    *Perf. 14*
2440 A1242 45c multi    1.10   .60
   Scouting, cent.

Bellevue Palace, Presidential Residence A1243

**2007, May 3**
2441 A1243 55c multi    1.45   .85

#### Coil Stamp
#### Self-Adhesive
*Die Cut Perf. 10x10¼*
2441A A1243 55c multi    1.60   .85

---

Moyland Castle, 700th Anniv. A1244

**2007, May 3**
2442 A1244 85c multi    1.35   .75

Hambacher Fest, 175th Anniv. A1245

**2007, May 3**     *Perf. 14*
2443 A1245 145c multi    3.50 2.00

#### Booklet Stamp
#### Self-Adhesive
*Die Cut Perf. 10x10¼*
2444 A1245 145c multi    3.75 2.00
  a.   Booklet pane of 10    35.00

Karl Valentin (1882-1948), Writer — A1246

**2007, June 14**    *Litho.*    *Perf. 13¾*
2445 A1246 45c multi    1.20   .70

Paul Klinger (1907-71), Film Actor — A1247

**2007, June 14**
2446 A1247 55c multi    3.00 1.90

### Lighthouses Type of 2004

Designs: 45c, Bremerhaven Oberfeuer. 55c, Hörnum.

**2007, July 12**     *Perf. 13¾*
2447 A1150 45c multi    1.20   .60
2448 A1150 55c multi    1.35   .75

UNESCO World Heritage Sites — A1248

Designs: 65c, Historic Center of Riga, Latvia. 70c, Historic Centers of Straslund and Wismar, Germany.

**2007, July 12**     *Perf. 14*
2449 A1248 65c multi    1.45   .90
2450 A1248 70c multi    1.60 1.00
   See Latvia Nos. 679-680.

Saale Valley Dam and Lake Bleiloch, 75th Anniv. A1249

**2007, Aug. 9**    *Litho.*    *Perf. 14*
2451 A1249 55c multi    1.35   .75

German Federal Bank, 50th Anniv. A1250

**2007, Aug. 9**
2452 A1250 55c multi    1.45   .75

Kaiser Wilhelm Bridge, Wilhelmshaven, Cent. — A1251

**2007, Aug. 9** Litho. & Engr.
2453 A1251 145c multi 3.75 2.25

**Letter Writing Type of 2007**

Designs: No. 2454, Postman delivering letter to woman. No. 2455, Woman reading letter.

**2007, Sept. 20** Litho. **Perf. 13¾**
2454 A1240 55c multi 1.20 .75
2455 A1240 55c multi 1.20 .75

For Children A1252

**2007, Sept. 20** **Perf. 14**
2456 A1252 55c multi 1.35 .75

Science Advisory Committee, 50th Anniv. A1253

**2007, Sept. 20**
2457 A1253 90c multi 2.40 1.50

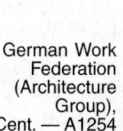

German Work Federation (Architecture Group), Cent. — A1254

**2007, Oct. 11** Litho. **Perf. 13¼**
2458 A1254 55c multi 1.35 .75

**Souvenir Sheet**

Frontiers of the Roman Empire UNESCO World Heritage Site — A1255

**2007, Oct. 11** **Perf. 14**
2459 A1255 55c multi 2.10 1.35

Heinrich Friedrich Carl Freiherr vom und zum Stein (1757-1831), Prussian Statesman — A1256

**2007, Oct. 11** **Perf. 13¾x14**
2460 A1256 145c multi 3.50 2.10

St. Elizabeth of Hungary (1207-31) — A1257

**2007, Nov. 8** Litho. **Perf. 13¾**
2461 A1257 55c multi 1.75 1.00

Astrid Lindgren (1907-2002), Writer — A1258

Litho. & Engr.
**2007, Nov. 8** **Perf. 13¾x14**
2462 A1258 100c multi 2.40 1.50

See Sweden No. 2572.

Brandenburg Gate, Designed by Carl Gotthard Langhans (1732-1808) A1259

**2007, Dec. 27** Litho. **Perf. 14**
2463 A1259 55c multi 1.45 .75

**Self-Adhesive**
**Booklet Stamp**
**Die Cut Perf. 10x10¼**
2464 A1259 55c multi 1.75 .75
a. Booklet pane of 10 17.00

Reichenau Monastic Island UNESCO World Heritage Site — A1260

**2008, Jan. 2** Litho. **Perf. 13**
2465 A1260 45c multi 1.10 .60

**Booklet Stamp**
**Self-Adhesive**
**Die Cut Perf. 10¾**
2466 A1260 45c multi 1.20 .70
a. Booklet pane of 10 12.00

Heinrich Zille (1858-1929), Illustrator — A1261

**2008, Jan. 2** **Perf. 13¾**
2467 A1261 55c multi 1.20 .75

Federal Cartel Office, 50th Anniv. — A1262

**2008** **Perf. 14**
2468 A1262 90c multi 2.00 1.30

**Booklet Stamp**
**Self-Adhesive**
**Die Cut Perf. 11¼x11**
2468A A1262 90c multi 2.40 1.35
b. Booklet pane of 10 26.00

Issued: No. 2468, 1/2; No. 2468A, 3/13.

Eichstätt, 1100th Anniv. — A1263

**2008, Jan. 2** **Perf. 13¾**
2469 A1263 145c multi 3.50 2.10

**Coil Stamp**
**Self-Adhesive**
**Die Cut Perf. 10¼**
2469A A1263 145c multi 3.75 2.25

Wenzel Jamnitzer (1508-85), Goldsmith A1264

**2008, Jan. 2** **Perf. 13¾x14**
2470 A1264 220c multi 5.50 3.50

"Congratulations" — A1265

"All the Best" — A1266

**2008, Feb. 7** **Perf. 14**
2471 A1265 55c multi 1.20 .75
2472 A1266 55c multi 1.20 .75

See Nos. 2487-2488.

Carl Spitzweg (1808-85), Painter — A1267

**2008, Feb. 7** Litho. **Perf. 13¾**
2473 A1267 55c multi 1.35 .75

**Coil Stamp**
**Self-Adhesive**
**Die Cut Perf. 10¼**
2474 A1267 55c multi 1.45 .75

Village Church, Bochum-Stiepel, 1000th Anniv. — A1268

**2008, Feb. 7** Litho. **Perf. 13¾**
2475 A1268 145c multi 3.75 2.25

Helmut Käutner (1908-80), Film Director A1269

**2008, Mar. 13** Litho. **Perf. 14**
2476 A1269 55c multi 1.35 .75

Frankfurt Zoo, 150th Anniv. — A1270

**2008, Mar. 13** **Perf. 13¼**
2477 A1270 65c multi 1.45 .90

Seebach Bird Sanctuary, Cent. — A1271

**2008, Apr. 10** Litho. **Perf. 14**
2478 A1271 45c multi 1.35 .60

Johann Hinrich Wichern (1808-81), Theologian A1272

**2008, Apr. 10**
2479 A1272 55c multi 1.35 .75

Max Planck (1858-1947), Physicist — A1273

**2008, Apr. 10** **Perf. 13¾**
2480 A1273 55c multi 1.35 .75

Oskar Schindler (1908-74), Industrialist Who Saved Jews From Holocaust A1274

**2008, Apr. 10** **Perf. 14x14¼**
2481 A1274 145c multi 3.25 2.00

First International Match of German Soccer Team, Cent. — A1275

**2008, Apr. 10** **Perf. 13¾**
2482 A1275 170c multi 5.00 3.00

Christoffel Blind Mission, Cent. A1276

**2008, May 8** Litho. **Perf. 13x13½**
2483 A1276 55c multi 1.35 .75

**Greetings Types of 2008 and**

"Kind Regards" A1277

"Thank You" — A1278

**2008, May 8** **Perf. 14**
2484 A1277 55c multi 1.35 .75
2485 A1278 55c multi 1.35 .75

**Booklet Stamps**
**Self-Adhesive**
**Die Cut Perf. 14**
2486 A1277 55c multi 1.35 .75
2487 A1265 55c multi 1.35 .75
2488 A1266 55c multi 1.35 .75
2489 A1278 55c multi 1.35 .75
a. Booklet pane of 20, 5 each #2486-2489 35.00
Nos. 2486-2489 (4) 5.40 3.00

Europa (Nos. 2484, 2486).

Honorary Offices A1279

**2008, June 12** Litho. **Perf. 14**
2490 A1279 55c multi 1.35 .75

Intl. Red Cross,
150th
Anniv. — A1440

**2013, Apr. 4**     **Perf. 13¾**
2725 A1440 58c black & red    1.50 .75

German Sports
Badge,
Cent. — A1441

**2013, Apr. 4**
2726 A1441 58c multi     1.50 .75

General German
Workers'
Association, 150th
Anniv. — A1442

**2013, Apr. 4**
2727 A1442 145c multi    3.75 1.90

Fehmarn Sound
Bridge — A1443

**2013, Apr. 4**     **Perf. 13¾**
2728 A1443 75c multi     2.00 1.00

**Booklet Stamp**
**Self-Adhesive**
**Size: 39x23mm**
**Die Cut Perf. 10**

2729 A1443 75c multi     2.00 1.00
   *a.*    Booklet pane of 10    20.00

Möhne
Reservoir
Dam — A1444

**2013**     **Perf. 13¾**
2730 A1444 90c multi     2.40 1.25

**Booklet Stamp**
**Self-Adhesive**
**Size: 39x23mm**
**Die Cut Perf. 10**

2731 A1444 90c multi     2.40 1.25
   *a.*    Booklet pane of 10    24.00

Issued: No. 2730, 4/4; No. 2731, 5/2.

Richard Wagner
(1813-83),
Composer
A1445

**2013, May 2**     **Perf. 13¾**
2732 A1445 58c multi     1.50 .75

Europa
A1446

**2013, May 2**     **Litho.**
2733 A1446 58c multi     1.50 .75

**Castles and Palaces Type of 2013**

Design: 45c, Glücksburg Castle (Schloss
Glücksburg).

**2013, June 6**     **Die Cut Perf. 10**
**Booklet Stamp**
**Self-Adhesive**
**Size: 39x23mm**

2734 A1432 45c multi     1.25 .60
   *a.*    Booklet pane of 10    12.50

---

German Rose
Show, Forst,
Cent. — A1447

**2013, June 6**     **Perf. 13¾**
2735 A1447 45c multi     1.25 .60

German Armed
Forces — A1448

**2013, June 6**
2736 A1448 58c multi     1.60 .80

**Lighthouses Type of 2004**

Designs: 45c, Flügge Lighthouse. 58c,
Büsum Lighthouse.

**2013, June 6**     **Perf. 13¾**
2737 A1150 45c multi     1.25 .60
2738 A1150 58c multi     1.60 .80

Temple of the
Sun, Bayreuth
A1449

Gyeongbokgung
Palace, Seoul,
South
Korea — A1450

**2013, June 6**     **Litho.**
2739 A1449 75c multi     2.00 1.00
2740 A1450 150c multi    4.00 2.00

See South Korea No. 2406.

Dessau, 800th
Anniv. — A1451

**2013, July 1**
2741 A1451 45c multi     1.25 .60

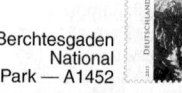

Berchtesgaden
National
Park — A1452

Wadden
Sea — A1453

**2013, July 1**     **Perf. 13¾**
2742 A1452 58c multi     1.50 .75
2743 A1453 58c multi     1.50 .75

Seascape, by
Gerhard Richter
A1454

**2013, July 1**     **Perf. 13¾**
2744 A1454 145c multi    3.75 1.90

**Booklet Stamp**
**Self-Adhesive**
**Size: 39x23mm**
**Die Cut Perf. 10**

2745 A1454 145c multi    3.75 1.90
   *a.*    Booklet pane of 10    37.50

---

Julius Cardinal
Dopfner (1913-
76) — A1455

**2013, Aug. 8**     **Perf. 13¾**
2746 A1455 58c multi     1.60 .80

Skat Card
Game, 200th
Anniv. — A1456

**2013, Sept. 5 Litho.**  **Perf. 13½x13¾**
2747 A1456 90c multi     2.40 1.25

Heidelberg — A1457

Designs: No. 2748, Heidelberg Castle and
Old Bridge, denomination at UL. No. 2749, Old
town, denomination at UR.

**2013, Sept. 5**
2748    58c multi     1.60 .80
2749    58c multi     1.60 .80
   *a.*    A1457 Horiz. pair, #2748-2749   3.20 1.60

Monument to the Battle of the Nations
(Battle of Leipzig), Leipzig,
Cent. — A1458

**2013, Oct. 10**     **Litho.**    **Perf. 13¾**
2750 A1458 45c multi     1.25 .60

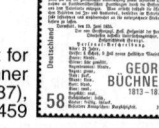

Arrest Warrant for
Georg Büchner
(1813-37),
Playwright — A1459

**2013, Oct. 10**     **Litho.**    **Perf. 13¾**
2751 A1459 58c blk & red    1.60 .80

Ludwig Leichhardt
(1813-48), Explorer
of Australian
Outback
Region — A1460

**2013, Oct. 10**     **Litho.**    **Perf. 13¾**
2752 A1460 75c multi     2.10 1.10

See Australia No. 4004.

Willy Brandt
(1913-92),
Chancellor of
Germany
A1461

**2013, Nov. 2**     **Litho.**    **Perf. 13¾**
2753 A1461 58c multi     1.60 .80

Discovery of Radio
Waves by Heinrich
Hertz, 125th
Anniv. — A1462

**2013, Nov. 2**     **Litho.**    **Perf. 14x13¾**
2754 A1462 58c multi     1.60 .80

---

Rahel Hirsch (1870-1953), First
Female Physician in Prussia
A1463

**2013, Nov. 2**  **Litho.**  **Perf. 13¾**
2755 A1463 145c multi    4.00 2.00

Christmas — A1464

**2013, Nov. 2**  **Litho.**  **Perf. 14x13¾**
2756 A1464 58c multi     1.60 .80

**Booklet Stamp**
**Self-Adhesive**
**Die Cut Perf. 11½x11¼**

2757 A1464 58c multi     1.60 .80
   *a.*    Booklet pane of 10    16.00

**Numeral Type of 2012**

**2013, Dec. 5**  **Litho.**  **Perf. 14x13½**
2758 A1426 2c multi     .25 .25

**Self-Adhesive**
**Die Cut Perf. 9¾**

2759 A1426 2c multi     .25 .25

Clouds in
Sky — A1465

**2013, Dec. 5**  **Litho.**  **Perf. 13¾**
2760 A1465 60c multi     1.75 .85

Reintroduction
of Atlantic
Salmon to
German
Rivers — A1466

**2014, Jan. 2 Litho.**  **Perf. 13½x13¾**
2761 A1466 45c multi     1.25 .60

Juvenile
Animals
A1467

Designs: Nos. 2762, 2764, Fox kits (fuchs).
Nos. 2763, 2765, Hedgehog hoglets (igel).

**2014, Jan. 2 Litho.**  **Perf. 13½x13¾**
2762 A1467 60c multi     1.75 .85
2763 A1467 60c multi     1.75 .85

**Booklet Stamps**
**Self-Adhesive**
**Size: 39x23mm**
**Die Cut Perf. 10**

2764 A1467 60c multi     1.75 .85
2765 A1467 60c multi     1.75 .85
   *a.*    Booklet pane of 20, 10 each
       #2764-2765    35.00

Lorsch Abbey
UNESCO World
Heritage
Site — A1468

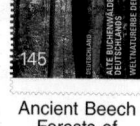

Ancient Beech
Forests of
Germany
UNESCO World
Heritage
Site — A1469

**2014, Jan. 2**  **Litho.**  **Perf. 13¾**
2766 A1468 60c multi     1.75 .85
2767 A1469 145c multi    4.00 2.00

## Coil Stamp
### Self-Adhesive
*Die Cut Perf. 10¼*

2768 A1468 60c multi 1.75 .85
Lorsch Abbey, 1250th anniv. See No. 2788.

Stolzenfels Castle — A1470

**2014, Jan. 2 Litho.** *Perf. 13½x13¾*
2769 A1470 75c multi 2.10 1.10

Lower Oder Valley Floodplain A1471

Devil's Table, Palatinate Forest — A1472

**2014, Feb. 6 Litho.** *Perf. 13½x13¾*
2770 A1471 60c multi 1.75 .85
2771 A1472 60c multi 1.75 .85
See Nos. 2784-2785.

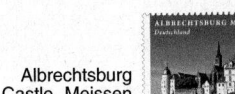

Albrechtsburg Castle, Meissen A1473

**2014, Mar. 1 Litho.** *Perf. 13½x13¾*
2772 A1473 90c multi 2.50 1.25

Protestant Brass Choirs — A1474

**2014, Mar. 1 Litho.** *Perf. 14x13¾*
2773 A1474 215c multi 6.00 3.00

"Happy Easter" A1475

"For You" — A1476

**2014, Mar. 1 Litho.** *Perf. 13½x13¾*
2774 A1475 45c multi 1.25 .60
2775 A1476 60c multi 1.75 .85

### Booklet Stamp
#### Self-Adhesive
Size: 39x22mm
*Die Cut Perf. 10*

2776 A1476 60c multi 1.75 .85
 a. Booklet pane of 10 17.50

A1477

**2014, Apr. 3 Litho.** *Perf. 13¾*
2777 A1477 60c multi 1.75 .85
Aktion Mensch (Action Man) Charity, 50th Anniv.

Max Weber (1864-1920), Sociologist — A1478

**2014, Apr. 3 Litho.** *Perf. 13¾*
2778 A1478 60c multi 1.75 .85

Dresden A1479

Boats on the Elbe River and: Nos. 2779, 2781, Crescent moon, Frauenkirche, denomination at UL. Nos. 2780, 2782, Hofkirche, Zwinger Palace and Semper Opera, denomination at UR

**2014, Apr. 3 Litho.** *Perf. 13¾*
2779 A1479 45c multi 1.25 .60
2780 A1479 45c multi 1.25 .60
 a. Horiz. pair, #2779-2780 2.50 1.25

### Booklet Stamps
#### Self-Adhesive
Size: 39x23mm
*Die Cut Perf. 9¾ on 3 Sides*

2781 A1479 45c multi 1.25 .60
2782 A1479 45c multi 1.25 .60
 a. Booklet pane of 10, 5 each
 #2781-2782 12.50

First Long Distance Railway Line in Germany, 175th Anniv. — A1480

**2014, Apr. 3 Litho.** *Perf. 13¾*
2783 A1480 145c multi 4.00 2.00

### Lower Oder Valley Floodplain and Devil's Table Types of 2014
#### Booklet Stamps
Self-Adhesive Size:39x23mm

**2014, May 8 Litho.** *Die Cut Perf. 10*
2784 A1471 60c multi 1.75 .85
2785 A1472 60c multi 1.75 .85
 a. Booklet pane of 10, 5 each
 #2784-2785 17.50

Two Women, Watercolor by Johann Gottfried Schadow (1764-1850) A1481

**2014, May 8 Litho.** *Perf. 13¾*
2786 A1481 60c multi 1.75 .85

Clarinet A1482

**2014, May 8 Litho.** *Perf. 13¾*
2787 A1482 60c multi 1.75 .85
Europa.

### Ancient Beech Forests Type of 2014
*Die Cut Perf. 10¼*

**2014, June 5 Litho.**

### Coil Stamp
#### Self-Adhesive
2788 A1469 145c multi 4.00 2.00

Orchestral Instruments and Silhouette of Richard Strauss (1864-1949), Composer — A1483

**2014, June 5 Litho.** *Perf. 13¾*
2789 A1483 60c multi 1.75 .85

Creation of the Animals, Detail of Altarpiece by Master Bertram (c. 1340-c. 1414) — A1484

**2014, June 5 Litho.** *Perf. 13¾*
2790 A1484 240c multi 6.75 3.50
See No. 2849.

Market Square, Bremen A1485

Designs: No. 2791, Deutsches Haus and adjoining buildings, denomination at UL. No. 2792, Town Hall, Statue of Roland, St. Peter's Cathedral, denomination at UR.

**2014, June 5 Litho.** *Perf. 13¾*
2791 A1485 60c multi 1.75 .85
2792 A1485 60c multi 1.75 .85
 a. Horiz. pair, #2791-2792 3.50 1.75

### Lighthouses Type of 2004
Designs: 45c, Buk Lighthouse. 60c, Pellworm Lighthouse.

**2014, July 3 Litho.** *Perf. 13¾*
2793 A1150 45c multi 1.25 .60
2794 A1150 60c multi 1.60 .80

Council of Constance, 600th Anniv. — A1486

**2014, July 3 Litho.** *Perf. 13¾*
2795 A1486 60c multi 1.60 .80

Opera Glasses and Silhouette of Christoph Willibald Gluck (1714-87), Opera Composer — A1487

**2014, July 3 Litho.** *Perf. 13¾*
2796 A1487 90c multi 2.40 1.25

Ricarda Huch (1864-1947), Writer — A1488

**2014, July 3 Litho.** *Perf. 13¾*
2797 A1488 145c blk & brt org 4.00 2.00

Victory of German Team at 2014 World Cup Soccer Championships — A1489

**2014, July 17 Litho.** *Perf. 14*
2798 A1489 60c multi 1.60 .80

Youth Fire Brigades, 50th Anniv. — A1490

**2014, Aug. 7 Litho.** *Perf. 13½x13¾*
2799 A1490 60c multi 1.60 .80

Never Again War, Poster by Käthe Kollwitz (1867-1945) A1491

**2014, Aug. 7 Litho.** *Perf. 13¾*
2800 A1491 75c multi 2.00 1.00
World War I, cent.

Coach of Lindau Messenger Courier Service A1492

**2014, Sept. 1 Litho.** *Perf. 13½x13¾*
2801 A1492 60c multi 1.60 .80
Stamp Day.

The Little Prince, by Antoine de Saint-Exupery (1900-44) — A1493

**2014, Sept. 1 Litho.** *Perf. 13¾*
2802 A1493 60c multi 1.60 .80

### Booklet Stamp
#### Self-Adhesive
*Die Cut Perf. 10¼*

2803 A1493 60c multi 1.60 .80
 a. Booklet pane of 10 16.00

Sunny Road, by August Macke — A1494

**2014, Sept. 1 Litho.** *Perf. 14*
2804 A1494 100c multi 2.75 1.40

Mittelland Canal Lock, Minden, Cent. — A1495

**2014, Oct. 2 Litho.** *Perf. 14*
2805 A1495 45c multi 1.25 .60

Fagus Factory UNESCO World Heritage Site — A1496

**2014, Oct. 2 Litho.** *Perf. 13½x13¾*
2806 A1496 60c multi 1.50 .75

External Auditing, 300th Anniv. — A1497

**2014, Oct. 2 Litho.** *Perf. 13¾x14*
2807 A1497 145c multi 3.75 1.90

Fahrenheit Temperature Scale, 300th Anniv. — A1498

**2014, Nov. 3    Litho.    Perf. 13¾**
2808 A1498 60c multi                1.50    .75

Julius Robert von Mayer (1814-78), Physicist A1499

**2014, Nov. 3    Litho.    Perf. 13¾**
2809 A1499 90c multi                2.25  1.10

Snowman A1500

**2014, Nov. 3    Litho.    Perf. 13¾x14**
2810 A1500 60c multi                1.50    .75

**Booklet Stamp**
**Self-Adhesive**
*Serpentine Die Cut*
2811 A1500 60c multi                1.50    .75
a.    Booklet pane of 10              15.00

Reintroduction of Sea Trout to German Rivers — A1501

**2014, Dec. 4    Litho.    Perf. 13¾**
2812 A1501 45c multi                1.10    .55

Visitation, by Rogier van der Weyden — A1502

**2014, Dec. 4    Litho.    Perf. 14**
2813 A1502 145c multi               3.50  1.75

**Flowers Type of 2005**

Designs: 62c, Pfingstrose (peony). 80c, Kugelprimel (drumstick primrose). 85c, Federnelke (pink). 395c, Purpurglöckchen (coral bells). 440c, Türkenbund (Turk's cap lily).

**2014, Dec. 4    Litho.    Perf. 14**
2814 A1165 62c multi                1.50    .75
2815 A1165 80c multi                2.00  1.00
2816 A1165 85c multi                2.10  1.10
2817 A1165 395c multi               9.50  4.75
2818 A1165 440c multi              11.00  5.50
    Nos. 2814-2818 (5)             26.10 13.10

**Self-Adhesive**
*Die Cut Perf. 10¼x10*
2819 A1165 62c multi                1.50    .75
a.    Booklet pane of 10             15.00

Western Pomerania Lagoon National Park — A1503

**2015, Jan. 2    Litho.    Perf. 13½x13¾**
2820 A1503 85c multi                2.10  1.10

**Booklet Stamp**
**Self-Adhesive**
Size: 39x23mm
*Die Cut Perf. 9¾*
2821 A1503 85c multi                2.10  1.10
a.    Booklet pane of 10             21.00

Juvenile Animals A1504

Designs: Nos. 2822, 2824, Squirrels (eichhörnchen). Nos. 2823, 2825, Wildcats (wildkatze).

**2015, Jan. 2    Litho.    Perf. 13½x13¾**
2822 A1504 62c multi                1.50    .75
2823 A1504 62c multi                1.50    .75

**Booklet Stamps**
**Self-Adhesive**
Size: 39x23mm
*Die Cut Perf. 9¾*
2824 A1504 62c multi                1.50    .75
2825 A1504 62c multi                1.50    .75
a.    Booklet pane of 20, 10 each
      #2824-2825                    30.00

Marksburg Castle — A1505

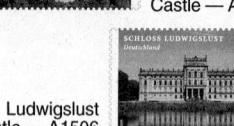

Ludwigslust Castle — A1506

**2015, Jan. 2    Litho.    Perf. 13½x13¾**
2826 A1505 62c multi                1.50    .75
2827 A1506 80c multi                2.00  1.00

**Coil Stamp**
**Self-Adhesive**
*Die Cut Perf. 10¾*
2828 A1505 62c multi                1.50    .75

**Booklet Stamp**
Size: 39x22mm
*Die Cut Perf. 9¾*
2829 A1506 80c multi                2.00  1.00
a.    Booklet pane of 10             20.00

Karl Leisner (1915-45), Priest Ordained While Interned at Dachau Concentration Camp — A1507

**2015, Feb. 5    Litho.    Perf. 13½x13¾**
2830 A1507 62c blue & blk           1.40    .70

Hildesheim Diocese, 1200th Anniv. — A1508

**2015, Mar. 2    Litho.    Perf. 14**
2831 A1508 62c blk & gold           1.40    .70

Felix the Rabbit, Children's Book Character by Annette Landen A1509

Designs: 45c, Felix in open suitcase. 62c, Felix writing letter.

**2015, Mar. 2    Litho.    Perf. 13½x13¾**
2832 A1509 45c multi                1.00    .50
2833 A1509 62c multi                1.40    .70

**Booklet Stamp**
**Self-Adhesive**
Size: 39x22mm
*Die Cut Perf. 9¾*
2834 A1509 62c multi                1.40    .70
a.    Booklet pane of 10             14.00

University of Kiel, 350th Anniv. — A1510

**2015    Litho.    Perf. 13½x13¾**
2835 A1510 62c multi                1.40    .70

**Booklet Stamp**
**Self-Adhesive**
Size: 39x22mm
*Die Cut Perf. 9¾*
2836 A1510 62c multi                1.40    .70
a.    Booklet pane of 10             14.00

Issued: No. 2835, 3/2; No. 2836, 5/7.

City of Köthen, 900th Anniv. — A1511

**2015, Mar. 2    Litho.    Perf. 13½x13¾**
2837 A1511 240c multi               5.50  2.75

Otto von Bismarck (1815-98), Chancellor A1512

**2015, Apr. 2    Litho.    Perf. 13½x13¾**
2838 A1512 62c multi                1.40    .70

Max and Moritz, by Wilhelm Busch, 150th Anniv. — A1513

**2015, Apr. 2    Litho.    Perf. 13¾x14**
2839 A1513 62c multi                1.40    .70

Automobiles A1514

Designs: Nos. 2840, 2842, 1956-59 BMW 507. Nos. 2841, 2843, Mercedes-Benz 220 S (W111).

**2015, Apr. 2    Litho.    Perf. 13½x13¾**
2840 A1514 145c multi               3.25  1.60
2841 A1514 145c multi               3.25  1.60

**Booklet Stamps**
**Self-Adhesive**
Size: 39x22mm
*Die Cut Perf. 9¾*
2842 A1514 145c multi               3.25  1.60
2843 A1514 145c multi               3.25  1.60
a.    Booklet pane of 10, 5 each
      #2842-2843                    32.50

German Maritime Search and Rescue Association, 150th Anniv. — A1515

**2015, May 7    Litho.    Perf. 13¾**
2844 A1515 62c multi                1.40    .70

Europa — A1516

**2015, May 7    Litho.    Perf. 13¾**
2845 A1516 62c multi                1.40    .70

Diplomatic Relations Between Germany and Israel, 50th Anniv. — A1517

**2015, May 7    Litho.    Perf. 14**
2846 A1517 80c multi                1.75    .90

See Israel No. 2062.

**Lighthouses Type of 2004**

Designs: 45c, Moritzburg Lighthouse. 62c, Lindau Lighthouse.

**2015, June 11    Litho.    Perf. 13¾**
2847 A1150 45c multi                1.00    .50
2848 A1150 62c multi                1.40    .70

**Master Bertram Altarpiece Type of 2014**
*Die Cut Perf. 11½*
**2015, June 11    Litho.**
**Booklet Stamp**
**Self-Adhesive**
2849 A1484 240c multi               5.25  2.60
a.    Booklet pane of 10             52.50

Young Scientists Competition, 50th Anniv. — A1518

**2015, June 11    Litho.    Perf. 14**
2850 A1518 62c multi                1.40    .70

First Bavarian Traditional Costume Association, 125th Anniv. — A1519

**2015, June 11    Litho.    Perf. 13¾**
2851 A1519 62c multi                1.40    .70

Kindergartens in Germany, 175th Anniv. — A1520

**2015, June 11    Litho.    Perf. 14**
2852 A1520 215c multi               4.75  2.40

Leipzig, 1000th Anniv. — A1521

**2015, July 1    Litho.    Perf. 13½x13¾**
2853 A1521 62c org & red            1.40    .70

Pina Bausch (1940-2009), Choreographer A1522

**2015, July 1    Litho.    Perf. 13½x13¾**
2854 A1522 85c multi                1.90    .95

Philipp Scheidemann (1865-1939), Chancellor — A1523

**2015, July 1    Litho.    Perf. 13¾**
2855 A1523 145c black & red         3.25  1.60

Chiemsee
A1524

Designs: Nos. 2856, 2858, Boat on Chiemsee (denomination at UL). Nos. 2857, 2859, Mountains near Chiemsee (denomination at UR).

**2015, July 1    Litho.    Perf. 13½x13¾**
2856  A1524  45c multi          1.00  .50
2857  A1524  45c multi          1.00  .50
  a.  Horiz. pair, #2856-2857   2.00  1.00

**Booklet Stamps**
**Self-Adhesive**
**Size: 39x22mm**
**Die Cut Perf. 9¾ on 3 Sides**
2858  A1524  45c multi          1.00  .50
2859  A1524  45c multi          1.00  .50
  a.  Booklet pane of 10, 5 each  10.00
      #2858-2859

International
Windjammer
Festival,
Bremerhaven
A1525

**2015, Aug. 6    Litho.    Perf. 13¾**
2860  A1525  62c multi          1.40  .70

Helmut Schön
(1915-96), Soccer
Coach — A1526

**2015, Sept. 1    Litho.    Perf. 13¾**
2861  A1526  62c multi          1.40  .70

Asterix, Comic Strip by René
Goscinny and Albert Uderzo
A1527

Characters: No. 2862a, Dogmatix carrying bone (35x35mm). Nos. 2862b, 2863, Obelix carrying boar (33x39mm). Nos. 2862c, 2864, Asterix the Gaul (33x39mm).

**Perf. 13¾ (21c), 14x13¾ (62c)**
**2015, Sept. 1    Litho.**
2862  A1527  Sheet of 3         3.25  3.25
  a.  21c multi                  .45  .25
  b.-c.  62c Either single      1.40  .70

**Booklet Stamps**
**Self-Adhesive**
**Die Cut Perf. 11¾x11¼**
2863  A1527  62c multi          1.40  .70
2864  A1527  62c multi          1.40  .70
  a.  Booklet pane of 10, 5 each  14.00
      #2863-2864

Altarpiece, St. Mary's Church,
Wittenberg, by Lucas Cranach the
Younger (1515-86)
A1528

**2015, Oct. 1    Litho.    Perf. 13½x13¾**
2865  A1528  45c multi          1.00  .50

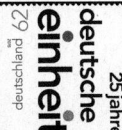

Reunification of
Germany, 25th
Anniv. — A1529

**2015, Oct. 1    Litho.    Perf. 13¾**
2866  A1529  62c multi          1.40  .70

Grieving
Women,
Sculpture by
Tilman
Riemenschneider
(c. 1460-1531)
A1530

Nativity with
Adoration of the
Shepherds, by
Martin
Schongauer (c.
1444-91)
A1531

**2015    Litho.    Perf. 14**
2867  A1530  62c multi          1.40  .70
2868  A1531  145c multi         3.25  1.60

Issued: 62c, 10/1; 145c, 11/2.

Christmas
A1532

**2015, Nov. 2    Litho.    Perf. 13½x13¾**
2869  A1532  62c multi          1.40  .70

**Booklet Stamp**
**Self-Adhesive**
**Size: 39x23mm**
**Die Cut Perf. 9¾**
2870  A1532  62c multi          1.40  .70
  a.  Booklet pane of 10        14.00

**Numeral Type of 2012**
**2015, Dec. 3    Litho.    Perf. 14x13½**
2871  A1426  8c multi           .25  .25

**Self-Adhesive**
**Die Cut Perf. 9¾**
2872  A1426  8c multi           .25  .25

Freiberg Universtiy of Mining and
Technology, 250th Anniv. — A1533

**2015, Dec. 3    Litho.    Perf. 13½x13¾**
2873  A1533  70c multi          1.60  .80

**Booklet Stamp**
**Self-Adhesive**
**Size: 39x23mm**
**Die Cut Perf. 10**
2874  A1533  70c multi          1.60  .80
  a.  Booklet pane of 10        16.00

Microscopic View
of
Diatom — A1534

Microscopic View
of Agrimony
Flower — A1535

**2015-16    Litho.    Perf. 14**
2875  A1534  70c multi          1.60  .80
2876  A1535  70c multi          1.60  .80

**Coil Stamps**
**Self-Adhesive**
**Die Cut Perf. 11x11½**
2877  A1534  70c multi          1.60  .80
2878  A1535  70c multi          1.60  .80
  a.  Horiz. pair, #2877-2878   3.20

Issued: Nos. 2875-2876, 12/3; Nos. 2877-2878, 1/2.16.

Sky Flowers Above
the Yellow House, by
Paul Klee (1879-
1940)
A1536

**2015, Dec. 3    Litho.    Perf. 14x13¾**
2879  A1536  240c multi         5.25  2.60

**Flowers Type of 2005**
Designs: 5c, Phlox. 70c, Schokoladen-kosmee (chocolate cosmos). 250c, Alpendistel (Alpine thistle). 260c, Madonnenlilie (Madonna lily). 400c, Fuchsie (fuschia). 450c, Bienenragwurz (bee orchid).

**2015-17    Litho.    Perf. 14**
2880  A1165  5c multi           .25  .25
2881  A1165  70c multi          1.60  .80
2882  A1165  250c multi         5.50  2.75
2883  A1165  260c multi         5.75  3.00
2884  A1165  400c multi         8.75  4.50
2885  A1165  450c multi         10.00  5.00
      Nos. 2881-2885 (5)        31.60  16.05

**Coil Stamp**
**Self-Adhesive**
**Die Cut Perf. 10¼x10**
2886  A1165  70c multi          1.60  .80

Issued: 70c, 400c, 450c, No. 2886, 12/3/15; 250c, 1/2/16; 260c, 2/11/16; 5c, 4/13/17.

Löwenburg
Castle, Kassel
A1537

**2016, Jan. 2    Litho.    Perf. 13½x13¾**
2887  A1537  90c multi          2.00  1.00

Bavarian
Forest — A1538

**2016, Jan. 2    Litho.    Perf. 13½x13¾**
2888  A1538  85c multi          1.90  .95

Automobiles
A1539

Designs: Nos. 2889, 2891, 1965 Porsche 911 Targa. Nos. 2890, 2892, 1969-73 Ford Capri 1.

**2016    Litho.    Perf. 13½x13¾**
2889  A1539  70c multi          1.60  .80
2890  A1539  70c multi          1.60  .80

**Booklet Stamps**
**Self-Adhesive**
**Size: 39x22mm**
**Die Cut Perf. 9¾**
2891  A1539  70c multi          1.60  .80
2892  A1539  70c multi          1.60  .80
  a.  Booklet pane of 20, 10 each  32.00
      #2891-2892

Issued: Nos. 2889-2890, 1/2; Nos. 2891-2892, 2/11.

Schwetzingen,
1250th
Anniv. — A1540

**2016    Litho.    Perf. 13½x13¾**
2893  A1540  145c multi         3.25  1.60

**Booklet Stamp**
**Self-Adhesive**
**Size: 39x22mm**
**Die Cut Perf. 9¾**
2894  A1540  145c multi         3.25  1.60
  a.  Booklet pane of 10        32.50

Issued: No. 2893, 1/2; No. 2894, 3/1.

112 European
Emergency Number,
25th
Anniv. — A1541

**2016, Feb. 11    Litho.    Perf. 13¾**
2895  A1541  45c red & dp ultra  1.00  .50

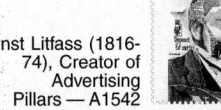

Ernst Litfass (1816-
74), Creator of
Advertising
Pillars — A1542

**2016, Feb. 11    Litho.    Perf. 13¾**
2896  A1542  70c multi          1.60  .80

Corvey Abbey
UNESCO World
Heritage
Site — A1543

**2016, Mar. 1    Litho.    Perf. 13½x13¾**
2897  A1543  70c multi          1.60  .80

Juvenile
Animals
A1544

Designs: Nos. 2898, 2900, Leverets. Nos. 2899, 2901, Greylag goslings.

**2016, Mar. 1    Litho.    Perf. 13½x13¾**
2898  A1544  70c multi          1.60  .80
2899  A1544  70c multi          1.60  .80

**Booklet Stamps**
**Self-Adhesive**
**Size: 39x22mm**
**Die Cut Perf. 9¾**
2900  A1544  70c multi          1.60  .80
2901  A1544  70c multi          1.60  .80
  a.  Booklet pane of 8, 4 each  13.00
      #2900-2901

Sanssouci
Palace,
Potsdam
A1545

**2016    Litho.    Perf. 13½x13¾**
2902  A1545  85c multi          1.90  .95

**Booklet Stamp**
**Self-Adhesive**
**Size: 39x22mm**
**Die Cut Perf. 9¾**
2903  A1545  85c multi          2.00  1.00
  a.  Booklet pane of 10        20.00

Issued: No. 2902, 3/1; No. 2903, 4/7.

Dresden
Frauenkirche,
Designed by George
Bähr (1666-1738)
A1546

**2016, Mar. 1    Litho.    Perf. 13¾**
2904  A1546  260c multi         5.75  3.00

**Booklet Stamp**
**Self-Adhesive**
**Die Cut Perf. 10¼**
2905  A1546  260c multi         5.75  3.00
  a.  Booklet pane of 10        57.50

Bavarian Beer Purity Laws, 500th Anniv. — A1547

**2016, Apr. 7 Litho. Perf. 14**
2906 A1547 45c multi 1.10 .55

Nelly Sachs (1891-1970), 1966 Nobel Laureate in Literature — A1548

**2016, Apr. 7 Litho. Perf. 13¾**
2907 A1548 70c multi 1.60 .80

Charles V, Holy Roman Emperor, by Titian — A1549

Ivory Frigate Carried by Neptune, by Jacob Zeller — A1550

**2016 Litho. Perf. 14**
2908 A1549 70c multi 1.60 .80
2909 A1550 145c multi 3.50 1.75

**Coil Stamp**
**Self-Adhesive**
**Die Cut Perf. 11½x11¼**
2910 A1550 145c multi 3.25 1.60

Issued: Nos. 2908-2909, 4/7; No. 2910, 6/2.

Bend in Moselle River Near Kröv — A1551

Designs: Nos. 2911, 2913, River bend and bridge, denomination at UL. Nos. 2912, 2914, River bend, no bridge, denomination at UR.

**2016 Litho. Perf. 13½x13¾**
2911 A1551 90c multi 2.10 1.10
2912 A1551 90c multi 2.10 1.10
a. Horiz. pair, #2911-2912 4.25 2.25

**Booklet Stamps**
**Self-Adhesive**
**Size: 39x22mm**
**Die Cut Perf. 9¾ on 3 Sides**
2913 A1551 90c multi 2.10 1.10
2914 A1551 90c multi 2.10 1.10
a. Booklet pane of 10, 5 each #2913-2914 21.00

Issued: Nos. 2911-2912, 4/7; Nos. 2913-2914, 5/2.

Europa A1552

**2016, May 2 Litho. Perf. 13½x13¾**
2915 A1552 70c multi 1.60 .80

Think Green Issue.

German Catholics' Day, Cent. — A1553

**2016, May 2 Litho. Perf. 13¾**
2916 A1553 70c multi 1.60 .80

Wedding Shoes — A1554

Birthday Cake — A1555

Flowers A1556

**2016, May 2 Litho. Perf. 13½x13¾**
2917 A1554 70c multi 1.60 .80
2918 A1555 70c multi 1.60 .80
2919 A1556 70c multi 1.60 .80
Nos. 2917-2919 (3) 4.80 2.40

**Booklet Stamps**
**Self-Adhesive**
**Size: 39x22mm**
**Die Cut Perf. 9¾**
2920 A1555 70c multi 1.60 .80
2921 A1556 70c multi 1.60 .80
a. Booklet pane of 10, 5 each #2920-2921 16.00

Black Madonna and Shrine of Our Lady of Altötting A1557

**2016, May 2 Litho. Perf. 13½x13¾**
2922 A1557 85c multi 2.00 1.00

Microscopic View of Moth's Antenna — A1558

Microscopic View of Radiolarian A1559

**2016, June 2 Litho. Perf. 14**
2923 A1558 70c multi 1.60 .80
2924 A1559 250c multi 5.75 3.00

Schrammsteine Rock Formation, Saxon Switzerland National Park — A1560

**2016, June 2 Litho. Perf. 13½x13¾**
2925 A1560 45c multi 1.00 .50

**Booklet Stamp**
**Self-Adhesive**
**Size:39x22mm**
**Die Cut Perf. 9¾**
2926 A1560 45c multi 1.00 .50
a. Booklet pane of 10 10.00

Polish-German Youth Office, 25th Anniv. — A1561

**2016, June 2 Litho. Perf. 13½x13¾**
2927 A1561 90c multi 2.00 1.00

See Poland No. 4229

**Lighthouses Type of 2004**
Designs: 45c, Staberhuk Lighthouse. 70c, Kampen Lighthouse.

**2016, July 7 Litho. Perf. 13¾**
2928 A1150 45c multi 1.00 .50
2929 A1150 70c multi 1.60 .80

First Glider of Otto Lilienthal (1848-96), 125th Anniv. — A1562

**2016, July 7 Litho. Perf. 14**
2930 A1562 145c multi 3.25 1.60

Münsterschwarzach Abbey, 1200th Anniv. — A1563

**2016, Aug. 4 Litho. Perf. 13½x13¾**
2931 A1563 70c multi 1.60 .80

Stamp Day — A1564

**2016, Sept. 1 Litho. Perf. 14**
2932 A1564 70c red & ol brown 1.60 .80

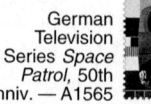

German Television Series Space Patrol, 50th Anniv. — A1565

**2016, Sept. 1 Litho. Perf. 13½x13¾**
2933 A1565 145c multi 3.25 1.60

**Souvenir Sheet**

Livestock Breeds A1566

No. 2934: a, Rhön sheep. b, German saddle pig.

**2016, Sept. 1 Litho. Perf. 13½x13¾**
2934 A1566 Sheet of 2 3.50 1.75
a. 70c multi 1.60 .80
b. 85c multi 1.90 .85

Naumburg Cathedral A1567

**2016, Oct. 6 Litho. Perf. 13½x13¾**
2935 A1567 45c multi 1.00 .50

"Song of Germany," German National Anthem, 175th Anniv. — A1568

**2016, Oct. 6 Litho. Perf. 13¾**
2936 A1568 70c gold & multi 1.60 .80

Electric Vehicles and Wind Generators — A1569

**2016, Oct. 6 Litho. Perf. 14**
2937 A1569 190c multi 4.25 2.10

To Beauty, Painting by Otto Dix (1891-1969) A1570

**2016, Nov. 2 Litho. Perf. 13½x13¾**
2938 A1570 85c multi 1.90 .95

Christmas A1571

**2016, Nov. 2 Litho. Perf. 13½x13¾**
2939 A1571 70c multi 1.50 .75

**Booklet Stamp**
**Self-Adhesive**
**Size:39x22mm**
**Die Cut Perf. 9¾**
2940 A1571 70c multi 1.50 .75
a. Booklet pane of 10 15.00

Steamship Die Weser, 200th Anniv. — A1572

**2016, Dec. 8 Litho. Perf. 13½x13¾**
2941 A1572 70c multi 1.50 .75

See No. 2944.

German Product Design — A1573

Designs: 70c, Loops Chair, by Luigi Colani. 145c, Glassware, by Hans Theo Baumann.

**2016, Dec. 8 Litho. Perf. 14**
2942 A1573 70c multi 1.50 .75
2943 A1573 145c multi 3.00 1.50

See No. 2989.

**Steamship Die Weser Type of 2016**
**Die Cut Perf. 9¾**
**2017, Jan. 2 Litho.**
**Booklet Stamp**
**Self-Adhesive**
**Size: 39x22mm**
2944 A1572 70c multi 1.50 .75
a. Booklet pane of 10 15.00

Topography of Terror Museum Foundation, 25th Anniv. — A1574

**2017, Jan. 2 Litho. Perf. 14**
2945 A1574 45c black .95 .45

Martin Luther's German Translation of the Bible — A1575

**2017, Jan. 2    Litho.    Perf. 14**
2946  A1575  260c multi          5.50  2.75
Protestant Reformation, 500th anniv.

Demoiselle Crane, Toucan and Tufted Crane, by Jean-Baptiste Oudry (1686-1755) A1576

The Girl with the Wine Glass, by Johannes Vermeer (1632-75) A1577

**2017, Jan. 2    Litho.    Perf. 14**
2947  A1576  70c multi          1.50  .75
2948  A1577  70c multi          1.50  .75

**Coil Stamps**
**Self-Adhesive**
**Die Cut Perf. 11¼x11½**
2949  A1576  70c multi          1.50  .75

**Die Cut Perf. 11½x11¼**
2950  A1577  70c multi          1.50  .75
  a.    Pair, #2949-2950          3.00

Opening of the Elbe Philharmonic Hall, Hamburg A1578

**2017    Litho.    Perf. 13½x13¾**
2951  A1578  145c multi         3.00  1.50

**Booklet Stamp**
**Self-Adhesive**
**Size: 39x22mm**
**Die Cut Perf. 10**
2952  A1578  145c multi         3.00  1.50
  a.    Booklet pane of 10       30.00

Issued: No. 2951, 1/2; No. 2952, 2/9.

Ludwigsburg Palace, Ludwigsburg A1579

**2017, Feb. 9    Litho.    Perf. 13½x13¾**
2953  A1579  70c multi          1.50  .75
See No. 2974.

Neunburg vorm Wald, 1000th Anniv. — A1580

**2017, Mar. 1    Litho.    Perf. 13½x13¾**
2954  A1580  45c blue & red vio      .95  .45

2017 German Presidency of G20 — A1581

**2017, Mar. 1    Litho.    Perf. 13¾**
2955  A1581  70c multi          1.50  .75

Gray Ottifant, Cartoon Elephant by Otto Waalkes A1582

---

**2017, Mar. 1    Litho.    Perf. 13½x13¾**
2956  A1582  70c multi          1.50  .75

**Booklet Stamp**
**Self-Adhesive**
**Size: 39x22mm**
**Die Cut Perf. 9¾**
2957  A1582  70c multi          1.50  .75
  a.    Booklet pane of 10       15.00

Juvenile Animals A1583

Designs: Nos. 2958, 2960, Wild boar squeakers (wildschwein). Nos. 2959, 2961, European polecat kits (iltis).

**2017, Mar. 1    Litho.    Perf. 13½x13¾**
2958  A1583  85c multi          1.90  .95
2959  A1583  85c multi          1.90  .95

**Booklet Stamp**
**Self-Adhesive**
**Size: 39x22mm**
**Die Cut Perf. 9¾**
2960  A1583  85c multi          1.90  .95
2961  A1583  85c multi          1.90  .95
  a.    Booklet pane of 10, 5 each
        #2960-2961             19.00

Martin Luther (1483-1546), Religious Reformer A1584

**2017, Apr. 13    Litho.    Perf. 13½x13¾**
2962  A1584  70c multi          1.60  .80
Protestant Reformation, 500th anniv. See Brazil No. 3351.

Automobiles A1585

Designs: Nos. 2963, 2965, 1974-83 Volkswagen Golf Series 1. Nos. 2964, 2966, 1970-75 Opel Manta A.

**2017, Apr. 13    Litho.    Perf. 13½x13¾**
2963  A1585  90c multi          2.00  1.00
2964  A1585  90c multi          2.00  1.00

**Booklet Stamps**
**Self-Adhesive**
**Size: 39x22mm**
**Die Cut Perf. 9¾**
2965  A1585  90c multi          2.00  1.00
2966  A1585  90c multi          2.00  1.00
  a.    Booklet pane of 10, 5 each
        #2965-2966             20.00

Mines of Rammelsberg, Historic Town of Goslar, and Upper Harz Water Management System UNESCO World Heritage Sites — A1586

**2017, Apr. 13    Litho.    Perf. 13¾x14**
2967  A1586  145c multi         3.25  1.60

**Flowers Type of 2005**
Designs: 10c, Winterling (winter aconite). 20c, Hasenglöckchen (bluebells). 45c, Seerose (water lily). 90c, Johanniskraut (St. John's wort).

**2017    Litho.    Perf. 14**
2968  A1165  10c multi          .25  .25
2969  A1165  20c multi          .45  .25
2970  A1165  45c multi         1.00  .50
2971  A1165  90c multi         2.00  1.00
Issued: 45c, 90c, 5/11. 10c, 20c, 6/8.

---

**Ludwigsburg Castle Type of 2017 and**

Wartburg Castle — A1587

**2017, May 11    Litho.    Perf. 13½x13¾**
2972  A1587  70c multi          1.60  .80
  a.    Booklet pane of 8, 4each
        #2962, 2972            13.00  —
        Complete booklet, #2972a  13.00

**Booklet Stamp**
**Self-Adhesive**
**Size: 39x22mm**
**Die Cut Perf. 9¾**
2973  A1587  70c multi          1.60  .80
2974  A1579  70c multi          1.60  .80
  a.    Booklet pane of 20, 10 each
        #2973-2974             32.00

Europa (Nos. 2972-2973). Issued: No. 2972a, 8/10.

Party Foods and Drinks — A1588

Lily — A1589

**2017, May 11    Litho.    Perf. 13½x13¾**
2975  A1588  70c multi          1.60  .80
2976  A1589  70c multi          1.60  .80

**Booklet Stamp**
**Self-Adhesive**
**Size: 39x22mm**
**Die Cut Perf. 9¾**
2977  A1589  70c multi          1.60  .80
  a.    Booklet pane of 10       16.00

**Lighthouse Type of 2004**
Designs: 45c, Kiel-Holtenau Lighthouse. 70c, Bremerhaven Unterfeuer Lighthouse.

**2017, June 8    Litho.    Perf. 13¾**
2978  A1150  45c multi          1.10  .55
2979  A1150  70c multi          1.60  .80

Heinz Sielmann (1917-2006), Biologist and Wildlife Documentary Filmmaker A1590

**2017, June 8    Litho.    Perf. 13½x13¾**
2980  A1590  45c multi          1.10  .55

**Booklet Stamp**
**Self-Adhesive**
**Size: 39x22mm**
**Die Cut Perf. 9¾**
2981  A1590  45c multi          1.10  .55
  a.    Booklet pane of 10       11.00

Invention of the Draisine by Karl Drais (1785-1851), 200th Anniv. — A1591

**2017, July 13    Litho.    Perf. 13¾**
2982  A1591  70c multi          1.75  .85

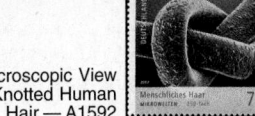

Microscopic View of Knotted Human Hair — A1592

---

Microscopic View of Vitamin C Crystal — A1593

**2017-18    Litho.    Perf. 14**
2983  A1592  70c multi          1.75  .85
2984  A1593  85c multi          2.00  1.00

**Coil Stamp**
**Self-Adhesive**
**Die Cut Perf. 11¼x11½**
2984A  A1593  85c multi         2.10  1.10
Issued: Nos. 2983, 2984, 7/13; No. 2984A, 2/1/18.

North German Confederation, 150th Anniv. — A1594

**2017, July 13    Litho.    Perf. 13¾**
2985  A1594  320c multi         7.75  4.00

**Flowers Type of 2005**
Design: 345c, Vergissmeinnicht (forget-me-not).

**2017, Aug. 10    Litho.    Perf. 14**
2986  A1165  345c multi         8.25  4.25

Color Television Broadcasting in Germany, 50th Anniv. — A1595

**Perf. 13½x13¾**
**2017, Aug. 10    Litho.**
2987  A1595  70c multi          1.75  .85

Fruitbearing Society, 400th Anniv. — A1596

**Perf. 13½x13¾**
**2017, Aug. 10    Litho.**
2988  A1596  145c multi         3.50  1.75

**German Product Design Type of 2016**
Design: Glassware, by Hans Theo Baumann.

**Die Cut Perf. 11½x11¼**
**2017, Aug. 10    Litho.**
**Coil Stamp**
**Self-Adhesive**
2989  A1573  145c multi         3.50  1.75

Wine Grapes — A1597

**2017, Sept. 7    Litho.    Perf. 13¾**
2990  A1597  70c multi          1.75  .85

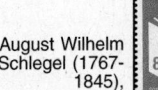

August Wilhelm Schlegel (1767-1845), Poet — A1598

**2017, Sept. 7    Litho.    Perf. 13¾**
2991  A1598  85c multi          2.00  1.00

Walther Rathenau (1867-1922), Foreign Minister — A1599

**2017, Sept. 7     Litho.     Perf. 13¾**
2992  A1599  250c multi          6.00 3.00

Baden Wine Route — A1600

Designs: No. 2993, Fields in valley (denomination at UL). No. 2994, Ölberg Chapel, Ehrenstetten (denomination at UR).

**2017, Oct. 12     Litho.     Perf. 13½x13¾**
2993  A1600  45c multi           1.10  .55
2994  A1600  45c multi           1.10  .55
  a.    Horiz. pair, #2993-2994   2.20 1.10

*Das Millionenspiel* (The Millions Game), 1970 Television Movie — A1601

**2017, Oct. 12     Litho.     Perf. 13½x13¾**
2995  A1601  70c multi           1.60  .80

Johann Joachim Winckelmann (1717-68), Archaeologist and Art Historian — A1602

**2017, Oct. 12     Litho.     Perf. 14**
2996  A1602  70c multi           1.60  .80

German Justitia et Pax Commission, 50th Anniv. — A1603

**2017, Oct. 12     Litho.     Perf. 14**
2997  A1603  145c multi          3.50 1.75

Mecklenburg Lake District A1604

Reinhardswald A1605

**2017, Nov. 2     Litho.     Perf. 13½x13¾**
2998  A1604  70c multi           1.75  .85
2999  A1605  90c multi           2.25 1.10

Theodor Mommsen (1817-1903), 1902 Nobel Laureate for Literature — A1606

**2017, Nov. 2     Litho.     Perf. 13¾**
3000  A1606  190c multi          4.50 2.25

---

Maria Rast Chapel, Krün — A1607

**2017, Nov. 2     Litho.     Perf. 13½x13¾**
3001  A1607  70c multi           1.75  .85

**Booklet Stamp**
**Self-Adhesive**
**Size: 39x22mm**
**Die Cut Perf. 9¾**
3002  A1607  70c multi           1.75  .85
  a.    Booklet pane of 10       17.50
       Christmas.

Heinrich Böll (1917-85), 1972 Nobel Laureate in Literature — A1608

**2017, Dec. 7     Litho.     Perf. 13½**
3003  A1608  70c multi           1.75  .85

Stuttgart Light Rail Train, Designed by Herbert Lindinger — A1609

**2017-18     Litho.     Perf. 14**
3004  A1609  145c multi          3.50 1.75

**Coil Stamp**
**Self-Adhesive**
**Die Cut Perf. 11½x11¼**
3005  A1609  145c multi          3.75 1.90
Issued: No. 3004, 12/7/17; No. 3005, 2/1/18.

Gaia Space Observatory A1610

Gravitational Waves — A1611

**Litho. With Foil Application**
                               **Perf. 13¾**
**2017-18**
3006  A1610  45c sil & multi     1.10  .55
**Litho.**
3007  A1611  70c multi           1.75  .85
**Booklet Stamp**
**Self-Adhesive**
**Size: 39x22mm**
**Die Cut Perf. 9¾x10**
3008  A1611  70c multi           1.75  .85
  a.    Booklet pane of 10       17.50
Isssued: Nos. 3006, 3007, 12/7; No. 3008, 1/2/18.

**Flowers Type of 2005**
Designs: 45c, Seerose (water lily). 100c, Alpenveilchen (cyclamen). 145c, Jungfer im Grünen (love-in-a-mist). 379c, Kokardenblume (Indian blanket).

**2018     Litho.     Perf. 14**
3009  A1165  100c multi          2.50 1.25
3010  A1165  145c multi          3.50 1.75
3011  A1165  379c multi          9.00 4.50
       Nos. 3009-3011 (3)       15.00 7.50
**Die Cut Perf. 10¼x10**
**Coil Stamp**
**Self-Adhesive**
3012  A1165  45c multi           1.10  .55
Issued: 45c, 4/12; 100c, 3/1; 145c, 1/2; 379c, 7/12.

---

Falkenlust Palace, Brühl — A1612

Friedenstein Palace, Gotha — A1613

**2018     Litho.     Perf. 13½x13¾**
3013  A1612  70c multi           1.75  .85
3014  A1613  70c multi           1.75  .85

**Booklet Stamps**
**Self-Adhesive**
**Size: 39x22mm**
**Die Cut Perf. 9¾**
3015  A1613  70c multi           1.75  .85
3016  A1612  70c multi           1.75  .85
  a.    Booklet pane of 20, 10 each
         #3015-3016              35.00
Issued: No. 3013, 1/2; No. 3014, 3/1; Nos. 3015-3016, 5/3.

Juvenile Animals A1614

Designs: Nos. 3017, 3019, Fawn (reh). No. 3018, Seal pups (seehund).

**2018     Litho.     Perf. 13½x13¾**
3017  A1614  85c multi           2.10 1.10
3018  A1614  85c multi           2.10 1.10

**Booklet Stamp**
**Self-Adhesive**
**Size: 39x22mm**
**Die Cut Perf. 9¾**
3019  A1614  85c multi           2.10 1.10
  a.    Booklet pane of 10       21.00
Issued: Nos. 3017-3018, 1/2; No. 3019, 4/12.

Five Slices of German Bread — A1615

**2018     Litho.     Perf. 13¾**
3020  A1615  260c multi          6.25 3.25

**Booklet Stamp**
**Self-Adhesive**
**Die Cut Perf. 10¼**
3021  A1615  260c multi          6.25 3.25
  a.    Booklet pane of 10       62.50
Issued: No. 3020, 1/2; No. 3021, 5/3.

University of Bonn (Rheinisch Friedrich-Wilhelms-Universität Bonn), 200th Anniv. — A1616

**2018, Feb. 1     Litho.     Perf. 13¾**
3022  A1616  45c multi           1.10  .55

Tafel Charity, 25th Anniv. — A1617

**2018, Feb. 1     Litho.     Perf. 14**
3023  A1617  70c multi           1.75  .85

---

Characters From *Peanuts* Comic Strip — A1618

Designs: 70c, Woodstock and Snoopy. 90c, Sally, Lucy, Woodstock, Snoopy, Linus, and Charlie Brown.

**2018, Mar. 1     Litho.     Perf. 13½x13¾**
3024  A1618  70c multi           1.75  .85
3025  A1618  90c multi           2.25 1.10
  a.    Souvenir sheet of 2, #3024-
         3025                     4.00 2.00
**Booklet Stamps**
**Self-Adhesive**
**Size: 39x22mm**
**Die Cut Perf. 9¾**
3026  A1618  70c multi           1.75  .85
  a.    Booklet pane of 10       17.50
3027  A1618  90c multi           2.25 1.10
  a.    Booklet pane of 10       22.50

Automobiles A1619

Designs: Nos. 3028, 3030, 1988-91 Wartburg 13. Nos. 3029, 3031 1980-91 Audi Quattro.

**2018     Litho.     Perf. 13½x13¾**
3028  A1619  145c sil & multi    3.50 1.75
3029  A1619  145c sil & multi    3.50 1.75
**Die Cut Perf. 9¾**
**Booklet Stamps**
**Self-Adhesive**
**Size: 39x22mm**
3030  A1619  145c multi          3.50 1.75
3031  A1619  145c multi          3.50 1.75
  a.    Booklet pane of 10, 5 each
         #3030-3031              35.00
Issued: Nos. 3028-3029, 3/1. Nos. 3030-3031, 4/12.

Peter Behrens (1868-1940), Architect and Designer A1620

**2018, Apr. 12     Litho.     Perf. 13½x13¾**
3032  A1620  70c multi           1.75  .85

Technical University of Munich, 150th Anniv. — A1621

**2018, Apr. 12     Litho.     Perf. 13½x13¾**
3033  A1621  150c multi          3.75 1.90

A1622

Design: Elisabeth Mann Borgese (1918-2002), expert on maritime law and environmental protection.

**2018, Apr. 12     Litho.     Perf. 13½x13¾**
3034  A1622  370c multi          9.00 4.50

Karl Marx (1818-83), Philosopher and Political Theorist A1623

**2018, May 3     Litho.     Perf. 13½x13¾**
3035  A1623  70c multi           1.75  .85

Rheinkniebrücke and Oberkassler Bridge, Düsseldorf — A1624

2018, May 3   Litho.   **Perf. 13½x13¾**
3036 A1624 70c multi          1.75  .85

Europa.

Gewandhaus Orchestra, Leipzig, 275th Anniv. — A1625

2018, May 3   Litho.   **Perf. 13¾**
3037 A1625 70c multi          1.75  .85

Music Day.

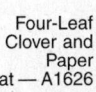

Four-Leaf Clover and Paper Boat — A1626

Gift — A1627

2018, May 3   Litho.   **Perf. 13½x13¾**
3038 A1626 70c multi          1.75  .85
3039 A1627 70c multi          1.75  .85
  a.   Booklet pane of 7, #2917-
       2919, 2975-2976, 3038-
       3039 + label            12.50   —
       Complete booklet, #3039a  12.50

**Lighthouses Type of 2004**

Designs: 45c, Darsser Ort Lighthouse. 70c, Wangerooge Lighthouse.

2018, June 7   Litho.   **Perf. 13¾**
3040 A1150 45c multi          1.10  .55
3041 A1150 70c multi          1.75  .85
         **Coil Stamp**
        **Self-Adhesive**
      **Die Cut Perf. 10¼**
3042 A1150 70c multi          1.75  .85

Rostock, 800th Anniv. — A1628

2018, June 7   Litho.   **Perf. 14**
3043 A1628 70c gold & brt blue  1.75  .85

Consecration of the Cathedral of Worms, 1000th Anniv. — A1629

2018, June 7   Litho.   **Perf. 13½x13¾**
3044 A1629 90c gold & brn gray  2.10  1.10
        **Booklet Stamp**
        **Self-Adhesive**
        **Size:39x22mm**
      **Die Cut Perf. 9¾**
3045 A1629 90c gold & brn gray  2.10  1.10
  a.   Booklet pane of 10       21.00

Goethe in the Campagna, by Johann Heinrich Wilhelm Tischbein (1751-1829) A1630

2018, June 7   Litho.   **Perf. 14**
3046 A1630 145c multi         3.50  1.75

**Die Cut Perf. 11¼x11½**
        **Coil Stamp**
        **Self-Adhesive**
3047 A1630 145c multi         3.50  1.75

Garden Kingdom of Dessau-Wörlitz UNESCO World Heritage Site — A1631

Buildings and: No. 3048, Boat on water. No. 3049, Boat and swan on water. No. 3050, Boat on water. No. 3051, Boat and swan on water.

2018, July 12   Litho.   **Perf. 13½x13¾**
3048 A1631 45c multi          1.10  .55
3049 A1631 45c multi          1.10  .55
  a.   Horiz. pair, #3048-3049  2.20  1.10
        **Booklet Stamps**
        **Self-Adhesive**
        **Size: 39x22mm**
   **Die Cut Perf. 9¾ on 3 Sides**
3050 A1631 45c multi          1.10  .55
3051 A1631 45c multi          1.10  .55
  a.   Booklet pane of 10, 5 each
       #3050-3051              11.00

Nelson Mandela (1918-2013), President of South Africa — A1632

2018, July 12   Litho.   **Perf. 13½x13¾**
3052 A1632 70c multi          1.75  .85

See South Africa No. 1575.

Magnus Hirschfeld (1868-1935), Sexologist — A1633

2018, July 12   Litho.   **Perf. 14**
3053 A1633 70c multi          1.75  .85

Braun World Receiver T1000, Designed by Dieter Rams — A1634

2018, July 12   Litho.   **Perf. 14**
3054 A1634 345c multi         8.00  4.00

Harz Mountain Spruce Forest — A1635

2018, Aug. 9   Litho.   **Perf. 13½x13¾**
3055 A1635 70c multi          1.75  .85

North German Confederation Nos. 4, 10, 15 and 19 — A1636

2018, Sept. 13   Litho.   **Perf. 13¾**
3056 A1636 70c multi          1.75  .85

North German Confederation postage stamps, 150th anniv., Stamp Day.

Microscopic View of Carbon Fibers — A1637

2018, Sept. 13   Litho.   **Perf. 14**
3057 A1637 90c multi          2.10  1.10

**Flowers Type of 2005**

Design: 10c, Winterling (winter aconite). 15c, Wiesenschaumkraut (cuckoo flower). 20c, Hasenglöckchen (bluebells). 220c, Hauswurz (amaranth).

2018             Litho.   **Perf. 14**
3058 A1165 15c multi          .35   .35
3059 A1165 220c multi        5.00  2.50
        **Booklet Stamps**
        **Self-Adhesive**
      **Die Cut Perf. 10¼x10**
3060 A1165 10c multi          .25   .25
  a.   Booklet pane of 10      2.40
3061 A1165 15c multi          .35   .25
  a.   Booklet pane of 10      3.50
3062 A1165 20c multi          .45   .25
  a.   Booklet pane of 10      4.50
       Nos. 3060-3062 (3)      1.05  .75

Issued: 10c, 15c, 20c, 12/18; 220c, 10/11.

Dinner for One, 1963 Television Show — A1638

2018, Oct. 11   Litho.   **Perf. 13½x13¾**
3063 A1638 45c multi          1.10  .55

Execution of Four Priests in Lübeck by Nazis, 75th Anniv. — A1639

2018, Oct. 11   Litho.   **Perf. 14**
3064 A1639 70c multi          1.60  .80

Die Prinzessinnengrupe (Prussian Princesses Louise and Frederica), Sculpture by Johann Gottfried Schadow (1764-1850) A1640

2018, Oct. 11   Litho.   **Perf. 14**
3065 A1640 85c multi          2.00  1.00

Friedrich Schleiermacher (1768-1834), Theologian A1641

2018, Nov. 2   Litho.   **Perf. 13½x13¾**
3066 A1641 70c multi          1.60  .80

Ernst Otto Fischer (1918-2007), 1973 Nobel Laureate in Chemistry — A1642

2018, Nov. 2   Litho.   **Perf. 13¾**
3067 A1642 70c multi          1.60  .80

Christmas A1643

2018, Nov. 2   Litho.   **Perf. 13½x13¾**
3068 A1643 70c multi          1.60  .80
        **Booklet Stamp**
        **Self-Adhesive**
        **Size: 39x22mm**
      **Die Cut Perf. 9¾**
3069 A1643 70c multi          1.60  .80
  a.   Booklet pane of 10      16.00

Moor on Hornisgrinde A1644

2018, Dec. 18   Litho.   **Perf. 13¾**
3070 A1644 70c multi          1.60  .80

Microscopic View of Liquid Crystal Display — A1645

2018, Dec. 18   Litho.   **Perf. 14**
3071 A1645 70c multi          1.60  .80

Helmut Schmidt (1918-2015), Chancellor — A1646

2018, Dec. 18   Litho.   **Perf. 13¾**
3072 A1646 70c multi          1.60  .80

Atacama Large Millimeter Array Observatory, Chile — A1647

Illustris Project Simulation of the Evolution of the Universe A1648

2018, Dec. 18   Litho.   **Perf. 13¾**
3073 A1647 145c multi         3.25  1.60
3074 A1648 145c multi         3.25  1.60

Porpoise A1649

2019, Jan. 2   Litho.   **Perf. 13½x13¾**
3075 A1649 45c multi          1.10  .55
        **Booklet Stamp**
        **Self-Adhesive**
        **Size: 39x22mm**
      **Die Cut Perf. 9¾**
3076 A1649 45c multi          1.10  .55
  a.   Booklet pane of 10      11.00

Woman Suffrage, Cent. — A1650

2019, Jan. 2   Litho.   **Perf. 13½x13¾**
3077 A1650 70c multi          1.60  .80

Juvenile Raccoons A1651

2019, Jan. 2   Litho.   **Perf. 13½x13¾**
3078 A1651 90c multi          2.10  1.10

The Lonely Tree, by Caspar David Friedrich (1774-1840) A1652

**2019, Jan. 2**    **Litho.**    *Perf. 14*
3079 A1652 145c multi    3.25 1.60

Rainbow and Cloud — A1653

Mirage — A1654

**2019, Feb. 7**   **Litho.**   *Perf. 13½x13¾*
3080 A1653 70c multi    1.60 .80
3081 A1654 70c multi    1.60 .80

**Booklet Stamps**
**Self-Adhesive**
**Size: 39x22mm**
*Die Cut Perf. 9¾*
3082 A1653 70c multi    1.60 .80
3083 A1654 70c multi    1.60 .80
   a.   Booklet pane of 20, 10 each
     #3082-3083    32.00

Else Lasker-Schüler (1869-1945), Poet — A1655

**2019, Feb. 7**    **Litho.**    *Perf. 14*
3084 A1655 70c multi    1.60 .80

**Flowers Type of 2005**
Design: 5c, Phlox. 120c, Traubenhyazinthe (grape hyacinth).

**2019**    **Litho.**    *Perf. 14*
3085 A1165 120c multi    2.75 1.40

**Booklet Stamp**
**Self-Adhesive**
*Die Cut Perf. 10¼x10*
3086 A1165 5c multi    .25 .25
   a.   Booklet pane of 10    1.10

   Issued: 120c, 3/1. No. 3086, 4/4.

Hannelore "Loki" Schmidt (1919-2010), Environmentalist and Wife of Chancellor Helmut Schmidt — A1656

**2019, Mar. 1**    **Litho.**    *Perf. 14*
3087 A1656 45c multi    1.00 .50
   a.   Souvenir sheet of 2, #3072,
     3087    2.60 2.60

Publication of *The Grüffalo*, Children's Book by Julia Donaldson, 20th Anniv. — A1657

**2019, Mar. 1**   **Litho.**   *Perf. 13½x13¾*
3088 A1657 70c multi    1.60 .80

**Booklet Stamp**
**Self-Adhesive**
**Size: 39x22mm**
*Die Cut Perf. 9¾*
3089 A1657 70c multi    1.60 .80
   a.   Booklet pane of 10    16.00

Blaibach Concert Hall, 5th Anniv. — A1658

**2019, Mar. 1**    **Litho.**    *Perf. 13¾*
3090 A1658 145c multi    3.25 1.60

University of Hamburg, Cent. — A1659

**2019, Mar. 1**    **Litho.**    *Perf. 14*
3091 A1659 260c multi    6.00 3.00

Emojis A1660

**2019, Apr. 4**    **Litho.**    *Perf. 13½x13¾*
3092 A1660 45c multi    1.00 .50

Rothenburg ob der Tauber A1661

   Various buildings with denomination at: No. 3093, UL. No. 3094, UR.

**2019, Apr. 4**   **Litho.**   *Perf. 13½x13¾*
3093 A1661 45c multi    1.00 .50
3094 A1661 45c multi    1.00 .50
   a.   Horiz. pair, #3093-3094    2.00 1.00

Adult Education Centers, Cent. — A1662

**2019, Apr. 4**    **Litho.**    *Perf. 13¾*
3095 A1662 70c multi    1.60 .80

Bauhaus Building, Dessau — A1663

**2019, Apr. 4**    **Litho.**    *Perf. 13¾*
3096 A1663 70c multi    1.60 .80

   Bauhaus Art School, cent.

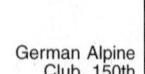

German Alpine Club, 150th Anniv. — A1664

**Litho. & Embossed**
**2019, Apr. 4**    *Perf. 13½x13¾*
3097 A1664 145c blue    3.25 1.60

Emberiza Citrinella A1665

**2019, May 2**    **Litho.**    *Perf. 13½x13¾*
3098 A1665 70c multi    1.60 .80

   Europa.

Huldrych Zwingli (1484-1531), Religious Reformer — A1666

**2019, May 2**    **Litho.**    *Perf. 13¾*
3099 A1666 150c multi    3.50 1.75

   See Switzerland No. 1721.

Campen Lighthouse A1667

**2019, June 6**    **Litho.**    *Perf. 13¾*
3100 A1667 70c multi    1.60 .80

Microscopic View of Palladium A1668

**2019, June 6**    **Litho.**    *Perf. 13¾*
3101 A1668 85c multi    2.00 1.00

House of the History of the Federal Republic of Germany, Bonn, 25th Anniv. — A1669

**2019, June 6**    **Litho.**    *Perf. 14*
3102 A1669 260c multi    6.00 3.00

**Flowers Type of 2005**
Designs: 60c, Kornblume (cornflower). 80c, Kapuzinerkresse (nasturtium). 95c, Flockenblume (knapweed). 110c, Wild-gladiole (wild gladiolus). 155c, Buschwindröschen (wood anemone). 170c, Stiefmütterchen (pansy). 190c, Löwenmäulchen (snapdragon). 270c, Habichtskraut (hawkweed).

**2019**    **Litho.**    *Perf. 14*
3103 A1165 60c multi    1.40 .70
3104 A1165 80c multi    1.90 .95
3105 A1165 95c multi    2.25 1.10
3106 A1165 110c multi    2.50 1.25
3107 A1165 155c multi    3.50 1.75
3108 A1165 170c multi    4.00 2.00
3109 A1165 190c multi    4.50 2.25
3110 A1165 270c multi    6.25 3.00
   *Nos. 3103-3110 (8)*    26.30 13.00

**Booklet Stamps**
**Self-Adhesive**
*Die Cut Perf. 10*
3111 A1165 60c multi    1.40 .70
   a.   Booklet pane of 10    14.00
3112 A1165 80c multi    1.90 .95
   a.   Booklet pane of 10    19.00
3113 A1165 95c multi    2.25 1.10
   a.   Booklet pane of 10    22.50
3114 A1165 110c multi    2.50 1.25
   a.   Booklet pane of 10    25.00
3115 A1165 155c multi    3.50 1.75
   a.   Booklet pane of 10    35.00
3116 A1165 270c multi    6.25 3.00
   a.   Booklet pane of 10    62.50
   *Nos. 3111-3116 (6)*    17.80 8.75

   Issued: Nos. 3114, 3115a, 3116, 8/1; Others, 7/1. Nos. 3111-3113, 3115 were also produced in coil rolls.

Rosetta Space Probe — A1670

Black Hole and Quasar A1671

Magnified Moon Rock — A1672

**2019, July 1**    **Litho.**    *Perf. 14*
3119 A1672 80c multi    1.90 .95

**2019, July 1**    **Litho.**    *Perf. 13¾*
3117 A1670 60c multi    1.40 .70
3118 A1671 110c multi    2.50 1.25

German Police System A1673

**Litho. With Foil Application**
**2019, July 1**    *Perf. 13¾*
3120 A1673 155c multi    3.50 1.75

 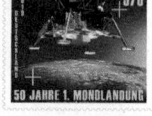

First Man on the Moon, 50th Anniv. — A1674

**Litho. With Foil Application**
**2019, July 1**    *Perf. 13¾*
3121 A1674 370c gold & multi    8.50 4.25
   a.   Souvenir sheet of 1    8.50 4.25

Weimar Constitution, Cent. — A1675

**2019, Aug. 1**    **Litho.**    *Perf. 14*
3122 A1675 95c gold & multi    2.10 1.10

Alexander von Humboldt (1769-1859), Naturalist A1676

**2019, Sept. 5**   **Litho.**   *Perf. 13½x13¾*
3123 A1676 80c multi    1.75 .85

Cards With Integrated Circuit Chips, 50th Anniv. — A1677

**2019, Sept. 5**   **Litho.**   *Perf. 13½x13¾*
3124 A1677 80c multi    1.75 .85

Clara Schumann (1819-96), Pianist and Composer A1678

**2019, Sept. 5**    **Litho.**    *Perf. 14*
3125 A1678 170c multi    3.75 1.90

A1679      Optical Illusions — A1680

**2019, Oct. 10**    **Litho.**    *Perf. 14*
3126 A1679 60c multi    1.40 .70
3127 A1680 80c multi    1.75 .90

Meeting of St. Francis of Assisi and the Sultan of Egypt, 800th Anniv. — A1681

| | | | |
|---|---|---|---|
| 2019, Oct. 10 | Litho. | | Perf. 14 |
| 3128 A1681 | 95c multi | 2.10 | 1.10 |

Annemarie Renger (1919-2008), First Female President of the Bundestag A1682

| | | | |
|---|---|---|---|
| 2019, Oct. 10 | Litho. | | Perf. 14 |
| 3129 A1682 | 155c blk & red | 3.50 | 1.75 |

**Flowers Type of 2005**

Designs: 30c, Taglilie (day lily). 370c, Fingerhut (foxglove).

| | | | |
|---|---|---|---|
| 2019-20 | Litho. | | Perf. 14 |
| 3130 A1165 | 30c multi | .70 | .35 |
| 3131 A1165 | 370c multi | 8.25 | 4.25 |

**Coil Stamp**
**Self-Adhesive**
*Die Cut Perf. 10¼x10*

| | | | |
|---|---|---|---|
| 3132 A1165 | 30c multi | .70 | .35 |

Issued: Nos. 3130, 3132, 1/2/20. 370c, 11/2.

Beat-Club, German Television Rock Music Series — A1683

| | | | |
|---|---|---|---|
| 2019, Nov. 2 | Litho. | | Perf. 13½x13¾ |
| 3133 A1683 | 110c multi | 2.50 | 1.25 |

Fritz Bauer (1903-68), Judge and Prosecutor A1684

| | | | |
|---|---|---|---|
| 2019, Nov. 2 | Litho. | | Perf. 13½x13¾ |
| 3134 A1684 | 270c multi | 6.00 | 3.00 |

Christmas A1685

| | | | |
|---|---|---|---|
| 2019, Nov. 2 | Litho. | | Perf. 13½x13¾ |
| 3135 A1685 | 80c multi | 1.75 | .90 |

**Booklet Stamp**
**Self-Adhesive**
**Size: 39x22mm**
*Die Cut Perf. 9¾*

| | | | |
|---|---|---|---|
| 3136 A1685 | 80c multi | 1.75 | .90 |
| a. | Booklet pane of 10 | 17.50 | |

Heidi, by Johanna Spyri (1827-1901) A1686

Pippi Longstocking, by Astrid Lindgren (1907-2002) A1687

| | | | |
|---|---|---|---|
| 2019, Dec. 5 | Litho. | | Perf. 13½x13¾ |
| 3137 A1686 | 60c multi | 1.40 | .70 |
| 3138 A1687 | 80c multi | 1.90 | .95 |

Characters from children's literature.

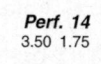

Theodor Fontane (1819-98), Writer — A1688

| | | | |
|---|---|---|---|
| 2019, Dec. 5 | Litho. | | Perf. 14 |
| 3139 A1688 | 155c multi | 3.50 | 1.75 |

Bonn and Siebengebirge (Seven Mountains) Area — A1689

Designs: Nos. 3140, 3142, Rhine River. Nos. 3141, 3143, Drachenburg Castle.

| | | | |
|---|---|---|---|
| 2020, Jan. 2 | Litho. | | Perf. 13¾ |
| 3140 A1689 | 60c multi | 1.40 | .70 |
| 3141 A1689 | 60c multi | 1.40 | .70 |
| a. | Horiz. pair, #3140-3141 | 2.80 | 1.40 |

**Booklet Stamps**
**Self-Adhesive**
**Size: 39x22mm**
*Die Cut Perf. 9¾ on 3 Sides*

| | | | |
|---|---|---|---|
| 3142 A1689 | 60c multi | 1.40 | .70 |
| 3143 A1689 | 60c multi | 1.40 | .70 |
| a. | Booklet pane of 10, 5 each #3142-3143 | 14.00 | |

Ludwig van Beethoven (1770-1827), Composer A1690

| | | | |
|---|---|---|---|
| 2020, Jan. 2 | Litho. | | Perf. 14 |
| 3144 A1690 | 80c multi | 1.90 | .95 |
| a. | Souvenir sheet of 1 | 1.90 | .95 |

**Booklet Stamp**
**Self-Adhesive**
*Die Cut Perf. 11¼x11¾*

| | | | |
|---|---|---|---|
| 3145 A1690 | 80c multi | 1.90 | .95 |
| a. | Booklet pane of 10 | 19.00 | |

Freedom of the Press — A1691

| | | | |
|---|---|---|---|
| 2020, Jan. 2 | Litho. | | Perf. 14 |
| 3146 A1691 | 95c multi | 2.10 | 1.10 |

Field with Poppies, by Vincent van Gogh (1853-90) A1692

| | | | |
|---|---|---|---|
| 2020, Jan. 2 | Litho. | | Perf. 14 |
| 3147 A1692 | 155c multi | 3.50 | 1.75 |

**Coil Stamp**
**Self-Adhesive**
*Die Cut Perf. 11¼x11½*

| | | | |
|---|---|---|---|
| 3148 A1692 | 155c multi | 3.50 | 1.75 |

Floating Angel, Sculpture by Ernst Barlach (1870-1938) — A1693

| | | | |
|---|---|---|---|
| 2020, Jan. 2 | Litho. | | Perf. 14 |
| 3149 A1693 | 270c multi | 6.00 | 3.00 |

**Booklet Stamp**
**Self-Adhesive**
*Die Cut Perf. 11¾x11¼*

| | | | |
|---|---|---|---|
| 3150 A1693 | 270c multi | 6.00 | 3.00 |
| a. | Booklet pane of 10 | 60.00 | |

Sustainable Development A1694

| | | | |
|---|---|---|---|
| 2020, Feb. 6 | Litho. | | Perf. 14 |
| 3151 A1694 | 80c multi | 1.75 | .90 |

Sesame Street, 50th Anniv. — A1695

| | | | |
|---|---|---|---|
| 2020, Mar. 2 | Litho. | | Perf. 13¾ |
| 3152 A1695 | 80c multi | 1.75 | .90 |

**Booklet Stamp**
**Self-Adhesive**
**Size: 39x22mm**
*Die Cut Perf. 10*

| | | | |
|---|---|---|---|
| 3153 A1695 | 80c multi | 1.75 | .90 |
| a. | Booklet pane of 10 | 17.50 | |

Lenticular Clouds A1696

Kelvin-Helmholtz Clouds — A1697

| | | | |
|---|---|---|---|
| 2020, Mar. 2 | Litho. | | Perf. 13¾ |
| 3154 A1696 | 80c multi | 1.75 | .90 |
| 3155 A1697 | 80c multi | 1.75 | .90 |

**Booklet Stamp**
**Self-Adhesive**
**Size: 39x22mm**
*Die Cut Perf. 10*

| | | | |
|---|---|---|---|
| 3156 A1696 | 80c multi | 1.75 | .90 |
| 3157 A1697 | 80c multi | 1.75 | .90 |
| a. | Booklet pane of 20, 10 each #3156-3157 | 35.00 | |

German Green Belt — A1698

| | | | |
|---|---|---|---|
| 2020, Mar. 2 | Litho. | | Perf. 13¾ |
| 3158 A1698 | 155c multi | 3.50 | 1.75 |

**Booklet Stamp**
**Self-Adhesive**
**Size: 39x22mm**
*Die Cut Perf. 9¾*

| | | | |
|---|---|---|---|
| 3159 A1698 | 155c multi | 3.50 | 1.75 |
| a. | Booklet pane of 10 | 35.00 | |

The German Green Belt was the land along the border between West and East Germany that remained undeveloped after reunification.

**Flowers Type of 2005**

Design: 50c, Zinnie (zinnia).

| | | | |
|---|---|---|---|
| 2020, Apr. 2 | Litho. | | Perf. 14 |
| 3160 A1165 | 50c multi | 1.10 | .55 |

Richard von Weizsäcker (1920-2015), German President A1699

| | | | |
|---|---|---|---|
| 2020, Apr. 2 | Litho. | | Perf. 13¾ |
| 3161 A1699 | 80c multi | 1.75 | .85 |

Marienplatz U-Bahn Station on Munich U3 and U6 Lines — A1700

| | | | |
|---|---|---|---|
| 2020, Apr. 2 | Litho. | | Perf. 13¾ |
| 3162 A1700 | 95c multi | 2.10 | 1.10 |

**Booklet Stamp**
**Self-Adhesive**
**Size: 39x22mm**
*Die Cut Perf. 9¾x10*

| | | | |
|---|---|---|---|
| 3163 A1700 | 95c multi | 2.10 | 1.10 |
| a. | Booklet pane of 10 | 21.00 | |

A1701

Optical Illusions — A1702

| | | | |
|---|---|---|---|
| 2020, Apr. 2 | Litho. | | Perf. 14 |
| 3164 A1701 | 110c multi | 2.40 | 1.25 |
| 3165 A1702 | 170c multi | 3.75 | 1.90 |

**Booklet Stamp**
**Self-Adhesive**
*Die Cut Perf. 11¼x11½*

| | | | |
|---|---|---|---|
| 3166 A1701 | 110c multi | 2.40 | 1.25 |
| a. | Booklet pane of 10 | 24.00 | |

Baron Hieronymus Karl Friedrich von Múnchausen (1720-97), Cavalry Captain and Teller of Implausible Stories of His Exploits — A1703

| | | | |
|---|---|---|---|
| 2020, May 7 | Litho. | | Perf. 13¾ |
| 3167 A1703 | 80c multi | 1.75 | .90 |

**Souvenir Sheet**

Thurn and Taxis Post Rider A1704

| | | | |
|---|---|---|---|
| 2020, May 7 | Litho. | | Perf. 13¾ |
| 3168 A1704 | 80c multi | 1.75 | .90 |

Europa.

Annaberger Kät Folk Festival, Annaberg-Buchholz, 500th Anniv. — A1705

| | | | |
|---|---|---|---|
| 2020, June 4 | Litho. | | Perf. 13¼ |
| 3169 A1705 | 95c multi | 2.10 | 1.10 |

St. Katharina Kasper (1820-98), Founder of Poor Handmaids of Jesus Christ — A1706

| | | | |
|---|---|---|---|
| 2020, June 4 | Litho. | | Perf. 13¼ |
| 3170 A1706 | 155c multi | 3.50 | 1.75 |

United Nations, 75th Anniv. — A1707

| | | | |
|---|---|---|---|
| 2020, June 4 | Litho. | | Perf. 13¼ |
| 3171 A1707 | 170c multi | 4.00 | 2.00 |

Schleimünde Lighthouse — A1708

**2020, July 2    Litho.    Perf. 13¾**
3172  A1708  60c multi                1.40  .70

**Coil Stamp**
**Self-Adhesive**
*Die Cut Perf. 10¼*

3173  A1708  60c multi                1.40  .70

German Presidency of the Council of the European Union — A1709

**2020, July 2    Litho.    Perf. 13½x13¾**
3174  A1709  80c multi                1.90  .95

Freiburg im Breisgau, 900th Anniv. — A1710

**2020, July 2    Litho.    Perf. 13½x13¾**
3175  A1710  80c multi                1.90  .95

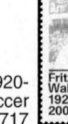

Outdoor Pool, Witten — A1711

Part of outdoor pool with denomination at: No. 3176, UL. No. 3177, LR.

**2020, July 2    Litho.    Perf. 13½x13¾**
3176  A1711  95c multi                2.25  1.10
3177  A1711  95c multi                2.25  1.10
  a.    Horiz. pair, #3176-3177       4.50  2.25

**Flowers Type of 2005**

Design: 200c, Purpur-knautie (knautia).

**2020, Aug. 6    Litho.    Perf. 14**
3178  A1165  200c multi               4.75  2.40

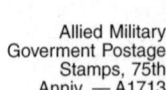

Georg Wilhem Friedrich Hegel (1770-1831), Philosopher A1712

**2020, Aug. 6    Litho.    Perf. 13¾**
3179  A1712  270c multi               6.50  3.25

Allied Military Goverment Postage Stamps, 75th Anniv. — A1713

**2020, Sept. 3    Litho.    Perf. 13¾**
3180  A1713  80c red & pale yel       1.90  .95

Stamp Day,

Juvenile Animals A1714

Designs: 80c, Juvenile otter. 95c, Juvenile dormouse.

**2020, Sept. 3    Litho.    Perf. 13½x13¾**
3181  A1714  80c multi                1.90  .95
3182  A1714  95c multi                1.90  1.10

Lore Lorentz (1920-94), Comedian A1715

**2020, Sept. 3    Litho.    Perf. 13¾x14**
3183  A1715  155c multi               3.75  1.90

Legend of Lorelei A1716

**2020, Oct. 1    Litho.    Perf. 13½x13¾**
3184  A1716  80c multi                1.90  .95

Fritz Walter (1920-2002), Soccer Player — A1717

**2020, Oct. 1    Litho.    Perf. 13¾**
3185  A1717  95c multi                2.25  1.10

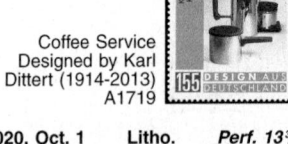

Women of the Reformation A1718

**2020, Oct. 1    Litho.    Perf. 13¾x14**
3186  A1718  370c multi               8.75  4.50

Coffee Service Designed by Karl Dittert (1914-2013) A1719

**2020, Oct. 1    Litho.    Perf. 13¾**
3187  A1719  155c multi               3.75  1.90

**Coil Stamp**
**Self-Adhesive**
*Die Cut Perf. 11½x11¼*

3188  A1719  155c multi               3.75  1.90

Tatort, German Television Series, 50th Anniv. — A1720

**2020, Nov. 2    Litho.    Perf. 13½x13¾**
3189  A1720  80c multi                1.90  .95

Christmas A1721

**2020, Nov. 2    Litho.    Perf. 13½x13¾**
3190  A1721  80c multi                1.90  .95

**Booklet Stamp**
**Self-Adhesive**
**Size: 39x22mm**
*Die Cut Perf. 9¾*

3191  A1721  80c multi                1.90  .95
  a.    Booklet pane of 10                 19.00

Vicky the Viking, Children's Book Character by Runer Jonsson A1722

Maya the Bee, Children's Book Character by Waldemar Bonsels A1723

**2020, Dec. 3    Litho.    Perf. 13½x13¾**
3192  A1722  60c multi                1.50  .75
3193  A1723  80c multi                2.00  1.00

The Pied Piper of Hamelin A1724

**2020, Dec. 3    Litho.    Perf. 13½x13¾**
3194  A1724  95c multi                2.40  1.25

Genuflection by Chancellor Willy Brandt (1913-92) at Memorial to Victims of Warsaw Ghetto Uprising, 50th Anniv. — A1725

**2020, Dec. 3    Litho.    Perf. 13¾**
3195  A1725  110c black               2.75  1.40
  a.    Souvenir sheet of 1           2.75  1.40

Housing Development Near Lübeck A1726

Aerial view of housing development with denomination at: Nos. 3196, 3198, UL. Nos. 3197, 3199, LR.

**2021, Jan. 7    Litho.    Perf. 13½x13¾**
3196  A1726  60c multi                1.50  .75
3197  A1726  60c multi                1.50  .75
  a.    Horiz. pair, #3196-3197       3.00  1.50

**Booklet Stamps**
**Self-Adhesive**
**Size: 39x23mm**
*Die Cut Perf. 9¾ on 3 Sides*

3198  A1726  60c multi                1.50  .75
3199  A1726  60c multi                1.50  .75
  a.    Booklet pane of 10, 5 each         15.00
        #3198-3199

Children's Mission Work, 175th Anniv. — A1727

**2021, Jan. 7    Litho.    Perf. 13½x13¾**
3200  A1727  80c yellow & black       2.00  1.00

Jewish Life in Germany, 1700th Anniv. — A1728

**2021, Feb. 4    Litho.    Perf. 13¾**
3201  A1728  80c multi                2.00  1.00

Friedrich Ebert (1871-1925), President of German Reich — A1729

**2021, Feb. 4    Litho.    Perf. 14x13¾**
3202  A1729  95c multi                2.40  1.25

"Digital Change" A1730

**2021, Feb. 4    Litho.    Perf. 13¾x14**
3203  A1730  80c multi                2.00  1.00

**Booklet Stamp**
**Self-Adhesive**
*Die Cut Perf. 13½x13¼*

3204  A1730  80c multi                2.00  1.00
  a.    Booklet pane of 10                 20.00
  b.    Die cut perf. 10              —    —
  c.    Booklet pane of 10 #3204b          —

No. 3204b also has a different dot structure than No. 3204, which is most noticeable in the denomination.

Beginning with Nos. 3203-3204, some German stamps will have printed on their right sides unique computer codes that will allow postal customers track postal mail bearing the stamps, and prevent the reuse of the stamps as each computer code is recorded as having gone through the mailstream.

"Die Sendung mit der Maus" Children's Television Series, 50th Anniv. A1731

**2021, Mar. 1    Litho.    Perf. 13¾x14**
3205  A1731  80c multi                2.00  1.00

**Booklet Stamp**
**Self-Adhesive**
*Die Cut Perf. 10¼x10*

3206  A1731  80c multi                2.00  1.00
  a.    Booklet pane of 10                 20.00

See footnote after No. 3204.

Uberseequartier U-Bahn Station on Hamburg U4 Line — A1732

Westend U-Bahn Station on Frankfurt C Line A1733

**2021, Mar. 1    Litho.    Perf. 13¾x14**
3207  A1732  95c multi                2.40  1.25
3208  A1733  270c multi               6.50  3.25

See footnote after No. 3204. See Nos. 3216, 3230.

Chess Matches Between Garry Kasparov and the Deep Blue Chess Supercomputer, 25th Anniv. — A1734

**2021, Mar. 1    Litho.    Perf. 13¾x14**
3209  A1734  110c multi               2.75  1.40

See footnote after No. 3204. See No. 3241.

2021 Federal Garden Show, Erfurt — A1735

**2021, Apr. 1    Litho.    Perf. 13½x13¾**
3210  A1735  80c multi                1.90  .95

Sebastian Kneipp
(1821-97), Priest
and Advocate of
Naturopathic
Medicine — A1736

**2021, Apr. 1    Litho.    Perf. 13¾**
3211  A1736  155c multi              3.75  1.90

Effelsberg Radio
Telescope, 50th
Anniv. — A1737

**2021, Apr. 1    Litho.    Perf. 14x13¾**
3212  A1737  155c multi              3.75  1.90
See No. 3227.

Invention of the
Harmonica, 200th
Anniv. — A1738

**2021, Apr. 1    Litho.    Perf. 14x13¾**
3213  A1738  190c multi              4.50  2.25

Endangered
Insects — A1739

**2021, May 6    Litho.    Perf. 14x13¾**
3214  A1739  80c multi               2.00  1.00
Europa.

Sophie Scholl
(1921-43), Executed
Anti-Nazi Political
Activist — A1740

**2021, May 6    Litho.    Perf. 13¾**
3215  A1740  80c multi               2.00  1.00

**Hamburg U-Bahn Station Type of 2020**
*Die Cut Perf. 10¼x10*
**2021, May 6    Litho.**
**Booklet Stamp**
**Self-Adhesive**
3216  A1732  95c multi               2.40  1.25
  a.    Booklet pane fo 10          24.00
See footnote after No. 3204.

Juvenile
European
Hamster
A1741

Juvenile
Alpine
Ibexes
A1742

**2021, June 10    Litho.    Perf. 13¾**
3217  A1741  60c multi               1.50  .75
3218  A1742  95c multi               2.25  1.10
See footnote after No. 3204. See No. 3229.

2020 European
Soccer
Championships
A1743

**2021, June 10    Litho.    Perf. 13¾**
3219  A1743  80c multi               1.90  .95
The 2020 European Soccer Championships were postponed until 2021 because of the COVID-19 pandemic.

Handstamps and
Signature of Joseph
Beuys (1921-86),
Painter and
Performance
Artist — A1744

**2021, June 10    Litho.    Perf. 13¾**
3220  A1744  155c multi              3.75  1.90

Diplomatic Relations Between
Germany and India, 70th
Anniv. — A1745

**2021, June 10    Litho.    Perf. 13¾**
3221  A1745  170c multi              4.00  2.00
See India No. 3254.

Tinsdal
Lighthouse — A1746

**2021, July 1    Litho.    Perf. 13¾**
3222  A1746  60c multi               1.50  .75

Thunderstorm — A1747

Supercell
A1748

**2021, July 1    Litho.    Perf. 13¾x14**
3223  A1747  80c multi               1.90  .95
3224  A1748  370c multi              8.75  4.50

**Booklet Stamp**
**Self-Adhesive**
*Die Cut Perf. 10¼x10*
3225  A1747  80c multi               1.90  .95
  a.    Booklet pane of 10          19.00
See footnote after No. 3204.

Automobile
Traffic and
Training
Route,
Cent.
A1750

**2021, July 1    Litho.    Perf. 13¾x14**
3226  A1750  155c multi              3.75  1.90
See footnote after No. 3204.

**Effelsberg Radio Telescope Type of 2021**
*Die Cut Perf. 11½x11¼*
**2021, Aug. 5    Litho.**
**Booklet Stamp**
**Self-Adhesive**
3227  A1737  155c multi              3.75  1.90
  a.    Booklet pane of 10          37.50

Fuggerei
Housing
Complex,
Augsburg, 500th
Anniv. — A1751

**2021, Aug. 5    Litho.    Perf. 13½x13¾**
3228  A1751  80c multi               1.90  .95

**Juvenile Alpine Ibexes Type of 2021**
*Die Cut Perf. 10¼x10*
**2021, Sept. 2    Litho.**
**Booklet Stamp**
**Self-Adhesive**
3229  A1742  95c multi               2.25  1.10
  a.    Booklet pane of 10          22.50
See footnote after No. 3204.

**Westend U-Bahn Station Type of 2021**
*Die Cut Perf. 10¼x10*
**2021, Sept. 2    Litho.**
**Booklet Stamp**
**Self-Adhesive**
3230  A1733  270c multi              6.25  3.25
  a.    Booklet pane of 10          62.50
See footnote after No. 3204.

Federal Training
Assistance Act, 50th
Anniv. — A1752

**2021, Sept. 2    Litho.    Perf. 14x13¾**
3231  A1752  80c multi               1.90  .95

Telephone Crisis
Counseling Hotlines,
65th Anniv. — A1753

**2021, Sept. 2    Litho.    Perf. 13¾**
3232  A1753  80c orange & lt orange  1.90  .95

Hildegard
Wegscheider (1871-
1953), Politician and
Equal Rights
Advocate — A1754

**2021, Sept. 2    Litho.    Perf. 13¾**
3233  A1754  95c multi               2.25  1.10

Optical
Illusion
A1755

**2021, Sept. 2    Litho.    Perf. 13¾x14**
3234  A1755  190c multi              4.50  2.25
See footnote after No. 3204.

Heinzelmännchen — A1756

Nibelungen
A1757

**2021, Oct. 7    Litho.    Perf. 13¾**
3235  A1756  60c multi               1.40  .70
3236  A1757  80c multi               1.90  .95
See footnote after No. 3204.

"Forests Protect the
Climate" — A1758

**2021, Oct. 7    Litho.    Perf. 13¾**
3237  A1758  80c multi               1.90  .95

Drops and
Rings, Mural by
1010 on
Building in
Berlin — A1759

**2021, Oct. 7    Litho.    Perf. 13¾**
3238  A1759  80c multi               1.90  .95
**Booklet Stamp**
**Self-Adhesive**
*Die Cut Perf. 10½*
3239  A1759  80c multi               1.90  .95
  a.    Booklet pane of 10          19.00
See footnote after No. 3204.

Butterflies, Mural by Youri Cansell on
Building in Thionville, France
A1760

**2021, Oct. 7    Litho.    Perf. 13¾**
3240  A1760  155c multi              3.75  1.90
See footnote after No. 3204.

**Deep Blue Chess Matches Type of 2021**
*Die Cut Perf. 10¼x10*
**2021, Nov. 2    Litho.**
**Booklet Stamp**
**Self-Adhesive**
3241  A1734  110c multi              2.50  1.25
  a.    Booklet pane of 10          25.00
See footnote after No. 3204.

German Dance
Sports Association,
Cent. — A1761

**2021, Nov. 2    Litho.    Perf. 13¾**
3242  A1761  80c multi               1.90  .95

"Polizeiruf
110,"
Television
Series,
50th Anniv.
A1762

**2021, Nov. 2    Litho.    Perf. 13¾**
3243  A1762  95c multi               2.25  1.10
See footnote after No. 3204.

## Souvenir Sheet

Robert Blum (1807-48),
Politician — A1763

**2021, Nov. 2**    **Litho.**    **Perf. 13¾**
3244 A1763 80c gold & multi    1.90   .95

Christmas
A1764

**2021, Nov. 2**    **Litho.**    **Perf. 13¾**
3245 A1764 80c multi    1.90   .95

### Booklet Stamp
### Self-Adhesive
### *Die Cut Perf. 10¼x10*
3246 A1764 80c multi    1.90   .95
*a.*   Booklet pane of 10    19.00

See footnote after No. 3204.

Bibi and Tina, Characters From
Children's Radio and Television Series
A1765

The Three Investigators, Children's
Audio Drama and Book
Series — A1766

**2021, Dec. 2**    **Litho.**    **Perf. 13¾**
3247 A1765 60c multi    1.40   .70
3248 A1766 80c multi    1.90   .95

See footnote after No. 3204.

Doctors Without
Borders, 50th
Anniv. — A1767

**2021, Dec. 2**    **Litho.**    **Perf. 13¾**
3249 A1767 270c multi    6.25 3.25

Water Lily With
Envelopes as
Petals
A1768

Origami Carrier
Pigeon
A1769

Ship with
Envelopes as
Sails — A1770

Envelope as
Kite — A1771

Pen as
Lighthouse — A1772

---

**2021-22**    **Litho.**    **Perf. 13¾x14**
3250 A1768   5c multi    .25   .25
3251 A1769   85c multi    2.00 1.00
3252 A1770 100c multi    2.25 1.10
3253 A1771 160c multi    3.75 1.90
3254 A1772 275c multi    6.25 3.25
   Nos. 3250-3254 (5)    14.50 7.50

### Booklet Stamps
### Self-Adhesive
### *Die Cut Perf. 10*
3255 A1768   5c multi    .25   .25
*a.*   Booklet pane of 10    1.25
3256 A1769   85c multi    2.00 1.00
*a.*   Booklet pane of 10    20.00
3257 A1770 100c multi    2.25 1.10
*a.*   Booklet pane of 10    22.50
3258 A1771 160c multi    3.75 1.90
*a.*   Booklet pane of 10    37.50
3259 A1772 275c multi    6.25 3.25
*a.*   Booklet pane of 10    62.50
   Nos. 3255-3259 (5)    14.50 7.50

See footnote after No. 3204. Issued: Nos.
3250-3253, 3255-3258, 12/2; No. 3254,
1/3/22.; No. 3259, 2/3/22.

### Flowers Type of 2005

Designs: 32c, Schneeglöckchen (snowdrops). 37c, Rotklee (red clover).

**2022, Jan. 3**    **Litho.**    **Perf. 14**
3260 A1165 32c multi    .75   .35
3261 A1165 37c multi    .85   .40

### Coil Stamps
### Self-Adhesive
### *Die Cut Perf. 10*
3262 A1165 32c multi    .75   .35
3263 A1165 37c multi    .85   .40

Annette von Droste-Hülshoff (1797-
1848), Poet — A1773

**2022, Jan. 3**    **Litho.**    **Perf. 13¾**
3264 A1773 70c multi    1.60   .80

See footnote after No. 3204.

David Bowie (1947-2016), Rock
Musician — A1774

**2022, Jan. 3**    **Litho.**    **Perf. 13¾**
3265 A1774 85c multi    2.00 1.00

See footnote after No. 3204.

Otto Braun (1872-1955), Prime
Minister of Prussia — A1775

**2022, Jan. 3**    **Litho.**    **Perf. 13¾**
3266 A1775 100c multi    2.25 1.10

See footnote after No. 3204.

Heinrich
Schliemann
(1822-90),
Archaeologist
and Discoverer
of
Troy — A1776

### Litho. & Engr.
**2022, Jan. 3**    **Perf. 13¾**
3267 A1776 110c multi    2.50 1.25

See footnote after No. 3204.

---

Stamp and
Pearl in Shell
A1777

Letters on Tree
A1779

Windmill With
Letters for
Blades
A1778

Envelope,
Letter and Pen
Orbiting Planet
A1780

Balloons With
Attached
Letters
A1781

Envelopes
Trailing Biplane
A1782

Letter Sunset
A1783

Envelopes and
Crescent Moon
A1784

Envelope, Colored
Pencils and Marker
Above Earth — A1785

**2022**    **Litho.**    **Perf. 13¾**
3268 A1777   32c multi    .65   .30
3269 A1778   37c multi    .75   .35
3270 A1779   45c multi    .90   .45
3271 A1780   70c multi    1.60   .80
3272 A1781   95c multi    1.90   .95
3273 A1782 110c multi    2.50 1.25
3274 A1783 170c multi    3.50 1.75
3275 A1784 195c multi    4.50 2.25
3276 A1785 225c multi    5.00 2.50
   Nos. 3268-3276 (9)    21.30 10.60

### Coil Stamps
### Self-Adhesive
### *Die Cut Perf. 10*
3277 A1777   32c multi    .65   .30
3278 A1778   37c multi    .75   .35
3279 A1779   45c multi    .90   .45
   Nos. 3277-3279 (3)    2.30 1.10

### Booklet Stamp
3280 A1780   70c multi    1.60   .80
*a.*   Booklet pane of 10    16.00

Issued: Nos. 3271, 3273, 3275, 3276, 3280,
3/1; Nos. 3268, 3269, 3270, 3272, 3277-3279,
8/4; No. 3274, 7/7.
See footnote after No. 3204.

Peacock and
Crane, Graffiti
Art by
Jeroo — A1786

**2022, Feb. 3**    **Litho.**    **Perf. 13¾**
3282 A1786 160c multi    3.75 1.90

See footnote after No. 3204.

---

Soccer Ball, Feet of Soccer Players
and Quotation of Sepp Herberger
A1787

**2022, Mar. 1**    **Litho.**    **Perf. 13¾**
3283 A1787 85c multi    1.90   .95

Sepp Herberger (1897-1977), soccer player
and manager. See footnote after No. 3204.

German
Children's
Fund, 50th
Anniv.
A1788

**2022, Mar. 1**    **Litho.**    **Perf. 13¾**
3284 A1788 85c multi    1.90   .95

See footnote after No. 3204.

Benjamin Blümchen, Character from
Animated Children's Television Show
A1789

**2022, Mar. 1**    **Litho.**    **Perf. 13¾**
3285 A1789 85c multi    1.90   .95

### Booklet Stamp
### Self-Adhesive
### *Die Cut Perf. 10¼x10*
3286 A1789 85c multi    1.90   .95
*a.*   Booklet pane of 10    19.00

See footnote after No. 3204.

Heidelberger Platz U-Bahn Station on
Berlin U3 Line — A1790

**2022, Mar. 1**    **Litho.**    **Perf. 13¾**
3287 A1790 275c multi    6.25 3.25

See footnote after No. 3204.

Juvenile
Badger
A1791

Juvenile
Lynx
A1792

**2022, Apr. 7**    **Litho.**    **Perf. 13¾**
3288 A1791 85c multi    1.90   .95
3289 A1792 85c multi    1.90   .95

See footnote after No. 3204.

Aurora
Borealis
A1793

**2022, Apr. 7**    **Litho.**    **Perf. 13¾**
3290 A1793 100c multi    2.10 1.10

See footnote after No. 3204.

Book and Duke Augustus II of
Brunswick-Wolfenbüttel (1579-
1666) — A1794

**2022, Apr. 7     Litho.     Perf. 13¾**
3291  A1794  195c multi          4.25  2.10
Herzog August Library, Wolfenbüttel, 450th
anniv. See footnote after No. 3204.

Swordsman
Battling
Dragon
A1795

**2022, May 5     Litho.     Perf. 13¾**
3292  A1795  85c multi          1.90  .95
Europa. See footnote after No. 3204.

Otl Aicher (1922-91), Graphic
Designer and Typographer — A1796

**2022, May 5     Litho.     Perf. 13¾**
3293  A1796  160c multi          3.50  1.75
See footnote after No. 3204.

Organ
Donation
A1797

**2022, June 2     Litho.     Perf. 13¾**
3294  A1797  85c multi          1.90  .95
See footnote after No. 3204.

Stockholm World Environment
Conference, 50th Anniv. — A1798

**2022, June 2     Litho.     Perf. 13¾**
3295  A1798  370c multi          8.00  4.00
See footnote after No. 3204.

Aerial View of
Sylvensteinsee — A1799

Part of aerial view of: No. 3296, Lake. No.
3297, Delta.

**2022, June 2     Litho.     Perf. 13¾**
3296  A1799  100c multi          2.25  1.10
3297  A1799  100c multi          2.25  1.10
a.    Horiz. pair, #3296-3297    4.50  2.25
See footnote after No. 3204.

48th Group of 7 Conference, Schloss
Elmau — A1800

**2022, June 23     Litho.     Perf. 13¾**
3298  A1800  85c multi          1.75  .90
See footnote after No. 3204.

Friedrichsort
Lighthouse — A1801

**2022, July 7     Litho.     Perf. 13¾**
3299  A1801  70c multi          1.50  .75
See footnote after No. 3204.

Spiderman
A1802

**2022, July 7     Litho.     Perf. 13¾**
3300  A1802  85c multi          1.75  .85
See footnote after No. 3204.

Winning Art in Children's Stamp
Design Contest with Theme of
Environmental Protection — A1803

**2022, July 7     Litho.     Perf. 13¾**
3301  A1803  85c multi          1.75  .85
See footnote after No. 3204.

Stendal,
1000th
Anniv.
A1804

**2022, July 7     Litho.     Perf. 13¾**
3302  A1804  85c multi          1.75  .85
See footnote after No. 3204.

Hans-Jürgen Wischnewski (1922-
2005), Minister for Economic
Cooperation — A1805

**2022, July 7     Litho.     Perf. 13¾**
3303  A1805  100c multi          2.10  1.10
See footnote after No. 3204.

Gregor
Mendel
(1822-84),
Abbot and
Biologist
A1806

**2022, July 7     Litho.     Perf. 13¾**
3304  A1806  110c multi          2.25  1.10
See footnote after No. 3204.

Heumarkt
U-Bahn
Station,
Cologne
A1807

**2022, Aug. 4     Litho.     Perf. 13¾x14**
3305  A1807  85c multi          1.75  .85
See footnote after No. 3204.

Plenary Assembly of World Council of
Churches, Karlsruhe
A1808

**2022, Aug. 4     Litho.     Perf. 13¾x14**
3306  A1808  160c multi          3.25  1.60
See footnote after No. 3204.

Message in a
Bottle
A1809

Pencils and
Letters on
Roller Coaster
A1810

Mountains
Made of Letters
and Delivery
Cyclist
A1811

Pencils With
Wings
A1812

Rainbow and
Open Envelope
A1813

Stamp as Hang
Glider
A1815

Butterfly
Envelope
A1814

Stamp in
Lightbulb
A1816

**2022-23     Litho.     Perf. 13¾x14**
3307  A1809  10c multi          .30  .30
3308  A1810  30c multi          .65  .35
3309  A1811  33c multi          .75  .35
3310  A1812  38c multi          .85  .40
3311  A1813  48c multi          1.10  .55
3312  A1814  50c multi          1.00  .50
3313  A1815  61c multi          1.40  .70
3314  A1816  370c multi          7.50  3.75
      Nos. 3307-3314 (8)          13.55 6.90

**Coil Stamps**
**Self-Adhesive**
**Die Cut Perf. 10**
3315  A1810  30c multi          .65  .35
3316  A1811  33c multi          .75  .35
3317  A1812  38c multi          .85  .40
3318  A1813  48c multi          1.10  .55
3319  A1815  61c multi          1.40  .70
      Nos. 3315-3319 (5)          4.75  2.35

Issued: 10c, 11/2; Nos. 3312, 3314,
9/1;Nos. 3308-3311, 3313, 3315-3319, 1/5/23.
See footnote after No. 3204.

Neuschwanstein Castle,
Hohenschwangau — A1817

**2022, Sept. 1     Litho.     Perf. 13¾x14**
3320  A1817  85c multi          1.75  .85
See footnote after No. 3204.

Pumuckl, Character From Children's
Radio and Film Series
A1818

The Smurfs, Characters From
Children's Comic, Television and Film
Series
A1819

**2022, Sept. 1     Litho.     Perf. 13¾x14**
3321  A1818  85c multi          1.75  .85
3322  A1819  85c multi          1.75  .85
See footnote after No. 3204.

1947 and 2015 Views of Cologne
Cathedral and Hohenzollern
Bridge — A1820

**2022, Oct. 6     Litho.     Perf. 13¾x14**
3323  A1820  70c multi          1.40  .70
See footnote after No. 3204.

Black
Panther
A1821

**2022, Oct. 6     Litho.     Perf. 13¾x14**
3324  A1821  85c multi          1.75  .85
See footnote after No. 3204.

Baden No.
4b — A1822

**2022, Oct. 6     Litho.     Perf. 13¾x14**
3325  A1822  85c multi          1.75  .85
a.    Souvenir sheet of 1          1.75  .85
Stamp Day. See footnote after No. 3204.

Postcrossing — A1823

**2022, Oct. 6     Litho.     Perf. 13¾x14**
3326  A1823  95c multi          1.90  .95
See footnote after No. 3204.

Diversity of Germany A1824

**2022, Nov. 2    Litho.    Perf. 13¾x14**
3327   A1824   85c multi           1.75   .85
See footnote after No. 3204.

German Caritas Association, 125th Anniv. — A1825

**2022, Nov. 2    Litho.    Perf. 13¾x14**
3328   A1825   85c multi           1.75   .90
See footnote after No. 3204.

"Rockpalast," German Rock Music Television Series — A1826

**2022, Nov. 2    Litho.    Perf. 13¾x14**
3329   A1826   160c multi          3.50   1.75
See footnote after No. 3204.

Christmas A1827

**2022, Nov. 2    Litho.    Perf. 13¾x14**
3330   A1827   85c multi           1.75   .90

**Booklet Stamp**
**Self-Adhesive**
*Die Cut Perf. 10¼x10*
3331   A1827   85c multi           1.75   .90
a.    Booklet pane of 10        17.50
See footnote after No. 3204.

Line from *Almansor,* Play by Heinrich Heine (1797-1856), Writer — A1828

**2022, Dec. 1    Litho.    Perf. 13¾x14**
3332   A1828   195c multi         4.00   2.00
See footnote after No. 3204.

Mainau Island A1829

Zollverein Colliery, Essen A1830

**2023, Jan. 5    Litho.    Perf. 13¾**
3333   A1829   85c multi          1.90   .95
3334   A1830   110c multi         2.40   1.25
See footnote after No. 3204.

Organ Building and Music, UNESCO Intangible Cultural Heritage A1831

**2023, Jan. 5    Litho.    Perf. 13¾**
3335   A1831   275c multi         6.00   3.00
See footnote after No. 3204.

## SEMI-POSTAL STAMPS

### Issues of the Republic

Nos. 83, 83d, 100, 100a, 100d Surcharged

**1919, May 1    Wmk. 125    Perf. 14**
B1   A16   10pf + 5pf on #83d    .75   4.25
B2   A22   15pf + 5pf on #100    .75   4.50
Set, never hinged              5.25

The surtax was for the war wounded.

"Planting Charity" — SP1

**1922, Dec. 11    Litho.    Wmk. 126**
B3   SP1   6m + 4m ultra & brn   .25   22.50
B4   SP1   12m + 8m red org & bl
             gray                .25   22.50
Set, never hinged              1.75

Nos. 221, 225 and 196 Surcharged

**1923, Feb. 19**
B5   A34   5m + 100m             .25   9.00
B6   A29   15m + 500m            .25   22.50
a.    Inverted surcharge       75.00
      Never hinged             190.00
B7   A32   20m + 1000m           2.00   82.50
a.    Inverted surcharge       975.00   3,750.
      Never hinged           2,100.
b.    Green background invert-
      ed                      375.00   1,700.
      Never hinged            750.00
      Nos. B5-B7 (3)           2.50   114.00
Set, never hinged              7.50

Note following No. 160 applies to Nos. B1-B7.

Feeding the Hungry — SP2

Designs: 10pf+30pf, Giving drink to the thirsty. 20pf+60pf, Clothing the naked. 50pf+1.50m, Healing the sick.

**1924, Feb. 25    Typo.    Perf. 14½x15**
B8    SP2   5pf + 15pf dk grn    1.75   3.50
B9    SP2   10pf + 30pf ver      1.75   3.50
B10   SP2   20pf + 60pf dk blue  5.75   8.25
B11   SP2   50pf + 1.50m red
             brn                22.50   65.00
      Nos. B8-B11 (4)          31.75   80.25
Set, never hinged             120.00

The surtax was used for emergency aid. See No. B58.

Prussia — SP6

**1925, Dec. 15    Perf. 14**
**Inscribed: "1925"**
B12   SP6   5pf + 5pf shown      .60   1.90
B13   SP6   10pf + 10pf Bavaria  1.75   1.90
B14   SP6   20pf + 20pf Saxony   9.00   13.50
a.    Bkt. pane of 2 + 2 labels 350.00  1,050.
      Never hinged             600.00
      Nos. B12-B14 (3)         11.35   17.30
Set, never hinged             37.50

**1926, Dec. 1    Inscribed: "1926"**
B15   SP6   5pf + 5pf Wurt-
             temberg            1.75   2.25
B16   SP6   10pf + 10pf Baden   2.25   3.00
a.    Bkt. pane of 6 + 2 labels 270.00  650.00
      Never hinged             450.00
B17   SP6   25pf + 25pf Thurin-
             gia                9.25   19.00
B18   SP6   50pf + 50pf Hesse   42.50   97.50
      Nos. B15-B18 (4)         55.75   121.75
Set, never hinged             175.00

Nos. B15-B16 are usually found with sideways watermarks. Both exist with an upright watermark, which is very scarce. No. B18 is usually found with an upright watermark. Examples of No. B18 with a sideways watermark are scarce.

See Nos. B23-B32.

Pres. Paul von Hindenburg — SP13

**1927, Sept. 26    Photo.**
B19   SP13   8pf dark green      .75   1.50
a.    Bkt. pane, 4 #B19, 3 #B20
      + label                 110.00   190.00
      Never hinged            180.00
B20   SP13   15pf scarlet       1.15   2.25
B21   SP13   25pf deep blue     9.50   21.00
B22   SP13   50pf bister brown  11.50   24.00
      Nos. B19-B22 (4)         22.90   48.75
Set, never hinged             90.00

80th birthday of Pres. Hindenburg. The stamps were sold at double face value. The surtax was given to a fund for War Invalids.

### Arms Type of 1925

Design: 8pf+7pf, Mecklenberg-Schwerin.

**1928, Nov. 15    Typo.**
**Design Type SP6**
**Inscribed: "1928"**
B23   5pf + 5pf Hamburg        .55   3.75
B24   8pf + 7pf multi          .45   3.75
a.    Bkt. pane, 4 #B24, 3 #B25 +
      label                   225.00   450.00
      Never hinged            400.00
B25   15pf + 15pf Oldenburg    .70   3.75
B26   25pf + 25pf Brunswick    14.50   50.00
B27   50pf + 50pf Anhalt       37.50   90.00
      Nos. B23-B27 (5)         53.70   151.25
Set, never hinged             180.00

Nos. B23-B26 are valued with sideways watermark. All exist with upright watermark, which is scarce to very rare.

**1929, Nov. 4    Inscribed: "1929"**
Coats of Arms: 8pf+4pf, Lippe-Detmold. 25pf+10pf, Mecklenburg-Strelitz. 50pf+40pf, Schaumburg-Lippe.

B28   SP6   5pf + 2pf Bremen    .75   1.90
a.    Bkt. pane of 6 + 2 labels 90.00   135.00
      Never hinged            150.00
B29   SP6   8pf + 4pf multi     .85   1.90
a.    Bkt. pane, 4 #B29, 3 #B30
      + label                 115.00   210.00
      Never hinged            190.00
B30   SP6   15pf + 5pf Lubeck   1.20   1.50
B31   SP6   25pf + 10pf multi   16.50   50.00
B32   SP6   50pf + 40pf choc,
             ocher & red        37.50   90.00
a.    "PE" for "PF"           150.00   375.00
      Never hinged            450.00
      Nos. B28-B32 (5)         56.80   145.30
Set, never hinged             180.00

Cathedral of Aachen SP24

Brandenburg Gate, Berlin SP25

Castle of Marienwerder SP26

Statue of St. Kilian and Marienburg Fortress at Würzburg SP27

**Souvenir Sheet**
**Wmk. 223**
**1930, Sept. 12    Engr.    Perf. 14**
B33   Sheet of 4              425.00   1,500.
      Never hinged          1,200.
a.    SP24 8pf + 4pf dark green  30.00   105.00
      Never hinged             82.50
b.    SP25 15pf + 5pf carmine  30.00   105.00
      Never hinged             82.50
c.    SP26 25pf + 10p dark blue  30.00   105.00
      Never hinged             82.50
d.    SP27 50pf + 40pf dark
             brown              30.00   105.00
      Never hinged             82.50

Intl. Phil. Exhib., Berlin, Sept. 12-21, 1930. No. B33 is watermarked Eagle on each stamp and "IPOSTA"-"1930" in the margins. Size: approximately 105x150. Each holder of an admission ticket was entitled to purchase one sheet. The ticket cost 1m and the sheet 1.70m (face value 98pf, charity 59pf, special paper 13pf).

The margin of the souvenir sheet is ungummed.

### Types of International Philatelic Exhibition Issue

**1930, Nov. 1    Wmk. 126**
B34   SP24   8 + 4pf dp green   .90   1.90
a.    Bkt. pane of 7 + label    82.50   170.00
      Never hinged            145.00
b.    Bkt. pane, 3 #B34, 4
      #B35 + label            105.00   180.00
      Never hinged            175.00
B35   SP25   15 + 5pf car      1.10   2.25
B36   SP26   25 + 10pf dk blue  7.75   22.50
B37   SP27   50 + 40pf dp brn  21.00   82.50
      Nos. B34-B37 (4)         30.75   109.15
Set, never hinged             105.00

The surtax was for charity.

The Zwinger at Dresden SP28

Breslau City Hall SP29

Heidelberg Castle SP30

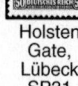

Holsten Gate, Lübeck SP31

**1931, Nov. 1**
B38   SP28   8 + 4pf dk grn    .55   2.25
a.    Bkt. pane of 7 + label    90.00   170.00
      Never hinged            150.00
b.    Bkt. pane, 3 #B38, 4
      #B39 + label             97.50   180.00
      Never hinged            170.00
B39   SP29   15 + 5pf carmine   .55   2.25
B40   SP30   25 + 10pf dk blue  9.50   30.00
B41   SP31   50 + 40pf dp
             brown             27.50   75.00
      Nos. B38-B41 (4)         38.10   109.50
Set, never hinged             180.00

The surtax was for charity.

Nos. B38-B39 Surcharged

**1932, Feb. 2**
B42   SP28   6 + 4pf on 8+4pf   4.25   9.75
B43   SP29   12 + 3pf on 15+5pf  5.00   11.50
Set, never hinged             45.00

Wartburg Castle SP32

Stolzenfels Castle SP33

Nuremberg Castle SP34

Lichtenstein Castle SP35

Marburg Castle — SP36

### 1932, Nov. 1 — Engr.

| | | | | |
|---|---|---|---|---|
| B44 | SP32 | 4 + 2pf lt blue | .80 | 1.90 |
| a. | | Bklt. pane, 5 #B44, 5 #B45 | 45.00 | 85.00 |
| | | Never hinged | 75.00 | |
| B45 | SP33 | 6 + 4pf olive grn | 1.00 | 1.90 |
| B46 | SP34 | 12 + 3pf lt red | .65 | 1.90 |
| b. | | Bklt. pane of 8 + 2 labels | 45.00 | 85.00 |
| | | Never hinged | 75.00 | |
| B47 | SP35 | 25 + 10pf dp blue | 8.00 | 18.00 |
| B48 | SP36 | 40 + 40pf brn vio | 21.00 | 65.00 |
| | | Nos. B44-B48 (5) | 37.95 | 88.70 |
| | | Set, never hinged | 145.00 | |

The surtax was for charity.

"Tannhäuser" — SP37

Designs: 4pf+2pf, "Der Fliegende Hollander." 5pf+2pf, "Das Rheingold." 6pf+4pf, "Die Meistersinger." 8pf+4pf, "Die Walküre." 12pf+3pf, "Siegfried." 20pf+10pf, "Tristan und Isolde." 25pf+15pf, "Lohengrin." 40pf+35pf, "Parsifal."

### Wmk. Swastikas (237)
### 1933, Nov. 1 — Perf. 13½x13

| | | | | |
|---|---|---|---|---|
| B49 | SP37 | 3 + 2pf bis brn | 3.75 | 5.75 |
| B50 | SP37 | 4 + 2pf dk blue | 2.50 | 2.25 |
| b. | | Bklt. pane, 5 #B50, 5 #B52 | 135.00 | 250.00 |
| | | Never hinged | 225.00 | |
| B51 | SP37 | 5 + 2pf brt grn | 6.25 | 6.75 |
| B52 | SP37 | 6 + 4pf gray grn | 2.50 | 2.25 |
| B53 | SP37 | 8 + 4pf dp org | 3.75 | 3.75 |
| b. | | Bklt. pane, 5 #B53, 4 #B54 + label | 135.00 | 250.00 |
| | | Never hinged | 225.00 | |
| B54 | SP37 | 12 + 3pf brn red | 3.75 | 2.60 |
| B55 | SP37 | 20 + 10pf blue | 190.00 | 190.00 |
| B56 | SP37 | 25 + 15pf ultra | 45.00 | 37.50 |
| B57 | SP37 | 40 + 35pf mag | 130.00 | 130.00 |
| | | Nos. B49-B57 (9) | 387.50 | 380.85 |
| | | Set, never hinged | 2,360. | |

### Perf. 13½x14

| | | | | |
|---|---|---|---|---|
| B50a | SP37 | 4 + 2pf dark blue | 2.75 | 3.00 |
| B52a | SP37 | 6 + 4pf gray grn | 2.75 | 5.00 |
| B53a | SP37 | 8 + 4pf dp org | 3.50 | 4.25 |
| B54a | SP37 | 12 + 3pf brn red | 3.50 | 6.50 |
| B55a | SP37 | 20 + 10pf blue | 135.00 | 97.50 |
| | | Nos. B50a-B55a (5) | 147.50 | 116.25 |
| | | Set, never hinged | 822.00 | |

### Types of Semi-Postal Stamps of 1924 Issue Overprinted
### Souvenir Sheet

### 1933, Nov. 29 — Typo. — Perf. 14½

| | | | | |
|---|---|---|---|---|
| B58 | | Sheet of 4 | 1,150. | 7,500. |
| | | Never hinged | 4,500. | |
| a. | SP2 | 5 + 15pf dark green | 90.00 | 375.00 |
| b. | SP2 | 10 + 30pf vermilion | 90.00 | 375.00 |
| c. | SP2 | 20 + 60pf dark blue | 90.00 | 375.00 |
| d. | SP2 | 50pf + 1.50m dk brown | 90.00 | 375.00 |
| | | Any single, never hinged | 225.00 | |

The Swastika watermark covers the four stamps and above them appears a further watermark "10 Jahre Deutsche Nothilfe" and "1923-1933" below. Sheet size: 208x148mm. The margin of the souvenir sheet is ungummed.

---

Businessman SP46

Judge SP54

Designs: 4pf+2pf, Blacksmith. 5pf+2pf, Mason. 6pf+4f, Miner. 8pf+4pf, Architect. 12pf+3pf, Farmer. 20pf+10pf, Agricultural Chemist. 25pf+15pf, Sculptor.

### 1934, Nov. 5 — Engr. — Perf. 13x13½

| | | | | |
|---|---|---|---|---|
| B59 | SP46 | 3 + 2pf brown | 1.30 | 1.50 |
| B60 | SP46 | 4 + 2pf black | .75 | 1.50 |
| a. | | Bklt. pane, 5 #B60, 5 #B62 | 52.50 | 102.50 |
| | | Never hinged | 90.00 | |
| B61 | SP46 | 5 + 2pf green | 5.75 | 7.50 |
| B62 | SP46 | 6 + 4pf dull grn | .75 | .60 |
| B63 | SP46 | 8 + 4pf org brn | 1.30 | 1.90 |
| a. | | Bklt. pane, 5 #B63, 4 #B64 + label | 82.50 | 150.00 |
| | | Never hinged | 135.00 | |
| B64 | SP46 | 12 + 3pf hn brn | .75 | .60 |
| B65 | SP46 | 20 + 10pf Prus bl | 15.00 | 21.00 |
| B66 | SP46 | 25 + 15pf ultra | 16.50 | 21.00 |
| B67 | SP54 | 40 + 35pf plum | 35.00 | 67.50 |
| | | Nos. B59-B67 (9) | 77.10 | 123.10 |
| | | Set, never hinged | 450.00 | |

### Souvenir Sheet

SP55

### 1935, June 23 — Wmk. 241 — Perf. 14

| | | | | |
|---|---|---|---|---|
| B68 | SP55 | Sheet of 4 | 975.00 | 825.00 |
| a. | | 3pf red brown | 34.00 | 37.50 |
| b. | | 6pf dark green | 34.00 | 37.50 |
| c. | | 12pf dark carmine | 34.00 | 37.50 |
| d. | | 25pf dark blue | 34.00 | 37.50 |

Watermarked cross on each stamp and "OSTROPA 1935" in the margins of the sheet. Size: 148x104mm. 1.70m was the price of a ticket of admission to the Intl. Exhib., Königsberg, June 23-July 3, 1935.

Because the gum on No. B68 contains sulphuric acid and tends to damage the sheet, most collectors prefer to remove it. **Catalogue unused values are for sheet and singles without gum.**

East Prussia — SP59

Designs (Costumes of Various Sections of Germany): 4pf+3pf, Silesia. 5pf+3pf, Rhineland. 6pf+4pf, Lower Saxony. 8pf+4pf, Brandenburg. 12pf+6pf, Black Forest. 15pf+10pf, Hesse. 25pf+15pf, Upper Bavaria. 30pf+20pf, Friesland. 40pf+35pf, Franconia.

### Wmk. Swastikas (237)
### 1935, Oct. 4 — Perf. 14x13½

| | | | | |
|---|---|---|---|---|
| B69 | SP59 | 3 + 2pf dk brown | .35 | .40 |
| a. | | Bklt. pane, 4 #B69, 5 #B74 + label | 42.50 | 75.00 |
| | | Never hinged | 67.50 | |
| B70 | SP59 | 4 + 3pf gray | 1.20 | 1.50 |
| B71 | SP59 | 5 + 3pf emerald | .35 | 1.00 |
| a. | | Bklt. pane, 5 #B71, 5 #B72 | 27.00 | 50.00 |
| | | Never hinged | 45.00 | |
| B72 | SP59 | 6 + 4pf dk green | .25 | .40 |
| B73 | SP59 | 8 + 4pf yel brn | 1.75 | 1.50 |
| B74 | SP59 | 12 + 6pf dk car | .25 | .40 |
| B75 | SP59 | 15 + 10pf red brn | 4.25 | 5.75 |
| B76 | SP59 | 25 + 15pf ultra | 8.25 | 6.00 |
| B77 | SP59 | 30 + 20pf olive brn | 9.25 | 19.50 |
| B78 | SP59 | 40 + 35pf plum | 8.50 | 14.50 |
| | | Nos. B69-B78 (10) | 34.40 | 50.95 |
| | | Set, never hinged | 135.00 | |

Skating — SP69

12+6pf, Ski jump. 25+15pf, Bobsledding.

---

### 1935, Nov. 25 — Perf. 13½

| | | | | |
|---|---|---|---|---|
| B79 | SP69 | 6 + 4pf green | .90 | 1.35 |
| B80 | SP69 | 12 + 6pf carmine | 1.75 | 1.20 |
| B81 | SP69 | 25 + 15pf ultra | 7.50 | 7.50 |
| | | Nos. B79-B81 (3) | 10.15 | 10.05 |
| | | Set, never hinged | 50.00 | |

Winter Olympic Games held in Bavaria, Feb. 6-16, 1936.

### 1936, May 8

Designs: 3pf+2pf, Horizontal bar. 4pf+3pf, Diving. 6pf+4pf, Soccer. 8pf+4pf, Throwing javelin. 12pf+6pf, Torch runner. 15pf+10pf, Fencing. 25pf+15pf, Sculling. 40pf+35pf, Equestrian.

| | | | | |
|---|---|---|---|---|
| B82 | SP69 | 3 + 2pf brown | .30 | .45 |
| a. | | Bklt. pane, 5 #B82, 5 #B86 | 27.00 | 50.00 |
| | | Never hinged | 45.00 | |
| B83 | SP69 | 4 + 3pf indigo | .25 | .75 |
| a. | | Bklt. pane, 5 #B83, 5 #B84 | 27.00 | 50.00 |
| | | Never hinged | 45.00 | |
| B84 | SP69 | 4 + 4pf green | .25 | .45 |
| B85 | SP69 | 8 + 4pf red org | 3.00 | 1.30 |
| B86 | SP69 | 12 + 6pf carmine | .40 | .45 |
| B87 | SP69 | 15 + 10pf brn vio | 5.50 | 3.00 |
| B88 | SP69 | 25 + 15pf ultra | 3.00 | 3.75 |
| B89 | SP69 | 40 + 35pf violet | 5.50 | 7.50 |
| | | Nos. B82-B89 (8) | 18.20 | 17.65 |
| | | Set, never hinged | 105.00 | |

Summer Olympic Games, Berlin, 8/1-16/36. See Nos. B91-B92.

### Souvenir Sheet

Horse Race — SP80

### 1936, June 22 — Wmk. 237 — Perf. 14

| | | | | |
|---|---|---|---|---|
| B90 | SP80 | 42pf brown | 12.00 | 13.50 |
| | | Never hinged | 24.00 | |

A surtax of 1.08m was to provide a 100,000m sweepstakes prize. Wmk. 237 appears on the stamp, with "München Riem 1936" watermarked on sheet margin. For overprint see No. B105.

### Types of 1936
### Souvenir Sheets

### 1936, Aug. 1 — Perf. 14x13½

| | | | | |
|---|---|---|---|---|
| B91 | SP69 | Sheet of 4 | 37.50 | 67.50 |
| B92 | SP69 | Sheet of 4 | 37.50 | 67.50 |
| | | Set, never hinged | 200.00 | |

11th Olympic Games, Berlin. No. B91 contains Nos. B82-B84, B89. No. B92 contains Nos. B85-B88.

Wmk. 237 appears on each stamp with "XI Olympische Spiele-Berlin 1936" watermarked on sheet margin. Sold for 1m each.

Frontier Highway, Munich — SP81

---

Designs: 4pf+3pf, Ministry of Aviation. 5pf+3pf, Nuremberg Memorial. 6pf+4pf, Bridge over the Saale, Saxony. 8pf+4pf, Germany Hall, Berlin. 12pf+6pf, German Alpine highway. 15pf+10pf, Fuhrer House, Munich. 25pf+15pf, Bridge over the Mangfall. 40pf+35pf, Museum of German Art, Munich.

### Perf. 13½x14

| | | | Unwmk. | |
|---|---|---|---|---|
| B93 | SP81 | 3pf + 2pf blk brn | .25 | .40 |
| a. | | Bklt. pane, 4 #B93 + 5 #B98 + label | 27.50 | 55.00 |
| | | | 45.00 | |
| B94 | SP81 | 4pf + 3pf black | .25 | .45 |
| B95 | SP81 | 5pf + 3pf brt grn | .25 | .40 |
| a. | | Bklt. pane, 5 #B95, 5 #B96) | 14.00 | 26.00 |
| | | Never hinged | 22.50 | |
| B96 | SP81 | 6pf + 4pf dk grn | .25 | .40 |
| B97 | SP81 | 8pf + 4pf brown | .95 | 1.30 |
| B98 | SP81 | 12pf + 6pf brn car | .25 | .40 |
| B99 | SP81 | 15pf + 10pf vio brn | 3.50 | 3.50 |
| B100 | SP81 | 25pf + 15pf indigo | 2.25 | 3.75 |
| B101 | SP81 | 40pf + 35pf rose vio | 3.75 | 5.75 |
| | | Nos. B93-B101 (9) | 11.70 | 16.35 |
| | | Set, never hinged | 60.00 | |

### Souvenir Sheets

Adolf Hitler SP90

### Wmk. 237
### 1937, Apr. 5 — Photo. — Perf. 14

| | | | | |
|---|---|---|---|---|
| B102 | SP90 | Sheet of 4 | 18.00 | 12.00 |
| | | Never hinged | 52.50 | |
| a. | | 6pf blksh blue green | 1.15 | 1.50 |
| | | Never hinged | 4.25 | |

48th birthday of Adolf Hitler. Sold for 1m. See Nos. B103-B104. For overprint see No. B106.

### 1937, Apr. 16 — Imperf.

| | | | | |
|---|---|---|---|---|
| B103 | SP90 | Sheet of 4 | 37.50 | 22.50 |
| | | Never hinged | 170.00 | |
| a. | | 6pf blksh blue green | 3.75 | 3.00 |
| | | Never hinged | 200.00 | |

German Natl. Phil. Exhib., Berlin, June 16-18, 1937 and the Phil. Exhib. of the Stamp Collectors Group of the Strength Through Joy Organization at Hamburg, Apr. 17-20, 1937. Sold at the Exhib. post offices for 1.50m.

---

APS 51900    Established 1964    ARA 1970

## STAMPS FOR THE DISCERNING COLLECTOR
# Laurence L. Winum

P.O. Box 247, Walden, NY 12586

## 1-800-914-8090

**FREE Price Lists for all areas of Germany:**

A. Germany Proper Part I all pre 1949 material Part II Scott from 665, B298
B. Berlin, DDR, Soviet Zone
B1. German States
C. Colonies, Offices & Occupied Territories
D. The Plebescites - Saar, Danzig, etc.
E. Zusammendrucke

Our frequent lists are for high quality stamps at competitive prices. Separate lists just for specialist material by Michel.

**FREE PRICE LISTS for French & Spanish Andorra, Austria, Canada, Denmark, France, Great Britain, Iceland, Japan, Monaco & Norway**

No. B102 with Marginal Inscriptions

### Perf. 14 and Rouletted
**1937, June 10**　　　　　**Wmk. 237**

| | | | |
|---|---|---|---|
| B104 | SP90 | Sheet of 4 | 75.00 67.50 |
| | | Never hinged | 240.00 |
| a. | | 6pf blksh blue grn + 25pf label | 3.75 6.75 |
| | | Never hinged | 15.00 |

No. B104 inscribed in the margin beside each stamp "25 Rpf. einschliesslich Kulturspende" in three lines.

The sheets were rouletted to allow for separation of each stamp with its component label. Sold at the post office as individual stamps with labels attached or in complete sheets.

### No. B90 Overprinted in Red

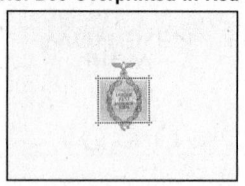

**1937, Aug. 1**　　　　　**Perf. 14**

| | | | |
|---|---|---|---|
| B105 | SP80 | 42pf brown | 52.50 97.50 |
| | | Never hinged | 135.00 |
| a. | | Inverted overprint | 14,500. |

4th running of the "Brown Ribbon" horse race at the Munich-Riem Race Course, Aug. 1, 1937.

### No. B104 Overprinted in Black on Each Stamp

### Perf. 14 and Rouletted
**1937, Sept. 3**　　　　　**Wmk. 237**

| | | | |
|---|---|---|---|
| B106 | SP90 | Sheet of 4 | 67.50 45.00 |
| | | Never hinged | 240.00 |
| a. | | 6pf blksh blue grn + 25pf label | 4.50 5.75 |
| | | Never hinged | 13.50 |

1937 Nazi Congress at Nuremburg.

 Lifeboat — SP91

Designs: 4pf+3pf, Lightship "Elbe I." 5pf+3pf, Fishing smacks. 6pf+4pf, Steamer. 8pf+4pf, Sailing vessel. 12pf+6pf, The "Tannenberg." 15pf+10pf, Sea-Train "Schwerin." 25pf+15pf, S. S. Hamburg. 40pf+35pf, S. S. Bremen.

### Perf. 13½
**1937, Nov. 4**　　**Engr.**　　**Unwmk.**

| | | | |
|---|---|---|---|
| B107 | SP91 | 3pf + 2pf dk brwn | .25 .40 |
| a. | | Bklt. pane, 4 #B107 + 5 #B112 + label | 27.00 50.00 |
| | | Never hinged | 45.00 |
| B108 | SP91 | 4pf + 3pf black | .85 1.15 |
| B109 | SP91 | 5pf + 3pf yel grn | .25 .40 |
| a. | | Bklt. pane, 5 #B109, 5 #B110 | 13.50 26.00 |
| | | Never hinged | 22.50 |
| B110 | SP91 | 6pf + 4pf bl grn | .25 .40 |
| B111 | SP91 | 8pf + 4pf orange | .55 1.15 |
| B112 | SP91 | 12pf + 6pf car lake | .25 .40 |
| B113 | SP91 | 15pf + 10pf vio brn | 1.10 3.75 |
| B114 | SP91 | 25pf + 15pf ultra | 2.50 3.75 |
| B115 | SP91 | 40pf + 35pf red vio | 4.25 7.50 |
| | | Nos. B107-B115 (9) | 10.25 18.90 |
| | | Set, never hinged | 75.00 |

No. B115 actually pictures the S.S. Europa.

Youth Carrying Torch and Laurel — SP100

### Wmk. 237
**1938, Jan. 28**　　**Photo.**　　**Perf. 14**

| | | | |
|---|---|---|---|
| B116 | SP100 | 6 + 4pf dk green | 1.15 1.90 |
| B117 | SP100 | 12 + 8pf brt car | 1.15 1.90 |
| | | Set, never hinged | 15.00 |

Assumption of power by the Nazis, 5th anniv.

Adolf Hitler — SP101

**1938, Apr. 13**　　**Engr.**　　**Unwmk.**

| | | | |
|---|---|---|---|
| B118 | SP101 | 12 + 38pf copper red | 1.90 2.60 |
| | | Never hinged | 9.75 |

Hitler's 49th birthday.

Horsewoman SP102

**1938, July 20**

| | | | |
|---|---|---|---|
| B119 | SP102 | 42 + 108pf dp brn | 21.00 45.00 |
| | | Never hinged | 115.00 |

5th "Brown Ribbon" at Munich.

Adolf Hitler — SP103

**1938, Sept. 1**

| | | | |
|---|---|---|---|
| B120 | SP103 | 6 + 19pf deep grn | 2.25 4.25 |

1938 Nazi Congress at Nuremberg. The surtax was for Hitler's National Culture Fund.

Theater at Saarbrücken — SP104

**1938, Oct. 9**　　**Photo.**　　**Wmk. 237**

| | | | |
|---|---|---|---|
| B121 | SP104 | 6 + 4pf blue grn | 1.40 1.90 |
| B122 | SP104 | 12 + 8pf dk car | 1.75 2.60 |
| | | Set, never hinged | 19.50 |

Inauguration of the theater of the District of Saarpfalz at Saarbrücken. The surtax was for Hitler's National Culture Fund.

Castle of Forchtenstein — SP105

Designs (scenes in Austria and various flowers): 4pf+3pf, Flexenstrasse in Vorarlberg. 5pf+3pf, Zell am See, Salzburg. 6pf+4pf, Grossglockner. 8pf+4pf, Ruins of Aggstein. 12pf+6pf, Prince Eugene Monument, Vienna. 15pf+10pf, Erzberg. 25pf+15pf, Hall, Tyrol. 40pf+35pf, Braunau.

### Unwmk.
**1938, Nov. 18**　　**Engr.**　　**Perf. 14**

| | | | |
|---|---|---|---|
| B123 | SP105 | 3 + 2pf ol brn | .25 .45 |
| a. | | Bklt. pane, 4 #B123, 5 #B128 + label | 27.00 50.00 |
| | | Never hinged | 45.00 |
| B124 | SP105 | 4 + 3pf indigo | 1.60 1.15 |
| B125 | SP105 | 5 + 3pf emer | .25 .45 |
| a. | | Bklt. pane, 5 #B125, 5 #B126 | 13.50 26.00 |
| | | Never hinged | 22.50 |

| | | | |
|---|---|---|---|
| B126 | SP105 | 6 + 4pf dk grn | .25 .40 |
| B127 | SP105 | 8 + 4pf red org | 1.60 1.15 |
| B128 | SP105 | 12 + 8pf dk car | .25 .45 |
| B129 | SP105 | 15 + 10pf dp cl | 3.00 4.50 |
| B130 | SP105 | 25 + 15pf dk bl | 2.60 4.50 |
| B131 | SP105 | 40 + 35pf plum | 6.00 7.50 |
| | | Nos. B123-B131 (9) | 15.80 20.55 |
| | | Set, never hinged | 75.00 |

The surtax was for "Winter Help."

Sudeten Couple — SP114

**1938, Dec. 2**　　**Photo.**　　**Wmk. 237**

| | | | |
|---|---|---|---|
| B132 | SP114 | 6 + 4pf blue grn | 1.50 3.00 |
| B133 | SP114 | 12 + 8pf dk car | 2.25 3.00 |
| | | Set, never hinged | 30.00 |

Annexation of the Sudeten Territory. The surtax was for Hitler's National Culture Fund.

Early Types of Automobiles SP115

Designs: 12pf+8pf, Racing cars. 25pf+10pf, Modern automobile.

**1939**

| | | | |
|---|---|---|---|
| B134 | SP115 | 6 + 4pf dk grn | 3.50 3.50 |
| B135 | SP115 | 12 + 8pf brt car | 3.50 3.50 |
| B136 | SP115 | 25 + 10pf dp blue | 6.00 6.00 |
| | | Nos. B134-B136 (3) | 13.00 13.00 |
| | | Set, never hinged | 82.50 |

Berlin Automobile and Motorcycle Exhibition. The surtax was for Hitler's National Culture Fund. For overprints see Nos. B141-B143.

Adolf Hitler — SP118

### Unwmk.
**1939, Apr. 13**　　**Engr.**　　**Perf. 14**

| | | | |
|---|---|---|---|
| B137 | SP118 | 12 + 38pf carmine | 1.50 4.50 |
| | | Never hinged | 8.25 |

Hitler's 50th birthday. The surtax was for Hitler's National Culture Fund.

Exhibition Building — SP119

**1939, Apr. 22**　　**Photo.**　　**Perf. 12½**

| | | | |
|---|---|---|---|
| B138 | SP119 | 6 + 4pf dk green | 1.20 3.00 |
| B139 | SP119 | 15 + 5pf dp plum | 1.75 3.75 |
| | | Set, never hinged | 15.00 |

Horticultural Exhib. held at Stuttgart. Surtax for Hitler's National Culture Fund.

Adolf Hitler — SP120

### Perf. 14x13½
**1939, Apr. 28**　　　　　**Wmk. 237**

| | | | |
|---|---|---|---|
| B140 | SP120 | 6 + 19pf black brn | 3.75 5.00 |
| | | Never hinged | 12.00 |

Day of National Labor. The surtax was for Hitler's National Culture Fund.
See No. B147.

Nos. B134-B136 Overprinted in Black

**1939, May 18**　　　　　**Perf. 14**

| | | | |
|---|---|---|---|
| B141 | SP115 | 6 + 4pf dk grn | 18.00 26.00 |
| B142 | SP115 | 12 + 8pf brt car | 18.00 26.00 |
| B143 | SP115 | 25 + 10pf dp bl | 18.00 26.00 |
| | | Nos. B141-B143 (3) | 54.00 78.00 |
| | | Set, never hinged | 210.00 |

Nurburgring Auto Races, 5/21, 7/23/39.

Racehorse "Investment" and Jockey — SP121

**1939, June 18**　　**Engr.**　　**Unwmk.**

| | | | |
|---|---|---|---|
| B144 | SP121 | 25 + 50pf ultra | 15.00 15.00 |
| | | Never hinged | 60.00 |

70th anniv. of the German Derby. The surtax was divided between Hitler's National Culture Fund and the race promoters.

Man Holding Rearing Horse — SP122

**1939, July 12**

| | | | |
|---|---|---|---|
| B145 | SP122 | 42 + 108pf dp brn | 15.00 24.00 |
| | | Never hinged | 60.00 |

6th "Brown Ribbon" at Munich.

"Venetian Woman" by Albrecht Dürer — SP123

**1939, July 12**　　**Photo.**　　**Wmk. 237**

| | | | |
|---|---|---|---|
| B146 | SP123 | 6 + 19pf dk grn | 5.25 9.75 |
| | | Never hinged | |

Day of German Art. The surtax was used for Hitler's National Culture Fund.

### Hitler Type of 1939
### Inscribed "Reichsparteitag 1939"
**1939, Aug. 25**　　　　　**Perf. 14x13½**

| | | | |
|---|---|---|---|
| B147 | SP120 | 6 + 19pf blk brn | 4.25 9.00 |
| | | Never hinged | 18.00 |

1939 Nazi Congress at Nuremberg.

Meeting in German Hall, Berlin — SP124

Designs: 4pf+3pf, Meeting of postal and telegraph employees. 5pf+3pf, Professional competitions. 6pf+4pf, 6pf+9pf, Professional camp. 8pf+4pf, 8pf+12pf, Gold flag competitions. 10pf+5pf, Awarding prizes. 12&f+6pf, 12pf+18pf, Automobile race. 15pf+10pf, Sports. 16pf+10pf, 16pf+24pf, Postal police. 20pf+10pf, 20pf+30pf, Glider workshops. 24pf+10pf, 24pf+36pf, Mail coach. 25pf+15pf, Convalescent home, Konigstein.

### Perf. 13½x14

| | | | | |
|---|---|---|---|---|
| **1939-41** | | **Unwmk.** | | **Photo.** |
| B148 | | 3 + 2pf bister brn | | 2.25 5.25 |
| B149 | | 4 + 3pf slate blue | | 2.00 5.25 |
| B150 | | 5 + 3pf brt bl grn | | .60 1.50 |
| B151 | | 6 + 4pf myrtle grn | | .75 1.50 |
| B151A | | 6 + 9pf dk grn ('41) | | .70 2.25 |
| B152 | | 8 + 4pf dp org | | .75 1.50 |
| B152A | | 8 + 12pf hn brn ('41) | | 1.05 1.50 |
| B153 | | 10 + 5pf dk brown | | .75 2.00 |
| B154 | | 12 + 6pf rose brown | | .85 2.00 |
| B154A | | 12 + 18pf dk car rose ('41) | | 1.05 1.90 |
| B155 | | 15 + 10pf dp red lilac | | .75 2.25 |
| B156 | | 16 + 10pf slate grn | | .75 2.25 |
| B156A | | 16 + 24pf black ('41) | | 1.05 3.75 |
| B157 | | 20 + 10pf ultra | | .75 2.25 |
| B157A | | 20 + 30pf ultra ('41) | | 1.40 3.75 |
| B158 | | 24 + 10pf ol grn | | 1.90 3.75 |

**B158A** 24 + 36pf pur ('41) 3.50 11.50
**B159** 25 + 15pf dk blue 1.90 3.00
*Nos. B148-B159 (18)* 22.75 57.15
Set, never hinged 110.00

The surtax was used for Hitler's National Culture Fund and the Postal Employees' Fund. See Nos. B273, B275-B277.

Elbogen Castle — SP136

Buildings: 4pf+3pf, Drachenfels on the Rhine. 5pf+3pf, Kaiserpfalz at Goslar. 6pf+4pf, Clocktower at Graz. 8pf+4pf, Town Hall, Frankfurt. 12pf+6pf, Guild House, Klagenfurt. 15pf+10pf, Ruins of Schreckenstein Castle. 25pf+15pf, Fortress of Salzburg. 40pf+35pf, Castle of Hohenzwiel.

**1939 Unwmk. Engr. Perf. 14**
**B160** SP136 3 + 2pf dk brn .25 .45
a. Bklt. pane, 4 #B160, 5 #B165+label 27.00 50.00
**B161** SP136 4 + 3pf gray blk 1.50 1.90
**B162** SP136 5 + 3pf emerald .35 .55
a. Bklt. pane, 5 #B162, 5 #B163 13.50 26.00
**B163** SP136 6 + 4pf slate grn .25 .40
**B164** SP136 8 + 4pf red org 1.50 1.60
**B165** SP136 12 + 6pf dk car .65 1.50
**B166** SP136 15 + 10pf brn vio 2.25 4.50
**B167** SP136 25 + 15pf ultra 1.75 4.50
**B168** SP136 40 + 35pf rose vio 2.50 6.00
*Nos. B160-B168 (9)* 11.00 21.40
Set, never hinged 45.00

Hall of Honor at Chancellery, Berlin — SP145

**1940, Mar. 28**
**B169** SP145 24 + 76pf dk grn 6.00 16.50
Never hinged 27.00
2nd National Stamp Exposition, Berlin.

Child Greeting Hitler — SP146

**Perf. 14x13½**
**1940, Apr. 10 Photo. Wmk. 237**
**B170** SP146 12 + 38pf cop red .30 6.00
Never hinged 12.00
51st birthday of Adolf Hitler.

Armed Warrior — SP147

**1940, Apr. 30 Unwmk. Perf. 14**
**B171** SP147 6 + 4pf sl grn & lt grn .30 1.30
Never hinged 1.35
Issued to commemorate May Day.

Horseman — SP148

**Perf. 14x13½**
**1940, June 22 Wmk. 237**
**B172** SP148 25 + 100pf dp ultra 4.25 11.00
Never hinged 19.50
Blue Ribbon race, Hamburg, June 30, 1940. Surtax for Hitler's National Culture Fund.

Chariot — SP149

**Unwmk.**
**1940, July 20 Engr. Perf. 14**
**B173** SP149 42 + 108pf brown 22.50 26.00
Never hinged 90.00
7th "Brown Ribbon" at Munich. The surtax was for Hitler's National Culture Fund and the promoters of the race.

View of Malmedy — SP150

Design: 12pf+8pf, View of Eupen.

**Perf. 14x13½**
**1940, July 25 Photo. Wmk. 237**
**B174** SP150 6 + 4pf dk green 1.15 3.00
**B175** SP150 12 + 8pf org red 1.15 3.00
Set, never hinged 9.75
Issued on the occasion of the reunion of Eupen-Malmedy with the Reich.

Rocky Cliffs of Heligoland — SP152

**1940, Aug. 9 Unwmk.**
**B176** SP152 6 + 94pf brt bl grn & red org 5.75 11.50
Never hinged 22.50
Heligoland's 50th year as part of Germany.

Artushof in Danzig — SP153

Buildings: 4pf+3pf, Town Hall, Thorn. 5pf+3pf, Castle at Kaub. 6pf+4pf, City Theater, Poznan. 8pf+4pf, Castle at Heidelberg. 12pf+6pf, Porta Nigra Trier. 15pf+10pf, New German Theater, Prague. 25pf+15pf, Town Hall, Bremen. 40pf+35pf, Town Hall, Munster.

**1940, Nov. 5 Engr. Perf. 14**
**B177** SP153 3 + 2pf dk brn .30 .45
a. Bklt. pane, 4 #B177 + 5 #B182 + label 27.00 50.00
Never hinged 45.00
**B178** SP153 4 + 3pf bluish blk .90 .75
**B179** SP153 5 + 3pf yel grn .30 .45
a. Bklt. pane, 5 #B179, 5 #B180 13.50 26.00
Never hinged 22.50
**B180** SP153 6 + 4pf dk grn .35 .45
**B181** SP153 8 + 4pf dp org 1.35 .85
**B182** SP153 12 + 6pf carmine .35 .45
**B183** SP153 15 + 10pf dk vio brn 1.50 2.60
**B184** SP153 25 + 15pf dp ultra 1.90 2.60
**B185** SP153 40 + 35pf red lil 3.75 6.00
*Nos. B177-B185 (9)* 10.70 14.60
Set, never hinged 30.00

von Behring — SP162

**1940, Nov. 26 Photo.**
**B186** SP162 6 + 4pf dp green 1.20 2.25
**B187** SP162 25 + 10pf brt ultra 1.75 2.25
Set, never hinged 11.50
Dr. Emil von Behring (1854-1917), bacteriologist.

Postilion — SP163

**1941, Jan. 12 Perf. 14x13½**
**B188** SP163 6 +24pf dp green 1.15 3.00
Never hinged 5.00
Postage Stamp Day. The surtax was for Hitler's National Culture Fund.

Benito Mussolini and Adolf Hitler — SP164

**Perf. 13½x14**
**1941, Jan. 30 Wmk. 237**
**B189** SP164 12 + 38pf rose brn 1.15 4.25
Never hinged 6.50
Issued as propaganda for the Rome-Berlin Axis. The surtax was for Hitler's National Culture Fund.

Adolf Hitler — SP165

**1941, Apr. 17 Perf. 14x13½**
**B190** SP165 12 + 38pf dk red 1.15 3.00
Never hinged 7.50
52nd birthday of Adolf Hitler. The surtax was for Hitler's National Culture Fund.

Race Horse — SP166

**Perf. 13½x14**
**1941, June 20 Engr. Unwmk.**
**B191** SP166 25 + 100pf sapphire 3.00 7.50
Never hinged 13.00
Issued in commemoration of the Blue Ribbon race held at Hamburg, June 29, 1941.

Amazons — SP167

**1941, July 20 Perf. 14**
**B192** SP167 42 + 108pf brown 1.90 5.00
Never hinged 9.00
8th "Brown Ribbon" at Munich.

Brandenburg Gate, Berlin — SP168

**1941, Sept. 9**
**B193** SP168 25 + 50pf dp ultra 2.60 6.75
Never hinged 10.50
Issued in honor of the Berlin races.

Marburg SP169 Veldes SP170

Pettau SP171 Triglav SP172

**1941, Sept. 29 Photo.**
**B194** SP169 3 + 7pf brown .75 2.25
**B195** SP170 6 + 9pf purple .75 2.25
**B196** SP171 12 + 13pf rose brn .75 2.60
**B197** SP172 25 + 15pf dk blue 1.45 2.60
*Nos. B194-B197 (4)* 3.70 9.70
Set, never hinged 15.00
Annexation of Styria and Carinthia.

View from Belvedere Palace, Vienna SP173

Belvedere Gardens, Vienna SP174

**1941, Sept. 16 Engr.**
**B198** SP173 12 + 8pf dp red 1.25 3.75
**B199** SP174 15 + 10pf violet 1.45 3.75
Set, never hinged 9.75
Issued to commemorate the Vienna Fair.

Mozart — SP175

**1941, Nov. 28**
**B200** SP175 6 + 4pf dk rose vio .25 .90
Never hinged .75
Wolfgang Amadeus Mozart (1756-91).

Philatelist — SP176

**1942, Jan. 11 Photo.**
**B201** SP176 6 + 24pf dp purple .55 3.00
Never hinged 3.00
To commemorate Stamp Day.

Soldier's Head — SP177

**1942, Mar. 10 Perf. 14x13½**
**B202** SP177 12 + 38pf slate blk .45 1.60
Never hinged 1.75
To commemorate Hero Memorial Day.

Adolf Hitler — SP178

**1942, Apr. 13**
**B203** SP178 12 + 38pf lake 1.50 6.00
Never hinged 11.50
To commemorate Hitler's 53rd birthday.

Racing Three-year-old
SP179

**1942, June 16** **Engr.** **Perf. 14**
B204 SP179 25 + 100pf dk bl 4.50 11.50
Never hinged 16.50

73rd Hamburg Derby.

Race Horses — SP180

**1942, July 14**
B205 SP180 42 + 108pf brown 1.50 5.25
Never hinged 7.50

9th "Brown Ribbon" at Munich.

Lüneburg Lion and Nuremberg Betrothal Cup — SP181

**1942, Aug. 8** **Photo.** **Perf. 14x13½**
B206 SP181 6 + 4pf copper red .35 1.50
B207 SP181 12 + 88pf green .45 2.25
Set, never hinged 3.50

10th anniv. of the German Goldsmiths' Society and the 1st Goldsmiths' Day in Germany. For overprint see Austria No. 394.

Henlein Monument, Nuremberg — SP182

**1942, Aug. 29** **Perf. 14**
B208 SP182 6 + 24pf rose vio .45 1.50
Never hinged 1.60

400th anniversary of the death of Peter Henlein, inventor of the pocket watch.

Postilion and Map of Europe SP183

Postilion and Globe SP184

Postilion — SP185

**Perf. 13½x14, 14x13½**
**1942, Oct. 12** **Photo.**
B209 SP183 3 + 7pf dull blue .25 1.50
**Engr.**
B210 SP184 6 + 14pf ultra & dp brn .35 1.50
B211 SP185 12 + 38pf rose red & dp brn .60 2.60
Nos. B209-B211 (3) 1.20 5.60
Set, never hinged 3.75

European Postal Congress, Vienna. For overprints see Austria Nos. 395, 397.

Nos. B209 to B211 Overprinted in Black

**1942, Oct. 19**
B212 SP183 3 + 7pf .70 2.60
B213 SP184 6 + 14pf .70 2.60
B214 SP185 12 + 38pf .90 4.50
Nos. B212-B214 (3) 2.30 9.70
Set, never hinged 7.50

To commemorate the signing of the European postal-telegraph agreement at Vienna.

Mail Coach — SP186

**1943, Jan. 10** **Engr.**
B215 SP186 6 + 24pf gray, brn & yel .25 .90
Never hinged .75

To commemorate Stamp Day. The surtax went to Hitler's National Culture Fund.

Brandenburg Gate — SP187

**1943, Jan. 26** **Photo.**
B216 SP187 54 + 96pf cop red .45 2.25
Never hinged 2.60

10th anniversary of the assumption of power by the Nazis.

Nazi Emblem — SP188

**1943, Jan. 26**
B217 SP188 3 + 2pf olive bister .25 .90
Never hinged .70

Used to secure special philatelic cancellations.

Submarine — SP189

Designs: 4pf+3pf, Schutz-Staffel Troops. 5pf+4pf, Motorized marksmen. 6pf+9pf, Signal Corps. 8pf+7pf, Engineer Corps. 12pf+8pf, Grenade assault. 15pf+10pf, Heavy artillery. 20pf+14pf, Anti-aircraft units in action. 25pf+15pf, Dive bombers. 30pf+30pf, Paratroops. 40pf+40pf, Tank. 50pf+50pf, Speed boat.

**1943, Mar. 21** **Engr.**
B218 SP189 3 + 2pf dk brn .50 1.20
B219 SP189 4 + 3pf brown .50 1.20
B220 SP189 5 + 4pf dk grn .40 1.20
B221 SP189 6 + 9pf dp violet .40 1.20
B222 SP189 8 + 7pf brn org .40 1.20
B223 SP189 12 + 8pf car lake .60 1.20
B224 SP189 15 + 10pf vio brn .60 1.20
B225 SP189 20 + 14pf slate bl .60 1.20
B226 SP189 25 + 15pf indigo .75 1.20
B227 SP189 30 + 30pf green .60 1.90
B228 SP189 40 + 40pf red lil .60 1.90
B229 SP189 50 + 50pf grnsh blk .60 3.00
Nos. B218-B229 (12) 6.55 17.60
Set, never hinged 16.50

Army Day and Hero Memorial Day. Nos. B220 and B224 exist imperf. Value, each $75.

Nazi Flag and Children — SP201

**1943, Mar. 26** **Photo.**
B230 SP201 6 + 4pf dk green .25 1.30
Never hinged 1.05

To commemorate the Day of Youth Obligation when all German boys and girls had to take an oath of allegiance to Hitler.

Adolf Hitler — SP202

**1943, Apr. 13**
B231 SP202 3 + 7pf brown blk .70 1.50
B232 SP202 6 + 14pf dk grn .45 1.50
B233 SP202 8 + 22pf dk chlky bl .45 1.50
B234 SP202 12 + 38pf cop red .45 1.50
B235 SP202 24 + 76pf vio brn .95 3.50
B236 SP202 40 + 160pf dk ol grn .95 3.50
Nos. B231-B236 (6) 3.95 13.00
Set, never hinged 10.50

Hitler's 54th birthday. No. B231 exists imperf. Value $100.

Reich Labor Service Corpsmen
SP203      SP204

Designs: 6pf+14pf, Corpsman chopping. 12pf+18pf, Corpsman with implements.

**1943, June 26** **Engr.**
B237 SP203 3 + 7pf bis brn .25 .75
B238 SP204 5 + 10pf pale ol grn .25 .75
B239 SP204 6 + 14pf dp blue .25 .75
B240 SP204 12 + 18pf dk red .30 1.35
Nos. B237-B240 (4) 1.05 3.60
Set, never hinged 3.00

Anniversary of Reich Labor Service. Nos. B237-B238, B240 exist imperf. Values: Nos. B237-B238, $45 each; No. B240, $60.

Rosegger's Birthplace, Upper Styria SP207

Peter Rosegger SP208

**Perf. 13½x14, 14x13½**
**1943, July 27** **Photo.**
B241 SP207 6 + 4pf green .25 .90
B242 SP208 12 + 8pf copper red .25 .90
Set, never hinged 1.50

Centenary of the birth of Peter Rosegger, Austrian writer.

Hunter — SP209

**1943, July 27** **Engr.**
B243 SP209 42 + 108pf brown .25 1.20
Never hinged .90

10th "Brown Ribbon" at Munich. No. B243 exists imperf. Value $200.

Race Horse — SP210

**1943, Aug. 14**
B244 SP210 6 + 4pf vio blk .25 1.20
B245 SP210 12 + 88pf dk car .25 1.20
Set, never hinged 1.60

Grand Prize of the Freudenau, the Vienna race track, Aug. 15, 1943.

Mother and Children — SP211

**1943, Sept. 1**
B246 SP211 12 + 38pf dark red .25 1.20
Never hinged .85

10th anniversary of Winter Relief.

St. George in Gold — SP212

**1943, Oct. 1**
B247 SP212 6 + 4pf dk ol grn .25 .75
B248 SP212 12 + 88pf vio brn .25 1.10
Set, never hinged 1.15

German Goldsmiths' Society.

Ancient Lübeck — SP213

**1943, Oct. 24** **Photo.**
B249 SP213 12 + 8pf copper red .25 1.15
Never hinged .70

Hanseatic town of Lubeck, 800th anniv. No. B249 exists imperf. Value, $110.

"And Despite All, You Were Victorious" — SP214

**1943, Nov. 5**
B250 SP214 24 + 26pf henna .25 1.50
Never hinged 1.15

20th anniv. of the Nazis' Munich beer-hall putsch and to honor those who died for the Nazi movement. No. B250 exists imperf; value, $100.

Dr. Robert Koch — SP215

**1944, Jan. 25** **Engr.** **Unwmk.**
B251 SP215 12 + 38pf sepia .25 1.15
Never hinged .75

Centenary of the birth of the bacteriologist, Robert Koch (1843-1910).

Hitler and Nazi Emblems — SP216

**1944, Jan. 29** **Photo.**
B252 SP216 54 + 96pf yel brn .25 2.25
Never hinged 1.50

Assumption of power by the Nazis, 11th anniv.

Airport Scene SP217

Seaplane SP218

Plane Seen from
Above — SP219

**Perf. 14x13½, 13½x14**

**1944, Feb. 11   Photo.   Unwmk.**
B252A SP217   6 + 4pf dk grn   .25  1.10
B252B SP218  12 + 8pf maroon   .25  1.10
B252C SP219  42 + 108pf dp
  slate bl   .30  2.25
  *Nos. B252A-B252C (3)*   .80  4.45
  Set, never hinged   2.25

25th anniv. of German air mail. The surtax
was for the National Culture Fund.

Infant's Crib — SP220

6pf+4pf, Public nurse. 12pf+8pf, "Mother &
Child" clinic. 15pf+10pf, Expectant mothers.

**1944, Mar. 2**
B253 SP220   3 + 2pf dk brn   .25  .75
B254 SP220   6 + 4pf dk grn   .25  .75
B255 SP220  12 + 8pf dp car   .25  .75
B256 SP220  15 + 10pf vio brn   .25  .75
  *Nos. B253-B256 (4)*   1.00  3.00
  Set, never hinged   1.50

10th anniv. of "Mother and Child" aid.

Assault
Boat — SP221

Designs: 4pf+3pf, Chain-wheel vehicle.
5pf+3pf, Paratroops. 6pf+4pf, Submarine
officer. 8pf+4pf, Schutz-Staffel grenade throwers. 10pf+5pf, Searchlight. 12pf+6pf, Infantry.
15pf+10pf, Self-propelled gun. 16pf+10pf,
Speed boat. 20pf+10pf, Sea raider. 24pf+10pf,
Railway artillery. 25pf+15pf, Rockets.
30pf+20pf, Mountain trooper.

**Inscribed: "Grossdeutsches Reich"**

**1944, Mar. 11**
B257 SP221   3 + 2pf yel brn   .30  1.15
B258 SP221   4 + 3pf royal bl   .30  1.15
B259 SP221   5 + 3pf dp yel
  grn   .25  .55
B260 SP221   6 + 4pf dp vio   .25  .55
B261 SP221   8 + 4pf org ver   .25  .55
B262 SP221  10 + 4pf choc   .25  .55
B263 SP221  12 + 6pf carmine   .25  .55
B264 SP221  15 + 10pf dp clar   .25  .75
B265 SP221  16 + 10pf dk bl
  grn   .25  1.20
B266 SP221  20 + 10pf brt bl   .35  1.90
B267 SP221  24 + 10pf dl org
  brn   .35  1.90
B268 SP221  25 + 15pf vio bl   .70  3.75
B269 SP221  30 + 20pf dl grn   .70  3.75
  *Nos. B257-B269 (13)*   4.45  18.35
  Set, never hinged   16.50

To commemorate Hero Memorial Day.

Flora Statue in
Fulda's Schloss
Garden — SP234

**1944, Mar. 11**
B270 SP234  12 + 38pf dp brown   .25  .90
  Never hinged   .60

1,200th anniversary of town of Fulda.

Adolf Hitler — SP235

**1944, Apr. 14   Engr.   Unwmk.**
B271 SP235  54 + 96pf rose car   .30  3.00
  Never hinged   1.75

To commemorate Hitler's 55th birthday.

**Type of 1939-41 and**

Woman Mail
Carrier
SP236

Field Post in
the East
SP237

Designs: 8pf+12pf, Mail coach. 16pf+24pf,
Automobile race. 20pf+30pf, Postal police.
24pf+36pf, Glider workshops.

**1944, May 3   Photo.**
**Designs measure 29½x24½mm**
B272 SP236   6 + 9pf vio bl   .25  .75
B273 SP124   8 + 12pf gray blk   .25  .75
B274 SP237  12 + 18pf dp plum   .25  .75
B275 SP124  16 + 24pf dk grn   .25  .75
B276 SP124  20 + 30pf blue   .25  1.35
B277 SP124  24 + 36pf dk pur   .25  1.35
  *Nos. B272-B277 (6)*   1.50  5.70
  Set, never hinged   3.00

Surtax for the Postal Employees' Fund.

Soldier and Tirolese
Rifleman — SP238

**1944, July**
B278 SP238   6 + 4pf dp grn   .25  .85
B279 SP238  12 + 8pf brn lake   .25  .85
  Set, never hinged   .85

7th National Shooting Matches at Innsbruck.

Albert I, Duke of
Prussia — SP239

**1944, July**
B280 SP239   6 + 4pf dk bl grn   .25  1.20
  Never hinged   .75

400th anniv. of Albert University, Königsberg.

Labor Corps
Girl
SP240

Labor
Corpsman
SP241

**1944, June   Engr.**
B281 SP240   6 + 4pf green   .25  .70
B282 SP241  12 + 8pf carmine   .25  .70
  Set, never hinged   .85

Issued to honor an exhibit of the Reich
Labor Service.

Race Horse and
Foal — SP242

**1944, July 23   Perf. 14x13½**
B283 SP242  42 + 108pf brown   .25  2.00
  Never hinged   1.05

11th "Brown Ribbon" at Munich.
For overprint see Austria No. 396.

Race Horse's Head in
Oak Wreath — SP243

**1944, Aug.   Photo.   Perf. 14**
B284 SP243   6 + 4pf Prus green   .25  1.05
B285 SP243  12 + 88pf car lake   .25  1.05
  Set, never hinged   1.05

Vienna Grand Prize Race.

Nautilus Cup in Green
Vault,
Dresden — SP244

**1944, Sept. 11**
B286 SP244   6 + 4pf dk grn   .25  1.05
B287 SP244  12 + 88pf car brn   .25  1.05
  Set, never hinged   1.00

German Goldsmiths' Society.
No. B287 exists imperf. Value $175.

Post Horn and
Letter — SP245

**1944, Oct. 2**
B288 SP245   6 + 24pf dk green   .25  1.20
  Never hinged   .70

To commemorate Stamp Day.

Eagle and
Serpent — SP246

**1944, Nov. 9**
B289 SP246  12 + 8pf rose red   .25  1.20
  Never hinged   .75

21st anniv. of the Munich putsch.

Count Anton
Günther — SP247

**1945, Jan. 6   Typo.   Perf. 13½x14**
B290 SP247   6 + 14pf brown vio   .25  1.20
  Never hinged   .75

600th anniv. of municipal law in Oldenburg.
Exists imperf. Value, $75.

People's
Army — SP248

**1945, Feb.   Photo.   Perf. 14x13½**
B291 SP248  12 + 8pf rose car   .30  2.60
  Never hinged   1.35

Proclamation of the People's Army (Volks-
turm) in East Prussia to fight the Russians.

Elite Storm
Trooper
(S. S.)
SP249

Storm
Trooper
(S. A.)
SP250

**1945, Apr. 21   Perf. 13½x14**
B292 SP249  12 + 38pf brt
  car   9.00  900.00
B293 SP250  12 + 38pf brt
  car   6.00  900.00
  Set, never hinged   60.00

12th anniv. of the assumption of power by
the Nazis. Nos. B292-B293 were on sale in
Berlin briefly before the collapse of that city.
Exist imperf unused. Value same as perf.
Forged cancels abound. Certificates of
authenticity mandatory for used stamps.

Two stamps were prepared, but not
issued, recognizing the National Socialist Motor Corps (NSKK) and the
National Socialist Flyers Corps (NSFK).
Value $15,000 each.

**Souvenir Sheets**

SP251

**Wmk. 284**
**1946, Dec. 8   Typo.   Perf. 14**
B294 SP251  Sheet of 3   19.00  130.00
  Never hinged   45.00

**Imperf**
B295 SP251  Sheet of 3   19.00  150.00
  Never hinged   45.00
  a.  A119 20pf light blue   4.50  37.50
  b.  A119 24pf orange brown   4.50  37.50
  c.  A119 40pf red violet   4.50  37.50

No. B294 contains Nos. 543, 544 and 548.
Nos. B294-B295 sold for 5m each. Surtax
for refugees and the aged.

Leipzig
Proclaimed
Market Place,
1160 — SP252

Design: 60pf+40pf, Foreign merchants displaying their wares, 1268.

**Wmk. 48**
**1947, Mar. 5   Engr.   Perf. 13**
B296 SP252  24 +26pf chestnut
  brn   .25  5.00
B297 SP252  60 + 40pf dp vio
  blue   .25  5.00
  Set, never hinged   2.25

1947 Leipzig Fairs.
No. B296 exists imperf. Value $150.
See Nos. 580-583, 10NB1-10NB2, 10NB4-
10NB5, 10NB12-10NB13 and German Democratic Republic Nos. B15-B16.

Madonna
SP254

Cathedral
Towers
SP255

Designs: 12pf+8pf, Three Kings. 24pf+16pf,
Cologne Cathedral.

**Wmk. 286**
**1948, Aug. 15   Typo.   Perf. 11**
B298 SP254   6 + 4pf org brn   .30  .75
  a.  "1948-1248"   4.25  19.00
    Never hinged   11.50
B299 SP254  12 + 8pf grnsh
  blue   .55  1.90
  a.  "1948-1948"   5.75  22.50
    Never hinged   15.00

B300 SP254 24 + 16pf car 1.15 *3.75*
B301 SP255 50 + 50pf blue 2.60 *9.00*
*Nos. B298-B301 (4)* 4.60 *15.40*
Set, never hinged 12.00

700th anniv. of the laying of the cornerstone of Cologne Cathedral. The surtax was to aid in its reconstruction.

Specialists collect Nos. B298-B301 with watermark in four positions: upright, D's facing left; upright, D's facing right; sideways, D's facing up; sideways, D's facing down. Two types of perforation: line and comb.

Brandenburg Gate, Berlin — SP256

**Perf. 10½x11½, 11**
**1948, Dec.** **Litho.**
B302 SP256 10 + 5pf green 2.40 *6.75*
B303 SP256 20 + 10pf rose car 2.40 *6.75*
Set, never hinged 12.00

The surtax was for aid to Berlin.

Bicycle Racers — SP257

**Wmk. 116**
**1949, May 15** **Engr.** **Perf. 14**
B304 SP257 10 + 5pf green 1.60 *6.00*
B305 SP257 20 + 10pf brn org 4.50 *15.00*
Set, never hinged 16.50

1949 Bicycle Tour of Germany.

Goethe at Rome SP258

Goethe SP259

30pf+15pf, Goethe portrait facing left.

**1949, Aug. 15**
B306 SP258 10 + 5pf green .80 *4.25*
B307 SP259 20 + 10pf red 1.20 *7.50*
B308 SP259 30 + 15pf blue 7.50 *22.50*
*Nos. B306-B308 (3)* 9.50 *34.25*
Set, never hinged 32.00

Bicentenary of the birth of Johann Wolfgang von Goethe.
The surtax was for the reconstruction of Goethe House, Frankfurt-on-Main.

**Federal Republic**

Bavaria Stamp of 1849 — SP260

**1949, Sept. 30** **Litho.** **Wmk. 285**
B309 SP260 10 + 2pf grn & blk 5.75 *22.50*
Never hinged 13.00

Centenary of German postage stamps.

St. Elisabeth — SP261

Designs: 10pf+5pf, Paracelsus. 20pf+10pf, F. W. A. Froebel. 30pf+15pf, J. H. Wichern.

**1949, Dec. 14** **Engr.** **Wmk. 286**
B310 SP261 8 + 2pf brn vio 5.50 *19.00*
B311 SP261 10 + 5pf yel grn 4.50 *10.50*
B312 SP261 20 + 10pf red 4.50 *10.50*

B313 SP261 30 + 15pf vio bl 23.00 *90.00*
*Nos. B310-B313 (4)* 37.50 *130.00*
Set, never hinged 82.50

The surtax was for welfare organizations.

Seal of Johann Sebastian Bach — SP262

**1950, July 28** **Perf. 14**
B314 SP262 10 + 2pf dk grn 17.50 *37.50*
B315 SP262 30 + 3pf dk car 17.50 *42.50*
Set, never hinged 82.50

Bicentenary of the death of Bach.

Frescoes from Marienkirche SP263

**1951, Aug. 30 Photo. Wmk. 286**
**Center in Gray**
B316 SP263 10 + 5pf green 28.00 *60.00*
B317 SP263 20 + 5pf brn lake 28.00 *65.00*
Set, never hinged 170.00

Construction of Marienkirche, Lübeck, 700th anniv.
The surtax aided in its reconstruction.

Stamps Under Magnifying Glass — SP264

**1951, Sept. 14** **Typo.** **Perf. 14**
B318 SP264 10 + 2pf multi 13.50 *37.50*
B319 SP264 20 + 3pf multi 15.00 *42.50*
Set, never hinged 67.50

Natl. Philatelic Exposition, Wuppertal, 1951.

St. Vincent de Paul — SP265

Portraits: 10pf+3pf, Friedrich von Bodelschwingh. 20pf+5pf, Elsa Brandstrom. 30pf+10pf, Johann Heinrich Pestalozzi.

**1951, Oct. 23** **Engr.**
B320 SP265 4 + 2pf brown 3.00 *7.50*
B321 SP265 10 + 3pf green 4.50 *6.00*
B322 SP265 20 + 5pf rose red 4.50 *6.00*
B323 SP265 30 + 10pf dp blue 37.50 *90.00*
*Nos. B320-B323 (4)* 49.50 *109.50*
Set, never hinged 105.00

The surtax was for charitable purposes.

Nuremberg Madonna — SP266

**1952, Aug. 9**
B324 SP266 10 + 5pf green 4.50 *15.00*
Never hinged 13.00

Centenary of the founding of the Germanic National Museum, Nuremberg. The surtax was for the museum.

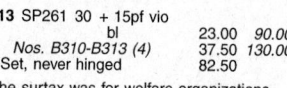

Boy Hikers and Youth Hostel — SP267

Design: 20pf+3pf, Girls and Hostel.

**1952, Sept. 17** **Perf. 13½x14**
B325 SP267 10 + 2pf green 7.50 *17.50*
B326 SP267 20 + 3pf dp car 7.50 *17.50*
Set, never hinged 34.00

The surtax was to aid the youth program of the Federal Republic.

Elizabeth Fry — SP268

10pf+5pf, Dr. Carl Sonnenschein. 20pf+10pf, Theodor Fliedner, Henri Dunant. 30pf+10pf,

**1952, Oct. 1**
B327 SP268 4 + 2pf org brn 4.00 *6.00*
B328 SP268 10 + 5pf green 4.00 *6.00*
B329 SP268 20 + 10pf brn car 5.25 *9.00*
B330 SP268 30 + 10pf dp bl 30.00 *60.00*
*Nos. B327-B330 (4)* 43.25 *81.00*
Set, never hinged 97.50

The surtax was for welfare organizations.

Owl and Cogwheel — SP269

**1953, May 7** **Wmk. 295** **Perf. 14**
B331 SP269 10 + 5pf dp grn 10.50 *24.00*
Never hinged 22.50

50th anniv. of the founding of the German Museum in Munich.

Thurn and Taxis Palace Gate — SP270

Design: 20pf+3pf, Telecommunications Bldg., Frankfurt-on-Main.

**Wmk. 285**
**1953, July 29** **Litho.** **Perf. 13½**
B332 SP270 10 + 2pf yel grn, bl & fawn 6.75 *21.00*
B333 SP270 20 + 3pf fawn, blk & gray 6.75 *21.00*
Set, never hinged 37.50

The surtax was for the International Stamp Exhibition, Frankfurt-on-Main, 1953.

August Hermann Francke — SP271

Designs: 10pf+5pf, Sebastian Kneipp. 20pf+10pf, Dr. Johann Christian Senckenberg. 30pf+10pf, Fridtjof Nansen.

**Wmk. 295**
**1953, Nov. 2** **Engr.** **Perf. 14**
B334 SP271 4 + 2pf choc 1.60 *7.50*
B335 SP271 10 + 5pf bl grn 2.25 *7.50*
B336 SP271 20 + 10pf red 5.00 *7.50*
B337 SP271 30 + 10pf blue 17.50 *57.50*
*Nos. B334-B337 (4)* 26.35 *80.00*
Set, never hinged 75.00

The surtax was for welfare organizations.

> **Catalogue values for unused stamps in this section, from this point to the end of the section, are for Never Hinged items.**

Käthe Kollwitz — SP272

Portraits: 10pf+5pf, Lorenz Werthmann. 20pf+10pf, Johann Friedrich Oberlin. 40pf+10pf, Bertha Pappenheim.

**1954, Dec. 28** **Perf. 13½x14**
B338 SP272 7pf + 3pf brown 2.60 2.60
B339 SP272 10pf + 5pf green 1.30 1.30
B340 SP272 20pf + 10pf red 9.00 4.50
B341 SP272 40pf + 10pf blue 28.00 34.00
*Nos. B338-B341 (4)* 40.90 42.40

The surtax was for welfare organizations.

Carrier Pigeon and Magnifying Glass — SP273

20pf+3pf, Post horn and stamp tongs.

**1955, Sept. 14** **Wmk. 304** **Perf. 14**
B342 SP273 10pf + 2pf green 4.25 5.25
B343 SP273 20pf + 3pf red 9.00 9.75

WESTROPA, 1955, philatelic exhibition at Dusseldorf. The surtax aided the Society of German Philatelists.

Amalie Sieveking — SP274

Portraits: 10pf+5pf, Adolph Kolping. 20pf+10pf, Dr. Samuel Hahnemann. 40pf+10pf, Florence Nightingale.

**1955, Nov. 15** **Photo. & Litho.**
B344 SP274 7 + 3pf olive bis 2.60 2.60
B345 SP274 10 + 5pf dk green 2.00 1.30
B346 SP274 20 + 10pf red org 2.00 1.30
B347 SP274 40 + 10pf grnsh blue 22.50 30.00
*Nos. B344-B347 (4)* 29.10 35.20

Surtax for independent welfare organizations.

Boy and Geometrical Designs — SP275

Design: 10pf+5pf, Girl playing flute.

**Unwmk.**
**1956, July 21** **Litho.** **Perf. 14**
B348 SP275 7pf + 3pf multi 1.75 2.60
B349 SP275 10pf + 5pf multi 5.75 7.50

The surtax was for the Youth Hostel Organization.

The Midwife — SP276

10+5pf, Ignaz Philipp Semmelweis.
20+10pf, The mother. 40+10pf, The children's
nurse.

**1956, Oct. 1**       **Photo.**
**Design and Inscription in Black**

| | | | |
|---|---|---|---|
| **B350** SP276 7pf + 3pf org brn | 1.30 | 2.00 |
| **B351** SP276 10pf + 5pf green | 1.00 | .65 |
| **B352** SP276 20pf + 10pf brt red | 1.00 | .65 |
| **B353** SP276 40pf + 10pf brt blue | 11.50 | 13.00 |
| *Nos. B350-B353 (4)* | 14.80 | 16.30 |

Issued to honor Ignaz Philipp Semmelweis,
the discoverer of the cause of puerperal fever.
Surtax for independent welfare organizations.

Children
Leaving — SP277

Design: 20pf+10pf, Child arriving.

**1957, Feb. 1**    **Litho.**    **Perf. 13½x13**

| | | | |
|---|---|---|---|
| **B354** SP277 10pf + 5pf gray grn & red org | 1.00 | 1.60 |
| **B355** SP277 20pf + 10pf red org & lt bl | 2.25 | 3.75 |

The surtax was for vacations for the children
of Berlin.

Young
Miner — SP278

10+5pf, Miner with drill. 20+10pf, Miner &
conveyor. 40+10pf, Miner & coal elevator.

**1957, Oct. 1**    **Wmk. 304**    **Perf. 14**

| | | | |
|---|---|---|---|
| **B356** SP278 7pf + 3pf bis brn & blk | 1.00 | 1.30 |
| **B357** SP278 10pf + 5pf blk & yel grn | .65 | .65 |
| **B358** SP278 20pf + 10pf black & red | 1.00 | .65 |
| **B359** SP278 40pf + 10pf black & blue | 13.50 | 16.50 |
| *Nos. B356-B359 (4)* | 16.15 | 19.10 |

Surtax for independent welfare organizations.

"A Hunter from the
Palatinate." — SP279

10pf + 5pf, "The Fox who Stole the Goose"

**1958, Apr. 1**      **Litho.**

| | | | |
|---|---|---|---|
| **B360** SP279 10pf + 5pf brn red, grn & blk | 1.30 | 1.60 |
| **B361** SP279 20pf + 10pf multi | 2.25 | 3.00 |

The surtax was to finance young peoples'
study trips to Berlin.

Friedrich
Wilhelm
Raiffeisen
SP280

Dairy Maid
SP281

Designs: 20pf+10pf, Girl picking grapes.
40pf+10pf, Farmer with pitchfork.

**1958, Oct. 1**    **Wmk. 304**    **Perf. 14**

| | | | |
|---|---|---|---|
| **B362** SP280 7pf + 3pf gldn brn & dk brn | .40 | .40 |
| **B363** SP281 10pf + 5pf grn, red & yel | .40 | .40 |
| **B364** SP281 20pf + 10pf red, yel & bl | .40 | .40 |
| **B365** SP281 40pf + 10pf blue & ocher | 6.00 | 7.25 |
| *Nos. B362-B365 (4)* | 7.20 | 8.45 |

Surtax for independent welfare organizations.

Stamp of Hamburg,
1859 — SP282

Design: 20pf+10pf, Stamp of Lübeck, 1859.

**1959**      **Engr.**      **Wmk. 304**

| | | | |
|---|---|---|---|
| **B366** SP282 10pf + 5pf yel green & brown | .25 | .65 |
|    **a.**   10pf + 5pf green & brown | .65 | 1.75 |
| **B367** SP282 20pf + 10pf red org & red brn | .25 | .65 |
|    **a.**   20pf + 10pf maroon & red brown | 1.00 | 1.75 |

"Interposa" Philatelic Exhibition, Hamburg,
May 22-31, 1959 for the cent. of the 1st
stamps of Hamburg and Lübeck.
The surtax on Nos. B366, B367 was for
vacations for the children of Berlin.
Issued: Nos. B366-B367, 8/22; Nos. B366a-
B367a, 5/22.

Girl Giving
Bread to
Beggar
SP283

Jacob and
Wilhelm Grimm
SP284

Designs (from "Star Dollars" fairy tale):
10pf+5pf, Girl giving coat to boy, 20pf+10pf,
Star-Money from Heaven.

**1959, Oct. 1**    **Litho.**    **Perf. 14**

| | | | |
|---|---|---|---|
| **B368** SP283 7pf + 3pf brn & yel | .25 | .35 |
| **B369** SP283 10pf + 5pf grn & yel | .25 | .35 |
| **B370** SP283 20pf + 10pf brick red & yel | .30 | .35 |
| **B371** SP284 40pf + 10pf bl, blk, ocher & emer | 2.60 | 4.50 |
| *Nos. B368-B371 (4)* | 3.40 | 5.55 |

Surtax for independent welfare organizations.

Little Red Riding
Hood and the
Wolf — SP285

Various Scenes from Little Red Riding
Hood.

**1960, Oct. 1**    **Wmk. 304**    **Perf. 14**

| | | | |
|---|---|---|---|
| **B372** SP285 7pf + 3pf brn ol, red & blk | .40 | .40 |
| **B373** SP285 10pf + 5pf grn, red & blk | .40 | .35 |
| **B374** SP285 20pf + 10pf brick red, emer & blk | .40 | .35 |
| **B375** SP285 40pf + 20pf brt bl, red & blk | 1.60 | 3.75 |
| *Nos. B372-B375 (4)* | 2.80 | 4.85 |

Surtax for independent welfare organizations.

**1961, Oct. 2**

Various Scenes from Hansel and Gretel.

| | | | |
|---|---|---|---|
| **B376** SP285 7pf + 3pf multi | .25 | .30 |
| **B377** SP285 10pf + 5pf multi | .25 | .30 |
| **B378** SP285 20pf + 10pf multi | .25 | .30 |
| **B379** SP285 40pf + 20pf multi | .80 | 1.60 |
| *Nos. B376-B379 (4)* | 1.55 | 2.50 |

Surtax for independent welfare organizations.
See B384-B387, B392-B395, B400-B403.

Fluorescent Paper
was introduced for semipostal
stamps, starting with No. B380.

Apollo — SP286

10pf+5pf, Camberwell beauty. 20pf+10pf,
Tortoise-shell. 40pf+20pf, Tiger swallowtail.

**Wmk. 304**
**1962, May 25**    **Litho.**    **Perf. 14**
**Butterflies in Natural Colors, Black**
**Inscriptions**

| | | | |
|---|---|---|---|
| **B380** SP286 7pf + 3pf bis brn | .35 | .55 |
| **B381** SP286 10pf + 5pf brt green | .35 | .55 |
| **B382** SP286 20pf + 10pf dp crim | .65 | 1.00 |
| **B383** SP286 40pf + 20pf brt blue | 1.00 | 1.60 |
| *Nos. B380-B383 (4)* | 2.35 | 3.70 |

Issued for the benefit of young people.
Nos. B381-B383 exist without watermark.
Value, each $900 unused, $975 used.

**Fairy Tale Type of 1960**

Scenes from Snow White (Schnee-
wittchen).

**1962, Oct. 10**      **Perf. 14**

| | | | |
|---|---|---|---|
| **B384** SP285 7pf + 3pf multi | .25 | .25 |
| **B385** SP285 10pf + 5pf multi | .25 | .25 |
| **B386** SP285 20pf + 10pf multi | .25 | .25 |
| **B387** SP285 40pf + 20pf multi | .65 | 1.05 |
| *Nos. B384-B387 (4)* | 1.40 | 1.80 |

Surtax for independent welfare organizations.

Hoopoe — SP287

Birds: 15pf+5pf, European golden oriole.
20pf+10pf, Bullfinch. 40pf+20pf, European
kingfisher.

**1963, June 12**    **Unwmk.**    **Perf. 14**

| | | | |
|---|---|---|---|
| **B388** SP287 10pf + 5pf multi | .40 | .55 |
| **B389** SP287 15pf + 5pf multi | .35 | .55 |
| **B390** SP287 20pf + 10pf multi | .35 | .55 |
| **B391** SP287 40pf + 20pf multi | 1.45 | 2.10 |
| *Nos. B388-B391 (4)* | 2.55 | 3.75 |

Issued for the benefit of young people.

**Fairy Tale Type of 1960**

Various Scenes from the Grimm Brothers'
"The Wolf and the Seven Kids."

**1963, Sept. 23**      **Litho.**

| | | | |
|---|---|---|---|
| **B392** SP285 10pf + 5pf multi | .25 | .25 |
| **B393** SP285 15pf + 5pf multi | .25 | .25 |
| **B394** SP285 20pf + 10pf multi | .25 | .25 |
| **B395** SP285 40pf + 20pf multi | .40 | 1.00 |
| *Nos. B392-B395 (4)* | 1.15 | 1.75 |

Surtax for independent welfare organizations.

Herring — SP288

Fish: 15pf+5pf, Rosefish. 20pf+10pf, Carp.
40pf+20pf, Cod.

**1964, Apr. 10**    **Unwmk.**    **Perf. 14**

| | | | |
|---|---|---|---|
| **B396** SP288 10pf + 5pf multi | .25 | .30 |
| **B397** SP288 15pf + 5pf multi | .25 | .30 |
| **B398** SP288 20pf + 10pf multi | .30 | .40 |
| **B399** SP288 40pf + 20pf multi | .80 | 1.60 |
| *Nos. B396-B399 (4)* | 1.60 | 2.60 |

Issued for the benefit of young people.

**Fairy Tale Type of 1960**

Various Scenes from Sleeping Beauty
(Dornroschen).

**1964, Oct. 6**      **Litho.**    **Perf. 14**

| | | | |
|---|---|---|---|
| **B400** SP285 10pf + 5pf multi | .25 | .25 |
| **B401** SP285 15pf + 5pf multi | .25 | .25 |
| **B402** SP285 20pf + 10pf multi | .25 | .25 |
| **B403** SP285 40pf + 20pf multi | .25 | .80 |
| *Nos. B400-B403 (4)* | 1.00 | 1.55 |

Surtax for independent welfare organizations.
See Berlin Nos. 9NB25-9NB28.

Woodcock — SP289

Birds: 15pf+5pf, Ring-necked pheasant.
20pf+10pf, Black grouse. 40pf+20pf,
Capercaillie.

**1965, Apr. 1**    **Unwmk.**    **Perf. 14**

| | | | |
|---|---|---|---|
| **B404** SP289 10pf + 5pf multi | .25 | .30 |
| **B405** SP289 15pf + 5pf multi | .25 | .30 |
| **B406** SP289 20pf + 10pf multi | .25 | .30 |
| **B407** SP289 40pf + 20pf multi | .25 | .80 |
| *Nos. B404-B407 (4)* | 1.00 | 1.70 |

Issued for the benefit of young people.
See Berlin Nos. 9NB29-9NB32.

Cinderella Feeding
Pigeons — SP290

Various Scenes from Cinderella.

**1965, Oct. 6**    **Litho.**    **Perf. 14**

| | | | |
|---|---|---|---|
| **B408** SP290 10pf + 5pf multi | .25 | .25 |
| **B409** SP290 15pf + 5pf multi | .25 | .25 |
| **B410** SP290 20pf + 10pf multi | .25 | .25 |
| **B411** SP290 40pf + 20pf multi | .30 | .60 |
| *Nos. B408-B411 (4)* | 1.05 | 1.35 |

Surtax for independent welfare organizations.
See Nos. B418-B421, B426-B429; Berlin
Nos. 9NB33-9NB36.

Roe Deer — SP291

Designs: 20pf+10pf, Chamois. 30pf+15pf,
Fallow deer. 50pf+25pf, Red deer.

**1966, Apr. 22**    **Litho.**    **Perf. 14**

| | | | |
|---|---|---|---|
| **B412** SP291 10pf + 5pf multi | .25 | .30 |
| **B413** SP291 20pf + 10pf multi | .25 | .30 |
| **B414** SP291 30pf + 15pf multi | .25 | .30 |
| **B415** SP291 50pf + 25pf multi | .55 | .80 |
| *Nos. B412-B415 (4)* | 1.30 | 1.70 |

Issued for the benefit of young people.
See Nos. B422-B425; Berlin Nos. 9NB37-
9NB40.

Prussian Letter
Carrier — SP292

Design: 30pf+15pf, Bavarian mail coach.

**1966**      **Litho.**    **Perf. 14**

| | | | |
|---|---|---|---|
| **B416** SP292 30pf + 15pf multi | .35 | .60 |
| **B417** SP292 50pf + 25pf multi | .50 | .60 |

Meeting of the Federation Internationale de
Philatelie (FIP), Munich, Sept. 26-29, and
stamp exhibition, Municipal Museum, Sept.
24-Oct. 1. The surcharge was for the Foundation for the Promotion of Philately and Postal
History.
Issued: No. B416, 9/24; No. B417, 7/13.

**Fairy Tale Type of 1965**

Various Scenes from The Princess and the
Frog.

**1966, Oct. 5**    **Litho.**    **Perf. 14**

| | | | |
|---|---|---|---|
| **B418** SP290 10pf + 5pf multi | .25 | .25 |
| **B419** SP290 20pf + 10pf multi | .25 | .25 |
| **B420** SP290 30pf + 15pf multi | .25 | .25 |
| **B421** SP290 50pf + 25pf multi | .30 | .40 |
| *Nos. B418-B421 (4)* | 1.05 | 1.55 |

Surtax for independent welfare organizations.
See Berlin Nos. 9NB41-9NB44.

**Animal Type of 1966**

10pf+5pf, Rabbit. 20pf+10pf, Ermine.
30pf+15pf, Hamster. 50pf+25pf, Red fox.

**1967, Apr. 4**    **Litho.**    **Perf. 14**

| | | | |
|---|---|---|---|
| **B422** SP291 10pf + 5pf multi | .25 | .35 |
| **B423** SP291 20pf + 10pf multi | .25 | .35 |
| **B424** SP291 30pf + 15pf multi | .40 | .65 |
| **B425** SP291 50pf + 25pf multi | .85 | 1.30 |
| *Nos. B422-B425 (4)* | 1.75 | 2.65 |

Issued for the benefit of young people.
See Berlin Nos. 9NB45-9NB48.

**Fairy Tale Type of 1965**

Various Scenes from Frau Holle.

**1967, Oct. 3    Litho.    Perf. 14**
B426 SP290 10pf + 5pf multi        .25    .25
B427 SP290 20pf + 10pf multi       .25    .25
B428 SP290 30pf + 15pf multi       .25    .25
B429 SP290 50pf + 25pf multi       .40   1.00
   Nos. B426-B429 (4)        1.15   1.75

Surtax for independent welfare organizations.
See Berlin Nos. 9NB49-9NB52.

Wildcat — SP293

Animals: 20pf+10pf, Otter. 30pf+15pf,
Badger. 50pf+25pf, Beaver.

**1968, Feb. 2    Photo.    Unwmk.**
B430 SP293 10pf + 5pf multi        .25    .40
B431 SP293 20pf + 15pf multi       .35    .65
B432 SP293 30pf + 15pf multi       .50    .95
B433 SP293 50pf + 25pf multi      1.30   2.60
   Nos. B430-B433 (4)        2.40   4.60

The surtax was for the benefit of young
people.
See Berlin Nos. 9NB53-9NB56.

### Olympic Games Type of Regular Issue

10pf+5pf, Karl-Friedrich Freiherr von
Langen, equestrian. 20pf+10pf, Rudolf Harbig,
runner. 30pf+15pf, Helene Mayer, fencer.
50pf+25pf, Carl Diem, sports organizer.

### Lithographed and Engraved
**1968, June 6    Unwmk.    Perf. 14**
B434 A285 10 + 5pf ol & dk brn     .55    .35
B435 A285 20 + 10pf dp emer &
       dk grn             .55    .35
B436 A285 30 + 15pf dp rose &
       dk red            1.00    .65
B437 A285 50 + 25pf brt bl & dk
       bl                1.00   1.00
   Nos. B434-B437 (4)        3.10   2.35

The surtax was for the Foundation for the
Promotion of the 1972 Olympic Games in
Munich.

Doll, c. 1878 — SP294

Various 19th Cent. Dolls. Nos. B438-B440
are from Germanic Natl. Museum, Nuremberg; No. B441 is from Altona Museum,
Hamburg.

**1968, Oct. 3    Litho.    Perf. 14**
B438 SP294 10pf + 5pf multi        .25    .25
B439 SP294 20pf + 10pf multi       .25    .25
B440 SP294 30pf + 15pf multi       .25    .25
B441 SP294 50pf + 25pf multi       .50    .80
   Nos. B438-B441 (4)        1.25   1.55

Surtax for independent welfare organizations.
See Berlin Nos. 9NB57-9NB60.

Pony — SP295

Horses: 20pf+10pf, Work horse. 30pf+15pf,
Hotblood. 50pf+25pf, Thoroughbred.

**1969, Feb. 6    Litho.    Perf. 14**
B442 SP295 10pf + 5pf multi        .30    .40
B443 SP295 20pf + 10pf multi       .30    .40
B444 SP295 30pf + 15pf multi       .50    .60
B445 SP295 50pf + 25pf multi      1.45   1.30
   Nos. B442-B445 (4)        2.55   2.75

Surtax for the benefit of young people.
See Berlin Nos. 9NB61-9NB64.

SP296

---

Olympic Rings and: 10pf+5pf, Track.
20pf+10pf, Hockey. 30pf+15pf, Archery.
50pf+25pf, Sailing.

**1969, June 4    Photo.    Perf. 14**
B446 SP296 10pf + 5pf dk brn &
       lem               .65    .50
B447 SP296 20pf + 10pf bl grn &
       emer              .65    .55
B448 SP296 30pf + 15pf mag &
       dp lil rose      1.00    .65
B449 SP296 50pf + 25pf dp bl &
       brt bl           1.60   1.30
   Nos. B446-B449 (4)        3.90   3.00

1972 Olympic Games in Munich. The surtax
was for the German Olympic Committee.

SP297

Tin Toys: 10pf+5pf, Locomotive. 20pf+10pf,
Gardener. 30pf+15pf, Bird seller. 50pf+25pf,
Knight on horseback.

**1969, Oct. 2    Litho.    Perf. 13½x14**
B450 SP297 10pf + 5pf multi        .25    .25
B451 SP297 20pf + 10pf multi       .25    .25
B452 SP297 30pf + 15pf multi       .30    .30
B453 SP297 50pf + 25pf multi       .75   1.00
   Nos. B450-B453 (4)        1.55   1.80

Surtax for independent welfare organizations.
See Berlin Nos. 9NB65-9NB68.

Tin Toy — SP297a

Christmas: 10pf+5pf, Jesus in Manger.

**1969, Nov. 13    Perf. 13½x14**
B454 SP297a 10pf + 5pf multi       .35    .30
   See Berlin No. 9NB69.
   Inscribed: "Weihnachtsmarke 1969"

Heinrich von
Rugge — SP298

Minnesingers: 20pf+10pf, Wolfram von
Eschenbach. 30pf+15pf, Walther von Metz.
50pf+25pf, Walther von der Vogelweide.

**1970, Feb. 5    Photo.    Perf. 13½x14**
B455 SP298 10pf + 5pf multi        .35    .30
B456 SP298 20pf + 10pf multi       .55    .35
B457 SP298 30pf + 15pf multi       .65    .55
B458 SP298 50pf + 25pf multi      1.45   1.30
   Nos. B455-B458 (4)        3.00   2.50

Surtax was for benefit of young people.
See Berlin Nos. 9NB70-9NB73.

Residenz
(Palace), Munich
SP299

Munich Buildings: 20pf+10pf, Propylaea.
30pf+15pf, Glyptothek.    50pf+25pf, Bavaria
Statue and Colonnade.

**1970, June 5    Engr.    Perf. 14**
B459 SP299 10pf + 5pf olive bis    .50    .35
B460 SP299 20pf + 10pf dk bl
       grn               .50    .35
B461 SP299 30pf + 15pf carmine    1.00   1.00
B462 SP299 50pf + 25pf dk blue    1.30   1.30
   Nos. B459-B462 (4)        3.30   3.00

The surtax was for the Foundation for the
Promotion of the 1972 Olympic Games in
Munich.

---

Jester — SP300

Puppets:        20pf+10pf,    "Hanswurst."
30pf+15pf, Clown. 50pf+25pf, Harlequin.

**1970, Oct. 6    Litho.    Perf. 13½x14**
B463 SP300 10pf + 5pf multi        .25    .25
B464 SP300 20pf + 10pf multi       .25    .30
B465 SP300 30pf + 15pf multi       .35    .65
B466 SP300 50pf + 25pf multi       .85    .85
   Nos. B463-B466 (4)        1.70   1.75

Surtax for independent welfare organizations.
See Berlin Nos. 9NB74-9NB77.

**1970, Nov. 12**

Christmas: 10pf+5pf, Rococo Angel, from
Ursuline Sisters' Convent, Innsbruck.
B467 SP300 10pf + 5pf multi        .35    .30
   See Berlin Nos. 9NB78.

King Caspar — SP301

Children's Drawings: 20pf+10pf, Flea.
30pf+15pf, Puss-in-Boots. 50pf+25pf, Snake.

**1971, Feb. 5    Litho.    Perf. 14**
B468 SP301 10pf + 5pf multi        .30    .30
B469 SP301 20pf + 10pf multi       .35    .35
B470 SP301 30pf + 15pf multi       .55    .55
B471 SP301 50pf + 25pf multi       .95    .95
   Nos. B468-B471 (4)        2.15   2.15

Surtax for the benefit of young people.
See Berlin Nos. 9NB79-9NB82.

Ski Jump — SP302

20pf+10pf, Figure skating. 30pf+15pf,
Downhill skiing. 50pf+25pf, Ice hockey.

### "1971" at Lower Right

**1971, June 4    Litho.    Perf. 14**
B472 SP302 10pf + 5pf brn org &
       blk               .30    .30
B473 SP302 20pf + 10pf grn &
       blk               .55    .40
B474 SP302 30pf + 15pf rose red
       & blk            .80    .65
B475 SP302 50pf + 25pf bl & blk   1.45   1.30
  a.  Souvenir sheet of 4    3.00   2.60
  b.  10pf + 5pf brown org & blk  .30  .30
  c.  20pf + 10pf green & black   .55  .40
  d.  30pf + 15pf rose red & black .80 .65
  e.  50pf + 25pf blue & black   1.45  1.20
   Nos. B472-B475 (4)        3.10   2.65

Olympic Games 1972.
No. B475a contains No. B475b-B475e
which lack the small date ("1971") at lower
right.

Women Churning
Butter — SP303

Wooden Toys: 25pf+10pf, Horseback rider.
30pf+15pf, Nutcracker. 60pf+30pf, Dovecot.

**1971, Oct. 5    Litho.    Perf. 14**
B476 SP303 20pf + 10pf multi       .25    .25
B477 SP303 25pf + 10pf multi       .25    .25
B478 SP303 30pf + 15pf multi       .40    .40
B479 SP303 60pf + 30pf multi      1.05   1.05
   Nos. B476-B479 (4)        1.95   1.95

Surtax for independent welfare organizations.
See Berlin Nos. 9NB83-9NB86.

---

**1971, Nov. 11**

Christmas: Christmas angel with lights.
B480 SP303 20pf + 10pf multi       .55    .35
   See Berlin No. 9NB87.

Ducks Crossing
Road — SP304

Designs: 25pf+10pf, Hunter chasing deer
and rabbits.  30pf+15pf, Girl protecting birds
from cat. 60pf+30pf, Boy annoying swans.

**1972, Feb. 4    Litho.    Perf. 14**
B481 SP304 20pf + 10pf multi       .50    .40
B482 SP304 25pf + 10pf multi       .50    .40
B483 SP304 30pf + 15pf multi       .65    .65
B484 SP304 60pf + 30pf multi      1.20   1.20
   Nos. B481-B484 (4)        2.85   2.65

Animal protection. Surtax for the benefit of
young people.
See Berlin Nos. 9NB88-9NB91.

Olympic Rings and
Wrestling — SP305

25pf+10pf, Sailing. 30pf+15pf, Gymnastics.
60pf+30pf, Swimming.

**1972, June 5    Photo.    Perf. 14**
B485 SP305 20pf + 10pf multi      1.30    .65
B486 SP305 25pf + 10pf multi      1.30    .65
B487 SP305 30pf + 15pf multi      1.30    .65
B488 SP305 60pf + 30pf multi      2.10   2.00
   Nos. B485-B488 (4)        6.00   3.95

20th Olympic Games, Munich, Aug. 26
Sept. 10. See No. B490.

### Souvenir Sheet

Olympic
Games
Site,
Munich
SP306

a, Gymnastics stadium. b, Soccer stadium.
c, Tent and lake. d, Television tower, vert.

**1972, July 5    Litho.    Perf. 14**
B489 SP306    Sheet of 4         5.00   5.00
  a.  25pf + 10pf multi        1.00   1.00
  b.  30pf + 15pf multi        1.00   1.00
  c.  40pf + 20pf multi        1.00   1.00
  d.  70pf + 35pf multi        1.00   1.00

20th Olympic Games, Munich. Surcharge
was for the Foundation for the Promotion of
the Munich Olympic Games.

### Olympic Games Type of 1972

a, Long jump, women's. b, Basketball. c,
Discus, women's. d, Canoeing.

### Souvenir Sheet

**1972, Aug. 18    Litho.    Perf. 14**
B490    Sheet of 4               4.50   4.50
  a.  SP305 25pf + 5pf multi     .40    .40
  b.  SP305 30pf + 10pf multi   1.05   1.05
  c.  SP305 40pf + 10pf multi   1.45   1.45
  d.  SP305 70pf + 10pf multi    .75    .75
  e.  Bklt. pane of 4, #B490a-B490d  7.50  7.50

20th Olympic Games, Munich.

Knight — SP307

**1972, Oct. 5**
B491 SP307 25pf + 10pf shown .30 .30
B492 SP307 30pf + 15pf Rook .30 .25
B493 SP307 40pf + 20pf Queen .50 .25
B494 SP307 70pf + 35pf King 1.60 1.60
Nos. B491-B494 (4) 2.70 2.40

19th cent. chess pieces made by Faience Works, Gien, France; now in Hamburg Museum. Surtax for independent welfare organizations.
See Berlin Nos. 9NB92-9NB95.

Adoration of the Kings — SP308

**1972, Nov. 10** Litho.
B495 SP308 30pf + 15pf multi .80 .50
Christmas.
See Berlin No. 9NB96.

Osprey — SP309

Birds of Prey: 30pf+15pf, Buzzard. 40pf+20pf, Red kite. 70pf+35pf, Montagu's harrier.

**1973, Feb. 6** Photo. Perf. 14
B496 SP309 25pf + 10pf multi .65 .65
B497 SP309 30pf + 15pf multi .80 .80
B498 SP309 40pf + 20pf multi 1.20 1.20
B499 SP309 70pf + 35pf multi 3.00 3.00
Nos. B496-B499 (4) 5.65 5.65

Surtax was for benefit of young people.
See Berlin Nos. 9NB97-9NB100.

Hesse-Kassel — SP310

Posthouse Signs: No. B501, Prussia. No. B502a, Württemberg. No. B502b, Bavaria.

**1973, Apr. 5** Litho. Perf. 14
B500 SP310 40pf + 20pf multi .60 .60
B501 SP310 70pf + 35pf multi 1.05 1.05
**Souvenir Sheet**
B502 Sheet of 2 3.00 3.00
a. SP310 40pf + 20pf multi 1.30 1.30
b. SP310 70pf + 35pf multi 1.30 1.30

IBRA München 1973 International Philatelic Exhibition, Munich, May 11-20. No. B502 sold for 2.20 mark.

French Horn, 19th Century — SP311

Musical Instruments: 30pf+15pf, Pedal piano, 18th century. 40pf+20pf, Violin, 18th century. 70pf+35pf, Pedal harp, 18th century.

**1973, Oct. 5** Litho. Perf. 14
B503 SP311 25pf + 10pf multi .50 .35
B504 SP311 30pf + 15pf multi .55 .35
B505 SP311 40pf + 20pf multi .65 .40
B506 SP311 70pf + 35pf multi 1.30 1.30
Nos. B503-B506 (4) 3.00 2.40

Surtax was for independent welfare organizations.
See Berlin Nos. 9NB101-9NB104.

Christmas Star — SP312

**1973, Nov. 9** Litho. & Engr.
B507 SP312 30pf + 15pf multi .80 .50
Christmas.
See Berlin No. 9NB105.

Young Builder — SP313

30+15pf, Girl in national costume. 40+20pf, Boy studying. 70+35pf, Girl with microscope.

**1974, Apr. 17** Photo. Perf. 14
B508 SP313 25pf + 10pf multi .50 .40
B509 SP313 30pf + 15pf multi .80 .65
B510 SP313 40pf + 20pf multi 1.30 1.20
B511 SP313 70pf + 35pf multi 2.40 2.40
Nos. B508-B511 (4) 5.00 4.65

Surtax was for benefit of young people.
See Berlin Nos. 9NB106-9NB109.

Campion — SP314

Flowers: 40pf+20pf, Foxglove. 50pf+25pf, Mallow. 70pf+35pf, Bellflower.

**1974, Oct. 15** Litho. Perf. 14
B512 SP314 30pf + 15pf multi .30 .30
B513 SP314 40pf + 20pf multi .35 .30
B514 SP314 50pf + 25pf multi .40 .35
B515 SP314 70pf + 35pf multi 1.15 1.15
Nos. B512-B515 (4) 2.20 2.10

Surtax was for independent welfare organizations.
See Berlin Nos. 9NB110-9NB113.

**1974, Oct. 29**
Christmas: 40pf+20pf, Poinsettia.
B516 SP314 40pf + 20pf multi .80 .50
See Berlin No. 9NB114.

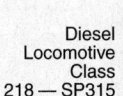

Diesel Locomotive Class 218 — SP315

Locomotives: 40pf+20pf, Electric engine Class 103. 50pf+25pf, Electric rail motor train Class 403. 70pf+35pf, Magnetic suspension train "Transrapid" (model).

**1975, Apr. 15** Litho. Perf. 14
B517 SP315 30pf + 15pf multi .30 .30
B518 SP315 40pf + 20pf multi .50 .40
B519 SP315 50pf + 25pf multi .65 .60
B520 SP315 70pf + 35pf multi 1.25 1.00
Nos. B517-B520 (4) 2.70 2.30

Surtax was for benefit of young people.
See Berlin Nos. 9NB115-9NB118.

Edelweiss — SP316

Alpine Flowers: 40pf+20pf, Trollflower. 50pf+25pf, Alpine rose. 70pf+35pf, Pasqueflower.

**1975, Oct. 15** Litho. Perf. 14
B521 SP316 30pf + 15pf multi .35 .30
B522 SP316 40pf + 20pf multi .35 .30
B523 SP316 50pf + 25pf multi .55 .40
B524 SP316 70pf + 35pf multi 1.20 1.20
Nos. B521-B524 (4) 2.45 2.20

Surtax was for independent welfare organizations.
See Berlin Nos. 9NB119-9NB122.

**1975, Nov. 14**
Christmas: Snow rose.
B525 SP316 40pf + 20pf multi 1.15 .80
See Berlin No. 9NB123.

Basketball — SP317

Designs: 40pf+20pf, Rowing. 50pf+25pf, Gymnastics, women's. 70pf+35pf, Volleyball.

**1976, Apr. 6** Litho. Perf. 14
B526 SP317 30pf + 15pf multi .40 .30
B527 SP317 40pf + 20pf multi .75 .55
B528 SP317 50pf + 25pf multi .95 .80
B529 SP317 70pf + 35pf multi 1.25 1.15
Nos. B526-B529 (4) 3.35 2.80

Youth training for Olympic Games. Surtax was for benefit of young people.
See Berlin Nos. 9NB124-9NB127.

Swimmer and Olympic Rings SP318

30pf+15pf, Hockey. 50pf+25pf, High jump. 70pf+35pf, Rowing, coxed four.

**1976, Apr. 6**
B530 SP318 40pf + 20pf multi 1.00 .65
B531 SP318 50pf + 25pf multi 1.30 1.00
**Souvenir Sheet**
B532 Sheet of 2 2.00 1.60
a. SP318 30pf + 15pf multi .80 .65
b. SP318 70pf + 35pf multi 1.05 1.00

21st Olympic Games, Montreal, Canada, July 17-Aug. 1. The surtax was for the German Sports Aid Foundation.

Phlox — SP319

Flowers: 40pf+20pf, Marigolds. 50pf+25pf, Dahlias. 70pf+35pf, Pansies.

**1976, Oct. 14** Litho. Perf. 14
B533 SP319 30pf + 15pf multi .40 .35
B534 SP319 40pf + 20pf multi .55 .50
B535 SP319 50pf + 25pf multi .60 .55
B536 SP319 70pf + 35pf multi 1.00 1.00
Nos. B533-B536 (4) 2.55 2.40

Surtax was for independent welfare organizations.

**Souvenir Sheet**

Nativity, Window, Frauenkirche, Esslingen — SP320

**1976, Nov. 16** Litho. & Engr.
B537 SP320 50pf + 25pf multi .80 .75
Christmas.
See Berlin No. 9NB132.

Wapen von Hamburg, c. 1730 — SP321

Historic Ships: 40pf+20pf, Preussen, 5-master, 1902. 50pf+25pf, Bremen, 1929. 70pf+35pf, Freighter Sturmfels, 1972.

**1977, Apr. 14** Litho. Perf. 14
B538 SP321 30pf + 15pf multi .50 .50
B539 SP321 40pf + 20pf multi .60 .55
B540 SP321 50pf + 25pf multi .80 .75
B541 SP321 70pf + 35pf multi 1.15 1.15
Nos. B538-B541 (4) 3.05 2.95

Surtax was for benefit of young people.
See Berlin Nos. 9NB133-9NB136.

Caraway — SP322

Meadow Flowers: 40pf+20pf, Dandelion. 50pf+25pf, Red clover. 70pf+35pf, Meadow sage.

**1977, Oct. 13** Litho. Perf. 14
B542 SP322 30pf + 15pf multi .60 .30
B543 SP322 40pf + 20pf multi .60 .35
B544 SP322 50pf + 25pf multi .60 .40
B545 SP322 70pf + 35pf multi 1.20 1.00
Nos. B542-B545 (4) 3.00 2.05

Surtax was for independent welfare organizations.
See Nos. B553-B556; Berlin Nos. 9NB137-9NB140.

**Souvenir Sheet**

King Caspar Offering Gold, Window, St. Gereon's, Cologne — SP323

**1977, Nov. 10**
B546 SP323 50pf + 25pf multi .75 .75
Christmas.
See Berlin No. 9NB141.

Giant Slalom — SP324

Design: No. B548, Steeplechase.

**1978** Litho. **Perf. 14**
B547 SP324 50pf + 25pf multi 1.20 1.00
B548 SP324 70pf + 35pf multi 2.60 2.25

Issued: No. B547, Jan. 12, No. B548, Apr. 13.

Surtax was for the German Sports Foundation.
See Berlin Nos. 9NB146-9NB147.

Balloon Ascent, Oktoberfest, Munich, 1820 — SP325

Designs: 40pf+20pf, Airship LZ 1, 1900. 50pf+25pf, Bleriot monoplane, 1909. 70pf+35pf, Grade monoplane, 1909.

**1978, Apr. 13** Litho. **Perf. 14**
B549 SP325 30pf + 15pf multi .40 .40
B550 SP325 40pf + 20pf multi .55 .55
B551 SP325 50pf + 25pf multi .75 .75
B552 SP325 70pf + 35pf multi 1.00 1.00
    Nos. B549-B552 (4) 2.70 2.70

Surtax was for benefit of young people.
See Berlin Nos. 9NB142-9NB145.

**Flower Type of 1977**

Woodland Flowers: 30pf+15pf, Arum. 40pf+20pf, Weaselsnout. 50pf+25pf, Turk's-cap lily. 70pf+35pf, Liverwort.

**1978, Oct. 12** Litho. **Perf. 14**
B553 SP322 30pf + 15pf multi .35 .30
B554 SP322 40pf + 20pf multi .50 .40
B555 SP322 50pf + 25pf multi .65 .60
B556 SP322 70pf + 35pf multi .85 .85
    Nos. B553-B556 (4) 2.35 2.15

Surtax was for independent welfare organizations.
See Berlin Nos. 9NB148-9NB151.

**Souvenir Sheet**

Christ Child, Window, Frauenkirche, Munich — SP326

**1978, Nov. 16** Litho. **Perf. 14**
B557 SP326 50pf + 25pf multi .95 .65

Christmas.
See Berlin No. 9NB152.

Dornier Wal, 1922 — SP327

Airplanes: 50pf+25pf, Heinkel HE70, 1932. 60pf+30pf, Junkers W33 Bremen, 1928. 90pf+45pf, Focke-Wulf FW61, 1936.

**1979, Apr. 5** Litho. **Perf. 14**
B558 SP327 40pf + 20pf multi .50 .50
B559 SP327 50pf + 25pf multi .65 .65
B560 SP327 60pf + 30pf multi .80 .80
B561 SP327 90pf + 45pf multi 1.05 1.05
    Nos. B558-B561 (4) 3.00 3.00

Surtax was for benefit of young people.
See Nos. B570-B573; Berlin Nos. 9NB153-9NB156.

Handball SP328

Design: 90pf+45pf, Canoeing.

**1979, Apr. 5** Litho.
B562 SP328 60pf + 30pf multi .80 .75
B563 SP328 90pf + 45pf multi 1.20 1.05

Surtax was for German Sports Foundation.
See Berlin Nos. 9NB157-9NB158.

Post House Sign, Altheim, Saar, 1754 — SP329

**1979, Oct. 11** Litho. **Perf. 14**
B564 SP329 60pf + 30pf multi .95 .95

Stamp Day. Surtax was for Foundation of Promotion of Philately and Postal History.

Red Beech — SP330

Woodland Plants: 50pf+25pf, English oak. 60pf+30pf, Hawthorn. 90pf+45pf, Mountain pine.

**1979, Oct. 11** Litho. **Perf. 14**
B565 SP330 40pf + 20pf multi .65 .40
B566 SP330 50pf + 25pf multi .65 .55
B567 SP330 60pf + 30pf multi .65 .60
B568 SP330 90pf + 45pf multi 1.00 1.00
    Nos. B565-B568 (4) 2.95 2.55

Surtax was for independent welfare organizations.
See Berlin Nos. 9NB159-9NB162.

Nativity, Medieval Manuscript SP331

**1979, Nov. 14** Litho. **Perf. 13½**
B569 SP331 60pf + 30pf multi .80 .80

Christmas.
See Berlin No. 9NB163.

**Aviation Type of 1979**

40pf+20pf, FS 24 Phoenix, 1957. 50pf+25pf, Lockheed Super Constellation, 1950. 60pf+30pf, Airbus A300, 1972. 90pf+45pf, Boeing 747, 1969.

**1980, Apr. 10** Litho. **Perf. 14**
B570 SP327 40 + 20pf multi .35 .35
B571 SP327 50 + 25pf multi .55 .55
B572 SP327 60 + 30pf multi .75 .75
B573 SP327 90 + 45pf multi 1.05 1.05
    Nos. B570-B573 (4) 2.70 2.70

Surtax was for benefit of young people.
See Berlin Nos. 9NB164-9NB167.

Soccer — SP332

Designs: 60pf+30pf, Equestrian. 90pf+45pf, Cross-country skiing.

**1980, May 8** Photo. **Perf. 14**
B574 SP332 50 + 25pf multi .50 .40
B575 SP332 60 + 30pf multi .65 .55
B576 SP332 90 + 45pf multi 1.20 1.20
    Nos. B574-B576 (3) 2.35 2.15

Surtax was for German Sports Foundation.
See Berlin Nos. 9NB168-9NB170.

Because of Germany's boycott of the 1980 Olympics in Russia, the postal administration pulled the planned 60+30pf semipostal before it was issued. A postal official used several examples, releasing them to collectors.

Ceratocephalus SP333

Wildflowers: 50pf+25pf, Climbing meadow pea. 60pf+30pf, Corn cockle. 90pf+45pf, Grape hyacinth.

**1980, Oct. 9** Litho. **Perf. 14**
B577 SP333 40 + 20pf multi .50 .40
B578 SP333 50 + 25pf multi .60 .55
B579 SP333 60 + 30pf multi .65 .65
B580 SP333 90 + 45pf multi 1.05 1.05
    Nos. B577-B580 (4) 2.80 2.65

Surtax was for independent welfare organizations.
See Berlin Nos. 9NB171-9NB174.

Post House Sign, 1754, Altheim, Saar — SP334

**1980, Nov. 13** Litho. **Perf. 14**
B581 SP334 60 + 30pf multi .65 .60

49th FIP Congress (Federation Internationale de Philatelie), Essen, Nov. 12-13.

Nativity, Altomunster Manuscript, 12th Century — SP335

**1980, Nov. 13** **Perf. 14x13½**
B582 SP335 60 + 30pf multi .85 .80

Christmas.
See Berlin No. 9NB175.

Borda Circle, 1800 — SP336

Historic Optical Instruments: 50pf+25pf, Reflecting telescope, 1770. 60pf+30pf, Binocular microscope, 1860. 90pf+45pf, Octant, 1775.

**1981, Apr. 10** Litho. **Perf. 13½**
B583 SP336 40 + 20pf multi .50 .35
B584 SP336 50 + 25pf multi .80 .65
B585 SP336 60 + 30pf multi .80 .65
B586 SP336 90 + 45pf multi 1.15 1.15
    Nos. B583-B586 (4) 3.25 2.80

Surtax was for benefit of young people.
See Berlin Nos. 9NB176-9NB179.

Rowing SP337

**1981, Apr. 10** **Perf. 14**
B587 SP337 60 + 30pf shown .65 .65
B588 SP337 90 + 45pf Gliding 1.05 1.05

Surtax was for the German Sports Foundation.
See Berlin Nos. 9NB180-9NB181.

Water Nut — SP338

Endangered Species: 50pf+25pf, Floating heart. 60pf+30pf, Water gillyflower. 90pf+45pf, Water lobelia.

**1981, Oct. 8** Litho.
B589 SP338 40 + 20pf multi .40 .35
B590 SP338 50 + 25pf multi .55 .50
B591 SP338 60 + 30pf multi .65 .65
B592 SP338 90 + 45pf multi 1.20 1.20
    Nos. B589-B592 (4) 2.80 2.70

Surtax was for independent welfare organizations.
See Berlin Nos. 9NB182-9NB185.

Nativity, 19th Cent. Painting — SP339

**1981, Nov. 12** Litho.
B593 SP339 60 + 30pf multi .85 .75

Christmas.
See Berlin No. 9NB186.

Antique Cars — SP340

Designs: 40+20pf, Benz, 1886. 50+25pf, Mercedes, 1913. 60+30pf, Hanomag, 1925. 90+45pf, Opel Olympia, 1937.

**1982, Apr. 15** Litho.
B594 SP340 40 + 20pf multi .50 .40
B595 SP340 50 + 25pf multi .60 .55
B596 SP340 60 + 30pf multi .75 .75
B597 SP340 90 + 45pf multi 1.45 1.45
    Nos. B594-B597 (4) 3.35 3.05

Surtax was for benefit of young people.
See Berlin Nos. 9NB187-9NB190.

Jogging SP341

**1982, Apr. 15** Litho.
B598 SP341 60 + 30pf shown .75 .75
B599 SP341 90 + 45pf Archery 1.15 1.15

Surtax was for the German Sports Foundation.
See Berlin Nos. 9NB191-9NB192.

Tea-rose Hybrid — SP342

60+30pf, Floribunda. 80f+40pf, Bourbon rose. 120+60pf, Polyantha hybrid.

**1982, Oct. 14** Litho. **Perf. 14**
B600 SP342 50 + 20pf multi .50 .40
B601 SP342 60 + 30pf multi .60 .55
B602 SP342 80 + 40pf multi .95 .85
B603 SP342 120 + 60pf multi 1.30 1.20
    Nos. B600-B603 (4) 3.35 3.00

Surtax was for independent welfare organizations.
See Berlin Nos. 9NB193-9NB196.

Christmas — SP343

Designs: Nativity, Oak altar, St. Peter's Church, Hamburg, 1380.

**1982, Nov. 10**
B604 SP343 80 + 40pf multi          1.30   .95
See Berlin No. 9NB197.

Historic Motorcycles SP344

Designs: 50pf+20pf, Daimler-Mayback, 1885. 60pf+30pf, NSU, 1901. 80pf+40pf, Megola-Sport, 1922. 120pf+60pf, BMW, 1936.

**1983, Apr. 12     Litho.     Perf. 14**
B605 SP344 50 + 20pf multi          .50   .40
B606 SP344 60 + 30pf multi          .60   .55
B607 SP344 80 + 40pf multi         1.05  1.00
B608 SP344 120 + 60pf multi        1.60  1.45
   Nos. B605-B608 (4)              3.75  3.40

Surtax was for benefit of young people. See Berlin Nos. 9NB198-9NB201.

1983 Sports Championships SP345

80+40pf, Gymnastics Festival. 120+60pf, Modern Pentathlon World Championships.

**1983, Apr. 12**
B609 SP345 80 + 40pf multi         1.00   .85
B610 SP345 120 + 60pf multi        1.60  1.45

Surtax was for German Sports Foundation. See Berlin Nos. 9NB202-9NB203.

Swiss Androsace — SP346

60+30pf, Krain groundsel. 80+40pf, Fleischer's willow herb. 120+60pf, Alpine sowthistle.

**1983, Oct. 13     Litho.     Perf. 14**
B611 SP346 50 + 20pf multi          .40   .40
B612 SP346 60 + 30pf multi          .55   .55
B613 SP346 80 + 40pf multi         1.00  1.00
B614 SP346 120 + 60pf multi        1.45  1.45
   Nos. B611-B614 (4)              3.40  3.40

Surtax was for welfare organizations. See Berlin Nos. 9NB204-9NB207.

Christmas — SP347

**1983, Nov. 10     Litho.**
B615 SP347 80 + 40pf Carolers   1.30  1.05

Surtax was for free welfare work. See Berlin No. 9NB208.

Insects — SP348

Designs: 50pf+20pf, Trichodes apoarius. 60pf+30pf, Vanessa atalanta. 80pf+40pf, Apis mellifera. 120pf+60pf, Chrysotoxum festivum.

**1984, Apr. 12          Litho.**
B616 SP348 50 + 20pf multi          .50   .50
B617 SP348 60 + 30pf multi          .85   .85
B618 SP348 80 + 40pf multi         1.15  1.15
B619 SP348 120 + 60pf multi        1.75  1.75
   Nos. B616-B619 (4)              4.25  4.25

Surtax was for German Youth Stamp Foundation. See Berlin Nos. 9NB209-9NB212.

Women's Discus — SP349

Olympic Sports: 80pf+40pf, Rhythmic gymnastics. 120pf+60pf, Wind surfing.

**1984, Apr. 12**
B620 SP349 60 + 30pf multi         1.30  1.00
B621 SP349 80 + 40pf multi         2.00  1.60
B622 SP349 120 + 60pf multi        3.75  2.60
   Nos. B620-B622 (3)              7.05  5.20

Surtax was for German Sports Foundation. See Berlin Nos. 9NB213-9NB215.

Orchids — SP350

Designs: 50pf+20pf, Aceras anthropophorum. 60pf+30pf, Orchis ustulata. 80pf+40pf, Limodorum abortivum. 120pf+60pf, Dactylorhiza sambucina.

**1984, Oct. 18     Litho.     Perf. 14**
B623 SP350 50 + 20pf multi          .60   .60
B624 SP350 60 + 30pf multi          .60   .60
B625 SP350 80 + 40pf multi          .95   .95
B626 SP350 120 + 60pf multi        2.00  2.00
   Nos. B623-B626 (4)              4.15  4.15

Surtax was for welfare organizations. See Berlin Nos. 9NB216-9NB219.

Christmas 1984 — SP351

No. B627, St. Martin.

**1984, Nov. 8          Litho.**
B627 SP351 80pf + 40pf multi   1.05  1.05

Surtax was for welfare organizations. See Berlin No. 9NB220.

Bowling SP352

No. B629, Kayaking.

**1985, Feb. 21          Photo.**
B628 SP352 80pf + 40pf multi    1.05   .95
B629 SP352 120pf + 60pf multi   1.75  1.60

Surtax was for German Sports Foundation. See Berlin Nos. 9NB221-9NB222.

Antique Bicycles — SP353

50pf+20pf, Draisienne, 1817. 60pf+30pf, NSU Germania, 1886. 80pf+40pf, Crossframe, 1887. 120pf+60pf, Adler tricycle, 1888.

**1985, Apr. 16**
B630 SP353 50pf + 20pf multi    .65   .65
B631 SP353 60pf + 30pf multi    .80   .80
B632 SP353 80pf + 40pf multi   1.05  1.05
B633 SP353 120pf + 60pf multi  2.10  2.10
   Nos. B630-B633 (4)          4.60  4.60

Surtax was for benefit of young people. Each stamp shows the Intl. Youth Year emblem. See Berlin Nos. 9NB223-9NB226.

MOPHILA '85, Hamburg, Sept. 11-15 — SP354

No. B634, Coachman, horses. No. 635, Stagecoach.

**1985, Aug. 13   Litho.   Perf. 14x14½**
B634 SP354 60 + 20pf multi      2.00  1.60
B635 SP354 80 + 20pf multi      2.00  1.60
   a. Pair, #B634-B635          4.50  3.75

Surtax for the benefit of the Philatelic & Postal History Foundation. No. B635a has continuous design.

SP355

Various ornamental borders, medieval prayer book, Prussian State Library, Berlin.

**1985, Oct. 15     Litho.     Perf. 14**
B636 SP355 50pf + 20pf multi    .80   .55
B637 SP355 60pf + 30pf multi    .80   .65
B638 SP355 80pf + 40pf multi    .95   .85
B639 SP355 120pf + 60pf multi  1.60  1.60
   Nos. B636-B639 (4)          4.15  3.65

Surtax for welfare organizations. See Berlin Nos. 9NB227-9NB230.

Christmas 1985 — SP356

Woodcut: The Birth of Christ, by Hans Baldung Grien (1485-1545), Freiburg Cathedral High Altar.

**1985, Nov. 12     Litho.     Perf. 14**
B640 SP356 80pf + 40pf multi   1.25  .125

Surtax for welfare organizations. See Berlin No. 9NB231.

European World Sports Championships SP357

No. B641, Running. No. B642, Bobsledding.

**1986, Feb. 13     Litho.     Perf. 14**
B641 SP357 80 + 40pf multi     1.30  1.30
B642 SP357 120 + 55pf multi    2.00  2.00

Surtax for the Natl. Sports Promotion Foundation. See Berlin Nos. 9NB232-9NB233.

Vocational Training SP358

No. B643, Optician. No. B644, Mason. No. B645, Beautician. No. B646, Baker.

**1986, Apr. 10**
B643 SP358 50 + 25pf multi      .85   .85
B644 SP358 60 + 30pf multi     1.00  1.00
B645 SP358 70 + 35pf multi     1.15  1.15
B646 SP358 80 + 40pf multi     1.45  1.45
   Nos. B643-B646 (4)          4.45  4.45

Surtax for German Youth Stamp Foundation. See Berlin Nos. 9NB234-9NB237.

Glassware in German Museums — SP359

No. B647, Ornamental flask, c. 300. No. B648, Goblet, c. 1650. No. B649, Imperial

eagle tankard, c. 1662. No. B650, Engraved goblet, c. 1720.

**1986, Oct. 16          Litho.**
B647 SP359 50 + 25pf multi      .60   .55
B648 SP359 60 + 30pf multi      .80   .75
B649 SP359 70 + 35pf multi      .95   .80
B650 SP359 80 + 40pf multi     1.05  1.00
   Nos. B647-B650 (4)          3.40  3.10

Surtax for public welfare organizations. See Berlin Nos. 9NB238-9NB241.

Christmas — SP360

Adoration of the Infant Jesus, Ortenberg Altarpiece, c. 1430, Hesse Museum, Darmstadt.

**1986, Nov. 13     Litho.     Perf. 14**
B651 SP360 80 + 40pf multi     1.20  1.15

Surtax for public welfare organizations. See Berlin No. 9NB242.

World Championships SP361

No. B652, Sailing. No. B653, Cross-country skiing.

**1987, Feb. 12          Litho.**
B652 SP361 80 + 40pf multi     1.15  1.15
B653 SP361 120 + 55pf multi    1.75  1.75

Surtax for the benefit of the national Sports Promotion Foundation. See Berlin Nos. 9NB243-9NB244.

Youth in Industry SP362

No. B654, Plumber. No. B655, Dental technician. No. B656, Butcher. No. B657, Bookbinder.

**1987, Apr. 9          Litho.**
B654 SP362 50 + 25pf multi     1.00   .95
B655 SP362 60 + 30pf multi     1.20  1.15
B656 SP362 70 + 35pf multi     1.30  1.20
B657 SP362 80 + 40pf multi     1.75  1.75
   Nos. B654-B657 (4)          5.25  5.05

Surtax for youth organizations. See Berlin Nos. 9NB245-9NB248.

Gold and Silver Artifacts SP363

No. B658, Roman bracelet, 4th cent. No. B659, Gothic buckle, 6th cent. No. B660, Merovingian disk fibula, 7th cent. No. B661, Purse-shaped reliquary, 8th cent.

**1987, Oct. 15**
B658 SP363 50 + 25pf multi     1.00  1.00
B659 SP363 60 + 30pf multi     1.00  1.00
B660 SP363 70 + 35pf multi     1.00  1.00
B661 SP363 80 + 40pf multi     1.30  1.30
   Nos. B658-B661 (4)          4.30  4.30

Surtax for welfare organizations sponsoring free museum exhibitions. See Berlin Nos. 9NB249-9NB252.

Christmas — SP364

Illustration from Book of Psalms, 13th cent., Bavarian Natl. Museum: Birth of Christ.

**1987, Nov. 6**
B662 SP364 80 + 40pf multi          1.20 1.20

Surtax for public welfare organizations. See Berlin No. 9NB253.

Sports — SP365

**1988, Feb. 18**                    **Litho.**
B663 SP365 60 + 30pf Soccer          2.25 1.60
B664 SP365 80 + 40pf Tennis          2.25 2.00
B665 SP365 120 + 55pf Diving         3.75 3.00
   *Nos. B663-B665 (3)*              8.25 6.60

Surtax for Stiftung Deutsche Sporthilfe, a foundation for the promotion of sports in Germany. See Berlin Nos. 9NB254-9NB256.

Rock Stars — SP366

No. B666, Buddy Holly (1936-59). No. B667, Elvis Presley (1935-77). No. B668, Jim Morrison (1943-71). No. B669, John Lennon (1940-80).

**1988, Apr. 14      Litho.      Perf. 14**
B666 SP366 50 + 25pf multi          1.00 1.20
B667 SP366 60 + 30pf multi          2.25 2.00
B668 SP366 70 + 35pf multi          1.20 1.30
B669 SP366 80 + 40pf multi          2.10 1.75
   *Nos. B666-B669 (4)*             6.55 6.25

Surtax for German Youth Stamp Foundation. See Berlin Nos. 9NB257-9NB260.

Gold and Rock Crystal Reliquary, c. 1200, Schnutgen Museum, Cologne — SP367

Gold and silver artifacts: No. B671, Bust of Charlemagne, 14th cent., Aachen cathedral. No. B672, Crown of Otto III, 10th cent., Essen cathedral. No. B673, Flower bouquet, c. 1620, Schmuck Museum, Pforzheim.

**1988, Oct. 13**                    **Litho.**
B670 SP367 50 + 25pf multi           .55  .55
B671 SP367 60 + 30pf multi           .80  .80
B672 SP367 70 + 35pf multi           .80  .80
B673 SP367 80 + 40pf multi          1.20 1.20
   *Nos. B670-B673 (4)*             3.35 3.35

Surtax for welfare organizations. See Berlin Nos. 9NB261-9NB264.

Christmas — SP368

Illumination from *The Gospel Book of Henry the Lion*, Helmarshausen, 1188, Prussian Cultural Museum, Bavaria: Adoration of the Magi.

**1988, Nov. 10**
B674 SP368 80 + 40pf multi          1.20 1.05

Surtax for public welfare organizations. See Berlin No. 9NB265.

World Championship Sporting Events Hosted by Germany SP369

No. B675, Table tennis. No. B676, Gymnastics.

**1989, Feb. 9**                     **Litho.**
B675 SP369 100pf + 50pf multi       1.45 1.45
B676 SP369 140pf + 60pf multi       2.25 2.25

Surtax for the Natl. Sports Promotion Foundation. See Berlin Nos. 9NB266-9NB267.

IPHLA Philatelic Literature Exhibition, Frankfurt, Apr. 19-23 — SP370

**1989, Apr. 20**                    **Litho.**
B677 SP370 100 + 50pf multi         2.25 2.10

Surtax benefited the Foundation for the Promotion of Philately and Postal History.

Circus — SP371

No. B678, Elephants. No. B679, Bareback rider. No. B680, Clown. No. B681, Caravans, big top.

**1989, Apr. 20**
B678 SP371 60 + 30pf multi          1.30 1.30
B679 SP371 70 + 30pf multi          1.60 1.60
B680 SP371 80 + 35pf multi          2.25 2.00
B681 SP371 100 + 50pf multi         3.75 2.25
   *Nos. B678-B681 (4)*             8.90 7.15

Surtax for natl. youth welfare organizations. See Berlin Nos. 9NB268-9NB271.

Mounted Courier of Thurn and Taxis, 18th Cent. — SP372

History of mail carrying: No. B683, Hamburg postal service messenger, 1808. No. B684, Bavarian mail coach, c. 1900.

**1989, Oct. 12**                    **Litho.**
B682 SP372 60 + 30pf multi          1.00  .95
B683 SP372 80 + 35pf multi          1.60 1.30
B684 SP372 100 + 50pf multi         2.60 2.10
   *Nos. B682-B684 (3)*             5.20 4.35

Surtax for the benefit of Free Welfare Work. See Berlin Nos. 9NB272-9NB274.

Christmas — SP373

Wood carvings by Veit Stoss in St. Lawrence's Church, Nuremburg, 1517-18: No. B685, Angel. No. B686, Adoration of the Kings.

**1989, Nov. 16**                    **Litho.**
B685 SP373 60 + 30pf multi          1.05  .95
B686 SP373 100 + 50pf multi         1.30 1.20

Surtax for benefit of the Federal Working Assoc. of Free Welfare Work. See Berlin Nos. 9NB275-9NB276.

Popular Sports — SP374

No. B687, Handball. No. B688, Physical fitness.

**1990, Feb. 15**                    **Litho.**
B687 SP374 100 + 50pf multi         2.10 1.30
B688 SP374 140 + 60pf multi         2.50 2.00

Surtax for the Natl. Sports Promotion Foundation. See Berlin Nos. 9NB277-9NB278.

*Max and Moritz*, by Wilhelm Busch, 125th Anniv. — SP375

No. B689, Widow Bolte. No. B690, Max. No. B691, Max and Moritz. No. B692, Max and Moritz, diff.

**1990, Apr. 19**                    **Litho.**
B689 SP375 60 + 30pf multi           .75  .75
B690 SP375 70 + 30pf multi          1.05 1.05
B691 SP375 80 + 35pf multi          1.45 1.30
B692 SP375 100 + 50pf multi         1.75 1.60
   *Nos. B689-B692 (4)*             5.00 4.70

Surcharge for the German Youth Stamp Foundation. See Berlin Nos. 9NB279-9NB282.

**Souvenir Sheet**

Dusseldorf '90 — SP376

**1990, June 21**                    **Litho.**
B693 SP376   Sheet of 6             16.50 19.00
   a.   100pf + 50pf multi          2.25 2.25

Surtax for the Foundation for Promotion of Philately and Postal History. 10th Intl. Philatelic Exhibition of Youth and 11th Natl. Philatelic Exhibition of Youth.

Post and Telecommunications SP377

Designs: 60pf+30pf, Postal vehicle, 1900. 80pf+35pf, Telephone exchange, 1890. 100pf+50pf, Post office, 1900.

**1990, Sept. 27   Litho.   Perf. 13½x14**
B694 SP377 60pf + 30pf multi         .75  .75
B695 SP377 80pf + 35pf multi        1.20 1.20
B696 SP377 100pf + 50pf multi       1.75 1.75
   *Nos. B694-B696 (3)*             3.70 3.70

Surtax for welfare organizations. See Berlin Nos. 9NB283-9NB285.

Christmas — SP378

No. B698, Smoking manikin. No. B699, Nutcracker. No. B700, Angel, diff.

**1990, Nov. 6      Litho.      Perf. 14**
B697 SP378 50pf + 20pf shown         .65  .65
B698 SP378 60pf + 30pf multi         .80  .80
B699 SP378 70pf + 30pf multi        1.05 1.05
B700 SP378 100pf + 50pf multi       1.60 1.60
   *Nos. B697-B700 (4)*             4.10 4.10

Surtax for welfare organizations.

Sports — SP379

No. B701, Weight lifting. No. B702, Cycling. No. B703, Basketball. No. B704, Wrestling.

**1991, Feb. 14      Litho.      Perf. 14**
B701 SP379 70 +30pf multi           1.30 1.30
B702 SP379 100 +50pf multi          1.30 1.30
B703 SP379 140 +60pf multi          2.00 2.00
B704 SP379 170 +80pf multi          2.00 2.00
   *Nos. B701-B704 (4)*             6.60 6.60

Surtax for the Foundation for the Promotion of Sports.

Endangered Butterflies — SP380

No. B705, Alpen gelbling, alpine sulphur. No. B706, Grosser eisvogel, Viceroy. No. B707, Grosser schillerfalter, purple emperor. No. B708, Blauschillernder beuerfalter, bluish copper. No. B709,Schwalben-schwanz, swallowtail. No. B710, Alpen apollo, alpine apollo. No. B711, Hochmoor gelbling, moor sulphur. No. B712, Grosser feuerfalter, large copper.

**1991, Apr. 9      Litho.      Perf. 13½**
B705 SP380 30 +15pf multi            .35  .35
B706 SP380 50 +25pf multi            .40  .40
B707 SP380 60 +30pf multi            .80  .80
B708 SP380 70 +30pf multi            .85  .85
B709 SP380 80 +35pf multi           1.05 1.05
B710 SP380 90 +45pf multi           1.30 1.30
B711 SP380 100 +50pf multi          1.60 1.60
B712 SP380 140 +60pf multi          2.00 2.00
   *Nos. B705-B712 (8)*             8.35 8.35

Surtax for German Youth Stamp Foundation. See Nos. B728-B732.

**Souvenir Sheet**

Otto Lilienthal's First Glider Flight, Cent. SP381

**1991, July 9      Litho.      Perf. 14**
B713 SP381 100pf +50pf multi        2.75 2.40

Surtax benefited Foundation of Philately and Postal History.

Post Offices — SP382

30pf+15pf, Bethel. 60pf+30pf, Budingen postal station. 70pf+30pf, Stralsund. 80pf+35pf, Lauscha. 100pf+50pf, Bonn. 140pf+60pf, Weilburg.

**1991, Oct. 10      Litho.      Perf. 14**
B714 SP382 30pf +15pf multi          .55  .55
B715 SP382 60pf +30pf multi          .80  .80
B716 SP382 70pf +30pf multi         1.00 1.00
B717 SP382 80pf +35pf multi         1.20 1.20
B718 SP382 100pf +50pf multi        1.60 1.60
B719 SP382 140pf +60pf multi        2.25 2.00
   *Nos. B714-B719 (6)*             7.40 7.15

Christmas — SP383

Paintings by Martin Schongauer (c. 1450-1491): 60pf+30pf, Angel of the Annunciation. 70pf+30pf, The Annunciation. 80pf+35pf, Angel. 100pf+50pf, Nativity.

**1991, Nov. 5      Litho.      Perf. 14**
B720 SP383 60pf +30pf multi          .85  .85
B721 SP383 70pf +30pf multi         1.05 1.00
B722 SP383 80pf +35pf multi         2.10 1.75
B723 SP383 100pf +50pf multi        2.60 2.25
   *Nos. B720-B723 (4)*             6.60 5.85

Surtax for Federal Working Association of Free Welfare Work.

Olympic
Sports — SP384

No. B724, Women's fencing. No. B725, Rowing coxed eights. No. B726, Dressage. No. B727, Men's slalom skiing.

**1992, Feb. 6**    **Litho.**    **Perf. 14**

| | | | | |
|---|---|---|---|---|
| B724 | SP384 | 60pf +30pf multi | .95 | .95 |
| B725 | SP384 | 80pf +40pf multi | 1.10 | 1.10 |
| B726 | SP384 | 100pf +50pf multi | 2.25 | 2.40 |
| B727 | SP384 | 170pf +80pf multi | 4.25 | 4.25 |
| | *Nos. B724-B727 (4)* | | 8.55 | 8.70 |

**Endangered Butterfly Type of 1991**

60+30pf, Purpurbar. 70+30pf, Labkraut schwarmer. 80+40pf, Silbermonch. 100+50pf, Schwarzer bar. 170+80pf, Rauschbeeren-fleckenspanner.

**1992, Apr. 9**    **Litho.**    **Perf. 13½**

| | | | | |
|---|---|---|---|---|
| B728 | SP380 | 60pf +30pf multi | 1.20 | 1.20 |
| B729 | SP380 | 70pf +30pf multi | 1.30 | 1.30 |
| B730 | SP380 | 80pf +40pf multi | 1.75 | 1.75 |
| B731 | SP380 | 100pf +50pf multi | 1.75 | 1.75 |
| B732 | SP380 | 170pf +80pf multi | 2.10 | 2.10 |
| | *Nos. B728-B732 (5)* | | 8.10 | 8.10 |

Surtax for German Youth Stamp Foundation.

Preservation of
Tropical Rain
Forests — SP385

**1992, June 11**    **Litho.**    **Perf. 13**

| | | | | |
|---|---|---|---|---|
| B733 | SP385 | 100pf +50pf multi | 1.60 | 1.75 |

Antique
Clocks — SP386

Antique clocks: 60pf+30pf, Turret, c. 1400. 70pf+30pf, Astronomical geographical mantelpiece, 1738. 80pf+40pf, Fluted, c. 1790. 100pf+50pf, Figurine, c. 1580. 170pf+80pf, Table, c. 1550.

**1992, Oct. 15**    **Litho.**    **Perf. 14**

| | | | | |
|---|---|---|---|---|
| B734 | SP386 | 60pf +30pf multi | .95 | .95 |
| B735 | SP386 | 70pf +30pf multi | 1.20 | 1.20 |
| B736 | SP386 | 80pf +40pf multi | 1.20 | 1.20 |
| B737 | SP386 | 100pf +50pf multi | 1.45 | 1.45 |
| B738 | SP386 | 170pf +80pf multi | 2.00 | 2.00 |
| | *Nos. B734-B738 (5)* | | 6.80 | 6.80 |

Surtax for welfare organizations.

Christmas — SP387

Carvings from Church of St. Anne, Annaberg-Buchholz, by Franz Maidburg: 60pf + 30pf, Adoration of the Magi. 100pf + 50pf, The Nativity.

**1992, Nov. 5**

| | | | | |
|---|---|---|---|---|
| B739 | SP387 | 60pf +30pf multi | .95 | .95 |
| B740 | SP387 | 100pf +50pf multi | 1.20 | 1.20 |

Surtax for benefit of free welfare work.

Sports — SP388

Designs: 60pf+30pf, Olympic ski jump, Garmisch-Partenkirchen. 80pf+40pf, Olympic Park, Munich. 100pf+50pf, Olympic Stadium, Berlin. 170pf+80pf, Olympic harbor, Kiel.

**1993, Feb. 11**    **Litho.**    **Perf. 13½**

| | | | | |
|---|---|---|---|---|
| B741 | SP388 | 60pf +30pf multi | 2.00 | 1.60 |
| B742 | SP388 | 80pf +40pf multi | 2.25 | 1.60 |
| B743 | SP388 | 100pf +50pf multi | 3.00 | 2.60 |
| B744 | SP388 | 170pf +80pf multi | 4.50 | 4.50 |
| | *Nos. B741-B744 (4)* | | 11.75 | 10.30 |

Surtax for Natl. Sports Promotion Foundation.

Beetles — SP389

Designs: No. B745, Alpenbock (Alpine sawyer). No. B746, Rosenkafer (rose chafer). No. B747, Hirschkafer (stag beetle). No. B748, Sandlaufkafer (tiger beetle). 200pf + 50pf, Maikafer (cockchafer).

**1993, Apr. 15**    **Litho.**    **Perf. 14**

| | | | | |
|---|---|---|---|---|
| B745 | SP389 | 80pf +40pf multi | 1.50 | 1.50 |
| B746 | SP389 | 80pf +40pf multi | 1.50 | 1.50 |
| B747 | SP389 | 100pf +50pf multi | 1.90 | 1.75 |
| B748 | SP389 | 100pf +50pf multi | 1.90 | 1.75 |
| B749 | SP389 | 200pf +50pf multi | 3.00 | 3.00 |
| | *Nos. B745-B749 (5)* | | 9.80 | 9.50 |

Surtax for German Youth Stamp Foundation.

Stamp
Day — SP390

**1993, Sept. 16**    **Litho.**    **Perf. 13½x14**

| | | | | |
|---|---|---|---|---|
| B750 | SP390 | 100pf +50pf multi | 1.60 | 1.75 |

Surtax for the Foundation for Promotion of Philately and Postal History.

Traditional
Costumes — SP391

Costumes from: No. B751, Rugen, Mecklenburg, Western Pomerania. No. B752, Fohr, Schleswig-Holstein. No. B753, Schwalm, Hesse. No. B754, Oberndorf, Bavaria. 200pf + 40pf, Ernstroda, Thuringia.

**1993, Oct. 14**       **Perf. 14**

| | | | | |
|---|---|---|---|---|
| B751 | SP391 | 80pf +40pf multi | 1.60 | 1.60 |
| B752 | SP391 | 80pf +40pf multi | 1.60 | 1.60 |
| B753 | SP391 | 100pf +50pf multi | 1.60 | 1.60 |
| B754 | SP391 | 100pf +50pf multi | 1.60 | 1.60 |
| B755 | SP391 | 200pf +50pf multi | 2.00 | 2.00 |
| | *Nos. B751-B755 (5)* | | 8.40 | 8.40 |

Surtax for welfare organizations. See Nos. B768-B772.

Christmas — SP392

Wings of high altar in choir of Blaubeuren Monastery: 80pf+40pf, Adoraration of Magi. 100pf+50pf, Nativity.

**1993, Nov. 10**    **Litho.**    **Perf. 14**

| | | | | |
|---|---|---|---|---|
| B756 | SP392 | 80pf +40pf multi | 1.00 | 1.00 |
| B757 | SP392 | 100pf +50pf multi | 1.75 | 1.75 |

Surtax for welfare organizations.

Figure
Skating — SP393

Sports: No. B759, Olympic Flame. No. B760, Soccer ball, World Cup Trophy. 200pf+80pf, Skiier.

**1994, Feb. 10**    **Litho.**    **Perf. 14x13½**

| | | | | |
|---|---|---|---|---|
| B758 | SP393 | 80pf +40pf multi | 3.00 | 1.60 |
| B759 | SP393 | 80pf +50pf multi | 3.00 | 1.60 |
| B760 | SP393 | 100pf +50pf multi | 3.00 | 1.60 |
| B761 | SP393 | 200pf +80pf multi | 4.00 | 3.25 |
| | *Nos. B758-B761 (4)* | | 13.00 | 8.05 |

1994 Winter Olympics, Lillehammer (No. B758). Intl. Olympic Committee, Cent. (No. B759). 1994 World Cup Soccer Championships, US (No. B760). 1994 Paralympics, Lillehammer (No. B761).

Heinrich Hoffmann
(1809-94),
Physician, Writer of
Children's
Books — SP394

Characters from "Slovenly Peter:" No. B762, Little Pauline. No. B763, Johnny Head-in-the-air. No. B764, Slovenly Peter. No. B765, Naughty Frederick. 200pf+80pf, The Fidget.

**1994, Apr. 14**    **Litho.**    **Perf. 13½**

| | | | | |
|---|---|---|---|---|
| B762 | SP394 | 80pf +40pf multi | 2.25 | 2.00 |
| B763 | SP394 | 80pf +40pf multi | 2.25 | 2.00 |
| B764 | SP394 | 100pf +50pf multi | 2.25 | 2.00 |
| B765 | SP394 | 100pf +50pf multi | 2.25 | 2.00 |
| B766 | SP394 | 200pf +80pf multi | 3.25 | 2.60 |
| | *Nos. B762-B766 (5)* | | 12.25 | 10.60 |

Surtax for German Youth Stamp Foundation.

Environmental
Protection — SP395

**1994, June 16**    **Litho.**    **Perf. 13**

| | | | | |
|---|---|---|---|---|
| B767 | SP395 | 100pf +50pf blk & grn | 1.60 | 1.60 |

**Traditional Costume Type 1993**

Costumes from: No. B768, Buckeburg. No. B769, Halle an der Saale. No. B770, Hoyerswerda. No. B771, Minden. 200pf+70pf, Betzingen.

**1994, Oct. 13**    **Litho.**    **Perf. 13½**

| | | | | |
|---|---|---|---|---|
| B768 | SP391 | 80pf +40pf multi | 1.20 | 1.20 |
| B769 | SP391 | 80pf +40pf multi | 1.20 | 1.20 |
| B770 | SP391 | 100pf +50pf multi | 1.60 | 1.60 |
| B771 | SP391 | 100pf +50pf multi | 1.60 | 1.60 |
| B772 | SP391 | 200pf +70pf multi | 2.60 | 2.60 |
| | *Nos. B768-B772 (5)* | | 8.20 | 8.20 |

Surtax for welfare organizations.

Christmas — SP396

Paintings by Hans Memling: 80pf+40pf, Adoration of the Magi. 100pf+50pf, Nativity Scene.

**1994, Nov. 9**    **Litho.**    **Perf. 13½**

| | | | | |
|---|---|---|---|---|
| B773 | SP396 | 80pf +40pf multi | 1.30 | 1.45 |
| B774 | SP396 | 100pf +50pf multi | 1.60 | 1.60 |

Sports — SP397

No. B775, Rowing. No. B776, Gymnastics. No. B777, Boxing. No. B778, Volleyball.

**1995, Feb. 9**    **Photo.**    **Perf. 13½**

| | | | | |
|---|---|---|---|---|
| B775 | SP397 | 80pf +40pf multi | 1.20 | 1.45 |
| B776 | SP397 | 100pf +50pf multi | 1.20 | 1.45 |
| B777 | SP397 | 100pf +50pf multi | 1.20 | 1.45 |
| B778 | SP397 | 200pf +80pf multi | 2.40 | 3.25 |
| | *Nos. B775-B778 (4)* | | | |

World Kayaking Championships, Duisburg (No. B775). Intl. Gymnastics Festival, Berlin (No. B776). World Amateur Boxing Championships, Berlin (No. B777). Volleyball, cent. (No. B778).

Dogs — SP398

No. B779, Munsterlander. No. B780, Schnauzer. No. B781, German shepherd. No. B782, Wire haired dachshund. 200pf+80pf, Wolf spitz.

**1995, June 8**    **Litho.**    **Perf. 13½**

| | | | | |
|---|---|---|---|---|
| B779 | SP398 | 80pf +40pf multi | 1.20 | 1.40 |
| B780 | SP398 | 80pf +40pf multi | 1.20 | 1.40 |
| B781 | SP398 | 100pf +50pf multi | 1.20 | 1.40 |
| B782 | SP398 | 100pf +50pf multi | 1.20 | 1.40 |
| B783 | SP398 | 200pf +80pf multi | 2.40 | 3.00 |
| | *Nos. B779-B783 (5)* | | 7.20 | 8.60 |

Surtax for benefit of German Youth Stamp Foundation. See Nos. B792-B796.

Stamp
Day — SP399

**1995, Sept. 6**    **Litho.**    **Perf. 13**

| | | | | |
|---|---|---|---|---|
| B784 | SP399 | 200pf +100pf multi | 3.00 | 3.25 |

Surtax for Foundation for Promotion of Philately and Postal History.

Farmhouses
SP400

No. B785, Eifel region. No. B786, Saxony. No. B787, Lower Germany. No. B788, Upper Bavaria. 200pf+70pf, Mecklenburg.

**1995, Oct. 12**    **Litho.**    **Perf. 14**

| | | | | |
|---|---|---|---|---|
| B785 | SP400 | 80pf +40pf multi | 1.35 | 1.35 |
| B786 | SP400 | 80pf +40pf multi | 1.35 | 1.35 |
| B787 | SP400 | 100pf +50pf multi | 1.35 | 1.35 |
| B788 | SP400 | 100pf +50pf multi | 1.35 | 1.35 |
| B789 | SP400 | 200pf +70pf multi | 2.25 | 2.25 |
| | *Nos. B785-B789 (5)* | | 7.65 | 7.65 |

Surtax for welfare organizations. See Nos. B802-B806.

Christmas — SP401

Stained glass windows, Augsburg Cathedral: 80pf+40pf, Annunciation. 100pf+50pf, Nativity.

**1995, Nov. 9**    **Litho.**    **Perf. 14**

| | | | | |
|---|---|---|---|---|
| B790 | SP401 | 80pf +40pf multi | 1.35 | 1.35 |
| B791 | SP401 | 100pf +50pf multi | 1.75 | 1.75 |

Surtax for welfare organizations.

**Dog Type of 1995**

No. B792, Borzoi. No. B793, Chow chow. No. B794, St. Bernard. No. B795, Collie. 200pf+80pf, Briard.

**1996, Feb. 8**    **Litho.**    **Perf. 13½**

| | | | | |
|---|---|---|---|---|
| B792 | SP398 | 80pf +40pf multi | 1.45 | 1.75 |
| B793 | SP398 | 80pf +40pf multi | 1.45 | 1.75 |
| B794 | SP398 | 100pf +50pf multi | 1.75 | 1.75 |
| B795 | SP398 | 100pf +50pf multi | 1.75 | 1.75 |
| B796 | SP398 | 200pf +80pf multi | 2.75 | 2.75 |
| | *Nos. B792-B796 (5)* | | 9.15 | 9.75 |

Surtax for benefit of German Youth Stamp Foundation.

Modern Olympic
Games,
Cent. — SP402

Olympic champions: 80pf+40pf, Carl Schuhmann (1869-1946), pommel horse. No. B798, Annie Hübler Horn (1885-1976), pairs figure skating. No. B799, Josef Neckermann (1912-92), equestrian. 200pf+80pf, Alfred Flatow (1869-1942), Gustav Felix Flatow (1875-1945), gymnastics.

| | | | | |
|---|---|---|---|---|
| **1996, June 13** | | **Photo.** | **Perf. 13½** | |
| B797 | SP402 | 80pf +40pf multi | 2.75 | 1.75 |
| B798 | SP402 | 100pf +50pf multi | 3.75 | 2.75 |
| B799 | SP402 | 100pf +50pf multi | 3.75 | 2.75 |
| B800 | SP402 | 200pf +80pf multi | 4.50 | 3.75 |
| | *Nos. B797-B800 (4)* | | 14.75 | 11.00 |

Preservation of Tropical Habitats — SP403

| | | | | |
|---|---|---|---|---|
| **1996, July 18** | | **Photo.** | **Perf. 14** | |
| B801 | SP403 | 100pf +50pf multi | 1.75 | 1.75 |

**Farmhouse Type of 1995**

Location: No. B802, Spree Forest. No. B803, Thuringia. No. B804, Black Forest. No. B805, Westphalia. 200pf+70pf, Schleswig-Holstein.

| | | | | |
|---|---|---|---|---|
| **1996, Oct. 9** | | **Litho.** | **Perf. 14** | |
| B802 | SP400 | 80pf +40pf multi | 1.10 | .90 |
| B803 | SP400 | 100pf +50pf multi | 1.10 | .90 |
| B804 | SP400 | 100pf +50pf multi | 1.35 | 1.10 |
| B805 | SP400 | 100pf +50pf multi | 1.35 | 1.10 |
| B806 | SP400 | 200pf +70pf multi | 2.40 | 2.40 |
| | *Nos. B802-B806 (5)* | | 7.30 | 6.40 |

Christmas — SP404

Illuminated pages from Henry II's book of pericopes (Gospels), 11th cent.: 80pf+40pf, Adoration of the Magi. 100pf+50pf, Nativity.

| | | | | |
|---|---|---|---|---|
| **1996, Nov. 14** | | **Litho.** | **Perf. 14** | |
| B807 | SP404 | 80pf +40pf multi | 1.25 | 1.45 |
| B808 | SP404 | 100pf +50pf multi | 1.45 | 1.75 |

Surtax for welfare organizations.

Sports — SP405

No. B809, Aerobics. No. B810, Inline skating. No. B811, Streetball. No. B812, Free climbing.

| | | | | |
|---|---|---|---|---|
| **1997, Feb. 4** | | **Litho.** | **Perf. 14x13½** | |
| B809 | SP405 | 80pf +40pf multi | 1.25 | 2.10 |
| B810 | SP405 | 100pf +50pf multi | 1.60 | 2.10 |
| B811 | SP405 | 100pf +50pf multi | 1.60 | 2.10 |
| B812 | SP405 | 200pf +80pf multi | 2.75 | 4.50 |
| | *Nos. B809-B812 (4)* | | 7.20 | 10.80 |

Horses — SP406

No. B813, Rheno-German draft. No. B814, Shetland pony. No. B815, Friesian. No. B816, Haflinger. No. B817, Hanoverian.

| | | | | |
|---|---|---|---|---|
| **1997, June 9** | | **Litho.** | **Perf. 14** | |
| B813 | SP406 | 80pf + 40pf multi | 2.25 | 1.75 |
| B814 | SP406 | 80pf + 40pf multi | 2.25 | 1.75 |
| B815 | SP406 | 100pf + 50pf multi | 2.25 | 1.75 |
| B816 | SP406 | 100pf + 50pf multi | 2.25 | 1.75 |
| B817 | SP406 | 200pf + 80pf multi | 4.50 | 3.75 |
| | *Nos. B813-B817 (5)* | | 13.50 | 10.75 |

**Arms Type of 1992 Redrawn and Inscribed "Hochwasserhilfe 1997" and "DEUTSCHLAND"**

| | | | | |
|---|---|---|---|---|
| **1997, Aug. 19** | | **Litho.** | **Perf. 13½** | |
| B818 | A739 | 110pf +90pf like #1702 | 2.10 | 3.25 |

**Souvenir Sheet**

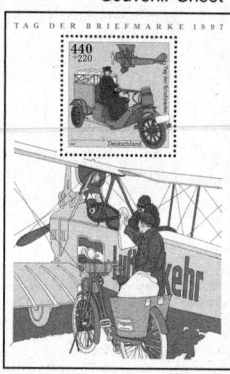

Stamp Day SP407

| | | | | |
|---|---|---|---|---|
| **1997, Sept. 17** | | **Litho.** | **Perf. 14** | |
| B819 | SP407 | 440pf +220pf multi | 6.50 | 7.75 |

Mills — SP408

Designs: 100pf+50pf, Black Forest. No. B821, Hesse. No. B822, Windmill, lower Rhine. No. B823, Scoop windmill, Schleswig-Holstein. 220pf+80pf, Dutch windmill.

| | | | | |
|---|---|---|---|---|
| **1997, Oct. 9** | | **Litho.** | **Perf. 13½x14** | |
| | | **Background Color** | | |
| B820 | SP408 | 100pf +50pf grn | 2.10 | 2.10 |
| B821 | SP409 | 110pf +50pf brn | 2.40 | 2.40 |
| B822 | SP408 | 110pf +50pf blue | 2.40 | 2.40 |
| B823 | SP408 | 110pf +50pf yel | 2.40 | 2.40 |
| B824 | SP408 | 220pf +80pf pink | 3.25 | 3.75 |
| | *Nos. B820-B824 (5)* | | 12.55 | 13.05 |

Christmas — SP409

| | | | | |
|---|---|---|---|---|
| **1997, Nov. 6** | | **Litho.** | **Perf. 14** | |
| B825 | SP409 | 100pf +50pf Magi | 1.45 | 1.45 |
| B826 | SP409 | 110pf +50pf Nativity | 1.75 | 1.75 |

Surtax for Federal Assoc. of Free Welfare Work in Bonn.

Sports — SP410

1998 Sporting events: 100pf+50pf, World Cup Soccer Championships, France. No. B828, Winter Olympic Games, Nagano. No. B829, Rowing Championships, Cologne. 300pf+100pf, Winter Paralympics, Nagano.

| | | | | |
|---|---|---|---|---|
| **1998, Feb. 5** | | **Photo.** | **Perf. 14** | |
| B827 | SP410 | 100pf +50pf multi | 3.25 | 2.25 |
| B828 | SP410 | 110pf +50pf multi | 3.25 | 2.25 |
| B829 | SP410 | 110pf +50pf multi | 3.25 | 2.25 |
| B830 | SP410 | 300pf +100pf multi | 7.25 | 7.25 |
| | *Nos. B827-B830 (4)* | | 17.00 | 14.00 |

**Declaration of Human Rights Type of 1998 Inscribed "KOSOVO-HILFE 1999"**

| | | | | |
|---|---|---|---|---|
| **1999, Apr. 27** | | **Litho.** | **Perf. 14** | |
| B848 | A958 | 110pf +100pf multi | 2.10 | 2.10 |

Sutax for aid to refugees from Kosovo.

Environmental Protection — SP411

| | | | | |
|---|---|---|---|---|
| **1998, May 7** | | **Litho.** | **Perf. 14** | |
| B831 | SP411 | 110pf +50pf multi | 2.25 | 3.00 |
| | See No. B907, B1078. | | | |

Cartoon Figures — SP412

No. B832, Mouse, Little Yellow Duck, Elephant. No. B833, Sandman. No. B834, Maja the Bee. No. B835, Captain Bluebear. No. B836, Pumuckl.

| | | | | |
|---|---|---|---|---|
| **1998, June 10** | | **Litho.** | **Perf. 14** | |
| B832 | SP412 | 100pf +50pf multi | 1.75 | 1.75 |
| B833 | SP412 | 100pf +50pf multi | 1.75 | 1.75 |
| B834 | SP412 | 110pf +50pf multi | 1.75 | 1.75 |
| B835 | SP412 | 110pf +50pf multi | 1.75 | 1.75 |
| B836 | SP412 | 220pf +50pf multi | 3.00 | 3.00 |
| | *Nos. B832-B836 (5)* | | 10.00 | 10.00 |

Surtax for the German Youth Stamp Foundation.

Welfare Stamps — SP413

Birds: 100pf+50pf, Hen-harrier. No. B838, Great bustard. No. B839, White-eyed duck. No. B840, Sedge warbler. 220pf+80pf, Woodchat shrike.

| | | | | |
|---|---|---|---|---|
| **1998, Oct. 8** | | **Litho.** | **Perf. 14** | |
| | | **Background Colors** | | |
| B837 | SP413 | 100pf +50pf tan | 1.75 | 1.75 |
| B838 | SP413 | 110pf +50pf gray grn | 1.75 | 1.75 |
| B839 | SP413 | 110pf +50pf gray blue | 1.75 | 1.75 |
| B840 | SP413 | 110pf +50pf blue grn | 1.75 | 1.75 |
| B841 | SP413 | 220pf +80pf lilac | 2.75 | 3.25 |
| | *Nos. B837-B841 (5)* | | 9.75 | 10.25 |

Christmas — SP414

No. B842, Shepherds. No. B843, Holy Child.

| | | | | |
|---|---|---|---|---|
| **1998, Nov. 12** | | | | |
| B842 | SP414 | 100pf +50pf multi | 1.45 | 1.45 |
| B843 | SP414 | 110pf +50pf multi | 1.45 | 1.45 |

Racing Sports — SP415

No. B844, Bicycles. No. B845, Cars. No. B846, Horses. No. B847, Motorcycles.

| | | | | |
|---|---|---|---|---|
| **1999, Feb. 18** | | **Photo.** | **Perf. 14** | |
| B844 | SP415 | 100pf +50pf multi | 1.75 | 2.25 |
| B845 | SP415 | 110pf +50pf multi | 1.75 | 2.25 |
| B846 | SP415 | 110pf +50pf multi | 1.75 | 2.25 |
| B847 | SP415 | 300pf +100pf multi | 3.75 | 4.25 |
| | *Nos. B844-B847 (4)* | | 9.00 | 11.00 |

**Souvenir Sheet**

IBRA '99, Intl. Stamp Exhibition, Nuremberg — SP416

Design: Bavaria #1 & Saxony #1.

| | | | | |
|---|---|---|---|---|
| **1999, Apr. 27** | | | **Perf. 13½** | |
| B849 | SP416 | 300pf +110pf multi | 5.50 | 7.75 |
| | German postage stamps, 150th anniv. | | | |

Cartoons — SP417

No. B850, The Little Polar Bear. No. B851, Rudi the Crow. No. B852, Mecki (hedgehog). No. B853, Twipsy, mascot of Expo 2000, Hanover. 220pf+80pf, Tabaluga (green dragon).

| | | | | |
|---|---|---|---|---|
| **1999, June 10** | | **Litho.** | **Perf. 13¾** | |
| B850 | SP417 | 100pf +50pf multi | 1.75 | 2.10 |
| B851 | SP417 | 100pf +50pf multi | 1.75 | 2.10 |
| B852 | SP417 | 110pf +50pf multi | 1.75 | 2.10 |
| B853 | SP417 | 110pf +50pf multi | 1.75 | 2.10 |
| B854 | SP417 | 220pf +80pf multi | 2.75 | 4.50 |
| | *Nos. B850-B854 (5)* | | 9.75 | 12.90 |

Surtax for the German Youth Stamp Foundation.

The Cosmos SP418

No. B855, Andromeda galaxy. No. B856, Cygnus constellation. No. B857, X-ray image of exploding star. No. B858, Collision of Comet Shoemaker-Levy 9 and Jupiter. 300pf + 100pf, Gamma ray image of entire sky, satellite.

| | | | | |
|---|---|---|---|---|
| **1999, Oct. 14** | | **Litho.** | **Perf. 14** | |
| B855 | SP418 | 100pf +50pf multi | 1.45 | 1.45 |
| B856 | SP418 | 100pf +50pf multi | 1.45 | 1.45 |
| B857 | SP418 | 110pf +50pf multi | 1.60 | 1.60 |
| B858 | SP418 | 110pf +50pf multi | 1.60 | 1.60 |
| B859 | SP418 | 300pf +100pf multi | 4.00 | 4.00 |
| | *Nos. B855-B859 (5)* | | 10.10 | 10.10 |

Surtax for the Federal Association of Free Welfare Work. Nos. B858-B859 have a holographic image. Soaking in water may affect hologram.

Christmas — SP419

| | | | | |
|---|---|---|---|---|
| **1999, Nov. 4** | | **Litho.** | **Perf. 13¾** | |
| B860 | SP419 | 100pf +50pf Angel | 1.45 | 1.60 |
| B861 | SP419 | 110pf +50pf Manger | 1.50 | 1.60 |

Sports SP420

Ancient art and: 100pf + 50pf, Swimmer. No. B863, Gymnast. No. B864, Sprinters. 300pf + 100pf, Hands.

| | | | | |
|---|---|---|---|---|
| **2000, Feb. 17** | | **Litho.** | **Perf. 13¾x14** | |
| B862 | SP420 | 100pf + 50pf multi | 2.40 | 2.10 |
| B863 | SP420 | 110pf + 50pf multi | 2.40 | 2.10 |
| B864 | SP420 | 110pf + 50pf multi | 2.40 | 2.10 |

B865 SP420 300pf + 100pf
multi 4.00 3.75
*Nos. B862-B865 (4)* 11.20 10.05

Surtax was for German Sports Federation.

Environmental Protection — SP421

**2000, May 12 Litho. Perf. 13¾x14**
B866 SP421 110pf +50pf multi 2.25 2.75

Expo
2000,
Hanover
SP422

No. B867, 4 backpackers. No. B868, Crowd.
No. B869, Map of Africa, words "see, come,
hear, feel." No. B870, Eye. No. B871, Abstract
with Chinese characters. No. B872, Abstract.

**2000, June 8 Litho. Perf. 13¾x14**
B867 SP422 100pf +50pf multi 1.75 1.75
B868 SP422 100pf +50pf multi 1.75 1.75
B869 SP422 110pf +50pf multi 1.75 1.75
B870 SP422 110pf +50pf multi 1.75 1.75
B871 SP422 110pf +50pf multi 1.75 1.75
B872 SP422 300pf +100pf
multi 2.75 2.75
*Nos. B867-B872 (6)* 11.50 11.50

Surtax for German Youth Stamp Foundation.

Actors and
Actresses
SP423

No. B873, Curd Jürgens (1915-82). No.
B874, Lilli Palmer (1914-86). No. B875, Heinz
Rühmann (1902-94). No. B876, Romy Schneider (1938-82). No. B877, Gert Fröbe (1913-
88).

**2000, Oct. 12 Litho. Perf. 14**
B873 SP423 100pf +50pf multi 1.75 1.75
B874 SP423 100pf +50pf multi 1.75 1.75
B875 SP423 110pf +50pf multi 1.75 1.75
B876 SP423 110pf +50pf multi 1.75 1.75
B877 SP423 300pf +100pf
multi 3.75 3.75
*Nos. B873-B877 (5)* 10.75 10.75

Surtax was for Federal Association of Welfare Work.

Christmas — SP424

Designs: 100pf+50pf, Birth of Christ, by
Conrad von Soest. 110pf+50pf, Nativity scene.

**2000, Nov. 9 Litho. Perf. 13¾**
B878 SP424 100pf +50pf multi 1.45 1.45
B879 SP424 110pf +50pf multi 1.45 1.45

Joint issue between Germany & Spain. Sur-
tax for the Federal Association of Voluntary
Welfare Work.
See Spain Nos. 3071-3072.

Sports
SP425

Designs: 100pf+50pf, Sports for schools.
No. B881, Sports for the disabled. No. B882,
Popular and leisure sports. 300pf+100pf,
Sports for senior citizens.

**2001, Feb. 8 Litho. Perf. 13¾x14**
B880 SP425 100pf +50pf multi 1.75 1.75
B881 SP425 110pf +50pf multi 1.75 1.75
B882 SP425 110pf +50pf multi 1.75 1.75
B883 SP425 300pf +100pf
multi 4.50 4.50
*Nos. B880-B883 (4)* 9.75 9.75

Surtax for German Sports Federation.
Nos B880-B883 with the text bar in turquoise blue were unissued. Value $20,000
each.

Wuppertal Suspension
Railway — SP426

**2001, Mar. 8**
B884 SP426 110pf +50pf multi 2.25 2.00

Surtax for the Foundation for Promotion of
Philately and Postal History.

Characters from
Children's
Stories — SP427

Designs: No. B885, Pinocchio. No. B886,
Pippi Longstockings. No. B887, Jim Knopf.
No. B888, Heidi. 300pf +100pf, Tom Sawyer
and Huckleberry Finn.

**2001, June 13 Litho. Perf. 13¾**
B885 SP427 100pf +50pf multi 2.00 2.00
B886 SP427 100pf +50pf multi 2.00 2.00
B887 SP427 110pf +50pf multi 2.00 2.00
B888 SP427 110pf +50pf multi 2.00 2.00
B889 SP427 300pf +100pf
multi 4.50 4.50
*Nos. B885-B889 (5)* 12.50 12.50

Surtax for the German Youth Stamp
Foundation.

Film
Stars — SP428

Designs: No. B890, Marilyn Monroe. No.
B891, Charlie Chaplin. No. B892, Film reel.
No. B893, Greta Garbo. 300pf+100pf, Jean
Gabin.

**2001, Oct. 11 Litho. Perf. 14**
B890 SP428 100pf +50pf multi 2.00 2.00
*a.* Perf. 13x13¼x13½x13¼ 4.00 4.00
B891 SP428 100pf +50pf multi 2.00 2.00
*a.* Perf. 13½x13¼ 4.00 4.00
B892 SP428 110pf +50pf multi 2.00 2.00
*a.* Perf. 13½x13¼ 4.00 4.00
B893 SP428 110pf +50pf multi 2.00 2.00
*a.* Perf. 13x13¼ 4.00 4.00
B894 SP428 300pf +100pf
multi 4.50 4.50
*a.* Perf. 13x13¼ 9.00 9.00
*b.* Booklet pane, #B890a-
B894a 16.00 16.00
Booklet, #B894b 20.00
*Nos. B890-B894 (5)* 12.50 12.50

Surtax for the Federal Association of Voluntary Welfare Work.

A stamp picturing Audrey Hepburn
originally was to have been included in
this set but was withdrawn. It was never
officially issued, nor were any examples
sold over post office counters. However,
30 examples from the original printing
were not recovered and destroyed as
ordered by the post office. Four of the
stamps have been found used on German mail. Value, $150,000.

Christmas — SP429

Designs: 100pf+50pf, Madonna and Child,
by Alfredo Roldán. 110pf+50pf, Adoration of
the Shepherds, by José de Ribera.

**2001, Nov. 8 Litho. Perf. 13¼**
B895 SP429 100pf +50pf multi 1.90 1.90
B896 SP429 110pf +50pf multi 1.90 1.90
*a.* Souvenir sheet (see footnote) 6.50 6.50

No. B896a contains Nos. B895-B896 and
lithographed and perf. 13¼ examples of Spain
Nos. 3123-3124. No. B896a sold for 4.45m.
See Spain Nos. 3123-3124.

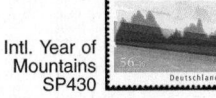

Intl. Year of
Mountains
SP430

**2002, Jan. 10 Litho. Perf. 14**
B897 SP430 56c +26c multi 2.00 1.90

Winter
Olympic
Sports
SP431

Designs: 51c+26c, Biathlon. No. B899,
56c+26c, Ski jumping. No. B900, 56c+26c,
Speed skating. 153c+51c, Luge.

**2002, Feb. 7 Litho. Perf. 13¾x14**
B898 SP431 51c +26c multi 2.00 2.00
B899 SP431 56c +26c multi 2.00 2.00
B900 SP431 56c +26c multi 2.00 2.00
B901 SP431 153c +51c multi 4.75 4.75
*a.* Booklet pane, #B898-B901 11.50 11.50
Booklet, #B901a 14.00
*Nos. B898-B901 (4)* 10.75 10.75

Surtax for German Sports Promotion
Foundation.

Toys and
Games — SP432

Designs: No. B902, Chess pieces. No.
B903, Toy truck. No. B904, Doll. No. B905,
Teddy bear. 153c+51c, Toy train.

**2002, June 6 Litho. Perf. 13¾**
B902 SP432 51c +26c multi 2.10 2.10
B903 SP432 51c +26c multi 2.10 2.10
B904 SP432 56c +26c multi 2.10 2.10
B905 SP432 56c +26c multi 2.10 2.10
B906 SP432 153c +51c multi 4.75 4.75
*Nos. B902-B906 (5)* 13.15 13.15

Surtax for German Youth Stamp Foundation.

**Environmental Protection Type of
1998 Inscribed "Hochwasserhilfe
2002"**

**2002, Aug. 30 Litho. Perf. 13x13½**
B907 SP411 56c +44c multi 3.00 2.50
*a.* Perf. 13x14

Surtax for flood victims relief.

Christmas — SP433

Details from paintings by Rogier van der
Weyden: 51c+26c, Annunciation to the Virgin.
56c+26c, Miraflores Altarpiece.

**2002, Nov. 7 Litho. Perf. 13¾**
B908 SP433 51c +26c multi 1.90 1.75
B909 SP433 56c +26c multi 1.90 1.75

Surtax for Federal Working Party on Independent Welfare.

Automobiles — SP434

Designs: 45c+20c, 1960 BMW Isetta 300.
No. B911, 55c+25c, 1961 VEB Sachsenring
Trabant P50. No. B912, 55c+25c, 1949 Volk-
swagen Beetle. No. B913, 55c+25c, 1954
Mercdes-Benz 300 SL. 144c+56c, 1957 Borg-
ward Isabella Coupe.

**2002, Dec. 5 Litho. Perf. 14**
B910 SP434 45c +20c multi 1.90 1.90
B911 SP434 55c +25c multi 2.00 2.00
B912 SP434 55c +25c multi 2.00 2.00
B913 SP434 55c +25c multi 2.00 2.00
B914 SP434 144c +56c multi 5.25 5.25
*Nos. B910-B914 (5)* 13.15 13.15

Surtax for Federal Working Party on Independent Welfare.
See Nos. B923-B927.

2006 World Cup Soccer
Championships, Germany — SP435

Designs: 45c+20c, Player kicking ball. No.
B916, Player heading ball. No. B917, Four
children playing soccer. No. B918, Fan celebrating. 144c+56c, Child and adult playing
soccer.

**2003, Mar. 6 Litho. Perf. 13x13½**
B915 SP435 45c +20c multi 2.10 2.10
B916 SP435 55c +25c multi 2.10 2.10
B917 SP435 55c +25c multi 2.10 2.10
B918 SP435 55c +25c multi 2.10 2.10
B919 SP435 144c +56c multi 4.75 4.75
*Nos. B915-B919 (5)* 13.15 13.15

Surtax for German Sports Promotion
Foundation.

First East-to-West
Non-Stop
Transatlantic Flight,
75th Anniv. — SP436

**2003, Apr. 10 Perf. 13¾**
B920 SP436 144c +56c multi 5.25 5.00

Surtax for German Organization for the
Enhancement of Philately and Postal History.

SP437

**2003, June 12 Photo. Perf. 14x14¼**
B921 SP437 55c +25c multi 2.10 2.10

June 17, 1953 Uprising in East Germany,
50th anniv.

## Souvenir Sheet

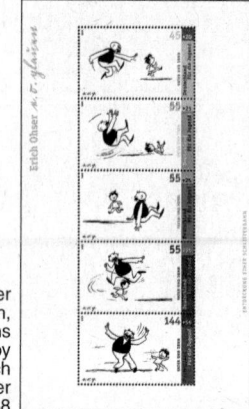

Father and Son, Cartoons by Ehrich Ohser SP438

No. B922: a, Father and son running in same direction. b, Father and son falling. c, Son running, father seated. d, Father and son running in different directions. e, Father and son with arms extended.

**2003, July 10    Litho.    Perf. 13x13½**
| | | | | | |
|---|---|---|---|---|---|
| B922 | SP438 | Sheet of 5 | | 13.00 | 13.00 |
| a. | | 45c +20c multi | | 2.10 | 2.10 |
| b.-d. | | 55c +25c any single | | 2.10 | 2.10 |
| e. | | 144c +56c multi | | 4.25 | 4.25 |

### Automobile Type of 2002

Designs: 45c+20c, Wartburg 311 Coupe. No. B924, Olympia Rekord P1. No. B925, 356 B Coupe. No. B926, 55c+25c, Taunus 17 M P3. 144c+56c, Auto Union 1000 S.

**2003, Oct. 9    Litho.    Perf. 14**
| | | | | | |
|---|---|---|---|---|---|
| B923 | SP434 | 45c +20c multi | | 1.90 | 1.90 |
| B924 | SP434 | 55c +25c multi | | 2.00 | 2.00 |
| B925 | SP434 | 55c +25c multi | | 2.00 | 2.00 |
| B926 | SP434 | 55c +25c multi | | 2.00 | 2.00 |
| B927 | SP434 | 144c +56c multi | | 5.25 | 5.25 |
| | | Nos. B923-B927 (5) | | 13.15 | 13.15 |

Christmas — SP439

Designs: 45c+20c, Adoration of the Shepherds. 55c+25c, Holy Family.

**2003, Nov. 13    Litho.    Perf. 13¾**
| | | | | | |
|---|---|---|---|---|---|
| B928 | SP439 | 45c +20c multi | | 1.75 | 1.75 |
| B929 | SP439 | 55c +25c multi | | 1.75 | 1.75 |

Wind Energy — SP440

**2004, Jan. 8    Litho.    Perf. 13¾**
| | | | | | |
|---|---|---|---|---|---|
| B930 | SP440 | 55c +25c multi | | 2.10 | 2.00 |

Sporting Events and Anniversaries — SP441

Designs: 45c+20c, European Soccer Championships, June 12-July 4, 2004. No. B932, Summer Olympic Games, Athens, Greece. No. B933, Paralympics, Athens, Greece. No. B934, First German World Cup Championship, 50th anniv. 144c+56c, FIFA (Fédération Internationale de Football Association), cent.

**2004, Feb. 5    Litho.    Perf. 13x13½**
| | | | | | |
|---|---|---|---|---|---|
| B931 | SP441 | 45c +20c multi | | 1.90 | 1.90 |
| B932 | SP441 | 55c +25c multi | | 2.00 | 2.00 |
| B933 | SP441 | 55c +25c multi | | 2.00 | 2.00 |
| B934 | SP441 | 55c +25c multi | | 2.00 | 2.00 |
| B935 | SP441 | 144c +56c multi | | 5.25 | 5.25 |
| | | Nos. B931-B935 (5) | | 13.15 | 13.15 |

Cats SP442

Designs: 45c+20c, Two cats playing with ball of string. No. B937, Cat, two kittens playing with ball. No. B938, Kitten on cat. No. B939, Cat licking paw. 144c+56c, Two cats sleeping.

**2004, June 3    Litho.    Perf. 13¾x14**
| | | | | | |
|---|---|---|---|---|---|
| B936 | SP442 | 45c +20c multi | | 1.90 | 1.90 |
| B937 | SP442 | 55c +25c multi | | 2.00 | 2.00 |
| B938 | SP442 | 55c +25c multi | | 2.00 | 2.00 |
| B939 | SP442 | 55c +25c multi | | 2.00 | 2.00 |
| B940 | SP442 | 144c +56c multi | | 5.25 | 5.25 |
| | | Nos. B936-B940 (5) | | 13.15 | 13.15 |

Landscapes — SP443

Designs: 45c+20c, Iceberg and pack ice. No. B942, Mountains and clouds. No. B943, Islands. No. B944, Sand dunes. 144c+56c, Tree tops.

**2004, Oct. 7    Litho.    Perf. 14**
| | | | | | |
|---|---|---|---|---|---|
| B941 | SP443 | 45c +20c multi | | 1.90 | 1.90 |
| B942 | SP443 | 55c +25c multi | | 2.00 | 2.00 |
| B943 | SP443 | 55c +25c multi | | 2.00 | 2.00 |
| B944 | SP443 | 55c +25c multi | | 2.00 | 2.00 |
| B945 | SP443 | 144c +56c multi | | 5.25 | 5.25 |
| | | Nos. B941-B945 (5) | | 13.15 | 13.15 |

Christmas — SP444

Paintings by Peter Paul Rubens: 45c+20c, The Flight Into Egypt. 55c+25c, Adoration of the Magi.

**2004, Nov. 4    Perf. 13¾**
| | | | | | |
|---|---|---|---|---|---|
| B946 | SP444 | 45c +20c multi | | 1.60 | 1.50 |
| B947 | SP444 | 55c +25c multi | | 1.90 | 1.75 |

See Belgium Nos. 2051-2053.

Sports SP445

Designs: 45c+20c, Soccer fans, mascot of 2006 World Cup Soccer Championships. No. B949, Soccer players, soccer ball globe. No. B950, Gymnasts, Brandenburg Gate, Berlin. No. B951, Ski jumper and ski jump. 144c+56c, Fencers, Leipzig Arena.

**2005, Feb. 10    Litho.    Perf. 13¾x14**
| | | | | | |
|---|---|---|---|---|---|
| B948 | SP445 | 45c +20c multi | | 1.90 | 1.90 |
| B949 | SP445 | 55c +25c multi | | 2.00 | 2.00 |
| B950 | SP445 | 55c +25c multi | | 2.00 | 2.00 |
| B951 | SP445 | 55c +25c multi | | 2.00 | 2.00 |
| B952 | SP445 | 144c +56c multi | | 5.25 | 5.25 |
| | | Nos. B948-B952 (5) | | 13.15 | 13.15 |

2006 World Cup Soccer Championships (Nos. B948-B949), Intl. Gymnastics Exhibition, Berlin (No. B950), Nordic Skiing World Championships, Oberstdorf (No. B951), Fencing World Championships, Leipzig (No. B952).

Stamp Day — SP446

**2005, May 12    Litho.    Perf. 14**
| | | | | | |
|---|---|---|---|---|---|
| B953 | SP446 | 55c +25c multi | | 2.00 | 2.00 |

Sailing Ships SP447

Designs: 45c+20c, Greif. No. B955, Rickmer Rickmers. No. B956, Passat. No. B957, Grossherzogin Elisabeth. 144c+56c, Deutschland.

**2005, June 2    Litho.    Perf. 13¾x14**
| | | | | | |
|---|---|---|---|---|---|
| B954 | SP447 | 45c +20c multi | | 1.90 | 1.90 |
| B955 | SP447 | 55c +25c multi | | 2.00 | 2.00 |
| B956 | SP447 | 55c +25c multi | | 2.00 | 2.00 |
| B957 | SP447 | 55c +25c multi | | 2.00 | 2.00 |
| B958 | SP447 | 144c +56c multi | | 5.25 | 5.25 |
| | | Nos. B954-B958 (5) | | 13.15 | 13.15 |

Christmas — SP448

Paintings by Stefan Lochner: 45c+20c, Adoration of the Child. 55c+25c, Madonna and Child in Rose Garden.

**2005, Nov. 3    Litho.    Perf. 13¾**
| | | | | | |
|---|---|---|---|---|---|
| B959 | SP448 | 45c +20c multi | | 1.60 | 1.50 |
| B960 | SP448 | 55c +25c multi | | 2.00 | 1.75 |

Butterflies SP449

Designs: 45c+20c, Zitronenfalter. No. B962, Russischer Bär. Nos. B963, B965, Tagpfauenauge. 145c+55c, Weisser Waldportier.

**2005, Dec. 1    Litho.    Perf. 14**
| | | | | | |
|---|---|---|---|---|---|
| B961 | SP449 | 45c +20c multi | | 1.75 | 1.75 |
| B962 | SP449 | 55c +25c multi | | 1.75 | 1.75 |
| B963 | SP449 | 55c +55c multi | | 1.75 | 1.75 |
| B964 | SP449 | 145c +55c multi | | 5.25 | 5.25 |
| | | Nos. B961-B964 (4) | | 10.50 | 10.50 |

**Self-Adhesive**
**Die Cut Perf. 11**
| | | | | | |
|---|---|---|---|---|---|
| B965 | SP449 | 55c +25c multi | | 2.10 | 2.00 |
| a. | | Booklet pane of 10 | | 21.00 | |

Protection of the Ozone Layer — SP450

**2006, Jan. 2    Perf. 14**
| | | | | | |
|---|---|---|---|---|---|
| B966 | SP450 | 55c +25c multi | | 2.10 | 2.00 |

Sports SP451

Designs: 45c+20c, Crowd waving German flags, stadium lights. No. B968, Stadium exterior, blurred athlete. No. B969, Stadium interior, players holding World Cup. No. B970, Horse and rider, rider's leg. 145c+55c, Emblem of 2006 World Cup Soccer Championships, blurred picture of soccer player kicking ball.

**2006, Feb. 9    Litho.    Perf. 13x13½**
| | | | | | |
|---|---|---|---|---|---|
| B967 | SP451 | 45c +20c multi | | 1.75 | 1.75 |
| B968 | SP451 | 55c +25c multi | | 1.75 | 1.75 |
| B969 | SP451 | 55c +25c multi | | 1.75 | 1.75 |
| B970 | SP451 | 55c +25c multi | | 1.75 | 1.75 |
| B971 | SP451 | 145c +55c multi | | 4.75 | 4.75 |
| a. | | Souvenir sheet, #B967-B969, B971 | | 10.00 | 10.00 |
| | | Nos. B967-B971 (5) | | 11.75 | 11.75 |

2006 World Cup Soccer Championships (Nos. B967-B969, B971), World Equestrian Championships, Aachen (No. B970). No. B971a issued 5/4.

Mammals SP452

Designs: 45c+20c, Pine marten. No. B973, Doe and fawn. No. B974, Hares. No. B975, Squirrel. 145c+55c, Wild pig and piglets.

**2006, June 8    Litho.    Perf. 14**
| | | | | | |
|---|---|---|---|---|---|
| B972 | SP452 | 45c +20c multi | | 1.50 | 1.50 |
| B973 | SP452 | 55c +25c multi | | 1.90 | 1.90 |
| B974 | SP452 | 55c +25c multi | | 1.90 | 1.90 |
| B975 | SP452 | 55c +25c multi | | 1.90 | 1.90 |
| B976 | SP452 | 145c +55c multi | | 4.75 | 4.75 |
| | | Nos. B972-B976 (5) | | 11.95 | 11.95 |

Surtax for the German Youth Stamp Foundation.

Trains SP453

Designs: 45c+20c, Fliegender Hamburger (VT 877). No. B978, Trans Europ Express (VT 11.5). Nos. B979, B981, InterCityExpress (ET403). 145c+55c, Henschel-Wegmann train (61 001).

**2006, Oct. 5    Litho.    Perf. 13¾x14**
| | | | | | |
|---|---|---|---|---|---|
| B977 | SP453 | 45c +20c multi | | 1.75 | 1.75 |
| B978 | SP453 | 55c +25c multi | | 1.75 | 1.75 |
| B979 | SP453 | 55c +25c multi | | 1.75 | 1.75 |
| B980 | SP453 | 145c +55c multi | | 4.75 | 4.75 |
| | | Nos. B977-B980 (4) | | 10.00 | 10.00 |

**Self-Adhesive**
**Die Cut Perf. 11**
| | | | | | |
|---|---|---|---|---|---|
| B981 | SP453 | 55c +25c multi | | 2.50 | 2.10 |
| a. | | Booklet pane of 10 | | 23.00 | |

Christmas SP454

15th Cent. altarpiece art by Meister Francke: 45c+20c, Nativity. 55c+25c, Adoration of the Magi.

**2006, Nov. 9    Litho.    Perf. 14**
| | | | | | |
|---|---|---|---|---|---|
| B982 | SP454 | 45c +20c multi | | 1.40 | 1.40 |
| B983 | SP454 | 55c +25c multi | | 1.75 | 1.75 |

SP455

Designs: 45c+20c, Canoe World Championships. No. B985, Handball World Championships. No. B986, Gymnastics World Championships. 145c+55c, Modern Pentathlon World Championships.

**2007    Litho.    Perf. 13x13½**
| | | | | | |
|---|---|---|---|---|---|
| B984 | SP455 | 45c +20c multi | | 1.75 | 1.75 |
| B985 | SP455 | 55c +25c multi | | 2.10 | 2.10 |
| B986 | SP455 | 55c +25c multi | | 2.00 | 2.00 |
| B987 | SP455 | 145c +55c multi | | 4.75 | 4.75 |
| a. | | Souvenir sheet, #B984-B987 | | 10.50 | 10.50 |
| | | Nos. B984-B987 (4) | | 10.60 | 10.60 |

Issued: B985, 1/2. B984, B986-B987, 2/8. B987a, 5/3.

## Souvenir Sheet

Graf Zeppelin and Itinerary of Flight to South America SP456

## Litho. & Engr.

**2007, Mar. 1**     *Perf. 14x14¼*
B988 SP456 170c +70c multi   6.50 6.50
Stamp Day.

### Souvenir Sheet

Hans Huckelbein, der Unglücksrabe,
by Wilhelm Busch — SP457

No. B989: a, Bird eating berry jam. b, Bird standing in jam. c, Bird tipping pan of jam. d, Bird dirtying clean laundry.

**2007, June 14**   Litho.   *Perf. 13¼*
B989 SP457 Sheet of 4   10.00 10.00
*a.*    45c +20c multi   1.75 1.75
*b.-c.*   55c +25c either single   1.75 1.75
*d.*    145c +55c multi   1.75 1.75

Christmas — SP458

Designs: 45c+20c, Magi. 55c+25c, Madonna and Child, donkey and bull.

**2007, Nov. 8**   Litho.   *Perf. 13¼*
B990 SP458 45c +20c multi   1.60 1.60
B991 SP458 55c +25c multi   1.90 1.90

Adult and
Juvenile
Animals
SP459

Designs: 45c+20c, Guinea pigs. Nos. B993, B996, Horses. No. B994, Dogs. 145c+55c, Rabbits.

**2007, Dec. 27**   Photo.   *Perf. 13¾x14*
B992 SP459 45c +20c multi   1.90 1.90
B993 SP459 55c +20c multi   1.90 1.90
B994 SP459 55c +25c multi   1.90 1.90
B995 SP459 145c +55c multi   5.25 5.25
   Nos. B992-B995 (4)   10.95 10.95

### Self-Adhesive
#### Die Cut Perf. 11
B996 SP459 55c +25c multi   2.25 2.10
*a.*   Booklet pane of 10   21.00

Sports Championships — SP460

Designs: 45c+20c, World Gliding Championships, Berlin. No. B998, Chess Olympiad, Dresden. No. B999, European Soccer Championships, Austria and Switzerland. 145c+55c, 2008 Summer Olympics, Beijing.

     *Perf. 13¼x13½*
**2008, Mar. 13**        Litho.
B997 SP460 45c +20c multi   1.75 1.75
B998 SP460 55c +25c multi   1.75 1.75
B999 SP460 55c +25c multi   1.75 1.75
B1000 SP460 145c +55c multi   4.25 4.25
   Nos. B997-B1000 (4)   9.50 9.50

Knut, Polar
Bear Cub in
Berlin
Zoo — SP461

**2008, Apr. 10**   Litho.   *Perf. 14*
B1001 SP461 55c +25c multi   2.10 2.10

---

Aircraft
SP462

Designs: 45c+20c, Dornier Do J Wal. No. B1003, Junkers Ju 52. Nos. B1004, B1006, Airbus A380. 145c+55c, Messerschmitt-Bölkow-Blohm BO 105 helicopter.

**2008, June 12**   Litho.   *Perf. 14*
B1002 SP462 45c +20c multi   1.60 1.60
B1003 SP462 55c +20c multi   1.75 1.75
B1004 SP462 55c +25c multi   1.75 1.75
B1005 SP462 145c +55c multi   4.25 4.25
   Nos. B1002-B1005 (4)   9.35 9.35

### Self-Adhesive
#### Die Cut Perf. 11
B1006 SP462 55c +25c multi   2.25 2.10
*a.*   Booklet pane of 10   21.00

### Miniature Sheet

Dinosaurs — SP463

No. B1007: a, Triceratops. b, Diplodocus. c, Tyrannosaurus rex. d, Plateosaurus.

**2008, Sept. 4**   Litho.   *Perf. 13x13½*
B1007 SP463 Sheet of 4   13.00 13.00
*a.*    45c +20c multi   2.50 2.50
*b.-c.*   55c +25c Either single   2.50 2.50
*d.*    145c +55c multi   5.25 5.25

Christmas — SP464

Designs: 45c+20c, Nativity, by Albrecht Dürer. 55c+25c, Adoration of the Magi, by Raphael, horiz.

**2008, Nov. 13**   Litho.   *Perf. 14*
B1008 SP464 45c +20c multi   1.45 1.45
B1009 SP464 55c +25c multi   1.75 1.75

See Vatican City Nos. 1399-1401.

Atmospheric Phenomena — SP465

Designs: 45c+20c, Rainbow. Nos. B1011, B1014, Clouds. No. B1012, Aurora borealis. 145c+55c, Lightning.

**2009, Jan. 2**   Litho.   *Perf. 14*
B1010 SP465 45c +20c multi   1.75 1.75
B1011 SP465 55c +25c multi   1.90 1.90
B1012 SP465 55c +25c multi   1.90 1.90
B1013 SP465 145c +55c multi   4.75 4.75
   Nos. B1010-B1013 (4)   10.30 10.30

### Self-Adhesive
#### Die Cut Perf. 11
B1014 SP465 55c +25c multi   1.90 1.75
*a.*   Booklet pane of 10   22.00

2009 World Track and Field
Championships, Berlin — SP466

Designs: 45c+20c, Hurdles. No. B1016, Pole vault. No. B1017, Runners. 145c+55c, Discus.

---

**2009, Apr. 9**      *Perf. 13x13½*
B1015 SP466 45c +20c multi   1.90 1.90
B1016 SP466 55c +25c multi   1.90 1.90
*a.*   Booklet pane of 8, 4 each
     #B1015-B1016   19.50 19.50
     Complete booklet,
     #B1016a   224.00
B1017 SP466 55c +25c multi   1.90 1.90
B1018 SP466 145c +55c multi   4.75 4.75
   Nos. B1015-B1018 (4)   10.45 10.45

Stamp
Day — SP467

**2009, May 7**   *Perf. 13¾ Syncopated*
B1019 SP467 55c +25c multi   2.00 1.75

"Our Sandman"
Children's
Television Show,
50th
Anniv. — SP468

Sandman: 45c+20c, On beach with boy. No. B1021, In flying suitcase. No. B1022, On train. 145c+55c, In spaceship.

**2009, Aug. 13**      *Perf. 13¼*
B1020 SP468 45c +20c multi   1.90 1.90
B1021 SP468 55c +25c multi   1.90 1.90
B1022 SP468 55c +25c multi   1.90 1.90
B1023 SP468 145c +55c multi   4.75 4.75
   Nos. B1020-B1023 (4)   10.45 10.45

Christmas
SP469

Illuminated manuscripts depicting: 45c+20c, Adoration of the Magi. 55c+25c, Nativity.

**2009, Nov. 12**      *Perf. 14*
B1024 SP469 45c +20c multi   1.45 1.45
B1025 SP469 55c +25c multi   1.75 1.75

Fruit
SP470

Blossom and fruit (whole and halved): 45c+20c, Apple (Malus domestica). No. B1027, Lemon (Citrus limon). Nos. B1028, B1030, Strawberry (Fragaria ananassa). 145c+55c, Blueberry (vaccinium myrtillus).

**2010, Jan. 2**   Litho.   *Perf. 14*
B1026 SP470 45c +20c multi   1.90 1.90
B1027 SP470 55c +25c multi   1.90 1.90
B1028 SP470 55c +25c multi   1.90 1.90
B1029 SP470 145c +55c multi   1.90 1.90
   Nos. B1026-B1029 (4)   7.60 7.60

### Self-Adhesive
#### Die Cut Perf. 10¾
B1030 SP470 55c +25c multi   2.10 1.75
*a.*   Booklet pane of 10   22.00

Nos. B1026-B1030 have a scratch-and-sniff coating on the whole and halved fruit parts of the vignette having the scent of the fruit shown.

Athletes
SP471

Designs: 45c+20c, Skier at Winter Paralympics, Vancouver. No B1032, Skier at 2010 Winter Olympics, Vancouver. Designs: No. B1033, Soccer players, 2010 World Cup Soccer Championships, South Africa. 145c+55c, Ice hockey players, 2010 World Ice Hockey Championships, Germany.

---

**2010**     Litho.     *Perf. 14*
B1031 SP471 45c +20c multi   1.75 1.45
B1032 SP471 55c +25c multi   1.90 1.75
B1033 SP471 55c +25c multi   1.75 1.45
B1034 SP471 145c +55c multi   5.00 4.50
   Nos. B1031-B1034 (4)   10.40 9.45

Issued: Nos. B1031-B1032, 2/11. Nos. B1033-B1034, 4/8.

Protection
of the
Seas
SP472

**2010, May 6**   Litho.   *Perf. 13x13½*
B1035 SP472 55c +25c multi   1.75 1.75

Steamers
SP473

Designs: 45c+20c, Deutschland. No. B1037, Aller. No. B1038, Imperator. 145c+55c, Columbus.

**2010, Aug. 12**   Litho.   *Perf. 13x13¼*
B1036 SP473 45c +20c multi   1.90 1.90
B1037 SP473 55c +25c multi   1.90 1.90
B1038 SP473 55c +25c multi   1.90 1.90
B1039 SP473 145c +55c multi   4.75 4.75
   Nos. B1036-B1039 (4)   10.45 10.45

Christmas
SP474

Creche figures: 45c+20c, Nativity. 55c+25c, Adoration of the Magi.

**2010, Nov. 11**   Litho.   *Perf. 13x13½*
B1040 SP474 45c +20c multi   1.45 1.45
B1041 SP474 55c +25c multi   1.75 1.75

Cartoons by Loriot (Bernhard-Viktor
von Bülow) — SP475

Designs: 45c+20c, Two men and talking dog. Nos. B1043, B1046, Two men at racetrack fence. No. B1044, Two naked men standing in bathtub. 145c+55c, Man and woman at breakfast table.

**2011, Jan. 3**   Litho.   *Perf. 13¾x14*
B1042 SP475 45c +20c multi   1.90 1.90
B1043 SP475 55c +25c multi   1.90 1.90
B1044 SP475 55c +25c multi   1.90 1.90
B1045 SP475 145c +55c multi   4.75 4.75
   Nos. B1042-B1045 (4)   11.75 11.75

### Self-Adhesive
#### Die Cut Perf. 11
B1046 SP475 55c +25c multi   1.75 1.75
*a.*   Booklet pane of 10   22.00

Athletes
SP476

Designs: 45c+20c, Goalie, 2011 Women's Soccer World Championships, Germany. No. B1048, Soccer players, 2011 Women's Soccer World Championships. No. B1049, Gymnasts, 2011 European Gymnastics Championships, Berlin. 145c+55c, Field hockey players, 2011 Men's European Field Hockey Championships, Mönchengladbach.

**2011, Apr. 7**     **Perf. 13¼x13½**
| | | | |
|---|---|---|---|
| B1047 | SP476 | 45c +20c multi | 2.00 2.00 |
| B1048 | SP476 | 55c +25c multi | 2.00 2.00 |
| a. | Booklet pane of 8, 4 each #B1047-B1048 | | 16.00 — |
| | Complete booklet, #B1048a | | 16.00 |
| B1049 | SP476 | 55c +25c multi | 2.00 2.00 |
| B1050 | SP476 | 145c +55c multi | 4.75 4.75 |
| | *Nos. B1047-B1050 (4)* | | 10.75 10.75 |

Issued: No. B1048a, 6/9.

Stamp Day, 75th Anniv. SP477

**2011, Aug. 11**     **Perf. 13½x13¾**
| | | | |
|---|---|---|---|
| B1051 | SP477 | 55c +25c multi | 2.00 2.00 |

Astronomy SP478

Designs: 45c+20c, Horeshead Nebula. No. B1053, Earth, Saturn, other planets, half of Sun. No. B1054, Jupiter, other planets, half of Sun. 145c+55c, Pleiades.

**2011, Aug. 11**     **Perf. 14**
| | | | |
|---|---|---|---|
| B1052 | SP478 | 45c +20c multi | 2.00 2.00 |
| B1053 | SP478 | 55c +25c multi | 2.00 2.00 |
| B1054 | SP478 | 55c +25c multi | 2.00 2.00 |
| a. | Horiz. pair, #B1053-B1054 | | 4.00 4.00 |
| B1055 | SP478 | 145c +55c multi | 5.00 5.00 |
| | *Nos. B1052-B1055 (4)* | | 11.00 11.00 |

Christmas SP479

Stained-glass windows depicting: 45c+20c, St. Martin. 55c+25c, St. Nicholas.

**2011, Nov. 10**     **Litho.**    **Perf. 13x13½**
| | | | |
|---|---|---|---|
| B1056 | SP479 | 45c +20c multi | 1.60 1.60 |
| B1057 | SP479 | 55c +25c multi | 2.00 2.00 |

Gems SP480

Designs: 55c+25c, Ruby. 90c+40c, Emerald. 145c+55c, Sapphire.

**2012, Jan. 2**     **Perf. 13¼x13½**
| | | | |
|---|---|---|---|
| B1058 | SP480 | 55c +25c multi | 2.10 2.10 |
| B1059 | SP480 | 90c +40c multi | 3.50 3.50 |
| B1060 | SP480 | 145c +55c multi | 5.25 5.25 |
| | *Nos. B1058-B1060 (3)* | | 10.85 10.85 |

**Self-Adhesive**
**Die Cut Perf. 11**
| | | | |
|---|---|---|---|
| B1061 | SP480 | 55c +25c multi | 2.10 2.10 |
| a. | Booklet pane of 10 | | 21.00 |

Sports SP481

Designs: 55c+25c, 2012 European Soccer Championships, Poland and Ukraine. 90c+40c, 2012 Summer Olympics, London. 145c+55c, 2012 World Team Table Tennis Championships, Dortmund.

**2012, Apr. 12**     **Perf. 13¼x13½**
| | | | |
|---|---|---|---|
| B1062 | SP481 | 55c +25c multi | 2.00 2.00 |
| B1063 | SP481 | 90c +40c multi | 3.25 3.25 |
| B1064 | SP481 | 145c +55c multi | 5.00 5.00 |
| | *Nos. B1062-B1064 (3)* | | 10.25 10.25 |

"Waste is Raw Material" — SP482

**2012, May 2**     **Litho.**    **Perf. 13¾**
| | | | |
|---|---|---|---|
| B1065 | SP482 | 55c +25c multi | 1.40 1.40 |

Historical Locomotives — SP483

Designs: 55c+25c, S3/6. 90c+40c, PTL 2/2. 145c+55c, Leopold Friedrich.

**2012, Aug. 9**     **Perf. 13¾x14**
| | | | |
|---|---|---|---|
| B1066 | SP483 | 55c +25c multi | 2.00 2.00 |
| B1067 | SP483 | 90c +40c multi | 3.25 3.25 |
| B1068 | SP483 | 145c +55c multi | 5.00 5.00 |
| | *Nos. B1066-B1068 (3)* | | 10.25 10.25 |

Christmas SP484

**2012, Nov. 2**     **Litho.**    **Perf. 13x13½**
| | | | |
|---|---|---|---|
| B1069 | SP484 | 55c +25c multi | 1.40 1.40 |

**Booklet Stamp**
**Self-Adhesive**
**Die Cut Perf. 11**
| | | | |
|---|---|---|---|
| B1070 | SP484 | 55c +25c multi | 1.40 1.40 |
| a. | Booklet pane of 10 | | 14.00 |

Trees SP485

Designs: 58c+27c, Linden tree. 90c+40c, Wild cherry tree. 145c+55c, Horse chestnut tree.

**2013, Feb. 7**     **Perf. 13¾x14**
| | | | |
|---|---|---|---|
| B1071 | SP485 | 58c +27c multi | 2.25 2.25 |
| B1072 | SP485 | 90c +40c multi | 3.50 3.50 |
| B1073 | SP485 | 145c +55c multi | 5.25 5.25 |
| | *Nos. B1071-B1073 (3)* | | 11.00 11.00 |

**Booklet Stamp**
**Self-Adhesive**
**Die Cut Perf. 10¾**
| | | | |
|---|---|---|---|
| B1074 | SP485 | 58c +27c multi | 2.25 2.25 |
| a. | Booklet pane of 10 | | 22.50 |

Sports SP486

Mouse: 58c+27c, In runner's starting blocks. 90c+40c, On sailboat with Swiss cheese sail. 145c+55c, On parallel bars.

**2013, May 2**     **Perf. 13¾**
| | | | |
|---|---|---|---|
| B1075 | SP486 | 58c +27c multi | 2.10 2.10 |
| B1076 | SP486 | 90c +40c multi | 3.25 3.25 |
| B1077 | SP486 | 145c +55c multi | 5.00 5.00 |
| | *Nos. B1075-B1077 (3)* | | 10.35 10.35 |

**Environmental Protection Type of 1998 Inscribed "Hochwasserhilfe 2013"**

**2013, July 18**     **Perf. 13x13½**
| | | | |
|---|---|---|---|
| B1078 | SP411 | 58c +42c multi | 2.50 2.50 |

Surtax for flood victims relief.

Birds — SP487

Designs: 58c+27c, Stieglitz (goldfinch). 90c+40c, Gimpel (bullfinch). 145c+55c, Blaumeise (blue tit).

**2013, Aug. 8**     **Perf. 13¾**
| | | | |
|---|---|---|---|
| B1079 | SP487 | 58c +27c multi | 2.25 2.25 |
| B1080 | SP487 | 90c +40c multi | 3.50 3.50 |
| B1081 | SP487 | 145c +55c multi | 5.50 5.50 |
| | *Nos. B1079-B1081 (3)* | | 11.25 11.25 |

Saxonia Steam Locomotive, 175th Anniv. — SP488

**2013, Sept. 5**     **Litho.**    **Perf. 13¾**
| | | | |
|---|---|---|---|
| B1082 | SP488 | 58c+27c multi | 2.25 2.25 |

Stamp Day.

Christmas — SP489

**2013, Nov. 2**     **Litho.**    **Perf. 13¾**
| | | | |
|---|---|---|---|
| B1083 | SP489 | 58c +27c multi | 2.25 2.25 |

**Booklet Stamp**
**Self-Adhesive**
**Die Cut Perf. 10½**
| | | | |
|---|---|---|---|
| B1084 | SP489 | 58c +27c multi | 2.25 2.25 |
| a. | Booklet pane of 10 | | 22.50 |

Hansel and Gretel — SP490

Designs: 60c+30c, Hansel and Gretel find witch's house. 90c+40c, Hansel imprisoned by witch. 145c+55c, Gretel riding on swan.

**2014, Feb. 6**     **Litho.**    **Perf. 13¾**
| | | | |
|---|---|---|---|
| B1085 | SP490 | 60c +30c multi | 2.50 2.50 |
| B1086 | SP490 | 90c +40c multi | 3.75 3.75 |
| B1087 | SP490 | 145c +55c multi | 5.50 5.50 |
| | *Nos. B1085-B1087 (3)* | | 11.75 11.75 |

**Self-Adhesive**
**Die Cut Perf. 10¼**
| | | | |
|---|---|---|---|
| B1088 | SP490 | 60c +30c multi | 2.50 2.50 |
| a. | Booklet pane of 10 | | 25.00 |

Surtax for Federal Association of Voluntary Welfare Work.

Protection of Water Resources — SP491

**2014, Apr. 3**     **Litho.**    **Perf. 13¾**
| | | | |
|---|---|---|---|
| B1089 | SP491 | 60c +30c multi | 2.50 2.50 |

Cartoon Mouse by Uli Stein — SP492

Mouse: 60c+30c, Running with sports trophy. 90c+40c, Wearing shirt in colors of German flag. 145c+55c, Cheering on victory stand.

**2014, May 8**     **Litho.**    **Perf. 13¾**
| | | | |
|---|---|---|---|
| B1090 | SP492 | 60c +30c multi | 2.50 2.50 |
| B1091 | SP492 | 90c +40c multi | 3.50 3.50 |
| B1092 | SP492 | 145c +55c multi | 11.50 11.50 |
| | *Nos. B1090-B1092 (3)* | | 11.50 11.50 |

The Dream Eater, by Michael Ende (1929-95) — SP493

Designs: 60c+30c, Princess Schlafittchen in bed. 90c+40c, Dream Eater. 145c+55c, Slumberland.

**2014, Aug. 7**     **Litho.**    **Perf. 13¾**
| | | | |
|---|---|---|---|
| B1093 | SP493 | 60c +30c multi | 2.40 2.40 |
| B1094 | SP493 | 90c +40c multi | 3.50 3.50 |
| B1095 | SP493 | 145c +55c multi | 5.25 5.25 |
| | *Nos. B1093-B1095 (3)* | | 11.15 11.15 |

Christmas SP494

**2014, Nov. 3**     **Litho.**    **Perf. 13½x13¾**
| | | | |
|---|---|---|---|
| B1096 | SP494 | 60c +30c multi | 2.25 2.25 |

**Booklet Stamp**
**Self-Adhesive**
**Size: 39x23mm**
**Die Cut Perf. 10**
| | | | |
|---|---|---|---|
| B1097 | SP494 | 60c +30c multi | 2.25 2.25 |
| a. | Booklet pane of 10 | | 22.50 |

Sleeping Beauty — SP495

Designs: 62c+30c, Sleeping Beauty, old woman and spinning wheel. 85c+40c, People at castle asleep. 145c+55c, Sleeping Beauty awakened by Prince's kiss.

**2015, Feb. 5**     **Perf. 13¾**
| | | | |
|---|---|---|---|
| B1098 | SP495 | 62c +30c multi | 2.10 2.10 |
| B1099 | SP495 | 85c +40c multi | 2.75 2.75 |
| B1100 | SP495 | 145c +55c multi | 4.50 4.50 |
| | *Nos. B1098-B1100 (3)* | | 9.35 9.35 |

**Self-Adhesive**
**Die Cut Perf. 10¼**
| | | | |
|---|---|---|---|
| B1101 | SP495 | 62c +30c multi | 2.10 2.10 |
| a. | Booklet pane of 10 | | 21.00 |

Surtax for Federal Association of Voluntary Welfare Work.

Sports for the Handicapped SP496

Designs: 62c+30c, Wheelchair tennis. 85c+40c, Runner with prosthetic legs. 145c+55c, Para-alpine skier.

**2015, May 7**     **Litho.**    **Perf. 13½x13¾**
| | | | |
|---|---|---|---|
| B1102 | SP496 | 62c +30c multi | 2.10 2.10 |
| B1103 | SP496 | 85c +40c multi | 2.75 2.75 |
| B1104 | SP496 | 145c +55c multi | 4.50 4.50 |
| | *Nos. B1102-B1104 (3)* | | 9.35 9.35 |

Fish — SP497

Designs: 62c+30c, Äsche (grayling). 85c+40c, Barbe (barbel). 145c+55c, Stör (sturgeon)

**2015, Aug. 6**     **Litho.**    **Perf. 13½x13¾**
| | | | |
|---|---|---|---|
| B1105 | SP497 | 62c +30c multi | 2.10 2.10 |
| B1106 | SP497 | 85c +40c multi | 3.00 3.00 |
| B1107 | SP497 | 145c +55c multi | 4.50 4.50 |
| a. | Booklet pane of 6, 5 #B1105 + 2 labels | | 15.00 — |
| | Complete booklet, #B1107a | | 15.00 |
| | *Nos. B1105-B1107 (3)* | | 9.60 9.60 |

See Nos. B1119-B1121.

Penny Black, 175th Anniv. — SP498

**2015, Sept. 1      Litho.      Perf. 14**
B1108  SP498 62c +30c multi        2.10  2.10
Stamp Day.

Christmas — SP499

**2015, Nov. 2      Litho.      Perf. 13¾**
B1109  SP499 62c +30c multi        2.10  2.10

**Booklet Stamp**
**Self-Adhesive**
*Die Cut Perf. 10½*
B1110  SP499 62c +30c multi        2.10  2.10
a.       Booklet pane of 10              21.00

Little Red Riding Hood — SP500

Designs: 70c+30c, Little Red Riding Hood and wolf in forest. 85c+40c, Little Red Riding Hood seeing wolf in grandmother's clothing. 145c+55c, Capture of wolf.

**2016, Feb. 11      Litho.      Perf. 13¾**
B1111  SP500  70c +30c multi        2.25  2.25
B1112  SP500  85c +40c multi        2.75  2.75
B1113  SP500  145c +55c multi       4.50  4.50
     *Nos. B1111-B1113 (3)*          9.50  9.50

**Self-Adhesive**
*Die Cut Perf. 10¼*
B1114  SP500  70c +30c multi        2.25  2.25
a.       Booklet pane of 10              22.50

Surtax for Federal Association of Voluntary Welfare Work. No. B1114 was also issued in coils.

Balls — SP501

Designs: 70c+30c, Soccer ball. 85c+40c, Rugby football. 145c+55c, Golf ball.

**2016, May 2      Litho.      Perf. 13¾**
B1115  SP501  70c +30c multi        2.40  2.40
B1116  SP501  85c +40c multi        3.00  3.00
B1117  SP501  145c +55c multi       4.75  4.75
     *Nos. B1115-B1117 (3)*          10.15 10.15

Protection of the Alps — SP502

**2016, June 2      Litho.      Perf. 14**
B1118  SP502 70c +30c multi        2.25  2.25
Surtax for fund for Alpine protection projects.

**Fish Type of 2015**
Designs: 70c+30c, Hering (herring). 85c+40c, Kabeljau (cod). 145c+55c, Scholle (plaice).

**2016, Aug. 4   Litho.   Perf. 13½x13¾**
B1119  SP497  70c +30c multi        2.25  2.25
B1120  SP497  85c +40c multi        2.75  2.75
B1121  SP497  145c +55c multi       4.50  4.50
     *Nos. B1119-B1121 (3)*          9.50  9.50

Christmas SP503

**2016, Nov. 2      Litho.      Perf. 13½x13¾**
B1122  SP503 70c+30c multi        2.25  2.25

**Booklet Stamp**
**Self-Adhesive**
**Size: 39x23mm**
*Die Cut Perf. 10*
B1123  SP503 70c+30c multi        2.25  2.25
a.       Booklet pane of 10              22.50

The Town Musicians of Bremen, Fairy Tale by the Brothers Grimm — SP504

Designs: 70c+30c, Donkey, cat, dog, rooster and windmills (Meeting friend). 85c+40c, Animals making thieves leave house (The attack). 145c+55c, Animals and house (In the new home).

**2017, Feb. 9      Litho.      Perf. 13¾**
B1124  SP504  70c +30c multi        2.10  2.10
B1125  SP504  85c +40c multi        2.75  2.75
B1126  SP504  145c +55c multi       4.25  4.25
     *Nos. B1124-B1126 (3)*          9.10  9.10

**Booklet Stamp**
**Self-Adhesive**
*Die Cut Perf. 10½*
B1127  SP504  70c +30c multi        2.10  2.10
a.       Booklet pane of 10              21.00

Surtax for Federal Association of Voluntary Welfare Work.

Athletes — SP505

Designs: 70c+30c, Swimmer. 85c+40c, Fencers. 145c+55c, Rowers.

**2017, May 11      Litho.      Perf. 13¾**
B1128  SP505  70c +30c multi        2.25  2.25
B1129  SP505  85c +40c multi        2.75  2.75
B1130  SP505  145c +55c multi       4.50  4.50
a.       Booklet pane of 6, #B1129,
         B1130, 4 #B1128 + 2 la-
         bels                            16.50   —
         Complete booklet,
         #B1130a                         16.50
     *Nos. B1128-B1130 (3)*          9.50  9.50

German Sport Aid, 50th anniv.

Augsburger Puppenkiste Marionette Theater SP506

Marionettes from: 70c+30c, *Urmel aus dem Eis.* 85c+40c, *Kleiner König Kalle Wirsch.* 145c+55c, *Kater Mikesch.*

**Perf. 13½x13¾**
**2017, Aug. 10                   Litho.**
B1131  SP506  70c +30c multi        2.40  2.40
B1132  SP506  85c +40c multi        3.00  3.00
B1133  SP506  145c +55c multi       4.75  4.75
     *Nos. B1131-B1133 (3)*          10.15 10.15

Fix and Foxi, Comic Strip Characters by Rolf Kauka (1917-2000) SP507

**2017, Sept. 7      Litho.      Perf. 14**
B1134  SP507 70c +30c multi        2.40  2.40
Stamp Day.

Adoration of the Magi, by Stefan Lochner (c. 1410-51) SP508

**2017, Nov. 2      Litho.      Perf. 13½x13¾**
B1135  SP508 70c +30c multi        2.40  2.40

**Booklet Stamp**
**Self-Adhesive**
**Size: 39x22mm**
*Die Cut Perf. 10*
B1136  SP508 70c+30c multi        2.40  2.40
a.       Booklet pane of 10              24.00
Christmas.

The Frog Prince, Fairy Tale by the Brothers Grimm — SP509

Frog Prince: 70c+30c, Holding golden ball. 85c+40c, Holding knife, fork and spoon. 145c+55c, Sleeping.

**2018, Feb. 1      Litho.      Perf. 13¾**
B1137  SP509  70c +30c multi        2.50  2.50
B1138  SP509  85c +40c multi        3.25  3.25
B1139  SP509  145c +55c multi       5.00  5.00
     *Nos. B1137-B1139 (3)*          10.75 10.75

**Self-Adhesive**
*Die Cut Perf. 10¼*
B1140  SP509  70c +30c multi        2.50  2.50
a.       Booklet pane of 10 + 2
         stickers                        25.00

Surtax for Federal Association of Voluntary Welfare. No. B1140 was also issued in coils.

German Victories in the World Cup Soccer Championships SP510

Broadcaster's quotes from covering championship of: 70c+30c, 1954. 85c+40c, 1974. 145c+55c, 1990.

**2018, May 3      Litho.      Perf. 13½x13¾**
B1141  SP510  70c +30c multi        2.40  2.40
B1142  SP510  85c +40c multi        3.00  3.00
B1143  SP510  145c +55c multi       4.75  4.75
a.       Booklet pane of 3,
         #B1141-B1143, + 5 la-
         bels                            10.50   —
         Complete booklet,
         #B1143a                         10.50
     *Nos. B1141-B1143 (3)*          10.15 10.15

Mushrooms SP511

Designs: 70c+30c, Echter pfifferling (chanterelle). 85c+40c, Echter steinpilz (porcini). 145c+55c, Maronen-Röhrling (chestnut pipe).

**2018, Aug. 9      Litho.      Perf. 13¾**
B1144  SP511  70c +30c multi        2.40  2.40
B1145  SP511  85c +40c multi        3.00  3.00
B1146  SP511  145c +55c multi       4.75  4.75
     *Nos. B1144-B1146 (3)*          10.15 10.15

A Large Piece of Turf, by Albrecht Dürer (1471-1528) SP512

**2018, Sept. 13      Litho.      Perf. 14**
B1147  SP512 70c +30c multi        2.40  2.40
Biodiversity.

Stained-glass Window — SP513

**2018, Nov. 2      Litho.      Perf. 13¾**
B1148  SP513 70c +30c multi        2.25  2.25

**Booklet Stamp**
**Self-Adhesive**
*Die Cut Perf. 10½x10¼*
B1149  SP513 70c +30c multi        2.25  2.25
a.       Booklet pane of 10              22.50
Christmas.

Brothers Grimm Fairy Tale "The Brave Little Tailor" — SP514

Designs: 70c+30c. Tailor, bird in window. 85c+40c, Tailor, pig, and fighting giants. 145c+55c, Tailor and his Princess wife dancing.

**2019, Feb. 7      Litho.      Perf. 13¾**
B1150  SP514  70c +30c multi        2.25  2.25
B1151  SP514  85c +40c multi        3.00  3.00
B1152  SP514  145c +55c multi       4.50  4.50
a.       Booklet pane of 3,
         #B1150-B1152                    9.75
         Complete booklet,
         #B1152a                         9.75
     *Nos. B1150-B1152 (3)*          9.75  9.75

**Self-Adhesive**
*Die Cut Perf. 10¼*
B1153  SP514  70c +30c multi        2.25  2.25
a.       Booklet pane of 10              22.50

Surtax for Federal Association of Free Welfare Care. No. B1153 was also available in coils.

Memorable Moments in German Olympic History SP515

Broadcaster's quotes from covering: 70c+30c, Show jumping at 1956 Summer Olympics. 85c+40c, Cross-country skiing at 1980 Winter Olympics. 145c+55c, Swimming at 1984 Summer Olympics.

**2019, May 2      Litho.      Perf. 13½x13¾**
B1154  SP515  70c +30c multi        2.25  2.25
B1155  SP515  85c +40c multi        3.00  3.00
B1156  SP515  145c +55c multi       4.50  4.50
     *Nos. B1154-B1156 (3)*          9.75  9.75

Bats — SP516

Designs: 80c+30c, Kleine hufeisennase (lesser horseshoe bat). 95c+40c, Graues langohr (gray long-eared bat). 155c+55c, Mopsfledermaus (western barbastelle bat).

**2019, Aug. 1      Litho.      Perf. 13¾**
B1157  SP516  80c +30c multi        2.50  2.50
B1158  SP516  95c +40c multi        3.00  3.00
B1159  SP516  155c +55c multi       4.75  4.75
a.       Booklet pane of 3,
         #B1157-B1159                    10.50   —
         Complete booklet,
         #B1159a                         10.50
     *Nos. B1157-B1159 (3)*          10.25 10.25

Stamp Day — SP517

**2019, Sept. 5      Litho.      Perf. 14**
B1160  SP517 155c +55c multi        4.75  4.75

Christmas
SP518

**2019, Oct. 10  Litho.  Perf. 13½x13¾**
B1161 SP518 80c +40c multi  2.75 2.75

**Booklet Stamp**
**Self-Adhesive**
**Size: 39x22mm**
**Die Cut Perf. 10**

B1162 SP518 80c +40c multi  2.75 2.75
*a.*    Booklet pane of 10  27.50

The Wolf and the
Seven Young Goats,
Fairy Tale by the
Brothers
Grimm — SP519

Designs: 80c+40c, Wolf, young goats in house. 95c+45c, Wolf in house, young goat hiding in clock. 155c+55c, Mother goat rescuing young goats from stomach of wolf.

**2020, Feb. 6  Litho.  Perf. 13¾**
B1163 SP519  80c +40c multi  2.75  2.75
B1164 SP519  95c +45c multi  3.25  3.25
B1165 SP519 155c +55c multi  4.75  4.75
      *Nos. B1163-B1165 (3)*  10.75 10.75

**Booklet Stamp**
**Self-Adhesive**
**Die Cut Perf. 10¼**

B1166 SP519  80c +40c multi  2.75  2.75
*a.*    Booklet pane of 10  27.50

Surtax for Federal Association of Voluntary Welfare.

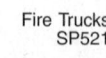

New Olympic
Sports — SP520

Designs: 80c+40c, Sport climbing. 95c+45c, Skateboarding. 155c+55c, Karate.

**2020, May 7  Litho.  Perf. 13¾**
B1167 SP520  80c +40c multi  2.75  2.75
B1168 SP520  95c +45c multi  3.25  3.25
B1169 SP520 155c +55c multi  4.75  4.75
*a.*    Booklet pane of 3,
        #B1167-B1169  11.00  —
        Complete booklet,
        #1169a  11.00
      *Nos. B1167-B1169 (3)*  10.75 10.75

Surtax for German Sports Aid Foundation.

Fire Trucks
SP521

Designs: 80c+40c, Volkswagen Type 2 T1 Bulli pumper truck. 95c+45c, Mercedes-Benz LF 16 MB pumper truck. 155c+55c, Werdau 16 W 50 multi-purpose truck.

**2020, Aug. 6  Litho.  Perf. 13¾**
B1170 SP521  80c +40c multi  3.00  3.00
B1171 SP521  95c +45c multi  3.50  3.50
B1172 SP521 155c +55c multi  5.00  5.00
      *Nos. B1170-B1172 (3)*  11.50 11.50

Surtax for the German Youth Stamp Foundation.

Environmental
Protection
Campaign — SP522

**2020, Sept. 3  Litho.  Perf. 14x13¾**
B1173 SP522  80c +40c multi  3.00  3.00

---

Christmas
SP523

**2020, Nov. 2  Litho.  Perf. 13½x13¾**
B1174 SP523 80c +40c multi  2.75 2.75

**Booklet Stamp**
**Self-Adhesive**
**Size: 39x22mm**
**Die Cut Perf. 10**

B1175 SP523 80c +40c multi  2.75 2.75
*a.*    Booklet pane of 10  27.50

Brothers Grimm
Fairy Tale *Frau
Holle* — SP524

Designs: 80c+40c, Widow's stepdaughter shaking apple tree and widow's daughter refusing task. 95c+45c, Stepdaughter shaking feathers from pillow and daughter resting. 155c+55c, Stepdaughter rewarded with gold and daughter receiving tar punishment.

**2021, Feb. 4  Litho.  Perf. 13¾**
B1176 SP524  80c +40c multi  3.00  3.00
B1177 SP524  95c +45c multi  3.50  3.50
B1178 SP524 155c +55c multi  5.00  5.00
      *Nos. B1176-B1178 (3)*  11.50 11.50

**Self-Adhesive**
**Die Cut Perf. 10¼**

B1179 SP524  80c +40c multi  3.00  3.00
*a.*    Booklet pane of 10  30.00

Surtax for Federal Association of Free Welfare Care.

New Sports for the
Summer
Olympics — SP525

Designs: 80c+40c, Baseball. 95c+45c, Softball. 155c+55c, Surfing.

**2021, May 6  Litho.  Perf. 13¾**
B1180 SP525  80c +40c multi  3.00  3.00
B1181 SP525  95c +45c multi  3.50  3.50
B1182 SP525 155c +55c multi  5.25  5.25
      *Nos. B1180-B1182 (3)*  11.75 11.75

Surtax for German Sports Aid Foundation.

Tractors
SP526

Designs: 80c+40c, 1958 Porsche Diesel Master tractor. 95c+45c, 1906 Bergmann Gaggenau tractor. 155c+55c, 1923 Lanz HP Knicklenker tractor.

**2021, Aug. 5  Litho.  Perf. 13½x13¾**
B1183 SP526  80c +40c multi  3.00  3.00
B1184 SP526  95c +45c multi  3.50  3.50
B1185 SP526 155c +55c multi  5.00  5.00
*a.*    Booklet pane of 3,
        #B1183-B1185  11.50  —
        Complete booklet,
        #B1185a  11.50
      *Nos. B1183-B1185 (3)*  11.50 11.50

Surtax for the German Youth Stamp Foundation.

Mauritius Nos. 1
and 2 on Cover to
Bordeaux,
France — SP527

**2021, Sept. 2  Litho.  Perf. 13¾x14**
B1186 SP527 80c +40c multi  2.75 2.75
*a.*    Souvenir sheet of 1  2.75 2.75

Stamp Day.

---

Angel of the
Annunciation,
Painting by Johann
Michael Hertz (1725-
90) — SP528

**2021, Nov. 2  Litho.  Perf. 13¾**
B1187 SP528 80c +40c gold &
              multi  2.75 2.75

**Booklet Stamp**
**Self-Adhesive**
**Die Cut Perf. 11½x11¼**

B1188 SP528 80c +40c gold &
              multi  2.75 2.75
*a.*    Booklet pane of 10  27.50

Christmas. Surtax for Federal Association of Free Welfare Care.

Rumplestiltskin, Fairy Tale by the
Brothers Grimm — SP529

Designs: 85c+40c, Miller's daughter and Rumplestiltskin spinning straw into gold. 100c+45c, Rumplestiltskin dancing around fire. 160c+55c, Queen revealing the name of Rumplestiltskin.

**2022, Feb. 3  Litho.  Perf. 13¾**
B1189 SP529  85c +40c multi  3.00  3.00
B1190 SP529 100c +45c multi  3.25  3.25
B1191 SP529 160c +55c multi  4.75  4.75
*a.*    Booklet pane of 3,
        #B1189-B1191  11.00  —
        Complete booklet,
        #B1191a  11.00
      *Nos. B1189-B1191 (3)*  11.00 11.00

**Booklet Stamp**
**Self-Adhesive**
**Die Cut Perf. 10¼**

B1192 SP529  85c +40c multi  3.00  3.00
*a.*    Booklet pane of 10  30.00

See footnote after No. 3204.

Non-Olympic Sports — SP530

Designs: 85c+40c, Skydiving. 100c+45c, Wakeboarding. 160c+55c, Fistball.

**2022, May 5  Litho.  Perf. 13¾**
B1193 SP530  85c +40c multi  2.75  2.75
B1194 SP530 100c +45c multi  3.25  3.25
B1195 SP530 160c +55c multi  4.75  4.75
      *Nos. B1193-B1195 (3)*  10.75 10.75

See footnote after No. 3204.

Protection
of
Antarctica
SP531

**2022, June 2  Litho.  Perf. 13¾**
B1196 SP531 85c +40c multi  2.75 2.75

See footnote after No. 3204.

Amphibians — SP532

Designs: 85c+40c, Bergmolch (mountain newt). 100c+45c, Laubfrosch (tree frog). 160c+55c, Feuersalamander (fire salamander).

---

**2022, Aug. 4  Litho.  Perf. 13¾x14**
B1197 SP532  85c +40c multi  2.50  2.50
B1198 SP532 100c +45c multi  3.00  3.00
B1199 SP532 160c +55c multi  4.50  4.50
      *Nos. B1197-B1199 (3)*  10.00 10.00

See footnote after No. 3204. Surtax for the German Youth Stamp Foundation.

Christmas
SP533

**2022, Nov. 2  Litho.  Perf. 13¾x14**
B1200 SP533 85c+40c multi  2.60 2.60

**Booklet Stamp**
**Self-Adhesive**
**Die Cut Perf. 10¼**

B1201 SP533 85c+40c multi  2.60 2.60
*a.*    Booklet pane of 10  26.00

See footnote after No. 3204.

---

**AIR POST STAMPS**

**Issues of the Republic**

Post Horn with        Biplane — AP2
Wings — AP1

**Perf. 15x14½**
**1919, Nov. 10  Typo.  Unwmk.**
C1 AP1 10pf orange  .25 2.60
C2 AP2 40pf dark green  .25 3.00
*a.*    Imperf.  1,900.
    Set, never hinged  1.35

No. C2a is ungummed.

Carrier Pigeon — AP3

**1922-23  Wmk. 126  Perf. 14, 14½**
**Size: 19x23mm**

C3 AP3  25(pf) chocolate  .45  18.00
C4 AP3  40(pf) orange  .40  24.00
C5 AP3  50(pf) violet  .25  8.25
C6 AP3  60(pf) carmine  .55  19.50
C7 AP3  80(pf) blue grn  .40  19.50

**Perf. 13x13½**
**Size: 22x28mm**

C8 AP3   1m dk grn & pale
             grn  .25  3.75
C9 AP3   2m lake & gray  .25  3.75
C10 AP3  3m dk blue &
             gray  .25  4.50
C11 AP3  5m red org & yel  2.60 105.00
C12 AP3 10m vio & rose
             ('23)  .25  9.00
C13 AP3 25m brn & yel
             ('23)  .25  8.25
C14 AP3 100m ol grn & rose
             ('23)  .25  6.75
      *Nos. C3-C14 (12)*  6.15 230.25
    Set, never hinged  13.50

**1923**
C15 AP3   5m vermilion  .25  42.50
C16 AP3  10m violet  .25  9.75
C17 AP3  25m dark brown  .25  9.75
C18 AP3 100m olive grn  .25  11.50
C19 AP3 200m deep blue  .25  34.00
*a.*    Imperf.  60.00
      *Nos. C15-C19 (5)*  1.25 107.50
    Set, never hinged  1.90

Issued: Nos. C15-C18, 6/1. No. C19, 7/25. Note following No. 160 applies to Nos. C1-C19.

**1924, Jan. 11  Perf. 14**
**Size: 19x23mm**

C20 AP3   5(pf) yellow grn  1.30  2.25
C21 AP3  10(pf) carmine  1.30  2.25
C22 AP3  20(pf) violet blue  6.75  5.25
C23 AP3  50(pf) orange  11.50  26.00
C24 AP3 100(pf) dull violet  30.00  57.50
C25 AP3 200(pf) grnsh bl  57.50  75.00

| | | | |
|---|---|---|---|
| **C26** AP3 | 300(pf) gray | 97.50 | 105.00 |
| *a.* | Imperf. | | 900.00 |
| | *Nos. C20-C26 (7)* | 205.85 | *273.25* |
| | Set, never hinged | 1,150. | |

German Eagle — AP4

### 1926-27

| | | | |
|---|---|---|---|
| **C27** AP4 | 5pf green | 1.15 | 1.15 |
| **C28** AP4 | 10pf rose red | 1.90 | 1.15 |
| *b.* | Tête bêche pair | 160.00 | 260.00 |
| | Never hinged | 260.00 | |
| *d.* | Bklt. pane 10 (6 No. C28 | | |
| | + 4 No. C29) | 225.00 | 340.00 |
| | Never hinged | 375.00 | |
| **C29** AP4 | 15pf lil rose ('27) | 1.90 | 1.90 |
| *a.* | Double impression | 1,375. | |
| **C30** AP4 | 20pf dull blue | 1.90 | 1.90 |
| *a.* | Tête bêche pair | 160.00 | 260.00 |
| | Never hinged | 260.00 | |
| *b.* | Bklt. pane 4 (4 No. C30 | | |
| | + 6 labels) | 225.00 | 340.00 |
| | Never hinged | 375.00 | |
| *c.* | Bklt. pane 5 (5 No. C30 | | |
| | + 5 labels) | 450.00 | 975.00 |
| | Never hinged | 900.00 | |
| **C31** AP4 | 50pf brown org | 18.00 | 5.25 |
| **C32** AP4 | 1m blk & sal | 18.00 | 6.00 |
| **C33** AP4 | 2m black & blue | 18.00 | 22.50 |
| **C34** AP4 | 3m blk & ol grn | 52.50 | 90.00 |
| | *Nos. C27-C34 (8)* | 113.35 | *129.85* |
| | Set, never hinged | 900.00 | |

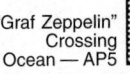

"Graf Zeppelin"
Crossing
Ocean — AP5

### 1928-31       Photo.

| | | | |
|---|---|---|---|
| **C35** AP5 | 1m carmine ('31) | 24.00 | *34.00* |
| **C36** AP5 | 2m ultra | 42.50 | *50.00* |
| **C37** AP5 | 4m black brown | 26.00 | *34.00* |
| | *Nos. C35-C37 (3)* | 92.50 | *118.00* |
| | Set, never hinged | 425.00 | |

Issued: 2m, 4m, Sept. 20. 1m, May 8.
For overprints see Nos. C40-C45.

AP6

### 1930, Apr. 19      Wmk. 126

| | | | |
|---|---|---|---|
| **C38** AP6 | 2m ultra | 250.00 | *300.00* |
| **C39** AP6 | 4m black brown | 250.00 | *300.00* |
| | Set, never hinged | 2,600. | |

First flight of Graf Zeppelin to South America. No. C38 is value with horizontal watermark. No. C39 is valued with vertical watermark. No. C38 with vertical watermark and No. C39 with horizontal watermark are worth 10%-20% more.
Counterfeits exist of Nos. C38-C45.

Nos. C35-C37
Overprinted in
Brown

### 1931, July 15

| | | | |
|---|---|---|---|
| **C40** AP5 | 1m carmine | 115.00 | 105.00 |
| **C41** AP5 | 2m ultra | 170.00 | *200.00* |
| **C42** AP5 | 4m black brown | 425.00 | *675.00* |
| | *Nos. C40-C42 (3)* | 710.00 | *980.00* |
| | Set, never hinged | 3,250. | |

Polar flight of Graf Zeppelin.

Nos. C35-C37
Overprinted

### 1933, Sept. 25

| | | | |
|---|---|---|---|
| **C43** AP5 | 1m carmine | 750.00 | *375.00* |
| **C44** AP5 | 2m ultra | 75.00 | *190.00* |
| **C45** AP5 | 4m black brown | 75.00 | *190.00* |
| | *Nos. C43-C45 (3)* | 900.00 | *755.00* |
| | Set, never hinged | 3,250. | |

Graf Zeppelin flight to Century of Progress International Exhibition, Chicago.

---

Swastika
Sun,
Globe and
Eagle
AP7

Otto Lilienthal
AP8

Design: 3m, Count Ferdinand von Zeppelin.

### Perf. 14, 13½x13

### 1934, Jan. 21    Typo.    Wmk. 237

| | | | |
|---|---|---|---|
| **C46** AP7 | 5(pf) brt green | 1.15 | .90 |
| **C47** AP7 | 10(pf) brt carmine | 1.15 | .90 |
| **C48** AP7 | 15(pf) ultra | 1.75 | 1.25 |
| **C49** AP7 | 20(pf) dull blue | 3.50 | 1.60 |
| **C50** AP7 | 25(pf) brown | 4.50 | 1.90 |
| **C51** AP7 | 40(pf) red violet | 6.75 | 1.15 |
| **C52** AP7 | 50(pf) dk green | 12.00 | .90 |
| **C53** AP7 | 80(pf) orange yel | 3.75 | 3.75 |
| **C54** AP7 | 100(pf) black | 7.50 | 2.60 |
| **C55** AP8 | 2m green & blk | 16.50 | *19.00* |
| **C56** AP8 | 3m blue & blk | 30.00 | *42.50* |
| | *Nos. C46-C56 (11)* | 88.55 | *76.45* |
| | Set, never hinged | 600.00 | |

"Hindenburg" — AP10

### Perf. 14, 14½x14

### 1936, Mar. 16      Engr.

| | | | |
|---|---|---|---|
| **C57** AP10 | 50pf dark blue | 18.00 | .75 |
| **C58** AP10 | 75pf dull green | 19.50 | 1.05 |

The note concerning gum after No. B68 also applies to Nos. C57-C58.
**Unused values are for stamps without gum.**

Count
Zeppelin
AP11

Airship
Gondola
AP12

### 1938, July 5    Unwmk.    Perf. 13½

| | | | |
|---|---|---|---|
| **C59** AP11 | 25pf dull blue | 2.75 | 1.50 |
| **C60** AP12 | 50pf green | 4.25 | 1.50 |
| | Set, never hinged | 42.50 | |

Count Ferdinand von Zeppelin (1838-1917), airship inventor and builder.

---

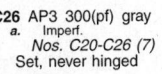

# GERMANY
# BERLIN & DDR

## ASK FOR OUR GERMANY PRICE LIST

### 1923 to Date Singles, Sets, Year Sets 1958 to 2022
(BERLIN & DDR 1958 TO 1990)

**Visit our Store on our Web Site
for Many Specialized Germany offers!**

## *https://bit.ly/hgpi-Germany*

### ALL OTHER GERMANY AVAILABLE

*German States, Empire, 3rd REICH, Propaganda Issues, Colonies, Occupation including Soviet Zone. Also Danzig, Memel & Saar. Want Lists welcomed by Scott or Michel Numbers
German Specimen Overprints – "Muestre"
Price List Available – Great for Topical Collectors
We have a large stock of German Zeppelin Flights listed on our Aerophilately & Zeppelin Price List. Ask for your copy today.*

**Better mint Germany & Area Urgently
Needed including Rarities**

**WE BUY**

3rd Reich in large quantities wanted! Top Prices Paid.

**1-800-94-STAMP (1-800-947-8267)**

## *Henry Gitner Philatelists, Inc.* HGPI

**P.O. Box 3077-S, Middletown, NY 10940
Tel: 845-343-5151   Fax: 845-343-0068   Toll Free: 1-800-947-8267**
*PayPal* E-mail: hgitner@hgitner.com    http://www.hgitner.com

**PHILATELY - THE QUIET EXCITEMENT!**

---

Catalogue values for unused stamps in this section, from this point to the end of the section, are for Never Hinged items.

### Federal Republic

Lufthansa
Emblem — AP13

### Perf. 13½x13

### 1955, Mar. 31   Litho.   Wmk. 295

| | | | |
|---|---|---|---|
| **C61** AP13 | 5pf lilac rose & blk | .95 | .70 |
| **C62** AP13 | 10pf green & blk | 1.15 | 1.05 |
| **C63** AP13 | 15pf blue & blk | 5.75 | 5.00 |
| **C64** AP13 | 20pf red & blk | 15.50 | 5.75 |
| | *Nos. C61-C64 (4)* | 23.35 | 12.50 |

Re-opening of German air service, Apr. 1.

---

### MILITARY AIR POST STAMP

Junkers 52
Transport — MAP1

### 1942    Unwmk.   Typo.    Perf. 13½

| | | | |
|---|---|---|---|
| **MC1** MAP1 | ultramarine | .30 | .45 |
| | Never hinged | .70 | |
| *a.* | Rouletted | .25 | .75 |
| | Never hinged | .45 | |

---

### MILITARY PARCEL POST STAMPS

Nazi Emblem — MPP1

### 1942    Unwmk.   Typo.    Perf. 13½
### Size: 28x23mm

| | | | |
|---|---|---|---|
| **MQ1** MPP1 | red brown | .30 | .30 |
| | Never hinged | .70 | |
| *a.* | Rouletted | .25 | 2.60 |
| | Never hinged | .45 | |

### 1944    Size: 22½x18mm    Perf. 14

| | | | |
|---|---|---|---|
| **MQ2** MPP1 | bright green | .60 | 1.90 |
| | Never hinged | 1.30 | |

No. 520 Overprinted in
Black

### 1944       Engr.

| | | | |
|---|---|---|---|
| **MQ3** A115 | on 40pf brt red vio | .55 | *3.00* |
| | Never hinged | 1.15 | |

Forged surcharges exist.
Used values for Nos. MQ1-MQ3 are for CTO examples. Postally used stamps are scarce and sell for much more.

---

### OFFICIAL STAMPS

### Issues of the Republic

In 1920 the Official Stamps of Bavaria and Wurttemberg then current were overprinted "Deutsches Reich" and made available for official use in all parts of Germany. They were, however, used almost exclusively in the two states where they originated and we have listed them among the issues of those states.

 O1   O2

O3  O4

O5  O6

O7  O8

O9  O10

 O11   O12

**1920-21  Typo.  Wmk. 125  Perf. 14**

| No. | Type | Description | Unused | Used |
|---|---|---|---|---|
| O1 | O1 | 5pf deep green | .90 | 13.50 |
| O2 | O2 | 10pf car rose | .25 | 1.60 |
| O3 | O2 | 10pf orange ('21) | .60 | 1.65 |
| O4 | O3 | 15pf violet brn | .25 | 2.25 |
| a. | | Imperf. ('21) | 750.00 | 750.00 |
| O5 | O4 | 20pf deep ultra | .25 | 1.90 |
| O6 | O5 | 30pf org, buff | .25 | 1.90 |
| O7 | O6 | 40pf carmine | .25 | 1.90 |
| O8 | O7 | 50pf violet, buff | .25 | 1.90 |
| O9 | O8 | 60pf red brn ('21) | .30 | 1.50 |
| O10 | O9 | 1m red, buff | .25 | 1.90 |
| O11 | O10 | 1.25m dk bl, yel | .25 | 3.75 |
| O12 | O11 | 2m dark blue | 4.25 | 3.00 |
| O13 | O12 | 5m brown, yel | .25 | 1.90 |
| | | Nos. O1-O13 (13) | 8.30 | 39.75 |
| | | Set, never hinged | 35.00 | |

The value of No. O4a is for a stamp postmarked at Bautzen.

See No. O15. For surcharges see Nos. O29-O33, O35-O36, O38. For overprints see Upper Silesia Nos. O39-O51.

---

**Postally Used vs. CTO**

Values quoted for canceled examples of Nos. O1-O46 are for postally used stamps. See note after No. 160.

---

 O13   O14

 O15

**Wmk. 126, 125 (#O16-O17)**

**1922-23**

| No. | Type | Description | Unused | Used |
|---|---|---|---|---|
| O14 | O13 | 75pf dark blue | .25 | 7.50 |
| O15 | O11 | 2m dark blue | .25 | 1.50 |
| a. | | Imperf. | 97.50 | |
| O16 | O14 | 3m brown, rose | .25 | 1.50 |
| O17 | O15 | 10m dk grn, rose | .25 | 1.50 |
| O18 | O15 | 10m dk grn, rose | .25 | 9.00 |
| O19 | O15 | 20m dk bl, rose | .25 | 1.50 |

| No. | Type | Description | Unused | Used |
|---|---|---|---|---|
| O20 | O15 | 50m vio, rose | .25 | 1.50 |
| a. | | Imperf. | 97.50 | — |
| O21 | O15 | 100m rose red, rose | .25 | 1.50 |
| a. | | Imperf. | 115.00 | 750.00 |
| | | Never hinged | 2.00 | 25.50 |
| | | Set, never hinged | 4.25 | |

Issue date: Nos. O18-O21, 1923.
Nos. O20-O21 exist imperf.
For surcharges see Nos. O34, O37, O39.

---

**Regular Issue of 1923**
**Overprinted — a**

**1923**

| No. | Type | Description | Unused | Used |
|---|---|---|---|---|
| O22 | A34 | 20m red lilac | .30 | 7.50 |
| O23 | A34 | 30m olive grn | .25 | 34.00 |
| O24 | A29 | 40m green | .30 | 3.00 |
| O25 | A35 | 200m car rose | .25 | 1.50 |
| O26 | A35 | 300m green | .25 | 1.50 |
| O27 | A35 | 400m dk brn | .25 | 1.50 |
| O28 | A35 | 500m red orange | .25 | 1.50 |
| | | Nos. O22-O28 (7) | 1.85 | 50.50 |
| | | Set, never hinged | 4.50 | |

**Official Stamps of 1920-23 Surcharged with New Values**

Abbreviations:
Th=(Tausend) Thousand
Mil=(Million) Million
Mlrd=(Milliarde) Billion

**1923  Wmk. 125**

| No. | Type | Description | Unused | Used |
|---|---|---|---|---|
| O29 | O12 | 5th m on 5m | .25 | 3.00 |
| a. | | Inverted surcharge | 50.00 | 2,250. |
| | | Never hinged | 115.00 | |
| O30 | O5 | 20th m on 30pf | .25 | 3.00 |
| a. | | Inverted surcharge | 52.50 | — |
| | | Never hinged | 130.00 | |
| b. | | Imperf. | 60.00 | — |
| O31 | O3 | 100th m on 15pf | .25 | 3.00 |
| a. | | Imperf. | 60.00 | — |
| | | Never hinged | 150.00 | |
| b. | | Inverted surcharge | 50.00 | — |
| | | Never hinged | 115.00 | |
| O32 | O2 | 250th m on 10pf car rose | .25 | 3.00 |
| a. | | Double surcharge | 37.50 | — |
| | | Never hinged | 90.00 | |
| O33 | O5 | 800th m on 30pf | .45 | 300.00 |

**Official Stamps and Types of 1920-23 Surcharged with New Values**
**Wmk. 126**

| No. | Type | Description | Unused | Used |
|---|---|---|---|---|
| O34 | O15 | 75th m on 50m | .25 | 3.00 |
| a. | | Inverted surcharge | 50.00 | — |
| | | Never hinged | 115.00 | |
| O35 | O3 | 400th m on 15pf brn | .25 | 27.00 |
| O36 | O5 | 800th m on 30pf org, buff | .30 | 4.50 |
| O37 | O13 | 1 mil m on 75pf | .25 | 37.50 |
| O38 | O2 | 2 mil m on 10pf car rose | .30 | 3.75 |
| a. | | Imperf. | 90.00 | — |
| | | Never hinged | 210.00 | |
| O39 | O15 | 5 mil m on 100m | .25 | 5.75 |
| | | Nos. O29-O39 (11) | 3.05 | 393.50 |
| | | Set, never hinged | 6.00 | |

The 10, 15 and 30 pfennig are not known with this watermark and without surcharge.

**Nos. 290-291, 295-299 Overprinted Type "a"**

**1923**

| No. | Type | Description | Unused | Used |
|---|---|---|---|---|
| O40 | A39 | 100 mil m | .25 | 150.00 |
| O41 | A39 | 200 mil m | .30 | 150.00 |
| O42 | A39a | 2 mlrd m | .25 | 115.00 |
| O43 | A39a | 5 mlrd m | .25 | 82.50 |
| O44 | A39a | 10 mlrd m | 3.75 | 135.00 |
| O45 | A39a | 20 mlrd m | 3.75 | 150.00 |
| O46 | A39a | 50 mlrd m | 1.90 | 200.00 |
| | | Nos. O40-O46 (7) | 10.45 | 982.50 |
| | | Set, never hinged | 34.50 | |

**Same Overprint on Nos. 323-328, Values in Rentenpfennig**

**1923**

| No. | Type | Description | Unused | Used |
|---|---|---|---|---|
| O47 | A40 | 3pf brown | .25 | .75 |
| O48 | A40 | 5pf dk green | .25 | .75 |
| a. | | Inverted overprint | 115.00 | 750.00 |
| | | Never hinged | 375.00 | |
| O49 | A40 | 10pf carmine | .25 | .75 |
| a. | | Inverted overprint | 115.00 | 300.00 |
| | | Never hinged | 300.00 | |
| b. | | Imperf. | 75.00 | — |
| | | Never hinged | 150.00 | |
| O50 | A40 | 20pf dp ultra | .60 | 1.15 |
| O51 | A40 | 50pf orange | .60 | 1.50 |
| O52 | A40 | 100pf brown vio | 3.75 | 7.50 |
| | | Nos. O47-O52 (6) | 5.70 | 12.40 |
| | | Set, never hinged | 22.50 | |

**Same Overprint On Issues of 1924**

**1924**

| No. | Type | Description | Unused | Used |
|---|---|---|---|---|
| O53 | A41 | 3pf lt brown | .70 | 2.25 |
| a. | | Inverted overprint | 60.00 | — |
| | | Never hinged | 300.00 | |

| No. | Type | Description | Unused | Used |
|---|---|---|---|---|
| O54 | A41 | 5pf lt green | .45 | .75 |
| a. | | Imperf. | 75.00 | |
| | | Never hinged | 225.00 | |
| b. | | Inverted overprint | 105.00 | |
| | | Never hinged | 300.00 | |
| O55 | A41 | 10pf vermilion | .30 | .75 |
| O56 | A41 | 20pf blue | .35 | .75 |
| O57 | A41 | 30pf rose lilac | 1.15 | .75 |
| O58 | A41 | 40pf olive green | 1.15 | .75 |
| O59 | A41 | 50pf orange | 5.75 | 3.75 |
| O60 | A47 | 60pf red brown | 2.25 | 3.75 |
| O61 | A47 | 80pf slate | 5.75 | 35.00 |
| | | Nos. O53-O61 (9) | 17.85 | 48.50 |
| | | Set, never hinged | 57.50 | |

 O16

**1927-33  Perf. 14**

| No. | Type | Description | Unused | Used |
|---|---|---|---|---|
| O62 | O16 | 3pf bister | .30 | .75 |
| O63 | O16 | 4pf lt bl ('31) | .40 | .90 |
| O64 | O16 | 4pf blue ('33) | 14.50 | 13.50 |
| O65 | O16 | 5pf green | .25 | .75 |
| O66 | O16 | 6pf pale ol grn ('32) | .70 | .90 |
| O67 | O16 | 8pf dk grn | .30 | .75 |
| O68 | O16 | 10pf carmine | 6.75 | 6.00 |
| O69 | O16 | 10pf ver ('29), wmk. upright | 17.00 | 26.00 |
| O70 | O16 | 10pf red vio ('30) | .40 | .90 |
| a. | | Imperf. | 225.00 | |
| | | Never hinged | 650.00 | |
| O71 | O16 | 10pf choc ('33) | 6.75 | 9.00 |
| O72 | O16 | 12pf org ('32) | .40 | .90 |
| O73 | O16 | 15pf vermilion | 1.50 | .90 |
| O74 | O16 | 15pf car ('29) | .35 | .90 |
| O75 | O16 | 20pf Prus grn, wmk. upright | 7.50 | 3.00 |
| O76 | O16 | 20pf gray ('30), wmk. upright | 1.90 | 1.15 |
| O77 | O16 | 30pf olive grn | .85 | .90 |
| O78 | O16 | 40pf violet, wmk upright | .95 | .90 |
| O79 | O16 | 60pf red brn ('28) | 1.25 | 1.90 |
| | | Nos. O62-O79 (18) | 62.05 | 70.00 |
| | | Set, never hinged | 210.00 | |

 Swastika — O17

**1934, Jan. 18  Wmk. 237**

| No. | Type | Description | Unused | Used |
|---|---|---|---|---|
| O80 | O17 | 3pf bister | .80 | 1.10 |
| O81 | O17 | 4pf dull blue | .25 | .90 |
| O82 | O17 | 5pf brt green | .25 | 1.10 |
| O83 | O17 | 6pf dk green | .25 | .90 |
| a. | | Imperf. | 150.00 | 525.00 |
| | | Never hinged | 375.00 | |
| O84 | O17 | 8pf vermilion | 1.75 | .90 |
| O85 | O17 | 10pf chocolate | .40 | 7.50 |
| O86 | O17 | 12pf brt carmine | 5.00 | 1.50 |
| a. | | Unwmkd. | .30 | .90 |
| O87 | O17 | 15pf claret | 1.20 | 9.00 |
| O88 | O17 | 20pf light blue | .45 | 1.50 |
| O89 | O17 | 30pf olive grn | .70 | 1.50 |
| O90 | O17 | 40pf red violet | .70 | 1.50 |
| O91 | O17 | 50pf orange yel | 1.20 | 3.75 |
| | | Nos. O80-O91 (12) | 12.95 | 31.15 |
| | | Set, never hinged | 37.50 | |

**1942  Unwmk.  Perf. 14**

| No. | Type | Description | Unused | Used |
|---|---|---|---|---|
| O92 | O17 | 3pf bister brn | .25 | 1.15 |
| O93 | O17 | 4pf dull blue | .25 | 3.00 |
| O94 | O17 | 5pf deep olive | .25 | 15.00 |
| O95 | O17 | 6pf deep violet | .25 | 1.15 |
| O96 | O17 | 8pf vermilion | .25 | 1.15 |
| O97 | O17 | 10pf chocolate | .40 | 11.50 |
| O98 | O17 | 12pf rose car | 1.60 | 22.50 |
| a. | | Wmk. 237 | 3.00 | 1.50 |
| O99 | O17 | 15pf brown car | 3.00 | 52.50 |
| O100 | O17 | 20pf light blue | .25 | 7.50 |
| O101 | O17 | 30pf olive grn | .25 | 7.50 |
| O102 | O17 | 40pf red violet | .50 | 19.00 |
| O103 | O17 | 50pf dk green | 4.00 | 300.00 |
| | | Nos. O92-O103 (12) | 11.25 | 441.95 |
| | | Set, never hinged | 42.50 | |

---

## LOCAL OFFICIAL STAMPS

### For Use in Prussia

("Nr. 21" refers to the district of Prussia) — LO1

**1903  Unwmk.  Typo.  Perf. 14, 14½**

| No. | Type | Description | Unused | Used |
|---|---|---|---|---|
| OL1 | LO1 | 2pf slate | 1.15 | 4.50 |
| OL2 | LO1 | 3pf bister brn | 1.15 | 4.50 |
| OL3 | LO1 | 5pf green | .25 | .55 |
| OL4 | LO1 | 10pf carmine | .25 | .55 |
| OL5 | LO1 | 20pf ultra | .25 | .55 |
| OL6 | LO1 | 25pf org & blk, yel | .75 | 1.60 |
| OL7 | LO1 | 40pf lake & blk | .75 | 2.00 |
| OL8 | LO1 | 50pf pur & blk, sal | .90 | 1.90 |
| | | Nos. OL1-OL8 (8) | 5.45 | 16.15 |
| | | Set, never hinged | 10.50 | |

 LO2   LO3

LO4  LO5

LO6  LO7

 LO8

**1920  Typo.  Wmk. 125  Perf. 14**

| No. | Type | Description | Unused | Used |
|---|---|---|---|---|
| OL9 | LO2 | 5pf green | .25 | 3.00 |
| OL10 | LO3 | 10pf carmine | .75 | 1.50 |
| OL11 | LO4 | 15pf vio brn | .25 | 2.25 |
| OL12 | LO5 | 20pf dp ultra | .25 | 1.90 |
| OL13 | LO6 | 30pf org, buff | .25 | 1.50 |
| OL14 | LO7 | 50pf brn lil, buff | .30 | 1.50 |
| OL15 | LO8 | 1m red, buff | 8.25 | 3.75 |
| | | Nos. OL9-OL15 (7) | 10.30 | 15.40 |
| | | Set, never hinged | 35.00 | |

For overprints see Upper Silesia Nos. O32-O38.

### For Use in Baden

 LO9

**1905  Unwmk.  Typo.  Perf. 14, 14½**

| No. | Type | Description | Unused | Used |
|---|---|---|---|---|
| OL16 | LO9 | 2pf gray blue | 52.50 | 75.00 |
| OL17 | LO9 | 3pf brown | 6.00 | 10.50 |
| OL18 | LO9 | 5pf green | 4.25 | 9.00 |
| OL19 | LO9 | 10pf rose | .75 | 2.10 |
| OL20 | LO9 | 20pf blue | 1.50 | 3.00 |
| OL21 | LO9 | 50pf org & blk, yel | 30.00 | 52.50 |
| | | Nos. OL16-OL21 (6) | 95.00 | 152.10 |
| | | Set, never hinged | 825.00 | |

---

## NEWSPAPER STAMPS

Newsboy and Globe — N1

**Wmk. Swastikas (237)**

**1939, Nov. 1  Photo.  Perf. 14**

| No. | Type | Description | Unused | Used |
|---|---|---|---|---|
| P1 | N1 | 5pf green | .60 | 5.25 |
| P2 | N1 | 10pf red brown | .60 | 5.25 |
| | | Set, never hinged | 4.50 | |

---

## POSTAL TAX STAMPS

On November 28, 1948, the "Notopfer Berlin" ("Berlin emergency levy") was enacted by the West German authorities to raise funds to subsidize civilian operations in West Berlin. Part of this levy was a 2pf surtax on virtually all types of internal mail in West Germany, except that of the military governments and foreign consulates and surface mail to Berlin. Initially applied to the Bizone (American and British administration), this levy was later extended to the French zone of occupation, and was continued by the Federal Republic of Germany after its formation in Sept. 1949.

From Dec. 1, 1948, until the expiration of the levy on March 31, 1956, most mail was required to carry one of the "Notopfer" tax stamps.

 PT1

### 1948     Wmk. 286     Typo.
*Imperf*

| | | | | |
|---|---|---|---|---|
| RA1 | PT1 | 2pf dk blue | .25 | .25 |
| | | Never hinged | | .75 |

*Compound Perf 12 and 14*

| | | | | |
|---|---|---|---|---|
| RA2 | PT1 | 2pf dk blue | .30 | .25 |
| | | Never hinged | | 1.50 |

No. RA2 also exists perf 9-10, 11, 11½x11, 11½, compund 11½ and 12, 12x11, 13½x11½ and rouletted, some of which were produced by local post offices or by private parties.
Issued: RA1, 12/1; RA2, 12/15.
Illustration PT1 actual size.

### 1948-50     Wmk. 285     Typo.
*Imperf*

| | | | | |
|---|---|---|---|---|
| RA3 | PT1 | 2pf dk blue | 19.00 | 1.50 |
| | | Never hinged | 45.00 | |

*Compound Perf 12 and 14*

| | | | | |
|---|---|---|---|---|
| RA4 | PT1 | 2pf dk blue ('49) | 15.00 | .90 |
| | | Never hinged | 60.00 | |

No. RA4 also exists perf 9½, 11, 11¼x11, 11½, 12, 12x11, 12x13½, 12¼ and rouletted, some of which were produced by local post offices or by private parties.

### Wmk. 285
### 1950, June 10     Litho.     *Perf. 14*

| | | | | |
|---|---|---|---|---|
| RA5 | PT1 | 2pf dk blue | .25 | .25 |
| | | Never hinged | | 1.15 |

### 1955, Aug. 8     Wmk. 295

| | | | | |
|---|---|---|---|---|
| RA6 | PT1 | 2pf dk blue | .25 | .25 |
| | | Never hinged | | .55 |

## FRANCHISE STAMPS

**For use by the National Socialist German Workers' Party**

Party Emblem — F1

### 1938    Typo.    Wmk. 237    *Perf. 14*

| | | | | |
|---|---|---|---|---|
| S1 | F1 | 1pf black | .75 | 3.00 |
| S2 | F1 | 3pf bister | .75 | 1.90 |
| S3 | F1 | 4pf dull blue | .90 | 1.50 |
| S4 | F1 | 5pf brt green | .35 | 1.50 |
| S5 | F1 | 6pf dk green | .35 | 1.50 |
| S6 | F1 | 8pf vermilion | 3.00 | 1.50 |
| S7 | F1 | 12pf brt car | 5.50 | 1.50 |
| S8 | F1 | 16pf gray | .65 | 9.00 |
| S9 | F1 | 24pf citron | 1.40 | 5.00 |
| S10 | F1 | 30pf olive | 1.10 | 7.50 |
| S11 | F1 | 40pf red violet | 1.30 | 11.50 |
| | | *Nos. S1-S11 (11)* | 16.05 | 45.40 |
| | | Set, never hinged | 127.00 | |

### 1942      Unwmk.

| | | | | |
|---|---|---|---|---|
| S12 | F1 | 1pf gray blk | .90 | 30.00 |
| S13 | F1 | 3pf bister brn | .25 | 1.15 |
| S14 | F1 | 4pf dk gray blue | .90 | 3.00 |
| S15 | F1 | 5pf gray green | .25 | 22.50 |
| S16 | F1 | 6pf violet | .25 | 2.25 |
| S17 | F1 | 8pf deep orange | .30 | 2.25 |
| a. | | Imperf. | 115.00 | |
| | | Never hinged | 340.00 | |
| S18 | F1 | 12pf carmine | .30 | 1.15 |
| S19 | F1 | 16pf blue green | 4.50 | 75.00 |
| S20 | F1 | 24pf yellow brn | .55 | 30.00 |
| S21 | F1 | 30pf dp olive grn | .70 | 22.50 |
| S22 | F1 | 40pf light rose vio | .70 | 45.00 |
| | | *Nos. S12-S22 (11)* | 9.60 | 234.80 |
| | | Set, never hinged | 37.50 | |

## GERMAN OCCUPATION STAMPS

---

100 Centimes = 1 Franc
100 Pfennig = 1 Mark

**Issued under Belgian Occupation**

Belgian Stamps of 1915-1920 Overprinted

### *Perf. 11½, 14, 14½*
### 1919-21      Unwmk.

| | | | | |
|---|---|---|---|---|
| 1N1 | A46 | 1c orange | .30 | .55 |
| 1N2 | A46 | 2c chocolate | .30 | .55 |
| 1N3 | A46 | 3c gray blk ('21) | .30 | 2.00 |
| 1N4 | A46 | 5c green | .60 | 1.00 |
| 1N5 | A46 | 10c carmine | 1.15 | 2.00 |
| 1N6 | A46 | 15c purple | .60 | 1.00 |
| 1N7 | A46 | 20c red violet | .90 | 1.00 |
| 1N8 | A46 | 25c blue | 1.15 | 1.60 |
| 1N9 | A54 | 25c dp blue ('21) | 3.75 | 9.75 |

Belgian Stamps of 1915-1920 Overprinted

| | | | | |
|---|---|---|---|---|
| 1N10 | A47 | 35c brn org & blk | 1.15 | 1.00 |
| 1N11 | A48 | 40c green & blk | 1.15 | 2.00 |
| 1N12 | A49 | 50c car rose & blk | 5.75 | 9.25 |
| 1N13 | A56 | 65c cl & blk ('21) | 3.00 | 9.75 |
| 1N14 | A50 | 1fr violet | 21.00 | 16.50 |
| 1N15 | A51 | 2fr slate | 37.50 | 40.00 |
| 1N16 | A52 | 5fr deep blue | 8.25 | 9.75 |
| 1N17 | A53 | 10fr brown | 45.00 | 52.50 |
| | | On cover | | 60.00 |
| | | *Nos. 1N1-1N17 (17)* | 131.85 | 160.20 |
| | | Set, never hinged | 450.00 | |

Nos. 1N1-1N17 were valid for postage until April 30, 1931, nearly one year after the Belgians and other occupation forces evacuated the Rhineland. Mixed frankings with Belgian stamps were permitted. The values for used stamps are for stamps with cancels from the Belgian military post offices in occupied Germany.

Nos. 1N14-1N17 exist with two overprint types: spacing between "Allemagne" and "Duitshland" 2mm (1919) and 1mm (1920).

### Belgian Stamps of 1915 Surcharged

Nos. 1N18-1N22

Nos. 1N23-1N24

### 1920      Black Surcharge

| | | | | |
|---|---|---|---|---|
| 1N18 | A46 | 5pf on 5c grn | .30 | .85 |
| 1N19 | A46 | 10pf on 10c car | .30 | 1.00 |
| 1N20 | A46 | 15pf on 15c pur | .55 | 1.30 |
| 1N21 | A46 | 20pf on 20c red vio | .55 | 1.60 |
| 1N22 | A46 | 30pf on 25c blue | .75 | 1.60 |

### Red Surcharge

| | | | | |
|---|---|---|---|---|
| 1N23 | A49 | 75pf on 50c car rose & blk | 15.00 | 16.50 |
| 1N24 | A50 | 1m25pf on 1fr vio | 21.00 | 17.00 |
| | | *Nos. 1N18-1N24 (7)* | 38.45 | 39.85 |
| | | Set, never hinged | 135.00 | |

### EUPEN ISSUE
**Belgian Stamps of 1915-20 Overprinted**

Nos. 1N25-1N36

Nos. 1N37-1N41

### 1920-21      *Perf. 11½, 14, 14½*

| | | | | |
|---|---|---|---|---|
| 1N25 | A46 | 1c orange | .40 | .80 |
| 1N26 | A46 | 2c chocolate | .40 | .80 |
| 1N27 | A46 | 3c gray blk ('21) | .60 | 3.25 |
| 1N28 | A46 | 5c green | .60 | .80 |

---

| | | | | |
|---|---|---|---|---|
| 1N29 | A46 | 10c carmine | 1.00 | 1.15 |
| 1N30 | A46 | 15c purple | 1.35 | 1.15 |
| 1N31 | A46 | 20c red violet | 1.50 | 1.30 |
| 1N32 | A46 | 25c blue | 1.35 | 1.60 |
| 1N33 | A54 | 25c dp blue ('21) | 4.50 | 14.50 |
| 1N34 | A47 | 35c brn org & blk | 1.90 | 1.60 |
| 1N35 | A48 | 40c green & blk | 2.25 | 2.00 |
| 1N36 | 49 | 50c car rose & blk | 6.00 | 6.50 |
| 1N37 | A56 | 65c cl & blk ('21) | 3.50 | 18.50 |
| 1N38 | A50 | 1fr violet | 24.00 | 16.50 |
| 1N39 | A51 | 2fr slate | 42.50 | 26.00 |
| 1N40 | A52 | 5fr deep blue | 13.50 | 9.75 |
| 1N41 | A53 | 10fr brown | 60.00 | 42.50 |
| | | *Nos. 1N25-1N41 (17)* | 165.35 | 148.70 |
| | | Set, never hinged | 320.00 | |

### MALMÉDY ISSUE
**Belgian Stamps of 1915-20 Overprinted**

Nos. 1N42-1N50

Nos. 1N51-1N53

Nos. 1N54-1N58

### 1920-21

| | | | | |
|---|---|---|---|---|
| 1N42 | A46 | 1c orange | .45 | .80 |
| 1N43 | A46 | 2c chocolate | .45 | .80 |
| 1N44 | A46 | 3c gray blk ('21) | .45 | 3.25 |
| 1N45 | A46 | 5c green | .70 | .80 |
| 1N46 | A46 | 10c carmine | 1.00 | 1.15 |
| 1N47 | A46 | 15c purple | 1.50 | 1.30 |
| 1N48 | A46 | 20c red violet | 1.90 | 1.60 |
| 1N49 | A46 | 25c blue | 1.50 | 1.60 |
| 1N50 | A54 | 25c dp blue ('21) | 4.50 | 14.50 |
| 1N51 | A47 | 35c brn org & blk | 1.90 | 1.60 |
| 1N52 | A48 | 40c green & blk | 1.90 | 2.00 |
| 1N53 | A49 | 50c car rose & blk | 7.50 | 6.50 |
| 1N54 | A56 | 65c cl & blk ('21) | 3.50 | 18.50 |
| 1N55 | A50 | 1fr violet | 24.00 | 16.50 |
| 1N56 | A51 | 2fr slate | 42.50 | 26.00 |
| 1N57 | A52 | 5fr deep blue | 13.50 | 14.50 |
| 1N58 | A53 | 10fr brown | 60.00 | 97.50 |
| | | *Nos. 1N42-1N58 (17)* | 167.25 | 208.90 |
| | | Set, never hinged | 320.00 | |

### OCCUPATION POSTAGE DUE STAMPS

Belgian Postage Due Stamps of 1919-20, Overprinted

### 1920      Unwmk.      *Perf. 14½*

| | | | | |
|---|---|---|---|---|
| 1NJ1 | D3 | 5c green | 1.00 | 1.00 |
| 1NJ2 | D3 | 10c carmine | 1.90 | 1.60 |
| 1NJ3 | D3 | 20c gray green | 3.75 | 4.00 |
| 1NJ4 | D3 | 30c bright blue | 3.75 | 4.00 |
| 1NJ5 | D3 | 50c gray | 19.00 | 13.00 |
| | | *Nos. 1NJ1-1NJ5 (5)* | 29.40 | 23.60 |
| | | Set, never hinged | 57.50 | |

Belgian Postage Due Stamps of 1919-20, Overprinted

###      Unwmk.

| | | | | |
|---|---|---|---|---|
| 1NJ6 | D3 | 5c green | 1.90 | 1.00 |
| 1NJ7 | D3 | 10c carmine | 3.75 | 1.60 |
| a. | | Inverted overprint | | |
| 1NJ8 | D3 | 20c gray green | 13.50 | 9.75 |
| 1NJ9 | D3 | 30c bright blue | 7.50 | 7.25 |
| 1NJ10 | D3 | 50c gray | 15.00 | 9.75 |
| | | *Nos. 1NJ6-1NJ10 (5)* | 41.65 | 29.35 |
| | | Set, never hinged | 82.50 | |

Nos. 1NJ1-1NJ10 were valid for postage until April 30, 1931, nearly one year after the Belgians and other occupation forces evacuated the Rhineland. Mixed frankings with Belgian stamps were permitted. The values for used stamps are for stamps with cancels from the Belgian military post offices in occupied Germany.

---

## A. M. G. ISSUE

Issued jointly by the Allied Military Government of the US and Great Britain, for civilian use in areas under Allied occupation.

 OS1

Type I. Thick paper, white gum.
Type II. Medium paper, yellow gum.
Type III. Medium paper, white gum.

### Type III, Brunswick Printing
### *Perf. 11, 11½ and Compound*
### 1945-46     Litho.     Unwmk.
**Size: 19-19½x22-22½mm**

| | | | | |
|---|---|---|---|---|
| 3N1 | OS1 | 1pf slate gray | .25 | 3.75 |
| 3N2 | OS1 | 3pf dull lilac | .25 | .90 |
| 3N3 | OS1 | 4pf lt gray | .25 | 1.10 |
| 3N4 | OS1 | 5pf emerald | .25 | 3.75 |
| 3N5 | OS1 | 6pf yellow | .25 | .90 |
| 3N6 | OS1 | 8pf orange | 1.90 | 30.00 |
| 3N7 | OS1 | 10pf yel brn | .25 | 1.50 |
| 3N8 | OS1 | 12pf rose vio | .25 | .75 |
| 3N9 | OS1 | 15pf rose car | .25 | 3.00 |
| 3N10 | OS1 | 16pf dp Prus grn | .25 | 11.00 |
| 3N11 | OS1 | 20pf blue | .25 | 3.75 |
| 3N12 | OS1 | 24pf choc | .25 | 10.00 |
| 3N13 | OS1 | 25pf brt ultra | .25 | 11.00 |

**Size: 21½x25mm**

| | | | | |
|---|---|---|---|---|
| 3N14 | OS1 | 30pf olive | .25 | 1.50 |
| 3N15 | OS1 | 40pf dp mag | .25 | 3.75 |
| 3N16 | OS1 | 42pf green | .25 | 1.50 |
| 3N17 | OS1 | 50pf slate grn | .25 | 13.50 |
| 3N18 | OS1 | 60pf vio brn | .50 | 15.00 |
| 3N19 | OS1 | 80pf bl blk | 9.00 | 225.00 |

**Size: 25x29½mm**

| | | | | |
|---|---|---|---|---|
| 3N20 | OS1 | 1m dk ol grn ('46) | 1.90 | 400.00 |
| | | *Nos. 3N1-3N20 (20)* | 17.30 | 741.65 |
| | | Set, never hinged | 40.00 | |

Most of Nos. 3N1-3N20 exist imperforate and part-perforate.

 OS1a

### Type I, Washington Printing
**Size: 19-19½x22-22½mm**
### *Perf. 11*

| | | | | |
|---|---|---|---|---|
| 3N2a | OS1a | 3pf lilac | .25 | 1.90 |
| 3N3a | OS1a | 4pf light gray | .25 | 1.50 |
| 3N4a | OS1a | 5pf emerald | .25 | .35 |
| 3N5a | OS1a | 6pf yellow | .25 | .35 |
| 3N6a | OS1a | 8pf deep orange | .25 | .35 |
| 3N7a | OS1a | 10pf brown | .25 | .35 |
| 3N8a | OS1a | 12pf rose violet | .25 | .35 |
| 3N9a | OS1a | 15pf cerise | .25 | 1.50 |
| 3N13a | OS1a | 25pf bright ultra | .25 | 1.50 |
| | | *Nos. 3N2a-3N13a (9)* | | 8.15 |
| | | Set, never hinged | 2.00 | |

### Type II, London Printing
**Size: 19-19½x22-22½mm**
### *Perf. 14, 14½ and Compound*
**Photo.**

| | | | | |
|---|---|---|---|---|
| 3N2b | OS1 | 3pf lilac | .25 | .60 |
| 3N3b | OS1 | 4pf light gray | .25 | .60 |
| 3N4b | OS1 | 5pf deep emerald | .25 | 11.00 |
| 3N5b | OS1 | 6pf orange yellow | .25 | .60 |
| 3N6b | OS1 | 8pf dark orange | .25 | 3.00 |
| 3N8b | OS1 | 12pf rose violet | .25 | .60 |
| | | *Nos. 3N2b-3N8b (6)* | 1.50 | 16.40 |
| | | Set, never hinged | 1.90 | |

### ISSUED UNDER FRENCH OCCUPATION

**Coats of Arms**

Rhine Province
OS3

Palatinate District
OS4

Saarland
OS5

Württemberg
OS6

Baden
OS7

Johann
Wolfgang
von Goethe
OS8

Friedrich
von Schiller
OS9

Heinrich
Heine
OS10

### Perf. 14x13½

| 1945-46 | | Unwmk. | | Typo. |
|---|---|---|---|---|
| 4N1 | OS3 | 1pf blk, grn & lem | .25 | .25 |
| 4N2 | OS4 | 3pf dk red, blk & dl yel | .25 | .25 |
| 4N3 | OS6 | 5pf brn, blk & org yel | .25 | .25 |
| 4N4 | OS7 | 8pf brn, yel & red | .25 | .25 |
| 4N5 | OS3 | 10pf brn, grn & lem | 5.25 | 50.00 |
| 4N6 | OS4 | 12pf red, blk & org yel | .25 | .25 |
| 4N7 | OS5 | 15pf blk, ultra & red ('46) | .25 | .25 |
| 4N8 | OS6 | 20pf red, org yel & blk | .25 | .25 |
| 4N9 | OS5 | 24pf blk, dp ultra & red ('46) | .25 | .25 |
| 4N10 | OS7 | 30pf blk, org yel & red | .25 | .25 |

### Perf. 13
### Engr.

| 4N11 | OS8 | 1m lilac brn | .90 | 16.00 |
|---|---|---|---|---|
| 4N12 | OS9 | 2m dp bl ('46) | .90 | 47.50 |
| 4N13 | OS10 | 5m dl red brn ('46) | 1.00 | 60.00 |
| | | Nos. 4N1-4N13 (13) | 10.30 | 175.75 |
| | | Set, never hinged | 21.00 | |

Exist imperf. Value for set of 13, $475 mint never hinged.

### BADEN

Johann
Peter
Hebel
OS1

Girl of
Constance
OS2

Hans
Baldung
Grien
OS3

Rastatt
Castle
OS4

Black Forest Scene
OS5

Cathedral
of
Freiburg
OS6

| 1947 | | Unwmk. | Photo. | Perf. 14 |
|---|---|---|---|---|
| 5N1 | OS1 | 2pf gray | .25 | .35 |
| 5N2 | OS2 | 3pf brown | .25 | .35 |
| 5N3 | OS3 | 10pf slate blue | .25 | .35 |
| 5N4 | OS1 | 12pf dk green | .25 | .35 |
| 5N5 | OS2 | 15pf purple | .25 | .35 |
| 5N6 | OS4 | 16pf olive green | .25 | 1.30 |
| 5N7 | OS3 | 20pf blue | .25 | .35 |
| 5N8 | OS4 | 24pf crimson | .25 | .35 |
| 5N9 | OS2 | 45pf cerise | .25 | .80 |
| 5N10 | OS1 | 60pf deep orange | .25 | .35 |
| 5N11 | OS3 | 75pf brt blue | .25 | 1.60 |
| 5N12 | OS5 | 84pf blue green | .25 | 1.60 |
| 5N13 | OS6 | 1m dark brown | .25 | .65 |
| | | Nos. 5N1-5N13 (13) | | 8.75 |
| | | Set, never hinged | 3.00 | |

Festival
Headdress
OS7

Grand
Duchess
Stephanie
OS8

| 1948 | | | | |
|---|---|---|---|---|
| 5N14 | OS1 | 2pf dp orange | .25 | .30 |
| 5N15 | OS2 | 6pf violet brn | .25 | .30 |
| 5N16 | OS7 | 8dpf blue green | .25 | 1.00 |
| 5N17 | OS3 | 10pf dark brown | .25 | .30 |
| 5N18 | OS1 | 12pf crimson | .25 | .30 |
| 5N19 | OS2 | 15pf blue | .25 | .55 |
| 5N20 | OS4 | 16dpf violet | .55 | 1.60 |
| 5N21 | OS3 | 20dpf brown | 2.25 | .85 |
| 5N22 | OS4 | 24pf dark green | .25 | .30 |
| 5N23 | OS7 | 30pf cerise | .55 | 1.00 |
| 5N24 | OS3 | 50pf brt blue | .55 | .30 |
| 5N25 | OS1 | 60dpf gray | 2.60 | .55 |
| 5N26 | OS5 | 84dpf rose brn | 3.00 | 4.00 |
| 5N27 | OS6 | 1dm brt blue | 3.00 | 4.00 |
| | | Nos. 5N14-5N27 (14) | 14.25 | 15.35 |
| | | Set, never hinged | 34.00 | |

| 1948-49 | | | Without "PF" | |
|---|---|---|---|---|
| 5N28 | OS1 | 2(pf) dp orange | .55 | .50 |
| 5N29 | OS4 | 4(pf) violet | .30 | .40 |
| 5N30 | OS2 | 5(pf) blue | .40 | .55 |
| 5N31 | OS2 | 6(pf) violet brn | 11.50 | 12.00 |
| 5N32 | OS7 | 8(pf) rose brn | .40 | .95 |
| 5N33 | OS3 | 10(pf) dark green | 1.60 | .50 |
| 5N37 | OS3 | 20(pf) cerise | .70 | .35 |
| 5N38 | OS4 | 40(pf) brown | 30.00 | 65.00 |
| 5N39 | OS1 | 80(pf) red | 3.75 | 5.25 |
| 5N40 | OS5 | 90(pf) rose brn | 29.00 | 65.00 |
| | | Nos. 5N28-5N40 (10) | 78.20 | 150.50 |
| | | Set, never hinged | 150.00 | |

Constance
Cathedral and
Insel
Hotel — OS9

Type I. Frameline thick and straight. Inscriptions thick. Shading dark. Upper part of "B" narrow.
Type II. Frameline thin and zigzag. Inscriptions fine. Shading light. Upper part of "B" wide.

**1949, June 22**

| 5N41 | OS9 | 30pf dark blue (I) | 9.00 | 57.50 |
|---|---|---|---|---|
| | | Never hinged | 19.50 | |
| a. | | Type II | 260.00 | 1,250. |
| | | Never hinged | 500.00 | |

Issued to publicize the International Engineering Congress, Constance, 1949.

Conradin Kreutzer — OS10

**1949, Aug. 27**

| 5N42 | OS10 | 10pf dark green | 1.50 | 9.75 |
|---|---|---|---|---|
| | | Never hinged | 3.50 | |

Conradin Kreutzer (1780-1849), composer.

Stagecoach
OS11

Design: 20pf, Post bus, trailer and plane.

**1949, Sept. 17**

| 5N43 | OS11 | 10pf green | 3.00 | 9.25 |
|---|---|---|---|---|
| 5N44 | OS11 | 20pf red brown | 3.00 | 9.25 |
| | | Set, never hinged | 11.50 | |

Centenary of German postage stamps.
See Rhine Palatinate Nos. 6N39-6N40;
Wurttemberg Nos. 8N38-8N39.

Globe, Olive Branch and
Post Horn — OS12

**1949, Oct. 4**

| 5N45 | OS12 | 20pf dark red | 3.00 | 9.25 |
|---|---|---|---|---|
| 5N46 | OS12 | 30pf deep blue | 3.00 | 8.00 |
| | | Set, never hinged | 12.00 | |

75th anniv. of the UPU.
See Rhine Palatinate Nos. 6N41-6N42;
Wurttemberg Nos. 8N40-8N41.

### OCCUPATION SEMI-POSTAL STAMPS

Arms of Baden — OSP1

### Perf. 13½x14
**1949, Feb. 25    Photo.    Unwmk.**
### Cross in Red

| 5NB1 | OSP1 | 10 + 20pf green | 9.00 | 65.00 |
|---|---|---|---|---|
| 5NB2 | OSP1 | 20 + 40pf lilac | 9.00 | 65.00 |
| 5NB3 | OSP1 | 30 + 60pf blue | 9.00 | 65.00 |
| 5NB4 | OSP1 | 40 + 80pf gray | 9.00 | 65.00 |
| a. | | Sheet of 4, #5NB1-5NB4, imperf. | 90.00 | 1,100. |
| | | Nos. 5NB1-5NB4 (4) | 36.00 | 260.00 |
| | | Set, never hinged | 82.50 | |

The surtax was for the Red Cross.
No. 5NB4a measures 90x101mm and has no gum.
See Rhine Palatinate Nos. 6NB3-6NB6;
Wurttemberg Nos. 8NB1-8NB4.

Cornhouse,
Freiburg — OSP2

10pf+20pf, Cathedral tower. 20pf+30pf, Trumpeting angel. 30pf+50pf, Fish pool.

**1949, Feb. 24    Perf. 14**

| 5NB5 | OSP2 | 4 + 16pf dk vio | 5.75 | 32.50 |
|---|---|---|---|---|
| 5NB6 | OSP2 | 10 + 20pf dk grn | 5.75 | 32.50 |
| 5NB7 | OSP2 | 20 + 30pf car | 5.75 | 32.50 |
| 5NB8 | OSP2 | 30 + 50pf blue | 6.25 | 40.00 |
| a. | | Sheet of 4, #5NB5-5NB8 | 26.00 | 180.00 |
| | | Never hinged | 57.50 | |
| b. | | As "a," imperf. | 26.00 | 180.00 |
| | | Never hinged | 57.50 | |
| | | Nos. 5NB5-5NB8 (4) | 23.50 | 137.50 |
| | | Set, never hinged | 52.50 | |

The surtax was for the reconstruction of historical monuments in Freiburg.

Carl Schurz at
Rastatt — OSP3

**1949, Aug. 23**

| 5NB9 | OSP3 | 10 + 5pf green | 4.75 | 25.00 |
|---|---|---|---|---|
| 5NB10 | OSP3 | 20 + 10pf cer | 4.75 | 25.00 |
| 5NB11 | OSP3 | 30 + 15pf blue | 6.00 | 25.00 |
| | | Nos. 5NB9-5NB11 (3) | 15.50 | 75.00 |
| | | Set, never hinged | 34.00 | |

Centenary of the surrender of Rastatt.

Goethe — OSP4

Various Portraits.

**1949, Aug. 12**

| 5NB12 | OSP4 | 10 + 5pf green | 4.75 | 16.50 |
|---|---|---|---|---|
| 5NB13 | OSP4 | 20 + 10pf cer | 4.75 | 16.50 |
| 5NB14 | OSP4 | 30 + 15pf blue | 6.00 | 40.00 |
| | | Nos. 5NB12-5NB14 (3) | 15.50 | 73.00 |
| | | Set, never hinged | 34.00 | |

Johann Wolfgang von Goethe (1749-1832).
See Rhine Palatinate Nos. 6NB7-6NB9;
Wurttemberg Nos. 8NB9-8NB11.

### RHINE PALATINATE

Beethoven
OS1

Wilhelm E.
F. von
Ketteler
OS2

Girl
Carrying
Grapes
OS3

Porta
Nigra,
Trier
OS4

Karl Marx
OS5

"Devil's
Table",
Near
Pirmasens
OS6

Street
Corner,
St. Martin
OS7

Cathedral
of Worms
OS8

Cathedral
of Mainz
OS9

Statue of
Johann
Gutenberg
OS10

Gutenfels and
Pfalzgrafenstein
Castles on
Rhine — OS11

Statue of
Charlemagne — OS12

**1947-48   Unwmk.   Photo.   Perf. 14**

| | | | | |
|---|---|---|---|---|
| 6N1 | OS1 | 2pf gray | .25 | .30 |
| 6N2 | OS2 | 3pf dk brown | .25 | .30 |
| 6N3 | OS3 | 10pf slate blue | .25 | .30 |
| 6N4 | OS4 | 12pf green | .25 | .30 |
| 6N5 | OS5 | 15pf purple | .25 | .30 |
| 6N6 | OS6 | 16pf lt ol grn | .25 | .95 |
| 6N7 | OS7 | 20pf brt blue | .25 | .30 |
| 6N8 | OS8 | 24pf crimson | .25 | .30 |
| 6N9 | OS10 | 30pf cerise ('48) | .25 | 2.00 |
| 6N10 | OS9 | 45pf cerise | .25 | .55 |
| 6N11 | OS9 | 50pf blue ('48) | .25 | 2.00 |
| 6N12 | OS1 | 60pf dp orange | .25 | .30 |
| 6N13 | OS10 | 75pf blue | .25 | .55 |
| 6N14 | OS11 | 84pf green | .25 | 1.20 |
| 6N15 | OS12 | 1m brown | .25 | .65 |
| | *Nos. 6N1-6N15 (15)* | | | 10.30 |
| | Set, never hinged | | 3.50 | |

Exist imperf. Value for set, $525 mint never hinged.

**1948**

| | | | | |
|---|---|---|---|---|
| 6N16 | OS1 | 2pf dp orange | .25 | .30 |
| 6N17 | OS2 | 6pf violet brn | .25 | .30 |
| 6N18 | OS4 | 8dpf blue green | .25 | 1.00 |
| 6N19 | OS3 | 10pf dk brown | .25 | .30 |
| 6N20 | OS5 | 12pf crim rose | .25 | .30 |
| 6N21 | OS5 | 15pf blue | .60 | .55 |
| 6N22 | OS6 | 16dpf dk violet | .30 | 1.20 |
| 6N23 | OS7 | 20dpf brown | 1.35 | .55 |
| 6N24 | OS8 | 24pf green | .25 | .30 |
| 6N25 | OS9 | 30pf cerise | .55 | .35 |
| 6N26 | OS10 | 50pf brt blue | .75 | .35 |
| 6N27 | OS1 | 60dpf gray | 4.50 | .35 |
| 6N28 | OS11 | 84dpf rose brown | 2.25 | 5.00 |
| 6N29 | OS12 | 1dm brt blue | 3.00 | 5.00 |
| | *Nos. 6N16-6N29 (14)* | | 14.80 | 15.85 |
| | Set, never hinged | | 30.00 | |

Exist imperf. Value for set, $500 mint never hinged.

**Types of 1947 Without "PF"**

**1948-49**

| | | | | |
|---|---|---|---|---|
| 6N30 | OS1 | 2(pf) dp org | .30 | .35 |
| 6N31 | OS6 | 4(pf) vio ('49) | .30 | .35 |
| 6N32 | OS5 | 5(pf) blue ('49) | .40 | .55 |
| 6N33 | OS2 | 6(pf) vio brn ('49) | 13.50 | 13.00 |
| 6N33A | OS4 | 8(pf) rose brn ('49) | 30.00 | 325.00 |
| 6N34 | OS3 | 10(pf) dk grn | .40 | .35 |
| *a.* | | Imperf. | 57.50 | 160.00 |
| | Never hinged | 115.00 | |
| 6N35 | OS7 | 20(pf) cerise | .40 | .35 |
| 6N36 | OS8 | 40(pf) brn ('49) | 1.35 | 3.25 |
| 6N37 | OS4 | 80(pf) red ('49) | 1.50 | 4.25 |
| 6N38 | OS11 | 90(pf) rose brn ('49) | 2.25 | 13.00 |
| | *Nos. 6N30-6N38 (10)* | | 50.40 | 360.45 |
| | Set, never hinged | | 115.00 | |

Stagecoach
OS13

**1949, Sept. 17**

| | | | | |
|---|---|---|---|---|
| 6N39 | OS13 | 10pf green | 5.00 | 16.50 |
| 6N40 | OS13 | 20pf red brown | 5.00 | 16.50 |
| | Set, never hinged | | 19.00 | |

See Baden Nos. 5N43-5N44; Wurttemberg Nos. 8N38-8N39.

Globe, Olive Branch and
Post Horn — OS14

**1949, Oct. 4**

| | | | | |
|---|---|---|---|---|
| 6N41 | OS14 | 20pf dark red | 3.75 | 9.75 |
| 6N42 | OS14 | 30pf deep blue | 3.75 | 8.50 |
| | Set, never hinged | | 15.00 | |

See Baden Nos. 5N45-5N46; Wurttemberg Nos. 8N40-8N41.

## OCCUPATION SEMI-POSTAL STAMPS

St. Martin — OSP1

Design: 30pf+50pf, St. Christopher.

**1948   Unwmk.   Photo.   Perf. 14**

| | | | | |
|---|---|---|---|---|
| 6NB1 | OSP1 | 20pf + 30pf dp cl | .75 | 50.00 |
| 6NB2 | OSP1 | 30pf + 50pf dp bl | .75 | 50.00 |
| | Set, never hinged | | 3.75 | |

The surtax was to aid victims of an explosion at Ludwigshafen.

Arms of Rhine
Palatinate — OSP2

**1949, Feb. 25   Perf. 13½x14**
**Cross in Red**

| | | | | |
|---|---|---|---|---|
| 6NB3 | OSP2 | 10pf + 20pf grn | 7.50 | 72.50 |
| 6NB4 | OSP2 | 20pf + 40pf lil | 7.50 | 72.50 |
| 6NB5 | OSP2 | 30pf + 60pf bl | 7.50 | 72.50 |
| 6NB6 | OSP2 | 40pf + 80pf gray | 7.50 | 72.50 |
| *a.* | | Sheet of 4, #6NB3-6NB6. | 82.50 | 925.00 |
| | *Nos. 6NB3-6NB6 (4)* | | 30.00 | 290.00 |
| | Set, never hinged | | 65.00 | |

The surtax was for the Red Cross.
No. 6NB6a measures 90x100mm and has no gum.

Goethe — OSP3

Various Portraits.

**1949, Aug. 12**

| | | | | |
|---|---|---|---|---|
| 6NB7 | OSP3 | 10pf + 5pf green | 2.60 | 16.00 |
| 6NB8 | OSP3 | 20pf + 10pf cerise | 2.60 | 16.00 |
| 6NB9 | OSP3 | 30pf + 15pf blue | 4.00 | 35.00 |
| | *Nos. 6NB7-6NB9 (3)* | | 9.20 | 67.00 |
| | Set, never hinged | | 26.00 | |

See Baden Nos. 5NB12-5NB14; Wurttemberg Nos. 8NB9-8NB11.

## WURTTEMBERG

Friedrich
von
Schiller
OS1

Castle of
Bebenhausen
OS2

Friedrich
Hölderlin
OS3

Town Gate
of
Wangen
(Allgäu)
OS4

Lichtenstein
Castle
OS5

Zwiefalten
Church
OS6

**1947-48   Unwmk.   Photo.   Perf. 14**

| | | | | |
|---|---|---|---|---|
| 8N1 | OS1 | 2pf gray ('48) | .25 | .55 |
| 8N2 | OS3 | 3pf brown ('48) | .25 | .30 |
| 8N3 | OS4 | 10pf slate bl ('48) | .25 | .35 |
| 8N4 | OS1 | 12pf dk green | .25 | .30 |
| 8N5 | OS3 | 15pf purple ('48) | .25 | .40 |
| 8N6 | OS2 | 16pf ol grn ('48) | .25 | 1.05 |
| 8N7 | OS4 | 20pf blue ('48) | .25 | 1.05 |
| 8N8 | OS1 | 24pf crimson | .25 | .30 |
| 8N9 | OS3 | 45pf cerise | .25 | 1.05 |
| 8N10 | OS1 | 60pf dp org ('48) | .25 | .65 |
| 8N11 | OS4 | 75pf brt blue | .25 | 1.20 |
| 8N12 | OS5 | 84pf blue grn | .25 | 1.20 |
| 8N13 | OS6 | 1m dk brown | .25 | 1.20 |
| | *Nos. 8N1-8N13 (13)* | | | 9.60 |
| | Set, never hinged | | 3.50 | |

Nos. 8N4 and 8N10 exist imperf. Value, each $37.50, mint never hinged.

Waldsee
OS7

Ludwig
Uhland
OS8

**1948**

| | | | | |
|---|---|---|---|---|
| 8N14 | OS1 | 2pf dp orange | .25 | .35 |
| 8N15 | OS3 | 6pf violet brn | .25 | .30 |
| 8N16 | OS7 | 8dpf blue grn | .40 | 2.00 |
| 8N17 | OS4 | 10pf dk brown | .25 | .35 |
| 8N18 | OS1 | 12pf crimson | .25 | .30 |
| 8N19 | OS3 | 15pf blue | .40 | .35 |
| 8N20 | OS2 | 16dpf dk violet | .40 | 1.30 |
| 8N21 | OS4 | 20dpf brown | 1.00 | 1.00 |
| 8N22 | OS4 | 24pf green | .45 | .55 |
| 8N23 | OS7 | 30pf cerise | .60 | .55 |
| 8N24 | OS1 | 50pf dull blue | 1.20 | .55 |
| 8N25 | OS1 | 60dpf gray | 5.75 | .55 |
| 8N26 | OS5 | 84dpf rose brn | 1.90 | 4.00 |
| 8N27 | OS6 | 1dm brt blue | 1.90 | 4.00 |
| | *Nos. 8N14-8N27 (14)* | | 15.00 | 16.15 |
| | Set, never hinged | | 30.00 | |

Nos. 8N14, 8N17, 8N22-8N23 exist imperf. Value, each $35, mint never hinged.

**1948-49                     Without "PF"**

| | | | | |
|---|---|---|---|---|
| 8N28 | OS1 | 2(pf) dp orange | .40 | .55 |
| 8N29 | OS2 | 4(pf) violet | 1.15 | .35 |
| 8N30 | OS2 | 5(pf) blue | 3.00 | 2.00 |
| 8N31 | OS3 | 6(pf) vio brown | 3.00 | 5.00 |
| 8N32 | OS7 | 8(pf) rose brn | 3.00 | 2.00 |
| 8N33 | OS4 | 10(pf) dk green | 3.00 | .35 |
| 8N34 | OS4 | 20(pf) cerise | 3.00 | .35 |
| 8N35 | OS2 | 40(pf) brown | 9.75 | 32.50 |
| 8N36 | OS1 | 80(pf) red | 19.00 | 32.50 |
| 8N37 | OS5 | 90(pf) rose brn | 30.00 | 85.00 |
| | *Nos. 8N28-8N37 (10)* | | 75.30 | 160.60 |
| | Set, never hinged | | 150.00 | |

Nos. 8N29 and 8N31 exist imperf. Value, respectively $75 and $57.50, mint never hinged.

Stagecoach
OS9

**1949, Sept. 17**

| | | | | |
|---|---|---|---|---|
| 8N38 | OS9 | 10pf green | 3.50 | 10.50 |
| 8N39 | OS9 | 20pf red brown | 3.50 | 10.50 |
| | Set, never hinged | | 13.50 | |

See Baden Nos. 5N43-5N44; Rhine Palatinate Nos. 6N39-6N40.

Globe, Olive Branch and
Post Horn — OS10

**1949, Oct. 4**

| | | | | |
|---|---|---|---|---|
| 8N40 | OS10 | 20pf dark red | 2.25 | 8.50 |
| 8N41 | OS10 | 30pf deep blue | 2.25 | 8.00 |
| | Set, never hinged | | 12.00 | |

See Baden Nos. 5N45-5N46; Rhine Palatinate Nos. 6N41-6N42.

## OCCUPATION SEMI-POSTAL STAMPS

Arms of
Württemberg — OSP1

**Perf. 13½x14**

**1949, Feb. 25   Photo.   Unwmk.**
**Cross in Red**

| | | | | |
|---|---|---|---|---|
| 8NB1 | OSP1 | 10 + 20pf grn | 15.00 | 80.00 |
| 8NB2 | OSP1 | 20 + 40pf lilac | 15.00 | 80.00 |
| 8NB3 | OSP1 | 30 + 60pf blue | 15.00 | 80.00 |
| 8NB4 | OSP1 | 40 + 80pf gray | 15.00 | 80.00 |
| *a.* | | Sheet of 4, imperf. | 115.00 | 1,200. |
| | *Nos. 8NB1-8NB4 (4)* | | 60.00 | 320.00 |
| | Set, never hinged | | 120.00 | |

The surtax was for the Red Cross.
No. 8NB4a measures 90x100mm and contains one each of Nos. 8NB1 to 8NB4, with red inscription in upper margin and no gum.
See Baden Nos. 5NB1-5NB4; Rhine Palatinate Nos. 6NB3-6NB6.

View of
Isny — OSP2

Design: 20pf+6pf, Skier and village.

**Wmk. 116**

**1949, Feb. 11   Typo.   Perf. 14**

| | | | | |
|---|---|---|---|---|
| 8NB5 | OSP2 | 10 + 4pf dl grn | 2.60 | 19.50 |
| 8NB6 | OSP2 | 20 + 6pf red brn | 2.60 | 19.50 |
| | Set, never hinged | | 15.00 | |

Issued to commemorate the 1948-49 German Ski Championship at Isny im Allgäu.

Gustav Werner — OSP3

**1949, Sept. 4**

| | | | | |
|---|---|---|---|---|
| 8NB7 | OSP3 | 10 + 5pf bl grn | 2.25 | 11.50 |
| 8NB8 | OSP3 | 20 + 10pf claret | 2.25 | 11.50 |
| | Set, never hinged | | 9.75 | |

Cent. of the founding of Gustav Werner's "Christianity in Action" and "House of Brotherhood."

Goethe — OSP4

Various Portraits.

**1949, Aug. 12**

| | | | | |
|---|---|---|---|---|
| 8NB9 | OSP4 | 10 + 5pf green | 3.75 | 16.50 |
| 8NB10 | OSP4 | 20 + 10pf cerise | 5.25 | 23.00 |
| 8NB11 | OSP4 | 30 + 15pf blue | 5.25 | 32.50 |
| | *Nos. 8NB9-8NB11 (3)* | | 14.25 | 72.00 |
| | Set, never hinged | | 26.00 | |

See Baden Nos. 5NB12-5NB14; Rhine Palatinate Nos. 6NB7-6NB9.

## OCCUPATION POSTAL TAX STAMPS

### Wohnungsbau Issues

During July 1-December 31, 1949, a postal tax was levied on most categories of mail, with proceeds going to the 'Social Housing' (*Socialen Wohnungsbau*) program, which provided interest-free loans for housing construction and renovation intended to provide housing for economically-disadvantaged families.

### Germany Nos. RA1, RA2, RA4 Overprinted in Red

### Overprint 18.7mm wide

#### Wmk. 286

| 1949, July 1 | Typo. | Imperf. | |
|---|---|---|---|
| 8NRA1 PT1 | 2pf dk blue | 225.00 | 350.00 |
| | Never hinged | 575.00 | |

#### Compound Perf 12, 14

| 8NRA2 PT1 | 2pf dk blue | 15.00 | 4.00 |
|---|---|---|---|
| | Never hinged | 45.00 | |

### Overprint 16.5 mm wide

| 1949, July 22 | Wmk. 285 | Perf. 12¼ | |
|---|---|---|---|
| 8NRA3 PT1 | 2pf dk blue | 5.00 | 3.00 |
| | Never hinged | 10.50 | |

OSPT1

| 1949 | | Perf. 12¼ | |
|---|---|---|---|
| 8NRA4 OSPT1 | 2pf yellow | .75 | 2.60 |
| | Never hinged | 2.25 | |
| *a.* | 2pf yellow orange | 11.00 | 12.00 |
| | Never hinged | 30.00 | |
| *b.* | 2pf orange | .75 | 2.60 |
| | Never hinged | 2.25 | |

Issued: No. 4, 8/22. No. 4a, 8/25. No. 4b, 10/4.
Illustration OSPT1 actual size.

---

## BERLIN

### Issued for Use in the American, British and French Occupation Sectors of Berlin

Germany Nos. 557-569, 571-573 Overprinted Diagonally in Black — a

#### Wmk. 284

| 1948, Sept. 1 | Typo. | Perf. 14 | |
|---|---|---|---|
| 9N1 A120 | 2pf brown blk | .90 | 4.00 |
| 9N2 A120 | 6pf purple | 1.90 | 4.00 |
| 9N3 A121 | 8pf red | .75 | 4.00 |
| 9N4 A121 | 10pf yellow grn | .75 | 1.20 |
| 9N5 A122 | 12pf gray | .75 | 1.20 |
| 9N6 A120 | 15pf chocolate | 4.25 | 52.50 |
| 9N7 A123 | 16pf dk blue grn | .90 | 1.60 |
| 9N8 A121 | 20pf blue | 2.00 | 6.00 |
| 9N9 A123 | 24pf brown org | .60 | .40 |
| 9N10 A120 | 25pf orange yel | 4.50 | 35.00 |
| 9N11 A122 | 30pf red | 1.75 | 6.50 |
| 9N12 A121 | 40pf red violet | 2.25 | 6.50 |
| 9N13 A123 | 50pf ultra | 2.60 | 19.50 |
| 9N14 A122 | 60pf red brown | 1.15 | .40 |
| 9N15 A122 | 80pf dark blue | 3.00 | 19.50 |
| 9N16 A123 | 84pf emerald | 3.75 | 65.00 |

Germany Nos. 574-577 Overprinted Diagonally in Black — b

#### Engr.

| 9N17 A124 | 1m yel ol | 13.00 | 105.00 |
|---|---|---|---|
| 9N18 A124 | 2m dk brn pur | 15.00 | 325.00 |
| 9N19 A124 | 3m copper red | 19.50 | 475.00 |
| 9N20 A124 | 5m dark blue | 26.00 | 500.00 |
| *Nos. 9N1-9N20 (20)* | | 105.30 | 1,632. |
| Set, never hinged | | 280.00 | |

Forged overprints and cancellations are found on Nos. 9N1-9N20.

---

## Stamps of Germany 1947-48 with "a" Overprint in Red

| 1948-49 | Wmk. 284 | Typo. | Perf. 14 | |
|---|---|---|---|---|
| 9N21 A120 | 2pf brn blk ('49) | | .75 | 2.00 |
| 9N22 A120 | 6pf purple ('49) | | 6.00 | 2.00 |
| 9N23 A121 | 8pf red ('49) | | 13.50 | 4.00 |
| 9N24 A121 | 10pf yellow grn | | 1.50 | 1.20 |
| 9N25 A121 | 15pf chocolate | | 3.00 | 1.60 |
| 9N26 A121 | 20pf blue | | 1.15 | 1.00 |
| 9N27 A120 | 25pf org yel ('49) | | 30.00 | 35.00 |
| 9N28 A122 | 30pf red ('49) | | 26.00 | 4.25 |
| 9N29 A121 | 40pf red vio ('49) | | 26.00 | 12.00 |
| 9N30 A123 | 50pf ultra ('49) | | 26.00 | 6.50 |
| 9N31 A122 | 60pf red brown | | 3.75 | .55 |
| 9N32 A122 | 80pf dk bl ('49) | | 42.50 | 6.50 |

### With "b" Overprint in Red
#### Engr.

| 9N33 A124 | 1m yel ol | 170.00 | 350.00 |
|---|---|---|---|
| 9N34 A124 | 2m dk brn pur | 75.00 | 180.00 |
| *Nos. 9N21-9N34 (14)* | | 425.15 | 606.60 |
| Set, never hinged | | 1,050. | |

Forgeries exist of the overprints on Nos. 9N21-9N34. No. 9N33 exists imperf.

A1

Statue of Heinrich von Stephan — A2

| 1949, Apr. 9 | Litho. | Perf. 14 | |
|---|---|---|---|
| 9N35 A1 | 12pf gray bl | 5.75 | 6.50 |
| 9N36 A1 | 16pf blue green | 11.50 | 13.00 |
| 9N37 A1 | 24pf orange | 7.50 | .65 |
| 9N38 A1 | 50pf brn olive | 50.00 | 32.50 |
| 9N39 A1 | 60pf brown red | 52.50 | 26.00 |
| 9N40 A2 | 1m olive | 26.00 | 80.00 |
| 9N41 A2 | 2m brown pur | 34.00 | 52.50 |
| *Nos. 9N35-9N41 (7)* | | 187.25 | 211.15 |
| Set, never hinged | | 575.00 | |

75th anniv. of the UPU.

Brandenburg Gate, Berlin — A3

Tempelhof Airport — A4

Designs: 4pf, 8pf, 40pf, Schoeneberg, Rudolf Wilde Square. 5pf, 25pf, 5m, Tegel Castle. 6pf, 50pf, Reichstag Building. 10pf, 30pf, Cloisters, Kleist Park. 15pf, Tempelhof Airport. 20pf, 80pf, 90pf, Polytechnic College, Charlottenburg. 60pf, National Gallery. 2m, Gendarmen Square. 3m, Brandenburg Gate.

| 1949 | Typo. | Wmk. 284 | |
|---|---|---|---|
| | Size: 22x18mm | | |
| 9N42 A3 | 1pf black | .25 | .35 |
| *a.* | Bklt. pane 5 + label | 9.00 | 52.50 |
| | Never hinged | 30.00 | |
| *b.* | Tête bêche | .40 | 2.00 |
| | Never hinged | 1.15 | |
| 9N43 A3 | 4pf yellow brn | .25 | .35 |
| *a.* | Bklt. pane 5 + label | 9.00 | 52.50 |
| | Never hinged | 30.00 | |
| *b.* | Tête bêche | 1.45 | 2.60 |
| | Never hinged | 4.50 | |
| 9N44 A3 | 5pf blue green | .25 | .35 |
| 9N45 A3 | 6pf red violet | .40 | 1.00 |
| 9N46 A3 | 8pf red orange | .40 | 1.00 |
| 9N47 A3 | 10pf yellow grn | .25 | .35 |
| *a.* | Bklt. pane 5 + label | 67.50 | 200.00 |
| | Never hinged | 135.00 | |
| 9N48 A3 | 15pf brown | 3.50 | .80 |
| 9N49 A3 | 20pf red | 1.35 | .35 |
| *a.* | Bklt. pane 5 + label | 67.50 | 200.00 |
| | Never hinged | 135.00 | |
| 9N50 A3 | 25pf orange | 6.00 | .80 |
| 9N51 A3 | 30pf violet bl | 3.00 | .65 |
| | Imperf. | 550.00 | |
| | Never hinged | 1,350. | |
| 9N52 A3 | 40pf carmine | 4.50 | .65 |
| 9N53 A3 | 50pf bister | 4.50 | .35 |
| 9N54 A3 | 60pf brown red | 15.00 | .35 |
| 9N55 A3 | 80pf dark blue | 3.00 | .65 |
| 9N56 A3 | 90pf emerald | 3.00 | .80 |

---

### Engr.
#### Size: 29¼-29¾x24-24½mm

| 9N57 A4 | 1m olive | 5.75 | 1.00 |
|---|---|---|---|
| 9N58 A4 | 2m brown pur | 15.00 | 1.30 |
| 9N59 A4 | 3m henna brn | 67.50 | 13.00 |
| 9N60 A4 | 5m deep blue | 34.00 | 13.00 |
| *Nos. 9N42-9N60 (19)* | | 167.90 | 37.10 |
| Set, never hinged | | 575.00 | |

See Nos. 9N101-9N102, 9N108-9N110.

Goethe and "Iphigenie" — A5

Designs (Goethe and scenes from his works): 20pf, "Reineke Fuchs." 30pf, "Faust."

| 1949, July 29 | Litho. | Perf. 14 | |
|---|---|---|---|
| 9N61 A5 | 10pf green | 30.00 | 47.50 |
| 9N62 A5 | 20pf carmine | 34.00 | 47.50 |
| 9N63 A5 | 30pf ultra | 7.50 | 32.50 |
| *Nos. 9N61-9N63 (3)* | | 71.50 | 127.50 |
| Set, never hinged | | 240.00 | |

Bicentenary of the birth of Johann Wolfgang von Goethe.

### Germany Nos. 550, 565, 572 and 576 Surcharged in Dark Green

| 1949, Aug. 1 | | Typo. | |
|---|---|---|---|
| 9N64 A119 | 5pf on 45pf | 1.15 | .35 |
| 9N65 A123 | 10pf on 24pf | 3.00 | .35 |
| 9N66 A122 | 20pf on 80pf | 15.00 | 11.50 |

#### Engr.

| 9N67 A124 | 1m on 3m | 37.50 | 14.50 |
|---|---|---|---|
| *Nos. 9N64-9N67 (4)* | | 56.65 | 26.70 |
| Set, never hinged | | 190.00 | |

Statue of Atlas, New York — A6

| 1950, Oct. 1 | Engr. | Wmk. 116 | |
|---|---|---|---|
| 9N68 A6 | 20pf dk carmine | 30.00 | 26.00 |
| | Never hinged | 75.00 | |

European Recovery Plan.

Albert Lortzing — A7

| 1951, Apr. 22 | | | |
|---|---|---|---|
| 9N69 A7 | 20pf red brown | 16.50 | 35.00 |
| | Never hinged | 45.00 | |

Centenary of the death of Albert Lortzing, composer.

Freedom Bell, Berlin — A8

---

| 1951 | | Perf. 14 | |
|---|---|---|---|
| 9N70 A8 | 5pf brown | .75 | 5.25 |
| 9N71 A8 | 10pf deep green | 3.75 | 16.50 |
| 9N72 A8 | 20pf rose red | 2.25 | 16.50 |
| 9N73 A8 | 30pf blue | 15.00 | 60.00 |
| 9N74 A8 | 40pf rose violet | 3.75 | 40.00 |
| *Nos. 9N70-9N74 (5)* | | 25.50 | 138.25 |
| Set, never hinged | | 75.00 | |

### Re-engraved

Bell clapper moved from left to right. Imprint "L. Schnell" in lower margin.

| 1951-52 | | | |
|---|---|---|---|
| 9N75 A8 | 5pf olive bis ('52) | .75 | 1.60 |
| 9N76 A8 | 10pf yellow grn | 2.25 | 3.25 |
| 9N77 A8 | 20pf brt red | 7.50 | 13.00 |
| 9N78 A8 | 30pf blue ('52) | 21.00 | 32.50 |
| 9N79 A8 | 40pf dp car ('52) | 7.50 | 13.00 |
| *Nos. 9N75-9N79 (5)* | | 39.00 | 63.35 |
| Set, never hinged | | 90.00 | |

No. 9N76 exists imperf. Value, $575 unused, $1,100 mint never hinged.
See Nos. 9N94-9N98.

Ludwig van Beethoven — A9

| 1952, Mar. 26 | Engr. | Unwmk. | |
|---|---|---|---|
| 9N80 A9 | 30pf blue | 13.00 | 19.50 |
| | Never hinged | 34.00 | |

125th anniversary of the death of Ludwig van Beethoven.

Olympic Symbols — A10

| 1952, June 20 | Litho. | Wmk. 116 | |
|---|---|---|---|
| 9N81 A10 | 4pf yellow brown | .30 | 1.60 |
| 9N82 A10 | 10pf lt green | 3.75 | 12.00 |
| 9N83 A10 | 20pf vermilion | 6.00 | 21.00 |
| *Nos. 9N81-9N83 (3)* | | 10.05 | 34.60 |
| Set, never hinged | | 22.50 | |

Pre-Olympic Festival Day, June 20, 1952.

Carl Friedrich Zelter — A11

Portraits: 5pf, Otto Lilienthal. 6pf, Walter Rathenau. 8pf, Theodor Fontane. 10pf, Adolph von Menzel. 15pf, Rudolf Virchow. 20pf, Werner von Siemens. 25pf, Karl Friedrich Schinkel. 30pf, Max Planck. 40pf, Wilhelm von Humboldt.

| 1952-53 | Engr. | Wmk. 284 | |
|---|---|---|---|
| 9N84 A11 | 4pf brown | .25 | .50 |
| 9N85 A11 | 5pf dp blue ('53) | .40 | .50 |
| 9N86 A11 | 6pf choc ('53) | 1.50 | 6.50 |
| 9N87 A11 | 8pf henna brn ('53) | .75 | 2.00 |
| 9N88 A11 | 10pf deep green | 1.15 | .50 |
| 9N89 A11 | 15pf dp lil ('53) | 4.50 | 12.00 |
| 9N90 A11 | 20pf brown red | .75 | .65 |
| 9N91 A11 | 25pf dp olive ('53) | 15.00 | 5.25 |
| 9N92 A11 | 30pf purple ('53) | 5.25 | 6.50 |
| 9N93 A11 | 40pf black ('53) | 6.75 | 2.00 |
| *Nos. 9N84-9N93 (10)* | | 36.30 | 36.40 |
| Set, never hinged | | 97.50 | |

## Bell Type of 1951-1952

Second Re-engraving

Bell clapper hangs straight down. Marginal imprint omitted.

| 1953 | Wmk. 284 | Perf. 14 | |
|---|---|---|---|
| 9N94 | A8 5pf brown | .40 | .85 |
| 9N95 | A8 10pf deep green | .75 | 1.30 |
| 9N96 | A8 20pf brt red | 2.25 | 2.60 |
| 9N97 | A8 30pf blue | 3.75 | 9.75 |
| 9N98 | A8 40pf rose violet | 16.50 | 23.00 |
| | Nos. 9N94-9N98 (5) | 23.65 | 37.50 |
| | Set, never hinged | 67.50 | |

For overprint & surcharge see Nos. 9N106, 9NB17.

Arms Breaking Chains — A12

Design: 30pf, Brandenburg Gate.

| 1953, Aug. 17 | | Typo. | |
|---|---|---|---|
| 9N99 | A12 20pf black | 2.25 | 1.30 |
| 9N100 | A12 30pf dp carmine | 8.75 | 25.00 |
| | Set, never hinged | 37.50 | |

Strike of East German workers, 6/17/53.

Exposition Halls — A12a

Designs: 20pf, Olympic Stadium, Berlin.

| 1953-54 | Wmk. 284 | Perf. 14 | |
|---|---|---|---|
| 9N101 | A12a 4pf yellow brn ('54) | 1.50 | 3.25 |
| 9N102 | A12a 20pf red | 16.50 | 2.00 |
| | Set, never hinged | 50.00 | |

**Catalogue values for unused stamps in this section, from this point to the end of the section, are for Never Hinged items.**

Allied Council Building — A13

| 1954, Jan. 25 | | Litho. | |
|---|---|---|---|
| 9N103 | A13 20pf red | 7.00 | 3.75 |

Four Power Conference, Berlin, 1954.

Prof. Ernst Reuter (1889-1953), Mayor of Berlin (1948-53) — A14

| 1954, Jan. 18 | Engr. | Wmk. 284 | |
|---|---|---|---|
| 9N104 | A14 20pf chocolate | 10.00 | 1.30 |

See No. 9N174.

Ottmar Mergenthaler and Linotype — A15

| 1954, May 11 | | | |
|---|---|---|---|
| 9N105 | A15 10pf dk blue grn | 3.00 | 2.00 |

Cent. of the birth of Ottmar Mergenthaler.

No. 9N96 Overprinted in Black

| 1954, July 17 | | Perf. 13½x14 | |
|---|---|---|---|
| 9N106 | A8 20pf bright red | 4.25 | 4.00 |

Issued to publicize the West German presidential election held in Berlin July 17, 1954.

Germany in Bondage — A16

| 1954, July 20 | | Typo. | |
|---|---|---|---|
| 9N107 | A16 20pf car & gray | 5.00 | 3.25 |

10th anniv. of the attempted assassination of Adolf Hitler.

Exposition Halls — A16a

Designs: 40pf, Memorial library. 70pf, Hunting lodge, Grunewald.

| 1954 | Wmk. 284 | Perf. 14 | |
|---|---|---|---|
| 9N108 | A16a 7pf turq blue | 5.25 | 1.30 |
| 9N109 | A16a 40pf rose lilac | 9.25 | 9.25 |
| 9N110 | A16a 70pf yel green | 85.00 | 16.50 |
| | Nos. 9N108-9N110 (3) | 99.50 | 20.40 |
| | Set, hinged | 40.00 | |

Richard Strauss — A17

| 1954, Sept. 18 | | Engr. | |
|---|---|---|---|
| 9N111 | A17 40pf violet blue | 8.50 | 3.00 |

5th anniv. of the death of Richard Strauss, composer.

Early Forge — A18

| 1954, Sept. 25 | | | |
|---|---|---|---|
| 9N112 | A18 20pf reddish brown | 6.50 | 1.45 |

Centenary of the death of August Borsig, industrial leader.

M. S. Berlin and Arms of Berlin — A19

| 1955, Mar. 12 | | Wmk. 284 | |
|---|---|---|---|
| 9N113 | A19 10pf dp blue grn | 1.05 | .65 |
| 9N114 | A19 25pf violet blue | 6.50 | 3.00 |

Issued to publicize the resumption of shipping under West German ownership.

Wilhelm Furtwängler — A20

| Perf. 13½x14 | | | |
|---|---|---|---|
| 1955, Sept. 17 | | Unwmk. | |
| 9N115 | A20 40pf dp ultra | 17.50 | 16.50 |

Issued to honor the conductor Wilhelm Furtwängler and to publicize the Berlin Music Festival, September 1955.

Arms of Berlin — A21

| 1955, Oct. 17 | Litho. | Wmk. 304 | |
|---|---|---|---|
| 9N116 | A21 10pf red, org yel & blk | .70 | .65 |
| 9N117 | A21 20pf red, org yel & blk | 4.25 | 7.25 |

Meeting of the German Bundestag in Berlin, Oct. 17-22, 1955.

Arms of Berlin — A22

| 1956, Mar. 16 | | | |
|---|---|---|---|
| 9N118 | A22 10pf red, ocher & blk | 1.05 | .65 |
| 9N119 | A22 25pf red, ocher & blk | 3.50 | 3.25 |

Meeting of the German Bundesrat in Berlin Mar. 16, 1956.

Radio Station, Berlin
A23          A24

A23 has no top inscription.
A24 has top inscription.

Free University A25        Monument of the Great Elector Frederick William A26

Designs: 1pf, 3pf, Brandenburg Gate. 5pf, General Post Office. 8pf, City Hall, Neukölln. 10pf, Kaiser Wilhelm Memorial Church. 15pf, Airlift memorial. 25pf, Lilienthal Monument. 30pf, Pfaueninsel Castle. 40pf, Charlottenburg Castle. 50pf, Reuter power plant. 60pf, Chamber of Commerce and Industry and Stock Exchange. 70pf, Schiller Theater. 3m, Congress Hall.

| Typo.; Litho. (3pf, #9N122) | | | |
|---|---|---|---|
| 1956-63 | Wmk. 304 | Perf. 14 | |
| 9N120 | A25 1pf gray ('57) | .25 | .25 |
| 9N120A | A25 3pf brt pur ('63) | .30 | .30 |
| 9N121 | A25 5pf rose lil ('57) | .25 | 2.00 |
| 9N122 | A23 7pf blue green | 7.00 | 2.00 |
| 9N123 | A24 7pf blue green | .25 | .25 |
| 9N124 | A24 8pf gray | .45 | .35 |
| 9N125 | A24 8pf red org ('59) | .30 | .35 |
| 9N126 | A24 10pf emerald | .25 | .25 |
| 9N127 | A24 15pf chlky blue | .45 | .25 |
| 9N128 | A24 20pf rose car | .45 | .25 |
| 9N129 | A24 25pf dull red brn | .45 | .40 |

| | Engr. | | |
|---|---|---|---|
| 9N130 | A24 30pf gray grn ('57) | .85 | .80 |
| 9N131 | A25 40pf blue ('57) | 8.50 | 6.50 |
| 9N132 | A24 50pf olive | .85 | .80 |
| 9N133 | A25 60pf lt brn ('57) | .85 | .80 |
| 9N134 | A25 70pf violet | 17.50 | 10.50 |
| 9N135 | A26 1m olive | 1.75 | 2.00 |

| | Size: 29x24½mm | | |
|---|---|---|---|
| 9N136 | A25 3m rose cl ('58) | 4.25 | 14.50 |
| | Nos. 9N120-9N136 (18) | 44.95 | 42.55 |

No. 9N120 exists on both ordinary and fluorescent paper; No. 9N120A on fluorescent paper only; others on ordinary paper.

Engineers' Society Emblem — A27

| 1956, May 12 | Engr. | Perf. 14 | |
|---|---|---|---|
| 9N140 | A27 10pf dark green | 1.60 | 1.40 |
| 9N141 | A27 20pf dark red | 3.00 | 3.75 |

Cent. of Soc. of German Civil Engineers.

Paul Lincke — A28

| 1956, Sept. 3 | | | |
|---|---|---|---|
| 9N142 | A28 20pf dark red | 2.00 | 2.25 |

Death of Paul Lincke, composer, 10th anniv.

Radio Station, Berlin-Nikolassee — A29

| 1956, Sept. 15 | | | |
|---|---|---|---|
| 9N143 | A29 25pf brown | 5.75 | 7.50 |

German Industrial Fair, Berlin, Sept. 15-30.

Spandau, 1850 — A30

| 1957, Mar. 7 | | | |
|---|---|---|---|
| 9N144 | A30 20pf gray ol & brn red | 2.10 | 3.25 |

725th anniversary of Spandau.

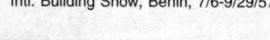

Hansa Model Town and "B" — A31

Designs: 20pf, View of exposition grounds and "B." 40pf, Auditorium and "B."

| 1957 | | Engr. | |
|---|---|---|---|
| 9N145 | A31 7pf violet brown | .35 | .35 |
| 9N146 | A31 20pf carmine | .65 | .65 |
| 9N147 | A31 40pf violet blue | 1.60 | 1.90 |
| | Nos. 9N145-9N147 (3) | 2.60 | 2.90 |

Intl. Building Show, Berlin, 7/6-9/29/57.

Famous Men — A32

Portraits: 7pf, Theodor Mommsen, historian. 8pf, Heinrich Zille, painter. 10pf, Ernst Reuter, mayor of Berlin. 15pf, Fritz Haber, chemist. 20pf, Friedrich Schleiermacher, theologian. 25pf, Max Reinhardt, theatrical director. 30pf, Friedrich Karl von Savigny, law teacher. 40pf, Alexander von Humboldt, naturalist and geographer. 50pf, Christian Daniel Rauch, sculptor.

| 1957-59 | Wmk. 304 | Perf. 14 | |
|---|---|---|---|
| **Portraits in Brown** | | | |
| 9N148 | A32 7pf blue grn ('58) | .25 | .25 |
| 9N149 | A32 8pf gray ('58) | .25 | .25 |
| 9N150 | A32 10pf yel grn ('58) | .25 | .25 |
| 9N151 | A32 15pf dark blue | .35 | .65 |
| 9N152 | A32 20pf red ('58) | .25 | .25 |
| 9N153 | A32 25pf carmine | .80 | .90 |
| 9N154 | A32 30pf gray green | 2.00 | 2.25 |
| 9N155 | A32 40pf Prus blue ('59) | .80 | .90 |
| 9N156 | A32 50pf olive | 4.00 | 5.75 |
| | Nos. 9N148-9N156 (9) | 8.95 | 11.45 |

Issued to honor famous men of Berlin. See No. 9NB19.

Uta Statue, Naumburg
Cathedral — A33

**1957, Aug. 6**
9N157　A33　25pf brown red　　.80　.95
Issued to publicize the annual meeting of
the East German Culture Society in Berlin.

"Unity and Justice and
Liberty" — A34

**1957, Oct. 15　　Litho.**
9N158　A34　10pf multicolored　1.00　.95
9N159　A34　20pf multicolored　3.00　3.00
1st meeting of the 3rd German Bundesrat,
Berlin, 10/15.

Postilion 1897-
1925 — A35

**1957, Oct. 23　Wmk. 304　Perf. 14**
9N160　A35　20pf multicolored　.95　.95
Issued for Stamp Day and BEPHILA stamp
exhibition, Berlin, Oct. 23-27.

World Veterans'
Federation
Emblem — A36

**1957, Oct. 28**
9N161　A36　20pf bl grn, ol grn &
　　　　　　　yel　　　　　1.00　.65
7th General Assembly of the World Veterans' Federation, Berlin, Oct. 24-Nov. 1.

Christ and the
Cosmos — A37

**1958, Aug. 13**
9N162　A37　10pf lt bl grn & blk　.50　.50
9N163　A37　20pf rose lilac & blk　.85　1.25
Issued in honor of the 78th German
Catholics Meeting, Berlin, Aug. 13-17.

Prof. Otto Suhr
(1894-1957), Mayor
of Berlin (1955-
57) — A38

**1958, Aug. 30　Engr.　Perf. 14**
9N164　A38　20pf rose red　　1.00　1.40

Pres. Heuss — A38a

**Litho., Engraved (40pf, 70pf)**
**1959**
9N165　A38a　7pf blue green　.30　.35
9N166　A38a　10pf green　　　.30　.35
9N167　A38a　20pf dk car rose　.50　.35

---

9N168　A38a　40pf blue　　　2.00　3.75
9N169　A38a　70pf dull purple　7.25　8.75
　Nos. 9N165-9N169 (5)　10.35　13.55
Nos. 9N168-9N169 were issued in sheets of
100 and in coils. Every fifth coil stamp has a
control number on the back.

Aerial Bridge to
Berlin — A39

**1959, May 12　　　Engr.**
9N170　A39　25pf maroon & blk　.55　.40
10th anniversary of Berlin Airlift.

Globe and
Brandenburg
Gate — A40

**1959, June 18　Litho.　Perf. 14**
9N171　A40　20pf lt blue & red　.75　.40
Issued to publicize the 14th International
Municipal Congress, Berlin, June 18-23.

Friedrich von Schiller
(1759-1805),
Poet — A41

**1959, Nov. 10　Engr.　Wmk. 304**
9N172　A41　20pf dull red & brn　.35　.40

Dr. Robert Koch
(1843-1910),
Bacteriologist — A42

**1960, May 27　　　Perf. 14**
9N173　A42　20pf rose lake　　.35　.40

A42a

Portrait: Dr. Walther Carl Rudolf Schreiber,
Mayor of Berlin, 1953-54.

**1960, June 30　Wmk. 304　Perf. 14**
9N174　A42a　20pf brown car　.50　.60

Hans Böckler (1875-
1951), Labor
Leader — A43

**1961, Feb. 16　Litho.　Perf. 14**
9N175　A43　20pf dk brick red &
　　　　　　　blk　　　　　　.30　.35
Hans Böckler (1875-1951), labor leader.

**Fluorescent Paper
was introduced for all stamps,
starting with No. 9N176, and including Nos. 9N120 and 9N120A.**

Albrecht Dürer — A44

Portraits: 5pf, Albertus Magnus. 7pf, St.
Elizabeth of Thuringia. 8pf, Johann
Gutenberg. 15pf, Martin Luther. 20pf, Johann
Sebastian Bach. 25pf, Balthasar Neumann.
30pf, Immanuel Kant. 40pf, Gotthold Ephraim
Lessing. 50pf, Johann Wolfgang von Goethe.

---

60pf, Friedrich von Schiller. 70pf, Ludwig van
Beethoven. 80pf, Heinrich von Kleist. 1m,
Annette von Droste-Hülshoff. 2m, Gerhart
Hauptmann.

**1961-62　　　Typo.　　Wmk. 304**
9N176　A44　5pf olive　　　.25　.25
9N177　A44　7pf dk bister　.25　.35
9N178　A44　8pf lilac　　　.25　.35
9N179　A44　10pf olive green　.25　.25
　b.　Tête bêche pair　　.90　1.90
9N180　A44　15pf blue　　　.25　.35
9N181　A44　20pf dark red　.25　.25
9N182　A44　25pf orange brn　.25　.35
　　　　　　　　Engr.
9N183　A44　30pf gray　　　.30　.45
9N184　A44　40pf blue　　　.50　.85
9N185　A44　50pf red brown　.35　.85
9N186　A44　60pf dk car rose
　　　　　　　('62)　　　　　.35　.95
9N187　A44　70pf green　　.50　.95
9N188　A44　80pf brown　　3.25　6.25
9N189　A44　1m violet blue　2.60　3.00
9N190　A44　2m yel grn ('62)　3.00　4.25
　Nos. 9N176-9N190 (15)　12.60　19.70
Nos. 9N176-9N182, 9N184 and 9N187
were issued in sheets and in coils. Every fifth
coil stamp has a black control number on the
back.

Louise
Schroeder — A45

**1961, June 3　　Engr.　Perf. 14**
9N192　A45　20pf dark brown　.40　.35
Issued to honor Louise Schroeder, acting
mayor of Berlin (1947-1948).

A46

Design: 10pf, Emblem and St. Mary's
Church. 20pf, Synod Emblem & Kaiser Wilhelm Memorial Church.

**1961, July 19　Litho.　Wmk. 304**
9N193　A46　10pf green & vio　.25　.25
9N194　A46　20pf rose claret & vio　.25　.25
10th meeting of German Protestants (Evangelical Synod), Berlin, July 19-23.

Berlin Bear with Record,
TV Set & Radio
Tower — A47

**1961, Aug. 3　　　　Engr.**
9N195　A47　20pf brn red & dk brn　.40　.40
German Radio, Television and Phonograph
Exhibition, Berlin, Aug. 25-Sept. 3.

Berlin, 1650 — A48

Views of Old Berlin: 10pf, Spree and
Waisenbrücke (Orphans' Bridge). 15pf, Mauer
Street, 1780. 20pf, Berlin Palace, 1703. 25pf,
Potsdam Square, 1825. 40pf, Bellevue Palace,
1800. 50pf, Fischer Bridge, 1830. 60pf, Halle
Gate, 1880. 70pf, Parochial Church, 1780.
80pf, University, 1825. 90pf, Opera House,
1780. 1m, Grunewald Lake, 1790.

**1962-63　　　Wmk. 304　Perf. 14**
9N196　A48　7pf dk gray & gldn
　　　　　　　brn　　　　　.25　.25
9N197　A48　10pf grn & dk gray　.25　.25
9N198　A48　15pf bluish gray & dk
　　　　　　　bl ('63)　　　.25　.25
9N199　A48　20pf org brn & sep　.25　.25
9N200　A48　25pf ol & gray ('63)　.25　.35
9N201　A48　40pf bluish gray & ul-
　　　　　　　tra　　　　　.25　.35
9N202　A48　50pf gray & dk brn
　　　　　　　('63)　　　　.35　.35

---

9N203　A48　60pf gray & car rose
　　　　　　　('63)　　　　.40　.40
9N204　A48　70pf dk gray & lilac　.40　.40
9N205　A48　80pf dk gray & dk red
　　　　　　　('63)　　　　.55　.60
9N206　A48　90pf sep & brn org　.65　.65
9N207　A48　1m ol gray & dp grn　.80　.95
　Nos. 9N196-9N207 (12)　4.65　4.95

Gelber Hund, 1912,
and Boeing
707 — A49

**1962, Sept. 12　　　Litho.**
9N208　A49　60pf brt blue & blk　.65　.45
50th anniv. of German airmail service.

Berlin Bear and Radio
Tower — A50

**1963, July 24　Unwmk.　Perf. 14**
9N209　A50　20pf bl, vio bl & gray　.40　.40
German Radio, Television and Phonograph
Exhibition, Berlin, Aug. 30-Sept. 8.

Schöneberg City Hall,
John F. Kennedy Place,
Berlin — A51

**1964, May 30　Engr.　Wmk. 304**
9N210　A51　20pf dk brn, cr　.40　.40
700th anniv. of the Schöneberg district of
Berlin. The Senate and House of Representatives of West Berlin meet at Schöneberg City
Hall.

Pres. Heinrich Lübke —
A51a

**1964, July 1　Litho.　Unwmk.**
9N211　A51a　20pf carmine　.25　.25
9N212　A51a　40pf ultra　　.35　.35
See Nos. 9N263-9N264.

Reichstag Building,
Berlin — A51b

**1964, Sept. 14　Litho.　Perf. 14**
9N213　A51b　20pf lt blue, blk &
　　　　　　　grn　　　　　.40　.40

Kennedy — A51c

**1964, Nov. 21　Engr.　Wmk. 304**
9N214　A51c　40pf dark blue　.40　.45

A52

A52a

Designs (German buildings through 12 centuries): 10pf, Wall pavilion, Zwinger, Dresden.
15pf, Tegel Castle, Berlin. 20pf, Portico,
Lorsch. 40pf, Trifels Fortress, Palatinate. 50pf,
Castle Gate, Ellwangen. 60pf, Treptow Gate,

Neubrandenburg. 70pf, Osthofen Gate, Soest. 80pf, Elling Gate, Weissenburg.

## 1964-65 Typo. Unwmk.
| | | | | |
|---|---|---|---|---|
| 9N215 | A52 | 10pf brown ('65) | .25 | .25 |
| a. | | Tête bêche pair | .55 | 1.60 |
| 9N216 | A52 | 15pf dk green ('65) | .25 | .25 |
| 9N217 | A52a | 20pf brn red ('65) | .25 | .25 |

### Engr.
| | | | | |
|---|---|---|---|---|
| 9N218 | A52a | 40pf vio bl ('65) | .55 | .95 |
| 9N219 | A52a | 50pf olive bis | 1.20 | 1.25 |
| 9N220 | A52a | 60pf rose red | .85 | .95 |
| 9N221 | A52a | 70pf dk green ('65) | 1.60 | 3.00 |
| 9N222 | A52a | 80pf chocolate | 1.60 | 1.25 |
| | Nos. 9N215-9N222 (8) | | 6.55 | 8.15 |

Nos. 9N215-9N218, 9N221 were issued in sheets of 100 and in coils. Every fifth coil stamp has a black control number on the back.

Kaiser Wilhelm Memorial Church — A53

The New Berlin: 15pf, German Opera House, horiz. 20pf, Philharmonic Hall, horiz. 30pf, Jewish Community Center, horiz. 40pf, Regina Martyrum Memorial, horiz. 50pf, Ernst Reuter Square, horiz. 60pf, Europa Center. 70pf, School of Engineering, horiz. 80pf, City Highway. 90pf, Planetarium and observatory, horiz. 1m, Schaeferberg radio tower, Wannsee. 1.10m, University clinic, Steglitz, horiz.

### Engraved and Lithographed
## 1965-66 Unwmk. Perf. 14
| | | | | |
|---|---|---|---|---|
| 9N223 | A53 | 10pf multi | .25 | .25 |
| 9N224 | A53 | 15pf multi | .25 | .25 |
| 9N225 | A53 | 20pf multi | .25 | .25 |
| 9N226 | A53 | 30pf multi ('66) | .25 | .25 |
| 9N227 | A53 | 40pf multi ('66) | .25 | .25 |
| 9N228 | A53 | 50pf multi | .25 | .25 |
| 9N229 | A53 | 60pf multi ('66) | .30 | .35 |
| 9N230 | A53 | 70pf multi ('66) | .40 | .40 |
| 9N231 | A53 | 80pf multi | .40 | .40 |
| 9N232 | A53 | 90pf multi ('66) | .50 | .65 |
| 9N233 | A53 | 1m multi ('66) | .50 | .75 |
| 9N234 | A53 | 1.10m multi ('66) | .50 | .85 |
| | Nos. 9N223-9N234 (12) | | 4.10 | 4.90 |

Nordertor, Flensburg — A54

5pf, Berlin Gate, Stettin. 8pf, Castle, Kaub on the Rhine. 10pf, Wall Pavilion, Zwinger, Dresden. 20pf, Portico, Lorsch. 40pf, Trifels Fortress, Palatinate. 50pf, Castle Gate, Ellwangen. 60pf, Treptow Gate, Neubrandenburg. 70pf, Osthofen Gate, Soest. 80pf, Elling Gate, Weissenburg. 90pf, Zschocke Ladies' Home, Königsberg. 1m, Melanchthon House, Wittenberg. 1.10m, Trinity Hospital, Hildesheim. 1.30m, Tegel Castle, Berlin. 2m, Löwenberg Town Hall, interior view.

## 1966-69 Engr. Perf. 14
| | | | | |
|---|---|---|---|---|
| 9N235 | A54 | 5pf olive | .25 | .25 |
| 9N236 | A54 | 8pf car rose | .25 | .25 |
| 9N237 | A54 | 10pf dk brn ('67) | .25 | .25 |
| 9N238 | A54 | 20pf dp grn ('67) | .25 | .25 |
| 9N239 | A54 | 30pf yellow grn | .25 | .25 |
| 9N240 | A54 | 30pf red ('67) | .25 | .25 |
| 9N241 | A54 | 40pf ol bis ('67) | .50 | .65 |
| 9N242 | A54 | 50pf blue ('67) | .35 | .40 |
| 9N243 | A54 | 60pf dp org ('67) | 1.30 | 1.60 |
| 9N244 | A54 | 70pf sl grn ('67) | .65 | .65 |
| 9N245 | A54 | 80pf red brn ('67) | .85 | 1.60 |
| 9N246 | A54 | 90pf black | .50 | .65 |
| 9N247 | A54 | 1m dull blue | .50 | .65 |
| 9N248 | A54 | 1.10m red brn | 1.20 | 1.15 |
| 9N249 | A54 | 1.30m green ('69) | 2.00 | 1.90 |
| 9N250 | A54 | 2m purple | 2.00 | 1.60 |
| | Nos. 9N235-9N250 (16) | | 11.35 | 12.35 |

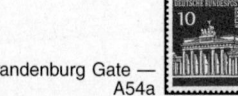

Brandenburg Gate — A54a

## 1966-70 Typo. Perf. 14
| | | | | |
|---|---|---|---|---|
| 9N251 | A54a | 10pf chocolate | .25 | .25 |
| a. | | Bklt. pane of 10 (4 #9N251, 2 #9N252, 4 #9N253) | 6.00 | 22.00 |
| b. | | Tête bêche pair | .80 | .95 |
| c. | | Bklt. pane of 6 (4 #9N251, 2 #9N253) ('70) | 2.60 | 6.25 |

| | | | | |
|---|---|---|---|---|
| 9N252 | A54a | 20pf dp green | .25 | .25 |
| a. | | Bklt. pane of 4 (2 #9N252, 2 #9N253) ('70) | 2.00 | 6.25 |
| 9N253 | A54a | 30pf red | .25 | .25 |
| a. | | Tête bêche pair | 1.20 | 2.25 |
| 9N254 | A54a | 50pf dk blue | .50 | .35 |
| 9N255 | A54a | 100pf dk blue | 4.00 | 4.25 |
| | Nos. 9N251-9N255 (5) | | 5.25 | 5.35 |

Nos. 9N251-9N255 were issued in sheets of 100 and in coils. Every fifth coil stamp has a black control number on the back.

A55

Designs: 10pf, Young Man, by Conrat Meit, 1520. 20pf, The Great Elector Friedrich Wilhelm (1640-88), head from monument by Andreas Schlüter. 30pf, The Evangelist Mark, by Tilman Riemenschneider. 50pf, Head of "Victory" from Brandenburg Gate, by Gottfried Schadow, 1793. 1m, Madonna, by Joseph Anton Feuchtmayer. 1.10m, Jesus and John, wood sculpture, anonymous, c. 1320.

## 1967 Engr. Perf. 14
| | | | | |
|---|---|---|---|---|
| 9N256 | A55 | 10pf sepia & lemon | .25 | .25 |
| 9N257 | A55 | 20pf sl grn & bluish gray | .25 | .25 |
| 9N258 | A55 | 30pf brown & olive | .25 | .25 |
| 9N259 | A55 | 50pf black & gray | .35 | .35 |
| 9N260 | A55 | 1m blue & chlky blue | .65 | .65 |

### Size: 22x40mm
| | | | | |
|---|---|---|---|---|
| 9N261 | A55 | 1.10m brown & buff | 1.00 | 1.20 |
| | Nos. 9N256-9N261 (6) | | 2.75 | 2.95 |

Issued to publicize Berlin art treasures.

A56

Berlin Radio Tower and Television Screens

## 1967, July 19 Litho. and Engr.
| | | | | |
|---|---|---|---|---|
| 9N262 | A56 | 30pf multicolored | .30 | .35 |

25th German Radio, Television and Phonograph Exhibition, Berlin, Aug. 25-Sept. 3.

Pres. Heinrich Lübke — A56a

## 1967, Oct. 14 Litho.
| | | | | |
|---|---|---|---|---|
| 9N263 | A56a | 30pf carmine | .25 | .25 |
| 9N264 | A56a | 50pf ultra | .35 | .40 |

Old Court Building (Berlin Museum) — A57

## 1968, Mar. 16 Engr. Perf. 14
| | | | | |
|---|---|---|---|---|
| 9N265 | A57 | 30pf black | .30 | .35 |

500th anniv. of the Berlin Court of Appeal.

Turners' Emblem — A58

## 1968, Apr. 29 Litho. Perf. 14
| | | | | |
|---|---|---|---|---|
| 9N266 | A58 | 20pf gray, blk & red | .30 | .35 |

Issued to publicize the German Turner Festival, Berlin, May 28-June 3.

Newspaper Vendor by Christian Wilhelm Allers — A59

19th Century Berliners: 5pf, Hack, by Heinrich Zille, horiz. No. 9N269, Horse omnibus, coachman and passengers, 1890, by C. W. Allers. No. 9N270, Cobbler's apprentice, by Franz Kruger. No. 9N271, Cobbler, by Adolph von Menzel. No. 9N272, Blacksmiths, by Paul Meyerheim. No. 9N273, Three Ladies, by Franz Kruger. 50pf, Strollers at Brandenburg Gate, by Christian W. Allers.

## 1969 Engr. Perf. 14
| | | | | |
|---|---|---|---|---|
| 9N267 | A59 | 5pf black | .25 | .25 |
| 9N268 | A59 | 10pf dp brown | .25 | .25 |
| 9N269 | A59 | 10pf brown | .25 | .25 |
| 9N270 | A59 | 20pf dk olive grn | .25 | .25 |
| 9N271 | A59 | 20pf green | .25 | .25 |
| 9N272 | A59 | 30pf dk red brown | .50 | .35 |
| 9N273 | A59 | 30pf red brown | .50 | .35 |
| 9N274 | A59 | 50pf ultra | 1.30 | 1.50 |
| | Nos. 9N267-9N274 (8) | | 3.55 | 3.45 |

### Souvenir Sheet

Berlin Zoo Animals — A60

Designs: 10pf, Orangutan family. 20pf, White pelicans. 30pf, Gaur and calf. 50pf, Zebra and foal.

### Engraved and Lithographed
## 1969, June 4 Perf. 14
| | | | | |
|---|---|---|---|---|
| 9N275 | A60 | Sheet of 4 | 1.60 | 1.60 |
| a. | | 10pf bister & black | .40 | .40 |
| b. | | 20pf light green & black | .40 | .40 |
| c. | | 30pf lilac rose & black | .40 | .40 |
| d. | | 50pf blue & black | .40 | .40 |

125th anniversary of the Berlin Zoo. The sheet was sold with a 20pf surtax for the benefit of the Zoo.

Australian Postman — A61

Designs: 20pf, African telephone operator. 30pf, Middle East telecommunications engineer. 50pf, Loading mail on plane.

## 1969, July 21 Litho. Perf. 14
| | | | | |
|---|---|---|---|---|
| 9N276 | A61 | 10pf ol & apple grn | .25 | .25 |
| 9N277 | A61 | 20pf dk brn, bis & brn | .25 | .25 |
| 9N278 | A61 | 30pf vio blk & bis | .50 | .50 |
| 9N279 | A61 | 50pf dk blue & blue | .95 | 1.00 |
| | Nos. 9N276-9N279 (4) | | 1.95 | 2.00 |

20th Congress of the Post Office Trade Union Federation, Berlin, July 7-11.

Joseph Joachim — A62

Design: 50pf, Alexander von Humboldt, painting by Joseph Stieler.

## 1969, Sept. 12 Photo. Perf. 14
| | | | | |
|---|---|---|---|---|
| 9N280 | A62 | 30pf multicolored | .50 | .40 |
| 9N281 | A62 | 50pf multicolored | .80 | 1.00 |

Cent. of the Berlin Music School and honoring its 1st director, Joseph Joachim (1831-1907), violinist, conductor and composer; Alexander von Humboldt (1769-1859), naturalist and explorer.

## 1970, Jan. 7

Theodor Fontane, painting by Hanns Fechner.

| | | | | |
|---|---|---|---|---|
| 9N282 | A62 | 20pf multicolored | .35 | .35 |

150th anniv. of the birth of Theodor Fontane (1819-1898), poet and writer. See No. 9N303.

Film Frame — A63

## 1970, June 18 Photo. Perf. 14
| | | | | |
|---|---|---|---|---|
| 9N283 | A63 | 30pf multicolored | .40 | .45 |

20th International Film Festival.

President Heinemann — A63a

## 1970-73 Engr. Perf. 14
| | | | | |
|---|---|---|---|---|
| 9N284 | A63a | 5pf dk gray | .25 | .25 |
| 9N285 | A63a | 8pf olive bis | .60 | .85 |
| 9N286 | A63a | 10pf brown | .25 | .25 |
| 9N286A | A63a | 15pf olive | .25 | .25 |
| 9N287 | A63a | 20pf green | .25 | .25 |
| 9N288 | A63a | 25pf dp yel grn | .75 | .45 |
| 9N289 | A63a | 30pf red brown | .85 | .45 |
| 9N290 | A63a | 40pf brown org | .50 | .25 |
| 9N291 | A63a | 50pf dark blue | .50 | .25 |
| 9N292 | A63a | 60pf blue | .75 | .45 |
| 9N293 | A63a | 70pf dk brown | .60 | .50 |
| 9N294 | A63a | 80pf slate grn | .80 | .75 |
| 9N295 | A63a | 90pf magenta | 1.60 | 1.90 |
| 9N296 | A63a | 1m olive | .80 | .60 |
| 9N296A | A63a | 110pf olive gray | 1.00 | .95 |
| 9N297 | A63a | 120pf ocher | 1.00 | .75 |
| 9N298 | A63a | 130pf ocher | 1.30 | 1.25 |
| 9N298A | A63a | 140pf dk blue grn | 1.30 | 1.25 |
| 9N299 | A63a | 150pf purple | 1.30 | .95 |
| 9N300 | A63a | 160pf orange | 1.75 | 1.60 |
| 9N300A | A63a | 170pf orange | 1.30 | 1.40 |
| 9N300B | A63a | 190pf dp claret | 1.60 | 2.25 |
| 9N301 | A63a | 2m dp violet | 1.60 | 1.15 |
| | Nos. 9N284-9N301 (23) | | 20.90 | 19.00 |

Issued: 5pf, 1m, 7/23; 10, 20pf, 10/23; 30, 90pf, 2m, 1/7/71; 8, 40, 50, 70, 80pf, 4/8/71; 60pf, 6/25/71; 25pf, 8/27/71; 120, 160pf, 3/8/72; 15, 130pf, 6/20/72; 150pf, 7/5/72; 170pf, 9/11/72; 110, 140, 190pf, 1/16/73.

Symbols of Dance, Theater & Art — A64

## 1970, Sept. 4 Litho. Perf. 13½x14
| | | | | |
|---|---|---|---|---|
| 9N302 | A64 | 30pf gray & multi | .50 | .45 |

20th Berlin Festival Weeks.

### Portrait Type of 1969

30pf, Leopold von Ranke, by Julius Schrage.

## 1970, Oct. 23 Photo. Perf. 13½x14
| | | | | |
|---|---|---|---|---|
| 9N303 | A62 | 30pf multicolored | .40 | .35 |

175th anniversary of the birth of Leopold von Ranke (1795-1886), historian.

Imperial Eagle — A64b

## 1971, Jan. 18 Litho. Perf. 13½x14
| | | | | |
|---|---|---|---|---|
| 9N304 | A64b | 30pf org, red, gray & blk | .50 | .45 |

Metropolitan Train, 1932 — A65

5pf, Suburban train, 1925. 10pf, Street cars, 1890. 20pf, Horsedrawn trolley. 50pf, Street car, 1950. 1m, Subway train, 1971.

| 1971 | Litho. | | Perf. 14 | |
|------|--------|--|----------|--|
| 9N305 | A65 | 5pf multicolored | .25 | .25 |
| 9N306 | A65 | 10pf multicolored | .25 | .25 |
| 9N307 | A65 | 30pf multicolored | .25 | .25 |
| 9N308 | A65 | 30pf multicolored | .40 | .35 |
| 9N309 | A65 | 50pf multicolored | 1.30 | 1.15 |
| 9N310 | A65 | 1m multicolored | 1.60 | 1.60 |
| | | *Nos. 9N305-9N310 (6)* | 4.05 | 3.85 |

Issued: 30pf, 1m, Jan. 18; others, May 3.

Bagpipe Player, by
Dürer — A66

| 1971, May 21 | Engr. | | Perf. 14 | |
|------|--------|--|----------|--|
| 9N311 | A66 | 10pf black & brown | .40 | .25 |

500th anniversary of the birth of Albrecht Dürer (1471-1528), painter and engraver.

Score from 2nd
Brandenburg
Concerto and
Bach — A67

| 1971, July 14 | Litho. | | Perf. 14 | |
|------|--------|--|----------|--|
| 9N312 | A67 | 30pf buff, brn & slate | .65 | .50 |

250th anniv. of 1st performance of Johann Sebastian Bach's 2nd Brandenburg Concerto.

A68

Telecommunications tower, Berlin.

| 1971, July 14 | | | Photo. | |
|------|--------|--|----------|--|
| 9N313 | A68 | 30pf dk blue, blk & car | .65 | .50 |

Intl. Broadcasting Exhibition, Berlin.

A69

**1971, Aug. 27**
| 9N314 | A69 | 25pf multicolored | .50 | .35 |
|------|--------|--|----------|--|

Hermann von Helmholtz (1821-94), scientist. See Nos. 9N332-9N333, 9N341.

**Souvenir Sheet**

Racing Cars — A70

a, Opel racer. b, Auto Union racer. c, Mercedes-Benz SSKL, 1931. d, Mercedes and Auto Union cars racing on North embankment.

| 1971, Aug. 27 | Litho. | Perf. 14 | |
|------|--------|--------|--|
| 9N315 | A70 | Sheet of 4 | 1.30 | 1.20 |
| a. | | 10pf multi | .25 | .25 |
| b. | | 25pf multi | .25 | .25 |
| c. | | 30pf multi | .35 | .25 |
| d. | | 60pf multi | .55 | .50 |

50th anniversary of Avus Race Track.

Accident Prevention —
A70a

---

5pf, "Matches cause fires." 10pf, Broken ladder. 20pf, Hand & circular saw. 25pf, "Alcohol & automobile." 30pf, Safety helmets prevent injury. 40pf, Defective plug. 50pf, Nail sticking from board. 60pf, 70pf, Traffic safety (ball rolling before car). 100pf, Hoisted cargo. 150pf, Fenced-in open manhole.

| 1971-73 | Typo. | | Perf. 14 | |
|------|--------|--|----------|--|
| 9N316 | A70a | 5pf orange | .25 | .25 |
| 9N317 | A70a | 10pf dk brn | .25 | .25 |
| a. | Bklt. pane, 2 each #9N317-9N318, 9N320-9N321 (74) | | 7.25 | 9.50 |
| 9N318 | A70a | 20pf purple | .25 | .25 |
| 9N319 | A70a | 25pf green | .35 | .50 |
| 9N320 | A70a | 30pf dk red | .35 | .40 |
| 9N321 | A70a | 40pf rose cl | .35 | .45 |
| 9N322 | A70a | 50pf Prus blue | 1.60 | .95 |
| 9N323 | A70a | 60pf vio bl | 1.60 | 1.90 |
| 9N323A | A70a | 70pf grn & vio bl | 1.20 | .90 |
| 9N324 | A70a | 100pf olive | 1.60 | .95 |
| 9N325 | A70a | 150pf red brn | 5.00 | 5.75 |
| | | *Nos. 9N316-9N325 (11)* | 12.80 | 12.55 |

Issued in sheets of 100 and coils. Every fifth coil stamp has a control number on the back. Value, set $29.

Issued: 25pf, 60pf, 9/10; 5pf, 10/29; 10pf, 30pf, 3/8/72; 40pf, 6/20/72; 20pf, 100pf, 7/5/72; 150pf, 9/11/72; 50pf, 1/16/73; 70pf, 6/5/73.

Microscope and Metal
Slide — A71

| 1971, Oct. 26 | Photo. | | Perf. 14 | |
|------|--------|--|----------|--|
| 9N326 | A71 | 30pf multicolored | .40 | .35 |

Materials Testing Laboratory centenary.

Friedrich Gilly, by
Gottfried
Schadow — A72

| 1972, Feb. 4 | Engr. | | Perf. 14 | |
|------|--------|--|----------|--|
| 9N327 | A72 | 30pf black & blue | .50 | .35 |

Friedrich Gilly (1772-1800), sculptor.

Grunewaldsee,
by Alexander
von
Riesen — A73

Paintings of Berlin Lakes: 25pf, Wannsee, by Max Liebermann. 30pf, Schlachtensee, by Walter Leistikow.

| 1972, Apr. 14 | Photo. | | Perf. 14 | |
|------|--------|--|----------|--|
| 9N328 | A73 | 10pf blue & multi | .25 | .25 |
| 9N329 | A73 | 25pf green & multi | .40 | .45 |
| 9N330 | A73 | 30pf black & multi | .70 | .50 |
| | | *Nos. 9N328-9N330 (3)* | 1.35 | 1.20 |

A74

**1972, May 18**
| 9N331 | A74 | 60pf violet & blk | .95 | .90 |
|------|--------|--|----------|--|

E. T. A. Hoffmann (1776-1822), writer and composer. (Portrait by Wilhelm Hensel.)

**Portrait Type of 1971**

Designs: No. 9N332, Max Liebermann (1847-1935), self-portrait. No. 9N333, Karl August, Duke of Hardenberg (1750-1822), Prussian statesman, by J. H. W. Tischbein.

| 1972 | Photo. | | Perf. 14 | |
|------|--------|--|----------|--|
| 9N332 | A69 | 40pf multicolored | .60 | .40 |
| 9N333 | A69 | 40pf multicolored | .55 | .40 |

Issued: No. 9N332, 7/18; No. 9N333, 11/10.

---

A75

| 1972, Oct. 20 | | Engr. & Litho. | | |
|------|--------|--|----------|--|
| 9N334 | A75 | 20pf Stamp-printing press | .55 | .25 |

Stamp Day 1972, and for the 5th National Youth Philatelic Exhib., Berlin, Oct. 26-29.

Streetcar,
1907 — A76

No. 9N336, Double-decker bus, 1919. No. 9N337, Double-decker bus, 1925. No. 9N338, Electrobus, 1933. No. 9N339, Double-decker bus, 1970. No. 9N340, Elongated bus, 1973.

| 1973, Apr. 30 | Litho. | | Perf. 14 | |
|------|--------|--|----------|--|
| 9N335 | A76 | 20pf gray & multi | .35 | .25 |
| 9N336 | A76 | 30pf gray & multi | .65 | .40 |
| 9N337 | A76 | 40pf gray & multi | 1.00 | .60 |

**1973, Sept. 14**
| 9N338 | A76 | 20pf gray & multi | .35 | .25 |
| 9N339 | A76 | 30pf gray & multi | 1.00 | .40 |
| 9N340 | A76 | 40pf gray & multi | 1.00 | .60 |
| | | *Nos. 9N335-9N340 (6)* | 4.35 | 2.50 |

Public transportation in Berlin.

**Portrait Type of 1971**

Design: 40pf, Ludwig Tieck (1773-1853), poet and writer, by Carl Christian Vogel von Vogelstein.

| 1973, May 25 | Photo. | | Perf. 14 | |
|------|--------|--|----------|--|
| 9N341 | A69 | 40pf multicolored | .60 | .40 |

Johann Joachim
Quantz (1697-1773),
Flutist and
Composer — A77

| 1973, June 12 | Engr. | | Perf. 14 | |
|------|--------|--|----------|--|
| 9N342 | A77 | 40pf black | .65 | .50 |

**Souvenir Sheet**

50 Years of Broadcasting — A78

a, Speaker, set, 1926. b, Hans Bredow. c, Girl, TV, tape recorder. d, TV camera.

| 1973, Aug. 23 | Litho. | Perf. 14 | |
|------|--------|--------|--|
| 9N343 | A78 | Sheet of 4 | 3.00 | 3.00 |
| a. | | A78 20pf multicolored | .75 | .50 |
| b. | | A78 30pf multicolored | .75 | .75 |
| c. | | A78 40pf multicolored | .75 | .75 |
| d. | | A78 70pf multicolored | .75 | 1.00 |

50 years of German broadcasting. Sold for 1.80m.

Georg W. von
Knobelsdorff — A79

| 1974, Feb. 15 | Engr. | | Perf. 14 | |
|------|--------|--|----------|--|
| 9N344 | A79 | 20pf chocolate | .35 | .25 |

275th anniversary of the birth of Georg Wenzelslaus von Knobelsdorff (1699-1753), architect.

---

Gustav R.
Kirchhoff — A80

| 1974, Feb. 15 | Litho. & Engr. | | | |
|------|--------|--|----------|--|
| 9N345 | A80 | 30pf gray & dk grn | .35 | .35 |

Sesquicentennial of the birth of Gustav Robert Kirchhoff (1824-1887), physicist.

Airlift Memorial, Allied
Flags — A81

| 1974, Apr. 17 | Photo. | | Perf. 14 | |
|------|--------|--|----------|--|
| 9N346 | A81 | 90pf multicolored | 2.00 | 1.25 |

End of the Allied airlift into Berlin, 25th anniv.

Adolf Slaby and
Waves — A82

| 1974, Apr. 17 | Litho. | | Perf. 14 | |
|------|--------|--|----------|--|
| 9N347 | A82 | 40pf black & red | .50 | .40 |

125th anniversary of the birth of Adolf Slaby (1849-1913), radio pioneer.

School Seal Showing
Athena and
Hermes — A83

| 1974, July 13 | Photo. | | Perf. 14 | |
|------|--------|--|----------|--|
| 9N348 | A83 | 50pf multicolored | .60 | .40 |

400th anniversary of the Gray Brothers' School, a secondary Franciscan school.

Berlin-Tegel
Airport — A84

**Lithographed and Engraved**
| 1974, Oct. 15 | | | Perf. 14 | |
|------|--------|--|----------|--|
| 9N349 | A84 | 50pf multicolored | .95 | .50 |

Opening of Berlin-Tegel Airport and Terminal, Nov. 1, 1974.

Venus, by F. E. Meyer,
c. 1775 — A85

Berlin Porcelain: 40pf, "Astronomy," by W. C. Meyer, c. 1772. 50pf, "Justice," by J. G. Müller, c. 1785.

| 1974, Oct. 29 | Litho. | | Perf. 14 | |
|------|--------|--|----------|--|
| 9N350 | A85 | 30pf carmine & multi | .40 | .40 |
| 9N351 | A85 | 40pf carmine & multi | .50 | .45 |
| 9N352 | A85 | 50pf carmine & multi | .60 | .60 |
| | | *Nos. 9N350-9N352 (3)* | 1.50 | 1.45 |

Gottfried Schadow — A86

**1975, Jan. 15    Engr.    Perf. 14**
9N353 A86 50pf maroon            .65  .45

Johann Gottfried Schadow (1764-1850), sculptor.

S.S. Princess Charlotte — A87

Ships: 40pf, S.S. Siegfried. 50pf, S.S. Sperber. 60pf, M.S. Vaterland. 70pf, M.S. Moby Dick.

**1975, Feb. 14    Litho.    Perf. 14**
9N354 A87 30pf gray & multi       .55  .25
9N355 A87 40pf olive & multi      .55  .25
9N356 A87 50pf ultra & multi      .80  .65
9N357 A87 60pf red brn & multi    .85  .65
9N358 A87 70pf dk blue & multi   1.20 1.15
  Nos. 9N354-9N358 (5)           3.95 2.95

Berlin passenger ships

Industry — A87a

5pf, Symphonie satellite. 10pf, Electric train. 20pf, Old Weser lighthouse. 30pf, Rescue helicopter. 40pf, Space shuttle. 50pf, Radar station. 60pf, X-ray machine. 70pf, Shipbuilding. 80pf, Tractor. 100pf, Coal excavator. 110pf, TV camera. 120pf, Chemical plant. 130pf, Brewery. 140pf, Heating plant. 150pf, Power shovel. 160pf, Blast furnace. 180pf, Payloader. 190pf, As #9N371. 200pf, Oil drill platform. 230pf, Frankfurt airport. 250pf, Airport. 300pf, Electric railroad. 500pf, Radio telescope.

**1975-82    Engr.    Perf. 14**
9N359 A87a 5pf ol grn            .25  .25
9N360 A87a 10pf red lilac        .25  .25
9N361 A87a 20pf red org          .25  .25
9N362 A87a 30pf dp vio           .30  .25
9N363 A87a 40pf pck blue         .40  .25
9N364 A87a 50pf rose             .40  .25
9N365 A87a 60pf red              .65  .35
9N366 A87a 70pf blue             .75  .40
9N367 A87a 80pf blue grn         .75  .25
9N368 A87a 100pf brown           .75  .40
9N368A A87a 110pf dp clar       1.15  .95
9N369 A87a 120pf blue vio       1.00  .75
9N369A A87a 130pf carmine       1.75 1.15
9N370 A87a 140pf red            1.00 1.10
9N371 A87a 150pf red brown      2.40  .95
9N372 A87a 160pf dull green     2.40 1.10
9N373 A87a 180pf brown          2.40 1.60
9N373A A87a 190pf org brn       2.40 1.90
9N374 A87a 200pf dp clar        1.30  .65
9N375 A87a 230pf reddsh
              pur               2.00 1.60
9N375A A87a 250pf green         3.25 1.90
9N375B A87a 300pf bister        3.25 1.90
9N376 A87a 500pf dark blue      4.75 3.25
  Nos. 9N359-9N376 (23)        33.80 21.70

Issued: 40, 50, 100pf, 5/15; 10, 30, 70pf, 8/14; 80, 120, 160pf, 10/15; 5, 140, 200pf, 11/14; 20, 500pf, 2/17/76; 60pf, 11/16/78; 230pf, 5/17/79; 150, 180pf, 7/12/79; 110, 130, 300pf, 6/16/82; 190, 250pf, 7/15/82.

Ferdinand Sauerbruch — A88

**Lithographed and Engraved**
**1975, May 15    Perf. 13½x14**
9N379 A88 50pf dull red & dk brn  .65  .45

Ferdinand Sauerbruch (1875-1951) surgeon, birth centenary.

---

Gymnasts' Emblem — A89

**1975, May 15    Photo.    Perf. 14**
9N380 A89 40pf grn, gold & blk    .50  .35

6th Gymnaestrada, Berlin, July 1-5.

Lovis Corinth (1858-1925), Self-portrait, 1900 — A90

**1975, July 15    Photo.    Perf. 14**
9N381 A90 50pf multicolored       .65  .45

Architecture A91

Design: Houses, Naunynstrasse, Berlin-Kreuzberg.

**1975, July 15    Litho. & Engr.**
9N382 A91 50pf multicolored       .65  .50

European Architectural Heritage Year.

Paul Löbe and Reichstag A92

**1975, Nov. 14    Engr.    Perf. 14**
9N383 A92 50pf copper red         .65  .45

Paul Löbe (1875-1967), president of German Parliament 1920-1932, birth centenary.

Grain — A93

**1976, Jan. 5    Photo.    Perf. 14**
9N384 A93 70pf green & yellow     .65  .65

Green Week International Agricultural Exhibition, Berlin, 50th anniversary.

Hockey — A94

**1976, May 13    Engr.    Perf. 14**
9N385 A94 30pf green              .65  .35

Women's World Hockey Championships.

Treble Clef — A95

**1976, May 13    Photo.**
9N386 A95 40pf multicolored       .65  .65

German Choir Festival.

---

Berlin Fire Brigade Emblem — A96

**1976, May 13    Litho.**
9N387 A96 50pf red & multi       1.00  .65

Berlin Fire Brigade, 125th anniversary.

Berlin Views — A97

Designs: 30pf, Sailboat on Havel River. 40pf, Spandau Castle. 50pf, Tiergarten.

**1976, Nov. 16    Engr.    Perf. 14**
9N388 A97 30pf blue & blk         .50  .35
9N389 A97 40pf brown & blk        .65  .35
9N390 A97 50pf green & blk        .75  .35
  Nos. 9N388-9N390 (3)           1.90 1.05

See Nos. 9N422-9N424.

Castles — A97a

10pf, Glücksburg. 20pf, 190pf, Pfaueninsel. 25pf, Gemen. 30pf, Ludwigstein. 40pf, Eltz. 50pf, Neuschwanstein. 60pf, Marksburg. 70pf, Mespelbrunn. 90pf, Vischering. 200pf, Bürresheim. 210pf, Schwanenburg. 230pf, Lichtenberg.

**1977-79    Typo.    Perf. 14**
9N391 A97a  10pf gray blue        .25  .25
  a.  Bklt. pane, 4 #9N391, 2
        each #9N394, 9N396       6.50 8.75
  b.  Bklt. pane, 4 #9N391, 2
        #9N394, 2 #9N440         3.25 5.75
  c.  Bklt. pane, 4 #9N391, 2
        #9N440, 2 #9N442        10.50 19.00
  d.  Bklt. pane, 2 each
        #9N391, 9N394, 9N440-
        9N441                   12.00 19.00
9N392 A97a 20pf orange           .25  .25
9N393 A97a 25pf crimson          .55  .35
9N394 A97a 30pf olive            .25  .25
9N395 A97a 40pf blue green       .30  .25
9N396 A97a 50pf rose car         .50  .25
9N397 A97a 60pf brown            .85  .40
9N398 A97a 70pf blue             .85  .40
9N399 A97a 90pf dark blue        .80  .65
9N400 A97a 190pf red brown      1.20 1.15
9N401 A97a 200pf green          1.20 1.15
9N402 A97a 210pf red brown      1.75 1.25
9N403 A97a 230pf dark green     1.75 1.25
  Nos. 9N391-9N403 (13)        10.50 7.85

Issued in sheets of 100 and coils. Every fifth coil stamp has a control number on the back. Issued: 60pf, 1/13; 40pf, 190pf, 2/16; 10pf, 20pf, 30pf, 4/14; 50pf, 70pf, 5/17; 230pf, 11/16/78; 25pf, 90pf, 1/11/79; 210pf, 2/14/79. See Nos. 9N438-9N445.

Eugenie d'Alton, by Rausch — A98

**1977, Jan. 13    Photo.    Perf. 14**
9N404 A98 50pf violet black       .65  .45

Christian Daniel Rausch (1777-1857), sculptor, birth bicentenary.

Eduard Gaertner (1801-77), Painter — A99

**1977, Feb. 16    Litho. & Engr.**
9N405 A99 40pf lt grn, grn & blk  .60  .35

---

Fountain, by Georg Kolbe — A100

**1977, Apr. 14    Photo.    Perf. 14**
9N406 A100 30pf dark olive        .50  .35

Georg Kolbe (1877-1947), sculptor.

"Bear each other's burdens" — A101

**1977, May 17    Litho.    Perf. 14**
9N407 A101 40pf green blk & yel   .50  .35

17th meeting of German Protestants (Evangelical Synod), Berlin.

Patent Office, Berlin-Kreuzberg A102

**1977, July 13    Litho. & Engr.**
9N408 A102 60pf gray & red       1.30  .60

Centenary of German patent laws.

Telephones, 1905 and 1977 — A103

**1977, July 13    Litho.**
9N409 A103 50pf multicolored     1.45  .85

International Broadcasting Exhibition, Berlin, Aug. 26-Sept. 4, and centenary of telephone in Germany.

Painting by George Grosz (1893-1959) — A104

**1977, July 13**
9N410 A104 70pf multicolored      .80  .85

15th European Art Exhibition, Berlin, Aug. 14-Oct. 16.

Rhinecanthus Aculeatus — A105

Designs: 30pf, Paddlefish. 40pf, Tortoise. 50pf, Rhinoceros iguana. Designs include statue of iguanodon from Aquarium entrance.

**1977, Aug. 16    Photo.    Perf. 14**
9N411 A105 20pf multicolored      .40  .40
9N412 A105 30pf multicolored      .60  .50
9N413 A105 40pf multicolored      .80  .65
9N414 A105 50pf multicolored     1.15  .75
  Nos. 9N411-9N414 (4)           2.95 2.30

25th anniv. of the reopening of Berlin Aquarium.

Walter Kollo (1878-1940), Composer — A106

**1978, Jan. 12　Engr.　Perf. 14**
9N415 A106 50pf brn, red & dk
　　　　　brn　　　　　.80　.65

Chamber of
Commerce
Emblem — A107

**1978, Apr. 13　Engr.　Perf. 14**
9N416 A107 90pf dk blue & red　1.00 1.00
American Chamber of Commerce in Germany, 75th anniversary.

Albrecht von
Graefe — A108

**1978, May 22　Engr.　Perf. 14**
9N417 A108 30pf red brn & blk　.50　.35
Dr. von Graefe (1828-70) ophthalmologist.

Friedrich Ludwig
Jahn — A109

**1978, July 13　Engr.　Perf. 14**
9N418 A109 50pf dk carmine　.65　.45
Friedrich Ludwig Jahn (1778-1852), founder of organized gymnastics.

Swimmers
A110

**1978, Aug. 17　Litho.　Perf. 14**
9N419 A110 40pf multicolored　.95　.65
3rd World Swimming Championships, Berlin, Aug. 18-28.

The Boat,
by Karl
Hofer
A111

**1978, Oct. 12　Photo.　Perf. 14**
9N420 A111 50pf multicolored　.65　.50
Karl Hofer (1878-1955), painter.

National
Library — A112

**1978, Nov. 16　Engr.　Perf. 14**
9N421 A112 90pf red & olive　1.20　.90
Opening of new National Library building.

Berlin Views —
A112a

Designs: 40pf, Belvedere, Charlottenburg Castle. 50pf, Shell House on Landwehr Canal. 60pf, Village Church, Alt-Lichtenrade.

**1978, Nov. 16**
9N422 A112a 40pf blue green &
　　　　　blk　　　　　.55　.35
9N423 A112a 50pf lilac & blk　.65　.50
9N424 A112a 60pf brown & blk　.80　.60
　　Nos. 9N422-9N424 (3)　2.00 1.45

International
Conference
Center — A113

**Photogravure and Engraved**
**1979, Feb. 14　　Perf. 14**
9N425 A113 60pf multicolored　.95　.60
Opening of Intl. Conference Center in Berlin.

German Eagles — A114

**1979, May 17　Litho.　Perf. 14**
9N426 A114 60pf multi　1.20　.90
Cent. of German Natl. Printing Bureau.

TV Screen,
Emblem — A115

**1979, July 12　Photo.　Perf. 14**
9N427 A115 60pf multi　.95　.65
Intl. Broadcasting Exhibition, Berlin.

Target and
Arrows — A116

**1979, July 12**
9N428 A116 50pf multicolored　.65　.45
World Archery Championships, Berlin.

Moses
Mendelssohn — A117

**1979, Aug. 9　Engr.　Perf. 14**
9N429 A117 90pf black　1.00　.65
Mendelssohn (1729-86), philosopher.

Gas Lamp — A118

Historic Street Lanterns: 40pf, Carbon arc lamp. 50pf, Hanging gas lamps. 60pf, 5-armed candelabra.

**1979, Aug. 9　　Litho.**
9N430 A118 10pf multicolored　.35　.25
9N431 A118 40pf multicolored　.65　.50
9N432 A118 50pf multicolored　1.00　.65
9N433 A118 60pf multicolored　1.00　.95
　　Nos. 9N430-9N433 (4)　3.00 2.35
300 years of street lighting in Berlin.

Orchid — A119

**1979, Aug. 9**
9N434 A119 50pf multicolored　.70　.45
Botanical Gardens, Berlin, 300th anniv.

Berlin Poster Columns,
125th
Anniversary — A120

**Lithographed and Engraved**
**1979, Nov. 14　　Perf. 14**
9N435 A120 50pf multicolored　1.00　.55

Castles — A120a

35pf, Lichtenstein. 40pf, Wolfsburg. 50pf, Inzlingen. 60pf, Rheydt. 80pf, Wilhelmsthal. 120pf, Charlottenburg. 280pf, Ahrensburg. 300pf, Herrenhausen.

**1979-82　　Typo.　Perf. 14**
9N438 A120a 35pf red brn　.30　.25
9N439 A120a 40pf brown　.50　.25
9N440 A120a 50pf green　.55　.25
9N441 A120a 60pf rose　.80　.40
9N442 A120a 80pf olive　.55　.25
9N443 A120a 120pf dk pur　.85　.75
9N444 A120a 280pf blue　3.00 1.90
9N445 A120a 300pf orange　3.00 1.90
　　Nos. 9N438-9N445 (8)　9.55 5.95
　Issued: 60pf, 11/14; 40pf, 50pf, 2/14/80; 35pf, 80pf, 30pf, 6/16/82; 120pf, 280pf, 7/15/82.

World Map Showing
Continental
Drift — A121

**1980, Feb. 14　Litho.　Perf. 14**
9N451 A121 60pf multicolored　1.15　.85
Alfred Wegener (1880-1930), geophysicist and meteorologist; founded theory of continental drift.

German Catholics
Day — A122

Cardinal Count Preysing (1880-1950).

**1980, May 8　Engr.　Perf. 14**
9N452 A122 50pf blk & car rose　.65　.45

Prussian Museum,
Berlin, 150th
Anniv. — A123

Designs: 40pf, Angel, enamel medallion, 12th cent. 60pf, Monks Reading, oak sculpture, by Ernest Barlach (1870-1938).

**1980, July 10　Litho.　Perf. 14**
9N453 A123 40pf multicolored　.55　.40
9N454 A123 60pf multicolored　.85　.50

Von Steuben Leading
Troops — A124

**1980, Aug. 14　Litho.　Perf. 14**
9N455 A124 40pf multicolored　.95　.45
Friedrich Wilhelm von Steuben (1730-94).

Robert Stolz (1880-
1975),
Composer — A125

**1980, Aug. 14**
9N456 A125 60pf dk blue & bis　.95　.65

Lilienthal
Memorial — A126

Designs: 50pf, Grosse Neugierde Memorial, 1835. 60pf, Lookout tower, Grunewald Memorial to Kaiser Wilhelm I.

**1980, Nov. 13　Engr.　Perf. 14**
9N457 A126 40pf dk green & blk　.65　.35
9N458 A126 50pf brown & blk　.75　.65
9N459 A126 60pf dk blue & blk　1.00　.65
　　Nos. 9N457-9N459 (3)　2.40 1.65

Von Gontard
and Kleist Park
Colonnades,
Berlin — A127

**1981, Jan. 15　Litho.　Perf. 14**
9N460 A127 50pf multicolored　.80　.50
Karl Philipp von Gontard (1731-91), architect.

Achim von Arnim
(1781-1831),
Poet — A128

**1981, Jan. 15　　Engr.**
9N461 A128 60pf dark green　.80　.50

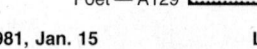

Adelbert von Chamisso
(1781-1838),
Poet — A129

**1981, Jan. 15　　Litho.**
9N462 A129 60pf brn & gldn brn　.80　.50

Berlin-Kreuzberg,
Liberation Monument,
1813 — A130

**1981, Feb. 12　Engr.　Perf. 14**
9N463 A130 40pf brown　.95　.65
Karl Friedrich Schinkel (1781-1841), architect, 400th anniversary of birth.

Arts and Science
Medal, Awarded 1842-
1933 — A131

**1981, July 16　Litho.　Perf. 14**
9N464 A131 40pf multicolored　.65　.45
"Prussia — an attempt at a balance" exhibition.

Amor and Psyche, by Reinhold Begas (1831-1911) — A132

**1981, July 16**      **Photo.**
9N465 A132 50pf multicolored    .65   .45

Intl. Telecommunications Exhibition — A133

**1981, July 16**      **Litho.**
9N466 A133 60pf multicolored    1.05   .65

Peter Beuth (1781-1853), Constitutional Law Expert — A134

**Lithographed and Engraved**
**1981, Nov. 12**      **Perf. 14**
9N467 A134 60pf gold & black    .65   .60

Nijinsky, by Georg Kolbe, 1914 — A135

20th Century Sculptures: 60pf, Mother Earth II, by Ernst Barlach, 1920. 90pf, Flora Kneeling, by Richard Scheibe, 1930.

**1981, Nov. 12**      **Photo.**
9N468 A135 40pf multicolored    .50   .35
9N469 A135 60pf multicolored    .80   .50
9N470 A135 90pf multicolored    1.05   .90
    Nos. 9N468-9N470 (3)    2.35 1.75

750th Anniv. of Spandau A136

**Lithographed and Engraved**
**1982, Feb. 18**      **Perf. 14**
9N471 A136 60pf multicolored    1.00   .75

Berlin Philharmonic Centenary — A137

**Lithographed and Embossed**
**1982, Apr. 15**      **Perf. 14**
9N472 A137 60pf multicolored    1.00   .65

Salzburg Emigration to Prussia, 250th Anniv. — A138

**& 1982, May 5**    **Litho.**    **Engr.**
9N473 A138 50pf multicolored    .65   .45

Italian Stone Carriers, by Max Pechstein A139

80pf, Two Girls Bathing, by Otto Mueller.

**1982, July 15**      **Litho.**     **Perf. 14**
9N474 A139 50pf multicolored    .80   .60
9N475 A139 80pf multicolored    1.20   .90

Villa Borsig — A140

60pf, Sts. Peter and Paul Church. 80pf, Villa von der Heydt.

**1982, Nov. 10**      **Engr.**     **Perf. 14**
9N476 A140 50pf shown    .90   .60
9N477 A140 60pf multicolored    .95   .70
9N478 A140 80pf multicolored    1.30   .75
    Nos. 9N476-9N478 (3)    3.15 2.05

State Theater, Charlottenburg, 1790 — A141

**1982, Nov. 10**      **Litho. & Engr.**
9N479 A141 80pf multicolored    1.30 1.00
Carl Gotthard Langhans (1732-1808), architect.

A142

Various street pumps and fire hydrants, 1900.

**1983, Jan. 13**      **Litho.**     **Perf. 14**
9N480 A142   50pf multi    1.00   .65
9N481 A142   60pf multi    1.15   .65
9N482 A142   80pf multi    1.30 1.00
9N483 A142 120pf multi    2.00 1.60
    Nos. 9N480-9N483 (4)    5.45 3.90

A142a

**1983, Feb. 8**      **Engr.**     **Perf. 14**
9N484 A142a 80pf dark brown    1.45 1.25
Berlin-Koblenz Telegraph Service sesquicentennial.

Portrait of Barbara Campanini, 1745, by Antoine Pesne (1683-1757) — A143

**1983, May 5**      **Photo.**     **Perf. 14**
9N485 A143 50pf multicolored    .80   .65

Joachim Ringelnatz (1883-1934), Painter and Writer — A144

**1983, July 14**      **Litho.**     **Perf. 14**
9N486 A144 50pf Silhouette    .95   .65

Intl. Radio Exhibition, Sept. 2-11 — A145

80pf, Nipkow's phototelegraphy diagram.

**1983, July 14**
9N487 A145 80pf multicolored    1.30 1.10

Ancient Artwork, Berlin Museum — A146

30pf, Bust of Queen Cleopatra VII, 69-30 B.C. 50pf, Statue of Egyptian Couple, Giza, 2400 B.C. 60pf, Stone God with Beaded Turban, Mexico, 300 B.C. 80pf, Enamel Plate, 16th cent.

**1984, Jan. 12**      **Litho.**     **Perf. 14**
9N488 A146 30pf multicolored    .80   .65
9N489 A146 50pf multicolored    1.05   .90
9N490 A146 60pf multicolored    1.30 1.15
9N491 A146 80pf multicolored    1.75 1.60
    Nos. 9N488-9N491 (4)    4.90 4.30

Electricity Centenary — A147

Design: Allegorical figure holding light bulb (symbol of electric power).

**1984, May 8**      **Litho.**     **Perf. 14**
9N492 A147 50pf black & org    .80   .65

Conference Emblem — A148

**1984, May 8**
9N493 A148 60pf multicolored    1.00   .65
European Ministers of Culture, 4th Conf.

Erich Klausener (1885-1934), Chairman of Catholic Action — A149

**1984, May 8**    **Engr.**    **Perf. 14x13½**
9N494 A149 80pf green    .95   .65

Alfred Brehm (1829-1884), Zoologist A150

**Lithographed and Engraved**
**1984, Apr. 18**      **Perf. 14**
9N495 A150 80pf Brehm, white    stork    1.45 1.10

Ernst Ludwig Heim (1747-1834), Botanist — A151

**1984, Aug. 21**      **Engr.**     **Perf. 14**
9N496 A151 50pf lake & blk    .95   .65

Sunflowers, by Karl Schmidt-Rottluff (1884-1976) — A152

**1984, Nov. 8**      **Litho.**     **Perf. 14**
9N497 A152 60pf multi    .95   .65

Bettina von Arnim (1785-1859), Writer — A153

**1985, Feb. 21**      **Litho. & Engr.**
9N498 A153 50pf multicolored    .80   .70

Wilhelm von Humboldt (1767-1835), Statesman — A154

**1985, Feb. 21**      **Engr.**
9N499 A154 80pf blue, blk & red    1.50 1.25

1985 Berlin Horticultural Show — A155

**1985, Apr. 16**      **Litho.**     **Perf. 14**
9N500 A155 80pf Symbolic flower 1.15   .90

Berlin Bourse, 300th Anniv. — A156

**1985, May 7**      **Litho. & Engr.**
9N501 A156 50pf multicolored    .95   .70

Otto Klemperer (1885-1973), Conductor A157

**1985, May 7**      **Engr.**
9N502 A157 60pf dp blue violet    1.15   .90

Telefunken Camera, 1936 — A158

**1985, July 16**      **Litho.**     **Perf. 14**
9N503 A158 80pf multicolored    1.60 1.25
German Television, 50th anniv., Intl. Telecommunications Exhibition, Berlin.

9th World Gynecological Congress — A159

Design: Emblem of the Intl. Federation for Gynecology and birth aid.

**1985, July 16**   **Photo.**   **Perf. 13½x14**
9N504 A159 60pf pale yel, ap grn    & dp grn    .95   .70

Edict of Potsdam, 300th Anniv. — A160

**Lithographed and Engraved**
**1985, Oct. 15**      **Perf. 14**
9N505 A160 50pf dk bluish lilac    .80   .60

Kurt Tucholsky (1890-1935), Novelist, Journalist — A161

**1985, Nov. 12    Litho.    Perf. 14**
9N506 A161 80pf multi         1.30  .90

Wilhelm Furtwangler (1886-1954), Composer A162

Score from Sonata in D Sharp.

**Lithographed and Engraved**
**1986, Jan. 16                    Perf. 14**
9N507 A162 80pf multi         1.60 1.40

Ludwig Mies van der Rohe (1886-1969), Architect A163

**1986, Feb. 13**
9N508 A163 50pf multi          .95  .95

New Natl. Gallery, Berlin.

16th European Communities Day — A164

**1986, Apr. 10    Litho.    Perf. 14**
9N509 A164 60pf Flags         .80  .85

Leopold von Ranke (1795-1886), Historian A165

Gottfried Benn (1886-1956), Writer and Physician A166

**1986, May 5                    Litho.**
9N510 A165 80pf brn blk & tan  1.30 1.10
**Engr.**
9N511 A166 80pf brt blue       1.30 1.10

Portals and Gateways — A167

50pf, Charlotteburg Gate. 60pf, Gryphon Gate, Glienicke Castle. 80pf, Elephant Gate, Berlin Zoo.

**1986, June 20          Litho. & Engr.**
9N512 A167 50pf multicolored   1.20 1.15
9N513 A167 60pf multicolored   1.20 1.15
9N514 A167 80pf multicolored   1.30 1.25
      *Nos. 9N512-9N514 (3)*    3.70 3.55

King Frederick the Great — A168

Painting: The Flute Concert (detail), by Adolph von Menzel.

**1986, Aug. 14    Litho.    Perf. 14**
9N515 A168 80pf multicolored   1.30 1.10

Famous Women — A168a

Designs: 5pf, Emma Ihrer (1857-1911), politician, labor leader. 10pf, Paula Modersohn-Becker (1876-1907), painter. 20pf, Cilly Aussem (1909-63), tennis champion. 40pf, Maria Sibylla Merian. 50pf, Christine Teusch. 60pf, Dorothea Erxleben (1715-62), physician. 80pf, Clara Schumann. 100pf, Therese Giehse (1898-1975), actress. 130pf, Lise Meitner (1878-1968), physicist. 140pf, Cecile Vogt (1875-1962), neurologist. 170pf, Hannah Arendt (1906-75), American political scientist. 180pf, Lotte Lehmann (1888-1976), soprano. 240pf, Mathilde Franziska Anneke, (1817-84), American author. 250pf, Queen Louise of Prussia (1776-1810). 300pf, Fanny Hensel (1805-1847), composer-conductor. 350pf, Hedwig Dransfeld (1871-1925), women's rights activist. 500pf, Alice Salomon (1872-1948), feminist and social activist.

**Type A168a**

**1986-89          Engr.          Perf. 14**
9N516    5pf bluish gray &
             org brn              .35  1.75
9N517   10pf vio & yel brn       .35  1.25
9N518   20pf lake & Prus bl     1.30  3.25
9N519   40pf dp bl & dk lil
             rose               1.05  3.25
9N520   50pf gray ol & Prus
             bl                 1.60  2.25
9N521   60pf dp vio & grnsh
             blk                1.00  3.25
9N522   80pf dk grn & lt red
             brn                1.00  2.25
9N523  100pf dk red & grnsh
             blk                1.60  1.25
9N524  130pf Prus bl & dk
             vio                3.00  9.50
9N525  140pf vio & org brn     4.00  9.50
9N526  170pf gray grn & dk
             brn                2.00  7.50
9N527  180pf bl & brn vio      3.00 11.00
9N528  240pf Prus bl & yel
             brn                2.60 11.00
9N529  250pf dp lil rose & dp
             bl                 6.25 17.50
9N530  300pf dk vio & sage
             grn                6.50 16.00
9N531  350pf gray grn & lake   4.75 12.50
9N532  500pf slate grn & brt
             ver                7.25 28.00
      *Nos. 9N516-9N532 (17)* 47.60 141.00

Issued: 50pf, 80pf, 11/1/86; 40pf, 9/17/87; 10pf, 4/4/88; 20pf, 130pf, 5/5/88; 60pf, 100pf, 170pf, 240pf, 350pf, 11/10/88; 500pf, 1/12/89; 5pf, 2/9/89; 180pf, 250pf, 7/13/89; 140pf, 300pf, 8/10/89.

Berlin 750th Anniv. — A168b

Designs: a, Berlin, 1650, engraving by Caspar Merian. b, Charlottenburg Castle, c. 1830. c, AEG Company turbine construction building, by architect Walter Behrens, 1909. d, Philharmonic Concert Hall and Chamber Music Rooms on the Kemperplatz, 1987.

**1987, Jan. 15    Litho.    Perf. 14**
9N536 A168b 80pf like #1496    1.60 1.25
**Souvenir Sheet**
**Perf. 14x14½**
9N537             Sheet of 4   4.00 3.75
   a.    A168b 40pf multicolored  .80  .65
   b.    A168b 50pf multicolored  .80  .65
   c.    A168b 60pf multicolored  .80  .75
   d.    A168b 80pf multicolored  .95 1.00

No. 9N537 contains four 43x25mm stamps.

Louise Schroeder (1887-1957), Politican — A169

**1987, Feb. 12    Engr.    Perf. 14**
9N538 A169 50pf sep & red      .95  .90

Settlement of Bohemians at Rixdorf, 250th Anniv. — A170

Bohemian refugees, bas-relief detail from monument to King Friedrich Wilhelm I of Prussia, 1912.

**1987, May 5          Litho. & Engr.**
9N539 A170 50pf sep & pale
             gray grn          .65  .75

1987 Intl. Architecture Exhibition A171

**1987, May 5    Litho.    Perf. 14x14½**
9N540 A171 80pf lt ultra, sil & blk  1.15  .95

14th Int'l. Botanical Congress — A172

**1987, July 16    Litho.    Perf. 14**
9N541 A172 60pf multicolored   .80  .85

Int'l. Radio Exhibition A173

80pf, Gramophone, compact disc.

**1987, Aug. 20**
9N542 A173 80pf multi         1.05  .95

Historic Sites and Objects — A174

Designs: 5pf, Brunswick Lion. 10pf, Frankfurt Airport. 20pf, No. 9N550, Queen Nefertiti, bust, Egyptian Museum, Berlin. 30pf, Corner tower, Celle Castle, 14th cent. 40pf, Chile House, Hamburg. 50pf, Filigree tracery on spires, Freiburg Cathedral. 60pf, Bavaria Munich, bronze statue above the Theresienwiese, Hall of Fame. No. 9N551, Heligoland. 80pf, Entrance to Zollern II, coal mine, Dortmund. 100pf, Altotting Chapel, Bavaria. 120pf, Schleswig Cathedral. 140pf, Bronze flagon from Reinheim. 300pf, Hambach Castle. 350pf, Externsteine Bridge near Horn-Bad Meinberg.

**Type A174**

**1987-90          Typo.          Perf. 14**
9N543    5pf Prus bl & gray    .30  .40
9N544   10pf lt chalky bl &
             slate bl          .35  .35
9N545   20pf dull blue & tan   .35  .65
9N546   30pf aqua & org brn    .85  .85
9N547   40pf ultra, dk red
             brn & org red    1.60 1.75
9N548   50pf ultra & yel brn  1.30  .95
9N549   60pf cob & pale gray  1.30  .95
9N550   70pf dull bl & fawn   1.30 2.25
9N551   70pf vio bl & henna
             brn              1.75 3.75
9N552   80pf cob & pale gray  1.30  .95
   a.   Bkt. pane of 8 (4 10pf, 2
             50pf, 2 80pf) ('89)  18.50 45.00
9N553  100pf brt bluish grn &
             olive bis        1.00 1.25
   a.   Bkt. pane of 8 (2 each 10pf,
             60pf, 80pf, 100pf)  40.00 75.00
9N554  120pf brn org & lt
             grnsh bl         2.00 3.00
9N555  140pf bis & yellow     2.00 3.50
9N556  300pf dk red brn &
             tan              4.00 3.75
9N557  350pf brt ultra & ol
             bis              3.75 6.25
      *Nos. 9N543-9N557 (15)* 23.15 30.60

Issued: 30pf, 50pf, 60pf, 80pf, 11/6/87; 10pf, 300pf, 1/14/88; No. 9N550, 120pf, 7/14/88; 20pf, 140pf, 1/12/89; 100pf, 350pf, 2/9/89; 5pf, 2/15/90; No. 9N551, 6/21/90.

European Culture — A175

**1988, Jan. 14    Litho.    Perf. 14**
9N568 A175 80pf Berlin Bear   1.60 1.60

Urania Science Museum, Cent. — A176

**1988, Feb. 18**
9N569 A176 50pf multicolored  1.20 1.10

A177

Design: Thoroughbred Foal, bronze sculpture by Renee Sintenis (1888-1965).

**1988, Feb. 18**
9N570 A177 60pf multicolored   .80  .75

A178

Design: The Great Elector with Family in Berlin Castle Gardens.

**1988, May 5          Litho. & Engr.**
9N571 A178 50pf multicolored   .95  .90

The Great Elector of Brandenburg (d. 1688).

Intl. Monetary Fund and World Bank Congress, Berlin — A179

**1988, Aug. 11                    Litho.**
9N572 A179 70pf multicolored  1.00  .85

Berlin-Potsdam Railway, 150th Anniv. — A180

**1988, Oct. 13                    Litho.**
9N573 A180 10pf multicolored   .55  .40

The Collector, 1913, by Ernst Barlach (1870-1938) — A181

**1988, Oct. 13**
9N574 A181 40pf multicolored   .60  .45

Berlin Airlift, 40th Anniv. — A182

**1989, May 5    Photo.    Perf. 14**
9N575 A182 60pf multicolored   .95 1.00

**1989, May 5**      **Litho.**
9N576 A183 80pf multicolored    1.45 1.25
13th Intl. Congress of the Supreme Audit Office, Berlin.

Ernst Reuter (1889-1953), Mayor of Berlin — A184

**Litho. & Engr.**
**1989, July 13**      **Perf. 14x14½**
9N577 A184 100pf multicolored    1.60 1.40

Intl. Radio Exhibition, Berlin — A185

**1989, July 13**      **Litho.**
9N578 A185 100pf multicolored    1.30 1.25

Plans of the Zoological Gardens, Berlin, and Designer Peter Joseph Lenne (1789-1866) A186

**Litho. & Engr.**
**1989, Aug. 10**      **Perf. 14**
9N579 A186 60pf multicolored    1.25 1.10

Carl von Ossietzky (1889-1938), Awarded Nobel Peace Prize of 1935 — A187

**1989, Aug. 10**      **Photo.**
9N580 A187 100pf multicolored    1.45 1.40

450th Anniv. of the Reformation — A188

Design: Nikolai Church, Spandau District.

**1989, Oct. 12**      **Litho.**
9N581 A188 60pf multicolored    1.00 .70

French Gymnasium, 300th Anniv. — A189

School from 1701 to 1873 and frontispiece of *Leges Gymnasie Gallici*, published in 1689.

**1989, Oct. 12**      **Litho. & Engr.**
9N582 A189 40pf multicolored    .80 .70

*Journalists*, 1925, by Hannah Hoch (1889-1978) — A190

**1989, Oct. 12**      **Litho.**    **Perf. 13½**
9N583 A190 100pf multicolored    1.60 1.25

European Postal Service 500th Anniv. — A190a

**Litho. & Engr.**
**1990, Jan. 12**      **Perf. 14**
9N584 A190a 100pf gray brn,
     blksh pur,
     beige    2.00 1.75

See Austria No. 1486, Belgium No. 1332, Germany No. 1592, and DDR No. 2791.

Public Transportation, 250th Anniv. — A191

**1990, Jan. 12**      **Litho.**
9N585 A191 60pf multicolored    1.60 1.25

Ernst Rudorff (1840-1916), Conservationist A192

**1990, Jan. 12**
9N586 A192 60pf multicolored    1.60 1.25

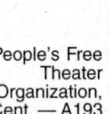

People's Free Theater Organization, Cent. — A193

**1990, Feb. 15**      **Perf. 13½**
9N587 A193 100pf multicolored    1.60 1.60

Parliament House, 40th Anniv. — A194

**1990, Feb. 15**      **Perf. 14x14½**
9N588 A194 100pf multicolored    2.25 1.60

Bicent. of the Invention of the Barrel Organ — A195

**1990, May 3**      **Litho.**    **Perf. 14**
9N589 A195 100pf multicolored    1.60 1.50

90th German Catholics Day — A196

**1990, May 3**
9N590 A196 60pf multicolored    1.45 1.40

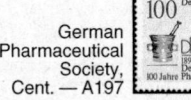

German Pharmaceutical Society, Cent. — A197

**1990, Aug. 9**      **Litho.**    **Perf. 14**
9N591 A197 100pf multicolored    3.25 2.50

Adolph Diesterweg (1790-1866), Educator — A198

**1990, Sept. 27**
9N592 A198 60pf multicolored    2.25 2.40

Stamps for Berlin were discontinued Oct. 3, 1990, when Germany and the German Democratic Republic merged. The stamps remained valid until Dec. 31, 1991.

---

## OCCUPATION SEMI-POSTAL STAMPS

Offering Plate and Berlin Bear — SP1

**Wmk. 284**
**1949, Dec. 1**      **Litho.**    **Perf. 14**
9NB1 SP1 10 + 5pf grn    26.00 120.00
9NB2 SP1 20 + 5pf car    29.00 120.00
9NB3 SP1 30 + 5pf blue    29.00 145.00
   a.   Souv. sheet of 3, #9NB1-
      9NB3    325.00   1,400.
      Never hinged    975.00
   Nos. 9NB1-9NB3 (3)    84.00 385.00
   Set, never hinged    230.00

The surtax was for Berlin victims of currency devaluation.

Harp and Laurel Branch SP2      "Singing Angels" SP3

**1950, Oct. 29**      **Engr.**    **Wmk. 116**
9NB4 SP2 10 + 5pf grn    13.00 25.00
9NB5 SP3 30 + 5pf dk sl bl    20.00 57.50
   Set, never hinged    92.50

The surtax was to aid in reestablishing the Berlin Philharmonic Orchestra.

Young Stamp Collectors — SP4

**1951, Oct. 7**      **Perf. 14**
9NB6 SP4 10 + 3pf grn    7.25 19.00
9NB7 SP4 20 + 2pf red    8.00 25.00
   Set, never hinged    35.00

Stamp Day, Berlin, Oct. 7, 1951.

Kaiser Wilhelm Memorial Church — SP5

Design: 20pf+10pf, 30pf+15pf, Ruins of Kaiser Wilhelm Memorial Church.

**1953, Aug. 9**      **Wmk. 284**
9NB8 SP5 4 + 1pf dk brn    .25 12.50
9NB9 SP5 10 + 5pf green    .50 34.00
9NB10 SP5 20 + 10pf car    .90 34.00
9NB11 SP5 30 + 15pf dp bl    5.75 62.50
   Nos. 9NB8-9NB11 (4)    7.40 143.00
   Set, never hinged    16.50

The surtax was to aid in reconstructing the church.

> **Catalogue values for unused stamps in this section, from this point to the end of the section, are for Never Hinged items.**

Prussian Postilion — SP6

**1954, Aug. 4**      **Litho.**    **Wmk. 284**
9NB12 SP6 20 + 10pf multi    12.00 24.00

National Stamp Exhibition, Berlin, Aug. 4-8.

Prussian Field Postilion — SP7

**Perf. 13½x14**
**1955, Oct. 27**      **Wmk. 304**
9NB13 SP7 25 + 10pf multi    5.00 11.50

The surtax was for the benefit of philately.

St. Otto, Bishop of Bamberg — SP8

Statues: 10pf+5pf, St. Hedwig, Duchess of Silesia. 20pf+10pf, St. Peter.

**1955, Nov. 26**      **Engr.**    **Perf. 14**
9NB14 SP8 7 + 3pf brown    .65 1.90
9NB15 SP8 10 + 5pf gray grn    1.00 2.25
9NB16 SP8 20 + 10pf rose lil    1.40 2.50
   Nos. 9NB14-9NB16 (3)    3.05 6.65

25th anniv. of the Bishopric of Berlin. The surtax was for the reconstruction of destroyed churches throughout the bishopric.

Bell Type of 1951 Surcharged

**Perf. 13½x14**
**1956, Aug. 9**      **Wmk. 284**
9NB17 OS8 20pf + 10pf citron    3.25 3.50

The surtax was for help for flood victims.

Postrider of Brandenburg, 1700 — SP9

**Wmk. 304**
**1956, Oct. 26**      **Litho.**    **Perf. 14**
9NB18 SP9 25pf + 10pf multi    2.60 3.00

The surtax was for the benefit of philately.

Ludwig Heck — SP10

**1957, Sept. 7    Engr.    Perf. 13½x14**
9NB19   SP10   20pf + 10pf red &
                dk brn      .65   .75

Dr. Ludwig Heck, zoologist and long-time director of the Berlin Zoo. The surtax was for the Zoo.

Elly Heuss-Knapp and Relaxing Mothers — SP11

**1957, Nov. 30        Perf. 14**
9NB20   SP11   20pf + 10pf dk red   1.30   2.10

The surtax was for welfare work among mothers.

Boy at Window — SP12

Designs: 10pf+5pf, Girl going to school. 20pf+10pf, Girl with flower and mountains. 40pf+20pf, Boy at seashore.

**1960, Sept. 15    Litho.    Wmk. 304**
9NB21   SP12   7pf + 3pf dk brn &
                brn        .25   .25
9NB22   SP12   10pf + 5pf ol grn &
                slate grn    .25   .25
9NB23   SP12   20pf + 10pf dk car
                & brn blk    .50   .45
9NB24   SP12   40pf + 20pf bl & ind   1.15   3.00
     Nos. 9NB21-9NB24 (4)     2.15   3.95

The surtax was for vacations for the children of Berlin.

**Fluorescent Paper was introduced for semipostal stamps, starting with Nos. 9NB25-9NB28.**

Sleeping Beauty — SP13

Various Scenes from Sleeping Beauty: No. 9NB25, The Curse Scene. No. 9NB26, Rose Pricks Her Finger. No. 9NB27, Prince Phillip standing above Sleeping Beauty. No. 9NB28, Cook, kid and black cat.

**1964, Oct. 6    Unwmk.    Perf. 14**
9NB25   SP13   10pf + 5pf multi    .25   .25
9NB26   SP13   15pf + 5pf multi    .25   .25
9NB27   SP13   20pf + 10pf multi   .35   .25
9NB28   SP13   40pf + 20pf multi   .50   .75
     Nos. 9NB25-9NB28 (4)     1.35   1.50

The surtax was for independent welfare organizations.

Beginning with 9NB25-9NB28 semipostals are types of Germany inscribed "Berlin" except Nos. 9NB129-9NB131.

Woodcock — SP14

Birds: 15pf+5pf, Ring-necked pheasant. 20pf+10pf, Black grouse. 40pf+20pf, Capercaillie.

---

**1965, Apr. 1    Litho.    Perf. 14**
9NB29   SP14   10pf + 5pf multi    .25   .25
9NB30   SP14   15pf + 5pf multi    .25   .25
9NB31   SP14   20pf + 10pf multi   .25   .25
9NB32   SP14   40pf + 20pf multi   .30   .65
     Nos. 9NB29-9NB32 (4)     1.05   1.40

Issued for the benefit of young people.

Cinderella — SP15

Various Scenes from Cinderella: No. 9NB33, Cinderella feeding birds. No. 9NB34, Two birds holding yellow dress while flying and Cinderella. No. 9NB35, Cinderella without slipper, Prince holding slipper. No. 9NB36, Cinderella and Prince on horse.

**1965, Oct. 6    Litho.    Perf. 14**
9NB33   SP15   10pf + 5pf multi    .25   .25
9NB34   SP15   15pf + 5pf multi    .25   .25
9NB35   SP15   20pf + 10pf multi   .30   .25
9NB36   SP15   40pf + 20pf multi   .30   .65
     Nos. 9NB33-9NB36 (4)     1.10   1.40

The surtax was for independent welfare organizations.

Roe Deer — SP16

20pf+10pf, Chamois. 30pf+15pf, Fallow deer. 50pf+25pf, Red deer.

**1966, Apr. 22    Litho.    Perf. 14**
9NB37   SP16   10pf + 5pf multi    .25   .25
9NB38   SP16   20pf + 10pf multi   .25   .25
9NB39   SP16   30pf + 15pf multi   .30   .25
9NB40   SP16   50pf + 25pf multi   .45   .65
     Nos. 9NB37-9NB40 (4)     1.25   1.40

Issued for the benefit of young people.

The Princess and the Frog — SP17

Various Scenes from The Princess and the Frog: No. 9NB41, The Princess and The Frog on edge of well. No. 9NB42, The Princess and The Frog at dining table. No. 9NB43, The Princess and The Prince. No. 9NB44, Princess and Prince in carriage.

**1966, Oct. 5    Litho.    Perf. 14**
9NB41   SP17   10pf + 5pf multi    .25   .25
9NB42   SP17   20pf + 10pf multi   .25   .25
9NB43   SP17   30pf + 15pf multi   .35   .25
9NB44   SP17   50pf + 25pf multi   .40   .65
     Nos. 9NB41-9NB44 (4)     1.25   1.40

Surtax for independent welfare organizations.

Rabbit — SP18

20pf+10pf, Ermine. 30pf+15pf, Hamster. 50pf+25pf, Red fox.

**1967, Apr. 4                Unwmk.**
9NB45   SP18   10pf + 5pf multi    .25   .25
9NB46   SP18   20pf + 10pf multi   .25   .25
9NB47   SP18   30pf + 15pf multi   .35   .25
9NB48   SP18   50pf + 25pf multi   .80   1.15
     Nos. 9NB45-9NB48 (4)     1.65   1.90

Issued for the benefit of young people.

Frau Holle — SP19

Various Scenes from Frau Holle: No. 9NB49, Frau Holle at spinning wheel. No. 9NB50, Frau Holle making it snow by shaking her pillow. No. 9NB51, Girl under gold rain. No. 9NB52, Girl is showered in tar.

---

**1967, Oct. 3    Litho.    Perf. 14**
9NB49   SP19   10pf + 5pf multi    .25   .25
9NB50   SP19   20pf + 10pf multi   .25   .25
9NB51   SP19   30pf + 15pf multi   .25   .35
9NB52   SP19   50pf + 25pf multi   .50   .65
     Nos. 9NB49-9NB52 (4)     1.25   1.50

The surtax was for independent welfare organizations.

Wildcat — SP20

Animals: 20pf+10pf, Otter. 30pf+15pf, Badger. 50pf+25pf, Beaver.

**1968, Feb. 2    Photo.    Perf. 14**
9NB53   SP20   10pf + 5pf multi    .25   .40
9NB54   SP20   20pf + 10pf multi   .30   .40
9NB55   SP20   30pf + 15pf multi   .50   .75
9NB56   SP20   50pf + 25pf multi   1.45   1.75
     Nos. 9NB53-9NB56 (4)     2.50   3.30

Surtax for benefit of young people.

Dolls — SP21

Various 19th century dolls in sitting position: No. 9NB57, Doll wearing maroon dress. No. 9NB58, Doll wearing olive green dress. No. 9NB59, Doll wearing bright carmine dress. No. 9NB60, Doll wearing blue dress and yellow hat.

**1968, Oct. 3    Litho.    Perf. 14**
9NB57   SP21   10pf + 5pf multi    .25   .25
9NB58   SP21   20pf + 10pf multi   .25   .25
9NB59   SP21   30pf + 15pf multi   .25   .30
9NB60   SP21   50pf + 25pf multi   .35   .65
     Nos. 9NB57-9NB60 (4)     1.10   1.45

The surtax was for independent welfare organizations.

Horses — SP22

10pf+5pf, Brown and white pony. 20pf+10pf, Brown work horse. 30pf+15pf, Black hotblood. 50pf+25pf, White thoroughbred.

**1969, Feb. 6    Litho.    Perf. 14**
9NB61   SP22   10pf + 5pf multi    .25   .25
9NB62   SP22   20pf + 10pf multi   .30   .45
9NB63   SP22   30pf + 15pf multi   .40   .65
9NB64   SP22   50pf + 25pf multi   1.05   1.25
     Nos. 9NB61-9NB64 (4)     2.00   2.60

Surtax for benefit of young people.

Tin Toys — SP23

10pf+5pf, Coach. 20pf+10pf, Woman feeding chickens. 30pf+15pf, Woman grocer. 50pf+25pf, Postilion on horseback.

**1969, Oct. 2    Litho.    Perf. 13½x14**
9NB65   SP23   10pf + 5pf multi    .25   .25
9NB66   SP23   20pf + 10pf multi   .25   .25
9NB67   SP23   30pf + 15pf multi   .35   .35
9NB68   SP23   50pf + 25pf multi   .85   .85
     Nos. 9NB65-9NB68 (4)     1.70   1.70

The surtax was for independent welfare organizations.

---

The Three Kings — SP24

**1969, Nov. 13    Litho.    Perf. 13½x14**
9NB69   SP24   10pf + 5pf multi    .35   .25

Christmas.

Heinrich von Stretlingen — SP25

Minnesingers (and their Ladies): 20pf+10pf, Meinloh von Sevelingen. 30pf+15pf, Burkhart von Hohenfels. 50pf+25pf, Albrecht von Johansdorf.

**1970, Feb. 5    Photo.    Perf. 13½x14**
9NB70   SP25   10pf + 5pf multi    .25   .25
9NB71   SP25   20pf + 10pf multi   .35   .40
9NB72   SP25   30pf + 15pf multi   .50   .50
9NB73   SP25   50pf + 25pf multi   1.05   1.20
     Nos. 9NB70-9NB73 (4)     2.15   2.35

Surtax for benefit of young people.

Puppets — SP26

10pf+5pf, "Kasperl." 20pf+10pf, Polichinelle. 30pf+5pf, Punch. 50pf+25pf, Pulcinella.

**1970, Oct. 6    Litho.    Perf. 13½x14**
9NB74   SP26   10pf + 5pf multi    .25   .25
9NB75   SP26   20pf + 10pf multi   .25   .25
9NB76   SP26   30pf + 15pf multi   .50   .40
9NB77   SP26   50pf + 25pf multi   .80   .90
     Nos. 9NB74-9NB77 (4)     1.80   1.80

Surtax for independent welfare organizations.

Christmas — SP27

10pf+5pf, Rococo angel, from Ursuline Sisters' Convent, Innsbruck.

**1970, Nov. 12**
9NB78   SP27   10pf + 5pf multi      .30   .25

Children's Drawings — SP28

10pf+5pf, Fly. 20pf+10pf, Fish. 30pf+15pf, Porcupine. 50pf+25pf, Cock. All stamps horizontal.

**1971, Feb. 5    Litho.    Perf. 14**
9NB79   SP28   10pf + 5pf multi    .30   .25
9NB80   SP28   20pf + 10pf multi   .30   .25
9NB81   SP28   30pf + 15pf multi   .40   .45
9NB82   SP28   50pf + 25pf multi   1.05   1.10
     Nos. 9NB79-9NB82 (4)     2.05   2.05

Surtax for the benefit of young people.

Wooden Toys — SP29

10pf+5pf, Movable dolls in box. 25pf+10pf, Knight on horseback. 30pf+15pf, Jumping jack. 60pf+30pf, Nurse rocking babies.

## 1971, Oct. 5
| | | | | |
|---|---|---|---|---|
| 9NB83 | SP29 | 10pf + 5pf multi | .25 | .25 |
| 9NB84 | SP29 | 25pf + 10pf multi | .25 | .35 |
| 9NB85 | SP29 | 30pf + 15pf multi | .50 | .45 |
| 9NB86 | SP29 | 60pf + 30pf multi | .85 | .95 |
| | *Nos. 9NB83-9NB86 (4)* | | 1.85 | 2.00 |

Christmas — SP30

10pf+5pf, Christmas angel with candles.

## 1971, Nov. 11
| | | | | |
|---|---|---|---|---|
| 9NB87 | SP30 | 10pf + 5pf multi | .35 | .30 |

Animal Protection — SP31

10pf+5pf, Boy trying to rob bird's nest. 25pf+10pf, Girl with kittens to be drowned. 30pf+15pf, Watch dog & man with whip. 60pf+30pf, Hedgehog & deer passing before car at night.

## 1972, Feb. 4
| | | | | |
|---|---|---|---|---|
| 9NB88 | SP31 | 10pf + 5pf multi | .25 | .25 |
| 9NB89 | SP31 | 25pf + 10pf multi | .30 | .25 |
| 9NB90 | SP31 | 30pf + 15pf multi | .50 | .45 |
| 9NB91 | SP31 | 60pf + 30pf multi | 1.00 | 1.10 |
| | *Nos. 9NB88-9NB91 (4)* | | 2.05 | 2.05 |

Surtax for the benefit of young people.

Chess — SP32

No. 9NB92, Knight. No. 9NB93, Rook. No. 9NB94, Queen. No. 9NB95, King.

## 1972, Oct. 5   Litho.   Perf. 14
| | | | | |
|---|---|---|---|---|
| 9NB92 | SP32 | 20pf + 10pf | .35 | .35 |
| 9NB93 | SP32 | 30pf + 15pf | .55 | .50 |
| 9NB94 | SP32 | 40pf + 20pf | 1.60 | 1.60 |
| 9NB95 | SP32 | 70pf + 35pf | 2.00 | 1.90 |
| | *Nos. 9NB92-9NB95 (4)* | | 4.50 | 4.35 |

Surtax for independent welfare organizations.

Holy Family — SP33

## 1972, Nov. 10   Litho.   Perf. 14
| | | | | |
|---|---|---|---|---|
| 9NB96 | SP33 | 20pf + 10pf multi | .50 | .40 |

Christmas.

Birds of Prey — SP34

20pf+10pf, Goshawk. 30pf+15pf, Peregrine falcon. 40pf+20pf, Sparrow hawk. 70pf+35pf, Golden eagle.

## 1973, Feb. 6   Photo.   Perf. 14
| | | | | |
|---|---|---|---|---|
| 9NB97 | SP34 | 20pf + 10pf multi | .40 | .40 |
| 9NB98 | SP34 | 30pf + 15pf multi | .55 | .60 |
| 9NB99 | SP34 | 40pf + 20pf multi | .80 | .85 |
| 9NB100 | SP34 | 70pf + 35pf multi | 1.30 | 1.40 |
| | *Nos. 9NB97-9NB100 (4)* | | 3.05 | 3.25 |

Surtax was for benefit of young people.

Musical Instruments — SP35

20+10pf, Hurdygurdy, 17th cent. 30+15pf, Drum, 16th cent. 40+20pf, Archlute, 18th cent. 70+35pf, Organ, 16th cent.

## 1973, Oct. 5   Litho.   Perf. 14
| | | | | |
|---|---|---|---|---|
| 9NB101 | SP35 | 20pf + 10pf multi | .35 | .35 |
| 9NB102 | SP35 | 30pf + 15pf multi | .65 | .65 |
| 9NB103 | SP35 | 40pf + 20pf multi | .65 | .75 |
| 9NB104 | SP35 | 70pf + 35pf multi | 1.05 | 1.15 |
| | *Nos. 9NB101-9NB104 (4)* | | 2.70 | 2.90 |

Surtax was for independent welfare organizations.

Christmas Star — SP36

## 1973, Nov. 9   Litho. & Engr.
| | | | | |
|---|---|---|---|---|
| 9NB105 | SP36 | 20pf + 10pf multi | .50 | .45 |

International Youth Work — SP37

Designs: 20pf+10pf, Boy photographing. 30pf+15pf, Boy athlete. 40pf+20pf, Girl violinist. 70pf+35pf, Nurse's aid.

## 1974, Apr. 17   Photo.   Perf. 14
| | | | | |
|---|---|---|---|---|
| 9NB106 | SP37 | 20pf + 10pf multi | .35 | .40 |
| 9NB107 | SP37 | 30pf + 15pf multi | .35 | .40 |
| 9NB108 | SP37 | 40pf + 20pf multi | .65 | .85 |
| 9NB109 | SP37 | 70pf + 35pf multi | 1.05 | 1.15 |
| | *Nos. 9NB106-9NB109 (4)* | | 2.40 | 2.80 |

Surtax was for benefit of young people.

Flowers — SP38

Designs: 30pf+15pf, Spring bouquet. 40pf+20pf, Autumn bouquet. 50pf+25pf, Roses. 70pf+35pf, Winter flowers. All horiz.

## 1974, Oct. 15   Litho.   Perf. 14
| | | | | |
|---|---|---|---|---|
| 9NB110 | SP38 | 30pf + 15pf multi | .35 | .35 |
| 9NB111 | SP38 | 40pf + 20pf multi | .65 | .65 |
| 9NB112 | SP38 | 50pf + 25pf multi | .65 | .65 |
| 9NB113 | SP38 | 70pf + 35pf multi | 1.60 | 1.60 |
| | *Nos. 9NB110-9NB113 (4)* | | 3.25 | 3.25 |

Surtax was for independent welfare organizations.

Christmas Bouquet — SP39

## 1974, Oct. 29
| | | | | |
|---|---|---|---|---|
| 9NB114 | SP39 | 30pf + 15pf multi | .65 | .75 |

Steam Locomotives SP40

30pf+15pf, Dragon. 40pf+20pf, Class 89 (70-75). 50pf+25pf, Class O50. 70pf+35pf, Class O10.

## 1975, Apr. 15   Litho.   Perf. 14
| | | | | |
|---|---|---|---|---|
| 9NB115 | SP40 | 30pf + 15pf multi | .65 | .50 |
| 9NB116 | SP40 | 40pf + 20pf multi | .65 | .65 |
| 9NB117 | SP40 | 50pf + 25pf multi | 1.30 | 1.10 |
| 9NB118 | SP40 | 70pf + 35pf multi | 1.60 | 1.90 |
| | *Nos. 9NB115-9NB118 (4)* | | 4.20 | 4.15 |

Surtax was for benefit of young people.

Alpine Flowers — SP41

30pf+15pf, Yellow gentian. 40pf+20pf, Arnica. 50pf+25pf, Cyclamen. 70pf+35pf, Blue gentian.

## 1975, Oct. 15   Litho.   Perf. 14
| | | | | |
|---|---|---|---|---|
| 9NB119 | SP41 | 30pf + 15pf multi | .50 | .45 |
| 9NB120 | SP41 | 40pf + 20pf multi | .40 | .40 |
| 9NB121 | SP41 | 50pf + 25pf multi | .55 | .50 |
| 9NB122 | SP41 | 70pf + 35pf multi | .95 | .90 |
| | *Nos. 9NB119-9NB122 (4)* | | 2.40 | 2.25 |

Surtax was for independent welfare organizations.

Snow Heather — SP42

## 1975, Nov. 14
| | | | | |
|---|---|---|---|---|
| 9NB123 | SP42 | 30pf + 15pf multi | .65 | .65 |

Christmas.

Sports — SP43

30+15pf, Shot put, women's. 40+20pf, Hockey. 50+25pf, Handball. 70+35pf, Swimming.

## 1976, Apr. 6   Litho.   Perf. 14
| | | | | |
|---|---|---|---|---|
| 9NB124 | SP43 | 30pf + 15pf multi | .55 | .60 |
| 9NB125 | SP43 | 40pf + 20pf multi | .55 | .60 |
| 9NB126 | SP43 | 50pf + 25pf multi | .55 | .65 |
| 9NB127 | SP43 | 70pf + 35pf multi | 1.20 | 1.25 |
| | *Nos. 9NB124-9NB127 (4)* | | 2.85 | 3.10 |

Youth training for Olympic Games. The surtax was for the benefit of young people.

Iris — SP44

Flowers: 40pf+20pf, Wallflower. 50pf+25pf, Dahlia. 70pf+35pf, Larkspur.

## 1976, Oct. 14   Litho.   Perf. 14
| | | | | |
|---|---|---|---|---|
| 9NB128 | SP44 | 30pf + 15pf | .35 | .35 |
| 9NB129 | SP44 | 40pf + 20pf | .35 | .35 |
| 9NB130 | SP44 | 50pf + 25pf | .55 | .65 |
| 9NB131 | SP44 | 70pf + 35pf | .80 | .90 |
| | *Nos. 9NB128-9NB131 (4)* | | 2.05 | 2.25 |

Surtax was for independent welfare organizations.

### Souvenir Sheet

Christmas — SP45

30pf+15pf, Annunciation to the Shepherds, stained-glass window, Frauenkirche, Esslingen.

## 1976, Nov. 16   Litho. & Engr.
| | | | | |
|---|---|---|---|---|
| 9NB132 | SP45 | 30pf + 15pf multi | .65 | .60 |

Historic Ships — SP46

30pf+15pf, Bremer Kogge, c. 1380. 40pf+20pf, Helena Sloman, 1850. 50pf+25pf, Passenger ship, Cap Polonio, 1914. 70pf+35pf, Freighter Widar, 1971.

## 1977, Apr. 14   Litho.   Perf. 14
| | | | | |
|---|---|---|---|---|
| 9NB133 | SP46 | 30pf + 15pf | .35 | .40 |
| 9NB134 | SP46 | 40pf + 20pf | .40 | .45 |
| 9NB135 | SP46 | 50pf + 25pf | .65 | .75 |
| 9NB136 | SP46 | 70pf + 35pf | .95 | .95 |
| | *Nos. 9NB133-9NB136 (4)* | | 2.35 | 2.55 |

Surtax was for benefit of young people.

Meadow Flowers — SP47

30pf+15pf, Daisy. 40pf+20pf, Cowslip. 50pf+25pf, Sainfoin. 70pf+35pf, Forget-me-not.

## 1977, Oct. 13   Litho.   Perf. 14
| | | | | |
|---|---|---|---|---|
| 9NB137 | SP47 | 30pf + 15pf | .30 | .25 |
| 9NB138 | SP47 | 40pf + 20pf | .50 | .45 |
| 9NB139 | SP47 | 50pf + 25pf | .55 | .65 |
| 9NB140 | SP47 | 70pf + 35pf | .80 | .95 |
| | *Nos. 9NB137-9NB140 (4)* | | 2.15 | 2.30 |

Surtax was for independent welfare organizations.
See Nos. 9NB148-9NB151.

### Souvenir Sheet

Christmas — SP48

30pf+15pf, Virgin and Child, stained-glass window, Sacristy of St. Gereon Basilica, Cologne.

## 1977, Nov. 10
| | | | | |
|---|---|---|---|---|
| 9NB141 | SP48 | 30pf + 15pf multi | .65 | .65 |

Aviation — SP49

Designs: 30pf+15pf, Montgolfier balloon, 1783. 40pf+20pf, Lilienthal's glider, 1891. 50pf+25pf, Wright brothers' plane, 1909. 70pf+35pf, Etrich/Rumpler Taube, 1910.

**1978, Apr. 13    Litho.    Perf. 14**
9NB142 SP49 30pf + 15pf    .35   .40
9NB143 SP49 40pf + 20pf    .50   .50
9NB144 SP49 50pf + 25pf    .60   .65
9NB145 SP49 70pf + 35pf    1.00 1.10
   Nos. 9NB142-9NB145 (4)   2.45 2.65

Surtax was for benefit of young people.

Sports — SP50

50+25pf, Bicycling. 70+35pf, Fencing.

**1978, Apr. 13    Litho.    Perf. 14**
9NB146 SP50 50pf + 25pf    .80   .50
9NB147 SP50 70pf + 35pf    1.05   .90

Surtax was for German Sports Foundation.

Woodland Flowers — SP51

30pf+15pf, Solomon's-seal. 40pf+20pf, Wood primrose. 50pf+25pf, Cephalanthera rubra (orchid). 70pf+35pf, Bugle.

**1978, Oct. 12    Litho.    Perf. 14**
9NB148 SP51 30pf + 15pf    .40   .40
9NB149 SP51 40pf + 20pf    .50   .45
9NB150 SP51 50pf + 25pf    .65   .70
9NB151 SP51 70pf + 35pf    1.00 1.00
   Nos. 9NB148-9NB151 (4)   2.55 2.55

Surtax was for independent welfare organizations.

Souvenir Sheet

Christmas — SP52

30pf+15pf, Adoration of the Kings, stained glass window, Frauenkirche, Munich.

**1978, Nov. 16    Litho.    Perf. 14**
9NB152 SP52 30pf + 15pf multi   .65   .65

Aviation — SP53

Airplanes: 40pf+20pf, Vampyr, 1921. 50pf+25pf, Junkers JU52/3M, 1932. 60pf+30pf, Messerschmitt BF/ME 108, 1934. 90pf+45pf, Douglas DC3, 1935.

---

**1979, Apr. 5    Litho.    Perf. 14**
9NB153 SP53 40pf + 20pf    .65   .65
9NB154 SP53 50pf + 25pf    1.00   .95
9NB155 SP53 60pf + 30pf    1.00   .95
9NB156 SP53 90pf + 45pf    1.30 1.25
   Nos. 9NB153-9NB156 (4)   3.95 3.80

Surtax was for benefit of young people.

Sports — SP54

60pf+30pf, Runners. 90pf+45pf, Archers.

**1979, Apr. 5**
9NB157 SP54 60pf + 30pf    .80   .85
9NB158 SP54 90pf + 45pf    1.05 1.10

Surtax was for German Sports Foundation.

Woodland Plants — SP55

40pf+20pf, Larch. 50pf+25pf, Hazelnut. 60pf+30pf, Horse chestnut. 90pf+45pf, Blackthorn.

**1979, Oct. 11    Litho.    Perf. 14**
9NB159 SP55 40pf + 20pf    .40   .40
9NB160 SP55 50pf + 25pf    .60   .60
9NB161 SP55 60pf + 30pf    .85   .85
9NB162 SP55 90pf + 45pf    1.15 1.10
   Nos. 9NB159-9NB162 (4)   3.00 2.95

Surtax was for independent welfare organizations.

Christmas — SP56

Design: Nativity, medieval manuscript, Cistercian Abby, Altenberg.

**1979, Nov. 14    Litho.    Perf. 13½**
9NB163 SP56 40pf + 20pf multi   .80   .65

Aviation — SP57

Designs: 40pf+20pf, Vickers Viscount, 1950. 50pf+25pf, Fokker 27 Friendship, 1955. 60pf+30pf, Sud Aviation Caravelle, 1955. 90pf+45pf, Sikorsky-55, 1949.

**1980, Apr. 10    Litho.    Perf. 14**
9NB164 SP57 40 + 20pf multi   .60   .60
9NB165 SP57 50 + 25pf multi   .65   .65
9NB166 SP57 60 + 30pf multi   .80   .85
9NB167 SP57 90 + 45pf multi   1.05 1.15
   Nos. 9NB164-9NB167 (4)   3.10 3.25

Surtax was for benefit of young people.

Sports — SP58

Designs: 50pf+25pf, Javelin. 60pf+30pf, Weight lifting. 90pf+45pf, Water polo.

**1980, May 8    Photo.    Perf. 14**
9NB168 SP58 50 + 25pf multi   .65   .65
9NB169 SP58 60 + 30pf multi   .65   .65
9NB170 SP58 90 + 45pf multi   .80   .80
   Nos. 9NB168-9NB170 (3)   2.10 2.10

Surtax was for German Sports Foundation.

Wildflower — SP59

---

Designs: 40pf+20pf, Orlaya. 50pf+25pf, Yellow gagea. 60pf+30pf, Summer pheasant's eye. 90pf+45pf, Small-flowered Venus' looking-glass.

**1980, Oct. 9    Litho.    Perf. 14**
9NB171 SP59 40 + 20pf multi   .60   .60
9NB172 SP59 50 + 25pf multi   .75   .70
9NB173 SP59 60 + 30pf multi   .75   .70
9NB174 SP59 90 + 45pf multi   1.25 1.20
   Nos. 9NB171-9NB174 (4)   3.35 3.20

Surtax was for independent welfare organizations.

Christmas — SP60

Design: 40pf+20pf, Annunciation to the Shepherds, from Altomunster manuscript, 12th century.

**1980, Nov. 13    Litho.    Perf. 14x13½**
9NB175 SP60 40 + 20pf multi   .80   .75

Optical Instruments — SP61

40pf+20pf, Theodolite, 1810. 50pf+25pf, Equatorial telescope, 1820. 60pf+30pf, Microscope, 1790. 90pf+45pf, Sextant, 1830.

**1981, Apr. 10    Litho.    Perf. 13½**
9NB176 SP61 40 + 20pf multi   .40   .45
9NB177 SP61 50 + 25pf multi   .60   .65
9NB178 SP61 60 + 30pf multi   .80   .85
9NB179 SP61 90 + 45pf multi   1.20 1.25
   Nos. 9NB176-9NB179 (4)   3.00 3.20

Surtax for benefit of young people.

Sports — SP62

Designs: 60pf+30pf, Women's gymnastics. 90pf+45pf, Cross-county running.

**1981, Apr. 10       Perf. 14**
9NB180 SP62 60 + 30pf multi   .80   .70
9NB181 SP62 90 + 45pf multi   1.20 1.10

Surtax for the German Sports Foundation.

Endangered Species — SP63

40pf+20pf, Common bistort. 50pf+25pf, Pedicularis sceptrum-carolinum. 60pf+30pf, Gladiolus palustris. 90pf+45pf, Iris sibirica.

**1981, Oct. 8           Litho.**
9NB182 SP63 40 + 20pf multi   .65   .65
9NB183 SP63 50 + 25pf multi   .65   .65
9NB184 SP63 60 + 30pf multi   .65   .65
9NB185 SP63 90 + 45pf multi   1.30 1.25
   Nos. 9NB182-9NB185 (4)   3.25 3.20

Surtax was for independent welfare organizations.

Christmas — SP64

Adoration of the Kings, 19th cent. painting.

**1981, Nov. 12          Litho.**
9NB186 SP64 40 + 20pf multi   .80   .65

---

Antique Cars — SP65

Designs: 40pf+20pf, Daimler, 1889. 50pf+25pf, Wanderer, 1911. 60pf+30pf, Adler limousine, 1913. 90pf+45pf, DKW-F, 1931.

**1982, Apr. 15          Litho.**
9NB187 SP65 40 + 20pf multi   .55   .60
9NB188 SP65 50 + 25pf multi   .60   .65
9NB189 SP65 60 + 30pf multi   .65   .75
9NB190 SP65 90 + 45pf multi   1.20 1.25
   Nos. 9NB187-9NB190 (4)   3.00 3.25

Surtax was for benefit of young people.

Sports — SP66

60pf+30pf, Sprinting. 90pf+45pf, Volleyball.

**1982, Apr. 15          Litho.**
9NB191 SP66 60 + 30pf multi   .80   .65
9NB192 SP66 90 + 45pf multi   1.20   .90

Surtax was for the German Sports Foundation.

Endangered Species — SP67

Designs: 50pf+20pf, Floribunda grandiflora. 60pf+30pf, Tea-rose hybrid, diff. 80pf+40pf, Floribunda, diff. 120pf+60pf, Miniature rose.

**1982, Oct. 14    Litho.    Perf. 14**
9NB193 SP67 50 + 20pf multi   .80   .75
9NB194 SP67 60 + 30pf multi   .80   .75
9NB195 SP67 80 + 40pf multi   1.30 1.25
9NB196 SP67 120 + 60pf multi   2.10 2.00
   Nos. 9NB193-9NB196 (4)   5.00 4.75

Surtax was for independent welfare organizations.

Christmas — SP68

Design: Adoration of the Kings, Oak altar, St. Peter's Church, Hamburg, 1380.

**1982, Nov. 10**
9NB197 SP68 50 + 20pf multi   .80   .65

Motorcycles SP69

Designs: 50pf+20pf, Hildebrand & Wolfmuller, 1894. 60pf+30pf, Wanderer, 1908. 80pf+40pf, DKW-Lomos, 1922. 120pf+60pf, Mars, 1925.

**1983, Apr. 12    Litho.    Perf. 14**
9NB198 SP69 50 + 20pf multi   .65   .45
9NB199 SP69 60 + 30pf multi   1.00   .85
9NB200 SP69 80 + 40pf multi   1.15   .85
9NB201 SP69 120 + 60pf multi   2.50 2.10
   Nos. 9NB198-9NB201 (4)   5.30 4.25

Surtax was for benefit of young people.

Sports — SP70

Designs: 80pf+40pf, European Latin American Dance Championship. 120pf+60pf, World Hockey Championship.

**1983, Apr. 12**
9NB202 SP70 80 + 40pf multi 1.20 .95
9NB203 SP70 120 + 60pf multi 1.75 1.60
Surtax was for German Sports Foundation.

Endangered Species — SP71

Designs: 50pf+20pf, Mountain wildflower. 60pf+30pf, Alpine auricula. 80pf+40pf, Little primrose. 120pf+60pf, Einsele's aquilegia.

**1983, Oct. 13    Litho.    Perf. 14**
9NB204 SP71 50 + 20pf multi .55 .50
9NB205 SP71 60 + 30pf multi .80 .75
9NB206 SP71 80 + 40pf multi 1.45 1.40
9NB207 SP71 120 + 60pf multi 2.00 2.10
  Nos. 9NB204-9NB207 (4) 4.80 4.75
Surtax was for welfare organizations.

Nativity — SP72

**1983, Nov. 10    Litho.**
9NB208 SP72 50 + 20pf multi .80 .75
Christmas.
Surtax was for free welfare work.

Insects — SP73

Designs: 50pf+20pf, Trichius fasciatus. 60pf+30pf, Agrumenia carniolioa. 80pf+40pf, Bombus terrestris. 120pf+60pf, Eristalis tenax.

**1984, Apr. 12    Litho.**
9NB209 SP73 50 + 20pf multi .85 .50
9NB210 SP73 60 + 30pf multi .85 .65
9NB211 SP73 80 + 40pf multi 1.30 1.15
9NB212 SP73 120 + 60pf multi 2.00 1.90
  Nos. 9NB209-9NB212 (4) 5.00 4.20
Surtax was for German Youth Stamp Foundation.

Olympics SP74

Women's Events: 60pf+30pf, Hurdles. 80pf+40pf, Cycling. 120pf+60pf, Kayak.

**1984, Apr. 12**
9NB213 SP74 60 + 30pf multi 1.30 .90
9NB214 SP74 80 + 40pf multi 1.30 .90
9NB215 SP74 120 + 60pf multi 2.25 2.25
  Nos. 9NB213-9NB215 (3) 4.85 4.05
Surtax was for German Sports Foundation.

Orchids — SP75

50+20pf, Listera cordata. 60pf+30pf, Ophrys insectifera. 80pf+40pf, Epipactis palustris. 120pf+60pf, Ophrys coriophora.

**1984, Oct. 18    Litho.    Perf. 14**
9NB216 SP75 50 + 20pf multi 1.20 .80
9NB217 SP75 60 + 30pf multi 1.20 .80
9NB218 SP75 80 + 40pf multi 1.90 1.75
9NB219 SP75 120 + 60pf multi 3.00 3.00
  Nos. 9NB216-9NB219 (4) 7.30 6.35
Surtax was for welfare organizations.

---

St. Nicholas — SP76

**1984, Nov. 8    Litho.**
9NB220 SP76 50 + 20pf multi .95 .90
Christmas.
Surtax was for welfare organizations.

Sports — SP77

No. 9NB221, Basketball. No. 9NB222, Table Tennis.

**1985, Feb. 21    Photo.**
9NB221 SP77 80 + 40pf multi 1.20 1.15
9NB222 SP77 120 + 60pf multi 2.00 1.90
Surtax was for German Sport Foundation.

Bicycles — SP78

50pf+20pf, Bussing bicycle, 1868. 60pf+30pf, Child's tricycle, 1885. 80pf+40pf, Jaray bicycle, 1925. 120pf+60pf, Opel racer, 1925.

**1985, Apr. 16    Litho.**
9NB223 SP78 50 + 20pf multi 1.00 .95
9NB224 SP78 60 + 30pf multi 1.00 .95
9NB225 SP78 80 + 40pf multi 1.30 1.40
9NB226 SP78 120 + 60pf multi 3.00 3.00
  Nos. 9NB223-9NB226 (4) 6.30 6.30
Surtax was for benefit of young people. Each stamp also shows the International Youth Year emblem.

Prayer Books — SP79

No. 9NB227, Red, blue and pink flowers, lady bugs. No. 9NB228, Red and blue flowers, bird and butterfly. No. 9NB229, Pink and blue flowers, butterfly and bee. No. 9NB230, Yellow and pink flowers, butterfly and snail.

**1985, Oct. 15    Litho.    Perf. 14**
9NB227 SP79 50 + 20pf multi 1.00 .95
9NB228 SP79 60 + 30pf multi 1.30 1.25
9NB229 SP79 80 + 40pf multi 1.30 1.25
9NB230 SP79 120 + 60pf multi 1.60 1.90
  Nos. 9NB227-9NB230 (4) 5.20 5.35
Surtax for welfare organizations.

Christmas — SP80

Woodcut: Worship of the Kings, Epiphany Altar, Frieburg Cathedral, by Hans Baldung Grien (1485-1545).

**1985, Nov. 12    Litho.    Perf. 14**
9NB231 SP80 50 + 20pf multi 1.00 .90
Surtax was for welfare organizations.

European Sports Championships SP81

No. 9NB232, Swimming. No. 9NB233, Show jumping.

---

**1986, Feb. 13    Litho.    Perf. 14**
9NB232 SP81 80 + 40pf multi 1.45 1.60
9NB233 SP81 120 + 55pf multi 1.75 1.90
Surtax for the Natl. Sports Promotion Foundation.

Vocational Training — SP82

No. 9NB234, Glass worker. No. 9NB235, Metal Worker. No. 9NB236, Tailor. No. 9NB237, Carpenter.

**1986, Apr. 10**
9NB234 SP82 50 + 25pf multi 1.00 1.10
9NB235 SP82 60 + 30pf multi 1.30 1.50
9NB236 SP82 70 + 35pf multi 1.30 1.50
9NB237 SP82 80 + 40pf multi 1.60 1.75
  Nos. 9NB234-9NB237 (4) 5.20 5.85
Surtax for German Youth Stamp Foundation.

Glassware — SP83

No. 9NB238, Cantharus, 1st cent. No. 9NB239, Tumbler, c. 200. No. 9NB240, Jug, 3rd cent. No. 9NB241, Diatreta, 4th cent.

**1986, Oct. 16    Litho.    Perf. 13x13½**
9NB238 SP83 50 + 25pf multi 1.00 .95
9NB239 SP83 60 + 30pf multi 1.30 1.25
9NB240 SP83 70 + 35pf multi 1.30 1.25
9NB241 SP83 80 + 40pf multi 1.30 1.60
  Nos. 9NB238-9NB241 (4) 4.90 5.05
Surtax for public welfare organizations.

Christmas — SP84

Design: Adoration of the Magi, Ortenberg Altarpiece, c. 1420.

**1986, Nov. 13    Litho.    Perf. 14**
9NB242 SP84 50 + 25pf multi .80 .85
Surtax for public welfare organizations.

Sports Championships SP85

No. 9NB243, Gymnastics. No. 9NB244, Judo.

**1987, Feb. 12    Litho.**
9NB243 SP85 80 + 40pf multi 1.30 1.25
9NB244 SP85 120 + 55pf multi 1.60 1.60
Surtax for the benefit of the national Sports Promotion Foundation.

Youth in Industry — SP86

No. 9NB245, Cooper. No. 9NB246, Stonemason. No. 9NB247, Furrier. No. 9NB248, Painter.

**1987, Apr. 9    Litho.**
9NB245 SP86 50 + 25pf multi .80 .95
9NB246 SP86 60 + 30pf multi .85 .95
9NB247 SP86 70 + 35pf multi 1.30 1.60
9NB248 SP86 80 + 40pf multi 1.30 1.25
  Nos. 9NB245-9NB248 (4) 4.25 4.75
Surtax for youth organizations.

---

Gold and Silver Artifacts — SP87

No. 9NB249, Bonnet ornament, 5th cent. No. 9NB250, Athena plate, 1st cent. B.C. No. 9NB251, Armilla armlet, c. 1180. No. 9NB252, Snake bracelet, 300 B.C.

**1987, Oct. 15**
9NB249 SP87 50 + 25pf multi .65 .65
9NB250 SP87 60 + 30pf multi 1.00 1.10
9NB251 SP87 70 + 35pf multi 1.20 1.40
9NB252 SP87 80 + 40pf multi 1.45 1.60
  Nos. 9NB249-9NB252 (4) 4.30 4.75
Surtax for welfare organizations sponsoring free museum exhibitions.

Christmas — SP88

Illustration from Book of Psalms, 13th cent., Bavarian Natl. Museum: Adoration of the Magi.

**1987, Nov. 6**
9NB253 SP88 50 + 25pf multi .80 .75
Surtax for public welfare ogranizations.

Sports — SP89

No. 9NB254, Trapshooting. No. 9NB255, Figure skating. No. 9NB256, Hammer throw.

**1988, Feb. 18    Litho.**
9NB254 SP89 60 + 30pf multi 1.20 1.15
9NB255 SP89 80 + 40pf multi 1.20 1.15
9NB256 SP89 120 + 60pf multi 1.60 1.60
  Nos. 9NB254-9NB256 (3) 4.00 3.90

Music — SP90

No. 9NB257, Piano terzet. No. 9NB258, Wind quintet. No. 9NB259, Guitar, mandolin, recorder. No. 9NB260, Children's choir.

**1988, Apr. 14    Litho.    Perf. 14**
9NB257 SP90 50 +25pf multi 1.00 .95
9NB258 SP90 60 +30pf multi 1.30 1.40
9NB259 SP90 70 +35pf multi 1.30 1.40
9NB260 SP90 80 +40pf multi 2.00 2.00
  Nos. 9NB257-9NB260 (4) 5.60 5.75
Surtax for German Youth Stamp Foundation.

Gold and Silver Artifacts — SP91

No. 9NB261, Brooch, c. 1700, Schmuck Jewelry Museum, Pforzheim. No. 9NB262, Lion, 1540, Kunstgewerbe Museum, Berlin. No. 9NB263, Lidded goblet, 1536, Kunstgewerbe Museum. No. 9NB264, Cope clasp, c. 1400, Aachen cathedral.

**1988, Oct. 13    Litho.**
9NB261 SP91 50 +25pf multi .80 .90
9NB262 SP91 60 +30pf multi .95 1.00
9NB263 SP91 70 +35pf multi 1.05 1.00
9NB264 SP91 80 +40pf multi 1.30 1.40
  Nos. 9NB261-9NB264 (4) 4.10 4.30
Surtax for welfare organizations.

Christmas — SP92

Illumination from *The Gospel Book of Henry the Lion*, Helmarshausen, 1188, Prussian Cultural Museum, Bavaria: Angels announce the birth of Christ to the shepherds.

**1988, Nov. 10**      **Litho.**
9NB265 SP92   50 +25pf multi    1.05 1.00

Surtax for public welfare organizations.

Sports — SP93

No. 9NB266, Volleyball. No. 9NB267, Hockey.

**1989, Feb. 9**      **Litho.**
9NB266 SP93 100 +50pf multi    2.00 1.90
9NB267 SP93 140 +60pf multi    2.60 3.00

Surtax for the Natl. Sports Promotion Foundation.

Circus — SP94

No. 9NB268, Tamer and tigers. No. 9NB269, Trapeze artists. No. 9NB270, Seals. No. 9NB271, Jugglers.

**1989, Apr. 20**      **Litho.**
9NB268 SP94   60 +30pf multi    1.30 1.25
9NB269 SP94   70 +30pf multi    1.60 1.60
9NB270 SP94   80 +35pf multi    2.25 2.50
9NB271 SP94 100 +50pf multi    2.60 3.00
    *Nos. 9NB268-9NB271 (4)*    7.75 8.35

Surtax for natl. youth welfare organizations.

Mail Transport — SP95

No. 9NB272, Messenger, 15th cent. No. 9NB273, Brandenburg mail wagon, c. 1700. No. 9NB274, Prussian postal workers, 19th cent.

**1989, Oct. 12**      **Litho.**
9NB272 SP95   60 +30pf multi    1.75 1.75
9NB273 SP95   80 +35pf multi    2.25 2.25
9NB274 SP95 100 +50pf multi    3.00 3.00
    *Nos. 9NB272-9NB274 (3)*    7.00 7.00

Surtax for the benefit of Free Welfare Work.

Christmas — SP96

Designs: No. 9NB275, Angel. No. 9NB276, Nativity.

**1989, Nov. 16**      **Litho.**
9NB275 SP96 40 +20pf multi    1.00  .95
9NB276 SP96 60 +30pf multi    1.60 1.40

Surtax for the benefit of the Federal Working Assoc. of Free Welfare Work.

Sports — SP97

Designs: No. 9NB277, Water polo. No. 9NB278, Wheelchair basketball.

---

**1990, Feb. 15**      **Litho.**
9NB277 SP97 100 +50pf multi    2.60 3.00
9NB278 SP97 140 +60pf multi    4.75 5.50

Surtax for the Natl. Sports Promotion Foundation.

Max and Moritz — SP98

No. 9NB279, Moritz filling pipe with gunpowder. No. 9NB280, Max & Moritz get baked into dough and eat their way out. No. 9NB281, Max & Moritz cutting holes in sack. No. 9NB282, The uncle and the May bug.

**1990, Apr. 19**      **Litho.**
9NB279 SP98   60 +30pf multi    1.45 *1.60*
9NB280 SP98   70 +30pf multi    2.25 2.25
9NB281 SP98   80 +35pf multi    2.25 2.25
9NB282 SP98 100 +50pf multi    2.25 2.25
    *Nos. 9NB279-9NB282 (4)*    8.20 8.35

Surcharge for the German Youth Stamp Foundation.

Post and Telecommunications SP99

Designs: 60pf + 30pf, Railway mail car, 1900. 80pf + 35pf, Telephone installation, 1900. 100pf + 50pf, Mail truck, 1900.

**1990, Sept. 27**   **Litho.**   *Perf. 13½x14*
9NB283 SP99   60 +30pf multi    1.60 1.75
9NB284 SP99   80 +35pf multi    2.25 2.25
9NB285 SP99 100 +50pf multi    3.00 3.00
    *Nos. 9NB283-9NB285 (3)*    6.85 7.00

Surtax for welfare organizations.

---

# GERMANY OFFICES ABROAD

---

## OFFICES IN CHINA

100 Pfennings = 1 Mark
100 Cents = 1 Dollar (1905)

Stamps of Germany, 1889-90, Overprinted in Black at 56 degree Angle

**1898**    **Unwmk.**     *Perf. 13½x14½*
1   A9   3pf dark brown    5.75   6.00
 *a.*   3pf yellow brown    12.00   12.00
 *b.*   3pf reddish ocher    37.50 125.00
2   A9   5pf green    3.25   3.25
3   A10 10pf carmine    5.75   6.25
4   A10 20pf ultramarine    17.00 16.50
5   A10 25pf orange    32.50 30.00
6   A10 50pf red brown    16.00 13.50
    *Nos. 1-6 (6)*    80.25 75.50

**Overprinted at 45 degree Angle**
1c   A9   3pf yellow brown   135.00 23,000.
1d   A9   3pf reddish ocher   375.00
 *e.*   3pf gray brown   1,850. 23,000.
2a   A9   5pf green   11.50 13.00
3a   A10 10pf carmine   32.50 10.50
4a   A10 20pf ultramarine   14.50 10.50
5a   A10 25pf orange   50.00 65.00
6a   A10 50pf red brown   21.00 17.50

Value for No. 1c used is for a stamp with small 1898 Shanghai cancel. Examples with other cancellations or later Shanghai cancels sell for about half the value quoted.

### Foochow Issue

Nos. 3 and 3a Handstamp Surcharged

---

**1900**
16   A10 5pf on 10pf, #3    550.00 *800.00*
 *a.*   On No. 3a    650.00 *950.00*

For similar 5pf surcharges on 10pf carmine, see Tsingtau Issue, Kiauchau.

### Tientsin Issue

German Stamps of 1900 Issue Handstamped

**1900**
17   A11   3pf brown    600.00 800.00
18   A11   5pf green    400.00 360.00
19   A11 10pf carmine    950.00 875.00
20   A11 20pf ultra    800.00 950.00
21   A11 30pf org & blk, *sal*   4,750. 4,750.
22   A11 50pf pur & blk, *sal*   16,000. 13,500.
23   A11 80pf lake & blk,
     *rose*    4,750. 4,750.

This handstamp is known inverted and double on most values. Used values for Nos. 16-23 are for postally used items, CTO on philatelic usage is about half.

Excellent faked handstamps are plentiful.

### Regular Issue

Germany No. 53 Overprinted

Germany No. 64 Ovptd.

Germany No. 65A Ovptd.

**1901**      *Perf. 14, 14½*
**Overprinted Horizontally in Black**
24   A11   3pf brown    1.50 2.10
 *a.*   3pf light red brown   105.00 45.00
25   A11   5pf green    1.50 1.60
26   A11 10pf carmine    2.40 1.25
27   A11 20pf ultra    3.25 1.60
28   A11 25pf org & blk, *yel*   9.50 16.00
29   A11 30pf org & blk, *sal*   9.50 13.00
30   A11 40pf lake & blk    9.50 9.50
31   A11 50pf pur & blk, *sal*   9.50 9.50
32   A11 80pf lake & blk,
     *rose*    11.00 11.00

**Overprinted in Black or Red**
33   A12 1m car rose    27.50 32.50
34   A13 2m gray blue    27.50 29.00
35   A14 3m blk vio (R)    47.50 65.00
36   A15 5m slate & car, I   1,350. 2,400.
 *b.*   Red and/or white re-
    touched    210.00 300.00
36A   A15 5m slate & car, II   210.00 325.00
    *Nos. 24-36A (14)*    1,720. 2,917.

See note after Germany No. 65A for information on retouches on No. 36. For description of the 5m Type I and Type II, see note above Germany No. 62.

### Surcharged on German Stamps of 1902 in Black or Red

a

b

c

**1905**      **Unwmk.**
37   A16(a)   1c on 3pf    3.00 *3.50*
38   A16(a)   2c on 5pf    3.00 1.60
39   A16(a)   4c on 10pf    5.50 1.60
40   A16(a) 10c on 20pf    3.00 1.75
41   A16(a) 20c on 40pf    19.00 7.25
42   A16(a) 40c on 80pf    30.00 13.50
43   A17(b)   ½d on 1m
     (26x17 perf.
     holes)    16.00 20.00

---

44   A21(b)   1d on 2m    16.00 22.50
45a   A19(c) 1 ½d on 1 ½d on 3m,
     25x16 perf. holes    17.00 47.50
46   A20(b) 2½d on 5m    100.00 300.00
    *Nos. 37-46 (10)*    212.50 419.20

### Surcharged on German Stamps of 1905 in Black or Red

**1906-13**      **Wmk. 125**
47   A16(a)   1c on 3pf    .65 *1.25*
48   A16(a)   2c on 5pf    .45 1.25
49   A16(a)   4c on 10pf    .80 1.60
50   A16(a) 10c on 20pf    .80 7.00
51   A16(a) 20c on 40pf    1.60 3.50
52   A16(a) 40c on 80pf    1.60 52.50
53   A17(b)   ½d on 1m    6.50 40.00
54   A21(b)   1d on 2m    10.50 40.00
55   A19(c) 1 ½d on 3m (R)   8.00 120.00
56   A20(b) 2 ½d on 5m (26x17
     perf. holes)    29.00 80.00
    *Nos. 47-56 (10)*    59.90 347.10

Forged cancellations exist.

# OFFICES IN MOROCCO

100 Centimos = 1 Peseta

Stamps of Germany
Surcharged in Black

### 1899      Unwmk.    Perf. 13½x14½

| | | | | |
|---|---|---|---|---|
| 1 | A9 | 3c on 3pf dk brn | 3.25 | 2.10 |
| 2 | A9 | 5c on 5pf green | 3.25 | 2.40 |
| 3 | A10 | 10c on 10pf car | 9.00 | 9.00 |
| 4 | A10 | 25c on 20pf ultra | 18.00 | 13.50 |
| 5 | A10 | 30c on 25pf orange | 27.50 | 32.50 |
| 6 | A10 | 60c on 50pf red brn | 22.50 | 37.50 |
| | | Nos. 1-6 (6) | 83.50 | 97.00 |

Before Nos. 1-6 were issued, the same six basic stamps of Germany's 1889-1900 issue were overprinted "Marocco" diagonally without the currency-changing surcharge line, but were not issued. Value, set $750.

### German Stamps of 1900 Surcharged in Black or Red

Germany No. 54 Srchd.

Germany No. 62 Srchd.

Germany No. 63 Srchd.

Germany No. 64 Srchd.

Germany No. 65A Srchd.

### 1900      Perf. 14, 14½

| | | | | |
|---|---|---|---|---|
| 7 | A11 | 3c on 3pf brn | 1.25 | 2.25 |
| 8 | A11 | 5c on 5pf grn | 1.50 | 1.50 |
| 9 | A11 | 10c on 10pf car | 2.25 | 1.50 |
| 10 | A11 | 25c on 20pf ultra | 3.00 | 2.75 |
| 11 | A11 | 30c on 25pf org & blk, yel | 9.00 | 15.00 |
| 12 | A11 | 35c on 30pf org & blk, sal | 6.75 | 6.00 |
| 13 | A11 | 50c on 40pf lake & blk | 6.75 | 6.00 |
| 14 | A11 | 60c on 50pf pur & blk, sal | 13.50 | 29.00 |
| 15 | A11 | 1p on 80pf lake & blk, rose | 12.00 | 10.50 |
| 16 | A12 | 1p25c on 1m car rose | 30.00 | 45.00 |
| 17 | A13 | 2p50c on 2m gray bl | 37.50 | 57.50 |
| 18 | A14 | 3p75c on 3m blk vio (R) | 45.00 | 65.00 |
| 19 | A15 | 6p25c on 5m sl & car, type I | 975.00 | 1,325. |
| b. | | Red and/or white re-touched | 165.00 | 300.00 |
| 19A | A15 | 6p25c on 5m sl & car, type II | 1,500. | — |
| | | Nos. 7-19A (14) | 2,644. | 1,567. |

See note after Germany No. 65A for information on retouches on No. 19. For description of the 5m Type I and Type II, see note above Germany No. 62.

Germany No. 54 Srchd.

Germany No. 62 Srchd.

---

Germany No. 63 Srchd.

Germany No. 64 Srchd.

Germany No. 65A Srchd.

### 1903     New Surcharge Plates

| | | | | |
|---|---|---|---|---|
| 8D | A11 | 5c on 5pf grn | 70.00 | 11.00 |
| 16D | A12 | 1p25c on 1m car rose | 350.00 | 180.00 |
| 17D | A13 | 2p50c on 2m gray bl | 500.00 | 110.00 |
| 18D | A14 | 3p75c on 3m blk vio (R) | 1,300. | 240.00 |
| 19D | A15 | 6p25c on 5m sl & car, type II | 200.00 | 260.00 |

The 1903 printing Nos. 8D, 16D-18D, 19D differs from Nos. 8, 16-18 and 19A in that the surcharge font is thicker, especially the "M" and "t".

### German Stamps of 1902 Surcharged in Black or Red

a

b

c

### 1905      Unwmk.

| | | | | |
|---|---|---|---|---|
| 20 | A16(a) | 3c on 3pf | 2.60 | 3.50 |
| 21 | A16(a) | 5c on 5pf | 4.50 | 1.10 |
| 22 | A16(a) | 10c on 10pf | 8.25 | 1.10 |
| 23 | A16(a) | 25c on 20pf | 18.00 | 3.25 |
| 24 | A16(a) | 30c on 25pf | 6.00 | 6.00 |
| 25 | A16(a) | 35c on 30pf | 9.00 | 5.50 |
| 26 | A16(a) | 50c on 40pf | 9.00 | 7.50 |
| 27 | A16(a) | 60c on 50pf | 20.00 | 22.50 |
| 28 | A16(a) | 1p on 80pf | 20.00 | 18.00 |
| 29 | A17(b) | 1p25c on 1m | 50.00 | 35.00 |
| 30 | A21(b) | 2p50c on 2m | 95.00 | 135.00 |
| 31 | A19(c) | 3p75c on 3m (R) | 42.50 | 52.50 |
| 32 | A20(b) | 6p25c on 5m | 150.00 | 200.00 |
| | | Nos. 20-32 (13) | 434.85 | 490.95 |

### Surcharged on Germany No. 54

| | | | | |
|---|---|---|---|---|
| 32A | A11(a) | 5c on 5pf | 7.50 | 24.00 |

German Stamps of 1905 Surcharged

### 1906-11      Wmk. 125

| | | | | |
|---|---|---|---|---|
| 33 | A16(a) | 3c on 3pf | 8.25 | 2.00 |
| 34 | A16(a) | 5c on 5pf | 6.50 | 1.10 |
| 35 | A16(a) | 10c on 10pf | 6.50 | 1.10 |
| 36 | A16(a) | 25c on 20pf | 19.00 | 7.50 |
| 37 | A16(a) | 30c on 25pf | 19.00 | 15.00 |
| 38 | A16(a) | 35c on 30pf | 15.00 | 9.75 |
| 39 | A16(a) | 50c on 40pf | 30.00 | 135.00 |
| 40 | A16(a) | 60c on 50pf | 22.50 | 17.00 |
| 41 | A16(a) | 1p on 80pf | 110.00 | 260.00 |
| 42 | A17(b) | 1p25c on 1m | 60.00 | 165.00 |
| 43 | A21(b) | 2p50c on 2m | 60.00 | 165.00 |
| 44 | A20(b) | 6p25c on 5m | 110.00 | 300.00 |
| | | Nos. 33-44 (12) | 466.75 | 1,078. |

Excellent forgeries exist of No. 41.

Surcharge Spelled "Marokko" in Black or Red

---

### 1911

| | | | | |
|---|---|---|---|---|
| 45 | A16(a) | 3c on 3pf | .55 | .75 |
| 46 | A16(a) | 5c on 5pf | .55 | 1.00 |
| 47 | A16(a) | 10c on 10pf | .55 | 1.10 |
| 48 | A16(a) | 25c on 20pf | .65 | 1.40 |
| 49 | A16(a) | 30c on 25pf | 1.50 | 16.00 |
| 50 | A16(a) | 35c on 30pf | 1.50 | 8.75 |
| 51 | A16(a) | 50c on 40pf | 1.25 | 5.25 |
| 52 | A16(a) | 60c on 50pf | 2.40 | 37.50 |
| 53 | A16(a) | 1p on 80pf | 1.60 | 24.00 |
| 54 | A17(b) | 1p25c on 1m | 4.50 | 65.00 |
| 55 | A21(b) | 2p50c on 2m | 6.00 | 47.50 |
| 56 | A19(c) | 3p75c on 3m (R) | 10.50 | 225.00 |
| 57 | A20(b) | 6p25c on 5m | 19.00 | 325.00 |
| | | Nos. 45-57 (13) | 50.55 | 758.25 |

Forged cancellations exist.

---

# OFFICES IN THE TURKISH EMPIRE

Unused values for Nos. 1-6 are for stamps with original gum. Stamps without gum sell for about one-third of the figures quoted.

40 Paras = 1 Piaster

### German Stamps of 1880-83 Surcharged in Black or Blue

Germany No. 30 Surcharged

Germany No. 31 Surcharged

### 1884      Unwmk.    Perf. 13½x14½

| | | | | |
|---|---|---|---|---|
| 1 | A6 | 10pa on 5pf dull vio | 52.50 | 30.00 |
| 2 | A7 | 20pa on 10pf rose | 75.00 | 75.00 |
| 3 | A7 | 1pi on 20pf ultra (Bk) | 60.00 | 7.50 |
| 4 | A7 | 1pi on 20pf ultra (Bl) | 2,250. | 72.50 |
| 5 | A7 | 1¼pi on 25pf brn | 120.00 | 260.00 |
| 6 | A7 | 2½pi on 50pf gray grn | 120.00 | 140.00 |
| a. | | 2½pi on 50pf deep olive grn | 275.00 | 210.00 |
| | | Nos. 1-6 (6) | 2,678. | 585.00 |

There are two types of the surcharge on the 1¼pi and 2½pi stamps, the difference being in the spacing between the figures and the word "PIASTER."

There are re-issues of these stamps which vary only slightly from the originals in overprint measurements.

### German Stamps of 1880-1900 Surcharged in Black

Germany No. 47 Surcharged

---

Germany No. 48 Surcharged

Germany No. 50 Surcharged

### 1889

| | | | | |
|---|---|---|---|---|
| 8 | A9 | 10pa on 5pf grn | 3.50 | 3.75 |
| 9 | A10 | 20pa on 10pf car | 9.00 | 3.25 |
| 10 | A10 | 1pi on 20pf ultra | 6.00 | 2.25 |
| 11 | A10 | 1¼pi on 25pf org | 22.50 | 20.00 |
| 12 | A10 | 2½pi on 50pf choc | 35.00 | 22.50 |
| a. | | 2½pi on 50pf copper brown | 190.00 | 110.00 |
| | | Nos. 8-12 (5) | 76.00 | 51.75 |

### German Stamps of 1900 Surcharged

Germany No. 55 Surcharged

Germany No. 62 Srchd.

Germany No. 63 Srchd.

Germany No. 64 Srchd.

Germany No. 65A Srchd.

### 1900      Perf. 14, 14½

### Black or Red Surcharge

| | | | | |
|---|---|---|---|---|
| 13 | A11 | 10pa on 5pf grn | 1.75 | 1.75 |
| 14 | A11 | 20pa on 10pf car | 2.75 | 2.25 |
| 15 | A11 | 1pi on 20pf ultra | 4.50 | 1.75 |
| 16 | A11 | 1¼pi on 25pf org & blk, yel | 6.00 | 4.50 |
| 17 | A11 | 1½pi on 30pf org & blk, sal | 6.00 | 4.50 |
| 18 | A11 | 2pi on 40pf lake & blk | 6.00 | 4.50 |
| 19 | A11 | 2½pi on 50pf pur & blk, sal | 12.00 | 13.00 |
| 20 | A11 | 4pi on 80pf lake & blk, rose | 13.50 | 13.00 |
| 21 | A12 | 5pi on 1m car rose | 35.00 | 37.50 |
| 22 | A13 | 10pi on 2m gray bl | 30.00 | 42.50 |
| 23 | A14 | 15pi on 3m blk vio (R) | 45.00 | 110.00 |

Search

PhilaSearch

www.Philasearch.com

| 24 | A15 | 25pi on 5m sl & car, type I | 640.00 | 1,250. |
|---|---|---|---|---|
| a. | | Double surcharge | | 9,000. |
| d. | | Red and/or white retouched | 175.00 | 250.00 |
| e. | | White only retouched | 290.00 | 500.00 |
| 24B | A15 | 25pi on 5m sl & car, type II | 290.00 | 500.00 |
| c. | | Double surcharge | 9,750. | |
| | | Nos. 13-24B (13) | 1,093. | 1,985. |

See note after Germany No. 65A for information on retouches on No. 24. For description of the 5m Type I & Type II, see note above Germany No. 62.

### German Stamps of 1900 Surcharged in Black

**1903-05**

| 25 | A11 | 10pa on 5pf green | 9.00 | 13.50 |
|---|---|---|---|---|
| 26 | A11 | 20pa on 10pf car | 30.00 | 19.00 |
| 27 | A11 | 1pi on 20pf ultra | 8.25 | 7.25 |

### German Stamps of 1900, 1905 Surcharged in Black

| 28 | A12 | 5pi on 1m car rose | 140.00 | 95.00 |
|---|---|---|---|---|
| 29 | A13 | 10pi on 2m bl ('05) | 150.00 | 260.00 |
| 30 | A15 | 25pi on 5m sl & car | 190.00 | 525.00 |
| a. | | Double surcharge | 4,500. | |
| | | Nos. 25-30 (6) | 527.25 | 919.75 |

The 1903-05 surcharges may be easily distinguished from those of 1900 by the added bar at the top of the letter "A."

### German Stamps of 1902 Surcharged in Black or Red

a          b

**1905**                                        **Unwmk.**

| 31 | A16(a) | 10pa on 5pf | 3.50 | 2.50 |
|---|---|---|---|---|
| 32 | A16(a) | 20pa on 10pf | 9.00 | 3.25 |
| 33 | A16(a) | 1pi on 20pf | 19.00 | 2.00 |
| 34 | A16(a) | 1¼pi on 25pf | 9.00 | 7.50 |
| 35 | A16(a) | 1½pi on 30pf | 13.50 | 15.00 |
| 36 | A16(a) | 2pi on 40pf | 22.50 | 15.00 |
| 37 | A16(a) | 2½pi on 50pf | 9.00 | 22.50 |
| 38 | A16(a) | 4pi on 80pf | 27.50 | 17.50 |
| 39 | A17(b) | 5pi on 1m | 45.00 | 45.00 |
| 40 | A21(b) | 10pi on 2m | 37.50 | 45.00 |
| 41 | A19(b) | 15pi on 3m (R) | 45.00 | 52.50 |
| 42 | A20(b) | 25pi on 5m | 225.00 | 525.00 |
| | | Nos. 31-42 (12) | 465.50 | 752.75 |

### German Stamps of 1905 Surcharged in Black or Red

**1906-12**                                    **Wmk. 125**

| 43 | A16(a) | 10pa on 5pf | 2.25 | .90 |
|---|---|---|---|---|
| 44 | A16(a) | 20pa on 10pf | 4.50 | .90 |
| 45 | A16(a) | 1pi on 20pf | 6.00 | .90 |
| 46 | A16(a) | 1¼pi on 25pf | 12.00 | 12.00 |
| 47 | A16(a) | 1½pi on 30pf | 12.00 | 10.00 |
| 48 | A16(a) | 2pi on 40pf | 6.00 | 1.75 |
| 49 | A16(a) | 2½pi on 50pf | 9.00 | 16.50 |
| 50 | A16(a) | 4pi on 80pf | 15.00 | 22.50 |
| 51 | A17(b) | 5pi on 1m | 35.00 | 30.00 |
| 52 | A21(b) | 10pi on 2m | 35.00 | 45.00 |
| 53 | A19(b) | 15pi on 3m (R) | 60.00 | 450.00 |
| 54 | A20(b) | 25pi on 5m | 30.00 | 75.00 |
| | | Nos. 43-54 (12) | 226.75 | 665.45 |

### German Stamps of 1905 Surcharged Diagonally in Black

**1908**

| 55 | A16 | 5c on 5pf | 1.90 | 2.75 |
|---|---|---|---|---|
| 56 | A16 | 10c on 10pf | 2.75 | 4.50 |
| 57 | A16 | 25c on 20pf | 6.00 | 22.50 |
| 58 | A16 | 50c on 40pf | 30.00 | 55.00 |
| 59 | A16 | 100c on 80pf | 52.50 | 60.00 |
| | | Nos. 55-59 (5) | 93.15 | 144.75 |

Forged cancellations exist on Nos. 37, 53-54, 57-59.

# GERMAN DEMOCRATIC REPUBLIC

LOCATION — Eastern Germany
GOVT. — Republic
AREA — 41,659 sq. mi.
POP. — 16,701,500 (1983)
CAPITAL — Berlin (Soviet sector)

100 Pfennigs = 1 Deutsche Mark (East)

100 Pfennigs = 1 Mark of the Deutsche Notenbank (MDN) (1965)

100 Pfennigs = 1 Mark of the National Bank (M) (1969)

100 Pfennigs = 1 Deutsche Mark (West) (1990)

**Catalogue values for unused stamps in this country are for Never Hinged items, beginning with Scott 48 in the regular postage section, Scott B14 in the semipostal section, Scott C1 in the air-post section, and Scott O1 official section.**

### Watermarks

Watermark 292, see Germany.

Wmk. 297 — DDR and Post Horn         Wmk. 313 — Quatrefoil and DDR

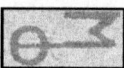

Wmk. 397

### FOR USE IN ALL PROVINCES IN THE RUSSIAN ZONE

When the mark was revalued in June, 1948, a provisional overprint, consisting of various city and town names and post office or zone numerals, was applied by hand in black, violet or blue at innumerable post offices to their stocks.

### Germany Nos. 557 to 573 Overprinted in Black

**1948, July 3     Wmk. 284     Perf. 14**

| 10N1 | A120 | 2pf brn blk | .25 | .25 |
|---|---|---|---|---|
| 10N2 | A120 | 6pf purple | .25 | .30 |
| 10N3 | A121 | 8pf red | .25 | .30 |
| 10N4 | A121 | 10pf yel grn | .25 | .30 |
| 10N5 | A122 | 12pf gray | .25 | .30 |
| 10N6 | A120 | 15pf choc | .25 | .30 |
| 10N7 | A123 | 16pf dk blue grn | .25 | .50 |
| 10N8 | A121 | 20pf blue | .25 | .30 |
| 10N9 | A123 | 24pf brn org | .25 | .25 |
| 10N10 | A122 | 25pf gray yel | .25 | .25 |
| 10N11 | A122 | 30pf red | .65 | .30 |
| 10N12 | A121 | 40pf red violet | .25 | .30 |
| 10N13 | A123 | 50pf ultra | .25 | .65 |
| 10N14 | A122 | 60pf red brn | .25 | .65 |
| a. | | 60pf brown red | 30.00 | 125.00 |
| 10N15 | A122 | 80pf dark blue | .80 | .80 |
| 10N16 | A123 | 84pf emerald | .80 | 1.10 |
| | | Nos. 10N1-10N16 (16) | 5.50 | 6.85 |
| | | Set, never hinged | 14.00 | |

### Same Overprint on Numeral Stamps of Germany, 1946

**1948, Sept.**

| 10N17 | A119 | 5pf yellow grn | .25 | .70 |
|---|---|---|---|---|
| 10N18 | A119 | 30pf olive | .40 | 2.00 |
| 10N19 | A119 | 45pf brt red | .25 | .80 |
| 10N20 | A119 | 75pf deep ultra | .25 | .80 |
| 10N21 | A119 | 84pf emerald | .40 | 1.60 |
| | | Nos. 10N17-10N21 (5) | 1.55 | 5.90 |
| | | Set, never hinged | 4.75 | |

Nos 10N1-10N21 all exist with inverted overprint, and majority with double overprint.

### Same Overprint on Berlin-Brandenburg Nos. 11N1-11N7

**1948, Sept.     Unwmk.     Litho.     Perf. 14**

| 10N22 | OS1 | 5pf green | .25 | .80 |
|---|---|---|---|---|
| a. | | Serrate roulette | .25 | .80 |
| 10N23 | OS1 | 6pf violet | .25 | .80 |
| 10N24 | OS1 | 8pf red | .25 | .80 |
| 10N25 | OS1 | 10pf brown | .25 | .80 |
| 10N26 | OS1 | 12pf rose | .25 | 1.20 |
| 10N27 | OS1 | 20pf blue | .25 | 1.20 |
| 10N28 | OS1 | 30pf olive | .25 | 1.20 |
| | | Nos. 10N22-10N28 (7) | 1.75 | 6.80 |
| | | Set, never hinged | 3.25 | |

The overprint made Nos. 10N22-10N28 valid for postage throughout the Russian Zone.

Gerhard Hauptmann — OS2

Designs: 2pf, 20pf, Käthe Kollwitz. 40pf, Gerhard Hauptmann. 8pf, 50pf, Karl Marx. 10pf, 84pf, August Bebel. 12pf, 30pf, Friedrich Engels. 15pf, 60pf, G. W. F. Hegel. 16pf, 25pf, Rudolf Virchow. 24pf, 80pf, Ernst Thälmann.

**1948     Typo.     Perf. 13x12½     Wmk. 292**

| 10N29 | OS2 | 2pf gray | .25 | 1.20 |
|---|---|---|---|---|
| 10N30 | OS2 | 6pf violet | .25 | 1.20 |
| 10N31 | OS2 | 8pf red brn | .25 | 1.20 |
| 10N32 | OS2 | 10pf blue grn | .25 | 1.00 |
| 10N33 | OS2 | 12pf blue | .80 | .80 |
| 10N34 | OS2 | 15pf brown | .30 | 1.75 |
| 10N35 | OS2 | 16pf turquoise | 1.75 | 1.75 |
| 10N36 | OS2 | 20pf maroon | .30 | 1.25 |
| 10N37 | OS2 | 24pf carmine | .60 | 1.20 |
| 10N38 | OS2 | 25pf olive grn | .35 | 2.00 |
| 10N39 | OS2 | 30pf red | .60 | 1.75 |
| 10N40 | OS2 | 40pf red violet | 4.00 | 2.50 |
| 10N41 | OS2 | 50pf dk ultra | .30 | 1.60 |
| 10N42 | OS2 | 60pf dull green | 1.75 | 2.00 |
| 10N43 | OS2 | 80pf dark blue | .30 | 1.75 |
| 10N44 | OS2 | 84pf brown lake | .30 | 3.50 |
| | | Nos. 10N29-10N44 (16) | 12.35 | 26.45 |
| | | Set, never hinged | 40.00 | |

See German Democratic Republic Nos. 122-136.

Karl Liebknecht and Rosa Luxemburg — OS3

**Perf. 13½x13**

**1949, Jan. 15     Litho.     Wmk. 292**

| 10N45 | OS3 | 24pf rose | .25 | .80 |
|---|---|---|---|---|
| | | Never hinged | .65 | |

30th anniv. of the death of Karl Liebknecht and Rosa Luxemburg, German socialists.

Dove and Laurel — OS4

**1949**

| 10N46 | OS4 | 24pf carmine rose | .45 | 1.75 |
|---|---|---|---|---|
| | | Never hinged | 1.25 | |

### Overprinted in Black: "3. Deutscher Volkskongress 29.-30. Mai 1949"

**1949, May 29**

| 10N47 | OS4 | 24pf carmine rose | .50 | 2.25 |
|---|---|---|---|---|
| | | Never hinged | 1.60 | |

Nos. 10N46 and 10N47 were issued for the 3rd German People's Congress.

# GERMAN DEMOCRATIC REPUBLIC

**Catalogue values for unused stamps in this section, from this point to the end of the section, are for Never Hinged items.**

Canceled to Order
The government stamp agency started in 1949 to sell canceled sets of new issues.
Used values are for CTO's for Nos. 48-2831, except for souvenir sheets, which are valued as postally used.

Pigeon, Letter and Globe — A5

**Wmk. Flowers Multiple (292)**

**1949, Oct. 9     Litho.     Perf. 13½**

| 48 | A5 | 50pf lt blue & dk blue | 8.50 | 8.50 |
|---|---|---|---|---|

75th anniv. of the UPU.

Letter Carriers — A6

**1949, Oct. 27     Perf. 13**

| 49 | A6 | 12pf blue | 6.00 | 6.00 |
|---|---|---|---|---|
| 50 | A6 | 30pf red | 8.50 | 12.00 |

"Day of the International Postal Workers' Trade Union," October 27-29, 1949.

Skier — A7

**1950, Mar. 2     Perf. 13**

| 51 | A7 | 12pf shown | 4.25 | 3.50 |
|---|---|---|---|---|
| 52 | A7 | 24pf Skater | 5.50 | 4.75 |

1st German Winter Sport Championship Matches, Schierke, 1950.

Globe and Sun — A8

**1950, May 1     Typo.**

| 53 | A8 | 30pf deep carmine | 12.00 | 11.00 |
|---|---|---|---|---|

60th anniv. of Labor Day.

A9                                Pres. Wilhelm Pieck — A10

**1950-51     Wmk. 292     Perf. 13x12½**

| 54 | A9 | 12pf dark blue | 15.00 | 1.50 |
|---|---|---|---|---|
| 55 | A9 | 24pf red brown | 21.00 | .95 |

**Perf. 13x13½**

| 56 | A10 | 1m olive green | 21.00 | 4.75 |
|---|---|---|---|---|

**Litho.**

| 57 | A10 | 2m red brown | 12.00 | 4.75 |
|---|---|---|---|---|

**Engr.**

| 57A | A10 | 5m deep blue ('51) | 6.00 | 1.20 |
|---|---|---|---|---|
| | | Nos. 54-57A (5) | 75.00 | 13.15 |

See Nos. 113-117, 120-121.

## Leonhard Euler — A11

Portraits: 5pf, Alexander von Humboldt. 6pf, Theodor Mommsen. 8pf, Wilhelm von Humboldt. 10pf, H. L. F. von Helmholtz. 12pf, Max Planck. 16pf, Jacob Grimm. 20pf, W. H. Nernst. 24pf, Gottfried von Leibnitz. 50pf, Adolf von Harnack.

**Wmk. 292**

| 1950, July 10 | | Litho. | Perf. 12½ | |
|---|---|---|---|---|
| 58 | A11 | 1pf gray | 3.00 | 1.20 |
| 59 | A11 | 5pf dp green | 4.25 | 3.00 |
| 60 | A11 | 6pf purple | 8.50 | 3.00 |
| 61 | A11 | 8pf orange brn | 9.50 | 6.00 |
| 62 | A11 | 10pf dk gray grn | 8.50 | 6.00 |
| 63 | A11 | 12pf dk blue | 6.00 | 2.50 |
| 64 | A11 | 16pf Prus blue | 12.00 | 12.00 |
| 65 | A11 | 20pf violet brn | 11.00 | 9.50 |
| 66 | A11 | 24pf red | 11.00 | 3.25 |
| 67 | A11 | 50pf dp ultra | 15.00 | 12.00 |
| | | Nos. 58-67 (10) | 88.75 | 58.45 |
| | | Set, hinged | 25.00 | |

250th anniv. of the founding of the Academy of Science, Berlin.
See Nos. 352-354.

## Miner — A12

Design: 24pf, Smelting copper.

| 1950, Sept. 1 | | | Perf. 13 | |
|---|---|---|---|---|
| 68 | A12 | 12pf blue | 4.25 | 4.75 |
| 69 | A12 | 24pf dark red | 6.50 | 4.75 |

750th anniv. of the opening of the Mannsfeld copper mines.

## Symbols of a Democratic Vote — A13

| 1950, Sept. 28 | | | | |
|---|---|---|---|---|
| 70 | A13 | 24pf brown red | 9.50 | 3.00 |

Publicizing the election of Oct. 15, 1950.

## Hand Between Dove and Tank — A14

Designs show hand shielding dove from: 8pf, Exploding shell. 12pf, Atomic explosion. 24pf, Cemetery.

| 1950, Dec. 15 | | Litho. | Perf. 13 | |
|---|---|---|---|---|
| 71 | A14 | 6pf violet blue | 3.00 | 2.00 |
| 72 | A14 | 8pf brown | 2.75 | 1.20 |
| 73 | A14 | 12pf blue | 3.25 | 2.15 |
| 74 | A14 | 24pf red | 3.50 | 1.75 |
| | | Nos. 71-74 (4) | 12.50 | 7.70 |

Issued to publicize the "Fight for Peace."

## Tobogganing — A15

Design: 24pf, Ski jump.

| 1951, Feb. 3 | | Litho. | Perf. 13 | |
|---|---|---|---|---|
| 76 | A15 | 12pf blue | 5.50 | 4.75 |
| 77 | A15 | 24pf rose | 7.25 | 6.00 |

Issued to publicize the second Winter Sports Championship Matches at Oberhof.

A16

| 1951, Mar. 4 | | Wmk. 292 | Perf. 13 | |
|---|---|---|---|---|
| 78 | A16 | 24pf rose carmine | 9.50 | 10.00 |
| 79 | A16 | 50pf violet blue | 10.00 | 10.00 |

Issued to publicize the 1951 Leipzig Fair.

## Pres. Wilhelm Pieck and Pres. Boleslaw Bierut Shaking Hands Across Oder-Neisse Frontier — A17

| 1951, Apr. 22 | | | Perf. 13 | |
|---|---|---|---|---|
| 80 | A17 | 24pf scarlet | 13.00 | 11.00 |
| 81 | A17 | 50pf blue | 13.00 | 11.00 |

Visit of Pres. Boleslaw Bierut of Poland to the Russian Zone of Germany.

## Mao Tse-tung — A18

## Redistribution of Chinese Land — A19

| 1951, June 27 | | | Perf. 13 | |
|---|---|---|---|---|
| 82 | A18 | 12pf dark green | 60.00 | 17.50 |
| 83 | A19 | 24pf deep carmine | 85.00 | 22.50 |
| 84 | A18 | 50pf violet blue | 60.00 | 22.50 |
| | | Nos. 82-84 (3) | 205.00 | 62.50 |
| | | Set, hinged | 65.00 | |

Issued to publicize East Germany's friendship toward Communist China.

## Boy Raising Flag — A20

Design: 24pf, 50pf, Girls dancing.

**1951, Aug. 3**
**Grayish Paper, Except 30pf**

| 85 | A20 | 12pf choc & org brn | 8.50 | 4.50 |
|---|---|---|---|---|
| 86 | A20 | 24pf dk car & yel grn | 8.50 | 2.50 |
| 87 | A20 | 30pf dk bl grn & org brn, cit | 9.75 | 5.00 |
| 88 | A20 | 50pf vio bl & dk car | 9.75 | 5.00 |
| | | Nos. 85-88 (4) | 36.50 | 17.00 |

3rd World Youth Festival, Berlin, 1951.

## 5-Year Plan Symbolism — A21

| 1951, Sept. 2 | | Typo. | Wmk. 292 | |
|---|---|---|---|---|
| 89 | A21 | 24pf multicolored | 3.25 | 2.00 |

East Germany's Five-Year Plan.

## Karl Liebknecht — A22

| 1951, Oct. 7 | | Litho. | Perf. 13½x13 | |
|---|---|---|---|---|
| 90 | A22 | 24pf red & blue gray | 4.00 | 2.00 |

Karl Liebknecht, socialist, 80th birth anniv.

## Father and Children with Stamp Collection — A23

| 1951, Oct. 28 | | | Perf. 13 | |
|---|---|---|---|---|
| 91 | A23 | 12pf deep blue | 4.50 | 2.00 |

Stamp Day, Oct. 28, 1951.

## Stalin and Wilhelm Pieck — A24

Design: 12pf, Pavel Bykov and Erich Wirth.

**1951**

| 92 | A24 | 12pf deep blue | 4.00 | 3.00 |
|---|---|---|---|---|
| 93 | A24 | 24pf red | 4.50 | 3.50 |

Month of East German-Soviet friendship. Issue dates: 12pf, Dec. 15, 24pf, Dec. 1.

## Winter Sports Championship Matches, Oberhof, 1952 — A25

Design: 12pf, Skier. 24pf, Ski jump.

| 1952, Jan. 12 | | | Wmk. 292 | |
|---|---|---|---|---|
| 94 | A25 | 12pf blue green | 4.00 | 3.00 |
| 95 | A25 | 24pf deep blue | 4.00 | 3.00 |

## Ludwig van Beethoven, 125th Death Anniv. — A26

Design: 12pf, Beethoven full face.

| 1952, Mar. 26 | | | Perf. 13½ | |
|---|---|---|---|---|
| 96 | A26 | 12pf bl gray & vio bl | 2.00 | .50 |
| 97 | A26 | 24pf gray & red brn | 2.25 | .75 |
| | | See Nos. 100-102. | | |

## Cyclists — A27

| 1952, May 5 | | Photo. | Perf. 13x13½ | |
|---|---|---|---|---|
| 98 | A27 | 12pf blue | 3.00 | 1.25 |

5th International Bicycle Peace Race, Warsaw-Berlin-Prague.

## Klement Gottwald — A28

| 1952, May 1 | | | | |
|---|---|---|---|---|
| 99 | A28 | 24pf violet blue | 2.25 | 1.40 |

Friendship between German Democratic Republic and Czechoslovakia.

**Type of 1952**

Portraits: 6pf, G. F. Handel. 8pf, Albert Lortzing. 50pf, C. M. von Weber.

| 1952, July 5 | | Litho. | Wmk. 297 | |
|---|---|---|---|---|
| 100 | A26 | 6pf brn buff & choc | 2.25 | 1.25 |
| 101 | A26 | 8pf pink & dp rose pink | 2.25 | 1.25 |
| 102 | A26 | 50pf bl gray & dp bl | 2.50 | 2.50 |
| | | Nos. 100-102 (3) | 7.00 | 6.00 |

## Victor Hugo — A29

Portraits: 20pf, Leonardo da Vinci. 24pf, Nicolai Gogol. 35pf, Avicenna.

**Wmk. 292**

| 1952, Aug. 11 | | Photo. | Perf. 13 | |
|---|---|---|---|---|
| 103 | A29 | 12pf brown | 2.50 | 2.75 |
| 104 | A29 | 20pf green | 2.50 | 2.75 |
| 105 | A29 | 24pf rose | 2.50 | 2.75 |
| 106 | A29 | 35pf blue | 4.00 | 4.00 |
| | | Nos. 103-106 (4) | 11.50 | 12.25 |

## Machine, Globe and Dove — A30

| 1952, Sept. 7 | | Wmk. 297 | Perf. 13 | |
|---|---|---|---|---|
| 108 | A30 | 24pf red | 2.00 | .75 |
| 109 | A30 | 35pf deep blue | 2.00 | 1.25 |

Issued to publicize the 1952 Leipzig Fair.

## Friedrich Ludwig Jahn — A31

| 1952, Oct. 15 | | | Litho. | |
|---|---|---|---|---|
| 110 | A31 | 12pf blue | 1.75 | 1.00 |

Jahn (1778-1852), introduced gymnastics to Germany, and was a politician.

## Halle University — A32

| 1952, Oct. 18 | | | Photo. | |
|---|---|---|---|---|
| 111 | A32 | 24pf green | 1.75 | .75 |

450th anniv. of the founding of Halle University, Wittenberg.

## Stamp, Flags, Wreath, Dove and Hammer — A33

| 1952, Oct. 26 | | | | |
|---|---|---|---|---|
| 112 | A33 | 24pf red brown | 2.25 | .85 |

Stamp Day, Oct. 26, 1952.

**Pieck Types of 1950**
**Perf. 13x12½**

| 1952-53 | | Wmk. 297 | Typo. | |
|---|---|---|---|---|
| 113 | A9 | 5pf blue green | 6.50 | 2.75 |
| 114 | A9 | 12pf dark blue | 17.50 | 1.25 |
| 115 | A9 | 24pf red brown | 17.50 | 1.25 |

**Perf. 13x13½**

| 116 | A10 | 1m olive green | 22.50 | 13.00 |
|---|---|---|---|---|

**Litho.** **Perf. 13**

| 117 | A10 | 2m red brown ('53) | 22.50 | 2.75 |
|---|---|---|---|---|
| | | Nos. 113-117 (5) | 86.50 | 21.00 |
| | | Set, hinged | 24.00 | |

## Globe, Dove and St. Stephen's Cathedral — A34

| 1952, Dec. 8 | | | Photo. | Perf. 13 | |
|---|---|---|---|---|---|
| 118 | A34 | 24pf brt carmine | 1.50 | 1.60 |
| 119 | A34 | 35pf deep blue | 1.50 | 3.00 |

Issued to publicize the Congress of Nations for Peace, Vienna, Dec. 12-19, 1952.

Pres. Wilhelm Pieck — A35

**1953**      *Perf. 13x13½*
| | | | | |
|---|---|---|---|---|
| 120 | A35 | 1m olive | 10.00 | .50 |
| a. | | 1m dark olive | 10.00 | .50 |
| 121 | A35 | 2m red brown | 7.00 | .50 |

See Nos. 339-340, 532.

### Portrait Types of Russian Occupation, 1948

Designs as before.

*Perf. 13x12½*

**1953**    **Typo.**     **Wmk. 297**
| | | | | |
|---|---|---|---|---|
| 122 | OS2 | 2pf gray | 2.50 | 2.75 |
| 123 | OS2 | 6pf purple | 2.50 | 1.75 |
| 124 | OS2 | 8pf red brown | 1.60 | 1.75 |
| 125 | OS2 | 10pf blue grn | 4.50 | 2.50 |
| 126 | OS2 | 12pf brown | 10.00 | 10.00 |
| 127 | OS2 | 16pf turquoise | 4.00 | 2.75 |
| 128 | OS2 | 20pf maroon | 6.50 | 1.75 |
| 129 | OS2 | 25pf olive grn | 130.00 | 175.00 |
| 130 | OS2 | 30pf red | 16.00 | 6.50 |
| 131 | OS2 | 40pf red violet | 3.25 | 3.25 |
| 132 | OS2 | 50pf dk ultra | 20.00 | 14.00 |
| 133 | OS2 | 60pf dull green | 4.00 | 2.75 |
| 134 | OS2 | 80pf dark blue | 4.00 | 1.75 |
| a. | | Varnish coating, dark ultramarine | 8.00 | 6.00 |
| 135 | OS2 | 80pf crimson | 10.00 | 6.50 |
| 136 | OS2 | 84pf brown lake | 52.50 | 65.00 |
| | | Nos. 122-136 (15) | 271.35 | 298.00 |
| | | Set, hinged | 85.00 | |

"Industry" and Red Flag A36

Karl Marx Speaking A38

Marx and Engels A37

Karl Marx Medallion A39

Designs: 12pf, Spasski tower and communist flag. 16pf, Marching workers. 24pf, Portrait of Karl Marx. 35pf, Marx addressing audience. 48pf, Karl Marx and Friedrich Engels. 60pf, Red banner above heads and shoulders of workers.

**1953**    **Photo.**     *Perf. 13*
| | | | | |
|---|---|---|---|---|
| 137 | A36 | 6pf grnsh gray & red | 1.00 | .65 |
| 138 | A37 | 10pf grnsh gray & dk brn | 3.25 | .65 |
| 139 | A36 | 12pf grn, dp plum & dk grn | .95 | .65 |
| 140 | A37 | 16pf vio bl & dk car | 2.50 | 1.75 |
| 141 | A38 | 20pf brown & buff | 1.00 | .65 |
| 142 | A38 | 24pf brown & red | 2.50 | .65 |
| 143 | A36 | 35pf dp pur & cr | 2.50 | 1.75 |
| 144 | A36 | 48pf dk ol grn & red brn | 1.25 | .65 |
| a. | | Souvenir sheets of 6 perf. & imperf. | 120.00 | 200.00 |
| | | Hinged | 45.00 | |
| 145 | A37 | 60pf vio brn & red | 3.25 | 2.25 |
| 146 | A37 | 84pf blue & brown | 2.50 | 1.75 |
| a. | | Souvenir sheets of 4 perf. & imperf. | 120.00 | 200.00 |
| | | Hinged | 45.00 | |
| | | Nos. 137-146 (10) | 20.70 | 11.40 |

No. 144a contains one each of the denominations in types A36 and A38. Perf. and imperf.

No. 146a contains one each of the denominations in types A37 and A39. Perf. and imperf.

Maxim Gorky — A40

**1953, Mar. 28**
| | | | | |
|---|---|---|---|---|
| 147 | A40 | 35pf brown | .45 | .40 |

Bicycle Racers — A41

24pf, 60pf, Different views of bicycle race.

**1953, May 2**    **Wmk. 297**    *Perf. 13*
| | | | | |
|---|---|---|---|---|
| 148 | A41 | 24pf bluish green | 2.00 | 1.25 |
| 149 | A41 | 35pf deep ultra | 1.00 | .80 |
| 150 | A41 | 60pf chocolate | 1.25 | 1.00 |
| | | Nos. 148-150 (3) | 4.25 | 3.05 |

6th International Bicycle Peace Race.

Heinrich von Kleist — A42

20pf, Evangelical Marienkirche. 24pf, Sailboat on Oder River. 35pf, City Hall, Frankfurt-on-Oder.

**1953, July 6**     **Litho.**
| | | | | |
|---|---|---|---|---|
| 151 | A42 | 16pf chocolate | 1.10 | 1.75 |
| 152 | A42 | 20pf blue green | .80 | 1.75 |
| 153 | A42 | 24pf rose red | 1.10 | 1.75 |
| 154 | A42 | 35pf violet blue | 1.25 | 2.25 |
| | | Nos. 151-154 (4) | 4.25 | 7.50 |

700th anniversary of the founding of Frankfurt-on-Oder.

Woman Mariner — A43

Designs: 1pf, Coal miner. 6pf, German and Soviet workers. 8pf, Mother teaching Marxist principles. 10pf, Machinists. 12pf, Worker, peasant and intellectual. 15pf, Teletype operator. 16pf, Steel worker. 20pf, Bad Elster. 24pf, Stalin Boulevard. 25pf, Locomotive building. 30pf, Dancing couple. 35pf, Sports Hall, Berlin. 40pf, Laboratory worker. 48pf, Zwinger Castle, Dresden. 60pf, Launching ship. 80pf, Agricultural workers. 84pf, Dove and East German family.

**1953**    **Litho.**     *Perf. 13x12½*
| | | | | |
|---|---|---|---|---|
| 155 | A43 | 1pf black brown | 1.25 | .25 |
| 156 | A43 | 5pf emerald | 1.60 | .25 |
| 157 | A43 | 6pf violet | 1.60 | .25 |
| 158 | A43 | 8pf orange brn | 2.25 | .25 |
| 159 | A43 | 10pf blue green | 1.60 | .25 |
| 160 | A43 | 12pf blue | 1.60 | .25 |
| 161 | A43 | 15pf purple | 2.60 | .25 |
| 162 | A43 | 16pf dk violet | 5.00 | .25 |
| 163 | A43 | 20pf olive | 3.75 | .25 |
| 163A | A43 | 24pf carmine | 7.00 | .25 |
| 164 | A43 | 25pf dk green | 5.00 | .25 |
| 165 | A43 | 30pf dp car | 15.00 | .25 |
| 166 | A43 | 35pf violet bl | 13.00 | .25 |
| 167 | A43 | 40pf rose red | 10.00 | .25 |
| 168 | A43 | 48pf rose red | 10.00 | .25 |
| 169 | A43 | 60pf deep blue | 10.00 | .25 |
| 170 | A43 | 80pf aqua | 12.00 | .25 |
| 171 | A43 | 84pf chocolate | 10.00 | .25 |
| | | Nos. 155-171 (18) | 113.25 | 4.50 |
| | | Set, hinged | | |

See Nos. 187-204, 227-230A, 330-338, 476-482. For surcharges see Nos. 216-223A. Used values of Nos. 155-171 are for cto reprints with printed cancellations, printed in 1957. The reprints differ slightly from originals in design and shade.

Power Shovel — A44

Design: 35pf, Road-building machine.

**1953, Aug. 29**    **Photo.**     *Perf. 13*
| | | | | |
|---|---|---|---|---|
| 172 | A44 | 24pf red brown | 2.00 | 2.00 |
| 173 | A44 | 35pf deep green | 2.00 | 2.00 |

The 1953 Leipzig Fair.

G. W. von Knobelsdorff and Berlin State Opera House — A45

Design: 35pf, Balthasar Neumann and Wurzburg bishop's palace.

**1953, Sept. 16**     *Perf. 13x12½*
| | | | | |
|---|---|---|---|---|
| 174 | A45 | 24pf cerise | 1.60 | .70 |
| 175 | A45 | 35pf dk slate blue | 1.60 | 1.10 |

200th anniv. of the deaths of G. W. von Knobelsdorff and Balthasar Neumann, architects.

Lucas Cranach — A46

**1953, Oct. 16**     *Perf. 13x13½*
| | | | | |
|---|---|---|---|---|
| 176 | A46 | 24pf brown | 2.50 | 1.25 |

400th anniversary of the death of Lucas Cranach (1472-1553), painter.

Nurse Applying Bandage — A47

*Perf. 13½x13*

**1953, Oct. 23**     **Wmk. 297**
| | | | | |
|---|---|---|---|---|
| 177 | A47 | 24pf brown & red | 2.10 | 1.25 |

Issued to honor the Red Cross.

Mail Delivery — A48

**1953, Oct. 25**     **Photo.**
| | | | | |
|---|---|---|---|---|
| 178 | A48 | 24pf blue gray | 2.25 | .60 |

Stamp Day, Oct. 24, 1953.

Lion and Lioness — A49

**1953, Nov. 2**     *Perf. 13x13½*
| | | | | |
|---|---|---|---|---|
| 179 | A49 | 24pf olive brown | 2.00 | .50 |

75th anniversary of Leipzig Zoo.

Thomas Muntzer and Attackers — A50

16pf, H. F. K. vom Stein. 20pf, Ferdinand von Schill leading cavalry. 24pf, G. L. Blucher and battle scene. 35pf, Students fighting for National Unity. 48pf, Revolution of 1848.

**1953, Nov.**    **Photo.**     *Perf. 13x12½*
| | | | | |
|---|---|---|---|---|
| 180 | A50 | 12pf brown red | 1.20 | .40 |
| 181 | A50 | 16pf dp brown | 1.20 | .40 |
| 182 | A50 | 20pf dk car rose | 1.20 | .30 |
| 183 | A50 | 24pf deep blue | 1.20 | .30 |
| 184 | A50 | 35pf dk green | 2.00 | 1.25 |
| 185 | A50 | 48pf blksh brn | 3.00 | 1.00 |
| | | Nos. 180-185 (6) | 9.80 | 3.65 |

Issued to honor German patriots.

Franz Schubert — A51

**1953, Nov. 13**     *Perf. 13½x13*
| | | | | |
|---|---|---|---|---|
| 186 | A51 | 48pf brt orange brn | 2.50 | 1.25 |

Death of Franz Schubert, 125th anniv.

### Types of 1953 Redrawn

Designs as before.

**1953-54**    **Typo.**     *Perf. 13x12½*
| | | | | |
|---|---|---|---|---|
| 187 | A43 | 1pf black brn | .60 | .25 |
| 188 | A43 | 5pf emerald | 2.00 | .25 |
| a. | | Bklt. pane, 3 #188 + 3 #227 | 24.00 | 28.00 |
| b. | | Bklt. pane, 3 #188 + 3 #228 | 24.00 | 28.00 |
| 189 | A43 | 6pf purple | 3.25 | .25 |
| 190 | A43 | 8pf orange brn | 3.25 | .25 |
| 191 | A43 | 10pf blue grn | 30.00 | .25 |
| 192 | A43 | 12pf grnsh blue | 4.50 | .25 |
| 193 | A43 | 15pf brt vio ('54) | 14.00 | .25 |
| 194 | A43 | 16pf dk purple | 3.25 | .25 |
| 195 | A43 | 20pf olive ('54) | 60.00 | .25 |
| 196 | A43 | 24pf carmine | 4.00 | .25 |
| 197 | A43 | 25pf dk bl grn | 3.25 | .25 |
| 198 | A43 | 30pf dp carmine | 6.50 | .25 |
| 199 | A43 | 35pf dp vio bl | 4.00 | .25 |
| 200 | A43 | 40pf rose red ('54) | 8.00 | .25 |
| 201 | A43 | 48pf rose vio | 8.00 | .25 |
| 202 | A43 | 60pf blue | 14.00 | .25 |
| 203 | A43 | 80pf aqua | 3.25 | .25 |
| 204 | A43 | 84pf chocolate | 13.00 | .25 |
| | | Nos. 187-204 (18) | 184.85 | 4.50 |
| | | Set, hinged | 50.00 | |

Nos. 155-171 were printed from screened halftones, and shading consists of dots. Shading in lines without screen on Nos. 187-204. Designers' and engravers' names added below design on all values except 6, 12, 16 and 35pf. There are many other minor differences.

See note on used values after No. 171.

Gotthold E. Lessing — A52

**1954, Jan. 20**    **Photo.**     *Perf. 13*
| | | | | |
|---|---|---|---|---|
| 205 | A52 | 20pf dark green | 2.00 | .75 |

225th anniversary of the birth of G. E. Lessing, dramatist.

Dove Over Conference Table — A53

**1954, Jan. 25**     *Perf. 12½x13*
| | | | | |
|---|---|---|---|---|
| 206 | A53 | 12pf blue | 1.40 | .75 |

Four Power Conference, Berlin, 1954.

Joseph V. Stalin — A54

**1954, Mar. 5**    **Typo.**     *Perf. 13x12½*
| | | | | |
|---|---|---|---|---|
| 207 | A54 | 20pf gray, dk brn & red org | 2.50 | .75 |

1st anniv. of the death of Joseph V. Stalin.

Cyclists — A55

Design: 24pf, Cyclists passing farm.

**1954, Apr. 30**     **Photo.**
| | | | | |
|---|---|---|---|---|
| 208 | A55 | 12pf brown | 1.20 | .60 |
| 209 | A55 | 24pf dull green | 1.75 | .85 |

7th International Bicycle Peace Race.

Dancers — A56

Design: 24pf, Boy, two girls and flag.

**1954, June 3**     *Perf. 13*
210 A56 12pf emerald    .95   .65
211 A56 24pf rose brown    .95   .65

Issued to publicize the 2nd German youth meeting for peace, unity and freedom.

Fritz Reuter — A57

**1954, July 12**
212 A57 24pf sepia    1.40   .75

Death of Fritz Reuter, writer, 80th anniv.

Ernst Thälmann — A58

**1954, Aug. 18**     *Perf. 13½x13*
213 A58 24pf red org & indigo   1.00   .60

10th anniv. of the death of Ernst Thälmann (1886-1944), Communist leader.

Hall of Commerce, Leipzig Fair — A59

**1954, Sept. 4**     *Perf. 13x13½*
214 A59 24pf dark red    .65   .50
215 A59 35pf gray blue    .65   .50

Issued to publicize the 1954 Leipzig Fair.

### Redrawn Types of 1953-54 Surcharged with New Value and "X" in Black

**1954**    Typo.     *Perf. 13x12½*
216 A43 5pf on 6pf violet    .90   .25
217 A43 5pf on 8pf org brn   1.10   .25
218 A43 10pf on 12pf blue   1.10   .25
219 A43 15pf on 16pf dk pur   .90   .25
220 A43 20pf on 24pf car    .90   .25
221 A43 40pf on 48pf rose vio   3.00   .25
222 A43 50pf on 60pf ultra   3.00   .25
223 A43 70pf on 84pf choc   8.50   .25
   *Nos. 216-223 (8)*    19.40   2.00

See note on used values after No. 171.

No. 163A Surcharged in Black

**1955**      Litho.
223A A43 20pf on 24pf car    .80   .45

Counterfeit surcharges exist on other values of the lithographed set (Nos. 155-171).

Pres. Wilhelm Pieck and Flags — A60

**1954, Oct. 6**     Photo.
224 A60 20pf brown    2.00   .65
225 A60 35pf greenish blue   2.00   .85

5th anniv. of the founding of the German Democratic Republic.

Cologne Cathedral, Leipzig Monument and Unissued Stamp Design — A61

**1954, Oct. 23**     *Perf. 13x13½*
226 A61 20pf brt car rose   1.25   .60
   a.   Souvenir sheet, imperf.   32.50   35.00

Stamp Day. No. 226a has frame and inscription in blue. Size: 60x80mm.

### Redrawn Types of 1953-54

Designs: 10pf, Worker, peasant and intellectual. 15pf, Steelworker. 20pf, Stalin Boulevard. 40pf, Zwinger Castle, Dresden. 50pf, Launching ship. 70pf, Dove and East German family.

**1955**    Typo.     *Perf. 13x12½*
227 A43 10pf blue    1.50   .25
   a.   Bklt. pane, 4 #227 + 2 #228   28.00   28.00
227B A43 15pf violet    2.75   .25
228 A43 20pf carmine    1.50   .25
229 A43 40pf rose violet   4.00   .25
230 A43 50pf deep blue   6.25   .25
230A A43 70pf chocolate   7.50   .25
   *Nos. 227-230A (6)*    23.50   1.50

See note on used values after No. 171.

Soviet Pavilion, Leipzig Spring Fair — A62

Design: 35pf, Chinese pavilion.

**1955, Feb. 21**    Photo.     *Perf. 13x13½*    Wmk. 297
231 A62 20pf rose violet    .90   .40
232 A62 35pf violet blue   1.10   .40

Issued to publicize the Leipzig Spring Fair.

Women of Three Nations — A63

**1955, Mar. 1**     *Perf. 13x13½*
233 A63 10pf green    .90   .30
234 A63 20pf red    .90   .30

International Women's Day, 45th year.

Workers' Demonstration A64

**1955, Mar. 15**     *Perf. 13x12½*
235 A64 10pf black & red    .90   .70

Intl. Trade Union Conference, Apr., 1955.

A65

Monument to the Victims of Fascism.

**1955, Apr. 9**     *Perf. 13½x13*
236 A65 10pf violet blue    .70   .60
237 A65 20pf cerise    1.00   .90
   a.   Souv. sheet of 2, #236-237, imperf.   15.00   15.00

No. 237a sold for 50pf.

A66

Russian War Memorial, Berlin.

**1955, Apr. 15**     *Perf. 12½x13*
238 A66 20pf lilac rose    1.30   .80

Nos. 236-238 issued for 10th anniv. of liberation, No. 237a for reconstruction of natl. memorial sites.

Cyclists — A67

**1955**    Wmk. 297     *Perf. 13½x13*
239 A67 10pf blue green    .80   .35
240 A67 20pf car rose    .80   .45

8th International Bicycle Peace Race, Prague-Berlin-Warsaw.

Starting with the 1955 issues, commemorative stamps which are valued in italics were sold on a restricted basis.

Friedrich von Schiller — A68

Various Portraits of Schiller.

**1955, Apr. 30**
241 A68 5pf dk gray grn    *2.00*   *1.75*
242 A68 10pf brt blue    .50   .25
243 A68 20pf chocolate    .50   .25
   a.   Souv. sheet, #241-243, imperf.   18.00   18.00
   *Nos. 241-243 (3)*    3.00   2.25

150th anniv. of the death of Friedrich von Schiller, poet.
No. 243a sold for 50pf.

Karl Liebknecht A69

Portraits: 10pf, August Bebel. 15pf, Franz Mehring. 20pf, Ernst Thalmann. 25pf, Clara Zetkin. 40pf, Wilhelm Liebknecht. 60pf, Rosa Luxemburg.

**1955, June 20**    Photo.     *Perf. 13x12½*
244 A69 5pf blue green    .30   .30
245 A69 10pf deep blue    .30   .30
246 A69 15pf violet    4.25   2.50
247 A69 20pf carmine    .40   .30
248 A69 25pf dk blue    .40   .30
249 A69 40pf rose carmine   2.00   .30
250 A69 60pf dk brown    .40   .30
   *Nos. 244-250 (7)*    8.05   4.30

Issued to honor German communists.

Optical Goods — A70

Design: 20pf, Pottery and china.

**1955, Aug. 29**    Photo.     *Perf. 13x13½*
253 A70 10pf dark blue    .60   .35
254 A70 20pf slate green    .60   .35

Issued to publicize the 1955 Leipzig Fair.

Farmer Receiving Deed A71     Harvesters A72

10pf, Construction of new farm community.

**1955, Sept. 3**     *Perf. 13½x13, 13x13½*
255 A71 5pf dull green    4.25   3.50
256 A71 10pf ultra    .60   .25
257 A72 20pf lake    .60   .25
   *Nos. 255-257 (3)*    5.45   4.00

10th anniv. of the Land-Reform Program.

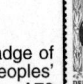

Man Holding Badge of Peoples' Solidarity — A73

          *Perf. 13½x13*
**1955, Oct. 10**     Wmk. 297
258 A73 10pf dark blue    .60   .40

10th anniv. of the "Peoples' Solidarity."

Engels at "First International," 1864 — A74

Designs: 10pf, Marx and Engels writing the Communist Manifesto. 15pf, Engels as newspaper editor. 20pf, Friedrich Engels. 30pf, Friedrich Engels. 70pf, Engels on the barricades in 1848.

**1955, Nov. 7**     *Perf. 13½x13*
259 A74 5pf dp blue & bis    .25   .25
260 A74 10pf vio & yel    .50   .25
261 A74 15pf sl blk & bis    .50   .25
262 A74 20pf brn pur & org   1.00   .25
263 A74 30pf org brn & gray     
      bl    6.00   5.00
264 A74 70pf gray & rose   3.00   .25
   a.   Souvenir sheet of 6, #259-264   60.00   120.00
   *Nos. 259-264 (6)*    11.25   6.25

Friedrich Engels, 135th birth anniv.

Cathedral at Magdeburg — A75

German Buildings: 10pf, German State Opera. 15pf, Old City Hall, Leipzig. 20pf, City Hall, Berlin. 30pf, Cathedral at Erfurt. 40pf, Zwinger at Dresden.

**1955, Nov. 14**
265 A75 5pf black brown    .65   .35
266 A75 10pf gray green    .65   .35
267 A75 15pf purple    .65   .65
268 A75 20pf carmine    .65   .65
269 A75 30pf dk red brown   6.00   8.50
270 A75 40pf indigo    1.25   .65
   *Nos. 265-270 (6)*    9.85   10.85

For surcharges see Nos. B29-B30.

Georgius Agricola — A76

**1955, Nov. 21**     Wmk. 297
271 A76 10pf brown    .60   .40

400th anniv. of the death of Georgius Agricola, mineralogist and scholar.

Paintings in Dresden Gallery — A77

Famous Paintings: 5pf, Portrait of a Young Man, by Dürer. 10pf, Chocolate Girl, by Liotard. 15pf, Portrait of a Boy, by Pinturicchio. 20pf, Self-portrait with Saskia, by Rembrandt. 40pf, Girl with Letter, by Vermeer. 70pf, Sistine Madonna, by Raphael.

**1955, Dec. 15**     *Perf. 13½x13*
272 A77 5pf dk red brown    .55   .25
273 A77 10pf chestnut    .55   .25
274 A77 15pf pale purple   19.00   19.00
275 A77 20pf brown    .55   .25
276 A77 40pf olive green    .55   .35
277 A77 70pf deep blue    1.25   .65
   *Nos. 272-277 (6)*    22.45   20.75

Issued to publicize the return of famous art works to the Dresden Art Gallery.
See Nos. 355-360, 439-443.

Mozart — A78

Designs: 20pf, Portrait facing left.

| 1956, Jan. 27 | | Photo. |
|---|---|---|
| 278 A78 10pf gray green | 9.00 | 6.00 |
| 279 A78 20pf copper brown | 3.00 | 1.50 |

200th anniv. of the birth of Wolfgang Amadeus Mozart, composer.

Flag and Schoenefeld Airport, Berlin — A79

Lufthansa Plane — A80

Designs: 15pf, Plane facing right. 20pf, Plane facing down and left.

| 1956, Feb. 1 | | Perf. 13x12½ |
|---|---|---|
| 280 A79 5pf multicolored | 11.00 | 8.00 |
| 281 A80 10pf gray green | .65 | .35 |
| 282 A80 15pf dull blue | .65 | .35 |
| 283 A80 20pf brown red | .65 | .35 |
| Nos. 280-283 (4) | 12.95 | 9.05 |

Issued to commemorate the opening of passenger service of the German Lufthansa.

Heinrich Heine — A81

Design: 20pf, Heine (different portrait.)

| 1956, Feb. 17 | | Perf. 13½x13 |
|---|---|---|
| 284 A81 10pf Prus green | 9.00 | 5.00 |
| 285 A81 20pf dark red | 2.00 | .50 |

Cent. of the death of Heinrich Heine, poet.

Railroad Cranes — A82

| 1956, Feb. 26 | | Perf. 13x13½ |
|---|---|---|
| 286 A82 20pf brown red | .60 | .40 |
| 287 A82 35pf violet blue | .90 | .75 |

Issued to publicize the Leipzig Spring Fair.

Ernst Thälmann — A83

| 1956, Apr. 16 | Litho. | Perf. 13x13½ |
|---|---|---|
| 288 A83 20pf blk ol & red | .60 | .35 |
| a. Souvenir sheet of 1, imperf | 8.00 | 22.50 |

Birth of Ernst Thälmann, 70th anniv.
No. 288a was sold at double face value. The proceeds were used for national memorials at former concentration camps.

Wheel, Hand and Olive Branch — A84

Design: 20pf, Wheel and coats of arms of Warsaw, Berlin, Prague.

### Perf. 13½x13

| 1956, Apr. 30 | | Wmk. 297 |
|---|---|---|
| 289 A84 10pf lt green | .65 | .25 |
| 290 A84 20pf brt carmine | .65 | .25 |

9th International Bicycle Peace Race, Warsaw-Berlin-Prague, May 1-15, 1956.

City Hall and Old Market — A85

Designs: 20pf, Hofkirche and Elbe Bridge. 40pf, Technical College.

| 1956, June 1 | | |
|---|---|---|
| 291 A85 10pf green | .35 | .25 |
| 292 A85 20pf carmine rose | .35 | .25 |
| 293 A85 40pf brt purple | 1.25 | 1.60 |
| Nos. 291-293 (3) | 1.95 | 2.10 |

750th anniversary of Dresden.

Worker Holding Cogwheel Emblem — A86

| 1956, June 30 | | Perf. 13½x13 |
|---|---|---|
| 294 A86 20pf rose red | .45 | .25 |

10th anniversary of nationalized industry.

Robert Schumann (Music by Schubert) — A87

| 1956, July 20 | | Perf. 13x13½ |
|---|---|---|
| 295 A87 10pf brt green | 1.60 | .90 |
| 296 A87 20pf rose red | 1.00 | .25 |

Centenary of the death of Robert Schumann, composer. See Nos. 303-304.

Soccer Players — A88

Designs: 10pf, Javelin Thrower. 15pf, Women Hurdlers. 20pf, Gymnast.

| 1956, July 25 | | Perf. 13½x13 |
|---|---|---|
| 297 A88 5pf green | .30 | .25 |
| 298 A88 10pf dk vio blue | .30 | .25 |
| 299 A88 15pf red violet | 1.75 | 1.10 |
| 300 A88 20pf rose red | .30 | .25 |
| Nos. 297-300 (4) | 2.65 | 1.85 |

Second Sports Festival, Leipzig, Aug. 2-5.

Thomas Mann — A89

| 1956, Aug. 13 | | Wmk. 297 |
|---|---|---|
| 301 A89 20pf bluish black | .85 | .45 |

Death of Thomas Mann, novelist, 1st anniv.

Jakub Bart Cisinski — A90

| 1956, Aug. 20 | | Photo. |
|---|---|---|
| 302 A90 50pf claret | .85 | .45 |

Birth centenary of Jakub Bart Cisinski, poet.

Robert Schumann (Music by Schumann) — A91

| 1956, Oct. 8 | | Perf. 13x13½ |
|---|---|---|
| 303 A91 10pf brt green | 4.75 | 1.25 |
| 304 A91 20pf rose red | 2.00 | .25 |

See Nos. 295, 296.

Lace — A92

Design: 20pf, Sailboat.

| 1956, Sept. 1 | Typo. | Perf. 13½x13 |
|---|---|---|
| 305 A92 10pf green & blk | .30 | .30 |
| 306 A92 20pf rose red & blk | .30 | .30 |

Leipzig Fair, Sept. 2-9.

Olympic Rings, Laurel and Torch — A93

Design: 35pf, Classic javelin thrower.

| 1956, Sept. 28 | | Litho. |
|---|---|---|
| 307 A93 20pf brown red | .45 | .35 |
| 308 A93 35pf slate blue | .65 | .45 |

16th Olympic Games at Melbourne, Nov. 22-Dec. 8, 1956.

Post Runner of 1450 — A94

| 1956, Oct. 27 | | |
|---|---|---|
| 309 A94 20pf red | .50 | .35 |

Issued to publicize the Day of the Stamp.

Greifswald University Seal — A95

| 1956, Oct. 17 | | Perf. 13x13½ |
|---|---|---|
| 310 A95 20pf magenta | .55 | .35 |

500th anniv. of Greifswald University.

Ernst Abbe A96     Zeiss Works, Jena A97

Portrait: 25pf, Carl Zeiss.

### Perf. 12½x13, 13x12½

| 1956, Nov. 9 | Photo. | Wmk. 297 |
|---|---|---|
| 311 A96 10pf dark green | .25 | .25 |
| 312 A97 20pf brown red | .25 | .25 |
| 313 A96 25pf bluish black | .35 | .30 |
| Nos. 311-313 (3) | .85 | .80 |

Carl Zeiss Optical Works, Jena, 110th anniv.

Chinese Girl with Flowers — A98

Designs: 10pf, Negro woman and child. 25pf, European man and dove.

| 1956, Dec. 10 | Litho. | Perf. 13 |
|---|---|---|
| 314 A98 5pf ol, *pale lem* | 1.10 | .75 |
| 315 A98 10pf brown, *pink* | .25 | .25 |
| 316 A98 25pf vio bl, *pale vio bl* | .25 | .25 |
| Nos. 314-316 (3) | 1.60 | 1.25 |

Issued for Human Rights Day.

Elephants A99

| 1956, Dec. 14 | Photo. | Perf. 13x12½ |
|---|---|---|
| **Design in Gray** | | |
| 317 A99 5pf shown | .25 | .25 |
| 318 A99 10pf Flamingoes | .25 | .25 |
| 319 A99 15pf White rhinoceros | 4.50 | 3.00 |
| 320 A99 20pf Mouflon | .25 | .25 |
| 321 A99 25pf Bison | .25 | .25 |
| 322 A99 30pf Polar bear | .25 | .25 |
| Nos. 317-322 (6) | 5.75 | 4.25 |

Issued to publicize the Berlin Zoo.

Freighter A100

Design: 25pf, Electric Locomotive.

| 1957, Mar. 1 | Litho. | Wmk. 313 |
|---|---|---|
| 323 A100 20pf rose red | .25 | .25 |
| 324 A100 25pf bright blue | .25 | .25 |

Leipzig Spring Fair.

Silver Thistle — A101

10pf, Emerald lizard. 20pf, Lady's-slipper.

| 1957, Apr. 12 | Photo. | Wmk. 313 |
|---|---|---|
| 325 A101 5pf chocolate | .25 | .25 |
| 326 A101 10pf dk slate grn | 2.00 | 1.75 |
| 327 A101 20pf red brown | .25 | .25 |
| Nos. 325-327 (3) | 2.50 | 2.25 |

Nature Conservation Week, Apr. 14-20.

Children at Play — A102

20pf, Friedrich Froebel and Children.

| 1957, Apr. 18 | Litho. | Perf. 13 |
|---|---|---|
| 328 A102 10pf black & olive | 1.00 | .25 |
| 329 A102 20pf black & brown red | .25 | .25 |

175th anniv. of the birth of Friedrich Froebel, educator.

### Redrawn Types of 1953

Designs: 5pf, Woman mariner. 10pf, Worker, peasant and intellectual. 15pf, Steel worker. 20pf, Stalin Boulevard. 25pf, Locomotive building. 30pf, Dancing couple. 40pf, Zwinger Castle, Dresden. 50pf, Launching ship. 70pf, Dove and East German family.

**Imprint: "E. Gruner K. Wolf"**
**No imprint on 10pf, 15pf**
### Perf. 13x12½, 14

| 1957-58 | Typo. | Wmk. 313 |
|---|---|---|
| 330 A43 5pf emerald | .60 | .25 |
| a. Bklt. pane, 3 #330 + 3 #331b | 27.50 | 27.50 |
| b. Bklt. pane, 3 #330 + 3 #333 | 27.50 | 27.50 |
| c. Booklet pane of 6 | 5.00 | 4.75 |
| 331 A43 10pf blue ('58) | .25 | .25 |
| a. Bklt. pane, 4 #331b + 2 #333 | 40.00 | 40.00 |
| b. Perf. 13x12½ | 5.50 | .25 |
| 332 A43 15pf violet ('58) | .60 | .25 |
| a. Perf. 13x12½ | .60 | .25 |
| 333 A43 20pf carmine | .25 | .25 |
| a. Bklt. pane, 5 #333 + 1 #477 | 4.00 | 8.00 |
| 334 A43 25pf bluish green | .30 | .25 |
| 335 A43 30pf dull red | .25 | .25 |
| 336 A43 40pf rose violet | .25 | .25 |

337 A43 50pf bright blue .25 .25
338 A43 70pf chocolate .25 .25
Nos. 330-338 (9) 3.00 2.25

No. 334 comes only perf 13x12½. Nos 330-333 and 335-338 come both perf 13x12½ and perf 14. Values are for the cheaper perf 14 varieties.
See Nos. 476-482.

**Pieck Type of 1953**
Photo.    Perf. 13x13½
339 A35 1m dk olive grn ('58) 1.75 .30
340 A35 2m red brown ('58) 3.75 .30

Bicycle Race Route — A103

Perf. 13x13½
**1957, Apr. 30    Litho.    Wmk. 313**
346 A103 5pf orange .35 .25

Issued to publicize the 10th International Bicycle Peace Race, Prague-Berlin-Warsaw.

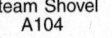

Steam Shovel          Miner
A104                   A105

Design: 20pf, Coal conveyor.

Perf. 13x12½, 13½x13 (25pf)
**1957, May 3**
347 A104 10pf green .25 .25
348 A104 20pf redsh brown .25 .25
349 A105 25pf blue violet 2.00 1.00
Nos. 347-349 (3) 2.50 1.50

Issued in honor of the coal mining industry.

Henri Dunant and Globe — A106

25pf, Henri Dunant facing right and globe.

**1957, May 7    Photo.    Perf. 13x12½**
350 A106 10pf green, red & blk .25 .25
351 A106 25pf brt blue, red & blk .25 .25
Tenth Red Cross world conference.

**Portrait Type of 1950, Redrawn**
Portraits: 5pf, Joachim Jungius. 10pf, Leonhard Euler. 20pf, Heinrich Hertz.

**1957, June 7    Litho.**
352 A11 5pf brown 1.25 .75
353 A11 10pf green .25 .25
354 A11 20pf henna brown .25 .25
Nos. 352-354 (3) 1.75 1.25

Issued to honor famous German scientists.

**Painting Type of 1955.**
Famous Paintings: 5pf, Holy Family, by Mantegna. 10pf, The Dancer Campani, by Carriera. 15pf, Portrait of Morette, by Holbein. 20pf, The Tribute Money, by Titian. 25pf, Saskia with Red Flower, by Rembrandt. 40pf, Young Standard Bearer, by Piazetta.

Perf. 13½x13
**1957, June 26    Photo.    Wmk. 313**
355 A77 5pf dk brown .30 .25
356 A77 10pf lt yellow grn .30 .25
357 A77 15pf brown olive .30 .25
358 A77 20pf rose brown .30 .25
359 A77 25pf deep claret .30 .25
360 A77 40pf dk blue gray 3.50 1.50
Nos. 355-360 (6) 5.00 2.75

Clara Zetkin — A107

**1957, July 5    Perf. 13x13½**
361 A107 10pf dk green & red .60 .25
Centenary of the birth of Clara Zetkin, politician and founder of the socialist women's movement.

Bertolt Brecht — A108

**1957, Aug. 14    Perf. 13½x13**
362 A108 10pf dark green .30 .25
363 A108 25pf deep blue .40 .25
Brecht (1898-1956), playwright and poet.

Congress Emblem — A109

**1957, Aug. 23    Litho.**
364 A109 20pf brt red & black .55 .25
4th Intl. Trade Union Congress, Leipzig, Oct. 4-15.

Fair Emblem — A110

**1957, Aug. 30    Wmk. 313**
365 A110 20pf crimson & ver .30 .25
366 A110 25pf brt blue & lt blue .30 .25
Issued to publicize the 1957 Leipzig Fair.

Savings Book — A111

**1957, Oct. 10    Perf. 13½x13**
367 A111 10pf grn & blk, gray .80 .50
368 A111 20pf rose car & blk, gray .30 .30
Issued to publicize "Savings Weeks."

Postrider, 1563 — A112

**1957, Oct. 25    Wmk. 313**
369 A112 5pf black, pale sepia .50 .25
Issued for the Day of the Stamp.

Sputnik I — A113

20pf, Stratospheric balloon above clouds. 25pf, Ship with plumb line exploring deep sea.

**1957-58    Perf. 12½x13**
370 A113 10pf blue black .40 .25
371 A113 20pf car rose ('58) .50 .25
372 A113 25pf brt blue ('58) 1.60 1.10
Nos. 370-372 (3) 2.50 1.60

IGY. The 10pf also for the launching of the 1st artificial satellite.

Storming of the Winter Palace — A114

**1957, Nov. 7    Photo.**
373 A114 10pf yellow grn & red .25 .25
374 A114 25pf brt blue & red .25 .25
40th anniv. of the Russian Revolution.

Guenther Ramin — A115

Portrait: 20pf, Hermann Abendroth.

Perf. 13½x13
**1957, Nov. 22    Litho.    Wmk. 313**
375 A115 10pf yellow grn & blk .85 .75
376 A115 20pf red orange & blk .25 .25
Ramin (1898-1956) and Abendroth (1883-1956), musicians, on the 1st anniv. of their death.

Dove and Globe — A116

**1958, Feb. 27    Perf. 13x13½**
377 A116 20pf rose red .30 .25
378 A116 25pf blue .30 .25
Issued to publicize the 1958 Leipzig Fair.

Radio Tower, Morse Code and Post Horn — A117

Design: 20pf, Radio tower and small post horn.

**1958, Mar. 6    Perf. 13x12½**
379 A117 5pf gray & blk .75 .45
380 A117 20pf crim rose & dk red .30 .25
Conf. of Postal Ministers of Communist countries, Moscow, Dec. 3-17, 1957.

Sketch by Zille — A118

Design: 20pf, Self-portrait of Zille.

**1958, Mar. 20    Perf. 13½x13**
381 A118 10pf green & gray 2.10 1.10
382 A118 20pf dp car & gray .55 .25
Centenary of the birth of Heinrich Zille, artist.

Symbolizing Quantum Theory — A119

Design: 20pf, Max Planck.

**1958, Apr. 23    Litho.**
383 A119 10pf gray green 1.00 .90
384 A119 20pf magenta .35 .25
Centenary of the birth of Max Planck, physicist.

Prize Cow — A120

10pf, Mowing machine. 20pf, Beet harvester.

Perf. 13x13½
**1958, June 4    Wmk. 313**
Size: 28x23mm
385 A120 5pf gray & blk 1.75 1.00
Size: 39x22mm
Perf. 13x12½
386 A120 10pf brt green .35 .25
387 A120 20pf rose red .35 .25
Nos. 385-387 (3) 2.45 1.50
6th Agricultural Show, Markkleeberg.

Charles Darwin — A121

Portrait: 20pf, Carl von Linné.

**1958, June 19    Perf. 13x13½**
388 A121 10pf green & black 1.20 .85
389 A121 20pf dk red & black .25 .25
Cent. of Darwin's theory of evolution and the bicent. of Linné's botanical system.

Seven Towers of Rostock and Ships — A122

10pf, Ship at pier. 25pf, Ships in harbor.

**1958    Perf. 13½x13**
390 A122 10pf emerald .25 .25
391 A122 20pf red orange .50 .25
392 A122 25pf lt blue .90 .90
Nos. 390-392 (3) 1.65 1.40
Establishment of Rostock as a seaport.
Issue dates: 20pf, July 5; 10pf and 25pf, Nov. 24.
For overprint see No. 500.

Congress Emblem — A123

**1958, June 25    Perf. 13x13½**
393 A123 10pf rose red .35 .30
5th congress of the Socialist Party of the German Democratic Republic (SED).

Mare and Foal — A124

Designs: 10pf, Trotter. 20pf, Horse race.

**1958, July 22    Photo.    Perf. 13x12½**
394 A124 5pf black brown 1.90 1.50
395 A124 10pf dk ol grn .25 .25
396 A124 20pf dark red brown .25 .25
Nos. 394-396 (3) 2.40 2.00
Grand Prize of the DDR, 1958.

Jan Amos Komensky (Comenius) — A125

Design: 20pf, Teacher and pupils, 17th cent.

**1958, Aug. 7　Litho.　Perf. 13x13½**
397　A125　10pf brt bl grn & blk　1.25　.90
398　A125　20pf org brn & blk　.25　.25

University
Seal — A126

Design: 20pf, Schiller University, Jena.

**1958, Aug. 19　　　Perf. 13x12½**
399　A126　5pf gray & black　1.20　.90
400　A126　20pf dark red & gray　.25　.25

Friedrich Schiller University in Jena, 400th anniv.

Soldier on Obstacle
Course — A127

Design: 20pf, Spartacist emblem. 25pf, Marching athletes, map and flag.

**Perf. 13½x13**
**1958, Sept. 19　Litho.　Wmk. 313**
401　A127　10pf emerald & brn　1.20　.75
402　A127　20pf brown red & yel　.25　.25
403　A127　25pf lt blue & red　.25　.25
　　　Nos. 401-403 (3)　1.70　1.25

1st Spartacist Sports Meet of Friendly Armies, Leipzig, Sept. 20-28.

Arms Breaking A-
Bomb — A128

**1958, Sept. 19　　　Perf. 13x13½**
404　A128　20pf rose red　.25　.25
405　A128　25pf blue　.40　.25

People's fight against atomic death.

Woman and
Leipzig Railroad
Station — A129

Design: 25pf, Woman in Persian lamb coat and old City Hall, Leipzig.

**1958, Aug. 29　　　Perf. 13x12½**
406　A129　10pf green, brn & blk　.25　.25
407　A129　25pf blue & black　.25　.25

Issued to publicize the 1958 Leipzig Fair.

Post Wagon,
17th
Century — A130

Design: 20pf, Mail train and plane.

**1958, Oct. 23　　　Wmk. 313**
408　A130　10pf green　1.60　1.00
409　A130　20pf lake　.35　.25

Issued for the Day of the Stamp.

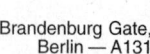

Brandenburg Gate,
Berlin — A131

**1958, Nov. 29　　　Perf. 13x13½**
410　A131　20pf rose red　.35　.25
411　A131　25pf dark blue　2.25　1.25

Issued to commemorate 10 years of democratic city administration of Berlin.

Head from Greek
Tomb — A132

20pf, Giant's head from Pergamum frieze.

**1958, Dec. 2　　　Perf. 13½x13**
412　A132　10pf blue grn & blk　1.20　.85
413　A132　20pf dp rose & black　.25　.25

Return of art treasures from Russia. See Nos. 484-486.

Negro and
Caucasian
Men — A133

Design: 25pf, Chinese and Caucasian girls.

**1958, Dec. 10　　　Perf. 13x12½**
414　A133　10pf brt blue grn & blk　.25　.25
415　A133　25pf blue & black　1.60　.90

10th anniv. of the signing of the Universal Declaration of Human Rights.

Worker and
Soldier — A134

**1958, Nov. 7　　　Perf. 12½x13**
416　A134　20pf blk, ver & dl pur　7.50　12.50

40th anniv. of the Revolution of Nov. 7. (Stamp inscribed Nov. 9.) Withdrawn from sale on day of issue.

Otto Nuschke — A135

**Perf. 13½x13**
**1958, Dec. 27　　　Wmk. 313**
417　A135　20pf red　.30　.25

First anniversary of the death of Otto Nuschke, vice president of the republic.

Communist
Newspaper,
"The Red
Flag" — A136

**1958, Dec. 30　　　Perf. 13x12½**
418　A136　20pf red　.35　.25

German Communist Party, 40th anniv.

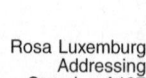

Rosa Luxemburg
Addressing
Crowd — A137

20pf, Karl Liebknecht addressing crowd.

**Perf. 13x13½**
**1959, Jan. 15　　　Wmk. 313**
419　A137　10pf blue green　1.75　1.10
420　A137　20pf henna brn & blk　.25　.25

40th anniversary of the death of Rosa Luxemburg and Karl Liebknecht.

Gewandhaus,
Leipzig — A138

Design: 25pf, Opening theme of Mendelssohn's A Major symphony.

**1959, Feb. 28　Engr.　Perf. 14**
421　A138　10pf green, grnsh　.35　.30
422　A138　25pf blue, bluish　1.25　2.25

150th anniversary of the birth of Felix Mendelssohn-Bartholdy, composer.

President Wilhelm
Pieck — A139

**1959, Jan. 3　Photo.　Perf. 13½x13**
423　A139　20pf henna brown　.40　.25

83rd birthday of President Wilhelm Pieck. See No. 511.

"Black Pump"
Plant — A140

Design: 25pf, Photographic equipment.

**1959, Feb. 28　　　Perf. 13x12½**
424　A140　20pf carmine rose　.25　.25
425　A140　25pf lt ultra　.35　.25

1959 Leipzig Spring Fair.

Boy and Girl — A141

**1959, Apr. 2　　　Perf. 13½x13**
426　A141　10pf blk, lt grn　1.25　.85
427　A141　20pf blk, salmon　.25　.25

5 years of the Youth Consecration ceremony.

Statue of Handel,
Halle — A142

20pf, Handel by Thomas Hudson, 1749.

**1959, Apr. 27　　　Wmk. 313**
428　A142　10pf bluish grn & blk　1.40　.90
429　A142　20pf rose & blk　.25　.25

Bicentenary of the death of George Frederick Handel, composer.

Alexander von Humboldt
and Central American
View — A143

Design: 20pf, Portrait and Siberian view.

**1959, May 6**
430　A143　10pf bluish grn　1.25　.90
431　A143　20pf rose　.30　.25

Centenary of the death of Alexander von Humboldt, naturalist and geographer.

Post Horn — A144

**1959, May 30　　　Perf. 13½x13**
432　A144　20pf scar, yel & blk　.30　.25
433　A144　25pf lt bl, yel & blk　.60　.60

Conference of socialist postal ministers.

Gray
Heron — A145

10pf, Bittern. 20pf, Lily of the valley & butterfly. 25pf, Beaver. 40pf, Pussy willows and bee.

**1959, June 26　　　Perf. 13x12½**
434　A145　5pf lt bl, blk & lil　.25　.25
435　A145　10pf grnsh bl, dk brn & org　.25　.25
436　A145　20pf org red, grn & vio　.25　.25
437　A145　25pf lilac, yel & blk　.35　.25
438　A145　40pf gray bl, yel & blk　4.75　3.00
　　　Nos. 434-438 (5)　5.85　4.00

Issued to publicize wildlife protection.

**Painting Type of 1955.**

Famous Paintings: 5pf, Portrait, by Angelica Kauffmann. 10pf, The Lady Lace Maker, by Gabriel Metsu. 20pf, Mademoiselle Lavergne, by Liotard. 25pf, Old Woman with Brazier, by Rubens. 40pf, Young Man in Black Coat, by Hals.

**1959, June 29　Photo.　Perf. 13½x13**
439　A77　5pf olive　.25　.25
440　A77　10pf green　.25　.25
441　A77　20pf dp org　.25　.25
442　A77　25pf chestnut　.35　.25
443　A77　40pf dp magenta　4.50　2.25
　　　Nos. 439-443 (5)　5.60　3.25

Great
Cormorant — A146

Birds: 10pf, Black Stork. 15pf, Eagle owl. 20pf, Black grouse. 25pf, Hoopoe. 40pf, Peregrine falcon.

**Perf. 13x13½**
**1959, July 2　Litho.　Wmk. 313**
**Designs in Black**
444　A146　5pf yellow　.25　.25
445　A146　10pf lt green　.25　.25
446　A146　15pf pale violet　4.25　2.50
447　A146　20pf deep pink　.25　.25
448　A146　25pf blue　.25　.25
449　A146　40pf vermilion　.25　.25
　　　Nos. 444-449 (6)　5.50　3.75

Protection of native birds.

Youths of Three
Races — A147

25pf, Swedish girl kissing African girl, horiz.

**1959, July 25　Perf. 12½x13, 13x12½**
450　A147　20pf crimson　.30　.25
451　A147　25pf bright blue　.75　.60

7th World Youth Festival, Vienna, 7/26-8/14.

Glass Tea
Service — A148

Design: 25pf, Distilling apparatus, vert.

**1959, Sept. 1　Perf. 13x12½, 12½x13**
452　A148　10pf bluish green　.25　.25
453　A148　25pf bright blue　1.60　1.00

75 years of Jena glassware.

Lunik 2
Hitting
Moon
A149

**1959, Sept. 21**     **Perf. 13½x13**
454 A149 20pf rose red    .50 .35
Landing of the Soviet rocket Lunik 2 on the moon, Sept. 13, 1959.

New Buildings,
Leipzig, Globe
and Fair
Emblem — A150

**1959, Aug. 17**     **Perf. 13x12½**
455 A150 20pf gray & rose    .35 .30
1959 Leipzig Fall Fair.

Flag and
Harvester — A151

10pf, Fritz Heckert rest home. 15pf, Zwinger, Dresden. 20pf, Steelworker. 25pf, Chemist. 40pf, Central Stadium, Leipzig. 50pf, Woman tractor driver. 60pf, Airplane. 70pf, Merchant ship. 1m, 1st atomic reactor of the DDR.

**1959, Oct. 6**     **Perf. 13½x13**
**Flag in Black, Red & Orange Yellow Inscription and Design in Black & Red**
| | | | |
|---|---|---|---|
| 456 A151 5pf yellow | | .25 | .25 |
| 457 A151 10pf gray | | .25 | .25 |
| 458 A151 15pf citron | | .25 | .25 |
| 459 A151 20pf gray | | .25 | .25 |
| 460 A151 25pf lt gray olive | | .25 | .25 |
| 461 A151 40pf citron | | .25 | .25 |
| 462 A151 50pf salmon | | .25 | .25 |
| 463 A151 60pf pale bluish grn | | .25 | .25 |
| 464 A151 70pf pale grnsh yel | | .25 | .25 |
| 465 A151 1m bister brn | | .35 | .40 |
| Nos. 456-465 (10) | | 2.60 | 2.65 |

German Democratic Republic, 10th anniv.

Johannes R.
Becher — A152

**1959, Oct. 28**   **Litho.**   **Perf. 13x13½**
466 A152 20pf red & slate   1.25 .25
1st anniversary of the death of Johannes R. Becher, writer.
Printed with alternating yellow labels. The label carries in blue a verse from the national anthem and Becher's signature.

Schiller's Home,
Weimar — A153

Design: 20pf, Friedrich von Schiller.

**1959, Nov. 10**   **Engr.**    **Perf. 14**
467 A153 10pf dl grn, *grnsh*   1.25 .90
468 A153 20pf lake, *pink*    .45 .25
Birth of Friedrich von Schiller, 200th anniv.

Post Rider and Mile
Stone, 18th
Century — A154

Design: 20pf, Motorized mailman.

---

**1959, Nov. 17**   **Litho.**   **Perf. 13½x13**
469 A154 10pf green   1.20 .85
470 A154 20pf dp rose red   .25 .25
Issued for the Day of the Stamp.

Red Squirrels
A155

**1959, Nov. 27**     **Perf. 13x12½**
| | | | |
|---|---|---|---|
| 471 A155 5pf shown | | .35 | .25 |
| 472 A155 10pf Hares | | .40 | .25 |
| 473 A155 20pf Roe deer | | .40 | .25 |
| 474 A155 25pf Red deer | | .45 | .25 |
| 475 A155 40pf Lynx | | 9.50 | 3.00 |
| Nos. 471-475 (5) | | 11.10 | 4.00 |

**Redrawn Types of 1953**
**Without Imprint**
**Perf. 14, 13x12½ (#477)**
**1959-60**    **Wmk. 313**    **Typo.**
| | | | |
|---|---|---|---|
| 476 A43 5pf emerald | | .25 | .25 |
| 477 A43 10pf lt bl grn (Machinists) | | .25 | .25 |
| a.   Perf. 14 | | 1.00 | .40 |
| b.   Bklt. pane of 6 #477 | | 6.00 | 4.75 |
| 478 A43 20pf carmine | | .25 | .25 |
| a.   Se-tenant with DEBRIA label | | .95 | .25 |
| 479 A43 30pf dull red | | .25 | .25 |
| 480 A43 40pf rose violet | | .25 | .25 |
| 481 A43 50pf brt blue | | .25 | .25 |
| 482 A43 70pf choc ('60) | | .25 | .25 |
| Nos. 476-482 (7) | | 1.75 | 1.75 |

No. 478a was issued Sept. 3, 1959, to commemorate the 2nd German Stamp Exhibition, Berlin. Sheet contains 60 stamps, 40 labels. Two other stamps without imprint are Nos. 331-332.

**Type of 1958 and**

Pergamum
Altar of
Zeus
A156

Designs: 5pf, Head of an Attic goddess, 580 B.C. 10pf, Head of a princess from Tell el Amarna, 1360 B.C. 20pf, Bronze figure from Toprak-Kale (Armenia), 7th century B.C.

**1959, Dec. 29**   **Litho.**   **Perf. 13½x13**
| | | | |
|---|---|---|---|
| 484 A132 5pf yellow & black | | .30 | .25 |
| 485 A132 10pf bluish grn & blk | | .30 | .25 |
| 486 A132 20pf rose & black | | .30 | .25 |
| 487 A156 25pf lt blue & blk | | .65 | .65 |
| Nos. 484-487 (4) | | 1.55 | 1.40 |

Boxing — A157

10pf, Sprinters. 20pf, Ski jump. 25pf, Sailboat.

**Perf. 13x13½**
**1960, Jan. 27**     **Wmk. 313**
| | | | |
|---|---|---|---|
| 488 A157 5pf brown & ocher | | 4.00 | 2.00 |
| 489 A157 10pf green & ocher | | .25 | .25 |
| 490 A157 20pf car & ocher | | .25 | .25 |
| 491 A157 25pf ultra & ocher | | .25 | .25 |
| Nos. 488-491 (4) | | 4.75 | 2.75 |

1960 Winter and Summer Olympic Games.

Technical Fair,
North Entrance
A158

Design: 25pf, "Ring" Fair building.

**1960, Feb. 17**     **Perf. 13x12½**
492 A158 20pf red & gray   .25 .25
493 A158 25pf lt blue & gray   .25 .25
1960 Leipzig Spring Fair.

---

Purple Foxglove — A159

Medicinal Plants: 10pf, Camomile. 15pf, Peppermint. 20pf, Poppy. 40pf, Dog rose.

**1960, Apr. 7**     **Perf. 12½x13**
| | | | |
|---|---|---|---|
| 494 A159 5pf grn, gray & car rose | | .25 | .25 |
| 495 A159 10pf citron, gray & grn | | .25 | .25 |
| 496 A159 15pf fawn, gray & grn | | .25 | .25 |
| 497 A159 20pf grnsh bl, gray & vio | | .25 | .25 |
| 498 A159 40pf brn, gray, grn & red | | 4.00 | 1.90 |
| Nos. 494-498 (5) | | 5.00 | 2.90 |

Lenin — A160

**1960, Apr. 22**   **Engr.**    **Perf. 14**
499 A160 20pf lake   .35 .25
90th anniversary of the birth of Lenin.

**No. 390 Overprinted:**
**"Inbetriebnahme des**
**Hochseehafens 1.Mai 1960"**
**1960, Apr. 28**   **Litho.**   **Perf. 13½x13**
500 A122 10pf emerald   .50 .35
Inauguration of the seaport Rostock.

Russian Soldier and
Liberated
Prisoner — A161

**1960, May 5**   **Litho.**    **Perf. 13x13½**
501 A161 20pf rose red   .35 .25
15th anniv. of Germany's liberation from fascism.

Model of
Vacation
Ship
A162

Designs: 25pf, Ship before Leningrad.

**Perf. 13½x13**
**1960, June 23**     **Wmk. 313**
| | | | |
|---|---|---|---|
| 502 A162 20pf slate, cit & blk | | .25 | .25 |
| 503 A162 25pf blk, yel & ultra | | 3.75 | 3.25 |
| Nos. 502-503,B58-B59 (4) | | 4.50 | 4.00 |

Launching of the trade union (FDGB) vacation ship, June 25, 1960.

Masked Dancer in
Porcelain — A163

Meissen porcelain: 10pf, Plate with Meissen mark and date. 15pf, Otter. 20pf, Potter. 25pf, Coffee pot.

**1960, July 28**     **Perf. 12½x13**
| | | | |
|---|---|---|---|
| 504 A163 5pf blue & orange | | .25 | .25 |
| 505 A163 10pf blue & emerald | | .25 | .25 |
| 506 A163 15pf blue & purple | | 3.00 | 3.00 |

---

| | | | |
|---|---|---|---|
| 507 A163 20pf blue & orange red | | .25 | .25 |
| 508 A163 25pf blue & apple grn | | .25 | .25 |
| Nos. 504-508 (5) | | 4.00 | 4.00 |

Meissen porcelain works, 250th anniv.

Lenin Monument,
Eisleben — A164

Design: 20pf, Thälmann monument, gift for Pushkin, USSR.

**Perf. 13x13½**
**1960, July 2**     **Wmk. 313**
509 A164 10pf dark green   .25 .25
510 A164 20pf bright red   .25 .25

**Pieck Type of 1959**
**1960, Sept. 10**   **Litho.**   **Perf. 13½x13**
511 A139 20pf black   .40 .30
  a.   Souv. sheet of 1, imperf.   1.20 1.90
Pres. Wilhelm Pieck (1876-1960).

Modern Postal
Trucks — A165

Design: 25pf, Railroad mail car, 19th cent.

**1960, Oct. 6**     **Perf. 13x12½**
512 A165 20pf car rose, blk & yel   .25 .25
513 A165 25pf blue, gray & blk   2.50 1.25
Issued for the Day of the Stamp, 1960.

New Opera
House,
Leipzig — A166

Design: 25pf, Car, sailboat, tent, campers.

**1960, Aug. 29**     **Wmk. 313**
514 A166 20pf rose brn & gray   .25 .25
515 A166 25pf blue & grysh brn   .30 .30
1960 Leipzig Fall Fair.

Hans Burkmair Medal,
1518 — A167

25pf, Dancing Peasants by Albrecht Dürer.

**1960, Oct. 20**   **Litho.**   **Perf. 12½x13**
516 A167 20pf buff, grn & ocher   .25 .25
517 A167 25pf lt blue & blk   1.25 1.50
400th anniv. of the Dresden Art Gallery.

Neidhardt von
Gneisenau — A168

20pf, Neidhardt von Gneisenau, horiz.

**1960, Oct. 27**   **Perf. 13x12½, 12½x13**
518 A168 20pf dk car & blk   .25 .25
519 A168 25pf ultra   1.10 1.10
200th anniversary of the birth of Count August Neidhardt von Gneisenau, Prussian Field Marshal.

Rudolf Virchow — A169

Humboldt University, Berlin — A170

10pf, Robert Koch. 25pf, Wilhelm & Alexander von Humboldt medal. 40pf, Wilheim Griesinger.

**1960, Nov. 4    Litho.    Perf. 13x12½**
520  A169  5pf ocher & blk          .25  .25
521  A169  10pf green & blk         .25  .25
522  A170  20pf cop red, gray &
            blk                           .25  .25
523  A170  25pf brt blue & blk           .25  .25
524  A169  40pf car rose & blk      2.00 1.20
       Nos. 520-524 (5)             3.00 2.20

Nos. 520, 521, 524 for the 250th anniv. of the Charité (hospital), Berlin; Nos. 522-523 the 150th anniv. of Humboldt University, Berlin. Nos. 520 and 523, and Nos. 521 and 522 are printed se-tenant.

Scientist and Chemical Formula — A171

Designs: 10pf, Chemistry worker (fertilizer). 20pf, Woman worker (automobile). 25pf, Laboratory assistant (synthetic fabrics).

**Perf. 13x13½**
**1960, Nov. 10          Wmk. 313**
525  A171  5pf dk red & gray        .25  .25
526  A171  10pf orange & brt grn    .25  .25
527  A171  20pf blue & red          .25  .25
528  A171  25pf yellow & ultra     1.50 1.75
       Nos. 525-528 (4)            2.25 2.50

Day of the Chemistry Worker.

"Young Socialists' Express" — A172

20pf, Sassnitz Harbor station & ferry. 25pf, Diesel locomotive & 1835 "Adler."

**Perf. 13x13½; 13x12½ (20pf)**
**1960, Dec. 5**
**Sizes: 10pf, 25pf, 28x23mm; 20pf, 38½x22mm**
529  A172  10pf emerald & blk       .25  .25
530  A172  20pf red & blk           .25  .25
531  A172  25pf blue & blk         4.00 3.50
       Nos. 529-531 (3)            4.50 4.00

125th anniv. of German railroads. No. 530 exists imperf. Values: unused $4; used $1.25.

**Pieck Type of 1953 with Dates Added**
**1961, Jan. 3    Photo.    Perf. 13x13½**
532  A35  20pf henna brn & blk     .40  .30

Issued on the 85th anniversary of the birth of Pres. Wilhelm Pieck (1876-1960).

380 Kilovolt Switch — A173

Design: 25pf, Leipzig Press Center.

**1961, Mar. 3    Litho.    Perf. 13½x13**
533  A173  10pf brt grn & dk gray   .30  .25
534  A173  25pf vio blue & dk gray  .30  .25

Leipzig Spring Fair of 1961.

Lilienstein — A174

---

Designs: 5pf, Rudelsburg on Saale. 10pf, Wartburg. No. 538, City Hall, Wernigerode. 25pf, Brocken, Harz Mts., horiz.

**1961          Typo.          Perf. 14**
535  A174  5pf gray              .25  .25
536  A174  10pf blue green       .25  .25
537  A174  20pf red brown        .25  .25
538  A174  20pf dull red         .25  .25
539  A174  25pf dark blue        .25  .25
       Nos. 535-539 (5)         1.25 1.25

Issued: No. 538, 25pf, 3/14; 5pf, 10pf, No. 537, 6/22.

Trawler — A176

Designs: 20pf, Fishermen. 25pf, S.S. Robert Koch. 40pf, Cannery worker.

**1961, Apr. 4    Engr.    Wmk. 313**
545  A176  10pf gray green       .25  .25
546  A176  20pf claret          .25  .25
547  A176  25pf slate           .25  .25
548  A176  40pf dull violet    1.90 1.40
       Nos. 545-548 (4)        2.65 2.15

Deep-sea fishing industry.

Vostok 1 Leaving Earth — A177

Designs: 20pf, Cosmonaut in capsule. 25pf, Parachute landing of capsule.

**1961, Apr.    Litho.    Perf. 13x12½**
549  A177  10pf lt blue grn & red  1.00  .65
550  A177  20pf red              1.00  .65
551  A177  25pf lt blue          3.50 3.25
       Nos. 549-551 (3)         5.50 4.55

1st man in space, Yuri A. Gagarin, 4/12/61. Issue dates: 10pf, Apr. 18; others, Apr. 20.

Zebra — A178

Dresden Zoo cent.: 20pf, Black-and-white colobus monkeys.

**1961, May 9**
552  A178  10pf green & blk     4.00 4.00
553  A178  20pf lilac rose & blk  .65  .40

Engels, Marx, Lenin and Crowd A179

**1961, Apr. 20    Litho.    Perf. 13½x13**
554  A179  20pf red             .40  .30

15th anniversary of Socialist Unity Party of Germany (SED).

Stag Leap — A180

Designs: 20pf, Arabesque. 25pf, Exercise on parallel bars, horiz.

**1961, June 3    Perf. 13½x13, 13x13½**
555  A180  10pf blue green      .25  .25
556  A180  20pf rose pink       .25  .25
557  A180  25pf brt blue       4.50 3.75
       Nos. 555-557 (3)        5.00 4.25

3rd Europa Cup for Women's Gymnastics.

---

Salt Miners and Castle Giebichenstein A181

20pf, Chemist and "Five Towers" of Halle.

**1961, June 22          Perf. 13x12½**
558  A181  10pf blk, grn & yel   1.20  .65
559  A181  20pf blk, dk red & yel 1.20  .65

1000th anniv. of the founding of Halle.

Kayak Slalom — A182

10pf, Canoe. 20pf, Two seater canoe.

**1961, July 6    Litho.    Wmk. 313**
560  A182  5pf gray & Prus bl   2.50 2.10
561  A182  10pf gray & olive    .25  .25
562  A182  20pf gray & car rose  .25  .25
       Nos. 560-562 (3)        3.00 2.60

Canoe Slalom and Rapids World Championships.

Target Line Casting — A183

Design: 20pf, River fishing.

**1961, July 21**
563  A183  10pf green & blue    2.50 2.00
564  A183  20pf dk red brn & blue  .30  .30

World Fishing Championships, Dresden.

Tulip — A184

**1961, Sept. 13    Photo.    Perf. 14**
565  A184  10pf shown           .35  .25
566  A184  20pf Dahlia          .35  .25
567  A184  40pf Rose           7.00 7.00
       Nos. 565-567 (3)        7.70 7.50

Intl. Horticulture Exhibition, Erfurt.

"Alte Waage," Historical Building, Leipzig — A185

Design: 25pf, Old Exchange Building.

**Perf. 13½x13**
**1961, Aug. 23    Litho.    Wmk. 313**
568  A185  10pf citron & bl grn  .25  .25
569  A185  25pf lt blue & ultra  .85  .30

1961 Leipzig Fall Fair. See Nos. 595-597.

Liszt's Hand, French Sculpture — A186

Designs: 5pf, Liszt and Hector Berlioz. 20pf, Franz Liszt, medallion by Ernst Rietschel, 1852. 25pf, Liszt and Frederic Chopin.

**1961, Oct.-Nov.    Engr.    Perf. 14**
570  A186  5pf gray             .25  .25
571  A186  10pf blue green     1.60 1.60
572  A186  20pf dull red        .25  .25
573  A186  25pf chalky blue    2.00 2.00
       Nos. 570-573 (4)        4.10 4.10

150th anniversary of the birth of Franz Liszt, composer.

---

Television Camera and Screen — A187

Design: 20pf, Microphone and radio dial.

**1961, Oct. 25          Perf. 13x13½**
574  A187  10pf brt green & blk  1.40 1.40
575  A187  20pf brick red & blk  .25  .25

Issued for Stamp Day, 1961.

Maj. Gherman Titov and Young Pioneers A188

10pf, Titov in Leipzig, vert. 15pf, Titov in spaceship. 20pf, Titov & Walter Ulbricht. 25pf, Spaceship Vostok 2. 40pf, Titov & Ulbricht in Berlin.

**1961, Dec. 11    Litho.    Perf. 13½**
576  A188  5pf carmine & vio    .25  .25
577  A188  10pf olive grn & car  .25  .25
578  A188  15pf blue & lilac   6.50 6.50
579  A188  20pf blue & car rose  .25  .25
580  A188  25pf carmine & blue  .25  .25
581  A188  40pf car & dk blue  1.20  .40
       Nos. 576-581 (6)        8.70 7.90

Visit of Russian Maj. Gherman Titov to the German Democratic Republic.

Chairman Walter Ulbricht — A189

**1961-67    Wmk. 313    Typo.    Perf. 14**
**Size: 17x21mm**
582   A189  5pf slate           .25  .25
 a.    Booklet pane of 8        24.00 32.50
583   A189  10pf brt green      .25  .25
 a.    Booklet pane of 8        10.50 16.00
584   A189  15pf red lilac      .25  .25
585   A189  20pf dark red       .30  .25
586   A189  25pf dull bl ('63)  .30  .25
587   A189  30pf car rose
              ('63)             .25  .25
588   A189  40pf brt vio ('63)  .25  .25
589   A189  50pf ultra ('63)    .25  .25
589A  A189  60pf dp yel grn
              ('64)             .30  .25
590   A189  70pf red brn ('63)  .30  .25
590A  A189  80pf brt blue ('67) .40  .40

**Engr.**
**Size: 24x28½mm**
590B  A189  1dm dull grn ('63)  .75  .35
590C  A189  2dm brown ('63)    1.50  .50
       Nos. 582-590C (13)      5.35 3.75

See Nos. 751-752, 1112A-1114A, 1483. Currency abbreviation is "DM" on Nos. 590B-590C, "MDN" on Nos. 751-752, "M" on Nos. 1113-1114A.

Red Ants — A190

**1962, Feb. 16                  Photo.**
591  A190  5pf shown           3.25 5.00
592  A190  10pf Weasels        .25  .25
593  A190  20pf Shrews         .25  .25
594  A190  40pf Bat            .45  .40
       Nos. 591-594 (4)        4.20 5.90

See Nos. 663-667.

**Type of 1961**
Buildings: 10pf, "Coffee Tree House." 20pf, Gohlis Castle. 25pf, Romanus House.

**1962, Feb. 22    Litho.    Perf. 13x13½**
595  A185  10pf olive grn & brn  .25  .25
596  A185  20pf org red & blk    .30  .25
597  A185  25pf brt blue & brn   .65  .65
       Nos. 595-597 (3)        1.20 1.15

Leipzig Spring Fair of 1962.

Air
Defense — A191

Designs: 10pf, Motorized infantry. 20pf, Soldier and worker as protectors. 25pf, Sailor and destroyer escort. 40pf, Tank and tankman.

**1962, Mar. 1**     **Perf. 13x12½**
| | | | | |
|---|---|---|---|---|
| 598 | A191 | 5pf light blue | .25 | .25 |
| 599 | A191 | 10pf bright green | .25 | .25 |
| 600 | A191 | 20pf red | .25 | .25 |
| 601 | A191 | 25pf ultra | .25 | .25 |
| 602 | A191 | 40pf brown | 1.25 | 1.20 |
| | | Nos. 598-602 (5) | 2.25 | 2.20 |

National People's Army, 6th anniv.

Cyclists and
Hradcany,
Prague — A192

25pf, Cyclist, East Berlin City Hall and dove.

**1962, Apr. 26**   **Litho.**   **Wmk. 313**
| | | | | |
|---|---|---|---|---|
| 603 | A192 | 10pf multicolored | .25 | .25 |
| 604 | A192 | 25pf multicolored | 1.10 | 1.10 |
| | | Nos. 603-604,B89 (3) | 1.60 | 1.60 |

15th International Bicycle Peace Race, Berlin-Warsaw-Prague.

Johann Gottlieb
Fichte — A193

10pf, Fichte's birthplace in Rammenau.

**1962, May 17**     **Perf. 13x13½**
| | | | | |
|---|---|---|---|---|
| 605 | A193 | 10pf brt green & blk | 1.20 | 1.50 |
| 606 | A193 | 25pf vermilion & blk | .25 | .25 |

Bicentenary of the birth of Johann Gottlieb Fichte, philosopher.

Cross, Crown of Thorns
and Rose — A194

**1962, June 7**     **Perf. 12½x13**
| | | | | |
|---|---|---|---|---|
| 607 | A194 | 20pf red & black | .25 | .25 |
| 608 | A194 | 25pf brt blue & blk | .80 | 1.00 |

20th anniversary of the destruction of Lidice in Czechoslovakia by the Nazis.

George Dimitrov at
Reichstag Trial,
Leipzig — A195

20pf, Dimitrov as Premier of Bulgaria.

**1962, June 18**   **Photo.**   **Perf. 14**
| | | | | |
|---|---|---|---|---|
| 609 | A195 | 5pf blue grn & blk | .45 | .35 |
| 610 | A195 | 20pf car rose & blk | .25 | .25 |
| a. | | Pair, #609-610, + label | 4.50 | 32.50 |

George Dimitrov, (1882-1949), communist leader and premier of the Bulgarian Peoples' Republic.
Nos. 609-610 also printed se-tenant, divided by a label inscribed with a Dimitrov quotation.

Corn
Planter — A196

20pf, Milking machine. 40pf, Combine harvester.

**1962, June 26**   **Litho.**   **Perf. 13x12½**
| | | | | |
|---|---|---|---|---|
| 611 | A196 | 10pf multicolored | .25 | .25 |
| 612 | A196 | 20pf multicolored | .25 | .25 |
| 613 | A196 | 40pf yel, grn & dk red | 1.25 | 1.20 |
| | | Nos. 611-613 (3) | 1.75 | 1.70 |

10th Agricultural Exhibition, Markkleeberg.

Map of Baltic Sea
and Emblem — A197

Designs: 20pf, Hotel, Rostock, vert. 25pf, Cargo ship "Frieden" in Rostock harbor.

**Perf. 13x13½, 13½x13 (20pf)**
**1962, July 2**     **Wmk. 313**
| | | | | |
|---|---|---|---|---|
| 614 | A197 | 10pf bluish grn & ultra | .25 | .25 |
| 615 | A197 | 20pf dk red & yellow | .25 | .25 |
| 616 | A197 | 25pf blue & bister | 1.75 | 1.60 |
| | | Nos. 614-616 (3) | 2.25 | 2.10 |

5th Baltic Sea Week, Rostock, July 7-15.

Brandenburg Gate,
Berlin — A198

No. 618 Heads of youths of three races. No. 619, Peace dove. No. 620, National Theater, Helsinki.

**1962, July 17**     **Perf. 13½x13**
| | | | | |
|---|---|---|---|---|
| 617 | A198 | 5pf multicolored | 1.60 | 2.50 |
| 618 | A198 | 5pf multicolored | 1.60 | 2.50 |
| 619 | A198 | 5pf multicolored | 1.60 | 2.50 |
| 620 | A198 | 5pf multicolored | 1.60 | 2.50 |
| a. | | Block of 4, #617-620 | 8.50 | 13.00 |
| | | Nos. 617-620 (4) | 6.40 | 10.00 |

8th Youth Festival for Peace and Friendship, Helsinki, July 28-Aug. 6, 1962.
No. 620a forms the festival flower emblem.

Free Style
Swimming — A199

Designs: 10pf, Back stroke. 25pf, Butterfly stroke. 40pf, Breast stroke. 70pf, Water polo.

**1962, Aug. 7**   **Litho.**   **Perf. 13x13½**
**Design in Greenish Blue**
| | | | | |
|---|---|---|---|---|
| 621 | A199 | 5pf orange | .25 | .25 |
| 622 | A199 | 10pf grnsh blue | .25 | .25 |
| 623 | A199 | 25pf ultra | .25 | .25 |
| 624 | A199 | 40pf brt violet | 1.00 | 1.00 |
| 625 | A199 | 70pf red brown | .25 | .25 |
| a. | | Block of 6, #621-625, B92 | 2.00 | 2.00 |
| | | Nos. 621-625,B92 (6) | 2.25 | 2.25 |

10th European Swimming Championships. Leipzig, Aug. 18-25.
Nos. 621-625, B92 each printed in sheets of 50, No. 625a in sheet of 60.

Municipal Store,
Leipzig — A200

Buildings: 20pf, Mädler Passage. 25pf, Leipzig Air Terminal and plane.

**Engr. & Photo.**
**1962, Aug. 28**   **Wmk. 313**   **Perf. 14**
| | | | | |
|---|---|---|---|---|
| 626 | A200 | 10pf black & emer-ald | .25 | .25 |
| 627 | A200 | 20pf black & red | .30 | .25 |
| 628 | A200 | 25pf black & blue | .65 | .50 |
| | | Nos. 626-628 (3) | 1.20 | 1.00 |

Leipzig Fall Fair of 1962.

"Transportation and
Communication"
A201

**1962, Oct. 3**   **Litho.**   **Perf. 13½x13**
| | | | | |
|---|---|---|---|---|
| 629 | A201 | 5pf light blue & black | .30 | .25 |

10th anniv. of the Friedrich List Transportation College.

Souvenir Sheet

Pavel R. Popovich, Andrian G.
Nikolayev and Space
Capsules — A202

**1962, Sept. 13**   **Wmk. 313**   **Imperf.**
| | | | | |
|---|---|---|---|---|
| 630 | A202 | 70pf dk blue, lt grn & yel | 2.75 | 5.00 |

1st Russian group space flight of Vostoks III and IV, Aug. 11-13, 1962.

DDR Television
Signal — A203

Young Collectors
and World
Map — A204

**1962, Oct. 25**     **Perf. 13½x13**
| | | | | |
|---|---|---|---|---|
| 631 | A203 | 20pf green & gray | .25 | .25 |
| 632 | A204 | 40pf brt pink & blk | 1.25 | 1.25 |

No. 631 for the 10th anniv. of television in the German Democratic Republic; No. 632 is for Stamp Day.

Gerhart
Hauptmann — A205

**1962, Nov. 15**     **Perf. 13x13½**
| | | | | |
|---|---|---|---|---|
| 633 | A205 | 20pf red & black | .35 | .25 |

Centenary of the birth of Gerhart Hauptmann, playwright.

Souvenir Sheet

Russian Space Flights and
Astronauts — A206

**1962, Dec. 28**   **Litho.**   **Perf. 12½x13**
| | | | | |
|---|---|---|---|---|
| 634 | A206 | Sheet of 8 | 25.00 | 32.50 |
| a. | | 5pf yellow | 1.00 | 1.00 |
| b. | | 10pf emerald | 1.00 | 1.00 |
| c. | | 15pf magenta | 2.25 | 2.25 |
| d. | | 20pf red | 2.25 | 2.25 |
| e. | | 25pf greenish blue | 2.25 | 2.25 |
| f. | | 30pf red brown | 2.25 | 2.25 |
| g. | | 40pf crimson | 1.00 | 1.00 |
| h. | | 50pf ultramarine | 1.00 | 1.00 |

Issued to show the development of Russian space flights from Sputnik 1 to Vostoks 3 and 4, and to honor the Russian astronauts Gagarin, Titov, Nikolayev and Popovich.

Pierre de
Coubertin — A207

Design: 25pf, Stadium and Olympic rings.

**1963, Jan. 2**     **Perf. 13½x13**
| | | | | |
|---|---|---|---|---|
| 635 | A207 | 20pf carmine & gray | .25 | .25 |
| 636 | A207 | 25pf blue & bister | 1.25 | 1.75 |

Baron Pierre de Coubertin, organizer of the modern Olympic Games, birth cent.

Congress Emblem,
Flag with Marx,
Engels and
Lenin — A208

**1963, Jan. 15**     **Perf. 13x13½**
| | | | | |
|---|---|---|---|---|
| 637 | A208 | 10pf yel, org, red & blk | .30 | .25 |

6th congress of Socialist Unity Party of Germany (SED).

World Map and
Exterminator
A209

Designs: 25pf, Map, cross and staff of Aesculapius. 50pf, Map, cross, mosquito.

**1963, Feb. 6**     **Perf. 13x12½**
| | | | | |
|---|---|---|---|---|
| 638 | A209 | 20pf dp org, dk red & blk | .25 | .25 |
| 639 | A209 | 25pf multicolored | .25 | .25 |
| 640 | A209 | 50pf multicolored | 1.00 | 1.00 |
| | | Nos. 638-640 (3) | 1.50 | 1.50 |

WHO drive to eradicate malaria.

Silver
Fox — A210

Design: 25pf, Karakul.

**1963, Feb. 14**   **Photo.**   **Perf. 14**
| | | | | |
|---|---|---|---|---|
| 641 | A210 | 20pf rose & black | .25 | .25 |
| 642 | A210 | 25pf blue & black | 1.50 | 1.50 |

Intl. Fur Auctions, Leipzig, 2/14-15, 4/21-24.

Barthels House,
Leipzig — A211

Designs: 20pf, New Leipzig City Hall. 25pf, Belltower Building.

**Engr. & Photo.**
**1963, Feb. 26**   **Wmk. 313**   **Perf. 14**
| | | | | |
|---|---|---|---|---|
| 643 | A211 | 10pf black & citron | .25 | .25 |
| 644 | A211 | 20pf black & red org | .30 | .25 |
| 645 | A211 | 25pf black & blue | 1.00 | 1.00 |
| | | Nos. 643-645 (3) | 1.55 | 1.50 |

1963 Leipzig Spring Fair.

Souvenir Sheet

On March 12, 1963, a souvenir sheet publicizing "Chemistry for Peace and Socialism" was issued. It contains two imperforate stamps, 50pf and 70pf, printed on ungummed synthetic tissue. Size: 105x74mm. Values: unused $4; used $20.

Richard Wagner
and "The Flying
Dutchman"
A213

Portrait & Scene from Play: 5pf, Johann Gottfried Seume (1763-1810). 10pf, Friedrich Hebbel (1813-63). 20pf, Georg Büchner (1813-37).

**1963, Apr. 9   Litho.   Perf. 13x12½**
| | | | | |
|---|---|---|---|---|
| 647 | A213 | 5pf brt citron & blk | .25 | .25 |
| 648 | A213 | 10pf brt green & blk | .25 | .25 |
| 649 | A213 | 20pf orange & blk | .25 | .25 |
| 650 | A213 | 25pf dull blue & blk | 1.25 | 1.50 |
| | | *Nos. 647-650 (4)* | 2.00 | 2.25 |

Anniversaries of German dramatists and the 150th anniv. of the birth of Richard Wagner, composer.

First Aid Station — A214

Design: 20pf, Ambulance and hospital.

**1963, May 14   Wmk. 313**
| | | | | |
|---|---|---|---|---|
| 651 | A214 | 10pf multicolored | 1.00 | 1.00 |
| 652 | A214 | 20pf red, blk & gray | .25 | .25 |

Centenary of International Red Cross.

Eugene Pottier, Writer — A215

25pf, Pierre-Chretien Degeyter, composer.

**1963, June 18   Perf. 13x13½**
| | | | | |
|---|---|---|---|---|
| 653 | A215 | 20pf vermilion & blk | .25 | .25 |
| 654 | A215 | 25pf vio blue & blk | 1.00 | 1.00 |

75th anniv. of the communist song "The International."

A216

No. 655, Valentina Tereshkova, Vostok 6.
No. 656, Valeri Bykovski, Vostok 5.

**1963, July 18   Photo.   Perf. 13½**
| | | | | |
|---|---|---|---|---|
| 655 | | 20pf blue, blk & gray bl | .65 | .25 |
| 656 | | 20pf blue, blk & gray bl | .65 | .25 |
| a. | | A216 Pair, #655-656 | 1.50 | .75 |

Space flights of Valeri Bykovski, June 14-19, and Valentina Tereshkova, 1st woman cosmonaut, June 16-19, 1963.

Motorcyclist in "Motocross" at Apolda — A217

20pf, Motorcyclist at Sachsenring, horiz. 25pf, 2 motorcyclists at Sachsenring, horiz.

**Engr. & Photo.**
**1963, July 30   Perf. 14**
**Size: 23x28mm**
| | | | | |
|---|---|---|---|---|
| 657 | | 10pf lt grn & dk grn | 2.50 | 3.00 |

**Size: 48½x21mm**
| | | | | |
|---|---|---|---|---|
| 658 | A217 | 20pf rose & dk red | .25 | .25 |
| 659 | A217 | 25pf lt blue & dk blue | .25 | .25 |
| | | *Nos. 657-659 (3)* | 3.00 | 3.50 |

Motorcycle World Championships.

Monument at Treblinka — A218

---

**Perf. 13x13½**
**1963, Aug. 20   Litho.   Wmk. 313**
| | | | | |
|---|---|---|---|---|
| 660 | A218 | 20pf brick red & dk blue | .30 | .25 |

Erection of a memorial at Treblinka (Poland) concentration camp.

A219

No. 661, Globe, car and train. No. 662, Globe, plane and bus.

**1963, Aug. 27   Perf. 13½x13**
| | | | | |
|---|---|---|---|---|
| 661 | | 10pf multicolored | .60 | .25 |
| 662 | | 10pf multicolored | .60 | .25 |
| a. | | A219 Pair, #661-662 | 1.90 | .40 |

Issued to publicize the 1963 Leipzig Fall Fair.

**Fauna Type of 1962**
10pf, Stag beetle. 20pf, Fire salamander. 30pf, Pond turtle. 50pf, Green toad. 70pf, Hedgehogs.

**1963, Sept. 10   Photo.   Perf. 14**
| | | | | |
|---|---|---|---|---|
| 663 | A190 | 10pf emer, brn & blk | .25 | .25 |
| 664 | A190 | 20pf crimson, blk & yel | .25 | .25 |
| 665 | A190 | 30pf multicolored | .25 | .25 |
| 666 | A190 | 50pf multicolored | 2.50 | 2.50 |
| 667 | A190 | 70pf claret brn, brn & | .55 | .55 |
| | | *Nos. 663-667 (5)* | 3.80 | 3.80 |

Neidhardt von Gneisenau and Gebhard Leberecht von Blücher A220

Designs: 10pf, Cossacks and home guard, Berlin. 20pf, Ernst Moritz Arndt and Baron Heinrich vom Stein. 25pf, Lützow's volunteers before battle. 40pf, Gerhard von Scharnhorst and Prince Mikhail I. Kutuzov.

**1963, Oct. 10   Litho.   Perf. 13½x13**
**Center in Tan and Black**
| | | | | |
|---|---|---|---|---|
| 668 | A220 | 5pf brt yellow | .25 | .25 |
| 669 | A220 | 10pf emerald | .25 | .25 |
| 670 | A220 | 20pf dp orange | .25 | .25 |
| 671 | A220 | 25pf dp ultra | .25 | .25 |
| 672 | A220 | 40pf dark red | 1.75 | 1.00 |
| | | *Nos. 668-672 (5)* | 2.75 | 2.00 |

150th anniversary of War of Liberation.

Valentina Tereshkova and Space Craft — A221

No. 674, Tereshkova and map of DDR, vert. No. 675, Yuri A. Gagarin and map of DDR, vert. 25pf, Tereshkova in space capsule.

**Size: 28x28mm (10pf, 25pf); 28x37mm (20pf)**
**1963   Perf. 13½x13, 13x13½**
| | | | | |
|---|---|---|---|---|
| 673 | A221 | 10pf ultra & green | .25 | .25 |
| 674 | A221 | 20pf red, blk & ocher | .25 | .25 |
| 675 | A221 | 20pf red, grn & ocher | .25 | .25 |
| 676 | A221 | 25pf orange & blue | 3.25 | 2.00 |
| | | *Nos. 673-676 (4)* | 4.00 | 2.75 |

Visit of astronauts Valentina Tereshkova and Yuri A. Gagarin to the German Democratic Republic.

Burning Synagogue and Star of David in Chains — A222

---

**Perf. 13½x13**
**1963, Nov. 8   Wmk. 313**
| | | | | |
|---|---|---|---|---|
| 677 | A222 | 10pf multicolored | .30 | .25 |

25th anniv. of the "Crystal Night," the start of the systematic persecution of the Jews in Germany. Inscribed: "Never again Crystal Night."

Letter Sorting Machine — A223

Design: 20pf, Mechanized mail loading.

**1963, Nov. 25   Perf. 13x12½**
| | | | | |
|---|---|---|---|---|
| 678 | A223 | 10pf multicolored | 1.40 | 1.40 |
| 679 | A223 | 20pf multicolored | .25 | .25 |

Issued for Stamp Day.

Ski Jump and Olympic Rings — A224

**1963, Dec. 16   Litho.   Perf. 13½x13**
| | | | | |
|---|---|---|---|---|
| 680 | A224 | 5pf shown | .25 | .25 |
| 681 | A224 | 10pf Start | .25 | .25 |
| 682 | A224 | 25pf Landing | 1.75 | 1.75 |
| | | *Nos. 680-682,B111 (4)* | 2.50 | 2.50 |

9th Winter Olympic Games, Innsbruck, Jan. 29-Feb. 9, 1964.

Admiral — A225

Butterflies: 15pf, Alpine Apollo. 20pf, Swallowtail. 25pf, Postilion. 40pf, Great fox.

**Wmk. 313**
**1964, Jan. 15   Photo.   Perf. 14**
**Butterflies in Natural Colors**
| | | | | |
|---|---|---|---|---|
| 683 | A225 | 10pf citron & blk | .35 | .25 |
| 684 | A225 | 15pf pale violet & blk | .35 | .25 |
| 685 | A225 | 20pf lt brick red & blk | .35 | .25 |
| 686 | A225 | 25pf lt blue & dk brn | .35 | .25 |
| 687 | A225 | 40pf lt ultra & blk | 5.00 | 2.00 |
| | | *Nos. 683-687 (5)* | 6.40 | 3.00 |

William Shakespeare A226

20pf, Quadriga, Brandenburg Gate, Berlin. 25pf, Keystone, History Museum (Zeughaus), Berlin.

**1964, Feb. 6   Litho.   Perf. 13x12½**
| | | | | |
|---|---|---|---|---|
| 688 | A226 | 20pf rose & dk blue | .25 | .25 |
| 689 | A226 | 25pf lt blue & mag | .25 | .25 |
| 690 | A226 | 40pf lt vio & dk bl grn | 1.10 | 1.00 |
| | | *Nos. 688-690 (3)* | 1.60 | 1.50 |

200th anniv. of the birth of the sculptor Johann Gottfried Schadow (20pf); 300th anniv. of the birth of the sculptor Andreas Schlüter (25pf); 400th anniv. of the birth of William Shakespeare, dramatist (40pf).

Electrical Engineering Exhibit — A227

20pf, Bräunigkes Court, exhibition hall, 1700.

**Perf. 13x13½**
**1964, Feb. 26   Wmk. 313**
| | | | | |
|---|---|---|---|---|
| 691 | A227 | 10pf brt green & blk | 2.00 | .25 |
| 692 | A227 | 20pf red & black | 2.00 | .25 |
| a. | | Block, 1 each #691-692 + 2 labels | 16.00 | 1.50 |

Leipzig Spring Fair, Mar. 1-10, 1964.

---

Khrushchev and Inventors — A228

40pf, Khrushchev, Tereshkova & Gagarin.

**1964, May 15   Perf. 13x13½**
| | | | | |
|---|---|---|---|---|
| 693 | A228 | 25pf blue | .25 | .25 |
| 694 | A228 | 40pf lilac & grnsh blk | 2.25 | 1.75 |

Issued in honor of Premier Nikita S. Khrushchev of the Soviet Union.

Youth Training for Leadership — A229

Designs: 20pf, Young athletes. 25pf, Accordion player and girl with flowers.

**1964, May 13   Litho.**
**Center in Black**
| | | | | |
|---|---|---|---|---|
| 695 | A229 | 10pf ultra, mag & emer | .25 | .25 |
| 696 | A229 | 20pf emer, ultra & mag | .25 | .25 |
| 697 | A229 | 25pf magenta, emer & ultra | 1.25 | .65 |
| | | *Nos. 695-697 (3)* | 1.75 | 1.15 |

German Youth Meeting, Berlin.

Television Antenna and Puppets — A230

Children's Day: Various characters from children's television programs.

**1964, June 1   Perf. 13x13½**
| | | | | |
|---|---|---|---|---|
| 698 | A230 | 5pf multicolored | .25 | .25 |
| 699 | A230 | 10pf multicolored | .25 | .25 |
| 700 | A230 | 15pf multicolored | .25 | .25 |
| 701 | A230 | 20pf multicolored | .25 | .25 |
| 702 | A230 | 40pf multicolored | 1.20 | 1.40 |
| | | *Nos. 698-702 (5)* | 2.20 | 2.40 |

Woman as Educator and Portrait of Jenny Marx — A231

Designs: 25pf, Women in industry and transistor diagram. 70pf, Women in agriculture.

**Perf. 13½x13**
**1964, June 26   Litho.   Wmk. 313**
| | | | | |
|---|---|---|---|---|
| 703 | A231 | 20pf crimson, gray & yel | .30 | .25 |
| 704 | A231 | 25pf lt blue, gray & red | .80 | .65 |
| 705 | A231 | 70pf emer, gray & yel | .55 | .25 |
| | | *Nos. 703-705 (3)* | 1.65 | 1.15 |

Congress of Women of the German Democratic Republic, June 25-27.

Bicycling A232

Diving A233

**Litho. & Engr.**
**1964, July 15   Perf. 14**
| | | | | |
|---|---|---|---|---|
| 706 | A232 | 5pf shown | .25 | .25 |
| 707 | A232 | 10pf Volleyball | .25 | .25 |
| 708 | A232 | 20pf Judo | .25 | .25 |
| 709 | A232 | 25pf Woman diver | .25 | .25 |
| 710 | A232 | 70pf Equestrian | 1.25 | 1.25 |
| | | *Nos. 706-710,B118 (6)* | 2.50 | 2.50 |

## Litho.
### Perf. 13x13½
| | | | | |
|---|---|---|---|---|
| 711 | A233 | 10pf shown | 2.25 | 2.25 |
| 712 | A233 | 10pf Volleyball | 2.25 | 2.25 |
| 713 | A233 | 10pf Bicycling | 2.25 | 2.25 |
| 714 | A233 | 10pf Judo | 2.25 | 2.25 |
| a. | | Block of 6, #711-714, B119-B120 | 17.00 | 17.00 |

18th Olympic Games, Tokyo, Oct. 10-25, 1964. See Nos. B118-B120. No. 714a printed in 2 horiz. rows: (1st: #711, #B119, #712. 2nd: #713, #B120, #714). The Olympic rings extend over the 6 stamps.

Monument, Leningrad — A234

**1964, Aug. 8   Litho.   Perf. 13x13½**
| | | | | |
|---|---|---|---|---|
| 715 | A234 | 25pf brt blue, blk & yel | .75 | .25 |

Issued to honor the victims of the siege of Leningrad, Sept. 1941-Jan. 1943.

Bertha von Suttner — A235

Designs: 20pf, Frederic Joliot Curie. 50pf, Carl von Ossietzky.

**1964, Sept. 1   Perf. 14**
| | | | | |
|---|---|---|---|---|
| 716 | A235 | 20pf red & black | .25 | .25 |
| 717 | A235 | 25pf ultra & black | .25 | .25 |
| 718 | A235 | 50pf lilac & black | 1.00 | .65 |
| | | Nos. 716-718 (3) | 1.50 | 1.15 |

Issued to promote World Peace.

Medieval Glazier and Goblet — A236

15pf, Jena glass for chemical industry.

**1964, Sept. 3   Perf. 14**
| | | | | |
|---|---|---|---|---|
| 719 | A236 | 10pf lt ultra & multi | .45 | .25 |
| 720 | A236 | 15pf red & multi | .45 | .25 |
| a. | | Pair, #719-720 + label | 2.00 | .70 |

Issued for the Leipzig Fall Fair, 1964.

Handstamp of First Socialist International, 1864 — A237

**1964, Sept. 16   Photo.   Wmk. 313**
| | | | | |
|---|---|---|---|---|
| 721 | A237 | 20pf orange red & blk | .25 | .25 |
| 722 | A237 | 25pf dull blue & blk | .55 | .55 |

Centenary of First Socialist International.

Stamp of 1955 (Dürer's Portrait of Young Man) — A238

**1964, Sept. 23   Litho.   Perf. 13x13½**
| | | | | |
|---|---|---|---|---|
| 723 | A238 | 50pf gray & dk red brn | 1.50 | 1.25 |
| | | Nos. 723,B124-B125 (3) | 2.05 | 1.75 |

Natl. Stamp Exhibition, Berlin, Oct. 3-18.

Coal Transport — A239

No. 724, Navigation. No. 725, Flag & new Berlin buildings. No. 727, Chemist. No. 728, Soldier. No. 729, Farm woman & cows. No. 730, Steel worker. No. 731, Woman scientist & lecture hall. No. 732, Heavy industry. No. 733, Optical industry. No. 734, Consumer goods (woman examining cloth). No. 735, Foreign trade, Leipzig fair emblem. No. 736, Buildings industry. No. 737, Sculptor. No. 738, Woman skier.

### Perf. 13½x13
**1964, Oct. 6   Litho.   Wmk. 313**
| | | | | |
|---|---|---|---|---|
| 724 | A239 | 10pf blue & multi | .30 | .30 |
| 725 | A239 | 10pf blue & multi | .30 | .30 |
| 726 | A239 | 10pf gray & multi | .30 | .30 |
| 727 | A239 | 10pf red & multi | .30 | .30 |
| 728 | A239 | 10pf red & multi | .30 | .30 |
| 729 | A239 | 10pf yel grn & multi | .30 | .30 |
| 730 | A239 | 10pf red & multi | .30 | .30 |
| 731 | A239 | 10pf red & multi | .30 | .30 |
| 732 | A239 | 10pf gray & multi | .30 | .30 |
| 733 | A239 | 10pf gray & multi | .30 | .30 |
| 734 | A239 | 10pf blue & multi | .30 | .30 |
| 735 | A239 | 10pf blue & multi | .30 | .30 |
| 736 | A239 | 10pf yel grn & multi | .30 | .30 |
| 737 | A239 | 10pf yel grn & multi | .30 | .30 |
| 738 | A239 | 10pf blue & multi | .30 | .30 |
| | | Nos. 724-738 (15) | 4.50 | 4.50 |

German Democratic Republic, 15th anniv. A souvenir sheet contains 15 imperf. stamps similar to Nos. 724-738. Size: 210x287mm. Values: $40 unused, $75 used. For surcharge see No. B134.

Man from Mönchgut, Rügen — A240

Regional Costumes: No. 740, Woman from Mönchgut, Rügen. No. 741, Man from Spreewald. No. 742, Woman from Spreewald. No. 743, Man from Thuringia. No. 744, Woman from Thuringia.

**1964, Nov. 25   Photo.   Perf. 14**
| | | | | |
|---|---|---|---|---|
| 739 | A240 | 5pf multicolored | 5.00 | 4.25 |
| 740 | A240 | 5pf multicolored | 5.00 | 4.25 |
| a. | | Pair, #739-740 | 25.00 | 10.00 |
| 741 | A240 | 10pf multicolored | 1.50 | .90 |
| 742 | A240 | 10pf multicolored | 1.50 | .90 |
| a. | | Pair, #741-742 | 7.50 | 3.00 |
| 743 | A240 | 20pf multicolored | 1.50 | .90 |
| 744 | A240 | 20pf multicolored | 1.50 | .90 |
| a. | | Pair, #739-740 | 7.50 | 3.00 |
| | | Nos. 739-744 (6) | 16.00 | 12.10 |

Printed in checkerboard arrangement. See Nos. 859-864.

### Souvenir Sheets

Exploration of Ionosphere — A241

Designs: 40pf, Exploration of sun activities. 70pf, Exploration of radiation belt.

**1964, Dec. 29   Litho.   Perf. 13½x13**
| | | | | |
|---|---|---|---|---|
| 745 | A241 | 25pf vio bl & yel | 4.50 | 8.00 |
| 746 | A241 | 40pf vio bl, yel & red | 2.25 | 4.00 |
| 747 | A241 | 70pf dp grn, vio bl & yel | 1.75 | 4.00 |
| | | Nos. 745-747 (3) | 8.50 | 16.00 |

Intl. Quiet Sun Year, 1964-65.

Albert Schweitzer as Physician — A242

Designs (Schweitzer): 20pf, As fighter against war and atom bomb. 25pf, At the organ with score of Organ Prelude by Bach.

### Wmk. 313
**1965, Jan. 14   Photo.   Perf. 14**
| | | | | |
|---|---|---|---|---|
| 748 | A242 | 10pf emerald, blk & bis | .50 | .25 |
| 749 | A242 | 20pf crimson, blk & bis | .50 | .25 |
| 750 | A242 | 25pf blue, blk & bis | 3.00 | 1.75 |
| | | Nos. 748-750 (3) | 4.00 | 2.25 |

90th birthday of Dr. Albert Schweitzer, medical missionary.

### Ulbricht Type of 1961-63
Currency in "Mark of the Deutsche Notenbank" (MDN)

**1965, Feb. 10   Engr.**
**Size: 24x28½mm**
| | | | | |
|---|---|---|---|---|
| 751 | A189 | 1mdn dull green | .40 | 1.00 |
| 752 | A189 | 2mdn brown | .50 | 1.50 |

See note below Nos. 590B-590C.

A243

10pf, Wilhelm Conrad Roentgen. No. 753A, Adolph von Menzel. 20pf, August Bebel. 25pf, Wilhelm Külz. 40pf, Erich Weinert. 50pf, Dante Alighieri.

**1965   Photo.   Perf. 14**
| | | | | |
|---|---|---|---|---|
| 753 | A243 | 10pf dk brn, yel & emer | .35 | .25 |
| 753A | A243 | 10pf dk brn, yel & org | .45 | .25 |
| 754 | A243 | 20pf ol brn, red & buff | .35 | .25 |
| 754A | A243 | 25pf ol brn, yel & bl | .75 | .25 |
| 754B | A243 | 40pf ol brn, buff & car rose | .40 | .25 |
| 755 | A243 | 50pf dk brn, yel & org | 1.25 | .25 |
| | | Nos. 753-755 (6) | 3.55 | 1.50 |

Roentgen (1845-1923), physicist, discoverer of X-rays. Sesquicentennial of the birth of Adolph von Menzel, painter and graphic artist. Bebel, labor leader (1840-1913). 90th anniv. of the birth of Wilhelm Külz, politician. 75th anniv. of the birth of Erich Weinert, poet. Alighieri (1265-1321), Italian poet.
Issued: No. 753, 3/24; No. 753A, 12/8; 20pf, 2/22; 25pf, 7/5; 40pf, 7/28; 50pf, 4/15.

A244

Designs: 10pf, Gold Medal, Leipzig Fair. 15pf, Obverse of medal, arms of German Democratic Republic. 25pf, Chemical plant.

**1965, Feb. 25   Litho.   Wmk. 313**
| | | | | |
|---|---|---|---|---|
| 756 | A244 | 10pf lilac rose & gold | .25 | .25 |
| 757 | A244 | 15pf lilac rose & gold | .25 | .25 |
| 758 | A244 | 25pf brt blue, yel & gold | .50 | .25 |
| | | Nos. 756-758 (3) | 1.00 | .75 |

1965 Leipzig Spring Fair; 800th anniv. of the Fair.

A245

Designs: 10pf, Giraffe. 25pf, Common iguana, horiz. 30pf, White-tailed gnu.

**1965, Mar. 24**
| | | | | |
|---|---|---|---|---|
| 759 | A245 | 10pf green & gray | .25 | .25 |
| 760 | A245 | 25pf dk vio bl & gray | .25 | .25 |
| 761 | A245 | 30pf brown & gray | 1.60 | 1.25 |
| | | Nos. 759-761 (3) | 2.10 | 1.75 |

10th anniversary of Berlin Zoo.

Col. Pavel Belyayev and Lt. Col. Alexei Leonov — A246

25pf, Lt. Col. Leonov floating in space.

### Perf. 13½x13
**1965, Apr. 15   Litho.   Wmk. 313**
| | | | | |
|---|---|---|---|---|
| 762 | A246 | 10pf red | .30 | .25 |
| 763 | A246 | 25pf dk ultra | 1.75 | 1.25 |

Space flight of Voskhod 2 and the first man walking in space, Lt. Col. Alexei Leonov.

Boxing Glove and Laurel Wreath — A247

**1965, Apr. 27   Photo.   Perf. 14**
| | | | | |
|---|---|---|---|---|
| 764 | A247 | 20pf blk, red & gold | .65 | .65 |

16th European Boxing Championship, Berlin, May, 1965. See No. B126.

Walter Ulbricht and Erich Weinert Distributing "Free Germany" Leaflets on the Eastern Front
A248

50pf, Liberation of concentration camps. 60pf, Russian soldiers raising flag on Reichstag, Berlin. 70pf, Political demonstration.

**1965, May 5   Photo.   Perf. 14**
**Flags in Red, Black & Yellow**
| | | | | |
|---|---|---|---|---|
| 765 | A248 | 40pf blue grn & red | .25 | .25 |
| 766 | A248 | 50pf dull blue & red | .25 | .25 |
| 767 | A248 | 60pf brown & red | 2.25 | 2.25 |
| 768 | A248 | 70pf vio blue & red | .25 | .25 |
| | | Nos. 765-768,B127-B131 (9) | 4.25 | 4.25 |

20th anniv. of liberation from fascism.

Radio Tower and Globe — A249

40pf, Workers & broadcasting equipment.

**1965, May 12   Litho.   Perf. 12½x13**
| | | | | |
|---|---|---|---|---|
| 769 | A249 | 20pf dk car rose & blk | .30 | .25 |
| 770 | A249 | 40pf vio bl & blk | 1.20 | .60 |

20th anniv. of the German Democratic broadcasting system.

ITU Emblem and Frequency Diagram — A250

25pf, ITU emblem & telephone diagram.

**1965, May 17**
771 A250 20pf olive, yel & blk .35 .25
772 A250 25pf vio, pale vio & blk 1.60 .40
Cent. of the ITU.

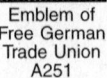

Emblem of Free German Trade Union A251

Hemispheres with Crowd of Workers A252

**1965, June 10   Photo.   Perf. 14**
773 A251 20pf red & gold .35 .25
774 A252 25pf gold, blue & blk 1.10 .45

20th anniv. of the Free German Trade Union (FDGB) and of the World Organization of Trade Unions.

Symbols of Industry — A253

Designs: 20pf, Red Tower. 25pf, City Hall.

**1965, June 16**
775 A253 10pf gold & emerald .25 .25
776 A253 20pf gold & crimson .25 .25
777 A253 25pf gold & brt blue .75 .45
Nos. 775-777 (3) 1.25 .95

800th anniv. of Chemnitz (Karl Marx City).

Marx and Lenin — A254

**1965, June 21   Litho.   Perf. 13½x13**
778 A254 20pf red, black & buff .45 .25

6th Conference of Postal Ministers of Communist Countries, Peking, June 21-July 15.

"Alte Waage" and New Building, Leipzig A255

25pf, Old City Hall. 40pf, Opera House & General Post Office. 70pf, Hotel "Stadt Leipzig."

**Unwmk.**
**1965, Aug. 25   Photo.   Perf. 14**
781 A255 10pf gold, cl brn & ultra .25 .25
a. Souv. sheet of 2, #781, 784 3.00 4.75
782 A255 25pf gold, brn, & ocher .25 .25
a. Souv. sheet of 2, #782-783 2.00 4.00
783 A255 40pf gold, brn, ocher & yel grn .25 .25
784 A255 70pf gold & ultra 1.60 .70
Nos. 781-784 (4) 2.35 1.45

800th anniv. of the City of Leipzig. No. 781a sold for 90pf; No. 782a for 80pf. The souvenir sheets were issued Sept. 4, 1965.

---

Cameras — A256

Leipzig Fall Fair: 15pf, Electric guitar and organ. 25pf, Microscope.

**1965, Sept. 9   Perf. 14**
785 A256 10pf green, blk & gold .25 .25
786 A256 15pf multicolored .25 .25
787 A256 25pf multicolored .70 .25
Nos. 785-787 (3) 1.20 .75

Equestrian — A257

**Perf. 13½x13**
**1965, Sept. 15   Litho.   Unwmk.**
789 A257 10pf shown .25 .25
790 A257 10pf Swimmer .25 .25
791 A257 10pf Runner 2.00 2.00
Nos. 789-791,B135-B136 (5) 3.00 3.00

Intl. Modern Pentathlon Championships, Leipzig.

Alexei Leonov and Brandenburg Gate — A258

Designs: No. 793, Pavel Belyayev and Berlin City Hall. 25pf, Leonov floating in space and space ship.

**Wmk. 313**
**1965, Oct. 1   Litho.   Perf. 14**
**Size: 23½x28½mm**
792 A258 20pf blue, sil & red .45 .55
793 A258 20pf blue, sil & red .45 .55
**Size: 51x28½mm**
794 A258 25pf blue, sil & red .45 .55
a. Strip of 3, #792-794 2.50 3.00

Visit of the Russian astronauts to the German Democratic Republic.

Memorial Monument, Putten — A259

**1965, Oct. 19   Perf. 13x13½**
795 A259 25pf brt bl, pale yel & blk .65 .25

Issued in memory of the victims of a Nazi attack on Putten, Netherlands, Sept. 30, 1944.

Furnace — A260

After old woodcuts: 15pf, Ore miners. 20pf, Proustite crystals. 25pf, Sulphur crystals.

**Perf. 13x12½**
**1965, Nov. 11   Litho.   Unwmk.**
796 A260 10pf black & multi .25 .25
797 A260 15pf black & multi .55 .55
798 A260 20pf black & multi .25 .25
799 A260 25pf black & multi .25 .25
Nos. 796-799 (4) 1.30 1.30

Mining Academy in Freiberg, bicent.

---

Red Kite — A261

Birds: 10pf, Lammergeier. 20pf, Buzzard. 25pf, Kestrel. 40pf, Northern goshawk. 70pf, Golden eagle.

**1965, Dec. 8   Photo.   Perf. 14**
**Gold Frame**
800 A261 5pf orange & blk .25 .25
801 A261 10pf emer, brn & blk .25 .25
802 A261 20pf car, red brn & blk .25 .25
803 A261 25pf blue, red brn & blk .25 .25
804 A261 40pf lilac, blk & dk red .35 .25
805 A261 70pf brn, blk & yel 3.00 1.75
Nos. 800-805 (6) 4.35 3.00

Otto Grotewohl — A262

**1965, Dec. 14   Photo.   Wmk. 313**
806 A262 20pf black .55 .25

Issued in memory of Otto Grotewohl (1894-1964), prime minister (1949-1964).

**Souvenir Sheet**

Spartacus Letter, Karl Liebknecht and Rosa Luxemburg — A263

**1966, Jan. 3   Unwmk.**
807 A263   Sheet of 2 1.75 5.00
a. 20pf red & black .35 .60
b. 50pf red & black .35 .60

50th anniv. of the natl. conf. of the Spartacus organization.

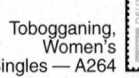

Tobogganing, Women's Singles — A264

20pf, Men's doubles. 25pf, Men's singles.

**Perf. 13½x13**
**1966, Jan. 25   Litho.   Unwmk.**
808 A264 10pf citron & dp grn .25 .25
809 A264 20pf car rose & dk vio bl .25 .25
810 A264 25pf blue & dk blue 1.00 .65
Nos. 808-810 (3) 1.50 1.15

10th Intl. Tobogganing Championships, Friedrichroda, Feb. 8-13.

Electronic Computer A265

Design: 15pf, Drill and milling machine.

**1966, Feb. 24   Perf. 13x12½**
811 A265 10pf multicolored .25 .25
812 A265 15pf multicolored .70 .25

Leipzig Spring Fair, 1966.

Jan Arnost Smoler and Linden Leaf — A266

25pf, House of the Sorbs, Bautzen, Saxony.

---

**1966, Mar. 1   Perf. 13x13½**
813 A266 20pf brt bl, blk & brt red .25 .25
814 A266 25pf brt red, blk & brt bl .55 .45

Smoler (1816-84), philologist of the Sorbian language. The Sorbs are a small group of slavic people in Saxony.

Soldier and National Gallery, Berlin — A267

Designs (Soldier and): 10pf, Brandenburg Gate. 20pf, Factory. 25pf, Combine.

**Wmk. 313**
**1966, Mar. 1   Photo.   Perf. 14**
815 A267 5pf ol gray, blk & yel .25 .25
816 A267 10pf ol gray, blk & yel .25 .25
817 A267 20pf ol gray, blk & yel .25 .25
818 A267 25pf ol gray, blk & yel .85 .65
Nos. 815-818 (4) 1.60 1.40

National People's Army, 10th anniversary.

Luna 9 on Moon — A268

**1966, Mar. 7   Unwmk.**
819 A268 20pf multicolored 1.75 .35

1st soft landing on the moon by Luna 9, 2/3/66.

Medal for Scholarship — A269

**1966, Mar. 7   Litho.   Perf. 13½x13**
820 A269 20pf multicolored .45 .25

20th anniv. of the State Youth Organization.

Traffic Signs — A270

Traffic safety: 15pf, Automobile and child with scooter. 25pf, Bicyclist and signaling hand. 50pf, Motorcyclist, ambulance and glass of beer.

**1966, Mar. 28   Litho.   Perf. 13**
821 A270 10pf dk & lt bl, red & blk .25 .25
822 A270 15pf brt grn, citron & blk .25 .25
823 A270 25pf ol bis, brt bl & blk .25 .25
824 A270 50pf car, yel, gray & blk .80 .45
Nos. 821-824 (4) 1.55 1.20

Marx, Lenin and Crowd A271

Designs: 5pf, Party emblem and crowd, vert. 15pf, Marx, Engels and title page of Communist Manifesto, vert. 20pf, Otto Grotewohl and Wilhelm Pieck shaking hands, and Party emblem, vert. 25pf, Chairman Walter Ulbricht receiving flowers.

**1966, Mar. 31   Photo.   Perf. 14**
825 A271 5pf multicolored .25 .25
826 A271 10pf multicolored .25 .25
827 A271 15pf green & blk .25 .25
828 A271 20pf dk carmine & blk .25 .25
829 A271 25pf multicolored 1.25 1.00
Nos. 825-829 (5) 2.25 2.00

20th anniversary of Socialist Unity Party of Germany (SED).

WHO Headquarters, Geneva — A272

**Perf. 13x12½**

| 1966, Apr. 26 | Litho. | Unwmk. | | |
|---|---|---|---|---|
| 830 | A272 | 20pf multicolored | .40 | .30 |

Inauguration of WHO Headquarters, Geneva.

Rügen Island, Königsstuhl A273

National Parks: 10pf, Spree River woodland. 20pf, Saxon Switzerland. 25pf, Dunes at Westdarss. 30pf, Thale in Harz, Devil's Wall. 50pf, Feldberg Lakes, Mecklenburg.

**Perf. 13x12½**

| 1966, May 17 | Litho. | Unwmk. | | |
|---|---|---|---|---|
| 831 | A273 | 10pf multicolored | .25 | .25 |
| 832 | A273 | 15pf multicolored | .25 | .25 |
| 833 | A273 | 20pf multicolored | .25 | .25 |
| 834 | A273 | 25pf multicolored | .25 | .25 |
| 835 | A273 | 30pf multicolored | 1.60 | .85 |
| 836 | A273 | 50pf multicolored | .25 | .25 |
| | | Nos. 831-836 (6) | 2.85 | 2.10 |

Plauen Lace — A274

Various Lace Designs.

| 1966, May 26 | | Perf. 13x13½ | | |
|---|---|---|---|---|
| 837 | A274 | 10pf green & lt green | .25 | .25 |
| 838 | A274 | 20pf dk blue & lt blue | .25 | .25 |
| 839 | A274 | 25pf brown red & ver | .25 | .25 |
| 840 | A274 | 50pf dk vio & bluish lil | 1.90 | 1.00 |
| | | Nos. 837-840 (4) | 2.65 | 1.75 |

Rhododendron A275

Flowers: 20pf, Lilies of the Valley. 40pf, Dahlias. 50pf, Cyclamen.

**Photo. & Engr.**

| 1966 | Unwmk. | Perf. 14x13½ | | |
|---|---|---|---|---|
| 841 | A275 | 20pf multicolored | .25 | .25 |
| 842 | A275 | 25pf multicolored | .25 | .25 |
| 843 | A275 | 40pf multicolored | .30 | .25 |
| 844 | A275 | 50pf multicolored | 3.00 | 2.90 |
| | | Nos. 841-844 (4) | 3.80 | 3.65 |

Intl. Flower Show, Erfurt.
Issued: 20pf, Aug. 16; others, June 28.

Parachutist Landing on Target — A276

15pf, Group parachute jump. 20pf, Free fall.

| 1966, July 12 | Litho. | Perf. 12½x13 | | |
|---|---|---|---|---|
| 845 | A276 | 10pf blue, blk & ol | .25 | .25 |
| 846 | A276 | 15pf multicolored | .45 | .45 |
| 847 | A276 | 20pf sky blue, blk & ol | .25 | .25 |
| | | Nos. 845-847 (3) | .95 | .95 |

8th Intl. Parachute Championships, Leipzig.

Hans Kahle, Song of German Fighters and Medal of Spanish Republic A277

15pf, Hans Beimler and street fighting in Madrid.

| 1966, July 15 | Photo. | Perf. 14 | | |
|---|---|---|---|---|
| 848 | A277 | 5pf multicolored | .25 | .25 |
| 849 | A277 | 15pf multicolored | .25 | .25 |
| | | Nos. 848-849,B137-B140 (6) | 2.50 | 2.25 |

German fighters in the Spanish Civil War.

Television Set — A278

Design: 15pf, Electric typewriter.

**Perf. 13x12½**

| 1966, Aug. 29 | Litho. | Unwmk. | | |
|---|---|---|---|---|
| 850 | A278 | 10pf brt grn, blk & gray | .25 | .25 |
| 851 | A278 | 15pf red, blk & gray | 1.20 | .25 |

1966 Leipzig Fall Fair.

Women's Doubles Kayak Race A279

| 1966, Aug. 16 | | | | |
|---|---|---|---|---|
| 852 | A279 | 15pf brt blue & multi | .90 | .75 |

7th Canoe World Championships, Berlin. See No. B141.

Oradour sur Glane Memorial and French Flag — A280

**Perf. 13x13½**

| 1966, Sept. 9 | | Wmk. 313 | | |
|---|---|---|---|---|
| 853 | A280 | 25pf ultra, blk & red | .50 | .25 |

Issued in memory of the victims of the Nazi attack on Oradour, France, June 10, 1944.

Emblem of the Committee for Health Education — A281

5pf, Symbolic blood donor & recipient, horiz.

| 1966, Sept. 13 | | Perf. 14 | | |
|---|---|---|---|---|
| 854 | A281 | 5pf brt green & red | .25 | .25 |
| 855 | A281 | 40pf brt blue & red | 1.40 | .45 |
| | | Nos. 854-855,B142 (3) | 2.00 | .95 |

Blood donations and health education.

Weight Lifter — A282

**Perf. 13½x13**

| 1966, Sept. 22 | Litho. | Unwmk. | | |
|---|---|---|---|---|
| 856 | A282 | 15pf lt brown & blk | 1.20 | 1.20 |

Intl. and European Weight Lifting Championships, Berlin. See No. B143.

Congress Hall A283

Emblem A284

| 1966, Oct. 10 | | Perf. 13 | | |
|---|---|---|---|---|
| 857 | A283 | 10pf multicolored | .40 | .35 |
| 858 | A284 | 20pf dk blue & yellow | .25 | .25 |

6th Cong. of the Intl. Organ. of Journalists, Berlin.

### Costume Type of 1964

Regional Costumes: 5pf, Woman from Altenburg. No. 860, Man from Altenburg. No. 861, Woman from Mecklenburg. 20pf, Man from Mecklenburg. 20pf, Woman from Magdeburg area. 30pf, Man from Magdeburg area.

| 1966, Oct. 25 | | Photo. | Perf. 14 | |
|---|---|---|---|---|
| 859 | A240 | 5pf multicolored | .35 | .25 |
| 860 | A240 | 10pf multicolored | .35 | .25 |
| a. | | Pair, #859-860 | 1.00 | .75 |
| 861 | A240 | 10pf lt green & multi | .35 | .25 |
| 862 | A240 | 15pf lt green & multi | .35 | .25 |
| a. | | Pair, #861-862 | 1.00 | .75 |
| 863 | A240 | 20pf yellow & multi | 1.60 | 1.25 |
| 864 | A240 | 30pf yellow & multi | 1.60 | 1.25 |
| a. | | Pair, #863-864 | 4.00 | 3.25 |
| | | Nos. 859-864 (6) | 4.60 | 3.50 |

Printed in checkerboard arrangement.

Megalamphodus Megalopterus A285

Various Tropical Fish in Natural Colors.

| 1966, Nov. 8 | Litho. | Perf. 13x12½ | | |
|---|---|---|---|---|
| 865 | A285 | 5pf lt blue & gray | .25 | .25 |
| 866 | A285 | 10pf blue & indigo | .25 | .25 |
| 867 | A285 | 15pf citron & blk | 2.00 | 1.60 |
| 868 | A285 | 20pf green & blk | .25 | .25 |
| 869 | A285 | 25pf ultra & blk | .25 | .25 |
| 870 | A285 | 40pf emerald & blk | .30 | .25 |
| | | Nos. 865-870 (6) | 3.30 | 2.85 |

Map of Oil Pipeline and Oil Field A286

Design: 25pf, Map of oil pipelines and "Walter Ulbricht" Leuna chemical factory.

| 1966, Nov. 8 | | Perf. 13½x13 | | |
|---|---|---|---|---|
| 871 | A286 | 20pf red & black | .25 | .25 |
| 872 | A286 | 25pf blue & black | .65 | .35 |

Chemical industry.

Detail from Ishtar Gate, Babylon, 580 B.C. A287

Designs from Babylon c. 580 B.C.: 20pf, Mythological animal from Ishtar Gate. 25pf, Lion facing right and ornaments, vert. 50pf, Lion facing left and ornaments, vert.

**Perf. 13½x14, 14x13½**

| 1966, Nov. 23 | | Photo. | | |
|---|---|---|---|---|
| 873 | A287 | 10pf multicolored | .25 | .25 |
| 874 | A287 | 20pf multicolored | .25 | .25 |
| 875 | A287 | 25pf multicolored | .25 | .25 |
| 876 | A287 | 50pf multicolored | .45 | .90 |
| | | Nos. 873-876 (4) | 1.20 | 1.65 |

Near East Museum, Berlin.

Wartburg, Thuringia — A288

Design: 25pf, Wartburg, Palace.

| 1966, Nov. 23 | Litho. | Perf. 13x13½ | | |
|---|---|---|---|---|
| 877 | A288 | 20pf olive | .25 | .25 |
| 878 | A288 | 25pf violet brown | .65 | .30 |
| | | Nos. 877-878,B145 (3) | 1.25 | .80 |

900th anniv. (in 1967) of the Wartburg (castle) near Eisenach, Thuringia.

Gentian — A289

Protected Flowers: 20pf, Cephalanthera rubra (orchid). 25pf, Mountain arnica.

### Black Background

| 1966, Dec. 8 | Litho. | Perf. 12½x13 | | |
|---|---|---|---|---|
| 879 | A289 | 10pf yel, grn & bl | .25 | .25 |
| 880 | A289 | 20pf yel, grn & red | .25 | .25 |
| 881 | A289 | 25pf red, yel & grn | 1.10 | .65 |
| | | Nos. 879-881 (3) | 1.60 | 1.15 |

Son Leaving Home — A290

Various Scenes from Fairy Tale "The Table, the Ass and the Stick."

| 1966, Dec. 8 | | Perf. 13½x13 | | |
|---|---|---|---|---|
| 882 | A290 | 5pf multicolored | .25 | .30 |
| 883 | A290 | 10pf multicolored | .25 | .30 |
| 884 | A290 | 20pf multicolored | .55 | .60 |
| 885 | A290 | 25pf multicolored | .55 | .60 |
| 886 | A290 | 30pf multicolored | .25 | .30 |
| 887 | A290 | 50pf multicolored | .25 | .30 |
| a. | | Sheet of 6, #882-887 | 2.50 | 4.00 |

See Nos. 968-973, 1063-1068, 1087-1092, 1176-1181, 1339-1344.

City Hall, Stralsund — A291

Buildings: 5pf, Wörlitz Castle, horiz. 15pf, Chorin Convent. 20pf, Ribbeck House, Berlin, horiz. 25pf, Moritzburg, Zeitz. 40pf, Old City Hall, Potsdam.

**Perf. 14x13½, 13½x14**

| 1967, Jan. 24 | | Photo. | | |
|---|---|---|---|---|
| 888 | A291 | 5pf multicolored | .25 | .25 |
| 889 | A291 | 10pf multicolored | .25 | .25 |
| 890 | A291 | 15pf multicolored | .25 | .25 |
| 891 | A291 | 20pf multicolored | .25 | .25 |
| 892 | A291 | 25pf multicolored | .25 | .25 |
| 893 | A291 | 40pf multicolored | 1.00 | .65 |
| | | Nos. 888-893 (6) | 2.25 | 1.90 |

See Nos. 1018, 1020, 1071-1076.

Rifle Shooting, Prone — A292

Designs: 20pf, Shooting on skis. 25pf, Relay race with rifles on skis.

| 1967, Feb. 15 | Litho. | Perf. 13x12½ | | |
|---|---|---|---|---|
| 894 | A292 | 10pf Prus bl gray & brt pink | .25 | .25 |
| 895 | A292 | 20pf sl grn, brt bl & grn | .25 | .25 |

| | | |
|---|---|---|
| 896 | A292 25pf ol grn, ol & grnsh bl | .60 .40 |
| | Nos. 894-896 (3) | 1.10 .90 |

World Biathlon Championships (skiing and shooting), Altenberg, Feb. 15-19.

Circular Knitting Machine — A293

Design: 15pf, Zeiss telescope and galaxy.

**1967, Mar. 2　　Perf. 13½x13**

| | | |
|---|---|---|
| 897 | A293 10pf dull mag & brt grn | .25 .25 |
| 898 | A293 15pf ultra & gray | .65 .25 |

Leipzig Spring Fair of 1967.

Mother and Child — A294

Design: 25pf, Working women.

**1967, Mar. 7　　Perf. 13x13½**

| | | |
|---|---|---|
| 899 | A294 20pf rose brn, red & gray | .25 .25 |
| 900 | A294 25pf dk bl, brt bl & brn | .65 .60 |

20th anniv. of the Democratic Women's Federation of Germany.

Marx, Engels, Lenin and Electronic Control Center — A295

Designs (Portraits and): 5pf, Farmer driving combine. No. 903, Students and teacher. 15pf, Family. No. 905, Soldier, sailor and aviator. No. 906, Ulbricht among workers. 40pf, Soldier, sailor, aviator and factories. 40pf, Farmers with modern equipment. Nos. 901, 903-905 are vertical.

**1967　　Photo.　　Perf. 14**

| | | |
|---|---|---|
| 901 | A295 5pf multicolored | .25 .25 |
| 902 | A295 5pf multicolored | .25 .25 |
| 903 | A295 10pf multicolored | .25 .25 |
| 904 | A295 15pf multicolored | .35 .40 |
| 905 | A295 20pf multicolored | .25 .25 |
| 906 | A295 20pf multicolored | .25 .25 |
| 907 | A295 25pf multicolored | .25 .25 |
| 908 | A295 25pf multicolored | .35 .60 |
| | Nos. 901-908 (8) | 2.20 2.50 |

7th congress of Socialist Unity Party of Germany (SED), Apr. 17.
Issued: No. 902, 906-908 3/22; Nos. 901, 903-905, 4/6.

Tahitian Women, by Paul Gauguin A296

Paintings from Dresden Gallery: 20pf, Young Woman, by Ferdinand Hodler. 25pf, Peter in the Zoo, by H. Hakenbeck. 30pf, Venetian Episode (woman feeding pigeons), by R. Bergander. 50pf, Grandmother and Granddaughter, by J. Scholtz. 70pf, Cairn in the Snow, by Caspar David Friedrich.

**1967, Mar. 29**

| | | |
|---|---|---|
| 909 | A296 20pf multi, vert. | .25 .25 |
| 910 | A296 25pf multi, vert. | .25 .25 |
| 911 | A296 30pf multi, vert. | .25 .25 |
| 912 | A296 40pf multi | .25 .25 |
| 913 | A296 50pf multi, vert. | 1.25 1.00 |
| 914 | A296 70pf multi | .30 .25 |
| | Nos. 909-914 (6) | 2.55 2.25 |

Barn Owl — A297

Protected Birds: 10pf, Eurasian crane. 20pf, Peregrine falcon. 25pf, Bullfinches. 30pf, European kingfisher. 40pf, European roller.

**1967, Apr. 27　　Photo.　　Perf. 14**
**Birds in Natural Colors**

| | | |
|---|---|---|
| 915 | A297 5pf gray blue | .25 .25 |
| 916 | A297 10pf gray blue | .25 .25 |
| 917 | A297 20pf gray blue | .25 .25 |
| 918 | A297 25pf gray blue | .25 .25 |
| 919 | A297 30pf gray blue | 3.25 1.75 |
| 920 | A297 40pf gray blue | .30 .25 |
| | Nos. 915-920 (6) | 4.55 3.00 |

Arms of Warsaw, Berlin and Prague — A298

Design: 25pf, Bicyclists and doves.

**Perf. 13x12½**

**1967, May 10　　Litho.　　Wmk. 313**

| | | |
|---|---|---|
| 921 | A298 10pf org, blk & lil | .25 .25 |
| 922 | A298 25pf lt bl & dk car | .40 .35 |

20th Intl. Bicycle Peace Race, Berlin-Warsaw-Prague.

Cat — A299

Children's Drawings: 10pf, Snow White and the Seven Dwarfs. 15pf, Fire truck. 20pf, Cock. 25pf, Flowers in vase. 30pf, Children playing ball.

**1967, June 1　　Unwmk.**

| | | |
|---|---|---|
| 923 | A299 5pf multicolored | .25 .25 |
| 924 | A299 10pf black & multi | .25 .25 |
| 925 | A299 15pf dk blue & multi | .25 .25 |
| 926 | A299 20pf orange & multi | .25 .25 |
| 927 | A299 25pf multicolored | .25 .25 |
| 928 | A299 30pf multicolored | .85 .65 |
| | Nos. 923-928 (6) | 2.10 1.90 |

Issued for International Children's Day.

Girl with Straw Hat, by Salomon Bray — A300

Paintings: 5pf, Three Horsemen, by Rubens, horiz. 10pf, Girl Gathering Grapes, by Gerard Dou. 20pf, Spring Idyl, by Hans Thoma, horiz. 25pf, Wilhelmine Schroder-Devrient, by Karl Begas. 50pf, The Four Evangelists, by Jacob Jordaens.

**1967, June 7　　Photo.　　Perf. 14**

| | | |
|---|---|---|
| 929 | A300 5pf lt & dk blue | .25 .25 |
| 930 | A300 10pf lt red brn & red brn | .25 .25 |
| 931 | A300 20pf lt & dp yel grn | .25 .25 |
| 932 | A300 25pf pale rose & rose lil | .25 .25 |
| 933 | A300 40pf pale grn & ol grn | .25 .25 |
| 934 | A300 50pf tan & sepia | 1.25 .75 |
| | Nos. 929-934 (6) | 2.50 2.00 |

Issued to publicize paintings missing from museums since World War II.

Exhibition Emblem and Map of DDR — A301

**Perf. 12½x13**

**1967, June 14　　Litho.　　Unwmk.**

| | | |
|---|---|---|
| 935 | A301 20pf dk grn, ocher & red | .35 .25 |

15th Agricultural Exhib., Markkleeberg.

Marie Curie — A302

Portraits: 5pf, Georg Herwegh, poet. 20pf, Käthe Kollwitz. 25pf, Johann J. Winckelmann, archaeologist. 40pf, Theodor Storm, writer.

**1967　　Engr.　　Perf. 14**

| | | |
|---|---|---|
| 936 | A302 5pf brown | .25 .25 |
| 937 | A302 10pf dark blue | .25 .25 |
| 938 | A302 20pf dull red | .25 .25 |
| 939 | A302 25pf gray | .25 .25 |
| 940 | A302 40pf slate green | .65 .45 |
| | Nos. 936-940 (5) | 1.65 1.45 |

150th anniv. of the birth of Herwegh, Winckelmann and Storm, and the birth centenaries of Curie and Kollwitz.

German Playing Cards — A303

Designs: Various German playing cards.

**1967, July 18　　Photo.**

| | | |
|---|---|---|
| 941 | A303 5pf red & multi | .25 .25 |
| 942 | A303 10pf green & multi | .25 .25 |
| 943 | A303 20pf multicolored | .25 .25 |
| 944 | A303 25pf multicolored | 4.00 2.75 |
| | Nos. 941-944 (4) | 4.75 3.50 |

Mare and Foal — A304

Horses: 10pf, Stallion. 20pf, Horse race finish. 50pf, Colts, vert.

**Perf. 13½x13, 13x13½**

**1967, Aug. 15　　Litho.　　Unwmk.**

| | | |
|---|---|---|
| 945 | A304 5pf multicolored | .25 .25 |
| 946 | A304 10pf org, blk & dk brn | .25 .25 |
| 947 | A304 20pf blue & multi | .25 .25 |
| 948 | A304 50pf multicolored | 2.60 1.60 |
| | Nos. 945-948 (4) | 3.35 2.35 |

Thoroughbred Horse Show of Socialist Countries, Hoppegarten, Berlin.

Small Electrical Appliances — A305

Leipzig Fall Fair: 15pf, Woman's fur coat and furrier's trademark.

**Perf. 14x13½**

**1967, Aug. 8　　Photo.　　Unwmk.**

| | | |
|---|---|---|
| 949 | A305 10pf brt bl, blk & yel | .35 .25 |
| 950 | A305 15pf yellow, brn & blk | .70 .35 |

Max Reichpietsch and Warship — A306

15pf, Albin Köbis, warship. 20pf, Sailors marching with red flag, warship.

**1967, Sept. 5　　Litho.　　Perf. 13½x13**
**Bluish Paper**

| | | |
|---|---|---|
| 951 | A306 10pf dk blue, gray & red | .25 .25 |
| 952 | A306 15pf dk blue, gray & red | .90 .45 |
| 953 | A306 20pf dk blue, gray & red | .35 .25 |
| | Nos. 951-953 (3) | 1.50 .95 |

50th anniv. of the sailors' uprising at Kiel.

Monument at Kragujevac — A307

**1967, Sept. 20　　Perf. 13x13½**

| | | |
|---|---|---|
| 954 | A307 25pf dk red, yel & blk | .60 .30 |

Issued in memory of the victims of the Nazis at Kragujevac, Yugoslavia, Oct. 21, 1941.

Worker and Symbols of Electrification A308

Communist Emblem and: 5pf, Worker, Communist newspaper masthead. 15pf, Russian War Memorial, Berlin-Treptow. 20pf, Russian and German soldiers, coat of arms. 40pf, Lenin, cruiser Aurora.

**1967, Oct. 6　　Photo.　　Perf. 14x14½**

| | | |
|---|---|---|
| 955 | A308 5pf multicolored | .25 .25 |
| 956 | A308 10pf multicolored | .25 .25 |
| 957 | A308 15pf multicolored | .25 .25 |
| 958 | A308 20pf multicolored | .30 .25 |
| 959 | A308 50pf multicolored | 2.00 1.60 |
| a. | Souvenir sheet of 2 | 1.25 2.50 |
| | Nos. 955-959 (5) | 3.05 2.60 |

50th anniv. of the Russian October Revolution. No. 959a contains 2 imperf. stamps similar to Nos. 958-959 with simulated perforations. It commemorates the Red October Jubilee Stamp Exhibition, Karl-Marx-Stadt, Oct. 6-15. Sold for 85pf.

Martin Luther, by Lucas Cranach — A309

Designs: 25pf, Luther's House, Wittenberg, horiz. 40pf, Castle Church, Wittenberg.

**Engraved and Photogravure**
**1967, Oct. 17　　Perf. 14**

| | | |
|---|---|---|
| 960 | A309 20pf black & rose lilac | .25 .25 |
| 961 | A309 25pf black & blue | .25 .25 |
| 962 | A309 40pf black & lemon | 1.75 .65 |
| | Nos. 960-962 (3) | 2.25 1.15 |

450th anniversary of the Reformation.

Young Inventors and Fair Emblem — A310

Designs: No. 964, Boy's and girl's heads and emblem of the Free German Youth Organization. 25pf, Young workers receiving awards, and medal.

**Size: 23x28½mm**

**1967, Nov. 15　　Unwmk.　　Perf. 14**

| | | |
|---|---|---|
| 963 | A310 20pf multicolored | .50 .40 |
| 964 | A310 20pf multicolored | .50 .40 |

**Size: 51x28½mm**

| | | |
|---|---|---|
| 965 | A310 25pf multicolored | .50 .40 |
| a. | Strip of 3, #963-965 | 3.00 3.00 |

Issued to publicize the 10th Masters of Tomorrow Fair, Leipzig, Nov. 15-26.

Goethe House, Weimar — A311

Design: 25pf, Schiller House, Weimar.

**1967, Nov. 27   Litho.   Perf. 13x12½**
966 A311 20pf gray, blk & brn .25 .25
967 A311 25pf citron, dk grn & brn 1.25 .40

Honoring German classical humanism.

**Fairy Tale Type of 1966**
Various Scenes from King Drosselbart.

**1967, Nov. 27   Perf. 13½x13**
968 A290 5pf multicolored .25 .25
969 A290 10pf multicolored .25 .25
970 A290 15pf multicolored .65 .80
971 A290 20pf multicolored .65 .80
972 A290 25pf multicolored .25 .25
973 A290 30pf multicolored .25 .25
a.    Sheet of 6, #968-973 4.50 4.50

Farmers, Stables and Silos — A312

**Perf. 13x12½**
**1967, Dec. 6   Litho.   Unwmk.**
974 A312 10pf multicolored .30 .25

1st agricultural co-operatives, 15th anniv.

Nutcracker and Figurines — A313

20pf, Candle holders: angel and miner.

**1967, Dec. 6   Photo.   Perf. 13½x14**
975 A313 10pf green & multi .65 .30
976 A313 20pf red & multi .25 .25

Issued to publicize local handicrafts of the Erzgebirge in Saxony (Ore Mountains).

Speed Skating — A314

Sport and Olympic Rings: 15pf, Slalom. 20pf, Ice hockey. 25pf, Figure skating, pair. 30pf, Long-distance skiing.

**Perf. 13½x13**
**1968, Jan. 17   Litho.   Unwmk.**
977 A314 5pf blue, dk bl & red .25 .25
978 A314 15pf multicolored .25 .25
979 A314 20pf grnsh bl, dk bl & red .25 .25
980 A314 25pf multicolored .25 .25
981 A314 30pf grnsh bl, vio bl & red 2.50 .90
Nos. 977-981,B146 (6) 3.75 2.15

10th Winter Olympic Games, Grenoble, France, Feb. 6-18.

Actinometer, Sun and Potsdam Meteorological Observatory — A315

Designs: 20pf, Antenna, Cloud Formation and Map of Europe. 25pf, Weather influence on farming (fields by day and night, produce).

**1968, Jan. 24   Perf. 13½x13**
**Size: 23x28mm**
982 A315 10pf brt mag, org & blk .40 .30
**Size: 50x28mm**
983 A315 20pf multicolored .40 .30

**Size: 23x28mm**
984 A315 25pf olive, blk & yel .40 .30
a.    Strip of 3, #982-984 3.50 3.50

75th anniversary of the Meteorological Observatory in Potsdam.

Venera 4 Interplanetary Station — A316

Design: 25pf, Earth satellites Kosmos 186 and 188 orbiting earth.

**1968, Jan. 24   Photo.   Perf. 14**
985 A316 20pf multicolored .25 .25
986 A316 25pf multicolored .70 .30

Russian space explorations.

Fighters of The Underground — A317

20pf, "The Liberation." 25pf, "The Partisans."

**1968, Feb. 21   Photo.   Perf. 14x13½**
987 A317 10pf black & multi .25 .25
988 A317 20pf black & multi .25 .25
989 A317 25pf black & multi .35 .25
Nos. 987-989 (3) .85 .75

The designs are from the stained glass window triptych by Walter Womacka in the Sachsenhausen Memorial Museum.

Diesel Locomotive — A318

Design: 15pf, Refrigerator fishing ship.

**1968, Feb. 29   Perf. 14**
990 A318 10pf multicolored .30 .25
991 A318 15pf multicolored .70 .35

The 1968 Leipzig Spring Fair.

Woman from Hoyerswerda — A319

Sorbian Regional Costumes: 20pf, Woman from Schleife. 40pf, Woman from Crostwitz. 50pf, Woman from Spreewald.

**1968, Mar. 14**
992 A319 10pf citron & multi .25 .25
993 A319 20pf fawn & multi .25 .25
994 A319 40pf blue grn & multi .25 .25
995 A319 50pf green & multi 2.00 .75
Nos. 992-995 (4) 2.75 1.50

Maxim Gorky and View of Gorky — A320

25pf, Stormy petrel and toppling towers.

**1968, Mar. 14   Engr.**
996 A320 20pf brown & rose car .25 .25
997 A320 25pf brown & rose car .55 .30

Maxim Gorky (1868-1936), Russian writer.

Ring-necked Pheasants — A321

15pf, Gray partridges. 20pf, Mallards. 25pf, Graylag geese. 30pf, Wood pigeons. 40pf, Hares.

**1968, Mar. 26   Litho.   Perf. 13½x13**
998 A321 10pf gray & multi .25 .25
999 A321 15pf gray & multi .25 .25
1000 A321 20pf gray & multi .25 .25
1001 A321 25pf gray & multi .25 .25
1002 A321 30pf gray & multi .30 .25
1003 A321 40pf gray & multi 2.25 4.25
Nos. 998-1003 (6) 3.55 5.50

Karl Marx — A322

Designs: 10pf, Title page of the "Communist Manifesto." 25pf, Title page of "Das Kapital."

**1968, Apr. 25   Photo.   Perf. 14**
1004 A322 10pf yel grn & blk .25 .25
1005 A322 20pf mag, yel & blk .25 .25
1006 A322 25pf lem, blk & red brn .25 .25
a.    Strip of three 1.25 3.25
b.    Souvenir sheet of 3 1.10 3.25

Karl Marx (1818-83). Nos. 1004-1006 are printed se-tenant. No. 1006a contains 3 imperf. stamps similar to Nos. 1004-1006 with simulated perforations.

Fritz Heckert — A323

Design: 20pf, Young workers, new apartment buildings and Congress emblem.

**1968, Apr. 25**
1007 A323 10pf multicolored .25 .25
1008 A323 20pf multicolored .25 .25

7th Congress of the Free German Trade Unions.

"Right to Work" — A324

Designs: 10pf, "Right to Live," tree and globe. 25pf, "Right for Peace," dove and sun.

**1968, May 8   Litho.   Perf. 13½x13**
1009 A324 5pf maroon & pink .25 .25
1010 A324 10pf brn ol & ol bister .25 .25
1011 A324 25pf Prus bl & lt bl .65 .35
Nos. 1009-1011 (3) 1.15 .85

International Human Rights Year.

Angler — A325

Designs: No. 1013, Rowing (woman). No. 1014, High jump (woman).

**Unwmk.**
**1968, June 6   Photo.   Perf. 14**
1012 A325 20pf ol grn, sl bl & dk red .40 .35
1013 A325 20pf Prus bl, dk bl & ol .25 .25

1014 A325 20pf cop red, dp cl & bl .25 .25
Nos. 1012-1014 (3) .90 .85

World angling championships, Gustrow (No. 1012); European women's rowing championships, Berlin (No. 1013); 2nd European youth athletic competition, Leipzig (No. 1014).

Brandenburg Gate, Torch — A326

Design: 25pf, Stadium and torch.

**1968, June 20   Litho.   Perf. 13½x13**
1015 A326 10pf multicolored .25 .25
1016 A326 25pf multicolored .70 .45

2nd Children's and Youths' Spartakiad, Berlin.

Youth Festival Emblem — A327

**1968, June 20**
1017 A327 25pf multicolored .60 .35

9th Youth Festival for Peace & Friendship, Sofia.
See No. B148.

**Type of 1967 and**

Moritzburg Castle, Dresden — A328

Buildings: 10pf, City Hall, Wernigerode, vert. 25pf, City Hall, Greifswald, vert. 30pf, Sanssouci Palace, Potsdam.

**1968, June 25   Photo.   Perf. 13½x14**
1018 A291 10pf multicolored .25 .25
1019 A328 20pf multicolored .25 .25
1020 A291 25pf multicolored .25 .25
1021 A328 30pf multicolored .60 .60
Nos. 1018-1021 (4) 1.35 1.35

Walter Ulbricht and Arms of Republic A329

**Photo. & Engr.**
**1968, June 27   Perf. 14**
1022 A329 20pf org, dp car & blk .45 .25

75th birthday of Walter Ulbricht, chairman of the Council of State, Communist party secretary and deputy prime minister.

Old Rostock and Arms — A330

Design: 25pf, Historic and modern buildings, 1968, and arms of Rostock.

**1968, July 9   Photo.**
1023 A330 20pf multicolored .25 .25
1024 A330 25pf multicolored .40 .35

750th anniv. of Rostock and to publicize the 11th Baltic Sea Week.

Karl Landsteiner, M.D. (1868-1943) — A331

Portraits: 15pf, Emanuel Lasker (1868-1941), chess champion and writer. 20pf,

Hanns Eisler (1898-1962), composer. 25pf,
Ignaz Semmelweis, M.D. (1818-1865). 40pf,
Max von Pettenkofer (1818-1901), hygienist.

**1968, July 17    Engr.    Perf. 14**
| | | | | |
|---|---|---|---|---|
| **1025** | A331 | 10pf gray green | .25 | .25 |
| **1026** | A331 | 15pf black | .25 | .25 |
| **1027** | A331 | 20pf brown | .25 | .25 |
| **1028** | A331 | 25pf gray blue | .25 | .25 |
| **1029** | A331 | 40pf rose lake | .60 | .50 |
| | *Nos. 1025-1029 (5)* | | 1.60 | 1.50 |

"Trener" Stunt
Plane — A332

25pf, 2 "Trener" stunt planes in parallel
flight.

**1968, Aug. 13   Litho.   Perf. 12½x13**
| | | | | |
|---|---|---|---|---|
| **1030** | A332 | 10pf multicolored | .25 | .25 |
| **1031** | A332 | 25pf blue & multi | .50 | .35 |

Peasant Woman, by
Wilhelm Leibl — A333

Paintings from Dresden Gallery: 10pf, "On
the Beach," by Walter Womacka, horiz. 15pf,
Mountain Farmers Mowing, by Albin Egger-
Lienz, horiz. 40pf, The Artist's daughter, by
Venturelli. 50pf, High School Girl, by Michae-
lis. 70pf, Girl with Guitar, by Castelli.

**Perf. 14x13½, 13½x14**

**1968, Aug. 20    Photo.**
| | | | | |
|---|---|---|---|---|
| **1032** | A333 | 10pf multicolored | .25 | .25 |
| **1033** | A333 | 15pf multicolored | .25 | .25 |
| **1034** | A333 | 25pf multicolored | .25 | .25 |
| **1035** | A333 | 40pf multicolored | .35 | .25 |
| **1036** | A333 | 50pf multicolored | .35 | .25 |
| **1037** | A333 | 70pf multicolored | 1.90 | .85 |
| | *Nos. 1032-1037 (6)* | | 3.35 | 2.10 |

Model Trains — A334

**1968, Aug. 29    Perf. 14x13½**
| | | | | |
|---|---|---|---|---|
| **1038** | A334 | 10pf lt ultra, red & blk | .30 | .25 |

The 1968 Leipzig Fall Fair.

Spremberg
Dam — A335

Designs: 10pf, Pöhl Dam, vert. 15pf, Ohra
Dam, vert. 20pf, Rappbode Dam.

**Perf. 13x12½, 12½x13**

**1968, Sept. 11    Litho.**
| | | | | |
|---|---|---|---|---|
| **1039** | A335 | 5pf multicolored | .25 | .25 |
| **1040** | A335 | 10pf multicolored | .25 | .25 |
| **1041** | A335 | 15pf multicolored | .35 | .35 |
| **1042** | A335 | 20pf multicolored | .25 | .25 |
| | *Nos. 1039-1042 (4)* | | 1.10 | 1.10 |

Issued to publicize dams built since 1945.

Runner — A336

Designs: 25pf, Woman gymnast, vert. 40pf,
Water polo, vert. 70pf, Sculling.

**1968, Sept. 18    Photo.    Perf. 14**
| | | | | |
|---|---|---|---|---|
| **1043** | A336 | 10pf multicolored | .25 | .25 |
| **1044** | A336 | 25pf multicolored | .25 | .25 |
| **1045** | A336 | 40pf multicolored | .35 | .25 |
| **1046** | A336 | 70pf blue & multi | 1.25 | 1.00 |
| | *Nos. 1043-1046,B149-B150 (6)* | | 2.50 | 2.25 |

19th Olympic Games, Mexico City, 10/12-27.

Monument, Fort
Breendonk,
Belgium — A337

**1968, Oct. 10    Litho.    Perf. 13x13½**
| | | | | |
|---|---|---|---|---|
| **1047** | A337 | 25pf multicolored | .35 | .25 |

Issued in memory of the victims of the Nazis
at the Fort Breendonk Concentration Camp.

Tiger Beetle — A338

Insects: 15pf, Ground beetle (Cychrus cara-
boides). 20pf, Ladybug. 25pf, Ground beetle
(Carabus arcensis hrbst.). 30pf, Hister beetle.
40pf, Checkered beetle.

**1968, Oct. 16    Perf. 13½x13**
| | | | | |
|---|---|---|---|---|
| **1048** | A338 | 10pf yellow & multi | .25 | .25 |
| **1049** | A338 | 15pf bluish lil & blk | .25 | .25 |
| **1050** | A338 | 20pf multicolored | .25 | .25 |
| **1051** | A338 | 25pf lt lilac & blk | 1.60 | 1.40 |
| **1052** | A338 | 30pf lt grn, blk & red | .25 | .25 |
| **1053** | A338 | 40pf pink & black | .25 | .25 |
| | *Nos. 1048-1053 (6)* | | 2.85 | 2.65 |

Lenin and Letter to
Spartacists — A339

Designs: 20pf, Workers, soldiers and sailors
with masthead and slogans. 25pf, Karl
Liebknecht and Rosa Luxemburg.

**1968, Oct. 29    Litho.    Perf. 13x12½**
| | | | | |
|---|---|---|---|---|
| **1054** | A339 | 10pf lemon, red & blk | .25 | .25 |
| **1055** | A339 | 20pf lemon, red & blk | .25 | .25 |
| **1056** | A339 | 25pf lemon, red & blk | .40 | .40 |
| | *Nos. 1054-1056 (3)* | | .90 | .90 |

November Revolution in Germany, 50th
anniv.

Cattleya
A340

Orchids: 10pf, Paphiopedilum albertianum.
15pf, Cattleya fabia. 20pf, Cattleya aclandiae.
40pf, Sobralia macrantha. 50pf, Dendrobium
alpha.

**1968, Nov. 12    Photo.    Perf. 13**
**Flowers in Natural Colors**
| | | | | |
|---|---|---|---|---|
| **1057** | A340 | 5pf bluish lilac | .25 | .25 |
| **1058** | A340 | 10pf green | .25 | .25 |
| **1059** | A340 | 15pf bister | .25 | .25 |
| **1060** | A340 | 20pf green | .25 | .25 |
| **1061** | A340 | 40pf light brown | .25 | .25 |
| **1062** | A340 | 50pf gray | 1.40 | 1.00 |
| | *Nos. 1057-1062 (6)* | | 2.65 | 2.25 |

**Fairy Tale Type of 1966**

Various Scenes from Puss in Boots.

**1968, Nov. 27    Litho.    Perf. 13½x13**
| | | | | |
|---|---|---|---|---|
| **1063** | A290 | 5pf multicolored | .25 | .25 |
| **1064** | A290 | 10pf multicolored | .25 | .25 |
| **1065** | A290 | 15pf multicolored | .80 | .80 |
| **1066** | A290 | 20pf multicolored | .80 | .80 |
| **1067** | A290 | 25pf multicolored | .25 | .25 |
| **1068** | A290 | 30pf multicolored | .25 | .25 |
| | *a.* | Sheet of 6, #1063-1068 | 4.25 | 7.50 |

Young
Pioneers — A341

Design: 15pf, Five Young Pioneers.

**1968, Dec. 3    Perf. 13x13½**
| | | | | |
|---|---|---|---|---|
| **1069** | A341 | 10pf blue & multi | .25 | .25 |
| **1070** | A341 | 15pf multicolored | .50 | .30 |

20th anniv. of the founding of the Ernst
Thalmann Young Pioneers' organization.

**Buildings Type of 1967**

Buildings: 5pf, City Hall, Tangermunde.
10pf, German State Opera, Berlin. 20pf, Wall
Pavilion, Dresden. 25pf, Burgher's House,
Luckau. 30pf, Rococo Palace, Dornburg. 40pf,
"Stockfish" House, Erfurt.

**1969, Jan. 1    Photo.    Perf. 14**
| | | | | |
|---|---|---|---|---|
| **1071** | A291 | 5pf multi | .25 | .25 |
| **1072** | A291 | 10pf multi, horiz. | .25 | .25 |
| **1073** | A291 | 20pf multi | .25 | .25 |
| **1074** | A291 | 25pf multi | .65 | .45 |
| **1075** | A291 | 30pf multi, horiz. | .25 | .25 |
| **1076** | A291 | 40pf multi | .25 | .25 |
| | *Nos. 1071-1076 (6)* | | 1.90 | 1.70 |

Martin Andersen
Nexö, Danish
Writer — A342

Portraits: 20pf, Otto Nagel (1894-1967),
painter. 25pf, Alexander von Humboldt (1769-
1859), naturalist, traveler, statesman. 40pf,
Theodor Fontane (1819-1898), writer.

**1969, Feb. 5    Engr.    Perf. 14**
| | | | | |
|---|---|---|---|---|
| **1077** | A342 | 10pf olive | .25 | .25 |
| **1078** | A342 | 20pf deep brown | .25 | .25 |
| **1079** | A342 | 25pf violet blue | .65 | .35 |
| **1080** | A342 | 40pf brown | .25 | .25 |
| | *Nos. 1077-1080 (4)* | | 1.40 | 1.10 |

Issued to honor famous men.

Be Attentive and
Considerate! — A343

10pf, Watch ahead! (car, truck & traffic signal). 20pf, Watch railroad crossings! (train &
car at crossing). 25pf, If in doubt don't pass!
(cars & truck).

**1969, Feb. 18    Litho.    Perf. 13x13½**
| | | | | |
|---|---|---|---|---|
| **1081** | A343 | 5pf lt blue & multi | .25 | .25 |
| **1082** | A343 | 10pf yellow & multi | .25 | .25 |
| **1083** | A343 | 20pf pink & multi | .25 | .25 |
| **1084** | A343 | 25pf multicolored | .40 | .35 |
| | *Nos. 1081-1084 (4)* | | 1.15 | 1.10 |

Traffic safety campaign.

Combine
A344

Leipzig Spring Fair: 15pf, Planeta-Variant
offset printing press.

**1969, Feb. 26    Photo.    Perf. 14**
| | | | | |
|---|---|---|---|---|
| **1085** | A344 | 10pf multicolored | .25 | .25 |
| **1086** | A344 | 15pf crimson, blk & bl | .25 | .25 |

Jorinde and
Joringel — A345

Various Scenes from Fairy Tale "Jorinde and
Joringel."

**1969, Mar. 18    Litho.    Perf. 13½x13**
| | | | | |
|---|---|---|---|---|
| **1087** | A345 | 5pf black & multi | .25 | .25 |
| **1088** | A345 | 10pf black & multi | .25 | .25 |
| **1089** | A345 | 15pf black & multi | .40 | .45 |
| **1090** | A345 | 20pf black & multi | .40 | .45 |

| | | | | |
|---|---|---|---|---|
| **1091** | A345 | 25pf black & multi | .25 | .25 |
| **1092** | A345 | 30pf black & multi | .25 | .25 |
| | *a.* | Sheet of 6, #1087-1092 | 2.25 | 2.75 |

See Nos. 1176-1181.

Spring
Snowflake — A346

Protected Plants: 10pf, Adonis. 15pf, Globe-
flowers. 20pf, Garden Turk's-cap. 25pf, Button
snakeroot. 30pf, Dactylorchis latifolia.

**1969, Apr. 4    Photo.    Perf. 14**
| | | | | |
|---|---|---|---|---|
| **1093** | A346 | 5pf green & multi | .25 | .25 |
| **1094** | A346 | 10pf green & multi | .25 | .25 |
| **1095** | A346 | 15pf green & multi | .25 | .25 |
| **1096** | A346 | 20pf green & multi | .25 | .25 |
| **1097** | A346 | 25pf green & multi | 2.10 | 1.25 |
| **1098** | A346 | 30pf green & multi | .30 | .25 |
| | *Nos. 1093-1098 (6)* | | 3.40 | 2.50 |

Red Cross, Crescent,
Lion and Sun
Emblems — A347

Design: 15pf, Large Red Cross, Red Crescent and Lion and Sun Emblems.

**1969, Apr. 23    Litho.    Perf. 12½x13**
| | | | | |
|---|---|---|---|---|
| **1099** | A347 | 10pf gray, red & yel | .25 | .25 |
| **1100** | A347 | 15pf multicolored | .90 | .40 |

League of Red Cross Societies, 50th anniv.

Conifer Nursery — A348

10pf, Forests as natural resources (timber &
resin). 20pf, Forests as regulators of climate.
25pf, Forests as recreation areas (tents along
lake).

**1969, Apr. 23**
| | | | | |
|---|---|---|---|---|
| **1101** | A348 | 5pf multicolored | .25 | .25 |
| **1102** | A348 | 10pf multicolored | .25 | .25 |
| **1103** | A348 | 20pf multicolored | .25 | .25 |
| **1104** | A348 | 25pf multicolored | 1.40 | .75 |
| | *Nos. 1101-1104 (4)* | | 2.15 | 1.50 |

Prevention of forest fires.

Erythrite from
Schneeberg — A349

Minerals: 10pf, Fluorite from Halsbrücke.
15pf, Galena from Neudorf. 20pf, Smoky
quartz from Lichtenberg. 25pf, Calcite from
Niederrabenstein. 50pf, Silver from Freiberg.

**1969, May 21    Photo.    Perf. 13½x14**
| | | | | |
|---|---|---|---|---|
| **1105** | A349 | 5pf tan & multi | .25 | .25 |
| **1106** | A349 | 10pf multicolored | .25 | .25 |
| **1107** | A349 | 15pf gray & multi | .25 | .25 |
| **1108** | A349 | 20pf lemon & multi | .25 | .25 |
| **1109** | A349 | 25pf multicolored | .65 | .45 |
| **1110** | A349 | 50pf lt blue & multi | .25 | .25 |
| | *Nos. 1105-1110 (6)* | | 1.90 | 1.70 |

Women and
Symbols of
Agriculture,
Science and
Industry — A350

Design: 25pf, Woman's head and symbols.

**1969, May 28      Engr.      Perf. 14**
1111  A350  20pf dk red & blue          .25  .25
1112  A350  25pf blue & dk red          .70  .30
2nd Women's Congress of the German Democratic Republic.

**Ulbricht Type of 1961-67**
**1969-71  Wmk. 313  Typo.  Perf. 14**
**Size: 17x21mm**
1112A  A189  35pf Prus blue
        ('71)                .45  .45
**Unwmk.**
**Engr.**
**Size: 24x28½mm**
1113  A189  1m dull green         .35  1.00
1114  A189  2m brown             .45  1.10
  Nos. 1112A-1114 (3)          1.25  2.55
See note below Nos. 590B-590C.

**Coil Stamp**
**1970, Jan. 20  Typo.  Wmk. 313**
**Size: 17x21mm**
1114A  A189  1m olive            .65  4.00

Emblem of DDR Philatelic Society — A351

**1969, June 4    Photo.    Unwmk.**
1115  A351  10pf red, gold & ultra   .30  .25
National Philatelic Exhibition "20 Years DDR," Magdeburg, Oct. 31-Nov. 9.

Worker Protecting Children — A352

25pf, Workers of various races. 20pf+5pf, Berlin buildings: Brandenburg Gate, Council of State, Soviet Cenotaph, Town Hall Tower, Television Tower, Teachers' Building & Hall.

**Size: 23x28mm**
**1969, June 4    Litho.    Perf. 13**
1116  A352  10pf lemon & multi      .45  .65
**Size: 50x28mm**
1117  A352  20pf + 5pf multi        .45  .65
**Size: 23x28mm**
1118  A352  25pf lemon & multi      .45  .65
  a.    Strip of 3, #1116-1118     3.00  3.25
Intl. Peace Meeting, Berlin. The surtax on No. 1117 was for the Peace Council of the German Democratic Republic.

Opening Ceremony before Battle of Leipzig Monument A353

15pf, Parading athletes & stadium. 25pf, Running, hurdling, javelin & flag waving. 30pf, Presentation of colors before old Leipzig Town Hall.

**Photo. & Engr.**
**1969, June 18               Perf. 14**
1119  A353  5pf multi & black       .25  .25
1120  A353  15pf multi & black      .25  .25
1121  A353  25pf multi & black     1.00  .40
1122  A353  30pf multi & black      .25  .25
  Nos. 1119-1122,B152-B153 (6)   2.25  1.65
5th German Gymnastic and Sports Festival, Leipzig.

Pierre de Coubertin, by Wieland Forster — A354

Design: 25pf, Coubertin column, Memorial Grove, Olympia.

**1969, June 6              Perf. 14x13½**
1123  A354  10pf black & lt blue    .25  .25
1124  A354  25pf black & sal pink   .70  .55
Revival of the Olympic Games, 75th anniv.

Knight — A355

No. 1126, Bicycle wheel. No. 1127, Volleyball.

**1969, July 29    Photo.    Perf. 14**
1125  A355  20pf red, gold & dk
        brn                 .25  .25
1126  A355  20pf green, gold &
        red                 .25  .25
1127  A355  20pf multicolored       .25  .25
  Nos. 1125-1127 (3)          .75  .75
16th Students' Chess World Championships, Dresden (No. 1125); Indoor Bicycle World Championships, Erfurt (No. 1126); 2nd Volleyball World Cup (No. 1127).

Merchandise — A356

**1969, Aug. 27   Litho.   Perf. 12½x13**
1128  A356  10pf multicolored       .30  .25
Leipzig Fall Fair, Aug. 31-Sept. 7, 1969.

Arms of Republic and View of Rostock — A357

1m, DDR Arms, Town Hall, Marienkirche and Television Tower, Berlin, vert.

**1969, Sept. 23   Photo.   Perf. 14**
1129  A357  10pf Rostock            .25  .25
1130  A357  10pf Neubrandenburg     .25  .25
1131  A357  10pf Potsdam            .25  .25
1132  A357  10pf Eisenhüttenstadt   .25  .25
1133  A357  10pf Hoyerswerda        .25  .25
1134  A357  10pf Magdeburg          .25  .25
1135  A357  10pf Halle-Neustadt     .25  .25
1136  A357  10pf Suhl               .25  .25
1137  A357  10pf Dresden            .25  .25
1138  A357  10pf Leipzig            .25  .25
1139  A357  10pf Karl-Marx-Stadt    .25  .25
1140  A357  10pf Berlin             .25  .25
  Nos. 1129-1140 (12)        3.00  3.00
**Souvenir Sheet**
1141  A357  1m multicolored        1.25  3.75
Nos. 1129-1141, 1142-1145 for 20th anniv. of the German Democratic Republic.
No. 1141 contains one 29x52mm stamp.

Television Tower, Berlin — A358

People and Flags A359

Designs: 20pf, Sphere of Television Tower and TV test picture. No. 1144, Television Tower and TV test picture.

**1969, Oct. 6              Perf. 14**
1142  A358  10pf multicolored       .25  .25
1143  A358  20pf multicolored       .25  .25
**Souvenir Sheets**
1144  A358  1m dk blue & multi     1.40  2.75
**Perf. 13x12½**
1145  A359  1m red & multi         1.10  3.25
No. 1144 contains one 21½x60mm stamp.

Cathedral, Otto von Guericke Monument and Hotel International, Magdeburg — A360

**1969, Oct. 28   Litho.   Perf. 13x12½**
1146  A360  20pf multicolored       .30  .25
Natl. Postage Stamp Exhibition in honor of the 20th anniv. of the German Democratic Republic, Magdeburg. Oct. 31-Nov. 9. See No. B154.

UFI Emblem — A361

**1969, Oct. 28             Perf. 13x13½**
1147  A361  10pf multicolored       .25  .25
1148  A361  15pf multicolored      1.10  .35
36th UFI Congress (Union des Foires Internationales), Leipzig, Oct. 28-30.

Memorial Monument, Copenhagen-Ryvangen — A362

**1969, Oct. 28             Perf. 13**
1149  A362  25pf multicolored       .60  .25
Issued in memory of the victims of the Nazis in Denmark.

Rostock University Seal and Building — A363

Design: 15pf, Steam turbine, curve and Rostock University emblem.

**1969, Nov. 12            Perf. 12½x13**
1150  A363  10pf brt blue & multi   .25  .25
1151  A363  15pf violet & multi     .80  .25
550th anniversary of Rostock University.

ILO Emblem — A364

**1969, Nov. 12            Perf. 13½x14**
1152  A364  20pf dp green & silver  .25  .25
1153  A364  25pf lil rose & silver 1.10  .30
50th anniv. of the ILO.

Mold for Christmas Cookies — A365

50pf, Negro couple, shaped spice cookie.

**1969, Nov. 25   Litho.   Perf. 13½x13**
1154  A365  10pf dull org, bl & red
        brn                 .80  .80
1155  A365  50pf lt blue & multi   1.25  1.25
  a.    Pair, #1154-1155         4.75  4.00
  Nos. 1154-1155,B155 (3)      2.35  2.35
Folk art of Lusatia.

Antonov An-24 — A366

Planes: 25pf, Ilyushin Il-18. 30pf, Tupolev Tu-134. 50pf, Mi-8 helicopter.

**1969, Dec. 2             Perf. 13x12½**
1156  A366  20pf blue, red & blk    .25  .25
1157  A366  25pf vio, red & blk     .90  .75
1158  A366  30pf ultra, red & blk   .25  .25
1159  A366  50pf olive, red & blk   .25  .25
  Nos. 1156-1159 (4)         1.65  1.50

Siberian Teacher, by D. K. Sveshnikov A367

Russian Paintings from Dresden Gallery of Modern Masters: 10pf, Steelworker, by V. A. Serov. 20pf, Still Life, by E. A. Aslamasjan. 25pf, Hot Day (boats on river), by J. D. Romas. 40pf, Spring is Coming (young woman and snow-covered street), by L. V. Kabatchek. 50pf, Man on River Bank, by V. J. Makovskij.

**1969, Dec. 10    Photo.    Perf. 13**
1160  A367  5pf gray & multi        .25  .25
1161  A367  10pf gray & multi       .25  .25
1162  A367  20pf gray & multi       .25  .25
1163  A367  25pf gray & multi       .80  .80
1164  A367  40pf gray & multi       .25  .25
1165  A367  50pf gray & multi       .25  .25
  Nos. 1160-1165 (6)         2.05  2.05

Ernst Barlach (1870-1938), Sculptor and Writer — A368

Portraits: 10pf, Johann Gutenberg (1400-68). 15pf, Kurt Tucholsky (1890-1935), writer. 20pf, Ludwig van Beethoven. 25pf, Friedrich Hölderlin (1770-1843), poet. 40pf, Georg Wilhelm Friedrich Hegel (1770-1831), philosopher.

**1970, Jan. 20    Engr.    Perf. 14**
1166  A368  5pf blue violet         .25  .25
1167  A368  10pf gray brown         .25  .25
1168  A368  15pf violet blue        .25  .25
1169  A368  20pf rose lilac         .30  .25
1170  A368  25pf blue green        1.60  .60
1171  A368  40pf rose claret        .30  .25
  Nos. 1166-1171 (6)         2.95  1.85

Rabbit
A369

**1970, Feb. 5** **Photo.** **Perf. 13½x14**
| | | | | |
|---|---|---|---|---|
| 1172 | A369 | 10pf shown | .25 | .25 |
| 1173 | A369 | 20pf Red fox | .25 | .25 |
| 1174 | A369 | 25pf Mink | 2.10 | 2.00 |
| 1175 | A369 | 40pf Hamster | .30 | .25 |
| | | Nos. 1172-1175 (4) | 2.90 | 2.75 |

525th International Fur Auctions, Leipzig.

**Fairy Tale Type of 1969**

Various Scenes from Fairy Tale "Little Brother and Sister."

**1970, Feb. 17** **Litho.** **Perf. 13½x13**
| | | | | |
|---|---|---|---|---|
| 1176 | A345 | 5pf lilac & multi | .25 | .25 |
| 1177 | A345 | 10pf lilac & multi | .25 | .25 |
| 1178 | A345 | 15pf lilac & multi | .45 | .50 |
| 1179 | A345 | 20pf lilac & multi | .45 | .50 |
| 1180 | A345 | 25pf lilac & multi | .25 | .25 |
| 1181 | A345 | 30pf lilac & multi | .25 | .25 |
| | a. | Sheet of 6, #1176-1181 | 5.50 | 3.75 |

Telephone Coordinating Station — A370

15pf, High voltage testing transformer, vert.

**1970, Feb. 24** **Perf. 13x12½, 12½x13**
| | | | | |
|---|---|---|---|---|
| 1182 | A370 | 10pf multicolored | .25 | .25 |
| 1183 | A370 | 15pf multicolored | .40 | .25 |

Leipzig Spring Fair, Mar. 1-10, 1970.

Horseman's Tombstone (700 A.D.) — A371

Treasures from the Halle Museum: 20pf, Helmet (500 A.D.). 25pf, Bronze basin (1000 B.C.). 40pf, Clay drum (2500 B.C.).

**1970, Mar. 3** **Photo.** **Perf. 13**
| | | | | |
|---|---|---|---|---|
| 1184 | A371 | 10pf dp grn, gray & dk brn | .25 | .25 |
| 1185 | A371 | 20pf multicolored | .25 | .25 |
| 1186 | A371 | 25pf yellow & multi | .50 | .90 |
| 1187 | A371 | 40pf multicolored | .25 | .25 |
| | | Nos. 1184-1187 (4) | 1.25 | 1.65 |

Lenin and Clara Zetkin A372

Designs: 10pf, Lenin, "ISKRA" (newspaper's name), composing frame and printing press. 25pf, Lenin and title page of German edition of "State and Revolution." 40pf, Lenin statue, Eisleben. 70pf, Lenin monument and Lenin Square, Berlin. 1m, Lenin portrait, vert.

**Photogravure and Engraved**

**1970, Apr. 16** **Perf. 14**
| | | | | |
|---|---|---|---|---|
| 1188 | A372 | 10pf multicolored | .25 | .25 |
| 1189 | A372 | 20pf multicolored | .25 | .25 |
| 1190 | A372 | 25pf multicolored | 1.25 | 1.00 |
| 1191 | A372 | 40pf multicolored | .25 | .25 |
| 1192 | A372 | 70pf multicolored | .30 | .25 |
| | | Nos. 1188-1192 (5) | 2.30 | 2.00 |

**Souvenir Sheet**

| | | | | |
|---|---|---|---|---|
| 1193 | A372 | 1m dk car & multi | 1.40 | 7.00 |

Sea Kale — A373

Protected Plants: 20pf, European pasqueflower. 25pf, Fringed gentian. 30pf, Galeate orchis. 40pf, Marsh tea. 70pf, Round-leaved wintergreen.

**1970, Apr. 28** **Photo.**
| | | | | |
|---|---|---|---|---|
| 1194 | A373 | 10pf multicolored | .25 | .25 |
| 1195 | A373 | 20pf violet & multi | .25 | .25 |
| 1196 | A373 | 25pf multicolored | 1.25 | 1.40 |
| 1197 | A373 | 30pf multicolored | .25 | .25 |
| 1198 | A373 | 40pf multicolored | .25 | .25 |
| 1199 | A373 | 70pf multicolored | .30 | .25 |
| | | Nos. 1194-1199 (6) | 2.55 | 2.65 |

Red Army Soldier Raising Flag over Berlin Reichstag — A374

20pf, Spasski Tower, Kremlin; State Council Building, Berlin; coats of arms of USSR and DDR, newspaper clipping about friendship treaty with USSR. 25pf, Mutual Economic Aid Building, Moscow, flags of member countries. 70pf, Memorial monument, Buchenwald.

**1970, May 5** **Litho.** **Perf. 13x13½**
| | | | | |
|---|---|---|---|---|
| 1200 | A374 | 10pf multi | .25 | .25 |
| 1201 | A374 | 20pf multi | .25 | .25 |
| 1202 | A374 | 25pf multi | .90 | .60 |
| | | Nos. 1200-1202 (3) | 1.40 | 1.10 |

**Souvenir Sheet**

| | | | | |
|---|---|---|---|---|
| 1203 | A374 | 70pf multi, horiz. | 1.25 | 4.50 |

25th anniv. of liberation from Fascism.

Shortwave Antenna, RBI Emblem and Globe — A375

15pf, Berlin Radio Station, emblems of Radio Berlin Intl. (RBI), Radio DDR & Radio Germany.

**1970, May 13** **Litho.** **Perf. 13½x13**
**Size: 23x28mm**
| | | | | |
|---|---|---|---|---|
| 1204 | A375 | 10pf grn, vio bl & bl | .45 | .45 |

**Size: 50x28mm**
| | | | | |
|---|---|---|---|---|
| 1205 | A375 | 15pf vio bl, dp rose & ap grn | .65 | .65 |
| | a. | Pair, #1204-1205 | 3.00 | 1.75 |

DDR broadcasting system, 25th anniv.

Grain and Globe — A376

25pf, House of Culture, Dresden, and grain.

**1970, May 19**
| | | | | |
|---|---|---|---|---|
| 1206 | A376 | 20pf vio bl, yel & bl | .60 | .60 |
| 1207 | A376 | 25pf vio bl, yel & bl | .60 | .60 |
| | a. | Strip of 2, #1206-1207 + label | 3.00 | 3.00 |

Issued to publicize the 5th World Cereal and Bread Congress, Dresden, May 24-29.

Fritz Heckert Medal — A377

Design: 25pf, Globes and "FSM."

**1970, June 9** **Perf. 13x12½**
| | | | | |
|---|---|---|---|---|
| 1208 | A377 | 20pf red, yel & bl | .25 | .25 |
| 1209 | A377 | 25pf red, bl & yel | .45 | .40 |

25th anniv. of the Free German Trade Union and of the World Organization of Trade Unions.

Traffic Policeman A378

Designs: 10pf, Young Pioneers congratulating police woman. 15pf, Volga police car. 20pf, Railroad policeman with radio-telephone. 25pf, River police in Volga wing-type boat.

**1970, June 23** **Litho.** **Perf. 13x12½**
| | | | | |
|---|---|---|---|---|
| 1210 | A378 | 5pf ocher & multi | .25 | .25 |
| 1211 | A378 | 10pf green & multi | .25 | .25 |
| 1212 | A378 | 15pf ultra & multi | .25 | .25 |
| 1213 | A378 | 20pf multicolored | .25 | .25 |
| 1214 | A378 | 25pf multicolored | 2.00 | .30 |
| | | Nos. 1210-1214 (5) | 3.00 | 1.30 |

25th anniversary of the People's Police.

Gods Amon, Shu and Tefnut A379

Designs from Lion Temple in Musawwarat: 15pf, Head of King Arnekhamani. 20pf, Cow from cattle frieze. 25pf, Head of Prince Arka. 30pf, Head of God Arensnuphis, vert. 40pf, Elephants and prisoners of war. 50pf, Lion God Apedemak.

**Perf. 13½x14, 14x13½**
**1970, June 23** **Photo.**
| | | | | |
|---|---|---|---|---|
| 1215 | A379 | 10pf multicolored | .25 | .25 |
| 1216 | A379 | 15pf multicolored | .25 | .25 |
| 1217 | A379 | 20pf multicolored | .25 | .25 |
| 1218 | A379 | 25pf multicolored | .60 | .50 |
| 1219 | A379 | 30pf multicolored | .25 | .25 |
| 1220 | A379 | 40pf multicolored | .25 | .25 |
| 1221 | A379 | 50pf multicolored | .25 | .25 |
| | | Nos. 1215-1221 (7) | 2.10 | 2.00 |

Archaeological work in the Sudan by the Humboldt University, Berlin.

Arms and Flags of DDR and Poland A380

**1970, July 1** **Litho.** **Perf. 13x12½**
| | | | | |
|---|---|---|---|---|
| 1222 | A380 | 20pf multicolored | .30 | .25 |

20th anniversary of the Görlitz Agreement concerning the Oder-Neisse border.

25th Anniv. of the German Kulturbund. — A381

Design: 10pf, Culture Association Emblem. 25pf, Johannes R. Becher medal.

**1970, July 1** **Photo.** **Perf. 14**
| | | | | |
|---|---|---|---|---|
| 1223 | | 10pf ultra, sil & brn | 1.40 | 1.40 |
| 1224 | | 25pf ultra, gold & brn | 1.40 | 1.40 |
| | a. | A381 Strip of 2, #1223-1224 + label | 7.00 | 8.50 |

Athlete on Pommel Horse — A382

**1970, July 1** **Perf. 14x13½**
| | | | | |
|---|---|---|---|---|
| 1225 | A382 | 10pf blk, yel & brn red | .30 | .25 |

Issued to publicize the 3rd Children's and Youths' Spartakiad. See No. B156.

Meeting of the American, British and Russian Delegations — A383

10pf, Cecilienhof Castle. 20pf, "Potsdam Agreement" in German, English, French & Russian.

**1970, July 28** **Litho.** **Perf. 13**
**Size: 23x28mm**
| | | | | |
|---|---|---|---|---|
| 1226 | | 10pf blk, cit & red | .25 | .25 |
| 1227 | | 20pf blk, cit & red | .25 | .25 |

**Size: 77x28mm**
| | | | | |
|---|---|---|---|---|
| 1228 | | 25pf red & blk | .25 | .25 |
| | a. | A383 Strip of 3, #1226-1228 | 1.40 | 2.25 |

25th anniv. of the Potsdam Agreement among the Allies concerning Germany at the end of WWII.

Men's Pocket and Wrist Watches — A384

**1970, Aug. 25** **Photo.** **Perf. 13½x14**
| | | | | |
|---|---|---|---|---|
| 1229 | A384 | 10pf ultra, blk & gold | .30 | .25 |

Leipzig Fall Fair, 1970.

Theodor Neubauer and Magnus Poser A385

"Homeland" from Soviet Cenotaph, Berlin-Treptow A386

**1970, Sept. 2** **Perf. 13x12½, 12½x13**
| | | | | |
|---|---|---|---|---|
| 1230 | A385 | 20pf dk bl, car & pale grn | .25 | .25 |
| 1231 | A386 | 25pf dp car, pale bl | .25 | .25 |

Issued in memory of fighters against "fascism and imperialistic wars."

Competition Map and Compass A387

Design: 25pf, Competition map and runner at 3 different stations.

**1970, Sept. 15** **Litho.** **Perf. 13x12½**
| | | | | |
|---|---|---|---|---|
| 1232 | A387 | 10pf yellow & multi | .25 | .25 |
| 1233 | A387 | 25pf yellow & multi | .90 | .30 |

World Orienting Championships.

Mother and Child, by Käthe Kollwitz — A388

Works of Art: 10pf, Forest Worker Scharf's Birthday, by Otto Nagel. 20pf, Portrait of a Girl, by Otto Nagel. 25pf, No More War, (Woman with raised arm) by Käthe Kollwitz. 40pf, Head from Gustrow Memorial, by Ernst Barlach. 50pf, The Flutist, by Ernst Barlach.

**Photo.; Litho. (25pf, 30pf)**
**1970, Sept. 22** **Perf. 14x13½**
| | | | | |
|---|---|---|---|---|
| 1234 | A388 | 10pf multicolored | .25 | .25 |
| 1235 | A388 | 20pf multicolored | .25 | .25 |
| 1236 | A388 | 25pf pink & dk brn | .65 | .75 |
| 1237 | A388 | 30pf sal & blk | .25 | .25 |
| 1238 | A388 | 40pf yel & blk | .25 | .25 |
| 1239 | A388 | 50pf yel & blk | .25 | .25 |
| | | Nos. 1234-1239 (6) | 1.90 | 2.00 |

Issued in memory of the artists Otto Nagel, Käthe Kollwitz and Ernst Barlach.

The Little Trumpeter — A389

**1970, Oct. 1**      **Photo.**
1240 A389 10pf dp ultra, brn & org   .25 .30

2nd Natl. Youth Stamp Exhib., Karl-Marx-Stadt, Oct. 4-11. The design shows the memorial in Halle for Fritz Weineck, trumpeter for the Red War Veterans' Organization. See No. B160.

Emblem with Flags of East Block Nations A390

**1970, Oct. 1**    **Litho.**    **Perf. 13x12½**
1241 A390 10pf carmine & multi   .25 .25
1242 A390 20pf multicolored   .25 .25

Issued to publicize the Brothers in Arms maneuvers of the East Bloc countries in the territory of the German Democratic Republic.

Musk Ox — A391

Berlin Zoo: 15pf, Shoebill. 20pf, Addax. 25pf, Malayan sun bear.

**1970, Oct. 6**    **Photo.**    **Perf. 14**
1243 A391 10pf blue & multi   .30 .25
1244 A391 15pf green & multi   .30 .25
1245 A391 20pf org & multi   .45 .30
1246 A391 25pf multicolored   4.25 4.25
    Nos. 1243-1246 (4)   5.30 5.05

UN Headquarters and Emblem — A392

**1970, Oct. 20**    **Photo.**    **Perf. 13**
1247 A392 20pf ultra & multi   .55 .25

25th anniversary of the United Nations.

Friedrich Engels — A393

20pf, Friedrich Engels and Karl Marx. 25pf, Engels and title page of his polemic against Dühring.

**Photogravure and Engraved**
**1970, Nov. 24**      **Perf. 14**
1248 A393 10pf ver, gray & blk   .25 .25
1249 A393 20pf ver, dk grn & blk   .25 .25
1250 A393 25pf ver, dk car rose
         & blk   .80 .65
    Nos. 1248-1250 (3)   1.30 1.15

Friedrich Engels (1820-1895), socialist, collaborator with Karl Marx.

Epiphyllum — A394

Flowering Cactus Plants: 10pf, Astrophytum myriostigma. 15pf, Echinocereus salm-dyckianus. 20pf, Selenicereus grandiflorus. 25pf, Hamatocactus setispinus. 30pf, Mamillaria boolii.

**1970, Dec. 2**    **Photo.**    **Perf. 14**
1251 A394 5pf multicolored   .25 .25
1252 A394 10pf dk blue & multi   .25 .25
1253 A394 15pf multicolored   .25 .25
1254 A394 20pf multicolored   .25 .25
1255 A394 25pf dk blue & multi   1.25 1.20
1256 A394 30pf purple & multi   .25 .25
    Nos. 1251-1256 (6)   2.50 2.45

**Souvenir Sheet**

Ludwig van Beethoven — A395

**1970, Dec. 10**    **Engr.**    **Perf. 14**
1257 A395 1m gray   1.40 2.75

Bicentenary of the birth of Ludwig van Beethoven (1770-1827), composer.

Dancer's Mask, South Seas — A396

Works from Ethnological Museum, Leipzig: 20pf, Bronze head, Africa. 25pf, Tea pot, Asia. 40pf, Clay figure (jaguar), Mexico.

**1971, Jan. 12**    **Photo.**    **Perf. 13**
1258 A396 10pf multicolored   .25 .25
1259 A396 20pf multicolored   .25 .25
1260 A396 30pf multicolored   .50 .40
1261 A396 40pf multicolored   .25 .25
    Nos. 1258-1261 (4)   1.25 1.15

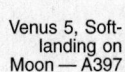

Venus 5, Soft-landing on Moon — A397

No. 1263, Model of space station. No. 1264, Luna 16 and Luna 10 satellites. No. 1265, Group flight of Sojuz 6, 7 and 8. No. 1266, Proton 1, radiation measuring satellite. No. 1267, Communications satellite Molniya 1. No. 1268, Yuri A. Gagarin, first flight of Vostok 1. No. 1269, Alexei Leonov walking in space, Voskhod 2.

**1971, Feb. 11**    **Litho.**    **Perf. 13x12½**
1262 A397 20pf dk blue & multi   .25 .25
1263 A397 20pf dk blue & multi   .25 .25
1264 A397 20pf dk blue & multi   .40 .40
1265 A397 20pf dk blue & multi   .40 .40
1266 A397 20pf dk blue & multi   .40 .40
1267 A397 20pf dk blue & multi   .40 .40
1268 A397 20pf dk blue & multi   .25 .25
1269 A397 20pf dk blue & multi   .25 .25
   a.   Sheet of 8, #1262-1269   4.25 4.25

Soviet space research.

Johannes R. Becher — A398

Portraits: 10pf, Heinrich Mann. 15pf, John Heartfield. 20pf, Willi Bredel. 25pf, Franz

Mehring. 40pf, Rudolf Virchow. 50pf, Johannes Kepler.

**1971**    **Engr.**      **Perf. 14**
1270 A398 5pf brown   .25 .25
1271 A398 10pf vio blue   .25 .25
1272 A398 15pf black   .25 .25
1273 A398 20pf rose lake   .25 .25
1274 A398 25pf green   .40 .35
1274A A398 40pf pale purple   .40 .25
1275 A398 50pf dp black   .25 .25
    Nos. 1270-1275 (7)   2.05 1.85

Honoring prominent Germans. See Nos. 1349-1353.

Karl Liebknecht — A399

Design: 25pf, Rosa Luxemburg.

**1971, Feb. 23**      **Photo.**
1276 A399 20pf gold, mag & blk   .35 .35
1277 A399 25pf gold, mag & blk   .35 .35
   a.   Pair, #1276-1277   .85 1.10

Karl Liebknecht (1871-1919) and Rosa Luxemburg (1871-1919), leaders of Spartacist Movement.

Soldier and Army Emblem A400

**1971, Mar. 1**      **Perf. 13½x14**
1278 A400 20pf gray & multi   .30 .25

15th anniv. of the National People's Army.

Crushing and Conveyor Plant, Magdeburg A401

Leipzig Spring Fair: 15pf, Dredger for low temperature work.

**1971, Mar. 9**    **Litho.**    **Perf. 13x12½**
1279 A401 10pf green & multi   .25 .25
1280 A401 15pf multicolored   .25 .25

Proclamation of the Commune, Town Hall, Paris — A402

Designs: 20pf, Barricade at Place Blanche, defended by women. 25pf, Illustration by Theophile A. Steinlen for the International. 30pf, Title page for "The Civil War in France," by Karl Marx.

**1971, Mar. 9**      **Perf. 13**
1281 A402 20pf red, bis & blk   .25 .25
1282 A402 20pf red, bis & blk   .25 .25
1283 A402 25pf red, buff & blk   .40 .35
1284 A402 30pf red, gray & blk   .25 .25
    Nos. 1281-1284 (4)   1.15 1.10

Centenary of the Paris Commune.

Lunokhod 1 on Moon — A403

**1971, Mar. 30**    **Photo.**    **Perf. 14**
1285 A403 20pf multicolored   .45 .30

Luna 17 unmanned, automated moon mission, Nov. 10-17, and the 24th Communist Party Congress of the Soviet Union.

Discobolus A404

**1971, Apr. 6**    **Litho.**    **Perf. 13½x13**
1286 A404 20pf dull bl, lt bl & buff   .55 .25

20th anniversary of the Olympic Committee of German Democratic Republic.

Köpenick Castle — A405

Berlin Buildings: 10pf, St. Mary's Church, vert. 20pf, Old Library. 25pf, Ermeler House, vert. 50pf, New Guard Memorial. 70pf, Natl. Gallery of Art.

**Perf. 13½x14, 14x13½**
**1971, Apr. 6**      **Photo.**
1287 A405 10pf multicolored   .25 .25
1288 A405 15pf multicolored   .25 .25
1289 A405 20pf multicolored   .25 .25
1290 A405 25pf multicolored   2.10 1.75
1291 A405 50pf multicolored   .25 .25
1292 A405 70pf multicolored   .30 .25
    Nos. 1287-1292 (6)   3.40 3.00

Clasped Hands — A406

**Lithographed and Embossed**
**1971, Apr. 20**      **Perf. 13x13½**
1293 A406 20pf red, blk & gold   .30 .25

25th anniversary of Socialist Unity Party of Germany (SED).

Dance Costume, Schleife — A407

Sorbian Dance Costumes from: 20pf, Hoyerswerda. 25pf, Cottbus. 40pf, Kamenz.

**1971, May 4**    **Litho.**    **Perf. 13½x13**
            **Size: 33x42mm**
1294 A407 10pf multicolored   .25 .25
1295 A407 20pf green & multi   .25 .25
1296 A407 25pf blue & multi   .45 .65
1297 A407 40pf multicolored   .25 .25
    Nos. 1294-1297 (4)   1.20 1.40

**1971, Nov. 23**      **Perf. 13½x13**
       **Booklet Stamps**
       **Size: 23x28mm**
1297A A407 10pf multicolored   .25 .25
  c.   Booklet pane of 4   1.40 1.10
  d.   Booklet pane, 2 #1297A, 2
       #1297B   3.25 2.50
1297B A407 20pf multicolored   .55 .40

Self-Portrait, by Dürer — A408

Art Works by Dürer: 40pf, Three Peasants. 70pf, Portrait of Philipp Melanchthon.

**1971, May 18**      *Perf. 12½x13*

| 1298 | A408 10pf multicolored | .25 | .25 |
|---|---|---|---|
| 1299 | A408 40pf brown & multi | .25 | .25 |
| 1300 | A408 70pf gray & multi | 1.25 | .65 |
| | *Nos. 1298-1300 (3)* | 1.75 | 1.15 |

500th anniversary of the birth of Albrecht Dürer (1471-1528), painter and engraver.

Building Industry A409

Congress Emblem A410

Designs: 10pf, Science and technology. No. 1303, Farming. 25pf, Civilian defense.

**1971, June 9**    *Photo.*    *Perf. 14*

| 1301 | A409 5pf cream, red & blk | .25 | .25 |
|---|---|---|---|
| 1302 | A409 10pf cream, red & blk | .25 | .25 |
| 1303 | A409 20pf cream, red, bl & blk | .25 | .25 |
| 1304 | A410 20pf gold, dp car & red | .25 | .25 |
| 1305 | A409 25pf cream, red & blk | .30 | .35 |
| | *Nos. 1301-1305 (5)* | 1.30 | 1.35 |

8th Congress of Socialist Unity Party of Germany (SED).

Treasures from the Green Vault, Dresden: 5pf, Cherry stone with 180 heads carved on it, 1590. 10pf, Golden Fleece, 1730. 15pf, Tankard, Nuremberg, 1530. 20pf, Moor with drums on horseback, 1720. 25pf, Decorated writing box, 1562. 30pf, St. George pendant, 1570.

**1971, June 22**      *Perf. 13*

| 1306 | A411 5pf dp car & multi | .25 | .25 |
|---|---|---|---|
| 1307 | A411 10pf green & multi | .25 | .25 |
| 1308 | A411 15pf violet & multi | .25 | .25 |
| 1309 | A411 20pf org red & multi | .25 | .25 |
| 1310 | A411 25pf brt bl grn & multi | .45 | .45 |
| 1311 | A411 30pf dp ultra & multi | .25 | .25 |
| | *Nos. 1306-1311 (6)* | 1.70 | 1.70 |

Prisoners, by Fritz Cremer — A412

Design: 25pf, Brutality in Buchenwald Concentration Camp, by Fritz Cremer.

**1971, June 22**    *Litho.*    *Perf. 13*

| 1312 | A412 20pf bister & blk | .40 | .45 |
|---|---|---|---|
| 1313 | A412 25pf lt blue & blk | .40 | .45 |
| a. | Pair, #1312-1313 with label between | 1.20 | 1.60 |

Intl. Federation of Resistance Fighters (FIR), 20th anniv.

Coat of Arms of Mongolia — A413

**1971, July 6**    *Litho.*    *Perf. 13*

| 1314 | A413 20pf dk red, yel & blk | .30 | .25 |
|---|---|---|---|

50th anniv. of the Mongolian People's Revolution.

Child's Head, UNICEF Emblem — A414

**1971, July 13**      *Photo.*

| 1315 | A414 20pf multicolored | .35 | .25 |
|---|---|---|---|

25th anniv. of UNICEF.

Militiaman, Soldier and Brandenburg Gate — A415

Design: 35pf, Brandenburg Gate and new buildings in East Berlin.

**1971, Aug. 12**

| 1316 | A415 20pf red & multi | .50 | .25 |
|---|---|---|---|
| 1317 | A415 35pf yel & multi | 1.25 | .90 |

10 years of Berlin Wall.

Passenger Ship Iwan Franko — A416

Ships: 15pf, Freighter, type 17. 20pf, Freighter Rostock, type XD. 25pf, Fish processing ship "Junge Welt." 40pf, Container cargo ship. 50pf, Explorer ship Akademik Kurtschatow.

**1971, Aug. 24**      *Engr.*

| 1318 | A416 10pf pale purple | .25 | .25 |
|---|---|---|---|
| 1319 | A416 15pf pale brn & ind | .25 | .25 |
| 1320 | A416 20pf gray green | .25 | .25 |
| 1321 | A416 25pf slate | .85 | .80 |
| 1322 | A416 40pf maroon | .25 | .25 |
| 1323 | A416 50pf grysh blue | .25 | .25 |
| | *Nos. 1318-1323 (6)* | 2.10 | 2.05 |

Shipbuilding industry.

Butadiene Plant — A417

Leipzig Fall Fair: 25pf, Refinery.

**1971, Sept. 2**    *Photo.*    *Perf. 13*

| 1324 | A417 10pf olive, vio & mag | .25 | .25 |
|---|---|---|---|
| 1325 | A417 25pf blue, vio & ol | .25 | .25 |

Raised Fists, Photo Montage by John Heartfield, 1937 — A418

**1971, Sept. 23**

| 1326 | A418 35pf grnsh bl, blk & sil | .30 | .25 |
|---|---|---|---|

Intl. Year Against Racial Discrimination.

Karl Marx Monument — A419

**1971, Oct. 5**    *Photo.*    *Perf. 14x13½*

| 1327 | A419 35pf vio brn, pink & buff | .35 | .25 |
|---|---|---|---|

Unveiling of Karl Marx memorial at Karl-Marx-Stadt (Chemnitz).

Wiltz Memorial, Flag of Luxembourg — A420

**1971, Oct. 5**

| 1328 | A420 25pf multicolored | .25 | .25 |
|---|---|---|---|

Memorial for Nazi victims, Wiltz, Luxembourg.

Postal Milestones, Saxony, and Zürner's Surveyor Carriage — A421

**Photo. & Engr.**

**1971, Oct. 5**      *Perf. 14*

| 1329 | A421 25pf blue, olive & lilac | .35 | .35 |
|---|---|---|---|

Philatelists' Day 1971. See No. B162.

Darbuka, North Africa — A422

Musical Instruments: 15pf, Two morin chuur, Mongolia. 20pf, Violin, Germany. 25pf, Mandolin, Italy. 40pf, Bagpipes, Bohemia. 50pf, Kasso, Sudan.

**1971, Oct. 26**    *Photo.*    *Perf. 14x13½*

| 1330 | A422 10pf multicolored | .25 | .25 |
|---|---|---|---|
| 1331 | A422 15pf multicolored | .25 | .25 |
| 1332 | A422 20pf ocher & multi | .25 | .25 |
| 1333 | A422 25pf blue & multi | .25 | .25 |
| 1334 | A422 40pf gray & multi | .25 | .25 |
| 1335 | A422 50pf multicolored | .75 | .65 |
| | *Nos. 1330-1335 (6)* | 2.00 | 1.90 |

Instruments from the Music Museum in Markneukirchen.

Geodetic Apparatus — A423

20pf, Ergaval microscope. 25pf, Planetarium.

**1971, Nov. 9**    *Photo.*    *Perf. 13½x14*
     **Size: 23½x28½mm**

| 1336 | A423 10pf blue, blk & red | .35 | .35 |
|---|---|---|---|
| 1337 | A423 20pf blue, blk & red | .35 | .35 |

     **Size: 50½x28½mm**

| 1338 | A423 25pf blue, vio bl & yel | .35 | .35 |
|---|---|---|---|
| a. | Strip of 3, #1336-1338 | 3.25 | 3.25 |

Carl Zeiss optical works in Jena, 125th anniv.

**Fairy Tale Type of 1966**

Designs: Various Scenes from Fairy Tale "The Bremen Town Musicians."

**1971, Nov. 23**    *Litho.*    *Perf. 13½x13*

| 1339 | A290 5pf multicolored | .25 | .25 |
|---|---|---|---|
| 1340 | A290 10pf ocher & multi | .25 | .25 |
| 1341 | A290 15pf gray & multi | .45 | .65 |
| 1342 | A290 20pf ver & multi | .45 | .65 |
| 1343 | A290 25pf violet & multi | .25 | .25 |
| 1344 | A290 30pf yellow & multi | .25 | .25 |
| a. | Sheet of 6, #1339-1344 | 3.00 | 8.00 |

Olympic Rings and Sledding A424

Olympic Rings and: 20pf, Long-distance skiing. 25pf, Biathlon. 70pf, Ski jump.

**1971, Dec. 7**      *Perf. 13½x14*

| 1345 | A424 5pf green, car & blk | .25 | .25 |
|---|---|---|---|
| 1346 | A424 20pf car rose, vio & blk | .25 | .25 |
| 1347 | A424 25pf vio, car & blk | 1.10 | .90 |
| 1348 | A424 70pf vio bl, vio & blk | .25 | .25 |
| | *Nos. 1345-1348,B163-B164 (6)* | 2.35 | 2.15 |

11th Winter Olympic Games, Sapporo, Japan, Feb. 3-13, 1972.

**Portrait Type of 1971**

Portraits: 10pf, Johannes Tralow (1882-1968), playwright. 20pf, Leonhard Frank (1882-1961), writer. 25pf, K. A. Kocor (1822-1904), composer. 35pf, Heinrich Schliemann (1822-1890), archaeologist. 50pf, F. Caroline Neuber (1697-1760), actress.

**1972, Jan. 25**    *Engr.*    *Perf. 14*

| 1349 | A398 10pf green | .25 | .25 |
|---|---|---|---|
| 1350 | A398 20pf rose claret | .25 | .25 |
| 1351 | A398 25pf dk blue | .25 | .25 |
| 1352 | A398 35pf brown | .25 | .25 |
| 1353 | A398 50pf rose violet | .65 | 1.00 |
| | *Nos. 1349-1353 (5)* | 1.65 | 2.00 |

Honoring famous personalities.

Gypsum, Eisleben — A425

Minerals found in East Germany: 10pf, Zinnwaldite, Zinnwald. 20pf, Malachite, Ullersreuth. 25pf, Amethyst, Wiesenbad. 35pf, Halite, Merkers. 50pf, Proustite, Schneeberg.

**1972, Feb. 22**    *Photo.*    *Perf. 13*

| 1354 | A425 5pf grnsh bl & brn blk | .25 | .25 |
|---|---|---|---|
| 1355 | A425 10pf citron, brn & blk | .25 | .25 |
| 1356 | A425 20pf multicolored | .25 | .25 |
| 1357 | A425 25pf multicolored | .25 | .25 |
| 1358 | A425 35pf lt green, ind & blk | .25 | .25 |
| 1359 | A425 50pf gray & multi | .80 | .85 |
| | *Nos. 1354-1359 (6)* | 2.05 | 2.10 |

Russian Pavilion and Fair Emblem — A426

Design: 25pf, Flags of East Germany and Russia, and Fair emblem.

**1972, Mar. 3**    *Photo.*    *Perf. 14*

| 1360 | A426 10pf vio blue & multi | .25 | .25 |
|---|---|---|---|
| 1361 | A426 25pf claret & multi | .25 | .25 |

50 years of Russian participation in the Leipzig Fair.

**Miniature Sheets**

Anemometer, 1896, and Meteorological Chart, 1876 — A427

Designs: 35pf, Dipole and cloud photograph taken by satellite. 70pf, Meteor weather satellite and weather map.

**1972, Mar. 23**    *Litho.*    *Perf. 13x12½*

| 1362 | A427 20pf multicolored | .60 | 1.00 |
|---|---|---|---|
| 1363 | A427 35pf multicolored | .60 | 1.00 |
| 1364 | A427 70pf green & multi | .60 | 1.00 |
| | *Nos. 1362-1364 (3)* | 1.80 | 3.00 |

Intl. Meteorologists' Cent. Meeting, Leipzig.

World Health Organization Emblem — A428

**1972, Apr. 4    Photo.    Perf. 13**
1365 A428 35pf lt bl, vio bl & sil    .30    .25
World Health Day.

Kamov Helicopter A429

Aircraft: 10pf, Agricultural spray plane. 35pf, Ilyushin jet. 1m, Jet and tail with Interflug emblem.

**1972, Apr. 25    Perf. 14**
1366 A429  5pf blue & multi    .25    .25
1367 A429 10pf multicolored    .25    .25
1368 A429 35pf blue grn & multi    .25    .25
1369 A429  1m multicolored    1.10    1.25
    Nos. 1366-1369 (4)    1.85    2.00

Wrestling and Olympic Rings A430

Sport and Olympic Rings: 20pf, Pole vault. 35pf, Volleyball. 70pf, Women's gymnastics.

**1972, May 16    Photo.    Perf. 13½x14**
1370 A430  5pf blue, gold & blk    .25    .25
1371 A430 20pf mag, gold & blk    .25    .25
1372 A430 35pf ol bis, gold & blk    .25    .25
1373 A430 70pf yel grn, gold & blk    2.25    1.40
    Nos. 1370-1373,B166-B167 (6)    3.50    2.65
20th Olympic Games, Munich, 8/26-9/11.

Flags of USSR and German Democratic Republic A431

20pf, Flags, Leonid Brezhnev & Erich Honecker.

**1972, May 24    Engr. & Photo.**
1374 A431 10pf red, yel & blk    .85    .65
1375 A431 20pf red, yel & blk    .85    .65
Soc. for German-Soviet Friendship, 25th anniv.

Workers — A432

Design: 35pf, Students.

**1972, May 24    Litho.    Perf. 13**
1376 A432 10pf dull yel, org & mag    .25    .25
1377 A432 35pf dull yel & ultra    .25    .25
    a.    Strip of 2, #1376-1377 + label    1.00    .85
8th Congress of Free German Trade Unions, Berlin.

Karneol Rose — A433

10pf, Berger's Erfurt Rose. 15pf, Charme. 20pf, Izetka Spree-Athens. 25pf, Kopenick summer. 35pf, Prof. Knoll.

**1972, June 13    Photo.    Perf. 13**
**Size: 36x36mm**
1378 A433  5pf shown    .25    .25
1379 A433 10pf multicolored    .25    .25
1380 A433 15pf multicolored    1.10    1.10
1381 A433 20pf multicolored    .25    .25
1382 A433 25pf multicolored    .25    .25
1383 A433 35pf multicolored    .25    .25
    Nos. 1378-1383 (6)    2.35    2.35
International Rose Exhibition.

**Redrawn**
**1972, Aug. 22    Perf. 13½x13**
**Booklet Stamps**
**Size: 23x28mm**
1383A A433 10pf multicolored    .25    .25
    d.    Booklet pane of 4    1.25    .80
1383B A433 25pf multicolored    .90    .35
    e.    Booklet pane of 4 (2 #1383B, 2 #1383C)    5.25    3.75
1383C A433 35pf multicolored    .90    .35
    Nos. 1383A-1383C (3)    2.05    .95

Young Mother and Child, by Cranach — A434

Paintings by Lucas Cranach: 5pf, Young man. 35pf, Margarete Luther (Martin's mother). 70pf, Reclining nymph, horiz.

**1972, July 4    Perf. 14x13½, 13½x14**
1384 A434  5pf gold & multi    .25    .25
1385 A434 20pf gold & multi    .25    .25
1386 A434 35pf gold & multi    .25    .25
1387 A434 70pf gold & multi    1.60    2.40
    Nos. 1384-1387 (4)    2.35    3.15
Lucas Cranach (1472-1553), painter.

Compass and Motorcyclist A435

Designs: 10pf, Parachute and light plane. 20pf, Target and military obstacle race. 25pf, Amateur radio transmitter, Morse key and tape. 35pf, Propeller and sailing ship.

**1972, Aug. 8    Photo.    Perf. 14**
1388 A435  5pf multicolored    .25    .25
1389 A435 10pf multicolored    .25    .25
1390 A435 20pf multicolored    .25    .25
1391 A435 25pf multicolored    .45    .45
1392 A435 35pf multicolored    .25    .25
    Nos. 1388-1392 (5)    1.45    1.45
Society for Sport and Technology.

Young Worker Reading, by Jutta Damme A436

**1972, Aug. 22    Photo.    Perf. 13½x14**
1393 A436 50pf multicolored    .45    .30
International Book Year 1972.

Polylux Writing Projector — A437

25pf, Pentacon-audiovision projector, horiz.

**Perf. 12½x13, 13x12½**
**1972, Aug. 29    Litho.**
1394 A437 10pf crimson & blk    .25    .25
1395 A437 25pf brt green & blk    .25    .25
Leipzig Fall Fair, 1972.

George Dimitrov — A438

**1972, Sept. 19    Perf. 13x13½**
1396 A438 20pf rose red & blk    .35    .25
George Dimitrov (1882-1949), Bulgarian Communist party leader.

Bird Catchers, Egypt, c. 2400 B.C. — A439

Design: 20pf, Tapestry with animal design, Anatolia, c. 1400 A.D.

**1972, Sept. 19    Photo.    Perf. 14**
1397 A439 10pf multicolored    .25    .25
1398 A439 20pf multicolored    .25    .25
    Nos. 1397-1398,B168-B169 (4)    1.40    1.30
Interartes Philatelic Exhib., Berlin, Oct. 4-Nov. 11.

Red Cross Trainees and Red Cross — A440

Designs: 15pf, Red Cross rescue launch in the Baltic. 35pf, Red Cross with world map, ship, plane and vehicles.

**1972, Oct. 3    Litho.    Perf. 13**
**Size: 23x28mm**
1399 A440 10pf grnsh bl, dk bl & red    .30    .25
1400 A440 15pf grnsh bl, dk bl & red    .30    .25
**Size: 50x28mm**
1401 A440 35pf grnsh bl, dk bl & red    .30    .25
    a.    Strip of 3, #1399-1401    1.50    1.75
Red Cross at work in the DDR.

Arab Celestial Globe, 1279 — A441

10pf, Globe, by Joachim R. Praetorius, 1568. 15pf, Globe clock, by Reinhold & Roll, 1586. 20pf, Globe clock, by J. Bürgi, c. 1590. 25pf, Armillary sphere, by J. Moeller, 1687. 35pf, Heraldic celestial globe, 1690.

**1972, Oct. 17    Photo.    Perf. 14x13½**
1402 A441  5pf gray & multi    .25    .25
1403 A441 10pf gray & multi    .25    .25
1404 A441 15pf gray & multi    1.60    2.25
1405 A441 20pf gray & multi    .25    .25
1406 A441 25pf gray & multi    .25    .25
1407 A441 35pf gray & multi    .25    .25
    Nos. 1402-1407 (6)    2.85    3.50
Celestial and terrestrial globes from the National Mathematical and Physics Collection, Dresden.

Anti-Fascists Monument — A442

**1972, Oct. 24    Litho.    Perf. 12½x13**
1408 A442 25pf multicolored    .35    .25
Monument for Polish soldiers and German anti-Fascists, unveiled in Berlin, May 14, 1972.

Young Workers Receiving Technical Education A443

25pf, Workers with modern welding machine.

**1972, Nov. 2    Photo.    Perf. 13½x14**
1409 A443 10pf blue & multi    .25    .25
1410 A443 25pf blue & multi    .25    .25
    a.    Strip of 2, #1409-1410 + label    .80    1.25
15th Central Fair of Masters of Tomorrow.

Mauz and Hoppel — A444

Children's television characters: 10pf, Fox and magpie. 15pf, Mr. Owl. 20pf, Mrs. Hedgehog and Borstel. 25pf, Schnuffel and Peips. 35pf, Paul from the Library.

**1972, Nov. 28    Litho.    Perf. 13½x13**
1411 A444  5pf shown    .25    .25
1412 A444 10pf multicolored    .25    .25
1413 A444 15pf multicolored    .60    .65
1414 A444 20pf multicolored    .60    .65
1415 A444 25pf multicolored    .25    .25
1416 A444 35pf multicolored    .25    .25
    a.    Sheet of 6, #1411-1416    2.40    2.60

Grandmother, Children, Magic Mirror — A445

Scenes from Hans Christian Andersen's "Snow Queen": 10pf, Kay and Snow Queen. 15pf, Gerda in magic garden. 20pf, Gerda and crows at palace. 25pf, Gerda and reindeer in Lapland. 35pf, Gerda and Kay at Snow Queen's palace.

**1972, Nov. 28    Perf. 13x13½**
1417 A445  5pf multicolored    .25    .25
1418 A445 10pf multicolored    .45    .65
1419 A445 15pf multicolored    .25    .25
1420 A445 20pf multicolored    .25    .25
1421 A445 25pf multicolored    .45    .65
1422 A445 35pf multicolored    .25    .25
    a.    Sheet of 6, #1417-1422    4.00    8.50
See designs A469, A490.

## Souvenir Sheet

Heinrich Heine
A446

**1972, Dec. 5          Perf. 12½x13**
1423  A446  1m brn ol, blk & red    1.25  2.00
150th anniversary of the birth of Heinrich Heine (1797-1856), poet.

Coat of Arms of
USSR — A447

**1972, Dec. 5    Photo.    Perf. 13½x14**
1424  A447  20pf red & multi         .35  .25
50th anniversary of the Soviet Union.

Michelangelo da
Caravaggio — A448

**1973        Litho.        Perf. 13½x13**
1425  A448  5pf brown              .50  .50
1426  A448  10pf dull green        .25  .25
1427  A448  20pf rose lilac        .25  .25
1428  A448  25pf blue              .25  .25
1429  A448  35pf brown red         .25  .25
1429A A448  40pf rose claret       .25  .25
        Nos. 1425-1429A (6)       1.75 1.75

Michelangelo da Caravaggio (1565(?)-1609), Italian painter (5pf). Friedrich Wolf (1888-1953), writer (10pf). Max Reger (1873-1916), composer (20pf). Max Reinhardt (1873-1943), Austrian theatrical director (25pf). Johannes Dieckmann (1893-1969), member and president of People's Chamber (35pf). Hermann Matern (1893-1971), vice-president of DDR (40pf).

Lenin Square,        Coat of Arms of
Berlin — A449        DDR — A449a

Designs: 5pf, Pelican, Berlin Zoo. 10pf, Neptune Fountain, City Hall Street. 15pf, Fisherman's Island, Berlin. 25pf, World clock, Alexander Square, Berlin. 30pf, Workers' Memorial, Halle. 35pf, Marx monument, Karl-Marx-Stadt. 40pf, Brandenburg Gate, Berlin. 50pf, New Guardhouse, Berlin. 60pf, Zwinger, Dresden. 70pf, Old Town Hall, Office Building, Leipzig. 80pf, Old and new buildings, Rostock-Warnemunde. 1m, Soviet War Memorial, Treptow.

**1973-74      Engr.      Perf. 14x13¾**
**Size: 29x23½mm**
1430  A449  5pf blue green      .25  .25
1431  A449  10pf emerald        .30  .25
1432  A449  15pf rose lilac     .35  .25
1433  A449  20pf rose mag       .65  .25
1434  A449  25pf grnsh blue     .65  .25
1435  A449  30pf orange         .35  .25
1436  A449  35pf grnsh blue     .65  .30
1437  A449  40pf dull violet    .35  .25
1438  A449  50pf blue, *bluish*  .40  .25
1439  A449  60pf lilac ('74)    .55  .30
1440  A449  70pf redsh brn      .45  .35
1441  A449  80pf vio blue
                    ('74)       .65  .30
1442  A449  1m olive            .75  .25

1443  A449a  2m lake            1.00  .25
1443A A449a  3m rose lil ('74)  3.25  .80
        Nos. 1430-1443A (15)   10.60 4.55
        See Nos. 1610-1617, 2071-2085.

Lebachia
Speciosa (Oldest
Conifer) — A450

Fossils from Natural History Museum, Berlin: 15pf, Sphenopteris hollandica (carbon fern). 20pf, Pterodactylus kochi (flying reptile). 25pf, Botryopteris (permian fern). 35pf, Archaeopteryx lithographica (primitive reptile-like bird). 70pf, Odontopieura ovata (trilobite).

**1973, Feb. 6      Photo.      Perf. 13**
1444  A450  10pf multicolored     .25  .25
1445  A450  15pf ultra, gray & blk .25  .25
1446  A450  20pf yellow & multi   .25  .25
1447  A450  25pf emer, blk & brn  .25  .25
1448  A450  35pf ocher & multi    .25  .25
1449  A450  70pf ind, blk & yel  1.20 1.20
        Nos. 1444-1449 (6)       2.45 2.45

Bobsled Track,
Oberhof — A451

**1973, Feb. 13   Litho.   Perf. 12½x13**
1450  A451  35pf dk bl, bl & org    .35  .30
15th Bobsledding Championships, Oberhof.

Combines
A452

Leipzig Spring Fair: 25pf, Computerized threshing and silage producing machine.

**1973, Mar. 6     Litho.    Perf. 13x12½**
1451  A452  10pf olive & multi     .25  .25
1452  A452  25pf blue & multi      .30  .30

Firecrests — A453

Songbirds: 10pf, White-winged crossbill. 15pf, Waxwing. 20pf, White-spotted and red-spotted bluethroats. 25pf, Goldfinch. 35pf, Golden oriole. 40pf, Gray wagtail. 50pf, Wall creeper.

**1973, Mar. 20   Photo.    Perf. 14x13½**
1453  A453  5pf multicolored         .25  .25
1454  A453  10pf multicolored        .25  .25
1455  A453  15pf multicolored        .25  .25
1456  A453  20pf multicolored        .25  .25
1457  A453  25pf multicolored        .25  .25
1458  A453  35pf multicolored        .25  .25
1459  A453  40pf multicolored        .25  .25
1460  A453  50pf ocher & multi      2.00 2.00
        Nos. 1453-1460 (8)          3.75 3.75

Copernicus and Title Page — A454

**1973, Feb. 13   Litho.   Perf. 13½x13**
1461  A454  70pf multicolored      .65  .35
500th anniversary of the birth of Nicolaus Copernicus (1473-1543), astronomer.

Electric Locomotive — A455

Railroad Cars Manufactured in DDR: 10pf, Refrigerator car. 20pf, Long-distance coach. 25pf, Multiple tank car with pneumatic filling device. 35pf, Two-story coach. 85pf, International coaches.

**1973, May 22    Litho.    Perf. 13x12½**
1462  A455  5pf gray & multi      .25  .25
1463  A455  10pf brt blue & multi .25  .25
1464  A455  20pf dk blue & multi  .25  .25
1465  A455  25pf gray & multi     .25  .25
1466  A455  35pf multicolored     .25  .25
1467  A455  85pf green & multi   1.60 1.60
        Nos. 1462-1467 (6)       2.85 2.85

King Lear, Staged
by Wolfgang
Langhoff — A456

Great Theatrical Productions: 25pf, Midsummer Marriage, staged by Walter Felsenstein. 35pf, Mother Courage, staged by Bertolt Brecht.

**1973, May 29    Photo.    Perf. 13**
1468  A456  10pf mar, rose & yel    .25  .25
1469  A456  25pf vio bl, lt bl &
                    rose            .25  .25
1470  A456  35pf dk gray, bis & bl  .60  .55
        Nos. 1468-1470 (3)         1.10 1.05

Goethe and his Home in
Weimar — A457

Designs (Portraits and Houses): 15pf, Christoph Martin Wieland. 20pf, Friedrich von Schiller. 25pf, Johann Gottfried Herder. 35pf, Lucas Cranach, the Elder. 50pf, Franz Liszt.

**1973, June 26   Litho.   Perf. 12½x13**
1471  A457  10pf blue & multi      .25  .25
1472  A457  15pf multicolored      .25  .25
1473  A457  20pf multicolored      .25  .25
1474  A457  25pf multicolored      .25  .25
1475  A457  35pf green & multi     .25  .25
1476  A457  50pf multicolored     1.60  .80
        Nos. 1471-1476 (6)        2.85 2.05
Famous men and their homes in Weimar.

Fireworks, TV Tower,
World Clock — A458

Designs (Festival Emblem and): 15pf, Vietnamese and European men, book and girder. 20pf, Construction workers and valve. 30pf, Negro and European students, dam and retort. 35pf, Emblems of World Federation of Democratic Youth and International Students Union. 50pf, Brandenburg Gate.

**1973**
1477  A458  5pf vio blue & multi   .25  .25
   *a.*  Booklet pane of 4        1.60 1.25
1478  A458  15pf olive & multi     .25  .25
1479  A458  20pf multicolored      .25  .25
   *a.*  Booklet pane of 4        1.60 1.25
1480  A458  30pf blue & multi      .70  .35
1481  A458  35pf green & multi     .25  .25
        Nos. 1477-1481 (5)        1.70 1.35

## Souvenir Sheet

1482  A458  50pf aqua & multi     1.00 1.60
10th Festival of Youths and Students, Berlin, July 1973.
Issued: Nos. 1477-1481, 7/3; No. 1482, 7/26.

## Ulbricht Type of 1961-67

**1973, Aug. 8      Engr.      Perf. 14**
**Size: 24x28½mm**
1483  A189  20pf black                .45  .30
In memory of Walter Ulbricht (1893-1973), chairman of Council of State.

Pylon, Map of Electric
Power System — A459

**1973, Aug. 14   Photo.   Perf. 14**
1484  A459  35pf mag, org & lt bl    .35  .30
10th anniversary of the united East European electric power system "Peace."

Sports
Equipment
A460

Design: 25pf, Sailboat, guitar, electric drill.

**1973, Aug. 28   Photo.   Perf. 14**
1485  A460  10pf multicolored     .25  .25
1486  A460  25pf multicolored     .30  .25
Leipzig Fall Fair and EXPOVITA exhibition for leisure time equipment.

Militiaman and
Emblem — A461

Designs: 20pf, Militia guarding border at Brandenburg Gate. 50pf, Representatives of Red Veterans' League, International Brigade in Spain and Workers' Militia in DDR, vert.

**1973, Sept. 11  Litho.   Perf. 13x12½**
1487  A461  10pf multicolored     .25  .25
1488  A461  20pf tan, red & blk   .30  .25

## Souvenir Sheet
**Perf. 12½x13**
1489  A461  50pf multicolored     .45 1.60
20th anniversary of Workers' Militia of the German Democratic Republic.

Globe and Red Flag
Emblem — A462

**1973, Sept. 11  Photo.   Perf. 13½x14**
1490  A462  20pf gold & red       .40  .25
15th anniversary of the review "Problems of Peace and Socialism," published in Prague in 28 languages.

Memorial, Langenstein-
Zwieberge — A463

**1973, Sept. 18          Perf. 14x13½**
1491  A463  25pf multicolored     .40  .25
In memory of the workers who perished in the subterranean munitions works at Langenstein-Zwieberge.

UN Headquarters, NY, UN and DDR Emblems — A464

**1973, Sept. 21**     **Perf. 13**
1492 A464 35pf multicolored    .40 .25
Admission of the DDR to the UN.

Union Emblem — A465

**1973, Oct. 11**   **Photo.**   **Perf. 14x13½**
1493 A465 35pf silver & multi    .35 .30
8th Congress of the World Federation of Trade Unions, Varna, Bulgaria.

Rocket Launching — A466

20pf, Emblem with map of Russia & hammer & sickle, horiz. 25pf, Oil refinery, Ryazan.

**1973, Oct. 23**     **Perf. 14**
1494 A466 10pf violet bl & multi    .25 .25
1495 A466 20pf vio bl, red & sil    .25 .25
1496 A466 25pf multicolored    .65 .55
    Nos. 1494-1496 (3)    1.15 1.05
Soviet Science & Technology Days in DDR.

Madonna with the Rose, by Parmigianino — A467

Paintings: 10pf Child with Doll, by Christian L. Vogel. 20pf, Woman with Plaited Blond Hair, by Rubens. 25pf, Lady in White, by Titian. 35pf, Archimedes, by Domenico Fetti. 70pf, Bouquet with Blue Iris, by Jan D. de Heem.

**1973, Nov. 13**   **Photo.**   **Perf. 14**
1497 A467 10pf gold & multi    .25 .25
1498 A467 15pf gold & multi    .25 .25
1499 A467 20pf gold & multi    .25 .25
1500 A467 25pf gold & multi    .25 .25
1501 A467 35pf gold & multi    .25 .25
1502 A467 70pf gold & multi    1.90 1.25
    Nos. 1497-1502 (6)    3.15 2.50

Human Rights Flame — A468

**1973, Nov. 20**     **Perf. 13**
1503 A468 35pf dp rose, dk car & sil    .40 .30
25th anniv. of the Universal Declaration of Human Rights.

At the Bidding of the Pike A469

Designs: Various scenes from Russian Folktale "At the Bidding of the Pike."

**1973, Dec. 4**   **Litho.**   **Perf. 13x13½**
1504 5pf multicolored    .25 .25
1505 10pf multicolored    .65 1.00
1506 15pf multicolored    .25 .25
1507 20pf multicolored    .65 1.00
1508 25pf multicolored    .25 .25
1509 35pf multicolored    .25 .25
   a. A469 Sheet of 6, #1504-1509    2.25 6.00

Edwin Hoernle — A470

No. 1511, Etkar Andre. No. 1512, Paul Merker. No. 1513, Hermann Duncker. No. 1514, Fritz Heckert. No. 1515, Otto Grotewohl. No. 1516, Wilhelm Florin. No. 1517, Georg Handke. No. 1518, Rudolf Breitscheid. No. 1519, Kurt Bürger. No. 1519A Carl Moltmann.

**1974**     **Litho.**   **Perf. 13½x13**
1510 A470 10pf gray green    .25 .25
1511 A470 10pf rose violet    .25 .25
1512 A470 10pf dark blue    .25 .25
1513 A470 10pf brown    .25 .25
1514 A470 10pf dull green    .25 .25
1515 A470 10pf red brown    .25 .25
1516 A470 10pf vio blue    .25 .25
1517 A470 10pf olive brown    .25 .25
1518 A470 10pf slate green    .25 .25
1519 A470 10pf dull violet    .25 .25
1519A A470 10pf brown    .25 .25
    Nos. 1510-1519A (11)    2.75 2.75
Leaders of German labor movement. Issued: Nos. 1510-1517, 1/8; others 7/9.

Flags of Comecon Members — A471

**1974, Jan. 22**   **Photo.**   **Perf. 13**
1520 A471 20pf red & multi    .35 .25
25th anniversary of the Council of Mutual Economic Assistance (Comecon).

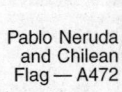

Pablo Neruda and Chilean Flag — A472

**1974, Jan. 22**     **Perf. 14**
1521 A472 20pf multicolored    .35 .25
Pablo Neruda (Neftali Ricardo Reyes, 1904-1973), Chilean poet.

Echinopsis Multiplex — A473

Various Flowering Cacti: 10pf, Lobivia haageana. 15pf, Parodia sanguiniflora. 20pf, Gymnocal. monvillei. 25pf, Neoporteria rapifera. 35pf, Notocactus concinnus.

**1974, Feb. 12**   **Photo.**   **Perf. 14**
1522 A473 5pf multicolored    .25 .25
1523 A473 10pf tan & multi    .25 .25
1524 A473 15pf green & multi    1.60 1.60
1525 A473 20pf multicolored    .25 .25
1526 A473 25pf violet & multi    .25 .25
1527 A473 35pf multicolored    .25 .25
    Nos. 1522-1527 (6)    2.85 2.85

Fieldball — A474

Design: Various fieldball scenes.

**1974, Feb. 26**   **Litho.**   **Perf. 13**
1528 A474 5pf green & multi    .30 .30
1529 A474 10pf green & multi    .30 .30
1530 A474 35pf green & multi    .30 .30
   a. Strip of 3, #1528-1530    1.00 1.10
8th World Fieldball Championships for Men.

Power Testing Station — A475

Leipzig Spring Fair: 25pf, Robotron EC 2040 data processer, horiz.

**1974, Mar. 5**   **Photo.**   **Perf. 14**
1531 A475 10pf multicolored    .25 .25
1532 A475 25pf multicolored    .30 .25

Poisonous European Mushrooms — A476

Designs: 5pf, Rhodophyllus Sinuatus. 10pf, Boletus satanas. 15pf, Amanita pantherina. 20pf, Amanita muscaria. 25pf, Gyromitra esculenta. 30pf, Inocybe patouillardii. 35pf, Amanita phalloides. 40pf, Clitocybe dealbata.

**1974, Mar. 19**   **Litho.**   **Perf. 13x13½**
1533 A476 5pf buff & multi    .25 .25
1534 A476 10pf buff & multi    .25 .25
1535 A476 15pf buff & multi    .25 .25
1536 A476 20pf buff & multi    .25 .25
1537 A476 25pf buff & multi    .25 .25
1538 A476 30pf buff & multi    .25 .25
1539 A476 35pf buff & multi    .25 .25
1540 A476 40pf buff & multi    1.25 .80
    Nos. 1533-1540 (8)    3.00 2.55

Gustav Robert Kirchhoff — A477

Portraits: 10pf, Immanuel Kant. 20pf, Ehm Welk. 25pf, Johann Gottfried Herder. 35pf, Lion Feuchtwanger.

**1974, Mar. 26**   **Litho.**   **Perf. 13½x13**
1541 A477 5pf black & gray    .25 .25
1542 A477 10pf vio bl & dull bl    .25 .25
1543 A477 20pf maroon & rose    .25 .25
1544 A477 25pf slate grn & grn    .25 .25
1545 A477 35pf brn & lt brn    .55 .40
    Nos. 1541-1545 (5)    1.55 1.40

"Peace" — A477a

**1974, Apr. 16**     **Perf. 13**
1548 A477a 35pf silver & multi    .35 .30
1st World Peace Congress, 25th anniv.

Oil Pipeline Operator and Arms of DDR — A477b

**1974, Apr. 30**   **Photo.**   **Perf. 13**
1549 A477b 10pf shown    .25 .25
1550 A477b 20pf Students    .25 .25
1551 A477b 25pf Woman worker    .25 .25
1552 A477b 35pf Family    .75 .65
    Nos. 1549-1552 (4)    1.50 1.40
25th anniv. of the DDR.

Buk Lighthouse, 1878, and Map — A478

Lighthouses, Maps and Nautical Charts: 15pf, Warnemünde, 1898. 20pf, Darsser Ort, 1848. 35pf, Arkona, 1827 and 1902. 40pf, Greifswalder Oie, 1855.

**1974, May 7**   **Litho.**   **Perf. 14**
1553 A478 10pf multicolored    .25 .25
1554 A478 15pf multicolored    .25 .25
1555 A478 20pf multicolored    .25 .25
1556 A478 35pf multicolored    .25 .25
1557 A478 40pf multicolored    .90 .80
    Nos. 1553-1557 (5)    1.90 1.80
Hydrographic Service of German Democratic Republic. See Nos. 1645-1649.

The Ages of Man, by C. D. Friedrich A479

C. D. Friedrich, Self-portrait — A480

Paintings by Friedrich: 10pf, Two Men Observing Moon. 25pf, The Heath near Dresden. 35pf, View of Elbe Valley.

**1974, May 21**   **Photo.**   **Perf. 13½**
1558 A479 10pf gold & multi    .25 .25
1559 A479 20pf gold & multi    .25 .25
1560 A479 25pf gold & multi    1.25 1.25
1561 A479 35pf gold & multi    .25 .25
    Nos. 1558-1561 (4)    2.00 2.00

**Souvenir Sheet**
**Engr.**
**Perf. 14x13½**
1562 A480 70pf sepia    1.10 2.00
Caspar David Friedrich (1774-1840), German Romantic painter.

Plauen Lace — A481

Designs: Various Plauen lace patterns.

**1974, June 11**   **Litho.**   **Perf. 13**
1563 A481 10pf violet, lil & blk    .25 .25
1564 A481 20pf brown ol & blk    .25 .25
1565 A481 25pf bl, lt bl & blk    1.00 .85
1566 A481 35pf lil rose, rose & blk    .25 .25
    Nos. 1563-1566 (4)    1.75 1.60

Trotter
A482

Designs: 10pf, Thoroughbred hurdling, vert. 25pf, Haflinger breed horses. 35pf, British thoroughbred race horse.

**Perf. 14x13½, 13½x14**

| 1974, Aug. 13 | | Photo. | | |
|---|---|---|---|---|
| 1570 | A482 | 10pf olive & multi | .25 | .25 |
| 1571 | A482 | 20pf multicolored | .25 | .25 |
| 1572 | A482 | lt blue & multi | 1.10 | 1.40 |
| 1573 | A482 | 35pf ocher & multi | .25 | .25 |
| | | Nos. 1570-1573 (4) | 1.85 | 2.15 |

International Horse Breeders' of Socialist Countries Congress, Berlin.

Crane Lifting Diesel Locomotive A483

Leipzig Fall Fair: 25pf, Sugar beet harvester, type KS6.

| 1974, Aug. 27 | | Litho. | Perf. 13x12½ | |
|---|---|---|---|---|
| 1574 | A483 | 10pf multicolored | .25 | .25 |
| 1575 | A483 | 25pf orange & multi | .30 | .25 |

Miniature China and Mirror Exhibits — A484

Scenes from 18th century Thuringia, Dolls' Village, Arnstadt Castle Museum: 10pf, Harlequin barker at Fair. 15pf, Wine tasters. 20pf, Cooper and apprentice. 25pf, Bagpiper. 35pf, Butcher and beggar, women.

| 1974, Sept. 10 | | Photo. | Perf. 14x13½ | |
|---|---|---|---|---|
| 1576 | A484 | 5pf shown | .25 | .25 |
| 1577 | A484 | 10pf multicolored | .25 | .25 |
| 1578 | A484 | 15pf multicolored | .25 | .25 |
| 1579 | A484 | 20pf multicolored | .25 | .25 |
| 1580 | A484 | 25pf multicolored | 1.00 | 1.00 |
| 1581 | A484 | 35pf multicolored | .25 | .25 |
| | | Nos. 1576-1581 (6) | 2.25 | 2.25 |

Bound Guerrillas, Ardeatine Caves, Rome A485

Design: No. 1583, Resistance Fighters, monument near Chateaubriant, France.

| 1974, Sept. 24 | | | Perf. 13½x14 | |
|---|---|---|---|---|
| 1582 | A485 | 35pf green, blk & red | .30 | .30 |
| 1583 | A485 | 35pf blue, blk & red | .30 | .30 |

International war memorials.

Souvenir Sheet

Family and Flag A486

| 1974, Oct. 3 | | Photo. | Perf. 13 | |
|---|---|---|---|---|
| 1584 | A486 | 1m multicolored | 1.25 | 3.00 |

25th anniv. of the DDR.

Freighter and Paddle Steamer — A487

Cent. of the UPU: 20pf, Old steam locomotive and modern Diesel. 25pf, Bi-plane and jet. 35pf, Mail coach and truck.

| 1974, Oct. 9 | | | Perf. 14 | |
|---|---|---|---|---|
| 1585 | A487 | 10pf green & multi | .25 | .25 |
| 1586 | A487 | 20pf multicolored | .25 | .25 |
| 1587 | A487 | blue & multi | .25 | .25 |
| 1588 | A487 | 35pf multicolored | .80 | .65 |
| | | Nos. 1585-1588 (4) | 1.55 | 1.40 |

"In Praise of Dialectics" — A488

Designs: 10pf+5pf, "Praise to the Revolutionaries." 25pf, "Praise to the Party." Designs are from bas-reliefs by Rossdeutscher, Jastram and Wetzel, illustrating poems by Bertholt Brecht.

| 1974, Oct. 24 | | Litho. | Perf. 13x13½ | |
|---|---|---|---|---|
| 1589 | A488 | 10pf + 5pf multi | .25 | .25 |
| 1590 | A488 | 20pf multicolored | .25 | .25 |
| 1591 | A488 | 25pf multicolored | .25 | .25 |
| a. | | Strip of 3, #1589-1591 | 1.00 | .85 |

DDR '74 Natl. Stamp Exhib., Karl-Marx-Stadt.

Souvenir Sheet

Drawings by Young Pioneers A489

a, Sun shines on everybody. b, My Friend Sascha. c, Carsten, the Best Swimmer. d, Me at the Blackboard.

| 1974, Nov. 26 | | Litho. | Perf. 14 | |
|---|---|---|---|---|
| 1592 | A489 | Sheet of 4 | 1.25 | 2.00 |
| a. | | 20pf multicolored | .30 | .30 |
| b. | | 20pf multicolored | .30 | .30 |
| c. | | 20pf multicolored | .30 | .30 |
| d. | | 20pf multicolored | .30 | .30 |

Young Pioneers' drawings (7-10 years old).

Man Cutting Tree, and Bird — A490

Designs: Various scenes from Russian folktale "Twittering To and Fro."

| 1974, Dec. 3 | | | Perf. 13x13½ | |
|---|---|---|---|---|
| 1593 | A490 | 10pf multicolored | .25 | .25 |
| 1594 | A490 | 15pf multicolored | .75 | .75 |
| 1595 | A490 | 20pf multicolored | .25 | .25 |
| 1596 | A490 | 30pf multicolored | .25 | .25 |
| 1597 | A490 | 35pf multicolored | .75 | .75 |
| 1598 | A490 | 40pf multicolored | .25 | .25 |
| a. | | Sheet of 6, #1593-1598 | 2.50 | 4.00 |

Meditating Girl, by Wilhelm Lachnit — A491

Paintings: 10pf, Still Life, by Ronald Paris, horiz. 20pf, Fisherman's House, Vitte, by Harald Hakenbeck. 35pf, Girl in Red, by

Rudolf Bergander, horiz. 70pf, The Artist's Parents, by Willi Sitte.

| 1974, Dec. 10 | | | Perf. 13½x14, 14x13½ | |
|---|---|---|---|---|
| 1599 | A491 | 10pf multicolored | .25 | .25 |
| 1600 | A491 | 15pf multicolored | .25 | .25 |
| 1601 | A491 | 20pf multicolored | .25 | .25 |
| 1602 | A491 | 35pf multicolored | .25 | .25 |
| 1603 | A491 | 70pf multicolored | 1.25 | 1.10 |
| | | Nos. 1599-1603 (5) | 2.25 | 2.10 |

Paintings in Berlin Museums.

Banded Jasper — A492

Minerals from the collection of the Mining Academy in Freiberg: 15pf, Smoky quartz. 20pf, Topaz. 25pf, Amethyst. 35pf, Aquamarine. 70pf, Agate.

| 1974, Dec. 17 | | Photo. | Perf. 14 | |
|---|---|---|---|---|
| 1604 | A492 | 10pf lt yellow & multi | .25 | .25 |
| 1605 | A492 | 15pf lt yellow & multi | .25 | .25 |
| 1606 | A492 | 20pf lt yellow & multi | .25 | .25 |
| 1607 | A492 | 25pf lt yellow & multi | .25 | .25 |
| 1608 | A492 | 35pf lt yellow & multi | .25 | .25 |
| 1609 | A492 | 70pf lt yellow & multi | 1.25 | 1.10 |
| | | Nos. 1604-1609 (6) | 2.50 | 2.35 |

**Type of 1973
Coil Stamps**

| 1974-75 | | Photo. | Perf. 14 | |
|---|---|---|---|---|
| | | **Size: 21x17½mm** | | |
| 1610 | A449 | 5pf blue grn ('74) | .25 | .25 |
| 1611 | A449 | 10pf emerald | .35 | .35 |
| 1612 | A449 | 20pf rose magenta | .35 | .35 |
| 1613 | A449 | 25pf green ('75) | .40 | .35 |
| 1615 | A449 | 50pf blue ('74) | .60 | .45 |
| 1617 | A449 | 1m olive ('74) | 1.25 | 1.25 |
| | | Nos. 1610-1617 (6) | 3.20 | 3.00 |

Black control number on back of every fifth stamp.
The 20pf was issued in sheets of 100 in 1975.

Martha Arendsee (1885-1953), Communist Politician — A493

| 1975, Jan. 14 | | Litho. | Perf. 13½x13 | |
|---|---|---|---|---|
| 1618 | A493 | 10pf dull red | .30 | .25 |

Souvenir Sheet

Peasants' War, Contemporary Woodcuts — A494

| 1975, Feb. 11 | | | Perf. 12½x13 | |
|---|---|---|---|---|
| 1619 | A494 | Sheet of 6 + label | 3.50 | 3.00 |
| a. | | 5pf Forced labor | .30 | .30 |
| b. | | 10pf Peasant paying tithe | .30 | .30 |
| c. | | 20pf Thomas Munzer | .30 | .30 |
| d. | | 25pf Armed peasants | .45 | .45 |
| e. | | 35pf Peasant, "Liberty" flag | .45 | .45 |
| f. | | 50pf Peasant on trial | .30 | .30 |

Peasants' War, 450th anniversary.

Black Women — A495

Designs: 20pf, Caucasian women. 25pf, Indian woman and child.

| 1975, Feb. 25 | | Litho. | Perf. 13 | |
|---|---|---|---|---|
| 1620 | A495 | 10pf red & multi | .25 | .25 |
| 1621 | A495 | 20pf red & multi | .25 | .25 |
| 1622 | A495 | 25pf red & multi | .25 | .25 |
| a. | | Strip of 3, Nos. 1620-1622 | .90 | .85 |

International Women's Year 1975.

Microfilm Pentakta Camera — A496

Leipzig Spring Fair: 25pf, Sket cement plant.

| 1975, Mar. 4 | | Photo. | Perf. 14 | |
|---|---|---|---|---|
| 1623 | A496 | 10pf ultra & multi | .25 | .25 |
| 1624 | A496 | 25pf orange & multi | .25 | .25 |

A497

Portraits: 5pf, Hans Otto (1900-33), actor. 10pf, Thomas Mann (1875-1955), writer. 20pf, Albert Schweitzer (1875-1965), medical missionary. 25pf, Michelangelo (1475-1564), painter and sculptor. 35pf, André Marie Ampère (1775-1836), scientist.

| 1975, Mar. 18 | | Litho. | Perf. 13½x13 | |
|---|---|---|---|---|
| 1625 | A497 | 5pf dk blue | .25 | .25 |
| 1626 | A497 | 10pf dk car rose | .25 | .25 |
| 1627 | A497 | 20pf dk green | .25 | .25 |
| 1628 | A497 | 25pf sepia | .25 | .25 |
| 1629 | A497 | 35pf vio blue | .65 | .40 |
| | | Nos. 1625-1629 (5) | 1.65 | 1.40 |

Famous men, birth anniversaries.

A498

German Zoological Gardens: 5pf, Blue and yellow macaws, Magdeburg Zoo. 10pf, Orangutan family, Dresden. 15pf, Siberian chamois, Halle. 20pf, Rhinoceros, Berlin. 25pf, Dwarf hippopotamus, Erfurt. 30pf, Baltic seal and pup, Rostock. 35pf, Siberian tiger, Leipzig. 50pf, Boehm's zebra, Cottbus. 20pf, 25pf, 30pf, 35pf are horiz.

| 1975, Mar. 25 | | | Perf. 13½x13, 13x13½ | |
|---|---|---|---|---|
| 1630 | A498 | 5pf multicolored | .25 | .25 |
| 1631 | A498 | 10pf multicolored | .25 | .25 |
| 1632 | A498 | 15pf multicolored | .25 | .25 |
| 1633 | A498 | 20pf multicolored | .25 | .25 |
| 1634 | A498 | 25pf multicolored | .25 | .25 |
| 1635 | A498 | 30pf multicolored | .25 | .25 |
| 1636 | A498 | 35pf multicolored | .25 | .25 |
| 1637 | A498 | 50pf multicolored | 1.25 | 1.25 |
| | | Nos. 1630-1637 (8) | 3.00 | 3.00 |

Soldiers, Industry and Agriculture A499

| 1975, May 6 | | Photo. | Perf. 13½x14 | |
|---|---|---|---|---|
| 1638 | A499 | 20pf multicolored | .85 | .30 |

20th anniv. of the signing of the Warsaw Treaty (Bulgaria, Czechoslovakia, DDR, Hungary, Poland, Romania, USSR).

Soviet War Memorial, Berlin-Treptow A500

Designs (Arms of German Democratic Rep. and): 20pf, Buchenwald Memorial (detail). 25pf, Woman reconstruction worker. 35pf, Skyscraper and statue at Orenburg (economic integration). 50pf, Soldier raising Red Flag on Reichstag Building, Berlin.

**1975, May 6**        **Perf. 14x13½**
1639 A500 10pf red & multi    .25 .25
1640 A500 20pf red & multi    .25 .25
1641 A500 25pf red & multi    .25 .25
1642 A500 35pf red & multi    .55 .40
    Nos. 1639-1642 (4)    1.30 1.15

**Souvenir Sheet**
*Imperf*
1643 A500 50pf red & multi    .80 1.75

30th anniversary of liberation from fascism.

Ribbons, Youth Organization Emblems of DDR and USSR — A501

**1975, May 13**        **Perf. 14**
1644 A501 10pf multicolored    .35 .25

Third Friendship Festival of Russian and German Youths, Halle, 1975.

**Lighthouse Type of 1974**

Lighthouses, Maps and Nautical Charts: 5pf, Timmendorf, 1872. 10pf, Gellen, 1905. 20pf, Sassnitz, 1904. 25pf, Dornbush, 1888. 35pf, Peenemünde, 1954.

**1975, May 13**     **Litho.**     **Perf. 14**
1645 A478 5pf multicolored    .25 .25
1646 A478 10pf multicolored    .25 .25
1647 A478 20pf multicolored    .25 .25
1648 A478 25pf multicolored    .25 .25
1649 A478 35pf multicolored    .65 .55
    Nos. 1645-1649 (5)    1.65 1.55

Hydrographic Service of the DDR.

Wilhelm Liebknecht, August Bebel — A502

20pf, Tivoli House & front page of Protocol of Gotha. 25pf, Karl Marx & Friedrich Engels.

**1975, May 21**        **Photo.**
1650 A502 10pf buff, brn & red    .25 .25
1651 A502 20pf sal, brn & red    .25 .25
1652 A502 25pf buff, brn & red    .25 .25
   a.    Strip of 3, #1650-1652    .85 .85

Centenary of the Congress of Gotha, the beginning of German Socialist Workers' Party.

Construction Workers, Union Emblem — A503

**1975, June 10**     **Photo.**     **Perf. 14**
1653 A503 20pf red & multi    .30 .25

Free German Association of Trade Unions (FDGB), 30th anniversary.

"Socialist Scientific Cooperation" Mosaic by Walter Womacka — A504

**1975, June 10**     **Litho.**     **Perf. 13**
1654 A504 20pf multicolored    .30 .25

Eisenhüttenstadt, first socialist city of DDR, 25th anniversary.

Automatic Clock by Paulus Schuster, 1585 — A505

Clocks, Dresden Museums: 10pf, Astronomical table clock, Augsburg, c. 1560. 15pf, Automatic clock, Hans Schlottheim, c. 1600. 20pf, Table clock, Johann Heinrich Köhler, c. 1720. 25pf, Table clock, Köhler, c. 1700. 35pf, Astronomical clock, Johannes Klein, 1738.

**1975, June 24**     **Photo.**     **Perf. 14**
1655 A505 5pf multicolored    .25 .25
1656 A505 10pf ultra & multi    .25 .25
1657 A505 15pf red & multi    1.00 1.00
1658 A505 20pf olive & multi    .25 .25
1659 A505 25pf multicolored    .25 .25
1660 A505 35pf ocher & multi    .25 .25
    Nos. 1655-1660 (6)    2.25 2.25

Dictionary, Compiled by Jacob and Wilhelm Grimm A506

20pf, Karl-Schwarzschild Observatory, Tautenburg near Jena. 25pf, Electron microscope & chemical plant (scientific & practical cooperation). 35pf, Intercosmos 10 satellite.

**1975, July 2**     **Litho.**     **Perf. 13½x13**
1661 A506 10pf plum, ol & blk    .25 .25
1662 A506 20pf vio bl & blk    .25 .25
1663 A506 25pf green, yel & blk    .25 .25
1664 A506 35pf blue & multi    .65 .60
    Nos. 1661-1664 (4)    1.40 1.35

German Academy of Sciences, 275th anniv.

Torch Bearer — A507

**1975, July 15**        **Perf. 13½x13**
1665 A507 10pf shown    .25 .25
1666 A507 20pf Hurdling    .25 .25
1667 A507 25pf Diving    .25 .25
1668 A507 35pf Gymnast on bar    .65 .60
    Nos. 1665-1668 (4)    1.40 1.35

5th Children and Youths Spartakiad.

Map of Europe — A508

**1975, July 30**     **Photo.**     **Perf. 13**
1669 A508 20pf multicolored    .40 .25

European Security and Cooperation Conference, Helsinki, July 30-Aug. 1.

China Aster — A509

**1975, Aug. 19**     **Photo.**     **Perf. 13½x14**
1670 A509 5pf shown    .25 .25
1671 A509 10pf Geranium    .25 .25
1672 A509 20pf Transvaal daisies    .25 .25
1673 A509 25pf Carnation    .25 .25
1674 A509 35pf Chrysanthemum    .25 .25
1675 A509 70pf Pansies    1.90 1.60
    Nos. 1670-1675 (6)    3.15 2.85

Medimorph Anesthesia Unit — A510

Leipzig Fall Fair: 25pf, Motorcycle, type MZ TS 250, horiz.

**1975, Aug. 28**        **Perf. 14**
1676 A510 10pf multicolored    .25 .25
1677 A510 25pf yellow & multi    .35 .25

Children and Child Crossing Guard — A511

Designs: 15pf, Traffic policewoman. 20pf, Policeman helping, motorist. 25pf, Motor vehicle inspection. 35pf, Volunteer instructor.

**1975, Sept. 9**     **Litho.**     **Perf. 13x12½**
1678 A511 10pf multicolored    .25 .25
1679 A511 15pf green & multi    1.00 .50
1680 A511 20pf brown & multi    .25 .25
1681 A511 25pf violet & multi    .25 .25
1682 A511 35pf multicolored    .25 .25
    Nos. 1678-1682 (5)    2.00 1.50

Traffic police serving and instructing the public.

Soyuz Take-off — A512

Designs: 20pf, Soyuz and Apollo in space. 70pf, Spacecraft after link-up, horiz., 79x28mm.

**Perf. 14x13½, 13½x14**
**1975, Sept. 15**        **Photo.**
1683 A512 10pf multicolored    .25 .25
1684 A512 20pf multicolored    .25 .25
1685 A512 70pf multicolored    1.25 1.20
    Nos. 1683-1685 (3)    1.75 1.70

Apollo Soyuz space test project (Russo-American space cooperation), launching July 15; link-up, July 17.

Weimar, 1630, after Merian A513

Designs: 20pf, Buchenwald Liberation Monument, vert. 35pf, Composite view of old and new buildings in Weimar.

**1975, Sept. 23**     **Litho.**     **Perf. 13½x13**
1686 A513 10pf green, gray & blk    .25 .25
1687 A513 20pf red & multi    .25 .25
1688 A513 35pf ultra & multi    .40 .40
    Nos. 1686-1688 (3)    .90 .85

Millennium of Weimar.

Monument, Vienna — A514

**1975, Oct. 14**     **Photo.**     **Perf. 14x13½**
1689 A514 35pf red & multi    .35 .25

Memorial for the victims of the struggle for a free Austria, 1934-1945.

Louis Braille and Dots — A515

Designs: 35pf, Hands reading Braille. 50pf, Eyeball and protective glasses.

**1975, Oct. 14**       
1690 A515 20pf gray & multi    .25 .25
1691 A515 35pf multicolored    .25 .25
1692 A515 50pf multicolored    1.00 .95
    Nos. 1690-1692 (3)    1.50 1.45

World Braille Year 1975. Sesquicentennial of the invention of Braille system of writing for the blind, by Louis Braille (1809-1852).

Post Office Bärenfels — A516

**1975, Oct. 21**     **Photo.**     **Perf. 14**
1693 A516 20pf multicolored    .35 .25

Philatelists' Day 1975. See No. B177.

Emperor Ordering Clothes A517

Designs: Scenes from "The Emperor's New Clothes," by Hans Christian Andersen and Andersen portrait.

**1975, Nov. 18**     **Litho.**     **Perf. 14x13**
1694 A517 20pf ocher & multi    .35 .35
1695 A517 35pf ocher & multi    .55 .55
1696 A517 50pf ocher & multi    .35 .35
   a.    Sheet of 3, #1694-1696    1.75 1.75

Tobogganing and Olympic Rings — A518

Olympic Rings and: 20pf, Speed-skating Rink, Berlin. 35pf, Figure-skating Hall, Karl-Marx Stadt. 70pf, Mass skiing at Schmiedefeld. 1m, Innsbruck & surrounding mountains.

**1975, Dec. 2**     **Photo.**     **Perf. 14**
1697 A518 5pf multicolored    .25 .25
1698 A518 20pf olive & multi    .25 .25
1699 A518 35pf multicolored    .25 .25
1700 A518 70pf multicolored    1.40 1.20
    Nos. 1697-1700,B178-B179 (6)    2.65 2.45

**Souvenir Sheet**
1701 A518 1m ultra & multi    1.75 1.25

12th Winter Olympic Games, Innsbruck, Austria, Feb. 4-15, 1976.
No. 1701 contains one 32x27mm stamp.

Pres. Wilhelm Pieck (1876-1960) — A519

**1975, Dec. 30**     **Litho.**     **Perf. 13½x13**
1702 A519 10pf lt ultra & blk    .25 .25

Ernst Thälmann (1886-1944) — A520

Labor Leaders: No. 1704, Georg Schumann (1886-1945). No. 1705, Wilhelm Koenen (1886-1963). No. 1706, John Schehr (1896-1934).

**1976, Jan. 13**     *Perf. 13½x13*
1703 A520 10pf rose & blk   .25 .25
1704 A520 10pf emerald & blk   .25 .25
1705 A520 10pf ocher & blk   .25 .25
1706 A520 10pf violet & blk   .25 .25
   *Nos. 1703-1706 (4)*   1.00 1.00
See Nos. 1852-1854.

Silbermann Organ,
Rötha — A521

Silbermann Organs: 20pf, Freiberg. 35pf,
Fraureuth. 50pf, Dresden.

**1976, Jan. 27**    **Photo.**    *Perf. 14*
1707 A521 10pf green & multi   .25 .25
1708 A521 20pf red & multi   .25 .25
1709 A521 35pf multicolored   .25 .25
1710 A521 50pf brown & multi   1.00 .65
   *Nos. 1707-1710 (4)*   1.75 1.40
Organs built by Gottfried Silbermann (1683-
1753).

**Souvenir Sheet**

Richard
Sorge
A522

**1976, Feb. 3**    **Litho.**    *Imperf.*
1711 A522 1m multicolored   1.50 3.25
Dr. Richard Sorge (1895-1944), Soviet intelligence agent. No. 1711 contains one stamp
with simulated perforations.

Military
Flag,
Sailor,
Soldier,
Aviator
A523

20pf, Military flag, ships, tanks, missile &
planes.

**1976, Feb. 24**    **Litho.**    *Perf. 13½x14*
1712 A523 10pf multicolored   .25 .25
1713 A523 20pf multicolored   .30 .25
National People's Army, 20th anniversary.

Telephone — A524

**1976, Mar. 2**     *Perf. 13*
1714 A524 20pf light blue   .30 .25
Centenary of first telephone call by Alexander Graham Bell, March 10, 1876.

Apartment House,
Leipzig — A525

Design: 25pf, Ocean super trawler, horiz.

**1976, Mar. 9**    **Photo.**    *Perf. 14*
1715 A525 10pf green & multi   .25 .25
1716 A525 25pf vio blue, blk & grn   .35 .25
Leipzig Spring Fair.

---

Palace of
the
Republic
A526

**1976, Apr. 22**    **Photo.**    *Perf. 14*
1717 A526 10pf vio blue & multi   .60 .25
Inauguration of Palace of the Republic, Berlin. See No. 1721.

Post Office Radar
Station — A527

**1976, Apr. 27**    **Photo.**    *Perf. 13½x14*
1718 A527 20pf multicolored   .30 .25
Intersputnik 1976.

Marx, Engels, Lenin
and Party
Flag — A528

20pf, New factories & apartment houses,
party flag, horiz. 1m, Palace of the Republic.

**1976, May 11**    *Perf. 14x13½, 13½x14*
1719 A528 10pf dp mag, gold &
   red   .25 .25
1720 A528 20pf multicolored   .25 .25

**Souvenir Sheet**
**Perf. 14**
1721 A526 1m multicolored   1.25 2.50
9th Congress of Unity Party (SED).

Peace
Bicycle
Race and
Olympic
Rings
A529

Designs: 20pf, Town and sport halls, Suhl.
25pf, Regatta course, Brandenburg. 70pf,
1500-meter race. 1m, Central Stadium,
Leipzig.

**1976, May 18**    **Photo.**    *Perf. 13½x14*
1722 A529 5pf green & multi   .25 .25
1723 A529 20pf blue & multi   .25 .25
1724 A529 25pf multicolored   .25 .25
1725 A529 70pf ultra & multi   1.75 1.50
   *Nos. 1722-1725,B180-B181 (6)*   3.00 2.75

**Souvenir Sheet**
**Perf. 14**
1726 A529 1m multicolored   1.25 1.10
21st Olympic Games, Montreal, Canada,
July 17-Aug. 1. No. 1726 contains one stamp
(32x27mm).

Ribbons and
Emblem — A530

Design: 20pf, Young man and woman,
industrial installations.

**1976, May 25**     *Perf. 14*
1727 A530 10pf blue & multi   .25 .25
1728 A530 20pf multicolored   .25 .25
10th Parliamentary Meeting of the Free German Youth Organization.

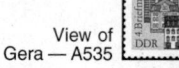

View of
Gera — A535

Design: 10pf+5pf, View of Gera, c. 1652.

---

European
orchids — A531

10pf, Himantoglossum Hircinum. 20pf,
Dactylorhiza incarnata. 25pf, Anacamptis
pyramidalis. 35pf, Dactylorhiza sambucina.
40pf, Orchis coriophora. 50pf, Cypripedium
calceolus.

**1976, June 15**    **Litho.**    *Perf. 12½x13*
1729 A531 10pf multi   .25 .25
1730 A531 20pf multi   .25 .25
1731 A531 25pf multi   .25 .25
1732 A531 35pf multi   .25 .25
1733 A531 40pf multi   .25 .25
1734 A531 50pf multi   1.90 1.25
   *Nos. 1729-1734 (6)*   3.15 2.50

Dancer at Rest, by
Walter
Arnold — A532

Small Sculptures: 10pf, Shetland Pony, by
Heinrich Drake, horiz. 25pf, "At the Beach," by
Ludwig Engelhardt. 35pf, Hermann Duncker,
by Walter Howard. 50pf, "The Conversation,"
by Gustav Weidanz.

**1976, June 22**    **Photo.**    *Perf. 14*
1735 A532 10pf blk & bl grn   .25 .25
1736 A532 20pf ocher & blk   .25 .25
1737 A532 25pf ocher & blk   .25 .25
1738 A532 35pf yel grn & blk   .25 .25
1739 A532 50pf brick red & blk   1.25 1.10
   *Nos. 1735-1739 (5)*   2.25 2.10

Marx, Engels, Lenin,
Red Flags, Berlin
Buildings — A533

**1976, June 29**    **Photo.**    *Perf. 14*
1740 A533 20pf blue, red & dk
   red   .35 .25
European Communist Workers' Congress,
Berlin.

Coronation
Coach,
1790 — A534

Historic Coaches: 20pf, Open carriage,
Russia, 1800. 25pf, Court landau, Saxony,
1840. 35pf, State carriage, Saxony, 1860.
40pf, Mail coach, 1850. 50pf, Town carriage,
Saxony, 1889.

**1976, July 27**
1741 A534 10pf multicolored   .25 .25
1742 A534 20pf multicolored   .25 .25
1743 A534 25pf multicolored   .25 .25
1744 A534 35pf multicolored   .25 .25
1745 A534 40pf multicolored   .25 .25
1746 A534 50pf multicolored   2.00 1.75
   *Nos. 1741-1746 (6)*   3.25 3.00

---

**1976, Aug. 5**    **Litho.**    *Perf. 13*
1747 A535 10pf + 5pf multi   .25 .25
1748 A535 20pf multicolored   .25 .25
   *a.*   Pair, #1747-1748 + label   .80 .65
4th German Youth Philatelic Exhib., Gera.

Boxer — A536

Dogs: 10pf, Airedale terrier. 20pf, German
shepherd. 25pf, Collie. 35pf, Giant schnauzer.
70pf, Great Dane.

**1976, Aug. 17**     *Perf. 14*
1749 A536 5pf multicolored   .25 .25
1750 A536 10pf multicolored   .25 .25
1751 A536 20pf multicolored   .25 .25
1752 A536 25pf multicolored   .25 .25
1753 A536 35pf multicolored   .25 .25
1754 A536 70pf multicolored   1.75 1.75
   *Nos. 1749-1754 (6)*   3.00 3.00

Oil Distillery
A537

Design: 25pf, German Library, Leipzig.

**1976, Sept. 1**     *Perf. 13x12½*
1755 A537 10pf multicolored   .25 .25
1756 A537 25pf multicolored   .30 .25
Leipzig Fall Fair.

Templin
Lake
Bridge
A538

Designs: 15pf, Overpass, Berlin-Adlergertell. 20pf, Elbe River Bridge, Rosslau. 25pf,
Göltzschtal Viaduct. 35pf, Elbe River Bridge,
Magdeburg. 50pf, Grosser Dreesch Overpass,
Schwerin.

**1976, Sept. 21**    **Photo.**    *Perf. 14*
1757 A538 10pf multicolored   .25 .25
1758 A538 15pf multicolored   .25 .25
1759 A538 20pf multicolored   .25 .25
1760 A538 25pf multicolored   .25 .25
1761 A538 35pf multicolored   .25 .25
1762 A538 50pf multicolored   1.25 1.25
   *Nos. 1757-1762 (6)*   2.50 2.50

Memorial
Monument
(detail),
Budapest
A539

**1976, Oct. 5**    **Photo.**    *Perf. 14*
1763 A539 35pf tan & multi   .35 .30
Memorial to World War II victims.

Brass Jug, c.
1500 — A540

Artistic Handicraft Works: 20pf, Faience
vase with lid, c. 1710. 25pf, Porcelain center-
piece (woman carrying bowl), c. 1768. 35pf,
Porter, gilded silver, c. 1700. 70pf, Art
Nouveau glass vase, c. 1900.

**1976, Oct. 19**
1764 A540 10pf dk car & multi   .25 .25
1765 A540 20pf ultra & multi   .25 .25
1766 A540 25pf green & multi   .25 .25
1767 A540 35pf vio blue & multi   .25 .25
1768 A540 70pf red brn & multi   1.40 1.40
   *Nos. 1764-1768 (5)*   2.40 2.40

Guppy — A541

Designs: Various guppies.

**1976, Nov. 9    Litho.    Perf. 13½x13**
1769  A541  10pf multicolored        .25   .25
1770  A541  15pf multicolored        .25   .25
1771  A541  20pf multicolored        .25   .25
1772  A541  25pf multicolored        .25   .25
1773  A541  35pf multicolored        .25   .25
1774  A541  70pf multicolored       1.50  1.25
      Nos. 1769-1774 (6)             2.75  2.50

Vessels, c. 3000 B.C. A542

20pf, Cult cart, c. 1300 B.C. 25pf, Roman gold coin, 270-273 A.D. 35pf, Gold pendant, 950 A.D. 70pf, Glass cup, 3rd cent. A.D.

**1976, Nov. 23    Photo.    Perf. 13**
1775  A542  10pf multicolored        .25   .25
1776  A542  20pf multicolored        .25   .25
1777  A542  25pf multicolored        .25   .25
1778  A542  35pf multicolored        .25   .25
1779  A542  70pf multicolored       1.40  1.40
      Nos. 1775-1779 (5)             2.40  2.40

Archaeological finds in DDR.

"Air," by Rosalba Carriera — A543

Paintings, Dresden Museum: 15pf, Virgin and Child, by Murillo. 20pf, Woman Viola da Gamba Player, by Bernardo Strozzi. 25pf, Ariadne Forsaken, by Angelica Kauffmann. 35pf, Old Man with Black Cap, by Bartolomeo Nazzari. 70pf, Officer Reading a Letter, by Gerard Terborch.

**1976, Dec. 14    Photo.    Perf. 13½x14**
1780  A543  10pf multicolored        .25   .25
1781  A543  15pf multicolored        .25   .25
1782  A543  20pf multicolored        .25   .25
1783  A543  25pf multicolored        .25   .25
1784  A543  35pf multicolored        .25   .25
1785  A543  70pf multicolored       1.60  1.20
      Nos. 1780-1785 (6)             2.85  2.45

Rumpelstiltskin and King — A544

Scenes from fairy tale "Rumpel-stiltskin."

**1976, Dec. 14    Litho.    Perf. 13**
1786  A544   5pf multicolored        .25   .25
1787  A544  10pf multicolored        .45   .45
1788  A544  15pf multicolored        .25   .25
1789  A544  20pf multicolored        .25   .25
1790  A544  25pf multicolored        .45   .45
1791  A544  30pf multicolored        .25   .25
   a.    Sheet of 6, #1786-1791     2.10  2.10

Arnold Zweig and Quotation A545

Designs: 20pf, Otto von Guericke and Magdeburg hemispheres. 35pf, Albrecht D. Thaer, wheat, plow and sheep. 40pf, Gustav Hertz and diagram of separation of isotopes.

**1977, Feb. 8    Litho.    Perf. 13x12½**
1792  A545  10pf rose & blk          .25   .25
1793  A545  20pf gray & blk          .25   .25
1794  A545  35pf lt green & blk      .25   .25
1795  A545  40pf blue & blk          .65   .65
      Nos. 1792-1795 (4)             1.40  1.40

Zweig (1887-1968), novelist; von Guericke (1602-86), physicist; Thaer (1752-1828), agronomist & physician; Hertz (1887-1975), physicist.

Spring near Plaue — A546

Natural Monuments: 20pf, Small Organ, Johnsdorf. 25pf, Ivenacker Oaks, Reuterstadt. 35pf, Stone Rose, Saalburg. 50pf, Rauenscher Stein (boulder), Furstenwalde.

**1977, Feb. 24    Litho.    Perf. 12½x13**
1796  A546  10pf multicolored        .25   .25
1797  A546  20pf multicolored        .25   .25
1798  A546  25pf multicolored        .25   .25
1799  A546  35pf multicolored        .25   .25
1800  A546  50pf multicolored       1.10  1.10
      Nos. 1796-1800 (5)             2.10  2.10

Fair Building, Book Fair — A547

Leipzig Spring Fair: 25pf, Wide aluminum roll casting machine, Nachterstedt factory.

**1977, Mar. 8    Photo.    Perf. 14**
1801  A547  10pf multicolored        .25   .25
1802  A547  25pf multicolored        .25   .25

Costume Senftenberg — A548

Sorbian Costumes from: 20pf, Bautzen. 25pf, Klitten. 35pf, Nochten. 70pf, Muskau.

**1977, Mar. 22**
1803  A548  10pf multicolored        .25   .25
1804  A548  20pf multicolored        .25   .25
1805  A548  25pf multicolored        .25   .25
1806  A548  35pf multicolored        .25   .25
1807  A548  70pf multicolored       1.75  1.25
      Nos. 1803-1807 (5)             2.75  2.25

Start after Wheel Change — A549

Designs: 20pf, Sprint. 35pf, At finish line.

**1977, Apr. 19    Photo.    Perf. 14**
1808  A549  10pf multicolored        .25   .25
1809  A549  20pf multicolored        .25   .25
1810  A549  35pf multicolored        .25   .25
   a.    Strip of 3. #1808-1810     1.10  1.10

30th International Peace Bicycling Race.

Carl Friedrich Gauss — A550

**1977, Apr. 19    Litho.    Perf. 13x12½**
1811  A550  20pf lt ultra & blk      .45   .25

Carl Friedrich Gauss (1777-1855), mathematician, 200th birth anniversary.

Flags and Handshake A551

**1977, May 3    Photo.    Perf. 13**
1812  A551  20pf vio bl & multi      .30   .25

9th German Trade Union Congress, Berlin.

VKM Channel Converter, Filter and ITU Emblem — A552

**1977, May 17    Litho.    Perf. 14**
1813  A552  20pf multicolored        .45   .25

International Telecommunications Day.

Pistol Shooting A553

Designs: 20pf, Deep-sea diver. 35pf, Radio controlled model boat.

**1977, May 17    Photo.**
1814  A553  10pf lt green & multi    .25   .25
1815  A553  20pf lt blue & multi     .25   .25
1816  A553  35pf salmon & multi      .60   .60
      Nos. 1814-1816 (3)             1.10  1.10

Organization for Physical and Technical Training.

Accordion, c. 1900 — A554

Designs: 20pf, Treble viola da gamba, 1747. 25pf, Oboe, 1785. Clarinet, 1830 and flute, 1817. 35pf, Concert zither, 1891. 70pf, Trumpet, 1860.

**1977, June 14**
1817  A554  10pf multicolored        .25   .25
1818  A554  20pf multicolored        .25   .25
1819  A554  25pf multicolored        .25   .25
1820  A554  35pf multicolored        .25   .25
1821  A554  70pf multicolored       1.60  1.50
      Nos. 1817-1821 (5)             2.60  2.50

Vogtland musical instruments from Markneukirchen Museum.

Mercury and Argus, by Rubens A555

Rubens Paintings in Dresden Gallery: 10pf, Bath of Bathsheba, vert. 20pf, The Drunk Hercules, vert. 25pf, Diana Returning from the Hunt. 35pf, Old Woman with Brazier, vert. 50pf, Leda and the Swan.

**1977, June 28    Photo.    Perf. 14**
1822  A555  10pf multicolored        .25   .25
1823  A555  15pf multicolored        .25   .25
1824  A555  20pf multicolored        .25   .25
1825  A555  25pf multicolored        .25   .25
1826  A555  35pf multicolored        .25   .25
1827  A555  50pf multicolored       2.60  1.75
      Nos. 1822-1827 (6)             3.85  3.00

Peter Paul Rubens (1577-1640), Flemish painter, 400th birth anniversary.

Souvenir Sheet

Wreath, Flags of USSR and DDR A556

**1977, June 28**
1828  A556  50pf multicolored        .75  1.60

Soc. for German-Soviet Friendship, 30th anniv.

Tractor with Plow A557

Designs: 20pf, Fertilizer-spreader. 25pf, Potato digger and loader. 35pf, High-pressure harvester. 50pf, Rotating milking machine.

**1977, July 12    Litho.    Perf. 13x12½**
1829  A557  10pf multicolored        .25   .25
1830  A557  20pf multicolored        .25   .25
1831  A557  25pf multicolored        .25   .25
1832  A557  35pf multicolored        .25   .25
1833  A557  50pf multicolored       1.40  1.25
      Nos. 1829-1833 (5)             2.40  2.25

Motorized modern agriculture.

High Jump — A558

Designs: 20pf, Hurdles, girls. 35pf, Dancing. 40pf, Torch bearer and flags.

**1977, July 19**
1834  A558   5pf red & multi         .25   .25
1835  A558  20pf lt green & multi    .25   .25
1836  A558  35pf green & multi       .25   .25
1837  A558  40pf blue & multi       1.25  1.25
      Nos. 1834-1837,B183-B184 (6)  2.50  2.50

6th Gymnastics and Sports Festival and 6th Children's and Youth Spartacist Games.

"Bread for all" by Wolfram Schubert — A559

Design: 25pf, "When Communists Dream," by Walter Womacka (detail) and Sozphilex emblem.

**1977, Aug. 16    Photo.    Perf. 14**
1838  A559  10pf multicolored        .25   .25
   a.    Souvenir sheet of 4         .90  1.25
1839  A559  25pf multicolored        .40   .35
   a.    Souvenir sheet of 4        1.75  1.60

SOZPHILEX '77 Philatelic Exhibition, Berlin, Aug. 19-28. See No. B185.

Konsument Department Store, Leipzig — A560

Design: 25pf, Glasses and wooden plate.

**1977, Aug. 30**
1840  A560  10pf blue & multi        .30   .25
1841  A560  25pf multicolored        .30   .25

Leipzig Fall Fair.

## Souvenir Sheet

Dzerzhinski and Quotation from Mayakovsky — A561

**1977, Sept. 6   Litho.   Perf. 12½x13**
| | | | | |
|---|---|---|---|---|
| 1842 | A561 | Sheet of 2 | 1.00 | 2.60 |
| a. | | 20pf multicolored | .40 | .65 |
| b. | | 35pf multicolored | .40 | .90 |

Feliks E. Dzerzhinski (1877-1926), organizer and head of Russian Secret Police (Cheka), birth centenary.

Muldenthal Locomotive, 1861 — A562

Designs: 10pf, Trolley car, Dresden, 1896. 20pf, First successful German plane, 1909. 25pf, 3-wheel car "Phäno-mobile," 1924. 35pf, Passenger steamship on the Elbe, 1837.

**1977, Sept. 13   Photo.   Perf. 14**
| | | | | |
|---|---|---|---|---|
| 1843 | A562 | 5pf green & multi | .25 | .25 |
| 1844 | A562 | 10pf green & multi | .25 | .25 |
| 1845 | A562 | 20pf green & multi | .25 | .25 |
| 1846 | A562 | 25pf green & multi | .25 | .25 |
| 1847 | A562 | 35pf green & multi | 2.00 | 1.60 |
| | | Nos. 1843-1847 (5) | 3.00 | 2.60 |

Transportation Museum, Dresden.

Cruiser "Aurora" — A563

Designs: 25pf, Storming of the Winter Palace. 1m, Lenin, vert.

**1977, Sept. 20**
| | | | | |
|---|---|---|---|---|
| 1848 | A563 | 10pf multicolored | .30 | .25 |
| 1849 | A563 | 25pf multicolored | .40 | .35 |

**Souvenir Sheet**
**Perf. 12½x13**
| | | | | |
|---|---|---|---|---|
| 1850 | A563 | 1m carmine & blk | 1.60 | 2.60 |

60th anniversary of the Russian Revolution.

Mother Russia and Obelisk — A564

**1977, Sept. 20   Litho.   Perf. 14**
| | | | | |
|---|---|---|---|---|
| 1851 | A564 | 35pf multicolored | .35 | .25 |

Soviet soldiers' memorial, Berlin-Schönholz.

### Labor Leaders Type of 1976

Portraits: No. 1852, Ernst Meyer (1887-1930). No. 1853, August Fröhlich (1877-1966). No. 1854, Gerhart Eisler (1897-1968).

**1977, Oct. 18   Litho.   Perf. 14**
| | | | | |
|---|---|---|---|---|
| 1852 | A520 | 10pf olive & brown | .25 | .25 |
| 1853 | A520 | 10pf rose & brown | .25 | .25 |
| 1854 | A520 | 10pf lt blue & blk brn | .25 | .25 |
| | | Nos. 1852-1854 (3) | .75 | .75 |

## Souvenir Sheet

Heinrich von Kleist, by Peter Friedl, 1801 A565

**1977, Oct. 18**
| | | | | |
|---|---|---|---|---|
| 1855 | A565 | 1m multicolored | 2.10 | 2.60 |

Heinrich von Kleist (1777-1811), poet and playwright, birth bicentenary.

Rocket — A566

Design: 20pf, as 10pf, design reversed.

**1977, Nov. 8   Photo.   Perf. 14**
| | | | | |
|---|---|---|---|---|
| 1856 | A566 | 10pf red, blk & sil | .25 | .25 |
| 1857 | A566 | 20pf ultra, blk & gold | .25 | .25 |
| a. | | Pair, #1856-1857 + label | .75 | .75 |

20th Central Young Craftsmen's Exhibition (Masters of Tomorrow).

A567

Hunting in East Germany: 10pf, Mouflons. 15pf, Red deer. 20pf, Retriever with pheasant, hunter. 25pf, Red fox, wild duck. 35pf, Tractor driver saving fawn. 70pf, Wild boars.

**1977, Nov. 15**
| | | | | |
|---|---|---|---|---|
| 1858 | A567 | 10pf multicolored | .25 | .25 |
| 1859 | A567 | 15pf multicolored | 1.60 | 1.60 |
| 1860 | A567 | 20pf multicolored | .25 | .25 |
| 1861 | A567 | 25pf multicolored | .25 | .25 |
| 1862 | A567 | 35pf multicolored | .25 | .25 |
| 1863 | A567 | 70pf multicolored | .30 | .25 |
| | | Nos. 1858-1863 (6) | 2.90 | 2.85 |

A568

Firemen's Activities: 10pf, Firemen racing with ladders. 20pf, Children Visiting Firehouse. 25pf, Fire engines fighting forest and brush fires. 35pf, Artificial respiration. 50pf, Fireboat alongside freighter.

**1977, Nov. 22   Litho.   Perf. 14**
| | | | | |
|---|---|---|---|---|
| 1864 | A568 | 10pf multi, horiz. | .25 | .25 |
| 1865 | A568 | 20pf multi | .25 | .25 |
| 1866 | A568 | 25pf multi, horiz. | .25 | .25 |
| 1867 | A568 | 35pf multi | .25 | .25 |
| 1868 | A568 | 50pf multi, horiz. | 1.60 | 1.40 |
| | | Nos. 1864-1868 (5) | 2.60 | 2.40 |

Knight and King — A569

Designs: Various scenes from fairytale: "Six Men Around the World."

**1977, Nov. 22   Perf. 13x13½**
| | | | | |
|---|---|---|---|---|
| 1869 | A569 | 5pf black & multi | .25 | .25 |
| 1870 | A569 | 10pf black & multi | .60 | .60 |
| 1871 | A569 | 20pf black & multi | .25 | .25 |
| 1872 | A569 | 25pf black & multi | .25 | .25 |
| 1873 | A569 | 35pf black & multi | .60 | .60 |
| 1874 | A569 | 60pf black & multi | .25 | .25 |
| a. | | Sheet of 6, #1869-1874 | 3.00 | 2.60 |

Hips and Dog Rose — A570

Medicinal Plants: 15pf, Birch. 20pf, Chamomile. 25pf, Coltsfoot. 35pf, Linden. 50pf, Elder.

**1978, Jan. 10   Photo.   Perf. 14**
| | | | | |
|---|---|---|---|---|
| 1875 | A570 | 10pf multicolored | .25 | .25 |
| 1876 | A570 | 15pf multicolored | .25 | .25 |
| 1877 | A570 | 20pf multicolored | .25 | .25 |
| 1878 | A570 | 25pf multicolored | .25 | .25 |
| 1879 | A570 | 35pf multicolored | .25 | .25 |
| 1880 | A570 | 50pf multicolored | 1.75 | 1.60 |
| | | Nos. 1875-1880 (6) | 3.00 | 2.85 |

Amilcar Cabral — A571

**1978, Jan. 17   Litho.   Perf. 14**
| | | | | |
|---|---|---|---|---|
| 1881 | A571 | 20pf multicolored | .35 | .30 |

Amilcar Cabral (1924-1973), freedom movement leader from Guinea-Bissau.

Town Hall, Suhl-Heinrichs — A572

Half-timbered Buildings, 17th-18th Centuries: 20pf, Farmhouse, Niederoderwitz. 25pf, Farmhouse, Strassen. 35pf, Townhouse, Quedlinburg. 40pf, Townhouse, Eisenach.

**1978, Jan. 24   Photo.   Perf. 14**
| | | | | |
|---|---|---|---|---|
| 1882 | A572 | 10pf multicolored | .25 | .25 |
| 1883 | A572 | 20pf multicolored | .25 | .25 |
| 1884 | A572 | 25pf multicolored | .25 | .25 |
| 1885 | A572 | 35pf multicolored | .25 | .25 |
| 1886 | A572 | 40pf multicolored | 1.60 | 1.50 |
| | | Nos. 1882-1886 (5) | 2.60 | 2.50 |

Mail Truck, 1921 — A573

Past and Present Mail Transport: 20pf, Mail truck, 1978. 25pf, Railroad mail car, 1896. 35pf, Railroad mail car, 1978.

**1978, Feb. 9   Litho.   Perf. 13x12½**
| | | | | |
|---|---|---|---|---|
| 1887 | A573 | 10pf brown & multi | .25 | .25 |
| 1888 | A573 | 20pf brown & multi | .35 | .35 |
| 1889 | A573 | 25pf brown & multi | .40 | .40 |
| 1890 | A573 | 35pf brown & multi | .55 | .55 |
| a. | | Block of 4, #1887-1890 | 2.25 | 2.25 |

Earring, 11th Century — A574

Archaeological Artifacts: 20pf, Earring, 10th century. 25pf, Bronze sheath, 10th century. 35pf, Bronze horse, 12th century. 70pf, Arabian coin, 8th century.

**1978, Feb. 21   Photo.   Perf. 14**
| | | | | |
|---|---|---|---|---|
| 1891 | A574 | 10pf multicolored | .25 | .25 |
| 1892 | A574 | 20pf multicolored | .25 | .25 |
| 1893 | A574 | 25pf multicolored | .25 | .25 |
| 1894 | A574 | 35pf multicolored | .25 | .25 |
| 1895 | A574 | 70pf multicolored | 1.25 | 1.25 |
| | | Nos. 1891-1895 (5) | 2.25 | 2.25 |

Treasures found on Slavic sites.

Royal House, Leipzig — A575

Leipzig Spring Fair: 25pf, Universal measuring instrument by Carl Zeiss.

**1978, Mar. 7**
| | | | | |
|---|---|---|---|---|
| 1896 | A575 | 10pf multicolored | .25 | .25 |
| 1897 | A575 | 25pf multicolored | .35 | .30 |

M-100 Meteorological Rocket — A576

Designs: 20pf, Intercosmos I satellite. 35pf, Meteor satellite with spectometric complex. 1m, MFK-6 multi-spectral camera over city.

**1978, Mar. 21   Photo.   Perf. 14x13½**
| | | | | |
|---|---|---|---|---|
| 1898 | A576 | 10pf multicolored | .25 | .25 |
| 1899 | A576 | 20pf multicolored | .25 | .25 |
| 1900 | A576 | 35pf multicolored | .80 | .80 |
| | | Nos. 1898-1900 (3) | 1.30 | 1.30 |

**Souvenir Sheet**
| | | | | |
|---|---|---|---|---|
| 1901 | A576 | 1m multicolored | 2.00 | 1.60 |

Achievements in atmospheric and space research.

Samuel Heinicke, Leipzig, c. 1800 — A577

25pf, Deaf child learning sign language.

**1978, Apr. 4   Litho.   Perf. 13x12½**
| | | | | |
|---|---|---|---|---|
| 1902 | A577 | 20pf multicolored | .25 | .25 |
| 1903 | A577 | 25pf multicolored | .55 | .55 |

National Institute for the Education of the Deaf, established by Samuel Heinicke, 200th anniversary.

Radio Tower, Dequede, TV Truck — A578

Design: 20pf, TV equipment and tower, vert.

**1978, Apr. 25   Perf. 13½x14, 14x13½**
| | | | | |
|---|---|---|---|---|
| 1904 | A578 | 10pf multicolored | .25 | .25 |
| 1905 | A578 | 20pf multicolored | .25 | .25 |

World Telecommunications Day.

Saxon Miner, 19th Century — A579

Dress Uniforms, 19th Century: 20pf, Foundry worker, Freiberg. 25pf, Mining Academy student. 35pf, Chief Inspector of Mines.

**1978, May 9   Perf. 12½x13**
| | | | | |
|---|---|---|---|---|
| 1906 | A579 | 10pf silver & multi | .25 | .25 |
| 1907 | A579 | 20pf silver & multi | .25 | .25 |
| 1908 | A579 | 25pf silver & multi | .25 | .25 |
| 1909 | A579 | 35pf silver & multi | 1.00 | .65 |
| | | Nos. 1906-1909 (4) | 1.75 | 1.40 |

Lion Cub — A580

Young Animals: 20pf, Leopard. 35pf, Tiger. 50pf, Snow leopard.

**1978, May 23** **Photo.** **Perf. 14**
1910 A580 10pf multicolored .25 .25
1911 A580 20pf multicolored .25 .25
1912 A580 35pf multicolored .25 .25
1913 A580 50pf multicolored 1.00 1.00
Nos. 1910-1913 (4) 1.75 1.75
Centenary of Leipzig Zoo.

Loading Container — A581

Designs: 20pf, Loading container on flatbed truck. 35pf, Container trains in terminal. 70pf, Loading container on ship.

**1978, June 13** **Litho.** **Perf. 12½x13**
1914 A581 10pf multicolored .25 .25
1915 A581 20pf multicolored .25 .25
1916 A581 35pf multicolored .25 .25
1917 A581 70pf multicolored 1.40 1.10
Nos. 1914-1917 (4) 2.15 1.85

Ceramic Bull — A582

Designs: 10pf, Woman's head, ceramic. 20pf, Gold armband, horiz. 25pf, Animal head, gold ring. 35pf, Seated family from signet ring. 40pf, Necklace, horiz.

**Perf. 14x13½, 13½x14**
**1978, June 20** **Photo.**
1918 A582 5pf multicolored .25 .25
1919 A582 10pf multicolored .25 .25
1920 A582 20pf multicolored .25 .25
1921 A582 25pf multicolored .25 .25
1922 A582 35pf multicolored .25 .25
1923 A582 40pf multicolored 1.00 1.00
Nos. 1918-1923 (6) 2.25 2.10

African art from 1st and 2nd centuries in Berlin and Leipzig Egyptian museums.

Old and New Buildings, Cottbus — A583

Design: 10pf + 5pf, View of Cottbus, 1730.

**1978, July 18** **Litho.** **Perf. 13x12½**
1924 10pf + 5pf multi .25 .25
1925 20pf multicolored .25 .25
a. A583 Pair, #1924-1925 + label .55 .55

5th Youth Philatelic Exhibition, Cottbus.

Justus von Liebig, Wheat and Retort — A584

Famous Germans: 10pf, Joseph Dietzgen (1828-1888) and title page. 15pf, Alfred Döblin (1878-1957) and title page. 20pf, Hans Loch (1898-1960) and signature, president of Liberal Democratic Party. 25pf, Dr. Theodor Brugsch (1878-1963), and blood circulation. 35pf, Friedrich Ludwig Jahn (1778-1852) and gymnast. 70pf, Dr. Albrecht von Graefe (1828-1870) and ophthalmological instruments.

**1978, July 18**
1926 A584 5pf yellow & blk .25 .25
1927 A584 10pf gray & blk .25 .25
1928 A584 15pf yel grn & blk .25 .25
1929 A584 20pf ultra & blk .25 .25
1930 A584 25pf salmon & blk .25 .25
1931 A584 35pf lt green & blk .25 .25
1932 A584 70pf ol & blk 1.10 1.00
Nos. 1926-1932 (7) 2.60 2.50

Festival Emblem and New Buildings, Havana — A585

35pf, Balloons and new buildings, Berlin.

**1978, July 25** **Litho.** **Perf. 13x12½**
1933 20pf multicolored .30 .30
1934 35pf multicolored .30 .30
a. A585 Strip of 2, #1933-1934 + label .90 .90

11th World Youth Festival, Havana, 7/28-8/5.

Foot Soldier, by Hans Schäufelein — A586

Etchings: 20pf, Woman Reading Letter, by Jean Antoine Watteau. 25pf, Seated Boy, by Gabriel Metsu. 30pf, Seated Young Man, by Cornelis Saftleven. 35pf, St. Anthony, by Matthias Grunewald. 50pf, Seated Man, by Abraham van Diepenbeeck.

**1978, July 25** **Perf. 13½x14**
1935 A586 10pf lemon & black .25 .25
1936 A586 20pf lemon & black .65 .65
1937 A586 25pf lemon & black .25 .25
1938 A586 30pf lemon & black .25 .25
1939 A586 35pf lemon & black .65 .65
1940 A586 50pf lemon & black .25 .25
a. A586 Sheet of 6, #1935-1940 2.40 2.40

Etchings from Berlin Museums.

Fair Building "Three Kings," Leipzig — A587

Leipzig Fall Fair: 10pf, IFA Multicar 25 truck, horiz.

**1978, Aug. 29** **Photo.** **Perf. 14**
1941 A587 10pf multicolored .25 .25
1942 A587 25pf multicolored .35 .30

Mauthausen Memorial — A588

**1978, Sept. 5** **Perf. 13½x14**
1943 A588 35pf multicolored .35 .25

International war memorials.

Soyuz, Intercosmos and German-Soviet Space Flight Emblems — A589

Soyuz, Camera and Space Complex — A590

Designs: 10pf, Soyuz and Albert Einstein. 20pf, Sigmund Jähn, 1st German cosmonaut, vert. 35pf, Salyut-Soyuz space station, Otto Lilienthal and his glider. 1m, Cosmonauts Bykovsky and Jähn and space ships.

**1978, Sept.** **Photo.** **Perf. 14**
1944 A589 20pf multicolored .35 .25

**Litho.**
**Perf. 13½x13**
1945 A590 5pf multicolored .25 .25
1946 A590 10pf multicolored .25 .25
1947 A590 25pf multicolored .25 .25
1948 A590 35pf multicolored .65 .65
Nos. 1944-1948 (5) 1.75 1.65

**Souvenir Sheet**
**Perf. 13½x14**
1949 A590 1m multicolored 1.60 3.25

1st German cosmonaut on Russian space mission. No. 1949 contains 1 54x33mm stamp.
Issued: No. 1944, 9/4; others, 9/21.

Marching Soldiers, Tractor, Factory — A591

Design: 35pf, Russian and German Soldiers, Communist war veteran, 1933.

**1978, Sept. 19** **Photo.** **Perf. 14**
1950 A591 20pf multicolored .35 .30
1951 A591 35pf multicolored .35 .35
a. Strip of 2, #1950-1951 + label 1.10 1.60

Workers' military units, 25th anniv.

Seven-person Pyramid — A592

10pf, Elephant on tricycle. 20pf, Dressage. 35pf, Polar bear kissing woman trainer.

**1978, Sept. 26** **Photo.** **Perf. 14**
1952 A592 5pf black & multi .30 .50
1953 A592 10pf black & multi .55 .75
1954 A592 20pf black & multi .90 1.25
1955 A592 35pf black & multi 1.25 2.25
a. Block of 4, #1952-1955 5.25 12.50

Circus in German Democratic Republic.

Construction of Gas Pipe Line, Drushba Section — A593

**1978, Oct. 3** **Litho.** **Perf. 13x12½**
1956 A593 20pf multicolored .35 .25

German youth helping to build gas pipe line from Orenburg to Russian border.

African Behind Barbed Wire — A594

**1978, Oct. 3** **Litho.** **Perf. 12½x13**
1957 A594 20pf multicolored .35 .25

Anti-Apartheid Year.

Papilio Hahneli — A595

20pf, Agama lehmanni (lizards). 25pf, Agate from Wiederau. 35pf, Paleobatrachus diluvianus. 40pf, Clock, 1720. 50pf, Table telescope, 1750.

**1978, Oct. 24** **Photo.** **Perf. 14**
1958 A595 10pf multicolored .25 .25
1959 A595 20pf multicolored .25 .25
1960 A595 25pf multicolored .25 .25
1961 A595 35pf multicolored .25 .25
1962 A595 40pf multicolored .25 .25
1963 A595 50pf multicolored 1.60 1.40
Nos. 1958-1963 (6) 2.85 2.65

Dresden Museum of Natural History, 250th anniversary.

Wheel Lock Gun, 1630 A596

Hunting Guns: 10pf, Double-barreled gun, 1978. 20pf, Spring-cock gun, 1780. 25pf, Superimposed double-barreled gun, 1978. 35pf, Percussion gun, 1850. 70pf, Three-barreled gun, 1978.

**1978, Nov. 21** **Photo.** **Perf. 14**
1964 A596 5pf silver & multi .25 .25
1965 A596 10pf silver & multi .25 .25
1966 A596 20pf silver & multi .25 .25
1967 A596 25pf silver & multi .30 .30
1968 A596 35pf silver & multi .35 .35
a. Vert. strip of 3, 5, 20, 35pf 1.10 1.10
1969 A596 70pf silver & multi .80 .80
a. Vert. strip of 3, 10, 25, 70pf 2.10 1.90
Nos. 1964-1969 (6) 2.20 2.20

Printed in sheets of 9.

Rapunzel's Father and Witch — A597

Designs: Scenes from fairy tale "Rapunzel."

**1978, Nov. 21** **Litho.** **Perf. 13**
1970 A597 10pf multicolored .25 .25
1971 A597 15pf multicolored .70 .70
1972 A597 20pf multicolored .25 .25
1973 A597 25pf multicolored .25 .25
1974 A597 35pf multicolored .70 .70
1975 A597 50pf multicolored .25 .25
a. Sheet of 6, #1970-1975 2.50 2.50

Chaffinches — A598

Song Birds: 10pf, Nuthatch. 20pf, Robin. 25pf, Bullfinches. 35pf, Blue tit. 50pf, Red linnets.

**1979, Jan. 9** **Photo.** **Perf. 13½x14**
1976 A598 5pf multicolored .25 .25
1977 A598 10pf multicolored .25 .25
1978 A598 20pf multicolored .25 .25
1979 A598 25pf multicolored .25 .25
1980 A598 35pf multicolored .25 .25
1981 A598 50pf multicolored 1.90 .95
Nos. 1976-1981 (6) 3.15 2.20

Chabo Cock — A599

German Cocks: 15pf, Kraienkopp. 20pf, Porcelain-colored bantam. 25pf, Saxonian. 35pf, Phoenix. 50pf, Striped Italian.

**1979, Jan. 23** **Perf. 14x13½**
1982 A599 10pf multicolored .25 .25
1983 A599 15pf multicolored .25 .25
1984 A599 20pf multicolored .25 .25
1985 A599 25pf multicolored .25 .25
1986 A599 35pf multicolored .25 .25
1987 A599 50pf multicolored 1.60 1.25
Nos. 1982-1987 (6) 2.85 2.50

Telephone Operators, 1900 and 1979 A600

35pf, Telegraph operators, 1880 and 1979.

**1979, Feb. 6** **Photo.** **Perf. 13½x14**
1988 A600 20pf multicolored .25 .25
1989 A600 35pf multicolored .60 .40

Development of German postal telephone and telegraph service.

## Souvenir Sheet

Albert Einstein (1879-1955),
Theoretical Physicist — A601

**1979, Feb. 20** **Litho.** **Perf. 14**
1990 A601 1m multicolored 1.75 3.00

Max Klinger House,
Leipzig — A602

Leipzig Spring Fair: 25pf, Horizontal drilling
and milling machine, horiz.

**1979, Mar. 6** **Litho.** **Perf. 14**
1991 A602 10pf multicolored .25 .25
1992 A602 25pf multicolored .30 .25

Container
Ship, Tug,
World Map
and IMCO
Emblem
A603

**1979, Mar. 20** **Photo.**
1993 A603 20pf multicolored .45 .25

World Navigation Day.

Otto Hahn and
Equation of
Nuclear
Fission — A604

Famous Germans: 10pf, Max von Laue
(1879-1969) and diagram of sulphide zinc.
20pf, Arthur Scheunert (1879-1957), symbol
of nutrition and health. 25pf, Friedrich August
Kekulé (1829-1896), and benzene ring. 35pf,
George Forster (1754-1794) and Capt. Cook's
ship Resolution. 70pf, Gotthold Ephraim Lessing (1729-1781) and title page for Nathan the
Wise.

**1979, Mar. 20** **Litho.** **Perf. 13x12½**
1994 A604 5pf pale salmon &
blk .25 .25
1995 A604 10pf blue gray & blk .25 .25
1996 A604 20pf lemon & blk .25 .25
1997 A604 25pf lt green & blk .25 .25
1998 A604 35pf lt blue & blk .25 .25
1999 A604 70pf pink & blk 1.60 1.00
Nos. 1994-1999 (6) 2.85 2.25

See Nos. 2088-2093.

## Miniature Sheet

A605

Design: 20pf, Horch 8, 1911. 35pf, Trabant
601S de luxe, 1978.

**1979, Apr. 3** **Litho.** **Perf. 14**
2000 A605 Sheet of 2 + label 1.60 1.25
a. 20pf multicolored .30 .30
b. 35pf multicolored .45 .45

Sachsenring automobile plant, Zwickau.

Self-Propelled
Car — A606

DDR Railroad Cars: 10pf, Self-unloading
freight car Us-y. 20pf, Diesel locomotive BR
110. 35pf, Laaes automobile carrier.

**1979, Apr. 17** **Litho.** **Perf. 13**
2001 A606 5pf multicolored .25 .25
2002 A606 10pf multicolored .25 .25
2003 A606 20pf multicolored .25 .25
2004 A606 35pf multicolored .65 .55
Nos. 2001-2004 (4) 1.40 1.30

Durga, 18th
Century — A607

Indian Miniatures in Berlin Museums: 35pf,
Mahavira, 15th-16th cents. 50pf, Todi Ragini,
17th cent. 70pf, Asavari Ragini, 17th cent.

**1979, May 8** **Photo.** **Perf. 14x13½**
2005 A607 20pf multicolored .25 .25
2006 A607 35pf multicolored .25 .25
2007 A607 50pf multicolored .25 .25
2008 A607 70pf multicolored 1.75 1.75
Nos. 2005-2008 (4) 2.50 2.50

Youth Gathering — A608

Design: 10pf+5pf, Torchlight parade of German youth, Oct. 7, 1949.

**1979, May 22** **Photo.** **Perf. 14**
2009 10pf + 5pf multi .25 .25
2010 20pf multicolored .25 .25
a. A608 Strip of 2, #2009-2010 + label .65 .65

National Youth Festival, Berlin.

Housing Project,
Berlin — A609

20pf, Berlin-Marzahn building site &
surveyors.

**1979, May 22** **Litho.** **Perf. 13x12½**
2011 A609 10pf multicolored .25 .25
2012 A609 20pf multicolored .30 .30

Berlin Project of Free German Youth.

Children Playing and
Reading — A610

20pf, Doctor with black & white children.

**1979, May 22** **Photo.** **Perf. 14**
2013 A610 10pf multicolored .25 .25
2014 A610 20pf multicolored .35 .35

International Year of the Child.

Exhibition
Emblem — A611

**1979, June 5**
2015 A611 10pf multicolored .35 .25

Agra '79 Agricultural Exhib., Markkleeberg.

Ferry Boats — A612

**1979, June 26** **Photo.** **Perf. 14**
2016 20pf Rostock .30 .30
2017 35pf Rugen .30 .30
a. A612 Strip of 2, #2016-2017 + label 1.20 .90

Railroad ferry from Sassnitz, DDR, to Trelleborg, Sweden, 70th anniversary.

Hospital
Classroom
A613

Design: 35pf, Handicapped workers.

**1979, June 26** **Litho.** **Perf. 13x12½**
2018 A613 10pf multicolored .25 .25
2019 A613 35pf multicolored .40 .35

Rehabilitation in DDR.

Bicyclists
A614

Design: 20pf, Roller skating.

**1979, July 3**
2020 A614 10pf multicolored .25 .25
2021 A614 20pf multicolored .40 .35

7th Children's and Youth Spartakiad, Berlin.

Dahlia
"Rubens" — A615

Dahlias: 20pf, Rosalie. 25pf, Corinna. 35pf,
Enzett-Dolli. 50pf, Enzett-Carola. 70pf, Don
Lorenzo.

**1979, July 17** **Photo.** **Perf. 13**
2022 A615 10pf multicolored .25 .25
2023 A615 20pf multicolored .25 .25
2024 A615 25pf multicolored .25 .25
2025 A615 35pf multicolored .25 .25
2026 A615 50pf multicolored .25 .25
2027 A615 70pf multicolored 2.00 1.75
Nos. 2022-2027 (6) 3.25 3.00

Dahlias shown at International Garden Exhibition, Erfurt.

Russian Alphabet
Around Congress
Emblem — A616

**1979, Aug. 7** **Photo.** **Perf. 13**
2028 A616 20pf multicolored .30 .25

4th International Congress of Teachers of
Russian Language and Literature, Berlin.

Dandelion Fountain,
Dresden — A617

**1979, Aug. 7** **Perf. 14**
2029 A617 20pf multicolored .25 .25

## Souvenir Sheet

Composite of Dresden
Buildings — A618

**1979, Aug. 7** **Litho.** **Perf. 13x12½**
2030 A618 1m multicolored 1.60 1.40

DDR '79, Natl. Stamp Exhib., Dresden.
See No. B187.

Italian Lira da
Gamba,
1592 — A619

Musical Instruments, Leipzig Museum: 25pf,
French "serpent," 17th-18th centuries. 40pf,
French barrel lyre, 18th century. 85pf, German
tenor trumpet, 19th century.

**1979, Aug. 21** **Perf. 14**
2031 A619 20pf multicolored .25 .25
2032 A619 25pf multicolored .25 .25
2033 A619 40pf multicolored .25 .25
2034 A619 85pf multicolored 1.90 1.40
Nos. 2031-2034 (4) 2.65 2.15

Galloping
A620

**1979, Aug. 21**
2035 A620 10pf shown .25 .25
2036 A620 25pf Dressage .65 .60

30th International Horse-breeding Congress
of Socialist Countries, Berlin.

Memorial Monument,
Nordhausen — A621

**1979, Aug. 28** **Photo.** **Perf. 14**
2037 A621 35pf dull vio & blk .40 .30

Memorial to World War II victims.

Teddy Bear — A622

Leipzig Autumn Fair: 25pf, Grosser Blumenberg (building), Leipzig, horiz.

**1979, Aug. 28**

| 2038 | A622 | 10pf multicolored | .25 | .25 |
| 2039 | A622 | 25pf multicolored | .25 | .25 |

Philipp Dengel (1888-1948) — A623

Working-Class Movement Leaders: No. 2041, Heinrich Rau (1899-1961). No. 2042, Otto Buchwitz (1879-1964). No. 2043, Bernard Koenen (1889-1964).

**1979, Sept. 11**       **Litho.**

| 2040 | A623 | 10pf multicolored | .25 | .25 |
| 2041 | A623 | 10pf multicolored | .25 | .25 |
| 2042 | A623 | 10pf multicolored | .25 | .25 |
| 2043 | A623 | 10pf multicolored | .25 | .25 |
| | | *Nos. 2040-2043 (4)* | 1.00 | 1.00 |

See Nos. 2166-2169, 2249-2253, 2314-2318, 2390-2392, 2452-2454.

DDR Arms and Flag, Worker — A624

DDR Arms, Flag and: 10pf, Young man and woman. 15pf, Soldiers. 20pf, Workers.

**1979, Oct. 2**       **Photo.**    **Perf. 13**

| 2044 | A624 | 5pf multicolored | .25 | .25 |
| 2045 | A624 | 10pf multicolored | .25 | .25 |
| 2046 | A624 | 15pf multicolored | .35 | .35 |
| 2047 | A624 | 20pf multicolored | .25 | .25 |
| | | *Nos. 2044-2047 (4)* | 1.10 | 1.10 |

**Souvenir Sheet**

| 2048 | A624 | 1m multicolored | 1.25 | 2.10 |

DDR, 30th anniv. No. 2048 contains one stamp (33x55mm).

Woman Applying Make-Up, 1967 — A625

Meissen Porcelain and Hallmark, 18th-20th Centuries: 10pf, Altozier coffee pot. 15pf, "Grosser Ausschnitt" coffee pot, 1974. 20pf, Covered vase. 25pf, Parrot. 35pf, Harlequin drinking. 50pf, Woman selling flowers. 70pf, Sake bottle.

**1979, Nov. 6**       **Photo.**    **Perf. 14**

| 2049 | A625 | 5pf multicolored | .25 | .25 |
| 2050 | A625 | 10pf multicolored | .25 | .25 |
| 2051 | A625 | 15pf multicolored | .25 | .25 |
| 2052 | A625 | 20pf multicolored | .30 | .30 |
| *a.* | | Block of 4, #2049-2052 | 2.60 | 2.00 |
| 2053 | A625 | 25pf multicolored | .35 | .35 |
| 2054 | A625 | 35pf multicolored | .55 | .55 |
| 2055 | A625 | 50pf multicolored | .75 | .75 |
| 2056 | A625 | 70pf multicolored | 1.00 | 1.00 |
| *a.* | | Block of 4, #2053-2056 | 5.25 | 5.00 |

Rag Doll, 1800 — A626

Historic Dolls: 15pf, Ceramic, 1960. 20pf, Wooden, 1780. 35pf, Straw, 1900. 50pf, Jointed, 1800. 70pf, Tumbler, 1820.

**1979, Nov. 20**       **Litho.**

| 2057 | A626 | 10pf multicolored | .25 | .25 |
| 2058 | A626 | 15pf multicolored | .80 | .80 |
| 2059 | A626 | 20pf multicolored | .25 | .25 |
| 2060 | A626 | 35pf multicolored | .25 | .25 |
| 2061 | A626 | 50pf multicolored | .80 | .80 |
| 2062 | A626 | 70pf multicolored | .25 | .25 |
| *a.* | | Sheet of 6, #2057-2062 | 3.00 | 3.00 |

Bobsledding, by Gunter Rechn, Olympic Rings — A627

Olympic Rings and: 20pf, Figure Skating, by Johanna Stake, vert. 35pf, Speed Skating, by Axel Wunsch, vert. 1m, Cross-country Skiing, by Lothar Zitzmann.

**1980, Jan. 15**       **Photo.**    **Perf. 14**

| 2063 | A627 | 10pf multicolored | .25 | .25 |
| 2064 | A627 | 20pf multicolored | .25 | .25 |
| 2065 | A627 | 35pf multicolored | 1.10 | 1.00 |
| | | *Nos. 2063-2065,B189 (4)* | 1.85 | 1.75 |

**Souvenir Sheet**

| 2066 | A627 | 1m multicolored | 1.75 | 3.25 |

13th Winter Olympic Games, Lake Placid, NY, Feb. 12-24. No. 2066 contains one 29x23½mm stamp. See Nos. 2098-2099, 2119-2121, B189-B190, B192.

"Quiet Music," Grossedlitz A628

Baroque Gardens: 20pf, Orange grove, Belvedere, Weimar. 50pf, Flower garden, Dornburg Castle. 70pf, Park, Rheinsberg Castle.

**1980, Jan. 29**

| 2067 | A628 | 10pf multicolored | .25 | .25 |
| 2068 | A628 | 20pf multicolored | .25 | .25 |
| 2069 | A628 | 50pf multicolored | .25 | .25 |
| 2070 | A628 | 70pf multicolored | 1.20 | 1.20 |
| | | *Nos. 2067-2070 (4)* | 1.95 | 1.95 |

**Type of 1973**

Designs as before and: 10pf, Palace of the Republic, Berlin.

**1980-81**       **Engr.**    **Perf. 14**
**Size: 22x17mm**

| 2071 | A449 | 5pf blue green | .25 | .25 |
| 2072 | A449 | 10pf emerald | .25 | .25 |
| 2073 | A449 | 15pf rose lilac | .25 | .25 |
| 2074 | A449 | 20pf rose mag | .40 | .25 |
| 2075 | A449 | 25pf grnsh bl | .35 | .30 |
| 2076 | A449 | 30pf org ('81) | .40 | .30 |
| 2077 | A449 | 35pf blue | .40 | .30 |
| 2078 | A449 | 40pf dull vio | .65 | .50 |
| 2079 | A449 | 50pf blue | .45 | .30 |
| 2080 | A449 | 60pf lilac ('81) | .55 | .30 |
| 2081 | A449 | 70pf redsh brn ('81) | .60 | .60 |
| 2082 | A449 | 80pf vio bl ('81) | .70 | .50 |
| 2083 | A449 | 1m olive | .80 | .45 |
| 2084 | A449a | 2m red | 1.40 | .55 |
| 2085 | A449a | 3m rose lil ('81) | 2.25 | .65 |
| | | *Nos. 2071-2085 (15)* | 9.70 | 5.75 |

Cable-Laying Vehicle, Dish Antenna — A629

20pf, Radio tower, television screen.

**1980, Feb. 5**       **Photo.**

| 2086 | A629 | 10pf multicolored | .25 | .25 |
| 2087 | A629 | 20pf multicolored | .25 | .25 |

**Famous Germans Type of 1979**

Designs: 5pf, Johann Wolfgang Dobereiner (1780-1849), chemist. 10pf, Frederic Joliot-Curie (1900-1958), French physicist. 20pf, Johann Friedrich Naumann (1780-1857), ornithologist. 25pf, Alfred Wegener (1880-1930), geophysicist and meteorologist. 35pf, Carl von Clausewitz (1780-1831), Prussian major general. 70pf, Helene Weigel (1900-1971), actress.

**1980, Feb. 26**     **Litho.**    **Perf. 13x12½**

| 2088 | A604 | 5pf pale yel & blk | .25 | .25 |
| 2089 | A604 | 10pf multicolored | .25 | .25 |
| 2090 | A604 | 20pf lt yel grn & blk | .25 | .25 |
| 2091 | A604 | 25pf multicolored | .25 | .25 |
| 2092 | A604 | 35pf lt blue & blk | .25 | .25 |
| 2093 | A604 | 70pf lt red brn & blk | 1.10 | .85 |
| | | *Nos. 2088-2093 (6)* | 2.35 | 2.10 |

Type ZT-303 Tractor — A630

1980 Leipzig Spring Fair: 10pf, Karl Marx University, Leipzig, vert.

**1980, Mar. 4**       **Photo.**    **Perf. 14**

| 2094 | A630 | 10pf multicolored | .25 | .25 |
| 2095 | A630 | 25pf multicolored | .30 | .25 |

Werner Eggerath (1900-1977), Labor Leader — A631

**1980, Mar. 18**       **Litho.**

| 2096 | A631 | 10pf brick red & blk | .40 | .30 |

**Souvenir Sheet**

Cosmonauts, Salyut 6 and Soyuz — A632

**1980, Apr. 11**     **Litho.**    **Perf. 14**

| 2097 | A632 | 1m multicolored | 1.60 | 2.60 |

Intercosmos cooperative space program.

**Olympic Type of 1980**

Designs: 10pf, On the Bars, by Erich Wurzer. 50pf, Scull's Crew, by Wilfried Falkenthal.

**1980, Apr. 22**     **Photo.**    **Perf. 14**

| 2098 | A627 | 10pf multicolored | .25 | .25 |
| 2099 | A627 | 50pf multicolored | 1.10 | .90 |
| | | *Nos. 2098-2099,B190 (3)* | 1.60 | 1.40 |

22nd Summer Olympic Games, Moscow, July 19-Aug. 3. See No. B190.

Flags of Member Countries — A633

**1980, May 13**       **Photo.**

| 2100 | A633 | 20pf multicolored | .40 | .25 |

Signing of Warsaw Pact (Bulgaria, Czechoslovakia, DDR, Hungary, Poland, Romania, USSR), 25th anniv.

Bauhaus Cooperative Society Building, 1928, Gropius — A634

Bauhaus Architecture: 10pf, Socialists' Memorial, 1926, by Mies van der Rohe, horiz. 15pf, Monument, 1922, by William Gropius. 20pf, Steel building, 1926, by Muche and Paulick, horiz. 35pf, Trade-Union School, 1928, by Meyer. 70pf, Bauhaus Building, 1926, by Gropius, horiz.

**1980, May 27**

| 2101 | A634 | 5pf multicolored | .25 | .25 |
| 2102 | A634 | 5pf multicolored | .25 | .25 |
| 2103 | A634 | 15pf multicolored | .25 | .25 |
| 2104 | A634 | 20pf multicolored | .25 | .25 |
| 2105 | A634 | 50pf multicolored | .30 | .25 |
| 2106 | A634 | 70pf multicolored | 1.60 | 1.40 |
| | | *Nos. 2101-2106 (6)* | 2.90 | 2.65 |

Rostock View — A635

**1980, June 10**     **Photo.**    **Perf. 14**

| 2107 | A635 | 10pf shown | .25 | .25 |
| 2108 | A635 | 20pf Dancers | .30 | .25 |

18th Workers' Festival, Rostock, June 27-29.

Dish Antenna, Interflug Airlines — A636

25pf, Jet. 35pf, Agricultural plane. 70pf, Aerial photography.

**1980, June 10**    **Litho.**    **Perf. 13x12½**

| 2109 | A636 | 10pf shown | .30 | .30 |
| 2110 | A636 | 25pf multi | .30 | .30 |
| 2111 | A636 | 35pf multi | .40 | .40 |
| 2112 | A636 | 70pf multi | .80 | .80 |
| *a.* | | Block of 4, #2109-2112 | 2.25 | 2.25 |

Interflug Airlines. See No. B191

Okapi — A637

10pf, Red pandas. 15pf, Prairie wolf. 20pf, Arabian oryx. 25pf, White-eared pheasant. 35pf, Musk oxen.

**1980, June 24**       **Perf. 14**

| 2113 | A637 | 5pf shown | .25 | .25 |
| 2114 | A637 | 10pf multi | .25 | .25 |
| 2115 | A637 | 15pf multi | .25 | .25 |
| 2116 | A637 | 20pf multi | .25 | .25 |
| 2117 | A637 | 25pf multi | .25 | .25 |
| 2118 | A637 | 35pf multi | 1.60 | 1.60 |
| | | *Nos. 2113-2118 (6)* | 2.85 | 2.85 |

**Olympic Type of 1980**

Designs: 10pf, Judo, by Erhard Schmidt. 50pf, Final Spurt, by Siegfried Schreiber. 1m, Spinnaker Yachts, by Karl Raetsch.

**1980, July 8**     **Photo.**    **Perf. 14**

| 2119 | A627 | 10pf multicolored | .25 | .25 |
| 2120 | A627 | 50pf multicolored | 1.10 | .90 |
| | | *Nos. 2119-2120,B192 (3)* | 1.60 | 1.40 |

**Souvenir Sheet**

| 2121 | A627 | 1m multicolored | 1.60 | 2.60 |

22nd Summer Olympic Games, Moscow, 7/19-8/3. No. 2121 contains one 29x24mm stamp.

6th National Youth Philatelic Exhibition, Suhl — A638

Design: 10pf + 5pf, View of Suhl, 1700. 20pf, Old and New Buildings, Suhl.

**1980, July 22**    **Litho.**    **Perf. 13x12½**

| 2122 | | 10pf + 5pf multi | .30 | .30 |
| 2123 | | 20pf multicolored | .30 | .30 |
| *a.* | A638 | Pair, #2122-2123 + label | 1.00 | .85 |

Surtax for East German Association of Philatelists.

Huntley Microscope, London, 1740 — A639

Optical Museum, Karl Zeiss Foundation, Jena: 25pf, Magny microscope, Paris, 1751. 35pf, Amici microscope, Modena, 1845. 70pf, Zeiss microscope, Jena, 1873.

**1980, Aug. 12**     **Photo.**    **Perf. 14**

| 2124 | A639 | 20pf multicolored | .30 | .30 |
| 2125 | A639 | 25pf multicolored | .30 | .30 |
| 2126 | A639 | 35pf multicolored | .45 | .45 |
| 2127 | A639 | 70pf multicolored | .65 | .65 |
| *a.* | | Block of 4, #2124-2127 | 3.00 | 3.00 |

Maidenek
Memorial
A640

**1980, Aug. 26**
2128 A640 35pf multicolored　　.40 .30

Leipzig 1980
Autumn Fair,
Information
Center — A641

**1980, Aug. 26**
2129 A641 10pf shown　　.25 .25
2130 A641 25pf Carpet loom　　.40 .25

67th Interparliamentary Conference,
Berlin — A642

**1980, Sept. 9　　Photo.　　Perf. 14**
2131 A642 20pf Republic Palace,
　　Berlin　　.60 .25

Paintings by Frans
Hals (1580-
1666) — A643

10pf, *Laughing Boy with Flute.* 20pf, *Man in Gray Coat.* 25pf, *The Mulatto.* 35pf, *Man in Black Coat.*
1m, *Self-portrait,* horiz.

**1980, Sept. 23**
2132 A643 10pf multicolored　　.25 .25
2133 A643 20pf multicolored　　.25 .25
2134 A643 25pf multicolored　　.25 .25
2135 A643 35pf multicolored　　.80 .65
　　Nos. 2132-2135 (4)　　1.55 1.40
**Souvenir Sheet**
2136 A643 1m multicolored　　1.60 3.25

A644

Edible Mushrooms: 5pf, Leccinum Testaceo Scabrum. 10pf, Boletus erythropus. 15pf, Agaricus campester. 20pf, Xerocomus badius. 35pf, Boletus edulis. 70pf, Cantharellus cibarius.

**1980, Oct. 28　　Litho.　　Perf. 13x13½**
2137 A644 5pf multicolored　　.25 .25
2138 A644 10pf multicolored　　.25 .25
2139 A644 15pf multicolored　　.25 .25
2140 A644 20pf multicolored　　.25 .25
2141 A644 35pf multicolored　　.25 .25
2142 A644 70pf multicolored　　1.40 1.25
　　Nos. 2137-2142 (6)　　2.65 2.50

Exploration of
Lignite Deposits
(Gravimetry)
A645

Geophysical Exploration: 25pf, Bore-hole measuring (water). 35pf, Seismic geology. (mineral oil, natural gas). 50pf, Seismology.

**1980, Nov. 11　　Litho.　　Perf. 13**
2143 A645 20pf multicolored　　.30 .30
2144 A645 25pf multicolored　　.35 .30
2145 A645 35pf multicolored　　.40 .40
2146 A645 50pf multicolored　　.65 .65
　　a.　Block of 4, #2143-2146　　3.00 2.40

Radebeul-Radeburg Railroad
Locomotive — A646

No. 1247 — b, Passenger car.
No. 1248 — a, Bad Doberan-Osteebad Kuhlungsborn Locomotive. b, Passenger car.

**1980, Nov. 25　　Perf. 13x12½**
2147　　Strip of 2 + label　　1.25 1.25
　　a. A646 20pf shown　　.30 .30
　　b. A646 25pf multi　　.30 .30
2148　　Strip of 2 + label　　1.25 1.25
　　a. A646 20pf multi　　.30 .30
　　b. A646 35pf multi　　.30 .30
Labels show maps of routes and Moritzburg Castle (No. 2147), Bad Doberan Street (No. 2148).
See Nos. 2205-2206.

A647

**1980, Dec. 9　　Perf. 14**
2149 A647　Sheet of 6　　2.60 2.50
　　a.　10pf Toy Locomotive, 1850　.30 .30
　　b.　20pf Airplane, 1914　　.80 .80
　　c.　25pf Steam roller, 1920　.30 .30
　　d.　35pf Ship, 1825　　.30 .30
　　e.　40pf Car, 1900　　.80 .80
　　f.　50pf Balloon, 1920　　.30 .30

**Souvenir Sheet**

Wolfgang
Amadeus
Mozart,
225th Birth
Anniv.
A648

**1981, Jan. 13　　Litho.**
2150 A648　1m multicolored　　2.00 3.00

St. John's Apple — A649

10pf, Snow drop, horiz. 20pf, Bladder bush. 25pf, Paulownia tomentose. 35pf, German honeysuckle, horiz. 50pf, Genuine spice bush.

**1981, Jan. 13　　Photo.**
2151 A649 5pf shown　　.25 .25
2152 A649 10pf multicolored　　.25 .25
2153 A649 20pf multicolored　　.25 .25
2154 A649 25pf multicolored　　.25 .25
2155 A649 35pf multicolored　　.25 .25
2156 A649 50pf multicolored　　1.60 1.40
　　Nos. 2151-2156 (6)　　2.85 2.65

Heinrich von Stephan
(1831-97), Founder of
UPU — A650

**1981, Jan. 20　　Litho.　　Perf. 13x13½**
2157 A650 10pf lt lemon & blk　　.45 .25

Dedication of National Commemorative
Plaza, Sachsenhausen
A651

**1981, Jan. 27　　Photo.　　Perf. 14**
2158 A651 10pf shown　　.25 .25
2159 A651 20pf Changing of
　　guard　　.30 .25
National People's Forces, 25th anniversary.

Socialist
Union
Party, 10th
Congress
A652

**1981, Feb. 10**
2160 A652 10pf multicolored　　.45 .25

Postal and
Newspaper
Apprentice
Training
A653

10pf, Telephone and telex service. 15pf, Radio communications. 20pf, School of Engineering, Leipzig. 25pf, Communications Academy, Dresden.

**1981, Feb. 10　　Litho.**
2161 A653 5pf shown　　.25 .25
2162 A653 10pf multicolored　　.25 .25
2163 A653 15pf multicolored　　.25 .25
2164 A653 20pf multicolored　　.25 .25
2165 A653 25pf multicolored　　.90 .65
　　Nos. 2161-2165 (5)　　1.90 1.65

**Working-class Leader Type of 1979**
Designs: No. 2166, Erich Baron (1881-1933). No. 2167, Conrad Blenkle (1901-1943). No. 2168, Arthur Ewert (1890-1959). No. 2169, Walter Stoecker (1891-1939).

**1981, Feb. 24　　Litho.　　Perf. 14**
2166 A623 10pf gray grn & blk　　.25 .25
2167 A623 10pf lemon & blk　　.25 .25
2168 A623 10pf bl vio & blk　　.25 .25
2169 A623 10pf lt red brn & blk　　.25 .25
　　Nos. 2166-2169 (4)　　1.00 1.00

Merkur Hotel,
Leipzig — A654

1981 Leipzig Spring Fair: 25pf, Takraf mining conveyor system, horiz.

**1981, Mar. 10　　Photo.　　Perf. 14**
2170 A654 10pf multicolored　　.25 .25
2171 A654 25pf multicolored　　.35 .25

Ernst Thälmann, by
Willi Sitte — A655

10th Communist Party Congress (Paintings): 20pf, Worker, by Bernhard Heising. 25pf, Festivities, by Rudolf Bergander. 35pf, Brotherhood in Arms, by Paul Michaelis. 1m, When Communists Dream, by Walter Womacka.

**1981, Mar. 24**
2172 A655 10pf multicolored　　.25 .25
2173 A655 20pf multicolored　　.25 .25
2174 A655 25pf multicolored　　.65 .55
2175 A655 35pf multicolored　　.25 .25
　　Nos. 2172-2175 (4)　　1.40 1.30
**Souvenir Sheet**
2176 A655 1m multicolored　　1.25 1.60

Souvenir Sheet

Opening of Sport and Recreation
Center, Berlin — A656

**1981, Mar. 24　　Litho.**
2177 A656 1m multicolored　　1.90 3.25

Energy
Conservation — A657

**1981, Apr. 21　　Litho.　　Perf. 12½x13**
2178 A657 10pf orange & blk　　.25 .25

Heinrich Barkhausen (1881-1956),
Physicist — A658

Famous Men: 20pf, Johannes R. Becher (1891-1958), poet. 25pf, Richard Dedekind (1831-1916), mathematician. 35pf, Georg Philipp Telemann (1681-1767), composer. 50pf, Adelbert V. Chamisso (1781-1838), botanist. 70pf, Wilhelm Raabe (1831-1910), writer.

**1981, May 5　　Perf. 13x12½**
2179 A658 10pf dull bl & blk　　.25 .25
2180 A658 20pf brick red & blk　　.25 .25
2181 A658 25pf dull brn & blk　　1.90 1.25
2182 A658 35pf lt vio & blk　　.25 .25
2183 A658 50pf yel grn & blk　　.30 .25
2184 A658 70pf ol bis & blk　　.40 .25
　　Nos. 2179-2184 (6)　　3.35 2.50

Free German
Youth Members
A659

**1981, May 19**
2185 A659 10pf shown　　.25 .25
2186 A659 20pf Youths, diff.　　.25 .25
　　a.　Pair, #2185-2186 + label　　.70 .65
Free German Youth, 11th Parliament, Berlin.

View and Map of Worlitz
Park — A660

**1981, June 9　　Litho.　　Perf. 12½x13**
2187 A660 5pf multicolored　　.25 .25
2188 A660 10pf Tiefurt　　.25 .25
2189 A660 15pf Marxwalde　　.25 .25
2190 A660 20pf Branitz　　.25 .25
2191 A660 25pf Treptow　　1.25 1.00
2192 A660 35pf Wiesenburg　　.25 .25
　　Nos. 2187-2192 (6)　　2.50 2.25

Artistic
Gymnastics
A661

8th Children's and Youth Spartacist Games:
No. 2193, children and youths.

**1981, June 23          Photo.          Perf. 14**
2193 A661 10pf + 5pf multi          .45     .35
2194 A661 20pf multicolored         .25     .25

Javelin Throwers
A662

**1981, June 23     Litho.     Perf. 13x12½**
2195 A662 5pf shown                 .25     .25
2196 A662 15pf Men at museum        .25     .25
   a.    Pair, #2195-2196 + label   .65     .50
   Intl. Year of the Disabled.

Schinkel's Berlin
Playhouse
A663

Karl Friedrich Schinkel, (1781-1841), Architect: 25pf, Old Museum, Berlin.

**1981, June 23          Litho. & Engr.**
2197 A663 10pf tan & blk           .70     .25
2198 A663 25pf tan & blk          1.60     .70

Sugar Loaf House,
Gross Zicker — A664

Frame Houses: 10pf, Zaulsdorf, 19th cent.,
vert. 25pf, Farmhouse, stable, Weckersdorf,
vert. 35pf, Restaurant (former farmhouse),
Pillgram. 50pf, Eschenbach, vert. 70pf, Farmhouse, Lüdersdorf.

**1981, July 7          Photo.**
2199 A664 10pf multicolored        .25     .25
2200 A664 20pf multicolored        .25     .25
2201 A664 25pf multicolored        .25     .25
2202 A664 35pf multicolored        .25     .25
2203 A664 50pf multicolored        .30     .25
2204 A664 70pf multicolored       2.25    1.75
   Nos. 2199-2204 (6)             3.55    3.00

**Railroad Type of 1980**
No. 2205 — a, Locomotive, Freital-Kurort-
Kipsdorf line. b, Luggage car.
No. 2206 — a, Locomotive, Putbus-Gohren
line. b, Passenger car.

**1981, July 21     Litho.     Perf. 13x12½**
2205      Strip of 2 + label       .70     .65
   a.    A646 5pf multi            .25     .25
   b.    A646 15pf multi           .25     .25
2206      Strip of 2 + label       .70     .65
   a.    A646 5pf multi            .25     .25
   b.    A646 20pf multi           .25     .25
   Labels show maps of train routes.

Ebers Papyrus (Egyptian
Medical Text, 1600 B.C.),
Leipzig — A665

Literary Treasures in DDR Libraries: 35pf,
Maya manuscript, 12th cent., Dresden. 50pf,
Petrarch sonnet illustration, 16th century
French manuscript, Berlin.

**1981, Aug. 18          Photo.          Perf. 14**
2207 A665 20pf multicolored        .25     .25
2208 A665 35pf multicolored        .25     .25
2209 A665 50pf multicolored       1.20    1.20
   Nos. 2207-2209 (3)             1.70    1.70

Chemical Plant — A666

Leipzig 1981 Autumn Fair: 25pf, Concert
Hall, Leipzig, horiz.

**1981, Aug. 18**
2210 A666 10pf multicolored        .25     .25
2211 A666 25pf multicolored        .35     .30

Anti-Fascist
Resistance
Monument,
Sassnitz — A667

**1981, Sept. 8          Photo.          Perf. 14**
2212 A667 35pf multicolored        .40     .30

Forceps, 18th Cent.,
Speculum, 17th
Cent. — A668

Historic Medical Instruments, Karl Sudhoff
Institute, Leipzig: 10pf, Henbana, censer, 16th
cent. 20pf, Pelican, dental elevator and extrac-
tors, 17th cent. 25pf, Seton forceps, 17th cent.
35pf, Lithotomy knife, 18th cent., hernia scissors, 17th cent. 85pf, Elevators, 17th cent.
10pf, 20pf, 25pf, 35pf horiz.

**1981, Sept. 22**
2213 A668 10pf multicolored        .25     .25
2214 A668 20pf multicolored        .25     .25
2215 A668 25pf multicolored        .25     .25
2216 A668 35pf multicolored        .25     .25
2217 A668 50pf multicolored       2.00    2.00
2218 A668 85pf multicolored        .45     .30
   Nos. 2213-2218 (6)             3.45    3.30

Philatelists'
Day — A669

10pf, Letter by Engels, 1840. 20pf, Postcard
by Marx, 1878.

**1981, Oct. 6          Photo.          Perf. 14**
2219 A669 10pf + 5pf multi         .65     .45
2220 A669 20pf multi               .25     .25

River
Boat — A670

**1981, Oct. 20**
2221 A670 10pf Tugboat             .25     .25
2222 A670 20pf Tugboat, diff.      .25     .25
2223 A670 25pf Diesel paddle
                liner              .25     .25
2224 A670 35pf Ice breaker         .25     .25
2225 A670 50pf Motor freighter     .30     .25
2226 A670 85pf Bucket dredger     2.10    2.00
   Nos. 2221-2226 (6)             3.40    3.25

Windmill, Dabel — A671

**1981, Nov. 10          Photo.          Perf. 14**
2227 A671 10pf shown               .25     .25
2228 A671 20pf Pahrenz             .25     .25
2229 A671 25pf Dresden-Gohlis      .25     .25
2230 A671 70pf Ballstadt          1.25    1.20
   Nos. 2227-2230 (4)             2.00    1.95

Toys — A672

**1981, Nov. 24     Litho.     Perf. 13½**
2231 A672  Sheet of 6             3.00    3.25
   a.    10pf Jointed snake, 1850  .30     .30
   b.    20pf Teddy bear, 1910     .30     .30
   c.    25pf Fish, 1935           .80     .80
   d.    35pf Hobby horse, 1850    .80     .80
   e.    40pf Cuckoo, 1800         .30     .30
   f.    70pf Frog, 1930           .30     .30

Meissen Porcelain
Teapot, 1715 — A673

20pf, Vase, 1715. 25pf, Oberon figurine,
1969. 35pf, Day and Night vase, 1979.

**1982, Jan. 26          Photo.          Perf. 14**
2232 A673 10pf shown               .25     .25
2233 A673 20pf multicolored        .30     .30
2234 A673 25pf multicolored        .40     .40
2235 A673 35pf multicolored        .55     .55
   a.    Block of 4, #2232-2235   1.90    1.60

**Souvenir Sheet**
2236      Sheet of 2              2.10    3.25
   a.    A673 50pf Portrait        .65    1.25
   b.    A673 50pf Emblem          .65    1.25
   Johann Friedrich Bottger (1682-1719),
inventor of Dresden china. No. 2236 contains
two 24x29mm stamps.

Post
Offices
A674

**1982, Feb. 9**
2237 A674 20pf Liebenstein        .25     .25
2238 A674 25pf Berlin             .25     .25
2239 A674 35pf Erfurt             .25     .25
2240 A674 50pf Dresden           1.60    1.10
   Nos. 2237-2240 (4)            2.35    1.85

Intl. Fur Auction,
Leipzig — A675

**1982, Feb. 23          Photo.          Perf. 14**
2241 A675 10pf Marmot, vert.      .25     .25
2242 A675 20pf Polecat            .25     .25
2243 A675 25pf Mink               .25     .25
2244 A675 35pf Stone marten      1.00     .85
   Nos. 2241-2244 (4)            1.75    1.60

**Souvenir Sheet**

Goethe-Schiller Awards, 1980-
1984 — A676

**1982, Mar. 9          Litho.**
2245 A676  Sheet of 2            2.25    3.25
   a.    50pf Goethe              .85    1.25
   b.    50pf Schiller            .85    1.25

1982 Leipzig
Spring
Fair — A677

**1982, Mar. 9          Perf. 13x12½**
2246 A677 10pf Entrance          .25     .25
2247 A677 25pf Exhibit           .30     .25

**Souvenir Sheet**

TB Bacillus Centenary — A678

**1982, Mar. 23          Perf. 14**
2248 A678  1m multi             1.60    3.25

**Working-class Leader Type of 1979**
No. 2249, Max Fechner (1892-1973). No.
2250, Ottomar Greschke (1882-1957). No.
2251, Helmut Lehmann (1882-1959). No.
2252, Herbert Warnke (1902-75). No. 2253,
Otto Winzer (1902-75).

**1982, Mar. 23          Engr.**
2249 A623 10pf dk red brn        .25     .25
2250 A623 10pf green             .25     .25
2251 A623 10pf violet            .25     .25
2252 A623 10pf dull blue         .25     .25
2253 A623 10pf gray olive        .25     .25
   Nos. 2249-2253 (5)           1.25    1.25

Poisonous Plants —
A679

**1982, Apr. 6          Litho.          Perf. 14**
2254 A679 10pf Meadow saffron    .25     .25
2255 A679 15pf Water arum        .25     .25
2256 A679 20pf Marsh tea         .25     .25
2257 A679 25pf White bryony      .25     .25
2258 A679 35pf Common monks-
                hood             .25     .25
2259 A679 50pf Henbane          1.25    1.10
   Nos. 2254-2259 (6)           2.50    2.35

Free Federation of
German Trade
Unions, 10th
Congress — A680

Paintings: 10pf, Mother and Child, by Walter
Womacka. 20pf, Discussion at the Innovator
Collective, by Willi Neubert, horiz. 25pf, Young
Couple, by Karl-Heinz Jacob.

**1982, Apr. 20          Photo.**
2260 A680 10pf multi             .25     .25
2261 A680 20pf multi             .25     .25
2262 A680 20pf multi             .45     .40
   Nos. 2260-2262 (3)            .95     .90

Intl. Book Art Exhibition,
Leipzig — A681

**1982, Apr. 20**
2263 A681 15pf "I"               .35     .35
2264 A681 35pf Emblem            .35     .35
   a.    Pair, #2263-2264 + label 1.10   1.00

A682

Protected species. 10pf, 25pf, 35pf vert.

**Perf. 13½x14, 14x13½**

| 1982, May 18 | | | Photo. | |
|---|---|---|---|---|
| **2265** | A682 | 10pf Fish hawk | .30 | .25 |
| **2266** | A682 | 20pf Sea eagle | .30 | .25 |
| **2267** | A682 | 25pf Little owl | .30 | .25 |
| **2268** | A682 | 35pf Eagle owl | 1.10 | 1.00 |
| | | Nos. 2265-2268 (4) | 2.00 | 1.75 |

 19th Workers' Festival, Neubrandenburg A683

10pf, View of Neubrandenburg. 20pf, Traditional costumes.

| 1982, June 8 | | | Photo. | |
|---|---|---|---|---|
| **2269** | A683 | 10pf multicolored | .25 | .25 |
| **2270** | A683 | 20pf multicolored | .35 | .30 |

### Souvenir Sheet

 Dimitrov Memorial Medal A684

| 1982, June 8 | | | |
|---|---|---|---|
| **2271** | A684 | 1m multi | 2.25 3.25 |

George Dimitrov (1882-1947), first prime minister of Bulgaria.

 Cargo Ship Frieden A685

| 1982, June 22 | | | | |
|---|---|---|---|---|
| **2272** | A685 | 5pf shown | .25 | .25 |
| **2273** | A685 | 10pf Fichtelberg | .25 | .25 |
| **2274** | A685 | 15pf Brocken | .25 | .25 |
| **2275** | A685 | 20pf Weimar | .25 | .25 |
| **2276** | A685 | 25pf Vorwarts | .25 | .25 |
| **2277** | A685 | 35pf Berlin | 1.10 | .90 |
| | | Nos. 2272-2277 (6) | 2.35 | 2.15 |

 Society for Sport & Technology A686

| 1982, June 22 | | Litho. | Perf. 13x12½ | |
|---|---|---|---|---|
| **2278** | A686 | 20pf multi | .35 | .25 |

  Bird Wedding A687

Sorbian Folklore: 20pf, Zampern masqueraders. 25pf, Easter egg game. 35pf, Painting Easter eggs. 40pf, St. John's Day parade. 50pf, Christmas celebration.

| 1982, July 6 | | Litho. | Perf. 13x12½ | |
|---|---|---|---|---|
| **2279** | A687 | Block of 6 | 3.25 | 3.00 |
| a. | | 10pf multi | .25 | .25 |
| b. | | 20pf multi | .25 | .25 |
| c. | | 25pf multi | .30 | .30 |
| d. | | 35pf multi | .45 | .45 |
| e. | | 40pf multi | .55 | .55 |
| f. | | 50pf multi | .65 | .65 |

 Views of Schwerin — A688

7th Youth Stamp Exhibition, Schwerin: No. 2280, View, 1640. No. 2281, Modern Schwerin.

| 1982, July 6 | | | | |
|---|---|---|---|---|
| **2280** | | 10pf + 5pf multi | .30 | .30 |
| **2281** | | 20pf multi | .30 | .30 |
| a. | | A688 Pair, #2280-2281 + label | 1.25 | 1.00 |

 7th Pioneer Meeting, Dresden — A689

No. 2282, Pioneers, banner. No. 2283, Bugle, pennant.

| 1982, July 20 | | Photo. | Perf. 14x13½ | |
|---|---|---|---|---|
| **2282** | A689 | 10pf + 5pf multi | .40 | .35 |
| **2283** | A689 | 20pf multi | .25 | .25 |

 Seascape, by Ludolf Backhuysen (1631-1708) — A690

17th Cent. Paintings in Natl. Museum, Schwerin: 10pf, Music Making at Home, by Frans van Mieris (1635-1681), vert. 20pf, The Gate Guard, by Carel Fabritius (1622-1654), vert. 25pf, Farmers Company, by Adriaen Brouwer (1606-1638). 35pf, Breakfast Table with Ham, by Willem Claesz Heda (1593-1680). 70pf, River Landscape, by Jan van Goyen (1596-1656).

| 1982, Aug. 10 | | | Perf. 14 | |
|---|---|---|---|---|
| **2284** | A690 | 5pf multi | .25 | .25 |
| **2285** | A690 | 10pf multi | .25 | .25 |
| **2286** | A690 | 20pf multi | .25 | .25 |
| **2287** | A690 | 25pf multi | .25 | .25 |
| **2288** | A690 | 35pf multi | .25 | .25 |
| **2289** | A690 | 70pf multi | 1.60 | 1.20 |
| | | Nos. 2284-2289 (6) | 2.85 | 2.45 |

  1982 Leipzig Autumn Fair — A691

| 1982, Aug. 24 | | Litho. | Perf. 13x12½ | |
|---|---|---|---|---|
| **2290** | A691 | 10pf Exhibition Hall | .25 | .25 |
| **2291** | A691 | 25pf Decorative box, ring | .25 | .25 |

 Karl-Marx-Stadt Buildings and Monument — A692

| 1982, Aug. 24 | | Photo. | Perf. 14 | |
|---|---|---|---|---|
| **2292** | A692 | 10pf multi + label | .30 | .25 |

Org. for the Cooperation of Socialist Countries and Posts and Telecommunications Dept., 13th Conference, Karl-Marx-Stadt, Sept. 6-11.

 Intl. Federation of Resistance Fighters, 9th Congress, Berlin — A693

| 1982, Sept. 7 | | Litho. | Perf. 14 | |
|---|---|---|---|---|
| **2293** | A693 | 10pf Emblem | .35 | .25 |

 Auschwitz- Birkenau Intl. Memorial — A694

| 1982, Sept. 7 | | | Photo. | |
|---|---|---|---|---|
| **2294** | A694 | 35pf multi | .35 | .30 |

 Autumn Flowers — A695

5pf, Autumn anemones. 10pf, Student flowers. 15pf, Hybrid gazanias. 20pf, Sunflowers. 25pf, Chrysanthemums. 35pf, Cosmos bipinnatus.

| 1982, Sept. 21 | | | | |
|---|---|---|---|---|
| **2295** | A695 | 5pf multicolored | .25 | .25 |
| **2296** | A695 | 10pf multicolored | .25 | .25 |
| **2297** | A695 | 15pf multicolored | .25 | .25 |
| **2298** | A695 | 20pf multicolored | .25 | .25 |
| **2299** | A695 | 25pf multicolored | .25 | .25 |
| **2300** | A695 | 35pf multicolored | 1.60 | 1.20 |
| | | Nos. 2295-2300 (6) | 2.85 | 2.45 |

 Ambulance A696

| 1982, Oct. 5 | | Litho. | Perf. 13x12½ | |
|---|---|---|---|---|
| **2301** | A696 | 5pf shown | .25 | .25 |
| **2302** | A696 | 10pf Street cleaner | .25 | .25 |
| **2303** | A696 | 20pf Bus | .25 | .25 |
| **2304** | A696 | 35pf Platform truck | .25 | .25 |
| **2305** | A696 | 35pf Platform truck, diff. | .25 | .25 |
| **2306** | A696 | 85pf Milk truck | 1.90 | 1.40 |
| | | Nos. 2301-2306 (6) | 3.15 | 2.65 |

 25th Masters of Tomorrow Central Fair — A697

| 1982, Oct. 19 | | | Perf. 14 | |
|---|---|---|---|---|
| **2307** | A697 | 20pf multicolored | .30 | .25 |

 Martin Luther (1483-1546) — A698

Designs: 10pf, Seal of Eisleben (town of birth and death). 20pf, Portrait, Eisenach, 1521. 35pf, Wittenberg seal, 1500. 85pf, Portrait, after Cranach, 1528.

| 1982, Nov. 23 | | Photo. | Perf. 14x13½ | |
|---|---|---|---|---|
| **2308** | A698 | 10pf multi | .25 | .25 |
| **2309** | A698 | 20pf multi | .25 | .25 |
| a. | | Miniature sheet of 10 | 6.50 | 6.50 |
| **2310** | A698 | 35pf multi | .35 | .25 |
| **2311** | A698 | 85pf multi | 2.60 | 1.90 |
| | | Nos. 2308-2311 (4) | 3.45 | 2.65 |

 A699

| 1982, Nov. 23 | | Litho. | Perf. 14 | |
|---|---|---|---|---|
| **2312** | A699 | Sheet of 6 | 3.00 | 3.00 |
| a. | | 10pf Toy Carpenter, 1830 | .25 | .25 |
| b. | | 20pf Cobbler | .90 | .90 |
| c. | | 25pf Baker | .25 | .25 |
| d. | | 35pf Cooper | .90 | .90 |
| e. | | 40pf Tanner | .90 | .90 |
| f. | | 70pf Carter | .25 | .25 |

### Souvenir Sheet

  Johannes Brahms (1833-1897), Composer — A700

| 1983, Jan. 11 | | Litho. | Perf. 14 | |
|---|---|---|---|---|
| **2313** | A700 | 1.15m multi | 2.25 | 4.00 |

### Working-class Leader Type of 1979

No. 2314, Franz Dahlem (1892-1981). No. 2315, Karl Maron (1903-75). No. 2316, Josef Miller (1883-1964). No. 2317, Fred Oelssner (1903-77). No. 2318, Siegfried Radel (1893-1943).

| 1983, Jan. 25 | | | Photo. | |
|---|---|---|---|---|
| **2314** | A623 | 10pf dark brown | .25 | .25 |
| **2315** | A623 | 10pf dark green | .25 | .25 |
| **2316** | A623 | 10pf dark olive grn | .25 | .25 |
| **2317** | A623 | 10pf deep plum | .25 | .25 |
| **2318** | A623 | 10pf dark blue | .25 | .25 |
| | | Nos. 2314-2318 (5) | 1.25 | 1.25 |

 World Communications Year — A701

5pf, Telephone receiver, buttons. 10pf, Rugen radio. 20pf, Surface and air mail. 35pf, Optical conductors.

| 1983, Feb. 8 | | Photo. | Perf. 14 | |
|---|---|---|---|---|
| **2319** | A701 | 5pf multicolored | .25 | .25 |
| **2320** | A701 | 10pf multicolored | .25 | .25 |
| **2321** | A701 | 20pf multicolored | .25 | .25 |
| **2322** | A701 | 35pf multicolored | 1.10 | .60 |
| | | Nos. 2319-2322 (4) | 1.85 | 1.35 |

 Otto Nuschke (1883-1957), Statesman — A702

| 1983, Feb. 8 | | | | |
|---|---|---|---|---|
| **2323** | A702 | 20pf red brn, bl & blk | .40 | .25 |

 Town Hall, Gera, 1576 — A703

10pf, Stolberg, 1482, horiz. 25pf, Possneck, 1486. 35pf, Berlin, 1869, horiz.

| 1983, Feb. 22 | | Photo. | Perf. 14 | |
|---|---|---|---|---|
| **2324** | A703 | 10pf multi | .25 | .25 |
| **2325** | A703 | 20pf shown | .25 | .25 |
| **2326** | A703 | 25pf multi | .25 | .25 |
| **2327** | A703 | 35pf multi | 1.10 | .85 |
| | | Nos. 2324-2327 (4) | 1.85 | 1.60 |

 1983 Leipzig Spring Fair — A704

10pf, Fair building. 25pf, Robotron microcomputer.

| 1983, Mar. 8 | | | | |
|---|---|---|---|---|
| **2328** | A704 | 10pf multi | .25 | .25 |
| **2329** | A704 | 25pf multi | .35 | .25 |

Paul Robeson (1898-1976), Singer — A705

**1983, Mar. 22   Litho.   Perf. 13x12½**
2330 A705 20pf multicolored .30 .25

**Souvenir Sheet**

Schulze-Boysen/Harnack Resistance Org. — A706

Arvid Harnack (1901-42), Harro Schulze-Boysen (1909-42), John Sieg (1903-42).

**1983, Mar. 22**
2331 A706 85pf multicolored 1.20 2.00

Karl Marx (1818-1883), and Newspaper Mastheads A707

Portraits and: 20pf, Lyons silk weavers' revolt, 1831, French-German Yearbook. 35pf, Engels, Communist Manifesto. 50pf, Das Kapital titlepage. 70pf, Program of German Workers' Movement text. 85pf, Engels, Lenin, globe. 1.15m Portrait (24x29mm).

**1983, Apr. 11   Photo.   Perf. 13x12½**
2332 A707 10pf multicolored .25 .25
2333 A707 20pf multicolored .25 .25
2334 A707 35pf multicolored .25 .25
2335 A707 50pf multicolored .25 .25
2336 A707 70pf multicolored .40 .25
2337 A707 85pf multicolored 2.00 2.00
    Nos. 2332-2337 (6) 3.40 3.25

**Souvenir Sheet**
**Litho.   Perf. 14**
2338 A707 1.15m multi 2.00 3.25

Works of Art from Berlin State Museums — A708

**1983, Apr. 19   Photo.   Perf. 14**
2339 A708 10pf Athena .25 .25
2340 A708 20pf Amazon, bronze, 430 BC .35 .25

Narrow-Gauge Railroads A709

No. 2341, Wernigerode-Nordhausen line. No. 2342, Zittau-Oybin/Johnsdorf line.

**1983, May 17   Litho.   Perf. 13x12½**
2341 Pair 1.25 1.00
  a. A709 15pf Locomotive .35 .35
  b. A709 20pf Passenger car .35 .35
2342 Pair 1.25 1.00
  a. A709 20pf Locomotive .35 .35
  b. A709 50pf Freight car .35 .35

Nos. 2341 and 2342 se-tenant with labels showing maps. See Nos. 2405-2406.

Sand Glasses and Sundials — A710

5pf, Sand glass, 1674. 10pf, Sand glass, 1700. 20pf, Sundial, 1611. 30pf, Sundial, 1750. 50pf, Sundial, 1760. 85pf, Sundial, 1800.

**1983, June 7   Photo.   Perf. 14**
2343 A710 5pf multi .25 .25
2344 A710 10pf multi .25 .25
2345 A710 20pf multi .25 .25
  a. Sheet of 8 2.00 2.00
2346 A710 30pf multi .25 .25
2347 A710 50pf multi .35 .25
2348 A710 85pf multi 2.10 2.00
    Nos. 2343-2348 (6) 3.45 3.25

Cacti — A711

5pf, Coryphantha elephantidens. 10pf, Thelocactus schwarzii. 20pf, Leuchtenbergia principis. 25pf, Submatucana madisoniorum. 35pf, Oroya peruviana. 50pf, Copiapoa cinerea.

**1983, June 21**
2349 A711 5pf multicolored .25 .25
2350 A711 10pf multicolored .25 .25
2351 A711 20pf multicolored .25 .25
2352 A711 25pf multicolored .25 .25
2353 A711 35pf multicolored .25 .25
2354 A711 50pf multicolored 1.25 1.20
    Nos. 2349-2354 (6) 2.50 2.45

Naumberg Cathedral Statues, 15th Cent. — A712

20pf, Thimo and Wilhelm. 25pf, Gepa and Gerburg. 35pf, Hermann and Reglindis. 85pf, Eckehard and Uta.

**1983, July 5   Photo.   Perf. 13**
2355 A712 20pf multicolored .35 .35
2356 A712 25pf multicolored .40 .40
2357 A712 35pf multicolored .45 .45
2358 A712 85pf multicolored 1.10 1.10
  a. Block of 4, #2355-2358 3.00 2.25

Technical Training, by Harald Metzkes (b. 1929) — A713

SOZPHILEX '83 Junior Stamp Exhibition, Berlin: 10pf+5pf, Glasewaldt and Zinna Defending the Barricade-18th March, 1848, by Theodor Hosemann, vert. Surtax was for exhibition.

**1983, July 5   Litho.   Perf. 13x12½**
2359 A713 10pf + 5pf multi .55 .45
2360 A713 20pf multi .25 .25

Volleyball — A714

**1983, July 19   Photo.   Perf. 14**
2361 A714 10pf + 5pf Passing beach balls .50 .40
2362 A714 20pf shown .25 .25

7th Gymnastic and Sports Meeting; 9th Children's and Youth Spartikiade, Leipzig.

Simon Bolivar (1783-1830) A715

35pf, Bolivar, Alexander von Humboldt.

**1983, July 19**
2363 A715 35pf multicolored .45 .30

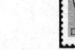

A715a      A716

City Arms

**1983, Aug. 9**
2364 A715a 50pf Berlin .65 .55
2365 A716 50pf Cottbus .65 .55
2366 A716 50pf Dresden .65 .55
2367 A716 50pf Erfurt .65 .55
2368 A716 50pf Frankfurt .65 .55
    Nos. 2364-2368 (5) 3.25 2.75

See Nos. 2398-2402, 2464-2468.

1983 Leipzig Autumn Fair — A717

10pf, Central Palace. 25pf, Microelectronic pattern.

**1983, Aug. 30**
2369 A717 10pf multicolored .25 .25
2370 A717 25pf multicolored .40 .25

Leonhard Euler (1707-1783), Mathematician A718

**1983, Sept. 6**
2371 A718 20pf multi .40 .25

**Souvenir Sheet**

30th Anniv. of Working-Class Brigade Groups — A719

**1983, Sept. 6   Litho.   Perf. 12½x13**
2372 A719 1m multicolored 1.90 2.25

Governmental Palaces, Potsdam Gardens — A720

10pf, Sanssouci Palace. 20pf, Chinese teahouse. 40pf, Charlottenhof Palace. 50pf, Royal Stables, Film Museum.

**1983, Sept. 20   Perf. 13x12½**
2373 A720 10pf multicolored .25 .25
2374 A720 20pf multicolored .25 .25
2375 A720 40pf multicolored .35 .25
2376 A720 50pf multicolored 2.00 2.00
    Nos. 2373-2376 (4) 2.85 2.75

Monument, Mamajew-Kurgan Hill — A721

**1983, Oct. 4   Perf. 14**
2377 A721 35pf Mother Home .40 .25

**Souvenir Sheet**

Martin Luther A722

**1983, Oct. 18   Litho.   Perf. 14**
2378 A722 1m multi 2.25 4.00

Margin shows title page from Luther Bible, 1541.

Thuringian Glass — A723

**1983, Nov. 8   Photo.   Perf. 13½x14**
2379 A723 10pf Cock .25 .25
2380 A723 20pf Cup .25 .25
2381 A723 25pf Vase .25 .25
2382 A723 70pf Ornamental Glass 1.60 1.25
    Nos. 2379-2382 (4) 2.35 2.00

**Souvenir Sheet**

New Year 1984 — A724

**1983, Nov. 22   Litho.   Perf. 14**
2383 A724 Sheet of 4 1.50 3.25
  a. 10pf multi .25 .25
  b. 20pf multi .25 .35
  c. 25pf multi .35 .65
  d. 35pf multi .45 .80

Winter Olympics 1984, Sarajevo A725

**1983, Nov. 22   Photo.   Perf. 14**
2384 A725 10pf + 5pf 2-man luge .25 .25
2385 A725 20pf + 10pf Ski jump .25 .25
2386 A725 25pf Skiing .25 .25
2387 A725 35pf Biathlon 1.25 .85
    Nos. 2384-2387 (4) 2.00 1.60

**Souvenir Sheet**
2388 A725 85pf Olympic Center 1.50 3.00

Jena Glass Centenary — A726

**1984, Jan. 10   Litho.   Perf. 12½x13**
2389 A726 20pf Otto Schott .35 .25

## Working-class Leader Type of 1979

Designs: No. 2390, Friedrich Ebert (1894-1979). No. 2391, Fritz Grosse (1904-1957). No. 2392, Albert Norden (1904-1982).

| | | | | |
|---|---|---|---|---|
| **1984, Jan. 24** | | **Engr.** | **Perf. 14** | |
| 2390 | A623 | 10pf black | .25 | .25 |
| 2391 | A623 | 10pf dark green | .25 | .25 |
| 2392 | A623 | 10pf dark blue | .25 | .25 |
| | | Nos. 2390-2392 (3) | .75 | .75 |

### Souvenir Sheet

Felix Mendelssohn (1809-1847), Composer — A727

| | | | | |
|---|---|---|---|---|
| **1984, Jan. 24** | | | **Litho.** | |
| 2393 | A727 | 85pf multi | .90 | 1.60 |

Margin shows Song Without Words score.

Postal Milestones — A728

Designs: 10pf, Muhlau, 1725; Oederan, 1722. 20pf, Johanngeorgenstadt, 1723; Schonbrunn, 1724. 35pf, Freiberg, 1723. 85pf, Pegau, 1723.

| | | | | |
|---|---|---|---|---|
| **1984, Feb. 7** | | **Photo.** | **Perf. 14** | |
| 2394 | A728 | 10pf multi | .25 | .25 |
| 2395 | A728 | 20pf multi | .30 | .25 |
| 2396 | A728 | 35pf multi | .35 | .30 |
| 2397 | A728 | 85pf multi | .65 | .65 |
| | | Nos. 2394-2397 (4) | 1.55 | 1.45 |

### City Arms Type of 1983

| | | | | |
|---|---|---|---|---|
| **1984, Feb. 21** | | | | |
| 2398 | A716 | 50pf Gera | .40 | .35 |
| 2399 | A716 | 50pf Halle | .40 | .35 |
| 2400 | A716 | 50pf Karl-Marx-Stadt | .40 | .35 |
| 2401 | A716 | 50pf Leipzig | .40 | .35 |
| 2402 | A716 | 50pf Magdeburg | .40 | .35 |
| | | Nos. 2398-2402 (5) | 2.00 | 1.75 |

1984 Leipzig Spring Fair — A729

| | | | | |
|---|---|---|---|---|
| **1984, Mar. 6** | | | **Perf. 14** | |
| 2403 | A729 | 10pf Old Town Hall | .25 | .25 |
| 2404 | A729 | 25pf Factory | .30 | .25 |

### Railroad Type of 1983

No. 2405: Cranzahl Oberwiesenthal Line — a, Locomotive. b, Passenger car. No. 2406: Selke Valley Line — a, Locomotive. b, Passenger car.

| | | | | |
|---|---|---|---|---|
| **1984, Mar. 20** | | **Litho.** | **Perf. 13x12½** | |
| 2405 | | Pair | 1.25 | 1.10 |
| a. | A709 | 30pf multi | .25 | .25 |
| b. | A709 | 80pf multi | .55 | .55 |
| 2406 | | Pair | 1.25 | .90 |
| a. | A709 | 40pf multi | .30 | .30 |
| b. | A709 | 60pf multi | .35 | .35 |

Labels show maps of routes.

Stone Door, Rostock — A730

Intl. Society of Monument Preservation 7th General Meeting: 10pf, Town Hall, Rostock. 15pf, Albrecht Castle, Meissen. 85pf, Stable Courtyard, Dresden. 10pf, 15pf, 85pf horiz.

| | | | | |
|---|---|---|---|---|
| **1984, Apr. 24** | | **Photo.** | **Perf. 14** | |
| 2407 | A730 | 10pf multi | .25 | .25 |
| 2408 | A730 | 15pf multi | .25 | .25 |
| 2409 | A730 | 40pf multi | .40 | .30 |
| 2410 | A730 | 85pf multi | 1.00 | .85 |
| | | Nos. 2407-2410 (4) | 1.90 | 1.65 |

Council Building — A731

| | | | | |
|---|---|---|---|---|
| **1984, May 8** | | | | |
| 2411 | A731 | 70pf multi | .70 | .30 |

Standing Commission of Posts and Telecommunications of Council of Mutual Economic Aid, 25th meeting.

Cast-iron Bowl, 19th Cent. — A732

Cast-Iron, Lauchhammer: 85pf, Ascending Man, by Fritz Cremer, 1967.

| | | | | |
|---|---|---|---|---|
| **1984, May 22** | | | | |
| 2412 | A732 | 20pf multi | .25 | .25 |
| 2413 | A732 | 85pf multi | .70 | .70 |

Marionette — A733

| | | | | |
|---|---|---|---|---|
| **1984, June 5** | | | | |
| 2414 | A733 | 50pf shown | .45 | .45 |
| 2415 | A733 | 80pf Puppet | .70 | .70 |

Natl. Youth Festival — A734

10pf + 5pf, Demonstration. 20pf, Construction workers.

| | | | | |
|---|---|---|---|---|
| **1984, June 5** | **Litho.** | | **Perf. 13x12½** | |
| 2416 | | 10pf + 5pf multi | .25 | .25 |
| 2417 | | 20pf multicolored | .25 | .25 |
| a. | | A734 Pair, #2416-2417 + label | 1.00 | .55 |

20th Workers' Festival — A735

| | | | | |
|---|---|---|---|---|
| **1984, June 19** | | | | |
| 2418 | | 10pf View of Gera | .25 | .25 |
| 2419 | | 20pf Traditional costumes | .25 | .25 |
| a. | | A735 Pair, #2418-2419 + label | .80 | .55 |

Natl. Stamp Exhib., Halle — A736

| | | | | |
|---|---|---|---|---|
| **1984, July 3** | | | **Perf. 13½x14** | |
| 2420 | A736 | 10pf + 5pf Salt carrier | .25 | .25 |
| 2421 | A736 | 20pf Wedding couple | .30 | .25 |

Historic Seals, 1442 — A737

5pf, Baker, Berlin. 10pf, Wool weaver, Berlin. 20pf, Wool weaver, Cologne. 35pf, Shoemaker, Cologne.

| | | | | |
|---|---|---|---|---|
| **1984, Aug. 7** | | **Litho.** | **Perf. 14** | |
| 2422 | A737 | 5pf multi | .30 | .25 |
| 2423 | A737 | 10pf multi | .45 | .30 |
| 2424 | A737 | 20pf multi | .85 | .35 |
| 2425 | A737 | 35pf multi | 1.40 | 1.25 |
| a. | | Block of 4, #2422-2425 | 4.25 | 3.25 |

Building Renovation and Construction — A738

Ironwork Collective Combine East — A739

No. 2428, Surface mining. No. 2429, Armed forces. No. 2430, Petro-chemical Collective Combine, Schwedt.
No. 2431, Privy Council Building. No. 2432, Family.

| | | | | |
|---|---|---|---|---|
| **Litho., Photo. (#2427, 2429, 25pf)** | | | | |
| **1984** | | | **Perf. 14x13½** | |
| 2426 | A738 | 10pf shown | .25 | .25 |
| 2427 | A739 | 10pf shown | .25 | .25 |
| 2428 | A738 | 20pf multicolored | .30 | .30 |
| 2429 | A739 | 20pf multicolored | .25 | .25 |
| 2430 | A739 | 25pf multicolored | .30 | .30 |
| | | Nos. 2426-2430 (5) | 1.35 | 1.35 |

### Souvenir Sheets

| | | | | |
|---|---|---|---|---|
| 2431 | A738 | 1m multicolored | 1.00 | 2.00 |
| 2432 | A739 | 1m multicolored | 1.00 | 2.00 |

DDR, 35th anniv. Issued: A738, 8/21; A739, 9/11.

1984 Leipzig Autumn Fair — A740

10pf, Frege House, Katharine St. 25pf, Crystal bowl, Olbernhau.

| | | | | |
|---|---|---|---|---|
| **1984, Aug. 28** | | **Photo.** | **Perf. 14** | |
| 2433 | A740 | 10pf multicolored | .25 | .25 |
| 2434 | A740 | 25pf multicolored | .30 | .25 |

Members of the Resistance, Sculpture by Arno Wittig — A741

| | | | | |
|---|---|---|---|---|
| **1984, Sept. 18** | | **Photo.** | **Perf. 14** | |
| 2435 | A741 | 35pf multi | .60 | .30 |

A742

No. 2436, View of Magdeburg. No. 2437, Old & modern buildings.

| | | | | |
|---|---|---|---|---|
| **1984, Oct. 4** | | **Litho.** | **Perf. 13x12½** | |
| 2436 | | 10pf + 5pf multi | .25 | .25 |
| 2437 | | 20pf multi | .25 | .25 |
| a. | | A742 Pair, #2436-2437 + label | .90 | .65 |

8th Youth Stamp Exhibition, Magdeburg.

35th Anniv. of Republic A743

10pf, Construction. 20pf, Military. 25pf, Heavy industry. 35pf, Agriculture.

1m, Arms, dove, vert.

| | | | | |
|---|---|---|---|---|
| **1984, Oct. 4** | | **Photo.** | **Perf. 14** | |
| 2438 | A743 | 10pf multicolored | .25 | .25 |
| 2439 | A743 | 20pf multicolored | .25 | .25 |
| 2440 | A743 | 25pf multicolored | .30 | .25 |
| 2441 | A743 | 35pf multicolored | .35 | .35 |
| | | Nos. 2438-2441 (4) | 1.15 | 1.15 |

### Souvenir Sheet

| | | | | |
|---|---|---|---|---|
| 2442 | A743 | 1m multicolored | .90 | 2.00 |

Figurines, Green Vault of Dresden — A744

| | | | | |
|---|---|---|---|---|
| **1984, Oct. 23** | | | | |
| 2443 | A744 | 10pf Spring | .25 | .25 |
| 2444 | A744 | 20pf Summer | .25 | .25 |
| a. | | Miniature sheet of 8, litho., perf. 12½x13 | 2.10 | 2.10 |
| 2445 | A744 | 35pf Autumn | .30 | .30 |
| 2446 | A744 | 70pf Winter | .65 | .65 |
| | | Nos. 2443-2446 (4) | 1.45 | 1.45 |

Falkenstein Castle — A745

| | | | | |
|---|---|---|---|---|
| **1984, Nov. 6** | | **Litho.** | **Perf. 14** | |
| 2447 | A745 | 10pf shown | .25 | .25 |
| 2448 | A745 | 20pf Kriebstein | .25 | .25 |
| 2449 | A745 | 35pf Ranis | .55 | .40 |
| 2450 | A745 | 80pf Neuenburg | .80 | .65 |
| | | Nos. 2447-2450 (4) | 1.85 | 1.55 |

See Nos. 2504-2507.

Dead Tsar's Daughter and the Seven Warriors A746

Various scenes from the fairytale.

| | | | | |
|---|---|---|---|---|
| **1984, Nov. 27** | | **Litho.** | **Perf. 13** | |
| 2451 | A746 | Sheet of 6 | 8.50 | 4.00 |
| a. | | 5pf multi | .35 | .35 |
| b. | | 10pf multi | .35 | .35 |
| c. | | 15pf multi | 2.25 | 1.25 |
| d. | | 20pf multi | 2.25 | 1.25 |
| e. | | 35pf multi | .35 | .35 |
| f. | | 50pf multi | .35 | .25 |

### Working-class Leader Type of 1979

Designs: No. 2452, Anton Ackermann (1905-1973). No. 2453, Alfred Kurella (1895-1975). No. 2454, Otto Schon (1905-1968).

| | | | | |
|---|---|---|---|---|
| **1985, Jan. 8** | | **Engr.** | **Perf. 14** | |
| 2452 | A623 | 10pf blk brn | .25 | .25 |
| 2453 | A623 | 10pf red brn | .25 | .25 |
| 2454 | A623 | 10pf gray vio | .25 | .25 |
| | | Nos. 2452-2454 (3) | .75 | .75 |

24th World Luge Championship A747

| | | | | |
|---|---|---|---|---|
| **1985, Jan. 22** | | | **Photo.** | |
| 2455 | A747 | 10pf Single seat luge | .30 | .25 |

Antique Mailboxes — A748

**1985, Feb. 5**    **Litho.**    **Perf. 14**

| 2456 | A748 | 10pf | 1850 | .25 | .25 |
|---|---|---|---|---|---|
| 2457 | A748 | 20pf | 1860 | .25 | .25 |
| 2458 | A748 | 35pf | 1900 | .30 | .30 |
| 2459 | A748 | 50pf | 1920 | .40 | .40 |
| a. | Block of 4, Nos. 2456-2459 | | | 1.20 | 1.60 |

**Souvenir Sheet**

Dresden Opera House
Reopening — A749

**1985, Feb. 12**    **Litho. & Engr.**    **Perf. 13**

| 2460 | A749 | 85pf multicolored | .85 | 1.50 |
|---|---|---|---|---|

1985 Leipzig Spring
Fair — A750

10pf, Statue of Bach, Leipzig. 25pf, Porcelain pot, Meissen.

**1985, Mar. 5**    **Photo.**    **Perf. 14**

| 2461 | A750 | 10pf multicolored | .25 | .25 |
|---|---|---|---|---|
| 2462 | A750 | 25pf multicolored | .30 | .25 |

**Souvenir Sheet**

Bach, Handel and Schutz
Tribute — A751

a, Bach. b, Handel. c, Heinrich Schutz
(1585-1672).

**1985, Mar. 19**    **Litho.**

| 2463 | A751 | Sheet of 3 | 2.00 | 3.00 |
|---|---|---|---|---|
| a. | 10pf multicolored | | .50 | .65 |
| b. | 20pf multicolored | | .50 | .65 |
| c. | 85pf multicolored | | .65 | 1.25 |

**City Arms Type of 1983**

**1985, Apr. 9**    **Photo.**    **Perf. 14**

| 2464 | A716 | 50pf Neubrandenburg | .40 | .35 |
|---|---|---|---|---|
| 2465 | A716 | 50pf Potsdam | .40 | .35 |
| 2466 | A716 | 50pf Rostock | .40 | .35 |
| 2467 | A716 | 50pf Schwerin | .40 | .35 |
| 2468 | A716 | 50pf Suhl | .65 | .65 |
| | Nos. 2464-2468 (5) | | 2.25 | 2.05 |

Seelow Heights
Memorial — A752

**1985, Apr. 16**    **Photo.**    **Perf. 14**

| 2469 | A752 | 35pf multi | .40 | .30 |
|---|---|---|---|---|

Egon Erwin
Kisch, Journalist
(1885-1948)
A753

**1985, Apr. 23**    **Photo.**    **Perf. 14**

| 2470 | A753 | 35pf multi | .30 | .25 |
|---|---|---|---|---|

No. 2470 was printed se-tenant with label
showing the house where Kisch was born.
Value, single with attached label: unused 50c;
used 40c.

Liberation from
Fascism, 40th
Anniv. — A754

Designs: 10pf, German and Soviet astronauts. 20pf, Coal miner Adolf Hennecke, symbols of industry and energy. 25pf, farm workers, symbols of socialist agriculture. 50pf, Technicians manufacturing microchips, science and technology.

1m, Berlin-Treptow Soviet Heroes
Monument.

**1985, May 7**    **Photo.**    **Perf. 14x13½**

| 2471 | A754 | 10pf multi | .25 | .25 |
|---|---|---|---|---|
| 2472 | A754 | 20pf multi | .30 | .30 |
| 2473 | A754 | 25pf multi | .30 | .30 |
| 2474 | A754 | 50pf multi | .40 | .40 |
| | Nos. 2471-2474 (4) | | 1.25 | 1.25 |

**Souvenir Sheet**
**Perf. 12½x13**

| 2475 | A754 | 1m multi | 1.00 | 2.00 |
|---|---|---|---|---|

Warsaw
Treaty,
30th
Anniv.
A755

20pf, Flags of pact nations.

**1985, May 14**    **Litho.**    **Perf. 13x12½**

| 2476 | A755 | 20pf multi | .35 | .25 |
|---|---|---|---|---|

Historical and Modern
Buildings — A756

12th Youth Parliament, Berlin: 20pf, Ernst
Thalmann, flags.

**1985, May 21**    **Litho.**

| 2477 | A756 | 10pf + 5pf multi | .25 | .25 |
|---|---|---|---|---|
| 2478 | A756 | 20pf multi | .25 | .25 |
| a. | Pair, #2477-2478 + label | | .55 | .55 |

Intl.
Olympic
Committee
90th
Meeting
A757

**1985, May 28**    **Litho.**    **Perf. 14**

| 2479 | A757 | 35pf Flag | .45 | .25 |
|---|---|---|---|---|

No. 2479 was printed setenant with label
depicting Olympic Torches. Value of single
with attached label: unused 85c; used 65c.

Free German Trade
Unions, 40th
Anniv. — A758

**1985, June 11**    **Photo.**

| 2480 | A758 | 20pf Red flags | .30 | .25 |
|---|---|---|---|---|

Wildlife
Preservation — A759

5pf, Harpy eagle, vert. 10pf, Red-necked
goose. 20pf, Spectacled bear. 50pf, Banteng
(Javanese) buffalo. 85pf, Sunda Straits
crocodile.

**1985, June 25**    **Photo.**

| 2481 | A759 | 5pf multicolored | .25 | .25 |
|---|---|---|---|---|
| 2482 | A759 | 10pf multicolored | .25 | .25 |
| 2483 | A759 | 20pf multicolored | .25 | .25 |
| 2484 | A759 | 50pf multicolored | .40 | .35 |
| 2485 | A759 | 85pf multicolored | .80 | .80 |
| | Nos. 2481-2485 (5) | | 1.95 | 1.90 |

19th Century
Steam
Engines — A760

10pf, Bock engine, vert. 85pf, Beam engine.

**1985, July 9**    **Photo.**

| 2486 | A760 | 10pf multicolored | .25 | .25 |
|---|---|---|---|---|
| 2487 | A760 | 85pf multicolored | .70 | .65 |

12th World Youth and Student Festival,
Moscow — A761

20pf + 5pf, Students reading. 50pf, Student
demonstration.

**1985, July 23**    **Litho.**    **Perf. 13x12½**

| 2488 | | 20pf + 5pf multi | .25 | .25 |
|---|---|---|---|---|
| 2489 | | 50pf multicolored | .35 | .35 |
| a. | A761 Pair, #2488-2489 + label | | .85 | .80 |

2nd World Orienteering and Deep-sea
Diving Championship — A762

10pf, Diver at turning buoy. 70pf, Long-distance divers.

**1985, Aug. 13**    **Photo.**    **Perf. 14**

| 2490 | A762 | 10pf multicolored | .25 | .25 |
|---|---|---|---|---|
| 2491 | A762 | 70pf multicolored | .65 | .65 |

Bose House Fair
Building, St. Thomas
Churchyard — A763

**1985, Aug. 27**    **Photo.**

| 2492 | A763 | 10pf shown | .25 | .25 |
|---|---|---|---|---|
| 2493 | A763 | 25pf Bach trumpet | .35 | .25 |

Leipzig Autumn Fair.

A764

SOZPHILEX '85: 19th century coach and
team, 1878, bas-relief by Hermann
Steinemann, in the court of the former Berlin
Post Office.

**1985, Sept. 10**    **Litho.**    **Perf. 13x12½**

| 2494 | | 5pf multi | .25 | .25 |
|---|---|---|---|---|
| 2495 | | 20pf + 5pf multi | .25 | .25 |
| a. | Miniature sheet of 4 #2495b | | .75 | .75 |
| b. | A764 Pair, #2494-2495 | | .45 | .45 |

No. 2495b has a continuous design.

German Railways 150th
Anniv. — A765

Socialist Railway Org.: 20pf, GS II signal
box, track diagram. 25pf, 1838 Saxonia, first
German locomotive, designer Johann
Andreas Schubert (1808-1870), Model 250
electric locomotive. 50pf, Helicopter lifting
cable drum, section electrification. 85pf, Leipzig Central Station.

**Litho.**
**Perf. 12½x13**

**1985, Sept. 24**

| 2496 | A765 | 20pf multi | .25 | .25 |
|---|---|---|---|---|
| 2497 | A765 | 25pf multi | .30 | .25 |
| 2498 | A765 | 50pf multi | .55 | .45 |
| 2499 | A765 | 85pf multi | .80 | .80 |
| | Nos. 2496-2499 (4) | | 1.90 | 1.75 |

Bridges in East
Berlin — A766

**Photo.; Litho. (#2501a)**

**1985, Oct. 8**    **Perf. 14**

| 2500 | A766 | 10pf Gertrauden | .25 | .25 |
|---|---|---|---|---|
| 2501 | A766 | 20pf Jungfern | .25 | .25 |
| a. | Min. sheet of 8, perf. 13x12½ | | 2.60 | 2.60 |
| 2502 | A766 | 35pf Weidendamm | .35 | .35 |
| 2503 | A766 | 70pf Marx-Engels | .55 | .55 |
| | Nos. 2500-2503 (4) | | 1.40 | 1.40 |

**Castles Type of 1984**

**1985, Oct. 15**    **Litho.**

| 2504 | A745 | 10pf Hohnstein | .25 | .25 |
|---|---|---|---|---|
| 2505 | A745 | 20pf Rochsburg | .25 | .25 |
| 2506 | A745 | 35pf Schwarzenberg | .30 | .30 |
| 2507 | A745 | 80pf Stein | .80 | .80 |
| | Nos. 2504-2507 (4) | | 1.60 | 1.60 |

Humboldt University,
175th Anniv. — A767

20pf, Administration building. 85pf, Charité
Hospital, Berlin, 275th anniv., buildings, 1897,
1982.

**1985, Oct. 22**    **Perf. 14**

| 2508 | A767 | 20pf multicolored | .30 | .25 |
|---|---|---|---|---|
| 2509 | A767 | 85pf multicolored | .80 | .80 |

Castle
Cacilienhof, UN
Emblem — A768

**1985, Oct. 22**    **Photo.**    **Perf. 13**

| 2510 | A768 | 85pf multi | .80 | .40 |
|---|---|---|---|---|

UN, 40th Anniv.

Circus Art — A769

10pf, Elephant training. 20pf, Trapeze artist.
35pf, Acrobats on unicycles. 50pf, Tiger
training.

**1985, Nov. 12**     **Perf. 14**
| | | | | |
|---|---|---|---|---|
| 2511 | A769 | 10pf multicolored | .30 | .30 |
| 2512 | A769 | 20pf multicolored | .40 | .40 |
| 2513 | A769 | 35pf multicolored | .80 | .80 |
| 2514 | A769 | 50pf multicolored | 1.10 | 1.10 |
| a. | | Block of 4, #2511-2514 | 5.00 | 11.00 |

### Souvenir Sheet

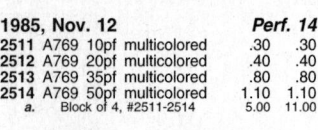

Brothers Grimm, Fabulists & Philologists — A770

Fairy tales compiled by Wilhelm (1786-1859) and Jacob (1785-1863) Grimm.

**1985, Nov. 26**    **Litho.**    **Perf. 13½x13**
| | | | | |
|---|---|---|---|---|
| 2515 | A770 | Sheet of 6 | 2.50 | 6.50 |
| a. | | 5pf Wilhelm & Jacob Grimm | .25 | .25 |
| b. | | 10pf Valiant Tailor | .25 | .25 |
| c. | | 20pf Lucky John | .45 | 1.25 |
| d. | | 25pf Puss-in-Boots | .45 | 1.25 |
| e. | | 35pf Seven Ravens | .25 | .25 |
| f. | | 85pf Sweet Porridge | .25 | .25 |

Monuments to Water Power — A772

Designs: 10pf, Cast iron hand pump, c. 1900. 35pf, Berlin-Altglienicke water tower, c. 1900. 50pf, Berlin-Friedrichshagen waterworks, 1893. 70pf, Rapphoden Hydro-electric Dam, 1959.

### Engr., Photo. & Engr. (35pf)
**1986, Jan. 21**     **Perf. 14**
| | | | | |
|---|---|---|---|---|
| 2516 | A772 | 10pf dk grn & lake | .25 | .25 |
| 2517 | A772 | 35pf buff, blk & dk grn | .30 | .30 |
| 2518 | A772 | 50pf dk red brn & lt ol grn | .45 | .45 |
| 2519 | A772 | 70pf dk bl & brn | .60 | .60 |
| | | Nos. 2516-2519 (4) | 1.60 | 1.60 |

Postal Uniforms, c. 1850 — A773

10pf, Saxon postillion. 20pf, Prussian postman. 85pf, Prussian P.O. clerk. 1m, Mecklenburg clerk.

**1986, Feb. 4**    **Photo.**    **Perf. 14**
| | | | | |
|---|---|---|---|---|
| 2520 | A773 | 10pf multicolored | .25 | .25 |
| a. | | Litho., perf. 12½x13 | .25 | .25 |
| 2521 | A773 | 20pf multicolored | .35 | .25 |
| a. | | Litho., perf. 12½x13 | .30 | .25 |
| 2522 | A773 | 85pf multicolored | .90 | .85 |
| a. | | Litho., perf. 12½x13 | .90 | .85 |
| 2523 | A773 | 1m multicolored | 1.20 | 1.20 |
| a. | | Litho., perf. 12½x13 | 1.20 | 1.20 |

Natl. People's Army, 30th Anniv. — A774

**1986, Feb. 18**     **Perf. 14**
| | | | | |
|---|---|---|---|---|
| 2524 | A774 | 20pf multi | .45 | .30 |

No. 2524 printed se-tenant with gold and red inscribed label. Value of single with attached label: unused 80c; used 45c.

Free German Youth Org., 40th Anniv. — A775

**1986, Feb. 18**
| | | | | |
|---|---|---|---|---|
| 2525 | A775 | 20pf multi | .40 | .30 |

Leipzig Spring Fair — A776

35pf, Fair grounds entrance, 1946. 50pf, Trawler Atlantik 488.

**1986, Mar. 11**    **Litho.**    **Perf. 13x12½**
| | | | | |
|---|---|---|---|---|
| 2526 | A776 | 35pf multicolored | .30 | .25 |
| 2527 | A776 | 50pf multicolored | .40 | .35 |

Manned Space Flight, 25th Anniv. A777

Designs: 40pf, Yuri Gagarin, Soviet cosmonaut, Vostok rocket, 1961. 50pf, Cosmonauts V. Bykowski, USSR, and S. Jahn, DDR, Vega probe, 1986, Intercosmos emblem. 70pf, Venera probe, Venus, spectrometer. 85pf, MKF-6 multi-spectral reconnaissance camera.

**1986, Mar. 25**     **Perf. 14**
| | | | | |
|---|---|---|---|---|
| 2528 | A777 | 40pf multi | .30 | .40 |
| 2529 | A777 | 50pf multi | .35 | .40 |
| 2530 | A777 | 70pf multi | .45 | .55 |
| 2531 | A777 | 85pf multi | .60 | .65 |
| a. | | Block of 4, #2528-2531 | 3.25 | 3.50 |

Socialist Unity 11th Party Day — A778

10pf, Marx, Engels & Lenin. 20pf, Ernst Thalmann. 50pf, Wilhelm Pieck & Otto Grotewohl, Uniting Party Day, 1946. 85pf,Family, motto. 1m, Construction worker, key to economic progress.

**1986, Apr. 8**     **Perf. 13½x13**
| | | | | |
|---|---|---|---|---|
| 2532 | A778 | 10pf multi | .25 | .25 |
| 2533 | A778 | 20pf multi | .25 | .25 |
| 2534 | A778 | 50pf multi | .40 | .40 |
| 2535 | A778 | 85pf multi | .80 | .80 |
| | | Nos. 2532-2535 (4) | 1.70 | 1.70 |

### Souvenir Sheet
**Perf. 13x14**
| | | | | |
|---|---|---|---|---|
| 2536 | A778 | 1m multi | .90 | 2.00 |

Ernst Thalmann Park Opening, Berlin — A779

**1986, Apr. 15**    **Photo.**    **Perf. 14**
| | | | | |
|---|---|---|---|---|
| 2537 | A779 | 20pf Memorial statue | .35 | .30 |

Trams and Streetcars A780

Designs: 10pf, Dresden horse-drawn tram, 1886. 20pf, Leipzig streetcar, 1896. 40pf, Berlin streetcar, 1919. 70pf, Halle streetcar, 1928.

**1986, May 20**    **Photo.**    **Perf. 14**
| | | | | |
|---|---|---|---|---|
| 2538 | A780 | 10pf multicolored | .25 | .25 |
| 2539 | A780 | 20pf multicolored | .25 | .25 |
| 2540 | A780 | 40pf multicolored | .45 | .45 |
| 2541 | A780 | 70pf multicolored | .65 | .65 |
| | | Nos. 2538-2541 (4) | 1.60 | 1.60 |

Dresden Zoo, 125th Anniv. — A781

**1986, May 27**    **Litho.**    **Perf. 14**
| | | | | |
|---|---|---|---|---|
| 2542 | A781 | 10pf Orangutan | .25 | .25 |
| 2543 | A781 | 20pf Colobus monkey | .35 | .30 |
| 2544 | A781 | 50pf Mandrill | .65 | .65 |
| 2545 | A781 | 70pf Lemur | .80 | .80 |
| | | Nos. 2542-2545 (4) | 2.05 | 2.00 |

Berlin, 750th Anniv. — A782

Designs: 10pf, City seal, 1253. 20pf, Map, 1648, horiz. 50pf, City arms, 1253, horiz. 70pf, Nicholas Church, 1832. 1m, Cabinet Council House.

### Litho. & Engr., Engr. (70pf, 1m)
**1986, June 3**    **Perf. 12½x13, 13x12½**
| | | | | |
|---|---|---|---|---|
| 2546 | A782 | 10pf multi | .25 | .25 |
| 2547 | A782 | 20pf multi | .40 | .25 |
| 2548 | A782 | 50pf multi | .80 | .55 |
| 2549 | A782 | 70pf multi | 1.25 | .85 |
| | | Nos. 2546-2549 (4) | 2.70 | 1.90 |

### Souvenir Sheet
| | | | | |
|---|---|---|---|---|
| 2550 | A782 | 1m multi | 1.10 | 1.60 |

21st Workers' Games, Magdeburg — A783

20pf, Couple in folk dress, house construction. 50pf, Magdeburg Port, River Elbe.

**1986, June 17**    **Litho.**    **Perf. 13x12½**
| | | | | |
|---|---|---|---|---|
| 2551 | | 20pf multicolored | .30 | .30 |
| 2552 | | 50pf multicolored | .30 | .30 |
| a. | | A783 Pair, #2551-2552 + label | .85 | .85 |

9th Youth Stamp Exhibition, Berlin — A784

10pf + 5pf, Berlin, c. 1652. 20pf, Art, architecture, 1986.

**1986, July 22**    **Litho.**    **Perf. 13x12½**
| | | | | |
|---|---|---|---|---|
| 2553 | | 10pf + 5pf multicolored | .25 | .25 |
| 2554 | | 20pf multicolored | .25 | .25 |
| a. | | A784 Pair, #2553-2554 + label | .55 | .65 |

Castles — A785

**1986, July 29**     **Perf. 13x12½**
| | | | | |
|---|---|---|---|---|
| 2555 | A785 | 10pf Schwerin | .25 | .25 |
| a. | | Miniature sheet of 4 | .55 | .55 |
| 2556 | A785 | 20pf Gustrow | .25 | .25 |
| a. | | Miniature sheet of 4 | .90 | .90 |
| 2557 | A785 | 85pf Rheinsberg | .80 | .80 |
| 2558 | A785 | 1m Ludwigslust | 1.00 | 1.00 |
| | | Nos. 2555-2558 (4) | 2.30 | 2.30 |

Intl. Peace Year — A786

**1986, Aug. 5**    **Photo.**    **Perf. 13**
| | | | | |
|---|---|---|---|---|
| 2559 | A786 | 35pf multi | .45 | .40 |

Berlin Wall, 25th Anniv. A787

20pf, Soldiers, Brandenburg Gate.

**1986, Aug. 5**    **Litho.**    **Perf. 14**
| | | | | |
|---|---|---|---|---|
| 2560 | A787 | 20pf multicolored | .80 | .40 |

### Souvenir Sheet

Leipzig Autumn Fair A788

**1986, Aug. 19**
| | | | | |
|---|---|---|---|---|
| 2561 | A788 | Sheet of 2 | 1.10 | 2.00 |
| a. | | 25pf Fair building | .25 | .40 |
| b. | | 85pf Cloth merchants, 15th cent. | .65 | 1.25 |

City Coins — A789

10pf, Rostock, 1637. 35pf, Nordhausen, 1660. 50pf, Erfurt, 1633. 85pf, Magdeburg, 1638. 1m, Stralsund, 1622.

**1986, Sept. 2**    **Photo.**    **Perf. 13**
| | | | | |
|---|---|---|---|---|
| 2562 | A789 | 10pf multi | .25 | .25 |
| 2563 | A789 | 35pf multi | .30 | .30 |
| 2564 | A789 | 50pf multi | .40 | .35 |
| 2565 | A789 | 85pf multi | .65 | .65 |
| 2566 | A789 | 1m multi | .90 | .90 |
| | | Nos. 2562-2566 (5) | 2.50 | 2.45 |

44th World Sports Shooting Championships, Suhl — A790

20pf, Rifle shooting. 70pf, Woman firing handgun. 85pf, Skeet-shooting.

**1986, Sept. 2**     **Perf. 14**
| | | | | |
|---|---|---|---|---|
| 2567 | A790 | 20pf multicolored | .25 | .25 |
| 2568 | A790 | 70pf multicolored | .65 | .55 |
| 2569 | A790 | 85pf multicolored | .80 | .70 |
| | | Nos. 2567-2569 (3) | 1.70 | 1.50 |

11th World Trade Unions Congress, Berlin A791

**1986, Sept. 9**
| | | | | |
|---|---|---|---|---|
| 2570 | A791 | 70pf multi + label | .45 | .45 |

Border Guards, 40th Anniv. — A792

**1986, Sept. 9**
| | | | | |
|---|---|---|---|---|
| 2571 | A792 | 20pf multi | .65 | .40 |

Intl. Brigades in Spain, 50th Anniv. — A793

20pf, Memorial, Friedrichshain.

**1986, Sept. 11**
| | | | | |
|---|---|---|---|---|
| 2572 | A793 | 20pf multicolored | .35 | .25 |

Natl. Memorial for Concentration Camp Victims, Sachsenhausem, 25th Anniv. — A794

**1986, Sept. 23**
2573 A794 35pf multicolored .40 .30

Mukran-Klaipeda Train-Ferry, Inauguration — A795

**1986, Sept. 23**
2574 A795 50pf Pier, Mukran .35 .35
2575 A795 50pf Ferry .35 .35
a. A795 Pair, #2574-2575 .70 .70

**Souvenir Sheet**

Carl Maria von Weber (1786-1826), Composer — A796

**1986, Nov. 4    Litho.    Perf. 14**
2576 A796 85pf multi 1.00 1.60

Indira Gandhi (1917-1984), Prime Minister of India — A797

**1986, Nov. 18    Photo.**
2577 A797 10pf multi .30 .25

**Miniature Sheet**

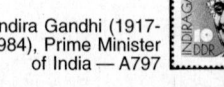

Chandeliers from the Ore Mountains — A798

Wrought iron candle-carrying chandeliers presented to Johann Georgenstadt miners annually by the mine blacksmith.

**1986, Nov. 18    Photo.    Perf. 14**
2578 A798 Sheet of 6 2.00 2.40
a. 10pf 1778 .25 .25
b. 20pf 1796 .25 .25
c. 25pf 1810 .45 .45
d. 35pf 1821 .45 .45
e. 40pf 1830 .25 .25
f. 85pf 1925 .25 .25

Statues of Roland, Medieval Hero — A799

10pf, Stendal, 1525. 20pf, Halle, 1719. 35pf, Brandenburg, 1474. 50pf, Quedlinburg, 1460.

---

**1987, Jan. 20    Photo.    Perf. 14½x14**
2579 A799 10pf multicolored .25 .25
2580 A799 20pf multicolored .25 .25
2581 A799 35pf multicolored .30 .30
2582 A799 70pf multicolored .45 .45
Nos. 2579-2582 (4) 1.25 1.25

See Nos. 2782-2785.

Historic Post Offices — A800

10pf, Freiberg, 1889. 20pf, Perleberg, 1897. 70pf, Weimar, 1889. 1.20m, Kirschau, 1926.

**1987, Feb. 3    Photo.    Perf. 14x14½**
2583 A800 10pf multi .25 .25
2584 A800 20pf multi .25 .25
2585 A800 70pf multi .45 .45
2586 A800 1.20m multi .90 .90
a. Block of 4, #2583-2586 2.00 2.00

Nos. 2583-2586 printed in sheets of fifty and se-tenant in sheets of 40.

Berlin, 750th Anniv. — A801

Architecture: 20pf, Reconstructed Palais Ephraim, Nikolai Quarter, demolished 1936, reopened 1987, vert. 35pf, Old Marzahn Village, modern housing. 70pf, Marx-Engels Forum, Central Berlin. 85pf, Reconstructed Friedrichstadt Palace Theater, reopened 1984.

**Perf. 12½x13, 13x12½**
**1987, Feb. 17    Engr.**
2587 A801 20pf vio brn & bluish grn .25 .25
2588 A801 35pf sage grn & dk rose brn .35 .25
2589 A801 70pf org & dk bl .65 .60
2590 A801 85pf dk ol grn & yel grn 1.00 .85
Nos. 2587-2590 (4) 2.25 1.95

See Nos. 2628-2631.

Democratic Women's Federation, 40th Anniv. — A802

**1987, Mar. 3    Litho.    Perf. 13½**
2591 A802 10pf sil, dk bl & brt red .30 .25

Leipzig Spring Fair — A803

35pf, New Fair Hall No. 20. 50pf, Traders at market, c. 1804.

**1987, Mar. 10    Perf. 13x12½**
2592 A803 35pf multicolored .30 .25
2593 A803 50pf multicolored .55 .55

Leaders of the German Workers' Movement — A804

No. 2594, Fritz Gabler (1897-1974). No. 2595, Robert Siewert (1887-1973). No. 2596, Walter Vesper (1897-1978). No. 2597, Clara Zetkin (1857-1933).

**1987, Mar. 24    Engr.    Perf. 14**
2594 A804 10pf brown black .25 .25
2595 A804 10pf dark green .25 .25
2596 A804 10pf blue black .25 .25
2597 A804 10pf vio black .25 .25
Nos. 2594-2597 (4) 1.00 1.00

See Nos. 2721-2724.

---

K.A. Lingner (1861-1916), Museum — A805

**1987, Apr. 7    Photo.    Perf. 14**
2598 A805 85pf multi .70 .65

German Hygiene Museum, Dresden, 75th anniv.

Free German Trade Unions 11th Congress — A806

**1987, Apr. 7    Litho.    Perf. 13x12½**
2599 20pf Construction .25 .25
2600 50pf Computer, ship .40 .40
a. A806 Pair, #2599-2600 + label .80 1.20

German Red Cross 10th Congress A807

**1987, Apr. 7    Photo.    Perf. 14**
2601 A807 35pf multi .40 .30

Agricultural Cooperative, 35th Anniv. — A808

**1987, Apr. 21    Litho.    Perf. 13x12½**
2602 A808 20pf multi .35 .30

Famous Men — A809

Designs: 10pf, Ludwig Uhland (1787-1862), poet, philologist. 20pf, Arnold Zweig (1887-1968), novelist. 35pf, Gerhart Hauptmann (1862-1946), 1912 Nobel laureate for literature, and scene from The Weavers. 50pf, Gustav Hertz (1887-1975), physicist, and atomic energy transmission diagram.

**1987, May 5**
2603 A809 10pf multi .25 .25
2604 A809 20pf multi .25 .25
2605 A809 35pf multi .35 .35
2606 A809 50pf multi .40 .40
Nos. 2603-2606 (4) 1.25 1.25

Freshwater Fish — A810

5pf, Abramis brama. 10pf, Salmo trutta fario. 20pf, Silurus glanis. 35pf, Thymallus thymallus. 50pf, Barbus barbus. 70pf, Esox lucius.

**1987, May 19    Litho.    Perf. 13x12½**
2607 A810 5pf multi .25 .25
2608 A810 10pf multi .25 .25
2609 A810 20pf multi .25 .25
2610 A810 35pf multi .35 .35
2611 A810 50pf multi .45 .35
2612 A810 70pf multi .65 .65
Nos. 2607-2612 (6) 2.20 2.10

Nos. 2608-2609 exist in sheets of 4.

Fire Engines — A811

10pf, Hand-operated, 1756. 25pf, Steam, 1903. 40pf, LF 15, 1919. 70pf, LF 16-TS 8, 1971.

**1987, June 16**
2613 A811 10pf multi .25 .25
2614 A811 25pf multi .25 .25
2615 A811 40pf multi .40 .40
2616 A811 70pf multi .65 .65
a. Block of 4, Nos. 2613-2616 2.25 2.25

---

**Souvenir Sheet**

Esperanto Movement, Cent. A812

**1987, July 7    Litho.    Perf. 14**
2617 A812 85pf L.L. Zamenhof, globe .80 1.60

World Wildlife Fund — A813

**1987, July 7    Photo.**
2618 A813 10pf Two otters .25 .25
2619 A813 25pf Otter swimming .25 .25
2620 A813 35pf Otter .35 .30
2621 A813 60pf Close-up of head .80 .80
Nos. 2618-2621 (4) 1.65 1.60

8th Sports Festival and 11th Youth Sports Championships, Leipzig — A814

**1987, July 21**
2622 A814 5pf Tug-of-war .25 .25
2623 A814 10pf Handball .25 .25
2624 A814 20pf + 5pf Girls' long jump .25 .25
2625 A814 35pf Table tennis .30 .25
2626 A814 40pf Bowling .40 .35
2627 A814 70pf Running .60 .60
Nos. 2622-2627 (6) 2.05 1.95

**Berlin Anniversary Type of 1987**
**Perf. 12½x13, 13x12½**
**1987, Feb. 17    Engr.**
2628 A801 10pf like No. 2587 .25 .25
a. Miniature sheet of 4 1.00 1.10
2629 A801 10pf like No. 2588 .25 .25
a. Miniature sheet of 4 1.00 1.10
2630 A801 20pf like No. 2589 .25 .25
a. Miniature sheet of 4 1.10 1.40
2631 A801 20pf like No. 2590 .25 .25
a. Miniature sheet of 4 1.00 1.40
Nos. 2628-2631 (4) 1.00 1.00

Assoc. of Sports and Science, 35th Anniv. — A815

**1987, Aug. 4    Litho.    Perf. 13x12½**
2632 A815 10pf multi .30 .25

Stamp Day — A816

Designs: 10pf+5pf, Court Post Office, Berlin, 1760. 20pf, Wartenberg Palace, former Prussian General Post Office, 1770.

**1987, Aug. 11    Photo.    Perf. 14**
2633 10pf +5pf multi .25 .25
2634 20pf multi .25 .25
a. A816 Pair, #2633-2634 + label .50 1.10

## Souvenir Sheet

Leipzig Autumn Fair A817

**1987, Aug. 25    Litho.    Perf. 13½**
2635 A817 Sheet of 2                 1.10 1.60
  a.    40pf multi                  .35  .45
  b.    50pf multi                  .45  .45

Intl. War Victims' Memorial, Budapest — A818

35pf, Statue by József Somogyi.

**1987, Sept. 8    Photo.    Perf. 14**
2636 A818 35pf multi                 .35  .25

## Souvenir Sheet

Thalmann Memorial — A819

**Litho. & Engr.**
**1987, Sept. 8               Perf. 14**
2637 A819 1.35m buff, ver & blk     1.25 2.25

City of Berlin, 750th anniv.

10th Natl. Art Exhibition, Berlin — A820

Designs: 10pf, Weidendamm Bridge, Berlin, 1986, by Arno Mohr. 50pf, They Only Wanted to Learn How to Read and Write, Nicaragua, 1985-86, by Willi Sitte. 70pf, Large Figure of a Man in Mourning, 1983, scupture by Wieland Forster. 1m, Ceramic bowl, 1986, by Gerd Lucke. Nos. 2638-2640, vert.

**1987, Sept. 28               Litho.**
2638 A820 10pf multi                 .25  .25
2639 A820 50pf multi                 .40  .45
2640 A820 70pf multi                 .55  .60
2641 A820 1m multi                   .80  .90
    Nos. 2638-2641 (4)         2.00 2.20

Lenin, Flag, Smolny Institute, Cruiser Aurora — A821

**1987, Oct. 27    Photo.    Perf. 14**
2642 A821 10pf shown                 .25  .25
2643 A821 20pf Spasski Tower         .25  .25

October Revolution, Russia, 70th anniv.

Robot ZIM 10-S Welding — A822

10pf, Personal computer.

**1987, Nov. 3    Litho.    Perf. 13x12½**
2644 A822 10pf multicolored          .25  .25
2645 A822 20pf shown                 .25  .25

30th MMM Science Fair and 10th Central Industrial Fair for Students and Youth Scientists, Leipzig.

## Miniature Sheet

Christmas Candle Carousels from the Ore Mountains — A823

Designs: 10pf, Annaberg, c. 1810. 20pf, Freiberg, c. 1830. 25pf, Neustadtel, c. 1870. 35pf, Schneeberg, c. 1870. 40pf, Lossnitz, c. 1880. 85pf, Seiffen, c. 1910.

**1987, Nov. 3    Litho.    Perf. 12½x13**
2646 A823 Sheet of 6                 2.25 2.60
  a.    10pf multi                  .25  .25
  b.    20pf multi                  .45  .55
  c.    25pf multi                  .25  .25
  d.    35pf multi                  .25  .25
  e.    40pf multi                  .45  .55
  f.    85pf multi                  .25  .25

1988 Winter Olympics, Calgary — A824

5pf, Ski jumping. 10pf, Speed skating. 20pf +10pf, 4-Man bobsled. 35pf, Biathlon. 1.20m, Single and double luge.

**1988, Jan. 19   Photo.    Perf. 14½x14**
2647 A824    5pf multi               .25  .25
2648 A824   10pf multi               .25  .25
2649 A824   20pf +10pf multi         .35  .30
2650 A824   35pf multi               .40  .35
    Nos. 2647-2650 (4)         1.25 1.15

## Souvenir Sheet
**Perf. 13x12½**
2651 A824 1.20m multi                1.25 2.00

No. 2649 surtaxed for the Olympic Promotion Society.

Postal Buildings, East Berlin — A825

15pf, Berlin-Buch post office. 20pf, Natl. Postal Museum. 50pf, General post office, Berlin-Marzahn.

**1988, Feb. 2                   Perf. 14**
2652 A825 15pf multicolored          .25  .25
2653 A825 20pf multicolored          .35  .25
2654 A825 50pf multicolored          .80  .55
    Nos. 2652-2654 (3)         1.40 1.05

## Souvenir Sheet

Bertolt Brecht (1898-1956), Playwright — A826

**1988, Feb. 2    Litho.    Perf. 13x12½**
2655 A826 70pf multicolored          .85 1.60

Flowering Plants — A827

10pf, Tillandsia macrochlamys. 25pf, Tillandsia bulbosa. 40pf, Tillandsia kalmbacheri. 70pf, Guzmania blassii.

**1988, Feb. 16   Photo.    Perf. 14**
2656 A827 10pf multicolored          .25  .25
2657 A827 25pf multicolored          .25  .25
2658 A827 40pf multicolored          .35  .35
2659 A827 70pf multicolored          .55  .55
    Nos. 2656-2659 (4)         1.40 1.40

Leipzig Spring Fair — A828

20pf, Entrance #8. 70pf, Faust & Mephistopheles, bronze statue by Matthieu Molitor.

**1988, Mar. 8    Litho.    Perf. 12½x13**
2660 A828 20pf multi                 .25  .25
2661 A828 70pf multi                 .80  .55

Madler Passage (arcade), 75th anniv.

## Souvenir Sheet

A829

**1988, Mar. 8                   Perf. 14**
2662 A829 70pf multi                 1.10 1.60

Joseph von Eichendorff (1788-1857), poet.

Seals — A830

10pf, Muhlhausen saddler, 1565. 25pf, Dresden butcher, 1564. 35pf, Nauen smith, 16th cent. 50pf, Frankfurt-Oder clothier, 16th cent.

**1988, Mar. 22   Photo.    Perf. 14**
2663 A830 10pf multicolored          .25  .25
2664 A830 25pf multicolored          .25  .25
2665 A830 35pf multicolored          .30  .30
2666 A830 50pf multicolored          .35  .35
  a.    Block of 4, #2663-2666      1.25 1.25

Georg Forster Antarctic Research Station — A831

**1988, Mar. 22   Litho.    Perf. 13x12½**
2667 A831 35pf multi                 .40  .30

District Capitals — A832

5pf, Wismar. 10pf, Anklam. 25pf, Ribnitz-Damgarten. 60pf, Stralsund. 90pf, Bergen. 1.20m, Greifswald.

**1988, Apr. 5    Photo.    Perf. 14**
2668 A832   5pf multi                .25  .25
2669 A832  10pf multi                .25  .25
2670 A832  25pf multi                .25  .25
2671 A832  60pf multi                .45  .40
2672 A832  90pf multi                .65  .65
2673 A832 1.20m multi                .85  .85
    Nos. 2668-2673 (6)         2.70 2.65

## Souvenir Sheet

Ulrich von Hutten (1488-1523), Promulgator of the Lutheran Movement — A833

**1988, Apr. 5    Litho.    Perf. 12½x13**
2674 A833 70pf multi                 .90 1.25

USSR-DDR Manned Space Flight, 10th Anniv. — A834

Designs: 5pf, Cosmonauts S. Jahn and Valery Bykowski, Soyuz-29 landing, Sept. 3, 1978. 10pf, MKS-M multi-channel spectrometer. 20pf, MIR space station.

**1988, June 21   Litho.    Perf. 14**
2675 A834   5pf multi                .25  .25
2676 A834  10pf multi                .25  .25
2677 A834  20pf multi                .25  .25
    Nos. 2675-2677 (3)          .75  .75

See Nos. 2698-2700.

10th Youth Stamp Exhibitions in Erfurt and Karl-Marx-Stadt A835

Designs: 10pf+5pf, Erfurt. c. 1520. 20+5pf, Chemnitz, c. 1620. 25pf, Historic and modern buildings of Erfurt. 50pf, Historic and modern buildings of Karl-Marx-Stadt.

**1988, June 21                  Photo.**
2678 A835 10pf +5pf multi            .25  .25
2679 A835 20pf +5pf multi            .25  .25
2680 A835 25pf multi                 .25  .25
  a.    Pair, #2678, 2680 + label   .60 1.00
2681 A835 50pf multi                 .45  .55
  a.    Pair, #2679, 2681 + label   .80 1.60

Nos. 2678-2679 surtaxed to benefit the Philatelists' League of the DDR Cultural Union.

22nd Workers' Games, Frankfurt-on-Oder — A836

**1988, June 7    Litho.    Perf. 13x12½**
2682  20pf multi                    .25  .25
2683  50pf multi, diff.             .45  .45
  a.  A836 Pair, #2682-2683 + label  .90  .80

Workers' Militia, 35th Anniv. — A837

5pf, Oath. 10pf, Ernst Thalmann tribute. 15pf, Roll call. 20pf, Weapons exchange.

**1988, July 5    Photo.    Perf. 14**
2684  A837  5pf multicolored       .25  .25
2685  A837  10pf multicolored      .25  .25
2686  A837  15pf multicolored      .25  .25
2687  A837  20pf multicolored      .25  .25
  Nos. 2684-2687 (4)             1.00  1.00

A838

No. 2688, 8th Young Pioneers' Congress, Karl-Marx-Stadt. No. 2689, Youths playing musical instruments.

**1988, July 19    Litho.    Perf. 13x12½**
2688  10pf multi                   .25  .25
2689  10pf +5pf multi              .25  .25
  a.  A838 Pair, #2688-2689 + label  1.00  1.00

Surtax financed the congress.

1988 Summer Olympics, Seoul — A839

5pf, Swimming. 10pf, Handball. 20pf +10pf, Hurdles. 25pf, Rowing. 35pf, Boxing. 50pf, Cycling.
85pf, Relay race.

**1988, Aug. 9    Photo.    Perf. 14**
2690  A839  5pf multi              .25  .25
2691  A839  10pf multi             .25  .25
2692  A839  20pf +10pf multi       .30  .30
2693  A839  25pf multi             .30  .30
2694  A839  35pf multi             .30  .30
2695  A839  50pf +20pf multi       .60  .60
  Nos. 2690-2695 (6)             2.00  2.00

**Souvenir Sheet**
**Litho.**
**Perf. 13x12½**
2696  A839  85pf multi           1.60  3.00

**Souvenir Sheet**

Leipzig Autumn Fair A840

**1988, Aug. 30    Litho.    Perf. 14**
2697  A840  Sheet of 3           1.60  2.00
  a.  5pf Fair, c. 1810           .25  .40
  b.  15pf Battle of Leipzig Memorial  .25  .40
  c.  1m Fair, c. 1820            .80  .80

**DDR-USSR Manned Space Flight Type**

**1988, Aug. 30    Litho.    Perf. 14**
2698  A834  10pf like No. 2675    .25  .25
  a.  Sheet of 3                  .85  1.00
2699  A834  20pf like No. 2676    .30  .30
  a.  Sheet of 3                 1.10  1.10
2700  A834  35pf like No. 2677    .40  .40
  a.  Sheet of 3                 2.10  2.10
  Nos. 2698-2700 (3)              .95  .95

Fascism Resistance Memorial, Como, Italy A841

**1988, Sept. 13    Photo.**
2701  A841  35pf multi            .35  .30

Memorial at Buchenwald, 30th Anniv. — A842

**1988, Sept. 13    Perf. 14**
2702  A842  10pf multi            .25  .25

Mariner's Soc., Stralsund, 500th Anniv. — A843

Paintings: 5pf, Adolph Friedrich at Stralsund, by C. Leplow. 10pf, Die Gartenlaube (built in 1872) at Stralsund, by J.F. Kruger. 70pf, Brigantine Auguste Mathilde (built in 1830) at Stralsund, by I.C. Grunwaldt. 1.20m, Brig Hoffnung at Cologne, by G.A. Luther.

**1988, Sept. 20    Litho.    Perf. 13½x13**
2703  A843  5pf multi             .30  .25
2704  A843  10pf multi            .30  .25
2705  A843  70pf multi            .65  .65
2706  A843  1.20m multi          1.00  1.00
  Nos. 2703-2706 (4)             2.25  2.15

Ship Lifts and Bridges — A844

5pf, Magdeburg. 10pf, Magdeburg-Rothensee. 35pf, Niederfinow. 70pf, Altfriesack. 90pf, Rugendamm.

**1988, Oct. 18    Photo.    Perf. 14x14½**
2707  A844  5pf multi             .25  .25
2708  A844  10pf multi            .25  .25
2709  A844  35pf multi            .30  .25
2710  A844  70pf multi            .55  .55
2711  A844  90pf multi            .65  .65
  Nos. 2707-2711 (5)             2.00  1.95

1st Nazi Pogrom (Kristallnacht), Nov. 9, 1938 — A845

**1988, Nov. 8    Perf. 14**
2712  A845  35pf Menorah          .40  .30

Paintings by Max Lingner (1888-1959) — A846

5pf, In the Boat, 1931. 10pf, Yvonne, 1939. 20pf, Free, Strong and Happy, 1944. 85pf, New Harvest, 1951.

**1988, Nov. 8**
2713  A846  5pf multicolored      .30  .25
2714  A846  10pf multicolored     .30  .25
2715  A846  20pf multicolored     .30  .25
2716  A846  85pf multicolored     .85  .70
  Nos. 2713-2716 (4)             1.75  1.45

**Souvenir Sheet**

Friedrich Wolf (1888-1953), Playwright — A847

**1988, Nov. 22    Litho.**
2717  A847  1.10m multi          1.00  3.00

WHO, 40th Anniv. — A848

**1988, Nov. 22    Photo.**
2718  A848  85pf multi            .80  .40

**Miniature Sheet**

Bone Lace from Erzgebirge — A849

Various lace designs.

**1988, Nov. 22    Litho.    Perf. 12½x13**
2719  A849    Sheet of 6        2.00  2.00
  a.  20pf multi                 .25  .25
  b.  25pf multi                 .45  .45
  c.  35pf multi                 .25  .25
  d.  40pf multi                 .25  .25
  e.  50pf multi                 .45  .45
  f.  85pf multi                 .25  .25

Council for Mutual Economic Aid, 40th Anniv. — A850

**1989, Jan. 10    Photo.    Perf. 13**
2720  A850  20pf multi            .40  .25

**Labor Leaders Type of 1987**

Portraits: No. 2721, Edith Baumann (1909-1973). No. 2722, Otto Meier (1889-1962). No. 2723, Fritz Selbmann (1899-1975). No. 2724, Alfred Oelssner (1879-1962).

**1989, Jan. 24    Engr.    Perf. 14**
2721  A804  10pf red brown        .25  .25
2722  A804  10pf gray grn         .25  .25
2723  A804  10pf blue             .25  .25
2724  A804  10pf dark brn         .25  .25
  Nos. 2721-2724 (4)             1.00  1.00

Telephones — A851

Designs: 10pf, Philipp Reis, 1861. 20pf, Siemens & Halske wall model, 1882. 50pf, Wall model OB 03, 1903. 85pf, Table model OB 05, 1905.

**1989, Feb. 7    Litho.**
2725  A851  10pf shown            .25  .25
2726  A851  20pf multi            .35  .25
2727  A851  50pf multi            .40  .40
2728  A851  85pf multi            .65  .65
  a.  Block of 4, #2725-2728     2.00  2.25

Famous Men — A852

No. 2729, Ludwig Renn (1889-1979). No. 2730, Carl von Ossietzky (1889-1938). No. 2731, Adam Scharrer (1889-1948). No. 2732, Rudolf Mauersberger (1889-1971). No. 2733, Johann Beckmann (1739-1811).

**1989, Feb. 28    Photo.**
2729  A852  10pf multicolored     .25  .25
2730  A852  10pf multicolored     .25  .25
2731  A852  10pf multicolored     .25  .25
2732  A852  10pf multicolored     .25  .25
2733  A852  10pf multicolored     .25  .25
  Nos. 2729-2733 (5)             1.25  1.25

Leipzig Spring Fair — A853

**1989, Mar. 7    Litho.**
2734  A853  70pf shown            .60  .50
2735  A853  85pf Buildings, 1690  .70  .70

Handelshof, 80th anniv. (70pf).

**Souvenir Sheet**

Thomas Muntzer (c. 1468-1525), Religious Reformer — A854

**1989, Mar. 21    Perf. 13x12½**
2736  A854  1.10m multi          1.10  2.25

1st Long-distance German Railway, Leipzig-Dresden, Sesquicentennial A855

15pf, Georg Friedrich List (1789-1846), industrialist, economist. 20pf, Dresden Station in Leipzig, 1839. 50pf, Leipzig Station in Dresden, 1839.

**1989, Apr. 4    Perf. 14**
2737  A855  15pf multi            .30  .25
2738  A855  20pf multi            .30  .25
2739  A855  50pf multi            .45  .45
  Nos. 2737-2739 (3)             1.05  .95

A856

Designs: Meissen Onion-pattern Porcelain, 250th anniv., and sword emblem.

**1989, Apr. 18    Litho.    Perf. 12½x13**
2740  A856  10pf Tea caddy        .25  .25
2741  A856  20pf Vase             .25  .30
2742  A856  35pf Breadboard       .35  .45
2743  A856  70pf Teapot           .65  .80
  Nos. 2740-2743 (4)             1.50  1.80

**Size: 33x56mm**
**Perf. 14**
2744    Block of 4              1.60  2.25
  a.  A856 10pf like No. 2740    .30  .30
  b.  A856 20pf like No. 2741    .25  .25
  c.  A856 35pf like No. 2742    .35  .35
  d.  A856 70pf like No. 2743    .75  .75

A857

**1989, May 2    Photo.    Perf. 14½x14**
2745 A857  20pf "I"                    .25   .25
2746 A857  50pf "B"                    .40   .35
2747 A857  1.35m "A"                  1.10  1.10
       Nos. 2745-2747 (3)             1.75  1.70

Intl. Book Fair (IBA), Leipzig.

Student Government — A858

No. 2748, 8th World Youth Festival, Pyongyang. No. 2749, Whitsun meeting of Free German Youth.

**1989, May 9    Litho.    Perf. 13½x12½**
2748      20pf multicolored            .30   .40
2749      20pf +5pf multi              .30   .40
  a.   A858 Pair, #2748-2749 + label   .60  1.25

Princess Luise — A859

Sculptures by Johann Gottfried Schadow (1764-1850), Prussian Court Sculptor — No. 2751, Princess Friederike.

**1989, May 16    Photo.    Perf. 14½x14**
2750 A859  50pf shown                  .55   .40
2751 A859  85pf multicolored           .90   .80

Carl Zeiss Foundation, Jena, Cent. — A860

Modern medical technology: 50pf, Interference microscope Jenaval. 85pf, Bicoordinate measuring instrument ZKM 01-250C.

**1989, May 16**
2752      50pf multi                   .35   .35
2753      85pf multi                   .65   .65
  a.   A860 Pair, #2752-2753 + label  1.25  2.00

Label pictures founder Ernst Abbe (1840-1905).

Jena University Inaugural Address, Bicent. — A861

**1989, May 23    Photo.    Perf. 14**
2754      25pf Frontispiece            .25   .25
2755      85pf Excerpt                 .60   .60
  a.   A861 Pair, #2754-2755 + label   .90   .90

Label pictures bust of Friedrich Schiller, author of the address.

Souvenir Sheet

Zoologists — A862

Designs: a, Alfred Brehm (1829-1884). b, Christian Brehm (1787-1864).

**1989, June 13    Litho.**
2756 A862  Sheet of 2                 1.60 10.00
  a.      50pf multicolored            .40  3.25
  b.      85pf multicolored            .80  5.25

French Revolution, Bicent. — A863

5pf, Storming of the Bastille, July 14, 1789. 20pf, Revolutionaries, flag bearer. 90pf, Storming Tuileries Palace, Aug. 10, 1792.

**1989, July 4    Photo.    Perf. 13**
2757 A863  5pf multi                   .25   .25
2758 A863  20pf multi                  .25   .25
2759 A863  90pf multi                  .65  1.10
       Nos. 2757-2759 (3)             1.15  1.60

Intl. Congress of Horse Breeders from Socialist States — A864

10pf, Haflinger. 20pf, English thoroughbred. 70pf, Cold blood. 110pf, Noble warm blood.

**1989, July 18    Litho.    Perf. 13½**
2760 A864  10pf multicolored           .25   .25
2761 A864  20pf multicolored           .25   .25
2762 A864  70pf multicolored           .55   .55
2763 A864  110pf multicolored          .85   .85
       Nos. 2760-2763 (4)             1.90  1.90

Natl. Stamp Exhibition, Magdeburg A865

20pf, Owlglass Fountain. 70pf +5pf, Demons Fountain.

**1989, Aug. 8    Litho.    Perf. 13x12½**
2764 A865  20pf multicolored           .25   .25
2765 A865  70pf +5pf multi             .65   .60

No. 2765 surtaxed for the philatelic unit of the Kulturbund.

Souvenir Sheet

Leipzig Autumn Fair A866

**1989, Aug. 22    Perf. 14**
2766 A866  Sheet of 2                 1.25  2.50
  a.      50pf Fairground              .45   .70
  b.      85pf Fairground, diff.       .65  1.25

Thomas Muntzer (1489-1525), Religious Reformer — A867

Various details of the painting *Early Bourgeois Revolution in Germany in 1525*, by W. Tubke.

**1989, Aug. 22**
2767 A867  5pf Globe                   .25   .25
2768 A867  10pf Fountain               .25   .25
2769 A867  20pf Battle scene           .25   .25
  a.      Souvenir sheet of 4         1.60  3.00
2770 A867  50pf Ark                    .40   .40
2771 A867  85pf Rainbow, battle        .85   .85
       Nos. 2767-2771 (5)             2.00  2.00

*Muttergruppe*, 1965, Bronze Statue in the Natl. Memorial, Ravensbruck — A868

**1989, Sept. 5    Photo.    Perf. 14**
2772 A868  35pf multi                  .35   .35

Natl. Memorial, Ravensbruck, 30th anniv.

Flowering Cacti (Epiphyllum) — A869

**1989, Sept. 19    Litho.    Perf. 13**
2773 A869  10m Adriana                 .25   .25
2774 A869  35m Feuerzauber             .40   .30
2775 A869  50m Franzisko               .55   .55
       Nos. 2773-2775 (3)             1.20  1.10

DDR, 40th Anniv. A870

**1989, Oct. 3    Perf. 14**
2776 A870  5pf Education               .25   .25
2777 A870  10pf Agriculture            .25   .25
2778 A870  20pf Construction           .30   .30
2779 A870  25pf Machinist, computer user    .30   .30
       Nos. 2776-2779 (4)             1.10  1.10

**Souvenir Sheet**
2780 A870  135pf Two workers          4.00  4.00

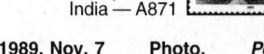

Jawaharlal Nehru, 1st Prime Minister of Independent India — A871

**1989, Nov. 7    Photo.    Perf. 14**
2781 A871  35pf multicolored           .35   .35

**Statues of Roland Type of 1987**

5pf, Zerbst, 1445. 10pf, Halberstadt, 1433. 20pf, Buch-Altmark, 1611. 50pf, Perleberg, 1546.

**1989, Nov. 7    Perf. 14½x14**
2782 A799  5pf multicolored            .25   .25
2783 A799  10pf multicolored           .25   .25
2784 A799  20pf multicolored           .25   .25
2785 A799  50pf multicolored           .40   .40
       Nos. 2782-2785 (4)             1.15  1.15

Miniature Sheet

Chandeliers from Erzgebirge — A872

Designs: a, Schneeburg, circa 1860. b, Schwarzenberg, circa 1850. c, Annaberg, circa 1880. d, Seiffen, circa 1900. e, Seiffen, circa 1930. f, Annaberg, circa 1925.

**Litho. & Engr.**

**1989, Nov. 28    Perf. 14**
2786 A872  Sheet of 6                 2.00  2.25
  a.      10pf multicolored            .25   .25
  b.      20pf multicolored            .45   .45
  c.      25pf multicolored            .25   .25
  d.      35pf multicolored            .25   .25
  e.      50pf multicolored            .45   .45
  f.      70pf multicolored            .25   .25

Bees Collecting Nectar — A873

5pf, Apple blossom. 10pf, Blooming heather. 20pf, Rape blossom. 50pf, Red clover.

**1990, Jan. 9    Litho.**
2787 A873  5pf multicolored            .25   .25
2788 A873  10pf multicolored           .25   .25
2789 A873  20pf multicolored           .25   .25
2790 A873  50pf multicolored           .55   .55
       Nos. 2787-2790 (4)             1.30  1.30

*The Young Post Rider*, an Engraving by Albrecht Durer — A874

**1990, Jan. 12    Litho.    Perf. 13**
2791 A874  35pf choc, gray brn,
            dark beige                 .40   .40

Postal communications in Europe, 500th anniv.
See Austria No. 1486, Belgium No. 1332, Germany No. 1592 and Berlin No. 9N584.

Labor Leaders — A875

Portraits: No. 2792, Bruno Leuschner (1910-65). No. 2793, Erich Weinert (1890-1953).

**1990, Jan. 16    Perf. 14**
2792 A875  10pf gray brown            .25   .25
2793 A875  10pf deep blue             .25   .25

Coats of Arms — A876

Early postal agency insignia: 10pf, Schwarzburg-Rudolstadt and Thurn & Taxis. 20pf, Royal Saxon letter collection. 50pf, Imperial Postal Agency. 1.10pf, Auxiliary post office.

**1990, Feb. 6    Photo.    Perf. 14**
2794 A876  10pf multicolored           .25   .25
2795 A876  20pf multicolored           .25   .25
2796 A876  50pf multicolored           .65   .55
2797 A876  110pf multicolored         1.25  1.20
       Nos. 2794-2797 (4)             2.40  2.25

**Size: 32x42mm**
**Perf. 13½**
**Litho.**
2798      Block of 4                  3.25  3.25
  a.   A876 10pf like No. 2794         .35   .25
  b.   A876 20pf like No. 2795         .35   .25
  c.   A876 50pf like No. 2796         .65   .55
  d.   A876 110pf like No. 2797       1.25  1.20

Posts & Telecommunications Workers' Day.

August Bebel (1840-1913), Co-founder of the Social Democratic Party — A877

**1990, Feb. 20    Photo.**
2799 A877  20pf multicolored           .40   .40

Flying Machine Designed by Leonardo da Vinci — A878

No. 2801, Melchior Bauer. No. 2802, Albrecht Berblinger. No. 2803, Otto Lilienthal.

**1990, Feb. 20    Litho.    Perf. 13½x13**
| 2800 | A878 | 20pf shown | .25 | .25 |
|------|------|------------|-----|-----|
| 2801 | A878 | 35pf +5pf multi | .40 | .40 |
| 2802 | A878 | 50pf multicolored | .55 | .45 |
| 2803 | A878 | 90pf multicolored | .90 | .90 |
| | | Nos. 2800-2803 (4) | 2.10 | 2.00 |

LILIENTHAL '91 airmail exhibition. No. 2801 surtaxed for philatelic promotion.

Leipzig Spring Fair Seals — A879

**1990, Mar. 6    Perf. 12½x13**
| 2804 | A879 | 70pf Seal, 1268 | 1.10 | .60 |
|------|------|------------|-----|-----|
| 2805 | A879 | 85pf Seal, 1497 | 1.20 | .70 |

City of Leipzig and the Leipzig Spring Fair, 825th anniv.

Dying Warriors — A880

Sculptures by Andreas Schluter.

**1990, Mar. 6    Photo.    Perf. 13½x14**
| 2806 | A880 | 40pf shown | .45 | .65 |
|------|------|------------|-----|-----|
| 2807 | A880 | 70pf multi, diff. | .65 | .80 |

Museum of German History in the Zeughaus of Berlin.

Famous Men — A881

Portraits: No. 2808, Friedrich Diesterweg (1790-1866), educator. No. 2809, Kurt Tucholsky (1890-1935), novelist, journalist.

**1990, Mar. 20    Photo.    Perf. 14**
| 2808 | A881 | 10pf multicolored | .30 | .30 |
|------|------|------------|-----|-----|
| 2809 | A881 | 10pf multicolored | .30 | .30 |

Labor Day, Cent. — A882

20pf, Flower, "1890/1990".

**1990, Apr. 3**
| 2810 | A882 | 10pf shown | .40 | .40 |
|------|------|------------|-----|-----|
| 2811 | A882 | 20pf red, sil & blk | .70 | .70 |

Dicraeosaurus A883

25pf, Kentrurosaurus. 35pf, Dysalotosaurus. 50pf, Brachiosaurus. 85pf, Brachiosaurus skull.

**Perf. 13x12½, 12½x13**
**1990, Apr. 17    Litho.**
| 2812 | A883 | 10pf shown | .25 | .25 |
|------|------|------------|-----|-----|
| 2813 | A883 | 25pf multicolored | .25 | .25 |
| a. | | Miniature sheet of 4 | 1.25 | 1.25 |
| 2814 | A883 | 35pf multicolored | .30 | .30 |
| 2815 | A883 | 40pf multicolored | .40 | .40 |
| 2816 | A883 | 85pf multicolored | .85 | .85 |
| | | Nos. 2812-2816 (5) | 2.05 | 2.05 |

Natural History Museum of Berlin, cent. Nos. 2815-2816 vert.

Penny Black, 150th Anniv. — A884

**1990, May 8    Perf. 14**
| 2817 | A884 | 20pf shown | .35 | .35 |
|------|------|------------|-----|-----|
| 2818 | A884 | 35pf +15pf Saxony #1 | .60 | .60 |
| 2819 | A884 | 110pf No. 48 | 1.60 | 1.60 |
| | | Nos. 2817-2819 (3) | 2.55 | 2.55 |

A885

Intl. Telecommunications Union, 125th Anniv.: 10pf, David Edward Hughes (1831-1900), type-printing telegraph, 1855. 20pf, Distribution linkage, Berlin-Kopenick post office. 25pf, TV and microwave tower. 50pf, Molniya news satellite, globe. 70pf, Philipp Reis (1834-1874), physicist, designed sound transmission equipment.

**1990, May 15**
| 2820 | A885 | 10pf multicolored | .30 | .30 |
|------|------|------------|-----|-----|
| 2821 | A885 | 20pf multicolored | .30 | .30 |
| 2822 | A885 | 25pf multicolored | .30 | .30 |
| 2823 | A885 | 50pf multicolored | .80 | .80 |
| | | Nos. 2820-2823 (4) | 1.70 | 1.70 |

**Souvenir Sheet**
| 2824 | A885 | 70pf multicolored | 1.75 | 3.00 |
|------|------|------------|-----|-----|

Pope John Paul II, 70th Birthday — A886

**1990, May 15**
| 2825 | A886 | 35pf multicolored | .80 | 1.00 |
|------|------|------------|-----|-----|

11th Youth Stamp Exhibition, Halle — A887

10pf +5pf, 18th cent. Halle. 20pf, 20th cent. Halle.

**1990, June 5    Perf. 13x12½**
| 2826 | | 10pf +5pf multi | .30 | .30 |
|------|------|------------|-----|-----|
| 2827 | | 20pf multi | .30 | .30 |
| a. | | A887 Pair, #2826-2827 + label | .65 | .85 |

Treasures in the German State Library, Berlin — A888

Designs: 20pf, Rules of an order, 1264. 25pf, Rudimentum novitiorum, 1475. 50pf, Chosrou wa Schirin, 18th cent. 110pf, Book-cover of Amalienbibliothek, 18th cent.

**1990, June 19**
| 2828 | A888 | 20pf multicolored | .40 | .25 |
|------|------|------------|-----|-----|
| 2829 | A888 | 25pf multicolored | .40 | .25 |
| 2830 | A888 | 50pf multicolored | 1.10 | .60 |
| 2831 | A888 | 110pf multicolored | 1.80 | 1.40 |
| | | Nos. 2828-2831 (4) | 3.70 | 2.50 |

Castle Albrechtsburg and Cathedral, Meissen — A889

30pf, Goethe-Schiller Monument, Weimar. 50pf, Brandenburg Gate, Berlin. 60pf, Kyffhauser Monument. 70pf, Semper Opera, Dresden. 80pf, Castle Sanssouci, Potsdam. 100pf, Wartburg, Eisenach. 200pf, Magdeburg Cathedral. 500pf, Schwerin Castle.

**1990, July 2    Photo.    Perf. 14**
| 2832 | A889 | 10pf ultramarine | .35 | .30 |
|------|------|------------|-----|-----|
| 2833 | A889 | 30pf olive green | .65 | .30 |
| 2834 | A889 | 50pf bluish green | .65 | .65 |
| 2835 | A889 | 60pf violet brown | .65 | .65 |
| 2836 | A889 | 70pf dark brown | .65 | .65 |
| 2837 | A889 | 80pf red brown | .65 | .65 |
| 2838 | A889 | 100pf dark carmine | 1.10 | 1.10 |
| 2839 | A889 | 200pf dark violet | 2.00 | 2.00 |
| 2840 | A889 | 500pf green | 4.00 | 4.00 |
| | | Nos. 2832-2840 (9) | 10.70 | 10.30 |

Nos. 2832-2852 have face values based on the Federal Republic's Deutsche mark and were valid for postage in both countries.

Postal System, 500th Anniv. — A890

30pf, 15th cent. postman. 50pf, 16th cent. postrider. 70pf, Post carriages c. 1595, 1750. 100pf, Railway mail carriages 1842, 1900.

**1990, Aug. 28    Litho.    Perf. 13x13½**
| 2841 | A890 | 30pf multicolored | .35 | .35 |
|------|------|------------|-----|-----|
| 2842 | A890 | 50pf multicolored | .45 | .45 |
| 2843 | A890 | 70pf multicolored | .60 | .60 |
| 2844 | A890 | 100pf multicolored | 1.00 | 1.00 |
| | | Nos. 2841-2844 (4) | 2.40 | 2.40 |

Louis Lewandowski (1821-94), Composer — A891

50pf+15pf, New Synagogue, Berlin.

**1990, Sept. 18    Perf. 14**
| 2845 | A891 | 30pf multicolored | .30 | .30 |
|------|------|------------|-----|-----|
| 2846 | A891 | 50pf +15pf multi | .55 | .55 |

Heinrich Schliemann (1822-1890), Archaeologist — A892

Design: 30pf, shown. 50pf, Schliemann, double pot c. 2600-1900 B.C., horiz.

**1990, Oct. 2    Photo.**
| 2847 | A892 | 30pf multicolored | .35 | .35 |
|------|------|------------|-----|-----|
| 2848 | A892 | 50pf multicolored | .65 | .65 |

Intl. Astronautics Federation, 41st Congress, Dresden — A893

**1990, Oct. 2**
| 2849 | A893 | 30pf Dresden skyline | .25 | .25 |
|------|------|------------|-----|-----|
| 2850 | A893 | 50pf Globe | .40 | .40 |
| 2851 | A893 | 70pf Moon | .65 | .65 |
| 2852 | A893 | 100pf Mars | .90 | .90 |
| | | Nos. 2849-2852 (4) | 2.20 | 2.40 |

Stamps of the German Democratic Republic were replaced starting Oct. 3, 1990 by those of the Federal Republic of Germany. Nos. 2832-2852 remained valid until Dec. 31, 1991.

## FOR USE IN ALL PROVINCES IN THE RUSSIAN ZONES

### SEMI-POSTALS
**Leipzig Fair Issue**
Type of German Semi-Postal Stamps

16pf+9pf, 1st New Year's Fair, 1459. 50pf+25pf, Arrival of clothmakers from abroad, 1469.

**Wmk. 292**
**1948, Aug. 29    Litho.    Perf. 13½**
| 10NB1 | SP252 | 16 + 9pf dk vio brn | .25 | .55 |
|------|------|------------|-----|-----|
| 10NB2 | SP252 | 50 + 25pf dl vio bl | .25 | .55 |
| | | Set, never hinged | | 1.20 |

The 1948 Leipzig Autumn Fair.

Emblem of Philatelic Institute — OSP1

**1948, Oct. 23    Perf. 13x13½**
| 10NB3 | OSP1 | 12 + 3pf red | .25 | .85 |
|------|------|------------|-----|-----|
| | | Never hinged | .65 | |

Stamp Day, Oct. 24, 1948.

### Type of German Semi-Postal Stamps of 1947

30pf+15pf, First fair in newly built Town Hall, 1556. 50pf+25pf, Italians at the Fair, 1536.

**1949, Mar. 6    Litho.    Perf. 13½**
| 10NB4 | SP252 | 30 + 15pf red | 1.00 | 3.50 |
|------|------|------------|-----|-----|
| 10NB5 | SP252 | 50 + 25pf blue | 1.25 | 4.00 |
| | | Set, never hinged | | 6.50 |

1949 Leipzig Spring Fair.

Goethe — OSP2

Designs: Different Goethe portraits.

**1949, July 20    Wmk. 292    Perf. 13**
| 10NB6 | OSP2 | 6 + 4pf dl vio | .80 | 2.25 |
|------|------|------------|-----|-----|
| 10NB7 | OSP2 | 12 + 8pf dl brn | .80 | 2.25 |
| 10NB8 | OSP2 | 24 + 16pf red brn | .65 | 2.00 |
| 10NB9 | OSP2 | 50 + 25pf dk bl | .65 | 2.00 |
| 10NB10 | OSP2 | 84 + 36pf ol gray | 1.00 | 4.00 |
| | | Nos. 10NB6-10NB10 (5) | 3.90 | 12.50 |
| | | Set, never hinged | 9.00 | |

Johann Wolfgang von Goethe, birth bicent.

### Souvenir Sheet

Profile of Goethe OSP3

**1949, Aug. 22    Engr.    Perf. 14**
| 10NB11 | OSP3 | 50pf + 4.50m blue | 100.00 | 400.00 |
|------|------|------------|-----|-----|
| | | Never hinged | 140.00 | |

The sheet measures 106x105mm. The surtax was for the reconstruction of Weimar.

### Type of German Semi-Postal Stamps

12pf+8pf, Russian merchants at the Fair, 1650. 24pf+16pf, Young Goethe at the Fair, 1765.

**1949, Aug. 30    Litho.    Perf. 13½**
| 10NB12 | SP252 | 12 + 8pf gray | 1.60 | 6.50 |
|------|------|------------|-----|-----|
| 10NB13 | SP252 | 24 + 16pf lake brn | 2.00 | 8.00 |
| | | Set, never hinged | | 10.50 |

1949 Leipzig Autumn Fair.

## GERMAN DEMOCRATIC REPUBLIC SEMI-POSTAL STAMPS

**Catalogue values for unused stamps in this section, from this point to the end of the section, are for Never Hinged items.**

Canceled to Order
Used values are for CTO's from No. B14 to No. B203.

Some se-tenants include a semi-postal stamp. To avoid splitting the se-tenant piece the semi-postal is listed with the regular issue.

Bavaria No. 1 and Magnifier — SP4

## Wmk. 292

**1949, Oct. 30　Litho.　Perf. 14**
B14　SP4　12pf + 3pf gray blk　5.25　5.25

Stamp Day, 1949. See No. B21a.

### Leipzig Fair Issue.
German Type of 1947
Inscribed: "Deutsche Demokratische
Republik"

Leipzig Spring Fair: 24pf+12pf, First porcelain at Fair, 1710. 30pf+14pf, First Fair at Municipal Store, 1894.

**1950, Mar. 5　　　　Perf. 13**
B15　SP252　24 + 12pf red vio　6.50　8.00
B16　SP252　30 + 14pf rose car　8.00　8.00

Shepherd Boy with
Double Flute — SP5

"Bach Year": 24pf+6pf, Girl with hand organ. 30pf+8pf, Johann Sebastian Bach. 50pf+16pf, Chorus.

**1950, June 14　　　　Perf. 14**
B17　SP5　12pf + 4pf bl grn　5.00　4.00
B18　SP5　24pf + 6pf olive　5.00　4.00
B19　SP5　30pf + 8pf dk red　6.50　6.50
B20　SP5　50pf + 16pf blue　13.00　12.00
　　　Nos. B17-B20 (4)　29.50　26.50

Saxony No. 1, Globe
and Dove — SP6

**1950, July 1　Photo.　Wmk. 292**
B21　SP6　84 + 41pf brn red　32.50　9.00
　a.　Souv. sheet of 2, #B14,
　　　B21, imperf.　100.00　110.00
　　　No. B21a hinged　25.00

German Stamp Exhib. (DEBRIA) held at Leipzig for the cent. of Saxony's 1st postage stamp.

Clearing Land — SP7

Reconstruction program: 24pf+6pf, Bricklaying. 30pf+10pf, Carpentry. 50pf+10pf, Inspecting plans.

**1952, May 1　　　　　Litho.**
B22　SP7　12pf + 3pf brt vio　2.25　.65
B23　SP7　24pf + 6pf henna brn　1.25　.65
B24　SP7　30pf + 10pf dp grn　2.25　.65
B25　SP7　50pf + 10pf vio bl　2.25　1.25
　　　Nos. B22-B25 (4)　8.00　3.20

Dam — SP8

**1954, Aug. 16　　　　Unwmk.**
B26　SP8　24pf + 6pf green　.60　.65

The surtax was for flood victims.

### Surcharged with New Value and "X"
**1955, Feb. 25**
B27　SP8　20 +5pf on 24+6pf　.75　.45

The surtax was for flood victims.

Buchenwald Memorial — SP9

---

## Perf. 13½x13

**1956, Sept. 8　　　　Wmk. 297**
B28　SP9　20pf + 80pf rose red　.90　3.25

The surtax was for the erection of national memorials at the concentration camps of Buchenwald, Ravensbruck and Sachsenhausen. See No. B43.

### Type of 1955 Surcharged "HELFT AGYPTEN +10" (#B29) or "HELFT DEM SOZIALISTISCHEN UNGARN +10" (#B30)
**Perf. 13½x13**

**1956, Dec. 20　　　　Wmk. 313**
B29　A75　20pf + 10pf carmine　.55　.35
B30　A75　20pf + 10pf carmine　.55　.35

Monument to
Ravensbrück — SP10

Memorial
Park and
Lake
SP11

### Perf. 13x13½, 13½x13

**1957, Apr. 25　　　　　　Litho.**
B31　SP10　5pf + 5pf green　.30　.25
B32　SP11　20pf + 10pf rose red　.35　.35

Intl. Day of Liberation. See Nos. B54, B70.

Ernst
Thälmann — SP12

Portraits: 25pf+15pf, Rudolf Breitscheid. 40pf+20pf, Rev. Paul Schneider.

**1957, Dec. 3　Photo.　Perf. 13**
### Portraits in Gray
B33　SP12　20pf + 10pf dp
　　　　　　plum　　　.25　.25
B34　SP12　25pf + 15pf dk
　　　　　　blue　　　.25　.25
B35　SP12　40pf + 20pf violet　.35　.35
　a.　Souv. sheet of 3, #B33-
　　　B35, imperf.　40.00　110.00
　　　Nos. B33-B35 (3)　.85　.85

No. B35a issued Sept. 15, 1958.

**1958, July 11　Wmk. 313　Perf. 13**
Portraits: 5pf+5pf, Albert Kuntz. 10pf+5pf, Rudi Arndt. 15pf+10pf, Kurt Adams. 20pf+10pf, Rudolf Renner. 25pf+15pf, Walter Stoecker.

### Portraits in Gray
B36　SP12　5pf + 5pf brn blk　.30　.65
B37　SP12　10pf + 5pf dk sl grn　.30　.65
B38　SP12　15pf + 10pf dp vio　.30　3.25
B39　SP12　20pf + 10pf brt
　　　　　　brn　　　.30　.65
B40　SP12　25pf + 15pf bl blk　.90　10.00
　　　Nos. B36-B40 (5)　2.10　15.20

Issued to honor the murdered victims of the Nazis at Buchenwald. The surtax was for the erection of national memorials.
See Nos. B49-B53, B55-B57, B60-B64, B71-B75, B79-B81.

Bugler, Flag and
Camp — SP13

Design: 20pf+10pf, Pioneers and flag.

---

**1958, Aug. 7　Litho.　Perf. 12½**
B41　SP13　10pf + 5pf green　.35　.25
B42　SP13　20pf + 10pf red　.35　.25

Pioneer organization, 10th anniversary.

### Type of 1956 Overprinted in Black "14. September 1958"
**Perf. 13½x13**

**1958, Sept. 15　　　　Unwmk.**
B43　SP9　20pf + 20pf rose red　.60　.55

Dedication of the memorial at Buchenwald concentration camp, Sept. 14, 1958.

Exercises with
Hoops — SP14

Designs: 10pf+5pf, High jump. 20pf+10pf Vaulting. 25pf+10pf, Girl gymnasts. 40pf+20pf, Leipzig stadium and fireworks.

### Perf. 13x13½

**1959, Aug. 10　Litho.　Wmk. 313**
B44　SP14　5pf + 5pf org　.25　.25
B45　SP14　10pf + 5pf grn　.25　.25
B46　SP14　20pf + 10pf brt car　.25　.25
B47　SP14　25pf + 10pf brt bl　.25　.25
B48　SP14　40pf + 20pf red vio　1.40　.45
　　　Nos. B44-B48 (5)　2.40　1.45

3rd German Sports Festival, Leipzig.

### Portrait Type of 1957-58
Portraits: 5pf+5pf, Tilde Klose. 10pf+5pf, Kathe Niederkirchner. 15pf+10pf, Charlotte Eisenblatter. 20pf+10pf, Olga Benario-Prestes. 25pf+15pf, Maria Grollmuss.

**1959, Sept. 3　Photo.　Perf. 13**
### Portraits in Gray
B49　SP12　5pf + 5pf sep　.25　.25
B50　SP12　10pf + 5pf dp grn　.25　.25
B51　SP12　15pf + 10pf dp vio　.25　.25
B52　SP12　20pf + 10pf mag　.25　.25
B53　SP12　25pf + 15pf dk bl　.35　.80
　　　Nos. B49-B53 (5)　1.35　1.80

Issued to honor women murdered by the Nazis at Buchenwald.

### Ravensbrück Type of 1957 Dated: "12. September 1959"
**Perf. 13½x13**

**1959, Sept. 11　Litho.　Wmk. 313**
B54　SP11　20pf + 10pf dp car &
　　　　　　blk　　　.45　.30

### Portrait Type of 1957-58
5pf+5pf, Lothar Erdmann. 10pf+5pf, Ernst Schneller. 20pf+10pf, Lambert Horn.

**1960, Feb. 25　Photo.　Perf. 13½x13**
### Portraits in Gray
B55　SP12　5pf + 5pf ol bis　.25　.25
B56　SP12　10pf + 5pf dk grn　.25　.25
B57　SP12　20pf + 10pf dl mag　.25　.25
　　　Nos. B55-B57 (3)　.75　.75

Issued to honor murdered victims of the Nazis at Sachsenhausen.

### Type of Regular Issue, 1960
Designs: 10pf+5pf, Vacation ship under construction, Wismar. 20pf+10pf, Ship before Stubbenkammer and sailboat.

### Wmk. 313
**1960, June 23　Litho.　Perf. 13**
B58　A162　10pf + 5pf blk, yel &
　　　　　　red　　　.25　.25
B59　A162　20pf + 10pf blk, red &
　　　　　　bl　　　.25　.25

### Portrait Type of 1957-58
Portraits: 10pf+5pf, Max Lademann. 15pf+5pf, Lorenz Breunig. 20pf+10pf, Mathias Thesen. 25pf+10pf, Gustl Sandtner. 40pf+20pf, Hans Rothbarth.

**1960　　Wmk. 313　　Perf. 13½x13**
### Portraits in Gray
B60　SP12　10pf + 5pf grn　.25　.25
B61　SP12　15pf + 5pf dp vio　.65　.45
B62　SP12　20pf + 10pf maroon　.25　.25
B63　SP12　25pf + 10pf dk bl　.25　.25
B64　SP12　40pf + 20pf lt red brn　1.40　2.00
　　　Nos. B60-B64 (5)　2.80　3.20

Issued to honor the murdered victims of the Nazis at Sachsenhausen.

---

Bicyclist — SP15

25pf+10pf, Bicyclists and spectators.

**1960, Aug. 3　Perf. 13x13½, 13x12½**
### Size: 28x23mm
B65　SP15　20pf + 10pf multi　.25　.25
### Size: 38½x21mm
B66　SP15　25pf + 10pf bl, gray
　　　　　　& brn　　　1.20　2.25

Bicycling World Championships, Aug. 3-14.

Rook and Congress
Emblem — SP16

20pf+10pf, Knight. 25pf+10pf, Bishop.

### Perf. 14x13½
**1960, Sept. 19　Engr.　Wmk. 313**
B67　SP16　10pf + 5pf blue green　.25　.25
B68　SP16　20pf + 10pf rose claret　.25　.25
B69　SP16　25pf + 10pf blue　.65　2.40
　　　Nos. B67-B69 (3)　1.15　2.90

14th Chess Championships, Leipzig.

### Type of 1957
Design: Monument and memorial wall of Sachsenhausen National Memorial.

**1960, Sept. 8　Litho.　Perf. 13½x13½**
B70　SP10　20pf + 10pf dp car　.35　.30

No. B70 was re-issued Apr. 20, 1961, with gray label adjoining each stamp in sheet, to commemorate the dedication of Sachsenhausen National Memorial. Values: unused 90c; used 40c.

### Type of 1957
Portraits: 5pf+5pf, Werner Kube. 10pf+5pf, Hanno Gunther. 15pf+5pf, Elvira Eisenschneider. 20pf+10pf, Hertha Lindner. 25pf+10pf, Herbert Tschäpe.

**1961, Feb. 6　　　　Perf. 13½x13**
### Portraits in Black
B71　SP12　5pf + 5pf brt grn　.25　.25
B72　SP12　10pf + 5pf bl grn　.25　.25
B73　SP12　15pf + 5pf brt lilac　.90　1.75
B74　SP12　20pf + 10pf rose　.25　.25
B75　SP12　25pf + 10pf brt bl　.25　.25
　　　Nos. B71-B75 (5)　1.90　2.75

Surtax for the erection of natl. memorials.

Pioneers Playing
Volleyball
SP17

Designs:　20pf+10pf,　Folk dancing. 25pf+10pf, Building model airplanes.

**1961, May 25　　　　Perf. 13x12½**
B76　SP17　10pf + 5pf multi　.25　.25
B77　SP17　20pf + 10pf multi　.25　.25
B78　SP17　25pf + 10pf multi　2.50　2.00
　　　Nos. B76-B78 (3)　3.00　2.50

Young Pioneers' meeting, Erfurt.

### Type of 1957 and

Sophie and
Hans
Scholl — SP18

Portraits: 5pf+5pf, Carlo Schönhaar. 10pf+5pf, Herbert Baum. 20pf+10pf, Liselotte Herrmann. 40pf+20pf, Hilde and Hans Coppi.

### Perf. 13½x13, 13x13½
**1961, Sept. 7　Litho.　Wmk. 313**
### Portraits in Black
B79　SP12　5pf + 5pf green　.25　.25
B80　SP12　10pf + 5pf bl grn　.25　.25
B81　SP12　20pf + 10pf rose car　.25　.25

**B82** SP18 25pf + 10pf blue .25 .25
**B83** SP18 40pf + 20pf rose brn 1.60 4.25
Nos. B79-B83 (5) 2.60 5.25

Surtax was the support of natl. memorials at Buchenwald, Ravensbrück & Sachsenhausen.

Danielle Casanova of
France — SP19

Portraits: 10pf+5pf, Julius Fucik, Czechoslo-vakia. 20pf+10pf, Johanna Jannetje Schaft, Netherlands. 25pf+10pf, Pawel Finder, Poland. 40pf+20pf, Soya Anatolyevna Kos-modemyanskaya, Russia.

**1962, Mar. 22    Engr.    Perf. 13½**
**B84** SP19 5pf + 5pf gray .25 .25
**B85** SP19 10pf + 5pf green .25 .25
**B86** SP19 20pf + 10pf maroon .25 .25
**B87** SP19 25pf + 10pf deep blue .25 .25
**B88** SP19 40pf + 20pf sepia 1.25 1.75
Nos. B84-B88 (5) 2.25 2.75

Issued in memory of foreign victims of the Nazis.

### Type of Regular Issue, 1962

Design: 20pf+10pf, Three cyclists and War-saw Palace of Culture and Science.

**Perf. 13x12½**
**1962, Apr. 26    Litho.    Wmk. 313**
**B89** A192 20pf + 10pf ver, bl, blk &
yel .25 .25

Folk Dance — SP20

15pf+5pf, Youths of three nations parading.

**1962, July 17    Wmk. 313    Perf. 14**
**B90** 10pf + 5pf multi .30 .25
**B91** 15pf + 5pf multi .30 .25
**a.** SP20 Pair, #B90-B91 1.00 .90

Issued to publicize the 8th Youth Festival for Peace and Friendship, Helsinki, July 28-Aug. 6, 1962.

No. B91a forms the festival emblem.

### Type of Regular Issue, 1962

Design: 20pf+10pf, Springboard diving.

**1962, Aug. 7    Wmk. 313    Perf. 13**
**B92** A199 20pf + 10pf lil rose &
grnsh bl .25 .25

René Blieck    Seven Cervi
of Belgium    Brothers of Italy
SP21    SP22

Portraits: 10pf+5pf, Dr. Alfred Klahr, Austria. 15pf+5pf, José Diaz, Spain. 20pf+10pf, Julius Alpari, Hungary.

**1962, Oct. 4    Engr.    Perf. 14**
**B93** SP21 5pf + 5pf dk bl gray .25 .25
**B94** SP21 10pf + 5pf bl grn .25 .25
**B95** SP21 15pf + 5pf vio .25 .25
**B96** SP21 20pf + 10pf red brn .25 .25
**B97** SP22 70pf + 30pf sepia 1.40 2.10
Nos. B93-B97 (5) 2.40 3.10

Issued to commemorate foreign victims of the Nazis.

Walter Bohne,
Runner — SP23

Portraits: 10pf+5pf, Werner Seelenbinder, wrestler. 15pf+5pf, Albert Richter, bicyclist. 20pf+10pf, Heinz Steyer, soccer player. 25pf+10pf, Kurt Schlosser, mountaineer.

---

**Engr. & Photo.**
**1963, May 27    Wmk. 313    Perf. 14**
**B98** SP23 5pf + 5pf yel & blk .25 .25
**B99** SP23 10pf + 5pf pale yel
grn & blk .25 .25
**B100** SP23 15pf + 5pf rose lil &
blk .25 .25
**B101** SP23 20pf + 10pf pink &
blk .25 .25
**B102** SP23 25pf + 10pf pale bl &
blk 1.60 4.00
Nos. B98-B102 (5) 2.60 5.00

Issued to commemorate sportsmen victims of the Nazis. Each stamp printed with alternat-ing label showing sporting events connected with each person honored. The surtax went for the maintenance of national memorials. See Nos. B106-B110.

Gymnasts — SP24

Designs: 20pf+10pf, Women gymnasts. 25pf+10pf, Relay race.

**1963, June 13    Litho.    Perf. 12½x13**
**B103** SP24 10pf + 5pf blk, yel
grn & lem .25 .25
**B104** SP24 20pf + 10pf blk, red
& vio .25 .25
**B105** SP24 25pf + 10pf blk, bl, &
gray 3.25 2.25
Nos. B103-B105 (3) 3.75 2.75

4th German Gymnastic and Sports Festival, Leipzig. The surtax went to the festival committee.

### Type of 1963

Portraits: 5pf+5pf, Hermann Tops, gymnas-tics instructor. 10pf+5pf, Käte Tucholla, field hockey players. 15pf+5pf, Rudolph Seiffert, long-distance swimmers. 20pf+10pf, Ernst Grube, sportsmen demonstrating for peace. 40pf+20pf, Kurt Biedermann, kayak in rapids.

**Engraved and Photogravure**
**1963, Sept. 24    Wmk. 313    Perf. 14**
**B106** SP23 5pf + 5pf yel & blk .25 .25
**B107** SP23 10pf + 5pf grn & blk .25 .25
**B108** SP23 15pf + 5pf lil & blk .25 .25
**B109** SP23 20pf + 10pf pale pink
& blk .25 .25
**B110** SP23 40pf + 20pf lt bl & blk 1.90 2.40
Nos. B106-B110 (5) 2.90 3.40

See note after No. B102.

### Type of Regular Issue, 1963

Design: 20pf+10pf, Ski jumper in mid-air.

**Perf. 13½x13**
**1963, Dec. 16    Litho.    Wmk. 313**
**B111** A224 20pf + 10pf multi .25 .25

Surtax for the Natl. Olympic Committee.

Anton Saefkow
SP25

Designs: 10pf+5pf, Franz Jacob. 15pf+5pf, Bernhard Bästlein. 20pf+5pf, Harro Schulze-Boysen. 25pf+10pf, Adam Kuckhoff. 40pf+10pf, Mildred and Arvid Harnack. Nos. B112-B114 show group posting anti-Hitler and pacifist posters. Nos. B115-B117 show pro-duction of anti-fascist pamphlets.

**1964, Mar. 24    Wmk. 313    Perf. 13**
**Size: 41x32mm**
**B112** SP25 5pf + 5pf .25 .25
**B113** SP25 5pf + 5pf .25 .25
**B114** SP25 15pf + 5pf .25 .25
**B115** SP25 20pf + 5pf .25 .25
**B116** SP25 25pf + 10pf .35 .25
**Size: 48½x28mm**
**B117** SP25 40pf + 10pf 1.00 1.25
Nos. B112-B117 (6) 2.35 2.50

The surtax was for the support of national memorials for victims of the Nazis.

---

### Olympic Types of Regular Issues

Designs: 40pf+20pf, Two runners. No. B119, Equestrian. No. B120, Three runners.

**Lithographed and Engraved**
**1964, July 15    Wmk. 313    Perf. 14**
**B118** A232 40pf + 20pf multi .25 .25
**Litho.**
**Perf. 13**
**B119** A233 10pf + 5pf multi 2.00 2.25
**B120** A233 10pf + 5pf multi 2.00 2.25
Nos. B118-B120 (3) 4.25 4.75

See note after No. 714.

Pioneers
Studying
SP26

Designs: 20pf+10pf, Pioneers planting tree. 25pf+10pf, Pioneers playing.

**1964, July 29**
**B121** SP26 10pf + 5pf multi 1.60 .35
**B122** SP26 20pf + 10pf multi 1.60 .35
**B123** SP26 25pf + 10pf multi 3.25 3.25
Nos. B121-B123 (3) 6.45 3.95

Fifth Young Pioneers Meeting, Karl-Marx-Stadt.

### Stamp Exhibition Type of 1964

Designs: 10pf+5pf, Stamp of 1958 (No. 390). 20pf+10pf, Stamp of 1950 (No. 73).

**Perf. 13x13½**
**1964, Sept. 23    Litho.    Wmk. 313**
**B124** A238 10pf + 5pf org & emer .25 .25
**B125** A238 20pf + 10pf brt pink &
bl .30 .25

### Boxing Type of Regular Issue

10pf+5pf, Two boxing gloves and laurel.

**Perf. 13½x14**
**1965, Apr. 27    Photo.    Wmk. 313**
**B126** A247 10pf + 5pf blk, gold,
red & blue .25 .25

The surtax went to the German Turner and Sport Organization.

### Type of Regular Issue, 1965

5pf+5pf, George Dimitrov at Leipzig trial & communist newspaper. 10pf+5pf, Anti-fascists clandestinely distributing leaflets. 15pf+5pf, Fighting in Spanish Civil War. 20pf+10pf, Ernst Thalman behind bars & demonstration for his release. 25pf+10pf, Founding of Natl. Committee for Free Germany & signatures.

**Wmk. 313**
**1965, May 5    Photo.    Perf. 14**
**Flags in Red, Black and Yellow**
**B127** A248 5pf + 5pf blk, org
& red .25 .25
**B128** A248 10pf + 5pf grn & red .25 .25
**B129** A248 15pf + 5pf lil, red &
yel .25 .25
**B130** A248 20pf + 10pf blk &
red .25 .25
**B131** A248 25pf + 10pf ol grn,
yel & blk .25 .25
Nos. B127-B131 (5) 1.25 1.00

The surtax went for the maintenance of national memorials.

Doves, Globe and
Finnish Flag — SP27

**1965, July 5    Litho.    Perf. 13x13½**
**B132** SP27 10pf + 5pf vio bl & em-
er .25 .25
**B133** SP27 20pf + 5pf red & vio bl .40 .30

World Peace Congress, Helsinki, July 10-17. The surtax went to the peace council of the DDR.

---

No. 725
Surcharged

**Perf. 13½x13**
**1965, Aug. 23    Wmk. 313**
**B134** A239 10pf + 10pf multi .35 .25

Surtax was for North Viet Nam.

### Sports Type of Regular Issue

**Perf. 13½x13**
**1965, Sept. 15    Litho.    Unwmk.**
**B135** A257 10pf + 5pf Fencer .25 .25
**B136** A257 10pf + 5pf Pistol
shooter .25 .25

International Modern Pentathlon Champion-ships, Leipzig.

### Type of Regular Issue

Designs: 10pf+5pf, Willi Bredel and instruc-tion of International Brigade. 20pf+10pf, Heinrich Rau and parade after battle of Brunete. 25pf+10pf, Hans Marchwitza, inter-national fighters and globe. 40pf+10pf, Artur Becker and battle on the Ebro.

**1966, July 15    Photo.    Perf. 14**
**B137** A277 10pf + 5pf multi .25 .25
**B138** A277 20pf + 10pf multi .25 .25
**B139** A277 25pf + 10pf multi .25 .25
**B140** A277 40pf + 10pf multi 1.25 1.00
Nos. B137-B140 (4) 2.00 1.75

The surtax was for the maintenance of national memorials.

### Canoe Type of Regular Issue

Design: 10pf+5pf, Men's single canoe race.

**Perf. 13x12½**
**1966, Aug. 16    Litho.    Unwmk.**
**B141** A279 10pf + 5pf multi .25 .25

### Red Cross Type of Regular Issue

Design: ICY Red Crescent, Red Cross, and Red Lion and Sun emblems, horiz.

**1966, Sept. 13    Wmk. 313    Perf. 14**
**B142** A281 20pf + 10pf vio & red .35 .25

International health cooperation. Surtax for German Red Cross.

### Sports Type of Regular Issue

Design: 20pf+5pf, Weight lifter.

**Perf. 13½x13**
**1966, Sept. 22    Litho.    Unwmk.**
**B143** A282 20pf + 5pf ultra & blk .35 .25

Armed Woman
Planting
Flower — SP28

**1966, Oct. 25    Perf. 13½x13**
**B144** SP28 20pf + 5pf blk & pink .50 .25

Surtax was for North Viet Nam.

### Wartburg Type of Regular Issue

Design: Wartburg, view from the East.

**1966, Nov. 23    Perf. 13x13½**
**B145** A288 10pf + 5pf slate .35 .25

See note after No. 878.

### Olympic Type of Regular Issue

Design: 10pf+5pf, Tobogganing.

**1968, Jan. 17    Litho.    Perf. 13½x13**
**B146** A314 10pf + 5pf grnsh bl, vio
bl & red .25 .25

The surtax was for the Olympic Committee of the German Democratic Republic.

Armed Mother and Child — SP29

**1968, May 8**      Perf. 13½x13
B147 SP29 10pf + 5pf yel & multi    .25 .25
Surtax was for North Viet Nam.

### Festival Type of Regular Issue
**1968, June 20   Litho.   Perf. 13½x13**
B148 A327 20pf + 5pf multi      .30 .25

### Olympic Games Type of Regular Issue, 1968
Designs: 10pf+5pf, Pole vault, vert. 20pf+10pf, Soccer, vert.

**1968, Sept. 18   Photo.   Perf. 14**
B149 A336 10pf + 5pf multi     .25 .25
B150 A336 20pf + 10pf multi    .25 .25
The surtax was for the Olympic Committee.

Armed Vietnamese Couple — SP30

**1969, June 4**
B151 SP30 10pf + 5pf multi      .30 .25
Surtax was for North Viet Nam.

### Sports Type of Regular Issue, 1969
Designs: 10pf+5pf, Gymnastics. 20pf+5pf, Art Exhibition with sports motifs.

### Photo. & Engr.
**1969, June 18      Perf. 14**
B152 A353 10pf + 5pf multi     .25 .25
B153 A353 20pf + 5pf multi     .25 .25
The surtax was for the German Gymnastic and Sports League.

Otto von Guericke's Vacuum Test with Magdeburg Hemispheres — SP31

**1969, Oct. 28   Litho.   Perf. 13x12½**
B154 SP31 40pf + 10pf multi    .85 .55
See note after No. 1146.

### Folk Art Type of Regular Issue
Design: 20pf+5pf, Decorative plate.

**1969, Nov. 25   Litho.   Perf. 13½x13**
B155 A365 20pf + 5pf yel blk & ultra    .30 .30

### Sports Type of Regular Issue
Design: 20pf+5pf, Children hurdling.

**1970, July 1   Photo.   Perf. 14x13½**
B156 A382 20pf + 5pf multi     .35 .25

6th Youth Pioneer Meeting, Cottbus — SP32

Design: 10pf+5pf, Pioneer Waving Kerchief, and Pioneer Activities. 25pf+5pf, Girl Pioneer holding kerchief, and Pioneer activities.

**1970, July 28   Litho.   Perf. 13x12½**
B157    10pf + 5pf multi     .25 .25
B158    25pf + 5pf multi     .25 .25
    a.   SP32 Pair, #B157-B158    .85 2.00
No. B158a has continuous design.

Ho Chi Minh — SP33

**1970, Sept. 2      Perf. 13x13½**
B159 SP33 20pf + 5pf rose, blk & red    .35 .25
Surtax was for North Viet Nam.

German Democratic Republic No. 460 — SP34

**1970, Oct. 1   Photo.   Perf. 14x13½**
B160 SP34 15pf + 5pf multi     .25 .30
2nd National Youth Philatelic Exhibition, Karl-Marx-Stadt, Oct. 4-11.

Mother and Child — SP35

### Photo. & Engr.
**1971, Sept. 2      Perf. 14**
B161 SP35 10pf + 5pf multi     .30 .25
Surtax was for North Viet Nam.

### Type of Regular Issue
10pf+5pf, Loading & unloading mail at airport.

### Photo. & Engr.
**1971, Oct. 5      Perf. 14**
B162 A421 10pf + 5pf multi     .25 .25

### Olympic Games Type of Regular Issue
Olympic Rings and: 10pf+5pf, Figure skating, pairs. 15pf+5pf, Speed skating.

**1971, Dec. 7   Photo.   Perf. 13½x14**
B163 A424 10pf + 5pf bl, car & blk    .25 .25
B164 A424 15pf + 5pf grn, blk & bl    .25 .25

Vietnamese Farm Woman — SP36

**1972, Feb. 22   Litho.   Perf. 13½x13**
B165 SP36 10pf + 5pf multi     .30 .25
Surtax was for North Viet Nam.

### Olympic Games Type of Regular Issue
Sport and Olympic Rings: 10pf+5pf, Diving. 25pf+10pf, Rowing.

**1972, May 16   Photo.   Perf. 13½x14**
B166 A430 10pf + 5pf grnsh bl, gold & blk    .25 .25
B167 A430 25pf + 10pf multi    .25 .25

### Interartes Type of Regular Issue
Designs: 15pf+5pf, Spear carrier, Persia, 500 B.C. 35pf+5pf, Grape Sellers, by Max Lingner, 1949, horiz.

**1972, Sept. 19   Photo.   Perf. 14**
B168 A439 15pf + 5pf multi     .65 .55
B169 A439 35pf + 5pf multi     .25 .25

Flags and World Time Clock — SP37

25pf+5pf, Youth group with guitar and dove.

**1973, Feb. 13   Litho.   Perf. 12½x13**
B170 SP37 10pf + 5pf multi     .25 .25
B171 SP37 25pf + 5pf multi     .30 .25
10th World Youth Festival, Berlin.

Young Couple, by Günter Glombitza — SP38

**1973, Oct. 4   Photo.   Perf. 13½x14**
B172 SP38 20pf + 5pf multi     .30 .25
Philatelists' Day and for the 3rd National Youth Philatelic Exhibition, Halle.

Child, Symbols of Reconstruction SP39

**1973, Oct. 11      Perf. 14x13½**
B173 SP39 10pf + 5pf multi     .30 .25
Surtax was for North Viet Nam.

Luis Corvalan, Red Flag — SP40

25pf+5pf, Salvador Allende, Chilean flag.

**1973, Nov. 5      Perf. 13½x14**
B174 SP40 10pf + 5pf multi     .25 .25
B175 SP40 25pf + 5pf multi     .35 .35
Solidarity with the people of Chile.

Raised Fist and Star — SP41

**1975, Sept. 23   Litho.   Perf. 13x13½**
B176 SP41 10pf + 5pf multi     .30 .25
Surtax was for the Solidarity Committee of the German Democratic Republic.

Restored Post Gate, Wurzen, 1734 — SP42

**1975, Oct. 21   Photo.   Perf. 14**
B177 SP42 10pf + 5pf multi     .35 .35
Philatelists' Day 1975.

### Olympic Games Type of 1975
Designs: 10pf+5pf, Luge run, Oberhof. 25pf+5pf, Ski jump, Rennsteig at Oberhof.

**1975, Dec. 2   Photo.   Perf. 14**
B178 A518 10pf + 5pf multi     .25 .25
B179 A518 25pf + 5pf multi     .25 .25

### Olympic Games Type of 1976
Designs: 10pf+5pf, Swimming pool, High School for Physical Education, Leipzig. 35pf+10pf, Rifle range, Suhl.

**1976, May 18   Photo.   Perf. 13½x14**
B180 A529 10pf + 5pf multi     .25 .25
B181 A529 35pf + 10pf multi    .25 .25

TV Tower, Berlin, and Perforations — SP43

**1976, Oct. 19   Litho.   Perf. 13**
B182 SP43 10pf + 5pf org & bl    .30 .25
Surtax was for Sozphilex 77, Philatelic Exhibition of Socialist Countries, in connection with 60th anniversary of October Revolution.

### Sports Type of 1977
10pf+5pf, Young milers. 25pf+5pf, Girls artistic gymnastic performance.

**1977, July 19   Litho.   Perf. 13x12½**
B183 A558 10pf + 5pf multi     .25 .25
B184 A558 25pf + 5pf multi     .25 .25

### Sozphilex Type of 1977
Souvenir Sheet
Design: 50pf+20pf, World Youth Song, by Lothar Zitzmann, horiz.

**1977, Aug. 16   Photo.   Perf. 13**
B185 A559 50pf + 20pf multi    1.10 2.60

Hand Holding Torch — SP44

**1977, Oct. 18   Litho.   Perf. 14**
B186 SP44 10pf + 5pf multi     .30 .25
Surtax was for East German Solidarity Committee.

### Fountain Type of 1979
Design: 10pf+5pf, Goose Boy Fountain.

**1979, Aug. 7   Photo.   Perf. 14**
B187 A617 10pf + 5pf multi     .40 .35

Vietnamese Soldier, Mother and Child — SP45

**1979, Nov. 6   Litho.   Perf. 14**
B188 SP45 10pf + 5pf red org & blk    .35 .25
Surtax was for Vietnam.

### Olympic Type of 1980
Ski Jump, sculpture by Gunther Schutz.

**1980, Jan. 15      Photo.**
B189 A627 25pf + 10pf multi    .25 .25

**1980, Apr. 22      Perf. 14**
Design: 20pf+5pf, Runners at the Finish, by Lothar Zitzmann.
B190 A627   20 + 5pf multi     .25 .25

### Interflug Type of 1980
Souvenir Sheet
**1980, June 10   Litho.   Perf. 13x12½**
B191 A636 1m + 10pf Jet, globe   1.90 4.00
AEROSOZPHILEX 1980 International Airpost Exhibition, Berlin, Aug. 1-10.

### Olympic Type of 1980
Design: Swimmer, by Willi Sitte, vert.

**1980, July 8     Photo.   Perf. 14**
B192 A627 10pf + 5pf multi     .25 .25
22nd Summer Olympic Games, Moscow, July 19-Aug. 3.

International Solidarity — SP46

**1980, Oct. 14        Photo.        Perf. 14**
B193 SP46 10pf + 5pf multi            .40   .25

International Solidarity — SP47

**1981, Oct. 6        Photo.        Perf. 14**
B194 SP47 10pf + 5pf multi            .35   .25

Palestinian Solidarity — SP48

Palestinian family, Tree of Life.

**1982, Sept. 21        Litho.        Perf. 14**
B195 SP48 10pf + 5pf multi            .35   .25

Nicaraguan Solidarity — SP49

Literacy, home defense.

**1983, Nov. 8        Litho.        Perf. 14x13½**
B196 SP49 10pf + 5pf multi            .30   .25

Solidarity — SP50

**1984, Oct. 23        Photo.        Perf. 14**
B197 SP50 10pf + 5pf Knot            .35   .25

Solidarity — SP51

10pf +5pf, Globe, peace dove.

**1985, May 28                    Photo.**
B198 SP51 10pf + 5pf multi            .25   .25
Surtax for the Solidarity Committee.

Technical Assistance to Developing Nations — SP52

**1986, Nov. 4                    Photo.**
B199 SP52 10pf + 5pf multi            .30   .25
Surtax for the Solidarity Committee.

Solidarity with South Africans Opposing Apartheid — SP53

**1987, June 16        Litho.        Perf. 14**
B200 SP53 10pf +5pf multi            .30   .25

---

Solidarity SP54

**1988, Oct. 4        Photo.        Perf. 14**
B201 SP54 10pf +5pf multi            .40   .40
Surtax for the Solidarity Committee. No. B201 printed se-tenant with label containing a Wilhelm Pieck quote.

UNICEF Emblem and Children of Africa — SP55

**1989, Sept. 5        Photo.        Perf. 14½x14**
B202 SP55 10pf +5pf multi            .30   .25
Surtax for the Solidarity Committee.

Leipzig Church, Municipal Arms — SP56

**1990, Feb. 28        Photo.        Perf. 13**
B203 SP56 35pf +15pf multi            .75   .55
We are the People.

Intl. Literacy Year — SP57

**1990, July 24        Photo.        Perf. 14**
B204 SP57 30pf+5pf on 10pf+5pf            .80   .80
Not issued without surcharge.

---

## AIR POST STAMPS

Catalogue values for all unused stamps in this section are for Never Hinged items.

Canceled to Order
Used values are for CTO's.

Stylized Plane
AP1                    AP2

**Perf. 13x12½, 13x13½ (AP2)**
**1957, Dec. 13        Litho.        Wmk. 313**
C1 AP1 5pf gray & blk            3.25   .25
C2 AP1 20pf brt car & blk            .25   .25
C3 AP1 35pf violet & blk            .25   .25
C4 AP1 50pf maroon & blk            .30   .25
C5 AP2 1m olive & yel            .90   .25
C6 AP2 3m choc & yel            1.40   .40
C7 AP2 5m dk bl & yel            3.25   .60
    Nos. C1-C7 (7)            9.60   2.25

Plane and Envelope — AP3

---

**1982-87        Photo.        Perf. 14**
C8 AP3 5pf lt bl & blk            .25   .25
C9 AP3 15pf brt rose lil & blk            .25   .30
C10 AP3 20pf ocher & blk            .25   .25
C11 AP3 25pf ol bis & blk            .30   .30
C12 AP3 30pf brt grn & blk            .25   .25
C13 AP3 40pf ol grn & blk            .30   .25
C14 AP3 1m blue & blk            .60   .40
C15 AP3 3m brown & blk            3.00   1.75
C16 AP3 5m dk red & blk            3.25   1.20
    Nos. C8-C16 (9)            8.45   4.95

Issued: 30, 40pf, 1m, 10/26; 5, 20pf, 10/4/83; 3m, 4/10/84; 5m, 9/10/85; 15, 25pf, 10/6/87.

---

## OFFICIAL STAMPS

While valid, these Official stamps were not sold to the public unused. After their period of use, some sets were sold abroad by the government stamp sales agency. Used values of Official stamps are for canceled-to-order examples. Reprints of type O1 stamps have printed cancellations.

Catalogue values for all unused stamps in this section are for Never Hinged items.

Arms of Republic — O1

**Perf. 13x12½**
**1954        Wmk. 297        Litho.**
O1 O1 5pf emerald            13.50   .25
O2 O1 6pf violet            6.50   .25
O3 O1 8pf org brown            9.00   .25
O4 O1 10pf lt bl grn            20.00   .25
O5 O1 12pf blue            32.50   .25
O6 O1 15pf dark violet            32.50   .25
O7 O1 16pf dark violet            6.50   .25
O8 O1 20pf olive            13.00   .25
O9 O1 24pf brown red            6.50   .25
O10 O1 25pf sage green            6.50   .25
O11 O1 30pf brown red            6.50   .25
O12 O1 40pf red            9.75   .25
O13 O1 48pf rose lilac            4.50   .65
O14 O1 50pf rose lilac            4.50   .25
O15 O1 60pf bright blue            4.00   .25
O16 O1 70pf brown            4.00   .25
O17 O1 84pf brown            10.00   2.00
    Nos. O1-O17 (17)            189.75   6.40

### Type of 1954 Redrawn

Arc of compass projects at right except on No. O22.

**1954-56                            Typo.**
O18 O1 5pf emer ('54)            3.25   .25
O19 O1 10pf bl grn            2.50   .25
O20 O1 12pf dk bl ('54)            2.50   .25
O21 O1 15pf dk vio            2.50   .25
O22 O1 20pf ol, arc at left ('55)            32.50   .25
a.   Arc of compass projects at right ('56)            325.00   .25
O23 O1 25pf dark green            2.00   .35
O24 O1 30pf brown red            4.00   .35
O25 O1 40pf red            5.25   .25
O26 O1 50pf rose lilac            2.00   .25
O27 O1 70pf brown            2.00   .25
    Nos. O18-O27 (10)            58.50   2.70

Shaded background of emblem consists of vertical lines; on Nos. O1-O17 it consists of dots.
Granite paper was used for a 1956 printing of the 5pf, 10pf, 15pf, 20pf and 40pf. Value for set unused $1,800, used $5.50.
See Nos. O37-O43.

O2

**1956        Wmk. 297        Perf. 13x12½**
O28 O2 5pf black            .25   .25
O29 O2 10pf black            .25   .25
O30 O2 20pf black            .30   .25
O31 O2 40pf black            .35   .25
O32 O2 70pf black            .40   .40
    Nos. O28-O32 (5)            1.55   1.40

O3

---

**1956        Litho.        Wmk. 297**
O33 O3 10pf lilac & black            .80   .65
O34 O3 20pf lilac & black            120.00   .65
O35 O3 40pf lilac & black            1.25   .65
O36 O3 70pf lilac & black            2.00   2.25
    Nos. O33-O36 (4)            124.05   4.20

Nos. O33-O36 exist also with black or violet overprint of 4-digit control number.
See Nos. O44-O45.
No. O34 was reprinted with watermark sideways ("DDR" vertical). Value $4.

### Redrawn Type of 1954-56
**Perf. 13x12½, 14**
**1957-60        Typo.        Wmk. 313**
**Granite Paper**
O37 O1 5pf emerald            .35   .25
O38 O1 10pf blue green            .35   .25
O39 O1 15pf dark vio            .35   .25
O40 O1 20pf olive            .35   .25
O41 O1 30pf dark red ('58)            .40   .25
O42 O1 40pf red            .35   .25
O42A O1 50pf rose lilac ('60)            1.10   1.60
O43 O1 70pf brown ('58)            1.10   1.60
    Nos. O37-O43 (8)            4.35   4.70

Nos. O37-O43 were all issued in perf. 13x12½. Nos. O37-O40 were also issued perf. 14. Values are the same. Postally used No. O42A is rare. Nos. O37-O41 are valued with Wmk. 313 reversed.
Nos. O37-O42 exist with Wmk. 313 normal, but overprinted cancel reprints value only slightly higher.

### Type of 1956
**1957        Litho.        Perf. 13x12½**
O44 O3 10pf lilac & black            .45   .35
O45 O3 20pf lilac & black            .45   .35

Nos. O44-O45 have black or violet overprint of four-digit control number.
Stamps similar to type O3 were issued later, with denomination expressed in dashes: one for 10pf, two for 20pf.

---

## ISSUED UNDER RUSSIAN OCCUPATION

### BERLIN-BRANDENBURG

Berlin Bear — OS1

6pf, Bear holding spade. 8pf, Bear on shield. 10pf, Bear holding brick. 12pf, Bear carrying board. 20pf, Bear on small shield. 30pf, Oak sapling, ruins.

**1945        Litho.        Perf. 14**
11N1 OS1 5pf green            .25   .45
11N2 OS1 6pf violet            .25   .45
11N3 OS1 8pf org red            .25   .35
11N4 OS1 10pf brown            .25   .35
11N5 OS1 12pf red            .25   .35
11N6 OS1 20pf blue            .25   .45
11N7 OS1 30pf olive            .25   .65
    Nos. 11N1-11N7 (7)                3.05
Set, never hinged            2.00

Issued: 5pf, 8pf, 6/9; 12pf, 7/5; others, 7/18.

**1945, Dec. 6        Serrate Roulette 13½**
11N1a OS1 5pf            .25   .55
11N2a OS1 6pf            3.75   90.00
11N3a OS1 8pf            2.25   90.00
11N4a OS1 10pf            3.75   90.00
11N5a OS1 12pf            4.50   125.00
11N6a OS1 20pf            3.00   97.50
11N7a OS1 30pf            4.50   125.00
    Nos. 11N1a-11N7a (7)            22.00   618.05
Set, never hinged            110.00

No. 11N1a comes with two different roulettes. The roulette that matches Nos. 11N2a-11N7a is valued at $2. No. 11N5a in the second roulette is rare.

---

### MECKLENBURG-VORPOMMERN

OS1

Plowman — OS2

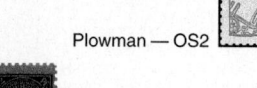

OS2a

## 1945-46        Typo.        Perf. 10½

| | | | | |
|---|---|---|---|---|
| **12N1** | OS1 | 6pf blk, *grn* | .25 | 2.00 |
| **12N2** | OS1 | 6pf purple | 1.00 | 3.25 |
| **12N3** | OS1 | 6pf pur, *grn* | 1.00 | 3.25 |
| **12N4** | OS2 | 8pf red, *rose* | .30 | 2.00 |
| a. | | 8pf red lilac, *rose* | .65 | |
| **12N5** | OS2 | 8pf blk, *rose* | 1.60 | 8.50 |
| **12N6** | OS2 | 8pf red lil, *grn* | .45 | 4.00 |
| **12N7** | OS2 | 8pf blk, *grn* | 2.60 | 13.00 |
| **12N8** | OS2 | 8pf brown | .40 | 4.00 |
| **12N9** | OS2a | 12pf blk | .25 | 2.00 |
| **12N10** | OS2a | 12pf brn lil | .30 | 2.00 |
| **12N11** | OS2a | 12pf red | 1.60 | 10.00 |
| **12N12** | OS2a | 12pf red, *rose* | .30 | 2.10 |
| | *Nos. 12N1-12N12 (12)* | | 10.05 | 56.10 |
| | Set, never hinged | | 30.00 | |

Many shades.

Issued: Nos. 12N1, 12N9, 8/28; No. 12N4, 10/6; No. 12N5, 10/19; No. 12N7, 11/2; No. 12N6, 11/3; No. 12N10, 11/9; No. 12N2, 11/16; No. 12N11, 12/20; No. 12N8, 1/7/46; No. 12N3, 1/11/46; No. 12N12, 1/30/46.

Buildings — OS3

Designs: 4pf, Deer. 5pf, Fishing boats. 6pf, Harvesting grain. 8pf, Windmill. 10pf, Two-horse plow. 12pf, Bricklayer on scaffolding. 15pf, Tractor plowing field. 20pf, Ship, warehouse. 30pf, Factory. 40pf, Woman spinning.

## 1946        Typo.        Imperf.

| | | | | |
|---|---|---|---|---|
| **12N13** | OS3 | 3pf brown | 1.00 | 37.50 |
| **12N14** | OS3 | 4pf blue | 12.00 | 52.50 |
| **12N15** | OS3 | 4pf red brown | 1.00 | 37.50 |
| **12N16** | OS3 | 5pf green | 1.00 | 37.50 |
| **12N17** | OS3 | 8pf orange | 1.00 | 37.50 |
| **12N18** | OS3 | 10pf brown | .80 | 37.50 |

### Perf. 10½

| | | | | |
|---|---|---|---|---|
| **12N19** | OS3 | 6pf purple | .65 | 6.00 |
| **12N20** | OS3 | 6pf blue | .65 | 6.00 |
| **12N21** | OS3 | 12pf red | .55 | 3.00 |
| **12N22** | OS3 | 15pf brown | .55 | 6.50 |
| **12N23** | OS3 | 20pf blue | .80 | 8.50 |
| **12N24** | OS3 | 30pf blue green | .65 | 10.00 |
| **12N25** | OS3 | 40pf red violet | .65 | 10.00 |
| | *Nos. 12N13-12N25 (13)* | | 21.30 | 290.00 |
| | Set, never hinged | | 62.50 | |

Issued: 3pf, No. 12N14, 5pf, 6pf, 8pf, 1/17; 10pf, 12pf, 40pf, 1/22; 15pf, 1/24; 30pf, 1/26; 20pf, 1/29; No. 12N15, 2/25.
Nos. 12N13-12N21 exist on both white and toned paper.

## MECKLENBURG-VORPOMMERN SEMI-POSTAL STAMPS

Rudolf Breitscheid (1874-1944), Politician — OSP1

Designs: 8pf+22pf, Dr. Erich Klausener (1885-1934), theologian. 12pf+28pf, Ernst Thalmann (1886-1944), politician.

## 1945, Oct. 21    Typo.    Perf. 10½x11

| | | | | |
|---|---|---|---|---|
| **12NB1** | OSP1 | 6 +14pf grn | 9.00 | 52.50 |
| **12NB2** | OSP1 | 8 +22pf pur | 9.00 | 52.50 |
| **12NB3** | OSP1 | 12 +28pf red | 9.00 | 52.50 |
| | *Nos. 12NB1-12NB3 (3)* | | 27.00 | 157.50 |
| | Set, never hinged | | 75.00 | |

Sower — OSP2

6pf+14pf, Horsedrawn Plow. 12pf+28pf, Reaper.

---

## 1945

| | | | | |
|---|---|---|---|---|
| **12NB4** | OSP2 | 6 +14pf bl grn | 1.60 | 35.00 |
| **12NB5** | OSP2 | 6 +14pf grn | 2.00 | 35.00 |
| **12NB6** | OSP2 | 8 +22pf brn | 2.00 | 35.00 |
| **12NB7** | OSP2 | 8 +22pf yel brn | 2.00 | 35.00 |
| **12NB8** | OSP2 | 12 +28pf red | 2.00 | 35.00 |
| **12NB9** | OSP2 | 12 +28pf org | 2.00 | 35.00 |
| | *Nos. 12NB4-12NB9 (6)* | | 11.60 | 210.00 |
| | Set, never hinged | | 32.50 | |

Issued: Nos. 12NB4, 12NB6, 12NB8, 12/8; others 12/31.

Child Welfare — OSP3

No. 12NB10, Child in hand. No. 12NB11, Girl in winter. No. 12NB12, Boy.

## 1945, Dec. 31        Perf. 11

| | | | | |
|---|---|---|---|---|
| **12NB10** | OSP3 | 6 +14pf org | 2.25 | 40.00 |
| **12NB11** | OSP3 | 8 +22pf ul-tra | .85 | 40.00 |
| **12NB12** | OSP3 | 12 +28pf car | .85 | 40.00 |
| | *Nos. 12NB10-12NB12 (3)* | | 3.95 | 120.00 |
| | Set, never hinged | | 10.00 | |

## SAXONY PROVINCE

Coat of Arms — OS1

### Perf. 13x12½

## 1945-46        Typo.        Wmk. 48

| | | | | |
|---|---|---|---|---|
| **13N1** | OS1 | 1pf slate | .25 | 2.00 |
| a. | | Imperf. | .25 | 4.00 |
| | | Never hinged | .55 | |
| **13N2** | OS1 | 3pf yellow brown | .25 | 2.00 |
| a. | | Imperf. | .25 | 2.60 |
| | | Never hinged | .55 | |
| **13N3** | OS1 | 5pf green | .25 | 2.00 |
| a. | | Imperf. | .45 | 10.00 |
| | | Never hinged | 1.25 | |
| **13N4** | OS1 | 6pf purple | .25 | 2.25 |
| a. | | Imperf. | .35 | 2.00 |
| | | Never hinged | .90 | |
| **13N5** | OS1 | 8pf orange | .25 | 2.25 |
| a. | | Imperf. | .25 | 2.60 |
| | | Never hinged | .55 | |
| **13N6** | OS1 | 10pf brown | .25 | 2.00 |
| a. | | Imperf. | 4.50 | 120.00 |
| | | Never hinged | 10.00 | |
| **13N7** | OS1 | 12pf red | .25 | 2.00 |
| a. | | Imperf. | .25 | 2.00 |
| | | Never hinged | .55 | |
| **13N8** | OS1 | 15pf red brown | .25 | 20.00 |
| **13N9** | OS1 | 20pf blue | .25 | 3.25 |
| **13N10** | OS1 | 24pf orange brown | .25 | 3.25 |
| **13N11** | OS1 | 30pf olive green | .25 | 3.25 |
| **13N12** | OS1 | 40pf lake | .55 | 6.50 |
| | *Nos. 13N1-13N12 (12)* | | 3.30 | 50.75 |
| | Set, never hinged | | 8.75 | |

Issued: Nos. 13N1-13N12, 12/1945; Nos. 13N1a-13N5a, 13N7a, 10/10/45; No. 13N6a, 1/1946.

Land Reform — OS2

## 1945-46        Unwmk.        Imperf.

| | | | | |
|---|---|---|---|---|
| **13N13** | OS2 | 6pf green | .25 | 1.90 |
| **13N14** | OS2 | 12pf red | .25 | 1.90 |

### On Thin Transparent Paper
### Wmk. 397
### Perf. 13x13½

| | | | | |
|---|---|---|---|---|
| **13N15** | OS2 | 6pf green | .25 | 1.90 |
| **13N16** | OS2 | 12pf red | .25 | 1.90 |
| | *Nos. 13N13-13N16 (4)* | | | 7.60 |
| | Set, never hinged | | 1.00 | |

Issued: Nos. 13N13-13N14, 12/17/45; others 2/21/46.

## SAXONY PROVINCE SEMI-POSTAL STAMPS

Reconstruction — OSP1

Designs: 6+4pf, Housing construction. 12+8pf, Bridge repair. 42+28pf, Locomotives.

## 1946, Jan. 19        Typo.        Perf. 13

| | | | | |
|---|---|---|---|---|
| **13NB1** | OSP1 | 6pf +4pf green | .25 | 1.90 |
| a. | | Imperf. | .25 | 16.00 |
| **13NB2** | OSP1 | 12pf +8pf red | .25 | 1.90 |
| a. | | Imperf. | .25 | 16.00 |
| **13NB3** | OSP1 | 42pf +28pf violet | .25 | 1.90 |
| a. | | Imperf. | .25 | 16.00 |
| | *Nos. 13NB1-13NB3 (3)* | | | 5.70 |
| | Set, never hinged | | .75 | |
| | Set, 13NB1a-13NB3a, never hinged | | 1.25 | |

Nos. 13NB1a-13NB3a issued Feb. 21.

---

## WEST SAXONY

OS1

## 1945    Typo.    Wmk. 48    Perf. 13x12½

| | | | | |
|---|---|---|---|---|
| **14N1** | OS1 | 3pf brown | .25 | 2.00 |
| **14N2** | OS1 | 4pf slate | .25 | 3.00 |
| **14N3** | OS1 | 5pf green | .25 | 2.00 |
| a. | | Imperf. | .25 | |
| | | Never hinged | .25 | |
| **14N4** | OS1 | 6pf violet | .25 | 2.00 |
| a. | | Imperf. | .25 | |
| | | Never hinged | .25 | |
| **14N5** | OS1 | 8pf orange | .25 | 4.00 |
| a. | | Imperf. | .25 | |
| | | Never hinged | .25 | |
| **14N6** | OS1 | 10pf gray | .25 | 3.50 |
| **14N7** | OS1 | 12pf red | .25 | 2.00 |
| a. | | Imperf. | .25 | |
| | | Never hinged | .25 | |
| **14N8** | OS1 | 15pf red brown | .30 | 3.50 |
| **14N9** | OS1 | 20pf blue | .25 | 3.25 |
| **14N10** | OS1 | 30pf olive green | .30 | 2.00 |
| **14N11** | OS1 | 40pf red lilac | .50 | 4.00 |
| **14N12** | OS1 | 60pf maroon | .30 | 16.00 |
| | *Nos. 14N1-14N12 (12)* | | 3.40 | 47.25 |
| | Set, never hinged | | 7.00 | |

Issued: 3-4, 20-30pf, 11/9; 5-8, 12pf, 11/12; 10, 15, 40-60pf, 11/15; imperfs., 9/28.

Leipzig Fair — OS2

## 1945, Oct. 18

| | | | | |
|---|---|---|---|---|
| **14N13** | OS2 | 6pf green | .30 | 2.50 |
| **14N14** | OS2 | 12pf red | .30 | 2.50 |
| | Set, never hinged | | 1.60 | |

Leipzig Arms — OS3

Designs: 5pf, 6pf, St. Nicholas Church. 8pf, 12pf, Leipzig Town Hall.

## 1946, Feb. 12

| | | | | |
|---|---|---|---|---|
| **14N15** | OS3 | 3pf brown | .25 | 5.00 |
| a. | | Unwatermarked | .25 | 7.50 |
| **14N16** | OS3 | 4pf slate | .25 | 5.00 |
| a. | | Unwatermarked | .25 | 7.50 |
| **14N17** | OS3 | 5pf green | .25 | 5.00 |
| a. | | Unwatermarked | .25 | 7.50 |
| **14N18** | OS3 | 6pf violet | .25 | 5.00 |
| a. | | Unwatermarked | .25 | 7.50 |
| **14N19** | OS3 | 8pf orange | .25 | 5.00 |
| a. | | Unwatermarked | .25 | 7.50 |
| **14N20** | OS3 | 12pf red | .25 | 5.00 |
| a. | | Unwatermarked | .25 | 7.50 |
| | *Nos. 14N15-14N20 (6)* | | | 30.00 |
| | Set, never hinged | | 2.40 | |
| | Set, 14NB15a-14NB20a, never hinged | | 2.40 | |

Nos. 14N15a-14N20a issued Mar. 15.

## WEST SAXONY SEMI-POSTAL STAMPS

OSP1

## 1946    Typo.    Wmk. 48    Perf. 13x12½

| | | | | |
|---|---|---|---|---|
| **14NB1** | OSP1 | 3 +2pf yel brn | .25 | 2.60 |
| **14NB2** | OSP1 | 4 +3pf slate | .25 | 2.60 |
| **14NB3** | OSP1 | 5 +3pf grn | .25 | 2.60 |
| **14NB4** | OSP1 | 6 +4pf violet | .25 | 2.60 |
| **14NB5** | OSP1 | 8 +4pf org | .25 | 2.60 |
| **14NB6** | OSP1 | 10 +5pf gray | .25 | 2.60 |
| **14NB7** | OSP1 | 12 +6pf red | .25 | 2.60 |
| **14NB8** | OSP1 | 15 +10pf red brn | .25 | 2.60 |
| **14NB9** | OSP1 | 20 +10pf blue | .25 | 2.60 |
| **14NB10** | OSP1 | 30 +20pf ol grn | .25 | 3.25 |
| **14NB11** | OSP1 | 40 +30pf red lilac | .25 | 2.60 |
| **14NB12** | OSP1 | 60 +40pf lake | .25 | 4.00 |
| | *Nos. 14NB1-14NB12 (12)* | | 3.00 | 33.25 |
| | Set, never hinged | | 5.75 | |

Issue dates: Nos. 14NB1, 14NB4, 14NB7, 14NB11, Jan. 7; others, Jan. 28.

Market, Old Town Hall — OSP2

## 1946, May 8        Perf. 13

| | | | | |
|---|---|---|---|---|
| **14NB13** | OSP2 | 6 +14pf vio | .25 | 2.25 |
| a. | | Imperf. | .35 | 12.00 |
| b. | | Unwatermarked | .35 | 3.00 |
| **14NB14** | OSP2 | 12 +18pf bl gray | .25 | 4.00 |
| a. | | Imperf. | .35 | 12.00 |
| b. | | Unwatermarked | .25 | 5.25 |
| **14NB15** | OSP2 | 24 +26pf org brn | .25 | 2.25 |
| a. | | Imperf. | .35 | 12.00 |
| b. | | Unwatermarked | .30 | 2.00 |
| **14NB16** | OSP2 | 84 +66pf grn | .25 | 6.50 |
| a. | | Imperf. | .35 | 24.00 |
| c. | | Sheet of 4, #14NB13a-14NB16a | 65.00 | 225.00 |
| | *Nos. 14NB13-14NB16 (4)* | | 1.00 | 15.00 |
| | Set, never hinged | | 1.25 | |
| | Set, 14NB13a-14NB16a, never hinged | | 3.25 | |
| | Set, 14NB13b-14NB15b, never hinged | | 2.40 | |

Issue date: Imperf., May 20.

---

## EAST SAXONY

OS1

## 1945, June 23    Photo.    Imperf.

| | | | | |
|---|---|---|---|---|
| **15N1** | OS1 | 12pf red | 160.00 | 525.00 |
| | | Never hinged | 400.00 | |

Withdrawn on day of issue.

OS2

### Litho. (3pf, #15N9), Photo.

## 1945-46

| | | | | |
|---|---|---|---|---|
| **15N2** | OS2 | 3pf sepia | .30 | 2.25 |
| **15N3** | OS2 | 4pf blue gray | .25 | 1.60 |
| a. | | 4pf gray | .25 | .95 |
| **15N4** | OS2 | 5pf brown | .30 | 1.75 |
| **15N5** | OS2 | 6pf green | 2.25 | 8.00 |
| **15N6** | OS2 | 6pf violet | .25 | 1.60 |
| **15N7** | OS2 | 8pf dark violet | .35 | 1.75 |
| **15N8** | OS2 | 10pf dark brown | .40 | 3.50 |
| **15N9** | OS2 | 10pf gray | .30 | 2.25 |
| **15N10** | OS2 | 12pf red | .30 | 1.75 |
| **15N11** | OS2 | 15pf lemon | .40 | 2.25 |
| **15N12** | OS2 | 20pf blue | .25 | 1.60 |
| a. | | 20pf gray blue | .25 | 5.25 |
| | | Never hinged | 1.10 | |
| **15N13** | OS2 | 25pf blue | .40 | 2.25 |
| **15N14** | OS2 | 30pf yellow | .25 | 1.60 |

| | | | | |
|---|---|---|---|---|
| 15N15 | OS2 | 40pf lilac | .40 | 2.25 |

**Typo.**

**Perf. 13x12½**

| | | | | |
|---|---|---|---|---|
| 15N16 | OS2 | 3pf brown | .25 | 1.60 |
| 15N17 | OS2 | 5pf green | .25 | 1.60 |
| 15N18 | OS2 | 6pf violet | .25 | 1.60 |
| 15N19 | OS2 | 8pf orange | .25 | 1.60 |
| 15N20 | OS2 | 12pf vermilion | .25 | 1.60 |
| | Nos. 15N2-15N20 (19) | | 7.65 | 42.40 |
| | Set, never hinged | | 20.00 | |

Issued: 12pf, 6/28; No. 15N5, 6/30; 8pf, No. 15N8, 7/3; 25pf, 7/5; 5pf, 6/6; 40pf, 7/7; 7pf, 7/10; No. 15N12a, 7/26; Nos. 15N9, 15N12, 15N17-15N20, 11/3; No. 15N3, 30pf, 11/5; 3pf, 12/5; No. 15N15, 12/21; No. 15N6, 1/22/46.

---

### EAST SAXONY SEMI-POSTAL STAMPS

Zwinger, Dresden — OSP1

Design: 12pf+88pf, Rathaus, Dresden.

**1946, Feb. 6    Photo.    Perf. 11**

| | | | | |
|---|---|---|---|---|
| 15NB1 | OSP1 | 6pf +44pf grn | .25 | 5.50 |
| 15NB2 | OSP1 | 12pf +88pf red | .25 | 5.50 |
| | Set, never hinged | | 1.75 | |

---

### THURINGIA

Fir Trees — OS1

Designs: 6pf, 8pf, Posthorn. 12pf, Schiller. 20pf, 30pf, Goethe.

**1945-46    Typo.    Perf. 11**

| | | | | |
|---|---|---|---|---|
| 16N1 | OS1 | 3pf brown | .25 | 2.60 |
| 16N2 | OS1 | 4pf black | .25 | 2.60 |
| 16N3 | OS1 | 5pf green | .25 | 3.25 |
| a. | Souvenir sheet of 3, #16N1-16N3 | | 140.00 | 725.00 |
| | Never hinged | | 300.00 | |
| 16N4 | OS1 | 6pf dark green | .25 | 2.00 |
| 16N5 | OS1 | 8pf orange | .25 | 2.00 |
| 16N6 | OS1 | 12pf red | .25 | 2.25 |
| 16N7 | OS1 | 20pf blue | .25 | 2.00 |
| a. | Imperf. | | .25 | 3.00 |
| | Never hinged | | .35 | |
| b. | Souv. sheet of 4, #16N2, 16N4, 16N6-16N7, rouletted x imperf. btwn. | | 525.00 | 2,150. |
| | Never hinged | | 1,150. | |
| 16N8 | OS1 | 30pf gray | .45 | 3.00 |
| a. | Imperf. | | 2.25 | 26.00 |
| | Never hinged | | 9.00 | |
| | Nos. 16N1-16N8 (8) | | 2.20 | 19.70 |
| | Set, never hinged | | 2.60 | |

No. 16N3a sold for 2m, No. 16N7b for 10m.
Issued: 6pf, 10/1; 12pf, 10/19; 5pf, 10/20; 8pf, 11/3; 20pf, 11/24; NOS. 16N3a, 16N7b, 12/18; 30pf, 12/22; 3pf, 4pf, 1/4/46.

---

### Souvenir Sheet

Rebuilding of German Natl. Theater, Weimar — OS2

a, 6pf, Schiller. b, 10pf, Goethe. c, 12pf, Liszt. d, 16pf, Wieland. e, 40pf, Natl. Theater.

---

**1946, Mar. 27    Wmk. 48    Imperf.**

| | | | | |
|---|---|---|---|---|
| 16N9 | OS2 | Sheet of 5, #a.- | | |
| | e. | | 13.00 | 52.50 |
| f. | Sheet, unwatermarked, rouletted | | 23.00 | 140.00 |
| | Never hinged | | 52.50 | |

No. 16N9 was issued without gum. Sold for 7.50 marks.

---

### THURINGIA SEMI-POSTAL STAMPS

Bridge Reconstruction OSP1

Designs: 10pf+60pf, Saalburg Bridge. 12pf+68pf, Camsdorf Bridge, Jena. 16pf+74pf, Goschwitz Bridge. 24pf+76pf, Ilm Bridge, Mellingen.

**1946, Mar. 30    Typo.    Imperf.**

| | | | | |
|---|---|---|---|---|
| 16NB1 | OSP1 | 10 +60pf red brn | .25 | 8.00 |
| 16NB2 | OSP1 | 12 +68pf red | .25 | 8.00 |
| 16NB3 | OSP1 | 16 +74pf dark grn | .25 | 8.00 |
| 16NB4 | OSP1 | 24 +76pf brn | .25 | 8.00 |
| a. | Souv. sheet of 4, #16NB1-16NB4 | | 130.00 | 1,100. |
| | Never hinged | | 275.00 | |
| | Nos. 16NB1-16NB4 (4) | | 2.60 | 32.00 |
| | Set, never hinged | | 2.60 | |

## Scott Postage Stamp Checklist

# $9.99-$19.99 *AA**

- Provides basic information about postage stamps listed with major numbers in the Scott *Standard Postage Stamp Catalogue*.

- Features the country name, issue date or year, the Scott number, a description and four checkboxes; unused and used. The other two boxes can be used to label other options such as never-hinged or on cover.

| | GREAT BRITAIN | | 9 |
|---|---|---|---|
| **DATE** | **SCOTT NO.** | **DESCRIPTION** | UNUSED USED |
| **Great Britain** | | | |
| 1865 | 43 | 4p vermilion (P12) | ☐ ☐ ☐ ☐ |
| 1865 | 44 | 3p rose (P4) | ☐ ☐ ☐ ☐ |
| 1865 | 45 | 6p lilac (P5) | ☐ ☐ ☐ ☐ |

# AmosAdvantage.com
## 1-800-572-6885

**ORDERING INFORMATION:** *AA prices apply to paid subscribers of Amos Media titles, or for orders placed online. Prices, terms and product availability subject to change. **SHIPPING & HANDLING:** U.S.: Orders total $0-$10.00 charged $4.99 shipping. U.S. Order total $10.01-$74.99 charged $9.99 shipping. Orders totaling $75+ will ship FREE! Taxes will apply in CA, OH, & IL. Canada: 20% of order total. Minimum charge $19.99 Maximum charge $200.00. Foreign orders are shipped via FedEx Intl. or USPS and billed actual freight.

# GHANA

'gä-nə

LOCATION — West Africa between Togo and Ivory Coast
GOVT. — Republic
AREA — 92,010 sq. mi.
POP. — 18,101,000 (1997 est.)
CAPITAL — Accra

Ghana is the former British colony of Gold Coast, which achieved independence March 6, 1957. It includes the former trusteeship territory of British Togoland.

12 Pence = 1 Shilling
20 Shillings = 1 Pound
100 Pesewas = 1 Cedi (1965, 1972)
100 New Pesewas = 1 New Cedi (1967)

**Used Values in Italics**

In 1961 the government canceled all remainder stocks, using cancellations that closely resemble genuine postmarks. Catalogue values in italics for these stamps (Nos. 1-13, 61-65, 67-77) are for canceled-to-order stamps. Postally used stamps are worth more.

> Catalogue values for all unused stamps in this country are for Never Hinged items.

## Watermark

Wmk. 325 — Stars and G Multiple

Kwame Nkrumah, Map and Palm-nut Vulture — A1

**Perf. 14x14½**

| | | | | |
|---|---|---|---|---|
| **1957, Mar. 6** | | **Wmk. 4** | | **Photo.** |
| 1 | A1 | 2p rose red | .25 | .25 |
| 2 | A1 | 2½p green | .25 | .25 |
| 3 | A1 | 4p brown | .25 | .25 |
| 4 | A1 | 1sh3p dark blue | .35 | .25 |
| | | Nos. 1-4 (4) | 1.10 | 1.00 |

Independence, Mar. 6, 1957.
For overprints see Nos. 28-31.

Stamps of Gold Coast, 1952-54, Overprinted in Black or Red

**Perf. 11½x12, 12x11½**

| | | | | |
|---|---|---|---|---|
| **1957, Mar. 6** | | | | **Engr.** |
| 5 | A14 | ½p yel brown & car | .50 | .25 |
| 6 | A14 | 1p deep blue (R) | .50 | .25 |
| 7 | A14 | 1½p green | .50 | .25 |
| 8 | A14 | 3p rose | .85 | .25 |
| 9 | A15 | 6p org & black (R) | .50 | .25 |
| 10 | A14 | 1sh red org & black | .50 | .25 |
| 11 | A14 | 2sh rose car & ol brn | 1.25 | .25 |
| 12 | A14 | 5sh gray & red vio | 2.00 | .25 |
| 13 | A15 | 10sh olive grn & black | 2.25 | .50 |
| | | Nos. 5-13 (9) | 8.85 | 2.50 |

Nos. 5-6 exist in vertical coils.
See Nos. 25-27.

Viking Ship and Angelfish — A2

1sh3p, Medieval galleon and swordfish. 5sh, Modern cargo ship and flyingfish.

**Perf. 12x11½**

| | | | | |
|---|---|---|---|---|
| **1957, Dec. 27** | | **Engr.** | | **Unwmk.** |
| 14 | A2 | 2½p emerald | .25 | .25 |
| 15 | A2 | 1sh3p dark blue | .30 | 1.25 |
| 16 | A2 | 5sh red lilac | .90 | 3.00 |
| | | Nos. 14-16 (3) | 1.45 | 4.50 |

Black Star Line inauguration.

Ambassador Hotel — A3

Coat of Arms — A4

Design: 2½p, Opening of Parliament. 1sh3p, National monument.

**Perf. 14x14½, 14½x14**

| | | | | |
|---|---|---|---|---|
| **1958, Mar. 6** | | **Photo.** | | **Wmk. 4** |
| 17 | A3 | ½p car rose & black | .25 | .40 |
| 18 | A3 | 2½p org yel, red & blk | .25 | .25 |
| 19 | A3 | 1sh3p blue & black | .25 | .25 |
| 20 | A4 | 2sh multicolored | .25 | .50 |
| | | Nos. 17-20 (4) | 1.00 | 1.40 |

First anniversary of Independence.

Map of Africa — A5

Map and Torch — A6

| | | | | |
|---|---|---|---|---|
| **1958, Apr. 15** | | | **Perf. 13½x14½** | |
| 21 | A5 | 2½p multicolored | .25 | .25 |
| 22 | A5 | 3p multicolored | .25 | .25 |
| 23 | A6 | 1sh multicolored | .25 | .25 |
| 24 | A6 | 2sh6p multicolored | .25 | .65 |
| | | Nos. 21-24 (4) | 1.00 | 1.40 |

1st conf. of Independent African States, Accra, Apr. 15-22.

**Gold Coast Nos. 151-152 and 154 Overprinted Like Nos. 5-13**
**Perf. 11½x12, 12x11½**

| | | | | |
|---|---|---|---|---|
| **1958, May 26** | | **Engr.** | | **Wmk. 4** |
| 25 | A15 | 2p chocolate | .50 | .35 |
| 26 | A15 | 2½p red | 1.25 | 1.40 |
| 27 | A14 | 4p deep blue | 6.00 | 9.00 |
| | | Nos. 25-27 (3) | 7.75 | 10.75 |

Nos. 25-27 were prepared in 1957 and some were sold without authorization. The set was officially released in 1958.

**Nos. 1-4 Overprinted "Prime Minister's Visit U. S. A. and Canada"**

| | | | | |
|---|---|---|---|---|
| **1958, July 18** | | **Photo.** | **Perf. 14x14½** | |
| 28 | A1 | 2p rose red | .25 | .40 |
| 29 | A1 | 2½p green | .25 | .30 |
| 30 | A1 | 4p brown | .25 | .50 |
| 31 | A1 | 1sh3p dark blue | .25 | .25 |
| | | Nos. 28-31 (4) | 1.00 | 1.45 |

Prime Minister Kwame Nkrumah's visit to the US and Canada, July, 1958.

Palm-nut Vulture over Globe — A7

"Britannia" Plane — A8

Designs: 2sh, Stratocruiser and albatross. 2sh6p, Palm-nut vulture and jet plane, horiz.

| | | | | |
|---|---|---|---|---|
| **1958, July 15** | **Perf. 14x14½, 14½x14** | | | |
| 32 | A7 | 2½p multicolored | .25 | .25 |
| 33 | A8 | 1sh3p multicolored | .35 | .25 |
| 34 | A8 | 2sh multicolored | .45 | .45 |
| 35 | A7 | 2sh6p olive bister & blk | .70 | .85 |
| | | Nos. 32-35 (4) | 1.75 | 1.80 |

Inauguration of Ghana Airways.

A9

**Perf. 14x14½**

| | | | | |
|---|---|---|---|---|
| **1958, Oct. 24** | | **Wmk. 4** | | **Litho.** |
| 36 | A9 | 2½p multicolored | .25 | .25 |
| 37 | A9 | 1sh3p multicolored | .25 | .25 |
| 38 | A9 | 2sh6p multicolored | .25 | .30 |
| | | Nos. 36-38 (3) | .75 | .80 |

United Nations Day, Oct. 24.

A10

Lincoln Memorial and Kwame Nkrumah.

**Perf. 14x14½**

| | | | | |
|---|---|---|---|---|
| **1959, Feb. 12** | | **Photo.** | | **Wmk. 325** |
| 39 | A10 | 2½p dp plum & brt pink | .25 | .25 |
| 40 | A10 | 1sh3p dp blue & lt bl | .25 | .25 |
| 41 | A10 | 2sh6p ol gray & org yel | .25 | .30 |
| a. | | Souv. sheet of 3, #39-41, imperf. | .80 | 1.50 |
| | | Nos. 39-41 (3) | .75 | .80 |

Lincoln's birth sesquicentennial.

Kente Cloth with Traditional Symbols A11

Symbol of Greeting A12

2½p, Talking drums and elephant horn-blower. 2sh, Map of Africa, flag and palm tree.

**Perf. 14½x14, 14x14½**

| | | | | |
|---|---|---|---|---|
| **1959, Mar. 6** | | **Photo.** | | **Wmk. 325** |
| 42 | A11 | ½p multicolored | .25 | .25 |
| 43 | A11 | 2½p multicolored | .25 | .25 |
| 44 | A12 | 1sh3p multicolored | .25 | .25 |
| 45 | A11 | 2sh multicolored | .25 | 1.00 |
| | | Nos. 42-45 (4) | 1.00 | 1.75 |

Independence, 2nd anniversary.

Flags of Independent States of Africa and Globe — A13

| | | | | |
|---|---|---|---|---|
| **1959, Apr. 15** | | | **Perf. 14½x14** | |
| 46 | A13 | 2½p multicolored | .25 | .25 |
| 47 | A13 | 8½p multicolored | .25 | .25 |

Africa Freedom Day, Apr. 15.

Kente Cloth and "God's Omnipotence" Symbol A13a

Nkrumah Statue, Accra A14

Shell Ginger — A15

Cacao — A16

"God's Omnipotence" Symbol — A16a

Blackwinged Red Bishop — A17

1½p, Ghana timber. 2p, Volta river. 4p, Diamond and mine. 11p, Golden spider lily. 2sh6p, Great blue turaco. 5sh, Tiger orchid. 10sh, Jewelfish (tropical African cichlid).

**Perf. 11½x12, 12x11½, 14x14½, 14½x14**

| | | | | |
|---|---|---|---|---|
| **1959, Oct. 5** | | | | **Wmk. 325** |
| **Size: 30½x21mm, 21x30½mm** | | | | |
| 48 | A13a | ½p multi (God's Omnipotence) | .25 | .25 |
| 49 | A14 | 1p multicolored | .30 | .25 |
| **Size: 26½x37mm, 37x26½mm** | | | | |
| 50 | A15 | 1½p multicolored | .25 | .25 |
| 51 | A16 | 2p multicolored | .25 | .25 |
| 52 | A16 | 2½p multicolored | 1.00 | .25 |
| 53 | A16a | 3p multi (God's Omnipotence) | .25 | .25 |
| 54 | A16 | 4p multicolored | 3.50 | .60 |
| 55 | A17 | 6p multicolored | 1.50 | .25 |
| a. | | Booklet pane of 4 | 6.50 | |
| 56 | A15 | 11p multicolored | .25 | .25 |
| 57 | A15 | 1sh multicolored | .25 | .25 |
| 58 | A17 | 2sh6p multicolored | 1.50 | .25 |
| 59 | A15 | 5sh multicolored | 2.25 | .60 |
| **Size: 45x26mm** | | | | |
| 60 | A16 | 10sh multicolored | 2.00 | .70 |
| | | Nos. 48-60,C1-C2 (15) | 16.30 | 5.05 |

Nos. 48 and 53 inscribed "God's Omnipotence." Nos. 95-96 inscribed "Gye Nyame."
For surcharges see Nos. 216-217, 219-225, 277-283.

Map and Gold Cup — A18

1p, Soccer players, vert. 3p, Flags and goalkeeper in stadium. 8p, Soccer player at goal. 2sh6p, Kwame Nkrumah Gold Cup, vert.

| | | | | |
|---|---|---|---|---|
| **1959, Oct. 15** | | **Perf. 14½x14, 14x14½** | | |
| 61 | A18 | ½p multicolored | .25 | .25 |
| 62 | A18 | 1p multicolored | .25 | .25 |
| 63 | A18 | 3p multicolored | .25 | .25 |
| 64 | A18 | 8p multicolored | .25 | .25 |
| 65 | A18 | 2sh6p multicolored | .25 | .30 |
| | | Nos. 61-65 (5) | 1.25 | 1.30 |

West African Soccer Competitions.

Prince Philip — A19

**Perf. 14½x14**

| | | | | |
|---|---|---|---|---|
| **1959, Nov. 24** | | | | **Wmk. 325** |
| 66 | A19 | 3p brt pink & black | .30 | .25 |

Visit of Prince Philip.

Talking Drums — A20

Designs: 6p, 1sh3p, Ghana flag and UN emblem, vert. 2sh6p, Pile of Ceremonial Stools and "UNTC," vert.

**1959, Dec. 10    Perf. 14½x14, 14x14½**
**Flag in Original Colors**

| 67 | A20 | 3p violet & org yel | .25 | .25 |
|----|-----|---------------------|-----|-----|
| 68 | A20 | 6p Prus green & blk | .25 | .25 |
| 69 | A20 | 1sh3p grnsh bl, blk & vio | .25 | .25 |
| 70 | A20 | 2sh6p dark blue & black | .25 | .25 |
| | | Nos. 67-70 (4) | 1.00 | 1.00 |

United Nations Trusteeship Council.

Three Flying Eagles — A21

Designs: 3p, Three clusters of fireworks. 1sh3p, Ghana flag forming "3" and dove. 2sh, Ghana flag forming triple sail of symbolic ship.

**Perf. 13½x14½**

**1960, Mar. 6          Wmk. 325**

| 71 | A21 | ½p multicolored | .25 | .25 |
|----|-----|-----------------|-----|-----|
| 72 | A21 | 3p multicolored | .25 | .25 |
| 73 | A21 | 1sh3p multicolored | .25 | .25 |
| 74 | A21 | 2sh multicolored | .25 | .25 |
| | | Nos. 71-74 (4) | 1.00 | 1.00 |

Independence, 3rd anniversary.

Flags Forming "A" and Map — A22

Designs: 6p, Letter "F." 1sh, "D."

**1960, Apr. 15    Photo.    Wmk. 325**
**Flags in Original Colors**

| 75 | A22 | 3p green, red & black | .25 | .25 |
|----|-----|----------------------|-----|-----|
| 76 | A22 | 6p rose & black | .25 | .25 |
| 77 | A22 | 1sh blue, black & red | .25 | .25 |
| | | Nos. 75-77 (3) | .75 | .75 |

Africa Freedom Day, Apr. 15.

President Kwame Nkrumah — A23

Designs: 1sh3p, Flag and star. 2sh, Hand holding torch. 10sh, Coat of Arms and flag of Ghana, horiz.

**Perf. 14x14½, 14½x14**

**1960, July 1          Litho.**

| 78 | A23 | 3p multicolored | .25 | .25 |
|----|-----|-----------------|-----|-----|
| 79 | A23 | 1sh3p multicolored | .25 | .25 |
| 80 | A23 | 2sh multicolored | .30 | .30 |
| 81 | A23 | 10sh multicolored | .70 | .70 |
| a. | | Souv. sheet of 4, #78-81, imperf. | .50 | 1.00 |
| | | Nos. 78-81 (4) | 1.50 | 1.50 |

Declaration of the Republic, July 1, 1960.

Olympic Rings and Hand Holding Torch — A24

Design: 1sh3p, 2sh6p, Runner, Map of Africa and Olympic Rings, horiz.

**1960, Aug. 15    Photo.    Wmk. 325**

| 82 | A24 | 3p multicolored | .25 | .25 |
|----|-----|-----------------|-----|-----|
| 83 | A24 | 6p multicolored | .25 | .25 |
| 84 | A24 | 1sh3p multicolored | .25 | .25 |
| 85 | A24 | 2sh6p multicolored | .35 | .25 |
| | | Nos. 82-85 (4) | 1.10 | 1.00 |

17th Olympic Games, Rome, Aug. 25-Sept. 11.

Map and Arch — A25

Designs: 3p, Flag and Kwame Nkrumah, horiz. 6p, Star and Nkrumah.

**1960, Sept. 21          Photo.**

| 86 | A25 | 3p multicolored | .25 | .25 |
|----|-----|-----------------|-----|-----|
| 87 | A25 | 6p multicolored | .25 | .25 |
| 88 | A25 | 1sh3p multicolored | .25 | .30 |
| | | Nos. 86-88 (3) | .75 | .80 |

Founder's Day, Sept. 21, birthday of Dr. Kwame Nkrumah.

UN Emblem and Ghana Flag — A26

6p, Flame & emblem. 1sh3p, UN Emblem.

**1960, Dec. 10          Perf. 14x14½**

| 89 | A26 | 3p multicolored | .25 | .25 |
|----|-----|-----------------|-----|-----|
| 90 | A26 | 6p multicolored | .25 | .25 |
| 91 | A26 | 1sh3p multicolored | .25 | .45 |
| | | Nos. 89-91 (3) | .75 | .95 |

Human Rights Day, Dec. 10, 1960.

Talking Drums and Map — A27

Designs: 6p, Map of Africa showing 25 independent states. 2sh, Map of Africa and flags of independent nations in 1958, horiz.

**Perf. 14x14½, 14½x14**

**1961, Apr. 15          Wmk. 325**

| 92 | A27 | 3p multicolored | .25 | .25 |
|----|-----|-----------------|-----|-----|
| 93 | A27 | 6p multicolored | .25 | .25 |
| 94 | A27 | 2sh multicolored | .25 | .35 |
| | | Nos. 92-94 (3) | .75 | .85 |

Africa Freedom Day, Apr. 15, 1961.

**Types of 1959 Redrawn and**

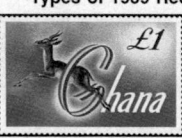

Red-fronted Gazelle A28

**Perf. 11½x12, 14½x14**

**1961, Apr. 29          Wmk. 325**

| 95 | A13a | ½p "Gye Nyame" | .25 | .25 |
|----|------|----------------|-----|-----|
| 96 | A16a | 3p "Gye Nyame" | .25 | .25 |
| a. | | Booklet pane of 4 | 1.00 | |

**Perf. 14x14½**

| 97 | A28 | £1 multicolored | 5.00 | 5.00 |
|----|-----|-----------------|------|------|
| | | Nos. 95-97 (3) | 5.50 | 5.50 |

Nos. 95-96 are the same sizes as Nos. 48 and 53 which are inscribed "God's Omnipotence."
For surcharges see Nos. 218, 226, 284.

Column, Eagle and Star — A29

Designs: 1sh3p, Symbolic flower and star. 2sh, Star and 3 Ghana flags.

**1961, July 1          Perf. 14x14½**

| 98 | A29 | 3p multicolored | .25 | .25 |
|----|-----|-----------------|-----|-----|
| 99 | A29 | 1sh3p multicolored | .25 | .25 |
| 100 | A29 | 2sh multicolored | .25 | 1.00 |
| | | Nos. 98-100 (3) | .75 | 1.50 |

First anniversary of the Republic.

Dove with Olive Branch — A30          World Map, Chain and Olive Branch — A31

Design: 5sh, Rostrum and olive branch.

**1961, Sept. 1    Perf. 14x14½, 14½x14**

| 101 | A30 | 3p green | .25 | .25 |
|-----|-----|----------|-----|-----|
| 102 | A31 | 1sh3p dark blue | .25 | .25 |
| 103 | A31 | 5sh rose carmine | .25 | .90 |
| | | Nos. 101-103 (3) | .75 | 1.40 |

Conference of Non-aligned Nations, Belgrade, Sept. 1961.

Kwame Nkrumah and Globe — A32

Designs: 1sh3p, Kente cloth and Nkrumah, vert. 5sh, Kwame Nkrumah, vert.

**Perf. 14½x14, 14x14½**

**1961, Sept. 21          Wmk. 325**

| 104 | A32 | 3p multicolored | .25 | .25 |
|-----|-----|-----------------|-----|-----|
| a. | | Souvenir sheet of 4, imperf. | 1.00 | 1.75 |
| 105 | A32 | 1sh3p multicolored | .25 | .25 |
| a. | | Souvenir sheet of 4, imperf. | 1.00 | 2.50 |
| 106 | A32 | 5sh multicolored | .40 | 2.00 |
| a. | | Souvenir sheet of 4, imperf. | 3.00 | 6.00 |
| | | Nos. 104-106 (3) | .90 | 2.50 |

Founder's Day.
The souvenir sheets contain four imperf. stamps each with simulated perforations.

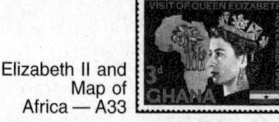

Elizabeth II and Map of Africa — A33

**1961, Nov. 10          Perf. 14½x14**
**Gold Inscriptions: Design in Black, Red, Yellow & Green**

| 107 | A33 | 3p claret | .25 | .25 |
|-----|-----|-----------|-----|-----|
| 108 | A33 | 1sh3p Prussian blue | .25 | .25 |
| 109 | A33 | 5sh violet blue | 1.00 | 1.00 |
| a. | | Souvenir sheet of 4 | 3.50 | 7.00 |
| | | Nos. 107-109 (3) | 1.50 | 1.50 |

Visit of Queen Elizabeth II to Ghana, Nov. 10-22.
No. 109a contains four imperf. examples of No. 109 with simulated perforations.

Map of Tema Harbor and Ships — A34

**Perf. 14x13**

**1962, Feb. 10    Litho.    Unwmk.**

| 110 | A34 | 3p multicolored | .25 | .25 |
|-----|-----|-----------------|-----|-----|
| | | Nos. 110,C3-C4 (3) | 1.45 | 1.45 |

Opening of Tema Harbor, as part of Volta River Project.

Dove Flying over Map of Africa — A35

**1962, Mar. 6          Perf. 13x14**

| 111 | A35 | 3p multicolored | .25 | .25 |
|-----|-----|-----------------|-----|-----|
| | | Nos. 111,C5-C6 (3) | 1.15 | 1.15 |

Conference of African heads of state at Casablanca, 1st anniv.

"Freedom" Illuminating Africa — A36

**Perf. 14x14½**

**1962, Apr. 15    Photo.    Wmk. 325**

| 112 | A36 | 3p multicolored | .25 | .25 |
|-----|-----|-----------------|-----|-----|
| 113 | A36 | 6p multicolored | .25 | .25 |
| 114 | A36 | 1sh3p multicolored | .25 | .25 |
| | | Nos. 112-114 (3) | .75 | .75 |

Africa Freedom Day, Apr. 15.

"Five Continents at Peace" — A37

Designs: 6p, Atom bomb blast in shape of skull. 1sh3p, Peace dove and globe.

**1962, June 21          Wmk. 325**

| 115 | A37 | 3p dp rose & blk | .25 | .25 |
|-----|-----|------------------|-----|-----|
| 116 | A37 | 6p black & dk red | .25 | .30 |
| 117 | A37 | 1sh3p greenish blue | .30 | .50 |
| | | Nos. 115-117 (3) | .80 | 1.05 |

Accra Assembly of Africans for a "World Without Bomb," June 21-28.

Patrice Lumumba — A38

**1962, June 30          Perf. 14½x14**

| 118 | A38 | 3p black & orange | .25 | .25 |
|-----|-----|-------------------|-----|-----|
| 119 | A38 | 6p mar, grn & blk | .25 | .30 |
| 120 | A38 | 1sh3p dk grn, pink & blk | .25 | .35 |
| | | Nos. 118-120 (3) | .75 | .90 |

1st anniv. (on Feb. 12) of the death of Patrice Lumumba, premier of Congo.

Arch and Star — A39

Designs: 6p, Torch in flag colors and globe. 1sh3p, Palm-nut vulture trailing flag, horiz.

**Perf. 13x13½, 13½x13**

**1962, July 1          Unwmk.**

| 121 | A39 | 3p multicolored | .25 | .25 |
|-----|-----|-----------------|-----|-----|
| 122 | A39 | 6p multicolored | .25 | .25 |
| 123 | A39 | 1sh3p multicolored | .25 | .35 |
| | | Nos. 121-123 (3) | .75 | .85 |

Second anniversary of the republic.

Kwame Nkrumah — A40

3p, Nkrumah medal. 1sh3p, Nkrumah's head & stars. 2sh, Hands with trowel & building block.

## 1962, Sept. 21    Litho.    Perf. 13x14

| 124 | A40 | 1p multicolored | .25 | .25 |
|---|---|---|---|---|
| 125 | A40 | 3p multicolored | .25 | .25 |
| 126 | A40 | 1sh3p ultra & black | .25 | .25 |
| 127 | A40 | 2sh multicolored | .25 | .25 |
| | | Nos. 124-127 (4) | 1.00 | 1.75 |

Founder's Day, Nkrumah's 53rd birthday.

Malaria Eradication Emblem — A41

### Perf. 14x14½

## 1962, Dec. 1    Photo.    Wmk. 325

| 128 | A41 | 1p carmine rose | .25 | .25 |
|---|---|---|---|---|
| 129 | A41 | 4p yellow green | .25 | 1.00 |
| 130 | A41 | 6p olive bister | .25 | .30 |
| 131 | A41 | 1sh3p violet | .25 | .80 |
| a. | | Souvenir sheet of 4, imperf. | 1.00 | 1.50 |
| | | Nos. 128-131 (4) | 1.00 | 2.35 |

WHO drive to eradicate malaria.

No. 131a contains one each of Nos. 128-131, with simulated perforation.

Wheat Emblem and Globe — A42

### Perf. 14x14½, 14½x14

## 1963, Mar. 21    Wmk. 325

| 132 | A42 | 1p multicolored | .30 | .25 |
|---|---|---|---|---|
| 133 | A42 | 4p multicolored | .45 | 1.00 |
| 134 | A42 | 1sh3p multicolored | 1.75 | 1.50 |
| | | Nos. 132-134 (3) | 2.50 | 2.75 |

FAO "Freedom from Hunger" campaign.

Map of Africa in Sun — A43

Designs: 4p, Symbolic wood carving, horiz. 1sh3p, Map of Africa and ceremonial fire. 2sh6p, Gazelle and flag.

## 1963, Apr. 15    Photo.

| 135 | A43 | 1p crimson & gold | .25 | .25 |
|---|---|---|---|---|
| 136 | A43 | 4p orange, blk & red | .25 | .25 |
| 137 | A43 | 1sh3p multicolored | .25 | .25 |
| 138 | A43 | 2sh6p multicolored | .25 | 1.00 |
| | | Nos. 135-138 (4) | 1.00 | 1.75 |

Africa Freedom Day, Apr. 15.

Cross, Flag and Centenary Emblem — A44

1 ½p, Centenary emblem, horiz. 4p, Family & emblem, horiz. 1sh3p, Emblem & globe.

### Perf. 14x14½, 14½x14

## 1963, May 28    Wmk. 325

| 139 | A44 | 1p multicolored | .45 | .25 |
|---|---|---|---|---|
| 140 | A44 | 1½p multicolored | .75 | 1.75 |
| 141 | A44 | 4p multicolored | 1.00 | .25 |
| 142 | A44 | 1sh3p multicolored | 2.00 | 2.00 |
| a. | | Souvenir sheet of 4, imperf. | 4.25 | 10.00 |
| | | Nos. 139-142 (4) | 4.20 | 4.25 |

Cent. of the founding of the Intl. Red Cross.

No. 142a contains one each of Nos. 139-142, with simulated perforation.

A45

Designs: 4p, Three flags. 1sh3p, Map of Africa with Ghana, vert. 2sh6p, Torch, vert.

### Perf. 14½x14, 14x14½

## 1963, July 1    Photo.

| 143 | A45 | 1p multicolored | .25 | .25 |
|---|---|---|---|---|
| 144 | A45 | 4p multicolored | .25 | .25 |
| 145 | A45 | 1sh3p multicolored | .25 | .25 |
| 146 | A45 | 2sh6p multicolored | .25 | 1.75 |
| | | Nos. 143-146 (4) | 1.00 | 2.50 |

The 3rd anniversary of the republic.

Dancers, Fireworks and Nkrumah — A46

1p, Nkrumah & streamer. 4p, Nkrumah & flag. 5sh, Wisdom symbol.

### Perf. 14x14½, 14½x14

## 1963, Sept. 21

| 147 | A46 | 1p multi, vert. | .25 | .25 |
|---|---|---|---|---|
| 148 | A46 | 4p multi, vert. | .25 | .25 |
| 149 | A46 | 1sh3p multi | .25 | .25 |
| 150 | A46 | 5sh multi | .25 | .40 |
| | | Nos. 147-150 (4) | 1.00 | 1.15 |

Founder's Day, Nkrumah's 54th birthday.

Ramses II at Abu Simbel — A47

Designs: 1½p, Rock painting, bird and fish, horiz. 2p, Queen Nefertari, horiz. 4p, Sphinx of Wadi es-Sebua. 1sh3p, Statues of Ramses II at Abu Simbel, horiz.

## 1963, Nov. 1    Unwmk.    Perf. 11½x11

| 151 | A47 | 1p multicolored | .25 | .25 |
|---|---|---|---|---|
| 152 | A47 | 1½p multicolored | .25 | .50 |
| 153 | A47 | 2p multicolored | .25 | .25 |
| 154 | A47 | 4p multicolored | .50 | .25 |
| 155 | A47 | 1sh3p multicolored | 1.50 | 1.00 |
| | | Nos. 151-155 (5) | 2.75 | 2.25 |

UNESCO world campaign to save historic monuments in Nubia.

Steam and Diesel Engines — A48

### Perf. 14½x14

## 1963, Nov. 1    Wmk. 325

| 156 | A48 | 1p multicolored | .25 | .25 |
|---|---|---|---|---|
| 157 | A48 | 6p multicolored | .65 | .25 |
| 158 | A48 | 1sh3p multicolored | 1.10 | .50 |
| 159 | A48 | 2sh6p multicolored | 1.40 | 1.40 |
| | | Nos. 156-159 (4) | 3.40 | 2.40 |

The 60th anniversary of Ghana's railroads.

Eleanor Roosevelt and Flame — A49

6p, Mrs. Roosevelt & flag. 1sh3p, Mrs. Roosevelt, flag, flame & Ghanaian symbols, horiz.

### Perf. 11½x11, 11x11½

## 1963, Dec. 10    Unwmk.

| 160 | A49 | 1p multicolored | .25 | .25 |
|---|---|---|---|---|
| 161 | A49 | 4p multicolored | .25 | .30 |
| 162 | A49 | 6p multicolored | .25 | .25 |
| 163 | A49 | 1sh3p multicolored | .25 | .25 |
| | | Nos. 160-163 (4) | 1.00 | 1.05 |

Eleanor Roosevelt; 15th anniv. of the Universal Declaration of Human Rights.

---

### Imperforates
### Starting in 1964, certain sets of Ghana exist imperf.

---

IQSY Emblem and Satellites — A50

## 1964, June 1    Photo.    Perf. 14

| 164 | A50 | 3p multicolored | .25 | .25 |
|---|---|---|---|---|
| 165 | A50 | 4p multicolored | .25 | .25 |
| 166 | A50 | 1sh3p multicolored | .25 | .25 |
| a. | | Souvenir sheet of 3 | .90 | 2.00 |
| | | Nos. 164-166 (3) | .75 | .75 |

Intl. Quiet Sun Year, 1964-65. No. 166a contains 4 imperf. stamps similar to No. 166 with simulated perforations.

See Nos. 186-188.

Harvest on State Farm — A51

Designs: 6p, Oil refinery, Tema. 1sh3p, Communal labor. 5sh, Ghana flag and people.

## 1964, July 1    Perf. 13x14

| 167 | A51 | 3p multicolored | .25 | .25 |
|---|---|---|---|---|
| 168 | A51 | 6p multicolored | .25 | .25 |
| 169 | A51 | 1sh3p multicolored | .25 | .25 |
| 170 | A51 | 5sh multicolored | .25 | .90 |
| a. | | Souvenir sheet of 4 | .80 | 1.50 |
| | | Nos. 167-170 (4) | 1.00 | 1.65 |

4th anniv. of the Republic. No. 170a contains four stamps similar to Nos. 167-170 with simulated perforations.

Dove, Globe, Olive Branch and Flag — A52

Designs: 6p, Map of Africa and quill pen, vert. 1sh3p, Knotted rope and map of Africa. 5sh, Hands planting symbolic tree, vert.

## 1964, July 6    Perf. 14

| 171 | A52 | 3p multicolored | .25 | .25 |
|---|---|---|---|---|
| 172 | A52 | 6p black & red | .25 | .25 |
| 173 | A52 | 1sh3p blue & multi | .25 | .25 |
| 174 | A52 | 5sh yel & multi | .25 | .60 |
| | | Nos. 171-174 (4) | 1.00 | 1.35 |

Signing of the African Unity Charter, 1st anniv.

Nkrumah and Hibiscus — A53

### Perf. 14x14½

## 1964, Sept. 21    Photo.    Wmk. 325
### Design in Brown, Green and Rose Red

| 175 | A53 | 3p light blue | .25 | .25 |
|---|---|---|---|---|
| 176 | A53 | 6p yellow | .25 | .25 |
| 177 | A53 | 1sh3p gray | .25 | .25 |
| 178 | A53 | 2sh6p emerald | .25 | .90 |
| a. | | Souvenir sheet of 4 | 1.10 | 2.00 |
| | | Nos. 175-178 (4) | 1.00 | 1.65 |

Founder's Day, Nkrumah's 55th birthday.

No. 178a contains four of No. 178 with simulated perforation.

Boxing — A54

Sport: 1p, Hurdling, horiz. 2½p, Running, horiz. 4p, Broad jump. 6p, Soccer. 1sh3p, Athlete with Olympic torch. 5sh, Banners and Tokyo Olympic emblem, horiz.

## 1964, Oct. 25    Perf. 14½x14

| 179 | A54 | 1p yellow & multi | .25 | .25 |
|---|---|---|---|---|
| 180 | A54 | 2½p multicolored | .25 | 1.00 |
| 181 | A54 | 3p red & multi | .25 | .25 |
| 182 | A54 | 4p blue & multi | .25 | .25 |
| 183 | A54 | 6p multicolored | .25 | .25 |
| 184 | A54 | 1sh3p blue & multi | .25 | .25 |
| 185 | A54 | 5sh gray & multi | .25 | 2.50 |
| a. | | Souvenir sheet of 3 | 1.30 | 2.25 |
| | | Nos. 179-185 (7) | 1.75 | 4.75 |

18th Olympic Games, Tokyo, Oct. 10-25. No. 185a contains stamps similar to Nos. 183-185 with simulated perforation.

### Quiet Sun Year Type of 1964
### Unwmk.

## 1964, Oct.    Photo.    Perf. 14

| 186 | A50 | 3p gray, bl, grn, yel & red | 1.25 | 1.25 |
|---|---|---|---|---|
| 187 | A50 | 6p pink, bl, grn, yel & red | 2.25 | 2.25 |
| 188 | A50 | 1sh3p tan, bl, grn, yel, & red | 3.50 | 3.50 |
| | | Nos. 186-188 (3) | 7.00 | 7.00 |

Each issued in sheets of 12, with star-strewn blue border inscribed "Ghana International Quiet Sun Year." Stamps arranged in square surrounding vignette of New York World's Fair Unisphere in blue.

G. W. Carver and Sweet Potato — A55

Design: 1sh3p, Albert Einstein, theory of relativity formula and atom symbol.

## 1964, Dec. 7    Wmk. 325    Perf. 14½

| 189 | A55 | 6p grn & dk blue | .30 | .30 |
|---|---|---|---|---|
| 190 | A55 | 1sh3p Prus bl & claret | .45 | .40 |
| 191 | A55 | 5sh org ver & brn blk | 1.50 | 3.00 |
| a. | | Souvenir sheet of 3 | 3.00 | 2.00 |
| | | Nos. 189-191 (3) | 2.25 | 3.70 |

Human Rights Day; Albert Einstein (1878-1955) and George Washington Carver (1864-1943), scientists.

No. 191a commemorates UNESCO Week and contains one each of Nos. 189-191 with simulated perforations.

Secretary Bird — A56

Designs: 1p, Elephant, vert. 2½p, Purple wreath, vert. 3p, Gray parrot, vert. 4p, Blue-naped mousebird. 6p, African tulip tree flowers. 1sh3p, Amethyst starling. 2sh6p, Hippopotamuses.

### Perf. 11½x11, 11x11½

## 1964, Dec. 14    Photo.    Unwmk.

| 192 | A56 | 1p blue & multi | .45 | .40 |
|---|---|---|---|---|
| 193 | A56 | 1½p org & multi | .65 | 1.40 |
| 194 | A56 | 2½p lt green & multi | .50 | .90 |
| a. | | Souv. sheet of 3, #192-194, imperf. | 2.75 | 2.75 |
| 195 | A56 | 3p lt green & multi | 1.10 | .50 |
| 196 | A56 | 4p multicolored | 1.10 | .70 |
| 197 | A56 | 6p multicolored | .50 | .30 |
| 198 | A56 | 1sh3p multicolored | 1.25 | 1.00 |
| 199 | A56 | 2sh6p multicolored | 1.25 | 3.50 |
| a. | | Souv. sheet of 5, #195-199, imperf. | 6.25 | 10.00 |
| | | Nos. 192-199 (8) | 6.80 | 8.70 |

ICY Emblem — A57

## 1965, Feb. 15   Litho.   *Perf. 14x13*
### Design in Black, Red and Green
| | | | | |
|---|---|---|---|---|
| 200 | A57 | 1p gray | .35 | .60 |
| 201 | A57 | 4p bister | 1.25 | 1.50 |
| 202 | A57 | 6p tan | 1.25 | .45 |
| 203 | A57 | 1sh3p light green | 1.60 | 2.25 |
| a. | | Souvenir sheet of 4 | 4.75 | 4.75 |
| | | Nos. 200-203 (4) | 4.45 | 4.80 |

Intl. Cooperation Year. No. 203a contains 4 imperf. stamps similar to No. 203.

ITU Emblem, Old and New Communication Equipment — A58

## 1965, Apr. 12     *Perf. 13½*
| | | | | |
|---|---|---|---|---|
| 204 | A58 | 1p multicolored | .25 | .25 |
| 205 | A58 | 6p multicolored | .25 | .25 |
| 206 | A58 | 1sh3p multicolored | .75 | .25 |
| 207 | A58 | 5sh multicolored | 2.00 | 2.00 |
| a. | | Souvenir sheet of 4 | 10.00 | 10.00 |
| | | Nos. 204-207 (4) | 3.25 | 2.75 |

Cent. of the ITU. No. 207a contains 4 imperf. stamps similar to Nos. 204-207 with simulated perforations.

Lincoln's Home, Springfield, Ill. — A59

1sh3p, Inaugural Address and Lincoln. 2sh, Lincoln and his signature. 5sh, Adaptation of 1869 US Lincoln stamp (No. 122).

### Wmk. 325
## 1965, Apr.   Photo.   *Perf. 12½*
| | | | | |
|---|---|---|---|---|
| 208 | A59 | 6p multicolored | .25 | .25 |
| 209 | A59 | 1sh3p multicolored | .25 | .25 |
| 210 | A59 | 2sh multicolored | .25 | .30 |
| 211 | A59 | 5sh red & black | .30 | 1.25 |
| a. | | Souvenir sheet of 4 | 1.25 | 2.25 |
| | | Nos. 208-211 (4) | 1.05 | 2.05 |

Centenary of death of Abraham Lincoln. No. 211a contains one each of Nos. 208-211 with simulated perforation.

5-Pesewa Coin, Nkrumah's Head — A60

Coins: 10pa, 10 pesewas. 25pa, 25 pesewas. 50pa, 50 pesewas.

### Perf. 11x13
## 1965, July 19   Unwmk.   Litho.
### Coin in Silver and Black
#### Size: 45x32mm
| | | | | |
|---|---|---|---|---|
| 212 | A60 | 5pa red, grn & lt grn | .25 | .25 |
| 213 | A60 | 10pa red, grn, & pink | .25 | .25 |

#### Size: 62x39mm
| | | | | |
|---|---|---|---|---|
| 214 | A60 | 25pa red, grn, & pink | .60 | .90 |

#### Size: 71x43½mm
| | | | | |
|---|---|---|---|---|
| 215 | A60 | 50pa red, grn & lt grn | 1.25 | 2.00 |
| | | Nos. 212-215 (4) | 2.35 | 3.40 |

Introduction of decimal currency.

### Regular Issue of 1959-61
Surcharged in Red, Blue, Brown, Black or White with New Value and: "Ghana New Currency / 19th July, 1965"
#### *Perf. 12x11½, 14½x14, 14x14½*
## 1965, July 19   Photo.   Wmk. 325
| | | | | |
|---|---|---|---|---|
| 216 | A14 | 1pa on 1p (R) | .25 | .25 |
| 217 | A16 | 2pa on 2p (Bl) | .25 | .25 |
| 218 | A16a | 3pa on 3p (#96, Br) | 1.00 | 5.50 |
| 219 | A16 | 4pa on 4p (Bl) | 4.50 | .50 |
| 220 | A17 | 6pa on 6p (Bk) | .50 | .25 |
| 221 | A15 | 11pa on 11p (W) | .25 | .25 |
| 222 | A15 | 12pa on 1sh (Bl) | .25 | .25 |
| 223 | A17 | 30pa on 2sh6p (Bl) | 4.50 | 8.00 |
| 224 | A15 | 60pa on 5sh (Bl) | 4.00 | .70 |

---

| | | | | |
|---|---|---|---|---|
| 225 | A16 | 1.20c on 10s (Bl) | .75 | 2.00 |
| 226 | A28 | 2.40c on £1 (Bl) | 1.00 | 6.25 |
| | | Nos. 216-226,C7-C8 (13) | 21.25 | 25.25 |

The two lines of the overprint are diagonal on the 1pa, 11pa, 12pa, 60pa, 1.20c and 2.40c.

The surcharge exists double or inverted on six or more denominations.

Numerous inverted surcharges, double surcharges, sideways surcharges, and surcharges on back exist on Nos. 216-226. Values, $10 to $200 each.

Summit Conference, Accra — A61

Map of Africa and Flags — A62

Designs: 2pa, "OAU" and three heads (triangle pointing up). 5pa, Symbol of African Unity. 15pa, Sunburst and map of Africa. 24pa, Map of Africa.

### Perf. 14, 14½x14
## 1965, Oct. 21     Photo.
### Ghana Flag in Red, Black & Green
| | | | | |
|---|---|---|---|---|
| 227 | A61 | 1pa multicolored | .25 | .25 |
| 228 | A61 | 2pa multicolored | .25 | .25 |
| 229 | A61 | 5pa multicolored | .25 | .25 |
| 230 | A62 | 6pa orange & black | .25 | .25 |
| 231 | A62 | 15pa light blue & blk | .25 | .30 |
| 232 | A62 | 24pa lt ultra & green | .25 | .60 |
| | | Nos. 227-232 (6) | 1.50 | 1.80 |

Summit Conference of the Organization for African Unity, Accra, Oct. 1965.

Soccer Goalkeeper A63

Designs: 15pa, Soccer player and cup, vert. 24pa, Two soccer players and cup.

### Perf. 14x13, 13x14
## 1965, Nov. 15     Unwmk.
| | | | | |
|---|---|---|---|---|
| 233 | A63 | 6pa ocher & multi | .25 | .25 |
| 234 | A63 | 15pa multicolored | .40 | .30 |
| 235 | A63 | 24pa lt blue & multi | .45 | .60 |
| | | Nos. 233-235 (3) | 1.10 | 1.15 |

African Soccer Cup competition. For overprints see Nos. 244-246.

John F. Kennedy and Eternal Flame — A64

Various Kennedy portraits.

## 1965, Dec. 15   Wmk. 325   *Perf. 12½*
| | | | | |
|---|---|---|---|---|
| 236 | A64 | 6pa blk, yel, gold & grn | .25 | .25 |
| 237 | A64 | 15pa vio, crim & brt grn | .25 | .30 |
| 238 | A64 | 24pa dp pur & blk | .25 | .25 |
| 239 | A64 | 30pa vio brn & blk | .25 | .80 |
| a. | | Souvenir sheet of 4 ('66) | 3.25 | 5.50 |
| | | Nos. 236-239 (4) | 1.00 | 1.85 |

President John F. Kennedy (1917-1963). No. 239a contains four imperf. stamps similar to Nos. 236-239.

Generators, Volta River Project — A65

Designs: 15pa, Dam and Lake Volta. 24pa, "Ghana" forming dam. 30pa, Grain.

---

### Perf. 11x11½
## 1966, Jan. 22     Unwmk.
| | | | | |
|---|---|---|---|---|
| 240 | A65 | 6pa sepia & multi | .25 | .25 |
| 241 | A65 | 15pa multicolored | .25 | .25 |
| 242 | A65 | 24pa multicolored | .25 | .25 |
| 243 | A65 | 30pa brt blue & blk | .30 | .50 |
| | | Nos. 240-243 (4) | 1.05 | 1.25 |

Opening of the Volta River dam and electric power station at Akosombo.

### Nos. 233-235 Overprinted Diagonally: "Black Stars Retain Africa Cup / 21st Nov. 1965"
## 1966, Feb. 7     *Perf. 14x13, 13x14*
| | | | | |
|---|---|---|---|---|
| 244 | A63 | 6pa ocher & multi | .25 | .25 |
| 245 | A63 | 15pa multicolored | .30 | .30 |
| 246 | A63 | 24pa lt bl & multi | .55 | .65 |
| | | Nos. 244-246 (3) | 1.10 | 1.20 |

Ghana's soccer victory, Nov. 21, 1965. Varieties exist, including overprint in green on No. 244.

Inauguration of WHO Headquarters, Geneva — A66

Designs: 24pa, 30pa, WHO Headquarters from the west and WHO emblem.

### Perf. 14x14½
## 1966, July 1   Photo.   Wmk. 325
| | | | | |
|---|---|---|---|---|
| 247 | A66 | 6pa multicolored | .55 | .25 |
| 248 | A66 | 15pa multicolored | 1.10 | .50 |
| 249 | A66 | 24pa multicolored | 1.30 | 1.30 |
| 250 | A66 | 30pa multicolored | 1.50 | 3.00 |
| a. | | Souvenir sheet of 4 | 28.00 | 28.00 |
| | | Nos. 247-250 (4) | 4.45 | 5.05 |

No. 250a contains 4 imperf. stamps similar to Nos. 247-250 with simulated perforations.

Herring, Fishermen and Flag — A67

Designs: 15pa, Flatfish and canoes. 24pa, Spadefish and schooner. 30pa, Red snapper and fishing trawler "Shama." 60pa, Mackerel and steamer.

## 1966, Aug. 10   Unwmk.   *Perf. 14x13*
| | | | | |
|---|---|---|---|---|
| 251 | A67 | 6pa ocher & multi | .25 | .25 |
| 252 | A67 | 15pa yel & multi | .40 | .25 |
| 253 | A67 | 24pa ver & multi | .50 | .30 |
| 254 | A67 | 30pa blue & multi | .70 | .70 |
| a. | | Souvenir sheet of 4 | 11.00 | 11.00 |
| 255 | A67 | 60pa green & multi | 1.00 | 3.00 |
| | | Nos. 251-255 (5) | 2.85 | 4.50 |

1966 Freedom from Hunger campaign "Young World Against Hunger." No. 254a contains 4 imperf. stamps similar to No. 254.

Flags of African Unity Charter Signers, Map and Diamond — A68

Designs: 6p, Ghana flag and links enclosing map of Africa, vert. 24p, Ship's wheel enclosing map of Africa, and cacao pod.

## 1966, Sept.   Unwmk.   *Perf. 13x13½*
| | | | | |
|---|---|---|---|---|
| 256 | A68 | 6pa brt blue & multi | .25 | .25 |
| 257 | A68 | 15pa blue & multi | .25 | .45 |
| 258 | A68 | 24pa dp green & multi | .25 | .50 |
| | | Nos. 256-258 (3) | .75 | 1.20 |

Signing of the African Unity Charter, 3rd anniv.

Soccer Player and Rimet Cup — A69

Various Soccer Scenes.

---

### Perf. 14½x14
## 1966, Nov. 14   Photo.   Wmk. 325
| | | | | |
|---|---|---|---|---|
| 259 | A69 | 5pa brown & multi | .25 | .25 |
| 260 | A69 | 15pa blue & multi | .70 | .30 |
| 261 | A69 | 24pa green & multi | .90 | .50 |
| 262 | A69 | 30pa brt rose & multi | 1.10 | 1.10 |
| 263 | A69 | 60pa lilac & multi | 1.25 | 4.00 |
| a. | | Souvenir sheet of 4 | 26.00 | 26.00 |
| | | Nos. 259-263 (5) | 4.20 | 6.15 |

World Cup Soccer Championship, Wembley, England, July 11-30. No. 263a contains 4 imperf. stamps similar to No. 263 with simulated perforations.

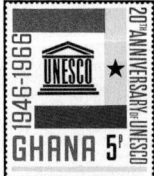

UNESCO Emblem — A70

## 1966, Dec. 23   Wmk. 325   *Perf. 14½*
| | | | | |
|---|---|---|---|---|
| 264 | A70 | 5pa multicolored | .25 | .25 |
| 265 | A70 | 15pa multicolored | .75 | .50 |
| 266 | A70 | 24pa multicolored | 1.00 | 1.00 |
| 267 | A70 | 30pa multicolored | 1.50 | 1.25 |
| 268 | A70 | 60pa multicolored | 2.25 | 5.00 |
| a. | | Souvenir sheet of 5 | 27.50 | 27.50 |
| | | Nos. 264-268 (5) | 5.75 | 8.00 |

UNESCO, 20th anniv. No. 268a contains 5 imperf. stamps similar to Nos. 264-268 with simulated perforations.

Packing Cases and Fair Emblem — A71

Fair Emblem and: 15pa, World map and trade routes to Accra. 24pa, Freighters and loading crane, vert. 36pa, Hand holding cargo net.

## 1967, Feb. 1     *Perf. 14½x14, 14x14½*
| | | | | |
|---|---|---|---|---|
| 269 | A71 | 5pa multicolored | .25 | .25 |
| 270 | A71 | 15pa multicolored | .25 | .25 |
| 271 | A71 | 24pa multicolored | .25 | .30 |
| 272 | A71 | 36pa multicolored | .30 | 1.50 |
| | | Nos. 269-272 (4) | 1.05 | 2.30 |

International Trade Fair, Accra, Feb. 1-19.

Eagle and Flag — A72

## 1967, Feb. 24   Photo.   *Perf. 14x14½*
### Flag in Red, Yellow, Black and Green
| | | | | |
|---|---|---|---|---|
| 273 | A72 | 1np gray bl & dk brn | .25 | .75 |
| 274 | A72 | 4np ocher & dk brn | .25 | .25 |
| 275 | A72 | 12½np ol grn & dk brn | .30 | .30 |
| 276 | A72 | 25np dl cl & dk brn | .50 | 2.25 |
| a. | | Souvenir sheet of 4, #273-276 | 6.50 | 8.00 |
| | | Nos. 273-276 (4) | 1.30 | 3.55 |

1st anniv. of the revolution which overthrew the regime of Kwame Nkrumah.

No. 276a has dull claret marginal inscriptions. An imperf. sheet similar to No. 276a has solid margins of dull claret, colorless inscriptions. Value $10.

### Nos. 51, 54-58, 60 and 97 Surcharged in Black, Red or White
Size: 30½x21mm, 21x30½mm
## 1967, Feb. 27   *Perf. 14½x14, 14x14½*
| | | | | |
|---|---|---|---|---|
| 277 | A16 | 1½np on 2p (B) | 2.00 | 10.00 |
| 278 | A16 | 3½np on 4p (B) | 8.00 | 4.00 |
| 279 | A17 | 5np on 6p (W) | 4.00 | 2.00 |
| 280 | A15 | 9np on 11p (W) | .30 | 1.00 |
| 281 | A15 | 10np on 1sh (W) | .35 | 2.00 |
| 282 | A17 | 25np on 2sh6p (R) | 3.00 | 8.00 |

#### Size: 45x26mm
| | | | | |
|---|---|---|---|---|
| 283 | A16 | 1nc on 10sh (R) | 2.50 | 16.00 |
| 284 | A28 | 2nc on £1 (R) | 4.00 | 25.00 |
| | | Nos. 277-284,C9-C10 (10) | 33.15 | 75.00 |

Corn
A73

Forest
Kingfisher
A74

Ghana Mace
(golden staff)
— A74a

Commelina
Flower — A74b

African
Lungfish — A75

Adomi Bridge, Volta
River — A75a

Chameleon —
A75b

Quay No. 2, Tema
Harbor — A75c

Cape Hare —
A75d

Black-winged
Stilt — A75e

Chief's Ceremonial
Stool — A75f

Frangipani —
A75g

State Chair — A75h

4np, Rufous-crowned roller, vert. 6np, Akosombo Dam, Volta River.

**Perf. 11½x12, 12x11½ (A73), 14x14½, 14½x14 (A74-A75)**

| | | | | |
|---|---|---|---|---|
| **1967** | | **Photo.** | **Wmk. 325** | |
| **286** | A73 | 1np multicolored | .25 | .25 |
| **287** | A74 | 1½np multicolored | 1.00 | 2.75 |
| **288** | A74a | 2np multicolored | .25 | .25 |
| **289** | A74b | 2½np multicolored | .40 | .25 |
| **290** | A75 | 3np multicolored | .25 | .45 |
| **291** | A74 | 4np multicolored | 1.50 | .25 |
| **292** | A75 | 6np multicolored | .25 | 1.75 |

| | | | | |
|---|---|---|---|---|
| **293** | A75a | 8np multicolored | .25 | .75 |
| **294** | A75b | 9np multicolored | .75 | .25 |
| **295** | A75c | 10np multicolored | .25 | .25 |
| **296** | A75d | 20np blue | .25 | .25 |
| **297** | A75e | 50np multicolored | 8.50 | 4.00 |
| **298** | A75f | 1nc multicolored | 2.00 | 1.00 |
| **299** | A75g | 2nc multicolored | 2.25 | 3.50 |
| **300** | A75h | 2.50nc multicolored | 2.50 | 11.00 |
| | | *Nos. 286-300 (15)* | 20.65 | 26.95 |

For overprints & surcharges see Nos. 356-370, 858, 1091, 1092A-1092C, 1092E-1093, 1095, 1096B.

Kumasi Fort,
1896 — A76

Castles on Ghana Coast: 12½np, Christiansborg Castle, 1659, and British galleon. 20np, Elmina Castle, 1482, and Portuguese galleon. 25np, Cape Coast Castle, 1664, and Spanish galleon.

| | | | | |
|---|---|---|---|---|
| **1967, June 12** | | | **Perf. 14½** | |
| **301** | A76 | 4np grnsh bl & multi | .25 | .25 |
| **302** | A76 | 12½np red org & multi | .70 | 1.00 |
| **303** | A76 | 20np brt grn & multi | 1.00 | 2.25 |
| **304** | A76 | 25np lt red brn & multi | 1.25 | 3.00 |
| | | *Nos. 301-304 (4)* | 3.20 | 6.50 |

Orbiter 1 Landing on
Moon — A77

Designs: 4np, Luna 10 on the moon, and globe. 12½np, Astronaut walking in space.

| | | | | |
|---|---|---|---|---|
| **1967, Aug. 16** | | **Unwmk.** | **Perf. 13½** | |
| **305** | A77 | 4np multicolored | .25 | .25 |
| **306** | A77 | 10np multicolored | .25 | .30 |
| **307** | A77 | 12½np multicolored | .25 | .60 |
| *a.* | | Souvenir sheet of 3 | 2.00 | 3.75 |
| | | *Nos. 305-307 (3)* | .75 | 1.15 |

Achievements in space. Issued in Ghana in sheets of 30. Sheets of 12 with ornamented, inscribed border also exist; these were sold in Ghana in 1968.
No. 307a contains 3 imperf. stamps similar to Nos. 305-307.

Boy Scouts at
Campfire — A78

Designs: 10np, Hiking Boy Scout. 12½np, Lord Baden-Powell.

| | | | | |
|---|---|---|---|---|
| **1967, Sept. 18** | | **Photo.** | **Perf. 14x13½** | |
| **308** | A78 | 4np multicolored | .25 | .25 |
| **309** | A78 | 10np multicolored | .35 | .35 |
| **310** | A78 | 12½np multicolored | .45 | .95 |
| *a.* | | Souvenir sheet of 3 | 6.00 | 8.50 |
| | | *Nos. 308-310 (3)* | 1.05 | 1.55 |

50th anniv. of the Ghana (Gold Coast) Boy Scouts. Issued in Ghana in sheets of 30. Sheets of 12 with ornamented, inscribed border also exist; these were sold in Ghana in 1968.
No. 310a contains 3 imperf. stamps similar to Nos. 308-310 with simulated perforations.

UN Secretariat
Building — A79

Design: 50np, 2.50nc, UN Headquarters.

| | | | | |
|---|---|---|---|---|
| **1967, Oct. 24** | | **Litho.** | **Perf. 13½x13** | |
| **311** | A79 | 4np multicolored | .25 | .25 |
| **312** | A79 | 10np multicolored | .25 | .25 |
| **313** | A79 | 50np multicolored | .30 | .40 |
| **314** | A79 | 2.50nc multicolored | .60 | 3.00 |
| *a.* | | Souvenir sheet | 4.00 | 9.00 |
| | | *Nos. 311-314 (4)* | 1.40 | 4.10 |

United Nations Day. No. 314a contains one imperf. stamp similar to No. 314 with simulated perforations.

Leopard
A80

Designs: 12½np, Christmas butterfly. 20np, Nubian carmine bee-eaters. 50np, Waterbuck.

**Wmk. 325**

| | | | | |
|---|---|---|---|---|
| **1967, Dec. 28** | | **Photo.** | **Perf. 12½** | |
| **315** | A80 | 4np multicolored | 1.25 | .25 |
| **316** | A80 | 12½np multicolored | 3.00 | 1.75 |
| **317** | A80 | 20np multicolored | 3.50 | 3.50 |
| **318** | A80 | 50np multicolored | 4.00 | 8.00 |
| *a.* | | Souvenir sheet of 3 | 22.00 | 25.00 |
| | | *Nos. 315-318 (4)* | 11.75 | 13.50 |

Intl. Tourist Year. No. 318a contains 3 imperf. stamps similar to Nos. 316-318 with simulated perforations.

Convoy
Entering
Accra — A81

12½np, Victory parade. 20np, Waving crowd. 40np, Singing and dancing crowd.

**Unwmk.**

| | | | | |
|---|---|---|---|---|
| **1968, Feb. 24** | | **Litho.** | **Perf. 14** | |
| **319** | A81 | 4np sal & multi | .25 | .25 |
| **320** | A81 | 12½np multicolored | .25 | .25 |
| **321** | A81 | 20np multicolored | .30 | .30 |
| **322** | A81 | 40np yel & multi | .65 | 1.75 |
| | | *Nos. 319-322 (4)* | 1.45 | 2.55 |

2nd anniversary of Feb. 24th Revolution.

Cacao Beans and
Microscope
A82

4np, 25np, Cacao tree & beans, microscope.

**Perf. 14½x14**

| | | | | |
|---|---|---|---|---|
| **1968, Mar. 18** | | **Photo.** | **Wmk. 325** | |
| **323** | A82 | 2½np grn & multi | .25 | 1.00 |
| **324** | A82 | 4np gray & multi | .25 | .25 |
| **325** | A82 | 10np scar & multi | .25 | .25 |
| **326** | A82 | 25np multicolored | .40 | 1.00 |
| *a.* | | Souvenir sheet of 4 | 3.25 | 3.25 |
| | | *Nos. 323-326 (4)* | 1.15 | 2.50 |

Issued to publicize Ghana's cocoa production. Sheets of 30.
No. 326a contains four imperf. stamps similar to Nos. 323-326 with simulated perforations.
Nos. 323-326 also exist in sheets of 12 believed not to have been on sale in Ghana.

Lt. Gen. E. K.
Kotoka — A83

Various portraits of Lt. Gen. Kotoka. 40np vert.

| | | | | |
|---|---|---|---|---|
| **1968, Apr. 17** | | **Unwmk.** | **Perf. 14** | |
| **327** | A83 | 4np pur & multi | .25 | .25 |
| **328** | A83 | 12½np grn & multi | .25 | .25 |
| **329** | A83 | 20np multicolored | .35 | .60 |
| **330** | A83 | 40np gray & multi | .50 | 2.00 |
| | | *Nos. 327-330 (4)* | 1.35 | 3.10 |

Lt. Gen. Emmanuel Kwasi Kotoka (1926-67), leader of the Revolution of 1966 against Nkrumah.

Tobacco — A84

Designs: 5np, Crested porcupine. 12½np, Tapped rubber tree. 20np, Cymothoe sangaris butterfly. 40np, Charaxes ameliae butterfly.

| | | | | |
|---|---|---|---|---|
| **1968, Aug.** | | **Photo.** | **Perf. 14x14½** | |
| **331** | A84 | 4np multicolored | .25 | .25 |
| **332** | A84 | 5np multicolored | .25 | 1.00 |
| **333** | A84 | 12½np multicolored | .75 | .75 |
| **334** | A84 | 20np multicolored | 2.25 | 2.75 |
| **335** | A84 | 40np multicolored | 2.50 | 5.00 |
| *a.* | | Souvenir sheet of 4 | 6.75 | 8.00 |
| | | *Nos. 331-335 (5)* | 6.00 | 9.75 |

No. 335a contains 4 stamps similar to Nos. 331, 332-335 with simulated perforations.
Nos. 331-335 exist imperf. Value, set $13.

Surgical
Team — A85

| | | | | |
|---|---|---|---|---|
| **1968, Nov. 11** | | | **Perf. 14x13** | |
| **336** | A85 | 4np grn & multi | .25 | .25 |
| **337** | A85 | 12½np multicolored | .55 | .30 |
| **338** | A85 | 20np pur & multi | .90 | .50 |
| **339** | A85 | 40np bl & multi | 1.50 | 2.50 |
| *a.* | | Souvenir sheet of 4 | 4.75 | 7.00 |
| | | *Nos. 336-339 (4)* | 3.20 | 4.05 |

WHO, 20th anniv. No. 339a contains 4 imperf. stamps similar to Nos. 336-339.

Hurdling — A86

12½np, Boxing. 20np, Torch bearer, flags & Olympic rings. 40np, Soccer.

| | | | | |
|---|---|---|---|---|
| **1968, Dec.** | | **Unwmk.** | **Perf. 14x14½** | |
| **340** | A86 | 4np gray & multi | .25 | .25 |
| **341** | A86 | 12½np gray & multi | .25 | .25 |
| **342** | A86 | 20np ultra & multi | .40 | .70 |
| **343** | A86 | 40np gray & multi | .60 | 2.50 |
| *a.* | | Souvenir sheet of 4 | 4.50 | 7.00 |
| | | *Nos. 340-343 (4)* | 1.50 | 3.70 |

19th Olympic Games, Mexico City, Oct. 12-27, 1968. No. 343a contains 4 imperf. stamps with simulated perforations similar to Nos. 340-343.

UN Headquarters and
Flags — A87

UN Day, 1968: 12np, UN emblem and Ghanaian staff and stool. 20np, UN Headquarters, New York, UN emblem and Ghana flag. 40np, UN emblem surrounded by flags.

| | | | | |
|---|---|---|---|---|
| **1969, Feb. 1** | | **Litho.** | **Perf. 13x13½** | |
| **344** | A87 | 4np multicolored | .25 | .25 |
| **345** | A87 | 12½np pink & multi | .25 | .25 |
| **346** | A87 | 20np blk & multi | .25 | .35 |
| **347** | A87 | 40np lt bl & multi | .25 | 1.75 |
| *a.* | | Souvenir sheet of 4 | 1.10 | 3.25 |
| | | *Nos. 344-347 (4)* | 1.00 | 2.60 |

No. 347a contains 4 imperf. stamps with simulated perforations similar to Nos. 344-347.
Nos. 344-347 exist imperf. Value, set $4.50.

Joseph Boakye
Danquah — A88

12½np, 20np, Dr. Martin Luther King, Jr., Human Rights flame & flag of Ghana.

## 1969, Mar. 7   Photo.   Perf. 14½x14

| 348 | A88 | 4np gray & multi | .25 | .25 |
|---|---|---|---|---|
| 349 | A88 | 12½np multicolored | .25 | .30 |
| 350 | A88 | 20np blue & multi | .50 | .75 |
| 351 | A88 | 40np grn & multi | .60 | 2.00 |
| a. | | Souvenir sheet of 4 | 1.50 | 3.50 |
| | | Nos. 348-351 (4) | 1.60 | 3.30 |

Intl. Human Rights Year, Rev. Martin Luther King, Jr. (1929-1968), American civil rights leader, and Joseph Boakye Danquah (1895-1965), lawyer, writer and Ghanaian political leader.

No. 351a contains 4 imperf. stamps with simulated perforations similar to Nos. 348-351.

Parliament — A89

Design: 12½np, 40np, Coat of Arms.

## 1969, Sept.   Wmk. 325   Perf. 14½x14

| 352 | A89 | 4np multicolored | .25 | .25 |
|---|---|---|---|---|
| 353 | A89 | 12½p multicolored | .25 | .25 |
| 354 | A89 | 20np multicolored | .25 | .25 |
| 355 | A89 | 40np multicolored | .25 | .60 |
| a. | | Souvenir sheet of 4 | 1.00 | 2.50 |
| | | Nos. 352-355 (4) | 1.00 | 1.35 |

3rd anniv. of the revolution. No. 355a contains 4 imperf. stamps with simulated perforations similar to Nos. 352-355.

Nos. 352-355 exist imperf. Value, set $5.

Nos. 286-300
Overprinted in Black,
Yellow or Red

## Perf. 11½x12, 12x11½ (A73), 14x14½, 14½x14 (A74-A75)
## 1969, Oct. 1   Photo.   Wmk. 325

| 356 | A73 | 1np multicolored | .25 | 2.25 |
|---|---|---|---|---|
| 357 | A74 | 1½np multicolored | 1.75 | 4.50 |
| 358 | A73 | 2np multicolored | .25 | 3.50 |
| 359 | A73 | 2½np multicolored | .25 | 2.25 |
| 360 | A73 | 3np multicolored | .70 | 2.50 |
| 361 | A73 | 4np multi (Y) | 2.25 | .75 |
| 362 | A75 | 6np multicolored | .25 | 2.75 |
| 363 | A75 | 8np multicolored | .25 | 3.00 |
| 364 | A75 | 9np multicolored | .25 | 3.00 |
| 365 | A75 | 10np multicolored | .25 | 3.00 |
| 366 | A74 | 20np blue | .65 | 2.25 |
| 367 | A74 | 50np multicolored | 5.00 | 8.50 |
| 368 | A74 | 1nc multicolored | 2.00 | 11.00 |
| 369 | A74 | 2nc multi (R) | 2.50 | 12.00 |
| 370 | A74 | 2.50nc multicolored | 2.50 | 13.00 |
| | | Nos. 356-370 (15) | 19.10 | 74.25 |

Overprint vertical on vertical stamps.
The 4np also exists with overprint in black and in red.

Map of Africa, Two
Ghana Flags Rising from
Ghana — A90

Designs: 12½np, "2" with laurel and star. 20np, Three hands and egg (symbol of rebirth) and Kente cloth. 40np, like 4np.

## Unwmk.
## 1969, Dec. 4   Litho.   Perf. 14

| 371 | A90 | 4np multicolored | .25 | .25 |
|---|---|---|---|---|
| 372 | A90 | 12½np bl & multi | .30 | .30 |
| 373 | A90 | 20np multicolored | .40 | .40 |
| 374 | A90 | 40np bl & multi | .80 | .80 |
| | | Nos. 371-374 (4) | 1.75 | 1.75 |

Inauguration of the 2nd Republic, Oct. 1969.

Cogwheels and
ILO
Emblem — A91

## Perf. 14½x14
## 1970, Jan. 5   Photo.   Wmk. 325

| 375 | A91 | 4np rose red & multi | .25 | .25 |
|---|---|---|---|---|
| 376 | A91 | 12½np multicolored | .25 | .45 |
| 377 | A91 | 20np multicolored | .30 | .90 |
| a. | | Souvenir sheet of 3 | 1.40 | 2.50 |
| | | Nos. 375-377 (3) | .80 | 1.60 |

ILO, 50th anniv. No. 377a contains 3 imperf. stamps similar to Nos. 375-377 with simulated perforations.

Nos. 375-377 printed in sheets of 12.

Red Cross
Helping
Wounded — A92

4np, Red Cross & globe, vert. 12½np, Henri Dunant, Red Cross, Red Crescent, Lion & Sun emblems. 40np, Red Cross and first aid.

## 1970, Feb. 2   Perf. 14x14½, 14½x14

| 378 | A92 | 4np gold & multi | .45 | .45 |
|---|---|---|---|---|
| 379 | A92 | 12½np gold & multi | .55 | .55 |
| 380 | A92 | 20np blue & multi | .65 | .85 |
| 381 | A92 | 40np multicolored | .85 | 2.50 |
| a. | | Souvenir sheet of 4 | 3.75 | 6.00 |
| | | Nos. 378-381 (4) | 2.50 | 4.35 |

League of Red Cross Societies, 50th anniv. No. 381a contains 4 imperf. stamps similar to Nos. 378-381 with simulated perforations.

Kotoka Airport,
Gen. Kotoka and
VC10 — A93

12½np, Control tower & tail section of VC10. 20np, Bird's eye view of airport and runway. 40np, Flags in front of Kotoka Airport.

## Perf. 13x14
## 1970, Apr.   Unwmk.   Litho.

| 382 | A93 | 4np multicolored | .25 | .25 |
|---|---|---|---|---|
| 383 | A93 | 12½np multicolored | .25 | .25 |
| 384 | A93 | 20np multicolored | .40 | .40 |
| 385 | A93 | 40np multicolored | .75 | .75 |
| | | Nos. 382-385 (4) | 1.65 | 1.65 |

Inauguration of Kotoka Airport.

Lunar Landing Module
and Spacecraft — A94

Designs: 12½np, Neil A. Armstrong stepping onto the moon. 20np, Scientific experiments on the moon, horiz. 40np, Neil A. Armstrong, Michael Collins and Edwin E. Aldrin, Jr., after return to earth, horiz.

## 1970, June 15   Litho.   Perf. 12½

| 386 | A94 | 4np multicolored | .25 | .25 |
|---|---|---|---|---|
| 387 | A94 | 12½np multicolored | .85 | .85 |
| 388 | A94 | 20np multicolored | 1.10 | 1.10 |
| 389 | A94 | 40np multicolored | 3.00 | 3.00 |
| a. | | Souvenir sheet of 4 | 6.25 | 10.00 |
| | | Nos. 386-389 (4) | 5.20 | 5.20 |

See note after US No. C76. No. 389a contains 4 imperf. stamps similar to Nos. 386-389. Exists with and without simulated perfs.

Nos. 386-389 and 389a were overprinted "PHILYMPIA/LONDON 1970" in black or silver in Sept. 1970. They are believed not to have been regularly issued. Value, set $20.

Adult
Education — A95

Education Year Emblem and: 12½np, Children of various races studying together. 20np, "Ntesie" symbol of wisdom and knowledge. 40np, Nursery school children.

## 1970, Aug. 10   Litho.   Perf. 13x12½

| 390 | A95 | 4np blue & multi | .25 | .25 |
|---|---|---|---|---|
| 391 | A95 | 12½np blue & multi | .25 | .25 |
| 392 | A95 | 20np blue & multi | .30 | .30 |
| 393 | A95 | 40np blue & multi | .45 | .45 |
| | | Nos. 390-393 (4) | 1.25 | 1.25 |

Issued for International Education Year.

Inauguration of
Second
Republic — A96

Designs: 12½np, Mace and words of proclamation by K. A. Busia. 20np, Mace and globe with doves. 40np, Opening of Parliament of Second Republic.

## 1970, Oct. 1   Litho.   Perf. 13

| 398 | A96 | 4np multicolored | .25 | .25 |
|---|---|---|---|---|
| 399 | A96 | 12½np multicolored | .25 | .25 |
| 400 | A96 | 20np multicolored | .40 | .40 |
| 401 | A96 | 40np lt bl & multi | .45 | .45 |
| | | Nos. 398-401 (4) | 1.35 | 1.35 |

First anniversary of the Second Republic.

Amaryllis — A97

## Perf. 14½x14
## 1970   Photo.   Wmk. 325

| 402 | A97 | 4np shown | 2.25 | |
|---|---|---|---|---|
| 403 | A97 | 12½np Lioness | 2.25 | 1.25 |
| 404 | A97 | 20np African orchid | 2.50 | 2.00 |
| 405 | A97 | 40np Elephant | 7.00 | 8.50 |
| | | Nos. 402-405 (4) | 14.00 | 12.00 |

Kuduo Brass
Casket — A98

Designs: 12½np, Akan traditional house, Danmun. 20np, Larabanga Mosque. 40np, Akan funerary clay head.

## 1970, Dec. 7   Litho.   Perf. 14½x14

| 406 | A98 | 4np gray & multi | .25 | .25 |
|---|---|---|---|---|
| 407 | A98 | 12½np blue & multi | .35 | .30 |
| 408 | A98 | 20np multicolored | .55 | .55 |
| a. | | Souvenir sheet of 4 | 7.00 | 9.50 |
| 409 | A98 | 40np blue & multi | 1.50 | 1.60 |
| | | Nos. 406-409 (4) | 2.65 | 2.70 |

No. 408a contains stamps similar to Nos. 406 and 408, a 12½np (Pompeii Basilica) and a 40np (Pompeii scene). Simulated perforation.

Fair Building and
Emblem — A99

Fair Emblem and: 12½np, Drugstore merchandise. 20np, Automotives and tools. 40np, Cranes and trucks. 50np, Cargo, ship and plane, vert.

## Perf. 14½x14, 14x14½
## 1971, Feb. 5   Photo.   Wmk. 325

| 410 | A99 | 4np multicolored | .25 | .25 |
|---|---|---|---|---|
| 411 | A99 | 12½np lilac & multi | .35 | .35 |
| 412 | A99 | 20np blue & multi | .60 | .60 |
| 413 | A99 | 40np multicolored | 1.25 | 1.25 |
| 414 | A99 | 50np multicolored | 1.50 | 1.50 |
| | | Nos. 410-414 (5) | 3.95 | 3.95 |

2nd Ghana International Trade Fair, Accra, Feb. 1-14, 1971.

Crucifixion — A100

Easter: 12½np, Jesus and disciples. 20np, Resurrection.

## Perf. 13½
## 1971, May 19   Litho.   Unwmk.

| 415 | A100 | 4np multicolored | .25 | .25 |
|---|---|---|---|---|
| 416 | A100 | 12½np multicolored | .40 | .40 |
| 417 | A100 | 20np multicolored | .70 | .70 |
| | | Nos. 415-417 (3) | 1.35 | 1.35 |

Corn and FAO
Emblem — A101

## Perf. 14x14½
## 1971, June   Wmk. 325   Photo.

| 418 | A101 | 4np lilac & multi | .25 | .25 |
|---|---|---|---|---|
| 419 | A101 | 12½np lt bl & multi | .30 | .30 |
| 420 | A101 | 20np multicolored | .55 | 1.25 |
| | | Nos. 418-420 (3) | 1.10 | 1.80 |

Freedom from Hunger, second development decade, 1970-1980.

The overprint "In Memoriam / Lord Boyd ORR / 1880-1971" was applied to Nos. 418-420 in October, 1971. The 4np was also surcharged "60NP."

Girl Guide Emblem
on Flag of
Ghana — A102

12½np, Mrs. Elsie Ofuatey-Kodjoe, national founder. 20np, Girl Guides at play. 40np, Campfire and tent. 50np, Girl Guides signalling.

## Unwmk.
## 1971, July 22   Litho.   Perf. 14

| 421 | A102 | 4np multicolored | .25 | .25 |
|---|---|---|---|---|
| 422 | A102 | 12½np yel & multi | .70 | .70 |
| 423 | A102 | 20np sal & multi | 1.40 | 1.40 |
| 424 | A102 | 40np multicolored | 2.25 | 2.25 |
| 425 | A102 | 50np lilac & multi | 2.40 | 2.40 |
| a. | | Souvenir sheet of 5 | 12.00 | 12.00 |
| | | Nos. 421-425 (5) | 7.00 | 7.00 |

50th anniversary of the Girl Guides of Ghana. No. 425a contains 5 imperf. stamps similar to Nos. 421-425.

Nos. 421-425 exist imperf. Value, set $24.

Child Care
Center — A103

YWCA Emblem and: 12½np, World Council Meeting and map of Ghana. 20np, Typing class. 40np, Building fund day.

## 1971, Aug. 5   Perf. 13

| 426 | A103 | 4np multicolored | .25 | .25 |
|---|---|---|---|---|
| 427 | A103 | 12½np ultra & multi | .25 | .25 |
| 428 | A103 | 20np blue & multi | .25 | .25 |
| 429 | A103 | 40np yel & multi | .40 | .80 |
| a. | | Souvenir sheet of 4 | 1.10 | 1.10 |
| | | Nos. 426-429 (4) | 1.15 | 1.55 |

World Council Meeting of Young Women's Christian Association, Accra, Aug. 5. No. 429a contains 4 stamps similar to Nos. 426-429 with simulated perforations.

Nos. 426-429 exist imperf. Value, set $5.

African Nativity
Scene — A104

Christmas: 1np, Fireworks, vert. 6np, Flight into Egypt.

## Perf. 14x14½, 14½x14
## 1971, Nov.   Photo.   Wmk. 325

| 433 | A104 | 1np multicolored | .25 | .70 |
|---|---|---|---|---|
| 434 | A104 | 3np orange & multi | .25 | .70 |
| 435 | A104 | 6np blue & multi | .25 | .70 |
| | | Nos. 433-435 (3) | .75 | 2.10 |

UNICEF Emblem,
and Child — A105

New Constitution (img: Nos. 286-300 overprinted, 1np New Constitution)

UNICEF Emblem and: 5np, Infant weighed in net scale, vert. 30np, Student midwife, vert. 50np, Boy in day care center.

**1971, Dec. 20 Litho. Unwmk.**
*Perf. 13½x13, 13x13½*

| | | | | |
|---|---|---|---|---|
| 436 | A105 | 5np grn & multi | .25 | .25 |
| 437 | A105 | 15np yel & multi | .25 | .30 |
| 438 | A105 | 30np pink & multi | .35 | .70 |
| 439 | A105 | 50np blue & multi | .50 | 1.75 |
| a. | Souvenir sheet of 4 | | 4.25 | 6.50 |
| | *Nos. 436-439 (4)* | | 1.35 | 3.00 |

25th anniv. of UNICEF. No. 439a contains 4 stamps with simulated perforations similar to Nos. 436-439.

Fair Emblem, Map of Africa, Symbol of Unity — A106

Fair Emblem and: 15np, Horn of Plenty. 30np, Fireworks over Africa. 60np, 1nc, Names of participating nations over map of Africa.

**1972, Feb. 23 Litho. Perf. 14**

| | | | | |
|---|---|---|---|---|
| 440 | A106 | 5np lt brn & multi | .25 | .25 |
| 441 | A106 | 15np lt bl & multi | .25 | .30 |
| 442 | A106 | 30np green & multi | .25 | .60 |
| 443 | A106 | 60np yel & multi | .25 | 1.25 |
| 444 | A106 | 1nc lt bl & multi | .35 | 1.75 |
| | *Nos. 440-444 (5)* | | 1.35 | 4.15 |

First All-Africa Trade Fair, Nairobi, Kenya, Feb. 23-Mar. 5.

Nos. 440-444 were overprinted "BELGICA 72" in red for release June 24, 1972. The regularity of this issue has been questioned. Value $7.50.

Nos. 440-444 exist imperf. Value, set $7.

Books for the Blind
A107

Book and Flame of Knowledge A108

Book Year Emblem and: 15p, Books for Children ("Anansi and Snake the Postman"). 30p, Books for Recreation (Accra Central Library). 50p, Books for Students (2 students).

**1972, Apr. 21 Perf. 13½**

| | | | | |
|---|---|---|---|---|
| 445 | A107 | 5p blue & multi | .25 | .25 |
| 446 | A107 | 15p yel & multi | .65 | .50 |
| 447 | A107 | 30p lilac & multi | .85 | 1.00 |
| 448 | A107 | 50p green & multi | 1.50 | 2.25 |
| 449 | A108 | 1ce blue & multi | 2.25 | 4.25 |
| a. | Souvenir sheet of 5 | | 9.00 | 12.00 |
| | *Nos. 445-449 (5)* | | 5.50 | 8.25 |

Intl. Book Year. No. 449a contains one each of Nos. 445-449 with simulated perforations.

Star Grass — A109

15p, Mona monkey. 30p, Amaryllis. 1ce, Side-striped squirrel.

**1972, July 3 Litho. Perf. 13½**

| | | | | |
|---|---|---|---|---|
| 450 | A109 | 5p shown | .25 | .25 |
| 451 | A109 | 15p multicolored | .65 | .65 |
| 452 | A109 | 30p multicolored | 4.25 | 4.25 |
| 453 | A109 | 1ce multicolored | 4.75 | 4.75 |
| | *Nos. 450-453 (4)* | | 9.90 | 9.90 |

Olympic Emblems, Soccer — A110

**1972, Sept. 5 Litho. Perf. 13½x13**

| | | | | |
|---|---|---|---|---|
| 454 | A110 | 5p shown | .25 | .25 |
| 455 | A110 | 15p Running | .25 | .25 |
| 456 | A110 | 30p Boxing | .35 | .45 |
| 457 | A110 | 50p Long jump | .70 | 1.75 |
| 458 | A110 | 1ce High jump | 1.50 | 3.00 |
| | *Nos. 454-458 (5)* | | 3.05 | 5.70 |

---

**Souvenir Sheet**

| | | | |
|---|---|---|---|
| 459 | Sheet of 2 | 3.25 | 6.00 |
| a. | A110 40p like 30p | 1.25 | 2.25 |
| b. | A110 60p like 5p | 1.75 | 3.00 |

20th Olympic Games, Munich, 8/26-9/11.

Senior and Cub Scouts, Badge — A111

Designs: 15p, Scout in front of tent. 30p, 40p, Sea Scouts in canoe. 50p, Cub Scouts with den mother. 60p, 1ce, Scouts studying.

**1972, Oct. Litho. Perf. 14**

| | | | | |
|---|---|---|---|---|
| 460 | A111 | 5p blue grn & multi | .25 | .25 |
| 461 | A111 | 15p ocher & multi | .45 | .45 |
| 462 | A111 | 30p lilac & multi | .85 | .85 |
| 463 | A111 | 50p rose & multi | 1.50 | 1.50 |
| 464 | A111 | 1ce blue & multi | 3.00 | 3.00 |
| | *Nos. 460-464 (5)* | | 6.05 | 6.05 |

**Souvenir Sheet**
*Perf. 13½*

| | | | |
|---|---|---|---|
| 465 | Sheet of 2 | 4.00 | 4.00 |
| a. | A111 40p brown & multi | 1.35 | 1.35 |
| b. | A111 60p green & multi | 2.25 | 2.25 |

Boy Scout Movement, 65th anniversary. For overprints see Nos. 484-489.

Virgin and Child, by Holbein the Younger — A112

Paintings: 1p, Holy Night, by Correggio. 15p, Virgin and Child, by Andrea Rico. 30p, Melchior. 60p, Virgin and Child with Caspar. 1ce, Balthasar. 30p, 60p, 1ce, are from early 16th century stained glass windows.

**1972, Dec. 2 Perf. 14x13½**

| | | | | |
|---|---|---|---|---|
| 466 | A112 | 1p black & multi | .25 | .25 |
| 467 | A112 | 3p black & multi | .25 | .25 |
| 468 | A112 | 15p black & multi | .30 | .30 |
| 469 | A112 | 30p black & multi | .60 | .60 |
| 470 | A112 | 60p black & multi | 1.40 | 1.40 |
| 471 | A112 | 1ce black & multi | 2.00 | 2.00 |
| a. | Souvenir sheet of 3 | | 7.25 | 7.25 |
| | *Nos. 466-471 (6)* | | 4.80 | 4.80 |

Christmas. No. 471a contains one each of Nos. 469-471 with simulated perforations.

Market — A113

Designs: 1p, Unity Declaration at Kumasi Durbar. 5p, Woman with child selling bananas, vert. 15p, Farmer at rest and produce, vert. 30p, Market. 40p, 1ce, Farmer cutting palm nuts with cutlass. 60p, Miners.

**1973, Apr. Litho.**
*Perf. 14x13½, 13½x14*

| | | | | |
|---|---|---|---|---|
| 472 | A113 | 1p multicolored | .25 | .25 |
| 473 | A113 | 3p multicolored | .25 | .25 |
| 474 | A113 | 5p multicolored | .25 | .25 |
| 475 | A113 | 15p multicolored | .25 | .25 |
| 476 | A113 | 30p multicolored | .25 | .40 |
| 477 | A113 | 1ce multicolored | .30 | 1.25 |
| | *Nos. 472-477 (6)* | | 1.55 | 2.65 |

**Souvenir Sheet**

| | | | |
|---|---|---|---|
| 478 | Sheet of 2 | 2.00 | 2.00 |
| a. | A113 40p multicolored | .70 | .70 |
| b. | A113 60p multicolored | 1.05 | 1.05 |

Operation "Feed Yourself" and for 1st anniv. of the Oct. 13 Revolution.
Nos. 472-477 exist imperf. Value, set $4.75.

---

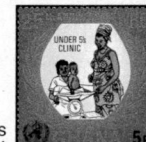

Children's Clinic — A114

WHO Emblem and: 15p, Radiology. 30p, Immunization. 50p, Fight against malnutrition (starving child). 1ce, WHO Headquarters, Geneva.

**1973, July Perf. 14x13½**

| | | | | |
|---|---|---|---|---|
| 479 | A114 | 5p rose red & multi | .25 | .25 |
| 480 | A114 | 15p blue & multi | .25 | .25 |
| 481 | A114 | 30p bister & multi | .30 | .40 |
| 482 | A114 | 50p green & multi | .50 | .70 |
| 483 | A114 | 1ce multicolored | .95 | 1.75 |
| | *Nos. 479-483 (5)* | | 2.25 | 3.40 |

WHO, 25th anniversary.

**Nos. 460-465 Overprinted: "1st WORLD SCOUTING CONFERENCE IN AFRICA"**

**1973, July Litho. Perf. 14**

| | | | | |
|---|---|---|---|---|
| 484 | A111 | 5p blue grn & multi | .25 | .25 |
| 485 | A111 | 15p ocher & multi | .25 | .50 |
| 486 | A111 | 30p lilac & multi | .50 | 1.25 |
| 487 | A111 | 50p rose & multi | .85 | 2.00 |
| 488 | A111 | 1ce blue & multi | 1.60 | 3.00 |
| | *Nos. 484-488 (5)* | | 3.45 | 7.00 |

**Souvenir Sheet**
*Perf. 13½*

| | | | |
|---|---|---|---|
| 489 | Sheet of 2 | 3.50 | 10.00 |
| a. | A111 40p brown & multi | 1.25 | 3.00 |
| b. | A111 60p green & multi | 1.75 | 6.00 |

24th Boy Scout World Conference (1st in Africa), Nairobi, Kenya, July 16-21.

Poultry Farming A115

FAO/UN Emblem and: 15p, 40p, Tractor. 50p, Cacao harvest. 60p, 1ce, FAO Headquarters, Rome.

**1973 Litho. Perf. 14½x14**

| | | | | |
|---|---|---|---|---|
| 490 | A115 | 5p blue & multi | .25 | .25 |
| 491 | A115 | 15p blue & multi | .25 | .25 |
| 492 | A115 | 50p blue & multi | .30 | .80 |
| 493 | A115 | 1ce blue & multi | .45 | 1.60 |
| | *Nos. 490-493 (4)* | | 1.25 | 2.90 |

**Souvenir Sheet**

| | | | |
|---|---|---|---|
| 494 | Sheet of 2 | 1.00 | 2.25 |
| a. | A115 40p blue & multi | .30 | .80 |
| b. | A115 60p blue & multi | .45 | 1.10 |

World Food Program, 10th anniversary.
Nos. 490-493 exist imperf. Value, set $4.75.

INTERPOL Emblem, Observer — A116

INTERPOL Emblem and: 30p, Judge's wig, poison bottle, handcuffs. 50p, photograph and fingerprint. 1ce, Corpse and question mark.

**1973 Perf. 13x13½**

| | | | | |
|---|---|---|---|---|
| 495 | A116 | 5p emerald & multi | .25 | .25 |
| 496 | A116 | 30p rose red & multi | .75 | .75 |
| 497 | A116 | 50p ultra & multi | 1.75 | 1.75 |
| 498 | A116 | 1ce gray & multi | 2.75 | 2.75 |
| | *Nos. 495-498 (4)* | | 5.50 | 5.50 |

50th anniv. the Intl. Criminal Police Org. (INTERPOL). Nos. 495-498 exist imperf. Value, set $7.50.

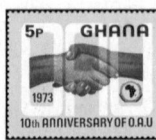

Handclasp and "OAU" — A117

"OAU" and: 30p, Africa Hall, Addis Ababa. 50p, OAU emblem (map of Africa). 1ce, "X" in Ghana flag colors.

**1973, Oct. 22 Litho. Perf. 14x14½**

| | | | | |
|---|---|---|---|---|
| 499 | A117 | 5p lt bl, blk & brn | .25 | .25 |
| 500 | A117 | 30p bluish grn, blk & brn | .25 | .30 |

---

| | | | | |
|---|---|---|---|---|
| 501 | A117 | 50p pink, black & ol | .25 | .75 |
| 502 | A117 | 1ce multicolored | .30 | 1.10 |
| | *Nos. 499-502 (4)* | | 1.05 | 2.40 |

Org. for African Unity, 10th anniv. Nos. 499-502 exist imperf. Value, set $5.00.

Weather Balloon, WMO Emblem — A118

WMO Emblem and: 15p, 40p, Tiros weather satellite. 30p, 60p, Computer weather map. 1ce, Radar cloud scanner.

**1973, Nov. 16**

| | | | | |
|---|---|---|---|---|
| 503 | A118 | 5p multicolored | .25 | .25 |
| 504 | A118 | 15p multicolored | .25 | .25 |
| 505 | A118 | 30p multicolored | .30 | .60 |
| 506 | A118 | 1ce multicolored | .55 | 1.75 |
| | *Nos. 503-506 (4)* | | 1.35 | 2.85 |

**Souvenir Sheet**

| | | | |
|---|---|---|---|
| 507 | Sheet of 2 | 1.50 | 3.25 |
| a. | A118 40p multicolored | .45 | .90 |
| b. | A118 60p multicolored | .85 | 1.60 |

Intl. meteorological cooperation, cent. No. 507 exists imperf.

Adoration of the Kings — A119

Christmas: 3p, 40p, Madonna and Child (contemporary). Nos. 510, 511d, Madonna and Child, by Murillo. No. 511, 60p, Adoration of the Kings, by Tiepolo. No. 511b as 1p.

**1973, Dec. 10 Perf. 14**

| | | | | |
|---|---|---|---|---|
| 508 | A119 | 1p black & multi | .25 | .25 |
| 509 | A119 | 3p gray & multi | .25 | .25 |
| 510 | A119 | 30p multicolored | .35 | .35 |
| 511 | A119 | 50p multicolored | .75 | .75 |
| | *Nos. 508-511 (4)* | | 1.60 | 1.60 |

**Souvenir Sheet**
*Imperf*

| | | | |
|---|---|---|---|
| 511A | Sheet of 4 | 2.00 | 2.00 |
| b. | A119 30p multicolored | .30 | .30 |
| c. | A119 40p gray & multi | .40 | .40 |
| d. | A119 50p multicolored | .50 | .50 |
| e. | A119 60p multicolored | .60 | .60 |

No. 511A has simulated perforations. Nos. 508-511 exist imperf. Value, set $5.

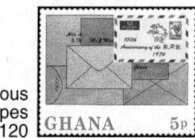

Various Envelopes A120

UPU Emblem and: 9p, 30p, UPU Headquarters, Bern. 40p, 50p, Airmail envelope with Ghana No. 296. 60p, 1ce, Ghana No. 296.

**1974, May Litho. Perf. 14½**

| | | | | |
|---|---|---|---|---|
| 512 | A120 | 5p blue, blk & org | .25 | .25 |
| 513 | A120 | 9p blue, blk & org | .25 | .25 |
| 514 | A120 | 50p blue, blk & org | .25 | .80 |
| 515 | A120 | 1ce blue, blk & org | .50 | 1.50 |
| | *Nos. 512-515 (4)* | | 1.25 | 2.80 |

**Souvenir Sheet**

| | | | |
|---|---|---|---|
| 515A | Sheet of 4 | .90 | 1.40 |
| b. | A120 20p blue, blk & org | .25 | .35 |
| c. | A120 30p blue, blk & org | .25 | .35 |
| d. | A120 40p blue, blk & org | .25 | .35 |
| e. | A120 60p blue, blk & org | .25 | .35 |

Centenary of Universal Postal Union. Nos. 512-515 exist imperf. Value, set $7. No. 515A exists imperf. Value $20. For overprints see Nos. 521-524A.

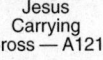

Jesus
Carrying
Cross — A121

The Betrayal
— A121a

Designs: 5p, 15p, Jesus Carrying Cross, painting by Thomas de Coloswar, 1427. 20p, 30p, The Betrayal. 25p, 50p, The Deposition. 40p, 1ce, Risen Christ and Mary Magdalene. The designs (except 5p, 15p) are from 15th century English ivory carvings.

**1974, Apr.      Litho.      Perf. 14**
| | | | |
|---|---|---|---|
| 516 | A121 | 5p black & multi | .25 .25 |
| 517 | A121a | 30p sil, ultra & brn | .25 .30 |
| 518 | A121a | 50p sil, red & brn | .25 .50 |
| 519 | A121a | 1ce silver, ol & brn | .35 .90 |
| | | Nos. 516-519 (4) | 1.10 1.95 |

**Souvenir Sheet**
**Imperf**
| | | | |
|---|---|---|---|
| 520 | | Sheet of 4 | 1.00 1.60 |
| a. | A121 | 15p black & multi | .25 .40 |
| b. | A121a | 20p silver, ultra & brn | .25 .40 |
| c. | A121a | 25p silver, red & brn | .25 .40 |
| d. | A121a | 40p silver, olive & brn | .25 .40 |

Easter. No. 520 contains 4 stamps with simulated perforations.
Nos. 516-519 exist imperf. Value, set $6.25.

**Nos. 512-515A Overprinted "INTERNABA 1974"**

**1974, June 7      Perf. 14½**
| | | | |
|---|---|---|---|
| 521 | A120 | 5p blue, blk & org | .25 .25 |
| 522 | A120 | 9p blue, blk & org | .25 .25 |
| 523 | A120 | 50p blue, blk & org | .30 .80 |
| 524 | A120 | 1ce blue, blk & org | .45 1.25 |
| | | Nos. 521-524 (4) | 1.25 2.55 |

**Souvenir Sheet**
| | | | |
|---|---|---|---|
| 524A | | Sheet of 4 | 1.75 3.50 |
| b. | A120 | 20p blue, blk & org | .25 .35 |
| c. | A120 | 30p blue, blk & org | .25 .35 |
| d. | A120 | 40p blue, blk & org | .25 .50 |
| e. | A120 | 60p blue, blk & org | .30 .60 |

INTERNABA 1974 International Philatelic Exhibition, Basel, June 7-16.
Overprint is applied to individual stamps of No. 524A.

Soccer and
World Cup
Emblem — A122

Designs: Various soccer scenes and world cup emblem.

**1974, June 17   Litho.   Perf. 14½, 13**
| | | | |
|---|---|---|---|
| 525 | A122 | 5p multicolored | .25 .25 |
| 526 | A122 | 30p multicolored | .25 .50 |
| 527 | A122 | 50p multicolored | .25 .75 |
| 528 | A122 | 1ce multicolored | .25 1.00 |
| | | Nos. 525-528 (4) | 1.00 2.50 |

**Souvenir Sheet**
**Perf. 14½**
| | | | |
|---|---|---|---|
| 529 | | Sheet of 4 | 1.75 3.00 |
| a. | A122 | 25p multicolored | .25 .30 |
| b. | A122 | 40p multicolored | .25 .40 |
| c. | A122 | 55p multicolored | .25 .45 |
| d. | A122 | 60p multicolored | .30 .50 |

World Cup Soccer Championship, June 13-July 7.
Nos. 525-528 were issued in sheets of 30, perf. 14½, and in sheets of 5 plus label, perf. 13.
For overprints, see Nos. 535-539, 549-553.

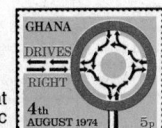

Traffic Diagram at
Traffic
Circle — A123

Designs: 15p, Traffic sign "Two-way traffic." 30p, "Change to right hand drive!," vert. 50p, Warning hands sign, vert. 1ce, 2 hands and car symbolizing traffic change, vert.

**1974, July 16      Perf. 13½**
**Size: 35x28½mm**
| | | | |
|---|---|---|---|
| 530 | A123 | 5p yel grn, red & blk | .25 .25 |
| 531 | A123 | 15p lilac, red & blk | .25 .30 |

**Size: 28½x41mm**
**Perf. 14½**
| | | | |
|---|---|---|---|
| 532 | A123 | 30p multicolored | .25 .25 |
| 533 | A123 | 50p multicolored | .60 .60 |
| 534 | A123 | 1ce red, green & blk | 1.25 1.25 |
| | | Nos. 530-534 (5) | 2.60 2.65 |

Publicity for change to right-hand driving, Aug. 4, 1974.

**Nos. 525-529 Overprinted: "WEST GERMANY WINNERS"**

**1974, Aug. 30   Litho.   Perf. 14½, 13**
| | | | |
|---|---|---|---|
| 535 | A122 | 5p multicolored | .25 .25 |
| 536 | A122 | 30p multicolored | .35 .35 |
| 537 | A122 | 50p multicolored | .55 .55 |
| 538 | A122 | 1ce multicolored | .90 .90 |
| | | Nos. 535-538 (4) | 2.05 2.05 |

**Souvenir Sheet**
| | | | |
|---|---|---|---|
| 539 | | Sheet of 4 | 1.75 1.75 |
| a. | A122 | 25p multicolored | .25 .25 |
| b. | A122 | 40p multicolored | .35 .35 |
| c. | A122 | 55p multicolored | .40 .40 |
| d. | A122 | 60p multicolored | .45 .45 |

World Cup Soccer Championship, 1974, victory of German Federal Republic. Overprint is applied to individual stamps of No. 539.

Family and WPY
Emblem — A124

30p, Clinic. 50p, Immunization of children. 1ce, Census.

**1974, Sept. 27      Perf. 12½**
| | | | |
|---|---|---|---|
| 540 | A124 | 5p shown | .25 .25 |
| 541 | A124 | 30p multicolored | .25 .30 |
| 542 | A124 | 50p multicolored | .25 .50 |
| 543 | A124 | 1ce multicolored | .40 1.25 |
| | | Nos. 540-543 (4) | 1.15 2.30 |

World Population Year.

Angel
A125

Nativity
A127

Three Kings,
Candles
A126

Design: 60p, 1ce, Annunciation.

**Perf. 13½, 14 (7p)**

**1974, Dec. 19                Litho.**
| | | | |
|---|---|---|---|
| 544 | A125 | 5p red & multi | .25 .25 |
| 545 | A126 | 7p blue & multi | .25 .25 |
| 546 | A127 | 9p orange & multi | .25 .25 |
| 547 | A127 | 1ce orange & multi | .40 1.25 |
| | | Nos. 544-547 (4) | 1.15 2.00 |

**Souvenir Sheet**
**Imperf**
| | | | |
|---|---|---|---|
| 548 | | Sheet of 4 | 1.15 2.00 |
| a. | A125 | 15p red & multi | .25 .50 |
| b. | A126 | 30p blue & multi | .25 .50 |
| c. | A127 | 45p orange & multi | .25 .50 |
| d. | A127 | 60p orange & multi | .25 .50 |

Christmas. No. 548 contains 4 stamps with simulated perforations.

**Nos. 525-529 Overprinted "APOLLO / SOYUZ / JULY 15, 1975"**

**1975, Aug. 15   Litho.   Perf. 14½, 13**
| | | | |
|---|---|---|---|
| 549 | A122 | 5p multicolored | .25 .25 |
| 550 | A122 | 30p multicolored | .25 .25 |
| 551 | A122 | 50p multicolored | .40 .50 |
| 552 | A122 | 1ce multicolored | .70 .70 |
| | | Nos. 549-552 (4) | 1.60 1.60 |

**Souvenir Sheet**
**Perf. 14½**
| | | | |
|---|---|---|---|
| 553 | | Sheet of 4 | 2.25 2.25 |
| a. | A122 | 25p multicolored | .25 .25 |
| b. | A122 | 40p multicolored | .30 .30 |
| c. | A122 | 50p multicolored | .50 .50 |
| d. | A122 | 60p multicolored | .55 .55 |

Apollo Soyuz space test project (Russo-American cooperation), launching July 15, link-up, July 17.
Overprint is applied to individual stamps of No. 553.
Nos. 549-552 with perf. 13 are from the sheets of 5 plus label. Nos. 549-553 exist imperf.

IWY Emblem,
Woman
Tractor
Driver — A128

Intl. Women's Year Emblem and: 15p, like 7p. 30p, 40p, Automobile mechanic. 60p, 65p, Factory workers. 80p, 1ce, Cocoa research.

**1975, Sept. 3     Litho.     Perf. 14**
| | | | |
|---|---|---|---|
| 554 | A128 | 7p multicolored | .25 .25 |
| 555 | A128 | 30p lt violet & multi | .45 .45 |
| 556 | A128 | 60p multicolored | 1.10 1.10 |
| 557 | A128 | 1ce lilac & multi | 1.75 1.75 |
| | | Nos. 554-557 (4) | 3.55 3.55 |

**Souvenir Sheet**
**Imperf**
| | | | |
|---|---|---|---|
| 558 | | Sheet of 4 | 3.25 5.00 |
| a. | A128 | 15p Prus green & multi | .25 .40 |
| b. | A128 | 40p light violet & multi | .60 .90 |
| c. | A128 | 65p dull green & multi | .85 1.25 |
| d. | A128 | 80p lilac & multi | 1.00 1.50 |

Intl. Women's Year. No. 558 contains 4 stamps with simulated perforations.

Angel over Child
in Crib — A129

Angel with
Harp — A130

Designs: 7p, 40p, Angels with lute and bell. 30p, 65p, Angel with viol. 1ce, 80p, Angels with trumpets. 15p, like 7p.

**1975, Dec. 31   Litho.   Perf. 14x13½**
| | | | |
|---|---|---|---|
| 559 | A129 | 2p org & multi | .25 .25 |
| 560 | A130 | 5p yel, brown & grn | .25 .25 |
| 561 | A130 | 7p yel, brown & grn | .25 .25 |
| 562 | A130 | 30p yel, brown & grn | .30 .25 |
| 563 | A130 | 1ce yel, brown & grn | .40 .75 |
| | | Nos. 559-563 (5) | 1.45 1.75 |

**Souvenir Sheet**
**Imperf**
| | | | |
|---|---|---|---|
| 564 | | Sheet of 4 | 1.60 2.50 |
| a. | A130 | 15p yellow, green & brown | .25 .25 |
| b. | A130 | 40p yellow, green & brown | .25 .25 |
| c. | A130 | 65p yellow, green & brown | .40 .65 |
| d. | A130 | 80p yellow, green & brown | .50 .75 |

Christmas. No. 564 has simulated perforations.

Boy Scouts
Reading
Map — A131

30p, 40p, Sailing. 60p, 65p, Hiking. 80p, 1ce, Life saving (swimmers). 15p, like 7p.

**1976, Jan. 5          Perf. 13½x14**
| | | | |
|---|---|---|---|
| 565 | A131 | 7p ocher & multi | .25 .25 |
| 566 | A131 | 30p blue & multi | .70 .70 |
| 567 | A131 | 60p green & multi | 1.45 1.45 |
| 568 | A131 | 1ce multicolored | 2.10 2.10 |
| | | Nos. 565-568 (4) | 4.50 4.50 |

**Souvenir Sheet**
| | | | |
|---|---|---|---|
| 569 | | Sheet of 4 | 4.00 6.00 |
| a. | A131 | 15p ocher & multi | .30 .50 |
| b. | A131 | 40p blue & multi | .70 1.10 |
| c. | A131 | 65p green & multi | 1.00 1.50 |
| d. | A131 | 80p rose claret & multi | 1.25 1.75 |

Nordjamb 75, 14th World Boy Scout Jamboree, Lillehammer, Norway, July 29-Aug. 7.

For overprints, see Nos. 578-582.

1¾ Pints
Equal 1
Liter — A132

Map of Ghana and: 30p, "2¼ lbs of jam a little more than a kilogram." 60p, "A meter of cloth will be a little more than 3 foot 3." 1ce, Thermometer, ice and boiling tea kettle.

**1976, Jan. 5     Litho.     Perf. 14x13½**
| | | | |
|---|---|---|---|
| 570 | A132 | 7p bluish gray & blk | .25 .25 |
| 571 | A132 | 30p vio blue & multi | .35 .35 |
| 572 | A132 | 60p ocher & multi | .70 .70 |
| 573 | A132 | 1ce multicolored | 1.25 1.25 |
| | | Nos. 570-573 (4) | 2.55 2.55 |

Introduction of metric system, Sept. 1975.

Fair Grounds
A133

Designs: Various exhibition halls.

**1976, Apr. 6     Litho.     Perf. 14**
| | | | |
|---|---|---|---|
| 574 | A133 | 7p multicolored | .25 .25 |
| 575 | A133 | 30p yellow & multi | .25 .25 |
| 576 | A133 | 60p multicolored | .25 .60 |
| 577 | A133 | 1ce salmon & multi | .35 1.00 |
| | | Nos. 574-577 (4) | 1.10 2.10 |

International Trade Fair, Accra, Feb. 1-15.

**Nos. 565-569 Overprinted in Violet Blue**

**1976, May 29   Litho.   Perf. 13½x14**
| | | | |
|---|---|---|---|
| 578 | A131 | 7p ocher & multi | .25 .25 |
| 579 | A131 | 30p blue & multi | .45 .45 |
| 580 | A131 | 60p green & multi | .90 .75 |
| 581 | A131 | 1ce multicolored | 1.25 1.25 |
| | | Nos. 578-581 (4) | 2.85 2.70 |

**Souvenir Sheet**
| | | | |
|---|---|---|---|
| 582 | | Sheet of 4 | 2.00 2.00 |
| a. | A131 | 15p ocher & multi | .25 .25 |
| b. | A131 | 40p blue & multi | .35 .35 |
| c. | A131 | 65p green & multi | .45 .45 |
| d. | A131 | 80p rose claret & multi | .45 .45 |

Interphil 76 International Philatelic Exhibition, Philadelphia, Pa., May 29-June 6. Overprint applied to individual stamps of No. 582.

Shot Put — A134

Olympic Rings, Map of Ghana and: 15p, like 7p. 30p, 40p, Soccer. 60p, 65p, Women's 1500 meters. 80p, 1ce, Boxing.

**1976, Aug. 9     Litho.     Perf. 14x13½**
| | | | |
|---|---|---|---|
| 583 | A134 | 7p lt blue & multi | .25 .25 |
| 584 | A134 | 30p yellow & multi | .25 .25 |
| 585 | A134 | 60p multicolored | .55 .55 |
| 586 | A134 | 1ce yellow & multi | .75 .75 |
| | | Nos. 583-586 (4) | 1.80 1.80 |

**Souvenir Sheet**
| | | | |
|---|---|---|---|
| 587 | | Sheet of 4 | 1.50 1.50 |
| a. | A134 | 15p light blue & multi | .25 .25 |
| b. | A134 | 40p yellow & multi | .25 .25 |
| c. | A134 | 65p emerald & multi | .25 .25 |
| d. | A134 | 80p yellow & multi | .30 .30 |

21st Olympic Games, Montreal, Canada, July 17-Aug. 1.
For overprints see Nos. 606-610.

Supreme Court, Accra — A135

Designs: Various views of Supreme Court Building, Scales of Justice, law book.

**1976, Sept. 7    Litho.    Perf. 14**
| | | | | |
|---|---|---|---|---|
| 588 | A135 | 8p lilac & multi | .25 | .25 |
| 589 | A135 | 30p blue & multi | .25 | .25 |
| 590 | A135 | 60p ver & multi | .30 | .50 |
| 591 | A135 | 1ce multicolored | .55 | 1.00 |
| | | Nos. 588-591 (4) | 1.35 | 2.00 |

Ghana Supreme Court, centenary.

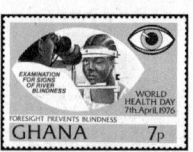

Examination for River Blindness A136

Designs: 30p, Ghanaian entomologist with microscope. 60p, Flowers. 1ce, Boatmen checking effectiveness of black fly larvae insecticide.

**1976, Oct. 28    Litho.    Perf. 14½x14**
| | | | | |
|---|---|---|---|---|
| 592 | A136 | 7p multicolored | .70 | .25 |
| 593 | A136 | 30p multicolored | 1.90 | 1.75 |
| 594 | A136 | 60p multicolored | 3.00 | 3.00 |
| 595 | A136 | 1ce multicolored | 5.00 | 5.00 |
| | | Nos. 592-595 (4) | 10.60 | 10.00 |

World Health Day. Prevention of blindness.

A137

A137a

Designs: 6p, 15p, Children with firecrackers. 30p, 65p, Children at Christmas dinner. 8p, 40p, 80p, 1ce, Children with Gifts and Christmas Tree.

**1976, Dec. 15    Litho.    Perf. 13½**
| | | | | |
|---|---|---|---|---|
| 596 | A137 | 6p multicolored | .25 | .25 |
| 597 | A137a | 8p multicolored | .25 | .25 |
| 598 | A137a | 30p multicolored | .50 | .50 |
| 599 | A137a | 1ce multicolored | 1.25 | 1.25 |
| | | Nos. 596-599 (4) | 2.25 | 2.25 |

**Souvenir Sheet**
**Imperf**
| | | | | |
|---|---|---|---|---|
| 600 | | Sheet of 4 | 2.50 | 2.50 |
| a. | | A137 15p multicolored | .25 | .25 |
| b. | | A137a 40p multicolored | .40 | .40 |
| c. | | A137a 65p multicolored | .70 | .70 |
| d. | | A137a 80p multicolored | 1.00 | 1.00 |

Christmas. No. 600 has simulated perfs.

1876 Gallows Frame Telephone and A. G. Bell — A138

A. G. Bell and: 15p, like 8p. 30p, 40p, 1895 telephone. 60p, 65p, 1929 telephone. 80p, 1ce, 1976 telephone.

**1976, Dec. 17    Perf. 14½**
| | | | | |
|---|---|---|---|---|
| 601 | A138 | 8p multicolored | .25 | .25 |
| 602 | A138 | 30p multicolored | .40 | .40 |
| 603 | A138 | 60p multicolored | 1.15 | 1.15 |
| 604 | A138 | 1ce multicolored | 1.35 | 1.35 |
| | | Nos. 601-604 (4) | 3.15 | 3.15 |

**Souvenir Sheet**
**Perf. 13**
| | | | | |
|---|---|---|---|---|
| 605 | | Sheet of 4 | 2.50 | 2.50 |
| a. | | A138 15p multicolored | .25 | .25 |
| b. | | A138 40p multicolored | .45 | .45 |
| c. | | A138 65p multicolored | .70 | .70 |
| d. | | A138 80p multicolored | .80 | .80 |

Centenary of first telephone call by Alexander Graham Bell, Mar. 10, 1876.
For overprints, see Nos. 616-620.

---

**Nos. 583-587 Overprinted**
a. EAST GERMANY / WINNERS
b. U.S.S.R. WINNERS
c. U.S.A. WINNERS

**1977, Feb. 22    Litho.    Perf. 14x13½**
| | | | | |
|---|---|---|---|---|
| 606 | A134(a) | 7p multicolored | .25 | .25 |
| 607 | A134(a) | 30p multicolored | .30 | .25 |
| 608 | A134(b) | 60p multicolored | .65 | .65 |
| 609 | A134(c) | 1ce multicolored | 1.30 | 1.30 |
| | | Nos. 606-609 (4) | 2.50 | 2.45 |

**Souvenir Sheet**
| | | | | |
|---|---|---|---|---|
| 610 | | Sheet of 4 | 3.00 | 3.00 |
| a. | | A134(a) 15p multicolored | .25 | .25 |
| b. | | A134(a) 40p multicolored | .60 | .60 |
| c. | | A134(b) 65p multicolored | .90 | .90 |
| d. | | A134(c) 80p multicolored | .95 | .95 |

1976 Montreal Olympic Games' winners.

Klama Dance, Dipo Tribe — A139

Festival Emblem and: 15p, like 8p. 30p, 40p, African artifacts. 60p, 65p, Acon dance. 80p, 1ce, Mud, straw and wooden huts.

**1977, Mar. 24    Litho.    Perf. 14x13½**
| | | | | |
|---|---|---|---|---|
| 611 | A139 | 8p multicolored | .25 | .25 |
| 612 | A139 | 30p multicolored | .40 | .60 |
| 613 | A139 | 60p multicolored | .65 | 1.10 |
| 614 | A139 | 1ce multicolored | 1.00 | 1.75 |
| | | Nos. 611-614 (4) | 2.30 | 3.70 |

**Souvenir Sheet**
| | | | | |
|---|---|---|---|---|
| 615 | | Sheet of 4 | 3.00 | 3.00 |
| a. | | A139 15p multicolored | .30 | .30 |
| b. | | A139 40p multicolored | .65 | .65 |
| c. | | A139 65p multicolored | .85 | .85 |
| d. | | A139 80p multicolored | 1.05 | 1.05 |

2nd World Black and African Festival of Arts and Culture, Lagos, Nigeria, Jan. 15-Feb. 12.

**Nos. 601-605 Overprinted: "PRINCE CHARLES / VISITS GHANA / 17th TO 25th / MARCH, 1977"**

**1977, June 2    Litho.    Perf. 14½**
| | | | | |
|---|---|---|---|---|
| 616 | A138 | 8p multicolored | .65 | .65 |
| 617 | A138 | 30p multicolored | 1.60 | 1.60 |
| 618 | A138 | 60p multicolored | 2.50 | 2.50 |
| 619 | A138 | 1ce multicolored | 3.25 | 3.25 |
| | | Nos. 616-619 (4) | 8.00 | 8.00 |

**Souvenir Sheet**
**Perf. 13**
| | | | | |
|---|---|---|---|---|
| 620 | | Sheet of 4 | 11.00 | 11.00 |
| a. | | A138 15p multicolored | 1.20 | 1.05 |
| b. | | A138 40p multicolored | 2.10 | 1.75 |
| c. | | A138 65p multicolored | 3.00 | 2.50 |
| d. | | A138 80p multicolored | 3.50 | 3.00 |

Visit of Prince Charles, Mar. 17-25. Overprint applied to individual stamps of No. 620.

Olive Colobus A140

Wildlife Fund Emblem and: 15p, like 8p. 20p, 40p, Ebien palm squirrel. 30p, 65p, African wild dog. 60p, 80p, West African manatee.

**1977, June 22    Litho.    Perf. 13½x14**
| | | | | |
|---|---|---|---|---|
| 621 | A140 | 8p multicolored | 2.75 | 1.50 |
| 622 | A140 | 20p multicolored | 5.75 | 1.75 |
| 623 | A140 | 30p multicolored | 7.25 | 4.50 |
| 624 | A140 | 60p multicolored | 11.00 | 6.50 |
| | | Nos. 621-624 (4) | 26.75 | 14.25 |

**Souvenir Sheet**
| | | | | |
|---|---|---|---|---|
| 625 | | Sheet of 4 | 18.00 | 18.00 |
| a. | | A140 15p multicolored | 2.00 | 2.00 |
| b. | | A140 40p multicolored | 3.75 | 3.75 |
| c. | | A140 65p multicolored | 4.50 | 4.50 |
| d. | | A140 80p multicolored | 5.50 | 5.50 |

Wildlife protection.
Nos. 621-624 exist imperf. Value, set $27.50.

Suzanne Fourment in Velvet Hat, by Rubens — A141

---

Paintings: 15p, like 8p. 30p, 40p, Isabella of Portugal, by Titian. 60p, 65p, Duke and Duchess of Cumberland, by Gainsborough. 80p, 1ce, Rubens and his wife Isabella, by Rubens.

**1977, Sept.    Litho.    Perf. 14x13½**
| | | | | |
|---|---|---|---|---|
| 626 | A141 | 8p lt blue & multi | .25 | .25 |
| 627 | A141 | 30p lt blue & multi | .50 | .50 |
| 628 | A141 | 60p lt blue & multi | 1.10 | 1.10 |
| 629 | A141 | 1ce lt blue & multi | 2.00 | 2.00 |
| | | Nos. 626-629 (4) | 3.85 | 3.85 |

**Souvenir Sheet**
| | | | | |
|---|---|---|---|---|
| 630 | | Sheet of 4 | 3.50 | 3.50 |
| a. | | A141 15p light blue & multi | .25 | .25 |
| b. | | A141 40p light blue & multi | .70 | .70 |
| c. | | A141 65p light blue & multi | 1.10 | 1.10 |
| d. | | A141 80p light blue & multi | 1.25 | 1.25 |

Painters, birth annivs.: Peter Paul Rubens (1577-1640); Titian (1477-1576); Thomas Gainsborough (1727-1788).

Adoration of the Kings — A142

Guild of the Good Shepherd, Abossey Okai — A143

Designs: 6p, 40p, Methodist Church, Wesley, Accra. 8p, Virgin and Child, and Star. 15p, like 2p. 30p, 65p, Holy Spirit Cathedral, Accra. 80p, 1ce, Ebenezer Presbyterian Church, Osu, Accra. Type A143 designs include score of "Hark the Herald Angels Sing."

**Perf. 14x14½, 14**
**1977, Dec. 30    Litho.**
| | | | | |
|---|---|---|---|---|
| 631 | A142 | 1p multicolored | .25 | .25 |
| 632 | A143 | 2p multicolored | .25 | .25 |
| 633 | A143 | 6p multicolored | .25 | .25 |
| 634 | A142 | 8p multicolored | .25 | .25 |
| 635 | A143 | 30p multicolored | .50 | .50 |
| 636 | A143 | 1ce multicolored | 1.50 | 1.50 |
| | | Nos. 631-636 (6) | 3.00 | 3.00 |

**Souvenir Sheet**
**Imperf**
| | | | | |
|---|---|---|---|---|
| 637 | | Sheet of 4 | 4.00 | 4.00 |
| a. | | A143 15p multicolored | .25 | .25 |
| b. | | A143 40p multicolored | .65 | .65 |
| c. | | A143 65p multicolored | 1.05 | 1.05 |
| d. | | A143 80p multicolored | 1.25 | 1.25 |

Christmas. No. 637 has simulated perfs.

**No. 631-637 Overprinted:**
**"REFERENDUM 1978 VOTE EARLY"**
**Perf. 14x14½, 14**
**1978, Mar. 28    Litho.**
| | | | | |
|---|---|---|---|---|
| 638 | A142 | 1p multicolored | .25 | .25 |
| 639 | A143 | 2p multicolored | .25 | .25 |
| 640 | A143 | 6p multicolored | .25 | .25 |
| 641 | A142 | 8p multicolored | .25 | .25 |
| 642 | A143 | 30p multicolored | .50 | .50 |
| 643 | A143 | 1ce multicolored | 1.75 | 1.75 |
| | | Nos. 638-643 (6) | 3.25 | 3.25 |

**Souvenir Sheet**
**Imperf**
| | | | | |
|---|---|---|---|---|
| 644 | | Sheet of 4 | 30.00 | 25.00 |
| a. | | A143 15p multicolored | 2.50 | 2.00 |
| b. | | A143 40p multicolored | 5.50 | 3.50 |
| c. | | A143 65p multicolored | 8.50 | 6.25 |
| d. | | A143 80p multicolored | 11.00 | 7.25 |

Banana Harvest A144

Designs: 8p, Vegetable garden. 30p, Produce market. 60p, Fishing. 1ce, Tractor.

**1978, May 15    Perf. 14**
| | | | | |
|---|---|---|---|---|
| 645 | A144 | 2p multicolored | .25 | .25 |
| 646 | A144 | 8p multicolored | .25 | .25 |
| 647 | A144 | 30p multicolored | .40 | .40 |
| 648 | A144 | 60p multicolored | .95 | .95 |
| 649 | A144 | 1ce multicolored | 1.60 | 1.60 |
| | | Nos. 645-649 (5) | 3.45 | 3.45 |

Operation feed yourself.

---

Wright Biplane and Crowd — A145

Planes and Crowd: 15p, like 8p. 30p, 40p, Heracles, 1st practical airliner. 60p, 65p, D. H. Comet, 1st jet airliner. 80p, 1ce, Concorde, 1st supersonic airliner.

**1978, June 6    Litho.    Perf. 14x13½**
| | | | | |
|---|---|---|---|---|
| 650 | A145 | 8p multicolored | .25 | .25 |
| 651 | A145 | 30p multicolored | .65 | .55 |
| 652 | A145 | 60p multicolored | 1.25 | 1.10 |
| 653 | A145 | 1ce multicolored | 2.00 | 1.60 |
| | | Nos. 650-653 (4) | 4.15 | 3.30 |

**Souvenir Sheet**
| | | | | |
|---|---|---|---|---|
| 654 | | Sheet of 4 | 6.00 | 3.25 |
| a. | | A145 15p multicolored | .35 | .25 |
| b. | | A145 40p multicolored | 1.10 | .60 |
| c. | | A145 65p multicolored | 1.90 | 1.00 |
| d. | | A145 80p multicolored | 2.10 | 1.10 |

75th anniversary of first powered flight. The cheering crowd forms a continuing design on Nos. 650-653.
Nos. 650-653 exist imperf. Value, set $6.

**Nos. 650-653, 654a-654d Overprinted: "CAPEX 78 / JUNE 9-18 1978"**

**1978, June 9**
| | | | | |
|---|---|---|---|---|
| 655 | A145 | 8p multicolored | .25 | .25 |
| 656 | A145 | 30p multicolored | .40 | .25 |
| 657 | A145 | 60p multicolored | .65 | .50 |
| 658 | A145 | 1ce multicolored | 1.75 | .80 |
| | | Nos. 655-658 (4) | 3.05 | 1.80 |

**Souvenir Sheet**
| | | | | |
|---|---|---|---|---|
| 659 | | Sheet of 4 | 2.50 | 2.25 |
| a. | | A145 15p multicolored | .25 | .25 |
| b. | | A145 40p multicolored | .45 | .40 |
| c. | | A145 65p multicolored | .70 | .65 |
| d. | | A145 80p multicolored | .90 | .80 |

CAPEX, Canadian International Philatelic Exhibition, Toronto, Ont., June 9-18.

Soccer, Africa Cup Emblem and Ghana Flag — A146

15p, like 8p. 30p, 40p, Three soccer players, Africa Cup emblem, Ghana flag. 60p, 65p, Two soccer players. Argentina '78 emblem, Argentine flag. 80p, 1ce, Goalkeeper, Argentina '78 emblem and Argentine flag.

**1978, July 1    Litho.    Perf. 13½x14**
| | | | | |
|---|---|---|---|---|
| 660 | A146 | 8p multicolored | .25 | .25 |
| 661 | A146 | 30p multicolored | .30 | .30 |
| 662 | A146 | 60p multicolored | .70 | .70 |
| 663 | A146 | 1ce multicolored | 1.30 | 1.30 |
| | | Nos. 660-663 (4) | 2.55 | 2.55 |

**Souvenir Sheet**
| | | | | |
|---|---|---|---|---|
| 664 | | Sheet of 4 | 1.75 | 1.75 |
| a. | | A146 15p multicolored | .25 | .25 |
| b. | | A146 40p multicolored | .35 | .35 |
| c. | | A146 65p multicolored | .55 | .55 |
| d. | | A146 80p multicolored | .60 | .60 |

11th African Cup of Nations, Ghana, Mar. 5-19, and 11th World Cup Soccer Championship, Argentina, June 1-25.
Nos. 660-663 exist imperf. Value, set $7.25.

**Nos. 660-661, 664a-664b Overprinted: "GHANA WINNERS"**
**Nos. 662-663, 664c-664d Overprinted: "ARGENTINA WINS"**

**1978, Aug. 21    Litho.    Perf. 13½x14**
| | | | | |
|---|---|---|---|---|
| 665 | A146 | 8p multicolored | .25 | .25 |
| 666 | A146 | 30p multicolored | .40 | .40 |
| 667 | A146 | 60p multicolored | .80 | .80 |
| 668 | A146 | 1ce multicolored | 1.40 | 1.40 |
| | | Nos. 665-668 (4) | 2.85 | 2.85 |

**Souvenir Sheet**
| | | | | |
|---|---|---|---|---|
| 669 | | Sheet of 4 | 1.50 | 1.50 |
| a. | | A146 15p multicolored | .25 | .25 |
| b. | | A146 40p multicolored | .25 | .25 |
| c. | | A146 65p multicolored | .35 | .35 |
| d. | | A146 80p multicolored | .55 | .55 |

Winners, 11th African Cup and 11th World Cup Soccer Championships.
Overprint on 60p and 65p is in two lines.

The Betrayal, by Dürer — A147

Etchings by Albrecht Dürer: 39p, The Crucifixion. 60p, The Deposition. 1ce, The Resurrection.

**1978, Sept. 1    Litho.    Perf. 14x13½**
| | | | |
|---|---|---|---|
| 670 | A147 11p lilac & black | .25 | .25 |
| 671 | A147 39p salmon & black | .30 | .30 |
| 672 | A147 60p orange & black | .45 | .45 |
| 673 | A147 1ce yel green & black | .75 | .75 |
| | Nos. 670-673 (4) | 1.75 | 1.75 |

Easter.

Bauhinia Purpurea — A148

Flowers: 39p, Cassia fistula. 60p, Frangipani. 1ce, Jacaranda mimosifolia.

**1978, Nov. 20    Litho.    Perf. 14x13½**
| | | | |
|---|---|---|---|
| 674 | A148 11p multicolored | .25 | .25 |
| 675 | A148 39p multicolored | .25 | .25 |
| 676 | A148 60p multicolored | .40 | .40 |
| 677 | A148 1ce multicolored | .60 | .60 |
| | Nos. 674-677 (4) | 1.50 | 1.50 |

Nos. 674-677 exist imperf. Value, set $10.

Mail Railroad Car — A149

Ghana railroad, 75th Anniv.: 39p, Pay and bank car. 60p, Locomotive, 1922. 1ce, Diesel locomotive, 1960.

**1978, Dec. 4    Litho.    Perf. 13½**
| | | | |
|---|---|---|---|
| 678 | A149 11p multicolored | .25 | .25 |
| 679 | A149 39p multicolored | .45 | .65 |
| 680 | A149 60p multicolored | .75 | 1.00 |
| 681 | A149 1ce multicolored | 1.10 | 1.50 |
| | Nos. 678-681 (4) | 2.55 | 3.40 |

Pioneer Venus Space Project — A150

15p, like 11p. 39p, 40p, Multiprobe spacecraft. 60p, 65p, Orbiter and Multiprobe circling Venus. 2ce, 3ce, Radar chart of Venus.

**1979, July 5    Litho.    Perf. 14x13½**
| | | | |
|---|---|---|---|
| 682 | A150 11p multicolored | .25 | .25 |
| 683 | A150 39p multicolored | .25 | .25 |
| 684 | A150 60p multicolored | .35 | .35 |
| 685 | A150 3ce multicolored | .55 | 1.10 |
| | Nos. 682-685 (4) | 1.40 | 1.95 |

**Souvenir Sheet**
**Imperf**
| | | | |
|---|---|---|---|
| 686 | Sheet of 4 | 1.90 | 1.90 |
| a. | A150 15p multicolored | .25 | .25 |
| b. | A150 40p multicolored | .25 | .25 |
| c. | A150 65p multicolored | .40 | .40 |
| d. | A150 2ce multicolored | .90 | .90 |

O Come All Ye Faithful — A152

Christmas Carols: 10p, O Little Town of Bethlehem. 15p, 65p, We Three Kings of Orient Are. 20p, I Saw Three Ships Come Sailing

By. 25p, like 8p. No. 696, 1ce, Away in a Manger. 4ce, No. 698d, Ding Dong Merrily on High.

**1979, Dec. 20    Perf. 14½**
| | | | |
|---|---|---|---|
| 692 | A152 8p multicolored | .25 | .25 |
| 693 | A152 10p multicolored | .25 | .25 |
| 694 | A152 15p multicolored | .25 | .25 |
| 695 | A152 20p multicolored | .25 | .25 |
| 696 | A152 2ce multicolored | .25 | .60 |
| 697 | A152 4ce multicolored | .25 | 1.10 |
| | Nos. 692-697 (6) | 1.50 | 2.70 |

**Souvenir Sheet**
| | | | |
|---|---|---|---|
| 698 | Sheet of 4 | 1.10 | 1.10 |
| a. | A152 25p multicolored | .25 | .25 |
| b. | A152 65p multicolored | .25 | .25 |
| c. | A152 1ce multicolored | .25 | .25 |
| d. | A152 2ce multicolored | .50 | .50 |

Christmas.
Nos. 692-697 exist imperf. Value, set $6.

J.B. Danquah (1895-1965) — A153

National Leaders: 65p, John Mensah Sarbah (1864-1910). 80p, J.E.K. Aggrey (1875-1925). 2ce, Kwame Nkrumah (1909-1972). 4ce, G.E. Grant (1878-1956).

**1980, Jan. 21    Litho.    Perf. 13½x14**
| | | | |
|---|---|---|---|
| 699 | A153 20p multicolored | .25 | .25 |
| 700 | A153 65p multicolored | .25 | .25 |
| 701 | A153 80p multicolored | .25 | .25 |
| 702 | A153 2ce multicolored | .35 | .35 |
| 703 | A153 4ce multicolored | .65 | .65 |
| | Nos. 699-703 (5) | 1.75 | 1.75 |

Man with Clack Bells, Hill — A154

Hill and: 25p, Man with clack bells. 50p, 65p, Chief, elephant staff. 1ce, 2ce, Drummer. 4ce, 5ce, Chief, ivory staff.

**1980, Mar. 12    Litho.    Perf. 14½**
| | | | |
|---|---|---|---|
| 704 | A154 20p multicolored | .25 | .25 |
| 705 | A154 65p multicolored | .25 | .25 |
| 706 | A154 2ce multicolored | .45 | .45 |
| 707 | A154 4ce multicolored | .80 | .80 |
| | Nos. 704-707 (4) | 1.75 | 1.75 |

**Souvenir Sheet**
| | | | |
|---|---|---|---|
| 708 | Sheet of 4 | 1.75 | 1.75 |
| a. | A154 25p multicolored | .25 | .25 |
| b. | A154 50p multicolored | .25 | .25 |
| c. | A154 1ce multicolored | .30 | .30 |
| d. | A154 5ce multicolored | .85 | .85 |

Sir Rowland Hill (1795-1879), originator of penny postage.
Nos. 708a-708d also exist perf 13½, issued in small individual sheetlets. Values slightly more than perf 14½.
For overprints see Nos. 714-718. Nos. 704-708 exist imperf. Value, set $14.

Students, IYC Emblem — A155

IYC Emblem and: 25p like 20p. 50p, 65p, Boys playing soccer. 1ce, 2ce, Boys in canoe. 3ce, 4ce, Mother and child.

**1980, Apr. 2    Litho.    Perf. 15**
| | | | |
|---|---|---|---|
| 709 | A155 20p multicolored | .25 | .25 |
| 710 | A155 65p multicolored | .25 | .30 |
| 711 | A155 2ce multicolored | .50 | .80 |
| 712 | A155 4ce multicolored | 1.05 | 1.60 |
| | Nos. 709-712 (4) | 2.05 | 2.95 |

**Souvenir Sheet**
| | | | |
|---|---|---|---|
| 713 | Sheet of 4 | 2.25 | 2.25 |
| a. | A155 25p multicolored | .25 | .25 |
| b. | A155 50p multicolored | .25 | .25 |
| c. | A155 1ce multicolored | .30 | .30 |
| d. | A155 3ce multicolored | .75 | .75 |

Intl. Year of the Child (in 1979).
For overprints see Nos. 719-723. Nos. 709-712 exist imperf. Value, set $9.50.

**Nos. 704-708 Overprinted: "LONDON 1980" / 6th-14th May 1980**

**1980, May 6    Litho.    Perf. 14½**
| | | | |
|---|---|---|---|
| 714 | A154 20p multicolored | .25 | .25 |
| 715 | A154 65p multicolored | .30 | .30 |
| 716 | A154 2ce multicolored | .75 | .75 |
| 717 | A154 4ce multicolored | 1.25 | 1.25 |
| | Nos. 714-717 (4) | 2.55 | 2.55 |

**Souvenir Sheet**
| | | | |
|---|---|---|---|
| 718 | Sheet of 4 | 3.00 | 3.00 |
| a. | A154 25p multicolored | .25 | .25 |
| b. | A154 50p multicolored | .25 | .25 |
| c. | A154 1ce multicolored | .25 | .25 |
| d. | A154 5ce multicolored | 1.90 | 1.90 |

London 1980 Intl. Stamp Exhib., May 6-14. Nos. 718a-718d also exist perf 13½, issued in small individual sheetlets. Value, unused or used, $15. Nos. 714-717 exist imperf. Value, set $8.50.

**Nos. 709-713 Overprinted: "PAPAL VISIT" / 8th-9th May / 1980**

**1980, May 8    Perf. 15**
| | | | |
|---|---|---|---|
| 719 | A155 20p multicolored | .75 | .25 |
| 720 | A155 65p multicolored | 1.40 | .70 |
| 721 | A155 2ce multicolored | 2.25 | 1.40 |
| 722 | A155 4ce multicolored | 3.50 | 2.25 |
| | Nos. 719-722 (4) | 7.90 | 4.60 |

**Souvenir Sheet**
| | | | |
|---|---|---|---|
| 723 | Sheet of 4 | 15.00 | 15.00 |
| a. | A155 25p multicolored | 1.00 | 1.00 |
| b. | A155 50p multicolored | 2.10 | 2.10 |
| c. | A155 1ce multicolored | 3.25 | 3.25 |
| d. | A155 3ce multicolored | 7.75 | 7.75 |

Visit of Pope John Paul II to Ghana, May 8-9.
Nos. 719-722 exist imperf. Value, set $12.50.

Parliament House — A156

**1980, Aug. 4    Litho.    Perf. 14**
| | | | |
|---|---|---|---|
| 724 | A156 20p shown | .25 | .25 |
| 725 | A156 65p Supreme Court | .25 | .25 |
| 726 | A156 2ce The Castle | .25 | .60 |
| | Nos. 724-726 (3) | .75 | 1.10 |

**Souvenir Sheet**
| | | | |
|---|---|---|---|
| 727 | Sheet of 3 | .65 | 1.00 |
| a. | A156 25p like #724 | .25 | .25 |
| b. | A156 1ce like #725 | .25 | .25 |
| c. | A156 3ce like #726 | .25 | .30 |

Third Republic.
Nos. 724-726 exist imperf. Value, $1.75.

Map of West African Member Countries, Flag of Ghana, Jet — A157

**1980, Nov. 5    Litho.    Perf. 14½**
| | | | |
|---|---|---|---|
| 728 | A157 20p shown | .25 | .25 |
| 729 | A157 65p Dish antenna | .25 | .25 |
| 730 | A157 80p Cogwheels | .25 | .25 |
| 731 | A157 2ce Corn | .25 | .25 |
| | Nos. 728-731 (4) | 1.00 | 1.00 |

5th Anniversary of ECOWAS (Economic Community of West African States).

A158

20p, "OAU". 65p, OAU Banner, Maps. 80p, Waves on map of Africa. 2ce, Flag, banner, map.

**1980, Nov. 26**
| | | | |
|---|---|---|---|
| 732 | A158 20p multicolored | .25 | .25 |
| 733 | A158 65p multicolored | .25 | .25 |
| 734 | A158 80p multicolored | .25 | .25 |
| 735 | A158 2ce multicolored | .25 | .25 |
| | Nos. 732-735 (4) | 1.00 | 1.00 |

Org. for African Unity summit conference, Lagos, Nigeria, Apr. 28-29. Nos. 732-735 exist imperf. Value, set $3.25.

A159

Christmas (Fra Angelico Paintings): 15p, 25p, Adoration of the Magi. 20p, 50p, Virgin and Child Enthroned with Four Angels. 1ce, 2ce, Virgin and Child Enthroned with Eight Angels. 3ce, 4ce, Annunciation.

**1980, Dec. 10    Perf. 14**
| | | | |
|---|---|---|---|
| 736 | A159 15p multicolored | .25 | .25 |
| 737 | A159 20p multicolored | .25 | .25 |
| 738 | A159 2ce multicolored | .35 | .60 |
| 739 | A159 4ce multicolored | .65 | 1.25 |
| | Nos. 736-739 (4) | 1.50 | 2.35 |

**Souvenir Sheet**
| | | | |
|---|---|---|---|
| 740 | Sheet of 4 | 1.00 | 1.00 |
| a. | A159 15p multicolored | .25 | .25 |
| b. | A159 50p multicolored | .25 | .25 |
| c. | A159 1ce multicolored | .25 | .25 |
| d. | A159 3ce multicolored | .30 | .30 |

Nos. 736-739 exist imperf. Value, set $5.50.

Nurse Weighing Newborn, Rotary Emblem — A160

65p, Map of Ghana and world. 2ce, Helping hands, world map. 4ce, Food distribution.

**1980, Dec. 18**
| | | | |
|---|---|---|---|
| 741 | A160 20p shown | .25 | .25 |
| 742 | A160 65p multicolored | .25 | .25 |
| 743 | A160 2ce multicolored | .45 | .75 |
| 744 | A160 4ce multicolored | .85 | 1.40 |
| | Nos. 741-744 (4) | 1.80 | 2.65 |

**Souvenir Sheet**
| | | | |
|---|---|---|---|
| 745 | Sheet of 4 | 2.00 | 2.00 |
| a. | A160 25p like #741 | .25 | .25 |
| b. | A160 50p like #742 | .25 | .25 |
| c. | A160 1ce like #743 | .25 | .25 |
| d. | A160 3ce like #744 | .80 | .80 |

Rotary International, 75th anniv.
Nos. 741-745 exist imperf. Value, set $11.50.

Narina Trogon — A161

65p, White-crowned robin-chat. 2ce, Swallow-tailed bee-eater. 4ce, Long-tailed parakeet.

**1981, Jan. 12    Litho.    Perf. 14**
| | | | |
|---|---|---|---|
| 746 | A161 20p shown | 1.25 | .25 |
| 747 | A161 65p multicolored | 2.50 | .60 |
| 748 | A161 2ce multicolored | 3.25 | 1.75 |
| 749 | A161 4ce multicolored | 4.50 | 3.25 |
| | Nos. 746-749 (4) | 11.50 | 5.85 |

**Souvenir Sheet**
| | | | |
|---|---|---|---|
| 750 | Sheet of 4 | 10.50 | 10.50 |
| a. | A161 25p like #746 | .40 | .30 |
| b. | A161 50p like #747 | 1.00 | .45 |
| c. | A161 1ce like #748 | 1.75 | .80 |
| d. | A161 3ce like #749 | 5.50 | 2.40 |

Nos. 746-749 exist imperf. Value, set $14.

Pope John Paul II, Pres. Limann, Archbishop of Canterbury A162

**1981, Mar. 3    Litho.    Perf. 14**
| | | | |
|---|---|---|---|
| 751 | A162 20p multicolored | .25 | .25 |
| 752 | A162 65p multicolored | .60 | .60 |
| 753 | A162 80p multicolored | .75 | .75 |
| 754 | A162 2ce multicolored | 2.40 | 2.40 |
| | Nos. 751-754 (4) | 4.00 | 4.00 |

Visit of Pope John Paul II, May 8-10, 1980. Nos. 751-754 exist imperf. Value, set $14.

Earth Satellite Station — A163

65p, Satellites orbiting earth. 80p, Satellite. 4ce, Satellite, earth.

| 1981, Sept. 28 | Litho. | Perf. 14 | |
|---|---|---|---|
| 755 | A163 20p shown | .25 | .25 |
| 756 | A163 65p multicolored | .25 | .25 |
| 757 | A163 80p multicolored | .25 | .25 |
| 758 | A163 4ce multicolored | 1.10 | 1.10 |
| | Nos. 755-758 (4) | 1.85 | 1.85 |

**Souvenir Sheet**

| 758A | | Sheet of 4 | 1.40 | 1.40 |
|---|---|---|---|---|
| b. | A163 25p like #755 | | .25 | .25 |
| c. | A163 50p like #756 | | .25 | .25 |
| d. | A163 1ce like #757 | | .25 | .25 |
| e. | A163 3ce like #758 | | .60 | .60 |

Earth Satellite Station commission.

Common Design Types pictured following the introduction.

**Royal Wedding Issue**
Common Design Type

| 1981 | Litho. | Perf. 14 | |
|---|---|---|---|
| 759 | CD331a 20p Couple | .25 | .25 |
| 759A | CD331a 65p like 20p | .25 | .25 |
| 760 | CD331a 80p Charles | .25 | .25 |
| 760A | CD331a 1ce like 80p | .25 | .25 |
| 760B | CD331a 3ce like 4ce | .40 | .40 |
| 761 | CD331a 4ce Royal yacht Britannia | .50 | .50 |
| | Nos. 759-761 (6) | 1.90 | 1.90 |

**Souvenir Sheet**

| 762 | CD331 7ce St. Paul's Cathedral | .80 | .80 |
|---|---|---|---|

**Booklet Stamps**

| 763 | CD331 2ce like 4ce | 1.10 | 1.10 |
|---|---|---|---|
| 764 | CD331 5ce like 20p | 2.40 | 2.40 |
| a. | Bkt. pane, 2 each #763-764 | 7.25 | 7.25 |

Nos. 759-761 each printed se-tenant with label showing heraldic design. Nos. 763-764 issued only in booklets.

Issued: 20p, 80p, 4ce, 7ce, 7/8; 65p, 1ce, 2ce, 3ce, 5ce, 9/16.

For surcharges see Nos. 859, 866, 871, 880, 1168-1169, 1195-1197.

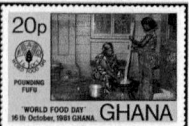

World Food Day — A164

20p, Women pounding fufu. 65p, Plucking cocoa. 80p, Preparing banku. 2ce, Processing garri.

| 1981, Oct. 16 | Litho. | Perf. 14 | |
|---|---|---|---|
| 765 | A164 20p multicolored | .25 | .25 |
| 766 | A164 65p multicolored | .25 | .25 |
| 767 | A164 80p multicolored | .40 | .40 |
| 768 | A164 2ce multicolored | .75 | .75 |
| | Nos. 765-768 (4) | 1.65 | 1.65 |

**Souvenir Sheet**

| 769 | | Sheet of 4 | 1.50 | 1.50 |
|---|---|---|---|---|
| a. | A164 25p like #765 | | .25 | .25 |
| b. | A164 50p like #766 | | .25 | .25 |
| c. | A164 1ce like #767 | | .30 | .30 |
| d. | A164 3ce like #768 | | .85 | .85 |

Nos. 765-768 exist imperf. Value, set $5.50.

Angelic Musicians Play for Mary and Child, by Aachener Altares (1480-1520) — A165

Christmas (Paintings): 15p, The Betrothal of St. Catherine of Alexandria, by Lucas Cranach (1472-1553). 65p, Child Jesus Embracing His Mother, by Gabriel Metsu (1629-1667). 80p, Virgin and Child, by Fra Filippo Lippi (1406-1469). $2, The Virgin with Infant Jesus, by Barnaba da Modena (1361-1383). $4, The Immaculate Conception, by Bartolome Murillo (1618-1682). $6, Virgin and Child, by Hans Memling (1430-1494).

| 1981, Nov. 26 | | Perf. 14 | |
|---|---|---|---|
| 770 | A165 15p multicolored | .25 | .25 |
| 771 | A165 20p multicolored | .25 | .25 |
| 772 | A165 65p multicolored | .25 | .25 |
| 773 | A165 80p multicolored | .25 | .25 |
| 774 | A165 $2 multicolored | .50 | .50 |
| 775 | A165 $4 multicolored | .65 | .65 |
| | Nos. 770-775 (6) | 2.15 | 2.15 |

**Souvenir Sheet**

| 776 | A165 $6 multicolored | 1.50 | 1.50 |
|---|---|---|---|

Intl. Year of the Disabled — A166

| 1982, Feb. 8 | Litho. | Perf. 14 | |
|---|---|---|---|
| 777 | A166 20p Blind man | .25 | .25 |
| 778 | A166 65p Woman, crutch | .30 | .30 |
| 779 | A166 80p Girl reading Braille | .40 | .40 |
| 780 | A166 4ce Couple | 1.50 | 1.50 |
| | Nos. 777-780 (4) | 2.45 | 2.45 |

**Souvenir Sheet**

| 781 | A166 6ce Group | 2.25 | 2.25 |
|---|---|---|---|

Clawless Otter — A167

| 1982, Feb. 22 | | | |
|---|---|---|---|
| 782 | A167 20p shown | .25 | .25 |
| 783 | A167 65p Bushbuck | .50 | .50 |
| 784 | A167 80p Aardvark | .60 | .60 |
| 785 | A167 1ce Scarlet bell tree | .80 | .80 |
| 786 | A167 2ce Glory lilies | 1.35 | 1.35 |
| 787 | A167 4ce Blue peas | 3.00 | 3.00 |
| | Nos. 782-787 (6) | 6.50 | 6.50 |

**Souvenir Sheet**

| 788 | A167 5ce Chimpanzees | 3.00 | 3.00 |
|---|---|---|---|

Nos. 782-787 exist imperf. Value, set $10.

Blue-spot Commodore — A168

65p, Emperor swallowtail. 2ce, Orange admiral. 4ce, Giant charaxes.

| 1982, Apr. 27 | Litho. | Perf. 14 | |
|---|---|---|---|
| 789 | A168 20p shown | .85 | .85 |
| 790 | A168 65p multicolored | 1.40 | 1.40 |
| 791 | A168 2ce multicolored | 2.50 | 2.50 |
| 792 | A168 4ce multicolored | 4.25 | 4.25 |
| | Nos. 789-792 (4) | 9.00 | 9.00 |

**Souvenir Sheet**
Perf. 14½

| 793 | | Sheet of 4 | 9.50 | 9.50 |
|---|---|---|---|---|
| a. | A168 25p like #789 | | .70 | .70 |
| b. | A168 50p like #790 | | 1.20 | 1.20 |
| c. | A168 1ce like #791 | | 1.90 | 1.90 |
| d. | A168 3ce like #792 | | 4.75 | 4.75 |

Nos. 789-792 exist imperf. Value, set $14.

Scouting Year — A169

| 1982, June 1 | Litho. | Perf. 15 | |
|---|---|---|---|
| 794 | A169 20p Tree planting | .25 | .25 |
| 795 | A169 65p Camping | .75 | .75 |
| 796 | A169 80p Sailing | .95 | .95 |
| 797 | A169 3ce Watching elephant | 2.50 | 2.50 |
| | Nos. 794-797 (4) | 4.45 | 4.45 |

**Souvenir Sheet**

| 798 | A169 5ce Baden-Powell, vert. | 4.25 | 4.25 |
|---|---|---|---|

For surcharges see Nos. 867, 870, 875, 877.

Kpong Hydroelectric Dam Opening — A170

| 1982, June 28 | Litho. | Perf. 14 | |
|---|---|---|---|
| 799 | A170 20p Cranes, lifts | .50 | .25 |
| 800 | A170 65p Construction | 1.00 | .55 |
| 801 | A170 80p Turbines | 1.50 | 1.50 |
| 802 | A170 2ce Aerial view | 3.00 | 3.00 |
| | Nos. 799-802 (4) | 6.00 | 5.30 |

Nos. 799-802 exist imperf. Value, set $6.

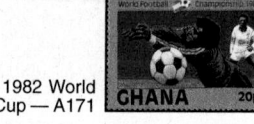

1982 World Cup — A171

**Perf. 15, 14½x15 (30p, No. 807, 1ce, 3ce)**

| 1982, July 19 | | Litho. | |
|---|---|---|---|
| 803 | A171 20p multi | .25 | .25 |
| 804 | A171 30p multi, like 20p | .25 | .25 |
| 805 | A171 65p multi | .80 | .80 |
| 806 | A171 80p multi, like 65p | 1.00 | 1.00 |
| 807 | A171 80p multi, diff. | .55 | .55 |
| 808 | A171 1ce multi, like #807 | .70 | .70 |
| 809 | A171 3ce multi | 1.60 | 1.60 |
| 810 | A171 4ce multi, like 3ce | 2.50 | 2.50 |
| | Nos. 803-810 (8) | 7.65 | 7.65 |

**Souvenir Sheet**

| 811 | A171 6ce multi | 2.10 | 2.10 |
|---|---|---|---|

Nos. 804, 806, 808-809 in sheets of 5 plus label.

For overprints & surcharges see Nos. 826-834, 861-862, 864-865, 868-869, 872-873, 878-879, 912-917.

TB Bacillus Centenary A172

20p, Child immunization. 65p, Koch, Berlin. 80p, Koch, Africa. 1ce, Looking through microscope. 2ce, Koch, 1905 Nobel medal.

| 1982, Aug. 9 | | Perf. 14 | |
|---|---|---|---|
| 812 | A172 20p multicolored | .50 | .50 |
| 813 | A172 65p multicolored | 1.40 | 1.40 |
| 814 | A172 80p multicolored | 1.75 | 1.75 |
| 815 | A172 1ce multicolored | 2.10 | 2.10 |
| 816 | A172 2ce multicolored | 3.50 | 3.50 |
| | Nos. 812-816 (5) | 9.25 | 9.25 |

Christmas — A173

| 1982, Dec. | | Litho. | Perf. 15 | |
|---|---|---|---|---|
| 817 | A173 15p Nativity | .25 | .25 |
| 818 | A173 20p Holy Family | .25 | .25 |
| 819 | A173 65p Three Kings | .30 | .30 |
| 820 | A173 4ce Angel with banner | 1.10 | 1.10 |
| | Nos. 817-820 (4) | 1.90 | 1.90 |

**Souvenir Sheet**

| 821 | A173 6ce Nativity, diff. | 2.00 | 2.00 |
|---|---|---|---|

Nos. 817-820 exist imperf. Value, set $3.75.

A173a

| 1983, Mar. 10 | | Litho. | Perf. 15 | |
|---|---|---|---|---|
| 822 | A173a 20p Flags | .25 | .25 |
| 823 | A173a 55p Aerial view | .45 | .45 |
| 824 | A173a 80p Minerals | 1.10 | 1.10 |
| 825 | A173a 3ce Eagle | 1.75 | 1.75 |
| | Nos. 822-825 (4) | 3.55 | 3.55 |

Commonwealth Day. For surcharges see Nos. 860, 863, 874, 876.

**Nos. 803-811 Overprinted in Gold: "WINNER ITALY / 3-1"**

| 1983, June | | | Litho. | |
|---|---|---|---|---|
| 826 | A171 20p multicolored | .25 | .25 |
| 827 | A171 30p multicolored | .25 | .25 |
| 828 | A171 65p multicolored | .40 | .40 |
| 829 | A171 80p multi, on #806 | .40 | .40 |
| 830 | A171 80p multi, on #807 | 1.25 | 1.25 |
| 831 | A171 1ce multicolored | 1.40 | 1.40 |
| 832 | A171 3ce multicolored | 2.75 | 2.75 |
| 833 | A171 4ce multicolored | 2.50 | 2.50 |
| | Nos. 826-833 (8) | 9.20 | 9.20 |

**Souvenir Sheet**

| 834 | A171 6ce multicolored | 3.50 | 3.50 |
|---|---|---|---|

Italy's victory in 1982 World Cup. For surcharges see Nos. 862, 865, 869, 873, 879, 913, 915, 917.

World Communications Year — A173b

1.40ce, Dish antenna. 2.30ce, Cable ship. 3ce, Switchboard. 5ce, Control tower. 6ce, Satellite.

| 1983, Dec. 13 | | Litho. | Perf. 14 | |
|---|---|---|---|---|
| 835 | A173b 1ce shown | .25 | .25 |
| 836 | A173b 1.40ce multicolored | .25 | .25 |
| 837 | A173b 2.30ce multicolored | .55 | .55 |
| 838 | A173b 3ce multicolored | .75 | .75 |
| 839 | A173b 5ce multicolored | 1.10 | 1.10 |
| | Nos. 835-839 (5) | 2.90 | 2.90 |

**Souvenir Sheet**

| 840 | A173b 6ce multicolored | .80 | .80 |
|---|---|---|---|

For surcharges see Nos. 1107-1111.

Coastal Marine Mammals A173c

1ce, Short fin pilot whale. 1.40ce, Gray dolphin. 2.30ce, False killer whale. 3ce, Spinner dolphin. 5ce, Atlantic humpback dolphin. 6ce, White Alantic humpback dolphin.

| 1983, Nov. 15 | | Litho. | Perf. 15 | |
|---|---|---|---|---|
| 841 | A173c 1ce multicolored | 1.75 | 1.75 |
| 842 | A173c 1.40ce multicolored | 1.90 | 1.90 |
| 843 | A173c 2.30ce multicolored | 2.25 | 2.25 |
| 844 | A173c 3ce multicolored | 2.75 | 2.75 |
| 845 | A173c 5ce multicolored | 3.50 | 3.50 |
| | Nos. 841-845 (5) | 12.15 | 12.15 |

**Souvenir Sheet**

| 846 | A173c 6ce multicolored | 5.25 | 5.25 |
|---|---|---|---|

For surcharges see Nos. 918-920.
Nos. 841-846 exist imperf. Value, set $22.

A174

Christmas — A175

70p, Children receiving gifts. 1ce, Nativity. 1.40ce, Children playing. 2.30ce, Family praying. 3ce, Bongo drums, festivities.

| 1983, Dec. 28 | Perf. 14x13½, 14½x14 | | |
|---|---|---|---|
| 852 | A174 70p multicolored | .25 | .25 |
| 853 | A175 1ce multicolored | .25 | .25 |
| 854 | A175 1.40ce multicolored | .40 | .40 |
| 855 | A175 2.30ce multicolored | .45 | .45 |
| 856 | A174 3ce multicolored | .50 | .50 |
| | Nos. 852-856 (5) | 1.85 | 1.85 |

**Souvenir Sheet**

| 857 | A175 6ce like #855 | .50 | .50 |
|---|---|---|---|

For surcharge see No. 2676.

## Surcharges

Many inverts, doubles, etc., exist on the surcharged stamps that follow.

### Previous Issues Surcharged

**1984, Feb. 8**

| | | | | |
|---|---|---|---|---|
| 858 | A74 | 1ce on 20np #296 | .40 | .25 |
| 859 | CD331 | 1ce on 20p #759 | 5.00 | 4.25 |
| 860 | A173a | 1ce on 20p #822 | .40 | .25 |
| 861 | A171 | 1ce on 20p #803 | .60 | .40 |
| 862 | A171 | 1ce on 20p #826 | .40 | .25 |
| 863 | A173a | 9ce on 55p #823 | .90 | .65 |
| 864 | A171 | 9ce on 65p #805 | 1.60 | 1.00 |
| 865 | A171 | 9ce on 65p #828 | .90 | .65 |
| 866 | CD331 | 9ce on 80p #760 | 6.25 | 5.50 |
| 867 | A169 | 10ce on 20p #794 | .90 | .65 |
| 868 | A171 | 10ce on 80p #806 | 1.60 | 1.00 |
| 869 | A171 | 10ce on 80p #830 | .90 | .65 |
| 870 | A169 | 19ce on 65p #795 | 1.75 | 1.25 |
| 871 | CD331 | 20ce on 4ce #761 | 8.00 | 8.75 |
| 872 | A171 | 20ce on 4ce #810 | 3.50 | 2.40 |
| 873 | A171 | 20ce on 4ce #833 | 1.75 | 1.25 |
| 874 | A173a | 30ce on 80p #824 | 3.50 | 2.40 |
| 875 | A169 | 30ce on 3ce #797 | 3.50 | 2.40 |
| 876 | A173a | 50ce on 3ce #825 | 6.00 | 4.00 |
| | | Nos. 858-876 (19) | 47.85 | 37.95 |

**Souvenir Sheets**

| | | | | |
|---|---|---|---|---|
| 877 | A169 | 60ce on 6ce #798 | 2.50 | 4.75 |
| 878 | A171 | 60ce on 6ce #811 | 2.50 | 3.25 |
| 879 | A171 | 60ce on 6ce #834 | 2.50 | 4.75 |
| 880 | CD331 | 60ce on 7ce #762 | 2.50 | 2.50 |

For surcharges ee Nos. 1092A-1092C.

Namibia Day — A176

50p, Soldiers raising rifles. 1ce, Soldiers, tank. 1.40ce, Machete cutting chains. 2.30ce, Namibian woman. 3ce, Soldiers in combat.

**1984, Jan. 26**     **Perf. 14**

| | | | | |
|---|---|---|---|---|
| 881 | A176 | 50p multicolored | .25 | .25 |
| 882 | A176 | 1ce multicolored | .25 | .25 |
| 883 | A176 | 1.40ce multicolored | .25 | .25 |
| 884 | A176 | 2.30ce multicolored | .25 | .25 |
| 885 | A176 | 3ce multicolored | .25 | .25 |
| | | Nos. 881-885 (5) | 1.25 | 1.25 |

Scorpion Weight — A177

5p, Hemichramis fasciatus, horiz. 10p, Hemichramis fasciatus, map, horiz. 20p, Haemanthus rupestris. 50p, Mounted warrior (gold statuette). 2ce, Jet, horiz. 3ce, Cercocebus torquatus. 4ce, Galagoides demidovii. 5ce, Kaempheria nigerica. 10ce, Camaroptera brevicaudata.

**1983, Dec. 12**    **Litho.**    **Perf. 14**

| | | | | |
|---|---|---|---|---|
| 886 | A177 | 5p multicolored | .35 | .25 |
| 887 | A177 | 10p multicolored | .60 | .25 |
| 888 | A177 | 20p multicolored | .70 | .25 |
| 889 | A177 | 50p multicolored | .70 | .30 |
| 890 | A177 | 1ce shown | .80 | .25 |
| 891 | A177 | 2ce multicolored | .80 | .30 |
| 892 | A177 | 3ce multicolored | 2.50 | .30 |
| 893 | A177 | 4ce multicolored | .70 | .40 |
| 894 | A177 | 5ce multicolored | .80 | .45 |
| 895 | A177 | 10ce multicolored | 1.00 | 1.00 |
| | | Nos. 886-895 (10) | 8.95 | 3.75 |

For surcharges see Nos. 1089A-1090, 1092, 1092D, 1093A-1094A, 1096-1096A.

Easter — A178

1ce, Cross, crown of thorns. 1.40ce, Jesus praying. 2.30ce, Jesus going to Jerusalem. 3ce, Jesus entering Jerusalem. 50ce, Jesus with Disciples.

60ce, Cross, crown of thorns.

**1984, Apr.**    **Litho.**    **Perf. 14½**

| | | | | |
|---|---|---|---|---|
| 906 | A178 | 1ce multicolored | .25 | .25 |
| 907 | A178 | 1.40ce multicolored | .25 | .25 |
| 908 | A178 | 2.30ce multicolored | .25 | .25 |
| 909 | A178 | 3ce multicolored | .25 | .25 |
| 910 | A178 | 50ce multicolored | .80 | 2.50 |
| | | Nos. 906-910 (5) | 1.80 | 3.50 |

**Souvenir Sheet**

| | | | | |
|---|---|---|---|---|
| 911 | A178 | 60ce multicolored | 3.25 | 3.25 |

### Nos. 804, 806, 809, 827, 829, 832 Surcharged

**1984, Feb. 8**      **Litho.**

| | | | | |
|---|---|---|---|---|
| 912 | A171 | 9ce on 3ce #809 | .85 | .85 |
| 913 | A171 | 9ce on 3ce #832 | .55 | .55 |
| 914 | A171 | 10ce on 30p #804 | .85 | .85 |
| 915 | A171 | 10ce on 30p #827 | .55 | .55 |
| 916 | A171 | 20ce on 80p #806 | 2.00 | 2.00 |
| 917 | A171 | 20ce on 80p #829 | 1.00 | 1.00 |
| | | Nos. 912-917 (6) | 5.80 | 5.80 |

### Nos. 844-846 Surcharged and Overprinted in Red with UPU Emblem and:"19th U.P.U. CONGRESS-HAMBURG"

**1984**      **Litho.**    **Perf. 14½**

| | | | | |
|---|---|---|---|---|
| 918 | A173c | 10ce on 3ce multi | .50 | .50 |
| 919 | A173c | 50ce on 5ce multi | 2.50 | 2.50 |

**Souvenir Sheet**

| | | | | |
|---|---|---|---|---|
| 920 | A173c | 60ce on 6ce multi | 3.00 | 3.00 |

Local Flowers — A179

1ce, Amorphophallus johnsonii. 1.40ce, Pancratium trianthum. 2.30ce, Eulophia cuculata. 3ce, Amorphophallus abyssinicus. 50ce, Chlorophytum togoense.

**1984, July**    **Litho.**    **Perf. 14**

| | | | | |
|---|---|---|---|---|
| 921 | A179 | 1ce multicolored | .25 | .25 |
| 922 | A179 | 1.40ce multicolored | .25 | .25 |
| 923 | A179 | 2.30ce multicolored | .25 | .25 |
| 924 | A179 | 3ce multicolored | .25 | .25 |
| 925 | A179 | 50ce multicolored | 2.50 | 2.75 |
| | | Nos. 921-925 (5) | 3.50 | 3.75 |

**Souvenir Sheet**

| | | | | |
|---|---|---|---|---|
| 926 | A179 | 60ce like 1ce | 2.75 | 2.75 |

Endangered Species — A180

1ce, Bongo. 2.30ce, Males locking horns. 3ce, Family. 20ce, Herd.
No. 931, Kob. No. 932, Bushbuck.

**1984, Aug.**      **Perf. 14**

| | | | | |
|---|---|---|---|---|
| 927 | A180 | 1ce multi | .55 | .55 |
| 928 | A180 | 2.30ce multi | 1.10 | 1.10 |
| 929 | A180 | 3ce multi | 1.35 | 1.35 |
| 930 | A180 | 20ce multi | 3.75 | 3.75 |
| | | Nos. 927-930 (4) | 6.75 | 6.75 |

**Souvenir Sheets**

| | | | | |
|---|---|---|---|---|
| 931 | A180 | 70ce multi | 6.00 | 6.00 |
| 932 | A180 | 70ce multi | 6.00 | 6.00 |

Nos. 927-930 exist imperf. Value: set, $21.

1984 Summer Olympics — A181

1ce, Running. 1.40ce, Boxing. 2.30ce, Field hockey. 3ce, Hurdles. 50ce, Rhythmic gymnastics.
70ce, Soccer.

**1984, Aug.**      **Perf. 15**

| | | | | |
|---|---|---|---|---|
| 933 | A181 | 1ce multi | .25 | .25 |
| 934 | A181 | 1.40ce multi | .25 | .25 |
| 935 | A181 | 2.30ce multi | .25 | .25 |
| 936 | A181 | 3ce multi | .25 | .25 |
| 937 | A181 | 50ce multi | 2.75 | 4.00 |
| | | Nos. 933-937 (5) | 3.75 | 5.00 |

**Souvenir Sheet**

| | | | | |
|---|---|---|---|---|
| 938 | A181 | 70ce multi | 2.50 | 2.50 |

For surcharges see Nos. 945-950, 1112-1116.

Native Dancers — A182

**1984, Sept.**      **Perf. 14**

| | | | | |
|---|---|---|---|---|
| 939 | A182 | 1ce Dipo | .30 | .25 |
| 940 | A182 | 1.40ce Adowa | .30 | .25 |
| 941 | A182 | 2.30ce Agbadza | .30 | .25 |
| 942 | A182 | 3ce Damba | .30 | .25 |
| 943 | A182 | 50ce Dipo, diff. | 2.00 | 3.00 |
| | | Nos. 939-943 (5) | 3.20 | 4.00 |

**Souvenir Sheet**

| | | | | |
|---|---|---|---|---|
| 944 | A182 | 70ce Mandolin player | 4.00 | 4.00 |

### Nos. 933-938 Ovptd. in Gold with Winner and Country

1ce, Valerie Brisco-Hooks, US. 1.40ce, US winners. 2.30ce, Pakistan, (field hockey). 3ce, Edwin Moses, US. 50ce, Lauri Fung, Canada. 70ce, France.

**1984, Dec. 3**    **Litho.**    **Perf. 15**

| | | | | |
|---|---|---|---|---|
| 945 | A181 | 1ce multicolored | .25 | .25 |
| 946 | A181 | 1.40ce multicolored | .25 | .25 |
| 947 | A181 | 2.30ce multicolored | .25 | .25 |
| 948 | A181 | 3ce multicolored | .25 | .25 |
| 949 | A181 | 50ce multicolored | 1.60 | 1.60 |
| | | Nos. 945-949 (5) | 2.60 | 2.60 |

**Souvenir Sheet**

| | | | | |
|---|---|---|---|---|
| 950 | A181 | 70ce multicolored | 2.50 | 2.50 |

Christmas — A183

70p, Adoration of the Magi. 1ce, Chorus of angels. 1.40ce, Adoration of the shepherds. 2.30ce, Flight into Egypt. 3ce, King holding Christ. 50ce, Adoration of the angels.

**1984, Nov. 19**      **Perf. 12x12½**

| | | | | |
|---|---|---|---|---|
| 951 | A183 | 70p multicolored | .25 | .25 |
| 952 | A183 | 1ce multicolored | .25 | .25 |
| 953 | A183 | 1.40ce multicolored | .25 | .25 |
| 954 | A183 | 2.30ce multicolored | .25 | .25 |
| 955 | A183 | 3ce multicolored | .25 | .25 |
| 956 | A183 | 50ce multicolored | 1.35 | 1.35 |
| | | Nos. 951-956 (6) | 2.60 | 2.60 |

**Souvenir Sheet**

| | | | | |
|---|---|---|---|---|
| 957 | A183 | 70ce like 70p | 2.60 | 2.60 |

Queen Mother, 85th Birthday — A184

Portraits.

**1985**      **Perf. 14**

| | | | | |
|---|---|---|---|---|
| 958 | A184 | 5ce multicolored | .25 | .25 |
| 959 | A184 | 8ce like 5ce | .25 | .25 |
| 960 | A184 | 12ce multicolored | .25 | .25 |
| 961 | A184 | 20ce like 12ce | .25 | .25 |
| 962 | A184 | 70ce multicolored | .90 | .90 |
| 963 | A184 | 100ce like 70ce | 1.10 | 1.10 |
| | | Nos. 958-963 (6) | 3.00 | 3.00 |

**Souvenir Sheet**

| | | | | |
|---|---|---|---|---|
| 964 | A184 | 110ce multicolored | 3.00 | 3.00 |

Issue dates: 5ce, 12ce, 100ce, 110ce, July 29. 8ce, 20ce, 70ce, Dec.
Nos. 959, 961-962 issued in sheets of 5 + label.
For surcharges see Nos. 1117-1119A, 1198-1200, 1311-1317.

Id-El-Fitr Islamic Festival — A185

5ce, Entering mosque. 8ce, Prayer rug. 12ce, Mosque. 18ce, Public Koran reading. 50ce, Map, Banda Nkwanta Mosque.

**1985, Aug. 1**

| | | | | |
|---|---|---|---|---|
| 965 | A185 | 5ce multicolored | .30 | .30 |
| 966 | A185 | 8ce multicolored | .40 | .40 |
| 967 | A185 | 12ce multicolored | .65 | .65 |
| 968 | A185 | 18ce multicolored | 1.15 | 1.15 |
| 969 | A185 | 50ce multicolored | 3.00 | 3.00 |
| | | Nos. 965-969 (5) | 5.50 | 5.50 |

Intl. Youth Year — A186

**1985, Aug. 9**

| | | | | |
|---|---|---|---|---|
| 970 | A186 | 5ce Street clean-up | .25 | .25 |
| 971 | A186 | 8ce Tree planting | .25 | .25 |
| 972 | A186 | 12ce Food production | .30 | .30 |
| 973 | A186 | 100ce Education | 1.25 | 2.50 |
| | | Nos. 970-973 (4) | 2.05 | 3.30 |

**Souvenir Sheet**

| | | | | |
|---|---|---|---|---|
| 974 | A186 | 110ce like 8ce | 2.00 | 2.00 |

Motorcycle Centenary A187

5ce, 1984 Honda Interceptor. 8ce, 1938 DKW. 12ce, 1923 BMW R 32. 100ce, 1900 NSU.
110ce, 1973 Zundapp.

**1985, Sept. 9**

| | | | | |
|---|---|---|---|---|
| 975 | A187 | 5ce multicolored | .50 | .50 |
| 976 | A187 | 8ce multicolored | .70 | .40 |
| 977 | A187 | 12ce multicolored | 1.10 | .85 |
| 978 | A187 | 100ce multicolored | 6.00 | 6.00 |
| | | Nos. 975-978 (4) | 8.30 | 7.55 |

**Souvenir Sheet**

| | | | | |
|---|---|---|---|---|
| 979 | A187 | 110ce multicolored | 5.25 | 5.25 |

Audubon Birth Bicent. — A188

5ce, York-tailed flycatcher. 8ce, Barred owl. 12ce, Black-throated mango. 100ce, White-crowned pigeon.
110ce, Downy woodpecker.

**1985, Oct. 16**

| | | | | |
|---|---|---|---|---|
| 980 | A188 | 5ce multicolored | 1.40 | 1.40 |
| 981 | A188 | 8ce multicolored | 2.25 | 2.25 |
| 982 | A188 | 12ce multicolored | 2.25 | 2.25 |
| 983 | A188 | 100ce multicolored | 5.50 | 5.50 |
| | | Nos. 980-983 (4) | 11.40 | 11.40 |

**Souvenir Sheet**

| | | | | |
|---|---|---|---|---|
| 984 | A188 | 110ce multicolored | 7.50 | 7.50 |

For surcharges see Nos. 1124-1127.

UN, 40th Anniv. — A189

5ce, UN building. 8ce, UN building, diff. 12ce, Dove. 18ce, General Assembly. 100ce, Flags.
110ce, UN No. 36.

**1985, Oct. 24**    *Perf. 14½x14*
| | | | | |
|---|---|---|---|---|
| 985 | A189 | 5ce multicolored | .25 | .25 |
| 986 | A189 | 8ce multicolored | .25 | .25 |
| 987 | A189 | 12ce multicolored | .25 | *.30* |
| 988 | A189 | 18ce multicolored | .25 | .25 |
| 989 | A189 | 100ce multicolored | 1.75 | *2.25* |
| | *Nos. 985-989 (5)* | | 2.75 | 3.45 |

**Souvenir Sheet**
| | | | | |
|---|---|---|---|---|
| 990 | A189 | 110ce multicolored | 1.75 | 1.75 |

UNCTAD, 20th Anniv. — A190

**1985, Nov. 4**    *Perf. 14*
| | | | | |
|---|---|---|---|---|
| 991 | A190 | 5ce Coffee | .25 | .25 |
| 992 | A190 | 8ce Cocoa | .25 | .25 |
| 993 | A190 | 12ce Lumber | .30 | .30 |
| 994 | A190 | 18ce Bauxite mining | 1.00 | 1.00 |
| 995 | A190 | 100ce Gold mining | 6.25 | 6.25 |
| | *Nos. 991-995 (5)* | | 8.05 | 8.05 |

**Souvenir Sheet**
*Perf. 15x14*
| | | | | |
|---|---|---|---|---|
| 996 | A190 | 110ce Produce | 2.50 | 2.50 |

UN Child Survival Campaign A191

5ce, Weighing. 8ce, Oral rehydration therapy. 12ce, Breast-feeding. 100ce, Immunization.
110ce, Emblem, pinwheel.

**1985, Dec. 16**    *Perf. 14*
| | | | | |
|---|---|---|---|---|
| 997 | A191 | 5ce multicolored | .25 | .25 |
| 998 | A191 | 8ce multicolored | .25 | .25 |
| 999 | A191 | 12ce multicolored | .50 | .50 |
| 1000 | A191 | 100ce multicolored | 3.75 | 3.75 |
| | *Nos. 997-1000 (4)* | | 4.75 | 4.75 |

**Souvenir Sheet**
*Perf. 15x14*
| | | | | |
|---|---|---|---|---|
| 1001 | A191 | 110ce multicolored | 2.10 | 2.10 |

AMERIPEX '86 — A192

5ce, Young collectors. 25ce, Earth, jet. 100ce, Stewardess, vert.
150ce, Young collectors, diff.

*Perf. 14½x14, 14x14½*
**1986, Oct. 27**    *Litho.*
| | | | | |
|---|---|---|---|---|
| 1002 | A192 | 5ce multicolored | .30 | .30 |
| 1003 | A192 | 25ce multicolored | .85 | .85 |
| 1004 | A192 | 100ce multicolored | 2.40 | 2.40 |
| | *Nos. 1002-1004 (3)* | | 3.55 | 3.55 |

**Souvenir Sheet**
| | | | | |
|---|---|---|---|---|
| 1005 | A192 | 150ce multicolored | 3.50 | 3.50 |

INTER-TOURISM '86, Nov. 8-17 — A193

Designs: 5ce, Kejetia Roundabout, Kumasi. 15ce, Fort St. Jago, Elmina. 25ce, Warriors. 100ce, Chief, retinue. 150ce, Elephants.

**1986, Nov. 10**    *Perf. 14*
| | | | | |
|---|---|---|---|---|
| 1006 | A193 | 5ce multi | .25 | .25 |
| 1007 | A193 | 15ce multi | .50 | .50 |
| 1008 | A193 | 25ce multi | .75 | .75 |
| 1009 | A193 | 100ce multi | 2.75 | 2.75 |
| | *Nos. 1006-1009 (4)* | | 4.25 | 4.25 |

**Souvenir Sheet**
*Perf. 15x14*
| | | | | |
|---|---|---|---|---|
| 1010 | A193 | 150ce multi | 4.75 | 4.75 |

1986 World Cup Soccer Championships, Mexico — A194

Various soccer plays.

**1987, Jan. 16**    *Litho.*    *Perf. 14x14½*
| | | | | |
|---|---|---|---|---|
| 1011 | A194 | 5ce multi | .30 | .30 |
| 1012 | A194 | 15ce multi | .35 | .35 |
| 1013 | A194 | 25ce multi | .55 | .55 |
| 1014 | A194 | 100ce multi | 2.00 | 2.00 |
| | *Nos. 1011-1014 (4)* | | 3.20 | 3.20 |

**Souvenir Sheet**
| | | | | |
|---|---|---|---|---|
| 1015 | A194 | 150ce multi | 2.40 | 2.40 |

For surcharges see Nos. 1120-1123D.

Fertility Dolls — A195

Various dolls.

**1987, Jan. 22**
| | | | | |
|---|---|---|---|---|
| 1016 | A195 | 5ce multi | .30 | .30 |
| 1017 | A195 | 15ce multi | .30 | .30 |
| 1018 | A195 | 25ce multi | .50 | .50 |
| 1019 | A195 | 100ce multi | 2.00 | 2.00 |
| | *Nos. 1016-1019 (4)* | | 3.10 | 3.10 |

**Souvenir Sheet**
| | | | | |
|---|---|---|---|---|
| 1020 | A195 | 150ce like #1016 | 2.00 | 2.00 |

Intl. Peace Year — A196

5ce, Children playing. 25ce, Plow. 100ce, Earth, doves, vert.
150ce, Dove, plow, vert.

*Perf. 14½x14, 14x14½*
**1987, Mar. 2**    *Litho.*
| | | | | |
|---|---|---|---|---|
| 1021 | A196 | 5ce multicolored | .30 | .30 |
| 1022 | A196 | 25ce multicolored | .85 | .85 |
| 1023 | A196 | 100ce multicolored | 3.00 | 3.00 |
| | *Nos. 1021-1023 (3)* | | 4.15 | 4.15 |

**Souvenir Sheet**
| | | | | |
|---|---|---|---|---|
| 1024 | A196 | 150ce multicolored | 2.50 | 2.50 |

GIFEX '87 — A197

5ce, Lumber, house construction. 15ce, Furniture. 25ce, Tree stumps. 200ce, Logs, art objects.

**1987, Mar. 10**    *Perf. 14*
| | | | | |
|---|---|---|---|---|
| 1025 | A197 | 5ce multicolored | .25 | .25 |
| 1026 | A197 | 15ce multicolored | .25 | .25 |
| 1027 | A197 | 25ce multicolored | .40 | .40 |
| 1028 | A197 | 200ce multicolored | 2.25 | 2.25 |
| | *Nos. 1025-1028 (4)* | | 3.15 | 3.15 |

Ghana Intl. Forestry Exposition, Accra.

A198

Halley's Comet A199

Designs: 5ce, Mikhail Vasilyevich Lomonosov (1711-1765), Russian scientist, and the Chamber of Curiosities. 25ce, Landing of the US probe Surveyor on the Moon's surface, 1966. 200ce, Wedgwood memorial to Sir Isaac Newton, the appearance of Halley's Comet in 1790 and US astronauts Armstrong and Aldrin landing Eagle on the Moon in 1969. 250ce, Comet over Fishermen near Christianborg Castle.

**1987, Apr. 8**    *Perf. 14½x14*
| | | | | |
|---|---|---|---|---|
| 1029 | A198 | 5ce multi | .30 | .25 |
| 1030 | A198 | 25ce multi | .90 | .90 |
| 1031 | A198 | 200ce multi | 4.25 | 4.25 |
| | *Nos. 1029-1031 (3)* | | 5.45 | 5.40 |

**Souvenir Sheet**
| | | | | |
|---|---|---|---|---|
| 1032 | A199 | 250ce multi | 5.00 | 5.00 |

For surcharges see Nos. 1128-1131,

Solidarity with South Africans for Abolition of Apartheid — A200

5ce, Liberated prisoner. 15ce, Miner, gold ingots. 25ce, Zulu warrior. 100ce, Nelson Mandela, shackles.
150ce, Mandela, map, star.

**1987, May 18**    *Perf. 14x14½*
| | | | | |
|---|---|---|---|---|
| 1033 | A200 | 5ce multicolored | .25 | .25 |
| 1034 | A200 | 15ce multicolored | .30 | .30 |
| 1035 | A200 | 25ce multicolored | .30 | .30 |
| 1036 | A200 | 100ce multicolored | 1.60 | 1.60 |
| | *Nos. 1033-1036 (4)* | | 2.45 | 2.45 |

**Souvenir Sheet**
| | | | | |
|---|---|---|---|---|
| 1037 | A200 | 150ce multicolored | 2.40 | 2.40 |

Traditional Musical Instruments A201

5ce, Horns. 15ce, Xylophone. 25ce, String instruments. 100ce, Drums.
200ce, Percussion instruments.

**1987, July 13**    *Perf. 14½x14*
| | | | | |
|---|---|---|---|---|
| 1038 | A201 | 5ce multicolored | .25 | .25 |
| 1039 | A201 | 15ce multicolored | .30 | .30 |
| 1040 | A201 | 25ce multicolored | .45 | .45 |
| 1041 | A201 | 100ce multicolored | 1.30 | 1.30 |
| | *Nos. 1038-1041 (4)* | | 2.30 | 2.30 |

**Souvenir Sheet**
| | | | | |
|---|---|---|---|---|
| 1042 | A201 | 200ce multicolored | 2.75 | 2.75 |

Intl. Year of Shelter for the Homeless A202

5ce, Public well. 15ce, Home construction. 25ce, Village, bridge, car. 100ce, Village, electric power lines.

**1987, Sept. 21**    *Litho.*    *Perf. 14*
| | | | | |
|---|---|---|---|---|
| 1043 | A202 | 5ce multicolored | .25 | .25 |
| 1044 | A202 | 15ce multicolored | .25 | .25 |
| 1045 | A202 | 25ce multicolored | .40 | .40 |
| 1046 | A202 | 100ce multicolored | 1.25 | 1.25 |
| | *Nos. 1043-1046 (4)* | | 2.15 | 2.15 |

Festivals — A203

Designs: Preparation of Kpokpoi, Homowo Festival. 15ce, Hunters with catch, Aboakyir Festival. 25ce, Chief dancing, Odwira Festival. 100ce, Chief held aloft in a palanquin, Yam Festival.

**1988, Jan. 6**    *Litho.*    *Perf. 15*
| | | | | |
|---|---|---|---|---|
| 1047 | A203 | 5ce multi | .25 | .25 |
| 1048 | A203 | 15ce multi | .25 | .25 |
| 1049 | A203 | 25ce multi | .35 | .35 |
| 1050 | A203 | 100ce multi | 1.15 | 1.15 |
| | *Nos. 1047-1050 (4)* | | 2.00 | 2.00 |

December 31, 1981 Revolution A203a

5ce, Ports. 15ce, Railways. 25ce, Cocoa industry. 100ce, Mining industry.

**1988, Jan. 26**    *Litho.*    *Perf. 13*
| | | | | |
|---|---|---|---|---|
| 1050A | A203a | 5ce multi | 1.50 | .50 |
| 1050B | A203a | 15ce multi | 13.50 | 3.00 |
| 1050C | A203a | 25ce multi | 2.75 | .75 |
| 1050D | A203a | 100ce multi | 16.00 | 16.00 |
| | *Nos. 1050A-1050D (4)* | | 33.75 | 20.25 |

UN Universal Immunization Campaign — A204

Child Survival Campaign emblem and: 5ce, Nurse immunizing woman. 15ce, Child receiving intramuscular vaccine. 25ce, Youth crippled by polio. 100ce, Nurse handing infant to mother.

**1988, Feb. 1**    *Perf. 15*
| | | | | |
|---|---|---|---|---|
| 1051 | A204 | 5ce multi | .25 | .25 |
| 1052 | A204 | 15ce multi | .25 | .25 |
| 1053 | A204 | 25ce multi | .40 | .40 |
| 1054 | A204 | 100ce multi | .90 | .90 |
| | *Nos. 1051-1054 (4)* | | 1.80 | 1.80 |

Intl. Fund for Agricultural Development A204a

5ce, Fishing. 15ce, Harvesting. 25ce, Cattle. 100ce, Granary.

**1988, Apr. 14**    *Perf. 13*
| | | | | |
|---|---|---|---|---|
| 1054A | A204a | 5ce multi | 1.75 | 1.75 |
| 1054B | A204a | 15ce multi | 3.00 | 3.00 |
| 1054C | A204a | 25ce multi | 5.00 | 5.00 |
| 1054D | A204a | 100ce multi | 11.00 | 11.00 |
| | *Nos. 1054A-1054D (4)* | | 20.75 | 20.75 |

Tribal Costumes — A205

**1988, May 9**    *Litho.*    *Perf. 14*
| | | | | |
|---|---|---|---|---|
| 1055 | A205 | 5ce Akwadjan | .25 | .25 |
| 1056 | A205 | 25ce Banaa | .50 | .50 |
| 1057 | A205 | 250ce Agwasen | 2.25 | 2.25 |
| | *Nos. 1055-1057 (3)* | | 3.00 | 3.00 |

For surcharges, see Nos. 2677, 2682.

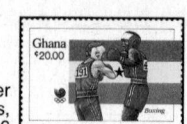

1988 Summer Olympics, Seoul — A206

**1988, Oct. 10**
| | | | | |
|---|---|---|---|---|
| 1058 | A206 | 20ce Boxing | .25 | .25 |
| 1059 | A206 | 60ce Running | .55 | .55 |
| 1060 | A206 | 80ce Discus | .70 | .70 |
| 1061 | A206 | 100ce Javelin | .90 | .90 |
| 1062 | A206 | 350ce Weight lifting | 3.00 | 3.00 |
| | *Nos. 1058-1062 (5)* | | 5.40 | 5.40 |

**Souvenir Sheet**
| | | | | |
|---|---|---|---|---|
| 1063 | A206 | 500ce like 80ce | 5.25 | 5.25 |

For overprints see Nos. 1084-1089.

Intl. Red Cross, 125th Anniv. — A207

20ce, Nutrition. 50ce, Voluntary service. 60ce, Disaster relief (flood). 200ce, Medical assistance.

**1988, Dec. 14**    Litho.    *Perf. 14*
| | | | | |
|---|---|---|---|---|
| 1064 | A207 | 20ce multicolored | .55 | .55 |
| 1065 | A207 | 50ce multicolored | 1.15 | 1.15 |
| 1066 | A207 | 60ce multicolored | 1.25 | 1.25 |
| 1067 | A207 | 200ce multicolored | 3.25 | 3.25 |
| | | Nos. 1064-1067 (4) | 6.20 | 6.20 |

Christmas Symbolism A208

60ce, Mother and child, vert. 80ce, Mother, child, tree, vert. 100ce, Magi follow star. 350ce, Abstract, diff., vert.
500ce, Mother and child, diff., vert.

**1988, Dec. 19**    Litho.    *Perf. 14*
| | | | | |
|---|---|---|---|---|
| 1068 | A208 | 20ce shown | .25 | .25 |
| 1069 | A208 | 60ce multicolored | .45 | .45 |
| 1070 | A208 | 80ce multicolored | .50 | .50 |
| 1071 | A208 | 100ce multicolored | .65 | .65 |
| 1072 | A208 | 350ce multicolored | 2.75 | 2.75 |
| | | Nos. 1068-1072 (5) | 4.60 | 4.60 |

**Souvenir Sheet**
| | | | | |
|---|---|---|---|---|
| 1073 | A208 | 500ce multicolored | 3.50 | 3.50 |

For surcharges see Nos. 2678, 2680-2681.

Organization of African Unity, 25th Anniv. — A209

20ce, Solidarity. 50ce, OAU, Addis Ababa. 60ce, Haile Selassie, Ethiopia. 200ce, Kwame Nkrumah, Ghana.

**1989, Jan. 3**
| | | | | |
|---|---|---|---|---|
| 1074 | A209 | 20ce multicolored | .25 | .25 |
| 1075 | A209 | 50ce multicolored | .25 | .25 |
| 1076 | A209 | 60ce multicolored | .35 | .35 |
| 1077 | A209 | 200ce multicolored | .55 | .55 |
| | | Nos. 1074-1077 (4) | 1.40 | 1.40 |

"Selassie" is spelled incorrectly on No. 1076. Nos. 1076-1077 horiz.

Titian, 500th Birth Anniv. (in 1988) — A210

20ce, Amor, 1515. 60ce, The Appeal. 80ce, Bacchus and Ariadne, c. 1523. 100ce, Portrait of a Musician, c. 1518. 350ce, Philip II Seated. 500ce, Portrait of a Gentleman, c. 1550.

**1989, Jan. 16**
| | | | | |
|---|---|---|---|---|
| 1078 | A210 | 20ce multicolored | .45 | .25 |
| 1079 | A210 | 60ce multicolored | .80 | .80 |
| 1080 | A210 | 80ce multicolored | 1.10 | 1.10 |
| 1081 | A210 | 100ce multicolored | 1.25 | 1.25 |
| 1082 | A210 | 350ce multicolored | 3.25 | 3.25 |
| | | Nos. 1078-1082 (5) | 6.85 | 6.65 |

**Souvenir Sheet**
| | | | | |
|---|---|---|---|---|
| 1083 | A210 | 500ce multicolored | 3.50 | 3.50 |

**Nos. 1058-1063 Ovptd. with Winners' Names**

20ce, "A. ZUELOW / DDR / 60 KG". 60ce, "G. BORDIN / ITALY / MARATHON". 80ce, "J. SCHULT / DDR". 100ce, "T. KORJUS / FINLAND". 350ce, "B. GUIDIKOV / BULGARIA / 75 KG".

---

**1989, Jan. 23**
| | | | | |
|---|---|---|---|---|
| 1084 | A206 | 20ce multicolored | .40 | .40 |
| 1085 | A206 | 60ce multicolored | .50 | .50 |
| 1086 | A206 | 80ce multicolored | .60 | .60 |
| 1087 | A206 | 100ce multicolored | .70 | .70 |
| 1088 | A206 | 350ce multicolored | 1.60 | 1.60 |
| | | Nos. 1084-1088 (5) | 3.80 | 3.80 |

**Souvenir Sheet**
| | | | | |
|---|---|---|---|---|
| 1089 | A206 | 500ce multi | 3.75 | 3.75 |

1988 Summer Olympics, Seoul. Margin of No. 1089 ovptd. "GOLD / J. SCHULT DDR / SILVER / R. OUBARTAS USSR / BRONZE / R. DANNEBERG W. GERMANY."

**Stamps of 1967-1984 Surcharged**

**1988-91**
| | | | | |
|---|---|---|---|---|
| 1089A | A177 | 20ce on 50p #889 | .35 | .30 |
| 1090 | A177 | 20ce on 1ce #890 | .35 | .30 |
| a. | | Double surcharge, one inverted | | — |
| 1091 | A75 | 50ce on 10np #295 | 2.00 | 2.00 |
| 1092 | A177 | 50ce on 10p #887 | 1.00 | 2.00 |
| f. | | 50ce' on 10p Denomination below obliterator | | — |
| 1092A | A74 | 50ce on 1ce #858 | 6.00 | 5.00 |
| 1092B | A74 | 50ce on 1ce #858 | 10.00 | 10.00 |
| 1092C | A74 | 50ce on 1ce #858 | 10.00 | 10.00 |
| 1092D | A177 | 50ce on 1ce #890 | 6.00 | .50 |
| 1092E | A73 | 60ce on 1np #286 | 6.00 | .50 |
| 1093 | A73 | 60ce on 4np #291 | 6.00 | .50 |
| 1093A | A177 | 60ce on 3ce #892 | 1.00 | .45 |
| 1094 | A177 | 80ce on 5p #886 | 1.00 | .45 |
| 1094A | A177 | 80ce on 5ce #894 | 10.00 | 10.00 |
| 1094B | A75 | 100ce on 3np #290 | — | — |
| 1095 | A74 | 100ce on 20np #296 | 10.00 | 10.00 |
| 1096 | A177 | 100ce on 20p #888 | 1.00 | 1.00 |
| 1096A | A177 | 100ce on 3ce #892 | 2.00 | 2.00 |
| 1096B | A75 | 200ce on 6np #292 | 8.00 | 8.00 |

Surcharge has no decimal on No. 1092A, is vertical on No. 1092B and horizontal on No. 1092C.
No. 1090 also exists with 5mm spacing between block and $20.00.
Surcharge on No. 1093A has decimal point. Unauthorized surcharges exist.
Issued: Nos. 1089A, 1096B, 7/1/88; Nos. 1092A, 1092B, 1092D, 1092E, 1094A, 1096A, 1990; No. 1092C, 1991; others, 1989.

Minamoto-no-Yoritomo, by Fujiwara-no-Takanobu (1142-1205) — A211

Paintings: 50ce, Takami Senseki, by Watanabe Kazan (1793-1841). 60ce, Ikkyu Sojum, by Bokusai, Muromachi period. 75ce, Nakamura Kuranosuke, by Ogata Korin (1658-1716). 125ce, Portrait of a Lady, Kyoto branch of Kano school, Momoyama period. 150ce, Portrait of Zemmui, anonymous, 12th cent. 200ce, Ono no Komachi, the Poetess, by Hokusai. No. 1104, Kobo Daisi as a Child, anonymous, Kamakura period. No. 1105, Portrait of Kodai-no-Kimi, attributed to Fujiwara-no-Nobuzane, 12th cent. No. 1106, Portrait of Emperor Hanazono, by Fujiwara-no-Goshin, 14th cent.

**1989, Aug. 21**    Litho.    *Perf. 13½x14*
| | | | | |
|---|---|---|---|---|
| 1097 | A211 | 20ce shown | .25 | .25 |
| 1098 | A211 | 50ce multi | .40 | .40 |
| 1099 | A211 | 60ce multi | .45 | .45 |
| 1100 | A211 | 75ce multi | .65 | .65 |

---

| | | | | |
|---|---|---|---|---|
| 1101 | A211 | 125ce multi | 1.00 | 1.00 |
| 1102 | A211 | 150ce multi | 1.40 | 1.40 |
| 1103 | A211 | 200ce multi | 1.60 | 1.60 |
| 1104 | A211 | 500ce multi | 2.25 | 2.25 |
| | | Nos. 1097-1104 (8) | 8.00 | 8.00 |

**Souvenir Sheets**
| | | | | |
|---|---|---|---|---|
| 1105 | A211 | 500ce multi | 6.00 | 6.00 |
| 1106 | A211 | 500ce multi | 6.00 | 6.00 |

Hirohito (1901-1989) and enthronement of Akihito as emperor of Japan.

**Nos. 835-838 and 840 Surcharged**

**1989, July 3**    Litho.    *Perf. 14*
| | | | | |
|---|---|---|---|---|
| 1107 | A173b | 60ce on 1ce | .90 | .60 |
| 1108 | A173b | 80ce on 1.40ce | 1.10 | .75 |
| 1109 | A173b | 200ce on 2.30ce | 2.75 | 2.75 |
| 1110 | A173b | 300ce on 3ce | 3.25 | 3.25 |
| | | Nos. 1107-1110 (4) | 8.00 | 7.35 |

**Souvenir Sheet**
| | | | | |
|---|---|---|---|---|
| 1111 | A173b | 500ce on 6ce | 6.50 | 6.50 |

**Nos. 933-936 and 938 Surcharged**

**1989, July 3**    *Perf. 15*
| | | | | |
|---|---|---|---|---|
| 1112 | A181 | 60ce on 1ce | .40 | .40 |
| 1113 | A181 | 80ce on 1.40ce | .60 | .60 |
| 1114 | A181 | 200ce on 2.30ce | 1.40 | 1.40 |
| 1115 | A181 | 300ce on 3ce | 1.90 | 1.90 |
| | | Nos. 1112-1115 (4) | 4.30 | 4.30 |

**Souvenir Sheet**
| | | | | |
|---|---|---|---|---|
| 1116 | A181 | 600ce on 70ce | 4.00 | 4.00 |

**Nos. 958, 960 and 963-964 Surcharged**

**1989, Nov. 20**    Litho.    *Perf. 14*
| | | | | |
|---|---|---|---|---|
| 1117 | A184 | 80ce on 5ce #958 | .60 | .60 |
| 1118 | A184 | 250ce on 12ce #960 | 1.90 | 1.90 |
| 1119 | A184 | 300ce on 100ce #963 | 2.10 | 2.10 |
| | | Nos. 1117-1119 (3) | 4.60 | 4.60 |

**Souvenir Sheet**
| | | | | |
|---|---|---|---|---|
| 1119A | A184 | 500ce on 110ce #964 | 4.75 | 4.75 |

**Nos. 1011-1013 and 1015 Surcharged**

**1989**    Litho.    *Perf. 14x14½*
| | | | | |
|---|---|---|---|---|
| 1120 | A194 | 60ce on 5ce #1011 | .60 | .60 |
| 1121 | A194 | 200ce on 15ce #1012 | 1.90 | 1.90 |
| 1122 | A194 | 300ce on 25ce #1013 | 2.50 | 2.50 |
| | | Nos. 1120-1122 (3) | 5.00 | 5.00 |

**Souvenir Sheet**
| | | | | |
|---|---|---|---|---|
| 1123 | A194 | 600ce on 150ce #1015 | 7.00 | 7.00 |

Nos. 1120-1123 Surcharged

**1989**    Litho.    *Perf. 14x14½*
| | | | | |
|---|---|---|---|---|
| 1123A | A194 | 60ce on 5ce | .90 | .90 |
| 1123B | A194 | 200ce on 15ce | 3.00 | 3.00 |
| 1123C | A194 | 300ce on 25ce | 4.75 | 4.75 |
| | | Nos. 1123A-1123C (3) | 8.65 | 8.65 |

**Souvenir Sheet**
| | | | | |
|---|---|---|---|---|
| 1123D | A194 | 600ce on 150ce | 10.00 | 10.00 |

**Nos. 980-982 and 984 Surcharged**

**1989, Nov. 20**    Litho.    *Perf. 14*
| | | | | |
|---|---|---|---|---|
| 1124 | A188 | 80ce on 5ce #980 | 1.75 | 1.75 |
| 1125 | A188 | 100ce on 8ce #981 | 3.25 | 3.25 |
| 1126 | A188 | 300ce on 12ce #982 | 3.50 | 3.50 |
| | | Nos. 1124-1126 (3) | 8.50 | 8.50 |

**Souvenir Sheet**
| | | | | |
|---|---|---|---|---|
| 1127 | A188 | 500ce on 110ce #984 | 9.50 | 9.50 |

**Nos. 1029-1032 Surcharged**

**1989, Nov. 20**    *Perf. 14½x14*
| | | | | |
|---|---|---|---|---|
| 1128 | A198 | 60ce on 5ce #1029 | 1.00 | 1.00 |
| a. | | With comet logo | 1.00 | 1.00 |
| 1129 | A198 | 80ce on 25ce #1030 | 1.25 | 1.25 |
| a. | | With comet logo | 1.25 | 1.25 |
| 1130 | A198 | 500ce on 200ce #1031 | 4.25 | 4.25 |
| a. | | With comet logo | 4.25 | 4.25 |
| | | Nos. 1128-1130 (3) | 6.50 | 6.50 |
| | | Nos. 1128a-1130a (3) | 6.50 | 6.50 |

**Souvenir Sheet**
| | | | | |
|---|---|---|---|---|
| 1131 | A199 | 750ce on 250ce #1032 | 6.00 | 6.00 |
| a. | | With comet logo | 6.00 | 6.00 |

---

PHILEXFRANCE '89, French Revolution Bicent. — A212

Emblems, French arms and flags: 20ce, Tube-mounted field carriage, flag of 1643 to 1790. 60ce, Infantryman, flag of 1789. 80ce, Handgun, flag of 1789, diff. 350ce, Musket, flag of 1794 to 1814 and 1848 to present. 600ce, Map of Paris.

**1989, Sept. 22**    Litho.    *Perf. 14*
| | | | | |
|---|---|---|---|---|
| 1132 | A212 | 20ce shown | .70 | .70 |
| 1133 | A212 | 60ce multi | 1.25 | 1.25 |
| 1134 | A212 | 80ce multi | 1.60 | 1.60 |
| 1135 | A212 | 350ce multi | 3.75 | 3.75 |
| | | Nos. 1132-1135 (4) | 7.30 | 7.30 |

**Souvenir Sheet**
| | | | | |
|---|---|---|---|---|
| 1136 | A212 | 600ce multi | 4.25 | 4.25 |

Mushrooms
A213      A214

20ce, Collybia. 50ce, Lawyer's wig. 60ce, Xerocomus subtomentosus. 80ce, Wood belwits. 150ce, Suillus placidus. 200ce, Lepista nuda. 300ce, Fairy rings. 500ce, Field mushroom.
No. 1145, Three Amanita species. No. 1146, Three Boletus species.

**1989, Oct. 2**    Litho.    *Perf. 14*
| | | | | |
|---|---|---|---|---|
| 1137 | A213 | 20ce multi | .25 | .25 |
| 1138 | A213 | 50ce multi | .35 | .35 |
| 1139 | A214 | 60ce multi | .40 | .40 |
| 1140 | A213 | 80ce multi | .60 | .60 |
| 1141 | A214 | 150ce multi | 1.20 | 1.20 |
| 1142 | A214 | 200ce multi | 1.50 | 1.50 |
| 1143 | A213 | 300ce multi | 2.10 | 2.10 |
| 1144 | A214 | 500ce multi | 3.50 | 3.50 |
| | | Nos. 1137-1144 (8) | 9.90 | 9.90 |

**Souvenir Sheets**
| | | | | |
|---|---|---|---|---|
| 1145 | A213 | 600ce multi | 4.25 | 4.25 |
| 1146 | A214 | 600ce multi | 4.25 | 4.25 |

**Souvenir Sheet**

*A Midsummer Night's Dream*, by Shakespeare — A215

Designs: a, "The course of true love never did run smooth." b, "Love looks not with the eye but with the mind." c, "Nature here shows art." d, "Things growing are not ripe till their season." e, "He is defiled that draws a sword on thee." f, "It is not enough to speak but to speak true." g, "Thou art wise as thou art beautiful." h, Leopard behind trees. i, Theseus. j, Boy holding flower, trees. k, Oberon and Titania among trees. l, Bottom wearing head of a jackass. m, Bottom's leg, leopard behind trees. n, Hippolyta. o, Leopard, tree trunk. p, Tree trunk, foliage, lower portion of Theseus's robe, q, Wisps of fragrance, clouds, hills, foliage. r, Wisps of fragrance, flowering plants. s, Flowering plants. t, Lion, foliage. u, Lion's mane, foliage.

**1989, Oct. 9**    *Perf. 13½x13*
| | | | | |
|---|---|---|---|---|
| 1147 | A215 | Sheet of 21 | 18.00 | 18.00 |
| a.-u. | | 40ce any single | .80 | .80 |

425th Birth anniv. of William Shakespeare, playwright.

Birds — A216

20ce, Spermestes cuculatus. 50ce, Motacilla aguimp. 60ce, Halcyon malimbicus. 80ce, Ispidina picta. 150ce, Striped kingfisher. 200ce, Shikra. 300ce, Gray parrot. 500ce, Black kite.
No. 1156, Four birds. No. 1157, Three birds.

| **1989, Oct. 16** | | **Perf. 14** | |
|---|---|---|---|
| 1148 | A216 | 20ce multicolored | .40 | .25 |
| 1149 | A216 | 50ce multicolored | .60 | .35 |
| 1150 | A216 | 60ce multicolored | 1.75 | 1.75 |
| 1151 | A216 | 80ce multicolored | 2.75 | 2.75 |
| 1152 | A216 | 150ce multicolored | 2.25 | 2.25 |
| 1153 | A216 | 200ce multicolored | 2.00 | 2.00 |
| 1154 | A216 | 300ce multicolored | 2.75 | 2.75 |
| 1155 | A216 | 500ce multicolored | 4.00 | 4.00 |
| *Nos. 1148-1155 (8)* | | | 16.50 | 16.10 |

**Souvenir Sheets**

| 1156 | A216 | 600ce multicolored | 8.25 | 8.25 |
|---|---|---|---|---|
| 1157 | A216 | 600ce multicolored | 8.25 | 8.25 |

Nos. 1152-1156 vert.

1st Moon Landing, 20th Anniv. — A217

Highlights of the Apollo 11 mission.

| **1989, Nov. 6** | | **Perf. 14** | |
|---|---|---|---|
| 1158 | A217 | 20ce Columbia | .25 | .25 |
| 1159 | A217 | 80ce Footprint | .75 | .75 |
| 1160 | A217 | 200ce Aldrin on Moon | 1.50 | 1.50 |
| 1161 | A217 | 300ce Splashdown | 2.25 | 2.25 |
| *Nos. 1158-1161 (4)* | | | 4.75 | 4.75 |

**Souvenir Sheets**

| 1162 | A217 | 500ce Liftoff, vert. | 4.00 | 4.00 |
|---|---|---|---|---|
| 1163 | A217 | 500ce Earth, vert. | 4.00 | 4.00 |

World Environment Day — A218

20ce, Desertification. 60ce, Bush fires. 400ce, Industrial pollution. 500ce, Soil erosion.

| **1989, Nov. 20** | | **Litho.** | **Perf. 14** |
|---|---|---|---|
| 1164 | A218 | 20ce multicolored | .25 | .25 |
| 1165 | A218 | 60ce multicolored | .60 | .60 |
| 1166 | A218 | 400ce multicolored | 3.50 | 3.50 |
| 1167 | A218 | 500ce multicolored | 4.50 | 4.50 |
| *Nos. 1164-1167 (4)* | | | 8.85 | 8.85 |

**Nos. 760 and 761 Surcharged**

| **1989, Nov. 20** | | **Litho.** | **Perf. 14** |
|---|---|---|---|
| 1168 | CD331a | 100ce on 80p | .90 | .90 |
| 1169 | CD331a | 500ce on 4ce | 4.75 | 4.75 |

French Revolution, Bicent. — A219

Designs: 20ce, Storming of the Bastille, vert. 60ce, Declaration of Human Rights and Citizenship, vert. 80ce, Storming of the Bastille, diff. 200ce, *Departure of the Volunteers in 1792*, high relief on the Arc de Triomphe, 1833-35, by Francis Rude. 350ce, Planting the Liberty Tree.

| **Perf. 14x13½, 13½x14** | | | |
|---|---|---|---|
| **1989, Sept. 22** | | | |
| 1170 | A219 | 20ce multicolored | .50 | .50 |
| 1171 | A219 | 60ce multicolored | 1.10 | 1.10 |
| 1172 | A219 | 80ce multicolored | 1.35 | 1.35 |
| 1173 | A219 | 200ce multicolored | 2.50 | 2.50 |
| 1174 | A219 | 350ce multicolored | 3.25 | 3.25 |
| *Nos. 1170-1174 (5)* | | | 8.70 | 8.70 |

Butterflies A220

20ce, Bebearia arcadius. 60ce, Charaxes laodice. 80ce, Euryphura porphyrion. 100ce, Neptis nicomedes. 200ce, Citrinophila erastus. 300ce, Epitola honorius. 300ce, Precis westermanni. 500ce, Cymothoe hypatha.
No. 1183, Telipna bimacula. No. 1184, Pentila phidia.

| **1990, Feb. 15** | | **Litho.** | **Perf. 14** |
|---|---|---|---|
| 1175 | A220 | 20ce multicolored | .50 | .50 |
| 1176 | A220 | 60ce multicolored | .65 | .65 |
| 1177 | A220 | 80ce multicolored | .85 | .85 |
| 1178 | A220 | 100ce multicolored | .95 | .95 |
| 1179 | A220 | 150ce multicolored | 1.10 | 1.10 |
| 1180 | A220 | 200ce multicolored | 1.60 | 1.60 |
| 1181 | A220 | 300ce multicolored | 2.10 | 2.10 |
| 1182 | A220 | 500ce multicolored | 2.75 | 2.75 |
| *Nos. 1175-1182 (8)* | | | 10.50 | 10.50 |

**Souvenir Sheets**

| 1183 | A220 | 600ce multicolored | 5.75 | 5.75 |
|---|---|---|---|---|
| 1184 | A220 | 600ce multicolored | 5.75 | 5.75 |

Seashells — A221

20ce, Cymbium glans. 60ce, Cardium costatum. 80ce, Conus genuanus. 200ce, Ancilla tankervillei. 350ce, Tectarius coronatus.

| **1990, Feb. 20** | | **Perf. 14x14½** | |
|---|---|---|---|
| 1185 | A221 | 20ce multicolored | .70 | .70 |
| 1186 | A221 | 60ce multicolored | 1.25 | 1.25 |
| 1187 | A221 | 80ce multicolored | 1.60 | 1.60 |
| 1188 | A221 | 200ce multicolored | 3.00 | 3.00 |
| 1189 | A221 | 350ce multicolored | 4.25 | 4.25 |
| *Nos. 1185-1189 (5)* | | | 10.80 | 10.80 |

Jawaharlal Nehru, 1st Prime Minister of Independent India — A222

Designs: 20ce, Greeting Pres. Kwame Nkrumah of Ghana. 60ce, Addressing Afro-Asian conference. 80ce, Return from tour of China, vert. 200ce, Releasing dove during a children's celebration in New Delhi, vert. 350ce, Portrait, vert.

| **Perf. 14½x14, 14x14½** | | | |
|---|---|---|---|
| **1990, Mar. 27** | | | **Litho.** |
| 1190 | A222 | 20ce shown | .75 | .75 |
| 1191 | A222 | 60ce multicolored | .90 | .90 |
| 1192 | A222 | 80ce multicolored | 1.10 | 1.10 |
| 1193 | A222 | 200ce multicolored | 1.60 | 1.60 |
| 1194 | A222 | 350ce multicolored | 2.25 | 2.25 |
| *Nos. 1190-1194 (5)* | | | 6.60 | 6.60 |

**Nos. 759A and 760A-760B Surcharged**

| **1990** | | | **Perf. 14** |
|---|---|---|---|
| 1195 | CD331a | 80ce on 65p | 1.00 | 1.00 |
| 1196 | CD331a | 100ce on 1ce | 1.40 | 1.40 |
| 1197 | CD331a | 300ce on 3ce | 4.25 | 4.25 |
| *Nos. 1195-1197 (3)* | | | 6.65 | 6.65 |

**Nos. 961, 959 and 962 Surcharged**

| **1990** | | | |
|---|---|---|---|
| 1198 | A184 | 80ce on 20ce | .75 | .75 |
| 1199 | A184 | 200ce on 8ce | 1.90 | 1.90 |
| 1200 | A184 | 250ce on 70ce | 2.40 | 2.40 |
| *Nos. 1198-1200 (3)* | | | 5.05 | 5.05 |

Penny Black, 150th Anniv. — A223

Great Britain No. 1 and: 20ce, City Medal containing portrait of Victoria by William Wyon adapted for use on the Penny Black. 60ce, No. 1208, Bath mail coach. 80ce, Leeds Mail coach. 200ce, Heath's engraving, based on the Wyon portrait. 350ce, Penny Black master die. 400ce, London mail coach. No. 1207, Printers and flat-bed presses of Perkins, Bacon & Petch, 1840.

| **1990, May 3** | | **Perf. 13½x14** | |
|---|---|---|---|
| 1201 | A223 | 20ce shown | .35 | .35 |
| 1202 | A223 | 60ce multicolored | .65 | .65 |
| 1203 | A223 | 80ce multicolored | .90 | .90 |
| 1204 | A223 | 200ce multicolored | 1.75 | 1.75 |
| 1205 | A223 | 350ce multicolored | 2.40 | 2.40 |
| 1206 | A223 | 400ce multicolored | 2.40 | 2.40 |
| *Nos. 1201-1206 (6)* | | | 8.45 | 8.45 |

**Souvenir Sheets**

| 1207 | A223 | 600ce multicolored | 4.75 | 4.75 |
|---|---|---|---|---|
| 1208 | A223 | 600ce multicolored | 4.75 | 4.75 |

June 4, Revolution, 10th Anniv. (in 1989) — A224

60ce, Pineapple, lobsters. 80ce, Corn, cacao beans. 200ce, Mining. 350ce, Scales, sword.

| **1990, June 5** | | **Litho.** | **Perf. 14½x14** |
|---|---|---|---|
| 1209 | A224 | 20ce shown | .25 | .25 |
| 1210 | A224 | 60ce multicolored | .50 | .50 |
| 1211 | A224 | 80ce multicolored | .65 | .65 |
| 1212 | A224 | 200ce multicolored | 1.60 | 1.60 |
| 1213 | A224 | 350ce multicolored | 2.50 | 2.50 |
| *Nos. 1209-1213 (5)* | | | 5.50 | 5.50 |

Intelsat, 25th Anniv. — A225

Satellites over: 60ce, Pacific Ocean. 80ce, Pacific, diff. 200ce, South Atlantic. 350ce, Pacific, Indian Oceans.

| **1990, July 12** | | **Perf. 14x14½** | |
|---|---|---|---|
| 1214 | A225 | 20ce multicolored | .25 | .25 |
| 1215 | A225 | 60ce multicolored | .50 | .50 |
| 1216 | A225 | 80ce multicolored | .60 | .60 |
| 1217 | A225 | 200ce multicolored | 1.40 | 1.40 |
| 1218 | A225 | 350ce multicolored | 2.00 | 2.00 |
| *Nos. 1214-1218 (5)* | | | 4.75 | 4.75 |

Introduction of Intl. Direct Dialing Service (in 1988) — A226

60ce, Man using telephone. 80ce, Man using pay telephone. 200ce, Telephone booths. 350ce, Satellite dish.

| **1990, July 16** | | | |
|---|---|---|---|
| 1219 | A226 | 20ce shown | .25 | .25 |
| 1220 | A226 | 60ce multicolored | .50 | .50 |
| 1221 | A226 | 80ce multicolored | .60 | .60 |
| 1222 | A226 | 200ce multicolored | 1.40 | 1.40 |
| 1223 | A226 | 350ce multicolored | 2.00 | 2.00 |
| *Nos. 1219-1223 (5)* | | | 4.75 | 4.75 |

**Miniature Sheet**

African Tropical Rain Forest — A227

Designs: No. 1224a, Blue fairy flycatcher. b, Boomslang. c, Superb sunbird. d, Bateleur eagle. e, Yellow-casqued hornbill. f, Salamis temora. g, Potto. h, Leopard. i, Bongo. j, Gray parrot. k, Okapi. l, Gorilla. m, Flap-necked chameleon. n, West African dwarf crocodile. o, Python. p, Giant pangolin. q, Pseudacraea boisduvali. r, African crested porcupine. s, Rosy-columned aerangis. t, Cymothoe sangaris.
No. 1225, Leopard, vert.

| **1990, Oct. 25** | | **Litho.** | **Perf. 14x14½** |
|---|---|---|---|
| 1224 | A227 | Sheet of 20 | 17.00 | 17.00 |
| *a.-t.* | | 40ce any single | .70 | .70 |

**Souvenir Sheet**

| 1225 | A227 | 600ce multicolored | 7.25 | 7.25 |
|---|---|---|---|---|

**Miniature Sheet**

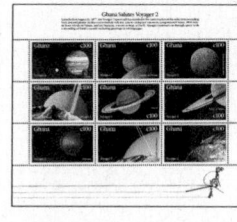

Voyager 2 A228

Photographs from Voyager 2: No. 1226a, Jupiter. b, Neptune, Triton. c, Ariel, moon of Uranus. d, Saturn, Mimas. e, Saturn. f, Rings of Saturn. g, Neptune. h, Uranus, Miranda. i, Volcano on Io.
No. 1227, Voyager 2 liftoff, vert. No. 1228, Voyager 2, vert.

| **1990, Dec. 13** | | **Litho.** | **Perf. 14** |
|---|---|---|---|
| 1226 | A228 | 100ce Sheet of 9, #1226a-1226i | 8.50 | 8.50 |

**Souvenir Sheets**

| 1227 | A228 | 600ce multi | 3.50 | 3.50 |
|---|---|---|---|---|
| 1228 | A228 | 600ce multi | 3.50 | 3.50 |

Orchids — A229

Designs: 20ce, Eulophia guineensis. 40ce, Eurychone rothschildiana. 60ce, Bulbophyllum barbigerum. 80ce, Polystachya galeata. 200ce, Diaphananthe kamerunensis. 300ce, Podangis dactyloceras. 400ce, Ancistrochilus rothschildianus. 500ce, Rangaeris muscicola. No. 1237, Bolusiella imbricata. No. 1238, Diaphananthe rutila.

| **1990, Dec. 17** | | | |
|---|---|---|---|
| 1229 | A229 | 20ce multicolored | .25 | .25 |
| 1230 | A229 | 40ce multicolored | .30 | .30 |
| 1231 | A229 | 60ce multicolored | .55 | .55 |
| 1232 | A229 | 80ce multicolored | .70 | .70 |
| 1233 | A229 | 200ce multicolored | 1.75 | 1.75 |
| 1234 | A229 | 300ce multicolored | 2.75 | 2.75 |
| 1235 | A229 | 400ce multicolored | 3.75 | 3.75 |
| 1236 | A229 | 500ce multicolored | 4.50 | 4.50 |
| *Nos. 1229-1236 (8)* | | | 14.55 | 14.55 |

**Souvenir Sheets**

| 1237 | A229 | 600ce multicolored | 7.25 | 7.25 |
|---|---|---|---|---|
| 1238 | A229 | 600ce multicolored | 7.25 | 7.25 |

Mushrooms A230

Designs: 20ce, Coprinus atramentarius. 50ce, Marasmius oreades. 60ce, Oudamansiella radicata. 80ce, Cep. 150ce, Hebeloma crustuliniforme. 200ce, Coprinus micaceus. 300ce, Lepiota procera. 500ce, Amanita phalloides.

| **1990, Dec. 18** | | | |
|---|---|---|---|
| 1239 | A230 | 20ce multicolored | .85 | .55 |
| 1240 | A230 | 50ce multicolored | 1.10 | .85 |
| 1241 | A230 | 60ce multicolored | 1.40 | .85 |
| 1242 | A230 | 80ce multicolored | 1.75 | 1.25 |
| 1243 | A230 | 150ce multicolored | 2.25 | 1.75 |
| 1244 | A230 | 200ce multicolored | 3.25 | 2.50 |
| 1245 | A230 | 300ce multicolored | 3.25 | 3.25 |
| *a.* | | Min. sheet of 4, #1240, 1243-1245 | 6.75 | 6.75 |
| 1246 | A230 | 500ce multicolored | 4.25 | 4.25 |
| *a.* | | Min. sheet of 4, #1239, 1241-1242, 1246 | 6.75 | 6.75 |
| *Nos. 1239-1246 (8)* | | | 18.10 | 15.25 |

World Cup Soccer Championships, Italy — A231

Players from participating countries: 20ce, Italy. 50ce, Egypt. 60ce, Cameroun. 80ce, Romania. 100ce, Yugoslavia. 150ce, Cameroun, vert. 400ce, South Korea. 600ce, West Germany.
No. 1255, UAE. No. 1256, Colombia.

## 1990, Dec. 18     Litho.     Perf. 14

| | | | | |
|---|---|---|---|---|
| 1247 | A231 | 20ce multi | .50 | .50 |
| 1248 | A231 | 50ce multi | .65 | .65 |
| 1249 | A231 | 60ce multi | .70 | .70 |
| 1250 | A231 | 80ce multi | .85 | .85 |
| 1251 | A231 | 100ce multi | 1.00 | 1.00 |
| 1252 | A231 | 150ce multi | 1.60 | 1.60 |
| 1253 | A231 | 400ce multi | 2.60 | 2.60 |
| 1254 | A231 | 600ce multi | 3.00 | 3.00 |
| | | Nos. 1247-1254 (8) | 10.90 | 10.90 |

### Souvenir Sheets

| | | | | |
|---|---|---|---|---|
| 1255 | A231 | 800ce multi | 5.00 | 5.00 |
| 1256 | A231 | 800ce multi | 5.00 | 5.00 |

Peter Paul Rubens (1577-1640), Painter — A232

Portraits by Rubens: 20ce, Duke of Mantua. 50ce, Jan Brant. 60ce, Young man. 80ce, Michel Ophovius. 100ce, Caspar Gevaerts. 200ce, Head of a warrior (detail). 300ce, Bearded man. 400ce, Paracelsus. No. 1265, Archduke Ferdinand. No. 1266, Warrior with Two Pages.

## 1990, Dec. 24     Litho.     Perf. 14

| | | | | |
|---|---|---|---|---|
| 1257 | A232 | 20ce multicolored | .25 | .25 |
| 1258 | A232 | 50ce multicolored | .40 | .40 |
| 1259 | A232 | 60ce multicolored | .50 | .50 |
| 1260 | A232 | 80ce multicolored | .60 | .60 |
| 1261 | A232 | 100ce multicolored | .75 | .75 |
| 1262 | A232 | 200ce multicolored | 1.75 | 1.25 |
| 1263 | A232 | 300ce multicolored | 2.25 | 2.25 |
| 1264 | A232 | 400ce multicolored | 3.25 | 3.25 |
| | | Nos. 1257-1264 (8) | 9.75 | 9.25 |

### Souvenir Sheets

| | | | | |
|---|---|---|---|---|
| 1265 | A232 | 600ce multicolored | 4.75 | 4.75 |
| 1266 | A232 | 600ce multicolored | 4.75 | 4.75 |

Minerals — A233

20ce, Manganese ore. 60ce, Iron ore. 80ce, Bauxite ore. 200ce, Gold ore. 350ce, Diamond. 600ce, Diamonds.

## 1991, May 2     Litho.     Perf. 14½x14

| | | | | |
|---|---|---|---|---|
| 1267 | A233 | 20ce multi | .55 | .55 |
| 1268 | A233 | 60ce multi | .70 | .70 |
| 1269 | A233 | 80ce multi | 1.25 | 1.25 |
| 1270 | A233 | 200ce multi | 3.00 | 3.00 |
| 1271 | A233 | 350ce multi | 4.00 | 4.00 |
| | | Nos. 1267-1271 (5) | 9.50 | 9.50 |

### Souvenir Sheet

| | | | | |
|---|---|---|---|---|
| 1272 | A233 | 600ce multi | 9.00 | 9.00 |

Tribal Drums — A234

## 1991, May 9

| | | | | |
|---|---|---|---|---|
| 1273 | A234 | 20ce Damba | .45 | .25 |
| 1274 | A234 | 60ce Atumpan | .85 | .55 |
| 1275 | A234 | 80ce Kroboto | 1.10 | .70 |
| 1276 | A234 | 200ce Asafo | 1.60 | 1.60 |
| 1277 | A234 | 350ce Obonu | 2.50 | 2.50 |
| | | Nos. 1273-1277 (5) | 6.50 | 5.60 |

### Souvenir Sheet

| | | | | |
|---|---|---|---|---|
| 1278 | A234 | 600ce Single drum | 6.50 | 6.50 |

Flowers — A235

20ce, Amorphophallus dracontioides. 60ce, Anchomanes difformis. 80ce, Kaemferia nigerica. 200ce, Aframomum sceptrum. 350ce, Amorphophallus flavovirens. 600ce, White flowers.

## 1991, May 15

| | | | | |
|---|---|---|---|---|
| 1279 | A235 | 20ce | .75 | .35 |
| 1280 | A235 | 60ce multicolored | 1.10 | .55 |
| 1281 | A235 | 80ce multicolored | 1.40 | .70 |
| 1282 | A235 | 200ce multicolored | 2.25 | 2.25 |
| 1283 | A235 | 350ce multicolored | 2.50 | 2.50 |
| | | Nos. 1279-1283 (5) | 8.00 | 6.35 |

### Souvenir Sheet

| | | | | |
|---|---|---|---|---|
| 1284 | A235 | 600ce multicolored | 6.00 | 6.00 |

## 1991, May 17     Litho.     Perf. 14½x14

20ce, Urginea indica. 60ce, Hymenocallis littoralis. 80ce, Crinum jagus. 200ce, Dipcadi tacazzeanum. 350ce, Haemanthus rupestris. 600ce, Red flowers.

| | | | | |
|---|---|---|---|---|
| 1285 | A235 | 20ce multicolored | .55 | .35 |
| 1286 | A235 | 60ce multicolored | 1.00 | .55 |
| 1287 | A235 | 80ce multicolored | 1.40 | .80 |
| 1288 | A235 | 200ce multicolored | 1.75 | 1.75 |
| 1289 | A235 | 350ce multicolored | 2.25 | 2.25 |
| | | Nos. 1285-1289 (5) | 6.95 | 5.70 |

### Souvenir Sheet

| | | | | |
|---|---|---|---|---|
| 1290 | A235 | 600ce multicolored | 6.00 | 6.00 |

A236

Designs: 20ce, Satellite transmissions, airplane. 60ce, Scientific research, honey bee. 80ce, Literacy instruction. 200ce, Agricultural development. 350ce, Industry.

## 1991, June 21     Litho.     Perf. 13½x14

| | | | | |
|---|---|---|---|---|
| 1291 | A236 | 20ce multicolored | .25 | .25 |
| 1292 | A236 | 60ce multicolored | .80 | .59 |
| 1293 | A236 | 80ce multicolored | .85 | .70 |
| 1294 | A236 | 200ce multicolored | 1.40 | 1.40 |
| 1295 | A236 | 350ce multicolored | 2.25 | 2.25 |
| | | Nos. 1291-1295 (5) | 5.55 | 5.15 |

UN Development Program, 40th anniv.

Lord Robert Baden-Powell (1857-1941), Founder of Boy Scouts — A237

Designs: 20ce, Sketch by Baden-Powell used in first scouting handbook, vert. 50ce, Portrait, vert. 80ce, Scout handbook illustration by Norman Rockwell. 100ce, Native runner, Cape of Good Hope #178. 200ce, Scouts aiding victims after V-1 attack, London, 1944. 500ce, Scout praying, vert. 600ce, Emblem, Cape of Good Hope No. 178 used. No. 1304, Cover with Cape of Good Hope No. 178 from Mafeking, 1900. No. 1305, Campsites, 17th World Scout Jamboree, Korea, 1991.

## 1991, July 16     Litho.     Perf. 14

| | | | | |
|---|---|---|---|---|
| 1296 | A237 | 20ce buff & black | .60 | .25 |
| 1297 | A237 | 50ce multicolored | .75 | .40 |
| 1298 | A237 | 60ce multicolored | .75 | .50 |
| 1299 | A237 | 80ce black & buff | 1.25 | .65 |
| 1300 | A237 | 100ce multicolored | 1.50 | 1.00 |
| 1301 | A237 | 200ce multicolored | 1.90 | 1.90 |
| 1302 | A237 | 500ce multicolored | 4.00 | 4.00 |
| 1303 | A237 | 600ce multicolored | 4.50 | 4.50 |
| | | Nos. 1296-1303 (8) | 15.25 | 13.20 |

### Souvenir Sheets

| | | | | |
|---|---|---|---|---|
| 1304 | A237 | 800ce multicolored | 4.75 | 4.75 |
| 1305 | A237 | 800ce multicolored | 4.75 | 4.75 |

For overprints see Nos. 1567-1572.

Chorkor Smoker — A238

Designs: 20ce, Placing fish on racks. 60ce, Preparing smokers. 80ce, Preparing fish. 200ce, Preparing racks for smoker. 350ce, Placing racks in smoker.

## 1991, July 22     Litho.     Perf. 14x14½

| | | | | |
|---|---|---|---|---|
| 1306 | A238 | 20ce multicolored | .40 | .25 |
| 1307 | A238 | 60ce multicolored | .70 | .45 |
| 1308 | A238 | 80ce multicolored | .80 | .65 |

| | | | | |
|---|---|---|---|---|
| 1309 | A238 | 200ce multicolored | 1.75 | 1.75 |
| 1310 | A238 | 350ce multicolored | 2.25 | 2.25 |
| | | Nos. 1306-1310 (5) | 5.90 | 5.35 |

### Nos. 958-964 Overprinted "90th Birthday / 4th August 1990" and Surcharged

### Perf. 14, 12½x12 (#1312-1313, 1315)

## 1991, July 22

| | | | | |
|---|---|---|---|---|
| 1311 | A184 | 20ce on 5ce #958 | .50 | .50 |
| 1312 | A184 | 20ce on 8ce #959 | .50 | .50 |
| 1313 | A184 | 40ce on 20ce #961 | .80 | .80 |
| 1314 | A184 | 60ce on 12ce #960 | 1.50 | 1.50 |
| 1315 | A184 | 80ce on 70ce #962 | 1.75 | 1.75 |
| 1316 | A184 | 150ce on 100ce #963 | 3.50 | 3.50 |
| | | Nos. 1311-1316 (6) | 8.55 | 8.55 |

### Souvenir Sheet

| | | | | |
|---|---|---|---|---|
| 1317 | A184 | 200ce on 110ce #964 | 5.00 | 5.00 |

Nos. 1312-1313, 1315 issued in sheets of 5 + label. Overprint is vertical on stamp in No. 1317, horizontal on sheet margin.
The status of this issue is uncertain.

Fish — A239

20ce, Cephalopholis taeniops. 50ce, Synodontis sorex. 80ce, Balistes forcipatus. 100ce, Petrocephalus bane. 200ce, Syngnathus rastellatus. 300ce, Gymnarchus niloticus. 400ce, Hemichromis bimaculatus. 500ce, Sphyrna zygaena.
No. 1326, Bagrus bayad. No. 1327, Dactylopterus orientalis.

## 1991, July 29     Litho.     Perf. 14

| | | | | |
|---|---|---|---|---|
| 1318 | A239 | 20ce multicolored | .25 | .25 |
| 1319 | A239 | 50ce multicolored | .35 | .35 |
| 1320 | A239 | 80ce multicolored | .35 | .35 |
| 1321 | A239 | 100ce multicolored | .45 | .45 |
| 1322 | A239 | 200ce multicolored | .85 | .85 |
| 1323 | A239 | 300ce multicolored | 2.25 | 2.25 |
| 1324 | A239 | 400ce multicolored | 3.00 | 3.00 |
| 1325 | A239 | 500ce multicolored | 2.50 | 2.50 |
| | | Nos. 1318-1325 (8) | 10.00 | 10.00 |

### Souvenir Sheets

| | | | | |
|---|---|---|---|---|
| 1326 | A239 | 800ce multicolored | 5.25 | 5.25 |
| 1327 | A239 | 800ce multicolored | 3.75 | 3.75 |

While Nos. 1320-1322, 1325, 1327 have the same issue date as Nos. 1318-1319, 1323-1324, 1326, the value of Nos. 1320-1322, 1325, 1327 was lower when they were released.
For overprints see Nos. 1573-1578.

Paintings by Vincent Van Gogh — A240

Designs: 20ce, Reaper with Sickle. 50ce, The Thresher. 60ce, The Sheaf Binder. 80ce, The Sheep Shearers. 100ce, Peasant Woman Cutting Straw. 200ce, The Sower. 500ce, The Plow and the Harrow, horiz. 600ce, The Woodcutter. No. 1336, Evening: The Watch. No. 1337, Evening: The End of the Day.

### Perf. 13x13½, 13½x13

## 1991, Aug. 12        Litho.

| | | | | |
|---|---|---|---|---|
| 1328 | A240 | 20ce multicolored | .25 | .25 |
| 1329 | A240 | 50ce multicolored | .40 | .40 |
| 1330 | A240 | 60ce multicolored | .50 | .50 |
| 1331 | A240 | 80ce multicolored | .65 | .65 |
| 1332 | A240 | 100ce multicolored | .80 | .80 |
| 1333 | A240 | 200ce multicolored | 1.60 | 1.60 |
| 1334 | A240 | 500ce multicolored | 3.25 | 3.25 |
| 1335 | A240 | 600ce multicolored | 4.00 | 4.00 |
| | | Nos. 1328-1335 (8) | 11.45 | 11.45 |

### Size: 106x80mm
### Imperf

| | | | | |
|---|---|---|---|---|
| 1336 | A240 | 800ce multicolored | 5.75 | 5.75 |
| 1337 | A240 | 800ce multicolored | 5.75 | 5.75 |

10th Non-aligned Ministers Conference, Accra — A241

Natl. Leaders: 20ce, Nasser, Egypt (1952-1970). 60ce, Tito, Yugoslavia (1945-1980). 80ce, Nehru, India (1947-1964). 200ce, Nkrumah, Ghana (1957-1966). 350ce, Sukarno, Indonesia (1945-1967).

## 1991, Sept. 2     Perf. 13½x14

| | | | | |
|---|---|---|---|---|
| 1338 | A241 | 20ce multicolored | .45 | .35 |
| 1339 | A241 | 60ce multicolored | .55 | .50 |
| 1340 | A241 | 80ce multicolored | 3.50 | 1.50 |
| 1341 | A241 | 200ce multicolored | 2.00 | 2.00 |
| 1342 | A241 | 350ce multicolored | 2.50 | 2.50 |
| | | Nos. 1338-1342 (5) | 9.00 | 6.85 |

Birds of Ghana — A242

Designs: No. 1343a, Melba finch. b, Orange-cheeked waxbill. c, Paradise flycatcher. d, Blue plantain-eater, e, Red bishop. f, Splendid glossy starling. g, Red-headed lovebird. h, Palm swift. i, Narina trogon. j, Tawny eagle. k, Bateleur eagle. l, Hoopoe. m, Secretary bird. n, White-backed vulture. o, Bare-headed rockfowl. p, Ground hornbill.
No. 1344a, Openbilled stork. b, African spoonbill. c, Pink-backed pelican. d, Little bittern. e, King reed-hen. f, Saddlebill stork. g, Glossy ibis. h, White-faced tree duck. i, Black-headed heron. j, Hammerkop. k, African darter. l, Woolly-necked stork. m, Yellow-billed stork. n, Black-winged stilt. o, Goliath heron. p, Lily trotter.
No. 1345a, Shikra. b, Abyssinian roller (c, g). c, Carmine bee-eater (g). d, Pintailed whydah (h). e, Purple glossy starling. f, Yellow-backed whydah (j). g, Pel's fishing owl. h, Verreaux's touraco (l). i, Red-cheeked cordon-bleu. j, Olive-bellied sunbird. k, Red-billed hornbill. l, Red-billed quelea. m, Crowned crane (i). n, Blue quail. o, Egyptian vulture (p). p, Helmeted guineafowl.
No. 1346, Marabou stork. No. 1347, Saddlebill stork, diff. No. 1348, African river eagle.

## 1991, Oct. 14     Litho.     Perf. 14½x14
### Sheets of 16

| | | | | |
|---|---|---|---|---|
| 1343 | A242 | 80ce #a.-p. | 7.50 | 7.50 |
| 1344 | A242 | 100ce #a.-p. | 11.50 | 11.50 |
| 1345 | A242 | 100ce #a.-p. | 13.50 | 13.50 |
| | | Nos. 1343-1345 (3) | 32.50 | 32.50 |

### Souvenir Sheets

| | | | | |
|---|---|---|---|---|
| 1346 | A242 | 800ce multicolored | 5.25 | 5.25 |
| 1347 | A242 | 800ce multicolored | 5.25 | 5.25 |
| 1348 | A242 | 800ce multicolored | 5.25 | 5.25 |

While No. 1344 has the same issue date as No. 1345, the value of No. 1344 was lower when it was released.

Insects — A243

20ce, Nularda. 50ce, Zonocrus. 60ce, Gryllotalpa africana. 80ce, Weevil. 100ce, Coenagrion. 150ce, Sahlbergella. 200ce, Anthia. 350ce, Megacephala. 600ce, Lacetus.

## 1991, Oct. 25     Perf. 14x13½

| | | | | |
|---|---|---|---|---|
| 1349 | A243 | 20ce multi | .75 | .25 |
| 1350 | A243 | 50ce multi | .90 | .40 |
| 1351 | A243 | 60ce multi | 1.25 | .50 |
| 1352 | A243 | 80ce multi | 1.75 | 1.25 |
| 1353 | A243 | 100ce multi | 2.25 | 2.00 |
| 1354 | A243 | 150ce multi | 2.50 | 2.25 |
| 1355 | A243 | 200ce multi | 3.00 | 3.00 |
| 1356 | A243 | 350ce multi | 4.00 | 3.00 |
| | | Nos. 1349-1356 (8) | 16.40 | 12.65 |

### Souvenir Sheet
### Perf. 13x12

| | | | | |
|---|---|---|---|---|
| 1357 | A243 | 600ce multi | 13.50 | 13.50 |

Landmarks — A243a

Leucodon Cowrie — A243b

Achatina Achatina — A243c

Designs: 50ce, Boti Falls, vert. 60ce, Larabanga Mosque. 80ce, Fort Sebastian, Shama. 100ce, Cape Coast Castle.

100ce exists in four types:
Type I, "G" has angled curve, bars in "A"s slope down to left, "c" has straight line, bottom inscription 10mm.
Type II, "G" is rounded, bars in "A"s slope down to right, "c" has slanted line, bottom inscription 13mm.
Type III, "G" is rounded, bars in "A"s slope down to right, "c" has straight line, bottom inscription 10mm.
Type IV, "G" rounded, but cut off at top, bars in "A"s slope to right, "c" with slanted line, bottom inscription 10mm.

200ce, 400ce
Nos. 1357E, 1357Ej, 1357F, Type I: "G" has angled curve, bar in "A"s slope down to left.
Nos. 1357Ek, 1357Fl, Type II: "G" is rounded, bars in "A"s slope down to right.

**Perf. 13¾x13½, 13½x13¾**

| | | | 1991 | | | Litho. |
|---|---|---|---|---|---|---|
| 1357A | A243a | 50ce multi | | — | — |
| | o. | Perf. 13¾x14¼ | | — | — |
| 1357B | A243a | 60ce multi | | — | — |
| | p. | Perf. 14¼x13¾ | | — | — |
| 1357C | A243a | 80ce multi | | — | — |
| 1357D | A243a | 100ce multi (I) | | — | — |
| | g. | Type II | | — | — |
| | h. | Type I, perf 14¼x13¾ | | — | — |
| | i. | Type III, perf 14¼x13¾ | | — | — |
| | m. | Type IV | | — | — |
| 1357E | A243b | 200ce multi (I) | | — | — |
| | j. | Type I, perf. 14¼x13¾ | | — | — |
| | k. | Type II, perf. 14¼x13¾ | | — | — |
| 1357F | A243c | 400ce multi (I) | | — | — |
| | l. | Type II, perf. 14¼x13¾ | | — | — |
| | n. | Type I, perf. 11½ | | — | — |

This set was printed locally. Shades exist.
Issue dates: 50ce, Nov. 21; others, Dec. 12. No. 1357Dm, 2004(?).
For surcharge, see No. 2687.

Adoration of the Magi by Hieronymus Bosch — A244

Details or entire paintings: 50ce, The Annunciation by Robert Campin. 60ce, Virgin and Child by Dirk Bouts. 80ce, Presentation in the Temple by Hans Memling. 100ce, The Virgin and Child Enthroned with an Angel and a Donor by Memling. 200ce, The Virgin and Child with Saints and a Donor by Jan van Eyck. 400ce, St. Luke Painting the Virgin by Rogier van der Weyden. 700ce, Virgin and Child by Bouts, diff. No. 1366, The Annunciation by Memling. No. 1367, The Virgin and Child Standing in a Niche by van der Weyden.

| | | | 1991, Dec. 23 | | Perf. 12 |
|---|---|---|---|---|---|
| 1358 | A244 | 20ce multicolored | .25 | .25 |
| 1359 | A244 | 50ce multicolored | .40 | .40 |
| 1360 | A244 | 60ce multicolored | .50 | .50 |
| 1361 | A244 | 80ce multicolored | .60 | .60 |
| 1362 | A244 | 100ce multicolored | .80 | .80 |
| 1363 | A244 | 200ce multicolored | 1.50 | 1.50 |
| 1364 | A244 | 400ce multicolored | 3.00 | 3.00 |
| 1365 | A244 | 700ce multicolored | 5.25 | 5.25 |
| | | Nos. 1358-1365 (8) | 12.30 | 12.30 |

**Souvenir Sheets**

**Perf. 14½**

| | | | | | |
|---|---|---|---|---|---|
| 1366 | A244 | 800ce multicolored | 5.50 | 5.50 |
| 1367 | A244 | 800ce multicolored | 5.50 | 5.50 |

Christmas.

Reunification of Germany A245

Designs: 20ce, Opening of German border, Nov. 9, 1989. 60ce, Signing of Two Plus Four Treaty, Sept. 12, 1990. 80ce, Opening of Brandenburg Gate, Dec. 22, 1989. 800ce, German leaders, Unity Day, Oct. 3, 1990. 1000ce, Currency union, July 1, 1990.
No. 1371Ab, USSR Pres. Mikhail Gorbachev, vert. c, Chancellor Helmut Kohl, vert. d, Map of West Germany, vert. e, Map of East Germany, vert.
No. 1371g, Doves. h, German Chancellor Helmut Kohl, Foreign Minister Hans-Dietrich Genscher.

| | | | 1992, Feb. 17 | | Litho. | Perf. 14 |
|---|---|---|---|---|---|---|
| 1368 | A245 | 20ce multi | | .30 | .25 |
| 1369 | A245 | 60ce multi | | .50 | .50 |
| 1370 | A245 | 80ce multi | | .70 | .70 |
| 1371 | A245 | 1000ce multi | | 8.00 | 8.00 |
| | | Nos. 1368-1371 (4) | | 9.50 | 9.45 |

**Souvenir Sheets**

| | | | | | |
|---|---|---|---|---|---|
| 1371A | A245 | 300ce Sheet of 4, #b.-e. | | 6.75 | 6.75 |
| 1371F | A245 | 400ce Sheet of 2, #g.-h. | | 2.00 | 2.00 |
| 1372 | A245 | 800ce multicolored | | 4.75 | 4.75 |

While No. 1371F has the same issue date as No. 1371A, the dollar value of No. 1371F was lower when it was released.

1992 Summer Olympics, Barcelona A246

Map and: 20ce, Eddie Blay, boxing, Ghana, 1964. 60ce, Mike Ahey, track, Ghana, 1964-1972. 80ce, T. Wilson, ski jumping, US, 1988. 100ce, East German 4-Man bobsled, 1988. 200ce, Greg Louganis, diving, US, 1984. 300ce, L. Visser, speed skating, Netherlands, 1988. 350ce, J. Passler, biathlon, Italy, 1988. 400ce, Mary Lou Retton, gymnastics, US, 1984. 500ce, Jurgen Hingsen, decathlon, Germany, 1984. 600ce, R. Neubert, heptathlon, West Germany, 1984. No. 1380, Jai alai player, vert. No. 1381, Windmill.

| | | | 1992, Mar. 3 | | Litho. | Perf. 14 |
|---|---|---|---|---|---|---|
| 1373 | A246 | 20ce multi | | .40 | .25 |
| 1373A | A246 | 60ce multi | | .50 | .45 |
| 1374 | A246 | 80ce multi | | .70 | .55 |
| 1375 | A246 | 100ce multi | | 1.00 | .90 |
| 1376 | A246 | 200ce multi | | 1.75 | 1.60 |
| 1377 | A246 | 300ce multi | | 1.75 | 2.10 |
| 1378 | A246 | 350ce multi | | 1.75 | 2.10 |
| 1378A | A246 | 400ce multi | | 2.40 | 2.75 |
| 1378B | A246 | 500ce multi | | 2.40 | 2.75 |
| 1379 | A246 | 600ce multi | | 2.40 | 2.75 |
| | | Nos. 1373-1379 (10) | | 15.05 | 16.20 |

**Souvenir Sheets**

| | | | | | |
|---|---|---|---|---|---|
| 1380 | A246 | 800ce multi | | 6.00 | 6.00 |
| 1381 | A246 | 800ce multi | | 6.00 | 6.00 |

While Nos. 1373A, 1378A-1378B have the same issue date as rest of the set the dollar value of Nos. 1373A, 1378A-1378B were lower when they were released.

Phila Nippon '91 — A247

60ce, Torii of Itsukushima Jingu shrine. 80ce, Geisha. 100ce, Samurai residence. 200ce, Bonsai tree. 400ce, Olympic sports hall. 500ce, Great Buddha. 600ce, Nagoya castle.
No. 1390, Takamatsu castle. No. 1391, Heian shrine.

| | | | 1992, Feb. 16 | | Litho. | Perf. 14 |
|---|---|---|---|---|---|---|
| 1382 | A247 | 20ce shown | | .25 | .25 |
| 1383 | A247 | 60ce multicolored | | .35 | .35 |
| 1384 | A247 | 80ce multicolored | | .45 | .45 |
| 1385 | A247 | 100ce multicolored | | .60 | .60 |
| 1386 | A247 | 200ce multicolored | | 1.40 | 1.40 |
| 1387 | A247 | 400ce multicolored | | 2.75 | 2.75 |
| 1388 | A247 | 500ce multicolored | | 3.25 | 3.25 |
| 1389 | A247 | 600ce multicolored | | 4.25 | 4.25 |
| | | Nos. 1382-1389 (8) | | 13.30 | 13.30 |

**Souvenir Sheets**

| | | | | | |
|---|---|---|---|---|---|
| 1390 | A247 | 800ce multicolored | | 6.00 | 6.00 |
| 1391 | A247 | 800ce multicolored | | 6.00 | 6.00 |

Ghana Natl. Railways — A248

Designs: 20c, Engine, 1903, Gold Coast Railway. 50c, Diesel passenger locomotive, Ghana Railways Corp. 60ce, First class coach, 1931 Gold Coast Railway. 80ce, Official inspection coach, Gold Coast Railway. 100ce, Engine No. 401 on turntable. 200c, Twin-bogie cocoa wagon, 1921, Gold Coast Railway. 500ce, Engine No. 223, "Prince of Wales." 600c, Twin-bogie cattle wagon, Gold Coast Railway. No. 1400, German-made locomotive, Gold Coast Railway. No. 1401, Beyer-Garratt #301, 1943, Gold Coast Railway.

| | | | 1992, Mar. 2 | | |
|---|---|---|---|---|---|
| 1392 | A248 | 20ce multicolored | .25 | .25 |
| 1393 | A248 | 50ce multicolored | .25 | .25 |
| 1394 | A248 | 60ce multicolored | .35 | .35 |
| 1395 | A248 | 80ce multicolored | .45 | .45 |
| 1396 | A248 | 100ce multicolored | .55 | .55 |
| 1397 | A248 | 200ce multicolored | 1.20 | 1.20 |
| 1398 | A248 | 500ce multicolored | 3.00 | 3.00 |
| 1399 | A248 | 600ce multicolored | 4.00 | 4.00 |
| | | Nos. 1392-1399 (8) | 10.05 | 10.05 |

**Souvenir Sheets**

| | | | | |
|---|---|---|---|---|
| 1400 | A248 | 800ce multicolored | 5.00 | 5.00 |
| 1401 | A248 | 800ce multicolored | 5.00 | 5.00 |

Decade of Revolutionary Progress — A249

20ce, Bore hole water. 50ce, Mining industry. 60ce, Small scale industry. 80ce, Timber industry. 200ce, Cocoa rehabilitation. 350ce, Rural electrification.

| | | | 1992, Feb. 2 | | Litho. | Perf. 14x13½ |
|---|---|---|---|---|---|---|
| 1402 | A249 | 20ce multicolored | | .25 | .25 |
| 1403 | A249 | 50ce multicolored | | .30 | .30 |
| 1404 | A249 | 60ce multicolored | | .40 | .40 |
| 1405 | A249 | 80ce multicolored | | .45 | .45 |
| 1406 | A249 | 200ce multicolored | | .80 | .80 |
| 1407 | A249 | 350ce multicolored | | 1.00 | 1.00 |
| | | Nos. 1402-1407 (6) | | 3.20 | 3.20 |

Reptiles — A251

20ce, Angides lugubris. 50ce, Kinixys erosa. 60ce, Agama agama. 80ce, Chameleo gracilis. 100ce, Naja melanleuca. 200ce, Crocodylus niloticus. 400ce, Chelonia mydas. 500ce, Varanus exanthematicus. 600ce, Snake & tortoise.

| | | | 1992, Mar. 30 | | Litho. | Perf. 14 |
|---|---|---|---|---|---|---|
| 1414 | A251 | 20ce multicolored | | .25 | .25 |
| 1415 | A251 | 50ce multicolored | | .35 | .35 |
| 1416 | A251 | 60ce multicolored | | .35 | .35 |
| 1417 | A251 | 80ce multicolored | | .45 | .45 |
| 1418 | A251 | 100ce multicolored | | .60 | .60 |
| 1419 | A251 | 200ce multicolored | | 1.00 | 1.00 |
| 1420 | A251 | 400ce multicolored | | 2.00 | 2.00 |
| 1421 | A251 | 500ce multicolored | | 2.50 | 2.50 |
| | | Nos. 1414-1421 (8) | | 7.50 | 7.50 |

**Souvenir Sheet**

| | | | | |
|---|---|---|---|---|
| 1422 | A251 | 600ce multicolored | 5.50 | 5.50 |

Numbers have been reserved for additional values in this set.

Easter — A252

Details from paintings: 20ce, The Four Apostles: Sts. John, Peter, Paul & Mark, by Durer. 50ce, The Last Judgment, by Rubens. 60ce, The Four Apostles: Sts. John, Peter, Paul and Mark, diff. by Durer. 80ce, The Last Judgment, diff. by Rubens. 100ce, Crucifixion, by Rubens. 200ce, The Last Judgment, diff. by Rubens. 600ce, The Last Judgment, diff. by Rubens. No. 1432, Last Communion of St. Francis of Assisi, by Rubens. No. 1432A, Scourging the Money Changers from the Temple, by El Greco, horiz.

| | | | 1992, Mar. 13 | | Perf. 13½x14 |
|---|---|---|---|---|---|
| 1424 | A252 | 20ce multi | | .25 | .25 |
| 1425 | A252 | 50ce multi | | .35 | .35 |
| 1426 | A252 | 60ce multi | | .45 | .45 |
| 1427 | A252 | 80ce multi | | .55 | .55 |

| | | | | | |
|---|---|---|---|---|---|
| 1428 | A252 | 100ce multi | | .65 | .65 |
| 1429 | A252 | 200ce multi | | 1.00 | 1.00 |
| 1430 | A252 | 500ce multi | | 2.50 | 2.50 |
| 1431 | A252 | 600ce multi | | 2.75 | 2.75 |
| | | Nos. 1424-1431 (8) | | 8.50 | 8.50 |

**Souvenir Sheets**

| | | | | |
|---|---|---|---|---|
| 1432 | A252 | 800ce multi | 5.25 | 5.25 |

**Perf. 14x13½**

| | | | | |
|---|---|---|---|---|
| 1432A | A252 | 800ce multi | 5.25 | 5.25 |

Spanish Art — A253

Paintings by Velazquez: 20ce, Two Men at Table. 60ce, Christ in the House of Mary and Martha (detail). 80ce, The Supper at Emmaus. 100ce, Three Muscians. 200ce, Old Woman Cooking Eggs, vert. 400ce, Old Woman Cooking Eggs (detail), vert. 500ce, The Surrender of Breda (detail) diff., vert. 600ce, The Surrender of Breda (detail), vert.
No. 1441, They Still Say that Fish is Expensive, by Joaquin Sorolla y Bastida. No. 1442, The Waterseller of Seville.

| | | | 1992, May 4 | | Perf. 13½ |
|---|---|---|---|---|---|
| 1433 | A253 | 20ce multicolored | | .25 | .25 |
| 1434 | A253 | 60ce multicolored | | .30 | .30 |
| 1435 | A253 | 80ce multicolored | | .35 | .35 |
| 1436 | A253 | 100ce multicolored | | .50 | .50 |
| 1437 | A253 | 200ce multicolored | | 1.10 | 1.10 |
| 1438 | A253 | 400ce multicolored | | 1.75 | 1.75 |
| 1439 | A253 | 500ce multicolored | | 2.25 | 2.25 |
| 1440 | A253 | 500ce multicolored | | 3.50 | 3.50 |

**Size: 120x95mm**

**Imperf**

| | | | | |
|---|---|---|---|---|
| 1441 | A253 | 900ce multicolored | 5.00 | 5.00 |
| 1442 | A253 | 900ce multicolored | 4.50 | 4.50 |
| | | Nos. 1433-1442 (10) | 19.50 | 19.50 |

Granada '92. While Nos. 1434-1435, 1438-1439, 1442 have the same issue date as Nos. 1433, 1436-1437, 1440-1441, the value in relation to the dollar of Nos. 1434-1435, 1438-1439, 1442 was lower when they were released.

Butterflies — A254

20ce, African monarch. 60ce, Mocker swallowtail. 80ce, Painted lady. 100ce, Mountain beauty. 200ce, Blue temora. 400ce, Foxy charaxes. 500ce, Blue pansy. 700ce, Golden pansy.
No. 1451, Gaudy commodore. No. 1452, Christmas butterfly.

| | | | 1992, May 25 | | Litho. | Perf. 14 |
|---|---|---|---|---|---|---|
| 1443 | A254 | 20ce multicolored | | .25 | .25 |
| 1444 | A254 | 60ce multicolored | | .40 | .40 |
| 1445 | A254 | 80ce multicolored | | .55 | .55 |
| 1446 | A254 | 100ce multicolored | | .65 | .65 |
| 1447 | A254 | 200ce multicolored | | 1.50 | 1.50 |
| 1448 | A254 | 400ce multicolored | | 3.00 | 3.00 |
| 1449 | A254 | 500ce multicolored | | 3.50 | 3.50 |
| 1450 | A254 | 700ce multicolored | | 4.75 | 4.75 |
| | | Nos. 1443-1450 (8) | | 14.60 | 14.60 |

**Souvenir Sheets**

| | | | | |
|---|---|---|---|---|
| 1451 | A254 | 900ce multicolored | 5.50 | 5.50 |
| 1452 | A254 | 900ce multicolored | 5.50 | 5.50 |

Genoa '92. For overprints see Nos. 1471-1480.

Dinosaurs — A255

20ce, Iguanodon. 50ce, Anchisaurus. 60ce, Heterodontosaurus. 80ce, Ouranosaurus. 100ce, Anatosaurus. 200ce, Elaphrosaurus. 500ce, Coelophysis. 600ce, Rhamphorynchus.

| | | | | |
|---|---|---|---|---|
| **1992, June 1** | | **Litho.** | *Perf. 14* | |
| 1453 | A255 | 20ce multi | .45 | .35 |
| 1454 | A255 | 50ce multi | .65 | .45 |
| 1455 | A255 | 60ce multi | .70 | .45 |
| 1456 | A255 | 80ce multi | .75 | .55 |
| 1457 | A255 | 100ce multi | 1.00 | .65 |
| 1458 | A255 | 200ce multi | 1.60 | 1.60 |
| 1459 | A255 | 500ce multi | 2.75 | 2.75 |
| 1460 | A255 | 600ce multi | 3.25 | 3.25 |
| | *Nos. 1453-1460 (8)* | | 11.15 | 10.05 |

**Souvenir Sheets**

| | | | | |
|---|---|---|---|---|
| 1461 | A255 | 1500ce like #1459 | 6.75 | 6.75 |
| 1462 | A255 | 1500ce like #1458 | 6.75 | 6.75 |

While Nos. 1453, 1456, 1458-1459 and 1462 have the same issue date as Nos. 1454-1455, 1457, 1460-1461, their value in relation to the dollar was lower when they were released.

Discovery of America, 500th Anniv. — A256

No. 1463: a, Capt. Martin Alonzo Pinzon, Pinta. b, Capt. Vicente Yanez Pinzon, Nina. c, Columbus, Fr. Marchena in La Rabida, 1485. d, Columbus in cabin. e, Land sighted, Oct. 12, 1492. f, Columbus lands on Samana Cay. g, Shipwreck of Santa Maria. h, Columbus returns to Spanish Court, 1493.
No. 1464, Columbus, ship.

| **1992, July** | | **Litho.** | *Perf. 14* | |
|---|---|---|---|---|
| 1463 | A256 | 200ce Sheet of 8, #a.-h. | 9.50 | 9.50 |

**Souvenir Sheet**

| 1464 | A256 | 500ce multicolored | 3.75 | 3.75 |
|---|---|---|---|---|

World Columbian Stamp Expo '92, Chicago.

Shells — A257

No. 1465, Olivancillaria hiatula. No. 1465A, Tympanotonus fuscatus. No. 1466, Donax rugosus. No. 1466A, Murex cornutus. No. 1467, Sigaretus concavus. No. 1467A, Tivela tripla. No. 1468, Pila africana. No. 1468A, Cypraea stercoraria. No. 1469, Thais hiatula. No. 1469A, Cassis tesselata.
No. 1470, Natica favel. No. 1470A, Semifusos morio.

| **1992, Oct. 5** | | **Litho.** | *Perf. 14* | |
|---|---|---|---|---|
| 1465 | A257 | 20ce multicolored | .25 | .25 |
| 1465A | A257 | 20ce multicolored | .25 | .25 |
| 1466 | A257 | 60ce multicolored | .35 | .35 |
| 1466A | A257 | 60ce multicolored | .35 | .35 |
| 1467 | A257 | 80ce multicolored | .45 | .45 |
| 1467A | A257 | 80ce multicolored | .45 | .45 |
| 1468 | A257 | 200ce multicolored | 1.10 | 1.10 |
| 1468A | A257 | 200ce multicolored | 1.10 | 1.10 |
| 1469 | A257 | 350ce multicolored | 1.75 | 1.75 |
| 1469A | A257 | 350ce multicolored | 1.75 | 1.75 |
| | *Nos. 1465-1469A (10)* | | 7.80 | 7.80 |

**Souvenir Sheet**

| 1470 | A257 | 600ce multicolored | 4.50 | 4.50 |
|---|---|---|---|---|
| 1470A | A257 | 600ce multicolored | 4.50 | 4.50 |

**Nos. 1443-1452 Ovptd. "40th / Anniversary / of the / Accession / of / HM Queen / Elizabeth II / 1952-1992" in Silver**

| **1992, Aug. 10** | | **Litho.** | *Perf. 14* | |
|---|---|---|---|---|
| 1471 | A254 | 20ce on #1443 | .25 | .25 |
| 1472 | A254 | 60ce on #1444 | .30 | .30 |
| 1473 | A254 | 80ce on #1445 | .40 | .40 |
| 1474 | A254 | 100ce on #1446 | .50 | .50 |
| 1475 | A254 | 200ce on #1447 | 1.00 | 1.00 |
| 1476 | A254 | 400ce on #1448 | 1.75 | 1.75 |
| 1477 | A254 | 500ce on #1449 | 2.50 | 2.50 |
| 1478 | A254 | 700ce on #1450 | 3.25 | 3.25 |
| | *Nos. 1471-1478 (8)* | | 9.95 | 9.95 |

**Souvenir Sheets**

| 1479 | A254 | 900ce on #1451 | 5.00 | 5.00 |
|---|---|---|---|---|
| 1480 | A254 | 900ce on #1452 | 5.00 | 5.00 |

Christmas — A259

Details or entire paintings: 20ce, Presentation in the Temple, by Master of Brunswick. 50ce, Presentation in the Temple, by Master of St. Severin. 60ce, The Visitation, by Sebastiano del Piombo. 80ce, The Visitation, by Giotto. 100ce, The Circumcision, by Studio of Giovanni Bellini. 200ce, The Circumcision, by Workshop of Benvenuto Garofalo. 500ce, The Visitation, by Workshop of Rogier van der Weyden. 800ce, The Visitation, by Workshop of Rogier Van der Weyden. No. 1491, The Visitation, by Giotto. No. 1492, The Presentation in the Temple, by Bartolo di Fredi.

| **1992** | | **Litho.** | *Perf. 13½x14* | |
|---|---|---|---|---|
| 1483 | A259 | 20ce multicolored | .25 | .25 |
| 1484 | A259 | 50ce multicolored | .30 | .30 |
| 1485 | A259 | 60ce multicolored | .35 | .35 |
| 1486 | A259 | 80ce multicolored | .40 | .40 |
| 1487 | A259 | 100ce multicolored | .50 | .50 |
| 1488 | A259 | 200ce multicolored | 1.00 | 1.00 |
| 1489 | A259 | 500ce multicolored | 2.75 | 2.75 |
| 1490 | A259 | 800ce multicolored | 4.25 | 4.25 |
| | *Nos. 1483-1490 (8)* | | 9.80 | 9.80 |

**Souvenir Sheet**

| 1491 | A259 | 900ce multicolored | 4.50 | 4.50 |
|---|---|---|---|---|
| 1492 | A259 | 900ce multicolored | 4.50 | 4.50 |

No. 1492 exists imperf.

Anniversaries and Events
A260 A261

Designs: 20ce, LZ3, floating hangar at Lake Constance, horiz. 100ce, Lift-off of Ariane 4 rocket, horiz. 200ce, Leopard in tree, horiz. 300ce, Roman Colosseum, fruits and vegetables, horiz. 400ce, Wolfgang Amadeus Mozart. 600ce, Lift-off of H-1 rocket, Japan. 800ce, LZ10, Schwaben, horiz. No. 1501, Scene from "The Marriage of Figaro." No. 1502, Space shuttle, US. No. 1503, Count Ferdinand von Zeppelin. No. 1504, Bongo, horiz.

| **1992, Dec.** | | **Litho.** | *Perf. 14* | |
|---|---|---|---|---|
| 1493 | A260 | 20ce multicolored | .30 | .30 |
| 1494 | A260 | 100ce multicolored | .60 | .60 |
| 1495 | A260 | 200ce multicolored | 1.15 | 1.15 |
| 1496 | A260 | 300ce multicolored | 1.75 | 1.75 |
| 1497 | A261 | 400ce multicolored | 2.60 | 2.60 |
| 1498 | A260 | 600ce multicolored | 4.00 | 4.00 |
| 1500 | A260 | 800ce multicolored | 5.25 | 5.25 |
| | *Nos. 1493-1500 (7)* | | 15.65 | 15.65 |

**Souvenir Sheets**

| 1501 | A261 | 900ce multicolored | 5.00 | 5.00 |
|---|---|---|---|---|
| 1502 | A260 | 900ce multicolored | 5.00 | 5.00 |
| 1503 | A260 | 900ce multicolored | 5.00 | 5.00 |
| 1504 | A260 | 900ce multicolored | 5.00 | 5.00 |

Count Ferdinand von Zeppelin, 75th anniv. of death (Nos. 1493, 1500, 1503). Intl. Space Year (Nos. 1494, 1499, 1502). UN Earth Summit, Rio de Janeiro (Nos. 1495, 1504). WHO, Intl. Conference on Nutrition, Rome (No. 1496). Mozart, bicent. of death (in 1991) (Nos. 1497, 1501).

Flowers — A262

Designs: Nos. 1505, 1514d (100ce), Lagerstroemia flos-reginae. No. 1506, Clerodendrum thomsoniae. Nos. 1507, 1514c (50ce), Spathodea campanulata. No. 1508, Cassia fistula. Nos. 1509, 1514e (150ce), Mellitea ferrugenea. Nos. 1510, 1514j (300ce), Hildegardia barteri. Nos. 1511, 1514i (150ce), Ipomoea asarifolia. No. 1512, Petrea volubilis. Nos. 1513, 1514f (300ce), Ritchiea reflexa.

Nos. 1514, 1514h (100ce), Bryphyllum pinnatum.

| **1993, Mar. 1** | | **Litho.** | *Perf. 14* | |
|---|---|---|---|---|
| 1505 | A262 | 20ce multicolored | .25 | .25 |
| 1506 | A262 | 20ce multicolored | .25 | .25 |
| 1507 | A262 | 60ce multicolored | .30 | .30 |
| 1508 | A262 | 60ce multicolored | .30 | .30 |
| 1509 | A262 | 80ce multicolored | .40 | .40 |
| 1510 | A262 | 80ce multicolored | .40 | .40 |
| 1511 | A262 | 200ce multicolored | .90 | .90 |
| 1512 | A262 | 200ce multicolored | .90 | .90 |
| 1513 | A262 | 350ce multicolored | 1.40 | 1.40 |
| 1514 | A262 | 350ce multicolored | 1.40 | 1.40 |
| | *Nos. 1505-1514 (10)* | | 6.50 | 6.50 |

**Souvenir Sheets**

| 1514A | A262 | Sheet of 4, #c.-f. | 3.50 | 3.50 |
|---|---|---|---|---|
| 1514B | A262 | Sheet of 4, #g.-j. | 3.50 | 3.50 |

Intl. Conference on Nutrition, Rome — A263

20ce, Energy foods. 60ce, Body-building foods. 80ce, Protective foods. 200ce, Disease prevention. 400ce, Food quality control, preservation.

| **1993, Jan.** | | **Litho.** | *Perf. 14* | |
|---|---|---|---|---|
| 1515 | A263 | 20ce multicolored | .25 | .25 |
| 1516 | A263 | 60ce multicolored | .30 | .30 |
| 1517 | A263 | 80ce multicolored | .40 | .40 |
| 1518 | A263 | 200ce multicolored | 1.00 | 1.00 |
| 1519 | A263 | 400ce multicolored | 1.75 | 1.75 |
| | *Nos. 1515-1519 (5)* | | 3.70 | 3.70 |

Crabs — A264

Designs: 20ce, Clappa rubroguttata. 60ce, Cardisoma amatum. 80ce, Maia squinado. 400ce, Ocypoda cursor. 800ce, Grapus grapus.

| **1993, Feb.** | | | *Perf. 14x13½* | |
|---|---|---|---|---|
| 1520 | A264 | 20ce multicolored | .25 | .25 |
| 1521 | A264 | 60ce multicolored | .35 | .35 |
| 1522 | A264 | 80ce multicolored | .45 | .45 |
| 1523 | A264 | 400ce multicolored | 2.10 | 2.10 |
| a. | | Souv. sheet of 4, #1520-1523 | 7.50 | 7.50 |
| 1524 | A264 | 800ce multicolored | 4.25 | 4.25 |
| | *Nos. 1520-1524 (5)* | | 7.40 | 7.40 |

Miniature Sheet of 8

Louvre Museum, Bicent. — A265

No. 1525 — Details or entire paintings, by Giovanni Domenico Tiepolo (1727-1804) (a-e) and Giovanni Battista Tiepolo (1696-1770) (f-h): a-c, Carnival Scene, (left, center, right). d-e, Tooth Puller, (left, right). f, Rebecca at the Well. g-h, Presenting Christ to the People, (left, right).
700ce, Chancellor Seguier, by Le Brun, horiz.

| **1993, Mar. 1** | | **Litho.** | *Perf. 12* | |
|---|---|---|---|---|
| 1525 | A265 | 200ce Sheet of 8, #a.-h. + label | 9.00 | 9.00 |

**Souvenir Sheet**
*Perf. 14½*

| 1526 | A265 | 700ce multicolored | 4.00 | 4.00 |
|---|---|---|---|---|

No. 1526 contains one 55x88mm stamp.

Oil Palm Fruit — A265a

| **1993, Apr.** | | **Litho.** | *Perf. 13½* | |
|---|---|---|---|---|
| 1526A | A265a | 20ce multi | | |

Faberge Eggs — A266

Easter: 50ce, Resurrection Egg. 80ce, Imperial Red Cross Egg with Resurrection Triptych. 100ce, Imperial Uspensky Cathedral Egg. 150ce, Imperial Red Cross Egg with portraits. 200ce, Orange Tree Egg. 250ce, Rabbit Egg. 400ce, Imperial Coronation Egg. 900ce, Silver-gilt enamel Easter Egg. No. 1535, Spring Flower Egg. No. 1536, Egg charms, horiz.

| **1993, Apr. 26** | | | *Perf. 14* | |
|---|---|---|---|---|
| 1527 | A266 | 50ce multi | .30 | .30 |
| 1528 | A266 | 80ce multi | .50 | .50 |
| 1529 | A266 | 100ce multi | .60 | .60 |
| 1530 | A266 | 150ce multi | .90 | .90 |
| 1531 | A266 | 200ce multi | 1.25 | 1.25 |
| 1532 | A266 | 250ce multi | 1.75 | 1.75 |
| 1533 | A266 | 400ce multi | 3.50 | 3.50 |
| 1534 | A266 | 400ce multi | 7.50 | 7.50 |
| | *Nos. 1527-1534 (8)* | | 16.30 | 16.30 |

**Souvenir Sheets**

| 1535 | A266 | 1000ce multi | 6.50 | 6.50 |
|---|---|---|---|---|
| 1536 | A266 | 1000ce multi | 6.50 | 6.50 |

Wild Animals — A267

20ce, African buffalo. 50ce, Giant forest hog. 60ce, Potto. 80ce, Bay duiker. 100ce, Royal antelope. 200ce, Serval. 500ce, Golden cat. 800ce, Megaloglossus woermanni.
No. 1545, Dormouse. No. 1546, White collared mangabey.

| **1993, May 24** | | **Litho.** | *Perf. 14* | |
|---|---|---|---|---|
| 1537 | A267 | 20ce multi | .25 | .25 |
| 1538 | A267 | 50ce multi | .50 | .50 |
| 1539 | A267 | 60ce multi | .60 | .60 |
| 1540 | A267 | 80ce multi | .80 | .80 |
| 1541 | A267 | 100ce multi | 1.00 | 1.00 |
| 1542 | A267 | 200ce multi | 2.00 | 2.00 |
| 1543 | A267 | 500ce multi | 5.00 | 5.00 |
| 1544 | A267 | 800ce multi | 8.00 | 8.00 |
| | *Nos. 1537-1544 (8)* | | 18.15 | 18.15 |

**Souvenir Sheets**

| 1545 | A267 | 900ce multi | 6.50 | 6.50 |
|---|---|---|---|---|
| 1546 | A267 | 900ce multi | 6.50 | 6.50 |

4th Republic — A268

50ce, Kwame Nkrumah Mausoleum, horiz. 100ce, Kwame Nkrumah Conference Center, horiz. 200ce, Constitution book. 350ce, Independence Square. 400ce, Christiansborg Castle.

| **1993, May** | | **Litho.** | *Perf. 14* | |
|---|---|---|---|---|
| 1547 | A268 | 50ce multicolored | .25 | .25 |
| 1548 | A268 | 100ce multicolored | .50 | .50 |
| 1549 | A268 | 200ce multicolored | 1.05 | 1.05 |
| 1550 | A268 | 350ce multicolored | 1.90 | 1.90 |
| 1551 | A268 | 400ce multicolored | 2.25 | 2.25 |
| | *Nos. 1547-1551 (5)* | | 5.95 | 5.95 |

A269

Aviation and
Automotive
Anniversaries
A270

50ce, Graf Zeppelin over Alps, vert. No.
1552, Mercedes Benz 300 SLR in 1955 Mille
Miglia. No. 1553, LZ7 Deutschland. No. 1554,
Vulcan bomber. No. 1555, Ford Tri-motor. No.
1556, 1920 Ford Depot Wagon. No. 1557,
Nieuport 27, vert. No. 1558, Graf Zeppelin tak-
ing aboard letters, vert. No. 1559, 1970 Ford
Mach 1 Mustang. No. 1560, LZ10 Schwaben.
No. 1561, Mercedes wins 1937 Monaco Grand
Prix.
No. 1562, Graf Zeppelin over Rome. No.
1563, 1955 Mercedes Benz Type 196. No.
1564, Early US air mail flight. No. 1565,
S.E.5A, 1918. No. 1566, 1910 Ford Super T,
999.

| 1993 | | Litho. | | Perf. 14 |
|------|------|--------|------|------|
| 1551A | A269 | 50ce multi | .35 | .35 |
| 1552 | A270 | 150ce multi | .90 | .90 |
| 1553 | A269 | 150ce multi | .90 | .90 |
| 1554 | A269 | 400ce multi | 2.75 | 2.75 |
| 1555 | A270 | 400ce multi | 2.75 | 2.75 |
| 1556 | A270 | 400ce multi | 2.75 | 2.75 |
| 1557 | A269 | 600ce multi | 4.00 | 4.00 |
| 1558 | A269 | 600ce multi | 4.00 | 4.00 |
| 1559 | A270 | 600ce multi | 4.00 | 4.00 |
| 1560 | A269 | 800ce multi | 5.00 | 5.00 |
| 1561 | A269 | 800ce multi | 5.00 | 5.00 |
| | Nos. 1551A-1561 (11) | | 32.40 | 32.40 |

**Souvenir Sheets**

| 1562 | A269 | 1000ce multi | 4.75 | 4.75 |
|------|------|--------------|------|------|
| 1563 | A270 | 1000ce multi | 4.75 | 4.75 |
| 1564 | A269 | 1000ce multi | 4.75 | 4.75 |
| 1565 | A269 | 1000ce multi | 4.75 | 4.75 |
| 1566 | A270 | 1000ce multi | 4.75 | 4.75 |

Capt. Hugo Eckener, 125th birth anniv.
(Nos. 1551A, 1553-1554, 1562). Benz's first
four-wheeled vehicle, cent. (Nos. 1552, 1561,
1563). Royal Air Force, 75th anniv. (Nos.
1554, 1557, 1564). Henry Ford's first gasoline
powered engine, cent. (Nos. 1556, 1559,
1566).
No. 1564 contains one 57x42mm stamp.
Nos. 1563, 1566 contains one 85x28mm
stamp.
Issued: Nos. 1555-1556, 1558-1559, 1565-
1566, May. Nos. 1551A-1554, 1557, 1560-
1564, June.

**Nos. 1300-1305 Ovptd.**

| 1993 | | Litho. | | Perf. 14 |
|------|------|--------|------|------|
| 1567 | A237 | 100ce multicolored | .65 | .65 |
| 1568 | A237 | 200ce multicolored | 1.60 | 1.60 |
| 1569 | A237 | 500ce multicolored | 3.25 | 3.25 |
| 1570 | A237 | 600ce multicolored | 4.50 | 4.50 |
| | Nos. 1567-1570 (4) | | 10.00 | 10.00 |

**Souvenir Sheet**

| 1571 | A237 | 800ce on #1304 | 5.50 | 5.50 |
|------|------|----------------|------|------|
| 1572 | A237 | 800ce on #1305 | 5.50 | 5.50 |

**Nos. 1321, 1323-1327 Ovptd.**

(a)

(b)

**1993**

| 1573 | A239(a) | 100ce multi | .75 | .75 |
|------|---------|-------------|------|------|
| 1574 | A239(b) | 300ce multi | 1.75 | 1.75 |
| 1575 | A239(b) | 400ce multi | 2.75 | 2.75 |
| 1576 | A239(a) | 500ce multi | 3.25 | 3.25 |
| | Nos. 1573-1576 (4) | | 8.50 | 8.50 |

**Souvenir Sheets**

| 1577 | A239(a) | 800ce on #1326 | 5.25 | 5.25 |
|------|---------|----------------|------|------|
| 1578 | A239(b) | 800ce on #1327 | 5.25 | 5.25 |

A271

Mushrooms — A272

Designs: 20ce, Cantharellus cibarius. 50ce,
Russula cyanoxantha. 60ce, Clitocybe
rivulosa. No. 1581, Boletus chrysenteron. No.
1582, Cortinarius elatior. No. 1583, Mycena
galericulata. No. 1584, Boletus edulis. No.
1585, Tricholoma gambosum. No. 1586,
Lepista saeva. 250ce, Gyroporus castaneus.
No. 1589, Nolanea sericea. No. 1590,
Hygrophorus puiceus. 500ce, Gomphidius glu-
tinosus. No. 1592, Russula olivacea. 1000ce,
Russula aurata.
No. 1594a, 100ce, Cantharellus cibarius. b,
150ce, Cortinarius elatior. c, 300ce,
Tricholoma gambosum. d, 600ce,
Hygrophorus puiceus.
No. 1595: a, 50ce, like #1581. b, 100ce, like
#1583. c, 150ce, like #1584. d, 1000ce, like
#1589.

| 1993, July 30 | | Litho. | | Perf. 14 |
|---------------|------|--------|------|------|
| 1579 | A271 | 20ce multi | .25 | .25 |
| 1580 | A271 | 50ce multi | .25 | .25 |
| 1581 | A271 | 60ce multi | .25 | .25 |
| 1582 | A271 | 80ce multi | .35 | .35 |
| 1583 | A271 | 80ce multi | .35 | .35 |
| 1584 | A271 | 200ce multi | .85 | .85 |
| 1585 | A271 | 200ce multi | .85 | .85 |
| 1586 | A272 | 200ce multi | .85 | .85 |
| 1587 | A272 | 250ce multi | 1.05 | 1.05 |
| 1588 | A271 | 300ce multi | 1.25 | 1.25 |
| 1589 | A271 | 350ce multi | 1.60 | 1.60 |
| 1590 | A271 | 350ce multi | 1.60 | 1.60 |
| 1591 | A272 | 500ce multi | 2.50 | 2.50 |
| 1592 | A272 | 600ce multi | 3.00 | 3.00 |
| 1593 | A272 | 1000ce multi | 5.00 | 5.00 |
| | Nos. 1579-1593 (15) | | 20.00 | 20.00 |

**Souvenir Sheets**

| 1594 | A271 | Sheet of 4, #a.-d. | 7.25 | 7.25 |
|------|------|---------------------|------|------|
| 1595 | A271 | Sheet of 4, #a.-d. | 7.25 | 7.25 |

Copernicus (1473-
1543) — A273

Designs: 20ce, Early astronomical instrument. 200ce, Telescope. No. 1598, Copernicus, long hair. No. 1599, Copernicus, shorter
hair.

| 1993, Oct. 19 | | Litho. | | Perf. 13½x14 |
|---------------|------|--------|------|------|
| 1596 | A273 | 20ce multicolored | .50 | .50 |
| 1597 | A273 | 200ce multicolored | 3.00 | 3.00 |

**Souvenir Sheets**
**Perf. 12x13**

| 1598 | A273 | 1000ce multicolored | 6.00 | 6.00 |
|------|------|---------------------|------|------|
| 1599 | A273 | 1000ce multicolored | 6.00 | 6.00 |

Picasso (1881-
1973) — A274

Paintings: 20ce, The Actor, 1905. 80ce, Portrait of Allen Stein, 1906. 800ce, Seated Male
Nude, 1908-09.
900ce, Man with a Javelin, 1958.

| 1993, Oct. 19 | | | | Perf. 14 |
|---------------|------|--------|------|------|
| 1600-1602 | A274 | Set of 3 | 5.50 | 5.50 |

**Souvenir Sheet**

| 1603 | A274 | 900ce multi | 5.50 | 5.50 |
|------|------|-------------|------|------|

Polska '93 — A275

Paintings: 200ce, Tattoo, by Sobocki, 1978.
600ce, Prison, by Blonder, 1934. 1000ce,
Fable of the Fortunate Man, by Michalak,
1925, horiz.

**1993, Oct. 19**

| 1604-1605 | A275 | Set of 2 | 5.00 | 5.00 |
|-----------|------|----------|------|------|

**Souvenir Sheet**

| 1606 | A275 | 1000ce multicolored | 5.00 | 5.00 |
|------|------|---------------------|------|------|

1994 World Cup
Soccer, US — A276

Designs: 50ce, Abedi Pele, Ghana. 80ce,
Pedro Troglio, Argentina. 100ce, Fernando
Alvez, Uruguay. 200ce, Franco Baresi, Italy.
250ce, Gomez, Colombia; Katanec, Yugoslavia. 600ce, Diego Maradona, Argentina.
800ce, Hasek, Czech Republic; Wynalda, US.
1000ce, Lothar Matthaeus, Germany.
No. 1615, Giuseppe Giannini, Italy. No.
1616, Rabie Yassein, Egypt; Ruud Gullit,
Holland.

| 1993, Dec. 1 | | | | Perf. 13½x14 |
|--------------|------|--------|------|------|
| 1607 | A276 | 50ce multi | .25 | .25 |
| 1608 | A276 | 80ce multi | .45 | .45 |
| 1609 | A276 | 100ce multi | .55 | .55 |
| 1610 | A276 | 200ce multi | 1.10 | 1.10 |
| 1611 | A276 | 250ce multi | 1.50 | 1.50 |
| 1612 | A276 | 600ce multi | 3.25 | 3.25 |
| 1613 | A276 | 800ce multi | 4.25 | 4.25 |
| 1614 | A276 | 1000ce multi | 5.00 | 5.00 |
| | Nos. 1607-1614 (8) | | 16.35 | 16.35 |

**Souvenir Sheets**
**Perf. 13**

| 1615 | A276 | 1200ce multi | 6.50 | 6.50 |
|------|------|--------------|------|------|
| 1616 | A276 | 1200ce multi | 6.50 | 6.50 |

Domestic
Animals — A277

Designs: 50ce, Meleagris gallopvo. 100ce,
Capra hircus. 150ce, Carina moschata. 200ce,
Eguus asinus. 250ce, Male gallus gallus.
300ce, Sus vittatus. 400ce, Numida meleagris.
600ce, Canis domesticus. 800ce, Female gal-
lus gallus. 1000ce, Ovis aries.
No. 1627: a, 100ce, Like #1618. b, 250ce,
Like #1624. c, 350ce, Like #1622. d, 500ce,
Like #1626.
No. 1628: a, 100ce, Like #1623. b, 250ce,
Like #1621. c, 350ce, Like #1625. d, 500ce,
Like #1617.

| 1993, Dec. 8 | | | | Perf. 14 |
|--------------|------|--------|------|------|
| 1617-1626 | A277 | Set of 10 | 18.00 | 18.00 |

**Souvenir Sheets**

| 1627 | A277 | Sheet of 4, #a-d | 7.00 | 7.00 |
|------|------|-------------------|------|------|
| 1628 | A277 | Sheet of 4, #a-d | 7.00 | 7.00 |

Arts and Crafts — A278

Designs: No. 1629, 50ce, Doll. No. 1630,
50ce, Pot and lid. No. 1631, 200ce, Beads.
No. 1632, 200ce, Snake charmers. No. 1633,
250ce, Hoe. No. 1634, 250ce, Scabbard. No.
1635, 600ce, Pipe. No. 1636, 600ce, Deer.
No. 1637, 1000ce, Mask. No. 1638, 1000ce,
Doll with baby.
No. 1639: a, 100ce, Like #1629. b, 250ce,
Like #1631. c, 350ce, Like #1633. d, 500ce,
Like #1635.
No. 1640: a, 100ce, Like #1630. b, 250ce,
Like #1632. c, 350ce, Like #1634. d, 500ce,
Like #1636.

| 1994, Jan. 24 | | Litho. | | Perf. 14 |
|---------------|------|--------|------|------|
| 1629-1638 | A278 | Set of 10 | 13.50 | 13.50 |

**Souvenir Sheets**

| 1639 | A278 | Sheet of 4, #a-d | 4.00 | 4.00 |
|------|------|-------------------|------|------|
| 1640 | A278 | Sheet of 4, #a-d | 4.00 | 4.00 |

Christmas — A279

Paintings and Woodcuts: 50ce, Adoration of
the Magi. 100ce, The Virgin and Child with
Saint John and an Angel, by Botticelli. 150ce,
Mary as Queen of Heaven. 200ce, Saint Anne.
250ce, The Madonna of the Magnificat, by
Botticelli. 400ce, The Madonna of the Gold-
finch, by Tiepolo. 600ce, The Virgin and the
Child with the Young St. John the Baptist, by
Correggio. 1000ce, Adoration of the
Shepherds.
No. 1649, Mystic Nativity (detail), by Botti-
celli, horiz. No. 1650, Madonna in a Circle, by
Durer.
Woodcuts (50ce, 150ce, 200ce, 1000ce)
are from Nuremberg Prayer Books, by Durer.

**Perf. 13½x14, 14x13½**

| 1993, Dec. 20 | | | Litho. |
|---------------|------|--------|------|
| 1641-1648 | A279 | Set of 8 | 13.00 | 13.00 |

**Souvenir Sheets**

| 1649 | A279 | 1000ce multicolored | 6.00 | 6.00 |
|------|------|---------------------|------|------|
| 1650 | A279 | 1000ce multicolored | 6.00 | 6.00 |

A280

Hong Kong
'94 — A281

Stamps, tram from Kennedy Town to Shau
Kei: No. 1651, Hong Kong #470, back of tram.
No. 1652, Front of tram, #1392.
No. 1653 — Imperial Palace clocks: a,
Windmill. b, Horse. c, Balloon. d, Zodiac. e,
Shar-Pei dog. f, Cat.

| 1994, Feb. 18 | | Litho. | | Perf. 14 |
|---------------|------|--------|------|------|
| 1651 | | 200ce multicolored | .90 | .90 |
| 1652 | | 200ce multicolored | .90 | .90 |
| a. | A280 | Pair, #1651-1652 | 1.80 | 1.80 |

**Miniature Sheet**

| 1653 | A281 | 100ce Sheet of 6, #a.-f. | 6.00 | 6.00 |
|------|------|--------------------------|------|------|

Nos. 1651-1652 issued in sheets of 5 pairs.
No. 1652a is a continuous design.
New Year 1994 (Year of the Dog) (No.
1653e).

Mickey Mouse,
65th
Birthday — A282

Mickey's films: 50ce, Steamboat Willie,
1928. 100ce, The Band Concert, 1937. 150ce,
Moose Hunters, 1937. 200ce, Brave Little Taylor, 1938. 250ce, Fantasia, 1940. 400ce, The
Nifty Nineties, 1941. 600ce, Canne Caddy,
1944. 1000ce, Mickey's Christmas Carol,
1983.
No. 1662, 1200ce, Mickey's Elephant, 1936.
No. 1663, 1200ce, Mickey's Amateurs, 1937.

**1994, Mar. 1    Litho.    Perf. 13½x14**
1654-1661  A282    Set of 8         11.50 11.50
**Souvenir Sheets**
1662-1663  A282    Set of 2         10.00 10.00

A283

Hummel Figurines: 50ce, Boy with backpack, walking stick. 100ce, Girl holding basket behind back. 150ce, Boy with rabbits. 200ce, Boy carrying chicks in basket. 250ce, Girl with chicks. 400ce, Girl petting lamb. 600ce, Lamb, girl waving handkerchief. 1000ce, Girl with basket, flowers.
No. 1672: a, 500ce, Like #1665; b, 150ce, Like #1671; c, 1200ce, Like #1667.
No. 1673: a, 300ce, Like #1668; b, 200ce, Like #1669; c, 500ce, Like #1670; d, 1000ce, Like #1666.

**1994, Apr. 6                    Perf. 14**
1664-1671  A283  Set of 8          9.50 9.50
**Souvenir Sheets**
1672  A283    Sheet of 4, #a.-c.,
                    #1664              5.00 5.00
1673  A283    Sheet of 4, #a.-d.     5.00 5.00

World Wildlife Fund — A284

Diana Monkeys: 50ce, Adult, young. 200ce, Sitting in tree. 500ce, Holding food. 800ce, Close-up of face.

**1994, May 16        Litho.       Perf. 14**
1674-1677  A284    Set of 4         7.50 7.50
1677a              Sheet, 3 each #1674-
                   1677             24.00 24.00

For surcharges see Nos. 2530-2533.

Wild Animals — A285

Designs: 100ce, Bushbuck. 150ce, Spotted hyena. 1000ce, Aardvark. No. 1681, 2000ce, Leopard, vert. No. 1682, 2000ce, Waterbuck, vert.

**1994, May 16**
1678-1680  A285    Set of 3         6.50 6.50
**Souvenir Sheets**
1681-1682  A285    Set of 2        13.00 13.00

Cats — A286

No. 1683, 200ce: a, Sorrel Abyssinian. b, Silver classic tabby. c, Chocolate-point Siamese. d, Brown tortie Burmese. e, Exotic shorthair. f, Havana brown. g, Devon rex. h, Black manx. i, British blue shorthair. j, Calico American wirehair. k, Spotted oriental Siamese. l, Red classic tabby.
No. 1684, 200ce: a, Norwegian forest cat. b, Blue longhair. c, Red self longhair. d, Black longhair. e, Chinchilla. f, Dilut calico longhair. g, Blue tabby-&-white longhair. h, Ruby somali. i, Blue smoke longhair. j, Calico longhair. k, Brown tabby longhair. l, Balinese.
No. 1685, 2000ce, Brown mackeral tabby Scottish fold. No. 1686, 2000ce, Seal-point colorpoint.

**1994, June 6        Litho.       Perf. 14**
**Sheets of 12, #a-l**
1683-1684  A286    Set of 2        16.00 16.00
**Souvenir Sheets**
1685-1686  A286    Set of 2        11.00 11.00

Birds — A287

No. 1687, 200ce: a, Red-bellied paradise flycatcher (b, e). b, Many-colored bush-shrike. c, Broad-tailed paradise whydah (b, e). d, White-crowned robin-chat. e, Violet plantain-eater. f, Village weaver. g, Fire-crowned bishop. h, Shoveler. i, Spur-winged goose (l). j, African crake. k, King reed-hen. l, Tiger bittern.
No. 1688, 200ce: a, Moho. b, Superb sunbird. c, Blue-breasted kingfisher. d, Blue cuckoo-shrike. e, Blue plantain-eater (d, g). f, Greater flamingo (i). g, Lily-trotter (j). h, Night heron. i, Black-winged stilt (l). j, White-spotted pigmy rail. k, Pigmy goose. k, Angola pitta.
No. 1689, 2000ce, Goliath heron. No. 1690, 2000ce, African spoonbill.

**1994, June 13            Sheets of 12, #a-l**
1687-1688  A287    Set of 2        19.00 19.00
**Souvenir Sheets**
1689-1690  A287    Set of 2        12.50 12.50

4th Republic, 1st Anniv. — A288

Designs: 50ce, Rural water projects. 100ce, Honoring farmers. 200ce, Rural electrification. 600ce, Rural bridge construction. 800ce, Natl. Theater. 1000ce, Lighting Perpetual Flame.

**1994, July 11        Litho.      Perf. 14**
1691-1696  A288    Set of 6         6.50 6.50

D-Day, 50th Anniv. — A289

Designs: 60ce, 15-inch Monitor HMS Roberts fires on Houlgate Battery. 100ce, HMS Warspite hits Villerville. 200ce, Flagship USS Augusta.
1500ce, USS Nevada bombards Utah Beach.

**1994, July 4        Litho.       Perf. 14**
1697-1699  A289    Set of 3         3.75 3.75
**Souvenir Sheet**
1700  A289  1500ce multicolored    7.00 7.00

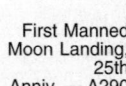

First Manned Moon Landing, 25th Anniv. — A290

No. 1701 — German, Japanese, scientist-astronauts: a, Sigmund Jahn. b, Ulf Merbold. c, Hans Wilhelm Schlegal. d, Ulrich Walter. e, Reinhard Furrer. f, Ernst Messerschmid. g, Mamoru Mohri. h, Klaus-Dietrich Flade. i, Chaiki Naito-Mukai.
2000ce, "Frau im Mond."

**1994, July 4**
1701  A290    300ce Sheet of 9,
                #a.-i.              8.75 8.75
**Souvenir Sheet**
1702  A290  2000ce multicolored    8.00 8.00

Duiker Antelopes A291

Designs: 50ce, Crowned. 100ce, Red-flanked. 200ce, Yellow-backed. 400ce, Ogilby's. 600ce, Bay. 800ce, Jentink's.
No. 1709, 2000ce, Cephalophus natalensis. No. 1710, 2000ce, Cephalophus niger.

**1994, May 16        Litho.       Perf. 14**
1703-1708  A291    Set of 6         7.00 7.00
**Souvenir Sheets**
1709-1710  A291    Set of 2        10.00 10.00

For surcharges see Nos. 2539-2544.

A292

Intl. Olympic Committee, Cent. — A293

Designs: 300ce, Dieter Modenburg, Germany, high jump, 1984. 400ce, Ruth Fuchs, German Democratic Republic, javelin, 1972, 1976.
1500ce, Jans Weissflog, Germany, large hill ski jump, 1994.

**1994, July 4        Litho.       Perf. 14**
1711  A292    300ce multicolored   1.10 1.10
1712  A292    400ce multicolored   1.40 1.40
**Souvenir Sheet**
1713  A293  1500ce multicolored    5.00 5.00

A294

PHILAKOREA '94 — A295

Designs: 20ce, Ch'unghak-dong village elder in traditional clothes. 150ce, Stone pagoda, Punhwangsa, Korea. 300ce, Traditional country house, Andong region.
No. 1717 — Letter pictures, eight-panel screen, Choson Dynasty, 20th cent: a, Shown. b, f, Birds. c, Rooster. d, Animal with antennae. e, g, Flowers. h, Fish.
1500ce, Temple judges determine final afterlife judgments, horiz.

**1994, July 4            Perf. 14, 13 (#1717)**
1714-1716  A294    Set of 3         2.00 2.00
1717  A295    250ce Sheet of 8,
                #a.-h.              7.25 7.25
**Souvenir Sheet**
1718  A294  1500ce multicolored    6.00 6.00

Miniature Sheet of 6

1994 World Cup Soccer Championships, US — A296

No. 1719: a, Dennis Bergkamp, Netherlands. b, Lothar Matthaus, Germany. c, Giuseppe Signori, Italy. d, Carlos Valderrama, Colombia. e, Jorge Campos, Mexico. f, Tony Meola, US.
No. 1720, 1200ce, Citrus Bowl, Orlando, FL, vert. No. 1721, 1200ce, Giants Stadium, Meadowlands, NJ, vert.

**1994, July 25                    Perf. 14**
1719  A296    200ce Sheet of 6,
                #a.-f.              4.00 4.00
**Souvenir Sheets**
1720-1721  A296    Set of 2         7.00 7.00

Christmas — A297

Italian art: 100ce, Madonna of the Annunciation, by Simone Martini. 200ce, Madonna and Child, by Niccolo di Pietro Gerini. 250ce, Virgin and Child on the Throne with Angels and Saints, by Raffaello Botticelli. 300ce, Madonna and Child with Saints, by Antonio Fiorentino. 400ce, Adoration of the Magi, by Bartolo di Fredi. 500ce, The Annunciation, by Cima da Congeliano. 600ce, Virgin and Child with the Young St. John the Baptist, by Workshop of Botticelli. 1000ce, The Holy Family, by Giorgione.
Details from Adoration of the Kings, by Giorgione: No. 1730, 2000ce, Presenting gifts. No. 1731, 20000ce, Madonna & Child.

**1994, Dec. 5     Litho.   Perf. 13½x14**
1722-1729  A297    Set of 8         9.00 9.00
**Souvenir Sheets**
1730-1731  A297    Set of 2        10.00 10.00

Intl. Year of the Family — A298

Designs: 50ce, Family. 100ce, Technical training. 200ce, Child care. 400ce, Care for the aged. 600ce, Vocational training. 1000ce, Adult education.

**1994, Dec. 20                    Perf. 14**
1732-1737  A298    Set of 6         6.00 6.00

Ghana Civil Aviation Authority, 50th Anniv. — A299

Designs: 100ce, Control tower. 400ce, Insignia, marker light. 1000ce, Airplane leaving runway.

**1994, Dec. 20**
1738-1740  A299    Set of 3         4.50 4.50

See Nos. 1766-1768. For surcharges see Nos. 2548-2550.

Red Cross & Red Crescent Societies in Ghana, 75th Anniv. — A300

Designs: 50ce, Transporting victim. 200ce, Aiding mother, children. 600ce, Erecting tents.

**1994, Dec. 20        Litho.       Perf. 14**
1741-1743  A300    Set of 3         4.00 4.00
**Souvenir Sheet**
1744          Sheet of 3, #1741-1742,
                1744a               6.50 6.50
   **a.** A300 1000ce like #1743    6.50 6.50

For surcharges see Nos. 2545-2547.

Fertility Dolls — A301

Various carvings with background colors of: 50ce, Green. 100ce, Yellow (red frame). 150ce, Blue (black doll). 200ce, Rose. 400ce, Dull orange. 600ce, Yellow green. 800ce, Yellow (green frame). 1000ce, Blue (white doll).

**1994, Dec. 20**

| 1745-1752 | A301 | Set of 8 | 9.00 | 9.00 |

**Souvenir Sheet**

| 1753 | | Sheet of 4, #1745, 1748-1749, 1753a | 6.75 | 6.75 |
| | *a.* | A301 250ce like #1752 | 1.60 | 1.60 |

For surcharges see Nos. 2551-2558.

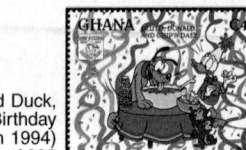

Donald Duck, 60th Birthday (in 1994) A302

Designs: 40ce, Pluto, Donald, Chip 'n Dale. 50ce, Mickey, pup. 60ce, Daisy. 100ce, Goofy. 150ce, Goofy. diff. 250ce, Donald, Goofy. 400ce, Ludwig Von Drake, Pluto. 500ce, Gramdma Duck, pups. 1000ce, Mickey, Minnie. 1500ce, Pluto.
No. 1764, 2000ce, Daisy, Donald, cake, Mickey, vert. No. 1765, 2000ce, Donald holding fork, spoon, vert.

**1995, Feb. 2     Litho.     Perf. 14x13½**

| 1754-1763 | A302 | Set of 10 | 10.00 | 10.00 |

**Souvenir Sheets**

**Perf. 13½x14**

| 1764-1765 | A302 | Set of 2 | 10.50 | 10.50 |

**Civil Aviation Authority Type of 1994 with ICAO Emblem and New Inscription**

Designs: 100ce, Like #1738. 400ce, Like #1739. 1000ce, Like #1740.

**1994, Dec. 20     Litho.     Perf. 14**

| 1766-1768 | A299 | Set of 3 | 9.00 | 9.00 |

Nos. 1766-1768 are inscribed "50th Anniversary of The International Civil Aviation Organization (ICAO)."
For surcharges see Nos. 2559-2561.

Panafest '94 — A303

Designs: 50ce, Northern region dancer. 100ce, Relics with landmark. 200ce, Chief sitting in state. 400ce, Royalist ceremonial dress. 600ce, Cape Coast Castle. 800ce, Clay figurines of West Africa.

**1994, Dec. 9     Litho.     Perf. 13½**

| 1769-1774 | A303 | Set of 6 | 8.50 | 8.50 |

Pan African Historical Theatre Festival, Dec. 1994.

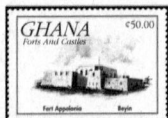

Forts — A304

Castles — A305

Forts: 50ce, Apolonia, Beyin. 200ce, Patience, Apam. 250ce, Amsterdam, Kormantin. 300ce, St. Jago, Elmina. 400ce, William, Anomabo. 600ce, Kumasi.
Castles: 150ce, Cochem, Germany. 600ce, Hohenzollern, Germany. 800ce, Uwajima, Japan. 100ce, Hohenschwangau, Germany.
Castles: No. 1785a, Windsor, England. b, Osaka, Japan. c, Vaj Dahunyad, Hungary. d, Karlstejn, Czech Republic. e, Kronborg, Denmark. f, Alcazar of Segovia, Spain. g, Chambourd, France. h, Linderhof, Bavaria. i, Red Fort, India.
No. 1786, 800ce, Elmira Castle. No. 1787, 1000ce, Fort St. Antonio, Axim. No. 1788,

2500ce, Himeji Castle, Japan. No. 1789, 2500ce, Neuschwanstein Castle, Germany.

**1995, Apr. 3     Perf. 14**

| 1775-1780 | A304 | Set of 6 | 5.50 | 5.50 |
| 1781-1784 | A305 | Set of 4 | 8.00 | 8.00 |
| 1785 | A305 | 500ce Sheet of 9, #a.-i. | 11.00 | 11.00 |

**Souvenir Sheets**

| 1786-1787 | A304 | Set of 2 | 4.50 | 4.50 |
| 1788-1789 | A305 | Set of 2 | 8.50 | 8.50 |

Water Birds — A306

Designs: 200ce, Eurasian pochard. 500ce, Maccoa duck. 800ce, Cape shoveler. 1000ce, Red-crested pochard.
No. 1794: a, African pygmy goose. b, Southern pochard. c, Cape teal. d, Ruddy shelduck. e, Fulvous whistling duck. f, White-faced whistling geese. g, Ferruginous white-eye. h, Hottentot teal. i, African black duck. j, Yellow-billed duck. k, White-checked pintail duck. l, Hartlaub's duck.
No. 1795, 2500ce, Roseate tern. No. 1796, 2500ce, Northern shoveler.

**1995, Apr. 28**

| 1790-1793 | A306 | Set of 4 | 7.00 | 7.00 |
| 1794 | A306 | 400ce Sheet of 12, #a.-l. | 10.50 | 10.50 |

**Souvenir Sheets**

| 1795-1796 | A306 | Set of 2 | 11.00 | 11.00 |

Nos. 1794-1796 have a continuous design. Nos. 1790-1793 have a white border.

1996 Summer Olympics, Atlanta
A307     A308

Athletes: 500ce, Carl Lewis. 800ce, Eric Liddell. 900ce, Runner. 1000ce, Jim Thorpe.
No. 1801: a, Cycling. b, Archery. c, Diving. d, Swimming. e, Gymnastics-Floor Exercise. f, Fencing. g, Boxing. h, Gymnastics-Rings. i, Javelin. j, Tennis. k, Soccer. l, Equestrian.
No. 1802, 1200ce, John Akii Bua. No. 1803, 1200ce, Pierre de Cobertin.

**1995, May 2**

| 1797-1800 | A307 | Set of 4 | 6.50 | 6.50 |
| 1801 | A308 | 300ce Sheet of 12, #a.-l. | 7.50 | 7.50 |

**Souvenir Sheets**

| 1802-1803 | A308 | Set of 2 | 5.00 | 5.00 |

UN, 50th Anniv. — A309

No. 1804 — Secretaries General: a, 200ce, Trygve Lie, Norway, 1946-52. b, 300ce, Dag Hammarskjold, Sweden, 1953-61. c, 400ce, U Thant, Burma, 1961-71. d, 500ce, Kurt Waldheim, Austria, 1972-81. e, 600ce, Javier Perez de Cuellar, Peru, 1982-91. f, 800ce, Boutros Boutros-Ghali, Egypt, 1992-.
No. 1805, UN flag, horiz.

**1995, July 6     Litho.     Perf. 14**

| 1804 | A309 | Sheet of 6, #a.-f. | 6.00 | 6.00 |

**Souvenir Sheet**

| 1805 | A309 | 1200ce multicolored | 3.00 | 3.00 |

**Miniature Sheets**

A310

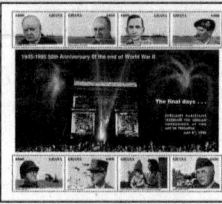

End of World War II, 50th Anniv. — A311

No. 1806 — Military decorations: a, US Navy Cross, US Purple Heart. b, UK Air Force Cross, UK Distinguished Flying Cross. c, US Navy and Marine Corps Medal, US Distinguished Service Cross. d, UK Distinguished Service Medal, UK Distinguished Conduct Medal. e, UK Military Medal, UK Military Cross. f, UK Distinguished Service Cross, UK Distinguished Service Order.
No. 1807: a, Churchill. b, Eisenhower. c, Air Chief Marshall Sir Arthur Tedder. d, Montgomery. e, Bradley. f, de Gaulle. g, French Resistance Organization. h, Patton.
No. 1808, 1200ce, U.S. Medal of Honor. No. 1809, 1200ce, Fuhrer's promise.

**1995, July 6     Litho.     Perf. 14**

| 1806 | A310 | 500ce Sheet of 6, #a.-f. + label | 7.50 | 7.50 |
| 1807 | A311 | 400ce Sheet of 8, #a.-h. + label | 7.50 | 7.50 |

**Souvenir Sheets**

| 1808-1809 | A310 | Set of 2 | 6.50 | 6.50 |

No. 1809 contains one 42x56mm stamp.

FAO, 50th Anniv. — A312

Designs: 200ce, Fish preservation. 300ce, Fishing. 400ce, Ox-drawn plow. 600ce, Harvesting. 800ce, Aforestation.
2000ce, Boat, shoreline, oxen, fruit.

**1995, July 6     Litho.     Perf. 14**

| 1810-1814 | A312 | Set of 5 | 4.75 | 4.75 |

**Souvenir Sheet**

| 1815 | A312 | 2000ce multicolored | 4.00 | 4.00 |

For surcharges see Nos. 2534-2538.

Rotary Intl., 90th Anniv. — A313

Designs: 600ce, Natl. flag, Rotary emblem. 1200ce, Rotary emblem on banner, vert.

**1995, July 6**

| 1816 | A313 | 600ce multicolored | 1.75 | 1.75 |

**Souvenir Sheet**

| 1817 | A313 | 1200ce multicolored | 3.00 | 3.00 |

1995 Boy Scout Jamboree, Holland — A314

No. 1818: a, 400ce, Two boys. 800ce, Two boys, one wearing glasses. c, 1000ce, Two boys facing left.

1200ce, Boy with bamboo poles.

**1995, July 6**

| 1818 | A314 | Strip of 3, #a.-c. | 4.50 | 4.50 |

**Souvenir Sheet**

| 1819 | A314 | 1200ce multicolored | 4.00 | 4.00 |

No. 1818 is a continuous design.

Queen Mother, 95th Birthday — A315

No. 1820: a, Drawing. b, Bright green blue hat. c, Formal portrait. d, Coral outfit. 2500ce, Pale blue outfit.

**1995, July 6     Perf. 13½x14**

| 1820 | A315 | 600ce Strip or block of 4, #a.-d. | 5.00 | 5.00 |

**Souvenir Sheet**

| 1821 | A315 | 2500ce multicolored | 4.50 | 4.50 |

No. 1820 was issued in sheets of 8 stamps. For surcharges see Nos. 2333-2334.

Singapore '95 — A316

No. 1822, 400ce: a, Seismosaurus (d-f). b, Supersaurus (a, d). c, Ultrasaurus (f). d, Saurolophus (e). e, Lambeosaurus (d, g-h). f, Parasaurolophus (e, i). g, Triceratops (h). h, Styracosaurus (e, g i). i, Pachyrhinosaurus (h).
No. 1823, 400ce: a, Peteinosaurus (b, d-e). b, Quetzalcoatlus (a, c, e). c, Eudimorphodon (b). d, Allosaurus (e-f, h-i). e, Daspletosaurus (f). f, Tarbosaurus (i). g, Velociraptor (h-i). h, Herrerasaurus (i). i, Coelophysis.
No. 1824, 2500ce, Albertosaur. No. 1825, 2500ce, Tyrannosaurus rex.

**1995, Aug. 8     Litho.     Perf. 14**

**Sheets of 9, #a-i**

| 1822-1823 | A316 | Set of 2 | 15.00 | 15.00 |

**Souvenir Sheets**

| 1824-1825 | A316 | Set of 2 | 10.00 | 10.00 |

Nobel Prize Recipients — A317

No. 1826: a, Nelson Mandela, peace, 1993. b, Albert Schweitzer, peace, 1952. c, Wole Soyinka, literature, 1986. d, Emil Fischer, chemistry, 1902. e, Rudolf Mossbauer, physics, 1961. f, Archbishop Desmond Tutu, peace, 1984. g, Max Born, physics, 1954. h, Max Planck, physics, 1918. i, Hermann Hesse, literature, 1946.
1200ce, Paul Ehrlich, medicine, 1908.

**1995, Oct. 2     Litho.     Perf. 14**

| 1826 | A317 | 400ce Sheet of 9, #a.-i. | 9.00 | 9.00 |

**Souvenir Sheet**

| 1827 | A317 | 1200ce multi | 3.50 | 3.50 |

Asantehene, 25th Anniv. — A318

Designs: 50ce, Emblem. 100ce, Silver casket. 200ce, Golden stool. 400ce, Busummuru sword bearer. 600ce, 800ce, Diff. portraits of Otumfuo Opoku Ware II. 1000ce, Mponponsuo sword bearer.

**1995**       *Perf. 13½x13*
1828-1834   A318   Set of 7     7.00   7.00

A319         Fauna — A319a

Designs: 400ce, Cymothoe beckeri. 500ce, Graphium policene. 1000ce, Urotriorchis macrourus, vert. 2000ce, Xiphias gladius. 3000ce, Monodoctylus sabee. 5000ce, Ardea purpurea, vert.
400ce exists in two types:
Type I — Large flower bud under second "A" in "Ghana," the top of which is above cross line of "A" (shown in illustration).
Type II — Small flower bud under second "A" in "Ghana," the top of which is below cross line of "A."

*Perf. 14¼x13¾, 13¾x14¼*
**1995, June 19**       **Litho.**
| | | | | |
|---|---|---|---|---|
| 1835 | A319 | 400ce multi | .80 | .80 |
| 1835A | A319 | 400ce multi, type II | — | |
| 1836 | A319 | 500ce multi | 1.00 | 1.00 |
| 1837 | A319 | 1000ce multi | 2.00 | 2.00 |
| a. | | Perf. 11½ | | |
| 1838 | A319a | 2000ce multi | 4.25 | 4.25 |
| 1839 | A319 | 3000ce multi | 6.00 | 6.00 |
| 1840 | A319 | 5000ce multi | 10.00 | 10.00 |
| | Nos. 1835-1840 (7) | | 24.05 | 24.05 |

No. 1838 has denomination at left. Compare with type A503. No. 1840 has green frame and "A's" of "Ghana" with cross lines sloping down to right.

Christmas — A320

Details or entire paintings: 50ce, The Infant Jesus and the Young St. John, by Murillo. 80ce, Rest on Flight to Egypt, by Memling. 300ce, Sacred Family, by Van Dyck. 600ce, The Virgin and the Infant, by Uccello. 800ce, The Virgin and the Infant, by Van Eyck. 1000ce, Head of Christ, by Rembrandt.
No. 1847, 2500ce, Madonna, by Montagna. No. 1848, 2500ce, The Holy Family, by Pulzone.

**1995, Dec. 1**   **Litho.**   *Perf. 13½x14*
1841-1846   A320   Set of 6    6.00   6.00
**Souvenir Sheets**
1847-1848   A320   Set of 2    17.00   17.00

Motion Pictures, Cent. — A321

No. 1849: a, 1903 H. Ernmann camera. b, Charles Chaplin. c, Rudolph Valentino. d, Will Rogers. e, Greta Garbo. f, Jackie Cooper. g, Bette Davis. h, John Barrymore. i, Shirley Temple.
No. 1850, Laurel and Hardy.

**1995, Dec. 8**
1849   A321   400ce Sheet of 9, #a.-i.    10.50   10.50
**Souvenir Sheet**
1850   A321   2500ce multi    7.00   7.00

A322       John Lennon (1940-80) — A323

No. 1852: a-g, i, Various portraits. h, Like No. 1851.
2000ce, Lennon playing guitar, water in background.

**1995, Dec. 8**       *Perf. 14*
1851   A322   400ce shown    3.50   3.50
**Miniature Sheet**
*Perf. 13½x14*
1852   A323   400ce Sheet of 9, #a.-i.    12.00   12.00
**Souvenir Sheet**
1853   A323   2000ce multi    9.00   9.00

No. 1851 was issued in sheets of 16.

Louis Pasteur (1822-95) — A324

No. 1854: a, In laboratory. b, Discovery of rabies virus and vaccine. c, Pneumococcus discovery, 1880. d, Development of first vaccine with birds. e, Perfection of brewer's yeast culture.

**1995, Dec. 13**       *Perf. 14*
1854   A324   600ce Sheet of 5, #a.-e.    7.25   7.25

Paintings from the Metropolitan Museum of Art — A325

No. 1855: a, 400ce: a, Portrait of a Man, by Van Der Goes. b, Paradise, by Giovanni di Paolo. c, Portrait of a Young Man, by Antonello da Messina. d, Tommaso Portinari, by Memling. e, Wife Maria Portinari, by Memling. f, Portrait of a Lady, by Ghirlandaio. g, St. Christopher & Infant Christ, by Ghirlandaio. h, Francesco D'Este, by van der Weyden.
No. 1856, 400ce: a, The Interrupted Sleep, by Boucher. b, Diana and Cupid, by Batoni. c, Boy Blowing Bubbles, by Chardin. d, Ancient Rome, by Pannini. e, Modern Rome, by Pannini. f, The Calmady Children, by Lawrence. g, The Triumph of Marius, by G.B. Tiepolo. h, Garden at Vaucresson, by E. Vuillard.
No. 1857, 2500ce, The Epiphany, by Giotto. No. 1858, 2500ce, The Calling of Matthew, by Hemessen.

**1996, Feb. 12**   **Litho.**   *Perf. 13½x14*
**Sheets of 8, #a-h, + Label**
1855-1856   A325   Set of 2    14.00   14.00
**Souvenir Sheets**
*Perf. 14*
1857-1858   A325   Set of 2    14.00   14.00
Nos. 1857-1858 each contain one 85x57mm stamp.

New Year 1996 (Year of the Rat) — A326

Nos. 1859-1860 — Stylized rats: a, With musical instruments, on horseback. b, Holding banners. c, Carrying rat in palanquin. d, Carrying box, holding fish.

1000ce, Four rats transporting rat in palanquin, horiz.

**1996, Jan. 28**   **Litho.**   *Perf. 14*
**Country Name in White**
1859   A326   250ce Strip of 4, #a.-d.    4.50   4.50
**Country Name in Red**
1860   A326   250ce Sheet of 4, #a.-d.    4.50   4.50
**Souvenir Sheet**
1861   A326   1000ce red, pink & yellow    4.50   4.50

No. 1859 was issued in sheets of 12 stamps.

Fauna of the Rainforest — A327

No. 1862, 400ce: a, Ramphastos toco. b, Choloepus didactylus. c, Pongo pygmaeus. d, Spiaetus cirrhatus. e, Panthera tigris. f, Ibis leucocephallus. g, Ara chloroptera. h, Saimiri sciureus. i, Macaca fascicularis. j, Cithaerias menander, ithomiidae. k, Cryptophanes cristatus, gekkonidae. l, Boa caninus.
No. 1863, 400ce: a, Opisthoccomus hoazin. b, Tarsius bancanus. c, Leontopithecus rosalia. d, Pteropus gouldii. e, Rupicola rupicola. f, Pharomachrus mocino. g, Hyla boans, dendrobates leucomeles. h, Lemur catta. i, Iguana iguana. j, Heliconius burneyi. k, Mellisuga minima. l, Propithecus verreauxi.
No. 1864, 3000ce, Sarcoramphus papa. No. 1865, 3000ce, Pteridophora alberti.

**1996, Apr. 15**   **Sheets of 12, #a-l**
1862-1863   A327   Set of 2    20.00   20.00
**Souvenir Sheets**
1864-1865   A327   Set of 2    14.00   14.00

China '96 — A328

No. 1866: a, Kaiyuan Si Temple, Fujian. b, Kaiyuan Si Temple, Hebei. c, Fogong Si Temple, Shanxi. d, Xiangshan, Beijing.
No. 1867, Baima Si Temple, Henan.

**1996, May 13**   **Litho.**   *Perf. 14*
1866   A328   400ce Strip of 4, #a.-d.    7.00   7.00
**Souvenir Sheet**
1867   A328   1000ce multicolored   5.50   5.50

No. 1866 was issued in sheets of 8 stamps. See No. 1913.

Queen Elizabeth II, 70th Birthday — A329

No. 1868: a, Portrait. b, Wearing blue hat, coat. c, Wearing printed dress, wide-brim hat. 2500ce, Riding in horse-drawn carriage, horiz.

**1996, June 10**   **Litho.**   *Perf. 13½x14*
1868   A329   1000ce Strip of 3, #a.-c.    7.00   7.00
**Souvenir Sheet**
*Perf. 14x13½*
1869   A329   2500ce multicolored   6.50   6.50
No. 1868 was issued in sheets of 9 stamps.

1996 Summer Olympics, Atlanta — A330

Designs: 300ce, Two wrestlers, javelin thrower, Bas Relief, 500BC. 500ce, Wilma Rudolph, gold medalist in track and field, Rome, 1960. 600ce, The Forum, St. Peter's Basilica, Colosseum, Olympic Stadium, Rome, 1960. 800ce, Soviet flag, ladies' kayak pairs gold medal winners, Rome, 1960.
No. 1874, 400ce — Medalists in swimming, diving: a, Aileen Riggin, springboard, 1920. b, Pat McCormick, platform, 1952. c, Dawn Fraser, 100m freestyle, 1956. d, Chris Von Saltza, 400m freestyle, 1960. e, Anita Lonsbrough, 200m breaststroke, 1960. f, Debbie Meyer, 400m freestyle, 1968. g, Shane Gould, 400m freestyle, 1972. h, Petra Thuemer, 800m freestyle, 1976. i, Marjorie Gestring, springboard, 1936.
No. 1875, 400ce, vert. — Soccer players: a, Abedi Pele, Ghana. b, Quico Navarez, Spain. c, Heino Hanson, Denmark. d, Mostafa Ismail, Egypt. e, Anthony Yeboah, Ghana. f, Jurgen Klinsmann, Germany. g, Cobi Jones, US. h, Franco Baresi, Italy. i, Igor Dobrovolski, Russia.
No. 1876, 2000ce, Kornella Ender, 200m freestyle gold medalist, 1976. No. 1877, 2000ce, Tracy Caulkins, 200m individual medlay gold medalist, 1984.

**1996, June 27**       *Perf. 14*
1870-1873   A330   Set of 4    4.50   4.50
**Sheets of 9, #a-i**
1874-1875   A330   Set of 2    17.00   17.00
**Souvenir Sheets**
1876-1877   A330   Set of 2    11.00   11.00

Intl. Amateur Boxing Assoc., 50th Anniv. — A331

Boxers: 300ce, Serafim Todorow, Bulgaria. 400ce, Oscar de La Hoya, US. 800ce, Ariel Hernandez, Cuba. 1500ce, Arnaldo Mesa, Cuba.
3000ce, Tadahiro Sasaki, Japan.

**1996, July 31**
1878-1881   A331   Set of 4    6.50   6.50
**Souvenir Sheet**
1882   A331   3000ce multicolored   6.50   6.50

UNESCO, 50th Anniv. A332

Designs: 400ce, The Citadel, Haiti, vert. 800ce, Aït-Ben-Haddou (Fortified Village), Morocco, vert. 1000ce, Spissky Hrad (exterior of castle), Slovakia.
2000ce, Cape Coast, Ghana.

**1996, July 31**   **Litho.**   *Perf. 14*
1883-1885   A332   Set of 3    6.50   6.50
**Souvenir Sheet**
1886   A332   2000ce multicolored   6.00   6.00

UNICEF, 50th Anniv. — A333

Designs: 400ce, Baby. 500ce, Mother, baby. 600ce, Mother, child drinking from glass. 1000ce, Child, diff.

**1996, July 31**
1887-1889   A333   Set of 3    3.00   3.00
**Souvenir Sheet**
1890   A333   1000ce multicolored   2.50   2.50

Jerusalem, 3000th Anniv. — A334

Landmark, flower: 400ce, St. Stephen's (Lion) Gate, Jasminum mesnyi. 600ce, Citadel and Tower of David, nerium oleander. 800ce, Chapel of the Ascension, romulea bulbocodium.
2000ce, Russian Church of St. Mary Magdalene.

**1996, July 31**
1891-1893 A334 Set of 3    4.50 4.50
**Souvenir Sheet**
1894 A334 2000ce multicolored    6.00 6.00
For overprints see Nos. 2032-2035.

Musical Instruments — A335

No. 1895: a, Fiddles. b, Proverbial drum. c, Double clapless bell & castanet. d, Gourd rattle. e, Horns.

**1996, Aug. 5**
1895 A335 500ce Sheet of 5, #a.-e.    5.00 5.00

Disney's Best Friends A336

No. 1896, 60ce, Ariel, Flounder, Sebastian. No. 1897, 60ce, Pinocchio, Jiminy Cricket. No. 1898, 60ce, Cogsworth, Lumiere. No. 1899, 60ce, Copper, Tod. No. 1900, 60ce, Pocahontas, Meeko, Flit. No. 1901, 60ce, Bambi, Flower, Thumper.
No. 1902: a, 450ce, Pocahontas, Meeko, Flit. b, 150ce, Pinocchio, Jiminy Cricket. c, 200ce, Copper, Tod. d, 600ce, Aladdin, Abu. e, 700ce, Penny, Rufus. f, 350ce, Cogsworth, Lumiere. g, 800ce, Mowgli, Baloo. h, 200ce, Ariel, Flounder, Sebastian, i, 300ce, Bambi, Flower, Thumper.
No. 1903, Winnie the Pooh, vert. No. 1904, Simba, Pumbaa.

**Perf. 14x13½, 13½x14**
**1996, Aug. 25**
1896-1901 A336 Set of 6    2.75 2.75
1902    A336 Sheet of 9, #a.-i.    8.50 8.50
**Souvenir Sheets**
1903 A336 3000ce multicolored    4.75 4.75
1904 A336 3000ce multicolored    4.75 4.75
Stampshow '96 (No. 1902).

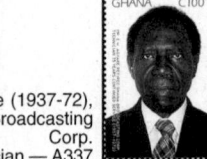

E.W. Agyare (1937-72), Ghana Broadcasting Corp. Technician — A337

**1996, July 31**    **Perf. 14**
1905 A337 100ce multicolored    .50 .50

Radio, Cent. — A338

Entertainers: 500ce, Frank Sinatra. No. 1907, 600ce, Judy Garland. No. 1908, 600ce, Bing Crosby. 800ce, Dean Martin, Jerry Lewis. 2000ce, Edgar Bergen, Charlie McCarthy.

**1996, July 31**    **Perf. 13½x14**
1906-1909 A338 Set of 4    3.25 3.25
**Souvenir Sheet**
1910 A338 2000ce multicolored    3.25 3.25

Sylvester Stallone in Movie, "Rocky II" — A339

**1996, Nov. 21**    **Litho.**    **Perf. 14**
1911 A339 2000ce multi    2.40 2.40
Issued in sheets of 3.

New Year 1997 (Year of the Ox) — A340

Various scenes from Chinese story, "Herd Boy and Girl Weaver."

**1997, Jan. 22**    **Litho.**    **Perf. 14**
1912 A340 500ce Sheet of 9, #a.-i.    7.00 7.00

**Souvenir Sheet**

China '96 — A341

Statue of the Devil.

**1996, May 13**    **Litho.**    **Perf. 14**
1913 A341 1000ce multicolored    3.25 3.25
No. 1913 was not available until March 1997.

African Hair Styles — A342

No. 1914, 1000ce: a, Dipo. b, Oduku. c, Dansinkran. d, Mbobom. e, Oduku 2.
No. 1915, 1000ce: a, African corn row. b, Chinese raster. c, Chinese raster 2. d, Corn row. e, Mbakaa.

**1997, Mar. 3**    **Sheets of 5, #a-e**
1914-1915 A342 Set of 2    9.00 9.00

Dr. Hideyo Noguchi (1876-1928), Pathologist — A343

No. 1916: a, Tomb. b, Portrait. c, Birth place. d, Noguchi Institute, Legon. e, Noguchi Gardens, Accra.
No. 1917, 3000ce, Dr. Noguchi in laboratory. No. 1918, 3000ce, Statue.

**1997, Mar. 3**
1916 A343 1000ce Sheet of 5, #a.-e.    6.50 6.50
**Souvenir Sheets**
1917-1918 A343 Set of 2    7.00 7.00

Independence, 40th Anniv. — A344

Designs: 200ce, Emblem. 550ce, Dr. Kwame Nkrumah, first president of Ghana, vert. 800ce, Achievement in education. 1100ce, Akosombo Dam.
2000ce, Declaration of independence, Old Polo Grounds, vert. 3000ce, Kofi Annan, UN Secretary General, vert.

**1997, Mar. 6**    **Litho.**    **Perf. 14**
1919-1922 A344 Set of 4    7.00 7.00
**Souvenir Sheets**
1923 A344 2000ce multicolored    2.75 2.75
1924 A344 3000ce multicolored    4.25 4.25

Deng Xiaoping (1904-97), Chinese Leader — A345

No. 1925: a, 300ce, Smiling. b, 600ce, Wearing glasses. c, 800ce, Like #1925b. d, 1000ce, Like #1925a.
No. 1926: a, 500ce, Lips pursed. b, 600ce, Teeth showing. c, 800ce, Like #1926b. d, 1000ce, Like #1926a.
No. 1927, Reading. No. 1928, Hand in air.

**1997, Apr. 28**    **Perf. 14x13½**
1925 A345 Sheet of 4, #a.-d.    3.50 3.50
1926 A345 Sheet of 4, #a.-d.    3.50 3.50
**Souvenir Sheets**
**Perf. 13½**
1927 A345 3000ce multicolored    3.50 3.50
1928 A345 4000ce multicolored    4.00 4.00
Nos. 1927-1928 each contain one 51x38mm stamp.

Paintings by Hiroshige (1797-1858) A346

No. 1929: a, Nihonbashi Bridge and Edobashi Bridge. b, View of Nihonbashi Tori 1-chome. c, Open Garden at Fukagawa Hachiman Shrine. d, Inari Bridge and Minato Shrine, Teppozu. e, Bamboo Yards, Kyobashi Bridge. f, Hall of Thirty-Three Bays, Fukagawa.
No. 1930, 3000ce, Teppozu and Tsukiji Honganji Temple. No. 1931, 3000ce, Sumiyoshi Festival, Tsukudajima.

**1997, May 29**    **Litho.**    **Perf. 13½x14**
1929 A346 600ce Sheet of 6, #a.-f.    5.00 5.00
**Souvenir Sheets**
1930-1931 A346 Set of 2    7.00 7.00

Queen Elizabeth II, Prince Philip, 50th Wedding Anniv. — A347

No. 1932: a, Queen. b, Royal Arms. c, Queen, Prince waving. d, Queen, Prince. e, Royal carriage. f, Portrait of Prince Philip. 3000ce, Portrait of Queen Elizabeth II.

**1997, May 29**    **Perf. 14**
1932 A347 800ce Sheet of 6, #a.-f.    5.50 5.50
**Souvenir Sheet**
1933 A347 3000ce multicolored    2.00 2.00

Heinrich von Stephan (1831-97), Founder of UPU — A348

No. 1934 — Portrait of Von Stephan and: a, Automobile used for postal delivery. b, UPU emblem. c, First airmail flight, Pierre Blanchard, 1784.
3000ce, African messenger with cleft stick.

**1997, May 29**    **Litho.**    **Perf. 14**
1934 A348 1000ce Sheet of 3, #a.-c.    3.50 3.50
**Souvenir Sheet**
1935 A348 3000ce multicolored    3.50 3.50
PACIFIC 97.

Paul P. Harris (1868-1947), Founder of Rotary Intl. — A349

Portrait of Harris, Rotary emblem and: 2000ce, PolioPlus oral vaccine administration, Egypt. 3000ce, Emblem for PolioPlus vaccine, "A world free of disease."

**1997, May 29**
1936 A349 2000ce multicolored    3.25 3.25
**Souvenir Sheet**
1937 A349 3000ce multicolored    3.25 3.25

Chernobyl, 10th Anniv. — A350

Designs: 800ce, UNESCO. 1000ce, Chabad's Children of Chernobyl.

**1997, May 29**    **Perf. 13½x14**
1938 A350 800ce multicolored    2.25 2.25
1939 A350 1000ce multicolored    2.50 2.50

Ajumpan Drums — A350a

Cyrestes Camillus — A350b

Kente Cloth — A350c

**Perf. 13½x14¼, 14¼x13½**
**1997**    **Litho.**
1939A A350a 550ce multi    — —
1939B A350b 800ce multi    — —
1939C A350c 1100ce multi    — —
Issued: 550ce, 5/30; 800ce, 6/4. 1100ce, 6/7. For surcharges see Nos. 2360, 2360A, 2675, 2684B.

A351

Entertainers — A352

No. 1940: a, Jackie Gleason. b, Danny Kaye. c, John Cleese. d, Lucille Ball. e, Jerry Lewis. f, Sidney James. g, Louis de Fuenes. h, Mae West. i, Bob Hope.

No. 1941: a, Professor Ajax Bukana with fingers making "V." b, Bukana with arms spread.

3000ce, Groucho Marx.

**1997, July 1**                  **Perf. 13½x14**
1940 A351   600ce Sheet of 9,
            #a.-i.                    7.00 7.00

**Souvenir Sheets**
**Perf. 14**
1941 A352  2000ce Sheet of 2,
            #a-b                      3.25 3.25
**Perf. 13½x14**
1942 A351  3000ce multicolored        2.25 2.25

Mushrooms — A353

Designs: 200ce, Galerina calyptrata. 300ce, Lepiota ignivolvata. 400ce, Omphalotus olearius. 550ce, Amanita phalloides. 600ce, Entoloma conferendum. 800ce, Entoloma nitidum.

No. 1949: a, Coprinus picaceus. b, Stropharia aurantiaca. c, Cortinarius splendens. d, Gomphidius roseus. e, Russula sardonia. f, Geastrum schmidelia.

No. 1950, 3000ce, Mycena crocata. No. 1951, 3000ce, Craterellus cornucopioides.

**1997, July 9**                  **Perf. 14**
1943-1948 A353  Set of 6             3.50 3.50
1949 A353  800ce Sheet of 6,
            #a.-f.                    5.50 5.50
**Souvenir Sheets**
1950-1951 A353  Set of 2             6.50 6.50

Fish — A354

Seabirds, Marine Life — A355

Designs: 400ce, African pygmy angelfish. 600ce, Angelfish. 800ce, Broomtail wrasse. 1000ce, Indian butterfly fish.

No. 1956: a, Violet crested turaco. b, Pied avocet. c, Bottle-nosed dolphin. d, Bottle-nosed dolphin, long-toed lapwing. e, Longfined spadefish (i). f, Imperial angelfish, manta ray. g, Raccoon butterfly fish, African pompano (h, k). h, Silvertip shark (g, l). i,

Longfin banner fish (e, j). j, Longfin banner fish, manta ray (f, i). k, Rusty parrot fish (j). l, Coral trout.

No. 1957, 3000ce, Crown butterfly fish. No. 1958, 3000ce, King angelfish.

**1997, July 15**
1952-1955 A354  Set of 4             3.50 3.50
1956 A355  500ce Sheet of 12,
            #a.-l.                    7.00 7.00
**Souvenir Sheets**
1957-1958 A355  Set of 2             8.00 8.00

Flowers — A356

Designs: 200ce, Eurychone rothschildiana. 550ce, Bulbophyllum lepidum. No. 1961, 800ce, Ansellia africana. 1100ce, Combretum grandiflorum.

No. 1963, vert: a, Strophanthus preusii. b, Ancistrochilus rothchildianus. c, Mussaendra arcuata. d, Microcoelia guyoniana. e, Gloriosa simplex. f, Brachycorythis kalbreyeri. g, Aframomum sceptrum. h, Thunbergia alata. i, Clerodendrum thomsoniae.

No. 1964, 3000ce, Kigelia africana. No. 1965, 3000ce, Spathodea campanulata.

**1997, Aug. 1**      **Litho.**      **Perf. 14½**
1959-1962 A356  Set of 4             3.75 3.75
1963 A356  800ce Sheet of 9,
            #a.-i.                    9.50 9.50
**Souvenir Sheets**
1964-1965 A356  Set of 2             7.50 7.50

1998 World Cup Soccer Championships, France — A357

Stadiums: 200ce, Azteca, Mexico, 1970, 1986. 300ce, Rose Bowl, US, 1994. 400ce, Giuseppe Meazza, Italy, 1990. 500ce, Olympic, Germany, 1974. 1000ce, Maracana, Brazil, 1950. 2000ce, Bernabeu, Spain, 1982.

No. 1972 — Soccer players: a, Patrick Kluivert, Holland. b, Roy Deane, Ireland. c, Abedi Pele Ayew, Ghana. d, Peter Schmeichel, Denmark. e, Roberto di Matteo, Italy. f, Bebeto, Brazil. g, Steve McManaman, England. h, George Appong Weah, Liberia.

No. 1973, 3000ce, Juninho, Brazil. No. 1974, 3000ce, Seaman, England.

**1997, July 12**               **Perf. 14x13½**
1966-1971 A357  Set of 6             4.50 4.50
1972 A357  600ce Sheet of 8,
            #a.-h. + la-
            bel                      4.50 4.50
**Souvenir Sheets**
1973-1974 A357  Set of 2             7.00 7.00

Nos. 1966-1971 were issued in sheets of 10 each.

Birds — A358

Designs: 200ce, Eurasian goldfinch. 300ce, Cape batis. 400ce, Bearded barbet. 500ce, White-necked raven. 600ce, Purple grenadier. 1000ce, Zebra waxbill.

No. 1981: a, Black bustard. b, Northern lapwing. c, Sandgrouse. d, Red-crested turaco. e, White-browed coucal. f, Lilac-breasted roller. g, Golden pipet. h, Crimson-breasted gonolek. i, Blackcap.

No. 1982, 3000ce, Nectarina famosa. No. 1983, 3000ce, Vidua regia.

**1997, Oct. 20**    **Litho.**      **Perf. 14**
1975-1980 A358  Set of 6             3.50 3.50
1981 A358  800ce Sheet of 9,
            #a.-i.                    8.00 8.00
**Souvenir Sheets**
1982-1983 A358  Set of 2             7.50 7.50

Cats and Dogs — A359

Cats, Nos. 1984-1989: 20ce, Havana. 50ce, Singapura. 100ce, Sphinx. 150ce, British white. 300ce, Snowshoe. 600ce, Persian.

Dogs, Nos. 1989A-1989F: 80ce, Papillon. 200ce, Bulldog. 400ce, Shetland sheepdog. 500ce, Schnauzer. 800ce, Shih tzu. 2000ce, Chow chow.

No. 1990, 1000ce — Dogs and cats: a, Russian wolfhound. b, Birman. c, Basset hound. d, Silver tabby. e, Afghan. f, Burmilla.

No. 1991, 1000ce: a, Abyssinian. b, Border terrier. c, Scottish fold. d, Boston terrier. e, Oriental. f, Keeshond.

No. 1992, 3000ce, Ragdoll. No. 1992A, 3000ce, Alaskan malamute.

**1997, Oct. 20**
1984-1989 A359  Set of 6             2.75 2.75
1989A-1989F A359  Set of 6           8.00 8.00
**Sheets of 6, #a-f**
1990-1991 A359  Set of 2             17.50 17.50
**Souvenir Sheets**
1992-1992A A359  Set of 2            8.00 8.00

Return of Hong Kong to China A360

No. 1993: a, Lin Tsi-Hsu (1785-1850). b, Gwan Tian-Pei.

**1997, Nov. 10**
1993 A360  1000ce Sheet of 4, 2
            each #a.-b.              7.00 7.00

Huang Binhong (1865-1955) A361

No. 1994 — Various details of "Color Landscape": a, 200ce. b, 300ce. c, 400ce. d, 500ce. e, 600ce. f, 800ce. g, 1000ce. h, 2000ce.

No. 1995: a, Detail with Chinese inscription. b, Detail without inscription.

**1997, Nov. 10**
1994 A361            Sheet of 8,
            #a.-h.                   7.00 7.00
**Souvenir Sheet**
1995 A361  2000ce Sheet of 2,
            #a.-b.                   5.50 5.50

Nos. 1994a-1994h are each 28x90mm.

Christmas — A362

Entire paintings or details: 200ce, Cupid by Botticelli. 550ce, Zephyr and Chloris, by Botticelli. 800ce, Trumphant Cupid, by Caravaggio. 1100ce, The Seven Works of Mercy, by Caravaggio. 1500ce, The Toilet of Venus, by Diego Velazquez. 2000ce, Freeing of Saint Peter, by Raphael.

Sculptures: No. 2002, 5000ce, The Cavalcant Annunciation, by Donatello. No. 2003, 5000ce, Isis and Nepthys Protecting the Cartouches of Tutankhamen with their Wings.

**1997, Dec. 8**     **Litho.**      **Perf. 14**
1996-2001 A362  Set of 6             6.00 6.00
**Souvenir Sheets**
2002-2003 A362  Set of 2            9.00 9.00

Diana, Princess of Wales (1961-97) — A363

Various portraits, background color of sheet margin: No. 2004, 1200ce, Pale pink. No. 2005, 1200ce, Pale blue.

Portraits with (in margin): No. 2006, 3000ce, Elizabeth Taylor. No. 2007, 3000ce, Henry Kissinger.

**1997, Dec. 22**               **Sheets of 6, #a-f**
2004-2005 A363  Set of 2             11.00 11.00
**Souvenir Sheets**
2006-2007 A363  Set of 2             7.00 7.00

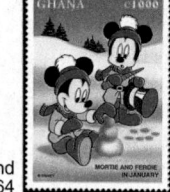

Mickey and Friends — A364

No. 2008, 1000ce — Characters, month: a, Mortie and Ferdie, Jan. b, Minnie, Feb. c, Goofy, Mar. d, Mickey, Minnie, & Pluto, Apr. e, Minnie, May. f, Daisy, June.

No. 2009, 1000ce: a, Donald, July. b, Donald and Daisy, Aug. c, Morty and Ferdie, Sept. d, Huey, Dewey, & Louie, Oct. e, Mickey, Nov. f, Mickey & Minnie, Dec.

Characters, season: No. 2010, 5000ce, Daisy, nephews, winter, horiz. No. 2011, 5000ce, Goofy, fall. No. 2012, 5000ce, Mickey, spring, horiz. No. 2013, 5000ce, Mickey, Minnie and Goofy in summer.

**Perf. 13½x14, 14x13½**
**1998, Jan. 29**                    **Litho.**
**Sheets of 6, #a-f**
2008-2009 A364  Set of 2   16.00 16.00
**Sheets of 6 With Added Marginal Inscription**
2008g-2009g       Set of 2   27.50 27.50
**Souvenir Sheets**
2010-2013 A364  Set of 4   28.00 28.00
**Souvenir Sheets With Added Marginal Inscriptions**
2012a-2013a       Set of 2   57.50 57.50

Nos. 2008g, 2009g, 2012a, 2013a have added inscription in sheet margin showing "Happy Birthday," Mickey Mouse, and "1998" in emblem.

Issued: Nos. 2008g, 2009g, 2012a, 2013a, 8/4/98.

Trains — A365

Designs: 300ce, Union Pacific SD60M, US. 500ce, ETR 450, Italy. No. 2018, 800ce, X200 Sweden. 1000ce, TGV Duplex, France. 2000ce, El Class Co-Co, Australia. 3000ce, Eurostar, Britain.

No. 2020, 800ce: a, SPS 4-4-0, Pakistan. b, Class WP 4-6-2, India. c, Class Ql 2-10-2, China. d, Class 12 4-4-2, Belgium. e, Class P8 4-6-0, Germany. f, Castle Class 4-6-0, Britain. g, Tank engine 2-6-0, Austria. h, Class P36 4-8-4, Russia. i, William Mason 4-4-0, US.

No. 2021, 800ce: a, AVE, Spain. b, Class 1600, Luxembourg. c, Bullet train, Japan. d, GM F7 Warbonnet, US. e, Class E1500, Morocco. f, Deltic, Great Britain. g, XPT, Australia. h, Le Shuttle, France/Britain. i, Class 201, Ireland.

No. 2022, 5500ce, Duchess Class 4-6-2, Britain. No. 2023, 5500ce, TGV, France.

**1998, Feb. 26**    **Litho.**      **Perf. 14**
2014-2019 A365  Set of 6             7.50 7.50

## Sheets of 9, #a-i

| | | | |
|---|---|---|---|
| 2020-2021 | A365 | Set of 2 | 13.50 13.50 |

### Souvenir Sheets

| | | | |
|---|---|---|---|
| 2022-2023 | A365 | Set of 2 | 10.00 10.00 |

Nos. 2022-2023 each contain one 57x42mm stamp.

Lunar New Year — A366

No. 2025 — Signs of Chinese zodiac: a, Horse. b, Monkey. c, Ram. d, Rooster. e, Dog. f, Ox. g, Rabbit. h, Boar. i, Snake. j, Dragon. k, Tiger. l, Rat.

**1998**    **Litho.**    *Perf. 13½*

| | | | |
|---|---|---|---|
| 2025 | A366 | 400ce Sheet of 12, #a.-l. | 6.00 6.00 |

Numbers have been reserved for additional values in this set.

Great Black Writers of the 20th Century — A368

No. 2027: a, Maya Angelou. b, Alex Haley. c, Charles Johnson. d, Richard Wright. e, Toni Cade Bambara. f, Henry Louis Gates, Jr.

**1998, Mar. 25**    **Litho.**    *Perf. 14*

| | | | |
|---|---|---|---|
| 2027 | A368 | 350ce Sheet of 6, #a.-f. | 5.00 5.00 |

Aircraft — A369

No. 2028, 800ce: a, Messerschmitt Bf 109 E-7. b, Lockheed PV-2 Harpoon. c, Airspeed Oxford MK1. d, Junkers Ju87D-1. e, Yakovlev Yak-9D. f, North American P-51D Mustang. g, Douglas A-20 Havoc. h, Supermarine Attacker F1. i, Mikoyan-Gurevich MIG-15.

No. 2029, 800ce: a, Breguet 14 B2. b, Curtiss BF2C-1 Goshawk. c, Supermarine Spitfire MK IX. d, Fiat G.50. e, Douglas B-18A. f, Boeing FB-5. g, Bristol F.2B. h, Hawker Fury 1. i, Fiat CR42.

No. 2030, 3000ce, Mitsubishi AGM8 Reisen. No. 2031, 3000ce, Supermarine Spitfire MK XIV, Supermarine Spitfire MK 1.

**1998, May 5**    **Sheets of 9, #a-i**

| | | | |
|---|---|---|---|
| 2028-2029 | A369 | Set of 2 | 13.50 13.50 |

### Souvenir Sheets

| | | | |
|---|---|---|---|
| 2030-2031 | A369 | Set of 2 | 5.50 5.50 |

Nos. 2030-2031 each contain one 57x42mm stamp.

Nos. 1891-1894 Overprinted

**1998, May 13**

| | | | |
|---|---|---|---|
| 2032 | A334 | 400ce multi | .90 .90 |
| 2033 | A334 | 600ce multi | 1.10 1.10 |
| 2034 | A334 | 800ce multi | 1.50 1.50 |

### Souvenir Sheet

| | | | |
|---|---|---|---|
| 2035 | A334 | 2000ce multi | 4.50 4.50 |

No. 2035 contains additional inscription in sheet margin: "ISRAEL 98 — WORLD STAMP

---

EXHIBITION / TEL-AVIV 13-21 MAY 1998." No. 2034 exists with an inverted surcharge.

Ships — A370

No. 2036, 800ce — Ocean liners: a, Empress of Ireland. b, Transylvania. c, Mauritania. d, Reliance. e, Aquitania. f, Lapland. g, Cap Polonio. h, France. i, Imperator.

No. 2037, 800ce — Warships: a, HMS Rodney. b, USS Alabama. c, HMS Nelson. d, SS Ormonde. e, USS Radford. f, SS Empress of Russia. g, Type XIV, Germany. h, Type A Midget, Japan. i, Brin, Italy.

No. 2038, 5500ce, Titanic. No. 2039, 5500ce, Amistad.

**1998, May 5**    **Litho.**    *Perf. 14*

### Sheets of 9, #a-i

| | | | |
|---|---|---|---|
| 2036-2037 | A370 | Set of 2 | 14.00 14.00 |

### Souvenir Sheets

| | | | |
|---|---|---|---|
| 2038-2039 | A370 | Set of 2 | 9.75 9.75 |

Nos. 2038-2039 each contain one 42x56mm stamp.

Orchids — A371

No. 2040, 800ce: a, Renanthera imschootiana. b, Arachnis flosaeris. c, Restrepia lansbergi. d, Paphiopedilum tonsum. e, Phalaenopsis ebauche. f, Pleione limprichti.

No. 2041, 800ce: a, Phragmipedium schroderae. b, Zygopetalum clayii. c, Vanda coerulea. d, Odontonia boussole. e, Disa uniflora. f, Dendrobium bigibbum.

No. 2042, 5500ce, Cypripedium calceolus. No. 2043, 5500ce, Sobralia candida.

**1998, June 2**    **Sheets of 6, #a-f**

| | | | |
|---|---|---|---|
| 2040-2041 | A371 | Set of 2 | 11.00 11.00 |

### Souvenir Sheets

| | | | |
|---|---|---|---|
| 2042-2043 | A371 | Set of 2 | 12.00 12.00 |

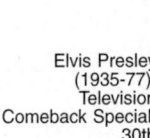

Elvis Presley (1935-77), Television Comeback Special, 30th Anniv. — A372

Various portraits during performance.

**1998, June 16**    **Litho.**    *Perf. 13½*

| | | | |
|---|---|---|---|
| 2044 | A372 | 800ce Sheet of 6, #a.-f. | 5.25 5.25 |

Japanese Flowers — A373

No. 2045, 2000ce — Predominant color of flowers, location of denomination : a, Green (bamboo), UR. b, Red, LR. c, Yellow, LR. d, Pale green & pink, UR.

No. 2046, 2000ce: a, Pale green, yellow & pink, LR. b, Red, UR. c, Pink, LR. d, White, LR.

No. 2047, 5500ce, Small pink & yellow, LR. No. 2048, 5500ce, Pink, UL.

**1998, June 2**    **Litho.**    *Perf. 14*

### Sheets of 4, #a-d

| | | | |
|---|---|---|---|
| 2045-2046 | A373 | Set of 2 | 13.50 13.50 |

### Souvenir Sheets

| | | | |
|---|---|---|---|
| 2047-2048 | A373 | Set of 2 | 11.00 11.00 |

---

Ghana Cocoa Board, 50th Anniv. — A374

Designs: 200ce, Tetteh Quarshie, pioneer of Ghana Cocoa industry. 550ce, Ripe hybrid cocoa pods. 800ce, Opening of cocoa pods. 1100ce, Fermenting cocoa beans. 1500ce, Shipment of cocoa.

**1998, July 8**    *Perf. 13x13½*

| | | | |
|---|---|---|---|
| 2049-2053 | A374 | Set of 5 | 5.00 5.00 |

Metropolitan Assembly, Cent. — A375

Designs: 200ce, AMA Centennial emblem. 550ce, King Tackie Tawiah I (1862-1902). 800ce, Achimota School, Accra. 1100ce, Korle Bu Hospital, Accra. 1500ce, Christianborg Castle, Accra.

**1998, July 8**

| | | | |
|---|---|---|---|
| 2054-2058 | A375 | Set of 5 | 4.50 4.50 |

Intl. Year of the Ocean — A376

No. 2059: a, Dolphins. b, Dolphin (f). c, Seagull. d, Least tern, seagulls. e, Emperor angelfish (i). f, Whit ear. g, Blue shark, diver (k). h, Parrotfish. i, Dottyback. j, Blue-spotted stingray (m, n). k, Masked butterfly fish. l, Jack knife fish (h). m, Octopus (i). n, Turkeyfish (lionfish) (j, k, o). o, Seadragon. p, Rock cod.

No. 2060, 3000ce, Devil ray. No. 2061, 3000ce, Great white shark.

**1998, Aug. 18**    *Perf. 14*

| | | | |
|---|---|---|---|
| 2059 | A376 | 500ce Sheet of 16, #a.-p. | 17.50 17.50 |

### Souvenir Sheets

| | | | |
|---|---|---|---|
| 2060-2061 | A376 | Set of 2 | 14.50 14.50 |

Inventors and Inventions — A377

No. 2062, 1000ce: a, Edison, light bulb. b, Peephole kinetoscope, Edison. c, Tesla coil, Tesla. d, Nikola Tesla (1856-1943). e, Gottlieb Wilhelm Daimler (1834-1900). f, Motorcycle, Daimler. g, Transmitter circuit for telescope, Marconi. h, Guglielmo Marconi.

No. 2063, 1000ce: a, Orville & Wright. b, 1st Flyer, Wright Brothers. c, Neon lighting and signs, Claude. d, Georges Claude (1870-1960). e, Alexander Graham Bell. f, The telephone, transmitter, Bell. g, Various uses of lasers, Townes. h, Charles Townes (b. 1915).

No. 2064, 5500ce, Robert Goddard (1882-1945), physicist. No. 2065, 5500ce, Paul Ehrlich (1854-1915), chemist, bacteriologist.

**1998, Sept. 1**    *Perf. 14*

### Sheets of 8, #a-h

| | | | |
|---|---|---|---|
| 2062-2063 | A377 | Set of 2 | 15.00 15.00 |

### Souenir Sheets

| | | | |
|---|---|---|---|
| 2064-2065 | A377 | Set of 2 | 10.00 10.00 |

Nos. 2062b-2062c, 2062f-2062g, 2063b-2063c, 2063f-2063g are each 53x38mm.

Christmas — A378

Cats and dogs in Christmas scenes: 500ce, British colorpoint. 600ce, American shorthair-

---

Dilute calico. 800ce, Peke-faced Persian. 1000ce, Small German spitz. 2000ce, British shorthair blue. 3000ce, Persian Dilute calico. No. 2072, 5500ce, English pointer. No. 2073, 5500ce, Rumpy max.

**1998, Dec. 1**    **Litho.**    *Perf. 14*

| | | | |
|---|---|---|---|
| 2066-2071 | A378 | Set of 6 | 10.00 10.00 |

### Souvenir Sheets

| | | | |
|---|---|---|---|
| 2072-2073 | A378 | Set of 2 | 13.00 13.00 |

Ferrari Automobiles — A378a

No. 2073A: c, Lampredi. d, 250 GT Cabriolet. e, 121 LM. 3000ce, 365 GTS/4 Spyder.

**1998, Dec. 24**    **Litho.**    *Perf. 14*

| | | | |
|---|---|---|---|
| 2073A | A378a | 2000ce Sheet of 3, #c-e | 5.00 5.00 |

### Souvenir Sheet

*Perf. 13¾x14¼*

| | | | |
|---|---|---|---|
| 2073B | A378a | 3000ce multi | 4.00 4.00 |

No. 2073A contains three 39x25mm stamps.

Diana, Princess of Wales (1961-97) — A379

No. 2074: a, Inscription panel at left. b, Panel at right.

**1998, Dec. 24**    **Litho.**    *Perf. 14½*

| | | | |
|---|---|---|---|
| 2074 | A379 | 1000ce Horiz. pair, #a-b | 3.50 3.50 |

No. 2074 was issued in sheets of 3 pairs.

Gandhi — A380

No. 2075: a, After 8 month prison term in Poona, 1931. b, On Salt March, 1930. c, Picking up natural salt at end of Salt March, 1930. d, After graduating from high school in Rajkot, 1887. 5500ce, At age 61, 1931.

**1998, Dec. 24**

| | | | |
|---|---|---|---|
| 2075 | A380 | 2000ce Sheet of 4, #a.-d. | 10.00 10.00 |

### Souvenir Sheet

| | | | |
|---|---|---|---|
| 2076 | A380 | 5500ce multi | 9.00 9.00 |

Nos. 2075b-2075c are each 53x38mm.

Pablo Picasso — A381

Designs: No. 2077, 1000ce, Collage, Composition with Butterfly, 1932. No. 2078, 1000ce, Sculpture, Mandolin and Clarinet, 1913, vert. 2000ce, Painting, Ballplayers on the Beach, 1931. 5500ce, Tomato Plant, 1944, vert.

**1998, Dec. 24**    *Perf. 14x14½*

| | | | |
|---|---|---|---|
| 2077-2079 | A381 | Set of 3 | 3.75 3.75 |

### Souenir Sheet

| | | | |
|---|---|---|---|
| 2080 | A381 | 5500ce multicolored | 5.25 5.25 |

19th World Scouting Jamboree, Chile — A382

No. 2081: a, Scout sign. b, Camping. c, Tying a bowline.
5000ce, Robert Baden-Powell.

**1998, Dec. 24**     **Perf. 14**
2081 A382 2000ce Sheet of 3,
   #a.-c.     5.50 5.50

**Souvenir Sheet**
2082 A382 5000ce multicolored    4.75 4.75

Royal Air Force, 80th Anniv. — A383

No. 2083: a, C130 Hercules. b, Chinook HC2. c, C130 Hercules W2. d, Panavia Tornado F3ADV.
No. 2084, 5500ce, Eurofighter 2000, Chipmunk. No. 2085, 5500ce, Hawk's head, biplane.

**1998, Dec. 24**
2083 A383 2000ce Sheet of 4,
   #a.-d.     7.25 7.25

**Souvenir Sheets**
2084-2085 A383   Set of 2    10.00 10.00

New Year 1999 (Year of the Rabbit) — A384

No. 2086 — Scenes showing farmer from "Farmer and Rabbit," by Han Fei Tzu: a, Working in field. b, Watching rabbit run into tree. c, Holding rabbit. d, Dreaming of rabbit.

**1999, Jan. 4**
2086 A384 1400ce Sheet of 4,
   #a.-d.     5.50 5.50

Dinosaurs A385

Designs: 400ce, Corythosaurus. 600ce, Struthiomimus. 1000ce, Lambeosaurus. No. 2089A, 2000ce, Hesperosuchus.
No. 2090, 800ce: a, Ankylosaurus. b, Anatosaurus. c, Diplodocus. d, Monoclonius. e, Tyrannosaurus. f, Camptosaurus. g, Ornitholestes. h, Archaeopteryx. i, Allosaurus.
No. 2091, 800ce: a, Pterodactylus. b, Scelidosaurus. c, Pteranodon. d, Plateosaurus. e, Ornithosuchus. f, Kentrosaurus. g, Hypsognathus. h, Erythrosuchus. i, Stegoceros.
No. 2092, 5000ce, Dimorphodon, vert. No. 2093, 5000ce, Apatosaurus.

**1999, Mar. 1**    **Litho.**    **Perf. 13½**
2087-
2089A   A385   Set of 4
    4.00 4.00
**Sheets of 9, #a-i**
2090-2091 A385   800ce Set of
    2    14.00 14.00
**Souvenir Sheets**
2092-2093 A385 5000ce Set of
    2    9.00 9.00

Australia '99, World Stamp Expo — A386

Butterflies: 300ce, California sister. 500ce, Red-splashed sulphur. 600ce, Checked white. 800ce, Blue emperor.

No. 2098, 1000ce, vert: a, Red admiral. b, Buckeye. c, Desert checkered skipper. d, Orange sulphur. e, Tiger swallowtail. f, Orange-bordered blue. g, Agraulis vanillae. h, Monarch.
No. 2099, 1000ce, vert: a, Small tortoiseshell. b, Brimstone. c, Camberwell beauty. d, Marbled white. e, Purple emperor. f, Clouded yellow. g, Ladoga camilla. h, Marsh fritillary.
No. 2100, 5000ce, Papilio homerus, vert. No. 2101, 5000ce, Blue copper.

**1999, Apr. 26**    **Litho.**    **Perf. 14**
2094-2097 A386   Set of 4    3.50 3.50
**Sheets of 8, #a-h**
2098-2099 A386   Set of 2    16.00 16.00
**Souvenir Sheets**
2100-2101 A386   Set of 2    10.00 10.00

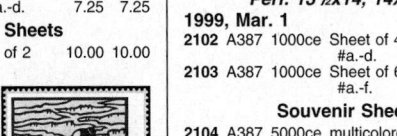

Shirley Temple as "Curly Top" — A387

No. 2102, vert.: a, Saying prayers. b, Actor John Boles looking at portrait. c, Taking Boles' hand. d, Dressed as old woman.
No. 2103: a, Hugging older sister. b, Dressed as a man. c, Looking at stuffed animals. d, Pulling Boles' tie. e, With family. f, Looking at sister and Boles together.
5000ce, In pink dress, vert.

**Perf. 13½x14, 14x13½**
**1999, Mar. 1**      **Litho.**
2102 A387 1000ce Sheet of 4,
   #a.-d.     3.50 3.50
2103 A387 1000ce Sheet of 6,
   #a.-f.     5.50 5.50
**Souvenir Sheet**
2104 A387 5000ce multicolored    5.50 5.50

Amorphophallus Flavovirens — A387a

**1999, May 6**    **Litho.**    **Perf. 14x14¼**
2104A A387a 200ce multi    —

Trains — A388

Designs: 400ce, ICE 2, Germany, 1966. 500ce, M41, Hungary, 1982. 600ce, DVR, Finland, 1963. 1000ce, AVE 100 class, Spain, 1982.
No. 2109, 1300ce: a, EMD GP7 Illinois Terminal RR, 1949-54. b, EMD SD 38-2, 1972-79. c, EMD SD 60M Soo Line, 1989-96. d, GE U25C, 1963-65. e, EMD GP 28, 1961-63. f, EMD SD 9, 1954-59.
No. 2110, 1300ce: a, Conrail EMD SD80, 1993-99. b, Columbus & Greenville RR EMD SDP35, 1964-66. c, Providence & Worcester RR, MLW M420 Loc. Works, 1973-77. d, Missouri Pacific C36-7, 1978-85. e, Alco C-420 Virginia & Maryland RR, 1963-68. f, Reading RR EMD GP30, 1961-63.
No. 2111, 5000ce, Swiss Federal RR Class RE 6/6 Co-Co, 1972. No. 2112, 5000ce, AGP44, ABB Traction, Inc. 1990-91.

**1999, May 10**      **Perf. 14**
2105-2108 A388   Set of 4    2.50 2.50
**Sheets of 6, #a-f**
2109-2110 A388   Set of 2    13.00 13.00
**Souvenir Sheets**
2111-2112 A388   Set of 2    9.00 9.00

Paintings by Hokusai (1760-1849) A389

No. 2113: a, Girl Picking Plum Blossoms. b, Surveying a Region. c, Sumo Wrestlers (rear view). d, Sumo Wrestlers (front view). e, Landscape with Seaside Village. f, Courtiers Crossing a Bridge.
No. 2114: a, Climbing the Mountain. b, Nakahara in Sagami Province. c, Sumo Wrestlers (2 fighting). d, An Oiran and Maid by a Fence. e, Fujiwara Yoshitaka.
No. 2115, 5000ce, Palanquin Bearers on a Steep Hill, vert. No. 2116, 5000ce, Three Ladies by a Well, vert.

**1999, Aug. 3**    **Litho.**    **Perf. 13¾**
2113 A389 1300ce Sheet of 6,
   #a.-f.     6.25 6.25
2114 A389 1300ce Sheet of 6,
   #a.-e., 2113c 6.25 6.25
**Souvenir Sheets**
2115-2116 A389   Set of 2    8.00 8.00

IBRA '99, World Philatelic Exhibition, Nuremberg — A390

Exhibition emblem, sailing ship Schomberg and: No. 2117, 500ce, Hanover #1. No. 2119, 1000ce, Lubeck #1.
Emblem, Class P8 4-6-0 locomotive and: No. 2118, 800ce, Hamburg #1. No. 2120, 2000ce, Heligoland #1A.
5000ce, Germany #66 tied to airmail label on cover, vert.

**1999, Aug. 3**      **Perf. 14x14½**
2117-2120 A390   Set of 4    4.00 4.00
**Souvenir Sheet**
**Perf. 14½x14**
2121 A390 5000ce multicolored    4.00 4.00

First Manned Moon Landing, 30th Anniv. — A391

No. 2122: a, Command Module. b, Lunar Module ascension. c, Giant moon rock. d, Lunar module signals home. e, Neil Armstrong. f, One small step.
5000ce, Earth rise, horiz.

**1999, Aug. 3**      **Perf. 14**
2122 A391 1300ce Sheet of 6,
   #a.-f.     8.00 8.00
**Souvenir Sheet**
2123 A391 5000ce multicolored    4.75 4.75

Queen Mother, 100th Birthday (in 2000) — A392

Queen Mother, 100th Birthday (in 2000) — No. 2124: a, Lady Elizabeth Bowles-Lyon with brother David, 1904. b, Queen Elizabeth, 1957. c, Queen Mother, 1970. d, Queen Mother, 1992.
5000ce, Queen Mother, 1970, diff.

**1999, Aug. 4**     **Gold Frames**
2124 A392 2000ce Sheet of 4,
   #a.-d. + label    7.25 7.25
**Souvenir Sheet**
2125 A392 5000ce multicolored    6.00 6.00

No. 2125 contains one 38x50mm stamp. Margins of sheets are embossed. See Nos. 2273-2274.

Fauna — A393

Designs: 200ce, Meles meles. 800ce, Vulpes vulpes.
No. 2128: a, Martes martes. b, Strix aluco. c, Sus scrofa. d, Accipiter gentilis. e, Eliomys quercinus. f, Lucanus cervus.
No. 2129: a, Merops apiaster. b, Upupa epops. c, Cervus elaphus. d, Circaetus gallicus. e, Lacerta ocellata. f, Lynx pardellus.
5000ce, Canis lupus, vert.

**1999, Mar. 29**    **Litho.**    **Perf. 14**
2126-2127 A393 Set of 2    2.00 2.00
2128 A393 1000ce Sheet of 6,
   #a.-f.     5.00 5.00
2129 A393 1000ce Sheet of 6,
   #a.-f.     5.00 5.00
**Souvenir Sheet**
2130 A393 5000ce multicolored    5.00 5.00

**1999**
Birds: 400ce, Cyanopica cyana. 600ce, Ciconia ciconia. 2000ce, Aegypius monachus, vert. 3000ce, Garrulus glandarius, vert. 5000ce, Aquila heliaca adalberti.

2131-2134 A393 Set of 4    5.50 5.50
**Souvenir Sheet**
2135 A393 5000ce multicolored    4.50 4.50

Rights of the Child — A394

No. 2136: a, Child, UN building. b, Dove, earth. c, Mother, child.
5000ce, Child.

**1999, Aug. 3**    **Litho.**    **Perf. 14**
2136 A394 3000ce Sheet of 3,
   #a.-c.     7.50 7.50
**Souvenir Sheet**
2137 A394 5000ce multicolored    5.00 5.00

**Souvenir Sheets**

PhilexFrance 99 — A395

Locomotives: No. 2138, 5000ce, 232-U1 Four cylinder compound 4-6-4. No. 2139, 5000ce, 0-6-0 Suburban tank engine.

**1999, Aug. 3**      **Perf. 14x13¾**
2138-2139 A395 Set of 2    15.00 15.00

Johann Wolfgang von Goethe (1749-1832), German Poet — A396

No. 2140: a, Wagner entreats Faust in his study. b, Goethe and Friedrich von Schiller. c, Mephistopheles disguised as the fool.
5000ce, Faust attended by spirits.

**1999, Aug. 3 Litho. Perf. 14**
2140 A396 2000ce Sheet of 3,
#a.-c. 5.75 5.75

**Souvenir Sheet**
2141 A396 5000ce multicolored 5.00 5.00

Return of Macao to People's Republic of China — A397

**1999, Aug. 20 Litho. Perf. 14x13¾**
2142 A397 1000ce multicolored 3.00 3.00

Issued in sheets of 4.

Save the Ozone Layer — A398

Designs: 200ce, Fish. 550ce, Earth surrounded by ozone layer, man. 800ce, Crying Earth. 1100ce, People holding up shield against sunlight. 1500ce, Objects with ozone-depleting and non-harmful chemicals.

**1999 Litho. Perf. 13½x13**
2143-2147 A398 Set of 5 8.50 8.50

SOS Children's Villages, 50th Anniv. — A399

Designs: 200ce, Grandma Alice. 550ce, Kindergarten. 800ce, SOS Children's Village founder Herrmann Gmeiner (1919-86), Asikawa SOS building. 1100ce, Food preparation.

**1999 Perf. 13x13½**
2148-2151 A399 Set of 4 3.00 3.00

Dr. Ephraim Apu, Musician, Birth Cent. — A400

Designs: 200ce, Apu, clef, note. 800ce, Apu playing Odurugya flute. 1100ce, Apu, indiginous flutes.

**1999 Perf. 13½x13**
2152-2154 A400 Set of 3 2.00 2.00

Millennium A401

Designs: 300ce, Millennium emblem, vert. 700ce, Emblem, Kwame Nkrumah. 1200ce, Emblem, University of Ghana, vert.

**1999, Dec. 28 Litho. Perf. 13¼**
2155-2157 A401 Set of 3 6.00 6.00

New Year 2000 — A402

Various scenes from Chinese story, "Daughter of the Dragon King." Stamps from

the two sheets are numbered 1-12 in Chinese numeral characters. The numerals are at the bottom of the top group of Chinese characters. See Chinese numerals in Illustrated Identifier.

**2000, Feb. 5 Perf. 14½x14¼**
2158 A402 1600ce Sheet of 6,
#a.-f. 5.00 5.00
2159 A402 1700ce Sheet of 6,
#a.-f. 5.50 5.50

Wildlife — A403

Designs: 300ce, Black-faced impala. 500ce, Cheetah. 1000ce, Wildebeest. 3000ce, Hippopotamus.
No. 2164, vert.: a, Chimpanzee. b, Boomslang. c, Vulture. d, Leopard. e, Rhinoceros. f, Zebra. g, Crowned crane. h, Lesser kudu.
No. 2165, vert.: a, Purple roller. b, Pelicans. c, Egrets. d, Orange-breasted waxbill. e, Giraffe, f, African buffalo. g, African elephant. h, African lion.
No. 2166, 7000ce, Waterbuck. No. 2167, 7000ce, Ostrich.

**2000, Feb. 28 Litho. Perf. 14**
2160-2163 A403 Set of 4 3.00 3.00
2164 A403 1100ce Sheet of 8,
#a.-h. 6.25 6.25
2165 A403 1200ce Sheet of 8,
#a.-h. 6.50 6.50

**Souvenir Sheets**
2166-2167 A403 each 8.00 8.00

Tourism — A404

Designs: No. 2168: a, 300ce, Building, palm trees. b, 300ce, Mud building, natives. c, 300ce, Elephants. d, 1100ce, Natives. e, 1200ce, Natives carrying animal. f, 1800ce, Natives, diff.

**2000 Litho. Perf. 13x13¼**
2168 A404 Booklet pane of 6,
#a.-f. 5.00 5.00
Complete booklet, 4 #2168 20.00

There are 2 types of No. 2168, which differ only by the arrangement of the stamps on the pane. The booklet contains 2 of each type.

Wildlife — A405

Designs: 500ce, Zebra duiker. 600ce, Leopard. 2000ce, Bush buck. 3000ce, African wood owl.
No. 2173, 1600ce: a, Blotted genet. b, Tree pangolin. c, Bongo. d, Elephant. e, Flap-necked chameleon. f, West African dwarf crocodile.
No. 2174, 1600ce: a, Lowe's monkey. b, Diana monkey. c, Potto. d, Moustached monkey. e, Thomas's galago. f, Chimpanzee.
No. 2175, 1600ce: a, Gray parrot. b, Hoopoe. c, European roller. d, European bee-eater. e, Blue-breasted kingfisher. f, White-throated bee-eater.
No. 2176, 6000ce, Hippopotamus, vert. No. 2177, 6000ce, Great blue turaco, vert.

**2000, May 1 Litho. Perf. 14**
2169-2172 A405 Set of 4 3.50 3.50
**Sheets of 6, #a.-f.**
2173-2175 A405 Set of 3 13.00 13.00
**Souvenir Sheets**
2176-2177 A405 Set of 2 7.50 7.50

Mushrooms — A406

No. 2178, horiz.: a, Slippery jack. b, Violet deceiver. c, Fairy stool. d, Honey fungus. e, Shaggy parasol. f, Russula sp.
No. 2179, horiz.: a, Grisette. b, Common puffball. c, Fan. d, Gray chanterelle. e, Fairies' bonnets. f, Russula sp., diff.
5000ce, Great orange elf-cup. 8000ce, Bitter boletus.

**2000, May 15**
2178 A406 1500ce Sheet of 6,
#a.-f. 6.00 6.00
2179 A406 2000ce Sheet of 6,
#a.-f. 8.00 8.00

**Souvenir Sheets**
2180 A406 5000ce multi 3.00 3.00
2181 A406 8000ce multi 4.00 4.00
The Stamp Show 2000, London.

Eurasian Goldfinch — A406a

**2000, June 1 Litho. Perf. 13¾x13¼**
2181A A406a 300ce multi — —

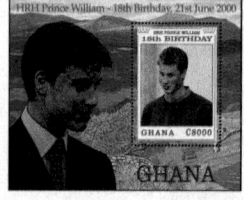

Prince William, 18th Birthday A407

No. 2182: a, In ski gear. b, With ribbons wrapped around fingers. c, With jacket, no tie. d, Close-up.
8000ce, In sweater.

**2000, June 26 Litho. Perf. 14**
2182 A407 2000ce Sheet of 4,
#a-d 5.50 5.50
**Souvenir Sheet**
**Perf. 13¾**
2183 A407 8000ce multi 5.50 5.50
No. 2182 contains four 28x42mm stamps.

First Zeppelin Flight, Cent. A408

No. 2184: a, LZ-129. b, LZ-9. c, LZ-4. 5000ce, LZ-11.

**2000, June 26 Perf. 13¾**
2184 A408 1600ce Sheet of 3,
#a-c 3.50 3.50
**Souvenir Sheet**
2185 A408 5000ce multi 4.25 4.25

Berlin Film Festival, 50th Anniv. A409

No. 2186: a, Wetherby. b, Die Frau und der Fremde. c, Hong Gao Liang (Red Sorghum). d, Skrivánci na Niti. e, Music Box. f, Tema. 6000ce, Justice Est Faite.

**2000, June 26 Perf. 14**
2186 A409 2000ce Sheet of 6,
#a-f 7.50 7.50
**Souvenir Sheet**
2187 A409 6000ce multi 4.00 4.00

Apollo-Soyuz Mission, 25th Anniv. — A410

No. 2188: a, Apollo 18. b, Docked spacecraft. c, Soyuz 19.
8000ce, Soyuz, Earth.

**2000, June 26**
2188 A410 4000ce Sheet of 3,
#a-c 6.50 6.50
**Souvenir Sheet**
2189 A410 8000ce multi 5.00 5.00

Souvenir Sheets

2000 Summer Olympics, Sydney — A411

No. 2190: a, Gymnastics. b, Long jump. c, Los Angeles Coliseum, and US flag. d, Ancient Greek chariot racer.

**2000, June 26**
2190 A411 1300ce Sheet of 4,
#a-d 4.50 4.50

Public Railways, 175th Anniv. — A412

No. 2191: a, Marc Seguin. b, Blenkinsop locomotive. c, Pumping station, Dawlish.

**2000, June 26**
2191 A412 4000ce Sheet of 3,
#a-c 7.00 7.00

Albert Einstein (1879-1955) — A413

**2000, June 26**      *Perf. 13¾*
2192 A413 8000ce multi    10.00 10.00

Ghana Home Economics Assoc. — A414

Designs: 300ce, Women, cooking pots. 700ce, Woman with home economics textbook, vert. 1200ce, Emblem, Alberta Ollennu, Patience A. Adow. 1800ce, Emblems, vert.

**2000**      *Perf. 13x13¼, 13¼x13*
2193-2196 A414 Set of 4    3.75 3.75

Space A415

No. 2197, horiz.: a, Mercury. b, Gemini. c, Apollo. d, Vostok. e, Voskhod 2. f, Soyuz.

**2000, June 26**   Litho.   *Perf. 14*
2197 A415 2000ce Sheet of 6,
       #a-f    7.75 7.75
**Souvenir Sheet**
2198 A415 2000ce Challenger
       51-L patch    6.00 6.00

World Stamp Expo 2000, Anaheim.

Cats and Dogs — A416

Designs: 1100ce, African shorthair. 1200ce, Russian Blue. 1800ce, Basenji. 2000ce, Basset hound.
No. 2203, horiz. a, 1600ce, Weimaraner. b, 1800ce, Keeshond. c, 1800ce, Fox terrier. d, 1800ce, Saluki. e, 1800ce, Dalmatian. f, 1800ce, English setter.
No. 2204, 1800ce, horiz.: a, Silver Persian. b, Creampoint Himalayan. c, British tortoiseshell shorthair. d, American shorthair tabby. e, Black Persian. f, Turkish Van.
No. 2205, 8000ce, Cocker spaniels. No. 2206, 8000ce, Lilac Persian.

**2000, Aug. 21**
2199-2202 A416 Set of 4    3.25 3.25
**Sheets of 6, #a-f**
2203-2204 A416 Set of 2    10.00 10.00
**Souvenir Sheets**
2205-2206 A416 Set of 2    8.00 8.00

Scenes from Tale of the White Snake A417

No. 2207, 2500ce: a, Xu Xian offers umbrella to White Lady and maid. b, White Lady (with basket) helps husband Xu Xian with business. c, Monk Fa Hai (with necklace) talks to Xu Xian. d, Xu Xian gives wine to wife. e, White Lady becomes snake, Xu Xian has heart attack. f, White Lady (with swords) trying to get medicinal herbs.
No. 2208, 2500ce: a, White Lady and maid at Fa Hai's temple. b, Maid threatens to kill Xu Xian. c, Fa Hai captures White Lady in bowl. d, Maid, Xu Xian at pagoda. e, Maid with sword attacks Fa Hai. f, Maid turns Fa Hai into crab. Illustration reduced.

**2001, Jan. 2**   Litho.   *Perf. 14*
**Sheets of 6, #a-f**
2207-2208 A417 Set of 2    8.50 8.50

New Year 2001 (Year of the snake).

Edward G. Robinson — A418

Color of photograph: a, Gray green. b, Lilac. c, Red violet (with hat). d, Brown (with cigar). e, Orange brown (with pipe). f, Blue green.

**2001, Apr. 16**   Litho.   *Perf. 14*
2209 A418 4000ce Sheet of 6,
       #a-f    6.00 6.00

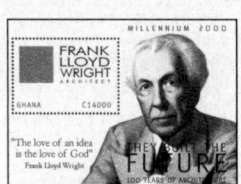

James Cagney A419

Color of photograph: a, Olive green. b, Emerald. c, Blue. d, Brown. e, Red violet. f, Orange.

**2001, Apr. 16**
2210 A419 4000ce Sheet of 6,
       #a-f    6.50 6.50

Millennium — A420

No. 2211, 2500ce — Architects: a, Walter Gropius. b, Aldo Rossi. c, Le Corbusier. d, Antonio Gaudi. e, Paolo Soleri. f, Ludwig Mies van de Rohe.
No. 2212, 2500ce — Artists: a, Wassily Kandinsky. b, Henry Moore. c, Marc Chagall. d, Norman Rockwell. e, Antonio López García. f, Frida Kahlo.
No. 2213, 14,000ce, Frank Lloyd Wright. No. 2214, 14,000ce, Pablo Picasso. No. 2215, 14,000ce, Human Genome Project.

**2001, Apr. 16**      **Sheets of 6, #a-f**
2211-2212 A420 Set of 2    8.00 8.00
**Souvenir Sheets**
2213-2215 A420 Set of 3    11.00 11.00

Jazz Musicians — A421

No. 2216, 4000ce: a, Scott Joplin. b, Clarence Williams. c, Sidney Bechet. d, Willie "The Lion" Smith. e, Ferdinand "Jelly Roll" Morton. f, Coleman "Bean" Hawkins.
No. 2217, 4000ce: a, Kid Ory. b, Earl "Fatha" Hines. c, Lil Hardin Armstrong. d, John Philip Sousa. e, James P. Johnson. f, Johnny St. Cyr.
No. 2218, 14,000ce, Joe "King" Oliver. No. 2219, 14,000ce, Louis "Satchmo" Armstrong.

**2001, Apr. 16**      **Sheets of 6, #a-f**
2216-2217 A421 Set of 2    12.50 12.50
**Souvenir Sheets**
2218-2219 A421 Set of 2    7.50 7.50

Oriental Art — A422

Designs: 500ce, Cranes, by Kano Eisenin Michinobu. 800ce, Flowers and Trees in Chen Chun's Style, by Tsubaki Chinzan. 1200ce, A Poetry Contest of 42 Matches, by unknown artist. 2000ce, Cranes, by Kano, diff. 5000ce, A Poetry Contest of 42 Matches, diff. 12,000ce, Plum Trees, by Tani Buncho.
No. 2226, 3000ce, vert. — The Tales of Ise, by Sumiyoshi Jokei: a, Chapter 1. b, Chapter 4. c, Chapter 6. d, Chapter 9 (Eastboud Trip, Mt. Utsu). e, Chapter 9, (Eastbound Trip, Mt. Fuji). f, Chapter 9, (Eastbound Trip, Blackheaded Gulls). g, Chapter 23, (Crossing Kawachi). h, Chapter 23, (By the Well Wall).
No. 2227, 4000ce, vert. — The Story of Sakyamuni, by unknown artist: a, Siddhartha's Excursion Through the South Gate. b, Siddhartha's Excursion Through the East Gate. c, Siddhartha's Excursion Through the North Gate. d, Siddhartha's Excursion Through the West Gate. e, Sakyamuni Entering Nirvana. f, Untitled.
No. 2228, 14,000ce, Cranes, by Kano (red denomination), diff. No. 2229, 14,000ce, Cranes, by Kano (yellow denomination), diff. No. 2230, 14,000ce, Chapter 1, by Sumiyoshi. No. 2231, Chapter 12, by Sumiyoshi.

**2001, Apr. 30**
2220-2225 A422 Set of 6    5.75 5.75
2226 A422 3000ce Sheet of 8,
       #a-h    6.50 6.50
2227 A422 4000ce Sheet of 6,
       #a-f    6.50 6.50
**Souvenir Sheets**
2228-2231 A422 Set of 4    14.00 14.00

Phila Nippon '01, Japan.

Automobiles A423

Designs: 2000ce, 1950 Bentley S Series convertible. 3000ce, 1948 Chrysler Town and Country. 5000ce, 1957 Lotus Elite. 6000ce, 1966 Chevrolet Corvette Sting Ray.
No. 2236, 4000ce: a, 1956-59 BMW 507. b, 1934 Bentley English Tourer. c, 1948 Morris Minor MM. d, 1954 Daimler SP-250 Dart. e, 1950 DeSoto custom convertible. f, 1955-60, Ford Thunderbird.
No. 2237, 4000ce: a,1959-63 Porshe 356B. b, 1962 Rolls-Royce Silver Cloud. c, 1958 Austin Healey Sprite MK-1. d, 1954-57 Mercedes 300SL. e, 1949 Citroen 2CV. f, 1949 Cadillac Series 62.

No. 2238, 14,000ce: a, 1933 Mercedes-Benz. No. 2239, 1953-55 Triumph TR-2.

**2001, June 18**
2232-2235 A423 Set of 4    4.50 4.50
**Sheets of 6, #a-f**
2236-2237 A423 Set of 2    12.50 12.50
**Souvenir Sheets**
2238-2239 A423 Set of 2    7.50 7.50

Belgica 2001 Intl. Stamp Exhibition, Brussels. No. 2238-2239 each contain one 85x28mm stamp.

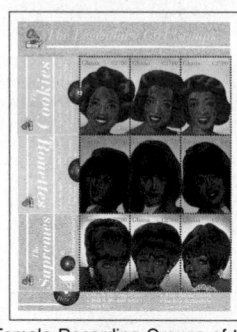

Female Recording Groups of the 1960s — A424

No. 2240 — Various members of: a-c, The Cookies. d-f, The Ronettes. g-i, The Supremes.

**2001, Apr. 16**   Litho.   *Perf. 14*
2240 A424 2700ce Sheet of 9,
       #a-i    6.50 6.50

Mao Zedong (1893-1976) — A425

No. 2241: a, With arm raised, orange and light orange background. b, Portrait. c, With arm raised, tan gray and blue background. 12,000ce, With flag.

**2001, Aug. 27**
2241 A425 7000ce Sheet of 3,
       #a-c    6.00 6.00
**Souvenir Sheet**
2242 A425 12,000ce multi    3.50 3.50

Giuseppe Verdi (1813-1901), Opera Composer — A426

No. 2243: a, Verdi. b, Scores for Aida and Rigoletto. c, Verdi's birthplace. d, Map of Italy. 13,000ce, Verdi and score.

**2001, Aug. 27**
2243 A426 5000ce Sheet of 4,
       #a-d    5.50 5.50
**Souvenir Sheet**
2244 A426 13,000ce multi    3.50 3.50

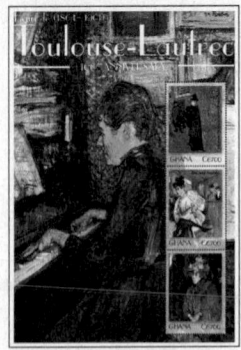

Toulouse-Lautrec Paintings — A427

No. 2245: a, Jane Avril Leaving the Moulin Rouge. b, Jane Avril Dancing. c, Jane Avril Entering the Moulin Rouge.

**2001, Aug. 27**     *Perf. 13¾*
2245 A427 6700ce Sheet of 3,
    #a-c     5.50 5.50

Monet Paintings — A428

No. 2246, horiz.: a, Zaandam. b, On the Seine at Bennecourt. c, The Studio Boat. d, Houses on the Waterfront, Zaandam.
15,000ce, Madame Gaudibert.

**2001, Aug. 27**
2246 A428 5000ce Sheet of 4,
    #a-d     5.50 5.50
    **Souvenir Sheet**
2247 A428 15,000ce multi     4.00 4.00

Queen Victoria (1819-1901) — A429

No. 2248: a, Victoria. b, Prince Albert. c, Albert and Victoria. d, Victoria and Albert on wedding day.
12,000ce, Victoria with green and white headpiece.

**2001, Aug. 27**     *Perf. 14*
2248 A429 5000ce Sheet of 4,
    #a-d     5.50 5.50
    **Souvenir Sheet**
2249 A429 12,000ce multi     3.25 3.25

Queen Elizabeth II, 75th Birthday A430

No. 2250, vert.: a, Bright pink hat. b, White hat. c, Peach hat. d, Crown. e, Blue and pink hat. f, In uniform.
15,000ce, with Prince Philip.

**2001, Aug. 27**
2250 A430 4000ce Sheet of 6,
    #a-f     6.50 6.50
    **Souvenir Sheet**
2251 A430 15,000ce multi     4.00 4.00

Whales — A431

Designs: 1000ce, Killer whale. 3000ce, Narwhal. 5000ce, Beluga. 6000ce, Bowhead whale.
No. 2256, 4000ce: a, Blue whale. b, Killer whale, diff. c, Northern bottlenose whale. d, Sperm whale. e, Southern right whale. f, Pygmy right whale.
No. 2257, 4000ce: a, Humpback whale. b, Fin whale. c, Bowhead whale, diff. d, Gray whale. e, Narwhal, diff. f, Beluga, diff.
No. 2258, 14,000ce, Sperm whale. No. 2259, 14,000ce, Blue whales.

**2001, Oct. 1**
2252-2255 A431   Set of 4    6.00 6.00
    **Sheets of 6, #a-f**
2256-2257 A431   Set of 2    19.00 19.00
    **Souvenir Sheets**
2258-2259 A431   Set of 2    13.00 13.00

Rotary Intl. In Ghana, 40th Anniv. (in 1998) — A432

Rotary Intl. emblem and: 300ce, Polio victim. 1100ce, Clean water. 1200ce, Founder Paul Harris. 1800ce, Blood donation.

**2001 ?**     *Perf. 13¼*
2260-2263 A432   Set of 4    2.25 2.25

Orchids — A433

Designs: 1100ce, Paphiopedilum hennisianum. 1200ce, Vuylstekeara cambria Plush. 1800ce, Cymbidium ormoulu. 2000ce, Phalaenopsis Barbara Moler.
No. 2268, 4500ce: a, Cattleya capra. b, Odontoglossum rossii. c, Epidendrum pseudepidendrum. d, Encyclia cochleata. e, Cymbidium baldoyle Melbury. f, Phalaenopsis asean.
No. 2269, 4500ce: a, Odontocidium Tigersun. b, Miltonia Emotion. c, Odontonia sappho Excul. d, Cymbidium Bulbarrow. e, Dendrobium nobile. f, Paphiopedilum insigne.
No. 2270, 15,000ce, Calanthe vestita. No. 2271, 15,000ce, Angraecum eburneum.

**2001, Oct. 30**   *Litho.*    *Perf. 14*
2264-2267 A433   Set of 4    2.75 2.75

    **Sheets of 6, #a-f**
2268-2269 A433   Set of 2    16.00 16.00
    **Souvenir Sheets**
2270-2271 A433   Set of 2    9.00 9.00

Musical Instruments — A434

No. 2272: a, Bamboo orchestra. b, Mmensuon. c, Fontomfrom. d, Pati.

**2001, Dec. 3**     *Perf. 14¼*
2272 A434 4000ce Sheet of 4,
    #a-d     4.50 4.50

**Queen Mother Type of 1999 Redrawn**

No. 2273: a, Lady Elizabeth Bowles-Lyon with brother David, 1904. b, In Rhodesia, 1957. c, In 1970. d, In 1992.
5000ce, In 1970, diff.

**2001, Dec.**     *Perf. 14*
    **Yellow Orange Frames**
2273 A392 2000ce Sheet of 4,
    #a-d, + label 4.50 4.50
    **Souvenir Sheet**
    *Perf. 13¾*
2274 A392 5000ce multi     3.00 3.00
Queen Mother's 101st birthday. No. 2274 contains one 38x50mm stamp with a darker background than on No. 2125. Sheet margins of Nos. 2273-2274 lack embossing and gold arms and frames found on Nos. 2124-2125.

Kwame Nkrumah University of Science and Technology, Kumasi, 50th Anniv. — A435

Designs: 300ce, Emblem. No. 2276, 700ce, No. 2280a, 4000ce, Main gate. No. 2277, 1100ce, No. 2280b, 4000ce, Dairy production. No. 2278, 1200ce, No. 2280c, 4000ce, Pharmacy Department. No. 2279, 1800ce, No. 2280d, 4000ce, Residence hall.

**2001**     *Perf. 13x13¼*
2275-2279 A435   Set of 5    2.00 2.00
    **Souvenir Sheet**
2280 A435 4000ce Sheet of 4,
    #a-d     4.25 4.25

For surcharge, see No. 2683.

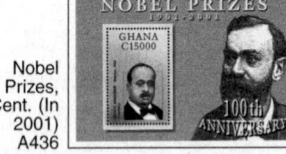

Nobel Prizes, Cent. (In 2001) A436

No. 2281, 4000ce — Chemistry laureates: a, George A. Olah, 1994. b, Kary Mullis, 1993. c, Sir Harold W. Kroto, 1996. d, Richard R. Ernst, 1991. e, Ahmed H. Zewail, 1999. f, Paul Crutzen, 1995.
No. 2282, 4000ce — Chemistry laureates: a, John E. Walker, 1997. b, Jens C. Skou, 1997. c, Alan G. MacDiarmid, 2000. d, Thomas Robert Cech, 1989. e, John Pole, 1998. f, Rudolph A. Marcus, 1992.
No. 2283, 4000ce — Chemistry laureates: a, Walter Kohn, 1998. b, F. Sherwood Rowland, 1995. c, Mario Molina, 1995. d, Hideki Shirakawa, 2000. e, Paul D. Boyer, 1997. f, Richard Smalley, 1996.
No. 2284, 15,000ce, Svante Arrhenius, Chemistry, 1903. No. 2285, 15,000ce, Alfred Werner, Chemistry, 1913. No. 2286, 15,000ce, Peter Debye, Chemistry, 1936. No. 2287, 15,000ce, Wole Soyinka, Literature, 1986. No. 2288, 15,000ce, Nelson Mandela, Peace, 1993.

**2002, Jan. 9**     *Perf. 14*
    **Sheets of 6, #a-f**
2281-2283 A436   Set of 3    19.00 19.00
    **Souvenir Sheets**
2284-2288 A436   Set of 5    20.00 20.00

Reign of Queen Elizabeth II, 50th Anniv. A437

No. 2289: a, Wearing pink dress. b, Sitting on horse. c, Looking at horses. d, In carriage with Prince Philip.
15,000ce, Sitting with Prince Philip (black and white photograph).

**2002, Feb. 6**   *Litho.*    *Perf. 14¼*
2289 A437 6500ce Sheet of 4,
    #a-d     7.00 7.00
    **Souvenir Sheet**
2290 A437 15,000ce multi     4.25 4.25

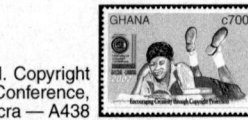

Intl. Copyright Conference, Accra — A438

Designs: 300ce, Conference emblem, vert. 700ce, Person reading. 1100ce, Spider, web, map of Ghana. 1200ce, Map of Ghana, Kente cloth. 1800ce, Drummer.

**2002, Feb. 20**   *Perf. 14¼x14, 14x14¼*
2291-2295 A438   Set of 5    1.75 1.75

2002 World Cup Soccer Championships, Japan and Korea — A439

World Cup trophy and: 100ce, Jay Jay Okacha, flag of Nigeria. 150ce, South African player and flag. 300ce, Pele, flag of Brazil. 400ce, Roger Milla, flag of Cameroun. 500ce, Bobby Charlton, flag of England. 800ce, Michel Platini, flag of France. 1000ce, Franz Beckenbauer, flag of West Germany. 1500ce, Ulsan Munsu Stadium, Korea, horiz. 2000ce, German player and flag. 3000ce, Brazilian player and flag. 4000ce, Korean player and flag. 5000ce, Yokohama Intl. Sports Stadium, Japan, horiz. 6000ce, Italian player and flag. 11,000ce, 1950 World Cup poster. 12,000ce, 1934 World Cup poster.
No. 2311, 15,000ce, Geoff Hurst's hat trick for England, 1966. No. 2312, 15,000ce, Gordon Banks making save on Pele, 1970.

**2002, Mar. 4**     *Perf. 14*
2296-2310 A439   Set of 15   12.50 12.50
    **Souvenir Sheets**
2311-2312 A439   Set of 2    8.50 8.50

Souvenir Sheet

New Year 2002 (Year of the Horse) A440

No. 2313: a, Brown panel at L, country name at LR. b, Brown panel at R, country name at UR. c, Brown panel at L, country name at LL. d, Brown panel at R, country name at LR.

**2002, Mar. 4**     **Perf. 13¾**
2313   A440 4000ce Sheet of 4, #a-d    4.75 4.75

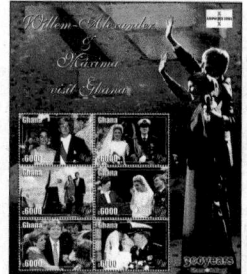

Visit of Netherlands Prince Willem-Alexander and Princess Máxima to Ghana — A441

Couple: a, With Prince wearing sash. b, Holding hands, Prince wearing hat. c, With windmills and flags. d, At wedding ceremony, with another man. e, In crowd. f, Kissing.

**2002**     **Perf. 14**
2314   A441 6000ce Sheet of 6, #a-f    8.50 8.50

Amphilex 2002 Intl. Stamp Show, Amsterdam.

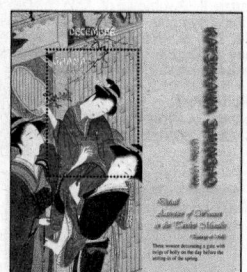

Paintings of Shunsho Katsukawa — A442

No. 2315, 9000ce — Activities of Women in the Twelve Months: a, Trying to retrieve a ball caught in a tree (March). b, Listening to a cuckoo in the bedroom (April). c, Holding a cage filled with fireflies for a woman to read a book (May).

No. 2316, 9000ce — Activities of Women in the Twelve Months: a, Mother and child taking a tub bath while woman holds a revolving lantern (June). b, Strips of paper with wishes and poems are tied on bamboo (July). c, Women enjoying the cool air on a boat (August).

No. 2317, 9000ce — Activities of Women in the Twelve Months: a, Celebrating Feast of the Chrysanthemum (September). b, Looking out for colored leaves (October). c, Mother reading picture book while sitting at a foot warmer (November).

No. 2318, 15,000ce, Three women decorating a gate (woman in blue kimono), from Activities of Women in the Twelve Months. No. 2319, 15,000ce, Part 1 (woman in red kimono) from Snow, Moonlight and Flowers. No. 2320, 15,000ce, Part 2 (woman in black kimono) from Snow, Moonlight and Flowers. No. 2321,

15,000ce, Part 3 (woman in gray kimono) from Snow, Moonlight and Flowers.

**2002, July 29**   **Litho.**   **Perf. 14¼**
**Sheets of 3, #a-c**
2315-2317 A442 Set of 3    19.00 19.00
**Souvenir Sheets**
2318-2321 A442 Set of 4    14.00 14.00

United We Stand — A443

**2002, Aug. 15**     **Perf. 14**
2322   A443 7000ce multi    3.25 3.25

Printed in sheets of 4.

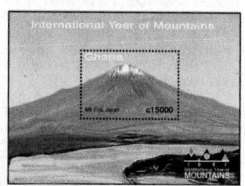

2002 Winter Olympics, Salt Lake City — A444

Designs: No. 2323, 7000ce, Figure skaters. No. 2324, 7000ce, Freestyle skier.

**2002, Aug. 15**
2323-2324 A444   Set of 2    3.50 3.50
2324a   Souvenir sheet, #2323-2324   3.75 3.75

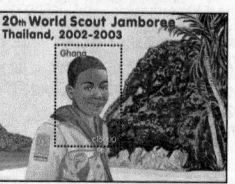

Intl. Year of Mountains — A445

No. 2325: a, Tateyama, Japan. b, Mt. Shivling, India. c, Wong Leng, Hong Kong. d, Mt. Blanc, France.
15,000ce, Mt. Fuji, Japan.

**2002, Aug. 15**
2325   A445   6000ce Sheet of 4, #a-d    6.00 6.00
**Souvenir Sheet**
2326   A445 15,000ce multi    3.75 3.75

20th World Scout Jamboree, Thailand — A446

No. 2327, horiz.: a, Scout with walking stick. b, Scout with backpack. c, Tent and campfire. d, Tent and scout tying knots.
15,000ce, Scout with red neckerchief.

**2002, Aug. 15**
2327   A446   6500ce Sheet of 4, #a-d    6.00 6.00
**Souvenir Sheet**
2328   A446 15,000ce multi    4.25 4.25

First Solo Transatlantic Flight, 75th Anniv. — A447

No. 2329, 8500ce, horiz.: a, Charles Lindbergh and Spirit of St. Louis. b, Charles and Anne Morrow Lindbergh in airplane.
15,000ce, Lindbergh wearing flying gear.

**2002, Aug. 15**
2329   A447   8500ce Sheet of 2, #a-b    4.00 4.00
**Souvenir Sheet**
2330   A447 15,000ce multi    3.75 3.75

Intl. Year of Ecotourism — A448

No. 2331: a, Nectarinia venusta. b, Panthera pardus. c, Kobus kob. d, Syncerus caffer. e, Pan troglodytes. f, Galago.
12,000ce, Loxodonta africana.

**2002, Aug. 15**
2331   A448   4000ce Sheet of 6, #a-f    9.50 9.50
**Souvenir Sheet**
2332   A448 12,000ce multi    5.00 5.00

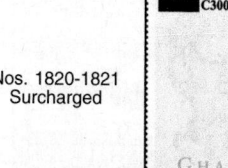

Nos. 1820-1821 Surcharged

**2002, Aug. 15**     **Perf. 13½x14**
2333    Strip or block of 4    3.00 3.00
  a.   A315 3000ce on 600ce #1820a   .75 .75
  b.   A315 3000ce on 600ce #1820b   .75 .75
  c.   A315 3000ce on 600ce #1820c   .75 .75
  d.   A315 3000ce on 600ce #1820d   .75 .75
**Souvenir Sheet**
2334   A315 20,000ce on 2500ce #1821    5.00 5.00

No. 2334 and sheets of No. 2333 are additionally overprinted in margin with black border and inscription "In Memoriam / 1900-2002."

Butterflies, Moths, Insects and Birds — A449

No. 2335, 4500ce — Butterflies: a, Iolaus menas. b, Neptis melicerta. c, Cymothoe lucasi. d, Euphaedra francina. e, Lilac nymph. f, Mocker swallowtail.

No. 2336, 4500ce — Moths: a, Phiala cunina. b, Mazuca strigicincta. c, Steindachner's emperor. d, Amphicallia pactolicus. e, Verdant sphinx. f, Oleander hawkmoth.

No. 2337, 4500ce — Insects: a, Bush hopper. b, Ant lion. c, Digger bee. d, Stag beetle. e, Mantis. f, Longhorn beetle.

No. 2338, 4500ce — Birds: a, Malachite kingfisher. b, Brown harrier eagle. c, Heuglin's masked weaver. d, Egyptian plover. e, Swallow-tailed bee-eater. f, Black-faced fire finch.

No. 2339, 15,000ce, Giant blue swallowtail butterfly. No. 2340, 15,000ce, African moon moth. No. 2341, 15,000ce, Mantis nymph. No. 2342, 15,000ce, Rufous fishing owl.

**2002, Aug. 26**     **Perf. 14**
**Sheets of 6, #a-f**
2335-2338 A449   Set of 4    25.00 25.00
**Souvenir Sheets**
2339-2342 A449   Set of 4    14.00 14.00

Edina Bakatue Festival — A450

Designs: No. 2343, 1000ce, No. 2349e, 4000ce, Casting of net. No. 2344, 2000ce, No. 2349b, 4000ce, Chief in palanquin. No. 2345, 2500ce, No. 2349c, 4000ce, Regatta. No. 2346, 3000ce, No. 2349d, 4000ce, Festival boat. No. 2347, 4000ce, Opening ritual. No. 2348, 5000ce, No. 2349a, 4000ce, Priestesses.

**2002, Oct. 21**     **Perf. 14x13½**
2343-2348 A450   Set of 6    4.00 4.00
2349   A450   Sheet of 6, #2347, 2349a-e    5.50 5.50

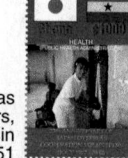

Japan Overseas Cooperation Volunteers, 25th Anniv. in Ghana — A451

Designs: No. 2350, 1000ce, Health. No. 2351, 1000ce, Education (Home economics). 2000ce, Education (Science and math). 2500ce, Education (Computer technology). 3000ce, Sports.

No. 2355 (without white inscriptions): a, Like 2000ce. b, Like No. 2350. c, Like 3000ce. d, Like 2500ce. e, Like No. 2351.

**2002, Oct. 23**     **Perf. 14**
2350-2354 A451   Set of 5    2.40 2.40
2355   A451 4000ce Sheet of 5, #a-e    5.00 5.00

Awarding of Nobel Peace Prize to UN Secretary General Kofi Annan — A452

Designs: 1000ce, With Ghana Pres. J. A. Kufuor at award ceremony. 2000ce, With Nobel medal and citation. 2500ce, Portrait. 3000ce, In academic procession at Kwame Nkrumah University.

**2002, Oct. 28**
2356-2359 A452   Set of 4    3.50 3.50

No. 1939C Surcharged

No. 1939B Surcharged

**Methods and Perfs As Before**
**2002, Mar. 7**
2360   A350c 1000ce on 1100ce multi, 10½x6mm obliterator   — —
  b.   Obliterator 10½x4mm   — —
2360A   A350b 2500ce on 800ce multi   — —

Obliterator on No. 2360 is 10½x6mm.

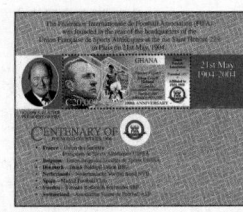

FIFA (Fédération Internationale de Football Association), Cent. — A484

No. 2460: a, Roberto Di Matteo. b, Marcel Desailly. c, Osei Kufuor. d, Eusebio. 20,000ce, Johan Cruyff.

**2005, Mar. 14**     **Perf. 13¼**
2460 A484   7500ce Sheet of 4,
     #a-d     7.25 7.25

**Souvenir Sheet**
2461 A484 20,000ce multi     4.75 4.75

Ipomoea Asarifolia — A485

**2005 ?**   **Litho.**   **Perf. 13¾x13½**
2462 A485 2000ce multi     — —

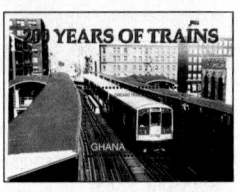

Trains A486

No. 2463, 5000ce: a, Stanier Class 5-4-6-0. b, Central Pacific Jupiter. c, Robe River RSC3 Class 9401. d, Bangkok BTS train. e, Stream-lined tank locomotive. f, ETR450.
No. 2464, 5000ce: a, Talgo train, Spain. b, VIA Turbotrain, Canada. c, Southern Pacific 4-8-4 #4449. d, Union Pacific "City of Portland." e, Shinkansen, Japan (white denomination). f, Deltic Diesel-electric engine, Great Britain.
No. 2465, 5000ce: a, Mogul 2-6-0. b, Milwaukee Railroad 4-6-2. c, Shinkansen (red denomination). d, Former Reading #2101 4-8-4. e, HST Inter-city 125. f, Daylight train.
No. 2466: a, Baldwin 4-6-0 steam train. b, Atchison, Topeka & Santa Fe 4-4-0 "American" steam train. c, Baldwin 4-6-0 Engine #44. d, Baldwin 2-6-0 #3 Three-spot.
No. 2467, 20,000ce, Chicago Transit Authority train. No. 2468, 20,000ce, Santa Fe train. No. 2469, 20,000ce, Empire Builder. No. 2470, 20,000ce, LMS 5305 steam train.

**2005, June 1**   **Litho.**   **Perf. 12¾**
    **Sheets of 6, #a-f**
2463-2465 A486   Set of 3   20.00 20.00
2466 A486 8000ce Sheet of 4,
     #a-d     7.00 7.00

**Souvenir Sheets**
2467-2470 A486   Set of 4   18.00 18.00

Motor Vehicles — A487

Designs: 2000ce, Setra State Transport bus. 4000ce, Albium double-decker bus. 4500ce, Bedford Mummy truck and trailer. 5000ce, 1925 Mail carrier. 6000ce, Morris truck.

**2005, June 21**   **Litho.**   **Perf. 13x13¼**
2471-2475 A487   Set of 5   5.00 5.00

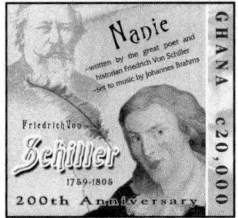

Friedrich von Schiller (1759-1805), Writer — A488

No. 2476: a, Schiller, with hand touching head. b, Schiller and birthplace. c, Brahms with beard.
20,000ce, Portraits of Schiller and Johannes Brahms.

**2005**   **Litho.**   **Perf. 13¼**
2476 A488 11,000ce Sheet of 3,
     #a-c     7.25 7.25

**Imperf**
2477 A488 20,000ce shown     4.75 4.75

No. 2476 contains three 42x28mm stamps.

World Cup Soccer Championships, 75th Anniv. — A489

No. 2478: a, 1938 Italian team. b, Scene from 1938 Italy vs. Hungary match. c, Olympic Stadium. d, Silvio Piola.
20,000ce, Italian team with World Cup.

**2005**     **Perf. 13¼**
2478 A489   8000ce Sheet of 4,
     #a-d     7.25 7.25

**Souvenir Sheet**
2479 A489 20,000ce multi     4.75 4.75

Panafest 05 — A489a

Inscriptions: No. 2479A, Biribi wo soro (a symbol of hope). No. 2479B, A royal entry, horiz. No. 2479C, 4000ce, Let's hold hands together, horiz. No. 2479D, 4500ce, Clarion call for Black Unity, horiz. No. 2479E, Sankofa (back to your roots). No. 2479F, Bi-nnka-bi (bite not one another), horiz. No. 2479G, 6000ce, Nkyinkyim (changing oneself; playing many roles).

    **Perf. 13½x13¼, 13¼x13½**
**2005 ?**     **Litho.**
2479A A489a 2000ce multi     —
2479B A489a 2000ce multi     —
2479C A489a 4000ce multi     —
2479D A489a 4500ce multi     —
2479E A489a 5000ce multi     —
2479F A489a 5000ce multi     —
2479G A489a 6000ce multi     —

The editors would like to examine any examples of any additional stamps that might exist in this set.

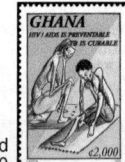

Disease Treatment and Prevention — A490

Designs: No. 2480, 2000ce, Emaciated people on rugs. No. 2481, 2000ce, Map of Ghana, symbols of medicine, red ribbon. No. 2482, 2000ce, People holding signs, horiz. 3000ce, Red ribbon, head. 4000ce, Maps of Africa and Ghana, arms, stylized people. No. 2485, 4500ce, Diseases on ladder destroying human body of bricks. No. 2486, 4500ce, Hand holding egg depicting health care workers. No. 2487, 5000ce, Emaciated man carrying bags of diseases. No. 2488, 5000ce, Heart, man lifting stylized globe. 6000ce, Whistle, hands holding cards with slogans.

**2006, Jan. 26**   **Perf. 13¼x13, 13x13¼**
2480-2489 A490   Set of 10   8.50 8.50

National Basketball Association Players and Team Emblems — A491

No. 2490, 3500ce: a, Carlos Boozer. b, Utah Jazz emblem
No. 2491, 3500ce: a, Carlos Arroyo. b, Detroit Pistons emblem.
No. 2492, 3500ce: a, Corey Magette. b, Los Angeles Clippers emblem.
No. 2493, 3500ce: a, David Wesley. b, Houston Rockets emblem.
No. 2494, 3500ce: a, Manu Ginobili. b, San Antonio Spurs emblem.
No. 2495, 3500ce: a, Al Harrington. b, Atlanta Hawks emblem.

**2006, Mar. 15**     **Perf. 13¼**
  **Sheets of 12, 10 each #a, 2 each #b**
2490-2495 A491   Set of 6   55.00 55.00

A492

A493

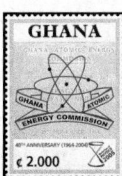

Elvis Presley (1935-77) — A494

No. 2496 — Background color: a, Lilac. b, Green. c, Yellow green. d, Blue.
No. 2497 — Face color: a, Lilac. b, Green. c, Yellow green. d, Blue.
No. 2498: a, Blue background. b, Green background with dark red halo, ghost image at right. c, Yellow background with orange halo. d, Green background with orange red halo, ghost image above head. e, Yellow background, ghost image showing teeth at left. f, Yellow background, gray area at right. g, Green background, blue halo.

**2006, Mar. 15**     **Perf. 14**
2496 A492 8000ce Sheet of 4,
     #a-d     7.00 7.00
2497 A493 8000ce Sheet of 4,
     #a-d     7.00 7.00
2498 A494 3500ce Sheet of 9,
     #a-f, 3 #g     7.00 7.00

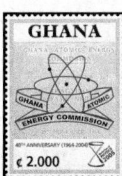

Intl. Year of Physics (in 2005) — A495

Designs: 2000ce, Emblem of Ghana Atomic Energy Commission. 4000ce, Ghana research reactor. 4500ce, Albert Einstein. 5000ce, Prof. Francis K. Allotey, physicist. 6000ce, Electricity experiment in physics laboratory.

**2006. Mar. 29**     **Perf. 13¼x14**
2499-2503 A495   Set of 5   7.25 7.25

Pope John Paul II (1920-2005) — A496

**2006, Apr. 7**     **Perf. 13¼**
2504 A496 12,000ce multi     2.75 2.75
    Printed in sheets of 4.

Battle of Trafalgar, Bicent. (in 2005) — A497

Designs: 2000ce, Sir John Jervis. 3000ce, Chase and Race. 5000ce, Goliath fires at Guerrier, horiz. 10,000ce, Death of Adm. Horatio Nelson, horiz.
20,000ce, Napoleon's flagships, Agamemnon. Vanguard, Elephant and Captain, horiz.

**2006, Apr. 7**   **Perf. 13x13¼, 13¼x13**
2505-2508 A497   Set of 4   4.50 4.50

**Souvenir Sheet**
    **Perf. 12**
2509 A497 20,000ce multi     4.50 4.50

Jules Verne (1828-1905), Writer — A498

No. 2510: a, Verne. b, Original book illustrations of balloons in flight. c, Montgolfier hot air balloon. d, Modern hot air balloon.
20,000ce, The Hindenburg.

**2006, Apr. 7**     **Perf. 12¾**
2510 A498 8000ce Sheet of 4,
     #a-d     7.50 7.50

**Souvenir Sheet**
2511 A498 20,000ce multi     5.00 5.00

2006 World Cup Soccer Championships, Germany — A499

Designs: No. 2512, 2000ce, Line of Ghana Black Stars players. No. 2513, 2000ce, Captain Stephen Appiah and opposing player, vert. No. 2514, 4000ce, Exchange of pennants. No. 2515, 4000ce, Joy of success. No. 2516, 4500ce, Michael Essien. No. 2517, 4500ce, Franz Beckenbauer, FIFA World Cup Stadium, Hanover. No. 2518, 5000ce, Scene from Ghana vs. Burkina Faso match. No. 2519, 5000ce, Black Stars team photo. No. 2520, 6000ce, Scene from Ghana vs. South Africa match. No. 2521, 6000ce, Fans celebrating Black Stars victory.
No. 2522, 4000ce: a, Appiah. b, Issah Ahmed. c, John Paintsil. d, Laryea Kingston. e, Essien, diff. f, Sule Ali Muntari. g, Joe Tex Frimpong. h, Coach Ratomir Dujkovic.
No. 2523, 4000ce: a, Asamoah Gyan. b, Sammy Adjei. c, Matthew Amoah. d, John Mensah. e, Emmanuel Pappoe. f, Mark Caniel

Edusei. g, Abubakari Yakubu. h, Godwin Attram.

**2006, May 18**     **Perf. 13½**
2512-2521 A499   Set of 10   9.50   9.50
**Sheets of 8, #a-h**
**Perf. 13¼**
2522-2523 A499   Set of 2   14.00   14.00
Nos. 2522-2523 each contain eight 42x28mm stamps.

Tympanotonus Fuscatus — A500

Synodontis Ocellifer — A500a

Musa Sapientum — A501

Gomphidius Glutinosus — A501a

Bebearia Arcadius — A502

Polemaetus Bellicosus — A502a

Xaphia Gladius (Denomination at Center) A503

Euphaedra Francina A504

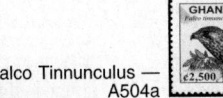

Falco Tinnunculus — A504a

Lagerstroemia Flos-reginae — A504b

Ardea Purpurea (With Brown Frame and "A's" of "Ghana" With Horizontal Cross Lines — A504c

Spathodea Campanulata — A505

**2003-07**    **Litho.**     **Perf. 13½**
2524   A500   500ce multi   27.50   5.00
2524A   A500a   500ce multi   27.50   5.00
2525   A501   800ce multi   10.00   5.00
2525A   A501a   1000ce multi
2526   A502   1500ce multi   27.50   5.00
2526A   A502a   1500ce multi   27.50   5.00
2527   A503   2000ce multi    —   —
2528   A504   2000ce multi    —   —
2528A   A504a   2500ce multi   27.50   5.00
2528B   A504b   4000ce multi    —   —
2528C   A504c   5000ce multi   16.50   5.00
2529   A505   6000ce multi    —   —
Nos. 2524-2529 (12)   136.50   30.00

Issued: No. 2524, July 2003; Nos. 2524A, 2528B, Oct. 2005. No. 2525A, 2529, 2006; Nos. 2526A, 2528A, 2528C, 2007; No. 2527, 2005.
Compare No. 2527 with No. 1838.

---

For surcharge see No. 2679.

Nos. 1674-1677 Surcharged

**2006, Aug. 28**    **Litho.**     **Perf. 14**
2530   A284   2000ce on 50ce
      #1674   29.00   10.00
2531   A284   2000ce on 200ce
      #1675   29.00   10.00
2532   A284   2000ce on 500ce
      #1676   29.00   10.00
2533   A284   2000ce on 800ce
      #1677   29.00   10.00
Nos. 2530-2533 (4)   116.00   40.00

**Nos. 1810-1814 Surcharged**

**2006, Aug. 28**    **Litho.**     **Perf. 14**
2534   A312   2000ce on 200ce
      #1810   .45   .45
2535   A312   2000ce on 300ce
      #1811   .45   .45
2536   A312   2000ce on 400ce
      #1812   .45   .45
2537   A312   2000ce on 600ce
      #1813   .45   .45
2538   A312   2000ce on 800ce
      #1814   .45   .45
Nos. 2534-2538 (5)   2.25   2.25

**Nos. 1703-1708 Surcharged**

**2006, Aug. 28**    **Litho.**     **Perf. 14**
2539   A291   3000ce on 50ce
      #1703   .65   .65
2540   A291   3000ce on 100ce
      #1704   .65   .65
2541   A291   3000ce on 200ce
      #1705   .65   .65
2542   A291   3000ce on 400ce
      #1706   .65   .65
2543   A291   3000ce on 600ce
      #1707   .65   .65
2544   A291   3000ce on 800ce
      #1708   .65   .65
Nos. 2539-2544 (6)   3.90   3.90

**Nos. 1741-1743 Surcharged**

**2006, Aug. 28**    **Litho.**     **Perf. 14**
2545   A300   4000ce on 50ce
      #1741   .90   .90
2546   A300   4000ce on 200ce
      #1742   .90   .90
2547   A300   4000ce on 600ce
      #1743   .90   .90
Nos. 2545-2547 (3)   2.70   2.70

**Nos. 1738-1740 Surcharged**

**2006, Aug. 28**    **Litho.**     **Perf. 14**
2548   A299   4500ce on 100ce
      #1738   1.00   1.00
2549   A299   4500ce on 400ce
      #1739   1.00   1.00

---

2550   A299   4500ce on 1000ce
      #1740   1.00   1.00
Nos. 2548-2550 (3)   3.00   3.00

Nos. 1745-1752 Surcharged

**2006, Aug. 28**    **Litho.**     **Perf. 14**
2551   A301   5000ce on 50ce
      #1745   1.10   1.10
2552   A301   5000ce on 100ce
      #1746   1.10   1.10
2553   A301   5000ce on 150ce
      #1747   1.10   1.10
2554   A301   5000ce on 200ce
      #1748   1.10   1.10
2555   A301   5000ce on 400ce
      #1749   1.10   1.10
2556   A301   5000ce on 600ce
      #1750   1.10   1.10
2557   A301   5000ce on 800ce
      #1751   1.10   1.10
2558   A301   5000ce on 1000ce
      #1752   1.10   1.10
Nos. 2551-2558 (8)   8.80   8.80

**Nos. 1766-1768 Surcharged**

**2006, Aug. 28**    **Litho.**     **Perf. 14**
2559   A299   6000ce on 100ce
      #1766   1.25   1.25
2560   A299   6000ce on 400ce
      #1767   1.25   1.25
2561   A299   6000ce on 1000ce
      #1768   1.25   1.25
Nos. 2559-2561 (3)   3.75   3.75

**Miniature Sheets**

Ghana Soccer Players A506

No. 2562, 4000ce: a, Asamoah Gyan. b, Sammy Adjei. c, Matthew Amoah. d, John Mensah. e, Emmanuel Pappoe. f, Mark Daniel Edusei. g, Abubakari Yakubu. h, Godwin Attram.
No. 2563, 4000ce: a, Stephen Appiah. b, Issah Ahmed. c, John Paintsil. d, Laryea Kingston. e, Michael Essien. f, Sule Ali Muntari. g, Joe Tex Frimpong. h, Ghana Team Coach Ratomir Dujkovic.

**2007, Jan. 22**    **Litho.**     **Perf. 13½**
**Sheets of 8, #a-h**
2562-2563 A506   Set of 2   14.00   14.00

Queen Elizabeth II, 80th Birthday A507

No. 2564: a, Holding flowers. b, Wearing purple hat. c, Wearing light green hat, denomination in purple. d, Wearing light green hat, denomination in white.
25,000ce, Wearing tiara.

**2007, Jan. 22**
2564   A507   6000ce Sheet of 4,
      #a-d   5.25   5.25
**Souvenir Sheet**
2565   A507   25,000ce multi   5.50   5.50

---

Marilyn Monroe (1926-62), Actress — A508

No. 2566: a, Wearing glasses. b, Wearing bathrobe. c, Looking left. d, Wearing red dress and earrings.
20,000ce, With eyes closed.

**2007, Jan. 22**
2566   A508   9000ce Sheet of 4,
      #a-d   8.00   8.00
**Souvenir Sheet**
2567   A508   20,000ce multi   4.50   4.50

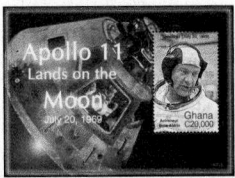

Space Achievements — A509

No. 2568, horiz. — Luna 9: a, Distant view of spacecraft and moon, denomination in black. b, Spacecraft, denomination in white. c, Close-up view of spacecraft and moon, denomination in black. d, Spacecraft in frame, denomination in white.
No. 2569, 6500ce, horiz. — Apollo-Soyuz Test Project: a, Apollo and Soyuz spacecraft docked. b, Mission emblem. c, Astronaut Tom Stafford. d, Cosmonaut Aleksei Leonov. e, Astronaut Deke Slayton. f, Astronaut Vance Brand and Cosmonaut Valeri Kubasov.
No. 2570, 6500ce — Giotto Comet Probe: a, Probe in space, black background. b, Comet, probe in space, red text at bottom. c, Top of probe, white background. d, Comet, probe in space, purple background. e, Probe and schematic diagram. f, Bottom of probe.
No. 2571, 20,000ce, Astronaut Buzz Aldrin. No. 2572, 20,000ce, Apollo-Soyuz crew members shaking hands in space, horiz. No. 2573, 20,000ce, Viking 1, horiz.

**2007, Jan. 22**
2568   A509   10,000ce Sheet of
      4, #a-d   8.75   8.75
**Sheets of 6, #a-f**
2569-2570 A509   Set of 2   17.00   17.00
**Souvenir Sheets**
2571-2573 A509   Set of 3   13.00   13.00

Scouting, Cent. A510

No. 2574, vert. — Dove, Scout emblem and Scout: a, Giving Scout sign. b, Blowing bugle. c, Carrying injured boy.
20,000ce, Scout emblem, Scout giving Scout sign.

**2007**                **Perf. 13¼**
2574   A510   12,000ce Sheet of 3,
      #a-c   8.00   8.00
**Souvenir Sheet**
2575   A510   20,000ce multi   4.50   4.50

Independence,
50th
Anniv. — A511

**2007, Sept. 15　　Litho.　　Perf. 13¼**
2576 A511 4000ce multi　　　　　.90　.90

Kente Cloth
Designs
A512

Designs: 4000ce, Sika ne Barima. 7300ce,
Edwene Si So. 7500ce, Dakoro Yesere. No.
2580, 9000ce, Agyenegyne Nsu. No. 2581,
9000ce, Nkatoa Sa. 10,000ce, Edwene Asa.

**2007, Sept. 15　　　Perf. 13½x13¼**
2577-2582 A512　Set of 6　　10.00 10.00

Aburi
Botanical
Gardens
A513

Designs: 4000ce, Bamboo groves. 7300ce,
School of Horticulture. 7500ce, Silk cotton
tree, vert. 9000ce, Royal Palm Walkway.
10,000ce, Famous ficus tree, vert.
No. 2588: a, Like 9000ce. b, Like 7300ce. c,
Silk cotton tree. d, Famous ficus tree. e, Like
4000ce. f, Sanatorium.

**Perf. 13¼x13½, 13½x13¼**
**2007, Sept. 15**
2583-2587 A513　Set of 5　　8.25 8.25
2588 A513 6000ce Sheet of 6,
　　#a-f　　　　　　　　7.75 7.75

Cocoa
A514

Designs: 4000ce, Cocoa beverages and
spread. 7300ce, Cocoa Pebbles. 7500ce,
Assorted chocolates. 9000ce, Man at cocoa
processing plant. 10,000ce, Finished cocoa
products.
No. 2594: a, Like 10,000ce. b, Cacao pods.
c, Like 7500ce. d, Like 9000ce. e, Like
7300ce. f, Workers packaging cocoa products.

**2007, Sept. 15　　　Perf. 13¼x13½**
2589-2593 A514　Set of 5　　8.25 8.25
2594 A514 6000ce Sheet of 6,
　　#a-f　　　　　　　　7.75 7.75

Cats and Dogs — A515

Designs: 6000ce, Chartreux cat. 7000ce,
Blue-mitted ragdoll cat. 8000ce, Blue lynx
point Birman cat, horiz. 9000ce, Norwegian
Forest cat.
No. 2599, horiz.: a, American bulldog. b, Old
English sheepdog. c, Shar-pei. d, Boston
terrier.
No. 2600, 20,000ce, Cinnamon point Sia-
mese cat. No. 2601, 20,000ce, Greyhound.

**2007, Sept. 15　　　Perf. 14**
2595-2598 A515　Set of 4　　6.50 6.50
2599 A515 7500ce Sheet of 4,
　　#a-d　　　　　　　　6.50 6.50
**Souvenir Sheets**
2600-2601 A515　Set of 2　　8.75 8.75

Orchids
A516

No. 2602: a, Epipactis atrorubens. b, Galeandra bicarinata. c, Platanthera tipuloides. d,
Platanthera ciliaris.
20,000ce, Spathoglottis plicata.

**2007, Sept. 15**
2602 A516　7500ce Sheet of 4,
　　#a-d　　　　　　　　6.50 6.50
**Souvenir Sheet**
2603 A516 20,000ce multi　　4.50 4.50

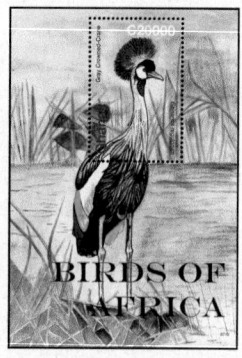

Birds
A517

No. 2604, horiz.: a, Red-billed hornbill. b,
Bearded barbet. c, Hoopoe. d, Pygmy
kingfisher.
20,000ce, Gray-crowned crane.

**2007, Sept. 15**
2604 A517　7500ce Sheet of 4,
　　#a-d　　　　　　　　6.50 6.50
**Souvenir Sheet**
2605 A517 20,000ce multi　　4.50 4.50

Traditional
Costumes — A518

Designs: 4000ce, War dress, Northern
Ghana. 7300ce, Woman. 7500ce, Mourning
wear. 9000ce, Smock. 10,000ce, Wulomo
costume.

**Perf. 13½x13¼**
**2007, Sept. 15　　　Litho.**
2606-2610 A518　Set of 5　　8.25 8.25

Famous
People — A519

Designs: No. 2611, 4000ce, Sir Arko Kor-
sah, first Chief Justice. No. 2612, 4000ce,
Amon Kotei, designer of national coat of arms.
No. 2613, 4000ce, Philip Gbeho, composer of
national anthem. 4500ce, F. K. Buah, historian. 6000ce, Prof. Albert Adu Boahene, historian and politician. 7300ce, Leticia Obeng,
aquatic biologist. 7500ce, Peter Cardinal
Appiah Turkson, first Ghanaian cardinal.
9000ce, Susanna Alhassan, first femal government minister.

**2007, Sept. 15　　　Perf. 13¼**
2611-2618 A519　Set of 8　　10.00 10.00

On July 3, 2007, Ghana's currency
was revalued at a rate of 10,000 old
cedis to 1 new cedi. Old cedis continued to be valid until Dec. 31, 2007. Nos.
2576-2618 and 2641-2646 were issued
after July 3, but have denominations
expressed in old cedis.

Antrak
Air — A520

Airplane: 40p, On ground. 73p, In flight.

**2007, Sept. 15　　　Perf. 13¼**
2619-2620 A520　Set of 2　　2.25 2.25

Accra Tourist
Attractions
A521

Designs: 20p, Independence Arch. 40p,
Independence Square. 73p, Supreme Court.
75p, National Theater. 90p, Intl. Conference
Center.

**2007, Sept. 15**
2621-2625 A521　Set of 5　　6.50 6.50

Agricultural
Development
Bank — A522

Designs: 40p, Emblem. 75p, Home Link
Account, vert. 90p, Young Farmers Program,
vert. 1ce, Gold Drive Motor Loan, vert.

**2007, Sept. 15**
2626-2629 A522　Set of 4　　6.75 6.75

Ghana
Commercial
Bank — A523

Designs: 40p, Emblem. 73p, Eagle, world
map. 75p, Ghana Commercial Bank Tower,
vert. 90p, Xpress Money Transfer, vert.

**2007, Sept. 15**
2630-2633 A523　Set of 4　　6.00 6.00

State Insurance
Company
A524

Designs: 40p, Emblem. 73p, Executives.
75p, New office building. 90p, Child pointing.
1ce, Three CIMG Awards, vert.

**2007, Sept. 15**
2634-2638 A524　Set of 5　　8.25 8.25

Ghanaian Heads of State — A525

Dr. Kwame Nkrumah and Pres. J. A.
Kufuor With State Sword
A526

No. 2639: a, Dr. Kwame Nkrumah. b, Lieu-
tenant General J. A. Ankrah. c, General A. A.
Afrifa. d, Dr. Kofi Abrefa Busia. e, General I. K.
Acheampong. f, Lieutenant General W. A.
Akuffo. g, Dr. Hilla Limann. h, Flight Lieutenant
J. J. Rawlings. i, Pres. J. A. Kufuor.

**2007, Sept. 15　　　Perf. 13½x13¼**
2639 A525 60p Sheet of 9, #a-
　　i　　　　　　　　　11.00 11.00
**Souvenir Sheet**
2640 A526 1ce multi　　　　1.10 1.10

Pope Benedict
XVI — A527

**2007, Nov. 15　　　Perf. 13¼**
2641 A527 4000ce multi　　　.90　.90
Printed in sheets of 8.

Gold — A528

Designs: 4000ce, Gold ore. 7300ce, Melting
gold ore. 7500ce, Woman holding gold bar.
9000ce, Entrance of Obuasi Gold Mines,
horiz. 10,000ce, Gold-plated chair.

**2007　　Perf. 13½x13¼, 13¼x13½**
2642-2646 A528　Set of 5　　8.25 8.25

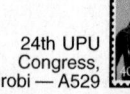

24th UPU
Congress,
Nairobi — A529

Designs: 40p, Dancers. 73p, Flags of
Ghana and Kenya, warrior with shield, vert.
75p, UPU emblem in opened box. 90p, UPU
emblem on map of Africa, vert.
No. 2651: a, Part of UPU emblem, folded
map of world, denomination at LL. b, Part of
UPU emblem, folded map of world, denomination at UR. c, Folded map of world, map and
flag of Kenya.

**2007, Dec. 3　　　Perf. 12½**
2647-2650 A529　Set of 4　　6.00 6.00
**Souvenir Sheet**
2651 A529 1ce Sheet of 3, #a-c　6.50 6.50

## Miniature Sheet

Wedding of Queen Elizabeth II and Prince Philip, 60th Anniv. (in 2007) A530

No. 2652: a, Queen, denomination in green. b, Couple, denomination in green. c, Couple, denomination in orange. d, Queen, denomination in orange. e, Queen, denomination in blue. f, Couple, denomination in blue.

**2008, Jan. 31    Litho.    Perf. 13¼x13½**
2652  A530  60p Sheet of 6, #a-f    7.75  7.75

Paintings by Qi Baishi (1864-1957) — A531

No. 2653: a, Top half of Lotus and Mandarin Ducks (lotus). b, Top half of River Landscape with Boats (boats). c, Bottom half of Lotus and Mandarin Ducks (ducks). d, Bottom half of River Landscape with Boats (trees). 3ce, Peony in a Dragon Vase.

**2008, Jan. 31    Perf. 12x11½**
2653  A531  90p Sheet of 4, #a-d    7.75  7.75

### Souvenir Sheet

**Perf. 11½**
2654  A531  3ce multi    6.50  6.50
No. 2653 contains four 30x40mm stamps.

### Miniature Sheet

2008 Summer Olympics, Beijing — A532

No. 2655: a, Boxing. b, Relay race. c, Long jump. d, Soccer.

**2008, May 8    Perf. 12¾**
2655  A532  40p Sheet of 4, #a-d    3.25  3.25

---

### Souvenir Sheet

Visit of US Pres. George W. Bush to Ghana A533

No. 2656: a, US Pres. George W. Bush. b, Ghana Pres. John Agyekum Kufuor.

**2008, Sept. 17    Perf. 13½**
2656  A533  1.25ce Sheet of 2, #a-b    4.50  4.50

Khilafat Ahmadiyya, Cent. — A533a

Designs: 40p, Flag, minaret, world map. 73p, T. I. Ahmadiyya Senior High School, Kumasi. 90p, Wheat. 1ce, Ahmadiuua Muslim Hospital, Daboase.

**2008    Litho.    Perf. 14½**
2656C-2656F  A533a    Set of 4    9.50  9.50

Coat of Arms A534

**2009, Mar. 31    Litho.    Perf. 14x15**
2657  A534  1ce gray + label    1.40  1.40

Vegetables A535

Designs: 1ce, Tomatoes. 1.20ce, Tomatoes and white eggplants. 1.30ce, White eggplants.

**2009, Mar. 31    Litho.    Perf. 14¾x14**
2658-2660  A535    Set of 3    5.00  5.00

Korle Bu Teaching Hospital — A536

Designs: 1ce, Medical block. No. 2662, 1.10ce, Cardiothoracic Center. No. 2663, 1.10ce, New administration block. 1.20ce, Prof. Frimpong Boateng, heart surgeon, vert.

**2009, Mar. 31    Perf. 14¾x14, 14x14¾**
2661-2664  A536    Set of 4    6.25  6.25

Tweneboa Kodua High School — A537

Designs: 1ce, Administration block. 1.10ce, Girls domitory. 1.20ce, Students at ICT Center. 1.30ce, Students playing volleyball.

**2009, Mar. 31    Perf. 14¾x14**
2665-2668  A537    Set of 4    6.50  6.50

Soccer Players — A538

Designs: No. 2669, 1ce, Edward Acquah. No. 2670, 1ce, Aggrey Fynn. No. 2671, 1ce,

---

Nana Gyamfi II. No. 2672, 1ce, Robert Mensah. No. 2673, 1ce, Baba Yara.

**2009, Mar. 31    Perf. 14x14¾**
2669-2673  A538    Set of 5    7.25  7.25

Peony — A539

**2009, Apr. 10    Perf. 13¼**
2674  A539  1ce multi    1.40  1.40
Printed in sheets of 8.

Pres. Kwame Nkrumah (1909-72) — A539a

Pres. Nkrumah: 1ce, At Afro-Asian Solidarity Conference. 1.10ce, And Africa Union emblem, horiz. 1.20ce, With Prince Philip at Balmoral Castle. 1.30ce, Signing Charter of African Unity. 1.40ce, With Mao Zedong.

**2009, Dec. 8    Litho.    Perf. 13¼x13**
2674A  A539a  1ce multi    —
2674B  A539a  1.10ce multi    —
2674C  A539a  1.20ce multi    —
2674D  A539a  1.30ce multi    —
2674E  A539a  1.40ce multi    —
  f.    Souvenir sheet of 5,    —    —
        #2674A-2674E

### Nos. 852, 1055, 1068, 1939B, and 2525 Surcharged

No. 2675

No. 2676

No. 2677        No. 2678

No. 2679

### Methods and Perfs. As Before 2009 ?
2675  A350a  20p on 800ce    —    —
              #1939B
2676  A174  1ce on 70p #852    —    —
2677  A205  1ce on 5ce    —    —
              #1055
2678  A208  1ce on 20ce    —    —
              #1068
2679  A501  1.20ce on 800ce    —    —
              #2525

The editors suspect more stamps may have been surcharged and would like to examine any examples.

### No. 1057 Surcharged Like No. 2677, Nos. 1069-1070 Surcharged Like No. 2678 and

No. 2683

---

### Methods and Perfs As Before 2009 ?
2680  A208  1ce on 60ce    —
              #1069
2681  A208  1ce on 80ce    —
              #1070
2682  A205  1ce on 250ce    —
              #1057
2683  A435  1.20ce on 1100ce    —
              #2277

The editors suspect more stamps may have been issued in this set and would like to examine any examples.

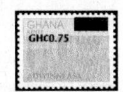

No. 1939C Surcharged

### Method and Perf. As Before 2009 ?
2684B  A350c  75p on 1100ce    —    —
              #1939C

Six additional stamps were issued in this set. The editors would like to examine any examples.

No. 1357Bp Surcharged

### Methods and Perfs As Before 2009 ?
2687  A243a  1.30ce on 60ce    —    —
              #1357Bp
  a.    Double surcharge    —    —

At least seven additional surcharges were issued in this set. The editors would like to examine any examples.

Volta River Authority — A539b

Designs: 1ce, Kwame Nkrumah switching on Akosombo Generating Station. 1.10ce, Takoradi Thermal Plant. 1.20ce, Kwame Nkrumah signing Akosombo Dam Agreement. 1.30ce, Akosombo Dam. 1.40ce, Akosombo Generating Station retrofit.

**2010, Mar. 2    Litho.    Perf. 13x13¼**
2689A  A539b  1ce multi    —
2689B  A539b  1.10ce multi    —
2689C  A539b  1.20ce multi    —
2689D  A539b  1.30ce multi    —
2689E  A539b  1.40ce multi    —

One additonal item was issued in this set. The editors would like to examine any examples. Numbers may change.

Friendship Between Ghana and People's Republic of China, 50th Anniv. — A539c

No. 2689F: g, Chinese symbol for friendship, Ghanaian unity symbol. h, National Theater, flags of People's Republic of China and Ghana. i, Kwame Nkrumah and Zhou Enlai, flags of People's Republic of China and Ghana. j, Great Wall of China.

**2010, July 8    Litho.    Perf. 12**
2689F    Horiz. strip of 4    —    —
  g.-h.  A539c  1ce Either single    —    —
  i.    A539c  1.30ce multi    —    —
  j.    A539c  1.40ce multi    —    —

A540

Wedding of Prince William and
Catherine Middleton — A541

Designs: Nos. 2690, 2692, Couple.
No. 2691: a, Prince William. b, Catherine
Middleton.
No. 2693, Couple, diff.

**2011, June 15    Litho.    Perf. 12**
2690  A540  3.50ce multi         4.75  4.75
2691  A541  3.50ce Horiz. pair,
                    #a-b           9.25  9.25
       **Souvenir Sheets**
2692  A540  12ce multi          16.00  16.00
2693  A541  12ce multi          16.00  16.00
No. 2690 was printed in sheets of 4. No.
2691 was printed in sheets containing 2 pairs.

2010 World Cup
Soccer
Championships,
South Africa —
A541a

Design: No. 2693A, Ghana Black Stars soccer team. No. 2693B, Michael Essien showing
sportsmanship. No. 2693C, Goalkeeper Richard Kingson in action. No. 2693D, Asamoah
Gyan and Nigerian players.
No. 2693E: f, Stephen Appiah. g, Agyeman
Badu and Egyptian player Ahmed Hassan. h,
Ghana soccer fans with flag of Ghana. i, Sul-
ley Muntari and opponent. j, Samuel Inkoom
and Didier Drogba. k, Anthony Annan and
opponent. l, Kwadwo Asamoah, Andre Dede
and opponent. m, Coach Milovan Rajevac.

**2011, Sept. 14    Litho.    Perf. 13x13¼**
2693A  A541a  1ce multi         —   —
2693B  A541a  1ce multi         —   —
2693C  A541a  1.20ce multi      —   —
2693D  A541a  1.40ce multi      —   —
       **Miniature Sheet**
2693E         Sheet of 8        —   —
f.-m.  A541a 50p Any single

2010 World Cup
Soccer
Championships,
South Africa —
A541b

Designs: No. 2693N, 1ce, Dominic Adiyiah
celebrating goal. No. 2693O,Team Captain
Andre Dede Ayew and opponent. No. 2693P,
Coach Sellas Tetteh being congratulated by
Brazilian coach. No. 2693Q, Players celebrat-
ing shootout with Brazil. No. 2693R: s,
Dominic Adiyiah and Ransford Osei. t, Adiyiah
and South African opponent. u, Players pray-
ing before penalty shootout against Brazil. v,
Players dancing after win against Brazil. w,
Goalkeeper Daniel Adjei. x, Players lifting
Coach Tetteh. y, Players holding trophy behind
chanpionship banner. z, Players holding tro-
phy, diff.

**2011, Sept. 14    Litho.    Perf. 13x13¼**
2693N  A541b  1ce multi         —   —
2693O  A541b  1ce multi         —   —
2693P  A541b  1.20ce multi      —   —
2693Q  A541b  1.40ce multi      —   —
       **Miniature Sheet**
2693R         Sheet of 8        —   —
s.-z.  A541b 50p Any single

Drafting of the Emancipation
Proclamation by Abraham Lincoln,
150th Anniv. — A542

No. 2694: a, 1863 *Harper's Weekly* illustra-
tion, by Thomas Nast. b, 1863 photograph of
Lincoln, by Thomas Le Mere. c, Watercolor by
Henry L. Stephens. d, First Reading of the

Emancipation Proclamation of President Lincoln, painting by Francis B. Carpenter.
No. 2695, horiz.: a, 1861 photograph of Lincoln, by Alexander Gardner. b, Text of Emancipation Proclamation from the *National
Republican*.

**2012, July 9              Perf. 14**
2694  A542  2ce Sheet of 4, #a-d   8.25  8.25
       **Souvenir Sheet**
2695  A542  3ce Sheet of 2, #a-b   6.25  6.25

Sinking
of the
Titanic,
Cent.
A543

No. 2696: a, Dollar bill recovered from the
Titanic wreckage. b, Captain Edward J. Smith.
c, Titanic at sea. d, Spoons recovered from the
Titanic wreckage.
5ce, Titanic at sea, horiz.

**2012, July 9              Perf. 12**
2696  A543  2ce Sheet of 4, #a-d   8.25  8.25
       **Souvenir Sheet**
2697  A543  5ce multi             5.25  5.25

Burning of the Hindenburg, 75th
Anniv. — A544

Hindenburg and: 2ce, Map of Europe. 5ce,
Spotlights, vert.

**2012, July 9              Perf. 12**
2698  A544  2ce multi             2.10  2.10
       **Souvenir Sheet**
2699  A544  5ce multi             5.25  5.25
No. 2699 contains one 30x50mm rectangular stamp.

Butterflies — A545

No. 2700: a, Acraea hypoleuca. b, Desmoly-
caena mazoensis. c, Aphnaeus erikssoni. d,
Lycaena gigantea. e, Mimacraea marshalli. f,
Iolaus alienus.
No. 2701: a, Female Durbania pallida. b,
Male Durbania pallida.

**2012, July 9    Perf. 13 Syncopated**
2700  A545  2ce Sheet of 6, #a-
                    f          12.50  12.50
       **Souvenir Sheet**
2701  A545  3ce Sheet of 2, #a-
                    b           6.25   6.25

Birds
A546

No. 2702: a, Hoopoe. b, Long-tailed glossy
starling. c, Northern carmine bee-eater. d,
Double-collared sunbird.
5ce, Ostrich.

**2012, July 9              Perf. 12**
2702  A546  2ce Sheet of 4, #a-d   8.25  8.25
       **Souvenir Sheet**
       **Perf. 12¾**
2703  A546  5ce multi             5.25  5.25
No. 2703 contains one 38x51mm stamp.

Parrots
A547

No. 2704: a, Cape parrot. b, Red-bellied
parrot. c, Meyer's parrot. d, Ruppell's parrot. e,
African gray parrot. f, Brown-headed parrot.
5ce, Senegal parrot.

**2012, July 9              Perf. 14**
2704  A547  2ce Sheet of 6, #a-
                    f          12.50  12.50
       **Souvenir Sheet**
       **Perf. 12**
2705  A547  5ce multi             5.25  5.25

Worldwide Fund for Nature
(WWF) — A548

No. 2706 — Bohor reedbuck: a, Three animals. b, Two animals butting heads. c, Two
animals running. d, One animal in water.

**2012, Aug. 21              Perf. 14**
2706  A548  1.50ce Block of 4,
                    #a-d        6.50  6.50
e.     Souvenir sheet of 8, 2 each
                    #a-d       13.00  13.00
       **Souvenir Sheets**

2012 Summer Olympics,
London — A549

Designs: No. 2707, 1.50ce, Basketball. No.
2708, 1.50ce, Table tennis. No. 2709, 1.50ce,
Synchronized swimming. No. 2710, 1.50ce,
Cycling.

**2012, Aug. 21              Perf. 14**
2707-2710  A549    Set of 4     6.50  6.50
       **Miniature Sheet**

Primates
A550

No. 2711: a, Mandrills. b, Chimpanzees. c,
Gorillas. d, Orangutans. e, Vervet monkeys.

**2012, Sept. 13              Litho.**
2711  A550  2ce Sheet of 5, #a-
                    e          10.50  10.50
       **Souvenir Sheet**

2009 Visit of President Barack Obama
to Ghana — A551

No. 2712: a, U.S. flag and President Barack
Obama. b, Ghana flag and Pres. John Atta
Mills.

**2012, Oct. 1              Perf. 12¾**
2712  A551  3ce Sheet of 2, #a-b   6.50  6.50
       **Souvenir Sheets**

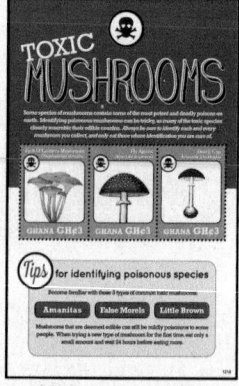

Mushrooms — A552

No. 2713, 3ce — Toxic mushrooms: a, Jack
o'lantern mushrooms. b, Fly agaric. c, Death
cap.
No. 2714, 3ce — Edible mushrooms: a,
Oyster mushrooms. b, Almond mushrooms. c,
Saffron milk caps.

**2012, Dec. 12              Perf. 12**
       **Sheets of 3, #a-c**
2713-2714  A552    Set of 2    19.00  19.00

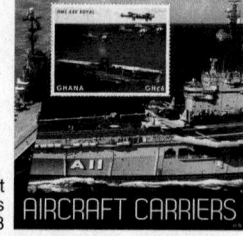

Aircraft
Carriers
A553

No. 2715: a, Arromanches. b, Béarn. c,
Commandant Teste. d, HMS Hermes.
6ce, HMS Ark Royal.

**2012, Dec. 12              Perf. 12**
2715  A553  2ce Sheet of 4, #a-d   8.50  8.50
       **Souvenir Sheet**
       **Perf. 12¾**
2716  A553  6ce multi             6.25  6.25
No. 2715 contains four 47x27mm stamps.

Completion of the Painting of the
Sistine Chapel, 500th Anniv. — A554

No. 2717: a, Libyan Sibyl. b, Cumaean
Sibyl. c, Delphic Sibyl.
7ce, First Day of Creation.

**2012, Dec. 12    Perf. 13 Syncopated**
2717  A554  2.75ce Sheet of 3,
                    #a-c        8.75  8.75
       **Souvenir Sheet**
2718  A554  7ce multi             7.50  7.50

Miniature Sheet

Muhammad Ali and His Boxing
Opponents — A554a

No. 2718A — Photographs from fights
between Ali and: b, Doug Jones, 1963. c,
Sonny Liston, 1965. d, Ernie Terrell, 1967. e,
Joe Frazier, 1975.

**2012** Litho. *Perf. 13 Syncopated*
2718A A554a 2ce Sheet of 4, #b-
e                            8.50 8.50

Fruits and
Vegetables — A555

Design: 10p, Pawpaws. 25p, Pineapples.
27p, Unripe oranges. 1ce, Shallot plants.
1.10ce, Tomatoes. 1.20ce, Shallots. 1.30ce,
Carrots. 1.40ce, Mangoes. 3ce, Avocados.
5ce, Coconuts.

**2012, Feb. 28** Litho. *Perf. 13¼x14*
2719 A555    10p multi            —
2720 A555    25p multi            —
2721 A555    27p multi            —
2722 A555    1ce multi            —
2723 A555    1.10ce multi         —
2724 A555    1.20ce multi         —
2725 A555    1.30ce multi    —    —
2726 A555    1.40ce multi    —    —
2727 A555    3ce multi            —
2728 A555    5ce multi            —

Souvenir Sheet

Statue of Lao Tsu and Hanguguan
Pass, Hanguguan, People's Republic
of China — A556

**2013, Jan. 1** Litho. *Perf. 12*
2729 A556 10ce multi        10.50 10.50

Rat — A557        Ox — A558

Chinese
Zodiac
Animals
A559

No. 2732: a, Rat. b, Ox. c, Tiger. d, Rabbit.
e, Dragon. f, Sanke. g, Horse. h, Sheep. i,
Monkey. j, Rooster. k, Dog. l, Boar.

**2013, Feb. 12** Litho. *Perf. 13¼x13*
2730 A557 50p multi          .55  .55
2731 A558 50p multi          .55  .55
          *Perf. 14*
2732 A559 50p Sheet of 12, #a-l 6.25 6.25
    2013 Beijing Intl. Philatelic Exhibition
(#2732).

World Environment Day — A560

No. 2733: a, Electical plug and socket. b,
Recycling bucket. c, Lightbulb. d, Hand and
faucet.
7ce, Wind generators.

**2013, Feb. 12** Litho. *Perf. 13¼*
2733 A560 2.25ce Sheet of 4,
              #a-d           9.50 9.50
    **Souvenir Sheet**
2734 A560    7ce multi       7.50 7.50

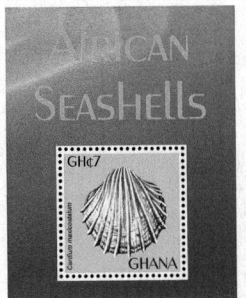

Shells
A561

No. 2735: a, Gymnobela abyssorum. b,
Cypraea stercoraria minima. c, Euspira
notabilis. d, Conus ateralbus.
7ce, Cardium maxicostatum.

**2013, Feb. 12** Litho. *Perf. 12½*
2735 A561 2.25ce Sheet of 4,
              #a-d           9.50 9.50
    **Souvenir Sheet**
2736 A561    7ce multi       7.50 7.50

London Underground, 150th
Anniv. — A562

No. 2737: a, Stockwell Staation, 1939. b,
Cannon Street Station, 1866. c, Passenger
drinking tea in train car, 1964. d, Bayswater
Station, 1868. e, Oxford Circus Station, 2012.
f, Escalators at Leicester Square Station,
1935.
7ce, Baker Street Station, 1863.

        *Perf. 12½x13¼*
**2013, Feb. 12** Litho.
2737 A562 2ce Sheet of 6, #a-
              f            12.50 12.50
    **Souvenir Sheet**
        *Perf. 13¼*
2738 A562    7ce multi       7.50 7.50
    No. 2738 contains one 51x38mm stamp.

Minerals
A563

No. 2739 — Agate with: a, Brown, blue and
orange rings. b, Purple rings with a dark
center. c, Greenish blue and white rings, dark
green blue center. d, Red violet and white
rings, red violet center. e, Brown ring with gray

blue crystals in center. f, Dark and light blue
rings.
7ce, Amethyst, vert.

**2013, May 1** Litho. *Perf. 13¾*
2739 A563 2ce Sheet of 6, #a-
              f            12.50 12.50
    **Souvenir Sheet**
        *Perf. 12½*
2740 A563    7ce multi       7.25 7.25
    No. 2740 contains one 38x51mm stamp.

Paintings by Edvard Munch (1863-
1944) — A564

No. 2741: a, Death in the Sickroom. b, Portrait of Friedrich Nietzsche. c, The Vampire.
7ce, The Scream.

**2013, May 1** Litho. *Perf. 12½*
2741 A564 2.75ce Sheet of 3,
              #a-c           8.50 8.50
    **Souvenir Sheet**
2742 A564    7ce multi       7.25 7.25

Souvenir Sheet

New Year 2013 (Year of the Snake)
A565

No. 2743: a, Head of snake. b, Tail of snake.

**2013, May 15** Litho. *Perf. 12½*
2743 A565 3.50ce Sheet of 2,
              #a-b           7.00 7.00

Lady Margaret Thatcher (1925-2013),
British Prime Minister — A566

No. 2744 — Thatcher meeting with: a,
Henry Kissinger, 1983. b, Pres. Ronald Reagan, 1983. c, Deng Xiaoping, 1982. d, Mikhail
Gorbachev, 1990.
7ce, Thatcher, vert.

**2013, June 24** Litho. *Perf. 12*
2744 A566 2.25ce Sheet4 of 4,
              #a-d           9.00 9.00
    **Souvenir Sheet**
        *Perf. 12½*
2745 A566    7ce black       7.00 7.00
    No. 2745 contains one 38x51mm stamp.

Reptiles
A567

No. 2746, 2.25ce: a, Desert monitor. b, Nile
crocodile. c, African slender-snouted crocodile. d, Ground agama.
No. 2747, 2.25ce: a, African striped skink. b,
Mwanza flat-headed agana. c, Red-headed
rock agama. d, Rock monitor.
No. 2748, 7ce, Yellow-throated day gecko.
No. 2749, 7ce, Mozambique spitting cobra,
vert.

**2013, July 7** Litho. *Perf. 14*
    Sheets of 4, #a-d
2746-2747 A567 Set of 2     18.00 18.00
    **Souvenir Sheets**
        *Perf. 12½*
2748-2749 A567 Set of 2     14.00 14.00
    No. 2748 contains one 51x38mm stamp.
No. 2749 contains one 38x51mm stamp.

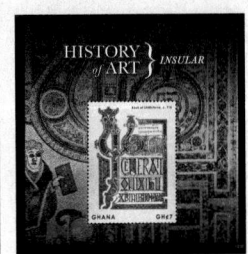

History
of Art
A568

No. 2750, 2.75ce — Byzantine art: a, St.
Acathius of Melitene. b, Menologion of Basil II.
c, Emperor Alexius I.
No. 2751, 2.75ce — Gothic art: a, Beata
Umilta Transports Bricks to the Monastery, by
Pietro Lorenzetti. b, Portrait of a Princess of
the House of Este, by Pisanello. c, Cambridge
Altarpiece, by Simone Martini.
No. 2752, 7ce, Book of Lindisfarne. No.
2753, 7ce, Illustration from Bury St. Edmunds
Bible, by Master Hugo, horiz.

**2013, July 7** Litho. *Perf. 12½*
    Sheets of 3, #a-c
2750-2751 A568 Set of 2     16.50 16.50
    **Souvenir Sheets**
2752-2753 A568 Set of 2     14.00 14.00

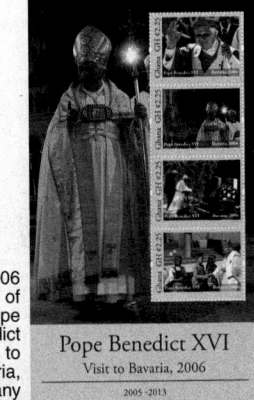

2006
Visit of
Pope
Benedict
XVI to
Bavaria,
Germany
A569

2008
Visit of
Pope
Benedict
XVI to
the
United
States
A570

No. 2754 — Pope Benedict XVI: a, Waving.
b, Wearing miter and holding crucifix. c, Kneel-
ing at gravesite. d, Greeting children.
No. 2755 — Pope Benedict XVI: a, With
New York City Mayor Michael Bloomberg. b,
Standing behind candle between two priests.
c, Holding censer. d, With arms extended.
No. 2756, Pope Benedict XVI and flower
bushes. No. 2757, Pope Benedict XVI with
Pres. George W. Bush.

## Perf. 13 Syncopated

**2013, July 19**      Litho.
2754 A569 2.25ce Sheet of 4,
     #a-d      8.75 8.75
2755 A570 2.25ce Sheet of 4,
     #a-d      8.75 8.75
**Souvenir Sheets**
2756 A569 7ce multi      6.75 6.75
2757 A570 7ce multi      6.75 6.75

A571

African Animals
A572

No. 2758: a, Lion. b, Cheetah. c, Impala. d, African elephant.
No. 2759: a, African elephant (30x80mm). b, Impala (30x40mm). c, Lesser flamingo (30x40mm). d, Rhinoceros (30x40mm). e, Cheetah (30x40mm).
No. 2760: a, Chimpanzee. b, Giraffe. c, Southern ground hornbill. d, Southern ground hornbill, tree in background. e, Zebra. f, Lion.
7ce, Meerkats.

## Perf. 12, 14 (A572)

**2013, Aug. 28**      Litho.
2758 A571 2.25ce Sheet of 4,
     #a-d      8.50 8.50
2759 A572 2.25ce Sheet of 5,
     #a-e      10.50 10.50
2760 A572 2.25ce Sheet of 6,
     #a-f      12.50 12.50
**Souvenir Sheet**
2761 A571 7ce multi      6.50 6.50

**Miniature Sheet**

Camellias — A573

No. 2762 — Camellia variety: a, Asmodee. b, Benaria Nova. c, Carlotta Nencini. d, Henry Clay. e, Imperatrice Eugenie. f, Isolina Corsi. g, L'Italia. h, Venetia la Bella. i, Brozzoni Nova.

**2013, Sept. 10**    Litho.    Perf. 13¾
2762 A573 2ce Sheet of 9, #a-i 16.50 16.50
     2013 China Intl. Collection Expo.

Pres. John F. Kennedy (1917-63) — A574

No. 2763 — Pres. Kennedy: a, Facing left, emblem at UR. b, Emblem at UL. c, Facing

---

left, flag in background, emblem at UR. d, Facing Right, emblem at LL. e, Clapping, emblem at LR.
7ce, Pres. Kennedy in rocking chair.

**2013, Sept. 10**    Litho.    Perf. 14
2763 A574 2ce Sheet of 5, #a-e   9.25 9.25
**Souvenir Sheet**
**Perf. 12**
2764 A574 7ce multi      6.50 6.50

UNESCO World Heritage Sites — A575

No. 2765: a, Mount Huangshan, People's Republic of China. b, Naeroyfjord, Norway. c, Thingvellir National Park, Iceland. d, Victoria Falls, Zambia and Zimbabwe.
No. 2766, 7ce, Cape Castle as seen from ocean, Ghana. No. 2767, 7ce, Larabanga Mosque, Ghana. No. 2768, 7ce, Cannons on Cape Castle.

**2013, Sept. 10**    Litho.    Perf. 12¾
2765 A575 2.25ce Sheet of 4,
     #a-d      8.50 8.50
**Souvenir Sheets**
2766-2768 A575 Set of 3   19.50 19.50

Birth of Prince George of Cambridge — A576

No. 2769: a, Head of Duchess of Cambridge. b, Head of Duke of Cambridge. c, Duke of Cambridge holding Prince George of Cambridge. d, Duke and Duchess of Cambridge, Prince George.
7ce, Prince George of Cambridge.

**2013, Oct. 1**    Litho.    Perf. 14
2769 A576 2.25ce Sheet of 4,
     #a-d      8.25 8.25
**Souvenir Sheet**
**Perf. 12**
2770 A576 7ce multi      6.50 6.50

John Atta Mills (1944-2012), President of Ghana — A576a

Design: 1.30ce, Mills meeting with United Nations Secretary-General Kofi Annan.

**2013, Oct. 9**    Litho.    Perf. 14
2770A A576a 1.30ce multi     —    —
Two strips of stamps, three sheets of four stamps and a souvenir sheet were issued in this set. The editors would like to examine examples of the strips and sheets in their entirety.

**Miniature Sheets**

A577

---

Mao Zedong (1893-1976), Chinese Communist Leader — A578

No. 2771: a, Photograph of Mao Zedong and three other people, 1949. b, Photograph of Mao Zedong on chair with three children, 1951. c, Painting o f Mao Zedong with arches in background. d, Painting of Mao Zedong, in brown coat, leading people. e, Painting of Mao Zedong, in black coat, leading people. f, Painting of Mao Zedong with people and horses.
No. 2772: a, Photograph from 1937. b, Photograph from 1953. c, Photograph of Mao Zedong, red brown panel. d, As "c," green panel. e, As "c," dull purple panel. f, As "c," dull brown panel.

**2013, Dec. 20**    Litho.    Perf. 14
2771 A577 50p Sheet of 6, #a-f   2.60 2.60
2772 A578 50p Sheet of 6, #a-f   2.60 2.60

Khon Masks — A579

No. 2773: a, Mask with three faces (35x70mm). b, Mask with green face (35x35mm). c, Mask with white face (35x35mm).
7ce, Mask, diff.

**2013, Sept. 1**    Litho.    Perf. 13¾
2773 A579 2.75ce Sheet of 3,
     #a-c      7.75 7.75
**Souvenir Sheet**
2774 A579 7ce multi      6.50 6.50
Thailand 2013 World Stamp Exhibition, Bangkok. No. 2774 contains one 35x70mm stamp.

**Souvenir Sheet**

Election of Pope Francis A580

No. 2775: a, Pope Francis. b, Arms of Pope Francis.

**2013**    Litho.    Imperf.
2775 A580 10ce Sheet of 2,
     #a-b      17.00 17.00

Dogs — A581

No. 2776: a, English pointer. b, Polish hound. c, Westphalian Dachsbracke. d, Pharaoh hound.
12ce, Welsh Springer spaniel.

**2014, Mar. 19**    Litho.    Perf. 14
2776 A581 4ce Sheet of 4,
     #a-d      13.00 13.00

---

**Souvenir Sheet**
**Perf. 12¾**
2777 A581 12ce multi      9.50 9.50
No. 2777 contains one 51x38mm stamp.

**Miniature Sheets**

Flowers — A582

No. 2778: a, Yellow disa. b, Blue disa. c, Flame lily. d, Sugarbush protea. e, Drip disa (large). f, Drip disa (small). g, Soprano lilac African spoon daisy.
No. 2779: a, Wood iris. b, Red disa. c, Comon sugarbush. d, Aloe. e, Ice plant.

**2014, Mar. 19**    Litho.    Perf. 14
2778 A582 3.50ce Sheet of 7,
     #a-g      19.50 19.50
2779 A582 4ce Sheet of 5,
     #a-e      16.00 16.00

Orchids A583

No. 2780, 4ce — Butterfly orchids of different colors with background color of: a, Dull green. b, Golden brown. c, Gray brown. d, Bright yellow green.
No. 2781, 4ce: a, Phalaenopsis. b, Cymbidium. c, Orchis mascula. d, Disa riette.
No. 2782, 12ce, Phalaenopsis, diff. No. 2783, 12ce, Butterfly orchid, diff., horiz.

**2014, Mar. 19**    Litho.    Perf. 14
     **Sheets of 4, #a-d**
2780-2781 A583 Set of 2   25.00 25.00
**Souvenir Sheets**
**Perf. 12½**
2782-2783 A583 Set of 2   19.00 19.00
No. 2782 contains one 38x51mm stamp. No. 2783 contains one 51x38mm stamp.

A584          A585

A586

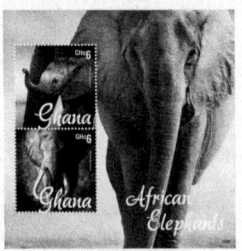

African Elephants — A587

No. 2784 — Elephants: a, Without tusks. b, With tusks.
No. 2785 — Elephant: a, Without tusks, b, With tusks.
No. 2786 — Elephant: a, With trunk raised. b, With trunk dangling.
No. 2787 — Elephants: a, Without tusks. b, With tusks.

**2014, Mar. 19    Litho.    Perf. 13¾**

| | | | | |
|---|---|---|---|---|
| 2784 | A584 | 4ce Pair, #a-b | 7.00 | 7.00 |
| 2785 | A585 | 4ce Pair, #a-b | 7.00 | 7.00 |

**Souvenir Sheets**

| | | | | |
|---|---|---|---|---|
| 2786 | A586 | 6ce Sheet of 2, #a-b | 10.00 | 10.00 |
| 2787 | A587 | 6ce Sheet of 2, #a-b | 10.00 | 10.00 |

Nos. 2784 and 2785 each were printed in sheets containing two pairs.

World War I, Cent. — A588

No. 2788, 2.75ce: a, King Albert I of Belgium. b, Field Marshal Paul von Hindenburg, Germany. c, Lord Horatio Kitchener, British War Secretary. d, Woodrow Wilson, U.S. President.
No. 2789, 2.75ce: a, U.S. soldiers in Renault FT-17 tank. b, British Mark IV Lodestar III tank. c, French Saint-Chomond tank. d, German A7V tank.
No. 2790, 4.50ce: a, Helmuth von Moltke, German Chief of Staff. b, Marshal Joseph Joffre, France.
No. 2791, 4.50ce: a, Hornsby chain track tractor. b, Mark V Hybrid Whippet tank.

**2014, Mar. 19    Litho.    Perf. 14**
**Sheets of 4, #a-d**

| | | | | |
|---|---|---|---|---|
| 2788-2789 | A588 | Set of 2 | 17.00 | 17.00 |

**Souvenir Sheets of 2, #a-b**
**Perf. 12½**

| | | | | |
|---|---|---|---|---|
| 2790-2791 | A588 | Set of 2 | 14.00 | 14.00 |

Nos. 2790-2791 each contain two 51x38mm stamps.

Pope Francis — A589

No. 2792, 2.75ce — Pope Francis: a, Wearing eyeglasses. b, Facing right. c, Waving. d, Holding icon.
No. 2793, 2.75ce — Pope Francis: a, With Italian Prime Minister Enrico Letta. b, Holding crucifix. c, Holding staff with crown. d, With Trinidad and Tobago President Anthony Carmona.
No. 2794, 4.50ce, horiz. — Pope Francis: a, With young boy. b, With Thailand Prime Minister Yingluck Shinawtra.

No. 2795, 4.50ce, horiz. — Pope Francis: a, Waving. b, With Lithuanian Prime Minister Algirdas Butkevicius.

**2014, Mar. 19    Litho.    Perf. 14**
**Sheets of 4, #a-d**

| | | | | |
|---|---|---|---|---|
| 2792-2793 | A589 | Set of 2 | 17.50 | 17.50 |

**Souvenir Sheets of 2, #a-b**

| | | | | |
|---|---|---|---|---|
| 2794-2795 | A589 | Set of 2 | 14.50 | 14.50 |

Paintings — A590

No. 2796, 3ce: a, Portrait of Félix Pissarro, by Camille Pissarro. b, Young Peasant at Her Toilette, by Pissarro. c, Brittany Peasant at the Pardon, by Childe Hassam.
No. 2797, 3ce: a, Marcella, by Ernst Ludwig Kirchner. b, The Arnolfini Portrait, by Jan van Eyck. c, Two Lovers, by Vincent van Gogh.
No. 2798, 9ce, Portrait of a Lute Player, by Francesco Salviati. No. 2799, 9ce, The Salon de la Rue des Moulins, by Henri de Toulouse-Lautrec.

**2014, Mar. 19    Litho.    Perf. 12¾**
**Sheets of 3, #a-c**

| | | | | |
|---|---|---|---|---|
| 2796-2797 | A590 | Set of 2 | 14.00 | 14.00 |

**Size: 100x100mm**
**Imperf**

| | | | | |
|---|---|---|---|---|
| 2798-2799 | A590 | Set of 2 | 14.00 | 14.00 |

Paintings by Qi Baishi (1864-1957) — A591

No. 2800, 2.75ce: a, Mother Hen, Chicks and Banana Leaves. b, Loquats in a Basket. c, Crows Returning to Wintry Trees. d, Mother and Child.
No. 2801, 2.75ce: a, Pomegranates. b, Mynahs and Amaranthus. c, Begonias and Rock. d, Camellias.
No. 2802, 4.50ce: a, Lotus and Mandarin Ducks. b, Magpie and Plum Blossoms.
No. 2803, 4.50ce: a, Autumn Landscape with Cormorants. b, Sunrise Over Water.

**2014, Mar. 19    Litho.    Perf. 14**
**Sheets of 4, #a-d**

| | | | | |
|---|---|---|---|---|
| 2800-2801 | A591 | Set of 2 | 17.00 | 17.00 |

**Souvenir Sheets of 2, #a-b**

| | | | | |
|---|---|---|---|---|
| 2802-2803 | A591 | Set of 2 | 14.00 | 14.00 |

Chinese Leaders — A592

Designs: No. 2804, Deng Xiaoping (1904-97), red brown background.
No. 2805: a, Deng Xiaoping, yellow orange background. b, Hu Jintao. c, Mao Zedong (1893-1976). d, Xi Jinping.

**Perf. 13 Syncopated**

| | | | |
|---|---|---|---|
| **2014, Sept. 4** | | | **Litho.** |
| 2804 | A592 | 2.75ce multi | 1.75  1.75 |
| 2805 | A592 | 2.75ce Sheet of 4, #a-d | 7.00  7.00 |

No. 2804 was printed in sheets of 4.

Mei Lanfang (1894-1961), Peking Opera Performer — A593

No. 2806: a, In costume with fan. b, In costume without fan.
9ce, Wearing suit and tie.

**2014, Sept. 4    Litho.    Perf. 12½**

| | | | | |
|---|---|---|---|---|
| 2806 | A593 | 2.75ce Pair, #a-b | 3.50 | 3.50 |

**Souvenir Sheet**

| | | | | |
|---|---|---|---|---|
| 2807 | A593 | 9ce multi | 5.75 | 5.75 |

No. 2806 was printed in sheets containing 3 pairs.

Endangered Animals of Africa — A594

No. 2808, 2.75ce: a, Addax. b, Bonobo. c, Wattled crane. d, West African giraffe.
No. 2809, 2.75ce: a, Dorcas gazelle. b, Eastern lowland gorilla. c, African penguin. d, White rhinoceros.
No. 2810, 4.50ce: a, Hartmann's mountain zebra. b, Verreaux's sifaka.
No. 2811, 4.50ce: a, Cheetah. b, Forest elephant.

**2014, Sept. 15    Litho.    Perf. 12**
**Sheets of 4, #a-d**

| | | | | |
|---|---|---|---|---|
| 2808-2809 | A594 | Set of 2 | 14.50 | 14.50 |

**Souvenir Sheets of 2, #a-b**

| | | | | |
|---|---|---|---|---|
| 2810-2811 | A594 | Set of 2 | 12.00 | 12.00 |

Fall of the Berlin Wall, 25th Anniv. — A595

No. 2812, 2.75ce: a, Brandenburg Gate. b, Pres. John F. Kennedy delivering speech at Berlin Wall, 1963. c, "Ich bin ein Berliner" quotation by Kennedy. d, Kennedy and others on platform with staircase.
No. 2813, 2.75ce: a, People on Berlin Wall, 1989. b, Pres. Ronald Reagan at podium in front of Berlin Wall, 1987. c, Quotation from Reagan's Berlin Wall speech. d, Reagan at podium in front of Brandenburg Gate, 1987.
No. 2814, 4.50ce, horiz.: a, Man waving German flag at fall of Berlin Wall, 1989. b, Sepia photograph of damaged segment of Berlin Wall.
No. 2815, 4.50ce, horiz.: a, People climbing on Berlin Wall, 1989. b, Color photograph of damaged segment of Berlin Wall.

**2014, Sept. 15    Litho.    Perf. 14**
**Sheets of 4, #a-d**

| | | | | |
|---|---|---|---|---|
| 2812-2813 | A595 | Set of 2 | 14.00 | 14.00 |

**Souvenir Sheets of 2, #a-b**
**Perf. 12**

| | | | | |
|---|---|---|---|---|
| 2814-2815 | A595 | Set of 2 | 11.50 | 11.50 |

Dinosaurs — A596

No. 2816, 2.75ce: a, Dilophosaurus. b, Tyrannosaurus. c, Ornitholestes. d, Compsognathus.
No. 2817, 2.75ce: a, Kentrosaurus. b, Achelousaurus. c, Brachiosaurus. d, Camarasaurus.
No. 2818, 4.50ce: a, Majungosaurus. b, Ceratosaurus.
No. 2819, 4.50ce, horiz.: a, Aucasaurus, country name at LL. b, Aucasaurus, country name at LR.

**2014, Sept. 15    Litho.    Perf. 14**
**Sheets of 4, #a-d**

| | | | | |
|---|---|---|---|---|
| 2816-2817 | A596 | Set of 2 | 14.00 | 14.00 |

**Souvenir Sheets of 2, #a-b**
**Perf. 12¾**

| | | | | |
|---|---|---|---|---|
| 2818-2819 | A596 | Set of 2 | 11.50 | 11.50 |

No. 2818 contains two 38x51mm stamps.
No. 2819 contains two 51x38mm stamps.

Frogs — A597

No. 2820, 2.50ce: a, Nest tree frog. b, Mababe River frog. c, Banana frog. d, African bullfrog. e, Banded grass frog.
No. 2821, 2.50ce: a, Snoring puddle frog. b, Mascarene grass frog. c, Painted reed frog. d, Nest frog. e, Spiny reed frog.
No. 2822, 2.50ce: a, Nosed grass frog. b, Water lily frog.

**2014, Sept. 15    Litho.    Perf. 13¾**
**Sheets of 5, #a-e**

| | | | | |
|---|---|---|---|---|
| 2820-2821 | A597 | Set of 2 | 17.00 | 17.00 |

**Souvenir Sheet**

| | | | | |
|---|---|---|---|---|
| 2822 | A597 | 4.50ce Sheet of 2, #a-b | 6.00 | 6.00 |

Statue of Four Sheep — A598

Woman and Goat — A599

Paintings by Qi Baishi (1864-1957) — A600

No. 2825 — Painting with: a, White goat. b, Black goat.

## 2014, Nov. 24 — Litho. — Perf. 12¾

2823 A598 2.75ce multi — 1.75 1.75

**Perf. 13¾**

2824 A599 3ce multi — 1.90 1.90

**Souvenir Sheet**
**Perf. 12**

2825 A600 4.50ce Sheet of 2, #a-b — 5.75 5.75

New Year 2015 (Year of the Goat). No. 2823 was printed in sheets of 4. No. 2824 was printed in sheets of 8 + 4 labels.

Lightning
A601

No. 2826 — Various lightning bolts, as shown.
9ce, Lightning, diff.

## 2015, Mar. 2 — Litho. — Perf. 14

2826 A601 3.50ce Sheet of 6, #a-f — 12.00 12.00

**Souvenir Sheet**
**Perf. 12**

2827 A601 9ce multi — 5.25 5.25

Snakes
A602

No. 2828, 4ce: a, Blotched snake. b, Caspian whipsnake. c, Grass snake. d, Longnosed viper.
No. 2829, 4ce: a, Smooth snake. b, Mangrove snake. c, Corn snake. d, Common garter snake.
No. 2830, 9ce, Aesculapian snake. No. 2831, 9ce, Royal python, vert.

## 2015, Mar. 2 — Litho. — Perf. 14
**Sheets of 4, #a-d**

2828-2829 A602 Set of 2 — 18.50 18.50

**Souvenir Sheets**
**Perf. 12**

2830-2831 A602 Set of 2 — 10.50 10.50

Horses
A603

No. 2832, 4ce: a, Mustang, North America. b, Fjord horse, Norway. c, Fell pony, England. d, Icelandic horse, Iceland.
No. 2833, 4ce, horiz.: a, Friesian horse, Netherlands. b, Thoroughbred, England. c, Andalusian horse, Iberian Peninsula. d, Arabian horse, Arabian Peninsula.
No. 2834, 9ce, Shire horse, England. No. 2835, 9ce, Appaloosa, United States, horiz.

## 2015, Mar. 2 — Litho. — Perf. 14
**Sheets of 4, #a-d**

2832-2833 A603 Set of 2 — 18.50 18.50

**Souvenir Sheets**
**Perf. 12**

2834-2835 A603 Set of 2 — 10.50 10.50

Sunbirds
A604

No. 2836: a, Variable sunbird. b, Southern double-collared sunbird. c, Scarlet-chested sunbird. d, Eastern olive sunbird. e, Amethyst sunbird. f, Malachite sunbird. g, Marico sunbird. h, Collared sunbird. i, Orange-breasted sunbird.
9ce, Splendid sunbird.

## 2015, Mar. 2 — Litho. — Perf. 14

2836 A604 2.50ce Sheet of 9, #a-i — 13.00 13.00

**Souvenir Sheet**

2837 A604 9ce multi — 5.25 5.25

**Miniature Sheets**

Characters From *Downton Abbey* Television Series — A605

No. 2838, 2ce: a, Earl of Grantham. b, Countess of Grantham. c, Lady Mary Crawley. d, Lady Edith Crawley. e, Lady Rose MacClare.
No. 2839, 2ce: a, Mr. Carson. b, Mrs. Hughes. c, Mr. Bates. d, Anna. e, Mrs. Patmore.
No. 2840, 2ce: a, Dowager Countess of Grantham. b, Mrs. Crawley. c, Mr. Barrow. d, Mr. Molesley. e, Daisy.

## 2015, Mar. 24 — Litho. — Perf.
**Sheets of 5, #a-e**

2838-2840 A605 Set of 3 — 16.00 16.00

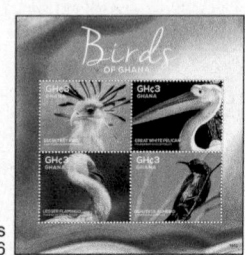

Birds
A606

No. 2841: a, Secretary bird. b, Great white pelican. c, Lesser flamingo. d, Beautiful sunbird.
7ce, Saddlebilled stork, vert.

## 2015, June 5 — Litho. — Perf. 14

2841 A606 3ce Sheet of 4, #a-d — 6.25 6.25

**Souvenir Sheet**

2842 A606 7ce multi — 3.75 3.75

No. 2842 contains one 30x80mm stamp.

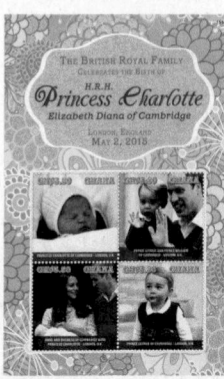

Birth of Princess Charlotte of Cambridge — A607

No. 2843: a, Princess Charlotte. b, Princes William and George. c, Duke and Duchess of Cambridge with Princess Charlotte. d, Prince George.
9ce, Duke and Duchess of Cambridge, Prince George, Princess Charlotte, horiz.

## 2015, June 5 — Litho. — Perf. 13¾

2843 A607 3.50ce Sheet of 4, #a-d — 7.25 7.25

**Souvenir Sheet**

2844 A607 9ce multi — 4.75 4.75

No. 2844 contains one 70x35mm stamp.

Palace Museum, Beijing, 50th Anniv.
A608

No. 2845: a, Buildings inside of walls of Forbidden City (1) (60x40mm). b, Painting of the Ming Dynasty Era Chinese official Xu Xianqing (2) (30x40mm). c, Sundial (3) (30x40mm). d, Portrait of Prince Zhu Youyuan (4) (30x40mm). e, Forbidden City Turret (5) (30x40mm). f, Neolithic era pot (6) (30x40mm). g, Painting of the Kangxi Emperor of the Qing Dynasty (7) (30x80mm). h, Forbidden City Main Gate Temple and Tiananmen Square (8) (60x40mm). i, Ornamented gate (9) (60x40mm). j, Lion-head handle on fire bowl (10) (30x40mm). k, Painting of the Ming Dynasty Era Chinese official Xu Xianqing (11) (30x40mm).
7ce, Portrait of the Qianlong Emperor in armor, horiz.

## 2015, June 5 — Litho. — Perf. 14

2845 A608 2ce Sheet of 11, #a-k — 11.50 11.50

**Souvenir Sheet**

2846 A608 7ce multi — 3.75 3.75

No. 2846 contains one 40x30mm stamp.

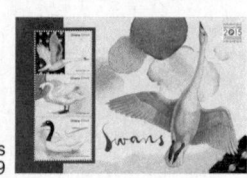

Swans
A609

No. 2847: a, Mute swan in flight. b, Mute swan standing. c, Black-necked swan.
9ce, Mute swan in flight, vert.

## 2015, Aug. 3 — Litho. — Perf. 12

2847 A609 4ce Sheet of 3, #a-c — 6.25 6.25

**Souvenir Sheet**

2848 A609 9ce multi — 4.75 4.75

Singapore 2015 Intl. Philatelic Exhibition.

Christmas — A610

Religious paintings by Sandro Botticelli: 2ce, Madonna and Child with Adoring Angel. 3ce, Madonna and Child. 4ce, Madonna of the Book. 5ce, The Adoration of the Magi.

## 2015, Sept. 2 — Litho. — Perf. 12½

2849-2852 A610 Set of 4 — 7.50 7.50

Butterflies — A611

No. 2853, 4ce: a, White morpho. b, Graphium. c, Thamyris morpho. d, Rice paper butterfly.
No. 2854, 4ce: a, Orange-barred sulphur. b, Leopard lacewing. c, Giant striped morpho. d, Orange albatross.

No. 2855, 12ce, Malachite. No. 2856, 12ce, Citrus swallowtail.

## 2015, Nov. 2 — Litho. — Perf. 12
**Sheets of 4, #a-d**

2853-2854 A611 Set of 2 — 16.50 16.50

**Souvenir Sheets**

2855-2856 A611 Set of 2 — 12.50 12.50

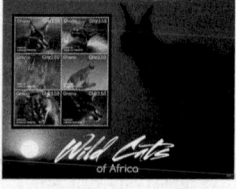

Wild Cats
A612

No. 2857 — Caracal: a, With both ears touching top of stamp. b, Facing left. c, Two juveniles. d, On tree branch. e, With mouth open. f, With one ear touching top of stamp.
No. 2858 — Lion: a, Female facing right with open mouth. b, Head of male. c, Male looking left. d, Female facing right with closed mouth.
No. 2859, 12ce, Jaguar. No. 2860, 12ce, Cheetah.

## 2015, Nov. 2 — Litho. — Perf. 14

2857 A612 3.50ce Sheet of 6, #a-f — 11.00 11.00

2858 A612 4ce Sheet of 4, #a-d — 8.25 8.25

**Souvenir Sheets**
**Perf. 12**

2859-2860 A612 Set of 2 — 12.50 12.50

No. 2860 contains one 50x30mm stamp.

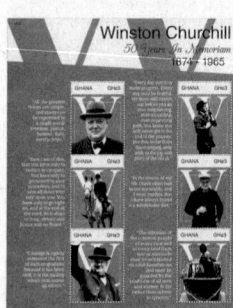

Sir Winston Churchill (1874-1965), British Prime Minister — A613

No. 2861 — Churchill: a, Wearing hat. b, Holding rifle. c, On horse. d, Holding cigar. e, Wearing hat, waving. f, In carriage, waving hat.
7ce, Churchill with cigar and cane.

## 2015, June 5 — Litho. — Perf. 14

2861 A613 3ce Sheet of 6, #a-f — 9.25 9.25

**Souvenir Sheet**

2862 A613 7ce multi — 3.75 3.75

**Souvenir Sheet**

New Year 2016 (Year of the Monkey)
A614

No. 2863: a, Monkey at left, with arm raised, Chinese characters at LL. b, Monkey with arm extended to left. c, Monkey with arm raised, Chinese characters at LR.

## 2015, Sept. 25 — Litho. — Perf. 12

2863 A614 4ce Sheet of 3, #a-c — 6.50 6.50

Mushrooms — A615

No. 2864: a, Shiitake mushroom. b, Chanterelle mushroom. c, Russula mushroom. d, Button mushroom. e, Oyster mushroom. f, Porcini mushroom.
9ce, Morel.

**2015, Nov. 2      Litho.      Perf. 14**
2864  A615  3.50ce  Sheet of 6,
                    #a-f                    11.00  11.00
**Souvenir Sheet**
**Perf. 12**
2865  A615      9ce multi                   4.75   4.75
No. 2865 contains one 50x30mm stamp. The mushroom on No. 2864c, Russula fellea, is inedible.

Pres. Abraham Lincoln (1809-65) — A616

No. 2866 — Various photographs of Lincoln, as shown.
9ce, Lincoln reading to son, Tad.

**2015, Nov. 2      Litho.      Perf. 14**
2866  A616  4ce Sheet of 4, #a-d            8.25   8.25
**Souvenir Sheet**
**Perf. 12**
2867  A616      9ce multi                   4.75   4.75

Sinking of the RMS Lusitania, Cent. — A617

No. 2868: a, Boat deck. b, First class dining room. c, Crowd on dock near Lusitania. d, Stern of Lusitania (no smokestacks). e, Midships of Lusitania. f, Bow of Lusitania (one smokestack).
9ce, Lusitania at sea.

**2015, Nov. 2      Litho.      Perf. 14**
2868  A617  3.50ce  Sheet of 6,
                    #a-f                    11.00  11.00
**Souvenir Sheet**
**Perf. 12½**
2869  A617      9ce multi                   4.75   4.75
No. 2869 contains one 51x38mm stamp.

Queen Elizabeth II, Longest-Reigning British Monarch — A618

No. 2870 — Queen Elizabeth II wearing hat with colors: a, Ultramarine and white. b, Pale blue. c, Yellow. d, Peach.
9ce, Queen Elizabeth II wearing cerise hat and coat.

**2015, Nov. 25      Litho.      Perf. 14**
2870  A618  4ce Sheet of 4, #a-d           8.25   8.25
**Souvenir Sheet**
2871  A618      9ce multi                   4.75   4.75

Visit of Pope Francis to New York City A619

No. 2872 — World Trade Center Memorial and: a, Pope not waving, rose at LR. b, Pope waving, hand at left, 2 roses behind head. c, Pope waving, hand at right, rose at LR. d, Pope not waving, rose at LL and at right. e, Pope waving, hand at left, rose at left and LR. f, Pope not waving, rose stem at right.
9ce, Pope Francis waving, buildings.

**2015, Nov. 25      Litho.      Perf. 14**
2872  A619  3.50ce  Sheet of 6,
                    #a-f                    11.00  11.00
**Souvenir Sheet**
**Perf. 12**
2873  A619      9ce multi                   4.75   4.75

Oct. 20, 2015 State Dinner at Buckingham Palace — A620

No. 2874: a, Duchess of Cambridge, hands not visible (35x35mm). b, Duchess of Cambridge holding glass (35x35mm). c, Duchess of Cambridge toasting Chinese President Xi Jinping (35x70mm).
9ce, Duchess of Cambridge, President Xi, Queen Elizabeth II, horiz.

**2015, Dec. 7      Litho.      Perf. 13¾**
2874  A620  4ce Sheet of 3, #a-c           6.25   6.25
**Souvenir Sheet**
**Perf. 14**
2875  A620      9ce multi                   4.75   4.75
No. 2875 contains one 80x30mm stamp.

Magna Carta, 800th Anniv. A621

No. 2876: a, Seal of King John of England (seated). b, People near King John, seated on throne. c, Seal of King John (on horse). d, King John signing Magna Carta.
9ce, King John.

**2015, Dec. 21      Litho.      Perf. 14**
2876  A621  4ce Sheet of 4, #a-d           8.50   8.50
**Souvenir Sheet**
**Perf. 12**
2877  A621      9ce multi                   4.75   4.75

New Horizons Space Probe A622

No. 2878: a, Atlas V on launchpad. b, Mission emblem. c, New Horizons over Pluto. d, New Horizons, Pluto and Charon.
9ce, New Horizons approaching Pluto.

**2015, Dec. 21      Litho.      Perf. 14**
2878  A622  4ce Sheet of 4, #a-d           8.50   8.50
**Souvenir Sheet**
**Perf. 12**
2879  A622      9ce multi                   4.75   4.75

Souvenir Sheets

Elvis Presley (1935-77) — A623

Inscriptions: No. 2880, 9ce, First recording session. No. 2881, 9ce, Purchases Rising Sun. No. 2882, 9ce, Promoted to Private First Class, vert. No. 2883, 9ce, Waterskiing on McKellar Lake.

**Perf. 12, 14 (#2883)**
**2015, Dec. 21              Litho.**
2880-2883  A623   Set of 4            19.00  19.00

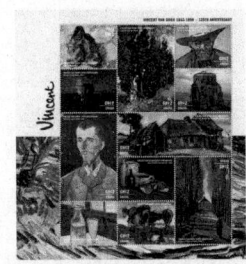

Paintings by Vincent van Gogh (1853-90) — A624

No. 2884: a, A Pair of Shoes, 1888 (40x30mm). b, Cypresses with Two Women, 1889 (40x60mm). c, Portrait of Patience Escalier, 1888 (40x30mm). d, Peasant Burning Weeds, 1883 (40x30mm). e, Country Churchyard and Old Church Tower, 1885 (40x30mm). f, Portrait of Eugene Boch, 1888 (40x60mm). g, Cottage with Decrepit Barn and Stooping Woman, 1885 (80x30mm). h, Still Life with Clogs and Pots, 1884 (40x30mm). i, Avenue of Poplars in Autumn, 1884 (40x60mm). j, Still Life with Absinthe, 1887 (40x30mm). k, Cows, 1890 (40x30mm).
9ce, Self-portrait with Gray Felt Hat, 1887.

**2015, Dec. 31      Litho.      Perf. 14**
2884  A624  2ce Sheet of 11,
                    #a-k                    11.50  11.50
**Souvenir Sheet**
**Perf. 12**
2885  A624      9ce multi                   4.75   4.75
No. 2885 contains one 40x60mm stamp. Inscription on No. 2884i is incorrect.

Gray-Crowned Crane — A625

No. 2886: a, Crane facing right, neck visible. b, Two cranes. c, Crane facing forward. d, Crane facing right, neck not visible.
12ce, Crane, diff.

**2016, Feb. 20      Litho.      Perf. 14**
2886  A625  4ce Sheet of 4, #a-d           8.25   8.25
**Souvenir Sheet**
**Perf. 12½**
2887  A625     12ce multi                   6.25   6.25
No. 2887 contains one 38x51mm stamp.

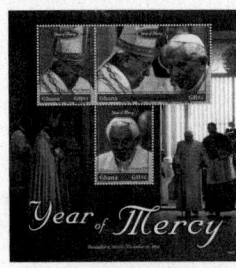

Extraordinary Jubilee of Mercy — A626

No. 2888: a, Pope Francis (30x40mm). b, Popes Francis and Benedict XVI (60x40mm). c, Pope Benedict XVI (30x40mm).
9ce, Popes Francis and Benedict XVI, vert.

**2016, Feb. 20      Litho.      Perf. 14**
2888  A626  4ce Sheet of 3, #a-c           6.25   6.25
**Souvenir Sheet**
**Perf. 12½**
2889  A626      9ce multi                   4.75   4.75
No. 2889 contains one 38x51mm stamp.

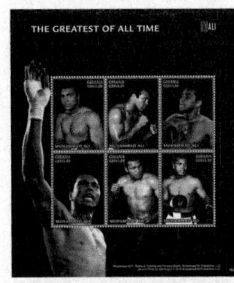

Muhammad Ali (1942-2016), Boxer — A627

No. 2890 — Various images of Ali, as shown.
9ce, Ali, horiz.

**2016, Mar. 8      Litho.      Perf. 14**
2890  A627  3.50ce  Sheet of 6,
                    #a-f                    11.00  11.00
**Souvenir Sheet**
2891  A627      9ce multi                   4.75   4.75
No. 2891 contains one 80x30mm stamp.

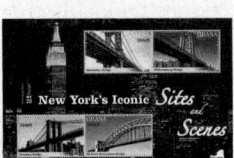

New York City Landmarks — A628

No. 2892: a, Manhattan Bridge. b, Williamsburg Bridge. c, Brooklyn Bridge. d, Hell Gate Bridge.
20ce, New York City skyline.

**2016, Apr. 8      Litho.      Perf. 12**
2892  A628  5ce Sheet of 4,
                    #a-d                   10.50  10.50
**Souvenir Sheet**
**Perf. 14**
2893  A628     20ce multi                  10.50  10.50
No. 2893 contains one 160x60mm stamp. Inscription on No. 2892d is incorrect.

Worldwide Fund for Nature (WWF) — A629

No. 2894 — Various depictions of Slender-snouted crocodile: a, Denomination at UR. b, Denomination at UL, crocodile facing left. c, Denomination at LR. d, Denomination at UL, crocodile facing right.

**2016, Apr. 8    Litho.    Perf. 14**
2894 A629 5ce Block of 4, #a-
d                                10.50 10.50
e.    Souvenir sheet of 8, 2 each
#2894a-2894d, perf. 12          21.00 21.00

Queen Elizabeth II, 90th Birthday A630

No. 2895 — Queen Elizabeth II: a, As child, with her mother (40x30mm). b, With Prince Charles and Princess Diana (40x30mm). c, With Duke and Duchess of Cambridge (80x30mm). d, With her family (40x30mm). e, With Duchess of Cambridge (40x30mm). 19ce, Queen Elizabeth II as infant, with parents.

**2016, May 16    Litho.    Perf. 14**
2895 A630 4.50ce Sheet of 5,
#a-e                             11.50 11.50
**Souvenir Sheet**
**Perf. 12½**
2896 A630 19ce multi             9.75  9.75
No. 2896 contains one 51x38mm stamp.

William Shakespeare (1564-1616), Writer — A631

No. 2897 — Scenes from: a, Coriolanus. b, The Taming of the Shrew. c, As You Like It. d, The Winter's Tale. e, The Tempest. f, Twelfth Night.
No. 2898 — Scenes from: a, Romeo and Juliet. b, Hamlet. c, Macbeth. d, King Lear. 19ce, First Folio, 1623, horiz.

**2016, May 16    Litho.    Perf. 13¾**
2897 A631 4ce Sheet of 6,
#a-f                             12.50 12.50
2898 A631 5ce Sheet of 4,
#a-d                             10.50 10.50
**Souvenir Sheet**
**Perf. 12½**
2899 A631 19ce multi             9.75  9.75
No. 2899 contains one 38x51mm stamp.

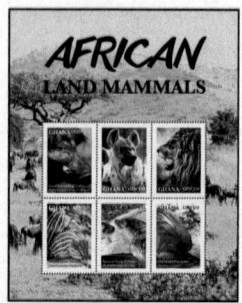

African Mammals — A632

No. 2900: a, Giant forest hog. b, Hyena. c, Lion. d, Striped grass mouse. e, Spotted-necked otter. f, Old World porcupine.
No. 2901, horiz.: a, Bat-eared fox. b, Cape hare. c, Caracal. d, Desert hedgehog. 9ce, Wildebeest.

**2016, May 16    Litho.    Perf. 14**
2900 A632 3.50ce Sheet of 6,
#a-f                             11.00 11.00

2901 A632    4ce Sheet of 4,
#a-d                             8.25  8.25
**Souvenir Sheet**
**Perf. 12**
2902 A632    9ce multi           4.75  4.75

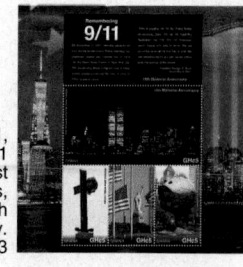

Sept. 11, 2001 Terrorist Attacks, 15th Anniv. A633

No. 2903: a, Nighttime New York City skyline with World Trade Center (90x50mm). b, Ground Zero steel cross (30x50mm). c, Statue of Liberty, flags at half-staff (30x50mm). d, World Trade Center bronze globe (30x50mm). 19ce, Ground Zero Tribute in Light.

**2016, May 16    Litho.    Perf. 12**
2903 A633 5ce Sheet of 4,
#a-d                             10.50 10.50
**Souvenir Sheet**
**Perf. 12**
2904 A633 19ce multi             9.75  9.75
No. 2904 contains one 60x50mm stamp.

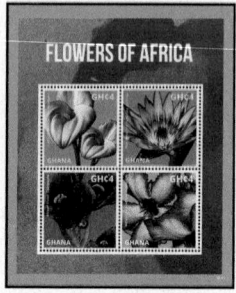

Flowers A634

No. 2905: a, Arum lily. b, Blue water lily. c, African violet. d, Impala lily. 9ce, Cape daisy, horiz.

**2016, May 30    Litho.    Perf. 13¾**
2905 A634 4ce Sheet of 4, #a-d   8.25  8.25
**Souvenir Sheet**
**Perf. 12½**
2906 A634 9ce multi              4.75  4.75
No. 2906 contains one 51x38mm stamp.

Statue of Liberty, 130th Anniv. A635

No. 2907: a, Entire statue. b, Tablet. c, Top of statue, torch touching top panel. d, Top of statue, torch below top panel. e, Torch. f, Head of statue.
9ce, Statue of Liberty, diff.

**2016, June 15    Litho.    Perf. 14**
2907 A635 4ce Sheet of 6, #a-
f                                12.50 12.50
**Souvenir Sheet**
**Perf.**
2908 A635 9ce multi              4.50  4.50
No. 2908 contains one 33x43mm oval stamp.

Funtunfunefu Symbol — A635a

Microphones, Pen, Paper and Computer — A635b — 2908B

Circle of People — A635c

Grieving Adult and Child — A635d

**LET GO!**    Map of Ghana — A635e

**2016, Aug. 17    Litho.    Perf. 14**
2908A A635a 2ce multi            —
2908B A635b 2ce multi            —
2908C A635c 2ce multi            —
2908D A635d 2ce multi            —
2908E A635e 3ce multi            —
2016 National Elections.

Voyager 2, 30th Anniv. (in 2017) A636

No. 2909: a, Trajectories of Voyagers 1 and 2, Pioneers 10 and 11. b, Voyager 2 flyby of Umbriel. c, Cover of Golden Record. d, Voyager 2 flyby of Ariel.
19ce, Launch of Voyager 2, vert.

**2016, Sept. 9    Litho.    Perf. 14**
2909 A636 5ce Sheet of 4,
#a-d                             10.00 10.00
**Souvenir Sheet**
2910 A636 19ce multi             9.50  9.50
Sheet margin of No. 2909 has incorrect information about launch date and a non-existent landing date.

Poisonous Plants — A637

No. 2911: a, Belladonna. b, Rosary pea plant. c, Wolfsbane. d, Strychnine tree.
No. 2912, horiz.: a, Castor oil plant. b, Angel's trumpet.
16ce, Yew tree.

**2016, Sept. 13    Litho.    Perf. 14**
2911 A637 8ce Sheet of 4,
#a-d                             16.00 16.00
**Souvenir Sheets**
**Perf. 12**
2912 A637 12ce Sheet of 2        12.00 12.00
2913 A637 16ce multi             8.00  8.00

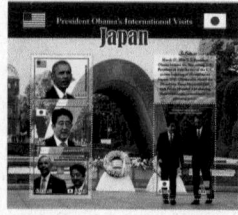

Visit of Pres. Barack Obama to Japan A638

No. 2914: a, 5ce, Pres. Obama, U.S. flag (40x30mm). b, 5ce, Japanese Prime Minister Shinzo Abe, Japanese flag (40x30mm). c, 5ce, Obama and Abe, flags (40x30mm). d, 10ce, Obama and Abe, flags, diff. (40x60mm).
No. 2915: a, Obama, Presidential Seal, U.S. flag. b, Abe, emblem of Prime Minister, Japanese flag.

**2016, Oct. 10    Litho.    Perf. 14**
2914 A638    Sheet of 4,
#a-d                             12.50 12.50

**Souvenir Sheet**
**Perf. 13¾**
2915 A638 10ce Sheet of 2,
#a-b                             10.00 10.00
No. 2915 contains two 35x35mm stamps.

Visit to Bhutan of Duke and Duchess of Cambridge — A639

No. 2916: a, Duke and Duchess of Cambridge, person behind Duchess. b, Duke of Cambridge. c, Duchess of Cambridge. d, Duke and Duchess, people in background.
No. 2917: a, Duke and Duchess, Duke holding jacket. b, Duke and Duchess, no hands visible.

**2016, Oct. 14    Litho.    Perf. 12**
2916 A639  8ce Sheet of 4,
#a-d                             16.00 16.00
**Souvenir Sheet**
**Perf. 13¾**
2917 A639 12ce Sheet of 2,
#a-b                             12.00 12.00
No. 2917 contains two 35x35mm stamps.

Patas Monkeys A640

No. 2918 — Monkey: a, Eating foliage, hand at mouth. b, Facing left with mouth open. c, Facing left with mouth closed. d, With food in mouth and hand near mouth. e, Facing right with mouth closed. f, Holding food with both hands.
No. 2919: a, Monkey on all fours. b, Monkey sitting.

**2016, Oct. 24    Litho.    Perf. 14**
2918 A640 3ce Sheet of 6, #a-f   9.00  9.00
**Souvenir Sheet**
2919 A640 8ce Sheet of 2, #a-b   8.00  8.00

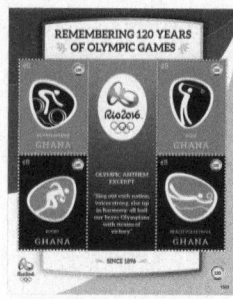

2016 Summer Olympics, Rio de Janeiro — A641

No. 2920, 8ce: a, Mountain biking. b, Golf. c, Rugby. d, Beach volleyball.
No. 2921, 8ce: a, Canoe sprint. b, Volleyball. c, Gymnastics. d, Equestrian eventing.
No. 2922: a, Greco-Roman wrestling. b, Kurt Leucht, Greco-Roman wrestler.

**2016, Nov. 14** Litho. **Perf. 14**
**Sheets of 4, #a-d**
2920-2921 A641 Set of 2 30.00 30.00
**Souvenir Sheet**
**Perf. 12½**
2922 A641 12ce Sheet of 2,
#a-b 11.50 11.50
No. 2922 contains two 38x51mm stamps.

*Star Trek* Television Series, 50th
Anniv. — A642

No. 2923 — Scenes from episode entitled:
a, Amok Time. b, Plato's Stepchildren. c,
Errand of Mercy. d, The Devil in the Dark. e,
The Doomsday Machine. f, Arena.
16ce, Where No Man Has Gone Before.

**2016, Oct. 24** Litho. **Perf. 14**
2923 A642 4ce Sheet of 6,
#a-f 12.00 12.00
**Souvenir Sheet**
**Perf. 12¾**
2924 A642 16ce multi 8.00 8.00
No. 2924 contains one 51x38mm stamp.

Christmas — A643

Designs: No. 2925, 5ce, Christmas tree. No.
2926, 5ce, Christmas ornaments, gifts and
holly. No. 2927, 8ce, Snowflake, Christmas
ornaments and text. No. 2928, 8ce, Bell and
text.

**2016, Dec. 5** Litho. **Perf. 12½**
2925-2928 A643 Set of 4 12.50 12.50

A644

New
Year
2017
(Year
of the
Rooster)
A645

No. 2929 — Rooster with: a, Head at left. b,
Head at right. c, Hen and chicks.
No. 2930 — Rooster facing: a, Right, pale
green background. b, Left, lavender gray back-
ground. c, Right, lavender gray background. d,
Left, pale green background.

**2016, Dec. 5** Litho. **Perf. 13¾**
2929 A644 8ce Sheet of 3, #a-
c 11.50 11.50
2930 A645 8ce Sheet of 4, #a-
d 15.50 15.50

**Miniature Sheet**

New
Year
Stamps
of
People's
Republic
of China
A646

No. 2931 — Stamps from People's Republic
of China: a, #3338, Monkey. b, #3418,
Rooster. c, #3466, Dog. d, #3557, Pig. e,
#3647, Rat. f, #3714, Ox. g, #3798, Tiger. h,
#3877, Rabbit. i, #3982, Dragon. j, #4061,
Snake. k, #4171, Horse. l, #4252, Sheep.

**2016, Dec. 28** Litho. **Perf. 12½**
2931 A646 2ce Sheet of 12,
#a-l 11.50 11.50

**Miniature Sheet**

Shengxiao Philatelic Society, 20th
Anniv. — A647

No. 2932 — Chinese person and: a, Rat. b,
Ox. c, Tiger. d, Rabbit. e, Dragon. f, Snake. g,
Horse. h, Sheep. i, Monkey. j, Rooster. k, Dog.
l, Pig.

**2016, Dec. 28** Litho. **Perf. 14**
2932 A647 2ce Sheet of 12,
#a-l 11.50 11.50
On No. 2932h the word "Sheep" is pink.

**Souvenir Sheet**

Monkey
King
A648

**2016, Dec. 28** Litho. **Perf. 13¾**
2933 A648 16ce multi 7.75 7.75

A649

Pres. John F. Kennedy (1917-
63) — A650

No. 2934: a, Pres. Kennedy with Dr. Martin
Luther King, Jr. and other civil rights leaders

(70x35mm). b, Pres. Kennedy and Nina
Khrushchev (35x35mm). c, Jacqueline Kennedy and Nikita Khrushchev (35x35mm). d,
Dr. King delivering "I Have a Dream" speech
(35x35mm). e, Pres. Kennedy (35x35mm). f,
Pres. Kennedy delivering speech in Berlin
(70x35mm).
No. 2935 — Civil rights leaders: a, Pres.
Barack Obama. b, Pres. Kennedy. c, Dr. King.
d, Pres. Abraham Lincoln.
16ce, Pres. Kennedy and Presidential seal.

**2017, Mar. 14** Litho. **Perf. 14x13¾**
2934 A649 5ce Sheet of 6,
#a-f 14.00 14.00
**Perf.**
2935 A650 7ce Sheet of 4,
#a-d 13.00 13.00
**Souvenir Sheet**
2936 A650 16ce multi 7.50 7.50
No. 2936 contains one 38mm diameter
stamp.

**Souvenir Sheets**

A652

Princess Diana (1961-97) — A653

**2017, Mar. 14** Litho. **Perf. 14**
2937 A651 16ce multi 7.50 7.50
**Perf. 12¾**
2938 A652 16ce multi 7.50 7.50
**Perf. 12**
2939 A653 16ce multi 7.50 7.50
Nos. 2937-2939 (3) 22.50 22.50

**Miniature Sheets**

A654

Elvis Presley (1935-77) — A655

No. 2940 — Presley wearing: a, Red shirt,
Turquoise green background. b, Brown red
shirt, dull scarlet background. c, Slate lilac
shirt, brick wall background. d, Suit and tie. e,
White shirt, red background with circles. f, Red
shirt and gray jacket.
No. 2941 — Presley wearing: a, Maroon
jacket, pale green background. b, Maroon shirt
and jacket, red background. c, Maroon shirt
and jacket, gray background. d, Maroon shirt
and gray sweater, red background.

**2017, June 3** Litho. **Perf. 14**
2940 A654 5ce Sheet of 6, #a-
f 14.00 14.00
2941 A655 8ce Sheet of 4, #a-d 15.00 15.00

**Miniature Sheet**

Birds
A656

No. 2942: a, Gouldian finch. b, Parrot finch.
c, Purple grenadier. d, Red bishop. e, Red-
crested cardinal. f, Spectacled monarch. g,
Crimson chat. h, Greater necklaced laughing-
thrush. i, Chestnut-backed jewel babbler.

**Perf. 13½x12½**
**2017, June 14** Litho.
2942 A656 4ce Sheet of 9, #a-i 16.50 16.50

Animals
A657

No. 2943: a, 6ce, Ashy-faced owl. b, 8ce,
Binturong. c, 12ce, Malachite green butterfly.
d, 14ce, Vancouver Island marmot.
25ce, Giant panda, vert.

**2017, July 21** Litho. **Perf. 12½**
2943 A657 Sheet of 4, #a-d 18.50 18.50
**Souvenir Sheet**
2944 A657 25ce multi 11.50 11.50

New
Year
2018
(Year of
the Dog)
A658

No. 2945 — Dogs: a, Shar pei. b, Peking-
ese. c, Chinese crested dog. d, Chinese
Chongqing dog.
No. 2946 — Dogs: a, Chow chow. b, Shih
Tzu.

**2017, Aug. 8** Litho. **Perf. 13¾**
2945 A658 8ce Sheet of 4,
#a-d 14.50 14.50
**Souvenir Sheet**
2946 A658 12ce Sheet of 2,
#a-b 11.00 11.00

Whales
A659

No. 2947: a, Humpback whale breaching surface. b, Orca. c, Humpback whale underwater.
20ce, Humpback whale, vert.

**2017, Sept. 11    Litho.    Perf. 14**
2947 A659 12ce Sheet of 3,
     #a-c      16.50 16.50

**Souvenir Sheet**
**Perf. 12**
2948 A659 20ce multi      9.25 9.25

No. 2948 contains one 30x50mm stamp.

Zeppelins — A660

No. 2949: a, Workers holding tether ropes of LZ-127 Graf Zeppelin. b, LZ-127 Graf Zeppelin in flight. c, LZ-127 Graf Zeppelin on beach. d, L-2 Zeppelin.
16ce, Count Ferdinand von Zeppelin (1838-1917), vert.

**2017, Oct. 26    Litho.    Perf. 12**
2949 A660 8ce Sheet of 4,
     #a-d      14.50 14.50

**Souvenir Sheet**
**Perf. 12½**
2950 A660 16ce multi      7.25 7.25

No. 2950 contains one 38x51mm stamp.

Butterflies — A661

No. 2951: a, Euphaedra janetta. b, Aeropetes tulbaghia. c, Colotis antevippe. d, Graphium leonidas.
16ce, Neptis nysiades.

**2017, Oct. 26    Litho.    Perf. 14**
2951 A661 8ce Sheet of 4,
     #a-d      14.50 14.50

**Souvenir Sheet**
**Perf. 12**
2952 A661 16ce multi      7.25 7.25

**Souvenir Sheets**

Elvis Presley (1935-77) — A662

Inscription: No. 2953, 16ce, Buys personal jet. No. 2954, 16ce, Made honorary Memphis Police Captain. No. 2955, 16ce, Wins third

Grammy Award. No. 2956, 16ce, Performs biggest concert ever.

**2017, Oct. 26    Litho.    Perf. 12¾**
2953-2956 A662 Set of 4      29.00 29.00

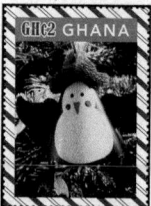

Christmas — A663

Designs: 2ce, Penguin. 3ce, Round Christmas ornaments. 4ce, Teddy bear and Christmas ornament on tree. 5ce, Santa Claus Christmas ornament.
10ce, Gingerbread man and house, horiz.

**2017, Dec. 25    Litho.    Perf. 12½**
2957-2960 A663 Set of 4      6.25 6.25

**Souvenir Sheet**
2961 A663 10ce multi      4.50 4.50

### SEMI-POSTAL STAMPS

Starlets, 1995 Under-17 World Soccer Champions — SP1

200ce+50ce, Holding gold cup won at Ecuador, vert. 550ce+50ce, Starlets '95 team photo. 800ce+50ce, Abu Idorisu, vert. 1100ce+50ce, Emmanuel Bentil, vert. 1500ce+50ce, Bashiru Gambo, vert.

**Perf. 13½x13, 13x13½**
**1997, Aug. 12      Litho.**
B1-B5 SP1 Set of 5      6.25 6.25

### AIR POST STAMPS

**Type of Regular Issue**
Designs: 1sh3p, Pennant-winged nightjar. 2sh, Crowned cranes, vert.

**Perf. 14½x14, 14x14½**
**1959, Oct. 5    Photo.    Wmk. 325**
C1 A17 1sh3p multicolored    1.50 .25
   a.   Booklet pane of 4      6.50
C2 A17 2sh multicolored      .25 .40
For surcharges see Nos. C7-C10.

Ships, Tema Harbor and Jet — AP1

**Perf. 14x13**
**1962, Feb. 10    Litho.    Unwmk.**
C3 AP1 1sh3p multicolored    .35 .35
C4 AP1 2sh6p multicolored    .85 .85
   Nos. C3-C4,110 (3)      1.60 1.60
Opening of Tema Harbor, as part of the Volta River Project.

**Type of Regular Issue, 1962**
**1962, Mar. 6      Perf. 13x14**
C5 A35 1sh3p multicolored    .30 .30
C6 A35 2sh6p multicolored    .60 .60

**Nos. C1-C2 Surcharged in White or Green with New Value and: "Ghana New Currency / 19th July, 1965"**
**Perf. 14½x14, 14x14½**
**1965, July 19    Photo.    Wmk. 325**
C7 A17 15pa on 1sh3p multi (W)   2.00 .70
C8 A17 24pa on 2sh multi (G)    .40 .35
The two lines of the overprint are diagonal on No. C8.

**Nos. C1, C8 Surcharged in White or Red**
**1967, Feb. 27    Photo.    Wmk. 325**
C9 A17 12½np on 1sh3p (W)    4.00 3.00
C10 A17 20np on 24pa on 2sh    5.00 4.00

### POSTAGE DUE STAMPS

**Gold Coast Nos. J2-J6 Overprinted "GHANA" and Bar in Red**
**Perf. 14**
**1958, June 25    Wmk. 4    Typo.**
J1 D1 1p black      .25 .45
J2 D1 2p black      .25 .45
J3 D1 3p black      .25 .45
J4 D1 6p black      .25 1.00
J5 D1 1sh black      .25 2.00
   Nos. J1-J5 (5)      1.25 4.35

**Type of Gold Coast Inscribed "Ghana"**
**1958, Dec. 1      Perf. 14**
J6 D1 1p carmine rose    .25 .45
J7 D1 2p green      .25 .45
J8 D1 3p orange      .25 .45
J9 D1 6p ultramarine    .25 1.00
J10 D1 1sh purple      .25 2.00
   Nos. J6-J10 (5)      1.25 4.35

**Nos. J6-J10 Surcharged in Black, Blue or Red with New Value and "Ghana New Currency / 19th July, 1965."**
**1965, July 19**
J11 D1 1pa on 1p car rose    .25 .75
J12 D1 2pa on 2p grn (Bl)    .25 1.40
J13 D1 3pa on 3p org (Bl)    .25 1.40
J14 D1 6pa on 6p ultra (R)    .35 2.50
J15 D1 12pa on 1sh pur (Bl)    .60 2.75
   Nos. J11-J15 (5)      1.70 8.80

Surcharge diagonal on Nos. J11 and J15.

No. J12 with additional surcharge, "1 ½Np" in red, was reported to have been used at one branch post office (Burma Camp) despite official intention. Four similar added surcharges were prepared: 1np on 1pa, 2½np on 3pa, 5np on 6pa, and 10np on 12pa.

D2

**1970    Unwmk.    Litho.    Perf. 14½x14**
J16 D2 1np carmine rose    1.30 5.00
J17 D2 1½np green      1.50 6.00
J18 D2 2½np orange      1.90 8.00
J19 D2 5np ultramarine    2.40 8.50
J20 D2 10np dull purple    3.50 9.50
   Nos. J16-J20 (5)      10.60 37.00

**1981      Litho.      Perf. 14½x14**
J21 D2 2p red orange      1.50 5.25
J22 D2 3p brown      1.50 5.25

# GIBRALTAR

jə-ˈbrol-tər

LOCATION — A fortified promontory, including the Rock, extending from Spain's southeast coast at the entrance to the Mediterranean Sea
GOVT. — British Crown Colony
AREA — 2.5 sq. mi.
POP. — 29,165 (1999 est.)
CAPITAL — Gibraltar

12 Pence = 1 Shilling
20 Shillings = 1 Pound
100 Centimos = 1 Peseta (1889-95)
100 Pence = 1 Pound (1971)

**Catalogue values for unused stamps in this country are for Never Hinged items, beginning with Scott 119 in the regular postage section and Scott J1 in the postage due section.**

GIBRALTAR

**Types of Bermuda Overprinted in Black**

**1886, Jan. 1    Wmk. 2    Perf. 14**
1 A6 ½p green      24.00 13.00
2 A1 1p rose      92.50 6.50
3 A2 2p violet brown    155.00 92.50
4 A8 2½p ultra      220.00 4.25
5 A7 4p orange brn    210.00 120.00
6 A4 6p violet      330.00 250.00
7 A5 1sh bister brn    500.00 400.00
   Nos. 1-7 (7)      1,532. 886.25

Forged overprints of No. 7 are plentiful.

Victoria
A6      A7

A8      A9

**1886-98      Typo.**
8 A6 ½p dull green ('87)    20.00 4.50
9 A6 ½p gray grn ('98)    14.50 2.00
10 A7 1p rose ('87)    52.50 5.00
11 A7 1p car rose ('98)    14.50 .55
12 A8 2p brn violet    35.00 36.00
13 A8 2p brn vio & ultra ('98)    30.00 2.75
14 A9 2½p brt ultra ('98)    47.50 .65
   a.   2½p ultramarine    95.00 3.25
16 A8 4p orange brn    90.00 90.00
17 A8 4p org brn & grn ('98)    21.00 5.25
18 A8 6p violet    145.00 150.00
19 A8 6p vio & car rose ('98)    47.50 25.00
20 A8 1sh bister    275.00 250.00
21 A8 1sh bis & car rose ('98)    47.50 11.00
   Nos. 8-14,16-21 (13)    840.00 582.70

**Stamps of 1886 Issue Surcharged in Black**

**1889, July**
22 A6 5c on ½p green    14.00 32.50
23 A7 10c on 1p rose    15.00 20.00
24 A8 25c on 2p brn vio    6.00 11.50
   a.   Small "I" in "CENTIMOS"    130.00 190.00
   b.   Broken "N"    130.00 190.00
25 A9 25c on 2½p ultra    30.00 2.75
   a.   Small "I" in "CENTIMOS"    400.00 125.00
   b.   Broken "N"    400.00 125.00
26 A8 40c on 4p org brn    62.50 87.50
27 A8 50c on 6p violet    67.50 87.50
28 A8 75c on 1sh bister    67.50 82.50
   Nos. 22-28 (7)    262.50 324.25
   Set, ovptd. "SPECIMEN"    375.00

There are two varieties of the figure "5" in the 5c, 25c, 50c and 75c.

A11

**1889-95**
29 A11 5c green      7.00 1.25
30 A11 10c rose      5.50 .60
   a.   Value omitted      7,000.
31 A11 20c ol green ('95)    19.00 100.00
31A A11 20c ol grn & brn ('95)    30.00 25.00
32 A11 25c ultra      27.50 .90
33 A11 40c orange brn    4.50 4.75
34 A11 50c violet      3.75 3.00
35 A11 75c olive green    37.50 37.50
36 A11 1p bister      90.00 24.00
36A A11 1p bis & bl ('95)    6.00 8.50
37 A11 2p blk & car rose ('95)    13.00 35.00
38 A11 5p steel blue    50.00 120.00
   Nos. 29-38 (12)    293.75 360.50

A12

FOUR SHILLINGS

King Edward VII — A13

### 1903, May 1

| | | | | |
|---|---|---|---|---|
| 39 | A12 | ½p grn & bl grn | 14.50 | 11.00 |
| 40 | A12 | 1p violet, *red* | 37.50 | .70 |
| 41 | A12 | 2p grn & car rose | 37.50 | 45.00 |
| 42 | A12 | 2½p vio & blk, *bl* | 8.75 | .70 |
| 43 | A12 | 6p violet & pur | 42.50 | 26.00 |
| 44 | A12 | 1sh blk & car rose | 32.50 | 42.50 |
| 45 | A13 | 2sh green & ultra | 200.00 | 275.00 |
| 46 | A13 | 4sh vio & green | 150.00 | 250.00 |
| 47 | A13 | 8sh vio & blk, *bl* | 170.00 | 200.00 |
| 48 | A13 | £1 vio & blk, *red* | 650.00 | 750.00 |

### 1904-12      Wmk. 3
### Ordinary or Chalky Paper

| | | | | |
|---|---|---|---|---|
| 49 | A12 | ½p blue grn ('07) | 16.00 | 2.00 |
| 49Ab | A12 | ½p dull grn & br grn ('04) | 14.00 | 9.00 |
| 50b | A12 | 1p vio, *red* ('05) | 8.50 | 1.00 |
| a. | | Bisected, used as ½p on card | | 1,800. |
| 51 | A12 | 1p car ('07) | 6.50 | .70 |
| 52a | A12 | 2p grn & car rose ('07) | 10.00 | 15.00 |
| 53 | A12 | 2p gray ('10) | 10.00 | 13.00 |
| 54 | A12 | 2½p vio & blk, *bl* ('07) | 45.00 | 110.00 |
| 55 | A12 | 2½p ultra ('07) | 9.00 | 1.90 |
| 56b | A12 | 6p vio & pur ('08) | 35.00 | 22.50 |
| a. | | 6p vio & red violet ('12) | 160.00 | 450.00 |
| 57a | A12 | 1sh blk & car rose ('06) | 57.50 | 25.00 |
| 58 | A12 | 1sh blk, *grn* ('10) | 27.50 | 24.00 |
| 59a | A13 | 2sh grn & ultra ('07) | 120.00 | 150.00 |
| 60 | A13 | 2sh vio & bl, *bl* ('10) | 67.50 | 57.50 |
| 61 | A13 | 4sh vio & grn ('10) | 350.00 | 425.00 |
| 62 | A13 | 4sh blk & red ('10) | 170.00 | 190.00 |
| 63 | A13 | 8sh vio & grn ('11) | 250.00 | 250.00 |
| 64 | A13 | £1 vio & blk, *red* | 650.00 | 700.00 |
| | | Nos. 49-64 (17) | 1,847. | 1,997. |

Nos. 51, 53, 55 are on ordinary paper. Nos. 54, 58, 60-64 are on chalky paper. Others come on both papers. The least expensive varieties are listed above. For detailed listings, see the *Scott Specialized Catalogue of Stamps and Covers.*

No. 56a, used, must have a 1912 cancellation. Stamps used later sell for about the same as unused.

A14

HALFPENNY

TWO SHILLINGS

King George V — A15

### 1912, July 17      Ordinary Paper

| | | | | |
|---|---|---|---|---|
| 66 | A14 | ½p green | 4.00 | .80 |
| 67 | A14 | 1p carmine | 4.75 | .90 |
| a. | | 1p scarlet ('16) | 10.00 | 1.60 |
| 68 | A14 | 2p gray | 21.00 | 1.75 |
| 69 | A14 | 2½p ultra | 11.00 | 3.00 |

### Chalky Paper

| | | | | |
|---|---|---|---|---|
| 70 | A14 | 6p dl vio & red vio | 11.00 | 19.00 |
| 71 | A14 | 1sh black, *green* | 19.50 | 4.00 |
| a. | | 1sh black, *emerald* ('24) | 32.50 | 110.00 |
| b. | | 1sh blk, *bl grn*, ol back ('19) | 29.00 | 27.50 |
| c. | | 1sh blk, *emer*, ol back ('23) | 32.50 | 92.50 |
| 72 | A15 | 2sh vio & ultra, *bl* | 30.00 | 4.50 |
| 73 | A15 | 4sh black & scar | 40.00 | 65.00 |
| 74 | A15 | 8sh vio & green | 110.00 | 130.00 |
| 75 | A15 | £1 vio & blk, *red* | 160.00 | 275.00 |
| | | Nos. 66-75 (10) | 411.25 | 503.95 |

### 1921-32      Ordinary Paper    Wmk. 4

| | | | | |
|---|---|---|---|---|
| 76 | A14 | ½p grn ('26) | 1.60 | 1.60 |
| 77 | A14 | 1p rose red | 2.10 | 1.25 |
| 78a | A14 | 1½p pale red brn ('22) | 2.25 | .60 |
| 79 | A14 | 2p gray | 1.60 | 1.60 |
| 80 | A14 | 2½p ultra | 22.50 | 60.00 |
| 81 | A14 | 3p ultra | 2.75 | 1.75 |

---

### Chalky Paper

| | | | | |
|---|---|---|---|---|
| 82 | A14 | 6p dl vio & red vio ('26) | 1.75 | 4.00 |
| a. | | 6p gray lilac & red violet ('23) | 7.00 | 6.50 |
| 83 | A14 | 1sh blk, *emer* | 12.00 | 26.00 |
| 84 | A14 | 1sh ol grn & blk | 17.50 | 42.50 |
| a. | | 1sh brn olive & black ('32) | 17.50 | 21.00 |
| 85a | A15 | 2sh red vio & ultra, *blue* ('25) | 8.25 | 47.50 |
| 86 | A15 | 2sh red brn & blk | 11.00 | 40.00 |
| 87 | A15 | 2sh6p grn & blk | 11.00 | 30.00 |
| 88 | A15 | 4sh blk & scar | 75.00 | 130.00 |
| 89 | A15 | 5sh car & blk | 19.00 | 75.00 |
| 90 | A15 | 8sh vio & grn | 325.00 | 550.00 |
| 91 | A15 | 10sh ultra & blk | 37.50 | 80.00 |
| 92 | A15 | £1 org & blk | 190.00 | 300.00 |
| 93 | A15 | £5 dl vio & blk | 1,750. | 6,000. |
| | | Nos. 76-92 (15) | 730.30 | 1,344. |

Years issued: Nos. 83, 85, 4sh, 8sh, 1924. 2sh6p, 5sh, 10sh, £5, 1925. £1, 1927. Nos. 84, 86, 1929.

No. 81 is inscribed "3 PENCE".

3 PENCE

No. 81

THREE PENCE

No. 94

### 1930, Apr. 12      Ordinary Paper
| | | | | |
|---|---|---|---|---|
| 94 | A14 | 3p ultramarine | 9.50 | 2.25 |

No. 94 is inscribed "THREE PENCE".

Rock of Gibraltar — A16

### 1931-33      Engr.      Perf. 14

| | | | | |
|---|---|---|---|---|
| 96 | A16 | 1p red | 2.75 | 3.00 |
| a. | | Perf. 13½x14 | 22.50 | 8.50 |
| 97 | A16 | 1½p red brown | 2.75 | 3.00 |
| a. | | Perf. 13½x14 | 18.00 | 5.00 |
| 98 | A16 | 2p gray ('32) | 13.50 | 2.00 |
| a. | | Perf. 13½x14 | 25.00 | 4.25 |
| 99 | A16 | 3p dk blue ('33) | 11.00 | 3.50 |
| a. | | Perf. 13½x14 | 45.00 | 42.50 |
| | | Nos. 96-99 (4) | 30.00 | 11.50 |
| | | Set, never hinged | 47.50 | |
| | | Nos. 96a-99a (4) | 110.50 | 60.25 |
| | | Set, never hinged | 185.00 | |

Common Design Types pictured following the introduction.

### Silver Jubilee Issue
### Common Design Type

### 1935, May 6      Perf. 11x12

| | | | | |
|---|---|---|---|---|
| 100 | CD301 | 2p black & ultra | 1.50 | 2.25 |
| 101 | CD301 | 3p ultra & brown | 3.25 | 4.50 |
| 102 | CD301 | 6p indigo & grn | 11.00 | 16.00 |
| 103 | CD301 | 1sh brn vio & ind | 13.00 | 20.00 |
| | | Nos. 100-103 (4) | 28.75 | 42.75 |
| | | Set, never hinged | 57.50 | |

### Coronation Issue
### Common Design Type

### 1937, May 12      Perf. 11x11½

| | | | | |
|---|---|---|---|---|
| 104 | CD302 | ½p deep green | .25 | .45 |
| 105 | CD302 | 2p gray black | .75 | 3.00 |
| 106 | CD302 | 3p deep ultra | 1.25 | 3.00 |
| | | Nos. 104-106 (3) | 2.25 | 6.45 |
| | | Set, never hinged | 4.50 | |

George VI — A17

Rock of Gibraltar — A18

Designs: 2p, Rock from north side. 3p, 5p, Europa Point. 6p, Moorish Castle. 1sh, Southport Gate. 2sh, Eliott Memorial. 5sh, Government House. 10sh, Catalan Bay.

---

### Perf. 13, 13½x14 (½p, No. 118), 14 (1½p)

### 1938-49      Engr.      Wmk. 4

| | | | | |
|---|---|---|---|---|
| 107 | A17 | ½p gray green | .25 | .40 |
| 108 | A18 | 1p red brn ('42) | .80 | .60 |
| a. | | 1p chestnut, perf. 14 | 20.00 | 2.75 |
| b. | | 1p chestnut, perf. 13½ | 20.00 | 2.50 |
| c. | | Perf. 13½, wmk. sideways ('40) | 4.50 | 7.75 |
| 109 | A18 | 1½p car rose ('43) | 20.00 | .90 |
| | | Perf. 13½ | 190.00 | 30.00 |
| 109A | A18 | 1½p gray vio ('43) | .45 | 1.60 |
| 110 | A18 | 2p dk gray ('43) | 1.40 | 1.50 |
| a. | | Perf. 14 | 22.00 | .55 |
| c. | | Perf. 13½ | 4.00 | .45 |
| d. | | Perf. 13½, wmk. sideways ('41) | 500.00 | 52.50 |
| 110B | A18 | 2p car rose ('44) | 1.00 | .55 |
| 111 | A18 | 3p blue ('42) | 2.00 | .35 |
| a. | | Perf. 14 | 100.00 | 6.00 |
| b. | | Perf. 13½ | 22.50 | 1.10 |
| 112 | A18 | 5p red org ('47) | 1.00 | 1.25 |
| 113 | A18 | 6p dl vio & car rose | 6.00 | 1.90 |
| a. | | Perf. 14 | 90.00 | 1.60 |
| b. | | Perf. 13½ | 30.00 | 4.00 |
| 114 | A18 | 1sh grn & blk ('42) | 2.25 | 4.50 |
| a. | | Perf. 14 | 30.00 | 27.50 |
| b. | | Perf. 13½ | 45.00 | 8.25 |
| 115 | A18 | 2sh org brn & blk ('42) | 6.00 | 6.50 |
| a. | | Perf. 14 | 40.00 | 30.00 |
| b. | | Perf. 13½ | 90.00 | 55.00 |
| 116 | A18 | 5sh dk car & blk ('44) | 12.50 | 14.00 |
| a. | | Perf 14 ('38) | 60.00 | 175.00 |
| b. | | Perf. 13½ | 35.00 | 16.00 |
| 117 | A18 | 10sh bl & blk ('43) | 22.50 | 22.50 |
| a. | | Perf. 14 | 45.00 | 150.00 |
| 118 | A17 | £1 orange | 30.00 | 55.00 |
| | | Nos. 107-118 (14) | 106.15 | 111.55 |
| | | Set, never hinged | 200.00 | |

Nos. 108c and 110d were issued in coils. No. 108 (1p, perf. 13) exists with watermark both normal and sideways. Nos. 110 and 110B (both 2p, perf. 13) have watermark sideways. For overprints see Nos. 127-130.

> **Catalogue values for unused stamps in this section, from this point to the end of the section, are for Never Hinged items.**

### Peace Issue
### Common Design Type

### 1946, Oct. 12      Perf. 13½x14

| | | | | |
|---|---|---|---|---|
| 119 | CD303 | ½p bright green | .30 | .50 |
| 120 | CD303 | 3p bright ultra | .45 | .50 |

### Silver Wedding Issue
### Common Design Types

### 1948, Dec. 1    Photo.    Perf. 14x14½
| | | | | |
|---|---|---|---|---|
| 121 | CD304 | ½p dark green | 1.00 | 3.00 |

### Engr.; Name Typo.    Perf. 11½x11
| | | | | |
|---|---|---|---|---|
| 122 | CD305 | £1 brown orange | 60.00 | 75.00 |
| | | Set, hinged | 40.00 | |

---

### UPU Issue
### Common Design Types
### Engr.; Name Typo. on 3p, 6p
### Perf. 13½, 11x11½

### 1949, Oct. 10      Wmk. 4

| | | | | |
|---|---|---|---|---|
| 123 | CD306 | 2p rose carmine | 1.25 | 1.25 |
| 124 | CD307 | 3p indigo | 2.00 | 1.50 |
| 125 | CD308 | 6p rose violet | 1.40 | 2.00 |
| 126 | CD309 | 1sh blue green | 1.25 | 4.00 |
| | | Nos. 123-126 (4) | 5.90 | 8.75 |

### Nos. 110B, 111, 113-114 overprinted in Black or Carmine

GIBRALTAR   NEW CONSTITUTION 1950

### 1950, Aug. 1      Perf. 13x12½

| | | | | |
|---|---|---|---|---|
| 127 | A18 | 2p carmine rose | .40 | 1.50 |
| 128 | A18 | 3p blue | .85 | 1.25 |
| 129 | A18 | 6p dl vio & car rose | 1.00 | 2.00 |
| a. | | Double overprint | 1,000. | 1,300. |
| 130 | A18 | 1sh grn & blk (C) | 1.25 | 2.00 |
| | | Nos. 127-130 (4) | 3.50 | 6.75 |

Adoption of Constitution of 1950.

### Coronation Issue
### Common Design Type

### 1953, June 2    Engr.    Perf. 13½x13
| | | | | |
|---|---|---|---|---|
| 131 | CD312 | ½p olive green & black | .50 | .50 |

GIBRALTAR

Wharves A26

Moorish Castle A27

Designs: 1p, South view. 1½p, Tunny fishing industry. 2p, Southport Gate. 2½p, Sailing in the bay. 3p, Ocean liner. 4p, Coaling wharf. 5p, Airport. 6p, Europa Point. 1sh, Strait from Buena Vista. 2sh, Rosia Bay. 5sh, Government House. £1, Arms of Gibraltar.

Search

PhilaSearch

www.PhilaSearch.com

**1953, Oct. 19**     *Perf. 13*

| | | | | |
|---|---|---|---|---|
| 132 | A26 | ½p dk grn & ind | .25 | .25 |
| 133 | A26 | 1p blue green | 1.60 | .95 |
| 134 | A26 | 1½p dark gray | 1.00 | 1.75 |
| 135 | A26 | 2p sepia | 2.00 | 1.25 |
| 136 | A26 | 2½p car lake | 3.25 | 1.00 |
| 137 | A26 | 3p grnsh blue | 4.50 | 1.25 |
| 138 | A26 | 4p ultra | 7.25 | 3.50 |
| 139 | A26 | 5p deep plum | 1.75 | 1.50 |
| 140 | A26 | 6p blue & black | 4.25 | 2.00 |
| 141 | A26 | 1sh red brn & bl | .90 | 1.25 |
| 142 | A26 | 2sh vio & org | 32.50 | 6.00 |
| 143 | A26 | 5sh dark brown | 40.00 | 15.00 |
| 144 | A27 | 10sh ultra & brn | 47.50 | 45.00 |
| 145 | A27 | £1 yellow & red | 57.50 | 55.00 |
| | | Nos. 132-145 (14) | 204.25 | 135.70 |
| | | Set, hinged | 100.00 | |

See Nos. 1390-1403.

**Inscribed: "ROYAL VISIT 1954"**

**1954, May 10**

| | | | | |
|---|---|---|---|---|
| 146 | A26 | 3p greenish blue | .50 | .30 |

Candytuft
A28

Rock and
Badge of
Gibraltar
Regiment
A30

Moorish
Castle — A29

Designs: 2p, St. George's Hall and cannons. 2½p, The keys. 3p, Rock by moonlight. 4p, Catalan Bay. 6p, Map. 7p, Air terminal. 9p, American war memorial. 1sh, Barbary ape. 2sh, Barbary partridge. 5sh, Blue rock thrush. 10sh, Narcissus.

**Wmk. 314**

**1960, Oct. 29**    Photo.    *Perf. 12½*

| | | | | |
|---|---|---|---|---|
| 147 | A28 | ½p brt green & lil | .25 | .50 |
| 148 | A29 | 1p black & yel grn | .25 | .25 |
| 149 | A29 | 2p org brn & sl | 1.00 | .25 |
| 150 | A28 | 2½p blue & black | 1.25 | .70 |
| 151 | A29 | 3p dk blue & ver | .30 | .25 |
| 152 | A29 | 4p choc & grnsh bl | 3.00 | .90 |
| a. | | Wmkd. sideways ('66) | .30 | 1.00 |
| 153 | A28 | 6p brown & emer | 1.00 | .70 |
| 154 | A28 | 7p gray & car | 2.50 | 1.75 |
| 155 | A28 | 9p grnsh blue & bluish gray | 1.00 | .95 |
| 156 | A29 | 1sh brown & green | 1.50 | .70 |
| 157 | A29 | 2sh dark red brn & ultra | 18.00 | 3.00 |
| 158 | A29 | 5sh ol & Prus grn | 8.50 | 7.00 |
| 159 | A28 | 10sh blue, yel & grn | 24.00 | 17.50 |

**Perf. 14**
**Engr.**

| | | | | |
|---|---|---|---|---|
| 160 | A30 | £1 org red & slate | 20.00 | 17.50 |
| | | Nos. 147-160 (14) | 82.55 | 51.95 |

For overprints see Nos. 165-166.

**Freedom from Hunger Issue**
Common Design Type

**1963, June 4**     *Perf. 14x14½*

| | | | | |
|---|---|---|---|---|
| 161 | CD314 | 9p sepia | 4.00 | 2.25 |

**Red Cross Centenary Issue**
Common Design Type

**1963, Sept. 2**    Litho.    *Perf. 13*

| | | | | |
|---|---|---|---|---|
| 162 | CD315 | 1p black & red | .75 | 1.40 |
| 163 | CD315 | 9p ultra & red | 5.50 | 4.00 |

**Shakespeare Issue**
Common Design Type

**1964, Apr. 23**    Photo.    *Perf. 14x14½*

| | | | | |
|---|---|---|---|---|
| 164 | CD316 | 7p brown | .65 | .55 |

Nos. 151 and 153
Overprinted

**1964, Oct. 16**     *Perf. 12½*

| | | | | |
|---|---|---|---|---|
| 165 | A29 | 3p dk blue & ver | .25 | .25 |
| 166 | A28 | 6p brown & emer | .35 | .50 |
| a. | | No period in overprint | 17.00 | 27.50 |

**ITU Issue**
Common Design Type

**Perf. 11x11½**

**1965, May 17**    Litho.    **Wmk. 314**

| | | | | |
|---|---|---|---|---|
| 167 | CD317 | 4p emerald & yel | 2.25 | .45 |
| 168 | CD317 | 2sh ap grn & dk bl | 6.75 | 5.50 |

**Intl. Cooperation Year Issue**
Common Design Type

**1965, Oct. 25**     *Perf. 14½*

| | | | | |
|---|---|---|---|---|
| 169 | CD318 | 1p lt violet & grn | .25 | 2.25 |
| 170 | CD318 | 4p blue green & cl | 1.00 | .50 |

**Churchill Memorial Issue**
Common Design Type

**1966, Jan. 24**    Photo.    *Perf. 14*
**Design in Black, Gold and Carmine Rose**

| | | | | |
|---|---|---|---|---|
| 171 | CD319 | ½p bright blue | .25 | 2.25 |
| 172 | CD319 | 1p green | .35 | .25 |
| 173 | CD319 | 4p brown | 1.35 | .30 |
| 174 | CD319 | 9p violet | 1.10 | 2.50 |
| | | Nos. 171-174 (4) | 3.05 | 5.30 |

**World Cup Soccer Issue**
Common Design Type

**1966, July 1**    Litho.    *Perf. 14*

| | | | | |
|---|---|---|---|---|
| 175 | CD321 | 2½p multicolored | .75 | 1.25 |
| 176 | CD321 | 6p multicolored | 1.10 | .50 |

Sea
Bream — A30a

7p, Orange scorpionfish. 1sh, Stone bass, vert.

**Perf. 14x13½, 13½x14**

**1966, Aug. 27**    Photo.    **Wmk. 314**

| | | | | |
|---|---|---|---|---|
| 177 | A30a | 4p ultra, rose red & blk | .30 | .25 |
| 178 | A30a | 7p ol, rose red & blk | .35 | .70 |
| a. | | Value omitted | 1,800. | |
| 179 | A30a | 1sh brt grn, brn & blk | .55 | .35 |
| | | Nos. 177-179 (3) | 1.20 | 1.30 |

European Sea Angling Championships, Gibraltar, Aug. 28-Sept. 3.

**WHO Headquarters Issue**
Common Design Type

**1966, Sept. 20**    Litho.    *Perf. 14*

| | | | | |
|---|---|---|---|---|
| 180 | CD322 | 6p multicolored | 2.75 | 1.50 |
| 181 | CD322 | 9p multicolored | 3.75 | 3.00 |

"Our Lady of
Europa" — A31

**Perf. 14x14½**

**1966, Nov. 15**    Photo.    **Wmk. 314**

| | | | | |
|---|---|---|---|---|
| 182 | A31 | 2sh ultra & black | .50 | .90 |

Enthronement of the recovered statue of the Madonna in its new shrine, cent.

**UNESCO Anniversary Issue**
Common Design Type

**1966, Dec. 1**    Litho.    *Perf. 14*

| | | | | |
|---|---|---|---|---|
| 183 | CD323 | 2p "Education" | .50 | .25 |
| 184 | CD323 | 7p "Science" | 2.00 | .25 |
| 185 | CD323 | 5sh "Culture" | 4.00 | 2.75 |
| | | Nos. 183-185 (3) | 6.50 | 3.25 |

Cable Ship
Mirror — A32

Ships and Arms of Gibraltar: ½p Victory, Nelson's flagship. 1p, S.S. Arab. 2p, H.M.S. Carmania. 2½p, M.V. Mons Calpe. 3p, S.S. Canberra. 4p, H.M.S. Hood. 6p, Xebec, Moorish vessel. 7p, Amerigo Vespucci, Italian training ship (sails). 9p, Raffaello, Italian liner. 1sh, H.M.S. Royal Katherine, 17th century British

warship. 2sh, H.M.S. Ark Royal, aircraft carrier. 5sh, H.M.S. Dreadnought, atomic submarine. 10sh, S.S. Neuralia, troopship. £1, Mary Celeste, 19th century mystery ship (sails).

**Perf. 14x14½**

**1967-69**    Photo.    **Wmk. 314**
**Design in Black, Red and Gold;**
**Background as Indicated**

| | | | | |
|---|---|---|---|---|
| 186 | A32 | ½p deep rose | .25 | .25 |
| 187 | A32 | 1p yellow | .25 | .25 |
| 188 | A32 | 2p ultra | .25 | .25 |
| 189 | A32 | 2½p orange | .40 | .30 |
| 190 | A32 | 3p violet | .25 | .25 |
| 191 | A32 | 4p rose | .35 | .25 |
| 191A | A32 | 5p brn & multi ('69) | 2.50 | .65 |
| 192 | A32 | 6p gray | .35 | .60 |
| 193 | A32 | 7p yellow grn | .35 | .50 |
| 194 | A32 | 9p green | .35 | .95 |
| 195 | A32 | 1sh rose brown | .35 | .35 |
| 196 | A32 | 2sh brt yellow | 4.00 | 2.50 |
| 197 | A32 | 5sh brick red | 3.50 | 6.75 |
| 198 | A32 | 10sh emerald | 12.00 | 18.50 |
| 199 | A32 | £1 lt ultra | 14.00 | 18.50 |
| | | Nos. 186-199 (15) | 39.15 | 50.85 |

Cable Car and ITY
Emblem — A33

ITY emblem and: 9p, Bull shark, horiz. 1sh, Skin diver, horiz.

**Perf. 14½x14, 14x14½**

**1967, June 15**    Photo.    **Wmk. 314**

| | | | | |
|---|---|---|---|---|
| 200 | A33 | 7p red brn, red & blk | .25 | .25 |
| 201 | A33 | 9p brt blue, blk & slate | .25 | .25 |
| 202 | A33 | 1sh emer, blk & org brn | .25 | .25 |
| | | Nos. 200-202 (3) | .75 | .75 |

International Tourist Year.

Holy Family — A34

Christmas: 6p, Church window, vert.

**1967, Nov. 1**     *Perf. 14½*

| | | | | |
|---|---|---|---|---|
| 203 | A34 | 2p dark red & multi | .25 | .25 |
| 204 | A34 | 6p dark green & multi | .25 | .25 |

General Eliott and
Map of Europe
and Great
Britain — A35

Designs: 9p, Eliott Memorial and tower. 1sh, Gen. Eliott and map of Gibraltar, vert. 2sh, Gen. Eliott directing rescue operations for enemy sailors during Great Siege 1779-83.

**Perf. 14½x14, 14x14½**

**1967, Dec. 11**    Photo.    **Wmk. 314**
**Size: 37x21mm, 21x37mm**

| | | | | |
|---|---|---|---|---|
| 205 | A35 | 4p multicolored | .25 | .25 |
| 206 | A35 | 9p multicolored | .25 | .25 |
| 207 | A35 | 1sh multicolored | .25 | .25 |

**Size: 58x21½mm**

| | | | | |
|---|---|---|---|---|
| 208 | A35 | 2sh multicolored | .30 | .25 |
| | | Nos. 205-208 (4) | 1.05 | 1.00 |

250th anniv. of the birth of General George Augustus Eliott (1717-1790), Governor of Gibraltar during Great Siege.

Lord Baden-
Powell — A36

Designs: 7p, Scout flag, Rock of Gibraltar and globe with map of Europe. 9p, Symbolic tents, heads and Scout salute. 1sh, Three Scout badges.

**Perf. 14x14½**

**1968, Mar. 27**    Photo.    **Wmk. 314**

| | | | | |
|---|---|---|---|---|
| 209 | A36 | 4p dull yellow & pur | .25 | .25 |
| 210 | A36 | 7p brn org, brn & grn | .25 | .25 |
| 211 | A36 | 9p ultra, black & org | .25 | .30 |
| 212 | A36 | 1sh yellow & emerald | 1.00 | 1.10 |
| | | Nos. 209-212 (4) | | |

60th anniv. of the Gibraltar Scout Assoc.

Nurse and
WHO
Emblem — A37

20th anniv. of WHO: 4p, Physician with microscope and WHO emblem.

**1968, July 1**    Photo.    **Wmk. 314**

| | | | | |
|---|---|---|---|---|
| 213 | A37 | 2p yellow, ultra & blk | .25 | .25 |
| 214 | A37 | 4p pink, black & slate | .25 | .25 |

King John Signing
Magna Carta — A38

Design: 2sh, Rock of Gibraltar, "Freedom" and Human Rights flame.

**1968, Aug. 26**     *Perf. 13½x14½*

| | | | | |
|---|---|---|---|---|
| 215 | A38 | 1sh org, gold & dk brn | .25 | .25 |
| 216 | A38 | 2sh brt green & gold | .40 | .40 |

International Human Rights Year.

Shepherd, Lamb and
Star — A39

Christmas: 9p, Mary, Jesus and lamb.

**1968, Nov. 1**     *Perf. 14x13½*

| | | | | |
|---|---|---|---|---|
| 217 | A39 | 4p lt brown & multi | .25 | .25 |
| 218 | A39 | 9p rose & multi | .25 | .25 |

Government
House,
Gibraltar — A40

9p, Rock of Gibraltar, Commonwealth Parliamentary Association emblem. 2sh, Big Ben, London, arms of Gibraltar.

**Perf. 14½x14, 14x14½**

**1969, May 26**    Photo.    **Wmk. 314**

| | | | | |
|---|---|---|---|---|
| 219 | A40 | 4p green & gold | .25 | .25 |
| 220 | A40 | 9p brt violet & gold | .25 | .25 |
| 221 | A40 | 2sh lt ultra, gold & red | .25 | .25 |
| | | Nos. 219-221 (3) | .75 | .75 |

Meeting of the Executive Committee of the General Council of the Commonwealth Parliamentary Assoc., Gibraltar, May 1969.

Rock of
Gibraltar — A41

**1969, July 30**     *Perf. 14½x13½*

| | | | | |
|---|---|---|---|---|
| 222 | A41 | ½p orange & gold | .25 | .25 |
| 223 | A41 | 5p emerald & silver | .25 | .25 |
| 224 | A41 | 7p brt rose lil & silver | .25 | .25 |
| 225 | A41 | 5sh ultra & gold | .85 | .85 |
| | | Nos. 222-225 (4) | 1.60 | 1.60 |

Gibraltar's new constitution.
Nos. 222-225 are valued with surrounding selvage.

Royal Artillery Officer, 1758 — A42

Uniforms: 6p, Contemporary soldier of the Royal Anglian Regiment. 9p, Soldier, Royal Engineers, 1786. 2sh, Private of Fox's Marines, 1704.

**1969, Nov. 6     Photo.     Perf. 14**
| | | | | |
|---|---|---|---|---|
| 226 | A42 | 1p gold & multi | .25 | .25 |
| 227 | A42 | 6p silver, gold & multi | .25 | .25 |
| 228 | A42 | 9p silver, gold & multi | .35 | .25 |
| 229 | A42 | 2sh gold & multi | .75 | .75 |
| | | Nos. 226-229 (4) | 1.60 | 1.50 |

Descriptions are printed on back on top of gum.

See Nos. 234-237, 276-279, 286-289, 299-302, 310-313, 318-321, 330-333.

Madonna della Seggiola, by Raphael — A43

Christmas (Paintings): 7p, Madonna and Child, by Luis Morales. 1sh, Virgin of the Rocks, by Leonardo da Vinci.

**1969, Dec. 1     Perf. 13½x14 Roulette 9**
| | | | | |
|---|---|---|---|---|
| 230 | A43 | 5p gold & multi | .25 | .25 |
| 231 | A43 | 7p gold & multi | .25 | .25 |
| 232 | A43 | 1sh gold & multi | .25 | .25 |
| a. | | Triptych, Nos. 230, 232, 231 | 1.10 | 1.10 |

## Europa Issue

Europa Point — A44

**1970, June 8     Perf. 13½**
| | | | | |
|---|---|---|---|---|
| 233 | A44 | 2sh multicolored | .45 | .40 |

### Uniform Type of 1969

Uniforms: 2p, Royal Scots officer, 1839. 5p, Private of South Wales Borderers. 7p, Private of Queen's Royal Regiment, 1742. 2sh, Piper of Royal Irish Rangers, 1969.

**1970, Aug. 28     Photo.     Perf. 14**
| | | | | |
|---|---|---|---|---|
| 234 | A42 | 2p gold & multi | .35 | .25 |
| 235 | A42 | 5p gold & multi | .50 | .25 |
| 236 | A42 | 7p gold & multi | .55 | .35 |
| 237 | A42 | 2sh gold & multi | 1.25 | 1.00 |
| | | Nos. 234-237 (4) | 2.65 | 1.85 |

Descriptions are printed on back on top of gum.

No. 178a and Rock of Gibraltar — A45

Design: 2sh, No. 30a and Moorish Castle.

**1970, Sept. 18     Perf. 13**
| | | | | |
|---|---|---|---|---|
| 238 | A45 | 1sh red & olive | .25 | .25 |
| 239 | A45 | 2sh ultra & rose | .40 | .55 |

Philympia, London Phil. Exhib., Sept. 18-26.

Virgin Mary by Gabriel Loire — A46

**1970, Dec. 1     Photo.     Perf. 13x14**
| | | | | |
|---|---|---|---|---|
| 240 | A46 | 2sh multicolored | .35 | .35 |

Christmas. The design is after a stained glass window in the Church of Our Lady of Perpetual Succour, Glasgow.

## Decimal Currency Issue

Prince George of Cambridge Quarters, and Trinity Church — A47

Designs show for each denomination a 19th century print and a contemporary photograph of the same view: ½p Battery Rosia. 1½p, Wellington Monument, Alameda Gardens. 2p, View from North Bastion. 2½p, Catalan Bay. 3p, Convent, seen from garden. 4p, The Exchange and Spanish Chapel. 5p, Commercial Square, Library and Main Guard. 7p, South Barracks and Rosia Magazine. 8p, Moorish Mosque and Castle. 9p, Europa Pass. 10p, South Barracks, from Rosia Bay. 12½p, Southport Gates. 25p, Guards on Alameda. 50p, Europa Pass Gorge, vert. £1 Prince Edward Gate, vert.

In the listing the 1st number is for the 19th cent. design, the 2nd for the 20th cent. design.

### Wmk. 314 Sideways
**1971, Feb. 15     Litho.     Perf. 14**
### Multicolored and:
| | | | |
|---|---|---|---|
| 241 | ½p brown red | .25 | .25 |
| 242 | ½p brown red | .25 | .25 |
| a. | A47 Pair, Nos. 241-242 | .50 | .50 |
| 243 | 1p light blue | .80 | .25 |
| 244 | 1p light blue | .80 | .25 |
| b. | A47 Pair, Nos. 243-244 | 1.75 | .60 |
| 245 | 1½p emerald | .25 | .25 |
| 246 | 1½p emerald | .25 | .25 |
| a. | A47 Pair, Nos. 245-246 | .50 | .90 |
| 247 | 2p dark brown | 1.25 | 2.25 |
| 248 | 2p dark brown | 1.25 | 2.25 |
| b. | A47 Pair, Nos. 247-248 | 3.00 | 5.75 |
| 249 | 2½p vermilion | .25 | .25 |
| 250 | 2½p vermilion | .25 | .35 |
| a. | A47 Pair, Nos. 249-250 | .50 | .75 |
| 251 | 3p pale green | .25 | .25 |
| 252 | 3p pale green | .25 | .25 |
| a. | A47 Pair, Nos. 251-252 | .50 | .40 |
| 253 | 4p gray | 1.40 | 2.50 |
| 254 | 4p gray | 1.40 | 2.50 |
| b. | A47 Pairs, Nos. 253-254 | 4.00 | 6.50 |
| 255 | 5p dark green | .35 | .35 |
| 256 | 5p dark green | .35 | .35 |
| a. | A47 Pair, Nos. 255-256 | .75 | .90 |
| 257 | 7p orange | .65 | .65 |
| 258 | 7p orange | .65 | .65 |
| a. | A47 Pair, Nos. 257-258 | 1.40 | 1.50 |
| 259 | 8p dark blue | .70 | .70 |
| 260 | 8p dark blue | .70 | .70 |
| a. | A47 Pair, Nos. 259-260 | 1.50 | 2.00 |
| 261 | 9p brick red | .70 | .70 |
| 262 | 9p brick red | .70 | .70 |
| a. | A47 Pair, Nos. 261-262 | 1.50 | 2.00 |
| 263 | 10p black | .80 | .80 |
| 264 | 10p black | .80 | .80 |
| a. | A47 Pair, Nos. 263-264 | 1.75 | 2.00 |
| 265 | 12½p bister | 1.00 | 1.75 |
| 266 | 12½p bister | 1.00 | 1.75 |
| a. | A47 Pair, Nos. 265-266 | 2.25 | 4.25 |
| 267 | 25p deep purple | 1.00 | 1.75 |
| 268 | 25p deep purple | 1.00 | 1.75 |
| a. | A47 Pair, Nos. 267-268 | 2.25 | 4.75 |
| 269 | 50p blue | 1.25 | 2.75 |
| 270 | 50p blue | 1.25 | 2.75 |
| a. | A47 Pair, Nos. 269-270 | 3.25 | 6.50 |
| 271 | £1 sepia | 2.25 | 4.00 |
| 272 | £1 sepia | 2.25 | 4.00 |
| a. | A47 Pair, Nos. 271-272 | 5.00 | 10.00 |
| | Nos. 241-272 (32) | 26.30 | 39.10 |

Se-tenant both horizontally and vertically.

**1973, Sept. 12     Wmk. 314 Upright**
| | | | | |
|---|---|---|---|---|
| 247a | A47 | 2p dark brown & multi | 1.50 | 2.50 |
| 248a | A47 | 2p dark brown & multi | 1.50 | 2.50 |
| c. | | Pair, Nos. 247a-248a | 4.00 | 6.50 |
| 253a | A47 | 4p gray & multi | 1.75 | 2.50 |
| 254a | A47 | 4p gray & multi | 1.75 | 2.50 |
| c. | | Pair, Nos. 253a-254a | 4.50 | 6.50 |
| | | Nos. 247a-254a (4) | 6.50 | 10.00 |

**1975, July 9     Wmk. 373**
| | | | | |
|---|---|---|---|---|
| 243a | A47 | 1p blue & multi | 1.60 | 2.50 |
| 244a | A47 | 1p blue & multi | 1.60 | 2.50 |
| c. | | Pair, Nos. 243a-244a | 4.50 | 7.00 |

Elizabeth II — A48

## Coil Stamps
**Perf. 14½x14**
**1971, Feb. 15     Photo.     Wmk. 314**
| | | | | |
|---|---|---|---|---|
| 273 | A48 | ½p red orange | .25 | .25 |
| 274 | A48 | 1p bright blue | .25 | .25 |
| 275 | A48 | 2p lt yellow green | .50 | .80 |
| a. | | Strip of 5 (½p, ½p, 1p, 1p, 2p) | 1.60 | 5.00 |
| | | Nos. 273-275 (3) | 1.00 | 1.30 |

### Uniform Type of 1969

Uniforms: 1p, Soldier, Black Watch, 1845. 2p, Drum Major with antelope mascot, Royal Fusiliers, 1971. 4p, Soldier, Kings Own Royal Border Regiment, 1704. 10p, Soldier, Devonshire and Dorset Regiment, 1801.

**1971, Sept. 6     Litho.     Perf. 14**
| | | | | |
|---|---|---|---|---|
| 276 | A42 | 1p silver & multi | .35 | .30 |
| 277 | A42 | 2p gold & multi | .60 | .30 |
| 278 | A42 | 4p gold & multi | .75 | .50 |
| 279 | A42 | 10p sil, gold & multi | 3.00 | 2.75 |
| | | Nos. 276-279 (4) | 4.70 | 3.85 |

Descriptions are printed on back on top of gum.

Regimental Coat of Arms — A49

**1971, Sept. 25     Perf. 13x12**
| | | | | |
|---|---|---|---|---|
| 280 | A49 | 3p red, bister & black | .50 | .35 |

Presentation of colors to Gibraltar Regiment, Sept. 25, 1971.

Nativity A50

Christmas: 5p, Journey to Bethlehem.

**1971, Dec. 1     Photo.     Perf. 13x13½**
| | | | | |
|---|---|---|---|---|
| 281 | A50 | 3p silver & multi | .50 | .50 |
| 282 | A50 | 5p gold & multi | .50 | .50 |

Artificer, 1773 — A51

3p, Tunneler with drill, 1969. 5p, Royal Engineers, 1772 and 1972, and regimental crest, horiz.

**1972, Mar. 6     Perf. 14x13½, 13½x14**
| | | | | |
|---|---|---|---|---|
| 283 | A51 | 1p dk blue & multi | .50 | .55 |
| 284 | A51 | 3p red & multi | .60 | .80 |
| 285 | A51 | 5p green & multi | .75 | .90 |
| | | Nos. 283-285 (3) | 1.85 | 2.25 |

Bicent. of the Royal Engineers in Gibraltar.

### Uniform Type of 1969

Uniforms: 1p, Soldier, Duke of Cornwall's Light Infantry, 1704. 3p, Officer, King's Royal Rifle Corps, 1830. 7p, Officer, 37th North Hampshire Regiment, 1825. 10p, Sailor, Royal Navy, 1972.

**1972, July 19     Litho.     Perf. 14**
| | | | | |
|---|---|---|---|---|
| 286 | A42 | 1p silver & multi | .55 | .25 |
| 287 | A42 | 3p slate & multi | 1.25 | .40 |
| 288 | A42 | 7p silver & multi | 2.10 | .70 |
| 289 | A42 | 10p gold & multi | 2.50 | 1.60 |
| | | Nos. 286-289 (4) | 6.40 | 2.95 |

Design descriptions printed on back of gum.

"Our Lady of Europa" — A52

**1972, Oct. 1     Perf. 14½x14**
| | | | | |
|---|---|---|---|---|
| 290 | A52 | 3p brown & multi | .25 | .25 |
| 291 | A52 | 5p green & multi | .25 | .35 |

Christmas. Design description printed on back.

## Silver Wedding Issue, 1972
### Common Design Type

Design: Queen Elizabeth II, Prince Philip, keys of Gibraltar and white narcissus.

**1972, Nov. 20     Photo.     Perf. 14x14½**
| | | | | |
|---|---|---|---|---|
| 292 | CD324 | 5p car rose & multi | .25 | .25 |
| 293 | CD324 | 7p slate green & multi | .25 | .25 |

Flags of EEC Members and EEC Emblem — A53

**Perf. 14½x14**
**1973, Feb. 22     Litho.     Unwmk.**
| | | | | |
|---|---|---|---|---|
| 294 | A53 | 5p red & multi | .55 | .40 |
| 295 | A53 | 10p ultra & multi | .60 | .60 |

Entry into European Economic Community.

Gibraltar Skull — A54

Designs: 6p, Head of Neanderthal man. 10p, Neanderthal family.

**1973, May 22     Wmk. 314     Perf. 13½**
| | | | | |
|---|---|---|---|---|
| 296 | A54 | 4p lilac rose & multi | 1.25 | .60 |
| 297 | A54 | 6p lt ultra & multi | 1.50 | 1.25 |
| 298 | A54 | 10p yel green & multi | 2.25 | 2.25 |
| | | Nos. 296-298 (3) | 5.00 | 4.10 |

125th anniv. of the discovery of the Gibraltar skull.

### Uniform Type of 1969

Uniforms: 1p, Fifer, King's Own Scottish Borderers, 1770. 4p, Officer, Royal Welsh Fusiliers, 1800. 6p, Soldier, Royal Northumberland Fusiliers, 1736. 10p, Private, Grenadier Guards, 1898.

**1973, Aug. 22     Litho.     Perf. 14**
| | | | | |
|---|---|---|---|---|
| 299 | A42 | 1p multicolored | .50 | .35 |
| 300 | A42 | 4p multicolored | 1.25 | .60 |
| 301 | A42 | 6p multicolored | 2.00 | 1.25 |
| 302 | A42 | 10p multicolored | 3.00 | 2.50 |
| | | Nos. 299-302 (4) | 6.75 | 4.70 |

Descriptions printed on back on top of gum.

Nativity, by Justus Danckerts A55

**1973, Oct. 17     Litho.     Perf. 12½x12**
| | | | | |
|---|---|---|---|---|
| 303 | A55 | 4p brown org & blue | .45 | .25 |
| 304 | A55 | 6p green & claret | .50 | .80 |

Christmas.

## Princess Anne's Wedding Issue
### Common Design Type

**1973, Nov. 14     Perf. 14**
| | | | | |
|---|---|---|---|---|
| 305 | CD325 | 6p bl grn & multi | .25 | .25 |
| 306 | CD325 | 14p brt grn & multi | .30 | .30 |

Wedding of Princess Anne and Capt. Mark Phillips, Nov. 14, 1973.

V.R. (Queen Victoria) Pillar Box — A56

Pillar Boxes: 6p, G.R. (King George). 14p, E.R. (Queen Elizabeth).

**1974, May 2     Litho.     Perf. 14**
| | | | | |
|---|---|---|---|---|
| 307 | A56 | 2p yel green & multi | .25 | .25 |
| 308 | A56 | 6p gray & multi | .25 | .30 |
| 309 | A56 | 14p dull yel & multi | .35 | .60 |
| a. | | Souvenir booklet | 11.00 | |
| | | Nos. 307-309 (3) | .85 | 1.15 |

UPU, cent.

No. 309a contains 2 self-adhesive panes printed on peelable paper backing with multicolored advertising on back. One pane of 6 contains 3 each similar to Nos. 307-308; the other pane of 3 contains one each similar to Nos. 307-309. Stamps are imperf. x roulette.

## Uniform Type of 1969

Uniforms: 4p, Officer, East Lancashire Regiment, 1742. 6p, Sergeant, Somerset Light Infantry, 1833. 10p, Company man, Royal Sussex Regiment, 1790. 16p, Officer, Royal Air Force, 1974.

**1974, Aug. 21**      *Perf. 14*
| | | | | |
|---|---|---|---|---|
| 310 | A42 | 4p silver & multi | .55 | .45 |
| 311 | A42 | 6p silver & multi | .80 | .60 |
| 312 | A42 | 10p silver & multi | 1.25 | 1.25 |
| 313 | A42 | 16p silver & multi | 3.00 | 3.25 |
| | | Nos. 310-313 (4) | 5.60 | 5.55 |

Descriptions are printed on back on top of gum.

Virgin with Green Cushion, Andrea Solario — A57

Christmas (Painting): 6p, Madonna of the Meadow, by Giovanni Bellini.

**1974, Nov. 5**      *Litho.*
| | | | | |
|---|---|---|---|---|
| 314 | A57 | 4p gold & multi | .40 | .30 |
| 315 | A57 | 6p gold & multi | .60 | .90 |

Churchill, Parliament and Big Ben — A58

20p, Churchill & George V-class battleship.

**1974, Nov. 30**      *Perf. 14x14½*
| | | | | |
|---|---|---|---|---|
| 316 | A58 | 6p violet & multi | .25 | .25 |
| 317 | A58 | 20p multicolored | .50 | .50 |
| a. | | Souvenir sheet of 2, #316-317 | 5.00 | 5.50 |

Sir Winston Churchill (1874-1965).

## Uniform Type of 1969

Uniforms: 4p, Officer, East Surrey Regiment, 1846. 6p, Private, Highland Light Infantry, 1777. 10p, Officer, Coldstream Guards, 1704. 20p, Sergeant, Gibraltar Regiment, 1974.

**1975, Mar. 14**     *Wmk. 373*     *Perf. 14*
| | | | | |
|---|---|---|---|---|
| 318 | A42 | 4p multicolored | .35 | .25 |
| 319 | A42 | 6p multicolored | .55 | .40 |
| 320 | A42 | 10p multicolored | .80 | .80 |
| 321 | A42 | 20p multicolored | 1.50 | 1.75 |
| | | Nos. 318-321 (4) | 3.20 | 3.20 |

Descriptions are printed on back on top of gum.

Girl Guides Emblem — A59

**1975, Oct. 10**      *Perf. 13½x13*
| | | | | |
|---|---|---|---|---|
| 322 | A59 | 5p violet, gold & blue | .30 | .40 |
| 323 | A59 | 7p red brn, gold & blk | .45 | .50 |
| 324 | A59 | 25p ocher, silver & blk | .75 | .90 |
| | | Nos. 322-324 (3) | 1.50 | 1.80 |

Girl Guides, 50th anniversary.

Child and Bird — A60

b, Angel playing lute. c, Singing boy. d, Mother & children. e, Praying child. f, Child & lamb.

---

**1975, Nov. 25**      *Perf. 14x14½*
| | | | |
|---|---|---|---|
| 325 | Block of 6 | 2.75 | 3.25 |
| a.-f. | A60 6p any single | .40 | .55 |

Christmas. No. 325 printed in sheets of 60 containing 10 blocks of 6 (3x2) stamps with horizontal and vertical gutters between blocks.

Bruges Madonna, by Michelangelo — A61

Sculptures by Michelangelo: 9p, Traddei Madonna. 15p, Pietà.

**1975, Dec. 17**      *Litho.*     *Perf. 14x13½*
| | | | | |
|---|---|---|---|---|
| 326 | A61 | 6p blue blk & multi | .25 | .25 |
| 327 | A61 | 9p black brn & multi | .25 | .40 |
| 328 | A61 | 12p dk purple & multi | .35 | .95 |
| a. | | Souvenir booklet | 5.50 | |
| | | Nos. 326-328 (3) | .85 | 1.60 |

500th birth anniv. of Michelangelo Buonarroti (1475-1564), Italian sculptor, painter and architect.

No. 328a contains 2 self-adhesive panes printed on peelable paper backing with stamp dealer's advertisements on back. One pane of 6 contains 2 each similar to Nos. 326-328; the other pane of 3 contains one each similar to Nos. 326-328. Stamps are imperf. x roulette.

American Bicentennial Emblem, Arms of Gibraltar — A62

**1976, May 28**      *Perf. 14x14½*
| | | | |
|---|---|---|---|
| 329 | A62 25p multicolored | .70 | .70 |
| a. | Souvenir sheet of 4 | 4.75 | 5.75 |

American Bicentennial. No. 329a is rouletted all around.

## Uniform Type of 1969

Uniforms: 1p, Suffolk Regiment, 1795. 6p, Northamptonshire Regiment, 1779. 12p, Lancashire Fusiliers, 1793. 25p, Royal Army Ordnance Corps. 1896.

**1976, July 21**      *Perf. 14*
| | | | | |
|---|---|---|---|---|
| 330 | A42 | 1p multicolored | .25 | .25 |
| 331 | A42 | 6p multicolored | .40 | .25 |
| 332 | A42 | 12p multicolored | .55 | .50 |
| 333 | A42 | 25p multicolored | .75 | 1.25 |
| | | Nos. 330-333 (4) | 1.95 | 2.25 |

Descriptions printed on back on top of gum.

Holy Family — A63

Stained Glass Windows: 9p, St. Bernard of Clairvaux. 12p, St. John the Evangelist. 20p, Archangel Michael.

**1976, Nov. 3**      *Litho.*     *Wmk. 373*
| | | | | |
|---|---|---|---|---|
| 334 | A63 | 6p ultra & multi | .25 | .25 |
| 335 | A63 | 9p brt green & multi | .30 | .25 |
| 336 | A63 | 12p orange & multi | .45 | .50 |
| 337 | A63 | 20p dk carmine & multi | .85 | 1.10 |
| | | Nos. 334-337 (4) | 1.85 | 2.10 |

Christmas.

Elizabeth II and Royal Crest — A64

---

**1977, Feb. 7**     *Litho.*     *Perf. 14x13½*
| | | | | |
|---|---|---|---|---|
| 338 | A64 | 6p multicolored | .25 | .25 |
| 339 | A64 | £1 multicolored | 1.40 | 1.50 |
| a. | | Souv. sheet of 2, #338-339, perf. | | |
| | | 13 | 2.00 | 2.50 |

25th anniv. of the reign of Queen Elizabeth II. Nos. 338-339 issued in sheets of 9.

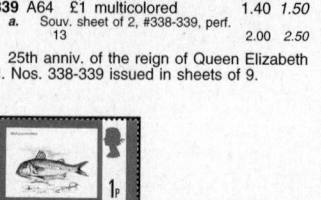

Red Mullet — A65

½p, Toothed orchid. 2p, Large blue. 2 ½p, Sardinian warbler. 3p, Giant squill. 4p, Gray wrasse. 5p, Red admiral. 6p, Black kite. 9p, Scorpion vetch. 10p, John Dory. 12p, Clouded yellow. 15p, Winged asparagus pea (inscr. "1980"). 20p, Andouin's gull. 25p, Barbary nut. 50p, Swordfish. £ 1, Swallowtail. £ 2, Hoopoe. £ 5, Coat of Arms (inscr. "1979").

½p, 3p, 9p, 15p, 25p, Flowers. 1p, 4p, 10p, 50p, Fish. 2p, 5p, 12p, £1, Butterflies. 2 ½p, 6p, 20p, £2, Birds. ½p, 2 ½p, 3p, 6p, 9p, 15p, 20p, 25p, £2, £5, vertical.

**1977-80**      *Perf. 14½x14, 14x14½*
**Inscribed "1977," except as noted**
| | | | | |
|---|---|---|---|---|
| 340 | A65 | ½p multi | .50 | 2.00 |
| a. | | Chalky paper, inscribed "1982" | 5.00 | 4.00 |
| 341 | A65 | 1p shown | .25 | .45 |
| 342 | A65 | 2p multi | .25 | 1.00 |
| 343 | A65 | 2 ½p multi | 1.00 | 1.50 |
| 344 | A65 | 3p multi | .25 | .25 |
| 345 | A65 | 4p multi | .25 | .25 |
| 346 | A65 | 5p multi | .40 | .80 |
| 347 | A65 | 6p multi | 1.50 | .45 |
| 348 | A65 | 9p multi | .50 | .55 |
| a. | | Inscribed "1978" | .60 | .60 |
| 349 | A65 | 10p multi | .35 | .25 |
| 350 | A65 | 12p multi | .75 | .35 |
| 350A | A65 | 15p multi | 1.25 | .45 |
| 351 | A65 | 20p multi | 1.50 | 2.75 |
| 352 | A65 | 25p multi | 1.00 | 2.00 |
| 353 | A65 | 50p multi | 1.50 | .80 |
| 354 | A65 | £1 multi | 3.50 | 5.00 |
| 355 | A65 | £2 multi | 7.25 | 11.00 |
| 355A | A65 | £5 multi | 9.00 | 12.00 |
| | | Nos. 340-355A (18) | 31.00 | 41.85 |

Issued: No. 348a, 2/1/78; £ 5, 5/16/79; 15p, 11/12/80; No. 340a, 2/22/82; others, 4/1/77.

### Inscribed "1981"

**1981, Apr. 21**      *Chalky Paper*
| | | | | |
|---|---|---|---|---|
| 345a | A65 | 4p multicolored | .50 | .70 |
| 349a | A65 | 10p multicolored | 1.00 | 1.50 |
| 350a | A65 | 15p multicolored | 4.00 | 4.00 |
| 352a | A65 | 25p multicolored | 5.00 | 5.50 |
| 353a | A65 | 50p multicolored | 6.50 | 6.50 |
| | | Nos. 345a-353a (5) | 17.00 | 18.20 |

Gibraltar No. 182 — A66

12p, Gibraltar #233. 25p, Gibraltar #294.

**1977, May 27**      *Litho.*     *Perf. 14*
| | | | | |
|---|---|---|---|---|
| 356 | A66 | 6p multi | .25 | .25 |
| 357 | A66 | 12p multi, vert. | .25 | .35 |
| 358 | A66 | 25p multi, vert. | .30 | .50 |
| | | Nos. 356-358 (3) | .80 | 1.10 |

Amphilex 77 Intl. Phil. Exhib., Amsterdam, May 26-June 5. Issued in sheets of 6.

Annunciation, by Rubens — A67

Rubens Paintings: 9p, Nativity. 12p, Adoration of the Kings. 15p, Holy Family under Apple Tree.

**1977, Nov. 2**      *Perf. 14x13½, 13½x14*     *Litho.*
| | | | | |
|---|---|---|---|---|
| 359 | A67 | 3p multi | .25 | .25 |
| 360 | A67 | 9p multi | .25 | .25 |
| 361 | A67 | 12p multi, horiz. | .25 | .25 |
| 362 | A67 | 15p multi | .35 | .35 |
| a. | | Souvenir sheet of 4, #359-362 | 3.75 | 3.75 |
| | | Nos. 359-362 (4) | 1.10 | 1.10 |

Christmas and 400th birth anniv. of Peter Paul Rubens.

---

Gibraltar from Space — A68

Design: 25p, Strait of Gibraltar, aerial view.

**1978, May 3**      *Litho.*     *Perf. 13½*
| | | | |
|---|---|---|---|
| 363 | A68 12p multicolored | .35 | .50 |

**Souvenir Sheet**
| | | | |
|---|---|---|---|
| 364 | A68 25p multicolored | .90 | .90 |

No. 363 issued in sheets of 10. No. 364 contains one stamp.

Holyroodhouse — A69

Royal Houses: 9p, St. James Palace. 12p, Sandringham House. 18p, Balmoral.

**1978, June 12**      *Litho.*     *Perf. 13½*
| | | | | |
|---|---|---|---|---|
| 365 | A69 | 6p multicolored | .25 | .25 |
| 366 | A69 | 9p multicolored | .25 | .25 |
| 367 | A69 | 12p multicolored | .35 | .30 |
| 368 | A69 | 18p multicolored | .40 | .40 |
| a. | | Souvenir booklet | 3.75 | |
| | | Nos. 365-368 (4) | 1.25 | 1.20 |

25th anniv. of coronation of Queen Elizabeth II. No. 368a contains 2 panes printed on peelable paper backing with pictures of castles. One pane contains 6 rouletted stamps, 3 each similar to Nos. 367-368; the other pane contains one 25p (Windsor Castle) rouletted stamp.

Sunderland Seaplane Landing — A70

Gibraltar and: 9p, Two-tiered Caudron taking off, 1918. 12p, Shackleton, 1953-1966. 16p, Hunter warplane, 1954-1966. 18p, Nimrod, 1969-1978.

**1978, Sept. 6**      *Litho.*     *Perf. 14*
| | | | | |
|---|---|---|---|---|
| 369 | A70 | 3p multicolored | .25 | .25 |
| 370 | A70 | 9p multicolored | .25 | .25 |
| 371 | A70 | 12p multicolored | .40 | .45 |
| 372 | A70 | 16p multicolored | .50 | .70 |
| 373 | A70 | 18p multicolored | .60 | .90 |
| | | Nos. 369-373 (5) | 2.00 | 2.65 |

Royal Air Force, 60th anniversary.

Madonna with Goldfinch, by Dürer — A71

Christmas (Paintings by Albrecht Dürer): 5p, Madonna with Animals. 9p, Nativity. 15p, Adoration of the Kings.

**1978, Nov. 1**      *Litho.*     *Perf. 14*
| | | | | |
|---|---|---|---|---|
| 374 | A71 | 5p multicolored | .25 | .25 |
| 375 | A71 | 9p multicolored | .25 | .25 |
| 376 | A71 | 12p multicolored | .30 | .35 |
| 377 | A71 | 15p multicolored | .35 | .75 |
| | | Nos. 374-377 (4) | 1.15 | 1.60 |

Rowland Hill and Gibraltar No. 10 — A72

Sir Rowland Hill (1795-1879), originator of penny postage and: 9p, Gibraltar No. 274. 12p, Parchment scroll with early postal regulations. 25p, "Barred G" cancellation used on British stamps in Gibraltar.

**1979, Feb. 7  Litho.  Perf. 13½**
378 A72 3p multicolored .25 .25
379 A72 9p multicolored .25 .25
380 A72 12p yellow grn & black .25 .25
381 A72 25p yellow & black .30 .45
 Nos. 378-381 (4) 1.05 1.20

Satellite Earth Station, Post Horn, Telephone A73

**1979, May 16  Perf. 13½x14**
382 A73 3p lt green & green .25 .25
383 A73 9p lt brown & brown .25 .55
384 A73 12p gray & ultra .30 .95
 Nos. 382-384 (3) .80 1.75

European telecommunications system.

Children, IYC Emblem, Nativity — A74

a, African girl. b, Chinese girl. c, Pacific islands girl. d, American Indian girl. e, Shown. f, Scandinavian boy.

**Litho.; Silver Embossed**
**1979, Nov. 14  Perf. 14**
385 Block of 6 1.75 1.75
 a.-f. A74 12p any single .25 .25

Christmas; IYC. No. 385 printed in sheets of 12 containing 2 No. 385 with vertical rouletted gutter between.

Officers, Exchange and Commercial Library, 1830 — A75

Gibraltar Police Force, 150th anniv.: 6p, Early and modern uniforms, Rock of Gibraltar. 12p, Traffic Officer, ambulance. 37p, Policeman and woman, Police Station, Irish Town.

**Perf. 14x14½**
**1980, Feb. 5  Litho.  Wmk. 373**
386 A75 3p multicolored .25 .25
387 A75 6p multicolored .25 .25
388 A75 12p multicolored .30 .35
389 A75 37p multicolored .50 .95
 Nos. 386-389 (4) 1.30 1.80

Archbishop Peter Amigo (1864-1949) — A76

Europa: No. 391, Gustavo Charles Bacarisas (1872-1971), artist. No. 392, John Mackintosh (1865-1940), philanthropist.

**1980, May 6  Wmk. 373  Perf. 14½**
390 A76 12p multicolored .25 .30
391 A76 12p multicolored .25 .30
392 A76 12p multicolored .25 .30
 Nos. 390-392 (3) .75 .90

**Queen Mother Elizabeth Birthday Issue**
**Common Design Type**
**1980, Aug. 4  Litho.  Perf. 14**
393 CD330 15p multicolored .35 .35

"Victory" and Rock of Gibraltar, by Monamy Swaine — A77

Paintings: 3p, Lord Nelson, by John Francis Rigaud, 1781, vert. 15p, Lord Nelson, by William Beechey, vert. 40p, Victory Towed into Gibraltar by Clarkson Stanfield.

**1980, Aug. 20  Litho.  Perf. 14**
394 A77 3p multicolored .25 .25
395 A77 9p multicolored .25 .25
396 A77 15p multicolored .35 .35
 a. Souvenir sheet 1.00 1.40
397 A77 40p multicolored .80 1.00
 Nos. 394-397 (4) 1.65 1.85

Horatio Nelson (1758-1805).

Holy Family — A78

**1980, Nov. 12**
398 A78 15p shown .25 .25
399 A78 15p Three kings .25 .25
 a. Pair, #398-399 .80 .80

Christmas. No. 399a has continuous design.

Hercules Separating Africa and Europe — A79

Europa: 15p, Hercules standing on Rock of Gibraltar and Morocco.

**Perf. 14x13½**
**1981, Feb. 24  Wmk. 373**
400 A79 9p multicolored .25 .25
401 A79 15p multicolored .30 .35

Dining Room, The Convent — A80

**1981, May 22  Litho.  Perf. 14½x14**
402 A80 4p shown .25 .25
403 A80 14p King's Chapel .25 .25
404 A80 15p Aerial view .30 .25
405 A80 55p Cloister .60 .70
 Nos. 402-405 (4) 1.40 1.45

450th anniv. of The Convent (Governor's residence, originally Franciscan monastery).

Prince Charles and Lady Diana — A81

**1981, July 27  Litho.  Perf. 14½**
406 A81 £1 multicolored 1.60 1.60

Royal wedding. Se-tenant with decorative label.

Queen Elizabeth II — A82

**1981, Sept. 29  Perf. 14½**
**Booklet Stamps**
407 A82 1p black .45 .45
 a. Bklt. pane of 10 + 2 labels (2 #407, 2 #408, 6 #409) 4.50
 b. Bklt. pane of 5 + label (#407, #408, 3 #409) 2.25
408 A82 4p dark blue .45 .45
409 A82 15p green .45 .45
 Nos. 407-409 (3) 1.35 1.35

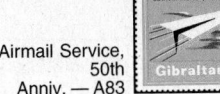

Airmail Service, 50th Anniv. — A83

14p, Paper plane. 15p, Envelopes, aerogram. 55p, Airplane circling globe.

**1981, Sept. 29  Perf. 14½**
410 A83 14p multicolored .25 .25
411 A83 15p multicolored .25 .25
412 A83 55p multicolored .80 .80
 Nos. 410-412 (3) 1.30 1.30

Intl. Year of the Disabled — A84

**1981, Nov. 19  Litho.  Wmk. 373**
413 A84 14p multicolored .30 .30

Christmas A85

15p, Children singing carols. 55p, Decorated mailbox, vert.

**1981, Nov. 19  Perf. 14**
414 A85 15p multicolored .30 .25
415 A85 55p multicolored 1.10 .75

Douglas DC-3 — A86

2p, Vickers Viking. 3p, Airspeed Ambassador. 4p, Vickers Viscount. 5p, Boeing 727. 10p, Vickers Vanguard. 14p, Short Solent. 15p, Fokker F-27 Friendship. 17p, Boeing 737. 20p, BAC One-eleven. 25p, Lockheed Constellation. 50p, De Havilland Comet 4B. £ 1, Saro Windhover. £ 2, Hawker Siddeley Trident 2. £ 5, DH-89A Dragon Rapide.

**1982, Feb. 10  Litho.  Perf. 14**
416 A86 1p shown .25 1.00
417 A86 2p multicolored .25 1.00
 a. Wmk. 384, dated 1986 ('87) 2.75 3.50
418 A86 3p multicolored .25 .50
419 A86 4p multicolored .40 .25
420 A86 5p multicolored .60 .30
 a. Wmk. 384, dated 1986 ('87) 2.75 3.50
421 A86 10p multicolored 1.10 .55
422 A86 14p multicolored 1.25 2.00
423 A86 15p multicolored 1.75 2.25
424 A86 17p multicolored .85 .90
425 A86 20p multicolored 1.25 .65
 a. Inscribed "1985" 1.60 1.60
426 A86 25p multicolored 3.50 4.25
427 A86 50p multicolored 3.75 2.25
428 A86 £1 multicolored 5.25 2.25
429 A86 £2 multicolored 6.50 5.25
430 A86 £5 multicolored 9.00 14.00
 Nos. 416-430 (15) 35.95 37.40

Royal Navy Ship Crests — A87

**1982, Apr. 14  Litho.  Perf. 14**
431 A87 ½p Opossum .25 .25
432 A87 15½p Norfolk .45 .50
433 A87 17p Fearless .55 .60
434 A87 60p Rooke 1.00 2.25
 Nos. 431-434 (4) 2.25 3.60

See Nos. 449-452, 465-468, 474-477, 492-495, 501-504, 528-531, 552-555, 574-577, 587-590.

Europa — A88

14p, Planes preparing for takeoff. 17p, Generals Eisenhower and Giraud.

**1982, June 11  Litho.  Perf. 14**
435 A88 14p multicolored .25 .60
436 A88 17p multicolored .35 .75

Operation Torch, 1943.

Chamber of Commerce Centenary — A89

Anniversaries: 15½p, British Forces Postal Service centenary. 60p, Scouting year.

**1982, Sept. 22**
437 A89 ½p multicolored .25 .25
438 A89 15½p multicolored .45 .35
439 A89 60p multicolored 1.25 1.50
 Nos. 437-439 (3) 1.95 2.10

Intl. Direct Telephone Dialing System Inauguration A90

**1982, Oct. 1  Perf. 14½**
440 A90 17p Map .45 .45

Christmas — A91

**Perf. 14x14½**
**1982, Nov. 18  Litho.  Wmk. 373**
441 A91 14p Holly .30 .25
442 A91 17p Mistletoe .40 .30

A92

4p, Local street. 14p, Scouts on parade. 17p, Flag, vert. 60p, Queen Elizabeth II, vert.

**1983, Mar. 14  Litho.  Perf. 14**
443 A92 4p multicolored .25 .25
444 A92 14p multicolored .25 .25
445 A92 17p multicolored .35 .30
446 A92 60p multicolored .95 1.10
 Nos. 443-446 (4) 1.80 1.90

Commonwealth Day.

Europa — A93

**1983, May 21  Perf. 14x13½**
447 A93 16p St. George's Hall .35 .35
448 A93 19p Water catchments .40 .45

**Royal Navy Crest Type of 1982**
**1983, July 1  Litho.  Perf. 14**
449 A87 4p Faulknor .40 .25
450 A87 14p Renown .60 .40
451 A87 17p Ark Royal .80 .50
452 A87 60p Sheffield 1.75 1.75
 Nos. 449-452 (4) 3.55 2.90

Fortresses A94

4p, Landport Gate, 1729. 17p, Koehler gun, 1782. 77p, King's Bastion, 1799.

**1983, Sept. 13  Perf. 13½x14**
453 A94 4p multicolored .25 .25
454 A94 17p multicolored .35 .25
455 A94 77p multicolored 1.30 1.25
 a. Souvenir sheet of 3, #453-455 3.00 3.00
 Nos. 453-455 (3) 1.90 1.75

Christmas A95

Raphael Paintings: 4p, Adoration of the Magi. 17p, Madonna of Foligno, vert. 60p, Sistine Madonna, vert.

**1983, Nov. 17    Litho.    Perf. 14**
| | | | | |
|---|---|---|---|---|
| 456 | A95 | 4p multicolored | .30 | .25 |
| 457 | A95 | 17p multicolored | .75 | .35 |
| 458 | A95 | 60p multicolored | 1.90 | 1.40 |
| | | *Nos. 456-458 (3)* | 2.95 | 2.00 |

Europa (1959-1984) — A96

Intl. Postal and Telecommunication Links — 17p, No. 98. 23p, Communications circuit.

**1984, Mar. 6    Litho.    Perf. 14½**
| | | | | |
|---|---|---|---|---|
| 459 | A96 | 17p multicolored | .40 | .50 |
| 460 | A96 | 23p multicolored | .50 | .90 |

Field Hockey — A97

**1984, May 25    Litho.    Perf. 14**
| | | | | |
|---|---|---|---|---|
| 461 | A97 | 20p shown | .65 | .70 |
| 462 | A97 | 21p Basketball | .65 | .70 |
| 463 | A97 | 26p Rowing | .65 | .90 |
| 464 | A97 | 29p Soccer | .75 | 1.25 |
| | | *Nos. 461-464 (4)* | 2.70 | 3.55 |

**Royal Navy Crest Type of 1982**
**1984, Sept. 21    Litho.    Perf. 13½x13**
| | | | | |
|---|---|---|---|---|
| 465 | A87 | 20p Active | 1.60 | 1.60 |
| 466 | A87 | 20p Foxhound | 1.60 | 1.60 |
| 467 | A87 | 26p Valiant | 1.90 | 1.90 |
| 468 | A87 | 29p Hood | 2.00 | 2.00 |
| | | *Nos. 465-468 (4)* | 7.10 | 7.10 |

Christmas — A98

**Perf. 14x14½**
**1984, Nov. 7    Litho.    Wmk. 373**
| | | | | |
|---|---|---|---|---|
| 469 | A98 | 20p Parade float | .45 | .45 |
| 470 | A98 | 80p Float, diff. | 2.00 | 2.00 |

**Europa Issue**

Musical Symbols — A99

**1985, Feb. 26    Photo.    Perf. 12½**
**Granite Paper**
| | | | | |
|---|---|---|---|---|
| 471 | A99 | 20p multi, diff. | .35 | .35 |
| 472 | A99 | 29p shown | .45 | 1.40 |

Save the Children Fund — A100

Globe and legend in various positions.

**1985, May 3    Litho.    Perf. 13x13½**
| | | | | |
|---|---|---|---|---|
| 473 | | Strip of 4 | 5.00 | 5.00 |
| a.-d. | | A100 26p any single | 1.00 | 1.00 |

---

**Royal Navy Crest Type of 1982**
**1985, July 3    Litho.    Perf. 14**
| | | | | |
|---|---|---|---|---|
| 474 | A87 | 4p Duncan | .75 | .50 |
| 475 | A87 | 9p Fury | 1.00 | 1.40 |
| 476 | A87 | 21p Firedrake | 2.50 | 2.75 |
| 477 | A87 | 80p Malaya | 4.25 | 5.00 |
| | | *Nos. 474-477 (4)* | 8.50 | 9.65 |

Intl. Youth Year — A101

4p, Emblem. 20p, Hands, diamond. 80p, Girl Guides anniv. emblem.

**1985, Sept. 6    Perf. 14½**
| | | | | |
|---|---|---|---|---|
| 478 | A101 | 4p multicolored | .50 | .25 |
| 479 | A101 | 20p multicolored | 1.50 | 1.25 |
| 480 | A101 | 80p multicolored | 4.00 | 3.00 |
| | | *Nos. 478-480 (3)* | 6.00 | 4.50 |

St. Joseph's Parish Church, Cent. — A102

**Perf. 13½; Roulette 7 Between**
**1985, Oct. 25    Wmk. 373    Litho.**
| | | | | |
|---|---|---|---|---|
| 481 | A102 | Pair | 2.00 | 2.50 |
| a. | | 4p Centenary seal | .75 | .60 |
| b. | | 4p Church | .75 | .60 |
| c. | | No. 481a, perf. 13½ on 4 sides | .80 | .60 |

Creche, Detail — A103

**Perf. 13½**
| | | | | |
|---|---|---|---|---|
| 482 | A103 | 80p multicolored | 5.25 | 5.25 |

Christmas. Nos. 481a-481b rouletted between. Printed in sheets of 10 pairs with the bottom row containing 5 No. 481c. Strips of 3, Nos. 481a-481c exist.

Europa — A104

**1986, Feb. 10    Litho.    Perf. 13x13½**
| | | | | |
|---|---|---|---|---|
| 483 | A104 | 22p Butterfly, house | .75 | .45 |
| 484 | A104 | 29p Seagull, hotel | 1.25 | 3.00 |

Postage Stamp Cent. — A105

**1986, Mar. 25    Perf. 13½x13**
| | | | | |
|---|---|---|---|---|
| 485 | A105 | 4p No. 18 | .35 | .25 |
| 486 | A105 | 22p No. 42 | 1.10 | 1.10 |
| 487 | A105 | 32p No. 67 | 1.75 | 2.00 |
| 488 | A105 | 36p No. 118 | 2.00 | 2.50 |

**Size: 32x48mm**
**Perf. 14**
| | | | | |
|---|---|---|---|---|
| 489 | A105 | 44p No. 131 | 2.25 | 3.00 |
| | | *Nos. 485-489 (5)* | 7.45 | 8.85 |

**Souvenir Sheet**
| | | | | |
|---|---|---|---|---|
| 490 | A105 | 29p No. 2 | 3.75 | 3.75 |

---

Elizabeth II, 60th Birthday — A106

**1986, May 22    Litho.    Perf. 14**
| | | | | |
|---|---|---|---|---|
| 491 | A106 | £1 multicolored | 2.25 | 3.00 |

**Royal Navy Crest Type of 1982**
**1986, Aug. 28    Litho.    Perf. 14**
| | | | | |
|---|---|---|---|---|
| 492 | A87 | 22p Lightning | 2.00 | 1.00 |
| 493 | A87 | 29p Hermione | 2.25 | 1.75 |
| 494 | A87 | 32p Laforey | 2.50 | 3.00 |
| 495 | A87 | 44p Nelson | 3.25 | 4.00 |
| | | *Nos. 492-495 (4)* | 10.00 | 9.75 |

Christmas, Intl. Peace Year — A107

18p, St. Mary the Crowned Cathedral. 32p, St. Andrew's Church.

**1986, Oct. 14    Litho.    Perf. 14½x14**
| | | | | |
|---|---|---|---|---|
| 496 | A107 | 18p multicolored | 1.00 | .50 |
| 497 | A107 | 32p multicolored | 1.50 | 2.75 |

**Souvenir Sheet**

Wedding of Prince Andrew and Sarah Ferguson A108

**1986, Aug. 28    Litho.    Perf. 15**
| | | | | |
|---|---|---|---|---|
| 498 | A108 | 44p multicolored | 1.50 | 2.00 |

Europa — A109

**1987, Feb. 17    Wmk. 384    Perf. 15**
| | | | | |
|---|---|---|---|---|
| 499 | A109 | 22p Neptune House | 1.25 | .90 |
| 500 | A109 | 29p Ocean Heights | 2.00 | 3.25 |

**Royal Navy Crest Type of 1982**
**1987, Apr. 2    Perf. 13½x13**
| | | | | |
|---|---|---|---|---|
| 501 | A87 | 18p Wishart | 1.75 | .70 |
| 502 | A87 | 22p Charybdis | 2.00 | 1.10 |
| 503 | A87 | 32p Antelope | 2.75 | 3.00 |
| 504 | A87 | 44p Eagle | 3.00 | 3.75 |
| | | *Nos. 501-504 (4)* | 9.50 | 8.55 |

Warrant Granted to the Royal Engineers, 200th Anniv. — A110

18p, Victoria Stadium. 32p, Casket, Freedom Scroll. 44p, Monogram.

**1987, Apr. 25    Wmk. 373    Perf. 14½**
| | | | | |
|---|---|---|---|---|
| 505 | A110 | 18p multicolored | 1.50 | .50 |
| 506 | A110 | 32p multicolored | 2.25 | 3.00 |
| 507 | A110 | 44p multicolored | 3.00 | 4.00 |
| | | *Nos. 505-507 (3)* | 6.75 | 7.50 |

Guns and Artillery — A111

Designs: 1p, 13-inch mortar, 1783. 2p, 6-inch Coast, 1909. 3p, 8-inch Howitzer, 1783.

---

4p, Bofors L40/70, 1951. 5p, 100-ton RML, 1882. 10p, 5.25 HAA, 1953. 18p, 25-pounder Gun-howitzer, 1943. 19p, 64-pounder RML, 1873. 22p, 12-pounder, 1758. 50p, 10-inch RML, 1870. £1, Russian 24-pounder, 1854. £3, 9.2-inch Coast Mk. 10, 1935. £5, 24-pounder, 1779.

**1987, June 1    Wmk. 373    Perf. 12½**
| | | | | |
|---|---|---|---|---|
| 508 | A111 | 1p multicolored | .25 | .60 |
| 509 | A111 | 2p multicolored | .35 | .50 |
| 510 | A111 | 3p multicolored | .35 | .95 |
| 511 | A111 | 4p multicolored | .45 | .25 |
| 512 | A111 | 5p multicolored | .45 | .65 |
| 513 | A111 | 10p multicolored | .45 | .50 |
| 514 | A111 | 18p multicolored | .70 | 1.40 |
| 515 | A111 | 19p multicolored | .70 | 1.00 |
| 516 | A111 | 22p multicolored | .70 | .50 |
| 517 | A111 | 50p multicolored | 1.40 | 2.25 |
| 518 | A111 | £1 multicolored | 2.50 | 2.50 |
| 519 | A111 | £3 multicolored | 4.50 | 6.00 |
| 520 | A111 | £5 multicolored | 8.00 | 15.00 |
| | | *Nos. 508-520 (13)* | 20.80 | 32.10 |

For surcharge see No. 595.

Christmas A112

**1987, Nov. 12    Wmk. 384    Perf. 14½**
| | | | | |
|---|---|---|---|---|
| 521 | A112 | 4p Three Wise Men | .25 | .25 |
| 522 | A112 | 22p Holy Family | 1.00 | .90 |
| 523 | A112 | 44p Shepherds | 1.90 | 2.75 |
| | | *Nos. 521-523 (3)* | 3.15 | 3.90 |

Europa A113

Transport and communication: No. 524, Rock of Gibraltar, Cruise Ship. No. 525, Passenger jet, yacht, dish aerial. No. 526, Bus, buggy. No. 527, Rock of Gibraltar, automobile, telephone.

**Perf. 14½x14 on 3 Sides; Rouletted Between**
**1988, Feb. 16    Litho.    Wmk. 373**
| | | | | |
|---|---|---|---|---|
| 524 | | 22p multicolored | 1.25 | 1.50 |
| 525 | | 22p multicolored | 1.25 | 1.50 |
| a. | | A113 Pair, #524-525 | 3.25 | 3.25 |
| 526 | | 32p multicolored | 1.75 | 2.00 |
| 527 | | 32p multicolored | 1.75 | 2.00 |
| a. | | A113 Pair, #526-527 | 4.25 | 4.25 |
| | | *Nos. 524-527 (4)* | 6.00 | 7.00 |

Nos. 525a, 527a have continuous design.

**Royal Navy Crest Type of 1982**
**Perf. 13½x13**
**1988, Apr. 7    Wmk. 384**
| | | | | |
|---|---|---|---|---|
| 528 | A87 | 18p Clyde | 1.75 | .65 |
| 529 | A87 | 22p Foresight | 2.25 | 1.25 |
| 530 | A87 | 32p Severn | 2.75 | 3.00 |
| 531 | A87 | 44p Rodney | 3.50 | 4.50 |
| | | *Nos. 528-531 (4)* | 10.25 | 9.40 |

Birds — A114

**1988, June 15    Wmk. 373    Perf. 14**
| | | | | |
|---|---|---|---|---|
| 532 | A114 | 4p Bee eater | 1.00 | .25 |
| 533 | A114 | 22p Common puffin | 2.00 | .85 |
| 534 | A114 | 32p Honey buzzard | 2.50 | 2.25 |
| 535 | A114 | 44p Blue rock thrush | 3.25 | 4.00 |
| | | *Nos. 532-535 (4)* | 8.75 | 7.35 |

Operation Raleigh, 1984-88 — A115

Designs: 19p, Square-rigger. 22p, Sir Walter Raleigh and expedition emblem. 32p, Maps and modern transport ship Sir Walter Raleigh. 44p, Ship Sir Walter Raleigh.

**Perf. 13x13½**
**1988, Sept. 14    Litho.    Wmk. 373**
| | | | | |
|---|---|---|---|---|
| 536 | A115 | 19p multicolored | .75 | .75 |
| 537 | A115 | 22p multicolored | .90 | .90 |
| 538 | A115 | 32p multicolored | 1.25 | 1.25 |
| | | *Nos. 536-538 (3)* | 2.90 | 2.90 |

**Souvenir Sheet**

**539** Sheet of 2, #537, 539a ... 5.25 5.25
**a.** A115 44p multicolored ... 2.25 2.25

400th anniv. of Sir Walter Raleigh's voyage to the New World to establish the 1st English-speaking colony, in what is now North Carolina.

Christmas — A116

Children's drawings: 4p, Snowman, by Rebecca Falero. 22p, Nativity, by Dennis Penalver. 44p, Santa Claus, by Gavin Key.

**1988, Nov. 2     Wmk. 384     Perf. 14**
**540** A116 4p multicolored ... .25 .25
**541** A116 22p multicolored ... .55 .55

**Size: 25x33mm**

**542** A116 44p multicolored ... 1.10 1.75
*Nos. 540-542 (3)* ... 1.90 2.55

Europa — A117

Toys: 32p, Doll, doll house, puppy, ball, boat.

**Perf. 13x13½**
**1989, Feb. 15     Wmk. 384**
**543** A117 25p shown ... 1.10 .75
**544** A117 32p multicolored ... 1.50 2.50

Gibraltar Regiment, 50th Anniv. — A118

4p, The Port Sergeant. 22p, Regimental colors, Queen's colors. 32p, Drum Major.

**Perf. 13½x13**
**1989, Apr. 28     Wmk. 373**
**545** A118 4p multicolored ... .50 .25
**546** A118 22p multicolored ... 1.50 1.00
**547** A118 32p multicolored ... 2.00 2.75
*Nos. 545-547 (3)* ... 4.00 4.00

**Souvenir Sheet**

**548** Sheet of 2, Nos. 546, 548a ... 5.75 5.75
**a.** A118 44p Regimental arms ... 2.50 2.50

Intl. Red Cross, 125th Anniv. — A119

25p, Mother and child. 32p, Malnourished children. 44p, Accident victims.

**Perf. 15x14½**
**1989, July 7     Wmk. 384**
**549** A119 25p multicolored ... 1.10 .60
**550** A119 32p multicolored ... 1.40 1.50
**551** A119 44p multicolored ... 1.75 2.50
*Nos. 549-551 (3)* ... 4.25 4.60

**Royal Navy Crest Type of 1982**

**1989, Sept. 7     Litho.     Perf. 14**
**552** A87 22p Blankney ... 1.75 .70
**553** A87 25p Deptford ... 1.75 1.50
**554** A87 32p Exmoor ... 2.50 2.50
**555** A87 44p Stork ... 3.50 4.25
*Nos. 552-555 (4)* ... 9.50 8.95

---

**Souvenir Sheets**

Coins — A120

No. 556: a, 1p Barbary Partridge. b, 2p Lighthouse at Europa Point. c, 10p Tower of Homage. d, 5p Barbary Ape.
No. 557: a, 50p Gibraltar Candytuft. b, £5 Pillars of Hercules. c, £2 Cannon from the Great Siege Period, 1779-1783. d, £1 Natl. coat of arms. e, Common obverse side of coins picturing Maklouf head of Queen Elizabeth II. f, 20p Our Lady of Europa.

**1989, Oct. 10     Perf. 14½x15**
**556** A120 Sheet of 4 ... 2.00 2.00
**a.-d.** 4p any single ... .50 .50
**557** A120 Sheet of 6 ... 6.75 6.75
**a.-f.** 22p any single ... 1.25 1.25

Christmas A121

4p, Santa's sleigh. 22p, Shepherds see star. 32p, Holy family. 44p, Adoration of the Magi.

**Wmk. 384**
**1989, Oct. 11     Litho.     Perf. 14½**
**558** A121 4p multicolored ... .25 .25
**559** A121 22p multicolored ... 1.10 .80
**560** A121 32p multicolored ... 1.75 1.90
**561** A121 44p multicolored ... 2.75 3.25
*Nos. 558-561 (4)* ... 5.85 6.20

Europa 1990 A122

Post offices: No. 562, G.P.O. exterior. No. 563, Carved crown and "VR" from p.o. archway and G.P.O. interior. No. 564, South District P.O. interior. No. 565, South District P.O. exterior.

**Perf. 14½, Rouletted 9½ Between**
**1990, Mar. 6     Litho.     Unwmk.**
**562** 22p multicolored ... 1.00 1.00
**563** 22p multicolored ... 1.00 1.00
**a.** A122 Pair, #562-563 ... 2.75 2.75
**564** 32p multicolored ... 1.25 1.25
**565** 32p multicolored ... 1.25 1.25
**a.** A122 Pair, #564-565 ... 3.75 3.75
*Nos. 562-565 (4)* ... 4.50 4.50

Pairs are rouletted between.

Early Fire Truck — A123

4p, Early firemen, hose, vert. 42p, Modern truck. 44p, Modern fireman, vert.

**1990, Apr. 2     Perf. 14½x14**
**566** A123 4p multicolored ... 1.00 .25
**567** A123 20p shown ... 2.50 1.00
**568** A123 42p multicolored ... 3.00 3.00
**569** A123 44p multicolored ... 3.25 3.25
*Nos. 566-569 (4)* ... 9.75 7.50

Fire Service, 125th anniv.

---

Penny Black, 150th Anniv. — A124

19p, Henry Corbould, Great Britain No. 1. 22p, 1st Royal Mail coach, Bristol-London. 32p, Sir Rowland Hill, Great Britain No. 1. 44p, Great Britain No. 1, Maltese Cross cancel.

**1990, May 3     Perf. 13½x14**
**570** A124 19p multicolored ... 1.00 .90
**571** A124 22p multicolored ... 1.25 .95
**572** A124 32p multicolored ... 2.50 2.50
*Nos. 570-572 (3)* ... 4.75 4.35

**Souvenir Sheet**

**573** A124 44p multicolored ... 6.25 6.25

**Royal Navy Crest Type of 1982**

**1990, July 10     Litho.     Perf. 14**
**574** A87 22p Calpe ... 2.00 .80
**575** A87 25p Gallant ... 2.25 1.90
**576** A87 32p Wrestler ... 2.75 3.00
**577** A87 44p Greyhound ... 3.50 4.00
*Nos. 574-577 (4)* ... 10.50 9.70

Europort Model — A125

23p, Building components. 25p, Land reclamation.

**1990, Oct. 10     Litho.     Perf. 14½**
**578** A125 22p multicolored ... .90 .80
**579** A125 23p multicolored ... .90 1.25
**580** A125 25p multicolored ... 1.00 1.25
*Nos. 578-580 (3)* ... 2.80 3.30

Christmas — A126

**1990, Oct. 10     Perf. 13½**
**581** A126 4p shown ... .25 .25
**582** A126 22p Santa Claus ... .80 .50
**583** A126 42p Christmas tree ... 1.75 2.25
**584** A126 44p Creche ... 1.75 2.25
*Nos. 581-584 (4)* ... 4.55 5.25

Europa — A127

25p, Spaceplane, satellite. 32p, ERS-1 satellite.

**1991, Feb. 26     Litho.     Perf. 13½**
**585** A127 25p multicolored ... .80 .60
**586** A127 32p multicolored ... 1.10 1.50

**Royal Navy Crest Type of 1982**
**1991, Apr. 9     Litho.     Perf. 13½x13**
**587** A87 4p Hesperus ... .60 .25
**588** A87 21p Forester ... 2.00 1.25
**589** A87 22p Furious ... 2.00 1.25
**590** A87 62p Scylla ... 4.50 6.00
*Nos. 587-590 (4)* ... 9.10 8.75

Birds — A128

**1991, May 30     Litho.     Perf. 13½**
**591** A128 13p Black stork ... 1.25 1.25
**592** A128 13p Egyptian vulture ... 1.25 1.25
**593** A128 13p Barbary partridge ... 1.25 1.25
**594** A128 13p Shag ... 1.25 1.25
**a.** Block of 4, #591-594 ... 6.50 7.50

World Wildlife Fund.

---

No. 519 Surcharged

**Wmk. 373**
**1991, May 30     Litho.     Perf. 12½**
**595** A111 £1.05 on £3 multi ... 5.75 2.75

Views of Gibraltar — A129

Paintings: 22p, North View of Gibraltar, by Gustavo Bacarisas (1873-1971). 26p, Parson's Lodge, by Elena Mifsud (1906-1989). 32p, Governor's Parade, by Jacobo Azabury, OBE (1890-1980). 42p, Waterport Wharf, by Rudesindo Mannia (1899-1982), vert.

**1991, Sept. 10     Litho.     Perf. 15x14**
**596** A129 22p multicolored ... 1.00 .50
**597** A129 26p multicolored ... 1.25 .90
**598** A129 32p multicolored ... 1.75 2.00

**Perf. 14x15**
**599** A129 42p multicolored ... 2.75 3.50
*Nos. 596-599 (4)* ... 6.75 6.90

Christmas — A130

Christmas carols: 4p, Once in Royal David's City. 24p, Silent Night. 25p, Angels We Have Heard on High. 49p, O Come All Ye Faithful.

**1991, Oct. 15     Litho.     Perf. 14½**
**600** A130 4p multicolored ... .40 .25
**601** A130 24p multicolored ... 1.50 .60
**602** A130 25p multicolored ... 1.50 .90
**603** A130 49p multicolored ... 3.00 4.00
*Nos. 600-603 (4)* ... 6.40 5.75

**Souvenir Sheet**

Phila Nippon '91 A131

**1991, Nov. 15**
**604** A131 £1.05 Plain tiger ... 4.75 4.75

**Queen Elizabeth II's Accession to the Throne, 40th Anniv.**
Common Design Type

**Wmk. 373**
**1992, Feb. 6     Litho.     Perf. 14**
**605** CD349 4p multicolored ... .25 .25
**606** CD349 20p multicolored ... .75 .75
**607** CD349 24p multicolored ... .90 1.00
**608** CD349 44p multicolored ... 1.50 1.50
**609** CD349 54p multicolored ... 1.75 2.00
*Nos. 605-609 (5)* ... 5.15 5.50

Discovery of America, 500th Anniv. — A132

No. 610, Columbus, Santa Maria. No. 611, Map, Nina. No. 612, Map, Pinta. No. 613, Map, sailor.

**1992, Feb. 6     Unwmk.     Perf. 14½**
**610** A132 24p multicolored ... 1.25 1.50
**611** A132 24p multicolored ... 1.25 1.50
**a.** Pair, #610-611 ... 3.50 3.75
**612** A132 34p multicolored ... 1.75 1.90
**613** A132 34p multicolored ... 1.75 1.90
**a.** Pair, #612-613 ... 4.00 4.00
*Nos. 610-613 (4)* ... 6.00 6.80

Europa. Printed in sheets containing 4 pairs.

Around the World Yacht Rally, 1991-92 — A133

Compass rose, sail and maps of routes through: 21p, Atlantic Ocean, vert. 24p, Malay Archipelago. 25p, Indian Ocean. 49p, Mediterranean and Red Seas, vert.

| 1992, Apr. 15 | Litho. | Perf. 13½ | | |
|---|---|---|---|---|
| 614 | A133 | 21p multicolored | .90 | .75 |
| 615 | A133 | 24p multicolored | 1.25 | 1.25 |
| 616 | A133 | 25p multicolored | 1.25 | 1.50 |
| | Nos. 614-616 (3) | | 3.40 | 3.50 |

**Souvenir Sheet**

| 617 | A133 | Sheet of 2, #614 & 617a | 3.00 | 3.00 |
|---|---|---|---|---|
| a. | | A133 49p multicolored | 2.00 | 2.00 |

Anglican Diocese of Gibraltar, 150th Anniv. — A134

4p, Holy Trinity Cathedral, vert. 24p, Crest and map. 44p, Construction work on Cathedral during 1800's. 54p, Bishop Tomlinson, first Bishop of Diocese (1842-1863), vert.

| 1992, Aug. 21 | Litho. | Perf. 14 | | |
|---|---|---|---|---|
| 618 | A134 | 4p multicolored | .40 | .25 |
| 619 | A134 | 24p multicolored | 1.10 | .60 |
| 620 | A134 | 44p multicolored | 2.00 | 2.25 |
| 621 | A134 | 54p multicolored | 2.25 | 3.00 |
| | Nos. 618-621 (4) | | 5.75 | 6.10 |

Christmas — A135

Designs: 4p, Church of the Sacred Heart of Jesus. 24p, Cathedral of St. Mary the Crowned. 34p, St. Andrew's Church. 49p, St. Joseph's Church.

| 1992, Nov. 10 | Litho. | Perf. 14 | | |
|---|---|---|---|---|
| 622 | A135 | 4p multicolored | .35 | .25 |
| 623 | A135 | 24p multicolored | 1.50 | .50 |
| 624 | A135 | 34p multicolored | 2.00 | 2.00 |
| 625 | A135 | 49p multicolored | 2.50 | 4.25 |
| | Nos. 622-625 (4) | | 6.35 | 7.00 |

Contemporary Art — A136

Europa: No. 626, Masks of Comedy and Tragedy, record. No. 627, Painting, dancer, pottery. No. 628, Architecture, sculpture. No. 629, Video camera, 35mm film.

| 1993, Mar. 2 | Litho. | Perf. 14½ | | |
|---|---|---|---|---|
| 626 | A136 | 24p multicolored | 1.50 | 1.50 |
| 627 | A136 | 24p multicolored | 1.50 | 1.50 |
| a. | | Pair, #626-627 | 3.50 | 4.25 |
| 628 | A136 | 34p multicolored | 1.75 | .200 |
| 629 | A136 | 34p multicolored | 1.75 | 2.00 |
| a. | | Pair, #628-629 | 4.50 | 5.25 |
| | Nos. 626-629 (4) | | 6.50 | 5.20 |

**Souvenir Sheet**

World War II Warships — A137

Designs: a, HMS Hood. b, HMS Ark Royal c, HMAS Waterhen. d, USS Gleaves.

---

| 1993, Apr. 27 | Litho. | Perf. 14 | | |
|---|---|---|---|---|
| 630 | A137 | 24p Sheet of 4, #a.-d. | 11.00 | 11.00 |

See Nos. 660, 684, 714, 732.

Architectural Heritage — A138

1p, Landport Gate. 2p, St. Mary the Crowned. 3p, Parsons Lodge Battery. 4p, Moorish Castle. 5p, General Post Office. 10p, South Barracks. 21p, American War Memorial. 24p, Garrison Library. 25p, Southport Gates. 26p, Casemates Gate. 50p, Central Police Station. £ 1, Prince Edward's Gate. £ 3, Lighthouse. £ 5, Coat of arms, keys to fortress, vert.

| 1993-94 | Litho. | Perf. 13 | | |
|---|---|---|---|---|
| 631 | A138 | 1p multicolored | .25 | .75 |
| 632 | A138 | 2p multicolored | .30 | .75 |
| 633 | A138 | 3p multicolored | .30 | .25 |
| 634 | A138 | 4p multicolored | .30 | .25 |
| 635 | A138 | 5p multicolored | .40 | .25 |
| 636 | A138 | 10p multicolored | .40 | .25 |
| 637 | A138 | 21p multicolored | 1.00 | .85 |
| 638 | A138 | 24p multicolored | 1.10 | .95 |
| 639 | A138 | 25p multicolored | 1.10 | .95 |
| 640 | A138 | 26p multicolored | 1.25 | 1.00 |
| 641 | A138 | 50p multicolored | 2.00 | 1.75 |
| 642 | A138 | £1 multicolored | 3.00 | 3.00 |
| 643 | A138 | £3 multicolored | 9.00 | 10.00 |
| 644 | A138 | £5 multicolored | 13.00 | 13.00 |
| | Nos. 631-644 (14) | | 33.40 | 34.00 |

Nos. 631, 635, 637, 639, 642-643 are vert. Portions of the design on No. 644 were applied by a thermographic process producing a shiny, raised effect.
Issued: £5, 6/6/94; others, 6/28/93.
See Nos. 686-693.

Anniversaries A139

21p, Coins. 24p, Jet, biplane fighters. 34p, Garrison Library. 49p, Churchill, searchlights.

| 1993, Sept. 21 | Litho. | Perf. 13 | | |
|---|---|---|---|---|
| 645 | A139 | 21p multicolored | 1.25 | .70 |
| 646 | A139 | 24p multicolored | 1.75 | .90 |
| 647 | A139 | 34p multicolored | 1.75 | 2.25 |
| 648 | A139 | 49p multicolored | 4.00 | 4.00 |
| | Nos. 645-648 (4) | | 8.75 | 7.85 |

First decimal coins, 25th anniv. Royal Air Force, 75th anniv. Garrison Library, bicent. Churchill's visit to Gibraltar, 50th anniv.

Christmas A140

Mice and: 5p, Christmas tree. 24p, Christmas cracker. 44p, Singing carols. 49p, Snowman.

| 1993, Nov. 16 | Litho. | Perf. 13½ | | |
|---|---|---|---|---|
| 649 | A140 | 5p multicolored | .25 | .25 |
| 650 | A140 | 24p multicolored | 1.00 | .70 |
| 651 | A140 | 44p multicolored | 2.00 | 2.50 |
| 652 | A140 | 49p multicolored | 3.00 | 3.00 |
| | Nos. 649-652 (4) | | 6.25 | 6.45 |

European Discoveries A141

Europa: No. 653, Atoms exploding, Lord Penney (1909-91). No. 654, Chemistry flasks, polonium, radium, Marie Curie. No. 655, Diesel engine, Rudolf Diesel. No. 656, Telescope, Galileo.

| 1994, Mar. 1 | Litho. | Perf. 13½ | | |
|---|---|---|---|---|
| 653 | A141 | 24p multicolored | 1.00 | 1.25 |
| 654 | A141 | 24p multicolored | 1.00 | 1.25 |
| a. | | Pair, #653-654 | 3.00 | 4.25 |
| 655 | A141 | 34p multicolored | 1.40 | 1.50 |
| 656 | A141 | 34p multicolored | 1.40 | 1.50 |
| a. | | Pair, #655-656 | 3.50 | 3.50 |
| | Nos. 653-656 (4) | | 4.80 | 5.50 |

---

1994 World Cup Soccer Championships, US — A142

26p, FIFA cup, US map, flag. 39p, Players, US map as playing field. 49p, Leg action.

| 1994, Apr. 19 | Litho. | Perf. 13½ | | |
|---|---|---|---|---|
| 657 | A142 | 26p multi | 1.00 | .65 |
| 658 | A142 | 39p multi | 1.50 | 2.00 |
| 659 | A142 | 49p multi, vert. | 2.00 | 2.75 |
| | Nos. 657-659 (3) | | 4.50 | 5.40 |

**World War II Warships Type of 1993**
**Souvenir Sheet**

Designs: a, 5p, HMS Penelope. b, 25p, HMS Warspite. c, 44p, USS McLanahan. d, 49p, HNLMS Isaac Sweers.

| 1994, June 6 | Litho. | Perf. 13½x13 | | |
|---|---|---|---|---|
| 660 | A137 | Sheet of 4, #a.-d. | 9.00 | 9.00 |

**Souvenir Sheet**

PHILAKOREA '94 — A143

| 1994, Aug. 16 | Litho. | Perf. 13 | | |
|---|---|---|---|---|
| 661 | A143 | £1.05 multicolored | 4.00 | 4.00 |

Marine Life — A144

21p, Golden star coral. 24p, Star fish. 34p, Gorgonian sea fan. 49p, Turkish wrasse.

| 1994, Sept. 27 | Litho. | Perf. 14 | | |
|---|---|---|---|---|
| 662 | A144 | 21p multicolored | .90 | .50 |
| 663 | A144 | 24p multicolored | 1.10 | .60 |
| 664 | A144 | 34p multicolored | 1.75 | 1.50 |
| 665 | A144 | 49p multicolored | 2.50 | 2.50 |
| | Nos. 662-665 (4) | | 6.25 | 5.10 |

Intl. Olympic Committee, Cent. — A145

| 1994, Nov. 22 | Litho. | Perf. 14 | | |
|---|---|---|---|---|
| 666 | A145 | 49p Discus | 2.50 | 2.25 |
| 667 | A145 | 54p Javelin | 2.50 | 2.50 |

Christmas Songbirds — A146

| 1994, Nov. 22 | | Perf. 13½ | | |
|---|---|---|---|---|
| 668 | A146 | 5p Great tit | .80 | .25 |
| 669 | A146 | 24p Robin, horiz. | 2.50 | .75 |
| 670 | A146 | 34p Blue tit, horiz. | 2.75 | 1.50 |
| 671 | A146 | 54p Goldfinch | 3.75 | 4.25 |
| | Nos. 668-671 (4) | | 9.80 | 6.75 |

New Members in European Union — A147

Flags: 24p, Austria. 26p, Finland. 34p, Sweden. 49p, Sweden, Austria, Finland, emblem of European Union.

---

| 1995, Jan. 3 | Litho. | Perf. 14 | | |
|---|---|---|---|---|
| 672 | A147 | 24p multicolored | .80 | .45 |
| 673 | A147 | 26p multicolored | .90 | .55 |
| 674 | A147 | 34p multicolored | 1.10 | 1.00 |
| 675 | A147 | 49p multicolored | 1.75 | 2.50 |
| | Nos. 672-675 (4) | | 4.55 | 4.50 |

Peace & Freedom — A148

Europa: No. 676, Cross, barbed wire, text. No. 677, Rainbow, dove, hands. No. 678, Shackles, text. No. 679, Doves, hands.

| 1995, Feb. 28 | Litho. | Perf. 13½ | | |
|---|---|---|---|---|
| 676 | | 24p multicolored | 1.25 | 1.25 |
| 677 | | 24p multicolored | 1.25 | 1.25 |
| a. | A148 | Pair, #676-677 | 3.25 | 3.00 |
| 678 | | 34p multicolored | 1.40 | 1.40 |
| 679 | | 34p multicolored | 1.40 | 1.40 |
| a. | A148 | Pair, #678-679 | 4.00 | 4.00 |
| | Nos. 676-679 (4) | | 5.30 | 5.30 |

Island Games — A149

| 1995, May 8 | Litho. | Perf. 14x13½ | | |
|---|---|---|---|---|
| 680 | A149 | 24p Sailing | .80 | .75 |
| 681 | A149 | 44p Running | 1.75 | 1.75 |
| 682 | A149 | 49p Swimming | 1.75 | 1.75 |
| | Nos. 680-682 (3) | | 4.30 | 4.25 |

| 680a | | Booklet pane of 3 | 3.75 | |
|---|---|---|---|---|
| 681a | | Booklet pane of 3 | 6.50 | |
| 682a | | Booklet pane of 3 | 8.00 | |
| 682b | | Bklt. pane, 1 ea. #680-682 | 6.00 | |
| | | Commemorative booklet, 1 each #680a-682b | 24.50 | |

**Souvenir Sheet**

VE Day, 50th Anniv. — A150

**1995, May 8**

| 683 | A150 | £1.05 multicolored | 5.00 | 5.00 |
|---|---|---|---|---|

**World War II Warships Type of 1993**

Designs: a, 5p, HMS Calpe. b, 24p, HMS Victorious. c, 44p, USS Weehawken. d, 49p, FFS Savorgnan de Brazza.

**Souvenir Sheet**

| 1995, June 6 | | Perf. 13½x14 | | |
|---|---|---|---|---|
| 684 | A137 | Sheet of 4, #a.-d. | 10.00 | 10.00 |

Singapore '95 — A151

Orchids: a, 22p, Bee. b, 23p, Brown bee. c, 24p, Pyramidal. d, 25p, Mirror. e, 26p, Sawfly.

| 1995, Sept. 1 | Litho. | Perf. 14x14½ | | |
|---|---|---|---|---|
| 685 | A151 | Strip of 5, #a.-e. | 8.25 | 8.25 |

**Architectural Heritage Type of 1993**

6p, House of Assembly. 7p, Bleak House. 8p, Bust of Gen. Eliott. 9p, Supreme Court Building. 20p, Convent. 30p, St. Bernard's Hospital. 40p, City Hall. £ 2, Church of Sacred Heart of Jesus.

| 1995, Sept. 1 | Litho. | Perf. 13 | | |
|---|---|---|---|---|
| 686 | A138 | 6p multicolored | .70 | .40 |
| 687 | A138 | 7p multicolored | .70 | .40 |
| 688 | A138 | 8p multicolored | .90 | .40 |
| 689 | A138 | 9p multicolored | 1.10 | .65 |
| 690 | A138 | 20p multicolored | 1.25 | .70 |
| 691 | A138 | 30p multicolored | 1.40 | 1.50 |
| 692 | A138 | 40p multicolored | 1.60 | 2.00 |
| 693 | A138 | £2 multicolored | 6.00 | 7.50 |
| | Nos. 686-693 (8) | | 13.65 | 13.55 |

Nos. 686, 688, 691, 693 are vert.

UN, 50th
Anniv. — A152

**1995, Oct. 24    Litho.    Perf. 13½**
694 A152 34p shown                  1.90 1.90
695 A152 49p Peace dove             2.00 2.00

**Miniature Sheets of 4 + 4 Labels**

Motion
Pictures,
Cent.
A153

Designs: No. 696: a, Ingrid Bergman. b, Vittorio De Sica. c, Marlene Dietrich. d, Laurence Olivier.
No. 697: a, 38p, Audrey Hepburn. b, 25p, Romy Schneider. c, 28p, Yves Montand. d, 5p, Marilyn Monroe.

**1995, Nov. 13    Litho.    Perf. 14½x14**
696 A153 24p #a.-d.                 3.50 3.50
697 A153     #a.-d.                 3.50 3.50

Christmas — A154

Designs: 5p, Santa Claus. 24p, Sack of toys. 34p, Reindeer. 54p, Santa with sleigh, reindeer flying over rooftops.

**1995, Nov. 27                    Perf. 14**
698 A154  5p multicolored            .45  .25
699 A154 24p multicolored           1.40  .55
700 A154 34p multicolored           2.00 1.50
701 A154 54p multicolored           3.00 4.00
      Nos. 698-701 (4)              6.85 6.30

**Miniature Sheet**

Puppies — A155

No. 702: a, 5p, Shih tzu. b, 21p, Dalmatian. c, Cocker spaniel. d, 25p, West Highland white terrier. e, 34p, Labrador. f, 35p, Boxer.

**1996, Jan. 24    Litho.    Perf. 14**
702 A155 Sheet of 6, #a.-f.         6.00 6.00

No. 702 is a continuous design.

Women of the
British Royal
Family — A156

**1996, Feb. 9    Litho.    Perf. 13½**
703 A156 24p Princess Anne          1.40 1.40
704 A156 24p Princess Diana         1.40 1.40
705 A156 34p Queen Mother           1.60 1.60
706 A156 34p Queen Elizabeth II     1.60 1.60
      Nos. 703-706 (4)              6.00 6.00

Europa.

European
Soccer — A157

Team members in action scenes: 21p, West Germany, 1980. 24p, France, 1964. 34p, Holland, 1988. £1.20, Denmark, 1992.

---

**1996, Apr. 2    Litho.    Perf. 13**
707 A157 21p multicolored            .60  .60
708 A157 24p multicolored            .85  .85
709 A157 34p multicolored           1.25 1.25
710 A157 £1.20 multicolored         3.25 3.25
  a.  Souvenir sheet, Nos. 707-710  9.00 9.00
      Nos. 707-710 (4)              5.95 5.95

Modern Olympic
Games,
Cent. — A158

34p, Ancient athletes. 49p, Athletes, 1896. £1.05, Athletes, 1990s.

**1996, May 2    Litho.    Perf. 13½**
711 A158   34p multi                1.10 1.10
712 A158   49p multi                1.60 1.60
713 A158 £1.05 multi                3.25 3.25
      Nos. 711-713 (3)              5.95 5.95

**World War II Warships Type of 1993**
**Souvenir Sheet**

a, 5p, HMS Starling. b, 25p, HMS Royalist. c, 49p, USS Philadelphia. d, 54p, HMCS Prescott.

**1996, June 8    Litho.    Perf. 13½x14**
714 A137 Sheet of 4, #a.-d.         7.50 7.50

UNICEF, 50th
Anniv. — A159

a, 21p, Girl, boy. b, 24p, Three children. c, 49p, Three children, diff. d, 54p, Girl, boy, diff.

**1996, June 8                    Perf. 13½x13**
715 A159 Strip of 4, #a.-d.         5.00 5.00

World Wildlife
Fund — A160

Red kite: a, In flight. b, One adult. c, One on rock, one in flight. d, Adults, young in nest.

**1996, July 12    Litho.    Perf. 14½**
716 A160 34p Block or strip of 4,
         #a.-d.                      7.00 7.00

Christmas Images
Formed with "Lego"
Blocks — A161

**1996, Nov. 27    Litho.    Perf. 14**
717 A161  5p Pudding                 .25  .25
718 A161 21p Snowman                 .65  .65
719 A161 24p Present                 .80  .80
720 A161 34p Santa Claus            1.00 1.00
721 A161 54p Candle                 1.50 1.50
      Nos. 717-721 (5)              4.20 4.20

Sailing Ship "Mary
Celeste" — A162

Europa: No. 722, "Mary Celeste" in rough seas. No. 723, Men on board ship. No. 724, Boat approaching "Mary Celeste." No. 725, In full sail.

**1997, Feb. 12    Litho.    Perf. 14**
722 A162 28p multicolored           1.00 1.00
723 A162 28p multicolored           1.00 1.00
724 A162 30p multicolored           1.10 1.10
725 A162 30p multicolored           1.10 1.10
      Nos. 722-725 (4)              4.20 4.20

---

Kittens — A163

Designs: a, 5p, Silver tabby American shorthair. b, 24p, "Rumpy" Manx red tabby. c, 26p, Blue point Birmans. d, 28p, Red self longhair. e, 30p, British shorthair, tortoiseshell & white. f, 35p, British bicolor shorthairs.

**1997, Feb. 12**
726 A163  Sheet of 6, #a.-f.        7.75 7.75
  g.  Bklt. pane of 3, #726a, 726c,
      726e                          3.00 3.00
  h.  Bklt. pane of 3, #726b, 726c,
      726d                          4.00
  i.  Bklt. pane of 4, #726a, 726b,
      726e, 726f                    4.75
  j.  Bklt. pane of 4, #726c, 726d,
      726e, 726f                    5.50
  k.  Booklet pane, #726            7.00
      Complete booklet, #726g-726k 24.00

Hong Kong '97. No. 726k is rouletted at left and does not have Hong Kong '97 emblem and inscription in bottom slevage.

Butterflies — A164

Designs: 23p, Anthocaris belia euphenoides. 26p, Charaxes jasius. 30p, Vanessa cardui. £1.20, Iphiclides podalirius.

**1997, Apr. 7    Litho.    Perf. 14x13½**
728 A164 23p multicolored            .75  .75
729 A164 26p multicolored            .90  .90
730 A164 30p multicolored           1.10 1.10
731 A164 £1.20 multicolored         3.75 3.75
  a.  Souvenir sheet of 4, #728-
      731                           8.00 8.00
      Nos. 728-731 (4)              6.50 6.50

**World War II Warships Type of 1993**
**Souvenir Sheet**

a, 24p, HMS Enterprise. b, 26p, HMS Cleopatra. c, 38p, USS Iowa. d, 50p, Polish Warship Orkan.

**1997, June 9    Litho.    Perf. 13½**
732 A137 Sheet of 4, #a.-d.         5.75 5.75

Queen Elizabeth II and Prince Philip,
50th Wedding Anniv. — A165

Designs: £1.20, Prince Philip driving a four-in-hand, Queen beside him. £1.40, Queen, Prince Philip at Royal Ascot, Queen "Trooping the Color."

**1997, July 10    Litho.    Perf. 14x13½**
733 A165 £1.20 multicolored         4.75 4.75
734     £1.40 multicolored         5.50 5.50
  a.  A165 Pair, #733-734          11.00 11.00

1997 Dior Fashion
Designs, by John
Galliano — A166

30p, Long black dress, hat. 35p, Mini skirt, lace top. 50p, Formal gown. 62p, Suit, hat. £1.20, Formal gown, diff.

**1997, Sept. 9    Litho.    Perf. 13½x13**
735 A166 30p multicolored            .85  .85
736 A166 35p multicolored           1.00 1.00
737 A166 50p multicolored           1.25 1.25
  a.  Pair, #735, 737               3.00 3.00
738 A166 62p multicolored           1.75 1.75
  a.  Pair, #736, 738               4.00 4.00
      Nos. 735-738 (4)              4.85 4.85

**Souvenir Sheet**
739 A166 £1.20 multicolored         4.00 4.00

---

Christmas — A167

Stained glass windows: 5p, Our Lady and St. Bernard. 26p, The Epiphany of the Lord. 38p, St. Joseph holding Jesus. 50p, The Holy Family. 62p, The Miraculous Medal Madonna.

**1997, Nov. 18    Litho.    Perf. 13½**
740 A167  5p multicolored            .25  .25
741 A167 26p multicolored           1.00 1.00
742 A167 38p multicolored           1.25 1.25
743 A167 50p multicolored           1.75 1.75
744 A167 62p multicolored           2.00 2.00
      Nos. 740-744 (5)              6.25 6.25

A168

**1997, Dec. 15    Litho.    Perf. 13**
745 A168 26p multicolored           1.20 1.20

Sir Joshua Hassan (1915-97), government leader.

A169

Scenes from previous World Cup Championships: 5p, Wales v. Brazil, 1958. 26p, N. Ireland v. France, 1958. 38p, Scotland v. Holland, 1978. £1.20, England v. W. Germany, 1966.

**1998, Jan. 23**
746 A169  5p multicolored            .35  .25
747 A169 26p multicolored           1.00 1.00
748 A169 38p multicolored           1.25 1.25
749 A169 £1.20 multicolored         3.50 3.50
  a.  Souvenir sheet, #746-749      6.50 6.50
      Nos. 746-749 (4)              6.10 6.00

1998 World Cup Soccer Championships, France.

**Diana, Princess of Wales (1961-97)**
**Common Design Type**

Various portraits: a, 26p, Wearing black & white outfit. b, 26p, Wearing pink & white outfit. c, 38p, In black dress. d, 38p, In blue & gold jacket.

**1998, Mar. 31    Litho.    Perf. 14½x14**
754 CD355 Sheet of 4, #a.-d.        4.75 4.75

The 20p surtax from international sales was donated to the Princess Diana Memorial Fund and the surtax from national sales was donated to a designated local charity.

**Royal Air Force, 80th Anniv.**
**Common Design Type of 1993 Re-inscribed**

Designs: 24p, Saro London. 26p, Fairey Fox. 38p, Handley Page Halifax GR.VI. 50p, Hawker Siddeley Buccaneer S.2B.
No. 759: a, 24p, Sopwith 1½ Strutter. b, 26p, Bristol M.1B. c, 38p, Supermarine Spitfire XII. d, 50p, Avro York.

**1998, Apr. 1                    Perf. 14**
755 CD350 24p multicolored           .80  .80
756 CD350 26p multicolored           .90  .90
757 CD350 38p multicolored          1.25 1.25
758 CD350 50p multicolored          1.75 1.75
      Nos. 755-758 (4)              4.70 4.70

**Souvenir Sheet of 4**
759 CD350     #a.-d.                5.00 5.00

Europa — A170

Costumes worn by Miss Gibraltar for National Day: No. 760, Military style. No. 761, Long skirt, long-sleeved top. No. 762, Short skirt, long cape. No. 763, Black lace scarf, ruffled petticoat.

| **1998, May 22** | **Litho.** | **Perf. 13** | |
|---|---|---|---|
| 760 | A170 | 26p multicolored | .90 .90 |
| 761 | A170 | 26p multicolored | .90 .90 |
| 762 | A170 | 38p multicolored | 1.30 1.30 |
| 763 | A170 | 38p multicolored | 1.30 1.30 |
| | *Nos. 760-763 (4)* | | 4.40 4.40 |

UNESCO 1998 Intl. Year of the Ocean — A171

Marine life: a, 5p, Striped dolphin. b, 26p, Killer whale, vert. c, £1.20, Blue whale. d, 5p, Common dolphin, vert.

| **1998, May 22** | | **Perf. 14** | |
|---|---|---|---|
| 764 | A171 | Sheet of 4, #a.-d. | 7.25 7.25 |

Italia '98 and Portugal '98.

Battle of the Nile — A172

| **1998, Aug. 1** | **Litho.** | **Perf. 13½** | |
|---|---|---|---|
| 765 | A172 | 12p Nileus | .85 .85 |
| 766 | A172 | 26p Lord Nelson | 1.10 1.10 |
| *a.* | | Booklet pane of 1 | 1.50 |
| 767 | A172 | 28p Frances Nisbet | 1.25 1.25 |
| *a.* | | Bklt. pane, #765-767 | 3.50 |
| 768 | A172 | 35p HMS Vanguard | 1.40 1.40 |

**Size: 45x27mm**

| 769 | A172 | 50p Battle of the Nile | 2.25 2.25 |
|---|---|---|---|
| *a.* | | Bklt. pane, #768-769, 2 #766 | 7.25 |
| *b.* | | Bklt. pane, #766, 768-769 | 5.75 |
| *c.* | | Bklt. pane, #765-769 | 8.00 |
| | | Complete booklet, #766a, 767a, 769a-769c | 26.00 |
| | *Nos. 765-769 (5)* | | 6.85 6.85 |

Quotations From Famous People — A173

No. 770, "Love comforts like sunshine after rain," Shakespeare. No. 771, "The price of greatness is responsibility," Churchill. No. 772, "Hate the sin, love the sinner," Gandhi. No. 773, "Imagination is more important than knowledge," Einstein.

| **1998, Oct. 6** | **Litho.** | **Perf. 14½** | |
|---|---|---|---|
| 770 | A173 | 26p multicolored | .90 .90 |
| 771 | A173 | 26p multicolored | .90 .90 |
| 772 | A173 | 38p multicolored | 1.50 1.50 |
| 773 | A173 | 38p multicolored | 1.50 1.50 |
| | *Nos. 770-773 (4)* | | 4.80 4.80 |

Nos. 770-773 were each printed in sheets of 6 with se-tenant labels.

A174

| **1998, Nov. 10** | **Litho.** | **Perf. 13** | |
|---|---|---|---|
| 774 | A174 | 5p Nativity | .45 .45 |
| 775 | A174 | 26p Star over manger | 1.10 1.10 |
| 776 | A174 | 30p Balthasar | 1.25 1.25 |
| 777 | A174 | 35p Melchior | 1.40 1.40 |
| 778 | A174 | 50p Caspar | 1.75 1.75 |
| | *Nos. 774-778 (5)* | | 5.95 5.95 |

Christmas.

A175

| **1999, Mar. 4** | **Litho.** | **Perf. 13½** | |
|---|---|---|---|
| 779 | A175 | 1p claret | .25 .25 |
| 780 | A175 | 2p brown | .25 .25 |
| 781 | A175 | 4p blue | .25 .25 |
| 782 | A175 | 5p green | .25 .25 |
| 783 | A175 | 10p brown orange | .40 .40 |
| 784 | A175 | 12p red | .45 .45 |
| 785 | A175 | 20p blue green | .75 .75 |
| 786 | A175 | 28p lilac rose | 1.00 1.00 |
| 787 | A175 | 30p vermilion | 1.10 1.10 |
| 788 | A175 | 40p gray olive | 1.50 1.50 |
| 789 | A175 | 42p slate | 1.60 1.60 |

**Size: 22½x28mm**

**Perf. 14½**

| 790 | A175 | 50p olive bister | 1.90 1.90 |
|---|---|---|---|
| 791 | A175 | £1 black | 3.75 3.75 |
| 792 | A175 | £3 ultramarine | 9.00 9.00 |

**Self-Adhesive**

***Die Cut Perf. 9x9½***

| 793 | A175 | 1st vermilion | 1.10 1.10 |
|---|---|---|---|
| | *Nos. 779-793 (15)* | | 23.55 23.55 |

No. 793 was valued at 26p on day of issue. See Nos. 885-886.

Nature Reserves — A176

| **1999, Mar. 4** | | **Perf. 13½x13** | |
|---|---|---|---|
| 794 | A176 | 30p Barbary macaque | 1.50 1.50 |
| 795 | A176 | 30p Dartford warbler | 1.50 1.50 |
| 796 | A176 | 42p Kingfisher | 1.90 1.90 |
| 797 | A176 | 42p Dusky perch | 1.90 1.90 |
| | *Nos. 794-797 (4)* | | 6.80 6.80 |

Europa.

Maritime Heritage — A177

Designs: 5p, Roman Anchorage. 30p, Medieval galley house. 42p, British relief ships. £1.20, HMS Berwick.

| **1999, Mar. 19** | | **Perf. 12½** | |
|---|---|---|---|
| 798 | A177 | 5p multicolored | .40 .25 |
| 799 | A177 | 30p multicolored | 1.25 .75 |
| 800 | A177 | 42p multicolored | 2.00 2.00 |
| 801 | A177 | £1.20 multicolored | 4.50 4.50 |
| *a.* | | Souvenir sheet, #798-801 | 8.75 8.75 |
| | *Nos. 798-801 (4)* | | 8.15 7.50 |

John Lennon (1940-80) — A178

Portraits: 20p, With flower over one eye. 30p, Black and white photo. 40p, Wearing glasses.

No. 805, Holding marriage license in front of Rock of Gibraltar. No. 806, Standing in front of airplane.

| **1999, Mar. 20** | | **Perf. 13** | |
|---|---|---|---|
| 802 | A178 | 20p multicolored | 1.00 .60 |
| 803 | A178 | 30p multicolored | 1.25 .90 |
| 804 | A178 | 40p multicolored | 1.50 1.50 |
| | *Nos. 802-804 (3)* | | 3.75 3.00 |

**Souvenir Sheets**

| 805 | A178 | £1 multicolored | 6.50 6.50 |
|---|---|---|---|
| 806 | A178 | £1 multicolored | 6.50 6.50 |

UPU, 125th Anniv. — A179

| **1999, June 7** | **Litho.** | **Perf. 12½** | |
|---|---|---|---|
| 807 | A179 | 5p Postal van | .25 .25 |
| 808 | A179 | 30p Space station | 1.25 1.25 |

Fighter Planes and Raptors — A180

Designs: No. 809, RAF Eurofighter 2000 Typhoon. No. 810, RAF F3 Tornado. No. 811, RAF GR7 Harrier II. No. 812, Lesser kestrel. No. 813, Peregrine falcon. No. 814, Kestrel.

| **1999, June 7** | | **Perf. 13x13¼** | |
|---|---|---|---|
| 809 | A180 | 30p multicolored | 1.00 1.00 |
| 810 | A180 | 30p multicolored | 1.00 1.00 |
| 811 | A180 | 30p multicolored | 1.00 1.00 |
| *a.* | | Sheet of 3, #809-811 | 3.25 3.25 |
| 812 | A180 | 42p multicolored | 1.10 1.10 |
| *a.* | | Pair, #809, 812 | 3.00 3.00 |
| 813 | A180 | 42p multicolored | 1.10 1.10 |
| *a.* | | Pair, #810, 813 | 3.00 3.00 |
| 814 | A180 | 42p multicolored | 1.10 1.10 |
| *a.* | | Pair, #811, 814 | 3.00 3.00 |
| *b.* | | Sheet of 3, #812-814 | 6.25 6.25 |

See Nos. 851-853, 887-889.

Wedding of Prince Edward and Sophie Rhys-Jones A181

**Perf. 13x13¼, 13¼x13**

| **1999, June 19** | | **Litho.** | |
|---|---|---|---|
| 815 | A181 | 30p shown | 1.40 1.40 |
| 816 | A181 | 42p Couple, vert. | 1.60 1.60 |

Sports in Gibraltar, Cent. — A182

| **1999, July 2** | | **Perf. 13** | |
|---|---|---|---|
| 817 | A182 | 30p Soccer | 1.00 1.00 |
| 818 | A182 | 42p Rowing | 1.50 1.50 |
| 819 | A182 | £1.20 Cricket | 3.50 3.50 |
| | *Nos. 817-819 (3)* | | 6.00 6.00 |

Wedding of Prince Edward to Sophie Rhys-Jones A183

**Perf. 13x13¼, 13¼x13**

| **1999, Oct. 11** | | **Litho.** | |
|---|---|---|---|
| 820 | A183 | 54p shown | 1.75 1.75 |
| 821 | A183 | 66p Couple standing, vert. | 2.25 2.25 |

Christmas and New Year's Greetings — A184

Designs: No. 822, "Happy Christmas," Santa, sleigh. No. 823, "Season's Greetings." No. 824, "Happy Millennium." No. 825, "Happy Christmas," Santa, reindeer. No. 826, "Yo ho ho." 54p, Santa, tree, fireplace.

| **1999, Nov. 11** | | **Litho.** | **Perf. 14** |
|---|---|---|---|
| 822 | A184 | 5p multicolored | .25 .25 |
| 823 | A184 | 5p multicolored | .25 .25 |
| 824 | A184 | 30p multicolored | 1.00 1.00 |
| 825 | A184 | 30p multicolored | 1.00 1.00 |
| 826 | A184 | 42p multicolored | 1.50 1.50 |
| 827 | A184 | 54p multicolored | 1.75 1.75 |
| | *Nos. 822-827 (6)* | | 5.75 5.75 |

Stampin' the Future Children's Stamp Design Contest Winners — A185

Artwork by: 30p, Colin Grech. 42p, Kim Barea. 54p, Stephan Williamson-Fa. 66p, Michael Podesta.

| **2000. Jan. 28** | | **Litho.** | **Perf. 14½x14** |
|---|---|---|---|
| 828 | A185 | 30p multi | 1.25 1.25 |
| 829 | A185 | 42p multi | 1.25 1.25 |
| 830 | A185 | 54p multi | 1.25 1.25 |
| 831 | A185 | 66p multi | 1.25 1.25 |
| *a.* | | Block or strip of 4, #828-831 | 7.25 7.25 |

European Soccer — A186

| **2000, Apr. 17** | | **Litho.** | **Perf. 12½** |
|---|---|---|---|
| 832 | A186 | 30p France | .85 .85 |
| 833 | A186 | 30p Holland | .95 .95 |
| 834 | A186 | 42p Denmark | 1.10 1.10 |
| 835 | A186 | 42p Germany | 1.25 1.25 |
| *a.* | | Souvenir sheet, #832-835 | 5.50 5.50 |
| 836 | A186 | 54p England | 1.50 1.50 |
| *a.* | | Souvenir sheet of 4 | 7.00 7.00 |
| | *Nos. 832-836 (5)* | | 5.65 5.65 |

The Stamp Show 2000, London (No. 836a).

Europa — A187

| **2000, Apr. 17** | | **Perf. 13¼x13** | |
|---|---|---|---|
| 837 | A187 | 30p Fountain | 1.00 .80 |
| 838 | A187 | 40p Hands | 1.25 1.25 |
| 839 | A187 | 42p Airplane | 1.50 1.50 |
| 840 | A187 | 54p Rainbow | 1.75 1.75 |
| | *Nos. 837-840 (4)* | | 5.50 5.30 |

Millennium — A188

History of Gibraltar: a, 3000-meter waterfall. b, The sandy plains. c, The Neanderthals. d, The Phoenicians. e, The Romans. f, The Arabs. g, Coat of arms, 1502. h, British Gibraltar. i, The great siege. j, Trafalgar. k, The city. l, Fortifications. m, The evacuation. n, The fortress. o, Queen Elizabeth II. p, European finance center.

| **2000, May 9** | | **Perf. 14** | |
|---|---|---|---|
| 841 | A188 | Sheet of 16 | 12.00 12.00 |
| *a.-h.* | | 5p Any single | .30 .30 |
| *i.-p.* | | 30p Any single | 1.25 1.25 |
| *q.* | | Souvenir booklet | 27.50 |

No. 841q contains a pane of 2 of each of Nos. 841a-841j and a pane of 3 of each of Nos. 841k-841p.

Prince William, 18th Birthday — A189

Designs: 30p, With Princess Diana. 42p, As child. 54p, With Prince Charles. 66p, In suit.

| **2000, June 21** | | **Litho.** | **Perf. 12½** |
|---|---|---|---|
| 842 | A189 | 30p multi | .80 .70 |
| 843 | A189 | 42p multi | 1.25 .85 |
| 844 | A189 | 54p multi | 1.50 1.50 |

| 845 | A189 | 66p multi | 1.75 | 1.75 |
| a. | | Souvenir sheet, #842-845 | 7.25 | 7.25 |
| | | Nos. 842-845 (4) | 5.30 | 4.80 |

Queen Mother, 100th Birthday — A190

Designs: 30p, As young woman. 42p, With King George VI. 54p, With blue hat. 66p, With orange hat.

**2000, Aug. 4**

| 846 | A190 | 30p multi | .85 | .75 |
| 847 | A190 | 42p multi | 1.25 | 1.00 |
| 848 | A190 | 54p multi | 1.50 | 1.50 |
| 849 | A190 | 66p multi | 1.75 | 1.75 |
| a. | | Souvenir sheet, #846-849 | 6.75 | 6.75 |
| | | Nos. 846-849 (4) | 5.35 | 5.00 |

Moorish Castle — A191

**Photo. & Engr.**

**2000, Sept. 15        Perf. 11½x11¾**

| 850 | A191 | £5 multi | 15.00 | 15.00 |

**Fighter Planes and Raptors Type**

No. 851: a, RAF "Gibraltar" Supermarine Spitfire. b, Male merlin.
No. 852: a, RAF "City of Lincoln" Avro Lancaster B1-3. b, Bonelli's eagle.
No. 853: a, RAF Hawker Hurricane MK IIC. b, Female merlin.

**2000, Sept. 15    Litho.    Perf. 14½x14**

| 851 | | Pair | 4.00 | 4.00 |
| a. | | A180 30p multi | 1.50 | 1.50 |
| b. | | A180 42p multi | 1.75 | 1.75 |
| 852 | | Pair | 4.00 | 4.00 |
| a. | | A180 30p multi | 1.50 | 1.50 |
| b. | | A180 42p multi | 1.75 | 1.75 |
| 853 | | Pair | 4.00 | 4.00 |
| a. | | A180 30p multi | 1.50 | 1.50 |
| b. | | A180 42p multi | 1.75 | 1.75 |
| c. | | Souvenir sheet, #851a, 852a, 853a | 5.00 | 5.00 |
| d. | | Souvenir sheet, #851b, 852b, 853b | 7.25 | 7.25 |
| | | Nos. 851-853 (3) | 12.00 | 12.00 |

Christmas — A192

5p, Baby Jesus. No. 855, 30p, Joseph, Mary, donkey. No. 856, 30p, Mary, Jesus. 40p, Joseph, Mary, innkeeper. 42p, Holy Family, donkey. 54p, Holy Family, Magi.

**2000, Nov. 13        Perf. 14**

| 854-859 | A192 | Set of 6 | 6.50 | 6.50 |

Queen Victoria (1819-1901) — A193

Designs: 30p, On wedding day. 42p, Portrait. 54p, In carriage. 66p, Jubilee portrait.

**2001, Jan. 22        Perf. 12¾**

| 860-863 | A193 | Set of 4 | 7.50 | 7.50 |

New Year 2001 (Year of the Snake) — A194

Snakes: No. 864, 5p, Grass. No. 865, 5p, Ladder. No. 866, 5p, Montpelier. No. 867, 30p, Viperine. No. 868, 30p, Southern smooth. No. 869, 30p, False smooth. 66p, Horseshoe whip.

**2001, Feb. 1    Litho.    Perf. 13¾**

| 864-870 | A194 | Set of 7 | 6.00 | 6.00 |
| 870a | | Souvenir sheet, #864-870 | 8.75 | 8.75 |

Size of No. 870: 31x62mm. Hong Kong 2001 Stamp Exhibition (No. 870a).

Europa — A195

Designs: 30p, Long-snouted seahorse. 40p, Snapdragon. 42p, Yellow-legged gull. 54p, Goldfish.

**2001, Feb. 1        Perf. 13¼x13**

| 871-874 | A195 | Set of 4 | 9.25 | 9.25 |

Queen Elizabeth II, 75th Birthday — A196

Designs: No. 875, 30p, As child. No. 876, 30p, As young woman. No. 877, 42p, In wedding dress. No. 878, 42p, At coronation. 54p, Wearing hat.
£2, In blue dress.

**2001, Apr. 21    Litho.    Perf. 14**

| 875-879 | A196 | Set of 5 | 6.75 | 6.75 |

**Souvenir Sheet**
**Perf. 13¾**

| 880 | A196 | £2 multi | 7.00 | 7.00 |

No. 880 contains one 35x48mm stamp.

Gibraltar Chronicle, Bicent. — A197

Designs: 30p, Battle of Trafalgar. 42p, Invention of the telephone. 54p, The end of World War II. 66p, First man on the Moon.

**2001, May 21        Perf. 14x14½**

| 881-884 | A197 | Set of 4 | 8.00 | 8.00 |

**Queen Type of 1999**

**2001, June 1    Litho.    Perf. 14x14¼**
**Size: 22x28mm**

| 885 | A175 | £1.20 carmine | 4.50 | 4.50 |
| 886 | A175 | £1.40 blue | 5.00 | 5.00 |

**Fighter Planes and Raptors Type of 1999**

No. 887: a, 40p, RAF Jaguar GR1B. b, 40p, Hobby.
No. 888: a, 40p, Royal Navy Sea Harrier FA MK 2. b, 40p, Marsh harrier.
No. 889: a, 40p, RAF Hawk T MK 1. b, 40p, Sparrowhawk.

**2001, Sept. 3    Litho.    Perf. 14½x14**
**Pairs, #a-b**

| 887-889 | A180 | Set of 3 | 8.75 | 8.75 |
| 889c | | Souvenir sheet #887a, 888a, 889a | 4.50 | 4.50 |
| 889d | | Souvenir sheet #887b, 888b, 889b | 4.50 | 4.50 |

Christmas — A198

Snoopy, from Peanuts comic strip: 5p, In Santa Claus suit ringing bell, Woodstock. 30p, Charlie Brown, Christmas tree. 40p, Wreath. 42p, In Santa Claus suit carrying cookies, Woodstock. 54p, On dog house.

**2001, Nov. 12        Perf. 14**

| 890-894 | A198 | Set of 5 | 6.50 | 6.50 |
| 894a | | Souvenir sheet, #890-894 | 7.50 | 7.50 |

**Souvenir Sheet**

Introduction of Euro Coinage to Europe — A199

Coins in denominations of: a, 5p, 1 cent. b, 12p, 2 cents. c, 30p, 5 cents. d, 35p, 10 cents. e, 40p, 20 cents. f, 42p, 50 cents. g, 54p, 1 euro. h, 66p, 2 euro.

**2002, Jan. 1    Litho.    Perf. 13¼x13**

| 895 | | Sheet of 8, #a-h | 10.00 | 10.00 |

A clear varnish was applied by a thermographic process producing a shiny, raised effect.

**Reign Of Queen Elizabeth II, 50th Anniv. Issue**
**Common Design Type**

Designs: No. 896, 30p, Princess Elizabeth in field, 1942. No. 897, 30p, Wearing tiara, 1961. No. 898, 30p, With Princess Margaret, microphones. No. 899, 30p, Wearing hat, 1993. 75p, 1955 portrait by Annigoni (38x50mm).

**Perf. 14¼x14½, 13¾ (75p)**

**2002, Feb. 6    Litho.    Wmk. 373**

| 896 | CD360 | 30p multicolored | 1.10 | 1.10 |
| 897 | CD360 | 30p multicolored | 1.10 | 1.10 |
| 898 | CD360 | 30p multicolored | 1.10 | 1.10 |
| 899 | CD360 | 30p multicolored | 1.10 | 1.10 |
| 900 | CD360 | 75p multicolored | 2.25 | 2.25 |
| 900a | | Souvenir sheet, #896-900 | 7.75 | 7.75 |

Europa — A200

Famous clowns: 30p, Joseph Grimaldi (1778-1831). 40p, Karl Adrien Wettach (1880-1959). 42p, Nicholai Polakovs (1900-74). 54p, Hubert Jean Charles Cairoli (1910-80).

**Perf. 13¼x13**

**2002, Mar. 4    Litho.    Unwmk.**

| 901-904 | A200 | Set of 4 | 6.00 | 6.00 |

Bobby Moore, English Soccer Player — A201

Moore in 1966: 30p, Holding up World Cup. 42p, Kissing World Cup. 54p, With Queen Elizabeth II. 66p, In action.

**Perf. 13¼x13**

**2002, May 1    Litho.    Unwmk.**

| 905-908 | A201 | Set of 4 | 7.00 | 7.00 |
| 908a | | Souvenir sheet, #905-908 | 7.00 | 7.00 |

Wildlife — A202

Designs: No. 909, 30p, Barbary macaque. No. 910, 30p, Red fox, horiz. 40p, White tooth shrew, horiz. £1, Rabbit.

**Perf. 14¼x14, 14x14¼**

**2002, June 6    Litho.    Unwmk.**

| 909-912 | A202 | Set of 4 | 7.50 | 7.50 |
| 912a | | Souvenir sheet, #909-912 | 7.50 | 7.50 |

Prince Harry, 18th Birthday — A203

Designs: 30p, As child in Princess Diana's arms. 42p, Waving. 54p, Wearing baseball cap. 66p, In suit and tie.

**2002, Sept. 15    Litho.    Perf. 12½**

| 913-916 | A203 | Set of 4 | 6.75 | 6.75 |
| 916a | | Souvenir sheet, #913-916 | 7.25 | 7.25 |

Rock of Gibraltar — A204

View of Rock from: a, North. b, South. c, East (46x38mm). d, West (46x38mm).

**2002, Sept. 15    Litho.    Perf. 13¼x13**

| 917 | | Horiz. strip of 4 | 9.50 | 9.50 |
| a.-b. | | A204 30p Either single | .90 | .90 |
| c.-d. | | A204 £1 Either single | 2.75 | 2.75 |

Particles of the Rock of Gibraltar were applied to portions of the designs by a thermographic process.

Christmas A205

Creche scenes from: 5p, Cathedral of St. Mary the Crowned. 30p, St. Joseph's Parish Church. 40p, St. Theresa's Parish Church. 42p, Our Lady of Sorrows Church, Catalan Bay. 52p, St. Bernard's Church. 54p, Cathedral of the Holy Trinity.

**2002, Nov. 13        Perf. 13**

| 918-923 | A205 | Set of 6 | 8.50 | 8.50 |

Coronation of Queen Elizabeth II, 50th Anniv. — A206

Designs: No. 924, 30p, Queen receiving crown. No. 925, 30p, Queen on throne. 40p, Queen holding orb. £1, Queen in profile.

**Perf. 12½**

**2003, Feb. 20    Litho.    Unwmk.**

| 924-927 | A206 | Set of 4 | 6.75 | 6.75 |
| 927a | | Souvenir sheet, #924-927 | 7.25 | 7.25 |

Europa — A207

Poster art for: 30p, Drama Festival. 40p, Spring Festival. 42p, Art Festival. 54p, Dance Festival.

**2003, Mar. 3        Perf. 14x14½**

| 928-931 | A207 | Set of 4 | 5.75 | 5.75 |

Powered Flight, Cent. — A208

Designs: 30p, Wright Flyer, 1903. No. 933, 40p, Charles Lindbergh and Spirit of St. Louis, 1927. No. 934, 40p, Boeing 314 Yankee Clipper, 1939. 42p, Saunders Roe SARO-21 Windhover Amphibian, 1931 (77x27mm). 44p, Concorde, 1976 (77x27mm). 66p, Space Shuttle Columbia, 1981, vert. (37x57mm).

**2003, Mar. 31  Litho.  Perf. 13x13¼**
932-937 A208  Set of 6  11.00 11.00
937a  Souvenir sheet of #932-937,  12.00 12.00
  perf. 12½

Martyrdom of St. George, 1700th Anniv. — A209

Designs: 30p, Cross of St. George. 40p, Constantinian Order of St. George. £1.20, Stained glass window depiction of St. George, vert. (31x63mm).

**2003, Apr. 23  Perf. 13¾**
938-940 A209  Set of 3  6.50 6.50
940a  Souvenir sheet, #938-940  7.00 7.00

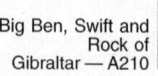

Big Ben, Swift and Rock of Gibraltar — A210

**Photo. & Engr.**
**2003, June 21  Perf. 11½**
941 A210  (£3) multi  10.50 10.50

Prince William, 21st Birthday — A211

Prince William: No. 942, 30p, As a child, with Princess Diana. No. 943, 30p, With hands in pockets. 40p, Close-up, wearing suit. £1, Wearing sweatshirt.

**2003, June 21  Litho.  Perf. 12½**
942-945 A211  Set of 4  10.00 10.00
945a  Souvenir sheet, #942-945  10.00 10.00

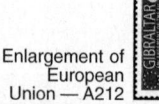

Enlargement of European Union — A212

National flowers of newly-added countries: 30p, Daisy (Latvia), Cornflower (Estonia), Rue (Lithuania). 40p, Rose (Cyprus), Maltese centaury (Malta). 42p, Tulip (Hungary), Carnation (Slovenia), Dog rose (Slovakia). 54p, Corn poppy (Poland), Scented thyme (Czech Republic).

**2003, Sept. 15  Litho.  Perf. 13¾**
946-949 A212  Set of 4  6.50 6.50

Mushrooms — A213

Designs: No. 950, 30p, Lepista nuda. No. 951, 30p, Clitocybe odora. No. 952, 30p, Hypholoma fasciculare. £1.20, Agaricus campestris.

**2003, Sept. 15  Perf. 14¼**
950-953 A213  Set of 4  8.75 8.75
953a  Souvenir sheet, #950-953  9.25 9.25

A214

---

Christmas — A215

Designs: 5p, Baby Jesus crib, Our Lady of Sorrows Church. 30p, Building a traditional creche at home. 40p, Three Kings Cavalcade on January 5. 42p, Children's provisions for Santa and reindeer on Christmas Eve. 54p, Christmas Eve midnight mass at the Cathedral of St. Mary the Crowned.

**2003, Nov. 17  Litho.  Perf. 14**
954-958 A214  Set of 5  6.00 6.00
**Souvenir Sheet**
**Perf. 12¼x12**
959 A215  £1 multi  4.75 4.75

Europa — A216

Designs: No. 960, 40p, Outdoor cafe. No. 961, 40p, St. Michael's Cave. No. 962, 54p, Seaside cafe. No. 963, 54p, Dolphin.

**2004, Feb. 20  Litho.  Perf. 14x14½**
960-963 A216  Set of 4  7.00 7.00

British Gibraltar, 300th Anniv. — A217

Designs: 8p, British flag, Gibraltar coat of arms.
No. 965: a, Ship with large flag. b, Ship, rowboat, cannons. c, Soldiers. d, Military uniform. e, Telephone booth, police hat. f, Mail box. g, Neckties, university documents, graduates in caps and gowns. h, Crowd waving flags. i, British flag.

**2004  Litho.  Perf. 13x13¼**
964 A217  8p multi  .70 .70
965  Sheet of 9  14.50 14.50
a.-h.  A217 30p Any single  1.00 1.00
i.  A217 £1.20 multi  4.00 4.00
j.  Souvenir sheet, #965i  5.25 5.25

Issued: Nos. 964-965i, 4/26. No. 965j, 9/10. Sir Elton John's Tercentenary Concert (No. 965j).
A perforated "black print" sheet of No. 965 exists with cancels.

Visit of Queen Elizabeth II to Gibraltar, 50th Anniv. — A218

Queen: 38p, Holding flowers. 40p, With arm extended. 47p, In limousine. £1, With children and soldiers.
£1.50, Standing in limousine with Prince Philip.

**2004, May 4  Perf. 12½**
966-969 A218  Set of 4  8.00 8.00
**Souvenir Sheet**
970 A218  £1.50 multi  6.00 6.00

European Soccer — A219

Designs: 30p, Goalie defending shot. No. 972, 40p, Players near side of goal. No. 973, 40p, Player making scissor kick. £1, Goalie playing ball near goal post.

---

£1.50, Player with arms extended, horiz.

**2004, June 6**
971-974 A219  Set of 4  7.50 7.50
974a  Souvenir sheet, #971-974  7.50 7.50
**Souvenir Sheet**
975 A219  £1.50 multi  5.00 5.00
  No. 975 contains one 48x37mm stamp.

D-Day, 60th Anniv. — A220

Designs: 38p, Soldiers leaving landing craft. 40p, Tank approaching beach. 47p, Airplane. £1, Ships.

**2004, June 6  Perf. 13x13¼**
976-979 A220  Set of 4  8.25 8.25
979a  Souvenir sheet, #976-979  8.25 8.25

Flowers — A221

Designs: 1p, Mallow-leaved bindweed. 2p, Gibraltar sea lavender. 5p, Gibraltar chickweed. G, Romulea. 10p, Common centaury. G1, Pyramidal orchid. S, Friar's cowl. UK, Corn poppy. E, Giant Tangier fennel. U, Snapdragon. 50p, Common gladiolus. £1, Yellow horned poppy. £3, Gibraltar candytuft.

**2004, Sept. 10  Litho.  Perf. 13¼**
980 A221  1p multi  .25 .25
  a.  Booklet pane of 1  .25 —
981 A221  2p multi  .25 .25
  a.  Booklet pane of 1  .25 —
982 A221  5p multi  .25 .25
  a.  Booklet pane of 1  .25 —
983 A221  G multi  .25 .25
  a.  Booklet pane of 1  .25 —
984 A221  10p multi  .40 .40
  a.  Booklet pane of 1  .40 —
985 A221  G1 multi  .55 .55
  a.  Booklet pane of 1  .55 —
986 A221  S multi  1.00 1.00
  a.  Booklet pane of 1  1.00 —
987 A221  UK multi  1.50 1.50
  a.  Booklet pane of 1  1.50 —
988 A221  E multi  1.60 1.60
  a.  Booklet pane of 1  1.60 —
989 A221  U multi  1.75 1.75
  a.  Booklet pane of 1  1.75 —
990 A221  50p multi  2.00 2.00
  a.  Booklet pane of 1  2.00 —
991 A221  £1 multi  3.50 3.50
  a.  Booklet pane of 1  3.50 —
992 A221  £3 multi  11.00 11.00
  a.  Booklet pane of 1  11.00 —
  Complete booklet, #980a-  28.00
  992a
  Nos. 980-992 (13)  24.30 24.30

Nos. 983, 985, 986, 987, 988 and 989 sold for 7p, 12p, 28p, 38p, 40p and 47p respectively on day of issue.
See Nos. 1033B-1036.

Ferrari Race Cars — A222

Designs: No. 993, 5p, F2003GA. No. 994, 5p, F2004. No. 995, 30p, F2001. No. 996, 30p, F2002. No. 997, 75p, F399. No. 998, 75p, F1-2000.

**2004, Nov. 12  Perf. 14¾x14¼**
993-998 A222  Set of 6  9.00 9.00
998a  Souvenir sheet, #993-998  9.00 9.00

Christmas — A223

Christmas tree ornaments: 7p, Santa Claus. 28p, Angel. 38p, Red star. 40p, Gold bell. 47p, Red ball. 53p, White star.

**2004, Nov. 12  Perf. 12½**
999-1004 A223  Set of 6  9.00 9.00

---

Battle of Trafalgar, Bicent. A224

Designs: 38p, Soldier guarding wine cask containing Admiral Horatio Nelson's body. 40p, HMS Entrepenante. 47p, Admiral Nelson, vert. £1.60, HMS Victory. £2, HMS Victory being towed to Gibraltar.

**2005, Jan. 29  Litho.  Perf. 13¼**
1005-1008 A224  Set of 4  14.50 14.50
**Souvenir Sheet**
**Perf. 13¾**
1009 A224  £2 multi  11.00 11.00

No. 1008 has particles of wood from the HMS Victory embedded in the areas covered by a thermographic process that produces a raised, shiny effect. No. 1009 contains one 44x44mm stamp.
See Nos. 1027-1028.

Europa — A225

Designs: No. 1010, 47p, Sherry trifle. No. 1011, 47p, Spinach pie. No. 1012, 47p, Veal birds. No. 1013, 47p, Grilled sea bass.

**Perf. 14¼x13¾**
**2005, Mar. 31  Litho.**
1010-1013 A225  Set of 4  8.25 8.25

V-E Day, 60th Anniv. — A226

Designs: 38p, Winston Churchill. 40p, Woman, children, British flags. 47p, Servicewomen in car waving flags. £1, People at dock.

**2005, May 8**
1014-1017 A226  Set of 4  9.00 9.00
1017a  Souvenir sheet, #1014-  9.00 9.00
  1017

Anniversaries A227

Designs: 38p, Royal Gibraltar Police, 175th anniv. 47p, Gibraltar Museum, 75th anniv. £1, Grant of Charter of Justice, 175th anniv.

**2005, June 17  Perf. 14¾x14¼**
1018-1020 A227  Set of 3  8.50 8.50

Cruise Ships — A228

Designs: 38p, Circassia. 40p, Nevassa. 47p, Black Prince. £1, Arcadia.

**2005, June 17  Perf. 13x13¼**
1021-1024 A228  Set of 4  9.75 9.75
1024a  Souvenir sheet, #1021-1024  9.75 9.75

Pope John Paul II
(1920-2005) — A229

**2005, July 15**     *Perf. 14¼x14¾*
1025 A229 75p multi     3.50 3.50

Printed in sheets of 6.

Europa
Stamps,
50th Anniv.
(in 2006)
A230

**Litho. With Foil Application**
**2005, Sept. 30**     *Perf. 14¼*
1026 A230 £5 multi     18.00 18.00

**Battle of Trafalgar Type of 2005**
**Souvenir Sheets**

Designs: Nos. 1027, 1028a, Admiral Nelson mortally wounded.

**2005, Oct. 21**     *Litho.*     *Perf. 13¼*
1027 A224 £1 multi     4.25 4.25
1028   Sheet, #1028a, Isle of
    Man #1127a     8.75 8.75
   *a.* A224 £1 multi, 47x30mm     4.25 4.25

No. 1028 has a Gibraltar Post emblem in sheet margin. See Isle of Man No. 1127.

Christmas — A231

Various angels: 7p, 38p, 40p, 47p, 53p.

**2005, Oct. 21**     *Perf. 13¼x13*
1029-1033 A231   Set of 5     8.00 8.00
*1033a*   Souvenir sheet, #1029-1033     8.75 8.75

**Flowers Type of 2004**

Designs: 3p, Gibraltar restharrow. 15p, Paper-white narcissus. 53p, Gibraltar campion. £1.60, Sea daffodil.

**2006, Jan. 31**     *Litho.*     *Perf. 13¼*
1033B A221   3p multi     .25 .25
1034 A221   15p multi     .55 .55
1035 A221   53p multi     1.90 1.90
1036 A221   £1.60 multi     5.75 5.75
   *Nos. 1033B-1036 (4)*     8.45 8.45

Worldwide Fund
for Nature
(WWF) — A232

Various depictions of Giant devil ray.

**2006, Feb. 20**     *Perf. 13x13¼*
1037    Strip of 4     11.00 11.00
   *a.* A232 38p multi     1.25 1.25
   *b.* A232 40p multi     1.50 1.50
   *c.* A232 47p multi     1.75 1.75
   *d.* A232 £1 multi     4.00 4.00

Queen Elizabeth
II, 80th
Birthday — A233

Various photographs.

**2006, Mar. 31**     *Perf. 14¾x14*
1038    Block of 4     10.50 10.50
   *a.* A233 38p multi     1.50 1.50
   *b.* A233 40p multi     1.75 1.75
   *c.* A233 47p multi     2.00 2.00
   *d.* A233 £1 multi     4.00 4.00

   *e.*   Souvenir sheet, #1038b,
     1038c     4.00 4.00
   *f.*   Souvenir sheet, #1038a,
     1038d     6.00 6.00

Miniature Sheet

2006 World Cup Soccer
Championships, Germany — A234

No. 1039 — Children with faces painted as flags of World Cup champions: a, Uruguay. b, Italy. c, Germany. d, Brazil. e, England. f, Argentina. g, France.

**2006, May 4**     *Perf. 15*
1039 A234   Sheet of 7     11.50 11.50
   *a.-g.*   38p Any single     1.50 1.50

Europa — A235

Children: No. 1040, 47p, Holding books and notebook paper. No. 1041, 47p, Playing musical instruments. No. 1042, 47p, Building birdhouse. No. 1043, 47p, Playing soccer.

**2006, June 30**     *Perf. 13x13¼*
1040-1043 A235   Set of 4     8.00 8.00

Gibraltar Packet
Agency,
Bicent: — A236

Ships: 8p, Cornwallis. 40p, Meteor. 42p, Carteret. 68p, Prince Regent.

     *Perf. 14¾x14¼*
**2006, Sept. 15**     *Litho.*
1044-1047 A236   Set of 4     9.00 9.00

Airmail Service,
75th
Anniv. — A237

Airplanes: 8p, Saro A21 Windhover. 40p, Vickers Vanguard. 49p, Vickers Viscount. £1.60, Boeing 737.

**2006, Sept. 15**
1048-1051 A237   Set of 4     14.00 14.00

Cruise
Ships — A238

Designs: 40p, Coral. 42p, Legend of the Seas. 66p, Saga Ruby. 78p, Costa Concordia.

**2006, Sept. 15**     *Perf. 13*
1052-1055 A238   Set of 4     12.00 12.00
*1055a*   Souvenir sheet, #1052-
    1055     12.50 12.50

See Nos. 1076-1079, 1153-1156.

Christopher
Columbus (1451-
1506),
Explorer — A239

Designs: 40p, Navigational equipment. 42p, Columbus on ship. 66p, Santa Maria. 78p, Columbus and Indian.
£1.60, Nina, Pinta and Santa Maria

**2006, Nov. 1**     *Litho.*     *Perf. 13x13¼*
1056-1059 A239   Set of 4     12.00 12.00
**Souvenir Sheet**
     *Perf. 13¼*
1060 A239 £1.60 multi     8.00 8.00

No. 1060 contains one 48x48mm stamp.

Christmas — A240

Various depictions of Santa Claus with panel colors of: 8p, Red brown. 40p, Prussian blue. 42p, Olive bister. 49p, Green. 55p, Gray blue.

**2006, Nov. 1**     *Perf. 13¼x13*
1061-1065 A240   Set of 5     9.50 9.50
*1065a*   Souvenir sheet, #1061-1065,
    perf. 13¼x12½     9.50 9.50

Miniature Sheet

Treaty of
Rome,
50th
Anniv.
A241

No. 1066 — European Union flag and flag of: a, Belgium. b, Germany. c, France. d, Italy. e, Luxembourg. f, Netherlands.

     *Perf. 14½x14¼*
**2007, Feb. 28**     *Litho.*
1066 A241 40p Sheet of 6, #a-
   f     10.50 10.50

Wedding of Queen
Elizabeth II and Prince
Philip, 60th
Anniv. — A242

Designs: 40p, Royal engagement, 1947. 42p, Royal wedding, 1947. 66p, Silver anniversary, 1972. 78p, Ruby anniversary, 1987. £1.60, Wedding party.

**2007, Feb. 28**     *Perf. 13½*
1067-1070 A242   Set of 4     10.00 10.00
**Souvenir Sheet**
     *Perf. 13½x13*
1071 A242 £1.60 multi     8.50 8.50

No. 1071 contains one 85x85mm diamond-shaped stamp.

Princess Diana
(1961-97) — A243

Various photographs: 8p, 40p, 42p, £1.60.

**2007, Mar. 31**     *Perf. 13½*
1072-1075 A243   Set of 4     11.00 11.00
*1075a*   Souvenir sheet, #1072-
    1075     11.00 11.00

**Cruise Ships Type of 2006**

Designs: 40p, Oriana. 42p, Oceana. 66p, Queen Elizabeth 2.78p, Queen Mary 2.

**2007, May 15**     *Litho.*     *Perf. 14¾x14*
1076-1079 A238   Set of 4     11.50 11.50
*1079a*   Souvenir sheet, #1076-
    1079     11.50 11.50

Europa — A244

Designs: 8p, Scout from 1908. 40p, Scout from 1950s. 42p, Sea Scout from 1980s. £1, Scout from 2007.

**2007, June 30**     *Litho.*     *Perf. 13*
1080-1083 A244   Set of 4     10.00 10.00

Gibraltar Postal
Anniversaries
A245

Designs: 8p, Last-day-of-validity postcard from Fez, Morocco (cessation of Gibraltar's responsibility for the British postal service in Morocco in 1907). 40p, Stampless cover with last Gibraltar datestamp of the Packet Agency (creation of Gibraltar Post Office in 1857). 42p, Cover franked with stamps of Great Britain (sale of British stamps in Gibraltar in 1857). £1, Cover to London from Morocco via Gibraltar (placement of British postal service in Morocco under control of Gibraltar in 1857).

**2007, Sept. 26**     *Perf. 14¾x14*
1084-1087 A245   Set of 4     11.50 11.50

Stork Carrying Baby, Baby Bottle,
Pacifier, Rubber Duck
A246

Diamond
Ring and
Heart
A247

Sheep,
Lion,
Dog at
Party
A248

Lamb,
Dolphins,
Rock of
Gibraltar
A249

Shell,
Crab and
Heart
A250

**2007, Sept. 26**     *Perf. 12½x13*
1088 A246 G multi + label     .40 .40
1089 A247 G multi + label     .40 .40
1090 A248 G multi + label     .40 .40
1091 A249 G multi + label     .40 .40
1092 A250 G multi + label     .40 .40
1093 A246 E multi + label     2.00 2.00
1094 A247 E multi + label     2.00 2.00
1095 A248 E multi + label     2.00 2.00
1096 A249 E multi + label     2.00 2.00
1097 A250 E multi + label     2.00 2.00
   *Nos. 1088-1097 (10)*     12.00 12.00

On day of issue Nos. 1088-1092 each sold for 8p, and Nos. 1093-1097 each sold for 42p. Labels shown with each stamp are the generic labels for that stamp type. Labels could be personalized for an additional fee.

Prehistoric Wildlife of Gibraltar — A251

Designs: 8p, Bears and dolphins. 40p, Eagle owl. 42p, Great auk and eagle. 55p, Red deer and bear. 78p, Wolf and vulture eating horse. £2, Ibex.

| 2007, Sept. 26 | | Perf. 13 | |
|---|---|---|---|
| 1098-1102 A251 | Set of 5 | 11.00 | 11.00 |
| 1098a | Booklet pane of 1 | .50 | — |
| 1099a | Booklet pane of 1 | 2.00 | — |
| 1100a | Booklet pane of 1 | 2.25 | — |
| 1101a | Booklet pane of 1 | 2.75 | — |
| 1102a | Booklet pane of 1 | 3.75 | — |
| | Complete booklet, #1098a-1103a, 1103b | 34.00 | |

**Souvenir Sheet**

| 1103 A251 | £2 multi | 11.00 | 11.00 |
|---|---|---|---|
| a. | Booklet pane of 1 | 11.00 | |
| b. | Booklet pane of 6, #1098-1102 | 11.00 | — |

No. 1103a has text in margin not found on the margin of No. 1103.

Views of Gibraltar A252

Trinity Lighthouse — A253

Various views: 40p, 42p, 55p, 78p.

| 2007, Nov. 2 | Litho. | Perf. 13¼ | |
|---|---|---|---|
| 1104-1107 A252 | Set of 4 | 10.50 | 10.50 |

**Souvenir Sheet**
**Perf. 13¼x13**

| 1108 A253 | £1.70 multi | 8.00 | 8.00 |
|---|---|---|---|

Christmas — A254

Porcelain Nativity figurines: No. 1109, 8p, Joseph. No. 1110, 8p, Baby Jesus. 40p, Mary. 42p, King Melchior. 49p, King Balthasar. 55p, King Gaspar.

| 2007, Nov. 2 | | Perf. 13¼x13 | |
|---|---|---|---|
| 1109-1114 A254 | Set of 6 | 9.50 | 9.50 |
| 1114a | Miniature sheet, #1109-1114 | 9.50 | 9.50 |

**Perf. 12½x13**
**Size: 32x32mm**

| 1114B A254 | 8p multi + label | .75 | .75 |
|---|---|---|---|
| 1114C A254 | 40p multi + label | 2.75 | 2.75 |

Nos. 1114B and 1114C were available with generic labels. Labels could be personalized for an additional fee.

Birds — A255

Designs: 1p, Woodchat shrike. 2p, Balearic shearwater. 5p, Eagle owl. G, European bee-eater. 10p, Razorbill. S, Egyptian vulture. UK, Blue rock thrush. E, Hoopoe. U, Bonelli's eagle. 50p, Greater flamingo. 55p, Mediterranean shag. £1, Honey buzzard. £5, Lesser kestrel.

| 2008, Feb. 15 | Litho. | Perf. 13x12½ | |
|---|---|---|---|
| 1115 A255 | 1p multi | .25 | .25 |
| 1116 A255 | 2p multi | .25 | .25 |
| 1117 A255 | 5p multi | .25 | .25 |
| 1118 A255 | G multi | .35 | .35 |
| 1119 A255 | 10p multi | .40 | .40 |
| 1120 A255 | S multi | 1.25 | 1.25 |
| 1121 A255 | UK multi | 1.60 | 1.60 |
| 1122 A255 | E multi | 1.75 | 1.75 |
| 1123 A255 | U multi | 1.90 | 1.90 |
| 1124 A255 | 50p multi | 2.00 | 2.00 |
| 1125 A255 | 55p multi | 2.25 | 2.25 |

**Size: 32x45mm**
**Perf. 13x13¼**

| 1126 A255 | £1 multi | 4.00 | 4.00 |
|---|---|---|---|
| 1127 A255 | £5 multi | 18.00 | 18.00 |
| | Nos. 1115-1127 (13) | 34.25 | 34.25 |

On day of issue Nos. 1118, 1120, 1121, 1122 and 1123 sold for 8p, 30p, 40p, 42p and 49p, respectively.
See Nos. 1202-1204, 1244-1246, 1326-1328. For surcharge, see No. 1412.

Admiral Horatio Nelson (1758-1805) — A256

Designs: No. 1128, 40p, HMS Agamemnon. No. 1129, 40p, HMS La Minerve. No. 1130, 42p, HMS Captain. No. 1131, 42p, HMS Vanguard. No. 1132, 49p, HMS Amphion. No. 1133, 49p, HMS Victory. £2, Nelson's Birthplace, Burnham Thorpe, England, horiz.

| | Perf. 14¼x14¾ | | |
|---|---|---|---|
| 2008, Mar. 15 | | Litho. | |
| 1128-1133 A256 | Set of 6 | 17.50 | 17.50 |

**Souvenir Sheet**
**Perf. 14¾x14¼**

| 1134 A256 | £2 multi | 13.50 | 13.50 |
|---|---|---|---|

Royal Air Force, 90th Anniv. — A257

Rock of Gibraltar and airplanes: No. 1135, 40p, Short 184. No. 1136, 40p, Spitfire IV, Hurricane IIc. No. 1137, 42p, Beaufighter II, Lancaster TS III. No. 1138, 42p, Hunter Mk. 6, Shackleton MR2. No. 1139, 49p, Vulcan, Mosquito. No. 1140, 49p, Tornado GR4, Jaguar GR3. £2, Felixstowe F3.

| 2008, Mar. 15 | | Perf. 14¼x14¾ | |
|---|---|---|---|
| 1135-1140 A257 | Set of 6 | 17.50 | 17.50 |

**Souvenir Sheet**

| 1141 A257 | £2 multi | 13.50 | 13.50 |
|---|---|---|---|

Europa — A258

Famous letter writers: 10p, Sir Winston Churchill. 42p, Admiral Horatio Nelson. 44p, Pres. John F. Kennedy. £1, Mohandas K. Gandhi.

| 2008, June 1 | Litho. | Perf. 14x14¾ | |
|---|---|---|---|
| 1142-1145 A258 | Set of 4 | 10.00 | 10.00 |

New Seven Wonders of the World — A259

Designs: No. 1146, 8p, Roman Colosseum. No. 1147, 8p, Christ the Redeemer Statue, Rio de Janeiro. No. 1148, 38p, Great Wall of China. No. 1149, 38p, Petra, Jordan. No. 1150, 40p, Chichen Itza Pyramid, Mexico. No. 1151, 40p, Machu Picchu, Peru. 66p, Taj Mahal, India.

| 2008, June 1 | | | |
|---|---|---|---|
| 1146-1152 A259 | Set of 7 | 13.50 | 13.50 |

**Cruise Ships Type of 2006**

Designs: 40p, Century. 42p, Grand Princess. 66p, Queen Victoria. 78p, Costa Mediterranea.

| 2008, Sept. 15 | Litho. | Perf. 13x13¼ | |
|---|---|---|---|
| 1153-1156 A238 | Set of 4 | 13.50 | 13.50 |
| 1156a | Souvenir sheet, #1153-1156 | 13.50 | 13.50 |

**Miniature Sheet**

National Aeronautics and Space Administration, 50th Anniv. — A260

No. 1157: a, Liftoff of Apollo 11. b, Earthrise from Moon. c, Lunar Module leaving Moon. d, US flag on Moon.

| 2008, Sept. 15 | | Perf. 13¼ | |
|---|---|---|---|
| 1157 A260 | Sheet of 4 | 13.50 | 13.50 |
| a. | 10p multi | .60 | .60 |
| b. | 17p multi | 1.00 | 1.00 |
| c. | 42p multi | 2.00 | 2.00 |
| d. | £2 multi | 9.50 | 9.50 |

Royal Gibraltar Regiment — A261

Designs: No. 1158, 10p, Gibraltar Volunteer Corps in World War I. No. 1159, 10p, Gibraltar Defense Force in World War II. No. 1160, 10p, National Service recruits at Buena Vista Barracks. No. 1161, 42p, Soldiers and large guns, Thomson's Battery of Gibraltar Regiment, 1958-91. No. 1162, 42p, Soldier from Infantry Company of Gibraltar Regiment, 1958-99. No. 1163, 44p, Soldier from Air Defense Troop of Gibraltar Regiment, 1958-91. No. 1164, 44p, Royal Gibraltar Regiment soldier guarding the rock. No. 1165, 51p, Royal Gibraltar Regiment soldier training African Peacekeepers. No. 1166, 51p, Royal Gibraltar Regiment soldier serving in operations in Iraq. £2, Royal Gibraltar Regiment soldier serving in operations in Afghanistan.

| 2008, Nov. 11 | Litho. | Perf. 15x14 | |
|---|---|---|---|
| 1158-1167 A261 | Set of 10 | 22.50 | 22.50 |

Christmas — A262

Songs: 10p, When Santa Got Stuck in a Chimney. 42p, Rudolph, the Red-nosed Reindeer. 44p, Oh, Christmas Tree. 51p, Away in a Manger. 59p, Jingle Bells.

| 2008, Nov. 11 | | Perf. 12½ | |
|---|---|---|---|
| 1168-1172 A262 | Set of 5 | 10.00 | 10.00 |

King Henry VIII, 500th Anniv. of Accession to the Throne — A263

Designs: No. 1173, 10p, Catherine of Aragon (first wife). No. 1174, 10p, Anne Boleyn (second wife). No. 1175, 42p, Jane Seymour (third wife). No. 1176, 42p, Anne of Cleves (fourth wife). No. 1177, 44p, Catherine Howard (fifth wife). No. 1178, 44p, Catherine Parr (sixth wife). No. 1179, 51p, Henry VIII. No. 1180, 51p, The Mary Rose.

£2, King Henry VIII at Hampton Court.

| 2009, Jan. 10 | Litho. | Perf. 12½ | |
|---|---|---|---|
| 1173-1180 A263 | Set of 8 | 16.00 | 16.00 |

**Souvenir Sheet**

| 1181 A263 | £2 multi | 10.50 | 10.50 |
|---|---|---|---|

Gibraltar Shrine to Our Lady of Europe, 700th Anniv. — A264

| 2009, Feb. 10 | | Perf. 14x14¾ | |
|---|---|---|---|
| 1182 A264 | 61p multi | 4.50 | 4.50 |

Printed in sheets of 4. See Vatican City No. 1402.

Naval Aviation, Cent. — A265

Designs: No. 1183, 42p, Short 184. No. 1184, 42p, Short S27. No. 1185, 42p, SS Type non-rigid airship. No. 1186, 42p, Caudron G-III. No. 1187, 42p, Avro 504. No. 1188, 42p, Morane-Saulnier L and Zeppelin LZ-37. £2, Short 184 and ships.

| 2009, Mar. 15 | | | |
|---|---|---|---|
| 1183-1188 A265 | Set of 6 | 16.00 | 16.00 |

**Souvenir Sheet**

| 1189 A265 | £2 multi | 12.00 | 12.00 |
|---|---|---|---|

Grandchildren of Queen Elizabeth II — A266

Designs: No. 1190, 42p, Prince William of Wales. No. 1191, 42p, Prince Henry of Wales. No. 1192, 42p, Princess Beatrice of York. No. 1193, 42p, Princess Eugenie of York. No. 1194, 42p, Viscount Severn. No. 1195, 42p, Lady Louise Windsor. No. 1196, 42p, Peter Phillips. No. 1197, 42p, Zara Phillips.

| 2009, May 1 | | Perf. 12½ | |
|---|---|---|---|
| 1190-1197 A266 | Set of 8 | 16.00 | 16.00 |

Europa — A267

Designs: 10p, Aristotle (384-322 B.C.), philosopher. 42p, Galileo Galilei (1564-1642), astronomer and physicist. 44p, Nicolaus Copernicus (1473-1543), astronomer. £1.50, Sir Isaac Newton (1642-1727), physicist and mathematician.

| 2009, June 1 | | Perf. 13x12½ | |
|---|---|---|---|
| 1198-1201 A267 | Set of 4 | 11.00 | 11.00 |

Intl. Year of Astronomy.

**Birds Type of 2008**

Designs: 10p, Black stork. £2, Northern gannet. £3, Osprey.

| 2009, Sept. 16 | Litho. | Perf. 13 | |
|---|---|---|---|
| 1202 A255 | 10p multi | .35 | .35 |

**Size: 32x45mm**
**Perf. 13x13¼**

| 1203 A255 | £2 multi | 6.50 | 6.50 |
|---|---|---|---|
| 1204 A255 | £3 multi | 9.50 | 9.50 |
| | Nos. 1202-1204 (3) | 16.35 | 16.35 |

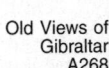

Old Views of Gibraltar
A268

Designs: No. 1205, 10p, Road to the frontier. No. 1206, 42p, Catalan Bay village. No. 1207, 44p, Rock of Gibraltar. 51p, Moorish Castle. 59p, South Barracks.

No. 1210: a, 10p, Garrison Library. b, 42p, Piazza. c, 44p, Piazza Casemates. d, £1, Main Street.

| 2009, Sept. 16 | | Perf. 14x14¾ | |
|---|---|---|---|
| 1205-1209 | A268 | Set of 5 | 10.00 10.00 |
| **Souvenir Sheet** | | | |
| 1210 | A268 | Sheet of 4, #a-d | 9.75 9.75 |

Charles Darwin (1809-82), Naturalist — A269

Darwin and: 10p, HMS Beagle, bird and books. 42p, Books and pages with scientific drawings. 44p, Books and pages with drawings of horse and bone. £2, Book, page with drawing of bird, notebook.
£2.42, Darwin, book and house.

| 2009, Nov. 12 | | Perf. 14x14¾ | |
|---|---|---|---|
| 1211-1214 | A269 | Set of 4 | 13.50 13.50 |
| **Souvenir Sheet** | | | |
| 1215 | A269 | £2.42 multi | 13.50 13.50 |

Christmas — A270

Christmas tree ornaments: 10p, Santa Claus. 42p, Angel. 44p, Teddy bear. 51p, Christmas tree. £2, Bells.

| 2009, Nov. 12 | | Perf. 13½x13 | |
|---|---|---|---|
| 1216-1220 | A270 | Set of 5 | 16.50 16.50 |

**Miniature Sheet**

100-Ton Guns of Gibraltar and Malta A271

No. 1221 — 100-ton gun from: a, Napier of Magdala Battery, Gibraltar, 1880. b, Napier of Magdala Battery, 2010. c, Fort Rinella, Malta, 2010. d, Fort Rinella, 1882.

| 2010, Feb. 19 | | Litho. | Perf. 13¾ | |
|---|---|---|---|---|
| 1221 | A271 | 75p Sheet of 4, #a-d | | 14.00 14.00 |

See Malta No. 1400.

Battle of Britain, 70th Anniv. — A272

Airplanes: No. 1222, 50p, Boulton Paul Defiant. No. 1223, 50p, Bristol Blenheim. No. 1224, 50p, Gloster Gladiator. No. 1225, 50p, Hawker Hurricane. No. 1226, 50p, Miles Master. No. 1227, 50p, Supermarine Spitfire. £2, Douglas Bader, British ace pilot, vert.

| 2010, Feb. 21 | | Perf. 14 | |
|---|---|---|---|
| 1222-1227 | A272 | Set of 6 | 16.00 16.00 |
| **Souvenir Sheet** | | | |
| 1228 | A272 | £2 multi | 10.50 10.50 |

Accession to Throne of King George V, Cent. — A273

King George V: 10p, As child, with family. 42p, Examining stamp collection. 44p, On horse, reviewing troops. £2, On deck of gunship.

| 2010, Mar. 26 | | Perf. 13 | |
|---|---|---|---|
| 1229-1232 | A273 | Set of 4 | 15.00 15.00 |

Europa — A274

Scenes from children's stories by Roald Dahl: 10p, Charlie and the Chocolate Factory. 42p, Matilda. 44p, The Twits. £1.50, The BFG.

| 2010, May 4 | | Litho. | Perf. 13 | |
|---|---|---|---|---|
| 1233-1236 | A274 | Set of 4 | | 10.50 10.50 |

**Miniature Sheet**

Sites in San Marino and Gibraltar A275

No. 1237: a, Second Tower, San Marino. b, Moorish Castle, Gibraltar. c, Mt. Titano, San Marino. d, Rock of Gibraltar.

| 2010, June 30 | | Perf. 14¾x14 | |
|---|---|---|---|
| 1237 | A275 | 75p Sheet of 4, #a-d | 13.50 13.50 |

See San Marino No. 1822.

**Souvenir Sheet**

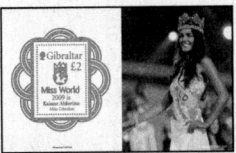

Emblem of Miss World Pageant and Name of 2009 Winner A276

**Litho. With Foil Application**

| 2010, June 30 | | Perf. 14x14¾ | |
|---|---|---|---|
| 1238 | A276 | £2 gold & black | 9.00 9.00 |

Aviation Centenaries A277

Designs: No. 1239, 10p, Airplane of Baroness Raymonde de Laroche, first woman to obtain pilot's license. No. 1240, 42p, LZ-7, first Zeppelin flight with fare-paying customers. No. 1241, 49p, Antoinette VII, airplane of Hubert Latham, setting altitude record of 4,541 feet. No. 1242, £2, Clément-Bayard No. 2, first airship to cross the English Channel.

No. 1243 — Seaplanes: a, 10p, Le Canard, seaplane of Henri Fabre, first seaplane to take off from water. b, 42p, Supermarine S.6B, first aircraft to surpass 400 miles per hour in speed. c, 49p, Short Sunderland of 204th Squadron. d, £2, Saunders-ROE Princess.

| 2010, Aug. 20 | | Litho. | Perf. 14¾x14 | |
|---|---|---|---|---|
| 1239-1242 | A277 | Set of 4 | | 13.50 13.50 |
| **Souvenir Sheet** | | | | |
| 1243 | A277 | Sheet of 4, #a-d | | 16.00 16.00 |

**Birds Type of 2008**

Designs: 59p, Barbary partridge. 76p, Ortolan bunting. £2, Pallid swift.

| 2010, Oct. 20 | | Litho. | Perf. 13 | |
|---|---|---|---|---|
| 1244 | A255 | 59p multi | 1.90 | 1.90 |
| 1245 | A255 | 76p multi | 2.50 | 2.50 |
| 1246 | A255 | £2 multi | 6.50 | 6.50 |
| *Nos. 1244-1246 (3)* | | | 10.90 | 10.90 |

Girl Guides, Cent. — A278

Uniform of: 10p, Rainbow. 42p, Brownie. 44p, Guide. £2, Senior.

| 2010, Oct. 20 | | Perf. 13½ | |
|---|---|---|---|
| 1247-1250 | A278 | Set of 4 | 13.50 13.50 |

**Souvenir Sheet**

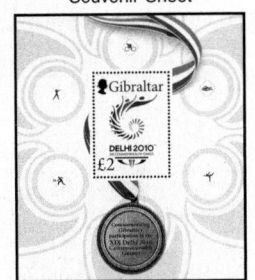

2010 Commonwealth Games, Delhi — A279

| 2010, Oct. 20 | | Perf. 14¼x14¾ | |
|---|---|---|---|
| 1251 | A279 | £2 multi | 10.50 10.50 |

**Souvenir Sheet**

Dicoese of Gibraltar, Cent. A280

| 2010, Nov. 16 | | Litho. | Perf. 15x14 | |
|---|---|---|---|---|
| 1252 | A280 | £2 multi | | 9.00 9.00 |

Christmas A281

Designs: 10p, Christmas crackers, gifts, ornaments, stocking, candle, bell and candy cane. 42p, Stockings hung on mantle. 44p, Santa Claus and reindeer in flight. 51p, Three snowmen.

| 2010, Nov. 26 | | Perf. 13x13¼ | |
|---|---|---|---|
| 1253-1256 | A281 | Set of 4 | 6.75 6.75 |

Royal British Legion — A282

British troops in action in: No. 1257, 50p, World War I. No. 1258, 50p, World War II. No. 1259, 50p, Northern Ireland. No. 1260, 50p, The Falkland Islands. No. 1261, 50p, The Gulf War. No. 1262, 50p, The Balkans. No. 1263, 50p, Afghanistan. No. 1264, 50p, Iraq. £2, Statue, poppies, words from poem, "In Flanders Fields."

| 2011, Jan. 14 | | Litho. | Perf. 13 | |
|---|---|---|---|---|
| 1257-1264 | A282 | Set of 8 | | 18.00 18.00 |
| **Souvenir Sheet** | | | | |
| | | | **Perf. 13x13½** | |
| 1265 | A282 | £2 multi | | 9.00 9.00 |

Nos. 1257-1264 each were printed in sheets of 6.

**Souvenir Sheet**

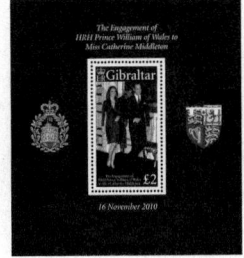

Engagement of Prince William and Catherine Middleton — A283

| 2011, Jan. 14 | | Perf. 14¾x14¼ | |
|---|---|---|---|
| 1266 | A283 | £2 multi | 9.50 9.50 |

Service of Queen Elizabeth II and Prince Philip A284

Designs: 10p, Queen Elizabeth II. 42p, Queen and Prince Philip. 44p, Queen and Prince Philip, diff. 51p, Queen and Prince Philip, diff. 55p, Queen and Prince Philip, diff. £2, Prince Philip.
£3, Queen and Prince Philip at wedding, diff.

| | | Perf. 13¼ | | |
|---|---|---|---|---|
| 2011, Feb. 6 | | Litho. | Unwmk. | |
| 1267-1272 | A284 | Set of 6 | 17.50 17.50 | |
| *1272a* | | Sheet of 6, #1267-1272, + 3 labels | 17.50 17.50 | |
| **Souvenir Sheet** | | | | |
| 1273 | A284 | £3 multi | 18.00 18.00 | |

Europa — A285

Designs: 10p, Alpine forest, Swiss National Forest, Switzerland. 42p, Amazon rainforest, Brazil. 44p, Forest and waterfall, Yosemite National Park, US. £1.50, Forest and waterfall, Plitvice Lakes National Park, Croatia.

| 2011, Apr. 4 | | Perf. 12½ | |
|---|---|---|---|
| 1274-1277 | A285 | Set of 4 | 8.25 8.25 |

Intl. Year of Forests.

Gibraltar Postage Stamps, 125th Anniv. — A286

Details from Gibraltar stamps: 10p, #7. 42p, #48. 44p, #93. 55p, #118. £1.50, #131.

| 2011, Apr. 15 | | Perf. 13¼ | |
|---|---|---|---|
| 1278-1282 | A286 | Set of 5 | 12.00 12.00 |

## Souvenir Sheet

Wedding of Prince William and Catherine Middleton — A287

**2011, July 15    Litho.    Perf. 14¾x14¼**
1283   A287   £3 multi      12.00   12.00

Endangered Animals A288

Designs: No. 1284, 42p, Asian elephant. No. 1285, 42p, Bengal tiger. No. 1286, 42p, Black rhinoceros. No. 1287, 42p, Giant panda. No. 1288, 42p, Polar bear. No. 1289, 42p, Sumatran orangutan.

**2011, July 31      Perf. 14x14¾**
1284-1289   A288   Set of 6    10.00   10.00
*1289a*     Souvenir sheet of 6,
     #1284-1289       10.00   10.00

See Nos. 1353-1358, 1405-1410.

Barbary Macaques — A289

Design: 10p, Macaque on tourist binoculars. 42p, Macaque on rock. 44p, Macaque on branch. 51p, Macaque on wall. 59p, Macaque on rock, diff. £1.50, Two macaques on rock.

**2011, Sept. 28      Perf. 15x14**
1290-1295   A289   Set of 6    12.00   12.00

Supermarine Spitfire Airplanes, 75th Anniv. — A290

Designs: 10p, Spitfire K5054 modified to Mk 1 standard, in flight. 42p, Pilot in Spitfire on ground for first flight, Mar. 5, 1936. 49p, Ground crew testing Spitfire before first flight.
No. 1300, £2, Pilot in Royal Air Force 92nd Squadron Spitfire Mk 1B.

**2011, Sept. 28      Perf. 14¾x14**
1296-1299   A290   Set of 4    10.00   10.00
**Souvenir Sheet**
1300   A290   £2 multi      7.00   7.00

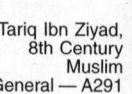

Tariq Ibn Ziyad, 8th Century Muslim General — A291

Scenes from Tariq Ibn Ziyad's invasion of Gibraltar in 711: 42p, Soldiers rowing boat. 44p, Boats on shore. 66p, Soldiers on horses. £2, Battle scene.

**2011, Nov. 7      Perf. 13¼**
1301-1304   A291   Set of 4    12.00   12.00

Christmas — A292

Nativity paintings by: 10p, Charles Le Brun. 42p, Lorenzo Lotto, 44p, Il Bronzino. 51p, Gerard van Honthorst. £2, Giorgione da Castelfranco.

**2011, Nov. 7      Perf. 14¼**
1305-1309   A292   Set of 5    12.00   12.00

Gibraltar Intl. Chess Festival, 10th Anniv. — A293

Chessboard positions in matches between: 2p, Viktor Bologan and Pia Cramling. 30p, Michael Adams and Natalia Zhukova. 75p, Fabiano Caruana and Viktor Korchnoi. £2, Vassily Ivanchuk and Nigel Short.

**2012, Jan. 23      Perf. 13x13¼**
1310-1313   A293   Set of 4    10.00   10.00

Sinking of the Titanic, Cent. — A294

Milestones in history of the Titanic: 10p, Fitting of Titanic completed Mar. 31, 1912. 42p, Titanic sets sail on maiden voyage, April 10, 1912. 44p, Iceberg strikes starboard bow, April 14, 1912. 54p, First lifeboats lowered to the sea, April 15, 1912. 66p, Stern rises and starts sinking, April 15, 1912.

**2012, Jan. 30      Perf. 13¼**
1314-1318   A294   Set of 5    7.00   7.00

Reign of Queen Elizabeth II, 60th Anniv. — A295

Queen Elizabeth II wearing: 10p, Light green hat. 42p, Tiara. 44p, Flowered hat. 51p, Large pendant earrings. 55p, Pearl necklace. £2, Red Cross hat.
£3, Queen Elizabeth II wearing sash and crown.

**2012, Feb. 27**
1319-1324   A295   Set of 6    13.00   13.00
*1324a*     Souvenir sheet of 6,
     #1319-1324, + 3 labels   13.00   13.00
**Souvenir Sheet**
1325   A295   £3 multi      9.50   9.50

### Birds Type of 2008

Designs: S, Red-necked nightjar. UK, Little owl. £3.44, Spotted flycatcher.

**2012, Apr. 16      Perf. 13x13¼**
1326   A255   S multi      1.00   1.00
1327   A255   UK multi      1.40   1.40
1328   A255   £3.44 multi      11.00   11.00
    Nos. 1326-1328 (3)      13.40   13.40

On day of issue, No. 1326 sold for 31p and No. 1327 sold for 41p. For surcharge, see No. 1411.

Royal Air Force Squadron Emblems and Aircraft — A296

Royal Air Force Squadron Emblems — A297

Designs: No. 1329, 10p, Westland WS-61 Sea King helicopter, emblem of 22nd Squadron. No. 1330, 42p, Gloster Javelin FAW.7 Mk IV airplane, emblem of 89th Squadron. No. 1331, 76p, Panavia tornado airplane, emblem of 111th Squadron. No. 1332, £2, Bristol Type 156 Beaufighter airplane, emblem of 248th Squadron.
No. 1333 — Emblem of: a, 22nd Squadron. b, 89th Squadron. c, 111th Squadron. d, 248th Squadron.

**2012, Apr. 16      Perf. 13¼**
1329-1332   A296   Set of 4    11.00   11.00
1333   A297   Sheet of 4    11.00   11.00
   *a.*    10p multi      .35   .35
   *b.*    42p multi      1.40   1.40
   *c.*    76p multi      2.50   2.50
   *d.*    £2 multi      6.50   6.50

See Nos. 1370-1374, 1477-1481, 1522-1526.

Tourism — A298

Designs: 10p, Aerial view of harbor, city and Rock of Gibraltar. 42p, Tower of Homage, Moorish Castle. 44p, Aerial view of city and Rock of Gibraltar. 51p, St. Michael's Cave. 54p, Trinity Lighthouse. 66p, Eliott's Column, Alameda Botanical Gardens.

**2012, June 15    Litho.    Perf. 13¼**
1334-1339   A298   Set of 6    8.25   8.25

Europa (42p, 44p).

Gibraltar Intl. Jazz Festival — A299

**2012, June 19      Perf. 13x13¼**
1340   A299   75p multi      2.40   2.40

Old Views of Gibraltar A300

Designs: No. 1341, 10p, Moorish Castle. 30p, Grand Casemates. 61p, Landing Pier. 78p, Waterport. £1.75, Alameda Gardens.
No. 1346: a, 10p, Marching band on Sand Hill Road. b, 42p, South Port Gates. c, 50p, Victoria Monument. d, £1, Hargraves Barracks.

**2012, Sept. 14      Perf. 13¼**
1341-1345   A300   Set of 5    11.50   11.50
**Souvenir Sheet**
1346   A300   Sheet of 4, #a-d   6.50   6.50

Charles Dickens (1812-70), Writer — A301

Photograph of Dickens and: 10p, Cover and illustration from *David Copperfield*. 42p, First page and illustration from *Oliver Twist*. 44p, Cover and first page from *A Tale of Two Cities*. No. 1350, £2, Cover and illustration from *A Christmas Carol*.
No. 1351, £2, Photograph of Dickens over book cover.

**2012, Sept. 14      Perf. 14¼x15**
1347-1350   A301   Set of 4    9.50   9.50
**Souvenir Sheet**
1351   A301   £2 multi      6.50   6.50

## Souvenir Sheet

Visit to Gibraltar of Earl and Countess of Wessex — A302

**2012, Sept. 14      Perf. 13¼**
1352   A302   £1 Sheet of 3, #a-c   9.75   9.75

### Endangered Animals Type of 2011

Designs: No. 1353, 42p, Arabian oryx. No. 1354, 42p, Asian one-horned rhinoceros. No. 1355, 42p, European wolf. No. 1356, 42p, Iberian lynx. No. 1357, 42p, Snow leopard. No. 1358, 42p, Western lowland gorilla.

**2012, Nov. 2      Perf. 13¼x13**
1353-1358   A288   Set of 6    8.25   8.25
*1358a*     Souvenir sheet of 6,
     #1353-1358       8.25   8.25

Christmas A303

Designs: 10p, Santa Claus, gifts and "Merry Christmas." 42p, Santa Claus with sack of gifts and lantern. 44p, Snowman, Christmas tree, gifts, flying sleigh and reindeer. 51p, Santa Claus in flying sleigh. £2, Reindeer, elf, Santa Claus holding bell.

**2012, Nov. 2      Perf. 13x13¼**
1359-1363   A303   Set of 5    11.50   11.50

New Year 2013 (Year of the Snake) A304

No. 1364: a, Head of snake. b, Entire snake.

### Litho. & Embossed With Foil Application

**2013, Jan. 30      Perf. 12¾**
1364   A304   Horiz. pair    4.75   4.75
   *a.*    42p multi      1.40   1.40
   *b.*    £1 multi      3.25   3.25

Coronation of Queen Elizabeth II, 60th Anniv. — A305

Various black-and-white photographs of Queen Elizabeth II on day of coronation: 10p, 42p, 44p, £1.50.
£3, Color photograph of Queen Elizabeth II.

**2013, Jan. 30    Litho.    Perf. 13¼**
1365-1368   A305   Set of 4    7.75   7.75
**Souvenir Sheet**
1369   A305   £3 multi      9.50   9.50

### Royal Air Force Squadrons Types of 2012

Designs: No. 1370, 10p, VS Spitfire 5C, emblem of 43rd Squadron. No. 1371, 42p, Hawker Hurricane, emblem of 87th Squadron. No. 1372, 76p, Consolidated PBY Catalina IV A, emblem of 210th Squadron. No. 1373, £2, Avro Shackleton MR2, emblem of 224th Squadron.
No. 1374 — Emblem of: a, 43rd Squadron. b, 87th Squadron. c, 210th Squadron. d, 224th Squadron.

| | | | |
|---|---|---|---|
| **2013, Mar. 25** | | **Perf. 13x13¼** | |
| 1370-1373 | A296 | Set of 4 | 10.00 10.00 |
| | | **Perf. 13¼** | |
| 1374 | A297 | Sheet of 4 | 10.00 10.00 |
| a. | | 10p multi | .30 .30 |
| b. | | 42p multi | 1.25 1.25 |
| c. | | 76p multi | 2.40 2.40 |
| d. | | £2 multi | 6.00 6.00 |

Gibraltar Literary Festival — A306

Designs: 10p, Open books. 42p, Braille print. £2, Book and electronic tablet.

| | | | |
|---|---|---|---|
| **2013, May 3** | | **Perf. 13x13¼** | |
| 1375-1377 | A306 | Set of 3 | 8.00 8.00 |

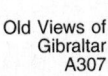

Old Views of Gibraltar A307

Designs: No. 1378, 10p, Moorish Castle and Landport. 30p, Casemates Square. 61p, Rock of Gibraltar and Victoria Gardens. 78p, Main Street. £1.75, Casemates Barracks.

No. 1383: a, 10p, Rock of Gibraltar and North Front Camp. b, 42p, Rosia Bay. c, 50p, Alameda Gardens. d, £1, Gunner's Parade.

| | | | |
|---|---|---|---|
| **2013, May 3** | | **Perf. 13¼** | |
| 1378-1382 | A307 | Set of 5 | 11.00 11.00 |
| **Souvenir Sheet** | | | |
| 1383 | A307 | Sheet of 4, #a-d | 6.25 6.25 |

Acceptance of Gibraltar to Union of European Football Associations (UEFA) — A308

| | | | |
|---|---|---|---|
| **2013, May 31** | | **Perf. 14¾x14** | |
| 1384 | A308 | 54p multi | 1.75 1.75 |

Treaty of Utrecht, 300th Anniv. A309

No. 1385: a, Union Jack. b, Text from treaty concerning permanence of transfer of control of Gibraltar from Spain to Great Britain.

| | | | |
|---|---|---|---|
| **2013, June 20** | | **Perf. 12¾** | |
| 1385 | A309 | Horiz. pair | 1.60 1.60 |
| a. | | 10p multi | .30 .30 |
| b. | | 42p multi | 1.25 1.25 |

Europa — A310

Postal vehicles: 10p, 1911 Dennis mail van. 42p, Horse-drawn mail cart. 44p, 1914 Rover motorcycle and sidecar. £1.75, 1928 Electromobile mail van.

| | | | |
|---|---|---|---|
| **2013, June 20** | | **Perf. 13x13¼** | |
| 1386-1389 | A310 | Set of 4 | 8.25 8.25 |

**Types of 1953**

Queen Elizabeth II and: 2p, Wharves. 10p, South view. 16p, Tunny fishing industry. 20p, Southport Gate. 22p, Sailing in the bay. 30p, Ocean liner. 42p, Airport. 44p, Coaling wharf. 50p, Europa Point. 58p, Strait from Buena Vista. 60p, Rosia Bay. £2, Government House. £3, Moorish Castle £5, Arms of Gibraltar.

| | | | |
|---|---|---|---|
| **2013, Aug. 1** | | **Perf. 12¾** | |
| 1390 | A26 | 2p dk grn & ind | .25 .25 |
| 1391 | A26 | 10p blk & bl grn | .30 .30 |
| 1392 | A26 | 16p brownish gray | .50 .50 |
| 1393 | A26 | 20p sepia | .65 .65 |

| | | | |
|---|---|---|---|
| 1394 | A26 | 22p car lake | .70 .70 |
| 1395 | A26 | 30p blue | .95 .95 |
| 1396 | A26 | 42p plum | 1.25 1.25 |
| 1397 | A26 | 44p ultra | 1.40 1.40 |
| 1398 | A26 | 50p blue & blk | 1.60 1.60 |
| 1399 | A26 | 58p red brn & bl | 1.75 1.75 |
| 1400 | A26 | 60p vio & org | 1.90 1.90 |
| 1401 | A26 | £2 dk brown | 6.25 6.25 |
| 1402 | A27 | £3 ultra & brn | 9.25 9.25 |
| 1403 | A27 | £5 org & org red | 15.50 15.50 |
| | | Nos. 1390-1403 (14) | 42.25 42.25 |

Birth of Prince George of Cambridge — A311

| | | | |
|---|---|---|---|
| **2013, Aug. 16** | | **Perf. 14x14¾** | |
| 1404 | A311 | £2 multi | 6.50 6.50 |

Printed in sheets of 6.

**Endangered Animals Type of 2011**

Designs: No. 1405, 42p, African penguin. No. 1406, 42p, Atlantic bluefin tuna. No. 1407, 42p, Asiatic cheetah. No. 1408, 42p, Chinese alligator. No. 1409, 42p, Red-crowned crane. No. 1410, 42p, Leatherneck sea turtle.

| | | | |
|---|---|---|---|
| **2013, Sept. 14** | | **Perf. 12½x13** | |
| 1405-1410 | A288 | Set of 6 | 8.00 8.00 |
| 1410a | | Souvenir sheet of 6, #1405-1410, perf. 13¼x13 | 8.00 8.00 |

Nos. 1117 and 1327 Surcharged in Gray or Black

**Methods and Perfs As Before**

| | | | |
|---|---|---|---|
| **2013, Nov. 2** | | | |
| 1411 | A255 | 14p on UK #1327 (G) | .45 .45 |
| 1412 | A255 | 28p on 5p #1117 | .90 .90 |

Ceremony of the Keys — A312

| | | | |
|---|---|---|---|
| **2013, Nov. 2** | | **Perf. 13¼** | |
| 1413 | A312 | £1 multi + 2 flanking labels | 3.25 3.25 |

Christmas A313

"Merry Christmas" and: 12p, Holly. 50p, Christmas tree and gifts. 54p, Santa Claus in sleigh. 64p, Christmas gift. £2.50, Christmas ornaments.

| | | | |
|---|---|---|---|
| **2013, Nov. 2** | | **Perf. 14x13½** | |
| 1414-1418 | A313 | Set of 5 | 14.00 14.00 |
| 1418a | | Souvenir sheet of 5, #1414-1418 | 14.00 14.00 |

New Year 2014 (Year of the Horse) A314

No. 1419: a, Horse's head. b, Horse.

| | | | |
|---|---|---|---|
| **2014, Jan. 31** | | **Perf. 12¾** | |
| 1419 | A314 | Horiz. pair | 5.00 5.00 |
| a. | | 50p multi | 1.60 1.60 |
| b. | | £1 multi | 3.25 3.25 |

Queen Elizabeth II
A315    A316

| | | | |
|---|---|---|---|
| **2014, Jan. 31** | | **Perf. 14x13½** | |
| **Self-Adhesive** | | | |
| 1420 | A315 | 2p rose car | .25 .25 |
| 1421 | A315 | 4p dp plum | .25 .25 |
| 1422 | A315 | 6p dk vio | .25 .25 |
| 1423 | A315 | 8p blk vio | .25 .25 |
| 1424 | A315 | 10p dk green | .35 .35 |
| 1425 | A316 | G blue | .40 .40 |
| 1426 | A316 | 14p red | .45 .45 |
| 1427 | A315 | 20p sl green | .65 .65 |
| 1428 | A315 | 28p dp plum | .90 .90 |
| 1429 | A315 | 40p dk brn | 1.40 1.40 |
| 1430 | A315 | 50p blue grn | 1.60 1.60 |
| 1431 | A316 | 54p car rose | 1.75 1.75 |
| 1432 | A315 | 64p sepia | 2.10 2.10 |
| 1433 | A316 | 70p blk vio | 2.25 2.25 |
| 1434 | A315 | £2 green | 6.50 6.50 |
| 1435 | A315 | £2.50 claret | 8.25 8.25 |
| | | Nos. 1420-1435 (16) | 27.60 27.60 |

No. 1425 sold for 12p on day of issue. See Nos. 1509-1512.

World War I, Cent. — A317

Inscriptions: 12p, Your Country Wants You. 40p, Joining up. 50p, Leaving family. 64p, Kitchener. 68p, Training. £1, Embarkation.

| | | | |
|---|---|---|---|
| **2014, Feb. 19** | | **Litho.** **Perf. 14** | |
| 1436-1441 | A317 | Set of 6 | 11.50 11.50 |

Nos. 1436-1441 each were printed in sheets of 8 + central label. See Nos. 1498-1503.

Royal Air Force Red Arrows, 50th Anniv. — A318

Royal Air Force roundel and various Red Arrows airplanes: 50p, 54p, 64p, 70p, £2.

| | | | |
|---|---|---|---|
| **2014, Mar. 20** | | **Litho.** **Perf. 13¼** | |
| 1442-1446 | A318 | Set of 5 | 14.50 14.50 |

Old Views of Gibraltar A319

Designs: No. 1447, 12p, Waterport Wharf. No. 1448, 40p, Eliott's Monument. No. 1449, 50p, Town area. 64p, Sandpits. 70p, Alameda Gardens.

No. 1452: a, 12p, Main Street. b, 40p, The Wharfs. c, 50p, The Market. d, £1, The Cascade.

| | | | |
|---|---|---|---|
| **2014, Mar. 20** | | **Litho.** **Perf. 13¼** | |
| 1447-1451 | A319 | Set of 5 | 8.00 8.00 |
| **Souvenir Sheet** | | | |
| 1452 | A319 | Sheet of 4, #a-d | 6.75 6.75 |

Europa — A320

Designs: 50p, Royal Gibraltar Regiment Band at Buckingham Palace. £1, Drum Corps.

| | | | |
|---|---|---|---|
| **2014, May 2** | | **Litho.** **Perf. 13¼x13** | |
| 1453-1454 | A320 | Set of 2 | 5.00 5.00 |

Dolphins — A321

Designs: 68p, Common dolphin. 84p, Striped dolphin. £2.50, Bottlenose dolphin.

| | | | |
|---|---|---|---|
| **2014, May 2** | | **Litho.** **Perf. 13¼x13½** | |
| 1455-1457 | A321 | Set of 3 | 13.50 13.50 |

William Shakespeare (1564-1616), Writer — A322

Various depictions of Shakespeare, quote and opening page from: 12p, *Macbeth.* 40p, *Hamlet.* 64p, *A Midsummer Night's Dream.* No. 1461, £2, *Romeo and Juliet.*

No. 1462, £2, Statue of Shakespeare, quote from *Twelfth Night.*

| | | | |
|---|---|---|---|
| **2014, June 2** | | **Litho.** **Perf. 12½** | |
| 1458-1461 | A322 | Set of 4 | 10.50 10.50 |
| **Souvenir Sheet** | | | |
| 1462 | A322 | £2 multi | 6.75 6.75 |

Flowers A323

Designs: 10p, Gibraltar saxifrage. 12p, Gibraltar restharrow. 50p, Gibraltar chickweed. 54p, Gibraltar candytuft. 64p, Gibraltar campion. 70p, Gibraltar thyme. £2, Gibraltar sea lavender.

| | | | |
|---|---|---|---|
| **2014, July 15** | | **Litho.** **Perf. 13¼** | |
| 1463-1469 | A323 | Set of 7 | 15.50 15.50 |

Evacuation of Gibraltar, 75th Anniv. — A324

Designs: 12p, People on gangplank. 50p, People hugging. 54p, People on ship waving. £1, People on gangplanks and stairs. £2, Family and text.

| | | | |
|---|---|---|---|
| | | **Perf. 13½x13¾** | |
| **2014, Sept. 10** | | **Litho.** | |
| 1470-1474 | A324 | Set of 5 | 13.50 13.50 |

Gibraltar Sea Scouts, Cent. — A325

Designs: 40p, Sea Scout leaders. 64p, Sea Scouts marching.

| | | | |
|---|---|---|---|
| **2014, Sept. 13** | | **Litho.** **Perf. 13¼x13** | |
| 1475-1476 | A325 | Set of 2 | 3.50 3.50 |

**Royal Air Force Squadrons Types of 2012**

Designs: No. 1477, 54p, British Aerospace Hawks, emblem of the 100th Squadron. No. 1478, 64p, Short/Saro London, emblem of the 202nd Squadron. No. 1479, 70p, Buccaneer S2s, emblem of 208th Squadron. No. 1480, £2, Lockheed Hudson V, emblem of 233rd Squadron.

No. 1481 — Emblem of: a, 100th Squadron. b, 202nd Squadron. c, 208th Squadron. d, 233rd Squadron.

| | | | |
|---|---|---|---|
| | | **Perf. 14¾x14¼** | |
| **2014, Sept. 15** | | **Litho.** | |
| 1477-1480 | A296 | Set of 4 | 12.50 12.50 |
| | | **Perf. 13¼** | |
| 1481 | A297 | Sheet of 4 | 12.50 12.50 |
| a. | | 54p multi | 1.75 1.75 |
| b. | | 64p multi | 2.00 2.00 |
| c. | | 70p multi | 2.25 2.25 |
| d. | | £2 multi | 6.50 6.50 |

Royal Marines, 350th
Anniv. — A326

**2014, Oct. 25    Litho.    Perf. 13¼x13**
1482 A326  £2 multi          6.50 6.50

Christmas — A327

Various details from artwork by disabled
people at the St. Bernadette Resource Center:
G, Santa Claus. 40p, Stars. 64p, Animals
wearing stocking caps. 70p, Three people.
80p, Christmas tree.
£3, Center section of entire work of art.

**2014, Nov. 3    Litho.    Perf. 12¾**
1483-1487 A327  Set of 5      8.75 8.75
**Souvenir Sheet**
1488 A327  £3 multi           9.50 9.50

No. 1483 sold for 22p on day of issue.

New Year 2015 (Year of the Goat)
A328

No. 1489: a, Goat's head. b, Goat.

**2015, Jan. 30    Litho.    Perf. 12¾**
1489 A328  Horiz. pair        4.50 4.50
  *a.*   50p multi            1.50 1.50
  *b.*   £1 multi             3.00 3.00

Gibraltar Fire
and Rescue
Service, 150th
Anniv.
A329

Designs: 10p, Firemen spraying water. 12p,
Firemen spraying foam. 40p, Rescue worker
tending to injured man. 50p, Helmet and visor.
54p, Rescue diver. 64p, Rescue workers at
automobile accident. 70p, Firemen in hazard-
ous material protective wear. £2, Fireman
spraying water on vehicle fire.

**2015, Feb. 11    Litho.    Perf. 13¼x13**
1490-1497 A329  Set of 8     15.50 15.50

**World War I, Cent. Type of 2014**

Inscriptions: 22p, Machine guns. 40p, Ships.
64p, Gas. 70p, Aircraft. 80p, Bayonets. £1.20,
Tanks.

**2015, Feb. 18    Litho.    Perf. 13**
1498-1503 A317  Set of 6     12.00 12.00

Nos. 1498-1503 each were printed in sheets
of 8 + central label.

Sir Winston Churchill
(1874-1965), British
Prime
Minister — A330

Churchill: 22p, On ship's deck. 64p, Inspecting military vehicles. 70p, Wearing helmet.
80p, Inspecting bombed buildings.
£3, Churchill giving "V for Victory" sign.

**2015, Mar. 20    Litho.    Perf. 12**
1504-1507 A330  Set of 4      7.00 7.00
**Souvenir Sheet**
1508 A330  £3 multi           7.00 7.00

---

**Queen Elizabeth II Type of 2014 and**

Queen Elizabeth II — A331

**2015, Apr. 24    Litho.    Perf. 14x13½**
**Self-Adhesive**
1509 A315  12p green          .40   .40
1510 A315  18p brown          .55   .55
1511 A315  80p blue          2.50  2.50
1512 A315  £3 red brown      9.25  9.25
**Die Cut**
1513 A331  £1 black          3.00  3.00
  Nos. 1509-1513 (5)        15.70 15.70

**Souvenir Sheet**

Penny
Black,
175th
Anniv.
A332

**2015, Apr. 24    Litho.    Perf. 13½**
1514 A332  £3 multi          9.25  9.25

Toys — A333

Designs: 14p, Soldier. 22p, Carousel. 64p,
Top. 70p, Teddy bear. 80p, Yo-yo. £1.20,
Wooden train cars.

**2015, May 5    Litho.    Perf. 14¼x14¾**
1515-1520 A333  Set of 6    11.50 11.50

Europa (Nos. 1517-1518).

Queen Elizabeth
II — A334

**Litho. With Foil Application**
**2015, May 30    Perf. 13**
1521 A334  £10 multi        30.00 30.00

**Royal Air Force Squadrons Type of
2012**

Designs: 54p, Handley Page Halifax Mk. V,
emblem of 520th Squadron. 64p, Vickers Wellington Mk. IV, emblem of 544th Squadron.
70p, Bristol Blenheim Mk. IV, emblem of 600th
Squadron. £2, De Havilland Vampire Mk. V,
emblem of 608th Squadron.
No. 1526 — Emblem of: a, 520th Squadron.
b, 544th Squadron. c, 600th Squadron. d,
608th Squadron.

**Perf. 14¾x14¼**
**2015, Aug. 31    Litho.**
1522-1525 A296  Set of 4    12.00 12.00
**Perf. 13¼**
1526 A297  Sheet of 4       12.00 12.00
  *a.*  54p multi           1.75  1.75
  *b.*  64p multi           2.00  2.00
  *c.*  70p multi           2.10  2.10
  *d.*  £2 multi            6.00  6.00

Rock of              Moorish Castle
Gibraltar                 A336
A335

---

Bouquet and Hands
of Bride and
Groom — A337

**2015, Sept. 7    Litho.    Perf. 14¼**
1527 A335  G multi           .70   .70
1528 A336  G multi           .70   .70
1529 A337  G multi           .70   .70
1530 A335  E multi          2.25  2.25
1531 A336  E multi          2.25  2.25
1532 A337  E multi          2.25  2.25
  Nos. 1527-1532 (6)        8.85  8.85

Nos. 1527-1529 each sold for 22p and Nos,
1530-1532 each sold for 70p on day of issue.
The stamps were available with adjacent
labels that could be personalized for an additional fee.
A 50p stamp of Type A335 was printed in
limited quantities in sheets of 4 having QR
codes in sheet margin.

Opening of
University of
Gibraltar — A338

**2015, Sept. 21    Litho.    Perf. 13¼**
1533 A338  80p multi        2.50  2.50

Christmas — A339

Designs: G, Christmas tree. 40p, Candy
canes, bow and holly leaves. 64p, Gift box.
70p, Reindeer. 80p, "Merry Christmas &
Happy New Year."

**2015, Nov. 2    Litho.    Perf. 14¼**
1534-1538 A339  Set of 5     8.50  8.50

No. 1534 sold for 22p on day of issue.

**Souvenir Sheet**

Magna
Carta,
800th
Anniv.
A340

No. 1539 — Text of illuminated Magna
Carta with panels at left in: a, Gray blue. b, Dull
brown.

**2015, Nov. 13    Litho.    Perf. 13x13¼**
1539 A340  £2 Sheet of 2, #a-
         b                  12.00 12.00

New Year 2016 (Year of the Monkey)
A341

No. 1540: a, Head of monkey. b, Entire
monkey.

**2016, Jan. 30    Litho.    Perf. 12½**
1540 A341  Horiz. pair      11.50 11.50
  *a.-b.*  £2 Either single  5.75  5.75

Queen Elizabeth II,
90th Birthday — A342

Various photographs of Queen Elizabeth II.

**2016, Feb. 19    Litho.    Perf. 12½**
1541 A342  12p multi         .35   .35
1542 A342  18p multi         .50   .50
1543 A342  22p multi         .65   .65

---

1544 A342  40p multi        1.10  1.10
1545 A342  50p multi        1.40  1.40
1546 A342  64p multi        1.75  1.75
1547 A342  70p multi        2.00  2.00
1548 A342  80p multi        2.25  2.25
1549 A342  £1 multi         3.00  3.00
**Size: 40x40mm**
**Perf. 13**
1550 A342  £5 multi        14.00 14.00
  Nos. 1541-1550 (10)      27.00 27.00

A343

Europa — A344

**2016, Mar. 30    Litho.    Perf. 14**
1551 A343  €1.50 multi      4.25  4.25
1552 A344  €1.50 multi      4.25  4.25

Think Green Issue.

Battle of the
Somme,
Cent. — A345

Poppies and various soldiers in battle: 22p,
64p, 70p, 80p, £2.

**2016, May 16    Litho.    Perf. 13¼x13½**
1553-1557 A345  Set of 5    12.50 12.50

**Souvenir Sheet**

Duke and Duchess of Cambridge, 5th
Wedding Anniversary — A346

**2016, May 16    Litho.    Perf. 14¾x14**
1558 A346  £2 multi         5.75  5.75

Alameda
Gardens,
200th Anniv.
A347

Designs: 64p, Gun at main entrance. 70p,
Prince of Wales' Summer House bandstand,
Aloe pseudorubroviolacea. 80p, Bridge, bust
of Giuseppe Codali, landscape gardener. £1,
Italian Garden. £2, Monument to General
George Augustus Elliott.

**2016, July 25    Litho.    Perf. 12½x13**
1559-1563 A347  Set of 5    13.50 13.50

Historic
Gates — A348

Designs: 22p, Rugged Staff Gates. 64p,
Prince Edward's Gate. 70p, Landport Gate.
80p, Grand Casemates Gates. £1, Old
Waterport Gates. £2, Southport Gates.

**2016, July 25    Litho.    Perf. 13x13¼**
1564-1569 A348  Set of 6    14.50 14.50

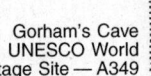

Gorham's Cave
UNESCO World
Heritage Site — A349

Designs: 22p, Sun and cave entrance. 64p, Archaeologists in cave. 70p, Rock of Gibraltar. 80p, Neanderthals. £2, Lines on cave wall.

**2016, Sept. 20   Litho.   Perf. 14¼**
1570-1574  A349   Set of 5          11.50  11.50

Pillar Boxes — A350

Pillar box from reign of: 22p, Queen Victoria. 64p, King Edward VII. 70p, King George V. 80p, King George VI. £2, Queen Elizabeth II.

**2016, Oct. 10   Litho.   Perf. 13¼**
1575-1579  A350   Set of 5          11.00  11.00

Historic
Streets of
Gibraltar
A351

Sign for: 22p, Cannon Lane. 40p, Castle Street. 50p, George's Lane. 54p, Cloister Ramp. 64p, Engineer Lane. 70p, Main Street. 80p, Flat Bastion Road. £2, Convent Place.

**2016, Oct. 10   Litho.   Perf. 13¼**
1580-1587  A351   Set of 8          14.50  14.50

Christmas — A352

Cookies shaped like: G, Santa Claus. 40p, Reindeer. 64p, Bell. 70p, Christmas tree. 80p, Star of Bethlehem. £2, Snowman.

**2016, Nov. 2   Litho.   Perf. 12½**
1588-1593  A352   Set of 6          12.00  12.00

No. 1588 sold for 22p on day of issue.

New Year 2017 (Year of the Rooster)
A353

No. 1594: a, Rooster's head. b, Rooster.

**2017, Jan. 30   Litho.   Perf. 12¾**
1594  A353   £2 Horiz. pair, #a-
          b                          10.00  10.00

A354

Moorish
Castle — A355

**2017, Feb. 6   Litho.   Perf. 12½**
1595  A354   £1.50 multi          3.75  3.75
1596  A355   £1.50 multi          3.75  3.75
Europa.

Accession of
Queen Elizabeth
II to the Throne,
65th
Anniv. — A356

Black-and-white photographs of Queen Elizabeth II: 22p, Holding flowers. 64p, Bowing. 70p, Wearing robe. 80p, Seated, wearing crown. £2, Wearing crown, holding orb. No. 1602, £3, Waving.
No. 1603, £3, Color photograph of Queen Elizabeth II wearing sash.

**2017, Feb. 6   Litho.   Perf. 13½**
1597-1602  A356   Set of 6          18.00  18.00
**Souvenir Sheet**
1603  A356   £3 multi             7.50  7.50

Ships Named
HMS Gibraltar
A357

Inscriptions: 22p, Edgar-class cruiser, 1892. 54p, 101-gun screw first rate, 1860. 64p, 80-gun Fénix. 70p, 14-gun brig, 1779. 80p, 45,000-ton aircraft carrier, 1943. £1, 20-gun sixth rate, 1711. £3, 20-gun sixth rate, 1754.

**2017, May 25   Litho.   Perf. 13¼x13½**
1604-1610  A357   Set of 7          18.00  18.00

70th Wedding
Anniversary of Queen
Elizabeth II and Prince
Philip — A358

Various wedding photographs: 22p, 40p, 50p, 64p, 70p, 80p, £1.50, £2. £3, Couple in coach.

**2017, May 25   Litho.   Perf. 13¼**
1611-1618  A358   Set of 8          17.50  17.50
**Souvenir Sheet**
1619  A358   £3 multi             7.75  7.75

A359

50th Anniversary of the 1967 Referendum

1967 Sovereignty Referendum, 50th
Anniv. — A360

Designs: £5, Queen Elizabeth II. No. 1621 — Union Jack pennants and various depictions of Gibraltarians showing British heritage.

**2017, June 19   Litho.   Perf. 13**
1620  A359   £5 multi            13.00  13.00
**Miniature Sheet**
**Perf. 12½**
1621  A360   Sheet of 4          9.50  9.50
   a.   22p multi                 .60   .60
   b.   64p multi                1.75  1.75
   c.   70p multi                1.90  1.90
   d.   £2 multi                 5.25  5.25

Miniature Sheet

House of
Windsor,
Cent.
A361

No. 1622: a, King George V. b, King Edward VIII. c, King George VI. d, Queen Elizabeth II.

**2017, June 19   Litho.   Perf. 12½**
1622  A361   Sheet of 4         11.00  11.00
   a.   64p multi                1.75  1.75
   b.   70p multi                1.90  1.90
   c.   80p multi                2.10  2.10
   d.   £2 multi                 5.75  5.75

Military Heritage
of
Gibraltar — A362

Designs: 18p, The Convent (home of Governor of Gibraltar). 22p, Cross of Sacrifice. 40p, 100-ton Victorian gun. 50p, Gibraltar War Memorial. 64p, Nelson's Anchorage. 70p, Parson's Lodge. 80p, Garrison Library. £1, Battle of Trafalgar Cemetery. £3, American War Memorial.

**2017, July 25   Litho.   Perf. 13x13½**
1623-1631  A362   Set of 9          20.00  20.00

Princess Diana
(1961-97) — A363

Various photographs of Princess Diana: 64p, 70p, £1, £2.

**2017, Aug. 31   Litho.   Perf. 12½**
1632-1635  A363   Set of 4          11.50  11.50

Upper Rock
Nature
Reserve
A364

Designs: 22p, Windsor Bridge. 50p, Great Siege tunnels. 64p, Apes den. 64p, Cable car. 80p, St. Michael's Cave. £1, Mediterranean Steps. £2, Moorish Castle.

**2017, Sept. 30   Litho.   Perf. 12**
1636-1642  A364   Set of 7          15.50  15.50

Christmas — A365

Decorated cupcakes featuring: 22p, Barbary macaque. 40p, Pan dulce cake. 64p, Snowman. 70p, Rock of Gibraltar. 80p, Penguin. £2, Legs of Santa Claus.

**2017, Nov. 2   Litho.   Perf. 13¼x13**
1643-1648  A365   Set of 6          13.00  13.00

Worldwide Fund
for Nature
(WWF) — A366

No. 1649: a, Schreiber's bent-winged bat. b, European free-tailed bat. c, Greater noctule bat. d, Isabelline serotine bat.

**2017, Nov. 30   Litho.   Perf. 13x13¼**
1649           Strip of 4         12.50  12.50
   a.   A366 70p multi            1.90  1.90
   b.   A366 80p multi            2.25  2.25
   c.   A366 £1 multi             2.75  2.75
   d.   A366 £2 multi             5.50  5.50

New
Year
2018
(Year of
the Dog)
A367

No. 1650: a, Dog's head. b, Dog.

**2018, Jan. 30   Litho.   Perf. 12¾**
1650  A367   £2 Horiz. pair, #a-
          b                       11.50  11.50

Europa — A368

Designs: No. 1651, 70p, Corral Road Bridge. No. 1652, 70p, Landport Bridge. No. 1653, £1.50, Montagu Curtain. No. 1654, £1.50, Windsor Bridge.

**2018, Feb. 6   Litho.   Perf. 12**
1651-1654  A368   Set of 4          12.00  12.00

Cannons — A369

Designs: 10p, 5.25 heavy anti-aircraft gun, 1953. 12p, 6-inch coast cannon, 1909. 18p, 8-inch howitzer, 1783. 22p, 9.2-inch coast MK 10 cannon, 1935. 40p, 10-inch rifled muzzle-loading gun, 1870. 50p, 12-pounder, 1758. 64p, 24-pounder, 1779. 70p, 13-inch mortar, 1783. 80p, 25-pounder gun-howitzer, 1943. £1, 64-pounder rifled muzzle-loading gun, 1873. £2, Bofors L40-70, 1951. £3, Russian 24-pounder, 1854.

**2018, Mar. 5   Litho.   Perf. 12**
1655-1666  A369   Set of 12          27.00  27.00

Souvenir Sheet

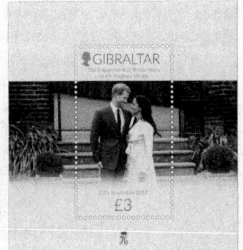

Engagement of Prince Harry and
Meghan Markle — A370

**2018, Mar. 5   Litho.   Perf. 13¼**
1667  A370   £3 multi             8.50  8.50

Coronation of Queen
Elizabeth II, 65th
Anniv. — A371

**2018, May 10   Litho.   Perf. 12**
1668  A371   £4 multi            11.00  11.00

## Souvenir Sheet

HMS Queen Elizabeth A372

**2018, May 10      Litho.      Perf. 12**
1669  A372  £3 multi          8.00  8.00

Royal Air Force, Cent. — A373

Designs: No. 1670, 22p, Supermarine Spitfire Mark V. No. 1671, 64p, Hawker Sea Hurricane Mark I in flight. No. 1672, 70p, Consolidated Catalina Mark I on water. No. 1673, 80p, Short Sunderland Mark I on water. £2, Vickers Wellington Mark IC. No. 1675, £3, Lockheed Hudson III (black-and-white photograph).
No. 1676: a, 64p, Eurofighter Typhoon T.1 on ground. b, 70p, Row of Hawker Siddeley Buccaneer S.2 on ground. c, 80p, Hawker Siddeley Nimrod MR in flight. d, £3, Two Boeing C-17A (color photograph).

**2018, May 18      Litho.      Perf. 12**
1670-1675  A373  Set of 6      20.00  20.00
  **Souvenir Sheet**
1676        Sheet of 4          14.00  14.00
  a.   A373 64p multi          1.75   1.75
  b.   A373 70p multi          1.90   1.90
  c.   A373 80p multi          2.25   2.25
  d.   A373 £3 multi           8.00   8.00

Rock of Gibraltar — A374

Designs: 22p, Rock of Gibraltar and Moorish Castle. 64p, Southern view from top of Rock of Gibraltar. 70p, Eastern side of Rock of Gibraltar. 80p, Rock of Gibraltar and Catalan Bay Beach. £1, Western side of Rock of Gibraltar (80x30mm). £2, Trinity Lighthouse at Europa Point (80x30mm).

**2018, July 31      Litho.      Perf. 13x13¼**
1677-1682  A374  Set of 6      14.00  14.00
1682a        Souvenir sheet of 6,
             #1677-1682        14.00  14.00

Prince Charles, 70th Birthday — A375

Various photographs of Prince Charles: 22p, 64p, 70p, 80p, £2, £3.

**2018, Sept. 21      Litho.      Perf. 12½**
1683-1688  A375  Set of 6      19.50  19.50

End of World War I, Cent. A376

No. 1689: a, Soldiers leaving trench. b, Ten soldiers marching. c, Six soldiers marching under clouds. d, Eleven soldiers standing.
No. 1690, Gibraltar Arboretum War Memorial.

**2018, Sept. 21      Litho.      Perf. 12½**
1689        Sheet of 4          14.50  14.50
  a.   70p multi               1.90   1.90
  b.   80p multi               2.10   2.10
  c.   £1 multi                2.60   2.60
  d.   £3 multi                7.75   7.75
  **Souvenir Sheet**
1690  A376  £3 multi           7.75   7.75

Christmas — A377

Painting by: 22p, Bernardino Luini. 40p, Fra Angelico. 64p, Gentile da Fabriano. 70p, Luini, diff. 80p, Fabriano, diff. £2, Giotto. £3, Johann Martin.

**2018, Nov. 2      Litho.      Perf. 12**
1691-1697  A377  Set of 7      20.00  20.00
1697a        Souvenir sheet of 7,
             #1691-1697        20.00  20.00

New Year 2019 (Year of the Pig) A378

No. 1699: a, Large pig, white rays to right of denomination. b, Small pig, yellow spiral to right of denomination and head of Queen Elizabeth II.

**2019, Jan. 30      Litho.      Perf. 12¾**
1699  A378  £2.60 Horiz. pair,
             #a-b              13.50  13.50

A379

Barbary Partridge — A380

Europa.

**2019, Feb. 5      Litho.      Perf. 13¼x13**
1700  A379  £1.66 multi       4.50   4.50
1701  A380  £1.66 multi       4.50   4.50
  a.   Souvenir sheet of 2, #1700-
       1701                   9.00   9.00

International Women's Day — A381

Winning art in school children's stamp design contest: 64p, Hands and slogan, by Sara Rumford. 80p, Woman's eye, by Kiarah Gomez. £2.80, Woman and slogan, by Eliana Medici.

**2019, Mar. 8      Litho.      Perf. 13x13¼**
1702-1704  A381  Set of 3      11.00  11.00

D-Day, 75th Anniv. A382

Map of coast of Normandy and: 70p, Soldiers on landing craft. 80p, Soldiers leaving landing craft. £2.86, Empty landing craft and soldiers heading for shore. £3.46, Soldiers near beach obstacles.

**2019, Mar. 8      Litho.      Perf. 14**
1705-1708  A382  Set of 4      20.50  20.50

Concorde, 50th Anniv. A383

Various photographs of the Concorde: 64p, 80p, £2.80, £3.40.

**2019, Apr. 20      Litho.      Perf. 14**
1709-1712  A383  Set of 4      20.00  20.00

18th Island Games, Gibraltar A384

Designs: 14p, Sprinter. 20p, Badminton, vert. 22p, Basketball, vert. 28p, Beach volleyball, vert. 40p, Bowling, vert. 50p, Cycling. 54p, Judo. 64p, Sailing. 70p, Shooting, vert. 80p, Squash, vert. £1, Swimming, vert. £2, Table tennis. £2.50, Tennis. £3, Triathlon.

**2019, Apr. 25      Litho.      Perf. 14**
1713-1726  A384  Set of 14     34.00  34.00

## Miniature Sheet

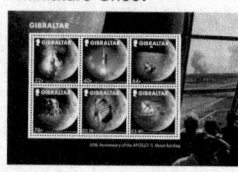

First Man on the Moon, 50th Anniv. A385

No. 1727: a, Apollo 11 on launch pad. b, Apollo 11 lifting off. c, Lunar Module over Moon. d, Lunar Module on Moon. e, Footprint on Moon. f, Retrieval of crew of Apollo 11.

**2019, July 5      Litho.      Perf. 12½**
1727  A385  Sheet of 6        18.50  18.50
  a.   22p multi              .55    .55
  b.   40p multi              .95    .95
  c.   64p multi              1.60   1.60
  d.   78p multi              1.90   1.90
  e.   £2.18 multi            5.25   5.25
  f.   £3.40 multi            8.25   8.25

Paintings by Leonardo da Vinci (1452-1519) — A386

Details from: 70p, St. John the Baptist. 80p, Virgin of the Rocks. £2.86, The Last Supper. £3.46, Mona Lisa.

**2019, Sept. 3      Litho.      Perf. 12½**
1728-1731  A386  Set of 4      19.00  19.00

Christmas — A387

Christmas carols: Nos, 1732a, 1733, 22p, Jingle Bells. Nos. 1732b, 1734, 40p, O Christmas Tree. Nos. 1732c, 1735, 64p, The Twelve Days of Christmas. Nos. 1732d, 1736, 70p, Deck the Hall. Nos. 1732e, 1737, 80p, Hark! The Herald Angels Sing. Nos. 1732e, 1738, £3, O Come All Ye Faithful.

**2019, Nov. 2      Litho.      Perf. 13½**
1732  A387  Sheet of 6        15.00  15.00
  a.   22p multi              .60    .60
  b.   40p multi              1.10   1.10
  c.   64p multi              1.60   1.60
  d.   70p multi              1.75   1.75
  e.   80p multi              2.10   2.10
  f.   £3 multi               7.75   7.75
  **Self-Adhesive**
1733-1738  A387  Set of 6      15.00  15.00

Great Siege Tunnels and Princess Anne's Battery — A388

**2019, Nov. 8      Litho.      Perf. 12½**
1739  A388  £1.06 multi       2.75   2.75

Gibraltar and Luxembourg joint issue.
See Luxembourg No. 1528.

Parks of Gibraltar and Romania A389

No. 1740: a, Upper Rock Nature Reserve, Gibraltar. b, Retezat National Park, Romania.

**2019, Nov. 12      Litho.      Perf. 12**
1740  A389  Horiz. pair        7.50   7.50
  a.   70p multi              1.75   1.75
  b.   £2.20 multi            5.75   5.75

See Romania Nos. 6337-6338.

New Year 2020 (Year of the Rat) A390

No. 1741: a, Head of rat. b, Rat.

**2020, Jan. 30      Litho.      Perf. 12¾**
1741  A390  Horiz. pair       17.00  17.00
  a.   £3 multi               8.00   8.00
  b.   £3.40 multi            9.00   9.00

VE (Victory in Europe) Day, 75th Anniv. — A391

Designs: 64p, Soldiers. 70p, Airplane, naval vessels, flag of British Royal Navy. 80p, Submarine. £2.86, Airplanes. £3.46, Coastal searchlights.
£4, Winston Churchill (1874-1965), British Prime Minister, signaling victory, vert.

**2020, Mar. 25      Litho.      Perf. 12**
1742-1746  A391  Set of 5      21.00  21.00
  **Souvenir Sheet**
1747  A391  £4 multi           9.75   9.75

Rosalind Franklin (1920-58), Chemist and Crystallographer A392

Florence Nightingale (1820-1910), Nurse A393

Ludwig van Beethoven (1770-1827), Composer — A394

**2020, Mar. 25      Litho.      Perf. 12**
1748  A392  80p multi         2.00   2.00
1749  A393  £2.86 multi       7.00   7.00
1750  A394  £3.46 multi       8.50   8.50
  Nos. 1748-1750 (3)          17.50  17.50

Schools
A395

Designs: 70p, St. Anne's School. 80p, Notre Dame School. £2.86, St. Bernard's School. £3.46, Bayside-Westside Schools.

**2020, Apr. 30    Litho.    Perf. 14**
1751-1754 A395    Set of 4    19.50 19.50

Europa
A396

Ships: £1.66, Lady Mary Wood, 1842. £2.86, SS Iberia, 1836.

**2020, May 8    Litho.    Perf. 12**
1755-1756 A396    Set of 2    11.50 11.50
*1756a*    Souvenir sheet of 2,
    #1755-1756    11.50 11.50

Ancient Postal Routes.

Crest of Government of
Gibraltar — A397

**2020, June 1    Litho.    Perf. 14x13½**
**Self-Adhesive**
**Color at Top of Stamp**
1757 A397    12p dark green    .30    .30
1758 A397    14p violet    .35    .35
1759 A397    18p dark red    .45    .45
1760 A397    30p dark red    .75    .75
1761 A397    60p bister    1.50    1.50
1762 A397    90p blue violet    2.25    2.25
1763 A397    £1 brnsh blk    2.50    2.50
1764 A397    £1.15 carmine    3.00    3.00
1765 A397    £2 blue    5.00    5.00
1766 A397    £4 blue green    10.00 10.00
*Nos. 1757-1766 (10)*    26.10 26.10

See Nos. 1804-1805.

Owls — A398

Designs: 30p, Scops owl. 60p, Little owl. 90p, Short-eared owl. £1, Barn owl. No. 1771, £4, Long-eared owl.
No. 1772: a, £2, Eagle owl. b, £4, Tawny owl.

**2020, Sept. 25    Litho.    Perf. 14**
1767-1771 A398    Set of 5    17.50 17.50
**Souvenir Sheet**
1772    Sheet of 2    16.00 16.00
*a.*    A398 £2 multi    5.25    5.25
*b.*    A398 £4 multi    10.50 10.50

Christmas — A399

Designs: Nos. 1773a, 1774, Santa Claus and reindeer. Nos. 1773b, 1775, Santa Claus in locomotive. Nos. 1773c, 1776, Santa Claus, reindeer, polar bear, elf, and penguin in gift box. Nos. 1773d, 1777, Christmas trees, and Santa Claus holding red gift box. Nos. 1773e, 1778, Christmas tree, and Santa Claus holding green gift box. Nos. 1773f, 1779, Santa Claus making snow angel.

**2020, Nov. 2    Litho.    Perf. 13¼x13½**
1773    Sheet of 6    21.00 21.00
*a.*    A399 30p multi    .80    .80
*b.*    A399 60p multi    1.60    1.60
*c.*    A399 90p multi    2.40    2.40
*d.*    A399 £1 multi    2.60    2.60
*e.*    A399 £1.15 multi    3.00    3.00

---

*f.*    A399 £4 multi    10.50 10.50
**Self-Adhesive**
1774 A399    30p multi    .80
1775 A399    60p multi    1.60
1776 A399    90p multi    2.40
1777 A399    £1 multi    2.60
1778 A399    £1.15 multi    3.00
1779 A399    £4 multi    10.50
*Nos. 1774-1779 (6)*    20.90

Values for Nos. 1774-1779 are for stamps on backing paper with back printing. Used examples of these stamps without backing paper are identical to Nos. 1773a-1773f.

Barbary
Macaques — A400

Various photographs of Barbary macaques: 30p, 90p, £1, £4.

**2020, Nov. 20    Litho.    Perf. 13½**
1780-1783 A400    Set of 4    16.50 16.50
See Nos. 1785-1786.

New
Year
2021
(Year of
the Ox)
A401

No. 1784: a, Ox. b, Ox with fireworks on horns.

**2021, Jan. 30    Litho.    Perf. 12½**
1784 A401    Horiz. pair    17.50 17.50
*a.*    £3 multi    8.25    8.25
*b.*    £3.40 multi    9.25    9.25

**Barbary Macaques Type of 2020
With Europa Emblem Added**

Various photographs of Barbary macaques: £1.96, £3.16.

**2021, Feb. 5    Litho.    Perf. 13½**
1785-1786 A400    Set of 2    14.50 14.50
*1786a*    Souvenir sheet of 2,
    #1785-1786    14.50 14.50

Queen Elizabeth II,
95th
Birthday — A402

Queen Elizabeth II: 30p, Wearing ambulance driver's uniform in World War II. 60p, Coronation photograph, 1952. 90p, With husband, Prince Philip. £1, Holding trophy. £1.15, Wearing Trooping the Color uniform. £4, Wearing purple hat and coat.

**2021, Feb. 9    Litho.    Perf. 13¼**
1787-1792 A402    Set of 6    22.50 22.50
See Isle of Man No. 2150a.

Duke and Duchess of
Cambridge, 10th
Wedding
Anniversary — A403

Designs: £1, Duchess of Cambridge in wedding dress, waving. £1.15, Duke of Cambridge in uniform, waving. £3.16, Duke of Cambridge placing wedding ring on wife's finger. No. 1796, £4, Couple in coach.
No. 1797, £4, Couple, diff.

**2021, Apr. 29    Litho.    Perf. 12**
1793-1796 A403    Set of 4    26.00 26.00
**Souvenir Sheet**
**Perf. 12½**
1797 A403    £4 multi    11.00 11.00
No. 1797 contains one 35x35mm stamp.

---

Souvenir Sheet

QR Code and Electronic Circuit
Diagram — A404

**2021, May 17    Litho.    Perf. 13½**
1798 A404    £4 multi + label    11.50 11.50
Crypto-currency.

Prince Philip (1921-
2021) — A405

Various photographs of Prince Philip, with blue green denominations: 90p, £1, £1.15, £4. No. 1803, £4, Prince Philip, with denomination in white.

**2021, June 10    Litho.    Perf. 12**
1799-1802 A405    Set of 4    19.50 19.50
**Souvenir Sheet**
1803 A405    £4 black    11.00 11.00

**Crest of Government Type of 2020**
**2021, Sept. 8    Litho.    Perf. 14x13½**
**Self-Adhesive**
**Color at Top of Stamp**
1804 A397    £3 dark brown    8.25    8.25
1805 A397    £5 brown    13.50 13.50

Old Maps
Depicting
Gibraltar
A406

Designs: 60p, 19th century map by William Hughes. 90p, French map published in late 1700s. £1, Map published by R. H. Laurie, 1823. £1.15, Map from 1726. £4, French map published in early 1700s.

**2021, Sept. 8    Litho.    Perf. 12**
1806-1810 A406    Set of 5    21.00 21.00

Christmas — A407

Designs: Nos. 1811a, 1812, Santa Claus carrying sack. Nos. 1811b, 1813, Santa Claus holding gift boxes. Nos. 1811c, 1814, Santa Claus, ringing bell. Nos. 1811d, 1815, Santa Claus, gift boxes and streamers. Nos. 1811e, 1816, Santa Claus checking list. Nos. 1811f, 1817, Santa Claus holding gift box and sack.

**2021, Nov. 2    Litho.    Perf. 13¼x13½**
1811    Sheet of 6    21.50 21.50
*a.*    A407 30p multi    .80    .80
*b.*    A407 60p multi    1.60    1.60
*c.*    A407 90p multi    2.40    2.40
*d.*    A407 £1 multi    2.75    2.75
*e.*    A407 £1.15 multi    3.25    3.25
*f.*    A407 £4 multi    10.50 10.50
**Self-Adhesive**
1812 A407    30p multi    .80
1813 A407    60p multi    1.60
1814 A407    90p multi    2.40
1815 A407    £1 multi    2.75
1816 A407    £1.15 multi    3.25
1817 A407    £4 multi    10.50
*Nos. 1812-1817 (6)*    21.30

Values for Nos. 1812-817 are for stamps on backing paper with back printing. Used examples of these stamps without backing paper are identical to Nos. 1811a-1811f.

---

City Council,
Cent. — A408

**2021, Nov. 11    Litho.    Perf. 12**
1818 A408    £4 multi    10.50 10.50

Torah Arks
and Bimahs
From
Synagogues
in Gibraltar
and Israel
A409

**2022, Feb. 15    Litho.    Perf. 14¼**
1819 A409    £4 multi    11.00 11.00
Joint issue between Gibraltar and Israel. See Israel No. 2306.

New Year 2022 (Year of the Tiger)
A410

No. 1820: a, Head of tiger. b, Tiger.

**2022, Feb. 25    Litho.    Perf. 12**
1820 A410    Horiz. pair    19.50 19.50
*a.*    £3.16 multi    8.50    8.50
*b.*    £4 multi    11.00 11.00

Europa — A411

Myth of the Pillars of Hercules: £1.96, Hecules touching pillar at left. £3.16, Hercules touching pillar at right.

**2022, Feb. 25    Litho.    Perf. 12**
1821-1822 A411    Set of 2    14.00 14.00
*1822a*    Souvenir sheet of 2,
    #1821-1822    14.00 14.00

Reign of Queen
Elizabeth II, 70th
Anniv. — A412

Queen Elizabeth II: £1, Wearing hat in black-and-white photograph. £1.15, Wearing pink hat. £3.16, Wearing red and black hat. No. 1826, £4, Wearing blue hat.
No. 1827, £4, Queen Elizabeth II wearing crown, vert.

**2022, Apr. 25    Litho.    Perf. 13**
1823-1826 A412    Set of 4    23.50 23.50
**Souvenir Sheet**
**Perf. 13x13¼**
1827 A412    £4 multi    10.00 10.00
No. 1827 contains one 29x48mm stamp.

Gibraltar International
Chess Festival, 20th
Anniv. — A413

Designs: 30p, Pawns. 60p, Rooks. 90p, Knights. £1, Bishops. £1.15, Queens. £4, Kings.

**2022, Apr. 25    Litho.    Perf. 12**
1828-1833 A413    Set of 6    20.00 20.00

Tourism — A414

Designs: £1, St. Michael's Cave. £1.15, Sandy Bay. £3.16, Man paddling on surfboard. No. 1837, £4, Barbary macaques. No. 1838, £4, Windsor Bridge.

**2022, Sept. 23　Litho.　Perf. 12½**
| 1834-1837 | A414 | Set of 4 | 21.00 | 21.00 |

**Souvenir Sheet**
| 1838 | A414 | £4 multi | 9.00 | 9.00 |

Paintings by Gustavo Bacarisas (1872-1971)
A415

Various unnamed paintings by Bacarisas: £1.15, £3.16, £4.
No. 1842, £4, Self-portrait, vert.

**2022, Oct. 20　Litho.　Perf. 12**
| 1839-1841 | A415 | Set of 3 | 19.50 | 19.50 |

**Souvenir Sheet**
| 1842 | A415 | £4 multi | 9.25 | 9.25 |

The Twelve Days of Christmas — A416

Items from song: No. 1843, 30p, A partridge in a pear tree. No. 1844, 60p, Two turtle doves. No. 1845, 90p, Three French hens. No. 1846, £1, Four calling birds. No. 1847, £1.15, Five gold rings. No. 1848, £4, Six geese a-laying.
No. 1849: a, 30p, Seven swans a-swimming. b, 60p, Eight maids a-milking. c, 90p, Nine ladies dancing. d, £1, Ten lords a-leaping. e, £1.15, Eleven pipers piping. f, £4, Twelve drummers drumming.

**2022, Nov. 2　Litho.　Perf. 13½**
| 1843-1848 | A416 | Set of 6 | 19.00 | 19.00 |

**Miniature Sheet**
| 1849 | A416 | Sheet of 6, #a-f | 19.00 | 19.00 |

Diwali — A417

Diwali candles with background color of: £1.15, Red. £3.16, Purple. £4, Orange.

**2022, Dec. 8　Litho.　Perf. 12½**
| 1850-1852 | A417 | Set of 3 | 20.00 | 20.00 |

---

## SEMI-POSTAL STAMPS

Souvenir Sheet

Calpe House, London
SP1

No B1: a, New Calpe House, London. b, Houses of Parliament and Westminster Bridge, London.

**2018, Nov. 2　Litho.　Perf. 12**
| B1 | SP1 | Sheet of 2 | 9.00 | 9.00 |
| a.-b. | | £1.50 Either single | 4.50 | 4.50 |

Calpe House, lodging for Gibraltar residents traveling to London for medical treatment. No. B1 sold for £3.50, with 50p going to the Friends of Calpe House Charity.

---

## POSTAGE DUE STAMPS

**Catalogue values for unused stamps in this section are for Never Hinged items.**

D1

**Perf. 14**
**1956, Dec. 1　Wmk. 4　Typo.**
**Chalky Paper**
| J1 | D1 | 1p green | 1.25 | 1.75 |
| J2 | D1 | 2p brown | 2.00 | 3.00 |
| J3 | D1 | 2½p ultramarine | 2.50 | 3.50 |
| | | Nos. J1-J3 (3) | 5.75 | 8.25 |

**"p" instead of "d"**
**Perf. 17½x18**
**1971, Feb. 15　Typo.　Wmk. 314**
**Chalky Paper**
| J4 | D1 | ½p green | .30 | .60 |
| J5 | D1 | 1p dark brown | .35 | .55 |
| J6 | D1 | 2p dark blue | .45 | .60 |
| | | Nos. J4-J6 (3) | 1.10 | 1.75 |

D2

**Perf. 14x13½**
**1976, Oct. 13　Litho.　Wmk. 373**
| J7 | D2 | 1p orange | .25 | .50 |
| J8 | D2 | 3p bright ultra | .25 | .50 |
| J9 | D2 | 5p vermilion | .25 | .65 |
| J10 | D2 | 7p bright red lilac | .25 | .75 |
| J11 | D2 | 10p gray | .35 | 1.50 |
| J12 | D2 | 20p green | .65 | 2.25 |
| | | Nos. J7-J12 (6) | 2.00 | 6.15 |

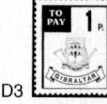
D3

**1984, July 2　　　　Perf. 14½x14**
| J13 | D3 | 1p black | .25 | .25 |
| J14 | D3 | 3p red | .25 | .25 |
| J15 | D3 | 5p ultra | .25 | .25 |
| J16 | D3 | 10p sky blue | .40 | .40 |
| J17 | D3 | 25p lilac | 1.00 | 1.25 |
| J18 | D3 | 50p orange | 1.75 | 2.00 |
| J19 | D3 | £1 green | 3.00 | 4.00 |
| | | Nos. J13-J19 (7) | 6.90 | 8.40 |

D4

Landmarks: 1p, Water Port Gates. 10p, HM Dockyard. 25p, Military Hospital. 50p, Governor's Cottage. £1, Laguna. £2, Catalan Bay.

**1996, Sept. 30　Litho.　Perf. 14½x14**
| J20 | D4 | 1p multicolored | .25 | .25 |
| J21 | D4 | 10p multicolored | .35 | .35 |
| J22 | D4 | 25p multicolored | .80 | .80 |
| J23 | D4 | 50p multicolored | 1.50 | 1.50 |
| J24 | D4 | £1 multicolored | 2.75 | 2.75 |
| J25 | D4 | £2 multicolored | 5.75 | 5.75 |
| | | Nos. J20-J25 (6) | 11.40 | 11.40 |

Finches — D5

Designs: 5p, Greenfinch. 10p, Serin. 20p, Siskin. 50p, Linnet. £1, Chaffinch. £2, Goldfinch.

**Perf. 13x13¼**
**2002, June 6　Litho.　Unwmk.**
| J26-J31 | D5 | Set of 6 | 14.00 | 14.00 |

---

## WAR TAX STAMP

No. 66 Overprinted

**1918, Apr.　　Wmk. 3　　Perf. 14**
| MR1 | A14 | ½p green | 1.75 | 2.40 |
| a. | | Double overprint | 900.00 | |

---

# GILBERT & ELLICE ISLANDS

ˈgil-bərt ənd ˌe-ləs ˈī-lənds

LOCATION — Groups of islands in the Pacific Ocean northeast of Australia
GOVT. — British Crown Colony
AREA — 375 sq. mi.
POP. — 57,816 (est. 1973)
CAPITAL — Tarawa

The Gilbert group of which Butaritari, Tarawa and Tamana are the more important, is on the Equator. Ellice Islands, Phoenix Islands, Line Islands (Fanning, Washington and Christmas), and Ocean Island are included in the Colony. The islands were annexed by Great Britain in 1892 and formed into the Gilbert and Ellice Islands Colony in 1915 on request of the native governments.
The colony divided into the Gilbert Islands and Tuvalu, Jan. 1, 1976.

12 Pence = 1 Shilling
20 Shillings = 1 Pound
100 Cents = 1 Dollar (1966)

**Catalogue values for unused stamps in this country are for Never Hinged items, beginning with Scott 52.**

Stamps and Type of Fiji Overprinted in Black or Red

**1911, Jan. 1　Wmk. 3　Perf. 14**
**Ordinary Paper**
| 1 | A22 | ½p green | 7.50 | 52.50 |
| 2 | A22 | 1p carmine | 52.50 | 30.00 |
| a. | | Pair, one without overprint | | |
| 3 | A22 | 2p gray | 22.50 | 17.50 |
| 4 | A22 | 2½p ultramarine | 18.50 | 52.50 |

**Chalky Paper**
| 5 | A22 | 5p violet & ol grn | 67.50 | 97.50 |
| 6 | A22 | 6p violet | 26.00 | 52.50 |
| 7 | A22 | 1sh black, green | 27.00 | 72.50 |
| | | Nos. 1-7 (7) | 221.50 | 375.00 |

Nos. 1-7 are known with a forged Ocean Island postmark dated "JY 15 11."

Pandanus — A2

**1911, Mar.　Engr.　Ordinary Paper**
| 8 | A2 | ½p green | 5.00 | 25.00 |
| 9 | A2 | 1p carmine | 2.75 | 12.50 |
| 10 | A2 | 2p gray | 1.75 | 7.50 |
| 11 | A2 | 2½p ultramarine | 13.00 | 17.50 |
| | | Nos. 8-11 (4) | 22.50 | 62.50 |

King George V — A3

For description of Dies I and II, see front section of the Catalogue.

---

**1912-24　　　　Die I　　　Typo.**
| 14 | A3 | ½p deep green | .60 | 6.00 |
| 15 | A3 | 1p carmine | 2.50 | 15.50 |
| a. | | 1p scarlet ('15) | 4.25 | 15.00 |
| 16 | A3 | 2p gray ('16) | 16.00 | 27.00 |
| 17 | A3 | 2½p ultra ('16) | 3.25 | 11.50 |

**Chalky Paper**
| 18 | A3 | 3p vio, yel ('19) | 2.75 | 13.50 |
| 19 | A3 | 4p blk & red, yel | .90 | 6.50 |
| 20 | A3 | 5p vio & ol grn | 2.00 | 6.25 |
| 21 | A3 | 6p vio & red vio | 1.50 | 6.75 |
| 22 | A3 | 1sh black, green | 1.50 | 5.25 |
| 23 | A3 | 2sh vio & ultra, bl | 15.00 | 36.00 |
| 24 | A3 | 2sh6p blk & red, bl | 23.00 | 26.00 |
| 25 | A3 | 5sh grn & red, yel | 37.50 | 67.50 |

**Die II**
| 26 | A3 | £1 vio & blk, red ('24) | 600.00 | 1,650. |
| | | Nos. 14-26 (13) | 706.50 | 1,878. |

**Die II**
**1921-27　Wmk. 4　Ordinary Paper**
| 27 | A3 | ½p green | 4.00 | 3.50 |
| 28 | A3 | 1p deep vio ('27) | 5.00 | 8.75 |
| 29 | A3 | 1½p scarlet ('24) | 8.50 | 3.75 |
| 30 | A3 | 2p gray | 8.00 | 47.50 |

**Chalky Paper**
| 31 | A3 | 10sh green & red, emer ('24) | 170.00 | 400.00 |
| | | Nos. 27-31 (5) | 195.50 | 463.50 |

**Common Design Types pictured following the introduction.**

**Silver Jubilee Issue**
**Common Design Type**
**1935, May 6　Engr.　Perf. 11x12**
| 33 | CD301 | 1p black & ultra | 2.40 | 17.50 |
| 34 | CD301 | 1½p car & blue | 1.90 | 3.50 |
| 35 | CD301 | 3p ultra & brn | 6.50 | 26.00 |
| 36 | CD301 | 1sh brn vio & in-digo | 26.00 | 20.00 |
| | | Nos. 33-36 (4) | 36.80 | 67.00 |
| | | Set, never hinged | 62.50 | |

**Coronation Issue**
**Common Design Type**
**1937, May 12　　　Perf. 13½x14**
| 37 | CD302 | 1p dark purple | .25 | .70 |
| 38 | CD302 | 1½p carmine | .25 | .70 |
| 39 | CD302 | 3p bright ultra | .35 | .75 |
| | | Nos. 37-39 (3) | .85 | 2.15 |
| | | Set, never hinged | 1.10 | |

Great Frigate Bird — A4　　Pandanus — A5

Designs: 1½p, Canoe crossing reef. 2p, Canoe and boat house. 2½p, Islander's house. 3p, Seascape. 5p, Ellice Islands canoe. 6p, Coconut trees. 1sh, Phosphate loading jetty, Ocean Island. 2sh, Cutter "Nimanoa." 2sh6p, Gilbert Islands canoe. 5sh, Coat of arms of colony.

**Perf. 11½x11 (Nos. 40, 43, 50), 12½ (Type A5), 13½ (Nos. 42, 44, 45, 48)**
**1939, Jan. 14　Engr.　Wmk. 4**
| 40 | A4 | ½p dk grn & sl bl | .35 | 1.00 |
| 41 | A4 | 1p dk vio & brt bl green | .25 | 1.50 |
| 42 | A4 | 1½p car & black | .25 | 1.25 |
| 43 | A4 | 2p black & brn | .75 | 1.00 |
| 44 | A4 | 2½p dp olive & blk | .55 | 1.00 |
| 45 | A4 | 3p ultra & black | .35 | 1.00 |
| a. | | Perf. 12 ('55) | .55 | 3.50 |
| 46 | A5 | 5p dk brn & dp ultra | 3.25 | 2.75 |
| 47 | A5 | 6p dl vio & olive | .40 | .60 |
| 48 | A4 | 1sh gray bl & blk | 8.00 | 3.75 |
| b. | | Perf. 12 ('51) | 1.75 | 20.00 |
| 49 | A5 | 2sh red org & ultra | 4.75 | 11.00 |
| 50 | A4 | 2sh6p brt bl grn & bl | 4.75 | 11.00 |
| 51 | A5 | 5sh dp blue & red | 6.50 | 16.00 |
| | | Nos. 40-51 (12) | 30.15 | 51.85 |
| | | Set, never hinged | | |

**Catalogue values for unused stamps in this section, from this point to the end of the section, are for Never Hinged items.**

## Peace Issue
### Common Design Type
**1946, Dec. 16**     **Perf. 13½x14**

| | | | | |
|---|---|---|---|---|
| 52 | CD303 | 1p deep magenta | .25 | .55 |
| 53 | CD303 | 3p deep blue | .25 | .55 |

## Silver Wedding Issue
### Common Design Types
**1949, Aug. 29**   **Photo.**   **Perf. 14x14½**

| | | | | |
|---|---|---|---|---|
| 54 | CD304 | 1p violet | .25 | 1.25 |

### Engraved; Name Typographed
**Perf. 11½x11**

| | | | | |
|---|---|---|---|---|
| 55 | CD305 | £1 red | 14.00 | 25.00 |

## UPU Issue
### Common Design Types
### Engr.; Name Typo. on 2p, 3p
**1949, Oct. 1**    **Perf. 13½, 11x11½**

| | | | | |
|---|---|---|---|---|
| 56 | CD306 | 1p rose violet | .70 | 2.50 |
| 57 | CD307 | 2p gray black | 2.00 | 4.00 |
| 58 | CD308 | 3p indigo | .85 | 4.00 |
| 59 | CD309 | 1sh blue | .75 | 2.50 |
| | | *Nos. 56-59 (4)* | 4.30 | 13.00 |

## Coronation Issue
### Common Design Type
**1953, June 2**   **Engr.**   **Perf. 13½x13**

| | | | | |
|---|---|---|---|---|
| 60 | CD312 | 2p gray & black | .65 | 2.25 |

## Types of 1939-42 with Portrait of Queen Elizabeth II, and

Canoe Crossing Reef — A6

**Perf. 11½x11 (Nos. 61, 63, 70), 12½ (Type A5), 12 (Nos. 64-65, 68, 72)**

**1956, Aug. 1**

| | | | | |
|---|---|---|---|---|
| 61 | A4 | ½p brt ultra & blk | .65 | 1.25 |
| 62 | A5 | 1p violet & olive | .60 | 1.25 |
| 63 | A4 | 2p dull pur & brt green | .90 | 2.50 |
| 64 | A4 | 2½p green & black | .50 | .65 |
| 65 | A5 | 3p dk car & black | .50 | .65 |
| 66 | A5 | 5p red org & brt ultra | 8.75 | 3.75 |
| 67 | A5 | 6p dk gray & red brn | .85 | 2.75 |
| 68 | A4 | 1sh ol green & blk | 3.00 | 1.25 |
| 69 | A5 | 2sh dk brn & brt ultra | 6.00 | 4.00 |
| 70 | A4 | 2sh6p dp ultra & rose red | 7.50 | 4.25 |
| 71 | A5 | 5sh green & blue | 8.50 | 6.00 |
| 72 | A6 | 10sh turq blue & blk | 29.00 | 10.00 |
| | | *Nos. 61-72 (12)* | 66.75 | 38.30 |

See Nos. 84-85.

Loading Phosphate on Freighter — A7

2½p, Original lump of phosphate. 1sh, Loading phosphate on truck, Ocean Island.

**Wmk. 314**
**1960, May 1**   **Photo.**   **Perf. 12**

| | | | | |
|---|---|---|---|---|
| 73 | A7 | 2p rose lilac & green | .80 | .85 |
| 74 | A7 | 2½p olive & black | .80 | .85 |
| 75 | A7 | 1sh grnsh blue & blk | .80 | .85 |
| | | *Nos. 73-75 (3)* | 2.40 | 2.55 |

60th anniversary of the discovery of phosphate deposits at Ocean Island.

## Freedom from Hunger Issue
### Common Design Type
**1963, June 4**     **Perf. 14x14½**

| | | | | |
|---|---|---|---|---|
| 76 | CD314 | 10p ultramarine | 1.40 | .40 |

## Red Cross Centenary Issue
### Common Design Type
**1963, Sept. 2**   **Litho.**   **Perf. 13**

| | | | | |
|---|---|---|---|---|
| 77 | CD315 | 2p black & red | .65 | 1.00 |
| 78 | CD315 | 10p ultra & red | 1.35 | 2.50 |

Plane and Fiji-Ellice-Gilbert Route — A8

---

Designs: 1sh, Eastern reef heron in flight, horiz. 3sh7p, Plane and Tarawa sailboat.

**1964, July 20**   **Perf. 11½x11, 11x11½**

| | | | | |
|---|---|---|---|---|
| 79 | A8 | 3p lt blue, bl & blk | .75 | .35 |
| 80 | A8 | 1sh dk blue, bl & blk | .90 | .35 |
| 81 | A8 | 3sh7p lt green, grn & blk | 1.50 | 1.50 |
| | | *Nos. 79-81 (3)* | 3.15 | 2.20 |

Inauguration of air service between Fiji and Gilbert and Ellice Islands.

## Queen Types of 1956
**Perf. 11½x11, 12½**
**1964-65**   **Engr.**   **Wmk. 314**

| | | | | |
|---|---|---|---|---|
| 84 | A4 | 2p dull pur & brt green | 1.10 | 1.40 |
| 85 | A5 | 6p dk gray & red brown | 1.50 | 1.50 |

Issue dates: 2p, Oct. 30. 6p, Apr. 1965.

## ITU Issue
### Common Design Type
**1965, June 4**   **Litho.**   **Perf. 11x11½**

| | | | | |
|---|---|---|---|---|
| 87 | CD317 | 3p dp org & turq blue | .25 | .25 |
| 88 | CD317 | 2sh6p grnsh bl & red lilac | .60 | .35 |

Village Elder Blowing Conch and Meeting House (Maneaba) — A9

Designs: 1p, Ellice Islanders torch fishing. 2p, Gilbertese girl weaving frangipani garland. 3p, Gilbertese woman dancing The Ruoia. 4p, Gilbertese man dancing. 5p, Gilbertese woman drawing water. 6p, Ellice kosu dance. 7p, Fatele taua dance, Ellice men. 1sh, Gilbertese woman harvesting taro roots (babai). 1sh6p, Ellice man and woman dancing fatele toka. 2sh, Ellice Islanders pounding taro roots. 3sh7p, Gilbertese sitting dance, ruoia, horiz. 5sh, Gilbertese boys playing stick game, horiz. 10sh, Ellice men beating box-drum, horiz. £1, Coat of arms, horiz.

**Perf. 12x11, 11x12**
**1965, Aug. 16**   **Litho.**   **Wmk. 314**

| | | | | |
|---|---|---|---|---|
| 89 | A9 | ½p blue grn & multi | .25 | .25 |
| 90 | A9 | 1p vio bl & multi | .25 | .25 |
| 91 | A9 | 2p lt olive & multi | .25 | .25 |
| 92 | A9 | 3p red & multi | .25 | .25 |
| 93 | A9 | 4p purple & multi | .25 | .25 |
| 94 | A9 | 5p car rose & multi | .25 | .25 |
| 95 | A9 | 6p multicolored | .25 | .25 |
| 96 | A9 | 7p brown & multi | .40 | .25 |
| 97 | A9 | 1sh bl vio & multi | .70 | .25 |
| 98 | A9 | 1sh6p yel & multi | 1.00 | 1.00 |
| 99 | A9 | 2sh multicolored | 1.15 | 1.40 |
| 100 | A9 | 3sh7p ultra & multi | 1.60 | .70 |
| 101 | A9 | 5sh multicolored | 1.75 | .90 |
| 102 | A9 | 10sh green & multi | 2.50 | 1.10 |
| 103 | A9 | £1 blue & multi | 3.00 | 1.90 |
| | | *Nos. 89-103 (15)* | 13.85 | 9.25 |

See Nos. 135-149. For surcharges see Nos. 110-124.

## Intl. Cooperation Year Issue
### Common Design Type
**1965, Oct. 25**   **Litho.**   **Perf. 14½**

| | | | | |
|---|---|---|---|---|
| 104 | CD318 | ½p blue grn & cl | .25 | .25 |
| 105 | CD318 | 3sh7p lt violet & grn | .60 | .35 |

## Churchill Memorial Issue
### Common Design Type
**1966, Jan. 24**   **Photo.**   **Perf. 14**
### Design in Black, Gold and Carmine Rose

| | | | | |
|---|---|---|---|---|
| 106 | CD319 | ½p brt blue | .25 | .25 |
| 107 | CD319 | 3p green | .30 | .25 |
| 108 | CD319 | 3sh brown | .45 | .40 |
| 109 | CD319 | 3sh7p violet | .50 | .50 |
| | | *Nos. 106-109 (4)* | 1.50 | 1.30 |

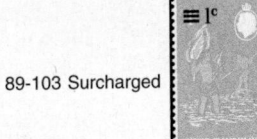

Nos. 89-103 Surcharged

---

**Perf. 12x11, 11x12**
**1966, Feb. 14**      **Litho.**

| | | | | |
|---|---|---|---|---|
| 110 | A9 | 1c on 1p multi | .25 | .25 |
| 111 | A9 | 2c on 2p multi | .25 | .25 |
| 112 | A9 | 3c on 3p multi | .25 | .25 |
| 113 | A9 | 4c on ½p multi | .25 | .25 |
| 114 | A9 | 5c on 6p multi | .25 | .25 |
| 115 | A9 | 6c on 4p multi | .25 | .25 |
| 116 | A9 | 8c on 5p multi | .25 | .25 |
| 117 | A9 | 10c on 1sh multi | .25 | .25 |
| 118 | A9 | 15c on 7p multi | .70 | 1.00 |
| 119 | A9 | 20c on 1sh6p multi | .50 | .40 |
| 120 | A9 | 25c on 2sh multi | .50 | .35 |
| 121 | A9 | 35c on 3sh7p multi | 1.10 | .35 |
| 122 | A9 | 50c on 5sh multi | .60 | .45 |
| 123 | A9 | $1 on 10sh multi | .60 | .50 |
| 124 | A9 | $2 on £1 multi | 2.00 | 3.25 |
| | | *Nos. 110-124 (15)* | 8.00 | 8.20 |

## World Cup Soccer Issue
### Common Design Type
**1966, July 1**   **Litho.**   **Perf. 14**

| | | | | |
|---|---|---|---|---|
| 125 | CD321 | 3c multicolored | .25 | .25 |
| 126 | CD321 | 35c multicolored | .45 | .35 |

## WHO Headquarters Issue
### Common Design Type
**1966, Sept. 20**   **Litho.**   **Perf. 14**

| | | | | |
|---|---|---|---|---|
| 127 | CD322 | 3c multicolored | .25 | .25 |
| 128 | CD322 | 12c multicolored | .55 | .45 |

## UNESCO Anniversary Issue
### Common Design Type
**1966, Dec. 1**   **Litho.**   **Perf. 14**

| | | | | |
|---|---|---|---|---|
| 129 | CD323 | 5c "Education" | .50 | .80 |
| 130 | CD323 | 10c "Science" | .75 | .25 |
| 131 | CD323 | 20c "Culture" | 1.25 | 1.40 |
| | | *Nos. 129-131 (3)* | 2.50 | 2.45 |

H.M.S. Royalist, 1892, and Union Jack — A10

10c, Cutter & canoe at trading post. 35c, Family.

**Perf. 14½x14**
**1967, Sept. 1**   **Photo.**   **Wmk. 314**

| | | | | |
|---|---|---|---|---|
| 132 | A10 | 3c green, blue & red | .25 | .50 |
| 133 | A10 | 10c multicolored | .25 | .25 |
| 134 | A10 | 35c multicolored | .25 | .50 |
| | | *Nos. 132-134 (3)* | .75 | 1.25 |

75th anniv. as a British Protectorate.

## Type of 1965
**Perf. 12x11, 11x12**
**1968, Jan. 1**   **Litho.**   **Wmk. 314**

| | | | | |
|---|---|---|---|---|
| 135 | A9 | 1c like 1p | .25 | .25 |
| 136 | A9 | 2c like 2p | .25 | .25 |
| 137 | A9 | 3c like 3p | .25 | .25 |
| 138 | A9 | 4c like ½p | .25 | .25 |
| 139 | A9 | 5c like 6p | .25 | .25 |
| 140 | A9 | 6c like 4p | .25 | .25 |
| 141 | A9 | 8c like 5p | .25 | .25 |
| 142 | A9 | 10c like 1sh | .25 | .25 |
| 143 | A9 | 15c like 7p | .50 | .25 |
| 144 | A9 | 20c like 1sh6p | .70 | .25 |
| 145 | A9 | 25c like 2sh | 1.25 | .25 |
| 146 | A9 | 35c like 3sh7p | 1.50 | .25 |
| 147 | A9 | 50c like 5sh | 1.50 | 2.50 |
| 148 | A9 | $1 like 10sh | 1.75 | 3.75 |
| 149 | A9 | $2 like £1 | 4.50 | 5.50 |
| | | *Nos. 135-149 (15)* | 13.70 | 14.75 |

Map of Tarawa Atoll — A11

Designs: 10c, US Marines wading ashore at Betio. 15c, Battle scene on Betio. 35c, Raising US and British flags on Betio.

**1968, Nov. 21**   **Photo.**   **Perf. 14**

| | | | | |
|---|---|---|---|---|
| 150 | A11 | 3c multicolored | .25 | .25 |
| 151 | A11 | 10c multicolored | .25 | .25 |
| 152 | A11 | 15c multicolored | .25 | .35 |
| 153 | A11 | 35c multicolored | .25 | .50 |
| | | *Nos. 150-153 (4)* | 1.00 | 1.35 |

Battle of Tarawa against Japan, 25th anniv.

---

School Boy and Map of Abemama Atoll — A12

Designs: 10c, Secondary school boy and girl on map of Tarawa, with rest of Gilbert and Ellice Islands. 35c, Student in cap and grown on main Fiji island (Viti Levu) and map of South Pacific Islands.

**1969, June 2**   **Litho.**   **Perf. 12½**

| | | | | |
|---|---|---|---|---|
| 154 | A12 | 3c dull org & multi | .25 | .25 |
| 155 | A12 | 10c black & multi | .25 | .25 |
| 156 | A12 | 35c dull grn & multi | .25 | .25 |
| | | *Nos. 154-156 (3)* | .75 | .85 |

1st anniv. of the University of the South Pacific in Fiji, and to show the progress of education in the area it serves.

Polynesian Madonna — A13

**1969, Oct. 20**     **Perf. 11½**

| | | | | |
|---|---|---|---|---|
| 157 | A13 | 2c multicolored | .25 | .25 |
| 158 | A13 | 10c multicolored | .25 | .25 |

Christmas.

---

### Canceled to Order
The Philatelic Bureau of Gilbert and Ellice Islands began in 1970 to sell canceled sets of new issues. Values in the second ("used") column are for these canceled-to-order stamps.

Mouth-to-Mouth Resuscitation A14

**1970, Mar. 9**   **Litho.**   **Perf. 14½**

| | | | | |
|---|---|---|---|---|
| 159 | A14 | 10c multi | .25 | .25 |
| 160 | A14 | 15c multi, diff. | .35 | .45 |
| 161 | A14 | 35c multi, diff. | .50 | .90 |
| | | *Nos. 159-161 (3)* | 1.10 | 1.60 |

Centenary of the British Red Cross.

Mother and Child Care — A15

Designs: 10c, Woman physician and laboratory equipment. 15c, Chest X-ray and technician. 35c, Map of Gilbert and Ellice Islands and UN emblem.

**Perf. 12½x13**
**1970, June 26**   **Litho.**   **Wmk. 314**

| | | | | |
|---|---|---|---|---|
| 162 | A15 | 5c lilac & multi | .25 | .25 |
| 163 | A15 | 10c black, gray & red | .25 | .25 |
| 164 | A15 | 15c yellow & multi | .25 | .25 |
| 165 | A15 | 35c blue grn, bl & blk | .30 | .45 |
| | | *Nos. 162-165 (4)* | 1.05 | 1.20 |

25th anniv. of the United Nations.

Map of Onotoa, Beru, Tamana and Arorae Islands — A16

Designs: 10c, Sailing ship "John Williams III," vert. 25c, Rev. Samuel James Whitmee, vert. 35c, Map of Islands and steamship "John Williams VII."

## Perf. 14x14½, 14½x14

**1970, Sept. 1    Litho.    Wmk. 314**

| 166 | A16 | 2c blue & multi | .25 | .25 |
|---|---|---|---|---|
| 167 | A16 | 10c brt green & black | .35 | .25 |
| 168 | A16 | 25c lt ultra & red brn | .25 | .25 |
| 169 | A16 | 35c ver, blk & lt gray | .55 | .65 |
| | | Nos. 166-169 (4) | 1.40 | 1.40 |

Centenary of the landing in the Southern Gilbert Islands by the first missionaries of the London Missionary Society.

**Island Child with Halo on Pandanus Mat — A17**

Christmas: 10c, Sanctuary of New Tarawa Cathedral. 35c, Three Gilbertese sailing canoes within Star of Bethlehem.

**1970, Oct. 3    Perf. 14½**

| 170 | A17 | 2c ocher & multi | .25 | .25 |
|---|---|---|---|---|
| 171 | A17 | 10c ocher & multi | .25 | .25 |
| 172 | A17 | 35c pink & multi | .25 | .25 |
| | | Nos. 170-172 (3) | .75 | .75 |

**Harvesting Copra — A18**     **Lagoon Fishing — A19**

3c, Women cleaning pandanus leaves. 4c, Fishermen casting nets. 5c, Gilbertese canoes. 6c, Dehusking coconuts. 8c, Woman weaving pandanus fronds. 10c, Basket weaving. 15c, Tiger shark. 20c, Beating rolled pandanus leaf. 25c, Loading copra. 35c, Night fishing. 50c, Local handicraft. $1, Woman weaving coconut screen. $2, Coat of arms.

**Wmk. 314 Upright (A18), Sideways (A19)**

**1971, May 31    Litho.    Perf. 14**

| 173 | A18 | 1c multicolored | .25 | .25 |
|---|---|---|---|---|
| 174 | A19 | 2c multicolored | .25 | .25 |
| 175 | A19 | 3c multicolored | .25 | .25 |
| 176 | A19 | 4c multicolored | .30 | .25 |
| 177 | A19 | 5c multicolored | .60 | .25 |
| 178 | A19 | 6c multicolored | .40 | .35 |
| 179 | A19 | 8c multicolored | .55 | .35 |
| 180 | A18 | 10c multicolored | .50 | .45 |
| 181 | A18 | 15c multicolored | 3.00 | .90 |
| 182 | A19 | 20c multicolored | 1.60 | 1.75 |
| 183 | A19 | 25c multicolored | 2.00 | 1.40 |
| 184 | A19 | 50c multicolored | 2.40 | 1.00 |
| 185 | A18 | 50c multicolored | 1.25 | 2.40 |
| 186 | A18 | $1 multicolored | 1.75 | 2.00 |
| 187 | A18 | $2 multicolored | 4.75 | 8.00 |
| | | Nos. 173-187 (15) | 19.85 | 19.85 |

**Wmk. 314 Upright (A19), Sideways (A18)**

**1972-73**

| 174a | A19 | 2c multicolored | 9.25 | 16.00 |
|---|---|---|---|---|
| 177a | A19 | 5c multicolored | 3.50 | 4.25 |
| 178a | A18 | 6c multicolored | 9.25 | 16.50 |
| 181a | A18 | 15c multicolored | 3.75 | 5.00 |
| 182a | A19 | 20c multicolored | 4.00 | 6.00 |
| | | Nos. 174a-182a (5) | 29.75 | 47.75 |

Issue dates: 9/7/72, 5c, 15c, 20c; 6/13/73, 2c, 6c.

**Legislative Council, 1971 (former House of Representatives) A20**

New Constitution: 10c, Meeting House.

**1971, Aug. 1    Wmk. 314    Perf. 14**

| 188 | A20 | 3c orange & multi | .25 | .25 |
|---|---|---|---|---|
| 189 | A20 | 10c green & multi | .25 | .25 |

**Nativity Scene — A21**

Christmas: 10c, Star of Bethlehem and palm fronds. 35c, Fishermen in outrigger canoe looking at Star.

**1971, Oct. 1**

| 190 | A21 | 3c vio blue, blk & yel | .25 | .35 |
|---|---|---|---|---|
| 191 | A21 | 10c grnsh bl, blk & gold | .25 | .25 |
| 192 | A21 | 35c car rose, blk & rose | .25 | .35 |
| | | Nos. 190-192 (3) | .75 | .95 |

**Children and UNICEF Emblem — A22**

25th Anniv. of UNICEF: 10c, Seated child. 35c, Child's head.

**1971, Dec. 11**

| 193 | A22 | 3c brt pink & multi | .25 | .80 |
|---|---|---|---|---|
| 194 | A22 | 10c black & multi | .25 | .25 |
| 195 | A22 | 35c blue & multi | .55 | .80 |
| | | Nos. 193-195 (3) | 1.05 | 1.85 |

**Commission Flag, Map of South Pacific — A23**

South Pacific Commission, 25th Anniv.: 10c, Island boats. 35c, Flags of 8 member nations plus Tonga, a non-member.

**1972, Feb. 21    Perf. 13½x14**

| 196 | A23 | 3c gray & multi | .25 | .30 |
|---|---|---|---|---|
| 197 | A23 | 10c tan, ultra & brown | .25 | .25 |
| 198 | A23 | 35c ultra & multi | .25 | .85 |
| | | Nos. 196-198 (3) | .75 | 1.40 |

**Corals — A24**

**1972, May 26    Perf. 14x14½**

| 199 | A24 | 3c Alveopora | .25 | .40 |
|---|---|---|---|---|
| 200 | A24 | 10c Euphyllia | .40 | .25 |
| 201 | A24 | 15c Melithea | .55 | .35 |
| 202 | A24 | 35c Spongodes | 1.50 | .90 |
| | | Nos. 199-202 (4) | 2.70 | 1.90 |

**"Peace" on Star of Bethlehem — A25**

Christmas: 10c, Holy Family, made of shells. 35c, Christ child sleeping in giant clam and covered with dawn cowrie, horiz.

**1972, Sept. 15    Perf. 13½**

| 203 | A25 | 3c gold & multi | .25 | .25 |
|---|---|---|---|---|
| 204 | A25 | 10c gold & multi | .25 | .25 |
| 205 | A25 | 35c gold & multi | .25 | .25 |
| | | Nos. 203-205 (3) | .75 | .75 |

**Silver Wedding Issue, 1972**
**Common Design Type**

Design: Queen Elizabeth II, Prince Philip and kaue floral headdress.

**1972, Nov. 20    Photo.    Perf. 14x14½**

| 206 | CD324 | 3c olive & multi | .25 | .25 |
|---|---|---|---|---|
| 207 | CD324 | 35c rose brown & multi | .25 | .25 |

**Funafuti, Land of Bananas — A26**

Designs: 10c, Butaritari, the smell of the sea. 25c, Tarawa, the center of the world. 35c, Abemama, the land of the moon.

**1973, Mar. 5    Litho.    Perf. 14½x14**

| 208 | A26 | 3c yellow & multi | .25 | .55 |
|---|---|---|---|---|
| 209 | A26 | 10c brt green & multi | .30 | .35 |
| 210 | A26 | 25c dull blue & multi | .40 | .60 |
| 211 | A26 | 35c orange & multi | .45 | .70 |
| | | Nos. 208-211 (4) | 1.40 | 2.20 |

Legends of island names.

**Ellice Dancer — A27**

Christmas (Within Outline of Nautilus Shell): 10c, Outrigger canoe in lagoon. 35c, Evening on the lagoon. 50c, Map of Christmas Island, Pacific Ocean.

**1973, Sept. 24    Perf. 14**

| 212 | A27 | 3c vio blue & multi | .25 | .25 |
|---|---|---|---|---|
| 213 | A27 | 10c multicolored | .25 | .25 |
| 214 | A27 | 35c multicolored | .25 | .25 |
| 215 | A27 | 50c vio blue & multi | .30 | 1.50 |
| | | Nos. 212-215 (4) | 1.05 | 2.25 |

**Princess Anne's Wedding Issue**
**Common Design Type**

**1973, Nov. 14    Perf. 14**

| 216 | CD325 | 3c brt green & multi | .25 | .25 |
|---|---|---|---|---|
| 217 | CD325 | 35c slate & multi | .25 | .25 |

**Meteorological Observation A28**

WMO Emblem and: 10c, Island observation station. 35c, Wind finding radar. 50c, Map of Gilbert and Ellice Islands world weather watch stations.

**1973, Nov. 26    Litho.    Perf. 14½**

| 218 | A28 | 3c orange & multi | .75 | .45 |
|---|---|---|---|---|
| 219 | A28 | 10c dp bister & multi | .80 | .30 |
| 220 | A28 | 35c gray & multi | 1.00 | .45 |
| 221 | A28 | 50c dk blue & multi | 1.50 | 1.50 |
| | | Nos. 218-221 (4) | 4.05 | 2.70 |

Cent. of intl. meteorological cooperation.

**Te-Mataaua Crest and Canoe — A29**

Designs: Various family crests and canoes.

**1974, Mar. 4    Litho.    Perf. 13½**

| 222 | A29 | 3c tan & multi | .25 | .25 |
|---|---|---|---|---|
| 223 | A29 | 10c lt blue & multi | .25 | .25 |
| 224 | A29 | 35c yellow & multi | .25 | .25 |
| 225 | A29 | 50c pink & multi | .25 | 1.50 |
| a. | | Souvenir sheet of 4, #222-225 | 6.25 | 7.50 |
| | | Nos. 222-225 (4) | 1.00 | 2.25 |

**UPU Emblem, "Te Koroba" and No. 26 — A30**

UPU cent.: 10c, Sailing ship "Kiakia" and No. 51. 25c, BAC 111 jet and No. 187. 35c, UPU emblem.

**1974, June 10    Perf. 14**

| 226 | A30 | 4c blue green & multi | .25 | .35 |
|---|---|---|---|---|
| 227 | A30 | 10c orange & multi | .25 | .25 |
| 228 | A30 | 25c dp blue & multi | .25 | .25 |
| 229 | A30 | 35c red orange & black | .35 | .45 |
| | | Nos. 226-229 (4) | 1.10 | 1.30 |

**Toy Canoe, Star and Boat — A31**

Star of Bethlehem and: 10c, Pinwheel and boat. 25c, Coconut ball (crate) and boat. 35c, Three boats (Wise Men) and stars.

**1974, Sept. 23**

| 230 | A31 | 4c yel green & multi | .25 | .25 |
|---|---|---|---|---|
| 231 | A31 | 10c red brown & multi | .25 | .25 |
| 232 | A31 | 25c multicolored | .25 | .45 |
| 233 | A31 | 35c red brown & multi | .25 | .55 |
| | | Nos. 230-233 (4) | 1.00 | 1.50 |

Christmas.

**Blenheim Palace, Entrance A32**     **Churchill Painting A33**

Design: 35c, Churchill Statue, London.

**1974, Nov. 30    Litho.    Perf. 14**

| 234 | A32 | 4c multicolored | .25 | .35 |
|---|---|---|---|---|
| 235 | A33 | 10c ultra & black | .25 | .25 |
| 236 | A33 | 35c blue, ocher & blk | .25 | .45 |
| | | Nos. 234-236 (3) | .75 | 1.05 |

Sir Winston Churchill (1874-1965).

**Carpilius Maculatus A34**

Crabs: 10c, Ranina ranina. 25c, Portunus pelagicus. 35c, Ocypode ceratophthalma.

**1975, Jan. 27    Litho.    Perf. 14**

| 237 | A34 | 4c violet & multi | .25 | 1.00 |
|---|---|---|---|---|
| 238 | A34 | 10c green & multi | .50 | .50 |
| 239 | A34 | 25c buff & multi | 1.25 | 1.25 |
| 240 | A34 | 35c lt blue & multi | 1.50 | 1.75 |
| | | Nos. 237-240 (4) | 3.50 | 4.50 |

**Living Cowries and Empty Shells — A35**

**1975, May 26    Wmk. 314    Perf. 14**

| 241 | A35 | 4c Cypraea argus | .55 | 1.00 |
|---|---|---|---|---|
| 242 | A35 | 10c Cypraea cribraria | .80 | .50 |
| 243 | A35 | 25c Cypraea talpa | 1.40 | 1.60 |
| 244 | A35 | 35c Cypraea mappa | 2.25 | 2.50 |
| a. | | Souvenir sheet of 4, #241-244 | 16.00 | 17.00 |
| | | Nos. 241-244 (4) | 5.00 | 5.60 |

**Map of Beru (The Bud) — A36**

Designs: 10c, Map of Onotoa (Six Giants). 25c, Map of Abaiang (Land to the North). 35c, Map of Marakei (Floating fish trap).

**Wmk. 314**

**1975, Aug. 1    Litho.    Perf. 14**

| 245 | A36 | 4c brt green & multi | .25 | .45 |
|---|---|---|---|---|
| 246 | A36 | 10c brown & multi | .25 | .25 |
| 247 | A36 | 25c vio blue & multi | .25 | .35 |
| 248 | A36 | 35c org red & multi | .40 | .50 |
| | | Nos. 245-248 (4) | 1.15 | 1.55 |

Legends of island names.

Christ Child Within
Coconut — A37

Christmas: 10c, Sadd Memorial Chapel (Protestant), Tarawa. 25c, R.C. Church, Ocean Island. 35c, Fishermen in outrigger canoes seeing canoes.

**1975, Sept. 22          Perf. 14**
249 A37 4c brown & multi          .25   .75
250 A37 10c brt blue & multi          .25   .25
251 A37 25c violet & multi          .35   .90
252 A37 35c green & multi          .45  1.50
          Nos. 249-252 (4)          1.30  3.40

## POSTAGE DUE STAMPS

D1

**1940, Aug.  Typo.  Wmk. 4  Perf. 12**
J1 D1 1p emerald          5.50  25.00
J2 D1 2p dark red          6.00  25.00
J3 D1 3p chocolate          8.25  25.00
J4 D1 4p deep blue          10.00  26.00
J5 D1 5p deep green          12.00  35.00
J6 D1 6p brt red vio          12.00  35.00
J7 D1 1sh dull violet          20.00  47.50
J8 D1 1sh6p turq green          30.00  90.00
          Nos. J1-J8 (8)          103.75 308.50
          Set, never hinged          180.00

## WAR TAX STAMP

No. 15a Overprinted

**1918          Wmk. 3          Perf. 14**
MR1 A3 1p scarlet          .70  6.75

## GILBERT ISLANDS

'gil-bərt 'ī-lənds

LOCATION — A group of islands in the Pacific Ocean northeast of Australia.
GOVT. — British Crown Colony
AREA — 270 sq. mi.
POP. — 52,000 (1973)
CAPITAL — Tarawa

The Gilbert Islands Colony consists of the Gilbert Islands, Phoenix, Ocean and Line Islands. They were part of the Gilbert and Ellice Islands colony until 1976. See Tuvalu.

**Catalogue values for all unused stamps in this country are for Never Hinged items.**

Stamps and Types of Gilbert and Ellice Islands 1971 Overprinted in Red, Black or Gold

**Wmk. 373; 314 (2c, 4c)**
**1976, Jan. 2          Litho.          Perf. 14**
253 A18 1c multi (R)          .25  1.60
    a.   Watermark 314          .25   .90
254 A19 2c multi (R)          .45   .30
    a.   Watermark upright          .55  2.40
255 A19 3c multi (R)          .40  2.50
    a.   Watermark 314          12.00 21.00

256 A19 4c multi (R)          .30  1.10
257 A19 5c multi (R)          .50   .90
258 A18 6c multi (B)          .50   .90
259 A18 8c multi (B)          .50  1.10
260 A18 10c multi (B)          .50  1.10
261 A18 15c multi (B)          2.75  1.40
262 A18 20c multi (B)          1.00  2.25
    a.   Watermark 314 sideways          6.25  3.25
    b.   Watermark 314 upright          125.00
263 A19 25c multi (B)          1.50  1.40
    a.   Watermark 314          29.00 50.00
264 A19 35c multi (G)          2.00  1.75
    a.   Watermark 314          950.00 1,000.
265 A18 50c multi (B)          1.75  2.25
    a.   Watermark 314          850.00 1,100.
266 A18 $1 multi (R)          3.75  7.75
          Nos. 253-266 (14)          16.15 26.30
          Location of overprint varies.

Maps of Tarawa and
Funafuti — A38

4c, Charts of Gilbert and Tuvalu Islands.

**1976, Jan. 2          Wmk. 373**
267 A38 4c multicolored          .55  1.00
268 A38 35c multicolored          .90  1.50

Separation of the Gilbert and Ellice Islands.

M.V.
Teraaka — A39

3c, M.V. Tautunu. 4c, Moorish idol. 5c, Hibiscus. 6c, Reef egret. 7c, Roman Catholic Cathedral, Tarawa. 8c, Frangipani. 10c, Maneaba meeting house. 12c, Betio Harbor. 15c, Sunset. 20c, Marakei Atoll. 35c, Chapel, Tangintebu. 40c, Flamboyant tree. 50c, Hypolimnas bolina elliciana (butterfly). $1, Landing craft, Tabakea. $2, Gilbert Islands flag.

**1976, July 1          Litho.          Perf. 14**
269 A39 1c multicolored          .40   .65
270 A39 3c multicolored          .60   .75
271 A39 4c multicolored          .35   .65
272 A39 5c multicolored          .40   .30
273 A39 6c multicolored          1.50   .90
274 A39 7c multicolored          .25   .30
275 A39 8c multicolored          .25   .30
276 A39 10c multicolored          .25   .30
277 A39 12c multicolored          .45   .45
278 A39 15c multicolored          .40   .45
279 A39 20c multicolored          .25   .35
280 A39 35c multicolored          .25   .40
281 A39 40c multicolored          .50   .50
282 A39 50c multicolored          1.40  1.75
283 A39 $1 multicolored          .90  2.50
284 A39 $2 multicolored          1.25  2.50
          Nos. 269-284 (16)          9.40 13.05

Church — A40

Children's Drawings: 15c, Feasting (vegetables, fish, pig, chicken), vert. 20c, Communal meeting house, vert. 35c, Children watching dancer.

**1976, Sept. 15          Litho.          Perf. 14**
285 A40 5c blue & multi          .25   .25
286 A40 15c green & multi          .40   .25
287 A40 20c rose & multi          .40   .35
288 A40 35c salmon & multi          .40   .50
          Nos. 285-288 (4)          1.45  1.35
          Christmas.

Porcupine Fish
Helmet — A41

Artifacts: 15c, Shark's teeth dagger. 20c, Fighting gauntlet. 35c, Coconut body armor.

**1976, Dec. 6          Litho.          Perf. 13½x13**
289 A41 5c multicolored          .25   .25
290 A41 15c multicolored          .35   .25
291 A41 20c multicolored          .35   .45
292 A41 35c multicolored          .25   .50
    a.   Souvenir sheet of 4, #289-292          8.25 11.00
          Nos. 289-292 (4)          1.55  1.50

Prince Charles, 1970
Visit — A42

Designs: 20c, Prince Philip, 1959 visit. 40c, Queen in coronation robes.

**1977, Feb. 7          Perf. 14**
293 A42 8c multicolored          .25   .25
294 A42 20c multicolored          .25   .25
295 A42 40c multicolored          .25   .35
          Nos. 293-295 (3)          .75   .85

Reign of Queen Elizabeth II, 25th anniv.

John Byron and
Dolphin,
1765 — A43

Explorers: 15c, Edmund Fanning, 1798, and "Betsey." 20c, Fabian Gottlieb von Bellingshausen, 1820, and "Vostok." 35c, Charles Wilkes, 1838-42, and "Vincennes."

**1977, June 1          Wmk. 373          Perf. 14**
296 A43 5c multicolored          .55  1.50
297 A43 15c multicolored          .65  2.75
298 A43 20c multicolored          .65  2.75
299 A43 35c multicolored          .90  4.00
          Nos. 296-299 (4)          2.75 11.00

Resolution and
Discovery off Christmas
Island — A44

15c, Capt. Cook's logbook entry, 1777. 20c, Capt. Cook on board ship. 40c, Capt. Cook landing on Christmas Island.

**1977, Sept. 12          Litho.          Perf. 14**
300 A44 8c multi          .40   .25
301 A44 15c multi, horiz          .40   .25
302 A44 20c multi          .60   .30
303 A44 40c multi, horiz.          .60   .65
    a.   Souvenir sheet of 4, #300-303          5.00  7.50
          Nos. 300-303 (4)          2.00  1.45

Christmas; bicentenary of Capt. Cook's discovery of Christmas Island.

Scout Emblem, Beach
Scene — A45

15c, Patrol meeting. 20c, Scout weaving mat. 40c, Canoeing.

**1977, Dec. 5          Litho.          Perf. 13**
304 A45 8c gold & multi          .30   .25
305 A45 15c gold & multi, horiz.          .40   .25
306 A45 20c gold & multi, horiz.          .40   .30
307 A45 40c gold & multi          .65   .65
          Nos. 304-307 (4)          1.75  1.45

50th anniversary of Gilbert Islands Scouting.

Taurus with
Aldebaran — A46

Night Sky over Gilbert Islands: 20c, Canis Major with Sirius. 25c, Scorpio with Antares. 45c, Orion with Betelgeuse and Rigel.

**1978, Feb. 20          Litho.          Perf. 14**
308 A46 10c blue & black          .50   .35
309 A46 20c dp rose & black          .55   .40
310 A46 25c olive grn & black          .60   .60
311 A46 45c orange & black          .80   .90
          Nos. 308-311 (4)          2.45  2.25

Common Design Types pictured following the introduction.

## Elizabeth II Coronation Anniversary
Common Design Types
Souvenir Sheet

**1978, Apr. 21          Unwmk.**
312          Sheet of 6          1.25  1.25
    a.   CD326 45c Unicorn of Scotland          .25   .25
    b.   CD327 45c Elizabeth II          .25   .25
    c.   CD328 45c Great frigate bird          .25   .25

Arrows, Tarawa
and Abemama
Islands, School
Insignia — A47

10c, Birds inscribed Bikenibeu, Abemama, Bairiki (school locations). 25c, Children greeting each other from maps of Islands. 45c, Abemama & Tarawa school buildings.

**Perf. 14x13½**
**1978, June 5          Wmk. 373**
313 A47 10c multicolored          .25   .25
314 A47 20c multicolored          .25   .25
315 A47 25c multicolored          .25   .25
316 A47 45c multicolored          .35   .35
          Nos. 313-316 (4)          1.10  1.10

King George V School, 25th anniversary of return from Abemama to Tarawa.

Garland — A48

Christmas: Various garlands.

**1978, Sept. 4          Litho.          Perf. 14**
317 A48 10c multicolored          .25   .25
318 A48 20c multicolored          .25   .25
319 A48 25c multicolored          .25   .25
320 A48 45c multicolored          .25   .30
    a.   Souvenir sheet of 4, #317-320, perf. 13x13½          1.75  4.25
          Nos. 317-320 (4)          1.00  1.05

Endeavour — A49

Designs: 20c, Green turtle. 25c, Quadrant. 45c, Capt. Cook after Flaxman/Wedgwood medallion.

**1979, Jan. 15          Litho.          Perf. 11**
321 A49 10c multicolored          .25   .25
322 A49 20c multicolored          .30   .30
323 A49 25c multicolored          .30   .45

**Litho.; Embossed**
324 A49 45c multicolored          .35   .80
          Nos. 321-324 (4)          1.20  1.80

Capt. Cook's voyages.
Gilbert Islands stamps were replaced in 1979 by those of Kiribati.

# GOLD COAST

'gōld 'kŏst

LOCATION — West Africa between Togo and Ivory Coast
GOVT. — Former British Crown Colony
AREA — 91,843 sq. mi.
POP. — 3,089,000 (1952)
CAPITAL — Accra

Attached to the colony were Ashanti and Northern Territories (protectorate). Togoland, under British mandate, was also included for administrative purposes.
Gold Coast became the independent state of Ghana in 1957.
See Ghana.

12 Pence = 1 Shilling
20 Shillings = 1 Pound

**Catalogue values for unused stamps in this country are for Never Hinged items, beginning with Scott 128.**

Queen Victoria — A1

#### Perf. 12½

**1875, July     Typo.     Wmk. 1**

| | | | | |
|---|---|---|---|---|
| 1 | A1 | 1p blue | 550.00 | 100.00 |
| 2 | A1 | 4p red violet | 525.00 | 150.00 |
| 3 | A1 | 6p orange | 825.00 | 82.50 |
| | | *Nos. 1-3 (3)* | 1,900. | 332.50 |

**1876-79          Perf. 14**

| | | | | |
|---|---|---|---|---|
| 4 | A1 | ½p bister ('79) | 100.00 | 42.50 |
| 5 | A1 | 1p blue | 42.50 | 8.00 |
| a. | | Half used as ½p on cover | | 4,500. |
| 6 | A1 | 2p green ('79) | 150.00 | 11.50 |
| a. | | Half used as 1p on cover | | 4,250. |
| b. | | Quarter used as ½p on cover | | 7,500. |
| 7 | A1 | 4p red violet | 275.00 | 7.25 |
| a. | | Quarter used as 1p on cover | | 10,000. |
| b. | | Half used as 2p on cover | | 8,000. |
| 8 | A1 | 6p orange | 325.00 | 28.00 |
| a. | | One sixth used as 1p on cover | | 13,000. |
| b. | | Half used as 3p on cover | | 10,000. |
| | | *Nos. 4-8 (5)* | 892.50 | 97.25 |

**Handstamp Surcharged "1D" in Black**

**1883, May**

| | | | | |
|---|---|---|---|---|
| 9 | A1 | 1p on 4p red violet | | |

Some experts question the status of No. 9. One canceled example is in the British Museum. Another example is supposed to exist (Ferrari).

**1883-91                Wmk. 2**

| | | | | |
|---|---|---|---|---|
| 10 | A1 | ½p bister ('83) | 275.00 | 85.00 |
| 11 | A1 | ½p green ('84) | 5.00 | 1.50 |
| 12 | A1 | 1p blue ('83) | 1,000. | 85.00 |
| 13 | A1 | 1p rose ('84) | 6.25 | .60 |
| a. | | Half used as ½p on cover | | 5,000. |
| 14 | A1 | 2p gray ('84) | 50.00 | 7.00 |
| b. | | Half used as 1p on cover | | 5,000. |
| 15 | A1 | 2½p ultral & org ('91) | 14.00 | .85 |
| 16 | A1 | 3p dl green ('89) | 27.50 | 15.00 |
| | | 3p olive bister | 27.50 | 13.00 |
| 17 | A1 | 4p dull vio ('84) | 29.00 | 4.25 |
| a. | | 4p claret | 35.00 | 8.00 |
| b. | | Half used as 2p on cover | | |
| 18 | A1 | 6p orange ('89) | 27.50 | 6.50 |
| a. | | One sixth used as 1p on cover | | |
| 19 | A1 | 1sh purple ('88) | 16.00 | 3.25 |
| a. | | 1sh violet | 50.00 | 15.00 |
| 20 | A1 | 2sh brown ('84) | 60.00 | 17.50 |
| a. | | 2sh yellow brown ('88) | 115.00 | 45.00 |

No. 18 Surcharged in Black

---

**1889, Mar.**

| | | | | |
|---|---|---|---|---|
| 21 | A1 | 1p on 6p orange | 150.00 | 60.00 |
| a. | | Double surcharge | | 4,750. |

The surcharge exists in two spacings between "PENNY" and bar: 7mm (normal) and 8mm.
No. 21a does not exist unused.

Queen Victoria — A3

**1889**

| | | | | |
|---|---|---|---|---|
| 22 | A3 | 5sh lilac & ultra | 82.50 | 30.00 |
| 23 | A3 | 10sh lilac & red | 145.00 | 18.00 |
| 24 | A3 | 20sh green & red | 3,500. | |

**1894**

| | | | | |
|---|---|---|---|---|
| 25 | A3 | 20sh vio & blk, *red* | 190.00 | 40.00 |

**1898-1902**

| | | | | |
|---|---|---|---|---|
| 26 | A3 | ½p lilac & green | 7.50 | 1.75 |
| 27 | A3 | 1p lil & car rose | 8.00 | .60 |
| 28 | A3 | 2p lil & red ('02) | 60.00 | 175.00 |
| 29 | A3 | 2½p lilac & ultra | 11.00 | 12.50 |
| 30 | A3 | 3p lilac & yel | 11.00 | 4.75 |
| 31 | A3 | 6p lilac & purple | 15.00 | 3.75 |
| 32 | A3 | 1sh gray grn & blk | 20.00 | 45.00 |
| 33 | A3 | 2sh grn grn & car rose | 37.50 | 45.00 |
| 34 | A3 | 5sh grn & lil ('00) | 110.00 | 65.00 |
| 35 | A3 | 10sh grn & brn ('00) | 225.00 | 72.50 |
| | | *Nos. 26-35 (10)* | 505.00 | 425.85 |

Numerals of 2p, 3p and 6p of type A3 are in color on colorless tablet.

Nos. 29 and 31 Surcharged in Black

**1901, Oct. 6**

| | | | | |
|---|---|---|---|---|
| 36 | A3 | 1p on 2½p lil & ultra | 12.00 | 8.00 |
| a. | | "ONE" omitted | 1,200. | |
| 37 | A3 | 1p on 6p lilac & pur | 12.00 | 5.50 |
| a. | | "ONE" omitted | 325.00 | 650.00 |

Beware of copies offered as No. 37a that have part of "ONE" showing.

King Edward VII — A5

**1902                     Wmk. 2**

| | | | | |
|---|---|---|---|---|
| 38 | A5 | ½p violet & green | 1.75 | .50 |
| 39 | A5 | 1p vio & car rose | 1.75 | .25 |
| 40 | A5 | 2p vio & red org | 47.50 | 8.50 |
| 41 | A5 | 2½p vio & ultra | 5.50 | 11.00 |
| 42 | A5 | 3p vio & orange | 7.50 | 3.00 |
| 43 | A5 | 6p violet & pur | 8.00 | 4.75 |
| 44 | A5 | 1sh green & blk | 25.00 | 4.50 |
| 45 | A5 | 2sh grn & car rose | 25.00 | 40.00 |
| 46 | A5 | 5sh green & violet | 67.50 | 120.00 |
| 47 | A5 | 10sh green & brn | 87.50 | 160.00 |
| 48 | A5 | 20sh blk & blk, *red* | 200.00 | 240.00 |
| | | *Nos. 38-48 (11)* | 477.00 | 590.75 |

Numerals of 2p, 3p, 6p and 2sh6p of type A5 are in color on colorless tablet.

**1904-07                    Wmk. 3**
**Chalky or Ordinary Paper**

| | | | | |
|---|---|---|---|---|
| 49 | A5 | ½p vio & grn ('07) | 3.00 | 8.50 |
| 50 | A5 | 1p vio & car rose | 17.50 | 2.75 |
| 51 | A5 | 2p vio & red org | 16.00 | 2.50 |
| 52 | A5 | 2½p vio & ultra ('06) | 65.00 | 80.00 |
| 53a | A5 | 3p vio & org ('06) | 29.00 | 1.50 |
| 54 | A5 | 6p vio & pur ('06) | 90.00 | 40.00 |
| 55 | A5 | 2sh6p grn & yel ('06) | 140.00 | 140.00 |
| | | *Nos. 49-55 (7)* | 255.50 | 244.25 |

Nos. 50, 51 and 54 exist on both ordinary and chalky paper. No. 55 is on chalky paper only. No. 53a, is the chalky-paper variety of the more expensive No. 53. For detailed listings, see the *Scott Classic Specialized Catalogue of Stamps and Covers.*

**1907-13              Ordinary Paper**

| | | | | |
|---|---|---|---|---|
| 56 | A5 | ½p green | 12.00 | .40 |
| 57 | A5 | 1p red | 20.00 | .50 |
| 58 | A5 | 2p gray ('09) | 3.00 | 1.00 |
| 59 | A5 | 2½p ultramarine | 22.50 | 5.25 |

**Chalky Paper**

| | | | | |
|---|---|---|---|---|
| 60 | A5 | 3p vio, *yel* ('09) | 9.50 | 1.25 |
| 61 | A5 | 6p dull vio ('08) | 42.50 | 2.25 |
| a. | | 6p dull violet & red violet | 8.50 | 8.00 |

---

| | | | | |
|---|---|---|---|---|
| 62 | A5 | 1sh blk, *grn* ('09) | 28.00 | 1.50 |
| 63a | A5 | 2sh Ordinary paper | 9.50 | 19.00 |
| 64 | A5 | 2sh6p blk & red, *blue* ('11) | 42.50 | 105.00 |
| 65 | A5 | 5sh grn & red, *yel* ('13) | 65.00 | 250.00 |
| | | *Nos. 56-65 (9)* | 245.00 | 367.15 |

King Edward VII — A6

**1908, Nov.          Ordinary Paper**

| | | | | |
|---|---|---|---|---|
| 66 | A6 | 1p carmine | 9.50 | .25 |

King George V
A7          A8

For description of Dies I and II, see front section of the Catalogue.

**Die I**

**1913-21           Ordinary Paper**

| | | | | |
|---|---|---|---|---|
| 69 | A7 | ½p green | 3.00 | 2.25 |
| 70 | A8 | 1p carmine | 2.25 | .25 |
| a. | | 1p scarlet | 4.25 | .60 |
| 71 | A7 | 2p gray | 12.50 | 3.00 |
| 72 | A7 | 2½p ultramarine | 16.00 | 2.75 |

**Chalky Paper**

| | | | | |
|---|---|---|---|---|
| 73 | A7 | 3p vio, *yel* ('15) | 4.50 | 1.00 |
| a. | | Die II ('19) | 65.00 | 6.75 |
| 74 | A7 | 6p dull vio & red vio | 14.00 | 3.00 |
| 75 | A7 | 1sh black, *green* | 6.75 | 2.75 |
| a. | | 1sh black, emerald | 4.00 | 2.50 |
| b. | | 1sh black, *bl grn*, ol back | 18.00 | .95 |
| c. | | Die II ('21) | 3.25 | .60 |
| 76 | A7 | 2sh vio & bl, *bl* | 14.00 | 5.25 |
| a. | | Die II ('21) | 190.00 | 77.50 |
| 77 | A7 | 2sh6p blk & red, *bl* | 14.50 | 16.00 |
| a. | | Die II ('21) | 45.00 | 45.00 |
| 78 | A7 | 5sh grn & red, *yel* | 30.00 | 70.00 |
| a. | | Die II ('21) | 52.50 | 180.00 |
| 79 | A7 | 10sh grn & red, *grn* ('16) | 70.00 | 120.00 |
| a. | | 10sh grn & red, emer | 50.00 | 200.00 |
| b. | | 10sh grn & red, *bl grn*, ol back | 45.00 | 100.00 |
| 80 | A7 | 20sh vio & blk, *red* ('16) | 175.00 | 120.00 |

**Surface-colored Paper**

| | | | | |
|---|---|---|---|---|
| 81 | A7 | 3p violet, *yel* | 2.10 | 1.00 |
| 82 | A7 | 5sh grn & red, *yel* | 30.00 | 72.50 |
| | | *Nos. 69-82 (14)* | 394.60 | 419.75 |

Numerals of 2p, 3p, 6p and 2sh6p of type A7 are in color on plain tablet.

**Die II**

**1921-25    Ordinary Paper    Wmk. 4**

| | | | | |
|---|---|---|---|---|
| 83 | A7 | ½p green ('22) | 1.50 | .75 |
| 84 | A8 | 1p brown ('22) | 1.00 | .25 |
| 85 | A7 | 1½p carmine ('22) | 2.75 | .25 |
| 86 | A7 | 2p gray | 2.60 | .40 |
| 87 | A7 | 2½p orange ('23) | 3.25 | 16.00 |
| 88 | A7 | 3p vio ('22) | 2.10 | 1.50 |

**Chalky Paper**

| | | | | |
|---|---|---|---|---|
| 89 | A7 | 6p dl vio & red vio ('22) | 5.00 | 3.50 |
| 90 | A7 | 1sh blk, *emer* ('25) | 11.00 | 4.25 |
| 91 | A7 | 2sh vio & bl, *bl* ('24) | 4.50 | 4.00 |
| 92 | A7 | 2sh6p blk & red, *bl* ('25) | 14.00 | 47.50 |
| 93 | A7 | 5sh grn & red, *yel* ('25) | 28.00 | 85.00 |

**Die I**

| | | | | |
|---|---|---|---|---|
| 94 | A7 | 15sh dl vio & grn ('21) | 200.00 | 700.00 |
| a. | | Die II ('25) | 140.00 | 700.00 |
| 95 | A7 | £2 grn & org | 550.00 | 2,000. |
| | | *Nos. 83-95 (13)* | 825.70 | 2,863. |

Christiansborg Castle — A9

**1928, Aug. 1  Photo.  Perf. 13½x14½**

| | | | | |
|---|---|---|---|---|
| 98 | A9 | ½p green | 1.50 | .50 |
| 99 | A9 | 1p red brown | 1.00 | .25 |
| 100 | A9 | 1½p scarlet | 4.50 | 1.60 |
| 101 | A9 | 2p slate | 4.50 | .25 |
| 102 | A9 | 2½p yellow | 4.75 | 3.50 |
| 103 | A9 | 3p ultramarine | 4.50 | .50 |
| 104 | A9 | 6p dull vio & blk | 5.25 | .50 |
| 105 | A9 | 1sh red org & blk | 8.00 | 1.90 |
| 106 | A9 | 2sh purple & black | 36.00 | 7.25 |
| 107 | A9 | 5sh ol green & car | 72.50 | 55.00 |
| | | *Nos. 98-107 (10)* | 142.50 | 71.25 |

---

Common Design Types pictured following the introduction.

**Silver Jubilee Issue**
Common Design Type

**1935, May 6   Engr.   Perf. 11x12**

| | | | | |
|---|---|---|---|---|
| 108 | CD301 | 1p brnsh blk & ultra | .75 | .60 |
| 109 | CD301 | 3p ultra & brown | 3.00 | 7.50 |
| 110 | CD301 | 6p indigo & grn | 17.00 | 30.00 |
| 111 | CD301 | 1sh brn vio & indigo | 5.00 | 40.00 |
| | | *Nos. 108-111 (4)* | 25.75 | 78.10 |
| | | Set, never hinged | 40.00 | |

**Coronation Issue**
Common Design Type

**1937, May 12        Perf. 11x11½**

| | | | | |
|---|---|---|---|---|
| 112 | CD302 | 1p brown | .85 | 2.50 |
| 113 | CD302 | 2p dark gray | 1.00 | 4.75 |
| 114 | CD302 | 3p deep ultra | 1.25 | 2.75 |
| | | *Nos. 112-114 (3)* | 3.10 | 10.00 |
| | | Set, never hinged | 6.00 | |

A10

George VI and Christiansborg Castle — A11

**Perf. 12x11½, 11½x12 (#123, 124, 125, 126, 127)**

**1938-41                       Wmk. 4**

| | | | | |
|---|---|---|---|---|
| 115 | A10 | ½p green | .35 | .50 |
| 116 | A10 | 1p red brown | .35 | .25 |
| 117 | A10 | 1½p rose red | .35 | .50 |
| 118 | A10 | 2p gray black | .35 | .25 |
| 119 | A10 | 3p ultramarine | .35 | .35 |
| 120 | A10 | 4p rose lilac | .70 | 1.25 |
| 121 | A10 | 6p rose violet | .70 | .25 |
| 122 | A10 | 9p red orange | 1.10 | .55 |
| 123 | A11 | 1sh gray grn & blk | 1.40 | .65 |
| 124 | A11 | 1sh3p turq grn & red brown | 1.75 | .50 |
| 125 | A11 | 2sh dk vio & dp bl | 4.00 | 21.00 |
| 126 | A11 | 5sh rose car & ol green | 7.50 | 24.00 |
| 127 | A11 | 10sh pur & blk | 7.50 | 32.50 |
| | | *Nos. 115-127 (13)* | 26.40 | 82.55 |
| | | Set, never hinged | 40.00 | |

Issued: 10sh, July, 1940; 1sh3p, Apr. 12, 1941; others, Apr. 1.

**Perf. 12**

| | | | | |
|---|---|---|---|---|
| 115a | A10 | ½p green | 7.50 | 4.00 |
| 116a | A10 | 1p red brown | 12.00 | .30 |
| 117a | A10 | 1½p rose red | 12.50 | 8.00 |
| 118a | A10 | 2p gray black | 10.00 | 2.00 |
| 119a | A10 | 3p ultramarine | 6.50 | 1.50 |
| 120a | A10 | 4p rose lilac | 6.50 | 4.50 |
| 121a | A10 | 6p rose violet | 15.00 | 2.00 |
| 122a | A10 | 9p red orange | 6.50 | 3.25 |
| 123a | A11 | 1sh gray grn & blk | 17.50 | 2.25 |
| 124a | A11 | 2sh dk vio & dp blue | 45.00 | 29.00 |
| 126a | A10 | 5sh rose car & ol grn | 65.00 | 35.00 |
| | | *Nos. 115a-126a (11)* | 204.00 | 91.80 |

**Catalogue values for unused stamps in this section, from this point to the end of the section, are for Never Hinged items.**

**Peace Issue**
Common Design Type

**1946, Oct. 14             Perf. 13½**

| | | | | |
|---|---|---|---|---|
| 128 | CD303 | 2p purple | .25 | .25 |
| a. | | Perf. 13½x14 | 25.00 | 3.00 |
| 129 | CD303 | 4p deep red violet | 1.60 | 3.50 |
| a. | | Perf. 13½x14 | 5.00 | 3.75 |
| | | *Nos. 128-129 (2)* | 1.85 | 3.75 |

A12

A13

½p, Mounted Constable. 1p, Christiansborg Castle. 1½p, Emblem of Joint Provincial Council. 2p, Talking Drums. 2½p, Map. 3p, Manganese mine. 4p, Lake Bosumtwi. 6p, Cacao farmer. 1sh, Breaking cacao pods. 2sh, Trooping the colors. 5sh, Surfboats. 10sh, Forest.

## 1948, July 1    Engr.    Perf. 12

| | | | | |
|---|---|---|---|---|
| 130 | A12 | ½p emerald | .25 | .60 |
| 131 | A13 | 1p deep blue | .25 | .25 |
| 132 | A13 | 1½p red | 1.50 | 1.50 |
| 133 | A12 | 2p chocolate | .65 | .25 |
| 134 | A13 | 2½p lt brown & red | 2.00 | 5.50 |
| 135 | A13 | 3p blue | 4.00 | 1.75 |
| 136 | A13 | 4p dk car rose | 4.75 | 6.00 |
| 137 | A12 | 6p org & black | 1.00 | .40 |
| 138 | A13 | 1sh red org & blk | 3.25 | .40 |
| 139 | A13 | 2sh rose car & ol brn | 11.00 | 4.75 |
| 140 | A13 | 5sh gray & red vio | 42.50 | 14.00 |
| 141 | A12 | 10sh ol grn & black | 22.00 | 17.00 |
| | | Nos. 130-141 (12) | 93.15 | 52.40 |

### Silver Wedding Issue
### Common Design Types

**1948, Dec. 20    Photo.    Perf. 14x14½**

| | | | | |
|---|---|---|---|---|
| 142 | CD304 | 1½p scarlet | .25 | .70 |

### Engraved; Name Typographed
### Perf. 11½x11

| | | | | |
|---|---|---|---|---|
| 143 | CD305 | 10sh dk brn olive | 35.00 | 47.50 |

### UPU Issue
### Common Design Types
### Engr.; Name Typo. on 2½p and 3p

**1949, Oct. 10    Perf. 13½, 11x11½**

| | | | | |
|---|---|---|---|---|
| 144 | CD306 | 2p red brown | .25 | .25 |
| 145 | CD307 | 2½p deep orange | 1.60 | 8.00 |
| 146 | CD308 | 3p indigo | .35 | 1.75 |
| 147 | CD309 | 1sh blue green | .35 | .35 |
| | | Nos. 144-147 (4) | 2.55 | 10.35 |

Map of West Africa
A14

Mounted Constable
A15

Designs: 1p, Christiansborg Castle. 1½p, Emblem of Joint Provincial Council. 2p, Talking drums. 3p, Manganese mine. 4p, Lake Bosumtwi. 6p, Cacao farmer. 1sh, Breaking cacao pods. 2sh, Trooping the colors. 5sh, Surfboats. 10sh, Forest.

### Perf. 11½x12, 12x11½

**1952-54    Engr.**

| | | | | |
|---|---|---|---|---|
| 148 | A14 | ½p yel brn & car | .25 | .25 |
| 149 | A14 | 1p deep blue | .40 | .25 |
| 150 | A14 | 1½p green | .40 | 1.50 |
| 151 | A15 | 2p chocolate | .40 | .25 |
| 152 | A14 | 2½p red | .45 | 1.50 |
| 153 | A14 | 3p rose | 1.25 | .25 |
| 154 | A14 | 4p deep blue | .50 | .45 |
| 155 | A14 | 6p orange & black | 1.00 | .25 |
| 156 | A14 | 1sh red org & black | 3.25 | .25 |
| 157 | A14 | 2sh rose car & ol brn | 16.00 | 1.00 |
| 158 | A14 | 5sh gray & red vio | 29.00 | 8.00 |
| 159 | A15 | 10sh olive grn & blk | 26.00 | 14.00 |
| | | Nos. 148-159 (12) | 78.90 | 27.95 |

Nos. 148-149 exist in vertical coils.
Issued: 2½p, 12/19/52; ½p, 1½p, 3p, 4p, 4/1/53; 1p, 2p, 6p, 1sh-10sh, 3/1/54.
For overprints see Ghana #5-13, 25-27.

### Coronation Issue
### Common Design Type

**1953, June 2    Perf. 13½x13**

| | | | | |
|---|---|---|---|---|
| 160 | CD312 | 2p dk brown & black | 1.00 | .25 |
| | | Nos. 160 (1) | 1.00 | .25 |

### POSTAGE DUE STAMPS

D1

**1923    Typo.    Wmk. 4    Perf. 14**
### Yellowish Toned Paper

| | | | | |
|---|---|---|---|---|
| J1 | D1 | ½p black | 20.00 | 125.00 |
| J2 | D1 | 1p black | .95 | 1.50 |
| J3 | D1 | 2p black | 13.00 | 3.00 |
| J4 | D1 | 3p black | 22.50 | 2.50 |
| | | Nos. J1-J4 (4) | 56.45 | 132.00 |

---

## 1951-52    Typo.    Wmk. 4    Perf. 14
### Chalk-Surfaced Paper

| | | | | |
|---|---|---|---|---|
| J5 | D1 | 2p black | 4.00 | 32.50 |
| a. | | Wmk. 4a (error) | 750.00 | |
| b. | | Wmk. 4, crown missing (error) | 1,600. | |
| J6 | D1 | 3p black | 4.50 | 30.00 |
| a. | | Wmk. 4a (error) | 700.00 | |
| b. | | Wmk. 4, crown missing (error) | 1,500. | |
| J7 | D1 | 6p black ('52) | 2.10 | 18.00 |
| a. | | Wmk. 4a (error) | 1,300. | |
| b. | | Wmk. 4, crown missing (error) | 2,250. | |
| J8 | D1 | 1sh black ('52) | 2.10 | 80.00 |
| a. | | Wmk. 4a (error) | 1,700. | |
| | | Nos. J5-J8 (4) | 12.70 | 160.50 |

Issued: Nos. J7-J8, 10/1.

---

### WAR TAX STAMP

Regular Issue of 1913 Surcharged

**1918, June    Wmk. 3    Perf. 14**

| | | | | |
|---|---|---|---|---|
| MR1 | A8 | 1p on 1p scarlet | 4.00 | 1.00 |

---

# GRAND COMORO

'grand 'kä-mə-ˌrō

LOCATION — One of the Comoro Islands in the Mozambique Channel between Madagascar and Mozambique.
GOVT. — French Colony
AREA — 385 sq. mi. (approx.)
POP. — 50,000 (approx.)
CAPITAL — Moroni

100 Centimes = 1 Franc

See Comoro Islands.

Navigation and Commerce — A1

### Perf. 14x13½

**1897-1907    Typo.    Unwmk.**
### Name of Colony in Blue or Carmine

| | | | | |
|---|---|---|---|---|
| 1 | A1 | 1c blk, *lil bl* | 1.25 | 1.25 |
| 2 | A1 | 2c brn, *buff* | 1.60 | 1.60 |
| 3 | A1 | 4c claret, *lav* | 2.25 | 2.25 |
| 4 | A1 | 5c grn, *grnsh* | 4.25 | 3.75 |
| 5 | A1 | 10c blk, *lavender* | 9.50 | 6.00 |
| 6 | A1 | 10c red ('00) | 11.00 | 11.00 |
| 7 | A1 | 15c blue, quadrille paper | 22.00 | 14.50 |
| 8 | A1 | 15c gray, *lt gray* ('00) | 11.00 | 11.00 |
| 9 | A1 | 20c red, *grn* | 12.50 | 12.50 |
| 10 | A1 | 25c blk, *rose* | 18.50 | 15.00 |
| 11 | A1 | 25c blue ('00) | 22.00 | 21.50 |
| 12 | A1 | 30c brn, *bister* | 23.00 | 20.00 |
| 13 | A1 | 35c blk, *yel* ('06) | 22.00 | 20.00 |
| 14 | A1 | 40c red, *straw* | 23.00 | 18.00 |
| 15 | A1 | 45c blk, *gray grn* ('07) | 80.00 | 70.00 |
| 16 | A1 | 50c car, *rose* | 40.00 | 24.00 |
| 17 | A1 | 50c brn, *bluish* ('00) | 45.00 | 40.00 |
| 18 | A1 | 75c dp vio, *org* | 60.00 | 40.00 |
| 19 | A1 | 1fr brnz grn, *straw* | 40.00 | 32.00 |
| | | Nos. 1-19 (19) | 448.85 | 364.35 |

Perf. 13½x14 stamps are counterfeits.

### Issues of 1897-1907 Surcharged in Black or Carmine

**1912**

| | | | | |
|---|---|---|---|---|
| 20 | A1 | 5c on 2c brn, *buff* | 1.50 | 1.50 |
| a. | | Inverted surcharge | 260.00 | |
| 21 | A1 | 5c on 4c cl, *lav* (C) | 1.25 | 1.25 |
| 22 | A1 | 5c on 15c blue (C) | 1.25 | 1.25 |

---

| | | | | |
|---|---|---|---|---|
| 23 | A1 | 5c on 20c red, *grn* | 1.25 | 1.25 |
| 24 | A1 | 5c on 25c blk, *rose* (C) | 1.50 | 1.50 |
| 25 | A1 | 5c on 30c brn, *bis* (C) | 1.50 | 1.50 |
| 26 | A1 | 10c on 40c red, *straw* | 1.50 | 1.50 |
| 27 | A1 | 10c on 45c blk, *gray grn* (C) | 2.50 | 2.50 |
| 28 | A1 | 10c on 50c car, *rose* | 2.00 | 2.00 |
| 29 | A1 | 10c on 75c dp vio, *org* | 2.50 | 2.50 |
| | | Nos. 20-29 (10) | 16.75 | 16.75 |

Two spacings between the surcharged numerals are found on Nos. 20-29. For detailed listings, see the *Scott Classic Specialized Catalogue of Stamps and Covers.*
Nos. 20-29 were available for use in Madagascar and the entire Comoro archipelago.
Stamps of Grand Comoro were superseded by those of Madagascar, and in 1950 by those of Comoro Islands.

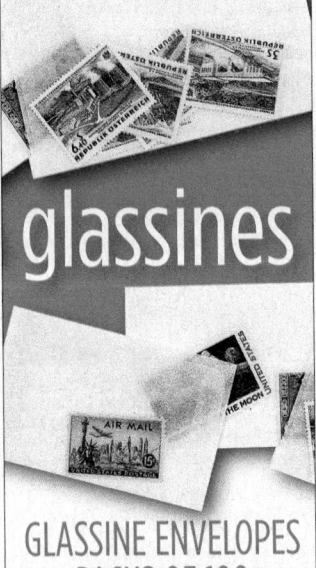

# glassines

## GLASSINE ENVELOPES PACKS OF 100

Perfect for organizing duplicates and sending approvals or mailing stamps.

| Item # | Description | Retail | AA |
|---|---|---|---|
| GE01 | #1 Glassine | $6.49 | $5.42 |
| GE02 | #2 Glassine | $7.25 | $6.16 |
| GE03 | #3 Glassine | $7.49 | $6.37 |
| GE04 | #4 Glassine | $8.49 | $7.22 |
| GE4H | #4.5 Glassine | $10.99 | $9.25 |
| GE05 | #5 Glassine | $10.25 | $8.71 |
| GE06 | #6 Glassine | $11.75 | $9.99 |
| GE07 | #7 Glassine | $12.75 | $10.84 |
| GE08 | #8 Glassine | $13.25 | $11.26 |
| GE10 | #10 Glassine | $17.99 | $16.99 |
| GE11 | #11 Glassine | $18.99 | $17.99 |

## GLASSINE ENVELOPES BOXES OF 1000

| Item # | Description | Retail | AA |
|---|---|---|---|
| GE01BOX | #1 Glassine | $54.99 | $50.59 |
| GE02BOX | #2 Glassine | $59.99 | $53.99 |
| GE03BOX | #3 Glassine | $61.99 | $55.79 |
| GE04BOX | #4 Glassine | $68.99 | $62.09 |
| GE4HBOX | #4.5 Glassine | $72.99 | $65.09 |
| GE05BOX | #5 Glassine | $84.99 | $78.19 |
| GE06BOX | #6 Glassine | $79.99 | $87.39 |
| GE07BOX | #7 Glassine | $94.99 | $87.99 |
| GE08BOX | #8 Glassine | $102.99 | $98.61 |
| GE10BOX | #10 Glassine | $149.99 | $149.99 |
| GE11BOX | #11 Glassine | $159.99 | $159.99 |

AmosAdvantage.com
1-800-572-6885

**ORDERING INFORMATION:** *AA prices apply to paid subscribers of Amos Media titles, or for orders placed online. Prices, terms and product availability subject to change.

# GREAT BRITAIN

'grāt 'bri-tən

### (United Kingdom)

LOCATION — Northwest of the continent of Europe and separated from it by the English Channel
GOVT. — Constitutional monarchy
AREA — 94,511 sq. mi.
POP. — 59,128,000 (1998 est.)
CAPITAL — London

12 Pence = 1 Shilling
20 Shillings = 1 Pound
100 Pence = 1 Pound (1970)

Catalogue values for unused stamps in this country are for Never Hinged items, beginning with Scott 264 in the regular postage section, Scott B1 in the semipostal section, Scott J34 in the postage due section, and Scott 93, Scott 246 and Scott 521 in British Offices in Morocco. All of the listings in British Offices — Middle East Forces, for Use in Eritrea, for Use in Somalia and for Use in Tripolitania are valued as neverhinged.

The letters in the corners of the early postage issues indicate position in the horizontal and vertical rows in which that particular specimen was placed.

In the case of illustration A1, this stamp came from the 15th horizontal row (O) and was the second stamp (B) from the left in that row. The left corner refers to the horizontal row and the right corner to the vertical row. Thus no two stamps on the plate bore the same combination of letters.

When four corner letters are used (starting in 1858), the lower ones indicate the stamp's position in the sheet and the top ones are the same letters reversed.

### Watermarks

Wmk. 18 — Small Crown

Wmk. 19 — V R

Wmk. 20 — Large Crown

Wmk. 21 — Small Garter

Wmk. 22 — Medium Garter

Wmk. 23 — Large Garter

Wmk. 24 — Heraldic Emblems

Wmk. 25 — Spray of Rose

Wmk. 26 — Maltese Cross

Wmk. 27 — "Half Penny" in Script

Wmk. 28 — Anchor

Wmk. 29 — Orb

Wmk. 30 — Imperial Crown

Wmk. 31 — Anchor

Wmk. 32 — Crown and GvR Multiple

Wmk. 33 — Crown and GvR

Wmk. 33 — In the normal watermark (sometimes termed the "repeated" watermark) the letters "GvR" are extended. The royal cyphers are placed one above the other and usually two appear on each stamp. In the multiple watermark the letters "GvR" are condensed, the cyphers are smaller and are so placed that those in each succeeding row are below the spaces between the cyphers in the row above.

Wmk. 34 — Large Crown and GvR

Wmk. 35 — Crown and Block GvR Multiple

Wmk. 219 — Large Crown and GvR

Wmk. 250 — Crown and E8R Multiple

Wmk. 251 — Crown and GviR Multiple

Wmk. 259 — Crown and Large G VI R

Wmk. 298 — Tudor Crown and E 2 R Multiple

Wmk. 308 — St. Edward's Crown and E 2 R Multiple

Wmk. 322 — St. Edward's Crown Multiple

Wmk. 401

Values for mint stamps of Great Britain are for stamps with original gum as defined in the catalogue introduction.

Values for unused and used stamps in this country are for examples with fresh color and all the attributes of fine-to-very fine condition (unless specified otherwise) through 1900 (Scott 126). All other stamps are for examples in the condition of very fine. Expect perforations to touch the design on one or two sides on all engraved stamps (Scott Nos. 8-21, 29-33 and 58) and early small format typographed stamps (Nos. 22-28, 34-56, 59-73, 78-89 and 94-95) because of the very narrow spacing between the stamps in the setting of the plates. Examples with margins clear of the design on all four sides range from scarce to very rare and command substantial premiums.

Cancellations on stamps from the 1847 issue to the 1900 issues, and in many cases beyond, are usually heavy. Values quoted are for stamps with better than average cancellations. **Poorly centered stamps and heavily canceled stamps might sell for 5 to 20 percent of the values listed here.**

Stamps with circular datestamps (especially those with a steel cds) range from scarce to very rare and command much higher prices. Premiums to be applied for fresh mint stamps with original gum and for used stamps that have both fine to very fine centering and circular datestamps can be found in footnotes for stamps from Scott 8 through Scott 126, including Official stamps for this period. For stamps that have both fine to very fine centering and circular datestamps, add the premiums together. Apply these premiums to covers, taking into account the overall condition of the cover and the stamps.

Queen Victoria — A1

**1840, May  Wmk. 18  Engr.  Imperf.**
**White Paper**

| | | | |
|---|---|---|---|
| 1 | A1 1p black | 12,500. | 375.00 |
| 2 | A1 2p blue | 38,000. | 975.00 |

No. 1 was printed from 11 plates; No. 2 from 2 plates. The 1p plates 1, 2, 5, 6, 8 and 9 can be found in two or more states. Stamp values are for the most common plates.
Issue dates: 1p, May 6; 2p, May 7.
See Nos. 3, 8-9, 11-12, 14, 16, 18, 20, O1. Compare designs A1-A2 with A8, A10.

A1a                A2

**1841**                **Bluish Paper**

| | | | |
|---|---|---|---|
| 3 | A1a 1p red brown | 625.00 | 32.50 |
| c. | Rouletted 12 | 26,000. | |
| d. | "A" missing in lower right corner (position BA, P77) | — | 27,500. |
| f. | On deep blue paper | 700.00 | 35.00 |
| g. | "Ivory Head" | 625.00 | 37.50 |
| 4 | A2 2p blue | 6,000. | 90.00 |
| c. | 2p violet blue | 27,500. | 1,800. |
| e. | "Ivory Head" | 6,500. | 100.00 |

No. 3 exists on silk thread paper, but was not regularly issued.
No. 4 was printed from two plates.
See Nos. 10, 13, 15, 17, 19, 21.
For shades, see the *Scott Classic Specialized Catalogue of Stamps and Covers.*

During the reigns of Victoria and Edward VII, many color trials were produced on perfed, gummed and watermarked papers.

Nos. 5-7 were printed one stamp at a time on the sheet. Space between the stamps usually is very small. Impressions that touch, or even overlap, are numerous.
Stamps with margins ½mm beyond the outer frame are considered as having full margins.
Values for Nos. 5-6 are for examples with complete frames and clear white margins on all four sides. Values for No. 7 are for examples with complete design but not necessarily clear margins around the design.

A3

**With Vertical Silk Threads**

**1847  Embossed  Unwmk.**

| | | | |
|---|---|---|---|
| 5 | A3 1sh pale green | 22,500. | 1,000. |
| a. | 1sh green | 22,500. | 1,000. |
| | Cut to shape | | 15.00 |

Die numbers (on base of bust): 1 and 2.

A3a

**1848**

| | | | |
|---|---|---|---|
| 6 | A3a 10p red brown | 12,000. | 1,500. |
| | Cut to shape | 500.00 | 20.00 |

Die numbers (on base of bust): 1, 2, 3, 4; also without die number.

A4

**1854**                **Wmk. 19**

| | | | |
|---|---|---|---|
| 7 | A4 6p red violet | 20,000. | 1,000. |
| a. | 6p dull violet | 20,000. | 1,000. |
| b. | 6p deep violet | 26,000. | 4,250. |
| | Cut to shape | | 10.00 |

**1854-55  Wmk. 18  Engr.  Perf. 16**
**Bluish Paper**

| | | | |
|---|---|---|---|
| 8 | A1 1p red brown | 350.00 | 35.00 |
| a. | 1p yellow brown | 475.00 | 55.00 |
| 9 | A1 1p red brn, re-engraved ('55) | 575.00 | 67.50 |
| a. | Imperf. | | |
| 10 | A2 2p blue | 5,000. | 110.00 |
| a. | 2p pale blue | 5,750. | 120.00 |

In the re-engraved 1p stamps, the lines of the features are deeper and stronger, the fillet behind the ear more distinct, the shading about the eye heavier, the line of the nostril is turned downward at right and an indentation of color appears between lower lip and chin.

# Easy Online Bidding

 **STANLEY GIBBONS** AUCTIONS

**ROUMET** R.H.P. *histoire postale*

 **PHILASEARCH**

**HEINRICH KÖHLER** *Deutschlands ältestes Briefmarken-Auktionshaus*

 **GM**

 **Postiljonen** AuctionHouse International *We value your collection*

**Philasearch.com**

 **FERRARIO**

*Argyll Etkin Limited*

**A.KARAMITSOS**

 **C.G.** Auctions

**ASTE BOLAFFI**

**SCHLEGEL** Berliner Auktionshaus für Philatelie GmbH

**LASER INVEST**

TEL AVIV STAMPS (Y. Tsachor) Ltd. בולי תל אביב (י.צחור) בע"מ

 **CERES Philatélie**

 **Aix–Phila**

# J&K

*Internationales Auktionshaus*

**Colonial Stamp Co.**

 **Auktionshaus Weiser**

 **ROMANO**

 **Lenz** SEIT 1958 | BRIEFMARKEN MÜNZEN FACHHANDEL AUKTIONEN

 **AB PHILEA**

François **FELDMAN**

**Briefmarken LOTH MAINZ**

 **NORDPHILA**

 Auktionshaus Dr. Reinhard Fischer

 SUOMEN FILATELIAPALVELU OY

 **classicphil**

**LE TIMBRE CLASSIQUE** Paris ◊ Genève

**LUGDUNUM** *Philatélie* Thierry LALLEVÉE

**GROSVENOR**

**BOULE**

 **SKANFIL** *Auksjoner as*

 **CHERRYSTONE** PHILATELIC AUCTIONEERS

*Robert A. Siegel* AUCTION GALLERIES. INC.

 **C O R B I T T S**

**LA POSTALE** PHILATÉLIE

 **David Feldman** Geneva ◆ Hong Kong ◆ New York

## and many more

## Perf. 14

| | | | | |
|---|---|---|---|---|
| 11 | A1 | 1p red brown ('55) | 1,250. | 110.00 |
| a. | | Imperf. | | |
| 12 | A1 | 1p red brn, re-engraved ('55) | 750.00 | 75.00 |
| a. | | 1p org brn, re-engraved | 2,000. | 250.00 |
| 13 | A2 | 2p blue ('55) | 15,000. | 375.00 |
| a. | | Imperf. (P5) | | 10,000. |

Wmk. 20 exists in two types. The first includes two vertical prongs, rising from the top of the crown's headband and extending into each of the two balancing midsections. The second type (illustrated), introduced in 1861, omits these prongs.

### 1855    Wmk. 20    Perf. 16
### Bluish Paper

| | | | | |
|---|---|---|---|---|
| 14 | A1 | 1p red brn, re-engraved | 2,750. | 140.00 |
| 15 | A2 | 2p blue | 20,000. | 500.00 |
| a. | | Imperf. (P5) | | 12,500. |

Some specialists regard No. 15a as a proof.

### 1855    Bluish Paper    Perf. 14

| | | | | |
|---|---|---|---|---|
| 16 | A1 | 1p red brn, re-engraved | 250.00 | 25.00 |
| a. | | 1p orange brn, re-engraved | 750.00 | 70.00 |
| b. | | 1p brown rose, re-engraved | 400.00 | 60.00 |
| c. | | Imperf. | 4,000. | 3,750. |
| 17 | A2 | 2p blue | 3,000. | 75.00 |

"Thick Line"

"Thin Line"

### Nos. 19, 21 With Lines Above and Below Head Thinner

### 1856-58    White Paper    Perf. 16

| | | | | |
|---|---|---|---|---|
| 18 | A1 | 1p rose red, re-engraved ('57) | 3,000. | 85.00 |
| 19 | A2 | 2p blue, thin lines ('58) | 15,000. | 375.00 |

### Perf. 14

| | | | | |
|---|---|---|---|---|
| 20 | A1 | 1p rose red, re-engraved ('57) | 45.00 | 9.00 |
| a. | | Imperf. | 4,500. | 3,500. |
| b. | | 1p red brown, re-engraved | 3,000. | 400.00 |
| 21 | A2 | 2p blue, thin lines ('57) | 3,250. | 75.00 |
| a. | | Imperf. | — | 14,000. |
| b. | | Vertical pair, imperf between | | 15,000. |

For examples of Nos. 8-21 with margins clear of the design on all four sides, add a 50 percent premium to the value listed. For stamps with clear circular datestamps, apply a 75 percent premium.

Queen Victoria — A5

### 1855    Typo.    Wmk. 21

| | | | | |
|---|---|---|---|---|
| 22 | A5 | 4p rose, *bluish* | 9,000. | 500.00 |
| 23 | A5 | 4p rose, *white* | 25,000. | 1,250. |

Compare design A5 with A11, A16, A31.

### 1856        Wmk. 22

| | | | | |
|---|---|---|---|---|
| 24 | A5 | 4p rose, *bluish* | 15,000. | 625. |
| 25 | A5 | 4p rose, *white* | 14,000. | 600. |

### 1857        Wmk. 23

| | | | | |
|---|---|---|---|---|
| 26 | A5 | 4p rose, *white* | 2,000. | 175.00 |

A6        A7

### 1856        Wmk. 24

| | | | | |
|---|---|---|---|---|
| 27 | A6 | 6p lilac | 1,500. | 140.00 |
| a. | | 6p deep lilac | 2,000. | 200.00 |
| b. | | Wmk. 3 roses and shamrock | — | — |

---

| | | | | |
|---|---|---|---|---|
| 28 | A7 | 1sh green | 3,500. | 400.00 |
| a. | | 1sh pale green | 3,500. | 400.00 |
| b. | | 1sh deep green | 6,000. | 600.00 |
| e. | | Imperf | — | |

Compare design A6 with A13, A18, A22. Compare A7 with A15, A21, A29.

A8

"Thick Line"

"Thin Line"

### 1858-69    Engr.    Wmk. 20    Perf. 14

| | | | | |
|---|---|---|---|---|
| 29 | A8 | 2p deep blue (P9) | 375.00 | 17.50 |
| | | Plate 7 | 2,250. | 70.00 |
| | | Plate 8 | 2,000. | 50.00 |
| | | Plate 12 | 3,500. | 150.00 |
| b. | | Imperf. (P9) | | 12,500. |

Plate numbers are contained in the scroll work at the sides of the stamp.

### Lines Above and Below Head Thinner

| | | | | |
|---|---|---|---|---|
| 30 | A8 | 2p blue ('69) (P13) | 400.00 | 35.00 |
| | | Plate 14 | 550.00 | 42.50 |
| | | Plate 15 | 575.00 | 42.50 |
| a. | | Imperf. (P13) | | 9,500. |

A9

### 1860-70

| | | | | |
|---|---|---|---|---|
| 31 | A9 | 1½p lil rose, *bluish* (P1) ('60) | 8,750. | 11,000. |
| 32 | A9 | 1½p dull rose ('70) (P3) | 550.00 | 80.00 |
| a. | | 1½p lake red | 650.00 | 80.00 |
| | | Plate 1 | 750.00 | 125.00 |
| c. | | Imperf (P1, 3) | 10,350. | |

The 1½p stamps from Plate 1 carry no plate number. The Plate 3 number is in the border at each side above the lower corner letters. No. 31 was prepared but not issued.

Queen Victoria — A10

### 1864

| | | | | |
|---|---|---|---|---|
| 33 | A10 | 1p rose red | 30.00 | 3.00 |
| a. | | 1p brick red | 30.00 | 3.00 |
| b. | | 1p lake red | 30.00 | 3.00 |
| c. | | Imperf. (P116, see footnote) | 6,000. | 3,750. |

Plate numbers are contained in the scroll work at the sides of the stamp.
No. 33 was printed from 1864 to 1879.
Thirty-nine plate numbers besides Plate 116 (No. 33c) are also known imperforate and used. Values for used examples start at $450.
Stamps from plate 177 have been altered and offered as plate 77.
For examples of Nos. 29-33 with margins clear of the design on all four sides, add a 50 percent premium to the value listed. For stamps with clear circular datestamps, apply a 75 percent premium.

### Plate Numbers

| | | |
|---|---|---|
| Plate 71 | 57.50 | 4.00 |
| Plate 72 | 62.50 | 5.00 |
| Plate 73 | 62.50 | 4.00 |
| Plate 74 | 62.50 | 3.00 |
| Plate 76 | 57.50 | 3.00 |
| Plate 77 | — | 750,000. |
| Plate 78 | 150.00 | 3.00 |
| Plate 79 | 52.50 | 3.00 |
| Plate 80 | 65.00 | 3.00 |
| Plate 81 | 65.00 | 3.00 |
| Plate 82 | 150.00 | 6.00 |
| Plate 83 | 175.00 | 10.00 |
| Plate 84 | 90.00 | 3.00 |
| Plate 85 | 62.50 | 4.00 |
| Plate 86 | 72.50 | 6.00 |
| Plate 87 | 52.50 | 3.00 |
| Plate 88 | 210.00 | 11.00 |
| Plate 89 | 62.50 | 3.00 |
| Plate 90 | 62.50 | 3.00 |
| Plate 91 | 85.00 | 8.00 |
| Plate 92 | 57.50 | 3.00 |

---

| | | |
|---|---|---|
| Plate 93 | 72.50 | 3.00 |
| Plate 94 | 70.00 | 7.00 |
| Plate 95 | 65.00 | 3.00 |
| Plate 96 | 65.00 | 3.00 |
| Plate 97 | 65.00 | 5.00 |
| Plate 98 | 75.00 | 7.50 |
| Plate 99 | 85.00 | 6.50 |
| Plate 100 | 90.00 | 3.00 |
| Plate 101 | 90.00 | 12.50 |
| Plate 102 | 70.00 | 3.00 |
| Plate 103 | 75.00 | 5.00 |
| Plate 104 | 110.00 | 6.50 |
| Plate 105 | 150.00 | 10.50 |
| Plate 106 | 85.00 | 3.00 |
| Plate 107 | 90.00 | 10.50 |
| Plate 108 | 125.00 | 3.00 |
| Plate 109 | 135.00 | 5.25 |
| Plate 110 | 90.00 | 12.50 |
| Plate 111 | 75.00 | 3.00 |
| Plate 112 | 100.00 | 3.00 |
| Plate 113 | 75.00 | 17.50 |
| Plate 114 | 375.00 | 17.50 |
| Plate 115 | 145.00 | 3.00 |
| Plate 116 | 110.00 | 12.50 |
| Plate 117 | 70.00 | 3.00 |
| Plate 118 | 75.00 | 3.00 |
| Plate 119 | 70.00 | 3.00 |
| Plate 120 | 30.00 | 3.00 |
| Plate 121 | 65.00 | 12.50 |
| Plate 122 | 30.00 | 3.00 |
| Plate 123 | 65.00 | 3.00 |
| Plate 124 | 50.00 | 3.00 |
| Plate 125 | 65.00 | 3.00 |
| Plate 127 | 85.00 | 3.00 |
| Plate 129 | 65.00 | 11.50 |
| Plate 130 | 85.00 | 3.00 |
| Plate 131 | 95.00 | 22.50 |
| Plate 132 | 210.00 | 32.50 |
| Plate 133 | 180.00 | 12.50 |
| Plate 134 | 30.00 | 3.00 |
| Plate 135 | 150.00 | 35.00 |
| Plate 136 | 150.00 | 26.00 |
| Plate 137 | 52.50 | 3.00 |
| Plate 138 | 37.50 | 3.00 |
| Plate 139 | 90.00 | 22.50 |
| Plate 140 | 37.50 | 3.00 |
| Plate 141 | 180.00 | 12.50 |
| Plate 142 | 105.00 | 35.00 |
| Plate 143 | 90.00 | 21.00 |
| Plate 144 | 150.00 | 27.50 |
| Plate 145 | 55.00 | 3.00 |
| Plate 146 | 65.00 | 7.50 |
| Plate 147 | 75.00 | 4.00 |
| Plate 148 | 65.00 | 4.00 |
| Plate 149 | 65.00 | 7.50 |
| Plate 150 | 32.50 | 3.00 |
| Plate 151 | 90.00 | 12.50 |
| Plate 152 | 90.00 | 9.00 |
| Plate 153 | 160.00 | 12.50 |
| Plate 154 | 75.00 | 3.00 |
| Plate 155 | 75.00 | 3.00 |
| Plate 156 | 70.00 | 3.00 |
| Plate 157 | 55.00 | 3.00 |
| Plate 158 | 55.00 | 3.00 |
| Plate 159 | 55.00 | 3.00 |
| Plate 160 | 55.00 | 3.00 |
| Plate 161 | 90.00 | 10.50 |
| Plate 162 | 75.00 | 10.50 |
| Plate 163 | 75.00 | 4.00 |
| Plate 164 | 75.00 | 4.00 |
| Plate 165 | 70.00 | 3.00 |
| Plate 166 | 70.00 | 7.50 |
| Plate 167 | 70.00 | 3.00 |
| Plate 168 | 75.00 | 11.50 |
| Plate 169 | 90.00 | 10.50 |
| Plate 170 | 60.00 | 3.00 |
| Plate 171 | 30.00 | 3.00 |
| Plate 172 | 55.00 | 3.00 |
| Plate 173 | 105.00 | 12.50 |
| Plate 174 | 57.50 | 3.00 |
| Plate 175 | 90.00 | 5.25 |
| Plate 176 | 90.00 | 3.00 |
| Plate 177 | 65.00 | 3.00 |
| Plate 178 | 90.00 | 5.25 |
| Plate 179 | 75.00 | 3.00 |
| Plate 180 | 90.00 | 8.00 |
| Plate 181 | 70.00 | 3.00 |
| Plate 182 | 140.00 | 8.00 |
| Plate 183 | 85.00 | 4.50 |
| Plate 184 | 55.00 | 3.00 |
| Plate 185 | 75.00 | 4.50 |
| Plate 186 | 100.00 | 3.00 |
| Plate 187 | 75.00 | 3.00 |
| Plate 188 | 105.00 | 14.50 |
| Plate 189 | 105.00 | 10.50 |
| Plate 190 | 75.00 | 8.50 |
| Plate 191 | 55.00 | 11.00 |
| Plate 192 | 75.00 | 3.00 |
| Plate 193 | 55.00 | 3.00 |
| Plates 194-195 | 75.00 | 11.50 |
| Plate 196 | 75.00 | 8.00 |
| Plate 197 | 85.00 | 12.50 |
| Plate 198 | 65.00 | 8.50 |
| Plate 199 | 85.00 | 8.50 |
| Plate 200 | 90.00 | 3.00 |
| Plate 201 | 55.00 | 7.50 |
| Plate 202 | 90.00 | 11.50 |
| Plate 203 | 55.00 | 23.00 |
| Plate 204 | 85.00 | 3.00 |
| Plate 205 | 85.00 | 4.50 |
| Plate 206 | 85.00 | 12.50 |
| Plate 207 | 90.00 | 12.50 |
| Plate 208 | 85.00 | 23.00 |
| Plate 209 | 70.00 | 11.50 |
| Plate 210 | 100.00 | 17.50 |
| Plate 211 | 105.00 | 30.00 |
| Plate 212 | 90.00 | 15.00 |
| Plate 213 | 90.00 | 15.00 |
| Plate 214 | 100.00 | 27.50 |
| Plate 215 | 100.00 | 27.50 |
| Plate 216 | 105.00 | 27.50 |
| Plate 217 | 105.00 | 11.00 |
| Plate 218 | 100.00 | 11.50 |
| Plate 219 | 140.00 | 95.00 |
| Plate 220 | 62.50 | 11.00 |
| Plate 221 | 105.00 | 25.00 |
| Plate 222 | 135.00 | 57.50 |
| Plate 223 | 150.00 | 85.00 |
| Plate 224 | 200.00 | 70.00 |
| Plate 225 | 3,750. | 875.00 |

A11

---

### 1862    Typo.       Wmk. 23

| | | | | |
|---|---|---|---|---|
| 34 | A11 | 4p vermilion | 2,250. | 150.00 |
| b. | | Hair lines (P4) | 2,300. | 170.00 |
| | | Imperf. (P4) | 2,600. | |

Hair lines on No. 34b are fine colorless lines drawn diagonally across the corners of the stamp. For more detail, see *Scott Classic Specialized Catalogue of Stamps & Covers 1840-1940.*

A12            A13

A14            A15

### 1862            Wmk. 24

| | | | | |
|---|---|---|---|---|
| 37 | A12 | 3p pale rose | 2,900. | 375.00 |
| a. | | 3p deep rose | 5,500. | 650.00 |
| b. | | With white dots under side ornaments | 52,500. | 20,000. |
| 39 | A13 | 6p lilac (P3) | 2,250. | 160.00 |
| c. | | 6p lilac, wmk. 3 roses & thistle | — | 7,000. |
| d. | | 6p lilac, hair lines (P4) ('64) | 3,500. | 275.00 |
| e. | | As "d," imperf. | 4,000. | |
| h. | | 6p deep lilac (P3) | 2,600. | 120.00 |
| 40 | A14 | 9p straw (p2) | 4,500. | 550.00 |
| d. | | 9p straw, wmk. 3 roses & thistle | — | |
| d. | | 9p bister (P2) | 7,000. | 700.00 |
| e. | | 9p bister, hair lines (P3) | 37,500. | 15,000. |
| 42 | A15 | 1sh green | 3,700. | 350.00 |
| a. | | 1sh deep green (P1) | 6,000. | 600.00 |
| c. | | 1sh deep green, with hair lines (P2) | 42,500. | |

Hair lines on Nos. 39d, 39e, 39f, 39g, 40e and 42c are fine colorless lines drawn diagonally across the corners of the stamp. For details, see *Scott Classic Specialized Catalogue of Stamps & Covers 1840-1940.*
Compare design A14 with A19.
Forgeries exist of Nos. 39a and 40a.

A16

### 1865            Wmk. 23

| | | | | |
|---|---|---|---|---|
| 43 | A16 | 4p vermilion (P12) | 600.00 | 62.50 |
| | | Plate 9 | 625.00 | 72.50 |
| | | Plate 10 | 850.00 | 150.00 |
| | | Plate 11 | 650.00 | 72.50 |
| | | Plate 13 | 375.00 | 47.50 |
| | | Plate 14 | 800.00 | 92.50 |
| a. | | 4p dull vermilion (P8) | 550.00 | 90.00 |
| | | Plate 7 | 600.00 | 100.00 |
| | | Plates 9 | 625.00 | 72.50 |
| | | Plate 10 | 850.00 | 150.00 |
| | | Plate 11 | 650.00 | 72.50 |
| | | Plate 12 | 600.00 | 62.50 |
| | | Plate 14 | 800.00 | 92.50 |
| | | Plate 13 | 375.00 | 47.50 |
| b. | | Imperf. (P11,12) | 7,750. | |

 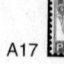

A17

(Hyphen after SIX) — A18

A19            A20

A21

### 1865            Wmk. 24

| | | | | |
|---|---|---|---|---|
| 44 | A17 | 3p rose (P4) | 3,000. | 275.00 |
| a. | | Wmk. error, 3 roses & shamrock | 8,000. | 1,450. |
| 45 | A18 | 6p lilac (P5) | 1,400. | 160.00 |
| a. | | 6p deep lilac | 2,400. | 240.00 |
| | | Plate 6 | 4,750. | 300.00 |

| | | | |
|---|---|---|---|
| b. | Double impression (P6) | | 14,500. |
| c. | Wmk. error, 3 roses & shamrock (P5) | | 2,750. |
| | As "c," Plate 6 | | 2,750. |
| 46 | A19 9p straw (P4) | 6,000. | 700.00 |
| | Plate 5 | 20,000. | |
| a. | Wmk. error, 3 roses & shamrock (P4) | | 3,000. |
| 47 | A20 10p red brn (P1) | | 67,500. |
| 48 | A21 1sh grn (P4) | 3,500. | 325.00 |
| b. | Wmk. error, 3 roses & shamrock | | 2,000. |
| c. | Vert. pair, imperf. btwn. | | 15,000. |

No. 46, plate 5 is from a proof sheet.
See Nos. 49-50, 52-54. Compare design A17 with A27.
For examples of Nos. 43-48 with margins clear of the design on all four sides, add a 40 percent premium to the value listed. For stamps with clear circular datestamps, apply a 60 percent premium.

(No hyphen after SIX) — A22

A23

**1867-80          Wmk. 25**

| | | | |
|---|---|---|---|
| 49 | A17 3p rose (P5) | 650.00 | 72.50 |
| a. | 3p deep rose | 950.00 | 115.00 |
| | Plate 4 | 2,250. | 350.00 |
| | Plate 6 | 675.00 | 85.00 |
| | Plate 7 | 775.00 | 85.00 |
| | Plate 8 | 750.00 | 72.50 |
| | Plate 9 | 750.00 | 85.00 |
| | Plate 10 | 1,050. | 175.00 |
| b. | Imperf. (P5,6,8,9) | 10,500. | |
| 50 | A18 6p dl vio (P6) | 2,400. | 210.00 |
| a. | 6p bright violet (P6) | 2,400. | 240.00 |
| b. | Imperf. (P6) | | 6,000. |
| 51 | A22 6p red vio ('69) (P9) | 850.00 | 110.00 |
| a. | 6p violet (P9) | 900.00 | 110.00 |
| | Plate 8 | 1,000. | 160.00 |
| | Plate 10 | | 45,000. |
| b. | Imperf. (P8, 9) | 11,000. | 5,000. |
| 52 | A19 9p bis (P4) ('67) | 2,900. | 350.00 |
| a. | Imperf. (P4) | 27,500. | |
| 53 | A20 10p red brn (P1) | 4,250. | 475.00 |
| a. | 10p deep red brown | 5,750. | 700.00 |
| b. | Imperf. (P1) | 20,000. | |
| 54 | A21 1sh grn (P4) | 1,125. | 75.00 |
| | Plate 5 | 925.00 | 52.50 |
| | Plate 6 | 1,400. | 52.50 |
| | Plate 7 | 1,625. | 105.00 |
| a. | 1sh deep green | 1,525. | 87.50 |
| b. | Imperf. (P4) | 9,000. | 5,750. |
| 55 | A23 2sh blue (P1) | 5,250. | 260.00 |
| a. | 2sh pale blue | 5,750. | 325.00 |
| | Plate 3 | | 19,250. |
| b. | Imperf. (P1) | 25,000. | |
| 56 | A23 2sh pale brn (P1) ('80) | 35,000. | 5,000. |
| a. | Imperf. | 35,000. | |

No. 51, plate 10 and No. 53, plate 2, are from proof sheets.
For examples of Nos. 49-56 with margins clear of the design on all four sides, add a 35 percent premium to the value listed. For stamps with clear circular datestamps, apply a 40 percent premium.

A24

**1867          Wmk. 26          Perf. 15½x15**

| | | | |
|---|---|---|---|
| 57 | A24 5sh rose (P1) | 11,000. | 775.00 |
| | Plate 2 | 17,500. | 1,750. |
| a. | 5sh pale rose | 11,000. | 775.00 |
| | Plate 2 | 17,500. | 1,750. |
| b. | Imperf. (P1) | 17,500. | |

See No. 90. Compare design A24 with A51.
For examples of No. 57 with margins clear of the design on all four sides, add a 50 percent premium to the value listed. For stamps with clear circular datestamps, apply a 50 percent premium.

A25

**1870          Engr.          Wmk. 27          Perf. 14**

| | | | |
|---|---|---|---|
| 58 | A25 ½p rose (P5) | 130.00 | 35.00 |
| | Plate 1 | 375.00 | 115.00 |
| | Plate 3 | 275.00 | 65.00 |
| | Plate 4 | 175.00 | 57.50 |
| | Plate 5 | 130.00 | 35.00 |
| | Plate 6 | 140.00 | 35.00 |
| | Plate 8 | 700.00 | 140.00 |
| | Plate 9 | 5,750. | 825.00 |
| | Plate 10 | 150.00 | 35.00 |
| | Plate 11, 13 | 140.00 | 35.00 |
| | Plate 12, 14 | 140.00 | 35.00 |
| | Plate 15 | 200.00 | 57.50 |
| | Plate 19 | 350.00 | 75.00 |
| | Plate 20 | 400.00 | 100.00 |
| a. | Imperf (see footnote) | — | |
| b. | Watermark inverted & reversed | 350.00 | 115.00 |

Plates 1, 4-6, 8, 13 and 14 are known imperf. Values: from $3,750 unused, $3,250 used.
For examples of No. 58 with margins clear of the design on all four sides, add a 125 percent premium to the value listed. For stamps with clear circular datestamps, apply a 75 percent premium.

A26

**1872-73          Wmk. 25          Typo.**

| | | | |
|---|---|---|---|
| 59 | A26 6p brown (P11) | 925.00 | 75.00 |
| | Plate 12 | | 4,400. |
| a. | 6p deep brown (P11) | 1,525. | 145.00 |
| | Plate 12 | | 4,075. |
| b. | 6p pale buff (P11) | 1,275. | 145.00 |
| | Plate 12 | 3,975. | 400.00 |
| 60 | A26 6p gray (P12) ('73) | 2,200. | 350.00 |
| a. | Imperf. | 17,500. | |

For examples of Nos. 59-60 with margins clear of the design on all four sides, add a 25 percent premium to the value listed. For stamps with clear circular datestamps, apply a 25 percent premium.

A27          A28

A29

Type A28 has a lined background.

**1873-80**

| | | | |
|---|---|---|---|
| 61 | A27 3p rose (shades) (P11) | 525.00 | 92.50 |
| | Plates 12 | 600.00 | 92.50 |
| | Plate 14 | 600.00 | 92.50 |
| | Plates 15-16 | 525.00 | 92.50 |
| | Plates 17-18 | 600.00 | 92.50 |
| | Plate 19 | 525.00 | 92.50 |
| | Plate 20 | 1,000. | 165.00 |
| 62 | A28 6p gray (P13-16) | 575.00 | 105.00 |
| | Plate 17 | 1,100. | 210.00 |
| 63 | A28 6p buff (P13) | | 29,000. |
| 64 | A29 1sh pale green (P12, 13) | 750.00 | 185.00 |
| | Plate 10 | 900.00 | 230.00 |
| | Plate 11 | 900.00 | 185.00 |
| | Plate 14 | | 46,000. |
| a. | 1sh deep green (P8, 9) | 1,275. | 265.00 |
| 65 | A29 1sh sal (P13) ('80) | 5,500. | 650.00 |

No. 63, plate 13, and No. 64, plate 14, are from proof sheets.
See Nos. 83, 86-87. For surcharges see Nos. 94-95. For overprints see Nos. O6, O30.
For examples of Nos. 61-65 with margins clear of the design on all four sides, add a 40 percent premium to the value listed. For stamps with clear circular datestamps, apply a 60 percent premium.

A30

**1875          Wmk. 28**

| | | | |
|---|---|---|---|
| 66 | A30 2½p claret (P1, 2) | 775.00 | 140.00 |
| | Plate 3 | 1,175. | 200.00 |
| a. | Bluish paper (P1) | 1,000. | 225.00 |
| | Plate 2 | 9,250. | 1,925. |
| | Plate 3 | | 6,500. |
| b. | Lettered "LH-FL" | 37,000. | 3,250. |

Forgeries exist of 66a.

**1876-80          Wmk. 29**

| | | | |
|---|---|---|---|
| 67 | A30 2½p claret (P4-9, 11-16) | 600.00 | 100.00 |
| | Plate 3 | 1,475. | 175.00 |
| | Plate 10 | 650.00 | 100.00 |
| | Plate 17 | 1,975. | 350.00 |
| 68 | A30 2½p ultra ('80) (P19, 20) | 675.00 | 65.00 |
| | Plate 17 | 675.00 | 87.50 |
| | Plate 18 | 675.00 | 65.00 |

See No. 82.

A31          A32

**1876-80          Wmk. 23**

| | | | |
|---|---|---|---|
| 69 | A31 4p vermilion (P15) | 3,500. | 550.00 |
| | Plate 16 | | 40,000. |
| 70 | A31 4p pale ol grn ('77) (P16) | 1,625. | 350.00 |
| | Plate 15 | 1,850. | 375.00 |
| | Plate 17 | | 23,000. |
| a. | Imperf (P15) | 1,400. | |
| 71 | A31 4p gray brn (P17) ('80) | 3,250. | 575.00 |
| 72 | A32 8p brn lilac (P1) ('76) | 8,750. | |
| 73 | A32 8p org (P1) ('76) | 2,150. | 400.00 |

Some specialists consider No. 70a a proof.
No. 72 was never placed in use.
No. 69, plate 16, is from proof sheets.
See No. 84.
For examples of Nos. 66-73 with margins clear of the design on all four sides, add a 50 percent premium to the value listed. For stamps with clear circular datestamps, apply a 50 percent premium. Add the two premiums together for covers with stamps having these attributes.

A33          A34

**1878          Wmk. 26          Perf. 15½x15**

| | | | |
|---|---|---|---|
| 74 | A33 10sh grnsh gray (P1) | 57,500. | 3,750. |
| 75 | A34 £1 brn lilac (P1) | 87,500. | 5,250. |

See Nos. 91-92. Compare design A34 with A52.
For examples of Nos. 74-75 with margins clear of the design on all four sides, add a 40 percent premium to the value listed. For stamps with clear circular datestamps, apply a 60 percent premium.

A35          A36

A37

A38

A39

**1880-81          Wmk. 30          Perf. 14**

| | | | |
|---|---|---|---|
| 78 | A35 ½p deep green | 65.00 | 26.00 |
| a. | Imperf. | 5,750. | |
| b. | No watermark | 11,500. | |
| 79 | A36 1p red brown | 40.00 | 17.50 |
| a. | Imperf. | 4,900. | |
| b. | Wmk. 29, error | | 31,500. |
| 80 | A37 1½p red brown | 290.00 | 70.00 |
| 81 | A38 2p lilac rose | 400.00 | 140.00 |
| 82 | A30 2½p ultra ('81) (P23) | 525.00 | 40.00 |
| | Plate 21 | 575.00 | 52.50 |
| | Plate 22 | 525.00 | 52.50 |
| a. | Imperf. (P23) | 750.00 | |
| 83 | A27 3p rose ('81) (P21) | 575.00 | 115.00 |
| | Plate 20 | 1,050. | 175.00 |
| 84 | A31 4p gray brown (P18) | 525.00 | 87.50 |
| 85 | A39 5p dp indigo ('81) | 850.00 | 200.00 |
| a. | Imperf. | 7,850. | 5,250. |
| 86 | A28 6p gray (P18) | 475.00 | 92.50 |
| | Plate 17 | 500.00 | 92.50 |
| 87 | A29 1sh salmon (P14) ('81) | 875.00 | 200.00 |
| | Plate 13 | 1,025. | 200.00 |
| | *Nos. 78-87 (10)* | *4,620.* | *988.50* |

Some specialists consider No. 82a a proof.
The 1sh in purple was not issued. Value, unused, $8,750.
See No. 98. For overprints, see Nos. O2-O3.
Compare design A35 with A54.
For examples of Nos. 78-87 with margins clear of the design on all four sides, add a 50 percent premium to the value listed. For stamps with clear circular datestamps, apply a 25 percent premium.

# Eastern Auctions Ltd.

In our Mail Auction, we offer about 2000 individually described and profusely illustrated lots approximately every six weeks. There is NO BUYER'S COMMISSION. We make every effort to present material for every collecting interest and budget. Large lots and individual stamps from worldwide countries and areas are always offered. Contact us to receive a complimentary catalogue of our next Mail Sale.

P.O. Box 250 - Bathurst - New Brunswick - E2A 3Z2 - Canada
Tel: 1(506) 548-8986 - Fax: 1(506) 546-6627
email: contact@easternauctions.com
website: www.easternauctions.com

Toll Free in North America
1(800) 667-8267

A40

Die I

Die II

**1881**

| 88 | A40 | 1p lilac (14 dots in each angle) | 260.00 | 52.50 |
|----|-----|-----|-----|-----|
| 89 | A40 | 1p lilac (16 dots in each angle) | 3.25 | 2.65 |
| a. | | Printed on both sides | 825. | |
| b. | | Imperf., pair | 8,750. | |
| c. | | Unwmkd. | 9,350. | |
| d. | | Bluish paper | 4,750. | |
| e. | | Printed on the gummed side | 825. | |

For overprints, see Nos. O4, O37, O45 and O55.

For examples of Nos. 88-89 with margins clear of the design on all four sides, add a 25 percent premium to the value listed. For stamps with clear circular datestamps, apply a 25 percent premium.

**1882-83** **Wmk. 31**

| 90 | A24 | 5sh rose, *bluish* (P4) | 41,000. | 4,700. |
|----|-----|-----|-----|-----|
| a. | | White paper | 32,500. | 4,500. |
| 91 | A33 | 10sh slate, *bluish* (P1) | 128,000. | 5,250. |
| a. | | White paper | 150,000. | 4,675. |
| 92 | A34 | £1 brown lilac, *bluish* (P1) | 162,500. | 8,750. |
| a. | | White paper | 187,500. | 8,000. |

A41

**1882** **Wmk. Two Anchors (31)**

| 93 | A41 | £5 brt org (P1) | 14,500. | 4,100. |
|----|-----|-----|-----|-----|
| a. | | £5 pale dull org, *bluish* | 70,000. | 14,500. |
| b. | | £5 bright org, *bluish* | 70,000. | 14,500. |

The paper of No. 93b is less bluish than that of No. 93a, and it is a later printing.

For examples of Nos. 90-93 with margins clear of the design on all four sides, add a 25 percent premium to the value listed. For stamps with clear circular datestamps, apply a 50 percent premium.

Types of 1873-80
Surcharged in Carmine

6d

**1883** **Wmk. 30**

| 94 | A27 | 3p on 3p violet | 750.00 | 185.00 |
|----|-----|-----|-----|-----|
| 95 | A28 | 6p on 6p violet | 775.00 | 175.00 |
| a. | | Double surcharge | 14,500. | |

For examples of Nos. 94-95 with margins clear of the design on all four sides, add a 40 percent premium to the value listed. For stamps with clear circular datestamps, apply a 50 percent premium.

A44

**1883** **Wmk. 31**

| 96 | A44 | 2sh6p lilac | 700.00 | 185.00 |
|----|-----|-----|-----|-----|
| a. | | Bluish paper | 7,000. | 1,750. |

For examples of No. 96 with margins clear of the design on all four sides, add a 25 percent premium to the value listed. For stamps with clear circular datestamps, apply a 25 percent premium.

---

**See British Offices Abroad for overprints on types A44-A133.**
**These overprints include "M.E.F.," "B.A.," "B.M.A.," "E.A.F.," "CHINA," "Morocco Agencies," "TANGIER," "LEVANT," "PARAS," and "PIASTRE(S)."**

Nos. 99-107 were printed by De La Rue in a newly invented doubly fugitive ink that was only available in lilac and green. The stamps were unpopular with the public and postal clerks because they were unattractive and the different denominations were difficult to distinguish from one another.

Values are for stamps of good color. Faded stamps sell for much less. **Soaking stamps will cause the color to run.**

A45

A46

A47

A48

A49

A50

**1883-84** **Wmk. 30**

| 98 | A35 | ½p slate bl ('84) | 40.00 | 11.75 |
|----|-----|-----|-----|-----|
| 99 | A45 | 1½p lilac ('84) | 145.00 | 52.50 |
| 100 | A46 | 2p lilac ('84) | 270.00 | 92.50 |
| 101 | A47 | 2½p lilac ('84) | 110.00 | 22.50 |
| 102 | A48 | 3p lilac ('84) | 325.00 | 115.00 |
| 103 | A49 | 4p green ('84) | 675.00 | 245.00 |
| 104 | A45 | 5p green ('84) | 675.00 | 245.00 |
| 105 | A46 | 6p green ('84) | 730.00 | 280.00 |
| 106 | A50 | 9p green | 1,450. | 550.00 |
| 107 | A48 | 1sh green ('84) | 1,875. | 380.00 |

For examples of Nos. 98-107 with margins clear of the design on all four sides, add a 50 percent premium to the value listed. For stamps with clear circular datestamps, apply a 50 percent premium.

Nos. 99-107 were printed by De La Rue in a newly invented doubly fugitive ink that was only available in lilac and green. The stamps were unpopular with the public and postal clerks because they were unattractive and the different denominations were difficult to distinguish from one another.

Values are for stamps of good color. Faded stamps sell for much less. Soaking stamps will cause the color to run.

No. 104 with line instead of period under "d" was not regularly issued. Value, $43,500.

Nos. 98-105 and 107 exist imperf. Values from $3,500 to $5,000 each for Nos. 98-105, $7,500 for No. 107.

For overprints see Nos. O5, O7, O27-O29.

A51

A52

**1884** **Wmk. 31**

| 108 | A51 | 5sh car rose | 1,150. | 290.00 |
|----|-----|-----|-----|-----|
| a. | | Bluish paper | 14,650. | 4,675. |
| 109 | A52 | 10sh ultra | 2,625. | 615.00 |
| a. | | 10sh cobalt | 49,000. | 9,650. |
| b. | | Bluish paper | 46,500. | 9,650. |
| c. | | As "a," bluish paper | 64,500. | 14,650. |

For overprints see Nos. O8-O9.

For examples of Nos. 108-109 with margins clear of the design on all four sides, add a 25 percent premium to the value listed. For stamps with clear circular datestamps, apply a 25 percent premium.

---

A53

**1884** **Wmk. 30**

| 110 | A53 | £1 brn violet | 32,500. | 3,500. |
|-----|-----|-----|-----|-----|

See Nos. 123-124. For overprints see Nos. O10, O13, O15.

For examples of No. 110 with margins clear of the design on all four sides, add a 25 percent premium to the value listed. For stamps with clear circular datestamps, apply a 25 percent premium.

The unpopular green and lilac issue (Nos. 98-107) were replaced by these stamps in colored inks and papers that made it easier to distinguish the different denominations. **Soaking these stamps will cause the color to run.**

**Queen Victoria Jubilee Issue**

A54

A55

A56

A57

A58

A59

A60

A61

A62

A63

A64

A65

Two types of 5p:
I — Squarish dots beside "d."
II — Tiny vertical dashes beside "d."

**1887-92** **Wmk. 30**

| 111 | A54 | ½p vermilion | 2.00 | 1.40 |
|-----|-----|-----|-----|-----|
| a. | | Printed on both sides | | |
| b. | | Double impression | 29,000. | |
| 112 | A55 | 1½p violet & grn | 21.00 | 9.25 |
| 113 | A56 | 2p grn & car rose | 40.00 | 17.50 |
| a. | | 2p green & vermilion | 500.00 | 305.00 |
| 114 | A57 | 2½p violet, *blue* | 29.00 | 5.75 |
| 115 | A58 | 3p violet, *yel* | 29.00 | 5.75 |
| a. | | 3p violet, *orange* | 925.00 | 175.00 |
| 116 | A59 | 4p brn & grn | 45.00 | 21.00 |
| 117 | A60 | 4½p car rose & grn ('92) | 12.75 | 52.50 |
| 118 | A61 | 5p lilac & bl, II | 49.00 | 17.50 |
| a. | | Type I | 925.00 | 140.00 |
| 119 | A62 | 6p violet, *rose* | 45.00 | 17.50 |
| 120 | A63 | 9p blue & lilac | 87.50 | 56.00 |

---

| 121 | A64 | 10p car rose & lilac ('90) | 70.00 | 52.50 |
|-----|-----|-----|-----|-----|
| 122 | A65 | 1sh green | 325.00 | 92.50 |
| | | Nos. 111-122 (12) | 755.25 | 349.15 |

See Nos. 125-126. For overprints see Nos. O11-O12, O14, O16-O18, O31-O36, O38, O44, O46-O48, O54, O56-O58, O65-O66.

**1888** **Wmk. Three Orbs (29)**

| 123 | A53 | £1 brown violet | 70,000. | 5,250. |
|-----|-----|-----|-----|-----|

**1891** **Wmk. 30**

| 124 | A53 | £1 green | 4,100. | 925.00 |
|-----|-----|-----|-----|-----|

**1900** **Wmk. 30**

| 125 | A54 | ½p blue green | 2.25 | 2.65 |
|-----|-----|-----|-----|-----|
| a. | | Imperf | 7,000. | |
| 126 | A65 | 1sh car rose & grn | 75.00 | 165.00 |

No. 125 in bright blue is a color changeling.

For examples of Nos. 111-126 with margins clear of the design on all four sides, add a 25 percent premium to the value listed. For stamps with clear circular datestamps, apply a 25 percent premium.

King Edward VII
A66    A67

A68

A69

A70

A71

A72

A73

A74

A75

A76

A77

A78

**1902-11** **Wmk. 30** **Perf. 14**
**Ordinary Paper**

| 127 | A66 | ½p gray green | 2.00 | 1.50 |
|-----|-----|-----|-----|-----|
| 128 | A66 | 1p scarlet | 2.00 | 1.50 |
| c. | | 1p aniline rose ('11) | 180.00 | 140.00 |
| e. | | Booklet pane of 6 | 60.00 | |
| f. | | No watermark ('11) | 50.00 | — |
| g. | | Imperf., pair | 30,000. | |
| 129 | A67 | 1½p vio & green | 50.00 | 24.00 |
| 130 | A68 | 2p yel grn & car | 70.00 | 25.00 |
| b. | | 2p deep grn & red ('11) | 28.00 | 22.00 |
| 131 | A66 | 2½p ultra | 20.00 | 15.00 |
| 132 | A69 | 3p dull pur, *org yel* | 50.00 | 18.00 |
| 133 | A70 | 4p gray brn & grn | 70.00 | 35.00 |
| 134 | A71 | 5p dull pur & ultra | 65.00 | 22.00 |
| 135 | A66 | 6p pale dull vio | 45.00 | 22.00 |
| a. | | 6p slate purple | 45.00 | 22.00 |
| b. | | 6p red violet | 45.00 | 28.00 |
| c. | | 6p dark violet | 45.00 | 28.00 |
| 136 | A72 | 9p ultra & dull vio | 140.00 | 75.00 |
| 137 | A73 | 10p car & dull pur | 150.00 | 75.00 |
| a. | | 10p scarlet & dull pur | 95.00 | 75.00 |

**138** A74 1sh car & dull grn 100.00 40.00
a. 1sh scar & dark green ('11) 120.00 60.00

**Wmk. 31**
**139** A75 2sh6p lilac 275.00 150.00
a. 2sh6p dark violet ('11) 325.00 190.00
**140** A76 5sh car rose 450.00 220.00
b. 5sh carmine 425.00 200.00
**141** A77 10sh ultra 1,000. 500.00

**Wmk. Three Imperial Crowns (30)**
**142** A78 £1 blue green 2,000. 825.00
Nos. 127-138 (12) 764.00 354.00

Nos. 129, 130 and 132 to 139 inclusive exist on both ordinary and chalky paper.
See Nos. 143, 144, 146-150. For overprints see Nos. O19-O26, O39-O43, O49-O53, O59-O64, O67-O83.

---

**See British Offices Abroad for overprints on types A44-A133.**
These overprints include "M.E.F.," "B.A.," "B.M.A.," "E.A.F.," "CHINA," "Morocco Agencies," "TANGIER," "LEVANT," "PARAS," and "PIASTRE(S)."

---

**Type of 1902-11 Issue**
**1904** **Wmk. 30**
**143** A66 ½p pale yel grn 2.00 1.50
b. Booklet pane of 5 + label 700.00
c. Booklet pane of 6 300.00
d. Double impression 20,000.
e. Imperf., pair 30,000.

Edward VII — A79

**1909-10**
**144** A70 4p pale orange ('10) 20.00 18.00
**145** A79 7p gray ('10) 17.25 25.00

**Type of 1902-11 Issue**
**1911** **Perf. 15x14**
**146** A66 ½p dull yel green 40.00 45.00
**147** A66 1p carmine rose 15.00 15.00
**148** A66 2½p brt ultra 22.00 15.00
**149** A69 3p violet, yellow 45.00 15.00
a. 3p gray, lemon 3,400.
**150** A70 4p orange 30.00 15.00
Nos. 146-150 (5) 152.00 105.00

King George V
A80  A81
Perf. 15x14

**1911, June 22** **Wmk. 30**
**151** A80 ½p yellow green 5.75 4.50
a. Booklet pane of 6 275.00
b. Perf. 14 (error) 18,500. 1,050.
**152** A81 1p carmine 5.25 3.00
a. Booklet pane of 6 275.00
b. Perf. 14 (error) —
c. 1p pale carmine 16.00 3.50
d. As "c," booklet pane of 6 125.00

**1912, Jan. 1** **Re-engraved**
**153** A80 ½p yellow green 10.00 4.50
**154** A81 1p scarlet 5.75 2.50
b. 1p aniline scarlet 180.00 110.00

In the re-engraved stamps the lines of the hair and beard are clearer. The re-engraved ½p has 3 lines of shading instead of 4 between the point of neck and frame; in the 1p the body of the lion is nearly covered with lines of shading.

**1912, Aug.** **Wmk. 33** **Perf. 15x14**
**Die I (Before Re-engraving)**
**155** A80 ½p yellow green 47.50 42.50
a. Booklet pane of 6 375.00
**156** A81 1p scarlet 32.50 32.50
a. Booklet pane of 6 275.00

**Die II (Re-engraved)**
**157** A80 ½p yellow green 9.00 4.50
**158** A81 1p scarlet 5.50 2.25

**1912, Sept.-Oct.** **Wmk. 32**
**158A** A80 ½p yellow green 15.50 9.25
e. Imperf., pair 375.00
**158B** A81 1p scarlet 20.00 11.50
e. Imperf., pair 325.00

---

A82  A83

A84  A85

A86  A87

A88  A89

King George V — A90

TWO PENCE:
Die I — Four horizontal lines above the head. Heavy colored lines above and below the bottom tablet. The inner frame line is closer to the central design than it is to the outer frame line.
Die II — Three lines above the head. Thinner lines above and below the bottom tablet. The inner frame line is midway between the central design and the outer frame line.

**1912-13** **Wmk. 33** **Perf. 15x14**
**159** A82 ½p green ('13) 1.10 1.10
a. Double impression 20,000.
b. Booklet pane of 6 110.00
**160** A83 1p scarlet 1.10 1.10
a. Booklet pane of 6 110.00
b. Tete beche pair 77,500.
**161** A84 1½p red brown 6.75 1.75
a. "PENCF" 325.00 275.00
b. 1½p orange brown 22.50 17.50
e. 1½p chocolate brown 12.50 2.25
f. As "e," Unwmkd. 290.00 275.00
g. Booklet pane of 6 140.00
h. Booklet pane of 4 + 2 labels 675.00
**162** A85 2p deep org (I) 5.00 3.50
a. 2p deep orange (II) ('21) 5.75 4.25
b. Booklet pane of 6 (I) 400.00
c. Booklet pane of 6 (II) 400.00
**163** A86 2½p ultramarine 14.00 4.50
**164** A87 3p bluish vio ('13) 9.00 3.25
**165** A88 4p slate green 17.50 2.25
**166** A89 5p yellow brown 17.50 5.75
a. Unwmkd. 1,300.
**167** A89 6p rose lilac 17.50 8.00
a. 6p dull violet ('13) 30.00 11.50
b. Perf. 14 100.00 125.00
**168** A89 7p ol grn ('13) 22.50 10.50
**169** A89 8p blk, yel ('13) 37.50 12.50
**170** A90 9p blk brn ('13) 17.50 6.75
**171** A90 10p light blue ('13) 25.00 22.50
**172** A90 1sh bister ('13) 40.00 13.50
Nos. 159-172 (14) 231.95 96.95

No. 167 is on chalky paper.
Nos. 159-172 were printed in a variety of shades.
See Nos. 177-178, 183, 187-200, 210, 212-220.
For overprints see Ireland Nos. 1-11, 15-35, 39-55, 59-62.
Compare design A82 with A97.

---

**See British Offices Abroad for overprints on types A44-A133.**
These overprints include "M.E.F.," "B.A.," "B.M.A.," "E.A.F.," "CHINA," "Morocco Agencies," "TANGIER," "LEVANT," "PARAS," and "PIASTRE(S)."

---

**Waterlow Brothers & Layton Printing (1913)**

"Britannia Rule the Waves" — A91

---

Measure 22mm vertically. Perforation holes are larger and evenly spaced.

**1913** **Engr.** **Wmk. 34** **Perf. 11x12**
**173** A91 2sh6p dk brn 325.00 160.00
**174** A91 5sh rose car 675.00 340.00
**175** A91 10sh indigo blue 1,100. 500.00
**176** A91 £1 green 3,000. 1,500.
Nos. 173-176 (4) 5,100. 2,500.

**De La Rue & Co. Printing (1915)**
Measure 22mm vertically. Gum tends to be yellowish and patchy. The top right and top left perf teeth are wider than the others. Perforation holes are smaller.

**1915** **Engr.** **Wmk. 34** **Perf. 11x12**
**173a** A91 2sh6p lt brn (worn plate) 350.00 240.00
**174a** A91 5sh br car 675.00 425.00
**175a** A91 10sh light blue 3,500. 900.00
See Nos. 179-181, 222-224.
For overprints see Ireland Nos. 12-14, 36-38, 56-58, 77-79.

**1913** **Wmk. 32** **Typo.** **Perf. 15x14**
**Coil Stamps**
**177** A82 ½p green 160.00 190.00
**178** A83 1p scarlet 240.00 240.00

**Bradbury, Wilkinson & Co. Printing (1918-19)**
**Seahorses Types of 1913-15**
**Retouched**
**1919** **Engr.** **Wmk. 34** **Perf. 11x12**
**179** A91 2sh6p olive brown 175.00 82.50
**180** A91 5sh car rose 350.00 145.00
**181** A91 10sh blue 525.00 190.00
Nos. 179-181 (3) 1,050. 417.50

The retouched stamps usually have a dot above the middle of the top frame. They are 22¾mm high, whereas Nos. 173-176 are 22mm high.

**Type of 1912-13**
**1922** **Typo.** **Wmk. 33** **Perf. 15x14**
**183** A90 9p olive green 120.00 32.00

**British Empire Exhibition Issue**

British Lion and George V — A92

**Wmk. 35**
**1924, Apr. 23** **Engr.** **Perf. 14**
**185** A92 1p vermilion 5.00 5.50
Never hinged 14.00
**186** A92 1½p dark brown 8.00 8.00
Never hinged 23.00
See Nos. 203-204.

**Types of 1912-13 Issue**
**1924** **Typo.** **Perf. 15x14**
**187** A82 ½p green 1.00 1.00
Never hinged 2.00
a. Wmk. sideways 9.00 3.25
Never hinged 18.00
b. Booklet pane of 6 85.00
Never hinged 120.00
c. Double impression 10,000.
**188** A83 1p scarlet 1.00 1.00
Never hinged 2.00
a. Wmk. sideways 20.00 15.00
Never hinged 40.00
b. Booklet pane of 6 85.00
Never hinged 120.00
**189** A84 1½p red brown 1.00 1.00
Never hinged 2.00
a. Tête bêche pair 500.00 800.00
Never hinged 775.00
b. Wmk. sideways 10.00 3.50
Never hinged 20.00
c. Booklet pane of 6 50.00
Never hinged 70.00
d. Bklt. pane of 4 + 2 labels 225.00
Never hinged 300.00
e. Double impression 19,000.
**190** A85 2p dp org (II) 2.50 2.50
Never hinged 4.00
a. Wmk. sideways 110.00 110.00
Never hinged 225.00
b. Unwatermarked 2,000.
Never hinged 2,400.
**191** A86 2½p ultra 5.00 3.00
Never hinged 10.00
a. Unwatermarked 3,000.
Never hinged 4,000.
**192** A87 3p violet 10.00 2.75
Never hinged 20.00
**193** A88 4p slate green 12.50 2.75
Never hinged 29.00
**194** A89 5p yel brown 22.50 3.25
Never hinged 42.50
**195** A89 6p dull violet 4.25 1.75
Never hinged 8.50
**198** A90 9p olive green 12.50 3.75
Never hinged 42.50

---

**199** A90 10p dull blue 42.50 42.50
Never hinged 90.00
**200** A90 1sh bister 24.00 3.25
Never hinged 55.00
Nos. 187-200 (12) 138.75 68.50

Nos. 187a, 188a, 189b, 190a issued in coils.
Inverted watermarks on the three lowest values are usually from booklet panes.
Nos. 188-189 were issued on experimental paper with variety of Wmk. 35: closer spacing; letters shorter, rounder.

**British Empire Exhibition Issue**
**Type of 1924, Dated "1925"**
**1925, May 9** **Engr.** **Perf. 14**
**203** A92 1p vermilion 11.50 23.00
Never hinged 28.75
**204** A92 1½p brown 28.00 50.00
Never hinged 69.00

A93  A94

A95

**1929, May 10** **Typo.** **Perf. 15x14**
**205** A93 ½p green 1.40 1.40
Never hinged 3.75
a. Wmk. sideways 60.00 55.00
Never hinged 85.00
b. Booklet pane of 6 200.00
**206** A94 1p scarlet 1.40 1.40
Never hinged 3.75
a. Wmk. sideways 100.00 95.00
Never hinged 145.00
b. Booklet pane of 6 200.00
**207** A94 1½p dark brown 1.40 1.10
Never hinged 3.75
a. Wmk. sideways 65.00 60.00
Never hinged 95.00
b. Booklet pane of 6 85.00
c. Booklet pane of 4 + 2 labels 400.00
**208** A95 2½p deep blue 6.50 6.50
Never hinged 17.50
Nos. 205-208 (4) 10.70 10.40
Set, never hinged 28.75

Inverted watermarks on the three lowest values are usually from booklet panes.
Nos. 205a, 206a and 207a were issued in coils.

St. George Slaying the Dragon — A96

**Wmk. 219**
**1929, May 10** **Engr.** **Perf. 12**
**209** A96 £1 black 750. 600.00
Never hinged 1,100.

Universal Postal Union, 9th Congress.

A97

Type A97 designs are re-engraved versions of the types of the 1912-13 issue, with the most obvious difference being the solid appearance of the central field. The backgrounds appear to be solid, although the photoengraving screen can be seen under magnification.

**Perf. 14½x14**
**1934-36** **Photo.** **Wmk. 35**
**210** A97 ½p dark green .50 .50
Never hinged 1.00
a. Wmk. sideways 10.00 5.00
Never hinged 17.50
b. Booklet pane of 6 90.00
**211** A97 1p carmine .50 .50
Never hinged 1.00
a. Wmk. sideways 20.00 13.00
Never hinged 40.00
b. Booklet pane of 6 85.00
c. Imperf., pair 7,250. 5,250.
d. Pair, imperf. btwn. 8,750. 9,000.
**212** A97 1½p red brown .50 .50
Never hinged 1.00
a. Imperf., pair 1,275. 1,400.
b. Wmk. sideways 10.00 5.00
Never hinged 15.00
c. Booklet pane of 6 32.50

|  |  |  |  |
|---|---|---|---|
| *d.* | Booklet pane of 4 + 2 labels | 200.00 |  |
| 213 | A97 2p red org ('35) | .75 | .75 |
|  | Never hinged | 1.50 |  |
| *a.* | Imperf., pair | 5,250. | 6,000. |
| *b.* | Wmk. sideways | 130.00 | 95.00 |
|  | Never hinged | 225.00 |  |
| 214 | A97 2½p ultra ('35) | 1.50 | 1.25 |
|  | Never hinged | 2.50 |  |
| 215 | A97 3p dk violet ('35) | 1.50 | 1.25 |
|  | Never hinged | 3.00 |  |
| 216 | A97 4p dk sl grn ('35) | 2.00 | 1.25 |
|  | Never hinged | 4.00 |  |
| 217 | A97 5p yel brown ('36) | 6.50 | 2.75 |
|  | Never hinged | 13.00 |  |
| 218 | A97 9p dk ol grn ('35) | 12.50 | 2.25 |
|  | Never hinged | 20.00 |  |
| 219 | A97 10p Prus blue ('36) | 15.00 | 10.00 |
|  | Never hinged | 30.00 |  |
| 220 | A97 1sh bister brn ('36) | 15.00 | 1.25 |
|  | Never hinged | 40.00 |  |
|  | *Nos. 210-220 (11)* | 56.25 | 22.25 |
|  | Set, never hinged | 117.00 |  |

The designs in this set are slightly smaller than the 1912-13 issue.

Inverted watermarks on the three lowest values are usually from booklet panes.

Nos. 210a, 211a, 212b and 213b were issued in coils.

### Britannia Type of 1913-19 Reengraved

**1934 Engr. Wmk. 34 Perf. 11x12**

|  |  |  |  |
|---|---|---|---|
| 222 | A91 2sh6p brown | 80.00 | 40.00 |
|  | Never hinged | 175.00 |  |
| 223 | A91 5sh carmine | 175.00 | 85.00 |
|  | Never hinged | 460.00 |  |
| 224 | A91 10sh dark blue | 350.00 | 80.00 |
|  | Never hinged | 575.00 |  |
|  | *Nos. 222-224 (3)* | 605.00 | 205.00 |

Printed by Waterlow & Sons. Can be distinguished by the crossed lines in background of portrait. Previous issues have horizontal lines only.

For overprints see Ireland Nos. 93-95.

### Silver Jubilee Issue

A98

**1935, May 7 Photo. Wmk. 35**

|  |  |  |  |
|---|---|---|---|
| 226 | A98 ½p dark green | .40 | .40 |
|  | Never hinged | .75 |  |
| *a.* | Booklet pane of 4 | 50.00 |  |
| 227 | A98 1p carmine | .75 | 2.00 |
|  | Never hinged | 1.50 |  |
| *a.* | Booklet pane of 4 | 45.00 |  |
| 228 | A98 1½p red brown | .50 | 1.00 |
|  | Never hinged | 1.00 |  |
| *a.* | Booklet pane of 4 | 18.00 |  |
| 229 | A98 2½p ultra | 3.50 | 6.50 |
|  | Never hinged | 6.25 |  |
| *a.* | 2½p Prussian blue | 13,500. | 15,000. |
|  | Never hinged | 16,500. |  |
|  | *Nos. 226-229 (4)* | 5.15 | 9.90 |
|  | Set, never hinged | 9.50 |  |

25th anniv. of the reign of George V. Device at right differs on 1½p and 2½p.

Inverted watermarks on the three lowest values are usually from booklet panes.

Edward VIII — A99

**1936 Wmk. 250**

|  |  |  |  |
|---|---|---|---|
| 230 | A99 ½p dark green | .25 | .25 |
|  | Never hinged | .25 |  |
| *a.* | Booklet pane of 6 | 16.00 |  |
|  | Never hinged | 30.00 |  |
| 231 | A99 1p crimson | .25 | .25 |
|  | Never hinged | .30 |  |
| *a.* | Booklet pane of 6 | 20.00 |  |
|  | Never hinged | 25.00 |  |
| 232 | A99 1½p red brown | .25 | .25 |
|  | Never hinged | .25 |  |
| *a.* | Booklet pane of 6 | 7.50 |  |
|  | Never hinged | 15.00 |  |
| *b.* | Booklet pane of 4 + 2 labels | 50.00 |  |
|  | Never hinged | 100.00 |  |
| *c.* | Booklet pane of 2 | 15.00 |  |
|  | Never hinged | 30.00 |  |
| 233 | A99 2½p bright ultra | .25 | .75 |
|  | Never hinged | .30 |  |
|  | *Nos. 230-233 (4)* | 1.00 | 1.50 |
|  | Set, never hinged | 1.10 |  |

Inverted watermarks on the three lowest values are usually from booklet panes.

King George VI and Queen Elizabeth — A100

**Perf. 14½x14**

**1937, May 13 Wmk. 251**

|  |  |  |  |
|---|---|---|---|
| 234 | A100 1½p purple brown | .30 | .25 |
|  | Never hinged | .30 |  |

Coronation of George VI and Elizabeth.

**See British Offices Abroad for overprints on types A44-A133.** These overprints include "M.E.F.," "B.A.," "B.M.A.," "E.A.F.," "CHINA," "Morocco Agencies," "TANGIER," "LEVANT," "PARAS," and "PIASTRE(S)."

A101     A102

King George VI — A103

Nos. 235-240 show face and neck highlighted, background solid.

**1937-39**

|  |  |  |  |
|---|---|---|---|
| 235 | A101 ½p deep green | .25 | .25 |
|  | Never hinged | .25 |  |
| *a.* | Wmk. sideways | .35 | .60 |
|  | Never hinged | .75 |  |
| *b.* | Booklet pane of 6 | 32.50 |  |
|  | Never hinged | 55.00 |  |
| *c.* | Booklet pane of 4 | 80.00 | 25.00 |
|  | Never hinged | 120.00 |  |
| *d.* | Booklet pane of 2 | 90.00 |  |
|  | Never hinged | 130.00 |  |
| 236 | A101 1p scarlet | .25 | .25 |
|  | Never hinged | .25 |  |
| *a.* | Wmk. sideways | 9.50 | 9.50 |
|  | Never hinged | 20.00 |  |
| *b.* | Booklet pane of 6 | 55.00 |  |
|  | Never hinged | 70.00 |  |
| *c.* | Booklet pane of 4 | 120.00 | 50.00 |
|  | Never hinged | 190.00 |  |
| *d.* | Booklet pane of 2 | 90.00 |  |
|  | Never hinged | 130.00 |  |
| 237 | A101 1½p red brown | .25 | .25 |
|  | Never hinged | .25 |  |
| *a.* | Wmk. sideways | .80 | 1.25 |
|  | Never hinged | 1.25 |  |
| *b.* | Booklet pane of 6 | 50.00 |  |
|  | Never hinged | 65.00 |  |
| *c.* | Booklet pane of 4 + 2 labels | 100.00 |  |
|  | Never hinged | 150.00 |  |
| *d.* | Booklet pane of 2 | 27.00 |  |
|  | Never hinged | 37.50 |  |
| 238 | A101 2p org ('38) | .70 | .55 |
|  | Never hinged | 1.40 |  |
| *a.* | Wmk. sideways | 37.50 | 45.00 |
|  | Never hinged | 80.00 |  |
| *b.* | Booklet pane of 6 | 145.00 |  |
|  | Never hinged | 190.00 |  |
| 239 | A101 2½p bright ultra | .25 | .25 |
|  | Never hinged | .40 |  |
| *a.* | Wmk. sideways | 37.50 | 37.50 |
|  | Never hinged | 80.00 |  |
| *b.* | Booklet pane of 6 | 110.00 |  |
|  | Never hinged | 160.00 |  |
| *c.* | Tête bêche pair | 22,000. |  |
| 240 | A101 3p dk pur ('38) | 2.50 | 1.10 |
|  | Never hinged | 5.25 |  |
| 241 | A102 4p gray grn ('38) | .25 | .80 |
|  | Never hinged | .65 |  |
| *a.* | Imperf., pair | 7,500. |  |
|  | Never hinged | 9,750. |  |
| *b.* | Horiz. pair, imperf. on 3 sides | 8,000. |  |
|  | Never hinged | 10,500. |  |
| 242 | A102 5p lt brn ('38) | 1.80 | .95 |
|  | Never hinged | 3.75 |  |
| *a.* | Imperf., pair | 7,000. |  |
|  | Never hinged | 9,250. |  |
| *b.* | Horiz. pair, imperf. on 3 sides | 7,500. |  |
|  | Never hinged | 9,750. |  |
| 243 | A102 6p rose lil ('39) | .80 | .65 |
|  | Never hinged | 1.60 |  |
| 244 | A103 7p emer ('39) | 2.00 | .65 |
|  | Never hinged | 5.50 |  |
| *a.* | Horiz. pair, imperf. on 3 sides | 7,500. |  |
|  | Never hinged | 9,750. |  |
| 245 | A103 8p brt rose ('39) | 3.00 | .85 |
|  | Never hinged | 8.00 |  |
| 246 | A103 9p dp ol grn ('39) | 2.75 | .85 |
|  | Never hinged | 7.00 |  |
| 247 | A103 10p royal bl ('39) | 2.75 | .85 |
|  | Never hinged | 7.50 |  |
| *a.* | Imperf., pair | 5,700. |  |
|  | Never hinged | 7,000. |  |

|  |  |  |  |
|---|---|---|---|
| 248 | A103 1sh brown ('39) | 2.75 | .80 |
|  | Never hinged | 9.75 |  |
| *a.* | Nos. 235-248 (14) | 20.30 | 9.05 |
|  | Set, never hinged | 51.55 |  |

Nos. 235a, 236a, 237a, 238a and 239a were issued in coils.

Nos. 235c and 236c are watermarked sideways.

The ½p, 1p, 1½p, 2p and 2½p with watermark inverted are from booklet panes.

No. 238 bisects were used in Guernsey from 12/27/40 to 2/24/41. Value, on cover $32.50.

See Nos. 258-263, 266, 280-285.

### Oman Surcharges

Various definitive and commemorative stamps between Nos. 243 and 372 were surcharged in annas (a), new paisa (np) and rupees (r) for use in Oman. The surcharges do not indicate where the stamps were used.

|  |  |
|---|---|
| King George VI and Royal Arms A104 | King George VI A105 |

**1939-42 Engr. Wmk. 259 Perf. 14**

|  |  |  |  |
|---|---|---|---|
| 249 | A104 2sh6p chestnut | 45.00 | 8.50 |
|  | Never hinged | 110.00 |  |
| 249A | A104 2sh6p yel grn ('42) | 6.50 | 1.60 |
|  | Never hinged | 16.00 |  |
| 250 | A104 5sh dull red | 9.50 | 2.20 |
|  | Never hinged | 22.50 |  |
| 251 | A105 10sh indigo | 135.00 | 24.00 |
|  | Never hinged | 275.00 |  |
| 251A | A105 10sh ultra ('42) | 15.00 | 5.50 |
|  | Never hinged | 47.50 |  |
|  | *Nos. 249-251A (5)* | 211.00 | 41.80 |
|  | Set, never hinged | 471.00 |  |

See No. 275.

Victoria and George VI — A106

**Perf. 14½x14**

**1940, May 6 Photo. Wmk. 251**

|  |  |  |  |
|---|---|---|---|
| 252 | A106 ½p deep green | .25 | .25 |
|  | Never hinged | .25 |  |
| 253 | A106 1p scarlet | .25 | .25 |
|  | Never hinged | .35 |  |
| 254 | A106 1½p red brown | .25 | .25 |
|  | Never hinged | .30 |  |
| 255 | A106 2p orange | .40 | .25 |
|  | Never hinged | .55 |  |
| 256 | A106 2½p brt ultra | .90 | .25 |
|  | Never hinged | 1.35 |  |
| 257 | A106 3p dark purple | 2.00 | 3.00 |
|  | Never hinged | 3.00 |  |
|  | *Nos. 252-257 (6)* | 4.05 | 4.25 |
|  | Set, never hinged | 5.80 |  |

Centenary of the postage stamp.

No. 255 bisects were used in Guernsey from 12/27/40 to 2/24/41. Value, on cover, $50.

### Type of 1937-39, with Background Lightened

**1941-42**

|  |  |  |  |
|---|---|---|---|
| 258 | A101 ½p green | .25 | .25 |
|  | Never hinged | .25 |  |
| *a.* | Booklet pane of 6 | 16.00 |  |
|  | Never hinged | 32.50 |  |
| *b.* | Booklet pane of 2 | 10.00 |  |
|  | Never hinged | 16.00 |  |
| *c.* | Imperf., pair | 6,500. |  |
|  | Never hinged | 9,250. |  |
| *d.* | Tete beche pair | 8,000. |  |
|  | Never hinged | 18,500. |  |
| *e.* | Booklet pane of 4 | 1,500. |  |
| 259 | A101 1p vermilion | .25 | .25 |
|  | Never hinged | .25 |  |
| *a.* | Wmk. sideways ('42) | 3.50 | 5.00 |
|  | Never hinged | 5.50 |  |
| *b.* | Booklet pane of 2 | 30.00 |  |
|  | Never hinged | 42.50 |  |
| *c.* | Imperf., pair | 6,500. |  |
|  | Never hinged | 8,750. |  |
| *d.* | Booklet pane of 4 | 1,500. |  |
| *e.* | Horiz. pair, imperf on 3 sides | 6,000. |  |
|  | Never hinged | 8,500. |  |
| 260 | A101 1½p lt red brn ('42) | .40 | .80 |
|  | Never hinged | .65 |  |
| *a.* | Booklet pane of 2 | 11.50 |  |
|  | Never hinged | 16.00 |  |
| *b.* | Booklet pane of 4 | 3,900. |  |

|  |  |  |  |
|---|---|---|---|
| 261 | A101 2p light orange | .30 | .55 |
|  | Never hinged | .55 |  |
| *a.* | Wmk. sideways ('42) | 22.50 | 22.00 |
|  | Never hinged | 30.00 |  |
| *b.* | Booklet pane of 6 | 20.00 |  |
|  | Never hinged | 32.50 |  |
| *c.* | Imperf., pair | 6,000. |  |
|  | Never hinged | 8,000. |  |
| *d.* | Tete beche pair | 16,000. |  |
|  | Never hinged | 18,500. |  |
| 262 | A101 2½p ultra | .25 | .25 |
|  | Never hinged | .25 |  |
| *a.* | Wmk. sideways ('42) | 12.00 | 13.00 |
|  | Never hinged | 16.00 |  |
| *b.* | Booklet pane of 6 | 16.00 |  |
|  | Never hinged | 22.50 |  |
| *c.* | Imperf., pair | 3,750. |  |
|  | Never hinged | 5,250. |  |
| *d.* | Tete beche pair | 12,000. |  |
|  | Never hinged | 18,500. |  |
| 263 | A101 3p violet | 1.75 | 1.10 |
|  | Never hinged | 2.75 |  |
|  | *Nos. 258-263 (6)* | 3.20 | 3.20 |
|  | Set, never hinged | 4.70 |  |

The ½p, 2p and 2½p with inverted watermarks are from booklet panes.

Nos. 259a, 261a and 262a were issued in coils.

Nos. 258b, 258e, 259b, 259d, 260a-260b are made from sheets.

> **Catalogue values for unused stamps in this section, from this point to the end of the section, are for Never Hinged items.**

### Peace Issue

A107

King George VI and Symbols of Peace and Industry — A108

**Perf. 14½x14**

**1946, June 11 Photo. Wmk. 251**

|  |  |  |  |
|---|---|---|---|
| 264 | A107 2½p bright ultra | .25 | .25 |
| 265 | A108 3p violet | .25 | .25 |

Return to peace at the close of WW II.

### George VI Type of 1939

**1947, Dec. 29**

|  |  |  |  |
|---|---|---|---|
| 266 | A103 11p violet brown | 3.25 | 3.00 |

A109

King George VI and Queen Elizabeth — A110

**1948, Apr. 26 Perf. 14½x14, 14x14½**

|  |  |  |  |
|---|---|---|---|
| 267 | A109 2½p brt ultra | .40 | .25 |
| 268 | A110 £1 dp chalky blue | 30.00 | 25.00 |

25th anniv. of the marriage of King George VI and Queen Elizabeth.

A111

Vraicking (Gathering Seaweed) A112

**1948, May 10 Perf. 14½x14**

|  |  |  |  |
|---|---|---|---|
| 269 | A111 1p red | .25 | .25 |
| 270 | A112 2½p bright ultra | .25 | .25 |

3rd anniversary of the liberation of the Channel Islands from German occupation.

Sold at post offices in the Channel Islands and at major philatelic windows in the United Kingdom, and valid for postage throughout Great Britain.

A113

A114

A115

A116

**1948, July 29**

| | | | | |
|---|---|---|---|---|
| 271 | A113 | 2½p bright ultra | .25 | .25 |
| 272 | A114 | 3p deep violet | .25 | .25 |
| 273 | A115 | 6p red violet | 2.75 | .90 |
| 274 | A116 | 1sh dark brown | 3.75 | 1.20 |
| | | Nos. 271-274 (4) | 7.00 | 2.60 |

1948 Olympic Games held at Wembley during July and August.

**George VI Type of 1939**
**Wmk. 259**

**1948, Oct. 1    Engr.    Perf. 14**

| | | | | |
|---|---|---|---|---|
| 275 | A105 | £1 red brown | 27.50 | 28.00 |

A117

A118

A119

A120

**Perf. 14½x14**

**1949, Oct. 10    Photo.    Wmk. 251**

| | | | | |
|---|---|---|---|---|
| 276 | A117 | 2½p bright ultra | .25 | .25 |
| 277 | A118 | 3p brt violet | .25 | .25 |
| 278 | A119 | 6p red violet | .35 | .25 |
| 279 | A120 | 1sh brown | .50 | .25 |
| | | Nos. 276-279 (4) | 1.35 | 1.00 |

UPU, 75th anniversary.

**Types of 1937**

**1950-51    Wmk. 251    Perf. 14½x14**

| | | | | |
|---|---|---|---|---|
| 280 | A101 | ½p light orange | .25 | .25 |
| a. | | Booklet pane of 2 | 16.50 | |
| b. | | Booklet pane of 4 | 16.50 | |
| c. | | Booklet pane of 6 | 11.00 | |
| d. | | Imperf., pair | 7,500. | |
| e. | | Tete beche pair | 18,000. | |
| 281 | A101 | 1p ultramarine | .25 | .25 |
| a. | | Wmk. sideways | 1.20 | 1.30 |
| b. | | Booklet pane of 2 | 16.50 | |
| c. | | Booklet pane of 4 | 22.50 | |
| d. | | Booklet pane of 6 | 45.00 | |
| e. | | Booklet pane of 3 + 3 labels | 20.00 | |
| f. | | Imperf., pair | 5,250. | |
| g. | | Horiz. pair, imperf on 3 sides | 7,000. | |
| 282 | A101 | 1½p green | .70 | .65 |
| a. | | Wmk. sideways | 3.50 | 5.50 |
| b. | | Booklet pane of 2 | 16.50 | |
| c. | | Booklet pane of 4 | 16.50 | |
| d. | | Booklet pane of 6 | 32.50 | |
| 283 | A101 | 2p lt red brown | .80 | .45 |
| a. | | Wmk. sideways | 1.90 | 2.25 |
| b. | | Booklet pane of 6 | 45.00 | |
| c. | | Tete beche pair | 18,000. | |
| d. | | Horiz. pair, imperf on 3 sides | 8,750. | |
| 284 | A101 | 2½p vermilion | .65 | .45 |
| a. | | Wmk. sideways | 1.90 | 1.90 |
| b. | | Booklet pane of 6 | 8.75 | |
| c. | | Tete beche pair | | |

---

| | | | | |
|---|---|---|---|---|
| 285 | A102 | 4p ultra ('50) | 2.20 | 1.90 |
| a. | | Double impression | 7,750. | |
| | | Nos. 280-285 (6) | 4.85 | 3.95 |

Inverted watermarks on Nos. 280-284 are usually from booklets.

Nos. 281a, 282a, 283a and 284a were issued in coils.

H.M.S.
Victory — A121

St. George
Slaying the
Dragon — A122

Royal
Arms — A123

Design: 5sh, White Cliffs, Dover.

**Perf. 11x12**

**1951, May 3    Engr.    Wmk. 259**

| | | | | |
|---|---|---|---|---|
| 286 | A121 | 2sh6p green | 7.50 | 1.00 |
| 287 | A121 | 5sh dull red | 16.00 | 1.00 |
| 288 | A122 | 10sh ultra | 22.50 | 8.00 |
| 289 | A123 | £1 lt red brown | 34.00 | 15.00 |
| | | Nos. 286-289 (4) | 80.00 | 25.00 |

Britannia, Symbols of Commerce and Prosperity, King George VI — A124

Festival
Symbol — A125

**Perf. 14½x14**

**1951, May 3    Photo.    Wmk. 251**

| | | | | |
|---|---|---|---|---|
| 290 | A124 | 2½p scarlet | .25 | .25 |
| 291 | A125 | 4p bright ultra | .25 | .25 |

Festival of Britain, 1951.

Queen Elizabeth
A126       A127

A128       A129

A130       A131

A132

The 2½d exists in two types: Type I, in the front cross of the diadem, the top line extends half the width of the cross; Type II, the top line extends across the full width of the top of the cross.

**Perf. 14½x14**

**1952-54    Photo.    Wmk. 298**

| | | | | |
|---|---|---|---|---|
| 292 | A126 | ½p red orange ('53) | .25 | .25 |
| a. | | Booklet pane of 2 | 5.00 | |
| b. | | Booklet pane of 4 | 8.50 | |
| c. | | Booklet pane of 6 | 4.25 | |

---

| | | | | |
|---|---|---|---|---|
| 293 | A126 | 1p ultra ('53) | .25 | .25 |
| a. | | Booklet pane of 2 | 5.25 | |
| b. | | Booklet pane of 4 | 12.50 | |
| c. | | Booklet pane of 6 | 37.50 | |
| d. | | Booklet pane 3 + 3 labels | 55.00 | |
| 294 | A126 | 1½p green ('52) | .25 | .25 |
| a. | | Booklet pane of 2 | 9.50 | |
| b. | | Booklet pane of 4 | 12.50 | |
| c. | | Booklet pane of 6 ('53) | 4.25 | |
| d. | | Wmk. sideways | 1.25 | 1.25 |
| e. | | As "c," imperf. (error) | 750.00 | |
| 295 | A126 | 2p red brn ('53) | .25 | .25 |
| a. | | Booklet pane of 6 | 65.00 | |
| b. | | Wmk. sideways | 2.25 | 2.25 |
| 296 | A127 | 2½p scarlet, Type I ('52) | .25 | .25 |
| a. | | Booklet pane of 6, Type II ('53) | 6.00 | |
| b. | | Wmk. sideways, Type I ('54) | 12.00 | 12.00 |
| c. | | Type II | 1.25 | 1.25 |
| 297 | A127 | 3p dk purple | .70 | .65 |
| 298 | A127 | 4p ultra ('53) | 2.50 | 1.10 |
| 299 | A129 | 5p lt brn ('53) | .65 | 1.50 |
| 300 | A129 | 6p lilac rose | 3.50 | .75 |
| 301 | A129 | 7p lt grn | 8.00 | 4.50 |
| 302 | A130 | 8p brt rose ('53) | .60 | .60 |
| 303 | A130 | 9p dp ol grn | 17.50 | 4.25 |
| 304 | A130 | 10p Prus blue | 15.00 | 4.00 |
| 305 | A130 | 11p vio brown | 27.50 | 11.50 |
| 306 | A131 | 1sh brown ('53) | .60 | .45 |
| 307 | A132 | 1sh3p dk grn ('53) | 4.25 | 2.50 |
| 308 | A131 | 1sh6p dk bl ('53) | 19.00 | 3.75 |
| | | Nos. 292-308 (17) | 101.05 | 36.80 |

Nos. 294d, 295b, 296b issued in coils.

Nos. 292-296 with watermark inverted are from booklets.

Type II stamps of No. 296 come only from booklet panes.

See Nos. 317-333, 353-369, 1801-1803, 2022-2023, 2086, 2125.

Compare design A128 with A139.

See regional issues, Guernsey, Jersey and Isle of Man for other stamps showing this portrait of the Queen, which have different frames or devices added to the design.

---

**See British Offices Abroad for overprints on types A44-A133.**

**These overprints include "M.E.F.," "B.A.," "B.M.A.," "E.A.F.," "CHINA," "Morocco Agencies," "TANGIER," "LEVANT," "PARAS," and "PIASTRE(S)."**

---

Windsor,
England — A133

Castles: 2sh6p, Carrickfergus, Ireland. 5sh, Caernarfon Castle, Wales. 10sh, Edinburgh, Scotland.

**1955    Engr.    Wmk. 308    Perf. 11x12**

| | | | | |
|---|---|---|---|---|
| 309 | A133 | 2sh6p dark brown | 12.50 | 1.50 |
| 310 | A133 | 5sh crimson | 37.50 | 4.25 |
| 311 | A133 | 10sh brt ultra | 80.00 | 9.00 |
| 312 | A133 | £1 intense blk | 110.00 | 37.50 |
| | | Nos. 309-312 (4) | 240.00 | 52.25 |

See Nos. 371-374, 525-528, 2278.

A134

A135

A136

A137

**Perf. 14½x14**

**1953, June 3    Photo.    Wmk. 298**

| | | | | |
|---|---|---|---|---|
| 313 | A134 | 2½p scarlet | .25 | .25 |
| 314 | A135 | 4p ultra | .90 | .45 |
| 315 | A136 | 1sh3p dark green | 3.25 | 1.10 |
| 316 | A137 | 1sh6p dark blue | 7.00 | 4.05 |
| | | Nos. 313-316 (4) | 11.40 | 4.05 |

See Nos. 1942, 2126.

---

**Types of 1952-54**

**1955-57    Wmk. 308    Perf. 14½x14**

| | | | | |
|---|---|---|---|---|
| 317 | A126 | ½p red org ('56) | .25 | .25 |
| a. | | Booklet pane of 6 | 4.25 | |
| b. | | Booklet pane of 4 | 8.50 | |
| d. | | Booklet pane of 2 | 27.50 | |
| 318 | A126 | 1p ultra ('56) | .35 | .25 |
| a. | | Bklt. pane of 3 + 3 labels | 19.00 | |
| b. | | Booklet pane of 6 | 5.50 | |
| c. | | Booklet pane of 4 | 11.00 | |
| e. | | Tete Beche pair | — | |
| f. | | Booklet pane of 2 | 27.50 | |
| 319 | A126 | 1½p green ('56) | .25 | .25 |
| a. | | Booklet pane of 6 | 4.50 | |
| b. | | Booklet pane of 4 | 1.50 | |
| c. | | Wmk. sideways ('56) | .30 | .65 |
| e. | | Tete beche pair | 3,000. | |
| f. | | Booklet pane of 2 | 6.50 | |
| 320 | A126 | 2p red brown | .30 | .35 |
| a. | | Wmk. sideways | .60 | .75 |
| b. | | Booklet pane of 6 | 3.75 | |
| d. | | Tete beche pair | 3,500. | |
| e. | | Vert. pair, imperf. between | 5,000. | |
| f. | | As "a," horiz. pair, imperf. between | 5,000. | |
| h. | | Imperf., pair | 350.00 | |
| 321 | A127 | 2½p scar, Type I ('56) | .25 | .25 |
| a. | | Booklet pane of 6, Type II | 3.75 | |
| b. | | Wmk. sideways, Type I ('56) | 1.50 | 1.75 |
| d. | | Type II | .55 | .40 |
| e. | | Tete beche pair | 3,500. | |
| f. | | Imperf., pair | 300.00 | |
| 322 | A127 | 3p dk pur ('56) | .30 | .25 |
| a. | | Booklet pane of 6 | 5.25 | |
| b. | | Booklet pane of 4 | 65.00 | |
| c. | | Wmk. sideways | 19.00 | 18.00 |
| e. | | Tete beche pair | 3,250. | |
| 323 | A128 | 4p ultra | 1.35 | .45 |
| 324 | A129 | 5p lt brn ('56) | 5.25 | 5.25 |
| 325 | A129 | 6p lil rose ('56) | 5.00 | 1.25 |
| 326 | A129 | 7p emerald | 45.00 | 10.00 |
| 327 | A130 | 8p brt rose ('56) | 6.50 | 1.10 |
| 328 | A130 | 9p dp ol grn ('56) | 18.00 | 2.75 |
| 329 | A130 | 10p royal bl ('56) | 18.00 | 2.75 |
| 330 | A130 | 11p vio brown | .75 | .85 |
| 331 | A131 | 1sh brown | 21.00 | .60 |
| 332 | A132 | 1sh3p dk grn ('56) | 25.00 | 1.50 |
| 333 | A131 | 1sh6p dark blue | 30.00 | 1.50 |
| | | Nos. 317-333 (17) | 177.55 | 29.60 |

Nos. 319c, 320a, 321b, 322c issued in coils.

Nos. 317-322 with watermark inverted are from booklets. See Nos. 353-369.

**Black Graphite Lines on Back**

**1957-59    Wmk. 308**

| | | | | |
|---|---|---|---|---|
| 317c | A126 | ½p red orange | .55 | .45 |
| p. | | Phosphor. ('59) | 4.50 | 4.50 |
| 318d | A126 | 1p ultra | .75 | .65 |
| p. | | Phosphor. ('59) | 12.00 | 12.00 |
| 319d | A126 | 1½p green | 2.25 | 1.90 |
| p. | | Phosphor. ('59) | 4.75 | 4.75 |
| 320c | A126 | 2p red brown | 2.75 | 2.75 |
| p. | | Phosphor. ('59) | 220.00 | 190.00 |
| 321c | A127 | 2½p scarlet (II) | 9.00 | 7.50 |
| 322d | A127 | 3p dark purple | 1.50 | 1.35 |
| | | Nos. 317c-322d (6) | 16.80 | 14.60 |

The vertical black graphite lines were applied to facilitate mail sorting by an electronic machine. The 2p has one line (at right, seen from back), the others two.

No. 321c exists with phosphor bands. This variety likely was not officially issued.

Phosphorescent bands were overprinted vertically in Nov. 1959 on the face of the preceding ½p, 1p, 1½p and 2p graphite-lined stamps, plus the 2p, 2½p, 3p, 4p and 4½p graphite-lined stamps with Wmk. 322, in a letter-sorting experiment. These faint bands can be seen best with an ultraviolet lamp; without it they can be seen best on unused stamps.

Scout Emblem and Rolling Hitch Knot — A138

4p, Swallows. 1sh3p, Globe encircled by compass.

**Perf. 14½x14**

**1957, Aug. 1    Wmk. 308**

| | | | | |
|---|---|---|---|---|
| 334 | A138 | 2½p scarlet | .25 | .25 |
| 335 | A138 | 4p ultra | .60 | .60 |
| 336 | A138 | 1sh3p dk green | 3.25 | 2.25 |
| | | Nos. 334-336 (3) | 4.10 | 3.10 |

50th anniv. of the Boy Scout movement and the World Scout Jubilee Jamboree, Sutton Coldfield, Aug. 1-12.

A139

**1957, Sept. 12** — **Photo.**
337 A139 4p ultra — .50 .50

46th Conf. of the Inter-Parliamentary Union, London, Sept. 12-19.

Welsh Dragon — A140

Designs: 6p, Flag with British Empire and Commonwealth Games Emblem. 1sh3p, Welsh dragon holding laurel.

**1958, July 18** — **Perf. 14½x14**
338 A140 3p dk purple — .25 .25
339 A140 6p red lilac — .25 .25
340 A140 1sh3p green — 1.75 1.15
Nos. 338-340 (3) — 2.25 1.65

6th British Empire and Commonwealth Games, Cardiff, July 18-26.

Regional Issues of Great Britain for Guernsey, Jersey, Isle of Man, Northern Ireland, Scotland and Wales-Monmouthshire are listed in separate sections following Great Britain Envelopes.

### Types of 1952-55
**Perf. 14½x14**

| | | | Photo. | Wmk. 322 |
|---|---|---|---|---|
| **1958-65** | | | | |
| 353 | A126 | ½p red orange | .25 | .25 |
| a. | | Booklet pane of 6 | 6.00 | |
| b. | | Booklet pane of 4 | 6.50 | |
| e. | | Booklet pane of 4 (3 No. 353 + No. 357) ('63) | 10.00 | 2.00 |
| g. | | Tete beche pair | 2,250. | |
| g. | | Booklet pane of 4 (2 Nos. 353 + 2 No. 357) ('64) | 2.45 | .80 |
| h. | | Wmk. sideways | .80 | .80 |
| 354 | A126 | 1p ultra ('59) | .25 | .25 |
| a. | | Booklet pane of 6 ('59) | 7.75 | |
| b. | | Booklet pane of 4 | 8.75 | |
| e. | | Imperf., pair | | |
| f. | | Bkit. pane, #2 #354, 2 #358 ('65) | 13.00 | 2.50 |
| f. | | Tête-beche pair | | |
| h. | | Wmk. sideways | 1.65 | 1.65 |
| s. | | As "f," booklet pane of 4 | 9.75 | 9.75 |
| 355 | A126 | 1½p green | .25 | .25 |
| a. | | Booklet pane of 6 | 11.00 | |
| b. | | Booklet pane of 4 | 11.00 | |
| e. | | Tête-beche pair | 3,000. | |
| g. | | Wmk. sideways | 37.50 | |
| 356 | A126 | 2p red brown | .25 | .25 |
| a. | | Wmk. sideways | 1.00 | 1.00 |
| b. | | Booklet pane of 6 | 110.00 | |
| 357 | A127 | 2½p scarlet, type II ('59) | .25 | .25 |
| a. | | Type I ('61) | .75 | .75 |
| b. | | Wmk. sideways, type I | .45 | .65 |
| c. | | Booklet pane of 6, Type II ('59) | 18.50 | |
| f. | | Tete beche pair, type II | 5,000. | |
| g. | | Booklet pane of 4, type II ('64) | 2.00 | |
| h. | | Imperf., pair | | |
| i. | | Wmk. sideways, type II ('59) | .75 | 1.35 |
| 358 | A127 | 3p dark purple | .25 | .25 |
| a. | | Booklet pane of 6 | 3.75 | |
| b. | | Booklet pane of 4 | 27.50 | |
| e. | | Imperf., pair | 250.00 | |
| g. | | Wmk. sideways | .55 | .60 |
| 359 | A128 | 4p ultra | .25 | .25 |
| b. | | Booklet pane of 6 ('65) | 6.50 | |
| c. | | Booklet pane of 4 ('65) | 7.50 | |
| d. | | Wmk. sideways | .75 | .60 |
| 360 | A128 | 4½p henna brn | .25 | .25 |
| 361 | A129 | 5p light brown | .30 | .40 |
| 362 | A129 | 6p lil rose ('59) | .25 | .25 |
| 363 | A129 | 7p emerald | .45 | .45 |
| 364 | A130 | 8p brt rose ('60) | .45 | .40 |
| 365 | A130 | 9p dp ol grn ('59) | .45 | .40 |
| 366 | A130 | 10p royal blue | .80 | .65 |
| 367 | A131 | 1sh brown | .45 | .35 |
| 368 | A132 | 1sh3p dk grn ('59) | .45 | .45 |
| 369 | A131 | 1sh6p dark blue | 5.25 | .60 |
| | | Nos. 353-369 (17) | 10.85 | 5.85 |

Nos. 356a and 357b were issued in coils. The 3p and 4p watermarked sideways may be from a coil or booklet pane of 4.
Booklet panes of this issue have watermarks upright, inverted or sideways.
Part perf. booklet panes exist of No. 353a and No. 354a.

### Black Graphite Lines on Back
**1958-59** — **Wmk. 322**

| | | | | | |
|---|---|---|---|---|---|
| 353c | A126 | ½p red orange ('59) | | 9.75 | 9.75 |
| d. | | Booklet pane of 6 | | 70.00 | |
| 354c | A126 | 1p ultra | | 2.25 | 1.65 |
| d. | | Booklet pane of 6 | | 22.00 | |
| 355c | A126 | 1½p green ('59) | | 100.00 | 87.50 |
| d. | | Booklet pane of 6 | | 525.00 | |

---

| | | | | | |
|---|---|---|---|---|---|
| 356c | A126 | 2p red brown | | 11.00 | 3.75 |
| cp. | | Phosphor. ('59) | | 6.50 | 4.50 |
| 357d | A127 | 2½p scarlet (II) ('59) | | 13.00 | 11.00 |
| dp. | | Phosphor. ('59) | | 24.00 | 19.75 |
| e. | | Booklet pane of 6 | | 130.00 | |
| 358c | A127 | 3p dark purple | | 1.00 | .70 |
| cp. | | Phosphor. ('59) | | 13.00 | 8.75 |
| d. | | Booklet pane of 6 | | 6.50 | |
| 359a | A128 | 4p ultra ('59) | | 6.00 | 5.50 |
| ap. | | Phosphor. ('59) | | 22.00 | 17.50 |
| 360a | A128 | 4½p henna brn ('59) | | 7.00 | 5.50 |
| ap. | | Phosphor. ('59) | | 32.50 | 22.00 |
| | | Nos. 353c-360a (8) | | 150.00 | 125.35 |

The vertical black graphite lines were applied to facilitate mail sorting by an electronic machine. The 2p has one line; the others two. Missing or misplaced lines occur on 1p, 3p and 4p.
Nos. 353c and 354c were issued only in booklets or coils; No. 355c only in booklets.
Booklet pane values are for panes with untrimmed perforations on all sides.

### Phosphorescent Stamps of 1958-65
**1960-67** — **Wmk. 322**

| | | | | |
|---|---|---|---|---|
| 353p | A126 | ½p red orange | .25 | .25 |
| ap. | | Booklet pane of 6 | 7.75 | |
| bp. | | Booklet pane of 6 | 50.00 | |
| hp. | | Wmk. sideways ('61) | 16.50 | 16.50 |
| 354p | A126 | 1p ultra | .25 | .25 |
| ap. | | Booklet pane of 6 | 7.50 | |
| bp. | | Booklet pane of 4 | 20.00 | |
| fp. | | Booklet pane of 2 each #354p, 358p | 20.00 | |
| hp. | | Wmk. sideways ('61) | 1.20 | 1.20 |
| 355p | A126 | 1½p green | .25 | .25 |
| ap. | | Booklet pane of 6 | 60.00 | |
| bp. | | Booklet pane of 4 | 87.50 | |
| fp. | | Wmk. sideways ('61) | 22.00 | 22.00 |
| 356p | A126 | 2p red brown | .25 | .25 |
| ap. | | Watermark sideways | 1.10 | 1.10 |
| 357p | A127 | 2½p scarlet (II) | .25 | .30 |
| ap. | | Type I ('61) | 47.50 | 42.50 |
| cp. | | Booklet pane of 6 | 130.00 | |
| 358p | A127 | 3p dark purple | .45 | .50 |
| ap. | | Booklet pane of 4 | 8.75 | |
| bp. | | Booklet pane of 4 | 32.50 | |
| gp. | | Watermark sideways | 1.90 | 1.90 |
| 359p | A128 | 4p ultramarine | .25 | .25 |
| bp. | | Booklet pane of 6 | 3.75 | |
| cp. | | Booklet pane of 4 | 16.50 | |
| dp. | | Watermark sideways | .30 | .50 |
| 360p | A128 | 4½p henna brown ('61) | .25 | .25 |
| 361p | A129 | 5p lt brown ('67) | .25 | .25 |
| 362p | A129 | 6p lilac rose | .35 | .30 |
| 363p | A129 | 7p emerald ('67) | .45 | .40 |
| 364p | A130 | 8p brt rose ('67) | .40 | .40 |
| 365p | A130 | 9p dp ol grn ('67) | .50 | .45 |
| 366p | A130 | 10p royal blue ('67) | .65 | .65 |
| 367p | A131 | 1sh brown ('67) | .45 | .35 |
| 368p | A132 | 1sh3p dark green | 1.90 | 2.50 |
| 369p | A131 | 1sh6p dark blue ('66) | 3.00 | 3.00 |
| | | Nos. 353p-369p (17) | 10.15 | 10.60 |

The 2p, 2½p (II) and 3p were issued with both one and two phosphorescent bands. The less expensive is valued here.
Watermarked sideways, the 2p is from a coil; the 3p and 4p from booklet pane or coil; the ½p, 1p and 1½p from booklet panes.
Booklet panes of 4 with phosphorescent bands;
No 354fp exists with 3p having one or two phosphorescent bands. No. 357cp exists with either one or two phosphorescent bands.

### Castle Type of 1955
**Perf. 11x12**

| | | | | Wmk. 322 |
|---|---|---|---|---|
| **1959-68** | | **Engr.** | | |
| 371 | A133 | 2sh6p dark brown | .40 | .40 |
| 372 | A133 | 5sh crimson | 1.40 | .50 |
| 373 | A133 | 10sh bright ultra | 4.75 | 4.75 |
| 374 | A133 | £1 intense blk | 14.50 | 9.00 |
| | | Nos. 371-374 (4) | 21.05 | 14.65 |

See Nos. 309-312, 525-528, 2278.

Postboy on Horseback A147

Queen Elizabeth II, Oak Leaves and 1660 Post Horn A148

**1960, July 7** — **Photo.** — **Wmk. 322**
**Perf. 14½x14, 14x14½**
375 A147 3p bright violet — .25 .25
376 A148 1sh3p dark green — 1.75 1.90

Tercentenary of the act establishing the General Letter Office (General Post Office).

---

Symbolic Wheel — CD3

**Perf. 14½x14**
**1960, Sept. 19** — **Wmk. 322**
377 CD3 6p red lilac & grn — 1.00 .25
378 CD3 1sh6p dk bl & red brn — 6.00 2.50

1st anniv. of the establishment of CEPT.

Symbolic Thrift Plant A150

Nut Tree, Nest, Squirrel, Owl A151

Thrift Plant — A152

**Perf. 14x14½, 14½x14**
**1961, Aug. 28** — **Photo.** — **Wmk. 322**
379 A150 2½p scar & blk — .25 .25
a. Black omitted — 27,500.
380 A151 3p pur & org — .25 .25
a. Orange omitted — 550.00
381 A152 1sh6p dk bl & ver — .95 .95
Nos. 379-381 (3) — 1.45 1.45

Centenary of Post Office Savings Bank.

CEPT Emblem — A153

Nineteen Doves Flying as One — CD4

Design: 10p, Queen at right.

**1961, Sept. 18** — **Perf. 14½x14**
382 A153 2p red brn, yel & rose — .25 .25
a. Orange omitted — 11,000.
383 CD4 4p ultra, pink & buff — .25 .25
384 CD4 10p dk bl, yel grn & Prus blue — .25 .25
a. Yellow green omitted — 17,500.
b. Dark blue omitted — 5,500.
Nos. 382-384 (3) — .75 .75

Hammer Beam Roof of Westminster Hall A155

Parliament A156

**Perf. 14½x14, 14x14½**
**1961, Sept. 25** — **Wmk. 322**
385 A155 6p red lil & gold — .25 .25
a. Gold omitted — 1,950.
386 A156 1sh3p grn & slate — 1.25 1.25
a. Slate (Queen's head) omitted — 27,500.
b. Green omitted —

7th Commonwealth Parliamentary Conf.

National Productivity Symbol — A157

Designs: 3p, Two arrows and map of the British Isles. 1sh3p, Five arrows pointing up.

---

Wheat Emblem and People — A158

**Perf. 14½x14**
**1962, Nov. 14** — **Photo.** — **Wmk. 322**
387 A157 2½p red & gray grn — .25 .25
388 A157 3p vio, lt blue & pur — .25 .25
a. Queen's head omitted — 4,675.
389 A157 1sh3p dk grn, red & lt bl — .85 .85
a. Queen's head omitted — 11,000.
Nos. 387-389 (3) — 1.35 1.35

### Phosphorescent

| | | | | |
|---|---|---|---|---|
| 387p | A157 | 2½p red & gray grn | .40 | .30 |
| 388p | A157 | 3p vio, lt blue & pur | .70 | .35 |
| 389p | A157 | 1sh3p dk grn, red & lt bl | 27.50 | 17.50 |
| | | Nos. 387p-389p (3) | 28.60 | 18.15 |

National Productivity Year. The watermark on Nos. 387-388 is inverted.

Phosphorescent Commemorative stamps between Nos. 387-493 were issued both with and without phosphorescence on the front unless otherwise noted with the issue.
Starting with No. 514, commemorative stamps were issued only with phosphorescence on the front unless otherwise noted.
Phosphorescent Regulars: Starting in 1967, all small stamps (lower values) of the regular series were issued only with phosphorescence.

1sh3p, Children of different races.

**1963, Mar. 21** — **Wmk. 322**
390 A158 2½p pink & dp car — .25 .25
p. Phosphor. — 1.00 1.00
391 A158 1sh3p yellow & brn — 1.00 1.00
p. Phosphor. — 19.00 14.00

FAO "Freedom from Hunger" campaign.

Paris Postal Conference A159

**1963, May 7** — **Wmk. 322**
392 A159 6p purple & green — .25 .25
p. Phosphor. — 4,125.
p. Phosphor. — 3.50 3.00

Cent. of the 1st Intl. Postal Conf., Paris, 1863, and Paris Postal Conf., May 7-9, 1963.

Buttercups, Daisies and Bee — A160

Design: 4½p, Badger, Fawn, woodpecker, lark, titmouse, butterfly, mouse and wild plants.

**1963, May 16** — **Perf. 14½x14**
393 A160 3p multicolored — .25 .25
p. Phosphor. — .35 .35
394 A160 4½p multicolored — .25 .25
p. Phosphor. — 1.50 1.50

Natl. Nature Week, May 18-25, and the importance of wildlife conservation.

Helicopter Lifting Man from Lifeboat — A161

Lifeboat Men — A162

Design: 4p, 19th cent. lifeboat under sail.

**1963, May 31** — **Photo.**
395 A161 2½p multicolored — .25 .25
396 A161 4p multicolored — .30 .30
397 A162 1sh6p multicolored — 1.65 1.65
Nos. 395-397 (3) — 2.20 2.20

**Phosphorescent**

| No. | Type | Denom | Description | Unused | Used |
|---|---|---|---|---|---|
| 395p | A161 | 2½p | multicolored | .55 | .60 |
| 396p | A161 | 4p | multicolored | .55 | .60 |
| 397p | A162 | 1sh6p | multicolored | 35.00 | 20.00 |
| | | Nos. 395p-397p (3) | | 36.10 | 21.20 |

9th Intl. Life-Boat Conf., Edinburgh, 6/3-5.

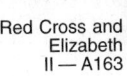
Red Cross and Elizabeth II — A163

1sh3p, Cross at UL. 1sh6p, Cross in center.

**1963, Aug. 15    Wmk. 322**
**Cross in Red**

| No. | Type | Denom | Description | Unused | Used |
|---|---|---|---|---|---|
| 398 | A163 | 3p | purple | .25 | .25 |
| a. | | | Red cross omitted | 13,000. | |
| 399 | A163 | 1sh3p | gray & blue | 1.35 | 1.35 |
| 400 | A163 | 1sh6p | dl bl & ol bister | 1.35 | 1.35 |
| | | Nos. 398-400 (3) | | 2.95 | 2.95 |

**Phosphorescent**

| No. | Type | Denom | Description | Unused | Used |
|---|---|---|---|---|---|
| 398p | A163 | 3p | purple | .50 | .50 |
| a. | | | Red cross omitted | 50,000. | |
| 399p | A163 | 1sh3p | gray & blue | 27.50 | 24.00 |
| 400p | A163 | 1sh6p | dull blue & ol bister | 20.00 | 12.00 |
| | | Nos. 398p-400p (3) | | 48.00 | 36.50 |

Red Cross Cent. Cong., Geneva, Sept. 2.

Cable Around World and Under Sea — A164

**1963, Dec. 3    Perf. 14½x14**

| No. | Type | Denom | Description | Unused | Used |
|---|---|---|---|---|---|
| 401 | A164 | 1sh6p | blue & blk | 1.35 | 1.35 |
| a. | | | Black omitted | 6,000. | |
| p. | | | Phosphor. | 8.00 | 7.75 |

Opening of the Commonwealth Pacific (telephone) cable service, COMPAC.

Puck and Bottom from "A Midsummer Night's Dream," Shakespeare A165

Hamlet Holding Yorick's Skull — A166

First Folio Portrait of Shakespeare and: 6p, Feste the Clown, from "Twelfth Night." 1sh3p, Romeo and Juliet. 1sh6p, Henry V praying at Agincourt.

**Perf. 14½x14**
**1964, Apr. 23    Photo.    Wmk. 322**

| No. | Type | Denom | Description | Unused | Used |
|---|---|---|---|---|---|
| 402 | A165 | 3p | multicolored | .25 | .25 |
| 403 | A165 | 6p | multicolored | .25 | .25 |
| 404 | A165 | 1sh3p | multicolored | .45 | .50 |
| 405 | A165 | 1sh6p | multicolored | .55 | .45 |

**Perf. 11x12**
**Engr.**

| No. | Type | Denom | Description | Unused | Used |
|---|---|---|---|---|---|
| 406 | A166 | 2sh6p | dark gray | 1.40 | 1.40 |
| | | Nos. 402-406 (5) | | 2.90 | 2.85 |

**Phosphorescent**

| No. | Type | Denom | Description | Unused | Used |
|---|---|---|---|---|---|
| 402p | A165 | 3p | multicolored | .25 | .25 |
| 403p | A165 | 6p | multicolored | .75 | .75 |
| 404p | A165 | 1sh3p | multicolored | 2.20 | 2.20 |
| 405p | A165 | 1sh6p | multicolored | 2.75 | 2.75 |
| | | Nos. 402p-405p (4) | | 5.95 | 5.95 |

400th anniv. of the birth of William Shakespeare. No. 406 was not issued with phosphorescence.

Apartment Buildings, London — A170

Designs: 4p, Shipyards, Belfast. 8p, Beddgelert Forest Park, Snowdonia. 1sh6p, Dounreay nuclear reactor and sheaves of wheat.

**1964, July 1    Photo.    Perf. 14½x14**

| No. | Type | Denom | Description | Unused | Used |
|---|---|---|---|---|---|
| 410 | A170 | 2½p | multicolored | .25 | .25 |
| 411 | A170 | 4p | multicolored | .25 | .25 |
| a. | | | Violet ("4d") omitted | 250.00 | |
| b. | | | Ocher omitted | 475.00 | |
| c. | | | Violet & ocher omitted | 550.00 | |
| 412 | A170 | 8p | multicolored | .50 | .50 |
| a. | | | Green omitted | 17,500. | |
| 413 | A170 | 1sh6p | multicolored | 2.00 | 2.00 |
| | | Nos. 410-413 (4) | | 3.00 | 3.00 |

**Phosphorescent**

| No. | Type | Denom | Description | Unused | Used |
|---|---|---|---|---|---|
| 410p | A170 | 2½p | multicolored | .25 | .35 |
| 411p | A170 | 4p | multicolored | .65 | .90 |
| 412p | A170 | 8p | multicolored | 1.60 | 2.75 |
| 413p | A170 | 1sh6p | multicolored | 17.50 | 12.00 |
| | | Nos. 410p-413p (4) | | 20.00 | 16.00 |

20th Intl. Geographical Cong., London, July 20-28.

Spring Gentian — A171

6p, Dog rose. 9p, Honeysuckle. 1sh3p, Fringed water lily.

**1964, Aug. 5    Wmk. 322**

| No. | Type | Denom | Description | Unused | Used |
|---|---|---|---|---|---|
| 414 | A171 | 3p | shown | .25 | .25 |
| a. | | | Blue omitted | 16,500. | |
| b. | | | Sage green omitted | 19,750. | |
| 415 | A171 | 6p | multi | .25 | .25 |
| 416 | A171 | 9p | multi | 1.10 | 1.25 |
| a. | | | Light green omitted | 17,500. | |
| 417 | A171 | 1sh3p | multi | 1.35 | 1.25 |
| a. | | | Yellow omitted | 50,000. | |
| | | Nos. 414-417 (4) | | 2.95 | 3.00 |

**Phosphorescent**

| No. | Type | Denom | Description | Unused | Used |
|---|---|---|---|---|---|
| 414p | A171 | 3p | Spring Gentian | .25 | .25 |
| 415p | A171 | 6p | Dog rose | 1.00 | 1.25 |
| 416p | A171 | 9p | Honeysuckle | 3.75 | 3.25 |
| 417p | A171 | 1sh3p | Fringed water lily | 14.00 | 9.50 |
| | | Nos. 414p-417p (4) | | 19.00 | 14.25 |

10th Intl. Botanical Cong., Edinburgh, Aug. 3-12.

Forth Road Bridge — A172

Design: 6p, Bridge and railroad bridge.

**1964, Sept. 4    Perf. 14½x14**

| No. | Type | Denom | Description | Unused | Used |
|---|---|---|---|---|---|
| 418 | A172 | 3p | blk, lil & blue | .25 | .25 |
| p. | | | Phosphor. | .50 | .50 |
| 419 | A172 | 6p | vio blk, grnsh bl & car lake | .25 | .25 |
| a. | | | Greenish blue omitted | 5,500. | 1,375. |
| p. | | | Phosphor. | 2.25 | 2.25 |

Opening of Forth Road Bridge, Scotland.

Winston Churchill — A173

Design: 1sh3p, Large portrait.

**1965, July 8    Photo.    Wmk. 322**

| No. | Type | Denom | Description | Unused | Used |
|---|---|---|---|---|---|
| 420 | A173 | 4p | dk brown & blk | .25 | .25 |
| p. | | | Phosphor. | .25 | .25 |
| 421 | A173 | 1sh3p | gray & black | .30 | .25 |
| p. | | | Phosphor. | 1.25 | 1.25 |

Sir Winston Spencer Churchill (1874-1965), statesman and WWII leader.

Seal of Simon de Montfort — A174

St. Stephen's Hall, Westminster Hall and Abbey, Engraving by Wenceslaus Hollar, 1647 — A175

**1965, July 19    Perf. 14½x14**

| No. | Type | Denom | Description | Unused | Used |
|---|---|---|---|---|---|
| 422 | A174 | 6p | dark olive | .25 | .25 |
| p. | | | Phosphor. | .55 | .55 |
| 423 | A175 | 2sh6p | brown black | .45 | .45 |

700th anniv. of Parliament. No. 423 was not issued with phosphorescence; size: 58x21mm.

Salvation Army Band and "Blood and Fire" Flag — A176

1sh6p, Salvation Army officers and flag.

**1965, Aug. 9**

| No. | Type | Denom | Description | Unused | Used |
|---|---|---|---|---|---|
| 424 | A176 | 3p | dk bl, yel & brt car | .25 | .25 |
| p. | | | Phosphor. | .25 | .25 |
| 425 | A176 | 1sh6p | red, yel & brt bl | .50 | .50 |
| p. | | | Phosphor. | 1.00 | 1.00 |

Centenary of the Salvation Army.

Lister's Carbolic Spray — A177

1sh, Joseph Lister & carbolic acid formula.

**1965, Sept. 1**

| No. | Type | Denom | Description | Unused | Used |
|---|---|---|---|---|---|
| 426 | A177 | 4p | gray, bluish blk & red brn | .25 | .25 |
| a. | | | Red brown (tubing) omitted | 525.00 | |
| b. | | | Bluish black omitted | 6,000. | |
| p. | | | Phosphor. | .25 | .25 |
| 427 | A177 | 1sh | blk, blue & pur | .45 | .45 |
| p. | | | Phosphor. | 1.10 | 1.10 |

Introduction of antiseptic surgery by Joseph Lister, cent.

Trinidad Folk Dancers, Shrove Monday Carnival — A178

Design: 1sh6p, French Canadian folk dancers, Les Feux Follets.

**Perf. 14½x14**
**1965, Sept. 1    Photo.    Wmk. 322**

| No. | Type | Denom | Description | Unused | Used |
|---|---|---|---|---|---|
| 428 | A178 | 6p | orange & blk | .25 | .25 |
| p. | | | Phosphor. | .45 | .45 |
| 429 | A178 | 1sh6p | brt vio & blk | .45 | .45 |
| p. | | | Phosphor. | 1.35 | 1.35 |

1st Commonwealth Arts Festival, 9/16-10/2.

Supermarine Spitfire Fighters — A179

Anti-Aircraft Gun Battery in Action — A180

Designs: No. 431, Pilot in cockpit of Hawker Hurricane fighter. No. 432, Wing tips of Messerschmitt ME-109 and Spitfire. No. 433, Two Spitfires attacking Heinkel HE-111 bomber. No. 434, Spitfire attacking Junkers JU-187B Stuka dive bomber. No. 435, Hurricanes returning over wreckage of Dornier DO-17 Z bomber. 1sh3p, Vapor trails over St. Paul's Cathedral, London.

**Perf. 14½x14**
**1965, Sept. 13    Photo.    Wmk. 322**

| No. | Type | Denom | Description | Unused | Used |
|---|---|---|---|---|---|
| 430 | A179 | 4p | slate & dk ol | .40 | .40 |
| 431 | A179 | 4p | slate & dk ol | .40 | .40 |
| 432 | A179 | 4p | sl, dk ol, brt bl & red | .40 | .40 |
| 433 | A179 | 4p | slate & dk ol | .40 | .40 |
| 434 | A179 | 4p | slate & dk ol | .40 | .40 |
| 435 | A179 | 4p | sl, dk ol & brt blue | .40 | .40 |
| a. | | | Bright blue omitted | 4,500. | |
| b. | | | Block of 6, #430-435 | 2.75 | 2.75 |
| 436 | A180 | 9p | vio bl, org & vio black | 1.75 | 1.75 |
| 437 | A180 | 1sh3p | brt bl, sl & grnsh gray | 1.75 | 1.75 |
| | | Nos. 430-437 (8) | | 5.90 | 5.90 |

**Phosphorescent**

| No. | Type | Denom | Description | Unused | Used |
|---|---|---|---|---|---|
| 430p | A179 | 4p | slate & dark ol | .90 | .90 |
| 431p | A179 | 4p | slate & dark ol | .90 | .90 |
| 432p | A179 | 4p | sl, dk ol, brt bl & red | .90 | .90 |
| 433p | A179 | 4p | slate & dark ol | .90 | .90 |
| 434p | A179 | 4p | slate & dark ol | .90 | .90 |
| 435p | A179 | 4p | sl, dk ol & brt bl | .90 | .90 |
| a. | | | Block of 6, #430p-435p | 4.25 | 4.25 |
| 436p | A180 | 9p | vio bl, org & vio black | 2.20 | 2.20 |

| No. | Type | Denom | Description | Unused | Used |
|---|---|---|---|---|---|
| 437p | A180 | 1sh3p | brt bl, slate & grnsh gray | 2.20 | 2.20 |
| | | Nos. 430p-437p (8) | | 9.80 | 9.80 |

25th anniv. of the Battle of Britain. Nos. 430-435 printed in blocks of 6 (3x2) in sheets of 120.

Post Office Tower and Georgian Buildings — A181

Design: 1sh3p, Post Office Tower and Nash Terrace, Regents Park, horiz.

**1965, Oct. 8    Perf. 14x14½, 14½x14**

| No. | Type | Denom | Description | Unused | Used |
|---|---|---|---|---|---|
| 438 | A181 | 3p | brt bl, ocher & ol green | .25 | .25 |
| a. | | | Lemon omitted | 5,250. | 2,000. |
| p. | | | Phosphor. | .25 | .25 |
| 439 | A181 | 1sh3p | grn, ol grn & bl | .25 | .25 |
| p. | | | Phosphor. | .25 | .25 |

Opening of the Post Office Tower, London.

UN Emblem — A182

ICY Emblem — A183

**1965, Oct. 25    Perf. 14½x14**

| No. | Type | Denom | Description | Unused | Used |
|---|---|---|---|---|---|
| 440 | A182 | 3p | multicolored | .25 | .25 |
| p. | | | Phosphor. | .25 | .25 |
| 441 | A183 | 1sh6p | multicolored | .40 | .40 |
| p. | | | Phosphor. | 1.10 | 1.10 |

20th anniv. of the UN and Intl. Cooperation Year, 1965.

"World Telecommunication Stations" — A184

ITU Cent.: 1sh6p, "Radio waves & switchboard."

**1965, Nov. 15    Photo.    Wmk. 322**

| No. | Type | Denom | Description | Unused | Used |
|---|---|---|---|---|---|
| 442 | A184 | 9p | multicolored | .25 | .25 |
| p. | | | Phosphor. | .50 | .50 |
| 443 | A184 | 1sh6p | bl, red, blk, ind & pink | .60 | .70 |
| a. | | | Pink omitted | 3,250. | 2,200. |
| p. | | | Phosphor. | 2.20 | 2.20 |

Robert Burns and Saltier Cross of St. Andrew — A185

Design: 1sh3p, Alexander Nasmyth portrait of Burns, his signature and symbols of his life. Portrait of Burns on 4p stamp is adaptation of Archibald Skirvings', chalk drawing, 1798.

**1966, Jan. 25    Perf. 14½x14**

| No. | Type | Denom | Description | Unused | Used |
|---|---|---|---|---|---|
| 444 | A185 | 4p | blue, blk & dk sl | .25 | .25 |
| p. | | | Phosphor. | .30 | .30 |
| 445 | A185 | 1sh3p | org, blk & Prus blue | .25 | .25 |
| p. | | | Phosphor. | 1.00 | 1.00 |

Robert Burns (1759-1796), Scottish national poet.

Westminster Abbey — A186

Fan Vaulting, Chapel of Henry VII — A187

**1966, Feb. 28　Photo.　Perf. 14½x14**

| | | | | |
|---|---|---|---|---|
| 452 | A186 | 3p blue, blk, & red brn | .25 | .25 |
| p. | | Phosphor. | .25 | .25 |

**Perf. 11x12**
**Engr.**

| | | | | |
|---|---|---|---|---|
| 453 | A187 | 2sh6p black | .35 | .35 |

900th anniv. of Westminster Abbey. No. 453 issued only without phosphor.

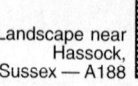

Landscape near Hassock, Sussex — A188

Views: 6p, Antrim, Northern Ireland. 1sh3p, Harlech Castle, Wales. 1sh6p, The Cairngorms (mountains), Scotland.

**Perf. 14½x14**

**1966, May 2　Photo.　Wmk. 322**

| | | | | |
|---|---|---|---|---|
| 454 | A188 | 4p multicolored | .25 | .25 |
| 455 | A188 | 6p multicolored | .25 | .25 |
| 456 | A188 | 1sh3p multicolored | .25 | .25 |
| 457 | A188 | 1sh6p multicolored | .25 | .25 |
| | | Nos. 454-457 (4) | 1.00 | 1.00 |

**Phosphorescent**

| | | | | |
|---|---|---|---|---|
| 454p | A188 | 4p multicolored | .25 | .25 |
| 455p | A188 | 6p multicolored | .25 | .25 |
| 456p | A188 | 1sh3p multicolored | .25 | .25 |
| 457p | A188 | 1sh6p multicolored | .25 | .25 |
| | | Nos. 454p-457p (4) | 1.00 | 1.00 |

Soccer Players A189

Players and Crowd A190

1sh3p, Goalkeeper and two players.

**Perf. 14x14½, 14½x14**

**1966, June 1　Photo.　Wmk. 322**

| | | | | |
|---|---|---|---|---|
| 458 | A189 | 4p multicolored | .25 | .25 |
| 459 | A190 | 6p multicolored | .25 | .25 |
| a. | | Black omitted | 175.00 | |
| b. | | Yellow green omitted | 5,500. | |
| c. | | Red omitted | 8,500. | |
| 460 | A190 | 1sh3p multicolored | .25 | .25 |
| a. | | Blue omitted | 325.00 | |
| | | Nos. 458-460 (3) | .75 | .75 |

**Phosphorescent**

| | | | | |
|---|---|---|---|---|
| 458p | A189 | 4p multicolored | .25 | .25 |
| 459p | A190 | 6p multicolored | .25 | .25 |
| d. | | Black omitted | 2,200. | |
| 460p | A190 | 1sh3p multicolored | .25 | .25 |
| | | Nos. 458p-460p (3) | .75 | .75 |

Final games of the 1965-66 World Soccer Championship for the Jules Rimet Cup, Wembley, July 11-30.
See No. 465.

Black-headed Gull — A191

**Perf. 14½x14**

**1966, Aug. 8　Photo.　Wmk. 322**
**Birds in Natural Colors**

| | | | | |
|---|---|---|---|---|
| 461 | A191 | 4p shown | .25 | .25 |
| p. | | Phosphor. | .25 | .25 |
| 462 | A191 | 4p Blue tit | .25 | .25 |
| p. | | Phosphor. | .25 | .25 |
| 463 | A191 | 4p European robin | .25 | .25 |
| p. | | Phosphor. | .25 | .25 |
| 464 | A191 | 4p European blackbird | .25 | .25 |
| p. | | Phosphor. | .25 | .25 |
| | | Block of 4, #461-464 | .50 | .50 |
| | | Block of 4, #461p-464p | .50 | .50 |

Seven colors have been found omitted (singly or in combinations) on Nos. 461-464: green, red, ultramarine, brown, red brown, yellow and black. Values range from $150 to $13,750.

---

Inscribed: "ENGLAND WINNERS" — A191a

**1966, Aug. 18　　　Perf. 14x14½**

| | | | | |
|---|---|---|---|---|
| 465 | A191a | 4p multicolored | .25 | .25 |

England's victory in the World Soccer Cup Championship.

Jodrell Bank Radio Telescope A192

Designs: 6p, Automobiles (Jaguar and 3 Mini-Minors). 1sh3p, SR N6 Hovercraft. 1sh6p, Windscale atomic reactor.

**1966, Sept. 19　　　Perf. 14½x14**

| | | | | |
|---|---|---|---|---|
| 466 | A192 | 4p yellow & blk | .25 | .25 |
| 467 | A192 | 6p org, red & dk bl | .25 | .25 |
| a. | | Red (Mini-Minors) omitted | 13,750. | |
| b. | | Dark blue (Jaguar & imprint) omitted | 11,000. | |
| 468 | A192 | 1sh3p sl, blk, org & bl | .25 | .25 |
| 469 | A192 | 1sh6p multicolored | .25 | .25 |
| | | Nos. 466-469 (4) | 1.00 | 1.00 |

**Phosphorescent**

| | | | | |
|---|---|---|---|---|
| 466p | A192 | 4p yellow & black | .25 | .25 |
| 467p | A192 | 6p org, red & dk bl | .25 | .25 |
| 468p | A192 | 1sh3p slate, blk, org & bl | .25 | .25 |
| 469p | A192 | 1sh6p multicolored | .25 | .25 |
| | | Nos. 466p-469p (4) | 1.00 | 1.00 |

British technology.

Battle of Hastings — A193

Battle of Hastings from Bayeux Tapestry: No. 471, Two knights on horseback, one killed, one attacking. No. 472, Slain Harold on horseback and knight with shield. No. 473, Knight with shield and axe fighting horseman. No. 474, Knight on foot killing man, and horseman attacking with lance. No. 475, Four knights and two horses in battle scene. 6p, Norman ship. 1sh3p, King Harold's housecarls (body guard) battling Normans.

**Photo.; Gold Impressed on 6p, 1sh3p**
**Perf. 14½x14**

**1966, Oct. 14　　　Wmk. 322**
**Size: 38½x22mm**

| | | | | |
|---|---|---|---|---|
| 470 | A193 | 4p multicolored | .25 | .25 |
| 471 | A193 | 4p multicolored | .25 | .25 |
| 472 | A193 | 4p multicolored | .25 | .25 |
| 473 | A193 | 4p multicolored | .25 | .25 |
| 474 | A193 | 4p multicolored | .25 | .25 |
| 475 | A193 | 4p multicolored | .25 | .25 |
| a. | | Strip of 6, #470-475 | 1.00 | 1.00 |
| 476 | A193 | 6p multi & gold | .25 | .25 |

**Size: 58x22mm**

| | | | | |
|---|---|---|---|---|
| 477 | A193 | 1sh3p multi & gold | .25 | .25 |
| | | Nos. 470-477 (8) | 2.00 | 2.00 |

**Phosphorescent**

| | | | | |
|---|---|---|---|---|
| 470p | A193 | 4p multicolored | .25 | .25 |
| 471p | A193 | 4p multicolored | .25 | .25 |
| 472p | A193 | 4p multicolored | .25 | .25 |
| 473p | A193 | 4p multicolored | .25 | .25 |
| 474p | A193 | 4p multicolored | .25 | .25 |
| 475p | A193 | 4p multicolored | .25 | .25 |
| b. | | Strip of 6, #470p-475p | 1.00 | 1.00 |
| 476p | A193 | 6p multi & gold | .25 | .25 |
| 477p | A193 | 1sh3p multi & gold | .25 | .25 |
| | | Nos. 470p-477p (8) | 2.00 | 2.00 |

900th anniv. of the Battle of Hastings.
Eight colors have been found omitted (singly or in pairs) on Nos. 470-475 and 470p-477p: gray, orange, blue, dark blue, bright green, olive green, brown and magenta. Also violet on 1sh3p. Values for various color-omitted examples of Nos. 470-475 and 470p-475p, $65-$75. Values for color-omitted examples of No. 477, $5,000.; No. 477p, $1,250.

---

**Gold Omitted**
The variety "Gold (Queen's head) omitted" can be forged by chemically removing the gold.

---

Christmas — A194

**Photo.; Gold Impressed**

**1966, Dec. 1　　　Perf. 14x14½**

| | | | | |
|---|---|---|---|---|
| 478 | A194 | 3p King | .25 | .25 |
| b. | | Green omitted | — | 3,500. |
| p. | | Phosphor. | .25 | .25 |
| 479 | A194 | 1sh6p Snowman | .25 | .25 |
| b. | | Pink omitted | 2,750. | |
| p. | | Phosphor. | .25 | .25 |

Loading Ship at Dock and Train — A195

Design: 1sh6p, Loading plane from trucks and flags of EFTA members.

**Perf. 14x14½**

**1967, Feb. 20　Photo.　Wmk. 322**

| | | | | |
|---|---|---|---|---|
| 480 | A195 | 9p blue & multi | .25 | .25 |
| p. | | Phosphor. | .25 | .25 |
| 481 | A195 | 1sh6p vio & multi | .25 | .25 |
| p. | | Phosphor. | .25 | .25 |

European Free Trade Assoc. Tariffs were abolished Dec. 31, 1966, among EFTA members (Austria, Denmark, Finland, Great Britain, Norway, Portugal, Sweden, Switzerland).
Colors omitted include: 9p — yellow, brown, light blue, light violet and green singly; black, brown, light blue and yellow simultaneously. 1sh6p — dark blue, bister, yellow, red, ultramarine and gray. 9p, value range for one-color omissions, $75 to $200. 1sh6p, value for red omitted $5,000 (used), dark blue omitted $500, value for other color-omitted errors $75 to $125 each.

Hawthorn and Wild Blackberry A196

Flowers: No. 489, Morning-glory and viper's bugloss. No. 490, Ox-eye daisy, coltsfoot and buttercup. No. 491, Bluebell, red campion and wood anemone. 9p, Dog violet. 1sh9p, Primrose.

**Perf. 14½x14**

**1967, Apr. 24　Photo.　Wmk. 322**

| | | | | |
|---|---|---|---|---|
| 488 | A196 | 4p multicolored | .25 | .25 |
| 489 | A196 | 4p multicolored | .25 | .25 |
| 490 | A196 | 4p multicolored | .25 | .25 |
| 491 | A196 | 4p multicolored | .25 | .25 |
| 492 | A196 | 9p multicolored | .25 | .25 |
| 493 | A196 | 1sh9p multicolored | .25 | .25 |
| | | Nos. 488-493 (6) | 1.50 | 1.50 |

**Phosphorescent**

| | | | | |
|---|---|---|---|---|
| 488p | A196 | 4p multicolored | .25 | .25 |
| 489p | A196 | 4p multicolored | .25 | .25 |
| 490p | A196 | 4p multicolored | .25 | .25 |
| 491p | A196 | 4p multicolored | .25 | .25 |
| 492p | A196 | 9p multicolored | .25 | .25 |
| 493p | A196 | 1sh9p multicolored | .25 | .25 |
| | | Nos. 488p-493p (6) | 1.50 | 1.50 |

Four colors have been found omitted on Nos. 488-491 and three on 488p-491p: dark brown, red, violet and dull purple. Values range from $475 to $4,500. No. 491 exists with the value omitted because of an obstruction during the printing process.

---

For QEII Machin definitives, see listings following Regional Issues and preceding Booklets.

---

Master Lambton, by Thomas Lawrence A198

Mares and Foals, by George Stubbs A199

---

Design: 1sh6p, Children Coming out of School, by Laurence Stephen Lowry.

**Photo.; Gold Impressed on 4p, 1sh6p**
**Perf. 14x14½, 14½x14**

**1967, July 10　　　Unwmk.**

| | | | | |
|---|---|---|---|---|
| 514 | A198 | 4p multi | .25 | .25 |
| a. | | Gold (Queen's head & value) omitted | 220.00 | |
| b. | | Blue omitted | 11,000. | |
| 515 | A199 | 9p multi | .25 | .25 |
| a. | | Black (Queen's head & value) omitted | 850.00 | |
| b. | | Black (Queen's head only) omitted | 1,650. | |
| 516 | A199 | 1sh6p multi | .25 | .25 |
| a. | | Blue omitted | 220.00 | |
| b. | | Gray omitted | 130.00 | |
| c. | | Gold (Queen's head) omitted | 13,500. | |
| | | Nos. 514-516 (3) | .75 | .75 |

See Nos. 568-571.

Gipsy Moth IV — A200

**1967, July 24　Photo.　Perf. 14½x14**

| | | | | |
|---|---|---|---|---|
| 517 | A200 | 1sh9p multicolored | .25 | .25 |

Sir Francis Chichester's one-man voyage around the world, Aug. 27, 1966-May 28, 1967.

Radar Screen — A201

British Discoveries: 1sh, Penicillin mold. 1sh6p, Vickers 10 twin jet engines. 1sh9p, Television camera, vert.

**Perf. 14½x14, 14x14½**

**1967, Sept. 19　Photo.　Wmk. 322**

| | | | | |
|---|---|---|---|---|
| 518 | A201 | 4p multi | .25 | .25 |
| 519 | A201 | 1sh multi | .25 | .25 |
| 520 | A201 | 1sh6p multi | .25 | .25 |
| 521 | A201 | 1sh9p multi | .25 | .25 |
| a. | | Gray omitted | 3,850. | |
| b. | | Orange (queen's head) omitted | 32,500. | |
| | | Nos. 518-521 (4) | 1.00 | 1.00 |

Adoration of the Shepherds, Ascribed to School of Seville A202

Adoration of the Shepherds, by Le Nain A203

Christmas 1967: 4p, Madonna and Child, by Murillo.

**Photo.; Gold Impressed**
**Perf. 14x14½, 14½x14**

**1967　　　　　　Unwmk.**

| | | | | |
|---|---|---|---|---|
| 522 | A202 | 3p multi | .25 | .25 |
| a. | | Gold (Queen's head & value) omitted | 100.00 | |
| b. | | Pink omitted | 3,500. | |
| 523 | A202 | 4p multi | .25 | .25 |
| a. | | Gold (Queen's head & value) omitted | 75.00 | |
| b. | | Gold ("4d" only) omitted | 1,900. | |
| c. | | Yellow omitted | 5,500. | |
| d. | | Greenish yellow & gold omitted | 11,000. | |
| 524 | A203 | 1sh6p multi | .25 | .25 |
| a. | | Gold (Queen's head & value) omitted | 11,000. | |
| b. | | Blue omitted | 625.00 | |
| c. | | Yellow omitted | 13,250. | |
| d. | | Gold (Queen's head only) omitted | 2,200. | |
| | | Nos. 522-524 (3) | .75 | .75 |

Issue dates: 4p, Oct. 18; 3p, 1sh6p, Nov. 27.

---

**Castle Type of 1955**
**Perf. 11x12**

**1967-68　　Engr.　　Unwmk.**

| | | | | |
|---|---|---|---|---|
| 525 | A133 | 2sh6p dk brown ('68) | .40 | .25 |
| 526 | A133 | 5sh crimson ('68) | .95 | .55 |

| | | | | |
|---|---|---|---|---|
| 527 | A133 | 10sh brt ultra ('68) | 4.75 | 2.20 |
| 528 | A133 | £1 intense black | 6.00 | 2.20 |
| | | Nos. 525-528 (4) | 12.10 | 5.20 |

See Nos. 309-312, 371-374, 2278.

Aberfeldy Bridge, Perthshire A204

Designs: 4p, Prehistoric Tarr Steps, Exmoor. 1sh6p, Menai Bridge, North Wales, 1826. 1sh9p, Viaduct, Highway M4.

**Perf. 14½x14**

**1968, Apr. 29 Photo. Unwmk.**

| | | | | |
|---|---|---|---|---|
| 560 | A204 | 4p gold & multi | .25 | .25 |
| 561 | A204 | 5p gold & multi | .25 | .25 |
| a. | | Blue omitted | | 5,500. |
| b. | | Gold (Queen's head) omitted | 250.00 | |
| 562 | A204 | 1sh6p gold & multi | .25 | .25 |
| a. | | Gold (Queen's head) omitted | 325.00 | |
| b. | | Red omitted | 325.00 | |
| 563 | A204 | 1sh9p gold & multi | .25 | .25 |
| a. | | Gold (Queen's head) omitted | 300.00 | |
| | | Nos. 560-563 (4) | 1.00 | 1.00 |

Emmeline Pankhurst Statue — A205

Designs: 4p, Letters "TUC" and faces. 1sh, Sopwith Camel 1914-1918 fighter plane and formation of Lightning jets. 1sh9p, Capt. Cook's "Endeavour" and signature.

**1968, May 29**

| | | | | |
|---|---|---|---|---|
| 564 | A205 | 4p brt grn, blk, ol & bl | .25 | .25 |
| 565 | A205 | 9p gray, violet & blk | .25 | .25 |
| 566 | A205 | 1sh gray, ol, red, bl & blk | .25 | .25 |
| 567 | A205 | 1sh9p blk & bister | .55 | .65 |
| | | Nos. 564-567 (4) | 1.30 | 1.40 |

Cent. of Trades Union Congress (4p); 50th anniv. of women's suffrage (9p); 50th anniv. of the Royal Air Force (1sh); bicent. of Captain Cook's first discovery voyage (1sh9p).

**Paintings Types of 1967**

Paintings: 4p, Elizabeth I, c. 1575, artist unknown. 1sh, Pinkie (Miss Sarah Moulton-Barrett) by Sir Thomas Lawrence. 1sh6p, St. Mary le Port, by John Piper. 1sh9p, The Hay Wain (landscape), by John Constable.

**Photo.; Gold Impressed**
**Perf. 14x14½, 14½x14**

**1968, Aug. 12**

| | | | | |
|---|---|---|---|---|
| 568 | A198 | 4p multi | .25 | .25 |
| a. | | Gold (Queen's head & value) omitted | 275.00 | |
| b. | | Vermilion omitted | 600.00 | |
| 569 | A198 | 1sh multi | .25 | .25 |
| a. | | Gold (Queen's head & value) omitted | 6,500. | |
| 570 | A198 | 1sh6p multi | .25 | .25 |
| a. | | Gold (Queen's head & value) omitted | 275.00 | |
| 571 | A199 | 1sh9p multi | .25 | .25 |
| a. | | Gold (Queen's head & value) omitted | 825.00 | |
| b. | | Red omitted | 7,250. | |
| | | Nos. 568-571 (4) | 1.00 | 1.00 |

Sizes: 4p, 27x37½mm; 1sh, 25½x37½mm; 1sh6p, 31x37½mm; 1sh9p, 38x28mm.

Boy and Girl with Rocking Horse A206

Girl Playing with Dolls and Dollhouse A207

Christmas: 1sh6p, Boy with toy train and building blocks.

**Perf. 14½x14, 14x14½**

**1968, Nov. 25 Photo.**

| | | | | |
|---|---|---|---|---|
| 572 | A206 | 4p gold & multi | .25 | .25 |
| a. | | Gold omitted | 4,250. | |
| b. | | Vermilion omitted | 500.00 | |
| c. | | Ultramarine omitted | 475.00 | |
| d. | | Bistre and orange omitted | — | |

---

| | | | | |
|---|---|---|---|---|
| 573 | A207 | 9p gold & multi | .25 | .25 |
| a. | | Yellow omitted | 165.00 | |
| b. | | Turquoise-green omitted | 16,500. | |
| 574 | A207 | 1sh6p gold & multi | .25 | .25 |
| | | Nos. 572-574 (3) | .75 | .75 |

British Ships A208

Designs: 5p, R.M.S. Queen Elizabeth 2. No. 576, Elizabethan Galleon. No. 577, East Indiaman. No. 578, Cutty Sark. No. 579, S.S. Great Britain. No. 580, R.M.S. Mauretania.

**1969, Jan. 15 Perf. 14½x14**
**Size: 58x22mm**

| | | | | |
|---|---|---|---|---|
| 575 | A208 | 5p multicolored | .25 | .25 |
| a. | | Black omitted | 3,100. | |
| b. | | Gray omitted | 200.00 | |
| c. | | Red omitted | 200.00 | |

**Size: 38½x22mm**

| | | | | |
|---|---|---|---|---|
| 576 | A208 | 9p multicolored | .25 | .25 |
| a. | | Red & blue omitted | 2,400. | |
| b. | | Blue omitted | 2,400. | |
| 577 | A208 | 9p multicolored | .25 | .25 |
| 578 | A208 | 9p multicolored | .25 | .25 |
| a. | | Strip of 3, #576-578 | .45 | |

**Size: 58x22mm**

| | | | | |
|---|---|---|---|---|
| 579 | A208 | 1sh multicolored | .25 | .25 |
| a. | | Greenish yellow omitted | 3,250. | |
| 580 | A208 | 1sh multicolored | .25 | .25 |
| a. | | Pair, #579-580 | .25 | |
| b. | | Carmine (hull overlay) omitted | 22,500. | |
| c. | | Red (funnels) omitted | 16,500. | |
| d. | | Carmine and red omitted | 16,500. | |
| | | Nos. 575-580 (6) | 1.50 | 1.50 |

British seamen and shipbuilders.

Concorde over Great Britain and France — A209

Designs: 9p, Concorde seen from above and from side, flags of France and Great Britain. 1sh6p, Outlines of plane's nose and tail superimposed.

**1969, Mar. 3 Photo. Perf. 14½x14**

| | | | | |
|---|---|---|---|---|
| 581 | A209 | 4p multicolored | .25 | .25 |
| a. | | Violet omitted | 625.00 | |
| b. | | Orange omitted | 625.00 | |
| 582 | A209 | 9p multicolored | .25 | .25 |
| 583 | A209 | 1sh6p multicolored | .25 | .25 |
| a. | | Silver omitted | 650.00 | |
| | | Nos. 581-583 (3) | .75 | .75 |

First flight of the prototype Concorde plane at Toulouse, France, Mar. 1, 1969.

Alcock, Brown, Daily Mail and Vickers Vimy Plane — A210

"EUROPA" and "CEPT" — CD12

Hand Holding Wrench — A212

Flags of NATO Nations Forming one Flag — A213

Vickers-Vimy Plane and Globe — A214

**1969, Apr. 2**

| | | | | |
|---|---|---|---|---|
| 584 | A210 | 5p multi | .25 | .25 |
| 585 | CD12 | 9p multi | .25 | .25 |
| 586 | A212 | 1sh multi | .25 | .25 |

---

| | | | | |
|---|---|---|---|---|
| 587 | A213 | 1sh6p multi | .25 | .25 |
| a. | | Black omitted | 110.00 | |
| b. | | Green omitted | 75.00 | |
| c. | | Yellow omitted | | 3,250. |
| 588 | A214 | 1sh9p multi | .25 | .25 |
| | | Nos. 584-588 (5) | 1.25 | 1.25 |

50th anniv. of the 1st non-stop Atlantic flight from Newfoundland to Ireland of Capt. John Alcock and Lt. Arthur Whitten Brown; 10th anniv. of the Conference of European Postal and Telecommunications Administrations; 50th anniv. of the ILO (1sh); 20th anniv. of NATO; 50th anniv. of the first England to Australia flight (1sh9p).

Durham Cathedral — A215

British Cathedrals: No. 590, York Minster. No. 591, St. Giles', Edinburgh. No. 592, Canterbury. 9p, St. Paul's. 1sh6p, Liverpool Metropolitan.

**Perf. 14½x14**

**1969, May 28 Photo. Unwmk.**

| | | | | |
|---|---|---|---|---|
| 589 | A215 | 5p multi | .25 | .25 |
| a. | | Bluish violet omitted | 8,250. | |
| 590 | A215 | 5p multi | .25 | .25 |
| a. | | Bluish violet omitted | 8,250. | |
| 591 | A215 | 5p multi | .25 | .25 |
| a. | | Green omitted | 100.00 | |
| 592 | A215 | 5p multi | .25 | .25 |
| a. | | Block of 4, #589-592 | .45 | .55 |
| 593 | A215 | 9p multi | .25 | .25 |
| a. | | Black (denomination) omitted | 220.00 | |
| 594 | A215 | 1sh6p multi | .25 | .25 |
| a. | | Black (denomination) omitted | 2,200. | |
| | | Nos. 589-594 (6) | 1.50 | 1.50 |

King's Gate, Caernarvon Castle, Wales A216

Celtic Cross, Margam Abbey, Glamorgan A217

Prince of Wales — A218

Designs: No. 596, Eagle Tower, Caernarvon Castle (2 flags). No. 597, Queen Eleanor's Gate, Caernarvon Castle.

**Perf. 14x14½**

**1969, July 1 Photo. Unwmk.**

| | | | | |
|---|---|---|---|---|
| 595 | A216 | 5p silver & multi | .25 | .25 |
| 596 | A216 | 5p silver & multi | .25 | .25 |
| 597 | A216 | 5p silver & multi | .25 | .25 |
| a. | | Strip of 3, #595-597 | .35 | .55 |
| 598 | A217 | 9p gold, gray & black | .25 | .25 |
| 599 | A218 | 1sh black & gold | .25 | .25 |
| | | Nos. 595-599 (5) | 1.25 | 1.25 |

Investiture of Prince Charles as Prince of Wales, July 1.

Mahatma Gandhi and Flag of India — A219

**1969, Aug. 13 Perf. 14½x14**

| | | | | |
|---|---|---|---|---|
| 600 | A219 | 1sh6p orange, blk & grn | .30 | .30 |

Mohandas K. Gandhi (1869-1948), leader in India's fight for independence.

Emblem of Post Office Bank — A220

---

International Subscriber Dialing — A221

Automatic Letter Sorting — A222

Design: 1sh, Telecommunications (pulse code modulation graph).

**Perf. 13½x14**

**1969, Oct. 1 Litho. Unwmk.**

| | | | | |
|---|---|---|---|---|
| 601 | A220 | 5p blue & multi | .25 | .25 |
| 602 | A221 | 9p ultra & multi | .25 | .25 |
| 603 | A221 | 1sh green & multi | .25 | .25 |
| 604 | A222 | 1sh6p multicolored | .25 | .25 |
| | | Nos. 601-604 (4) | 1.00 | 1.00 |

Technological advancements of the British Post Office, transfer of responsibility from the government to the Post Office Corporation.

Angel — A223

Christmas: 5p, Three shepherds. 1sh6p, The Three Kings.

**Photo.; Gold Embossed**

**1969, Nov. 26 Perf. 14x15**

| | | | | |
|---|---|---|---|---|
| 605 | A223 | 4p multicolored | .25 | .25 |
| 606 | A223 | 5p multicolored | .25 | .25 |
| 607 | A223 | 1sh6p multicolored | .25 | .25 |
| | | Nos. 605-607 (3) | .75 | .75 |

Fife Harling House, Scotland — A224

British Rural Architecture: 9p, Cotswold limestone house, Gloucestershire, England. 1sh, Aberaeron town house, Wales ("Stwco Cymreig Welsh Stucco"). 1sh6p, Irish cottage with Ulster thatching.

**Perf. 14x15**

**1970, Feb. 11 Photo. Unwmk.**
**Size: 38½x22mm**

| | | | | |
|---|---|---|---|---|
| 608 | A224 | 5p multicolored | .25 | .25 |
| 609 | A224 | 9p multicolored | .25 | .25 |

**Size: 38½x27mm**

| | | | | |
|---|---|---|---|---|
| 610 | A224 | 1sh multicolored | .25 | .25 |
| 611 | A224 | 1sh6p multicolored | .25 | .25 |
| | | Nos. 608-611 (4) | 1.00 | 1.00 |

Mayflower Leaving Plymouth, England — A225

Designs: 5p, Signing of the Declaration of Arbroath. 9p, Florence Nightingale and soldiers in Scutari Hospital. 1sh, Earl Grey, Great Britain; Charles Robert, France; Victor Bohmert, Germany; De Keussler, Russia, and document in 4 languages. 1sh9p, Sir William Herschel, Francis Bailey, Sir John Herschel and telescope.

**Photo.; Gold Embossed**

**1970, Apr. 1 Perf. 14x15**

| | | | | |
|---|---|---|---|---|
| 612 | A225 | 5p red & multi | .25 | .25 |
| 613 | A225 | 9p blue & multi | .25 | .25 |
| 614 | A225 | 1sh lt blue & multi | .25 | .25 |
| 615 | A225 | 1sh6p olive & multi | .25 | .25 |
| 616 | A225 | 1sh9p brt pink & multi | .25 | .25 |
| | | Nos. 612-616 (5) | 1.25 | 1.25 |

650th anniv. of the Declaration of Arbroath (5p); Florence Nightingale (1820-1910), nurse and hospital reformer (9p); Intl.Cooperative Alliance, 75th anniv. (1sh); 350th anniv. of Mayflower sailing (1sh6p); sesquicentennial of the Royal Astronomical Soc. (1sh9p).

Missing colors or embossing occur on each denomination.

"The Pickwick Papers," by Dickens A226

Wordsworth's Grasmere, Lake District A227

Designs: No. 618, Mr. and Mrs. Micawber ("David Copperfield"). No. 619, David Copperfield and Betsy Trotwood ("David Copperfield"). No. 620, "Oliver Twist."

### Perf. 14x14½

**1970, June 3    Photo.    Unwmk.**

| | | | | |
|---|---|---|---|---|
| 617 | A226 | 5p orange & multi | .25 | .25 |
| 618 | A226 | 5p lil rose & multi | .25 | .25 |
| 619 | A226 | 5p grnsh blue & multi | .25 | .25 |
| 620 | A226 | 5p lemon & multi | .25 | .25 |
| a. | | Block of 4, #617-620 | .45 | .65 |
| 621 | A227 | 1sh6p citron & multi | .25 | .25 |
| | | Nos. 617-621 (5) | 1.25 | 1.25 |

Charles Dickens (1812-70), novelist. William Wordsworth (1770-1850), poet, No. 621. No. 620a exists imperf. Value $2,250.

Athletics — A228

**1970, July 15    Litho.    Perf. 14x14½**

| | | | | |
|---|---|---|---|---|
| 639 | A228 | 5p shown | .25 | .25 |
| 640 | A228 | 1sh6p Swimming | .25 | .25 |
| 641 | A228 | 1sh9p Bicycling | .25 | .25 |
| | | Nos. 639-641 (3) | .75 | .75 |

9th British Commonwealth Games, Edinburgh, July 16-25.

Philympia, London Phil. Exhib., Sept. 18-26 — A229

5p, Penny black. 9p, 1847 1-shilling stamp, #5. 1sh6p, 1855 4-pence stamp, #22.

**1970, Sept. 18    Photo.    Perf. 14x14½**

| | | | | |
|---|---|---|---|---|
| 642 | A229 | 5p multicolored | .25 | .25 |
| 643 | A229 | 9p multicolored | .25 | .25 |
| 644 | A229 | 1sh6p multicolored | .25 | .25 |
| | | Nos. 642-644 (3) | .75 | .75 |

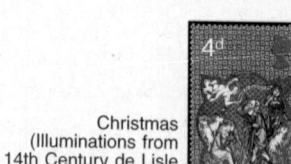

Christmas (Illuminations from 14th Century de Lisle Psalter) — A230

Designs: 4p, Angel and Shepherds. 5p, Nativity. 1sh6p, Adoration of the Kings.

**1970, Nov. 25    Photo.    Perf. 14x14½**

| | | | | |
|---|---|---|---|---|
| 645 | A230 | 4p red & multi | .25 | .25 |
| 646 | A230 | 5p violet & multi | .25 | .25 |
| a. | | Imperf., pair | 325.00 | |
| 647 | A230 | 1sh6p olive & multi | .25 | .25 |
| | | Nos. 645-647 (3) | .75 | .75 |

### Decimal Currency Issue

Mountain Road, by T.P. Flanagan — A231

Paintings from Northern Ireland: 7½p, Deer's Meadow, by Thomas Carr. 9p, Tollymore Forest Park, by Colin Middleton.

### "P" instead of "D"

**1971, June 16    Photo.    Perf. 14½x14**

| | | | | |
|---|---|---|---|---|
| 648 | A231 | 3p multicolored | .25 | .25 |
| 649 | A231 | 7½p multicolored | .25 | .25 |
| 650 | A231 | 9p multicolored | .25 | .25 |
| | | Nos. 648-650 (3) | .75 | .75 |

Ulster '71 Festival, Belfast, May-Oct.

John Keats (1795-1821) A232

Writers and their signatures: 5p, Thomas Gray (1716-71). 7½p, Sir Walter Scott (1771-1832).

**1971, July 28    Photo.    Perf. 14½x14**

| | | | | |
|---|---|---|---|---|
| 651 | A232 | 3p dull bl, blk & gold | .25 | .25 |
| 652 | A232 | 5p olive, blk & gold | .25 | .25 |
| 653 | A232 | 7½p yel brn, blk & gold | .25 | .25 |
| | | Nos. 651-653 (3) | .75 | .75 |

Soldier, Sailor, Airman, Nurse, 1921, and Poppy — A233

Designs: 7½p, Roman centurion on horseback, York Castle and coat of arms. 9p, Rugby players 100 years ago, and rose.

**1971, Aug. 25**

| | | | | |
|---|---|---|---|---|
| 654 | A233 | 3p ultra & multi | .25 | .25 |
| 655 | A233 | 7½p ocher & multi | .25 | .25 |
| 656 | A233 | 9p olive & multi | .25 | .25 |
| | | Nos. 654-656 (3) | .75 | .75 |

50th anniv. of the British Legion (3p); 1900th anniv. of the founding of York (7½p); cent. of the Rugby Football Union (9p).

Physical Sciences Building, University College of Wales, Aberystwyth A234

Modern University Buildings: 5p, Faraday Building, Engineering Faculty, University of Southampton. 7½p, Engineering Building, University of Leicester. 9p, Hexagon Restaurant, University of Essex.

**1971, Sept. 22    Photo.    Perf. 14½x14**

| | | | | |
|---|---|---|---|---|
| 657 | A234 | 3p citron & multi | .25 | .25 |
| 658 | A234 | 5p rose vio & multi | .25 | .25 |
| 659 | A234 | 7½p dp brn & multi | .25 | .25 |
| 660 | A234 | 9p dk blue & multi | .25 | .25 |
| | | Nos. 657-660 (4) | 1.00 | 1.00 |

No. 658 exists with large "p" in "5p." These are from plate combination 1A1B1C1D and were not officially issued.

Dream of the Kings — A235

Christmas (from Stained Glass Windows, Canterbury Cathedral): 3p, Adoration of the Kings. 7½p, Journey of the Kings.

**1971, Oct. 13**

| | | | | |
|---|---|---|---|---|
| 661 | A235 | 2½p scarlet & multi | .25 | .25 |
| 662 | A235 | 3p ultra & multi | .25 | .25 |
| 663 | A235 | 7½p green & multi | .25 | .25 |
| | | Nos. 661-663 (3) | .75 | .75 |

James Clark Ross (1800-1862) and Map of South Polar Sea — A236

British Polar Explorers: 5p, Martin Frobisher (1535-1594), and Desceliers map, 1550. 7½p, Henry Hudson (c. 1560-1611) and Petrus Plancius map, 1592. 9p, Robert Falcon Scott (1868-1912) and map of Antarctica.

**1972, Feb. 16     Perf. 14x14½**

| | | | | |
|---|---|---|---|---|
| 664 | A236 | 3p dp bister & multi | .25 | .25 |
| 665 | A236 | 5p brick red & multi | .25 | .25 |
| 666 | A236 | 7½p violet & multi | .25 | .25 |
| 667 | A236 | 9p blue & multi | .25 | .25 |
| | | Nos. 664-667 (4) | 1.00 | 1.00 |

See Nos. 689-693.

Head of Tutankhamen as Fisherman A237

Coast Guard — A238

Ralph Vaughan Williams and "Sea Symphony" A239

**1972, Apr. 26    Photo.    Perf. 14½x14**

| | | | | |
|---|---|---|---|---|
| 668 | A237 | 3p gold & multi | .25 | .25 |

### Photo.; Queen's Head Gold Embossed

| | | | | |
|---|---|---|---|---|
| 669 | A238 | 7½p blue & multi | .25 | .25 |
| 670 | A239 | 9p multicolored | .25 | .25 |
| | | Nos. 668-670 (3) | .75 | .75 |

50th anniv. of the discovery of the tomb of Tutankhamen by Howard Carter and Lord Carnarvon; sesquicentennial of the British Coast guard; Ralph Vaughan Williams (1872-1958), composer.

St. Andrew's, Greensted-Juxta-Ongar A240

Old Village Churches: 4p, All Saints, Earls Barton. 5p, St. Andrew's, Letheringsett. 7½p, St. Andrew's, Helpringham. 9p, St. Mary the Virgin, Huish Episcopi.

### Photo.; Queen's Head Gold Embossed

**1972, June 21     Perf. 14x14½**

| | | | | |
|---|---|---|---|---|
| 671 | A240 | 3p dull blue & multi | .25 | .25 |
| 672 | A240 | 4p olive & multi | .25 | .25 |
| 673 | A240 | 5p dp grn & multi | .25 | .25 |
| 674 | A240 | 7½p red & multi | .25 | .25 |
| 675 | A240 | 9p blue & multi | .25 | .25 |
| | | Nos. 671-675 (5) | 1.25 | 1.25 |

Various BBC Microphones A241

Designs: 5p, Wooden horn loudspeaker 1925. 7½p, Color TV camera, 1972. 9p, Marconi's oscillator and spark transmitter, 1897.

**1972, Sept. 13    Photo.    Perf. 14x14½**

| | | | | |
|---|---|---|---|---|
| 676 | A241 | 3p black, brn & yel | .25 | .25 |
| 677 | A241 | 5p henna brn & blk | .25 | .25 |
| 678 | A241 | 7½p black & magenta | .25 | .25 |
| 679 | A241 | 9p black & yel | .25 | .25 |
| | | Nos. 676-679 (4) | 1.00 | 1.00 |

Daily broadcasting in the United Kingdom, 50th anniv. (British Broadcasting Corp., Nos. 676-678), Marconi-Kemp experiments resulting in the 1st radio transmission across water, 75th anniv. (No. 679).

Angel with Trumpet — A242

### Photo.; Gold Embossed

**1972, Oct. 18     Perf. 14x14½**

| | | | | |
|---|---|---|---|---|
| 680 | A242 | 2½p shown | .25 | .25 |
| 681 | A242 | 3p Angel with lute | .25 | .25 |
| 682 | A242 | 7½p Angel with harp | .25 | .25 |
| | | Nos. 680-682 (3) | .75 | .75 |

Christmas.

Queen Elizabeth II, Prince Philip — A243

**1972, Nov. 20    Photo.    Perf. 14x14½**

| | | | | |
|---|---|---|---|---|
| 683 | A243 | 3p dk bl, sep & sil | .25 | .25 |
| 684 | A243 | 20p dk pur, sepia & sil | .70 | .70 |

25th anniv. of the marriage of Queen Elizabeth II and Prince Philip. No. 684 is without phosphor.

Britain as Part of European Community — A244

**1973, Jan. 3**

| | | | | |
|---|---|---|---|---|
| 685 | A244 | 3p brown org & multi | .25 | .25 |
| 686 | A244 | 5p blue & multi | .25 | .25 |
| 687 | A244 | 5p emerald & multi | .25 | .25 |
| a. | | Pair, #686-687 | .40 | .50 |
| | | Nos. 685-687 (3) | .75 | .75 |

Britain's entry into the European Community.

Oak — A245

**1973, Feb. 28    Photo.    Perf. 14½x14**

| | | | | |
|---|---|---|---|---|
| 688 | A245 | 9p multicolored | .25 | .25 |

Tree Planting Year.

### Explorer Type of 1972

British Explorers: No. 689, David Livingstone and map of Africa. No. 690, Henry Stanley and map of Africa. 5p, Sir Francis Drake and world map. 7½p, Sir Walter Raleigh and world map. 9p, Charles Sturt and map of Australia.

**1973, Apr. 8    Photo.    Perf. 14x14½**

| | | | | |
|---|---|---|---|---|
| 689 | A236 | 3p multicolored | .25 | .25 |
| 690 | A236 | 3p multicolored | .25 | .25 |
| a. | | Pair, #689-690 | .30 | .30 |
| 691 | A236 | 5p multicolored | .25 | .25 |
| 692 | A236 | 7½p multicolored | .25 | .25 |
| 693 | A236 | 9p multicolored | .25 | .25 |
| | | Nos. 689-693 (5) | 1.25 | 1.25 |

William Gilbert Grace — A246

Designs: Caricatures of William Gilbert Grace, the Great Cricketer, by Harry Furniss.

**1973, May 16    Photo.    Perf. 14x14½**

| | | | | |
|---|---|---|---|---|
| 694 | A246 | 3p brown & black | .25 | .25 |
| 695 | A246 | 7½p green & black | .40 | .40 |
| 696 | A246 | 9p blue & black | .55 | .60 |
| | | Nos. 694-696 (3) | 1.20 | 1.25 |

Centenary of British County Cricket.

Sir Joshua Reynolds, Self-portrait — A247

Paintings: 5p, Sir Henry Raeburn (1756-1823), self-portrait. 7½p, Nelly O'Brien, by Reynolds (1723-92). 9p, Rev. R. Walker (The Skater), by Raeburn.

**1973, July 4    Photo.    Perf. 14x14½**
| | | | | |
|---|---|---|---|---|
| 697 | A247 | 3p multicolored | .25 | .25 |
| 698 | A247 | 5p multicolored | .25 | .25 |
| 699 | A247 | 7½p multicolored | .25 | .25 |
| 700 | A247 | 9p gray & multi | .25 | .25 |
| | | Nos. 697-700 (4) | 1.00 | 1.00 |

Tuscan Portico, St. Paul's Church, Covent Garden — A248

Designs: No. 701, Costumes for Oberon and Titania. No. 703, Prince's Lodging, Newmarket. No. 704, Stage scenery for Oberon.

**Litho. and Typo.**
**1973, Aug. 15    Perf. 14½x14**
| | | | | |
|---|---|---|---|---|
| 701 | A248 | 3p black, pur & gold | .25 | .25 |
| 702 | A248 | 3p gold, brn & blk | .25 | .25 |
| a. | | Pair, #701-702 | .50 | .50 |
| 703 | A248 | 5p black, blue & gold | .25 | .25 |
| 704 | A248 | 5p gold, olive & blk | .25 | .25 |
| a. | | Pair, #703-704 | .50 | .50 |
| | | Nos. 701-704 (4) | 1.00 | 1.00 |

400th birth anniv. of Inigo Jones (1573-1652), architect and designer.

Parliament, from Millbank — A249

Design: 8p, Parliament, from Whitehall.

**1973, Sept. 12    Engr. and Typo.**
| | | | | |
|---|---|---|---|---|
| 705 | A249 | 8p buff, gray & blk | .25 | .25 |
| 706 | A249 | 10p black & gold | .25 | .25 |

Opening by the Queen of the 19th Commonwealth Parliamentary Assoc. Conf., Westminster Hall.

Princess Anne and Mark Phillips — A250

**1973, Nov. 14    Photo.    Perf. 14½x14**
| | | | | |
|---|---|---|---|---|
| 707 | A250 | 3½p violet & silver | .25 | .25 |
| 708 | A250 | 20p brown & silver | .35 | .35 |

Wedding of Princess Anne and Captain Mark Phillips, Nov. 14, 1973.

Good King Wenceslas A251

Illustrations for Christmas carol "Good King Wenceslas" showing king and page: No. 710, Page looking out of window. No. 711, Page leaving castle. No. 712, Page in storm. No. 713, Page bringing gifts. No. 714, Page and peasant.

**1973, Nov. 28**
| | | | | |
|---|---|---|---|---|
| 709 | A251 | 3p shown | .30 | .30 |
| 710 | A251 | 3p multicolored | .30 | .30 |
| 711 | A251 | 3p multicolored | .30 | .30 |
| 712 | A251 | 3p multicolored | .30 | .30 |
| 713 | A251 | 3p multicolored | .30 | .30 |
| a. | | Strip of 5, #709-713 | 1.50 | 1.50 |
| 714 | A251 | 3½p multicolored | .30 | .30 |
| | | Nos. 709-714 (6) | 1.80 | 1.80 |

Horse Chestnut — A252

**1974, Feb. 27    Photo.    Perf. 14½x14**
| | | | | |
|---|---|---|---|---|
| 715 | A252 | 10p green & multi | .30 | .25 |

Fire Engine, 1766 — A253

Designs: 3½p, First motorized fire engine, 1904. 5½p, Prize winning Sutherland fire engine, 1863. 8p, First steam engine, 1830.

**1974, Apr. 24**
| | | | | |
|---|---|---|---|---|
| 716 | A253 | 3½p multicolored | .25 | .25 |
| 717 | A253 | 5½p multicolored | .25 | .25 |
| 718 | A253 | 8p multicolored | .25 | .25 |
| 719 | A253 | 10p multicolored | .25 | .25 |
| | | Nos. 716-719 (4) | 1.00 | 1.00 |

Fire Prevention (Metropolis) Act, bicent.

Packet "Peninsular," 1888, and "Southampton Packet Letter" Postmark — A254

Development of Overseas Mail Transport: 5½p, Farnham Biplane and "Aerial Post" postmark. 8p, Truck and pillar box for airmail and "London F.S. Air Mail" postmark. 10p, Imperial Airways flying boat and "Southampton Airport" postmark.

**1974, June 12    Perf. 14½x14**
| | | | | |
|---|---|---|---|---|
| 720 | A254 | 3½p multicolored | .25 | .25 |
| 721 | A254 | 5½p multicolored | .25 | .25 |
| 722 | A254 | 8p multicolored | .25 | .25 |
| 723 | A254 | 10p multicolored | .25 | .25 |
| | | Nos. 720-723 (4) | 1.00 | 1.00 |

UPU, Cent.

Robert the Bruce — A255

"Great Britons" on caparisoned chargers.

**1974, July 10    Perf. 14½x14**
| | | | | |
|---|---|---|---|---|
| 724 | A255 | 4½p shown | .25 | .25 |
| 725 | A255 | 5½p Owain Glyndwr | .25 | .25 |
| 726 | A255 | 8p King Henry V | .25 | .25 |
| 727 | A255 | 10p Black Prince | .25 | .25 |
| | | Nos. 724-727 (4) | 1.00 | 1.00 |

Churchill, Lord Warden of the Cinque Ports, 1942 — A256

Designs (Churchill): 5½p, with bowler and cigar, 1940. 8p, with top hat, as Secretary of War and Air, 1919. 10p, in uniform of South African Light Horse Regiment, 1899.

**1974, Oct. 9    Photo.    Perf. 14x14½**
| | | | | |
|---|---|---|---|---|
| 728 | A256 | 4½p silver & multi | .25 | .25 |
| 729 | A256 | 5½p silver & multi | .25 | .25 |
| 730 | A256 | 8p silver & multi | .30 | .25 |
| 731 | A256 | 10p silver & multi | .35 | .25 |
| | | Nos. 728-731 (4) | 1.15 | 1.00 |

Sir Winston Spencer Churchill (1874-1965).

Adoration of the Kings, York Minster, c. 1355 — A257

Christmas (Roof Bosses): 4½p, Nativity, St. Helen's, Norwich, c. 1480. 8p, Virgin and

Child, Church of Ottery St. Mary, Devonshire, c. 1350. 10p, Virgin and Child, Lady Chapel, Worcester Cathedral, c. 1224.

**1974, Nov. 27    Perf. 14½x14**
| | | | | |
|---|---|---|---|---|
| 732 | A257 | 3½p gold & multi | .25 | .25 |
| 733 | A257 | 4½p gold & multi | .25 | .25 |
| 734 | A257 | 8p gold & multi | .25 | .25 |
| 735 | A257 | 10p gold & multi | .25 | .25 |
| | | Nos. 732-735 (4) | 1.00 | 1.00 |

"Peace-Burial at Sea," by Turner — A258

Paintings: 5½p, "Snowstorm-Steamer off a Harbour's Mouth." 8p, "Arsenal, Venice." 10p, "View of St. Laurent."

**1975, Feb. 19    Photo.    Perf. 14½x14**
| | | | | |
|---|---|---|---|---|
| 736 | A258 | 4½p multicolored | .25 | .25 |
| 737 | A258 | 5½p multicolored | .25 | .25 |
| 738 | A258 | 8p multicolored | .25 | .25 |
| 739 | A258 | 10p multicolored | .25 | .25 |
| | | Nos. 736-739 (4) | 1.00 | 1.00 |

Birth bicent. of Joseph Mallord William Turner (1775-1851), painter.

Charlotte Square, Edinburgh A259

National Theater, London — A260

Designs: No. 740, The Rows, Chester (double-storied medieval shopping streets). 8p, Sir Christopher Wren's Flamsteed House, Royal Observatory, Greenwich. 10p, St. George's Chapel, Windsor.

**1975, Apr. 23    Perf. 14½x14**
| | | | | |
|---|---|---|---|---|
| 740 | A259 | 7p multicolored | .25 | .25 |
| 741 | A259 | 7p multicolored | .25 | .25 |
| a. | | Pair, #740-741 | .50 | .50 |
| 742 | A259 | 8p multicolored | .25 | .25 |
| 743 | A259 | 10p multicolored | .25 | .25 |
| 744 | A260 | 12p multicolored | .25 | .25 |
| | | Nos. 740-744 (5) | 1.25 | 1.25 |

European Architectural Heritage Year 1975. Nos. 740-741 printed se-tenant in sheets of 100. 300th anniv. of Royal Observatory, (No. 742) and 500th anniv. of St. George's Chapel (No. 743).

Dinghies — A261

**1975, June 11    Photo. & Engr.**
| | | | | |
|---|---|---|---|---|
| 745 | A261 | 7p shown | .25 | .25 |
| 746 | A261 | 8p Racing keelboats | .25 | .25 |
| 747 | A261 | 10p Cruising yachts | .25 | .25 |
| 748 | A261 | 12p Multihulls | .25 | .25 |
| | | Nos. 745-748 (4) | 1.00 | 1.00 |

Royal Thames Yacht Club bicent. and other sailing club anniversaries.

Stephenson's Locomotion, 1825 — A262

Locomotives: 8p, Abbotsford, Waverley Class, 1876. 10p, Caerphilly Castle, 1923. 12p, High-speed train, 1975.

**1975, Aug. 13    Photo.    Perf. 14½x14**
| | | | | |
|---|---|---|---|---|
| 749 | A262 | 7p multicolored | .25 | .25 |
| 750 | A262 | 8p multicolored | .25 | .25 |
| 751 | A262 | 10p multicolored | .25 | .25 |
| 752 | A262 | 12p multicolored | .35 | .35 |
| | | Nos. 749-752 (4) | 1.10 | 1.10 |

Sesquicentennial of public railroads in Great Britain.

Parliament A263

**1975, Sept. 3**
| | | | | |
|---|---|---|---|---|
| 753 | A263 | 12p multicolored | .30 | .30 |

62nd Inter-Parliamentary Conference, London, Sept. 1975.

Emma and Mr. Woodhouse from "Emma" — A264

Designs (Illustrations by Barbara Brown of Characters from Jane Austen's Novels): 10p, Catherine Morland from "Northanger Abbey." 11p, Mr. Darcy from "Pride and Prejudice." 13p, Mary and Henry Crawford from "Mansfield Park."

**1975, Oct. 22    Photo.    Perf. 14x14½**
| | | | | |
|---|---|---|---|---|
| 754 | A264 | 8½p multicolored | .25 | .25 |
| 755 | A264 | 10p multicolored | .25 | .25 |
| 756 | A264 | 11p multicolored | .25 | .25 |
| 757 | A264 | 13p multicolored | .25 | .25 |
| | | Nos. 754-757 (4) | 1.00 | 1.00 |

Jane Austen (1775-1817), novelist.

Angels with Lute and Harp — A265

Christmas: 8½p, Angel with mandolin. 11p, Angel with horn. 13p, Angel with trumpet.

**1975, Nov. 26    Photo.    Perf. 14½x14**
| | | | | |
|---|---|---|---|---|
| 758 | A265 | 6½p violet & multi | .25 | .25 |
| 759 | A265 | 8½p multicolored | .25 | .25 |
| 760 | A265 | 11p multicolored | .25 | .25 |
| 761 | A265 | 13p ocher & multi | .25 | .25 |
| | | Nos. 758-761 (4) | 1.00 | 1.00 |

Woman Making Social Call — A266

Designs: 10p, Policeman making emergency call. 11p, District nurse making social welfare call. 13p, Refinery worker making field call.

**1976, Mar. 10    Photo.    Perf. 14½x14**
| | | | | |
|---|---|---|---|---|
| 777 | A266 | 8½p multicolored | .25 | .25 |
| 778 | A266 | 10p multicolored | .25 | .25 |
| 779 | A266 | 11p multicolored | .25 | .25 |
| 780 | A266 | 13p multicolored | .25 | .25 |
| | | Nos. 777-780 (4) | 1.00 | 1.00 |

1st telephone call by Alexander Graham Bell, Mar. 10, 1876.

Coal Miner's Hands (Thomas Hepburn) — A267

Designs: 10p, Child's hands, textile mill (Robert Owen). 11p, Boy's hand sweeping chimney (Lord Shaftesbury). 13p, Woman's hands holding prison bars (Elizabeth Frey).

**1976, Apr. 28    Photo.    Perf. 14½x14**
| | | | | |
|---|---|---|---|---|
| 781 | A267 | 8½p gray & black | .25 | .25 |
| 782 | A267 | 10p multicolored | .25 | .25 |
| 783 | A267 | 11p multicolored | .25 | .25 |
| 784 | A267 | 13p multicolored | .25 | .25 |
| | | Nos. 781-784 (4) | 1.00 | 1.00 |

19th cent. industrial & social reformers: Hepburn formed 1st miners' union in 1831; Owen, improved working conditions in his mill and established schools; Lord Shaftesbury, philanthropist and sponsor of reform work laws; Frey, pioneer of women's prison reforms.

Benjamin Franklin, by Jean-Jacques Caffieri — A268

**1976, June 2**     *Perf. 14x14½*
785 A268 11p multicolored    .30 .30
American Bicentennial.

Royal National Rose Society, Centenary — A269

Roses Painted by Kristin Rosenberg — 8½p, Elizabeth of Glamis Rose. 10p, Grandpa Dickson. 11p, Rosa Mundi. 13p, Sweet Briar.

**1976, June 30 Photo.**   *Perf. 14x14½*
786 A269 8½p multicolored   .25 .25
787 A269 10p multicolored   .25 .25
788 A269 11p multicolored   .25 .25
789 A269 13p multicolored   .25 .25
   Nos. 786-789 (4)   1.00 1.00

Archdruid, Eisteddfod A270

Morris Dancing A271

British Cultural Traditions: 11p, Piper and dancers, Highland gathering. 13p, Woman playing Welsh harp (telyn), Eisteddfod.

**1976, Aug. 4 Photo.**   *Perf. 14x14½*
790 A270 8½p multicolored   .25 .25
791 A271 10p multicolored   .25 .25
792 A271 11p multicolored   .25 .25
793 A270 13p multicolored   .25 .25
   Nos. 790-793 (4)   1.00 1.00

Squire, from Canterbury Tales — A272

Designs: 10p, Page from Tretyse of Love, c. 1493, set in Caxton typeface. 11p, Philosopher, from The Game and Playe of Chesse, c. 1483. 13p, Printing press and printers, early 16th century woodcut.

**Photo.; Queen's Head Gold Embossed**
**1976, Sept. 29**     *Perf. 14x14½*
794 A272 8½p blue & indigo   .25 .25
795 A272 10p olive & dk grn   .25 .25
796 A272 11p gray & black   .25 .25
797 A272 13p ocher & red brn   .25 .25
   Nos. 794-797 (4)   1.00 1.00
500 years of British printing, introduced by William Caxton (1422-1491).

Virgin and Child, Clare Chasuble — A273

Christmas (English medieval embroideries): 8½p, Angel with crown. 11p, Angel appearing to the shepherds. 13p, Three Kings bringing gifts, Butler-Bowden cope.

**1976, Nov. 24 Photo.**
798 A273 6½p multicolored   .25 .25
799 A273 8½p multicolored   .25 .25
800 A273 11p multicolored   .25 .25
801 A273 13p multicolored   .25 .25
   Nos. 798-801 (4)   1.00 1.00

Racket Sports — A274

**1977, Jan. 12 Photo.**   *Perf. 14½x14*
802 A274 8½p Tennis   .25 .25
803 A274 10p Table tennis   .25 .25
804 A274 11p Squash   .25 .25
805 A274 13p Badminton   .25 .25
   Nos. 802-805 (4)   1.00 1.00
Wimbledon Tennis Championships, cent. and 1977 World Table Tennis Championships, Birmingham.

Steroids Conformational Analysis — A275

Designs: 10p, Vitamin C synthesis (formula and orange). 11p, Starch chromatography. 13p, Salt crystallography.

**1977, Mar. 2 Photo.**   *Perf. 14½x14*
806 A275 8½p multicolored   .25 .25
807 A275 10p multicolored   .25 .25
808 A275 11p multicolored   .25 .25
809 A275 13p multicolored   .25 .25
   Nos. 806-809 (4)   1.00 1.00
British chemists who won Nobel prize. Derek Barton, 1969 (8½p); Walter Norman Haworth, 1937 (10p); Archer J. P. Martin and Richard L. M. Synge, 1952 (11p); William and Lawrence Bragg, 1915 (13p).

Queen Elizabeth II — A276

**1977**    **Photo.**   *Perf. 14½x14*
810 A276 8½p silver & multi   .25 .25
811 A276 9p silver & multi   .30 .30
812 A276 10p silver & multi   .25 .25
813 A276 11p silver & multi   .25 .25
814 A276 13p silver & multi   .25 .25
   Nos. 810-814 (5)   1.30 1.30
25th anniv. of the reign of Elizabeth II. Issue dates: 9p, June 15; others, May 11.

Pentagons, Symbolic of Continents and Nations — A277

**1977, June 8 Photo.**   *Perf. 14x14½*
815 A277 13p multicolored   .25 .25
Summit Conference of Commonwealth Heads of Government, London, June 1977.

Wildlife Protection — A278

**1977, Oct. 5 Photo.**   *Perf. 14x14½*
816 A278 9p Hedgehog   .25 .25
817 A278 9p Brown hare   .25 .25
818 A278 9p Red squirrel   .25 .25
819 A278 9p Otter   .25 .25
820 A278 9p Badger   .25 .25
  *a.*   Strip of 5, #816-820   1.00

"Two Turtle Doves, Three French Hens. . ." — A279

The Twelve Days of Christmas: No. 822, 4 colly birds, 5 gold rings, 6 geese a-laying. No. 823, 7 swans a-swimming, 8 maids a-milking. No. 824, 9 drummers drumming, 10 pipers piping. No. 825, 11 ladies dancing, 12 lords a-leaping. 9p, A partridge in a pear tree.

**1977, Nov. 23 Photo.**   *Perf. 14½x14*
821 A279 7p multicolored   .25 .25
822 A279 7p multicolored   .25 .25
823 A279 7p multicolored   .25 .25
824 A279 7p multicolored   .25 .25
825 A279 7p multicolored   .25 .25
  *a.*   Strip of 5, #821-825   1.25
826 A279 9p multicolored   .25 .25
   Nos. 821-826 (6)   1.50 1.50

Oil Production Platform, North Sea — A280

Designs: 10½p, Coal, pithead. 11p, Natural gas, flame. 13p, Electricity-producing nuclear power plant and uranium atom diagram.

**1978, Jan. 25 Photo.**   *Perf. 14x14½*
827 A280 9p multicolored   .25 .25
828 A280 10½p multicolored   .25 .25
829 A280 11p multicolored   .25 .25
830 A280 13p multicolored   .25 .25
   Nos. 827-830 (4)   1.00 1.00
Great Britain's wealth of energy resources.

Tower of London — A281

British Architecture: 10½p, Abbey and Palace, Holyrood House, Edinburgh. 11p, Caernarvon Castle, Wales. 13p, Hampton Court Palace, London.

**1978, Mar. 1 Photo.**   *Perf. 14½x14*
831 A281 9p multicolored   .25 .25
832 A281 10½p multicolored   .25 .25
833 A281 11p multicolored   .25 .25
834 A281 13p multicolored   .25 .25
  *a.*   Souv. sheet of 4, #831-834   1.10 1.10
   Nos. 831-834 (4)   1.00 1.00
No. 834a issued to publicize London 1980 Intl. Stamp Exhib. and sold for 53½p. The surtax went to exhibition fund.

Gold State Coach — A282

Designs: 10½p, St. Edward's crown. 11p, Orb. 13p, Imperial State crown.

**1978, May 31 Photo.**   *Perf. 14x14½*
835 A282 9p vio blue & gold   .25 .25
836 A282 10½p car lake & gold   .25 .25
837 A282 11p dp green & gold   .25 .25
838 A282 13p purple & gold   .25 .25
   Nos. 835-838 (4)   1.00 1.00
25th anniv. of coronation of Elizabeth II.

Shire Horse — A283

British Horses: 10½p, Shetland pony. 11p, Merlyn Cymreig Welsh pony. 13p, Thoroughbred.

**1978, July 5 Photo.**   *Perf. 14½x14*
839 A283 9p multicolored   .25 .25
840 A283 10½p multicolored   .25 .25
841 A283 11p multicolored   .25 .25
842 A283 13p multicolored   .25 .25
   Nos. 839-842 (4)   1.00 1.00

"Penny-farthing," 19th Century — A284

British bicycles: 10½p, 1920 touring bicycles. 11p, Modern small-wheel bicycles. 13p, Road racers.

**1978, Aug. 2 Photo.**   *Perf. 14½x14*
843 A284 9p multicolored   .25 .25
844 A284 10½p multicolored   .25 .25
845 A284 11p multicolored   .25 .25
846 A284 13p multicolored   .25 .25
   Nos. 843-846 (4)   1.00 1.00
Cent. of 1st natl. cycling organizations: British Cycling Fed. and Cyclists Touring Club.

Carolers Around Christmas Tree — A285

Christmas: 9p, Christmas waits (watchmen). 11p, 18th century carolers. 13p, Boar's head carol.

**1978, Nov. 22 Photo.**   *Perf. 14½x14*
847 A285 7p multicolored   .25 .25
848 A285 9p multicolored   .25 .25
849 A285 11p multicolored   .25 .25
850 A285 13p multicolored   .25 .25
   Nos. 847-850 (4)   1.00 1.00

Old English Sheepdog A286

British dogs: 10½p, Welsh springer spaniel. 11p, West Highland white terrier. 13p, Irish setter.

**1979, Feb. 7 Photo.**   *Perf. 14½x14*
851 A286 9p multicolored   .25 .25
852 A286 10½p multicolored   .25 .25
853 A286 11p multicolored   .25 .25
854 A286 13p multicolored   .25 .25
   Nos. 851-854 (4)   1.00 1.00

British Wild Flowers — A287

**1979, Mar. 21 Photo.**   *Perf. 14x14½*
855 A287 9p Primroses   .25 .25
856 A287 10½p Daffodils   .25 .25
857 A287 11p Bluebells   .25 .25
858 A287 13p Snowdrops   .25 .25
   Nos. 855-858 (4)   1.00 1.00

Flags of Member Nations as Ballots — A288

Flags of European Community Members: United Kingdom, Italy, Denmark, Belgium, Fed. Rep. of Germany, France, Netherlands, Ireland, Luxembourg. Positions of hands and flags different on each denomination.

**1979, May 9 Photo.**   *Perf. 14½x14*
859 A288 9p multicolored   .25 .25
860 A288 10½p multicolored   .25 .25
861 A288 11p multicolored   .25 .25
862 A288 13p multicolored   .25 .25
   Nos. 859-862 (4)   1.00 1.00
European Parliament, 1st direct elections, 6/7-10.

Saddling of
Mahmoud, 1936
Derby, by Alfred
Munnings — A289

200th Anniv. of the Derby: 10½p, Liverpool
Great National Steeple Chase, 1839, aquatint
by F. C. Turner. 11p, First Spring Meeting,
Newmarket, 1793, by J. N. Sartorius. 13p,
Charles II watching racing at Dorsett Ferry,
Windsor, 1684, by Francis Barlow.

**1979, June 6   Photo.   Perf. 14½x14**
863  A289   9p multicolored         .25   .25
864  A289  10½p multicolored        .25   .25
865  A289  11p multicolored         .25   .25
866  A289  13p multicolored         .25   .25
      Nos. 863-866 (4)             1.00  1.00

Peter Rabbit — A290

Children's books: 10½p, The Wind in the
Willows. 11p, Winnie the Pooh. 13p, Alice's
Adventures in Wonderland.

**1979, July 11   Photo.   Perf. 14x14½**
867  A290   9p multicolored         .25   .25
868  A290  10½p multicolored        .30   .25
869  A290  11p multicolored         .30   .25
870  A290  13p multicolored         .40   .25
      Nos. 867-870 (4)             1.25  1.00

International Year of the Child.

Rowland Hill — A291

Designs: 11½p, Bellman, early 19th cent.
13p, London post office and mailman, early
19th cent. 15p, Victorian woman and child
mailing letter.

**1979, Aug. 22   Photo.   Perf. 14x14½**
871  A291  10p multicolored         .25   .25
872  A291  11½p multicolored        .25   .25
873  A291  13p multicolored         .25   .25
874  A291  15p multicolored         .30   .25
 a.     Souvenir sheet of 4, #871-874   1.05  1.00
      Nos. 871-874 (4)             1.05  1.00

Sir Rowland Hill (1795-1879), originator of
penny postage.
No. 874a issued 10/24/79 to publicize
London 1980 Intl. Stamp Exhib. and sold for
59½p. The surtax went to exhibition fund.

Police Constable
and
Children — A292

Designs: 11½p, Police constable directing
traffic. 13p, Police woman on horseback. 15p,
River patrol boat.

**1979, Sept. 26   Photo.   Perf. 14½x14**
875  A292  10p multicolored         .25   .25
876  A292  11½p multicolored        .25   .25
877  A292  13p multicolored         .30   .25
878  A292  15p multicolored         .35   .25
      Nos. 875-878 (4)             1.15  1.00

London Metropolitan Police, 150th anniv.

Three Kings
Following
Star — A293

Christmas: 10p, Angel appearing before the
shepherds. 11½p, Nativity. 13p, Joseph and
Mary traveling to Bethlehem. 15p,
Annunciation.

**1979, Nov. 21   Photo.   Perf. 14½x14**
879  A293   8p multicolored         .25   .25
880  A293  10p multicolored         .25   .25
881  A293  11½p multicolored        .25   .25
882  A293  13p multicolored         .25   .25
883  A293  15p multicolored         .25   .25
      Nos. 879-883 (5)             1.25  1.25

Kingfisher — A294

**1980, Jan. 16   Photo.   Perf. 14x14½**
884  A294  10p shown                .25   .25
885  A294  11½p Dipper              .25   .25
886  A294  13p Moorhen              .25   .25
887  A294  15p Yellow wagtail       .35   .25
      Nos. 884-887 (4)             1.10  1.00

"Rocket"
Locomotive
A295

No. 905, 1st, 2nd class cars. No. 906, 3rd
class and sheep cars. No. 907, Flat cars. No.
908, Flat car, mail coach.

**1980, Mar. 12   Photo.   Perf. 14½x14**
904  A295  12p shown                .25   .25
905  A295  12p multicolored         .25   .25
906  A295  12p multicolored         .25   .25
907  A295  12p multicolored         .25   .25
908  A295  12p multicolored         .25   .25
 a.     Strip of 5, #904-908        1.35  1.35

Liverpool-Manchester Railroad, 150th
anniv. No. 908a has a continuous design.

London
View — A296

**1980, Apr. 9   Engr.   Perf. 14½**
909  A296  50p brown               1.10  1.00
 a.     Souvenir sheet             1.25  1.00

London 1980, Intl. Stamp Exhib., May 6-14.
No. 909a, issued May 7, sold for 75p.

Buckingham
Palace — A297

12p, Albert Memorial. 13½p, Royal Opera
House. 15p, Hampton Court. 17½p, Kensington Palace.

**1980, May 7   Photo.   Perf. 14x14½**
910  A297  10½p shown               .25   .25
911  A297  12p multicolored         .25   .25
912  A297  13½p multicolored        .25   .25
913  A297  15p multicolored         .30   .25
914  A297  17½p multicolored        .30   .25
      Nos. 910-914 (5)             1.30  1.25

Emily Bronte and
"Wuthering
Heights" — A298

Victorian novelists and scenes from their
novels: 12p, Charlotte Bronte, "Jane Eyre."
13½p, George Eliot, "The Mill on the Floss."
17½p, Mrs. Gaskell, "North and South." 12p
and 13½p show CEPT (Europa) emblem.

**1980, July 9   Photo.   Perf. 15x14**
915  A298  12p multicolored         .25   .25
916  A298  13½p multicolored        .30   .25
917  A298  15p multicolored         .35   .30
918  A298  17½p multicolored        .40   .35
      Nos. 915-918 (4)             1.30  1.15

Queen Mother
Elizabeth, 80th
Birthday — A299

**1980, Aug. 4   Photo.   Perf. 14x14½**
919  A299  12p multicolored         .40   .25

English
Conductors — A300

Designs: 12p, Henry Wood (1869-1944).
13½p, Thomas Beecham (1879-1961). 15p,
Malcolm Sargent (1895-1967). 17½p, John
Barbirolli (1899-1970).

**1980, Sept. 10**
920  A300  12p multicolored         .25   .25
921  A300  13½p multicolored        .30   .25
922  A300  15p multicolored         .35   .25
923  A300  17½p multicolored        .40   .25
      Nos. 920-923 (4)             1.30  1.05

Running — A301

**1980, Oct. 10   Litho.   Perf. 14x14½**
924  A301  12p shown                .25   .25
925  A301  13½p Rugby              .30   .25
926  A301  15p Boxing              .35   .30
927  A301  17½p Cricket            .40   .30
      Nos. 924-927 (4)             1.30  1.10

Centenaries: Amateur Athletics Assoc.;
Welsh Rugby Union; Amateur Boxing Assoc.;
1st cricket test match against Australia.

Christmas Tree
with
Candles — A302

Christmas (Traditional Decorations): 12p,
Candles, ivy, ribbons. 13½p, Mistletoe,
apples. 15p, Paper chain and bell. 17½p, Holly
wreath.

**1980, Nov. 19   Photo.   Perf. 14½x14**
928  A302  10p multicolored         .25   .25
929  A302  12p multicolored         .25   .25
930  A302  13½p multicolored        .25   .25
931  A302  15p multicolored         .30   .25
932  A302  17½ multicolored        .40   .30
      Nos. 928-932 (5)             1.45  1.30

Lovebirds, Angels
and Heart
(Valentine's
Day) — A303

Folklore: 18p, Morris Dancers, 16th century
window, Shropshire. 22p, Wheat, fruit, farm
couple dancing (Lammastide). 25p, Medieval
mummers, 14th century manuscript illustration. 14p and 18p show CEPT (Europa)
emblem.

**1981, Feb. 6   Photo.   Perf. 14½x14**
933  A303  14p multicolored         .30   .30
934  A303  18p multicolored         .40   .35
935  A303  22p multicolored         .50   .40
936  A303  25p multicolored         .50   .40
      Nos. 933-936 (4)             1.70  1.45

Guide Dog
Leading Blind
Man — A304

**1981, Mar. 25   Photo.**
937  A304  14p shown                .30   .25
938  A304  18p Sign language       .35   .25
939  A304  22p Man in wheelchair   .50   .40
940  A304  25p Foot painting       .55   .45
      Nos. 937-940 (4)             1.70  1.35

International Year of the Disabled.

Small
Tortoiseshell — A305

**1981, May 13   Perf. 14x14½**
941  A305  14p shown                .30   .25
942  A305  18p Large blue          .35   .30
943  A305  22p Peacock             .50   .40
944  A305  25p Checkered skipper   .55   .45
      Nos. 941-944 (4)             1.70  1.40

Glenfinnan,
Highlands,
Scotland — A306

50th anniv. of National Trust for Scotland:
18p, Derwentwater, Lake District, England.
20p, Stackpole Head, Dyfed, Wales. 22p,
Giant's Causeway, County Antrim, Northern
Ireland. 25p, St. Kilda, Scotland.

**1981, June 24   Photo.   Perf. 14½x14**
945  A306  14p multicolored         .25   .25
946  A306  18p multicolored         .35   .35
947  A306  20p multicolored         .40   .30
948  A306  22p multicolored         .45   .40
949  A306  25p multicolored         .50   .45
      Nos. 945-949 (5)             1.95  1.75

Prince Charles and
Lady Diana — A307

**1981, July 22   Photo.   Perf. 14x14½**
950  A307  14p multicolored         .25   .25
951  A307  25p multicolored         .75   .50

Wedding of Charles, Prince of Wales, and
Lady Diana Spencer, St. Paul's Cathedral,
July 29.

Hikers Reading
Map — A308

18p, Girl at potter's wheel. 22p, Woman
administering artificial respiration. 25p,
Hurdler.

**1981, Aug. 12   Litho.   Perf. 14**
952  A308  14p shown                .25   .25
953  A308  18p multicolored         .35   .30
954  A308  22p multicolored         .45   .35
955  A308  25p multicolored         .55   .45
      Nos. 952-955 (4)             1.60  1.35

The Duke of Edinburgh's Awards (expeditions, skills, service, recreation), 25th anniv.

Cockle
Dredging — A309

**1981, Sept. 23 Photo. Perf. 14½x14**

| | | | | |
|---|---|---|---|---|
| 956 | A309 | 14p shown | .25 | .25 |
| 957 | A309 | 18p Hauling trawl net | .35 | .30 |
| 958 | A309 | 22p Lobster potting | .45 | .35 |
| 959 | A309 | 25p Hauling seine net | .55 | .45 |
| | | Nos. 956-959 (4) | 1.60 | 1.35 |

Fishermen's Year and Royal Natl. Mission to Deep Sea Fishermen centenary.

Santa Claus — A309a

Joseph and Mary Arriving at Bethlehem

Christmas: Children's Drawings.

**1981, Nov. 18 Photo.**

| | | | | |
|---|---|---|---|---|
| 960 | A309a | 11½p Santa Claus | .25 | .25 |
| 961 | A309a | 14p Jesus | .25 | .25 |
| 962 | A309a | 18p Angel | .35 | .30 |
| 963 | A310 | 22p shown | .50 | .45 |
| 964 | A309a | 25p Three Kings | .55 | .50 |
| | | Nos. 960-964 (5) | 1.90 | 1.75 |

Death Centenary of Charles Darwin (1809-1882) A311

**1982, Feb. 10 Photo.**

| | | | | |
|---|---|---|---|---|
| 965 | A311 | 15½p Giant tortoises | .30 | .30 |
| 966 | A311 | 19½p Iguanas | .40 | .40 |
| 967 | A311 | 26p Darwin's finches | .60 | .50 |
| 968 | A311 | 29p Skulls | .65 | .60 |
| | | Nos. 965-968 (4) | 1.95 | 1.80 |

Youth Organizations — A312

**1982, Mar. 24 Photo. Perf. 14x14½**

| | | | | |
|---|---|---|---|---|
| 983 | A312 | 15½p Boy's Brigade | .30 | .35 |
| 984 | A312 | 19½p Girl's Brigade | .40 | .40 |
| 985 | A312 | 26p Boy Scouts | .60 | .50 |
| 986 | A312 | 29p Girl Guides | .65 | .60 |
| | | Nos. 983-986 (4) | 1.95 | 1.85 |

75th anniv. of scouting and 125th birth anniv. of founder Robert Baden-Powell (26p).

Performing Arts — A313

15½p, Ballet. 19½p, Pantomime. 26p, Shakespearean drama. 29p, Opera.

**1982, Apr. 28 Photo. Perf. 14x14½**

| | | | | |
|---|---|---|---|---|
| 987 | A313 | 15½p multicolored | .25 | .25 |
| 988 | A313 | 19½p multicolored | .35 | .35 |
| 989 | A313 | 26p multicolored | .45 | .45 |
| 990 | A313 | 29p multicolored | .60 | .60 |
| | | Nos. 987-990 (4) | 1.65 | 1.65 |

Nos. 987-990 show CEPT (Europa) emblem.

King Henry VIII and the Mary Rose — A314

19½p, Admiral Blake, Triumph. 24p, Lord Nelson, Victory. 26p, Lord Fisher, Dreadnought. 29p, Viscount Cunningham, Warspite.

**1982, June 16 Perf. 14½x14**

| | | | | |
|---|---|---|---|---|
| 991 | A314 | 15½p shown | .35 | .25 |
| 992 | A314 | 19½p multicolored | .45 | .35 |
| 993 | A314 | 24p multicolored | .45 | .40 |
| 994 | A314 | 26p multicolored | .50 | .50 |
| 995 | A314 | 29p multicolored | .65 | .60 |
| | | Nos. 991-995 (5) | 2.40 | 2.10 |

Textile Designs — A315

15½p, Strawberry Thief, 1883. 19½p, Tulips, 1906. 26p, Cherry Orchard, 1930. 29p, Chevron, 1973.

**1982, July 23 Photo. Perf. 14x14½**

| | | | | |
|---|---|---|---|---|
| 996 | A315 | 15½p multicolored | .30 | .25 |
| 997 | A315 | 19½p multicolored | .45 | .35 |
| 998 | A315 | 26p multicolored | .55 | .45 |
| 999 | A315 | 29p multicolored | .60 | .55 |
| | | Nos. 996-999 (4) | 1.90 | 1.60 |

Information Technology — A316

15½p, Hieroglyphics, library, word processor. 26p, Viewdata set, satellite, laser pen.

**1982, Sept. 8 Photo.**

| | | | | |
|---|---|---|---|---|
| 1000 | A316 | 15½p multicolored | .30 | .30 |
| 1001 | A316 | 26p multicolored | .55 | .50 |

Austin's Seven (1922) and Metro — A317

Cars: 19½p, Ford Model T (1913) and Escort. 26p, Jaguar SS (1931) and XJ6 (1967). 29p, Rolls-Royce Silver Ghost (1907) and Silver Spirit (1982).

**1982, Oct. 13 Litho. Perf. 14½x14**

| | | | | |
|---|---|---|---|---|
| 1002 | A317 | 15½p multicolored | .30 | .25 |
| 1003 | A317 | 19½p multicolored | .50 | .40 |
| 1004 | A317 | 26p multicolored | .55 | .45 |
| 1005 | A317 | 29p multicolored | .65 | .55 |
| | | Nos. 1002-1005 (4) | 2.00 | 1.65 |

Christmas 1982 — A318

Christmas carols — No. 1006, While Shepherds Watched. No. 1007, The Holly and the Ivy. No. 1008, I Saw Three Ships. No. 1009, We Three Kings. No. 1010, Good King Wenceslas.

**1982, Nov. 17 Photo.**

| | | | | |
|---|---|---|---|---|
| 1006 | A318 | 12½p multi | .25 | .25 |
| 1007 | A318 | 15½p multi | .30 | .25 |
| 1008 | A318 | 19½p multi | .40 | .35 |
| 1009 | A318 | 26p multi | .50 | .40 |
| 1010 | A318 | 29p multi | .55 | .50 |
| | | Nos. 1006-1010 (5) | 2.00 | 1.75 |

River Fish — A319

**1983, Jan. 26 Photo. Perf. 15x14**

| | | | | |
|---|---|---|---|---|
| 1011 | A319 | 15½p Salmon | .30 | .25 |
| 1012 | A319 | 19½p Pike | .40 | .45 |
| 1013 | A319 | 26p Trout | .60 | .45 |
| 1014 | A319 | 29p Perch | .65 | .50 |
| | | Nos. 1011-1014 (4) | 1.95 | 1.65 |

Commonwealth Day — A320

Landscapes by Donald Hamilton Fraser.

**1983, Mar. 9 Photo. Perf. 14x14½**

| | | | | |
|---|---|---|---|---|
| 1015 | A320 | 15½p Tropical island | .30 | .30 |
| 1016 | A320 | 19½p Desert | .40 | .45 |
| 1017 | A320 | 26p Farmland | .55 | .55 |
| 1018 | A320 | 29p Mountains | .60 | .60 |
| | | Nos. 1015-1018 (4) | 1.85 | 1.90 |

Engineering Achievements (Europa) — A321

16p, Humber Bridge. 20½p, Thames Flood Barrier. 28p, Emergency oil rig support vessel Lolair.

**1983, May 25 Photo. Perf. 15x14**

| | | | | |
|---|---|---|---|---|
| 1019 | A321 | 16p multicolored | .40 | .25 |
| 1020 | A321 | 20½p multicolored | .50 | .50 |
| 1021 | A321 | 28p multicolored | .70 | .70 |
| | | Nos. 1019-1021 (3) | 1.60 | 1.45 |

A322

Designs: 16p, The Royal Scots (Royal Regiment). 20½p, Royal Welsh Fusiliers. 26p, Royal Green Jackets. 28p, Irish Guards. 31p, Parachute Regiment.

**1983, July 6 Perf. 14x14½**

| | | | | |
|---|---|---|---|---|
| 1022 | A322 | 16p multicolored | .30 | .30 |
| 1023 | A322 | 20½p multicolored | .45 | .45 |
| 1024 | A322 | 26p multicolored | .50 | .50 |
| 1025 | A322 | 28p multicolored | .55 | .55 |
| 1026 | A322 | 31p multicolored | .65 | .65 |
| | | Nos. 1022-1026 (5) | 2.45 | 2.45 |

A323

Designs: 16p, 20th cent. garden, Sissinghurst. 20½p, Biddulph Grange, 19th cent. 28p, Blenheim, 18th cent. 31p, Pitmeeden, 17th cent.

**1983, Aug. 24 Litho. Perf. 14**

| | | | | |
|---|---|---|---|---|
| 1027 | A323 | 16p multicolored | .35 | .25 |
| 1028 | A323 | 20½p multicolored | .45 | .40 |
| 1029 | A323 | 28p multicolored | .60 | .45 |
| 1030 | A323 | 31p multicolored | .65 | .50 |
| | | Nos. 1027-1030 (4) | 2.05 | 1.60 |

British Fairs — A324

16p, Merry-go-round. 20½p, Animals, rides. 28p, Games. 31p, Ancient market fair.

**1983, Oct. 5 Photo. Perf. 14½x14**

| | | | | |
|---|---|---|---|---|
| 1031 | A324 | 16p multicolored | .35 | .25 |
| 1032 | A324 | 20½p multicolored | .45 | .40 |
| 1033 | A324 | 28p multicolored | .60 | .45 |
| 1034 | A324 | 31p multicolored | .65 | .45 |
| | | Nos. 1031-1034 (4) | 2.05 | 1.60 |

850th anniv. of St. Bartholomew's Fair.

Christmas A325

12½p, Birds mailing cards. 16p, Three Kings chimney pots. 20½p, Birds under umbrella. 28p, Birds under street lamp. 31p, Topiary dove.

**1983, Nov. 16 Photo.**

| | | | | |
|---|---|---|---|---|
| 1035 | A325 | 12½p multicolored | .25 | .25 |
| 1036 | A325 | 16p multicolored | .30 | .25 |
| 1037 | A325 | 20½p multicolored | .45 | .35 |
| 1038 | A325 | 28p multicolored | .55 | .50 |
| 1039 | A325 | 31p multicolored | .55 | .50 |
| | | Nos. 1035-1039 (5) | 2.10 | 1.85 |

Heraldry — A326

Designs: 16p, Arms of The College of Arms. 20½p, Arms of Richard III, founder. 28p, Arms of The Earl Marshal. 31p, Arms of The City of London.

**1984, Jan. 17 Photo. Perf. 14½**

| | | | | |
|---|---|---|---|---|
| 1040 | A326 | 16p multicolored | .30 | .25 |
| 1041 | A326 | 20½p multicolored | .40 | .35 |
| 1042 | A326 | 28p multicolored | .60 | .45 |
| 1043 | A326 | 31p multicolored | .65 | .50 |
| | | Nos. 1040-1043 (4) | 1.95 | 1.55 |

National Cattle Breeders' Association A327

16p, Highland Cow. 20½p, Chillingham Wild Bull. 26p, Hereford Bull. 28p, Welsh Black Bull. 31p, Irish Moiled Cow.

**1984, Mar. 6 Litho. Perf. 15x14½**

| | | | | |
|---|---|---|---|---|
| 1044 | A327 | 16p multicolored | .25 | .25 |
| 1045 | A327 | 20½p multicolored | .40 | .35 |
| 1046 | A327 | 26p multicolored | .55 | .40 |
| 1047 | A327 | 28p multicolored | .60 | .45 |
| 1048 | A327 | 31p multicolored | .60 | .45 |
| | | Nos. 1044-1048 (5) | 2.40 | 1.90 |

Royal Institute of British Architects Sesquicentennial A328

Urban renewal projects and plans.

**1984, Apr. 3 Photo.**

| | | | | |
|---|---|---|---|---|
| 1049 | A328 | 16p Liverpool | .30 | .25 |
| 1050 | A328 | 20½p Durham | .45 | .40 |
| 1051 | A328 | 28p Bristol | .55 | .50 |
| 1052 | A328 | 31p Perth | .65 | .55 |
| | | Nos. 1049-1052 (4) | 1.95 | 1.70 |

Europa (1959-1984) A329

No. 1053, No. 1055, Bridge. No. 1054, No. 1056, Abduction of Europa.

**1984, May 9 Photo. Perf. 14½x14**

| | | | | |
|---|---|---|---|---|
| 1053 | A329 | 16p gray, dk bl, blk | .30 | .30 |
| 1054 | A329 | 16p gray, dk bl, blk | .30 | .30 |
| a. | | Pair, #1053-1054 | .65 | .65 |
| 1055 | A329 | 20½p brn rose, dp car, blk | .40 | .40 |
| 1056 | A329 | 20½p brn rose, dp car, blk | .40 | .40 |
| a. | | Pair, #1055-1056 | .75 | .75 |
| | | Nos. 1053-1056 (4) | 1.40 | 1.40 |

Nos. 1054, 1056 also for 2nd Election of the European Parliament.

London Economic Summit, June 7-9 — A330

**1984, June 5      Photo.      Perf. 14x15**
1057 A330 31p Lancaster House      .70   .75

Greenwich Meridian, Cent. — A331

16p, View from Apollo 11. 20½p, English Channel map. 28p, Greenwich Observatory. 31p, Airy's transit telescope, 1850.

**1984, June 26      Litho.      Perf. 14x14½**
1058 A331  16p multicolored      .30   .30
1059 A331  20½p multicolored     .45   .50
1060 A331  28p multicolored      .60   .50
1061 A331  31p multicolored      .70   .60
      Nos. 1058-1061 (4)          2.05  1.90

Bath-Bristol-London Mail Coach Bicentenary — A332

18th century drawings by James Pollard — No. 1062, Bath, 1784. No. 1063, Exeter, 1816. No. 1064, Norwich, 1827. No. 1065, Holyhead & Liverpool. No. 1066, Edinburgh, 1831.

**Photo. & Engr.**
**1984, July 31            Perf. 14½x14**
1062 A332 16p multicolored       .35   .35
1063 A332 16p multicolored       .35   .35
1064 A332 16p multicolored       .35   .35
1065 A332 16p multicolored       .35   .35
1066 A332 16p multicolored       .35   .35
   a.   Strip of 5, #1062-1066   1.50  1.50

50th Anniv. of British Council — A333

17p, Education for development. 22p, Promoting the arts. 31p, Technical training. 34p, Language & libraries.

**1984, Sept. 25            Photo.**
1067 A333 17p multicolored       .30   .30
1068 A333 22p multicolored       .40   .40
1069 A333 31p multicolored       .55   .55
1070 A333 34p multicolored       .80   .80
      Nos. 1067-1070 (4)          2.05  2.05

Christmas 1984 — A334

Crayon Sketches by Yvonne Gilbert: 13p, Holy Family. 17p, Arrival in Bethlehem. 22p, Shephard and Lamb. 31p, Virgin and child. 34p, Offering Frankincense.

**1984, Nov. 20      Photo.      Perf. 15x14**
1088 A334 13p multicolored       .25   .25
   a.   Booklet pane of 20 (BK770)   6.00
1089 A334 17p multicolored       .35   .30
1090 A334 22p multicolored       .40   .50
1091 A334 31p multicolored       .65   .55
1092 A334 34p multicolored       .75   .70
      Nos. 1088-1092 (5)          2.40  2.30

Bklt. of 20 13p sold at 30p discount. Stamps have blue stars printed on the back.

Great Western Railway Sesquicentennial A335

**1985, Jan. 22      Photo.      Perf. 15x14**
1093 A335 17p Flying Scotsman     .35   .35
1094 A335 22p Golden Arrow        .55   .50
1095 A335 29p Cheltenham Flyer    .60   .60
1096 A335 31p Royal Scot          .80   .75
1097 A335 34p Cornish Riviera     .80   .80
      Nos. 1093-1097 (5)          3.10  3.00

Insects — A336

17p, Buff tailed bumble bee. 22p, Seven spotted ladybird. 29p, Wart-biter bush-cricket. 31p, Stag beetle. 34p, Emperor dragonfly.

**1985, Mar. 12      Photo.      Perf. 15x14½**
1098 A336 17p multicolored       .30   .25
1099 A336 22p multicolored       .45   .50
1100 A336 29p multicolored       .55   .60
1101 A336 31p multicolored       .70   .70
1102 A336 34p multicolored       .75   .75
      Nos. 1098-1102 (5)          2.75  2.80

Music Year (Europa) — A337

British Composers: 17p, Water Music, by George Frideric Handel. 22p, The Planets Suite, by Gustav Holst. 31p, The First Cookoo, by Frederick Delius. 34p, Sea Pictures, by Edward Elgar.

**1985, May 14            Perf. 14½**
1103 A337 17p Reflections in
                  pool           .40   .35
1104 A337 22p View of planets    .85   .65
1105 A337 31p Roosting cuckoo   1.00  1.00
1106 A337 34p Waves, wing       1.00  1.05
      Nos. 1103-1106 (4)         3.25  3.05

Safety at Sea — A338

17p, Lifeboat. 22p, Beachy Head Lighthouse, chart. 31p, Marecs-A satellite. 34p, Signal buoy, yacht.

**1985, June 18      Litho.      Perf. 14**
1107 A338 17p multicolored       .30   .35
1108 A338 22p multicolored       .45   .50
1109 A338 31p multicolored       .75   .70
1110 A338 34p multicolored       .75   .70
      Nos. 1107-1110 (4)          2.25  2.25

Royal Mail Service, 350th Anniv. — A339

Designs: 17p, Royal Mail Datapost motorcyclist and plane. 22p, Postbus on country road. 31p, Parcel service delivery. 34p, Postman delivering mail.

**1985, July 30      Photo.      Perf. 14x14½**
1111 A339 17p multicolored       .30   .35
   a.   Booklet pane of 10 (BK631)   4.50
1112 A339 22p multicolored       .50   .50
1113 A339 31p multicolored       .65   .60
1114 A339 34p multicolored       .75   .75
      Nos. 1111-1114 (4)          2.20  2.20

Arthurian Legends — A340

Designs: 17p, Arthur consulting with Merlin. 22p, The Lady of the Lake with the sword "Excalibur." 31p, Guinevere and Lancelot fleeing from Camelot. 34p, Sir Galahad praying during his quest for the Holy Grail.

**1985, Sept. 3      Photo.      Perf. 15x14**
1115 A340 17p multicolored       .35   .35
1116 A340 22p multicolored       .45   .50
1117 A340 31p multicolored       .70   .70
1118 A340 34p multicolored       .70   .70
      Nos. 1115-1118 (4)          2.20  2.25

500th anniv. of William Caxton's edition of Le Morte D'Arthur, by Sir Thomas Mallory.

20th Cent. Stars and Directors of Film — A341

Photographs: 17p, Peter Sellers (1925-80). 22p, David Niven (1910-83). 29p, Charlie Chaplin (1889-1977). 31p, Vivien Leigh (1913-67). 34p, Sir Alfred Hitchcock (1899-1980), director.

**1985, Oct. 8      Photo.      Perf. 14½**
1119 A341 17p multicolored       .30   .30
1120 A341 22p multicolored       .40   .45
1121 A341 29p multicolored       .75   .70
1122 A341 31p multicolored       .75   .70
1123 A341 34p multicolored       .80   .80
      Nos. 1119-1123 (5)          3.00  2.95

Christmas Pantomime A342

**1985, Nov. 19      Photo.      Perf. 15x14½**
1124 A342 12p Principal boy       .25   .25
   a.   Booklet pane of 20 (BK 780)   5.50
1125 A342 17p Genie               .30   .30
1126 A342 22p Grande dame         .45   .45
1127 A342 31p Good fairy          .65   .60
1128 A342 34p Cat                 .70   .65
      Nos. 1124-1128 (5)          2.35  2.25

No. 1124a has random star design printed on back.

Industry Year — A343

17p, North Sea oil rig, light bulb. 22p, Medical research lab, thermometer. 31p, Steel mill, garden hoe. 34p, Cornfield, bread.

**1986, Jan. 14      Litho.      Perf. 15x14**
1129 A343 17p multicolored       .30   .30
1130 A343 22p multicolored       .45   .50
1131 A343 31p multicolored       .70   .55
1132 A343 34p multicolored       .80   .65
      Nos. 1129-1132 (4)          2.25  2.00

Halley's Comet — A344

Designs: 17p, Caricature, Edmond Halley (1656-1742), astronomer. 22p, European Space Agency Giotto spacecraft pursuing comet. 31p, Comet and legend, Maybe Twice in a Lifetime. 34p, Comet orbiting sun.

**1986, Feb. 18            Photo.**
1133 A344 17p multicolored       .30   .30
1134 A344 22p multicolored       .50   .45
1135 A344 31p multicolored       .70   .65
1136 A344 34p multicolored       .80   .70
      Nos. 1133-1136 (4)          2.30  2.10

A345

Queen Elizabeth II, 60th Birthday — A346

**1986, Apr. 21            Photo.**
1137 A345 17p multicolored       .45   .55
1138 A346 17p multicolored       .45   .55
   a.   Pair, #1137-1138          .90  1.10
1139 A345 34p multicolored       .85   .85
1140 A346 34p multicolored       .85   .85
   a.   Pair, #1139-1140         1.55  1.90

Europa — A347

Designs: 17p, Barn owl. 22p, Pine marten. 31p, Wild cat. 34p, Natterjack toad.

**1986, May 20      Photo.      Perf. 14½**
1141 A347 17p gold & multi       .35   .35
1142 A347 22p gold & multi       .40   .40
1143 A347 31p gold & multi       .50   .50
1144 A347 34p gold & multi       .60   .60
      Nos. 1141-1144 (4)          1.85  1.85

Domesday Book, 900th Anniv. — A348

**1986, June 17            Photo.**
1145 A348 17p Peasant            .35   .35
1146 A348 22p Freeman            .50   .50
1147 A348 31p Knight             .70   .70
1148 A348 34p Lord               .75   .75
      Nos. 1145-1148 (4)          2.30  2.30

Domesday Book, first nationwide survey in British history.

Sports — A349

**1986, July 15      Photo.      Perf. 15x14**
1149 A349 17p Track and field    .30   .30
1150 A349 22p Rowing             .40   .55
1151 A349 29p Weight lifting     .60   .55
1152 A349 31p Shooting           .70   .55
1153 A349 34p Field hockey       .70   .70
      Nos. 1149-1153 (5)          2.70  2.65

1986 Commonwealth Games, Edinburgh. World Hockey Cup, London.

Wedding of Prince Andrew and Sarah Ferguson — A350

**1986, July 22            Perf. 14x15**
1154 A350 12p multicolored       .40   .35
1155 A350 17p multicolored       .50   .55

Commonwealth Parliamentary Assoc. Conf., London — A351

**1986, Aug. 19    Litho.    Perf. 14x14½**
1156  A351  34p multicolored          .80   .85

Royal Air Force Commanders and Aircraft — A352

Designs: 17p, Lord Dowding (1882-1970), Hurricane. 22p, Lord Tedder (1890-1967), Hawker Typhoon. 29p, Lord Trenchard (1873-1956), De Havilland 9A World War I bomber. 31p, Sir Arthur Harris (1892-1984), Avro Lancaster. 34p, Lord Portal (1893-1971), De Havilland Mosquito.

**1986, Sept. 16    Photo.    Perf. 14½**
1157  A352  17p multicolored          .30   .30
1158  A352  22p multicolored          .50   .55
1159  A352  29p multicolored          .65   .60
1160  A352  31p multicolored          .75   .70
1161  A352  34p multicolored          .80   .85
       Nos. 1157-1161 (5)            3.00  3.00

Christmas A353

Customs: 12p, 13p, Glastonbury Thorn. 18p, Tanad Valley Plygain. 22p, Hebrides Tribute. 31p, Dewsbury Church Knell. 34p, Hereford Boy Bishop.

**1986, Nov. 18    Photo.    Perf. 15x14½**
1162  A353  12p multicolored          .25   .25
1163  A353  13p multicolored          .25   .25
    a.     Pane of 36               12.50
1164  A353  18p multicolored          .35   .35
1165  A353  22p multicolored          .55   .45
1166  A353  31p multicolored          .65   .55
1167  A353  34p multicolored          .65   .60
       Nos. 1162-1167 (6)            2.70  2.45

No. 1163a printed in two panes of 18 with gutter between, stars on back; folded and sold in discount booklet for £4.30.

Flora — A354

Photographs by Alfred Lammer.

**1987, Jan. 20    Photo.    Perf. 14½**
1168  A354  18p Gaillardia           .30   .30
1169  A354  22p Echinops             .50   .50
1170  A354  31p Echeveria            .65   .65
1171  A354  34p Colchicum            .80   .80
       Nos. 1168-1171 (4)            2.25  2.25

Sir Isaac Newton (1642-1727), Physicist, Mathematician — A355

Manuscripts and principles: 18p, Philosophiae Naturalis Principia Mathematica, 1687. 22p, Motion of bodies in ellipses. 31p, Optics Treatise of the Refraction, Reflections and Colors of Light. 34p, The System of the World.

**1987, Mar. 24    Photo.    Perf. 14**
1172  A355  18p multicolored         .35   .35
1173  A355  22p multicolored         .50   .50
1174  A355  31p multicolored         .65   .65
1175  A355  34p multicolored         .75   .75
       Nos. 1172-1175 (4)            2.25  2.25

Europa — A356

Modern architecture: 18p, Willis Faber & Dumas Building, Ipswich, designed by Norman Foster. 22p, Pompidou Centre, Paris, designed by Richard Rogers and Renzo Piano. 31p, Staatsgalerie, Stuttgart, designed by James Stirling and Michael Wilford. 34p, European Investment Bank, Luxembourg, designed by Sir Denys Lasdun.

**1987, May 12    Photo.    Perf. 15x14**
1176  A356  18p multicolored         .30   .30
1177  A356  22p multicolored         .55   .55
1178  A356  31p multicolored         .65   .65
1179  A356  34p multicolored         .85   .85
       Nos. 1176-1179 (4)            2.35  2.35

St. John Ambulance, Cent. — A357

First aid: 18p, Ambulance, 1887. 22p, War victims, 1940. 31p, Public event, 1965. 34p, Transplant organ flight, 1987.

**1987, June 16    Litho.    Perf. 14x14½**
1180  A357  18p multicolored         .35   .35
1181  A357  22p multicolored         .50   .50
1182  A357  31p multicolored         .65   .65
1183  A357  34p multicolored         .75   .75
       Nos. 1180-1183 (4)            2.25  2.25

Order of the Thistle, Scotland, 300th Anniv. of Revival — A358

Coats of arms: 18p, Lord Lyon, King of Arms, 1687. 22p, Duke of Rothesay, bestowed on Prince Charles in 1974. 31p, Royal Scottish Academy of Painting, Sculpture & Architecture, 1826. 34p, The Royal Society of Edinburgh, 1783.

**1987, July 21    Photo.    Perf. 14½**
1184  A358  18p multicolored         .35   .35
1185  A358  22p multicolored         .50   .50
1186  A358  31p multicolored         .65   .65
1187  A358  34p multicolored         .75   .75
       Nos. 1184-1187 (4)            2.25  2.25

Accession of Queen Victoria, 150th Anniv. — A359

Portraits of Victoria and: 18p, Great Exhibition (1851) at the Crystal Palace, Grace Darling's rescue (1838) of the Forfarshire's survivors, and Monarch of the Glen, by Sir Edwin Henry Landseer. 22p, Launching of Brunel's ship Great Eastern, portrait of Prince Consort Albert, Mrs. Beeton's Book of Household Management (1889). 31p, The Albert Memorial, Prime Minister Disraeli and 1st ballot box. 34p, The Boer War, Guglielmo Marconi's wireless telegraph communications linking Paris and London (1898), and diamond jubilee emblem.

**Photo. & Engr.**
**1987, Sept. 8              Perf. 15x14**
1188  A359  18p multicolored         .35   .35
1189  A359  22p multicolored         .50   .50
1190  A359  31p multicolored         .65   .65
1191  A359  34p multicolored         .80   .75
       Nos. 1188-1191 (4)            2.30  2.25

Europa 1988 — A365

Transportation and communication, 1938: 18p, Mallard locomotive. 26p, Queen Elizabeth ocean liner. 31p, Tram No. 1173, Glasgow. 34p, Handley Page aircraft, Croydon Airport.

**1988, May 10              Perf. 15x14**
1213  A365  18p multicolored         .30   .35
1214  A365  26p multicolored         .55   .50
1215  A365  31p multicolored         .65   .65
1216  A365  34p multicolored         .80   .80
       Nos. 1213-1216 (4)            2.30  2.30

**1987, Oct. 13    Photo.    Perf. 14½**
1192  A360  18p Bernard Leach        .35   .35
1193  A360  26p Elizabeth Fritsch    .60   .60
1194  A360  31p Lucie Rie            .65   .65
1195  A360  34p Hans Coper           .70   .70
       Nos. 1192-1195 (4)            2.30  2.30

Christmas A361

Childhood memories: 13p, Decorating tree. 18p, Looking out window, Christmas eve. 26p, Sweet dreams. 31p, Reading new book to toys, Christmas morning. 34p, Playing horn, snowman.

**1987, Nov. 17    Photo.    Perf. 15x14**
1196  A361  13p multicolored         .25   .25
    a.     Pane of 36               12.50
1197  A361  18p multicolored         .35   .35
1198  A361  26p multicolored         .50   .50
1199  A361  31p multicolored         .60   .55
1200  A361  34p multicolored         .70   .70
       Nos. 1196-1200 (5)            2.40  2.35

No. 1196a printed in two panes of 18 with gutter between, stars on back; folded and sold in discount booklets for £4.30.

Linnean Society of London, 200th Anniv. — A362

**1988, Jan. 19              Perf. 15x14½**
1201  A362  18p Bull-rout fish       .35   .35
1202  A362  26p Yellow waterlily     .50   .50
1203  A362  31p Bewick's swan        .65   .65
1204  A362  34p Morel                .70   .70
       Nos. 1201-1204 (4)            2.20  2.20

Linnaeus (Carl von Linne, 1707-78), inventor of system of taxonomic nomenclature.

Welsh Bible, 400th Anniv. — A363

**1988, Mar. 1    Photo.    Perf. 14½**
1205  A363  18p William Morgan       .35   .35
1206  A363  26p William Salesbury    .55   .50
1207  A363  31p Richard Davies       .65   .60
1208  A363  34p Richard Parry        .65   .70
       Nos. 1205-1208 (4)            2.20  2.15

Sports — A364

**1988, Mar. 22    Photo.    Perf. 14½**
1209  A364  18p Balance beam         .30   .30
1210  A364  26p Downhill skiing      .55   .50
1211  A364  31p Tennis               .65   .65
1212  A364  34p Soccer               .70   .70
       Nos. 1209-1212 (4)            2.20  2.15

Ski Club of Great Britain and centenaries of the British Amateur Gymnastics Assoc., Lawn Tennis Assoc. and the Soccer League.

A366

Designs: No. 1217, Armada approaching The Lizard, July 19, 1588. No. 1218, Royal Navy vessels sailing from Plymouth to engage Spaniards in battle, July 21. No. 1219, Battle scene off the Isle of Wight, July 25. No. 1220, Battle scene off Calais, France, July 28-29. No. 1221, Spanish ships foundering in the North Sea storms, July 30-Aug. 2. Printed in a continuous design.

**1988, July 19**
1217  A366  18p multicolored         .40   .55
1218  A366  18p multicolored         .40   .55
1219  A366  18p multicolored         .40   .55
1220  A366  18p multicolored         .40   .55
1221  A366  18p multicolored         .40   .55
       Strip of 5, Nos. 1217-1221   2.00  2.20

Defeat of the Spanish Armada by the Royal Navy, 400th Anniv.

Australia Bicentennial — A367

Designs: No. 1222, Colonist, First Fleet vessel. No. 1223, British and Australian parliaments, Queen Elizabeth II. No. 1224, Cricketer W.G. Grace. No. 1225, John Lennon (1940-1980), William Shakespeare (1564-1616) and Sydney Opera House. Flag of Australia appears on Nos. 1223a, 1225a.

**1988, June 21    Litho.    Perf. 14½**
1222  A367  18p multicolored         .35   .35
1223  A367  18p multicolored         .35   .35
    a.     Pair, #1222-1223          .75   .75
1224  A367  34p multicolored         .75   .75
1225  A367  34p multicolored         .75   .75
    a.     Pair, #1224-1225         1.60  1.60
       Nos. 1222-1225 (4)            2.20  2.20

See Australia Nos. 1082-1085.

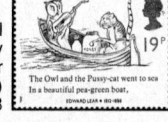

Nonsensical Drawings by Edward Lear (1812-1888) — A368

Illustrations and text: 19p, The Owl and the Pussycat, 1867. 27p, Self-portrait as a bird, pen-and-ink sketch from a letter. 32p, "C" is for Cat, alphabet book character. 35p, Girl, birds and part of a limerick.

**1988, Sept. 6    Photo.    Perf. 15x14**
1226  A368  19p multicolored         .30   .30
1227  A368  27p multicolored         .55   .50
1228  A368  32p multicolored         .75   .70
1229  A368  35p multicolored         .80   .75
    a.     Souv. sheet of 4, #1226-
           1229                      3.75  4.00
       Nos. 1226-1229 (4)            2.40  2.25

No. 1229a sold for £1.35. The surtax benefited Stamp World London '90.

Photographs of Castles by Prince Andrew — A369

£1, Carrickfergus. £1.50, Caernarfon. £2, Edinburgh. £5, Windsor.

**1988, Oct 18              Engr.**
1230  A369  £1 green               3.75   .30
1231  A369  £1.50 maroon           4.00   .55
1232  A369  £2 Prus blue           7.00   .80
1233  A369  £5 brown              18.50  1.65
       Nos. 1230-1233 (4)          33.25  3.30

See Nos. 1445-1448.

Christmas Cards — A370

14p, Journey to Bethlehem. 19p, Shepherds see star. 27p, Magi follow star. 32p, Nativity. 35p, The Annunciation.

**1988, Nov. 15  Photo.  Perf. 15x14½**

| 1234 | A370 | 14p multicolored | .25 | .25 |
|------|------|------------------|-----|-----|
| 1235 | A370 | 19p multicolored | .40 | .30 |
| 1236 | A370 | 27p multicolored | .50 | .50 |
| 1237 | A370 | 32p multicolored | .65 | .60 |
| 1238 | A370 | 35p multicolored | .80 | .85 |
| | | *Nos. 1234-1238 (5)* | 2.60 | 2.50 |

Birds — A371

**1989, Jan. 17  Perf. 14x15**

| 1239 | A371 | 19p Puffin | .35 | .35 |
|------|------|------------|-----|-----|
| 1240 | A371 | 27p Avocet | .50 | .50 |
| 1241 | A371 | 32p Oystercatcher | .70 | .70 |
| 1242 | A371 | 35p Gannet | .80 | .75 |
| | | *Nos. 1239-1242 (4)* | 2.35 | 2.35 |

Special Occasions A372

**1989, Jan. 31  Photo.  Perf. 15x14**
**Booklet Stamps**

| 1243 | A372 | 19p Rose | 2.25 | 2.00 |
|------|------|----------|------|------|
| 1244 | A372 | 19p Cupid | 2.25 | 2.00 |
| 1245 | A372 | 19p Ships | 2.25 | 2.00 |
| 1246 | A372 | 19p Fruit bowl | 2.25 | 2.00 |
| 1247 | A372 | 19p Teddy Bear | 2.25 | 2.00 |
| a. | | Bklt. pane of 10 (2 each #1243-1247) +12 labels (BK733) | 29.00 | |
| | | *Nos. 1243-1247 (5)* | 11.25 | 10.00 |

Labels inscribed "CONGRATULATIONS," "BEST WISHES," "HAPPY BIRTHDAY," "HAPPY ANNIVERSARY," "WITH LOVE," or "THANK YOU."

No. 1247a is valued with perfs guillotined. Full perfs sell for more.

Food and Farming Year — A373

Foods and tile mosaics in agricultural motifs.

**1989, Mar. 7  Photo.  Perf. 14½**

| 1248 | A373 | 19p Fruit and vegetables | .35 | .40 |
|------|------|--------------------------|-----|-----|
| 1249 | A373 | 27p Meat, fish, fruit | .65 | .60 |
| 1250 | A373 | 32p Dairy products | .70 | .65 |
| 1251 | A373 | 35p Breads, cake, cereal | .70 | .75 |
| | | *Nos. 1248-1251 (4)* | 2.40 | 2.40 |

Fireworks — A374

**1989, Apr. 11  Photo.  Perf. 14x14½**

| 1252 | A374 | 19p Mortarboard | .30 | .25 |
|------|------|-----------------|-----|-----|
| 1253 | A374 | 19p "X" on ballot | .30 | .25 |
| a. | | Pair, #1252-1253 | .65 | .65 |
| 1254 | A374 | 35p Posthorn | .50 | .50 |
| 1255 | A374 | 35p Globe | .50 | .50 |
| a. | | Pair, #1254-1255 | 1.25 | 1.25 |
| | | *Nos. 1252-1255 (4)* | 1.60 | 1.50 |

Public education in England and Wales, 150th anniv. (No. 1252); European Parliament 3rd elections (No. 1253); 26th world congress of Postal Telegraph and Telephone Intl., Brighton, Sept. 18-23 (No. 1254); Interparliamentary Union Cent. Conf., 82nd session, Sept. 4-9 (No. 1255).

Europa 1989 — A375

Children's toys: 19p, Airplane, locomotive. 27p, Building-block tower. 32p, Checkerboard, die, ladder, chips. 35p, Doll house, boat, robot.

**1989, May 16  Perf. 14x15**

| 1256 | A375 | 19p multicolored | .30 | .30 |
|------|------|------------------|-----|-----|
| 1257 | A375 | 27p multicolored | .40 | .40 |
| 1258 | A375 | 32p multicolored | .55 | .55 |
| 1259 | A375 | 35p multicolored | .70 | .70 |
| | | *Nos. 1256-1259 (4)* | 1.95 | 1.95 |

Industrial Archaeology — A376

**1989, July 4  Photo.  Perf. 14x15**

| 1280 | A376 | 19p Ironbridge | .40 | .40 |
|------|------|----------------|-----|-----|
| 1281 | A376 | 27p Tin Mine | .60 | .60 |
| 1282 | A376 | 32p Mills | .65 | .65 |
| 1283 | A376 | 35p Pontcysyllte Aqueduct | .70 | .80 |
| | | *Nos. 1280-1283 (4)* | 2.35 | 2.45 |

**1989, July 25  Souvenir Sheet**

| 1284 | | Sheet of 4 | 3.75 | 4.00 |
|------|------|------------|------|------|
| a. | | A376 19p like #1280, horiz. | .50 | .50 |
| b. | | A376 27p like #1281, horiz. | .75 | .75 |
| c. | | A376 32p like #1282, horiz. | 1.00 | .95 |
| d. | | A376 35p like #1283, horiz. | 1.20 | 1.00 |

No. 1284 sold for £1.40.

Microscopy — A377

Specimens under magnification: 19p, Snowflake, the soc. emblem. 27p, Blue fly. 32p, Blood cells. 35p, Microchip.

**1989, Sept. 5  Litho.  Perf. 14½x14**

| 1285 | A377 | 19p multicolored | .40 | .40 |
|------|------|------------------|-----|-----|
| 1286 | A377 | 27p multicolored | .60 | .60 |
| 1287 | A377 | 32p multicolored | .65 | .65 |
| 1288 | A377 | 35p multicolored | .75 | .75 |
| | | *Nos. 1285-1288 (4)* | 2.40 | 2.40 |

Royal Microscopical Soc., 150th anniv.

The Lord Mayor's Show, London — A378

Procession of the Lord Mayor's coach from Guildhall to the Law Courts in the Strand: No. 1289, Royal mail coach and The Guildhall. No. 1290, Drummer, cavalrymen and Mansion House. No. 1291, Gold coach, 1757, and The Royal Exchange. No. 1292, Coachman and St. Paul's Cathedral. No. 1293, Drummer, cavalryman and the Law Courts.

**1989, Oct. 17  Litho.  Perf. 14x15**

| 1289 | A378 | 20p multicolored | .40 | .45 |
|------|------|------------------|-----|-----|
| a. | | Perf. 14x14¼ | 1.50 | 1.50 |
| b. | | Booklet pane of 4 #1289a (BK189) | 6.00 | — |
| 1290 | A378 | 20p multicolored | .40 | .45 |
| 1291 | A378 | 20p multicolored | .40 | .45 |
| 1292 | A378 | 20p multicolored | .40 | .45 |
| 1293 | A378 | 20p multicolored | .40 | .45 |
| a. | | Strip of 5, #1289-1293 | 2.10 | 2.25 |

Issued. Nos. 1289a, 1289b, 8/19/09.

Ely Cathedral, Cambridgeshire, 800th Anniv. — A379

**1989, Nov. 14  Photo.  Perf. 15x14**

| 1294 | A379 | 15p Gothic arches, 4 peasants | .30 | .25 |
|------|------|-------------------------------|-----|-----|
| | | *Nos. 1294,B2-B5 (5)* | 2.50 | 2.50 |

Christmas.

For stamps and souvenir sheets with the design shown above, see Nos. MH190-MH198A in the Machins section.

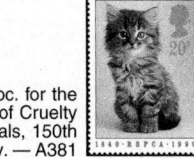

Royal Soc. for the Prevention of Cruelty to Animals, 150th Anniv. — A381

**1990, Jan. 23  Litho.  Perf. 14x15**

| 1300 | A381 | 20p Kitten | .40 | .40 |
|------|------|------------|-----|-----|
| 1301 | A381 | 29p Rabbit | .65 | .65 |
| 1302 | A381 | 34p Duckling | .80 | .80 |
| 1303 | A381 | 37p Puppy | 1.00 | 1.00 |
| | | *Nos. 1300-1303 (4)* | 2.85 | 2.85 |

A382

A382a

A382b

A382c

A382d

A382e

A382f

A382g

A382h

Famous Smiles — A382i

No. 1304, Teddy bear. No. 1305, Dennis the Menace. No. 1306, Mr. Punch. No. 1307, Cheshire Cat. No. 1308, Man in the Moon. No. 1309, The Laughing Policeman. No. 1310, Clown. No. 1311, Mona Lisa. No. 1312, Queen of Hearts. No. 1313, Stan Laurel.

**1990, Feb. 6  Photo.  Perf. 15x14**

| 1304 | A382 | 20p multi | 1.10 | 1.00 |
|------|------|-----------|------|------|
| 1305 | A382a | 20p multi | 1.10 | 1.00 |
| 1306 | A382b | 20p multi | 1.10 | 1.00 |
| 1307 | A382c | 20p multi | 1.10 | 1.00 |
| 1308 | A382d | 20p multi | 1.10 | 1.00 |
| 1309 | A382e | 20p multi | 1.10 | 1.00 |
| 1310 | A382f | 20p multi | 1.10 | 1.00 |
| 1311 | A382g | 20p multi | 1.10 | 1.00 |
| 1312 | A382h | 20p multi | 1.10 | 1.00 |
| 1313 | A382i | 20p multi | 1.10 | 1.00 |
| a. | | Pane of 10, #1304-1313 | 11.00 | 10.00 |
| | | *Nos. 1304-1313 (10)* | 11.00 | 10.00 |

No. 1313a sold folded and unattached in booklet cover.
See Nos. 1364-1373.

A383

Europa 1990: No. 1314, Alexandra Palace. No. 1315, School of Art, Glasgow. 29p, British Philatelic Bureau, Edinburgh. 37p, Templeton Carpet Factory, Glasgow.

**1990, Mar. 6  Photo.  Perf. 14x15**

| 1314 | A383 | 20p sil & multi | .30 | .30 |
|------|------|-----------------|-----|-----|
| a. | | Bklt. pane of 4 + printed margin | 1.75 | |
| 1315 | A383 | 20p sil & multi | .30 | .30 |
| 1316 | A383 | 29p sil & multi | .45 | .45 |
| 1317 | A383 | 37p sil & multi | .60 | .60 |
| | | *Nos. 1314-1317 (4)* | 1.65 | 1.65 |

Stamp World '90, London (No. 1314); Glasgow, European City of Culture (Nos. 1315, 1317).

For Prestige booklet containing pane No. 1314a, see listings in the Booklets section.

Queen's Awards for Export and Technological Achievement, 25th Anniv. — A384

No. 1318, No. 1320, Export. No. 1319, No. 1321, Technology.

**1990, Apr. 10  Litho.**

| 1318 | | 20p yel & blue, sil | .40 | .40 |
|------|------|---------------------|-----|-----|
| 1319 | | 20p yel & blue, sil | .40 | .40 |
| a. | | A384 Pair, #1318-1319 | 1.00 | 1.00 |
| 1320 | | 37p blue, yel, sil | .90 | .80 |
| 1321 | | 37p blue, yel, sil | .90 | .80 |
| a. | | A384 Pair, #1320-1321 | 2.00 | 2.00 |
| | | *Nos. 1318-1321 (4)* | 2.60 | 2.40 |

Se-tenant pairs have continuous designs.

Kew Gardens, 150th
Anniv. — A385

**1990, June 5** **Photo.**
1322 A385 20p Cycad .40 .35
1323 A385 29p Stone pine .60 .60
1324 A385 34p Willow tree .70 .70
1325 A385 37p Blue cedar .75 .75
　　　Nos. 1322-1325 (4) 2.45 2.40

Thomas Hardy (1840-
1928), Writer and
Clyffe Clump,
Dorset — A386

**1990, July 10** **Photo.** **Perf. 14x15**
1326 A386 20p multicolored .45 .45

Queen Mother, 90th
Birthday — A387

Portraits of Queen Elizabeth, The Queen
Mother: 20p, Recent portrait. 29p, As Queen
Consort, 1937. 34p, As Duchess of York. 37p,
As Lady Elizabeth Bowes-Lyon.

**1990, Aug. 2** **Perf. 14x15, 14½**
1327 A387 20p multicolored .60 .65
1328 A387 29p multicolored .90 .90
1329 A387 34p multicolored 1.05 1.05
1330 A387 37p multicolored 1.25 1.20
　　　Nos. 1327-1330 (4) 3.80 3.80

Gallantry
Awards — A388

Designs: No. 1331, Victoria Cross. No.
1332, George Cross. No. 1333, Military Cross,
Military Medal. No. 1334, Distinguished Flying
Cross, Distinguished Flying Medal. No. 1335,
Distinguished Service Cross, Distinguished
Service Medal. Nos. 1333-1335 horiz.

**1990, Sept. 11** **Perf. 14x15, 15x14**
1331 A388 20p multicolored .45 .45
　a. Litho., perf. 14x14¼, black
　　denomination ('06) 4.50 4.25
　b. Booklet pane of 4 #1331a
　　(BK180) 18.00 —
1332 A388 20p multicolored .45 .45
1333 A388 20p multicolored .45 .45
1334 A388 20p multicolored .45 .45
1335 A388 20p multicolored .45 .45
　　　Nos. 1331-1335 (5) 2.25 2.25

Denomination on No. 1331 is gray.
Nos. 1331a, 1331b issued 9/21/2006.

Astronomy — A389

Designs: 22p, Armagh Observatory, Jodrell
Bank and La Palma telescopes. 26p, Early tel-
escope, celestial diagram. 31p, Greenwich
Old Observatory, sextant, chronometer. 37p,
Stonehenge, celestial navigation.

**1990, Oct. 16** **Perf. 14**
1336 A389 22p multicolored .40 .50
1337 A389 26p multicolored .50 .50
1338 A389 31p multicolored .70 .70
1339 A389 37p multicolored .80 .70
　　　Nos. 1336-1339 (4) 2.40 2.40

Christmas
A390

17p, Building snowman. 22p, Carrying
Christmas tree. 26p, Caroling. 31p, Sledding.
37p, Ice skating.

**1990, Nov. 13** **Litho.** **Perf. 15x14**
1340 A390 17p multicolored .30 .30
　a. Booklet pane of 20 8.25
1341 A390 22p multicolored .40 .40
1342 A390 26p multicolored .55 .50
1343 A390 31p multicolored .65 .60
1344 A390 37p multicolored .75 .70
　　　Nos. 1340-1344 (5) 2.65 2.50

Dogs — A391

Paintings by George Stubbs: 22p, King
Charles Spaniel. 26p, A Pointer. 31p, Two
Hounds in a Landscape. 33p, A Rough Dog.
37p, Fino and Tiny.

**1991, Jan. 8** **Photo.** **Perf. 14x14½**
1345 A391 22p multicolored .40 .40
1346 A391 26p multicolored .50 .45
1347 A391 31p multicolored .65 .65
1348 A391 33p multicolored .65 .65
1349 A391 37p multicolored .70 .70
　　　Nos. 1345-1349 (5) 2.90 2.85

Royal Veterinary College bicentennial,
National Canine Defense League and Cruft's
Dog Show, centennial.

Symbols of Good
Luck — A392

No. 1351, Shooting star, rainbow. No. 1352,
Bird, charm bracelet. No. 1353, Black cat. No.
1354, Bluebird, key. No. 1355, Duck, frog. No.
1356, Black boot, shamrocks. No. 1357, Rainbow, pot of gold. No. 1358, Peacock moths.
No. 1359, Wishing well, sixpence.

**1991, Feb. 5** **Photo.** **Perf. 15x14**
**Booklet Stamps**
1350 A392 1st shown 1.60 1.50
1351 A392 1st multicolored 1.60 1.50
1352 A392 1st multicolored 1.60 1.50
1353 A392 1st multicolored 1.60 1.50
1354 A392 1st multicolored 1.60 1.50
1355 A392 1st multicolored 1.60 1.50
1356 A392 1st multicolored 1.60 1.50
1357 A392 1st multicolored 1.60 1.50
1358 A392 1st multicolored 1.60 1.50
1359 A392 1st multicolored 1.60 1.50
　a. Bkt. pane of 10, #1350-1359
　　(BK1160) 16.50

No. 1359a printed se-tenant with 12 greetings labels. No. 1359a sold for £2.20 at date of
issue.

Scientists & Their
Technology — A393

Designs: No. 1360, Michael Faraday, electricity. No. 1361, Charles Babbage, computers. 31p, Radar, developed by Robert Wat-
son-Watt. 37p, Jet engine developed by Frank
Whittle.

**1991, Mar. 5** **Perf. 14x15**
1360 A393 22p multicolored .45 .45
1361 A393 22p multicolored .45 .45
1362 A393 31p multicolored .70 .70
1363 A393 37p multicolored .80 .80
　　　Nos. 1360-1363 (4) 2.40 2.40

**Famous Smiles Type of 1990**

No. 1364, Teddy bear. No. 1365, Dennis the
Menace. No. 1366, Mr. Punch. No. 1367,
Cheshire Cat. No. 1368, Man in the Moon. No.
1369, The Laughing Policeman. No. 1370,

Clown. No. 1371, Mona Lisa. No. 1372,
Queen of Hearts. No. 1373, Stan Laurel.

**1991, Mar. 26** **Photo.** **Perf. 15x14**
**Booklet Stamps**
1364 A382 1st multicolored 1.35 1.20
　a. Sheet of 20 + 20 labels,
　　litho., perf. 14¼x14 37.50 —
1365 A382a 1st multicolored 1.35 1.20
　a. Sheet, 10 each #1364-1365
　　+ 20 labels 32.50
　b. Sheet of 20 + 20 labels,
　　litho., perf. 14¼x14 37.50 —
1366 A382b 1st multicolored 1.35 1.20
1367 A382c 1st multicolored 1.35 1.20
1368 A382d 1st multicolored 1.35 1.20
1369 A382e 1st multicolored 1.35 1.20
1370 A382f 1st multicolored 1.35 1.20
1371 A382g 1st multicolored 1.35 1.20
1372 A382h 1st multicolored 1.35 1.20
1373 A382i 1st multicolored 1.35 1.20
　a. Booklet pane of 10 13.50
　b. Sheet, #1364-1373 + 10 la-
　　bels 22.00

No. 1373a sold for £2.20 at date of issue.
No. 1373a was affixed to booklet cover and
was printed se-tenant with 12 greetings labels.
No. 1373b issued 5/22/00. Labels depict ribbons and are inscribed "The Stamp Show /
2000". The sheet with ribbon labels sold for
£2.95, while the sheet with personalized labels
sold for £5.95.
A sheet similar to No. 1373b with labels
inscribed "Collect British Stamps" was specially produced for stamp dealers. Value,
$225.
No. 1365a issued 2002. It sold for £5.95 and
had labels that could be personalized.
Nos. 1364a, 1365b issued 2002. Each sold
for £14.95 and has labels that can be
personalized.

A394

Space
A395

**1991, Apr. 23** **Photo.** **Perf. 14x15**
1374 22p Planets .45 .45
1375 22p Stars .45 .45
　a. A394 Pair, #1374-1375 .95 .95
1376 37p shown .80 .80
1377 37p Crescent eye .80 .80
　a. A395 Pair, #1376-1377 1.75 1.75

Europa.

Nos. 1374-1377 (4) 2.50 2.50

Sports — A396

**1991, June 11** **Photo.** **Perf. 14½x14**
1378 A396 22p Fencing .45 .50
1379 A396 26p Hurdling .60 .55
1380 A396 31p Diving .75 .70
1381 A396 37p Rugby .80 .85
　　　Nos. 1378-1381 (4) 2.60 2.60

World Student Games, Nos. 1378-1380.
Rugby World Cup, No. 1381.

Roses — A397

22p, Silver Jubilee. 26p, Mme. Alfred Car-
riere. 31p, Rosa moyesii. 33p, Harvest Fayre.
37p, Mutabilis.

**1991, July 16** **Litho.** **Perf. 14½x14**
1382 A397 22p multicolored .40 .40
1383 A397 26p multicolored .75 .75
1384 A397 31p multicolored .60 .60

1385 A397 33p multicolored .60 .60
1386 A397 37p multicolored .70 .70
　　　Nos. 1382-1386 (5) 3.05 3.05

Dinosaurs — A398

**1991, Aug. 20** **Photo.** **Perf. 14½x14**
1387 A398 22p Iguanodon .50 .50
1388 A398 26p Stegosaurus .60 .60
1389 A398 31p Tyrannosaurus .70 .70
1390 A398 33p Protoceratops .75 .75
1391 A398 37p Triceratops .85 .85
　　　Nos. 1387-1391 (5) 3.40 3.40

First use of word "dinosaur" by Sir Richard
Owen, 150th anniv.

Ordnance Survey
Maps,
Bicent. — A399

Maps of village of Hamstreet, Kent.

**1991, Sept. 17** **Litho. & Engr.**
1392 A399 24p 1816 .50 .50
**Litho.**
1393 A399 28p 1906 .60 .60
1394 A399 33p 1959 .75 .75
1395 A399 39p 1991 .90 .90
　　　Nos. 1392-1395 (4) 2.75 2.75

Christmas
A400

Illuminated letters from Venetian manuscript
"Acts of Mary and Jesus": 18p, "P," Adoration
of the Magi. 24p, "M," Mary placing Jesus in
manger. 28p, "A," Angel warning Joseph. 33p,
"Q," The Annunciation. 39p, "N," Flight into
Egypt.

**1991, Nov. 12** **Photo.** **Perf. 15x14**
1416 A400 18p multicolored .35 .30
　a. Booklet pane of 20 8.00
1417 A400 24p multicolored .50 .45
1418 A400 28p multicolored .55 .50
1419 A400 33p multicolored .70 .70
1420 A400 39p multicolored .75 .80
　　　Nos. 1416-1420 (5) 2.85 2.75

Animals in
Winter — A401

18p, Fallow deer. 24p, Brown hare. 28p,
Fox. 33p, Redwing. 39p, Welsh mountain
sheep.

**1992, Jan. 14** **Photo.** **Perf. 15x14**
1421 A401 18p multicolored .40 .35
1422 A401 24p multicolored .50 .50
1423 A401 28p multicolored .60 .55
1424 A401 33p multicolored .75 .75
1425 A401 39p multicolored .80 .90
　a. Booklet pane of 4 2.75
　　　Nos. 1421-1425 (5) 3.05 3.05

For Prestige booklet containing pane No.
1425a, see BK156.
Issue date: No. 1425a, Mar. 1.

Memories
A402

No. 1426, Flowers. No. 1427, Locket. No.
1428, Key. No. 1429, Model car. No. 1430,
Compass, 4-leaf clover. No. 1431, Pocket
watch. No. 1432, Envelope, fountain pen. No.
1433, Buttons, pearls. No. 1434, Marbles. No.
1435, Starfish, shovel and bucket.

## 1992, Jan. 28    Litho.    *Perf. 15x14*
### Booklet Stamps
| | | | | |
|---|---|---|---|---|
| 1426 | A402 | 1st multicolored | 1.35 | 1.20 |
| 1427 | A402 | 1st multicolored | 1.35 | 1.20 |
| 1428 | A402 | 1st multicolored | 1.35 | 1.20 |
| 1429 | A402 | 1st multicolored | 1.35 | 1.20 |
| 1430 | A402 | 1st multicolored | 1.35 | 1.20 |
| 1431 | A402 | 1st multicolored | 1.35 | 1.20 |
| 1432 | A402 | 1st multicolored | 1.35 | 1.20 |
| 1433 | A402 | 1st multicolored | 1.35 | 1.20 |
| 1434 | A402 | 1st multicolored | 1.35 | 1.20 |
| 1435 | A402 | 1st multicolored | 1.35 | 1.20 |
| *a.* | | Bklt. pane of 10, #1426-1435 (BK1171) | 13.50 | |

No. 1435a printed se-tenant with 12 greeting labels and sold for £2.40 at date of issue.

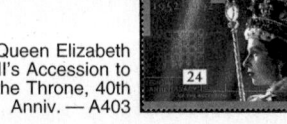

Queen Elizabeth II's Accession to the Throne, 40th Anniv. — A403

Queen Elizabeth II: No. 1436, In coronation regalia. No. 1437, Facing right, wearing garter robes as head of Church of England. No. 1438, Holding infant Prince Andrew. No. 1439, Wearing military uniform at Trooping of the Color. No. 1440, Wearing purple hat.

## 1992, Feb. 6    Litho.    *Perf. 14½x14*
| | | | | |
|---|---|---|---|---|
| 1436 | A403 | 24p multicolored | .65 | .65 |
| 1437 | A403 | 24p multicolored | .65 | .65 |
| 1438 | A403 | 24p multicolored | .65 | .65 |
| 1439 | A403 | 24p multicolored | .65 | .65 |
| 1440 | A403 | 24p multicolored | .65 | .65 |
| *a.* | | Strip of 5, #1436-1440 | 3.25 | 3.25 |

Alfred, Lord Tennyson, Death Cent. — A404

Portraits and illustrations for poems: 24p, The Beguiling of Merlin by Sir Edward Burne-Jones. 28p, April Love by Arthur Hughes. 33p, The Lady of Shalott by John William Waterhouse. 39p, Mariana by Dante Gabriel Rossetti.

## 1992, Mar. 10    Photo.
| | | | | |
|---|---|---|---|---|
| 1441 | A404 | 24p multicolored | .50 | .50 |
| 1442 | A404 | 28p multicolored | .65 | .60 |
| 1443 | A404 | 33p multicolored | .75 | .80 |
| 1444 | A404 | 39p multicolored | .90 | .90 |
| | | *Nos. 1441-1444 (4)* | 2.80 | 2.80 |

### Castle Type of 1988
Nos. 1445-1448 have been re-engraved to show greater detail than on Nos. 1230-1233. The silhouette of the Queen's head on Nos. 1445-1448 is printed in a special ink that changes color from green to gold.

### *Perf. 15x14 Syncopated*
#### 1992-95                         Engr.
| | | | | |
|---|---|---|---|---|
| 1445 | A369 | £1 like #1230 | 3.25 | .80 |
| 1446 | A369 | £1.50 like #1231 | 5.00 | 1.00 |
| 1447 | A369 | £2 like #1232 | 6.75 | .95 |
| 1447A | A369 | £3 like #1232 | 12.00 | 1.75 |
| 1448 | A369 | £5 like #1233 | 14.00 | 2.25 |
| | | *Nos. 1445-1448 (5)* | 41.00 | 6.75 |

Nos. 1445-1447, 1448 were re-issued 12/6/94 with lines strengthened. Castles appear darker than on original issue. Etching in queen's head is square shaped instead of diamond shaped. Values, set: unused $39, used $8.

Issued: £3, 8/22/95; others, 3/24/92.

### Castle Type Re-engraved
#### 1997, July 29
| | | | | |
|---|---|---|---|---|
| 1446a | A369 | £1.50 Caernarfon | 9.75 | 5.75 |
| 1447b | A369 | £2 Edinburgh | 12.00 | 1.50 |
| 1447Ac | A369 | £3 Carrickfergus | 25.00 | 1.90 |
| 1448a | A369 | £5 Windsor | 30.00 | 6.00 |

Queen's head is silkscreened and feels smooth on Nos. 1446a, 1447b, 1447Ac, 1448a. Letters "C" and "S" in Castle do not have serifs. Letters in castle names also differ from the 1992 and 1995 printings. The elliptical perforation begins one perf hole higher than on the earlier printings.

Discovery of America, 500th Anniv. — A405

Design: 39p, Sailing ship, Operation Raleigh Grand Regatta.

### Litho. & Engr.
## 1992, Apr. 7                     *Perf. 14½*
| | | | | |
|---|---|---|---|---|
| 1449 | A405 | 24p multicolored | .50 | .40 |
| 1450 | A405 | 39p multicolored | .70 | .90 |

Europa.

Events — A406

Designs: No. 1451, British Olympic Assoc. flag. No. 1452, Flying torch flag of British Paralympic Assoc. No. 1453, British pavilion.

## 1992, Apr. 7                     Litho.
| | | | | |
|---|---|---|---|---|
| 1451 | A406 | 24p multicolored | .30 | .30 |
| 1452 | A406 | 24p multicolored | .30 | .30 |
| *a.* | | Pair, #1451-1452 | .90 | .90 |
| 1453 | A406 | 39p multicolored | .75 | .75 |
| | | *Nos. 1451-1453 (3)* | 1.35 | 1.35 |

1992 Summer Olympics (No. 1451) and Paralympics (No. 1452), Barcelona. Expo '92, Seville (No. 1453).

English Civil War, 350th Anniv. — A407

## 1992, June 16    Photo.    *Perf. 14½*
| | | | | |
|---|---|---|---|---|
| 1454 | A407 | 24p Pikeman | .50 | .50 |
| 1455 | A407 | 28p Drummer | .65 | .60 |
| 1456 | A407 | 33p Musketeer | .75 | .75 |
| 1457 | A407 | 39p Standard bearer | .85 | .90 |
| | | *Nos. 1454-1457 (4)* | 2.75 | 2.75 |

Yeoman of the Guard, by Gilbert & Sullivan — A408

Scenes from comic operas: 24p, The Gondoliers. 28p, The Mikado. 33p, The Pirates of Penzance. 39p, Iolanthe.

## 1992, July 21    Photo.    *Perf. 14½x14*
| | | | | |
|---|---|---|---|---|
| 1458 | A408 | 18p multicolored | .35 | .35 |
| 1459 | A408 | 24p multicolored | .50 | .50 |
| 1460 | A408 | 28p multicolored | .65 | .65 |
| 1461 | A408 | 33p multicolored | .70 | .70 |
| 1462 | A408 | 39p multicolored | .80 | .80 |
| | | *Nos. 1458-1462 (5)* | 3.00 | 3.00 |

Sir Arthur Sullivan, 150th anniv. of birth.

Protect the Environment — A409

Children's drawings: 24p, Acid rain kills. 28p, Ozone layer. 33p, Greenhouse effect. 39p, Bird of hope.

## 1992, Sept. 15    Photo.    *Perf. 14½*
| | | | | |
|---|---|---|---|---|
| 1463 | A409 | 24p multicolored | .45 | .45 |
| 1464 | A409 | 28p multicolored | .60 | .60 |
| 1465 | A409 | 33p multicolored | .75 | .70 |
| 1466 | A409 | 39p multicolored | .90 | .85 |
| | | *Nos. 1463-1466 (4)* | 2.70 | 2.60 |

Single European Market — A410

## 1992, Oct. 13    Photo.    *Perf. 15x14*
| | | | | |
|---|---|---|---|---|
| 1467 | A410 | 24p multicolored | .55 | .55 |

Christmas A411

Stained glass windows: 18p, Angel Gabriel. 24p, Madonna and Child. 28p, King offering gold crown. 33p, Shepherds. 39p, Kings offering frankincense and myrrh.

## 1992, Nov. 10    Photo.    *Perf. 15x14*
| | | | | |
|---|---|---|---|---|
| 1468 | A411 | 18p multicolored | .40 | .30 |
| *a.* | | Booklet pane of 20 | 8.00 | |
| 1469 | A411 | 24p multicolored | .50 | .50 |
| 1470 | A411 | 28p multicolored | .60 | .60 |
| 1471 | A411 | 33p multicolored | .75 | .75 |
| 1472 | A411 | 39p multicolored | .80 | .90 |
| | | *Nos. 1468-1472 (5)* | 3.05 | 3.05 |

Mute Swans — A412

Designs: 18p, Male, St. Catherine's Chapel, Abbotsbury. 24p, Cygnet, reed bed, Abbotsbury Swannery. 28p, Pair, cygnet. 33p, Eggs in nest, Tithe Barn. 39p, Head of young swan.

## 1993, Jan. 19    Photo.    *Perf. 14x15*
| | | | | |
|---|---|---|---|---|
| 1473 | A412 | 18p multicolored | .45 | .45 |
| 1474 | A412 | 24p multicolored | .65 | .65 |
| 1475 | A412 | 28p multicolored | .75 | .75 |
| 1476 | A412 | 33p multicolored | .90 | .90 |
| 1477 | A412 | 39p multicolored | 1.00 | 1.00 |
| | | *Nos. 1473-1477 (5)* | 3.75 | 3.75 |

Abbotsbury Swannery, 600th anniv.

Britannia A413

### Litho., Typo. and Embossed
### *Perf. 14x14½ Syncopated*
#### 1993, Mar. 2              Granite Paper
| | | | | |
|---|---|---|---|---|
| 1478 | A413 | £10 multicolored | 27.50 | 12.50 |
| *a.* | | Silver (Queen's head, security crosses) omitted | 3,250. | |

Soaking may damage these stamps.

A414

A414a

A414b

A414c

A414d

A414e

A414f

A414g

A414h

A414i — Greetings Stamps

Children's Characters: No. 1479, Long John Silver, parrot. No. 1480, Tweedledum, Tweedledee. No. 1481, Just William, Violet Elizabeth. No. 1482, Toad, Mole. No. 1483, Bash Street Kids, teacher. No. 1484, Peter Rabbit, Mrs. Rabbit. No. 1485, Father Christmas, Snowman. No. 1486, Big Friendly Giant, Sophie. No. 1487, Rupert Bear, Bill Badger. No. 1488, Aladdin, Genie.

### *Perf. 15x14 Syncopated*
#### 1993, Feb. 2                     Litho.
| | | | | |
|---|---|---|---|---|
| 1479 | A414 | (1st) multicolored | 1.35 | 1.20 |
| 1480 | A414a | (1st) multicolored | 1.35 | 1.20 |
| 1481 | A414b | (1st) multicolored | 1.35 | 1.20 |
| 1482 | A414c | (1st) multicolored | 1.35 | 1.20 |
| 1483 | A414d | (1st) multicolored | 1.35 | 1.20 |
| 1484 | A414e | (1st) multicolored | 1.35 | 1.20 |
| *a.* | | Booklet pane of 4 (BK158) | 8.75 | |
| 1485 | A414f | (1st) multicolored | 1.35 | 1.20 |
| 1486 | A414g | (1st) multicolored | 1.35 | 1.20 |
| 1487 | A414h | (1st) multicolored | 1.35 | 1.20 |
| 1488 | A414i | (1st) multicolored | 1.35 | 1.20 |
| *a.* | | Booklet pane of 10, #1479-1488 (BK1172) | 16.50 | |

No. 1479-1488 sold for 24p on day of issue. No. 1488a printed se-tenant with 20 greetings labels. See note above No. 1445.

Issue date: No. 1484a, Aug. 10.

For booklets containing panes of No. 1484a and No. 1488a, see BK158 and BK1172, respectively.

Marine Chronometer No. 4 — A415

Designs: 24p, Face. 28p, Escapement, remontoire and fusee. 33p, Balance spring, temperature compensator. 39p, Back of movement.

**1993, Feb. 16   Litho.   Perf. 14½**
| | | | | |
|---|---|---|---|---|
| 1489 | A415 | 24p multicolored | .50 | .50 |
| 1490 | A415 | 28p multicolored | .60 | .60 |
| 1491 | A415 | 33p multicolored | .70 | .70 |
| 1492 | A415 | 39p multicolored | .80 | .80 |
| | *Nos. 1489-1492 (4)* | | 2.60 | 2.60 |

John Harrison (1693-1776), inventor of marine chronometer.

Orchids — A416

14th World Orchid Conf., Glasgow: 18p, Dendrobium hellwigianum. 24p, Paphiopedilum Maudiae "Magnificum." 28p, Cymbidium lowianum. 33p, Vanda Rothschildiana. 39p, Dendrobium vexillarius.

**1993, Mar. 16   Litho.   Perf. 15x14**
| | | | | |
|---|---|---|---|---|
| 1493 | A416 | 18p multicolored | .35 | .35 |
| 1494 | A416 | 24p multicolored | .50 | .50 |
| 1495 | A416 | 28p multicolored | .60 | .55 |
| 1496 | A416 | 33p multicolored | .75 | .75 |
| 1497 | A416 | 39p multicolored | .80 | .85 |
| | *Nos. 1493-1497 (5)* | | 3.00 | 2.95 |

Contemporary Art — A417

Europa: 24p, Sculpture, Family Group, by Henry Moore. 28p, Print, Kew Gardens, by Edward Bawden. 33p, Painting, St. Francis and the Birds, by Stanley Spencer. 39p, Painting, Still Life, Odyssey 1, by Ben Nicholson.

**1993, May 11   Photo.   Perf. 14x14½**
| | | | | |
|---|---|---|---|---|
| 1498 | A417 | 24p multicolored | .55 | .50 |
| 1499 | A417 | 28p multicolored | .60 | .60 |
| 1500 | A417 | 33p multicolored | .75 | .70 |
| 1501 | A417 | 39p multicolored | .90 | .90 |
| | *Nos. 1498-1501 (4)* | | 2.80 | 2.70 |

Roman Artifacts — A418

24p, Gold aureus of Claudius. 28p, Bronze bust of Hadrian. 33p, Gemstone carved with head of Roma. 39p, Mosaic of Christ.

**1993, June 15   Photo.   Perf. 14½x14**
| | | | | |
|---|---|---|---|---|
| 1502 | A418 | 24p multicolored | .50 | .50 |
| 1503 | A418 | 28p multicolored | .60 | .55 |
| 1504 | A418 | 33p multicolored | .75 | .70 |
| 1505 | A418 | 39p multicolored | .90 | 1.00 |
| | *Nos. 1502-1505 (4)* | | 2.75 | 2.75 |

British Canals, Bicent. — A419

Designs: 24p, Grand Junction Canal boats. 28p, Stainforth and Keadby Canal. 33p, Brecknock and Abergavenny Canal boats, horse. 39p, Crinan Canal, steamers and fishing boats.

**1993, July 20   Litho.   Perf. 14½x14**
| | | | | |
|---|---|---|---|---|
| 1506 | A419 | 24p multicolored | .50 | .50 |
| 1507 | A419 | 28p multicolored | .60 | .55 |
| 1508 | A419 | 33p multicolored | .75 | .70 |
| 1509 | A419 | 39p multicolored | .90 | 1.00 |
| | *Nos. 1506-1509 (4)* | | 2.75 | 2.75 |

Autumn Fruits — A420

**1993, Sept. 14   Photo.   Perf. 15x14**
| | | | | |
|---|---|---|---|---|
| 1510 | A420 | 18p Horse chestnut | .35 | .30 |
| 1511 | A420 | 24p Blackberries | .50 | .50 |
| 1512 | A420 | 28p Filbert | .65 | .65 |

| | | | | |
|---|---|---|---|---|
| 1513 | A420 | 33p Rowanberries | .70 | .70 |
| 1514 | A420 | 39p Pears | .85 | .90 |
| | *Nos. 1510-1514 (5)* | | 3.05 | 3.05 |

Sherlock Holmes — A421

Holmes and: No. 1515, Dr. Watson, The Reigate Squire. No. 1516, Sir Henry, The Hound of the Baskervilles. No. 1517, Lestrade, The Six Napoleons. No. 1518, Mycroft, The Greek Interpreter. No. 1519, Moriarty, The Final Problem.

**1993, Oct. 12   Litho.   Perf. 14x14½**
| | | | | |
|---|---|---|---|---|
| 1515 | A421 | 24p multicolored | .60 | .60 |
| 1516 | A421 | 24p multicolored | .60 | .60 |
| 1517 | A421 | 24p multicolored | .60 | .60 |
| 1518 | A421 | 24p multicolored | .60 | .60 |
| 1519 | A421 | 24p multicolored | .60 | .60 |
| *a.* | Strip of 5, #1515-1519 | | 3.00 | 3.00 |

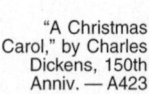

"A Christmas Carol," by Charles Dickens, 150th Anniv. — A423

Designs: 19p, Tiny Tim, Bob Cratchit. 25p, Mr. & Mrs. Fezziwig. 30p, Scrooge. 35p, Prize Turkey. 41p, Mr. Scrooge's Nephew.

**1993, Nov. 9   Photo.   Perf. 15x14**
| | | | | |
|---|---|---|---|---|
| 1528 | A423 | 19p multicolored | .40 | .30 |
| *a.* | Booklet pane of 20 | | 8.75 | |
| 1529 | A423 | 25p multicolored | .50 | .50 |
| 1530 | A423 | 30p multicolored | .65 | .65 |
| 1531 | A423 | 35p multicolored | .75 | .70 |
| 1532 | A423 | 41p multicolored | .90 | .85 |
| | *Nos. 1528-1532 (5)* | | 3.20 | 3.00 |

For booklet containing No. 1528a, see BK857.
No. BK803 contains No. 1529.

Age of Steam — A424

Designs: 19p, Tandem locomotives, West Highland Line, North British Railway. 25p, Locomotive No. 60149, Kings Cross Station, London. 30p, Locomotive No. 43000 on turntable, Blyth North engine shed. 35p, Locomotive entering station. 41p, Locomotive on bridge over Worcester & Birmingham Canal.

**1994, Jan. 18   Photo.   Perf. 14½**
| | | | | |
|---|---|---|---|---|
| 1533 | A424 | 19p black & green | .40 | .40 |
| 1534 | A424 | 25p black & purple | .50 | .50 |
| 1535 | A424 | 30p black & red brn | .65 | .65 |
| 1536 | A424 | 35p black & red violet | .70 | .70 |
| 1537 | A424 | 41p black & dark blue | .80 | .80 |
| | *Nos. 1533-1537 (5)* | | 3.05 | 3.05 |

Dan Dare — A425

The Three Bears — A426

Rupert the Bear — A427

Alice in Wonderland A428

Noggin the Nog — A429

Peter Rabbit — A430

Little Red Riding Hood — A431

Orlando, the Marmalade Cat — A432

Biggles — A433

Paddington A434

**Perf. 15x14 Syncopated**
**1994, Feb. 1     Photo.**
**Booklet Stamps**
| | | | | |
|---|---|---|---|---|
| 1538 | A425 | (1st) multicolored | 1.45 | 1.25 |
| 1539 | A426 | (1st) multicolored | 1.45 | 1.25 |
| 1540 | A427 | (1st) multicolored | 1.45 | 1.25 |
| 1541 | A428 | (1st) multicolored | 1.45 | 1.25 |
| 1542 | A429 | (1st) multicolored | 1.45 | 1.25 |
| 1543 | A430 | (1st) multicolored | 1.45 | 1.25 |
| 1544 | A431 | (1st) multicolored | 1.45 | 1.25 |
| 1545 | A432 | (1st) multicolored | 1.45 | 1.25 |
| 1546 | A433 | (1st) multicolored | 1.45 | 1.25 |
| 1547 | A434 | (1st) multicolored | 1.45 | 1.25 |
| *a.* | Bklt. pane of 10, #1538-1547 | | 14.50 | |

Nos. 1538-1547 sold for 25p on day of issue. No. 1547a was printed se-tenant with 20 greetings labels.
For booklet containing No. 1547a, see BK1182.

Investiture of Prince of Wales, 25th Anniv. — A435

Watercolor landscapes, by Prince Charles: 19p, Chirk Castle, Clwyd, Wales. 25p, Ben Arkle, Sutherland, Scotland. 30p, Mourne Mountains, County Down, Northern Ireland. 35p, Dersingham, Norfolk, England. 41p, Dolwyddelan, Gwynedd, Wales.

**1994, Mar. 1   Photo.   Perf. 15x14**
| | | | | |
|---|---|---|---|---|
| 1548 | A435 | 19p multicolored | .35 | .35 |
| 1549 | A435 | 25p multicolored | .50 | .50 |
| 1550 | A435 | 30p multicolored | .65 | .70 |
| *a.* | Booklet pane of 4 | | 2.75 | |
| 1551 | A435 | 35p multicolored | .80 | .80 |
| 1552 | A435 | 41p multicolored | .90 | .90 |
| | *Nos. 1548-1552 (5)* | | 3.20 | 3.30 |

For booklet containing pane No. 1550a, see No. BK159.

British Picture Postcards, Cent. — A436

Seaside characters: 19p, "Bather at Blackpool." 25p, "Where's my Little Lad." 30p, "Wish You Were Here." 35p, "Punch and Judy Show." 41p, "The Tower Crane."

**1994, Apr. 12   Litho.   Perf. 14x14½**
| | | | | |
|---|---|---|---|---|
| 1553 | A436 | 19p multicolored | .35 | .35 |
| 1554 | A436 | 25p multicolored | .50 | .55 |
| 1555 | A436 | 30p multicolored | .65 | .70 |
| 1556 | A436 | 35p multicolored | .80 | .80 |
| 1557 | A436 | 41p multicolored | .90 | .90 |
| | *Nos. 1553-1557 (5)* | | 3.20 | 3.30 |

Blackpool Tower, cent. (No. 1553). Tower Bridge, cent. (No. 1557).

Opening of Channel Tunnel — A437

Nos. 1558, 1560, British lion, French rooster, meeting over Channel. Nos. 1559, 1561, Joined hands above speeding train.

**1994, May 3   Photo.   Perf. 14x14½**
| | | | | |
|---|---|---|---|---|
| 1558 | | 25p dk blue & multi | .35 | .35 |
| 1559 | | 25p dk blue & multi | .50 | .55 |
| *a.* | A437 Pair, #1558-1559 | | 1.10 | 1.10 |
| 1560 | | 41p lt blue & multi | .65 | .65 |
| 1561 | | 41p multicolored | .80 | .75 |
| *a.* | A437 Pair, #1560-1561 | | 1.60 | 1.60 |
| | *Nos. 1558-1561 (4)* | | 2.30 | 2.30 |

See France Nos. 2421-2424.

D-Day, 50th Anniv. — A438

Photographs from Imperial War Museum's archives: No. 1562, Ground crew reloading FAF Bostons. No. 1563, Coastal bombardment by HMS Warspite. No. 1564, Commandos landing on Gold Beach. No. 1565, Infantry regrouping on Sword Beach. No. 1566, Advancing inland from Ouistreham.

**1994, June 6   Litho.   Perf. 14**
| | | | | |
|---|---|---|---|---|
| 1562 | A438 | 25p multicolored | .50 | .50 |
| 1563 | A438 | 25p multicolored | .50 | .50 |
| 1564 | A438 | 25p multicolored | .50 | .50 |
| 1565 | A438 | 25p multicolored | .50 | .50 |
| 1566 | A438 | 25p multicolored | .50 | .50 |
| *a.* | Strip of 5, #1562-1566 | | 2.50 | 2.50 |

Honorable Company of Edinburgh Golfers, 250th Anniv. — A439

Golf courses: 19p, St. Andrews, old course. 25p, Muirfield, 18th hole. 30p, Carnoustie, 15th hole. 35p, Royal Troon, "postage stamp" 8th hole. 41p, Turnberry, 9th hole.

**1994, July 5   Photo.   Perf. 14**
| | | | | |
|---|---|---|---|---|
| 1567 | A439 | 19p multicolored | .35 | .35 |
| 1568 | A439 | 25p multicolored | .50 | .55 |
| 1569 | A439 | 30p multicolored | .70 | .70 |
| 1570 | A439 | 35p multicolored | .80 | .75 |
| 1571 | A439 | 41p multicolored | .90 | .90 |
| | *Nos. 1567-1571 (5)* | | 3.25 | 3.25 |

Summertime Events — A440

Designs: 19p, Royal Welsh Agricultural Show, Llanelwedd. 25p, Wimbledon. 30p, Yachts on Solent during Cowes Week. 35p,

Cricket at Lord's. 41p, Scottish Highland Games, Braemar.

**1994, Aug. 2**    **Perf. 14½x14**
| | | | |
|---|---|---|---|
| 1572 | A440 | 19p multicolored | .35 .35 |
| 1573 | A440 | 25p multicolored | .50 .50 |
| 1574 | A440 | 30p multicolored | .65 .65 |
| 1575 | A440 | 35p multicolored | .75 .75 |
| 1576 | A440 | 41p multicolored | .85 .85 |
| | | Nos. 1572-1576 (5) | 3.10 3.10 |

Medical Discoveries A441

Europa: 25p, Ultrasonic imaging. 30p, Scanning electron microscopy. 35p, Magnetic resonance imaging. 41p, Computed tomography.

**1994, Sept. 27 Photo.**    **Perf. 14x14½**
| | | | |
|---|---|---|---|
| 1577 | A441 | 25p multicolored | .50 .60 |
| 1578 | A441 | 30p multicolored | .75 .70 |
| 1579 | A441 | 35p multicolored | .80 .80 |
| 1580 | A441 | 41p multicolored | 1.00 1.00 |
| | | Nos. 1577-1580 (4) | 3.05 3.10 |

Christmas A442

School children portraying: 19p, Mary, Joseph, with infant Jesus. 25p, Magi. 30p, Mary holding Jesus. 35p, Shepherds. 41p, Angels.

**1994, Nov. 1 Photo.**    **Perf. 15x14**
| | | | |
|---|---|---|---|
| 1581 | A442 | 19p multicolored | .35 .35 |
| a. | | Booklet pane of 20 | 8.00 |
| 1582 | A442 | 25p multicolored | .50 .50 |
| 1583 | A442 | 30p multicolored | .65 .65 |
| 1584 | A442 | 35p multicolored | .70 .70 |
| 1585 | A442 | 41p multicolored | .90 .90 |
| | | Nos. 1581-1585 (5) | 3.10 3.10 |

For booklet containing No. 1581a, see No. BK858.
No. BK804 contains No. 1582.

Cats — A443

Designs: 19p, Black cat. 25p, Siamese, tabby cats. 30p, Yellow cat. 35p, Calico, Abyssinian cats. 41p, Black & white cat.

**1995, Jan. 17 Litho.**    **Perf. 15x14**
| | | | |
|---|---|---|---|
| 1586 | A443 | 19p multicolored | .35 .35 |
| 1587 | A443 | 25p multicolored | .50 .50 |
| 1588 | A443 | 30p multicolored | .70 .70 |
| 1589 | A443 | 35p multicolored | .80 .80 |
| 1590 | A443 | 41p multicolored | .90 .90 |
| | | Nos. 1586-1590 (5) | 3.25 3.25 |

Springtime A444

Sculptures from natural materials, by Andy Goldsworthy: 19p, Dandelions. 25p, Chestnut leaves. 30p, Garlic leaves. 35p, Hazel leaves. 41p, Spring grass.

**1995, Mar. 14 Photo.**    **Perf. 15x14**
| | | | |
|---|---|---|---|
| 1591 | A444 | 19p multicolored | .35 .30 |
| 1592 | A444 | 25p multicolored | .50 .50 |
| 1593 | A444 | 30p multicolored | .70 .70 |
| 1594 | A444 | 35p multicolored | .75 .75 |
| 1595 | A444 | 41p multicolored | .90 .90 |
| | | Nos. 1591-1595 (5) | 3.20 3.15 |

La Danse a la Campagne, by Renoir — A445

---

Troilus and Criseyde, by Peter Brookes — A446

The Kiss, by Rodin — A447

Girls on the Town, by Beryl Cook — A448

Jazz, by Andrew Mockett — A449

Girls Performing aKathal Dance (Aurangzeb Period) — A450

Alice Keppel with her Daughter, by Alice Hughes — A451

Children Playing, by L.S. Lowry — A452

Circus Clowns, by Emily Firmin and Justin Mitchell — A453

Decoration from All the Love Poems of Shakespeare, by Eric Gill — A454

**Perf. 14 Syncopated**
**1995, Mar. 21**    **Litho.**
| | | | |
|---|---|---|---|
| 1596 | A445 | 1st multicolored | 1.65 1.65 |
| 1597 | A446 | 1st multicolored | 1.65 1.65 |
| 1598 | A447 | 1st multicolored | 1.65 1.65 |
| 1599 | A448 | 1st multicolored | 1.65 1.65 |
| 1600 | A449 | 1st multicolored | 1.65 1.65 |
| 1601 | A450 | 1st multicolored | 1.65 1.65 |
| 1602 | A451 | 1st multicolored | 1.65 1.65 |
| 1603 | A452 | 1st multicolored | 1.65 1.65 |
| 1604 | A453 | 1st multicolored | 1.65 1.65 |
| 1605 | A454 | 1st multicolored | 1.65 1.65 |
| a. | | Bklt. pane of 10, #1596-1605 | 16.50 |

Complete booklet sold for £2.50 on day of issue.
For booklet containing No. 1605a, see No. BK1183.

National Trust, Cent. — A455

Designs: 19p, Celebrating 100 years. 25p, Protecting land. 30p, Conserving art. 35p, Saving coast. 41p, Repairing buildings.

---

**1995, Apr. 11 Photo.**    **Perf. 14x15**
| | | | |
|---|---|---|---|
| 1606 | A455 | 19p multicolored | .35 .30 |
| 1607 | A455 | 25p multicolored | .50 .50 |
| a. | | Booklet pane of 6 | 3.00 |
| 1608 | A455 | 30p multicolored | .65 .70 |
| 1609 | A455 | 35p multicolored | .75 .75 |
| 1610 | A455 | 41p multicolored | .90 .90 |
| | | Nos. 1606-1610 (5) | 3.15 3.15 |

For booklet containing panes No. 1607a, see No. BK160.
Issued: No. 1607a, 4/25/95.

Peace & Freedom — A456

Designs: No. 1611, Hands, British Red Cross 1870-1995. No. 1612, British troops, people celebrating liberation of Paris. No. 1613, Dove, outstretched hand, UN, 1945-95. No. 1614, St. Paul's Cathedral, floodlights forming Victory V. 30p, Hands above earth, UN 1945-95.

**1995, May 2 Photo.**    **Perf. 14½x14**
| | | | |
|---|---|---|---|
| 1611 | A456 | 19p multicolored | .35 .35 |
| 1612 | A456 | 19p multicolored | .35 .35 |
| 1613 | A456 | 25p multicolored | .55 .55 |
| 1614 | A456 | 25p multicolored | .55 .55 |
| 1615 | A456 | 30p multicolored | .65 .65 |
| | | Nos. 1611-1615 (5) | 2.45 2.45 |

End of World War II, 50th anniv. (Nos. 1612, 1614), Europa (Nos. 1613, 1615).
See No. 2294a.

H. G. Wells (1866-1946), Science Fiction Writer — A457

Novels: 25p, The Time Machine. 30p, The First Men on the Moon. 35p, The War of the Worlds. 41p, The Shape of Things to Come.

**1995, June 6 Litho.**    **Perf. 14½x14**
| | | | |
|---|---|---|---|
| 1616 | A457 | 25p multicolored | .50 .50 |
| 1617 | A457 | 30p multicolored | .60 .60 |
| 1618 | A457 | 35p multicolored | .70 .70 |
| 1619 | A457 | 41p multicolored | .80 .80 |
| | | Nos. 1616-1619 (4) | 2.60 2.60 |

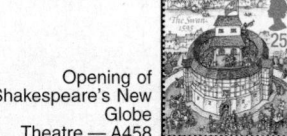

Opening of Shakespeare's New Globe Theatre — A458

Bankside theatres: No. 1620, Swan, 1595. No. 1621, The Rose, 1595. No. 1622, The Globe, 1599. No. 1623, The Hope, 1613. No. 1624, The Globe, 1614.

**1995, Aug. 8 Litho.**    **Perf. 14½x14**
| | | | |
|---|---|---|---|
| 1620 | A458 | 25p multicolored | .50 .45 |
| 1621 | A458 | 25p multicolored | .50 .45 |
| 1622 | A458 | 25p multicolored | .50 .45 |
| 1623 | A458 | 25p multicolored | .50 .45 |
| 1624 | A458 | 25p multicolored | .50 .45 |
| a. | | Strip of 5, #1620-1624 | 2.60 2.75 |

Pioneers of Communication A459

Designs: 19p, Sir Rowland Hill, introduction of uniform penny postage. 25p, Hill as older man, design A1. 41p, Guglielmo Marconi, early wireless equipment. 60p, Marconi as older man using radiophone, sinking *Titanic.*

**Litho. & Engr.**
**1995, Sept. 5**    **Perf. 14½**
| | | | |
|---|---|---|---|
| 1625 | A459 | 19p multicolored | .35 .35 |
| 1626 | A459 | 25p multicolored | .55 .55 |
| 1627 | A459 | 41p multicolored | .90 .90 |
| 1628 | A459 | 60p multicolored | 1.20 1.20 |
| | | Nos. 1625-1628 (4) | 3.00 3.00 |

---

Rugby League, Cent. — A460

**1995, Oct. 3 Photo.**    **Perf. 14x14½**
| | | | |
|---|---|---|---|
| 1629 | A460 | 19p Harold Wagstaff | .35 .35 |
| 1630 | A460 | 25p Gus Risman | .50 .55 |
| 1631 | A460 | 30p Jim Sullivan | .65 .65 |
| 1632 | A460 | 35p Billy Batten | .70 .65 |
| 1633 | A460 | 41p Brian Bevan | .85 .85 |
| | | Nos. 1629-1633 (5) | 3.05 3.05 |

Christmas A461

Designs showing robin in winter scene: 19p, In pillar box. 25p, On fence rail, holly bush. 30p, Standing on snow covered milk bottle. 41p, Sitting on snow covered road sign, blue fence. 60p, Sitting on door knob, Chistmas decoration on door.

**1995, Oct. 30 Photo.**    **Perf. 14¾x14**
| | | | |
|---|---|---|---|
| 1634 | A461 | 19p multicolored | .35 .35 |
| a. | | Booklet pane of 20 | 8.50 |
| b. | | Sheet of 20 + 20 labels | 225.00 |
| 1635 | A461 | 25p multicolored | .50 .50 |
| 1636 | A461 | 30p multicolored | .65 .65 |
| 1637 | A461 | 41p multicolored | .90 .90 |
| 1638 | A461 | 60p multicolored | 1.20 1.20 |
| a. | | Booklet pane of 4 | 7.25 |
| | | Nos. 1634-1638 (5) | 3.60 3.60 |

No. 1634b was issued 10/3/00. It sold for £3.99 and has labels that read "Seasons Greetings" and "Glad Tidings." Sheets with personalized labels were made available only to select Royal Post customers via mail order purchases, and sold for more.
For booklets containing Nos. 1634a and 1638a, see Nos. BK859 and BK792, respectively.
No. BK805 contains No. 1635.

Robert Burns (1759-1796), Poet — A462

Lines from poems: 19p, "Wee sleeket, cowran, tim'rous beastie." 25p, "O my luve's like a red, red rose." 41p, "Scots, wha hae wi Wallace bled." 60p, "Should auld acquaintance be forgot."

**1996, Jan. 25 Litho.**    **Perf. 14½**
| | | | |
|---|---|---|---|
| 1639 | A462 | 19p multicolored | .40 .40 |
| 1640 | A462 | 25p multicolored | .55 .60 |
| 1641 | A462 | 41p multicolored | 1.00 1.00 |
| 1642 | A462 | 60p multicolored | 1.30 1.25 |
| | | Nos. 1639-1642 (4) | 3.25 3.25 |

Greetings Cartoons — A463

No. 1643, More Love. No. 1644, Sincerely. No. 1645, Human condition. No. 1646, Mental Floss. No. 1647, Don't ring. No. 1648, Dear lottery prize winner. No. 1649, I'm writing to you... No. 1650, Fetch this... No. 1651, My day starts... No. 1652, The check in the post.

**Perf. 14½ Syncopated**
**1996-2001**    **Litho.**
| | | | |
|---|---|---|---|
| 1643 | A463 | 1st black & lilac | 1.35 1.20 |
| 1644 | A463 | 1st black & green | 1.35 1.20 |
| 1645 | A463 | 1st black & blue | 1.35 1.20 |
| 1646 | A463 | 1st black & purple | 1.35 1.20 |
| 1647 | A463 | 1st black & red | 1.35 1.20 |
| 1648 | A463 | 1st black & blue | 1.35 1.20 |
| 1649 | A463 | 1st black & red | 1.35 1.20 |
| 1650 | A463 | 1st black & purple | 1.35 1.20 |
| 1651 | A463 | 1st black & green | 1.35 1.20 |
| 1652 | A463 | 1st black & lilac | 1.35 1.20 |
| a. | | Booklet pane, #1643-1652+20 labels | 13.50 |
| b. | | Sheet of 10, #1643-1652, + 10 labels, perf. 14½x14 | 12.50 — |

*c.* Sheet of 20, 2 each #1643-
1652, + 20 labels, perf.
14¼ — —

Issued: No. 1652b, 12/18/01. 1652a,
2/26/96. 1652c, 7/29/03.
No. 1652b lacks perforation syncopation.
Labels could be personalized for an additional
amount.
Nos. 1643-1652 sold for 25p on day of
issue.
No. 1652c sold for £6.15.
For booklet containing No. 1652a, see No.
BK1184.
No. 1652a was issued on phosphored
paper. Booklet panes with two phosphor
bands exist. Value, $27.50.

Wildfowl and
Wetlands Trust,
50th Anniv. — A464

Paintings by Charles Tunnicliffe RA (1901-
79): 19p, Muscovy duck. 25p, Lapwing. 30p,
White-fronted goose. 35p, Bittern. 41p,
Whooper swan.

**1996, Mar. 12　Photo.　Perf. 14x14½**
1653 A464 19p multicolored .35 .35
1654 A464 25p multicolored .50 .50
1655 A464 30p multicolored .65 .65
1656 A464 35p multicolored .75 .75
1657 A464 41p multicolored .90 .90
　*Nos. 1653-1657 (5)* 3.15 3.15

Motion Pictures,
Cent. — A465

Designs: 19p, Exterior of Odeon at Harro-
gate, 1930s theater. 25p, Laurance Olivier,
Vivien Leigh in scene from "That Hamilton
Woman." 30p, Cinema ticket from "The Picture
House." 35p, Rooster emblem of Pathe News,
motion picture newsreels. 41p, Theater
marquee.

**1996, Apr. 16　Photo.　Perf. 14x14½**
1658 A465 19p multicolored .40 .40
1659 A465 25p multicolored .55 .55
1660 A465 30p multicolored .70 .70
1661 A465 35p multicolored .75 .75
1662 A465 41p multicolored .85 .85
　*Nos. 1658-1662 (5)* 3.25 3.25

1996 European
Soccer
Championships
A466

Legendary players: 19p, Dixie Dean (1907-
80). 25p, Bobby Moore (1941-93). 35p,
Duncan Edwards (1936-58). 41p, Billy Wright
(1924-94). 60p, Danny Blanchflower (1926-
93).

**1996, May 14　Litho.　Perf. 15x14**
1663 A466 19p gray, red & blk .40 .35
　*a.* Bklt. pane of 4 + printed mar-
　　gin (BK161) 1.60
1664 A466 25p gray, grn & blk .55 .55
　*a.* Bklt. pane of 4 + printed mar-
　　gin (BK161) 2.25
1665 A466 35p gray, yel & blk .75 .75
1666 A466 41p blk, blue & gray .90 .90
1667 A466 60p gray, org & blk 1.20 1.20
　*a.* Bklt. pane, 2 ea #1665-1667
　　(BK161) 5.75
　*Nos. 1663-1667 (5)* 3.80 3.75

1996 Summer
Olympic,
Paralympic
Games,
Atlanta — A467

**1996, July 9　Litho.　Perf. 15x14**
1688 A467 26p Sprinting .50 .50
1689 A467 26p Javelin .50 .50
1690 A467 26p Basketball .50 .50
1691 A467 26p Swimming .50 .50
1692 A467 26p Victorious athlete .50 .50
　*a.* Strip of 5, #1688-1692 2.75 2.80

Compare with Type A588.

20th Century
Women of
Achievement
A468

Designs: 20p, Dorothy Hodgkin (1910-94),
chemist. 26p, Margot Fonteyn (1919-91), ballerina. 31p, Elisabeth Frink (1930-93), sculptor. 37p, Daphne du Maurier (1907-89), novelist. 43p, Marea Hartman (1920-94), sports
administrator.

**1996, Aug. 6　Photo.　Perf. 14½**
1693 A468 20p multicolored .50 .50
1694 A468 26p multicolored .55 .55
1695 A468 31p multicolored .70 .70
1696 A468 37p multicolored .80 .80
1697 A468 43p multicolored .95 .95
　*Nos. 1693-1697 (5)* 3.50 3.50

Europa, Nos. 1694-1695.

British Television
Programs for
Children, 50th
Anniv. — A469

Designs: 20p, Annette Mills, "Muffin the
Mule." 26p, Sooty. 31p, String puppets Troy
Tempest and Lord Titan. 37p, The Clangers.
43p, Dangermouse.

**1996, Sept. 3　Perf. 14½x14**
1698 A469 20p multicolored .45 .45
　*a.* Pane of 4 #1698b + printed
　　margin 3.00
　*b.* Perf. 15x14 .75 .75
1699 A469 26p multicolored .50 .55
1700 A469 31p multicolored .65 .70
1701 A469 37p multicolored .70 .75
1702 A469 43p multicolored .95 1.00
　*Nos. 1698-1702 (5)* 3.25 3.45

For Prestige booklet containing pane No.
1698a, see BK162.
Issued: No. 1698a, 9/23/97.

Classic British
Sports Cars — A470

Designs: 20p, 1955 Triumph TR3. 26p, MG
TD. 37p, Austin-Healy 100. 43p, 1948 Jaguar
XK 120. 63p, Morgan Plus Four.

**1996, Oct. 1　Photo.　Perf. 14½**
1703 A470 20p multicolored .45 .35
1704 A470 26p multicolored .55 .55
1705 A470 37p multicolored .75 .75
1706 A470 43p multicolored .90 1.00
1707 A470 63p multicolored 1.30 1.30
　*Nos. 1703-1707 (5)* 3.95 3.95

Christmas
A471

Designs: 2nd, Three kings, star. 1st, The
Annunciation. 31p, Mary, Joseph on journey to
Bethlehem. 43p, Madonna and Child. 63p,
Angel telling shepherds of Christ's birth.

**1996, Oct. 28　Photo.　Perf. 14½x14**
1708 A471 2nd multicolored .85 .65
　*a.* Booklet pane of 20 23.00
1709 A471 1st multicolored 1.05 .95
1710 A471 31p multicolored .65 .70
1711 A471 43p multicolored .90 .95
1712 A471 63p multicolored 1.20 1.20
　*Nos. 1708-1712 (5)* 4.65 4.45

Nos. 1708-1709 sold for 20p and 26p
respectively on day of issue.
For booklet containing No. 1708a, see No.
BK1220.
No. BK1194 contains No. 1709.

Gentiana
Acaulis — A472

Magnolia
Altissima — A473

Camellia
Japonica — A474

Tulip — A475

Fuchsia "Princess
of Wales" — A476

Le Perroquet
Rouge — A477

Gazania
Splendens
A478

Iris
Latifolia — A479

Amaryllis
Bresiliensis
A480

Granadilla
A481

**Perf. 14½x14 Syncopated**
**1997, Jan. 6　Litho.**
　　**Booklet Stamps**
1713 A472 1st multicolored 1.30 1.20
　*a.* Perf 15x14 4.75 4.75
1714 A473 1st multicolored 1.30 1.20
1715 A474 1st multicolored 1.30 1.20
1716 A475 1st multicolored 1.30 1.20
　*a.* Perf 15x14 2.50 2.50
1717 A476 1st multicolored 1.30 1.20
1718 A477 1st multicolored 1.30 1.20
1719 A478 1st multicolored 1.30 1.20
1720 A479 1st multicolored 1.30 1.20
　*a.* Perf 15x14 4.75 4.75
　*b.* Booklet pane, #1713a, 1720a,
　　2 #1716a (BK176) 15.00 —
1721 A480 1st multicolored 1.30 1.20
1722 A481 1st multicolored 1.30 1.20
　*a.* Bklt. pane of 10, #1713-1722 13.00
　*b.* Sheet, 2 each #1713-1722, +
　　20 labels, perf. 14¼ 37.50

Nos. 1713-1722, 1722a issued 1/9/97.
1722a sold for £2.50 on day of issue, but
stamps each had 26p of franking value.
No. 1722b issued 2003. It sold for £14.95
and had labels that could be personalized.
No. 1720a issued 5/25/04. 1720a sold for
£1.12 on day of issue.
For booklet containing No. 1722a, see No.
BK1195.
See Nos. 2671-2672.

King Henry VIII
and His Six
Wives — A482

**1997, Jan. 21　Photo.　Perf. 15**
1723 A482 26p shown .70 .70
　　**Size: 27x38mm**
　　**Perf. 14x15**
1724 A482 26p Catherine of Ara-
　　gon .70 .70
1725 A482 26p Anne Boleyn .70 .70
1726 A482 26p Jane Seymour .70 .70
1727 A482 26p Anne of Cleves .70 .70
1728 A482 26p Catherine How-
　　ard .70 .70
1729 A482 26p Catherine Parr .70 .70
　*a.* Strip of 6, #1724-1729 4.25 4.25
　*Nos. 1723-1729 (7)* 4.90 4.90

St. Augustine of
Canterbury & St.
Columba of
Iona — A483

Designs: 26p, St. Columba's journey across
Irish Sea to Iona. 37p, St. Columba at work,
Ionian Sea. 43p, St. Augustine baptizing King
Ethelbert. 63p, St. Augustine outside Cathe-
dral at Canterbury, Kent coastline.

**1997, Mar. 11　Photo.　Perf. 14½x14**
1730 A483 26p multicolored .60 .60
1731 A483 37p multicolored .80 .80
1732 A483 43p multicolored 1.05 1.05
1733 A483 63p multicolored 1.30 1.30
　*Nos. 1730-1733 (4)* 3.75 3.75

Stories and
Legends — A484

Europa: 26p, Dracula. 31p, Frankenstein.
37p, Dr. Jekyll and Mr. Hyde. 43p, The Hound
of the Baskervilles.

**1997, May 13　Photo.　Perf. 14x15**
1754 A484 26p multicolored .55 .55
1755 A484 31p multicolored .65 .65
1756 A484 37p multicolored .80 .80
1757 A484 43p multicolored 1.10 1.10
　*Nos. 1754-1757 (4)* 3.10 3.10

Aircraft,
Designers
A485

20p, Supermarine Spitfire, R.J. Mitchell.
26p, Avro Lancaster, Roy Chadwick. 37p,
DeHavilland Mosquito, R.E. Bishop. 43p,
Gloster Meteor, George Carter. 63p, Hawker
Hunter, Sidney Camm.

**1997, June 10　Photo.　Perf. 15x14**
1758 A485 20p multicolored .45 .35
　*a.* Litho., perf. 14¼x14 (#2587b)
　　('08) 2.50 2.50
1759 A485 26p multicolored .55 .55
1760 A485 37p multicolored .75 .80
1761 A485 43p multicolored 1.05 1.00
1762 A485 63p multicolored 1.45 1.40
　*Nos. 1758-1762 (5)* 4.25 4.10

Issued: No. 1758a, 9/18/08.
On Nos. 1758-1762 the face of the aircraft
designer was hidden in the clouds.

All the Queen's
Horses — A486

20p, 43p, Carriage horses from Royal Mews. 26p, 63p, Mount horses from Household Cavalry.

**1997, July 9    Litho.    Perf. 14x14½**

| | | | | |
|---|---|---|---|---|
| 1763 | A486 | 20p multicolored | .45 | .45 |
| 1764 | A486 | 26p multicolored | .50 | .50 |
| 1765 | A486 | 43p multicolored | .90 | .90 |
| 1766 | A486 | 63p multicolored | 1.25 | 1.25 |
| | *Nos. 1763-1766 (4)* | | 3.10 | 3.10 |

British Horse Society, 50th anniv.

Post Offices — A487

Designs: 20p, Haroldswick, Shetland Islands, Scotland. 26p, Painswick, Gloucestershire, England. 43p, Beddgelert, Gwynedd, Wales. 63p, Ballyroney, County Down, Northern Ireland.

**1997, Aug. 12    Litho.    Perf. 14½x14**

| | | | | |
|---|---|---|---|---|
| 1767 | A487 | 20p multicolored | .45 | .35 |
| 1768 | A487 | 26p multicolored | .60 | .60 |
| 1769 | A487 | 43p multicolored | 1.05 | 1.10 |
| 1770 | A487 | 63p multicolored | 1.40 | 1.40 |
| | *Nos. 1767-1770 (4)* | | 3.50 | 3.45 |

Enid Blyton, Author of Children's Stories, Birth Cent. — A488

Characters from books: 20p, "Noddy." 26p, "Famous Five." 37p, "Secret Seven." 43p, "Faraway Tree." 63p, "Malory Towers."

**1997, Sept. 9    Litho.    Perf. 14x14½**

| | | | | |
|---|---|---|---|---|
| 1771 | A488 | 20p multicolored | .45 | .40 |
| 1772 | A488 | 26p multicolored | .50 | .60 |
| 1773 | A488 | 37p multicolored | .75 | .85 |
| 1774 | A488 | 43p multicolored | 1.00 | 1.05 |
| 1775 | A488 | 63p multicolored | 1.30 | 1.35 |
| | *Nos. 1771-1775 (5)* | | 4.00 | 4.25 |

Christmas Crackers — A489

Designs: 2nd, Santa as Man in Moon sharing cracker with two children. 1st, Santa bursting through wrapping paper with cracker. 31p, Santa riding across sky on giant cracker. 43p, Santa on giant snowball holding cracker. 63p, Santa climbing into chimney with sack full of crackers.

**1997, Oct. 27    Photo.    Perf. 15x14**

| | | | | |
|---|---|---|---|---|
| 1776 | A489 | 2nd multicolored | .85 | .65 |
| a. | | Booklet pane of 20 | 23.00 | |
| 1777 | A489 | 1st multicolored | 1.00 | .90 |
| b. | | Sheet of 10 + 10 labels | 200.00 | |
| c. | | Sheet of 20 + 20 labels, litho., perf 14½x14 | 40.00 | |
| 1778 | A489 | 31p multicolored | .65 | .70 |
| 1779 | A489 | 43p multicolored | 1.00 | 1.00 |
| 1780 | A489 | 63p multicolored | 1.15 | 1.25 |
| | *Nos. 1776-1780 (5)* | | 4.65 | 4.50 |

Nos. 1776-1777 were sold for 20p and 26p, respectively, on day of issue.

No. 1777b was sold for 10/3/00. It sold for £2.95 and has labels that read "Seasons Greetings" and "Ho Ho Ho." Sheets with personalized labels were made available only to select Royal Post customers via mail order purchases, and sold for more.

No. 1777c issued 2003. It sold for £5.95 and had labels that could be personalized.

For booklet containing No. 1776a, see No. BK1221.

No. BK1198 contains No. 1777.

Queen Elizabeth II, Prince Philip, 50th Wedding Anniv. — A490

Designs: 20p, 43p, Wedding portrait, 1947. 26p, 63p, Anniversary portrait, 1997.

**1997, Nov. 13    Photo.    Perf. 15**

| | | | | |
|---|---|---|---|---|
| 1781 | A490 | 20p multicolored | .65 | .50 |
| 1782 | A490 | 26p multicolored | .75 | .75 |
| 1783 | A490 | 43p multicolored | 1.50 | 1.45 |
| 1784 | A490 | 63p multicolored | 2.00 | 1.75 |
| | *Nos. 1781-1784 (4)* | | 4.90 | 4.45 |

Endangered Species — A491

Designs: 20p, Common dormouse. 26p, Lady's slipper orchid. 31p, Song thrush. 37p, Shining ram's horn snail. 43p, Mole cricket. 63p, Devil's bolete.

**1998, Jan. 20    Litho.    Perf. 14x14½**

| | | | | |
|---|---|---|---|---|
| 1785 | A491 | 20p multicolored | .45 | .45 |
| 1786 | A491 | 26p multicolored | .55 | .55 |
| 1787 | A491 | 31p multicolored | .70 | .70 |
| 1788 | A491 | 37p multicolored | .80 | .80 |
| 1789 | A491 | 43p multicolored | 1.00 | 1.00 |
| 1790 | A491 | 63p multicolored | 1.25 | 1.25 |
| | *Nos. 1785-1790 (6)* | | 4.75 | 4.75 |

Diana, Princess of Wales (1961-97) — A492

Portraits of Diana wearing: No. 1791, Choker. No. 1792, Blue dress. No. 1793, Tiara. No. 1794, Checked dress. No. 1795, Black dress.

**1998, Feb. 3    Photo.    Perf. 14x15**

| | | | | |
|---|---|---|---|---|
| 1791 | A492 | 26p multicolored | .60 | .60 |
| 1792 | A492 | 26p multicolored | .60 | .60 |
| 1793 | A492 | 26p multicolored | .60 | .60 |
| 1794 | A492 | 26p multicolored | .60 | .60 |
| 1795 | A492 | 26p multicolored | .60 | .60 |
| a. | | Strip of 5, #1791-1795 | 3.00 | 3.00 |
| b. | | As "a," imperf. | 13,500. | |

Order of the Garter, 650th Anniv. — A493

Queen's Beasts (supporters of Royal Arms created for Queen Elizabeth II's coronation in 1953): No. 1796, Lion of England, Griffin of Edward III. No. 1797, Falcon of Plantagenet, Bull of Clarence. No. 1798, Lion of Mortimer, Yale of Beaufort. No. 1799, Greyhound of Richmond, Dragon of Wales. No. 1800, Unicorn of Scotland, Horse of Hanover.

**Litho. & Engr.**

**1998, Feb. 24    Perf. 15x14**

| | | | | |
|---|---|---|---|---|
| 1796 | A493 | 26p multicolored | .60 | .60 |
| 1797 | A493 | 26p multicolored | .60 | .60 |
| 1798 | A493 | 26p multicolored | .60 | .60 |
| 1799 | A493 | 26p multicolored | .60 | .60 |
| 1800 | A493 | 26p multicolored | .60 | .60 |
| a. | | Strip of 5, #1796-1800 | 3.75 | 3.75 |

**Queen Type of 1952 with Face Values in Decimal Currency**

**Perf. 14 Syncopated**

**1998, Mar. 10    Litho.**

| | | | | |
|---|---|---|---|---|
| 1801 | A129 | 20p dk grn & lt grn | .45 | .45 |
| a. | | Booklet pane of 6 + printed margin (BK163) | 3.50 | |
| 1802 | A129 | 26p dk brn & lt brn | .60 | .60 |
| a. | | Booklet pane of 9 + printed margin (BK163) | 6.50 | |
| 1803 | A129 | 37p dk red lil & lt lil | 1.60 | 1.60 |
| a. | | Booklet pane 3 each #1802-1803 + printed margin (BK163) | 8.50 | |
| b. | | Booklet pane, 4 #1801, 2 ea #1802-1803 + printed margin (BK163) | 7.75 | |

Lighthouses — A494

**1998, Mar. 24    Perf. 14x14½**

| | | | | |
|---|---|---|---|---|
| 1804 | A494 | 20p St. John's Point | .50 | .40 |
| 1805 | A494 | 26p The Smalls | .60 | .60 |
| 1806 | A494 | 37p Needles Rocks | .80 | .85 |
| 1807 | A494 | 43p Bell Rock | 1.15 | 1.20 |
| 1808 | A494 | 63p Eddystone | 1.50 | 1.50 |
| | *Nos. 1804-1808 (5)* | | 4.55 | 4.55 |

Comedians A495

20p, Tommy Cooper (1922-84). 26p, Eric Morecambe (1926-84). 37p, Joyce Grenfell (1910-79). 43p, Les Dawson (1933-93). 63p, Peter Cook (1937-95).

**1998, Apr. 23    Litho.    Perf. 14½x14**

| | | | | |
|---|---|---|---|---|
| 1809 | A495 | 20p multicolored | .45 | .45 |
| 1810 | A495 | 26p multicolored | .55 | .55 |
| 1811 | A495 | 37p multicolored | .70 | .70 |
| 1812 | A495 | 43p multicolored | 1.00 | 1.00 |
| 1813 | A495 | 63p multicolored | 1.30 | 1.30 |
| | *Nos. 1809-1813 (5)* | | 4.00 | 4.00 |

National Health Service, 50th Anniv. — A496

Designs: 20p, Hands forming heart, "10,000 donors give blood every day." 26p, Adult hand clasping child's, "1,700,000 prescriptions dispensed every day." 43p, Hands forming cradle, "2,000 babies delivered every day." 63p, Taking pulse, "130,000 hospital outpatients seen every day."

**1998, June 23    Litho.    Perf. 14x14½**

| | | | | |
|---|---|---|---|---|
| 1814 | A496 | 20p multicolored | .40 | .40 |
| 1815 | A496 | 26p multicolored | .50 | .50 |
| 1816 | A496 | 43p multicolored | .95 | .95 |
| 1817 | A496 | 63p multicolored | 1.20 | 1.20 |
| | *Nos. 1814-1817 (4)* | | 3.05 | 3.05 |

Magical World of Children's Literature A496a

Stories depicted: 20p, "The Hobbit," by J.R.R. Tolkien. 26p, "The Lion, The Witch and the Wardrobe," by C.S. Lewis. 37p, "The Phoenix and the Carpet," by E. Nesbit. 43p, "The Borrowers," by Mary Norton. 63p, "Through the Looking Glass," by Lewis Carroll.

**1998, July 21    Photo.    Perf. 15x14**

| | | | | |
|---|---|---|---|---|
| 1820 | A496a | 20p multicolored | .50 | .40 |
| 1821 | A496a | 26p multicolored | .60 | .60 |
| 1822 | A496a | 37p multicolored | .85 | .85 |
| 1823 | A496a | 43p multicolored | 1.10 | 1.10 |
| 1824 | A496a | 63p multicolored | 1.40 | 1.40 |
| | *Nos. 1820-1824 (5)* | | 4.45 | 4.35 |

Notting Hill Carnival — A497

Expressionist photographic images of dancers, color of costumes: 20p, Yellow. 26p, Blue. 43p, Gold and white. 63p, Green.

**1998, Aug. 25    Perf. 14x14½**

| | | | | |
|---|---|---|---|---|
| 1825 | A497 | 20p multicolored | .45 | .45 |
| 1826 | A497 | 26p multicolored | .50 | .50 |
| 1827 | A497 | 43p multicolored | 1.00 | 1.00 |
| 1828 | A497 | 63p multicolored | 1.30 | 1.30 |
| | *Nos. 1825-1828 (4)* | | 3.25 | 3.25 |

Europa (Nos. 1825-1826).

Land Speed Records — A498

Car, driver, year, record speed: 20p, Bluebird, Sir Malcolm Campbell, 1925, 151 mph. 26p, Red Sunbeam, Sir Henry Segrave, 1926, 152 mph. 30p, Babs, John G. Parry Thomas, 1926, 171 mph. 43p, Railton Mobil Special, John R. Cobb, 1947, 394 mph. 63p, Bluebird CN7, Donald Campbell, 1964, 403 mph.

**1998, Sept. 29    Photo.    Perf. 15x14**

| | | | | |
|---|---|---|---|---|
| 1829 | A498 | 20p multicolored | .45 | .35 |
| a. | | Perf. 14½x13½ | 1.40 | 1.40 |
| b. | | As "a," booklet pane of 4 + printed margin (BK164) | 5.75 | |
| 1830 | A498 | 26p multicolored | .55 | .55 |
| 1831 | A498 | 30p multicolored | .65 | .65 |
| 1832 | A498 | 43p multicolored | 1.05 | 1.05 |
| 1833 | A498 | 63p multicolored | 1.35 | 1.35 |
| | *Nos. 1829-1833 (5)* | | 4.05 | 3.95 |

Christmas Angels — A499

**1998, Nov. 2    Photo.    Perf. 15x14**

| | | | | |
|---|---|---|---|---|
| 1834 | A499 | 20p shown | .45 | .45 |
| a. | | Booklet pane of 20 | 14.00 | |
| 1835 | A499 | 26p Praying | .50 | .50 |
| 1836 | A499 | 30p Playing flute | .55 | .55 |
| 1837 | A499 | 43p Playing lute | 1.00 | 1.00 |
| 1838 | A499 | 63p Praying, diff. | 1.30 | 1.30 |
| | *Nos. 1834-1838 (5)* | | 3.80 | 3.80 |

No. BK1199 contains No. 1835.

British Achievements During Past 1000 Years — A500

Inventions: 20p, Timekeeping, John Harrison's chronometer. 26p, Development of steam power. 43p, William Henry Fox Talbot's use of negatives to create photographs. 63p, Development of computers.

Transportation: 20p, Jet travel. 26p, Development of bicycle. 43p, Isambard Kingdom Brunel's Clifton Suspension Bridge, Great Western Railway. 63p, Capt. Cook's expeditions.

Health care: 20p, First smallpox vaccination, by Edward Jenner. 26p, Development of nursing care. 43p, Discovery of penicillin, by Alexander Fleming. 63p, First "test tube" baby (in-vitro fertilization), pioneered by Patrick Steptoe and Robert Edwards.

Emigration: 20p, Migration to Scotland. 26p, Pilgrim fathers. 43p, Destination Australia. 63p, Migration to UK.

Workers: 19p, Weavers. 26p, Mill towns. 44p, Ship building. 64p, City finance.

Entertainment and sports: 19p, Freddie Mercury, lead singer of Queen. 26p, Bobby Moore, 1966 World Cup Soccer Champions. 44p, Dalek from "Dr. Who" television series. 64p, Charlie Chaplin.

Citizens' Rights: 19p, Equal rights. 26p, Right to health. 44p, Right to learn. 64p, First rights.

Scientists: 19p, Decoding DNA. 26p, Darwin's theory. 44p, Faraday's electricity. 64p, Newton, Hubble Telescope.

Farmers: 19p, Strip farming (Europa). 26p, Mechanical farming. 44p, Food from afar. 64p, Satellite agriculture.

Soldiers: 19p, Battle of Bannockburn. 26p, Civil War. 44p, World Wars, cemetery. 64p, Peace keeping.

Christians: 19p, John Wesley (1703-91), founder of Methodism, and "Hark, The Herald Angels Sing," hymn by brother Charles (1707-88). 26p, King James Bible. 44p, St. Andrews Pilgrimage. 64p, First Christmas.

Artists: 19p, World of the stage. 26p, World of music. 44p, World of literature. 64p, New worlds.

**1999    Photo.    Perf. 14¼x14½**

**Inventions**

| | | | | |
|---|---|---|---|---|
| 1839 | A500 | 20p multi (48) | .50 | .50 |
| 1840 | A500 | 26p multi (47) | .50 | .50 |
| 1841 | A500 | 43p multi (46) | .95 | .95 |
| 1842 | A500 | 63p multi (45) | 1.30 | 1.30 |
| a. | | Perf. 13¾ | 3.00 | 3.00 |
| b. | | Booklet pane, 4 #1842a (BK166) | 12.00 | |

**Transportation**

| | | | | |
|---|---|---|---|---|
| 1843 | A500 | 20p multi (44) | .50 | .50 |
| 1844 | A500 | 26p multi (43) | .50 | .50 |
| 1845 | A500 | 43p multi (42) | .95 | .95 |
| 1846 | A500 | 63p multi (41) | 1.30 | 1.30 |

**Health Care**

**Perf. 13¾x14**

| | | | | |
|---|---|---|---|---|
| 1847 | A500 | 20p multi (40) | .50 | .50 |
| a. | | Booklet pane of 4 (BK166) | 2.25 | |

| | | | |
|---|---|---|---|
| 1848 | A500 26p multi (39) | .50 | .50 |
| 1849 | A500 43p multi (38) | .95 | .95 |
| 1850 | A500 63p multi (37) | 1.30 | 1.30 |

### Emigration
#### Perf. 14¼x14½

| | | | |
|---|---|---|---|
| 1851 | A500 20p multi (36) | .50 | .50 |
| 1852 | A500 26p multi (35) | .50 | .50 |
| 1853 | A500 43p multi (34) | .95 | .95 |
| 1854 | A500 63p multi (33) | 1.30 | 1.30 |

### Workers
#### Perf. 14¼x14½

| | | | |
|---|---|---|---|
| 1855 | A500 19p multi (32) | .50 | .50 |
| 1856 | A500 26p multi (31) | .50 | .50 |
| a. | Booklet pane #1852, 1856 (BK1141) | 1.25 | |
| 1857 | A500 44p multi (30) | .95 | .95 |
| 1858 | A500 64p multi (29) | 1.30 | 1.30 |

### Entertainment & Sports
#### Perf. 14¼x14½

| | | | |
|---|---|---|---|
| 1859 | A500 19p multi (28) | .50 | .50 |
| 1860 | A500 26p multi (27) | .50 | .50 |
| 1861 | A500 44p multi (26) | .95 | .95 |
| 1862 | A500 64p multi (25) | 1.30 | 1.30 |

### Citizen's Rights
#### Perf. 14¼x14½

| | | | |
|---|---|---|---|
| 1863 | A500 19p multi (24) | .50 | .50 |
| 1864 | A500 26p multi (23) | .50 | .50 |
| 1865 | A500 44p multi (22) | .95 | .95 |
| 1866 | A500 64p multi (21) | 1.30 | 1.30 |

### Scientists
#### Perf. 14¼ (#1868-1869), 13¾ (#1867, 1870)

| | | | |
|---|---|---|---|
| 1867 | A500 19p multi (20) | .50 | .50 |
| 1868 | A500 26p multi (19) | .50 | .50 |
| a. | Perf. 14¼x14 | 2.25 | 2.25 |
| b. | Booklet pane, 4 #1868a (BK166) | 9.00 | |
| 1869 | A500 44p multi (18) | .95 | .95 |
| a. | Perf. 14¼x14 | 2.75 | 2.75 |
| b. | Booklet pane, 4 #1869a (BK166) | 11.00 | |
| 1870 | A500 64p multi (17) | 1.30 | 1.30 |
| a. | Perf. 14¼ | 4.50 | 4.50 |
| b. | Souvenir sheet, 4 #1870a | 12.25 | 12.25 |

### Farmers
#### Perf. 14¼x14½

| | | | |
|---|---|---|---|
| 1871 | A500 19p multi (16) | .50 | .50 |
| 1872 | A500 26p multi (15) | .50 | .50 |
| a. | Booklet pane of 2 (BK1142) | 1.25 | |
| 1873 | A500 44p multi (14) | .95 | .95 |
| 1874 | A500 64p multi (13) | 1.30 | 1.30 |

Europa, No. 1871.

### Soldiers
#### Perf. 14¼x14½

| | | | |
|---|---|---|---|
| 1875 | A500 19p multi (12) | .50 | .50 |
| 1876 | A500 26p multi (11) | .50 | .50 |
| 1877 | A500 44p multi (10) | .95 | .95 |
| 1878 | A500 64p multi (9) | 1.50 | 1.60 |

### Christians
#### | | | | |
|---|---|---|---|
| 1879 | A500 19p multi (8) | .50 | .50 |
| a. | Booklet pane of 20 | 11.00 | |
| 1880 | A500 26p multi (7) | .50 | .50 |
| 1881 | A500 44p multi (6) | .95 | .95 |
| 1882 | A500 64p multi (5) | 1.30 | 1.30 |

### Artists
#### Perf. 14¼x14½

| | | | |
|---|---|---|---|
| 1883 | A500 19p multi (4) | .50 | .50 |
| 1884 | A500 26p multi (3) | .50 | .50 |
| 1885 | A500 44p multi (2) | .95 | .95 |
| 1886 | A500 64p multi (1) | 1.30 | 1.30 |
| | Nos. 1839-1886 (48) | 39.20 | 39.30 |

Issued: Nos. 1839-1842, 1/12; Nos. 1843-1846, 2/2; Nos. 1847-1850, 3/2; Nos. 1851-1854, 4/6; Nos. 1855-1858, 5/4; Nos. 1859-1862, 6/1; Nos. 1863-1866, 7/6; Nos. 1867-1870, 8/3; Nos. 1871-1874, 9/7; Nos. 1870b, 8/11; Nos. 1875-1878, 10/5; Nos. 1879-1882, 11/2; Nos. 1883-1886, 12/7.
See Nos. 1889, 1890-1937, 1938.
No. BK1200 contains No. 1880.

Marriage of Prince Edward and Sophie Rhys-Jones
A501

**1999, June 15    Photo.    Perf. 15x14**

| | | | |
|---|---|---|---|
| 1887 | A501 26p shown | .60 | .75 |
| 1888 | A501 64p Profile portrait | 1.50 | 1.50 |

---

### Souvenir Sheet

Millennium — A502

Clock and globe showing: a, North America. b, Southeast Asia. c, Middle East. d, Europe.

#### Perf. 14¼x14½

**1999, Dec. 14    Photo.**

| | | | |
|---|---|---|---|
| 1889 | A502 Sheet of 4 | 14.75 | 14.75 |
| a.-d. | 64p any single | 3.50 | 3.50 |

No. 1889 exists overprinted "EARLS COURT, LONDON...STAMP SHOW 2000." It was sold at a substantial premium as part of a premium entrance fee. Value, $18.75.

Millennium Projects — A503

Above and Beyond: 19p, Barn owl's head, 3rd Millennium conservation projects, Muncaster. 26p, Night sky, National Space Center, Leicester. 44p, Buildings and waterfall, Torrs Walkway project, Derbyshire. 64p, Sea birds, Scottish Sea Bird Center.
Fire & Light: 19p, Beacon, Beacon Millennium project. 26p, Rheilffordd Eryri / Snowdonia, Welsh Highland Railway rebuilding project. 44p, Lightning bolt, Dynamic Earth project. 64p, Lights, Croydon Skyline project.
Water & Coast: 19p, Stones, Durham Coast restoration project. 26p, Frog, flowers, National Pondlife Center, conservation project. 44p, Parc Arfordirol project. 64p, Portsmouth Harbor project.
Life & Earth: 2nd, Wetlands, ECOS/Ballymena Project. 1st, Ants, Web of Life Exhibition at London Zoo. 44p, Solar cells, Earth Center, Doncaster. 64p, Plant leaves in water, Project SUZY, Teeside.
Art & Craft: 2nd, Ceramica project, Stoke-on-Trent. 1st, Tate Gallery of Modern Art, London. 45p, Cycle Network Artworks Project. 65p, The Lowry Arts Complex, Balford.
People & Place: 2nd, Millennium Greens project. 1st, Gateshead Millennium Bridge, Newcastle. 45p, Mile End Park, London. 65p, On the Line project.
Stone & Soil: 2nd, Raising of Strangford Stone, Killyleagh, Northern Ireland. 1st, Trans Pennine Trail project. 45p, Kingdom of Fife Cycle Ways project, Scotland. 65p, Changing Places project of Groundwork Foundation.
Tree & Leaf: 2nd, Yews for the Millennium project. 1st, Eden Project, St. Austell. 45p, Millennium Seed Bank project, Ardingly. 65p, Forest for Scotland project.
Mind & Matter: 2nd, Ant's head, Wildscreen at Bristol Project. 1st, People in rowboat, Norfolk and Norwich Project, Newport. 45p, X-ray image of hand and computer mouse, Millennium Point Project, Birmingham. 65p, Plaid globe, Scottish Cultural Resources Access Network.
Body & Bone: 2nd, Dancers, Millennium Dome project, Greenwich. 1st, Soccer players, Hampden Park project, Glasgow. 45p, Bath Spa project. 65p, Center for Life, Newcastle.
Spirit & Faith: 2nd, Stained glass window, St. Edmundsbury Cathedral project. 1st, Church floodlighting project. 45p, St. Patrick Center project, Downpatrick. 65p, York mystery plays.
Sound & Vision: 2nd, Bells, Ringing in the Millennium project. 1st, Eye, Year of the Artist. 45p, Harp, Camofym Millennium Center, Cardiff. 65p, TS2K Talent and Skills project.

### Above & Beyond
#### Photo., Litho. (#1892, 1900, 1911, 1913)
#### Perf. 13¾x14, 14¼x14½ (#1892)

**2000**

| | | | |
|---|---|---|---|
| 1890 | A503 19p multi (1) | .50 | .50 |
| 1891 | A503 26p multi (2) | .60 | .60 |
| 1892 | A503 44p multi (3) | 1.15 | 1.15 |
| 1893 | A503 64p multi (4) | 1.60 | 1.60 |

#### Perf. 14¼x14½
### Fire & Light

| | | | |
|---|---|---|---|
| 1894 | A503 19p multi (5) | .50 | .50 |
| 1895 | A503 26p multi (6) | .60 | .60 |
| 1896 | A503 44p multi (7) | 1.15 | 1.15 |
| 1897 | A503 64p multi (8) | 1.60 | 1.60 |

---

### Water & Coast

| | | | |
|---|---|---|---|
| 1898 | A503 19p multi (9) | .50 | .50 |
| 1899 | A503 26p multi (10) | .60 | .60 |
| 1900 | A503 44p multi (11) | 1.15 | 1.15 |
| 1901 | A503 64p multi (12) | 1.60 | 1.60 |

### Life & Earth

| | | | |
|---|---|---|---|
| 1902 | A503 2nd multi (13) | .85 | .75 |
| 1903 | A503 1st multi (14) | 1.00 | 1.05 |
| 1904 | A503 44p multi (15) | 1.10 | 1.10 |
| 1905 | A503 64p multi (16) | 1.60 | 1.60 |

### Art & Craft

| | | | |
|---|---|---|---|
| 1906 | A503 2nd multi (17) | .85 | .75 |
| 1907 | A503 1st multi (18) | 1.00 | 1.05 |
| 1908 | A503 45p multi (19) | 1.10 | 1.10 |
| 1909 | A503 65p multi (20) | 1.60 | 1.60 |

### People & Place

| | | | |
|---|---|---|---|
| 1910 | A503 2nd multi (21) | .85 | .75 |
| 1911 | A503 1st multi (22) | 1.00 | 1.05 |
| 1912 | A503 45p multi (23) | 1.10 | 1.10 |
| 1913 | A503 65p multi (24) | 1.60 | 1.60 |

### Stone & Soil

| | | | |
|---|---|---|---|
| 1914 | A503 2nd multi (25) | .85 | .75 |
| 1915 | A503 1st multi (26) | 1.00 | 1.05 |
| 1916 | A503 45p multi (27) | 1.10 | 1.10 |
| 1917 | A503 65p multi (28) | 1.60 | 1.60 |
| a. | Booklet pane of 2 (BK169) | 3.25 | |

### Tree & Leaf

| | | | |
|---|---|---|---|
| 1918 | A503 2nd multi (29) | .85 | .75 |
| a. | Bklt. pane of 4 (BK169) | 1.75 | |
| 1919 | A503 1st multi (30) | 1.00 | 1.05 |
| a. | Bklt. pane, #1915, 1919 (BK1202) | 2.00 | |
| 1920 | A503 45p multi (31) | 1.10 | 1.10 |
| a. | Bklt. pane of 4 (BK169) | 4.50 | |
| 1921 | A503 65p multi (32) | 1.60 | 1.60 |
| a. | Bklt. pane of 2 (BK169) | 3.25 | |

### Mind & Matter
#### Litho.

| | | | |
|---|---|---|---|
| 1922 | A503 2nd multi (33) | .85 | .80 |
| 1923 | A503 1st multi (34) | 1.10 | 1.10 |
| 1924 | A503 45p multi (35) | 1.15 | 1.15 |
| 1925 | A503 65p multi (36) | 1.60 | 1.60 |

### Body & Bone

| | | | |
|---|---|---|---|
| 1926 | A503 2nd multi (37) | .80 | .80 |

#### Photo.
#### Perf. 13¾

| | | | |
|---|---|---|---|
| 1927 | A503 1st multi (38) | 1.00 | 1.00 |
| 1928 | A503 45p multi (39) | 1.10 | 1.10 |
| 1929 | A503 65p multi (40) | 1.60 | 1.60 |

#### Perf. 14¼
### Spirit & Faith

| | | | |
|---|---|---|---|
| 1930 | A503 2nd multi (41) | .85 | .80 |
| a. | Bklt. pane of 20 (BK1211) | 16.00 | |
| 1931 | A503 1st multi (42) | 1.00 | 1.00 |
| 1932 | A503 45p multi (43) | 1.10 | 1.10 |
| 1933 | A503 65p multi (44) | 1.60 | 1.60 |

### Sound & Vision

| | | | |
|---|---|---|---|
| 1934 | A503 2nd multi (45) | .85 | .80 |
| 1935 | A503 1st multi (46) | 1.00 | 1.00 |
| 1936 | A503 45p multi (47) | 1.10 | 1.10 |
| 1937 | A503 65p multi (48) | 1.60 | 1.60 |
| | Nos. 1890-1937 (48) | 52.60 | 52.20 |

Nos. 1902, 1906, 1910, 1914, 1918, 1922, 1926, 1930, 1934 sold for 19p; No. 1903, sold for 26p; Nos. 1907, 1911, 1915, 1919, 1923, 1927, 1931, 1935 sold for 27p on day of issue.
Issued: Nos. 1890-1893, 1/18; Nos. 1894-1897, 2/1; Nos. 1898-1901, 3/7; Nos. 1902-1905, 4/4; Nos. 1906-1909, 5/2; Nos. 1910-1913, 6/6; Nos. 1914-1917, 7/4; Nos. 1918-1921, 8/1; Nos. 1917a-1921a, 9/18; Nos. 1922-1925, 9/5; Nos. 1926-1929, 10/3; Nos. 1930-1933, 11/7; Nos. 1934-1937, 12/5.
No. BK1203 contains No. 1931.

**2000-02    Photo.    Perf. 14¼x14½**

| | | | |
|---|---|---|---|
| 1938 | A503 (1st) Like #1891 | 3.50 | 3.50 |
| a. | Booklet pane, #1903, 1938 (BK1201) | 8.75 | |
| b. | Booklet pane of 4 (BK172) | 16.00 | |

Issued: No. 1938, 5/26. No. 1938b, 9/24/02.
Nos. 1938 sold for 27p on day of issue, and was issued only in booklets.

### Souvenir Sheet
### Types of 1953 and 2000

Stamp Show 2000, London — A503a

**2000, May 23    Photo.    Perf. 14¾x14**

| | | | |
|---|---|---|---|
| 1942 | A136 Sheet, #1942a, 4 #MH335 | 10.75 | 10.75 |
| a. | £1 dark green | 10.00 | 10.00 |

---

### Souvenir Sheet

Queen Mother's 100th Birthday
A504

Designs: a, Queen Elizabeth II. b, Prince William. c, Queen Mother. d, Prince Charles.

**2000, Aug. 4    Photo.    Perf. 14½**

| | | | |
|---|---|---|---|
| 1943 | A504 Sheet of 4 | 6.75 | 7.00 |
| a.-d. | 27p single | 1.75 | 1.65 |
| e. | Booklet pane, #1943 with silver border (BK168) | 8.25 | 8.25 |
| f. | Booklet pane, 4 #1943c (BK168) | 7.00 | |

Millennium 2001 — A505

Painted faces of children: 2nd, Flower. 1st, Tiger. 45p, Owl. 65p, Butterfly.

#### Perf. 14¼x14½

**2001, Jan. 16    Photo.**

| | | | |
|---|---|---|---|
| 1944 | A505 2nd multi | .85 | .75 |
| 1945 | A505 1st multi | 1.10 | 1.10 |
| 1946 | A505 45p multi | 1.15 | 1.15 |
| 1947 | A505 65p multi | 1.60 | 1.60 |
| | Nos. 1944-1947 (4) | 4.70 | 4.60 |

Stamps inscribed "2nd" and "1st" sold for 19p and 27p respectively on day of issue.

Greetings A506

**2001, Feb. 6    Photo.    Perf. 14¼**

| | | | |
|---|---|---|---|
| 1948 | A506 1st shown | 1.45 | 1.45 |
| 1949 | A506 1st Cheers | 1.45 | 1.45 |
| 1950 | A506 1st Love | 1.45 | 1.45 |
| 1951 | A506 1st Thanks | 1.45 | 1.45 |
| 1952 | A506 1st Welcome | 1.45 | 1.45 |
| a. | Sheet, 4 vert. strips #1948-1952 + 20 labels, litho. | 200.00 | 25.00 |
| | Nos. 1948-1952 (5) | 7.25 | 7.25 |

Nos. 1948-1952 each sold for 27p on day of issue.
No. 1952a issued 6/5/01. No. 1952a sold for £5.95.
A sheet containing No. 1949 and 3 No. 1951 + 10 labels depicting Spiderman was specially produced for stamp dealers.

Dogs and Cats — A507

Designs: No. 1953, Dog and man on park bench. No. 1954, Dog in bathtub. No. 1955, Dog looking over carrel. No. 1956, Cat in handbag. No. 1957, Cat on fence. No. 1958, Dog in automobile. No. 1959, Cat in curtained window. No. 1960, Dog looking over fence. No. 1961, Cat looking at bird through window. No. 1962, Cat in sink.

**2001, Feb. 13    Die Cut Perf. 14½x14**
**Self- Adhesive**
**Booklet Stamps**

| | | | |
|---|---|---|---|
| 1953 | A507 1st blk & sil | 1.45 | 1.20 |
| 1954 | A507 1st blk & sil | 1.45 | 1.20 |
| 1955 | A507 1st blk & sil | 1.45 | 1.20 |
| 1956 | A507 1st blk & sil | 1.45 | 1.20 |
| 1957 | A507 1st blk & sil | 1.45 | 1.20 |
| 1958 | A507 1st blk & sil | 1.45 | 1.20 |
| 1959 | A507 1st blk & sil | 1.45 | 1.20 |
| 1960 | A507 1st blk & sil | 1.45 | 1.20 |
| 1961 | A507 1st blk & sil | 1.45 | 1.20 |
| 1962 | A507 1st blk & sil | 1.45 | 1.20 |
| a. | Booklet, #1953-1962 | 14.50 | |
| b. | Booklet, #1953-1962, 2 #MH297 | 30.00 | |
| | Nos. 1953-1962 (10) | 14.50 | 12.00 |

Nos. 1953-1962 each sold for 27p on day of issue.

The Weather — A508

Designs: 19p, Rain. 27p, Fair. 45p, Much rain, storms. 65p, Very dry, set fair.

**Perf. 14¼x14½**

| | | | **2001, Mar. 13** | **Photo.** |
|---|---|---|---|---|
| **1963** | A508 | 19p multi | .45 | .45 |
| **1964** | A508 | 27p multi | .60 | .60 |
| **1965** | A508 | 45p multi | 1.25 | 1.25 |
| **1966** | A508 | 65p multi | 2.05 | 2.05 |
| *a.* | Souvenir sheet, #1963-1966 | | 11.50 | 11.50 |
| | *Nos. 1963-1966 (4)* | | 4.35 | 4.35 |

Purple cloud at bottom of No. 1964 is printed with thermochromic ink and changes color to blue when warmed.

Submarines A509

Designs: 2nd, Vanguard Class, 1992. 1st, Swiftsure Class, 1973. 45p, Unity Class, 1939. 65p, Holland Class, 1901.

| **2001** | | **Photo.** | **Perf. 14¾x14** | |
|---|---|---|---|---|
| **1967** | A509 | 2nd multi | 1.15 | .50 |
| *a.* | Perf. 15¼x14¾ | | 3.25 | 3.25 |
| **1968** | A509 | 1st multi | 1.35 | .65 |
| *a.* | Perf. 15¼x14¾ | | 2.25 | 2.25 |
| **1969** | A509 | 45p multi | .95 | 1.40 |
| *a.* | Perf. 15¼x14¾ | | 3.25 | 3.25 |
| *b.* | Booklet pane, 2 each #1967a, 1969a (BK170) | | 13.00 | |
| **1970** | A509 | 65p multi | 1.35 | 2.25 |
| *a.* | Perf. 15¼x14¾ | | 3.25 | 3.25 |
| *b.* | Booklet pane, 2 each #1968a, 1970a (BK170) | | 11.00 | |
| | *Nos. 1967-1970 (4)* | | 4.80 | 4.80 |

**Self-Adhesive**
**Die Cut Perf. 15½x14¼**

| **1971** | A509 | 1st multi | 35.00 | 35.00 |
|---|---|---|---|---|
| *a.* | Booklet, 2 #1971, 4 #MH298 | | 85.00 | |

Issued: Nos. 1967-1970, 4/10; No. 1971, 4/17; Nos. 1967a, 1968a, 1969a, 1970a, 10/22/01.

On day of issue No. 1967 sold for 19p and Nos. 1968 and 1971 sold for 27p.

Buses — A510

Designs: No. 1972, Blue and red Leyland X-type (half), London General (No. 11), yellow green and orange Leyland Titan, dark green and yellow AEC Regent I (half). No. 1973, AEC Regent I (half), Daimler COG5 (No. 8), Guy Arab Mk II (No. 51), green and yellow AEC Regent (half). No. 1974, AEC Regent (half), Bristol KSW 5G (No. 68), AEC Routemaster (No. 21), red and yellow Bristol Lodekka (half). No. 1975, Bristol Lodekka (half), Leyland Titan (No. 12B), Leyland Atlantean (No. 53X), red and yellow Daimler Fleetline (half). No. 1976, Daimler Fleetline (half), MCW Metrobus (No. 770), Leyland Olympian (No. 12), red and blue Dennis Trident (half).

| **2001, May 15** | | **Photo.** | **Perf. 14¼x14** | |
|---|---|---|---|---|
| **1972** | A510 | 1st multi | 1.45 | 1.45 |
| **1973** | A510 | 1st multi | 1.45 | 1.45 |
| **1974** | A510 | 1st multi | 1.45 | 1.45 |
| **1975** | A510 | 1st multi | 1.45 | 1.45 |
| **1976** | A510 | 1st multi | 1.45 | 1.45 |
| *a.* | Horiz. strip, #1972-1976 | | 7.25 | 7.25 |
| *b.* | Souvenir sheet, #1972-1976 | | 8.25 | 8.25 |

Nos. 1972-1976 each sold for 27p on day of issue.

Women's Hats — A511

Hats designed by: 1st, Pip Hackett. E, Dai Rees. 45p, Stephen Jones. 65p, Philip Treacy.

**Perf. 14½x14¼**

| **2001, June 19** | | | | **Litho.** |
|---|---|---|---|---|
| **1977** | A511 | 1st multi | 1.25 | 1.25 |
| **1978** | A511 | E multi | 1.75 | 1.50 |
| **1979** | A511 | 45p multi | 1.15 | 1.25 |
| **1980** | A511 | 65p multi | 1.60 | 1.50 |
| | *Nos. 1977-1980 (4)* | | 5.75 | 5.75 |

Nos. 1977 and 1978 sold for 27p and 36p respectively on day of issue.

Europa — A512

| **2001, July 10** | | **Photo.** | **Perf. 14¾x14** | |
|---|---|---|---|---|
| **1981** | A512 | 1st Frog | 1.10 | 1.10 |
| **1982** | A512 | E Great diving beetle | 1.40 | 1.40 |
| **1983** | A512 | 45p Stickleback | 1.10 | 1.10 |
| **1984** | A512 | 65p Dragonfly | 1.65 | 1.65 |
| | *Nos. 1981-1984 (4)* | | 5.25 | 5.25 |

Nos. 1981 and 1982 sold for 27p and 36p respectively on day of issue.

Puppets — A513

| **2001, Sept. 4** | | **Photo.** | **Perf. 14x15** | |
|---|---|---|---|---|
| **1985** | A513 | 1st Policeman | 1.20 | 1.10 |
| **1986** | A513 | 1st Clown | 1.20 | 1.10 |
| **1987** | A513 | 1st Punch | 1.20 | 1.10 |
| **1988** | A513 | 1st Judy | 1.20 | 1.10 |
| **1989** | A513 | 1st Beadle | 1.20 | 1.10 |
| **1990** | A513 | 1st Crocodile | 1.20 | 1.10 |
| *a.* | Horiz. strip of 6, #1985-1990 | | 7.50 | 6.75 |
| | *Nos. 1985-1990 (6)* | | 7.20 | 6.60 |

**Booklet Stamps**
**Self-Adhesive**
**Die Cut Perf. 14x15½**

| **1991** | A513 | 1st Punch | 9.50 | 9.50 |
|---|---|---|---|---|
| **1992** | A513 | 1st Judy | 9.50 | 9.50 |
| *a.* | Booklet, #1991-1992, 4 #MH298 | | 20.00 | |

Nos. 1985-1992 sold for 27p on day of issue.

Nobel Prizes, Cent. — A514

Items symbolic of prize categories: 2nd, Carbon 60 molecule (Chemistry). 1st, Globe (Economics). E, Dove (Peace). 40p, Crosses (Physiology or Medicine). 45p, The Addressing of Cats, by T.S. Eliot (Literature). 65p, Boron atom (Physics)

| **2001, Oct. 2** | | **Photo.** | **Perf. 14½x14¼** | |
|---|---|---|---|---|
| **1993** | A514 | 2nd multi | 1.25 | 1.25 |

**Photo. & Engr.**

| **1994** | A514 | 1st multi | 1.60 | 1.30 |
|---|---|---|---|---|

**Photo. & Embossed**

| **1995** | A514 | E multi | 2.00 | 1.45 |
|---|---|---|---|---|

**Photo.**

| **1996** | A514 | 40p multi | 1.60 | 1.60 |
|---|---|---|---|---|
| **1997** | A514 | 45p multi | 1.90 | 1.90 |

**Photo. With Hologram Affixed**

| **1998** | A514 | 65p multi | 2.50 | 2.50 |
|---|---|---|---|---|
| | *Nos. 1993-1998 (6)* | | 10.85 | 10.00 |

Nos. 1993-1995 each sold for 19p, 27p and 37p respectively on day of issue. Molecule on No. 1993 is covered with a thermochromic film that changes color when warmed. No. 1996 has a scrach and sniff coating with a eucalyptus odor. Soaking in water may affect holographic images.

Flags A515

Designs: Nos. 1999a, 2001, White ensign. No. 1999b, Union flag. Nos. 1999c, 2000, Jolly Roger. No. 1999d, Flag of the Chief of the Defense Staff.

| **2001, Oct. 22** | **Photo.** | **Perf. 14¾** | |
|---|---|---|---|
| **1999** | A515 Sheet of 4 | 7.25 | 7.25 |
| *a.-d.* | 1st Any single | 1.90 | 1.25 |
| *e.* | Booklet pane, #1999 + selvage at L (BK170) | 8.25 | |
| *f.* | Sheet of 20 #1999b + 20 labels, litho. | 50.00 | — |
| *g.* | Sheet of 20 #1999a + 20 labels, litho. | 27.50 | — |
| *h.* | Booklet pane of 3 #1999a, litho. (BK178) | 5.75 | — |
| *i.* | Booklet pane of 4, 2 each #1999a, 1999b, litho. (BK184) | 7.75 | — |
| *j.* | Booklet pane of 4, 2 each #1999a, 1999b, litho. (BK190) | 12.00 | |

**Booklet Stamps**
**Self-Adhesive**
**Die Cut Perf. 14¾**

| **2000** | A515 | 1st multi | 9.50 | 9.50 |
|---|---|---|---|---|
| **2001** | A515 | 1st multi | 9.50 | 9.50 |
| *a.* | Booklet, #2000-2001, 4 #MH298 | | 20.00 | |

Nos. 1999a-1999d, 2000-2001 each sold for 27p on day of issue. The left edge of No. 1999 is straight while rouletting separates the selvage from the sheet on No. 1999e.

No. 1999f issued 2004. It sold for £14.95 and has labels that can be personalized.

No. 1999h issued 10/18/2005. No. 1999i issued 1/8/2008. No. 1999j issued 9/17/2009.

Christmas — A516

Robins and: 2nd, Snowman. 1st, Birdhouse. E, Birdbath. 45p, Suet ball. 65b, Nest.

**Die Cut Perf. 14¼x14½**

| **2001, Nov. 6** | | | | **Photo.** |
|---|---|---|---|---|
| | | **Self-Adhesive** | | |
| **2002** | A516 | 2nd multi | 1.05 | .90 |
| *a.* | Booklet of 24 | | 26.00 | |
| *b.* | Sheet of 20 + 20 labels, litho. | | 24.00 | — |
| **2003** | A516 | 1st multi | 1.25 | 1.15 |
| *a.* | Booklet of 12 | | 19.00 | |
| *b.* | Sheet of 20 + 20 labels, litho. | | 26.00 | |
| *c.* | Sheet, 10 each #2002-2003 +20 labels, litho. | | 14.00 | — |
| **2004** | A516 | E multi | 2.25 | 1.45 |
| **2005** | A516 | 45p multi | .85 | 1.15 |
| **2006** | A516 | 65p multi | 1.25 | 1.75 |
| | *Nos. 2002-2006 (5)* | | 6.65 | 6.40 |

Nos. 2002-2004 each sold for 19p, 27p, and 37p respectively on day of issue.

Issued: No. 2003b, 9/30/03. No. 2003b sold for £6.15 and had labels that could be personalized.

Issued: No. 2202b, 2203c, 2005. No. 2002b sold for £9.95 and had labels that could be personalized. No. 2003c sold for £5.60.

Just So Stories, by Rudyard Kipling, Cent. — A517

Designs: No. 2007, How the Whale Got His Throat (whale in bed). No. 2008, How the Camel Got His Hump (genie, camel). No. 2009, How the Rhinoceros Got His Skin (man in palm tree, rhinoceros). No. 2010, How the Leopard Got His Spots (man putting spots on leopard). No. 2011, The Elephant's Child (crocodile, elephant, snake). No. 2012, The Sing-song of Old Man Kangaroo (dog chasing kangaroo). No. 2013, The Beginning of the Armadilloes (jaguar, armadillo). No. 2014, The Crab That Played With the Sea (people in boat, giant crab). No. 2015, The Cat That

Walked by Himself (people, dog, cat and shadow in cave). No. 2016, The Butterfly That Stamped (castle, giant butterfly).

**Serpentine Die Cut 14½x14**

| **2002, Jan. 15** | | | | **Photo.** |
|---|---|---|---|---|
| | | **Booklet Stamps** | | |
| | | **Self-Adhesive** | | |
| **2007** | A517 | 1st multi | 1.45 | 1.10 |
| **2008** | A517 | 1st multi | 1.45 | 1.10 |
| **2009** | A517 | 1st multi | 1.45 | 1.10 |
| **2010** | A517 | 1st multi | 1.45 | 1.10 |
| **2011** | A517 | 1st multi | 1.45 | 1.10 |
| **2012** | A517 | 1st multi | 1.45 | 1.10 |
| **2013** | A517 | 1st multi | 1.45 | 1.10 |
| **2014** | A517 | 1st multi | 1.45 | 1.10 |
| **2015** | A517 | 1st multi | 1.45 | 1.10 |
| **2016** | A517 | 1st multi | 1.45 | 1.10 |
| *a.* | Booklet, #2007-2016 | | 14.50 | |

Nos. 2007-2016 each sold for 27p on day of issue. Titles of stories are not on stamps, but in margin.

Reign of Queen Elizabeth II, 50th Anniv. — A518

Photographs of Queen by: 2nd, Dorothy Wilding, 1952. 1st, Cecil Beaton, 1968. E, Lord Snowdon, 1978. 45p, Yousuf Karsh, 1984. 65p, Tim Graham, 1996.

**Perf. 14½x14¼**

| **2002, Feb. 6** | | **Photo.** | **Wmk. 401** | |
|---|---|---|---|---|
| **2017** | A518 | 2nd blk & sil | 1.20 | .90 |
| **2018** | A518 | 1st blk & sil | 1.35 | 1.10 |
| **2019** | A518 | E blk & sil | 2.50 | 1.35 |
| **2020** | A518 | 45p blk & sil | 1.00 | 1.70 |
| *a.* | Booklet pane, #2017-2020 (BK171) | | 13.50 | 13.50 |
| **2021** | A518 | 65p blk & sil | 1.35 | 2.25 |
| *a.* | Booklet pane, #2018-2021 (BK171) | | 14.00 | 14.00 |
| | *Nos. 2017-2021 (5)* | | 7.40 | 6.80 |

Nos. 2017-2019 each sold for 19p, 27p, and 37p respectively on day of issue.

Stamps in Nos. 2020a and 2021a have an upright watermark. Compare Nos. 2017-2018 with Nos. 4299-4300.

**Queen Types of 1952**
**Tan Surface-colored Paper**
**Perf. 14¾x14 Syncopated**

| **2002, Feb. 6** | | **Photo.** | **Wmk. 401** | |
|---|---|---|---|---|
| **2022** | A127 | 2nd red | 2.00 | 1.00 |
| **2023** | A126 | 1st green | 2.50 | 1.50 |
| *a.* | Booklet pane, 5 #2022, 4 #2023, + label (BK171) | | 25.00 | |

Nos. 2022 and 2023 sold for 19p and 27p respectively on day of issue.

A New Baby — A519

Hello — A520

Moving — A521

Best Wishes — A522

Love — A523

## Perf. 14¾x14

| 2002-3 | Litho. | Unwmk. | | |
|---|---|---|---|---|
| **2024** | A519 | 1st multi | 1.30 | 1.20 |
| *a.* | | Perf. 14¼ + label | 2.50 | 2.50 |
| **2025** | A520 | 1st multi | 1.30 | 1.20 |
| *a.* | | Perf. 14¼ + label | 2.50 | 2.50 |
| **2026** | A521 | 1st multi | 1.30 | 1.20 |
| *a.* | | Perf. 14¼ + label | 2.50 | 2.50 |
| **2027** | A522 | 1st multi | 1.30 | 1.20 |
| *a.* | | Perf. 14¼ + label | 2.50 | 2.50 |
| **2028** | A523 | 1st multi | 1.30 | 1.20 |
| *a.* | | Perf. 14¼ + label | 2.50 | 2.50 |
| *c.* | | Sheet of 20, 4 each #2024-2028, + 20 labels, perf. 14¼ | 50.00 | — |
| | *Nos. 2024-2028 (5)* | | 6.50 | 6.00 |

### Self-Adhesive
### Booklet Stamp
*Die Cut Perf. 14¾x14*

| **2028A** | A520 | 1st multi | 5.75 | 5.00 |
|---|---|---|---|---|
| *b.* | | Booklet pane, 2 #2028A, 4 #MH300 | 10.00 | |

Nos. 2024-2028A each sold for 27p on day of issue.

Nos. 2024a-2028a each sold for £14.95 and have labels that can be personalized. No. 2028c sold for £5.95.

Sheets of No. 2025a with a Washington 2006 World Philatelic Exhibition margin and labels sold for £6.95. Value $27.50. Sheets with other margins exist.

Issued, Nos. 2024-2028, 3/5/02; No. 2028c, 4/23/02; Nos. 2024a-2028a, 2002; No. 2028A, 3/4/03.

Aerial Photographs of Coastline — A524

| 2002, Mar. 19 | | | Perf. 14¼x14½ | |
|---|---|---|---|---|
| **2029** | A524 | 27p Studland Bay | .70 | .70 |
| **2030** | A524 | 27p Luskentyre | .70 | .70 |
| **2031** | A524 | 27p Dover | .70 | .70 |
| **2032** | A524 | 27p Padstow | .70 | .70 |
| **2033** | A524 | 27p Broadstairs | .70 | .70 |
| **2034** | A524 | 27p St. Abb's Head | .70 | .70 |
| **2035** | A524 | 27p Dunster Beach | .70 | .70 |
| **2036** | A524 | 27p Newquay | .70 | .70 |
| **2037** | A524 | 27p Portrush | .70 | .70 |
| **2038** | A524 | 27p Conwy | .70 | .70 |
| *a.* | | Block of 10, #2029-2038 | 7.00 | 7.00 |

Circus — A525

Designs: 2nd, High wire performer. 1st, Lion tamer. E, Trick tricyclists. 45p, Krazy kar. 65p, Equestrienne.

| 2002, Apr. 9 | Photo. | Perf. 14¼x14½ | | |
|---|---|---|---|---|
| **2039** | A525 | 2nd multi | 1.00 | 1.00 |
| **2040** | A525 | 1st multi | 1.20 | 1.20 |
| **2041** | A525 | E multi | 1.50 | 1.50 |
| **2042** | A525 | 45p multi | 1.30 | 1.30 |
| **2043** | A525 | 65p multi | 1.75 | 1.75 |
| | *Nos. 2039-2043 (5)* | | 6.75 | 6.75 |

Europa (Nos. 2040-2041). Nos. 2039-2041 sold for 19p, 27p and 37p respectively on day of issue.

First day covers of Nos. 2039-2043 bear an April 9, 2001, date, but the issue of the stamps was delayed until April 10 due to the funeral of the Queen Mother.

Queen Mother (1900-2002) — A526

| 2002, Apr. 25 | | | Perf. 14x14¾ | |
|---|---|---|---|---|
| **2044** | A526 | 1st 1990 photo | 1.25 | .90 |
| **2045** | A526 | E 1948 photo | 2.25 | 1.40 |
| **2046** | A526 | 45p 1930 photo | .90 | 1.40 |
| **2047** | A526 | 65p 1907 photo | 1.30 | 1.40 |
| | *Nos. 2044-2047 (4)* | | 5.70 | 5.10 |

Nos. 2044-2045 sold for 27p and 37p respectively on day of issue. Compare with Type A387.

Jet Aircraft — A527

Designs: 2nd, Airbus A340-600, 2002. 1st, Concorde, 1976. E, Trident, 1964. 45p, VC10, 1964. 65p, Comet, 1952.

| 2002, May 2 | | | Perf. 14½ | |
|---|---|---|---|---|
| **2048** | A527 | 2nd multi | 1.10 | 1.10 |
| **2049** | A527 | 1st multi | 1.35 | 1.35 |
| *a.* | | Litho. (#2619a) ('09) | 9.50 | 9.50 |
| **2050** | A527 | E multi | 1.60 | 1.60 |
| **2051** | A527 | 45p multi | 1.50 | 1.50 |
| **2052** | A527 | 65p multi | 2.50 | 2.50 |
| *a.* | | Souvenir sheet, #2048-2052 | 10.00 | 9.50 |
| | *Nos. 2048-2052 (5)* | | 8.05 | 8.05 |

### Booklet Stamp
### Self-Adhesive
*Die Cut Perf. 14½*

| **2053** | A527 | 1st multi | 4.75 | 4.75 |
|---|---|---|---|---|
| *a.* | | Booklet, 2 #2053, 4 #MH297 | 10.00 | |

Nos. 2048-2052 sold for 19p, 27p and 37p respectively on day of issue.

No. 2049a issued 1/13/09. No. 2049a sold for 36p on day of issue.

A528　　　2002 World Cup Soccer Championships, Japan and Korea — A529

Soccer ball and: Nos. 2056a, 2057, Upper left portion of English flag. Nos. 2056b, 2058, Upper right portion of English flag. No. 2056c, Lower left portion of English flag. Nos. 2055, 2056d, Lower right portion of English flag.

### Photo., Litho. (#2055)

| 2002, May 21 | | | Perf. 14¼ | |
|---|---|---|---|---|
| **2054** | A528 | 1st multi | 2.00 | 2.00 |
| **2055** | A529 | 1st dull blue & multi | 2.00 | 2.00 |

### Souvenir Sheet

| **2056** | | Sheet, #2054, #2056a-2056d | 6.50 | 6.50 |
|---|---|---|---|---|
| *a.-d.* | | A529 1st deep blue & multi, perf. 14¾x14, any single | 1.50 | 1.50 |

### Booklet Stamps
*Die Cut Perf. 14¾x14*
### Self-Adhesive

| **2057** | A529 | 1st dp blue & multi | 4.25 | 4.25 |
|---|---|---|---|---|
| **2058** | A529 | 1st dp blue & multi | 4.25 | .425 |
| *a.* | | Booklet, #2057, 2058, 4 #MH298 | 10.00 | |

Nos. 2054, 2056a-2056d, 2057-2058 sold for 27p on day of sale. No. 2055 was issued only in sheets of 20 stamps + 16 labels that sold for £5.95, and which could have the labels personalized for an additional fee.

17th Commonwealth Games, Manchester — A530

Designs: 2nd, Swimming. 1st, Running. E, Cycling. 47p, Long jump. 68p, Wheelchair racing.

| 2002, July 16 | | | Perf. 14¾x14¼ | Photo. |
|---|---|---|---|---|
| **2059** | A530 | 2nd multi | 1.10 | .80 |
| **2060** | A530 | 1st multi | 1.25 | 1.00 |
| **2061** | A530 | E multi | 2.25 | 1.20 |
| **2062** | A530 | 47p multi | 1.00 | 1.35 |
| **2063** | A530 | 68p multi | 1.40 | 2.10 |
| | *Nos. 2059-2063 (5)* | | 7.00 | 6.45 |

Nos. 2059-2061 each sold for 19p, 27p and 37p respectively on day of issue.

Peter Pan, by J. M. Barrie, 150th Anniv. — A531

Designs: 2nd, Tinkerbell. 1st, Darling children. E, Crocodile and clock. 47p, Captain Hook. 68p, Peter Pan.

| | Perf. 14¾x14¼ | | | Photo. |
|---|---|---|---|---|
| 2002, Aug. 20 | | | | |
| **2064** | A531 | 2nd multi | 1.05 | 1.05 |
| **2065** | A531 | 1st multi | 1.35 | 1.05 |
| **2066** | A531 | E multi | 1.60 | 1.25 |
| **2067** | A531 | 47p multi | 1.35 | 1.45 |
| **2068** | A531 | 68p multi | 1.95 | 2.45 |
| | *Nos. 2064-2068 (5)* | | 7.30 | 7.25 |

Nos. 2064-2066 each sold for 19p, 27p and 37p respectively on day of issue.

 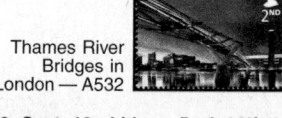

Thames River Bridges in London — A532

| 2002, Sept. 10 | Litho. | | Perf. 14¾x14 | |
|---|---|---|---|---|
| **2069** | A532 | 2nd Millennium | 1.00 | .75 |
| **2070** | A532 | 1st Tower | 1.25 | 1.25 |
| **2071** | A532 | E Westminster | 2.00 | 2.00 |
| **2072** | A532 | 47p Blackfriars | 2.25 | 2.25 |
| **2073** | A532 | 68p London | 2.75 | 2.75 |
| | *Nos. 2069-2073 (5)* | | 9.25 | 9.00 |

### Booklet Stamp
*Serpentine Die Cut 14¾x14*

| **2074** | A532 | 1st Tower | 4.75 | 4.75 |
|---|---|---|---|---|
| *a.* | | Booklet, 2 #2074, 4 #MH300 | 10.00 | |

Nos. 2070 and 2074 sold for 27p; Nos. 2069, 2071 sold for 19p and 37p respectively on day of sale.

### Souvenir Sheet

Astronomy — A533

No. 2075: a, Planetary nebula in Aquila. b, Seyfert 2 galaxy in Pegasus. c, Planetary nebula in Norma. d, Seyfert 2 galaxy in Circinus.

| | Perf. 14¾x14¼ | | | Photo. |
|---|---|---|---|---|
| 2002, Sept. 24 | | | | |
| **2075** | A533 | Sheet of 4 | 5.00 | 6.00 |
| *a.-d.* | | (1st) Any single | 1.20 | 1.20 |
| *e.* | | Booklet pane, #2075, rouletted at left (BK172) | 5.25 | |

Nos. 2075a-2075d each sold for 27p on day of issue.

Pillar Boxes, 150th Anniv. — A534

Designs: 2nd, Decorative box, 1857. 1st, Mainland box, 1874. E, Airmail box, 1934. 47p, Oval dual-aperture box, 1939. 68p, Modern box, 1980.

### Litho. & Engr.

| 2002, Oct. 8 | | | Perf. 14x14¼ | |
|---|---|---|---|---|
| **2076** | A534 | 2nd multi | 1.10 | .90 |
| **2077** | A534 | 1st multi | 1.25 | 1.15 |
| **2078** | A534 | E multi | 2.40 | 1.40 |
| **2079** | A534 | 47p multi | 1.00 | 1.40 |
| **2080** | A534 | 68p multi | 1.40 | 1.75 |
| | *Nos. 2076-2080 (5)* | | 7.15 | 6.60 |

Nos. 2076-2078 each sold for 19p, 27p and 37p on day of issue.

Christmas — A535

*Die Cut Perf. 14½x14*

| 2002, Nov. 5 | | | | Photo. |
|---|---|---|---|---|
| | | **Self-Adhesive** | | |
| **2081** | A535 | 2nd Spruce branches | 1.25 | 1.00 |
| *a.* | | Booklet pane of 24 | 26.50 | |
| **2082** | A535 | 1st Holly | 1.45 | 1.20 |
| *a.* | | Booklet pane of 12 | 19.00 | |
| **2083** | A535 | E Ivy | 2.60 | 1.45 |
| **2084** | A535 | 47p Mistletoe | 1.05 | 1.45 |
| **2085** | A535 | 68p Pine cone | 1.50 | 1.75 |
| | *Nos. 2081-2085 (5)* | | 7.85 | 6.85 |

Nos. 2081-2085 each sold for 19p, 27p and 37p on day of issue.

### Types of 1952-54
### Souvenir Sheet
**Tan Surface-colored Paper**

*Perf. 14¾x14 Syncopated*

| 2002, Dec. 5 | Photo. | | Wmk. 401 | |
|---|---|---|---|---|
| **2086** | | Sheet of 9, #2022-2023, 2086a-2086g + label | 7.50 | 6.50 |
| *a.* | | A126 1p red orange | .25 | .25 |
| *b.* | | A126 2p ultramarine | .25 | .25 |
| *c.* | | A126 5p brown | .25 | .25 |
| *d.* | | A129 33p light brown | 1.20 | .90 |
| *e.* | | A130 37p bright rose | 1.50 | 1.00 |
| *f.* | | A131 47p brown | 1.80 | 1.10 |
| *g.* | | A132 50p dark green | 2.05 | 1.25 |

Barn Owl in Flight — A536

Barn Owl in Flight — A537

Barn Owl in Flight — A538

Barn Owl in Flight — A539

Barn Owl in Flight — A540

Kestrel in Flight — A541

Kestrel in Flight — A542

Kestrel in
Flight — A543

Kestrel in
Flight — A544

Kestrel in
Flight — A545

**2003, Jan. 14   Litho.   Perf. 14¼x14½**

| | | | | |
|---|---|---|---|---|
| 2087 | A536 | 1st multi | 1.40 | 1.10 |
| 2088 | A537 | 1st multi | 1.40 | 1.10 |
| 2089 | A538 | 1st multi | 1.40 | 1.10 |
| 2090 | A539 | 1st multi | 1.40 | 1.10 |
| 2091 | A540 | 1st multi | 1.40 | 1.10 |
| 2092 | A541 | 1st multi | 1.40 | 1.10 |
| 2093 | A542 | 1st multi | 1.40 | 1.10 |
| 2094 | A543 | 1st multi | 1.40 | 1.10 |
| 2095 | A544 | 1st multi | 1.40 | 1.10 |
| 2096 | A545 | 1st multi | 1.40 | 1.10 |
| a. | | Block of 10, #2087-2096 | 14.25 | 12.00 |

Nos. 2087-2096 each sold for 27p on day of issue.

Check-off
Slogans — A546

Designs: No. 2097, Gold star, See me, Playtime. No. 2098, I love you, XXXX, S.W.A.L.K. No. 2099, Angel, Poppet, Little terror. No. 2100, Yes, No, Maybe. No. 2101, Oops!, Sorry, Will try harder. No. 2102, I did it!, You did it, We did it!

**2003, Feb. 4   Litho.   Perf. 14¼x14**

| | | | | |
|---|---|---|---|---|
| 2097 | A546 | 1st multi | 1.35 | 1.15 |
| 2098 | A546 | 1st multi | 1.35 | 1.15 |
| 2099 | A546 | 1st multi | 1.35 | 1.15 |
| 2100 | A546 | 1st multi | 1.35 | 1.15 |
| 2101 | A546 | 1st multi | 1.35 | 1.15 |
| 2102 | A546 | 1st multi | 1.35 | 1.15 |
| a. | | Block of 6, #2097-2102 | 8.00 | 7.00 |
| b. | | Sheet, 3 each #2097, 2099, 2101-2102, 4 each #2098, 2100 + 20 labels | 30.00 | |

No. 2102b sold for £5.95 and had labels that could be personalized.

Genetics — A548

Designs: 2nd, Scientists with jigsaw puzzle. 1st, Chimpanzee and scientist. E, Scientist, DNA double helix, snake. 47p, Scientists with animals. 68p, Scientist with doctor's satchel, crystal ball.

**Perf. 14¼x14½**

| | | | | Litho. |
|---|---|---|---|---|
| 2103 | A548 | 2nd multi | 1.10 | .90 |
| 2104 | A548 | 1st multi | 1.25 | 1.15 |
| a. | | Booklet pane, 2 each #2103-2104 (BK173) | 4.75 | |
| 2105 | A548 | E multi | 2.25 | 1.40 |
| a. | | Booklet pane of 4 (BK173) | 9.00 | |
| 2106 | A548 | 47p multi | 1.00 | 1.40 |
| 2107 | A548 | 68p multi | 1.35 | 1.75 |
| | | Nos. 2103-2107 (5) | 6.95 | 6.60 |

Nos. 2103-2105 sold for 19p, 27p and 37p respectively on day of issue.

Fruit and
Vegetables
A549

**Die Cut Perf. 14¼x14**

**2003, Mar. 25                     Photo.**

**Self-Adhesive**
**Booklet Stamps**

| | | | | |
|---|---|---|---|---|
| 2108 | A549 | 1st Strawberry | 1.40 | 1.00 |
| 2109 | A549 | 1st Potato | 1.40 | 1.00 |
| 2110 | A549 | 1st Apple | 1.40 | 1.00 |
| 2111 | A549 | 1st Pepper | 1.40 | 1.00 |
| 2112 | A549 | 1st Pear | 1.40 | 1.00 |
| 2113 | A549 | 1st Orange | 1.40 | 1.00 |
| 2114 | A549 | 1st Tomato | 1.40 | 1.00 |
| 2115 | A549 | 1st Lemon | 1.40 | 1.00 |
| 2116 | A549 | 1st Brussels sprout | 1.40 | 1.00 |
| 2117 | A549 | 1st Eggplant | 1.40 | 1.00 |
| a. | | Pane, #2108-2117 + 76 stickers | 14.25 | |
| b. | | Sheet, 2 each #2108-2117, litho., + 20 labels +93 stickers ('06) | 26.00 | |

Nos. 2108-2117 each sold for 27p on day of issue.

No. 2117b issued 3/7/06. No. 2117b sold for £6.55.

Adventurers — A550

Designs: 2nd, Amy Johnson (1903-41), first woman to fly to Australia. 1st, British Mount Everest expedition of 1953. E, Freya Stark (1893-1993), Middle East traveler and writer. 42p, Ernest Shackleton (1874-1922), Antarctic explorer. 47p, Francis Chichester (1901-72), sailor. 68p, Robert Falcon Scott (1868-1912), Antarctic explorer.

**Perf. 14¾x14¼**

**2003, Apr. 29     Photo.     Unwmk.**

| | | | | |
|---|---|---|---|---|
| 2118 | A550 | 2nd multi | 1.30 | 1.10 |
| 2119 | A550 | 1st multi | 1.50 | 1.35 |
| 2120 | A550 | E multi | 2.75 | 1.60 |
| 2121 | A550 | 42p multi | 1.00 | 1.50 |
| 2122 | A550 | 47p multi | 1.10 | 1.60 |
| 2123 | A550 | 68p multi | 1.60 | 2.00 |
| | | Nos. 2118-2123 (6) | 9.25 | 9.15 |

**Booklet Stamp**
**Self-Adhesive**
**Die Cut Perf. 14¾x14¼**

| | | | | |
|---|---|---|---|---|
| 2124 | A550 | 1st multi | 4.50 | 4.50 |
| a. | | Booklet pane, 2 #2124, 4 #MH300 | 10.00 | |

Nos. 2118-2120 sold for 19p, 27p and 38p respectively on day of issue.

**Types of 1952-54**

A550a

**Perf. 14¾x14 Syncopated**
**2003, May 20    Photo.    Wmk. 401**
**Tan Surface-colored Paper**
**Souvenir Sheet**

| | | | | |
|---|---|---|---|---|
| 2125 | A550a | Sheet of 9 + label | 7.00 | 7.50 |
| a. | A127 | 4p purple | .25 | .25 |
| b. | A128 | 8p ultramarine | .25 | .25 |
| c. | A129 | 10p lilac rose | .25 | .25 |
| d. | A129 | 20p emerald | .50 | .25 |
| e. | A130 | 28p deep olive green | .65 | .35 |
| f. | A130 | 34p violet brown | .80 | .45 |
| g. | A128 | E henna brown | 1.10 | .55 |
| h. | A130 | 42p royal blue | 1.05 | .50 |
| i. | A131 | 68p dark blue | 1.85 | .85 |

**Booklet Stamp**
**Perf. 14¾x14**

| | | | | |
|---|---|---|---|---|
| 2126 | A136 | £1 dark green | 42.50 | 42.50 |
| a. | | Booklet pane, #2126, 2 each #2086f, 2125i (BK174) | 52.50 | 52.50 |

No. 2125g sold for 38p on day of issue.

Coronation of
Queen Elizabeth II,
50th Anniv. — A551

Designs: No. 2127, Aerial view of parade entering circle. No. 2128, Children reading coronation party sign. No. 2129, Queen at coronation. No. 2130, Children at wall of pictures. No. 2131, Queen holding orb and scepter. No. 2132, Children running in street. No. 2133,

Royal carriage under arch. No. 2134, Children standing in front of house. No. 2135, Royal carriage. No. 2136, Children at party.

**Perf. 14½x14¼**

**2003, June 2    Photo.    Wmk. 401**

| | | | | |
|---|---|---|---|---|
| 2127 | A551 | 1st multi | 1.45 | 1.20 |
| 2128 | A551 | 1st multi | 1.45 | 1.20 |
| 2129 | A551 | 1st multi | 1.45 | 1.20 |
| 2130 | A551 | 1st multi | 1.45 | 1.20 |
| 2131 | A551 | 1st multi | 1.45 | 1.20 |
| 2132 | A551 | 1st multi | 1.45 | 1.20 |
| 2133 | A551 | 1st multi | 1.45 | 1.20 |
| 2134 | A551 | 1st multi | 1.45 | 1.20 |
| a. | | Booklet pane, #2127, 2129, 2132, 2134 (BK174) | 8.00 | |
| 2135 | A551 | 1st multi | 1.45 | 1.20 |
| 2136 | A551 | 1st multi | 1.45 | 1.20 |
| a. | | Block of 10, #2127-2136 | 14.50 | 12.00 |
| b. | | Booklet pane, #2128, 2131, 2133, 2136 (BK174) | 8.00 | |

Nos. 2127-2136 each sold for 28p on day of issue.

Prince William, 21st
Birthday — A552

Various portraits.

**2003, June 17    Photo.    Perf. 14¼**
**Background Color**

| | | | | |
|---|---|---|---|---|
| 2137 | A552 | 28p silver | 1.30 | 1.30 |
| 2138 | A552 | E brown | 2.50 | 1.65 |
| 2139 | A552 | 47p green | 2.35 | 2.65 |
| 2140 | A552 | 68p olive green | 2.95 | 3.15 |
| | | Nos. 2137-2140 (4) | 9.10 | 8.75 |

No. 2138 sold for 38p on day of issue. Background colors are printed with Iriodin ink, giving the stamp a three dimensional appearance.

Scottish
Scenery — A553

Designs: 2nd: Loch Assynt, Sutherland. 1st, Ben More, Isle of Mull. E, Rothiemurchus, Cairngorms. 42p, Dalveen Pass, Lowther Hills. 47p, Glenfinnan Viaduct, Lochaber. 68p, Papa Little, Shetland Islands.

**2003, July 15    Photo.    Perf. 14½**

| | | | | |
|---|---|---|---|---|
| 2141 | A553 | 2nd multi | 1.10 | .90 |
| 2142 | A553 | 1st multi | 1.30 | 1.15 |
| 2143 | A553 | E multi | 2.25 | 1.40 |
| 2144 | A553 | 42p multi | .85 | 1.25 |
| 2145 | A553 | 47p multi | .95 | 1.40 |
| 2146 | A553 | 68p multi | 1.40 | 1.75 |
| | | Nos. 2141-2146 (6) | 7.85 | 7.85 |

**Booklet Stamp**
**Self-Adhesive**
**Die Cut Perf. 14½**

| | | | | |
|---|---|---|---|---|
| 2147 | A553 | 1st multi | 5.00 | 5.25 |
| a. | | Booklet pane, 2 #2147, 4 #MH300 | 10.00 | |

Nos. 2141 and 2143 each sold for 20p and 38p respectively on day of issue, while Nos. 2142 and 2147 sold for 28p on day of issue.

Pub Signs — A554

Designs: 1st, The Station, Thurnscoe. E, Black Swan, Lincoln. 42p, The Cross Keys, London. 47p, The Mayflower, Southsea. 68p, The Barley Sheaf, Bodmin.

**2003, Aug. 12    Photo.    Perf. 14x14¼**

| | | | | |
|---|---|---|---|---|
| 2148 | A554 | 1st multi | 1.30 | 1.15 |
| a. | | Booklet pane of 4 (BK175) | 6.00 | — |
| 2149 | A554 | E multi | 2.75 | 1.45 |
| 2150 | A554 | 42p multi | 1.00 | 1.60 |
| 2151 | A554 | 47p multi | 1.10 | 1.70 |
| 2152 | A554 | 68p multi | 1.60 | 2.10 |
| | | Nos. 2148-2152 (5) | 7.95 | 8.00 |

Europa (Nos. 2148-2149).

Nos. 2148 and 2149 each sold for 28p and 38p, respectively, on day of issue.

Toys — A555

Designs: 1st, Meccano Constructor Biplane, c. 1931. E, Wells-Brimtoy Clockwork Double-decker Omnibus, c. 1938. 42p, Hornby M1 Clockwork Locomotive and Tender, c. 1948. 47p, Dinky Toys Ford Zephyr, c. 1956. 68p, Mettoy Friction drive Space Ship Eagle c. 1960.

**2003, Sept. 18   Photo.   Perf. 14¼x14**

| | | | | |
|---|---|---|---|---|
| 2153 | A555 | 1st multi | 1.50 | 1.25 |
| 2154 | A555 | E multi | 2.75 | 1.85 |
| 2155 | A555 | 42p multi | 1.05 | 1.10 |
| 2156 | A555 | 47p multi | 1.40 | 1.40 |
| 2157 | A555 | 68p multi | 1.70 | 1.60 |
| a. | | Souvenir sheet, #2153-2157 | 8.50 | 8.50 |
| | | Nos. 2153-2157 (5) | 8.40 | 7.40 |

**Booklet Stamp**
**Self-Adhesive**
**Die Cut Perf. 14¼x14**

| | | | | |
|---|---|---|---|---|
| 2158 | A555 | 1st multi | 4.50 | 4.50 |
| a. | | Booklet, 2 #2158, 4 #MH300 | 10.00 | |

Nos. 2153 and 2158 each sold for 28p on day of issue. No. 2154 sold for 38p on day of issue.

British Museum, 250th
Anniv. — A556

Museum Exhibits: 2nd, Coffin of Denytenamun, c. 900 B.C. 1st, Bust of Alexander the Great, c. 200 B.C. E, Sutton Hoo Helmet, c. 600. 42p, Sculpture of Indian Goddess Parvati, c. 1500. 47p, Mask of Xiuhtecuhtli, c. 1500. 68p, Hoa Hakananai'a Easter Island moai, c. 1000.

**2003, Oct. 7                 Perf. 14x14¼**

| | | | | |
|---|---|---|---|---|
| 2159 | A556 | 2nd multi | .85 | .85 |
| 2160 | A556 | 1st multi | 1.30 | 1.30 |
| 2161 | A556 | E multi | 1.75 | 1.50 |
| 2162 | A556 | 42p multi | 1.40 | 1.40 |
| 2163 | A556 | 47p multi | 1.50 | 1.50 |
| 2164 | A556 | 68p multi | 2.00 | 2.00 |
| | | Nos. 2159-2164 (6) | 8.80 | 8.55 |

Nos. 2159-2161 each sold for 20p, 28p and 38p respectively on day of issue.

Christmas — A557

Ice and snow sculptures by Andy Goldsworthy: 2nd, Ice Spiral. 1st, Icicle Star. E, Wall of Frozen Snow. 53p, Ice Ball. 68p, Ice Hole. £1.12, Snow Pyramids.

**Die Cut Perf. 14¼x14**

**2003, Nov. 4                     Photo.**
**Self-Adhesive**

| | | | | |
|---|---|---|---|---|
| 2165 | A557 | 2nd multi | .85 | .85 |
| a. | | Booklet pane of 24 | 26.00 | |
| b. | | Sheet of 20 + 20 labels, litho. | 17.50 | |
| 2166 | A557 | 1st multi | 1.30 | 1.30 |
| a. | | Booklet pane of 12 | 19.00 | |
| b. | | Sheet of 20 + 20 labels, litho. | 26.00 | |
| 2167 | A557 | E multi | 1.75 | 1.50 |
| 2168 | A557 | 53p multi | 1.50 | 1.50 |
| 2169 | A557 | 68p multi | 1.90 | 1.60 |
| 2170 | A557 | £1.12 multi | 3.00 | 2.75 |
| | | Nos. 2165-2170 (6) | 10.30 | 9.50 |

Nos. 2165-2167 sold for 20p, 28p and 38p respectively on day of issue.

Nos. 2165b and 2166b sold for £4.20 and £6.15 respectively and had labels that could be personalized.

## Souvenir Sheet

England, Winners of 2003 Rugby
World Cup Championships — A558

No. 2171: a, English flags. b, Players with
red shirts in huddle. c, World Cup. d, Players
in white jerseys, celebrating.

**2003, Dec. 19 Litho. Perf. 13¾x14**
| | | | | | |
|---|---|---|---|---|---|
| 2171 | A558 | Sheet of 4 | | 10.50 | 10.50 |
| a.-b. | | 1st Either single | | 1.75 | 1.75 |
| c.-d. | | 68p Either single | | 3.50 | 3.50 |

Nos. 2171a-2171b sold for 28p on day of
issue.

Locomotives — A559

Designs: 20p, Dolgoch 0-4-0T. 28p, CR 439
0-4-4T. E, GCR 8K 2-8-0. 42p, GWR Manor 4-
6-0. 47p, SR West Country 4-6-2. 68p, BR
Standard 4 2-6-4T.

**2004, Jan. 13 Litho. Perf. 14¾x14¼**
| | | | | | |
|---|---|---|---|---|---|
| 2172 | A559 | 20p | multi | .65 | .65 |
| 2173 | A559 | 28p | multi | .85 | .85 |
| 2174 | A559 | E | multi | 1.65 | 1.10 |
| 2175 | A559 | 42p | multi | 1.40 | 1.55 |
| a. | | Booklet pane, #2173-2175 | | | |
| | | (BK175) | | 3.75 | — |
| 2176 | A559 | 47p | multi | 1.65 | 1.85 |
| 2177 | A559 | 68p | multi | 2.10 | 2.10 |
| a. | | Souvenir sheet, #2172-2177 | | 14.50 | 14.50 |
| | | Nos. 2172-2177 (6) | | 8.30 | 8.10 |

First steam locomotive, bicent. No. 2174
sold for 38p on day of issue.

Special
Occasions — A560

**2004, Feb. 3 Litho. Perf. 14¼x14**
| | | | | | |
|---|---|---|---|---|---|
| 2178 | A560 | 1st Postman | | 1.40 | 1.15 |
| 2179 | A560 | 1st Face | | 1.40 | 1.15 |
| 2180 | A560 | 1st Duck | | 1.40 | 1.15 |
| 2181 | A560 | 1st Baby | | 1.40 | 1.15 |
| 2182 | A560 | 1st Airplane | | 1.40 | 1.15 |
| a. | | Horiz. strip of 5, #2178-2182 | | 7.00 | 5.75 |
| c. | | Sheet, 4 each #2178-2182, + | | | |
| | | 20 labels | | 24.00 | — |

Nos. 2178-2182 each sold for 28p on day of
issue. No. 2182c sold for £6.15 and had labels
that could not be personalized.

| Map | Forest of |
|---|---|
| A561 | Lothlórien |
| | A562 |

| The Fellowship of | Rivendell — A564 |
|---|---|
| the Ring — A563 | |

| Hall at Bag- | Orthanc — A566 |
|---|---|
| End — A565 | |

| Doors of Durin | Barad-Dur |
|---|---|
| A567 | A568 |

| Minas | Fangorn |
|---|---|
| Tirith — A569 | Forest — A570 |

**2004, Feb. 26 Perf. 14½x14¼**
| | | | | | |
|---|---|---|---|---|---|
| 2183 | A561 | 1st | multi | 1.45 | 1.20 |
| 2184 | A562 | 1st | multi | 1.45 | 1.20 |
| 2185 | A563 | 1st | multi | 1.45 | 1.20 |
| 2186 | A564 | 1st | multi | 1.45 | 1.20 |
| 2187 | A565 | 1st | multi | 1.45 | 1.20 |
| 2188 | A566 | 1st | multi | 1.45 | 1.20 |
| 2189 | A567 | 1st | multi | 1.45 | 1.20 |
| 2190 | A568 | 1st | multi | 1.45 | 1.20 |
| 2191 | A569 | 1st | multi | 1.45 | 1.20 |
| 2192 | A570 | 1st | multi | 1.45 | 1.20 |
| a. | | Block of 10, #2183-2192 | | 14.50 | 12.00 |

Publication of *The Lord of the Rings*, by
J.R.R. Tolkien, 50th anniv. Nos. 2183-2192
each sold for 28p on day of issue.

Northern Ireland
Scenery — A571

Designs: 2nd, Ely, Island, Lower Lough
Erne. 1st, Giant's Causeway, Antrim Coast. E,
Slemish, Antrim Mountains. 42p, Banns Road,
Mourne Mountain. 47p, Glenelly Valley, Sper-
rins. 68p, Islandmore, Strangford Lough.

**2004, Mar. 16 Photo. Perf. 14½**
| | | | | | |
|---|---|---|---|---|---|
| 2193 | A571 | 2nd | multi | 1.10 | 1.10 |
| 2194 | A571 | 1st | multi | 1.35 | 1.10 |
| 2195 | A571 | E | multi | 2.35 | 1.55 |
| 2196 | A571 | 42p | multi | .90 | .90 |
| 2197 | A571 | 47p | multi | 1.00 | 1.10 |
| 2198 | A571 | 68p | multi | 1.40 | 1.55 |
| | | Nos. 2193-2198 (6) | | 8.10 | 7.30 |

### Booklet Stamp
### Self-Adhesive
### Die Cut Perf. 14½
| | | | | | |
|---|---|---|---|---|---|
| 2199 | A571 | 1st | multi | 4.50 | 4.50 |
| a. | | Booklet, 2 #2199, 4 #MH300 | | 10.00 | |

Nos. 2193-2195 each sold for 20p, 28p and
38p respectively on day of issue.

Entente Cordiale,
Cent. — A572

Designs: 28p, Lace 1 (trial proof) 1968, by
Sir Terry Frost. 57p, Coccinelle, by Sonia
Delaunay.

**2004, Apr. 6 Photo. Perf. 14x14¼**
| | | | | | |
|---|---|---|---|---|---|
| 2200 | A572 | 28p | multi | .80 | .80 |
| 2201 | A572 | 57p | multi | 1.60 | 1.60 |

See France Nos. 3009-3010.

Ocean
Liners — A573

Designs: 1st, RMS Queen Mary 2, 2004. E,
SS Canberra, 1961. 42p, RMS Queen Mary,
1936. 47p, RMS Mauretania, 1907. 57p, SS
City of New York, 1888. 68p, PS Great Western, 1838.

**2004, Apr. 13 Perf. 14¼x14**
| | | | | | |
|---|---|---|---|---|---|
| 2202 | A573 | 1st | multi | 1.00 | .85 |
| 2203 | A573 | E | multi | 1.90 | 1.05 |
| 2204 | A573 | 42p | multi | 1.15 | 1.15 |
| 2205 | A573 | 47p | multi | 1.15 | 1.15 |
| 2206 | A573 | 57p | multi | 1.30 | 1.30 |
| 2207 | A573 | 68p | multi | 1.60 | 1.60 |
| a. | | Souvenir sheet, #2202-2207 | | 9.75 | 9.75 |
| b. | | Litho. (from #2356a) | | 5.50 | 5.50 |
| | | Nos. 2202-2207 (6) | | 8.10 | 7.10 |

### Booklet Stamp
### Self-Adhesive
### Serpentine Die Cut 14¼x14
| | | | | | |
|---|---|---|---|---|---|
| 2208 | A573 | 1st | multi | 4.50 | 4.50 |
| a. | | Booklet pane, 2 #2208, 4 | | | |
| | | #MH300 | | | |

Nos. 2202 and 2203 sold for 28p and 40p
respectively on day of issue.
No. 2207b is contained in the booklet pane
No. 2356a, issued 2/23/06.

Royal Horticultural
Society,
Bicent. — A574

Designs: 2nd, Dianthus Allwoodii Group.
1st, Dahlia "Garden Princess." E, Clematis
"Arabella." 42p, Miltonia "French Lake." 47p,
Lilium "Lemon Pixie." 68p, Delphinium "Clifford
Sky."

**2004, May 25 Photo. Perf. 14½**
| | | | | | |
|---|---|---|---|---|---|
| 2209 | A574 | 2nd | multi | .95 | .90 |
| 2210 | A574 | 1st | multi | 1.20 | 1.10 |
| a. | | Perf. 14¼ + label, litho. | | 3.50 | 3.25 |
| 2211 | A574 | E | multi | 1.75 | 1.40 |
| 2212 | A574 | 42p | multi | 1.25 | 1.20 |
| 2213 | A574 | 47p | multi | 1.40 | 1.30 |
| a. | | Booklet pane, 2 each | | | |
| | | #2210, 2213 (BK176) | | 5.50 | — |
| 2214 | A574 | 68p | multi | 1.75 | 1.60 |
| a. | | Souvenir sheet, #2209-2214 | | 9.75 | 9.75 |
| b. | | Booklet pane, #2209, 2211, | | | |
| | | 2212, 2214 (BK176) | | 6.00 | — |
| | | Nos. 2209-2214 (6) | | 8.30 | 7.50 |

Nos. 2209-2211 each sold for 21p, 28p and
40p respectively on day of issue.
No. 2210a was printed in sheets of 20
stamps + 20 labels that sold for £6.15.

Wales
Scenery — A575

Designs: 2nd, Barmouth Bridge. 1st,
Hyddgen, Plynlimon. 40p, Brecon Beacons
National Park. 43p, Pen-pych, Rhondda Val-
ley. 47p, Rhewl, Dee Valley. 68p, Marloes
Sands.

**2004, June 15 Photo. Perf. 14½**
| | | | | | |
|---|---|---|---|---|---|
| 2215 | A575 | 2nd | multi | .90 | .80 |
| 2216 | A575 | 1st | multi | 1.10 | 1.00 |
| 2217 | A575 | 40p | multi | 1.00 | .95 |
| 2218 | A575 | 43p | multi | 1.20 | 1.10 |
| 2219 | A575 | 47p | multi | 1.30 | 1.20 |
| 2220 | A575 | 68p | multi | 1.60 | 1.50 |
| | | Nos. 2215-2220 (6) | | 7.10 | 6.55 |

### Booklet Stamp
### Self-Adhesive
### Die Cut Perf. 14½
| | | | | | |
|---|---|---|---|---|---|
| 2221 | A575 | 1st | multi | 5.75 | 5.75 |
| a. | | Booklet pane, 2 #2221, 4 | | | |
| | | #MH300 | | 10.00 | |

Europa (Nos. 2216, 2217, 2221). Nos.
2215-2216 each sold for 21p and 28p respectively on day of issue.

Royal Society of
Arts, 250th
Anniv. — A576

Designs: 1st, Great Britain #1. 40p, William
Shipley, Society founder. 43p, Stylized typewriter keys, shorthand. 47p, Apparatus for
sweeping chimneys invented by George
Smart. 57p, Typeface designed by Eric Gill.
68p, Zero waste.

**2004, Aug. 10 Perf. 13¾x14¼**
| | | | | | |
|---|---|---|---|---|---|
| 2222 | A576 | 1st | multi | 1.00 | .85 |
| 2223 | A576 | 40p | multi | 1.35 | 1.35 |
| 2224 | A576 | 43p | multi | 1.25 | 1.25 |
| 2225 | A576 | 47p | multi | 1.35 | 1.35 |
| 2226 | A576 | 57p | multi | 1.50 | 1.50 |
| 2227 | A576 | 68p | multi | 1.70 | 1.70 |
| | | Nos. 2222-2227 (6) | | 8.15 | 8.00 |

No. 2222 sold for 28p on day of issue.

Mammals — A577

**2004, Sept. 16 Perf. 14½x14¼ Photo.**
| | | | | | |
|---|---|---|---|---|---|
| 2228 | A577 | 1st | Pine marten | 1.40 | 1.20 |
| 2229 | A577 | 1st | Roe deer | 1.40 | 1.20 |
| 2230 | A577 | 1st | Badger | 1.40 | 1.20 |
| 2231 | A577 | 1st | Yellow-necked | | |
| | | | mouse | 1.40 | 1.20 |
| 2232 | A577 | 1st | Wild cat | 1.40 | 1.20 |
| 2233 | A577 | 1st | Red squirrel | 1.40 | 1.20 |
| 2234 | A577 | 1st | Stoat | 1.40 | 1.20 |
| 2235 | A577 | 1st | Natterer's bat | 1.40 | 1.20 |
| 2236 | A577 | 1st | Mole | 1.40 | 1.20 |
| 2237 | A577 | 1st | Fox | 1.40 | 1.20 |
| a. | | Block of 10, #2228-2237 | | 14.25 | 12.25 |

Nos. 2228-2237 each sold for 28p on day of
issue.

Crimean War, 150th
Anniv. — A578

Photographs of Crimean War heroes: 2nd,
Private Michael MacNamara. 1st, Piper David
Muir. 40p, Sergeant Major Edward Edwards.
57p, Sergeant William Powell. 68p, Sergeant
Major John Poole. £1.12, Sergeant Robert
Glasgow.

**2004, Oct. 12 Litho. Perf. 14x13¾**
| | | | | | |
|---|---|---|---|---|---|
| 2238 | A578 | 2nd | multi | 1.00 | .80 |
| 2239 | A578 | 1st | multi | 1.25 | 1.00 |
| 2240 | A578 | 40p | multi | 1.20 | .95 |
| 2241 | A578 | 57p | multi | 1.60 | 1.30 |
| 2242 | A578 | 68p | multi | 1.80 | 1.50 |
| 2243 | A578 | £1.12 | multi | 3.00 | 2.50 |
| | | Nos. 2238-2243 (6) | | 9.85 | 8.05 |

Nos. 2238-2239 each sold for 21p and 28p
respectively on day of issue.

Christmas — A579

Santa Claus: Nos. 2244a, 2245, Walking
toward chimney in snow. Nos. 2244b, 2246,
Looking at rising sun. Nos. 2244c, 2247, In
wind. Nos. 2244d, 2248, With umbrella in rain
storm. Nos. 2244e, 2249, With flashlight in
fog. Nos. 2244f, 2250, Taking protection from
hail storm.

**2004, Nov. 2 Photo. Perf. 14½x14**
| | | | | | |
|---|---|---|---|---|---|
| 2244 | | Sheet of 6 | | 10.00 | 10.00 |
| a. | A579 | (2nd) multi | | 1.30 | 1.30 |
| b. | A579 | (1st) multi | | 1.60 | 1.60 |
| c. | A579 | 40p multi | | 1.15 | 1.15 |
| d. | A579 | 57p multi | | 1.45 | 1.45 |
| e. | A579 | 68p multi | | 1.60 | 1.60 |
| f. | A579 | £1.12 multi | | 3.00 | 3.00 |

## Self-Adhesive
### Die Cut Perf. 14½x14

| | | | | |
|---|---|---|---|---|
| 2245 | A579 | (2nd) multi | 1.00 | 1.00 |
| a. | | Booklet pane of 24 | 26.00 | |
| b. | | Sheet of 20 + 20 personal-<br>ized labels, litho. | 30.00 | |
| 2246 | A579 | (1st) multi | 1.25 | 1.25 |
| a. | | Booklet pane of 12 | 19.00 | .25 |
| b. | | Sheet, 10 each #2245-2246,<br>+ 20 labels, litho. | 23.00 | |
| c. | | Sheet of 20 + 20 personal-<br>ized labels, litho. | 40.00 | |
| 2247 | A579 | 40p multi | 1.20 | 1.05 |
| 2248 | A579 | 57p multi | 1.60 | 1.60 |
| 2249 | A579 | 68p multi | 2.25 | 2.40 |
| 2250 | A579 | £1.12 multi | 2.75 | 2.40 |
| | | *Nos. 2245-2250 (6)* | 10.05 | 8.90 |

Nos. 2244a and 2245 each sold for 21p and Nos. 2244b and 2246 each sold for 28p on day of issue.

No. 2245b sold for £9.95; No. 2246b sold for £5.40; No. 2246c sold for £14.95.

Farm Animals — A580

Designs: No. 2251, British Saddleback pigs. No. 2252, Two Khaki Campbell ducks. No. 2253, Clydesdale horses. No. 2254, Shorthorn cattle. No. 2255, Border collie. No. 2256, Chicks. No. 2257, Suffolk sheep. No. 2258, Bagot goat. No. 2259, Norfolk Black turkeys. No. 2260, Three Embden geese.

### 2005, Jan. 11    Photo.    Perf. 14½

| | | | | |
|---|---|---|---|---|
| 2251 | A580 | 1st multi | 1.45 | 1.30 |
| 2252 | A580 | 1st multi | 1.45 | 1.30 |
| 2253 | A580 | 1st multi | 1.45 | 1.30 |
| 2254 | A580 | 1st multi | 1.45 | 1.30 |
| 2255 | A580 | 1st multi | 1.45 | 1.30 |
| 2256 | A580 | 1st multi | 1.45 | 1.30 |
| 2257 | A580 | 1st multi | 1.45 | 1.30 |
| 2258 | A580 | 1st multi | 1.45 | 1.30 |
| 2259 | A580 | 1st multi | 1.45 | 1.30 |
| 2260 | A580 | 1st multi | 1.45 | 1.30 |
| a. | | Block of 10, #2251-2260 | 14.50 | 13.50 |
| b. | | Sheet, 2 each #2251-2260<br>+ 20 labels, litho. | 30.00 | |

Nos. 2251-2260 each sold for 28p on day of issue. No. 2260b sold for £6.15.

Southwestern England Scenery — A581

Designs: 2nd, Old Harry Rocks, Studland Bay. 1st, Wheal Coates mine, St. Agnes. 40p, Start Point and Start Bay. 43p, Norton Down, Wiltshire. 57p, Chiselcombe, Exmoor. 68p, St. James Stone, Lundy.

### 2005, Feb. 8    Photo.    Perf. 14½

| | | | | |
|---|---|---|---|---|
| 2261 | A581 | 2nd multi | 1.00 | 1.00 |
| 2262 | A581 | 1st multi | 1.25 | 1.25 |
| 2263 | A581 | 40p multi | 1.20 | 1.20 |
| 2264 | A581 | 43p multi | 1.35 | 1.35 |
| 2265 | A581 | 57p multi | 1.60 | 1.60 |
| 2266 | A581 | 68p multi | 1.90 | 1.90 |
| | | *Nos. 2261-2266 (6)* | 8.30 | 8.30 |

Nos. 2261 and 2262 sold for 21p and 28p respectively on day of issue.

Jane Eyre, by Charlotte Bronte (1816-55) — A582

Various characters.

### 2005, Feb. 24    Litho.    Perf. 14¼

| | | | | |
|---|---|---|---|---|
| 2267 | A582 | 2nd multi | 1.00 | 1.00 |
| 2268 | A582 | 1st multi | 1.25 | 1.25 |
| a. | | Booklet pane, 2 each #2267-<br>2268 (BK177) | 6.00 | — |
| 2269 | A582 | 40p multi | 1.20 | 1.20 |
| 2270 | A582 | 57p multi | 1.60 | 1.60 |
| 2271 | A582 | 68p multi | 1.80 | 1.80 |
| 2272 | A582 | £1.12 multi | 3.00 | 3.00 |
| a. | | Souvenir sheet, #2267-2272 | 9.50 | 9.50 |
| b. | | Booklet pane, #2269-2272<br>(BK177) | 10.00 | |
| | | *Nos. 2267-2272 (6)* | 9.85 | 9.85 |

Nos. 2267 and 2268 sold for 21p and 28p respectively on day of issue.

Magic Tricks — A583

Designs: 1st, Magician, "heads or tails" coin. 40p, Rabbit and hat. 47p, Popper. 68p, Ace of Hearts. £1.12, Pyramids and fezzes.

### 2005, Mar. 15    Photo.    Perf. 14¼x14

| | | | | |
|---|---|---|---|---|
| 2273 | A583 | 1st multi, un-<br>scratched<br>coin | 1.10 | 1.05 |
| a. | | Scratched coin, heads | 1.10 | 1.05 |
| b. | | Scratched coin, tails | 1.10 | 1.05 |
| c. | | Vert. pair, unscratched | 2.25 | 2.10 |
| d. | | Sheet of 20 + 20 labels, un-<br>scratched, litho. | 40.00 | |
| 2274 | A583 | 40p multi | 1.30 | 1.20 |
| 2275 | A583 | 47p multi | 1.60 | 1.50 |
| 2276 | A583 | 68p multi | 2.00 | 1.90 |
| 2277 | A583 | £1.12 multi | 3.00 | 2.75 |
| | | *Nos. 2273-2277 (5)* | 9.00 | 8.40 |

No. 2273 sold for 28p on day of issue. No. 2273 has a chalky covering over the coin that can be scratched away with a coin or other metal object to reveal a "heads" picture, showing a face composed of a planet, star and a crescent, or a "tails" picture, showing a shooting star. The chalky covering may, like earlier British chalky paper stamps, dissolve in any fluid.

No. 2273c will have both versions of the stamp. Vertical or horizontal pairs from No. 2273d will have both versions of the stamp. No. 2273d sold for £6.15.

Portions of the designs of Nos. 2275 and 2277 are printed with a thermochromic ink that changes color when warmed.

### Castles Type of 1955
### Miniature Sheet
### Litho. & Engr.
### 2005, Mar. 22    Perf. 11x11¾
### On Cream-Colored Paper

| | | | | |
|---|---|---|---|---|
| 2278 | | Sheet of 4 | 7.00 | 7.75 |
| a. | A133 | 50p Carrickfergus<br>(brown) | .85 | 1.00 |
| b. | A133 | 50p Windsor (black) | 2.75 | 2.00 |
| c. | A133 | £1 Caernarfon (red) | 1.75 | 2.00 |
| d. | A133 | £1 Edinburgh (blue) | 1.75 | 2.00 |
| e. | | Booklet pane of 4 #2278b<br>(BK197) | 11.00 | |

Issued: No. 2278e, 9/9/11. Stamps from No. 2278e have a pale yellow background.
See Nos. 309-312, 371-374, 525-528.

### Miniature Sheet

Wedding of Prince Charles and Camilla Parker Bowles A584

No. 2279 — Couple: a, 30p, Prince wearing blue, red and green tie. b, 68p, Prince wearing vest.

### 2005, Apr. 8    Litho.    Perf. 13½x14

| | | | | |
|---|---|---|---|---|
| 2279 | A584 | Sheet, 2 each #a-b | 6.00 | 6.00 |
| a. | | 30p multi | 1.55 | 1.55 |
| b. | | 68p multi | 2.45 | 2.45 |

The marginal inscription states that the wedding took place on Apr. 8, but it was delayed until Apr. 9, due to Prince Charles's attendance at the Apr. 8 funeral of Pope John Paul II. Post offices were requested not to sell the stamps until Apr. 9, but first day covers have Apr. 8 cancels.

UNESCO World Heritage Sites in Great Britain and Australia — A585

Designs: No. 2280, Hadrian's Wall, England. No. 2281, Ayers Rock, Uluru-Kata Tjuta National Park, Australia. No. 2282,

Stonehenge, England No. 2283, Wet Tropics of Queensland, Australia. No. 2284, Blenheim Palace, England. No. 2285, Greater Blue Mountains Area, Australia. No. 2286, Heart of Neolithic Orkney, Scotland. No. 2287, Purnululu National Park, Australia.

### 2005, Apr. 21    Perf. 14½

| | | | | |
|---|---|---|---|---|
| 2280 | A585 | 2nd multi | .85 | .80 |
| 2281 | A585 | 2nd multi | .85 | .80 |
| a. | | Horiz. pair, #2280-2281 | 1.75 | 1.60 |
| 2282 | A585 | 1st multi | 1.05 | 1.00 |
| 2283 | A585 | 1st multi | 1.05 | 1.00 |
| a. | | Horiz. pair, #2282-2283 | 2.10 | 2.00 |
| 2284 | A585 | 47p multi | 1.30 | 1.20 |
| 2285 | A585 | 47p multi | 1.30 | 1.20 |
| a. | | Horiz. pair, #2284-2285 | 2.60 | 2.40 |
| 2286 | A585 | 68p multi | 1.60 | 1.50 |
| 2287 | A585 | 68p multi | 1.60 | 1.50 |
| a. | | Horiz. pair, #2286-2287 | 3.25 | 3.00 |
| | | *Nos. 2280-2287 (8)* | 9.60 | 9.00 |

Nos. 2280 and 2281 each sold for 21p, and Nos. 2282 and 2283 each sold for 30p on day of issue.
See Australia Nos. 2369-2376.

Trooping the Color Ceremony — A586

Designs: 2nd, Soldier holding regimental flag. 1st, Queen Elizabeth II saluting. 42p, Bugler on horseback. 60p, Soldier holding scabbard. 68p, Queen on horseback. £1.12, Queen and soldier in phaeton.

### 2005, June 7    Litho.    Perf. 14½

| | | | | |
|---|---|---|---|---|
| 2288 | A586 | 2nd multi | .85 | .80 |
| 2289 | A586 | 1st multi | 1.05 | .85 |
| 2290 | A586 | 42p multi | 1.05 | 1.05 |
| 2291 | A586 | 60p multi | 1.50 | 1.50 |
| 2292 | A586 | 68p multi | 1.60 | 1.60 |
| 2293 | A586 | £1.12 multi | 2.35 | 2.35 |
| a. | | Souvenir sheet, #2288-2293 | 8.25 | 8.25 |
| | | *Nos. 2288-2293 (6)* | 8.40 | 8.20 |

Nos. 2288 and 2289 sold for 21p and 30p respectively on day of issue.

### St. Paul's Cathedral Type of 1995
### Souvenir Sheet
### 2005, July 5    Photo.    Perf. 14½

| | | | | |
|---|---|---|---|---|
| 2294 | | Sheet of 6, #2294a, 5<br>#MH287 | 7.75 | 7.75 |
| a. | A456 | (1st) deep blue & silver | 1.60 | 1.60 |

No. 2294a issued 6/21/2005 and sold for 30p on day of issue. End of World War II, 60th anniv.

Motorcycles A587

Designs: 1st, 1991 Norton F.1. 40p, 1969 BSA Rocket 3. 42p, 1949 Vincent Black Shadow. 47p, 1938 Triumph Speed Twin. 60p, 1930 Brough Superior. 68p, 1914 Royal Enfield.

### 2005, July 19    Litho.    Perf. 13¾x14

| | | | | |
|---|---|---|---|---|
| 2295 | A587 | 1st multi | 1.15 | 1.15 |
| 2296 | A587 | 40p multi | 1.10 | 1.05 |
| 2297 | A587 | 42p multi | 1.15 | 1.15 |
| 2298 | A587 | 47p multi | 1.40 | 1.35 |
| 2299 | A587 | 60p multi | 1.50 | 1.50 |
| 2300 | A587 | 68p multi | 1.75 | 1.75 |
| | | *Nos. 2295-2300 (6)* | 8.05 | 7.95 |

No. 2295 sold for 30p on day of issue.

### Miniature Sheet

Selection of London as Host of 2012 Summer Olympics A588

No. 2301: a, Javelin. b, Swimming. c, Sprinting. d, Basketball. e, Victorious athlete.

### 2005, Aug. 5    Perf. 14¼

| | | | | |
|---|---|---|---|---|
| 2301 | A588 | Sheet of 6, #a-d,<br>2 #e | 8.00 | 8.00 |
| a.-e. | | 1st Any single | 1.25 | 1.25 |

Nos. 2301a-2301e each sold for 30p on day of issue. Compare with Type A467.

Changing Tastes in Britain — A589

Designs: 2nd, Woman with rice bowl and chopsticks. 1st, Woman with mug of tea. 42p, Man eating sushi. 47p, Woman with pasta bowl and wine glass. 60p, Woman with bag of French fries. 68p, Man with bowl of fruit.

### 2005, Aug. 23    Photo.    Perf. 14½

| | | | | |
|---|---|---|---|---|
| 2302 | A589 | 2nd multi | .90 | .90 |
| 2303 | A589 | 1st multi | 1.15 | 1.15 |
| 2304 | A589 | 42p multi | 1.15 | 1.15 |
| 2305 | A589 | 47p multi | 1.50 | 1.50 |
| 2306 | A589 | 60p multi | 1.50 | 1.50 |
| 2307 | A589 | 68p multi | 1.75 | 1.75 |
| | | *Nos. 2302-2307 (6)* | 7.95 | 7.95 |

Europa (Nos. 2303, 2304). Nos. 2302 and 2303 sold for 21p and 30p respectively on day of issue.

Television Shows — A590

Designs: 2nd, Inspector Morse. 1st, Emmerdale. 42p, Rising Damp. 47p, The Avengers. 60p, The South Bank Show. 68p, Who Wants To Be a Millionaire?

### 2005, Sept. 15    Litho.    Perf. 14¼x14

| | | | | |
|---|---|---|---|---|
| 2308 | A590 | 2nd multi | .85 | .80 |
| 2309 | A590 | 1st multi | 1.05 | 1.00 |
| a. | | Sheet of 20 + 20 labels | 21.00 | |
| 2310 | A590 | 42p multi | 1.30 | 1.20 |
| 2311 | A590 | 47p multi | 1.30 | 1.20 |
| 2312 | A590 | 60p multi | 1.45 | 1.35 |
| 2313 | A590 | 68p multi | 1.60 | 1.50 |
| | | *Nos. 2308-2313 (6)* | 7.55 | 7.05 |

Independent Television, 50th anniv. Nos. 2308 and 2309 sold for 21p and 30p respectively on day of issue. No. 2309a sold for £6.65.
Labels on No. 2309a could be personalized for a fee.

Flower A591

Hello A592

Love A593

Teddy Bear A595

Flag A594

Bird A596

### Serpentine Die Cut 14¾x14
### 2005, Oct. 4    Photo.
### Self-Adhesive
### Booklet Stamps

| | | | | |
|---|---|---|---|---|
| 2314 | A591 | 1st multi | 2.75 | 2.75 |
| a. | | Sheet of 20 + 20 labels, litho. | 57.50 | |
| 2315 | A592 | 1st multi | 2.75 | 2.75 |
| a. | | Sheet of 20 + 20 labels, litho. | 57.50 | |
| 2316 | A593 | 1st multi | 2.75 | 2.75 |
| a. | | Sheet of 20 + 20 labels, litho. | 57.50 | |
| 2317 | A594 | 1st multi | 2.75 | 2.75 |
| a. | | Sheet of 20 + 20 labels, litho. | 57.50 | |
| 2318 | A595 | 1st multi | 2.75 | 2.75 |
| a. | | Sheet of 20 + 20 labels, litho. | 57.50 | |
| 2319 | A596 | 1st multi | 2.75 | 2.75 |
| a. | | Booklet pane, #2314-2319 | 12.50 | |
| b. | | Sheet of 20 + 20 labels, litho. | 57.50 | |

c. Sheet, 4 each #2315-2316, 3
each #2314, 2317-2319, +
20 labels, litho. ('06)     55.00

Each stamp sold for 30p on day of issue.
Nos. 2314a-2318a, 2319b each sold for
£14.95 and had labels that could be
personalized.
No. 2319 issued 7/4/06. No. 2319c sold for
£6.95.
See Nos. 2427, 2537-2538a, 2545, 2793,
3452.

### Souvenir Sheet

**Great Britain's Victory Over Australia
in Ashes Cricket Test Match Series
A597**

No. 2320: a, Players celebrating with trophy.
b, Players celebrating. c, Batsman. d, Players
in action.

| | | | | | |
|---|---|---|---|---|---|
| **2005, Oct. 6** | | **Litho.** | | **Perf. 14¼x14** | |
| 2320 | A597 | Sheet of 4 | | 5.75 | 5.75 |
| a.-b. | | 1st Either single | | 1.20 | 1.20 |
| c.-d. | | 68p Either single | | 1.60 | 1.60 |

Nos. 2320a and 2320b each sold for 30p on
day of issue.

**Battle of Trafalgar, Bicent. A598**

Designs: No. 2321, Ships in battle. No.
2322, Wounded Admiral Horatio Nelson on
deck of HMS Victory. No. 2323, Ship on fire.
No. 2324, Ships in battle, diff. No. 2325, Columns of British ships. No. 2326, French and
Spanish ships.

| | | | | | |
|---|---|---|---|---|---|
| **2005, Oct. 18** | | **Litho.** | | **Perf. 14¾x14¼** | |
| 2321 | A598 | 1st multi | | 1.00 | .90 |
| 2322 | A598 | 1st multi | | 1.00 | .90 |
| a. | | Horiz. pair, #2321-2322 | | 2.00 | 1.90 |
| 2323 | A598 | 42p multi | | 1.20 | 1.15 |
| 2324 | A598 | 42p multi | | 1.20 | 1.15 |
| a. | | Horiz. pair, #2323-2324 | | 2.40 | 2.30 |
| 2325 | A598 | 68p multi | | 2.00 | 1.90 |
| a. | | Booklet pane, #2321, 2323, 2325 (BK178) | | 4.25 | — |
| 2326 | A598 | 68p multi | | 2.00 | 1.90 |
| a. | | Horiz. pair, #2325-2326 | | 4.00 | 4.00 |
| b. | | Booklet pane, #2322, 2324, 2326 (BK178) | | 4.25 | — |
| c. | | Souvenir sheet #2321-2326 | | 9.00 | 9.00 |
| | | Nos. 2321-2326 (6) | | 8.40 | 7.90 |

Nos. 2321-2322 each sold for 30p on day of
issue.

**Christmas — A599**

Madonna and Child in artistic style of: 2nd,
Haiti. 1st, Europe. 42p, Europe. 60p, Native
Americans. 68p, India. £1.12, Australian
Aborigines.

| | | | | | |
|---|---|---|---|---|---|
| **2005, Nov. 1** | | **Photo.** | | **Perf. 14½x14** | |
| 2327 | | Sheet of 6 | | 10.00 | 10.00 |
| a. | A599 | 2nd multi | | 1.40 | 1.40 |
| b. | A599 | 1st multi | | 1.75 | 1.75 |
| c. | A599 | 42p multi | | 1.05 | 1.05 |
| d. | A599 | 60p multi | | 1.40 | 1.40 |
| e. | A599 | 68p multi | | 1.60 | 1.60 |
| f. | A599 | £1.12 multi | | 2.90 | 2.90 |

### Self-Adhesive
### Die Cut Perf. 14½x14

| | | | | | |
|---|---|---|---|---|---|
| 2328 | A599 | 2nd multi | | .95 | .85 |
| a. | | Booklet pane of 24 | | 26.00 | |
| 2329 | A599 | 1st multi | | 1.25 | 1.05 |
| a. | | Booklet pane of 12 | | 19.00 | |
| 2330 | A599 | 42p multi | | 1.25 | 1.05 |
| 2331 | A599 | 60p multi | | 1.60 | 1.40 |
| 2332 | A599 | 68p multi | | 1.75 | 1.60 |
| 2333 | A599 | £1.12 multi | | 3.00 | 2.50 |
| | | Nos. 2328-2333 (6) | | 9.80 | 8.45 |

Nos. 2327a and 2328 each sold for 21p and
Nos. 2327b and 2329 each sold for 30p on day
of issue.

**Animals From Children's Books — A600**

Designs: No. 2334, Jeremy Fisher, from *The
Tale of Mr. Jeremy Fisher*, by Beatrix Potter.
No. 2335, Kipper, from *Kipper*, by Mick Inkpen.
No. 2336, The Enormous Crocodile, from *The
Enormous Crocodile*, by Roald Dahl. No.
2337, Paddington Bear, from *More About Pad-
dington*, by Michael Bond. No. 2338, Boots,
from *The Comic Adventures of Boots*, by
Satoshi Kitamura. No. 2339, White Rabbit,
from *Alice's Adventures in Wonderland*, by
Lewis Carroll. No. 2340, The Very Hungry Cat-
erpillar, from *The Very Hungry Caterpillar*, by
Eric Carle. No. 2341, Maisy, from *Maisy's
ABC*, by Lucy Cousins.
No. 2342, Like #2337.

| | | | | | |
|---|---|---|---|---|---|
| **2006, Jan. 10** | | **Litho.** | | **Perf. 14½** | |
| 2334 | A600 | 2nd multi | | .85 | .75 |
| 2335 | A600 | 2nd multi | | .85 | .75 |
| a. | | Horiz. pair, #2334-2335 | | 1.75 | 1.50 |
| 2336 | A600 | 1st multi | | 1.00 | .95 |
| 2337 | A600 | 1st multi | | 1.00 | .95 |
| a. | | Horiz. pair, #2336-2337 | | 2.00 | 1.90 |
| 2338 | A600 | 42p multi | | 1.25 | 1.20 |
| 2339 | A600 | 42p multi | | 1.25 | 1.20 |
| a. | | Horiz. pair, #2338-2339 | | 2.50 | 2.40 |
| 2340 | A600 | 68p multi | | 2.00 | 1.90 |
| 2341 | A600 | 68p multi | | 2.00 | 1.90 |
| a. | | Horiz. pair, #2340-2341 | | 4.00 | 4.00 |
| | | Nos. 2334-2341 (8) | | 10.20 | 9.60 |

### Self-Adhesive
### Serpentine Die Cut 14½

| | | | | | |
|---|---|---|---|---|---|
| 2342 | A600 | 1st multi + label | | 2.75 | 2.75 |

Nos. 2334-2335 each sold for 21p, and Nos.
2336-2337 each sold for 30p on day of issue.
No. 2340 has two die cut holes resenting
holes eaten by the caterpillar.
See United States Nos. 3987, 3990.
No. 2342 had a franking value of 30p on the
day of issue, and was issued in sheets of 20
stamps + 20 different labels that sold for
£6.55.

**English Scenery — A601**

Designs: No. 2343, Carding Mill Valley,
Shropshire. No. 2344, Beachy Head, Sussex
coast. No. 2345, St. Paul's Cathedral, London.
No. 2346, Brancastle, Norfolk coast. No. 2347,
Derwent Edge, Peak District. No. 2348, Robin
Hood's Bay, Yorkshire coast. No. 2349, But-
termere, Lake District. No. 2350, Chipping
Campden, Cotswolds. No. 2351, St. Boniface
Down, Isle of Wight. No. 2352, Chamberlain
Square, Birmingham.

| | | | | | |
|---|---|---|---|---|---|
| **2006, Feb. 7** | | **Photo.** | | **Perf. 14½** | |
| 2343 | A601 | 1st multi | | 1.40 | 1.20 |
| 2344 | A601 | 1st multi | | 1.40 | 1.20 |
| 2345 | A601 | 1st multi | | 1.40 | 1.20 |
| 2346 | A601 | 1st multi | | 1.40 | 1.20 |
| 2347 | A601 | 1st multi | | 1.40 | 1.20 |
| 2348 | A601 | 1st multi | | 1.40 | 1.20 |
| 2349 | A601 | 1st multi | | 1.40 | 1.20 |
| 2350 | A601 | 1st multi | | 1.40 | 1.20 |
| 2351 | A601 | 1st multi | | 1.40 | 1.20 |
| 2352 | A601 | 1st multi | | 1.40 | 1.20 |
| a. | | Block of 10, #2343-2352 | | 14.25 | 12.25 |
| | | Nos. 2343-2352 (10) | | 14.00 | 12.00 |

Nos. 2343-2352 each sold for 30p on day of
issue.

**Isambard Kingdom Brunel (1806-
1859), Engineer — A602**

Engineering projects of Brunel: 1st, Royal
Albert Bridge. 40p, Box Tunnel. 42p, Paddington Station. 47p, PSS Great Eastern. 60p, Clifton Suspension Bridge design. 68p, Maiden-
head Bridge.

| | | | | | |
|---|---|---|---|---|---|
| **2006, Feb. 23** | | **Litho.** | | **Perf. 14x13¼** | |
| 2353 | A602 | 1st multi | | .85 | .70 |
| 2354 | A602 | 60p multi | | .95 | .95 |
| 2355 | A602 | 42p multi | | .95 | .95 |
| 2356 | A602 | 47p multi | | 1.15 | 1.15 |
| a. | | Booklet pane, #2356, 2 #2207b (BK179) | | 12.50 | — |

| | | | | | |
|---|---|---|---|---|---|
| 2357 | A602 | 60p multi | | 1.30 | 1.30 |
| a. | | Booklet pane, #2354, 2356, 2357 (BK179) | | 4.25 | |
| 2358 | A602 | 68p multi | | 1.55 | 1.55 |
| a. | | Souvenir sheet, #2353-2358 | | 7.00 | 7.00 |
| b. | | Booklet pane, #2353, 2355, 2358 (BK179) | | 4.00 | |
| | | Nos. 2353-2358 (6) | | 6.75 | 6.60 |

No. 2353 sold for 30p on day of issue.

**Ice Age Animals — A603**

Designs: 1st, Saber-tooth cat. 42p, Giant
deer. 47p, Woolly rhinoceros. 68p, Woolly
mammoth. £1.12, Cave bear.

| | | | | | |
|---|---|---|---|---|---|
| **2006, Mar. 21** | | | | **Perf. 14¼x14½** | |
| | | | | | |
| **2006, Mar. 21** | | | | | **Litho.** |
| 2359 | A603 | 1st gray & blk | | 1.30 | 1.15 |
| 2360 | A603 | 42p gray & blk | | 1.30 | 1.15 |
| 2361 | A603 | 47p gray & blk | | 1.60 | 1.40 |
| 2362 | A603 | 68p gray & blk | | 2.00 | 1.75 |
| 2363 | A603 | £1.12 gray & blk | | 3.50 | 2.90 |
| | | Nos. 2359-2363 (5) | | 9.70 | 8.35 |

No. 2359 sold for 30p on day of issue.

**Queen Elizabeth II, 80th Birthday — A604**

Queen: No. 2364, Wearing sunglasses,
1972. No. 2365, With horse, 1985. No. 2366,
Wearing hat, 2001. No. 2367, As child, with
mother, 1931. No. 2368, Wearing tiara, 1951.
No. 2369, Wearing hat, 1960. No. 2370, As
teenager, 1940. No. 2371, With Prince Philip,
1950.

| | | | | | |
|---|---|---|---|---|---|
| **2006, Apr. 18** | | **Photo.** | | **Perf. 14¼x14** | |
| 2364 | A604 | 2nd gray & blk | | .90 | .80 |
| 2365 | A604 | 2nd gray & blk | | .90 | .80 |
| a. | | Horiz. pair, #2364-2365 | | 2.00 | 1.60 |
| 2366 | A604 | 1st gray & blk | | 1.10 | 1.00 |
| 2367 | A604 | 1st gray & blk | | 1.10 | 1.00 |
| a. | | Horiz. pair, #2366-2367 | | 2.25 | 2.00 |
| 2368 | A604 | 44p gray & blk | | 1.25 | 1.15 |
| 2369 | A604 | 44p gray & blk | | 1.25 | 1.15 |
| a. | | Horiz. pair, #2368-2369 | | 2.60 | 2.40 |
| 2370 | A604 | 72p gray & blk | | 1.90 | 1.75 |
| 2371 | A604 | 72p gray & blk | | 1.90 | 1.75 |
| a. | | Horiz. pair, #2370-2371 | | 4.00 | 3.50 |
| | | Nos. 2364-2371 (8) | | 10.30 | 9.40 |

On day of issue, Nos. 2364-2365 each sold
of 23p; Nos. 2366-2367 each sold for 32p.

**2006 World Cup Soccer Championships, Germany — A605**

Globe, soccer player and flag from: 1st,
England. 42p, Italy. 44p, Argentina. 50p, Germany. 64p, France. 72p, Brazil.

| | | | | | |
|---|---|---|---|---|---|
| **2006, June 6** | | **Litho.** | | **Perf. 14½** | |
| 2372 | A605 | 1st multi | | 1.05 | 1.00 |
| a. | | Sheet of 20 + 20 labels | | 40.00 | |
| 2373 | A605 | 42p multi | | 1.30 | 1.20 |
| 2374 | A605 | 44p multi | | 1.35 | 1.25 |
| 2375 | A605 | 50p multi | | 1.60 | 1.50 |
| 2376 | A605 | 64p multi | | 1.90 | 1.75 |
| 2377 | A605 | 72p multi | | 2.40 | 2.25 |
| | | Nos. 2372-2377 (6) | | 9.60 | 8.95 |

No. 2372 sold for 32p on day of issue.
No.2372a sold for £6.95.

**Modern Architecture — A606**

Designs: 1st, 30 St. Mary Axe, London,
designed by Sir Norman Foster. 42p, Maggie's
Center, Dundee, designed by Frank Gehry.
44p, Selfridges, Birmingham, designed by
Future Systems. 50p, Downland Gridshell,
Chichester, by Edward Cullinan. 64p, An
Turas, Isle of Tiree, by Sutherland Hussey

Architects. 72p, The Deep Hull, by Terry Farrell and Partners.

| | | | | | |
|---|---|---|---|---|---|
| **2006, June 20** | | | | **Photo.** | |
| 2378 | A606 | 1st multi | | 1.00 | .95 |
| 2379 | A606 | 42p multi | | 1.15 | 1.15 |
| 2380 | A606 | 44p multi | | 1.40 | 1.40 |
| 2381 | A606 | 50p multi | | 1.50 | 1.50 |
| 2382 | A606 | 64p multi | | 1.75 | 1.90 |
| 2383 | A606 | 72p multi | | 1.75 | 1.90 |
| | | Nos. 2378-2383 (6) | | 8.55 | 8.80 |

No. 2378 sold for 32p on day of issue.

**National Portrait Gallery,
150th Anniv. — A607**

Famous Britons in art from National Portrait
Gallery: No. 2384, Sir Winston Churchill, by
Walter Sickert. No. 2385, Self-portrait of Sir
Joshua Reynolds. No. 2386, T. S. Eliot, by
Patrick Heron. No. 2387, Emmeline Pank-
hurst, by Georgina Brakenbury. No. 2388, Vir-
ginia Woolf, photograph by George Beresford.
No. 2389, Sir Walter Scott, bust by Sir Francis
Chantry. No. 2390, Mary Seacole, by Albert
Challen. No. 2391, William Shakespeare, by
John Taylor. No. 2392, Dame Cicely Saun-
ders, by Catherine Goodman. No. 2393,
Charles Darwin, by John Collier.

| | | | | | |
|---|---|---|---|---|---|
| **2006, July 18** | | | | **Perf. 14¼** | |
| 2384 | A607 | 1st multi | | 1.40 | 1.30 |
| 2385 | A607 | 1st multi | | 1.40 | 1.30 |
| 2386 | A607 | 1st multi | | 1.40 | 1.30 |
| 2387 | A607 | 1st multi | | 1.40 | 1.30 |
| 2388 | A607 | 1st multi | | 1.40 | 1.30 |
| 2389 | A607 | 1st multi | | 1.40 | 1.30 |
| 2390 | A607 | 1st multi | | 1.40 | 1.30 |
| 2391 | A607 | 1st multi | | 1.40 | 1.30 |
| 2392 | A607 | 1st multi | | 1.40 | 1.30 |
| 2393 | A607 | 1st multi | | 1.40 | 1.30 |
| a. | | Block of 10, #2384-2393 | | 14.00 | 13.00 |
| | | Nos. 2384-2393 (10) | | 14.00 | 13.00 |

Nos. 2384-2393 each sold for 32p on day of
issue.

**Recipients of Victoria Cross — A608**

Designs: No. 2394, Corporal Agansing Rai.
No. 2395, Boy Seaman First Class Jack
Cornwell. No. 2396, Midshipman Charles
Lucas. No. 2397, Captain Noel Chavasse. No.
2398, Captain Albert Ball. No. 2399, Captain
Charles Upham.

| | | | | | |
|---|---|---|---|---|---|
| **2006, Sept. 21** | | **Litho.** | | **Perf. 14¼x14** | |
| 2394 | A608 | 1st multi | | 1.10 | .90 |
| 2395 | A608 | 1st multi | | 1.10 | .90 |
| a. | | Horiz. pair, #2394-2395 | | 2.25 | 1.90 |
| 2396 | A608 | 64p multi | | 1.75 | 1.60 |
| 2397 | A608 | 64p multi | | 1.75 | 1.60 |
| a. | | Horiz. pair, #2396-2397 | | 3.50 | 3.25 |
| 2398 | A608 | 72p multi | | 2.10 | 2.00 |
| a. | | Booklet pane, #2394, 2396, 2398 (BK180) | | 5.00 | — |
| 2399 | A608 | 72p multi | | 2.60 | 2.40 |
| a. | | Horiz. pair, #2398-2399 | | 4.75 | 4.50 |
| b. | | Booklet pane, #2395, 2397, 2399 (BK180) | | 5.50 | — |
| c. | | Souvenir sheet, #1331a, 2394-2399 | | 11.00 | 10.50 |
| | | Nos. 2394-2399 (6) | | 10.40 | 9.40 |

Nos. 2394-2395 each sold for 32p on day of
issue.

**Musicians and
Dancers — A609**

Designs: 1st, Sitar player and dancer. 42p,
Guitarist and drummer. 50p, Violinist and
harpist. 72p, Saxophone player and guitarist.
£1.19, Maracas player and dancers.

| | | | | | |
|---|---|---|---|---|---|
| **2006, Oct. 3** | | | | **Perf. 14¼x14½** | |
| 2400 | A609 | 1st multi | | 1.10 | .95 |
| 2401 | A609 | 42p multi | | 1.35 | 1.25 |
| 2402 | A609 | 50p multi | | 1.90 | 1.60 |
| 2403 | A609 | 72p multi | | 2.20 | 1.90 |
| 2404 | A609 | £1.19 multi | | 2.75 | 2.50 |
| | | Nos. 2400-2404 (5) | | 9.30 | 8.20 |

Europa (No. 2402).

Thematica 2006

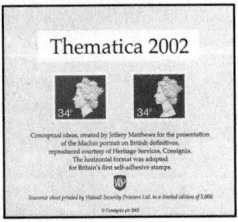

Thematica 2002

The gummed souvenir sheets shown above, created for the 2002 and 2006 Thematica stamp shows, contain invalid imperforate stamps with simulated perforations that were never issued by Royal Mail. The stamps on these sheets have no obliterators.

The gummed 2005 Thematica sheet reproduces reduced versions of Nos. 440, 441, 683, 1040 and 1796. These reproduced images lack obliterators, and are also invalid for postage.

Gummed Thematica sheets for other years exist, each showing reproductions of other stamps with obliterators to invalidate the images.

"New Baby" A610

"Thank You" A612

Fireworks A614

"Best Wishes" A611

Balloons A613

Flowers, Butterflies and Champagne Bottle A615

**Die Cut Perf. 14¾x14¼**

| | | | 2006, Oct. 17 | Photo. |
|---|---|---|---|---|
**Self-Adhesive**

| 2405 | A610 | 1st multi | 2.25 | 1.15 |
|---|---|---|---|---|
| 2406 | A611 | 1st multi | 2.25 | 1.15 |
| 2407 | A612 | 1st multi | 2.25 | 1.15 |
| 2408 | A613 | 1st multi | 2.25 | 1.15 |
| 2409 | A614 | 1st multi | 2.25 | 1.15 |
| 2410 | A615 | 1st multi | 2.25 | 1.15 |
| a. | Booklet pane, #2405-2410 | | 10.00 | |
| b. | Sheet, 3 each #2406-2409, 4 each #2405, 2410 + 20 labels, litho. | | 45.00 | |
| | Nos. 2405-2410 (6) | | 13.50 | 6.90 |

Nos. 2405-2410 each sold for 32p on day of issue. No. 2410b sold for £6.95. See Nos. 2546-2548, 2794.

Christmas
A616        A617

Designs: Nos. 2411a, 2411c, 2412, 2414, Snowman. Nos. 2411b, 2411d, 2413, 2415, Santa Claus. Nos. 2411e, 2416, Reindeer. Nos. 2411f, 2417, Christmas tree.

| | | | 2006, Nov. 7 | Photo. | Perf. 14¾x14 |
|---|---|---|---|---|---|
| 2411 | | Sheet of 6 | | 10.00 | 9.75 |
| a. | A616 | 2nd multi | | .95 | .95 |
| b. | A616 | 1st multi | | 1.20 | 1.20 |
| c. | A617 | 2nd Large multi | | 1.35 | 1.35 |
| d. | A617 | 1st Large multi | | 1.90 | 1.90 |
| e. | A616 | 72p multi | | 1.75 | 1.90 |
| f. | A616 | £1.19 multi | | 2.75 | 2.60 |

**Self-Adhesive**
**Die Cut Perf. 14¾x14**

| 2412 | A616 | 2nd multi | | .95 | .95 |
|---|---|---|---|---|---|
| a. | | Booklet pane of 12 | | 16.00 | |
| 2413 | A616 | 1st multi | | 1.20 | 1.15 |
| a. | | Booklet pane of 12 | | 19.00 | |
| b. | | Sheet, 10 each #2412-2413, + 20 labels, litho. | | 29.00 | — |
| 2414 | A617 | 2nd Large multi | | 1.35 | 1.30 |
| 2415 | A617 | 1st Large multi | | 1.75 | 1.75 |
| 2416 | A616 | 72p multi | | 1.75 | 1.75 |
| 2417 | A616 | £1.19 multi | | 2.90 | 2.75 |
| | Nos. 2412-2417 (6) | | | 9.90 | 9.65 |

On day of issue, Nos. 2411a and 2412 each sold for 23p, Nos. 2411b and 2413 each sold for 32p, Nos. 2411c and 2414 each sold for 37p, and Nos. 2411d and 2415 each sold for 44p. No. 2413b sold for £6.

**Souvenir Sheet**

Battle of the Somme, 90th Anniv. A618

**Perf. 14½x14¼ (#2418a), 14¾x14**
**Syncopated**

| | | | 2006, Nov. 9 | | Photo. |
|---|---|---|---|---|---|
| 2418 | A618 | Sheet of 5 | | 11.00 | 11.00 |
| a. | | 1st Poppies | | 2.75 | 2.75 |
| b. | | Sheet of 20 #2418a + 20 labels, litho. | | 55.00 | |
| c. | | Single stamp, litho. (#2614b) ('08) | | 1.90 | 1.90 |

No. 2418 contains #2418a, England #13, Northern Ireland #24, Scotland #27 and Wales & Monmouthshire #27. No. 2418a sold for 32p on day of issue. No. 2418b sold for £6.95.
No. 2418c issued 11/6/08. It sold for 36p on day of issue.

**Souvenir Sheet**

Heritage of Scotland A619

No. 2419: a, National flag (Scotland type A5). b, St. Andrew (58x22mm). c, Edinburgh Castle (58x22mm).

**Perf. 14¾x14 Syncopated, 14¾x14 (#2419b, 2419c)**

| | | | 2006, Nov. 30 | | Photo. |
|---|---|---|---|---|---|
| 2419 | A619 | Sheet of 4, #2419a-2419c, Scotland #21 | | 7.50 | 7.50 |
| a. | | 1st multi | | 1.75 | 1.50 |
| b.-c. | | 72p Either single | | 2.75 | 2.00 |
| e. | | As "a," litho. (2744k, MH440a) | | 2.00 | 2.00 |

No. 2419a sold for 32p on day of issue. Issued: No. 2419e, 5/9/13.

Beatles Memorabilia — A620

Beatles Album Covers — A621

No. 2420: a, Toy guitar, button. b, Lunch box, buttons. c, 45RPM record of "Love Me Do." d, Tray picturing the Beatles, buttons.
No. 2421, "With The Beatles." No. 2422, "Sgt. Pepper's Lonely Hearts Club Band." No. 2423, "Help!" No. 2424, "Abbey Road." No. 2425, "Let It Be." No. 2426, "Revolver."

| | | | 2007, Jan. 9 | Litho. | Perf. 14 |
|---|---|---|---|---|---|
| 2420 | A620 | Sheet of 4 | | 5.50 | 5.50 |
| a.-d. | | 1st Any single | | 1.25 | 1.25 |

**Self-Adhesive**
**Photo.**
**Die Cut Perf. 13x13¾**

| 2421 | A621 | 1st multi | | 1.25 | 1.25 |
|---|---|---|---|---|---|
| 2422 | A621 | 1st multi | | 1.25 | 1.25 |
| 2423 | A621 | 64p multi | | 1.90 | 1.90 |
| 2424 | A621 | 64p multi | | 1.90 | 1.90 |
| 2425 | A621 | 72p multi | | 2.00 | 2.00 |
| 2426 | A621 | 72p multi | | 2.00 | 2.00 |
| | Nos. 2421-2426 (6) | | | 10.30 | 10.30 |

Nos. 2420a-2420d, 2421-2422 each sold for 32p on day of issue.

**Love Type of 2005**
**Serpentine Die Cut 14¾x14**
**Syncopated**
**Booklet Stamp**

| | | | 2007-08 | Photo. | Self-Adhesive |
|---|---|---|---|---|---|
| 2427 | A593 | 1st multi | | 7.50 | 7.50 |
| a. | | Booklet pane, #2427, 5 #MH380 | | 22.00 | |
| b. | | Booklet pane, 2 #2427, 4 #MH300 + 3 labels | | 20.00 | |
| c. | | As #2427, litho. (from 2538a) | | 11.00 | 11.00 |

No. 2427 sold for 32p on day of issue. Compare with No. 2316 which is not syncopated.
Issued: Nos. 2427, 2427a, 1/16/07. Nos. 2427b, 2427c, 1/15/08.
No. 2427c had a franking value of 34p on day of issue.

Marine Life — A622

Designs: No. 2428, Moon jellyfish. No. 2429, Common starfish. No. 2430, Beadlet anemone. No. 2431, Bass. No. 2432, Thornback ray. No. 2433, Lesser octopus. No. 2434, Common mussels. No. 2435, Gray seal. No. 2436, Shore crab. No. 2437, Common sun star.

| | | | 2007, Feb. 1 | Litho. | Perf. 14½ |
|---|---|---|---|---|---|
| 2428 | A622 | 1st multi | | 1.40 | 1.20 |
| 2429 | A622 | 1st multi | | 1.40 | 1.20 |
| 2430 | A622 | 1st multi | | 1.40 | 1.20 |
| 2431 | A622 | 1st multi | | 1.40 | 1.20 |
| 2432 | A622 | 1st multi | | 1.40 | 1.20 |
| 2433 | A622 | 1st multi | | 1.40 | 1.20 |
| 2434 | A622 | 1st multi | | 1.40 | 1.20 |
| 2435 | A622 | 1st multi | | 1.40 | 1.20 |
| 2436 | A622 | 1st multi | | 1.40 | 1.20 |
| 2437 | A622 | 1st multi | | 1.40 | 1.20 |
| a. | | Block of 10, #2428-2437 | | 14.25 | 12.00 |

Nos. 2428-2437 each sold for 32p on day of issue.

Astronomical Objects — A623

Designs: No. 2438, Saturn Nebula (C55). No. 2439, Eskimo Nebula (C39). No. 2440, Cat's Eye Nebula (C6). No. 2441, Helix Nebula (C63). No. 2442, Flaming Star Nebula (C31). No. 2443, Spindle Galaxy (C53).

**Serpentine Die Cut 14¼x14**

| | | | 2007, Feb. 13 | | Photo. |
|---|---|---|---|---|---|
| 2438 | A623 | 1st multi | | 1.45 | 1.30 |
| 2439 | A623 | 1st multi | | 1.45 | 1.30 |
| 2440 | A623 | 50p multi | | 1.75 | 1.60 |
| 2441 | A623 | 50p multi | | 1.75 | 1.60 |
| 2442 | A623 | 72p multi | | 2.25 | 2.10 |
| 2443 | A623 | 72p multi | | 2.25 | 2.10 |
| | Nos. 2438-2443 (6) | | | 10.90 | 10.90 |

Nos. 2438-2439 each sold for 32p on day of issue.

World of Invention — A624

Designs: Nos. 2444, 2450, Man thinking about bridge. Nos. 2445, 2451, Locomotive and tracks. Nos. 2446, 2452, People using telephones, maps of Great Britain, Ireland and Australia. Nos. 2447, 2453, Television camera, man with microphone, man watching television. Nos. 2448, 2454, Man at computer with cord in large ball. Nos. 2449, 2455, Man and woman travelers on cratered planet.

| | | | 2007, Mar. 1 | Photo. | Perf. 14½x14 |
|---|---|---|---|---|---|
| 2444 | A624 | 1st multi | | 1.30 | .90 |
| 2445 | A624 | 1st multi | | 1.30 | .90 |
| 2446 | A624 | 64p multi | | 2.50 | 2.50 |
| 2447 | A624 | 64p multi | | 2.50 | 2.50 |
| a. | | Booklet pane, #2444-2447 (BK181) | | 9.00 | |
| 2448 | A624 | 72p multi | | 4.50 | 4.50 |
| 2449 | A624 | 72p multi | | 4.50 | 4.50 |
| a. | | Souvenir sheet, #2444-2449 | | 17.50 | 17.50 |
| b. | | Booklet pane, #2444-2445, 2448-2449 | | 13.50 | — |
| | Nos. 2444-2449 (6) | | | 16.60 | 15.80 |

**Self-Adhesive**
**Die Cut Perf. 14½x14**

| 2450 | A624 | 1st multi | | 1.30 | .90 |
|---|---|---|---|---|---|
| 2451 | A624 | 1st multi | | 1.90 | 1.75 |
| 2452 | A624 | 64p multi | | 1.90 | 1.75 |
| 2453 | A624 | 64p multi | | 1.30 | 1.25 |
| 2454 | A624 | 72p multi | | 2.10 | 2.10 |
| 2455 | A624 | 72p multi | | 2.10 | 2.10 |
| | Nos. 2450-2455 (6) | | | 10.60 | 9.85 |

Nos. 2444-2445, 2450-2451 each sold for 32p on day of issue.

Abolition of the Slave Trade, Bicent. — A625

Designs: No. 2456, William Wilberforce (1759-1833), abolitionist leader in Parliament, and poster. No. 2457, Olaudah Equiano (c. 1750-97), freed slave and abolitionist writer, and map. No. 2458, Granville Sharp (1735-1813), abolitionist, and ship. No. 2459, Thomas Clarkson (1760-1846), abolitionist and diagram of slaves in slave ship. No. 2460, Hannah More (1745-1833), religious writer, and illustration from Cheap Repository Tracts. No. 2461, Ignatius Sancho (c. 1729-80), abolitionist and actor, poster for performance by Sancho.

| | | | 2007, Mar. 22 | Litho. | Perf. 14¼ |
|---|---|---|---|---|---|
| 2456 | A625 | 1st multi | | 1.20 | 1.20 |
| 2457 | A625 | 1st multi | | 1.20 | 1.20 |
| a. | | Horiz. pair, #2456-2457 | | 2.50 | 2.50 |
| 2458 | A625 | 50p multi | | 1.40 | 1.40 |
| 2459 | A625 | 50p multi | | 1.40 | 1.40 |
| a. | | Horiz. pair, #2458-2459 | | 3.00 | 3.00 |
| 2460 | A625 | 72p multi | | 1.90 | 1.90 |
| 2461 | A625 | 72p multi | | 1.90 | 1.90 |
| a. | | Horiz. pair, #2460-2461 | | 4.00 | 4.00 |
| | Nos. 2456-2461 (6) | | | 9.00 | 9.00 |

Nos. 2456-2457 each sold for 32p on day of issue.

**Souvenir Sheet**

Heritage of England A626

No. 2462: a, English flag (18x22mm). b, St. George slaying dragon (59x22mm). c, Parliament (59x22mm).

**Perf. 14 Syncopated, 14¾x14 (#2462b, 2462c)**

| | | | 2007, Apr. 23 | | Photo. |
|---|---|---|---|---|---|
| 2462 | A626 | Sheet of 4, #2462a-2462c, England #7 | | 6.75 | 6.75 |
| a. | | 1st multi | | 1.50 | 1.50 |
| b.-c. | | 78p Either single | | 1.90 | 1.90 |
| e. | | As "a," litho. (MH440a) | | 1.70 | 1.70 |

On day of issue, No. 2462a and England No. 7 sold for 34p.
Issued: No. 2462e, 5/9/13.

Seaside Resort Scenes — A627

Designs: 1st, Giant ice cream cone. 46p, Sand castle. 48p, Carousel horses. 54p, Beach cabins. 69p, Beach chairs. 78p, Hitched donkeys.

**2007, May 15    Photo.    Perf. 14½**

| | | | | |
|---|---|---|---|---|
| 2463 | A627 | 1st multi | 1.20 | 1.20 |
| 2464 | A627 | 46p multi | 1.35 | 1.35 |
| 2465 | A627 | 48p multi | 1.35 | 1.35 |
| 2466 | A627 | 54p multi | 1.50 | 1.50 |
| 2467 | A627 | 69p multi | 1.90 | 1.90 |
| 2468 | A627 | 78p multi | 2.10 | 2.10 |
| | | Nos. 2463-2468 (6) | 9.40 | 9.40 |

No. 2463 sold for 34p on day of issue. See No. 2573.

Crowned Lion of England A628

**2007, May 17    Litho.    Perf. 14½x14¼**

| | | | | |
|---|---|---|---|---|
| 2469 | A628 | 1st gray bl & dk red + label | 2.75 | 2.75 |

**Souvenir Sheet**
**Photo.**

| | | | | |
|---|---|---|---|---|
| 2470 | | Sheet, #2470a, 2 each England #6, 15 + label | 8.50 | 8.50 |
| a. | | A628 1st bl grn & brt red | 2.00 | .70 |

No. 2469 was issued in sheets of 20 stamps + 20 labels that sold for £7.35. No. 2470 sold for £2.38 on day of issue. Nos. 2469 and 2470 each had a franking value of 34p on day of issue.

**Souvenir Sheet**

Definitive Stamps Designed by Arnold Machin, 40th Anniv. — A629

Design: No. 2472, Arnold Machin.

**Perf. 14½x14¼ (#2471a-2471b, 2472)**
**Photo. & Embossed (#2471a-2471b)**
**2007, June 5**

| | | | | |
|---|---|---|---|---|
| 2471 | A629 | Sheet, #2471a, 2471b, MH237, MH373 | 8.00 | 8.00 |
| a. | | 1st Arnold Machin | 2.50 | 2.50 |
| b. | | 1st #MH6 | 2.50 | 2.50 |
| c. | | Booklet pane, 2 each #2471a, 2471b (BK182) | 10.00 | — |

**Photo.**

| | | | | |
|---|---|---|---|---|
| 2472 | A629 | 1st multi + label | 2.75 | 2.75 |

Nos. 2471a and 2471b each sold for 34p on day of issue and were only issued in the souvenir sheet and the booklet pane.

No. 2472, having a franking value of 34p on day of issue, was issued only in sheets of 20 stamps + 20 labels. The sheets sold for £7.35.

Grand Prix Race Cars and Drivers — A630

Designs: No. 2473, 1957 Vanwall 2.5-liter, Stirling Moss. No. 2474, 1962 BRM P57, Graham Hill. No. 2475, 1963 Lotus 25 Climax, Jim Clark. No. 2476, 1973 Tyrrell 006/2, Jackie Stewart. No. 2477, 1976 McLaren M23, James Hunt. No. 2478, 1986 Williams FW11, Nigel Mansell.

**2007, July 3    Litho.    Perf. 14¼x14**

| | | | | |
|---|---|---|---|---|
| 2473 | A630 | 1st multi | 1.15 | 1.15 |
| 2474 | A630 | 1st multi | 1.15 | 1.15 |
| 2475 | A630 | 54p multi | 1.50 | 1.50 |
| 2476 | A630 | 54p multi | 1.50 | 1.50 |

| | | | | |
|---|---|---|---|---|
| 2477 | A630 | 78p multi | 2.10 | 2.10 |
| 2478 | A630 | 78p multi | 2.10 | 2.10 |
| | | Nos. 2473-2478 (6) | 9.50 | 9.50 |

Nos. 2473 and 2474 each sold for 34p on day of issue.

Publication of Last Harry Potter Novel by J. K. Rowling A631

Coats of Arms From Harry Potter Novels A632

Novels: No. 2479, Harry Potter and the Philosopher's Stone. No. 2480, Harry Potter and the Chamber of Secrets. No. 2481, Harry Potter and the Prisoner of Azkaban. No. 2482, Harry Potter and the Goblet of Fire. No. 2483, Harry Potter and the Order of the Phoenix. No. 2484, Harry Potter and the Half-Blood Prince. No. 2485, Harry Potter and the Deathly Hallows.

Arms of: Nos. 2486a, 2487, Gryffindor. Nos. 2486b, 2488, Hufflepuff. Nos. 2486c, 2489, Hogwarts. Nos. 2486d, 2490, Ravenclaw. Nos. 2486e, 2491, Slytherin.

**2007, July 17    Perf. 14x14¼**

| | | | | |
|---|---|---|---|---|
| 2479 | A631 | 1st multi | 1.40 | 1.50 |
| 2480 | A631 | 1st multi | 1.40 | 1.50 |
| 2481 | A631 | 1st multi | 1.40 | 1.50 |
| 2482 | A631 | 1st multi | 1.40 | 1.50 |
| 2483 | A631 | 1st multi | 1.40 | 1.50 |
| 2484 | A631 | 1st multi | 1.40 | 1.50 |
| 2485 | A631 | 1st multi | 1.40 | 1.50 |
| a. | | Horiz. strip of 7, #2479-2485 | 10.00 | 10.50 |

**Souvenir Sheet**
**Perf. 14¾x14**

| | | | | |
|---|---|---|---|---|
| 2486 | | Sheet of 5 | 7.25 | 6.75 |
| a.-e. | | A632 1st Any single | 1.45 | 1.25 |

**Self-Adhesive**
**Die Cut Perf. 14¾x14**

| | | | | |
|---|---|---|---|---|
| 2487 | A632 | 1st multi + label | 1.90 | 1.90 |
| 2488 | A632 | 1st multi + label | 1.90 | 1.90 |
| 2489 | A632 | 1st multi + label | 1.90 | 1.90 |
| 2490 | A632 | 1st multi + label | 1.90 | 1.90 |
| 2491 | A632 | 1st multi + label | 1.90 | 1.90 |
| a. | | Vert. strip of 5, #2487-2491, + 5 labels | 10.00 | |
| | | Nos. 2487-2491 (5) | 9.50 | 9.50 |

Nos. 2479-2485, 2486a-2486e, each sold for 34p on day of issue. Nos. 2487-2491, having a franking value of 34p on day of issue, were sold in a sheet of 20 stamps + 20 labels that sold for £7.35. Labels could be personalized for an extra fee.

Scouting, Cent. — A633

Designs: 1st, Scouts around campfire. Scout looking at sky. 46p, Scouts climbing rocks. 48p, Scout planting tree. 54p, Scout learning archery from volunteer. 69p, Scouts and glider. 78p, Nine Scouts.

**2007, July 26    Perf. 14¼x14**

| | | | | |
|---|---|---|---|---|
| 2492 | A633 | 1st multi | 1.20 | 1.20 |
| 2493 | A633 | 46p multi | 1.30 | 1.30 |
| 2494 | A633 | 48p multi | 1.30 | 1.30 |
| 2495 | A633 | 54p multi | 1.50 | 1.50 |
| 2496 | A633 | 69p multi | 1.90 | 1.90 |
| 2497 | A633 | 78p multi | 3.00 | 3.00 |
| | | Nos. 2492-2497 (6) | 10.20 | 10.20 |

Europa (Nos. 2492, 2494). No. 2492 sold for 34p on day of issue.

Endangered Birds — A634

**2007, Sept. 4    Litho.    Perf. 14½**

| | | | | |
|---|---|---|---|---|
| 2498 | A634 | 1st White-tailed eagle | 1.50 | 1.30 |
| 2499 | A634 | 1st Bearded tit | 1.50 | 1.30 |

| | | | | |
|---|---|---|---|---|
| 2500 | A634 | 1st Red kite | 1.50 | 1.30 |
| 2501 | A634 | 1st Cirl bunting | 1.50 | 1.30 |
| 2502 | A634 | 1st Marsh harrier | 1.50 | 1.30 |
| 2503 | A634 | 1st Avocet | 1.50 | 1.30 |
| 2504 | A634 | 1st Bittern | 1.50 | 1.30 |
| 2505 | A634 | 1st Dartford warbler | 1.50 | 1.30 |
| 2506 | A634 | 1st Corncrake | 1.50 | 1.30 |
| 2507 | A634 | 1st Peregrine falcon | 1.50 | 1.30 |
| a. | | Block of 10, #2498-2507 | 15.00 | 13.00 |

Nos. 2498-2507 each sold for 34p on day of issue.

British Army Uniforms — A635

Designs: No. 2508, Non-commissioned officer, Royal Military Police, 1999. No. 2509, Tank commander, 5th Royal Tank Regiment, 1944. No. 2510, Observer, Royal Field Artillery, 1917. No. 2511, Rifleman, 95th Rifles, 1813. No. 2512, Grenadier, Royal Regiment of Foot of Ireland, 1704. No. 2513, Trooper, Earl of Oxford's Horse, 1661.

**2007, Sept. 20    Litho.    Perf. 14¼**

| | | | | |
|---|---|---|---|---|
| 2508 | A635 | 1st multi | 1.30 | 1.30 |
| 2509 | A635 | 1st multi | 1.30 | 1.30 |
| 2510 | A635 | 1st multi | 1.30 | 1.30 |
| a. | | Horiz. strip of 3, #2508-2510 | 4.00 | 4.00 |
| b. | | Booklet pane of 3, #2508-2510 (BK183) | 4.00 | |
| c. | | Booklet pane of 4 (BK208) | 5.25 | — |
| 2511 | A635 | 78p multi | 2.00 | 2.00 |
| 2512 | A635 | 78p multi | 2.00 | 2.00 |
| 2513 | A635 | 78p multi | 1.75 | 1.75 |
| a. | | Horiz. strip of 3, #2511-2513 | 6.00 | 6.00 |
| b. | | Booklet pane of 3, #2511-2513 (BK183) | 5.75 | — |
| | | Nos. 2508-2513 (6) | 9.65 | 9.65 |

Issued: No. 2510c, 5/14/15. Nos. 2508-2510 each sold for 34p on day of sale.

Wedding of Queen Elizabeth II and Prince Philip, 60th Anniv. — A636

Royal Family A637

Various photographs of couple from: No. 2514, 2006. No. 2515, 1997. No. 2516, 1980. No. 2517, 1969. No. 2518, 1961. No. 2519, 1947.

No. 2520: a, Royal family, log and flowers (35x35mm). b, Queen Elizabeth II and Prince Philip (40x30mm). c, Royal family, baby carriage (41x30mm). d, Queen Elizabeth II, Prince Philip, Princess Anne and Prince Charles (27x38mm).

**2007, Oct. 26    Litho.    Perf. 14¼x14**

| | | | | |
|---|---|---|---|---|
| 2514 | A636 | 1st black | 1.20 | 1.10 |
| 2515 | A636 | 1st black | 1.20 | 1.10 |
| a. | | Horiz. pair, #2514-2515 | 2.50 | 2.25 |
| 2516 | A636 | 54p black | 1.50 | 1.40 |
| 2517 | A636 | 54p black | 1.50 | 1.40 |
| a. | | Horiz. pair, #2516-2517 | 3.00 | 2.90 |
| 2518 | A636 | 78p black | 2.25 | 2.00 |
| 2519 | A636 | 78p black | 2.25 | 2.00 |
| a. | | Horiz. pair, #2518-2519 | 4.50 | 4.00 |
| | | Nos. 2514-2519 (6) | 9.90 | 9.00 |

**Souvenir Sheet**
**Self-Adhesive**

| | | | | |
|---|---|---|---|---|
| 2520 | A637 | Sheet of 4 | 7.00 | 7.00 |
| a. | | 1st multi, die cut perf. 14½ | 1.40 | 1.40 |
| b. | | 1st multi, die cut perf. 14½x14¼ | 1.40 | 1.40 |
| c. | | 69p multi, die cut perf. 14¼x14 | 1.90 | 1.90 |
| d. | | 78p multi, die cut perf. 14¼ | 2.25 | 2.25 |

Nos. 2514-2515, 2520a and 2520b each sold for 34p on day of sale.

Madonna and Child, by William Dyce A638

Madonna of Humility, by Lippo di Dalmasio A639

**Die Cut Perf. 14¾x14 Syncopated**
**2007, Nov. 6    Photo.**
**Self-Adhesive**

| | | | | |
|---|---|---|---|---|
| 2521 | A638 | 2nd multi | 1.35 | 1.35 |
| 2522 | A639 | 1st multi | 1.65 | 1.50 |

On day of issue, No. 2521 sold for 24p; No. 2522 for 34p.

Christmas
A640    A641

Angels with banners inscribed: Nos. 2523a, 2523c, 2524, 2526, Peace. Nos. 2523b, 2523d, 2525, 2527, Goodwill. Nos. 2523e, 2528, Joy. Nos. 2523f, 2529, Glory.

**2007, Nov. 6    Photo.    Perf. 14¾x14**

| | | | | |
|---|---|---|---|---|
| 2523 | | Sheet of 6 | 10.75 | 10.75 |
| a. | | A640 2nd multi | 1.00 | 1.00 |
| b. | | A640 1st multi | 1.25 | 1.25 |
| c. | | A641 2nd Large multi | 1.40 | 1.40 |
| d. | | A641 1st Large multi | 1.90 | 1.90 |
| e. | | A640 78p multi | 2.00 | 2.00 |
| f. | | A640 £1.24 multi | 3.25 | 3.25 |

**Self-Adhesive**
**Die Cut Perf. 14¾x14**

| | | | | |
|---|---|---|---|---|
| 2524 | A640 | 2nd multi | .90 | .90 |
| a. | | Booklet pane of 12 | 16.00 | |
| b. | | Sheet of 20 + 20 labels, litho. | 20.00 | |
| 2525 | A640 | 1st multi | 1.10 | 1.10 |
| a. | | Booklet pane of 12 | 19.00 | |
| b. | | Sheet of 20 + 20 labels, litho. | 25.00 | |
| 2526 | A641 | 2nd Large multi | 1.35 | 1.35 |
| 2527 | A641 | 1st Large multi | 1.75 | 1.75 |
| 2528 | A640 | 78p multi | 2.00 | 2.00 |
| a. | | Sheet, 8 each #2524-2525, 4 #2528, + 20 labels, litho. | 25.00 | |
| b. | | Sheet of 10 + 10 labels, litho. | 30.00 | |
| 2529 | A640 | £1.24 multi | 3.50 | 3.50 |
| | | Nos. 2524-2529 (6) | 10.60 | 10.60 |

On day of issue, Nos. 2523a and 2524 sold for 24p, Nos. 2523b and 2425 sold for 34p, Nos. 2523c and 2426 sold for 40p, Nos. 2523d and 2427 sold for 48p. No. 2528a sold for £8.30. No. 2524b sold for £8.50, Nos. 2525b and 2528b each sold for £13.50. Labels on Nos. 2524b, 2525b, and 2528b were personalizable.

Poppy and Soldiers — A642

**2007, Nov. 8    Litho.    Perf. 14½x14¼**

| | | | | |
|---|---|---|---|---|
| 2530 | A642 | 1st multi | 2.75 | 2.75 |
| a. | | Souvenir sheet of 5 | 10.50 | 10.50 |

Battle of Passchendaele, 90th anniv. No. 2530a contains #2530, England #15, Northern Ireland #26, Scotland #29, and Wales & Monmouthshire #30. No. 2530 was also printed in a sheet of 20 + 5 labels that sold for £7.35, and a limited-quantity privately-contracted sheet of 10 + 10 labels, that sold for £28.50.

Book Covers of James Bond Novels by Ian Fleming A643

Designs: No. 2531, Casino Royale. No. 2532, Doctor No. No. 2533, Goldfinger. No. 2534, Diamonds Are Forever. No. 2535, For Your Eyes Only. No. 2536, From Russia, with Love.

**2008, Jan. 8    Litho.    Perf. 14¾x14¼**

| 2531 | A643 | 1st multi | 1.25 | 1.25 |
|------|------|-----------|------|------|
| 2532 | A643 | 1st multi | 1.25 | 1.25 |
| 2533 | A643 | 54p multi | 1.60 | 1.60 |
| 2534 | A643 | 54p multi | 1.40 | 1.40 |
| 2535 | A643 | 78p multi | 2.25 | 2.25 |
| a. | | Booklet pane of 3, #2531, 2533, 2535 (BK184) | 5.25 | — |
| 2536 | A643 | 78p multi | 1.90 | 1.90 |
| a. | | Miniature sheet of 6, #2531-2536 | 14.50 | 13.50 |
| b. | | Booklet pane of 3, #2532, 2534, 2536 (BK184) | 4.50 | — |
| | | Nos. 2531-2536 (6) | 9.65 | 9.65 |

On day of issue, Nos. 2531-2532 each sold for 34p.

### Hello and Flag Types of 2005
*Die Cut Perf 14¾x14 Syncopated*

**2008, Jan. 15                    Litho.**

**Self-Adhesive**

| 2537 | A592 | 1st Hello | 2.75 | 2.50 |
|------|------|-----------|------|------|
| a. | | Sheet of 20 + 20 labels | 55.00 | |
| 2538 | A594 | 1st Flag | 2.75 | 2.50 |
| a. | | Sheet, 8 #2427c, 6 each #2537-2538, + 20 labels | 55.00 | |

Issued: No. 2537a, 5/8/10. No. 2537a sold for £8.50. Labels could not be personalized. No. 2538a sold for £7.35. Nos. 2537-2538 each had a franking value of 34p on day of issue.

Working Dogs — A644

Designs: 1st, Assistance dog. 46p, Mountain rescue dog. 48p, Police dog. 54p, Customs dog. 69p, Sheepdog. 78p, Guide dog.

**2008, Feb. 5    Litho.    Perf. 14¼x14½**

| 2539 | A644 | 1st multi | 1.30 | 1.30 |
|------|------|-----------|------|------|
| 2540 | A644 | 46p multi | 1.25 | 1.25 |
| 2541 | A644 | 48p multi | 1.25 | 1.25 |
| 2542 | A644 | 54p multi | 1.50 | 1.50 |
| 2543 | A644 | 69p multi | 1.90 | 1.90 |
| 2544 | A644 | 78p multi | 2.10 | 2.10 |
| | | Nos. 2539-2544 (6) | 9.30 | 8.95 |

No. 2539 sold for 34p on day of issue. Europa (No. 2539).

### Types of 2005-06
*Die Cut Perf. 14¾x14 Syncopated*

**2008, Feb. 28                    Litho.**

**Booklet Stamps**

**Self-Adhesive**

| 2545 | A591 | 1st Flower | 7.50 | 7.50 |
|------|------|------------|------|------|
| 2546 | A613 | 1st Balloons | 7.50 | 7.50 |
| 2547 | A614 | 1st Fireworks | 7.50 | 7.50 |
| a. | | Sheet of 20 + 20 labels | 150.00 | |
| 2548 | A615 | 1st Champagne bottle | 7.50 | 7.50 |
| a. | | Booklet pane of 6, #2537-2538, 2545-2548 | 37.50 | |

On day of issue, Nos. 2545-2548 each sold for 34p.

Issued: No. 2547a, 1/20/12. No. 2547a sold for £11.47. Labels could not be personalized.

British Royalty and History — A645

Designs: No. 2549, King Henry IV. No. 2550, King Henry V. No. 2551, King Henry VI. No. 2552, King Edward IV. No. 2553, King Edward V. No. 2554, King Richard III.

No. 2555: a, Owen Glendower (Owain Glyn Dwr). b, Welsh rebel. b, Battle of Agincourt. c, Battle of Tewkesbury. d, William Caxton, first English printer.

**2008, Feb. 28    Litho.    Perf. 14¼**

| 2549 | A645 | 1st multi | 1.00 | .95 |
|------|------|-----------|------|-----|
| 2550 | A645 | 1st multi | 1.00 | .95 |
| 2551 | A645 | 54p multi | 1.50 | 1.50 |
| 2552 | A645 | 54p multi | 1.50 | 1.50 |
| 2553 | A645 | 69p multi | 1.90 | 2.00 |
| 2554 | A645 | 69p multi | 1.90 | 2.00 |
| | | Nos. 2549-2554 (6) | 8.80 | 8.90 |

**Souvenir Sheet**

| 2555 | | Sheet of 4 | 6.25 | 6.25 |
|------|---|-----------|------|------|
| a.-b. | | A645 1st Either single | 1.00 | .90 |
| c.-d. | | A645 78p Either single | 2.25 | 2.00 |

On day of issue, Nos. 2549, 2550, 2555a and 2555b each sold for 34p.

---

See Nos. 2653-2659, 2767-2774, 2807-2814, 2940-2946, 2990-2995.

**Souvenir Sheet**

Heritage of Northern Ireland A646

No. 2556: a, Carrickfergus Castle (18x21mm). b, Giant's Causeway, ocean and sky (18x21mm). c, St. Patrick (57x21mm). d, Queen's Bridge and Friendship Beacon, Belfast (57x21mm).

**Perf. 14¾x14¼ Syncopated, 14¾x14¼ (78p)**

**2008, Mar. 11                    Litho.**

| 2556 | A646 | Sheet of 4 | 7.25 | 7.25 |
|------|------|-----------|------|------|
| a.-b. | | 1st Either single | 1.10 | 1.00 |
| c.-d. | | 78p Either single | 2.50 | 2.40 |

On day of issue Nos. 2556a-2556b each sold for 34p.

Rescue at Sea — A647

Sea rescuers in action near: 1st, Barra. 46p, Appledore. 48p, Portland. 54p, St. Ives. 69p, Lee-on-Solent. 78p, Tenby.

**Perf. 14¼x14 Syncopated**

**2008, Mar. 13**

| 2557 | A647 | 1st multi | 1.00 | .95 |
|------|------|-----------|------|-----|
| 2558 | A647 | 46p multi | 1.30 | 1.30 |
| 2559 | A647 | 48p multi | 1.35 | 1.35 |
| 2560 | A647 | 54p multi | 1.50 | 1.50 |
| 2561 | A647 | 69p multi | 2.00 | 2.00 |
| 2562 | A647 | 78p multi | 2.25 | 2.25 |
| | | Nos. 2557-2562 (6) | 9.40 | 9.35 |

No. 2557 sold for 34p on day of issue.

Endangered Insects — A648

Designs: No. 2563, Adonis blue butterfly. No. 2564, Southern damselfly. No. 2565, Red-barbed ant. No. 2566, Barberry carpet moth. No. 2567, Stag beetle. No. 2568, Hazel pot beetle. No. 2569, Field cricket. No. 2570, Silver-spotted skipper. No. 2571, Purbeck mason wasp. No. 2572, Noble chafer.

**2008, Apr. 15    Litho.    Perf. 14½**

| 2563 | A648 | 1st multi | 1.50 | 1.30 |
|------|------|-----------|------|------|
| 2564 | A648 | 1st multi | 1.50 | 1.30 |
| 2565 | A648 | 1st multi | 1.50 | 1.30 |
| 2566 | A648 | 1st multi | 1.50 | 1.30 |
| 2567 | A648 | 1st multi | 1.50 | 1.30 |
| 2568 | A648 | 1st multi | 1.50 | 1.30 |
| 2569 | A648 | 1st multi | 1.50 | 1.30 |
| 2570 | A648 | 1st multi | 1.50 | 1.30 |
| 2571 | A648 | 1st multi | 1.50 | 1.30 |
| 2572 | A648 | 1st multi | 1.50 | 1.30 |
| a. | | Block of 10, #2563-2572 | 15.00 | 13.00 |

Nos. 2563-2572 each sold for 36p on day of issue.

### Seaside Resorts Type of 2007
*Die Cut Perf. 14½*

**2008, May 13                    Photo.**

**Booklet Stamp**

**Self-Adhesive**

| 2573 | A627 | 1st Like #2463 | 3.75 | 3.75 |
|------|------|----------------|------|------|
| a. | | Booklet pane, 2 #2573, 4 #MH300 | 10.00 | |

No. 2573 sold for 36p on day of issue.

A649

---

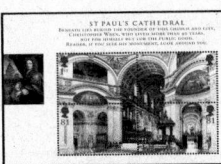

Cathedrals — A650

Designs: No. 2574, Lichfield Cathedral. 48p, Belfast Cathedral. 50p, Gloucester Cathedral. 56p, St. David's Cathedral, Wales. 72p, Westminster Cathedral. 81p, St. Magnus Cathedral, Orkney.

No. 2580 — St. Paul's Cathedral: a, Ceiling, denomination at UL. b, Ceiling, denomination at UR. c, Floor, denomination at UL. d, Floor, denomination at UR.

**2008, May 13    Litho.    Perf. 14¼**

| 2574 | A649 | 1st black | 1.25 | 1.10 |
|------|------|-----------|------|------|
| 2575 | A649 | 48p black | 1.50 | 1.40 |
| 2576 | A649 | 50p black | 1.60 | 1.40 |
| 2577 | A649 | 56p black | 1.75 | 1.60 |
| 2578 | A649 | 72p black | 2.25 | 2.00 |
| 2579 | A649 | 81p black | 2.60 | 2.25 |
| | | Nos. 2574-2579 (6) | 10.95 | 9.75 |

**Souvenir Sheet**

| 2580 | A650 | Sheet of 4 | 7.00 | 7.00 |
|------|------|-----------|------|------|
| a.-b. | | 1st Either single | 1.10 | 1.00 |
| c.-d. | | 81p Either single | 2.40 | 2.25 |

Nos. 2574, 2580a-2580b each sold for 36p on day of issue.

Posters of British Comedy and Horror Films — A651

Poster for: 1st, Carry On Sergeant. 48p, Dracula. 50p, Carry On Cleo. 56p, The Curse of Frankenstein. 72p, Carry On Screaming. 81p, The Mummy.

**2008, June 10    Litho.    Perf. 13¾x14**

| 2581 | A651 | 1st multi | 1.00 | .85 |
|------|------|-----------|------|-----|
| 2582 | A651 | 48p multi | 1.35 | 1.20 |
| 2583 | A651 | 50p multi | 1.40 | 1.25 |
| 2584 | A651 | 56p multi | 1.50 | 1.40 |
| 2585 | A651 | 72p multi | 2.00 | 1.75 |
| 2586 | A651 | 81p multi | 2.25 | 2.00 |
| | | Nos. 2581-2586 (6) | 9.50 | 8.45 |

No. 2581 sold for 36p on day of issue.

First Powered Flight in Great Britain, Cent. — A652

Air displays: 1st, Red Arrow aerobatic team. 48p, Royal Air Force Falcons parachuting squad. 50p, Boy watching airplanes in formation. 56p, Avro Vulcans and Avro 707s in flight. 72p, Parachutist Robert Wyndham on wing of Avro 504 biplane. 81p, Blériot airplane and air race tower.

**2008, July 17    Photo.    Perf. 14¼x14**

| 2587 | A652 | 1st multi | 1.00 | .90 |
|------|------|-----------|------|-----|
| a. | | Sheet of 20 + 17 labels, litho. | 22.00 | |
| b. | | Litho. | 3.60 | 3.60 |
| c. | | Booklet pane of 4, 2 each #1758a, 2587b (BK185) | 12.00 | |
| 2588 | A652 | 48p multi | 1.35 | 1.20 |
| 2589 | A652 | 50p multi | 1.40 | 1.25 |
| 2590 | A652 | 56p multi | 1.50 | 1.40 |
| 2591 | A652 | 72p multi | 2.00 | 1.75 |
| 2592 | A652 | 81p multi | 2.25 | 2.00 |
| | | Nos. 2587-2592 (6) | 9.50 | 8.50 |

No. 2587 sold for 36p on day of issue. No. 2587a sold for £7.75. Labels could not be personalized. No. 2587c issued 9/18.

**Souvenir Sheet**

2008 Olympic Games, Beijing and 2012 Olympic Games, London A653

---

No. 2593: a, National Stadium, Beijing. b, London Eye. c, Tower of London. d, Corner Tower, Forbidden City, Beijing.

**Litho. & Silk Screened**

**2008, Aug. 22                    Perf. 14½**

| 2593 | A653 | Sheet of 4 | 6.50 | 6.50 |
|------|------|-----------|------|------|
| a.-d. | | 1st Any single | 1.60 | 1.50 |

On day of issue Nos. 2593a-2593d each sold for 36p.

Royal Air Force Uniforms — A654

Designs: No. 2594, Drum major, Royal Air Force Central Band, 2007. No. 2595, Helicopter rescue winchman, 1984. No. 2596, Hawker Hunter pilot, 1951. No. 2597, Lancaster air gunner, 1944. No. 2598, Plotter, Women's Army Air Force, 1940. No. 2599, Pilot, 1918.

**2008, Sept. 18    Litho.    Perf. 14¼**

| 2594 | A654 | 1st multi | 1.00 | .95 |
|------|------|-----------|------|-----|
| 2595 | A654 | 1st multi | 1.00 | .95 |
| 2596 | A654 | 1st multi | 1.00 | .95 |
| a. | | Horiz. strip of 3, #2594-2596 | 3.25 | 3.00 |
| b. | | Booklet pane of 3, #2594-2596 (BK185) | 3.25 | |
| 2597 | A654 | 81p multi | 2.25 | 2.10 |
| 2598 | A654 | 81p multi | 2.25 | 2.10 |
| 2599 | A654 | 81p multi | 2.25 | 2.10 |
| a. | | Horiz. strip of 3, #2597-2599 | 7.00 | 6.50 |
| b. | | Booklet pane of 3, #2597-2599 (BK185) | 7.00 | |
| | | Nos. 2594-2599 (6) | 9.75 | 9.15 |

Nos. 2594-2596 each sold for 36p on day of issue.

**Miniature Sheet**

Country Definitive Stamps, 50th Anniv. A655

**Perf. 14¾x14 Syncopated**

**2008, Sept. 29                    Photo.**

**Buff Paper**

| 2600 | A655 | Sheet of 9 + label | 14.50 | 14.00 |
|------|------|--------------------|-------|-------|
| a. | | 1st Wales & Monmouthshire Type A1 | 1.50 | 1.50 |
| b. | | 1st Scotland Type A1 | 1.50 | 1.50 |
| c. | | 1st Wales & Monmouthshire Type A3 | 1.50 | 1.50 |
| d. | | 1st Scotland Type A3 | 1.50 | 1.50 |
| e. | | 1st Northern Ireland Type A1 | 1.50 | 1.50 |
| f. | | 1st Wales & Monmouthshire Type A2 | 1.50 | 1.50 |
| g. | | 1st Scotland Type A2 | 1.50 | 1.50 |
| h. | | 1st Northern Ireland Type A2 | 1.50 | 1.50 |
| i. | | 1st Northern Ireland Type A3 | 1.50 | 1.50 |
| j. | | As #2600e, litho., white paper | 1.60 | 1.60 |
| k. | | As #2600i, litho., white paper | 1.60 | 1.60 |
| l. | | As #2600h, litho., white paper | 1.60 | 1.60 |
| m. | | As #2600a, litho., white paper | 1.60 | 1.60 |
| n. | | As #2600c, litho., white paper | 1.60 | 1.60 |
| o. | | As #2600f, litho., white paper | 1.60 | 1.60 |
| p. | | As #2600b, litho., white paper | 1.60 | 1.60 |
| q. | | As #2600d, litho., white paper | 1.60 | 1.60 |
| r. | | As #2600g, litho., white paper | 1.60 | 1.60 |
| s. | | Booklet pane of 9, #2600j-2600r (BK186) | 16.00 | |
| t. | | Booklet pane of 6, #2600p-2600r, 3 Scotland #21a (BK186) | 11.00 | |
| u. | | Booklet pane of 6, #2600j-2600l, 3 Northern Ireland #18a (BK186) | 9.75 | |
| v. | | Booklet pane of 6, #2600m-2600o, 3 Wales & Monmouthshire #21b (BK186) | 14.00 | |

Nos. 2600a-2600r each sold for 36p on day of issue.

Famous Women — A656

Designs: 1st, Millicent Garrett Fawcett (1847-1929), suffragist. 48p, Elizabeth Garrett Anderson (1836-1917), first female physician in Britain. 50p, Marie Stopes (1880-1958), birth control advocate. 56p, Eleanor Rathbone (1872-1946), politician and advocate for family allowance. 72p, Claudia Jones (1915-64), civil rights activist. 81p, Barbara Castle (1910-2002), politician and advocate for equal pay for women.

### Perf. 14¼x14½

| | | | | Photo. |
|---|---|---|---|---|
| **2008, Oct. 14** | | | | |
| 2601 | A656 | 1st multi | 1.00 | .95 |
| 2602 | A656 | 48p multi | 1.35 | 1.25 |
| 2603 | A656 | 50p multi | 1.40 | 1.30 |
| 2604 | A656 | 56p multi | 1.60 | 1.50 |
| 2605 | A656 | 72p multi | 2.00 | 1.90 |
| 2606 | A656 | 81p multi | 2.25 | 2.10 |
| | | Nos. 2601-2606 (6) | 9.60 | 9.00 |

On day of issue, No. 2601 sold for 36p.

Christmas
A657    A658

Pantomime actors: Nos. 2607a, 2607c, 2608, 2610, Ugly sisters from Cinderella. Nos. 2607b, 2607e, 2609, 2612, Genie from Aladdin. 50p, Captain Hook from Peter Pan. 81p, Wicked queen from Snow White.

### 2008, Nov. 4   Photo.   Perf. 14¾x14

| 2607 | | Sheet of 6 | 9.25 | 9.25 |
|---|---|---|---|---|
| a. | A657 | 2nd multi | .90 | .75 |
| b. | A657 | 1st multi | 1.15 | 1.15 |
| c. | A658 | 2nd Large multi | 1.35 | 1.35 |
| d. | A657 | 50p multi | 1.60 | 1.60 |
| e. | A658 | 1st Large multi | 1.60 | 1.60 |
| f. | A657 | 81p multi | 2.60 | 2.60 |

### Self-Adhesive
### Die Cut Perf. 14¾x14 Syncopated

| 2608 | A657 | 2nd multi | .90 | .75 |
|---|---|---|---|---|
| a. | | Booklet pane of 12 | 16.00 | |
| b. | | Litho. + label | .85 | .75 |
| 2609 | A657 | 1st multi | 1.15 | 1.15 |
| a. | | Booklet pane of 12 | 19.00 | |
| b. | | Litho. + label | 1.00 | 1.00 |
| 2610 | A658 | 2nd Large multi | 1.35 | 1.35 |
| 2611 | A657 | 50p multi | 1.60 | 1.60 |
| 2612 | A658 | 1st Large multi | 1.60 | 1.60 |
| 2613 | A657 | 81p multi | 2.60 | 2.60 |
| a. | | Litho. + label | 2.25 | 2.50 |
| b. | | Sheet of 20, 8 each #2608b, 2609b, 4 #2613a + 20 labels | 24.00 | — |
| | | Nos. 2608-2613 (6) | 9.20 | 9.05 |

On day of issue, the franking value of Nos. 2607a, 2608, and 2608b was 27p, and that of Nos. 2607b, 2609 and 2609b was 36p. On day of issue, Nos. 2607c and 2610 sold for 42p, and Nos. 2607e and 2612 sold for 52p. No. 2613b sold for £8.85. Labels could not be personalized.

No. 2608 was also printed in sheets of 20 stamps + 20 labels that could be personalized. No. 2609b was also printed in sheets of 10 stamps + 10 labels and 20 stamps + 20 labels that could be personalized. No. 2613a was also available in a sheet of 10 stamps + 10 labels that could be personalized.

Poppy With Soldier's Face — A659

### 2008, Nov. 6   Litho.   Perf. 14½x14¼

| 2614 | A659 | 1st multi | 2.50 | 1.00 |
|---|---|---|---|---|
| a. | | Souvenir sheet of 5 | 10.00 | 10.00 |
| b. | | Horiz. strip of 5, #2418c, 2530, 2614 | 5.00 | 4.50 |
| c. | | Booklet pane of 4, #2418c, 2614, 2 #2530 (BK217) | 7.50 | — |

End of World War I, 90th anniv. On day of issue, No. 2614 sold for 36p. No. 2614a contains #2614, England #18, Northern Ireland #29, Scotland #32, and Wales and Monmouthshire #32. No. 2614 also was printed in a sheet of 20 + 5 labels that sold for £7.75, and in a series of limited-quantity privately contracted sheets of 10 + 10 labels that sold for various prices.

Issued: No. 2614c, 7/31/17.

British Design — A660

---

Designs: No. 2615, Supermarine Spitfire, designed by R. J. Mitchell. No. 2616, Miniskirt, designed by Mary Quant. No. 2617, Mini Cooper, designed by Sir Alec Issigonis. No. 2618, Anglepoise lamp, designed by George Carwardine. No. 2619, Concorde, designed by Aérospatiale-BAC. No. 2620, K2 telephone kiosk, designed by Sir Giles Gilbert Scott. No. 2621, Polypropylene chair, designed by Robin Day. No. 2622, Penguin books, designed by Edward Young. No. 2623, London Underground map, designed by Harry Beck. No. 2624, Routemaster Bus, designed by AAM Durrant.

### 2009, Jan. 13   Litho.   Perf. 14½

| 2615 | A660 | 1st multi | 1.40 | 1.20 |
|---|---|---|---|---|
| a. | | Sheet of 20 + 20 labels | 30.00 | — |
| 2616 | A660 | 1st multi | 1.40 | 1.20 |
| 2617 | A660 | 1st multi | 1.40 | 1.20 |
| a. | | Sheet of 20 + 20 labels | 30.00 | — |
| 2618 | A660 | 1st multi | 1.40 | 1.20 |
| 2619 | A660 | 1st multi | 1.40 | 1.20 |
| a. | | Booklet pane of 4, 2 each #2049A, 2619 (BK187) | 21.00 | — |
| b. | | Sheet of 20 + 20 labels | 30.00 | — |
| 2620 | A660 | 1st multi | 1.40 | 1.20 |
| 2621 | A660 | 1st multi | 1.40 | 1.20 |
| 2622 | A660 | 1st multi | 1.40 | 1.20 |
| 2623 | A660 | 1st multi | 1.40 | 1.20 |
| a. | | Booklet pane of 6, #2616, 2618, 2620-2623 (BK187) | 8.50 | — |
| 2624 | A660 | 1st multi | 1.40 | 1.20 |
| a. | | Block of 10, #2615-2624 | 14.00 | 14.00 |
| b. | | Booklet pane of 4, #2615, 2617, 2 #2624 (BK187) | 5.75 | — |

On day of issue, Nos. 2615-2624 each sold for 36p. Nos. 2617a, 2619b sold for £7.74. Labels on No. 2617a, No. 2619b could not be personalized.

Issued: No. 2619b, 3/2/09. No. 2615a, 9/15/10. No. 2615a sold for £8.50 and labels could not be personalized.

See Nos. 2640-2644, 2833.

### Miniature Sheet

Robert Burns (1759-96), Poet — A661

No. 2625: a, Man with plow, text, "A Man's a Man for a' that". b, Portrait of Burns by Alexander Naysmith.

### Perf. 14½ (#2625a, 2625b), 14¾x14 Syncopated

| | | | | Photo. |
|---|---|---|---|---|
| **2009, Jan. 22** | | | | |
| 2625 | A661 | Sheet of 6, #2625a, 2625b, Scotland #20, 21, 31, 32 | 8.00 | 8.00 |
| a.-b. | | 1st Either single | 1.25 | 1.25 |

On day of issue, Nos. 2625a and 2625b each sold for 36p.

### Miniature Sheet

Wildlife and HMS Beagle Map of Galapagos Islands — A662

No. 2626: a, Flightless cormorant. b, Giant tortoise, cactus finch. c, Marine iguana. d, Floreana mockingbird.

### 2009, Feb. 12   Perf. 14¼

| 2626 | A662 | Sheet of 4 | 7.00 | 7.00 |
|---|---|---|---|---|
| a.-b. | | 1st Either single | 1.10 | 1.00 |
| c.-d. | | 81p Either single | 2.40 | 1.25 |
| e. | | Booklet pane, #2626, litho. (BK188) | 7.25 | — |

On day of issue, Nos. 2626a and 2626b each sold for 36p. No. 2626e has a rouletted label to the left of the sheet.

Charles Darwin (1809-82), Naturalist — A663

Designs: Nos. 2627, 2633, Photograph of Darwin. Nos. 2628, 2634, Head of marine

---

iguana (zoology). Nos. 2629, 2635, Heads of finches (ornithology). Nos. 2630, 2636, Island (geology). Nos. 2631, 2637, Bee orchid (botany). Nos. 2632, 2638, Orangutan (anthropology).

### 2009, Feb. 12   Perf. 14 Syncopated
### Booklet Stamps (#2627-2632)

| 2627 | A663 | 1st multi (2632a) | 5.75 | 5.75 |
|---|---|---|---|---|
| 2628 | A663 | 48p multi (2630a) | 6.90 | 6.90 |
| 2629 | A663 | 50p multi (2630a) | 7.35 | 7.35 |
| 2630 | A663 | 56p multi (2630a) | 7.85 | 7.85 |
| a. | | Booklet pane of 3, #2628-2630 (BK188) | 21.00 | |
| 2631 | A663 | 72p multi (2632a) | 8.35 | 8.35 |
| 2632 | A663 | 81p multi (2632a) | 9.15 | 9.15 |
| a. | | Booklet pane of 3, #2627, 2631, 2632 (BK188) | 22.50 | — |
| | | Nos. 2627-2632 (6) | 45.35 | 45.35 |

### Self-Adhesive
### Die Cut Perf. 14 Syncopated

| 2633 | A663 | 1st multi | 1.40 | 1.40 |
|---|---|---|---|---|
| 2634 | A663 | 48p multi | 1.35 | 1.35 |
| 2635 | A663 | 50p multi | 1.45 | 1.45 |
| 2636 | A663 | 56p multi | 1.60 | 1.60 |
| 2637 | A663 | 72p multi | 2.00 | 2.00 |
| 2638 | A663 | 81p multi | 2.25 | 2.25 |
| | | Nos. 2633-2638 (6) | 10.05 | 10.05 |

On day of issue, Nos. 2627 and 2633 each sold for 36p.

### Miniature Sheet

Heritage of Wales A664

No. 2639: a, Flag of Wales (18x22mm). b, Red dragon (18x21mm). c, St. David (58x22mm). d, Welsh Assembly, Cardiff (58x22mm).

### Perf. 14¾x14 Syncopated (#2639a), 14¾x14 (#2639b, 2639c)

| | | | | Litho. |
|---|---|---|---|---|
| **2009, Feb. 26** | | | | |
| 2639 | A664 | Sheet of 4 | 7.00 | 7.00 |
| a.-b. | | 1st Either single | .95 | .95 |
| c.-d. | | 81p Either single | 2.35 | 2.35 |

On day of issue, Nos. 2639a and 2639b each sold for 36p.

### British Design Types of 2009

Designs: No. 2640, K2 telephone kiosk. No. 2641, Routemaster Bus. No. 2642, Mini Cooper automobile. No. 2643, Concorde. No. 2644, Miniskirt.

### 2009   Photo.   Die Cut Perf. 14½
### Booklet Stamps
### Self-Adhesive

| 2640 | A660 | 1st multi | 3.00 | 3.00 |
|---|---|---|---|---|
| 2641 | A660 | 1st multi | 3.00 | 3.00 |
| a. | | Booklet pane, #2640-2641, 4 #MH384 | 10.00 | |
| 2642 | A660 | 1st multi | 3.00 | 3.00 |
| a. | | Booklet pane, 2 #2642, 4 #MH384 | 10.00 | |
| 2643 | A660 | 1st multi | 3.00 | 3.00 |
| a. | | Booklet pane of 6, 2 #2643, 4 #MH384 | 10.00 | |
| 2644 | A660 | 1st multi | 3.00 | 3.00 |
| a. | | Booklet pane of 6, 2 #2644, 4 #MH384 | 10.00 | |

Issued: Nos. 2640, 2641, 2641a, 3/10; Nos. 2642, 2642a, 4/21; Nos. 2643, 2643a, 8/18; Nos. 2644, 2644a, 9/17. On day of issue, Nos. 2640-2641 each sold for 36p; Nos. 2642, 2643, 2644 sold for 39p.

Pioneers of the Industrial Revolution — A665

Designs: No. 2645, Matthew Boulton (1728-1809), steam engine manufacturer. No. 2646, James Watt (1736-1819), steam engine pioneer and inventor. No. 2647, Richard Arkwright (1732-92), inventor of textile machines. No. 2648, Josiah Wedgwood (1730-95), manufacturer of decorative ceramics. No. 2649, George Stephenson (1781-1848), steam locomotive inventor. No. 2650, Henry Maudslay (1771-1831), engineer and machine tool inventor. No. 2651, James Brindley (1716-72), canal engineer. No. 2652, John McAdam (1756-1836), engineer, road builder.

---

### Perf. 14¼x14½

| | | | | Litho. |
|---|---|---|---|---|
| **2009, Mar. 10** | | | | |
| 2645 | A665 | 1st multi | 1.00 | 1.00 |
| 2646 | A665 | 1st multi | 1.00 | 1.00 |
| a. | | Horiz. pair, #2645-2646 | 2.00 | 2.00 |
| 2647 | A665 | 50p multi | 1.40 | 1.40 |
| 2648 | A665 | 50p multi | 1.40 | 1.40 |
| a. | | Horiz. pair, #2647-2648 | 3.00 | 3.00 |
| 2649 | A665 | 56p multi | 1.60 | 1.60 |
| 2650 | A665 | 56p multi | 1.60 | 1.60 |
| a. | | Horiz. pair, #2649-2650 | 3.25 | 3.25 |
| 2651 | A665 | 72p multi | 2.00 | 2.00 |
| 2652 | A665 | 72p multi | 2.00 | 2.00 |
| a. | | Horiz. pair, #2651-2652 | 4.00 | 4.00 |
| | | Nos. 2645-2652 (8) | 12.00 | 12.00 |

On day of issue, Nos. 2645-2646 each sold for 36p.

### British Royalty and History Type of 2008

Designs: No. 2653, King Henry VII. No. 2654, King Henry VIII. No. 2655, King Edward VI. No. 2656, Lady Jane Grey. No. 2657, Queen Mary I. No. 2658, Queen Elizabeth I. No. 2659: a, Warship Mary Rose. b, Field of Cloth of Gold Royal Conference. c, Royal Exchange. d, Sir Francis Drake, first English circumnavigator.

### 2009, Apr. 21   Perf. 14¼

| 2653 | A645 | 1st multi | 1.00 | .90 |
|---|---|---|---|---|
| 2654 | A645 | 1st multi | 1.00 | .90 |
| 2655 | A645 | 62p multi | 1.75 | 1.50 |
| 2656 | A645 | 62p multi | 1.75 | 1.50 |
| 2657 | A645 | 81p multi | 2.25 | 2.00 |
| 2658 | A645 | 81p multi | 2.25 | 2.00 |
| | | Nos. 2653-2658 (6) | 10.00 | 8.80 |

### Souvenir Sheet

| 2659 | | Sheet of 4 | 7.25 | 6.50 |
|---|---|---|---|---|
| a.-b. | A645 | 1st Either single | 1.10 | 1.00 |
| c.-d. | A645 | 90p Either single | 2.60 | 2.25 |

On day of issue, Nos. 2653, 2654, 2659a and 2659b sold for 39p.

Endangered Plants — A666

Designs: No. 2660, Round-headed leek. No. 2661, Floating water plantain. No. 2662, Lady's slipper orchid. No. 2663, Dwarf milkwort. No. 2664, Marsh saxifrage. No. 2665, Downy woundwort. No. 2666, Upright spurge. No. 2667, Plymouth pear. No. 2668, Sea knotgrass. No. 2669, Deptford pink.

### 2009, May 19   Perf. 14¼

| 2660 | A666 | 1st multi | 1.40 | 1.25 |
|---|---|---|---|---|
| 2661 | A666 | 1st multi | 1.40 | 1.25 |
| 2662 | A666 | 1st multi | 1.40 | 1.25 |
| 2663 | A666 | 1st multi | 1.40 | 1.25 |
| 2664 | A666 | 1st multi | 1.40 | 1.25 |
| 2665 | A666 | 1st multi | 1.40 | 1.25 |
| 2666 | A666 | 1st multi | 1.40 | 1.25 |
| 2667 | A666 | 1st multi | 1.40 | 1.25 |
| 2668 | A666 | 1st multi | 1.40 | 1.25 |
| 2669 | A666 | 1st multi | 1.40 | 1.25 |
| a. | | Block of 10, #2660-2669 | 14.00 | 12.50 |

On day of issue, Nos. 2660-2669 each sold for 39p.

### Miniature Sheet

Royal Botanic Gardens, Kew A667

No. 2670: a, Palm House. b, Millennium Seed Bank, Wakehurst Place. c, Pagoda. d, Sackler Crossing.

### 2009, May 19   Perf. 14¼x14½

| 2670 | A667 | Sheet of 4 | 7.50 | 6.75 |
|---|---|---|---|---|
| a.-b. | | 1st Either single | 1.10 | 1.00 |
| c.-d. | | 90p Either single | 2.60 | 2.25 |

On day of issue, Nos. 2670a and 2670b each sold for 39p.

## Flowers Type of 1997
*Die Cut Perf. 14½x14 Syncopated*
**2009, May 21**      **Photo.**

**Booklet Stamps**
**Self-Adhesive**

| | | | | |
|---|---|---|---|---|
| 2671 | A475 | 1st multi | 4.95 | 4.95 |
| 2672 | A479 | 1st multi | 5.10 | 5.10 |
| a. | | Booklet pane, #2671-2672, 4 #MH384 | 12.50 | |

On day of issue Nos. 2671-2672 each sold for 39p.

Mythical Creatures — A668

**2009, June 16**    **Photo.**    *Perf. 14½*

| | | | | |
|---|---|---|---|---|
| 2673 | A668 | 1st Dragon | 1.10 | .95 |
| 2674 | A668 | 1st Unicorn | 1.10 | .95 |
| 2675 | A668 | 62p Giant | 1.75 | 1.50 |
| 2676 | A668 | 62p Pixie | 1.75 | 1.50 |
| 2677 | A668 | 90p Mermaid | 2.50 | 2.25 |
| 2678 | A668 | 90p Fairy | 2.50 | 2.25 |
| | | Nos. 2673-2678 (6) | 10.70 | 9.40 |

On day of issue, Nos. 2673-2674 each sold for 39p.

### Miniature Sheet

Post Boxes A669

No. 2679: a, George V type B wall box. b, Edward VII Ludlow box. c, Victorian lamp box. d, Elizabeth II type A wall box.

**2009, Aug. 18**    **Litho.**    *Perf. 14¼*

| | | | | |
|---|---|---|---|---|
| 2679 | A669 | Sheet of 4 | 7.50 | 7.50 |
| a. | | 1st multi | 1.15 | 1.15 |
| b. | | 56p multi | 1.60 | 1.60 |
| c. | | 81p multi | 2.25 | 2.25 |
| d. | | 90p multi | 2.50 | 2.50 |
| e. | | Booklet pane of 4, #2679a-2679d (BK189) | 7.50 | |
| f. | | Sheet of 20 #2679a + 20 labels | 30.00 | — |

No. 2679 sold for 39p on day of issue. No. 2679f sold for £8.35 on day of issue and its labels could not be personalized.

Fire and Rescue Service — A670

Designs: 1st, Firefighting. 54p, Chemical fire. 56p, Emergency rescue. 62p, Flood rescue. 81p, Search and rescue. 90p, Fire safety.

*Perf. 14¼x14½*
**2009, Sept. 1**      **Photo.**

| | | | | |
|---|---|---|---|---|
| 2680 | A670 | 1st multi | 1.10 | 1.00 |
| 2681 | A670 | 54p multi | 1.50 | 1.40 |
| 2682 | A670 | 56p multi | 1.60 | 1.45 |
| 2683 | A670 | 62p multi | 1.80 | 1.60 |
| 2684 | A670 | 81p multi | 2.25 | 2.10 |
| 2685 | A670 | 90p multi | 2.60 | 2.25 |
| | | Nos. 2680-2685 (6) | 10.85 | 9.80 |

No. 2680 sold for 39p on day of issue.

Royal Navy Uniforms — A671

Designs: No. 2686, Flight deck officer, 2009. No. 2687, Captain, 1941. No. 2688, Second officer WRNS, 1918. No. 2689, Able seaman, 1880. No. 2690, Royal Marine, 1805. No. 2691, Admiral, 1795.

**2009, Sept. 17**    **Litho.**    *Perf. 14¼*

| | | | | |
|---|---|---|---|---|
| 2686 | A671 | 1st multi | 1.10 | .95 |
| 2687 | A671 | 1st multi | 1.10 | .95 |
| 2688 | A671 | 1st multi | 1.10 | .95 |
| a. | | Horiz. strip of 3, #2686-2688 | 3.50 | 3.00 |
| b. | | Booklet pane of 3, #2686-2688 (BK190) | 3.50 | — |

| | | | | |
|---|---|---|---|---|
| 2689 | A671 | 90p multi | 2.40 | 2.25 |
| 2690 | A671 | 90p multi | 2.40 | 2.25 |
| 2691 | A671 | 90p multi | 2.40 | 2.25 |
| a. | | Horiz. strip of 3, #2689-2691 | 7.50 | 7.00 |
| b. | | Booklet pane of 3, #2689-2691 (BK190) | 10.50 | 9.60 |
| | | Nos. 2686-2691 (6) | 10.50 | 9.60 |

Nos. 2686-2688 each sold for 39p on day of issue.

Famous People — A672

Designs: No. 2692, Fred Perry (1909-95), tennis player. No. 2693, Henry Purcell (1659-95), composer and musician. No. 2694, Sir Matt Busby (1909-94), soccer player and manager. No. 2695, William Gladstone (1809-98), prime minister. No. 2696, Mary Wollstonecraft (1759-97), writer on feminist themes. No. 2697, Sir Arthur Conan Doyle (1859-1930), writer and creator of Sherlock Holmes stories. No. 2698, Donald Campbell (1921-67), breaker of land and water speed records. No. 2699, Judy Fryd (1909-2000), founder of Royal Society for Mentally Handicapped Children. No. 2700, Samuel Johnson (1709-84), lexicographer, critic and poet. No. 2701, Sir Martin Ryle (1918-84), radio astronomer.

**2009, Oct. 8**    **Litho.**    *Perf. 14½*

| | | | | |
|---|---|---|---|---|
| 2692 | A672 | 1st multi | 1.45 | 1.25 |
| 2693 | A672 | 1st multi | 1.45 | 1.25 |
| 2694 | A672 | 1st multi | 1.45 | 1.25 |
| 2695 | A672 | 1st multi | 1.45 | 1.25 |
| 2696 | A672 | 1st multi | 1.45 | 1.25 |
| a. | | Horiz. strip of 5, #2692-2696 | 7.25 | 6.25 |
| 2697 | A672 | 1st multi | 1.45 | 1.25 |
| 2698 | A672 | 1st multi | 1.45 | 1.25 |
| 2699 | A672 | 1st multi | 1.45 | 1.25 |
| 2700 | A672 | 1st multi | 1.45 | 1.25 |
| 2701 | A672 | 1st multi | 1.45 | 1.25 |
| a. | | Horiz. strip of 5, #2697-2701 | 7.25 | 6.25 |
| | | Nos. 2692-2701 (10) | 14.50 | 12.50 |

On day of issue, Nos. 2692-2701 each sold for 39p. Europa (No. 2701).

Sports of the 2012 Summer Olympics and Paralympics, London — A673

Olympics or Paralympics emblem and: No. 2702, Canoe slalom. Nos. 2703, 2713, Archery (Paralympics). Nos. 2704, 2714, Track. No. 2705, Aquatics. No. 2706, Boccie (Paralympics). Nos. 2707, 2712, Judo. No. 2708, Equestrian (Paralympics). No. 2709, Badminton. No. 2710, Weight lifting. Nos. 2711, 2715, Basketball.

**2009-10**    **Litho.**    *Perf. 14½*

| | | | | |
|---|---|---|---|---|
| 2702 | A673 | 1st multi | 1.45 | 1.25 |
| 2703 | A673 | 1st multi | 1.45 | 1.25 |
| 2704 | A673 | 1st multi | 1.45 | 1.25 |
| 2705 | A673 | 1st multi | 1.45 | 1.25 |
| 2706 | A673 | 1st multi | 1.45 | 1.25 |
| a. | | Horiz. strip of 5, #2702-2706 | 7.25 | 6.25 |
| 2707 | A673 | 1st multi | 1.45 | 1.25 |
| 2708 | A673 | 1st multi | 1.45 | 1.25 |
| a. | | Booklet pane of 2, #2703, 2708 (BK200) | 2.75 | — |
| 2709 | A673 | 1st multi | 1.45 | 1.25 |
| 2710 | A673 | 1st multi | 1.45 | 1.25 |
| 2711 | A673 | 1st multi | 1.45 | 1.25 |
| a. | | Horiz. strip of 5, #2707-2711 | 7.25 | 6.25 |
| | | Nos. 2702-2711 (10) | 14.50 | 12.50 |

**Booklet Stamps**
**Self-Adhesive**
**Photo.**
*Die Cut Perf. 14½*

| | | | | |
|---|---|---|---|---|
| 2712 | A673 | 1st multi (2713a) | 1.40 | 1.35 |
| 2713 | A673 | 1st multi (2713a) | 1.40 | 1.35 |
| a. | | Booklet pane of #2712, 2713, 4 #MH384 | 10.00 | |
| 2714 | A673 | 1st multi | 1.40 | 1.35 |
| 2715 | A673 | 1st multi | 1.40 | 1.35 |
| a. | | Booklet pane of 6, #2714-2715, 4 #MH384 | 10.00 | |

On day of issue, Nos. 2702-2715 each sold for 39p. Issued: Nos. 2702-2711, 10/22; Nos. 2712-2713, 1/7/10; Nos. 2714-2715, 2/25/10. No. 2708a, 7/27/12.

See Nos. 2815-2826, 2840-2841, 2916-2927.

Christmas
A674      A675

Stained-glass windows: Nos. 2716a, 2716c, 2717, 2719, Angel, Church of St. James, Staveley. Nos. 2716b, 2716e, 2718, 2721, Madonna and Child, Church of Ormesby St. Michael, Great Yarmouth. 56p, Joseph, Church of St. Michael, Minehead. 90p, Wise Man, Church of St. Mary the Virgin, Rye. £1.35, Shepherd, Church of St. Mary's, Upavon.

*Perf. 14¾x14 Syncopated*
**2009, Nov. 3**      **Photo.**

| | | | | |
|---|---|---|---|---|
| 2716 | | Sheet of 7 | 13.00 | 11.50 |
| a. | | A674 2nd multi | .85 | .75 |
| b. | | A674 1st multi | 1.05 | .95 |
| c. | | A675 2nd Large multi | 1.30 | 1.15 |
| d. | | A674 56p multi | 1.50 | 1.40 |
| e. | | A675 1st Large multi | 1.60 | 1.50 |
| f. | | A674 90p multi | 2.50 | 2.25 |
| g. | | A674 £1.35 multi | 3.75 | 3.25 |
| h. | | As "a," litho. (2716i) | 1.90 | 1.90 |
| i. | | Booklet pane of 4 #2716h + label | 7.75 | — |

**Self-Adhesive**
*Die Cut Perf. 14¾x14 Syncopated*

| | | | | |
|---|---|---|---|---|
| 2717 | A674 | 2nd multi | .85 | .80 |
| a. | | Booklet pane of 12 | 16.00 | |
| b. | | Litho., serpentine die cut 14¾x14 + label | .85 | .75 |
| 2718 | A674 | 1st multi | 1.15 | 1.00 |
| a. | | Booklet pane of 12 | 19.00 | |
| b. | | Litho., serpentine die cut 14¾x14 + label | 1.10 | 1.00 |
| 2719 | A675 | 2nd Large multi | 2.25 | .75 |
| 2720 | A674 | 56p multi | 1.60 | 1.45 |
| a. | | Litho., serpentine die cut 14¾x14 + label | 1.50 | 1.45 |
| 2721 | A675 | 1st Large multi | 1.75 | 1.60 |
| 2722 | A674 | 90p multi | 2.60 | 2.40 |
| a. | | Litho., serpentine die cut 14¾x14 + label | 2.50 | 2.40 |
| b. | | Sheet of 20, 8 each #2717b, 2718b, 2 each #2720a, 2722a, + 20 labels | 25.00 | |
| 2723 | A674 | £1.35 multi | 4.00 | 3.50 |
| | | Nos. 2717-2723 (7) | 14.20 | 11.50 |

On day of issue, Nos. 2716a and 2717 each sold for 30p; Nos. 2716b and 2718, 39p; Nos. 2716c and 2719, 47p; Nos. 2716e and 2721, 61p. No. 2722b sold for £9, and contains 20 labels that could not be personalized. No. 2717b was additionally sold in a sheet of 20 + 20 labels that could be personalized that sold for £9.50. No. 2718b was additionally sold in a sheet of 20 + 20 labels that could be personalized that sold for £13.50. No. 2720a was additionally sold in a sheet of 10 + 10 labels that could be personalized that sold for £9.50. No. 2722b was additionally sold in a sheet of 10 + 10 labels that could be personalized that sold for £13.50.

Issued: Nos. 2716h, 2716i, 5/5/11.

Let It Bleed, by The Rolling Stones — A676    Led Zeppelin IV, by Led Zeppelin — A677

The Rise and Fall of Ziggy Stardust and the Spiders from Mars, by David Bowie — A678    Power, Corruption and Lies, by New Order — A679

Screamadelica, by Primal Scream — A680    The Division Bell, by Pink Floyd — A681

Tubular Bells, by Mike Oldfield — A682    London Calling, by The Clash — A683

Parklife, by Blur — A684    A Rush of Blood to the Head, by Coldplay — A685

*Perf. 14¾ Syncopated*
**2010, Jan. 7**      **Litho.**

| | | | | |
|---|---|---|---|---|
| 2724 | A676 | 1st multi | 2.50 | 1.90 |
| 2725 | A677 | 1st multi | 2.50 | 1.90 |
| 2726 | A678 | 1st multi | 2.50 | 1.90 |
| 2727 | A679 | 1st multi | 2.50 | 1.90 |
| 2728 | A680 | 1st multi | 2.50 | 1.90 |
| 2729 | A681 | 1st multi | 2.50 | 1.90 |
| a. | | Booklet pane of 6, #2724-2729 (BK191) | 15.00 | — |
| b. | | Souvenir sheet of 10 #2729 | 25.00 | — |

No. 2729b sold for £4.75.

| | | | | |
|---|---|---|---|---|
| 2730 | A682 | 1st multi | 2.50 | 1.90 |
| 2731 | A683 | 1st multi | 2.50 | 1.90 |
| 2732 | A684 | 1st multi | 2.50 | 1.90 |
| 2733 | A685 | 1st multi | 2.50 | 1.90 |
| a. | | Booklet pane of 4, #2730-2733 (BK191) | 10.00 | — |
| b. | | Souvenir sheet of 4, #2724-2733 | 33.00 | 33.00 |

No. 2733b has simulated creases and toning at the sides and corners of the album cover sheet margin.

**Self-Adhesive**
**Photo.**
*Die Cut Perf. 14¾*

| | | | | |
|---|---|---|---|---|
| 2734 | A681 | 1st multi | 1.60 | 1.35 |
| 2735 | A685 | 1st multi | 1.60 | 1.35 |
| 2736 | A684 | 1st multi | 1.60 | 1.35 |
| 2737 | A679 | 1st multi | 1.60 | 1.35 |
| 2738 | A676 | 1st multi | 1.60 | 1.35 |
| a. | | Horiz. strip of 5, #2734-2738 | 8.25 | 6.75 |
| 2739 | A683 | 1st multi | 1.60 | 1.35 |
| 2740 | A682 | 1st multi | 1.60 | 1.35 |
| 2741 | A677 | 1st multi | 1.60 | 1.35 |
| 2742 | A680 | 1st multi | 1.60 | 1.35 |
| 2743 | A678 | 1st multi | 1.60 | 1.35 |
| a. | | Horiz. strip of 5, #2739-2743 | 8.25 | 6.75 |

On day of issue, Nos. 2724-2743 each sold for 39p.

### Miniature Sheet

A686

Nos. 2744 and 2745: a, Airplane with propellers. b, Automobile. c, Sealing wax with crown impression. d, Birthday cake. e, Steam locomotive. f, Ocean liner. g, Poppies. h, Gift box. i, Bird carrying airmail letter. j, "Hello" in airplane's contrail.

*Perf. 14¾x14 Syncopated*
**2010, Jan. 26**      **Litho.**

| | | | | |
|---|---|---|---|---|
| 2744 | A686 | Sheet of 10 | 17.00 | 15.00 |
| a.-h. | | 1st Any single | 1.50 | 1.25 |
| i. | | (56p) multi | 1.90 | 1.75 |
| j. | | (90p) multi | 3.00 | 2.75 |
| k. | | Booklet pane of 8, #2419e, 2462a, 2639a, Northern Ireland #18, 4 #2744g (BK213) | 12.50 | |
| l. | | Booklet pane of 8 #2744g + central label (BK217) | 14.50 | |
| m. | | Booklet pane of 8, 4 each #2744g, MH440 (BK221) | 15.00 | |

**Self-Adhesive**
*Die Cut Perf. 14¾x14 Syncopated*

| | | | | |
|---|---|---|---|---|
| 2745 | A686 | Sheet of 20, 2 each #a-j, + 20 labels | 42.50 | |
| a.-h. | | 1st Any single + label | 2.00 | 1.40 |
| i. | | (56p) multi + label | 2.00 | 2.00 |
| j. | | (90p) multi + label | 3.25 | 3.25 |
| k. | | Sheet of 20 #2745d + 20 labels | 44.00 | |
| l. | | Sheet of 20 #2745g + 20 labels | 44.00 | |
| m. | | Sheet of 10 #2745h + 10 labels | 31.00 | |

| | | | |
|---|---|---|---|
| n. | Sheet of 10 #2745i + 10 labels | 44.00 | |
| o. | Sheet of 20 #2745c + 20 labels | 40.00 | |

On day of issue, Nos. 2744a-2744h sold for 39p. No. 2745 sold for £9.70, and Nos. 2745a-2745h had a franking value of 39p. Labels could not be personalized.

Nos. 2745k and 2745l each sold for £13.63; No. 2745m for £9.58; and No. 2745n for £13.60. Labels could be personalized on Nos. 2745k-2745n.

Issued: No. 2744k, 6/21/16; No. 2744l, 7/31/17; No. 2744m, 9/13/18; No. 2745l, 9/15/11. No. 2745o sold for £9.50. Labels could not be personalized.

No. 2745g has value and Queen's head in grayish black, die cut perfs at the left side of the stamp are incomplete to keep the label attached. Compare with No. 3118A.

### Miniature Sheet

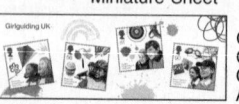

Girl Guides, Cent. A687

No. 2746 — Girl Guides and: a, Kite, handprint, drawing of flower. b, Cupcake, magnifying glass, leaves, colored pencils. c, Archery target, climber's rope. d, Photographs, swimming goggles, map of Manchester.

**2010, Feb. 2**     *Perf. 14¼x14½*
| | | | | |
|---|---|---|---|---|
| 2746 | A687 | Sheet of 4 | 6.30 | 6.50 |
| a. | | 1st multi | .95 | .95 |
| b. | | 56p multi | 1.30 | 1.40 |
| c. | | 81p multi | 1.95 | 1.95 |
| d. | | 90p multi | 2.10 | 2.25 |

No. 2746a sold for 39p on day of issue.

Royal Society, 350th Anniv. — A688

Scientists: No. 2747, Robert Boyle (1627-91), air pump. No. 2748, Sir Isaac Newton (1642-1727), color spectrum and optics diagram. No. 2749, Benjamin Franklin (1706-90), lightning. No. 2750, Edward Jenner (1749-1823), smallpox virus. No. 2751, Charles Babbage (1792-1871), gear diagram. No. 2752, Alfred Russel Wallace (1823-1913), oak tree. No. 2753, Sir Joseph Lister (1827-1912), spray. No. 2754, Ernest Rutherford (1871-1937), atom. No. 2755, Dorothy Hodgkin (1910-94), crystal diagram. No. 2756, Sir Nicholas Shackleton (1937-2006), microfossils.

**2010, Feb. 25**    *Litho.*    *Perf. 14½*
| | | | | |
|---|---|---|---|---|
| 2747 | A688 | 1st multi | 1.60 | 1.50 |
| 2748 | A688 | 1st multi | 1.60 | 1.50 |
| 2749 | A688 | 1st multi | 1.60 | 1.50 |
| 2750 | A688 | 1st multi | 1.60 | 1.50 |
| 2751 | A688 | 1st multi | 1.60 | 1.50 |
| 2752 | A688 | 1st multi | 1.60 | 1.50 |
| 2753 | A688 | 1st multi | 1.60 | 1.50 |
| 2754 | A688 | 1st multi | 1.60 | 1.50 |
| a. | | Booklet pane of 4, #2748, 2749, 2 #2754 (BK192) | 6.50 | — |
| 2755 | A688 | 1st multi | 1.60 | 1.50 |
| a. | | Booklet pane of 4, #2753, 2755, 2 #2750 (BK192) | 6.50 | — |
| 2756 | A688 | 1st multi | 1.60 | 1.50 |
| a. | | Block of 10, #2747-2756 | 16.00 | 15.00 |
| b. | | Booklet pane of 4, #2747, 2751, 2752, 2756 (BK192) | 6.50 | — |
| | | Nos. 2747-2756 (10) | 16.00 | 15.00 |

On day of issue, Nos. 2747-2756 each sold for 39p.

Battersea Dogs and Cats Home, 150th Anniv. — A689

Designs: No. 2757, Pixie (dog). No. 2758, Button (cat). No. 2759, Herbie (dog). No. 2760, Mr. Tumnus (cat). No. 2761, Tafka (dog). No. 2762, Boris (dog). No. 2763, Casey (dog). No. 2764, Tigger (cat). No. 2765, Leonard (dog). No. 2766, Tia (dog).

**2010, Mar. 11**     *Perf. 14½*
| | | | | |
|---|---|---|---|---|
| 2757 | A689 | 1st multi | 1.50 | 1.40 |
| 2758 | A689 | 1st multi | 1.50 | 1.40 |
| 2759 | A689 | 1st multi | 1.50 | 1.40 |
| 2760 | A689 | 1st multi | 1.50 | 1.40 |
| 2761 | A689 | 1st multi | 1.50 | 1.40 |
| 2762 | A689 | 1st multi | 1.50 | 1.40 |

---

| | | | | |
|---|---|---|---|---|
| 2763 | A689 | 1st multi | 1.50 | 1.40 |
| 2764 | A689 | 1st multi | 1.50 | 1.40 |
| 2765 | A689 | 1st multi | 1.50 | 1.40 |
| 2766 | A689 | 1st multi | 1.50 | 1.40 |
| a. | | Block of 10, #2757-2766 | 15.00 | 14.00 |
| | | Nos. 2757-2766 (10) | 15.00 | 14.00 |

On day of issue, Nos. 2757-2766 each sold for 39p.

### British Royalty and History Type of 2008

Designs: No. 2767, King James I of Scotland (1406-37). No. 2768, King James II of Scotland (1437-60). No. 2769, King James III. No. 2770, King James IV. No. 2771, King James V. No. 2772, Mary, Queen of Scots. No. 2773, King James VI.

No. 2774: a, Founding of St. Andrew's University, 1413. b, College of Surgeons, Edinburgh, 1505. c, Court of Session, 1532. d, John Knox, religious reformer.

**2010, Mar. 23**     *Perf. 14¼*
| | | | | |
|---|---|---|---|---|
| 2767 | A645 | 1st multi | 1.10 | 1.00 |
| 2768 | A645 | 1st multi | 1.10 | 1.00 |
| 2769 | A645 | 1st multi | 1.10 | 1.00 |
| 2770 | A645 | 62p multi | 1.75 | 1.60 |
| 2771 | A645 | 62p multi | 1.75 | 1.60 |
| 2772 | A645 | 81p multi | 2.40 | 2.10 |
| 2773 | A645 | 81p multi | 2.40 | 2.10 |
| | | Nos. 2767-2773 (7) | 11.60 | 10.40 |

### Souvenir Sheet
| | | | | |
|---|---|---|---|---|
| 2774 | | Sheet of 4 | 7.50 | 7.00 |
| a.-b. | A645 | 1st Either single | 1.25 | 1.10 |
| c.-d. | A645 | 81p Either single | 2.50 | 2.25 |

On day of issue, Nos. 2767-2769, 2774a-2774b each sold for 39p.

Land and Sea Mammals — A690

Designs: No. 2775, Humpback whale. No. 2776, Wildcat. No. 2777, Brown long-eared bat. No. 2778, Polecat. No. 2779, Sperm whale. No. 2780, Water vole. No. 2781, Greater horseshoe bat. Nos. 2782, 2785, Otter. No. 2783, Dormouse. Nos. 2784, 2786, Hedgehog.

**2010**     *Perf. 14½*
| | | | | |
|---|---|---|---|---|
| 2775 | A690 | 1st multi | 1.50 | 1.40 |
| 2776 | A690 | 1st multi | 1.50 | 1.40 |
| 2777 | A690 | 1st multi | 1.50 | 1.40 |
| 2778 | A690 | 1st multi | 1.50 | 1.40 |
| 2779 | A690 | 1st multi | 1.50 | 1.40 |
| 2780 | A690 | 1st multi | 1.50 | 1.40 |
| 2781 | A690 | 1st multi | 1.50 | 1.40 |
| 2782 | A690 | 1st multi | 1.50 | 1.40 |
| 2783 | A690 | 1st multi | 1.50 | 1.40 |
| 2784 | A690 | 1st multi | 1.50 | 1.40 |
| a. | | Block of 10, #2775-2784 | 15.00 | 14.00 |
| | | Nos. 2775-2784 (10) | 15.00 | 14.00 |

### Photo.
### Booklet Stamps
### Self-Adhesive
### *Die Cut Perf. 14½*
| | | | | |
|---|---|---|---|---|
| 2785 | A690 | 1st multi | 4.75 | 4.25 |
| 2786 | A690 | 1st multi | 4.75 | 4.25 |
| a. | | Booklet pane of 6, #2785-2786, 4 #MH384 | 13.50 | |

Issued: Nos. 2775-2784, 4/13; Nos. 2785-2786, 6/15. On day of issue, Nos. 2775-2786 each sold for 41p.

King George V and Queen Elizabeth II — A691

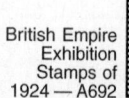

British Empire Exhibition Stamps of 1924 — A692

"Britannia Rules the Waves" Stamps of 1913 — A693

---

Heads of King George V and Lion From Types A81 and A82 — A694

Designs: No. 2788, Great Britain #185. No. 2789, Great Britain #186. No. 2790, Great Britain #176. No. 2791, Great Britain #175.

*Perf. 14½x14 (#2787, 2792), 14¾x14¼*
### Litho. (#2787, 2792), Litho. & Engr.
**2010**
| | | | | |
|---|---|---|---|---|
| 2787 | A691 | 1st red | 2.00 | 1.00 |
| 2788 | A692 | 1st multi | 2.00 | 1.00 |
| 2789 | A692 | 1st multi | 2.00 | 1.00 |
| a. | | Booklet pane of 4, 2 each #2788-2789 (BK193) | 8.00 | |
| 2790 | A693 | £1 multi | 4.50 | 2.60 |
| 2791 | A693 | £1 multi | 4.50 | 2.60 |
| a. | | Souvenir sheet of 4, #2788-2791 | 10.00 | 9.00 |
| b. | | Booklet pane of 2, #2790-2791 (BK193) | 9.00 | |
| 2792 | A694 | £1 brown & silver | 4.50 | 2.60 |
| a. | | Souvenir sheet of 2, #2787, 2792 | 5.75 | 5.00 |
| b. | | Booklet pane of 6, 3 each #2787, 2792 (BK193) | 19.50 | — |
| | | Nos. 2787-2792 (6) | 19.50 | 10.80 |

Issued: No. 2787, 5/6; others, 5/8. London 2010 Festival of Stamps. Nos. 2787-2789 each sold for 41p on day of issue.

### Bird and Thank You Types of 2005-06

*Die Cut Perf. 14¾x14 Syncopated*
**2010, May 8**    *Litho.*
### Self-Adhesive
| | | | | |
|---|---|---|---|---|
| 2793 | A596 | 1st multi + label (2794a) | 19.50 | 5.00 |
| 2794 | A612 | 1st multi + label (2794a) | 19.50 | 5.00 |
| a. | | Sheet of 20, #2427, 2546, 2547, 2793, 2794, 2 each #2745i, 2745j, 3 #2538, 4 each #2745d, 2745g + 20 labels | 32.50 | |

No. 2794a sold for £10. Labels could not be personalized. Nos. 2793 and 2794 each had a franking value of 41p on day of issue.

Britain in World War II — A695

Designs: No. 2795, Prime Minister Winston Churchill reviewing troops. No. 2796, Girl on tractor. No. 2797, Home Guard. No. 2798, Evacuees. No. 2799, Air raid warden. No. 2800, Woman in factory. No. 2801, Firemen at fire. No. 2802, Royal broadcast.

No. 2803, Soldiers in water. No. 2804, Flotilla of small boats. No. 2805, Soldiers in boat. No. 2806, Soldiers on two boats.

**2010, May 13**     *Perf. 14½*
| | | | | |
|---|---|---|---|---|
| 2795 | A695 | 1st multi | 1.75 | 1.25 |
| 2796 | A695 | 1st multi | 1.75 | 1.25 |
| 2797 | A695 | 60p multi | 1.75 | 1.35 |
| 2798 | A695 | 60p multi | 1.75 | 1.35 |
| 2799 | A695 | 67p multi | 2.00 | 1.50 |
| 2800 | A695 | 67p multi | 2.00 | 1.50 |
| 2801 | A695 | 97p multi | 2.90 | 2.10 |
| a. | | Booklet pane of 4, #2797-2799, 2801 (BK194) | 8.50 | |
| 2802 | A695 | 97p multi | 2.90 | 2.10 |
| a. | | Booklet pane of 4, #2795-2796, 2800, 2802 (BK194) | 8.50 | |

### Inscribed "Dunkirk"
| | | | | |
|---|---|---|---|---|
| 2803 | A695 | 1st multi | 1.75 | 1.25 |
| 2804 | A695 | 1st multi | 1.75 | .85 |
| 2805 | A695 | 88p multi | 2.60 | 1.25 |
| 2806 | A695 | 97p multi | 2.90 | 2.10 |
| a. | | Souvenir sheet of 4, #2803-2806 | 9.75 | 9.75 |
| b. | | Booklet pane of 4, #2803-2806 (BK194) | 9.00 | — |
| | | Nos. 2795-2806 (12) | 25.80 | 17.85 |

Nos. 2795, 2796 and 2803 each sold for 41p on day of issue.

### British Royalty and History Type of 2008

Designs: No. 2807, King James I of Great Britain (1603-25). No. 2808, King Charles I. No. 2809, King Charles II. No. 2810, King James II of Great Britain (1685-88). No. 2811, King William III. No. 2812, Queen Mary II. No. 2813, Queen Anne.

No. 2814: a, William Harvey, discoverer of blood circulation, 1628. b, Civil War Battle of

---

Naseby, 1645. c, John Milton, author of Paradise Lost, 1667. d, Castle Howard, designed by John Vanbrugh.

**2010, June 15**     *Perf. 14¼*
| | | | | |
|---|---|---|---|---|
| 2807 | A645 | 1st multi | 1.50 | .90 |
| 2808 | A645 | 1st multi | 1.50 | .90 |
| 2809 | A645 | 60p multi | 1.75 | 1.35 |
| 2810 | A645 | 60p multi | 1.75 | 1.35 |
| 2811 | A645 | 67p multi | 2.00 | 1.50 |
| 2812 | A645 | 67p multi | 2.00 | 1.50 |
| 2813 | A645 | 88p multi | 2.60 | 2.00 |
| | | Nos. 2807-2813 (7) | 13.10 | 9.50 |

### Souvenir Sheet
| | | | | |
|---|---|---|---|---|
| 2814 | | Sheet of 4 | 8.75 | 8.75 |
| a. | A645 | 1st multi | 1.50 | .90 |
| b. | A645 | 60p multi | 1.80 | 1.35 |
| c. | A645 | 88p multi | 2.60 | 2.00 |
| d. | A645 | 97p multi | 2.90 | 2.25 |

On day of issue, Nos. 2807, 2808 and 2814a each sold for 41p.

### Sports of the 2012 Olympics and Paralympics Type of 2009-10

Olympics or Paralympics emblem and: Nos. 2815, 2825, Rowing (Paralympics). No. 2816, Shooting. Nos. 2817, Modern pentathlon. No. 2818, Taekwondo. No. 2819, Cycling. Nos. 2820, 2826, Table tennis (Paralympics). No. 2821, Field hockey. No. 2822, Soccer. No. 2823, Goalball (Paralympics). No. 2824, Boxing.

**2010, July 27**    *Litho.*    *Perf. 14½*
| | | | | |
|---|---|---|---|---|
| 2815 | A673 | 1st multi | 1.55 | 1.20 |
| 2816 | A673 | 1st multi | 1.55 | 1.20 |
| 2817 | A673 | 1st multi | 1.55 | 1.20 |
| 2818 | A673 | 1st multi | 1.55 | 1.20 |
| 2819 | A673 | 1st multi | 1.55 | 1.20 |
| a. | | Horiz. strip of 5, #2815-2819 | 7.75 | 6.00 |
| 2820 | A673 | 1st multi | 1.55 | 1.20 |
| 2821 | A673 | 1st multi | 1.55 | 1.20 |
| 2822 | A673 | 1st multi | 1.55 | 1.20 |
| a. | | Booklet pane of 2, #2704, 2822 (BK200) | 2.75 | — |
| 2823 | A673 | 1st multi | 1.55 | 1.20 |
| 2824 | A673 | 1st multi | 1.55 | 1.20 |
| a. | | Horiz. strip of 5, #2820-2824 | 7.75 | 6.00 |
| | | Nos. 2815-2824 (10) | 15.50 | 12.00 |

### Booklet Stamps
### Self-Adhesive
### Photo.
### *Die Cut Perf. 14½*
| | | | | |
|---|---|---|---|---|
| 2825 | A673 | 1st multi (2826a) | 3.75 | 1.00 |
| 2826 | A673 | 1st multi (2826a) | 3.75 | 1.00 |
| a. | | Booklet pane of 6, #2825, 2826, 4 #MH384 | 10.00 | |

Nos. 2815-2826 each sold for 41p on day of issue. See Nos. 2840-2841.
Issued: No. 2822a, 7/27/12.

Locomotives A696

Designs: No. 2827, London Midland and Scottish Railway Coronation Class. No. 2828, British Rail Class 9F. No. 2829, Great Western Railway King Class. No. 2830, London North Eastern Railway Class A1. No. 2831, London Midland and Scottish Railway Northern Counties Committee Class WT. No. 2832, Southern Railway King Arthur Class.

**2010, Aug. 19**   *Photo.*   *Perf. 14¼x14*
| | | | | |
|---|---|---|---|---|
| 2827 | A696 | 1st multi | 1.30 | .95 |
| 2828 | A696 | 1st multi | 1.30 | .95 |
| 2829 | A696 | 67p multi | 2.00 | 1.50 |
| 2830 | A696 | 67p multi | 2.00 | 1.50 |
| 2831 | A696 | 97p multi | 2.90 | 2.25 |
| 2832 | A696 | 97p multi | 2.90 | 2.25 |
| | | Nos. 2827-2832 (6) | 12.40 | 9.40 |

Nos. 2827-2828 each sold for 41p on day of issue.

### British Design Type of 2009

Design: Supermarine Spitfire.

### *Die Cut Perf. 14½*
**2010, Sept. 15**     *Photo.*
### Booklet Stamp
### Self-Adhesive
| | | | | |
|---|---|---|---|---|
| 2833 | A660 | 1st multi | 4.25 | 1.00 |
| a. | | Booklet pane of 6, 2 #2833, 4 #MH384 | 10.00 | |

No. 2833 sold for 41p on day of issue.

Medical
Breakthroughs
A697

Designs: 1st, Heart-regulating beta blockers synthesized by Sir James Black, 1962. 58p, Antibiotic properties of penicillin discovered by Sir Alexander Fleming, 1928. 60p, Total hip replacement operation pioneered by Sir John Charnley, 1962. 67p, Artificial lens implant surgery pioneered by Sir Harold Ridley, 1949. 88p, Malaria parasite transmitted by mosquitoes proved by Sir Ronald Ross, 1897. 97p, Computed tomography scanner invented by Sir Godfrey Hounsfield, 1971.

### *Perf. 14¼x14½*

| 2010, Sept. 16 | | | Litho. | |
|---|---|---|---|---|
| 2834 | A697 | 1st multi | 1.30 | .95 |
| 2835 | A697 | 58p multi | 1.75 | 1.30 |
| 2836 | A697 | 60p multi | 1.80 | 1.35 |
| 2837 | A697 | 67p multi | 2.00 | 1.50 |
| 2838 | A697 | 88p multi | 2.60 | 2.00 |
| 2839 | A697 | 97p multi | 2.90 | 2.25 |
| | *Nos. 2834-2839 (6)* | | 12.35 | 9.35 |

No. 2834 sold for 41p on day of issue. See No. 2866.

### Sports of the 2012 Olympics and Paralympics Type of 2009-10

Designs: No. 2840, Soccer. No. 2841, Cycling.

### *Die Cut Perf. 14½*

| 2010, Oct. 12 | | | Photo. | |
|---|---|---|---|---|
| | **Booklet Stamps** | | | |
| | **Self-Adhesive** | | | |
| 2840 | A673 | 1st multi (2841a) | 3.75 | 1.00 |
| 2841 | A673 | 1st multi (2841a) | 3.75 | 1.00 |
| *a.* | | Booklet pane of 6, #2840, 2841, 4 #MH384 | 10.00 | |

Nos. 2840-2841 each sold for 41p on day of issue.

Characters From
Winnie-the-Pooh
Stories by A. A.
Milne — A698

Winnie-the-Pooh and: No. 2842, Christopher Robin. 58p, Piglet. No. 2844, Rabbit. 67p, Eeyore. No. 2846, Friends. No. 2847, Tigger.

No. 2848 — Winnie-the-Pooh and Christopher Robin with inscriptions: a, Wherever I am, there's always Pooh. b, There's always Pooh and Me, Whatever I do, he wants to do. c, "Where are you going to-day?" says Pooh: "Well, that's very odd 'cos I was too." d, "Let's go together," says Pooh, says he. "Let's go together," says Pooh.

| 2010, Oct. 12 | Litho. | | *Perf. 14¼x14½* | |
|---|---|---|---|---|
| 2842 | A698 | 1st multi | 1.30 | .95 |
| 2843 | A698 | 58p multi | 1.75 | 1.30 |
| 2844 | A698 | 60p multi | 1.80 | 1.35 |
| 2845 | A698 | 67p multi | 2.00 | 1.50 |
| 2846 | A698 | 88p multi | 2.60 | 2.00 |
| 2847 | A698 | 97p multi | 2.90 | 2.25 |
| | *Nos. 2842-2847 (6)* | | 12.35 | 9.35 |

**Souvenir Sheet**
### *Perf. 14½*

| 2848 | | Sheet of 4 | 8.75 | 8.25 |
|---|---|---|---|---|
| *a.* | A698 | 1st multi | 1.30 | .95 |
| *b.* | A698 | 60p multi | 1.80 | 1.35 |
| *c.* | A698 | 88p multi | 2.60 | 2.00 |
| *d.* | A698 | 97p multi | 2.90 | 2.25 |

Europa (Nos. 2842, 2848a). Nos. 2842 and 2848a each sold for 41p on day of issue.

Christmas
A699          A700

Designs: 2nd, Wallace and Gromit singing Christmas carols. 1st, Gromit mailing Christmas cards. 2nd Large, Wallace and Gromit singing Christmas carols, Christmas tree at left. 60p, Wallace and Gromit decorating Christmas tree. 1st Large, Gromit mailing Christmas cards, Feathers McGraw at left. 97p, Gromit carrying Christmas pudding. £1.46, Gromit wearing large sweater.

### *Perf. 14¾x14 Syncopated*

| 2010, Nov. 2 | | | Photo. | |
|---|---|---|---|---|
| 2849 | | Sheet of 7 | 15.00 | 11.00 |
| *a.* | A699 | 2nd multi | 1.00 | .75 |
| *b.* | A699 | 1st multi | 1.30 | .95 |
| *c.* | A700 | 2nd Large multi | 1.60 | 1.15 |
| *d.* | A699 | 60p multi | 1.80 | 1.35 |
| *e.* | A700 | 1st Large multi | 2.00 | 1.50 |
| *f.* | A699 | 97p multi | 2.90 | 2.25 |
| *g.* | A699 | £1.46 multi | 4.75 | 2.40 |

**Self-Adhesive**
### *Die Cut Perf. 14¾x14 Syncopated*

| 2850 | A699 | 2nd multi | 1.00 | .75 |
|---|---|---|---|---|
| *a.* | | Booklet pane of 12 | 16.00 | |
| *b.* | | Litho., serpentine die cut 14¾x14 syncopated, + label (2855b) | 1.25 | 1.25 |
| *c.* | | Sheet of 20 #2850b | 19.00 | — |
| 2851 | A699 | 1st multi | 1.30 | .95 |
| *a.* | | Booklet pane of 12 | 15.50 | |
| *b.* | | Litho., serpentine die cut 14¾x14 syncopated, + label (2855b) | 2.25 | 2.25 |
| *c.* | | Sheet of 20 #2851b | 42.50 | — |
| 2852 | A700 | 2nd Large multi | 1.60 | 1.15 |
| 2853 | A699 | 60p multi | 1.80 | 1.35 |
| *a.* | | Litho., serpentine die cut 14¾x14 syncopated, + label (2855b) | 2.00 | 2.00 |
| *b.* | | Sheet of 10 #2853a | 30.00 | |
| 2854 | A700 | 1st Large multi | 2.00 | 1.50 |
| 2855 | A699 | 97p multi | 2.90 | 2.25 |
| *a.* | | Litho., serpentine die cut 14¾x14 syncopated, + label (2855b) | 3.50 | 3.50 |
| *b.* | | Sheet of 20, 8 each #2850b, 2851b, 2 each #2853a, 2855a, + 20 labels | 40.00 | |
| *c.* | | Sheet of 10 #2855a | 45.00 | |
| 2856 | A699 | £1.46 multi | 4.50 | 3.25 |
| | *Nos. 2850-2856 (7)* | | 15.10 | 11.20 |

On day of issue, Nos. 2849a and 2850 sold for 32p, Nos. 2849b and 2851 each sold for 41p, Nos. 2849c and 2852 each sold for 51p, and Nos. 2849e and 2854 each sold for 66p. No. 2855b sold for £9.30 and contained 20 labels that could not be personalized.

Nos. 2850c, 2851c, 2853b and 2855c had labels that could be personalized. Nos. 2850a and 2853b each sold for £9.95; No. 2851c sold for £13.95; No. 2855c sold for £14.50. Sheets of 10 No. 2850b were also sold but these were halves of No. 2850c torn along the sheet's central row of rouletting. Nos. 2853b and 2855c have rouletting along the left or right side of the sheet, but these stamps were not sold in sheets of 20.

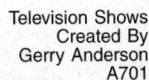

Television Shows
Created By
Gerry Anderson
A701

Designs: No. 2857, Joe 90. No. 2858, Captain Scarlet. No. 2859, 2864, Thunderbirds. No. 2860, Stingray. No. 2861, Fireball XL5. No. 2862, Supercar.
No. 2863 — Opening sequence of show depicting Thunderbird: a, "4." b, "3." c, "2." d, "1."

| 2011, Jan. 11 | Litho. | | *Perf. 14¼* | |
|---|---|---|---|---|
| 2857 | A701 | 1st multi | 1.05 | .90 |
| 2858 | A701 | 1st multi | 1.05 | .90 |
| 2859 | A701 | 1st multi | 1.05 | .90 |
| *a.* | | Horiz. strip of 3, #2857-2859 | 3.25 | 2.80 |
| 2860 | A701 | 97p multi | 2.30 | 1.75 |
| 2861 | A701 | 97p multi | 2.30 | 1.75 |
| 2862 | A701 | 97p multi | 2.30 | 1.75 |
| *a.* | | Horiz. strip of 3, #2860-2862 | 7.00 | 5.25 |
| | *Nos. 2857-2862 (6)* | | 13.95 | 6.90 |

**Souvenir Sheet**
**Litho. With Three-Dimensional
Plastic Affixed**

| 2863 | | Sheet of 4 | 8.75 | 8.75 |
|---|---|---|---|---|
| *a.* | A701 | 41p multi | 1.30 | 1.30 |
| *b.* | A701 | 60p multi | 1.80 | 1.80 |
| *c.* | A701 | 88p multi | 2.00 | 2.00 |
| *d.* | A701 | 97p multi | 2.90 | 2.90 |

**Booklet Stamp**
**Self-Adhesive**
### *Die Cut Perf. 14¼x14*

| 2864 | A701 | 1st multi | 4.00 | 1.00 |
|---|---|---|---|---|
| *a.* | | Booklet pane of 6, 2 #2864, 4 #MH384 | 10.00 | |

On day of issue, Nos. 2857-2859, 2864 each sold for 41p.

### Miniature Sheet

Locomotives — A702

No. 2865: a, British Railways Dean Goods No. 2532. b, Peckett R2 Thor. c, Lancashire &

Yorkshire Railway 1093 No. 1100. d, British Railways WD No. 90662.

| 2011, Feb. 1 | Litho. | | *Perf. 14¼* | |
|---|---|---|---|---|
| 2865 | A702 | Sheet of 4 | 8.75 | 8.25 |
| *a.* | | 1st multi | 1.30 | 1.00 |
| *b.* | | 60p multi | 1.80 | 1.75 |
| *c.* | | 88p multi | 2.00 | 1.50 |
| *d.* | | 97p multi | 2.90 | 2.75 |
| *e.* | | Booklet pane of 4, 2 each #2865a, 2865b (BK204) | 6.25 | |

No. 2865a sold for 41p on day of issue. Issued: No. 2865e, 2/20/14. See No. 2930.

### Medical Breakthroughs Type of 2010

Design: Heart-regulating beta blockers synthesized by Sir James Black, 1962.

### *Die Cut Perf. 14¼x14½*

| 2011, Feb. 24 | | | Photo. | |
|---|---|---|---|---|
| | **Booklet Stamp** | | | |
| | **Self-Adhesive** | | | |
| 2866 | A697 | 1st multi | 4.00 | 1.00 |
| *a.* | | Booklet pane of 6, 2 #2866, 4 #MH384 | 10.00 | |

No. 2866 sold for 41p on day of issue.

Musicals — A703

Designs: No. 2867, Oliver! No. 2868, Blood Brothers. No. 2869, We Will Rock You. No. 2870, Monty Python's Spamalot. No. 2871, Rocky Horror Show. No. 2872, Me and My Girl. No. 2873, Return to the Forbidden Planet. No. 2874, Billy Elliot.

| 2011, Feb. 24 | Litho. | | *Perf. 14¼* | |
|---|---|---|---|---|
| 2867 | A703 | 1st multi | 1.30 | .95 |
| 2868 | A703 | 1st multi | 1.30 | .95 |
| 2869 | A703 | 1st multi | 1.30 | .95 |
| 2870 | A703 | 1st multi | 1.30 | .95 |
| 2871 | A703 | 97p multi | 2.90 | 2.25 |
| 2872 | A703 | 97p multi | 2.90 | 2.25 |
| 2873 | A703 | 97p multi | 2.90 | 2.25 |
| 2874 | A703 | 97p multi | 2.90 | 2.25 |
| | *Nos. 2867-2874 (8)* | | 16.80 | 12.80 |

On day of issue, Nos. 2867-2870 each sold for 41p.

Fictional Wizards
and
Magicians — A704

Designs: No. 2875, Rincewind, from Discworld, by Terry Pratchett. No. 2876, Nanny Ogg, from Discworld. No. 2877, Dumbledore, from Harry Potter stories, by J.K. Rowling. No. 2878, Lord Voldemort, from Harry Potter stories. No. 2879, Merlin, from Arthurian legend. No. 2880, Morgan Le Fay, from Arthurian legend. No. 2881, Aslan, from Narnia, by C. S. Lewis. No. 2882, The White Witch, from Narnia.

| 2011, Mar. 8 | Photo. | | *Perf. 14½* | |
|---|---|---|---|---|
| 2875 | A704 | 1st multi | 1.30 | .95 |
| 2876 | A704 | 1st multi | 1.30 | .95 |
| *a.* | | Vert. pair, #2875-2876 | 2.60 | 1.90 |
| 2877 | A704 | 1st multi | 1.30 | .95 |
| 2878 | A704 | 1st multi | 1.30 | .95 |
| *a.* | | Vert. pair, #2877-2878 | 2.60 | 1.90 |
| 2879 | A704 | 60p multi | 1.80 | 1.35 |
| 2880 | A704 | 60p multi | 1.80 | 1.35 |
| *a.* | | Vert. pair, #2879-2880 | 2.75 | 2.75 |
| 2881 | A704 | 97p multi | 2.90 | 2.25 |
| 2882 | A704 | 97p multi | 2.90 | 2.25 |
| *a.* | | Vert. pair, #2881-2882 | 6.00 | 4.50 |
| | *Nos. 2875-2882 (8)* | | 14.60 | 11.00 |

On day of issue, Nos. 2875-2878 each sold for 41p.

A705

Worldwide Fund for Nature (WWF),
50th Anniv. — A706

Designs: No. 2883, African elephant. No. 2884, Mountain gorilla. No. 2885, Siberian tiger. No. 2886, Polar bear. No. 2887, Amur leopard. No. 2888, Iberian lynx. No. 2889, Red panda. No. 2890, Black rhinoceros. No. 2891, African wild dog. No. 2892, Golden lion tamarin.
No. 2893, a, Spider monkey. b, Hyacinth macaw. c, Poison dart frog. d, Jaguar.

| 2011, Mar. 22 | Litho. | | *Perf. 14½* | |
|---|---|---|---|---|
| 2883 | A705 | 1st multi | 1.50 | 1.30 |
| 2884 | A705 | 1st multi | 1.50 | 1.30 |
| 2885 | A705 | 1st multi | 1.50 | 1.30 |
| 2886 | A705 | 1st multi | 1.50 | 1.30 |
| 2887 | A705 | 1st multi | 1.50 | 1.30 |
| *a.* | | Horiz. strip of 5, #2883-2887 | 7.75 | 6.75 |
| 2888 | A705 | 1st multi | 1.50 | 1.30 |
| 2889 | A705 | 1st multi | 1.50 | 1.30 |
| 2890 | A705 | 1st multi | 1.50 | 1.30 |
| *a.* | | Booklet pane of 6, #2885-2890 (BK195) | 8.00 | |
| 2891 | A705 | 1st multi | 1.50 | 1.30 |
| 2892 | A705 | 1st multi | 1.50 | 1.30 |
| *a.* | | Horiz. strip of 5, #2888-2892 | 7.75 | 6.75 |
| *b.* | | Booklet pane of 6, #2883-2884, 2891-2892 (BK195) | 5.25 | |
| | *Nos. 2883-2892 (10)* | | 15.00 | 13.00 |

### *Perf. 14¼*

| 2893 | A706 | Sheet of 4 | 7.00 | 7.00 |
|---|---|---|---|---|
| *a.* | | 1st multi | 1.05 | 1.05 |
| *b.* | | 60p multi | 1.45 | 1.45 |
| *c.* | | 88p multi | 1.60 | 1.60 |
| *d.* | | 97p multi | 2.30 | 2.30 |
| *e.* | | Booklet pane of 4, #2893a-2893d (BK195) | 8.75 | |

Europa (nos. 2893a, 2893e). On day of issue, Nos. 2883-2892 and 2893a each sold for 41p. No. 2893e is 150x96mm, and has additional printing in booklet pane margin beyond that shown in illustration A706.

A707

Royal Shakespeare Company,
Stratford-on-Avon, 50th Anniv. — A708

Line from play by William Shakespeare and: No. 2894, David Tennant in *Hamlet*. 66p, Anthony Sher in *The Tempest*. No. 2896, Chuk Iwuji in *Henry VI*. No. 2897, Paul Schofield in *King Lear*. No. 2898, Sarah Kestelman in *A Midsummer Night's Dream*. £1.10, Ian McKellen and Francesca Annis in *Romeo and Juliet*.
No. 2900: a, Janet Suzman in *Hamlet* at Royal Shakespeare Theater. b, Patrick Stewart in *Antony and Cleopatra* at Swan Theater. c, Geoffrey Streatfeild in *Henry V* at the Courtyard Theater. d, Dame Judi Dench in *Macbeth* at the Other Place.

| 2011, Apr. 12 | Photo. | | *Perf. 14½* | |
|---|---|---|---|---|
| 2894 | A707 | 1st red & black | 1.50 | 1.05 |
| 2895 | A707 | 66p black & red | 2.00 | 1.50 |
| 2896 | A707 | 68p red & black | 2.00 | 1.50 |
| 2897 | A707 | 76p black & red | 2.25 | 1.75 |
| 2898 | A707 | £1 red & black | 3.00 | 2.25 |
| 2899 | A707 | £1.10 black & red | 3.25 | 2.50 |
| | *Nos. 2894-2899 (6)* | | 14.00 | 10.55 |

### Litho.
### *Perf. 14¼*

| 2900 | A708 | Sheet of 4 | 8.75 | 8.50 |
|---|---|---|---|---|
| *a.* | | 1st multi | 1.50 | 1.05 |
| *b.* | | 68p multi | 2.00 | 1.50 |
| *c.* | | 76p multi | 2.25 | 1.75 |
| *d.* | | £1 multi | 3.00 | 2.25 |

On day of issue, Nos. 2894 and 2900 sold for 46p.

## Souvenir Sheet

Wedding of Prince William and Catherine Middleton — A709

**Perf. 14½x14¼**

**2011, Apr. 21**       **Photo.**
2901 A709   Sheet of 4, 2     each #a-b     9.50   9.50
    a.   1st Couple     1.50   1.00
    b.   £1.10 Couple, diff.     3.25   2.50

No. 2901a sold for 46p on day of issue.

William Morris & Company, 150th Anniv. — A710

Designs: No. 2902, Floral fabric design, by William Morris, 1884. No. 2903, Cherry tree wall panel design, by Philip Webb, 1867. No. 2904, Floral wallpaper design, by John Henry Dearle, 1901. No. 2905, Floral ceramic tile design, by Kate Faulkner. No. 2906, Floral glazed tile design, by Morris and William De Morgan, 1876. No. 2907, The Merchant's Daughter, stained-glass by Edward Burne-Jones, c. 1864.

**2011, May 5**   **Litho.**    **Perf. 14¼**
2902 A710   1st multi    1.40   1.00
2903 A710   1st multi    1.40   1.00
2904 A710   76p multi    2.15   1.75
2905 A710   76p multi    2.15   1.75
2906 A710   £1.10 multi    3.10   2.50
   a.   Booklet pane of 4, #2902,    2904, 2905, 2906    (BK196)    9.25   —
2907 A710   £1.10 multi    3.10   2.50
   a.   Booklet pane of 4, 2 each    #2903, 2907 (BK196)    9.50   —
   Nos. 2902-2907 (6)    13.30   10.50

No. 2902 sold for 46p on day of issue.

A711

Thomas the Tank Engine Children's Book Characters, by Rev. Wilbert Awdry (1911-97) — A712

Designs: No. 2908, Thomas. 66p, James. No. 2910, Percy. No. 2911, Daisy. No. 2912, Toby. £1, Gordon.

No. 2914 — Inscriptions: a, "Goodbye, Bertie," called Thomas. b, James was more dirty than hurt. c, "Yes, Sir," Percy shivered miserably. d, They told Henry, "We shall leave you there for always."

No. 2915, Like No. 2914a.

**2011, June 14**     **Perf. 14¾x14¼**
2908 A711   1st multi    1.40   1.00
2909 A711   66p multi    1.90   1.50
2910 A711   68p multi    1.90   1.50
2911 A711   76p multi    2.15   1.75
2912 A711   £1 multi    2.85   2.25
2913 A711   £1.10 multi    3.10   2.50
   Nos. 2908-2913 (6)    13.30   10.50
     **Perf. 14¼**
2914 A712   Sheet of 4    8.50   8.25
   a.   1st multi    1.40   1.00
   b.   68p multi    2.00   1.50
   c.   76p multi    2.25   1.75
   d.   £1 multi    3.00   2.25

---

## Booklet Stamp
## Self-Adhesive
### Photo.
### Die Cut Perf. 14¼

2915 A712   1st multi    4.00   1.25
   a.   Booklet pane of 6, 2 #2915, 4    #MH384    10.00

On day of issue, Nos. 2908, 2914a and 2915 each sold for 46p.

## Sports of the 2012 Summer Olympics and Paralympics Type of 2009-10

Olympics or Paralympics emblem and: Nos. 2916, 2927, Sailing (Paralympics). No. 2917, High jump. No. 2918, Volleyball. Nos. 2919, 2926, Wheelchair rugby (Paralympics). No. 2920, Wrestling. No. 2921, Wheelchair tennis (Paralympics). Nos. 2922, 2929, Fencing. Nos. 2923, 2928, Gymnastics. No. 2924, Triathlon. No. 2925, Handball.

**2011**    **Litho.**    **Perf. 14½**
2916 A673   1st multi    1.75   1.00
2917 A673   1st multi    1.75   1.00
   a.   Booklet pane of 2, #2705,    2917 (BK200)    3.00   —
2918 A673   1st multi    1.75   1.00
2919 A673   1st multi    1.75   1.00
2920 A673   1st multi    1.75   1.00
   a.   Horiz. strip of 5, #2916-   2920    8.75   5.00
2921 A673   1st multi    1.75   1.00
2922 A673   1st multi    1.75   1.00
2923 A673   1st multi    1.75   1.00
2924 A673   1st multi    1.75   1.00
2925 A673   1st multi    1.75   1.00
   a.   Horiz. strip of 5, #2921-   2925    8.75   5.00
   b.   Sheet of 30, #2702-2711,    2815-2824, 2916-2925    42.50   —
   Nos. 2916-2925 (10)    17.50   10.00

## Booklet Stamps
## Self-Adhesive
### Photo.
### Die Cut Perf. 14½

2926 A673   1st multi    3.75   1.00
2927 A673   1st multi    3.75   1.00
   a.   Booklet pane of 6, #2926-   2927, 4 #MH384    10.00
2928 A673   1st multi    3.75   1.00
2929 A673   1st multi    3.75   1.00
   a.   Booklet pane of 6, #2928-   2929, + 4 #MH384    10.00

Issued: Nos. 2916-2927, 7/27. Nos. 2928-2929, 9/15. No. 2917a, 7/27/12. No. 2925b, 7/27. Nos. 2916-2929 each sold for 46p on day of issue. No. 2925b sold for £13.80.

## Locomotives Type of 2011

Design: British Railways Dean Goods No. 2532.

### Die Cut Perf. 14¼
**2011, Aug. 23**      **Photo.**
## Booklet Stamp
## Self-Adhesive
2930 A702   1st multi    3.75   1.00
   a.   Booklet pane of 6, 2 #2930, 4    #MH384    10.00

No. 2930 sold for 46p on day of issue.

British Crown Jewels — A713

Designs: No. 2931, Sovereign's scepter with cross. No. 2932, St. Edward's crown. No. 2933, Rod and scepter with doves. No. 2934, Queen Mary's crown. No. 2935, Sovereign's orb. No. 2936, Jeweled sword of offering. No. 2937, Imperial state crown. No. 2938, Coronation spoon.

### Perf. 14¼x14½
**2011, Aug. 23**      **Litho.**
2931 A713   1st multi    1.45   1.00
2932 A713   1st multi    1.45   1.00
2933 A713   68p multi    1.90   1.50
2934 A713   68p multi    1.90   1.50
2935 A713   76p multi    2.15   1.75
2936 A713   76p multi    2.15   1.75
2937 A713   £1.10 multi    3.10   2.50
2938 A713   £1.10 multi    3.10   2.50
   Nos. 2931-2938 (8)    17.20   13.50

On day of issue Nos. 2931-2932 each sold for 46p.

---

## Miniature Sheet

First Air Mail Flight in Great Britain, Cent. A714

No. 2939: a, Pilot Gustav Hamel receives first mail bag. b, Hamel in plane ready to leave Hendon Aerodrome. c, Clement Greswell near his Blériot airplane at Windsor Castle. d, Air mail delivered at Windsor Castle.

**2011, Sept. 9**   **Litho.**    **Perf. 14¼x14**
2939 A714   Sheet of 4    13.00   7.50
   a.   1st multi    2.00   1.00
   b.   68p multi    2.65   1.50
   c.   £1 multi    4.00   2.25
   d.   £1.10 multi    4.35   2.50
   e.   Booklet pane of 3, #2939c,    2 #2939b (BK197)    12.00   —
   f.   Booklet pane of 3, #2939d,    2 #2939a (BK197)    12.75   —

No. 2939a sold for 46p on day of issue.

## British Royalty and History Type of 2008

Designs: No. 2940, King George I. No. 2941, King George II. No. 2942, King George III. No. 2943, King George IV. No. 2944, King William IV. No. 2945, Queen Victoria.

No. 2946: a, Robert Walpole, first Prime Minister. b, Interior of Kedleston Hall, designed by architect Robert Adam. c, Great Britain #1. d, Queen Victoria in 1897.

**2011, Sept. 15**     **Perf. 14¼**
2940 A645   1st multi    1.50   1.00
2941 A645   1st multi    1.50   1.00
2942 A645   76p multi    2.25   1.75
2943 A645   76p multi    2.25   1.75
2944 A645   £1.10 multi    3.25   2.50
2945 A645   £1.10 multi    3.25   2.50
   Nos. 2940-2945 (6)    14.00   10.50
2946    Sheet of 4    8.25   8.00
   a.   A645 1st multi    1.40   1.00
   b.   A645 68p multi    1.90   1.50
   c.   A645 76p multi    2.10   1.75
   d.   A645 £1 multi    2.85   3.25

On day of issue, Nos. 2940, 2941 and 2946a each sold for 46p.

Great Britain Landmarks in Alphabetical Order — A715

Designs: No. 2947, Angel of the North sculpture, Gateshead. No. 2948, Blackpool Tower. No. 2949, Carrick-a-Rede rope bridge, near Ballintoy, Northern Ireland. No. 2950, 10 Downing Street (Prime Minister's residence, London). No. 2951, Edinburgh Castle. No. 2952, Forth Railway Bridge. No. 2953, Glastonbury Tor. No. 2954, Harlech Castle. No. 2955, Ironbridge. No. 2956, Jodrell Bank radio telescope. No. 2957, Kursaal, Southend. No. 2958, Lindisfarne Priory, Lindisfarne Island. No. 2959, Manchester Town Hall. No. 2960, Narrow Water Castle, near Warrenpoint, Northern Ireland. No. 2961, Old Bailey Courthouse, London. No. 2962, Portmeirion, Wales. No. 2963, Queen's College, Oxford University. No. 2964, Roman Baths, Bath. No. 2965, Stirling Castle, Stirling, Scotland. No. 2966, Tyne Bridge, Newcastle. No. 2967, Urquhart Castle, near Drumnadrochit, Scotland. No. 2968, Victoria and Albert Museum, London. No. 2969, White Cliffs of Dover. No. 2970, Station X, Bletchley Park. No. 2971, York Minster. No. 2972, ZSL London Zoo.

**2011**        **Perf. 14½**
2947 A715   1st multi    1.50   1.00
2948 A715   1st multi    1.50   1.00
2949 A715   1st multi    1.50   1.00
2950 A715   1st multi    1.50   1.00
2951 A715   1st multi    1.50   1.00
2952 A715   1st multi    1.50   1.00
   a.   Horiz. strip of 6, #2947-   2952    9.00   6.25
2953 A715   1st multi    1.50   1.00
2954 A715   1st multi    1.50   1.00
2955 A715   1st multi    1.50   1.00
2956 A715   1st multi    1.50   1.00
2957 A715   1st multi    1.50   1.00
2958 A715   1st multi    1.50   1.00
   a.   Horiz. strip of 6, #2953-   2958    9.00   6.25
   Nos. 2947-2958 (12)    18.00   12.00
2959 A715   1st multi    1.50   1.00
2960 A715   1st multi    1.50   1.00
2961 A715   1st multi    1.50   1.00

---

2962 A715   1st multi    1.50   1.00
2963 A715   1st multi    1.50   1.00
2964 A715   1st multi    1.50   1.00
   a.   Horiz. strip of 6, #2959-   2964    9.00   6.25
2965 A715   1st multi    1.50   1.00
2966 A715   1st multi    1.50   1.00
2967 A715   1st multi    1.50   1.00
2968 A715   1st multi    1.50   1.00
2969 A715   1st multi    1.50   1.00
2970 A715   1st multi    1.50   1.00
   a.   Horiz. strip of 6, #2965-   2970    9.00   6.25
2971 A715   1st multi    1.50   1.00
2972 A715   1st multi    1.50   1.00
   a.   Horiz. pair, #2971-2972    3.00   2.00
   b.   Sheet of 26, #2947-2972, +    4 labels    90.00   90.00
   Nos. 2959-2972 (14)    21.00   14.00
   Nos. 2947-2972 (26)    39.00   26.00

Europa (No. 2968).

Issued: Nos. 2947-2958, 10/13. Nos. 2959-2972, 4/10/12. On day of issue, Nos. 2947-2972 each sold for 46p.

A716

A717

Designs: Nos. 2973a, 2973c, 2974, 2976, Angel visiting Joseph. Nos. 2973b, 2975, Madonna and Child, Nos. 2973e, 2978, Madonna and Child, livestock, dove. 68p, Baby Jesus in manger, livestock. £1.10, Angel visiting shepherds. £1.65, Magi and Star of Bethlehem.

### Perf. 14¾x14 Syncopated
**2011, Nov. 8**      **Photo.**
2973    Sheet of 7    17.00   12.50
   a.   A716 2nd multi    1.20   .80
   b.   A716 1st multi    1.50   1.00
   c.   A717 2nd Large multi    1.75   1.30
   d.   A716 68p multi    2.00   1.50
   e.   A717 1st Large multi    2.25   1.75
   f.   A716 £1.10 multi    3.25   2.50
   g.   A716 £1.65 multi    5.00   3.75

### Self-Adhesive
### Die Cut Perf. 14¾x14 Syncopated
2974 A716   2nd multi    1.20   .80
   a.   Booklet pane of 12    16.00
   b.   Sheet of 20 #2974c + 20 labels    48.00
   b.   Litho. + label    2.40   2.40
2975 A716   1st multi    1.50   1.00
   a.   Booklet pane of 12    19.00
   b.   Sheet of 10 #2975c + 10 labels    30.00
   b.   Litho. + label    3.00   3.00
2976 A717   2nd Large multi    1.75   1.30
2977 A716   68p multi    2.00   1.50
   a.   Sheet of 10 #2977b + 10 labels    40.00
   b.   Litho. + label    4.00   4.00
2978 A717   1st Large multi    2.25   1.75
2979 A716   £1.10 multi    3.25   2.50
   a.   Sheet of 20, 8 each #2974c-   2975c, 2 each #2977b,    2979c + 20 labels    65.00
   b.   Sheet of 10 #2979c + 10 labels    65.00
   b.   Litho. + label    6.50   6.50
2980 A716   £1.65 multi    5.00   3.75
   Nos. 2974-2980 (7)    16.95   12.60

On day of issue, Nos. 2973a and 2974 each sold for 36p; Nos. 2973b and 2975 for 46p; Nos. 2973c and 2976 for 58p; Nos. 2973e and 2978 for 75p. No. 2979a sold for £10.45. Labels on No. 2979a could not be personalized.

Nos. 2974b, 2975b, 2977a and 2979b had labels that could be personalized. No. 2974b sold for £10.95; No. 2975b, for £8.30; No. 2977a, for £10.75; and No. 2979b, for £15.80. No. 2975b was half of a larger sheet of 20 stamps and 20 labels that sold for £14.95, which was torn along central row of rouletting. Nos. 2977a and 2979b have rouletting along the left or right side of the sheet, but these stamps were not sold in sheets of 20.

Emblem of 2012 Summer Olympics A718

Emblem of 2012 Paralympics A719

## Die Cut Perf. 14¾x14 Syncopated
**2012, Jan. 5**      **Photo.**

### Self-Adhesive

| | | | | |
|---|---|---|---|---|
| 2981 | A718 | 1st gray, org & blk | 1.50 | 1.00 |
| 2982 | A719 | 1st gray, org & blk | 1.50 | 1.00 |
| a. | | Booklet pane of 6, 3 each #2981-2982, #2981 at UL | 11.00 | |
| b. | | As "a," #2982 at UL | 11.00 | 11.00 |

Nos. 2981 and 2982 each sold for 46p on day of issue.
See Nos. 3044-3045, C6-C9.

Illustrations From Children's Books by Roald Dahl (1916-90) — A720

Designs: 1st, Charlie and the Chocolate Factory. 66p, Fantastic Mr. Fox. 68p, James and the Giant Peach. 76p, Matilda. £1, The Twits. £1.10, The Witches.
No. 2989 — Scenes from The BFG (Big Friendly Giant): a, Giant holding Sophie in hand. b, Big Friendly Giant and Sophie awakening other Giants. c, Sophie on Queen's window sill. d, Giant and Sophie at desk.

**2012, Jan. 10**    **Litho.**    **Perf. 14¼**

| | | | | |
|---|---|---|---|---|
| 2983 | A720 | 1st multi | 1.50 | 1.00 |
| 2984 | A720 | 66p multi | 2.00 | 1.50 |
| 2985 | A720 | 68p multi | 2.00 | 1.50 |
| 2986 | A720 | 76p multi | 2.25 | 1.75 |
| a. | | Booklet pane of 3, #2983, 2985, 2986 (BK198) | 5.75 | — |
| 2987 | A720 | £1 multi | 3.00 | 2.25 |
| 2988 | A720 | £1.10 multi | 3.25 | 2.40 |
| a. | | Booklet pane of 3, #2984, 2987, 2988 (BK198) | 8.25 | — |
| | | Nos. 2983-2988 (6) | 14.00 | 10.40 |

### Souvenir Sheet
**Perf. 14¼x14½**

| | | | | |
|---|---|---|---|---|
| 2989 | | Sheet of 4 | 11.00 | 8.50 |
| a. | A720 | 1st multi | 1.90 | 1.00 |
| b. | A720 | 68p multi | 2.50 | 1.50 |
| c. | A720 | 76p multi | 2.85 | 1.75 |
| d. | A720 | £1 multi | 3.75 | 2.25 |
| e. | | Booklet pane of 4, #2989a-2989d (BK198) | 8.75 | — |

On day of issue, Nos. 2983 and 2989a sold for 46p. No. 2989 contains four 36x35mm stamps.

### British Royalty and History Type of 2008

Designs: No. 2990, King Edward VII. No. 2991, King George V. No. 2992, King Edward VIII. No. 2993, King George VI. £1.10, Queen Elizabeth II.
No. 2995: a, 1912 Scott Expedition to the South Pole. b, King George VI and Queen Mary talking with man amidst World War II damage. c, Victory of 1966 English World Cup soccer team. d, Opening of Channel Tunnel, 1994.

**2012, Feb. 2**    **Litho.**    **Perf. 14¼**

| | | | | |
|---|---|---|---|---|
| 2990 | A645 | 1st multi | 1.50 | 1.00 |
| 2991 | A645 | 68p multi | 2.00 | 1.50 |
| 2992 | A645 | 76p multi | 2.25 | 1.75 |
| 2993 | A645 | £1 multi | 3.00 | 2.25 |
| 2994 | A645 | £1.10 multi | 3.25 | 2.50 |
| | | Nos. 2990-2994 (5) | 12.00 | 9.00 |

### Souvenir Sheet

| | | | | |
|---|---|---|---|---|
| 2995 | | Sheet of 4 | 8.75 | 8.75 |
| a. | A645 | 1st multi | 1.50 | 1.00 |
| b. | A645 | 68p multi | 2.00 | 1.50 |
| c. | A645 | 76p multi | 2.25 | 1.75 |
| d. | A645 | £1 multi | 3.00 | 2.25 |

On day of issue, Nos. 2990 and 2995a each sold for 46p.

### Miniature Sheet

Reign of Queen Elizabeth II, 60th Anniv. A721

No. 2996 — Image of Queen Elizabeth II: a, Great Britain Type A131 redrawn. b, From 1960 one-pound banknote ("ND" at upper left). c, From 1971 five-pound banknote. d, From coin, without tiara. e, From coin, with tiara. f, Great Britain Type MH2 with iridescent overprint of "Diamond Jubilee" in wavy lines.

**Perf. 14¾x14 Syncopated**
**2012, Feb. 6**      **Photo.**

| | | | | |
|---|---|---|---|---|
| 2996 | A721 | Sheet of 6 | 9.75 | 6.50 |
| a.-f. | | 1st Any single | 1.50 | 1.00 |

---

| | | | | |
|---|---|---|---|---|
| 2996G | A721 | 1st As #2996a, litho. | | |
| | | (2996Gh) | 3.50 | 2.00 |
| h. | | Booklet pane of 8, 4 each #2996G, MH419, + central label (BK199) | 30.00 | — |

Nos. 2996a-2996f each sold for 46p on day of issue.
Issued: No. 2996G, 2996Gh, 5/31. No. 2996G sold for 60p on day of issue.

Britons of Distinction — A722

Designs: No. 2997, New Coventry Cathedral, designed by Sir Basil Spence (1907-76). No. 2998, Frederick Delius (1862-1934), composer. No. 2999, Orange Tree embroidery by Mary "May" Morris (1862-1938), designer and textile artist. No. 3000, Odette Hallowes (1912-95), Special Operations Executive agent in World War II. No. 3001, Atmospheric steam engine invented by Thomas Newcomen (1664-1729). No. 3002, Kathleen Ferrier (1912-53), opera singer. No. 3003, Interior of Palace of Westminster, designed by Augustus Pugin (1812-53). No. 3004, Montague Rhodes James (1862-1936), medieval scholar and writer of ghost stories. No. 3005, Bombe code-breaking machine designed by Alan Turing (1912-54), mathematician and cryptanalyst. No. 3006, Joan Mary Fry (1862-1955), relief worker and social reformer.

**2012, Feb. 23**    **Litho.**    **Perf. 14½**

| | | | | |
|---|---|---|---|---|
| 2997 | A722 | 1st multi | 1.70 | 1.00 |
| 2998 | A722 | 1st multi | 1.70 | 1.00 |
| 2999 | A722 | 1st multi | 1.70 | 1.00 |
| 3000 | A722 | 1st multi | 1.70 | 1.00 |
| 3001 | A722 | 1st multi | 1.70 | 1.00 |
| a. | | Horiz. strip of 5, #2997-3001 | 8.50 | 5.00 |
| 3002 | A722 | 1st multi | 1.70 | 1.00 |
| 3003 | A722 | 1st multi | 1.70 | 1.00 |
| 3004 | A722 | 1st multi | 1.70 | 1.00 |
| 3005 | A722 | 1st multi | 1.70 | 1.00 |
| 3006 | A722 | 1st multi | 1.70 | 1.00 |
| a. | | Horiz. strip of 5, #3002-3006 | 8.50 | 5.00 |
| | | Nos. 2997-3006 (10) | 17.00 | 10.00 |

Nos. 2997-3006 each sold for 46p on day of issue.

### Miniature Sheet

Scottish Locomotives — A723

No. 3007: a, British Railways D34 Nos. 62471 and 62496. b, British Railways D40 No. 62276. c, Andrew Barclay No. 807. d, British Railways 4P No. 54767.

**2012, Mar. 8**      **Perf. 14¼**

| | | | | |
|---|---|---|---|---|
| 3007 | A723 | Sheet of 4 | 9.50 | 7.50 |
| a. | | 1st multi | 1.45 | 1.00 |
| b. | | 68p multi | 1.95 | 1.50 |
| c. | | £1 multi | 2.90 | 2.25 |
| d. | | £1.10 multi | 3.15 | 2.50 |
| e. | | Booklet pane of 4, 2 each #3007a, 3007b (BK204) | 7.25 | — |

No. 3007a sold for 46p on day of issue. Issued: No. 3007e, 2/20/14. See No. 3111.

Comic Book Covers and Characters — A724

Designs: No. 3008, The Dandy. No. 3009, The Beano. No. 3010, Eagle. No. 3011, The Topper. No. 3012, Tiger. No. 3013, Bunty. No. 3014, Buster. No. 3015, Valiant. No. 3016, Twinkle. No. 3017, 2000 A.D.

**2012, Mar. 20**      **Perf. 14½**

| | | | | |
|---|---|---|---|---|
| 3008 | A724 | 1st multi | 1.75 | 1.00 |
| 3009 | A724 | 1st multi | 1.75 | 1.00 |
| 3010 | A724 | 1st multi | 1.75 | 1.00 |
| 3011 | A724 | 1st multi | 1.75 | 1.00 |
| 3012 | A724 | 1st multi | 1.75 | 1.00 |
| a. | | Horiz. strip of 5, #3008-3012 | 8.75 | 5.00 |
| 3013 | A724 | 1st multi litho. | 1.75 | 1.00 |
| 3014 | A724 | 1st multi | 1.75 | 1.00 |
| 3015 | A724 | 1st multi | 1.75 | 1.00 |
| 3016 | A724 | 1st multi | 1.75 | 1.00 |

---

| | | | | |
|---|---|---|---|---|
| 3017 | A724 | 1st multi | 1.75 | 1.00 |
| a. | | Horiz. strip of 5, #3013-3017 | 8.75 | 5.00 |
| | | Nos. 3008-3017 (10) | 17.50 | 10.00 |

Nos. 3008-3017 each sold for 46p on day of issue.

Fashion — A725

Clothing designed by: No. 3018, Hardy Amies. No. 3019, Norman Hartnell. No. 3020, Granny Takes a Trip. No. 3021, Ossie Clark. No. 3022, Tommy Nutter. No. 3023, Jean Muir. No. 3024, Zandra Rhodes. No. 3025, Vivienne Westwood. No. 3026, Paul Smith. No. 3026, Alexander McQueen.

**2012, May 15**    **Litho.**    **Perf. 14½**

| | | | | |
|---|---|---|---|---|
| 3018 | A725 | 1st multi | 1.75 | 1.35 |
| 3019 | A725 | 1st multi | 1.75 | 1.35 |
| 3020 | A725 | 1st multi | 1.75 | 1.35 |
| 3021 | A725 | 1st multi | 1.75 | 1.35 |
| 3022 | A725 | 1st multi | 1.75 | 1.35 |
| a. | | Horiz. strip of 5, #3018-3022 | 8.75 | 6.75 |
| 3023 | A725 | 1st multi | 1.75 | 1.35 |
| 3024 | A725 | 1st multi | 1.75 | 1.35 |
| 3025 | A725 | 1st multi | 1.75 | 1.35 |
| 3026 | A725 | 1st multi | 1.75 | 1.35 |
| 3027 | A725 | 1st multi | 1.75 | 1.35 |
| a. | | Horiz. strip of 5, #3023-3027 | 8.75 | 6.75 |
| | | Nos. 3018-3027 (10) | 17.50 | 13.50 |

Nos. 3018-3027 each sold for 60p on day of issue.

Reign of Queen Elizabeth II, 60th Anniv. — A726

Photographs of Queen Elizabeth II at: Nos. 3028, 3036, Golden Jubilee, 2002. No. 3029, Trooping the Color, 1967. No. 3030, The Royal Welsh, 2007. No. 3031, First Christmas TV Broadcast, 1957. No. 3032, Silver Jubilee Walkabout, 1977. No. 3033, Garter Ceremony, 1997. No. 3034, United Nations Address, 1957. No. 3035, Commonwealth Games, 1982.

**Perf. 14¼x14½**

**2012, May 31**      **Photo.**

| | | | | |
|---|---|---|---|---|
| 3028 | A726 | 1st multi | 1.90 | 1.35 |
| a. | | Litho. (3034b) | 2.10 | 2.10 |
| 3029 | A726 | 1st black | 1.90 | 1.35 |
| a. | | Litho. (3030b) | 2.10 | 2.10 |
| b. | | Horiz. pair, #3028-3029 | 4.00 | 2.75 |
| 3030 | A726 | 77p multi | 2.40 | 1.75 |
| a. | | Litho. (3030b) | 2.60 | 2.60 |
| b. | | Booklet pane of 2, #3029a, 3030a (BK199) | 4.75 | — |
| 3031 | A726 | 77p black | 2.40 | 1.75 |
| a. | | Litho. (3035c) | 2.60 | 2.60 |
| b. | | Horiz. pair, #3030-3031 | 5.00 | 3.50 |
| 3032 | A726 | 87p black | 2.60 | 2.00 |
| a. | | Litho. (3034b) | 2.60 | 2.60 |
| b. | | Horiz. pair, #3032-3033 | 5.25 | 4.00 |
| 3033 | A726 | 87p multi | 2.60 | 2.00 |
| a. | | Litho. (3034b) | 2.60 | 2.60 |
| b. | | Booklet pane of 4, #3028a, 3032a, 3033a, 3034a (BK199) | 12.00 | — |
| 3034 | A726 | £1.28 black | 4.00 | 2.90 |
| a. | | Litho. (3035c) | 4.50 | 4.50 |
| b. | | Horiz. pair, #3034-3035 | 8.00 | 6.00 |
| 3035 | A726 | £1.28 multi | 4.00 | 2.90 |
| a. | | Litho. (3035c) | 4.50 | 4.50 |
| c. | | Booklet pane of 2, #3031a, 3035a (BK199) | 7.25 | — |
| | | Nos. 3028-3035 (8) | 21.80 | 16.00 |

### Booklet Stamp
### Self-Adhesive
**Die Cut Perf. 14¾x14½**

| | | | | |
|---|---|---|---|---|
| 3036 | A726 | 1st multi | 4.50 | 1.35 |
| a. | | Booklet pane of 6, 2 #3036, 4 #MH414 | 10.00 | |

On day of issue, Nos. 3028, 3029 and 3036 each sold for 60p.

A727

---

Nicholas Nickleby 1st

Characters and Scenes From Novels by Charles Dickens (1812-70) — A728

Designs: 2nd, Mr. Bumble from Oliver Twist. No. 3038, Mr. Pickwick from The Pickwick Papers. 77p, The Marchioness from The Old Curiosity Shop. 87p, Mrs. Gamp from Martin Chuzzlewit. £1.28, Captain Cuttle from Dombey and Son. £1.90, Mr. Micawber from David Copperfield.
No. 3043 — Scenes from: a, Nicholas Nickleby. b, Bleak House. c, Little Dorrit. d, A Tale of Two Cities.

**2012, June 19**    **Litho.**    **Perf. 14¼**

| | | | | |
|---|---|---|---|---|
| 3037 | A727 | 2nd multi | 1.55 | 1.15 |
| 3038 | A727 | 1st multi | 1.85 | 1.35 |
| 3039 | A727 | 77p multi | 2.20 | 1.75 |
| 3040 | A727 | 87p multi | 2.50 | 2.00 |
| 3041 | A727 | £1.28 multi | 3.85 | 2.90 |
| 3042 | A727 | £1.90 multi | 5.55 | 4.25 |
| | | Nos. 3037-3042 (6) | 17.50 | 13.40 |

### Miniature Sheet

| | | | | |
|---|---|---|---|---|
| 3043 | | Sheet of 4 | 7.50 | 7.50 |
| a.-d. | A728 | 1st Any single | 1.90 | .95 |

On day of issue No. 3037 sold for 50p, and Nos. 3038, 3043a-3043d each sold for 60p.

### Olympics and Paralympics Emblems Type of 2012
**Perf. 14¾x14 Syncopated**
**2012, July 27**      **Litho.**

### Booklet Stamps

| | | | | |
|---|---|---|---|---|
| 3044 | A718 | 1st gray, org & blk (C9a) | 4.75 | 4.75 |
| 3045 | A719 | 1st gray, org & blk (C9a) | 4.75 | 4.75 |

On day of issue Nos. 3044-3045 each sold for 60p.

### Miniature Sheet

Welcome to the Summer Olympics A729

No. 3046: a, Fencing, Tower Bridge. b, Runners, Olympic Stadium. c, Diver, Tate Modern Museum. d, Cyclist at left, London Eye.

**2012, July 27**    **Litho.**    **Perf. 14¾**

| | | | | |
|---|---|---|---|---|
| 3046 | A729 | Sheet of 4 | 11.50 | 11.50 |
| a.-b. | | 1st Either single | 1.75 | 1.35 |
| c.-d. | | £1.28 Either single | 3.75 | 2.90 |

On day of issue Nos. 3046a-3046b each sold for 60p.

British Gold Medalists at 2012 Summer Olympics A730

Photographs of gold medalists and inscription: No. 3047, Team GB, Rowing, Women's Pairs. No. 3048, Bradley Wiggins, Cycling: Road, Men's Time Trial. No. 3049, Team GB, Canoe Slalom: Men's, Canoe Double (C2). No. 3050, Peter Wilson, Shooting: Shotgun, Men's Double Trap. No. 3051, Team GB, Cycling: Track, Men's Team Sprint. No. 3052, Team GB, Rowing, Women's Double Sculls. No. 3053, Team GB, Cycling: Track, Men's Team Pursuit. No. 3054, Victoria Pendleton, Cycling: Track, Women's Keirin. No. 3055, Team GB, Rowing, Men's Fours. No. 3056, Team GB, Rowing: Lightweight Women's Double Sculls. No. 3057, Team GB, Cycling: Track Women's Team Pursuit. No. 3058, Jessica Ennis, Athletics: Combined Women's Heptathlon. No. 3059, Greg Rutherford, Athletics: Field, Men's Long Jump. No. 3060, Mo Farah, Athletics: Track, Men's 10,000m. No. 3061, Ben Ainslie, Sailing: Finn, Men's Heavyweight Dinghy. No. 3062, Andy Murray, Tennis, Men's Singles. No. 3063, Team GB, Equestrian: Jumping, Team. No. 3064, Jason Kenny, Cycling: Track, Men's Sprint. No. 3065, Alistair Brownlee, Triathlon, Men's. No. 3066, Team GB, Equestrian: Dressage, Team. No. 3067, Laura Trott, Cycling: Track, Women's Omnium. No. 3068, Chris Hoy, Cycling: Track, Men's Keirin. No. 3069, Charlotte Dujardin, Equestrian: Dressage, Individual. No. 3070, Nicola Adams, Boxing, Women's Flyweight. No. 3071, Jade Jones, Taekwondo, Women's

Under 57kg. No. 3072, Ed McKeever, Canoe Sprint: Men's, Kayak Single (K1) 200m. No. 3073, Mo Farah, Athletics: Track, Men's 5000m. No. 3074, Luke Campbell, Boxing, Men's Bantamweight. No. 3075, Anthony Joshua, boxing, Men's Super Heavyweight.

### Litho. With Digital Printing

| 2012 | | Die Cut Perf. 14¾x14½ | | |
|---|---|---|---|---|
| | | Self-Adhesive | | |
| 3047 | A730 | 1st multi | 1.75 | 1.35 |
| 3048 | A730 | 1st multi | 1.75 | 1.35 |
| 3049 | A730 | 1st multi | 1.75 | 1.35 |
| 3050 | A730 | 1st multi | 1.75 | 1.35 |
| 3051 | A730 | 1st multi | 1.75 | 1.35 |
| 3052 | A730 | 1st multi | 1.75 | 1.35 |
| 3053 | A730 | 1st multi | 1.75 | 1.35 |
| 3054 | A730 | 1st multi | 1.75 | 1.35 |
| 3055 | A730 | 1st multi | 1.75 | 1.35 |
| 3056 | A730 | 1st multi | 1.75 | 1.35 |
| 3057 | A730 | 1st multi | 1.75 | 1.35 |
| 3058 | A730 | 1st multi | 1.75 | 1.35 |
| 3059 | A730 | 1st multi | 1.75 | 1.35 |
| 3060 | A730 | 1st multi | 1.75 | 1.35 |
| 3061 | A730 | 1st multi | 1.75 | 1.35 |
| 3062 | A730 | 1st multi | 1.75 | 1.35 |
| 3063 | A730 | 1st multi | 1.75 | 1.35 |
| 3064 | A730 | 1st multi | 1.75 | 1.35 |
| 3065 | A730 | 1st multi | 1.75 | 1.35 |
| 3066 | A730 | 1st multi | 1.75 | 1.35 |
| 3067 | A730 | 1st multi | 1.75 | 1.35 |
| 3068 | A730 | 1st multi | 1.75 | 1.35 |
| 3069 | A730 | 1st multi | 1.75 | 1.35 |
| 3070 | A730 | 1st multi | 1.75 | 1.35 |
| 3071 | A730 | 1st multi | 1.75 | 1.35 |
| 3072 | A730 | 1st multi | 1.75 | 1.35 |
| 3073 | A730 | 1st multi | 1.75 | 1.35 |
| 3074 | A730 | 1st multi | 1.75 | 1.35 |
| 3075 | A730 | 1st multi | 1.75 | 1.35 |
| | | Nos. 3047-3075 (29) | 50.75 | 39.15 |

Issued: Nos. 3047-3048, 8/2; Nos. 3049-3051, 8/3; Nos. 3052-3055, 8/4; Nos. 3056-3060, 8/5; Nos. 3061-3062, 8/6; Nos. 3063-3064, 8/7; Nos. 3065-3068, 8/8; Nos. 3069-3071, 8/10; Nos. 3072-3075, 8/12.

Nos. 3047-3075 were each issued in sheets of six. Each stamp sold for 60p on day of issue

### Miniature Sheet

Welcome to the Paralympics — A731

No. 3076: a, Runner with artificial leg, Olympic Stadium. b, Wheelchair basketball player, Palace of Westminster. c, Weight lifter, St. Paul's Cathedral and Millennium Bridge. d, London Eye, cyclist on right.

| 2012, Aug. 29 | | Litho. | Perf. 14¾ | |
|---|---|---|---|---|
| 3076 | A731 | Sheet of 4 | 11.50 | 11.50 |
| a.-b. | | 1st Either single | 1.75 | 1.35 |
| c.-d. | | £1.28 Either single | 3.75 | 2.90 |

On day of issue Nos. 3076a-3076b each sold for 60p.

British Gold Medalists at 2012 Summer Paralympics A732

Photograph of gold medalist and inscription: No. 3077, Sarah Storey, Cycling: Track, Women's C5 Pursuit. No. 3078, Jonathan Fox, Swimming: Men's, 100m Backstroke, S7. No. 3079, Mark Colbourne, Cycling: Track, Men's C1 Pursuit. No. 3080, Hannah Cockroft, Athletics: Track, Women's 100m, T34. No. 3081, Paralympics GB, Cycling: Track, Men's B 1km Time Trial. No. 3082, Richard Whitehead, Athletics: Track, Men's 200m, T42. No. 3083, Natasha Baker, Equestrian: Individual, Championship Test, Grade II. No. 3084, Sarah Storey, Cycling: Track, Women's C4-5 500m Time Trial. No. 3085, Ellie Simmonds, Swimming: Women's, 400m Freestyle, S6. No. 3086, Paralympics GB, Rowing: Mixed, Coxed Four, LTA Mix 4+. No. 3087, Aled Davies, Athletics: Field, Men's Discus, F42. No. 3088, Paralympics GB, Cycling: Track, Men's B Sprint. No. 3089, Jessica-Jane Applegate, Swimming: Women's, 200m Freestyle, S14. No. 3090, Sophie Christiansen, Equestrian: Individual, Championship Test, Grade Ia. No. 3091, David Weir, Athletics: Track, Men's 5000m, T54. No. 3092, Natasha Baker, Equestrian: Individual, Freestyle Test, Grade II. No. 3093, Ellie Simmonds, Swimming: Women's, 200m Individual Medley, SM6. No. 3094, Mickey Bushell, Athletics: Track, Men's 100m, T53. No. 3095, Danielle Brown, Archery: Women's, Individual Compound, Open. No. 3096, Heather Frederiksen, Swimming: Women's, 100m Backstroke, S8. No. 3097, Sophie Christiansen, Equestrian: Individual, Freestyle Test, Grade Ia. No. 3098, David

Weir, Athletics: Track, Men's 1500m, T54. No. 3099, Sarah Storey, Cycling: Road, Women's C5 Time Trial. No. 3100, Ollie Hynd, Swimming: Men's, 200m Individual Medley, SM8. No. 3101, Paralympics GB, Equestrian: Team, Open. No. 3102, Helena Lucas, Sailing: Single-person, Keelboat 2.4mR. No. 3103, Sarah Storey, Cycling: Road, Women's C4-5 Road Race. No. 3104, Josef Craig, Swimming: Men's, 400m Freestyle, S7. No. 3105, Hannah Cockroft, Athletics: Track, Women's 200m, T34. No. 3106, David Weir, Athletics: Track, Men's 800m, T54. No. 3107, Jonnie Peacock, Athletics: Track, Men's 100m, T44. No. 3108, Josie Pearson, Athletics: Field, Women's Discus, F51/52/53. No. 3109, David Stone, Cycling: Road, Mixed T1-2 Road Race. No. 3110, David Weir, Athletics: Road, Men's Marathon, T54.

### Litho. With Digital Printing

| 2012 | | Die Cut Perf. 14¾x14½ | | |
|---|---|---|---|---|
| | | Self-Adhesive | | |
| 3077 | A732 | 1st multi | 2.00 | 1.35 |
| 3078 | A732 | 1st multi | 2.00 | 1.35 |
| 3079 | A732 | 1st multi | 2.00 | 1.35 |
| 3080 | A732 | 1st multi | 2.00 | 1.35 |
| 3081 | A732 | 1st multi | 2.00 | 1.35 |
| 3082 | A732 | 1st multi | 2.00 | 1.35 |
| 3083 | A732 | 1st multi | 2.00 | 1.35 |
| 3084 | A732 | 1st multi | 2.00 | 1.35 |
| 3085 | A732 | 1st multi | 2.00 | 1.35 |
| 3086 | A732 | 1st multi | 2.00 | 1.35 |
| 3087 | A732 | 1st multi | 2.00 | 1.35 |
| 3088 | A732 | 1st multi | 2.00 | 1.35 |
| 3089 | A732 | 1st multi | 2.00 | 1.35 |
| 3090 | A732 | 1st multi | 2.00 | 1.35 |
| 3091 | A732 | 1st multi | 2.00 | 1.35 |
| 3092 | A732 | 1st multi | 2.00 | 1.35 |
| 3093 | A732 | 1st multi | 2.00 | 1.35 |
| 3094 | A732 | 1st multi | 2.00 | 1.35 |
| 3095 | A732 | 1st multi | 2.00 | 1.35 |
| 3096 | A732 | 1st multi | 2.00 | 1.35 |
| 3097 | A732 | 1st multi | 2.00 | 1.35 |
| 3098 | A732 | 1st multi | 2.00 | 1.35 |
| 3099 | A732 | 1st multi | 2.00 | 1.35 |
| 3100 | A732 | 1st multi | 2.00 | 1.35 |
| 3101 | A732 | 1st multi | 2.00 | 1.35 |
| 3102 | A732 | 1st multi | 2.00 | 1.35 |
| 3103 | A732 | 1st multi | 2.00 | 1.35 |
| 3104 | A732 | 1st multi | 2.00 | 1.35 |
| 3105 | A732 | 1st multi | 2.00 | 1.35 |
| 3106 | A732 | 1st multi | 2.00 | 1.35 |
| 3107 | A732 | 1st multi | 2.00 | 1.35 |
| 3108 | A732 | 1st multi | 2.00 | 1.35 |
| 3109 | A732 | 1st multi | 2.00 | 1.35 |
| 3110 | A732 | 1st multi | 2.00 | 1.35 |
| | | Nos. 3077-3110 (34) | 68.00 | 45.90 |

Issued: No. 3077, 8/31; No. 3078, 9/1; Nos. 3079-3085, 9/3; Nos. 3086-3093, 9/4; Nos. 3094-3097, 9/5; Nos. 3098-3101, 9/7. Nos. 3102-3105, 9/8; Nos. 3106-3110, 9/10.

Nos. 3077-3110 were each issued in sheets of two. Each stamp sold for 60p on day of issue

### Scottish Locomotives Type of 2012

Design: British Railways D34 Nos. 62471 and 62496.

| | Die Cut Perf. 14¼ | | | |
|---|---|---|---|---|
| 2012, Sept. 27 | | | Photo. | |
| | | Booklet Stamp | | |
| | | Self-Adhesive | | |
| 3111 | A723 | 1st multi | 3.75 | 1.35 |
| a. | | Booklet pane of 6, 2 #3111, 4 #MH414 | 10.00 | |

No. 3111 sold for 60p on day of issue.

### Miniature Sheet

Scenes From 2012 Summer Olympics and Paralympics — A733

No. 3112: a, British Paralympics Team in procession. b, Athletes walking near stadium. c, Paralympic Games Opening Ceremonies. d, Olympic Closing Ceremony.

| 2012, Sept. 27 | | Litho. | Perf. 14¾ | |
|---|---|---|---|---|
| 3112 | A733 | Sheet of 4 | 11.50 | 11.50 |
| a.-b. | | 1st Either single | 1.75 | 1.35 |
| c.-d. | | £1.28 Either single | 3.75 | 2.90 |

On day of issue Nos. 3112a-3112b each sold for 60p.

Astronomical Bodies — A734

Designs: No. 3113, Sun. No. 3114, Venus. No. 3115, Mars. No. 3116, Asteroid Lutetia. No. 3117, Saturn. No. 3118, Titan, moon of Saturn.

| 2012, Oct. 10 | | | Perf. 14¼x14 | |
|---|---|---|---|---|
| 3113 | A734 | 1st multi | 1.60 | 1.35 |
| 3114 | A734 | 1st multi | 1.60 | 1.35 |
| 3115 | A734 | 77p multi | 2.20 | 1.75 |
| 3116 | A734 | 77p multi | 2.20 | 1.75 |
| 3117 | A734 | £1.28 multi | 3.45 | 2.90 |
| 3118 | A734 | £1.28 multi | 3.45 | 2.90 |
| | | Nos. 3113-3118 (6) | 14.50 | 12.00 |

First British satellite, 50th anniv. On day of issue, Nos. 3113-3114 each sold for 60p.

### Poppy Type of 2010

| | Die Cut Perf14¾x14 Syncopated | | | |
|---|---|---|---|---|
| 2012, Dec. 23 | | | Litho. | |
| 3118A | A686 | 1st multi | 2.25 | 2.25 |

No. 3118A has value and Queen's head in silver, die cuts are complete. There is no attached label.

Christmas
A735          A736

Designs: 2nd, Reindeer with Christmas ornaments on antlers. 1st, Bird on hand of Santa Claus. 2nd Large, Reindeer with Christmas ornaments on antlers, trees. 87p, Penguin and snowman. 1st Large, Bird on hand of Santa Claus, tree. £1.28, Bird carrying star Christmas ornament on holly branch. £1.90, Cat, mouse and Christmas tree.

| | Perf. 14¾x14 Syncopated | | | |
|---|---|---|---|---|
| 2012, Nov. 6 | | | Photo. | |
| 3119 | | Sheet of 7 | 18.50 | 18.50 |
| a. | A735 | 2nd multi | 1.50 | 1.15 |
| b. | A735 | 1st multi | 1.75 | 1.35 |
| c. | A735 | 2nd Large multi | 2.10 | 1.60 |
| d. | A735 | 87p multi | 2.60 | 2.00 |
| e. | A736 | 1st Large multi | 2.75 | 2.00 |
| f. | A735 | £1.28 multi | 3.75 | 2.90 |
| g. | A735 | £1.90 multi | 5.75 | 4.25 |

### Self-Adhesive

| | Die Cut Perf. 14¾x14 Syncopated | | | |
|---|---|---|---|---|
| 3120 | A735 | 2nd multi | 1.35 | 1.15 |
| a. | | Booklet pane of 12 | 16.00 | |
| b. | | Litho. + label (3125b) | 3.00 | 3.00 |
| 3121 | A735 | 1st multi | 1.60 | 1.35 |
| a. | | Booklet pane of 12 | 19.00 | |
| b. | | Litho. + label (3125b) | 3.50 | 3.50 |
| 3122 | A736 | 2nd Large multi | 1.90 | 1.60 |
| a. | | Litho. + label (3125b) | 5.50 | 5.50 |
| 3123 | A735 | 87p multi | 2.40 | 2.00 |
| a. | | Litho. + label (3125b) | 5.50 | 5.50 |
| 3124 | A736 | 1st Large multi | 2.50 | 2.00 |
| 3125 | A735 | £1.28 multi | 3.45 | 2.00 |
| a. | | Litho. + label (3125b) | 8.00 | 8.00 |
| b. | | Sheet of 20, 8 each #3120b, 3121b, 2 each #3123a, 3125a, + 20 labels | 80.00 | |
| 3126 | A735 | £1.90 multi | 5.25 | 4.25 |
| | | Nos. 3120-3126 (7) | 18.45 | 15.25 |

On day of issue, Nos. 3119a and 3120 each sold for 50p, Nos. 3119b and 3121 each sold for 60p, Nos. 3119c and 3122 each sold for 69p, and Nos. 3119e and 3124 each sold for 90p. No. 3125b sold for £13.60. Labels could not be personalized.

London Underground, 150th Anniv. — A737

Advertisements in London Underground — A738

Designs: No. 3127, Train and cars in tunnel, 1863. No. 3128, Workers tunneling under London streets, 1898. No. 3129, Suburban commuters in train car, 1911. Nos. 3130, 3134, Boston Manor Art Deco station exterior, 1934. No. 3131, Train cars, 1938. No. 3132, Escalators at Canary Wharf Jubilee Line Station, 1999.

No. 3133 — Underground emblem and various advertising posters promoting travel on the Underground.

| 2013, Jan. 9 | | Litho. | Perf. 14¼ | |
|---|---|---|---|---|
| 3127 | A737 | 2nd multi | 1.50 | 1.15 |
| 3128 | A737 | 2nd multi | 1.50 | 1.15 |
| 3129 | A737 | 1st multi | 1.75 | 1.35 |
| 3130 | A737 | 1st multi | 1.75 | 1.35 |
| 3131 | A737 | £1.28 multi | 3.75 | 2.90 |
| 3132 | A737 | £1.28 multi | 3.75 | 2.90 |
| | | Nos. 3127-3132 (6) | 14.00 | 10.80 |

### Miniature Sheet

| | Perf. 14¾ | | | |
|---|---|---|---|---|
| 3133 | A738 | Sheet of 4 | 10.50 | 10.50 |
| a. | | 1st multi | 1.75 | 1.35 |
| b. | | 77p multi | 2.40 | 1.75 |
| c. | | 87p multi | 2.60 | 2.00 |
| d. | | £1.28 multi | 3.75 | 2.90 |

### Booklet Stamp
### Self-Adhesive

| | Die Cut Perf. 14¼ | | | |
|---|---|---|---|---|
| 3134 | A737 | 1st multi | 4.50 | 1.75 |
| a. | | Booklet pane of 6, 2 #3134, 4 #MH426 | 10.00 | |

On day of issue, Nos.3127-3128 each sold for 50p, and Nos, 3129-3130, 3133a and 3134 each sold for 60p.

Scenes From Novels by Jane Austen — A739

Scene from: No. 3135, Sense and Sensibility. No. 3136, Pride and Prejudice. No. 3137, Mansfield Park. No. 3138, Emma. No. 3139, Northanger Abbey. No. 3140, Persuasion.

| 2013, Feb. 21 | | | Perf. 14¼ | |
|---|---|---|---|---|
| 3135 | A739 | 1st multi | 1.55 | 1.35 |
| 3136 | A739 | 1st multi | 1.55 | 1.35 |
| 3137 | A739 | 77p multi | 2.15 | 1.75 |
| 3138 | A739 | 77p multi | 2.15 | 1.75 |
| 3139 | A739 | £1.28 multi | 3.50 | 2.90 |
| 3140 | A739 | £1.28 multi | 3.50 | 2.90 |
| | | Nos. 3135-3140 (6) | 16.60 | 8.40 |

On day of issue, Nos. 3135-3136 each sold for 60p.

Matt Smith, Eleventh Doctor Who — A740

David Tennant, Tenth Doctor Who — A741

Christopher Eccleston, Ninth Doctor Who — A742

Paul McGann, Eighth Doctor Who — A743

Sylvester McCoy, Seventh Doctor Who — A744

Colin Baker, Sixth Doctor Who — A745

Peter Davison, Fifth Doctor Who — A746

Tom Baker,
Fourth Doctor
Who — A747

Jon Pertwee,
Third Doctor
Who — A748

Patrick Troughton,
Second Doctor
Who — A749

William Hartnell,
First Doctor
Who — A750

Doctor Who Props and
Characters — A751

Designs: Nos. 3152, 3153e, 3156, TARDIS (police call box). No. 3153a, Dalek. No. 3153b, Ood. No. 3153c, Weeping Angel. No. 3153d, Cyberman.

| 2013, Mar. 26 | | Perf. 14¼x14 | |
|---|---|---|---|
| 3141 A740 | 1st multi | 1.75 | 1.35 |
| 3142 A741 | 1st multi | 1.75 | 1.35 |
| 3143 A742 | 1st multi | 1.75 | 1.35 |
| a. | Horiz. strip of 3, #3141-3143 | 5.50 | 4.25 |
| b. | Booklet pane of 3, #3141-3143 (BK201) | 5.50 | — |
| 3144 A743 | 1st multi | 1.75 | 1.35 |
| 3145 A744 | 1st multi | 1.75 | 1.35 |
| 3146 A745 | 1st multi | 1.75 | 1.35 |
| a. | Horiz. strip of 4, #3144-3147 | 7.25 | 5.50 |
| b. | Booklet pane of 4, #3144-3147 (BK201) | 7.25 | — |
| 3148 A747 | 1st multi | 1.75 | 1.35 |
| 3149 A748 | 1st multi | 1.75 | 1.35 |
| 3150 A749 | 1st black | 1.75 | 1.35 |
| 3151 A750 | 1st black | 1.75 | 1.35 |
| a. | Horiz. strip of 4, #3148-3151 | 7.25 | 5.50 |
| b. | Booklet pane of 4, #3148-3151 (BK201) | 7.25 | — |
| Nos. 3141-3151 (11) | | 19.25 | 14.85 |

### Booklet Stamp
### Perf. 14¾x14 Syncopated

| 3152 A751 | 1st multi (3152a) | 2.40 | 2.40 |
|---|---|---|---|
| a. | Booklet pane of 8, #MH429-MH432, 4 #3152, + label (BK201) | 21.50 | — |

### Miniature Sheet
### Self-Adhesive
### Photo.
### Die Cut Perf. 14½ Syncopated (#3153a-3153d), Die Cut Perf. 14¾x14 Syncopated (#3153e)

| 3153 A751 | Sheet of 5 | 8.00 | 8.00 |
|---|---|---|---|
| a.-d. | 2nd Any single | 1.50 | 1.15 |
| e. | 1st multi | 1.75 | 1.35 |
| f.-i. | 2nd As #3153a-3153d, any single, litho. (3153k) | 1.60 | 1.60 |
| j. | 1st As #3153e, litho., die cut perf. 14¾ syncopated (3153k) | 1.90 | 1.90 |
| k. | Booklet pane of 5, #3153f-3153j (BK201) | 8.75 | |
| l. | Sheet of 20 #3153e + 20 labels | 36.00 | |

### Booklet Stamps
### Photo.
### Die Cut Perf. 14¼

| 3154 A740 | 1st multi | 6.00 | 1.75 |
|---|---|---|---|
| 3155 A750 | 1st multi | 6.00 | 1.75 |

### Die Cut Perf. 14¾x14 Syncopated

| 3156 A751 | 1st multi | 6.00 | 1.75 |
|---|---|---|---|
| a. | Booklet pane of 6, #3154-3155, 4 #3156 | 17.50 | |
| Nos. 3154-3156 (3) | | 18.00 | 5.25 |

Doctor Who television set, 50th anniv. On day of issue, Nos. 3153a-3153d, 3153f-3153i each had a franking value of 50p, and Nos.

---

3141-3152, 3153e, 3153j, 3154-3156 each had a franking value of 60p. No. 3153l sold for £12.50 and labels could be personalized for an additional fee.

Famous
People — A752

Designs: No. 3157, Norman Parkinson (1913-90), photographer. No. 3158, Vivien Leigh (1913-67), actress. No. 3159, Peter Cushing (1913-94), actor. No. 3160, David Lloyd George (1863-1945), prime minister. No. 3161, Elizabeth David (1913-92), cookbook writer. No. 3162, John Archer (1863-1932), politician. No. 3163, Benjamin Britten (1913-76), composer. No. 3164, Mary Leakey (1913-96), anthropologist. No. 3165, Bill Shankly (1913-81), soccer player and manager. No. 3166, Richard Dimbleby (1913-65), broadcast journalist.

| 2013, Apr. 16 | | Litho. | Perf. 14½ | |
|---|---|---|---|---|
| 3157 A752 | 1st multi | | 1.75 | 1.35 |
| 3158 A752 | 1st multi | | 1.75 | 1.35 |
| 3159 A752 | 1st multi | | 1.75 | 1.35 |
| 3160 A752 | 1st multi | | 1.75 | 1.35 |
| 3161 A752 | 1st multi | | 1.75 | 1.35 |
| a. | Horiz. strip of 5, #3157-3161 | | 9.00 | 6.75 |
| 3162 A752 | 1st multi | | 1.75 | 1.35 |
| 3163 A752 | 1st multi | | 1.75 | 1.35 |
| 3164 A752 | 1st multi | | 1.75 | 1.35 |
| 3165 A752 | 1st multi | | 1.75 | 1.35 |
| 3166 A752 | 1st multi | | 1.75 | 1.35 |
| a. | Horiz. strip of 5, #3162-3166 | | 9.00 | 6.75 |
| Nos. 3157-3166 (10) | | | 17.50 | 13.50 |

On day of issue, Nos. 3157-3166 each sold for 60p.

Soccer
Players — A753

Designs: Nos. 3167, 3178, Jimmy Greaves, England. Nos. 3168, 3179, John Charles (1931-2004), Wales. Nos. 3169, 3183, Gordon Banks, England. Nos. 3170, 3184, George Best (1946-2005), Northern Ireland. Nos. 3171, 3185, John Barnes, England. Nos. 3172, 3180, Kevin Keegan, England. No. 3173, 3181, Denis Law, Scotland. Nos. 3174, 3182, 3190, Bobby Moore (1941-93), England. Nos. 3175, 3186, Bryan Robson, England. Nos. 3176, 3187, Dave Mackay, Scotland. Nos. 3177, 3188, Bobby Charlton, England.

| 2013, May 9 | | Litho. | Perf. 14¾x14½ | |
|---|---|---|---|---|
| 3167 A753 | 1st multi | | 1.90 | 1.40 |
| 3168 A753 | 1st multi | | 1.90 | 1.40 |
| 3169 A753 | 1st multi | | 1.90 | 1.40 |
| 3170 A753 | 1st multi | | 1.90 | 1.40 |
| 3171 A753 | 1st multi | | 1.90 | 1.40 |
| a. | Horiz. strip of 5, #3167-3171 | | 9.50 | 7.00 |
| 3172 A753 | 1st multi | | 1.90 | 1.40 |
| 3173 A753 | 1st multi | | 1.90 | 1.40 |
| 3174 A753 | 1st multi | | 1.90 | 1.40 |
| 3175 A753 | 1st multi | | 1.90 | 1.40 |
| 3176 A753 | 1st multi | | 1.90 | 1.40 |
| 3177 A753 | 1st multi | | 1.90 | 1.40 |
| a. | Horiz. strip of 6, #3172-3177 | | 11.50 | 8.50 |
| b. | Souvenir sheet of 11, #3167-3177 | | 20.00 | 16.00 |
| Nos. 3167-3177 (11) | | | 20.90 | 15.40 |

### Booklet Stamps
### Self-Adhesive
### Die Cut Perf. 14¾x14½

| 3178 A753 | 1st multi | 2.75 | 2.75 |
|---|---|---|---|
| 3179 A753 | 1st multi | 2.75 | 2.75 |
| 3180 A753 | 1st multi | 2.75 | 2.75 |
| 3181 A753 | 1st multi | 2.75 | 2.75 |
| 3182 A753 | 1st multi | 2.75 | 2.75 |
| a. | Booklet pane of 5, #3178-3182 (BK202) | 14.00 | |
| 3183 A753 | 1st multi | 2.75 | 2.75 |
| 3184 A753 | 1st multi | 2.75 | 2.75 |
| 3185 A753 | 1st multi | 2.75 | 2.75 |
| 3186 A753 | 1st multi | 2.75 | 2.75 |
| 3187 A753 | 1st multi | 2.75 | 2.75 |
| 3188 A753 | 1st multi | 2.75 | 2.75 |
| a. | Booklet pane of 6, #3183-3188 (BK202) | 17.00 | |

---

### Photo.
### Die Cut Perf. 14¾x14

| 3189 A753 | 1st multi | 5.00 | 2.00 |
|---|---|---|---|
| 3190 A753 | 1st multi | 5.00 | 2.00 |
| a. | Booklet pane of 6, #3189-3190, 4 #MH426 | 13.50 | |
| Nos. 3178-3190 (13) | | 40.25 | 34.25 |

On day of issue, Nos. 3172-3190 each had a franking value of 60p. See Nos. 3266-3267.

Portraits of Queen
Elizabeth II — A754

Portrait by: 2nd, Terence Cuneo, 1953. 1st, Nicky Philipps, 2013. 78p, Andrew Festing, 1999. 88p, Pietro Annigoni, 1955. £1.28, Sergei Pavlenko, 2000. £1.88, Richard Stone, 1992.

| 2013, May 30 | | Photo. | Perf. 14¼ | |
|---|---|---|---|---|
| 3191 A754 | 2nd multi | | 1.40 | 1.15 |
| 3192 A754 | 1st multi | | 1.65 | 1.35 |
| 3193 A754 | 78p multi | | 2.25 | 1.65 |
| 3194 A754 | 88p multi | | 2.40 | 2.00 |
| 3195 A754 | £1.28 multi | | 3.75 | 2.90 |
| 3196 A754 | £1.88 multi | | 5.35 | 4.25 |
| Nos. 3191-3196 (6) | | | 16.80 | 13.40 |

On day of issue, No. 3191 sold for 50p, and No. 3192 sold for 60p.

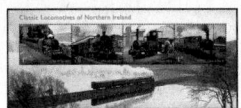

Northern Ireland Steam
Locomotives — A755

Designs: 1st, Ulster Transport Authority W No. 103. 78p, Ulster Transport Authority SG3 No. 35. 88p, Peckett No. 2. £1.28, County Donegal Railways Joint Commission Class 5 No. 4.

| 2013, June 18 | | Litho. | Perf. 14¼ | |
|---|---|---|---|---|
| 3197 A755 | Sheet of 4 | | 10.00 | 8.00 |
| a. | 1st multi | | 1.75 | 1.35 |
| b. | 78p multi | | 2.40 | 1.75 |
| c. | 88p multi | | 2.60 | 2.00 |
| d. | £1.28 multi | | 4.00 | 2.90 |
| e. | Booklet pane of 4, 2 each #3197a, 3197b (BK204) | | 8.25 | — |

### Booklet Stamp
### Self-Adhesive
### Photo.
### Die Cut Perf. 14¼

| 3198 A755 | 1st multi | 3.75 | 1.75 |
|---|---|---|---|
| a. | Booklet pane of 6, 2 #3198, 4 #MH426 | 10.00 | |

On day of issue Nos. 3197a and 3198 each sold for 60p. Issued: No. 3197e, 2/20/14.

Butterflies — A756

Designs: Nos. 3199, 3210, Comma butterfly. No. 3200, Orange-tip butterfly. No. 3201, Small copper butterfly. Nos. 3202, 3209, Chalkhill blue butterfly. No. 3203, Swallowtail butterfly. No. 3204, Purple emperor butterfly. No. 3205, Marsh fritillary butterfly. No. 3206, Brimstone butterfly. No. 3207, Red admiral butterfly. No. 3208, Marbled white butterfly.

| 2013, July 11 | | Litho. | Perf. 14¼ | |
|---|---|---|---|---|
| 3199 A756 | 1st multi | | 1.75 | 1.35 |
| 3200 A756 | 1st multi | | 1.75 | 1.35 |
| 3201 A756 | 1st multi | | 1.75 | 1.35 |
| 3202 A756 | 1st multi | | 1.75 | 1.35 |
| 3203 A756 | 1st multi | | 1.75 | 1.35 |
| a. | Horiz. strip of 5, #3199-3203 | | 9.00 | 6.75 |
| 3204 A756 | 1st multi | | 1.75 | 1.35 |
| 3205 A756 | 1st multi | | 1.75 | 1.35 |
| 3206 A756 | 1st multi | | 1.75 | 1.35 |
| 3207 A756 | 1st multi | | 1.75 | 1.35 |
| 3208 A756 | 1st multi | | 1.75 | 1.35 |
| a. | Horiz. strip of 5, #3204-3208 | | 9.00 | 6.75 |
| Nos. 3199-3208 (10) | | | 17.50 | 13.50 |

---

### Booklet Stamps
### Self-Adhesive
### Die Cut Perf. 14¼

| 3209 A756 | 1st multi | 3.75 | 1.75 |
|---|---|---|---|
| 3210 A756 | 1st multi | 3.75 | 1.75 |
| a. | Booklet pane of 6, #3209-3210, 4 #MH426 | 10.00 | |

Nos. 3199-3210 each sold for 60p on day of issue.

### Miniature Sheet

Victory of Andy Murray in 2013
Wimbledon Men's Singles Tennis
Final — A757

No. 3211 — Murray: a, Kissing trophy. b, Serving. c, Chasing shot. d, Holding trophy.

| 2013, Aug. 8 | | Litho. | Perf. 14¾ | |
|---|---|---|---|---|
| 3211 A757 | Sheet of 4 | | 10.00 | 8.50 |
| a.-b. | 1st Either single | | 1.75 | 1.35 |
| c.-d. | £1.28 Either single | | 4.00 | 2.90 |

On day of issue, Nos. 3211a-3211b each sold for 60p.

A758

Motor
Vehicles
A759

Designs: No. 3212, 1961 Jaguar E-Type. No. 3213, 1965 Rolls-Royce Silver Shadow. No. 3214, 1963, Aston Martin DB5. No. 3215, 1962 MG MGB. No. 3216, 1968 Morgan Plus 8. No. 3217, 1976 Lotus Esprit.
No. 3218: a, 1953-71 Morris Minor Van. b, 1958-97 Austin FX4. c, 1959-67 Ford Anglia 105E. d, 1990-2013 Land Rover Defender 110.

| 2013, Aug. 13 | | Litho. | Perf. 13¼ | |
|---|---|---|---|---|
| 3212 A758 | 1st multi | | 1.65 | 1.35 |
| 3213 A758 | 1st multi | | 1.65 | 1.35 |
| 3214 A758 | 1st multi | | 1.65 | 1.35 |
| a. | Horiz. strip of 3, #3212-3214 | | 5.00 | 4.25 |
| 3215 A758 | £1.28 multi | | 3.85 | 2.90 |
| 3216 A758 | £1.28 multi | | 3.85 | 2.90 |
| 3217 A758 | £1.28 multi | | 3.85 | 2.90 |
| a. | Horiz. strip of 3, #3215-3217 | | 11.50 | 8.75 |
| Nos. 3212-3217 (6) | | | 16.50 | 12.75 |

### Miniature Sheet
### Perf. 14¼x14

| 3218 A759 | Sheet of 4 | 7.25 | 5.50 |
|---|---|---|---|
| a.-d. | 1st Any single | 1.75 | 1.35 |

Europa (#3218a). On day of issue, Nos. 3212-3214 and 3218a-3218d each sold for 60p.
See No. 3226.

Merchant Navy
Ships — A760

World
War II
Atlantic
and
Arctic
Convoys
A761

Ships: No. 3219, Atlas, 1813. No. 3220, Britannia, 1840. No. 3221, Cutty Sark, 1870. No. 3222, Clan Matheson, 1919. No. 3223, Queen Elizabeth. No. 3224, Lord Hinton.
No. 3225: a, Ships in convoy, flag flying on ship at UL. b, Sailor signaling another ship with semaphore flag. c, Sailors removing snow from deck of ship. d, Convoy of ships.

| | | | | |
|---|---|---|---|---|
| **2013, Sept. 19** | | **Litho.** | **Perf. 14¼x14** | |
| 3219 | A760 | 1st multi | 1.65 | 1.35 |
| 3220 | A760 | 1st multi | 1.65 | 1.35 |
| 3221 | A760 | 1st multi | 1.65 | 1.35 |
| *a.* | | Booklet pane of 3, #3219-3221 (BK203) | 5.00 | — |
| 3222 | A760 | £1.28 multi | 3.85 | 2.90 |
| 3223 | A760 | £1.28 multi | 3.85 | 2.90 |
| 3224 | A760 | £1.28 multi | 3.85 | 2.90 |
| *a.* | | Booklet pane of 3, #3222-3224 (BK203) | 11.50 | — |
| | | Nos. 3219-3224 (6) | 16.50 | 12.75 |
| | | **Souvenir Sheet** | | |
| 3225 | A761 | Sheet of 4 | 7.25 | 5.50 |
| *a.-d.* | | 1st Any single | 1.75 | 1.35 |
| *e.* | | Booklet pane of 4, #3225a-3225d (BK203) | 7.25 | |

On day of issue Nos. 3219-3221, 3225a-3225d each sold for 60p. Margin on No. 3225e differs from that on No. 3225.

See No. 3227.

### Motor Vehicles and Merchant Navy Types of 2013

Designs: No. 3226, Morris Minor Van. No. 3227, Britannia.

| | | | | |
|---|---|---|---|---|
| | | *Die Cut Perf. 14¼x14* | | |
| **2013, Sept. 19** | | | **Photo.** | |
| | | **Booklet Stamps** | | |
| | | **Self-Adhesive** | | |
| 3226 | A759 | 1st multi | 6.00 | 2.25 |
| 3227 | A760 | 1st multi | 6.00 | 2.25 |
| *a.* | | Booklet pane of 6, #3226-3227, 4 #MH426 | 17.50 | |

On day of issue, Nos. 3226-3227 each sold for 60p. Europa (#3226).

Dinosaurs — A762

Designs: No. 3228, Polacanthus. No. 3229, Ichthyosaurus. No. 3230, Iguanodon. No. 3231, Ornithocheirus. No. 3232, Baryonyx. No. 3233, Dimorphodon. No. 3234, Hypsilophodon. No. 3235, Cetiosaurus. No. 3236, Megalosaurus. No. 3237, Pleisiosaurus.

| | | | | |
|---|---|---|---|---|
| | | *Die Cut Perf. 13½x14* | | |
| **2013, Oct. 10** | | | **Photo.** | |
| | | **Self-Adhesive** | | |
| 3228 | A762 | 1st multi | 1.75 | 1.35 |
| 3229 | A762 | 1st multi | 1.75 | 1.35 |
| 3230 | A762 | 1st multi | 1.75 | 1.35 |
| 3231 | A762 | 1st multi | 1.75 | 1.35 |
| 3232 | A762 | 1st multi | 1.75 | 1.35 |
| *a.* | | Horiz. strip of 5, #3228-3232 | 9.00 | 6.75 |
| 3233 | A762 | 1st multi | 1.75 | 1.35 |
| 3234 | A762 | 1st multi | 1.75 | 1.35 |
| 3235 | A762 | 1st multi | 1.75 | 1.35 |
| 3236 | A762 | 1st multi | 1.75 | 1.35 |
| 3237 | A762 | 1st multi | 1.75 | 1.35 |
| *a.* | | Horiz. strip of 5, #3233-3237 | 9.00 | 6.75 |
| | | Nos. 3228-3237 (10) | 17.50 | 13.50 |

On day of issue, Nos. 3228-3237 each sold for 60p.

A763

Christmas — A764

Details from paintings: Nos. 3238a, 3238c, 3239, 3241, Virgin and Child with the Young St. John the Baptist, by Antoniazzo Romano. Nos. 3238b, 3238e, 3240, 3243, Madonna and Child, by Francesco Granacci. 88p, St. Roch Praying to the Virgin for an End to the Plague, by Jacques-Louis David. £1.28, La Vierge au Lys, by William-Adolphe Bouguereau. £1.88, Theotokos, Mother of God, by Fadi Mikhail.

| | | | | |
|---|---|---|---|---|
| **2013, Nov. 5** | **Photo.** | | **Perf. 14½x15** | |
| 3238 | | Sheet of 7 | 20.00 | 20.00 |
| *a.* | A763 | 2nd multi | 1.50 | 1.15 |
| *b.* | A763 | 1st multi | 1.75 | 1.35 |
| *c.* | A764 | 2nd Large multi | 2.10 | 1.60 |
| *d.* | A763 | 88p multi | 2.60 | 2.00 |
| *e.* | A764 | 1st Large multi | 2.75 | 2.00 |

| | | | | |
|---|---|---|---|---|
| *f.* | A763 | £1.28 multi | 4.00 | 2.90 |
| *g.* | A763 | £1.88 multi | 5.75 | 4.25 |
| | | **Self-Adhesive** | | |
| | | *Die Cut Perf. 14½x15* | | |
| 3239 | A763 | 2nd multi | 1.50 | 1.15 |
| *a.* | | Booklet pane of 12 | 16.00 | |
| *b.* | | Litho., die cut perf. 14½x15 syncopated, + label (#3245b) | 2.25 | 2.25 |
| 3240 | A763 | 1st multi | 1.75 | 1.35 |
| *a.* | | Booklet pane of 12 | 19.00 | |
| *b.* | | Litho., die cut perf. 14½x15 syncopated, + label (#3245b) | 2.50 | 2.50 |
| 3241 | A764 | 2nd Large multi | 2.10 | 1.60 |
| 3242 | A763 | 88p multi | 2.60 | 2.00 |
| *a.* | | Litho., die cut perf. 14½x15 syncopated, + label (#3245b) | 4.50 | 4.50 |
| 3243 | A764 | 1st Large multi | 2.75 | 2.00 |
| 3244 | A763 | £1.28 multi | 4.00 | 2.90 |
| *a.* | | Litho., die cut perf. 14½x15 syncopated, + label (#3245b) | 8.50 | 8.50 |
| 3245 | A763 | £1.88 multi | 5.75 | 4.25 |
| *a.* | | Litho., die cut perf. 14½x15 syncopated, + label (#3245b) | 12.50 | 12.50 |
| *b.* | | Sheet of 20 + 20 labels, #3244a, 3245a, 2 #3242a, 8 each #3239b, 3240b | 50.00 | |
| | | Nos. 3239-3245 (7) | 20.45 | 15.25 |

On day of issue, Nos. 3238a and 3239 each sold for 50p, Nos. 3238b and 3240 each sold for 60p, Nos. 3238c and 3241 each sold for 69p, and Nos. 3238e and 3241 each sold for 90p. No. 3245b sold for £14.22. Labels could not be personalized.

Christmas A765

Winning art in children's Christmas stamp design contest: 2nd, Angels, by Rosie Hargreaves. 1st, Santa Claus, by Molly Robson.

| | | | | |
|---|---|---|---|---|
| | | *Die Cut Perf. 14¾* | | |
| **2013, Nov. 5** | | | **Photo.** | |
| 3246 | A765 | 2nd multi | 2.50 | 1.50 |
| 3247 | A765 | 1st multi | 3.00 | 1.75 |

On day of issue, No. 3246 sold for 50p and No. 3247 sold for 60p.

Children's Television Characters — A766

Designs: No. 3248, Andy Pandy and Teddy. No. 3249, Ivor the Engine. No. 3250, Dougal from *The Magic Roundabout*. No. 3251, Windy Miller from *Camberwick Green*. No. 3252, Mr. Benn. No. 3253, Great Uncle Bulgaria from *The Wombles*. No. 3254, Bagpuss. No. 3255, Paddington Bear. No. 3256, Postman Pat and cat, Jess. No. 3257, Bob the Builder. No. 3258, Peppa Pig. No. 3259, Shaun the Sheep.

| | | | | |
|---|---|---|---|---|
| | | *Die Cut Perf. 15* | | |
| **2014, Jan. 17** | | | **Photo.** | |
| | | **Self-Adhesive** | | |
| 3248 | A766 | 1st black | 1.75 | 1.35 |
| 3249 | A766 | 1st multi | 1.75 | 1.35 |
| 3250 | A766 | 1st multi | 1.75 | 1.35 |
| 3251 | A766 | 1st multi | 1.75 | 1.35 |
| 3252 | A766 | 1st multi | 1.75 | 1.35 |
| 3253 | A766 | 1st multi | 1.75 | 1.35 |
| *a.* | | Horiz. strip of 6, #3248-3253 | 11.00 | 8.25 |
| 3254 | A766 | 1st multi | 1.75 | 1.35 |
| 3255 | A766 | 1st multi | 1.75 | 1.35 |
| 3256 | A766 | 1st multi | 1.75 | 1.35 |
| 3257 | A766 | 1st multi | 1.75 | 1.35 |
| 3258 | A766 | 1st multi | 1.75 | 1.35 |
| 3259 | A766 | 1st multi | 1.75 | 1.35 |
| *a.* | | Horiz. strip of 6, #3254-3259 | 11.00 | 8.25 |
| | | Nos. 3248-3259 (12) | 21.00 | 16.20 |

On day of issue, Nos. 3248-3259 each sold for 60p.

Horses — A767

Inscriptions: No. 3260, Riding for the Disabled Association. No. 3261, The King's Troop Ceremonial Horses. No. 3262, Dray Horses. No. 3263, Royal Mews Carriage Horses. No. 3264, Police Horses. No. 3265, Forestry Horse.

| | | | | |
|---|---|---|---|---|
| **2014, Feb. 4** | | **Litho.** | **Perf. 14¼x14** | |
| 3260 | A767 | 1st multi | 1.75 | 1.35 |
| 3261 | A767 | 1st multi | 1.75 | 1.35 |
| 3262 | A767 | 88p multi | 2.75 | 2.00 |
| 3263 | A767 | 88p multi | 2.75 | 2.00 |
| 3264 | A767 | £1.28 multi | 4.00 | 2.90 |
| 3265 | A767 | £1.28 multi | 4.00 | 2.90 |
| | | Nos. 3260-3265 (6) | 17.00 | 12.50 |

On day of issue Nos. 3260 and 3261 each sold for 60p.

### Soccer Players Type of 2013

Designs: No. 3266, John Charles (1931-2004), Wales. No. 3267, Dave Mackay, Scotland.

| | | | | |
|---|---|---|---|---|
| | | *Die Cut Perf. 14¾x14* | | |
| **2014, Feb. 20** | | | **Photo.** | |
| | | **Booklet Stamps** | | |
| | | **Self-Adhesive** | | |
| 3266 | A753 | 1st multi | 4.50 | 1.90 |
| 3267 | A753 | 1st multi | 4.50 | 1.90 |
| *a.* | | Booklet pane of 6, #3266-3267, 4 #MH426 | 13.50 | |

On day of issue, Nos. 3266-3267 each sold for 60p.

### Miniature Sheet

Locomotives of Wales — A768

No. 3268: a, LMS No. 7720. b, Hunslet No. 589 Blanche. c, Welshpool & Llanfair Light Railway No. 822 The Earl. d, British Railways 5600 No. 5652.

| | | | | |
|---|---|---|---|---|
| **2014, Feb. 20** | | **Litho.** | **Perf. 14¼** | |
| 3268 | A768 | Sheet of 4 | 11.00 | 8.00 |
| *a.* | | 1st multi | 1.75 | 1.35 |
| *b.* | | 78p multi | 2.40 | 1.75 |
| *c.* | | 88p multi | 2.75 | 2.00 |
| *d.* | | £1.28 multi | 4.00 | 2.90 |
| *e.* | | Booklet pane of 4, 2 each #3268a, 3268b (BK204) | 8.50 | — |

On day of issue No. 3268a sold for 60p. See No. 3320.

Famous People — A769

Designs: No. 3269, Roy Plomley (1914-84), broadcaster, writer. No. 3270, Barbara Ward (1914-81), economist, broadcaster. No. 3271, Joe Mercer (1914-90), Soccer player, team manager. No. 3272, Kenneth More (1914-82), actor. No. 3273, Dylan Thomas (1914-53), poet, writer. No. 3274, Sir Alec Guinness (1914-2000), actor. No. 3275, Noorunissa Inayat Khan (1914-44), Special Operations Executive agent. No. 3276, Max Perutz (1914-2002), molecular biologist, 1962 Nobel laureate in Chemistry. No. 3277, Joan Littlewood (1914-2002), theater director, writer. No. 3278, Abram Games (1914-96), graphic designer.

| | | | | |
|---|---|---|---|---|
| **2014, Mar. 25** | | **Litho.** | **Perf. 14½** | |
| 3269 | A769 | 1st black | 1.75 | 1.35 |
| 3270 | A769 | 1st black | 1.75 | 1.00 |
| 3271 | A769 | 1st black | 1.75 | 1.00 |
| 3272 | A769 | 1st black | 1.75 | 1.00 |
| 3273 | A769 | 1st black | 1.75 | 1.00 |
| *a.* | | Horiz. strip of 5, #3269-3273 | 9.00 | 6.75 |
| 3274 | A769 | 1st black | 1.75 | 1.35 |
| 3275 | A769 | 1st black | 1.75 | 1.35 |
| 3276 | A769 | 1st black | 1.75 | 1.35 |
| 3277 | A769 | 1st black | 1.75 | 1.35 |
| 3278 | A769 | 1st black | 1.75 | 1.35 |
| *a.* | | Horiz. strip of 5, #3274-3278 | 9.00 | 6.75 |
| | | Nos. 3269-3278 (10) | 17.50 | 12.10 |

Nos. 3269-3278 each sold for 60p on day of issue.

Historic Views of Exterior of Buckingham Palace — A770

Rooms in Buckingham Palace — A771

Image of Buckingham Palace from: No. 3279, 2014. No. 3280, Circa 1862. No. 3281, 1846. No. 3282, 1819 (Buckingham House). No. 3283, 1714 (Buckingham House). No. 3284, Circa 1700 (Buckingham House).

No. 3285: a, Throne Room. b, Grand Staircase. c, Blue Drawing Room. d, Green Drawing Room.

No. 3286, Like #3285b. No. 3287, Like #3285a.

| | | | | |
|---|---|---|---|---|
| **2014, Apr. 15** | | **Litho.** | **Perf. 14¾** | |
| 3279 | A770 | 1st multi | 1.90 | 1.40 |
| *a.* | | Perf. 14x13¼ (#3280b) | 2.00 | 2.00 |
| 3280 | A770 | 1st multi | 1.90 | 1.40 |
| *a.* | | Perf. 14x13¼ (#3280b) | 2.00 | 2.00 |
| *b.* | | Booklet pane of 2 each #3279a-3280a (BK205) | 8.00 | — |
| 3281 | A770 | 1st multi | 1.90 | 1.40 |
| *a.* | | Perf. 14x13¼ (#3284c) | 2.00 | 2.00 |
| *b.* | | Horiz. strip of 3, #3279-3281 | 5.75 | 4.25 |
| 3282 | A770 | 1st multi | 1.90 | 1.40 |
| *a.* | | Perf. 14x13¼ (#3284c) | 2.00 | 2.00 |
| 3283 | A770 | 1st multi | 1.90 | 1.40 |
| *a.* | | Perf. 14x13¼ (#3284c) | 2.00 | 2.00 |
| 3284 | A770 | 1st multi | 1.90 | 1.40 |
| *a.* | | Perf. 14x13¼ (#3284c) | 2.00 | 2.00 |
| *b.* | | Horiz. strip of 3, #3282-3284 | 5.75 | 4.25 |
| *c.* | | Booklet pane of 4, #3281a, 3282a, 3283a, 3284a (BK205) | 8.00 | — |
| | | Nos. 3279-3284 (6) | 11.40 | 8.40 |
| | | **Perf. 14¼x14** | | |
| 3285 | | Sheet of 4 | 7.50 | 5.75 |
| *a.-d.* | A771 | 1st Any single | 1.90 | 1.40 |
| *e.* | | Booklet pane of 4, #3285a-3285d (BK205) | 7.50 | |
| | | **Photo.** | | |
| | | **Booklet Stamps** | | |
| | | **Self-Adhesive** | | |
| | | *Die Cut Perf. 14¼x14* | | |
| 3286 | A771 | 1st multi | 4.00 | 1.90 |
| 3287 | A771 | 1st multi | 4.00 | 1.90 |
| *a.* | | Booklet pane of 6, #3286-3287, 4 #MH426 | 10.00 | |

Nos. 3279-3284, 325a-3285d, 3286-3287 each sold for 62p on day of issue.

Scenes From British Films A772

Scenes From Films Made by General Post Office Film Unit A773

Scene from: No. 3288, *A Matter of Life and Death*. No. 3289, *Lawrence of Arabia*. No. 3290, *2001: A Space Odyssey*. No. 3291, *Chariots of Fire*. No. 3292, *Secrets & Lies*. No. 3293, *Bend It Like Beckham*.

No. 3294 — Scenes from: a, *Night Mail*. b, *Love on the Wing*. c, *A Colour Box*. d, *Spare Time*.

| | | | | |
|---|---|---|---|---|
| **2014, May 13** | | **Litho.** | **Perf. 14¾** | |
| 3288 | A772 | 1st multi | 1.90 | 1.40 |
| 3289 | A772 | 1st multi | 1.90 | 1.40 |
| 3290 | A772 | 1st multi | 1.90 | 1.40 |
| *a.* | | Horiz. strip of 3, #3288-3290 | 5.75 | 4.25 |
| 3291 | A772 | £1.28 multi | 4.00 | 2.90 |
| 3292 | A772 | £1.28 multi | 4.00 | 2.90 |
| 3293 | A772 | £1.28 multi | 4.00 | 2.90 |
| *a.* | | Horiz. strip of 3, #3291-3293 | 12.00 | 8.75 |
| | | Nos. 3288-3293 (6) | 17.70 | 12.90 |
| | | **Miniature Sheet** | | |
| | | **Perf. 14¼x14** | | |
| 3294 | A773 | Sheet of 4 | 7.50 | 5.75 |
| *a.-d.* | | 1st Any single | 1.90 | 1.40 |

Nos. 3288-3290 and 3294a-3294d each sold for 62p on day of issue.

Fish — A774

Designs: No. 3295, Herrings. No. 3296, Red gurnard. No. 3297, Dab. No. 3298, Poutings. No. 3299, Cornish sardines. No. 3300, Common skate. No. 3301, Spiny dogfish. No. 3302, Wolffish. No. 3303, Sturgeon. No. 3304, Conger eel.

**2014, June 5     Litho.     Perf. 14¼**

| | | | | |
|---|---|---|---|---|
| 3295 | A774 | 1st multi | 1.90 | 1.40 |
| 3296 | A774 | 1st multi | 1.90 | 1.40 |
| 3297 | A774 | 1st multi | 1.90 | 1.40 |
| 3298 | A774 | 1st multi | 1.90 | 1.40 |
| 3299 | A774 | 1st multi | 1.90 | 1.40 |
| a. | | Horiz. strip of 5, #3295-3299 | 9.50 | 7.00 |
| 3300 | A774 | 1st multi | 1.90 | 1.40 |
| 3301 | A774 | 1st multi | 1.90 | 1.40 |
| 3302 | A774 | 1st multi | 1.90 | 1.40 |
| 3303 | A774 | 1st multi | 1.90 | 1.40 |
| 3304 | A774 | 1st multi | 1.90 | 1.40 |
| a. | | Horiz. strip of 5, #3300-3304 | 9.50 | 7.00 |
| | | Nos. 3295-3304 (10) | 19.00 | 14.00 |

Nos. 3295-3304 each sold for 62p on day of issue. See Nos. 3318-3319.

20th Commonwealth Games, Glasgow — A775

Designs: 2nd, Judo. 1st, Swimming. 97p, Track. £1.28, Squash. £1.47, Netball. £2.15, Cycling.

**2014, July 17     Litho.     Perf. 14¼**

| | | | | |
|---|---|---|---|---|
| 3305 | A775 | 2nd multi | 1.60 | 1.20 |
| 3306 | A775 | 1st multi | 1.90 | 1.40 |
| 3307 | A775 | 97p multi | 2.90 | 2.25 |
| 3308 | A775 | £1.28 multi | 4.00 | 2.90 |
| 3309 | A775 | £1.47 multi | 4.50 | 3.25 |
| 3310 | A775 | £2.15 multi | 6.50 | 4.75 |
| | | Nos. 3305-3310 (6) | 21.40 | 15.75 |

**Photo.**
**Booklet Stamp**
**Self-Adhesive**
**Die Cut Perf. 14¼**

| | | | | |
|---|---|---|---|---|
| 3311 | A775 | 1st multi | 4.00 | 1.90 |
| a. | | Booklet pane of 6, 2 #3311, 4 #MH426 | 10.00 | |

No. 3305 sold for 53p and Nos. 3306 and 3311 each sold for 62p on day of issue.

Poppy, Painting by Fiona Strickland A776

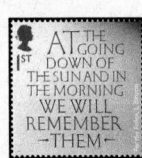

Line From *For the Fallen*, Poem by Laurence Binyon A777

Private William Cecil Tickle A778

*A Star Shell*, Painting by Christopher Richard Wynne Nevinson A779

*The Response*, Sculpture by William Goscombe John — A780

Princess Mary's Gift Fund Box — A781

**2014, July 28     Litho.     Perf. 14¼**

| | | | | |
|---|---|---|---|---|
| 3312 | A776 | 1st multi | 1.90 | 1.40 |
| 3313 | A777 | 1st multi | 1.90 | 1.40 |
| 3314 | A778 | 1st multi | 1.90 | 1.40 |
| a. | | Booklet pane of 3, #3312-3314 (BK206) | 5.75 | — |

| | | | | |
|---|---|---|---|---|
| 3315 | A779 | £1.47 multi | 4.50 | 3.25 |
| 3316 | A780 | £1.47 multi | 4.50 | 3.25 |
| 3317 | A781 | £1.47 multi | 4.50 | 3.25 |
| a. | | Booklet pane of 3, #3315-3317 (BK206) | 13.50 | — |
| | | Nos. 3312-3317 (6) | 19.20 | 13.95 |

World War I, cent. Nos. 3312-3314 each sold for 62p on day of issue. See No. 3778.

### Fish Type of 2014

Designs: No. 3318, Common skate. No. 3319, Cornish sardines.

**Die Cut Perf. 14¼**

**2014, Aug. 18     Photo.**
**Booklet Stamps**
**Self-Adhesive**

| | | | | |
|---|---|---|---|---|
| 3318 | A774 | 1st multi | 4.50 | 1.90 |
| 3319 | A774 | 1st multi | 4.50 | 1.90 |
| a. | | Booklet pane of 6, #3318-3319, 4 #MH426 | 13.50 | |

Nos. 3318-3319 each sold for 62p on day of issue.

### Locomotives of Wales Type of 2014

Design: No. 3320, LMS No. 7720.

**Die Cut Perf. 14¼**

**2014, Sept. 18     Photo.**
**Booklet Stamp**
**Self-Adhesive**

| | | | | |
|---|---|---|---|---|
| 3320 | A768 | 1st multi | 5.00 | 2.00 |
| a. | | Booklet pane of 6, 2 #3320, 4 #MH426 | 10.00 | |

No. 3320 sold for 62p on day of issue.

Seaside Architecture A782

Designs: No. 3321, Eastbourne Bandstand. No. 3322, Tinside Lido, Plymouth. No. 3323, Bangor Pier. No. 3324, Southwold Lighthouse. No. 3325, Casino, Blackpool Pleasure Beach. No. 3326, Shelter, Bexhill-on-Sea.

No. 3327: a, Llandudno Pier. b, Worthing Pier. c, Dunoon Pier. d, Brighton Pier.

**2014, Sept. 18     Litho.     Perf. 14¼**

| | | | | |
|---|---|---|---|---|
| 3321 | A782 | 1st multi | 1.90 | 1.40 |
| 3322 | A782 | 1st multi | 1.90 | 1.40 |
| 3323 | A782 | 97p multi | 2.90 | 2.25 |
| 3324 | A782 | 97p multi | 2.90 | 2.25 |
| 3325 | A782 | £1.28 multi | 4.00 | 2.90 |
| 3326 | A782 | £1.28 multi | 4.00 | 2.90 |
| | | Nos. 3321-3326 (6) | 17.60 | 13.10 |
| 3327 | | Sheet of 4 | 11.50 | 8.75 |
| a.-b. | A782 | 1st Either single | 1.90 | 1.40 |
| c.-d. | A782 | £1.28 Either single | 4.00 | 2.90 |

Europa (No. 3321). Nos. 3321, 3322, 3327a and 3327b each sold for 62p on day of issue.

Prime Ministers — A783

Designs: No. 3328, Lady Margaret Thatcher (1925-2013). No. 3329, Harold Wilson (1916-95). No. 3330, Clement Attlee (1883-1967). No. 3331, Sir Winston Churchill (1874-1965). No. 3332, William Gladstone (1809-98). No. 3333, Sir Robert Peel (1788-1850). No. 3334, Charles Grey, 2nd Earl Grey (1764-1845). No. 3335, William Pitt, the Younger (1759-1806).

**2014, Oct. 14     Litho.     Perf. 14½**

| | | | | |
|---|---|---|---|---|
| 3328 | A783 | 1st multi | 1.90 | 1.40 |
| 3329 | A783 | 1st multi | 1.90 | 1.40 |
| 3330 | A783 | 1st multi | 1.90 | 1.40 |
| 3331 | A783 | 1st multi | 1.90 | 1.40 |
| a. | | Horiz. strip of 4, #3328-3331 | 7.75 | 5.75 |
| 3332 | A783 | 97p multi | 2.90 | 2.25 |
| 3333 | A783 | 97p multi | 2.90 | 2.25 |
| 3334 | A783 | 97p multi | 2.90 | 2.25 |
| 3335 | A783 | 97p multi | 2.90 | 2.25 |
| a. | | Horiz. strip of 4, #3332-3335 | 12.00 | 9.00 |
| | | Nos. 3328-3335 (8) | 19.20 | 14.60 |

Nos. 3328-3331 each sold for 62p on day of issue.

A784

Christmas — A785

Designs: Nos. 3336a, 3336c, 3337, 3339, Collecting a Christmas tree. Nos. 3336b, 3336d, 3338, 3340, Posting Christmas cards. £1.28, Building a snowman. £1.47, Carolers. £2.15, Ice skaters.

**2014, Nov. 4     Photo.     Perf. 14½x15**

| | | | | |
|---|---|---|---|---|
| 3336 | | Sheet of 7 | 23.00 | 23.00 |
| a. | A784 | 2nd multi | 1.60 | 1.20 |
| b. | A784 | 1st multi | 1.90 | 1.40 |
| c. | A785 | 2nd Large multi | 2.25 | 1.60 |
| d. | A785 | 1st Large multi | 2.75 | 2.10 |
| e. | A784 | £1.28 multi | 4.00 | 2.90 |
| f. | A784 | £1.47 multi | 4.50 | 3.25 |
| g. | A784 | £2.15 multi | 6.50 | 5.00 |

**Self-Adhesive**
**Die Cut Perf. 14½x15**

| | | | | |
|---|---|---|---|---|
| 3337 | A784 | 2nd multi | 1.60 | 1.20 |
| a. | | Booklet pane of 12 | 16.00 | |
| b. | | Litho., die cut perf. 14½x15 syncopated, + label (3342b) | 2.75 | 2.75 |
| 3338 | A784 | 1st multi | 1.90 | 1.40 |
| a. | | Booklet pane of 12 | 19.00 | |
| b. | | Litho., die cut perf. 14½x15 syncopated, + label (3342b) | 3.25 | 3.25 |
| 3339 | A785 | 2nd Large multi | 2.25 | 1.60 |
| 3340 | A785 | 1st Large multi | 2.75 | 2.10 |
| 3341 | A784 | £1.28 multi | 4.00 | 2.90 |
| a. | | Litho., die cut perf. 14½x15 syncopated, + label (3342b) | 6.75 | 6.75 |
| 3342 | A784 | £1.47 multi | 4.50 | 3.25 |
| a. | | Litho., die cut perf. 14½x15 syncopated, + label (3342b) | 7.50 | 7.50 |
| b. | | Sheet of 20, 8 each #3337b, 3338b, 2 each #3341a, 3342a, + 20 labels | 77.50 | |
| 3343 | A784 | £2.15 multi | 6.50 | 5.00 |
| | | Nos. 3337-3343 (7) | 23.50 | 17.45 |

On day of issue, Nos. 3336a and 3337 each sold for 53p, Nos. 3336b and 3338 each sold for 62p, Nos. 3336c and 3339 each sold for 73p, and Nos. 3336d and 3340 each sold for 93p. No. 3342b sold for £15.20 and labels could not be personalized.

Publication of *Alice's Adventures in Wonderland*, by Lewis Carroll, 150th Anniv. — A786

Designs: No. 3344, Alice and the White Rabbit. No. 3345, Alice falling down the Rabbit Hole. Nos. 3346, 3353B, Alice holding bottle with tag inscribed "Drink Me." Nos. 3347, 3353C, Alice bent over in the White Rabbit's house. No. 3348, Alice and the Cheshire Cat. No. 3349, Alice, March Hare, Dormouse and the Hatter at the Tea Party. No. 3350, Queen of Hearts. No. 3351, Alice and flamingo at the Queen's Croquet Ground. No. 3352, Alice giving evidence at the trial of the Knave of Hearts. No. 3353, Alice and playing cards.

**2015, Jan. 6     Litho.     Perf. 14½**

| | | | | |
|---|---|---|---|---|
| 3344 | A786 | 2nd multi | 1.60 | 1.20 |
| 3345 | A786 | 2nd multi | 1.60 | 1.20 |
| a. | | Vert. pair, #3344-3345 | 3.20 | 2.40 |
| 3346 | A786 | 1st multi | 1.90 | 1.40 |
| 3347 | A786 | 1st multi | 1.90 | 1.40 |
| a. | | Vert. pair, #3346-3347 | 3.80 | 2.90 |
| 3348 | A786 | 81p multi | 2.50 | 1.90 |
| 3349 | A786 | 81p multi | 2.50 | 1.90 |
| a. | | Vert. pair, #3348-3349 | 5.00 | 4.00 |
| 3350 | A786 | £1.28 multi | 4.00 | 3.00 |
| 3351 | A786 | £1.28 multi | 4.00 | 3.00 |
| a. | | Vert. pair, #3350-3351 | 8.00 | 6.00 |
| 3352 | A786 | £1.47 multi | 4.50 | 3.25 |
| 3353 | A786 | £1.47 multi | 4.50 | 3.25 |
| a. | | Vert. pair, #3352-3353 | 9.00 | 6.75 |
| | | Nos. 3344-3353 (10) | 29.00 | 21.50 |

**Photo.**
**Booklet Stamps**
**Self-Adhesive**
**Die Cut Perf. 14½**

| | | | | |
|---|---|---|---|---|
| 3353B | A786 | 1st multi | 6.50 | 4.00 |
| 3353C | A786 | 1st multi | 6.50 | 4.00 |
| d. | | Booklet pane of 6, #3353B-3353C, 4 #MH426 | 14.50 | |

On day of issue, Nos. 3344 and 3345 each sold for 53p and Nos. 3346, 3347, 3353B and 2253C each sold for 62p.

A787

A788

A789

A790

A791

A792

A793

A794

**Perf. 14¾x14 Syncopated**

**2015, Jan. 20     Litho.**

| | | | | |
|---|---|---|---|---|
| 3354 | | Sheet of 8 | 15.50 | 11.50 |
| a. | A787 | 1st multi | 1.90 | 1.40 |
| b. | A788 | 1st multi | 1.90 | 1.40 |
| c. | A789 | 1st multi | 1.90 | 1.40 |
| d. | A790 | 1st multi | 1.90 | 1.40 |
| e. | A791 | 1st multi | 1.90 | 1.40 |
| f. | A792 | 1st multi | 1.90 | 1.40 |
| g. | A793 | 1st multi | 1.90 | 1.40 |
| h. | A794 | 1st multi | 1.90 | 1.40 |

**Photo.**
**Booklet Stamps**
**Self-Adhesive**
**Die Cut Perf. 14¾x14**

| | | | | |
|---|---|---|---|---|
| 3355 | A791 | 1st multi | 2.50 | 1.90 |
| 3356 | A787 | 1st multi | 2.50 | 1.90 |
| 3357 | A790 | 1st multi | 2.50 | 1.90 |
| 3358 | A794 | 1st multi | 2.50 | 1.90 |
| 3359 | A788 | 1st multi | 2.50 | 1.90 |
| 3360 | A789 | 1st multi | 2.50 | 1.90 |
| 3361 | A793 | 1st multi | 2.50 | 1.90 |
| 3362 | A792 | 1st multi | 2.50 | 1.90 |
| a. | | Booklet pane of 12, #3356, 3359, 3361, 3362, 2 each #3355, 3357, 3358, 3360 | 22.50 | |
| b. | | Sheet of 20, 3 each #3355, 3357, 3358, 3360, 2 each #3356, 3359, 3361, 3362, + 20 labels, litho. | 60.00 | |
| | | Nos. 3355-3362 (8) | 20.00 | 15.20 |

On day of issue, Nos. 3354a-3354h, 3355-3362 each sold for 62p. No. 3362b sold for £12.90. Labels could not be personalized.

Inventions — A795

Designs: No. 3363, Colossus computer. No. 3364, World Wide Web. No. 3365, Catseye reflectors. No. 3366, Fiber optics. No. 3367, Stainless steel. No. 3368, Carbon fiber. No. 3369, DNA sequencing. No. 3370, I-limb bionic hand.

**2015, Feb. 19     Litho.     Perf. 14½**

| | | | | |
|---|---|---|---|---|
| 3363 | A795 | 1st multi | 1.90 | 1.40 |
| a. | | Booklet pane of 4 #2970, 3363, 2 #3005 (BK207) | 6.50 | — |
| 3364 | A795 | 1st multi | 1.90 | 1.40 |
| a. | | Horiz. pair, #3363-3364 | 3.80 | 2.90 |
| 3365 | A795 | 81p multi | 2.50 | 1.90 |
| 3366 | A795 | 81p multi | 2.50 | 1.90 |
| a. | | Horiz. pair, #3365-3366 | 5.00 | 4.00 |
| 3367 | A795 | £1.28 multi | 4.00 | 3.00 |
| 3368 | A795 | £1.28 multi | 4.00 | 3.00 |
| a. | | Horiz. pair, #3367-3368 | 8.00 | 6.00 |
| 3369 | A795 | £1.47 multi | 4.50 | 3.50 |
| a. | | Booklet pane of 4, #3365, 3366, 3368, 3369 (BK207) | 14.50 | |
| 3370 | A795 | £1.47 multi | 4.50 | 3.50 |
| a. | | Horiz. pair, #3369-3370 | 9.00 | 7.00 |
| b. | | Booklet pane of 4, #3363, 3364, 3367, 3370 (BK207) | 13.00 | |
| | | Nos. 3363-3370 (8) | 25.80 | 19.60 |

Nos. 3363-3364 each sold for 62p on day of issue.

Bridges — A796

Designs: No. 3371, Tarr Steps Bridge over Barle River. No. 3372, Row Bridge over Mosedale Beck. No. 3373, Pulteney Bridge over Avon River. No. 3374, Craigellachie Bridge over Spey River. No. 3375, Menai Suspension Bridge over Menai Strait. No. 3376, High Level Bridge over Tyne River. No. 3377, Royal Border Bridge over Tweed River. No. 3378, Tees Transporter Bridge over Tees River. No. 3379, Humber Bridge over Humber River. No. 3380, Peace Bridge over Foyle River.

| 2015, Mar. 5 | Litho. | | Perf. 14½x14¼ | |
|---|---|---|---|---|
| 3371 | A796 | 1st multi | 1.90 | 1.40 |
| 3372 | A796 | 1st multi | 1.90 | 1.40 |
| 3373 | A796 | 1st multi | 1.90 | 1.40 |
| 3374 | A796 | 1st multi | 1.90 | 1.40 |
| 3375 | A796 | 1st multi | 1.90 | 1.40 |
| a. | | Horiz. strip of 5, #3371-3375 | 9.50 | 7.00 |
| 3376 | A796 | 1st multi | 1.90 | 1.40 |
| 3377 | A796 | 1st multi | 1.90 | 1.40 |
| 3378 | A796 | 1st multi | 1.90 | 1.40 |
| 3379 | A796 | 1st multi | 1.90 | 1.40 |
| 3380 | A796 | 1st multi | 1.90 | 1.40 |
| a. | | Horiz. strip of 5, #3376-3380 | 9.50 | 7.00 |
| | Nos. 3371-3380 (10) | | 19.00 | 14.00 |

Nos. 3371-3380 each sold for 62p on day of issue.

Comedians
A797

Designs: No. 3381, Spike Milligan (1918-2002). No. 3382, Ronnie Corbett and Ronnie Barker (1929-2005) (The Two Ronnies). No. 3383, Billy Connolly. No. 3384, 3392, Eric Morecambe (1926-84) and Ernie Wise (1925-99). Nos. 3385, 3391, Norman Wisdom (1915-2010). No. 3386, Lenny Henry. No. 3387, Peter Cook (1937-95) and Dudley Moore (1935-2002). No. 3388, Monty Python. No. 3389, Dawn French and Jennifer Saunders. No. 3390, Victoria Wood.

| 2015, Apr. 1 | Litho. | | Perf. 14¼ | |
|---|---|---|---|---|
| 3381 | A797 | 1st multi | 1.90 | 1.40 |
| 3382 | A797 | 1st multi | 1.90 | 1.40 |
| 3383 | A797 | 1st multi | 1.90 | 1.40 |
| 3384 | A797 | 1st multi | 1.90 | 1.40 |
| 3385 | A797 | 1st multi | 1.90 | 1.40 |
| a. | | Horiz. strip of 5, #3381-3385 | 9.50 | 7.00 |
| 3386 | A797 | 1st multi | 1.90 | 1.40 |
| 3387 | A797 | 1st multi | 1.90 | 1.40 |
| 3388 | A797 | 1st multi | 1.90 | 1.40 |
| 3389 | A797 | 1st multi | 1.90 | 1.40 |
| 3390 | A797 | 1st multi | 1.90 | 1.40 |
| a. | | Horiz. strip of 5, #3386-3390 | 9.50 | 7.00 |
| | Nos. 3381-3390 (10) | | 19.00 | 14.00 |

Photo.
Booklet Stamps
Self-Adhesive
Die Cut Perf. 14¼x14

| 3391 | A797 | 1st multi | 4.00 | 3.00 |
|---|---|---|---|---|
| 3392 | A797 | 1st multi | 4.00 | 3.00 |
| a. | | Booklet pane of 6, #3391, 3392, 4 #MH426 | 18.00 | |

Nos. 3381-3392 each sold for 63p on day of issue.

Penny Black, 175th Anniv. A798

Designs: Nos. 3393a, 3394, 3396, Great Britain #1. Nos. 3393b, 3395, Great Britain #2.

Perf. 14¾x14 Syncopated

| 2015, May 6 | | | Litho. | |
|---|---|---|---|---|
| 3393 | A798 | Sheet of 4, 2 each #3393a-3393b | 7.75 | 6.00 |
| a.-b. | | 1st Either single | 1.90 | 1.40 |

Self-Adhesive
Die Cut Perf. 14¾x14 Syncopated

| 3394 | A798 | 1st multi + label | 6.25 | 4.00 |
|---|---|---|---|---|
| 3395 | A798 | 1st multi + label | 6.25 | 4.00 |

Photo.
Booklet Stamp

| 3396 | A798 | 1st reddish brown & black | 2.50 | 1.90 |
|---|---|---|---|---|
| a. | | Booklet pane of 6 | 16.00 | |

Nos. 3393a, 3393b, 3394-3396 each had a franking value of 63p on day of issue. Nos. 3394 and 3395 were printed together in sheets containing 10 of each stamp + 20 labels that could not be personalized. The sheet sold for £13.10. No. 3394 was also printed in sheets of 10 + 10 labels that could be personalized that sold for £10.20, and sheets of 20 + 20 labels that could be personalized that sold for £18.65.

No. 3393a was issued in a sheet of 25 stamps on 3/10/20.
See No. 3946.

World War I, Cent. — A799

Designs: No. 3397, Poppies, painting by Howard Hodgkin. No. 3398, Line from poem, All the Hills and Vales Along, by Charles Sorley. No. 3399, Kulbir Thapa, Nepalese Gurkha rifleman. No. 3400, The Kensingtons at Laventie, painting by Eric Kennington. No. 3401, Soldier at grave, Cape Helles, Gallipoli, Turkey. No. 3402, London Irish Rifles' soccer ball from Battle of Loos.

| 2015, May 14 | Litho. | | Perf. 14¼ | |
|---|---|---|---|---|
| 3397 | A799 | 1st multi | 1.90 | 1.40 |
| 3398 | A799 | 1st multi | 1.90 | 1.40 |
| 3399 | A799 | 1st multi | 1.90 | 1.40 |
| a. | | Booklet pane of 3, #3397-3399 (BK208) | 5.75 | — |
| 3400 | A799 | £1.52 multi | 4.50 | 3.50 |
| 3401 | A799 | £1.52 multi | 4.50 | 3.50 |
| 3402 | A799 | £1.52 multi | 4.50 | 3.50 |
| a. | | Booklet pane of 3, #3400-3402 (BK208) | 13.50 | — |
| | Nos. 3397-3402 (6) | | 19.20 | 14.70 |

On day of issue, Nos. 3397-3399 each sold for 63p.

Magna Carta, 800th Anniv. A800

Designs: No. 3403, Farmer, quotation from Magna Carta. No. 3404, King and nobleman, quotation from Simon de Montfort's Parliament. No. 3405, Man and woman, quotation from British Bill of Rights. No. 3406, Man and jail cell, quotation from American Bill of Rights. No. 3407, Dove, quotation from Universal Declaration of Human Rights. No. 3408, Women, quotation from Charter of the Commonwealth.

| 2015, June 2 | Litho. | | Perf. 14¾ | |
|---|---|---|---|---|
| 3403 | A800 | 1st multi | 1.90 | 1.40 |
| 3404 | A800 | 1st multi | 1.90 | 1.40 |
| 3405 | A800 | £1.33 multi | 4.00 | 3.00 |
| 3406 | A800 | £1.33 multi | 4.00 | 3.00 |
| 3407 | A800 | £1.52 multi | 4.50 | 3.50 |
| 3408 | A800 | £1.52 multi | 4.50 | 3.50 |
| | Nos. 3403-3408 (6) | | 20.80 | 15.80 |

On day of issue, Nos. 3403 and 3404 each sold for 63p.

A801

Battle of Waterloo, 200th Anniv. — A802

Paintings: No. 3409, The Defense of Hougoumont. No. 3410, The Scots Greys During the Charge of the Union Brigade. No. 3411, The French Cavalry's Assault on Allied Defensive Squares. No. 3412, The Defense of La Haye Sainte by the King's German Legion. No. 3413, The Capture of Plancenoit by the Prussians. No. 3414, The French Imperial Guard's Final Assault.

No. 3415 — Soldier from: a, Prussian Army 15th Infantry Regiment, IV Corps. b, Anglo-Allied Army King's German Legion Light Infantry. c, Anglo-Allied Army 92nd Gordon Highlanders. d, French Army Imperial Guard Grenadiers.

| 2015, June 18 | Litho. | | Perf. 14¾ | |
|---|---|---|---|---|
| 3409 | A801 | 1st multi | 1.90 | 1.40 |
| 3410 | A801 | 1st multi | 1.90 | 1.40 |
| 3411 | A801 | £1 multi | 3.00 | 2.25 |
| 3412 | A801 | £1 multi | 3.00 | 2.25 |
| 3413 | A801 | £1.52 multi | 4.50 | 3.50 |
| a. | | Booklet pane of 4, #3410-3413 (BK209) | 12.50 | |
| 3414 | A801 | £1.52 multi | 4.50 | 3.50 |
| a. | | Booklet pane of 2, #3409, 3414 (BK209) | 6.50 | — |
| | Nos. 3409-3414 (6) | | 18.80 | 14.30 |

Miniature Sheet
Perf. 14¼

| 3415 | A802 | Sheet of 4 | 12.00 | 9.00 |
|---|---|---|---|---|
| a.-b. | | 1st Either single | 1.90 | 1.40 |
| c.-d. | | £1.33 Either single | 4.00 | 3.00 |
| e. | | Booklet pane of 4, #3415a-3415d (BK209) | 12.00 | |

On day of issue, Nos. 3409-3410, 3415a-3415b each sold for 63p.

Miniature Sheet

Battle of Britain, 75th Anniv. A803

No. 3416: a, Pilots scramble to their Hurricanes. b, Supermarine Spitfires on patrol. c, Armorer replaces ammunition boxes. d, Spotters of the Auxiliary Territorial Service. e, Operations Room at Bentley Priory. f, Pilots of 32 Squadron await orders.

| 2015, July 16 | Litho. | | Perf. 14¼ | |
|---|---|---|---|---|
| 3416 | A803 | Sheet of 6 | 18.00 | 13.50 |
| a.-c. | | 1st Any single | 1.90 | 1.40 |
| d.-f. | | £1.33 Any single | 4.00 | 3.00 |
| g. | | Booklet pane of 4, #3416a, 3416c, 2 #3416b (BK220) | 7.50 | — |

On day of issue, Nos. 3416a-3416c each sold for 63p.
Issued: No. 3416g, 3/20/18.

A804

Bees
A805

Designs: 2nd, Scabious bee on field scabious. Nos. 3418, 3424, Great yellow bumblebee on bird's foot trefoil. £1, Northern Colletes bee on wild carrot. No. 3420, Bilberry bumblebee on bilberry. £1.52, Large mason bee on horseshoe vetch. £2.25, Potter flower bee on ground ivy.

No. 3423: a, Waggle dance. b, Pollination. c, Making honey. d, Tending young.

Perf. 14¼x14½

| 2015, Aug. 18 | | | Litho. | |
|---|---|---|---|---|
| 3417 | A804 | 2nd multi | 1.60 | 1.20 |
| 3418 | A804 | 1st multi | 1.90 | 1.40 |
| 3419 | A804 | £1 multi | 3.00 | 2.25 |
| 3420 | A804 | £1.33 multi | 4.00 | 3.00 |
| 3421 | A804 | £1.52 multi | 4.50 | 3.50 |
| 3422 | A804 | £2.25 multi | 6.75 | 5.00 |
| | Nos. 3417-3422 (6) | | 21.75 | 16.35 |

Miniature Sheet

| 3423 | A805 | Sheet of 4 | 12.00 | 9.00 |
|---|---|---|---|---|
| a.-b. | | 1st Either single | 1.90 | 1.40 |
| c.-d. | | £1.33 Either single | 4.00 | 3.00 |

Photo.
Booklet Stamp
Self-Adhesive
Die Cut Perf. 14¼x14½

| 3424 | A804 | 1st multi | 3.00 | 2.00 |
|---|---|---|---|---|
| a. | | Booklet pane of 6, #3424, 4 #MH426 | 10.00 | |

On day of issue, No. 3417 sold for 54p; Nos. 3418, 3423a, 3423b and 3424, for 63p each.

2015 Rugby World Cup, Great Britain — A806

Designs: No. 3425, Tackle. No. 3426, Scrum. Nos. 3427, 3433, Try. No. 3428, 3434, Conversion attempt. No. 3429, Pass. No. 3430, Drop goal. No. 3431, Ruck. No. 3432, Line-out.

| 2015, Sept. 18 | Litho. | | Perf. 14¼ | |
|---|---|---|---|---|
| 3425 | A806 | 2nd multi | 1.60 | 1.20 |
| 3426 | A806 | 2nd multi | 1.60 | 1.20 |
| a. | | Horiz. pair, #3425-3426 | 3.25 | 2.50 |
| 3427 | A806 | 1st multi | 1.90 | 1.40 |
| 3428 | A806 | 1st multi | 1.90 | 1.40 |
| a. | | Horiz. pair, #3427-3428 | 4.00 | 2.90 |
| 3429 | A806 | £1 multi | 3.00 | 2.25 |
| 3430 | A806 | £1 multi | 3.00 | 2.25 |
| a. | | Horiz. pair, #3429-3430 | 6.00 | 4.50 |
| 3431 | A806 | £1.52 multi | 4.50 | 3.50 |
| 3432 | A806 | £1.52 multi | 4.50 | 3.50 |
| a. | | Horiz. pair, #3431-3432 | 9.00 | 7.00 |
| | Nos. 3425-3432 (8) | | 22.00 | 16.70 |

Photo.
Booklet Stamps
Self-Adhesive
Die Cut Perf 14¼

| 3433 | A806 | 1st multi | 3.50 | 2.00 |
|---|---|---|---|---|
| 3434 | A806 | 1st multi | 3.50 | 2.00 |
| a. | | Booklet pane of 6, #3433, 3434, 4 #MH457 | 14.50 | |

On day of issue, Nos. 3425-3426 each sold for 54p and Nos. 3427-3428, 3433-3434 each sold for 63p.

A807

Premiere of Movie Star Wars: The Force Awakens
A808

Designs: Nos. 3435, 3448, Darth Vader. Nos. 3436, 3447, Yoda. No. 3437, Obi-Wan Kenobi. Nos. 3438, 3450, Stormtrooper. Nos. 3439, 3449, Han Solo. No. 3440, Rey. No. 3441, Princess Leia. No. 3442, The Emperor. No. 3443, Luke Skywalker. No. 3444, Boba Fett. No. 3445, Finn. No. 3446, Kylo Ren.

No. 3451: a, X-Wing Starfighter with red stripe (60x21mm). b, AT-AT walkers (41x30mm). c, TIE Fighters (27x36mm). d, TIE Fighters and Death Star (35x36mm). e, X-Wing Starfighter and planet (60x21mm). f, Millennium Falcon (60x30mm).

| 2015, Oct. 20 | Litho. | | Perf. 14½ | |
|---|---|---|---|---|
| 3435 | A807 | 1st multi | 1.90 | 1.40 |
| 3436 | A807 | 1st multi | 1.90 | 1.40 |
| 3437 | A807 | 1st multi | 1.90 | 1.40 |
| 3438 | A807 | 1st multi | 1.90 | 1.40 |
| 3439 | A807 | 1st multi | 1.90 | 1.40 |
| 3440 | A807 | 1st multi | 1.90 | 1.40 |
| a. | | Horiz. strip of 6, #3435-3440 | 11.50 | 8.50 |
| 3441 | A807 | 1st multi | 1.90 | 1.40 |
| 3442 | A807 | 1st multi | 1.90 | 1.40 |
| 3443 | A807 | 1st multi | 1.90 | 1.40 |
| a. | | Booklet pane of 6, #3436, 3438, 3439, 3441, 3442, 3443 (BK210) | 11.50 | — |
| 3444 | A807 | 1st multi | 1.90 | 1.40 |
| 3445 | A807 | 1st multi | 1.90 | 1.40 |
| 3446 | A807 | 1st multi | 1.90 | 1.40 |
| a. | | Horiz. strip of 6, #3441-3446 | 11.50 | 8.50 |
| b. | | Booklet pane of 6, #3435, 3437, 3440, 3444, 3445, 3446 (BK210) | 11.50 | — |
| | Nos. 3435-3446 (12) | | 22.80 | 16.80 |

Self-Adhesive
Die Cut Perf. 14½

| 3447 | A807 | 1st multi + label | 3.00 | 3.00 |
|---|---|---|---|---|
| 3448 | A807 | 1st multi + label | 3.00 | 3.00 |
| 3449 | A807 | 1st multi + label | 3.00 | 3.00 |
| 3450 | A807 | 1st multi + label | 3.00 | 3.00 |
| a. | | Sheet of 10, 3 each #3447-3448, 2 each #3449-3450, + 10 labels | 20.00 | |
| | Nos. 3447-3450 (4) | | 12.00 | 12.00 |

## Miniature Sheet
### Die Cut Perf. 14¼, 14½ (#3451a-3451e), 14¾ (#3451f)

| | | | | |
|---|---|---|---|---|
| 3451 | | Sheet of 6 | 11.50 | 11.50 |
| a.-f. | | 1st Any single | 1.90 | 1.40 |
| g. | | Booklet pane of 3, #3451a-3451c (BK210) | 5.75 | |
| h. | | Booklet pane of 3, #3451d-3451f (BK210) | 5.75 | |

Issued: Nos. 3443a, 3446b, 3451g, 12/17. On day of issue, Nos. 3435-3436, 3451a-3451f each sold for 63p. Nos. 3447-3450 each had a franking value of 63p on day of issue. No. 3450a sold for £6.80 and labels could not be personalized.

### Flag Type of 2005
### Perf. 14¾x14 Syncopated

**2015, Dec. 17** — Litho.
### Booklet Stamp

| | | | | |
|---|---|---|---|---|
| 3452 | A594 | 1st multi | 2.40 | 2.00 |
| a. | | Booklet pane of 8, 4 #3452, 2 each #MH401Cf, MH440, + label (BK210) | 25.00 | — |

No. 3452 had a franking value of 63p on day of issue.

A809

Christmas — A810

Designs: Nos. 3453a, 3453c, 3454, 3456, Journey to Bethlehem. Nos. 3453b, 3453d, 3455, 3457, Nativity. £1, Animals and palm tree. £1.33, Shepherds and angel. £1.52, Magi and Star of Bethlehem. £2.25, Annunciation.

**2015, Nov. 3** — Photo. — Perf. 14½x15
### Miniature Sheet

| | | | | |
|---|---|---|---|---|
| 3453 | | Sheet of 8 | 27.50 | 21.00 |
| a. | A809 | 2nd multi | 1.60 | 1.20 |
| b. | A809 | 1st multi | 1.90 | 1.40 |
| c. | A810 | 2nd Large multi | 2.25 | 1.65 |
| d. | A810 | 1st Large multi | 2.90 | 2.10 |
| e. | A809 | £1 multi | 3.00 | 2.25 |
| f. | A809 | £1.33 multi | 4.00 | 3.00 |
| g. | A809 | £1.52 multi | 4.50 | 3.50 |
| h. | A809 | £2.25 multi | 6.75 | 5.00 |

### Self-Adhesive
### Die Cut Perf. 14½x15

| | | | | |
|---|---|---|---|---|
| 3454 | A809 | 2nd multi | 1.60 | 1.20 |
| a. | | Booklet pane of 12 | 16.00 | |
| b. | | Litho., die cut perf. 14½x15 syncopated + label (3461b) | 2.00 | 2.00 |
| 3455 | A809 | 1st multi | 1.90 | 1.40 |
| a. | | Booklet pane of 12 | 19.00 | |
| b. | | Litho., die cut perf. 14½x15 syncopated + label (3461b) | 2.25 | 2.25 |
| 3456 | A810 | 2nd Large multi | 2.25 | 1.65 |
| 3457 | A810 | 1st Large multi | 2.90 | 2.10 |
| 3458 | A809 | £1 multi | 3.00 | 2.25 |
| a. | | Litho., die cut perf. 14½x15 syncopated + label (3461b) | 5.50 | 5.50 |
| 3459 | A809 | £1.33 multi | 4.00 | 3.00 |
| a. | | Litho., die cut perf. 14½x15 syncopated + label (3461b) | 7.50 | 7.50 |
| 3460 | A809 | £1.52 multi | 4.50 | 3.50 |
| a. | | Litho., die cut perf. 14½x15 syncopated + label (3461b) | 8.00 | 8.00 |
| 3461 | A809 | £2.25 multi | 6.75 | 5.00 |
| a. | | Litho., die cut perf. 14½x15 syncopated + label (3461b) | 12.50 | 12.50 |
| b. | | Sheet of 20, #3458a, 3459a, 3460a, 3461a, 8 each #3454b, 3455b, + 20 labels | 67.50 | |
| | | Nos. 3454-3461 (8) | 26.90 | 20.10 |

On day of issue, Nos. 3453a and 3454 each sold for 54p; Nos. 3453b and 3455, for 63p; Nos. 3453c and 3456, for 74p; and Nos. 3453d and 3457, for 95p. No. 3461b sold for £15.96 and labels could not be personalized.

Ernest Shackleton and the Endurance Expedition, Cent. — A811

Designs: No. 3462, Entering the Antarctic ice, December 1914. No. 3463, Endurance frozen in pack ice, January 1915. No. 3464, Striving to free Endurance, February 1915.

No. 3465, Trapped in a pressure crack, October 1915. No. 3466, Patience Camp, December 1915-April 1916. No. 3467, Safe arrival at Elephant Island, April 1916. No. 3468, Setting out for South Georgia, April 1916. No. 3469, Rescue of Endurance crew, August 1916.

**2016, Jan. 7** — Litho. — Perf. 14¼x14½

| | | | | |
|---|---|---|---|---|
| 3462 | A811 | 1st multi | 1.90 | 1.40 |
| 3463 | A811 | 1st multi | 1.90 | 1.40 |
| a. | | Horiz. pair, #3462-3463 | 3.80 | 2.90 |
| 3464 | A811 | £1 multi | 3.00 | 2.25 |
| 3465 | A811 | £1 multi | 3.00 | 2.25 |
| a. | | Horiz. pair, #3464-3465 | 6.00 | 4.50 |
| 3466 | A811 | £1.33 multi | 4.00 | 3.00 |
| 3467 | A811 | £1.33 multi | 4.00 | 3.00 |
| a. | | Horiz. pair, #3466-3467 | 8.00 | 6.00 |
| 3468 | A811 | £1.52 multi | 4.50 | 3.50 |
| 3469 | A811 | £1.52 multi | 4.50 | 3.50 |
| a. | | Horiz. pair, #3468-3469 | 9.00 | 7.00 |
| | | Nos. 3462-3469 (8) | 26.80 | 20.30 |

On day of issue, Nos. 3462-3463 each sold for 63p.

Royal Mail, 500th Anniv. — A812

Post Office Posters A813

Designs: No. 3470, Sir Brian Tuke, 16th Century Master of the Posts. No. 3471, Packet ship. No. 3472, Penfold pillar box. No. 3473, River post. No. 3474, Mail coach. No. 3475, Medway Mail Center.

No. 3476 — Inscriptions: a, "Quickest way by air mail." b, "Addrerss your letters plainly." c, "Pack your parcels carefully. d, "Stamps in books save time."

### Perf. 14½x14¼

**2016, Feb. 17** — Litho.

| | | | | |
|---|---|---|---|---|
| 3470 | A812 | 1st multi | 1.75 | 1.40 |
| 3471 | A812 | 1st multi | 1.75 | 1.40 |
| 3472 | A812 | 1st multi | 1.75 | 1.40 |
| 3473 | A812 | £1.52 multi | 4.25 | 3.50 |
| a. | | Booklet pane of 3, #3470, 3472, 3473 (BK211) | 9.25 | |
| 3474 | A812 | £1.52 multi | 4.25 | 3.50 |
| 3475 | A812 | £1.52 multi | 4.25 | 3.50 |
| a. | | Booklet pane of 3, #3471, 3474, 3475 (BK211) | 12.00 | |
| | | Nos. 3470-3475 (6) | 18.00 | 14.70 |

### Miniature Sheet

| | | | | |
|---|---|---|---|---|
| 3476 | A813 | Sheet of 4 | 11.00 | 11.00 |
| a.-b. | | 1st Either single | 1.75 | 1.40 |
| c.-d. | | £1.33 Either single | 3.75 | 2.90 |
| e. | | Booklet pane of 4, #3476a-3476d (BK211) | 13.00 | |

On day of issue, Nos. 3470-3472, 3476a and 3476b each sold for 63p.

Penny Red (Great Britain No. 3), 175th Anniv. — A814

### Perf. 14¾x14 Syncopated

**2016, Feb. 18** — Litho.
### Booklet Stamps

| | | | | |
|---|---|---|---|---|
| 3477 | A814 | 1st multi | 2.50 | 2.50 |
| a. | | Booklet pane of 8, 2 #3393a, 3 each #3393b, 3477, + central label (BK211) | 20.00 | — |

### Self-Adhesive
### Photo.
### Die Cut Perf. 14¾x14 Syncopated

| | | | | |
|---|---|---|---|---|
| 3478 | A814 | 1st multi | 2.50 | 2.00 |
| a. | | Booklet pane of 6 | 12.75 | |
| b. | | Litho., pane of 20 + 20 labels | 37.00 | |

Nos. 3477-3478 had a franking value of 63p on day of issue. No. 3478b sold for £13.10, and labels could not be personalized.

Humanitarians A815

Designs: No. 3479, Sir Nicholas Winton (1909-2015), rescuer of children in World War II. No. 3480, Sue Ryder (1924-2000), charity founder. No. 3481, John Boyd Orr (1880-1971), Director General of United Nations Food and Agriculture Organization. No. 3482, Eglantyne Jebb (1876-1928), founder of Save the Children Fund. No. 3483, Joseph Rowntree (1836-1925), philanthropist. No. 3484, Josephine Butler (1828-1906), social reformer and feminist.

### Perf. 14½x14¼

**2016, Mar. 15** — Litho.

| | | | | |
|---|---|---|---|---|
| 3479 | A815 | 1st black | 1.90 | 1.40 |
| 3480 | A815 | 1st black | 1.90 | 1.40 |
| 3481 | A815 | 1st black | 1.90 | 1.40 |
| a. | | Horiz. strip of 3, #3479-3481 | 5.75 | 4.25 |
| 3482 | A815 | £1.33 black | 3.75 | 2.90 |
| 3483 | A815 | £1.33 black | 3.75 | 2.90 |
| 3484 | A815 | £1.33 black | 3.75 | 2.90 |
| a. | | Horiz. strip of 3, #3482-3484 | 11.50 | 8.75 |
| | | Nos. 3479-3484 (6) | 16.95 | 12.90 |

On day of issue, Nos. 3479-3481 each sold for 63p.

Quotations From Works by William Shakespeare (1564-1616) — A816

Quotation from: No. 3485, Hamlet. No. 3486, Julius Caesar. No. 3487, Romeo and Juliet. No. 3488, As You Like It. No. 3489, Much Ado About Nothing. No. 3490, Sonnet 30. No. 3491, Venus and Adonis. No. 3492, The Tempest. No. 3493, Macbeth. No. 3494, Richard III.

**2016, Apr. 5** — Litho. — Perf. 14½x14¼

| | | | | |
|---|---|---|---|---|
| 3485 | A816 | 1st multi | 1.90 | 1.40 |
| 3486 | A816 | 1st multi | 1.90 | 1.40 |
| 3487 | A816 | 1st multi | 1.90 | 1.40 |
| 3488 | A816 | 1st multi | 1.90 | 1.40 |
| 3489 | A816 | 1st multi | 1.90 | 1.40 |
| a. | | Horiz. strip of 5, #3485-3489 | 9.50 | 7.00 |
| 3490 | A816 | 1st multi | 1.90 | 1.40 |
| 3491 | A816 | 1st multi | 1.90 | 1.40 |
| 3492 | A816 | 1st multi | 1.90 | 1.40 |
| 3493 | A816 | 1st multi | 1.90 | 1.40 |
| 3494 | A816 | 1st multi | 1.90 | 1.40 |
| a. | | Horiz. strip of 5, #3490-3494 | 9.50 | 7.00 |
| | | Nos. 3485-3494 (10) | 19.00 | 14.00 |

On day of issue, Nos. 3485-3494 each sold for 64p.

Princess Elizabeth and King George VI, c. 1930 — A817

Queen Elizabeth II at State Opening of Parliament, 2012 — A818

Queen Elizabeth II, Princess Anne, Prince Charles, 1952 — A819

Queen Elizabeth II Visiting New Zealand, 1977 — A820

Queen Elizabeth II and Prince Philip, 1957 — A821

Queen Elizabeth II and Nelson Mandela, 1996 — A822

Queen Elizabeth II and Heirs to the Throne A823

Designs: Nos. 3501a, 3502, Prince Charles. Nos. 3501b, 3503, Queen Elizabeth II. Nos. 3501c, 3504, Prince George of Cambridge. Nos. 3501d, 3505, Prince William of Cambridge.

**2016** — Litho. — Perf. 14¼x14½

| | | | | |
|---|---|---|---|---|
| 3495 | A817 | 1st multi | 1.90 | 1.40 |
| 3496 | A818 | 1st multi | 1.90 | 1.40 |
| 3497 | A819 | 1st multi | 1.90 | 1.40 |
| a. | | Horiz. strip of 3, #3495-3497 | 5.75 | 4.25 |
| b. | | Booklet pane of 4, #3028a, 3029a, 3496, 3497 (BK1237) | 10.00 | — |
| 3498 | A820 | £1.52 multi | 4.50 | 3.50 |
| 3499 | A821 | £1.52 multi | 4.50 | 3.50 |
| a. | | Booklet pane of 2, #3498-3499 (BK212) | 9.50 | |
| 3500 | A822 | £1.52 multi | 4.50 | 3.50 |
| a. | | Horiz. strip of 3, #3498-3500 | 13.50 | 10.50 |
| b. | | Booklet pane of 4, #3495, 3496, 3497, 3500 (BK212) | 10.50 | — |
| | | Nos. 3495-3500 (6) | 19.20 | 14.70 |

### Miniature Sheet
### Perf. 14¼

| | | | | |
|---|---|---|---|---|
| 3501 | A823 | Sheet of 4 | 7.75 | 7.75 |
| a.-d. | | 1st Any single | 1.90 | 1.40 |
| e. | | Booklet pane of 4, #3501a-3501d (BK212) | 7.75 | |

### Booklet Stamps
### Self-Adhesive
### Photo.
### Die Cut Perf. 14¼

| | | | | |
|---|---|---|---|---|
| 3502 | A823 | 1st multi | 3.00 | 1.40 |
| 3503 | A823 | 1st multi | 3.00 | 1.40 |
| a. | | Booklet pane of 6, #3502, 3503, 4 #MH457 | 11.50 | |
| 3504 | A823 | 1st multi | 3.00 | 1.40 |
| 3505 | A823 | 1st multi | 3.00 | 1.40 |
| a. | | Booklet pane of 6, #3504, 3505, 4 #MH457 | 10.50 | |
| | | Nos. 3502-3505 (4) | 12.00 | 5.60 |

90th birthday of Queen Elizabeth II. Issued: Nos. 3495-3503, 4/21; Nos. 3504-3505, 6/9; No. 3497b, 2/4/22. On day of issue, Nos. 3495-3497, 3501a-3501d, 3502-2505 each sold for 64p.

### Miniature Sheet

Animals A824

No. 3506: a, Woodpecker (36x40mm). b, Snake (31x49mm). c, Chimpanzee (39x50mm). d, Bat (26x49mm). e, Orangutan (29x50mm). f, Koalas (41x35mm).

### Die Cut Perf. 14¾x14¼ Syncopated

**2016, May 17** — Litho.
### Self-Adhesive

| | | | | |
|---|---|---|---|---|
| 3506 | A824 | Sheet of 6 | 18.00 | |
| a.-b. | | 1st Either single | 1.90 | 1.40 |
| c.-d. | | £1.05 Either single | 3.00 | 2.25 |
| e.-f. | | £1.33 Either single | 4.00 | 3.00 |

On day of issue, Nos. 3506a-3506b each sold for 64p.

World War I, Cent. — A825

Post Office at War, 1914-18 A826

Designs: No. 3507, Munitions worker Lottie Meade. No. 3508, Quotation from "To My Brother," by Vera Brittain. No. 3509, Battlefield Poppy, by Giles Revell. No. 3510, Battle of Jutland commemorative medal. No. 3511, Thiepval Memorial, Somme, France. No. 3512, Travoys Arriving with Wounded, by Sir Stanley Spencer.

No. 3513: a, Post Office Rifles. b, Soldier writing a letter from the Western Front. c,

Delivering the mail on the home front. d, Home Depot at Regent's Park, London.

**2016, June 21    Litho.    Perf. 14¼**

| 3507 | A825 | 1st multi | 1.75 | 1.35 |
|---|---|---|---|---|
| 3508 | A825 | 1st multi | 1.75 | 1.35 |
| 3509 | A825 | 1st multi | 1.75 | 1.35 |
| a. | | Booklet pane of 3, #3507-3509 (BK213) | 5.50 | — |
| 3510 | A825 | £1.52 multi | 4.00 | 3.00 |
| 3511 | A825 | £1.52 multi | 4.00 | 3.00 |
| 3512 | A825 | £1.52 multi | 4.00 | 3.00 |
| a. | | Booklet pane of 3, #3510-3512 (BK213) | 12.50 | |

**Miniature Sheet**
**Perf. 14¼x14**

| 3513 | A826 | Sheet of 4 | 10.50 | 10.50 |
|---|---|---|---|---|
| a.-b. | | 1st Either single | 1.75 | 1.35 |
| c.-d. | | £1.33 Either single | 3.50 | 2.60 |
| e. | | Booklet pane of 4, #3513a-3513d (BK213) | 11.00 | |

On day of issue, Nos. 3507-3509, 3513a, 3513b each sold for 64p.

Pink Floyd Concerts A827

The Piper at the Gates of Dawn, by Pink Floyd, 1967 — A828

Atom Heart Mother, by Pink Floyd, 1970 — A829

The Dark Side of the Moon, by Pink Floyd, 1973 — A830

Wish You Were Here, by Pink Floyd, 1975 — A831

Animals, by Pink Floyd, 1977 — A832

The Endless River, by Pink Floyd, 2014 — A833

No. 3514: a, UFO Club concert, 1966. b, The Dark Side of the Moon tour, 1973. c, The Wall tour, 1981. d, The Division Bell tour, 1994.

**2016, July 7    Litho.    Perf. 14¾x14½**

| 3514 | A827 | Sheet of 4 | 11.50 | 11.50 |
|---|---|---|---|---|
| a.-b. | | 1st Either single | 1.75 | 1.35 |
| c.-d. | | £1.52 Either single | 4.00 | 3.00 |

**Self-Adhesive**
**Photo.**
**Die Cut Perf. 14¾ Syncopated**

| 3515 | A828 | 1st multi | 1.75 | 1.35 |
|---|---|---|---|---|
| 3516 | A829 | 1st multi | 1.75 | 1.35 |
| 3517 | A830 | 1st multi | 1.75 | 1.35 |
| 3518 | A831 | £1.52 multi | 4.00 | 3.00 |
| 3519 | A832 | £1.52 multi | 4.00 | 3.00 |
| 3520 | A833 | £1.52 multi | 4.00 | 3.00 |
| | | Nos. 3515-3520 (6) | 17.25 | 13.05 |

On day of issue, Nos. 3514a-3514b, 3515-3517 each sold for 64p. A sheet of ten perf. 14¾x14½ stamps with water-activated gum of type A830 sold for £12.95.

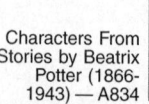

Characters From Stories by Beatrix Potter (1866-1943) — A834

Designs: Nos. 3521, 3528, Peter Rabbit. Nos. 3522, 3529, Mrs. Tiggy-Winkle. No. 3523, Squirrel Nutkin. No. 3524, Jemima Puddle-Duck. No. 3525, Tom Kitten. No. 3526, Benjamin Bunny.

No. 3527 — Scenes from The Tale of Peter Rabbit: a, Mother Rabbit adjusting coat on

Peter Rabbit. b, Peter Rabbit and potted plants. c, Peter Rabbit crawling under fence. d, Farmer chasing Peter Rabbit.

**2016, July 28    Litho.    Perf. 14½x14¼**

| 3521 | A834 | 1st multi | 1.75 | 1.35 |
|---|---|---|---|---|
| 3522 | A834 | 1st multi | 1.75 | 1.35 |
| a. | | Horiz. pair, #3521-3522 | 3.50 | 2.75 |
| 3523 | A834 | £1.33 multi | 3.50 | 2.60 |
| 3524 | A834 | £1.33 multi | 3.50 | 2.60 |
| a. | | Horiz. pair, #3523-3524 | 7.00 | 5.25 |
| 3525 | A834 | £1.52 multi | 4.00 | 3.00 |
| a. | | Booklet pane of 3, #3522, 3524, 3525 (BK214) | 10.00 | |
| 3526 | A834 | £1.52 multi | 4.00 | 3.00 |
| a. | | Booklet pane of 3, #3525-3526 | 8.00 | 6.00 |
| b. | | Booklet pane of 3, #3521, 3523, 3526 (BK214) | 10.00 | |
| | | Nos. 3521-3526 (6) | 18.50 | 13.90 |

**Miniature Sheet**

| 3527 | | Sheet of 4 | 10.50 | 10.50 |
|---|---|---|---|---|
| a.-b. | | A834 1st Either single | 1.75 | 1.35 |
| c.-d. | | A834 £1.33 Either single | 3.50 | 2.60 |
| e. | | Booklet pane of 4, #3527a-3527d (BK214) | 11.00 | |

**Booklet Stamps**
**Self-Adhesive**
**Photo.**
**Die Cut Perf. 14½x14¼**

| 3528 | A834 | 1st multi | 4.25 | 1.75 |
|---|---|---|---|---|
| 3529 | A834 | 1st multi | 4.25 | 1.75 |
| a. | | Booklet pane of 6, #3528, 3529, 4 #MH457 | 12.00 | |

On day of issue, Nos. 3521-3522, 3527a-3527b, 3528-3529 each sold for 64p.

Landscape Gardens Designed by Lancelot "Capability" Brown (c. 1716-83) — A835

Designs: No. 3530, Blenheim Palace. No. 3531, Longleat. No. 3532, Compton Verney. Nos. 3533, 3539, Highclere Castle. No. 3534, Alnwick Castle. No. 3535, Berrington Hall. No. 3536, Stowe. No. 3537, Croome Park.

**2016, Aug. 16    Litho.    Perf. 14¼x14**

| 3530 | A835 | 2nd multi | 1.50 | 1.10 |
|---|---|---|---|---|
| 3531 | A835 | 2nd multi | 1.50 | 1.10 |
| a. | | Horiz. pair, #3530-3531 | 3.00 | 2.25 |
| 3532 | A835 | 1st multi | 1.75 | 1.35 |
| 3533 | A835 | 1st multi | 1.75 | 1.35 |
| a. | | Horiz. pair, #3532-3533 | 3.50 | 2.75 |
| 3534 | A835 | £1.05 multi | 2.75 | 2.00 |
| 3535 | A835 | £1.05 multi | 2.75 | 2.00 |
| a. | | Horiz. pair, #3534-3535 | 5.50 | 4.00 |
| 3536 | A835 | £1.33 multi | 3.50 | 2.60 |
| 3537 | A835 | £1.33 multi | 3.50 | 2.60 |
| a. | | Horiz. pair, #3536-3537 | 7.00 | 5.25 |
| | | Nos. 3530-3537 (8) | 19.00 | 14.10 |

**Booklet Stamps**
**Self-Adhesive**
**Photo.**
**Die Cut Perf. 14¼x14¼**

| 3538 | A835 | 1st multi | 4.50 | 1.75 |
|---|---|---|---|---|
| 3539 | A835 | 1st multi | 4.50 | 1.75 |
| a. | | Booklet pane of 6, #3538, 3539, 4 #MH457 | 12.00 | |

Nos. 3530-3531 each sold for 55p and Nos. 3532-3533 and 3538-3539 each sold for 64p on day of issue.

Great Fire of London, 350th Anniv. — A836

Cartoon depictions of fire events with map features: No. 3540, Pudding Lane and Thames Street. No. 3541, River Thames. No. 3542, Finch Lane, Birchin Lane, Cornhill. No. 3543, Paternoster Row. No. 3544, Moorfields. No. 3545, Whitehall.

**2016, Sept. 2    Litho.    Perf. 14½x14¼**

| 3540 | A836 | 1st multi | 1.75 | 1.35 |
|---|---|---|---|---|
| 3541 | A836 | 1st multi | 1.75 | 1.35 |
| a. | | Horiz. pair, #3540-3541 | 3.50 | 2.75 |
| 3542 | A836 | £1.05 multi | 2.75 | 2.00 |
| 3543 | A836 | £1.05 multi | 2.75 | 2.00 |
| a. | | Horiz. pair, #3542-3543 | 5.50 | 4.00 |
| 3544 | A836 | £1.52 multi | 4.00 | 3.00 |
| 3545 | A836 | £1.52 multi | 4.00 | 3.00 |
| a. | | Horiz. pair, #3544-3545 | 8.00 | 6.00 |
| | | Nos. 3540-3545 (6) | 17.00 | 12.70 |

On day of issue, Nos. 3540-3541 each sold for 64p.

Scenes From Novels by Agatha Christie (1890-1976) — A837

Scene from: No. 3546, Murder on the Orient Express. No. 3547, And Then There Were None. No. 3548, The Mysterious Affair at Styles. No. 3549, The Murder of Roger Ackroyd. No. 3550, The Body in the Library. No. 3551, A Murder is Announced.

**Perf. 14¾x14½**

**2016, Sept. 15    Litho.**

| 3546 | A837 | 1st multi | 1.75 | 1.35 |
|---|---|---|---|---|
| 3547 | A837 | 1st multi | 1.75 | 1.35 |
| a. | | Vert. pair, #3546-3547 | 3.50 | 2.75 |
| 3548 | A837 | £1.33 multi | 3.50 | 2.00 |
| 3549 | A837 | £1.33 multi | 3.50 | 2.00 |
| a. | | Vert. pair, #3548-3549 | 7.00 | 4.00 |
| 3550 | A837 | £1.52 multi | 4.00 | 3.00 |
| 3551 | A837 | £1.52 multi | 4.00 | 3.00 |
| a. | | Vert. pair, #3550-3551 | 8.00 | 6.00 |
| | | Nos. 3546-3551 (6) | 18.50 | 12.70 |

On day of issue, Nos. 3546-3547 each sold for 64p.

Children's Book Characters by Roger Hargreaves — A838

Designs: Nos. 3552, 3562a, 3563, Mr. Happy. Nos. 3553, 3562b, Little Miss Naughty. Nos. 3554, 3562c, Mr. Bump. Nos. 3555, 3562d, Little Miss Sunshine. Nos. 3556, 3562e, 3564, Mr. Tickle. Nos. 3557, 3562f, Mr. Grumpy. Nos. 3558, 3562g, Little Miss Princess. Nos. 3559, 3562h, Mr. Strong. Nos. 3560, 3562i, Little Miss Christmas. Nos. 3561, 3562j, Mr. Messy.

**2016, Oct. 20    Litho.    Perf. 14½**

| 3552 | A838 | 1st multi | 1.75 | 1.35 |
|---|---|---|---|---|
| 3553 | A838 | 1st multi | 1.75 | 1.35 |
| 3554 | A838 | 1st multi | 1.75 | 1.35 |
| 3555 | A838 | 1st multi | 1.75 | 1.35 |
| 3556 | A838 | 1st multi | 1.75 | 1.35 |
| a. | | Horiz. strip of 5, #3552-3556 | 8.75 | 6.75 |
| 3557 | A838 | 1st multi | 1.75 | 1.35 |
| 3558 | A838 | 1st multi | 1.75 | 1.35 |
| 3559 | A838 | 1st multi | 1.75 | 1.35 |
| 3560 | A838 | 1st multi | 1.75 | 1.35 |
| 3561 | A838 | 1st multi | 1.75 | 1.35 |
| a. | | Horiz. strip of 5, #3557-3561 | 8.75 | 1.35 |
| | | Nos. 3552-3561 (10) | 17.50 | 13.50 |

**Self-Adhesive**
**Litho.**
**Die Cut Perf. 14½**

| 3562 | | Sheet of 10 + 10 labels | 17.50 | |
|---|---|---|---|---|
| a.-j. | | A838 1st Any single + label | 1.75 | 1.75 |

**Booklet Stamps**
**Photo.**

| 3563 | A838 | 1st multi | 3.75 | 2.50 |
|---|---|---|---|---|
| 3564 | A838 | 1st multi | 3.75 | 2.50 |
| a. | | Booklet pane of 6, #3563-3564, 4 #MH426 | 10.00 | |

On day of issue, Nos. 3552-3561 and 3563-3564 each sold for 64p. No. 3562 sold for £6.90, and Nos. 3562a-3562j each have a franking value of 64p. Nos. 3563 and 3564 each have a fuzzy dot structure most visible on the thin black lines of the Hargreaves signature.

A839

Christmas — A840

Designs: Nos. 3565a, 3565c, 3566, 3568, Snowman. Nos. 3565b, 3565d, 3567, 3569, Robin. £1.05, Christmas tree. £1.33, Christmas lantern. £1.52, Christmas stocking. £2.25, Christmas pudding.

**2016, Nov. 8    Photo.    Perf. 14½x15**
**Miniature Sheet**

| 3565 | | Sheet of 8 | 23.50 | 12.00 |
|---|---|---|---|---|
| a. | | A839 2nd multi | 1.60 | 1.20 |
| b. | | A839 1st multi | 1.75 | 1.35 |
| c. | | A839 2nd Large multi | 2.10 | 1.60 |
| d. | | A840 1st Large multi | 2.60 | 2.00 |
| e. | | A839 £1.05 multi | 3.00 | 2.10 |
| f. | | A839 £1.33 multi | 3.75 | 2.90 |
| g. | | A839 £1.52 multi | 4.25 | 3.25 |
| h. | | A839 £2.25 multi | 6.25 | 4.75 |

**Self-Adhesive**
**Die Cut Perf. 14½x15**

| 3566 | A839 | 2nd multi | 1.60 | 1.60 |
|---|---|---|---|---|
| a. | | Booklet pane of 12 | 16.00 | |
| b. | | Litho., die cut perf. 14½x15 syncopated + label (3567c) | 1.75 | 1.75 |
| 3567 | A839 | 1st multi | 1.75 | 1.35 |
| a. | | Booklet pane of 12 | 19.00 | |
| b. | | Litho., die cut perf. 14½x15 syncopated + label (3567c) | 1.75 | 1.75 |
| c. | | Sheet of 20, 10 each #3566b, 3567b + 20 labels, litho. | 35.00 | |
| 3568 | A840 | 2nd Large multi | 2.10 | 1.60 |
| 3569 | A840 | 1st Large multi | 2.60 | 2.00 |
| 3570 | A839 | £1.05 multi | 3.00 | 2.10 |
| a. | | Litho., die cut perf. 14½x15 syncopated + label (3573b) | 4.75 | 4.75 |
| 3571 | A839 | £1.33 multi | 3.75 | 2.90 |
| a. | | Litho., die cut perf. 14½x15 syncopated + label (3573b) | 6.00 | 6.00 |
| 3572 | A839 | £1.52 multi | 4.25 | 3.25 |
| a. | | Litho., die cut perf. 14½x15 syncopated + label (3573b) | 6.75 | 6.75 |
| 3573 | A839 | £2.25 multi | 6.25 | 4.75 |
| a. | | Litho., die cut perf. 14½x15 syncopated + label (3573b) | 10.00 | 10.00 |
| b. | | Sheet of 20, #3570a, 3571a, 3572a, 3573a, 8 each #3566b, 3567b + 20 labels | 55.00 | |
| | | Nos. 3566-3573 (8) | 25.30 | 19.55 |

On day of issue, Nos. 3565a and 3566 each sold for 55p; Nos. 3565b and 3567, for 64p; Nos. 3565c and 3568, for 76p; and Nos. 3565d and 3569, for 95p. No. 3567c sold for £12.40 and labels could not be personalized. No. 3573b sold for £16.21 and labels could not be personalized.

Ancient Britain — A841

Designs: No. 3574, Battersea shield, London, 350-50 B.C. No. 3575, Skara Brae village, Orkney Islands, 3100-2500 B.C. No. 3576, Star Carr headdress, Yorkshire, 9000 B.C. No. 3577, Maiden Castle hill fort, Dorset, 400 B.C. No. 3578, Avebury stone circles, Wiltshire, 2500 B.C. No. 3579, Drumbest horns, County Antrim, 800 B.C. No. 3580, Grime's Graves flint mines, Norfolk, 2500 B.C. No. 3581, Mantell yr Wydddrug Mold cape, Flintshire, 1900-1600 B.C.

**2017, Jan. 17    Litho.    Perf. 14¼**

| 3574 | A841 | 1st multi | 1.75 | 1.35 |
|---|---|---|---|---|
| 3575 | A841 | 1st multi | 1.75 | 1.35 |
| a. | | Horiz. pair, #3574-3575 | 3.50 | 2.75 |
| 3576 | A841 | £1.05 multi | 3.00 | 2.25 |
| 3577 | A841 | £1.05 multi | 3.00 | 2.25 |
| a. | | Horiz. pair, #3576-3577 | 6.00 | 4.50 |
| 3578 | A841 | £1.33 multi | 3.75 | 2.90 |
| 3579 | A841 | £1.33 multi | 3.75 | 2.90 |
| a. | | Horiz. pair, #3578-3579 | 7.50 | 6.00 |
| 3580 | A841 | £1.52 multi | 4.25 | 3.25 |
| 3581 | A841 | £1.52 multi | 4.25 | 3.25 |
| a. | | Horiz. pair, #3580-3581 | 8.50 | 6.50 |
| | | Nos. 3574-3581 (8) | 25.50 | 19.50 |

On day of issue, Nos. 3574-3575 each sold for 64p.

Windsor Castle A842

St. George's Chapel, Windsor Castle A843

Designs: No. 3582, Long Walk. No. 3583, Round Tower. No. 3584, Norman Gate.

No. 3585, St. George's Hall. No. 3586, Queen's Ballroom. No. 3587, Waterloo Chamber.

No. 3588: a, Sir Reginald Bray roof boss. b, Fan-vaulted roof. c, Garter banners. d, St. George's Cross roof boss.

No. 3589, Like #3588a. No. 3590, Like #3588b.

| 2017, Feb. 15 | | Litho. | Perf. 14¾ | |
|---|---|---|---|---|
| 3582 | A842 | 1st multi | 1.60 | 1.20 |
| 3583 | A842 | 1st multi | 1.60 | 1.20 |
| 3584 | A842 | 1st multi | 1.60 | 1.20 |
| a. | | Horiz. strip of 3, #3582-3584 | 4.80 | 3.60 |
| 3585 | A842 | £1.52 multi | 3.75 | 2.75 |
| a. | | Booklet pane of 2, #3582, 3585 (BK215) | 5.75 | — |
| 3586 | A842 | £1.52 multi | 3.75 | 2.75 |
| 3587 | A842 | £1.52 multi | 3.75 | 2.75 |
| a. | | Horiz. strip of 3, #3585-3587 | 11.50 | 8.25 |
| b. | | Booklet pane of 4, #3583-3584, 3586-3587 (BK215) | 11.50 | — |
| | | Nos. 3582-3587 (6) | 16.05 | 11.85 |

**Miniature Sheet**
**Perf. 14¼**

| 3588 | A843 | Sheet of 4 | 9.75 | 9.75 |
|---|---|---|---|---|
| a.-b. | | 1st Either single | 1.60 | 1.20 |
| c.-d. | | £1.33 Either single | 3.25 | 2.50 |
| e. | | Booklet pane of 4, #3588a-3588d (BK215) | 10.50 | — |

**Booklet Stamps**
**Self-Adhesive**
**Photo.**
**Die Cut Perf. 14¼**

| 3589 | A843 | 1st multi | 4.00 | 1.50 |
|---|---|---|---|---|
| 3590 | A843 | 1st multi | 4.00 | 1.50 |
| a. | | Booklet pane of 6, #3589-3590, 4 #M426 | 10.00 | |

Europa (No. 3584). On day of issue, Nos. 3582-3584, 3588a-3588b, 3589-3590 each sold for 64p. Complete booklet sold for £14.58.

David Bowie (1947-2016), Rock Musician — A844

Hunky Dory, by Bowie, 1971 — A845

Aladdin Sane, by Bowie, 1973 — A846

"Heroes," by Bowie, 1977 — A847

Let's Dance, by Bowie, 1983 — A848

Earthling, by Bowie, 1997 — A849

Blackstar, by Bowie, 2016 — A850

No. 3591: a, Ziggy Stardust tour, 1973. b, Serious Moonlight tour, 1983. c, Stage tour, 1978. d, A Reality tour, 2004.

| 2017, Mar. 14 | | Litho. | Perf. 14½ | |
|---|---|---|---|---|
| 3591 | A844 | Sheet of 4 | 11.00 | 8.25 |
| a.-b. | | 1st Either single | 1.60 | 1.20 |
| c.-d. | | £1.52 Either single | 3.75 | 2.75 |

**Perf. 14½ Syncopated**

| 3591E | | Sheet of 6 | 97.50 | — |
|---|---|---|---|---|
| f. | | A845 1st multi | 9.00 | 8.75 |
| g. | | A846 1st multi | 9.00 | 8.75 |
| h. | | A847 1st multi | 9.00 | 8.75 |
| i. | | A848 £1.52 multi | 20.00 | 20.00 |
| j. | | A849 £1.52 multi | 20.00 | 20.00 |
| k. | | A850 £1.52 multi | 20.00 | 20.00 |

No. 3591E sold for £12.95. The franking value of Nos. 3591Ef-3591Eh was 64p. Sheets containing five examples of Nos. 3591Ef-3591Eh each sold for £7.50.

**Photo.**
**Self-Adhesive**
**Die Cut Perf. 14¾ Syncopated**

| 3592 | A845 | 1st multi | 1.60 | 1.20 |
|---|---|---|---|---|
| 3593 | A846 | 1st multi | 1.60 | 1.20 |
| 3594 | A847 | 1st multi | 1.60 | 1.20 |
| a. | | Booklet pane of 6, #3593-3594, 4 #MH426 | 10.00 | |
| 3595 | A848 | £1.52 multi | 3.75 | 2.75 |
| 3596 | A849 | £1.52 multi | 3.75 | 2.75 |
| 3597 | A850 | £1.52 multi | 3.75 | 2.75 |
| | | Nos. 3592-3597 (6) | 16.05 | 11.85 |

On day of issue, Nos. 3591a-3591b, 3592-3594 each sold for 64p.

Famous Race Horses — A851

Designs: No. 3598, Frankel. No. 3599, Red Rum. No. 3600, Shergar. No. 3601, Kauto Star. No. 3602, Desert Orchid. No. 3603, Brigadier Gerard. No. 3604, Arkle. No. 3605, Estimate.

| 2017, Apr. 6 | | Litho. | Perf. 14¼ | |
|---|---|---|---|---|
| 3598 | A851 | 1st multi | 1.75 | 1.30 |
| 3599 | A851 | 1st multi | 1.75 | 1.30 |
| 3600 | A851 | £1.17 multi | 3.00 | 2.25 |
| 3601 | A851 | £1.17 multi | 3.00 | 2.25 |
| 3602 | A851 | £1.40 multi | 3.75 | 2.75 |
| 3603 | A851 | £1.40 multi | 3.75 | 2.75 |
| 3604 | A851 | £1.57 multi | 4.25 | 3.25 |
| 3605 | A851 | £1.57 multi | 4.25 | 3.25 |
| | | Nos. 3598-3605 (8) | 25.50 | 19.10 |

On day of issue, Nos. 3598-3599 each sold for 65p.

Songbirds — A852

Designs: No. 3606, Great tit. No. 3607, Wren. No. 3608, Willow warbler. No. 3609, Goldcrest. No. 3610, Skylark. No. 3611, Blackcap. No. 3612, Song thrush. No. 3613, Nightingale. No. 3614, Cuckoo. No. 3615, Yellowhammer.

| 2017, May 4 | | Litho. | Perf. 14½ | |
|---|---|---|---|---|
| 3606 | A852 | 1st multi | 1.75 | 1.30 |
| 3607 | A852 | 1st multi | 1.75 | 1.30 |
| 3608 | A852 | 1st multi | 1.75 | 1.30 |
| 3609 | A852 | 1st multi | 1.75 | 1.30 |
| 3610 | A852 | 1st multi | 1.75 | 1.30 |
| a. | | Horiz. strip of 5, #3606-3610 | 8.75 | 6.50 |
| 3611 | A852 | 1st multi | 1.75 | 1.30 |
| 3612 | A852 | 1st multi | 1.75 | 1.30 |
| 3613 | A852 | 1st multi | 1.75 | 1.30 |
| 3614 | A852 | 1st multi | 1.75 | 1.30 |
| 3615 | A852 | 1st multi | 1.75 | 1.30 |
| a. | | Horiz. strip of 5, #3611-3615 | 8.75 | 6.50 |
| | | Nos. 3606-3615 (10) | 17.50 | 13.00 |

On day of issue, Nos. 3606-3615 each sold for 65p.

Mills — A853

Designs: No. 3616, Nutley Windmill, East Sussex. No. 3617, New Abbey Corn Mill, Dumfries and Galloway. No. 3618, Ballycopeland Windmill, County Down. No. 3619, Cheddleton Flint Mill, Staffordshire. No. 3620, Woodchurch Windmill, Kent. No. 3621, Felin Cochwillan Mill, Gwynedd.

**Perf. 14½x14¼**

| 2017, June 20 | | Litho. | | |
|---|---|---|---|---|
| 3616 | A853 | 1st multi | 1.75 | 1.30 |
| 3617 | A853 | 1st multi | 1.75 | 1.30 |
| a. | | Vert. pair, #3616-3617 | 3.50 | 2.60 |
| 3618 | A853 | £1.40 multi | 3.75 | 2.75 |
| 3619 | A853 | £1.40 multi | 3.75 | 2.75 |
| a. | | Vert. pair, #3618-3619 | 7.50 | 5.50 |
| 3620 | A853 | £1.57 multi | 4.25 | 3.25 |
| 3621 | A853 | £1.57 multi | 4.25 | 3.25 |
| a. | | Vert. pair, #3620-3621 | 8.50 | 6.50 |
| | | Nos. 3616-3621 (6) | 19.50 | 14.60 |

On day of issue, Nos. 3616-3617 each sold for 65p.

Contemporary Architecture — A854

Designs: No. 3622, London Aquatics Center. No. 3623, Library of Birmingham. No. 3624, SEC Armadillo, Glasgow. No. 3625, Scottish Parliament, Edinburgh. No. 3626, Giant's Causeway Visitor Center, Northern Ireland. No. 3627, National Assembly for Wales, Cardiff. No. 3628, Eden Project, St. Austell. No. 3629, Everyman Theater, Liverpool. No. 3630, IWM (Imperial War Museum) North, Manchester. No. 3631, Switch House, Tate Modern Art Gallery, London.

| 2017, July 13 | | Litho. | Perf. 14½ | |
|---|---|---|---|---|
| 3622 | A854 | 1st multi | 1.75 | 1.30 |
| 3623 | A854 | 1st multi | 1.75 | 1.30 |
| 3624 | A854 | 1st multi | 1.75 | 1.30 |
| 3625 | A854 | 1st multi | 1.75 | 1.30 |
| 3626 | A854 | 1st multi | 1.75 | 1.30 |
| a. | | Horiz. strip of 5, #3622-3626 | 8.75 | 6.50 |
| 3627 | A854 | 1st multi | 1.75 | 1.30 |
| 3628 | A854 | 1st multi | 1.75 | 1.30 |
| 3629 | A854 | 1st multi | 1.75 | 1.30 |
| 3630 | A854 | 1st multi | 1.75 | 1.30 |
| 3631 | A854 | 1st multi | 1.75 | 1.30 |
| a. | | Horiz. strip of 5, #3627-3631 | 8.75 | 6.50 |
| | | Nos. 3622-3631 (10) | 17.50 | 13.00 |

On day of issue, Nos. 3622-3631 each sold for 65p.

World War I, Cent. — A855

Designs: No. 3632, Shattered Poppy, by J. Ross. No. 3633, Dead Man's Dump, by I. Rosenberg. No. 3634, Nurses Elsie Knocker and Mairi Chisholm. No. 3635, Dry Docked for Scaling and Painting, by E. Wadsworth. No. 3636, Tyne Cot Cemetery, Belgium. No. 3637, Private Lemuel Thomas Rees's life-saving Bible.

| 2017, July 31 | | Litho. | Perf. 14½ | |
|---|---|---|---|---|
| 3632 | A855 | 1st multi | 1.75 | 1.30 |
| 3633 | A855 | 1st multi | 1.75 | 1.30 |
| a. | | Booklet pane of 4, #3313, 3398, 3508, 3633 (BK221) | 7.50 | — |
| 3634 | A855 | 1st multi | 1.75 | 1.30 |
| a. | | Booklet pane of 3, #3632-3634 (BK217) | 5.50 | — |
| 3635 | A855 | £1.57 multi | 4.25 | 3.25 |
| 3636 | A855 | £1.57 multi | 4.25 | 3.25 |
| 3637 | A855 | £1.57 multi | 4.25 | 3.25 |
| a. | | Booklet pane of 3, #3635-3637 (BK217) | 13.50 | — |
| | | Nos. 3632-3637 (6) | 18.00 | 13.65 |

Issued: No. 3633a, 9/13/18. On day of issue, Nos. 3632-3634 each sold for 65p.

Toys — A856

Designs: No. 3638, Merrythought teddy bear. No. 3639, Sindy Weekender doll. No. 3640, Spirograph. No. 3641, Stickle Bricks. No. 3642, Herald Trojan warriors. No. 3643, Spacehopper. No. 3644, Fuzzy-Felt farm set. No. 3645, Meccano Ferris wheel. No. 3646, Action Man Red Devil parachutist. No. 3647, Hornby Dublo electric trains.

| 2017, Aug. 22 | | Litho. | Perf. 14½ | |
|---|---|---|---|---|
| 3638 | A856 | 1st multi | 1.75 | 1.30 |
| 3639 | A856 | 1st multi | 1.75 | 1.30 |
| 3640 | A856 | 1st multi | 1.75 | 1.30 |
| 3641 | A856 | 1st multi | 1.75 | 1.30 |
| 3642 | A856 | 1st multi | 1.75 | 1.30 |
| a. | | Horiz. strip of 5, #3638-3642 | 8.75 | 6.50 |
| 3643 | A856 | 1st multi | 1.75 | 1.30 |
| 3644 | A856 | 1st multi | 1.75 | 1.30 |
| 3645 | A856 | 1st multi | 1.75 | 1.30 |
| 3646 | A856 | 1st multi | 1.75 | 1.30 |
| 3647 | A856 | 1st multi | 1.75 | 1.30 |
| a. | | Horiz. strip of 5, #3643-3647 | 8.75 | 6.50 |
| | | Nos. 3638-3647 (10) | 17.50 | 13.00 |

On day of issue, Nos. 3638-3647 each sold for 65p.

Ladybird Books — A857

Various children's books, with book series inscription at lower left of: No. 3648, Adventures from History. No. 3649, Well-loved Tales. No. 3650, Key Words Reading Scheme. No. 3651, Early Tales and Rhymes. No. 3652, Hobbies and How It Works. No. 3653, People at Work. No. 3654, Nature and Conservation. No. 3655, Achievements.

| 2017, Sept. 14 | | Litho. | Perf. 14¼ | |
|---|---|---|---|---|
| 3648 | A857 | 2nd multi | 1.50 | 1.15 |
| 3649 | A857 | 2nd multi | 1.50 | 1.15 |
| a. | | Horiz. pair, #3648-3649 | 3.00 | 2.30 |
| 3650 | A857 | 1st multi | 1.75 | 1.30 |
| 3651 | A857 | 1st multi | 1.75 | 1.30 |
| a. | | Horiz. pair, #3650-3651 | 3.50 | 2.60 |
| 3652 | A857 | £1.40 multi | 3.75 | 2.75 |
| 3653 | A857 | £1.40 multi | 3.75 | 2.75 |
| a. | | Horiz. pair, #3652-3653 | 7.50 | 5.50 |
| 3654 | A857 | £1.57 multi | 4.25 | 3.25 |
| 3655 | A857 | £1.57 multi | 4.25 | 3.25 |
| a. | | Horiz. pair, #3654-3655 | 8.50 | 6.50 |
| | | Nos. 3648-3655 (8) | 22.50 | 16.90 |

On day of issue, Nos. 3648-3649 each sold for 56p; Nos. 3650-3651, for 65p.

Droids and Aliens From *Star Wars* Movies — A858

Designs: Nos. 3656, 3664a, BB-8. Nos. 3657, 3664g, R2-D2. Nos. 3658, 3664h, C-3PO. Nos. 3659, 3664b, K-2S0. Nos. 3660, 3664c, Maz Kanata. Nos. 3661, 3664d, Chewbacca. Nos. 3662, 3664e, Supreme Leader Snoke. Nos. 3663, 3664f, Porg.

| 2017, Oct. 12 | | Litho. | Perf. 14½ | |
|---|---|---|---|---|
| 3656 | A858 | 1st multi | 1.75 | 1.30 |
| 3657 | A858 | 1st multi | 1.75 | 1.30 |
| 3658 | A858 | 1st multi | 1.75 | 1.30 |
| a. | | Booklet pane of 4, #3439, 3441, 3657, 3658 (BK218) | 7.75 | — |
| 3659 | A858 | 1st multi | 1.75 | 1.30 |
| a. | | Horiz. strip of 4, #3656-3659 | 7.00 | 5.25 |
| 3660 | A858 | 1st multi | 1.75 | 1.30 |
| 3661 | A858 | 1st multi | 1.75 | 1.30 |
| 3662 | A858 | 1st multi | 1.75 | 1.30 |
| a. | | Booklet pane of 4, #3436, 3440, 3660, 3662 (BK218) | 7.75 | — |
| 3663 | A858 | 1st multi | 1.75 | 1.30 |
| a. | | Horiz. strip of 4, #3660-3663 | 7.00 | 5.25 |
| b. | | Sheet of 20, #3435-3448, 3656-3663 | 35.00 | 35.00 |
| c. | | Booklet pane of 4, #3656, 3659, 3661, 3663 (BK218) | 7.75 | — |
| | | Nos. 3656-3663 (8) | 14.00 | 10.40 |

**Self-Adhesive**
**Litho.**
**Die Cut Perf. 14½**

| 3664 | | Sheet of 10, #3664c-3664h, 2 each #3664a-3664b, + 10 labels | 19.00 | |
|---|---|---|---|---|
| a.-h. | | A858 1st Any single | 1.90 | 1.90 |
| i. | | Like #3664a, photo. (3664k) | 3.00 | 2.25 |
| j. | | Like #3664g, photo. (3664n) | 3.00 | 2.25 |
| k. | | Booklet pane of 6, #3664i, 3664j, 4 #MH426 | 10.00 | |
| l. | | Like #3664c, photo. (3664m) | 3.00 | 2.25 |
| m. | | Like #3664d, photo. (3664n) | 3.00 | 2.25 |
| n. | | Booklet pane of 6, #3664l, 3664m, 4 #MH426 | 10.00 | |

On day of issue, Nos. 3646-3663, 3664a-3664j, 3664m-3664n had a franking value of 65p. No. 3664 has 10 labels that could not be personalized, and sold for £7. The lithogrpahed stamps, Nos. 3664a-3664h, have a smaller dot size than photogravure stamps, 3664i-3664j, 3664l-3664m.

Virgin and Child, Attributed to Gerard David A859

Madonna and Child, by William Dyce A860

Family of Snowmen, by Arwen Wilson A867

Santa Claus, by Ted Lewis-Clark A868

Virgin and Child, Attributed to Gerard David — A861

Madonna and Child, by William Dyce — A862

Family of Snowmen, by Arwen Wilson A869

Santa Claus, by Ted Lewis-Clark A870

Virgin Mary and Child, Attributed to Quentin Massys A863

Small Cowper Madonna, by Raphael A864

Madonna and Child, by Il Sassoferrato A865

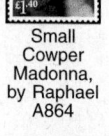
Virgin and Child, by Jakob von Steinle A866

**2017, Nov. 7   Photo.   Perf. 14½x15**

| | | | |
|---|---|---|---|
| 3665 | | Sheet of 8 | 26.00 26.00 |
| a. | A859 | 2nd multi | 1.50 1.15 |
| b. | A860 | 1st multi | 1.75 1.30 |
| c. | A861 | 2nd Large multi | 2.10 1.60 |
| d. | A862 | 1st Large multi | 2.75 2.10 |
| e. | A863 | £1.17 multi | 3.25 2.75 |
| f. | A864 | £1.40 multi | 3.75 2.75 |
| g. | A865 | £1.57 multi | 4.25 3.25 |
| h. | A866 | £2.27 multi | 6.25 4.75 |

**Self-Adhesive**
**Die Cut Perf. 14½x15**

| | | | |
|---|---|---|---|
| 3666 | A859 | 2nd multi | 1.50 1.10 |
| a. | | Booklet pane of 12 | 16.00 |
| b. | | Litho. die cut perf. 14½x15 syncopated + label (3673b) | 1.60 1.60 |
| 3667 | A860 | 1st multi | 1.75 1.30 |
| a. | | Booklet pane of 12 | 19.00 |
| b. | | Litho. die cut perf. 14½x15 syncopated + label (3673b) | 1.75 1.75 |
| 3668 | A861 | 2nd Large multi | 2.10 1.60 |
| 3669 | A862 | 1st Large multi | 2.75 2.10 |
| 3670 | A863 | £1.17 multi | 3.25 2.50 |
| a. | | Litho. die cut perf. 14½x15 syncopated + label (3673b) | 5.25 5.25 |
| 3671 | A864 | £1.40 multi | 3.75 2.75 |
| a. | | Litho. die cut perf. 14½x15 syncopated + label (3673b) | 6.25 6.25 |
| 3672 | A865 | £1.57 multi | 4.25 3.25 |
| a. | | Litho. die cut perf. 14½x15 syncopated + label (3673b) | 7.00 7.00 |
| 3673 | A866 | £2.27 multi | 6.25 4.75 |
| a. | | Litho. die cut perf. 14½x15 syncopated + label (3673b) | 10.50 10.50 |
| b. | | Sheet of 20, #3670a, 3671a, 3672a, 3673a, 8 each #3666b, 3667b, + 20 labels | 57.50 |
| | | Nos. 3666-3673 (8) | 25.60 19.35 |

Christmas. On day of issue, Nos. 3665a and 3666 each sold for 56p; Nos. 3665b and 3667, for 65p; Nos. 3665c and 3668, for 76p; Nos. 3665d and 3669, for 98p.

No. 3673b sold for £16.40 and labels could not be personalized.

**Die Cut Perf. 14½x15**

**2017, Nov. 7** Photo.

**Self-Adhesive**

| | | | |
|---|---|---|---|
| 3674 | A867 | 2nd multi | 1.50 1.10 |
| a. | | Booklet pane of 12, 6 each #3666, 3674 | 16.00 |
| b. | | Litho. die cut perf. 14½x15 syncopated + label (3675c) | 1.60 1.60 |
| 3675 | A868 | 1st multi | 1.75 1.30 |
| a. | | Booklet pane of 12, 6 each #3667, 3675 | 19.00 |
| b. | | Litho. die cut perf. 14½x15 syncopated + label (3675c) | 1.75 1.75 |
| c. | | Sheet of 20, 10 each #3674b, 3675b, + 20 labels | 33.50 |
| 3676 | A869 | 2nd Large multi | 2.10 1.60 |
| 3677 | A870 | 1st Large multi | 2.75 2.10 |
| | | Nos. 3674-3677 (4) | 8.10 6.10 |

Christmas. On day of issue, No. 3674 sold for 56p; No. 3675, for 65p; No. 3676, for 76p; No. 3677, for 98p.

No. 3675c sold for £12.60 and labels could not be personalized.

**Miniature Sheet**

70th Wedding Anniversary of Queen Elizabeth II and Prince Philip — A871

No. 3678: a, Princess Elizabeth and Duke of Edinburgh walking. b, Wedding procession. c, Princess Elizabeth and Duke of Edinburgh on bench on honeymoon. d, Engagement of Princess Elizabeth and Duke of Edinburgh seated, diff. e, Princess Elizabeth in wedding dress with Duke of Ediburgh. f, Princess Elizabeth holding arm of Duke of Edinbugh on honeymoon.

**2017, Nov. 20   Litho.   Perf. 14¼**

| | | | |
|---|---|---|---|
| 3678 | A871 | Sheet of 6 | 18.00 18.00 |
| a.-c. | | 1st Any single | 1.75 1.30 |
| d.-f. | | £1.57 Any single | 4.25 3.25 |

On day of issue, Nos. 3678a-3678c each sold for 65p.

Characters From *Game of Thrones* Television Series A872

Iron Throne A873

Characters From *Game of Thrones* Television Series — A874

Designs: No. 3679, Sansa Stark. No. 3680, Jon Snow. No. 3681, Eddard Stark. No. 3682, Olenna Tyrell. No. 3683, Tywin Lannister. No. 3684, Tyrion Lannister. No. 3685, Cersei Lannister. No. 3686, Arya Stark. No. 3687, Jaime Lannister. No. 3688, Daenerys Targaryen.

Nos. 3690, 3695a, Night King and White Walkers. Nos. 3691, 3695b, Giants. Nos. 3692, 3695c, Direwolves. Nos. 3693, 3695d, Dragons.

No. 3694: a, Sansa Stark. b, Jon Snow. c, Eddard Stark. d, Olenna Tyrell. e, Tywin Lannister. f, Tyrion Lannister. g, Cersei Lannister. h, Arya Stark. i, Jaime Lannister. j, Daenerys Targaryen.

**2018, Jan. 23   Litho.   Perf. 14¼x14**

| | | | |
|---|---|---|---|
| 3679 | A872 | 1st multi | 1.90 1.40 |
| 3680 | A872 | 1st multi | 1.90 1.40 |
| 3681 | A872 | 1st multi | 1.90 1.40 |
| 3682 | A872 | 1st multi | 1.90 1.40 |
| 3683 | A872 | 1st multi | 1.90 1.40 |
| a. | | Horiz. strip of 5, #3679-3683 | 9.50 7.00 |
| 3684 | A872 | 1st multi | 1.90 1.40 |
| 3685 | A872 | 1st multi | 1.90 1.40 |
| 3686 | A872 | 1st multi | 1.90 1.40 |
| a. | | Booklet pane of 6, #3679-3681, 3684-3686 (BK219) | 12.00 |
| 3687 | A872 | 1st multi | 1.90 1.40 |
| 3688 | A872 | 1st multi | 1.90 1.40 |
| a. | | Horiz. strip of 5, #3684-3688 | 9.50 7.00 |
| b. | | Booklet pane of 4, #3682-3683, 3687-3688 (BK219) | 8.00 |
| | | Nos. 3679-3688 (10) | 19.00 14.00 |

**Booklet Stamps**
**Perf. 14¾x14 Syncopated**

| | | | |
|---|---|---|---|
| 3689 | A873 | 1st multi | 2.80 1.50 |
| a. | | Booklet pane of 8, #MH255a, MH471, 2 each #3689, MH429, Northern Ireland 17, + central label (BK219) | 13.00 — |

**Perf. 14¾**

| | | | |
|---|---|---|---|
| 3690 | A874 | 1st multi | 2.75 1.40 |
| 3691 | A874 | 1st multi | 2.75 1.40 |
| 3692 | A874 | 1st multi | 2.75 1.40 |
| 3693 | A874 | 1st multi | 2.75 1.40 |
| a. | | Booklet pane of 4, #3690-3693 (BK219) | 8.00 — |
| | | Nos. 3689-3693 (5) | 13.80 7.10 |

**Die Cut Perf. 14¼x14½**

| | | | |
|---|---|---|---|
| 3694 | | Sheet of 10 + 10 labels | 21.00 |
| a.-j. | A872 | 1st Any single + label | 2.10 2.10 |

**Self-Adhesive**
**Die Cut Perf. 14¾, Die Cut Perf. 14¾x14 Syncopated (#3695e)**

| | | | |
|---|---|---|---|
| 3695 | | Sheet of 5 | 9.50 |
| a.-d. | A874 | 1st Any single | 1.90 1.40 |
| e. | A873 | 1st multi | 1.90 1.40 |
| f. | | As "e," photo. | 1.90 1.40 |
| g. | | Booklet pane of 6 #3695f | 11.50 |

On day of issue, Nos. 3679-3688, 3695a-3695f each sold for 65p, and Nos. 3689-3693 each had a franking value of 65p.

No. 3694 sold for £7.50. Nos. 3694a-3694j each had a franking value of 65p on day of issue.

No. 3695f has larger dots than No. 3695e.

Woman Suffrage, Cent. — A875

Designs: No. 3696, Lone suffragette in Whitehall, c. 1908. No. 3697, The Great Pilgrimage of Suffragists, 1913. No. 3698, Suffragette leaders at Earl's Court, 1908. No. 3699, Women's Freedom League Poster Parade, 1907. No. 3700, Welsh suffragettes in Coronation procession, 1911. No. 3701, Mary Leigh (1885-1978) and Edith New (1877-1951) released from prison, 1908. No. 3702, Sophia Duleep Singh (1876-1948) sells *The Suffragette,* 1913. No. 3703, Suffragette Prisoners' Pageant, 1911.

**2018, Feb. 15   Litho.   Perf. 14¼x14**

| | | | |
|---|---|---|---|
| 3696 | A875 | 2nd multi | 1.60 1.20 |
| 3697 | A875 | 2nd multi | 1.60 1.20 |
| a. | | Horiz. pair, #3696-3697 | 3.20 2.40 |
| 3698 | A875 | 1st multi | 1.75 1.30 |
| 3699 | A875 | 1st multi | 1.75 1.30 |
| a. | | Horiz. pair, #3698-3699 | 3.50 2.60 |
| 3700 | A875 | £1.40 multi | 4.00 3.00 |
| 3701 | A875 | £1.40 multi | 4.00 3.00 |
| a. | | Horiz. pair, #3700-3701 | 8.00 6.00 |
| 3702 | A875 | £1.57 multi | 4.50 3.50 |
| 3703 | A875 | £1.57 multi | 4.50 3.50 |
| a. | | Horiz. pair, #3702-3703 | 9.00 7.00 |
| | | Nos. 3696-3703 (8) | 23.70 18.00 |

On day of issue Nos. 3696-3697 each sold for 56p; Nos. 3698-3699, for 65p.

Royal Air Force, Cent. — A876

Royal Air Force Red Arrows Aerobatic Team — A877

Designs: Nos. 3704, 3712, Lightning F6. Nos. 3705, 3711, Hurricane MK I. No. 3706, Vulcan B2. No. 3707, Typhoon FGR4. No. 3708, Sopwith Camel F1. No. 3709, Nimrod MR2.

Nos. 3710a, 3713, Flypast. Nos. 3710b, 3714, Swan. No. 3710c, Synchro. No. 3710d, Python.

**2018   Litho.   Perf. 14¼x14**

| | | | |
|---|---|---|---|
| 3704 | A876 | 1st multi | 1.90 1.40 |
| 3705 | A876 | 1st multi | 1.90 1.40 |
| a. | | Horiz. pair, #3704-3705 | 3.80 2.80 |
| 3706 | A876 | £1.40 multi | 4.00 3.00 |
| 3707 | A876 | £1.40 multi | 4.00 3.00 |
| b. | | Horiz. pair, #3706-3707 | 8.00 6.00 |
| a. | | Booklet pane of 4, 2 each #3704, 3707 (BK220) | 11.50 — |
| 3708 | A876 | £1.57 multi | 4.50 3.50 |
| 3709 | A876 | £1.57 multi | 4.50 3.50 |
| a. | | Horiz. pair, #3708-3709 | 9.00 7.00 |
| b. | | Booklet pane of 4, #3705, 3706, 3708, 3709 (BK220) | 15.00 — |
| | | Nos. 3704-3709 (6) | 20.80 15.80 |

**Miniature Sheet**

| | | | |
|---|---|---|---|
| 3710 | A877 | Sheet of 4 | 12.00 12.00 |
| a.-b. | | 1st Either single | 1.90 1.40 |
| c.-d. | | £1.40 Either single | 4.00 3.00 |
| e. | | Booklet pane of 4, #3710a-3710d (BK220) | 11.50 |

**Booklet Stamps**
**Self-Adhesive**
**Die Cut Perf. 14¼x14**

| | | | |
|---|---|---|---|
| 3711 | A876 | 1st multi | 4.00 2.25 |
| 3712 | A876 | 1st multi | 4.00 2.25 |
| a. | | Booklet pane of 6, #3711, 3712, 4 #MH426 | 10.00 |
| 3713 | A877 | 1st multi | 4.00 2.25 |
| 3714 | A877 | 1st multi | 4.00 2.25 |
| a. | | Booklet pane of 6, #3713, 3714, 4 #MH426 | 15.00 |
| | | Nos. 3711-3714 (4) | 16.00 9.00 |

Issued: Nos. 3704-3712, 3/20; Nos. 3713-3714, 5/11. Nos. 3704, 3705, 3710a, 3710b, 3711, 3712 each sold for 65p on day of issue. Nos. 3713, 3714 each sold for 67p on day of issue.

Reintroduced Species — A878

Designs: No. 3715, Osprey. No. 3716, Large blue butterfly. No. 3717, Eurasian beaver. No. 3718, Pool frog. No. 3719, Stinking hawk's beard. No. 3720, Sand lizard.

**2018, Apr. 17   Litho.   Perf. 14¼**

| | | | |
|---|---|---|---|
| 3715 | A878 | 1st multi | 1.90 1.40 |
| 3716 | A878 | 1st multi | 1.90 1.40 |
| a. | | Horiz. pair, #3715-3716 | 3.80 2.80 |
| 3717 | A878 | £1.45 multi | 4.00 3.00 |
| 3718 | A878 | £1.45 multi | 4.00 3.00 |
| a. | | Horiz. pair, #3717-3718 | 8.00 6.00 |
| 3719 | A878 | £1.55 multi | 4.25 3.25 |
| 3720 | A878 | £1.55 multi | 4.25 3.25 |
| a. | | Horiz. pair, #3719-3720 | 8.50 6.50 |
| | | Nos. 3715-3720 (6) | 20.30 15.30 |

On day of issue, Nos. 3715-3716 each sold for 67p.

Adult Barn Owl — A879

Adult Little Owl — A880

Adult Tawny Owl — A881

Adult Short-eared Owl — A882

Adult Long-eared Owl — A883

Juvenile Barn Owls — A884

Juvenile Little Owls — A885

Juvenile Tawny Owl — A886

Juvenile Short-eared Owl — A887

Juvenile Long-eared Owl — A888

**2018, May 11        Litho.        Perf. 14¼**

| | | | | |
|---|---|---|---|---|
| 3721 | A879 | 1st multi | 1.90 | 1.40 |
| 3722 | A880 | 1st multi | 1.90 | 1.40 |
| 3723 | A881 | 1st multi | 1.90 | 1.40 |
| 3724 | A882 | 1st multi | 1.90 | 1.40 |
| 3725 | A883 | 1st multi | 1.90 | 1.40 |
| *a.* | | Horiz. strip of 5, #3721-3725 | 9.50 | 7.00 |
| 3726 | A884 | 1st multi | 1.90 | 1.40 |
| 3727 | A885 | 1st multi | 1.90 | 1.40 |
| 3728 | A886 | 1st multi | 1.90 | 1.40 |
| 3729 | A887 | 1st multi | 1.90 | 1.40 |
| 3730 | A888 | 1st multi | 1.90 | 1.40 |
| *a.* | | Horiz. strip of 5, #3726-3730 | 9.50 | 7.00 |
| | | *Nos. 3721-3730 (10)* | 19.00 | 14.00 |

On day of issue, Nos. 3721-3730 each sold for 67p.

**Miniature Sheet**

Wedding of Prince Harry and Meghan Markle A889

No. 3731 — Photograph of couple in: a, Color. b, Black-and-white.

**2018, May 19        Litho.        Perf. 14¼**

| | | | | |
|---|---|---|---|---|
| 3731 | A889 | Sheet of 4, 2 each #a-b | 12.50 | 12.50 |
| *a.* | | 1st multi | 1.90 | 1.40 |
| *b.* | | £1.55 multi | 4.25 | 3.25 |

On day of issue, No. 3731a sold for 67p.

Royal Academy of Arts, 250th Anniv. — A890

Designs: No. 3732, Summer Exhibition, by Grayson Perry. No. 3733, Queen of the Sky, by Fiona Rae. No. 3734, St. Kilda: The Great Sea Stacs, by Norman Ackroyd. No. 3735, Inverleith Allotments and Edinburgh Castle, by Barbara Rae. No. 3736, Queuing at the RA, by Yinka Shonibare. No. 3737, Saying Goodbye, by Tracey Emin.

**2018, June 5        Litho.        Perf. 14¼**

| | | | | |
|---|---|---|---|---|
| 3732 | A890 | 1st multi | 1.75 | 1.40 |
| 3733 | A890 | 1st multi | 1.75 | 1.40 |
| *a.* | | Vert. pair, #3732-3733 | 3.50 | 2.80 |
| 3734 | A890 | £1.25 multi | 3.25 | 2.50 |
| 3735 | A890 | £1.25 multi | 3.25 | 2.50 |
| *a.* | | Vert. pair, #3734-3735 | 6.50 | 5.00 |
| 3736 | A890 | £1.55 multi | 4.25 | 3.25 |
| 3737 | A890 | £1.55 multi | 4.25 | 3.25 |
| *a.* | | Vert. pair, #3736-3737 | 8.50 | 6.50 |
| | | *Nos. 3732-3737 (6)* | 18.50 | 14.30 |

On day of issue, Nos. 3732-3733 each sold for 67p.

*Dad's Army* Television Series, 50th Anniv. — A891

Characters: No. 3738, Sergeant Wilson. No. 3739, Private Pike. Nos. 3740, 3746, Captain Mainwaring. Nos. 3741, 3747, Lance Corporal Jones. No. 3742, Private Walker. No. 3743, Private Frazer. No. 3744, Private Godfrey. No. 3745, Chief Warden Hodges.

**2018, June 26        Litho.        Perf. 14¼x14**

| | | | | |
|---|---|---|---|---|
| 3738 | A891 | 2nd multi | 1.60 | 1.20 |
| 3739 | A891 | 2nd multi | 1.60 | 1.20 |
| *a.* | | Horiz. pair, #3738-3739 | 3.20 | 2.40 |
| 3740 | A891 | 1st multi | 1.75 | 1.30 |
| 3741 | A891 | 1st multi | 1.75 | 1.30 |
| *a.* | | Horiz. pair, #3740-3741 | 3.50 | 2.60 |
| 3742 | A891 | £1.45 multi | 3.75 | 2.75 |
| 3743 | A891 | £1.45 multi | 3.75 | 2.75 |
| *a.* | | Horiz. pair, #3742-3743 | 7.50 | 5.50 |
| 3744 | A891 | £1.55 multi | 4.25 | 3.25 |
| 3745 | A891 | £1.55 multi | 4.25 | 3.25 |
| *a.* | | Horiz. pair, #3744-3745 | 8.50 | 6.50 |
| | | *Nos. 3738-3745 (8)* | 22.70 | 17.00 |

**Self-Adhesive**

**Photo.**

**Die Cut Perf. 14¼x14**

| | | | | |
|---|---|---|---|---|
| 3746 | A891 | 1st multi (3747c) | 4.00 | 2.25 |
| *a.* | | Litho., die cut perf. 14¼x14¾ + label | 3.50 | 2.00 |
| 3747 | A891 | 1st multi (3747c) | 4.00 | 2.25 |
| *a.* | | Litho., die cut perf. 14¼x14¾ + label | 3.50 | 2.00 |
| *b.* | | Sheet of 10, 5 each #3746a, 3747a + 10 labels | 35.00 | |
| *c.* | | Booklet pane, #3746, 3747, 4 #MH426 | 10.00 | |

No. 3747b sold for £7.50. Labels on No. 3746a and 3747a could not be personalized. On day of issue, Nos. 3738-3739 each sold for 58p, and Nos. 3740-3741, 3746-3747 each sold for 67p.

Hampton Court Palace A892

Hampton Court Palace A893

Designs: No. 3748, South Front. No. 3749, West Front. No. 3750, East Front. No. 3751, Pond Gardens. No. 3752, Palace Maze. No. 3753, Great Fountain Garden.
Nos. 3754a, 3755, Great Hall. No. 3754b, 3756, King's Great Bedchamber. No. 3754c, Chapel Royal. No. 3754d, King's Staircase.

**2018, July 31        Litho.        Perf. 14½x14¾**

| | | | | |
|---|---|---|---|---|
| 3748 | A892 | 1st multi | 1.75 | .90 |
| 3749 | A892 | 1st multi | 1.75 | .90 |
| 3750 | A892 | 1st multi | 1.75 | .90 |
| *a.* | | Horiz. strip of 3, #3748-3750 | 5.25 | 2.75 |
| 3751 | A892 | £1.55 multi | 4.25 | 2.10 |
| 3752 | A892 | £1.55 multi | 4.25 | 2.10 |
| 3753 | A892 | £1.55 multi | 4.25 | 2.10 |
| *a.* | | Horiz. strip of 3, #3751-3753 | 12.75 | 6.50 |
| | | *Nos. 3748-3753 (6)* | 18.00 | 9.00 |

**Miniature Sheet**

**Perf. 14¼**

| | | | | |
|---|---|---|---|---|
| 3754 | A893 | Sheet of 4 | 11.50 | 6.00 |
| *a.-b.* | | 1st Either single | 1.75 | .90 |
| *c.-d.* | | £1.45 Either single | 4.00 | 2.00 |

**Booklet Stamps**
**Self-Adhesive**
**Photo.**

**Die Cut Perf. 14¼**

| | | | | |
|---|---|---|---|---|
| 3755 | A893 | 1st multi | 4.00 | 2.00 |
| 3756 | A893 | 1st multi | 4.00 | 2.00 |
| *a.* | | Booklet pane of 6, #3755-3756, 4 #MH426 | 10.00 | |

On day of issue, Nos. 3748-3750, 3754a, 3754b, 3755-3756 each sold for 67p.

A894

Voyage of the Endeavour, 250th Anniv. — A895

Designs: No. 3757, Painting of Joseph Banks (1743-1820), naturalist, by Sir Joshua Reynolds, red-tailed tropicbird, red passion flowers. No. 3758, Chief mourner of Tahiti and canoe. No. 3759, Painting of Captain James Cook (1728-79), by Nathaniel Dance, and Triumph of the Navigators, by Robin Brooks. No. 3760, Sextant and drawings of the transit of Venus. No. 3761, Drawings of Scarlet clianthus and Maori Chief by Sydney Parkinson. No. 3762, Blue-black grassquit and self-portrait by Parkinson.
No. 3763: a, Map of Endeavour's voyage around Australia and New Zealand. b, Raiatea boathouse and canoes. c, Maori fort on rock arch. d, Repairing of the Endeavour on the Endeavour River, Australia.

**2018, Aug. 16        Litho.        Perf. 14¼**

| | | | | |
|---|---|---|---|---|
| 3757 | A894 | 2nd multi | 1.50 | .75 |
| 3758 | A894 | 2nd multi | 1.50 | .75 |
| *a.* | | Horiz. pair, #3757-3758 | 3.00 | 1.50 |
| 3759 | A894 | 1st multi | 1.75 | .85 |
| 3760 | A894 | 1st multi | 1.75 | .85 |
| *a.* | | Horiz. pair, #3759-3760 | 3.50 | 1.75 |
| 3761 | A894 | £1.45 multi | 3.75 | 1.90 |
| 3762 | A894 | £1.45 multi | 3.75 | 1.90 |
| *a.* | | Horiz. pair, #3761-3762 | 7.50 | 3.80 |
| | | *Nos. 3757-3762 (6)* | 14.00 | 7.00 |

**Miniature Sheet**

| | | | | |
|---|---|---|---|---|
| 3763 | A895 | Sheet of 4 | 11.00 | 5.50 |
| *a.-b.* | | 1st Either single | 1.75 | .90 |
| *c.-d.* | | £1.45 Either single | 3.75 | 1.90 |

On day of issue, Nos. 3757-3758 each sold for 58p, and Nos. 3759-3760 and 3763a-3763b each sold for 67p.

Old Vic Theater, London, 200th Anniv. — A896

Designs: No. 3764, Laurence Olivier in 1967 production of *The Dance of Death.* No. 3765, Glenda Jackson in 2016 production of *King Lear.* No. 3766, Albert Finney in 1975 production of *Hamlet.* No. 3767, Maggie Smith in 1970 production of *Hedda Gabler.* No. 3768, John Gielgud and Ralph Richardson in 1975 production of *No Man's Land.* No. 3769, Sharon Benson in 1991 production of *Carmen Jones.* No. 3770, Judi Dench and John Stride in 1960 production of *Romeo and Juliet.* No. 3771, Richard Burton in 1955 production of *Henry V.*

**2018, Aug. 30        Litho.        Perf. 14¼**

| | | | | |
|---|---|---|---|---|
| 3764 | A896 | 1st multi | 1.75 | .85 |
| 3765 | A896 | 1st multi | 1.75 | .85 |
| *a.* | | Horiz. pair, #3764-3765 | 3.50 | 1.75 |
| 3766 | A896 | £1.25 multi | 3.25 | 1.60 |
| 3767 | A896 | £1.25 multi | 3.25 | 1.60 |
| *a.* | | Horiz. pair, #3766-3767 | 6.50 | 3.25 |
| 3768 | A896 | £1.45 multi | 3.75 | 1.90 |
| 3769 | A896 | £1.45 multi | 3.75 | 1.90 |
| *a.* | | Horiz. pair, #3768-3769 | 7.50 | 3.80 |
| 3770 | A896 | £1.55 multi | 4.00 | 2.00 |
| 3771 | A896 | £1.55 multi | 4.00 | 2.00 |
| *a.* | | Horiz. pair, #3770-3771 | 8.00 | 4.00 |
| | | *Nos. 3764-3771 (8)* | 25.50 | 12.70 |

On day of issue, No. 3764-3765 each sold for 67p.

World War I, Cent. — A897

Designs: Nos. 3772, 3779. Image from *100 Poppies,* photograph by Zafer and Barbara Baran. No. 3773, Line from poem, "Anthem for Doomed Youth," by Wilfred Owen. No. 3774, Second Lieutenanat Walter Tull. No. 3775, *We Are Making a New World,* painting by Paul Nash. No. 3776, Grave of the Unknown Warrior, Westminster Abbey. No. 3777, Goggles of pilot Lieutenant Francis Hopgood.

**2018, Sept. 13        Litho.        Perf. 14¼**

| | | | | |
|---|---|---|---|---|
| 3772 | A897 | 1st multi | 1.75 | .85 |
| 3773 | A897 | 1st multi | 1.75 | .85 |
| 3774 | A897 | 1st multi | 1.75 | .85 |
| *a.* | | Booklet pane of 3, #3772-3774 (BK221) | 5.50 | — |
| 3775 | A897 | £1.55 multi | 4.00 | 2.00 |
| 3776 | A897 | £1.55 multi | 4.00 | 2.00 |
| 3777 | A897 | £1.55 multi | 4.00 | 2.00 |
| *a.* | | Booklet pane of 3, #3775-3777 (BK221) | 13.00 | — |
| *b.* | | Sheet of 30, #3312-3317, 3397-3402, 3507-3512, 3632-3637, 3772-3777 | 87.50 | 87.50 |
| | | *Nos. 3772-3777 (6)* | 17.25 | 8.55 |

**Booklet Stamps**
**Self-Adhesive**
**Photo.**

**Die Cut Perf. 14¼**

| | | | | |
|---|---|---|---|---|
| 3778 | A776 | 1st multi | 4.00 | 2.00 |
| 3779 | A897 | 1st multi | 4.00 | 2.00 |
| *a.* | | Booklet pane of 3, #3778-3779, 4 #MH426 | 10.00 | |

On day of issue, Nos. 3772-3774, 3778-3779 each sold for 67p.

A898

Characters from *Harry Potter* Movies — A899

Designs: Nos. 3780, 3791a, 3791k, Hermione Granger. Nos. 3781, 3791c, Hogwarts Express. Nos. 3782, 3791e, 3791l, Harry Potter. Nos. 3783, 3791g, Flying Ford Anglia. Nos. 3784, 3791i, Ron Weasley. Nos. 3785, 3791b, Hagrid's Motorbike. Nos. 3786, 3791d, Ginny Weasley. Nos. 3787, 3791f, Triwizard Cup. Nos. 3788, 3791h, Neville Longbottom. Nos. 3789, 3791j, Knight Bus.
No. 3790: a, Pomona Sprout. b, Horace Slughorn. c, Sybill Trelawney. d, Remus Lupin. e, Severus Snape.

**2018        Litho.        Perf. 14¼**

| | | | | |
|---|---|---|---|---|
| 3780 | A898 | 1st multi | 1.75 | .85 |
| 3781 | A898 | 1st multi | 1.75 | .85 |
| 3782 | A898 | 1st multi | 1.75 | .85 |
| 3783 | A898 | 1st multi | 1.75 | .85 |
| 3784 | A898 | 1st multi | 1.75 | .85 |
| *a.* | | Horiz. strip of 5, #3780-3784 | 8.75 | 4.25 |
| 3785 | A898 | 1st multi | 1.75 | .85 |
| 3786 | A898 | 1st multi | 1.75 | .85 |
| 3787 | A898 | 1st multi | 1.75 | .85 |
| 3788 | A898 | 1st multi | 1.75 | .85 |
| *a.* | | Booklet pane of 5, #3780, 3782, 3784, 3786, 3788 (BK222) | 9.50 | — |
| 3789 | A898 | 1st multi | 1.75 | .85 |
| *a.* | | Horiz. strip of 5, #3785-3789 | 8.75 | 4.25 |
| *b.* | | Booklet pane of 5, #3781, 3783, 3785, 3787, 37898 (BK222) | 9.50 | — |
| | | *Nos. 3780-3789 (10)* | 17.50 | 8.50 |

**Miniature Sheets**
**Self-Adhesive**

**Die Cut Perf. 14¼**

| | | | | |
|---|---|---|---|---|
| 3790 | A899 | Sheet of 5 | 8.75 | |
| *a.-e.* | | 1st Any single | 1.75 | .85 |
| *f.* | | Booklet pane of 3, #3790a-3790c (BK222) | 3.75 | |
| *g.* | | Booklet pane of 3, #3790d-3790e (BK222) | 3.75 | |
| 3791 | | Sheet of 10 + 10 labels | 20.00 | |
| *a.-j.* | | A898 1st Any single | 2.00 | 2.00 |
| *k.* | | As #3791a, photo. (#3791m) | 4.00 | 2.25 |
| *l.* | | As #3791e, photo. (#3791m) | 4.00 | 2.25 |
| *m.* | | Booklet pane of 6, #3791k, 3791l, 4 #MH426 | 10.00 | |

Issued: Nos. 3788a, 3789a, 3790f, 3790g, 12/4; others, 10/16. Nos. 3780-3790, 3790a-3790e, 3791k-3791l each sold for 67p on day of issue. No. 3791 sold for £7.70.

A900

Christmas — A901

People in winter near mailboxes from: Nos. 3792a, 3792c, 3793, 3795, King Edward VII era. Nos. 3792b, 3792d, 3794, 3796, Queen Elizabeth II era. £1.25, King George VI era. £1.45, Queen Victoria era. £1.55, King Edward VIII era. £2.25, King George V era.

**2018, Nov. 1**    **Litho.**    **Perf. 14½x15**

| | | | |
|---|---|---|---|
| 3792 | Sheet of 8 | 25.00 | 25.00 |
| a. | A900 2nd multi | 1.50 | .75 |
| b. | A900 1st multi | 1.75 | .85 |
| c. | A901 2nd Large multi | 2.10 | 1.10 |
| d. | A901 1st Large multi | 2.60 | 1.40 |
| e. | A900 £1.25 multi | 3.25 | 1.60 |
| f. | A900 £1.55 multi | 3.75 | 1.90 |
| g. | A900 £1.55 multi | 4.00 | 2.00 |
| h. | A900 £2.25 multi | 6.00 | 3.00 |

**Photo.**

**Self-Adhesive**

**Die Cut Perf. 14½x15**

| | | | |
|---|---|---|---|
| 3793 | A900 2nd multi | 1.50 | .75 |
| a. | Booklet pane of 12 | 18.00 | |
| b. | Litho., die cut perf. 14½x15 syncopated + label (#3800b) | | |
| | | 1.60 | 1.60 |
| 3794 | A900 1st multi | 1.75 | .85 |
| a. | Booklet pane of 12 | 21.00 | |
| b. | Litho., die cut perf. 14½x15 syncopated + label (#3800b) | | |
| | | 1.90 | 1.90 |
| 3795 | A901 2nd Large multi | 2.10 | 1.10 |
| 3796 | A901 1st Large multi | 2.60 | 1.40 |
| 3797 | A900 £1.25 multi | 3.25 | 1.60 |
| a. | Litho., die cut perf. 14½x15 syncopated + label (#3800b) | | |
| | | 3.50 | 3.50 |
| 3798 | A900 £1.45 multi | 3.75 | 1.90 |
| a. | Litho., die cut perf. 14½x15 syncopated + label (#3800b) | | |
| | | 4.00 | 4.00 |
| 3799 | A900 £1.55 multi | 4.00 | 2.00 |
| a. | Litho., die cut perf. 14½x15 syncopated + label (#3800b) | | |
| | | 4.25 | 4.25 |
| 3800 | A900 £2.25 multi | 6.00 | 3.00 |
| a. | Litho., die cut perf. 14½x15 syncopated + label (#3800b) | | |
| | | 6.25 | 6.25 |
| b. | Sheet of 20, #3797a, 3798a, 3799a, 3800a, 8 each #3793b, 3794b + 20 labels | 46.00 | |
| | Nos. 3793-3800 (8) | 24.95 | 12.60 |

On day of issue, Nos. 3792a and 3793 each sold for 58p; Nos. 3792b and 3794, for 67p; Nos. 3792c and 3795, for 79p; Nos. 3792d and 3796, for £1.01. No. 3800b sold for £17.50 and labels could not be personalized.

**Miniature Sheet**

Prince Charles, 70th Birthday
A902

No. 3801: a, Prince Charles wearing blue suit. b, Prince Charles with wife, the Duchess of Cornwall. c, Prince Charles with sons, Princes William and Harry, in military uniforms. d, Prince Charles with sons in sports shirts. e, Prince Charles at Castle of Mey. f, Prince Charles and children waving Welsh flags.

**Die Cut Perf. 14¼x14**

**2018, Nov. 14**      **Litho.**

**Self-Adhesive**

| | | | |
|---|---|---|---|
| 3801 | A902 Sheet of 6 | 17.50 | |
| a.-c. | 1st Any single | 1.75 | .85 |
| d.-f. | £1.55 Any single | 4.00 | 2.00 |

On day of issue, Nos. 3801a-3801c each sold for 67p.

**Miniature Sheet**

Classic British Stamps
A903

No. 3802: a, Great Britain #124 (73x30mm). b, Unissued 2p stamp depicting King Edward VII prepared in 1910 (31x30mm). c, Great Britain #173 (52x30mm). d, Great Britain #232 (33x30mm). e, Great Britain #252 (42x30mm). f, Great Britain #313 (52x30mm).

**2019, Jan. 15**    **Litho.**    **Perf. 14x13½**

| | | | |
|---|---|---|---|
| 3802 | A903 Sheet of 6 + label | 17.50 | 17.50 |
| a.-c. | 1st Any single | 1.75 | 1.40 |
| d.-f. | £1.55 Any single | 4.00 | 3.00 |
| g. | As #3802, with Stampex International 2019 emblem added to label | 25.00 | 25.00 |

On day of issue, Nos. 3802a-3802c each sold for 67p. Issued: No. 3802g, 2/13. No. 3802g was sold only at the Stampex International 2019 Stamp Exhibition, and the sheet margin shows a serial number.

---

The Skull Sectioned, 1489
A904

A Sprig of Guelder-Rose, c. 1506-12
A905

Studies of Cats, c. 1517-18
A906

A Star of Bethlehem and Other Plants, c. 1506-12
A907

The Anatomy of the Shoulder and Foot, c. 1510-11
A908

The Head of Leda, c. 1505-08
A909

The Head of a Bearded Man, c. 1517-18
A910

The Skeleton, c. 1510-11
A911

The Head of St. Philip, c. 1495
A912

A Woman in a Landscape, c. 1517-18
A913

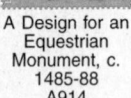

A Design for an Equestrian Monument, c. 1485-88
A914

The Fall of Light on a Face, c. 1488
A915

**2019, Feb. 13**    **Litho.**    **Perf. 14½**

| | | | |
|---|---|---|---|
| 3803 | A904 1st multi | 1.75 | 1.40 |
| 3804 | A905 1st multi | 1.75 | 1.40 |
| 3805 | A906 1st multi | 1.75 | 1.40 |
| 3806 | A907 1st multi | 1.75 | 1.40 |
| 3807 | A908 1st multi | 1.75 | 1.40 |
| 3808 | A909 1st multi | 1.75 | 1.40 |
| a. | Horiz. strip of 6, #3803-3808 | 10.50 | 8.50 |
| 3809 | A910 1st multi | 1.75 | 1.40 |
| 3810 | A911 1st multi | 1.75 | 1.40 |
| 3811 | A912 1st multi | 1.75 | 1.40 |
| 3812 | A913 1st multi | 1.75 | 1.40 |
| a. | Booklet pane of 4, #3808-3809, 3811-3812 (BK223) | 7.75 | — |
| 3813 | A914 1st multi | 1.75 | 1.40 |
| a. | Booklet pane of 4, #3804-3806, 3813 (BK223) | 7.75 | — |
| 3814 | A915 1st multi | 1.75 | 1.40 |
| a. | Horiz. strip of 6, #3809-3814 | 10.50 | 8.50 |
| b. | Booklet pane of 4, #3803, 3807, 3810, 3814 (BK223) | 7.75 | — |
| | Nos. 3803-3814 (12) | 21.00 | 16.80 |

Drawings by Leonardo da Vinci (1452-1519) in the Royal Collection. Nos. 3803-3814 each sold for 67p on day of issue.

---

Marvel Comics Superheroes
A916

Designs: Nos. 3815, 3826a, 3826k, Spiderman. No. 3816, 3826b, Captain Marvel. Nos. 3817, 3826c, 3826l, Hulk. Nos. 3818, 3826d, Doctor Strange. Nos. 3819, 3826e, Captain Britain. Nos. 3820, 3826f, Peggy Carter. Nos. 3821, 3826g, Iron Man. Nos. 3822, 3826h, Union Jack. Nos. 3823, 3826i, Black Panther. Nos. 3824, 3826j, Thor.

No. 3825 — Text in word bubble: a, He's strong (60x21mm). b, . . . Thanos (27x37mm). c, But we're stronger. . . (27x37mm). d, . . . Together (41x30mm). e, Fury, a portal is opening (60x21mm).

**2019, Mar. 14**    **Litho.**    **Perf. 14¼**

| | | | |
|---|---|---|---|
| 3815 | A916 1st multi | 1.75 | 1.40 |
| 3816 | A916 1st multi | 1.75 | 1.40 |
| 3817 | A916 1st multi | 1.75 | 1.40 |
| 3818 | A916 1st multi | 1.75 | 1.40 |
| 3819 | A916 1st multi | 1.75 | 1.40 |
| a. | Horiz. strip of 5, #3815-3819 | 8.75 | 7.00 |
| 3820 | A916 1st multi | 1.75 | 1.40 |
| 3821 | A916 1st multi | 1.75 | 1.40 |
| a. | Booklet pane of 6, #3815-3817, 3819-3821 (BK224) | 11.50 | — |
| 3822 | A916 1st multi | 1.75 | 1.40 |
| 3823 | A916 1st multi | 1.75 | 1.40 |
| 3824 | A916 1st multi | 1.75 | 1.40 |
| a. | Horiz. strip of 5, #3820-3824 | 8.75 | 7.00 |
| b. | Booklet pane of 4, #3818, 3822-3824 (BK224) | 7.75 | — |
| | Nos. 3815-3824 (10) | 17.50 | 14.00 |

**Self-Adhesive**

**Die Cut Perf. 14½x14¼ (#3825a, 3825e), 14¼ (#3825b, 3825c), 14¼x14 (3825d)**

| | | | |
|---|---|---|---|
| 3825 | Sheet of 5 | 12.50 | |
| a.-c. | A916 1st Any single | 1.75 | 1.40 |
| d. | A916 £1.25 multi | 3.25 | 2.50 |
| e. | A916 £1.45 multi | 4.00 | 3.00 |
| f. | Booklet pane of 2, #3825b, 3825e (BK224) | 6.25 | |
| g. | Booklet pane of 3, #3825a, 3825c, 3825d (BK224) | 7.50 | |

**Die Cut Perf. 14¼**

| | | | |
|---|---|---|---|
| 3826 | Sheet of 10 + 10 labels | 25.00 | |
| a.-j. | A916 1st Any single + label | 2.00 | 2.00 |
| k. | Like No. 3815, photo. (3826m) | 5.00 | 1.40 |
| l. | Like No. 3817, photo. (3826m) | 5.00 | 1.40 |
| m. | Booklet pane of 6, #3826k, 3826l, 4 #MH426 | 12.00 | |

On day of issue, Nos. 3815-3824, 3825a-3825c, 3826a-3826l had a franking value of 67p. No. 3826 sold for £7.70 and its labels could not be personalized.

Birds of Prey — A917

Designs: No. 3827, White-tailed eagle. No. 3828, Merlin. No. 3829, 3838, Hobby. Nos. 3830, 3837, Buzzard. No. 3831, Golden eagle. No. 3832, Kestrel. No. 3833, Goshawk. No. 3834, Sparrowhawk. No. 3835, Red kite. No. 3836, Peregrine falcon.

**2019, June 4**    **Litho.**    **Perf. 14x14¼**

| | | | |
|---|---|---|---|
| 3827 | A917 1st multi | 1.90 | 1.40 |
| 3828 | A917 1st multi | 1.90 | 1.40 |
| 3829 | A917 1st multi | 1.90 | 1.40 |
| 3830 | A917 1st multi | 1.90 | 1.40 |
| 3831 | A917 1st multi | 1.90 | 1.40 |
| a. | Horiz. strip of 5, #3827-3831 | 9.50 | 7.00 |
| 3832 | A917 1st multi | 1.90 | 1.40 |
| 3833 | A917 1st multi | 1.90 | 1.40 |
| 3834 | A917 1st multi | 1.90 | 1.40 |
| 3835 | A917 1st multi | 1.90 | 1.40 |
| 3836 | A917 1st multi | 1.90 | 1.40 |
| a. | Horiz. strip of 5, #3832-3836 | 9.50 | 7.00 |
| | Nos. 3827-3836 (10) | 19.00 | 14.00 |

**Booklet Stamps**
**Self-Adhesive**

**Photo.**

**Die Cut Perf. 14¼**

| | | | |
|---|---|---|---|
| 3837 | A917 1st multi | 10.00 | 1.40 |
| 3838 | A917 1st multi | 10.00 | 1.40 |
| a. | Booklet pane of 6, #3837-3838, 4 #MH426 | 42.00 | |

On day of issue, Nos. 3827-3838 each sold for 70p.

---

British Engineering Achievements
A918

Designs: No. 3839, Raspberry Pi microcomputer. No. 3840, Falkirk Wheel rotating boat lift. No. 3841, Three-way catalytic converter. No. 3842, Crossrail tunnel boring project. No. 3843, Superconducting magnet for use in magnetic resonance imaging machine. No. 3844, Synthetic bone-graft material.

**2019, May 2**    **Litho.**    **Perf. 14¼x14**

| | | | |
|---|---|---|---|
| 3839 | A918 1st multi | 1.75 | 1.40 |
| 3840 | A918 1st multi | 1.75 | 1.40 |
| a. | Horiz. pair, #3839-3840 | 3.50 | 2.80 |
| 3841 | A918 £1.55 multi | 4.00 | 3.00 |
| 3842 | A918 £1.55 multi | 4.00 | 3.00 |
| a. | Horiz. pair, #3841-3842 | 8.00 | 6.00 |
| 3843 | A918 £1.60 multi | 4.00 | 3.00 |
| 3844 | A918 £1.60 multi | 4.00 | 3.00 |
| a. | Horiz. pair, #3843-3844 | 8.00 | 6.00 |
| | Nos. 3839-3844 (6) | 19.50 | 14.80 |

On day of issue, Nos. 3839-3840 each sold for 70p.

**Miniature Sheet**

Harrier Jump Jet. 50th Anniv.
A919

No. 3845 — Harrier GR3: a, Performing short take-off. b, In conventional flight. c, Transitioning to landing. d, Performing vertical landing.

**2019, May 2**    **Litho.**    **Perf. 14¼x14**

| | | | |
|---|---|---|---|
| 3845 | A919 Sheet of 4 | 11.50 | 11.50 |
| a.-b. | 1st Either single | 1.75 | 1.40 |
| c.-d. | £1.55 Either single | 4.00 | 3.00 |

On day of issue, Nos. 3845a-3845b each sold for 70p.

Queen Victoria (1819-1901)
A920

Legacy of Prince Albert (1819-61) — A921

Paintings: No. 3846, Queen Victoria, 1890, by Heinrich von Angeli. No. 3847, Queen Victoria and Benjamin Disraeli, 1878, by Theodore Blake Wirgman. No. 3848, Queen Victoria on Horseback, with John Brown, 1876, by Charles Burton Barber. No. 3849, Queen Victoria Wearing Robes of State, 1859, by Franz Xaver Winterhalter. No. 3850, The Marriage of Queen Victoria, 1840, by Sir George Hayter. No. 3851, Queen Victoria When a Girl, 1830, by Richard Westall.

No. 3852 — Buildings: a, Model Lodge, Kennington. b, Balmoral Castle, Scotland. c, New Crystal Palace, Sydenham. d, Royal Albert Hall, London.

**2019, May 24**    **Litho.**    **Perf. 14¼**

| | | | |
|---|---|---|---|
| 3846 | A920 1st multi | 1.75 | 1.40 |
| 3847 | A920 1st multi | 1.75 | 1.40 |
| a. | Horiz. pair, #3846-3847 | 3.50 | 2.80 |
| 3848 | A920 £1.35 multi | 3.50 | 2.60 |
| a. | Booklet pane of 3, #3846-3848 (BK1225) | 7.50 | — |
| 3849 | A920 £1.35 multi | 3.50 | 2.60 |
| a. | Horiz. pair, #3848-3849 | 7.00 | 5.25 |
| 3850 | A920 £1.60 multi | 4.00 | 3.00 |
| 3851 | A920 £1.60 multi | 4.00 | 3.00 |
| a. | Horiz. pair, #3850-3851 | 8.00 | 6.00 |
| b. | Booklet pane of 3, #3849-3851 (BK1225) | 13.00 | — |
| | Nos. 3846-3851 (6) | 18.50 | 14.00 |

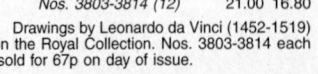

## Miniature Sheet
### Perf. 14¼x14

| | | | | |
|---|---|---|---|---|
| 3852 | A921 | Sheet of 4 | 11.50 | 11.50 |
| a.-b. | | 1st Either single | 1.75 | 1.40 |
| c.-d. | | £1.55 Either single | 4.00 | 3.00 |
| e. | | Booklet pane of 4, #3852a-3852d (BK1225) | 12.50 | — |

On day of issue, Nos. 3846-3847, 3852a-3852b each sold for 70p.

A922

D-Day, 75th Anniv. A923

Designs: No. 3853, British soldiers being briefed before embarkation. No. 3854, HMS Warspite shelling in support of beach landings. No. 3855, Paratroopers synchronizing watches. No. 3856, Soldiers wading ashore at Juno Beach. No. 3857, American light bomber providing air support. No. 3858, British troops taking cover as they advance inland.

No. 3859 — Scenes of soldiers at landing sites: a, Utah Beach. b, Omaha Beach. c, Gold Beach. d, Juno Beach. e, Sword Beach. No. 3860, Like No. 3859c. No. 3861, Like No. 3859e.

### 2019    Litho.    Perf. 14¾x14½

| | | | | |
|---|---|---|---|---|
| 3853 | A922 | 1st multi | 1.75 | 1.40 |
| 3854 | A922 | 1st multi | 1.75 | 1.40 |
| a. | | Vert. pair, #3853-3854 | 3.50 | 2.80 |
| 3855 | A922 | £1.35 multi | 3.50 | 2.60 |
| 3856 | A922 | £1.35 multi | 3.50 | 2.60 |
| a. | | Vert. pair, #3855-3856 | 7.00 | 5.25 |
| 3857 | A922 | £1.60 multi | 4.00 | 3.00 |
| 3858 | A922 | £1.60 multi | 4.00 | 3.00 |
| a. | | Vert. pair, #3857-3858 | 8.00 | 6.00 |
| | | Nos. 3853-3858 (6) | 18.50 | 14.00 |

### Miniature Sheet
#### Perf. 14¼

| | | | | |
|---|---|---|---|---|
| 3859 | A923 | Sheet of 5 | 20.00 | 20.00 |
| a.-e. | | 1st Any single | 3.50 | 1.75 |
| f. | | As #3859, with Stampex International 2019 emblem in sheet margin | 20.00 | 20.00 |

### Self-Adhesive
### Booklet Stamps
### Photo.
#### Die Cut Perf. 14¼

| | | | | |
|---|---|---|---|---|
| 3860 | A923 | 1st multi | 5.00 | 1.40 |
| 3861 | A923 | 1st multi | 5.00 | 1.40 |
| a. | | Booklet pane of 6, #3860-3861, 4 #MH426 | 12.50 | |

Issued: Nos. 3853-3859, 3860-3861, 6/6; No. 3859f, 9/11. On day of issue, Nos. 3853-3854, 3859a-3859e, 3860-3861 each sold for 70p. No. 3859f was sold only at the 2019 Stampex International Stamp Exhibition, and also has a serial number in sheet margin.

Burning of the Clocks Winter Solstice Festival, Brighton — A924

'Obby 'Oss Festival, Padstow — A925

World Gurning Chanpionships, Egremont A926

Up Helly Aa Fire Festival, Lerwick A927

Cheese Rolling Contest, Cooper's Hill, Brockworth A928

Halloween, Londonderry A929

Horn Dance, Abbots Bromley — A930

World Bog Snorkelling Championships, Llanwrtyd Wells — A931

### 2019, July 9    Litho.    Perf. 14¼

| | | | | |
|---|---|---|---|---|
| 3862 | A924 | 2nd multi | 1.50 | 1.10 |
| 3863 | A925 | 2nd multi | 1.50 | 1.10 |
| a. | | Horiz. pair, #3862-3863 | 3.00 | 2.25 |
| 3864 | A926 | 1st multi | 1.75 | 1.40 |
| 3865 | A927 | 1st multi | 1.75 | 1.40 |
| a. | | Horiz. pair, #3864-3865 | 3.50 | 2.80 |
| 3866 | A928 | £1.55 multi | 3.75 | 2.75 |
| 3867 | A929 | £1.55 multi | 3.75 | 2.75 |
| a. | | Horiz. pair, #3866-3867 | 7.50 | 5.50 |
| 3868 | A930 | £1.60 multi | 4.00 | 3.00 |
| 3869 | A931 | £1.60 multi | 4.00 | 3.00 |
| a. | | Horiz. pair, #3868-3869 | 8.00 | 6.00 |
| | | Nos. 3862-3869 (8) | 22.00 | 16.50 |

On day of issue, Nos. 3862-3863 each sold for 61p, and Nos. 3864-3865 each sold for 70p.

Forests A932

Designs: No. 3870, Glen Affric National Nature Reserve, Inverness-shire. No. 3871, Westonbirt National Arboretum, Gloucestershire. No. 3872, Sherwood Forest, Nottinghamshire. No. 3873, Coed y Brenin (King's Forest), Gwynedd. No. 3874, Glenariff Forest Park, County Antrim. No. 3875, Kielder Forest, Northumberland.

### Perf. 14¾x14½
### 2019, Aug. 13    Litho.

| | | | | |
|---|---|---|---|---|
| 3870 | A932 | 1st multi | 1.75 | 1.40 |
| 3871 | A932 | 1st multi | 1.75 | 1.40 |
| a. | | Vert. pair, #3870-3871 | 3.50 | 2.80 |
| 3872 | A932 | £1.55 multi | 3.75 | 2.75 |
| 3873 | A932 | £1.55 multi | 3.75 | 2.75 |
| a. | | Vert. pair, #3872-3873 | 7.50 | 5.50 |
| 3874 | A932 | £1.60 multi | 4.00 | 3.00 |
| 3875 | A932 | £1.60 multi | 4.00 | 3.00 |
| a. | | Vert. pair, #3874-3875 | 8.00 | 6.00 |
| | | Nos. 3870-3875 (6) | 19.00 | 14.30 |

On day of issue, Nos. 3870-3871 each sold for 70p.

Honky Château, by Elton John, 1972 — A933

Goodbye Yellow Brick Road, by Elton John, 1973 — A934

Caribou, by Elton John, 1974 — A935

Captain Fantastic and the Brown Dirt Cowboy, by Elton John, 1975 — A936

Sleeping with the Past, by Elton John, 1989 — A937

The One, by Elton John, 1992 — A938

Made in England, by Elton John, 1995 — A939

Songs from the West Coast, by Elton John, 2001 — A940

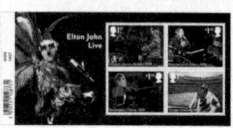

Elton John in Concert A941

No. 3884 — Performance at: a, Madison Square Garden, New York, 2018. b, Dodger Stadium, Los Angeles, 1975. c, Hammersmith Odeon, London, 1973. d, Buckingham Palace, London, 2012.

### 2019, Sept. 3    Litho.    Perf. 14¼x14

| | | | | |
|---|---|---|---|---|
| 3876 | A933 | 1st multi | 1.75 | 1.40 |
| 3877 | A934 | 1st multi | 1.75 | 1.40 |
| 3878 | A935 | 1st multi | 1.75 | 1.40 |
| 3879 | A936 | 1st multi | 1.75 | 1.40 |
| a. | | Horiz. strip of 4, #3876-3879 | 7.00 | 5.60 |
| 3880 | A937 | £1.55 multi | 3.75 | 2.75 |
| 3881 | A938 | £1.55 multi | 3.75 | 2.75 |
| 3882 | A939 | £1.55 multi | 3.75 | 2.75 |
| 3883 | A940 | £1.55 multi | 3.75 | 2.75 |
| a. | | Horiz. strip of 4, #3880-3883 | 15.00 | 11.00 |
| b. | | Souvenir sheet of 8, #3876-3883 | 30.00 | 30.00 |
| | | Nos. 3876-3883 (8) | 22.00 | 16.60 |

### Miniature Sheet

| | | | | |
|---|---|---|---|---|
| 3884 | A941 | Sheet of 4 | 11.00 | 11.00 |
| a.-b. | | 1st Either single | 1.75 | 1.40 |
| c.-d. | | £1.55 Either single | 3.75 | 2.75 |

### Booklet Stamps
### Self-Adhesive
### Photo.
#### Die Cut Perf. 14¼x14

| | | | | |
|---|---|---|---|---|
| 3885 | A934 | 1st multi | 4.00 | 1.40 |
| 3886 | A936 | 1st multi | 4.00 | 1.40 |
| a. | | Booklet pane of 6, #3885-3886, 4 #MH426 | 15.00 | |

On day of issue, Nos. 3876-3879, 3885-3886 each sold for 70p. A sheet of four of No. 3877 and a sheet of four of No. 3879 were each sold for £7.50.

Royal Navy Ships — A942

Designs: Nos. 3887, 3895, Mary Rose, 1511. Nos. 3888, 3896, HMS Queen Elizabeth, 2014. No. 3889, HMS Victory, 1765. No. 3890, HMS Dreadnought, 1906. No. 3891, HMS Warrior, 1860. No. 3892, Sovereign of the Seas, 1637. No. 3893, HMS King George V, 1939. No. 3894, HMS Beagle, 1820.

### 2019, Sept. 19    Litho.    Perf. 14¼x14

| | | | | |
|---|---|---|---|---|
| 3887 | A942 | 1st multi | 1.75 | 1.40 |
| 3888 | A942 | 1st multi | 1.75 | 1.40 |
| a. | | Horiz. pair, #3887-3888 | 3.50 | 2.80 |
| 3889 | A942 | £1.35 multi | 3.25 | 2.50 |
| 3890 | A942 | £1.35 multi | 3.25 | 2.50 |
| a. | | Horiz. pair, #3889-3890 | 6.50 | 5.00 |
| 3891 | A942 | £1.55 multi | 3.75 | 2.75 |
| 3892 | A942 | £1.55 multi | 3.75 | 2.75 |
| a. | | Horiz. pair, #3891-3892 | 7.50 | 5.50 |
| 3893 | A942 | £1.60 multi | 4.00 | 3.00 |
| 3894 | A942 | £1.60 multi | 4.00 | 3.00 |
| a. | | Horiz. pair, #3893-3894 | 8.00 | 6.00 |
| | | Nos. 3887-3894 (8) | 25.50 | 19.30 |

### Booklet Stamps
### Self-Adhesive
### Photo.
#### Die Cut Perf. 14¼x14

| | | | | |
|---|---|---|---|---|
| 3895 | A942 | 1st multi | 9.50 | 1.40 |
| 3896 | A942 | 1st multi | 9.50 | 1.40 |
| a. | | Booklet pane of 6, #3895-3896, 4 #MH426 | 25.00 | |

On day of issue, Nos. 3887-3888, 3895-3896 each sold for 70p.

### Miniature Sheets

Victory of England's Men's Cricket Team in 2019 Cricket World Cup — A943

Victory of England's Women's Cricket Team in 2017 Cricket World Cup — A944

No. 3897: a, Team photo, player holding Cricket World Cup above head. b, Team photo, player holding Cricket World Cup at level of his chest. c, Players celebrating, no uniform numbers visible. d, Players celebrating, player Adil Rashid at right.

No. 3898: a, Team with Cricket World Cup, behind letters spelling "CHAMPIONS." b, Players Jenny Gunn and Natalie Sciver celebrating with teammates. c, Seven players celebrating. d, Team with Cricket World Cup on balcony.

#### Perf. 14¾x14½

### 2019, Sept. 26    Litho.

| | | | | |
|---|---|---|---|---|
| 3897 | A943 | Sheet of 4 | 11.50 | 11.50 |
| a.-b. | | 1st Either single | 1.75 | 1.40 |
| c.-d. | | £1.60 Either single | 4.00 | 3.00 |
| 3898 | A944 | Sheet of 4 | 11.50 | 11.50 |
| a.-b. | | 1st Either single | 1.75 | 1.40 |
| c.-d. | | £1.60 Either single | 4.00 | 3.00 |

On day of issue, Nos. 3897a-3897b, 3898a-3898b each sold for 70p.

A945

Characters from The Gruffalo, Children's Book by Julia Donaldson — A946

Inscriptions: No. 3899, Scrambled snake! No. 3900, Gruffalo crumble! No. 3901, All was quiet in the deep dark wood. No. 3902, A mouse took a stroll. No. 3903, Roasted fox! No. 3904, Owl ice cream? Nos. 3905 and 3906: a, Owl. b, Mouse. c, Snake. d, Fox.

### 2019, Oct. 10    Litho.    Perf. 14

| | | | | |
|---|---|---|---|---|
| 3899 | A945 | 1st multi | 1.90 | 1.40 |
| 3900 | A945 | 1st multi | 1.90 | 1.40 |
| 3901 | A945 | 1st multi | 1.90 | 1.40 |
| a. | | Horiz. strip of 3, #3899-3901 | 5.75 | 4.25 |
| 3902 | A945 | £1.60 multi | 4.25 | 3.25 |
| 3903 | A945 | £1.60 multi | 4.25 | 3.25 |
| 3904 | A945 | £1.60 multi | 4.25 | 3.25 |
| a. | | Horiz. strip of 3, #3902-3904 | 13.00 | 9.75 |
| | | Nos. 3899-3904 (6) | 18.45 | 13.95 |

### Miniature Sheets
#### Perf. 14¼

| | | | | |
|---|---|---|---|---|
| 3905 | A946 | Sheet of 4 | 12.00 | 12.00 |
| a.-b. | | 1st Either single | 1.90 | 1.40 |
| c.-d. | | £1.55 Either single | 4.00 | 3.00 |

## Self-Adhesive
### Die Cut Perf. 14¼

| | | | |
|---|---|---|---|
| 3906 A946 | Sheet of 10, 3 each #3906a-3906b, 2 each #3906c-3906d, + 10 labels | 30.00 | |
| a.-b. | 1st Either single | 2.00 | 2.00 |
| c.-d. | £1.55 Either single | 4.50 | 4.50 |

On day of issue, Nos. 3899-3901, 3905a-3905b each sold for 70p. No. 3906 sold for £11.50, with Nos. 3906a-3906b each having a franking value of 70p on day of issue. Labels on No. 3906 could not be personalized.

A947

Christmas — A948

Designs: Nos. 3907a, 3907c, 3908, 3910, Angel, shepherd and sheep. Nos. 3907b, 3907d, 3909, 3911, Madonna and Child. Nos. 3907e, 3912, St. Joseph with staff. Nos. 3907f, 3913, Infant Jesus, ox and donkey. Nos. 3907g, 3914, Shepherds and sheep. Nos. 3907h, 3915, Magi.

**2019, Nov. 5   Litho.   Perf. 14½x15**

| | | | |
|---|---|---|---|
| 3907 | Sheet of 8 | 26.50 | 26.50 |
| a. A947 | 2nd multi | 1.60 | 1.25 |
| b. A947 | 1st multi | 1.90 | 1.50 |
| c. A948 | 2nd Large multi | 2.25 | 1.75 |
| d. A948 | 1st Large multi | 2.75 | 2.10 |
| e. A947 | £1.35 multi | 3.50 | 2.60 |
| f. A947 | £1.55 multi | 4.00 | 3.00 |
| g. A947 | £1.60 multi | 4.25 | 3.25 |
| h. A947 | £2.30 multi | 6.00 | 4.50 |

### Self-Adhesive
### Die Cut Perf. 14½x15
### Photo.

| | | | |
|---|---|---|---|
| 3908 A947 | 2nd multi | 1.60 | 1.25 |
| a. | Booklet pane of 12 | 19.50 | |
| b. | Litho., die cut perf. 14½x15 syncopated, + label | 1.75 | 1.75 |
| 3909 A947 | 1st multi | 1.90 | 1.50 |
| a. | Booklet pane of 12 | 23.00 | |
| b. | Litho., die cut perf. 14½x15 syncopated, + label | 2.00 | 2.00 |
| 3910 A948 | 2nd Large multi | 2.25 | 1.75 |
| 3911 A948 | 1st Large multi | 2.75 | 2.10 |
| 3912 A947 | £1.35 multi | 3.50 | 2.60 |
| a. | Litho., die cut perf. 14½x15 syncopated, + label | 3.75 | 3.75 |
| 3913 A947 | £1.55 multi | 4.00 | 3.00 |
| a. | Litho., die cut perf. 14½x15 syncopated, + label | 4.25 | 4.25 |
| 3914 A947 | £1.60 multi | 4.25 | 3.25 |
| a. | Litho., die cut perf. 14½x15 syncopated, + label | 4.50 | 4.50 |
| 3915 A947 | £2.30 multi | 6.00 | 4.50 |
| a. | Litho., die cut perf. 14½x15 syncopated, + label | 6.50 | 6.50 |
| b. | Sheet of 20, #3912a, 3913a, 3914a, 3915a, 8 each #3908b, 3909b, + 20 labels | 49.00 | |
| | Nos. 3908-3915 (8) | 26.25 | 19.95 |

On day of issue, Nos. 3907a and 3908 sold for 61p; Nos. 3907b and 3909, 70p; Nos. 3907c and 3910, 83p; Nos. 3907d and 3911, £1.06. No. 3915b sold for £18.40, with Nos. 3907b having a franking value on the day of issue of 61p; and No. 3908b having a franking value of 70p on the day of issue. Labels on No. 3915b could not be personalized.

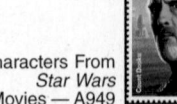

Characters From Star Wars Movies — A949

Modes of Transportation From Star Wars Movies — A950

Designs: Nos. 3916, 3927a, Count Dooku. Nos. 3917, 3927b, Lando Calrissian. Nos. 3918, 3927c, Sith trooper. Nos. 3919, 3927d, Jannah. Nos. 3920, 3927e, Grand Moff Tarkin. Nos. 3921, 3927f, Darth Maul. Nos. 3922, 3927g, Zorii. Nos. 3923, 3927h, Wicket W. Warrick. Nos. 3924, 3927i, 3927l, Poe Dameron. Nos. 3925, 3927j, Queen Amidala.

No. 3926: a, Poe's X-wing fighter (41x30mm). b, Jedi starfighter (27x36mm). c, Slave I (27x36mm). d, TIE silencer (41x30mm). e, Podracers (60x21mm). f, Speeder bikes (60x21mm).

**2019, Nov. 26   Litho.   Perf. 14½**

| | | | |
|---|---|---|---|
| 3916 A949 | 1st multi | 1.90 | 1.50 |
| 3917 A949 | 1st multi | 1.90 | 1.50 |
| 3918 A949 | 1st multi | 1.90 | 1.50 |
| 3919 A949 | 1st multi | 1.90 | 1.50 |
| 3920 A949 | 1st multi | 1.90 | 1.50 |
| a. | Horiz. strip of 5, #3916-3920 | 9.50 | 7.50 |
| 3921 A949 | 1st multi | 1.90 | 1.50 |
| 3922 A949 | 1st multi | 1.90 | 1.50 |
| 3923 A949 | 1st multi | 1.90 | 1.50 |
| 3924 A949 | 1st multi | 1.90 | 1.50 |
| a. | Booklet pane of 6, #3916, 3918, 3919, 3920, 3923, 3924 (BK1226) | 12.00 | — |
| 3925 A949 | 1st multi | 1.90 | 1.50 |
| a. | Horiz. strip of 5, #3921-3925 | 9.50 | 7.50 |
| b. | Booklet pane of 4, #3917, 3921, 3922, 3925 (BK1226) | 8.00 | — |
| c. | Sheet of 30, #3435-3446, 3656-3663, 3916-3925 | 57.00 | 57.00 |
| | Nos. 3916-3925 (10) | 19.00 | 15.00 |

### Miniature Sheets
### Self-Adhesive
### Die Cut Perf. 14¼ (#3926a-3926d), 14¾x14¼ (#3926e-3926f)

| | | | |
|---|---|---|---|
| 3926 A950 | Sheet of 6 | 11.50 | |
| a.-f. | 1st Any single | 1.90 | 1.50 |
| g. | Booklet pane of 3, #3926a, 3926b, 3926e (BK1226) | 6.00 | |
| h. | Booklet pane of 3, #3926c, 3926d, 3926f (BK1226) | 6.00 | |

### Die Cut Perf. 14½

| | | | |
|---|---|---|---|
| 3927 | Sheet of 10 + 10 labels | 21.00 | |
| a.-j. | A949 1st Any single + label | 2.10 | 2.10 |
| k. | Photo. (3927m) | 3.75 | 1.50 |
| l. | Photo. (3927m) | 3.75 | 1.50 |
| m. | Booklet pane of 6, #3927k, 3927l, 4 #MH426 | 10.00 | |

On day of issue, Nos. 3916-3925, 3926a-3926f, 3927k and 3927l each sold for 70p. No. 3927 sold for £8.10 with Nos. 3927a-3927j each having a franking value of 70p. Labels on No. 3927 could not be personalized.

A951

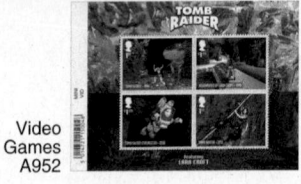

Video Games A952

Designs: No. 3928, Elite, 1984. No. 3929, Worms, 1995. No. 3930, Sensible Soccer, 1992. No. 3931, Lemmings, 1991. No. 3932, Wipeout, 1995. No. 3933, Micro Machines, 1991. No. 3934, Dizzy, 1987. No. 3935, Populous, 1989.

Nos. 3936a, 3937a, 3937e, Tomb Raider, 1996. Nos. 3936b, 3937f, Tomb Raider, 2013. Nos. 3936c, 3937c, Adventures of Lara Croft, 1998. Nos. 3936d, 3937d, Tomb Raider Chronicles, 2000.

**2020, Jan. 21   Litho.   Perf. 14**

| | | | |
|---|---|---|---|
| 3928 A951 | 2nd multi | 1.60 | 1.25 |
| 3929 A951 | 2nd multi | 1.60 | 1.25 |
| a. | Vert. pair, #3928-3929 | 3.20 | 2.50 |
| 3930 A951 | 1st multi | 1.90 | 1.40 |
| 3931 A951 | 1st multi | 1.90 | 1.40 |
| a. | Vert. pair, #3930-3931 | 3.80 | 2.80 |
| 3932 A951 | £1.55 multi | 4.00 | 3.00 |
| 3933 A951 | £1.55 multi | 4.00 | 3.00 |
| a. | Vert. pair, #3932-3933 | 8.00 | 6.00 |
| 3934 A951 | £1.60 multi | 4.25 | 3.25 |
| 3935 A951 | £1.60 multi | 4.25 | 3.25 |
| a. | Vert. pair, #3934-3935 | 8.50 | 6.50 |
| | Nos. 3928-3935 (8) | 23.50 | 17.80 |

### Miniature Sheets
### Perf. 14¼

| | | | |
|---|---|---|---|
| 3936 A952 | Sheet of 4 | 12.00 | 12.00 |
| a.-b. | 1st Either single | 1.90 | 1.40 |
| c.-d. | £1.55 Either single | 4.00 | 3.00 |

### Self-Adhesive
### Die Cut Perf. 14¼x14½

| | | | |
|---|---|---|---|
| 3937 A952 | Sheet of 10, 3 each #3937a-3937b, 2 each #3937c-3937d, + 10 labels | 30.00 | |
| a.-b. | 1st Either single | 2.00 | 2.00 |
| c.-d. | £1.55 Either single | 4.50 | 4.50 |
| e. | Photo., die cut perf. 14¼ | 3.75 | 1.40 |
| f. | Photo., die cut perf. 14¼ | 3.75 | 1.40 |
| g. | Booklet pane of 6, #3937e, 3937f, 4 #MH426 | 17.50 | |

On day of issue, Nos. 3928-3929 each sold for 61p, and Nos. 3930-3931, 3936a-3936b, 3937e-3937f each sold for 70p. On day of issue, Nos. 3937a-3937b had a franking value of 70p. No. 3937 sold for £11.40 and contains labels that cannot be personalized.

Visions of the Universe A953

Cat's Eye Nebula is composed of dust and gas.

Designs: No. 3938, Cat's Eye Nebula. No. 3939, Enceladus. No. 3940, Pulsar. No. 3941, Black hole. No. 3942, Aurora on Jupiter. No. 3943, Gravitational lensing. No. 3944, Comet 67P. No. 3945, Galaxy Cygnus A.

**2020, Feb. 11   Litho.   Perf. 14**

| | | | |
|---|---|---|---|
| 3938 A953 | 2nd multi | 1.60 | 1.25 |
| 3939 A953 | 2nd multi | 1.60 | 1.25 |
| a. | Horiz. pair, #3938-3939 | 3.20 | 2.50 |
| 3940 A953 | 1st multi | 1.90 | 1.40 |
| 3941 A953 | 1st multi | 1.90 | 1.40 |
| a. | Horiz. pair, #3940-3941 | 3.80 | 2.80 |
| 3942 A953 | £1.55 multi | 4.00 | 3.00 |
| 3943 A953 | £1.55 multi | 4.00 | 3.00 |
| a. | Booklet pane of 4, #3938, 3940, 3942, 3944 (BK1227) | 12.50 | — |
| 3945 A953 | £1.60 multi | 4.25 | 3.25 |
| a. | Horiz. pair, #3944-3945 | 8.50 | 6.50 |
| b. | Booklet pane of 4, #3939, 3941, 3943, 3945 (BK1227) | 12.50 | — |
| | Nos. 3938-3945 (7) | 19.25 | 14.55 |

Royal Astronomical Society, 200th anniv. On day of issue, Nos. 3938-3939 each sold for 61p, and Nos. 3940-3941 each sold for 70p.

### Penny Black, 175th Anniv. Type of 2015
### Die Cut Perf. 14¾x14 Syncopated
**2020, Mar. 10   Photo.**
### Booklet Stamp
### Self-Adhesive

| | | | |
|---|---|---|---|
| 3946 A798 | 1st Like #3396, beige & black | 3.75 | 1.40 |
| a. | Booklet pane of 6, 2 each #3396, 3478, 3946 | 10.50 | |

No. 3946 sold for 70p on day of issue.

Actors Who Have Portrayed James Bond in Movies — A954

Means of Transportation in James Bond Movies — A955

Designs: No. 3947, Daniel Craig in Casino Royale, 2006. No. 3948, Pierce Brosnan in GoldenEye, 1995. No. 3949, Timothy Dalton in The Living Daylights, 1987. No. 3950, Roger Moore in Live or Let Die, 1973. No. 3951, George Lazenby in On Her Majesty's Secret Service, 1969. No. 3952, Sean Connery in Goldfinger, 1964.

Nos. 3953a, 3954, Connery in Bell-Textron Jet Pack from Thunderball, 1965 (40x30mm). Nos. 3953b, 3955, Craig near Aston Martin D85 from Skyfall, 2012 (40x30mm). No. 3953c, Lotus Esprit Submarine from The Spy Who Loved Me, 1977 (60x30mm). No. 3953d, Connery in Little Nellie autogyro from You Only Live Twice, 1967 (60x30mm).

**2020, Mar. 17   Litho.   Perf. 14¾**

| | | | |
|---|---|---|---|
| 3947 A954 | 1st multi | 1.75 | 1.40 |
| 3948 A954 | 1st multi | 1.75 | 1.40 |
| 3949 A954 | 1st multi | 1.75 | 1.40 |
| a. | Horiz. strip of 3, #3947-3949 | 5.25 | 4.25 |
| 3950 A954 | £1.60 multi | 4.00 | 3.00 |
| a. | Booklet pane of 4, #3947-3950 (BK1228) | 10.00 | — |
| 3951 A954 | £1.60 multi | 4.00 | 3.00 |
| 3952 A954 | £1.60 multi | 4.00 | 3.00 |
| a. | Horiz. strip of 3, #3950-3952 | 12.00 | 9.00 |
| b. | Booklet pane of 2, #3951-3952 (BK1228) | 8.75 | — |
| c. | Sheet of 10, #3948-3951, 3 each #3947, 3952, +10 labels, perf. 14¼x14 | 32.00 | 32.00 |
| | Nos. 3947-3952 (6) | 17.25 | 13.20 |

### Miniature Sheet
### Perf. 14¼x14¾

| | | | |
|---|---|---|---|
| 3953 A955 | Sheet of 4 | 11.00 | 11.00 |
| a.-b. | 1st Either single | 1.75 | 1.40 |
| c.-d. | £1.55 Either single | 3.75 | 2.75 |
| e. | Booklet pane of 4, #3953a-3953d (BK1228) | 12.50 | — |

### Booklet Stamps
### Self-Adhesive
### Photo.
### Die Cut Perf. 14¼

| | | | |
|---|---|---|---|
| 3954 A955 | 1st multi | 4.00 | 1.40 |
| 3955 A955 | 1st multi | 4.00 | 1.40 |
| a. | Booklet pane of 6, #3954-3955, 4 #MH426 | 10.50 | |
| b. | Litho. single + label | 2.40 | 2.40 |
| c. | Sheet of 10 #3955b + 10 labels | 24.00 | |

On day of issue, Nos. 3947-3949, 3953a-3953b, 3954 and 3955 each sold for 70p. No. 3952c sold for £12.90 and labels could not be personalized. Perforations in one corner of Nos. 3953a-3953d were substituted with "007" perforations. No. 3955c sold for £9.70. Labels could not be personalized.

Lines of Romantic Poetry — A956

For every thing I felt a love The weeds below the birds above. 'The Progress of Rhyme' by John Clare

Designs: No. 3956, "For every thing I felt a love The weeds below the birds above," from The Progress of Rhyme by John Clare (1793-1864). No. 3957, "The frost performs its secret ministry Unhelped by any wind," from Frost at Midnight, by Samuel Taylor Coleridge (1772-1834). No. 3958, "To see a world in a grain of sand And a heaven in a wild flower," from Auguries of Innocence, by William Blake (1757-1827). No. 3959, "And mountains, that like giants stand, To sentinel enchanted land," from The Lady of the Lake, by Walter Scott (1771-1832). No. 3960, "Higher still and higher From the earth thou springest Like a cloud of fire," from To a Skylark, by Percy Bysshe Shelley (1792-1822). No. 3961, "My heart leaps up when I behold A rainbow in the sky," from The Rainbow, by William Wordsworth (1770-1850). No. 3962, "The snowdrop, Winter's timid child, Awakes to life, bedew'd with tears," from Ode to the Snowdrop, by Mary Robinson (1757-1800). No. 3963, "Absence is The moonlight of affection," from The Fate of Adelaide, by Letitia Elizabeth Landon (1802-38). No. 3964, "Beauty is Truth, Truth Beauty — That is all Ye know on earth, and all ye need to know," from Ode on a Grecian Urn, by John Keats (1795-1821). No. 3965, "She walks in beauty, like the night Of cloudless climes and starry skies," from She Walks in Beauty, by Lord Byron (1788-1824).

**2020, Apr. 17   Litho.   Perf. 14¼**

| | | | |
|---|---|---|---|
| 3956 A956 | 1st black & org brown | 1.90 | 1.40 |
| 3957 A956 | 1st black & org brown | 1.90 | 1.40 |
| 3958 A956 | 1st org brown & black | 1.90 | 1.40 |
| 3959 A956 | 1st black & org brown | 1.90 | 1.40 |
| 3960 A956 | 1st black & org brown | 1.90 | 1.40 |
| a. | Horiz. strip of 5, #3956-3960 | 9.50 | 7.00 |
| 3961 A956 | 1st black & org brown | 1.90 | 1.40 |
| 3962 A956 | 1st org brown & black | 1.90 | 1.40 |
| 3963 A956 | 1st black & org brown | 1.90 | 1.40 |
| 3964 A956 | 1st black & org brown | 1.90 | 1.40 |
| 3965 A956 | 1st black & org brown | 1.90 | 1.40 |
| a. | Horiz. strip of 5, #3961-3965 | 9.50 | 7.00 |
| | Nos. 3956-3965 (10) | 19.00 | 14.00 |

On day of issue, Nos. 3956-3965 each sold for 76p.

A957

**End of World War II, 75th Anniv.**
**A958**

Designs: No. 3966, Servicemen welcomed home. No. 3967, Nurses celebrate. No. 3968, Jubilant public. No. 3969, Evacuees return home. No. 3970, Troops parade at end of war. No. 3971, Demobilized servicemen. No. 3972, Allied prisoners of war liberated. No. 3973, Navy personnel celebrate.

No. 3974: a, Hall of Names, Holocaust History Museum, Yad Vashem, Jerusalem. b, Runnymede Memorial. c, Plymouth Naval Memorial. d, Rangoon Memorial, Myanmar.

| 2020, May 8 | Litho. | | Perf. 14¼ | |
|---|---|---|---|---|
| 3966 | A957 | 2nd multi | 1.60 | 1.25 |
| 3967 | A957 | 2nd multi | 1.60 | 1.25 |
| a. | | Vert. pair, #3966-3977 | 3.20 | 1.25 |
| 3968 | A957 | 1st multi | 1.90 | 1.40 |
| 3969 | A957 | 1st multi | 1.90 | 1.40 |
| a. | | Vert. pair, #3968-3969 | 3.80 | 2.80 |
| b. | | Booklet pane of 4, #3966-3969 (BK1229) | 7.50 | — |
| 3970 | A957 | £1.42 multi | 3.50 | 2.60 |
| 3971 | A957 | £1.42 multi | 3.50 | 2.60 |
| a. | | Vert. pair, #3970-3971 | 7.00 | 5.20 |
| 3972 | A957 | £1.63 multi | 4.00 | 3.00 |
| 3973 | A957 | £1.63 multi | 4.00 | 3.00 |
| b. | | Vert. pair, #3972-3973 | 8.00 | 6.00 |
| b. | | Booklet pane of 4, #3970-3973 (BK1229) | 16.50 | — |
| | | Nos. 3966-3973 (8) | 22.00 | 16.50 |
| | | **Miniature Sheet** | | |
| | | **Perf. 14¾** | | |
| 3974 | A958 | Sheet of 4 | 12.00 | 12.00 |
| a.-b. | | 1st Either single | 1.90 | 1.40 |
| c.-d. | | £1.63 Either single | 4.00 | 3.00 |
| | | Booklet pane of 4, #3974a-3974d (BK1229) | 13.00 | — |

On day of issue. Nos. 3966-3967 each sold for 65p, and Nos. 3968-3969, 3974a-3974b each sold for 76p.

A959

*Coronation Street* Television Series, 60th Anniv. — A960

Characters and lines from the program: No. 3975, Ena Sharples and Elsie Tanner, "That woman's tongue. If it was a bit longer she could shave with it." No. 3976, Stan and Hilda Ogden, "Woman, Stanley, woman." Nos. 3977, 3984, Vera and Jack Duckworth, " Vera, my little swamp duck." Nos. 3978, 3985, Deirdre and Ken Barlow, "Ken! Do something!" No. 3979, Rita Sullivan and Norris Cole, "I can't abide to see people gossiping." No. 3980, Hayley and Roy Cropper, "Be nice if every day I have left would be like this." No. 3981, Sunita and Dev Alahan, "I love you. We shouldn't be apart a minute longer." No. 3982, Tracy Barlow and Steve McDonald, "I always thought that I'd be the person you'd cheat with, not on!"

No. 3983 — Characters: a, Bet Lynch. b, Raquel Watts. c, Liz McDonald. d, Gemma Winter.

| 2020, May 28 | Litho. | | Perf. 14¼ | |
|---|---|---|---|---|
| 3975 | A959 | 2nd multi | 1.60 | 1.25 |
| 3976 | A959 | 2nd multi | 1.60 | 1.25 |
| a. | | Horiz. pair, #3975-3976 | 3.20 | 2.50 |
| 3977 | A959 | 1st multi | 1.90 | 1.40 |
| 3978 | A959 | 1st multi | 1.90 | 1.40 |
| a. | | Horiz. pair, #3977-3978 | 3.80 | 2.80 |
| 3979 | A959 | £1.42 multi | 3.50 | 2.60 |
| 3980 | A959 | £1.42 multi | 3.50 | 2.60 |
| a. | | Horiz. pair, #3979-3980 | 7.00 | 5.20 |
| 3981 | A959 | £1.63 multi | 4.00 | 3.00 |
| 3982 | A959 | £1.63 multi | 4.00 | 3.00 |
| a. | | Horiz. pair, #3981-3982 | 8.00 | 6.00 |
| | | Nos. 3975-3982 (8) | 22.00 | 16.50 |
| | | **Miniature Sheet** | | |
| 3983 | A960 | Sheet of 4 | 11.00 | 11.00 |
| a.-b. | | 1st Either single | 1.90 | 1.40 |
| c.-d. | | £1.42 Either single | 3.50 | 2.60 |
| | | **Booklet Stamps** | | |
| | | **Self-Adhesive** | | |
| | | **Photo.** | | |
| | | **Die Cut Perf. 14¼** | | |
| 3984 | A959 | 1st multi | 4.50 | 1.40 |
| a. | | Litho. + label, perf. 14¼x14½ | 2.25 | 2.25 |

| 3985 | A959 | 1st multi | 4.50 | 1.40 |
|---|---|---|---|---|
| a. | | Booklet pane of 6, #3984-3985, 4 #MH426 | 11.50 | |
| b. | | Litho. + label, perf. 14¼x14½ | 2.25 | 2.25 |

On day of issue, Nos. 3975-3976 each sold for 65p, and Nos. 3977-3978, 3984-3985 each sold for 76p. A sheet containing 5 each of Nos. 3984a and 3985b, + 10 labels that could not be personalized sold for £8.80.

**Artifacts of Roman Era in Britain — A961**

Designs: No. 3986, Dover Lighthouse. No. 3987, Bignor Mosaic depicting Venus. No. 3988, Amphitheater, Isca Fortress, Caerleon, Wales. No. 3989, Ribchester helmet. No. 3990, Bridgeness distance slab. No. 3991, Warrior god, Cambridgeshire. No. 3992, Gorgon's head, Bath. No. 3993, Hadrian's Wall.

| 2020, June 18 | Litho. | | Perf. 14¼ | |
|---|---|---|---|---|
| 3986 | A961 | 2nd multi | 1.60 | 1.25 |
| 3987 | A961 | 2nd multi | 1.60 | 1.25 |
| a. | | Horiz. pair, #3986-3987 | 3.20 | 2.50 |
| 3988 | A961 | 1st multi | 1.90 | 1.40 |
| 3989 | A961 | 1st multi | 1.90 | 1.40 |
| a. | | Horiz. pair, #3988-3989 | 3.80 | 2.80 |
| 3990 | A961 | £1.63 multi | 4.00 | 3.00 |
| 3991 | A961 | £1.63 multi | 4.00 | 3.00 |
| a. | | Horiz. pair, #3990-3991 | 8.00 | 6.00 |
| 3992 | A961 | £1.68 multi | 4.25 | 3.25 |
| 3993 | A961 | £1.68 multi | 4.25 | 3.25 |
| a. | | Horiz. pair, #3992-3993 | 8.50 | 6.50 |
| | | Nos. 3986-3993 (8) | 23.50 | 17.80 |

On day of issue, Nos. 3986-3987 each sold for 65p and Nos. 3988-3989 each sold for 76p.

*Queen II*, by Queen, 1974 — A962

*Sheer Heart Attack*, by Queen, 1974 — A963

*A Night at the Opera*, by Queen, 1975 — A964

*News of the World*, by Queen, 1977 — A965

*The Game*, by Queen, 1980 — A966

*Greatest Hits*, by Queen, 1981 — A967

*The Works*, by Queen, 1984 — A968

*Innuendo*, by Queen, 1991 — A969

Members of Queen A970

Designs: No. 4002a, Freddie Mercury performing during 1986 Magic Tour (35x35mm). No. 4002b, Roger Taylor performing during 1976 Hyde Park Concert (35x35mm). Nos. 4002c, 4004, 1974 photograph of band (21x24mm). No. 4002d, John Deacon performing during 1975 A Night at the Opera Tour (35x35mm). No. 4002e, Brian May performing during 1986 Magic Tour (35x35mm).

| 2020, July 9 | Litho. | | Perf. 14¼ | |
|---|---|---|---|---|
| 3994 | A962 | 1st multi | 2.00 | 1.50 |
| 3995 | A963 | 1st multi | 2.00 | 1.50 |
| 3996 | A964 | 1st multi | 2.00 | 1.50 |
| 3997 | A965 | 1st multi | 2.00 | 1.50 |
| a. | | Horiz. strip of 4, #3994-3997 | 8.00 | 6.00 |
| b. | | Booklet pane of 4, #3994-3997 (BK1230) | 8.75 | |
| 3998 | A966 | £1.63 multi | 4.25 | 3.25 |
| 3999 | A967 | £1.63 multi | 4.25 | 3.25 |
| 4000 | A968 | £1.63 multi | 4.25 | 3.25 |
| 4001 | A969 | £1.63 multi | 4.25 | 3.25 |
| a. | | Horiz. strip of 4, #3998-4001 | 17.00 | 13.00 |
| b. | | Souvenir sheet of 8, #3994-4001 | 37.50 | 37.50 |
| c. | | Booklet pane of 4, #3998-4001 (BK1230) | 18.50 | — |
| | | Nos. 3994-4001 (8) | 25.00 | 19.00 |
| | | **Miniature Sheet** | | |
| | | **Perf. 14½, 14¾x14 Syncopated (#4002c)** | | |
| 4002 | A970 | Sheet of 5 | 14.50 | 14.50 |
| a.-c. | | 1st Any single | 2.00 | 1.50 |
| d.-e. | | £1.63 Either single | 4.25 | 3.25 |
| f. | | Booklet pane of 6, #4002a, 4002b, 4002d, 4002e (BK1230) | 13.50 | — |
| g. | | Booklet pane of 8, 4 each #4002c, MH438 (BK1230) | 9.00 | — |
| | | **Self-Adhesive** | | |
| | | **Die Cut Perf. 13¼x13 Syncopated** | | |
| 4003 | | Sheet of 10, #4003a, 4003b, 4003d, 4003e, 4003g, 4003h, 2 each #4003c, 40003f + 10 labels | 35.00 | |
| a. | | 4962 1st multi | 2.25 | 2.25 |
| b. | | 4963 1st multi | 2.25 | 2.25 |
| c. | | 4964 1st multi | 2.25 | 2.25 |
| d. | | 4965 1st multi | 2.25 | 2.25 |
| e. | | 4966 £1.63 multi | 4.75 | 4.75 |
| f. | | 4967 £1.63 multi | 4.75 | 4.75 |
| g. | | 4968 £1.63 multi | 4.75 | 4.75 |
| h. | | 4969 £1.63 multi | 4.75 | 4.75 |
| i. | | 4962 1st Photo, die cut perf. 14¼x14 | 2.00 | 1.50 |
| j. | | 4964 1st Photo, die cut perf. 14¼x14 | 2.00 | 1.50 |
| k. | | Booklet pane of 6, #4003i, 4003j, 4 #MH426 | 12.00 | |
| | | **Die Cut Perf. 14¾x14 Syncopated** | | |
| 4004 | A970 | 1st multi + label | 2.25 | 2.25 |
| a. | | Photo. (booklet stamp) | 2.40 | 1.90 |
| b. | | Booklet pane of 6, #4004a | 14.50 | |

On day of issue, Nos. 3994-3997, 4002a, 4002b, 4003i and 4003j each sold for 76p. No. 4003 sold for £13.15 and Nos. 4003a-4003d had a franking value of 76p. Labels on No. 4003 could not be personalized. No. 4004 had a franking value of 76p, and was printed in sheets of 10 + 10 labels that could not be personalized. The sheet sold for £8.80. A sheet of 4 of No. 3996 sold for £7.50.

Issued: Nos. 4004a, 4004b, 3/29/21. No. 4004b sold for £5.10, and contained six stamps that had a franking value of 85p. This booklet was issued after the 1st rate had been increased from the 76p franking value that No. 4004 had when it was issued.

A971

**Palace of Westminster — A972**

Designs: No. 4005, View from Old Palace Yard. No. 4006, River Thames view. No. 4007, Elizabeth Tower. No. 4008, Commons Chamber. No. 4009, Central Lobby. No. 4010, Lords Chamber.

No. 4011: a, Norman Porch. b, Chapel of St. Mary undercroft. c, St. Stephen's Hall. d, Royal Gallery.

| 2020, July 30 | Litho. | | Perf. 14¾ | |
|---|---|---|---|---|
| 4005 | A971 | 1st multi | 2.00 | 1.50 |
| 4006 | A971 | 1st multi | 2.00 | 1.50 |
| 4007 | A971 | 1st multi | 2.00 | 1.50 |
| a. | | Horiz. strip of 3, #4005-4007 | 6.00 | 4.50 |
| 4008 | A971 | £1.68 multi | 4.50 | 3.50 |
| 4009 | A971 | £1.68 multi | 4.50 | 3.50 |
| 4010 | A971 | £1.68 multi | 4.50 | 3.50 |
| a. | | Horiz. strip of 3, #4008-4010 | 13.50 | 10.50 |
| | | Nos. 4005-4010 (6) | 19.50 | 15.00 |
| | | **Miniature Sheet** | | |
| | | **Perf. 14¼** | | |
| 4011 | A972 | Sheet of 4 | 12.50 | 12.50 |
| a.-b. | | 1st Either single | 2.00 | 1.50 |
| c.-d. | | £1.63 Either single | 4.25 | 3.25 |

On day of issue, Nos. 4005-4007, 4011a-4011b each sold for 76p.

A973

**Sherlock Holmes Mystery Stories by Sir Arthur Conan Doyle (1859-1930) — A974**

Designs: Nos. 4012, 4019a, The Reichenbach Fall. Nos. 4013, 4019b, A Study in Pink. Nos. 4014, 4019c, The Great Game. Nos. 4015, 4019d, The Empty Hearse. Nos. 4016, 4019e, A Scandal in Belgravia. Nos. 4017, 4019f, The Final Problem.

Nos. 4018a, 4021, The Adventure of the Speckled Band. Nos. 4018b, 4020, The Red-Headed League. No. 4018c, The Adventure of the Second Stain. No. 4018d, The Adventure of the Dancing Men.

| 2020, Aug. 18 | Litho. | | Perf. 14¾ | |
|---|---|---|---|---|
| 4012 | A973 | 1st multi | 2.10 | 1.60 |
| 4013 | A973 | 1st multi | 2.10 | 1.60 |
| a. | | Vert. pair, #4012-4013 | 4.20 | 3.20 |
| 4014 | A973 | £1.42 multi | 4.00 | 3.00 |
| 4015 | A973 | £1.42 multi | 4.00 | 3.00 |
| a. | | Vert. pair, #4014-4015 | 8.00 | 6.00 |
| 4016 | A973 | £1.68 multi | 4.50 | 3.50 |
| 4017 | A973 | £1.68 multi | 4.50 | 3.50 |
| a. | | Vert. pair, #4016-4017 | 9.00 | 7.00 |
| | | Nos. 4012-4017 (6) | 21.20 | 16.20 |
| | | **Souvenir Sheet** | | |
| | | **Perf. 14x14¼** | | |
| 4018 | A974 | Sheet of 4 | 13.50 | 13.50 |
| a.-b. | | 1st Either single | 2.10 | 1.60 |
| c.-d. | | £1.68 Either single | 4.50 | 3.50 |
| | | **Self-Adhesive** | | |
| | | **Die Cut Perf. 14** | | |
| 4019 | | Sheet of 10, #4019c-2 #4019a, 2 #4019b, + 10 labels | 33.50 | |
| a.-b. | | A973 1st Either single | 2.25 | 2.25 |
| c.-d. | | A973 £1.42 Either single | 4.25 | 4.25 |
| e.-f. | | A973 £1.68 Either single | 5.75 | 5.75 |
| | | **Booklet Stamps** | | |
| | | **Photo.** | | |
| | | **Die Cut Perf. 14x14¼** | | |
| 4020 | A974 | 1st multi | 4.50 | 1.60 |
| 4021 | A974 | 1st multi | 4.50 | 1.60 |
| a. | | Booklet pane of 6, #4020-4021, 4 #MH426 | 13.50 | |

On day of issue, Nos. 4012-4013, 4018a-4018b, 4020-4021 each sold for 76p. No. 4019 sold for £11.95, and Nos. 4019a-4019b each had a franking value of 76p. Labels on No. 4019 could not be personalized.

**Rupert Bear Comic Strips by Mary Tourtel (1874-1948), Cent. — A975**

Inscriptions: No. 4022, Then with a terrifying roar, the water bursts in through the door. No. 4023, The bath is rocked from side to side, and Pompey quite enjoys his ride. No. 4024, Then Algy looks a trifle glum, "I'm going home," he tells his chum. No. 4025, The large bird says "Our king will know; climb on my back and off we'll go." No. 4026, "There's something puzzling all of you," says Rupert. "So please tell me too." No. 4027, "My cuckoo's back again — hooray! He didn't really go away!" No. 4028, Though Rupert searches all around, there's not one spruce tree to be found. No. 4029, The tree is such a lovely sight, that Rupert's chums gaze with delight.

| 2020, Sept. 3 | Litho. | | Perf. 14¼ | |
|---|---|---|---|---|
| 4022 | A975 | 2nd multi | 1.75 | 1.40 |
| 4023 | A975 | 2nd multi | 1.75 | 1.40 |
| a. | | Horiz. pair, #4022-4023 | 3.50 | 2.80 |
| 4024 | A975 | 1st multi | 2.00 | 1.50 |
| 4025 | A975 | 1st multi | 2.00 | 1.50 |
| a. | | Horiz. pair, #4024-4025 | 4.00 | 3.00 |
| 4026 | A975 | £1.45 multi | 3.75 | 2.75 |
| 4027 | A975 | £1.45 multi | 3.75 | 2.75 |
| a. | | Horiz. pair, #4026-4027 | 7.50 | 5.50 |

| | | | | | |
|---|---|---|---|---|---|
| **4028** | A975 | £1.70 multi | | 4.50 | 3.50 |
| **4029** | A975 | £1.70 multi | | 4.50 | 3.50 |
| *a.* | Horiz. pair, #4028-4029 | | | 9.00 | 7.00 |
| | *Nos. 4022-4029 (8)* | | | 24.00 | 18.30 |

On day of issue, Nos. 4022-4023 each sold for 65p, and Nos. 4024-4025 each sold for 76p.

**Pollinators — A976**

Designs: No. 4030, Common carder bee. No. 4031, Painted lady butterfly. No. 4032, Longhorn beetle. No. 4033, Elephant hawkmoth. No. 4034, Marmalade hoverfly. No. 4035, Ruby-tailed wasp.

| **2020, Oct. 1** | | **Litho.** | | **Perf. 14¼** | |
|---|---|---|---|---|---|
| **4030** | A976 | 1st multi | | 2.00 | 1.50 |
| **4031** | A976 | 1st multi | | 2.00 | 1.50 |
| *a.* | Vert. pair, #4030-4031 | | | 4.00 | 3.00 |
| **4032** | A976 | £1.45 multi | | 3.75 | 2.75 |
| **4033** | A976 | £1.45 multi | | 3.75 | 2.75 |
| *a.* | Vert. pair, #4032-4033 | | | 7.50 | 5.50 |
| **4034** | A976 | £1.70 multi | | 4.50 | 3.50 |
| **4035** | A976 | £1.70 multi | | 4.50 | 3.50 |
| *a.* | Vert. pair, #4034-4035 | | | 9.00 | 7.00 |
| | *Nos. 4030-4035 (6)* | | | 20.50 | 15.50 |

On day of issue, Nos. 4030-4031 each sold for 76p.

A977

**Christmas — A978**

Stained-glass windows depicting Madonna and Child from: Nos. 4036a, 4036c, 4037, 4039, St. Andrew's Church, East Lexham. Nos. 4036b, 4036d, 4038, 4040, St. Andrew's church, Coln Rogers. Nos. 4036e, 4041, Church of St. James, Hollowell. Nos. 4036f, 4042, All Saints Church, Otley. Nos. 4036g, 4043, St. Columba's Church, Topcliffe. Nos. 4036h, Christ Church, Coalville.

| **2020, Nov. 3** | | **Litho.** | | **Perf. 14½x15** | |
|---|---|---|---|---|---|
| **4036** | | Sheet of 8 | | 30.50 | 30.50 |
| *a.* | A977 2nd multi | | | 1.75 | 1.40 |
| *b.* | A977 1st multi | | | 2.00 | 1.50 |
| *c.* | A978 2nd Large multi | | | 2.25 | 1.75 |
| *d.* | A978 1st Large multi | | | 3.00 | 2.25 |
| *e.* | A977 £1.45 multi | | | 3.75 | 2.75 |
| *f.* | A977 £1.70 multi | | | 4.50 | 3.50 |
| *g.* | A977 £2.50 multi | | | 6.50 | 5.00 |
| *h.* | A977 £2.55 multi | | | 6.75 | 5.00 |

**Photo.**
**Self-Adhesive**
***Die Cut Perf. 14½x15***

| | | | | | |
|---|---|---|---|---|---|
| **4037** | A977 | 2nd multi | | 1.75 | 1.40 |
| *a.* | Booklet pane of 12 | | | 21.00 | |
| *b.* | Litho., die cut perf. 14½x15 syncopated, + label (#4044b) | | | 1.90 | 1.90 |
| **4038** | A977 | 1st multi | | 2.00 | 1.50 |
| *a.* | Booklet pane of 12 | | | 24.00 | |
| *b.* | Litho., die cut perf. 14½x15 syncopated, + label (#4044b) | | | 2.10 | 2.10 |
| **4039** | A978 | 2nd Large multi | | 2.25 | 1.75 |
| **4040** | A978 | 1st Large multi | | 3.00 | 2.25 |
| **4041** | A977 | £1.45 multi | | 3.75 | 2.75 |
| *a.* | Litho., die cut perf. 14½x15 syncopated, + label (#4044b) | | | 4.00 | 4.00 |
| **4042** | A977 | £1.70 multi | | 4.50 | 3.50 |
| *a.* | Litho., die cut perf. 14½x15 syncopated, + label (#4044b) | | | 4.75 | 4.75 |
| **4043** | A977 | £2.50 multi | | 6.50 | 5.00 |
| *a.* | Litho., die cut perf. 14½x15 syncopated, + label (#4044b) | | | 7.00 | 7.00 |
| **4044** | A977 | £2.55 multi | | 6.75 | 5.00 |
| *a.* | Litho., die cut perf. 14½x15 syncopated, + label (#4044b) | | | 7.00 | 7.00 |
| *b.* | Sheet of 20, #4041a, 4042a, 4043a, 4044a, 8 each #4037b, 4038b, + 20 labels | | | 55.00 | |
| | *Nos. 4037-4044 (8)* | | | 30.50 | 23.15 |

On day of issue, Nos. 4036a and 4037 each sold for 65p; Nos. 4036b and 4038, for 76p; Nos. 4036c and 4039, for 88p; Nos. 4036d and 4040, for £1.15. No. 4044b sold for £20.60 and labels could not be personalized.

A979

**Characters From *Star Trek* Television Series and Movies — A980**

Designs: Nos. 4045, 4058a, 4058g, Captain James T. Kirk. Nos. 4046, 4058b, 4058h, Captain Jean-Luc Picard. Nos. 4047, 4058c, Captain Benjamin Sisko. Nos. 4048, 4058d, Capatin Kathryn Janeway. Nos. 4049, 4058e, Captain Jonathan Archer. Nos. 4050, 4058f, Captain Gabriel Lorca. No. 4051, Spock. No. 4052, Deanna Troi. No. 4053, Dr. Julian Bashir. No. 4054, Malcolm Reed. No. 4055, Michael Burnham. No. 4056, Ash Tyler.
No. 4057: a, Montgomery Scott (60x21mm). b, Shinzon (60x21mm). c, Tolian Soran (22x37mm). d, Chancellor Gorkon (22x37mm). e, Carol Marcus (22x37mm). f, Krall (22x37mm).

| **2020, Nov. 13** | | **Litho.** | | **Perf. 14½** | |
|---|---|---|---|---|---|
| **4045** | A979 | 1st multi | | 2.10 | 1.60 |
| **4046** | A979 | 1st multi | | 2.10 | 1.60 |
| **4047** | A979 | 1st multi | | 2.10 | 1.60 |
| **4048** | A979 | 1st multi | | 2.10 | 1.60 |
| **4049** | A979 | 1st multi | | 2.10 | 1.60 |
| **4050** | A979 | 1st multi | | 2.10 | 1.60 |
| *a.* | Horiz. strip of 6, #4045-4050 | | | 13.00 | 9.75 |
| *b.* | Booklet pane of 6, #4045-4050 (BK1231) | | | 13.00 | |
| **4051** | A979 | 1st multi | | 2.10 | 1.60 |
| **4052** | A979 | 1st multi | | 2.10 | 1.60 |
| **4053** | A979 | 1st multi | | 2.10 | 1.60 |
| **4054** | A979 | 1st multi | | 2.10 | 1.60 |
| **4055** | A979 | 1st multi | | 2.10 | 1.60 |
| **4056** | A979 | 1st multi | | 2.10 | 1.60 |
| *a.* | Horiz. strip of 6, #4051-4056 | | | 13.00 | 9.75 |
| *b.* | Booklet pane of 6, #4051-4056 (BK1231) | | | 13.00 | |
| | *Nos. 4045-4056 (12)* | | | 25.20 | 19.20 |

**Self-Adhesive**
***Die Cut Perf. 14¾x14¼ (#4057a-4057b), 14¼ (#4057c-4057f)***

| | | | | | |
|---|---|---|---|---|---|
| **4057** | A980 | Sheet of 6 | | 13.00 | |
| *a.-f.* | 1st Any single | | | 2.10 | 1.60 |
| *g.* | Booklet pane of 6, #4057a-4057f (BK1231) | | | 13.00 | |

***Die Cut Perf. 14½***

| | | | | | |
|---|---|---|---|---|---|
| **4058** | | Sheet of 10, #4058c-4058f, 3 each #4058a-4058b, + 10 labels | | 26.00 | |
| *a.-f.* | A979 1st Any single + label | | | 2.60 | 2.60 |
| *g.* | A979 1st Photo. (booklet stamp) | | | 2.10 | 1.60 |
| *i.* | A979 1st Photo. (booklet stamp) | | | 2.10 | 1.60 |
| *i.* | Booklet pane of 6, #4058g-4058h, 4 #MH426 | | | | |

On day of issue, Nos. 4045-4056, 4057a-4057f each sold for 76p. No. 4058 sold for £9.70 and labels could not be personalized.

**National Parks — A981**

Designs: No. 4059, Dartmoor National Park. No. 4060, New Forest National Park. No. 4061, Lake District National Park. No. 4062, Loch Lomond & the Trossachs National Park. Nos. 4063, 4070, Snowdonia National Park. No. 4064, North York Moors National Park. No. 4065, South Downs National Park. Nos. 4066, 4069, Peak District National Park. No. 4067, Pembrokeshire Coast National Park. No. 4068, Broads National Park.

| **2021, Jan. 14** | | **Litho.** | | **Perf. 14½** | |
|---|---|---|---|---|---|
| **4059** | A981 | 1st multi | | 2.40 | 1.75 |
| **4060** | A981 | 1st multi | | 2.40 | 1.75 |
| **4061** | A981 | 1st multi | | 2.40 | 1.75 |
| **4062** | A981 | 1st multi | | 2.40 | 1.75 |
| **4063** | A981 | 1st multi | | 2.40 | 1.75 |
| *a.* | Horiz. strip of 5, #4059-4063 | | | 12.00 | 8.75 |
| **4064** | A981 | 1st multi | | 2.40 | 1.75 |
| **4065** | A981 | 1st multi | | 2.40 | 1.75 |
| **4066** | A981 | 1st multi | | 2.40 | 1.75 |
| **4067** | A981 | 1st multi | | 2.40 | 1.75 |
| **4068** | A981 | 1st multi | | 2.40 | 1.75 |
| *a.* | Horiz. strip of 5, #4064-4068 | | | 12.00 | 8.75 |
| | *Nos. 4059-4068 (10)* | | | 24.00 | 17.50 |

**Photo.**
**Booklet Stamp**
**Self-Adhesive**
***Die Cut Perf. 14½***

| | | | | | |
|---|---|---|---|---|---|
| **4069** | A981 | 1st multi | | 4.50 | 1.75 |
| **4070** | A981 | 1st multi | | 4.50 | 1.75 |
| *a.* | Booklet pane of 6, #4069-4070, 4 #MH426 | | | 14.50 | |

On day of issue, Nos. 4059-4070 each sold for 85p.

**Miniature Sheet**

**Strengths and Accomplishments — A982**

No. 4071 — Inscriptions: a, Great Sport. b, Great Creativity. c, Great Community. d, Great Industry and Innovation.

| **2021, Jan. 15** | | **Litho.** | | **Perf. 15x14¾** | |
|---|---|---|---|---|---|
| **4071** | A982 | Sheet of 4 | | 14.50 | 14.50 |
| *a.-b.* | 1st Either single | | | 2.40 | 1.75 |
| *c.-d.* | £1.70 Either single | | | 4.75 | 3.50 |

On day of issue, Nos. 4071a-4071b each sold for 85p.

A983

***Only Fools and Horses* Television Series, 40th Anniv. — A984**

Lines from show characters: No. 4072, "I knew you was cheating, Boycie." and "Because that wasn't the hand I dealt you." No. 4073, "Don't worry, he's house-trained." and "Hey, we live in a flat!" No. 4074, "Play it nice and cool, son, nice and cool." No. 4075, "Now brace yourself, Rodney, brace yourself." No. 4076, "Our coach has just blown up!" No. 4077, " What have you been doing?" and "I've been skateboarding, Cassandra." No. 4078, "It's a baby, Raquel!" and "I've been wondering what that swelling was." No. 4079, "That's just over three million each!"
Nos. 4080a, 4081, Del Boy and "This time next year, we'll be millionaires!" Nos. 4080b, 4082, Rodney and "Cosmic!" No. 4080c, Uncle Albert and "During the war. . ." No. 4080d, Grandad and "I've always wanted to go to Benidorm. Where is it?"

| **2021, Feb. 16** | | **Litho.** | | **Perf. 14** | |
|---|---|---|---|---|---|
| **4072** | A983 | 1st multi | | 2.40 | 1.75 |
| **4073** | A983 | 1st multi | | 2.40 | 1.75 |
| *a.* | Vert. pair, #4072-4073 | | | 4.80 | 3.50 |
| **4074** | A983 | 1st multi | | 2.40 | 1.75 |
| **4075** | A983 | 1st multi | | 2.40 | 1.75 |
| *a.* | Vert. pair, #4074-4075 | | | 4.80 | 3.50 |
| *b.* | Booklet pane of 4, #4072-4075 (BK1232) | | | 10.50 | — |
| **4076** | A983 | £1.70 multi | | 4.75 | 3.50 |
| **4077** | A983 | £1.70 multi | | 4.75 | 3.50 |
| *a.* | Vert. pair, #4076-4077 | | | 9.50 | 7.00 |
| **4078** | A983 | £1.70 multi | | 4.75 | 3.50 |
| **4079** | A983 | £1.70 multi | | 4.75 | 3.50 |
| *a.* | Vert. pair, #4078-4079 | | | 9.50 | 7.00 |
| *b.* | Booklet pane of 4, #4076-4079 (BK1232) | | | 20.50 | — |
| | *Nos. 4072-4079 (8)* | | | 28.60 | 21.00 |

**Miniature Sheet**
***Perf. 14½x14***

| | | | | | |
|---|---|---|---|---|---|
| **4080** | A984 | Sheet of 4 | | 14.50 | 14.50 |
| *a.-b.* | 1st Either single | | | 2.40 | 1.75 |
| *c.-d.* | £1.70 Either single | | | 4.75 | 3.50 |
| *e.* | Booklet pane of 4, #4080a-4080d (BK1232) | | | 15.50 | — |

**Self-Adhesive**
**Photo.**
***Die Cut Perf. 14½x14***

| | | | | | |
|---|---|---|---|---|---|
| **4081** | A984 | 1st multi | | 4.50 | 1.75 |
| *a.* | Litho. + label, die cut perf. 14½ | | | 2.75 | 2.75 |
| **4082** | A984 | 1st multi | | 4.50 | 1.75 |
| *a.* | Booklet pane of 6, #4081-4082, 4 #MH426 | | | 14.50 | |
| *b.* | Litho. + label, die cut perf. 14½ | | | 2.75 | 2.75 |

On day of issue, Nos. 4072-4075, 4080a-4080b, 4081-4082 each sold for 85p. Nos. 4081-4082 were only issued in booklets. Nos. 4081a and 4082b were printed in sheets containing five of each stamp + 10 labels that could not be personalized. That sheet sold for £9.60.

**The Legend of King Arthur — A985**

Designs: No. 4083, Merlin and the baby Arthur. No. 4084, Arthur draws the sword from the stone. No. 4085, Arthur takes Excalibur. No. 4086, Arthur marries Guinevere. No. 4087, Sir Gawain and the Green Knight. No. 4088, Knights of the Round Table. No. 4089, Sir Lancelot defeats the dragon. No. 4090, Sir Galahad and the Holy Grail. No. 4091, Arthur battles Mordred. No. 4092, The death of King Arthur.

| **2021, Mar. 16** | | **Litho.** | | **Perf. 14½** | |
|---|---|---|---|---|---|
| **4083** | A985 | 1st multi | | 2.40 | 1.90 |
| **4084** | A985 | 1st multi | | 2.40 | 1.90 |
| **4085** | A985 | 1st multi | | 2.40 | 1.90 |
| **4086** | A985 | 1st multi | | 2.40 | 1.90 |
| **4087** | A985 | 1st multi | | 2.40 | 1.90 |
| *a.* | Horiz. strip of 5, #4083-4087 | | | 12.00 | 9.50 |
| **4088** | A985 | £1.70 multi | | 4.75 | 3.75 |
| **4089** | A985 | £1.70 multi | | 4.75 | 3.75 |
| **4090** | A985 | £1.70 multi | | 4.75 | 3.75 |
| **4091** | A985 | £1.70 multi | | 4.75 | 3.75 |
| **4092** | A985 | £1.70 multi | | 4.75 | 3.75 |
| *a.* | Horiz. strip of 5, #4088-4092 | | | 24.00 | 19.00 |
| | *Nos. 4083-4092 (10)* | | | 35.75 | 28.25 |

Nos. 4083-4087 each sold for 85p on day of issue.

**Science Fiction Novels by British Authors — A986**

Designs: No. 4093, *Frankenstein*, by Mary Shelley (1797-1851). No. 4094, *The Time Machine*, by H. G. Wells (1866-1946). No. 4095, *Brave New World*, by Aldous Huxley (1894-1963). No. 4096, *The Day of the Triffids*, by John Wyndham (1903-69). No. 4097, *Childhood's End*, by Arthur C. Clarke (1917-2008). No. 4098, *Shikasta*, by Doris Lessing (1919-2013).

| **2021, Apr. 15** | | **Litho.** | | **Perf. 14¼** | |
|---|---|---|---|---|---|
| **4093** | A986 | 1st multi | | 2.40 | 2.40 |
| **4094** | A986 | 1st multi | | 2.40 | 2.40 |
| *a.* | Horiz. pair, #4093-4094 | | | 4.80 | 4.80 |
| **4095** | A986 | £1.70 multi | | 4.75 | 4.75 |
| **4096** | A986 | £1.70 multi | | 4.75 | 4.75 |
| *a.* | Horiz. pair, #4095-4096 | | | 9.50 | 9.50 |
| **4097** | A986 | £2.55 multi | | 7.00 | 7.00 |
| **4098** | A986 | £2.55 multi | | 7.00 | 7.00 |
| *a.* | Horiz. pair, #4097-4098 | | | 14.00 | 14.00 |
| | *Nos. 4093-4098 (6)* | | | 28.30 | 28.30 |

On day of issue, Nos. 4093-4094 each sold for 85p.

**15th Century Battles A987**

Designs: No. 4099, Battle of Bosworth, 1485. No. 4100, Battle of Tewkesbury, 1471. No. 4101, Battle of Barnet, 1471. No. 4102, Battle of Edgecote Moor, 1469. No. 4103, Battle of Towton, 1461. No. 4104, Battle of Wakefield, 1460. No. 4105, Battle of Northampton, 1460. No. 4106, First Battle of St. Albans, 1455.

| **2021, May 4** | | **Litho.** | | **Perf. 14** | |
|---|---|---|---|---|---|
| **4099** | A987 | 2nd multi | | 1.90 | 1.90 |
| **4100** | A987 | 2nd multi | | 1.90 | 1.90 |
| *a.* | Horiz. pair, #4099-4100 | | | 3.80 | 3.80 |
| **4101** | A987 | 1st multi | | 2.40 | 2.40 |
| **4102** | A987 | 1st multi | | 2.40 | 2.40 |
| *a.* | Horiz. pair, #4101-4102 | | | 4.80 | 4.80 |
| **4103** | A987 | £1.70 multi | | 5.00 | 5.00 |
| **4104** | A987 | £1.70 multi | | 5.00 | 5.00 |
| *a.* | Horiz. pair, #4103-4104 | | | 10.00 | 10.00 |
| **4105** | A987 | £2.55 multi | | 7.25 | 7.25 |
| **4106** | A987 | £2.55 multi | | 7.25 | 7.25 |
| *a.* | Horiz. pair, #4105-4106 | | | 14.50 | 14.50 |
| | *Nos. 4099-4106 (8)* | | | 33.10 | 33.10 |

On day of issue, Nos. 4099-4100 each sold for 66p, and Nos. 4101-4102 each sold for 85p.

*McCartney*, by
Paul McCartney,
1970 — A988

*Ram*, by Paul and
Linda McCartney,
1971 — A989

*Venus and Mars*,
by Paul
McCartney and
Wings,
1975 — A990

*McCartney II*, by
Paul McCartney,
1980 — A991

*Tug of War*, by
Paul McCartney,
1982 — A992

*Flaming Pie*, by
Paul McCartney,
1997 — A993

*Egypt Station*, by
Paul McCartney,
2018 — A994

*McCartney III*, by
Paul McCartney,
2020 — A995

McCartney in Recording
Studio — A996

No. 4115 — Photo of McCartney recording:
a, *McCartney*, 1970. b, *Ram*, 1971. c, *McCartney II*, 1980. d, *Flaming Pie*, 1997.

**2021, May 28      Litho.      Perf. 14¼**

| 4107 | A988 | 1st multi | 2.40 | 2.40 |
|---|---|---|---|---|
| 4108 | A989 | 1st multi | 2.40 | 2.40 |
| 4109 | A990 | 1st multi | 2.40 | 2.40 |
| 4110 | A991 | 1st multi | 2.40 | 2.40 |
| a. | | Horiz. strip of 4, #4107-4110 | 9.75 | 9.75 |
| b. | | Booklet pane of 4, #4107-4110 (BK1233) | 11.00 | — |
| 4111 | A992 | £1.70 multi | 5.00 | 5.00 |
| 4112 | A993 | £1.70 multi | 5.00 | 5.00 |
| 4113 | A994 | £1.70 multi | 5.00 | 5.00 |
| 4114 | A995 | £1.70 multi | 5.00 | 5.00 |
| a. | | Horiz. strip of 4, #4111-4114 | 20.00 | 20.00 |
| b. | | Booklet pane of 4, #4111-4114 (BK1233) | 21.50 | — |
| c. | | Sheet of 8, #4107-4114 | 39.95 | 39.95 |
| d. | | Sheet of 10, #4109-4114, 2 each #4107-4108, + 10 labels | 37.00 | 37.00 |
| e. | | Sheet of 4 #4114 | 28.50 | 28.50 |
| | | Nos. 4107-4114 (8) | 29.60 | 29.60 |

**Miniature Sheet**

| 4115 | A996 | Sheet of 4 | 15.00 | 15.00 |
|---|---|---|---|---|
| a.-b. | | 1st Either single | 2.40 | 2.40 |
| c.-d. | | £1.70 Either single | 5.00 | 5.00 |
| e. | | Booklet pane of 4, #4115a-4115d (BK1233) | 16.00 | |

**Booklet Stamps
Self-Adhesive
Photo.
Die Cut Perf. 14¼**

| 4116 | A988 | 1st multi | 4.50 | 2.40 |
|---|---|---|---|---|
| 4117 | A991 | 1st multi | 4.50 | 2.40 |
| a. | | Booklet pane of 6, #4116-4117, 4 #MH426 | 14.50 | |

On day of issue, Nos. 4107-4110, 4115a-4115b, 4116-4117 each sold for 85p. No. 4114c sold for £10.90. No. 4114d sold for £13 and has labels that could not be personalized. No. 4114e sold for £7.50. A sheet containing four examples of No. 4108 sold for £7.50.

---

**Miniature Sheet**

Prince Philip (1921-2021) — A997

Various photographs of Prince Philip.

**2021, June 24      Litho.      Perf. 14¼**

| 4118 | A997 | Sheet of 4 | 16.50 | 16.50 |
|---|---|---|---|---|
| a. | | 2nd black | 1.90 | 1.90 |
| b. | | 1st black | 2.40 | 2.40 |
| c. | | £1.70 black | 4.75 | 4.75 |
| d. | | £2.55 black | 7.00 | 7.00 |

On day of issue, No. 4118a sold for 66p and No. 4118b sold for 85p.

A998

*Dennis the Menace* Comic Strips, 70th
Anniv.
A999

Inscriptions: No. 4119, Dennis's first comic strip, 1951. No. 4120, Dennis adopts Gnasher, 1968. No. 4121, Dennis's front cover debut, 1974. No. 4122, Dennis adopts Rasher the Pig, 1979. No. 4123, Dennis meets his sister Bea, 1998. No. 4124, Dennis reveals his dad was Dennis, 2015.
Nos. 4125: a, Dennis. b, Gnasher. c, Minnie the Minx. d, Dennis, his parents and sister, Bea.

**2021, July 1      Litho.      Perf. 14**

| 4119 | A998 | 1st multi | 2.40 | 2.40 |
|---|---|---|---|---|
| 4120 | A998 | 1st multi | 2.40 | 2.40 |
| 4121 | A998 | 1st multi | 2.40 | 2.40 |
| a. | | Horiz. strip of 3, #4119-4121 | 7.25 | 7.25 |
| 4122 | A998 | £1.70 multi | 4.75 | 4.75 |
| 4123 | A998 | £1.70 multi | 4.75 | 4.75 |
| 4124 | A998 | £1.70 multi | 4.75 | 4.75 |
| a. | | Horiz. strip of 3, #4122-4124 | 14.50 | 14.50 |

**Miniature Sheet
Self-Adhesive
Die Cut Perf. 14¼**

| 4125 | A999 | Sheet of 4 | 14.50 | 14.50 |
|---|---|---|---|---|
| a.-b. | | 1st Either single | 2.40 | 2.40 |
| c.-d. | | £1.70 Either single | 4.75 | 4.75 |
| e. | | Sheet of 10, 5 each #4125a-4125b, + 10 labels | 27.50 | |
| f. | | Like #4125a, photo.( from booklet pane) | 2.40 | 2.40 |
| g. | | Like #4125b, photo. (from booklet pane) | 2.40 | 2.40 |
| h. | | Booklet pane of 6, #4125f, 4125g, 4 #MH426 | 14.50 | |

On day of issue, Nos. 4119-4121, 4125a, 4125b, 4125f, 4125g each sold for 85p. No. 4125e sold £9.70 and the labels could not be personalized.

A1000

Coastal and Marine Animals
A1001

Designs: Nos. 4126, 4137a, Northern gannet. Nos. 4127, 4137b, Common cuttlefish. Nos. 4128, 4137c, 4137l, Gray seal. Nos. 4129, 4137d, Bottlenose dolphin. Nos. 4130, 4137e, Spiny spider crab. Nos. 4131, 4137f, Long-snouted seahorse. Nos. 4132, 4137g, 4137k Orca. Nos. 4133, 4137h, Fried-egg anemone. Nos. 4134, 4137i, Cuckoo wrasse. Nos. 4135, 4137j, Cold-water coral reef.
No. 4136: a, Phytoplankton. b, Zooplankton. c, Atlantic herring. d, Harbor porpoises.

---

**2021, July 22      Litho.      Perf. 14¼**

| 4126 | A1000 | 1st multi | 2.40 | 2.40 |
|---|---|---|---|---|
| 4127 | A1000 | 1st multi | 2.40 | 2.40 |
| 4128 | A1000 | 1st multi | 2.40 | 2.40 |
| 4129 | A1000 | 1st multi | 2.40 | 2.40 |
| 4130 | A1000 | 1st multi | 2.40 | 2.40 |
| a. | | Horiz. strip of 5, #4126-4130 | 12.00 | 12.00 |
| 4131 | A1000 | 1st multi | 2.40 | 2.40 |
| 4132 | A1000 | 1st multi | 2.40 | 2.40 |
| 4133 | A1000 | 1st multi | 2.40 | 2.40 |
| 4134 | A1000 | 1st multi | 2.40 | 2.40 |
| 4135 | A1000 | 1st multi | 2.40 | 2.40 |
| a. | | Horiz. strip of 5, #4131-4135 | 12.00 | 12.00 |
| | | Nos. 4126-4135 (10) | 24.00 | 24.00 |

**Miniature Sheets
Perf. 14¼x14**

| 4136 | A1001 | Sheet of 4 | 14.50 | 14.50 |
|---|---|---|---|---|
| a.-b. | | 1st Either single | 2.40 | 2.40 |
| c.-d. | | £1.70 Either single | 4.75 | 4.75 |

**Self-Adhesive
Die Cut Perf. 14¼**

| 4137 | | Sheet of 10 + 10 labels | 27.50 | |
|---|---|---|---|---|
| a.-j. | | A1000 1st Any single + label | 2.75 | 2.75 |
| k. | | A1000 Photo. (from booklet pane) | 2.40 | 2.40 |
| l. | | A1000 Photo. (from booklet pane) | 2.40 | 2.40 |
| m. | | Booklet pane of 6, #4137k, 4137l, 4 #MH426 | 14.50 | |

On day of issue, Nos. 4126-4135, 4136a-4136b, 4137k, 4137l each sold for 85p. No. 4137 sold for £9.70 and labels could not be personalized. Nos. 4137a-4137j had a franking value of 85p.

Inventions and Innovations of the
Industrial Revolution — A1002

Inventions and Innovations of the
Electrical Revolution — A1003

Designs: No. 4138, Henry Bessemer process for production of steel, 1856. No. 4139, James Watt's rotative steam engine, 1780s. No. 4140, Richard Trevithick's Penydarren locomotive, 1804. No. 4141, Jame's Hargreaves's spinning jenny, c. 1764. No. 4142, John and Thomas Lombe's silk mill, c. 1721. No. 4143, Joseph Aspdin's Portland cement, 1824.
No. 4144: a, Michael Faraday's apparatus for generating electricity with coiled wire and magnet, 1831. b, Trans-atlantic cable, 1858. c, Deptford Power Station alternating current dynamo, 1889. d, Joseph Swan's incandescent light bulb, 1880.

**2021, Aug. 12      Litho.      Perf. 14½**

| 4138 | A1002 | 2nd multi | 1.90 | 1.90 |
|---|---|---|---|---|
| 4139 | A1002 | 2nd multi | 1.90 | 1.90 |
| a. | | Vert. pair, #4138-4139 | 3.80 | 3.80 |
| 4140 | A1002 | 1st multi | 2.40 | 2.40 |
| 4141 | A1002 | 1st multi | 2.40 | 2.40 |
| a. | | Vert. pair, #4140-4141 | 4.80 | 4.80 |
| b. | | Booklet pane of 4, #4138-4141 (BK1234) | 9.25 | — |
| 4142 | A1002 | £1.70 multi | 4.75 | 4.75 |
| 4143 | A1002 | £1.70 multi | 4.75 | 4.75 |
| a. | | Vert. pair, #4142-4143 | 9.50 | 9.50 |
| b. | | Booklet pane of 4, #4140-4143 (BK1234) | 15.50 | |

**Miniature Sheet
Perf. 14**

| 4144 | A1003 | Sheet of 4 | 14.50 | 14.50 |
|---|---|---|---|---|
| a. | | 2nd multi | 1.90 | 1.90 |
| b. | | 1st multi | 2.40 | 2.40 |
| c. | | £1.70 multi | 2.40 | 2.40 |
| d. | | £2.55 multi | 7.00 | 7.00 |
| e. | | Booklet pane of 4, #4144a-4144d (BK1234) | 17.50 | |

On day of issue, Nos. 4138-4139, 4144a each sold for 66p, and Nos. 4140-4141, 4144b each sold for 85p.

Army Tanks
A1004

---

Army
Vehicles
and
Aircraft
A1005

Designs: No. 4145, Mk IV tank. No. 4146, Matilda Mk II tank. No. 4147, Churchill AVRE tank. No. 4148, Centurion Mk 9 tank. No. 4149, Scorpion tank. No. 4150, Chieftain Mk 5 tank. No. 4151, Challenger 2 tank. No. 4152, Ajax tank.
No. 4153: a, Coyote tactical support vehicle. b, Army Wildcat reconnaisance helicopter. c, Trojan tank. d, Foxhound light protected patrol vehicle.

**2021, Sept. 2      Litho.      Perf. 14**

| 4145 | A1004 | 1st multi | 2.40 | 2.40 |
|---|---|---|---|---|
| 4146 | A1004 | 1st multi | 2.40 | 2.40 |
| 4147 | A1004 | 1st multi | 2.40 | 2.40 |
| 4148 | A1004 | 1st multi | 2.40 | 2.40 |
| a. | | Horiz. strip of 4, #4145-4148 | 9.75 | 9.75 |
| 4149 | A1004 | £1.70 multi | 4.75 | 4.75 |
| 4150 | A1004 | £1.70 multi | 4.75 | 4.75 |
| 4151 | A1004 | £1.70 multi | 4.75 | 4.75 |
| 4152 | A1004 | £1.70 multi | 4.75 | 4.75 |
| a. | | Horiz. strip of 4, #4149-4152 | 19.00 | 19.00 |
| | | Nos. 4145-4152 (8) | 28.60 | 28.60 |

**Miniature Sheet
Perf. 14¼x14**

| 4153 | A1005 | Sheet of 4 | 14.50 | 14.50 |
|---|---|---|---|---|
| a.-b. | | 1st Either single | 2.40 | 2.40 |
| c.-d. | | £1.70 Either single | 4.75 | 4.75 |

On day of issue, Nos. 4145-4148, 4153a-4153b each sold for 85p.

DC Comics Heroes
and
Villains — A1006

DC Comics Justice League
Characters — A1007

Designs: Nos. 4154, 4167a, 4167m, Batman. Nos. 4155, 4167b, Batwoman. Nos. 4156, 4167c, 4167n, Robin. Nos. 4157, 4167d, Batgirl. Nos. 4158, 4167e, Alfred. Nos. 4159, 4167f, Nightwing. Nos. 4160, 4167g, The Joker. Nos. 4161, 4167h, Harley Quinn. Nos. 4162, 4167i, The Penguin. Nos. 4163, 4167j, Poison Ivy. Nos. 4164, 4167k, Catwoman. Nos. 4165, 4167l, The Riddler.
No. 4166: a, Batman, diff. (50x30mm). b, Wonder Woman (35x35mm). c, Superman (65x23mm). d, Green Lantern and The Flash (50x30mm). e, Cyborg and Aquaman (35x42mm). f, Supergirl and Shazam! (27x42mm).

**2021, Sept. 17      Litho.      Perf. 14¼**

| 4154 | A1006 | 1st multi | 2.40 | 2.40 |
|---|---|---|---|---|
| 4155 | A1006 | 1st multi | 2.40 | 2.40 |
| 4156 | A1006 | 1st multi | 2.40 | 2.40 |
| 4157 | A1006 | 1st multi | 2.40 | 2.40 |
| 4158 | A1006 | 1st multi | 2.40 | 2.40 |
| 4159 | A1006 | 1st multi | 2.40 | 2.40 |
| a. | | Horiz. strip of 6, #4154-4159 | 14.50 | 14.50 |
| b. | | Booklet pane of 6, #4154-4159 (BK1235) | 15.00 | |
| 4160 | A1006 | 1st multi | 2.40 | 2.40 |
| 4161 | A1006 | 1st multi | 2.40 | 2.40 |
| 4162 | A1006 | 1st multi | 2.40 | 2.40 |
| 4163 | A1006 | 1st multi | 2.40 | 2.40 |
| 4164 | A1006 | 1st multi | 2.40 | 2.40 |
| 4165 | A1006 | 1st multi | 2.40 | 2.40 |
| a. | | Horiz. strip of 6, #4160-4165 | 14.50 | 14.50 |
| b. | | Booklet pane of 6, #4160-4165 (BK1235) | 15.00 | |
| | | Nos. 4154-4165 (12) | 28.80 | 28.80 |

**Miniature Sheet
Self-Adhesive
Die Cut Perf. 14 (#4166a, 4166d, 4166f), Die Cut Perf. 14¼ (#4166b, 4166c, 4166e, 4166h)**

| 4166 | A1007 | Sheet of 6 | 14.50 | |
|---|---|---|---|---|
| a.-f. | | 1st Any single | 2.40 | 2.40 |
| g. | | Booklet pane of 2, #4166a, 4166d (BK1235) | 5.00 | — |
| h. | | Booklet pane of 4, #4166b, 4166c, 4166e, 4166f (BK1235) | 10.00 | — |
| i. | | Like #4166b, photo. (from booklet pane) | 2.40 | 2.40 |

| | | | | |
|---|---|---|---|---|
| j. | Booklet pane of 6, 2 #4166j, 4 #MH426 | | 14.50 | |
| | **Die Cut Perf. 14½** | | | |
| 4167 | Sheet of 12 + 12 labels | | 31.00 | |
| a.-l. | A1006 1st Any single + label | | 2.60 | 2.60 |
| m. | A1006 1st Photo. (from booklet pane) | | 2.40 | 2.40 |
| n. | A1006 1st Photo. (from booklet pane) | | 2.40 | 2.40 |
| o. | Booklet pane of 6, #4167m, 4167n, 4 #MH426 | | 14.50 | |

On day of issue, Nos. 4154-4165, 4166a-4166f, 4166i, 4167m, 4167n each sold for 85p. No. 4167 sold for £11.40 and labels could not be personalized. Nos. 4167a-4167l each had a franking value of 85p.

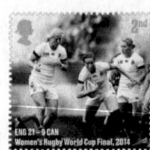

**Famous Rugby Matches — A1008**

Scene from: No. 4168, England defeating Canada in the 2014 Women's Rugby World Cup Final. No. 4169, Wales defeating England in the 1970 Five Nations Championship. No. 4170, Ireland defeating Scotland in 2015 Women's Six Nations Championship. No. 4171, Scotland defeating Ireland in the 1984 Five Nations Championship. No. 4172, Scotland defeating England in the 1998 Women's Home Nations Championship. No. 4173, Ireland defeating England in the 1994 Five Nations Championship. No. 4174, Wales defeating England in the 2009 Women's Six Nations Championship. No. 4175, England defeating Australia in the 2003 Rugby World Cup Final.

**2021, Oct. 19    Litho.    Perf. 14¼**

| | | | | |
|---|---|---|---|---|
| 4168 | A1008 | 2nd multi | 1.90 | 1.40 |
| 4169 | A1008 | 2nd multi | 1.90 | 1.40 |
| a. | Horiz. pair, #4168-4169 | | 3.80 | 2.80 |
| 4170 | A1008 | 1st multi | 2.40 | 1.90 |
| 4171 | A1008 | 1st multi | 2.40 | 1.90 |
| a. | Horiz. pair, #4170-4171 | | 4.80 | 3.80 |
| 4172 | A1008 | £1.70 multi | 4.75 | 3.75 |
| 4173 | A1008 | £1.70 multi | 4.75 | 3.75 |
| a. | Horiz. pair, #4172-4173 | | 9.50 | 7.50 |
| 4174 | A1008 | £2.55 multi | 7.00 | 5.25 |
| 4175 | A1008 | £2.55 multi | 7.00 | 5.25 |
| a. | Horiz. pair, #4174-4175 | | 14.00 | 10.50 |
| | Nos. 4168-4175 (8) | | 32.10 | 24.60 |

Rugby Football Union and first international match between England and Scotland, 150th anniv. On day of issue, Nos. 4168-4169 each sold for 66p, and Nos. 4170-4171 each sold for 85p.

A1009

**Christmas — A1010**

Designs: Nos. 4176, 4177, Angels. Nos. 4178, 4179, Madonna and Child. No. 4180, Journey to Bethlehem. No. 4181, Visitation of the Shepherds. £1.70, Magi following Star of Bethlehem. £2.55, Adoration of the Shepherds.

**Die Cut Perf. 15x14½ (A1009), Die Cut Perf. 14½x15 (A1010)**

**2021, Nov. 2                Photo.**

**Self-Adhesive**

| | | | | |
|---|---|---|---|---|
| 4176 | A1009 | 2nd multi | 1.75 | 1.30 |
| a. | Litho. | | 1.75 | 1.30 |
| 4177 | A1010 | 2nd multi | 1.75 | 1.30 |
| a. | Litho. | | 1.75 | 1.30 |
| b. | Litho., die cut perf. 14½x15 syncopated | | 1.90 | 1.90 |
| c. | Booklet pane of 12 #4177 | | 21.00 | |
| 4178 | A1009 | 1st multi | 2.25 | 1.75 |
| a. | Litho. | | 2.25 | 1.75 |
| 4179 | A1010 | 1st multi | 2.25 | 1.75 |
| a. | Litho. | | 2.25 | 1.75 |
| b. | Litho., die cut perf. 14½x15 syncopated | | 2.40 | 2.40 |
| c. | Booklet pane of 12 #4179 | | 27.00 | |
| 4180 | A1009 | 2nd Large multi | 2.60 | 2.00 |
| a. | Litho. | | 2.60 | 2.00 |
| 4181 | A1010 | 1st Large multi | 3.50 | 2.60 |
| a. | Litho. | | 3.50 | 2.60 |
| 4182 | A1010 | £1.70 multi | 4.50 | 3.50 |
| a. | Litho. | | 4.50 | 3.50 |
| b. | Litho., die cut perf. 14½x15 syncopated | | 4.75 | 4.75 |

| | | | | |
|---|---|---|---|---|
| 4183 | A1010 | £2.55 multi | 6.75 | 5.00 |
| a. | Litho. | | 6.75 | 5.00 |
| b. | Litho., die cut perf. 14½x15 syncopated | | 7.25 | 7.25 |
| c. | Souvenir sheet of 8, #4176a, 4177a, 4178a, 4179a, 4180a, 4181a, 4182a, 4183a | | 25.50 | |
| d. | Sheet of 20, 8 each #4177b, 4179b, 2 each #4182b, 4183b, + 20 labels | | 58.50 | |
| | Nos. 4176-4183 (8) | | 25.35 | 19.20 |

On day of issue, Nos. 4176, 4176a, 4177, 4177a, each sold for 66p; Nos. 4178, 4178a, 4179, 4179a, for 85p; Nos. 4180, 4180a, for 96p; Nos. 4181, 4181a, for £1.29. No. 4183d sold for £21.75, and its labels could not be personalized. On day of issue, the franking value of Nos. 4177b, 4179b, 4182b and 4183b were the same as the selling price of Nos. 4177, 4179, 4182, and 4183 respectively. See footnote after No. MH498.

Rolling Stones Concert, London, 1969 A1011

Rolling Stones Concert, East Rutherford, NJ, 2019 A1012

Rolling Stones Concert, Rotterdam, Netherlands, 1995 A1013

Rolling Stones Concert, Tokyo, 1995 A1014

Rolling Stones Concert, New York, NY, 1972 A1015

Rolling Stones Concert, Oslo, Norway, 2014 A1016

Rolling Stones Concert, Knebworth, England, 1976 A1017

Rolling Stones Concert, Düsseldorf, Germany, 2017 A1018

**Rolling Stones Band Members and Tour Posters A1019**

No. 4192: a, Charlie Watts (1941-2021), Ron Wood, Mick Jagger, and Keith Richards. b, Wood, Jagger, Richards and Watts. c, Posters for 1990 Urban Jungle Tour and 1975 Tour

of the Americas. d, Posters for 1970 UK Tour and 1981 American Tour.

**2022, Jan. 20    Litho.    Perf. 14**

| | | | | |
|---|---|---|---|---|
| 4184 | A1011 | 1st multi | 2.25 | 1.75 |
| 4185 | A1012 | 1st multi | 2.25 | 1.75 |
| 4186 | A1013 | 1st multi | 2.25 | 1.75 |
| 4187 | A1014 | 1st multi | 2.25 | 1.75 |
| a. | Horiz. strip of 4, #4184-4187 | | 9.00 | 7.00 |
| 4188 | A1015 | £1.70 multi | 4.25 | 3.50 |
| 4189 | A1016 | £1.70 multi | 4.25 | 3.50 |
| a. | Booklet pane of 4, #4184-4185, 4188-4189 (BK1236) | | 15.00 | — |
| 4190 | A1017 | £1.70 multi | 4.25 | 3.50 |
| 4191 | A1018 | £1.70 multi | 4.25 | 3.50 |
| a. | Horiz. strip of 4, #4188-4191 | | 19.00 | 14.00 |
| b. | Booklet pane of 4, #4186-4187, 4190-4191 (BK1236) | | 15.00 | — |
| | Nos. 4184-4191 (8) | | 26.00 | 21.00 |

**Miniature Sheets**

**Perf. 14½**

| | | | | |
|---|---|---|---|---|
| 4192 | A1019 | Sheet of 4 | 14.00 | 14.00 |
| a.-b. | 1st Either single | | .25 | 1.75 |
| c.-d. | £1.70 Either single | | 4.75 | 3.50 |
| e. | Booklet pane of 4, #4192a-4192d (BK1236) | | 15.00 | |

**Self-Adhesive**

**Die Cut Perf. 14**

| | | | | |
|---|---|---|---|---|
| 4193 | | Sheet of 8 + 8 labels, with stamps and labels alternating horizontally | 31.50 | |
| a. | A1011 1st multi + label | | 2.60 | 2.60 |
| b. | A1012 1st multi + label | | 2.60 | 2.60 |
| c. | A1013 1st multi + label | | 2.60 | 2.60 |
| d. | A1014 1st multi + label | | 2.60 | 2.60 |
| e. | A1015 1.70 multi + label | | 5.25 | 5.25 |
| f. | A1016 £1.70 multi + label | | 5.25 | 5.25 |
| g. | A1017 £1.70 multi + label | | 5.25 | 5.25 |
| h. | A1018 £1.70 multi + label | | 5.25 | 5.25 |
| i. | As #4193, with stamps in center columns, labels at sides | | 31.50 | |

On day of issue, Nos. 4184-4187, 4192a and 4192b each sold for 85p. Nos. 4193 and 4193i each sold for £11.50, and their labels could not be personalized. Images on labels and marginal markings of Nos. 4193 and 4193i differ. The franking values of each of Nos. 4193a-4193d was 85p on the day of issue. Nos. 4184 and 4187 were each printed in sheets of 3 that sold for £7.

Reign of Queen Elizabeth II (1926-2022), 70th Anniv. — A1020

Queen Elizabeth II: No. 4194, Visiting headquarters of MI5, 2020. No. 4195, With Prince Philip on tour of United States, 1957. No. 4196, Walking in Worcester, 1980. No. 4197, At Trooping the Color ceremony, 1978. No. 4198, At Provincial Museum of Alberta, 2005. No. 4199, At Silver Jubilee celebrations, 1977. No. 4200, Touring St. Vincent, 1966. No. 4201, At Order of the Garter ceremony, 1999.

**2022, Feb. 4    Litho.    Perf. 14½**

| | | | | |
|---|---|---|---|---|
| 4194 | A1020 | 1st multi | 2.25 | 1.75 |
| 4195 | A1020 | 1st multi | 2.25 | 1.75 |
| 4196 | A1020 | 1st multi | 2.25 | 1.75 |
| 4197 | A1020 | 1st multi | 2.25 | 1.75 |
| a. | Horiz. strip of 4, #4194-4197 | | 9.00 | 7.00 |
| 4198 | A1020 | £1.70 multi | 4.75 | 3.75 |
| 4199 | A1020 | £1.70 multi | 4.75 | 3.75 |
| 4200 | A1020 | £1.70 multi | 4.75 | 3.75 |
| a. | Booklet pane of 4, #4195-4196, 4199-4200 (BK1237) | | 15.00 | — |
| 4201 | A1020 | £1.70 multi | 4.75 | 3.75 |
| a. | Horiz. strip of 4, #4198-4201 | | 19.00 | 15.00 |
| b. | Booklet pane of 4, #4194, 4197-4198, 4201 (BK1237) | | 15.00 | — |
| | Nos. 4194-4201 (8) | | 28.00 | 22.00 |

On day of issue, Nos. 4194-4197 each sold for 85p.

**Miniature Sheet**

**Stamps Designed by David Gentleman — A1021**

No. 4202: a, 1962 3p stamp (Great Britain #388). b, 1969 9p stamp (Great Britain #576). c, 1973 9p stamp (Great Britain #781). e, 1966 8½p stamp (Great Britain #476). f, 1965 4p stamp (Great Britain #430).

**2022, Feb. 18    Litho.    Perf. 14x14¾**

| | | | | |
|---|---|---|---|---|
| 4202 | A1021 | Sheet of 6 | 17.50 | 17.50 |
| a.-b. | 2nd Either single | | 1.75 | 1.30 |
| c.-d. | 1st Either single | | 2.25 | 1.75 |
| e.-f. | £1.70 Either single | | 4.75 | 3.75 |
| g. | As #4802, with London 2022 Stamp Exhibition emblem and serial number in sheet margin | | 17.50 | 17.50 |

On day of issue, Nos. 4202a-4202b each sold for 66p, and Nos. 4202c-4202d each sold for 85p. No. 4202g lacks the barcode tab at left.

A1022

**Football Association Challenge Cup, 150th Anniv. — A1023**

Designs: No. 4203, Arsenal players Charlie George and Frank McLintock holding FA Cup, 1971. No. 4204, Wembley Stadium, 1923. No. 4205, Fans of West Bromwich Albion cheering, 1968. No. 4206, Keith Houchen scoring goal for Coventry City, 1987. No. 4207, Lincoln City players celebrating victory over Burnley in quarter-final match, 2017. No. 4208, King George VI and Queen Elizabeth presenting FA Cup to Sunderland captain Raich Carter, 1937.

No. 4209: a, Ticket stub for 1959 final match, ribbon rosettes and painted rattle. b, Replica of first FA Cup trophy, winner's medal. c, Soccer ball from 1903 final match, FA steward's badge, Manchester City player's shirt from 1969 final. d, 1927 souvenir porcelain replica of FA Cup, souvenir gramophone record of 1932 final match, and Leeds United pennant, 1972.

**2022, Mar. 8    Litho.    Perf. 14¾**

| | | | | |
|---|---|---|---|---|
| 4203 | A1022 | 1st multi | 2.25 | 1.75 |
| 4204 | A1022 | 1st multi | 2.25 | 1.75 |
| a. | Vert. pair, #4203-4204 | | 4.50 | 3.50 |
| 4205 | A1022 | £1.70 multi | 4.50 | 3.50 |
| 4206 | A1022 | £1.70 multi | 4.50 | 3.50 |
| a. | Vert. pair, #4205-4206 | | 9.00 | 7.00 |
| 4207 | A1022 | £2.55 multi | 6.75 | 5.25 |
| 4208 | A1022 | £2.55 multi | 6.75 | 5.25 |
| a. | Vert. pair, #4207-4208 | | 13.50 | 10.50 |
| | Nos. 4203-4208 (6) | | 27.00 | 21.00 |

**Miniature Sheet**

**Perf. 14¼x14**

| | | | | |
|---|---|---|---|---|
| 4209 | A1023 | Sheet of 4 | 13.50 | 13.50 |
| a.-b. | 1st Either single | | 2.25 | 1.75 |
| c.-d. | £1.70 Either single | | 4.50 | 3.50 |

On day of issue, Nos. 4203-4204, 4209a-4209b each sold for 85p.

Winning Art in Children's Stamp Design Contest With Theme of COVID-19 Pandemic Heroes — A1024

Designs: No. 4210, National Health Service Workers, by Jessica Roberts. No. 4211, Captain Sir Tom Moore, by Shachow Ali. No. 4212, National Health Service Hospital Cleaners, by Raphael Valle Martin. No. 4213, National Health Service Worker/My Mum, by Alfie Craddock. No. 4214, Lab Technician, by Logan Pearson. No. 4215, Delivery Driver, by Isabella Grover. No. 4216, National Health Service Worker, by Connie Stuart. No. 4217, Doctors and Nurses, by Ishan Bains.

**2022, Mar. 23    Litho.    Perf. 14¼**

| | | | | |
|---|---|---|---|---|
| 4210 | A1024 | 1st multi | 2.25 | 1.75 |
| 4211 | A1024 | 1st multi | 2.25 | 1.75 |
| 4212 | A1024 | 1st multi | 2.25 | 1.75 |
| 4213 | A1024 | 1st multi | 2.25 | 1.75 |
| a. | Horiz. strip of 4, #4210-4213 | | 9.00 | 7.00 |
| 4214 | A1024 | 1st multi | 2.25 | 1.75 |
| 4215 | A1024 | 1st multi | 2.25 | 1.75 |
| 4216 | A1024 | 1st multi | 2.25 | 1.75 |
| 4217 | A1024 | 1st multi | 2.25 | 1.75 |
| a. | Horiz. strip of 4, #4214-4217 | | 9.00 | 7.00 |
| | Nos. 4210-4217 (8) | | 18.00 | 14.00 |

On day of issue, Nos. 4210-4217 each sold for 85p.

Birds — A1025

Designs: No. 4218, Nightjar. No. 4219, Pied flycatcher. No. 4220, Swift. No. 4221, Yellow wagtail. No. 4222, Arctic skua. No. 4223, Stone-curlew. No. 4224, Arctic tern. No. 4225, Swallow. No. 4226, Turtle dove. No. 4227, Montagu's harrier.

| 2022, Apr. 7 | Litho. | | Perf. 14¼x14 | |
|---|---|---|---|---|
| 4218 | A1025 | 1st multi | 2.40 | 1.60 |
| 4219 | A1025 | 1st multi | 2.40 | 1.60 |
| 4220 | A1025 | 1st multi | 2.40 | 1.60 |
| 4221 | A1025 | 1st multi | 2.40 | 1.60 |
| 4222 | A1025 | 1st multi | 2.40 | 1.60 |
| a. | Horiz. strip of 5, #4218-4222 | | 12.00 | 8.00 |
| 4223 | A1025 | 1st multi | 2.40 | 1.60 |
| 4224 | A1025 | 1st multi | 2.40 | 1.60 |
| 4225 | A1025 | 1st multi | 2.40 | 1.60 |
| 4226 | A1025 | 1st multi | 2.40 | 1.60 |
| 4227 | A1025 | 1st multi | 2.40 | 1.60 |
| a. | Horiz. strip of 5, #4223-4227 | | 12.00 | 8.00 |
| | Nos. 4218-4227 (10) | | 24.00 | 16.00 |

On day of issue, Nos. 4218-4227 each sold for 95p.

A1026

Women in World War II A1027

Inscriptions: No. 4228, Protecting civilians. No. 4229, Nursing on the front line. No. 4230, Repairing Army vehicles. No. 4231, Arming the fleet. No. 4232, Powering the war effort. No. 4233, Deciphering enemy messages. No. 4234, Supplying military production. No. 4235, Lighting the way to victory. No. 4236, Maintaining RAF aircraft. No. 4237, Meeting Britain's demand.

No. 4238: a, Pilots meet in their Ferry Pool meeting room. b, Pilot climbing into the cockpit of a Supermarine Spitfire. c, Pilot completing her post-flight paperwork in a Lockheed Hudson. d, Pilots of the No. 5 Ferry Pool disembarking from an Avro Anson.

| 2022, May 5 | Litho. | | Perf. 14½ | |
|---|---|---|---|---|
| 4228 | A1026 | 1st multi | 2.40 | 1.60 |
| 4229 | A1026 | 1st multi | 2.40 | 1.60 |
| 4230 | A1026 | 1st multi | 2.40 | 1.60 |
| 4231 | A1026 | 1st multi | 2.40 | 1.60 |
| 4232 | A1026 | 1st multi | 2.40 | 1.60 |
| a. | Horiz. strip of 5, #4228-4232 | | 12.00 | 8.00 |
| 4233 | A1026 | 1st multi | 2.40 | 1.60 |
| 4234 | A1026 | 1st multi | 2.40 | 1.60 |
| 4235 | A1026 | 1st multi | 2.40 | 1.60 |
| a. | Booklet pane of 6, #4228-4230, 4233-4235 (BK1238) | | 15.50 | — |
| 4236 | A1026 | 1st multi | 2.40 | 1.60 |
| 4237 | A1026 | 1st multi | 2.40 | 1.60 |
| a. | Horiz. strip of 5, #4233-4237 | | 12.00 | 8.00 |
| b. | Booklet pane of 4, #4231-4232, 4236-4237 (BK1238) | | 10.50 | — |
| | Nos. 4228-4237 (10) | | 24.00 | 16.00 |

**Miniature Sheet**
**Perf. 14¼x14**

| 4238 | A1027 | Sheet of 4 | 14.50 | 14.50 |
|---|---|---|---|---|
| a.-b. | 1st Either single | | 2.40 | 1.60 |
| c.-d. | £1.85 Either single | | 4.75 | 3.75 |
| e. | Booklet pane of 4, #4238-4238d (BK1238) | | 15.50 | — |

On day of issue, Nos. 4228-4237, 4238a-4238b each sold for 95p.

Cats — A1028

Designs: Nos. 4239, 4247a, Siamese cat grooming. Nos. 4240, 4247b, Tabby cat stalking. Nos. 4241, 4247c, Ginger cat playing. Nos. 4242, 4247d, British shorthair cat sleeping. Nos. 4243, 4247e, Maine Coon cat staring. Nos. 4244, 4247f, Black-and-white cat on alert. Nos. 4245, 4247g, Bengal cat being

curious. Nos. 4246, 4247h, Tabby-and-white cat stretching.

| 2022, June 9 | Litho. | | Perf. 14¼x14 | |
|---|---|---|---|---|
| 4239 | A1028 | 2nd multi | 1.75 | 1.30 |
| 4240 | A1028 | 2nd multi | 1.75 | 1.30 |
| a. | Vert. pair, #4239-4240 | | 3.50 | 2.60 |
| 4241 | A1028 | 1st multi | 2.40 | 1.60 |
| 4242 | A1028 | 1st multi | 2.40 | 1.60 |
| a. | Vert. pair, #4241-4242 | | 4.80 | 3.20 |
| 4243 | A1028 | £1.85 multi | 4.50 | 3.50 |
| 4244 | A1028 | £1.85 multi | 4.50 | 3.50 |
| a. | Vert. pair, #4243-4244 | | 9.00 | 7.00 |
| 4245 | A1028 | £2.55 multi | 6.25 | 4.75 |
| 4246 | A1028 | £2.55 multi | 6.25 | 4.75 |
| a. | Vert. pair, #4245-4246 | | 12.50 | 9.50 |
| | Nos. 4239-4246 (8) | | 29.80 | 22.30 |

**Miniature Sheet**
**Self-Adhesive**
**Die Cut Perf. 14¼x15**

| 4247 | Sheet of 10, #4247a-4247b, 4247e-4247h, 2 each #4247c-4247d, + 10 labels | | 31.50 | |
|---|---|---|---|---|
| a.-b. | 1028 2nd Either single + label | | 1.90 | 1.90 |
| c.-d. | 1028 1st Either single + label | | 2.50 | 2.50 |
| e.-f. | 1028 £1.85 Either single + label | | 5.00 | 5.00 |
| g.-h. | 1028 £2.55 Either single + label | | 6.75 | 6.75 |

On day of issue, Nos. 4239-4240 each sold for 68p and Nos. 4241-4242 each sold for 95p. No. 4247 sold for £15.20, with Nos. 4247a-4247b each having a franking value of 68p, and Nos. 4247c-4247d each having a franking value of 95p. Labels on No. 4247 could not be personalized.

A1029

A1030

A1031

A1032

A1033

A1034

A1035

First Gay Pride Rally in Great Britain, 50th Anniv. A1036

| 2022, July 1 | Litho. | | Perf. 14 | |
|---|---|---|---|---|
| 4248 | A1029 | 1st multi | 2.40 | 1.60 |
| 4249 | A1030 | 1st multi | 2.40 | 1.60 |
| a. | Horiz. pair, #4248-4249 | | 4.80 | 3.20 |
| 4250 | A1031 | 1st multi | 2.40 | 1.60 |
| 4251 | A1032 | 1st multi | 2.40 | 1.60 |
| a. | Horiz. pair, #4250-4251 | | 4.80 | 3.20 |
| 4252 | A1033 | £1.85 multi | 4.50 | 3.50 |
| 4253 | A1034 | £1.85 multi | 4.50 | 3.50 |
| a. | Horiz. pair, #4252-4253 | | 9.00 | 7.00 |
| 4254 | A1035 | £1.85 multi | 4.50 | 3.50 |
| 4255 | A1036 | £1.85 multi | 4.50 | 3.50 |
| a. | Horiz. pair, #4254-4255 | | 9.00 | 7.00 |
| | Nos. 4248-4255 (8) | | 27.60 | 20.40 |

**Miniature Sheet**
**Self-Adhesive**
**Die Cut Perf. 14**

| 4256 | Sheet of 8 + 8 labels | | 30.50 | |
|---|---|---|---|---|
| a. | A1029 1st multi + label | | 2.60 | 2.60 |
| b. | A1030 1st multi + label | | 2.60 | 2.60 |
| c. | A1031 1st multi + label | | 2.60 | 2.60 |
| d. | A1032 1st multi + label | | 2.60 | 2.60 |
| e. | A1033 £1.85 multi + label | | 5.00 | 5.00 |
| f. | A1034 £1.85 multi + label | | 5.00 | 5.00 |
| g. | A1035 £1.85 multi + label | | 5.00 | 5.00 |
| h. | A1036 £1.85 multi + label | | 5.00 | 5.00 |

On day of issue, Nos. 4248-4251 each sold for 95p. No. 4256 sold for £12.60, and the labels could not be personalized. Nos. 4256a-4256d each had a franking value of 95p on day of issue.

2022 Commonwealth Games, Birmingham A1037

Designs: No. 4257, Diving. No. 4258, Boxing. No. 4259, Para table tennis. No. 4260, Para powerlifting. No. 4261, Women's gymnastics. No. 4262, Mountain biking. No. 4263, Relay race. No. 4264, Wheelchair basketball.

| 2022, July 28 | Litho. | | Perf. 14¼ | |
|---|---|---|---|---|
| 4257 | A1037 | 1st multi | 2.40 | 1.60 |
| 4258 | A1037 | 1st multi | 2.40 | 1.60 |
| 4259 | A1037 | 1st multi | 2.40 | 1.60 |
| 4260 | A1037 | 1st multi | 2.40 | 1.60 |
| a. | Horiz. strip of 4, #4257-4260 | | 9.60 | 6.40 |
| 4261 | A1037 | £1.85 multi | 4.50 | 3.50 |
| 4262 | A1037 | £1.85 multi | 4.50 | 3.50 |
| 4263 | A1037 | £1.85 multi | 4.50 | 3.50 |
| 4264 | A1037 | £1.85 multi | 4.50 | 3.50 |
| a. | Horiz. strip of 4, #4261-4264 | | 18.00 | 14.00 |
| | Nos. 4257-4264 (8) | | 27.60 | 20.40 |

On day of issue, Nos. 4257-4260 each sold for 95p.

A1038

Transformers — A1039

Designs: Nos. 4265, 4274a, Optimus Prime. Nos. 4266, 4274b, Megatron. Nos. 4267, 4274c, Bumblebee. Nos. 4268, 4274d, Starscream. Nos. 4269, 4274e, Grimlock. Nos. 4270, 4274f, Shockwave. Nos. 4271, 4274g, Arcee. Nos. 4272, 4274h, Soundwave.

No. 4273: a, Swoop. b, Slug. c, Sludge. d, Grimlock, diff. e, Snarl.

| 2022, Sept. 1 | Litho. | | Perf. 14 | |
|---|---|---|---|---|
| 4265 | A1038 | 1st multi | 2.25 | 1.10 |
| 4266 | A1038 | 1st multi | 2.25 | 1.10 |
| a. | Horiz. pair, #4265-4266 | | 4.50 | 2.20 |
| 4267 | A1038 | 1st multi | 2.25 | 1.10 |
| 4268 | A1038 | 1st multi | 2.25 | 1.10 |
| a. | Horiz. pair, #4267-4268 | | 4.50 | 2.20 |
| b. | Booklet pane of 4, #4265-4268 (BK1239) | | 9.50 | |
| 4269 | A1038 | £1.85 multi | 4.25 | 2.10 |
| 4270 | A1038 | £1.85 multi | 4.25 | 2.10 |
| a. | Horiz. pair, #4269-4270 | | 8.50 | 4.20 |
| 4271 | A1038 | £1.85 multi | 4.25 | 2.10 |
| 4272 | A1038 | £1.85 multi | 4.25 | 2.10 |
| a. | Horiz. pair, #4271-4272 | | 8.50 | 4.20 |
| b. | Booklet pane of 4, #4269-4272 (BK1239) | | 18.50 | — |
| | Nos. 4265-4272 (8) | | 26.00 | 12.80 |

**Miniature Sheet**
**Self-Adhesive**
**Die Cut Perf. 14**

| 4273 | A1039 | Sheet of 5 | 13.00 | |
|---|---|---|---|---|
| a. | 2nd multi | | 1.60 | .80 |
| b.-d. | 1st Any single | | 2.25 | 1.10 |
| e. | £1.85 multi | | 4.25 | 2.10 |
| f. | Booklet pane of 2, #4273a-4273b (BK1239) | | 4.25 | — |
| g. | Booklet pane of 2, #4273c-4273e (BK1239) | | 9.50 | |

| 4274 | Sheet of 8 + 8 labels | | 27.00 | |
|---|---|---|---|---|
| a.-d. | A1038 1st Any single + label | | 2.25 | 2.25 |
| e.-h. | A1038 £1.85 Any single + label | | 4.50 | 4.50 |

On day of issue, No. 4273a sold for 68p and Nos. 4265-4268, 4273b-4273d each sold for 95p. No. 4274 sold for £11.50 and Nos. 4274a-4274d had a franking value of 95p on the day of issue. Labels on No. 4274 could not be personalized.

A1040

Royal Marines Commandos — A1041

Inscriptions: No. 4275, Aviation operations. No. 4276, Cold-weather operations. No. 4277, Mountain operations. No. 4278, Arid-climate operations. No. 4279, Commando training. No. 4280, Band service. No. 4281, Amphibious operations. No. 4282, Maritime security operations.

No. 4283: a, Sea soldier, Duke of York and Albany's Maritime Regiment of Foot, 1664. b, Grenadier, Chatham Division, His Majesty's Marine Forces, 1775. c, Sergeant, 4th Battalion, Royal Marines, 1918. d, Officer, 48th Royal Marine Commando, 1944.

| 2022, Sept. 29 | Litho. | | Perf. 14¼x14 | |
|---|---|---|---|---|
| 4275 | A1040 | 1st multi | 2.25 | 1.10 |
| 4276 | A1040 | 1st multi | 2.25 | 1.10 |
| 4277 | A1040 | 1st multi | 2.25 | 1.10 |
| 4278 | A1040 | 1st multi | 2.25 | 1.10 |
| a. | Horiz. strip of 4, #4275-4278 | | 9.00 | 4.40 |
| 4279 | A1040 | £1.85 multi | 4.25 | 2.10 |
| 4280 | A1040 | £1.85 multi | 4.25 | 2.10 |
| 4281 | A1040 | £1.85 multi | 4.25 | 2.10 |
| 4282 | A1040 | £1.85 multi | 4.25 | 2.10 |
| a. | Horiz. strip of 4, #4279-4282 | | 17.00 | 8.40 |
| | Nos. 4275-4282 (8) | | 26.00 | 12.80 |

**Miniature Sheet**
**Perf. 14x14¼**

| 4283 | A1041 | Sheet of 4 | 13.00 | 13.00 |
|---|---|---|---|---|
| a.-b. | 1st Either single | | 2.25 | 1.10 |
| c.-d. | £1.85 Either single | | 4.25 | 2.10 |

On day of issue, Nos. 4275-4278 and Nos. 4283a-4283b each sold for 95p.

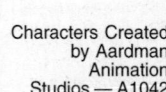

Characters Created by Aardman Animation Studios — A1042

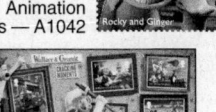

Animated Motion Pictures by Aardman Animation Studios — A1043

Designs: No. 4284, Rocky and Ginger. No. 4285, Feathers McGraw. No. 4286, Wallace and Gromit. No. 4287, Frank the Tortoise. No. 4288, Timmy. No. 4289, Morph and Chas. No. 4290, Robin. No. 4291, Shaun the Sheep and Bitzer.

No. 4292: a, A Close Shave. b, A Matter of Loaf and Death, horiz. c, The Wrong Trousers, horiz. d, A Grand Day Out, horiz.

**Die Cut Perf. 13½x14**

| 2022, Oct. 19 | | | Litho. | |
|---|---|---|---|---|
| | | **Self-Adhesive** | | |
| 4284 | A1042 | 2nd multi | 1.60 | .80 |
| 4285 | A1042 | 2nd multi | 1.60 | .80 |
| a. | Horiz. pair, #4284-4285 | | 3.20 | |
| 4286 | A1042 | 1st multi | 2.25 | 1.10 |
| 4287 | A1042 | 1st multi | 2.25 | 1.10 |
| a. | Horiz. pair, #4286-4287 | | 4.50 | |
| 4288 | A1042 | £1.85 multi | 4.25 | 2.10 |
| 4289 | A1042 | £1.85 multi | 4.25 | 2.10 |
| a. | Horiz. pair, #4288-4289 | | 8.50 | |

| | | | | |
|---|---|---|---|---|
| 4290 | A1042 | £2.55 multi | 6.00 | 3.00 |
| 4291 | A1042 | £2.55 multi | 6.00 | 3.00 |
| a. | | Horiz. pair, #4290-4291 | 12.00 | |
| b. | | Sheet of 8, #4284-4291 + 8 labels | 31.00 | |
| | | Nos. 4284-4291 (8) | 28.20 | 14.00 |

**Miniature Sheet**
***Die Cut Perf. 14x14¼***

| | | | | |
|---|---|---|---|---|
| 4292 | A1043 | Sheet of 4 | 13.00 | |
| a.-b. | | 1st Either single | 2.25 | 1.10 |
| c.-d. | | £1.85 Either single | 4.25 | 2.10 |

On day of issue, Nos. 4284-4285 each sold for 68p and Nos. 4286-4287, 4292a-4292b each sold for 95p. No. 4291b sold for £13.25 and its labels could not be personalized.

Christmas
A1044

Designs: 2nd, Annunciation. 1st, Holy Family. 2nd Large, Journey to Bethlehem. 1st Large, Angel. £1.85, Angel and shepherds. £2.55, Magi.

***Die Cut Perf. 15x14½***

**2022, Nov. 1**        Photo.

**Self-Adhesive**

| | | | | |
|---|---|---|---|---|
| 4293 | A1044 | 2nd multi | 1.60 | 1.25 |
| a. | | Booklet pane of 8 | 13.00 | |
| b. | | Litho., die cut perf. 14½x14x14 | 1.75 | 1.75 |
| 4294 | A1044 | 1st multi | 2.25 | 1.75 |
| a. | | Booklet pane of 8 | 18.00 | |
| b. | | Litho., die cut perf. 14½x14 | 2.40 | 2.40 |
| 4295 | A1044 | 2nd Large multi | 2.50 | 1.90 |
| 4296 | A1044 | 1st Large multi | 3.50 | 2.60 |
| 4297 | A1044 | £1.85 Large multi | 4.25 | 3.25 |
| a. | | Litho., die cut perf. 14½x14 | 4.50 | 4.50 |
| 4298 | A1044 | £2.55 Large multi | 6.00 | 4.50 |
| a. | | Souvenir sheet of 6, #4293-4298 | 20.50 | |
| b. | | Litho., die cut perf. 14½x14 | 6.25 | 6.25 |
| c. | | Sheet of 20, 8 each #4293b, 4294b, 2 each #4297a, 4298b | 55.00 | |
| | | Nos. 4293-4298 (6) | 20.10 | 15.25 |

On day of issue, No. 4293 sold for 68p; No. 4294, 95p; No. 4295, £1.05; No. 4296, £1.45. No. 4298c sold for £23.05, with No. 4293b having a franking value of 68p, and No. 4294b having a franking value of 95p.

Queen Elizabeth II
(1926-2022)
A1045

Photographs of Queen Elizabeth II by: 2nd, Dorothy Wilding, 1952. 1st, Cecil Beaton, 1968. £1.85, Yousuf Karsh, 1984. £2.55, Tim Graham, 1996.

***Perf. 14½x14¼***

**2022, Nov. 10**        Litho.

| | | | | |
|---|---|---|---|---|
| 4299 | A1045 | 2nd black | 1.75 | 1.30 |
| 4300 | A1045 | 1st black | 2.25 | 1.75 |
| 4301 | A1045 | £1.85 black | 4.50 | 3.50 |
| 4302 | A1045 | £2.55 black | 6.25 | 4.75 |
| | | Nos. 4299-4302 (4) | 14.75 | 11.30 |

On day of issue, No. 4299 sold for 68p for No. 4300, 95p. Compare Nos. 4299-4300 with Nos. 2017-2018.

Items From Tomb of
King Tutankhamun
A1046

Discovery of Tomb of King
Tutankhamun, Cent. — A1047

Designs: No. 4303, Wood sculpture of head of King Tutankhamun. No. 4304, Inlaid fan. No. 4305, Gold funerary mask. No. 4306, Falcon pendant. No. 4307, Detail of lion couch. No.

4308, Detail of throne. No. 4309, Boat model. No. 4310, Guardian statue.

No. 4311: a, Objects in tomb's antechamber. b, Head of the outermost coffin. c, Examination of the innermost coffin. d, Moving of small shrine to laboratory.

***Perf. 14¼x14½***

**2022, Nov. 24**        Litho.

| | | | | |
|---|---|---|---|---|
| 4303 | A1046 | 2nd multi | 1.75 | 1.30 |
| 4304 | A1046 | 2nd multi | 1.75 | 1.30 |
| a. | | Horiz. pair, #4303-4304 | 3.50 | 2.60 |
| 4305 | A1046 | 1st multi | 2.25 | 1.75 |
| 4306 | A1046 | 1st multi | 2.25 | 1.75 |
| a. | | Horiz. pair, #4305-4306 | 4.50 | 3.50 |
| 4307 | A1046 | £1.85 multi | 4.50 | 3.50 |
| 4308 | A1046 | £1.85 multi | 4.50 | 3.50 |
| a. | | Horiz. pair, #4307-4308 | 9.00 | 7.00 |
| b. | | Booklet pane of 4, #4305-4308 (BK1240) | 14.50 | — |
| 4309 | A1046 | £2.55 multi | 6.25 | 4.75 |
| 4310 | A1046 | £2.55 multi | 6.25 | 4.75 |
| a. | | Horiz. pair, #4309-4310 | 12.50 | 9.50 |
| b. | | Booklet pane of 4, #4303-4304, 4309-4310 (BK1240) | 17.00 | — |
| | | Nos. 4303-4310 (8) | 29.50 | 22.60 |

**Miniature Sheet**
***Perf. 14¼***

| | | | | |
|---|---|---|---|---|
| 4311 | A1047 | Sheet of 4 | 13.50 | 13.50 |
| a.-b. | | 1st Either single | 2.25 | 1.75 |
| c.-d. | | £1.85 Either single | 4.50 | 3.50 |
| e. | | Booklet pane of 4, #4311a-4311d (BK1240) | 14.50 | — |

On day of issue, Nos.4303-4304 each sold for 68p and Nos. 4305-4306, 4311a-4311b each sold for 95p.

Iron Maiden
in Concert
A1048

Eddie,
Mascot
of Iron
Maiden
A1049

Iron Maiden in concert at: Nos. 4312, 4321a, Vancouver, British Columbia, 2010. Nos. 4313, 4321b, Hammersmith Odeon Theater, London, 1983. Nos. 4314, 4321c, Pamplona, Spain, 1988. Nos. 4315, 4321d, Quito, Ecuador, 2009. Nos. 4316, 4321e, Rio de Janeiro, Brazil, 2001. Nos. 4317, 4321f, Helsinki, Finland, 2018. Nos. 4318, 4321g, Twickenham Stadium, London, 2008. No. 4319, 4321h, Birmingham, England, 2018.

No. 4320 — Eddie: a, Holding Union Jack (1983 artwork for "The Trooper"). b, In cockpit of Spitfire airplane (1984 artwork for "Aces High"). c, In front of brick wall (1980 Iron Maiden album artwork). d, With sword and quiver of arrows (2021 artwork for Senjutsu album).

**2023, Jan. 12**     Litho.     **Perf. 14**

| | | | | |
|---|---|---|---|---|
| 4312 | A1048 | 1st multi | 2.40 | 1.90 |
| 4313 | A1048 | 1st multi | 2.40 | 1.90 |
| 4314 | A1048 | 1st multi | 2.40 | 1.90 |
| 4315 | A1048 | 1st multi | 2.40 | 1.90 |
| a. | | Horiz. strip of 4, #4312-4315 | 9.60 | 7.60 |
| 4316 | A1048 | £1.85 multi | 4.75 | 3.75 |
| 4317 | A1048 | £1.85 multi | 4.75 | 3.75 |
| 4318 | A1048 | £1.85 multi | 4.75 | 3.75 |
| 4319 | A1048 | £1.85 multi | 4.75 | 3.75 |
| a. | | Horiz. strip of 4, #4316-4319 | 19.00 | 15.00 |
| | | Nos. 4312-4319 (8) | 28.60 | 22.60 |

**Miniature Sheets**
***Perf. 14¼x14½***

| | | | | |
|---|---|---|---|---|
| 4320 | A1049 | Sheet of 4 | 14.50 | 14.50 |
| a.-b. | | 1st Either single | 2.40 | 1.90 |
| c.-d. | | £1.85 Either single | 4.75 | 3.75 |

**Self-Adhesive**
***Die Cut Perf. 14***

| | | | | |
|---|---|---|---|---|
| 4321 | | Sheet of 8 + 8 labels | 31.50 | |
| a.-d. | | A1048 1st Any single | 2.60 | 2.60 |
| e.-h. | | A1048 £1.85 Any single | 5.25 | 5.25 |

On day of issue, Nos. 4312-4315, 4320a-4320b each sold for 95p. No. 4321 sold for £12.40 and Nos. 4321a-4321d each had a franking value fo 95p. Two versions on No. 4321 exist, having different sheet margins, labels that could not be personalized, and placement of stamps on the sheet. Value for No. 4321 is for either sheet.

**SEMI-POSTAL STAMPS**

**Catalogue values for unused stamps in this section are for Never Hinged items.**

Handicapped
Person — SP1

***Perf. 14½x14***

**1975, Jan. 22**     Photo.     Unwmk.

| | | | | |
|---|---|---|---|---|
| B1 | SP1 | 4½p +1½p blue & lt blue | .25 | .25 |

For the benefit of health and handicap charities. No. B1 is phosphorescent.

**Christmas Type of 1989**

Ely Cathedral, Cambridgeshire: No. B2, Romanesque arches, west front. No. B3, Central tower. No. B4, Interlocking arches, Romanesque arcades, west transept. No. B5, Peasant, stained-glass window in triple arch, west front.

**1989, Nov. 14**     Photo.     **Perf. 15x14**

| | | | | |
|---|---|---|---|---|
| B2 | A379 | 15p +1p multicolored | .30 | .30 |
| B3 | A379 | 20p +1p multicolored | .45 | .45 |
| B4 | A379 | 34p +1p multicolored | .70 | .70 |
| B5 | A379 | 37p +1p multicolored | .75 | .80 |
| | | Nos. B2-B5 (4) | 2.20 | 2.25 |

**AIR POST STAMPS**

Queen Elizabeth II
AP1     AP2

***Serpentine Die Cut 14¾x14 Syncopated***

**2003, Mar. 27**        Photo.

**Self-Adhesive**
**Booklet Stamps**

| | | | | |
|---|---|---|---|---|
| C1 | AP1 | (52p) blue & red | 4.50 | 4.50 |
| a. | | Booklet pane of 4 | 15.00 | |
| C2 | AP2 | (£1.12) red & blue | 6.50 | 6.00 |
| a. | | Booklet pane of 4 | 22.50 | |

Queen Elizabeth II — AP3

***Die Cut Perf. 14¾x14 Syncopated***

**2004, Apr. 1**        Photo.

**Self-Adhesive**

| | | | | |
|---|---|---|---|---|
| C3 | AP3 | (43p) blk, red & blue | 4.00 | 1.75 |
| a. | | Booklet of 4 + 4 etiquettes | 13.00 | |

Nos. C1-C3 were sold for 52p, £1.12 and 43p, respectively, when issued.

Queen Elizabeth II
AP4     AP5

***Die Cut Perf. 14¾x14 Syncopated***

**2010, Mar. 30**        Photo.

**Booklet Stamps**
**Self-Adhesive**

| | | | | |
|---|---|---|---|---|
| C4 | AP4 | (60p) grn, red & blue | 4.00 | 1.90 |
| a. | | Booklet pane of 4 | 18.00 | |
| C5 | AP5 | (97p) pur, red & blue | 5.50 | 3.00 |
| a. | | Booklet pane of 4 | 18.50 | |

Emblem       Emblem
of 2012       of 2012
Olympics     Paralympics
AP6           AP7

***Die Cut Perf. 14¾x14 Syncopated***

**2012, Jan. 5**        Photo.

**Self-Adhesive**

| | | | | |
|---|---|---|---|---|
| C6 | AP6 | (£1.10) multi | 6.00 | 4.00 |
| C7 | AP7 | (£1.10) multi | 6.00 | 4.00 |
| a. | | Sheet of 20, 8 each #2981-2982, 2 each #C6-C7, + 20 labels, litho. | 47.50 | |

Issued: No. C7a, 7/27/12. No. C7a sold for £15.22. Labels on No. C7a could not be personalized.

**Olympic and Paralympic Emblems**
**Type of 2012**
***Perf. 14¾x14 Syncopated***

**2012, July 27**        Litho.

**Booklet Stamps**

| | | | | |
|---|---|---|---|---|
| C8 | AP6 | (£1.28) multi | 15.50 | 15.50 |
| C9 | AP7 | (£1.28) multi | 15.50 | 15.50 |
| a. | | Booklet pane of 8, #C8, C9, 3 each #3044-3045 (BK200) | 45.00 | — |

On day of issue Nos. C8-C9 each had a franking value of £1.28.

**SPECIAL DELIVERY STAMPS**

Queen Elizabeth II
SD1     SD2

***Die Cut Perf. 14¾x14 Syncopated***

**2010, Oct. 26**        Photo.

**Self-Adhesive**

| | | | | |
|---|---|---|---|---|
| E1 | SD1 | (£5.05) dk bl & gray | 15.00 | 10.00 |
| E2 | SD2 | (£5.50) gray & dk bl | 17.00 | 12.00 |

**POSTAGE DUE STAMPS**

The watermarks on Nos. J1-J67 are sideways.

D1

***Perf. 14x14½***

**1914-24**     Typo.     **Wmk. 33**

| | | | | |
|---|---|---|---|---|
| J1 | D1 | ½p emerald | .90 | .30 |
| | | Never hinged | 3.00 | |
| J2 | D1 | 1p rose | .90 | .25 |
| | | Never hinged | 3.00 | |
| J3 | D1 | 1½p red brown ('22) | 50.00 | 20.00 |
| | | Never hinged | 160.00 | |
| J4 | D1 | 2p brown black | .85 | .25 |
| | | Never hinged | 3.00 | |
| J5 | D1 | 3p violet ('18) | 11.00 | 2.00 |
| | | Never hinged | 30.00 | |
| J6 | D1 | 4p gray green ('21) | 50.00 | 3.00 |
| | | Never hinged | 325.00 | |
| J7 | D1 | 5p org brown | 7.00 | 2.00 |
| | | Never hinged | 27.50 | |
| J8 | D1 | 1sh blue ('15) | 50.00 | 4.50 |
| | | Never hinged | 170.00 | |
| | | Nos. J1-J8 (8) | 170.65 | 32.30 |

Values for No. J6 are for stamps with sideways inverted watermark. No. J6 also exists on paper with sideways watermark. Values thus: $150 unused, $50 used.

From the front of the stamp the sideways watermark reads up in normal type. From the back, the watermark still reads up, but the letters are reversed. The sideways inverted watermark reads down.

D2

**1924-30**        **Wmk. 35**

| | | | | |
|---|---|---|---|---|
| J9 | D1 | ½p emerald | .75 | .60 |
| | | Never hinged | 3.00 | |
| J10 | D1 | 1p car rose | .65 | .30 |
| | | Never hinged | 3.00 | |
| J11 | D1 | 1½p red brown | 52.50 | 22.50 |
| | | Never hinged | 175.00 | |
| J12 | D1 | 2p black brown | 1.60 | .30 |
| | | Never hinged | 10.00 | |
| J13 | D1 | 3p violet | 1.75 | .30 |
| | | Never hinged | 17.50 | |
| a. | | Experimental wmk. | 110.00 | 110.00 |
| | | Never hinged | 190.00 | |
| b. | | Printed on the gummed side | 135.00 | |
| | | Never hinged | 190.00 | |

| | | | | |
|---|---|---|---|---|
| J14 | D1 | 4p deep green | 15.00 | 2.75 |
| | | Never hinged | 65.00 | |
| J15 | D1 | 5p org brown ('30) | 55.00 | 37.50 |
| | | Never hinged | 175.00 | |
| J16 | D1 | 1sh blue | 9.50 | .75 |
| | | Never hinged | 37.50 | |
| J17 | D2 | 2sh6p brown, yellow | 75.00 | 1.90 |
| | | Never hinged | 275.00 | |
| | | Nos. J9-J17 (9) | 211.75 | 66.90 |

The experimental watermark of No. J13a resembles Wmk. 35 but is spaced more closely, with letters short and rounded, crown with flat arch and sides high, lines thicker.

**1936-37** — **Wmk. 250**

| | | | | |
|---|---|---|---|---|
| J18 | D1 | ½p emerald ('37) | 9.75 | 10.00 |
| | | Never hinged | 20.00 | |
| J19 | D1 | 1p car rose ('37) | 1.15 | 1.75 |
| | | Never hinged | 2.25 | |
| J20 | D1 | 2p blk brn ('37) | 9.00 | 9.50 |
| | | Never hinged | 17.50 | |
| J21 | D1 | 3p violet ('37) | 1.10 | 1.40 |
| | | Never hinged | 2.25 | |
| J22 | D1 | 4p slate green | 21.00 | 30.00 |
| | | Never hinged | 72.50 | |
| J23 | D1 | 5p bister ('37) | 20.00 | 26.00 |
| | | Never hinged | 45.00 | |
| a. | | 5p orange brown | 37.50 | 30.00 |
| | | Never hinged | 100.00 | |
| J24 | D1 | 1sh blue ('36) | 6.25 | 8.50 |
| | | Never hinged | 27.50 | |
| J25 | D2 | 2sh6p brn, yel ('37) | 100.00 | 15.50 |
| | | Never hinged | 375.00 | |
| | | Nos. J18-J25 (8) | 168.25 | 102.65 |

**1938-39** — **Wmk. 251**

| | | | | |
|---|---|---|---|---|
| J26 | D1 | ½p emerald | 8.75 | 5.50 |
| | | Never hinged | 15.00 | |
| J27 | D1 | 1p carmine rose | 1.50 | .40 |
| | | Never hinged | 3.25 | |
| J28 | D1 | 2p black brown | 1.15 | .40 |
| | | Never hinged | 3.00 | |
| J29 | D1 | 3p violet | 6.00 | .45 |
| | | Never hinged | 12.50 | |
| J30 | D1 | 4p slate green | 30.00 | 8.50 |
| | | Never hinged | 125.00 | |
| J31 | D1 | 5p bister ('39) | 6.75 | 1.60 |
| | | Never hinged | 19.00 | |
| J32 | D1 | 1sh blue | 20.00 | 1.00 |
| | | Never hinged | 90.00 | |
| J33 | D2 | 2sh6p brown, yel ('39) | 40.00 | 1.75 |
| | | Never hinged | 95.00 | |
| | | Nos. J26-J33 (8) | 114.15 | 19.60 |

> **Catalogue values for unused stamps in this section, from this point to the end of the section, are for Never Hinged items.**

**1951-52**

| | | | | |
|---|---|---|---|---|
| J34 | D1 | ½p orange | 3.75 | 3.75 |
| J35 | D1 | 1p violet blue | 1.60 | .40 |
| J36 | D1 | 1½p green ('52) | 2.25 | 2.25 |
| J37 | D1 | 4p bright blue | 55.00 | 25.00 |
| J38 | D1 | 1sh olive bister | 30.00 | 6.00 |
| | | Nos. J34-J38 (5) | 92.60 | 37.80 |

**1954-55** — **Wmk. 298**

| | | | | |
|---|---|---|---|---|
| J39 | D1 | ½p orange ('55) | 8.75 | 6.00 |
| J40 | D1 | 2p brn blk ('55) | 29.00 | 26.00 |
| J41 | D1 | 3p purple ('55) | 82.50 | 65.00 |
| J42 | D1 | 4p brt blue ('55) | 29.00 | 35.00 |
| a. | | Imperf., pair | 275.00 | |
| J43 | D1 | 5p bis brn ('55) | 22.50 | 22.50 |
| J44 | D2 | 2sh6p dk pur brn, yel | 165.00 | 7.00 |
| | | Nos. J39-J44 (6) | 336.75 | 161.50 |

**1955-57** — **Wmk. 308** — **Perf. 14x14½**

| | | | | |
|---|---|---|---|---|
| J45 | D1 | ½p orange ('56) | 3.00 | 3.50 |
| J46 | D1 | 1p ultra ('56) | 5.50 | 1.65 |
| J47 | D1 | 1½p green ('56) | 9.25 | 7.75 |
| J48 | D1 | 2p brown blk ('56) | 50.00 | 3.75 |
| J49 | D1 | 3p purple ('56) | 6.50 | 1.65 |
| J50 | D1 | 4p brt blue ('56) | 27.50 | 6.75 |
| J51 | D1 | 5p bister brn ('56) | 29.00 | 22.00 |
| J52 | D1 | 1sh dp olive bister | 72.50 | 2.50 |
| J53 | D2 | 2sh6p dk red brn, yel ('57) | 220.00 | 9.00 |
| J54 | D2 | 5sh red, yellow | 165.00 | 35.00 |
| | | Nos. J45-J54 (10) | 588.25 | 93.55 |

**1959-63** — **Wmk. 322** — **Perf. 14x14½**

| | | | | |
|---|---|---|---|---|
| J55 | D1 | ½p orange ('61) | .25 | .25 |
| J56 | D1 | 1p ultra ('60) | .25 | .25 |
| J57 | D1 | 1½p green ('60) | 2.60 | 2.90 |
| J58 | D1 | 2p brown black | 1.10 | .40 |
| J59 | D1 | 3p purple | .25 | .25 |
| J60 | D1 | 4p brt blue ('60) | .30 | .35 |
| J61 | D1 | 5p bister brn ('62) | .40 | .45 |
| J62 | D1 | 6p dp mag ('62) | .45 | .35 |
| J63 | D1 | 1sh dp ol bis ('60) | .75 | .25 |
| J64 | D2 | 2sh6p dk red brn, yel ('61) | .80 | .55 |
| J65 | D2 | 5sh red, yellow ('61) | 5.75 | .85 |
| J66 | D2 | 10sh ultra, yel ('63) | 15.00 | 3.50 |
| J67 | D2 | £1 blk, yellow ('63) | 34.00 | 8.50 |
| | | Nos. J55-J67 (13) | 64.10 | 18.85 |

Nos. J1-J67 are watermarked sideways.

---

**Perf. 14x14½**

**1968-69** — **Unwmk.** — **Typo.**

| | | | | |
|---|---|---|---|---|
| J68 | D1 | 2p greenish black | .80 | 1.10 |
| J69 | D1 | 3p purple | 1.10 | 1.10 |
| J70 | D1 | 4p bright blue | 1.10 | 1.10 |
| J71 | D1 | 5p brown org ('69) | 8.75 | 12.00 |
| J72 | D1 | 6p deep magenta | 2.50 | 1.90 |
| J73 | D1 | 1sh bister ('69) | 4.50 | 2.75 |
| | | Nos. J68-J73 (6) | 18.75 | 19.95 |

**1968-69** — **Photo.**

| | | | | |
|---|---|---|---|---|
| J74 | D1 | 4p bright blue ('69) | 7.75 | 7.50 |
| J75 | D1 | 8p bright red | .55 | 1.10 |

D3

D4

D4a

**Perf. 14x14½**

**1970-75** — **Photo.** — **Unwmk.**

| | | | | |
|---|---|---|---|---|
| J79 | D3 | ½p grnsh blue ('71) | .25 | .60 |
| J80 | D3 | 1p magenta ('71) | .25 | .60 |
| J81 | D3 | 2p green ('71) | .25 | .25 |
| J82 | D3 | 3p ultra ('71) | .25 | .25 |
| J83 | D3 | 4p bister brown ('71) | .25 | .25 |
| J84 | D3 | 5p violet ('71) | .25 | .25 |
| J85 | D3 | 7p brown red ('74) | .35 | .40 |
| J86 | D4 | 10p carmine rose | .35 | .25 |
| J87 | D4 | 11p slate grn ('75) | .60 | .60 |
| J88 | D4 | 20p olive brn | .50 | .35 |
| J89 | D4 | 50p dp blue | 1.40 | .75 |
| J90 | D4 | £1 black | 2.50 | .75 |
| J91 | D4a | £5 org & black ('73) | 20.00 | 3.25 |
| | | Nos. J79-J91 (13) | 27.20 | 8.20 |

D5

D5a

**1982, June 9** — **Photo.** — **Perf. 14x14½**

| | | | | |
|---|---|---|---|---|
| J92 | D5 | 1p brn lil | .25 | .25 |
| J93 | D5 | 2p ultramarine | .25 | .25 |
| J94 | D5 | 3p deep rose lilac | .25 | .25 |
| J95 | D5 | 4p dk gray blue | .25 | .25 |
| J96 | D5 | 5p sepia | .25 | .25 |
| J97 | D5 | 10p yel brn | .25 | .25 |
| J98 | D5 | 20p dark ol green | .45 | .40 |
| J99 | D5 | 25p slate blue | .70 | .70 |
| J100 | D5 | 50p black | 1.25 | 1.20 |
| J101 | D5a | £1 vermilion | 1.90 | 1.00 |
| J102 | D5a | £2 greenish blue | 4.00 | 3.25 |
| J103 | D5a | £5 orange brown | 9.50 | 1.50 |
| | | Nos. J92-J103 (12) | 19.30 | 9.55 |

D6

**Perf. 15x14 Syncopated, Type C (2 Sides)**

**1994, Feb. 15** — **Photo. & Embossed**

| | | | | |
|---|---|---|---|---|
| J104 | D6 | 1p ver & org | .25 | .60 |
| J105 | D6 | 2p red lilac & red | .25 | .60 |
| J106 | D6 | 5p yel & brn | .40 | .75 |
| J107 | D6 | 10p yel & brn | .50 | .75 |
| J108 | D6 | 20p green & violet | 1.10 | 2.90 |
| J109 | D6 | 25p rose & red | 2.40 | 3.00 |
| J110 | D6 | £1 vio & red lilac | 6.00 | 6.50 |
| J111 | D6 | £1.20 bl grn & grn | 7.00 | 7.00 |
| J112 | D6 | £5 pale grn & blk | 20.00 | 7.50 |
| | | Nos. J104-J112 (9) | 37.90 | 29.20 |

## OFFICIAL STAMPS

**Type of Regular Issue of 1840 "V R" in Upper Corners**

O1

**1840** — **Wmk. 18** — **Imperf.**

| | | | | |
|---|---|---|---|---|
| O1 | O1 | 1p black | 23,000. | 26,000. |

No. O1 was never placed in use but examples are known used and on covers that passed through the mails by oversight. The

---

stamp also was used experimentally to test cancellations.

Postage stamps perforated with a crown and initials "H.M.O.W.," "O.W.," "B.T." or "S.O.," or with only the initials "H.M.S.O." or "D.S.I.R.," were used for official purposes.

> Counterfeits exist of Nos. O2-O83.

### Inland Revenue
#### Regular Issues Overprinted in Black

a

b

Type "a" is overprinted on the stamps of ½ penny to 1 shilling inclusive, type "b" on the higher values.

**1882-85** — **Wmk. 30** — **Perf. 14**

| | | | | |
|---|---|---|---|---|
| O2 | A35 | ½p pale green | 135.00 | 65.00 |
| O3 | A35 | ½p slate bl | 120.00 | 37.50 |
| O4 | A40 | 1p lilac | 8.50 | 6.50 |
| a. | | "OFFICIAL" omitted | | 14,000. |
| b. | | Ovpt. lines transposed | | |
| O5 | A47 | 2½p lilac ('85) | 575.00 | 200.00 |
| O6 | A28 | 5p gray | 625.00 | 155.00 |
| O7 | A48 | 1sh green ('85) | 6,500. | 2,100. |

**Wmk. 31**

| | | | | |
|---|---|---|---|---|
| O8 | A51 | 5sh car rose ('85) | 13,000. | 2,750. |
| a. | | Bluish paper | 20,000. | 7,250. |
| O9 | A52 | 10sh ultra | 11,500. | 3,600. |
| a. | | 10sh cobalt | 25,000. | 9,000. |
| b. | | Bluish paper | 42,500. | 10,000. |

**Wmk. Three Imperial Crowns (30)**

| | | | | |
|---|---|---|---|---|
| O10 | A53 | £1 brown vio | 67,500. | 25,000. |

**1888-89** — **Wmk. 30**

| | | | | |
|---|---|---|---|---|
| O11 | A54 | ½p vermilion | 16.00 | 7.75 |
| a. | | "I.R." omitted | 8,000. | |
| O12 | A65 | 1sh green ('89) | 1,100. | 425.00 |

**1890** — **Wmk. Three Orbs (29)**

| | | | | |
|---|---|---|---|---|
| O13 | A53 | £1 brown vio | 95,000. | 35,000. |

**1891** — **Wmk. 30**

| | | | | |
|---|---|---|---|---|
| O14 | A57 | 2½p violet, blue | 200.00 | 32.50 |

**Wmk. Three Imperial Crowns (30)**

**1892**

| | | | | |
|---|---|---|---|---|
| O15 | A53 | £1 green | 14,000. | 2,750. |
| a. | | No period after "R" | | 4,500. |

For examples of Nos. O2-O15 with margins clear of the design on all four sides, add a 20 percent premium to the value listed. For stamps with clear circular datestamps, apply a 20 percent premium. Add the two premiums together for covers with stamps having these attributes.

**1901** — **Wmk. 30**

| | | | | |
|---|---|---|---|---|
| O16 | A54 | ½p blue green | 22.50 | 16.50 |
| O17 | A62 | 1p violet, rose | 700.00 | 165.00 |
| O18 | A65 | 1sh car rose & green | 4,750. | 2,000. |

**1902-04**

| | | | | |
|---|---|---|---|---|
| O19 | A66 | ½p gray grn | 35.00 | 5.00 |
| O20 | A66 | 1p carmine | 24.00 | 3.50 |
| O21 | A66 | 2½p ultra | 1,150. | 310.00 |
| O22 | A66 | 6p dull vio ('04) | 575,000. | 345,000. |
| O23 | A74 | 1sh car rose & grn | 4,250. | 1,025. |

**Wmk. 31**

| | | | | |
|---|---|---|---|---|
| O24 | A76 | 5sh car rose | 42,500. | 11,500. |
| O25 | A77 | 10sh ultra | 97,500. | 50,000. |

**Wmk. Three Imperial Crowns (30)**

| | | | | |
|---|---|---|---|---|
| O26 | A78 | £1 green | 57,500. | 20,000. |

Nos. O4, O8, O9 and O13 also exist with overprint in blue black.

#### Government Parcels

Overprinted

GOVᵀ PARCELS

---

**1883-86** — **Wmk. 30**

| | | | | |
|---|---|---|---|---|
| O27 | A45 | 1½p lilac ('86) | 450.00 | 115.00 |
| O28 | A46 | 6p green ('86) | 4,000. | 1,600. |
| O29 | A50 | 9p green | 3,000. | 1,350. |
| O30 | A29 | 1sh sal (P13) | 2,000. | 350.00 |
| | | Plate 14 | 4,000. | 675.00 |
| | | Nos. O27-O30 (4) | 9,450. | 3,415. |

**1887-92**

| | | | | |
|---|---|---|---|---|
| O31 | A55 | 1½p vio & grn | 195.00 | 35.00 |
| O32 | A56 | 2p grn & car rose ('91) | 290.00 | 57.50 |
| O33 | A60 | 4½p grn & car grn ('92) | 450.00 | 310.00 |
| O34 | A62 | 6p violet, rose | 310.00 | 85.00 |
| O35 | A63 | 9p blue & lil ('88) | 475.00 | 135.00 |
| O36 | A65 | 1sh green | 800.00 | 310.00 |
| | | Nos. O31-O36 (6) | 2,520. | 932.50 |

**1897**

| | | | | |
|---|---|---|---|---|
| O37 | A40 | 1p lilac | 115.00 | 35.00 |
| a. | | Inverted overprint | 8,500. | 4,000. |

**1900**

| | | | | |
|---|---|---|---|---|
| O38 | A65 | 1sh car rose & grn | 725.00 | 310.00 |
| a. | | Inverted overprint | | 17,500. |

For examples of Nos. O27-38 with margins clear of the design on all four sides, add a 25 percent premium to the value listed. For stamps with clear circular datestamps, apply a 100 percent premium. Add the two premiums together for covers with stamps having these attributes.

**1902**

| | | | | |
|---|---|---|---|---|
| O39 | A66 | 1p carmine | 85.00 | 25.00 |
| O40 | A68 | 2p green & car | 250.00 | 67.50 |
| O41 | A66 | 6p dull violet | 310.00 | 67.50 |
| O42 | A72 | 9p ultra & violet | 725.00 | 200.00 |
| O43 | A74 | 1sh car rose & grn | 1,550. | 325.00 |
| | | Nos. O39-O43 (5) | 2,920. | 685.00 |

#### Office of Works

Overprinted

O.W. OFFICIAL

**1896**

| | | | | |
|---|---|---|---|---|
| O44 | A54 | ½p vermilion | 400.00 | 165.00 |
| O45 | A40 | 1p lilac | 550.00 | 165.00 |

For examples of Nos. O44-O45 with margins clear of the design on all four sides, add a 20 percent premium to the value listed. For stamps with clear circular datestamps, apply a 15 percent premium. Add the two premiums together for covers with stamps having these attributes.

O.W. OFFICIAL

**1901-02**

| | | | | |
|---|---|---|---|---|
| O46 | A54 | ½p blue green | 525.00 | 250.00 |
| O47 | A61 | 5p lilac & ultra | 4,500. | 1,550. |
| O48 | A64 | 10p car rose & lil | 8,250. | 2,500. |

**1902**

| | | | | |
|---|---|---|---|---|
| O49 | A66 | ½p gray grn | 650.00 | 205.00 |
| O50 | A66 | 1p carmine | 650.00 | 205.00 |
| O51 | A68 | 2p grn & car | 2,250. | 500.00 |
| O52 | A66 | 2½p ultra | 4,000. | 750.00 |
| O53 | A73 | 10p car rose & vio | 45,000. | 8,000. |

#### Army
Overprinted

| | |
|---|---|
| a | b |

**1896**

| | | | | |
|---|---|---|---|---|
| O54 | A54(a) | ½p vermilion | 8.75 | 3.50 |
| a. | | "OFFICIAl" | 315.00 | 150.00 |

| | | | |
|---|---|---|---|
| O55 | A40(a) | 1p lilac | 8.75 | 7.75 |

| | | |
|---|---|---|
| *a.* | "OFFICIAI" | 275.00 170.00 |
| O56 | A57(b) 2½p violet, *blue* | 57.50 39.00 |
| | *Nos. O54-O56 (3)* | 75.00 50.25 |

**1900**

| | | | |
|---|---|---|---|
| O57 | A54(a) | ½p blue green | 11.00 *17.00* |

For examples of Nos. O54-O57 with margins clear of the design on all four sides, add a 20 percent premium to the value listed. For stamps with clear circular datestamps, apply a 15 percent premium. Add the two premiums together for covers with stamps having these attributes.

**1901**

| | | | |
|---|---|---|---|
| O58 | A62(b) | 6p violet, *rose* | 125.00 67.50 |

**1902**

| | | | |
|---|---|---|---|
| O59 | A66(a) | ½p gray green | 6.75 2.75 |
| O60 | A66(a) | 1p carmine | 6.75 2.75 |

| | | |
|---|---|---|
| *a.* | "ARMY" omitted | — |
| O61 | A66(a) 6p dull violet | 200.00 90.00 |
| | *Nos. O59-O61 (3)* | 213.50 95.50 |

Overprinted

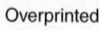

**1903**

| | | | |
|---|---|---|---|
| O62 | A66 | 6p dull violet | 3,250. 1,800. |

**Royal Household**

Overprinted

**1902**

| | | | |
|---|---|---|---|
| O63 | A66 | ½p gray green | 425.00 220.00 |
| O64 | A66 | 1p carmine | 350.00 190.00 |

**Board of Education**

Overprinted

**1902**

| | | | |
|---|---|---|---|
| O65 | A61 | 5p lilac & ultra | 6,500. 1,700. |
| O66 | A65 | 1sh car rose & grn | 13,500. 6,750. |

**1902-04**

| | | | |
|---|---|---|---|
| O67 | A66 | ½p gray green | 200.00 50.00 |
| O68 | A66 | 1p carmine | 200.00 50.00 |
| O69 | A66 | 2½p ultramarine | 5,750. 525.00 |
| O70 | A71 | 5p lilac & ultra ('04) | 34,000. 9,500. |
| O71 | A74 | 1sh car rose & grn | 180,000. — |

**Admiralty**

Overprinted

**1903**

| | | | |
|---|---|---|---|
| O72 | A66 | ½p gray green | 32.50 16.50 |
| O73 | A66 | 1p carmine | 22.50 11.00 |
| O74 | A67 | 1½p vio & green | 350.00 170.00 |
| O75 | A68 | 2p green & car | 375.00 180.00 |
| O76 | A66 | 2½p ultra | 525.00 170.00 |
| O77 | A69 | 3p violet, *yel* | 475.00 180.00 |
| | *Nos. O72-O77 (6)* | 1,780. 727.50 |

Overprinted

**1903**

| | | | |
|---|---|---|---|
| O78 | A66 | ½p gray green | 67.50 30.00 |
| O79 | A66 | 1p carmine | 67.50 30.00 |
| O80 | A67 | 1½p vio & grn | 2,100. 725.00 |
| O81 | A68 | 2p grn & car | 3,000. 1,000. |
| O82 | A66 | 2½p ultramarine | 3,250. 1,050. |
| O83 | A69 | 3p violet, *yel* | 2,900. 450.00 |

The two types of the "Admiralty Official" overprint differ principally in the shape of the letter "M."

---

## ENVELOPES

Britannia Sending Letters to World (William Mulready, Designer)
E1

**1840**

| | | |
|---|---|---|
| U1 | E1 1p black | 400.00 *600.00* |
| U2 | E1 2p blue | 500.00 *2,800.* |

---

## LETTER SHEETS

| | | |
|---|---|---|
| U3 | E1 1p black | 400.00 *600.00* |
| U4 | E1 2p blue | 475.00 *2,500.* |

---

## REGIONAL ISSUES

Sold only at post offices within the respective regions, but valid for postage throughout Great Britain. Issues for Guernsey, Jersey and Isle of Man are listed with the Bailiwick issues that follow.

Starting in 1967, all Regional stamps were issued only with phosphorescence.

> **Catalogue values for unused stamps in this section are for Never Hinged items.**

## ENGLAND

Three Lions — A1

*Perf. 15x14 Syncopated*

**2001-02**                                              **Photo.**

| | | | | |
|---|---|---|---|---|
| 1 | A1 | 2nd shown | 1.40 | 1.40 |
| 2 | A1 | 1st Crowned Lion | 1.75 | 1.75 |
| 3 | A1 | E Oak tree | 2.75 | 2.90 |
| 4 | A1 | 65p Tudor rose | 2.90 | 2.90 |
| 5 | A1 | 68p Tudor rose | 2.90 | 2.90 |
| | | *Nos. 1-5 (5)* | 11.70 | 11.85 |

Issued: Nos. 1-4, 4/23/01. No. 5, 7/4/02. Nos. 1-3 sold for 19p, 27p and 36p respectively on day of issue.

Three Lions A2

Crowned Lion A3

Oak Tree A4

Tudor Rose A5

*Perf. 14¾x14 Syncopated*

**2003, Oct. 14**

| | | | | |
|---|---|---|---|---|
| 6 | A2 | 2nd multi | 1.40 | 1.40 |
| 7 | A3 | 1st multi | 1.75 | 1.75 |
| *a.* | Litho. (Wales #21a) | 3.00 | 3.00 |
| 8 | A4 | E multi | 2.75 | 2.75 |
| 9 | A5 | 68p multi | 2.75 | 2.25 |
| | | *Nos. 6-9 (4)* | 8.65 | 8.15 |

Nos. 6-8 each sold for 20p, 28p and 38p respectively on day of issue.

---

**2004, May 11**

| | | | |
|---|---|---|---|
| 10 | A4 40p multi | 1.60 | 1.50 |
| *a.* | Booklet pane, 2 each #6, 10 + label (BK177) | 8.00 | — |

No. 10a issued 2/24/05.

**2005, Apr. 5**

| | | |
|---|---|---|
| 11 | A4 42p multi | 1.75 1.75 |

**2006, Mar. 28**

| | | |
|---|---|---|
| 12 | A4 44p multi | 1.90 1.90 |
| 13 | A5 72p multi | 2.50 2.50 |

**2007**

| | | |
|---|---|---|
| 14 | A4 48p multi | 1.75 *1.90* |
| 15 | A5 78p multi | 2.50 2.50 |

**Litho.**
**Self-Adhesive**
*Die Cut Perf. 14¾x14*
**Stamp + Label**

| | | |
|---|---|---|
| 16 | A3 1st multi | 2.25 2.00 |

Issued: Nos. 14, 15, 3/27; No. 16, 4/23. No. 16 was issued in sheets of 20 stamps + 20 labels that sold for £7.35 and had a franking value of 34p on day of issue.

*Perf. 14¾x14 Syncopated*

**2008, Apr. 1**                               **Photo.**

| | | |
|---|---|---|
| 17 | A4 50p multi | 1.90 1.75 |
| 18 | A5 81p multi | 2.75 2.50 |

**Litho.**
**Self-Adhesive**
**Stamp + Label**
*Die Cut Perf. 14¾x14 Syncopated*

| | | |
|---|---|---|
| 18A | A3 1st multi | 3.50 3.50 |

Issued: No. 18A, 9/29/08. See Wales & Monmouthshire No. 32Ab.

**2009, Mar. 31**

| | | |
|---|---|---|
| 19 | A4 56p multi | 1.75 1.75 |
| 20 | A5 90p multi | 2.75 2.75 |

**Heritage of England Type of 2007**

Design: English flag (like #2462a).

**Self-Adhesive**
*Die Cut Perf. 14¾x14*

**2009, Apr. 21**                               **Litho.**

| | | |
|---|---|---|
| 21 | A626 1st multi + label | 2.50 2.50 |

No. 21 was issued in a sheet of 20 stamps + 20 labels that sold for £8.35, and had a franking value of 39p on day of issue.

**Types of 2003**
*Perf. 14¾x14 Syncopated*

**2010, Mar. 30**                               **Photo.**

| | | |
|---|---|---|
| 22 | A4 60p multi | 1.90 1.75 |
| 23 | A5 97p multi | 3.00 2.75 |

**2011, Mar. 29**                               **Litho.**

| | | |
|---|---|---|
| 24 | A4 68p multi | 2.25 2.00 |
| 25 | A5 £1.10 multi | 3.50 3.50 |

**2012, Apr. 25**

| | | |
|---|---|---|
| 26 | A4 87p multi | 4.25 3.75 |
| 27 | A5 £1.28 multi | 3.90 3.50 |

**2013, Mar. 27**

| | | |
|---|---|---|
| 28 | A4 88p multi | 2.75 2.10 |

**2014, Mar. 26**

| | | |
|---|---|---|
| 29 | A4 97p multi | 3.25 2.50 |

**Types of 2003**
*Perf. 14¾x14 Syncopated*

**2015, Mar. 24**                               **Litho.**

| | | |
|---|---|---|
| 30 | A4 £1 multi | 2.60 2.60 |
| 31 | A5 £1.33 multi | 3.50 3.50 |

**Oak Tree Type of 2003**
*Perf. 14¾x14 Syncopated*

**2016, Mar. 22**                               **Litho.**

| | | |
|---|---|---|
| 32 | A4 £1.05 multi | 2.75 2.75 |

**Types of 2003**
*Perf. 14¾x14 Syncopated*

**2017, Mar. 21**                               **Litho.**

| | | |
|---|---|---|
| 33 | A4 £1.17 multi | 3.00 1.50 |
| 34 | A5 £1.40 multi | 3.50 1.75 |

---

Three Lions A6

Crowned Lion A7

Oak Tree A8

Tudor Rose A9

*Perf. 14¾x14 Syncopated*

**2018, Mar. 20**                               **Litho.**

| | | | |
|---|---|---|---|
| 35 | A6 | 2nd multi | 1.60 .80 |
| 36 | A7 | 1st multi | 1.90 .95 |
| 37 | A8 | £1.25 multi | 3.50 1.75 |
| 38 | A9 | £1.45 multi | 4.25 2.10 |
| | | *Nos. 35-38 (4)* | 11.25 5.60 |

On day of issue, No. 35 sold for 56p and No. 36 sold for 65p.

**Oak Tree and Tudor Rose Types of 2018**
*Perf. 14¾x14 Syncopated*

**2019, Mar. 19**                               **Litho.**

| | | | |
|---|---|---|---|
| 39 | A8 | £1.35 multi | 3.50 2.60 |
| 40 | A9 | £1.55 multi | 4.25 3.25 |

**Oak Tree and Tudor Rose Types of 2018**
*Perf. 14¾x14 Syncopated*

**2020, Mar. 17**                               **Litho.**

| | | | |
|---|---|---|---|
| 41 | A8 | £1.42 multi | 3.50 2.60 |
| 42 | A9 | £1.63 multi | 4.00 3.00 |

**Oak Tree Type of 2018**
*Perf. 14¾x14 Syncopated*

**2020, Dec. 23**                               **Litho.**

| | | | |
|---|---|---|---|
| 43 | A8 | £1.70 multi | 4.75 3.75 |

Three Lions and Matrix Code — A10

Crowned Lion and Matrix Code — A11

Oak Tree and Matrix Code — A12

*Die Cut Perf. 15x14½ Syncopated*

**2022, Aug. 11**                               **Litho.**
**Self-Adhesive**

| | | | |
|---|---|---|---|
| 44 | A10 | 2nd multi | 1.60 .80 |
| 45 | A11 | 1st multi | 2.25 1.10 |
| 46 | A12 | £1.85 multi | 4.25 2.10 |

On day of issue, No. 44 sold for 68p and No. 45 sold for 95p.

---

## NORTHERN IRELAND

A1

A2

Flax and Red Hand of Ulster — A3

*Perf. 15x14*

**1958-67**              **Photo.**              **Wmk. 322**

| | | | | |
|---|---|---|---|---|
| 1 | A1 | 3p dark purple | .25 | .25 |
| *p.* | Phosphor. ('67) | .25 | .25 |

| 2 | A1 | 4p ultra ('66) | .25 | .25 |
|---|----|----|----|----|
| p. | | Phosphor. ('67) | .25 | .25 |
| 3 | A2 | 6p rose lilac | .30 | .30 |
| 4 | A2 | 9p dk green ('67) | .25 | .35 |
| 5 | A3 | 1sh3p dark green | .35 | .45 |
| 6 | A3 | 1sh6p dark blue ('67) | .25 | .35 |
| | | Nos. 1-6 (6) | 1.65 | 1.95 |

Nos. 4, 6 and following are phosphorescent. For stamps with denomination of "1st" see No. 2600.

**1968-69**       **Unwmk.**

Design: 1sh6p, Flax plant, Red Right Hand of Ulster and Ulster field gate.

| 7 | A1 | 4p ultramarine | .25 | .25 |
|---|----|----|----|----|
| 8 | A1 | 4p olive brown | .25 | .25 |
| 9 | A1 | 4p bright red ('69) | .25 | .25 |
| 10 | A1 | 5p dark green | .25 | .25 |
| 11 | A3 | 1sh6p dark blue ('69) | 2.00 | 2.10 |
| | | Nos. 7-11 (5) | 3.00 | 3.10 |

Giant's Causeway — A4

**Perf. 14¾x14 Syncopated**

**2001-02**       **Litho.**

| 12 | A4 | 2nd shown | 1.45 | 1.45 |
|----|----|----|----|----|
| 13 | A4 | 1st Farm fields | 1.75 | 1.75 |
| a. | | Booklet pane, 5 #12, 4 #13 (BK173) | 14.50 | |
| 14 | A4 | E Linen | 2.40 | 2.40 |
| 15 | A4 | 65p Parian China | 3.00 | 3.00 |
| 16 | A4 | 68p Parian China | 3.25 | 3.25 |
| | | Nos. 12-16 (5) | 11.85 | 11.85 |

Issued: Nos. 12-15, 3/6/01; No. 16, 7/4/02; No. 13a, 2/25/03.

Nos. 12-14 sold for 19p, 27p and 36p respectively on day of issue.

Giant's Causeway A5      Farm Fields A6

Linen A7      Parian China A8

**2003, Oct. 14**

| 17 | A5 | 2nd multi | 1.45 | 1.45 |
|----|----|----|----|----|
| a. | | Photo. | 1.45 | 1.45 |
| 18 | A6 | 1st multi | 1.75 | 1.75 |
| a. | | Photo. ('07) | 1.60 | 1.60 |
| 19 | A7 | E multi | 2.75 | 2.75 |
| 20 | A8 | 68p multi | 2.75 | 2.75 |
| | | Nos. 17-20 (4) | 8.70 | 8.70 |

Nos. 17-19 each sold for 20p, 28p and 38p respectively on day of issue.

**2004, May 11**

| 21 | A7 | 40p multi | 1.90 | 1.90 |
|----|----|----|----|----|

**2005, Apr. 5**

| 22 | A7 | 42p multi | 2.60 | 2.60 |
|----|----|----|----|----|

**2006, Mar. 28**

| 23 | A7 | 44p multi | 1.75 | 1.75 |
|----|----|----|----|----|
| 24 | A8 | 72p multi | 3.25 | 3.25 |

**2007, Mar. 27**       **Photo.**

| 25 | A7 | 48p multi | 1.50 | 1.50 |
|----|----|----|----|----|
| 26 | A8 | 78p multi | 2.50 | 2.50 |

**Self-Adhesive**
**Stamp + Label**
**Die Cut Perf. 14¾x14**

**2008, Mar. 11**       **Litho.**

| 27 | A6 | 1st multi | 2.75 | 2.75 |
|----|----|----|----|----|

No. 27 was issued in sheets of 20 stamps + 20 labels that sold for £7.35, and had a franking value of 34p on day of issue.

**Perf. 14¾x14 Syncopated**

**2008, Apr. 1**       **Photo.**

| 28 | A7 | 50p multi | 1.60 | 1.60 |
|----|----|----|----|----|
| 29 | A8 | 81p multi | 2.60 | 2.60 |

**2009**

| 30 | A7 | 56p multi | 1.75 | 1.75 |
|----|----|----|----|----|

| 31 | A8 | 90p multi | 2.75 | 2.75 |
|----|----|----|----|----|

**Litho.**
**Self-Adhesive**
**Stamp + Label**
**Die Cut Perf. 14¾x14 Syncopated**

| 32 | A6 | 1st multi | 2.25 | 2.25 |
|----|----|----|----|----|

Issued: Nos. 30-31, 3/31; No. 32, 4/21. No. 32 was issued in a sheet of 20 stamps + 20 labels that sold for £8.35, and had a franking value of 39p on day of issue.

**Perf. 14¾x14 Syncopated**

**2010, Mar. 30**       **Photo.**

| 33 | A7 | 60p multi | 1.90 | 1.90 |
|----|----|----|----|----|
| 34 | A8 | 97p multi | 2.75 | 2.75 |

**2011, Mar. 29**       **Litho.**

| 35 | A7 | 68p multi | 2.25 | 1.90 |
|----|----|----|----|----|
| 36 | A8 | £1.10 multi | 3.50 | 3.50 |

**2012, Apr. 25**

| 37 | A7 | 87p multi | 4.00 | 4.00 |
|----|----|----|----|----|
| 38 | A8 | £1.28 multi | 3.75 | 3.75 |

**2013, Mar. 27**

| 39 | A7 | 88p multi | 3.25 | 3.25 |
|----|----|----|----|----|

**2014, Mar. 26**       **Litho.**

| 40 | A7 | 97p multi | 3.50 | 3.50 |
|----|----|----|----|----|

**Types of 2003**
**Perf. 14¾x14 Syncopated**

**2015, Mar. 24**       **Litho.**

| 41 | A7 | £1 multi | 3.00 | 2.60 |
|----|----|----|----|----|
| 42 | A8 | £1.33 multi | 3.75 | 3.25 |

**Linen Type of 2003**
**Perf. 14¾x14 Syncopated**

**2016, Mar. 22**       **Litho.**

| 43 | A7 | £1.05 multi | 3.00 | 2.60 |
|----|----|----|----|----|

**Types of 2003**
**Perf. 14¾x14 Syncopated**

**2017, Mar. 21**       **Litho.**

| 44 | A7 | £1.17 multi | 3.00 | 1.50 |
|----|----|----|----|----|
| 45 | A8 | £1.40 multi | 3.50 | 1.75 |

Giant's Causeway A9      Farm Fields A10

Linen A11      Parian China A12

**Perf. 14¾x14 Syncopated**

**2018, Mar. 20**       **Litho.**

| 46 | A9 | 2nd multi | 1.60 | .80 |
|----|----|----|----|----|
| 47 | A10 | 1st multi | 1.90 | .95 |
| 48 | A11 | £1.25 multi | 3.50 | 1.75 |
| 49 | A12 | £1.45 multi | 4.25 | 2.10 |
| | | Nos. 46-49 (4) | 11.25 | 5.60 |

On day of issue, No. 46 sold for 56p and No. 47 sold for 65p.

**Linen and Parian China Types of 2018**
**Perf. 14¾x14 Syncopated**

**2019, Mar. 19**       **Litho.**

| 50 | A11 | £1.35 multi | 3.50 | 2.60 |
|----|----|----|----|----|
| 51 | A12 | £1.55 multi | 4.25 | 3.25 |

**Linen and Parian China Types of 2018**
**Perf. 14¾x14 Syncopated**

**2020, Mar. 17**       **Litho.**

| 52 | A11 | £1.42 multi | 3.50 | 2.60 |
|----|----|----|----|----|
| 53 | A12 | £1.63 multi | 4.00 | 3.00 |

**Linen Type of 2018**
**Perf. 14¾x14 Syncopated**

**2020, Dec. 23**       **Litho.**

| 54 | A11 | £1.70 multi | 4.75 | 3.75 |
|----|----|----|----|----|

Giant's Causeway and Matrix Code — A13      Farm Fields and Matrix Code — A14

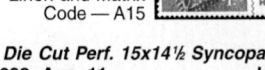

Linen and Matrix Code — A15

**Die Cut Perf. 15x14½ Syncopated**

**2022, Aug. 11**       **Litho.**

**Self-Adhesive**

| 55 | A13 | 2nd multi | 1.60 | .80 |
|----|----|----|----|----|
| 56 | A14 | 1st multi | 2.25 | 1.10 |
| 57 | A15 | £1.85 multi | 4.25 | 2.10 |

On day of issue, No. 55 sold for 68p and No. 56 sold for 95p.

---

# SCOTLAND

St. Andrew's Cross and Thistle — A1

A2            A3

**Perf. 15x14**

**1958-67**       **Photo.**       **Wmk. 322**

| 1 | A1 | 3p dark purple | .25 | .25 |
|---|----|----|----|----|
| p. | | Phosphor. | .25 | .25 |
| 2 | A1 | 4p ultra ('66) | .25 | .25 |
| p. | | Phosphor. ('67) | .25 | .25 |
| 3 | A2 | 6p rose lilac | .25 | .25 |
| p. | | Phosphor. ('63) | .25 | .25 |
| 4 | A2 | 9p dark green ('67) | .40 | .40 |
| 5 | A3 | 1sh3p dark green | .40 | .40 |
| p. | | Phosphor. ('63) | .40 | .40 |
| 6 | A3 | 1sh6p dark blue ('67) | .45 | .45 |
| | | Nos. 1-6 (6) | 2.00 | 2.00 |

The 3p with two phosphorescent bands was issued in 1963; with one side band in 1965, and one center band in 1967. The value of No. 1p is for one center band. Nos. 4, 6 and following are phosphorescent. For stamps with denomination of "1st" see No. 2600.

**1967-70**       **Unwmk.**

| 7 | A1 | 3p purple ('68) | .25 | .25 |
|---|----|----|----|----|
| 8 | A1 | 4p ultramarine | .25 | .25 |
| 9 | A1 | 4p olive brown ('68) | .25 | .25 |
| 10 | A1 | 4p brt red ('69) | .25 | .25 |
| 11 | A1 | 5p dark blue ('68) | .25 | .25 |
| 12 | A2 | 9p dark green ('70) | 3.75 | 3.75 |
| 13 | A3 | 1sh6p dark blue ('68) | 1.10 | 1.10 |
| | | Nos. 7-13 (7) | 6.10 | 6.10 |

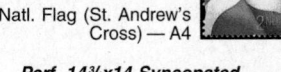

Natl. Flag (St. Andrew's Cross) — A4

**Perf. 14¾x14 Syncopated**

**1999-2002**       **Photo.**

| 14 | A4 | (2nd) shown | 1.45 | 1.45 |
|----|----|----|----|----|
| 15 | A4 | (1st) Lion Rampant | 1.75 | 1.60 |
| a. | | Booklet pane, #15, 4 England #1, 4 England #2 (BK172) | 14.50 | |
| 16 | A4 | (E) Thistle | 2.25 | 2.25 |
| a. | | Booklet pane, 4 each #15-16, + label (BK170) | 16.00 | |
| 17 | A4 | 64p Tartan | 8.00 | 8.00 |
| 18 | A4 | 65p As #17 | 2.60 | 2.60 |
| a. | | Booklet pane, 6 #14, 2 #18 + label (BK168) | 14.00 | |
| 19 | A4 | 68p Tartan | 3.25 | 3.25 |
| | | Nos. 14-19 (6) | 39.10 | 19.15 |

nos. 14-16 sold for 19p, 26p, & 30p, respectively on day of issue.

Issued: Nos. 14-17, 6/8; No. 18, 4/25/00; No. 18a, 8/4/00; No. 16a, 10/22/01. No. 19, 7/4/02. No. 15a, 9/24/02.

Natl. Flag (St. Andrew's Cross) A5      Lion Rampant A6

Thistle A7        Tartan A8

**2003, Oct. 14**

| 20 | A5 | 2nd multi | 1.45 | 1.45 |
|----|----|----|----|----|
| a. | | Booklet pane, 3 each England #9, Scotland #20 (BK175) | 12.50 | — |
| 21 | A6 | 1st multi | 1.75 | 1.75 |
| a. | | Litho. (Wales #21a, GB 2600t) | 2.00 | 2.00 |
| 22 | A7 | E multi | 2.90 | 2.90 |
| 23 | A8 | 68p multi | 2.10 | 1.75 |
| | | Nos. 20-23 (4) | 9.00 | 9.00 |

Nos. 20-22 each sold for 20p, 28p and 38p respectively on day of issue.

No. 20a issued 3/16/04. No. 21a issued 9/28/08.

See Great Britain No. 2419a for National Flag stamp inscribed "1st."

**2004, May 11**

| 24 | A7 | 40p multi | 1.75 | 1.35 |
|----|----|----|----|----|
| a. | | Souvenir sheet, #20, 2 each #21, 24 | 6.00 | 6.00 |

No. 24a issued 10/5/04.

**2005, Apr. 5**

| 25 | A7 | 42p multi | 1.90 | 1.40 |
|----|----|----|----|----|

**2006, Mar. 28**

| 26 | A7 | 44p multi | 1.75 | 1.75 |
|----|----|----|----|----|
| 27 | A8 | 72p multi | 2.90 | 2.90 |

**2007, Mar. 27**

| 28 | A7 | 48p multi | 1.75 | 1.75 |
|----|----|----|----|----|
| 29 | A8 | 78p multi | 2.75 | 2.75 |

**Self-Adhesive**
**Stamp + Label**
**Die Cut Perf. 14¾x14**

**2007, Nov. 30**       **Litho.**

| 30 | A6 | 1st multi | 2.75 | 2.75 |
|----|----|----|----|----|

No. 30 was issued in sheets of 20 stamps + 20 labels that sold for £8.50, and had a franking value of 34p on day of issue.

**Perf. 14¾x14 Syncopated**

**2008, Apr. 1**       **Photo.**

| 31 | A7 | 50p multi | 1.90 | 1.75 |
|----|----|----|----|----|
| 32 | A8 | 81p multi | 2.75 | 2.75 |

**Litho.**
**Self-Adhesive**
**Stamp + Label**
**Die Cut Perf. 14¾x14 Syncopated**

| 32A | A6 | 1st multi | 3.75 | 2.90 |
|----|----|----|----|----|

Issued: No. 32A, 9/29/08. See Wales & Monmouthshire No. 32Ab.

**2009, Mar. 31**

| 33 | A7 | 56p multi | 1.90 | 1.90 |
|----|----|----|----|----|
| 34 | A8 | 90p multi | 2.75 | 2.75 |

Flag of Scotland A9

| 35 | A9 | 1st multi + label | 2.00 | 2.00 |
|----|----|----|----|----|

No. 35 was printed in a sheet of 20 + 20 labels that could not be personalizd that sold for £8.35. See No. 2419a for similar stamp with water-activated gum.

**Types of 2003**

**2010, Mar. 30**       **Photo.**

| 36 | A7 | 60p multi | 2.40 | 1.90 |
|----|----|----|----|----|
| 37 | A8 | 97p multi | 3.75 | 2.90 |

**2011, Mar. 29**       **Litho.**

| 38 | A7 | 68p multi | 2.40 | 2.40 |
|----|----|----|----|----|
| 39 | A8 | £1.10 multi | 3.50 | 3.50 |

**2012, Apr. 25**

| | | | | |
|---|---|---|---|---|
| 40 | A7 | 87p multi | 4.25 | 3.25 |
| 41 | A8 | £1.28 multi | 3.75 | 2.60 |

**2013, Mar. 27**

| | | | | |
|---|---|---|---|---|
| 42 | A7 | 88p multi | 2.75 | 2.00 |

**2014, Mar. 26**

| | | | | |
|---|---|---|---|---|
| 43 | A7 | 97p multi | 3.25 | 2.25 |

**Types of 2003**
*Perf. 14¾x14 Syncopated*

**2015, Mar. 24**     **Litho.**

| | | | | |
|---|---|---|---|---|
| 44 | A7 | £1 multi | 3.00 | 2.25 |
| 45 | A8 | £1.33 multi | 4.00 | 3.00 |

**Thistle Type of 2003**
*Perf. 14¾x14 Syncopated*

**2016, Mar. 22**     **Litho.**

| | | | | |
|---|---|---|---|---|
| 46 | A7 | £1.05 multi | 3.00 | 2.25 |

**Types of 2003**
*Perf. 14¾x14 Syncopated*

**2017, Mar. 21**     **Litho.**

| | | | | |
|---|---|---|---|---|
| 47 | A7 | £1.17 multi | 3.00 | 1.50 |
| 48 | A8 | £1.40 multi | 3.50 | 1.75 |

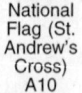

National Flag (St. Andrew's Cross) A10

Lion Rampant A11

Thistle A12

Tartan A13

*Perf. 14¾x14 Syncopated*

**2018, Mar. 20**     **Litho.**

| | | | | |
|---|---|---|---|---|
| 49 | A10 | 2nd multi | 1.60 | .80 |
| 50 | A11 | 1st multi | 1.90 | .95 |
| 51 | A12 | £1.25 multi | 3.50 | 1.75 |
| 52 | A13 | £1.45 multi | 4.25 | 2.10 |
| | | *Nos. 49-52 (4)* | 11.25 | 5.60 |

On day of issue, No. 49 sold for 56p and No. 50 sold for 65p.

**Thistle and Tartan Types of 2018**
*Perf. 14¾x14 Syncopated*

**2019, Mar. 19**     **Litho.**

| | | | | |
|---|---|---|---|---|
| 53 | A12 | £1.35 multi | 3.50 | 2.60 |
| 54 | A13 | £1.55 multi | 4.25 | 3.25 |

**Thistle and Tartan Types of 2018**
*Perf. 14¾x14 Syncopated*

**2020, Mar. 17**     **Litho.**

| | | | | |
|---|---|---|---|---|
| 55 | A12 | £1.42 multi | 3.50 | 2.60 |
| 56 | A13 | £1.63 multi | 4.00 | 3.00 |
| a. | | Souvenir sheet of 4, Scotland #49, 50, 55, 56 | 11.00 | 11.00 |

Declaration of Arbroath, 700th anniv. (No. 56a).

**Thistle Type of 2018**
*Perf. 14¾x14 Syncopated*

**2020, Dec. 23**     **Litho.**

| | | | | |
|---|---|---|---|---|
| 57 | A12 | £1.70 multi | 4.75 | 3.75 |

National Flag (St. Andrew's Cross) and Matrix Code — A14

Lion Rampant and Matrix Code — A15

Thistle and Matrix Code — A16

---

*Die Cut Perf. 15x14½ Syncopated*

**2022, Aug. 11**     **Litho.**

**Self-Adhesive**

| | | | | |
|---|---|---|---|---|
| 58 | A14 | 2nd multi | 1.60 | .80 |
| 59 | A15 | 1st multi | 2.25 | 1.10 |
| 60 | A16 | £1.85 multi | 4.25 | 2.10 |

On day of issue, No. 58 sold for 68p and No. 59 sold for 95p.

---

# WALES & MONMOUTHSHIRE

A1

A2

Welsh Dragon — A3

Designs: 6p, 9p, Dragon in rectangular panel at bottom. 1sh3p, 1sh6p, Dragon and leek.

*Perf. 15x14*

**1958-67**     **Photo.**     **Wmk. 322**

| | | | | |
|---|---|---|---|---|
| 1 | A1 | 3p dark purple | .25 | .25 |
| p. | | Phosphor. band ('67) | .25 | .25 |
| 2 | A1 | 4p ultra ('66) | .25 | .25 |
| p. | | Phosphor. bands ('67) | .25 | .25 |
| 3 | A2 | 6p rose lilac | .40 | .35 |
| 4 | A2 | 9p dark green ('67) | .40 | .40 |
| 5 | A3 | 1sh3p dark green | .50 | .50 |
| 6 | A3 | 1sh6p dark blue ('67) | .40 | .40 |
| | | *Nos. 1-6 (6)* | 2.20 | 2.15 |

Nos. 4, 6 and following are phosphorescent. For stamps with denomination of "1st" see No. 2600.

**1967-69**     **Unwmk.**

| | | | | |
|---|---|---|---|---|
| 7 | A1 | 3p dark purple | .25 | .25 |
| 8 | A1 | 4p ultra ('68) | .25 | .25 |
| 9 | A1 | 4p olive brown ('68) | .25 | .25 |
| 10 | A1 | 4p brt red ('69) | .25 | .25 |
| 11 | A1 | 5p dark blue ('68) | .25 | .25 |
| 12 | A3 | 1sh6p dark blue ('69) | 3.50 | 3.50 |
| | | *Nos. 7-12 (6)* | 4.75 | 4.75 |

Leek — A4

*Perf. 15x14 Syncopated*

**1999-2002**     **Photo.**

| | | | | |
|---|---|---|---|---|
| 13 | A4 | 2nd shown | 1.40 | 1.40 |
| 14 | A4 | 1st Dragon | 1.75 | 1.75 |
| 15 | A4 | E Daffodil | 2.25 | 2.25 |
| 16 | A4 | 64p Prince of Wales feathers | 8.00 | 7.50 |
| 17 | A4 | 65p Prince of Wales feathers | 3.00 | 3.00 |
| | | *Nos. 13-17 (5)* | 16.40 | 15.90 |
| 18 | A2 | 2nd Leek, perf 13¾x14¼ | 3.75 | 3.00 |
| a. | | Booklet pane, 4 each #18, MH336 + label (BK169) | 23.00 | |
| 19 | A4 | 68p Prince of Wales Feathers | 3.00 | 3.00 |

Nos. 13, 18 sold for 19p; No. 14, 26p; & No. 15, 30p, on day of issue.
Issued: Nos. 13-16, 6/8; No. 17, 4/25/00; No. 19, 7/4/02.
No. 18 is a booklet stamp.

Leek A5

Dragon A6

Daffodil A7

Prince of Wales Feathers A8

*Perf. 14¾x14 Syncopated*

**2003, Oct. 14**

| | | | | |
|---|---|---|---|---|
| 20 | A5 | 2nd multi | 1.45 | 1.45 |
| 21 | A6 | 1st multi | 1.90 | 1.75 |
| a. | | Booklet pane, litho., England #7a, Northern Ireland #18, Scotland, #21a, Wales & Monmouthshire #21b, + 5 labels (BK183) ('07) | 9.75 | |
| b. | | Litho. (#21a, GB #2600v) ('07) | 3.00 | 3.00 |
| 22 | A7 | E multi | 2.90 | 2.90 |
| 23 | A8 | 68p multi | 2.25 | 2.00 |
| a. | | Souvenir sheet, #20, 2 each #21, 23 ('06) | 7.00 | 7.00 |
| | | *Nos. 20-23 (4)* | 8.50 | 8.10 |

Nos. 20-22 each sold for 20p, 28p and 38p respectively on day of issue.
No. 23a issued 3/1/06. No. 21b issued 9/28/08

**2004, May 11**

| | | | | |
|---|---|---|---|---|
| 24 | A7 | 40p multi | 1.75 | 1.75 |

**2005, Apr. 5**

| | | | | |
|---|---|---|---|---|
| 25 | A7 | 42p multi | 2.25 | 2.25 |

**2006-07**

| | | | | |
|---|---|---|---|---|
| 26 | A7 | 44p multi | 1.75 | 1.75 |
| a. | | Booklet pane, 3 each Scotland #20, Wales & Monmouthshire #26 (BK181) ('07) | 11.50 | — |
| 27 | A8 | 72p multi | 2.50 | 2.25 |

**Self-Adhesive**
**Litho.**
**Stamp + Label**
*Die Cut Perf. 14¾x14*

| | | | | |
|---|---|---|---|---|
| 28 | A6 | 1st multi | 2.75 | 2.25 |

No. 28 was issued in a sheet of 20 stamps + 20 different se-tenant labels that sold for £6.95. The franking value of No. 28 was 32p on day of issue.
Issued: Nos. 26, 27, 3/28; Nos. 26a, 28 issued 3/1/07.

*Perf. 14¾x14 Syncopated*

**2007, Mar. 27**     **Photo.**

| | | | | |
|---|---|---|---|---|
| 29 | A7 | 48p multi | 1.90 | 1.75 |
| 30 | A8 | 78p multi | 2.50 | 2.50 |

**2008, Apr. 1**

| | | | | |
|---|---|---|---|---|
| 31 | A7 | 50p multi | 1.90 | 1.75 |
| 32 | A8 | 81p multi | 3.25 | 2.40 |

**Litho.**
**Self-Adhesive**
**Stamp + Label**
*Die Cut Perf. 14¾x14 Syncopated*

| | | | | |
|---|---|---|---|---|
| 32A | A6 | 1st multi | 3.25 | 3.25 |
| b. | | Sheet, 5 each #32A, England #18A, Northern Ireland #32, Scotland #32A, + 20 labels | 27.50 | — |

Issued: No. 32A, 9/29/08.
No. 32Ab sold for £7.74. Labels could not be personalized.

**2009, Mar. 31**

| | | | | |
|---|---|---|---|---|
| 33 | A7 | 56p multi | 1.75 | 1.75 |
| 34 | A8 | 90p multi | 2.75 | 2.75 |

Flag of Wales A9

*Die Cut Perf. 14¾x14 Syncopated*

**2010, Mar. 1**     **Self-Adhesive**     **Litho.**

| | | | | |
|---|---|---|---|---|
| 35 | A9 | 1st multi + label | 2.25 | 1.75 |

Issued: No. 32A, 9/29/08. No. 35 was printed in a sheet of 20 + 20 labels that could not be personalizd that sold for £8.35. See No. 2639a for similar stamp with water-activated gum.

**Types of 2003**
*Perf. 14¾x14 Syncopated*

**2010, Mar. 30**     **Photo.**

| | | | | |
|---|---|---|---|---|
| 36 | A7 | 60p multi | 1.90 | 1.40 |
| 37 | A8 | 97p multi | 3.00 | 2.25 |

**2011, Mar. 29**     **Litho.**

| | | | | |
|---|---|---|---|---|
| 38 | A7 | 68p multi | 2.40 | 1.90 |
| 39 | A8 | £1.10 multi | 3.50 | 2.60 |

**2012, Apr. 25**

| | | | | |
|---|---|---|---|---|
| 40 | A7 | 87p multi | 4.25 | 3.25 |
| 41 | A8 | £1.28 multi | 3.75 | 2.90 |

**2013, Mar. 27**

| | | | | |
|---|---|---|---|---|
| 42 | A7 | 88p multi | 2.75 | 2.10 |

**2014, Mar. 26**

| | | | | |
|---|---|---|---|---|
| 43 | A7 | 97p multi | 3.50 | 2.60 |

**Types of 2003**
*Perf. 14¾x14 Syncopated*

**2015, Mar. 24**     **Litho.**

| | | | | |
|---|---|---|---|---|
| 44 | A7 | £1 multi | 3.00 | 2.25 |
| 45 | A8 | £1.33 multi | 4.00 | 3.25 |

**Daffodil Type of 2003**
*Perf. 14¾x14 Syncopated*

**2016, Mar. 22**     **Litho.**

| | | | | |
|---|---|---|---|---|
| 46 | A7 | £1.05 multi | 3.00 | 2.25 |

**Types of 2003**
*Perf. 14¾x14 Syncopated*

**2017, Mar. 21**     **Litho.**

| | | | | |
|---|---|---|---|---|
| 47 | A7 | £1.17 multi | 3.00 | 1.50 |
| 48 | A8 | £1.40 multi | 3.50 | 1.75 |

Leek A10

Dragon A11

Daffodil A12

Prince of Wales Feathers A13

*Perf. 14¾x14 Syncopated*

**2018, Mar. 20**     **Litho.**

| | | | | |
|---|---|---|---|---|
| 49 | A10 | 2nd multi | 1.60 | .80 |
| 50 | A11 | 1st multi | 1.90 | .95 |
| 51 | A12 | £1.25 multi | 3.50 | 1.75 |
| 52 | A13 | £1.45 multi | 4.25 | 2.10 |
| | | *Nos. 49-52 (4)* | 11.25 | 5.60 |

On day of issue, No. 49 sold for 56p and No. 50 sold for 65p.

**Daffodil and Prince of Wales Feathers Types of 2018**
*Perf. 14¾x14 Syncopated*

**2019, Mar. 19**     **Litho.**

| | | | | |
|---|---|---|---|---|
| 53 | A12 | £1.35 multi | 3.50 | 2.60 |
| 54 | A13 | £1.55 multi | 4.25 | 3.25 |

**Daffodil and Prince of Wales Feathers Types of 2018**
*Perf. 14¾x14 Syncopated*

**2020, Mar. 17**     **Litho.**

| | | | | |
|---|---|---|---|---|
| 55 | A12 | £1.42 multi | 3.50 | 2.60 |
| 56 | A13 | £1.63 multi | 4.00 | 3.00 |

**Daffodil Type of 2018**
*Perf. 14¾x14 Syncopated*

**2020, Dec. 23**     **Litho.**

| | | | | |
|---|---|---|---|---|
| 57 | A12 | £1.70 multi | 4.75 | 3.75 |

Leek and Matrix Code — A14

Dragon and Matrix Code — A15

Daffodil and Matrix Code — A16

*Die Cut Perf. 15x14½ Syncopated*

**2022, Aug. 11**     **Litho.**

**Self-Adhesive**

| | | | | |
|---|---|---|---|---|
| 58 | A14 | 2nd multi | 1.60 | .80 |
| 59 | A15 | 1st multi | 2.25 | 1.10 |
| 60 | A16 | £1.85 multi | 4.25 | 2.10 |

On day of issue, No. 58 sold for 68p and No. 59 sold for 95p.

# MACHINS

## MACHIN DEFINITIVE STAMPS

### Sterling Currency Issue

MA1

Type I      Type II

Two types of 2p:
Type I — Head off-center to right. Foot of "2" 1mm from left margin.
Type II — Head centered. Foot of "2" ½mm from left margin.

MH21      MH168

Two types of "£" symbol:
No. MH21 has a loop at the bottom and the numeral is a figure "1."
No. MH168 has no loop and numeral is like a capital "I."

### *Perf. 15x14*

| 1967-69 | Photo. | Unwmk. |
|---|---|---|
| | **Size: 17½x21½mm** | |
| MH1 | ½p brown orange | .30 | .25 |
| MH2 | 1p olive | .30 | .25 |
| *a.* | Booklet pane of 6 (BK101-BK104, BK121) | 1.00 | |
| MH3 | 2p maroon (I) | .30 | .25 |
| MH4 | 2p maroon (II) | .30 | .25 |
| MH5 | 3p dark violet | .30 | .25 |
| *a.* | Booklet pane of 6 (BK121) | 1.25 | |
| *b.* | Booklet pane, 2 ea #MH2, MH5 (BK83) | .80 | |
| *c.* | imperf. pair | 850.00 | |
| MH6 | 4p brown black | .30 | .25 |
| *a.* | Bkt. pane of 2 + 2 labels (BK84) | .50 | |
| *b.* | Bkt. pane of 4 (BK83-BK84) | 1.00 | |
| *c.* | Booklet pane of 6 (BK101-BK102, BK114-BK115, BK121-BK122) | 1.25 | |
| *d.* | Booklet pane, 4 #MH2, 2 #MH6 (BK122) | 1.50 | |
| MH7 | 4p bright red | .30 | .25 |
| *a.* | Bkt. pane of 2 + 2 labels (BK85) | .50 | |
| *b.* | Booklet pane of 4 (BK85) | 1.00 | |
| *c.* | Booklet pane of 6 (BK103-BK104, BK116-BK117, BK123-BK124) | 1.50 | |
| *d.* | Booklet pane of 15 + recipe (BK125-BK126) | 3.00 | |
| *e.* | Booklet pane, 4 #MH2, 2 #MH7 (BK123-BK124) | 1.50 | |
| *f.* | Coil strip of 5, #MH2, MH5, #MH7, 2 #MH4 | 1.25 | |
| MH8 | 5p dark blue | .30 | .25 |
| *a.* | Booklet pane of 6 (BK110-BK112, BK122-BK124) | 1.50 | |
| *b.* | Booklet pane, 6 each #MH2, #MH7, 3 #MH8 + recipe (BK125-BK126) | 3.00 | |
| *c.* | Booklet pane of 15 + recipe (BK125-BK126) | 3.00 | |
| MH9 | 6p magenta | .30 | .25 |
| MH10 | 7p bright green | .35 | .35 |
| MH11 | 8p scarlet | .25 | .50 |
| MH12 | 8p lt greenish blue | .40 | .50 |
| MH13 | 9p dark green | .40 | .30 |
| MH14 | 10p gray | .75 | .75 |
| MH15 | 1sh light violet | .45 | .30 |
| MH16 | 1sh6p indigo & lt bl | .50 | .50 |
| *a.* | Greenish blue omitted | 150.00 | |
| MH17 | 1sh9p blk & org | .60 | .50 |

### *Perf. 12*

### Engr.

### *Size: 27x31mm*

| MH18 | 2sh6p brown | .45 | .25 |
|---|---|---|---|
| MH19 | 5sh dark carmine | 1.40 | .70 |
| MH20 | 10sh dp ultra | 4.75 | 4.75 |
| MH21 | £1 bluish black | 2.90 | 1.75 |
| *Nos. MH1-MH21 (21)* | | 15.90 | 13.40 |

Nos. MH10-MH13 have denomination at right. Many of Nos. MH1-MH17 exist with phosphor bands omitted in error.
Issued: ½p, 1p, No. MH3, 6p, 2/5/68; No. MH4, 8/27/69; 3p, 4/6/68; No. MH6, 1sh,

---

1sh9p, 6/5/67; Nos. MH7, MH12, 1/6/69; 5p, 7p, No. MH11, 1/6/69; 10p, 7/1/68; 9p, 1sh6p, 8/8/67; Nos. MH18-MH21, 3/5/69.

### Decimal Currency Issues
### (P Instead of D)

MA2

Original

Type MA2: Upper lip not defined by sharp line, nostril is incomplete, hairlines not sharply defined, upper corners of cross formeé are widely separated.
Nos. MH22-MH189, MH199-MH243 are Type MA2.
Redrawn portrait: Upper lip sharply outlined, nostril is complete and defined by two lines, hairlines are sharply defined, upper corners of cross formeé are close together so they nearly complete a square.
See listings begining with No. MH245 for Type MA2 Redrawn.
Specialized illustrations are shown for identification purposes.
Two types of 1p: Type I: Thick numeral and "p," which are 2½mm from bottom of design. Type II: Thinner numeral and "p," which are 3mm from bottom of design.

### *Perf. 15x14*

| 1970-95 | Photo. | Unwmk. |
|---|---|---|
| | **Size: 17½x21½mm** | |
| MH22 | ½p greenish blue | .30 | .25 |
| *a.* | Booklet pane of 5 + label (BK129-BK130, BK132, BK138, BK143) | 1.25 | |
| MH23 | 1p magenta, Type I | .30 | .25 |
| MH23A | 1p magenta, Type II | .45 | .45 |
| MH24 | 1½p black | .30 | .25 |
| *a.* | Booklet pane, 2 each #MH23-MH24 (BK127-BK128) | 1.00 | |

Issued: ½p, No. MH23, 1½p, 2/15/71. No. MH23A, 8/4/80.

2ᴾ    2ᴾ

a      b

2ᴾ

c

Three types of 2p:
a, Wide "2," thick at bottom of curve.
b, Wide "2," thin at bottom of curve.
c, Narrow "2."

| MH25 | 2p light green (a) | .30 | .25 |
|---|---|---|---|
| *a.* | Coil strip, 2 ea #MH22-MH23, 1 #MH25 | .90 | |
| MH26 | 2p light green (b) | .55 | .25 |
| *a.* | Booklet pane, 2 each #MH22, MH26(BK127-BK128) | 1.50 | |
| *b.* | Booklet pane of 6 + printed margin (BK145) | 3.50 | |
| MH27 | 2p dark green (c) | .35 | .25 |
| MH28 | 2p dark green (c) | 9.75 | 9.75 |

### Litho.

| MH29 | 2p grn, perf 14 (a) | .45 | .25 |
|---|---|---|---|
| MH30 | 2p green (a) | .40 | .25 |
| MH31 | 2p dark green (c) | .75 | .65 |
| MH31A | 2p dk grn, perf 14 (c) | 2.00 | .25 |

Nos. MH24a, MH26a exist with with stamps se-tenant vertically or horizontally.
Issued: No. MH25, 12/12/79; No. MH26, 2/15/71; No. MH27, 9/5/88; No. MH28, 7/26/88; No. MH29, 5/21/80; No. MH30, 7/10/84; No. MH31, 2/23/88; No. MH31A, 2/9/93.
No. MH31A comes from No. MH128a (BK420) only.

---

2½ᴾ    2½ᴾ

a      b

2½ᴾ

c

Three types of 2½p:
a, Thick numerals & "P," end of curve of small "2" is thick.
b, Thinner numerals & "P," end of curve of small "2" is thin.
c, Very thin numerals & "P," end of curve of small "2" is pointy.

| MH32 | 2½p pink (a) | .40 | .40 |
|---|---|---|---|
| *a.* | Booklet pane of 4 + 2 labels (BK129-BK130, BK132) | 1.75 | |
| *b.* | Booklet pane of 5 + label (BK129-BK130, BK132, BK138, BK143) | 2.00 | |
| MH33 | 2½p pink (b) | .30 | .60 |
| MH34 | 2½p pink (c) | 1.25 | 1.75 |
| *a.* | Booklet pane, 3 #MH22, 9 #MH34 + printed margin (BK144) | 27.50 | |
| *b.* | Booklet pane, 4 #MH22, 2 #MH34 + printed margin (BK144) | 47.50 | |

Nos. MH34a, MH34b valued in F-VF condition.

| MH35 | 2½p vermilion (b) | .30 | .40 |
|---|---|---|---|

Issued: No. MH32 2/15/71; No. MH33, 5/21/75; No. MH34, 5/24/72; No. MH35, 1/14/81.
No. MH34 issued only in booklets.

3ᴾ    3ᴾ

a      b

Two types of 3p:
a, Thick numeral with top serif.
b, Thin numeral without serif.

| MH36 | 3p dp ultra (a) | .30 | .25 |
|---|---|---|---|
| *a.* | Booklet pane, 2 #MH32, 4 #MH36 (BK138, BK143) | 2.50 | |
| *b.* | Booklet pane, 5 + label (BK131, BK133-BK136, BK139) | 2.00 | |
| *c.* | Bkt. pane of 6 (BK138, BK143) | 1.50 | |
| *d.* | Booklet pane of 12, 6 each #MH34, #MH36 + printed margin (BK144) | 20.00 | |
| *e.* | Booklet pane of 12 + printed margin (BK144) | 5.50 | |
| MH37 | 3p magenta (a) | .30 | .25 |
| *a.* | Coil strip, #MH35, 3 #MH37 | .90 | .90 |
| MH38 | 3p magenta (a) | 2.25 | .75 |

Issued: No. MH36, 9/10/73; No. MH37, 10/22/80; No. MH38, 1/21/92.

3½ᴾ    3½ᴾ

a      b

Two types of 3½p:
a, Numerals in fraction aligned diagonally.
b, Numerals in fraction aligned vertically.

| MH39 | 3½p gray green (a) | .40 | .40 |
|---|---|---|---|
| *a.* | Booklet pane of 5 + label (BK137, BK139-BK141) | 2.25 | |
| MH40 | 3½p brown rose (b) | .45 | .55 |

Issued: No. MH39, 6/24/74; No. MH40, 3/30/83.

4ᴾ    4ᴾ

a      b

4ᴾ

c

Three types of 4p:
a, Wide "4" with large serif and thick crossbar.
b, Wide "4" with small serif and thin crossbar.

---

c, Narrow "4."

| MH41 | 4p bister brown (a) | .30 | .25 |
|---|---|---|---|
| *a.* | Imperf., pair | | |
| MH42 | 4p greenish blue (a) | .60 | .75 |
| *a.* | Coil strip, #MH22, 3 MH42 | 1.25 | 2.50 |
| MH43 | 4p lt greenish bl (a) | .50 | .60 |
| *a.* | Coil strip, #MH23, 3 MH43 | 1.50 | |
| *b.* | Coil strip, #MH28, 3 MH43 | 8.25 | |
| MH44 | 4p greenish blue (b) | 1.60 | 1.90 |
| MH45 | 4p lt grnish bl (c) | 1.50 | 1.90 |
| MH46 | 4p bright blue (c) | .40 | .25 |
| *a.* | Coil strip, #MH38, 3 #MH46 | 4.00 | |
| MH47 | 4p Turq blue, litho., perf 13½x14 (b) | .30 | .30 |
| MH48 | 4p Turq blue, litho. (c) | .95 | .30 |
| MH49 | 4½p grayish blue | .25 | .25 |
| *a.* | Booklet pane of 5 + label (BK140, BK142) | 9.75 | |

Issued: No. MH41, 2/15/71; Nos. MH42-MH42a, 12/30/81; Nos. MH43-MH43a, 8/14/84; No. MH43b, 9/5/88. No. MH44, 8/26/81; No. MH45, 9/3/84; No. MH46, 7/26/88; No. MH46a, 9/19/89. No. MH47, 1/30/80; No. MH48, 5/13/86; 4 1/2p, 10/24/73.
No. MH43 issued only in strips.

5ᴾ    5ᴾ

a      b

5ᴾ

c

Three types of 5p:
a, 5p is 3.25mm wide.
b, 5p is 2.75mm wide.
c, 5p is 3mm wide (see No. MH248B).

| MH50 | 5p bluish lilac (a) | .30 | .25 |
|---|---|---|---|
| MH51 | 5p lilac, perf 13½x14 (a) | .45 | .45 |
| MH52 | 5p claret, litho., perf 13½x14 (a) | .60 | .60 |
| MH53 | 5p claret, litho. (a) | .70 | .60 |
| MH54 | 5p lt red brown (b) | 2.25 | 1.25 |
| MH55 | 5p pale red brn (b) | .45 | .35 |
| *a.* | Coil strip, #MH55, 3 #MH46 | 2.00 | |
| *b.* | Coil strip, 2 ea #MH46, MH55 | 2.00 | |
| *c.* | Coil strip, #MH46, 3 MH55 | 2.00 | |
| MH56 | 5½p dark violet | .35 | .35 |

Issued: No. MH50, 2/15/71; No. MH51, 5/21/80; No. MH52, 1/27/82; No. MH53, 2/21/84; No. MH54, 10/20/86; No. MH55, 7/26/88; No. MH55a, 11/27/90; No. MH55b, 10/1/91. No. MH55c, 1/31/95. 5 1/2p, 10/24/73.

6ᴾ    6ᴾ

a      b

6ᴾ

c

Three types of 6p:
a, Thick numeral and "P."
b, Thinner numeral and "P," numeral is pointed at top and very thin where loop joins.
c, Narrow numeral.

| MH57 | 6p light emerald (a) | .35 | .25 |
|---|---|---|---|
| MH58 | 6p light emerald (b) | .75 | .25 |
| *a.* | Booklet pane, #MH58, 2 MH22, 3 MH23 (BK225) | 1.75 | |
| *b.* | Coil strip, #MH23, MH26, MH58, 2 MH22 | | |
| MH59 | 6p brt olive green (c) | .40 | .25 |
| MH60 | 6½p greenish blue | .30 | .40 |

Issued: No. MH57, 2/15/71; No. MH58, 6/9/76; No. MH58b, 12/3/75. No. MH59, 9/10/91; 6 1/2p, 9/4/74.
No. MH58 issued only in booklets and strips.

7ᴾ    7ᴾ

a      b

Two types of 7p:
a, Wide numeral.
b, Narrow numeral.

| MH61 | 7p brown purple (a) | .30 | .30 |
|---|---|---|---|
| *a.* | Coil strip, #MH61, 2 ea MH22-MH23 | .95 | |

b. Booklet pane, #MH61, 2 ea MH22-MH23 + label (BK226) .75

MH62 7p henna brown (b) .85 1.50
MH63 7½p lt red brown .35 .40
MH64 8p scarlet .30 .25
  a. Coil strip, #MH64, 2 MH23 + 2 labels .75
  b. Booklet pane, #MH64, 2 MH23 + label (BK227) .75
MH65 8½p yellow green .35 .25
  b. Bklt. pane, 3 #MH22-MH23, MH60, 4 MH65 (BK228) 2.60

No. MH65a exists with the four 8½p stamps se-tenant on either the left or right side of the pane.

MH66 9p black & salmon .50 .25
MH67 9p violet blue .35 .25
  a. Booklet pane, 3 ea MH61, MH67 (BK229-BK230) 2.25
  b. Booklet pane, 10 ea #MH61, MH67 (BK672) 5.50

No. MH67a exists with the three 9p stamps se-tenant on either the left or right side of the pane.

MH68 9½p reddish purple .40 .50

Issued: No. MH61, 1/15/75; No. MH61a, 12/14/77; No. MH62, 10/29/85; 7 7/2p, 2/15/71; 8p, 10/24/73; No. MH64a, 1/16/80. 8½p, 9/24/75; No. MH66, 2/15/71; No. MH67, 9 1/2p, 2/25/76.

a        b

c

Three types of 10p:
a, Round "0."
b, Thin part of "0" at upper left, lower right.
c, Thin part of "0" at top, bottom.

MH69 10p org brn & lt org (a) .50 .35
MH70 10p salmon (b) .40 .30
  a. Bklt. pane of 9 + printed margin (BK145) 3.75
  b. Booklet pane, 2 ea #MH26, MH64, 3 #MH70 + label (BK231-BK232) 2.25
  c. Booklet pane, 10 ea #MH64, MH70 (BK709) 6.00
MH70D 10p light org brn (c) 26.00 20.00

No. MH70b exists with the three 10p stamps se-tenant on either the left or right side of the pane.

MH71 10p brn orange (c) .55 .50
MH72 10½p yellow .50 .50
MH73 10½p gray blue .65 .60
MH74 11p rose .50 .25

Issued: No. MH69, 8/11/71; Nos. MH70, MH72, 11p, 2/25/76; No. MH71, 9/4/90; No. MH73, 4/26/78; No. MH70D, 9/4/84.

a        b

Two types of 11½p:
a, Thin numerals in fraction.
b, Thick numerals in fraction.

MH75 11½p bister brown (a) .55 .55
MH76 11½p gray brown (a) .45 .40
  a. Booklet pane, 2 #MH44, 3 each MH35, MH76 (BK236) 

No. MH76a exists with the three 11½p stamps se-tenant on either the left or right side of the pane.

MH77 11½p gray brown (b) 1.00 .25

No. MH77 comes from No. MH86c (BK826), only.

Issued: No. MH75, 8/15/79; No. MH76, 1/14/81; No. MH77, 11/11/81;

a        b

Two types of 12p:
a, Wide numerals.
b, Narrow, thin numerals.

MH78 12p yellow green (a) .55 .50
  a. Booklet pane of 9 + printed margin (BK145) 5.00

b. Booklet pane of 9 (#MH26, 4 each #MH70, MH78) + printed margin (BK145) 4.50
c. Booklet pane of 10 each #MH70, MH78 (BK759) 9.50
d. Booklet pane, 3 each MH70, MH78 + label (BK233) 3.50

No. MH78d exists with the three 2p stamps se-tenant on either the left or right side of the pane.

MH79 12p bright green (b) .55 .35
  a. Booklet pane of 9 + printed margin (BK140) 5.00
  b. Booklet pane, 2 #MH23, 4 MH79 (BK245) 9.50

Issued: No. MH78, 1/30/80; No. MH79, 10/29/85.

a        b

Two types of 12½p:
a, Thin, narrow numerals.
b, Thick, wider numerals.

MH80 12½p light emerald (a) .55 .25
  a. Booklet pane of 6 + printed margin (BK146-BK147) 3.50
  b. Booklet pane of 9, #MH25, MH37, 7 MH80 + printed margin (BK146) 4.25
  c. Booklet pane, #MH22, 4 MH37, 3 MH80 (BK237-BK238) 2.75
  e. Booklet pane of 20 (BK760) 11.00

No. MH80c exists with the three 12½p stamps se-tenant on either the left or right side of the pane. Booklets with 20 No. MH80 were sold at a discount. Stamps in these booklets had 5-point double-lined stars printed on the reverse.

MH81 12½p green (b) .75 .25
  a. Booklet pane, 2 #MH23, 3 each MH40, MH81 (BK239+) 5.00

No. MH81 comes from Nos. BK239, BK513-BK514 and from No. MH93d (BK572-BK574).
Issued: No. MH80, 1/27/82; No. MH81, 2/1/82.

a        b

Two types of 13p:
a, "3" with serif.
b, "3" without serif.

MH82 13p olive gray (a) .65 .55
MH83 13p lt red brown (b) .50 .25
  a. Booklet pane of 6 + printed margin (BK148, BK151) 3.00
  b. Booklet pane of 9 + printed margin (BK149, BK151) 4.50
  c. Booklet pane, 2 #MH45, 3 each MH23, MH83 (BK240) 5.00
  d. Booklet pane, #MH23, 2 MH54, 3 MH83 (BK244, BK248) 6.25
  e. Booklet pane of 4, margins all around (BK285) 2.00
  f. Booklet pane of 10, margins all around (BK534) 5.00
  g. As "d," imperf edges (BK248A, BK250-BK251) 5.25

Panes of No. MH83 with stars printed on the reverse were sold at a discount.

MH84 13p lt red brn, litho. (b) .75 .85
  a. Booklet pane of 6 + printed margin (BK152) 4.50
MH85 13½p brown purple .70 .70

Issued: No. MH82, 8/15/79; No. MH83, 8/28/84; No. MH84, 2/9/88; 13½p, 1/30/80.

a        b

Two types of 14p:
a, Wide "4."
b, Narrow "4."

MH86 14p gray blue (a) .60 .60
  a. Bklt. pane, #MH22-MH23, MH86, 3 MH76 (BK234-BK235) 2.40
  b. Booklet pane, 4 #MH76, 6 MH86 (BK524) 5.50
  c. Booklet pane, 10 each #MH77, MH86 (BK826) 16.00

No. MH86a exists with the three 11½p stamps se-tenant on either the left or right side of the pane.

MH87 14p dark blue (b) .60 .40
  a. Booklet pane of 4, margins all around (BK295) 4.75
  b. Booklet pane of 4, imperf on T, B (BK296) 5.75

c. Booklet pane of 4, imperf on T, B, R (BK297) 27.00
d. Boolet pane of 10, margins all around (BK558) 12.00
e. Booklet pane of 10, imperf on T, B (BK560) 7.50

MH88 14p dark blue, litho. 2.25 2.00
MH89 14p dark blue, litho., perf 14 (b) 6.75 1.00

No. MH89 comes from No. MH108a (BK412), only.

MH90 15p deep ultramarine .65 .65
MH91 15p bright blue .80 .80

Issued: No. MH86, 1/14/81; No. MH87, 9/5/88; No. MH88, 10/11/88; No. MH89, 4/25/89; No. MH90, 8/15/79; No. MH91, 9/26/89.

a        b

Two types of 15½p:
a, Thin numerals in fraction, top bar of "5" thin.
b, Thick numerals in fraction, top bar of "5" thick.

MH92 15½p light violet (a) .60 .50
  a. Booklet pane of 6 + printed margin (BK146) 3.75
  b. Booklet pane of 9 + printed margin (BK146) 5.50
MH93 15½p light violet (b) .90 .75
  d. Booklet pane, 4 #MH81, 6 MH93 (BK572-BK574) 6.50
  e. Booklet pane, 10 each #MH80, MH93 (BK802) 12.00

No. MH93e was printed with 10-point single-line blue stars on the reverse over the gum.

MH94 16p brownish gray .65 .65
  a. Booklet pane, #MH37, 2 MH40 6 MH94 + printed margin (BK147) 5.00
  b. Booklet pane of 9 + printed margin (BK147) 5.75
  c. Booklet pane, 4 #MH80, 6 MH94 (BK594) 6.75

Panes of No. MH94 with double-line D printed on reverse were sold at a discount in BK584.

MH95 16½p brown rose .80 .85

Issued: No. MH92, 1/14/81; No. MH93, 2/1/82; 16p, 3/30/83; 16½p, 1/27/82. No. MH93 issued only in booklets.

a        b

Two types of 17p:
a, Wide "7."
b, Narrow "7."

MH96 17p light green (a) .75 .80
MH97 17p blue gray (b) .50 .50
  a. Booklet pane of 3 + label (star printed on reverse-BK241-BK242) 2.75
  b. Booklet pane of 9 + printed margin (BK149-BK150) 4.50
  c. Booklet pane of 6 + printed margin (BK148-BK150) 3.00
  d. Booklet pane, #MH70D, MH83, 7 MH97 + printed margin (BK148) 33.00
  e. Booklet pane, 4 #MH79, 6 MH97 (BK616-BK618) 5.25
  f. Booklet pane, 4 #MH23, 6 MH97 (BK641) 5.00
  g. Booklet pane of 10 (double-lined "D" printed on reverse-BK652) 5.00
MH98 17p dark blue (b) 1.10 1.00
  a. Bklt. pane of 3 + label (BK256) 7.00
MH99 17p dk bl, litho. (b) .95 .95
  a. Booklet pane of 6 + printed margin (BK155) 5.75
MH100 17½p brown rose 1.00 1.00
MH101 18p violet blue .80 .80
MH102 18p olive green .60 .50
  a. Booklet pane of 9 + printed margin (BK151) 5.50
  b. Booklet pane, #MH23, MH83, 2 MH102 (BK246-BK247, BK249) 3.00
  c. Booklet pane of 4, margins all around (BK328) 3.00
  d. Booklet pane, #MH83, 5 MH102 (BK406-BK407) 4.00
  e. Booklet pane of 10, margins all around (BK714) 6.00
  f. As "d," imperf edges (BK408-BK410) 6.00
MH103 18p ol grn, litho. .80 .90
  a. Booklet pane of 6 + printed margin (BK152) 5.00
  b. Booklet pane of 9 + printed margin (BK152) 7.25
MH104 18p brt yel grn .85 .85
MH105 18p brt yel grn, litho. .95 1.00
  a. Booklet pane of 6 + printed margin (BK157) 5.75

MH106 19p brt orange .75 .50
  a. Bklt. pane, #MH87, 2 #MH106 + label (BK252-BK253) 6.25
  b. Booklet pane, 2 #MH87, 4 MH106 (BK411, BK413) 5.25
  c. Booklet pane of 4, margins all around (BK348) 5.25
  d. Booklet pane of 4, imperf on T, B (BK349) 6.50
  e. Booklet pane of 4, imperf on T, B, R (BK350) 26.00
  f. Booklet pane of 10, margins all around (BK729) 8.50
  g. Booklet pane of 10, imperf on T, B (BK730) 9.25
MH107 19p red org, litho. 2.00 2.00
MH108 19p red org, litho., perf 14 3.25 3.25
  a. Booklet pane, 2#MH89, 4 #MH108 (BK412) 26.50
MH110 19½p olive gray 1.75 1.50

Issued: No. MH96, 1/30/80; No. MH97, 3/30/80; No. MH98, 9/4/90; No. MH99, 3/19/91; 17½p, 1/30/80; No. MH101, 1/14/81; No. MH102, 8/28/84; No. MH103, 2/9/88; No. MH104, 9/10/91; No. MH105, 10/27/92; No. MH106, 8/3/88; No. MH107, 10/11/88; No. MH108, 4/25/89; 19½p, 1/27/82.
Nos. MH99, MH103, MH105, MH108 issued only in booklets.

a        b

Two types of 20p:
a, Thin part of "0" at upper left, lower right.
b, Thin part of "0" at top, bottom.

MH111 20p dp pur brn (a) .95 .95
MH112 20p dp pur brn, litho., perf 13¾x14 (a) 1.40 1.40
MH113 20p dp pur brn, litho., perf 15x14 (b) 2.00 1.75
MH114 20p Turq grn (b) .85 .80
MH115 20p brown black (b) .90 .90
  a. Booklet pane, 2 #MH91, MH115 + label (BK254) 13.00
  b. Booklet pane of 5 + label (BK414) 6.25
MH116 20½p ultramarine 1.20 1.20
MH117 22p dark blue .85 .85
MH118 22p yellow green .90 .90
MH119 22p yel grn, litho. (MH150a) 13.00 9.00
MH120 22p orange red .95 .90
  a. Booklet pane, 2 #MH98, 3 MH120 + 3 labels (BK417) 5.25
MH121 22p org red, litho. 1.00 1.00
  a. Booklet pane of 9 + printed margin (BK155) 9.00
MH122 23p rose pink 1.25 1.10
MH123 23p brt yel grn 1.25 1.25
MH124 24p violet 1.75 1.40
MH125 24p brown red 2.00 2.00
MH126 24p red brown .95 .90
  a. Booklet pane, 2 each #MH23, MH126 (BK257-BK259) 2.25
  b. Booklet pane, 2 #MH27, 4 MH126 + 2 labels (BK418-BK419) 4.50
MH127 24p red brn, litho. 1.00 1.00
  a. Booklet pane of 6 + printed margin (BK157) 6.00
MH128 24p red brn, litho. perf 14 1.25 1.25
  a. Booklet pane, 2 #MH31A, 4 MH128 + 2 labels (BK420) 9.00
MH129 25p reddish pur 1.00 1.10
MH129A 25p salmon 14.50 14.00

Issued: No. MH111, 2/25/76; No. MH112, 5/21/80; No. MH113, 5/13/86; No. MH114, 8/23/88; No. MH115, 9/26/89; 20½p, 3/30/83; No. MH117, 10/22/80; No. MH118, 8/28/84; No. MH119, 2/6/92; No. MH120, 9/4/90; No. MH121, 3/19/91; No. MH122, 3/30/83; No. MH123, 8/3/88; No. MH124, 8/28/84; No. MH125, 9/26/89; No. MH126, 9/10/91; No. MH127, 10/27/92; No. MH128, 2/9/93; 25p, 1/14/81.

Nos. MH119, MH121, MH127 issued only in booklets.
No. MH129A was issued 2/6/96 only in coils.

a        b

Two types of 26p:
a, Wide numerals.

b, Narrow numerals.

| MH130 | 26p red (a) | .95 | .70 |
|---|---|---|---|
| a. | Booklet pane, #MH23, MH130, 2 MH83, 5 MH102 + printed margin (BK151) | 5.50 | |
| MH131 | 26p red (b) | 4.75 | 3.75 |
| a. | Booklet pane of 4, margins all around (BK446) | 15.00 | |
| MH132 | 26p gray brown (b) | 1.10 | 1.00 |
| MH133 | 27p red brown | 1.10 | 1.10 |
| a. | Booklet pane of 4, margins all around (BK456) | 8.25 | |
| b. | Booklet pane of 4, horiz. edges imperf (BK457) | 25.00 | |
| MH134 | 27p violet | 1.10 | 1.00 |
| MH135 | 28p violet blue | .95 | .95 |
| MH136 | 28p yellow brown | 1.10 | 1.10 |
| MH137 | 28p dp bluish gray | 1.10 | 1.10 |

Issued: No. MH130, 1/27/82; No. MH131, 8/4/87; No. MH132, 9/4/90; No. MH133, 8/3/88; No. MH134, 9/4/90; No. MH135, 3/30/83; No. MH136, 8/23/88; No. MH137, 9/10/91.

No. MH131 issued only in booklets.

Two types of 29p:
a, Wide numerals.
b, Narrow numerals.

| MH138 | 29p brown olive (a) | 1.40 | 1.25 |
|---|---|---|---|
| MH139 | 29p dp rose lilac (b) | 1.75 | 1.75 |
| MH140 | 29p dp rose lilac, litho., perf 14 (b) | 3.00 | 3.00 |
| a. | Booklet pane of 4, imperf edges (BK478) | 12.50 | |
| MH141 | 30p dk olive green | 1.15 | 1.15 |
| MH142 | 31p brt rose lilac | 1.15 | 1.15 |
| a. | Bkt. pane, #MH142, 6 MH79, 2 MH97 + printed margin (BK150) | 5.50 | |
| MH143 | 31p ultramarine | 1.60 | 1.60 |
| MH144 | 31p ultra, litho., perf 14 | 1.90 | 1.90 |
| a. | Booklet pane of 4, imperf on T, B (BK503) | 7.75 | |
| MH145 | 32p Prussian blue | 1.40 | 1.20 |
| MH146 | 33p emerald | 1.40 | 1.20 |
| MH147 | 33p emerald, litho. | 2.00 | 2.00 |
| a. | Bkt. pane, 6 #MH121, 2 MH147 + label, printed margin (BK155) | 10.00 | |
| MH148 | 33p emer., litho. perf 14 | 2.10 | 2.10 |
| a. | Booklet pane of 4, imperf. on T, B (BK544) | 8.50 | |
| MH149 | 34p brown | 1.35 | 1.35 |
| a. | Bkt. pane, #MH149, 2 MH45, 4 MH83, 2 MH97 + printed margin (BK149) | 7.50 | |
| MH150 | 34p brown, litho. | 11.50 | 9.00 |
| a. | Booklet pane, 6 #MH84, 1 ea MH103, MH119, MH150 + printed margin (BK152) | 30.00 | |
| MH151 | 34p dp grayish blue | 2.00 | 2.00 |
| MH152 | 34p brt rose lilac | 1.75 | 1.75 |
| MH153 | 35p dark brown | 1.75 | 1.75 |
| MH154 | 35p dull orange | 1.75 | 1.75 |
| MH155 | 37p scarlet | 1.75 | 1.50 |
| MH156 | 39p brt rose lilac | 1.90 | 1.90 |
| MH157 | 39p brt rose lil, litho. perf 14 | 2.25 | 2.25 |
| a. | Booklet pane of 4, imperf on T, B (BK662) | 9.00 | |
| MH158 | 39p brt rose lil, litho. (MH178a, MH187b) | 2.00 | 2.00 |

Issued: No. MH138, 1/27/82; No. MH139, 9/26/89; No. MH140, 10/2/89; No. MH141, 9/4/90; No. MH142, 3/30/83; No. MH143, 9/4/90; No. MH144, 9/17/90; No. MH145, 8/23/88; No. MH146, 9/4/90; No. MH147, 3/19/91; No. MN148, 9/16/91; No. MH149, 8/28/84; No. MH150, 2/9/88; No. MH151, 9/26/89; No. MH152, 9/10/91; No. MH153, 8/23/88; No. MH154, 9/10/91; No. MH155, 9/26/89; No. MH156, 9/10/91; No. MH157, 9/16/91; No. MH158, 10/27/92.

Nos. MH144, MH147-MH148, MH150 issued only in booklets.

Two types of 50p:
a, Wide numerals.
b, Narrow numerals.

| MH159 | 50p bister brown (a) | 2.25 | .75 |
|---|---|---|---|
| MH160 | 50p ocher (b) | 4.00 | 1.60 |

Issued: No. MH159, 2/2/77; No. MH160, 5/21/80.

Two types of 75p:
a, Wide numerals.
b, Narrow numerals.

| MH161 | 75p black, litho., perf 13½x14 (a) | 3.00 | 1.50 |
|---|---|---|---|
| MH162 | 75p black, litho. (a) | 3.25 | 2.00 |
| MH163 | 75p black, litho. (b) | 9.50 | 9.50 |
| MH164 | 75p black (b) | 7.50 | 2.00 |

Issued: No. MH161, 3/1/80; No. MH162, 2/21/84; No. MH163, 2/23/88; No. MH164, 7/26/88.

### Engr.
### Perf. 12
### Size: 27x31mm

| MH165 | 10p carmine rose | .75 | 1.00 |
|---|---|---|---|
| MH166 | 20p olive | .80 | .25 |
| MH167 | 50p ultramarine | 1.60 | .60 |
| p. | Phosphor | 2.00 | .60 |
| MH168 | £1 bluish black | 3.75 | 1.00 |

For illustration of £1, see above No. MH1.
No. MH168, imperf, are from printers' waste.

Issued: Nos. MH165-MH167, 6/17/70; £1, 12/6/72.

### Photo.
### Perf. 14x15
### Size: 27x38mm

| MH169 | £1 olive grn & yel | 2.75 | .25 |
|---|---|---|---|
| MH170 | £1.30 slate bl & buff | 4.50 | 6.00 |
| MH171 | £1.33 black & pale rose lilac | 6.75 | 7.25 |
| MH172 | £1.41 indigo & buff | 7.75 | 7.75 |
| MH173 | £1.50 blk & lt pink | 5.75 | 5.00 |
| MH174 | £1.60 indigo & buff | 5.75 | 6.25 |
| MH175 | £2 red brn & pale yel grn | 5.50 | .75 |
| MH176 | £5 dk bl & pink | 13.50 | 2.75 |

Issued: £1, 2/2/77; £1.30, 8/3/83; £1.33, 8/28/84; £1.41, 9/17/85; £1.50, 9/2/86; £1.60, 9/15/87; £2, £5, 2/2/77.

### 2nd or 1st Class (Non-Denominated)

2nd and 1st class stamps sell for the current rates and remain valid indefinitely for the indicated service.

| 1989-90 | | Perf. 15x14 | |
|---|---|---|---|
| MH177 | 2nd bright blue | 1.45 | 1.45 |
| a. | Booklet pane of 4, imperf on T, B, R (BK961) | 32.50 | |
| b. | Booklet pane of 10, imperf on T, B (BK1028, BK1037) | 14.50 | |
| MH178 | 2nd bright blue, litho. | 1.60 | 1.60 |
| a. | Booklet pane, 2 each #MH105, MH147, MH158, MH178 + label, printed margin (BK158) | 13.00 | |
| MH179 | 2nd bright blue, litho., perf 14 | 1.40 | 1.40 |
| a. | Booklet pane of 4, imperf on T, B, R (BK960) | 5.75 | |
| b. | Booklet pane of 4, imperf on T, B (BK963-BK964) | 5.75 | |
| c. | Booklet pane of 10, imperf on T, B (BK1034-BK1035) | 14.00 | |

Nos. MH177-MH179 each sold for 14p on day of issue.

| MH180 | 2nd dark blue | 1.75 | 1.75 |
|---|---|---|---|
| a. | Booklet pane of 10, imperf on T, B (BK1030) | 17.50 | |
| MH181 | 2nd dark blue, litho. | 2.75 | 2.75 |
| MH182 | 2nd dark blue, litho., perf 14 | 1.35 | 1.00 |
| a. | Booklet pane of 4, imperf on T, B (BK962) | 5.50 | |
| b. | Booklet pane of 10, imperf on T, B (BK1032) | 13.50 | |

Nos. MH180-MH182 each sold for 15p on day of issue.

| MH183 | 1st brown black | 2.00 | 1.60 |
|---|---|---|---|
| a. | Booklet pane of 4, imperf on T, B, R (BK995) | 35.00 | |
| b. | Booklet pane of 10, imperf on T, B (BK1041) | 16.00 | |
| MH184 | 1st brown black, litho., perf 14 | 2.75 | 2.75 |
| a. | Booklet pane of 4, imperf on T, B, R (BK994) | 11.00 | |
| MH185 | 1st brown black, litho. | 2.25 | 2.25 |

Nos. MH183-MH185 each sold for 19p on day of issue.

Issued: No. MH183c, 6/5/17.

| MH186 | 1st orange red | 1.60 | 1.60 |
|---|---|---|---|
| a. | Booklet pane of 10, imperf on T, B (BK1068, BK1091) | 16.00 | |
| MH187 | 1st orange red, litho. | 1.60 | 1.60 |
| a. | Booklet pane, 3 each #MH178, MH187 + printed margin (BK158) | 9.75 | |
| b. | Booklet pane, #MH178, MH187, 2 ea MH105, MH127, MH158 + label, printed margin (BK157) | 15.00 | |

| c. | Booklet pane of 8+ label, printed margin (BK156) | 11.50 | |
|---|---|---|---|
| d. | Booklet pane of 10, imperf on T, B (BK1092-BK1093) | 16.00 | |

No. MH187c contains Nos. MH178, MH187, 2 each Nos. MH147, WMMH34, WMMH45.

| MH188 | 1st orange red, litho., perf 14 | 1.60 | 1.60 |
|---|---|---|---|
| a. | Booklet pane of 4, imperf on T, B (BK996-BK997) | 6.50 | |
| b. | Booklet pane of 10, imperf on T, B (BK1070) | 16.00 | |
| MH189 | 1st orange red, litho., perf 13x13½ | 5.25 | 5.00 |
| a. | Booklet pane of 4, imperf. on T, B (BK996A) | 20.00 | — |

Nos. MH186-MH189 each sold for 20p on day of issue.
Distance of denomination to the margin and bust may vary on different printings of the same stamp.

Issued: No. MH177, 8/22/89; No. MH178, 9/18/89; No. MH179, 8/22/89; No. MH180-MH182, 8/7/90; Nos. MH183-MH184, 8/22/89; No. MH185, 9/19/89; Nos. MH186-MH188, 8/7/90; No. MH189, 10/90.

Nos. MH177-MH189 issued only in booklets.

 Victoria and Elizabeth II — MA3

| 1990-2000 | Photo. | Perf. 15x14 | |
|---|---|---|---|
| MH190 | 15p bright blue | .85 | .85 |
| a. | Booklet pane of 10, imperf on T, B (BK619) | 8.50 | |
| MH191 | 15p brt bl, litho., perf 14 | 1.50 | 1.75 |
| a. | Booklet pane of 4 with imperf on T, B, R (BK307) | 6.00 | |
| b. | Booklet pane of 10 with imperf on T, B (BK621) | 15.00 | |
| MH192 | 15p bright blue, litho. | 2.25 | 2.50 |
| a. | Booklet pane of 10 (BK621) | 22.50 | |
| MH193 | 20p blk & brn blk | .90 | .90 |
| a. | Booklet pane, #MH193, 2 MH190 + label (BK255) | 10.50 | |
| b. | Booklet pane of 4 with imperf on T, B (BK371) | 7.00 | |
| c. | Bkt. pane of 5 + label (BK415) | 8.50 | |
| d. | Booklet pane of 6 + printed margin (BK154) | 6.75 | |
| e. | Booklet pane of 10 with imperf on T, B (BK743) | 9.00 | |
| f. | Souvenir sheet of 1 | 3.50 | 3.75 |
| MH194 | 20p blk & brn blk, litho., perf 14 | 1.50 | 1.75 |
| a. | Booklet pane of 4 with imperf on T, B, R (BK372) | 6.50 | |
| b. | Bkt. pane of 5 + label (BK416) | 14.00 | |
| c. | Booklet pane of 10 with imperf on T, B, R (BK744) | 17.50 | |
| MH195 | 20p blk & brn blk, litho. | 2.50 | 2.60 |
| a. | Booklet pane of 10 (BK745) | 25.00 | |
| MH196 | 29p dp rose lil | 1.60 | 1.60 |
| a. | Booklet pane, #MH91, MH115, MH160, MH177, MH183, MH190, MH193, MH196 + label, printed margin (BK154) | 15.50 | |
| MH197 | 20p dull blue green | 1.90 | 1.90 |
| MH198 | 37p scarlet | 2.00 | 2.00 |

### Perf. 13¾x14¼ Syncopated

| MH198A | 1st blk & yel | 2.50 | 2.50 |
|---|---|---|---|
| b. | Booklet pane of 6 (BK167) | 16.50 | |

Nos. MH191-MH192, MH194-MH195, MH198A were issued only in booklets.
No. MH198A sold for 26p on day of issue.
No. MH198A is redrawn.

Issued: Nos. MH190, MH193, MH196-MH198, 1/10; Nos. MH191, MH194, 1/30; Nos. MH192, MH195, 4/17; No. MH198A, 2/15/00; No. MH193c, 6/5/17.

 Queen Elizabeth II

### Syncopated Perf. 15x14

| 1993-97 | | Type MA2 | |
|---|---|---|---|
| MH199 | 1p magenta | .30 | .25 |
| MH200 | 1p mag, litho. (MH216b) | .90 | .90 |
| MH201 | 2p dark green | .30 | .30 |
| MH202 | 4p Prussian blue | .45 | .45 |
| MH203 | 5p rose brown | .35 | .35 |
| MH204 | 6p brt ol grn | .45 | .45 |
| MH205 | 6p brt ol grn, litho. (MH214a) | 14.00 | 14.00 |
| MH206 | 10p brown orange | .45 | .45 |
| MH207 | 10p brn ol grn, litho. (MH231a) | 7.00 | 7.00 |
| MH208 | 19p olive green | .70 | .70 |
| MH209 | 19p ol grn, litho. (MH214a, MH231a) | 1.25 | 1.25 |
| a. | Booklet pane of 6 + printed margin (BK160) | 7.50 | |

| MH210 | 20p Turq grn | .95 | .95 |
|---|---|---|---|
| MH211 | 20p bright yel grn | 1.75 | 1.75 |
| MH212 | 20p brt yel grn, litho. (MH216a-MH216b) | 3.75 | 3.50 |
| MH213 | 25p salmon | .90 | .90 |
| a. | Booklet pane of 2 + 2 labels (BK260-BK262) | 1.90 | |
| MH214 | 25p sal, litho. (MH231a) | .95 | .95 |
| a. | Bklt. pane, #MH205, MH209, 4 MH214 + printed margin (BK159) | 19.50 | |
| b. | Booklet pane of 8 + label, printed margin (see footnote) (BK161) | 7.75 | |

No. MH214b contains 2 each Nos. MH214, NIMH59, SMH65, WMMH60.

| MH215 | 26p lake brn | 1.60 | 1.60 |
|---|---|---|---|
| MH216 | 26p lake brn, litho. | 1.25 | 1.25 |
| a. | Bklt. pane, #MH212, 7 MH216 (BK749) | 12.50 | |
| b. | Bklt. pane, #MH200, 3 MH216 + 2 labels (BK426) | 9.25 | |
| MH218 | 29p gray | 1.25 | 1.25 |
| MH219 | 30p olive green | 1.25 | 1.25 |
| MH220 | 30p olive green, litho. (MH231a) | 7.00 | 7.00 |
| MH221 | 31p purple | 1.75 | 1.75 |
| MH222 | 35p yellow orange | 1.75 | 1.75 |
| MH223 | 35p org yel, litho. | 1.90 | 1.90 |
| a. | Booklet pane of 4 (BK562-BK563) | 7.75 | |
| MH224 | 36p blue | 1.75 | 1.75 |
| MH225 | 37p bright rose lilac | 2.00 | 2.00 |
| MH226 | 37p redsh pur, litho. | 4.10 | 4.10 |
| a. | Booklet pane of 4 (BK605) | 17.00 | |
| MH227 | 38p brt rose red | 1.90 | 1.90 |
| MH228 | 39p magenta | 2.00 | 2.00 |
| MH230 | 41p drab | 2.00 | 2.00 |
| MH231 | 41p drab, litho. | 2.25 | 2.25 |
| a. | Booklet pane, #MH207, MH220, MH223, MH231, 2 each MH209, MH214 + label, printed margin (BK160) | 22.50 | |
| b. | Booklet pane of 4 (BK685-BK686) | 9.00 | |
| MH232 | 43p dark brown | 2.50 | 2.50 |
| MH233 | 50p ocher | 2.60 | 2.60 |
| MH234 | 60p slate blue, litho. | 2.75 | 2.75 |
| a. | Booklet pane of 4 (BK790-BK791) | 11.00 | |
| MH235 | 63p bright green | 3.25 | 3.25 |
| MH236 | 63p brt grn, litho. | 4.50 | 4.50 |
| a. | Bklt. pane of 4 (BK815) | 18.00 | |
| MH237 | £1 violet | 4.75 | 4.75 |

No. MH237 is printed with Iriodin ink, giving stamp design a three dimensional appearance.

| MH238 | 2nd bright blue | 1.35 | 1.35 |
|---|---|---|---|
| MH239 | 2nd bright blue, litho. | 1.35 | 1.35 |
| MH240 | 1st orange red | 1.60 | 1.60 |
| MH241 | 1st orange red, litho. | 1.60 | 1.60 |
| a. | Miniature sheet of 1 | 7.00 | 7.00 |
| b. | Booklet pane of 4 + label (BK1000, BK1002, BK1004) | 6.50 | |
| c. | Booklet pane of 9 + printed margin (BK165) | 14.50 | |

No. MH241a was sold for £1 on day of issue in pre-packaged greeting cards at Boots pharmacy. Unfolded examples were later sold by British Philatelic Bureau. Value indicated is for unfolded example.

MH243                    MH309

### Size: 21½x17½mm
### Die Cut 14x15 Syncopated
### Litho.
### Self-Adhesive

| MH243 | 1st orange red | 1.75 | 1.75 |
|---|---|---|---|
| a. | Booklet pane of 20 | 20.00 | |

Nos. MH238-MH239 each sold for 18p on day of issue; Nos. MH240-MH241, MH243 each for 24p.

Issued: No. MH201, 4/11/95; No. MH204, 4/27/93; No. MH219, 7/27/93; No. MH222, 8/17/93; No. MH234, 8/9/94; No. MH237, 8/22/95; No. MH238, 9/7/93; No. MH241, 9/6/93. No. MH241c, 2/16/99.

Nos. MH239, MH240, 4/6/93.
Nos. MH199, MH203, MH206, 6/8/93.
No. MH243, 10/19/93.
Nos. MH208, MH213, MH218, MH224, MH227, MH230, 10/26/93.
Nos. MH202, MH221, MH223, 11/1/93.
Nos. MH202, MH210, MH233, 12/14/93.
Nos. MH205, MH209, 7/26/94.
Nos. MH207, MH220, 4/25/95.
Nos. MH215, MH221, MH225, MH228, MH232, MH235, 6/25/96.
Nos. MH200, MH212, MH216, MH226, MH236, 7/8/96.
Nos. MH200, MH205, MH207, MH209, MH212, MH216, MH219, MH226, MH231, MH236 issued only in booklets.
No. MH243a is a complete booklet.

| | | | |
|---|---|---|---|
| NIMH34 | 18p bright yel grn (II) | .85 | .90 |
| NIMH35 | 18p bright yel grn, perf 13½x14 (II) | .85 | .85 |
| NIMH36 | 19p red orange (II) | 1.25 | 1.25 |
| NIMH37 | 19½p olive brn, perf 13½x14 (I) | 1.00 | 1.00 |
| NIMH38 | 20p brown black (II) | .95 | .75 |
| NIMH39 | 20½p ultramarine, perf 13½x14 (I) | 2.50 | 2.25 |
| NIMH40 | 22p dark blue, perf 13½x14 (I) | .90 | .90 |
| NIMH41 | 22p yellow green (I) | 3.00 | 3.00 |
| NIMH42 | 22p red orange (I) | .95 | .70 |
| NIMH43 | 23p bright yel grn (II) | 1.00 | .80 |
| NIMH44 | 24p brown red (II) | 1.30 | 1.10 |
| NIMH45 | 24p brown (II) | .95 | .80 |
| a. | Bklt. pane, see footnote (BK158) | 5.50 | |

No. NIMH45a contains Nos. NIMH34, NIMH45, SMH35, SMH47, WMMH34, WMMH45.

| | | | |
|---|---|---|---|
| NIMH46 | 26p red, perf 13½x14 (I) | 1.00 | 1.00 |
| NIMH47 | 26p red (II) | 2.95 | 2.95 |
| NIMH48 | 26p drab (II) | 1.30 | 1.30 |
| NIMH49 | 28p viol bl, perf 13½x14 (I) | 1.10 | 1.10 |
| NIMH50 | 28p vio blue (II) | 1.60 | 1.60 |
| NIMH51 | 28p grnsh slate (II) | 1.10 | .90 |
| NIMH52 | 31p dp mag (I) | 2.20 | 1.75 |
| a. | Type II | 175.00 | 175.00 |
| NIMH53 | 32p greenish blue (I) | 1.50 | 1.50 |
| NIMH54 | 34p grnsh slate (II) | 1.75 | 1.75 |
| NIMH55 | 37p scarlet (II) | 1.85 | 1.85 |
| NIMH56 | 39p dp mag (II) | 2.00 | 2.00 |

Issued: Nos. NIMH1, NIMH9, 3p, 5p, 7/7/71; Nos. NIMH3, NIMH6, 8p, 1/23/74; No. NIMH4, 11/6/74;

Nos. NIMH7, NIMH11, 1/14/76; 10p, 11p, 10/20/76; 7p, 9p, NIMH14, 1/18/78.

Nos. NIMH17, NIMH22, NIMH25, 7/23/80; Nos. NIMH16, NIMH23, NIMH32, NIMH40, 4/8/81; No. NIMH19, 1/24/82; No. NIMH27, NIMH28, NIMH31, NIMH46, 2/24/82; Nos. NIMH39, NIMH49, 4/27/83;

Nos. NIMH20, NIMH29, 2/28/84; 13p, Nos. NIMH30, NIMH41, 31p, 10/23/84; No. NIMH18, 1/7/86; No. NIMH33, 1/6/87; No. NIMH50, 1/27/87; No. NIMH24, 19p, 23p, 32p, 11/8/88; Nos. NIMH26, NIHM44, 20p, 34p, 11/28/89; Nos. NIMH31, NIMH42, NIMH48, 37p, 12/4/90; Nos. NIMH34, NIMH45, NIMH51, 39p, 12/3/91; Nos. NIMH35, NIMH45a, 8/10/93; No. NIMH47, 12/7/93.

### Perf. 15x14 Syncopated

| 1993-96 | | Litho. | |
|---|---|---|---|
| NIMH57 | 19p olive brown | 1.10 | 1.00 |
| NIMH58 | 20p brt yel green | 1.75 | 1.75 |
| NIMH59 | 25p rose red | .90 | .90 |
| a. | Bklt. pane, see footnote (BK160) | 6.00 | |

No. NIMH59a contains Nos. NIMH57, NIMH59, SMH63, SMH65, WMMH58, WMMH60 + label, printed margin.

| | | | |
|---|---|---|---|
| NIMH60 | 26p red brown | 2.20 | 2.20 |
| NIMH61 | 30p olive green | 1.95 | 1.95 |
| NIMH62 | 37p dp mag | 3.25 | 3.00 |
| NIMH63 | 41p drab | 2.20 | 2.20 |
| a. | Bklt. pane, #NIMH61, NIMH63, 2 #NIMH57, 4 #NIMH59 + label, printed margin (BK159) | 9.00 | |
| b. | Bklt. pane, #NIMH57, NIMH59, NIMH61, NIMH63 + printed margin (BK159) | 5.25 | |
| NIMH64 | 63p emerald | 4.75 | 4.75 |

Issued: 19p, 25p, 30p, 41p, 12/7/93; No. NIMH59a, 4/25/95; 20p, 26, 37p, 63p, 7/23/96.

### Queen Design of 1970 with Redrawn Portrait

### Perf. 15x14 Syncopated

| 1997-2000 | | Photo. | |
|---|---|---|---|
| NIMH68 | 19p olive green | 4.75 | 4.75 |
| NIMH69 | 20p brt yel grn | 4.00 | 1.50 |
| NIMH70 | 20p brt yel grn, perf 14 | 6.00 | 6.00 |
| NIMH73 | 26p red brown | 2.60 | 2.25 |
| NIMH74 | 26p brown, perf 14 | 6.00 | 6.00 |
| NIMH81 | 37p bright rose lilac | 3.00 | 3.00 |
| a. | Bklt. pane, see footnote (BK162) | 16.00 | |

No. NIMH81a contains Nos. NIMH73, NIMH81, SMH79, SMH87, WMMH74, WMMH82 + printed margin.

| | | | |
|---|---|---|---|
| NIMH82 | 38p ultramarine | 9.25 | 9.25 |
| NIMH83 | 40p chalky blue | 5.50 | 5.50 |
| NIMH91 | 63p emerald | 6.50 | 6.50 |
| NIMH92 | 64p turq grn | 10.00 | 10.00 |
| NIMH93 | 65p Prussian blue | 4.75 | 4.75 |

Issued: Nos. NIMH69, NIMH73, 37p, 63p, 7/1/97; No. NIMH81a, 9/24/97; Nos. NIMH70, NIMH74, 10/13/98; Nos. NIMH68, NIMH82, NIMH92, 6/8/99; 40p, 65p, 4/25/00.

Nos. NIMH70, NIMH74 issued only in booklets (BK164).

### Perf. 13¾x14¼ Syncopated

| 2000 | | Photo. | |
|---|---|---|---|
| NIMH96 | 1st org red (WM-MH96a) | 3.50 | 3.50 |

### Perf. 15x14 Syncopated

| | | | |
|---|---|---|---|
| NIMH99 | 1st org red | 10.00 | 10.00 |

Nos. NIMH96, NIMH99 sold for 26p on day of issue. No. NIMH96 issued only in booklets.

Issued: No. NIMH96, 2/15/00; No. NIMH99, 4/25/00.

# SCOTLAND

All stamps are Design MA2 unless noted.

Type I      Type II

Two types of lion (1983-93):

Type I: Thin tongue, no line across bridge of nose, three "feathers" on left of tail are widely separated.

Type II: Thick tongue where it enters mouth, eye connected to background by solid line, three "feathers" on left of tail are close together.

Photogravure stamps in this section have a mottled background that is neither solid nor composed of distinct dots. The outside edges of the numerals have a jagged appearance. Some lithographed stamps, specifically Nos. SMH20-21a, SMH28-30, SMH38, SMH52-53, SMH56-57, have a background composed of fine dots giving the impression of a phtogravure printing. The images on these stamps, however, are more finely detailed than those on a photogravure printing. The outside edges of the numerals are smooth. All other lithographed stamps in this section have a solid background.

| 1971-93 | | Photo. | Perf. 15x14 | |
|---|---|---|---|---|
| SMH1 | 2½p magenta | | .30 | .25 |
| SMH2 | 3p ultramarine | | .30 | .25 |
| SMH3 | 3½p olive | | .30 | .25 |
| SMH4 | 4½p indigo | | .30 | .25 |
| SMH5 | 5p violet | | .65 | .65 |
| SMH6 | 5½p dark violet | | .30 | .25 |
| SMH7 | 6½p grnsh blue | | .30 | .25 |
| SMH8 | 7p dark red brn | | .30 | .30 |
| SMH9 | 7½p chestnut | | .75 | 1.00 |
| SMH10 | 8p red | | .30 | .25 |
| SMH11 | 8½p yellow green | | .35 | .35 |
| SMH12 | 9p violet blue | | .35 | .40 |
| SMH13 | 10p orange brown | | .35 | .40 |
| SMH14 | 10½p gray blue | | .50 | .55 |
| SMH15 | 11p red | | .50 | .55 |
| SMH16 | 11½p gray brn, litho., perf 13½x14 (I) | | .65 | .65 |
| SMH17 | 12p yellow green | | .50 | .55 |
| SMH18 | 12p emer, litho., perf 13½x14 (II) | | 1.10 | 1.10 |
| SMH19 | 12p green, litho. (II) | | 1.50 | 1.60 |
| SMH20 | 12½p lt emer, litho., perf 13½x14 (I) | | .65 | .75 |
| SMH21 | 13p lt red brown, litho., perf 13½x14 (I) | | .90 | .80 |
| a. | Type II | | 10.00 | 10.00 |
| SMH22 | 13p lt red brn, litho. (II) | | .95 | 1.00 |
| SMH23 | 13½p brown purple | | .70 | .80 |
| SMH24 | 14p gray blue, litho., perf 13½x14 (I) | | .55 | .55 |
| SMH25 | 14p Prus bl, litho. | | .55 | .55 |
| a. | Booklet pane of 6 + printed margin (BK153) | | 3.50 | |
| SMH26 | 15p blue black | | .55 | .65 |

**Litho.**

| | | | |
|---|---|---|---|
| SMH27 | 15p bright blue (II) | .70 | .70 |

**Perf. 13½x14**

| | | | |
|---|---|---|---|
| SMH28 | 15½p lilac (II) | .70 | .75 |
| SMH29 | 16p brownish gray (II) | .70 | .75 |
| SMH30 | 17p blue gray (II) | 2.00 | 2.00 |
| a. | Type I | 2.00 | 2.00 |

**Perf. 15x14**

| | | | |
|---|---|---|---|
| SMH31 | 17p blue gray (II) | 2.50 | 2.50 |
| SMH32 | 17p dark blue (II) | .90 | .90 |
| SMH33 | 18p violet blue, perf 13½x14 | .90 | .90 |
| SMH34 | 18p olive green (II) | .85 | .65 |
| SMH35 | 18p bright yel grn (II) | .85 | .60 |
| SMH36 | 18p brt yel grn, perf 13½x14 (II) | 1.25 | 1.25 |
| SMH37 | 19p red orange (II) | .75 | .75 |
| a. | Booklet pane of 6 + printed margin (BK153) | 4.50 | |
| b. | Booklet pane of 9 + printed margin (BK153) | 6.75 | |
| SMH38 | 19½p olive gray, perf 13½x14 (I) | .95 | .95 |
| SMH39 | 20p brown black | .90 | .90 |

**Perf. 13½x14**

| | | | |
|---|---|---|---|
| SMH40 | 20½p ultra (II) | 2.75 | 2.75 |
| SMH41 | 22p Prussian blue (I) | .90 | .90 |
| SMH42 | 22p yel grn (II) | 3.00 | 3.00 |
| a. | Type II | 22.50 | 22.50 |

**Perf. 15x14**

| | | | |
|---|---|---|---|
| SMH43 | 22p dk yel grn (II) | 1.90 | 1.90 |
| SMH44 | 22p red orange (II) | .85 | .65 |
| SMH45 | 23p bright yel grn (II) | 1.00 | .85 |
| a. | Booklet pane #SMH45, 2 #SMH37, 5 #SMH25 + printed margin (BK153) | 4.50 | |
| SMH46 | 24p brown red (II) | 1.25 | 1.25 |
| SMH47 | 24p brown (II) | .95 | .95 |
| SMH48 | 24p chestnut, perf 13½x14 (II) | 9.00 | 9.00 |
| SMH49 | 26p red, perf 13½x14 (I) | 1.00 | 1.00 |
| SMH50 | 26p red (II) | 3.00 | 3.25 |
| SMH51 | 26p olive gray (II) | 1.30 | 1.30 |
| SMH52 | 28p dp vio bl, perf 13½x14 (I) | 1.10 | 1.10 |
| SMH53 | 28p lt violet (II) | 1.60 | 1.60 |
| SMH54 | 28p grnsh slate (II) | 1.35 | 1.60 |
| SMH55 | 28p grnsh slate, perf 13½x14 (II) | 11.00 | 11.00 |
| SMH56 | 31p mag, perf 13½x14 (II) | 2.25 | 2.25 |
| a. | Type II | 200.00 | 175.00 |
| SMH57 | 31p mag (II) | 2.25 | 2.25 |
| SMH58 | 32p greenish blue (II) | 1.65 | 1.65 |
| SMH59 | 34p grnsh slate (II) | 1.75 | 1.75 |
| SMH60 | 37p scarlet (II) | 1.90 | 1.90 |
| SMH61 | 39p dp mag (II) | 2.00 | 2.00 |
| SMH62 | 39p dp mag, perf 13½x14 (II) | 19.00 | 19.00 |

Issued: Nos. SMH1, SMH9, 3p, 5p, 7/7/71; Nos. SMH3, SMH6, 8p, 1/6/74; No. SMH4, 11/6/74; Nos. SMH7, SMH11, 1/14/76; 10p, 11p, 10/20/76; 7p, 9p, SMH14, 1/18/78; Nos. SMH17, SMH23, SMH26, 7/23/80.

Nos. SMH16, SMH24, SMH33, SMH41, 4/8/81; Nos. SMH20, SMH28, SMH38, No. SMH49, 2/24/82;

16p, Nos. SMH40, SMH52, 4/27/83; Nos. SMH21, SMH30, SMH42, SMH46, 10/23/84; No. SMH18, 1/7/86; No. SMH19, 1/24/86; No. SMH31, SMH57, 4/29/86; No. SMH22, 11/4/86; No. SMH34, 1/6/87.

Nos. SMH43, SMH50, SMH53, 1/27/87; No. SMH25, 19p, 23p, 32p, 11/8/88; Nos. SMH27, SMH46, 20p, 34p, 11/28/89; Nos. SMH32, SMH44, SMH51, 37p, 12/4/90;

Nos. SMH3, SMH47, SMH54, SMH61, 12/3/91; No. SMH36, 9/26/92; No. SMH48, 10/92; No. SMH62, 11/92; No. SMH55, 2/18/93.

### Perf. 15x14 Syncopated

| 1993-96 | | Litho. | |
|---|---|---|---|
| SMH63 | 19p olive brown | 1.10 | 1.00 |
| SMH64 | 20p brt yel green | 1.75 | 1.75 |
| SMH65 | 25p rose red | .95 | .85 |
| SMH66 | 26p red brown | 2.25 | 2.25 |
| SMH67 | 30p olive green | 2.00 | 2.00 |
| SMH68 | 37p bright rose lilac | 3.25 | 3.25 |
| SMH69 | 41p drab | 2.25 | 2.25 |
| SMH70 | 63p emerald | 4.75 | 4.75 |

Issued: 19p, 20p, 30p, 41p, 12/7/93; 20p, 26p, 37p, 63p, 7/23/96.

### Queen Design of 1970 with Redrawn Portrait

### Perf. 15x14 Syncopated

| 1997-98 | | Photo. | |
|---|---|---|---|
| SMH75 | 20p yel green | 1.50 | 1.10 |
| SMH76 | 20p brt yel grn, perf 14 | 6.00 | 6.00 |
| SMH79 | 26p brown | 2.25 | 1.90 |
| SMH80 | 26p brown, perf 14 | 6.00 | 6.00 |
| SMH87 | 37p dp magenta | 3.00 | 3.00 |
| SMH97 | 63p emerald | 6.00 | 6.00 |

Issued: Nos. SMH75, SMH79, 37p, 63p, 7/1/97; Nos. SMH76, SMH80, 10/13/98.

Nos. SMH76, SMH80 issued only in booklets (BK164).

### Perf. 13¾x14¼ Syncopated

| 2000 | | Photo. | |
|---|---|---|---|
| SMH101 | 1st org red (WM-MH96a) | 3.50 | 3.50 |

Issued: No. SMH96, 2/15/00. No. SMH96 sold for 26p on day of issue and was issued only in booklets.

# WALES & MONMOUTHSHIRE

All stamps are Design MA2 unless noted.

Type I      Type II

Two types of dragon (1981-91):

Type I: Eye is complete with white dot in center. No line across bridge of nose. Wing tips, tail and tongue are thin.

Type II: Eye is connected to nose by solid line. Wing tips, tail and tongue are thick.

Photogravure stamps in this section have a mottled background that is neither solid nor composed of distinct dots. The outside edges of the numerals have a jagged appearance. Some lithographed stamps, specifically Nos. WMMH16, WMMH19, WMMH21, WMMH23, WMMH27-30, WMMH32, WMMH37, WMMH40, WMMH50, have a background composed of fine dots giving the impression of a phtogravure printing. The images on these stamps, however, are more finely detailed than those on a photogravure printing. The outside edges of the numerals are smooth. All other lithographed stamps in this section have a solid background.

| 1971-93 | | Photo. | Perf. 15x14 | |
|---|---|---|---|---|
| WMMH1 | 2½p magenta | | .30 | .25 |
| WMMH2 | 3p ultra | | .30 | .25 |
| WMMH3 | 3½p olive | | .30 | .30 |
| WMMH4 | 4½p indigo | | .30 | .30 |
| WMMH5 | 5p brt violet | | .70 | .70 |
| WMMH6 | 5½p dark violet | | .30 | .30 |
| WMMH7 | 6½p grnsh blue | | .30 | .25 |
| WMMH8 | 7p dark red brn | | .30 | .25 |
| WMMH9 | 7½p chestnut | | 1.00 | 1.00 |
| WMMH10 | 8p red | | .30 | .35 |
| WMMH11 | 8½p yel grn | | .35 | .35 |
| WMMH12 | 9p violet blue | | .30 | .30 |
| WMMH13 | 10p orange brn | | .35 | .45 |
| WMMH14 | 10½p gray blue | | .50 | .60 |
| WMMH15 | 11p red | | .50 | .60 |
| WMMH16 | 11½p drab, litho., perf 13½x14 (I) | | .85 | .90 |
| WMMH17 | 12p yel grn | | .50 | .60 |

**Litho.**

| | | | |
|---|---|---|---|
| WMMH18 | 12p emer (I) | .95 | .95 |
| WMMH19 | 12½p lt emer, perf 13½x14 (I) | .55 | .55 |
| WMMH20 | 12½p lt emer (I) | 3.25 | 3.00 |
| WMMH21 | 13p lt red brn (I) | .60 | .60 |
| a. | Type II | 2.25 | 2.00 |

**Photo.**

| | | | |
|---|---|---|---|
| WMMH22 | 13½p brown pur | .70 | .80 |
| WMMH23 | 14p gray blue, litho., perf 13½x14 (I) | .70 | .70 |
| WMMH24 | 14p Prus blue, litho. (II) | .70 | .70 |
| WMMH25 | 15p deep ultra | .70 | .80 |

**Litho.**

| | | | |
|---|---|---|---|
| WMMH26 | 15p brt blue (II) | .75 | .65 |
| WMMH27 | 15½p lt vio, perf 13½x14 (I) | .75 | .75 |
| WMMH28 | 16p brnsh gray, perf 13½x14 (I) | 1.10 | 1.10 |
| WMMH29 | 16p brnsh gray (I) | 1.10 | 1.10 |
| WMMH30 | 17p blue gray (I) | .85 | .95 |
| a. | Type II | 57.50 | 55.00 |
| WMMH31 | 17p Prussian blue | .80 | .70 |
| WMMH32 | 18p vio bl, perf 13½x14 (I) | 1.00 | .95 |
| WMMH33 | 18p ol grn (II) | .90 | .85 |
| WMMH34 | 18p brt yel grn (II) | .90 | .90 |
| a. | Booklet pane of 6 + printed margin (BK156) | 5.50 | |

| | | | |
|---|---|---|---|
| WMMH35 | 18p brt yel grn, perf 13½x14 (II) | 11.00 | 11.00 |
| WMMH36 | 19p red org (II) | .85 | .95 |
| WMMH37 | 19½p ol gray, perf 13½x14 (I) | 1.00 | 1.25 |
| WMMH38 | 20p brn blk (II) | .95 | .95 |
| WMMH39 | 20½p ultra (I) | 2.50 | 2.50 |
| WMMH40 | 20p Prus bl, perf 13½x14 (I) | 1.10 | 1.25 |
| WMMH41 | 22p yel grn (I) | 1.10 | 1.25 |
| WMMH42 | 22p org red (II) | .90 | 1.00 |
| WMMH43 | 23p brt yel grn (II) | 1.00 | 1.10 |
| WMMH44 | 24p brown red (II) | 1.45 | 1.45 |
| WMMH45 | 24p red brn (II) | .90 | .90 |
| a. | Booklet pane of 6 + printed margin (BK156) | 5.50 | |
| WMMH46 | 24p red brn, perf 13½x14 (II) | 10.00 | 10.00 |
| WMMH47 | 26p red, perf 13½x14 (I) | 1.00 | 1.00 |
| WMMH48 | 26p red (II) | 4.25 | 4.50 |
| WMMH49 | 26p gray brn (II) | 1.75 | 1.75 |
| WMMH50 | 28p dp vio bl, perf 13½x14 (I) | 1.50 | 1.50 |
| WMMH51 | 28p dp vio bl (II) | 1.90 | 1.90 |
| WMMH52 | 28p grnsh slate (II) | 1.25 | 1.25 |
| WMMH53 | 31p brt rose lil (I) | 1.35 | 1.35 |
| WMMH54 | 32p grnsh blue (II) | 1.60 | 1.60 |
| WMMH55 | 34p grnsh slate (II) | 1.75 | 1.75 |
| WMMH56 | 37p scarlet (II) | 2.00 | 2.00 |
| WMMH57 | 39p dp mag (II) | 2.00 | 2.00 |

Issued: Nos. WMMH1, WMMH9, 3p, 5p, 7/7/71; Nos. WMMH3, WMMH6, 8p, 1/23/74; No. WMMH4, 11/6/74; Nos. WMMH7, WMMH11, 1/14/76; 10p, 11p, 10/20/76.

7p, 9p, No. WMMH14, 1/18/78; Nos. WMMH17, WMMH22, WMMH25, 7/23/80; Nos. WMMH16, WMMH23, WMMH32, WMMH40, 4/8/81;

Nos. WMMH19, WMMH27, WMMH37, WMMH47, 2/24/82; Nos. WMMH28, WMMH39, WMMH50, 4/27/83; Nos. WMMH20, WMMH29, 1/10/84.

Nos. WMMH30, WMMH41, 31p, 10/23/84; No. WMMH18, 1/7/86; No. WMMH33, 1/6/87; Nos. WMMH48, WMMH51, 1/27/87; No. WMMH24, 19p, 23p, 32p, 8/11/88; Nos. WMMH26, 20p, WMMH44, 34p, 11/28/89.

Nos. WMMH31, WMMH42, WMMH49, 37p, 12/4/90; Nos. WMMH34, WMMH45, WMMH52, 39p, 12/3/91; No. WMMH46, 9/14/92; No. WMMH35, 1/12/93.

### Perf. 15x14 Syncopated

| 1993-96 | | Litho. | |
|---|---|---|---|
| WMMH58 | 19p olive green | 1.10 | 1.00 |
| WMMH59 | 20p brt yel grn | 1.75 | 1.75 |
| WMMH60 | 25p rose red | .95 | .75 |
| WMMH61 | 26p brown | 2.25 | 2.25 |
| WMMH62 | 30p olive green | 2.00 | 2.00 |
| WMMH63 | 37p dp mag | 3.25 | 3.25 |
| WMMH64 | 41p gray brown | 2.25 | 2.25 |
| WMMH65 | 63p emerald | 5.00 | 5.00 |

Issued: 19p, 25p, 30p, 41p, 12/7/93. 20p, 26p, 37p, 63p, 7/23/96.

### Queen Design of 1970 with Redrawn Portrait
### "P" Removed
### Perf. 15x14 Syncopated

| 1997-98 | | Photo. | |
|---|---|---|---|
| WMMH70 | 20p brt yel grn | 1.75 | 1.75 |
| WMMH71 | 20p brt yel grn, perf 14 | 6.00 | 6.00 |
| WMMH74 | 26p red brown | 2.00 | 2.00 |
| WMMH75 | 26p red brn, perf 14 | 6.00 | 6.00 |
| WMMH82 | 37p dp mag | 2.75 | 2.75 |
| WMMH92 | 63p emerald | 6.00 | 6.00 |

Issued: Nos. WMMH70, WMMH74, 37p, 63p, 7/1/97; Nos. WMMH71, WMMH75, 10/13/98.

Nos. WMMH71, WMMH75 issued only in booklets (BK164).

### Perf. 13¾x14¼ Syncopated

| 2000 | | Photo. | |
|---|---|---|---|
| WMMH96 | 1st orange red | 3.50 | 3.00 |
| a. | Bklt. pane, 3 ea #NIMH96, SMH101, WMMH96 (BK167) | 32.00 | |

Issued: No. WMMH96, 2/15/00. No. WMMH96 sold for 26p on day of issue and was issued only in booklets.

See Isle of Man Nos. 8-11 for additional Machin Head definitives.

---

## GREAT BRITAIN BOOKLETS

Booklets are listed in denomination sequence by reign. Numbers in parenthesis following each listing reflect the number of cover varieties or edition numbers that apply to each cover style.

Values shown for complete booklets are for examples containing most panes having full perforations on two edges of the pane only. Booklets containing most or all panes with very fine, full perforations on all sides are scarce and will sell for more. Also, in booklets where most of the value is contained in only one pane of several, it is assumed that this pane has full perforations on two sides only. If this pane is very fine, the booklet will be worth a considerable premium over the value given.

Beginning with No. BK128, values for complete booklets are sometimes less than the sum of the individual panes. This is primarily due to market demand for a particular pane in the booklet or, in some cases, a single stamp found only in the booklet. Under these conditions, the value for the intact booklet reflects the market value for the key stamp or pane in the booklet.

This section does not contain complete booklets consisting solely of self-adhesive stamps. These are catalogued as minors under stamp listings.

### Sterling Currency

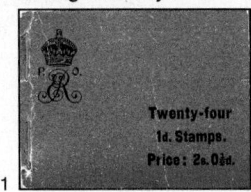

BC1

| 1904 | | | |
|---|---|---|---|
| BK1 | BC1 | 2sh½p red, 4 #128e | 500.00 |

| 1906-11 | | | |
|---|---|---|---|
| BK2 | BC1 | 2sh red, 2 #128e, 3 #143c, #143b | 2,200. |
| BK3 | BC1 | 2sh red, 3 #128e, 1 each #143b-143c (4) | 2,750. |

Cover inscription on Nos. BK2-BK3 revised to reflect changed contents.

| 1911 | | | |
|---|---|---|---|
| BK4 | BC1 | 2sh red, 2#151a, 3 #152a | 2,750. |

BC2

| 1912-13 | | | |
|---|---|---|---|
| BK5 | BC2 | 2sh red, 2 #151a, 3 #152a | 1,600. |
| BK6 | BC2 | 2sh red, 2 #155a, 3 #156a (4) | 1,300. |

Cover inscription on Nos. BK5-BK6 shows only Inland Postage Rates.

| 1913 | | | |
|---|---|---|---|
| BK7 | BC2 | 2sh red, 2 #159b, 3 #160a (35) | 1,400. |
| BK8 | BC2 | 2sh org, 2 #159b,3 #160a (20) | 1,250. |

BC3

| 1917 | | | |
|---|---|---|---|
| BK9 | BC3 | 2sh org, 2 #159b, 3 #160a (17) | 1,400. |

BC4

| 1924-34 | | | |
|---|---|---|---|
| BK10 | BC4 | 2sh blue, #159b, 160a, 161g-161h (2) | 2,750. |
| BK11 | BC4 | 2sh blue, #187b, 188b, 189c-189d (277) | 1,000. |

BC5

| 1929 | | | |
|---|---|---|---|
| BK12 | BC5 | 2sh blue, buff, #205b-207b, 207c | 600.00 |

| 1935 | | | |
|---|---|---|---|
| BK13 | BC4 | 2sh blue, #210b-211b, 212c-212d (58) | 600.00 |

BC6

| 1935 | | | |
|---|---|---|---|
| BK14 | BC6 | 2sh blue, buff, #226a-227a, 3 #228a | 100.00 |

| 1918-19 | | | |
|---|---|---|---|
| BK15 | BC4 | 3sh org, 2 each #159b, 160a, 161g (11) | 2,000. |
| BK16 | BC4 | 3sh org, #159b, 160a, 3 #161g (15) | 2,000. |

Cover used for Nos. BK15-BK16 does not have inscription above top line.

| 1921 | | | |
|---|---|---|---|
| BK17 | BC4 | 3sh blue, 3 #162b (3) | 2,500. |
| BK18 | BC4 | 3sh blue, 3 #162c (3) | 2,500. |

| 1922 | | | |
|---|---|---|---|
| BK19 | BC4 | 3sh scar, #159b, 160a, 3 #161g (33) | 900.00 |
| BK20 | BC4 | 3sh blue, 4 #161g (2) | 950.00 |

| 1924-34 | | | |
|---|---|---|---|
| BK21 | BC4 | 3sh scar, #187b-188b, 3 #189c (237) | 550.00 |

| 1929 | | | |
|---|---|---|---|
| BK22 | BC5 | 3sh blue, buff, #205b-206b, 3 #207b (5) | 475.00 |

| 1935 | | | |
|---|---|---|---|
| BK23 | BC4 | 3sh scar, #210b-211b, 3 #212c (27) | 550.00 |
| BK24 | BC6 | 3sh red, buff, #226a-227a, 5 #228a (4) | 100.00 |

| 1920 | | | |
|---|---|---|---|
| BK25 | BC4 | 3sh6p org, #160a, 3 #162b (6) | 2,400. |

Cover used for No. BK25 does not have inscription above top line.

| 1921 | | | |
|---|---|---|---|
| BK26 | BC4 | 3sh6p org red, #159b, 160a, 161g, 2 #162b (7) | 2,400. |
| BK27 | BC4 | 3sh6p org red, #159b, 160a, 161g, 2 #162c (13) | 2,400. |

| 1931-35 | | | |
|---|---|---|---|
| BK28 | BC4 | 5sh grn, #187b-188b, 189d, 5 #189c | 6,750. |
| BK29 | BC4 | 5sh buff, #187b-188b, 189d, 5 #189c (7) | 2,400. |
| BK30 | BC4 | 5sh buff, #210b-211b, 212d, 5 #212c (7) | 725.00 |

BC7

| 1936 | | | |
|---|---|---|---|
| BK31 | BC7 | 6p buff, 2 #232c | 70.00 |

BC8

| | | | |
|---|---|---|---|
| BK32 | BC8 | 2sh blue, #230a-231a, #232a-232b (31) | 150.00 |
| BK33 | BC8 | 3sh scar, #230a-231a, 3 #232a (12) | 130.00 |
| BK34 | BC8 | 5sh buff, #230a-231a, 6 #232a (2) | 300.00 |

| 1938-40 | | | |
|---|---|---|---|
| BK35 | BC7 | 6p buff, 2 #237d | 75.00 |
| BK36 | BC7 | 6p pink, #235d-237d | 325.00 |
| BK37 | BC7 | 6p pale grn, #235c-236c | 165.00 |

No. BK37 is 53x41mm.

| 1947-51 | | | |
|---|---|---|---|
| BK38 | BC7 | 1sh buff, 2 each #258b-259b, 260a | 30.00 |
| BK39 | BC7 | 1sh buff, 2 each #280a, 281b-282b | 30.00 |
| BK40 | BC7 | 1sh buff, #258e, 259d, 260b | 10,000. |
| BK41 | BC7 | 1sh buff, #280b-282b | 57.50 |

Nos. BK40-BK41 are 53x41mm.

Round GPO Emblem
BC9

| 1952-53 | | | |
|---|---|---|---|
| BK42 | BC9 | 1sh buff, #280b, 281c-282c | 27.50 |
| a. | Inland postage rate corrected in ink on inside booklet cover | 30.00 | |

Oval GPO Emblem
BC10

| 1954 | | | |
|---|---|---|---|
| BK43 | BC10 | 1sh buff, #280b, 281c-282c | 40.00 |

**1937**
BK44 BC8 2sh *blue,* #235b-
236b, #237b-
237c (26) 1,200.

BC11

**1938**
BK45 BC11 2sh *blue,* #235b-
236b, #237b-
237c (95) 1,200.

**1940-42**          **2sh6p Booklets**
BK46 BC11 *scar,* #235b,
#238b-239b (7) 1,900.
BK47 BC11 *blue,* #235b,
#238b-239b (6) 1,900.

Denomination part of cover of Nos. BK46-
BK47 is printed in white on black background.

BK48 BC11 *grn,* #235b,
#238b-239b (80) 1,100.
BK49 BC11 *grn,* #258a,
#261b-262b
(120) 1,100.

BC12

**1943**
BK50 BC12 *grn,* #258a,
#261b-262b (90) 100.00

With booklets issued in August and September 1943, commercial advertising on British
booklets was discontinued. Covers and interleaving were used for Post Office slogans.
Booklets were no longer numbered, but carried the month and year of issue.

**1951-52**
BK51 BC12 *grn,* #280c, #283b-
284b (10) 60.00
BK52 BC12 *grn,* #280c, 281e,
#282d, 284b (15) 45.00

**1937-38**          **3sh Booklets**
BK53 BC8 *scar,* #235b-236b,
3 #237b (10) 2,150.
BK54 BC11 *scar,* #235b-236b,
3 #237b (34) 2,150.

**1937-43**          **5sh Booklets**
BK55 BC8 *buff,* #235b-236b,
237c, 5 #237b (3) 2,250.
BK56 BC11 *buff,* #235b-236b,
237c, 5 #237b (9) 2,250.
BK57 BC11 *buff,* #235b, 238b,
3 #239b (16) 2,250.
BK58 BC11 *buff,* #258a, 261b,
3 #262b (20) 2,250.

**1943-53**
BK59 BC12 *tan,* #258a, 261b,
3 #262b (49) 147.50
BK60 BC12 *tan,* #258a, 261b,
3 #262b (20) 6,000.

Cover on No. BK60 has thick horizontal
lines separating the GPO emblem and the
various inscriptions.

BK61 BC12 *tan,* #280a, 283b,
3 #284b (5) 72.50
BK62 BC12 *tan,* #280c, 281e,
282d, 3 #284b (5) 62.50
BK63 BC12 *tan,* #280c, 281d-
282d, 283b, 2
#284b (2) 72.50

BC13

**1953-54**          **2sh6p Booklets**
BK64 BC12 *grn,* #280c, 281e,
294c, #296a (6) 30.00
BK65 BC13 *grn,* #280c, 281e,
294c, 296a (7) 60.00
BK66 BC13 *grn,* #281e, 292c,
294c, 296a 375.00

**5sh Booklets**
BK67 BC12 *grn,* #280c, 281d,
283b, 294c, 2
#296a (3) 45.00
BK68 BC13 *brn,* #280c, 281d,
283b, 294c, 2
#296a (2) 55.00
BK69 BC13 *brn,* #281d, 283b,
292c, 294c, 2
#296a 300.00
BK70 BC13 *brn,* #283b, 292c-
294c, 2 #296a 165.00

**1953-57**          **1sh Booklets**
BK71 BC7 *buff,* 2 each
#292a-294a 6.50
BK72 BC7 *buff,* 2 each #317d,
318f, 319f 45.00

**1954-59**
BK73 BC10 *buff,* #292b-294b (2) 8.75
BK74 BC10 *buff,* #317b, 318c,
319b (3) 7.25
BK75 BC10 *buff,* #353b-355b (2) 7.25

**1959**          **2sh Booklets**
BK76 BC10 *salmon,* #317b,
318c, 319b, 322b 6.75

BC14

**1960-65**          **2sh Booklets**
BK77 BC14 *sal,* #353b-355b,
358b 6.75
BK77A BC14 *pale yel,* 353b-
355b, 358b 7.25
BK78 BC14 *red, pale yel,*
#353e, 2 #357g 7.25
a. White stiching 7.25
BK79 BC14 *pale yel,* #353b-
355b, 358b (17) 35.00
a. #353bp-355bp, 358bp (13) 65.00
BK80 BC14 *red, pale yel,* 4
#353g 2.75
BK81 BC14 *org yel,* #354f,
359c (7) 5.50
a. #354fp, 359cp (12) 3.50
BK82 BC14 *red, org yel,* 2
#358b 8.75

No. BK77A has an upright watermark, No.
BK79 a sideways watermark.

**1968-69**
BK83 BC14 *org yel,* #MH5b,
MH6b (3) 1.25
BK84 BC14 *gray,* #MH6a-MH6b
(5) 1.00
BK85 BC14 *gray,* #MH7a-MH7b
(12) 1.50

**1954, Mar.**          **2sh6p Booklets**
BK86 BC13 *grn,* #292c, 293d,
294c, 296a (19) 57.50

No. BK86 inscribed Apr. 1954 through Aug.
1955 are valued. Booklet inscribed Mar. 1954
is valued at $365.
No. BK86 inscribed Aug. 1955 through Nov.
1955, may contain one or more panes
watermarked 308 substituted for those listed.
Value $60.

**1955, Dec.**
BK87 BC13 *grn,* #317a, 318b,
319a, 321a (16) 35.00

No. BK87 inscribed Dec. 1955 through June
1956 may contain one or more panes
watermarked 298 substituted for those listed.
Value $15.

**1957**
BK88 BC13 *grn,* #317a, 320b, 321a
(9) 35.00

**1958, Jan.**          **3sh Booklets**
BK89 BC13 *red,* #317a, 318b,
319a, 322a (9) 30.00

No. BK89 inscribed Nov. 1958, may contain
one or more panes watermarked 322 substituted for those listed. Value $15.

**1958, Dec.-59**
BK90 BC13 *red,* #353a-355a,
358a (5) 40.00
a. #353d, 354d, 355d, 358d (2) 275.00

No. BK90 dated Dec. 1958, may contain
one or more panes watermarked 308 substituted for those listed. Value $16.

BK91 BC13 *brick red,* #353a-355a,
358a (14) 45.00
a. #353d, 354d, 355d, 358d (4) 350.00
b. #353ap, 354ap, 355ap, 358ap
(2) 87.50

BC15

**1960**
BK92 BC15 *brick red,* #353a-355a,
358a (46) 47.50
a. #353ap-355ap, 358ap (35) 72.50

**1953, Nov.**          **3sh9p Booklets**
BK93 BC13 *red,* 3 #296a (10) 45.00

No. BK93 inscribed Oct. or Dec. 1955 may
contain one or more panes watermarked 308
substituted for those listed. Value $16.

**1956, Feb.**
BK94 BC13 *red,* 3 #321a (10) 20.00

**4sh6p Booklets**

**1957, Oct.-Dec. 1960**
BK95 BC13 *dull mauve,* 3 #322a
(7) 32.50
BK96 BC13 *dull mauve,* 3 #358a 145.00
BK97 BC13 *dull mauve,* 3 #358a
(4) 30.00
a. 3 #358d 42.50
BK98 BC14 *pale reddish lil,* 3
358a (9) 32.50
a. 3 #358d (4) 27.50
b. 3 #358ap 55.00
BK99 BC15 *pale reddish lil,* 3
#358a (36) 42.50
a. 3 #358ap (31) 42.50

**1965**
BK100 BC15 *slate bl,* #354a, 2
#359b (7) 32.50
a. #354ap, 2 #359bp (13) 17.00

**1968**
BK101 BC15 *slate bl,* #MH2a, 2
#MH6c 4.25

Ship with
GPO
Emblem
BC16

**1968-70**          **4sh6p Booklets**
BK102 BC16 *blue,* #MH2a, 2
#MH6c (3) 1.00
BK103 BC16 *blue,* #MH2a, 2
#MH7c (9) 1.00

**Ship Type with St. Edward's Crown
instead of GPO emblem**
BK104 BC16 *blue,* #MH2a, 2
#MH7c (2) 6.00

**1954, Mar.**          **5sh Booklets**
BK105 BC13 *brn,* #292c-294c,
295a-296a (10) 105.00

No. BK105 inscribed Sept. 1955 may contain one or more panes watermarked 308 substituted for those listed. Value $16.

**1955, Nov.**
BK106 BC13 *brn,* #317a, 318b,
319a, 320b, 321a
(14) 52.50

No. BK106 inscribed Nov. 1955, Jan. 1956
or May 1956 may contain one or more panes
watermarked 298 substituted for those listed.
Value $17.

**1958**
BK107 BC13 *brn,* #317a, 318b,
321a, 2 #322a (5) 32.00

No. BK107 inscribed July or Nov. 1958 may
contain one or more panes watermarked 322
substituted for those listed. Value $17.50.

**1959, Jan.**
BK108 BC14 *bl,* #353a-354a,
357c, 2 #358a (11) 37.50
a. #353d-354d, 357e, 2 #358d (3) 140.00
b. #353ap-354ap, 357cp, 2
#358ap 140.00

No. BK108 inscribed Jan. 1959 may contain
one or more panes watermarked 308 substituted for those listed. Value $17.50.

**1961, Jan.**
BK109 BC15 *bl,* #353a-354a,
357c, 2 #358a (27) 65.00
a. #353ap-354ap, 357cp, 2
#358ap (24) 175.00

House
with
GPO
Emblem
BC17

**1968-70**
BK110 BC17 *org brn,* 2 #MH8a
(5) 2.25

**House Type with St. Edward's
Crown instead of GPO Emblem**
BK111 BC17 5sh *org brn,* 2 #MH8a
(7) 3.00

BC18

**1970**
BK112 BC18 *org brn,* 2 #MH8a 3.00

**1965**          **6sh Booklets**
BK113 BC15 *claret,* 3 #359b (23) 50.00
a. 3 #359bp (27) 50.00

**1967**
BK114 BC15 *claret,* 3 #MH6c (10) 20.00

Bird with
GPO
Emblem
BC19

**1968-70**
BK115 BC19 *org,* 3 #MH6c (8) 2.00
BK116 BC19 *org,* 3 #MH7c (5) 3.50

**Bird Type with St. Edward's Crown
instead of GPO Emblem**
BK117 BC19 *org,* 3 #MH7c (5) 4.00

**1961-67**          **10sh Booklets**
BK118 BC15 *grn,* #353a-355a,
356b, 5 #358a (2) 165.00
BK119 BC15 *gray grn,* #354a-
355a, 357c, 5
#358a (7) 145.00
BK120 BC15 *tan,* #354a, 358a, 4
#359b (5) 42.50
a. #354ap, 358ap, 4 #359bp (3) 7.75

Explorers with GPO Emblem — BC20

## 1968-70
**BK121** BC20   *pur,* #MH2a,
    MH5a, 4 #MH6c
    (2)         6.00

### Explorer Type with clear GPO Emblem
**BK122** BC20   *yel grn,* #MH6d, 2
    ea #MH6c,
    #MH8a     4.00
**BK123** BC20   *yel grn,* #MH7c,
    MH7e, MH8a (4)   3.50

### Explorer Type with St. Edward's Crown instead of GPO Emblem
**BK124** BC20   *yel grn,* #MH7e, 2
    ea #MH7c,
    MH8a (2)    6.50

BC21

## 1969           £1 Booklets
**BK125** BC21   multi, 2 #MH7d,
    MH8b-MH8c    7.50
**BK126** BC21   2 #MH7d, MH8b-
    MH8c, stapled   350.00

### Decimal Currency Booklets (Stitched)

BC22

## 1971-74
**BK127** BC22   *10p org yel,*
    #MH24a,
    MH26a (21)    1.50

BC23

## 1974-76
**BK128** BC23   *10p org yel,*
    #MH24a,
    MH26a (9)     .75

BC24

## 1971-73
**BK129** BC24   *25p dull purple* (12)   4.00
    Contents: Nos. MH22a, MH32a-MH32b.

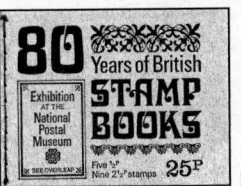

BC25

## 1971
**BK130** BC25   *25p dull purple*   4.50
    Contents: Nos. MH22a, MH32a-MH32b.
**BK131** BC25   *30p bright pur,* 2
    #MH36b     5.00

---

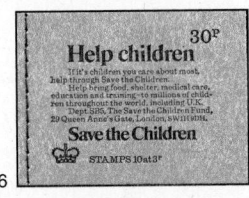

BC26

## 1973-74
**BK132** BC26   *25p dull mauve*   8.00
    Contents: Nos. MH22a, MH32a-MH32b.
**BK133** BC26   *30p vermilion,* 2
    #MH36b     3.75

### Bird Type with St. Edward's Crown instead of GPO Emblem
## 1971-73
**BK134** BC19   *30p pur,* 2
    #MH36b (16)   3.75
**BK135** BC19   *30p buff,* 2
    #MH36b     7.75

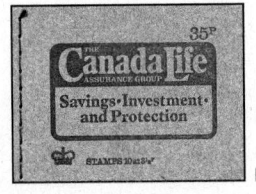

BC27

## 1973-74
**BK136** BC27   *30p red,* 2
    #MH36b     4.75
**BK137** BC27   *35p blue,* 2
    #MH39a     3.25
**BK138** BC27   *50p pale bluish
    grn*     7.00
    Contents: Nos. MH22a, MH32b, MH36a,
MH36c (4).
**BK139** BC27   *50p pale grn,*
    MH36b, 2
    #MH39a (2)   4.75
**BK140** BC27   *85p purple,*
    #MH39a, 3
    #MH49a     8.00

BC28

## 1973-74
**BK141** BC28   *35p bl,* 2 #MH39a
    (3)       3.00
**BK142** BC28   *45p yel brn,* 2
    #MH49a (3)    3.75
    **a.**   *45p org brn,* MH49a (1)   19.50

BC29

## 1971-72
**BK143** BC29   *50p pale bluish
    green*     6.00
    Contents: Nos. MH22a, MH32b, MH36a,
MH36c (8).

---

### Prestige Booklets

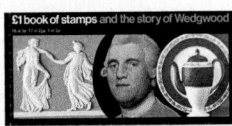

BC30

## 1972, May 24
**BK144** BC30   £1  *Wedgwood*   60.00
    Contents: Nos. MH34a-MH34b, #MH36d-
MH36e. Valued with full perforations on the ½p
stamps.

BC31

## 1980, Apr. 16
**BK145** BC31   £3  *Wedgwood*   5.00
    Contents: Nos. MH26b, MH70a, MH78a-
MH78b.

## 1982, May 19
**BK146**   £4  *Stanley Gibbons*   6.25
    Contents: Nos. MH80a-MH80b, MH92a-
MH92b.

## 1983, Sept. 14
**BK147**   £4  *Royal Mint*   6.25
    Contents: Nos. MH94a-MH94b, 2 #MH80a.

## 1984, Sept. 4
**BK148**   £4  *Christian Heritage*   29.50
    Contents: Nos. MH97c-MH97d, 2 No.
MH83a.

## 1985, Jan. 8
**BK149**   £5  *The Times*   12.50
    Contents: Nos. MH83b, MH97b-MH97c,
MH149a.

## 1986, Mar. 18
**BK150**   £5  *British Rail*   17.50
    Contents: Nos. MH79a, MH97b-MH97c,
MH142a.

## 1987, Mar. 3
**BK151**   £5  *P & O*   14.95
    Contents: Nos. MH83a-MH83b, MH102a,
MH130a.

---

## 1988, Feb. 9
**BK152**   £5  *The Financial
    Times*     32.50
    Contents: Nos. MH84a, MH103a-MH103b,
MH150a.

## 1989, Mar. 21
**BK153**   £5  *Scots Connection*   15.95
    Contents: Nos. SMH25a, SMH37a-
SMH37b, SMH45a.

## 1990, Mar. 20
**BK154**   £5  *London Life*   20.00
    Contents: Nos. 1314a, MH196a, 2 No.
MH193d.

## 1991, Mar. 19
**BK155**   £6  *Agatha Christie*   15.00
    Contents: Nos. MH121a, MH147a, 2 No.
MH99a.

## 1992, Feb. 25
**BK156**   £6  *Cymru-Wales*   15.00
    Contents: Nos. 1425a, MH187c,
WMMH34a, WMMH45a.

## 1992, Oct. 27
**BK157**   £6  *J.R.R. Tolkien*   15.50
    Contents: Nos. MH105a, MH187b, 2 No.
MH127a.

## 1993, Aug. 10
**BK158**   £5.64  *Beatrix Potter*   19.00
    Although inscribed £6 on the cover, No.
BK158 was sold for £5.64, the face value of its
contents, which were Nos. 1484a, MH178a,
MH187a, NIMH45a.

## 1994, July 26
**BK159**   £6.04  *N. Ireland*   22.50
    Contents: Nos. 1550a, MH214a, NIMH63a-
NIMH63b, 2 postal cards.

## 1995, Apr. 25
**BK160**   £6  *National Trust*   21.50
    Contents: Nos. 1607a, MH209a, MH231a,
NIMH59a.

## 1996, May 14
**BK161**   £6.48  *European Soc-
    cer Champi-
    onships*     13.00
    Contents: Nos. 1663a, 1664a, 1667a,
MH214b.

## 1997, Sept. 23
**BK162**   £6.15  *75th Anniv. of
    BBC*     16.00
    Contents: Nos. 1698a, MH287a, MH257a,
NIMH81a.

## 1998, Mar. 10
**BK163**   £7.49  *Definitive Por-
    trait*     17.50
    Contents: Nos. 1801a, 1802a, 1803a-1803b.

## 1998, Oct. 13
**BK164**   £6.16  *Breaking Barri-
    ers*     32.50
    Contents: Nos. 1829b, MH269a, MH285a-
MH285b.

## 1999, Feb. 16
**BK165**   (£7.54)  *Profile on
    Print*     32.50
    Contents: Nos. MH241c, MH288a,
MH310a-MH312a.

## 1999, Sept. 21
**BK166**   (£6.99)  *World
    Changers*     22.00
    Contents: Nos. 1842b, 1847a, 1868b,
1869b, MH257f.

## 2000, Feb. 15
**BK167**   (£7.50)  *Special by Design*  34.50
    Contents: Nos. MH198Ab, MH264Bc,
MH336b, WMMH96a.

**2000, Aug. 4**
BK168    (£7.03)  *The Life of the Century*    23.50
Contents: Nos. 1943e, 1943f, Scotland 18a, MH335b.

**2000, Sept. 18**
BK169    (£7)  *A Treasury of Trees*    24.50
Contents: Nos. 1917a, 1918a, 1920a, 1921a, Wales and Monmouthshire 18a.

**2001, Oct. 22**
BK170    (£6.76)  *Unseen and Unheard*    33.50
Contents: Nos. 1969b, 1970b, 1999e, Scotland 16a.

**2002, Feb. 6**
BK171    (£7.23)  *A Gracious Accession*    29.00
Contents: Nos. 2020a, 2021a, 2023a, MH290b.

**2002, Sept. 24**
BK172    (£6.83)  *Across the Universe*    27.50
Contents: 1938b, 2075e, Scotland 15a, MH290c.

**2003, Feb. 25**
BK173    (£6.99)  *Microcosmos*    27.00
Contents: Nos. 2104a, 2105a, Northern Ireland 13a, MH290c.

**2003, June 2**
BK174    (£7.46)  *A Perfect Coronation*    62.50
Contents: Nos. 2126a, 2134a, 2136b, MH287b.

**2004, Mar. 16**
BK175    (£7.44)  *Letters by Night*    23.50
Contents: Nos. 2148a, 2175a, Scotland 20a, MH287c.

**2004, May 25**
BK176    (£7.23)  *The Glory of the Garden*    26.00
Contents: Nos. 1720b, 2213a, 2214b, MH287d.

**2005, Feb. 24**
BK177    (£7.43)  *The Bronte Sisters*    24.00
Contents: Nos. 2268a, 2272b, England 10a, MH354a.

**2005, Oct. 18**
BK178    (£7.26)  *Battle of Trafalgar*    24.00
Contents: Nos. 1999h, 2325a, 2326b, MH287e.

**2006, Feb. 23**
BK179    (£7.40)  *Isambard Kingdom Brunel*    22.50
Contents: Nos. 2356a, 2357a, 2358b, MH355a.

**2006, Sept. 21**
BK180    (£7.44)  *Victoria Cross*    24.00
Contents: Nos. 1331b, 2398a, 2399b, MH376a.

**2007, Mar. 1**
BK181    (£7.49)  *World of Invention*    29.50
Contents: Nos. 2447a, 2449b, Wales & Monmouthshire 26a, MH376b.

**2007, June 5**
BK182    (£7.66)  *The Machin*    23.00
Contents: Nos. 2471c, MH363a, MH373a, MH378a.

**2007, Sept. 20**
BK183    (£7.66)  *British Army Uniforms*    24.00
Contents: Nos. 2510b, 2513b, MH366a, Wales & Monmouthshire 21a.

**2008, Jan. 8**
BK184    (£7.40)  *Ian Fleming's James Bond*    27.50
Contents: Nos. 1999i, 2535a, 2536b, MH287f.

**2008, Sept. 18**
BK185    (£7.15)  *RAF Uniforms*    27.50
Contents: Nos. 2587c, 2596b, 2599b, MH287h.

**2008, Sept. 29**
BK186    (£9.72)  *The Regional Definitives: Heraldry and Symbol*    35.00
Contents: Nos. 2600s, 2600t, 2600u, 2600v.

**2009, Jan. 13**
BK187    (£7.68)  *British Design Classics*    32.50
Contents: Nos. 2619a, 2623a, 2624b, MH365b.

**2009, Feb. 12**
BK188    (£7.75)  *Charles Darwin*    29.50
Contents: Nos. 2626e, 2630a, 2632a, MH363c.

**2009, Aug. 18**
BK189    (£8.18)  *Treasures of the Archive*    26.00
Contents: Nos. 1289b, 2679e, MH368b, MH394a.

**2009, Sept. 17**
BK190    (£7.93)  *Royal Navy Uniforms*    25.00
Contents: Nos. 1999j, 2688b, 2691b, MH372Ac.

**2010, Jan. 7**
BK191    (£8.06)  *Classic Album Covers*    40.00
Contents: Nos. 2729a, 2733a, MH350Ad, MH368c.

**2010, Feb. 25**
BK192    (£7.72)  *The Royal Society*    26.00
Contents: Nos. 2754a, 2755a, 2756b, MH366Bc.

**2010, May 8**
BK193    (£11.15)  *King George V*    32.50
Contents: Nos. 2792b, 2791b, 2789a, MH385a.

**2010, May 13**
BK194    (£9.76)  *Britain Alone*    30.00
Contents: Nos. MH397b, 2802a, 2801a, 2806b.

**2011, Mar. 11**
BK195    (£9.05)  *WWF For a Living Planet*    29.50
Contents: Nos. 2890a, 2892b, 2893e, MH400b.

**2011, May 5**
BK196    (£9.44)  *Morris & Co.*    28.00
No. BK196 sold for £9.99. Contents: Nos. 2716i, 2906a, 2907a, MH405a.

**2011, Sept. 9**
BK197    (£9.02)  *First United Kingdom Aerial Post*    52.50
No. BK197 sold for £9.97. Contents: Nos. 2278e, 2939e, 2939f, MH412a.

**2012, Jan. 10**
BK198    (£10.52)  *Roald Dahl: Master Storyteller*    36.00
No. BK198 sold for £11.47. Contents: Nos. 2986a, 2988a, 2989e, MH413a.

**2012, May 31**
BK199    (£11.84)  *The Diamond Jubilee*    37.50
No. BK199 sold for £12.77. Contents: Nos. 2996Gh, 3030b, 3034b, 3035c.

**2012, July 27**
BK200    (£9.76)  *Keeping the Flame Alive*    52.50
No. BK200 sold for £10.71. Contents: Nos. 2708a, 2822a, 2917a, C9a.

**2013, Mar. 26**
BK201    (£12.82)  *50 Years of Doctor Who*    37.50
No. BK201 sold for £13.77. Contents: Nos. 3143b, 3147b, 3151b, 3152a, 3153k.

**2013, May 9**
BK202    (£10.56)  *Football Heroes*    39.00
No. BK202 sold for £11.11. Contents: Nos. 3182a, 3188a, MH439a, MH440a.

**2013, Sept. 19**
BK203    (£10.24)  *Merchant Navy*    33.50
No. BK203 sold for £11.19. Contents: Nos. 3221a, 3224a, 3225e, MH441a.

**2014, Feb. 20**
BK204    (£13.02)  *Classic Locomotives of the United Kingdom*    41.00
No. BK204 sold for £13.97. Contents: Nos. 2865e, 3007e, 3197e, 3268e, MH248c.

**2014, Apr. 15**
BK205    (£10.44)  *Buckingham Palace*    33.50
No. BK205 sold for £11.39. Contents: Nos. 3280b, 3284c, 3285e, MH446a.

**2014, July 28**
BK206    (£10.35)  *The Great War 1914*    33.50
No. BK206 sold for £11.30. Contents: Nos. 3314a, 3317a, MH431a, MH446b.

**2015, Feb. 19**
BK207    (£13.67)  *Inventive Britain*    42.50
No. BK207 sold for £14.60. Contents: Nos. 3363a, 3369a, 3370b, MH448a.

**2015, May 14**
BK208    (£13.01)  *The Great War 1915*    37.50
No. BK208 sold for £13.96. Contents: Nos. 2510c, 3399a, 3402a, MH455a.

**2015, June 18**
BK209    (£12.12)  *The Battle of Waterloo 1815*    37.50
No. BK209 sold for £14.47. Contents: Nos. 3513a, 3514a, 3515e, MH446c.

**2015, Dec. 17**
BK210    (£16.20)  *The Making of Star Wars The British Story*    42.50
No. BK210 sold for £16.99. Contents: Nos. 3443a, 3446b, 3451g, 3451h, 3452a.

**2016, Feb. 18**
BK211    (£15.41)  *500 Years of Royal Mail*    41.00
No. BK211 sold for £16.36. Contents: Nos. 3473a, 3475a, 3476e, 3477a.

**2016, Apr. 21**
BK212    (£14.16)  *HM The Queen's 90th Birthday*    45.00
No. BK212 sold for £15.11. Contents: Nos. 3499a, 3500b, 3501e, MH459a.

**2016, June 21**
BK213    (£15.54)  *The Great War 1916*    41.00
No. BK213 sold for £16.49. Contents: Nos. 2744k, 3509a, 3512a, 3513e.

**2016, July 28**
BK214    (£14.42)  *The Tale of Beatrix Potter*    37.50
No. BK214 sold for £15.37. Contents: Nos. 3525a, 3526b, 3527e, MH460a.

**2017, Feb. 15**
BK215    (£13.63)  *Windsor Castle*    34.00
No. BK215 sold for £14.58. Contents: Nos. 3585a, 3587b, 3588e, MH460b.

**2017, June 5**
BK216    (£14.64)  *The Machin Definitive: 50th Anniversary*    37.50
No. BK216 sold for £15.59. Contents: Nos. MH440d, MH467a MH468g, MH468h, MH469c.

**2017, July 31**
BK217    (£14.46)  *The Great War 1917*    36.00
No. BK217 sold for £15.41. Contents: Nos. 2614c, 2744l, 3634a, 3637a.

**2017, Dec. 14**
BK218    (£14.22)  *Star Wars: The Making of the Droids, Aliens and Creatures*    37.50
No. BK218 sold for £15.95. Contents: Nos. 3658a, 3662a, 3663c, MH470a.

**2018, Jan. 23**
BK219    (£12.99)  *Game of Thrones*    34.50
No. BK219 sold for £13.95. Contents: Nos. 3686a, 3688b, 3689a, 3693a.

**2018, Mar. 20**
BK220    (£18.54)  *The RAF Centenary*    46.00
No. BK220 sold for £18.69. Contents: Nos. 3416g, 3707b, 3709b, 3710e, MH471a.

**2018, Sept. 13**
BK221    (£14.70)  *The Great War 1918*    36.00
No. BK221 sold for £15.65. Contents: Nos. 2744m, 3633a, 3774a, 3777a.

**2018, Dec. 4**
BK222    (£13.97)  *The Marauder's Map*    36.00
No. BK222 sold for £15.50. Contents: Nos. 3788a, 3789b, 3790f, 3790g, MH476a.

**2019, Feb. 13**
BK223    (£11.64)  *Leonardo da Vinci 500 Years*    39.00
No. BK223 sold for £13.10. Contents: Nos. 3812a, 3813a, 3814b, MH477a.

**2019, Mar. 14**
BK224    (£15.98)  *Make Mine Marvel*    41.00
No. BK224 sold for £17.45. Contents: Nos. 3821a, 3824b, 3825f, 3825g, MH478a.

Additional prestige booklets can be found starting with No. BK1225.

———

### Decimal Currency Booklets (Folded)

Booklets are listed in denomination sequence in chronological order in this section.

BC32

**1976-77**
BK225 BC32 10p red, gray,
#MH58a (3) .50

BC33

**1978**
BK226 BC33 10p brn, bl, #MH61b
(6) .40

**1979-80**
BK227 BC33 10p London '80,
#MH64b (2) .35

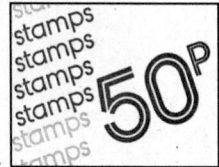

BC34

**1977**
BK228 BC34 50p #MH65a 1.80
BK229 BC34 50p #MH67a 1.80

Nos. BK228-BK238 exist with either version of Nos. MH65a, MH67a, MH70b, MH76a, MH78d, MH80c, MH86a. See the notes following the listings for these panes.

Commercial
Vehicles
BC35

**50p Booklets, Cover BC35**

**1978-95**
| BK230 | Commercial Vehicles, #MH67a (6) | 1.80 |
|---|---|---|
| BK231 | Commercial Vehicles, #MH70b | 1.80 |
| BK232 | Veteran Cars, #MH70b | 1.80 |
| BK233 | Veteran Cars, #MH78d (3) | 1.80 |
| BK234 | Veteran Cars, #MH86a (2) | 1.80 |
| BK235 | Follies, #MH86a | 1.80 |
| BK236 | Follies, #MH76a (2) | 5.00 |
| BK237 | Follies, #MH80c (4) | 1.20 |
| BK238 | Rare Farm Animals, #MH80c | 2.10 |
| BK239 | Rare Farm Animals, #MH81a (4) | 4.20 |
| BK240 | Orchids, #MH83c (4) | 3.00 |
| BK241 | Pillar Box, #MH97a | 3.25 |
| BK242 | Pond Life, #MH97a (2) | 2.10 |

Nos. BK241-BK242 sold for a 1p discount. Some panes have stars on reverse.

| BK244 | Pond Life, #MH83d (2) | 4.25 |
|---|---|---|
| BK245 | Roman Britain, #MH79b | 7.75 |
| BK246 | Roman Britain, #MH102b (2) | 2.75 |
| BK247 | Marylebone Cricket Club, #MH102b (4) | 2.25 |
| BK248 | Botanical Gardens, #MH83d (2) | 3.90 |
| BK248A | Botanical Gardens, #MH83g (2) | 2.10 |
| BK249 | London Zoo, #MH102b (2) | 2.40 |
| BK250 | London Zoo, #MH83g | 2.40 |
| BK251 | Marine Life, #MH83g | 2.40 |
| BK252 | Marine Life, #MH106a | 6.00 |

| BK253 | Gilbert & Sullivan Operas, #MH106a (3) | 6.00 |
|---|---|---|
| BK254 | Aircraft, #MH115a | 9.00 |
| BK255 | Aircraft, #MH193a | 12.00 |
| BK256 | Aircraft, #MH98a (2) | 12.00 |
| BK257 | Archaeology, #MH126a (4) | 1.80 |
| BK258 | Sheriff's Millennium, #MH126a | 1.90 |
| BK259 | Postal History, #MH126a (3) | 1.80 |
| BK260 | Postal History, #MH213a | 1.80 |
| BK261 | Coaching Inns, #MH213a (4) | 1.80 |
| BK262 | Sea Charts, #MH213a (4) | 1.80 |

With
Window
BC36

Without
Window
BC37

**1987**
BK285 BC36 52p #MH83e 2.75

**1988-89**
BK295 BC36 56p #MH87a (2) 4.25
BK296 BC37 56p #MH87b 4.75
BK297 BC37 56p #MH87c 24.00

**1990**
BK307 BC37 60p #MH191a 4.50

**1976-77**
BK317 BC34 65p 10 #MH60 6.30
BK325 BC34 70p 10 #MH61 4.00

Nos. BK317, BK325-BK327, BK370, BK394, BK404-BK405, BK467-BK468, BK488-BK492, BK513-BK514, BK524-BK533, BK554-BK557, BK573-BK574, BK584, BK594, BK616-BK618, BK631, BK641, BK651-BK652, BK673-BK675, BK696-BK699, BK709-BK713, BK715-BK718, BK728, BK732-BK733 exist with stamps affixed to cover by selvage at either right or left edges of block or pane of stamps.

BC38

**1978-79** **70p Booklets**
BK326 BC38 Country Crafts, 10 #MH61 (6) 3.75
BK327 BC38 Derby Mechanized Letter Office, 10 #MH61 6.75

**1987**
BK338 BC36 72p red, yel & blk, #MH102c 2.75

**1988-89**
BK348 BC36 76p #MH106c (2) 4.75
BK349 BC37 76p #MH106d 6.00
BK350 BC37 76p #MH106e 24.00

BC39

**1992**
BK360 BC39 78p 2 #MH157 4.75

Cover of No. BK360 does not show the numeral four. Contents of Nos. BK360 is 1/2 of Nos. MH157a, the right hand vertical pair of stamps being removed.

**1979**
BK370 BC38 80p Military Aircraft, 10 #MH64 2.75

**1990**
BK371 BC37 80p red, yel & blk, #MH193b 5.50
BK372 BC37 80p red, yel & blk, #MH194a 6.00

**1976-79**
BK382 BC34 85p gray & ol grn, 10 #MH65 6.75
BK392 BC34 90p lt & dk bl, 10 #MH67 4.25
BK393 BC38 90p British Canals, 10 #MH67 (6) 3.75
BK394 BC38 90p Derby Letter Office, 10 #MH67 8.50

**1979-95** **£1 Booklets**
| BK403 | BC38 | Industrial Archaeology, 10 #MH70 | 3.00 |
|---|---|---|---|
| BK404 | BC38 | Military Aircraft, 10 #MH70 (3) | 3.00 |
| BK405 | BC35 | Violin, 6 #MH97 | 3.60 |
| BK406 | BC35 | Musical Instruments, #MH102d (2) | 3.60 |
| BK407 | BC35 | Sherlock Holmes, #MH102d (2) | 3.60 |
| BK408 | BC35 | Sherlock Holmes, #MH102f (2) | 3.60 |
| BK409 | BC35 | London Zoo, #MH102f | 3.60 |
| BK410 | BC35 | Oliver Twist, #MH102f | 4.50 |
| BK411 | BC35 | Nicholas Nickleby, #MH106b (2) | 4.50 |
| BK412 | BC35 | Great Expectations, #MH108a | 10.25 |
| BK413 | BC35 | Marine Life, #MH106b | 4.50 |
| BK414 | BC35 | Wicken Fen, #MH115b | 4.75 |
| BK415 | BC35 | Click Mill, #MH193c | 7.25 |
| BK416 | BC35 | Wicken Fen, #MH194b | 11.50 |
| BK417 | BC35 | Jack & Jill Mills, #MH120a (2) | 3.60 |
| BK418 | BC35 | Punch Magazine, #MH126b (4) | 2.40 |
| BK419 | BC35 | Sheriff's Millennium, #MH126b | 2.40 |
| BK420 | BC35 | Educational Institutions, #MH128a (3) | 4.80 |
| BK421 | BC35 | Educational Institutions, 4 #MH214 | 4.50 |
| BK422 | BC35 | Prime Ministers, 4 #MH214 | 2.10 |
| BK423 | BC35 | Prime Ministers, 4 #MH213 (3) | 2.10 |
| BK424 | BC35 | End of World War II, 4 #MH213 (4) | 2.10 |

BC40

**1996-2000**
BK425 BC40 £1 multi, 4 #MH214 4.80
BK426 BC40 £1 multi, #MH216b 4.50
BK427 BC40 £1 multi, #MH257b 24.00
BK428 BC40 £1 multi, #MH257d 7.25
BK429 BC40 £1 #MH288d 8.00

**1987-88** **£1.04 Booklet**
BK446 BC36 #MH131a 29.00

**£1.08 Booklets**
BK456 BC36 #MH133a 9.75
BK457 BC37 #MH133b 24.00

**1981** **£1.15 Booklets**
BK467 BC38 Military Aircraft, 10 #MH76 (2) 3.60
BK468 BC38 Museums, 10 #MH76 (2) 3.60

**1989** **£1.16 Booklet**
BK478 BC37 multi, #MH140a 14.50

**1980-86** **£1.20 Booklets**
BK488 BC38 Industrial Archaeology, 10 #MH78 (3) 3.60
BK489 BC38 Pillar Box, 10 #MH79 5.50
BK490 BC38 National Gallery, 10 #MH79 5.00
BK491 BC38 Handwriting, 10 #MH79 5.00
BK492 BC38 Christmas, 10 #MH83 5.50

No. BK492 was sold at a discount. Each stamp has a blue double-line star printed on reverse.

BC41

**1998** **£1.20 Booklet**
BK493 BC41 multi, 4 #MH259 2.75

**1990** **£1.24 Booklet**
BK503 BC39 multi, #MH144a 4.75

**1982-83** **£1.25 Booklets**
BK513 BC38 Museums, 10 #MH81 (4) 3.25
BK514 BC38 Railway Engines, 10 #MH81 (5) 4.80

**1981-88** **£1.30 Booklets**
BK524 BC38 Postal History, #MH86b (2) 3.25
BK525 BC38 Trams, 10 #MH83 (4) 3.25
BK526 BC38 Books for Children, 10 #MH83 3.25
BK527 BC38 Keep in Touch, 10 #MH83 3.25
BK528 BC38 Ideas for your Garden, 10 #MH83 3.25
BK529 BC38 Brighter Writer, 10 #MH83 3.25
BK530 BC38 Jolly Postman, 10 #MH83 3.25
BK531 BC38 Linnean Society, 10 #MH83 4.25
BK532 BC38 Recipe Cards, 10 #MH83 3.25
BK533 BC38 Party Pack, 10 #MH83 3.25
BK534 BC36 red, yel & blk, #MH83f 4.25

**1991** **£1.32 Booklet**
BK544 BC39 multi, #MH148a 4.25

**1981-89** **£1.40 Booklets**
BK554 BC38 Industrial Archaeology, 10 #MH86 (2) 3.25
BK555 BC38 Women's Costumes, 10 #MH86 (2) 3.25
BK556 BC38 Pocket Planner, 10 #MH87 3.25
BK557 BC38 William Henry Fox Talbot, 10 #MH87 3.25

**1988-95** **£1.40 Booklets**
BK558 BC36 #MH87d 10.25
BK559 BC36 10 #MH88 10.25
BK560 BC37 #MH87e 6.75
BK561 BC37 10 #MH88 12.00
BK562 BC39 #MH223a 4.00
BK563 BC41 #MH223a (2) 4.00

**1982** **£1.43 Booklets**
BK572 BC38 Postal History, #MH93d 3.60
BK573 BC38 Postal History, #MH93d (5) 3.60

**BK574** BC38   *Holiday Postcard Stamp Book,* #MH93d   3.60

No. BK574 contains a postcard voucher on the back cover.

**1983**      **£1.45 Booklet**
**BK584** BC38   *Britain's Country- side,* 10 #MH94   5.75

Stamps in No. BK584 have double-lined D printed on reverse.
No. BK584 had a face value of £1.60.

**1983**      **£1.46 Booklet**
**BK594** BC38   *Postal History,* #MH94c (4)   5.75

BC42

**1996-97**      **£1.48 Booklets**
**BK605** BC41   #MH226a (2)   6.50
**BK606** BC42   4 #MH262   4.50

**1986-90**      **£1.50 Booklets**
**BK616** BC38   *Pillar Box,* #MH97e   4.25
**BK617** BC38   *National Gallery,* #MH97e   4.25
**BK618** BC38   *Handwriting,* #MH97e   4.25
**BK619** BC37   #MH190a   6.75
**BK620** BC37   #MH191b   7.50
**BK621** BC37   #MH192a   12.00

**1999**      **£1.52 Booklet**
**BK630** BC41   4 #MH264   4.00

**1985**      **£1.53 Booklet**
**BK631** BC38   *Royal Mail, 350th Anniv.,* #1111a   4.50

**1984**      **£1.54 Booklet**
**BK641** BC38   *Postal History,* #MH97f (4)   3.75

**1982-85**      **£1.55 Booklets**
**BK651** BC38   *Women's Cos- tumes,* 10 #MH93 (4)   3.25
**BK652** BC38   *Social Letter Writ- ing,* 10 #MH97g   4.25

No. BK652 sold for a 15p discount. Panes have double-lined "D" printed on reverse.

**1991**      **£1.56 Booklet**
**BK662** BC39   #MH157a   7.00

**1978-2000**      **£1.60 Booklets**
**BK672** BC38   *Christmas,* #MH67b   3.00
**BK673** BC38   *Birthday Box,* 10 #MH97 (2)   4.25
**BK674** BC38   *Britain's Country- side,* 10 #MH94   3.60
**BK675** BC38   *Write It,* 10 #MH97   4.25
**BK676** BC41   #MH266a   4.75

**1993-96**      **£1.64 Booklets**
**BK685** BC39   #MH231b   3.60
**BK686** BC41   #MH231b (2)   3.60

**1984-86**      **£1.70 Booklets**
**BK696** BC38   *Love Letters,* 10 #MH97 (2)   4.25
**BK697** BC38   *Pillar Box,* 10 #MH97 (2)   4.00
**BK698** BC38   *National Gallery,* 10 #MH97   4.25
**BK699** BC38   *Handwriting,* 10 #MH97   4.25

**1979-88**      **£1.80 Booklets**
**BK709** BC38   *Christmas,* #MH70c   3.75
**BK710** BC38   *Books for Chil- dren,* 10 #MH102   4.50
**BK711** BC38   *Keep in Touch,* 10 #MH102   4.50
**BK712** BC38   *Ideas for your Garden,* 10 #MH102   4.50
**BK713** BC38   *Brighter Writer,* 10 #MH102   4.50
**BK714** BC36   red, yel & blk, #MH102e   6.00

**BK715** BC38   *Jolly Postman,* 10 #MH102   4.50
**BK716** BC38   *Linnean Society,* 10 #MH102   4.50
**BK717** BC38   *Recipe Cards,* 10 #MH102   4.50
**BK718** BC38   *Party Pack,* 10 #MH102   4.50

**1988-89**      **£1.90 Booklets**
**BK728** BC38   *Pocket Planner,* 10 #MH106   5.50
**BK729** BC36   red, yel & blk, #MH106f   8.00
**BK730** BC37   #MH106g   8.00
**BK731** BC37   10 #MH107   15.00
**BK732** BC38   *William Henry Fox Talbot,* 10 #MH106   5.50

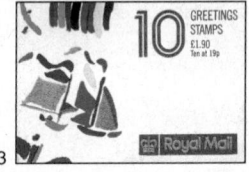
BC43

**1989**      **£1.90 Booklet**
**BK733** BC43   *Greetings,* #1247a   29.00

Artwork for No. BC43 spanned six booklet covers. Only portions of the design appear on each cover.
Value is for pane with perfs guillotined. Value for booklet with pane having full perfs is approximately 60% more.

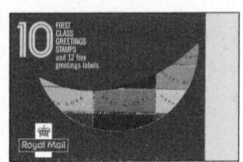
BC44

**1990-96**      **£2 Booklets**
**BK742** BC44   #1313a   16.25
**BK743** BC37   #MH193e   7.50
**BK744** BC37   #MH194c   11.00
**BK745** BC37   #MH195a   14.50
**BK746** BC35   *Postal Vehicles,* 8 #965/213 (3)   4.00
**BK747** BC35   *Rowland Hill,* 8 #965/213 (4)   4.00
**BK748** BC40   8 #MH214   4.50
**BK749** BC40   #MH216a   4.50

**1998-2000**
**BK751** BC40   #MH257c   24.00
**BK752** BC40   #MH257e   8.00
**BK753** BC40   #MH288e   10.25

**1980-93**      **£2.20 Booklets**
**BK759** BC38   *Christmas,* #MH78c   4.00
**BK760** BC38   *Christmas,* #MH80e   5.50

**£2.30 Booklet**
**BK770** BC38   *Christmas,* #1088a   6.00

**£2.40 Booklet**
**BK780** BC38   *Christmas,* #1124a   5.50

Stamps in Nos. BK760, BK770, BK780 have double-line star printed on reverse over gum.

BC45

**1994-95**      **£2.40 Booklets**
**BK790** BC39   #MH234a (2)   5.50
**BK791** BC41   #MH234a (2)   5.50
**BK792** BC45   #1638a   4.50

**1981-94**      **£2.50 Booklets**
**BK802** BC38   *Christmas,* #MH93e   6.00

No. BK802 was sold for a 30p discount. Stamps in No. BK802 have a 10-point single-line blue star printed on reverse over gum.

**BK803** BC45   *Santa, Reindeer,* 10 #1529   6.00

**BK804** BC45   *Christmas Play Props,* 10 #1582   4.75
**BK805** BC45   *Christmas Robin,* 10 #1635   4.50

**1996-97**      **£2.52 Booklet**
**BK815** BC41   #MH236a (3)   9.75

**1981**      **£2.55 Booklet**
**BK826** BC38   *Christmas,* #MH86c   5.25

**1999**      **£2.56 Booklet**
**BK827** BC41   4 #MH276   6.50

**2000**      **£2.60 Booklet**
**BK830** BC41   #MH277a   7.50

**1990-95**      **£3.40 Booklet**
**BK836** BC45   *Snowman,* #1340a   6.75

**£3.60 Booklets**
**BK846** BC45   *Holly,* #1416a   7.00
**BK847** BC45   *Santa, Reindeer,* #1468a   7.00

**£3.80 Booklets**
**BK857** BC45   *Santa, Reindeer,* #1528a   6.25
**BK858** BC45   *Christmas Play Props,* #1581a   6.50
**BK859** BC45   *Christmas Robin,* #1634a   7.25

---

## No-Value Indicated Booklets

BC46

**1989-2000**
**BK960** BC37   (56p) #MH179a   6.50
**BK961** BC37   (60p) #MH177a   26.50
**BK962** BC39   (60p) #MH182a   6.00
**BK963** BC39   (68p) #MH179b   6.00
**BK964** BC46   (72p) #MH179b   6.75
**BK965** BC39   (72p) 4 #MH238   6.00
**BK966** BC39   (72p) 4 #MH239   6.00
**BK967** BC41   (76p) 4 #MH238   6.00
**BK968** BC41   (76p) 4 #MH239 (2)   6.00
**BK969** BC41   (80p) 4 #MH284 (4)   6.00
**BK994** BC37   (76p) #MH184a   9.50
**BK995** BC37   (80p) #MH183a   26.50
**BK996** BC39   (80p) #MH188a (2)   7.25
**BK996A** BC39   (80p) #MH189a   14.50
**BK997** BC46   (96p) #MH188a   7.25
**BK998** BC39   (96p) 4 #MH240   7.25
**BK999** BC39   (96p) 4 #MH241   7.25
**BK1000** BC39   (£1) #MH241b (Bank of England)   7.25
**BK1001** BC41   (£1) 4 #MH241 (4)   7.25
**BK1002** BC41   (£1) #MH241b (4)   7.25

**(£1.04) Booklets**
**BK1003** BC41   4 #MH241   7.25
**BK1004** BC41   #MH241b (Rugby World Cup)   7.25
**BK1005** BC41   4 #MH288   7.25
**BK1006** BC41   4 #MH288+label   7.25
**BK1007** BC41   #MH335c   7.25

**(£1.20) Booklet**
**BK1010** BC41   #MH290a   12.00

**(£1.40) Booklets**
**BK1028** BC37   #MH177b   11.50
**BK1029** BC37   10 #MH178   11.50

**(£1.50) Booklets**
**BK1030** BC39   #MH180a   12.00
**BK1031** BC39   10 #MH181   12.50
**BK1032** BC39   #MH182b   11.50

**(£1.70) Booklets**
**BK1033** BC39   10 #MH178   11.50
**BK1034** BC39   10 #MH179c   11.50

**(£1.80) Booklets**
**BK1035** BC46   #MH179c   11.50
**BK1036** BC46   10 #MH178   11.50
**BK1037** BC39   #MH177b   11.50
**BK1038** BC39   10 #MH239 (3)   11.50

**(£1.90) Booklets**
**BK1039** BC41   10 #MH239 (5)   11.50
**BK1040** BC41   10 #MH238 (4)   11.50
**BK1041** BC37   #MH183b   14.50

**(£2) Booklets**
**BK1068** BC39   #MH186a (2)   14.50
**BK1069** BC39   10 #MH187 (3)   14.50
**BK1070** BC39   #MH188b (3)   14.50
**BK1071** BC41   10 #MH284   11.50
**BK1072** BC41   10 #MH285   12.00

**(£2.40) Booklets**
**BK1091** BC46   #MH186a   14.50
**BK1092** BC46   #MH187d   14.50
**BK1093** BC39   #MH187d   14.50
**BK1094** BC39   10 #MH240   13.00
**BK1095** BC39   10 #MH241 (11)   13.00

**(£2.50) Booklets**
**BK1116** BC41   10 #MH240 (11)   14.50
**BK1117** BC41   10 #MH241 (12)   14.50

**(£2.60) Booklets**
**BK1137** BC41   10 #MH287 (3)   14.50
**BK1139** BC41   10 #MH288   14.50
**BK1139A** BC41   #MH289a   14.50
**BK1140** BC41   10 #MH288   14.50
**BK1141** BC41   #1856a, MH288b   16.25
**BK1142** BC41   #1872a, MH288b   16.25
**BK1143** BC41   10 #MH335   14.50
**BK1144** BC41   #MH336a   14.50

BC47

**1991-2000**      **(£2.20) Booklets**
**BK1160** BC47   #1359a   16.50
**BK1161** BC47   *Laughing Pillar Box,* #1373a   16.50

**(£2.40) Booklets**
**BK1171** BC47   *Memories,* #1435a   16.50
**BK1172** BC47   *Rupert Bear,* #1488a (3)   16.50

**(£2.50) Booklets**
**BK1182** BC47   *Rupert Bear, Paddington Bear,* #1547a   16.50
**BK1183** BC47   *Clown,* #1605a   16.50
**BK1184** BC47   *More Love,* #1652a   16.50

**(£2.60) Booklets**
**BK1194** BC47   *Christmas,* 10 #1709   16.25
**BK1195** BC47   *Flower,* #1722a (4)   16.50
**BK1196** BC47   *Chocolates,* #1722a   17.00
**BK1197** BC47   *Memorable Post,* #1722a   17.00
**BK1198** BC47   *Santa Claus,* 10 #1777   16.25
**BK1199** BC47   *Christmas,* 10 #1835   5.00
**BK1200** BC47   10 #1880   5.00

**(£2.70) Booklets**
**BK1201** BC41   #1938a, MH335a   16.25
**BK1202** BC47   #1919a, MH335a   16.25
**BK1203** BC47   10 #1931   16.25

**(£3.80) Booklet**
**BK1210** BC47   #1879a   7.25
**BK1211** BC47   #1930a   23.00

**(£4) Booklets**
**BK1220** BC47   *Magi,* #1708a   23.00
**BK1221** BC47   *Santa Claus, Children,* #1776a   23.00
**BK1222** BC47   *Christmas,* #1834a   7.50

---

## Additional Prestige Booklets

**2019, May 24**
**BK1225**   (£15.64) *Victoria A Long and Glorious Reign*   55.00

No. BK1225 sold for £17.20. Contents: Nos. 3848a, 3851b, 3852e, MH485a.

**2019, Nov. 26**
BK1226 (£16.08) *Star Wars: The Making of the Vehicles* 42.50

No. BK1226 sold for £17.65. Contents: Nos. 3924a, 3925b, 3926g, 3926h, MH471b.

**2020, Feb. 11**
BK1227 (£14.82) *Visions of the Universe* 37.50

No. BK1227 sold for £16.10. Contents: Nos. 3944a, 3945b, MH430a, MH486a.

**2020, Mar. 17**
BK1228 (£15.28) *Behind the Scenes of James Bond* 39.50

No. BK1228 sold for £16.99. Contents: Nos. 3950a, 3952b, 3953e, MH439b.

**2020, May 8**
BK1229 (£18.16) *End of the Second World War* 45.00

No. BK1229 sold for £19.80. Contents: Nos. 3969b, 3973b, 3974e, MH434a.

**2020, July 9**
BK1230 (£17.42) *Queen* 42.50

No. BK1230 sold for £19.10. Contents: Nos. 3997b, 4001c, 4002f, 4002g.

**2020, Nov. 13**
BK1231 (£17.17) *Star Trek* 41.00

No. BK1231 sold for £18.35. Contents: Nos. 4050b, 4056b, 4057g, MH441b.

**2021, Feb. 16**
BK1232 (£19.77) *Only Fools and Horses* 52.50

No. BK1232 sold for £21.70. Contents: Nos. 4075b, 4079b, 4080e, MH440e.

**2021, May 28**
BK1233 (£18.24) *Paul McCartney* 57.50

No. BK1233 sold for £20.25. Contents: Nos. 4110b, 4114b, 4115e, MH441c.

**2021, Aug. 12**
BK1234 (£16.38) *Industrial Revolutions* 50.00

No. BK1234 sold for £18.03. Contents: Nos. 4141b, 4143b, 4144e, MH499a.

**2021, Sept. 17**
BK1235 (£19.58) *DC Collection* 50.00

No. BK1235 sold for £21.20. Contents: Nos. 4159b, 4165b, 4166g, 4166h, MH440f.

**2022, Jan. 20**
BK1236 (£18.90) *The Rolling Stones* 56.00

No. BK1236 sold for £20.85. Contents: Nos. 4189a, 4191b, 4192e, MH446d.

**2022, Feb. 4**
BK1237 (£17.84) *Her Majesty The Queen's Platinum Jubilee* 52.50

No. BK1237 sold for £19.50. Contents: Nos. 3497b, 4200a, 4201b, MH504a.

**2022, May 5**
BK1238 (£19.10) *Unsung Heroes Women of World War II* 52.50

No. BK1238 sold for £20.75. Contents: Nos. 4235a, 4237b, 4238e, MH511a.

**2022, Sept. 1**
BK1239 (£19.58) *Transformers* 49.50

No. BK1239 sold for £21.25. Contents: Nos. 4268b, 4272b, 4273f, 4273g, MH511b.

**2022, Dec. 21**
BK1240 (£20.11) *Tutankhamun Finding a Pharaoh* 52.50

No. BK1240 sold for £21.55. Contents: Nos. 4308b, 4310b, 4311e, MH521a. No. BK1240 was supposed to have been issued on Nov. 24, 2022 but its release was delayed.

## SCOTT
# Great Britain Album Set
## 1840-2015

### Item #: 200SET

Save when you purchase the complete Great Britain Album Set covering 1840-2015 in 490 Scott Specialty Series album pages. Also includes Great Britain Machin album pages 1967-2015, 2 large Scott 3-Ring, metal hinged, Binders with matching slipcases and binder labels.

### Retail: $609.49

### AA Price: $518.07
*(prices are subject to change)*

## Looking for just pages for individual year sets?

| Item | Retail | AA |
|---|---|---|
| 200GBR1 – 1840-1973 | $74.72 | **$63.51** |
| 200GBR2 – 1974-1996 | $64.65 | **$54.95** |
| 200GBR3 – 1997-2003 | $50.34 | **$42.79** |
| 200GBR4 – 2004-2009 | $64.65 | **$54.95** |
| 200GBR5 – 2010-2015 | $107.05 | **$90.99** |
| 200GBR6 – 2016-2020 | $64.65 | **$54.95** |

# AmosAdvantage.com
# 1-800-572-6885

**ORDERING INFORMATION:** *AA prices apply to paid subscribers of Amos Media titles, or for orders placed online. Prices, terms and product availability subject to change. See AmosAdvantage.com for up-to-date pricing.

# GREAT BRITAIN OFFICES ABROAD

---

## OFFICES IN AFRICA

---

> Catalogue values for unused stamps in this section are for Never Hinged stamps.

### MIDDLE EAST FORCES

For use in Ethiopia, Cyrenaica, Eritrea, the Dodecanese and Somalia

Stamps of Great Britain, 1937-42 Overprinted in Black or Blue Black

**London Printing — ovpt. 14mm long, square dots**

**1942-43   Wmk. 251   Perf. 14½x14**

| | | | | |
|---|---|---|---|---|
| 1 | A101 | 1p scarlet | 3.50 | 4.75 |
| 2 | A101 | 2p orange | 3.00 | 6.00 |
| 3 | A101 | 2½p bright ultra | 3.00 | 2.00 |
| 4 | A101 | 3p dark purple | 2.75 | .35 |
| a. | | Double overprint | | 6,400. |
| 5 | A102 | 5p lt brn (Blk) | 2.75 | 1.00 |
| a. | | Blue black overprint ('43) | 4.25 | .25 |
| 6 | A102 | 6p rose lilac ('43) | .65 | .25 |
| 7 | A102 | 9p dp olive grn ('43) | 1.00 | .25 |
| 8 | A103 | 1sh brown ('43) | .40 | .25 |

**Wmk. 259**
**Perf. 14**

| | | | | |
|---|---|---|---|---|
| 9 | A104 | 2sh6p yel green ('43) | 6.50 | .90 |
| | | Nos. 1-9 (9) | 23.55 | 15.75 |

**Same Overprint in Blue Black on Nos. 259, 261, 262 and 263**

**1943, Jan. 1   Wmk. 251**

| | | | | |
|---|---|---|---|---|
| 10 | A101 | 1p vermilion | 1.50 | .25 |
| 11 | A101 | 2p light orange | 2.25 | 1.25 |
| 12 | A101 | 2½p ultramarine | 2.50 | .25 |
| 13 | A101 | 3p violet | 2.00 | .25 |
| | | Nos. 10-13 (4) | 8.25 | 2.00 |

There were two printings of Nos. 1-5, both issued Mar. 2, 1942, and both black. Nos. 5a and 6-13 compose a third printing, also made in London. On these stamps, issued Jan. 1, 1943, the overprint is 13½mm wide. The 2sh6p overprint is black, the others blue black.

**Same Ovpt. in Black on #250, 251A**

**1947   Wmk. 259   Perf. 14**

| | | | | |
|---|---|---|---|---|
| 14 | A104 | 5sh dull red | 40.00 | 17.00 |
| 15 | A105 | 10sh ultramarine | 60.00 | 8.50 |

In 1950 Nos. 1-15 were declared valid for use in Great Britain. Used values are for stamps postmarked in territory of issue. Others sell for about 25 percent less.

### POSTAGE DUE STAMPS

> Catalogue values for unused stamps in this section are for Never Hinged items.

Postage Due Stamps of Great Britain Overprinted in Blue

**1942   Wmk. 251   Perf. 14x14½**

| | | | | |
|---|---|---|---|---|
| J1 | D1 | ½p emerald | .40 | 17.00 |
| J2 | D1 | 1p carmine rose | .40 | 3.00 |
| J3 | D1 | 2p black brown | 1.75 | 2.75 |
| J4 | D1 | 3p violet | .40 | 4.90 |
| J5 | D1 | 1sh blue | 3.75 | 17.00 |
| | | Nos. J1-J5 (5) | 6.70 | 44.65 |

No. J1-J5 were used in Eritrea.

### FOR USE IN ERITREA

> Catalogue values for unused stamps in this section are for Never Hinged items.

---

**100 Cents = 1 Shilling**

Stamps of Great Britain 1937-42 Surcharged — a

**Perf. 14½x14**

**1948, June -49   Wmk. 251**

| | | | | |
|---|---|---|---|---|
| 1 | A101 | 5c on ½p green (II) | 2.75 | .75 |
| 2 | A101 | 10c on 1p vermilion (II) | 2.00 | 2.75 |
| 3 | A101 | 20c on 2p light org (II) | 3.00 | 2.50 |
| 4 | A101 | 25c on 2½p ultra (II) | 2.00 | .70 |
| 5 | A101 | 30c on 3p violet (II) | 2.50 | 5.00 |
| 6 | A101 | 40c on 5p light brn | 2.75 | 4.75 |
| 7 | A101 | 50c on 6p rose lilac | 2.25 | 1.10 |
| 8 | A103 | 75c on 9p dp ol grn | 3.75 | .85 |
| 9 | A103 | 1sh on 1sh brown | 2.50 | .55 |

Great Britain Nos. 249A, 250 and 251A Surcharged

**Wmk. 259**
**Perf. 14**

| | | | | |
|---|---|---|---|---|
| 10 | A104 | 2sh50c on 2sh6p yel grn | 13.00 | 11.50 |
| 11 | A104 | 5sh on 5sh dl red | 14.00 | 25.00 |
| 12 | A105 | 10sh on 10sh ultra | 30.00 | 25.00 |

**Great Britain No. 245 Surcharged Type "a"**

**Wmk. 251**
**Perf. 14½x14**

| | | | | |
|---|---|---|---|---|
| 13 | A103 | 65c on 8p brt rose ('49) | 6.75 | 2.00 |
| | | Nos. 1-13 (13) | 87.25 | 82.45 |

"B. M. A." stands for British Military Administration.

Stamps of Great Britain 1937-42 Surcharged — c

**1950, Feb. 6**

| | | | | |
|---|---|---|---|---|
| 14 | A101 | 5c on ½p green (II) | 1.50 | 9.25 |
| 15 | A101 | 10c on 1p ver (II) | .45 | 3.50 |
| 16 | A101 | 20c on 2p lt org (II) | 1.50 | .90 |
| 17 | A101 | 25c on 2½p ultra (II) | 1.00 | .70 |
| 18 | A101 | 30c on 3p violet (II) | .45 | 2.50 |
| 19 | A102 | 40c on 5p light brown | 3.00 | 2.00 |
| 20 | A102 | 50c on 6p rose lilac | .45 | .25 |
| 21 | A103 | 65c on 8p bright rose | 6.50 | 1.75 |
| 22 | A103 | 75c on 9p dp ol grn | 2.00 | .30 |
| 23 | A103 | 1sh on 1sh brown | .45 | .25 |

Great Britain Nos. 249A, 250, 251A Surcharged

**Wmk. 259**
**Perf. 14**

| | | | | |
|---|---|---|---|---|
| 24 | A104 | 2sh50c on 2sh6p yel grn | 9.75 | 5.50 |
| 25 | A104 | 5sh on 5sh dl red | 9.75 | 14.00 |
| 26 | A105 | 10sh on 10sh ultra | 80.00 | 70.00 |
| | | Nos. 14-26 (13) | 116.80 | 110.90 |

**Great Britain Nos. 280, 281, 283 and 284 Surcharged Type "c"**

**Perf. 14½x14**

**1951, May 3   Wmk. 251**

| | | | | |
|---|---|---|---|---|
| 27 | A101 | 5c on ½p lt orange | 3.50 | 8.00 |
| 28 | A101 | 10c on 1p ultra | 2.75 | 1.00 |
| 29 | A101 | 20c on 2p lt red brown | 3.50 | .50 |
| 30 | A101 | 25c on 2½p vermilion | 3.50 | .50 |

**Great Britain Nos. 286-288 Surcharged**

---

**Perf. 11x12**

**1951, May 31   Wmk. 259**

| | | | | |
|---|---|---|---|---|
| 31 | A121 | 2sh50c on 2sh6p grn | 21.00 | 42.50 |
| 32 | A121 | 5sh on 5sh dl red | 24.00 | 47.50 |
| 33 | A122 | 10sh on 10sh ultra | 30.00 | 52.50 |
| | | Nos. 27-33 (7) | 88.25 | 152.50 |

Surcharge arranged to fit the design on No. 33.

---

### POSTAGE DUE STAMPS

> Catalogue values for unused stamps in this section are for Never Hinged items.

Great Britain Nos. J26-J29, J32 Surcharged

**1948   Wmk. 251   Perf. 14x14½**

| | | | | |
|---|---|---|---|---|
| J1 | D1 | 5c on ½p emer | 11.00 | 25.00 |
| J2 | D1 | 10c on 1p car rose | 11.00 | 27.50 |
| J3 | D1 | 20c on 2p blk brn | 16.50 | 18.00 |
| J4 | D1 | 30c on 3p violet | 13.00 | 16.50 |
| J5 | D1 | 1sh on 1sh blue | 20.00 | 35.00 |
| a. | | No period after "A" | — | 650.00 |
| | | Nos. J1-J5 (5) | 71.50 | 122.00 |

Great Britain Nos. J26 to J29 and J32 Surcharged

**1950, Feb. 6**

| | | | | |
|---|---|---|---|---|
| J6 | D1 | 5c on ½p emer | 15.50 | 65.00 |
| J7 | D1 | 10c on 1p car rose | 15.50 | 21.00 |
| a. | | "C" of CENTS omitted | 5,000. | |
| | | Lightly hinged | 3,000. | |
| J8 | D1 | 20c on 2p blk brn | 16.00 | 24.00 |
| a. | | No period after "A" | 450.00 | — |
| J9 | D1 | 30c on 3p violet | 19.50 | 45.00 |
| J10 | D1 | 1sh on 1sh blue | 21.00 | 45.00 |
| | | Nos. J6-J10 (5) | 87.50 | 200.00 |

## EAST AFRICAN FORCES

### FOR USE IN SOMALIA (ITALIAN SOMALILAND)

> Catalogue values for unused stamps in this section are for Never Hinged items.

**12 Pence = 1 Shilling**
**100 Cents = 1 Shilling**

Stamps of Great Britain 1938-42 Overprinted in Blue

**Perf. 14½x14**

**1943, Jan. 15   Wmk. 251**

| | | | | |
|---|---|---|---|---|
| 1 | A101 | 1p vermilion | 1.40 | 2.75 |
| 2 | A101 | 2p light orange | 1.75 | 1.75 |
| 3 | A101 | 2½p ultramarine | 2.00 | 3.75 |
| 4 | A101 | 3p violet | 1.50 | .25 |
| 5 | A101 | 5p light brown | 2.25 | .45 |
| 6 | A101 | 6p rose lilac | 2.00 | 1.40 |
| 7 | A103 | 9p dp olive green | 2.50 | 3.75 |
| 8 | A103 | 1sh brown | 3.50 | .25 |

**On Great Britain No. 249A**

**1946   Wmk. 259   Perf. 14**

| | | | | |
|---|---|---|---|---|
| 9 | A104 | 2sh6p yellow green | 35.00 | 12.50 |
| | | Nos. 1-9 (9) | 51.90 | 26.85 |

Stamps of Great Britain, 1937-42 Surcharged

**Perf. 14½x14**

**1948, May 27   Wmk. 251**

| | | | | |
|---|---|---|---|---|
| 10 | A101 | 5c on ½p grn (II) | 1.40 | 2.15 |
| 11 | A101 | 15c on 1½p lt red brn (II) | 2.00 | 17.50 |
| 12 | A101 | 20c on 2p lt org (II) | 3.50 | 6.50 |
| 13 | A101 | 25c on 2½p ultra (II) | 2.50 | 5.00 |

---

| | | | | |
|---|---|---|---|---|
| 14 | A101 | 30c on 3p vio (II) | 2.50 | 10.50 |
| 15 | A101 | 40c on 5p lt brown | 1.40 | .25 |
| 16 | A102 | 50c on 6p rose lilac | .55 | 2.25 |
| 17 | A103 | 75c on 9p dp ol grn | 2.25 | 27.50 |
| 18 | A103 | 1sh on 1sh brown | 1.40 | .25 |

Great Britain Nos. 249A and 250 Surcharged

**Wmk. 259   Perf. 14**

| | | | | |
|---|---|---|---|---|
| 19 | A104 | 2sh50c on 2sh6p yel grn | 11.00 | 29.00 |
| 20 | A104 | 5sh on 5sh dl red | 21.00 | 65.00 |
| | | Nos. 10-20 (11) | 49.50 | 165.90 |

Stamps of Great Britain 1937-42 Surcharged

**Perf. 14½x14**

**1950, Jan. 2   Wmk. 251**

| | | | | |
|---|---|---|---|---|
| 21 | A101 | 5c on ½p grn (II) | .25 | 3.50 |
| 22 | A101 | 15c on 1½p lt red brn (II) | .85 | 19.00 |
| 23 | A101 | 20c on 2p lt org (II) | .85 | 8.50 |
| 24 | A101 | 25c on 2½p ultra (II) | .55 | 13.50 |
| 25 | A101 | 30c on 3p violet (II) | 1.40 | 9.75 |
| 26 | A102 | 40c on 5p light brn | .65 | 2.50 |
| 27 | A102 | 50c on 6p rose lilac | .55 | 1.10 |
| 28 | A103 | 75c on 9p deep ol grn | 2.25 | 13.00 |
| 29 | A103 | 1sh on 1sh brown | .70 | 1.75 |

Great Britain Nos. 249A and 250 Surcharged

**Wmk. 259   Perf. 14**

| | | | | |
|---|---|---|---|---|
| 30 | A104 | 2sh50c on 2sh 6p yel grn | 8.50 | 37.50 |
| 31 | A104 | 5sh on 5sh dull red | 22.00 | 55.00 |
| | | Nos. 21-31 (11) | 38.55 | 165.10 |

### FOR USE IN TRIPOLITANIA

> Catalogue values for unused stamps in this section are for Never Hinged items.

Stamps of Great Britain, 1937-42, Surcharged

**M.A.L. = Military Authority Lire**

**Perf. 14½x14**

**1948, July 1   Wmk. 251**

| | | | | |
|---|---|---|---|---|
| 1 | A101 | 1 l on ½p green (II) | 1.00 | 6.00 |
| 2 | A101 | 2 l on 1p ver (II) | .50 | .25 |
| 3 | A101 | 3 l on 1½p lt red brn (II) | .50 | .50 |
| 4 | A101 | 4 l on 2p lt org (II) | .50 | .90 |
| 5 | A101 | 5 l on 2½p ultra (II) | .50 | .25 |
| 6 | A101 | 6 l on 3p violet (II) | .50 | .45 |
| 7 | A102 | 10 l on 5p lt brown | .50 | .25 |
| 8 | A102 | 12 l on 6p rose lilac | .50 | .25 |
| 9 | A103 | 18 l on 9p dp ol grn | 1.50 | 1.75 |
| 10 | A103 | 24 l on 1sh brown | 2.50 | 3.00 |

Great Britain Nos. 249A, 250 and 251A Surcharged

**Wmk. 259   Perf. 14**

| | | | | |
|---|---|---|---|---|
| 11 | A104 | 60 l on 2sh6p yel grn | 9.25 | 16.50 |
| 12 | A104 | 120 l on 5sh dl red | 28.00 | 30.00 |
| 13 | A105 | 240 l on 10sh ultra | 32.50 | 150.00 |
| | | Nos. 1-13 (13) | 78.25 | 210.10 |

Stamps of Great Britain
1937-42 Surcharged

**Perf. 14½x14**

| | | | | |
|---|---|---|---|---|
| **1950, Feb. 6** | | | **Wmk. 251** | |
| 14 | A101 | 1 l on ½p green (II) | 6.00 | 13.00 |
| 15 | A101 | 2 l on 1p ver (II) | 5.00 | .45 |
| 16 | A101 | 3 l on 1½p lt red brn (II) | 4.00 | 13.00 |
| 17 | A101 | 4 l on 2p lt org (II) | 4.25 | 4.40 |
| 18 | A101 | 5 l on 2½p ultra (II) | 2.25 | .75 |
| 19 | A101 | 6 l on 3p violet (II) | 3.75 | 3.25 |
| 20 | A102 | 10 l on 5p lt brown | 3.75 | 4.00 |
| 21 | A102 | 12 l on 6p rose lilac | 5.00 | .50 |
| 22 | A103 | 18 l on 9p dp ol grn | 7.75 | 2.75 |
| 23 | A103 | 24 l on 1sh brown | 7.25 | 3.75 |

Great Britain Nos.
249A, 250 and 251A
Surcharged

| | | | | |
|---|---|---|---|---|
| | | **Wmk. 259** | **Perf. 14** | |
| 24 | A104 | 60 l on 2sh6p yel grn | 20.00 | 10.00 |
| 25 | A104 | 120 l on 5sh dl red | 40.00 | 42.50 |
| 26 | A105 | 240 l on 10sh ultra | 55.00 | 90.00 |
| | | Nos. 14-26 (13) | 164.00 | 188.35 |

Great Britain Nos. 280-284
Surcharged like Nos. 14-23

**Perf. 14½x14**

| | | | | |
|---|---|---|---|---|
| **1951, May 3** | | | **Wmk. 251** | |
| 27 | A101 | 1 l on ½p lt org | .55 | 10.00 |
| 28 | A101 | 2 l on 1p ultra | .55 | 1.10 |
| 29 | A101 | 3 l on 1½p orange | .55 | 9.25 |
| 30 | A101 | 4 l on 2p lt red brown | .55 | 1.40 |
| 31 | A101 | 5 l on 2½p ver | 1.25 | 8.50 |

Great Britain Nos. 286-288
Surcharged

| | | | | |
|---|---|---|---|---|
| **1951, May 3** | **Wmk. 259** | | **Perf. 11x12** | |
| 32 | A121 | 60 l on 2sh6p grn | 20.00 | 40.00 |
| 33 | A121 | 120 l on 5sh dl red | 20.00 | 45.00 |
| 34 | A122 | 240 l on 10sh ultra | 50.00 | 85.00 |
| | | Nos. 27-34 (8) | 93.45 | 200.25 |

Surcharge arranged to fit the design on No. 34.

---

### POSTAGE DUE STAMPS

> **Catalogue values for unused stamps in this section are for Never Hinged items.**

Great Britain Nos. J26-
J29, J32 Surcharged

| | | | | |
|---|---|---|---|---|
| **1948** | **Wmk. 251** | | **Perf. 14x14½** | |
| J1 | D1 | 1 l on ½p emer | 7.50 | 65.00 |
| J2 | D1 | 2 l on 1p car rose | 2.50 | 57.50 |
| J3 | D1 | 4 l on 2p blk brn | 13.50 | 52.50 |
| a. | | No period after "A" | 170.00 | — |
| b. | | No period after "M" | 325.00 | 375.00 |
| J4 | D1 | 6 l on 3p violet | 8.00 | 30.00 |
| J5 | D1 | 24 l on 1sh blue | 30.00 | 115.00 |
| | | Nos. J1-J5 (5) | 61.50 | 320.00 |

Great Britain Nos. J26-
J29, J32 Surcharged

| | | | | |
|---|---|---|---|---|
| **1950, Feb. 6** | | | | |
| J6 | D1 | 1 l on ½p emer | 17.50 | 140.00 |
| J7 | D1 | 2 l on 1p car rose | 10.00 | 47.50 |
| J8 | D1 | 4 l on 2p blk brn | 12.00 | 65.00 |

| | | | | |
|---|---|---|---|---|
| J9 | D1 | 6 l on 3p violet | 20.00 | 100.00 |
| J10 | D1 | 24 l on 1sh blue | 57.50 | 225.00 |
| | | Nos. J6-J10 (5) | 117.00 | 577.50 |

### CHINA

100 Cents = 1 Dollar

Stamps of Hong Kong,
1912-14, Overprinted

| | | | | |
|---|---|---|---|---|
| **1917** | | **Wmk. 3** | **Perf. 14** | |
| **Ordinary Paper** | | | | |
| 1 | A11 | 1c brown | 15.00 | 1.25 |
| a. | | Broken crown at right | | |
| 2 | A11 | 2c deep green | 17.50 | .25 |
| 3 | A12 | 4c scarlet | 12.00 | .25 |
| 4 | A13 | 6c orange | 9.00 | 1.50 |
| 5 | A12 | 8c gray | 14.00 | 1.40 |
| 6 | A11 | 10c ultramarine | 17.50 | .25 |
| **Chalky Paper** | | | | |
| 7 | A14 | 12c violet, yel | 17.00 | 10.00 |
| 8 | A14 | 20c olive grn & vio | 24.00 | 1.25 |
| 9 | A15 | 25c red vio & dl vio (on #117) | 15.00 | 15.00 |
| 10 | A13 | 30c orange & violet | 47.50 | 10.00 |
| 11 | A14 | 50c black, emerald | 50.00 | 6.00 |
| a. | | 50c blk, blue green, ol back | 75.00 | 1.75 |
| b. | | 50c blk, emerald, ol back | 60.00 | 9.75 |
| 12 | A11 | $1 blue & vio, bl | 80.00 | 2.90 |
| 13 | A12 | $2 black & red | 250.00 | 75.00 |
| 14 | A13 | $3 violet & grn | 675.00 | 275.00 |
| 15 | A14 | $5 red & grn, bl grn, ol back | 375.00 | 375.00 |
| 16 | A13 | $10 blk & vio, red | 750.00 | 750.00 |
| | | Nos. 1-16 (16) | 2,369. | 1,525. |

Stamps of Hong Kong,
1921-26, Overprinted

| | | | | |
|---|---|---|---|---|
| **1922-27** | **Ordinary Paper** | | **Wmk. 4** | |
| 17 | A11 | 1c brown | 3.25 | 7.00 |
| 18 | A11 | 2c green | 8.00 | 2.00 |
| 19 | A12 | 4c scarlet | 20.00 | 3.00 |
| 20 | A13 | 6c orange | 7.00 | 6.50 |
| 21 | A12 | 8c gray | 14.00 | 17.50 |
| 22 | A11 | 10c ultramarine | 22.00 | 4.25 |
| **Chalky Paper** | | | | |
| 23 | A14 | 20c ol grn & vio | 22.00 | 4.75 |
| 24 | A15 | 25c red violet & dull vio | 26.00 | 80.00 |
| 25 | A14 | 50c blk, emerald ('27) | 55.00 | 325.00 |
| 26 | A11 | $1 ultra & vio, bl | 75.00 | 75.00 |
| 27 | A14 | $2 black & red | 200.00 | 250.00 |
| | | Nos. 17-27 (11) | 452.25 | 775.00 |

### MOROCCO

100 Centimos = 1 Peseta
12 Pence = 1 Shilling
20 Shillings = 1 Pound
100 Centimes = 1 Franc

These stamps were issued for various purposes:

a — For general use at the British Post Offices throughout Morocco.

b — For use in the Spanish Zone of Northern Morocco.

c — For use in the French Zone of Southern Morocco.

d — For use in the International Zone of Tangier.

For convenience these stamps are listed in four groups according to the coinage expressed or surcharged on the stamps, namely:

#1-108: Value expressed in Spanish currency.

#201-280: Value in British currency.

#401-440: Value in French currency.

#501-611: Stamps overprinted "Tangier."

**Spanish Currency**

Gibraltar Stamps of 1889-
95 Overprinted

| | | | | |
|---|---|---|---|---|
| **1898** | | **Wmk. 2** | **Perf. 14** | |
| **Black Overprint** | | | | |
| 1 | A11 | 5c green | 5.00 | 6.00 |
| 2 | A11 | 10c carmine rose | 10.00 | 3.00 |
| b. | | Double overprint | 950.00 | 800.00 |

| | | | | |
|---|---|---|---|---|
| 3 | A11 | 20c olive green | 17.50 | 12.50 |
| 4 | A11 | 25c ultramarine | 8.00 | 2.00 |
| 5 | A11 | 40c orange brown | 7.00 | 3.75 |
| 6 | A11 | 50c violet | 16.00 | 22.00 |
| 7 | A11 | 1pe bister & blue | 20.00 | 30.00 |
| 8 | A11 | 2pe blk & car rose | 32.50 | 35.00 |
| | | Nos. 1-8 (8) | 116.00 | 114.25 |
| **Dark Blue Overprint** | | | | |
| 9 | A11 | 40c orange brown | 50.00 | 40.00 |
| 10 | A11 | 50c violet | 22.50 | 20.00 |
| 11 | A11 | 1pe bister & blue | 225.00 | 400.00 |
| **Inverted "V" for "A"** | | | | |
| 1a | A11 | 5c | 70.00 | 90.00 |
| 2a | A11 | 10c | 300.00 | 350.00 |
| 3a | A11 | 20c | 150.00 | 150.00 |
| 4a | A11 | 25c | 175.00 | 160.00 |
| 5a | A11 | 40c | 225.00 | 250.00 |
| 6a | A11 | 50c | 350.00 | 450.00 |
| 7a | A11 | 1pe | 350.00 | 450.00 |
| 8a | A11 | 2pe | 450.00 | 550.00 |

**Overprinted in Black**

(Narrower "M," ear of "g" horiz.)

| | | | | |
|---|---|---|---|---|
| **1899** | | | | |
| 12 | A11 | 5c green | 3.75 | 3.75 |
| 13 | A11 | 10c carmine rose | 5.00 | 4.00 |
| 14 | A11 | 20c olive green | 14.00 | 4.75 |
| 15 | A11 | 25c ultramarine | 10.00 | 1.45 |
| 16 | A11 | 40c orange brown | 47.50 | 63.00 |
| 17 | A11 | 50c violet | 15.00 | 8.50 |
| 18 | A11 | 1pe bister & blue | 32.50 | 57.50 |
| 19 | A11 | 2pe blk & car rose | 62.50 | 75.00 |
| | | Nos. 12-19 (8) | 190.25 | 217.95 |
| **"M" with long serif** | | | | |
| 12a | A11 | 5c | 13.00 | 22.50 |
| 13a | A11 | 10c | 17.00 | 22.50 |
| 14a | A11 | 20c | 72.50 | 69.00 |
| 15a | A11 | 25c | 62.50 | 69.00 |
| 16a | A11 | 40c | 315.00 | 375.00 |
| 17a | A11 | 50c | 150.00 | 160.00 |
| 18a | A11 | 1pe | 205.00 | 345.00 |
| 19a | A11 | 2pe | 400.00 | 425.00 |

**Type of Gibraltar, 1903, with Value in Spanish Currency, Overprinted**

| | | | | |
|---|---|---|---|---|
| **1903-05** | | | | |
| 20 | A12 | 5c gray grn & bl grn | 11.00 | 3.25 |
| 21 | A12 | 10c violet, red | 9.75 | .45 |
| 22 | A12 | 20c gray grn & car rose ('04) | 20.00 | 57.50 |
| 23 | A12 | 25c vio & blk, bl | 9.25 | .35 |
| 24 | A12 | 50c pur & vio | 75.00 | 375.00 |
| 25 | A12 | 1pe blk & car rose | 30.00 | 315.00 |
| 26 | A12 | 2pe black & ultra | 45.00 | 285.00 |
| | | Nos. 20-26 (7) | 200.00 | 1,037. |
| **"M" with long serif** | | | | |
| 20a | A12 | 5c | 69.00 | 72.50 |
| 21a | A12 | 10c | 69.00 | 50.00 |
| 22a | A12 | 20c | 170.00 | 315.00 |
| 23a | A12 | 25c | 72.50 | 55.00 |
| 24a | A12 | 50c | 425.00 | — |
| 25a | A12 | 1pe | 250.00 | — |
| 26a | A12 | 2pe | 315.00 | — |

| | | | | |
|---|---|---|---|---|
| **1905-06** | **Wmk. 3** | | **Chalky Paper** | |
| 27 | A12 | 5c gray grn & bl grn | 20.00 | 12.50 |
| 28 | A12 | 10c violet, red | 22.50 | 1.75 |
| 29 | A12 | 20c gray grn & car rose ('06) | 9.00 | 35.00 |
| 30 | A12 | 25c vio & blk, bl ('06) | 65.00 | 8.00 |
| 31 | A12 | 50c pur & vio | 10.00 | 60.00 |
| 32 | A12 | 1pe blk & car rose | 50.00 | 87.50 |
| 33 | A12 | 2pe black & ultra | 27.50 | 37.50 |
| | | Nos. 27-33 (7) | 204.00 | 242.25 |

No. 29 is on ordinary paper. Nos. 27 and 28 are on both ordinary and chalky paper.

| | | | | |
|---|---|---|---|---|
| **"M" with long serif** | | | | |
| 27a | A12 | 5c | 135.00 | 105.00 |
| 28a | A12 | 10c | 115.00 | 47.50 |
| 29a | A12 | 20c | 95.00 | 250.00 |
| 30a | A12 | 25c | 550.00 | 195.00 |
| 31a | A12 | 50c | 205.00 | 460.00 |
| 32a | A12 | 1pe | 370.00 | 575.00 |
| 33a | A12 | 2pe | 285.00 | 345.00 |

Numerous other minor overprint varieties exist of Nos. 1-33.

**British Stamps of 1902-10 Surcharged in Spanish Currency**

a                                b

| | | | | |
|---|---|---|---|---|
| **1907-10** | | | **Wmk. 30** | |
| 34(a) | A66 | 5c on ½p pale grn | 12.50 | .25 |
| 35(a) | A66 | 10c on 1p car | 20.00 | .25 |
| 36(a) | A67 | 15c on 1½p vio & grn | 7.50 | .25 |
| a. | | "1" of "15" omitted | 7,500. | |
| 37(a) | A68 | 20c on 2p grn & car | 6.00 | 2.50 |
| 38(a) | A66 | 25c on 2½p ultra | 3.00 | .25 |
| 39(a) | A70 | 40c on 4p brn & grn | 3.00 | 6.00 |
| 40(a) | A70 | 40c on 4p org | 1.25 | 2.00 |
| 41(a) | A71 | 50c on 5p lil & ultra | 10.00 | 10.00 |
| 42(a) | A73 | 1pe on 10p car rose & vio | 20.00 | 22.50 |
| **Wmk. 31** | | | | |
| 43(b) | A75 | 3pe on 2sh6p vio | 24.00 | 40.00 |
| 44(b) | A76 | 6pe on 5sh car rose | 32.50 | 47.50 |
| 45(b) | A77 | 12pe on 10sh ultra | 75.00 | 80.00 |
| | | Nos. 34-45 (12) | 214.75 | 211.50 |

Nos. 36-37, 39-43 are on chalky paper.

Great Britain Nos. 153, 154 and 148
Surcharged

| | | | | |
|---|---|---|---|---|
| **1912** | | **Wmk. 30** | **Perf. 15x14** | |
| 46(a) | A80 | 5c on ½p yel grn | 6.00 | .25 |
| 47(a) | A81 | 10c on 1p scarlet | 1.75 | .25 |
| 48(a) | A66 | 25c on 2½p ultra | 65.00 | 62.50 |
| | | Nos. 46-48 (3) | 72.75 | 63.00 |

**British Stamps of 1912-18 Surcharged in Black or Carmine**

c                                d

e

| | | | | |
|---|---|---|---|---|
| **1914-18** | | | **Wmk. 33** | |
| 49 | A82(a) | 5c on ½p grn | 3.50 | .25 |
| 50 | A83(d) | 10c on 1p scar | 5.75 | .25 |
| 51 | A84(c) | 15c on 1½p red brn ('15) | 1.75 | .25 |
| 52 | A85(d) | 20c on 2p grn (I) | 2.00 | .25 |
| 53 | A86(d) | 25c on 2½p ultra | 4.25 | .25 |
| 54 | A90(d) | 1pe on 10p 1t bl | 11.50 | 20.00 |
| **Wmk. 34** | | | | |
| **Perf. 11x12** | | | | |
| 55 | A91(e) | 3pe on 2sh6p lt brn | 57.50 | 160.00 |
| a. | | 3pe on 2sh6p dark brown | 57.50 | 160.00 |
| 56 | A91(e) | 6pe on 5sh car | 45.00 | 62.50 |
| 57 | A91(e) | 12pe on 10sh dk bl (C) | 150.00 | 225.00 |
| a. | | 12pe on 10sh blue | 125.00 | 225.00 |
| | | Nos. 49-57 (9) | 281.25 | 468.75 |

Great Britain Nos. 159, 165
Surcharged in Spanish Currency

f                                g

| | | | | |
|---|---|---|---|---|
| **1917-23** | **Wmk. 33** | | **Perf. 15x14** | |
| 58 | A82(f) | 3c on ½p grn | 4.00 | 17.00 |
| 59 | A88(g) | 40c on 4p sl green | 12.50 | 4.50 |

Great Britain Nos. 189, 191, 179
Surcharged in Spanish Currency

| | | | | |
|---|---|---|---|---|
| **1926** | | | **Wmk. 35** | |
| 60 | A84(c) | 15c on 1½p red brn | 8.50 | 26.50 |
| 61 | A86(d) | 25c on 2½p ultra | 9.00 | 2.75 |
| **Wmk. 34** | | | | |
| **Perf. 11x12** | | | | |
| 62 | A91(e) | 3pe on 2sh6p brn | 34.50 | 107.50 |
| | | Nos. 60-62 (3) | 52.00 | 136.75 |

British Stamps of 1924 Surcharged
in Spanish Currency

| | | | | |
|---|---|---|---|---|
| **1929-31** | | **Wmk. 35** | **Perf. 15x14** | |
| 63 | A82(a) | 5c on ½p grn ('31) | 11.50 | 40.00 |
| 64 | A83(d) | 10c on 1p scar | 45.00 | 45.00 |
| 65 | A85(d) | 20c on 2p org (II) ('31) | 3.50 | 17.00 |

| 66 | A88(g) | 40c on 4p sl grn | | |
|---|---|---|---|---|
| | | ('30) | 9.75 | 2.75 |
| | | Nos. 63-66 (4) | 69.75 | 104.75 |

### Silver Jubilee Issue

Great Britain Nos. 226-229 Srchd. in Blue or Red

**1935, May 8** — *Perf. 14½x14*

| 67 | A98 | 5c on ½p dk grn | 1.10 | 1.20 |
|---|---|---|---|---|
| 68 | A98 | 10c on 1p car | 2.50 | 2.50 |
| a. | | Pair, one reading "CEN- | | |
| | | TIMES" | 1,900. | 2,875. |
| 69 | A98 | 15c on 1½p red brn | 7.00 | 25.00 |
| 70 | A98 | 25c on 2½p ultra (R) | 3.00 | 2.00 |
| | | Nos. 67-70 (4) | 13.60 | 30.70 |

25th anniv. of the reign of King George V.

> Catalogue values for unused stamps in this section, from this point to the end of the section, are for Never Hinged items.

Great Britain Nos. 210-214, 216, 219 Surcharged in Spanish Currency

**1935-37** — *Photo.*

| 71 | A97(a) | 5c on ½p dk grn | | |
|---|---|---|---|---|
| | | ('36) | 1.50 | 22.50 |
| 72 | A97(d) | 10c on 1p car | 5.00 | 22.50 |
| 73 | A97(c) | 15c on 1½p red | | |
| | | brn | 12.50 | 3.00 |
| 74 | A97(d) | 20c on 2p red org ('36) | .60 | .30 |
| 75 | A97(d) | 25c on 2½p ultra ('36) | 1.00 | 12.50 |
| 76 | A97(d) | 40c on 4p dk sl grn ('37) | .40 | 7.50 |
| 77 | A97(d) | 1pe on 10p Prus bl ('37) | 5.00 | 4.00 |
| | | Nos. 71-77 (7) | 26.00 | 72.30 |

Great Britain Nos. 230-233 Surcharged

### "MOROCCO" 14mm

**1936** — *Wmk. 250*

| 78 | A99 | 5c on ½p dk green | .25 | .25 |
|---|---|---|---|---|
| 79 | A99 | 10c on 1p crimson | .40 | 1.75 |
| a. | | "Morocco" 15mm long | 4.00 | 16.00 |
| 80 | A99 | 15c on 1½p red brown | .25 | .25 |
| 81 | A99 | 25c on 2½p brt ultra | .25 | .25 |
| | | Nos. 78-81 (4) | 1.15 | 2.50 |

### Great Britain #234 Surcharged in Blue

*Perf. 14½x14*

**1937, May 13** — *Wmk. 251*

| 82 | A100 | 15c on 1½p purple brn | .80 | .60 |
|---|---|---|---|---|

Coronation of George VI and Elizabeth.

Great Britain Nos. 235-237, 239, 241, 244 Surcharged in Blue or Black

h

**1937-40**

| 83 | A101 | 5c on ½p dp grn (Bl) | 1.10 | .35 |
|---|---|---|---|---|
| 84 | A101 | 10c on 1p scarlet | .90 | .25 |
| 85 | A101 | 15c on 1½p red brown (Bl) | 3.00 | .25 |
| 86 | A101 | 25c on 2½p brt ultra | 1.90 | 1.40 |
| 87 | A102 | 40c on 4p gray grn ('40) | 45.00 | 20.00 |
| 88 | A103 | 70c on 7p emer ('40) | 4.00 | 27.50 |
| | | Nos. 83-88 (6) | 55.90 | 49.75 |

Great Britain Nos. 252-254, 256 Surcharged in Blue or Black

**1940, May 6**

| 89 | A106 | 5c on ½p dp grn (Bl) | .35 | 2.50 |
|---|---|---|---|---|
| 90 | A106 | 10c on 1p scarlet | 4.25 | 5.50 |
| 91 | A106 | 15c on 1½p red brn | .60 | 7.00 |
| 92 | A106 | 25c on 2½p brt ultra | 1.00 | 5.50 |
| | | Nos. 89-92 (4) | 6.20 | 20.50 |

Centenary of the postage stamp.

### Great Britain Nos. 267 and 268 Surcharged in Black

i              j

*Perf. 14½x14, 14x14½*

**1948, Apr. 26** — *Wmk. 251*

| 93 | A109(i) | 25c on 2½p | 1.10 | .75 |
|---|---|---|---|---|
| 94 | A110(j) | 45pe on £1 | 16.00 | 25.00 |

25th anniv. of the marriage of King George VI and Queen Elizabeth.

### Great Britain Nos. 271-274 Surcharged "MOROCCO AGENCIES" and New Value

**1948, July 29** — *Perf. 14½x14*

| 95 | A113 | 25c on 2½p brt ultra | .55 | 1.40 |
|---|---|---|---|---|
| 96 | A114 | 30c on 3p dp vio | .55 | 1.40 |
| 97 | A115 | 60c on 6p red vio | .55 | 1.40 |
| 98 | A116 | 1.20pe on 1sh dk brn | .55 | 1.40 |
| a. | | Double surcharge | 1,250. | |
| | | Nos. 95-98 (4) | 2.20 | 5.60 |

1948 Olympic Games, Wembley, July-Aug. A square of dots obliterates the original denomination on No. 98.

### Great Britain Nos. 280-282, 284-285, 247 Surcharged Type "h"

**1951-52** — *Wmk. 251* — *Perf. 14½x14*

| 99 | A101 | 5c on ½p lt org | 1.80 | 8.00 |
|---|---|---|---|---|
| 100 | A101 | 10c on 1p ultra | 3.00 | 10.00 |
| 101 | A101 | 15c on 1½p green | 1.60 | 27.50 |
| 102 | A101 | 25c on 2½p ver | 1.50 | 27.00 |
| 103 | A102 | 40c on 4p ultra ('52) | .80 | 14.50 |
| 104 | A103 | 1pe on 10p ryl bl ('52) | 2.50 | 14.50 |
| | | Nos. 99-104 (6) | 11.20 | 101.50 |

### Great Britain Nos. 292-293 Surcharged Type "h"

**1954-55** — *Wmk. 298*

| 105 | A126 | 5c on ½c red org | .30 | 4.50 |
|---|---|---|---|---|
| 106 | A126 | 10c on 1p red ('55) | .75 | 3.25 |

### Great Britain Nos. 317 and 323 Surcharged type "h"

**1956** — *Wmk. 308* — *Perf. 14x14½*

| 107 | A126 | 5c on ½p red org | .25 | 6.50 |
|---|---|---|---|---|
| 108 | A128 | 40c on 4p ultra | .60 | 6.50 |

### BRITISH CURRENCY

Stamps of Morocco Agencies were accepted for postage in Great Britain, starting in mid-1950. Examples with contemporaneous Morocco cancellations sell for more.

### British Stamps of 1902-11 Overprinted

a              b

Overprint "a" 14½mm long

**1907-12** — *Wmk. 30* — *Perf. 14*
### Ordinary Paper

| 201 | A66 | ½p pale yel grn | 2.50 | 13.00 |
|---|---|---|---|---|
| 202 | A66 | 1p carmine | 9.00 | 9.50 |

### Chalky Paper

| 203 | A68 | 2p green & car | 11.50 | 6.25 |
|---|---|---|---|---|
| 204 | A70 | 4p brown & grn | 4.25 | 4.50 |
| 205 | A70 | 4p orange ('12) | 11.50 | 20.00 |
| a. | | Perf. 15x14 | 55.00 | 40.00 |
| 206 | A66 | 6p dull vio | 17.00 | 35.00 |
| 207 | A74 | 1sh car rose & grn | 30.00 | 17.50 |

### Overprinted Type "b" Wmk. 31

| 208 | A75 | 2sh6p violet | 92.50 | 160.00 |
|---|---|---|---|---|
| | | Nos. 201-208 (8) | 178.25 | 265.75 |

### British Stamps of 1912-18 Overprinted Type "a"
*Perf. 14½x14, 15x14*

**1914-21** — *Wmk. 33*

| 209 | A82 | ½p green ('18) | 7.50 | .55 |
|---|---|---|---|---|
| 210 | A83 | 1p scarlet ('17) | 2.00 | .25 |
| 211 | A84 | 1½p red brn ('21) | 7.50 | 17.50 |
| 212 | A85 | 2p orange ('18) | 5.00 | .70 |
| 213 | A87 | 3p violet ('21) | 1.75 | .75 |
| 214 | A88 | 4p slate grn ('21) | 8.50 | 1.40 |
| 215 | A89 | 6p dull vio ('21) | 10.00 | 17.50 |
| 216 | A90 | 1sh bister ('17) | 15.00 | 2.25 |

c

*Wmk. 34* — *Perf. 11x12*

| 217 | A91 | 2sh6p violet | 60.00 | 45.00 |
|---|---|---|---|---|
| | | Nos. 209-217 (9) | 117.25 | 85.90 |

### Same Overprint on Great Britain Nos. 179-180

**1925-31**

| 218 | A91 | 2sh6p gray brown | 52.50 | 35.00 |
|---|---|---|---|---|
| 219 | A91 | 5sh car rose ('31) | 62.50 | 135.00 |

### British Stamps of 1924 Overprinted Type "a" (14½mm long)

**1925-31** — *Wmk. 35* — *Perf. 15x14*

| 220 | A82 | ½p green | 3.50 | .55 |
|---|---|---|---|---|
| 221 | A84 | 1½p red brn ('31) | 13.50 | 18.00 |
| 222 | A85 | 2p dp org (Die II) | 2.50 | 1.10 |
| 223 | A86 | 2½p ultra | 10.00 | 4.00 |
| 224 | A89 | 6p red vio ('31) | 4.00 | 10.00 |
| 225 | A90 | 1sh bister | 19.00 | 7.00 |
| | | Nos. 220-225 (6) | 52.50 | 40.65 |

### Silver Jubilee Issue

Great Britain Nos. 226-229 Overprinted in Blue or Red

**1935, May 8** — *Perf. 14½x14*

| 226 | A98 | ½p dark green (Bl) | 1.40 | 7.50 |
|---|---|---|---|---|
| 227 | A98 | 1p carmine (Bl) | 1.40 | 15.00 |
| 228 | A98 | 1½p red brown (Bl) | 6.00 | 30.00 |
| 229 | A98 | 2½p ultramarine (R) | 7.50 | 3.50 |
| | | Nos. 226-229 (4) | 16.30 | 56.00 |

25th anniversary of the reign of King George V.

### British Stamps of 1924 Overprinted Type "a" (15½mm long)

**1935-36**

| 230 | A82 | ½p green | 25.00 | 75.00 |
|---|---|---|---|---|
| 231 | A86 | 2½p ultra | 110.00 | 20.00 |
| 232 | A88 | 4p slate green | 14.00 | 47.50 |
| 233 | A89 | 6p red violet | 2.00 | .70 |
| 234 | A90 | 1sh bister | 62.50 | 70.00 |
| | | Nos. 230-234 (5) | 213.50 | 213.20 |

### British Stamps of 1934-36 Overprinted "MOROCCO AGENCIES"

**1935-36**

| 235 | A97 | 1p carmine | 3.50 | 25.00 |
|---|---|---|---|---|
| 236 | A97 | 1½p red brn ('36) | 6.00 | 32.50 |
| 237 | A97 | 2p red org ('36) | 1.40 | 20.00 |
| 238 | A97 | 2½p ultra ('36) | 1.60 | 4.75 |
| 239 | A97 | 3p dk vio ('36) | .55 | .35 |
| 240 | A97 | 4p dk sl grn ('36) | .55 | .35 |
| 241 | A97 | 1sh bis brn ('36) | 1.00 | 10.00 |

### Overprinted Type "c" Wmk. 34
*Perf. 11x12*

| 242 | A91 | 2sh6p brown | 62.50 | 85.00 |
|---|---|---|---|---|
| 243 | A91 | 5sh car ('37) | 35.00 | 160.00 |
| | | Nos. 235-243 (9) | 112.10 | 337.95 |

> Catalogue values for unused stamps in this section, from this point to the end of the section, are for Never Hinged items.

Great Britain Nos. 231, 233 Overprinted

### "MOROCCO" 14mm

**1936** — *Wmk. 250* — *Perf. 14½x14*

| 244 | A99 | 1p crimson | .25 | .30 |
|---|---|---|---|---|
| a. | | "Morocco" 15mm long | 7.00 | 27.50 |
| 245 | A99 | 2½p bright ultra | .25 | .25 |
| a. | | "Morocco" 15mm long | 1.10 | 6.00 |

Great Britain Nos. 258-263, 241-248, 266, 249A-250 Overprinted "MOROCCO AGENCIES" (14½mm long)

**1949, Aug. 16** — *Wmk. 251*

| 246 | A101 | ½p green | 2.00 | 8.00 |
|---|---|---|---|---|
| 247 | A101 | 1p vermilion | 3.00 | 10.00 |
| 248 | A101 | 1½p lt red brown | 3.00 | 9.50 |
| 249 | A101 | 2p lt orange | 3.50 | 12.50 |
| 250 | A101 | 2½p ultra | 3.00 | 12.50 |
| 251 | A101 | 3p violet | 1.40 | 2.75 |
| 252 | A102 | 4p gray green | .55 | 1.40 |
| 253 | A102 | 5p lt brown | 2.75 | 16.00 |
| 254 | A102 | 6p rose lilac | 1.40 | 2.25 |
| 255 | A103 | 7p emerald | .55 | 18.00 |
| 256 | A103 | 8p brt rose | 2.75 | 7.50 |
| 257 | A103 | 9p dp olive grn | .55 | 11.00 |
| 258 | A103 | 10p royal blue | .55 | 11.00 |
| 259 | A103 | 11p violet brn | .65 | 10.00 |
| 260 | A103 | 1sh brown | 3.00 | 7.00 |

### "MOROCCO AGENCIES" 17½mm long
Wmk. 259
*Perf. 14*

| 261 | A104 | 2sh6p yellow grn | 20.00 | 42.50 |
|---|---|---|---|---|
| 262 | A104 | 5sh dull red | 37.50 | 70.00 |
| | | Nos. 246-262 (17) | 86.15 | 255.40 |

Great Britain Nos. 280-284, 286-287 Overprinted "MOROCCO AGENCIES" (14½mm long)
*Perf. 14½x14*

**1951, May 3** — *Wmk. 251*

| 263 | A101 | ½p lt orange | 2.00 | 1.00 |
|---|---|---|---|---|
| 264 | A101 | 1p ultra | 2.00 | 1.50 |
| 265 | A101 | 1½p green | 2.00 | 12.50 |
| 266 | A101 | 2p lt red brown | 2.25 | 7.75 |
| 267 | A101 | 2½p vermilion | 2.25 | 7.50 |

### "MOROCCO AGENCIES" 17½mm long
Wmk. 259
*Perf. 11x12*

| 268 | A121 | 2sh6p green | 15.00 | 27.50 |
|---|---|---|---|---|
| 269 | A121 | 5sh dull red | 17.50 | 30.00 |
| | | Nos. 263-269 (7) | 43.00 | 87.75 |

Great Britain Nos. 292-296, 298-300, 302 and 306 Overprinted "MOROCCO AGENCIES" (14½mm long)

**1952-55** — *Wmk. 298* — *Perf. 14½x14*

| 270 | A126 | ½p red orange | .25 | .25 |
|---|---|---|---|---|
| 271 | A126 | 1p ultramarine | .25 | 1.50 |
| 272 | A126 | 1½p green ('52) | .25 | .25 |
| 273 | A126 | 2p red brown | .30 | 2.25 |
| 274 | A127 | 2½p scarlet ('52) | .25 | 1.00 |
| 275 | A128 | 4p ultra ('55) | 4.25 | 5.00 |
| 276 | A129 | 5p light brown | .50 | 1.40 |
| 277 | A129 | 6p lilac rose ('55) | 1.25 | 4.00 |
| 278 | A130 | 8p bright rose | .50 | 1.25 |
| 279 | A131 | 1sh brown | .50 | 1.75 |
| | | Nos. 270-279 (10) | 8.30 | 18.65 |

### Same Ovpt. on Great Britain No. 321

**1956** — *Wmk. 308*

| 280 | A127 | 2½p scarlet | 2.50 | 6.00 |
|---|---|---|---|---|

## French Currency

British Stamps of 1912-22 Surcharged in French Currency in Red or Black

h

i

| | | | Perf. 14½x14, 15x14 | | |
|---|---|---|---|---|---|
| **1917-24** | | | | **Wmk. 33** | |
| 401 | A82(h) | 3c on ½p grn (R) | | 3.00 | 2.75 |
| 402 | A82(h) | 5c on ½p green | | .60 | .25 |
| 403 | A83(h) | 10c on 1p scarlet | | 4.75 | .30 |
| 404 | A84(h) | 15c on 1½p red brn | | 4.25 | .25 |
| 405 | A86(h) | 25c on 2½p ultra | | 1.25 | .25 |
| 406 | A88(h) | 40c on 4p slate grn | | 1.75 | .25 |
| 407 | A89(h) | 50c on 5p yel brn ('23) | | .75 | 2.50 |
| 408 | A90(h) | 75c on 9p ol grn ('24) | | .80 | .60 |
| 409 | A90(i) | 1fr on 10p lt blue | | 12.50 | 4.00 |
| | | Nos. 401-409 (9) | | 29.65 | 11.15 |

### Great Britain No. 179 Surcharged

k

| | | | | | |
|---|---|---|---|---|---|
| **1924** | | **Wmk. 34** | | **Perf. 11x12** | |
| 410 | A91(k) | 3fr on 2sh6p brn | | 6.50 | 2.50 |

### British Stamps of 1924 Surcharged in French Currency as in 1917-24

| | | | | | |
|---|---|---|---|---|---|
| **1925-26** | | **Wmk. 35** | | **Perf. 15x14** | |
| 411 | A82(h) | 5c on ½p green | | .25 | 6.00 |
| 412 | A83(h) | 10c on 1p scarlet | | .25 | 1.75 |
| 413 | A84(h) | 15c on 1½p red brn | | 2.50 | 1.25 |
| 414 | A86(h) | 25c on 2½p ultra | | 3.75 | .35 |
| 415 | A88(h) | 40c on 4p sl green | | .60 | .70 |
| 416 | A89(h) | 50c on 5p yel brn | | 1.30 | .25 |
| 417 | A90(h) | 75c on 9p ol green | | 15.00 | .25 |
| 418 | A90(i) | 1fr on 10p dl blue | | 1.50 | .25 |
| | | Nos. 411-418 (8) | | 25.15 | 10.80 |

### Great Britain Nos. 180, 198 and 200 Surcharged type "k"

| | | | | | |
|---|---|---|---|---|---|
| **1932** | | **Wmk. 34** | | **Perf. 11x12** | |
| 419 | A91 | 6fr on 5sh car rose | | 40.00 | 55.00 |

| | | | | | |
|---|---|---|---|---|---|
| **1934** | | **Wmk. 35** | | **Perf. 14½x14** | |
| 420 | A90 | 90c on 9p ol green | | 21.00 | 15.00 |
| 421 | A90 | 1.50fr on 1sh bister | | 19.00 | 2.00 |

### Silver Jubilee Issue

Great Britain Nos. 226-229 Surcharged in Blue or Red

| | | | | | |
|---|---|---|---|---|---|
| **1935, May 8** | | | | **Perf. 14½x14** | |
| 422 | A98 | 5c on ½p dk green | | .25 | .25 |
| 423 | A98 | 10c on 1p carmine | | 6.00 | .60 |
| 424 | A98 | 15c on 1½p red brn | | 2.75 | 2.75 |
| 425 | A98 | 25c on 2½p ultra (R) | | .35 | .35 |
| | | Nos. 422-425 (4) | | 9.35 | 3.95 |

25th anniv. of the reign of King George V.

### British Stamps of 1934-36 Surcharged Types "h" or "k"

| | | | Perf. 14½x14 | | |
|---|---|---|---|---|---|
| **1935-37** | | **Photo.** | | **Wmk. 35** | |
| 426 | A97(h) | 5c on ½p dk grn | | .65 | 8.00 |
| 427 | A97(h) | 10c on 1p car ('36) | | .30 | .25 |
| 428 | A97(h) | 15c on 1½p red brn | | 12.00 | 5.25 |
| 429 | A97(h) | 25c on 2½p ultra | | .25 | .25 |
| 430 | A97(h) | 40c on 4p dk sl grn | | .25 | .25 |
| 431 | A97(h) | 50c on 5p yel brn | | .25 | .25 |
| 432 | A97(h) | 90c on 9p dk ol grn | | .65 | 1.75 |
| 433 | A97(k) | 1fr on 10p Prus bl | | .25 | .25 |
| 434 | A97(h) | 1.50fr on 1sh bister brn ('37) | | .65 | 3.25 |

### Waterlow Printing

| | | | | | |
|---|---|---|---|---|---|
| | | **Wmk. 34** | | **Perf. 11x12** | |
| 435 | A91(k) | 3fr on 2sh6p brn | | 5.00 | 11.00 |
| 436 | A91(k) | 6fr on 5sh car ('36) | | 11.00 | 22.50 |
| | | Nos. 426-436 (11) | | 31.25 | 53.00 |

### Great Britain Nos. 230, 232 Surcharged

| | | | | | |
|---|---|---|---|---|---|
| **1936** | | **Wmk. 250** | | **Perf. 14½x14** | |
| 437 | A99 | 5c on ½p dark green | | .25 | .25 |
| 438 | A99 | 15c on 1½p red brown | | .25 | .25 |

### Great Britain No. 234 Surcharged in Blue

| | | | | | |
|---|---|---|---|---|---|
| **1937, May 13** | | | | **Wmk. 251** | |
| 439 | A100 | 15c on 1½p pur brn | | .50 | .25 |

Coronation of George VI and Elizabeth.

### Great Britain No. 235 Surcharged in Blue

| | | | | |
|---|---|---|---|---|
| **1937** | | | | |
| 440 | A101 | 5c on ½p deep green | 5.50 | 6.00 |

### For Use in the International Zone of Tangier

### Great Britain Nos. 187-190 Overprinted in Black — a

| | | | | | |
|---|---|---|---|---|---|
| **1927** | | **Wmk. 35** | | **Perf. 15x14** | |
| 501 | A82 | ½p green | | 7.50 | .25 |
| 502 | A83 | 1p scarlet | | 10.00 | .25 |
| 503 | A84 | 1½p red brown | | 8.00 | 12.50 |
| 504 | A85 | 2p orange (II) | | 3.00 | .25 |
| | | Nos. 501-504 (4) | | 28.50 | 13.25 |

### Same Overprint on Great Britain Nos. 210-212

| | | | Perf. 14½x14 | | |
|---|---|---|---|---|---|
| **1934-35** | | **Photo.** | | | |
| 505 | A97 | ½p dark green | | 1.00 | 3.00 |
| 506 | A97 | 1p carmine | | 12.00 | 3.75 |
| 507 | A97 | 1½p red brown | | .60 | .25 |
| | | Nos. 505-507 (3) | | 13.60 | 7.00 |

### Silver Jubilee Issue

Great Britain Nos. 226-228 Overprinted in Blue

b

| | | | | |
|---|---|---|---|---|
| **1935, May 8** | | | | |
| 508 | A98 | ½p dark green | 2.50 | 9.00 |
| 509 | A98 | 1p carmine | 22.50 | 22.50 |
| 510 | A98 | 1½p red brown | 1.00 | 2.00 |
| | | Nos. 508-510 (3) | 26.00 | 33.50 |

25th anniv. of the reign of King George V.

### Great Britain Nos. 230-232 Overprinted Type "a"

| | | | | |
|---|---|---|---|---|
| **1936** | | | | **Wmk. 250** |
| 511 | A99 | ½p dark green | .25 | .25 |
| 512 | A99 | 1p crimson | .25 | .25 |
| 513 | A99 | 1½p red brown | .25 | .25 |
| | | Nos. 511-513 (3) | .75 | .75 |

### Great Britain No. 234 Overprinted Type "b" in Blue

| | | | | |
|---|---|---|---|---|
| **1937, May 13** | | | | **Wmk. 251** |
| 514 | A100 | 1½p purple brown | 1.25 | .50 |

Coronation of George VI and Elizabeth.

### Great Britain Nos. 235-237 Overprinted in Blue or Black — c

| | | | Perf. 14½x14 | | |
|---|---|---|---|---|---|
| **1937** | | | | | |
| 515 | A101 | ½p deep green (Bl) | | 8.00 | 3.00 |
| 516 | A101 | 1p scarlet (Bk) | | 25.00 | 3.00 |
| 517 | A101 | 1½p red brown (Bl) | | 2.50 | .75 |
| | | Nos. 515-517 (3) | | 35.50 | 6.75 |

### Great Britain Nos. 252-254 Ovptd. Type "a" in Blue or Black

| | | | | |
|---|---|---|---|---|
| **1940, May 6** | | | | |
| 518 | A106 | ½p deep green (Bl) | .25 | 8.50 |
| 519 | A106 | 1p scarlet (Bk) | .80 | .80 |
| 520 | A106 | 1½p red brown (Bl) | 1.75 | 12.50 |
| | | Nos. 518-520 (3) | 2.80 | 21.80 |

Centenary of the postage stamp.

### Great Britain Nos. 258 and 259 Overprinted Type "c" in Blue or Black

| | | | | |
|---|---|---|---|---|
| **1944-45** | | | | |
| 521 | A101 | ½p green (Bl) | 11.50 | 6.75 |
| 522 | A101 | 1p ver (Bk) ('45) | 11.50 | 6.75 |

> Catalogue values for unused stamps in this section, from this point to the end of the section, are for Never Hinged items.

### Great Britain Nos. 264-265 Overprinted

d

e

| | | | | |
|---|---|---|---|---|
| **1946, June 11** | | | | |
| 523 | A107(d) | 2½p bright ultra | 1.00 | .55 |
| 524 | A108(e) | 3p violet | 1.00 | 2.00 |

Return to peace at close of World War II.

### Great Britain Nos. 267 and 268 Overprinted Type "a"

| | | | Perf. 14½x14, 14x14½ | | |
|---|---|---|---|---|---|
| **1948, Apr. 26** | | | | | |
| 525 | A109 | 2½p bright ultra | | .40 | .25 |
| a. | | Pair, one without overprint | | 10,000. | |
| 526 | A110 | £1 dp chalky bl | | 22.50 | 32.50 |

25th anniv. of the marriage of King George VI and Queen Elizabeth.

### Great Britain Nos. 271 to 274 Overprinted Type "a"

| | | | Perf. 14½x14 | | |
|---|---|---|---|---|---|
| **1948, July 29** | | | | | |
| 527 | A113 | 2½p bright ultra | | 1.00 | 1.80 |
| 528 | A114 | 3p deep violet | | 1.00 | 2.00 |
| 529 | A115 | 6p red violet | | 1.00 | 2.00 |
| 530 | A116 | 1sh dark brown | | 1.00 | 2.00 |
| | | Nos. 527-530 (4) | | 4.00 | 7.80 |

1948 Olympic Games, Wembley, July-Aug.

### Stamps of Great Britain, 1937-47, and Nos. 249A, 250 and 251A Overprinted Type "c"

| | | | | |
|---|---|---|---|---|
| **1949, Jan. 1** | | | | |
| 531 | A101 | 2p lt org (II) | 8.00 | 10.50 |
| 532 | A101 | 2½p ultra (II) | 6.00 | 10.50 |
| 533 | A101 | 3p violet (II) | .60 | 1.00 |
| 534 | A102 | 4p gray green | 10.00 | 16.00 |
| 535 | A102 | 5p light brown | 5.00 | 33.00 |
| 536 | A102 | 6p rose lilac | 1.25 | .25 |
| 537 | A103 | 7p emerald | 2.25 | 18.00 |
| 538 | A103 | 8p bright rose | 4.50 | 16.00 |
| 539 | A103 | 9p deep ol grn | 2.25 | 16.00 |
| 540 | A103 | 10p royal blue | 2.50 | 15.50 |
| 541 | A103 | 11p violet brn | 4.00 | 24.00 |
| 542 | A103 | 1sh brown | 1.25 | 2.50 |

| | | | | |
|---|---|---|---|---|
| | | **Wmk. 259** | | |
| | | **Perf. 14** | | |
| 543 | A104 | 2sh6p yellow grn | 9.00 | 27.00 |
| 544 | A104 | 5sh dull red | 20.00 | 45.00 |
| 545 | A105 | 10sh ultra | 50.00 | 130.00 |
| | | Nos. 531-545 (15) | 126.60 | 365.25 |

### Great Britain Nos. 276 to 279 Overprinted Type "a"

| | | | Perf. 14½x14 | | |
|---|---|---|---|---|---|
| **1949, Oct. 10** | | | | **Wmk. 251** | |
| 546 | A117 | 2½p bright ultra | | .65 | 4.50 |
| 547 | A118 | 3p bright violet | | .65 | 7.50 |
| 548 | A119 | 6p red violet | | .65 | 1.00 |
| 549 | A120 | 1sh brown | | .65 | 3.00 |
| | | Nos. 546-549 (4) | | 2.60 | 16.00 |

### Great Britain Nos. 280-288 Overprinted Type "c" or "a" (Shilling Values)

| | | | | |
|---|---|---|---|---|
| **1950-51** | | | | |
| 550 | A101 | ½p lt orange | .90 | 1.35 |
| 551 | A101 | 1p ultra | 1.10 | 2.75 |
| 552 | A101 | 1½p green | 1.10 | 22.50 |
| 553 | A101 | 2p lt red brn | 1.10 | 4.50 |
| 554 | A101 | 2½p vermilion | 1.10 | 10.00 |
| 555 | A102 | 4p ultra ('50) | 4.00 | 2.75 |

| | | | | |
|---|---|---|---|---|
| | | **Wmk. 259** | | |
| | | **Perf. 11x12** | | |
| 556 | A121 | 2sh6p green | 9.00 | 4.50 |
| 557 | A121 | 5sh dull red | 16.00 | 14.00 |
| 558 | A122 | 10sh ultra | 30.00 | 14.00 |
| | | Nos. 550-558 (9) | 64.30 | 76.35 |

### Great Britain Nos. 292-308 Overprinted Type c

| | | | Perf. 14½x14 | | |
|---|---|---|---|---|---|
| **1952-54** | | **Wmk. 298** | | | |
| 559 | A126 | ½p red org ('53) | | .25 | .40 |
| 560 | A126 | 1p ultra ('53) | | .25 | .40 |
| 561 | A126 | 1½p green ('52) | | .25 | .25 |
| 562 | A126 | 2p red brn ('53) | | .25 | 1.00 |
| 563 | A127 | 2½p scarlet ('52) | | .25 | .90 |
| 564 | A127 | 3p dk pur (Dk Bl) | | .25 | 1.00 |
| 565 | A128 | 4p ultra ('53) | | .50 | 4.00 |
| 566 | A129 | 5p lt brown ('53) | | .25 | .90 |
| 567 | A129 | 6p lilac rose | | .50 | .25 |
| 568 | A129 | 7p emerald | | .90 | 4.00 |
| 569 | A130 | 8p brt rose ('53) | | .50 | 1.30 |
| 570 | A130 | 9p dp olive grn | | 1.25 | 1.50 |
| 571 | A130 | 10p royal blue | | 1.25 | 2.50 |
| 572 | A130 | 11p violet brn | | 1.25 | 3.00 |
| 573 | A131 | 1sh brown ('53) | | .50 | .60 |
| 574 | A132 | 1sh3p dk grn ('53) | | .90 | 7.00 |
| 575 | A131 | 1sh6p dk blue ('53) | | 1.30 | 2.00 |
| | | Nos. 559-575 (17) | | 10.85 | 31.00 |

### Stamp and Type of Great Britain 1955 Overprinted Type a

| | | | Perf. 11x12 | | |
|---|---|---|---|---|---|
| **1955, Sept. 23** | | **Engr.** | | **Wmk. 308** | |
| 576 | A133 | 2sh6p dark brown | | 3.00 | 11.00 |
| 577 | A133 | 5sh crimson | | 4.00 | 32.50 |
| 578 | A133 | 10sh brt ultra | | 17.00 | 37.50 |
| | | Nos. 576-578 (3) | | 24.00 | 81.00 |

### Coronation Issue

### Great Britain Nos. 313-316 Overprinted Type a

| | | | | |
|---|---|---|---|---|
| **1953, June 3** | | **Photo.** | | **Wmk. 298** |
| 579 | A134 | 2½p scarlet | .90 | .55 |
| 580 | A135 | 4p brt ultra | 4.00 | 1.00 |
| 581 | A136 | 1sh3p dark green | 3.00 | 1.50 |
| 582 | A137 | 1sh6p dark blue | 3.00 | 2.25 |
| | | Nos. 579-582 (4) | 10.90 | 5.30 |

### Great Britain Nos. 317-323, 325 and 332 Overprinted Type c

| | | | Perf. 14½x14 | | |
|---|---|---|---|---|---|
| **1956** | | **Wmk. 308** | | | |
| 583 | A126 | ½p red orange | | .25 | 1.25 |
| 584 | A126 | 1p ultramarine | | .25 | .65 |
| 585 | A126 | 1½p green | | .30 | 4.25 |
| 586 | A126 | 2p red brown | | 1.10 | 1.60 |
| 587 | A127 | 2½p scarlet | | .30 | .45 |
| 588 | A127 | 3p dark purple | | .30 | 7.00 |
| 589 | A128 | 4p ultra | | .55 | 1.70 |
| 590 | A129 | 6p lilac rose | | .40 | 7.00 |
| 591 | A132 | 1sh3p dark green | | 1.50 | 14.00 |
| | | Nos. 583-591 (9) | | 4.95 | 37.95 |

### Great Britain Nos. 317-333 and 309-311 Overprinted 1857-1957 TANGIER

| | | | | |
|---|---|---|---|---|
| **1957, Apr. 1** | | **Photo.** | | **Wmk. 308** |
| 592 | A126 | ½p red orange | .25 | .25 |
| 593 | A126 | 1p ultramarine | .25 | .25 |
| 594 | A126 | 1½p green | .25 | .25 |
| 595 | A126 | 2p red brown | .25 | .25 |
| 596 | A127 | 2½p scarlet | .25 | 1.00 |
| 597 | A127 | 3p dark purple | .25 | .35 |
| 598 | A128 | 4p ultramarine | .30 | .35 |
| 599 | A129 | 5p lt brown | .30 | .35 |
| 600 | A129 | 6p lilac rose | .30 | .45 |
| 601 | A129 | 7p emerald | .30 | .35 |
| 602 | A130 | 8p brt rose | .30 | .80 |
| 603 | A130 | 9p dp olive grn | .30 | .35 |
| 604 | | "TANGIER" omitted | 7,000. | |
| | A130 | 10p royal blue | .30 | .30 |
| 605 | A130 | 11p violet brown | .30 | .30 |
| 606 | A131 | 1sh brown | .30 | .30 |
| 607 | A132 | 1sh3p dark green | .40 | 4.75 |
| 608 | A131 | 1sh6p dark blue | .45 | 1.50 |

**Engr.**
**Perf. 11x12**

| | | | | |
|---|---|---|---|---|
| **609** | A133 | 2sh6p dark brown | 1.75 | 9.50 |
| **610** | A133 | 5sh crimson | 2.50 | 18.00 |
| **611** | A133 | 10sh ultramarine | 3.50 | 18.00 |
| | | Nos. 592-611 (20) | 12.80 | 57.45 |

Centenary of British P.O. in Tangier.
Nos. 609-611 are found with hyphen omitted (one stamp in sheet of 40).
British stamps overprinted "Tangier" were discontinued Apr. 30, 1957.

## TURKISH EMPIRE

40 Paras = 1 Piaster
12 Pence = 1 Shilling (1905)

    a         b

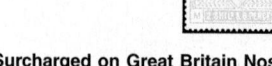
    c

**Surcharged on Great Britain Nos. 101, 104, 96**

**1885, Apr. 1**    **Wmk. 30**    **Perf. 14**

| | | | | |
|---|---|---|---|---|
| **1** | A47(a) | 40pa on 2½p lil | 180.00 | 1.50 |
| **2** | A45(b) | 80pa on 5p grn | 275.00 | 11.00 |
| | | **Wmk. 31** | | |
| **3** | A44(c) | 12pi on 2sh6p lil | 75.00 | 32.50 |
| a. | | Bluish paper | 650.00 | 350.00 |
| | | Nos. 1-3 (3) | 530.00 | 45.00 |

**Great Britain Nos. 114, 118 Surcharged**

**1887**    **Wmk. 30**

| | | | | |
|---|---|---|---|---|
| **4** | A57(a) | 40pa on 2½p vio, bl | 22.50 | 1.00 |
| a. | | Double surcharge | 2,250. | 2,750. |
| **5** | A61(b) | 80pa on 5p lil & bl | 20.00 | 1.00 |
| a. | | Small "0" in "80" | 425.00 | 105.00 |

**Great Britain No. 111 Handstamp Surcharged — d**

**1893, Feb. 25**

| | | | | |
|---|---|---|---|---|
| **6** | A54(d) | 40pa on ½p ver | 525.00 | 140.00 |

No. 6 was a provisional, made and used at Constantinople for five days. Excellent forgeries are known.

**Great Britain No. 121 Surcharged — e**

**1896**

| | | | | |
|---|---|---|---|---|
| **7** | A64(e) | 4pi on 10p car rose & lil | 50.00 | 10.00 |

**British Stamps of 1902 Surcharged**

**1902-05**    **Wmk. 30**

| | | | | |
|---|---|---|---|---|
| **8** | A66(a) | 40pa on 2½p ultra | 25.00 | 1.00 |
| a. | | Double surcharge | — | 2,500. |
| **9** | A71(b) | 80pa on 5p lil & bl | 20.00 | 2.00 |
| a. | | Small "0" in "80" | 375.00 | 225.00 |
| **10** | A73(e) | 4pi on 10p car rose & vio | 25.00 | 4.00 |
| | | **Wmk. 31** | | |
| **11** | A75(c) | 12pi on 2sh6p vio ('03) | 50.00 | 45.00 |
| **12** | A76(c) | 24pi on 5sh car rose ('05) | 45.00 | 50.00 |
| | | Nos. 8-12 (5) | 165.00 | 102.00 |

**Great Britain Nos. 131, 134 Surcharged — f**

**1906**    **Wmk. 30**

| | | | | |
|---|---|---|---|---|
| **13** | A66(f) | 1pi on 2½p ultra | 35.00 | .80 |
| a. | | Double surcharge | 2,250. | |
| **14** | A71(f) | 2pi on 5p lil & ultra | 35.00 | 3.00 |

Nos. 10, 11, 14 are on both ordinary and chalky paper.

**Great Britain Nos. 127-135, 138 Overprinted — g**

**1905**

| | | | | |
|---|---|---|---|---|
| **15** | A66 | ½p pale green | 8.00 | .80 |
| **16** | A66 | 1p carmine | 13.00 | .80 |
| **17** | A67 | 1½p violet & grn | 6.50 | 2.25 |
| **18** | A68 | 2p green & car | 4.00 | 9.00 |
| **19** | A66 | 2½p ultra | 8.00 | 18.00 |
| **20** | A69 | 3p violet, yel | 6.50 | 11.00 |
| **21** | A70 | 4p brown & grn | 9.00 | 65.00 |
| **22** | A71 | 5p lilac & ultra | 15.00 | 37.50 |
| **23** | A66 | 6p dull violet | 11.00 | 23.00 |
| **24** | A74 | 1sh car rose & grn | 40.00 | 50.00 |
| | | Nos. 15-24 (10) | 121.00 | 217.35 |

Nos. 17, 18 and 24 are on both ordinary and chalky paper.

**No. 18 Surcharged**

**1906, July 2**

| | | | | |
|---|---|---|---|---|
| **25** | A68 | 1pi on 2p grn & car | 1,750. | 825.00 |

**British Stamps of 1902-09 Surcharged**

    j         k

**1909**

| | | | | |
|---|---|---|---|---|
| **26** | A67 | 30pa on 1½p vio & grn | 20.00 | 1.00 |
| **27** | A69 | 1pi10pa on 3p vio, yel | 17.50 | 55.00 |
| **28** | A70 | 1pi30pa on 4p brn & grn | 8.50 | 25.00 |
| **29** | A70 | 1pi30pa on 4p org | 25.00 | 80.00 |
| **30** | A66 | 2pi20pa on 6p dl vio | 30.00 | 80.00 |
| **31** | A74 | 5pi on 1sh car rose & grn | 7.50 | 20.00 |
| | | Nos. 26-31 (6) | 108.50 | 261.00 |

No. 29 is on ordinary paper, the others are on chalky paper.

**Great Britain Nos. 132, 144, 135 Surcharged**

    m         n

**1910**

| | | | | |
|---|---|---|---|---|
| **32** | A69(m) | 1¼pi on 3p vio, yel | .90 | 1.25 |
| **33** | A70(n) | 1¾pi on 4p orange | .55 | .75 |
| **34** | A66(n) | 2½pi on 6p dl vio | 5.00 | .75 |
| | | Nos. 32-34 (3) | 6.45 | 2.75 |

There are three different varieties of "4" in the fraction of the 1¾ piastre.

**Great Britain Nos. 151-154 Overprinted Type g**

**1911-12**    **Perf. 15x14**

| | | | | |
|---|---|---|---|---|
| **35** | A80 | ½p yellow green | 4.00 | 5.25 |
| **36** | A81 | 1p carmine | .75 | 9.50 |
| | | **Re-engraved** | | |
| **37** | A80 | ½p yel grn ('12) | 4.50 | .75 |
| **38** | A81 | 1p scarlet ('12) | 3.50 | 1.75 |

**Great Britain No. 148 Surcharged — o**

| | | | | |
|---|---|---|---|---|
| **39** | A66(o) | 1pi on 2½p ultra | 40.00 | 5.00 |
| | | Nos. 35-39 (5) | 52.75 | 22.25 |

The surcharge on No. 39 exists in two types with the letters 2½ and 3mm high respectively.

The stamp also differs from No. 13 in the perforation.

**British Stamps of 1912-13 Surcharged with New Values**

**1913-14**    **Wmk. 33**

| | | | | |
|---|---|---|---|---|
| **40** | A84(j) | 30pa on 1½p red brn | 4.00 | 15.00 |
| **41** | A86(o) | 1pi on 2½p ultra | 16.00 | .25 |
| **42** | A87(m) | 1¼pi on 3p vio | 10.00 | 5.00 |
| **43** | A88(m) | 1¾pi on 4p sl grn | 5.00 | 10.00 |
| **44** | A90(o) | 4pi on 10p lt bl | 16.00 | 32.50 |
| **45** | A90(o) | 5pi on 1sh bis | 57.50 | 95.00 |
| | | Nos. 40-45 (6) | 108.50 | 157.75 |

**British Stamps of 1912-19 Overprinted Type "g"**

**1913-21**

| | | | | |
|---|---|---|---|---|
| **46** | A82 | ½p green | 2.50 | 4.00 |
| **47** | A83 | 1p scarlet | .40 | 9.00 |
| **48** | A85 | 2p orange ('21) | 2.50 | 60.00 |
| **49** | A87 | 3p violet ('21) | 9.00 | 13.00 |
| **50** | A88 | 4p sl grn ('21) | 5.75 | 32.50 |
| **51** | A89 | 5p yel brn ('21) | 14.00 | 35.00 |
| **52** | A89 | 6p dl vio ('21) | 27.50 | 50.00 |
| **53** | A90 | 1sh bister ('21) | 25.00 | 10.00 |
| | | **Wmk. 34** | | |
| | | **Perf. 11x12** | | |
| **54** | A91 | 2sh6p brn ('21) | 45.00 | 130.00 |
| | | Nos. 46-54 (9) | 131.65 | 343.50 |

**British Stamps of 1912-19 Surcharged as in 1909-10 and**

    p         q

**1921**    **Wmk. 33**    **Perf. 14½x14**

| | | | | |
|---|---|---|---|---|
| **55** | A82(j) | 30pa on ½p grn | 1.00 | 20.00 |
| **56** | A83(j) | 1½pi on 1p scar | 2.00 | 2.25 |
| **57** | A86(o) | 3¾pi on 2½p ultra | 1.75 | .50 |
| **58** | A87(m) | 4½pi on 3p vio | 2.75 | 4.00 |
| **59** | A89(p) | 7½p on 5p yel brn | .75 | |
| **60** | A90(p) | 15pi on 10p lt bl | 1.00 | .50 |
| **61** | A90(p) | 18¾pi on 1sh bis | 5.00 | 6.50 |
| | | **Wmk. 34** | | |
| | | **Perf. 11x12** | | |
| **62** | A91(q) | 45pi on 2sh6p brown | 27.50 | 52.50 |
| **63** | A91(q) | 90pi on 5sh car rose | 32.50 | 35.00 |
| **64** | A91(q) | 180pi on 10sh blue | 52.50 | 52.50 |
| | | Nos. 55-64 (10) | 126.75 | 174.25 |

## GUERNSEY

'gərn-zē

LOCATION — A group of islands in the English Channel
GOVT. — Dependent territory (bailiwick) of the British Crown
AREA — 30 sq. mi.
POP. — 58,681 (1996)
CAPITAL — St. Peter Port

The bailiwick includes the islands of Guernsey, Alderney, Sark, Herm, Jethou and Lithou.

Following the establishment of the British General Post Office as a public corporation on October 1, 1969, the post office of the Bailiwick of Guernsey became a separate entity and British postage stamps ceased to be valid.

> **Catalogue values for unused stamps in this country are for Never Hinged items.**

**Watermark**

Wmk. 396 — Link Fence

**British Regional Issue**

Guernsey Lily and Crown of William the Conqueror
    A1         A2

**1958-69**    **Photo.**    **Wmk. 322**

| | | | | |
|---|---|---|---|---|
| **1** | A1 | 2½p rose red ('64) | .45 | .45 |
| **2** | A2 | 3p light purple | .35 | .35 |
| p. | | Phosphor. ('67) | .25 | .25 |
| **3** | A2 | 4p ultra ('66) | .30 | .30 |
| p. | | Phosphor. ('67) | .25 | .25 |
| | | **Unwmk.** | | |
| **4** | A2 | 4p ultra ('68) | .25 | .25 |
| **5** | A2 | 4p olive brown ('68) | .25 | .25 |
| **6** | A2 | 4p bright red ('69) | .30 | .30 |
| **7** | A2 | 5p dark blue ('68) | .25 | .25 |
| | | Nos. 1-7 (7) | 2.15 | 2.15 |

Nos. 4-7 are phosphorescent.
Sold to the general public only at post offices within Guernsey; Philatelic Bureau, Edinburgh; and Philatelic Centre, London, but valid for postage throughout Great Britain.
See also Great Britain Nos. 269-270, which were sold only in the Channel Islands and at a few philatelic windows in Great Britain, and may be considered to be precursors to the regional issues.

**Bailiwick Issues**

William the Conqueror, Queen Elizabeth II and Map of Bailiwick — A3

Creux Harbor, Sark — A4

Designs (Queen Elizabeth II and): ½p, Castle Cornet and Edward the Confessor. 1½p, Martello Tower and Henry II. 2p, Arms of Sark and King John. 3p, Arms of Alderney and Edward III. 4p, Guernsey lily and Henry V. 5p, Arms of Guernsey and Queen Elizabeth I. 6p, Arms of Alderney and Charles II. 9p, Arms of Sark and George III. 1sh, Arms of Guernsey and Queen Victoria. 1sh6p, Map of Bailiwick and William I. 1sh9p, Guernsey lily and Queen Elizabeth I. 2sh6p, Martello Tower and King John. 10sh, Braye Harbor, Alderney. £1, St. Peter Port, Guernsey.

**Perf. 14½x14**

**1969-70**    **Photo.**    **Unwmk.**

| | | | | |
|---|---|---|---|---|
| **8** | A3 | ½p magenta & blk | .25 | .25 |
| **9** | A3 | 1p ultra & black | .25 | .25 |
| **10** | A3 | 1½p bister & blk | .25 | .25 |
| **11** | A3 | 2p dk blue & multi | .25 | .25 |
| **12** | A3 | 3p deep org & multi | .25 | .25 |
| **13** | A3 | 4p yel green & multi | .25 | .25 |
| a. | | Booklet pane of 1 | .60 | .60 |
| **14** | A3 | 5p vio blue & multi | .25 | .25 |
| a. | | Booklet pane of 1 | .75 | .75 |
| **15** | A3 | 6p ol green & multi | .35 | .35 |
| **16** | A3 | 9p plum & multi | .35 | .35 |
| **17** | A3 | 1sh dk olive & multi | .35 | .35 |
| **18** | A3 | 1sh6p blue grn & blk | .35 | .35 |
| **19** | A3 | 1sh9p magenta & multi | 1.00 | 1.00 |
| **20** | A3 | 2sh6p purple & blk | 4.00 | 3.50 |
| | | **Perf. 12½** | | |
| **21** | A4 | 5sh multicolored | 2.60 | 2.50 |
| **22** | A4 | 10sh multicolored | 13.00 | 13.00 |
| a. | | Perf. 13½x13 | 42.50 | 40.00 |
| | | **Perf. 13½x13** | | |
| **23** | A4 | £1 multicolored | 2.40 | 2.25 |
| a. | | Perf. 12½ | 4.50 | 3.50 |
| | | Nos. 8-23 (16) | 26.15 | 25.40 |

Issued: Nos. 22a, 23, 3/4/70; others, 10/1/69.
Nos. 9 and 18 are inscribed "40o 30' N."
See Nos. 28-29, 41-55, 749.

Col. Isaac Brock — A5

Designs: 5p, Sir Isaac Brock as major general. 1sh9p, as ensign, flags of 1789 and 1969. 2sh6p, Regimental coat of arms and flags, horiz.

### Perf. 14x13½, 13½x14
**1969, Dec. 1    Litho.    Unwmk.**

| 24 | A5 | 4p multicolored | .25 | .25 |
|----|----|----|----|----|
| 25 | A5 | 5p black & multi | .25 | .25 |
| 26 | A5 | 1sh9p dp blue & multi | .60 | .55 |
| 27 | A5 | 2sh6p purple & multi | .60 | .55 |
| | | Nos. 24-27 (4) | 1.70 | 1.60 |

Sir Isaac Brock (1769-1812), born on Guernsey, commander of Quebec garrison.

### Map Type of 1969 Redrawn
**1969-70    Photo.    Perf. 14½x14**

| 28 | A3 | 1p "49o 30'N" | .30 | .30 |
|----|----|----|----|----|
| a. | | Booklet pane of 1 | .45 | .45 |
| | | Complete booklet, 3 #13a, 2 #14a, 2 #28a | 3.50 | |
| | | Complete booklet, 6 #13a, 4 #14a, 4 #28a | 10.00 | |
| | | Complete booklet, 9 #13a, 6 #14a, 6 #28a | 12.00 | |
| 29 | A3 | 1sh6p "49o 30'N" | 1.65 | 1.65 |

Issued: No. 28a, 12/12/69; Nos. 28-29, 2/4/70.

Nos. 9 and 18 are inscribed "40o 30' N." Booklets issued in 1970 have different covers from those issued in 1969.

Destroyer "Bulldog" near Castle Cornet — A6

Designs: 5p, Liberation fleet in roadsteads between Guernsey, Herm and Jethou. 1sh6p, Brigadier A. E. Snow reading proclamation of King George VI on steps of Elizabeth College in Guernsey, vert.

**1970, May 9    Photo.    Perf. 11½**

| 30 | A6 | 4p vio blue & lt blue | .25 | .25 |
|----|----|----|----|----|
| 31 | A6 | 5p dp plum & gray | .25 | .25 |
| 32 | A6 | 1sh6p dk brown & bis | 1.00 | .90 |
| | | Nos. 30-32 (3) | 1.50 | 1.40 |

25th anniv. of Guernsey's liberation from the Germans.

Guernsey Cow — A7

**1970, Aug. 12    Photo.    Perf. 11½**

| 33 | A7 | 4p Tomatoes | .35 | .30 |
|----|----|----|----|----|
| 34 | A7 | 5p shown | .50 | .30 |
| 35 | A7 | 9p Guernsey bull | 1.90 | .85 |
| 36 | A7 | 1sh6p Freesias | 2.00 | 1.60 |
| | | Nos. 33-36 (4) | 4.75 | 3.05 |

For similar design see No. 68.

St. Anne, Alderney — A8

Christmas (Churches): 5p, St. Peter, Town Church, Guernsey. 9p, St. Peter, Sark, vert. 1sh6p, St. Tugual Chapel, Herm, vert.

**1970, Nov. 11    Photo.    Perf. 11½**

| 37 | A8 | 4p blue, gold & brn | .25 | .25 |
|----|----|----|----|----|
| 38 | A8 | 5p brt grn, gold & brn | .25 | .25 |
| 39 | A8 | 9p rose red, gold & brown | .75 | .70 |
| 40 | A8 | 1sh6p brt pur, gold & brn | 1.05 | 1.00 |
| | | Nos. 37-40 (4) | 2.30 | 2.20 |

### Decimal Currency Issue
### Types of 1969
### "p" instead of "d"

Designs: ½p, Castle Cornet and Edward the Confessor. 1p, 5p, Map of Bailiwick and William the Conqueror. 1½p, Martello Tower and Henry II. 2p, Guernsey lily and Henry V. 2½p, Arms of Guernsey and Elizabeth I. 3p, Arms of Alderney and Edward III. 3½p, Guernsey lily and Elizabeth I. 4p, Arms of Sark and King John. 6p, Arms of Alderney and Charles II. 7½p, Arms of Guernsey and Queen Victoria. 9p, Arms of Sark and George III. 10p, Martello Tower and King John. 20p, Creux Harbor. 50p, Braye Harbor.

**1971    Photo.    Perf. 14½x14**

| 41 | A3 | ½p magenta & blk | .25 | .25 |
|----|----|----|----|----|
| a. | | Booklet pane of 1 | .25 | |

| 42 | A3 | 1p ultra & black | .25 | .25 |
|----|----|----|----|----|
| 43 | A3 | 1½p bister & blk | .25 | .25 |
| 44 | A3 | 2p yel green & multi | .25 | .25 |
| a. | | Booklet pane of 1 | .30 | |
| 45 | A3 | 2½p vio blue & multi | .25 | .25 |
| a. | | Booklet pane of 1 | .30 | |
| | | Complete booklet, 2 each #41a, 44a, 45a | .75 | |
| | | Complete booklet, 4 each #41a, 44a, 45a | 1.00 | |
| | | Complete booklet, 6 each #41a, 44a, 45a | 1.00 | |
| 46 | A3 | 3p dp orange & multi | .25 | .25 |
| 47 | A3 | 3½p magenta & multi | .25 | .25 |
| 48 | A3 | 4p dk blue & multi | .25 | .25 |
| 49 | A3 | 5p brt green & multi | .25 | .25 |
| 50 | A3 | 6p dk green & multi | .25 | .25 |
| 51 | A3 | 7½p brn olive & multi | .75 | .75 |
| 52 | A3 | 9p plum & multi | .25 | .25 |
| 53 | A3 | 10p purple & black | 1.40 | 1.40 |

### Perf. 13

| 54 | A4 | 20p dk red & multi | .60 | .60 |
|----|----|----|----|----|
| 55 | A4 | 50p multicolored | 1.50 | 1.50 |
| | | Nos. 41-55 (15) | 7.00 | 7.00 |

Issued: Nos. 53-55, 1/6; others 2/15. Stamps from the booklets reprinted in 1973 are printed on whiter, chalk-surfaced paper, with different covers.

Thomas de la Rue, Hong Kong No. 1 — A9

Thomas de la Rue and: 2½p, GB No. 22. 4p, Italy No. 26. 7½p, US Confederate States No. 6.

**1971, June 2    Engr.    Perf. 14x13½**

| 56 | A9 | 2p brown | .25 | .25 |
|----|----|----|----|----|
| 57 | A9 | 2½p carmine | .25 | .25 |
| 58 | A9 | 4p dark green | .90 | .75 |
| 59 | A9 | 7½p deep blue | 1.05 | 1.00 |
| | | Nos. 56-59 (4) | 2.45 | 2.25 |

Thomas de la Rue (1793-1866), founder of Thomas de la Rue & Co., Ltd., security printers.

Ebenezer Methodist Church — A10

Historic Churches of Guernsey: 2½p, St. Pierre du Bois. 5p, St. Joseph's, vert. 7½p, St. Philippe de Torteval, vert.

**1971, Oct. 27    Photo.    Perf. 11½**

| 60 | A10 | 2p green, sil & blk | .25 | .25 |
|----|----|----|----|----|
| 61 | A10 | 2½p blue, sil & blk | .25 | .25 |
| 62 | A10 | 5p pur, silver & blk | .95 | .95 |
| 63 | A10 | 7½p red, silver & blk | 1.30 | 1.20 |
| | | Nos. 60-63 (4) | 2.75 | 2.65 |

Christmas 1971.

Earl of Chesterfield, 1794 — A11

Mail Boats — 2½p, Dasher, 1827. 7½p, Ibex, 1891. 9p, Alberta, 1900.

**1972, Feb. 10    Photo.    Perf. 11½**

| 64 | A11 | 2p shown | .25 | .25 |
|----|----|----|----|----|
| 65 | A11 | 2½p multicolored | .25 | .25 |
| 66 | A11 | 7½p multicolored | .25 | .25 |
| 67 | A11 | 9p multicolored | .40 | .40 |
| | | Nos. 64-67 (4) | 1.15 | 1.15 |

See Nos. 77-80.

Guernsey Bull — A12

**1972, May 22    Photo.    Perf. 11½**

| 68 | A12 | 5p brown & multi | .40 | .35 |
|----|----|----|----|----|

Guernsey Breeders, 2nd World Conf. For similar designs see Nos. 33-36.

Wild Flowers — A13

2p, Sorrel (Oxalis pes-caprae). 2½p, heath spotted orchid (Orchis maculata), vert. 7½p, kafir fig (Carpobrotus edulis). 9p, scarlet pimpernel (Anagallis arvensi), vert.

**1972, May 24**

| 69 | A13 | 2p multicolored | .25 | .25 |
|----|----|----|----|----|
| 70 | A13 | 2½p multicolored | .25 | .25 |
| 71 | A13 | 7½p multicolored | .30 | .30 |
| 72 | A13 | 9p multicolored | .30 | .30 |
| | | Nos. 69-72 (4) | 1.10 | 1.10 |

Angels, St. Martin's Church — A14

Stained Glass Windows from Guernsey Churches: 2½p, Virgin and Child, St. André's. 7½p, Virgin Mary, St. Sampson's. 9p, Christ Victorious, St. Pierre's.

**1972, Nov. 20    Photo.    Perf. 11½**

| 73 | A14 | 2p brick red & multi | .25 | .25 |
|----|----|----|----|----|
| 74 | A14 | 2½p lt violet & multi | .25 | .25 |
| 75 | A14 | 7½p yellow & multi | .25 | .25 |
| 76 | A14 | 9p lt green & multi | .25 | .25 |
| | | Nos. 73-76 (4) | 1.00 | 1.00 |

Christmas 1972 and for the 25th anniv. of the marriage of Queen Elizabeth II and Prince Philip.

### Mail Boat Type of 1972

2½p, St. Julien, 1925. 3p, Isle of Guernsey, 1932. 7½p, St. Patrick, 1947. 9p, Sarnia, 1961.

**1973, Mar. 9    Photo.    Perf. 11½**

| 77 | A11 | 2½p multicolored | .25 | .25 |
|----|----|----|----|----|
| 78 | A11 | 3p multicolored | .25 | .25 |
| 79 | A11 | 7½p multicolored | .25 | .25 |
| 80 | A11 | 9p multicolored | .30 | .30 |
| | | Nos. 77-80 (4) | 1.05 | 1.05 |

No. 78 is incorrectly inscribed "Isle of Guernsey 1930."

Supermarine Sea Eagle — A15

Airplanes: 3p, Westland Wessex. 5p, De Havilland Rapide. 7½p, Douglas Dakota. 9p, Vickers Viscount.

**1973, July 4    Photo.    Perf. 11½**

| 81 | A15 | 2½p multicolored | .25 | .25 |
|----|----|----|----|----|
| 82 | A15 | 3p multicolored | .25 | .25 |
| 83 | A15 | 5p multicolored | .25 | .25 |
| 84 | A15 | 7½p multicolored | .30 | .30 |
| 85 | A15 | 9p multicolored | .40 | .40 |
| | | Nos. 81-85 (5) | 1.45 | 1.45 |

50th anniversary of air service to Guernsey.

The Good Shepherd, St. Michel du Valle — A16

Stained-glass Windows from Guernsey Churches: 3p, Jesus preaching, St. Marie du Castel. 7½p, St. Dominic, Notre Dame du Rosaire. 20p, Virgin and Child, St. Sauveur.

**1973, Oct. 24    Photo.    Perf. 11½**

| 86 | A16 | 2½p salmon & multi | .25 | .25 |
|----|----|----|----|----|
| 87 | A16 | 3p blue & multi | .25 | .25 |
| 88 | A16 | 7½p yellow & multi | .25 | .25 |
| 89 | A16 | 20p multicolored | .35 | .35 |
| | | Nos. 86-89 (4) | 1.10 | 1.10 |

Christmas 1973.

Princess Anne and Mark Phillips — A17

**1973, Nov. 14**

| 90 | A17 | 25p blue & multi | .60 | .60 |
|----|----|----|----|----|

Wedding of Princess Anne and Capt. Mark Phillips, Nov. 14, 1973.

"John Lockett," 1875 — A18

Guernsey Lifeboats: 3p, "Arthur Lionel," 1875. 8p, "Euphrosyne Kendal," 1954. 10p, "Arun," 1972.

**1974, Jan. 15    Photo.    Perf. 11½**
### Granite Paper

| 91 | A18 | 2½p multicolored | .25 | .25 |
|----|----|----|----|----|
| 92 | A18 | 3p multicolored | .25 | .25 |
| 93 | A18 | 8p multicolored | .25 | .25 |
| 94 | A18 | 10p multicolored | .25 | .25 |
| | | Nos. 91-94 (4) | 1.00 | 1.00 |

Sesqui. of Royal Natl. Lifeboat Institution.

A19    Militia — A20

**1974-78    Photo.    Perf. 11½**
### Granite Paper (Nos. 95-107)

| 95 | A19 | ½p 1815 | .25 | .25 |
|----|----|----|----|----|
| 96 | A19 | 1p 1825 | .25 | .25 |
| 97 | A19 | 1½p 1787 | .25 | .25 |
| 98 | A19 | 2p 1815 | .25 | .25 |
| 99 | A19 | 2½p Royal, 1868 | .25 | .25 |
| | | Complete booklet, pane of 8 (5 #95, 3 #99) ('74) | .30 | |
| 100 | A19 | 3p Royal, 1895 | .25 | .25 |
| | | Complete booklet, pane of 16 (4 #95, 6 #99 and 6 #100) ('74) | .90 | |
| 101 | A19 | 3½p Royal, 1867 | .25 | .25 |
| 102 | A19 | 4p 1822 | .25 | .25 |
| 102A | A19 | 5p Royal, 1895 | .25 | .25 |
| | | Complete booklet, pane of 8 (4 #96, 2 #100, 2 #102A) ('77) | .75 | |
| | | Complete booklet, pane of 4 (#96, 2 #98, #102A) ('77) | .50 | |
| 103 | A19 | 5½p Royal, 1833 | .25 | .25 |
| 104 | A19 | 6p Royal, 1832 | .25 | .25 |
| 104A | A19 | 7p 1822 | .35 | .35 |
| 105 | A19 | 8p Royal, 1868 | .25 | .25 |
| 106 | A19 | 9p 1785 | .25 | .25 |
| 107 | A19 | 10p 1824 | .25 | .25 |

### Perf. 13x13½, 13½x13

| 108 | A20 | 20p Royal, 1848, vert. | .50 | .50 |
|----|----|----|----|----|
| 109 | A20 | 50p Royal, 1868, vert. | 1.25 | 1.25 |
| 110 | A20 | £1 1814 | 2.10 | 2.00 |
| | | Nos. 95-110 (18) | 7.70 | 7.60 |

Issued: Nos. 95-107, 4/2/74; No. 108-110, 4/1/75; No. 102A, 104A, 5/29/76; No. 96a, 2/8/77; No. 96b, 2/7/78.

Stamps in booklet panes are from special sheets of 80 (two 8x5 panes) which were sold separately. The booklets following Nos. 99 and 100 come from panes of 88 with no gutter.

Bailiwick Seal and UPU Emblem A21

UPU Cent.: 3p, Map of Guernsey. 8p, UPU Headquarters, Bern, flag of Guernsey. 10p, Legislative Chamber, Parliament.

**1974, June 11    Photo.    Perf. 11½**
### Granite Paper

| 111 | A21 | 2½p multicolored | .25 | .25 |
|----|----|----|----|----|
| 112 | A21 | 3p ultra & multi | .25 | .25 |
| 113 | A21 | 8p multicolored | .25 | .25 |
| 114 | A21 | 10p multicolored | .25 | .25 |
| | | Nos. 111-114 (4) | 1.00 | 1.00 |

Postal Independence, 40th Anniv. — A222

"1969" and "2009" with inscription: 36p, The Psychedelic 60's. 43p, God Save the 70's. 51p, The POPular 80's. 54p, The Urban 90's. 56p, The Seductive 00's. 77p, Looking to the Future.

| | | | **2009, July 30 Litho.** | **Perf. 14x13¾** | |
|---|---|---|---|---|---|
| 1051 | A222 | 36p multi | | 1.00 | 1.00 |
| 1052 | A222 | 43p multi | | 1.15 | 1.15 |
| 1053 | A222 | 51p multi | | 1.35 | 1.35 |
| 1054 | A222 | 54p multi | | 1.45 | 1.45 |
| 1055 | A222 | 56p multi | | 1.60 | 1.60 |
| 1056 | A222 | 77p multi | | 2.00 | 2.00 |
| | | *Nos. 1051-1056 (6)* | | 8.55 | 8.55 |

### Seaside Views Type of 2007

Designs: 36p, Jerbourg Point. 43p, Vazon Bay. 51p, Saints Bay Moorings. 54p, Le Jaonnet Bay. 56p, Rocquaine Bay. 77p, Bordeaux Harbor.

| | | | **2009, Sept. 16 Litho.** | **Perf. 13½** | |
|---|---|---|---|---|---|
| 1057 | A209 | 36p multi | | 1.00 | 1.00 |
| 1058 | A209 | 43p multi | | 1.10 | 1.10 |
| 1059 | A209 | 51p multi | | 1.30 | 1.30 |
| 1060 | A209 | 54p multi | | 1.45 | 1.45 |
| 1061 | A209 | 56p multi | | 1.55 | 1.55 |
| 1062 | A209 | 77p multi | | 2.00 | 2.00 |
| | | *Nos. 1057-1062 (6)* | | 8.40 | 8.40 |

Christmas
A223

Designs: No. 1063, St. Martin's Church. No. 1064, Castel Church. No. 1065, Torteval Church. No. 1066, St. John's Church. No. 1067, St. Peter Port Church. No. 1068, St. Sampson's Church. 36p, St. Matthew's Church. 43p, St. Saviour's Church. 51p, Forest Church. 54p, St. Andrew's Church. 56p, Vale Church. 77p, St. Peter's Church.

**2009, Oct. 29**

| | | | | | |
|---|---|---|---|---|---|
| 1063 | A223 | 31p multi | | .85 | .85 |
| 1064 | A223 | 31p multi | | .85 | .85 |
| 1065 | A223 | 31p multi | | .85 | .85 |
| 1066 | A223 | 31p multi | | .85 | .85 |
| 1067 | A223 | 31p multi | | .85 | .85 |
| 1068 | A223 | 31p multi | | .85 | .85 |
| 1069 | A223 | 36p multi | | .95 | .95 |
| 1070 | A223 | 43p multi | | 1.10 | 1.10 |
| 1071 | A223 | 51p multi | | 1.35 | 1.35 |
| 1072 | A223 | 54p multi | | 1.35 | 1.35 |
| 1073 | A223 | 56p multi | | 1.50 | 1.50 |
| 1074 | A223 | 77p multi | | 2.00 | 2.00 |
| | | *Nos. 1063-1074 (12)* | | 13.35 | 13.35 |

### Souvenir Sheet

Asian Elephant A224

| | | | **2010, Feb. 25 Litho.** | **Perf. 14** | |
|---|---|---|---|---|---|
| 1075 | A224 | £3.07 multi | | 8.00 | 8.00 |

Views of Guernsey — A225

Designs: Nos. 1076, 1082a, Port à la Jument, Sark. Nos. 1077, 1082b, Dog and Lion Rocks. Nos. 1078, 1082c, Fort Grey. Nos. 1079, 1082d, West coast of Guernsey. Nos. 1080, 1082e, Slipway, Havelet Bay. Nos. 1081, 1082f, Castle Cornet.

| | | | **2010, Mar. 18** | **Perf. 13¼** | |
|---|---|---|---|---|---|
| 1076 | A225 | (48p) multi | | 1.30 | 1.30 |
| 1077 | A225 | (48p) multi | | 1.30 | 1.30 |
| *a.* | | Vert. pair, #1076-1077 | | 2.60 | 2.60 |
| 1078 | A225 | (50p) multi | | 1.40 | 1.40 |
| 1079 | A225 | (58p) multi | | 1.55 | 1.55 |

| 1080 | A225 | (58p) multi | | 1.55 | 1.55 |
|---|---|---|---|---|---|
| *a.* | | Vert. pair, #1079-1080 | | 3.10 | 3.10 |
| 1081 | A225 | (80p) multi | | 2.20 | 2.20 |
| | | *Nos. 1076-1081 (6)* | | 9.30 | 9.30 |

#### Self-Adhesive
*Serpentine Die Cut 12½*

| 1082 | | Sheet of 6 | 9.50 | |
|---|---|---|---|---|
| *a.-b.* | A225 | (48p) Either single | 1.50 | 1.50 |
| *c.* | A225 | (50p) multi | 1.60 | 1.60 |
| *d.-e.* | A225 | (58p) Either single | 1.75 | 1.75 |
| *f.* | A225 | (80p) multi | 2.50 | 2.50 |
| *g.* | | Booklet pane of 4, 2 each #1082a-1082b | 6.00 | |
| *h.* | | Booklet pane of 4, 2 each #1082d-1082e | 7.00 | |

Nos. 1076-1077, 1082a-1082b are inscribed "GY LARGE"; Nos. 1078, 1082c, "EUR"; Nos. 1079-1080, 1082d-1082e, "UK LARGE"; Nos. 1081, 1082f, "ROW."

Nos. 1082a-1082b, 1082d-1082e were issued in complete booklets of 50 consisting of 5 panes of 10 stamps. Each pane contained 5 of each denomination.

The Adventures of Penny the Postie — A226

Children on treasure chest with sail and: 45p, Volcano. 50p, Map. £2, Pirate and ship.

| | | | **2010, May 4 Litho.** | **Perf. 13¼** | |
|---|---|---|---|---|---|
| 1083 | A226 | 45p multi | | 1.20 | 1.20 |

**Size: 38x51mm**
**Perf. 14¼**

| 1084 | A226 | 50p multi | | 1.30 | 1.30 |
|---|---|---|---|---|---|
| 1085 | A226 | £2 multi | | 5.50 | 5.50 |
| *a.* | | Souvenir sheet, #1083-1085 | | 8.00 | 8.00 |
| | | *Nos. 1083-1085 (3)* | | 8.00 | 8.00 |

Europa (Nos. 1083-1084).

Girl Guides, Cent. — A227

Designs: 36p, Outdoor activities. 45p, Help during World Wars I and II. 48p, Crystal Palace Maze. 50p, Agnes Baden-Powell. 58p, Mount Everest. 80p, Queen's Guide award.

| | | | **2010, May 27 Litho.** | **Perf. 13¼** | |
|---|---|---|---|---|---|
| 1086 | A227 | 36p multi | | 1.00 | 1.00 |
| 1087 | A227 | 45p multi | | 1.10 | 1.10 |
| 1088 | A227 | 48p multi | | 1.25 | 1.25 |
| 1089 | A227 | 50p multi | | 1.50 | 1.50 |
| 1090 | A227 | 58p multi | | 1.60 | 1.60 |
| 1091 | A227 | 80p multi | | 2.25 | 2.25 |
| | | *Nos. 1086-1091 (6)* | | 8.70 | 8.70 |

National Trust of Guernsey, 50th Anniv. — A228

Designs: 36p, Victorian Shop, 26 Cornet Street, St. Peter Port. 45p, Field, Jerbourg. 48p, Martello Tower, Fermain Bay. 50p, Ivy Gates. 58p, Pleinmont Headland. 80p, Moulin de Quanteraine.

| | | | **2010, July 5 Litho.** | **Perf. 13½** | |
|---|---|---|---|---|---|
| 1092 | A228 | 36p multi | | 1.05 | 1.05 |
| 1093 | A228 | 45p multi | | 1.15 | 1.15 |
| 1094 | A228 | 48p multi | | 1.30 | 1.30 |
| 1095 | A228 | 50p multi | | 1.50 | 1.50 |
| 1096 | A228 | 58p multi | | 1.60 | 1.60 |
| 1097 | A228 | 80p multi | | 2.25 | 2.25 |
| | | *Nos. 1092-1097 (6)* | | 8.85 | 8.85 |

### Seaside Views Type of 2007

Design: Point Robert Lighthouse, Sark.

| | | | **2010, June 18** | **Perf. 13¾x13½** | |
|---|---|---|---|---|---|
| 1098 | A209 | 55p multi | | 1.45 | 1.45 |

Evacuation of Guernsey, 70th Anniv. — A229

Designs: 36p, Gas masks being loaded onto a truck, 1939. 45p, Guernsey children waiting to leave, 1940. 48p, German soldiers leaving Guernsey, 1945. 50p, Evacuees arriving back in Guernsey, 1945. 58p, Royal visit to Guernsey, June 1945. 80p, Liberation Day, 1946.

| | | | **2010, July 29** | **Perf. 13¾** | |
|---|---|---|---|---|---|
| 1099 | A229 | 36p multi | | 1.05 | 1.05 |
| 1100 | A229 | 45p multi | | 1.15 | 1.15 |
| 1101 | A229 | 48p multi | | 1.30 | 1.30 |
| 1102 | A229 | 50p multi | | 1.40 | 1.40 |
| 1103 | A229 | 58p multi | | 1.65 | 1.65 |
| 1104 | A229 | 80p multi | | 2.10 | 2.10 |
| | | *Nos. 1099-1104 (6)* | | 8.65 | 8.65 |

2010 Commonwealth Games, Delhi — A230

Designs: 36p, Tennis. 45p, Lawn bowling. 48p, Shooting. 50p, Swimming. 58p, Track. 80p, Cycling.

| | | | **2010, Sept. 23** | **Perf. 13½** | |
|---|---|---|---|---|---|
| 1105 | A230 | 36p multi | | .95 | .95 |
| *a.* | | Booklet pane of 4 | | 4.00 | |
| 1106 | A230 | 45p multi | | 1.25 | 1.25 |
| *a.* | | Booklet pane of 4 | | 5.25 | |
| 1107 | A230 | 48p multi | | 1.40 | 1.40 |
| *a.* | | Booklet pane of 4 | | 5.75 | |
| 1108 | A230 | 50p multi | | 1.50 | 1.50 |
| *a.* | | Booklet pane of 4 | | 6.25 | |
| 1109 | A230 | 58p multi | | 1.60 | 1.60 |
| *a.* | | Booklet pane of 4 | | 6.50 | |
| 1110 | A230 | 80p multi | | 2.25 | 2.25 |
| *a.* | | Booklet pane of 4 | | 9.25 | |
| | | Complete booklet, #1005a, 1106a, 1107a, 1108a, 1109a, 1110a | | 32.50 | |
| | | *Nos. 1105-1110 (6)* | | 8.95 | 8.95 |

Christmas Carols — A231

Designs: 31p, The Holly and the Ivy. 36p, Little Donkey. 45p, Silent Night. 48p, I Saw Three Ships. 50p, Joy to the World. 58p, Ding Dong Merrily on High. 80p, We Three Kings.

| | | | **2010, Nov. 4 Litho.** | **Perf. 13¼x14** | |
|---|---|---|---|---|---|
| 1111 | A231 | 31p multi | | 1.00 | 1.00 |
| 1112 | A231 | 36p multi | | 1.10 | 1.10 |
| 1113 | A231 | 45p multi | | 1.25 | 1.25 |
| 1114 | A231 | 48p multi | | 1.40 | 1.40 |
| 1115 | A231 | 50p multi | | 1.50 | 1.50 |
| 1116 | A231 | 58p multi | | 1.60 | 1.60 |
| 1117 | A231 | 80p multi | | 2.00 | 2.00 |
| | | *Nos. 1111-1117 (7)* | | 11.45 | 11.45 |

Royal British Legion, 90th Anniv. A232

Emblem, soldiers or veterans and word: 36p, Hope. 45p, Reflection. 52p, Comradeship. 58p, Selflessness. 65p, Service. 70p, Dedication.

| | | | **2011, Feb. 23 Litho.** | **Perf. 13¼x13** | |
|---|---|---|---|---|---|
| 1118 | A232 | 36p multi | | 1.10 | 1.10 |
| 1119 | A232 | 45p multi | | 1.25 | 1.25 |
| 1120 | A232 | 52p multi | | 1.40 | 1.40 |
| 1121 | A232 | 58p multi | | 1.50 | 1.50 |
| 1122 | A232 | 65p multi | | 1.75 | 1.75 |
| 1123 | A232 | 70p multi | | 2.00 | 2.00 |
| *a.* | | Souvenir sheet of 6, #1118-1123 | | 9.00 | 9.00 |
| | | *Nos. 1118-1123 (6)* | | 9.00 | 9.00 |

### Souvenir Sheet

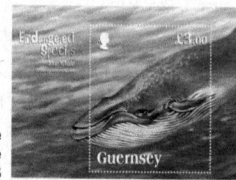

Blue Whale A233

| | | | **2011, Feb. 23** | **Perf. 13¼** | |
|---|---|---|---|---|---|
| 1124 | A233 | £3 multi | | 8.25 | 8.25 |

Intl. Year of Forests — A234

Designs: 45p, Oak leaves, acorn. 52p, Hazel leaves, hazel nut. £2, Horse chestnut leaves and horse chestnut.

| | | | **2011, May 4** | **Perf. 13¾** | |
|---|---|---|---|---|---|
| 1125 | A234 | 45p multi | | 1.15 | 1.15 |
| 1126 | A234 | 52p multi | | 1.60 | 1.60 |
| 1127 | A234 | £2 multi | | 5.25 | 5.25 |
| *a.* | | Souvenir sheet of 3, #1125-1127 | | 8.00 | 8.00 |
| | | *Nos. 1125-1127 (3)* | | 8.00 | 8.00 |

Europa (Nos. 1125-1126).

### Souvenir Sheets

Wedding of Prince William and Catherine Middleton — A235

Designs: No. 1128, Engagement photo. No. 1129, Bride and groom on wedding day.

| | | | **2011, June 2** | **Perf. 14** | |
|---|---|---|---|---|---|
| 1128 | A235 | £2 multi | | 5.25 | 5.25 |
| 1129 | A235 | £2 multi | | 5.25 | 5.25 |

The Guernsey Literary and Potato Peel Pie Society, Book by Mary Ann Shaffer and Annie Barrows — A236

Depictions of scenes from book: 36p, How to roast your pig. 47p, The books enjoyed by the Guernsey Literary and Potato Peel Pie Society. 48p, Juliet arrives at St. Peter Port weaing her red cloak. 52p, The view through Elizabeth's cottage window. 61p, Juliet and Dawsey's pivotal moment on the cliffs. 65p, Isola's legendary parrot, Zenobia.

| | | | **2011, July 28** | **Perf. 13¼** | |
|---|---|---|---|---|---|
| 1130 | A236 | 36p multi | | .95 | .95 |
| 1131 | A236 | 47p multi | | 1.05 | 1.05 |
| 1132 | A236 | 48p multi | | 1.30 | 1.30 |
| 1133 | A236 | 52p multi | | 1.40 | 1.40 |
| 1134 | A236 | 61p multi | | 1.60 | 1.60 |
| 1135 | A236 | 65p multi | | 1.75 | 1.75 |
| | | *Nos. 1130-1135 (6)* | | 8.05 | 8.05 |

### Seaside Views Type of 2007

Designs: 36p, Victoria Marina, St. Peter Port. 45p, L'Ancresse Bay. 52p, Bordeaux Harbor Slipway. 58p, South Coast sunset. 65p, Salerie Harbor. 70p, Petit Port.

| | | | **2011, Sept. 28 Litho.** | **Perf. 14¼** | |
|---|---|---|---|---|---|
| 1136 | A209 | 36p multi | | 1.00 | 1.00 |
| 1137 | A209 | 45p multi | | 1.25 | 1.25 |
| 1138 | A209 | 52p multi | | 1.35 | 1.35 |
| 1139 | A209 | 58p multi | | 1.40 | 1.40 |
| 1140 | A209 | 65p multi | | 1.65 | 1.65 |
| 1141 | A209 | 70p multi | | 1.90 | 1.90 |
| | | *Nos. 1136-1141 (6)* | | 8.55 | 8.55 |

### British Formula 1 World Championship Cars and Drivers Type of 2007

Driver and championship year: 36p, Lewis Hamilton, 2008 (red background). 47p, Jenson Button, 2009 (purple background). 61p, Hamilton, 2008 (blue background). 65p, Button, 2009 (orange background).

| | | | **2011, Oct. 27** | **Perf. 13¼x13** | |
|---|---|---|---|---|---|
| 1142 | A206 | 36p multi | | .95 | .95 |
| 1143 | A206 | 47p multi | | 1.15 | 1.15 |
| 1144 | A206 | 61p multi | | 1.65 | 1.65 |
| 1145 | A206 | 65p multi | | 1.85 | 1.85 |
| *a.* | | Souvenir sheet of 4, #1142-1145 | | 5.75 | 5.75 |
| | | *Nos. 1142-1145 (4)* | | 5.60 | 5.60 |

Guernsey in Winter — A237

Winning entries in "Guernsey in Winter" photography contest: 31p, Forest Church, by John Shakerley. 36p, L'Ancresse Common, by Nigel Byrom. 47p, Guernsey Cows, by Sarah Plumley. 48p, St. Peter Port, by Karen Millard. 52p, La Coupée, by Sue Daly. 61p, St. Peter's Church, by Jason Bishop. 65p, Cobo Bay, by Eric Ferbrache.

**2011, Oct. 27**     **Perf. 13½x13¼**

| | | | |
|---|---|---|---|
| 1146 | A237 | 31p multi | .90 | .90 |
| 1147 | A237 | 36p multi | 1.00 | 1.00 |
| 1148 | A237 | 47p multi | 1.15 | 1.15 |
| 1149 | A237 | 48p multi | 1.30 | 1.30 |
| 1150 | A237 | 52p multi | 1.40 | 1.40 |
| 1151 | A237 | 61p multi | 1.45 | 1.45 |
| 1152 | A237 | 65p multi | 1.85 | 1.85 |
| | | Nos. 1146-1152 (7) | 9.05 | 9.05 |

**Souvenir Sheet**

Bengal Tiger A238

**2012, Feb. 22**     **Perf. 13¾**

| 1153 | A238 | £3 multi | 8.50 | 8.75 |
|---|---|---|---|---|

Reign of Queen Elizabeth II, 60th Anniv. — A239

Gem and: 36p, Queen at coronation, birth of Prince Andrew. 47p, Queen presenting Jules Rimet trophy to captain of British soccer team, ocean liner Queen Elizabeth 2. 48p, Queen, Sydney Opera House, emblem of 1976 Montreal Summer Olympics. 52p, Queen riding horse, Princes William and Harry in school uniforms, 1989. 61p, Queen, Queen Mother, Nelson Mandela. 65p, Queen at Guernsey Liberation Day, Queen with Pres. Barack Obama.

**2012, Feb. 22**     **Perf. 12½**

| 1154 | A239 | 36p multi | .95 | .95 |
|---|---|---|---|---|
| 1155 | A239 | 47p multi | 1.20 | 1.20 |
| 1156 | A239 | 48p multi | 1.35 | 1.35 |
| 1157 | A239 | 52p multi | 1.45 | 1.45 |
| 1158 | A239 | 61p multi | 1.65 | 1.65 |
| 1159 | A239 | 65p multi | 1.90 | 1.90 |
| a. | | Souvenir sheet of 6, #1154-1159 | 8.50 | 8.50 |
| | | Nos. 1154-1159 (6) | 8.50 | 8.50 |

Tourist Attractions A240

Designs: (39p), Surfer, Vazon Bay. (52p), Shell Beach, Herm. (53p), Grande Greve Beach, Sark. (59p), Bluestone Bay, Alderney. (69p), Sailboat off the coast of Herm. (74p), La Coupée, Sark.

**2012, May 1**     **Perf. 13x13¼**

| 1160 | A240 | (39p) multi | 1.20 | 1.20 |
|---|---|---|---|---|
| 1161 | A240 | (52p) multi | 1.40 | 1.40 |
| 1162 | A240 | (53p) multi | 1.55 | 1.55 |
| 1163 | A240 | (59p) multi | 1.65 | 1.65 |
| 1164 | A240 | (69p) multi | 1.95 | 1.95 |
| 1165 | A240 | (74p) multi | 2.25 | 2.25 |
| a. | | Souvenir sheet of 6, #1160-1165 | 10.00 | 10.00 |
| | | Nos. 1160-1165 (6) | 10.00 | 10.00 |

Europa (53p, 59p). Inscriptions on: No. 1160, "GY Letter"; No. 1161, "GY Large"; No. 1162, "UK Letter"; No. 1163, "INT Letter 20G"; No. 1164, "UK Large"; No. 1165, "INT Letter 40G."

Duke of Cambridge, 30th Birthday — A241

Prince William: 36p, Carrying log, Chile, 2006. 47p, At St. Andrews University graduation ceremonies, 2005. 48p, Playing soccer,

2006. 52p, Climbing mountain, 2007. 67p, Riding motorcycle at Endura Africa Charity Motorcycle Ride, 2008. 65p, As rescue pilot, 2010.

**2012, May 8**     **Perf. 13½**

| 1166 | A241 | 36p multi | 1.00 | 1.00 |
|---|---|---|---|---|
| a. | | Booklet pane of 4 | 4.25 | |
| 1167 | A241 | 47p multi | 1.10 | 1.10 |
| a. | | Booklet pane of 4 | 4.50 | |
| 1168 | A241 | 48p multi | 1.50 | 1.50 |
| a. | | Booklet pane of 4 | 6.00 | |
| 1169 | A241 | 52p multi | 1.60 | 1.60 |
| a. | | Booklet pane of 4 | 6.50 | |
| 1170 | A241 | 61p multi | 1.75 | 1.90 |
| a. | | Booklet pane of 4 | 7.25 | |
| 1171 | A241 | 65p multi | 2.00 | 2.10 |
| a. | | Booklet pane of 4 | 8.00 | |
| b. | | Complete booklet, #1166a, 1167a, 1168a, 1169a, 1170a, 1171a | 35.00 | |
| | | Nos. 1166-1171 (6) | 8.95 | 9.20 |

War of 1812 A242

No. 1172: a, Sir Isaac Brock (1769-1812), British Major General. b, Tecumseh (1768-1813), leader of Indian confederacy.

**2012, June 15**     **Perf. 13¼x12½**

| 1172 | A242 | Horiz. pair | 5.75 | 6.75 |
|---|---|---|---|---|
| a.-b. | | £1 Either single | 2.75 | 2.75 |

See Canada Nos. 2554-2555.

Royal Channel Islands Yacht Club, 150th Anniv. A243

Various sailors on yachts.

**2012, July 25**     **Perf. 13¼x13½**
**Denomination Color**

| 1173 | A243 | 39p purple | 1.25 | 1.35 |
|---|---|---|---|---|
| 1174 | A243 | 52p blue gray | 1.40 | 1.50 |
| 1175 | A243 | 53p blue | 1.50 | 1.60 |
| 1176 | A243 | 59p blue | 1.75 | 1.90 |
| 1177 | A243 | 69p olive green | 1.90 | 2.00 |
| 1178 | A243 | 74p orange brown | 2.00 | 2.10 |
| | | Nos. 1173-1178 (6) | 9.80 | 10.45 |

A244

Floral Guernsey, 20th Anniv. — A245

Designs: 39p, Flowers in wheelbarrow. 52p, Flowers and Seigneurie, home of Lord of Sark. 53p, Flower display and rope. 59p, Flowers and sea. 69p, Potted flowers in and near shelf. 74p, Flowers and building, diff. £3, Floral Guernsey daffodil.

**2012, Sept. 27**     **Perf. 13½**

| 1179 | A244 | 39p multi | 1.25 | 1.35 |
|---|---|---|---|---|
| 1180 | A244 | 52p multi | 1.40 | 1.50 |
| 1181 | A244 | 53p multi | 1.50 | 1.60 |
| 1182 | A244 | 59p multi | 1.75 | 1.90 |
| 1183 | A244 | 69p multi | 1.90 | 2.00 |
| 1184 | A244 | 74p multi | 2.00 | 2.10 |
| | | Nos. 1179-1184 (6) | 9.80 | 10.45 |

**Souvenir Sheet**
**Perf. 14**

| 1185 | A245 | £3 multi | 8.50 | 9.50 |
|---|---|---|---|---|

Christmas — A246

Designs: 34p, Annunciation. 39p, Innkeeper shows Mary and Joseph to the stable. 52p, Jesus is born in a stable. 53p, Angels come down amongst the shepherds. 59p, The Three Kings. 69p, Mary and baby Jesus with Angels. 74p, Flight to Egypt.

**2012, Oct. 31**     **Perf. 13¼x13**

| 1186 | A246 | 34p multi | 1.05 | 1.10 |
|---|---|---|---|---|
| 1187 | A246 | 39p multi | 1.15 | 1.20 |
| 1188 | A246 | 52p multi | 1.45 | 1.50 |
| 1189 | A246 | 53p multi | 1.60 | 1.60 |
| 1190 | A246 | 59p multi | 1.60 | 1.75 |
| 1191 | A246 | 69p multi | 1.75 | 1.90 |
| 1192 | A246 | 74p multi | 2.10 | 2.10 |
| | | Nos. 1186-1192 (7) | 10.70 | 11.15 |

**Souvenir Sheet**

Giant Panda A247

**2013, Feb. 20**     **Perf. 14x14¼**

| 1193 | A247 | £3 multi | 8.00 | 8.00 |
|---|---|---|---|---|

Fish — A248

Designs: 39p, Tompot blenny. 52p, Leopard-spotted goby. 53p, Red gurnard. 59p, Female cuckoo wrasse. 69p, Male cuckoo wrasse. 74p, John Dory. £5, Black-face blenny.

**2013, Feb. 20**     **Perf. 12½**

| 1194 | A248 | 39p multi | 1.10 | 1.10 |
|---|---|---|---|---|
| 1195 | A248 | 52p multi | 1.40 | 1.40 |
| 1196 | A248 | 53p multi | 1.40 | 1.40 |
| 1197 | A248 | 59p multi | 1.55 | 1.55 |
| 1198 | A248 | 69p multi | 1.70 | 1.70 |
| 1199 | A248 | 74p multi | 1.85 | 1.85 |
| | | Nos. 1194-1199 (6) | 10.55 | 10.55 |

**Souvenir Sheet**
**Perf. 13¼x13½**

| 1200 | A248 | £5 multi | 13.50 | 13.50 |
|---|---|---|---|---|

No. 1200 contains one 48x66mm stamp.

**Souvenir Sheet**

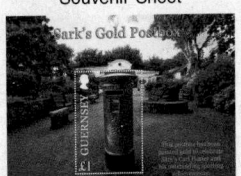

Mailbox on Sark Painted Gold to Commemorate Olympic Gold Medalist Carl Hester — A249

**2013, Mar. 20**     **Perf. 14¾x14¼**

| 1201 | A249 | £1 multi | 2.75 | 2.75 |
|---|---|---|---|---|

No. 1201 was sent free of charge to Guernsey Post standing order customers in February 2013. It was offered for sale starting March 20 through online sales only.

Postal Vehicles — A250

Designs: (40p), Guernsey Post Daihatsu Hijet van, GY Letter. (53p), La Poste Citroen 2CV van, France, GY Large Letter. (55p),

Royal Mail Morris 6cwt O Type van, Great Britain, UK Letter. (63p), Deutsche Post Volkswagen Beetle van, Germany, Int Letter 20g. (71p), Posten AB Kalmar Tjorven van, Sweden, UK Large Letter. (79p), United States Post Office Studebaker Zip van, Int Letter 40g.

**2013, May 8**     **Perf. 13¼x13**

| 1202 | A250 | (40p) multi | 1.10 | 1.10 |
|---|---|---|---|---|
| 1203 | A250 | (53p) multi | 1.55 | 1.55 |
| 1204 | A250 | (55p) multi | 1.55 | 1.55 |
| 1205 | A250 | (63p) multi | 1.75 | 1.75 |
| 1206 | A250 | (71p) multi | 1.95 | 1.95 |
| 1207 | A250 | (79p) multi | 2.20 | 2.20 |
| a. | | Souvenir sheet of 6, #1202-1207 | 10.25 | 10.25 |
| | | Nos. 1202-1207 (6) | 10.10 | 10.10 |

Europa (Nos. 1204-1205).

Herm Island — A251

Designs: 40p, Mermaid Tavern sign. 53p, Shell Beach. 55p, Belvoir Bay. 63p, Harbor moorings. 71p, Fishermans Beach. 79p, Gift shop.

**2013, May 29**     **Perf. 13x12½**

| 1208 | A251 | 40p multi | 1.05 | 1.05 |
|---|---|---|---|---|
| 1209 | A251 | 53p multi | 1.50 | 1.50 |
| 1210 | A251 | 55p multi | 1.50 | 1.50 |
| 1211 | A251 | 63p multi | 1.70 | 1.70 |
| 1212 | A251 | 71p multi | 1.90 | 1.90 |
| 1213 | A251 | 79p multi | 2.15 | 2.15 |
| | | Nos. 1208-1213 (6) | 9.80 | 9.80 |

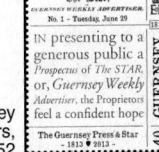

Guernsey Newspapers, Bicent. — A252

Designs: 40p, Text from first edition of The Star, 1813. 53p, Text and illustration from The Star announcing Diamond Jubilee of Queen Victoria. 55p, Guernsey #N1, Text from The Evening Press announcing occupation of Guernsey. 63p, Text from The Guernsey Press announcing bicentennial of newspaper. 71p, Text and illustration from Guernsey Evening Press announcing coronation of Queen Elizabeth II. 79p, Text and illustration from Guernsey Evening Press announcing end of World War II in Europe.

**2013, July 31**    **Litho.**    **Perf. 13**

| 1214 | A252 | 40p gray & blk | 1.05 | 1.05 |
|---|---|---|---|---|
| 1215 | A252 | 53p gray & blk | 1.50 | 1.50 |
| 1216 | A252 | 55p multi | 1.50 | 1.50 |
| 1217 | A252 | 63p multi | 1.70 | 1.70 |
| 1218 | A252 | 71p gray & blk | 1.90 | 1.90 |
| 1219 | A252 | 79p gray & blk | 2.15 | 2.15 |
| | | Nos. 1214-1219 (6) | 9.80 | 9.80 |

West Show, Cent. — A253

Designs: 40p, Farmers looking at tractors and hay-kicker. 53p, Prize-winning produce. 55p, Brewery dray and shire horses. 63p, Guernsey cows. 71p, Steam tractor engine. 79p, Haymaking.

**2013, Sept. 24**    **Litho.**    **Perf. 13**

| 1220 | A253 | 40p multi | 1.05 | 1.05 |
|---|---|---|---|---|
| 1221 | A253 | 53p multi | 1.50 | 1.50 |
| 1222 | A253 | 55p multi | 1.50 | 1.50 |
| 1223 | A253 | 63p multi | 1.70 | 1.70 |
| 1224 | A253 | 71p multi | 1.90 | 1.90 |
| 1225 | A253 | 79p multi | 2.15 | 2.15 |
| | | Nos. 1220-1225 (6) | 9.80 | 9.80 |

## Souvenir Sheet

Birth of Prince George of Cambridge — A254

**2013, Sept. 24**   Litho.   *Perf. 12½*
1226 A254 £3 multi    8.25 8.25

Clematis Varieties Developed by Raymond Evison — A255

Clematis variety: 40p, Samaritan Jo. 53p, Anna Louise. 55p, Chelsea. 63p, Edda. 71p, The Countess of Wessex. 79p, Giselle.

**2013, Nov. 13**   Litho.   *Perf. 13¾*
| | | | |
|---|---|---|---|
| 1227 | A255 40p multi | 1.15 | 1.15 |
| a. | Booklet pane of 4 | 4.75 | |
| 1228 | A255 53p multi | 1.45 | 1.45 |
| a. | Booklet pane of 4 | 5.75 | |
| 1229 | A255 55p multi | 1.55 | 1.55 |
| a. | Booklet pane of 4 | 6.25 | |
| 1230 | A255 63p multi | 1.75 | 1.75 |
| a. | Booklet pane of 4 | 7.00 | |
| 1231 | A255 71p multi | 1.95 | 1.95 |
| a. | Booklet pane of 4 | 8.00 | |
| 1232 | A255 79p multi | 2.15 | 2.15 |
| a. | Booklet pane of 4 | 8.75 | |
| | Complete booklet, #1227a, 1228a, 1229a, 1230a, 1231a, 1232a | 37.50 | |
| | Nos. 1227-1232 (6) | 10.00 | 10.00 |

Christmas A256

Santa Claus: 35p, Outside of sleeping child's bedroom window. 40p, On roof. 53p, Stuck in chimney. 55p, Being pulled out of chimney by children. 63p, Sneezing. 71p, Placing gifts under Christmas tree. 79p, Above houses in flying sleigh.

**2013, Nov. 13**   Litho.   *Perf. 13x13½*
| | | | |
|---|---|---|---|
| 1233 | A256 35p multi | 1.10 | 1.10 |
| 1234 | A256 40p multi | 1.20 | 1.20 |
| 1235 | A256 53p multi | 1.50 | 1.50 |
| 1236 | A256 55p multi | 1.65 | 1.65 |
| 1237 | A256 63p multi | 1.80 | 1.80 |
| 1238 | A256 71p multi | 2.10 | 2.10 |
| 1239 | A256 79p multi | 2.25 | 2.25 |
| | Nos. 1233-1239 (7) | 11.60 | 11.60 |

New Year 2014 (Year of the Horse) — A257

Chinese character for "horse" and various depictions of horses.

**2014, Jan. 8**   Litho.   *Perf. 13*
| | | | |
|---|---|---|---|
| 1240 | A257 40p multi | 1.20 | 1.20 |
| 1241 | A257 53p multi | 1.50 | 1.50 |
| 1242 | A257 55p multi | 1.60 | 1.60 |
| 1243 | A257 63p multi | 1.80 | 1.80 |
| 1244 | A257 71p multi | 2.05 | 2.05 |
| 1245 | A257 79p multi | 2.20 | 2.20 |
| a. | Souvenir sheet of 6, #1240-1245 | 10.50 | 10.50 |
| | Nos. 1240-1245 (6) | 10.35 | 10.35 |

## Souvenir Sheet

Sumatran Orangutan — A258

**2014, Feb. 12**   Litho.   *Perf. 14x14¼*
1246 A258 £3 multi    8.25 8.25

---

Chifournie — A259

Designs: 40p, Chifournie keys. 53p, Chifournie wooden pegs and turning handle. 55p, Chifournie rotating wheel. 63p, Chifournie wheel and strings. 71p, Chifournie turning handle and wheel. 79p, Entire chifournie.

**2014, May 8**   Litho.   *Perf. 13x13¼*
| | | | |
|---|---|---|---|
| 1247 | A259 40p multi | 1.20 | 1.20 |
| 1248 | A259 53p multi | 1.50 | 1.50 |
| 1249 | A259 55p multi | 1.60 | 1.60 |
| 1250 | A259 63p multi | 1.75 | 1.75 |
| 1251 | A259 71p multi | 2.05 | 2.05 |
| 1252 | A259 79p multi | 2.35 | 2.35 |
| a. | Souvenir sheet of 6, #1247-1252 | 10.50 | 10.50 |
| | Nos. 1247-1252 (6) | 10.45 | 10.45 |

Europa (55p, 63p).

Postcrossing — A260

**2014, May 28**   Litho.   *Perf. 13¼*
1253 A260 (66p) multi    2.25 2.25

Britain in Bloom Horticultural Campaign, 50th Anniv. — A261

Designs: (41p), St. Peter Port Marina. (54p), White House view, Herm. (55p), Mermaid Tavern, Herm. (66p), St. Pierre du Bois. (74p), St. Martin's Church. (83p), Albion Tavern, St. Peter Port.

**2014, May 28**   Litho.   *Perf. 13½*
| | | | |
|---|---|---|---|
| 1254 | A261 (41p) multi | 1.20 | 1.20 |
| 1255 | A261 (54p) multi | 1.65 | 1.65 |
| 1256 | A261 (55p) multi | 1.65 | 1.65 |
| 1257 | A261 (66p) multi | 1.95 | 1.95 |
| 1258 | A261 (74p) multi | 2.20 | 2.20 |
| 1259 | A261 (83p) multi | 2.40 | 2.40 |
| | Nos. 1254-1259 (6) | 11.05 | 11.05 |

Inscriptions: No. 1254, "GY Letter." No. 1255, "GY Large Letter." No. 1256, "UK Letter." No. 1257, "Int Letter 20g." No. 1258, "UK Large Letter." No. 1259, "Int Letter 40g."

Crustaceans — A262

Designs: 41p, Chancre (brown crab). 54p, Lobster. 55p, Velvet swimming crab. 66p, Hermit crab. 74p, Squat lobster. 83p, Spider crab. £3, Anemone shrimp.

**2014, July 30**   Litho.   *Perf. 12½*
| | | | |
|---|---|---|---|
| 1260 | A262 41p multi | 1.20 | 1.20 |
| 1261 | A262 54p multi | 1.65 | 1.65 |
| 1262 | A262 55p multi | 1.65 | 1.65 |
| 1263 | A262 66p multi | 1.95 | 1.95 |
| 1264 | A262 74p multi | 2.15 | 2.15 |
| 1265 | A262 83p multi | 2.40 | 2.40 |
| | Nos. 1260-1265 (6) | 11.00 | 11.00 |

### Souvenir Sheet
*Perf. 13¼x13¾*
1266 A262 £3 multi    9.00 9.00

No. 1266 contains one 48x66mm stamp.

Views of Guernsey, Alderney, Herm and Sark — A263

No. 1267: a, Little Chapel and cow. b, Bec du Néz. c, Torteval Church. d, Moulin Huet. e, St. Peter Port Harbor. f, Fisherman's Beach, Herm. g, Creux Harbor, Sark. h, Fort Essex,

---

Alderney. i, Vazon Bay, Guernsey. j, Petit Bot, Guernsey.

### Serpentine Die Cut 12½
**2014, July 30**    Litho.
**Self-Adhesive**
| | | | |
|---|---|---|---|
| 1267 | Sheet of 10 | 14.50 | |
| a.-e. | A263 (41p) Any single | 1.25 | 1.25 |
| f.-j. | A263 (55p) Any single | 1.70 | 1.70 |
| k. | Booklet pane of 10, 2 each #1267a-1267e | 12.50 | |
| l. | Booklet pane of 10, 2 each #1267f-1267j | 16.75 | |

Nos. 1267a-1267e are inscribed "GY"; Nos. 1267f-1267j, "UK."

Christmas — A264

Children's art depicting: 36p, Rudolph, the Red-nosed Reindeer and stars, by Katka Devon. 41p, Robins in tree, by Patience Ogler. 54p, Rudolph and candy canes, by Georgia Winstanley. 55p, Santa Claus, by Mali Chatterton. 66p, Robin in stocking cap, by Ruby Parker. 74p, Snowman and candy canes, by Giselle Fuller. 83p, Robin on chimney, by Keone Hardy.

### Serpentine Die Cut
**2014, Nov. 6**    Litho.
**Self-Adhesive**
| | | | |
|---|---|---|---|
| 1268 | A264 36p multi | 1.15 | 1.15 |
| 1269 | A264 41p multi | 1.30 | 1.30 |
| 1270 | A264 54p multi | 1.60 | 1.60 |
| 1271 | A264 55p multi | 1.60 | 1.60 |
| 1272 | A264 66p multi | 1.95 | 1.95 |
| 1273 | A264 74p multi | 2.25 | 2.25 |
| 1274 | A264 83p multi | 2.40 | 2.40 |
| | Nos. 1268-1274 (7) | 12.25 | 12.25 |

World War I, Cent. — A265

Designs: 41p, Private Yves Cataroche. 54p, Major George Le Page. 55p, Munitions worker Dorothy Nicolls. 66p, Lieutenant Frank Lainé. 74p, Salvation Army worker Ada Le Poidevin. 83p, Private Latimer Le Poidevin.

**2014, Nov. 11**   Litho.   *Perf. 14x14¾*
| | | | |
|---|---|---|---|
| 1275 | A265 41p multi | 1.15 | 1.15 |
| a. | Booklet pane of 4 | 4.75 | — |
| 1276 | A265 54p multi | 1.60 | 1.60 |
| a. | Booklet pane of 4 | 6.50 | — |
| 1277 | A265 55p multi | 1.60 | 1.60 |
| a. | Booklet pane of 4 | 6.50 | — |
| 1278 | A265 66p multi | 1.90 | 1.90 |
| a. | Booklet pane of 4 | 7.75 | — |
| 1279 | A265 74p multi | 2.20 | 2.20 |
| a. | Booklet pane of 4 | 8.75 | — |
| 1280 | A265 83p multi | 2.40 | 2.40 |
| a. | Booklet pane of 4 | 9.75 | — |
| | Complete booklet, #1275a, 1276a, 1277a, 1278a, 1279a, 1280a | 45.00 | |
| | Nos. 1275-1280 (6) | 10.85 | 10.85 |

See Nos. 1320-1325, 1367-1372, 1409-1414, 1455-1460.

### Souvenir Sheet

Sir Winston Churchill (1874-1965), British Prime Minister — A266

No. 1281 — Churchill: a, Walking in garden (40x30mm). b, Painting picture (40x30mm). c, Wearing military cap (60x48mm).

**2015, Jan. 22**   Litho.   *Perf. 13x13¼*
| | | | |
|---|---|---|---|
| 1281 | A266 Sheet of 3 | 9.00 | 9.00 |
| a.-c. | £1 Any single | 3.00 | 3.00 |

---

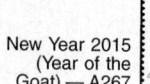

New Year 2015 (Year of the Goat) — A267

Various depictions of goats.

**2015, Jan. 28**   Litho.   *Perf. 13x13¼*
| | | | |
|---|---|---|---|
| 1282 | A267 41p red & gold | 1.25 | 1.25 |
| 1283 | A267 54p red & gold | 1.60 | 1.60 |
| 1284 | A267 55p red & gold | 1.75 | 1.75 |
| 1285 | A267 66p red & gold | 2.00 | 2.00 |
| 1286 | A267 74p red & gold | 2.25 | 2.25 |
| 1287 | A267 83p red & gold | 2.50 | 2.50 |
| a. | Souvenir sheet of 6, #1282-1287 | 11.50 | 11.50 |
| | Nos. 1282-1287 (6) | 11.35 | 11.35 |

Toys of the Royal Family — A268

Designs: 41p, Prince George's rocking horse, c. 2013. 54p, Princess Victoria's wooden dolls, c. 1831. 55p, Prince Charles's toy car, c. 1950. 66p, Teddy bear from Royal Nursery. 74p, Princess Elizabeth's toy baker's wagon, c. 1930. 83p, Silver rattles, c. 1774, 1763 and 2003.

**2015, May 1**   Litho.   *Perf. 13¾*
| | | | |
|---|---|---|---|
| 1288 | A268 41p multi | 1.25 | 1.25 |
| 1289 | A268 54p multi | 1.60 | 1.60 |
| 1290 | A268 55p multi | 1.75 | 1.75 |
| 1291 | A268 66p multi | 2.00 | 2.00 |
| 1292 | A268 74p multi | 2.25 | 2.25 |
| 1293 | A268 83p multi | 2.50 | 2.50 |
| a. | Souvenir sheet of 6, #1288-1293 | 11.50 | 11.50 |
| | Nos. 1288-1293 (6) | 11.35 | 11.35 |

Europa (Nos. 1290-1291).

Liberation of Guernsey, 70th Anniv. A269

Designs: (41p), Two boys enjoying chocolate for first time. (54p), Duke of Cornwall's Light Infantry Band. (55p), Col. H. R. Power tours St. Peter Port seafront. (66p), Petty Officer J. D. Langlois enjoying the moment. (74p), US 516 docks in St. Peter Port harbor. (83p), King George VI and Queen Elizabeth.

**2015, May 1**   Litho.   *Perf. 13¼x13½*
| | | | |
|---|---|---|---|
| 1294 | A269 (41p) multi | 1.25 | 1.25 |
| a. | Booklet pane of 4 | 5.00 | — |
| 1295 | A269 (54p) multi | 1.60 | 1.60 |
| a. | Booklet pane of 4 | 6.50 | — |
| 1296 | A269 (55p) multi | 1.75 | 1.75 |
| a. | Booklet pane of 4 | 7.00 | — |
| 1297 | A269 (66p) multi | 2.00 | 2.00 |
| a. | Booklet pane of 4 | 8.00 | — |
| 1298 | A269 (74p) multi | 2.25 | 2.25 |
| a. | Booklet pane of 4 | 9.00 | — |
| 1299 | A269 (83p) multi | 2.50 | 2.50 |
| a. | Booklet pane of 4 | 10.00 | — |
| | Complete booklet, #1294a, 1295a, 1296a, 1297a, 1298a, 1299a | 46.00 | |
| | Nos. 1294-1299 (6) | 11.35 | 11.35 |

Inscriptions on: No. 1294, "GY Letter." No. 1295, "GY Large Letter." No. 1296, "UK Letter." No. 1297, "EUR Letter." No. 1298, "UK Large Letter." No. 1299, "ROW Letter."

### Souvenir Sheet

Penny Black, 175th Anniv. A270

**2015, May 1**   Litho.   *Perf. 12½*
1300 A270 £2 multi    6.25 6.25

Paintings A271

Designs: 42p, Moulin Huet Bay, by John Paul Jacob Naftel. 56p, La Moye Harbor, Le Gouffre, by Peter Le Lievre. 57p, Cradle Rock & Pea Stacks, by William John Caparne. 62p, La Saignée, Sark, by William A. Toplis. 68p, Grand Rocques Old Fort, by Ethel Cheeswright. 77p, Moulin Huet Bay, by Pierre-Auguste Renoir.

**2015, July 22    Litho.    Perf. 14**

| | | | | |
|---|---|---|---|---|
| 1301 | A271 | 42p multi | 1.40 | 1.40 |
| 1302 | A271 | 56p multi | 1.75 | 1.75 |
| 1303 | A271 | 57p multi | 1.75 | 1.75 |
| 1304 | A271 | 62p multi | 2.00 | 2.00 |
| 1305 | A271 | 68p multi | 2.10 | 2.10 |
| 1306 | A271 | 77p multi | 2.40 | 2.40 |
| | Nos. 1301-1306 (6) | | 11.40 | 11.40 |

A272

Sark as a Fief of the Crown, 450th Anniv. A273

Designs: 42p, St. Magloire, patron saint of Sark. 57p, Sark in the 15th century. 62p, French invasion of Sark. 68p, Le Manoir, home of first seigneur of Sark. 77p, Silver and copper mine on Little Sark.

No. 1312: a, Bronze cannon, c. 1572 (40x26mm). b, Queen Elizabeth I (32x40mm).

**2015, July 22    Litho.    Perf. 13x13¼**

| | | | | |
|---|---|---|---|---|
| 1307 | A272 | 42p multi | 1.40 | 1.40 |
| 1308 | A272 | 57p multi | 1.75 | 1.75 |
| 1309 | A272 | 62p multi | 2.00 | 2.00 |
| 1310 | A272 | 68p multi | 2.10 | 2.10 |
| 1311 | A272 | 77p multi | 2.40 | 2.40 |
| | Nos. 1307-1311 (5) | | 9.65 | 9.65 |

**Souvenir Sheet**

**Perf. 13 (#1312a), 12½ (#1312b)**

| | | | | |
|---|---|---|---|---|
| 1312 | A273 | Sheet of 2 | 9.50 | 9.50 |
| a. | | £1 multi | 3.25 | 3.25 |
| b. | | £2 multi | 6.25 | 6.25 |

Christmas — A274

St. Stephen's Church stained-glass windows by William Morris: 37p, Annunciation. 42p, Adoration of the Magi. 56p, Angels with harps. 57p, Angels and crucified Christ. 62p, Saint and angel. 68p, Church. 77p, Christ the King and angels.

**Serpentine Die Cut 14¼**

**2015, Nov. 6    Litho.**

**Self-Adhesive**

| | | | | |
|---|---|---|---|---|
| 1313 | A274 | 37p multi | 1.10 | 1.10 |
| 1314 | A274 | 42p multi | 1.25 | 1.25 |
| 1315 | A274 | 56p multi | 1.75 | 1.75 |
| 1316 | A274 | 57p multi | 1.75 | 1.75 |
| 1317 | A274 | 62p multi | 1.90 | 1.90 |
| 1318 | A274 | 68p multi | 2.10 | 2.10 |
| 1319 | A274 | 77p multi | 2.40 | 2.40 |
| | Nos. 1313-1319 (7) | | 12.25 | 12.25 |

**World War I, Cent. Type of 2014**

Map, poppy and: 42p, Private Philip Carré, Christmas greetings from postmaster. 56p, Mailboat SS Vera. 57p, Christmas card from Lieutenant Peter Le Page, embroidered sampler. 62p, Post Office Rifles. 68p, Field service postcard noting status of Private Yves Cataroche. 77p, Robert and Ethel Bynam, Great Britain #128.

**2015, Nov. 11    Litho.    Perf. 14x14¾**

| | | | | |
|---|---|---|---|---|
| 1320 | A265 | 42p multi | 1.25 | 1.25 |
| a. | | Booklet pane of 4 | 5.00 | — |
| 1321 | A265 | 56p multi | 1.75 | 1.75 |
| a. | | Booklet pane of 4 | 7.00 | — |
| 1322 | A265 | 57p multi | 1.75 | 1.75 |
| a. | | Booklet pane of 4 | 7.00 | — |
| 1323 | A265 | 62p multi | 1.90 | 1.90 |
| a. | | Booklet pane of 4 | 7.75 | — |
| 1324 | A265 | 68p multi | 2.10 | 2.10 |
| a. | | Booklet pane of 4 | 8.50 | — |

| | | | | |
|---|---|---|---|---|
| 1325 | A265 | 77p multi | 2.40 | 2.40 |
| a. | | Booklet pane of 4 | 9.75 | — |
| | | Complete booklet, #1320a, 1321a, 1322a, 1323a, 1324a, 1325a | 45.00 | |
| | Nos. 1320-1325 (6) | | 11.15 | 11.15 |

New Year 2016 (Year of the Monkey) — A275

Designs: 42p, Three Plenties Monkey. 56p, Fire Monkey. 57p, Aristocratic Monkey. 62p, Noble and Successful Monkey. 68p, Mother and Baby Monkey. 77p, Three Wealthy Monkeys.

**2016, Jan. 20    Litho.    Perf. 13**

| | | | | |
|---|---|---|---|---|
| 1326 | A275 | 42p red & gold | 1.25 | 1.25 |
| 1327 | A275 | 56p red & gold | 1.60 | 1.60 |
| 1328 | A275 | 57p red & gold | 1.75 | 1.75 |
| 1329 | A275 | 62p red & gold | 1.90 | 1.90 |
| 1330 | A275 | 68p red & gold | 2.00 | 2.00 |
| 1331 | A275 | 77p red & gold | 2.25 | 2.25 |
| a. | | Souvenir sheet of 6, #1326-1331 | 11.00 | 11.00 |
| | Nos. 1326-1331 (6) | | 10.75 | 10.75 |

**Souvenir Sheet**

Philippine Eagle — A276

**2016, Feb. 17    Litho.    Perf. 14x14¼**

| | | | | |
|---|---|---|---|---|
| 1332 | A276 | £3 multi | 8.50 | 8.50 |

Scenes from *Toilers of the Sea,* by Victor Hugo — A277

Designs: 43p, Gilliatt the Fisherman. 57p, Durande wrecked. 58p, Great Douvres. 64p, Great storm. 70p, Devilish octopus. 78p, Déruchette sails away.

**2016, May 6    Litho.    Perf. 13¾x13½**

| | | | | |
|---|---|---|---|---|
| 1333 | A277 | 43p multi | 1.25 | 1.25 |
| a. | | Booklet pane of 4 | 5.00 | — |
| 1334 | A277 | 57p multi | 1.75 | 1.75 |
| a. | | Booklet pane of 4 | 7.00 | — |
| 1335 | A277 | 58p multi | 1.75 | 1.75 |
| a. | | Booklet pane of 4 | 7.00 | — |
| 1336 | A277 | 64p multi | 1.90 | 1.90 |
| a. | | Booklet pane of 4 | 7.75 | — |
| 1337 | A277 | 70p multi | 2.00 | 2.00 |
| a. | | Booklet pane of 4 | 8.00 | — |
| 1338 | A277 | 78p multi | 2.25 | 2.25 |
| a. | | Booklet pane of 4 | 9.00 | — |
| | | Complete booklet, #1333a, 1334a, 1335a, 1336a, 1337a, 1338a | 44.00 | |
| | Nos. 1333-1338 (6) | | 10.90 | 10.90 |

Europa — A278

**2016, May 6    Litho.    Perf. 13¼x13½**

| | | | | |
|---|---|---|---|---|
| 1339 | A278 | 64p multi | 1.90 | 1.90 |

Think Green Issue.

Four Seasons — A279

Designs: 43p, Bluebell Woods in spring. 57p, Petit Port Bay in summer. 64p, Sausmarez Park in autumn. 70p, St. Peter Port Lighthouse in winter.

**2016, May 25    Litho.    Perf. 12½x13¼**

| | | | | |
|---|---|---|---|---|
| 1340 | A279 | 43p multi | 1.25 | 1.25 |
| 1341 | A279 | 57p multi | 1.75 | 1.75 |
| 1342 | A279 | 64p multi | 1.90 | 1.90 |
| 1343 | A279 | 70p multi | 2.00 | 2.00 |
| | Nos. 1340-1343 (4) | | 6.90 | 6.90 |

**Souvenir Sheet**

Guernsey Cow — A280

**2016, May 25    Litho.    Perf. 14¾**

| | | | | |
|---|---|---|---|---|
| 1344 | A280 | £2 multi | 5.75 | 5.75 |

World Stamp Show 2016, New York.

Postcrossing A281

Designs: (64p), Bird and fish. (70p), Butterfly, bee and bird.

**2016, July 14    Litho.    Perf. 13¼**

| | | | | |
|---|---|---|---|---|
| 1345 | A281 | (64p) multi | 1.75 | 1.75 |
| 1346 | A281 | (70p) multi | 1.90 | 1.90 |

No. 1345 is inscribed "EUR;" No. 1346, "ROW."

Island of Herm — A282

Designs: 43p, Oysters. 57p, Mint sauce worms. 58p, Cowrie shells. 64p, Burial chamber. 70p, Common tern. 78p, Burnet roses.

**2016, July 27    Litho.    Perf. 12½x13**

| | | | | |
|---|---|---|---|---|
| 1347 | A282 | 43p multi | 1.25 | 1.25 |
| 1348 | A282 | 57p multi | 1.50 | 1.50 |
| 1349 | A282 | 58p multi | 1.50 | 1.50 |
| 1350 | A282 | 64p multi | 1.75 | 1.75 |
| 1351 | A282 | 70p multi | 1.90 | 1.90 |
| 1352 | A282 | 78p multi | 2.10 | 2.10 |
| a. | | Souvenir sheet of 6, #1347-1352, perf. 13 | 10.00 | 10.00 |
| | Nos. 1347-1352 (6) | | 10.00 | 10.00 |

Royal Mail, 500th Anniv. — A283

Designs: 43p, Royal Mail coach, 1784. 57p, Royal Mail steamboat Ariadne, 1824. 58p, Smith Street Post Office, St. Peter Port, 1883. 64p, Royal Mail underground train, 1927. 70p, Post Office Tower, London, 1965. 78p, Heathrow Distribution Center, 2003.

£2, Union Street pillar box installed in 1853, St. Peter Port, vert.

**2016, July 27    Litho.    Perf. 13¼**

| | | | | |
|---|---|---|---|---|
| 1353 | A283 | 43p multi | 1.25 | 1.25 |
| 1354 | A283 | 57p multi | 1.50 | 1.50 |
| 1355 | A283 | 58p multi | 1.50 | 1.50 |
| 1356 | A283 | 64p multi | 1.75 | 1.75 |
| 1357 | A283 | 70p multi | 1.90 | 1.90 |
| 1358 | A283 | 78p multi | 2.10 | 2.10 |
| | Nos. 1353-1358 (6) | | 10.00 | 10.00 |

**Souvenir Sheet**

| | | | | |
|---|---|---|---|---|
| 1359 | A283 | £2 multi | 5.25 | 5.25 |

No. 1359 contains one 52x52mm stamp.

Christmas — A284

Bells and: 38p, Holly. 43p, Christmas tree. 57p, Gift. 58p, Santa Claus. 64p, Reindeer. 70p, Snowman. 78p, Stars.

**Litho. With Foil Application**
***Serpentine Die Cut 7¼***

**2016, Nov. 8    Self-Adhesive**

| | | | | |
|---|---|---|---|---|
| 1360 | A284 | 38p gold & green | 1.00 | 1.00 |
| 1361 | A284 | 43p green & gold | 1.10 | 1.10 |
| 1362 | A284 | 57p gold & green | 1.50 | 1.50 |
| 1363 | A284 | 58p green & gold | 1.50 | 1.50 |
| 1364 | A284 | 64p gold & green | 1.60 | 1.60 |
| 1365 | A284 | 70p green & gold | 1.75 | 1.75 |
| 1366 | A284 | 78p gold & green | 2.00 | 2.00 |
| | Nos. 1360-1366 (7) | | 10.45 | 10.45 |

**World War I, Cent. Type of 2014**

Semaphore flag and men from Guernsey in British Navy: 43p, Seaman James Gale. 57p, Stoker First Class George Arthur Hicks. 58p, Sailors T. Gibson and H. Broadbent and other submariners. 64p, Seaman Wilfred Cochrane. 70p, First Class Petty Officer Harold de Putron Taylor and Lord Kitchener. 78p, Seaman John Helman.

**2016, Nov. 11    Litho.    Perf. 14x14¾**

| | | | | |
|---|---|---|---|---|
| 1367 | A265 | 43p multi | 1.10 | 1.10 |
| a. | | Booklet pane of 4 | 4.50 | |
| 1368 | A265 | 57p multi | 1.50 | 1.50 |
| a. | | Booklet pane of 4 | 6.00 | — |
| 1369 | A265 | 58p multi | 1.50 | 1.50 |
| a. | | Booklet pane of 4 | 6.00 | — |
| 1370 | A265 | 64p multi | 1.60 | 1.60 |
| a. | | Booklet pane of 4 | 6.50 | |
| 1371 | A265 | 70p multi | 1.75 | 1.75 |
| a. | | Booklet pane of 4 | 7.00 | |
| 1372 | A265 | 78p multi | 2.00 | 2.00 |
| a. | | Booklet pane of 4 | 8.00 | — |
| | | Complete booklet, #1367a, 1368a, 1369a, 1370a, 1371a, 1372a | 38.00 | |
| | Nos. 1367-1372 (6) | | 9.45 | 9.45 |

New Year 2017 (Year of the Rooster) — A285

Various depictions of roosters.

**2017, Jan. 18    Litho.    Perf. 13**

| | | | | |
|---|---|---|---|---|
| 1373 | A285 | 43p gold & scar | 1.10 | 1.10 |
| 1374 | A285 | 57p gold & scar | 1.50 | 1.50 |
| 1375 | A285 | 58p gold & scar | 1.50 | 1.50 |
| 1376 | A285 | 64p gold & scar | 1.60 | 1.60 |
| 1377 | A285 | 70p gold & scar | 1.75 | 1.75 |
| 1378 | A285 | 78p gold & scar | 2.00 | 2.00 |
| a. | | Souvenir sheet of 6, #1373-1378 | 9.50 | 9.50 |
| | Nos. 1373-1378 (6) | | 9.45 | 9.45 |

Worldwide Fund for Nature (WWF) — A286

Meadow Pipit: 43p, Chick. 57p, On branch. 64p, In flight. 70p, Head with mouth open.

***Perf. 13¼x13½***

**2017, Feb. 15    Litho.**

| | | | | |
|---|---|---|---|---|
| 1379 | A286 | 43p multi | 1.10 | 1.10 |
| 1380 | A286 | 57p multi | 1.40 | 1.40 |
| 1381 | A286 | 64p multi | 1.60 | 1.60 |
| 1382 | A286 | 70p multi | 1.75 | 1.75 |
| a. | | Souvenir sheet of 4, #1379-1382 | 6.00 | 6.00 |
| | Nos. 1379-1382 (4) | | 5.85 | 5.85 |

A sheet of 8 containing 2 imperforate examples of each of Nos. 1379-1382 was produced in limited quantities.

Castle Cornet — A287

Designs: 44p, Soldiers and cannon. 59p, Shrubs in garden. 60p, Dancers in circle. 73p, Audience watching historical presentation. 80p, Garden. 90p, Actors in historical presentation.

£3, Castle at night.

**2017, May 4    Litho.    Perf. 13¾**

| | | | | |
|---|---|---|---|---|
| 1383 | A287 | 44p multi | 1.10 | 1.10 |
| 1384 | A287 | 59p multi | 1.50 | 1.50 |
| 1385 | A287 | 60p multi | 1.60 | 1.60 |
| 1386 | A287 | 73p multi | 1.90 | 1.90 |
| 1387 | A287 | 80p multi | 2.10 | 2.10 |
| 1388 | A287 | 90p multi | 2.40 | 2.40 |
| | Nos. 1383-1388 (6) | | 10.60 | 10.60 |

## Souvenir Sheet
### Perf. 13½

| | | | | |
|---|---|---|---|---|
| 1389 | A287 | £3 multi | 7.75 | 7.75 |

Europa (Nos. 1384, 1386). No. 1389 contains one 45x45mm stamp.

### Guernsey and Flag — A288

Sweater, measuring tape and flag of: 44p, Guernsey. 59p, Australia. 73p, United States. 80p, Japan.

**2017, May 17    Litho.    Perf. 13½**

| | | | | |
|---|---|---|---|---|
| 1390 | A288 | 44p multi | 1.10 | 1.10 |
| 1391 | A288 | 59p multi | 1.50 | 1.50 |
| 1392 | A288 | 73p multi | 1.90 | 1.90 |
| 1393 | A288 | 80p multi | 2.10 | 2.10 |
| | *Nos. 1390-1393 (4)* | | 6.60 | 6.60 |

Values are for stamps with side selvage.

### Folklore — A289

Designs: 44p, The De Garis Family and the Pouques. 59p, The Fairies' Bat. 60p, The Fairy Invasion of Guernsey. 73p, The Fairies' Gallows. 80p, Pierre Dumont and Le P'tit Colin. 90p, The Devil's Hoofprint. £3, The Corner of the Goat, horiz.

**2017, July 19    Litho.    Perf. 13x13¼**

| | | | | |
|---|---|---|---|---|
| 1394 | A289 | 44p multi | 1.25 | 1.25 |
| 1395 | A289 | 59p multi | 1.60 | 1.60 |
| 1396 | A289 | 60p multi | 1.60 | 1.60 |
| 1397 | A289 | 73p multi | 2.00 | 2.00 |
| 1398 | A289 | 80p multi | 2.10 | 2.10 |
| 1399 | A289 | 90p multi | 2.40 | 2.40 |
| | *Nos. 1394-1399 (6)* | | 10.95 | 10.95 |

### Souvenir Sheet
#### Perf. 13¼

| | | | | |
|---|---|---|---|---|
| 1400 | A289 | £3 multi | 8.00 | 8.00 |

No. 1400 contains one 36x30mm stamp.

### Coastal Scenes — A290

No. 1401: a, Rocquaine Bay, two boats at LL. b, Rocquaine Bay, one boat at LL. c, Rocquaine Bay, three boats at LL. d, Rocquaine Bay, two boats and boat ramp at LL. e, Fort Grey. f, Albert Marina. g, Victoria Marina, one boat and two gangways. h, Victoria Marina, sailboat and motorboat. h, Victoria Marina, sailboat and two gangways. i, Careening Hard.

### Serpentine Die Cut 11
**2017, Sept. 1                          Litho.**
### Booklet Stamps
### Self-Adhesive

| | | | | |
|---|---|---|---|---|
| 1401 | | Booklet pane of 10 | 13.50 | |
| a.-e. | A290 GY Any single | | 1.10 | 1.10 |
| f.-j. | A290 UK Any single | | 1.60 | 1.60 |
| k. | Booklet pane of 10, 2 each #1401a-1401e | | 11.00 | |
| l. | Booklet pane of 10, 2 each #1401f-1401j | | 16.00 | |

On day of issue, Nos. 1401a-1401e each sold for 44p; Nos. 1401f-1401j, 59p.

### Princess of Wales's Royal Regiment, 25th Anniv. — A291

Designs: 44p, Carol service in Canterbury Cathedral. 59p, Presentation of colors. 60p, Flying Tigers Parachute Display Team. 73p, Homecoming. 80p, Formal parade. 90p, Infantry exercise. £3, Princess Diana (1961-97).

---

**2017, Sept. 1    Litho.    Perf. 13x12½**

| | | | | |
|---|---|---|---|---|
| 1402 | A291 | 44p multi | 1.10 | 1.10 |
| 1403 | A291 | 59p multi | 1.60 | 1.60 |
| 1404 | A291 | 60p multi | 1.60 | 1.60 |
| 1405 | A291 | 73p multi | 1.90 | 1.90 |
| 1406 | A291 | 80p multi | 2.10 | 2.10 |
| 1407 | A291 | 90p multi | 2.40 | 2.40 |
| | *Nos. 1402-1407 (6)* | | 10.70 | 10.70 |

### Souvenir Sheet
#### Perf. 13¼x13½

| | | | | |
|---|---|---|---|---|
| 1408 | A291 | £3 multi | 7.75 | 7.75 |

No. 1408 contains one 36x44mm stamp.

### World War I, Cent. Type of 2014

Designs: 44p, Captain Wilfred Picton-Warlow. 59p, Picture of Flight Lieutenant Charles Collet in airplane from *Navy and Army Illustrated*. 60p, Alfred, Harold and Frederick Crespin and drawing of airplane. 73p, Captain Adrian Le Patourel Jones. 80p, Pilot and seaplane. 90p, Sergeant Frederick Fieldhouse Smith.

**2017, Nov. 8    Litho.    Perf. 14x14¼**

| | | | | |
|---|---|---|---|---|
| 1409 | A265 | 44p multi | 1.25 | 1.25 |
| a. | Booklet pane of 4 | | 5.00 | |
| 1410 | A265 | 59p multi | 1.60 | 1.60 |
| a. | Booklet pane of 4 | | 6.50 | — |
| 1411 | A265 | 60p multi | 1.60 | 1.60 |
| a. | Booklet pane of 4 | | 6.50 | — |
| 1412 | A265 | 73p multi | 2.00 | 2.00 |
| a. | Booklet pane of 4 | | 8.00 | — |
| 1413 | A265 | 80p multi | 2.25 | 2.25 |
| a. | Booklet pane of 4 | | 9.00 | — |
| 1414 | A265 | 90p multi | 2.50 | 2.50 |
| a. | Booklet pane of 4 | | 10.00 | — |
| | Complete booklet, #1409a, 1410a, 1411a, 1412a, 1413a, 1414a | | 45.00 | |
| | *Nos. 1409-1414 (6)* | | 11.20 | 11.20 |

### 70th Wedding Anniversary of Queen Elizabeth II and Prince Philip — A292

Photograph of Queen Elizabeth II and Prince Philip from: 44p, 1951. 59p, 1965. 60p, 1976. 73p, 1977. 80p, 2010. 90p, 2016.

### Litho. With Foil Application
**2017, Nov. 8                          Perf. 14x13½**

| | | | | |
|---|---|---|---|---|
| 1415 | A292 | 44p sil & multi | 1.25 | 1.25 |
| 1416 | A292 | 59p sil & multi | 1.60 | 1.60 |
| 1417 | A292 | 60p sil & multi | 1.60 | 1.60 |
| 1418 | A292 | 73p sil & multi | 2.00 | 2.00 |
| 1419 | A292 | 80p sil & multi | 2.25 | 2.25 |
| 1420 | A292 | 90p sil & multi | 2.50 | 2.50 |
| | *Nos. 1415-1420 (6)* | | 11.20 | 11.20 |

### Christmas — A293

Lyrics from "Good King Wenceslas" and: 39p, King Wenceslas. 44p, Man carrying wood in snow. 59p, King Wenceslas and page. 60p, Page and King Wenceslas carrying wood near castle. 73p, Page and King Wenceslas carrying wood in forest. 80p, King Wenceslas, page, bird in tree. 90p, King Wenceslas and page bringing wood to man's house.

### Serpentine Die Cut 10x9½
**2017, Nov. 8                          Litho.**
### Self-Adhesive

| | | | | |
|---|---|---|---|---|
| 1421 | A293 | 39p multi | 1.10 | 1.10 |
| 1422 | A293 | 44p multi | 1.25 | 1.25 |
| 1423 | A293 | 59p multi | 1.60 | 1.60 |
| 1424 | A293 | 60p multi | 1.60 | 1.60 |
| 1425 | A293 | 73p multi | 2.00 | 2.00 |
| 1426 | A293 | 80p multi | 2.25 | 2.25 |
| 1427 | A293 | 90p multi | 2.50 | 2.50 |
| | *Nos. 1421-1427 (7)* | | 12.30 | 12.30 |

### New Year 2018 (Year of the Dog) — A294

Various depictions of dogs.

---

**2018, Feb. 1    Litho.    Perf. 13**

| | | | | |
|---|---|---|---|---|
| 1428 | A294 | 44p red & gold | 1.25 | 1.25 |
| 1429 | A294 | 59p red & gold | 1.75 | 1.75 |
| 1430 | A294 | 60p red & gold | 1.75 | 1.75 |
| 1431 | A294 | 73p red & gold | 2.10 | 2.10 |
| 1432 | A294 | 80p red & gold | 2.25 | 2.25 |
| 1433 | A294 | 90p red & gold | 2.60 | 2.60 |
| a. | Souvenir sheet of 6, #1428-1433 | | 12.00 | 12.00 |
| | *Nos. 1428-1433 (6)* | | 11.70 | 11.70 |

### Souvenir Sheet

### Black Rhinoceros — A295

**2018, Feb. 14    Litho.    Perf. 14**

| | | | | |
|---|---|---|---|---|
| 1434 | A295 | £3 multi | 8.50 | 8.50 |

### Royal Air Force, Cent. — A296

Designs: 46p, Nimrod MR2P providing search and rescue. 63p, Sunderland attack on U-boat, 1943. 63p, London Flying Boat on first affiliation visit, 1939. 76p, Major William Barker's Victoria Cross action, 1918. 85p, First Squadron RNAS trench strafing, 1917. 94p, Flight Sub-Lieutenant Warneford attacking Zeppelin, 1915. £3, Cargo airplane over Guernsey.

**2018, Apr. 3    Litho.    Perf. 13¾**

| | | | | |
|---|---|---|---|---|
| 1435 | A296 | 46p multi | 1.25 | 1.25 |
| 1436 | A296 | 62p multi | 1.75 | 1.75 |
| 1437 | A296 | 63p multi | 1.75 | 1.75 |
| 1438 | A296 | 76p multi | 2.10 | 2.10 |
| 1439 | A296 | 85p multi | 2.40 | 2.40 |
| 1440 | A296 | 94p multi | 2.60 | 2.60 |
| | *Nos. 1435-1440 (6)* | | 11.85 | 11.85 |

### Souvenir Sheet

| | | | | |
|---|---|---|---|---|
| 1441 | A296 | £3 multi | 8.25 | 8.25 |

### Causeways and Bridges — A297

Designs: 46p, Lihou Causeway. 62p, Castle Cornet. 63p, Fort Clonque Causeway. 76p, Reservoir Bridge. 85p, Fort Grey Causeway. 94p, Sark Coupée.

**2018, May 2    Litho.    Perf. 13x13¼**

| | | | | |
|---|---|---|---|---|
| 1442 | A297 | 46p multi | 1.25 | 1.25 |
| 1443 | A297 | 62p multi | 1.75 | 1.75 |
| 1444 | A297 | 63p multi | 1.75 | 1.75 |
| 1445 | A297 | 76p multi | 2.00 | 2.00 |
| 1446 | A297 | 85p multi | 2.25 | 2.25 |
| 1447 | A297 | 94p multi | 2.50 | 2.50 |
| a. | Souvenir sheet of 6, #1442-1447 | | 11.50 | 11.50 |
| | *Nos. 1442-1447 (6)* | | 11.50 | 11.50 |

Europa (62p, 76p).

### Souvenir Sheet

### Wedding of Prince Harry and Meghan Markle A298

No. 1448 — Couple looking at: a, Each other. b, Camera.

**2018, May 2    Litho.    Perf. 14½**

| | | | | |
|---|---|---|---|---|
| 1448 | A298 | Sheet of 2 | 11.00 | 11.00 |
| a.-b. | £2 Either single | | 5.50 | 5.50 |

---

### Aerial Views A299

Designs: 46p, Vale Castle. 62p, Rousse. 63p, Torteval Church. 76p, Reservoir. 85p, Pembroke. 94p, Beaucette Marina.

**2018, Aug. 1    Litho.    Perf. 13¼x13**

| | | | | |
|---|---|---|---|---|
| 1449 | A299 | 46p multi | 1.25 | 1.25 |
| 1450 | A299 | 62p multi | 1.60 | 1.60 |
| 1451 | A299 | 63p multi | 1.75 | 1.75 |
| 1452 | A299 | 76p multi | 2.00 | 2.00 |
| 1453 | A299 | 85p multi | 2.25 | 2.25 |
| 1454 | A299 | 94p multi | 2.50 | 2.50 |
| | *Nos. 1449-1454 (6)* | | 11.35 | 11.35 |

### World War I, Cent. Type of 2014

"Lest we forget" and details of war memorials: 46p, Royal Guernsey Light Infantry Memorial, St. Peter Port. 62p, Guernsey Post Office Roll of Honor. 63p, Elizabeth College Roll of Honor. 76p, Alderney Stone. 85p, Guernsey War Memorial. 94p, Memorial Window, St. Peter's Church, Sark.

**2018, Nov. 8    Litho.    Perf. 14x14¼**

| | | | | |
|---|---|---|---|---|
| 1455 | A265 | 46p multi | 1.25 | 1.25 |
| a. | Booklet pane of 4 | | 5.00 | — |
| 1456 | A265 | 62p multi | 1.60 | 1.60 |
| a. | Booklet pane of 4 | | 6.50 | — |
| 1457 | A265 | 63p multi | 1.75 | 1.75 |
| a. | Booklet pane of 4 | | 7.00 | — |
| 1458 | A265 | 76p multi | 2.00 | 2.00 |
| a. | Booklet pane of 4 | | 8.00 | — |
| 1459 | A265 | 85p multi | 2.25 | 2.25 |
| a. | Booklet pane of 4 | | 9.00 | — |
| 1460 | A265 | 94p multi | 2.50 | 2.50 |
| a. | Booklet pane of 4 | | 10.00 | — |
| | Complete booklet, #1455a, 1456a, 1457a, 1458a, 1459a, 1460a | | 46.00 | |
| | *Nos. 1455-1460 (6)* | | 11.35 | 11.35 |

### Prince Charles, 70th Birthday — A300

Photograph of Prince Charles from: 46p, 2012. 62p, 1998. 63p, 1986. 76p, 1987. 85p, 1980. 94p, 2005.

**2018, Nov. 8    Litho.    Perf. 13¼**

| | | | | |
|---|---|---|---|---|
| 1461 | A300 | 46p gold & multi | 1.25 | 1.25 |
| 1462 | A300 | 62p gold & multi | 1.60 | 1.60 |
| 1463 | A300 | 63p gold & multi | 1.75 | 1.75 |
| 1464 | A300 | 76p gold & multi | 2.00 | 2.00 |
| 1465 | A300 | 85p gold & multi | 2.25 | 2.25 |
| 1466 | A300 | 94p gold & multi | 2.50 | 2.50 |
| | *Nos. 1461-1466 (6)* | | 11.35 | 11.35 |

### Scenes From *The Nutcracker and the Mouse King*, by E. T. A. Hoffmann (1776-1822) A301

Designs: 41p, Fritz breaks the Nutcracker. 46p, The battle. 62p, Nutcracker repaired. 63p, The Mouse Queen and Pirlipat. 76p, Breaking the spell. 85p, Mouse King visits Marie. 94p, Drosselmeier's nephew and Marie.

### Serpentine Die Cut 9½x10
**2018, Nov. 8                          Litho.**
### Self-Adhesive

| | | | | |
|---|---|---|---|---|
| 1467 | A301 | 41p multi | 1.10 | 1.10 |
| 1468 | A301 | 46p multi | 1.25 | 1.25 |
| 1469 | A301 | 62p multi | 1.60 | 1.60 |
| 1470 | A301 | 63p multi | 1.75 | 1.75 |
| 1471 | A301 | 76p multi | 2.00 | 2.00 |
| 1472 | A301 | 85p multi | 2.25 | 2.25 |
| 1473 | A301 | 94p multi | 2.50 | 2.50 |
| | *Nos. 1467-1473 (7)* | | 12.45 | 12.45 |

Christmas.

### New Year 2019 (Year of the Pig) — A302

Various depictions of pigs.

**2019, Jan. 22    Litho.    Perf. 12½x13**

| | | | | |
|---|---|---|---|---|
| 1474 | A302 | 46p multi | 1.25 | 1.25 |
| a. | | Perf. 13x13¼ | 1.25 | 1.25 |
| 1475 | A302 | 62p multi | 1.60 | 1.60 |
| a. | | Perf. 13x13¼ | 1.60 | 1.60 |
| 1476 | A302 | 63p multi | 1.60 | 1.60 |
| a. | | Perf. 13x13¼ | 1.60 | 1.60 |
| 1477 | A302 | 76p multi | 1.90 | 1.90 |
| a. | | Perf. 13x13¼ | 1.90 | 1.90 |
| 1478 | A302 | 85p multi | 2.25 | 2.25 |
| a. | | Perf. 13x13¼ | 2.25 | 2/25 |
| 1479 | A302 | 94p multi | 2.40 | 2.40 |
| a. | | Perf. 13x13¼ | 2.40 | 2.40 |
| b. | | Souvenir sheet of 6, #1474a-1479a | 11.00 | 11.00 |
| | | Nos. 1474-1479 (6) | 11.00 | 11.00 |

Guernsey Buildings Designed by John Wilson (1781-1866) A303

Designs: 46p, St. James Church. 62p, Les Arcades. 63p, Elizabeth College. 76p, St. George. 85p, Roseneath. 94p, Bonamy House. £1.54, Meat Market. £2.31, Castle Carey.

**2019, Feb. 13    Litho.    Perf. 12**

| | | | | |
|---|---|---|---|---|
| 1480 | A303 | 46p multi | 1.25 | 1.25 |
| 1481 | A303 | 62p multi | 1.60 | 1.60 |
| 1482 | A303 | 63p multi | 1.75 | 1.75 |
| 1483 | A303 | 76p multi | 2.00 | 2.00 |
| 1484 | A303 | 85p multi | 2.25 | 2.25 |
| 1485 | A303 | 94p multi | 2.50 | 2.50 |
| 1486 | A303 | £1.54 multi | 4.00 | 4.00 |
| 1487 | A303 | £2.31 multi | 6.00 | 6.00 |
| | | Nos. 1480-1487 (8) | 21.35 | 21.35 |

Birds — A304

Designs: 48p, Puffin. 65p, Linnet. 66p, Bullfinch. 80p, Goldfinch. 90p, Starling. 98p, Kingfisher.

**2019, Apr. 1    Litho.    Perf. 14½**

| | | | | |
|---|---|---|---|---|
| 1488 | A304 | 48p multi | 1.25 | 1.25 |
| 1489 | A304 | 65p multi | 1.75 | 1.75 |
| 1490 | A304 | 66p multi | 1.75 | 1.75 |
| 1491 | A304 | 80p multi | 2.10 | 2.10 |
| a. | | Souvenir sheet of 2, #1489, 1491 | 4.00 | 4.00 |
| 1492 | A304 | 90p multi | 2.40 | 2.40 |
| 1493 | A304 | 98p multi | 2.60 | 2.60 |
| a. | | Souvenir sheet of 6, #1488-1493 | 12.00 | 12.00 |
| | | Nos. 1488-1493 (6) | 11.85 | 11.85 |

Europa (Nos. 1489, 1491).

Queen Victoria (1819-1901) and Prince Albert (1819-61) — A305

Designs: 48p, Bust of Queen Victoria, by Joseph Durham. 65p, Photogrpah of Queen Victoria and Prince Albert. 66p, Photograph of Prince Albert. 80p, Photograph of Queen Victoria and Prince Albert, diff. 90p, Portrait of Queen Victoria. 98p, Bust of Prince Albert, by Durham.

**2019, May 29    Litho.    Perf. 13¼**

| | | | | |
|---|---|---|---|---|
| 1494 | A305 | 48p sil & multi | 1.25 | 1.25 |
| 1495 | A305 | 65p sil & multi | 1.75 | 1.75 |
| 1496 | A305 | 66p sil & multi | 1.75 | 1.75 |
| 1497 | A305 | 80p sil & multi | 2.00 | 2.00 |
| 1498 | A305 | 90p sil & multi | 2.25 | 2.25 |
| 1499 | A305 | 98p sil & multi | 2.50 | 2.50 |
| | | Nos. 1494-1499 (6) | 11.50 | 11.50 |

First Man on the Moon, 50th Anniv. — A306

Quadrant of Moon and: 48p, Astronaut on ladder of Lunar Module. 65p, Astronaut. 80p, Footprint on Moon. 90p, Earth.

**2019, July 20    Litho.    Perf. 13¼**

| | | | | |
|---|---|---|---|---|
| 1500 | A306 | 48p multi | 1.35 | 1.35 |
| a. | | Booklet pane of 4 | 5.45 | |
| 1501 | A306 | 65p multi | 1.75 | 1.75 |
| a. | | Booklet pane of 4 | 7.00 | |
| 1502 | A306 | 80p multi | 2.20 | 2.20 |
| a. | | Booklet pane of 4 | 8.75 | |
| 1503 | A306 | 90p multi | 2.45 | 2.45 |
| a. | | Booklet pane of 4 | 9.90 | |
| | | Complete booklet, #1500a, 1501a, 1502a, 1503a | 31.00 | |
| b. | | Souvenir sheet of 4, #1500-1503 | 7.90 | 7.25 |
| | | Nos. 1500-1503 (4) | 7.75 | 7.75 |

**Souvenir Sheet**

Hauteville House, Home of Victor Hugo (1802-85), Writer — A307

No. 1504: a, Garden and terrace. b, The Look-out. c, The Red Room.

**2019, July 24    Litho.    Perf. 12**

| | | | | |
|---|---|---|---|---|
| 1504 | A307 | Sheet of 3 | 8.50 | 8.50 |
| a. | | 80p gold & multi | 2.00 | 2.00 |
| b. | | 98p gold & multi | 2.40 | 2.40 |
| c. | | £1.59 gold & multi | 4.00 | 4.00 |

**Souvenir Sheet**

Investiture of Prince Charles as Prince of Wales, 50th Anniv. — A308

**2019, July 24    Litho.    Perf. 11½x11¾**

| | | | | |
|---|---|---|---|---|
| 1505 | A308 | £2 multi | 5.00 | 5.00 |

Postal Independence of Guernsey, 50th Anniv. — A309

Designs: 48p, Workers painting mail box blue, 1980. 65p, Introduction of local post codes, 1995. 66p, Introduction of automated postal equipment, 2003. 80p, Introduction of electric vans to postal vehicle fleet, 2017. 90p, Increase of parcel delivery because of internet ordering. 98p, Commercialization of Guernsey Post Office and move of headquarters, 2001.

**2019, Oct. 1    Litho.    Perf. 12**

| | | | | |
|---|---|---|---|---|
| 1506 | A309 | 48p multi | 1.25 | 1.25 |
| 1507 | A309 | 65p multi | 1.60 | 1.60 |
| 1508 | A309 | 66p multi | 1.60 | 1.60 |
| 1509 | A309 | 80p multi | 2.00 | 2.00 |
| 1510 | A309 | 90p multi | 2.25 | 2.25 |
| 1511 | A309 | 98p multi | 2.40 | 2.40 |
| a. | | Souvenir sheet of 6, #1506-1511 | 11.50 | 11.50 |
| | | Nos. 1506-1511 (6) | 11.10 | 11.10 |

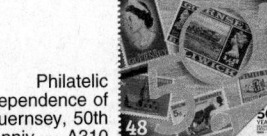

Philatelic Independence of Guernsey, 50th Anniv. — A310

Stamp under magnifying glass: 48p, Guernsey #8. 65p, Guernsey #182. 66p, Guernsey #429. 80p, Guernsey #703. 90p, Guernsey #859. 98p, Guernsey #1506.

**Litho. & Embossed With Foil Application**

**2019, Oct. 1    Perf. 14½x14¼**

| | | | | |
|---|---|---|---|---|
| 1512 | A310 | 48p gold & multi | 1.25 | 1.25 |
| 1513 | A310 | 65p gold & multi | 1.60 | 1.60 |
| 1514 | A310 | 66p gold & multi | 1.60 | 1.60 |
| 1515 | A310 | 80p gold & multi | 2.00 | 2.00 |
| 1516 | A310 | 90p gold & multi | 2.25 | 2.25 |
| 1517 | A310 | 98p gold & multi | 2.40 | 2.40 |
| | | Nos. 1512-1517 (6) | 11.10 | 11.10 |

Christmas A311

Designs: 43p, Nativity. 48p, Journey to Bethlehem. 65p, Bethlehem. 66p, No room at the inn. 80p, Shepherd and sheep. 90p, Magi. 98p, Nativity, diff.

**Serpentine Die Cut 14½**

**2019, Oct. 30    Litho.**

**Self-Adhesive**

| | | | | |
|---|---|---|---|---|
| 1518 | A311 | 43p multi | 1.10 | 1.10 |
| 1519 | A311 | 48p multi | 1.25 | 1.25 |
| 1520 | A311 | 65p multi | 1.75 | 1.75 |
| 1521 | A311 | 66p multi | 1.75 | 1.75 |
| 1522 | A311 | 80p multi | 2.10 | 2.10 |
| 1523 | A311 | 90p multi | 2.40 | 2.40 |
| 1524 | A311 | 98p multi | 2.60 | 2.60 |
| | | Nos. 1518-1524 (7) | 12.95 | 12.95 |

New Year 2020 (Year of the Rat) — A312

Various depictions of rats.

**2020, Jan. 8    Litho.    Perf. 13**

| | | | | |
|---|---|---|---|---|
| 1525 | A312 | 48p gold & multi | 1.25 | 1.25 |
| 1526 | A312 | 65p gold & multi | 1.75 | 1.75 |
| 1527 | A312 | 66p gold & multi | 1.75 | 1.75 |
| 1528 | A312 | 80p gold & multi | 2.10 | 2.10 |
| 1529 | A312 | 90p gold & multi | 2.40 | 2.40 |
| 1530 | A312 | 98p gold & multi | 2.60 | 2.60 |
| a. | | Souvenir sheet of 6, #1525-1530 | 12.00 | 12.00 |
| | | Nos. 1525-1530 (6) | 11.85 | 11.85 |

A313          A314

A315

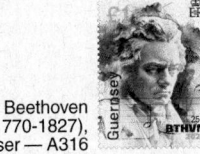

Ludwig van Beethoven (1770-1827), Composer — A316

**2020    Litho.    Perf. 14**

| | | | | |
|---|---|---|---|---|
| 1531 | A313 | £1 multi | 2.60 | 2.60 |
| a. | | Booklet pane of 4 | 10.50 | — |
| 1532 | A314 | £1 multi | 2.50 | 2.50 |
| a. | | Booklet pane of 4 | 10.50 | — |
| 1533 | A315 | £1 multi | 2.60 | 2.60 |
| a. | | Booklet pane of 4 | 10.50 | — |
| 1534 | A316 | £1 multi | 2.60 | 2.60 |
| a. | | Booklet pane of 4 | 10.50 | — |
| | | Complete booklet, #1531a, 1532a, 1533a, 1534a | 42.00 | |
| b. | | Souvenir sheet of 4, #1531-1534 | 10.50 | 10.50 |
| | | Nos. 1531-1534 (4) | 10.30 | 10.30 |

Issued: No. 1531, 1/21; No. 1532, 5/2; No. 1533, 7/21; Nos. 1531a, 1532a, 1534, 1534a, 1534b, 10/28.

Mail Ships — A317

Ships: 50p, Earl of Chesterfield. 68p, Ariadne. 70p, Antelope. 85p, Alberta. 95p, Isle of Guernsey. £1.02, Sarnia.

**2020, Apr. 1    Litho.    Perf. 13½x13¾**

| | | | | |
|---|---|---|---|---|
| 1535 | A317 | 50p multi | 1.25 | 1.25 |
| 1536 | A317 | 68p multi | 1.75 | 1.75 |
| 1537 | A317 | 70p multi | 1.75 | 1.75 |
| 1538 | A317 | 85p multi | 2.10 | 2.10 |
| 1539 | A317 | 95p multi | 2.40 | 2.40 |
| 1540 | A317 | £1.02 multi | 2.50 | 2.50 |
| a. | | Souvenir sheet of 6, #1535-1540 | 12.00 | 12.00 |
| | | Nos. 1535-1540 (6) | 11.75 | 11.75 |

Europa (68p, 85p).

Liberation of Guernsey, 75th Anniv. — A318

Designs: 50p, Quote and "V" for "Victory" hand gesture of Prime Minister Winston Churchill (1874-1965). 68p, Hands holding flags of Guernsey. 70p, Military band. 85p, Soldiers in jeep, flags of Guernsey and Great Britain, airplane, crackers. 95p, Microphone, people dancing. £1.02, Fireworks.

**2020, May 2    Litho.    Perf. 12¼x12**

| | | | | |
|---|---|---|---|---|
| 1541 | A318 | 50p multi | 1.25 | 1.25 |
| 1542 | A318 | 68p multi | 1.75 | 1.75 |
| 1543 | A318 | 70p multi | 1.75 | 1.75 |
| 1544 | A318 | 85p multi | 2.10 | 2.10 |
| 1545 | A318 | 95p multi | 2.40 | 2.40 |
| 1546 | A318 | £1.02 multi | 2.60 | 2.60 |
| | | Nos. 1541-1546 (6) | 11.85 | 11.85 |

**Souvenir Sheet**

Kordofan Giraffe A319

**2020, May 2    Litho.    Perf. 14**

| | | | | |
|---|---|---|---|---|
| 1547 | A319 | £3 multi | 7.50 | 7.50 |

Paintings — A320

Designs: 50p, Catskin, by Frances Lemmon. 68p, Dusk, by Keith Langlois. 70p, Cobo Gold, by James Colmer. 85p, Cobo Wild Flowers in Pink Pot, by Olympia McEwan. 95p, Fishing Boat, by Richard Le Goupillot. £1.02, Guernsey Grockles: Vazon Vera, by Yasmin Mariess.

**2020, July 21    Litho.    Perf. 13¼x13**

| | | | | |
|---|---|---|---|---|
| 1548 | A320 | 50p multi | 1.30 | 1.30 |
| 1549 | A320 | 68p multi | 1.75 | 1.75 |
| 1550 | A320 | 70p multi | 1.90 | 1.90 |
| 1551 | A320 | 85p multi | 2.25 | 2.25 |
| 1552 | A320 | 95p multi | 2.50 | 2.50 |
| 1553 | A320 | £1.02 multi | 2.75 | 2.75 |
| | | Nos. 1548-1553 (6) | 12.45 | 12.45 |

Rupert Bear, Comic Strip by Mary Tourtel (1874-1948), Cent. — A321

Designs: 50p, Rupert Bear. 68p, Podgy Pig. 70p, Edward Trunk. 85p, Bill the Badger. 95p, Algy Pug. £1.02, Rupert Bear, diff. £3, Rupert Bear, diff.

**2020, July 21    Litho.    Perf. 12**

| | | | | |
|---|---|---|---|---|
| 1554 | A321 | 50p multi | 1.30 | 1.30 |
| 1555 | A321 | 68p multi | 1.75 | 1.75 |
| 1556 | A321 | 70p multi | 1.90 | 1.90 |
| 1557 | A321 | 85p multi | 2.25 | 2.25 |
| 1558 | A321 | 95p multi | 2.50 | 2.50 |
| 1559 | A321 | £1.02 multi | 2.75 | 2.75 |
| | | Nos. 1554-1559 (6) | 12.45 | 12.45 |

**Souvenir Sheet**

**Perf. 11½**

| | | | | |
|---|---|---|---|---|
| 1560 | A321 | £3 multi | 7.75 | 7.75 |

No. 1560 contains one 38x49mm stamp.

Children's Art — A322

Children's art by: No. 1561, Kahlan Marriott. No. 1562, Olivia Le Tissier. No. 1563, Alexis Drummy. No. 1564, Danny King. No. 1565, Joe De Carteret. No. 1566, Lily-Ella O'Brien. No. 1567, Oliver Blake. No. 1568, Phoebe Smart.

**Serpentine Die Cut 14½**

**2020, Aug. 19**     Litho.

**Self-Adhesive**

| | | | | |
|---|---|---|---|---|
| 1561 | A322 | 50p multi | 1.40 | 1.40 |
| 1562 | A322 | 50p multi | 1.40 | 1.40 |
| a. | | Horiz. pair, #1561-1562 | 2.80 | |
| 1563 | A322 | 68p multi | 1.90 | 1.90 |
| 1564 | A322 | 68p multi | 1.90 | 1.90 |
| a. | | Horiz. pair, #1563-1564 | 3.80 | |
| 1565 | A322 | 85p multi | 2.25 | 2.25 |
| 1566 | A322 | 85p multi | 2.25 | 2.25 |
| a. | | Horiz. pair, #1565-1566 | 4.50 | |
| 1567 | A322 | 95p multi | 2.60 | 2.60 |
| 1568 | A322 | 95p multi | 2.60 | 2.60 |
| a. | | Horiz. pair, #1567-1568 | 5.20 | |
| | | Nos. 1561-1568 (8) | 16.30 | 16.30 |

Proceeds from the sale of Nos. 1561-1568 were donated to the Guernsey COVID-19 Response Appeal and the Social Investment Fund COVID-19 Community Charity Appeal.

Christmas A323

Designs: 45p, Santa Claus on Royal National Lifeboat Institute vessel. 50p, Santa Claus driving Guernsey Post van. 68p, Santa Claus climbing Les Hanois Lighthouse. 70p, Santa Claus on donkey in Market Square. 85p, Reindeer firing Noonday Gun. 95p, Elves putting fake antlers on Guernsey cow. £1.02, Santa Claus and reindeer skating on frozen reservoir.

**Serpentine Die Cut 14¼**

**2020, Oct. 28**     Litho.

**Self-Adhesive**

| | | | | |
|---|---|---|---|---|
| 1569 | A323 | 45p multi | 1.25 | 1.25 |
| 1570 | A323 | 50p multi | 1.30 | 1.30 |
| 1571 | A323 | 68p multi | 1.75 | 1.75 |
| 1572 | A323 | 70p multi | 1.90 | 1.90 |
| 1573 | A323 | 85p multi | 2.25 | 2.25 |
| 1574 | A323 | 95p multi | 2.50 | 2.50 |
| 1575 | A323 | £1.02 multi | 2.75 | 2.75 |
| | | Nos. 1569-1575 (7) | 13.70 | 13.70 |

New Year 2021 (Year of the Ox) — A324

Various depictions of oxen.

**2021, Jan. 26**   Litho.   **Perf. 13½x13¼**

| | | | | |
|---|---|---|---|---|
| 1576 | A324 | 50p scar & ol bis | 1.30 | 1.30 |
| 1577 | A324 | 68p scar & ol bis | 1.75 | 1.75 |
| 1578 | A324 | 70p scar & ol bis | 1.90 | 1.90 |
| 1579 | A324 | 85p scar & ol bis | 2.25 | 2.25 |
| 1580 | A324 | 95p scar & ol bis | 2.50 | 2.50 |
| 1581 | A324 | £1.02 scar & ol bis | 2.75 | 2.75 |
| a. | | Souvenir sheet of 6, #1576-1581 | 12.50 | 12.50 |
| | | Nos. 1576-1581 (6) | 12.45 | 12.45 |

Birds — A325

Designs: 1p, House sparrow. 2p, Pied wagtail. 3p, Great tit. 4p, Long-tailed tit. 5p, Green finch. 6p, Song thrush. 7p, Blackbird. 8p, Swallow. 9p, Magpie. 10p, Common tern. 20p, Lapwing. 30p, Cormorant. 40p, Pale phase buzzard. 50p, Common buzzard. £1, Gray heron. £2, Lesser black-backed gull. £4, Gannets.

---

**2021, Feb. 17**     Litho.     **Perf. 12**

| | | | | |
|---|---|---|---|---|
| 1582 | A325 | 1p multi | .25 | .25 |
| 1583 | A325 | 2p multi | .25 | .25 |
| 1584 | A325 | 3p multi | .25 | .25 |
| 1585 | A325 | 4p multi | .25 | .25 |
| 1586 | A325 | 5p multi | .25 | .25 |
| 1587 | A325 | 6p multi | .25 | .25 |
| 1588 | A325 | 7p multi | .25 | .25 |
| 1589 | A325 | 8p multi | .25 | .25 |
| 1590 | A325 | 9p multi | .25 | .25 |
| 1591 | A325 | 10p multi | .25 | .25 |
| 1592 | A325 | 20p multi | .50 | .50 |
| 1593 | A325 | 30p multi | .75 | .75 |
| 1594 | A325 | 40p multi | 1.00 | 1.00 |
| 1595 | A325 | 50p multi | 1.30 | 1.30 |
| 1596 | A325 | £1 multi | 2.60 | 2.60 |
| 1597 | A325 | £2 multi | 5.25 | 5.25 |
| 1598 | A325 | £4 multi | 10.50 | 10.50 |
| | | Nos. 1582-1598 (17) | 24.40 | 24.40 |

Wreath of Poppies and Royal Air Force Spitfires A326

Wreath of Poppies and Royal Air Force Hurricane — A327

Wreath of Poppies and British Soldiers in Afghanistan — A328

Wreath of Poppies and HMS Ardent in 1982 Falkland Islands Conflict A329

**2021**     Litho.     **Perf. 13**

| | | | | |
|---|---|---|---|---|
| 1599 | A326 | £1 multi | 2.60 | 2.60 |
| 1600 | A327 | £1 multi | 2.50 | 2.50 |
| 1601 | A328 | £1 multi | 2.75 | 2.75 |
| 1602 | A329 | £1 multi | 2.75 | 2.75 |
| a. | | Souvenir sheet of 4, #1599-1602 | 11.00 | 11.00 |
| | | Nos. 1599-1602 (4) | 10.60 | 10.60 |

Royal British Legion, cent. Issued: No. 1599, 2/17; No. 1600, 5/15; No. 1601, 9/1; No. 1602, 11/11.

**Souvenir Sheet**

Clematis "Sarah Elizabeth" — A330

**2021, Feb. 17**     Litho.     **Perf. 14x13½**

| | | | | |
|---|---|---|---|---|
| 1604 | A330 | £3 multi | 7.75 | 7.75 |

Endangered Wildlife — A331

Designs: 50p, European herring gull. 70p, Scaly cricket. 73p, Basking shark. £1, European eel. £1.15, Black-backed meadow ant. £1.20, Harbor porpoise. £2.20, Glanville fritillary. £3.50, Porbeagle shark.

---

**2021, Apr. 7**     Litho.     **Perf. 14¼**

| | | | | |
|---|---|---|---|---|
| 1605 | A331 | 50p multi | 1.25 | 1.25 |
| 1606 | A331 | 70p multi | 1.75 | 1.75 |
| 1607 | A331 | 73p multi | 1.90 | 1.90 |
| 1608 | A331 | £1 multi | 2.50 | 2.50 |
| a. | | Souvenir sheet of 2, #1607-1608 | 4.50 | 4.50 |
| 1609 | A331 | £1.15 multi | 3.00 | 3.00 |
| 1610 | A331 | £1.20 multi | 3.00 | 3.00 |
| 1611 | A331 | £2.20 multi | 5.50 | 5.50 |
| 1612 | A331 | £3.50 multi | 8.75 | 8.75 |
| | | Nos. 1605-1612 (8) | 27.65 | 27.65 |

Europa (Nos. 1607, 1608, 1608a).

Queen Elizabeth II, 95th Birthday — A332

Photograph of: 50p, Princess Elizabeth at age 10, with her dog. 70p, Queen Elizabeth II at coronation, 1953. 73p, Queen Elizabeth II and Prince Philip, 1952. £1, Queen Elizabeth II, 2016. £1.15, Queen Elizabeth II on horse at Trooping the Colors ceremony. £1.20, Queen Elizabeth II, 2015.

**2021, Apr. 21**     Litho.     **Perf. 13¼**

| | | | | |
|---|---|---|---|---|
| 1613 | A332 | 50p multi | 1.25 | 1.25 |
| 1614 | A332 | 70p multi | 1.75 | 1.75 |
| 1615 | A332 | 73p multi | 1.90 | 1.90 |
| 1616 | A332 | £1 multi | 2.50 | 2.50 |
| 1617 | A332 | £1.15 multi | 3.00 | 3.00 |
| 1618 | A332 | £1.20 multi | 3.00 | 3.00 |
| | | Nos. 1613-1618 (6) | 13.40 | 13.40 |

See Isle of Man No. 2150a.

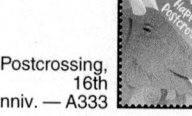

Postcrossing, 16th Anniv. — A333

Guernsey post box and: UK, Golden Guernsey goat with postcard, Torteval Church. EUR, Chance crab with postcard, Pleinmont Observation Tower. ROW, Atlantic puffin with postcard, sailboat, Herm and Jethou.

**2021, June 10**     Litho.     **Perf. 12**

| | | | | |
|---|---|---|---|---|
| 1619 | A333 | UK multi | 1.90 | 1.90 |
| 1620 | A333 | EUR multi | 2.50 | 2.50 |
| 1621 | A333 | ROW multi | 2.75 | 2.75 |
| | | Nos. 1619-1621 (3) | 7.15 | 7.15 |

On day of issue, Nos. 1619-1621 each sold for 73p, £1, and £1.20, respectively.

Designation of Sark as First Dark Sky Island, 10th Anniv. — A334

Photograph of night sky taken: 50p, Near Monk Rock. 70p, Near Point Robert Lighthouse. 73p, Near La Coupée. £1, Near Mer Tower. £1.15, On Little Sark. £1.20, Near La Seigneurie.

**2021, June 10**     Litho.     **Perf. 14**

| | | | | |
|---|---|---|---|---|
| 1622 | A334 | 50p multi | 1.25 | 1.25 |
| a. | | Booklet pane of 4 | 5.00 | — |
| 1623 | A334 | 70p multi | 1.75 | 1.75 |
| a. | | Booklet pane of 4 | 7.00 | — |
| 1624 | A334 | 73p multi | 1.90 | 1.90 |
| a. | | Booklet pane of 4 | 7.75 | — |
| 1625 | A334 | £1 multi | 2.50 | 2.50 |
| a. | | Booklet pane of 4 | 10.00 | — |
| 1626 | A334 | £1.15 multi | 3.00 | 3.00 |
| a. | | Booklet pane of 4 | 12.00 | — |
| 1627 | A334 | £1.20 multi | 3.00 | 3.00 |
| a. | | Booklet pane of 4 | 12.00 | — |
| | | Complete booklet, #1622a, 1623a, 1624a, 1625a, 1626a, 1627a | 54.00 | |

Historic Maps by John Speed (1552-1629) A335

Maps detailing: 50p, Area near Vale Castle (Northeastern Guernsey). 70p, Herm, Sark, Jethou and Brecqhou Islands. 73p, The Town and Castle Cornet (Western Guernsey). £1, Guernsey and nearby islands. £1.15, Southwestern Guernsey. £1.20, Lihou Island and nearby Guernsey coast.

---

**2021, Sept. 1**     Litho.     **Perf. 12**

| | | | | |
|---|---|---|---|---|
| 1628 | A335 | 50p multi | 1.40 | 1.40 |
| 1629 | A335 | 70p multi | 2.00 | 2.00 |
| 1630 | A335 | 73p multi | 2.00 | 2.00 |
| 1631 | A335 | £1 multi | 2.75 | 2.75 |
| 1632 | A335 | £1.15 multi | 3.25 | 3.25 |
| 1633 | A335 | £1.20 multi | 3.50 | 3.50 |
| | | Nos. 1628-1633 (6) | 14.90 | 14.90 |

Christmas — A336

Designs: 45p, Nativity. 50p, Anunciation. 70p, Joseph dreaming. 73p, Journey to Bethlehem. £1, Madonna and Child in manger. £1.15, Angel appearing to shepherd. £1.20, Magi following Star of Bethlehem.

**Serpentine Die Cut 14¼**

**2021, Nov. 3**     Litho.

**Self-Adhesive**

| | | | | |
|---|---|---|---|---|
| 1634 | A336 | 45p multi | 1.25 | 1.25 |
| 1635 | A336 | 50p multi | 1.40 | 1.40 |
| 1636 | A336 | 70p multi | 1.90 | 1.90 |
| 1637 | A336 | 73p multi | 2.00 | 2.00 |
| 1638 | A336 | £1 multi | 2.75 | 2.75 |
| 1639 | A336 | £1.15 multi | 3.00 | 3.00 |
| 1640 | A336 | £1.20 multi | 3.25 | 3.25 |
| | | Nos. 1634-1640 (7) | 15.55 | 15.55 |

New Year 2022 (Year of the Tiger) — A337

Various depictions of tigers.

**2022, Jan. 19**   Litho.   **Perf. 13½x13¼**

| | | | | |
|---|---|---|---|---|
| 1641 | A337 | 50p scar & ol bis | 1.40 | 1.40 |
| 1642 | A337 | 70p scar & ol bis | 1.90 | 1.90 |
| 1643 | A337 | 73p scar & ol bis | 2.00 | 2.00 |
| 1644 | A337 | £1 scar & ol bis | 2.75 | 2.75 |
| 1645 | A337 | £1.15 scar & ol bis | 3.25 | 3.25 |
| 1646 | A337 | £1.20 scar & ol bis | 3.25 | 3.25 |
| a. | | Souvenir sheet of 6, #1641-1646 | 15.00 | 15.00 |
| | | Nos. 1641-1646 (6) | 14.55 | 14.55 |

Bird and Tree — A338

Butterfly and Forest — A339

Insects, Tree Trunk and Leaves — A340

Butterfly and Flowers — A341

**2022**     Litho.     **Perf. 13½x13¼**

| | | | | |
|---|---|---|---|---|
| 1647 | A338 | £1 multi | 2.75 | 2.75 |
| 1648 | A339 | £1 multi | 2.50 | 2.50 |
| 1649 | A340 | £1 multi | 2.40 | 2.40 |
| 1650 | A341 | £1 multi | 2.40 | 2.40 |
| a. | | Souvenir sheet of 4, #1647-1650 | 10.00 | 10.00 |
| | | Nos. 1647-1650 (4) | 10.05 | 10.05 |

Issued: No. 1647, 2/9; No. 1648, 4/4; No. 1649, 8/24; Nos. 1650, 1650a, 11/2.

## Souvenir Sheet

Clematis "Samaritan Jo" — A342

**2022, Feb. 9    Litho.    Perf. 12**
1651  A342  £3 multi                    8.00  8.00

Native Speakers of Guernsey Patois — A343

Designs: 52p, Roy Le Prevost. 73p, Joan Lacey. 79p, Fred Gallienne. £1.10, Lloyd Le Poidevin. £1.26, Ivan De La Mare. £1.35, Jean De Garis. £2.20, Joyce Girard. £3.50, Alan Le Ray.

**2022, Apr. 4    Litho.    Perf. 12**
1652  A343  52p multi              1.30  1.30
1653  A343  73p multi              1.90  1.90
1654  A343  79p multi              2.00  2.00
1655  A343  £1.10 multi            2.75  2.75
1656  A343  £1.26 multi            3.25  3.25
1657  A343  £1.35 multi            3.50  3.50
1658  A343  £2.20 multi            5.50  5.50
1659  A343  £3.50 multi            8.75  8.75
    Nos. 1652-1659 (8)           28.95  28.95

Witches — A344

Designs: 52p, Le Sabbat des sorciers. 73p, Witches flying. 79p, Witches and witch standing on witch's seat. £1.10, Witch in the hedge. £1.26, Jean Falla and witches. £1.35, Witch's ghost.

**2022, May 21    Litho.    Perf. 12**
1660  A344  52p multi              1.30  1.30
1661  A344  73p multi              1.90  1.90
1662  A344  79p multi              2.00  2.00
1663  A344  £1.10 multi            2.75  2.75
   a.   Souvenir sheet of 2, #1662-
        1663                       4.75  4.75
1664  A344  £1.26 multi            3.25  3.25
1665  A344  £1.35 multi            3.50  3.50
    Nos. 1660-1665 (6)           14.70  14.70

Europa (Nos. 1662-1663).

Falkland Islands War, 40th Anniv. — A345

Designs: 52p, HMS Ardent. 73p, HMS Ardent Memorial at National Arboretum. 79p, HMS Ardent Memorial, Campito Hill, Falkland Islands. £1.10, Type 21 Memorial Bench, Plymouth. £1.26, Petty Officer P. I. H. Brouard Memorial, Le Foulon Cemetery, St. Peter Port. £1.35, Bell of HMS Ardent.

**2022, May 21    Litho.    Perf. 14½**
1666  A345  52p multi              1.30  1.30
   a.   Booklet pane of 4          5.25   —
1667  A345  73p multi              1.90  1.90
   a.   Booklet pane of 4          7.75   —
1668  A345  79p multi              2.00  2.00
   a.   Booklet pane of 4          8.00   —
1669  A345  £1.10 multi            2.75  2.75
   a.   Booklet pane of 4         11.00   —
1670  A345  £1.26 multi            3.25  3.25
   a.   Booklet pane of 4         13.00   —
1671  A345  £1.35 multi            3.50  3.50
   a.   Booklet pane of 4         14.00   —
   Complete booklet, #1666a,
   1667a, 1668a, 1669a,
   1670a, 1671a                   59.00
    Nos. 1666-1671 (6)           14.70  14.70

Seagulls — A346

Seagull and: 52p, Piece of gâche (raisin bread). 79p, Fish. £1.10, Beer can. £1.35, Ice cream cone.

**2022, June 22    Litho.    Perf. 12**
1672  A346  52p multi              1.25  1.25
1673  A346  79p multi              1.90  1.90
1674  A346  £1.10 multi            2.75  2.75
1675  A346  £1.35 multi            3.25  3.25
    Nos. 1672-1675 (4)            9.15  9.15

Illustrations From *The Book of Ebenezer Le Page,* by Gerald Basil Edwards — A347

Illustrations: 52p, Ebby on the Common. 73p, La Hetty and La Prissy. 79p, Liza Quéripel. £1.10, Liberation Day. £1.26, Neville Falla. £1.35, Old Ebenezer and Liza.

**2022, Aug. 24    Litho.    Perf. 13¼x13**
1676  A347  52p multi              1.25  1.25
1677  A347  73p multi              1.75  1.75
1678  A347  79p multi              1.90  1.90
1679  A347  £1.10 multi            2.60  2.60
1680  A347  £1.26 multi            3.00  3.00
1681  A347  £1.35 multi            3.25  3.25
    Nos. 1676-1681 (6)           13.75  13.75

Christmas — A348

Scenes from pantomime production of *Sleeping Beauty:* 47p, Good Fairy casting spell on Princess. 52p, Evil Fairy placing curse on Princess. 73p, Sixteenth birthday celebrations of the Princess. 79p, Princess pricks finger on spinning wheel. £1.10, Prince cutting through briar rose hedge. £1.26, Prince approaches sleeping Princess. £1.35, Prince and Princess dancing.

**Serpentine Die Cut 14¼**
**2022, Nov. 16                 Litho.**
**Self-Adhesive**
1682  A348  47p multi              1.10  1.10
1683  A348  52p multi              1.25  1.25
1684  A348  73p multi              1.75  1.75
1685  A348  79p multi              1.90  1.90
1686  A348  £1.10 multi            2.75  2.75
1687  A348  £1.26 multi            3.00  3.00
1688  A348  £1.35 multi            3.25  3.25
    Nos. 1682-1688 (7)           15.00  15.00

New Year 2023 (Year of the Rabbit) — A349

Various depictions of rabbits.

**2023, Jan. 5    Litho.    Perf. 14**
1689  A349  56p red & gold         1.40  1.40
1690  A349  79p red & gold         1.90  1.90
1691  A349  87p red & gold         2.10  2.10
1692  A349  £1.21 red & gold       3.00  3.00
1693  A349  £1.39 red & gold       3.50  3.50
1694  A349  £1.50 red & gold       3.75  3.75
   a.   Souvenir sheet of 6, #1689-
        1694                      16.00  16.00
    Nos. 1689-1694 (6)           15.65  15.65

## POSTAGE DUE STAMPS

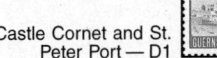

Castle Cornet and St. Peter Port — D1

---

**Perf. 12½x12**
**1969, Oct. 1    Photo.    Unwmk.**
**Black Numeral**
J1  D1  1p deep magenta            1.25  1.25
J2  D1  2p yellow green            1.40  1.40
J3  D1  3p red                     2.20  2.20
J4  D1  4p ultra                   3.00  3.00
J5  D1  5p yellow bister           4.00  4.00
J6  D1  6p greenish blue           4.50  4.50
J7  D1  1sh red brown              8.75  8.75
    Nos. J1-J7 (7)               25.10  25.10

**Type of 1969**
**"p" instead of "d"**
**1971-76                 Black Numeral**
J8   D1  ½p deep magenta            .25   .25
J9   D1  1p yellow green            .25   .25
J10  D1  2p red                     .25   .25
J11  D1  3p ultra                   .25   .25
J12  D1  4p yellow bister           .25   .25
J13  D1  5p greenish blue           .25   .25
J14  D1  6p purple ('76)            .25   .25
J15  D1  8p orange ('75)            .25   .35
J16  D1  10p red brown              .25   .40
J17  D1  15p gray ('76)             .25   .40
    Nos. J8-J17 (10)              2.50  2.90

Town Church, St. Peter Port — D2

**1977-80    Photo.    Perf. 13½x13**
**Arms and Denomination in Black**
J18  D2  ½p red brown               .25   .25
J19  D2  1p lilac rose              .25   .25
J20  D2  2p orange                  .25   .25
J21  D2  3p red                     .25   .25
J22  D2  4p greenish blue           .25   .25
J23  D2  5p olive green             .25   .25
J24  D2  6p greenish blue           .25   .25
J25  D2  8p ocher                   .25   .25
J26  D2  10p dark blue              .30   .30
J27  D2  14p green ('80)            .30   .30
J28  D2  15p purple                 .30   .30
J29  D2  16p salmon rose ('80)      .35   .35
    Nos. J18-J29 (12)             3.25  3.25

Woman Milking Cow — D3

2p, Vale Mill. 3p, Sark cottage. 4p, St. Peter Port. 5p, Well, Moulin Huet. 16p, Seaweed gathering. 18p, Upper Walk, White Rock. 20p, Cobo Bay. 25p, Saints' Bay. 30p, La Coupee, Sark. 50p, Old Harbor, St. Peter Port. £1, Greenhouses, Victoria Tower.

**1982, July 13    Litho.    Perf. 14½**
J30  D3  1p shown                   .25   .25
J31  D3  2p multicolored            .25   .25
J32  D3  3p multicolored            .25   .25
J33  D3  4p multicolored            .25   .25
J34  D3  5p multicolored            .25   .25
J35  D3  16p multicolored           .30   .30
J36  D3  18p multicolored           .35   .35
J37  D3  20p multicolored           .40   .40
J38  D3  25p multicolored           .45   .45
J39  D3  30p multicolored           .55   .55
J40  D3  50p multicolored           .80   .80
J41  D3  £1 multicolored           1.80  1.80
    Nos. J30-J41 (12)             5.90  5.90

## OCCUPATION STAMPS

**Issued Under German Occupation**

Bisects of Great Britain Nos. 238 and 255 were used in Guernsey from 12/27/40 to 2./24/41. Values, on cover or postcard: No. 238, $45; No. 255, $40.

Catalogue values for unused stamps in this section are for hinged items.

OS1

---

**Rouletted 14x7**
**1941-44    Typo.    Unwmk.**
N1  OS1  ½p light green             4.00  4.00
N2  OS1  1p red                     3.25  2.25
N3  OS1  2½p ultramarine           12.75  17.25
    Nos. N1-N3 (3)               20.00  23.50

Issued: No. N1, from 7/43; No. N2, 2/18/41; No. N3, 4/12/44.

Additional shades and papers exist. The rouletting is very crude and may not be measurable. This is not a defect.

For detailed listings, see the Scott Classic Specialized catalogue.

**Bluish French Bank Note Paper**

**Wmk. 396 Chain Link Fence**
**1942                 Rouletted 14x7**
N4  OS1  ½p green                  27.50  28.75
N5  OS1  1p red                    18.75  28.75

Issue dates: ½p, Mar. 11; 1p, Apr. 9.
Nos. N1-N5 remained valid until 4/13/46.

# ALDERNEY

'ol-dər-nē

LOCATION — Northernmost of the Channel Islands in the Guernsey Bailiwick
GOVT. — Dependent territory under Bailiwick of Guernsey.
AREA — 3 sq. mi.
POP. — 2,373 (1994 est.)
CAPITAL — St. Anne's

Part of the Bailiwick of Guernsey, this island began issuing its own stamps.

Catalogue values for unused stamps in this section are for Never Hinged items.

Map of Alderney, Arms — A1

**1983, June 14    Litho.    Perf. 11¾**

| 1 | A1 | 1p shown | .25 | .25 |
|---|----|----|----|----|
| 2 | A1 | 4p Hanging Rock | .25 | .25 |
| 3 | A1 | 9p States Building | .25 | .25 |
| 4 | A1 | 10p St. Anne's Church | .25 | .25 |
| 5 | A1 | 11p Yachts, Braye Bay | .35 | .35 |
| 6 | A1 | 12p Victoria St., St. Anne | .35 | .35 |
| 7 | A1 | 13p Map, arms | .35 | .35 |
| 8 | A1 | 14p Ft. Clonque | .40 | .40 |
| 9 | A1 | 15p Corblets Bay Port | .40 | .40 |
| 10 | A1 | 16p Old Tower, St. Anne | .40 | .40 |
| 11 | A1 | 17p Essex Castle Golf Course | .45 | .45 |
| 12 | A1 | 18p Ships in Old Harbor | .45 | .45 |
| | | Nos. 1-12 (12) | 4.15 | 4.15 |

See Nos. 42-46, which is considered to be the higher-denomination continuation of this definitive set.

Oystercatcher, Telegraph Bay — A2

13p, Turnstone, Corblets Bay. 26p, Ringed plover, Corblets Bay. 28p, Dunlin, Arch Bay. 31p, Curlew, Old Harbor.

**1984, June 12    Perf. 14½**

| 13 | A2 | 9p shown | .75 | .75 |
|----|----|----|----|----|
| 14 | A2 | 13p multicolored | .75 | .75 |
| 15 | A2 | 26p multicolored | 1.50 | 1.50 |
| 16 | A2 | 28p multicolored | 1.50 | 1.50 |
| 17 | A2 | 31p multicolored | 1.50 | 1.50 |
| | | Nos. 13-17 (5) | 6.00 | 6.00 |

Alderney Airport, 50th Anniv. — A3

Aircraft: 9p, Wessex helicopter of the Queen's Flight, 1984. 13p, Aurigny Air Joey Britten-Norman Trislander, 1981. 29p, Morton Air Services DeHavilland Heron, 1946. 31p, DeHavilland Dragon Rapide, c. 1930. 34p, Saunders-Roe Saro Windhover, 1935.

**1985, Mar. 19    Perf. 12x11½**

| 18 | A3 | 9p multicolored | 1.00 | 1.00 |
|----|----|----|----|----|
| 19 | A3 | 13p multicolored | 1.25 | 1.25 |
| 20 | A3 | 29p multicolored | 2.15 | 2.15 |
| 21 | A3 | 31p multicolored | 2.30 | 2.30 |
| 22 | A3 | 34p multicolored | 2.30 | 2.30 |
| | | Nos. 18-22 (5) | 9.00 | 9.00 |

Regimental Uniforms, Alderney Garrison — A4

9p, Royal Engineers, 1890. 14p, Duke of Albany's Own Highlanders, 1856. 29p, Royal

Artillery, 1855. 31p, South Hampshire Regiment, 1810. 34p, Royal Irish Regiment, 1782.

**1985, Sept. 24    Perf. 14½**

| 23 | A4 | 9p multicolored | .25 | .25 |
|----|----|----|----|----|
| 24 | A4 | 14p multicolored | .70 | .70 |
| 25 | A4 | 29p multicolored | .70 | .70 |
| 26 | A4 | 31p multicolored | 1.00 | 1.00 |
| 27 | A4 | 34p multicolored | 1.15 | 1.15 |
| | | Nos. 23-27 (5) | 3.80 | 3.80 |

Forts — A5

**1986, Sept. 23    Litho.    Perf. 13x13½**

| 28 | A5 | 10p Grosnez | .75 | .75 |
|----|----|----|----|----|
| 29 | A5 | 14p Tourgis | .75 | .75 |
| 30 | A5 | 31p Clonque | 1.50 | 1.50 |
| 31 | A5 | 34p Albert | 1.50 | 1.50 |
| | | Nos. 28-31 (4) | 4.50 | 4.50 |

Shipwrecks — A6

11p, Liverpool, 1902. 15p, Petit Raymond, 1906. 29p, Maina, 1910. 31p, Burton, 1911. 34p, Point Law, 1975.

**1987, May 5    Litho.    Perf. 14½**

| 32 | A6 | 11p multicolored | 1.40 | 1.40 |
|----|----|----|----|----|
| 33 | A6 | 15p multicolored | 1.50 | 1.50 |
| 34 | A6 | 29p multicolored | 2.80 | 2.80 |
| 35 | A6 | 31p multicolored | 3.00 | 3.00 |
| 36 | A6 | 34p multicolored | 3.25 | 3.25 |
| | | Nos. 32-36 (5) | 11.95 | 11.95 |

18th-20th Cent. Maps — A7

Designs: 12p, Herman Moll map, 1724. 18p, Survey by J.H. Bastide, 1739. 27p, Land survey by M.P. Goodwin, 1831. 32p, Wartime occupation map, 1943. 35p, Ordnance survey, 1988.

**1989, July 7    Litho.    Perf. 13½x14**

| 37 | A7 | 12p multicolored | .35 | .35 |
|----|----|----|----|----|
| 38 | A7 | 18p multicolored | .50 | .50 |
| 39 | A7 | 27p multicolored | .90 | .90 |
| 40 | A7 | 32p multicolored | 1.00 | 1.00 |
| 41 | A7 | 35p multicolored | 1.25 | 1.25 |
| | | Nos. 37-41 (5) | 4.00 | 4.00 |

Quesnard Lighthouse — A8

Designs: 21p, Inner Harbor, Braye. 23p, The Island Hall, Alderney. 24p, Alderney Railway locomotive, J. T. Daly. 28p, Lifeboat, Louis Marchesi of Round Table.

**1989-93    Litho.    Perf. 15x14**

| 42 | A8 | 20p multicolored | 1.00 | 1.00 |
|----|----|----|----|----|
| 43 | A8 | 21p multicolored | 1.00 | 1.00 |
| 44 | A8 | 23p multicolored | .80 | .80 |
| 45 | A8 | 24p multicolored | 1.75 | 1.75 |
| 46 | A8 | 28p multicolored | 2.25 | 2.25 |
| | | Nos. 42-46 (5) | 6.80 | 6.80 |

Issued: 20p, 12/27; 21p, 4/2/91; 23p, 2/6/92; 24p, 28p, 3/3/93.

Ships Called HMS Alderney — A9

14p, Bomb ketch, 1738. 20p, Sixth-rate, 1742. 29p, Sloop, 1755. 34p, A-Class submarine, 1945. 37p, Fishery protection vessel, 1979.

**1990, May 3    Litho.    Perf. 13½**

| 55 | A9 | 14p multicolored | .40 | .25 |
|----|----|----|----|----|
| 56 | A9 | 20p multicolored | .55 | .40 |
| 57 | A9 | 29p multicolored | 1.00 | 1.00 |
| 58 | A9 | 34p multicolored | 1.25 | 1.25 |
| 59 | A9 | 37p multicolored | 1.40 | 1.40 |
| | | Nos. 55-59 (5) | 4.60 | 4.30 |

Automation of Casquets Lighthouse A10

21p, Wreck of HMS Victory, 1744. 26p, Returning by rowboat. 31p, Helicopter relief. 37p, Lighthouse, birds. 50p, MV Patricia.

**1991, Apr. 30    Litho.    Perf. 14x13½**

| 60 | A10 | 21p multicolored | 1.10 | .65 |
|----|----|----|----|----|
| 61 | A10 | 26p multicolored | 1.90 | 1.60 |
| 62 | A10 | 31p multicolored | 2.25 | 2.25 |
| 63 | A10 | 37p multicolored | 2.25 | 2.25 |
| 64 | A10 | 50p multicolored | 2.50 | 2.50 |
| | | Nos. 60-64 (5) | 10.00 | 9.25 |

Battle of La Hogue, 300th Anniv. — A11

23p, 28p, and 33p, Various details from painting by unknown artist. 50p, Entire painting.

**1992, Sept. 18    Litho.    Perf. 13½**

| 65 | A11 | 23p multicolored | 1.00 | 1.00 |
|----|----|----|----|----|
| 66 | A11 | 28p multicolored | 1.85 | 1.85 |
| 67 | A11 | 33p multicolored | 2.00 | 2.00 |

**Size: 45x30mm**
**Perf. 14x14½**

| 68 | A11 | 50p multicolored | 2.65 | 2.65 |
|----|----|----|----|----|
| | | Nos. 65-68 (4) | 7.50 | 7.50 |

Marine Life — A12

Designs: a, 24p, Palinurus elephas. b, 28p, Metridium senile. c, 33p, Luidia ciliaris. d, 39p, Psammechinus miliaris.

**1993, Nov. 2    Litho.    Perf. 15x14½**

| 69 | A12 | Strip of 4, #a.-d. | 4.25 | 4.25 |
|----|----|----|----|----|

Flora and Fauna — A13

Designs: 1p, Ischnura elegans, ranunculus trichophyllus, sparganium erectum. 2p, Crocidura russula, hypericum linarifolium. 3p, Fulmarus glacialis, carpobrotus edulis. 4p, Colias croceus, trifolium pratense. 5p, Bombus lucorum, orobanche rapum-genistae, cytisus scoparius. 6p, Sylvia undata, cuscuta epithymum, ulex europaeus. 7p, Inachis io, cirsium acaule. 8p, Talpa europaea, endymion non-scripta. 9p, Tettigonia viridissima, ulex europaeus. 10p, Zygaena filipendulae, echium vulgare. 16p, Polyommatus icarus, anacamptis pyramidalis. 20p, Oryctolagus cuniculus, rannunculus repens, pteridium aquilinum. 24p, Larus marinus, romulea columnae. 30p, Fratercula arctica, sedum anglicum. 40p, Saturnia pavonia, rubus fruticosus. 50p, Erinaceus europaeus, oxalis articulata. £1, Sterna hirundo, cynodon dactylon, horiz. £2, Morus bassanus, fucus vesiculosus.

**1994-95    Litho.    Perf. 14½x14¼**

| 70 | A13 | 1p multicolored | .25 | .25 |
|----|----|----|----|----|
| 71 | A13 | 2p multicolored | .25 | .25 |
| 72 | A13 | 3p multicolored | .25 | .25 |
| 73 | A13 | 4p multicolored | .25 | .25 |
| 74 | A13 | 5p multicolored | .25 | .25 |
| 75 | A13 | 6p multicolored | .25 | .25 |
| 76 | A13 | 7p multicolored | .25 | .25 |
| 77 | A13 | 8p multicolored | .30 | .30 |
| 78 | A13 | 9p multicolored | .35 | .35 |
| 79 | A13 | 10p multicolored | .30 | .30 |
| 80 | A13 | 16p multicolored | .50 | .50 |
| a. | | Perf. 14x15 on three sides | .65 | .65 |
| b. | | As "a," booklet pane of 8 | 3.50 | |
| | | Complete booklet, #80b | 3.50 | |
| 81 | A13 | 20p multicolored | .40 | .40 |
| a. | | Perf. 14x15 on three sides | .65 | .65 |
| b. | | As "a," booklet pane of 8 | 3.50 | |
| | | Complete booklet, #81b | 3.50 | |
| 82 | A13 | 24p multicolored | .55 | .55 |
| a. | | Perf. 14x15 on three sides | .70 | .70 |
| b. | | As "a," booklet pane of 8 | 4.50 | |
| | | Complete booklet, #82b | 4.50 | |
| 83 | A13 | 30p multicolored | .75 | .75 |
| 84 | A13 | 40p multicolored | .90 | .90 |
| 85 | A13 | 50p multicolored | 1.50 | 1.50 |
| 86 | A13 | £1 multicolored | 2.50 | 2.50 |
| | | **Perf. 14x15** | | |
| 87 | A13 | £2 multicolored | 6.00 | 6.00 |
| | | Nos. 70-87 (18) | 15.80 | 15.80 |

No. 81 is dated "1994." Nos. 81a-81b are dated "1998."
Issued: £2, 2/28/95; others, 5/5/94.
See Nos. 98-100.

Career of Flt. Lt. Tommy Rose DFC (1895-1968) A14

No. 88: a, 1917-18 Royal Flying Corps. b, 1939-45 Chief Test Pilot. c, Phillips & Powis (Miles) Aircraft.
No. 89: a, Winner, 1935 King's Cup Air Race. b, Winner, 1947 Manx Air Derby. c, UK-Cape-UK Speed Record, 1936.

**1995, Sept. 1    Litho.    Perf. 14x15**

| 88 | A14 | 35p Strip of 3, #a.-c. | 3.25 | 3.25 |
|----|----|----|----|----|
| 89 | A14 | 41p Strip of 3, #a.-c. | 4.00 | 4.00 |

Nos. 88-89 printed in sheets of 12 stamps + 3 labels.

**Souvenir Sheet**

Return of Islanders, 50th Anniv. — A15

**1995, Nov. 16    Litho.    Perf. 13½**

| 90 | A15 | £1.65 multicolored | 4.75 | 4.75 |
|----|----|----|----|----|

A16

a, 24p, Training. b, 41p, Natl. contingencies overseas. c, 60p, Strategic communications. d, 75p, UN operations.

**1996, Jan. 24    Litho.    Perf. 14**

| 91 | A16 | Strip of 4, #a.-d. | 5.75 | 5.75 |
|----|----|----|----|----|

30th Signal Regiment Activities in Alderney, 25th Anniv.

Domestic Cats — A17

16p, Butterfly, brown & white cat. 24p, Gray cat on table. 25p, Two cats on chair. 35p, Cat pulling on table cloth. 41p, Calico cat in toy cart, white cat. 60p, Siamese cat with yarn.

**1996, July 19    Litho.    Perf. 13½**

| 92 | A17 | 16p multicolored | .60 | .60 |
|----|----|----|----|----|
| 93 | A17 | 24p multicolored | .95 | .95 |
| 94 | A17 | 25p multicolored | 1.00 | 1.00 |
| 95 | A17 | 35p multicolored | 1.25 | 1.25 |
| 96 | A17 | 41p multicolored | 1.50 | 1.50 |
| 97 | A17 | 60p multicolored | 2.00 | 2.00 |
| a. | | Souvenir sheet, #92-97 | 7.50 | 7.50 |
| | | Nos. 92-97 (6) | 7.30 | 7.30 |

No. 97a is a continuous design.

## Fauna and Flora Type of 1994

Designs: 18p, Aglais urticae, Buddleja davidii. 25p, Anthus petrosus, matthiola incana. 26p, Ammophila sabulosa, calystegia soldanella, horiz.

| | | | |
|---|---|---|---|
| **1997, Jan. 2** | **Litho.** | **Perf. 14½x14¼** | |
| **98** A13 18p multicolored | | .50 | .50 |
| a. | Perf. 14x15 on 3 sides | .90 | |
| b. | As "a," booklet pane of 8 | 3.50 | |
| | Complete booklet, #98b | 3.50 | |
| **99** A13 25p multicolored | | .80 | .80 |
| a. | Perf. 14x15 on 3 sides | .90 | |
| b. | As "a," booklet pane of 8 | 4.50 | |
| | Complete booklet, #99b | 4.50 | |
| **100** A13 26p multicolored | | .80 | .80 |
| *Nos. 98-100 (3)* | | 2.10 | 2.10 |

Alderney Cricket Club, 150th Anniv. — A18

| | | | |
|---|---|---|---|
| **1997, Aug. 21** | **Litho.** | **Perf. 13½** | |
| **101** A18 18p Harold Larwood | | .50 | .50 |
| **102** A18 25p John Arlott | | .65 | .65 |
| **103** A18 37p Pelham J. Warner | | 1.25 | 1.25 |
| **104** A18 43p W.G. Grace | | 1.50 | 1.50 |
| **105** A18 63p John Wisden | | 2.00 | 2.00 |
| a. | Souvenir sheet, #101-105 + label | 7.50 | 7.50 |
| *Nos. 101-105 (5)* | | 5.90 | 5.90 |

Garrison Island — A19

No. 106, Founding of the harbor. No. 107, Ariadne at anchor. No. 108, Quarrying at Mannez. No. 109, Earliest train ferrying stone. No. 110, Queen Victoria arrives ashore. No. 111, Royal yacht at anchor. No. 112, Railway and quarry workers greet the Queen. No. 113, Queen Victoria tours the island.

| | | | |
|---|---|---|---|
| **1997, Nov. 20** | **Litho.** | **Perf. 14½x14** | |
| **106** A19 18p multicolored | | .60 | .60 |
| **107** A19 18p multicolored | | .60 | .60 |
| a. | Pair, #106-107 | 1.25 | 1.25 |
| **108** A19 25p multicolored | | .70 | .70 |
| **109** A19 25p multicolored | | .70 | .70 |
| a. | Pair, #108-109 | 1.50 | 1.50 |
| b. | Booklet pane, #107a, 109a ('98) | 3.00 | 3.00 |
| **110** A19 26p multicolored | | .80 | .80 |
| **111** A19 26p multicolored | | .80 | .80 |
| a. | Pair, #110-111 | 1.75 | 1.75 |
| b. | Booklet pane, #107a, 111a ('98) | 3.50 | 3.50 |
| **112** A19 31p multicolored | | .90 | .90 |
| **113** A19 31p multicolored | | .90 | .90 |
| a. | Pair, #112-113 | 2.00 | 2.00 |
| b. | Booklet pane, #111a, 113a ('98) | 3.75 | 3.75 |
| c. | Booklet pane, #109a, 113a ('98) | 3.50 | 3.50 |
| *Nos. 106-113 (8)* | | 6.00 | 6.00 |

Nos. 109b, 111b, 113b, 113c issued 11/10/98.
See Nos. 119-126, 134-141, 155-162, 176-183.

Alderney Diving Club, 21st Anniv. — A20

20p, Modern superlite helmet. 30p, Cousteau-Gagnan demand valve, 1943. 37p, Heinke closed helmet, 1845. 43p, Siebe closed helmet, 1840. 63p, Deane open helmet, 1829.

| | | | |
|---|---|---|---|
| **1998, Feb. 10** | **Litho.** | **Perf. 13** | |
| **114** A20 20p multicolored | | .60 | .60 |
| **115** A20 30p multicolored | | .85 | .85 |
| **116** A20 37p multicolored | | 1.25 | 1.25 |
| **117** A20 43p multicolored | | 1.60 | 1.60 |
| **118** A20 63p multicolored | | 2.00 | 2.00 |
| a. | Souvenir sheet, #114-118 + label | 7.50 | 7.50 |
| *Nos. 114-118 (5)* | | 6.30 | 6.30 |

## Garrison Island Type of 1997

No. 119, Alderney Post Office. No. 120, Traders in Victoria Street. No. 121, Court House. No. 122, Police Station and Fire Service. No. 123, St. Anne's Church. No. 124, Wedding Party at The Albert Gate. No. 125, SS Courier unloading. No. 126, Fishermen at quay.

| | | | |
|---|---|---|---|
| **1998, Nov. 10** | **Litho.** | **Perf. 14½x14** | |
| **119** A19 20p multicolored | | .60 | .60 |
| **120** A19 20p multicolored | | .60 | .60 |
| a. | Pair, #119-120 | 1.40 | 1.40 |
| **121** A19 25p multicolored | | .70 | .70 |
| **122** A19 25p multicolored | | .70 | .70 |
| a. | Pair, #121-122 | 1.50 | 1.50 |
| b. | Booklet pane, #120a, 122a | 3.00 | 3.00 |
| **123** A19 30p multicolored | | .80 | .80 |
| **124** A19 30p multicolored | | .80 | .80 |
| a. | Pair, #123-124 | 1.75 | 1.75 |
| b. | Booklet pane, #120a, 124a | 3.50 | 3.50 |
| **125** A19 37p multicolored | | .90 | .90 |
| **126** A19 37p multicolored | | .90 | .90 |
| a. | Pair, #125-126 | 2.00 | 2.00 |
| b. | Booklet pane, #124a, 126a | 3.75 | 3.75 |
| c. | Booklet pane, #122a, 126a | 3.50 | 3.50 |
| | Complete booklet, #109b, 111b, 113b, 113c, 122b, 124b, 126b, 126c | 24.00 | |
| *Nos. 119-126 (8)* | | 6.00 | 6.00 |

Booklet sold for £8.48.

### Souvenir Sheet

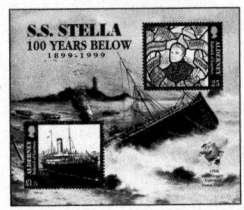

The Wreck of the SS Stella, Cent. A21

a, 25p, Stained glass window, Anglican Cathedral, Liverpool, dedicated to Mary Rogers, chief stewardess. b, £1.75, Ship leaving Southampton.

| | | | |
|---|---|---|---|
| **1999, Feb. 4** | **Litho.** | **Perf. 14** | |
| **127** A21 Sheet of 2, #a.-b. | | 6.50 | 6.50 |

UPU, 125th Anniv.

Total Solar Eclipse — A22

Stages of eclipse on 8/11/99: 20p, 10:15. 25p, 10:51. 30p, 11:14. 38p, 11:16. 44p, 11:17. 64p, 11:36.

| | | | |
|---|---|---|---|
| **1999, Apr. 27** | **Litho.** | **Perf. 13½x13** | |
| **128** A22 20p multicolored | | .45 | .45 |
| **129** A22 25p multicolored | | .60 | .60 |
| **130** A22 30p multicolored | | 1.00 | 1.00 |
| **131** A22 38p multicolored | | 1.25 | 1.25 |
| **132** A22 44p multicolored | | 1.40 | 1.40 |
| **133** A22 64p multicolored | | 1.75 | 1.75 |
| a. | Souvenir sheet, #128-133 + label | 6.75 | 6.75 |
| *Nos. 128-133 (6)* | | 6.45 | 6.45 |

IBRA '99, Nuremberg; Philex '99, Paris (No. 133a).

## Garrison Island Type of 1997

Designs: No. 134, Fort Grosnez, c. 1855. No. 135, Ninth Battalion, Royal Garrison Artillery. No. 136, Arsenal, Fort Albert. No. 137, Royal Engineer Unit. No. 138, Fort Tourgis, c. 1865. No. 139, Second Battalion, Royal Scots Regiment. No. 140, Fort Houmet Herbé, c. 1870. No. 141, Royal Alderney Artillery Militia.

| | | | |
|---|---|---|---|
| **1999, Oct. 19** | **Litho.** | **Perf. 14¼x13¾** | |
| **134** A19 20p multicolored | | .60 | .60 |
| **135** A19 20p multicolored | | .60 | .60 |
| a. | Pair, #134-135 | 1.40 | 1.40 |
| **136** A19 25p multicolored | | .70 | .70 |
| **137** A19 25p multicolored | | .70 | .70 |
| a. | Pair, #136-137 | 1.50 | 1.50 |
| b. | Booklet pane, #135a, 137a | 3.00 | 3.00 |
| **138** A19 30p multicolored | | .80 | .80 |
| **139** A19 30p multicolored | | .80 | .80 |
| a. | Pair, #138-139 | 1.75 | 1.75 |
| b. | Booklet pane, #135a, 139a | 3.50 | 3.50 |
| c. | Booklet pane, #137a, 139a | 3.25 | 3.25 |
| **140** A19 38p multicolored | | .90 | .90 |
| **141** A19 38p multicolored | | .90 | .90 |
| a. | Pair, #140-141 | 2.00 | 2.00 |
| b. | Booklet pane, #135a, 141a | 3.75 | 3.75 |
| c. | Booklet pane, #137a, 141a | 3.50 | 3.50 |
| d. | Booklet pane, #139a, 141a | 3.75 | 3.75 |
| | Complete booklet, #137b, 139b, 139c, 141b, 141c, 141d | 17.50 | |
| *Nos. 134-141 (8)* | | 6.00 | 6.00 |

Booklet sold for £6.78.

Peregrine Falcon — A23

Falcons: 21p, Attacking turnstone near lighthouse. 26p, With prey. 34p, With eggs. 38p, With chicks. 44p, With young near Fort Clonque. 64p, Preparing to fly.

| | | | |
|---|---|---|---|
| **2000, Feb. 4** | **Litho.** | **Perf. 14½x14** | |
| **142** A23 21p multicolored | | .50 | .50 |
| a. | Booklet pane of 10 | 4.75 | |
| | Complete booklet | 5.25 | |
| **143** A23 26p multicolored | | .55 | .55 |
| a. | Booklet pane of 10 | 5.50 | |
| | Complete booklet | 6.00 | |
| **144** A23 34p multi | | .85 | .85 |
| **145** A23 38p multi | | 1.05 | 1.05 |
| **146** A23 44p multi | | 1.50 | 1.50 |
| **147** A23 64p multi | | 1.95 | 1.95 |
| *Nos. 142-147 (6)* | | 6.40 | 6.40 |

Worldwide Fund for Nature, Nos. 144-147.

The Wombles on Vacation — A24

Wombles: 21p, With map. 26p, On beach. 36p, At lighthouse. 40p, Picnicking. 45p, On golf course. 65p, At airport.

| | | | |
|---|---|---|---|
| **2000, Apr. 28** | **Litho.** | **Perf. 14¼x13¾** | |
| **148** A24 21p multi | | .70 | .70 |
| **149** A24 26p multi | | .80 | .80 |
| **150** A24 36p multi | | .90 | .90 |
| **151** A24 40p multi | | 1.15 | 1.15 |
| **152** A24 45p multi | | 1.45 | 1.45 |
| **153** A24 65p multi | | 1.80 | 1.80 |
| a. | Souvenir sheet, #148-153 | 7.75 | 7.75 |
| *Nos. 148-153 (6)* | | 6.80 | 6.80 |

The Stamp Show 2000, London (No. 153a).

### Souvenir Sheet

Queen Mother, 100th Birthday A25

### Litho. with Foil Application

| | | | |
|---|---|---|---|
| **2000, Aug. 4** | | **Perf. 13¼** | |
| **154** A25 £1.50 multi | | 5.00 | 5.00 |

## Garrison Island Type of 1997

No. 155, Regimental boxing tournament. No. 156, Sports Day of Alderney Gala Week, 1924. No. 157, Regimenal Band of 15th entertains. No. 158, Garrison Ball, 1873, Fort Albert mess room. No. 159, Garrison assembly for Queen's birthday celebrations, 1859. No. 160, Demonstration of field guns on the Butes. No. 161, Inspection of honor guard, 1863. No. 162, Arrival of Lt. Gov. Major Gen. Marcus Slade.

| | | | |
|---|---|---|---|
| **2000, Oct. 19** | **Litho.** | **Perf. 13¼x13** | |
| **155** A19 21p multi | | .65 | .65 |
| **156** A19 21p multi | | .65 | .65 |
| a. | Pair, #155-156 | 1.30 | 1.30 |
| **157** A19 26p multi | | .75 | .75 |
| **158** A19 26p multi | | .75 | .75 |
| a. | Pair, #157-158 | 1.50 | 1.50 |
| b. | Booklet pane, #156a, 158a | 3.00 | 3.00 |
| **159** A19 36p multi | | .85 | .85 |
| **160** A19 36p multi | | .85 | .85 |
| a. | Pair, #159-160 | 1.90 | 1.90 |
| b. | Booklet pane, #158a, 160a | 3.75 | 3.75 |
| **161** A19 40p multi | | .95 | .95 |
| **162** A19 40p multi | | .95 | .95 |
| a. | Pair, #161-162 | 2.15 | 2.15 |
| b. | Booklet pane, #156a, 162a | 3.50 | 3.50 |
| c. | Booklet pane, #160a, 162a | 4.00 | 4.00 |
| | Booklet, #158b, 162c, 2 each #160b, 162b | 17.50 | |
| *Nos. 155-162 (8)* | | 6.40 | 6.40 |

Booklet sold for £7.38. Each of the two panes of Nos. 160b and 162b in the booklet have different selvages.

### Souvenir Sheet

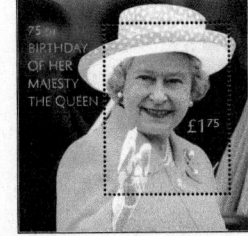

Queen Elizabeth, 75th Birthday — A26

| | | | |
|---|---|---|---|
| **2001, Feb. 1** | **Litho.** | **Perf. 14¼** | |
| **163** A26 £1.75 multi | | 5.25 | 5.25 |

Community Health Services — A27

Health care workers and: 22p, Hospital x-ray department. 27p, Mignot Memorial Hospital in 1980s. 36p, Princess Anne visiting hospital, 1972. 40p, Nurse with infant, 1960s. 45p, Queen Elizabeth II laying hospital cornerstone, 1957. 65p, Opening of original hospital, 1920s.

| | | | |
|---|---|---|---|
| **2001-02** | **Litho.** | **Perf. 14¼x14½** | |
| **164** A27 22p multi | | .75 | .75 |
| a. | Perf. 13¼x13 | 1.10 | 1.10 |
| **165** A27 27p multi | | .85 | .85 |
| a. | Perf. 13¼x13 | 1.25 | 1.25 |
| **166** A27 36p multi | | 1.00 | 1.00 |
| a. | Perf. 13¼x13 | 1.50 | 1.50 |
| **167** A27 40p multi | | 1.30 | 1.30 |
| a. | Perf. 13¼x13 | 2.50 | 2.50 |
| b. | Booklet pane, #164a, 165a, 166a, 167a | 6.50 | |
| **168** A27 45p multi | | 1.50 | 1.50 |
| a. | Perf. 13¼x13 | 2.25 | 2.25 |
| **169** A27 65p multi | | 1.85 | 1.85 |
| a. | Perf. 13¼x13 | 2.75 | 2.75 |
| b. | Booklet pane, #166a, 167a, 168a, 169a | 9.00 | 9.00 |
| c. | Booklet pane, #164a, 165a, 168a, 169a | 7.50 | 7.50 |
| *Nos. 164-169 (6)* | | 7.25 | 7.25 |

Issued: Nos. 164-169, 4/26/01; Nos. 164a-169a, 10/17/02.
See Nos. 196-201, 215-220, 239-244.

Alderney Golf Club — A28

Designs: 22p, Golf ball with core of feathers, 1901. 27p, Golfing fashions, 1920s. 36p, Player and ball on Alderney Golf Club green, 1970s. 40p, Modern putter. 45p, Golf accessories. 65p, Modern lofted wood.

| | | | |
|---|---|---|---|
| **2001, Aug. 1** | **Litho.** | **Perf. 14¾** | |
| **170** A28 22p multi | | .65 | .65 |
| **171** A28 27p multi | | .85 | .85 |
| **172** A28 36p multi | | 1.05 | 1.05 |
| **173** A28 40p multi | | 1.30 | 1.30 |
| **174** A28 45p multi | | 1.50 | 1.50 |
| **175** A28 65p multi | | 1.90 | 1.90 |
| a. | Souvenir sheet, #170-175 | 7.50 | 7.50 |
| *Nos. 170-175 (6)* | | 7.25 | 7.25 |

Phila Nippon '01 (No. 175a).

## Garrison Island Type of 1997

Designs: No. 176, Work continues at the breakwater. No. 177, Officials observe work in progress. No. 178, Steam frigate Emerald grounded. No. 179, Soldiers disembarking Emerald. No. 180, Torpedo boats moored at breakwater. No. 181, Railway provides mobile artillery. No. 182, HMS Majestic at anchor, 1901. No. 183, Torpedo boats maneuver at speed.

| | | | |
|---|---|---|---|
| **2001, Oct. 16** | **Litho.** | **Perf. 13¼x13** | |
| **176** A19 22p multi | | .65 | .65 |
| **177** A19 22p multi | | .65 | .65 |
| a. | Pair, #176-177 | 1.40 | 1.40 |
| **178** A19 27p multi | | .75 | .75 |
| **179** A19 27p multi | | .75 | .75 |
| a. | Pair, #178-179 | 1.60 | 1.60 |
| b. | Booklet pane, #177a, 179a | 3.25 | |
| **180** A19 36p multi | | .90 | .90 |
| **181** A19 36p multi | | .90 | .90 |
| a. | Pair, #180-181 | 2.00 | 2.00 |
| b. | Booklet pane, #179a, 181a | 3.75 | — |

| | | | |
|---|---|---|---|
| **182** | A19 | 40p multi | 1.00 1.00 |
| **183** | A19 | 40p multi | 1.00 1.00 |
| *a.* | | Pair, #182-183 | 2.25 2.25 |
| *b.* | | Booklet pane, #177a, 183a | 3.75 — |
| *c.* | | Booklet pane, #179a, 183a | 4.00 — |
| *d.* | | Booklet pane, #181a, 183a | 4.25 — |
| | | Booklet, #179b, 181b, 183c, 183d, 2 #183b | 17.50 |
| | | *Nos. 176-183 (8)* | 6.60 6.60 |

Booklet sold for £7.50. Each of the two panes of No. 183b in the booklet have different selvages.

### Souvenir Sheet

Reign of Queen Elizabeth II, 50th Anniv. — A29

**2002, Feb. 6** **Litho.** **Perf. 13¾x13½**
| | | | |
|---|---|---|---|
| **184** | A29 | £2 multi | 6.50 6.50 |
| *a.* | | Booklet pane of 1 | 6.50 |
| | | Complete booklet, #184a, Guernsey #773a, 774a, 774b, 774c | 25.00 |

No. 184a is sewn into booklets, but is otherwise identical to No. 184.

Issued: No. 184: 2/6; No. 184a, 4/30.

Birds — A30

**2002, Apr. 30** **Perf. 13¾**
| | | | |
|---|---|---|---|
| **185** | A30 | 22p Hobby | .50 .50 |
| **186** | A30 | 27p Black kite | .75 .75 |
| **187** | A30 | 36p Merlin | 1.00 1.00 |
| **188** | A30 | 40p Honey buzzard | 1.10 1.10 |
| **189** | A30 | 45p Osprey | 1.40 1.40 |
| **190** | A30 | 65p Marsh harrier | 2.00 2.00 |
| *a.* | | Souvenir sheet, #185-190 | 9.00 9.00 |
| | | *Nos. 185-190 (6)* | 6.75 6.75 |

See Nos. 209-214, 233-238, 256-261.

Lighting at Les Casquets Lighthouse — A31

Designs: 22p, Coal fire, 1725. 27p, Oil lantern, 1779. 36p, Argand lamp, 1790. 45p, Revolving apparatus, 1818. 65p, Electrification, 1952.

**2002, July 30** **Perf. 12¾x13¼**
| | | | |
|---|---|---|---|
| **191** | A31 | 22p multi | .70 .70 |
| **192** | A31 | 27p multi | .85 .85 |
| **193** | A31 | 36p multi | 1.25 1.25 |
| **194** | A31 | 45p multi | 1.45 1.45 |
| **195** | A31 | 65p multi | 2.00 2.00 |
| | | *Nos. 191-195 (5)* | 6.25 6.25 |

Emergency Medical Services — A32

Designs: 22p, Ambulance technician, crew running to ambulance. 27p, Emergency medical technician on radio, ambulance on road. 36p, Doctor, transfer of patient to airplane. 40p, Pilot, Aurigny Trislander airplane. 45p, Emergency dispatch operator, transfer of patient to lifeboat. 65p, Lifeboat crewman, speeding lifeboat.

**2002, Oct. 17** **Litho.** **Perf. 14x14½**
| | | | |
|---|---|---|---|
| **196** | A32 | 22p multi | .70 .70 |
| *a.* | | Perf. 13¼x13 | 1.05 1.05 |
| **197** | A32 | 27p multi | .85 .85 |
| *a.* | | Perf. 13¼x13 | 1.25 1.25 |
| **198** | A32 | 36p multi | 1.20 1.20 |
| *a.* | | Perf. 13¼x13 | 1.75 1.75 |
| **199** | A32 | 40p multi | 1.35 1.35 |
| *a.* | | Perf. 13¼x13 | 2.00 2.00 |
| *b.* | | Booklet pane, #196a, 197a, 198a, 199a | 6.00 6.00 |
| **200** | A32 | 45p multi | 1.50 1.50 |
| *a.* | | Perf. 13¼x13 | 2.25 2.25 |
| **201** | A32 | 65p multi | 2.15 2.15 |
| *a.* | | Perf. 13¼x13 | 4.00 4.00 |
| *b.* | | Booklet pane, #198a, 199a, 200a, 201a | 9.00 — |
| *c.* | | Booklet pane, #196a, 197a, 200a, 201a | 7.50 — |

| | | |
|---|---|---|
| | Complete booklet, #167b, 169b, 169c, 199b, 201b, 201c | 30.00 |
| | *Nos. 196-201 (6)* | 7.75 7.75 |

### Souvenir Sheet

Coronation of Queen Elizabeth II, 50th Anniv. — A33

### Litho. & Embossed

**2003, Jan. 30** **Perf. 13½**
| | | | |
|---|---|---|---|
| **202** | A33 | £2 multi | 6.50 6.50 |

Powered Flight, Cent. — A34

Designs: 22p, Wright Flyer, 1903. 27p, Vickers Vimy, 1919. 36p, Douglas DC-3, 1936. 40p, Comet, 1946. 45p, Concorde, 1969. 65p, Airbus A380.

**2003, Apr. 10** **Litho.**
| | | | |
|---|---|---|---|
| **203** | A34 | 22p multi | .65 .65 |
| **204** | A34 | 27p multi | .80 .80 |
| **205** | A34 | 36p multi | 1.10 1.10 |
| **206** | A34 | 40p multi | 1.20 1.20 |
| **207** | A34 | 45p multi | 1.30 1.30 |
| **208** | A34 | 65p multi | 1.95 1.95 |
| | | *Nos. 203-208 (6)* | 7.00 7.00 |

### Bird Type of 2002

**2003, July 3** **Perf. 13¾**
| | | | |
|---|---|---|---|
| **209** | A30 | 22p Arctic tern | .70 .70 |
| **210** | A30 | 27p Great skua | .80 .80 |
| **211** | A30 | 36p Sandwich tern | 1.10 1.10 |
| **212** | A30 | 40p Sooty shearwater | 1.30 1.30 |
| **213** | A30 | 45p Arctic skua | 1.40 1.40 |
| **214** | A30 | 65p Manx shearwater | 2.00 2.00 |
| *a.* | | Souvenir sheet, #209-214 | 8.50 8.50 |
| | | *Nos. 209-214 (6)* | 7.30 7.30 |

Island Police — A35

Police officer and: 22p, Policemen patrolling streets. 27p, Police vehicle. 36p, Member of forensics team. 40p, Policeman assisting child on bicycle. 45p, Police at car accident. 65p, Policeman working with customs officer.

**2003, Oct. 16** **Litho.** **Perf. 13¼x13**
| | | | |
|---|---|---|---|
| **215** | A35 | 22p multi | .70 .70 |
| **216** | A35 | 27p multi | .80 .80 |
| **217** | A35 | 36p multi | 1.15 1.15 |
| **218** | A35 | 40p multi | 1.30 1.30 |
| *a.* | | Booklet pane, #215-218 | 4.00 — |
| **219** | A35 | 45p multi | 1.40 1.40 |
| *a.* | | Booklet pane, #215-217, 219 | 4.25 — |
| **220** | A35 | 65p multi | 1.95 1.95 |
| *a.* | | Booklet pane, #215-216, 219-220 | 5.00 — |
| *b.* | | Booklet pane, #217-220 | 5.75 — |
| *c.* | | Booklet pane, #215-216, 218, 220 | 4.75 — |
| | | Complete booklet, #218a, 219a, 220a, 220c, 2 #220b | 25.00 |
| | | *Nos. 215-220 (6)* | 7.30 7.30 |

The two examples of No. 220b in the booklet have different margins.

Fungi — A36

Designs: 22p, Sulphur tuft. 27p, Orange peel fungus. 36p, Shining ink-cap. 40p, Giant puffball. 45p, Parasol. 65p, Candle snuff fungus.

**2004, Jan. 29** **Litho.** **Perf. 13¼**
| | | | |
|---|---|---|---|
| **221** | A36 | 22p multi | .70 .70 |
| **222** | A36 | 27p multi | .80 .80 |
| **223** | A36 | 36p multi | 1.15 1.15 |
| **224** | A36 | 40p multi | 1.30 1.30 |
| **225** | A36 | 45p multi | 1.40 1.40 |
| **226** | A36 | 65p multi | 2.00 1.00 |
| | | *Nos. 221-226 (6)* | 7.35 7.35 |

FIFA (Fédération Internationale de Football Association), Cent. — A37

Designs: 26p, Challenge on Tourgis Close. 32p, Soccer on the beach. 36p, Playground school soccer. 40p, Friendly kickabout. 45p, Turning the defender. 65p, Tackling Dad at Arch Bay.

**2004, May 12** **Litho.** **Perf. 13¼**
| | | | |
|---|---|---|---|
| **227** | A37 | 26p multi | .80 .80 |
| **228** | A37 | 32p multi | 1.00 1.00 |
| **229** | A37 | 36p multi | 1.10 1.10 |
| **230** | A37 | 40p multi | 1.25 1.25 |
| **231** | A37 | 45p multi | 1.40 1.40 |
| **232** | A37 | 65p multi | 2.00 2.00 |
| | | *Nos. 227-232 (6)* | 7.55 7.55 |

Values are for stamps with surrounding selvage.

### Birds Type of 2002

**2004, July 29** **Litho.** **Perf. 13¼**
| | | | |
|---|---|---|---|
| **233** | A30 | 26p Wheatear | .80 .80 |
| **234** | A30 | 32p Redstart | 1.00 1.00 |
| **235** | A30 | 36p Yellow wagtail | 1.10 1.10 |
| **236** | A30 | 40p Hoopoe | 1.25 1.25 |
| **237** | A30 | 45p Ring ouzel | 1.40 1.40 |
| **238** | A30 | 65p Sand martin | 1.95 1.95 |
| *a.* | | Souvenir sheet, #233-238 | 8.00 8.00 |
| | | *Nos. 233-238 (6)* | 7.50 7.50 |

Fire Services — A38

Designs: 26p, Fireman and fire truck. 32p, Firemen and fire truck. 36p, Fireman and airport fire truck. 40p, Fire chief, fire truck at station. 45p, Training grounds at airport. 65p, Road accicent training exercise.

**2004, Oct. 28** **Litho.** **Perf. 13¼x13**
| | | | |
|---|---|---|---|
| **239** | A38 | 26p multi | .80 .80 |
| **240** | A38 | 32p multi | 1.00 1.00 |
| **241** | A38 | 36p multi | 1.15 1.15 |
| **242** | A38 | 40p multi | 1.25 1.25 |
| *a.* | | Booklet pane, #239-242 | 4.25 |
| **243** | A38 | 45p multi | 1.45 1.45 |
| *a.* | | Booklet pane, #239-241, 243 | 4.50 |
| **244** | A38 | 65p multi | 2.00 2.00 |
| *a.* | | Booklet pane, #239-240, 243-244 | 5.50 — |
| *b.* | | Booklet pane, #241-244 | 5.75 — |
| *c.* | | Booklet pane, #239-240, 242, 244 | 5.25 — |
| | | Complete booklet, #242a, 243a, 244a, 244c, 2 #244b | 27.50 |
| | | *Nos. 239-244 (6)* | 7.65 7.65 |

The two examples of No. 244b in the complete booklet have different margins.

Hans Christian Andersen (1805-75), Author — A39

Scenes from "The Little Mermaid": 26p, Mermaid, fish, castle. 32p, Mermaid rescues prince. 36p, Mermaid and sea witch. 40p, Mermaid and prince on land. 65p, Dead mermaid and angels.

**2005, Feb. 3** **Litho.** **Perf. 13½**
| | | | |
|---|---|---|---|
| **245** | A39 | 26p multi | .80 .80 |
| **246** | A39 | 32p multi | 1.00 1.00 |
| **247** | A39 | 36p multi | 1.15 1.15 |
| **248** | A39 | 40p multi | 1.30 1.30 |
| **249** | A39 | 65p multi | 2.10 2.10 |
| | | *Nos. 245-249 (5)* | 6.35 6.35 |

Battle of Trafalgar, Bicent. — A40

Designs: 26p, Admiral Horatio Nelson. 32p, HMS Victory. 36p, Enemy in sight. 40p, Fall of Nelson. 45p, Breaking the line. 65p, Admiral James de Saumarez.

**2005, May 9** **Litho.** **Perf. 14x13¼**
| | | | |
|---|---|---|---|
| **250** | A40 | 26p multi | .80 .80 |
| **251** | A40 | 32p multi | .95 .95 |
| **252** | A40 | 36p multi | 1.10 1.10 |

| | | | |
|---|---|---|---|
| **253** | A40 | 40p multi | 1.20 1.20 |
| *a.* | | Booklet pane, #250-253 | 4.25 |
| **254** | A40 | 45p multi | 1.40 1.40 |
| **255** | A40 | 65p multi | 1.95 1.95 |
| *a.* | | Booklet pane, #250-251, 254-255 | 5.25 — |
| *b.* | | Booklet pane, #252-255 | 5.75 |
| *c.* | | Booklet pane, #251-252, 254-255 | 5.75 |
| *d.* | | Booklet pane, #250, 253-255 | 5.00 |
| | | Complete booklet, #255a, 255b, 255c, 255d, 2 #253a | 24.00 |
| | | *Nos. 250-255 (6)* | 7.40 7.40 |

The two examples of No. 253a in the complete booklet have different pane margins.

### Bird Type of 2002

26p, Little stint. 32p, Greenshank. 36p, Golden plover. 40p, Bar-tailed godwit. 45p, Green sandpiper. 65p, Sanderling.

**2005, July 21** **Perf. 13¼**
| | | | |
|---|---|---|---|
| **256** | A30 | 26p multicolored | .80 .80 |
| **257** | A30 | 32p multicolored | 1.05 1.05 |
| **258** | A30 | 36p multicolored | 1.10 1.10 |
| **259** | A30 | 40p multicolored | 1.30 1.30 |
| **260** | A30 | 45p multicolored | 1.50 1.50 |
| **261** | A30 | 65p multicolored | 2.00 2.00 |
| *a.* | | Souvenir sheet, #256-261 | 8.50 8.50 |
| | | *Nos. 256-261 (6)* | 7.75 7.75 |

### Souvenir Sheet

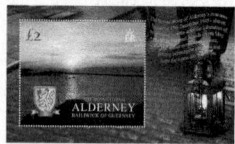

Homecoming of World War II Evacuees, 60th Anniv. — A41

**2005, Oct. 27** **Perf. 13¾**
| | | | |
|---|---|---|---|
| **262** | A41 | £2 multi | 6.50 6.50 |

T.H. White, Author of *The Once and Future King*, Birth Centenary — A42

Authorian legends: 29p, King Arthur. 34p, Merlyn. 38p, Morgause. 42p, Queen Guenever. 47p, Lancelot. 68p, Mordred.

**2006, Feb. 16** **Litho.** **Perf. 13½x14**
| | | | |
|---|---|---|---|
| **263** | A42 | 29p multi | .80 .80 |
| **264** | A42 | 34p multi | 1.00 1.00 |
| **265** | A42 | 38p multi | 1.05 1.05 |
| **266** | A42 | 42p multi | 1.15 1.15 |
| **267** | A42 | 47p multi | 1.35 1.35 |
| **268** | A42 | 68p multi | 1.95 1.95 |
| *a.* | | Souvenir sheet, #263-268 | 7.50 7.50 |
| | | *Nos. 263-268 (6)* | 7.30 7.30 |

Queen Elizabeth II, 80th Birthday A43

Various photographs of Queen with predominant background colors of:
No. 269: a, Blue violet. b, Red violet.
No. 270: a, Green. b, Orange brown.
No. 271: a, Yellow brown. b, Bright red.
No. 272: a, Red. b, Violet.

**2006, Apr. 21** **Perf. 13¾**
| | | | |
|---|---|---|---|
| **269** | A43 | Horiz. pair | 1.65 1.65 |
| *a.-b.* | | 29p Either single | .80 .80 |
| **270** | A43 | Horiz. pair | 2.20 2.20 |
| *a.-b.* | | 34p Either single | 1.10 1.10 |
| **271** | A43 | Horiz. pair | 2.40 2.40 |
| *a.-b.* | | 42p Either single | 1.20 1.20 |
| **272** | A43 | Horiz. pair | 2.60 2.60 |
| *a.-b.* | | 45p Either single | 1.30 1.30 |
| | | *Nos. 269-272 (4)* | 8.85 8.85 |

Birds — A44

Designs: 29p, Fulmar. 34p, Gannet. 42p, Lesser black-backed gull. 45p, Storm petrel. 47p, Kittiwake. 68p, Puffin.

**2006, July 27    Litho.    Perf. 13¾**

| | | | | |
|---|---|---|---|---|
| 273 | A44 | 29p multi | .85 | .85 |
| a. | | Booklet pane of 4 | 3.25 | — |
| 274 | A44 | 34p multi | 1.10 | 1.10 |
| a. | | Booklet pane of 4 | 4.25 | — |
| 275 | A44 | 42p multi | 1.15 | 1.15 |
| a. | | Booklet pane of 4 | 4.75 | — |
| 276 | A44 | 45p multi | 1.30 | 1.30 |
| a. | | Booklet pane of 4 | 5.50 | — |
| 277 | A44 | 47p multi | 1.45 | 1.45 |
| a. | | Booklet pane of 4 | 5.75 | — |
| 278 | A44 | 68p multi | 2.10 | 2.10 |
| a. | | Booklet pane of 4 | 8.25 | — |
| | | Complete booklet, #273a, 274a, 275a, 276a, 277a, 278a | 25.00 | |
| | | Nos. 273-278 (6) | 7.95 | 7.95 |

See Nos. 297-302, 319-324, 344-349.

Corals and Anemones — A45

Designs: 1p, Burrowing anemone. 2p, Colonial anemone. 3p, Jewel anemone. 4p, Sagartia elegans. 5p, Red fingers. 6p, Plumose anemone. 7p, Fan coral. 8p, Jewel anemone, diff. 9p, Actinothoe sphyrodeta. 10p, Snakelocks anemone. £1, Beadlet anemone. £2, Sunset cup coral.

**2006, Nov. 2    Litho.    Perf. 13x13½**

| | | | | |
|---|---|---|---|---|
| 279 | A45 | 1p multi | .25 | .25 |
| 280 | A45 | 2p multi | .25 | .25 |
| 281 | A45 | 3p multi | .25 | .25 |
| 282 | A45 | 4p multi | .25 | .25 |
| 283 | A45 | 5p multi | .25 | .25 |
| 284 | A45 | 6p multi | .25 | .25 |
| 285 | A45 | 7p multi | .25 | .25 |
| 286 | A45 | 8p multi | .25 | .25 |
| 287 | A45 | 9p multi | .25 | .25 |
| 288 | A45 | 10p multi | .30 | .30 |

**Litho. & Embossed**
**Size: 22x27mm**
**Perf. 12¾x13¼**

| | | | | |
|---|---|---|---|---|
| 289 | A45 | £1 multi | 3.00 | 3.00 |
| 290 | A45 | £2 multi | 6.25 | 6.25 |
| | | Nos. 279-290 (12) | 11.80 | 11.80 |

See Nos. 303-306.

Alderney Wetlands — A46

Designs: 32p, Cushion starfish. 37p, Gannet. 45p, Spiny squat lobster. 48p, Gray seal. 50p, Golden samphire. 71p, Little egret.

**2007, Mar. 8    Litho.    Perf. 13¼**

| | | | | |
|---|---|---|---|---|
| 291 | A46 | 32p multi | .90 | .90 |
| 292 | A46 | 37p multi | 1.10 | 1.10 |
| 293 | A46 | 45p multi | 1.30 | 1.30 |
| 294 | A46 | 48p multi | 1.40 | 1.40 |
| 295 | A46 | 50p multi | 1.45 | 1.45 |
| 296 | A46 | 71p multi | 2.00 | 2.00 |
| a. | | Souvenir sheet, #291-296 | 8.50 | 8.50 |
| | | Nos. 291-296 (6) | 8.15 | 8.15 |

Addition of Alderney Wetlands and Burhou Islands to Ramsar Convention Protected Wetlands List.

**Birds Type of 2006**

Designs: 32p, Blackbird. 37p, Dartford warbler. 45p, Blue tit. 48p, Wren. 50p, House sparrow. 71p, Jackdaw.

**2007, May 24    Litho.    Perf. 13¾**

| | | | | |
|---|---|---|---|---|
| 297 | A44 | 32p multi | 1.00 | 1.00 |
| a. | | Booklet pane of 4 | 4.00 | — |
| 298 | A44 | 37p multi | 1.20 | 1.20 |
| a. | | Booklet pane of 4 | 5.00 | — |
| 299 | A44 | 45p multi | 1.45 | 1.45 |
| a. | | Booklet pane of 4 | 5.75 | — |
| 300 | A44 | 48p multi | 1.60 | 1.60 |
| a. | | Booklet pane of 4 | 6.25 | — |
| 301 | A44 | 50p multi | 1.60 | 1.60 |
| a. | | Booklet pane of 4 | 6.25 | — |
| 302 | A44 | 71p multi | 2.50 | 2.50 |
| a. | | Booklet pane of 4 | 9.75 | — |
| | | Complete booklet, #297a-302a | 27.50 | |
| | | Nos. 297-302 (6) | 9.35 | 9.35 |

**Corals and Anemones Type of 2006**

Designs: 20p, Devonshire cup coral. 40p, Fried egg anemone. 50p, Parasitic anemone. £4, Strawberry anemone.

**2007, Aug. 2    Litho.    Perf. 14**
**Size: 27x23mm**

| | | | | |
|---|---|---|---|---|
| 303 | A45 | 20p multi | .70 | .70 |
| 304 | A45 | 40p multi | 1.35 | 1.35 |
| 305 | A45 | 50p multi | 1.70 | 1.70 |

**Litho. & Embossed**
**Size: 27x28mm**

| | | | | |
|---|---|---|---|---|
| 306 | A45 | £4 multi | 13.00 | 13.00 |
| | | Nos. 303-306 (4) | 16.75 | 16.75 |

Just So Stories, by Rudyard Kipling — A47

Designs: 32p, How the Camel Got His Hump. 37p, How the Whale Got His Throat. 45p, The Elephant's Child. 48p, How the Leopard Got His Spots. 50p, The Cat That Walked by Himself. 71p, How the Rhinoceros Got His Skin.

**2007, Oct. 25    Litho.    Perf. 13x13¼**

| | | | | |
|---|---|---|---|---|
| 307 | A47 | 32p multi | 1.10 | 1.10 |
| 308 | A47 | 37p multi | 1.15 | 1.15 |
| 309 | A47 | 45p multi | 1.50 | 1.50 |
| 310 | A47 | 48p multi | 1.50 | 1.50 |
| 311 | A47 | 50p multi | 1.65 | 1.65 |
| 312 | A47 | 71p multi | 2.40 | 2.40 |
| a. | | Miniature sheet, #307-312 | 9.00 | 9.00 |
| | | Nos. 307-312 (6) | 9.30 | 9.30 |

Butterflies — A48

Butterflies: 34p, Painted lady. 40p, Grayling. 48p, Green hairstreak. 51p, Speckled wood. 53c, Common blue. 74p, Glanville fritillary.

**2008, Feb. 28    Litho.    Perf. 13¾**

| | | | | |
|---|---|---|---|---|
| 313 | A48 | 34p multi | 1.05 | 1.05 |
| 314 | A48 | 40p multi | 1.25 | 1.25 |
| 315 | A48 | 48p multi | 1.50 | 1.50 |
| 316 | A48 | 51p multi | 1.50 | 1.50 |
| 317 | A48 | 53p multi | 1.60 | 1.60 |
| 318 | A48 | 74p multi | 2.35 | 2.35 |
| a. | | Miniature sheet, #313-318 | 9.00 | 9.00 |
| | | Nos. 313-318 (6) | 9.25 | 9.25 |

**Birds Type of 2006**

Designs: 34p, Common buzzard. 40p, Peregrine falcon. 48p, Kestrel. 51p, Barn owl. 53p, Long-eared owl. 74p, Sparrowhawk.

**2008, May 15    Litho.    Perf. 13¾**

| | | | | |
|---|---|---|---|---|
| 319 | A44 | 34p multi | 1.05 | 1.05 |
| a. | | Booklet pane of 4 | 4.25 | — |
| 320 | A44 | 40p multi | 1.20 | 1.20 |
| a. | | Booklet pane of 4 | 4.75 | — |
| 321 | A44 | 48p multi | 1.35 | 1.35 |
| a. | | Booklet pane of 4 | 5.50 | — |
| 322 | A44 | 51p multi | 1.45 | 1.45 |
| a. | | Booklet pane of 4 | 5.75 | — |
| 323 | A44 | 53p multi | 1.60 | 1.60 |
| a. | | Booklet pane of 4 | 6.50 | — |
| 324 | A44 | 74p multi | 2.30 | 2.30 |
| a. | | Booklet pane of 4 | 9.25 | — |
| | | Complete booklet, #319a-324a | 32.50 | |
| | | Nos. 319-324 (6) | 8.95 | 8.95 |

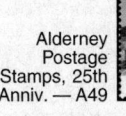

Alderney Postage Stamps, 25th Anniv. — A49

Flag and tourist sites: 34p, Old Harbor. 40p, Breakwater. 48p, Fort Clonque Causeway. 51p, Golf course. 53p, Hanging Rock. 74p, Fort Clonque.

**2008, June 14    Litho.    Perf. 14x13¾**

| | | | | |
|---|---|---|---|---|
| 325 | A49 | 34p multi | 1.05 | 1.05 |
| 326 | A49 | 40p multi | 1.20 | 1.20 |
| 327 | A49 | 45p multi | 1.45 | 1.45 |
| 328 | A49 | 51p multi | 1.45 | 1.45 |
| 329 | A49 | 53p multi | 1.55 | 1.55 |
| 330 | A49 | 74p multi | 2.25 | 2.25 |
| | | Nos. 325-330 (6) | 8.95 | 8.95 |

See No. 376.

Heraldic Lion — A50

**Litho. & Embossed With Foil Application**

**2008, June 14    Perf. 14¼x13½**

| | | | | |
|---|---|---|---|---|
| 331 | A50 | £5 multi | 13.50 | 13.50 |

Aurigny Air Services, 40th Anniv. — A51

Airplanes: 34p, Britten-Norman Islander. 40p, Britten-Norman Trislander. 48p, DHC-6 Twin Otter. 51p, Short 360. 53p, Saab 340. 74p, ATR 72.

**2008, Oct. 30    Litho.    Perf. 13½**

| | | | | |
|---|---|---|---|---|
| 332 | A51 | 34p multi | .95 | .95 |
| 333 | A51 | 40p multi | 1.05 | 1.05 |
| 334 | A51 | 48p multi | 1.35 | 1.35 |
| 335 | A51 | 51p multi | 1.50 | 1.50 |
| 336 | A51 | 53p multi | 1.50 | 1.50 |
| 337 | A51 | 74p multi | 2.00 | 2.00 |
| a. | | Souvenir sheet, #332-337 | 8.50 | 8.50 |
| | | Nos. 332-337 (6) | 8.35 | 8.35 |

Bees — A52

Flowers and: 36p, Tawny mining bee. 43p, Early bumblebee. 51p, Bug mining bee. 54p, Cuckoo bee. 56p, Solitary bee. 77p, Honey bee.

**2009, Feb. 26    Litho.    Perf. 13¾**

| | | | | |
|---|---|---|---|---|
| 338 | A52 | 36p multi | 1.00 | 1.00 |
| 339 | A52 | 43p multi | 1.10 | 1.10 |
| 340 | A52 | 51p multi | 1.35 | 1.35 |
| 341 | A52 | 54p multi | 1.45 | 1.45 |
| 342 | A52 | 56p multi | 1.45 | 1.45 |
| 343 | A52 | 77p multi | 2.00 | 2.00 |
| a. | | Miniature sheet of 6, #338-343 | 8.50 | 8.50 |
| | | Nos. 338-343 (6) | 8.35 | 8.35 |

**Birds Type of 2006**

Designs: 36p, Turnstone. 43p, Curlew. 51p, Oystercatcher. 54p, Snipe. 56p, Dunlin. 77p, Ringed plover.

**2009, May 28    Litho.    Perf. 13¾**

| | | | | |
|---|---|---|---|---|
| 344 | A44 | 36p multi | 1.00 | 1.00 |
| a. | | Booklet pane of 4 | 4.00 | — |
| 345 | A44 | 43p multi | 1.10 | 1.10 |
| a. | | Booklet pane of 4 | 4.50 | — |
| 346 | A44 | 51p multi | 1.25 | 1.25 |
| a. | | Booklet pane of 4 | 5.00 | — |
| 347 | A44 | 54p multi | 1.45 | 1.45 |
| a. | | Booklet pane of 4 | 5.75 | — |
| 348 | A44 | 56p multi | 1.55 | 1.55 |
| a. | | Booklet pane of 4 | 6.25 | — |
| 349 | A44 | 77p multi | 2.00 | 2.00 |
| a. | | Booklet pane of 4 | 8.00 | — |
| | | Complete booklet, #344a-349a | 30.00 | |
| | | Nos. 344-349 (6) | 10.40 | 10.40 |

Naval Aviation, Cent. — A53

Designs: 36p, Flying Boat over Castle Cornet. 43p, Fairey Swordfish attacking U-boat. 51p, Skuas divebombing Scharnhorst. 54p, Sea Fury over Alderney. 56p, Sea Hawk and Sea Fury. 77p, Merlin helicopter landing on HMS Daring.

**2009, July 30    Perf. 14¼x13¾**

| | | | | |
|---|---|---|---|---|
| 350 | A53 | 36p multi | .95 | .95 |
| 351 | A53 | 43p multi | 1.15 | 1.15 |
| 352 | A53 | 51p multi | 1.35 | 1.35 |
| 353 | A53 | 54p multi | 1.45 | 1.45 |
| 354 | A53 | 56p multi | 1.45 | 1.45 |
| 355 | A53 | 77p multi | 2.00 | 2.00 |
| | | Nos. 350-355 (6) | 10.90 | 10.90 |

Scenes From Sherlock Holmes and the Curious Case of the Alderney Bull, by Sir Arthur Conan Doyle (1859-1930) — A54

Designs: 36p, Alice West reporting theft to Holmes. 43p, Holmes and policeman studying message, arrest of suspect. 51p, Holmes looking for clues with magnifying glass. 54p, Holmes with two men outside building. 56p, Holmes pointing to partially-built lighthouse. 77p, Holmes pointing to thief.

**2009, Oct. 29    Litho.    Perf. 13¼x13**

| | | | | |
|---|---|---|---|---|
| 356 | A54 | 36p multi | 1.05 | 1.05 |
| 357 | A54 | 43p multi | 1.30 | 1.30 |
| 358 | A54 | 51p multi | 1.50 | 1.50 |
| 359 | A54 | 54p multi | 1.60 | 1.60 |
| 360 | A54 | 56p multi | 1.60 | 1.60 |
| 361 | A54 | 77p multi | 2.25 | 2.25 |
| | | Nos. 356-361 (6) | 10.90 | 10.90 |

A miniature sheet of six containing one of each stamp was sold together with a special lens and a DVD for £9.99. The sheet was not available separately. Value, sheet $27.50.

Dragonflies — A55

Designs: 36p, Common darter. 45p, Emperor dragonfly. 56p, Blue-tailed damselfly. 66p, Brown hawker. 75p, Black-tailed skimmer. 83p, Red-veined darter.

**2010, Feb. 25    Litho.    Perf. 13¾**

| | | | | |
|---|---|---|---|---|
| 362 | A55 | 36p multi | .95 | .95 |
| 363 | A55 | 45p multi | 1.20 | 1.20 |
| 364 | A55 | 56p multi | 1.50 | 1.50 |
| 365 | A55 | 66p multi | 1.70 | 1.70 |
| 366 | A55 | 75p multi | 2.00 | 2.00 |
| 367 | A55 | 83p multi | 2.20 | 2.20 |
| a. | | Souvenir sheet, #362-367 | 9.75 | 9.75 |
| | | Nos. 362-367 (6) | 11.25 | 11.25 |

Battle of Britain, 70th Anniv. — A56

Designs: 36p, Pilot Keith Gilman. 45p, Hawker Hurricanes in flight. 48p, Pilots scrambling to planes. 50p, Spitfire sortie. 58p, Air raid warden. 80p, Evacuees. £2, Sir Douglas Bader, vert.

**2010, May 4    Perf. 14**

| | | | | |
|---|---|---|---|---|
| 369 | A56 | 36p blk & gray | 1.00 | 1.00 |
| 370 | A56 | 45p blk & gray | 1.30 | 1.30 |
| 371 | A56 | 48p blk & gray | 1.40 | 1.40 |
| 372 | A56 | 50p blk & gray | 1.40 | 1.40 |
| 373 | A56 | 58p blk & gray | 1.60 | 1.60 |
| 374 | A56 | 80p blk & gray | 2.20 | 2.20 |
| | | Nos. 369-374 (6) | 9.65 | 9.65 |

**Souvenir Sheet**

| | | | | |
|---|---|---|---|---|
| 375 | A56 | £2 blk & gray | 6.75 | 6.75 |

**Alderney Postage Stamps, 25th Anniv. Type of 2008**

Design: Hanging Rock.

**2010, June 18    Perf. 14x13¾**

| | | | | |
|---|---|---|---|---|
| 376 | A49 | 55p multi | 1.50 | 1.50 |

Florence Nightingale (1820-1910), Nurse — A57

Various quotes of Nightingale and: 36p, Hand carrying lantern. 45p, Hand reaching out. 48p, Hand holding bucket. 50p, Hands unwrapping gauze bandage. 58p, Hand writing. 80p, Hands in prayer.

**2010, July 29    Perf. 14½x14**

| | | | | |
|---|---|---|---|---|
| 377 | A57 | 36p multi | 1.00 | 1.00 |
| 378 | A57 | 45p multi | 1.25 | 1.25 |
| 379 | A57 | 48p multi | 1.35 | 1.35 |
| 380 | A57 | 50p multi | 1.45 | 1.45 |
| 381 | A57 | 58p multi | 1.70 | 1.70 |
| 382 | A57 | 80p multi | 2.25 | 2.25 |
| | | Nos. 377-382 (6) | 10.00 | 10.00 |

Peter Pan, by Sir James M. Barrie (1860-1937) — A58

Designs: 36p, Children flying above London. 45p, Captain Hook and crocodile. 48p, Peter Pan visits Captain Hook's ship. 50p, Peter Pan waving a rainbow. 58p, Children on Neverpeak. 80p, Bonfire. £3, Peter Pan, vert.

**2010, Nov. 4    Litho.    Perf. 13¼x13½**
| | | | | |
|---|---|---|---|---|
| 383 | A58 | 36p multi | 1.05 | 1.05 |
| 384 | A58 | 45p multi | 1.25 | 1.25 |
| 385 | A58 | 48p multi | 1.35 | 1.35 |
| 386 | A58 | 50p multi | 1.35 | 1.35 |
| 387 | A58 | 58p multi | 1.60 | 1.60 |
| 388 | A58 | 80p multi | 2.20 | 2.20 |
| | | Nos. 383-388 (6) | 10.45 | 10.45 |

**Souvenir Sheet**
**Perf. 13½x13¼**
| | | | | |
|---|---|---|---|---|
| 389 | A58 | £3 multi | 8.75 | 8.75 |

Christmas Carols — A59

Designs: 31p, O Christmas Tree. 36p, Away in a Manger. 45p, While Shepherds Watched Their Flocks By Night. 48p, Hark the Herald Angels Sing. 50p, O Holy Night. 58p, O Little Town of Bethlehem. 80p, Good King Wenceslas.

**2010, Nov. 4    Litho.    Perf. 13¼x14**
| | | | | |
|---|---|---|---|---|
| 390 | A59 | 31p multi | .85 | .85 |
| 391 | A59 | 36p multi | 1.10 | 1.10 |
| 392 | A59 | 45p multi | 1.30 | 1.30 |
| 393 | A59 | 48p multi | 1.40 | 1.40 |
| 394 | A59 | 50p multi | 1.40 | 1.40 |
| 395 | A59 | 58p multi | 1.65 | 1.65 |
| 396 | A59 | 80p multi | 2.25 | 2.25 |
| | | Nos. 390-396 (7) | 11.45 | 11.45 |

Hawk Moths — A60

Designs: 36p, Elephant hawkmoth. 45p, Hummingbird hawkmoth. 52p, Convolvulus hawkmoth. 58p, Poplar hawkmoth. 65p, Striped hawkmoth. 70p, Privet hawkmoth.

**2011, Feb. 23    Litho.    Perf. 13¾**
| | | | | |
|---|---|---|---|---|
| 397 | A60 | 36p multi | 1.05 | 1.05 |
| 398 | A60 | 45p multi | 1.30 | 1.30 |
| 399 | A60 | 52p multi | 1.50 | 1.50 |
| 400 | A60 | 58p multi | 1.60 | 1.60 |
| 401 | A60 | 65p multi | 1.75 | 1.75 |
| 402 | A60 | 70p multi | 1.90 | 1.90 |
| a. | | Souvenir sheet of 6, #397-402 | 9.25 | 9.25 |
| | | Nos. 397-402 (6) | 9.10 | 9.10 |

See Nos. 440-445.

Birds — A61

Designs: 36p, Mediterranean gull. 45p, Shelduck. 48p, Firecrest. 52p, Balearic shearwater. 58p, Woodcock. 65p, Little grebe.

**2011, May 4**
| | | | | |
|---|---|---|---|---|
| 403 | A61 | 36p multi | 1.05 | 1.05 |
| 404 | A61 | 45p multi | 1.30 | 1.30 |
| 405 | A61 | 48p multi | 1.35 | 1.35 |
| 406 | A61 | 52p multi | 1.50 | 1.50 |
| 407 | A61 | 58p multi | 1.60 | 1.60 |
| 408 | A61 | 65p multi | 1.80 | 1.80 |
| a. | | Souvenir sheet of 6, #403-408 | 8.75 | 8.75 |
| | | Nos. 403-408 (6) | 8.60 | 8.60 |

Queen Elizabeth II, 85th Birthday, Prince Philip, 90th Birthday — A62

Various photographs of Queen and Prince.

---

**2011, June 2    Perf. 13¾x13¼**
| | | | | |
|---|---|---|---|---|
| 409 | A62 | 36p silver & sepia | 1.00 | 1.00 |
| a. | | Booklet pane of 4 | 4.00 | — |
| 410 | A62 | 45p silver & sepia | 1.20 | 1.20 |
| a. | | Booklet pane of 4 | 4.80 | — |
| 411 | A62 | 48p silver & sepia | 1.30 | 1.30 |
| a. | | Booklet pane of 4 | 5.25 | — |
| 412 | A62 | 52p silver & sepia | 1.40 | 1.40 |
| a. | | Booklet pane of 4 | 5.60 | — |
| 413 | A62 | 58p silver & sepia | 1.50 | 1.50 |
| a. | | Booklet pane of 4 | 6.25 | — |
| 414 | A62 | 65p silver & sepia | 1.70 | 1.70 |
| a. | | Booklet pane of 4 | 6.75 | — |
| | | Complete booket, #409a, 410a, 411a, 412a, 413a, 414a | 32.50 | |
| | | Nos. 409-414 (6) | 8.10 | 8.10 |

Red Cross Uniforms, Cent. — A63

Designs: 36p, Women's Voluntary Aid Detachment uniform, c. 1915. 47p, Men's Voluntary Aid Detachment uniform, 1915. 48p, Nurse's uniform, c. 1966-78. 52p, Women's uniform, 1981-2001. 61p, Man's uniform, c. 2001. 65p, Women's uniform, c. 2011.

**2011, July 28    Perf. 14¼x13¾**
| | | | | |
|---|---|---|---|---|
| 415 | A63 | 36p multi | 1.00 | 1.00 |
| 416 | A63 | 47p multi | 1.20 | 1.20 |
| 417 | A63 | 48p multi | 1.30 | 1.30 |
| 418 | A63 | 52p multi | 1.40 | 1.40 |
| 419 | A63 | 61p multi | 1.60 | 1.60 |
| 420 | A63 | 65p multi | 1.70 | 1.70 |
| | | Nos. 415-420 (6) | 8.20 | 8.20 |

Alderney in Winter — A64

Designs: 31p, Victoria Street. 36p, St. Anne's Church. 47p, Les Estacs Gannet Colonies, reindeer in flight. 48p, Reindeer pulling Santa's sleigh, Mannez Lighthouse. 52p, Alderney train. 61p, Children playing in snow, snowman. 65p, Boat in harbor.

**2011, Oct. 27    Litho.    Perf. 13½x14¼**
| | | | | |
|---|---|---|---|---|
| 421 | A64 | 31p multi | .85 | .85 |
| 422 | A64 | 36p multi | 1.05 | 1.05 |
| 423 | A64 | 47p multi | 1.25 | 1.25 |
| 424 | A64 | 48p multi | 1.35 | 1.35 |
| 425 | A64 | 52p multi | 1.50 | 1.50 |
| 426 | A64 | 61p multi | 1.70 | 1.70 |
| 427 | A64 | 65p multi | 1.75 | 1.75 |
| | | Nos. 421-427 (7) | 9.45 | 9.45 |

Sinking of the Titanic, Cent. — A65

Designs: 36p, Titanic leaving port. 47p, Rocket exploding over Titanic. 48p, Grand staricase. 52p, Musicians. 61p, Capt. Edward J. Smith. 65p, Lifeboat near sinking Titanic.

**2012, Feb. 22    Perf. 13¼x13¾**
| | | | | |
|---|---|---|---|---|
| 428 | A65 | 36p multi | 1.00 | 1.00 |
| a. | | Booklet pane of 4 | 4.00 | — |
| 429 | A65 | 47p multi | 1.20 | 1.20 |
| a. | | Booklet pane of 4 | 4.75 | — |
| 430 | A65 | 48p multi | 1.30 | 1.30 |
| a. | | Booklet pane of 4 | 5.25 | — |
| 431 | A65 | 52p multi | 1.40 | 1.40 |
| a. | | Booklet pane of 4 | 5.75 | — |
| 432 | A65 | 61p multi | 1.60 | 1.60 |
| a. | | Booklet pane of 4 | 6.50 | — |
| 433 | A65 | 65p multi | 1.70 | 1.70 |
| a. | | Booklet pane of 4 | 7.00 | — |
| | | Complete booklet, #428a, 429a, 430a, 431a, 432a, 433a | 32.50 | |
| | | Nos. 428-433 (6) | 8.20 | 8.20 |

Charles Dickens (1812-70), Writer — A66

Various illustrations by George Cruikshank for original printing of Oliver Twist.

---

**2012, May 8    Perf. 14**
| | | | | |
|---|---|---|---|---|
| 434 | A66 | 36p blk & ol brn | 1.00 | 1.00 |
| 435 | A66 | 47p blk & ol brn | 1.35 | 1.35 |
| 436 | A66 | 48p blk & ol brn | 1.35 | 1.35 |
| 437 | A66 | 52p blk & ol brn | 1.40 | 1.40 |
| 438 | A66 | 61p blk & ol brn | 1.70 | 1.70 |
| 439 | A66 | 65p blk & ol brn | 1.80 | 1.80 |
| | | Nos. 434-439 (6) | 8.60 | 8.60 |

**Moths Type of 2011**

Designs: 39p, Garden tiger moth. 52p, Cream spot tiger moth. 53p, Buff ermine. 59p, Ruby tiger moth. 69p, Jersey tiger moth. 74p, Cinnabar.

**2012, July 25    Perf. 13¾**
| | | | | |
|---|---|---|---|---|
| 440 | A60 | 39p multi | 1.10 | 1.10 |
| 441 | A60 | 52p multi | 1.40 | 1.40 |
| 442 | A60 | 53p multi | 1.50 | 1.50 |
| 443 | A60 | 59p multi | 1.65 | 1.65 |
| 444 | A60 | 69p multi | 1.95 | 1.95 |
| 445 | A60 | 74p multi | 2.05 | 2.05 |
| a. | | Souvenir sheet of 6, #440-445 | 10.00 | 10.00 |
| | | Nos. 440-445 (6) | 9.65 | 9.65 |

Alderney Harbor — A67

Designs: 39p, Douglas Quay, Braye Harbor, c.1800. 52p, Breakwater completed, 1856. 53p, SS Courier, c. 1926. 59p, Little Crabby Harbor, 1985. 69p, RNLI Lifeboat Roy Baker I, c. 1995. 74p, Commercial Quay, 2011.

**2012, Oct. 31**
| | | | | |
|---|---|---|---|---|
| 446 | A67 | 39p multi | 1.05 | 1.05 |
| 447 | A67 | 52p multi | 1.50 | 1.50 |
| 448 | A67 | 53p multi | 1.50 | 1.50 |
| 449 | A67 | 59p multi | 1.60 | 1.60 |
| 450 | A67 | 69p multi | 1.90 | 1.90 |
| 451 | A67 | 74p multi | 2.05 | 2.05 |
| a. | | Souvenir sheet of 6, #446-451 | 10.00 | 10.00 |
| | | Nos. 446-451 (6) | 9.60 | 9.60 |

Christmas — A68

Designs: 34p, Annunciation. 39p, No room at the inn. 52p, Birth of Jesus. 53p, Whilst shepherds watch their flocks. 59p, The Three Kings. 69p, Children of Bethlehem visiting baby Jesus. 74p, Flight to Egypt.

**2012, Oct. 31    Perf. 13¼x12½**
| | | | | |
|---|---|---|---|---|
| 452 | A68 | 34p multi | .95 | .95 |
| 453 | A68 | 39p multi | 1.05 | 1.05 |
| 454 | A68 | 52p multi | 1.50 | 1.50 |
| 455 | A68 | 53p multi | 1.50 | 1.50 |
| 456 | A68 | 59p multi | 1.60 | 1.60 |
| 457 | A68 | 69p multi | 1.90 | 1.90 |
| 458 | A68 | 74p multi | 2.05 | 2.05 |
| | | Nos. 452-458 (7) | 10.55 | 10.55 |

Beetles — A69

Designs: 39p, Rose chafer. 52p, Burying beetle. 53p, Green tiger beetle. 59p, May bug. 69p, Netocia moria. 74p, Oil beetle.

**2013, Feb. 20    Perf. 13¾**
| | | | | |
|---|---|---|---|---|
| 459 | A69 | 39p multi | 1.10 | 1.10 |
| 460 | A69 | 52p multi | 1.40 | 1.40 |
| 461 | A69 | 53p multi | 1.40 | 1.40 |
| 462 | A69 | 59p multi | 1.50 | 1.50 |
| 463 | A69 | 69p multi | 1.85 | 1.85 |
| 464 | A69 | 74p multi | 1.95 | 1.95 |
| a. | | Souvenir sheet of 6, #459-464 | 9.50 | 9.50 |
| | | Nos. 459-464 (6) | 10.55 | 10.55 |

Coronation of Queen Elizabeth II, 60th Anniv. — A70

---

Designs: 40p, Queen Elizabeth II wearing crown. 53p, Silversmith working on regalia. 55p, Queen Eliabeth II wearing George IV diadem. 63p, Queen Elizabeth II and clergymen. 71p, Administration of oath. 79p, Queen Elizabeth II holding orb and scepter.

**2013, May 29    Perf. 13½**
| | | | | |
|---|---|---|---|---|
| 465 | A70 | 40p multi | 1.05 | 1.05 |
| a. | | Booklet pane of 4 | 4.25 | — |
| 466 | A70 | 53p multi | 1.50 | 1.50 |
| a. | | Booklet pane of 4 | 6.00 | — |
| 467 | A70 | 55p multi | 1.50 | 1.50 |
| a. | | Booklet pane of 4 | 6.00 | — |
| 468 | A70 | 63p multi | 1.70 | 1.70 |
| a. | | Booklet pane of 4 | 7.00 | — |
| 469 | A70 | 71p multi | 1.90 | 1.90 |
| a. | | Booklet pane of 4 | 7.75 | — |
| 470 | A70 | 79p multi | 2.10 | 2.10 |
| a. | | Booklet pane of 4 | 8.50 | — |
| | | Complete booklet, #465a-470a | 35.00 | |
| | | Nos. 465-470 (6) | 9.75 | 9.75 |

Beatrix Potter (1866-1943), Children's Book Author — A71

Potter and: 40p, Rabbit and signpost. 53p, Duck. 55p, Mouse and onions. 63p, Dog. 71p, Cat. 79p, Chicken.

**2013, July 31**
| | | | | |
|---|---|---|---|---|
| 471 | A71 | 40p multi | 1.05 | 1.05 |
| 472 | A71 | 53p multi | 1.50 | 1.50 |
| 473 | A71 | 55p multi | 1.50 | 1.50 |
| 474 | A71 | 63p multi | 1.70 | 1.70 |
| 475 | A71 | 71p multi | 1.90 | 1.90 |
| 476 | A71 | 79p multi | 2.10 | 2.10 |
| a. | | Souvenir sheet of 6, #471-476 | 10.00 | 10.00 |
| | | Nos. 471-476 (6) | 9.75 | 9.75 |

Christmas — A72

Scenes from "Rudolph the Red-Nosed Reindeer": 35p, Santa Claus tending to Rudolph.. 40p, Elf comforting Rudolph. 53p, Rudolph and snowmen. 55p, Reindeer mocking Rudolph. 63p, Santa Claus surveying fog. 71p, Santa looking at Rudolph's nose. 79p, Rudolph leading reindeer in flight.

**Perf. 13½x13¼**
**2013, Nov. 13    Litho.**
| | | | | |
|---|---|---|---|---|
| 477 | A72 | 35p multi | 1.10 | 1.10 |
| 478 | A72 | 40p multi | 1.25 | 1.25 |
| 479 | A72 | 53p multi | 1.55 | 1.55 |
| 480 | A72 | 55p multi | 1.70 | 1.70 |
| 481 | A72 | 63p multi | 1.85 | 1.85 |
| 482 | A72 | 71p multi | 2.10 | 2.10 |
| 483 | A72 | 79p multi | 2.30 | 2.30 |
| | | Nos. 477-483 (7) | 11.85 | 11.85 |

Ladybugs — A73

Designs: 40p, Seven-spot ladybug. 53p, Newly-hatched seven-spot ladybug. 55p, Two-spot ladybug. 63p, Orange ladybug. 71p, Harlequin ladybugs. 79p, Harlequin ladybugs, diff.

**2014, Feb. 12    Litho.    Perf. 13¾**
| | | | | |
|---|---|---|---|---|
| 484 | A73 | 40p multi | 1.25 | 1.25 |
| 485 | A73 | 53p multi | 1.55 | 1.55 |
| 486 | A73 | 55p multi | 1.70 | 1.70 |
| 487 | A73 | 63p multi | 1.90 | 1.90 |
| 488 | A73 | 71p multi | 2.15 | 2.15 |
| 489 | A73 | 79p multi | 2.30 | 2.30 |
| a. | | Souvenir sheet of 6, #484-489 | 11.25 | 11.25 |
| | | Nos. 484-489 (6) | 10.85 | 10.85 |

Final Panel of the Bayeux Tapestry, Fabric Art by Kate Russell and Pauline Black — A74

Details from tapestry: 40p, William the Conqueror dining with family after Battle of Hastings victory. 53p, William the Conqueror and knights. 55p, London nobles submitting to William's rule. 63p, Blessing at coronation. 71p,

Coronation of William. 79p, People acclaiming William as King.

£3, People acclaiming William as King, vert.

**2014, May 28    Litho.    Perf. 13¼x13**

| | | | | |
|---|---|---|---|---|
| 490 | A74 | 40p multi | 1.20 | 1.20 |
| a. | | Booklet pane of 4 | 5.00 | — |
| 491 | A74 | 53p multi | 1.50 | 1.50 |
| a. | | Booklet pane of 4 | 6.00 | — |
| 492 | A74 | 55p multi | 1.60 | 1.60 |
| a. | | Booklet pane of 4 | 6.50 | — |
| 493 | A74 | 63p multi | 1.75 | 1.75 |
| a. | | Booklet pane of 4 | 7.00 | — |
| 494 | A74 | 71p multi | 2.00 | 2.00 |
| a. | | Booklet pane of 4 | 8.00 | — |
| 495 | A74 | 79p multi | 2.35 | 2.35 |
| a. | | Booklet pane of 4 | 9.50 | — |
| | | Complete booklet, #490a, 491a, 492a, 493a, 494a, 495a | 34.00 | |
| | | Nos. 490-495 (6) | 10.40 | 10.40 |

**Souvenir Sheet
On Cotton-Faced Paper
Perf. 14x14¼**

| | | | | |
|---|---|---|---|---|
| 496 | A74 | £3 multi | 10.00 | 10.00 |

No. 496 contains one 30x41mm stamp.

First Birthday of Prince George of Cambridge — A75

No. 497: a, Prince George, Prince William, Prince Charles and Queen Elizabeth II. b, Prince George, Prince William and Duchess of Cambridge.

**2014, July 22    Litho.    Perf. 14¼**

| | | | | |
|---|---|---|---|---|
| 497 | A75 | Horiz. pair | 3.50 | 3.50 |
| a.-b. | | 55p Either single | 1.75 | 1.75 |

Ian Fleming (1908-64), Writer — A76

Photograph of Fleming and inscription: 41p, Commander in Naval Intelligence during World War II. 54p, Well traveled, he wrote vividly about the places he visited. 55p, In Jamaica, where all of the James Bond novels were written. 66p, Holding his son, Caspar, in 1952. 74p, Journalist and writer at his desk in London. 83p, As a journalist abroad.

£3, Fleming driving Bentley convertible.

**Litho. With Foil Application
2014, July 30    Perf. 13¼**

| | | | | |
|---|---|---|---|---|
| 498 | A76 | 41p blk & gold | 1.20 | 1.20 |
| 499 | A76 | 54p blk & gold | 1.50 | 1.50 |
| 500 | A76 | 55p blk & gold | 1.60 | 1.60 |
| 501 | A76 | 66p blk & gold | 1.90 | 1.90 |
| 502 | A76 | 74p blk & gold | 2.10 | 2.10 |
| 503 | A76 | 83p blk & gold | 2.35 | 2.35 |
| | | Nos. 498-503 (6) | 10.65 | 10.65 |

**Souvenir Sheet
Perf. 14¼**

| | | | | |
|---|---|---|---|---|
| 504 | A76 | £3 blk & gold | 8.50 | 8.50 |

No. 504 contains one 43x43mm stamp. The stamp also was sold as an imperf. press sheet for £26 and a gold foil replica of the sheet for £95.

Christmas — A77

Children's art depicting: 36p, North Pole, by Alexandra Campbell, Joe Blackham and Ian Adamson. 41p, Santa and snowman on a starry night, by Louis Smart, Danielle Allen, and Lydia Jenkins. 54p, Snowman and house, by Holly Neil, Libby Needham, Rosie Williams and Kamil Olbrycht. 55p, Snowmen and trees, by Sian Craig, Amber Shaw, Grace Millan, Cameron Tugby-Maloy, Keira Scott, and Harvey Olliver. 66p, Elves' Workshop, by Jasmine Sayer, Frankie Jenkins, Matthew Burke, Cameron Bunrham, Florence Carpenter, Scarlett Oldfield, Carl Evans, Andrew Page, and Chloe Faulkner. 74p, Alderney Lighthouse and children at mailbox, by Katie Shaw ans Kiri Winder. 83p, Bright Lights and Decorations, by Amelie Carpenter, Erin Atkinson, Bennett Blackham, and Owen Carré.

**2014, Nov. 6    Litho.    Perf. 13¼x12¾
Self-Adhesive**

| | | | | |
|---|---|---|---|---|
| 505 | A77 | 36p multi | 1.25 | 1.25 |
| 506 | A77 | 41p multi | 1.40 | 1.40 |
| 507 | A77 | 54p multi | 1.75 | 1.75 |
| 508 | A77 | 55p multi | 1.75 | 1.75 |
| 509 | A77 | 66p multi | 2.10 | 2.10 |
| 510 | A77 | 74p multi | 2.40 | 2.40 |
| 511 | A77 | 83p multi | 2.60 | 2.60 |
| | | Nos. 505-511 (7) | 13.25 | 13.25 |

Alice's Adventures in Wonderland, by Lewis Carroll, 150th Anniv. — A78

Designs: 41p, Alice and flamingo. 54p, White Rabbit. 55p, Caterpillar. 66p, Cheshire Cat. 74p, Mad Hatter. 83p, Queen of Hearts. £3, Alice at tea party.

**2015, Feb. 22    Litho.    Perf. 13¼x13**

| | | | | |
|---|---|---|---|---|
| 512 | A78 | 41p multi | 1.25 | 1.25 |
| 513 | A78 | 54p multi | 1.60 | 1.60 |
| 514 | A78 | 55p multi | 1.75 | 1.75 |
| 515 | A78 | 66p multi | 2.00 | 2.00 |
| 516 | A78 | 74p multi | 2.25 | 2.25 |
| 517 | A78 | 83p multi | 2.60 | 2.60 |
| | | Nos. 512-517 (6) | 11.45 | 11.45 |

**Souvenir Sheet
Perf. 13½x13¼**

| | | | | |
|---|---|---|---|---|
| 518 | A78 | £3 multi | 9.25 | 9.25 |

No. 518 contains one 28x42mm stamp.

Flora and Fauna — A79

Designs: (41p), Alderney sea lavender. (54p), Blonde hedgehog. (55p), Dwarf thistle. (66p), Black rabbit. (74p), Spotted rock rose. (83p), Mole.

**2015, May 1    Litho.    Perf. 13¾**

| | | | | |
|---|---|---|---|---|
| 519 | A79 | (41p) multi | 1.25 | 1.25 |
| 520 | A79 | (54p) multi | 1.60 | 1.60 |
| 521 | A79 | (55p) multi | 1.75 | 1.75 |
| 522 | A79 | (66p) multi | 2.00 | 2.00 |
| 523 | A79 | (74p) multi | 2.25 | 2.25 |
| 524 | A79 | (83p) multi | 2.50 | 2.50 |
| a. | | Souvenir sheet of 6, #519-524 | 11.50 | 11.50 |
| | | Nos. 519-524 (6) | 11.35 | 11.35 |

Inscriptions on: No. 519, "Local Letter." No. 520, "Local Large Letter." No. 521, "UK Letter." No. 522, "EUR Letter." No. 523, "UK Large Letter." No. 524, "ROW Letter."

Forts — A80

Designs: 42p, Fort Tourgis. 56p, Fort Clonque. 57p, Fort Grosnez. 62p, Fort Houmet Herbé. 68p, Fort Château à l'Etoc. 77p, Nunnery Roman Fort.

**2015, July 22    Litho.    Perf. 14¾x14¼**

| | | | | |
|---|---|---|---|---|
| 525 | A80 | 42p multi | 1.40 | 1.40 |
| 526 | A80 | 56p multi | 1.75 | 1.75 |
| 527 | A80 | 57p multi | 1.75 | 1.75 |
| 528 | A80 | 62p multi | 2.00 | 2.00 |
| 529 | A80 | 68p multi | 2.10 | 2.10 |
| 530 | A80 | 77p multi | 2.40 | 2.40 |
| | | Nos. 525-530 (6) | 11.40 | 11.40 |

Queen Elizabeth II, Longest-Reigning British Monarch — A81

**Litho. With Foil Application
2015, Sept. 9    Perf. 12½**

| | | | | |
|---|---|---|---|---|
| 531 | A81 | £10 multi | 28.50 | 28.50 |

Christmas — A82

Various stained-glass windows in St. Anne's Church dedicated to Anne French.

**2015, Nov. 6    Litho.    Perf. 14¾**

| | | | | |
|---|---|---|---|---|
| 532 | A82 | 37p multi | 1.10 | 1.10 |
| 533 | A82 | 42p multi | 1.25 | 1.25 |
| 534 | A82 | 56p multi | 1.75 | 1.75 |
| 535 | A82 | 57p multi | 1.75 | 1.75 |
| 536 | A82 | 62p multi | 1.90 | 1.90 |
| 537 | A82 | 68p multi | 2.10 | 2.10 |
| 538 | A82 | 77p multi | 2.40 | 2.40 |
| | | Nos. 532-538 (7) | 12.25 | 12.25 |

**Souvenir Sheet**

Alderney Homecoming, 70th Anniv. — A83

**2015, Nov. 10    Litho.    Perf. 13¼**

| | | | | |
|---|---|---|---|---|
| 539 | A83 | £3 multi | 9.00 | 9.00 |

Flora and Fauna of Longis Nature Reserve — A84

Designs: 42p, Eelgrass. 56p, Glanville fritillary. 57p, Yarrow broomrape. 62p, Meadow pipit. 68p, Sand crocus. 77c, Greater white-toothed shrew.

**2016, Feb. 17    Litho.    Perf. 13¼**

| | | | | |
|---|---|---|---|---|
| 540 | A84 | 42p multi | 1.25 | 1.25 |
| 541 | A84 | 56p multi | 1.60 | 1.60 |
| 542 | A84 | 57p multi | 1.60 | 1.60 |
| 543 | A84 | 62p multi | 1.75 | 1.75 |
| 544 | A84 | 68p multi | 1.90 | 1.90 |
| 545 | A84 | 77p multi | 2.25 | 2.25 |
| a. | | Souvenir sheet of 6, #540-545 | 10.50 | 10.50 |
| | | Nos. 540-545 (6) | 10.35 | 10.35 |

Queen Elizabeth II, 90th Birthday — A85

Photographs of Queen Elizabeth II from: 43p, Trooping the Color, 2011. 57p, Birthday Parade, 2012. 58p, Birthday Parade, 2013. 64p, Trooping the Color, 2014. 70p, Birthday Parade, 2015. 78p, Sept. 9, 2015 (day she became longest-reigning British monarch).

**2016, May 25    Litho.    Perf. 14¼x14**

| | | | | |
|---|---|---|---|---|
| 546 | A85 | 43p sil & multi | 1.25 | 1.25 |
| a. | | Booklet pane of 4 | 5.00 | — |
| 547 | A85 | 57p sil & multi | 1.75 | 1.75 |
| a. | | Booklet pane of 4 | 7.00 | — |
| 548 | A85 | 58p sil & multi | 1.75 | 1.75 |
| a. | | Booklet pane of 4 | 7.00 | — |
| 549 | A85 | 64p sil & multi | 1.90 | 1.90 |
| a. | | Booklet pane of 4 | 7.75 | — |
| 550 | A85 | 70p sil & multi | 2.00 | 2.00 |
| a. | | Booklet pane of 4 | 8.00 | — |
| 551 | A85 | 78p sil & multi | 2.25 | 2.25 |
| a. | | Booklet pane of 4 | 9.00 | — |
| | | Complete booklet, #546a, 547a, 548a, 549a, 550a, 551a | 44.00 | |
| | | Nos. 546-551 (6) | 10.90 | 10.90 |

Battle of Hastings, 950th Anniv. — A86

Designs: 43p, William the Conqueror lands in England at Pevensey. 57p, King Harold II rides south from the Stamford Bridge. 58p, Norman knights charge the Saxon shield wall.

64p, Saxon fyrd shield breaks to attack fleeing Bretons. 70p, William lifts helmet to show he's still alive. 78p, Harold hard-pressed in shield wall.

**2016, Sept. 14    Litho.    Perf. 13x13½**

| | | | | |
|---|---|---|---|---|
| 552 | A86 | 43p multi | 1.10 | 1.10 |
| 553 | A86 | 57p multi | 1.50 | 1.50 |
| 554 | A86 | 58p multi | 1.50 | 1.50 |
| 555 | A86 | 64p multi | 1.75 | 1.75 |
| 556 | A86 | 70p multi | 1.90 | 1.90 |
| 557 | A86 | 78p multi | 2.00 | 2.00 |
| a. | | Souvenir sheet of 6, #552-557 | 9.75 | 9.75 |

Christmas — A87

Snowflake and: 38p, Holly. 43p, Christmas tree. 57p, Gifts. 58p, Santa Claus. 64p, Reindeer and Christmas ornaments. 70p, Snowman. 78p, Stars.

**Litho. With Foil Application
2016, Nov. 8    Perf. 13¼
Self-Adhesive**

| | | | | |
|---|---|---|---|---|
| 558 | A87 | 38p sil & dp blue | 1.00 | 1.00 |
| 559 | A87 | 43p dp blue & sil | 1.10 | 1.10 |
| 560 | A87 | 57p sil & dp blue | 1.50 | 1.50 |
| 561 | A87 | 58p dp blue & sil | 1.50 | 1.50 |
| 562 | A87 | 64p sil & dp blue | 1.60 | 1.60 |
| 563 | A87 | 70p dp blue & sil | 1.75 | 1.75 |
| 564 | A87 | 78p sil & dp blue | 2.00 | 2.00 |
| | | Nos. 558-564 (7) | 10.45 | 10.45 |

Map of Alderney and Burhou, by Addison Warren — A88

Designs: 43p, Braye Bay area. 57p, Alderney Aerodrome area. 58p, St. Anne area. 64p, Northeastern area. 70p, Burhou and other islands. 78p, Entire map.

£3, Area south of Braye Bay and east of St. Anne, vert.

**2017, Feb. 1    Litho.    Perf. 13½**

| | | | | |
|---|---|---|---|---|
| 565 | A88 | 43p brz & multi | 1.10 | 1.10 |
| 566 | A88 | 57p brz & multi | 1.50 | 1.50 |
| 567 | A88 | 58p brz & multi | 1.50 | 1.50 |
| 568 | A88 | 64p brz & multi | 1.60 | 1.60 |
| 569 | A88 | 70p brz & multi | 1.75 | 1.75 |
| 570 | A88 | 78p brz & multi | 2.00 | 2.00 |
| | | Nos. 565-570 (6) | 9.45 | 9.45 |

**Souvenir Sheet
Perf. 14**

| | | | | |
|---|---|---|---|---|
| 571 | A88 | £3 brz & multi | 7.75 | 7.75 |

No. 571 contains one 29x43mm stamp.

Tourist Attractions — A89

Designs: 44p, Victoria Street, St. Anne. 59p, Château à l'Etoc and Saye Beach. 60p, Alderney Week, St. Anne. 73p, Pepperpot, Essex Castle. 80p, Alderney Railway, Mannez Quarry. 90p, Mannez Lighthouse, Quesnard Point.

**2017, May 17    Litho.    Perf. 14x14¼**

| | | | | |
|---|---|---|---|---|
| 572 | A89 | 44p multi | 1.10 | 1.10 |
| a. | | Booklet pane of 4 | 4.50 | — |
| 573 | A89 | 59p multi | 1.50 | 1.50 |
| a. | | Booklet pane of 4 | 6.00 | — |
| 574 | A89 | 60p multi | 1.60 | 1.60 |
| a. | | Booklet pane of 4 | 6.50 | — |
| 575 | A89 | 73p multi | 1.90 | 1.90 |
| a. | | Booklet pane of 4 | 7.75 | — |
| 576 | A89 | 80p multi | 2.10 | 2.10 |
| a. | | Booklet pane of 4 | 8.50 | — |
| 577 | A89 | 90p multi | 2.40 | 2.40 |
| a. | | Booklet pane of 4 | 9.75 | — |
| | | Complete booklet, #572a, 573a, 574a, 575a, 576a, 577a | 43.00 | |
| | | Nos. 572-577 (6) | 10.60 | 10.60 |

Views of August 21, 2017 Solar Eclipse From Various Cities — A90

View of eclipse from: 44p, Vancouver, B.C., Canada. 59p, Miami, Florida. 60p, Hamilton, Bermuda. 73p, Dakar, Senegal. 80p, St. Anne, Alderney. 90p, Anadyr, Russia.

**2017, July 19 Litho. Perf. 13¾x13¼**
| | | | | |
|---|---|---|---|---|
| 578 | A90 | 44p multi | 1.25 | 1.25 |
| 579 | A90 | 59p multi | 1.60 | 1.60 |
| 580 | A90 | 60p multi | 1.60 | 1.60 |
| 581 | A90 | 73p multi | 2.00 | 2.00 |
| 582 | A90 | 80p multi | 2.10 | 2.10 |
| 583 | A90 | 90p multi | 2.40 | 2.40 |
| a. | | Souvenir sheet of 6, #578-583 | 11.00 | 11.00 |
| | | Nos. 578-583 (6) | 10.95 | 10.95 |

Portions of the vignettes of Nos. 578-573 were printed with a circle of thermochromic ink, which when warmed, allows the moon to be seen.

Christmas — A91

Lyrics from "The Holly and the Ivy" and: 39p, Holly on trees. 44p, Bird, holly on tree. 59p, Deers standing in forest. 60p, Deers running in forest. 73p, Pipe organ. 80p, Choir holding candles. 90p, Madonna and Child.

**2017, Nov. 8 Litho. Perf. 13¼x13**
| | | | | |
|---|---|---|---|---|
| 584 | A91 | 39p multi | 1.10 | 1.10 |
| 585 | A91 | 44p multi | 1.25 | 1.25 |
| 586 | A91 | 59p multi | 1.60 | 1.60 |
| 587 | A91 | 60p multi | 1.60 | 1.60 |
| 588 | A91 | 73p multi | 2.00 | 2.00 |
| 589 | A91 | 80p multi | 2.25 | 2.25 |
| 590 | A91 | 90p multi | 2.50 | 2.50 |
| | | Nos. 584-590 (7) | 12.30 | 12.30 |

Wombles, Characters From Children's Books by Elizabeth Beresford — A92

Design and inscription: (44p), Uncle Bulgaria (Local Letter). (59p), Bungo and Orinoco (UK Letter). (60p), Madame Cholet (Local Large Letter). (73p), Uncle Bulgaria and Cousin Yellowstone (EUR Letter). (80p), Tobermoy and Bungo (ROW Letter). (90p), Tomsk (UK Large Letter).

**Perf. 13¾x13¼**
**2018, Feb. 14 Litho.**
| | | | | |
|---|---|---|---|---|
| 591 | A92 | (44p) multi | 1.25 | 1.25 |
| 592 | A92 | (59p) multi | 1.75 | 1.75 |
| 593 | A92 | (60p) multi | 1.75 | 1.75 |
| 594 | A92 | (73p) multi | 2.10 | 2.10 |
| 595 | A92 | (80p) multi | 2.25 | 2.25 |
| 596 | A92 | (90p) multi | 2.60 | 2.60 |
| a. | | Souvenir sheet of 6, #591-596 | 12.00 | 12.00 |
| | | Nos. 591-596 (6) | 11.70 | 11.70 |

**Souvenir Sheet**

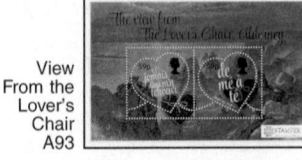

View From the Lover's Chair A93

No. 597 — Rocks, hearts and inscription: a, "à jomais dàns m'n tchoeur." b, "de mé à té."

**2018, Feb. 14 Litho. Perf. 13¾**
| | | | | |
|---|---|---|---|---|
| 597 | A93 | Sheet of 2 | 3.50 | 3.50 |
| a.-b. | | 59p Either single | 1.75 | 1.75 |

Spring 2018 Stampex Philatelic Exhibition, London.

Coronation of Queen Elizabeth II, 65th Anniv. — A94

Photograph of Queen Elizabeth II from: 46p, 2001. 62p, 1954. 63p, 2012. 76p, 1971. 85p, 2002. 94p, 2006.

**2018, May 23 Litho. Perf. 13¼x13¾**
| | | | | |
|---|---|---|---|---|
| 598 | A94 | 46p multi | 1.25 | 1.25 |
| 599 | A94 | 62p multi | 1.75 | 1.75 |
| 600 | A94 | 63p multi | 1.75 | 1.75 |
| 601 | A94 | 76p multi | 2.00 | 2.00 |
| 602 | A94 | 85p multi | 2.25 | 2.25 |
| 603 | A94 | 94p multi | 2.50 | 2.50 |
| | | Nos. 598-603 (6) | 11.50 | 11.50 |

Alderney Week — A95

Designs: 46p, Festival of Color. 62p, Cavalcade. 63p, Man-powered flight. 76p, Decorated float. 85p, Daft rafts. 94p, Torchlight parade.

**2018, Aug. 1 Litho. Perf. 13½x13¼**
| | | | | |
|---|---|---|---|---|
| 604 | A95 | 46p multi | 1.25 | 1.25 |
| a. | | Booklet pane of 4 | 5.00 | — |
| 605 | A95 | 62p multi | 1.60 | 1.60 |
| a. | | Booklet pane of 4 | 6.50 | — |
| 606 | A95 | 63p multi | 1.75 | 1.75 |
| a. | | Booklet pane of 4 | 7.00 | — |
| 607 | A95 | 76p multi | 2.00 | 2.00 |
| a. | | Booklet pane of 4 | 8.00 | — |
| 608 | A95 | 85p multi | 2.25 | 2.25 |
| a. | | Booklet pane of 4 | 9.00 | — |
| 609 | A95 | 94p multi | 2.50 | 2.50 |
| a. | | Booklet pane of 4 | 10.00 | — |
| | | Complete booklet, #604a, 605a, 606a, 607a, 608a, 609a | 46.00 | |
| | | Nos. 604-609 (6) | 11.35 | 11.35 |

Scenes From *A Christmas Carol,* by Charles Dickens (1812-70) — A96

Designs: 41p, Bob Cratchit and Tiny Tim. 46p, Bob Cratchit and Ebenezer Scrooge. 62p, Visit of Marley's ghost. 63p, Ghost of Christmas Past. 76p, Ghost of Christmas Present. 85p, Ghost of Christmas Future. 94p, Christmas celebration.

**2018, Nov. 8 Litho. Perf. 13¼**
| | | | | |
|---|---|---|---|---|
| 610 | A96 | 41p multi | 1.10 | 1.10 |
| 611 | A96 | 46p multi | 1.25 | 1.25 |
| 612 | A96 | 62p multi | 1.60 | 1.60 |
| 613 | A96 | 63p multi | 1.75 | 1.75 |
| 614 | A96 | 76p multi | 2.00 | 2.00 |
| 615 | A96 | 85p multi | 2.25 | 2.25 |
| 616 | A96 | 94p multi | 2.50 | 2.50 |
| | | Nos. 610-616 (7) | 12.45 | 12.45 |

Christmas.

Sinking of the SS Stella, 120th Anniv. — A97

Designs: 46p, SS Stella at Southampton Docks. 62p, SS Stella at sea. 63p, Lookout at ship's bow. 76p, Mary giving up her lifevest. 85p, Reverend and passengers praying. 94p, Ship sinking.

**2019, Feb. 13 Litho. Perf. 14**
| | | | | |
|---|---|---|---|---|
| 617 | A97 | 46p multi | 1.25 | 1.25 |
| 618 | A97 | 62p multi | 1.60 | 1.60 |
| 619 | A97 | 63p multi | 1.75 | 1.75 |
| 620 | A97 | 76p multi | 2.00 | 2.00 |
| 621 | A97 | 85p multi | 2.25 | 2.25 |
| 622 | A97 | 94p multi | 2.50 | 2.50 |
| a. | | Souvenir sheet of 6, #617-622 | 11.50 | 11.50 |
| | | Nos. 617-622 (6) | 11.35 | 11.35 |

D-Day, 75th Anniv. — A98

Designs: 48p, Mosquito attacking E-boats. 65p, Pegasus Bridge. 66p, Invasion begins. 80p, Commandos come ashore at Sword Beach. 90p, Soldiers at outskirts of Villers-Bocage. 98p, Typhoon attacks Tiger tank. £3, Liberation of Arromanches.

**2019, May 29 Litho. Perf. 14¼x14**
| | | | | |
|---|---|---|---|---|
| 623 | A98 | 48p multi | 1.25 | 1.25 |
| 624 | A98 | 65p multi | 1.75 | 1.75 |
| 625 | A98 | 66p multi | 1.75 | 1.75 |
| 626 | A98 | 80p multi | 2.10 | 2.10 |
| 627 | A98 | 90p multi | 2.25 | 2.25 |
| 628 | A98 | 98p multi | 2.50 | 2.50 |
| | | Nos. 623-628 (6) | 11.60 | 11.60 |

**Souvenir Sheet**
| | | | | |
|---|---|---|---|---|
| 629 | A98 | £3 multi | 7.75 | 7.75 |

No. 629 contains one 48x41mm stamp.

Odes Written by John Keats (1795-1821) in 1819, 200th Anniv. — A99

Designs: 48p, Ode on a Grecian Urn. 65p, Ode to Indolence. 66p, Ode on Melancholy. 80p, Ode to a Nightingale. 90p, Ode to Psyche. 98p, To Autumn.

**2019, July 24 Litho. Perf. 13½**
| | | | | |
|---|---|---|---|---|
| 630 | A99 | 48p multi | 1.25 | 1.25 |
| a. | | Booklet pane of 4 | 5.00 | |
| 631 | A99 | 65p multi | 1.60 | 1.60 |
| a. | | Booklet pane of 4 | 6.50 | |
| 632 | A99 | 66p multi | 1.60 | 1.60 |
| a. | | Booklet pane of 4 | 6.50 | |
| 633 | A99 | 80p multi | 2.00 | 2.00 |
| a. | | Booklet pane of 4 | 8.00 | |
| 634 | A99 | 90p multi | 2.25 | 2.25 |
| a. | | Booklet pane of 4 | 9.00 | |
| 635 | A99 | 98p multi | 2.40 | 2.40 |
| a. | | Booklet pane of 4 | 9.75 | |
| | | Complete booklet, #630a, 631a, 632a, 633a, 634a, 635a | 45.00 | |
| | | Nos. 630-635 (6) | 11.10 | 11.10 |

A100

Christmas — A101

Designs: 43p, Nativity. 48p, Journey to Bethlehem. 65p, Bethlehem. 66p, No room at the inn. 80p, Shepherd and sheep. 90p, Magi. 98p, Nativity, diff. £1, Nativity and Magi.

**2019, Oct. 30 Litho. Perf. 13¼x13½**
| | | | | |
|---|---|---|---|---|
| 636 | A100 | 43p multi | 1.10 | 1.10 |
| 637 | A100 | 48p multi | 1.25 | 1.25 |
| 638 | A100 | 65p multi | 1.75 | 1.75 |
| 639 | A100 | 66p multi | 1.75 | 1.75 |
| 640 | A100 | 80p multi | 2.10 | 2.10 |
| 641 | A100 | 90p multi | 2.40 | 2.40 |
| 642 | A100 | 98p multi | 2.60 | 2.60 |
| | | Nos. 636-642 (7) | 12.95 | 12.95 |

**Souvenir Sheet**
**Perf.**
| | | | | |
|---|---|---|---|---|
| 643 | A101 | £1 multi | 2.60 | 2.60 |

**Souvenir Sheet**

Armistice Day Poppy A102

**2019, Nov. 11 Litho. Perf.**
| | | | | |
|---|---|---|---|---|
| 644 | A102 | £2 multi | 5.25 | 5.25 |

Remembrance Day, cent.

Birds — A103

Designs: 1p, Dunnock. 2p, Robin. 3p, Black redstart. 4p, Whinchat. 5p, Kingfisher. 6p, Yellow wagtail. 7p, Goldfinch. 8p, Meadow pipit. 9p, Blue tit. 10p, Puffin. 20p, Turnstone. 40p, Ringed plover. 50p, Shag. £1, Kestrel. £2, Barn owl. £4, Long-eared owl.

**2020, Jan. 21 Litho. Perf. 12**
| | | | | |
|---|---|---|---|---|
| 645 | A103 | 1p multi | .25 | .25 |
| 646 | A103 | 2p multi | .25 | .25 |
| 647 | A103 | 3p multi | .25 | .25 |
| 648 | A103 | 4p multi | .25 | .25 |
| 649 | A103 | 5p multi | .25 | .25 |
| 650 | A103 | 6p multi | .25 | .25 |
| 651 | A103 | 7p multi | .25 | .25 |
| 652 | A103 | 8p multi | .25 | .25 |
| 653 | A103 | 9p multi | .25 | .25 |
| 654 | A103 | 10p multi | .25 | .25 |
| 655 | A103 | 20p multi | .50 | .50 |
| 656 | A103 | 40p multi | 1.00 | 1.00 |
| 657 | A103 | 50p multi | 1.40 | 1.40 |
| 658 | A103 | £1 multi | 2.60 | 2.60 |
| 659 | A103 | £2 multi | 5.25 | 5.25 |
| 660 | A103 | £4 multi | 10.50 | 10.50 |
| | | Nos. 645-660 (16) | 23.75 | 23.75 |

Sea Life — A104

Designs: 48p, Gray seal pup. 65p, Shore crab. 66p, Gannet. 80p, Beadlet anemone. 90p, Ormer. 98p, Cushion stars.

**2020, Jan. 21 Litho. Perf. 12**
| | | | | |
|---|---|---|---|---|
| 661 | A104 | 48p multi | 1.25 | 1.25 |
| 662 | A104 | 65p multi | 1.75 | 1.75 |
| 663 | A104 | 66p multi | 1.75 | 1.75 |
| 664 | A104 | 80p multi | 2.10 | 2.10 |
| 665 | A104 | 90p multi | 2.40 | 2.40 |
| 666 | A104 | 98p multi | 2.60 | 2.60 |
| a. | | Souvenir sheet of 6, #661-666 | 12.00 | 12.00 |
| | | Nos. 661-666 (6) | 11.85 | 11.85 |

Lines of Poetry by William Wordsworth (1770-1850) — A105

Wordsworth and: 50p, "The flower that smells the sweetest is shy and lowly." 68p, "Strongest minds are often those whom the noisy world hears least." 70p, "The mind that is wise mourns less for what age takes away than what it leaves behind." 85p, "Poetry is the spontaneous overflow of powerful feelings." 95p, "Nature never did betray the heart that loved her." £1.02, "Wisdom is oft-times nearer when we stoop than when we soar."

**2020, Apr. 1 Litho. Perf. 13½**
| | | | | |
|---|---|---|---|---|
| 667 | A105 | 50p multi | 1.25 | 1.25 |
| 668 | A105 | 68p multi | 1.75 | 1.75 |
| 669 | A105 | 70p multi | 1.75 | 1.75 |
| 670 | A105 | 85p multi | 2.10 | 2.10 |
| 671 | A105 | 95p multi | 2.40 | 2.40 |
| 672 | A105 | £1.02 multi | 2.50 | 2.50 |
| | | Nos. 667-672 (6) | 11.75 | 11.75 |

**Battle of Britain, 80th Anniv. — A106**

Designs: 50p, Royal Observer Corps member searching for enemy aircraft. 68p, Supermarine Spitfire and Hawker Hurricane. 70p, Postman collecting mail from box amidst rubble in London. 85p, British aircraft shooting at German Heinkel He 111. 95p, St. Paul's Cathedral shrouded in smoke. £1.02, Lancaster bomber under attack from German airplane.

**2020, July 21   Litho.   Perf. 13½x13¼**
| | | | | |
|---|---|---|---|---|
| 673 | A106 | 50p multi | 1.30 | 1.30 |
| a. | | Booklet pane of 4 | 5.25 | — |
| 674 | A106 | 68p multi | 1.75 | 1.75 |
| a. | | Booklet pane of 4 | 7.00 | — |
| 675 | A106 | 70p multi | 1.90 | 1.90 |
| a. | | Booklet pane of 4 | 7.75 | — |
| 676 | A106 | 85p multi | 2.25 | 2.25 |
| a. | | Booklet pane of 4 | 9.00 | — |
| 677 | A106 | 95p multi | 2.50 | 2.50 |
| a. | | Booklet pane of 4 | 10.00 | — |
| 678 | A106 | £1.02 multi | 2.75 | 2.75 |
| a. | | Booklet pane of 4 | 11.00 | — |
| | | Complete booklet, #673a, 674a, 675a, 676a, 677a, 678a | 50.00 | |

**Children's Art — A107**

Children's art by: 50p, Grace Chapman. 68p, Eli Maurice. 85p, Hollie Maurice. 95p, Isla Cauvain.

*Serpentine Die Cut 14½*
**2020, Aug. 19   Litho.**
**Self-Adhesive**
| | | | | |
|---|---|---|---|---|
| 679 | A107 | 50p multi | 1.40 | 1.40 |
| 680 | A107 | 68p multi | 1.90 | 1.90 |
| 681 | A107 | 85p multi | 2.25 | 2.25 |
| 682 | A107 | 95p multi | 2.60 | 2.60 |
| | | Nos. 679-682 (4) | 8.15 | 8.15 |

Proceeds of sales of Nos. 679-682 were donated to the Alderney Helping Hands Appeal.

**Souvenir Sheet**

**St. Anne's Church, 170th Anniv. A108**

**2020, Oct. 28   Litho.   Perf. 12**
| | | | | |
|---|---|---|---|---|
| 683 | A108 | £3 multi | 7.75 | 7.75 |

**Christmas A109**

Designs: 45p, Hedgehog and snowman. 50p, Santa Claus in flying sleigh. 68p, Santa Claus flying around Mannez Lighthouse. 70p, Santa Claus taking picture of himself near telephone booth and mailbox. 85p, Santa Claus and reindeer at Bonne Terre Watermill. 95p, Santa Claus driving Alderney train. £1.02, Santa Claus leaving St. Anne's Church.

**2020, Oct. 28   Litho.   Perf. 13½x13¼**
| | | | | |
|---|---|---|---|---|
| 684 | A109 | 45p multi | 1.25 | 1.25 |
| 685 | A109 | 50p multi | 1.30 | 1.30 |
| 686 | A109 | 68p multi | 1.75 | 1.75 |
| 687 | A109 | 70p multi | 1.90 | 1.90 |
| 688 | A109 | 85p multi | 2.25 | 2.25 |
| 689 | A109 | 95p multi | 2.50 | 2.50 |
| 690 | A109 | £1.02 multi | 2.75 | 2.75 |
| | | Nos. 684-690 (7) | 13.70 | 13.70 |

**Decimalization of Guernsey's Currency, 50th Anniv. — A110**

Guernsey's 1971: 50p, 50-pence coin. 68p, 10-pence coin. 70p, 5-pence coin. 85p, 2-pence coin. 95p, 1-penny coin. £1.02, Half-penny coin.

**2021, Feb. 15   Litho.   Perf. 13¾**
| | | | | |
|---|---|---|---|---|
| 691 | A110 | 50p multi | 1.30 | 1.30 |
| 692 | A110 | 68p multi | 1.90 | 1.90 |
| 693 | A110 | 70p multi | 2.00 | 2.00 |
| 694 | A110 | 85p multi | 2.40 | 2.40 |
| 695 | A110 | 95p multi | 2.75 | 2.75 |
| 696 | A110 | £1.02 multi | 3.00 | 3.00 |
| a. | | Souvenir sheet of 6, #691-696 | 13.50 | 13.50 |
| | | Nos. 691-696 (6) | 13.35 | 13.35 |

**International Year of Fruits and Vegetables A111**

Designs: 50p, Strawberries. 70p, Physalis. 73p, Peas. £1, Tomatoes. £1.15, Oranges. £1.20, Quinces. £2.20, Carrots. £3.50, Onions and garlic.

**2021, Apr. 7   Litho.   Perf. 13x13½**
| | | | | |
|---|---|---|---|---|
| 697 | A111 | 50p multi | 1.25 | 1.25 |
| 698 | A111 | 70p multi | 1.75 | 1.75 |
| 699 | A111 | 73p multi | 1.90 | 1.90 |
| 700 | A111 | £1 multi | 2.50 | 2.50 |
| 701 | A111 | £1.15 multi | 3.00 | 3.00 |
| 702 | A111 | £1.20 multi | 3.00 | 3.00 |
| 703 | A111 | £2.20 multi | 5.50 | 5.50 |
| 704 | A111 | £3.50 multi | 8.75 | 8.75 |
| | | Nos. 697-704 (8) | 27.65 | 27.65 |

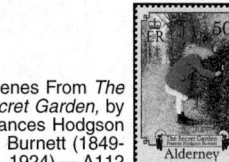

**Scenes From *The Secret Garden*, by Frances Hodgson Burnett (1849-1924) — A112**

Designs: 50p, Mary Lennox with key to open door to secret garden. 70p, Mary and Dickon Sowerby in garden with animals. 73p, Mary discovering the sick Colin Craven. £1, Dickon, holding lamb, meeting colin. £1.15, Dickon singing to Ben Weatherstaff, Mary and Colin. £1.20, Burnett in 1886.

**2021, Sept. 1   Litho.   Perf. 13¼x13½**
| | | | | |
|---|---|---|---|---|
| 705 | A112 | 50p multi | 1.40 | 1.40 |
| 706 | A112 | 70p multi | 2.00 | 2.00 |
| 707 | A112 | 73p multi | 2.00 | 2.00 |
| 708 | A112 | £1 multi | 2.75 | 2.75 |
| 709 | A112 | £1.15 multi | 3.25 | 3.25 |
| 710 | A112 | £1.20 multi | 3.50 | 3.50 |
| | | Nos. 705-710 (6) | 14.90 | 14.90 |

**Prince Philip (1921-2021) — A113**

Prince Philip: 50p, Holding trophy. 73p, In military uniform, saluting. £1, With Queen Elizabeth II. £1.20, Standing on airplane's wing.

**2021, Sept. 1   Litho.   Perf. 13½x13¼**
| | | | | |
|---|---|---|---|---|
| 711 | A113 | 50p multi | 1.40 | 1.40 |
| 712 | A113 | 73p multi | 2.00 | 2.00 |
| 713 | A113 | £1 multi | 2.75 | 2.75 |
| 714 | A113 | £1.20 multi | 3.50 | 3.50 |
| a. | | Souvenir sheet of 4, #711-714 | 9.75 | 9.75 |
| | | Nos. 711-714 (4) | 9.65 | 9.65 |

**Christmas — A114**

Stained-glass window and Biblical passage on the birth of Jesus: 45p, Luke 2:14. 50p, Luke 1:30. 70p, Luke 1:31. 73p, Luke 2:7. £1, Luke 2:10. £1.15, Matthew 2:9. £1.20, Matthew 2:14.

**2021, Nov. 3   Litho.   Perf. 14¼**
| | | | | |
|---|---|---|---|---|
| 715 | A114 | 45p multi | 1.25 | 1.25 |
| 716 | A114 | 50p multi | 1.40 | 1.40 |
| 717 | A114 | 70p multi | 1.90 | 1.90 |
| 718 | A114 | 73p multi | 2.00 | 2.00 |
| 719 | A114 | £1 multi | 2.75 | 2.75 |
| 720 | A114 | £1.15 multi | 3.00 | 3.00 |
| 721 | A114 | £1.20 multi | 3.25 | 3.25 |
| | | Nos. 715-721 (7) | 15.55 | 15.55 |

**Reign of Queen Elizabeth II (1926-2022), 70th Anniv. — A115**

**Queen Victoria's Diamond Jubilee Necklace A116**

Color photograph of Queen Elizabeth II from: 50p, 1965. 70p, 1972. 73p, 1977. £1, 2000. £1.15, 2004. £1.20, 2013.

**Litho. With Foil Application**
**2022, Feb. 4   Perf. 13¼x14**
| | | | | |
|---|---|---|---|---|
| 722 | A115 | 50p sil & multi | 1.40 | 1.40 |
| a. | | Booklet pane of 4 | 5.75 | — |
| 723 | A115 | 70p sil & multi | 1.90 | 1.90 |
| a. | | Booklet pane of 4 | 7.75 | — |
| 724 | A115 | 73p sil & multi | 2.00 | 2.00 |
| a. | | Booklet pane of 4 | 8.00 | — |
| 725 | A115 | £1 sil & multi | 2.75 | 2.75 |
| a. | | Booklet pane of 4 | 11.00 | — |
| 726 | A115 | £1.15 sil & multi | 3.25 | 3.25 |
| a. | | Booklet pane of 4 | 13.00 | — |
| 727 | A115 | £1.20 sil & multi | 3.25 | 3.25 |
| a. | | Booklet pane of 4 | 13.00 | — |
| | | Complete booklet, #722a, 723a, 724a, 725a, 726a, 727a | 58.50 | |
| | | Nos. 722-727 (6) | 14.55 | 14.55 |

**Souvenir Sheet**
**Litho., Sheet Margin Litho. With Foil Application**
**Perf. 14¼x14¾**
| | | | | |
|---|---|---|---|---|
| 728 | A116 | £2.20 sil & multi | 6.00 | 6.00 |

Examples of Nos. 722-727 with a black-and-white photograph were produced in limited quantities. These stamps were not sold to customers, but one stamp of the black-and-white set was given away to standing order customers and customers who ordered any products from the Platinum Jubilee issue within the first three months after issuance.

**Alderney Patois — A117**

English translation of Alderney patois inscription: 52p, Health to your friends and family. 73p, Bells sounding midnight at St. Anne. 79p, My grandmother has too many fish. £1.10, The man in the moon doesn't wear trousers. £1.26, Puffins on Burhou. £1.35, A fishing boat in Braye Harbor. £2.20, Blonde hedgehogs on Platte Saline. £3.50, Alderney cow at the Marais.

**2022, Apr. 4   Litho.   Perf. 13x13¼**
| | | | | |
|---|---|---|---|---|
| 729 | A117 | 52p multi | 1.30 | 1.30 |
| 730 | A117 | 73p multi | 1.90 | 1.90 |
| 731 | A117 | 79p multi | 2.00 | 2.00 |
| 732 | A117 | £1.10 multi | 2.75 | 2.75 |
| 733 | A117 | £1.26 multi | 3.25 | 3.25 |
| 734 | A117 | £1.35 multi | 3.50 | 3.50 |
| 735 | A117 | £2.20 multi | 5.50 | 5.50 |
| 736 | A117 | £3.50 multi | 8.75 | 8.75 |
| | | Nos. 729-736 (8) | 28.95 | 28.95 |

**Alderney Wildlife Trust, 20th Anniv. — A118**

Inscriptions: 52p, Seabird monitoring, conservation through science. 79p, Learning through nature in the community woodland. £1.10, Learning can be fun, pond dipping, Longis Nature Reserve. £1.35, Planting woodland for the next generation.

**2022, June 9   Litho.   Perf. 13¾**
| | | | | |
|---|---|---|---|---|
| 737 | A118 | 52p multi | 1.25 | 1.25 |
| 738 | A118 | 79p multi | 1.90 | 1.90 |
| 739 | A118 | £1.10 multi | 2.75 | 2.75 |
| 740 | A118 | £1.35 multi | 3.25 | 3.25 |
| | | Nos. 737-740 (4) | 9.15 | 9.15 |

**Alderney Breakwater, 175th Anniv. — A119**

Designs: 52p, Breakwater wall, walkway and arches. 79p, Waves hitting breakwater. £1.10, Breakwater and harbor. £1.35, End of breakwater.

**2022, Aug. 24   Litho.   Perf. 12**
| | | | | |
|---|---|---|---|---|
| 741 | A119 | 52p multi | 1.25 | 1.25 |
| 742 | A119 | 79p multi | 1.90 | 1.90 |
| 743 | A119 | £1.10 multi | 2.60 | 2.60 |
| 744 | A119 | £1.35 multi | 3.25 | 3.25 |
| a. | | Souvenir sheet of 4, #741-744 | 9.00 | 9.00 |
| | | Nos. 741-744 (4) | 9.00 | 9.00 |

**Christmas — A120**

Scenes from pantomime production of *Robin Hood*: 47p, Marriage of Robin Hood. 52p, Robin Hood and Little John. 73p, Sheriff of Nottingham taking from the poor. 79p, Robin Hood holding bow and arrow. £1.10, Robin Hood taking from the rich. £1.26, Maid Marion in jail. £1.35, Friar Tuck and Dame drinking.

**2022, Nov. 16   Litho.   Perf. 12**
| | | | | |
|---|---|---|---|---|
| 745 | A120 | 47p multi | 1.10 | 1.10 |
| 746 | A120 | 52p multi | 1.25 | 1.25 |
| 747 | A120 | 73p multi | 1.75 | 1.75 |
| 748 | A120 | 79p multi | 1.90 | 1.90 |
| 749 | A120 | £1.10 multi | 2.75 | 2.75 |
| 750 | A120 | £1.26 multi | 3.00 | 3.00 |
| 751 | A120 | £1.35 multi | 3.25 | 3.25 |
| | | Nos. 745-751 (7) | 15.00 | 15.00 |

# JERSEY

jər-zē

LOCATION — Island in the English Channel
GOVT. — Dependent territory (bailiwick) of the British Crown
AREA — 45 sq. mi.
POP. — 89,721 (1999 est.)
CAPITAL — St. Helier

Following the establishment of the British General Post Office as a public corporation on October 1, 1969, the post office of the Bailiwick of Jersey became a separate entity and British postage stamps ceased to be valid.

Catalogue values for unused stamps in this country are for Never Hinged items.

## British Regional Issue

A1

Royal Mace and Arms of Jersey — A2

### Perf. 15x14
**1958-69    Photo.    Wmk. 322**

| | | | | |
|---|---|---|---|---|
| 1 | A1 | 2½p rose red ('64) | .50 | .50 |
| 2 | A2 | 3p light purple | .35 | .35 |
| p. | | Phosphor. ('67) | .25 | .25 |
| 3 | A2 | 4p ultra ('66) | .30 | .30 |
| p. | | Phosphor. ('67) | .30 | .30 |

### Unwmk.

| | | | | |
|---|---|---|---|---|
| 4 | A2 | 4p olive brown ('68) | .25 | .25 |
| 5 | A2 | 4p brt red ('69) | .25 | .25 |
| 6 | A2 | 5p dark blue ('68) | .25 | .25 |
| | | Nos. 1-6 (6) | 1.90 | 1.90 |

Nos. 4-6 are phosphorescent.
Sold to the general public only at post offices within Jersey, but valid for postage throughout Great Britain.
See also Great Britain Nos. 269-270, which were sold only in the Channel Islands and at a few philatelic windows in Great Britain, and may be considered to be precursors to the regional issues.

## Bailiwick Issues

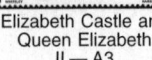

Elizabeth Castle and Queen Elizabeth II — A3

Queen Elizabeth II — A4

Designs (Queen Elizabeth II and): 1p, La Hougue Bie (prehistoric tomb). 2p, Portelet Bay. 3p, La Corbière Lighthouse. 4p, Mont Orgueil by night. 5p, Arms of Jersey and Royal Mace. 6p, Jersey cow. 9p, 1sh6p, Map of English Channel with Jersey. 1sh, Mont Orgueil. 2sh6p, Airport. 5sh, Legislative Chamber. 10sh, Royal Court. £1, Queen Elizabeth II, photograph by Cecil Beaton.

### Perf. 14½
**1969, Oct. 1    Photo.    Unwmk.**

| | | | | |
|---|---|---|---|---|
| 7 | A3 | ½p ocher & multi | .25 | .25 |
| 8 | A3 | 1p brown & multi | .25 | .25 |
| a. | | Booklet pane of 1 | .35 | |
| b. | | Booklet pane of 2 | .90 | |
| 9 | A3 | 2p multicolored | .25 | .25 |
| 10 | A3 | 3p dp blue & multi | .25 | .25 |
| a. | | Orange omitted | | |
| 11 | A3 | 4p multicolored | .25 | .25 |
| a. | | Booklet pane of 1 | .60 | |
| | | Complete booklet, 4 #8a, 5 #11a | 2.00 | |
| b. | | Booklet pane of 2 | 1.10 | |
| c. | | Gold omitted | — | |
| 12 | A3 | 5p multicolored | .25 | .25 |
| a. | | Booklet pane of 2 | 1.75 | |
| | | Complete booklet, 3 each #8b & 12a, 6 #11b | 17.50 | |

| | | | | |
|---|---|---|---|---|
| | | Complete booklet, 2 #8b, 7 #11b, 6 #12a | 12.50 | |
| b. | | Gold omitted | — | |
| 13 | A3 | 6p multicolored | .25 | .25 |
| 14 | A3 | 9p multicolored | .25 | .25 |
| 15 | A3 | 1sh lilac & multi | .25 | .25 |
| 16 | A3 | 1sh6p green & multi | .75 | .75 |
| 17 | A4 | 1sh9p multicolored | 1.05 | 1.05 |

### Perf. 12

| | | | | |
|---|---|---|---|---|
| 18 | A3 | 2sh6p multicolored | 1.55 | 1.55 |
| 19 | A3 | 5sh multicolored | 6.25 | 6.25 |
| 20 | A3 | 10sh gray & multi | 13.25 | 13.25 |
| a. | | 10sh green & multi (error) | 5,500. | |
| 21 | A4 | £1 tan & multi | 1.75 | 1.75 |
| | | Nos. 7-21 (15) | 26.85 | 26.85 |

A second post-1971 printing of No. 21 shows the background drapery less purple and more blue. Value, $3.
See Nos. 34-48, 107-109.

Jersey Post Office First Day Cover — A5

**1969, Oct. 1    Perf. 14½**

| | | | | |
|---|---|---|---|---|
| 22 | A5 | 4p multicolored | .25 | .25 |
| 23 | A5 | 5p blue & multi | .25 | .25 |
| 24 | A5 | 1sh6p brown & multi | .50 | .50 |
| 25 | A5 | 1sh9p emerald & multi | .80 | .80 |
| | | Nos. 22-25 (4) | 1.80 | 1.80 |

Inauguration of independent postal service.

Jersey Woman Reaching for Royal Mace, Flags of USSR, US and Great Britain — A6

4p, Lord Coutanche, Bailiff of Jersey, by James Gunn, vert. 5p, Sir Winston Churchill, by D. Van Praag, vert. 1sh9p, Swedish Red Cross ship "Vega."

**1970, May 9    Photo.    Perf. 11½**

| | | | | |
|---|---|---|---|---|
| 26 | A6 | 4p gold & multi | .25 | .25 |
| 27 | A6 | 5p gold & multi | .25 | .25 |
| 28 | A6 | 1sh6p gold & multi | .65 | .65 |
| 29 | A6 | 1sh9p gold & multi | .65 | .65 |
| | | Nos. 26-29 (4) | 1.80 | 1.80 |

25th anniv. of Jersey's liberation from the Germans.

"Rags to Riches" Cinderella A7

Designs (Parade Floats Made of Flowers): 4p, "A Tribute to Enid Blyton," author of children's books. 1sh6p, "Gourmet's Delight." 1sh9p, "We're the Greatest" (ostriches and trees).

**1970, July 28    Photo.    Perf. 11½**

| | | | | |
|---|---|---|---|---|
| 30 | A7 | 4p gold & multi | .25 | .25 |
| 31 | A7 | 5p gold & multi | .25 | .25 |
| 32 | A7 | 1sh6p gold & multi | 2.50 | 1.75 |
| 33 | A7 | 1sh9p gold & multi | 2.50 | 2.00 |
| | | Nos. 30-33 (4) | 5.50 | 4.25 |

"Battle of Flowers" annual parade.

## Decimal Currency Issue
### Types of 1969
### "p" instead of "d"

Designs: ½p, Elizabeth Castle. 1p, La Corbière Lighthouse. 1½p, Jersey cow. 2p, Mont Orgueil by night. 2½p, Arms of Jersey and Royal Mace. 3p, La Hougue Bie. 3½p, Portelet Bay. 4p, 7½p, Map of English Channel and Jersey. 5p, Mont Orgueil by day. 6p, Martello Tower at Archirondel. 9p, Queen Elizabeth II, by Cecil Beaton. 10p, Airport. 20p, Legislative Chamber. 50p, Royal Court.

**1970-75    Photo.    Perf. 14½**

| | | | | |
|---|---|---|---|---|
| 34 | A3 | ½p ocher & multi ('71) | .25 | .25 |
| a. | | Booklet pane of 1 | .25 | |
| 35 | A3 | 1p multicolored ('71) | .25 | .25 |
| a. | | Booklet pane of 2 ('75) | .25 | |
| b. | | Booklet pane of 4 ('75) | .35 | |
| c. | | Orange omitted | — | |
| 36 | A3 | 1½p multicolored ('71) | .25 | .25 |
| 37 | A3 | 2p multicolored ('71) | .25 | .25 |
| a. | | Booklet pane of 1 | .25 | |
| b. | | Booklet pane of 2 | .35 | |

| | | | | |
|---|---|---|---|---|
| 38 | A3 | 2½p multicolored ('71) | .25 | .25 |
| a. | | Booklet pane of 1 | .35 | |
| | | Complete booklet, 2 each #34a, 37a, 38a | 1.25 | |
| b. | | Booklet pane of 2 | .45 | |
| | | Complete booklet,5 #37b, 3 #38b | 1.75 | |
| | | Complete booklet,5 #37b, 6 #38b | 3.75 | |
| | | Complete booklet, 4 #38b | 4.00 | |
| 39 | A3 | 3p brn & multicolored ('71) | .25 | .25 |
| a. | | Booklet pane of 1 ('72) | .35 | |
| | | Complete booklet, 3 #34a, 1 #38a, 2 #39a | 1.00 | |
| b. | | Booklet pane of 2 ('72) | .45 | |
| | | Complete booklet, 5 #39b | 4.00 | |
| | | Complete booklet, 4 #38b, 5 #39b | 4.00 | |
| 40 | A3 | 3½p multicolored ('71) | .25 | .25 |
| a. | | Booklet pane of 1 ('74) | .35 | |
| | | Complete booklet, 3 #39a, 2 #40a | 1.00 | |
| | | Booklet pane of 2 ('74) | .60 | |
| | | Complete booklet, 2 #39a, 4 #40a | .90 | |
| b. | | Booklet pane of 2 ('74) | .50 | |
| | | Complete booklet, 3 #39b, 6 #40b | 3.00 | |
| 41 | A3 | 4p multicolored ('71) | .25 | .25 |
| a. | | Booklet pane of 2 ('75) | .50 | |
| b. | | Booklet pane of 4 ('75) | .75 | |
| 42 | A3 | 5p lilac & multi ('71) | .25 | .25 |
| a. | | Booklet pane of 2 ('75) | .55 | |
| | | Complete booklet, 3 each #35a, #41a, 2 #42a | 2.75 | |
| b. | | Booklet pane of 4 ('75) | .95 | |
| | | Complete booklet, 2 each #35b, 41b, 3 #42b | 5.00 | |
| 43 | A3 | 6p green & multi ('71) | .25 | .25 |
| 44 | A3 | 7½p multicolored ('71) | .25 | .25 |
| 45 | A4 | 9p multicolored ('71) | .35 | .35 |

### Perf. 12

| | | | | |
|---|---|---|---|---|
| 46 | A3 | 10p multicolored | .40 | .40 |
| 47 | A3 | 20p multicolored | .75 | .75 |
| 48 | A3 | 50p multicolored | 1.50 | 1.50 |
| | | Nos. 34-48 (15) | 5.75 | 5.75 |

See also Nos. 107-109.

White-eared Pheasant — A8

2½p, Thick-billed parrots, vert. 7½p, Ursine colobus monkeys, vert. 9p, Ring-tailed lemurs.

**1971, Mar. 9    Photo.    Perf. 11½**

| | | | | |
|---|---|---|---|---|
| 49 | A8 | 2p deep plum & multi | .25 | .25 |
| 50 | A8 | 2½p dark gray & multi | .25 | .25 |
| 51 | A8 | 7½p olive & multi | 1.75 | 1.75 |
| 52 | A8 | 9p vio blue & multi | 4.00 | 4.00 |
| | | Nos. 49-52 (4) | 6.25 | 6.25 |

Jersey Wildlife Preservation Trust.
See Nos. 65-68.

British Legion Emblem — A9

2½p, Poppy field & poppy emblem. 7½p, Jack Counter (1899-1970) & Victoria Cross. 9p, Flags of France & Great Britain.

**1971, June 15    Litho.    Perf. 14½**

| | | | | |
|---|---|---|---|---|
| 53 | A9 | 2p multicolored | .25 | .25 |
| 54 | A9 | 2½p multicolored | .25 | .25 |
| 55 | A9 | 7½p multicolored | 1.10 | 1.10 |
| 56 | A9 | 9p multicolored | 1.10 | 1.10 |
| | | Nos. 53-56 (4) | 2.70 | 2.70 |

50th anniversary of the British Legion.

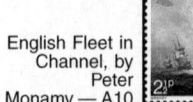

English Fleet in Channel, by Peter Monamy — A10

Paintings by Jersey Artists: 2p, Tante Elizabeth (women in farm kitchen), by Edmund Blampied, vert. 7½p, Boyhood of Raleigh (man and boys at seashore), by Sir John Millais. 9p, The Blind Beggar (old man and girl), by W. W. Ouless, vert.

**1971, Oct. 5    Photo.    Perf. 11½**

| | | | | |
|---|---|---|---|---|
| 57 | A10 | 2p gold & multi | .25 | .25 |
| 58 | A10 | 2½p gold & multi | .25 | .25 |
| 59 | A10 | 7½p gold & multi | .95 | .95 |
| 60 | A10 | 9p gold & multi | 1.25 | 1.25 |
| | | Nos. 57-60 (4) | 2.70 | 2.70 |

Jersey Fern — A11

Jersey Wild Flowers: 5p, Thrift. 7½p, Orchid (laxiflora). 9p, Viper's bugloss.

**1972, Jan. 18**
### Flowers in Natural Colors

| | | | | |
|---|---|---|---|---|
| 61 | A11 | 3p brown & blk | .25 | .25 |
| 62 | A11 | 5p lt blue & blk | .25 | .25 |
| 63 | A11 | 7½p lilac & blk | .70 | .70 |
| 64 | A11 | 9p green & blk | .95 | .95 |
| | | Nos. 61-64 (4) | 2.15 | 2.15 |

### Wildlife Type of 1971

2½p, Cheetahs. 3p, Rothschild's mynahs, vert. 7½p, Spectacled bear. 9p, Tuatara reptiles.

**1972, Mar. 17    Photo.    Perf. 11½**
### Queen's Head in Gold

| | | | | |
|---|---|---|---|---|
| 65 | A8 | 2½p Prus blue & multi | .25 | .25 |
| 66 | A8 | 3p dk pur & multi | .25 | .25 |
| 67 | A8 | 7½p yel bis & multi | .50 | .50 |
| 68 | A8 | 9p multicolored | .75 | .75 |
| | | Nos. 65-68 (4) | 1.75 | 1.75 |

Jersey Wildlife Preservation Trust.

Jersey Royal Artillery Shako — A12

3p, 2nd North Regiment. 7½p, South West Regiment. 9p, 3rd (South) Light Infantry.

**1972, June 27**

| | | | | |
|---|---|---|---|---|
| 69 | A12 | 2½p shown | .25 | .25 |
| 70 | A12 | 3p multicolored | .25 | .25 |
| 71 | A12 | 7½p multicolored | .30 | .30 |
| 72 | A12 | 9p multicolored | .50 | .50 |
| | | Nos. 69-72 (4) | 1.30 | 1.30 |

Royal Jersey Militia shakos of 19th century.

Princess Anne — A13

Designs: 3p, Queen Elizabeth II and Prince Philip, horiz. 7½p, Prince Charles. 20p, Queen Elizabeth II and family, horiz.

**1972, Nov. 1    Photo.    Perf. 11½**

| | | | | |
|---|---|---|---|---|
| 73 | A13 | 3p citron & multi | .25 | .25 |
| 74 | A13 | 3p rose & multi | .25 | .25 |
| 75 | A13 | 7½p blue & multi | .25 | .25 |
| 76 | A13 | 20p gray & multi | .25 | .25 |
| | | Nos. 73-76 (4) | 1.00 | 1.00 |

25th anniversary of the marriage of Queen Elizabeth II and Prince Philip.

Silver Wine and Christening Cups, 18th Century — A14

Designs: 3p, Gold torque, Bronze Age, vert. 7½p, Seal of Charles II, 1659, vert. 9p, Armorican (Brittany) coins, c. 55 B.C.

**1973, Jan. 23    Photo.    Perf. 11½**

| | | | | |
|---|---|---|---|---|
| 77 | A14 | 3p ultra & multi | .25 | .25 |
| 78 | A14 | 3p dp car & multi | .25 | .25 |
| 79 | A14 | 7½p org & multi | .25 | .25 |
| 80 | A14 | 9p blue & multi | .25 | .25 |
| | | Nos. 77-80 (4) | 1.00 | 1.00 |

Cent. of the Jersey Soc. Designs are from exhibits in the Soc. museum in St. Helier.

Balloon, Letter to Jersey from Siege of Paris, 1870 — A15

5p, Astra seaplane, 1912. 7½p, Supermarine Sea Eagle, 1923. 9p, De Havilland DH86, 1933.

**1973, May 16    Photo.    Perf. 11½**
| | | | | |
|---|---|---|---|---|
| 81 | A15 | 3p brt blue & multi | .25 | .25 |
| 82 | A15 | 5p blue grn & multi | .25 | .25 |
| 83 | A15 | 7½p ultra & multi | .25 | .25 |
| 84 | A15 | 9p vio blue & multi | .35 | .35 |
| | | *Nos. 81-84 (4)* | 1.10 | 1.10 |

Aviation history connected with Jersey before 1939.

19th Century Locomotives A16

**1973, Aug. 6    Photo.    Perf. 11½**
| | | | | |
|---|---|---|---|---|
| 85 | A16 | 2½p North Western | .25 | .25 |
| 86 | A16 | 3p Calvados | .25 | .25 |
| 87 | A16 | 7½p Carteret | .30 | .30 |
| 88 | A16 | 9p Caesarea | .35 | .35 |
| | | *Nos. 85-88 (4)* | 1.15 | 1.15 |

Centenary of Jersey Eastern Railroad.

Princess Anne and Mark Phillips — A17

**1973, Nov. 14    Photo.    Perf. 11½**
| | | | | |
|---|---|---|---|---|
| 89 | A17 | 3p lt blue & multi | .25 | .25 |
| 90 | A17 | 20p pink & multi | .60 | .60 |

Wedding of Princess Anne and Capt. Mark Phillips, Nov. 14, 1973.

Spider Crab — A18

**1973, Nov. 15    Photo.    Perf. 11½**
| | | | | |
|---|---|---|---|---|
| 91 | A18 | 2½p shown | .25 | .25 |
| 92 | A18 | 3p Conger eel | .25 | .25 |
| 93 | A18 | 7½p Lobster | .25 | .25 |
| 94 | A18 | 20p Ormer | .25 | .25 |
| | | *Nos. 91-94 (4)* | 1.00 | 1.00 |

Jersey Spring Flowers — A19

**1974, Feb. 13    Photo.    Perf. 12x11½**
| | | | | |
|---|---|---|---|---|
| 95 | A19 | 3p Freesias | .25 | .25 |
| 96 | A19 | 5½p Anemones | .25 | .25 |
| 97 | A19 | 8p Carnations & gladioli | .25 | .25 |
| 98 | A19 | 10p Daffodils & iris | .25 | .25 |
| | | *Nos. 95-98 (4)* | 1.00 | 1.00 |

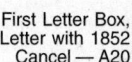

First Letter Box, Letter with 1852 Cancel — A20

UPU Cent.: 3p, Postmen, 1862 and 1969. 5½p, Contemporary pillar box and first day cover of No. 101. 20p, BAC 111 and paddle steamer "Aquila," 1874.

**1974, June 7    Photo.    Perf. 11½**
| | | | | |
|---|---|---|---|---|
| 99 | A20 | 2½p multicolored | .25 | .25 |
| 100 | A20 | 3p ultra & multi | .25 | .25 |
| 101 | A20 | 5½p olive & multi | .25 | .25 |
| 102 | A20 | 20p gray & multi | .25 | .25 |
| | | *Nos. 99-102 (4)* | 1.00 | 1.00 |

John Wesley — A21

**Lithographed and Engraved**
**1974, July 31    Perf. 13½x14**
| | | | | |
|---|---|---|---|---|
| 103 | A21 | 3p shown | .25 | .25 |
| 104 | A21 | 3½p Hillary | .25 | .25 |
| 105 | A21 | 8p Wace | .25 | .25 |
| 106 | A21 | 20p Churchill | .25 | .25 |
| a. | | Pale buff omitted | | |
| | | *Nos. 103-106 (4)* | 1.00 | 1.00 |

Anniversaries: Methodism in Jersey, bicen.; John Wesley, theologian, founder of Methodism. Sesquicentennial of Royal Natl. Lifeboat Institution, Lt. Col. Sir William Hillary, founder. 800th death anniv. of Canon Wace, poet and chronicler. Sir Winston Churchill, birth centenary.

**Type of 1969**

4½p, Arms of Jersey and Royal Mace. 5p, Jersey cow. 8p, Mont Orgueil by night.

**1974, Oct. 31    Photo.    Perf. 14½**
| | | | | |
|---|---|---|---|---|
| 107 | A3 | 4½p olive & multi | .25 | .25 |
| 108 | A3 | 5½p magenta & multi | .25 | .25 |
| 109 | A3 | 8p yellow & multi | .25 | .25 |
| | | *Nos. 107-109 (3)* | .75 | .75 |

English Yacht, 1660, by Peter Monamy — A22

Marine paintings by Peter Monamy (d. 1749): 5½p, French ship. 8p, Dutch ship, horiz. 25p, Naval battle, 1662.

**1974, Nov. 22    Photo.    Perf. 11½**
**Size: 31x38, 38x31mm**
| | | | | |
|---|---|---|---|---|
| 116 | A22 | 3½p gold & multi | .25 | .25 |
| 117 | A22 | 5½p gold & multi | .25 | .25 |
| 118 | A22 | 8p gold & multi | .25 | .25 |

**Size: 54x25mm**
| | | | | |
|---|---|---|---|---|
| 119 | A22 | 25p gold & multi | .50 | .50 |
| | | *Nos. 116-119 (4)* | 1.25 | 1.25 |

Potato Digger — A23

19th cent. farming tools: 3½p, Cider apple crusher. 8p, Six-horse plow. 10p, Hay cart.

**1975, Feb. 25    Photo.    Perf. 11½**
| | | | | |
|---|---|---|---|---|
| 120 | A23 | 3p multicolored | .25 | .25 |
| 121 | A23 | 3½p multicolored | .25 | .25 |
| 122 | A23 | 8p multicolored | .25 | .25 |
| 123 | A23 | 10p multicolored | .25 | .25 |
| | | *Nos. 120-123 (4)* | 1.00 | 1.00 |

Shell Design as Letter "J" — A24

Posters: 8p, Beach umbrella. 10p, Beach chair. 12p, Sand castle with Union Jacks & Jersey flag.

**1975, June 8    Photo.    Perf. 11½**
| | | | | |
|---|---|---|---|---|
| 124 | A24 | 5p multicolored | .25 | .25 |
| 125 | A24 | 8p multicolored | .25 | .25 |
| 126 | A24 | 10p multicolored | .25 | .25 |
| 127 | A24 | 12p multicolored | .25 | .25 |
| a. | | Souvenir sheet of 4 | 1.10 | 1.10 |
| | | *Nos. 124-127 (4)* | 1.00 | 1.00 |

Tourist publicity. No. 127a contains Nos. 124-127 in continuous design extending into margin.

Queen Mother Elizabeth — A25

**1975, May 30    Photo.    Perf. 11½**
| | | | | |
|---|---|---|---|---|
| 128 | A25 | 20p multicolored | .60 | .60 |

Visit of Queen Mother Elizabeth to Jersey.

Common Tern — A26

**1975, July 28    Photo.    Perf. 11½**
| | | | | |
|---|---|---|---|---|
| 129 | A26 | 4p shown | .25 | .25 |
| 130 | A26 | 5p Storm petrel | .25 | .25 |
| 131 | A26 | 8p Brent geese | .25 | .25 |
| 132 | A26 | 25p Shag | .35 | .35 |
| | | *Nos. 129-132 (4)* | 1.10 | 1.10 |

Siskin 3A, 1925 — A27

R.A.F. Planes: 5p, Southampton 1, 1925. 10p, Spitfire 1, 1931. 25p, Gnat T.1, 1962.

**1975, Oct. 30    Photo.    Perf. 11½**
| | | | | |
|---|---|---|---|---|
| 133 | A27 | 4p blue & multi | .25 | .25 |
| 134 | A27 | 5p lt green & multi | .25 | .25 |
| 135 | A27 | 10p yellow & multi | .25 | .35 |
| 136 | A27 | 25p ultra & multi | .35 | .35 |
| | | *Nos. 133-136 (4)* | 1.10 | 1.20 |

Royal Air Force Assoc., Jersey Branch, 50th anniv.

Map of Jersey with 12 Parishes — A28        Arms of Trinity and Zoo — A29

Queen Elizabeth II — A30

Arms and scene: 5p, Church of St. Mary. 6p, Grouville, Seymour Tower. 7p, St. Brelade, La Corbière Lighthouse. 8p, Church of St. Saviour. 9p, St. Helier, Elizabeth Castle. 10p, St. Martin, Gorey Harbor. 11p, St. Peter, Jersey Airport. 12p, St. Ouen, Grosnez Castle. 13p, St. John, Bonne Nuit Harbor. 14p, St. Clement and Le Hocq Tower. 15p, St. Lawrence, Morel Farm. 20p, 12 Parishes, view of harbor. 30p, Jersey flag, map of Island. 40p, Postal Administration emblem, PO Headquarters. 50p, Jersey, Parliament and Royal Court. £1, Flag of Lt.-Governor, Government House.

**1976-77    Litho.    Perf. 14½**
**Size: 33x23mm**
| | | | | |
|---|---|---|---|---|
| 137 | A28 | ½p lt blue & multi | .25 | .25 |
| 138 | A29 | 1p bister & multi | .25 | .25 |
| a. | | Bkt. pane of 2 + 2 labels | .80 | |
| b. | | Booklet pane of 4 | .80 | |
| 139 | A29 | 5p rose & multi | .25 | .25 |
| a. | | Booklet pane of 4 | .80 | |
| 140 | A29 | 6p vio blue & multi | .25 | .25 |
| a. | | Booklet pane of 4 ('78) | 1.00 | |
| | | Complete booklet, #138b, 4 #140a | 3.75 | |
| 141 | A29 | 7p fawn & multi | .25 | .25 |
| a. | | Booklet pane of 4 | 1.10 | |
| | | Complete booklet, #138a, 139a, 141a | 2.25 | |
| | | Complete booklet, #138b, 2 each #139a, 141a | 4.00 | |
| 142 | A29 | 8p yel grn & multi | .25 | .25 |
| a. | | Booklet pane of 4 ('78) | 1.10 | |
| | | Complete booklet, #138b, 3 #142a | 3.75 | |

| | | | | |
|---|---|---|---|---|
| | | Complete booklet, 2 each #138b, 140a, 142a | 5.00 | |
| 143 | A29 | 9p lil rose & multi | .25 | .25 |
| a. | | Booklet pane of 4 ('80) | 1.25 | |
| | | Complete booklet, 3 #138b, 2 each #141a, 143a | 5.50 | |
| 144 | A29 | 10p ol bis & multi | .25 | .25 |
| 145 | A29 | 11p bl grn & multi | .25 | .25 |
| 146 | A29 | 12p org & multi | .25 | .25 |
| 147 | A29 | 13p blue & multi | .25 | .25 |
| 148 | A29 | 14p yel org & multi | .40 | .40 |
| 149 | A29 | 15p vio & multi | .40 | .40 |

**Photo.**
**Perf. 12**
**Size: 41x26mm, 26x41mm**
| | | | | |
|---|---|---|---|---|
| 150 | A29 | 20p gold & multi | .45 | .45 |
| 151 | A28 | 30p gold & multi | .55 | .55 |
| 152 | A29 | 40p gold & multi | .80 | .80 |
| 153 | A29 | 50p gold & multi | 1.00 | 1.00 |
| 154 | A29 | £1 gold & multi | 2.75 | 2.75 |
| 155 | A30 | £2 multicolored ('77) | 4.00 | 4.00 |
| | | *Nos. 137-155 (19)* | 13.10 | 13.10 |

Issue dates: Nos. 137-149, Jan. 29; Nos. 150-154, Aug. 20. No. 155, Nov. 16.
Booklet panes Nos. 138a, 138b, 140a, 142a exist with no date in the bottom selvage, while panes Nos. 138b, 143a and 146a have "May 1980" at bottom.

Sir Walter Raleigh and Old Map of Virginia A31

US Bicentennial: 7p, Sir George Carteret and old map of New Jersey. 11p, Philippe Dauvergne and ships landing on Long Island. 13p, John Singleton Copley and his "Death of Major Pierson."

**1976, May 29    Photo.    Perf. 11½**
| | | | | |
|---|---|---|---|---|
| 160 | A31 | 5p multicolored | .25 | .25 |
| 161 | A31 | 7p multicolored | .25 | .25 |
| 162 | A31 | 11p multicolored | .25 | .25 |
| 163 | A31 | 13p multicolored | .35 | .35 |
| | | *Nos. 160-163 (4)* | 1.10 | 1.10 |

Dr. Grandin, Central and Southern China Map — A32

7p, Yangtze River journey. 11p, On horseback to Chaotung. 13p, Dr. Grandin holding infant.

**1976, Nov. 25    Photo.    Perf. 11½**
| | | | | |
|---|---|---|---|---|
| 164 | A32 | 5p multicolored | .25 | .25 |
| 165 | A32 | 7p multicolored | .25 | .25 |
| 166 | A32 | 11p multicolored | .25 | .25 |
| 167 | A32 | 13p multicolored | .35 | .35 |
| | | *Nos. 164-167 (4)* | 1.10 | 1.10 |

Lilian Mary Grandin (1876-1924), Jersey-born missionary doctor in China.

Queen Wearing St. Edward's Crown — A33

7p, Queen with Jersey Bailiff Sir Alexander Coutanche, 1957. 25p, Portrait, 1976.

**1977, Feb. 7    Photo.    Perf. 11½**
| | | | | |
|---|---|---|---|---|
| 168 | A33 | 5p multicolored | .25 | .25 |
| 169 | A33 | 7p multicolored | .30 | .30 |
| 170 | A33 | 25p multicolored | .50 | .50 |
| | | *Nos. 168-170 (3)* | 1.05 | 1.05 |

25th anniv. of the reign of Elizabeth II.

1/13th sh, 1871 and ½th sh, 1877 — A34

Coins: 7p, 1/13th sh, 1949. 11p, Silver crown, 1966. 13p, Silver £2, 1972.

**1977, Mar. 25    Litho.    Perf. 14**

| | | | | |
|---|---|---|---|---|
| 171 | A34 | 5p multicolored | .25 | .25 |
| 172 | A34 | 7p multicolored | .25 | .25 |
| 173 | A34 | 11p multicolored | .25 | .25 |
| 174 | A34 | 13p multicolored | .30 | .30 |
| | | Nos. 171-174 (4) | 1.05 | 1.05 |

Centenary of Jersey's currency reform.

Sir William Weston and Santa Anna, 1530 — A35

Designs: 7p, Sir William Drogo and horse-drawn ambulance, 1877. 11p, Duke of Connaught and Jersey ambulance, 1917. 13p, Richard, Duke of Gloucester and ambulance team, 1977.

**1977, June 24    Litho.    Perf. 14x13½**

| | | | | |
|---|---|---|---|---|
| 175 | A35 | 5p multicolored | .25 | .25 |
| 176 | A35 | 7p multicolored | .25 | .25 |
| 177 | A35 | 11p multicolored | .25 | .25 |
| 178 | A35 | 13p multicolored | .35 | .35 |
| | | Nos. 175-178 (4) | 1.10 | 1.10 |

St. John Ambulance Assoc. cent. (in GB).

Victoria and Albert Arriving in Jersey, 1846 — A36

Designs: 10½p, Victoria College, 1852. 11p, Statue of Sir Galahad near college gate, vert. 13p, College Hall, interior, vert.

**1977, Sept. 29    Litho.    Perf. 14½**

| | | | | |
|---|---|---|---|---|
| 179 | A36 | 7p multicolored | .25 | .25 |
| 180 | A36 | 10½p multicolored | .25 | .25 |
| 181 | A36 | 11p multicolored | .25 | .25 |
| 182 | A36 | 13p multicolored | .35 | .35 |
| | | Nos. 179-182 (4) | 1.10 | 1.10 |

Jersey Victoria College, 125th anniv.

Harry Vardon Statuette, Layout of Golf Course — A37

Designs: 8p, Golf grip and swing perfected by Vardon. 11p, Vardon's putting grip and stance. 13p, Vardon's British and US Open Golf trophies, his book "The Complete Golfer" and biography.

**1978, Feb. 28    Litho.    Perf. 14**

| | | | | |
|---|---|---|---|---|
| 183 | A37 | 6p multicolored | .25 | .25 |
| 184 | A37 | 8p multicolored | .25 | .25 |
| 185 | A37 | 11p multicolored | .25 | .25 |
| 186 | A37 | 13p multicolored | .35 | .35 |
| | | Nos. 183-186 (4) | 1.10 | 1.10 |

Cent. of Royal Jersey Golf Club and to honor Vardon (1870-1937), Jersey-born golfer.

Mont Orgueil — A38

Europa: 8p, St. Aubin's Fort. 10½p, Elizabeth Castle.

**1978, May 1    Photo.    Perf. 11½**

| | | | | |
|---|---|---|---|---|
| 187 | A38 | 6p multicolored | .25 | .25 |
| 188 | A38 | 8p multicolored | .25 | .25 |
| 189 | A38 | 10½p multicolored | .25 | .25 |
| | | Nos. 187-189 (3) | .75 | .75 |

Gaspe Basin, by P. J. Ouless — A39

8p, Early map of Gaspe Peninsula, after Capt. Cook. 10½p, Sailing ship Century. 11p, Early map of Jersey. 13p, St. Aubin's Bay Town & Harbor.

**1978, June 9    Litho.    Perf. 14x15**

| | | | | |
|---|---|---|---|---|
| 190 | A39 | 6p multicolored | .25 | .25 |
| 191 | A39 | 8p multicolored | .25 | .25 |
| 192 | A39 | 10½p multicolored | .25 | .25 |
| 193 | A39 | 11p multicolored | .25 | .25 |
| 194 | A39 | 13p multicolored | .35 | .35 |
| | | Nos. 190-194 (5) | 1.35 | 1.25 |

Jersey's links with Canada and for CAPEX, Canadian Intl. Phil. Exhib., Toronto, Ont., June 9-18.

Elizabeth II, Hallmarks of the reign,1953 and 1977 — A40

Design: 8p, Elizabeth II and Prince Philip.

**1978, June 27    Photo.    Perf. 11½**

| | | | | |
|---|---|---|---|---|
| 195 | A40 | 8p car, sil & black | .25 | .25 |
| 196 | A40 | 25p blue, sil & black | .75 | .70 |

25th anniv. of coronation of Queen Elizabeth II and for Royal visit, June 27.

Mail Cutter — A41

Packets: 8p, Flamer, paddle vessel. 10½p, Diana, screw steamer. 11p, Ibex, steamer. 13p, Caesarea, mini-liner.

**1978, Oct. 18    Litho.    Perf. 14½x14**

| | | | | |
|---|---|---|---|---|
| 197 | A41 | 6p multicolored | .25 | .25 |
| 198 | A41 | 8p multicolored | .25 | .25 |
| 199 | A41 | 10½p multicolored | .25 | .25 |
| 200 | A41 | 11p multicolored | .25 | .25 |
| 201 | A41 | 13p multicolored | .35 | .25 |
| | | Nos. 197-201 (5) | 1.35 | 1.25 |

First Government packet between Britain and Jersey, bicentenary.

Jersey Pillar Box, 1860 — A42

Europa: No. 203, Mailman emptying 1979 mailbox. No. 204, Telephone switchboard, c. 1900. No. 205, Technician working on contemporary telecommunications system.

**Perf. 14, 14½x15**

**1979, Mar. 1    Litho.**

| | | | | |
|---|---|---|---|---|
| 202 | A42 | 8p yellow & blk | .25 | .25 |
| 203 | A42 | 8p carmine & blk | .25 | .25 |
| a. | | Pair, #202-203 | .50 | .50 |
| 204 | A42 | 10½p violet & blk | .25 | .25 |
| 205 | A42 | 10½p blue & blk | .25 | .25 |
| a. | | Pair, #204-205 | .75 | .75 |
| | | Nos. 202-205 (4) | 1.00 | 1.00 |

Nos. 203a, 205a have continuous design. Both exist perf. 14 and 14½x15.

Soft-colored Jersey Heifer — A43

25p, Milk-laden Jersey cow with 1st Prize ribbon.

**Perf. 14 (#206), 13¾ (#207)**

**1979, Mar. 1**

| | | | | |
|---|---|---|---|---|
| 206 | A43 | 6p multicolored | .25 | .25 |

**Size: 48x31mm**

| | | | | |
|---|---|---|---|---|
| 207 | A43 | 25p multicolored | .75 | .75 |

30th anniv. of 1st Intl. Conf. of Jersey Breed Societies and 9th Conf. of the World Jersey Cattle Bureau.

Percival Mew Gull — A44

Planes: 8p, De Havilland Chipmunk. 10½p, Druine D-31 Turbulent. 11p, De Havilland Tiger Moth. 13p, North American Harvard Mk. 4.

**1979, Apr. 24    Photo.    Perf. 11½**

| | | | | |
|---|---|---|---|---|
| 208 | A44 | 6p multicolored | .25 | .25 |
| 209 | A44 | 8p multicolored | .25 | .25 |
| 210 | A44 | 10½p multicolored | .25 | .25 |
| 211 | A44 | 11p multicolored | .25 | .25 |
| 212 | A44 | 13p multicolored | .35 | .35 |
| | | Nos. 208-212 (5) | 1.35 | 1.35 |

25th International Air Rally.

My First Sermon, by Millais — A45

Paintings by Millais: 10½p, Orphan. 11p, The Princes in the Tower. 25p, Jesus in the Home of His Parents, horiz.

**1979, Aug. 13    Photo.    Perf. 11½**
**Size: 25x35mm**

| | | | | |
|---|---|---|---|---|
| 213 | A45 | 8p multicolored | .25 | .25 |
| 214 | A45 | 10½p multicolored | .25 | .25 |
| 215 | A45 | 11p multicolored | .25 | .25 |

**Size: 49x30mm**
**Perf. 12x12½**

| | | | | |
|---|---|---|---|---|
| 216 | A45 | 25p multicolored | .60 | .60 |
| | | Nos. 213-216 (4) | 1.35 | 1.35 |

IYC and for John Everett Millais (1829-96).

Waldrapp Ibis — A46

6p, Pink pigeons. 8p, Orangutans. 13p, Lowland gorillas. 15p, Rodrigues fruit bats.

**1979, Nov. 8    Photo.    Perf. 11½**

| | | | | |
|---|---|---|---|---|
| 217 | A46 | 6p multicolored | .25 | .25 |
| 218 | A46 | 8p multicolored | .25 | .25 |
| 219 | A46 | 11½p shown | .25 | .25 |
| 220 | A46 | 13p multicolored | .35 | .35 |
| 221 | A46 | 15p multicolored | .40 | .40 |
| | | Nos. 217-221 (5) | 1.50 | 1.50 |

Nos. 217-218, 220-221 vertical.

Mont Orgueil Fortress — A47

Fortresses, 300th Anniversary: 11½p, St. Aubin Tower. 13p, Elizabeth. 25p, Map of Jersey showing fortress locations.

**1980, Feb. 5    Litho.    Perf. 14½x13½**

| | | | | |
|---|---|---|---|---|
| 222 | A47 | 8p multicolored | .25 | .25 |
| 223 | A47 | 11½p multicolored | .25 | .25 |
| 224 | A47 | 13p multicolored | .35 | .35 |

**Perf. 13½x14**
**Size: 37½x26mm**

| | | | | |
|---|---|---|---|---|
| 225 | A47 | 25p multicolored | .60 | .60 |
| | | Nos. 222-225 (4) | 1.45 | 1.45 |

Potato Harvest — A48

Royal Jersey Potato Cent.: 7p, Planting potatoes. 17½p, Loading dock, Weighbridge.

**1980, May 6    Litho.    Perf. 14**

| | | | | |
|---|---|---|---|---|
| 226 | A48 | 8p multicolored | .25 | .25 |
| 227 | A48 | 15p multicolored | .30 | .30 |
| 228 | A48 | 17½p multicolored | .35 | .35 |
| | | Nos. 226-228 (3) | .90 | .90 |

A49

Europa (Wax Figures from Mont Orgueil and Elizabeth Castles): No. 229a, Sir Walter Raleigh; 229b, Paul Ivy. No. 230a, Charles II and Sir George Carteret; 230b, Lady Carteret. Pairs in continuous design.

**1980, May 6**

| | | | | |
|---|---|---|---|---|
| 229 | A49 | Pair | .50 | .50 |
| a.-b. | | 9p any single | .25 | .25 |
| 230 | A49 | Pair | .60 | .60 |
| a.-b. | | 13½p any single | .30 | .30 |

Three-lap Motorcycle Race — A51

9p, Intl. road race. 13½p, Motorcycle scrambling. 15p, Sand racing, saloon cars. 17½p, Natl. Hill climb.

**1980, July 24    Litho.    Perf. 12**
**Granite Paper**

| | | | | |
|---|---|---|---|---|
| 231 | A51 | 7p shown | .25 | .25 |
| 232 | A51 | 9p multicolored | .25 | .25 |
| 233 | A51 | 13½p multicolored | .25 | .25 |
| 234 | A51 | 15p multicolored | .30 | .30 |
| 235 | A51 | 17½p multicolored | .35 | .35 |
| | | Nos. 231-235 (5) | 1.40 | 1.40 |

Jersey Motorcycle and Light Car Club, 60th anniv.

"Eye of the Wind" Leaving St. Helier — A52

Designs: 9p, Medical research, Cuna Indians, Panama. 13½p, Exploration, Papua New Guinea. 14p, Capt. Scott's ship, Antarctica. 15p, Conservation, Sulawesi. 17½p, Marine studies.

**1980, Oct. 1    Litho.    Perf. 14½**

| | | | | |
|---|---|---|---|---|
| 236 | A52 | 7p multicolored | .25 | .25 |
| 237 | A52 | 9p multicolored | .25 | .25 |
| 238 | A52 | 13½ multicolored | .25 | .25 |
| 239 | A52 | 14p multicolored | .30 | .30 |
| 240 | A52 | 15p multicolored | .30 | .30 |
| 241 | A52 | 17½p multicolored | .40 | .40 |
| | | Nos. 236-241 (6) | 1.75 | 1.75 |

Operation Drake, a two-year, round-the-world scientific expedition in tribute to Royal Geographic Society sesquicentennial.

Armed Soldiers and Wounded Drummer — A53

Designs: Details from The Death of Major Peirson, by John Singleton Copley.

**1981, Jan. 6    Photo.    Perf. 12½**
**Granite Paper**

| | | | | |
|---|---|---|---|---|
| 242 | A53 | 7p multicolored | .25 | .25 |
| 243 | A53 | 10p multicolored | .25 | .25 |
| 244 | A53 | 15p multicolored | .35 | .35 |
| 245 | A53 | 17½p multicolored | .45 | .45 |
| a. | | Souvenir sheet of 4, #242-245 | 1.50 | 1.50 |
| | | Nos. 242-245 (4) | 1.30 | 1.30 |

Battle of Jersey bicentenary. No. 245a has continuous design.

De Bagot
Family
Arms
A54

Jersey, Channel
Map
A54a

Queen Elizabeth II,
by Norman
Hepple — A54b

| | | | |
|---|---|---|---|
| **1981-83** | | **Litho.** | **Perf. 14** |
| 246 | A54 | ½p shown | .25 .25 |
| 247 | A54 | 1p De Carteret | .25 .25 |
| *a.* | | Booklet pane of 6 | .35 |
| 248 | A54 | 2p La Cloche | .25 .25 |
| *a.* | | Booklet pane of 6 | .55 |
| 249 | A54 | 3p Dumaresq | .25 .25 |
| *a.* | | Booklet pane of 6 | .65 |
| 250 | A54 | 4p Payn | .25 .25 |
| 251 | A54 | 5p Janvrin | .25 .25 |
| 252 | A54 | 6p Poingdestre | .25 .25 |
| 253 | A54 | 7p Pipon | .25 .25 |
| *a.* | | Booklet pane of 6 | 1.90 |
| 254 | A54 | 8p Marett | .25 .25 |
| *a.* | | Booklet pane of 6 ('83) | 2.40 |
| 255 | A54 | 9p Le Breton | .25 .25 |
| 256 | A54 | 10p Le Maistre | .35 .25 |
| *a.* | | Booklet pane of 6 | 2.75 |
| | | Complete booklet, 2 #247a, 1 each #249a, 253a, 256a | 6.00 |
| | | Complete booklet #247a, 248a, 253a, 256a | 6.00 |
| 257 | A54 | 11p Bisson | .35 .25 |
| *b.* | | Booklet pane of 6 ('83) | 3.25 |
| | | Complete booklet, #247a, #248a, 254a, 257b | 6.00 |
| 258 | A54 | 12p Robin | .35 .25 |
| 259 | A54 | 13p Herault | .40 .25 |
| 260 | A54 | 14p Messervy | .45 .25 |
| 261 | A54 | 15p Fiott | .50 .30 |
| 262 | A54 | 20p Badier | .65 .30 |
| 263 | A54 | 25p L'Arbalestier | .80 .30 |
| 264 | A54 | 30p Journeaulx | 1.00 .50 |
| 265 | A54 | 40p Lempriere | 1.10 .50 |
| 266 | A54 | 50p D'Auvergne | 1.25 .60 |
| 267 | A54a | £1 shown | 2.50 1.25 |

| | | **Photo.** | |
|---|---|---|---|
| | | **Perf. 12½x12** | |
| 268 | A54b | £5 multi | 12.00 8.00 |
| | | *Nos. 246-268 (23)* | 24.20 15.35 |

Issued: Nos. 246-256, 2/24; No. 248a, 12/1; Nos. 257-262, 7/28; Nos. 263-267, 2/23/82; Nos. 254a, 257a, 4/19/83; £5, 11/17/83.

| | | | |
|---|---|---|---|
| **1984-88** | | | **Perf. 15x14** |
| 247b | A54 | 1p ('88) | .30 .30 |
| 248b | A54 | 2p Bklt. pane of 6 ('86) | .65 |
| 248c | A54 | 2p ('84) | .25 .25 |
| 249b | A54 | 3p Bklt. pane of 6 ('84) | .75 |
| 249c | A54 | 3p ('84) | .25 .25 |
| 250a | A54 | 4p Bklt. pane of 6 ('87) | 1.00 |
| 250b | A54 | 4p ('86) | .25 .25 |
| 251a | A54 | 5p ('86) | .30 .25 |
| 252a | A54 | 6p ('86) | .35 .35 |
| 255a | A54 | 9p Bklt. pane of 6 ('84) | 2.50 |
| 255b | A54 | 9p ('84) | .40 .40 |
| 256b | A54 | 10p Bklt. pane of 6 ('86) | 1.50 |
| 256c | A54 | 10p ('86) | .40 .30 |
| 257a | A54 | 11p Bklt. pane of 6 ('87) | 2.00 |
| 257c | A54 | 11p ('87) | .45 .45 |
| 258a | A54 | 12p Bklt. pane of 6 ('84) | 3.00 |
| | | Complete booklet, 2 each #249b, 255a, 1 #258a | 14.50 |
| 258b | A54 | 12p ('84) | .50 .50 |
| 259a | A54 | 13p ('84) | .50 .25 |
| 260a | A54 | 14p Bklt. pane of 6 ('86) | 2.50 |
| | | Complete booklet, 2 each #248b, 256b, 1 #260a | 9.50 |
| 260b | A54 | 14p ('84) | .40 .25 |
| 261a | A54 | 15p ('87) | .45 .45 |
| 261b | A54 | 15p Bklt. pane of 6 ('87) | 2.50 |
| | | Complete booklet, 2 each #250a, 257a, 1 #261b | 11.00 |
| 262a | A54 | 20p ('86) | .85 .60 |
| 264a | A54 | 30p ('86) | 1.00 1.00 |
| 265a | A54 | 40p ('87) | 1.50 1.50 |
| 266a | A54 | 50p ('87) | 2.00 2.00 |

Issued: Nos. 251a, 252a, 262a, 264a, 3/4.
No. 247a dated "February 1981," "December 1981" or "April 1983;" No. 248a dated "December 1981" or "April 1983;" Nos. 253a, 256a dated "February 1981" or "December 1981;" No. 250a dated "April 1987" or "May 1988." No. 258a dated "April 1984" or "May 1988."
See Nos. 381-388.

Knight of Hamby
Killing the
Dragon — A55

Europa (Legends): 10p, La Hougue Bie. 18p, Easter Voyage of St. Brelade. No. 272, Servant killing Knight of Hamby. No. 273, Shipwreck of St. Brelade. No. 274, Whale, ships' departure.

| | | | |
|---|---|---|---|
| **1981, Apr. 7** | | | **Perf. 14½** |
| 271 | A55 | 10p multicolored | .25 .25 |
| 272 | A55 | 10p multicolored | .25 .25 |
| *a.* | | Pair, #271-272 | .60 .60 |
| 273 | A55 | 18p multicolored | .30 .30 |
| 274 | A55 | 18p multicolored | .30 .30 |
| *a.* | | Pair, #273-274 | 1.00 1.00 |
| | | *Nos. 271-274 (4)* | 1.10 1.10 |

Royal Square by
Gaslight — A56

| | | | |
|---|---|---|---|
| **1981, May 22** | | **Photo.** | **Perf. 12** |
| | | **Granite Paper** | |
| 275 | A56 | 7p The Harbor | .25 .25 |
| 276 | A56 | 10p The Quay | .25 .25 |
| 277 | A56 | 18p shown | .40 .40 |
| 278 | A56 | 22p Halkett Place | .45 .45 |
| 279 | A56 | 25p Central Market | .65 .65 |
| | | *Nos. 275-279 (5)* | 2.00 2.00 |

Gas light sesquicentennial.

Prince Charles
and Lady
Diana — A57

| | | | |
|---|---|---|---|
| **1981, July 28** | | **Photo.** | **Perf. 12** |
| | | **Granite Paper** | |
| 280 | A57 | 10p multicolored | .25 .25 |
| 281 | A57 | 25p multicolored | 1.00 1.00 |

Royal Wedding.

Christmas Tree, Royal
Square, St. Helier — A58

10p, East window, St. Helier's Church, choir. 18p, Boxing Day, Jersey Drag Hunt.

| | | | |
|---|---|---|---|
| **1981, Sept. 29** | | **Litho.** | **Perf. 14½** |
| 282 | A58 | 7p shown | .25 .25 |
| 283 | A58 | 10p multicolored | .25 .25 |
| 284 | A58 | 18p multicolored | .45 .45 |
| | | *Nos. 282-284 (3)* | .95 .95 |

Christmas 1981.

Europa
1982 — A59

Designs: Maps showing formation of Channel Islands resulting from rise in sea level.

| | | | |
|---|---|---|---|
| **1982, Apr. 20** | | **Litho.** | **Perf. 14½** |
| 285 | A59 | 11p 16,000 BC | .25 .25 |
| 286 | A59 | 11p 10,000 BC, vert. | .25 .25 |
| 287 | A59 | 19½p 7,000 BC, vert. | .50 .50 |
| 288 | A59 | 19½p 4,000 BC | .50 .50 |
| | | *Nos. 285-288 (4)* | 1.50 1.50 |

Rollon Duke of Normandy, William the
Conqueror, Clameur de Haro (Plea of
Injunction)
A60

Links with France: No. 290, Kings John and Philippe Auguste, Siege of Rouen. No. 291, Jean Martell (1694-1753), brandy merchant. No. 292, Victor Hugo. No. 293, Pierre Teilhard de Chardin (1881-1955), theologian. No. 294, Charles Rey (1897-1981), meteorologist.

| | | | |
|---|---|---|---|
| **1982, June 11** | | **Litho.** | **Perf. 14** |
| 289 | A60 | 8p multicolored | .25 .25 |
| 290 | A60 | 8p multicolored | .25 .25 |
| *a.* | | Bklt. pane of 4+label, 2 each #289-290 | 1.00 1.00 |
| *b.* | | Pair, #289-290 | .50 .50 |
| 291 | A60 | 11p multicolored | .30 .25 |
| 292 | A60 | 11p multicolored | .30 .25 |
| *a.* | | Bklt. pane of 4+label, 2 each #291-292 | 1.50 1.50 |
| *b.* | | Pair, #291-292 | .70 .70 |
| 293 | A60 | 19½p multicolored | .45 .30 |
| 294 | A60 | 19½p multicolored | .45 .30 |
| *a.* | | Bklt. pane of 4+label, 2 each #293-294 | 2.25 2.25 |
| *b.* | | Pair, #293-294 | 1.00 1.00 |
| | | Complete booklet, 2 each #290a, 292a, 294a | 10.00 |
| | | *Nos. 289-294 (6)* | 2.00 1.60 |

Issue date: Nos. 290a-294a, Sept. 7. Two versions of Nos. 290a, 292a and 294a exist: the label is inscribed in English or French.

Scouting
Year — A61

Designs: 8p, Sir William Smith (Boys Brigade founder). 11p, Liberation parade, 1945, vert. 24p, Boys Brigade annual display, 1903. 26p, The Baden-Powells, 1924, vert. 29p, Scouts.

| | | | |
|---|---|---|---|
| **1982, Nov. 18** | | **Photo.** | **Perf. 12** |
| | | **Granite Paper** | |
| 295 | A61 | 8p multicolored | .25 .25 |
| 296 | A61 | 11p multicolored | .25 .25 |
| 297 | A61 | 24p multicolored | .50 .50 |
| 298 | A61 | 26p multicolored | .65 .65 |
| 299 | A61 | 29p multicolored | .85 .85 |
| | | *Nos. 295-299 (5)* | 2.50 2.50 |

Port
Egmont — A62

250th Birth Anniv. of Capt. Philippe de Carteret (1733-97): 18th cent. engravings — 11p, Dolphin, Swallow. 19½p, Discovering Pitcairn Island. 24p, English Cove, New Ireland. 26p, Sinking pirate ship. 29p, Endymion.

| | | | |
|---|---|---|---|
| **1983, Feb. 15** | | **Litho.** | **Perf. 14¼** |
| 300 | A62 | 8p shown | .25 .25 |
| 301 | A62 | 11p multicolored | .30 .25 |
| 302 | A62 | 19½p multicolored | .50 .40 |
| 303 | A62 | 24p multicolored | .55 .50 |
| 304 | A62 | 26p multicolored | .65 .50 |
| 305 | A62 | 29p multicolored | .80 .65 |
| | | *Nos. 300-305 (6)* | 3.05 2.55 |

No. 19 — A63

Royal Mace — A64

| | | | |
|---|---|---|---|
| **1983, Apr. 19** | | | **Litho.** |
| 306 | A63 | 11p shown | .30 .30 |
| 307 | A64 | 11p shown | .30 .30 |
| *a.* | | Pair, #306-307 | 1.00 1.00 |
| 308 | A63 | 19½p No. 20a | .40 .40 |
| 309 | A64 | 19½p Bailiff's seal | .40 .40 |
| *a.* | | Pair, #308-309 | 1.10 1.10 |
| | | *Nos. 306-309 (4)* | 1.40 1.40 |

Europa.

World
Communications
Year — A65

1st Postmaster Charles William LeGeyt (1733-1827): 8p, Commanding Grenadier Co., 25th Foot, Battle of Minden, 1759. 11p, London-Weymouth mail coach. 24p, PO Mail

Packet attacked by French privateer. 26p, Hue St. PO. 29p, St. Helier Harbor.

| | | | |
|---|---|---|---|
| **1983, June 21** | | **Litho.** | **Perf. 14** |
| 310 | A65 | 8p multicolored | .25 .25 |
| 311 | A65 | 11p multicolored | .30 .30 |
| 312 | A65 | 24p multicolored | .55 .55 |
| 313 | A65 | 26p multicolored | .65 .65 |
| 314 | A65 | 29p multicolored | .80 .80 |
| | | *Nos. 310-314 (5)* | 2.55 2.55 |

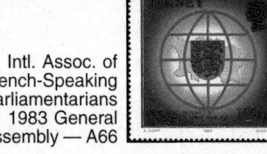

Intl. Assoc. of
French-Speaking
Parliamentarians
1983 General
Assembly — A66

| | | | |
|---|---|---|---|
| **1983, June 21** | | | **Perf. 15** |
| 315 | A66 | 19½p multicolored | .70 .70 |

Cardinal Newman, by
Walter William Ouless
(1848-1933) — A67

11p, M. De Cazotte and his Daughter. 20½p, Thomas Hardy. 31p, David with the Head of Goliath.

| | | | |
|---|---|---|---|
| **1983, Sept. 20** | | **Photo.** | **Perf. 11½** |
| 316 | A67 | 8p shown | .25 .25 |
| 317 | A67 | 11p multicolored | .40 .40 |
| 318 | A67 | 20½p multicolored | .60 .60 |
| | | **Size: 41x34mm** | |
| 319 | A67 | 31p multicolored | .80 .80 |
| | | *Nos. 316-319 (4)* | 2.05 2.05 |

Jersey Wildlife
Preservation
Trust — A68

9p, Golden Lion Tamarin. 12p, Snow Leopard. 20½p, Jamaican Boa. 26p, Round Island Gecko. 28p, Coscoroba Swan. 31p, St. Lucia Parrot.

| | | | |
|---|---|---|---|
| **1984, Jan. 17** | | **Litho.** | **Perf. 14** |
| 320 | A68 | 9p multicolored | .25 .25 |
| 321 | A68 | 12p multicolored | .25 .25 |
| 322 | A68 | 20½p multicolored | .60 .60 |
| 323 | A68 | 26p multicolored | .75 .75 |
| 324 | A68 | 28p multicolored | .80 .80 |
| 325 | A68 | 31p multicolored | 1.00 1.00 |
| | | *Nos. 320-325 (6)* | 3.65 3.65 |

Europa 1984 (25th
Anniv.) — A69

| | | | |
|---|---|---|---|
| **1984, Mar. 12** | | | **Perf. 14½x15** |
| 326 | A69 | 9p multicolored | .30 .30 |
| 327 | A69 | 12p multicolored | .35 .35 |
| 328 | A69 | 20½p multicolored | .55 .55 |
| | | *Nos. 326-328 (3)* | 1.20 1.20 |

**Souvenir Sheet**

Jersey Links with the
Commonwealth — A70

| | | | |
|---|---|---|---|
| **1984, Mar. 12** | | | **Perf. 15x14½** |
| 329 | A70 | 75p multicolored | 2.00 2.00 |

Commonwealth Postal Administrations Conf.

Royal Natl. Lifeboat Institution Centenary — A71

Rescue Scenes (Lifeboats and Ships): No. 330, Sarah Brooshoft, Demie de Pas Light. No. 331, Hearts of Oak, Maurice Georges. No. 332, Elizabeth Rippon, Hanna. No. 333, Elizabeth Rippon, Santa Maria. No. 334, Elizabeth Rippon, Bacchus. No. 335, Thomas James King, Cythara.

**1984, June 1    Litho.     Perf. 14½**

| | | | | |
|---|---|---|---|---|
| 330 | A71 | 9p multicolored | .25 | .25 |
| 331 | A71 | 9p multicolored | .25 | .25 |
| 332 | A71 | 12p multicolored | .35 | .35 |
| 333 | A71 | 12p multicolored | .35 | .35 |
| 334 | A71 | 20½p multicolored | .60 | .60 |
| 335 | A71 | 20½p multicolored | .60 | .60 |
| | | Nos. 330-335 (6) | 2.40 | 2.40 |

40th Anniv. of Intl. Civil Aviation Org. — A72

9p, Bristol Type 170. 12p, Airspeed AS-57 Ambassador 2. 26p, De Havilland Heron 1B, De Havilland DH89A Dragon Rapide, 31p,

**1984, July 24    Litho.     Perf. 14**
**Granite Paper**

| | | | | |
|---|---|---|---|---|
| 336 | A72 | 9p multicolored | .25 | .25 |
| 337 | A72 | 12p multicolored | .35 | .35 |
| 338 | A72 | 26p multicolored | .75 | .75 |
| 339 | A72 | 31p multicolored | 1.00 | 1.00 |
| | | Nos. 336-339 (4) | 2.35 | 2.35 |

Robinson Crusoe, by John Alexander Gilfillan (1793-1864) A73

"Links with Australia" paintings by J.A. Gilfillan: 12p, Edinburgh Castle. 20½p, Maori Village. 26p, Australian Landscape. 28p, Waterhouse's Corner, Adelaide. 31p, Capt. Cook at Botany Bay.

**1984, Sept. 21    Photo.     Perf. 11½**

| | | | | |
|---|---|---|---|---|
| 340 | A73 | 9p shown | .25 | .25 |
| 341 | A73 | 9p multicolored | .30 | .25 |
| 342 | A73 | 20½p multicolored | .60 | .60 |
| 343 | A73 | 26p multicolored | .75 | .75 |
| 344 | A73 | 28p multicolored | .85 | .85 |
| 345 | A73 | 31p multicolored | .85 | .85 |
| | | Nos. 340-345 (6) | 3.60 | 3.55 |

Christmas 1984 — A74

**1984, Nov. 15    Photo.     Perf. 12x11½**

| | | | | |
|---|---|---|---|---|
| 346 | A74 | 9p St. Helier orchid | .30 | .30 |
| 347 | A74 | 12p Mt. Bingham orchid | .60 | .60 |

Ship Paintings by Philip John Ouless (1817-85) A75

**1985, Feb. 26    Photo.     Perf. 14x14½**

| | | | | |
|---|---|---|---|---|
| 348 | A75 | 9p Hebe, 1874 | .25 | .25 |
| 349 | A75 | 12p Gaspe | .30 | .30 |
| 350 | A75 | 22p London, 1856 | .60 | .60 |
| 351 | A75 | 31p Rambler | .90 | .90 |
| 352 | A75 | 34p Elizabeth Castle | 1.10 | 1.10 |
| | | Nos. 348-352 (5) | 3.15 | 3.15 |

Europa 1985 — A76

Performing Arts: 10p, John Ireland, composer (1879-1962). 13p, Ivy St. Helier, actress (1886-1971). 22p, Claude Debussy, composer.

**1985, Apr. 23    Litho.     Perf. 14**

| | | | | |
|---|---|---|---|---|
| 353 | A76 | 10p multicolored | .30 | .30 |
| 354 | A76 | 13p multicolored | .35 | .35 |
| 355 | A76 | 22p multicolored | .65 | .65 |
| | | Nos. 353-355 (3) | 1.30 | 1.30 |

Intl. Youth Year — A77

10p, Girls' Brigade. 13p, Girl Guides. 29p, Jersey Youth Service. 31p, Sea Cadet Corps. 34p, Air Training Corps.

**1985, May 30    Litho.     Perf. 14½**

| | | | | |
|---|---|---|---|---|
| 356 | A77 | 10p multicolored | .35 | .35 |
| 357 | A77 | 13p multicolored | .40 | .40 |
| 358 | A77 | 29p multicolored | .80 | .80 |
| 359 | A77 | 31p multicolored | .90 | .90 |
| 360 | A77 | 34p multicolored | 1.10 | 1.10 |
| | | Nos. 356-360 (5) | 3.55 | 3.55 |

Railway History — A78

10p, Duke of Normandy, Cheapside. 13p, Saddletank, First Tower. 22p, La Moye, Millbrook. 29p, St. Helier's, St. Aubin. 34p, St. Aubyns, Corbiere.

**1985, July 16    Photo.     Perf. 12x11½**

| | | | | |
|---|---|---|---|---|
| 361 | A78 | 10p multicolored | .35 | .35 |
| 362 | A78 | 13p multicolored | .45 | .45 |
| 363 | A78 | 22p multicolored | .80 | .80 |
| 364 | A78 | 29p multicolored | 1.00 | 1.00 |
| 365 | A78 | 34p multicolored | 1.10 | 1.10 |
| | | Nos. 361-365 (5) | 3.70 | 3.70 |

Centenary of Jersey's first train from St. Helier to Corbiere.

Huguenot Heritage — A79

300th anniv. of revocation of the Edict of Nantes (religious tolerance) by King Louis XIV of France: No. 366, James Hemery (1814-1849), Dean of Jersey, Rector of St. Helier, Memorial window, St. Helier Town Church. No. 367, Francis Henry Jeune, Baron St. Helier, law lord and junior counsel in the Tichbourne case, houses of Parliament, Westminster. No. 368, Francois Voisin, merchant, Great Fair, Nijni-Novgorod, Russia. No. 369, Pierre Amiraux, silversmith, silver coffee pot, pitcher. No. 370, George Henry Ingouville, Victoria Cross recipient, Naval Battle of Viborg. No. 371, Robert Brohier, co-founder of Schweppes soft-drink company, glass bottles, carbonated water commercial patent.

**1985, Sept. 10    Litho.     Perf. 14**

| | | | | |
|---|---|---|---|---|
| 366 | A79 | 10p multicolored | .35 | .35 |
| a. | | Booklet pane of 4 | 1.40 | |
| 367 | A79 | 10p multicolored | .35 | .35 |
| a. | | Booklet pane of 4 | 1.40 | |
| 368 | A79 | 13p multicolored | .40 | .40 |
| a. | | Booklet pane of 4 | 1.60 | |
| 369 | A79 | 13p multicolored | .40 | .40 |
| a. | | Booklet pane of 4 | 1.60 | |
| 370 | A79 | 22p multicolored | .60 | .60 |
| a. | | Booklet pane of 4 | 2.50 | |
| 371 | A79 | 22p multicolored | .60 | .60 |
| a. | | Booklet pane of 4 | 2.50 | |
| | | Complete booklet, #366a-371a | 11.00 | |
| | | Nos. 366-371 (6) | 2.70 | 2.70 |

Thomas Benjamin Frederick Davis (1867-1942), Shipping Magnate, Philanthropist A80

Portrait and endowments: 10p, Howard Davis Hall, Victoria College. 13p, Yacht, racing schooner Westward. 31p, Howard Davis Park,

St. Helier. 34p, Howard Davis Agricultural Development Farm, Trinity.

**1985, Oct. 25     Perf. 13½**

| | | | | |
|---|---|---|---|---|
| 372 | A80 | 10p multicolored | .35 | .35 |
| 373 | A80 | 13p multicolored | .40 | .40 |
| 374 | A80 | 31p multicolored | .95 | .95 |
| 375 | A80 | 34p multicolored | 1.10 | 1.10 |
| | | Nos. 372-375 (4) | 2.80 | 2.80 |

50th anniv. of Howard Davis Hall, Victoria College, donated by Davis in memory of his son.

### Arms Type of 1981-82 and

Elizabeth II, 60th Birthday — A80a

16p, Malet. 17p, Mabon. 18p, De St. Martin. 19p, Hamptonne. 26p, De Bagot. 75p, Remon.

**1985-91    Litho.     Perf. 15x14**

| | | | | |
|---|---|---|---|---|
| 381 | A54 | 16p multicolored | .55 | .35 |
| a. | | Booklet pane of 6 ('88) | 3.50 | |
| | | Complete booklet, 2 each #250a, 258a, 381a | 15.00 | |
| 382 | A54 | 17p multicolored | .55 | .45 |
| 383 | A54 | 18p multi ('88) | .80 | .75 |
| 384 | A54 | 19p multi ('88) | .95 | .80 |
| 386 | A54 | 26p multi ('88) | .80 | .65 |
| 388 | A54 | 75p multi ('87) | 2.40 | 1.75 |

**Perf. 11½x12**

| | | | | |
|---|---|---|---|---|
| 389 | A80a | £1 multicolored | 3.50 | 3.25 |

**Photo.**
**Granite Paper**

| | | | | |
|---|---|---|---|---|
| 390 | A80a | £2 multicolored | 6.00 | 4.00 |
| | | Nos. 381-390 (8) | 15.55 | 12.00 |

Issued: 16, 17p, 10/25; £1, 4/21/86; 75p, 4/23/87; 18, 19, 26p, 4/26/88; £2, 3/19/91. No. 381a inscribed "May 1988."

Jersey Lily — A81

Lillie Langtry, by Sir John Millais — A82

**1986, Jan. 28    Litho.     Perf. 15x14½**

| | | | | |
|---|---|---|---|---|
| 391 | A81 | 13p multicolored | .45 | .45 |
| 392 | A82 | 34p multicolored | 1.00 | 1.00 |
| a. | | Souvenir sheet of 5 (4 13p, 34p) | 3.50 | 3.50 |

Intl. Flower Gala, June 10-14.

Halley's Comet Sightings — A83

Comet and coinciding historic events: 10p, Conquest of England, Bayeux Tapestry, A.D. 912 and 1066 sightings. 22p, Lady Carteret signing New Jersey over to William Penn, Edmond Halley observing comet, comets of 1301 & 1682. 31p, Giotto spacecraft and technology developed in 1910, 1986. Caesarea maiden voyage.

**1986, Mar. 4     Perf. 13½x13**

| | | | | |
|---|---|---|---|---|
| 393 | A83 | 10p multicolored | .35 | .35 |
| 394 | A83 | 22p multicolored | .80 | .80 |
| 395 | A83 | 31p multicolored | 1.00 | 1.00 |
| | | Nos. 393-395 (3) | 2.15 | 2.15 |

Europa 1986 — A84

**1986, Apr. 21     Perf. 14½**

| | | | | |
|---|---|---|---|---|
| 396 | A84 | 10p Dwarf pansy | .30 | .30 |
| 397 | A84 | 14p Sea stock | .40 | .40 |
| 398 | A84 | 22p Sand crocus | .65 | .65 |
| | | Nos. 396-398 (3) | 1.35 | 1.35 |

Environmental conservation.

Jersey Natl. Trust, 50th Anniv. — A85

10p, Le Rat cottage. 14p, The Elms, headquarters. 22p, Morel Farm entrance. 29p, Quetivel Mill. 31p, La Vallette.

**1986, June 17    Litho.     Perf. 13½x13**

| | | | | |
|---|---|---|---|---|
| 399 | A85 | 10p multicolored | .25 | .25 |
| 400 | A85 | 14p multicolored | .35 | .35 |
| 401 | A85 | 22p multicolored | .60 | .60 |
| 402 | A85 | 29p multicolored | .75 | .75 |
| 403 | A85 | 31p multicolored | .85 | .85 |
| | | Nos. 399-403 (5) | 2.80 | 2.80 |

Wedding of Prince Andrew and Sarah Ferguson — A86

**1986, July 23     Perf. 13½**

| | | | | |
|---|---|---|---|---|
| 404 | A86 | 14p multicolored | .40 | .40 |
| 405 | A86 | 40p multicolored | 1.20 | 1.20 |

Paintings by Edmund Blampied (1886-1966), Artist — A87

10p, Gathering Vraic. 14p, Driving Home in the Rain. 29p, The Miller. 31p, The Joy Ride. 34p, Tante Elizabeth.

**1986, Aug. 28    Litho.     Perf. 14**

| | | | | |
|---|---|---|---|---|
| 406 | A87 | 10p multicolored | .25 | .25 |
| 407 | A87 | 14p multicolored | .40 | .40 |
| 408 | A87 | 29p multicolored | .75 | .75 |
| 409 | A87 | 31p multicolored | .90 | .90 |
| 410 | A87 | 34p multicolored | 1.00 | 1.00 |
| | | Nos. 406-410 (5) | 3.30 | 3.30 |

Christmas, Intl. Peace Year — A88

**1986, Nov. 4     Perf. 14½**

| | | | | |
|---|---|---|---|---|
| 411 | A88 | 10p Dove, map, flower | .30 | .25 |
| 412 | A88 | 14p Lovebirds | .50 | .40 |
| 413 | A88 | 34p Dove, noise-maker | 1.10 | .90 |
| | | Nos. 411-413 (3) | 1.90 | 1.55 |

Racing Schooner Westward — A89

10p, Under full sail. 14p, T.B. Davis, owner. 31p, Overhauling Britannia. 34p, Dry dock, St. Helier.

**1987, Jan. 15    Litho.     Perf. 13½**

| | | | | |
|---|---|---|---|---|
| 414 | A89 | 10p multicolored | .35 | .35 |
| 415 | A89 | 14p multicolored | .45 | .45 |
| 416 | A89 | 31p multicolored | .95 | .95 |
| 417 | A89 | 34p multicolored | 1.05 | 1.05 |
| | | Nos. 414-417 (4) | 2.80 | 2.80 |

Jersey Airport, 50th Anniv. — A90

10p, DH86 Belcroute Bay. 14p, Boeing 757, Douglas DC-9. 22p, Britten Norman Trislander, Islander. 29p, Short SD330, Vickers Viscount. 31p, BAC1-11, HPR.7 Dart Herald.

**1987, Mar. 3    Litho.    Perf. 14**
| | | | |
|---|---|---|---|
| 418 | A90 | 10p multicolored | .30 .30 |
| 419 | A90 | 14p multicolored | .45 .45 |
| 420 | A90 | 22p multicolored | .55 .55 |
| 421 | A90 | 29p multicolored | .90 .90 |
| 422 | A90 | 31p multicolored | 1.00 1.00 |
| | | Nos. 418-422 (5) | 3.20 3.20 |

Europa 1987 — A91

Modern architecture: 11p, St. Mary and St. Peter's Church. 15p, Villa Devereux. 22p, Fort Regent, St. Helier.

**1987, Apr. 23    Perf. 15x14**
| | | | |
|---|---|---|---|
| 423 | A91 | 11p multicolored | .35 .35 |
| 424 | A91 | 15p multicolored | .45 .45 |

**Size: 61x31mm**
| | | | |
|---|---|---|---|
| 425 | A91 | 22p multicolored | .60 .60 |
| | | Nos. 423-425 (3) | 1.40 1.40 |

Adm. Philippe D'Auvergne (1754-1816) A92

Ships: 11p, Racehorse trapped in the Arctic. 15p, Alarm burned at Rhode Island. 29p, Arethusa wrecked off Ushant, France. 31p, Rattlesnake stranded on Trinidad. 34p, Mont Orgueil Castle.

**1987, July 9    Perf. 14**
| | | | |
|---|---|---|---|
| 426 | A92 | 11p multicolored | .35 .35 |
| 427 | A92 | 15p multicolored | .45 .45 |
| 428 | A92 | 29p multicolored | .75 .75 |
| 429 | A92 | 31p multicolored | .90 .90 |
| 430 | A92 | 34p multicolored | .95 .95 |
| | | Nos. 426-430 (5) | 3.40 3.40 |

William the Conqueror (c. 1028-87), King of England (1066-87) A93

Designs in the style of the Bayeux Tapestry: 11p, King Charles negotiating peace with the Vikings, 911, and cession of Jersey to Rollo's son William, 933. 15p, Duke Robert I and King Edward ashore Jersey after storm, 1030; Edward's succession to the throne of England, 1042. 22p, William the Conqueror's coronation, 1066, and succession of William II, 1087. 29p, Death of King William Rufus, and Henry defeating Duke Robert to unite England and Normandy, 1106. 31p, Death of Henry, battle for the throne and succession of King Stephen, 1135. 34p, Successions of Henry II, 1154, and John Lackland, 1189.

**1987    Perf. 13½**
| | | | |
|---|---|---|---|
| 431 | A93 | 11p multicolored | .35 .35 |
| a. | | Booklet pane of 4 + label | .95 |
| 432 | A93 | 15p multicolored | .40 .40 |
| a. | | Booklet pane of 4 + label | 1.10 |
| 433 | A93 | 22p multicolored | .80 .65 |
| a. | | Booklet pane of 4 + label | 2.25 |
| 434 | A93 | 29p multicolored | .85 .85 |
| a. | | Booklet pane of 4 + label | 2.40 |
| 435 | A93 | 31p multicolored | .95 .95 |
| a. | | Booklet pane of 4 + label | 2.75 |
| 436 | A93 | 34p multicolored | 1.10 1.10 |
| a. | | Booklet pane of 4 + label | 3.00 |
| | | Complete booklet, #431a-436a | 15.00 |
| | | Nos. 431-436 (6) | 4.45 4.30 |

Paintings by John Le Capelain (1812-1848) A94

11p, Grosnez Castle. 15p, St. Aubin's Bay. 22p, Mt. Orgueil Castle. 31p, Town Fort and Harbor, St. Helier. 34p, The Hermitage.

**1987, Nov. 3    Photo.    Perf. 12x11½**
| | | | |
|---|---|---|---|
| 437 | A94 | 11p multicolored | .35 .35 |
| 438 | A94 | 15p multicolored | .50 .50 |
| 439 | A94 | 22p multicolored | .65 .65 |
| 440 | A94 | 31p multicolored | .85 .85 |
| 441 | A94 | 34p multicolored | 1.00 1.00 |
| | | Nos. 437-441 (5) | 3.35 3.35 |

Christmas.

Hybrids, Eric Young Orchid Foundation, Trinity — A95

11p, Cymbidium pontac. 15p, Odontioda Eric Young, vert. 29p, Lycaste auburn Seaford and Ditchling. 31p, Odontoglossum St. Brelade, vert. 34p, Cymbidium mavourneen Jester.

**1988, Jan. 12    Litho.    Perf. 14**
| | | | |
|---|---|---|---|
| 442 | A95 | 11p multicolored | .45 .45 |
| 443 | A95 | 15p multicolored | .55 .55 |
| 444 | A95 | 29p multicolored | .95 .95 |
| 445 | A95 | 31p multicolored | 1.00 1.00 |
| 446 | A95 | 34p multicolored | 1.20 1.20 |
| | | Nos. 442-446 (5) | 4.15 4.15 |

Jersey Dog Club, Cent. — A96

11p, Labrador retriever. 15p, Wire-haired dachshund. 22p, Pekingese. 31p, Cavalier King Charles spaniel. 34p, Dalmatian.

**1988, Mar. 2**
| | | | |
|---|---|---|---|
| 447 | A96 | 11p multicolored | .40 .40 |
| 448 | A96 | 15p multicolored | .50 .50 |
| 449 | A96 | 22p multicolored | .75 .75 |
| 450 | A96 | 31p multicolored | 1.00 1.00 |
| 451 | A96 | 34p multicolored | 1.10 1.10 |
| | | Nos. 447-451 (5) | 3.75 3.75 |

Europa 1988 — A97

Nos. 453 and 455 vert.

**Perf. 14x13½, 13½x14**
**1988, Apr. 26    Litho.**
| | | | |
|---|---|---|---|
| 452 | A97 | 16p De Havilland DHC 7 | .35 .35 |
| 453 | A97 | 16p Weather radar and unstrument landing system | .35 .35 |
| 454 | A97 | 22p Hydrofoil | .65 .65 |
| 455 | A97 | 22p Port control tower | .65 .65 |
| | | Nos. 452-455 (4) | 2.00 2.00 |

Wildlife Preservation Trust, 25th Anniv. — A98

12p, Rodrigues fody, vert. 16p, Volcano rabbit. 29p, White-faced marmoset, vert. 31p, Ploughshare tortoise. 34p, Mauritius kestrel, vert.

**1988, July 6    Litho.**
| | | | |
|---|---|---|---|
| 456 | A98 | 12p multicolored | .40 .40 |
| 457 | A98 | 16p multicolored | .50 .50 |
| 458 | A98 | 29p multicolored | .95 .95 |
| 459 | A98 | 31p multicolored | .95 .95 |
| 460 | A98 | 34p multicolored | 1.05 1.05 |
| | | Nos. 456-460 (5) | 3.85 3.85 |

Operation Raleigh — A99

Activities: 12p, Rain Forest Leaf Frog, Costa Rica. 16p, Archaeological Survey, Peru. 22p,

Glacier Climbing, Chile. 29p, Medical Assistance, Solomon Isls. 31p, Underwater Exploration, Australia. 34p, Zebu returns to St. Helier, Jersey.

**1988, Sept. 27    Photo.    Perf. 12**
| | | | |
|---|---|---|---|
| 461 | A99 | 12p multicolored | .45 .45 |
| 462 | A99 | 16p multicolored | .50 .50 |
| 463 | A99 | 22p multicolored | .75 .75 |
| 464 | A99 | 29p multicolored | .90 .90 |
| 465 | A99 | 31p multicolored | .95 .95 |
| 466 | A99 | 34p multicolored | 1.20 1.20 |
| | | Nos. 461-466 (6) | 4.75 4.75 |

Operation Raleigh: voyage of the Zebu, on which youths were trained with the aim of removativing them and helping them to earn new self-respect.
WHO 40th anniv. (29p).

Parish Churches — A100

**1988, Nov. 15    Litho.    Perf. 14**
| | | | |
|---|---|---|---|
| 467 | A100 | 12p St. Clement | .45 .45 |
| 468 | A100 | 16p St. Ouen | .55 .55 |
| 469 | A100 | 31p St. Brelade | 1.00 1.00 |
| 470 | A100 | 34p St. Lawrence | 1.10 1.10 |
| | | Nos. 467-470 (4) | 3.10 3.10 |

Christmas. See Nos. 549-552, 610-613.

Classic Cars — A101

Designs: 12p, 1912 Talbot Tourer, seaweed harvest at Le Hocq. 16p, 1920 De Dion Bouton, Grosnez Castle ruins. 23p, 1926 Austin Chummy, brick kiln at Mont a l'Abbe. 30p, 1926 Ford Model T, harvest of the Jersey royal potato crop. 32p, 1930 Bentley 8-Litre, Guard House and Gate at Government House. 35p, 1931 Cadillac V16 Fleetwood Sports Phaeton, St. Ouen's Manor.

**1989, Jan. 31**
| | | | |
|---|---|---|---|
| 471 | A101 | 12p multicolored | .45 .45 |
| 472 | A101 | 16p multicolored | .55 .45 |
| 473 | A101 | 23p multicolored | .70 .55 |
| 474 | A101 | 30p multicolored | 1.00 .80 |
| 475 | A101 | 32p multicolored | 1.00 1.00 |
| 476 | A101 | 35p multicolored | 1.10 1.10 |
| | | Nos. 471-476 (6) | 4.80 4.35 |

See Nos. 604-609, 903-908.

Scenic Views A102

Coronation of Queen Elizabeth II, 40th Anniv. A102a

Royal Arms — A102b

1p, Belcroute Bay. 2p, High St., St. Aubin. 4p, Royal Jersey Golf Course. 5p, Portelet Bay. 10p, Les Charrieres D'Anneport. 13p, St. Helier Marina. 14p, St. Ouen's Bay. 15p, Rozel Harbor. 16p, St. Aubin's Harbor. 17p, Jersey Airport. 18p, Corbiere Lighthouse. 19p, Val de la Mare. 20p, Elizabeth Castle. 21p, Greve de Lecq. 22p, Samares Manor. 23p, Bonne Nuit Harbor. 24p, Grosnez Castle. 25p, Augres Manor. 26p, Central Market. 27p, St. Brelade's Bay. 30p, St. Ouen's Manor. 40p, La Hougue Bie. 50p, Mont Orgueil Castle. 75p, Royal Square.

| | | | |
|---|---|---|---|
| 477 | A102 | 1p multicolored | .25 .25 |
| 478 | A102 | 2p multicolored | .25 .25 |
| 480 | A102 | 4p multicolored | .25 .25 |
| a. | | Booklet pane of 6 | .80 |
| 481 | A102 | 5p multicolored | .25 .25 |
| a. | | Booklet pane of 6 | 1.40 |
| 485 | A102 | 10p multicolored | .35 .35 |
| 486 | A102 | 13p multicolored | .45 .45 |
| 487 | A102 | 14p multicolored | .45 .45 |
| a. | | Booklet pane of 6 | 3.00 3.00 |
| b. | | Booklet pane of 8 | 3.75 3.75 |
| | | Complete booklet, #487b ('92) | 3.75 |
| 488 | A102 | 15p multicolored | .50 .50 |
| a. | | Booklet pane of 6 | 3.25 3.25 |
| 489 | A102 | 16p multicolored | .55 .55 |
| a. | | Booklet pane of 8 | 5.00 5.00 |
| | | Complete booklet, #489a ('92) | 5.00 |
| 490 | A102 | 17p multicolored | .55 .55 |
| 491 | A102 | 18p multicolored | .60 .60 |
| a. | | Booklet pane of 6 | 4.25 4.25 |
| | | Complete booklet, 2 each #480a, 487a, 491a ('90) | 17.50 |
| 492 | A102 | 19p multicolored | .60 .60 |
| 493 | A102 | 20p multicolored | .50 .50 |
| a. | | Booklet pane of 6 | 3.25 3.25 |
| | | Complete booklet, 2 each #481a, 488a, 493a ('91) | 20.00 |
| 494 | A102 | 21p multicolored | .55 .55 |
| 495 | A102 | 22p multicolored | .50 .50 |
| a. | | Booklet pane of 8 | 4.50 4.50 |
| | | Complete booklet, #495a ('92) | 4.50 |
| 496 | A102 | 23p multicolored | .85 .85 |
| 497 | A102 | 24p multicolored | .70 .70 |
| 498 | A102 | 25p multicolored | .80 .80 |
| 499 | A102 | 26p multicolored | .90 .90 |
| 500 | A102 | 27p multicolored | .90 .90 |
| 501 | A102 | 30p multicolored | 1.00 1.00 |
| 502 | A102 | 40p multicolored | 1.20 1.20 |
| 503 | A102 | 50p multicolored | 1.60 1.60 |
| 504 | A102 | 75p multicolored | 2.50 2.50 |

**Perf. 14½**
| | | | |
|---|---|---|---|
| 505 | A102a | £1 multicolored | 4.50 4.50 |

**Perf. 15x14**
| | | | |
|---|---|---|---|
| 506 | A102b | £4 multicolored | 8.50 8.50 |
| | | Nos. 477-506 (26) | 30.05 30.05 |

Pane Nos. 480a, 487a and 491a issued for Stamp World London '90 and are inscribed "May 1990."
Issued: 1p-20p, 3/21/89; 21p-27p, 1/16/90; 30p-75p, 3/13/90; Nos. 481a, 488a, 493a, 2/12/91; £1, 6/2/93; £4, 1/2/95. Nos. 487b, 489a, 495a were released on May 22, but were not readily available until September 1992. Other booklet panes, 1990.

World Wildlife Fund — A103

No. 507, Large checkered skipper. No. 508, Agile frog, horiz. No. 509, Green lizard, horiz. No. 510, Barn owl.

**1989, Apr. 25    Litho.    Perf. 13x13¼**
| | | | |
|---|---|---|---|
| 507 | A103 | 13p multicolored | 1.10 1.10 |

**Perf. 13¼x13**
| | | | |
|---|---|---|---|
| 508 | A103 | 13p multicolored | 1.10 1.10 |
| 509 | A103 | 17p multicolored | 1.10 1.10 |

**Perf. 13½x13¾**
| | | | |
|---|---|---|---|
| 510 | A103 | 17p multicolored | 1.10 1.10 |
| | | Nos. 507-510 (4) | 4.40 4.40 |

Europa 1989 — A104

Children's games — No. 511, Playpen. No. 512, Playground. No. 513, Magician, games. No. 514, Cricket, rugby, tennis.

**1989, Apr. 25    Perf. 14**
| | | | |
|---|---|---|---|
| 511 | A104 | 17p multicolored | .55 .55 |
| 512 | A104 | 17p multicolored | .55 .55 |
| 513 | A104 | 23p multicolored | .80 .80 |
| 514 | A104 | 23p multicolored | .80 .80 |
| | | Nos. 511-514 (4) | 2.70 2.70 |

Visit of Queen Elizabeth II — A105

£1, Ferry Terminal, St. Helier.

**1989, May 24    Litho.    Perf. 14½**
515  A105  £1 multicolored                         2.75  2.75

French
Revolution,
Bicent. — A106

Designs: 13p, D'Auvergne meets Louis XVI, 1786. 17p, Storming the Bastille, 1789. 23p, Marie de Bouillon at the Chateau de Navarre, 1790. 30p, Mission from Mont Orgueil, 1795. 32p, Support for the Chouans, 1796. 35p, The last Chouannerie, 1799.

**1989, July 7                    Perf. 13½**
516  A106  13p multicolored              .40    .30
    a.    Booklet pane of 4            1.20
517  A106  17p multicolored              .50    .40
    a.    Booklet pane of 4            1.50
518  A106  23p multicolored              .60    .50
    a.    Booklet pane of 4            1.90
519  A106  30p multicolored              .95    .95
    a.    Booklet pane of 4            3.00
520  A106  32p multicolored             1.00   1.00
    a.    Booklet pane of 4            3.00
521  A106  35p multicolored             1.25   1.25
    a.    Booklet pane of 4            3.75
          Complete booklet, #516a-521a   15.00
          Nos. 516-521 (6)             4.70   4.40

Great Western Railway Steamer
Service Between Weymouth and the
Channel Isls., Cent. — A107

Steamers: 13p, St. Helier, 1925. 17p, Caesarea II, 1910. 27p, Reindeer, 1897. 32p, Ibex & Frederica, 1891. 35p, Lynx, 1889.

**1989, Sept. 5    Litho.    Perf. 13½x14**
522  A107  13p multicolored              .40    .30
523  A107  17p multicolored              .35    .35
524  A107  27p multicolored              .80    .80
525  A107  32p multicolored             1.00   1.00
526  A107  35p multicolored             1.20   1.20
          Nos. 522-526 (5)             3.75   3.65

Paintings by
Sarah Louisa
Kilpack (1839-
1909)
A108

**1989, Oct. 24    Litho.    Perf. 13x12½**
527  A108  13p Gorey Harbour            .30    .30
528  A108  17p La Corbiere              .35    .35
529  A108  23p Greve de Lecq            .80    .80
530  A108  32p Bouley Bay              1.00   1.00
531  A108  35p Mont Orgueil            1.10   1.10
          Nos. 527-531 (5)             3.55   3.55

Europa
1990 — A109

Post offices — No. 532, Broad Street, 1969, vert. No. 533, Mont Millais, 1990, vert. No. 534, Hue Street, 1815. No. 535, Halkett Place, 1890.

**Perf. 13½x14, 14x13½**
**1990, Mar. 13                   Litho.**
532  A109  18p multicolored              .55    .55
533  A109  18p multicolored              .55    .55
534  A109  24p multicolored              .65    .65
535  A109  24p multicolored              .65    .65
          Nos. 532-535 (4)             2.40   2.40

Festival of
Tourism — A110

**1990, May 3    Litho.    Perf. 14x13½**
536  A110  18p Battle of Flowers        .65    .65
537  A110  24p Recreation               .80    .80
538  A110  29p History                  .95    .95
539  A110  32p Salon Culinaire         1.00   1.00
    a.    Souvenir sheet of 4, #536-539  3.50  3.50
          Nos. 536-539 (4)             3.40   3.40

News Media
A111

14p, Print (newspapers), 1784-1889. 18p, The Evening Post, 1890. 34p, BBC Radio Jersey, 1982. 37p, Channel Television, 1962.

**1990, June 26    Litho.    Perf. 13½**
540  A111  14p multicolored              .50    .50
541  A111  18p multicolored              .50    .50
542  A111  34p multicolored             1.00   1.00
543  A111  37p multicolored             1.10   1.10
          Nos. 540-543 (4)             3.10   3.10

UNESCO World Literacy Year.

Battle of Britain,
50th
Anniv. — A112

**1990, Sept. 4                    Perf. 14**
544  A112  14p Hawk                     .40    .40
545  A112  18p Spitfire                 .55    .55
546  A112  24p Hurricane                .85    .85
547  A112  34p Wellington              1.35   1.35
548  A112  37p Lancaster               1.40   1.40
          Nos. 544-548 (5)             4.55   4.55

**Parish Churches Type of 1988**
**1990, Nov. 13    Litho.    Perf. 13½x14**
549  A100  14p St. Helier              .45    .45
550  A100  18p Grouville               .45    .45
551  A100  34p St. Saviour            1.05   1.05
552  A100  37p St. John              1.30   1.30
          Nos. 549-552 (4)             3.25   3.25

Christmas.

Prince's Tower, La
Hougue Bie,
1801 — A113

Philippe d'Auvergne: 20p, Arrested in Paris, 1802. 26p, Plotting against Napoleon, 1803. 31p, Execution of Cadoudal, 1804. 37p, H.M. Cutter Surly, 1809. 44p, Prince de Bouillon, 1816.

**1991, Jan. 22    Litho.    Perf. 13½**
553  A113  15p multicolored              .50    .40
554  A113  20p multicolored              .60    .60
555  A113  26p multicolored              .80    .80
556  A113  31p multicolored             1.00   1.00
557  A113  37p multicolored             1.25   1.25
558  A113  44p multicolored             1.40   1.40
          Nos. 553-558 (6)             5.55   5.45

A114

Europa (Satellites and their functions): No. 559, ERS-1, oceanography. No. 560, Landsat, Earth resources. No. 561, Meteosat, meteorology. No. 562, Olympus, communications.

**1991, Mar. 19    Litho.    Perf. 14½x13**
559  A114  20p multicolored              .60    .60
560  A114  20p multicolored              .60    .60
561  A114  26p multicolored              .80    .80
562  A114  26p multicolored              .80    .80
          Nos. 559-562 (4)             2.80   2.80

A115

15p, German Occupation Stamps for Jersey, 50th anniv. 20p, Eastern Railway extension to Gorey Pier, 100th anniv. 26p, Jersey Herd Book, 125th anniv. 31p, Victoria Harbor, 150th anniv. 53p, Hospital bequest of Marie Bartlett, 250th anniv.

**1991, May 16    Litho.    Perf. 13½**
563  A115  15p multicolored              .35    .35
564  A115  20p multicolored              .60    .60
565  A115  26p multicolored              .75    .75
566  A115  31p multicolored              .90    .90
567  A115  53p multicolored             1.50   1.50
          Nos. 563-567 (5)             4.10   4.10

Butterflies &
Moths — A116

15p, Glanville fritillary. 20p, Jersey tiger. 37p, Small elephant hawk-moth. 57p, Peacock.

**1991, July 9    Litho.    Perf. 13x12½**
568  A116  15p multicolored              .40    .40
569  A116  20p multicolored              .50    .50
570  A116  37p multicolored             1.50   1.50
571  A116  57p multicolored             1.75   1.75
          Nos. 568-571 (4)             4.15   4.15

See Nos. 727-731.

Overseas
Aid — A117

Designs: 15p, Water drilling rig, Ethiopia. 20p, Construction work, Rwanda. 26p, Technical school, Kenya. 31p, Leprosy and eye care, Tanzania. 37p, Agriculture and cultivation aid, Zambia. 44p, Health care and immunization, Lesotho.

**1991, Sept. 3    Litho.    Perf. 13½**
572  A117  15p multicolored              .50    .50
573  A117  20p multicolored              .55    .55
574  A117  26p multicolored              .75    .75
575  A117  31p multicolored              .90    .90
576  A117  37p multicolored             1.10   1.10
577  A117  44p multicolored             1.25   1.25
          Nos. 572-577 (6)             5.05   5.05

Christmas — A118

Illustrations by Edmund Blampied from Peter Pan: 15p, This is the place for me. 20p, The Island Come True. 37p, The Never Bird. 53p, The Great White Father.

**1991, Nov. 5    Litho.    Perf. 14**
578  A118  15p multicolored              .40    .40
579  A118  20p multicolored              .70    .70
580  A118  37p multicolored             1.20   1.20
581  A118  53p multicolored             1.60   1.60
          Nos. 578-581 (4)             3.90   3.90

Winter Birds — A119

**1992, Jan. 7    Litho.    Perf. 13½x14**
582  A119  16p Pied wagtail            .55    .55
583  A119  22p Firecrest               .75    .75
584  A119  28p Snipe                   .95    .95

585  A119  39p Lapwing               1.40   1.40
586  A119  57p Fieldfare             2.00   2.00
          Nos. 582-586 (5)             5.65   5.65

Shanghai Harbor,
1860 — A120

William Mesny, 150th birth anniv: No. 588, Running the Taiping blockade, 1862. No. 589, General Mesny, River Gate, 1874. No. 590, Mesny accompanying Gill to Burma, 1877. No. 591, Mesny advises Governor Chang, 1882. No. 592, Mesny, Mandarin First Class, 1886.

**1992, Feb. 25    Litho.    Perf. 13½**
587  A120  16p multicolored              .45    .45
588  A120  16p multicolored              .45    .45
589  A120  22p multicolored              .70    .70
590  A120  22p multicolored              .70    .70
591  A120  33p multicolored              .95    .95
592  A120  33p multicolored              .95    .95
          Nos. 587-592 (6)             4.20   4.20

587a  Booklet pane of 4               .95    .95
588a  Booklet pane of 4               .95    .95
589a  Booklet pane of 4              1.55   1.55
590a  Booklet pane of 4              1.55   1.55
591a  Booklet pane of 4              2.15   2.15
592a  Booklet pane of 4              2.15   2.15
      Complete booklet, #587a-592a   11.00

Discovery of
America, 500th
Anniv. — A121

Columbus, ship and: 22p, John Bertram (1796-1882). 28p, Sir George Carteret (1610-1680). 39p, Sir Walter Raleigh (1554-1618).

**1992, Apr. 14    Litho.    Perf. 14½**
593  A121  22p multicolored              .70    .70
594  A121  28p multicolored              .75    .75
595  A121  39p multicolored             1.20   1.20
          Nos. 593-595 (3)             2.65   2.65

Europa.

Jersey-Built
Sailing
Ships — A122

**1992, Apr. 14    Litho.    Perf. 14**
596  A122  16p Tickler                  .55    .55
597  A122  22p Hebe                     .85    .85
598  A122  50p Gemini                  1.60   1.60
599  A122  57p Percy Douglas           1.90   1.90
    a.    Souvenir sheet of 4, #596-599  4.50  4.50
          Nos. 596-599 (4)             4.90   4.90

Batik — A123

16p, Snow leopards. 22p, Three elements. 39p, Three men in a tub. 57p, Cockatoos.

**1992, June 23    Litho.    Perf. 14½**
600  A123  16p multicolored              .50    .50
601  A123  22p multicolored              .70    .70
602  A123  39p multicolored             1.25   1.25
603  A123  57p multicolored             1.60   1.60
          Nos. 600-603 (4)             4.05   4.05

**Classic Car Type of 1989**
Designs: 16p, 1925 Morris Cowley "Bullnose." 22p, 1932 Rolls Royce 20/25. 28p, 1924 Chenard & Walcker T5. 33p, 1932 Packard 900 Series Light Eight. 39p, 1927 Lanchester 21. 50p, 1913 Buick 30 Roadster.

**1992, Sept. 8    Litho.    Perf. 13x12½**
604  A101  16p multicolored              .30    .30
605  A101  22p multicolored              .50    .50
606  A101  28p multicolored              .80    .80
607  A101  33p multicolored             1.00   1.00
608  A101  39p multicolored             1.15   1.15
609  A101  50p multicolored             1.50   1.50
          Nos. 604-609 (6)             5.25   5.25

## Parish Church Type of 1988

**1992, Nov. 3    Litho.    Perf. 13½x14**
610 A100 16p Trinity .45 .45
611 A100 22p St. Mary .60 .60
612 A100 39p St. Martin 1.10 1.10
613 A100 57p St. Peter 1.50 1.50
    Nos. 610-613 (4) 3.65 3.65
    Christmas.

Non-Value Indicator
Stamps — A124

Scenic views: No. 614, Building with arches. No. 615, Cemetery. Trinity Church. No. 616, Daffodils, cattle. No. 617, Cattle in pasture.
Beach scenes: No. 618, People lying on beach with umbrella. No. 619, Man with windsurfer. No. 620, Crab facing right. No. 621, Crab, facing left.
Parade floats: No. 622, Smiling face, rainbow. No. 623, Dragon head, Oriental theme. No. 624, Umbrellas, Asian theme. No. 625, Elephant's tusks, African theme.

**1993, Jan. 11    Litho.    Perf. 13½**
614 A124 (17p) Bailiwick .55 .55
615 A124 (17p) Bailiwick .55 .55
616 A124 (17p) Bailiwick .55 .55
617 A124 (17p) Bailiwick .55 .55
    a. Block of 4, #614-617 2.25 2.25
    b. Booklet pane of 8, 2 each
        #614-617 4.50
        Complete booklet, #617b 5.00
618 A124 (23p) UK .70 .70
619 A124 (23p) UK .70 .70
620 A124 (23p) UK .70 .70
621 A124 (23p) UK .70 .70
    a. Block of 4, #618-621 3.00 3.00
    b. Booklet pane of 8, 2 each
        #618-621 6.00
        Complete booklet, #621b 6.75
622 A124 (28p) European .85 .85
623 A124 (28p) European .85 .85
624 A124 (28p) European .85 .85
625 A124 (28p) European .85 .85
    a. Block of 4, #622-625 3.25 3.25
    b. Booklet pane of 8, 2 each
        #622-625 7.00 7.00
        Complete booklet, #625b 7.75
    Nos. 614-625 (12) 8.40 8.40

The minimum postage rate is represented for each area where mail is delivered.

Orchids — A125

17p, Phragmipedium Eric Young "Jersey." 23p, Odontoglossum Augres "Trinity." 28p, Miltonia Saint Helier "Colomberie." 39p, Phragmipedium pearcei. 57p, Calanthe Grouville "Gorey."

**1993, Jan. 26    Litho.    Perf. 14½x13**
626 A125 17p multicolored .50 .50
627 A125 23p multicolored .70 .70
628 A125 28p multicolored .85 .85
629 A125 39p multicolored 1.25 1.25
630 A125 57p multicolored 1.75 1.75
    Nos. 626-630 (5) 5.05 5.05

Europa — A126

Contemporary Art: 23p, Jersey Opera House, by Ian Rolls. 28p, The Ham and Tomato Bap, by Jonathan Hubbard. 39p, Vase of Flowers, by Neil MacKenzie.

**1993, Apr. 1    Litho.    Perf. 13½x14**
631 A126 23p multicolored .65 .65
632 A126 28p multicolored .75 .75
633 A126 39p multicolored 1.25 1.25
    Nos. 631-633 (3) 2.65 2.65

Royal Air Force,
75th
Anniv. — A127

Designs: 17p, Douglas Dakota. 23p, Wight Seaplane. 28p, Avro Shakleton AEW2. 33p, Gloster Meteor, DeHavilland Vampire. 39p, BAe Harrier GR1A. 57p, Panavia Tornado F3.

**1993, Apr. 1    Perf. 14**
634 A127 17p multicolored .50 .50
635 A127 23p multicolored .60 .60
636 A127 28p multicolored .75 .75
637 A127 33p multicolored .80 .80
638 A127 39p multicolored 1.05 1.05
639 A127 57p multicolored 1.65 1.65
    a. Souvenir sheet of 2, #635, 639 5.50 5.50
    Nos. 634-639 (6) 5.35 5.35

Stamps from No. 639a do not have white border.

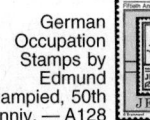

German
Occupation
Stamps by
Edmund
Blampied, 50th
Anniv. — A128

**1993, June 2    Litho.    Perf. 13½**
640 A128 17p No. N3 .40 .40
641 A128 23p No. N4 .60 .60
642 A128 28p No. N5 .80 .80
643 A128 33p No. N6 1.00 1.00
644 A128 39p No. N7 1.40 1.40
645 A128 50p No. N8 1.60 1.60
    Nos. 640-645 (6) 5.80 5.80

Birds — A129

17p, Short-toed treecreeper. 23p, Dartford warbler. 28p, Wheatear. 39p, Cirl bunting. 57p, Jay.

**1993, Sept. 7    Litho.    Perf. 13½x14**
646 A129 17p multicolored .50 .50
647 A129 23p multicolored .75 .75
648 A129 28p multicolored .90 .90
649 A129 39p multicolored 1.25 1.25
650 A129 57p multicolored 2.00 2.00
    Nos. 646-650 (5) 5.40 5.40

Christmas — A130

Stained glass windows by Henry Bosdet, from St. Aubin on the Hill.

**1993, Nov. 2    Litho.    Perf. 14½x13**
651 A130 17p multicolored .50 .50
652 A130 23p multicolored .75 .75
653 A130 39p multicolored 1.25 1.25
654 A130 57p multicolored 2.00 2.00
    Nos. 651-654 (4) 4.50 4.50

Mushrooms — A131

**1994, Jan. 11    Litho.    Perf. 14½**
655 A131 18p Shaggy ink cap .45 .45
656 A131 23p Fly agaric .60 .60
657 A131 30p Chanterelle .80 .80
658 A131 41p Parasol mushroom 1.15 1.15
659 A131 60p Latticed stinkhorn 1.55 1.55
    Nos. 655-659 (5) 4.55 4.55

Souvenir Sheet

New
Year
1994
(Year of
the Dog)
A132

**1994, Feb. 18    Litho.    Perf. 15x14½**
660 A132 £1 multicolored 2.75 2.75
    Hong Kong '94.

Cats — A133

18p, Maine coon, vert. 23p, British shorthair. 35p, Persian, vert. 41p, Siamese. 60p, Non-pedigree, vert.

**1994, Apr. 5    Litho.    Perf. 13½**
661 A133 18p multicolored .50 .50
662 A133 23p multicolored .75 .75
663 A133 35p multicolored .95 .95
664 A133 41p multicolored 1.40 1.40
665 A133 60p multicolored 1.40 1.40
    Nos. 661-665 (5) 5.00 5.00

Jersey Cat Club, 21st anniv., and 4th Championship Show.

Europa — A134

Designs: No. 666, Mammoths on cliff, c. 250,000 B.C. No. 667, Paleolithic hunters dragging mammoth by tusks. No. 668, Neolithic dolmen, "La Hougue Bie," c. 4,000 B.C. No. 669, Exterior of "La Hougue Bie," during construction.

**1994, Apr. 5    Litho.    Perf. 13½x14**
666 23p multicolored .60 .60
667 23p multicolored .60 .60
    a. A134 Pair, #666-667 1.20 1.20
668 30p multicolored .90 .90
669 30p multicolored .90 .90
    a. A134 Pair, #668-669 1.80 1.80
    Nos. 666-669 (4) 3.00 3.00

D-Day, 50th
Anniv. — A135

No. 670, Airborne Forces enroute to drop zones. No. 671, Allied Fleet off Normandy Coast. No. 672, Coming ashore, Gold Beach. No. 673, Coming ashore, Sword Beach. No. 674, Spitfires on beachead patrol. No. 675, Normandy invasion map.

**1994, June 6    Litho.    Perf. 13½**
670 A135 18p multicolored .55 .55
671 A135 18p multicolored .55 .55
    a. Bklt. pane, 3 each #670-671 3.00
672 A135 23p multicolored .75 .75
673 A135 23p multicolored .75 .75
    a. Bklt. pane, 3 each #672-673 4.75
674 A135 30p multicolored .85 .85
675 A135 30p multicolored .85 .85
    a. Bklt. pane, 3 each #674-675 5.00
    b. Bklt. pane of 6, #670-675 5.00
        Complete booklet, #671a,
        673a, 675a, 675b 17.00
    Nos. 670-675 (6) 4.30 4.30

No. 675b also sold by the Philatelic Bureau separate from the booklet, without stitching, as a souvenir sheet.

Intl. Olympic
Committee,
Cent. — A136

**1994, June 6    Perf. 14**
676 A136 18p Sailing .45 .45
677 A136 23p Rifle shooting .65 .65
678 A136 30p Hurdles .85 .85

679 A136 41p Swimming 1.25 1.25
680 A136 60p Field hockey 1.75 1.75
    Nos. 676-680 (5) 4.95 4.95

Marine
Life — A137

Designs: 18p, Strawberry anemone. 23p, Hermit crab, parasitic anemone. 41p, Velvet swimming crab. 60p, Common jellyfish.

**1994, Aug. 2    Litho.    Perf. 13½x13**
681 A137 18p multicolored .45 .45
682 A137 23p multicolored .70 .70
683 A137 41p multicolored 1.40 1.40
684 A137 60p multicolored 1.90 1.90
    Nos. 681-684 (4) 4.45 4.45

Postal
Independence,
25th
Anniv. — A138

Designs: 18p, Condor 10 Wavepiercer. 23p, Map of Jersey, postbox. 35p, BEA "Vanguard" aircraft. 41p, Aurigny "Short 360" aircraft. 60p, Sealink vessel "Caesarea."

**1994, Oct. 1    Litho.    Perf. 14**
685 A138 18p multicolored .50 .50
686 A138 23p multicolored .60 .60
687 A138 35p multicolored .85 .85
688 A138 41p multicolored 1.05 1.05
689 A138 60p multicolored 1.70 1.70
    a. Souvenir sheet, #685-689 + label 5.00 5.00
    Nos. 685-689 (5) 4.70 4.70

See Guernsey Nos. 536-540a.

Christmas
A139

Christmas carols: 18p, "Away in the manger..." 23p, "Hark! the herald angels sing..." 41p, "While shepherds watched..." 60p, "We three kings of Orient are..."

**1994, Nov. 8**
690 A139 18p multicolored .40 .40
691 A139 23p multicolored .50 .50
692 A139 41p multicolored 1.20 1.20
693 A139 60p multicolored 1.50 1.50
    Nos. 690-693 (4) 3.60 3.60

Greetings
Stamps — A140

Designs: No. 694, Dog, "Good Luck." No. 695, Rose, "With Love." No. 696, Chick, "Congratulations." No. 697, Bouquet of flowers, "Thank You."
No. 698, Dove, "With love." No. 699, Cat, "Good Luck." No. 700, Carnations, "Thank You." No. 701, Parrot, "Congratulations." 60p, Boar, "Happy New Year."

**1995, Jan. 24    Litho.    Perf. 13½x13**
694 A140 18p multicolored .50 .50
695 A140 18p multicolored .50 .50
696 A140 18p multicolored .50 .50
697 A140 18p multicolored .50 .50
    a. Strip of 4, #694-697 3.25 3.25
698 A140 23p multicolored .80 .80
699 A140 23p multicolored .80 .80
700 A140 23p multicolored .80 .80
701 A140 23p multicolored .80 .80
    a. Strip of 4, #698-701 3.25 3.25
    **Size: 25x64mm**
702 A140 60p multicolored .80 .80
    a. Booklet pane, #697a, #701a,
        #702 6.75
        Complete booklet, #702a 6.75
    Nos. 694-702 (9) 6.00 6.00

New Year 1995 (Year of the Boar) (No. 702).

Camellias — A141

18p, Captain Rawes. 23p, Brigadoon. 30p, Elsie Jury. 35p, Augusto L'Gouveia Pinto. 41p, Bella Romana.

**1995, Mar. 21    Litho.    Perf. 14**
| | | | |
|---|---|---|---|
| 703 | A141 | 18p multicolored | .50 .50 |
| 704 | A141 | 23p multicolored | .70 .70 |
| 705 | A141 | 30p multicolored | .80 .80 |
| 706 | A141 | 35p multicolored | .95 .95 |
| 707 | A141 | 41p multicolored | 1.00 1.00 |
| | | Nos. 703-707 (5) | 3.95 4.00 |

International Camellia Society conference, Jersey, Mar. 30-Apr. 4, 1995.

Liberation, by Philip Jackson — A142

**1995, May 9    Litho.    Perf. 13½**
| | | | |
|---|---|---|---|
| 708 | A142 | 23p gray & black | .65 .65 |
| 709 | A142 | 30p pink & black | .85 .85 |

Europa.

Liberation, 50th Anniv. — A143

No. 710, Bailiff, Crown Officers taken to HMS Beagle. No. 711, Red Cross ship SS Vega. No. 712, Germans surrender on board HMS Beagle. No. 713, First troops of task force 135, Ordinance Yard, St. Helier. No. 714, Royal visitors, June 1945. No. 715, Supplies come ashore from LSTs, Operation Nestegg. £1, Princess Elizabeth, Queen Elizabeth, Winston Churchill, King George VI, Princess Margaret at Buckingham Palace, VE Day.

**1995, May 9    Litho.    Perf. 14½x14**
| | | | |
|---|---|---|---|
| 710 | A143 | 18p multicolored | .45 .45 |
| 711 | A143 | 18p multicolored | .45 .45 |
| a. | | Bklt. pane, 3 each #710-711 | 2.60 |
| 712 | A143 | 23p multicolored | .60 .60 |
| 713 | A143 | 23p multicolored | .60 .60 |
| a. | | Bklt. pane, 3 each #712-713 | 3.70 |
| 714 | A143 | 60p multicolored | 1.50 1.50 |
| 715 | A143 | 60p multicolored | 1.50 1.50 |
| a. | | Bklt. pane, 3 each #714-715 | 9.50 |
| | | Nos. 710-715 (6) | 5.10 5.10 |

**Souvenir Sheet**
| | | | |
|---|---|---|---|
| 716 | A143 | £1 multicolored | 3.25 3.25 |
| a. | | Booklet pane, #716 | 2.60 |
| | | Complete booklet, #711a, #713a, #715a, #716a | 15.00 |

No. 716 contains one 81x29mm stamp.

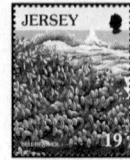

Wild Flowers — A144

No. 717, Bell heather. No. 718, Sea campion. No. 719, Spotted rock-rose. No. 720, Thrift. No. 721, Sheep's-bit scabious. No. 722, Field bind-weed. No. 723, Common bird's-foot trefoil. No. 724, Sea holly. No. 725, Common centaury. No. 726, Dwarf pansy.

**1995, July 4    Litho.    Perf. 13½**
| | | | |
|---|---|---|---|
| 717 | A144 | 19p multicolored | .45 .25 |
| 718 | A144 | 19p multicolored | .45 .25 |
| 719 | A144 | 19p multicolored | .45 .25 |
| 720 | A144 | 19p multicolored | .45 .25 |
| 721 | A144 | 19p multicolored | .45 .25 |
| a. | | Strip of 5, #717-721 | 2.75 2.75 |
| 722 | A144 | 23p multicolored | .60 .25 |
| 723 | A144 | 23p multicolored | .60 .25 |
| 724 | A144 | 23p multicolored | .60 .25 |
| 725 | A144 | 23p multicolored | .60 .25 |
| 726 | A144 | 23p multicolored | .60 .25 |
| a. | | Strip of 5, #722-726 | 3.00 3.00 |
| | | Nos. 717-726 (10) | 5.25 2.50 |

**Butterfly & Moth Type of 1991**

19p, Peacock pansy. 23p, Green-barred swallowtail. 30p, Orange emigrant. 41p, Scarlet mormon. 60p, Common birdwing.

**1995, Sept. 1    Litho.    Perf. 14**
| | | | |
|---|---|---|---|
| 727 | A116 | 19p multicolored | .60 .60 |
| 728 | A116 | 23p multicolored | .65 .65 |
| 729 | A116 | 30p multicolored | .90 .90 |
| 730 | A116 | 41p multicolored | 1.20 1.20 |
| 731 | A116 | 60p multicolored | 1.90 1.90 |
| a. | | Souvenir sheet of 2, #730-731 | 3.25 3.25 |
| | | Nos. 727-731 (5) | 5.25 5.25 |

Singapore '95 (No. 731a).
Stamps from No. 731a do not have border around the designs or inscriptions at bottom.

Christmas Pantomimes A145

Childrens' stories: 19p, Puss in Boots. 23p, Cinderella. 41p, Sleeping Beauty. 60p, Aladdin.

**1995, Oct. 24    Litho.    Perf. 13½**
| | | | |
|---|---|---|---|
| 732 | A145 | 19p multicolored | .60 .60 |
| 733 | A145 | 23p multicolored | .65 .65 |
| 734 | A145 | 41p multicolored | 1.15 1.15 |
| 735 | A145 | 60p multicolored | 1.45 1.45 |
| | | Nos. 732-735 (4) | 3.85 3.85 |

UN, 50th Anniv. — A146

Nos. 736, 739, Doves, emblem. Nos 737, 738, Wheat ear, emblem.

**1995, Oct. 24    Litho.    Perf. 13x14**
| | | | |
|---|---|---|---|
| 736 | A146 | 19p dk blue, lt blue | .60 .60 |
| 737 | A146 | 23p emer, turq grn | .65 .65 |
| 738 | A146 | 41p turq grn, emer | 1.15 1.15 |
| 739 | A146 | 60p lt blue, dk blue | 1.45 1.45 |
| | | Nos. 736-739 (4) | 3.85 3.85 |

UNICEF, 50th Anniv. — A147

Children, map areas of UNICEF activities: 19p, Africa. 23p, Globe. 30p, Europe, Balkans. 35p, South America, Caribbean. 41p, South Asia. 60p, Australasia, South Pacific.

**1996, Feb. 19    Litho.    Perf. 14½**
| | | | |
|---|---|---|---|
| 740 | A147 | 19p multicolored | .55 .50 |
| 741 | A147 | 23p multicolored | .65 .50 |
| 742 | A147 | 30p multicolored | .85 .75 |
| 743 | A147 | 35p multicolored | 1.10 1.10 |
| 744 | A147 | 41p multicolored | 1.20 1.20 |
| 745 | A147 | 60p multicolored | 1.75 1.75 |
| | | Nos. 740-745 (6) | 6.10 5.80 |

**Souvenir Sheet**

New Year 1996 (Year of the Rat) A148

**1996, Feb. 19    Perf. 14**
| | | | |
|---|---|---|---|
| 746 | A148 | £1 multicolored | 3.00 3.00 |

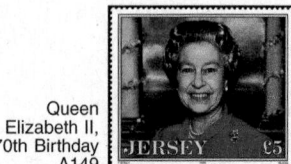

Queen Elizabeth II, 70th Birthday A149

**1996, Apr. 21    Litho.    Perf. 14x15**
| | | | |
|---|---|---|---|
| 747 | A149 | £5 multicolored | 13.00 13.00 |

Women of Achievement A150

Europa: 23p, Elizabeth Garrett, first British woman physician. 30p, Emmeline Pankhurst (1858-1928), suffragist.

**1996, Apr. 25    Perf. 14**
| | | | |
|---|---|---|---|
| 748 | A150 | 23p multicolored | .65 .65 |
| 749 | A150 | 30p multicolored | 1.00 1.00 |

1996 European Soccer Chamionships A151

Various soccer plays.

**1996, Apr. 25**
| | | | |
|---|---|---|---|
| 750 | A151 | 19p multicolored | .55 .55 |
| 751 | A151 | 23p multicolored | .70 .70 |
| 752 | A151 | 35p multicolored | 1.15 1.15 |
| 753 | A151 | 41p multicolored | 1.15 1.15 |
| 754 | A151 | 60p multicolored | 1.80 1.80 |
| | | Nos. 750-754 (5) | 5.35 5.35 |

Modern Olympic Games, Cent. — A152

**1996, June 8    Litho.    Perf. 14**
| | | | |
|---|---|---|---|
| 755 | A152 | 19p Rowing | .60 .60 |
| 756 | A152 | 23p Judo | .70 .70 |
| 757 | A152 | 35p Fencing | 1.15 1.15 |
| 758 | A152 | 41p Boxing | 1.15 1.15 |
| 759 | A152 | 60p Basketball | 1.85 1.85 |
| | | Nos. 755-759 (5) | 5.45 5.45 |

**Souvenir Sheet**
| | | | |
|---|---|---|---|
| 760 | A152 | £1 Olympic torch, flame | 3.50 3.50 |

Intl. Amateur Boxing Assoc., 50th anniv. (No. 758). CAPEX '96 (No. 760). No. 760 contains one 50x38mm stamp.

Tourism — A153

19p, North Coast. 23p, Portelet Bay. 30p, Greve de Lecq Bay. 35p, Beauport Beach. 41p, Plemont Bay. 60p, St. Brelade's Bay.

**1996, June 8    Litho.    Perf. 14**
| | | | |
|---|---|---|---|
| 761 | A153 | 19p multi | .55 .55 |
| 762 | A153 | 23p multi | .65 .65 |
| a. | | Bklt. pane, 3 each #761-762 | 3.85 |
| 763 | A153 | 30p multi | .90 .90 |
| 764 | A153 | 35p multi | 1.05 1.05 |
| a. | | Bklt. pane, 3 each #763-764 | 5.75 |
| 765 | A153 | 41p multi | 1.20 1.20 |
| 766 | A153 | 60p multi | 1.75 1.75 |
| a. | | Bklt. pane, 1 each #761-766 | 6.25 |
| b. | | Bklt. pane, 3 each #765-766 | 9.00 |
| | | Complete booklet, #762a, 764a, 766a, 766b | 17.50 |
| | | Nos. 761-766 (6) | 6.10 6.10 |

Horses — A154

**1996, Sept. 13    Litho.    Perf. 13½x14**
| | | | |
|---|---|---|---|
| 767 | A154 | 19p Drag hunt | .60 .60 |
| 768 | A154 | 23p Horse driving | .70 .70 |
| 769 | A154 | 30p Race training | 1.00 1.00 |
| 770 | A154 | 41p Show jumping | 1.20 1.20 |
| 771 | A154 | 41p Pony club | 1.30 1.30 |
| 772 | A154 | 60p Shire horses | 1.90 1.90 |
| | | Nos. 767-772 (6) | 6.70 6.70 |

Christmas A155

19p, Journey to Bethlehem. 23p, Archangel Gabriel visits shepherds. 30p, Nativity. 60p, Magi.

**1996, Nov. 12    Perf. 13x13½**
| | | | |
|---|---|---|---|
| 773 | A155 | 19p multicolored | .55 .55 |
| 774 | A155 | 23p multicolored | .65 .65 |
| 775 | A155 | 30p multicolored | 1.00 1.00 |
| 776 | A155 | 60p multicolored | 1.60 1.60 |
| | | Nos. 773-776 (4) | 3.80 3.80 |

**Souvenir Sheet**

New Year 1997 (Year of the Ox) A156

**1997, Feb. 7    Litho.    Perf. 13½**
| | | | |
|---|---|---|---|
| 777 | A156 | £1 multicolored | 3.50 3.50 |
| a. | | With added inscription in sheet margin | 3.75 3.75 |

No. 777a inscribed in sheet margin with "JERSEY AT HONG KONG '97" in red and Hong Kong '97 emblem in black.

Birds — A157

1p, Red-breasted merganser. 10p, Common tern. 15p, Black-headed gull. 20p, Dunlin. 24p, Puffin. 37p, Oystercatcher. 75p, Redshank. £2, Shag.

**Inscribed "1997"**

**1997, Feb. 12    Perf. 14½**
| | | | |
|---|---|---|---|
| 778 | A157 | 1p multicolored | .25 .25 |
| 779 | A157 | 10p multicolored | .25 .25 |
| 780 | A157 | 15p multicolored | .45 .45 |
| 781 | A157 | 20p multicolored | .80 .80 |
| 782 | A157 | 24p multicolored | .90 .90 |
| 783 | A157 | 37p multicolored | 1.05 1.05 |
| 784 | A157 | 75p multicolored | 2.75 2.75 |
| 785 | A157 | £2 multicolored | 6.75 6.75 |
| a. | | Souv. sheet of 8, #778-785 | 12.00 12.00 |
| b. | | As "a," with added inscription in sheet margin | 12.50 12.50 |

No. 785b contains PACIFIC '97 World Philatelic Exhibition emblem in sheet margin. Issued: 5/29.
See Nos. 825-832, 864-871, 909-916.

**1998, Apr. 2    Inscribed "1998"**
| | | | |
|---|---|---|---|
| 781a | A157 | 20p Dunlin | .75 .80 |
| 782a | A157 | 24p Puffin | .75 .80 |

Lillie the Cow — A158

Designs: No. 786, Building sand castle. No. 787, Taking photographs. No. 788, Lying on beach. No. 789, In restaurant.

**1997, Feb. 12    Die Cut Perf 9½x9 Self-Adhesive**
**Inscribed "1997"**
| | | | |
|---|---|---|---|
| 786 | A158 | (23p) multicolored | .80 .80 |
| 787 | A158 | (23p) multicolored | .80 .80 |
| 788 | A158 | (23p) multicolored | .80 .80 |
| 789 | A158 | (23p) multicolored | .80 .80 |
| b. | | Strip of 4, #786-789 | 3.25 |

Peelable backing is rouletted 9 between stamps.

**1999, Apr. 16    Inscribed "1999" ©**
| | | | |
|---|---|---|---|
| 786d | | (25p) multi | 6.00 6.00 |
| 787d | | (25p) multi | 6.00 6.00 |
| 788d | | (25p) multi | 6.00 6.00 |
| 789d | | (25p) multi | 6.00 6.00 |
| 789e | | Strip of 4, #786d-789d | 24.00 |

**2000, Dec. 9    Coil Stamps**
**Inscribed "2000" ©**
| | | | |
|---|---|---|---|
| 786f | | (26p) Die cut perf. 8¾x9 | 7.00 7.00 |
| 787f | | (26p) Die cut perf. 8¾x9 | 7.00 7.00 |
| 788f | | (26p) Die cut perf. 8¾x9 | 7.00 7.00 |
| 789f | | (26p) Die cut perf. 8¾x9 | 7.00 7.00 |
| 789g | | Strip of 4, #786f-789f | 27.50 |

Nos. 786-789 are inscribed "U.K. MINIMUM POSTAGE PAID."

Jersey Airport, 60th Anniv. — A159

**1997, Mar. 10    Litho.    Perf. 13½x14**
| | | | | |
|---|---|---|---|---|
| 790 | A159 | 20p DH95 Flamingo | .50 | .50 |
| 791 | A159 | 24p HPR1 Marathon | .60 | .60 |
| 792 | A159 | 31p DH114 Heron | .75 | .75 |
| 793 | A159 | 37p Boeing 737-236 | 1.05 | 1.05 |
| 794 | A159 | 43p BN Trislander | 1.25 | 1.25 |
| 795 | A159 | 63p BAe 146-200 | 1.95 | 1.95 |
| | | Nos. 790-795 (6) | 6.10 | 6.10 |

Stories and Legends — A160

Europa: 20p, Bull of St. Clement. 24p, Black Horse of St. Ouen. 31p, Black Dog of Bouley Bay. 63p, Les Fontaines des Mittes.

**1997, Apr. 15    Litho.    Perf. 14½x14**
| | | | | |
|---|---|---|---|---|
| 796 | A160 | 20p multicolored | .70 | .65 |
| 797 | A160 | 24p multicolored | .85 | .75 |
| 798 | A160 | 31p multicolored | 1.10 | 1.10 |
| 799 | A160 | 63p multicolored | 1.40 | 1.40 |
| | | Nos. 796-799 (4) | 4.05 | 3.90 |

1997 Jersey Island Games — A161

**1997, June 28    Litho.    Perf. 13½x14**
| | | | | |
|---|---|---|---|---|
| 800 | A161 | 20p Cycling | .55 | .55 |
| 801 | A161 | 24p Archery | .65 | .65 |
| a. | | Booklet pane, 3 each #800-801 | 2.60 | |
| 802 | A161 | 31p Windsurfing | .80 | .80 |
| 803 | A161 | 37p Gymnastics | 1.00 | 1.00 |
| a. | | Booklet pane, 3 each #802-803 | 3.75 | |
| 804 | A161 | 43p Volleyball | 1.10 | 1.10 |
| 805 | A161 | 63p Running | 1.75 | 1.75 |
| a. | | Booklet pane, 3 each #804-805 | 6.25 | — |
| b. | | Booklet pane, #800-805 | 4.00 | — |
| | | Complete booklet, #801a, 803a, 805a-805b | 18.00 | |
| | | Nos. 800-805 (6) | 5.85 | 5.85 |

Jesey Wildlife Preservation Trust — A162

Endangered species: 20p, Mallorcan midwife toad. 24p, Aye-aye. 31p, Echo parakeet. 37p, Pigmy hog. 43p, St. Lucia whip-tail. 63p, Madagascar teal.

**1997, Sept. 2    Litho.    Perf. 13**
| | | | | |
|---|---|---|---|---|
| 806 | A162 | 20p multicolored | .55 | .50 |
| 807 | A162 | 24p multicolored | .65 | .55 |
| 808 | A162 | 31p multicolored | 1.00 | 1.00 |
| 809 | A162 | 37p multicolored | 1.10 | 1.10 |
| 810 | A162 | 43p multicolored | 1.25 | 1.25 |
| 811 | A162 | 63p multicolored | 1.90 | 1.90 |
| | | Nos. 806-811 (6) | 6.45 | 6.30 |

Trees — A163

**1997, Sept. 2    Perf. 14½**
| | | | | |
|---|---|---|---|---|
| 812 | A163 | 20p Ash | .55 | .50 |
| 813 | A163 | 24p Elder | .65 | .55 |
| 814 | A163 | 31p Beech | 1.00 | 1.00 |
| 815 | A163 | 37p Sweet chestnut | 1.10 | 1.10 |
| 816 | A163 | 43p Hawthorn | 1.25 | 1.25 |
| 817 | A163 | 63p Common oak | 1.90 | 1.90 |
| | | Nos. 812-817 (6) | 6.45 | 6.30 |

Christmas A164

Santa Claus at various Jersey landmarks: 20p, Jersey Airport. 24p, St. Aubin's Harbor. 31p, Mont Orgueil Castle. 63p, Royal Square, St. Helier.

**1997, Nov. 11    Litho.    Perf. 14**
| | | | | |
|---|---|---|---|---|
| 818 | A164 | 20p multicolored | .60 | .60 |
| 819 | A164 | 24p multicolored | .70 | .70 |
| 820 | A164 | 31p multicolored | 1.00 | 1.00 |
| 821 | A164 | 63p multicolored | 1.90 | 1.90 |
| | | Nos. 818-821 (4) | 4.20 | 4.20 |

Queen Elizabeth II and Prince Philip, 50th Wedding Anniv. — A165

Designs: No. 822, Wedding portrait. No. 823, Anniversary portrait. £1.50, Full length wedding portrait, vert.

**1997, Nov. 20    Litho.    Perf. 14½**
| | | | | |
|---|---|---|---|---|
| 822 | A165 | 50p multicolored | 1.50 | 1.50 |
| 823 | A165 | 50p multicolored | 1.50 | 1.50 |
| a. | | Pair, #822-823 | 3.50 | 3.50 |

**Souvenir Sheet**
**Perf. 13½x14**
| | | | | |
|---|---|---|---|---|
| 824 | A165 | £1.50 multicolored | 4.50 | 4.50 |

No. 824 contains one 38x51mm stamp.

**Bird Type of 1997**

2p, Sanderling. 5p, Great crested grebe. 21p, Sandwich tern. 25p, Brent goose. 30p, Fulmar. 40p, Turnstone. 60p, Avocet. £1, Razorbill.

**1998, Jan. 28    Litho.    Perf. 14½**
| | | | | |
|---|---|---|---|---|
| 825 | A157 | 2p multicolored | .25 | .25 |
| 826 | A157 | 5p multicolored | .25 | .25 |
| 827 | A157 | 21p multicolored | .50 | .50 |
| 828 | A157 | 25p multicolored | .65 | .65 |
| 829 | A157 | 30p multicolored | .80 | .80 |
| 830 | A157 | 40p multicolored | 1.05 | 1.05 |
| 831 | A157 | 60p multicolored | 1.50 | 1.50 |
| 832 | A157 | £1 multicolored | 3.25 | 3.25 |
| a. | | Souvenir sheet of 8, #825-832 | 8.75 | 8.75 |
| | | Nos. 825-832 (8) | 8.25 | 8.25 |

**Souvenir Sheet**

New Year 1998 (Year of the Tiger) A166

**1998, Jan. 28    Perf. 14**
| | | | | |
|---|---|---|---|---|
| 833 | A166 | £1 multicolored | 3.50 | 3.50 |

Buses — A167

Designs: 20p, JMT Bristol 4 Tonner, 1923. 24p, SCS Regent Double Decker, 1934. 31p, Slade's Dennis Lancet, 1936. 37p, Tantivy Leyland PLSC Lion, 1947. 43p, JBS Morris Bus, 1958. 63p, JMT Leyland Titan TD4 Double Decker, 1961.

**1998, Apr. 2    Litho.    Perf. 14**
| | | | | |
|---|---|---|---|---|
| 834 | A167 | 20p multicolored | .65 | .55 |
| 835 | A167 | 24p multicolored | .75 | .60 |
| a. | | Bklt. pane, 3 each #834-835 | 3.50 | |
| 836 | A167 | 31p multicolored | .85 | .80 |
| 837 | A167 | 37p multicolored | 1.20 | 1.20 |
| a. | | Bklt. pane, 3 each #836-837 | 4.00 | |
| 838 | A167 | 43p multicolored | 1.25 | 1.25 |
| 839 | A167 | 63p multicolored | 1.75 | 1.75 |
| a. | | Bklt. pane, 3 each #838-839 | 6.00 | |
| b. | | Bklt. pane, 1 each #834-839 | 3.75 | |
| | | Complete booklet, #835a, 837a, 839a, 839b | 18.00 | |
| | | Nos. 834-839 (6) | 6.45 | 6.15 |

National Festivals — A168

Europa: 20p, Creative Arts Festival. 24p, Jazz Festival. 31p, Good Food Festival. 63p, Floral Festival.

**1998, Apr. 2    Perf. 14x13½**
| | | | | |
|---|---|---|---|---|
| 840 | A168 | 20p multicolored | .65 | .45 |
| 841 | A168 | 24p multicolored | .70 | .55 |
| 842 | A168 | 31p multicolored | .90 | .90 |
| 843 | A168 | 63p multicolored | 1.75 | 1.75 |
| | | Nos. 840-843 (4) | 4.00 | 3.65 |

Yachting — A169

Nos. 844-848: Various Hobie Cats sailing in St. Aubin's Bay.
Nos. 849-853: Various yachts racing in annual "Lombard Challenge."

**1998, May 18    Litho.    Perf. 13**
| | | | | |
|---|---|---|---|---|
| 844 | A169 | 20p multicolored | .50 | .50 |
| 845 | A169 | 20p multicolored | .50 | .50 |
| 846 | A169 | 20p multicolored | .50 | .50 |
| 847 | A169 | 20p multicolored | .50 | .50 |
| 848 | A169 | 20p multicolored | .50 | .50 |
| a. | | Strip of 5, #844-848 | 3.25 | 3.25 |
| 849 | A169 | 24p multicolored | .55 | .55 |
| 850 | A169 | 24p multicolored | .55 | .55 |
| 851 | A169 | 24p multicolored | .55 | .55 |
| 852 | A169 | 24p multicolored | .55 | .55 |
| 853 | A169 | 24p multicolored | .55 | .55 |
| a. | | Strip of 5, #849-853 | 3.50 | 3.50 |

"Days Gone By" — A170

Jersey lily and: No. 854, Cider making. No. 855, Potato barrels transported by horse and cart. No. 856, Gathering seaweed for fertilizer. No. 857, Milking Jersey cows by hand.

***Serpentine Die Cut Perf. 11¼***
**1998, Aug. 11    Litho.**
**Self-Adhesive**
**Inscribed "1998"**
| | | | | |
|---|---|---|---|---|
| 854 | A170 | (20p) multicolored | .90 | .90 |
| 855 | A170 | (20p) multicolored | .90 | .90 |
| 856 | A170 | (20p) multicolored | .90 | .90 |
| 857 | A170 | (20p) multicolored | .90 | .90 |
| a. | | Strip of 4, #854-857 | 4.00 | |

**Inscribed "1999"**
| | | | | |
|---|---|---|---|---|
| 854b | | (20p) multi | 5.50 | 5.50 |
| 855b | | (20p) multi | 5.50 | 5.50 |
| 856b | | (20p) multi | 5.50 | 5.50 |
| 857b | | (20p) multi | 5.50 | 5.50 |
| 857c | | Strip of 4, #854b-857b | 22.50 | |

Issued: 7/16/99.

**Inscribed "2000"**
| | | | | |
|---|---|---|---|---|
| 854d | | (20p) multi | 6.50 | 6.50 |
| 855d | | (20p) multi | 6.50 | 6.50 |
| 856d | | (20p) multi | 6.50 | 6.50 |
| 857d | | (20p) multi | 6.50 | 6.50 |
| 857e | | Strip of 4, #854d-857d | 26.00 | |

Issued: 11/3/00.

**Inscribed "2001"**
| | | | | |
|---|---|---|---|---|
| 854f | | (20p) multi | 5.00 | 5.00 |
| 855f | | (20p) multi | 5.00 | 5.00 |
| 856f | | (20p) multi | 5.00 | 5.00 |
| 857f | | (20p) multi | 5.00 | 5.00 |
| 857g | | Strip of 4, #854f-857f | 22.50 | |

Issued: 11/19/01.

**Inscribed "2003"**
| | | | | |
|---|---|---|---|---|
| 854h | | (20p) multi | 2.25 | 2.25 |
| 855h | | (20p) multi | 2.25 | 2.25 |
| 856h | | (20p) multi | 2.25 | 2.25 |
| 857h | | (20p) multi | 2.25 | 2.25 |
| 857i | | Strip of 4, #854h-857h | 10.00 | |

Nos. 854-857h are inscribed "Bailiwick / Minimum Postage Paid."
Issued: 4/4/03.

Marine Life — A171

**1998, Aug. 11    Litho.    Perf. 15x14½**
| | | | | |
|---|---|---|---|---|
| 858 | A171 | 20p Bass | .45 | .45 |
| 859 | A171 | 24p Red gurnard | .70 | .70 |
| 860 | A171 | 31p Skate | .90 | .90 |
| 861 | A171 | 37p Mackerel | 1.10 | 1.10 |
| 862 | A171 | 43p Tope | 1.20 | 1.20 |
| 863 | A171 | 63p Cuckoo wrasse | 1.75 | 1.75 |
| | | Nos. 858-863 (6) | 6.10 | 6.10 |

Intl. Year of the Ocean.

**Bird Type of 1997**

4p, Gannet. 22p, Ringed plover. 26p, Grey plover. 31p, Golden plover. 32p, Greenshank. 35p, Curlew. 44p, Herring gull. 50p, Great black-backed gull.

**1998, Aug. 11    Perf. 14½**
| | | | | |
|---|---|---|---|---|
| 864 | A157 | 4p multicolored | .30 | .30 |
| 865 | A157 | 22p multicolored | .55 | .55 |
| 866 | A157 | 26p multicolored | .70 | .70 |
| 867 | A157 | 31p multicolored | 1.00 | 1.00 |
| 868 | A157 | 32p multicolored | 1.00 | 1.00 |
| 869 | A157 | 35p multicolored | 1.05 | 1.05 |
| 870 | A157 | 44p multicolored | 1.35 | 1.35 |
| 871 | A157 | 50p multicolored | 1.45 | 1.45 |
| a. | | Souvenir sheet of 8, #864-871 | 7.50 | 7.50 |
| | | Nos. 864-871 (8) | 7.40 | 7.40 |

Jersey Autumn Flowers — A172

20p, Iris. 24p, Carnations. 31p, Chrysanthemums. 37p, Pinks. 43p, Roses. 63p, Lilies. £1.50, Lilium star gazer.

**1998, Oct. 23    Litho.    Perf. 14½**
| | | | | |
|---|---|---|---|---|
| 872 | A172 | 20p multi | .60 | .45 |
| 873 | A172 | 24p multi | .70 | .60 |
| 874 | A172 | 31p multi | .90 | .90 |
| 875 | A172 | 37p multi | 1.10 | 1.10 |
| 876 | A172 | 43p multi | 1.25 | 1.25 |
| 877 | A172 | 63p multi | 1.75 | 1.75 |
| | | Nos. 872-877 (6) | 6.30 | 5.95 |

**Souvenir Sheet**
**Perf. 14**
| | | | | |
|---|---|---|---|---|
| 878 | A172 | £1.50 multi | 4.75 | 4.75 |

No. 878 contains one 50x38mm stamp. Italia '98 (No. 878).

Christmas A173

Island manger (crib), service club sponsor: 20p, Central Market, Jersey Round Table. 24p, St. Thomas' Church, Soroptimist Intl. of Jersey. 31p, Trinity Parish Church, Rotary Club of Jersey. 63p, Royal Square, Lions Club of Jersey.

**1998, Nov. 10    Perf. 13x13½**
| | | | | |
|---|---|---|---|---|
| 879 | A173 | 20p multicolored | .45 | .45 |
| 880 | A173 | 24p multicolored | .60 | .60 |
| 881 | A173 | 31p multicolored | .80 | .80 |
| 882 | A173 | 63p multicolored | 1.90 | 1.90 |
| | | Nos. 879-882 (4) | 3.75 | 3.75 |

**Souvenir Sheet**

New Year 1999 (Year of the Rabbit) A174

**1999, Feb. 16    Litho.    Perf. 13½**
| | | | | |
|---|---|---|---|---|
| 883 | A174 | £1 multicolored | 3.25 | 3.25 |

UPU, 125th Anniv. — A175

Jersey mail transport: 20p, Eastern Railway train. 24p, Mail steamer, "Brighton." 43p, DH 86A, first airmail arrival. 63p, Morris Minor P.O. van.

**1999, Feb. 16    Perf. 14**
| | | | | |
|---|---|---|---|---|
| 884 | A175 | 20p multicolored | .60 | .55 |
| 885 | A175 | 24p multicolored | .70 | .70 |
| 886 | A175 | 43p multicolored | 1.10 | 1.10 |
| 887 | A175 | 63p multicolored | 1.75 | 1.75 |
| | | Nos. 884-887 (4) | 4.15 | 4.05 |

Royal Natl. Lifeboat Institution, 175th Anniv. — A176

75p, Jessica Eliza, St. Catherine. £1, Alexander Coutanche, St. Helier.

**1999, Feb. 16** | | | **Perf. 14½** | |
---|---|---|---|---
888 | A176 | 75p multicolored | 2.25 | 1.00
889 | A176 | £1 multicolored | 3.00 | 1.25
a. | | Pair, #888-889 | 5.50 | 5.50

Orchids — A177

Designs: 21p, Cymbidium Maufant "Jersey." 25p, Miltonia Millbrook "Jersey." 31p, Paphiopedilum Transvaal. 37p, Paphiopedilum Elizabeth Castle. 43p, Calanthe Five Oaks. 63p, Cymbidium Icho Tower "Trinity." £1.50, Miltonia Portelet.

**Perf. 14¼x13¼**
**1999, Mar. 19** | | | **Litho.** |
---|---|---|---|---
890 | A177 | 21p multicolored | .65 | .50
891 | A177 | 25p multicolored | .65 | .50
892 | A177 | 31p multicolored | .90 | .70
893 | A177 | 37p multicolored | 1.00 | .80
894 | A177 | 43p multicolored | 1.10 | .90
895 | A177 | 63p multicolored | 2.50 | 2.00
 | | Nos. 890-895 (6) | 6.80 | 5.40

**Souvenir Sheet**
**Perf. 13½**
896 | A177 | £1.50 multicolored | 5.25 | 5.25

Australia '99 World Stamp Expo (No. 896).

IBRA'99 Intl. Philatelic Exhibition, Nuremberg A178

National Parks: 21p, Howard Davis Park. 25p, Sir Winston Churchill Memorial Park. 31p, Coronation Park. 63p, La Collette Gardens.

**1999, Apr. 27** | | | **Perf. 13x13½** |
---|---|---|---|---
897 | A178 | 21p multicolored | .55 | .55
898 | A178 | 25p multicolored | .75 | .75
899 | A178 | 31p multicolored | 1.15 | 1.15
900 | A178 | 63p multicolored | 2.05 | 2.05
 | | Nos. 897-900 (4) | 4.50 | 4.50

Europa (Nos. 898-899).

Wedding of Prince Edward and Sophie Rhys-Jones A179

**1999, June 19** | | | **Litho.** | **Perf. 14½** |
---|---|---|---|---
901 | A179 | 35p yellow & multi | 1.10 | 1.10
902 | A179 | 35p blue & multi | 1.10 | 1.10
a. | | Pair, #901-902 | 2.25 | 2.25

**Classic Car Type of 1989**

Designs: 21p, 1899 Jersey-built Benz. 25p, 1910 Star Tourer. 31p, 1938 Citroen "Traction Avant." 37p, 1937 Talbot BG110 Tourer. 43p, 1934 Morris Cowley Six Special Coupé. 63p, 1946 Ford Anglia E04A Saloon.

**1999, July 2** | | | **Litho.** | **Perf. 14** |
---|---|---|---|---
903 | A101 | 21p multicolored | .55 | .45
904 | A101 | 25p multicolored | .65 | .65
a. | | Bklt. pane, 3 each #903-904 | 2.50 |
905 | A101 | 31p multicolored | .80 | .80
906 | A101 | 37p multicolored | 1.25 | 1.00
a. | | Bklt. pane, 3 each #905-906 | 4.00 |
907 | A101 | 43p multicolored | 1.50 | 1.25
908 | A101 | 63p multicolored | 1.75 | 1.50
a. | | Bklt. pane, 3 each #907-908 | 6.50 |
b. | | Booklet pane, #903-908 | 4.00 |
 | | Complete booklet, #904a, 906a, 908a, 908b | 17.50 |
 | | Nos. 903-908 (6) | 6.50 | 5.50

PhilexFrance '99 (Nos. 904a, 906a, 908a-908b).

---

**Bird Type of 1997**

23p, Bar-tailed godwit. 27p, Common scoter. 28p, Lesser black-backed gull. 29p, Little egret. 33p, Little grebe. 34p, Cormorant. 45p, Rock pipit. 65p, Gray heron.

**1999, Aug. 21** | | | **Litho.** | **Perf. 14¾** |
---|---|---|---|---
909 | A157 | 23p multicolored | .65 | .65
910 | A157 | 27p multicolored | .75 | .75
911 | A157 | 28p multicolored | .85 | .85
912 | A157 | 29p multicolored | .85 | .85
913 | A157 | 33p multicolored | .90 | .90
914 | A157 | 34p multicolored | .90 | .90
915 | A157 | 45p multicolored | 1.35 | 1.35
916 | A157 | 65p multicolored | 1.70 | 1.70
a. | | Souvenir sheet of 8, #909-916 | 8.50 | 8.50
 | | Nos. 909-916 (8) | 7.95 | 7.95

Small Mammals — A180

Designs: 21p, Hedgehog. 25p, Red squirrel. 31p, Nathusius pipestrelle. 37p, Jersey bank vole. 43p, Lesser white-toothed shrew. 63p, Common mole.

**1999, Aug. 21** | | | **Litho.** | **Perf. 13¼x13** |
---|---|---|---|---
917 | A180 | 21p multicolored | .50 | .50
918 | A180 | 25p multicolored | .60 | .60
919 | A180 | 31p multicolored | 1.60 | 1.60
920 | A180 | 37p multicolored | 1.10 | 1.10
921 | A180 | 43p multicolored | 1.10 | 1.10
922 | A180 | 63p multicolored | 2.25 | 2.25
 | | Nos. 917-922 (6) | 7.15 | 7.15

Lighthouses — A181

**1999, Oct. 5** | | | **Litho.** | **Perf. 14** |
---|---|---|---|---
923 | A181 | 21p Gorey Pierhead | .55 | .45
924 | A181 | 25p La Corbiere | .65 | .55
925 | A181 | 34p Noirmont Point | .90 | .75
926 | A181 | 38p Demie de Pas | 1.25 | 1.00
927 | A181 | 44p Greve d'Azette | 1.50 | 1.25
928 | A181 | 64p Sorel Point | 2.50 | 2.00
 | | Nos. 923-928 (6) | 7.35 | 6.00

Christmas — A182

Poinsettias and: 21p, Mistletoe. 25p, Holly. 34p, Ivy. 64p, Christmas rose.

**1999, Nov. 9** | | | **Litho.** | **Perf. 13¾** |
---|---|---|---|---
929 | A182 | 21p multi | .50 | .50
930 | A182 | 25p multi | .60 | .60
931 | A182 | 34p multi | 1.30 | 1.30
932 | A182 | 64p multi | 1.85 | 1.85
 | | Nos. 929-932 (4) | 4.25 | 4.25

Coat of Arms — A183

**Litho. & Embossed with Foil Application**
**2000, Jan. 1** | | | **Perf. 13¼** |
---|---|---|---|---
933 | A183 | £10 gold & multi | 27.00 | 27.00

Millennium.

---

**Souvenir Sheet**

New Year 2000 (Year of the Dragon) A184

**2000, Feb. 5** | | | **Litho.** | **Perf. 13¾** |
---|---|---|---|---
934 | A184 | £1 multi | 3.25 | 3.25

**Europa Issue**
**Common Design Type and**

A185

**2000, May 9** | | | | **Perf. 13¼x13** |
---|---|---|---|---
935 | A185 | 26p multi | 1.00 | 1.00
936 | CD17 | 34p multi | 1.40 | 1.40

Stampin' the Future — A186

Children's Stamp Design Contest Winners: No. 937, Ocean Adventure, by Gemma Carré. No. 938, Solar Power, by Chantal Varley-Best. No. 939, Floating City and Space Cars, by Nicola Singleton. No. 940, Conservation, by Carly Logan.

**2000, May 9** | | | **Litho.** | **Perf. 14** |
---|---|---|---|---
937 | A186 | 22p multi | .75 | .65
938 | A186 | 22p multi | .75 | .65
939 | A186 | 22p multi | .75 | .65
940 | A186 | 22p multi | .75 | .65
a. | | Souvenir sheet, #937-940 | 3.00 | 3.00
 | | Nos. 937-940 (4) | 3.00 | 2.60

Ships — A187

No. 941, Roman merchant ship. No. 942, Viking long boat. No. 943, Warship, 13th cent. No. 944, Merchant ship, 14th-15th cent. No. 945, Tudor warship, 16th cent.
No. 946, Warship, 17th cent. No. 947, Navy cutter, 18th cent. No. 948, Barque, 19th cent. No. 949, Oyster cutter, 19th cent. No. 950, Ketch, 20th cent.

**2000, May 22** | | | | **Perf. 13¾** |
---|---|---|---|---
941 | A187 | 22p multi | .55 | .25
942 | A187 | 22p multi | .55 | .25
943 | A187 | 22p multi | .55 | .25
944 | A187 | 22p multi | .55 | .25
945 | A187 | 22p multi | .55 | .25
a. | | Strip of 5, #941-945 | 2.75 | 2.75
946 | A187 | 26p multi | .60 | .25
947 | A187 | 26p multi | .60 | .25
948 | A187 | 26p multi | .60 | .25
949 | A187 | 26p multi | .60 | .25
a. | | Booklet pane, #941-944, 946-949 | 4.75 |
950 | A187 | 26p multi | .60 | .25
a. | | Strip of 5, #946-950 | 5.00 | 5.00
b. | | Souvenir sheet, #941-950 | 7.50 | 7.50
c. | | Booklet pane, #941-942, 944-946, 948-950 | 4.00 |
d. | | Booklet pane, #941, 943-947, 949-950 | 5.00 | 5.00
e. | | Booklet pane, #941-943, 945-948, 950 | 4.00 |
f. | | Bklt. pane, #942-945, 947-950 | 5.00 |
 | | Booklet, #949a, 950c-950f | 23.00 |
g. | | As "b," with London Stamp Show 2000 emblem added in sheet margin | 7.50 | 7.50

London 2000 Stamp Show.

Marine Mammals A188

---

Designs: 22p, Bottle-nosed dolphin. 26p, Long-finned pilot whale. 34p, Harbor porpoise. 38p, Atlantic gray seal. 44p, Risso's dolphin. 64p, White-beaked dolphin. £1.50, Common dolphin.

**2000, June 5** | | | | **Perf. 14¾x14** |
---|---|---|---|---
951 | A188 | 22p multi | .65 | .65
952 | A188 | 26p multi | .70 | .70
953 | A188 | 34p multi | 1.05 | 1.05
954 | A188 | 38p multi | 1.40 | 1.40
955 | A188 | 44p multi | 1.55 | 1.55
956 | A188 | 64p multi | 1.95 | 1.95
 | | Nos. 951-956 (6) | 7.30 | 7.30

**Souvenir Sheet**
957 | A188 | £1.50 multi | 5.25 | 5.25
a. | | As #957, with World Stamp Expo 2000 emblem in margin | 5.75 | 5.75

No. 957 contains one 81x29mm stamp. Issued: No. 957a, 7/7/00.

Prince William, 18th Birthday A189

William &: No. 958, Mountain. No. 959, Polo player. No. 960, Fireworks. No. 961, Beaumarais Castle.

**2000, June 21** | | | | **Perf. 14¼x14¼** |
---|---|---|---|---
958 | A189 | 75p multi | 2.25 | 1.50
959 | A189 | 75p multi | 2.25 | 1.50
960 | A189 | 75p multi | 2.25 | 1.50
961 | A189 | 75p multi | 2.25 | 1.50
 | | Nos. 958-961 (4) | 9.00 | 6.00

Queen Mother, 100th Birthday — A190

**Litho. with Foil Application**
**2000, Aug. 4** | | | | **Perf. 14½x14¼** |
---|---|---|---|---
962 | A190 | 50p Purple hat | 1.50 | 1.25
963 | A190 | 50p Pink hat | 1.50 | 1.25
a. | | Souvenir sheet, #962-963 | 3.00 | 3.00

Battle of Britain, 60th Anniv. — A191

Designs: 22p, Supermarine Spitfire Mk. I. 26p, Hawker Hurricane Mk. I. 36p, Bristol Blenheim Mk. IV. 40p, Vickers Wellington Mk. Ic. 45p, Boulton Paul Defiant Mk. I. 65p, Short Sunderland Mk. I.

**2000, Sept. 15** | | | **Litho.** | **Perf. 14¼x14** |
---|---|---|---|---
964 | A191 | 22p multi | .75 | .75
965 | A191 | 26p multi | .85 | .85
966 | A191 | 36p multi | 1.15 | 1.15
967 | A191 | 40p multi | 1.25 | 1.25
968 | A191 | 45p multi | 1.40 | 1.40
969 | A191 | 65p multi | 2.15 | 2.15
 | | Nos. 964-969 (6) | 7.55 | 7.55

Christmas — A192

**2000, Nov. 7** | | | | **Perf. 13** |
---|---|---|---|---
970 | A192 | 22p Virgin Mary | .70 | .70
971 | A192 | 26p Shepherd | .80 | .65
972 | A192 | 36p Angel | 1.25 | 1.00
973 | A192 | 65p Magus | 2.00 | 1.60
 | | Nos. 970-973 (4) | 4.75 | 3.80

## Souvenir Sheet

New Year 2001 (Year of the Snake) A193

**2001, Jan. 24**    **Litho.**    **Perf. 13¾**
974 A193 £1 multi     3.25 3.25

Steamships on Jersey-France Route — A194

**2001, Jan. 24**     **Perf. 13x13¼**
| | | | | |
|---|---|---|---|---|
| 975 | A194 | 22p Rose | .60 | .55 |
| 976 | A194 | 26p Comete | .75 | .65 |
| 977 | A194 | 36p Cygne | .95 | .85 |
| 978 | A194 | 40p Victoria | 1.10 | .95 |
| 979 | A194 | 45p Attala | 1.40 | 1.25 |
| 980 | A194 | 65p Brittany | 2.00 | 1.60 |
| | | *Nos. 975-980 (6)* | 6.80 | 5.85 |

Agricultural Products — A195

No. 981: a, Jersey cows. b, Royal potatoes. c, Tomatoes. d, Cauliflower and purple broccoli. e, Zucchini and peppers.

### Serpentine Die Cut 11¼

**2001, Apr. 3**     **Self-Adhesive**
**Inscribed "2001"**
| | | | |
|---|---|---|---|
| 981 | | Strip of 5 | 20.00 |
| a.-e. | A195 (26p) Any single | 1.75 | 1.75 |
| f. | As No. 981, inscribed "2002" | 14.00 | |
| g. | As No. 981, inscribed "2003" | 9.00 | |
| h. | As No. 981, inscribed "2005" | 8.00 | |

Issued: No. 981f, 10/4/02; No. 981g, 4/4/03; No. 981h, 10/21/05.

Navy Ships Named Jersey — A196

Ships in service from: 23p, 1654-91. 26p, 1694-98. 37p, 1698-1731. 41p, 1736-83. 46p, 1860-73. 66p, 1938-41.

**2001, Apr. 3**     **Perf. 14**
| | | | | |
|---|---|---|---|---|
| 982 | A196 | 23p multi | .60 | .55 |
| 983 | A196 | 26p multi | .75 | .65 |
| 984 | A196 | 37p multi | .95 | .85 |
| 985 | A196 | 41p multi | 1.25 | .95 |
| 986 | A196 | 46p multi | 1.40 | 1.25 |
| 987 | A196 | 66p multi | 2.00 | 1.60 |
| | | *Nos. 982-987 (6)* | 6.95 | 5.85 |

Queen Elizabeth II, 75th Birthday A197

**2001, Apr. 21**     **Perf. 14x14¾**
988 A197 £3 multi    8.75 8.75

Pond Life — A198

Designs: 23p, Agile frog. 26p, Trout. 37p, White water lily. 41p, Common blue damselfly. 46p, Palmate newt. 66p, Tufted duck. £1.50, Kingfisher.

---

**2001, May 22**     **Perf. 14¾x14**
| | | | | |
|---|---|---|---|---|
| 989 | A198 | 23p multi | .70 | .70 |
| 990 | A198 | 26p multi | .80 | .80 |
| 991 | A198 | 37p multi | 1.15 | 1.15 |
| 992 | A198 | 41p multi | 1.30 | 1.30 |
| 993 | A198 | 46p multi | 1.30 | 1.30 |
| 994 | A198 | 66p multi | 2.30 | 2.30 |
| | | *Nos. 989-994 (6)* | 7.55 | 7.55 |

### Souvenir Sheet
### Perf. 14¼

| | | | | |
|---|---|---|---|---|
| 995 | A198 | £1.50 multi | 5.00 | 5.00 |
| a. | As #995, with Belgica 2001 emblem in margin | | 6.00 | 6.00 |

Europa (Nos. 990-991). No. 995 contains one 38x50mm stamp.
Issued: No. 995a, 6/9/01.

Birds of Prey — A199

Designs: 23p, Long-eared owl. 26p, Peregrine falcon. 37p, Short-eared owl. 41p, Marsh harrier. 46p, Sparrowhawk. 66p, Tawny owl. £1.50, Barn owl.

**2001, July 3**    **Litho.**    **Perf. 13½**
| | | | | |
|---|---|---|---|---|
| 996 | A199 | 23p multi | .50 | .50 |
| 997 | A199 | 26p multi | .65 | .65 |
| 998 | A199 | 37p multi | .90 | .90 |
| 999 | A199 | 41p multi | 1.10 | 1.10 |
| 1000 | A199 | 46p multi | 1.35 | 1.35 |
| a. | Booklet pane of #997, 998, 2 each #996, 1000 | | 6.75 | |
| 1001 | A199 | 66p multi | 1.70 | 1.70 |
| a. | Booklet pane of #996-1001 | | 6.75 | |
| b. | Booklet pane, 2 each #996, 998, 1001 | | 6.75 | |
| c. | Booklet pane, #996-998, 1001, 2 #999 | | 6.25 | |
| | | *Nos. 996-1001 (6)* | 6.20 | 6.20 |
| 1002 | A199 | £1.50 Booklet pane of 1 | 6.50 | |
| | Booklet, #1000a, 1001a, 1001b, 1001c, 1002 | | 22.50 | |

### Souvenir Sheet

| | | | | |
|---|---|---|---|---|
| 1003 | A199 | £1.50 multi | 5.25 | 5.25 |
| a. | Like #1003, with Hafnia 01 emblem | | 5.25 | 5.25 |

Issued: No. 1003a, 10/16/01.
On No. 1002, "Tyto" is 4mm from the owl's head (owl is in center of stamp), while on No. 1003, it is 9mm from the head (owl is at right of stamp). The size of No. 1002 is 154x100mm, while the size of No. 1003 is 110x75.

### Souvenir Sheet

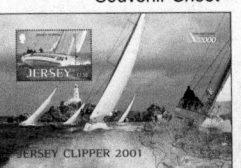

Racing Yacht Jersey Clipper A200

**2001, Sept. 17**     **Perf. 13¾**
1004 A200 £1.50 multi    5.00 5.00

Fire Engines — A201

Designs: 23p, Tilley 26 manual, c. 1845. 26p, Albion Merriweather, c. 1935. 37p, Dennis Ace, c. 1940. 41p, Dennis F8 pump escape, c. 1952. 46p, Land Rover Merryweather, c. 1968. 66p, Dennis Carmichael, c. 1989.

**2001, Sept. 25**     **Perf. 13x13¼**
| | | | | |
|---|---|---|---|---|
| 1005 | A201 | 23p multi | .60 | .60 |
| 1006 | A201 | 26p multi | .80 | .80 |
| 1007 | A201 | 37p multi | 1.05 | 1.05 |
| 1008 | A201 | 41p multi | 1.20 | 1.20 |
| 1009 | A201 | 46p multi | 1.35 | 1.35 |
| 1010 | A201 | 66p multi | 2.05 | 2.05 |
| | | *Nos. 1005-1010 (6)* | 7.05 | 7.05 |

Christmas — A202

---

No. 1011: a, Nativity. b, Street decorations. c, Carolers. d, Santa Claus. e, Bells and other ornaments on Christmas tree.
No. 1012: a, Adoration of the Shepherds. b, Carolers, Santa Claus, reindeer. c, Bell ornament, Christmas tree with candles. d, Church bells. e, Cracker with bells on wrapper.

### Serpentine Die Cut 11x11¼
**2001, Nov. 6**     **Self-Adhesive**
### Coil Stamps
**Inscribed "2001"**
| | | | |
|---|---|---|---|
| 1011 | | Horiz. strip of 5 | 4.25 |
| a.-e. | A202 (23p) green & multi, any single | .75 | .75 |
| 1012 | | Horiz. strip of 5 | 5.25 |
| a.-e. | A202 (29p) red & multi, any single | 1.00 | .75 |
| f. | Booklet pane of 16, 2 each #1011a, 1011c-1011e, 1012a-1012b, 1012d-1012e | 15.00 | |

On Nos. 1011-1012, the matrix was stripped from around the stamps; on the booklets, the matrix remains surrounding the stamps.

**2002, Nov. 23**     **Inscribed "2002"**
| | | | |
|---|---|---|---|
| 1011f | | Horiz. strip of 5 | 9.00 |
| g.-k. | A202 (23p) any single | 1.75 | .75 |
| 1012g | | Horiz. strip of 5 | 11.00 |
| h.-l. | A202 (29p) any single | 2.00 | .75 |

**2003, Nov. 10**     **Inscribed "2003"**
| | | | |
|---|---|---|---|
| 1011l | | Horiz. strip of 5 | 12.00 |
| m.-q. | A202 (23p) any single | 2.00 | .75 |

Jersey State Vessels — A203

Designs: 23p, Launch "Duchess of Normandy." 29p, Tugboat "Duke of Normandy." 38p, Customs patrol boat "Challenger." 47p, Pilot boat "Le Fret." 68p, Sea fisheries protection boat "Norman Le Brocq."

**2002, Jan. 22**    **Litho.**    **Perf. 13x13¼**
| | | | | |
|---|---|---|---|---|
| 1013 | A203 | 23p multi | .60 | .55 |
| 1014 | A203 | 29p multi | .80 | .70 |
| 1015 | A203 | 38p multi | .95 | .85 |
| 1016 | A203 | 47p multi | 1.40 | 1.25 |
| 1017 | A203 | 68p multi | 2.00 | 1.90 |
| | | *Nos. 1013-1017 (5)* | 5.75 | 5.25 |

Reign of Queen Elizabeth II, 50th Anniv. — A204

### Litho. & Embossed With Foil Application

**2002, Feb. 6**     **Perf. 13¼**
1018 A204 £3 multi    8.50 8.50

### Souvenir Sheet

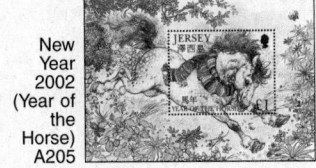

New Year 2002 (Year of the Horse) A205

**2002, Feb. 12**    **Litho.**    **Perf. 13¾**
1019 A205 £1 multi    3.00 3.00

Battle of Flowers Depictions of Circus Figures — A206

**2002, Mar. 12**    **Litho.**    **Perf. 13¾**
| | | | | |
|---|---|---|---|---|
| 1020 | A206 | 23p Elephant, cats | .65 | .65 |
| 1021 | A206 | 29p Clown | .80 | .80 |
| 1022 | A206 | 38p Clown, diff. | 1.30 | 1.30 |
| 1023 | A206 | 68p Seal | 2.20 | 2.20 |
| | | *Nos. 1020-1023 (4)* | 4.95 | 4.95 |

Europa (Nos. 1021-1022).

---

La Moye Golf Club, Cent. — A207

Designs: 23p, Aubrey Boomer. 29p, Harry Vardon. 38p, Sir Henry Cotton. 47p, Golfer's swing. 68p, Golfer addressing ball.

**2002, Apr. 16**     **Perf. 14**
| | | | | |
|---|---|---|---|---|
| 1024 | A207 | 23p multi | .60 | .60 |
| 1025 | A207 | 29p multi | .90 | .90 |
| 1026 | A207 | 38p multi | 1.10 | 1.10 |
| 1027 | A207 | 47p multi | 1.50 | 1.50 |
| 1028 | A207 | 68p multi | 2.25 | 2.25 |
| | | *Nos. 1024-1028 (5)* | 6.35 | 6.35 |

Police Vehicles — A208

Designs: 23p, Vauxhall 12, c. 1952. 29p, 1959-60 Jaguar 2.4 MkII. 38p, 1972-73 Austin 1800. 40p, Ford Cortina MkIV, c. 1978. 47p, 1995-2000 Honda motorcycle. 68p, 1998-2000 Vauxhall Vectra.

**2002, May 24**    **Litho.**    **Perf. 13x13¼**
| | | | | |
|---|---|---|---|---|
| 1029 | A208 | 23p multi | .65 | .55 |
| 1030 | A208 | 29p multi | .85 | .70 |
| 1031 | A208 | 38p multi | 1.00 | .85 |
| 1032 | A208 | 40p multi | 1.20 | .80 |
| 1033 | A208 | 47p multi | 1.40 | 1.10 |
| 1034 | A208 | 68p multi | 2.00 | 1.75 |
| | | *Nos. 1029-1034 (6)* | 7.10 | 5.75 |

Insects — A209

Designs: 23p, Honeybee. 29p, Seven-spot ladybug. 38p, Great green bush cricket. 40p, Greater horntail. 47p, Emperor dragonfly. 68p, Hawthorn shield bug.

**2002, June 18**     **Perf. 14¾x14**
| | | | | |
|---|---|---|---|---|
| 1035 | A209 | 23p multi | .65 | .55 |
| 1036 | A209 | 29p multi | .85 | .70 |
| 1037 | A209 | 38p multi | 1.00 | .85 |
| 1038 | A209 | 40p multi | 1.20 | .80 |
| 1039 | A209 | 47p multi | 1.40 | 1.10 |
| 1040 | A209 | 68p multi | 2.00 | 1.75 |
| | | *Nos. 1035-1040 (6)* | 7.10 | 5.75 |

Queen Mother Elizabeth (1900-2002) A210

### Litho. with Foil Application
**2002, Aug. 4**     **Perf. 14x14¾**
1041 A210 £2 multi    5.75 5.75

Battle of Flowers, Cent. — A211

Designs: 23p, Hydrangeas. 29p, Chrysanthemums. 38p, Hare's tails, pampas grass. 40p, Asters. 47p, Carnations. 68p, Gladioli. £2, Float "Zanzibar."

**2002, Aug. 8**    **Litho.**    **Perf. 13x13¼**
| | | | | |
|---|---|---|---|---|
| 1042 | A211 | 23p multi | .65 | .55 |
| 1043 | A211 | 29p multi | .85 | .70 |
| 1044 | A211 | 38p multi | 1.00 | .85 |
| 1045 | A211 | 40p multi | 1.20 | .80 |
| 1046 | A211 | 47p multi | 1.40 | 1.10 |
| 1047 | A211 | 68p multi | 2.00 | 1.75 |
| a. | Booklet pane, #1042-1047 | | 6.25 | |
| | | *Nos. 1042-1047 (6)* | 7.10 | 5.75 |

### Souvenir Sheet
### Perf. 13

| | | | | |
|---|---|---|---|---|
| 1048 | A211 | £2 multi | 4.00 | 4.00 |
| a. | Booklet pane of 1 | | 4.00 | |
| | Booklet, #1048a, 3 #1047a | | 17.50 | |

No. 1047a has three different layouts of stamps on pane. No. 1048 contains one 76x39mm stamp. No. 1048a is larger than No.

1048, having extra selvage at left, with rouletting separating the selvage from the rest of the sheet.

Cats — A212

Designs: 23p, British dilute tortoiseshell. 29p, Cream Persian. 38p, Blue exotic shorthair. 40p, Black smoke Devon Rex. 47p, British silver tabby. 68p, Usual Abyssinian. £2, British cream and white bi-color, vert.

| | | **2002, Oct. 12** | **Perf. 14¾x14¼** |
|---|---|---|---|
| 1049 | A212 | 23p multi | .65 | .65 |
| 1050 | A212 | 29p multi | .80 | .80 |
| 1051 | A212 | 38p multi | 1.05 | 1.05 |
| 1052 | A212 | 40p multi | 1.15 | 1.15 |
| 1053 | A212 | 47p multi | 1.35 | 1.35 |
| 1054 | A212 | 68p multi | 2.05 | 2.05 |
| | | Nos. 1049-1054 (6) | 7.05 | 7.05 |

**Souvenir Sheet**
**Perf. 14¼**

| 1055 | A212 | £2 multi | 6.00 | 6.00 |
|---|---|---|---|---|

No. 1055 contains one 38x50mm stamp.

Letter Boxes, 150th
Anniv. — A213

Designs: 23p, Pillar box, Central Market. 29p, Wall box, Colomberie. 38p, Wall box, St. Clement's Inner Road. 40p, Ship box. 47p, Pillar box, Parade, 1952. 68p, Pillar box, La Collette, 2000. £2, First letter box, David Place, 1852.

| | | **2002, Nov. 23** | **Perf. 14½x14¼** |
|---|---|---|---|
| 1056 | A213 | 23p multi | .65 | .65 |
| 1057 | A213 | 29p multi | .80 | .80 |
| 1058 | A213 | 38p multi | 1.05 | 1.05 |
| 1059 | A213 | 40p multi | 1.15 | 1.15 |
| 1060 | A213 | 47p multi | 1.35 | 1.35 |
| 1061 | A213 | 68p multi | 2.05 | 2.05 |
| | | Nos. 1056-1061 (6) | 7.05 | 7.05 |

**Souvenir Sheet**
**Perf. 14¾**

| 1062 | A213 | £2 multi | 6.00 | 6.00 |
|---|---|---|---|---|

No. 1062 contains one 39x76mm stamp.

Airplanes — A214

Designs: 23p, Sanchez-Besa Hydroplane. 29p, Supermarine S.6B. 38p, De Havilland DH84 Dragon. 40p, De Havilland DH89a Rapide. 47p, Vickers 701 Viscount. 68p, BAC One-Eleven.
£2, 1906 Biplane of Jacob Christian Hansen Ellehammer.

| | | **2003, Jan. 21** | **Litho.** | **Perf. 13x13¼** |
|---|---|---|---|---|
| 1063 | A214 | 23p multi | .60 | .55 |
| 1064 | A214 | 29p multi | .80 | .70 |
| 1065 | A214 | 38p multi | 1.10 | .85 |
| 1066 | A214 | 40p multi | 1.10 | .90 |
| 1067 | A214 | 47p multi | 1.20 | 1.10 |
| 1068 | A214 | 68p multi | 1.90 | 1.60 |
| a. | | Booklet pane, #1063-1068 | 4.25 | — |
| | | Nos. 1063-1068 (6) | 6.70 | 5.70 |

**Souvenir Sheet**
**Perf. 13¼x13**

| 1069 | A214 | £2 multi | 5.75 | 5.75 |
|---|---|---|---|---|
| a. | | Booklet pane, #1069 | 4.75 | — |
| | | Complete booklet, #1069a, 3 #1068a | 17.50 | |

No. 1069 contains one 60x40mm stamp. The booklet contains three examples of No. 1068a, each with different margins. No. 1069a has a larger margin than No. 1069, which contains additional text and illustrations. The £2 stamp from the booklet pane No. 1069a has the date under the second "e" of "Ellehammer," while the date on the stamp from the souvenir sheet No. 1069 has the date under the first "m" of "Ellehammer."

---

**Souvenir Sheet**

New Year 2003 (Year of the Ram) A215

| | | **2003, Feb. 1** | **Perf. 13¾** |
|---|---|---|---|
| 1070 | A215 | £1 multi | 3.00 | 3.00 |

Poster Art — A216

Designs: 23p, Portelet, c. 1935. 29p, Southern British Railways, c. 1952, vert. 38p, Chemins de Fer de l'Ouest, c. 1910, vert. 68p, Jersey, the Sunny Channel Island, c. 1947.

| | | **2003, Mar. 11** | **Perf. 13½** |
|---|---|---|---|
| 1071 | A216 | 23p multi | .50 | .50 |
| 1072 | A216 | 29p multi | .80 | .80 |
| 1073 | A216 | 38p multi | 1.25 | 1.25 |
| 1074 | A216 | 68p multi | 1.75 | 1.75 |
| | | Nos. 1071-1074 (4) | 4.30 | 4.30 |

Europa (29p, 38p).

Lighthouses and Buoys — A217

No. 1075: a, St. Catherine's Breakwater Light. b, Violet Channel Buoy.
No. 1076: a, Mont Ubé Lighthouse. b, Frouquie Aubert Buoy.
No. 1077: a, Gronez Point Lighthouse. b, Banc des Ormes Buoy.

| | | **2003, Apr. 15** | **Perf. 13¾** |
|---|---|---|---|
| 1075 | A217 | Horiz. pair | 1.50 | 1.50 |
| a.-b. | | 29p Either single | .60 | .60 |
| 1076 | A217 | Horiz. pair | 1.50 | 1.50 |
| a.-b. | | 30p Either single | .60 | .60 |
| 1077 | A217 | Horiz. pair | 2.50 | 2.50 |
| a.-b. | | 48p Either single | 1.00 | 1.00 |
| | | Nos. 1075-1077 (3) | 5.50 | 5.50 |

Wild Orchids — A218

Designs: 29p, Southern-marsh orchid. 30p, Loose-flowered orchid. 39p, Spotted orchid. 50p, Autumn Ladies Tresses. 53p, Greenwinged orchid. 69p, Pyramidal orchid.
£2, Loose-flowered orchid, diff.

| | | **2003, May 13** | **Perf. 13¼x13** |
|---|---|---|---|
| 1078 | A218 | 29p multi | .80 | .65 |
| 1079 | A218 | 30p multi | .85 | .65 |
| 1080 | A218 | 39p multi | 1.10 | .85 |
| 1081 | A218 | 50p multi | 1.40 | 1.10 |
| 1082 | A218 | 53p multi | 1.40 | 1.25 |
| 1083 | A218 | 69p multi | 1.90 | 1.50 |
| | | Nos. 1078-1083 (6) | 7.45 | 6.00 |

**Souvenir Sheet**

| 1084 | A218 | £2 multi | 5.50 | 5.50 |
|---|---|---|---|---|
| a. | | As #1084, with added marginal inscription | 5.50 | 5.50 |

No. 1084a has Bangkok 2003 Philatelic Exhibition emblem and text, "Jersey at Bangkok 2003," added in margin. Issued, 10/4.

Coronation of Queen Elizabeth II, 50th Anniv. — A219

Designs: 29p, Sovereign's orb. 30p, St. Edward's Crown. 39p, Scepter with Cross. 50p, Ampulla and Spoon. 53p, Sovereign's Ring. 69p, Armills.

---

**Litho. With Foil Application**

| | | **2003, June 2** | **Perf. 14¾x14** |
|---|---|---|---|
| 1085 | A219 | 29p multi | .80 | .65 |
| 1086 | A219 | 30p multi | .85 | .65 |
| 1087 | A219 | 39p multi | 1.10 | .85 |
| 1088 | A219 | 50p multi | 1.40 | 1.10 |
| 1089 | A219 | 53p multi | 1.40 | 1.25 |
| 1090 | A219 | 69p multi | 1.90 | 1.50 |
| a. | | Souvenir sheet, #1085-1090 | 7.50 | 7.50 |
| | | Nos. 1085-1090 (6) | 7.45 | 6.00 |

**Souvenir Sheet**

Prince William, Prince Charles and Queen Elizabeth II
A220

| | | **2003, June 21** | **Litho.** | **Perf. 13¾** |
|---|---|---|---|---|
| 1091 | A220 | £2 multi | 5.50 | 5.50 |

Prince William, 21st birthday.

Offshore Reefs and Flowers — A221

No. 1092: a, Les Ecrehous Reef, tree mallow. b, Les Minquiers Reef, smooth sow-thistle. c, Les Minquiers Reef, thrift. d, Paternosters Reef, rock samphire. e, Les Ecrehous Reef, bluebells.
Nos. 1092g, 1092m, Like No. 1092a. Nos. 1092h, 1092n, Like No. 1092b. Nos. 1092i, 1092o, Like No. 1092c. Nos. 1092j, 1092p, Like No. 1092d. Nos. 1092k, 1092q, Like No. 1092e.

**Serpentine Die Cut 11**
**2003, Aug. 5    Photo.    Coil Stamps**
**Self-Adhesive**

| 1092 | | Horiz. strip of 5 | 5.50 | 5.50 |
|---|---|---|---|---|
| a.-e. | A221 | (29p) Any single | 1.00 | 1.00 |
| f. | | Like #1092, serp. die cut 11¼, inscribed "2004" | 8.00 | |
| g.-k. | A221 | (32p) Any single, serp. die cut 11¼ | 1.40 | 1.40 |
| l. | | Like #1092, serp. die cut 11¼, inscribed "2006" | 7.00 | |
| m.-q. | A221 | (32p) Any single, serp. die cut 11¼, inscribed "2006" | 1.40 | 1.40 |

Nos. 1092f-1092k issued 11/3/04. Nos. 1092l-1092q issued 11/16/06.

Pets — A222

Designs: 29p, Albino Rex rabbit. 30p, Labrador retriever. 38p, Canary and budgerigar. 53p, Hamster. 69p, Guinea pig.
£2, Border collie.

| | | **2003, Sept. 9** | **Litho.** | **Perf. 13¾** |
|---|---|---|---|---|
| 1093 | A222 | 29p multi | .80 | .80 |
| 1094 | A222 | 30p multi | .80 | .80 |
| 1095 | A222 | 38p multi | 1.00 | 1.00 |
| 1096 | A222 | 53p multi | 1.50 | 1.50 |
| 1097 | A222 | 69p multi | 1.90 | 1.90 |
| | | Nos. 1093-1097 (5) | 6.00 | 6.00 |

**Souvenir Sheet**
**Perf. 13¼**

| 1098 | A222 | £2 multi | 5.75 | 5.75 |
|---|---|---|---|---|

No. 1098 contains one 39x51mm stamp.

Winter Flowers — A223

Designs: 29p, Japanese quince. 30p, Winter jasmine. 39p, Snowdrop. 48p, Winter heath. 53p, Chinese witch hazel. 69p, Winter daphne.

---

| | | **2003, Nov. 10** | **Perf. 14¼** |
|---|---|---|---|
| 1099 | A223 | 29p multi | .75 | .65 |
| 1100 | A223 | 30p multi | .80 | .65 |
| 1101 | A223 | 39p multi | 1.10 | .85 |
| 1102 | A223 | 48p multi | 1.20 | 1.00 |
| 1103 | A223 | 53p multi | 1.40 | 1.10 |
| 1104 | A223 | 69p multi | 1.90 | 1.50 |
| | | Nos. 1099-1104 (6) | 7.15 | 5.75 |

**Souvenir Sheet**

New Year 2004 (Year of the Monkey) A224

| | | **2004, Jan. 22** | **Litho.** | **Perf. 13¾** |
|---|---|---|---|---|
| 1105 | A224 | £1 multi | 3.00 | 3.00 |

British Chess Federation, Cent. — A225

| | | **2004, Jan. 22** | |
|---|---|---|---|
| 1106 | A225 | 29p Rook | .85 | .85 |
| 1107 | A225 | 30p Knight | .85 | .85 |
| 1108 | A225 | 39p Bishop | 1.10 | 1.10 |
| 1109 | A225 | 48p Pawn | 1.30 | 1.30 |
| 1110 | A225 | 53p Queen | 1.55 | 1.55 |
| 1111 | A225 | 69p King | 1.75 | 1.75 |
| | | Nos. 1106-1111 (6) | 7.40 | 7.40 |

Tourist Attractions
A226

Designs: 29p, St. Aubin's Harbor. 30p, Mont Orgueil Castle. 39p, Corbiere Lighthouse. 69p, Rozel Harbor.

| | | **2004, Mar. 9** | **Perf. 13x13¼** |
|---|---|---|---|
| 1112 | A226 | 29p multi | .85 | .85 |
| 1113 | A226 | 30p multi | .85 | .85 |
| 1114 | A226 | 39p multi | 1.10 | 1.10 |
| 1115 | A226 | 69p multi | 2.20 | 2.20 |
| | | Nos. 1112-1115 (4) | 5.00 | 5.00 |

Europa (Nos. 1113, 1114).

Waterfowl
A227

Designs: 32p, Eurasian teal. 33p, Mute swan. 40p, Northern shoveler. 49p, Common pochard. 62p, Black swan. 70p, Eurasian wigeon.
£2, Mallard, vert.

| | | **2004, Apr. 6** | **Perf. 14¾x14** |
|---|---|---|---|
| 1116 | A227 | 32p multi | .90 | .90 |
| 1117 | A227 | 33p multi | 1.00 | 1.00 |
| 1118 | A227 | 40p multi | 1.10 | 1.10 |
| 1119 | A227 | 49p multi | 1.45 | 1.45 |
| 1120 | A227 | 62p multi | 1.80 | 1.80 |
| 1121 | A227 | 70p multi | 2.00 | 2.00 |
| | | Nos. 1116-1121 (6) | 8.25 | 8.25 |

**Souvenir Sheet**
**Perf. 14¼**

| 1122 | A227 | £2 multi | 6.25 | 6.25 |
|---|---|---|---|---|

No. 1122 contains one 38x50mm stamp.

Orchids — A228

Designs: 32p, Cymbidium lowianum "Concolor." 33p, Phragmipedium besseae var. flavum. 40p, Peristeria elata. 54p, Cymbidium tracyanum. 62p, Paphiopedilum "Victoria Village Isle of Jersey." 70p, Paphiopedilum hirsutissimum.

£2, Phragmipedium "Jason Fischer."

**2004, May 25**     *Perf. 13x13¼*
| | | | | |
|---|---|---|---|---|
| 1123 | A228 | 32p multi | .90 | .90 |
| 1124 | A228 | 33p multi | .95 | .95 |
| 1125 | A228 | 40p multi | 1.10 | 1.10 |
| 1126 | A228 | 54p multi | 1.55 | 1.55 |
| 1127 | A228 | 62p multi | 1.75 | 1.75 |
| 1128 | A228 | 70p multi | 1.95 | 1.95 |
| a. | | Booklet pane #1123-1128 | 5.00 | — |
| | | Nos. 1123-1128 (6) | 8.20 | 8.20 |

**Souvenir Sheet**
| | | | | |
|---|---|---|---|---|
| 1129 | A228 | £2 multi | 6.00 | 6.00 |
| a. | | Booklet pane #1129 | 6.00 | — |
| | | Complete booklet, #1129a, 3 #1128a | 22.50 | |
| b. | | Like #1129, with added marginal inscription | 6.50 | 6.50 |

The booklet contains three examples of No. 1128a each with different arrangements of the stamps. No. 1129a has a larger margin than No. 1129.

No. 1129b issued 6/26. It is inscribed "Jersey at / Le Salon du Timbre 2004" in margin.

**Souvenir Sheet**

D-Day, 60th Anniv. A229

**2004, June 4**     *Perf. 13*
| | | | | |
|---|---|---|---|---|
| 1130 | A229 | £2 multi | 5.75 | 5.75 |

Mont Orgueil Castle and Monarchs — A230

No. 1131: a, Castle in 13th century (49x32mm). b, King John, vert. (29x32mm).
No. 1132: a, Castle in 17th century (49x32mm). b, King Charles II, vert. (29x32mm).
No. 1133: a, Castle in 21st century (49x32mm). b, Queen Elizabeth II, vert. (29x32mm).

**2004, June 25**     *Perf. 14¾*
| | | | | |
|---|---|---|---|---|
| 1131 | A230 | Horiz. pair | 1.80 | 1.80 |
| a.-b. | | 32p Either single | .90 | .90 |
| 1132 | A230 | Horiz. pair | 1.80 | 1.80 |
| a.-b. | | 33p Either single | .90 | .90 |
| 1133 | A230 | Horiz. pair | 2.50 | 2.50 |
| a.-b. | | 40p Either single | 1.25 | 1.25 |
| | | Nos. 1131-1133 (3) | 6.10 | 6.10 |

Worldwide Fund for Nature (WWF) — A231

Designs: 32p, Wall lizard. 33p, Ant lion. 49p, Field cricket. 70p, Dartford warbler.

**2004, July 27**     *Perf. 14¾x14*
| | | | | |
|---|---|---|---|---|
| 1134 | A231 | 32p multi | 1.05 | 1.05 |
| 1135 | A231 | 33p multi | 1.05 | 1.05 |
| 1136 | A231 | 49p multi | 1.70 | 1.70 |
| 1137 | A231 | 70p multi | 2.35 | 2.35 |
| a. | | Miniature sheet, 2 each #1134-1137 | 12.50 | 12.50 |
| | | Nos. 1134-1137 (4) | 6.15 | 6.15 |

Corals — A232

Designs: 32p, Dead man's fingers. 33p, Devonshire cup. 40p, White sea fan. 54p, Pink sea fan. 62p, Sunset cup. 70p, Red fingers.

**2004, Sept. 28**    **Litho.**    *Perf. 13x13¼*
| | | | | |
|---|---|---|---|---|
| 1138 | A232 | 32p multi | .90 | .90 |
| 1139 | A232 | 33p multi | .90 | .90 |
| 1140 | A232 | 40p multi | 1.15 | 1.15 |
| 1141 | A232 | 50p multi | 1.50 | 1.50 |
| 1142 | A232 | 62p multi | 1.80 | 1.80 |
| 1143 | A232 | 70p multi | 1.95 | 1.95 |
| a. | | Souvenir sheet, #1141-1143 | 6.25 | 6.25 |
| | | Nos. 1138-1143 (6) | 8.20 | 8.20 |

---

Christmas — A233

No. 1144: a, Nativity. b, Street with Christmas decorations. c, Santa Claus, children, Christmas tree. d, Church interior. e, Candles and holly. Each inscribed "Jersey Minimum Postage Paid."
No. 1145: a, Madonna and Child, lilies. b, Christmas stocking on mantle. c, Candles and flowers. d, Angel and candle. e, Candles in window. Each inscribed "U.K. Minimum Postage Paid."

*Serpentine Die Cut 11¼x11½*
**2004, Nov. 2**    **Litho.**    **Self-Adhesive Coil Stamps**
| | | | | |
|---|---|---|---|---|
| 1144 | | Horiz. strip of 5 | 5.00 | |
| a.-e. | | A233 (32p) Any single | 1.10 | 1.10 |
| f. | | Like #1144, inscribed "2005" | 6.00 | |
| g.-k. | | A233 (32p) Any single | 1.25 | 1.25 |
| l. | | Like #1144, inscribed "2006" | 6.00 | |
| m.-q. | | A233 (32p) Any single | 1.25 | 1.25 |
| 1145 | | Horiz. strip of 5 | 5.25 | |
| a.-e. | | A233 (33p) Any single | 1.10 | 1.10 |
| f. | | Like #1145, inscribed "2005" | 6.25 | |
| g.-k. | | A233 (33p) Any single | 1.25 | 1.25 |
| l. | | Like #1145, inscribed "2006" | 6.25 | |
| m.-q. | | A233 (33p) Any single | 1.25 | 1.25 |

Nos. 1144f-1144k, 1145f-1145k issued 10/21/05. Nos. 1144l-1144q, 1145l-1145q issued 10/31/06.

Rescue Craft — A234

Designs: 32p, Channel Islands Air Search airplane. 33p, Burby helicopter. 40p, Beach Lifeguard Service Surf Rescue boat. 49p, Fire Rescue inflatable boat. 70p, Royal Air Force Sea King helicopter.

**2005, Jan. 18**    **Litho.**    *Perf. 13x13¼*
| | | | | |
|---|---|---|---|---|
| 1146 | A234 | 32p multi | .70 | .70 |
| 1147 | A234 | 33p multi | .70 | .70 |
| 1148 | A234 | 40p multi | .90 | .85 |
| 1149 | A234 | 49p multi | 1.60 | 1.50 |
| 1150 | A234 | 70p multi | 1.90 | 1.75 |
| | | Nos. 1146-1150 (5) | 5.80 | 5.50 |

**Souvenir Sheet**

New Year 2005 (Year of the Rooster) A235

**2005, Feb. 9**     *Perf. 14¼*
| | | | | |
|---|---|---|---|---|
| 1151 | A235 | £1 multi | 3.00 | 3.00 |

Gastronomy — A236

Designs: 32p, Conger eel soup. 33p, Oysters. 40p, Bean crock. 70p, Bourdélots with black butter.

**2005, Mar. 8**    **Litho.**    *Perf. 13¾*
| | | | | |
|---|---|---|---|---|
| 1152 | A236 | 32p multi | .90 | .70 |
| 1153 | A236 | 33p multi | .90 | .70 |
| 1154 | A236 | 40p multi | 1.20 | .85 |
| 1155 | A236 | 70p multi | 2.00 | 1.50 |
| | | Nos. 1152-1155 (4) | 5.00 | 3.75 |

Europa (33p, 40p).

Fairy Tales — A237

Designs: 33p, Little Red Riding Hood. 34p, The Little Mermaid. 41p, Beauty and the

---

Beast. 50p, Rumpelstiltskin. 73p, The Goose That Laid the Golden Egg. £2, The Ugly Duckling.

**2005, Apr. 2**     *Perf. 13x13¼*
| | | | | |
|---|---|---|---|---|
| 1156 | A237 | 33p multi | .70 | .70 |
| 1157 | A237 | 34p multi | .75 | .75 |
| 1158 | A237 | 41p multi | .85 | .85 |
| 1159 | A237 | 50p multi | 1.60 | 1.60 |
| 1160 | A237 | 73p multi | 2.10 | 2.10 |
| | | Nos. 1156-1160 (5) | 6.00 | 6.00 |

**Souvenir Sheet**
*Perf. 13¼*
| | | | | |
|---|---|---|---|---|
| 1161 | A237 | £2 multi | 5.75 | 5.75 |
| a. | | As No. 1161, with Nordia 2005 emblem in sheet margin | 6.00 | 6.00 |

No. 1161 contains one 49x35mm stamp, and has a hologram applied in the sheet margin. Hans Christian Andersen, birth bicentennial.
No. 1161a issued 5/26.

**Souvenir Sheet**

Jersey Soccer Association and Muratti Vase Soccer Competition, Cent. — A238

**2005, Apr. 27**     *Perf.*
| | | | | |
|---|---|---|---|---|
| 1162 | A238 | £2 multi | 5.75 | 5.75 |

**Souvenir Sheet**

End of World War II, 60th Anniv. A239

**2005, May 9**    **Litho.**    *Perf. 14¼*
| | | | | |
|---|---|---|---|---|
| 1163 | A239 | £2 multi | 5.75 | 5.75 |

Jersey Motor Festival — A240

Automobiles: 33p, MGB GT. 34p, Mini Cooper. 41p, Citroen DS. 50p, Jaguar E Type. 56p, Volkswagen Beetle. 73p, Aston Martin DB5.

**2005, June 6**     *Perf. 13x13¼*
| | | | | |
|---|---|---|---|---|
| 1164 | A240 | 33p multi | 1.10 | .70 |
| 1165 | A240 | 34p multi | 1.00 | .75 |
| 1166 | A240 | 41p multi | 1.25 | .85 |
| 1167 | A240 | 50p multi | 1.50 | 1.50 |
| 1168 | A240 | 56p multi | 1.75 | 1.75 |
| 1169 | A240 | 73p multi | 2.25 | 2.25 |
| a. | | Booklet pane, #1164-1169 | 6.00 | — |
| | | Complete booklet, 3 #1169a | 18.00 | |
| | | Nos. 1164-1169 (6) | 8.85 | 7.80 |

Complete booklet contains three examples of No. 1169a, each with a different margin and layout of the stamps.

Flowers — A241

Designs: 2p, Scarlet pimpernel. 4p, Common knapweed. 20p, Greater stitchwort. 30p, Common mallow. 40p, White campion. 50p, Common dog-violet. 65p, Herb Robert. £1, Three-cornered garlic.

**2005, July 19**     *Perf. 13¼*
| | | | | |
|---|---|---|---|---|
| 1170 | A241 | 2p multi | .25 | .25 |
| 1171 | A241 | 4p multi | .25 | .25 |
| 1172 | A241 | 20p multi | .55 | .55 |
| 1173 | A241 | 30p multi | .80 | .80 |
| 1174 | A241 | 40p multi | 1.05 | 1.05 |
| 1175 | A241 | 50p multi | 2.40 | 2.40 |
| 1176 | A241 | 65p multi | 1.65 | 1.65 |

---

| | | | | |
|---|---|---|---|---|
| 1177 | A241 | £1 multi | 2.65 | 2.65 |
| a. | | Souvenir sheet, #1170-1177 | 9.75 | 9.75 |
| | | Nos. 1170-1177 (8) | 9.60 | 9.60 |

See Nos. 1228-1235a, 1267-1274a.

Martello Towers — A242

**2005, Aug. 9**     *Perf. 13¾*
| | | | | |
|---|---|---|---|---|
| 1178 | A242 | 33p Le Hocq | .95 | .95 |
| 1179 | A242 | 34p Seymour | .95 | .95 |
| 1180 | A242 | 41p Archirondel | 1.20 | 1.20 |
| 1181 | A242 | 56p Kempt | 1.65 | 1.65 |
| 1182 | A242 | 73p Le Rocco | 2.10 | 2.10 |
| | | Nos. 1178-1182 (5) | 6.85 | 6.85 |

Mushrooms — A243

Designs: 33p, Pink waxcap. 34p, Boletus erythropus. 41p, Inocybe godeyi. 50p, Pepperpot earthstar. 56p, White elfin saddle. 73p, Red waxy cap.
£2, Fairy ring mushrooms, horiz.

**2005, Sept. 13**     *Perf. 13¾*
| | | | | |
|---|---|---|---|---|
| 1183 | A243 | 33p multi | .95 | .95 |
| 1184 | A243 | 34p multi | .95 | .95 |
| 1185 | A243 | 41p multi | 1.15 | 1.15 |
| 1186 | A243 | 50p multi | 1.40 | 1.40 |
| 1187 | A243 | 56p multi | 1.65 | 1.65 |
| 1188 | A243 | 73p multi | 2.10 | 2.10 |
| | | Nos. 1183-1188 (6) | 8.20 | 8.20 |

**Souvenir Sheet**
*Perf. 14¼*
| | | | | |
|---|---|---|---|---|
| 1189 | A243 | £2 multi | 6.50 | 6.50 |

No. 1189 contains one 50x38mm stamp.

Battle of Trafalgar, Bicent. — A244

Designs: 33p, HMS Belleisle. 34p, HMS Royal Sovereign. 41p, HMS Neptune. 50p, HMS Euryalus. 73p, HMS Mars. £2, HMS Victory.

**2005, Oct. 21**     *Perf. 14*
| | | | | |
|---|---|---|---|---|
| 1190 | A244 | 33p multi | .90 | .90 |
| 1191 | A244 | 34p multi | .90 | .90 |
| 1192 | A244 | 41p multi | 1.15 | 1.15 |
| 1193 | A244 | 50p multi | 1.60 | 1.60 |
| 1194 | A244 | 73p multi | 2.05 | 2.05 |
| | | Nos. 1190-1194 (5) | 6.60 | 6.60 |

**Souvenir Sheet**
*Perf. 14¼*
| | | | | |
|---|---|---|---|---|
| 1195 | A244 | £2 multi | 6.00 | 6.00 |

No. 1195 contains one 50x38mm stamp.

Royal Jersey Militia Uniforms and Badges — A245

Uniforms and badges from: 33p, Royal Jersey Regiment, ca. 1830. 34p, Royal Jersey Regiment, ca. 1844. 41p, Royal Jersey Artillery, ca. 1881. 50p, Royal Jersey Light Infantry ca. 1890. 73p, Royal Engineers, present day.

**2006, Jan. 6**    **Litho.**    *Perf. 13¼*
| | | | | |
|---|---|---|---|---|
| 1196 | A245 | 33p multi | .90 | .90 |
| 1197 | A245 | 34p multi | .90 | .90 |
| 1198 | A245 | 41p multi | 1.15 | 1.15 |
| 1199 | A245 | 50p multi | 1.60 | 1.60 |
| 1200 | A245 | 73p multi | 2.05 | 2.05 |
| | | Nos. 1196-1200 (5) | 6.60 | 6.60 |

## Souvenir Sheet

New Year 2006 (Year of the Dog) A246

**2006, Jan. 29     Litho.     Perf. 14¼**
1201 A246 £1 multi                3.00 3.00

## Souvenir Sheet

Victoria Cross, 150th Anniv. A247

**2006, Jan. 29          Perf. 13¼x14**
1202 A247 £2 multi                6.00 6.00

Multiculturalism A248

Designs: 33p, Chinese costumes. 34p, Portuguese Fado Music Festival. 41p, Polish Pisanki Easter egg tradition. 73p, Indian costumes.

**2006, Mar. 7          Perf. 14**
1203 A248 33p multi          1.00   .70
1204 A248 34p multi          1.00   .75
1205 A248 41p multi          1.25   .85
1206 A248 73p multi          2.25  2.00
     Nos. 1203-1206 (4)      5.50  4.30

Europa (34p, 41p).

Shells — A249

Designs: 34p, Flat periwinkle. 37p, Painted top shell. 42p, Dog cockle. 51p, Variegated scallop. 57p, Blue-rayed limpet. 74p, European cowrie. £2, Ormer shell.

**2006, Apr. 4     Litho.     Perf. 13x13¼**
1207 A249 34p multi          1.00   .75
1208 A249 37p multi          1.10   .80
1209 A249 42p multi          1.25   .90
1210 A249 51p multi          1.50  1.10
1211 A249 57p multi          1.75  1.20
1212 A249 74p multi          2.25  1.60
     Nos. 1207-1212 (6)      8.85  6.35

### Souvenir Sheet
### Litho. & Embossed With Hologram Affixed
**Perf.**
1213 A249 £2 multi                6.00  6.00
   a.  Like #1213, with Belgica '06
        emblem added in sheet
        margin                     6.75  6.75

Portions of the designs of Nos. 1207-1212 were applied by a thermographic process producing a shiny, raised effect. No. 1213 contains one 46x30 oval stamp.
Issued: No. 1213a, 11/16.

Wedding of Prince Charles and Camilla Parker-Bowles, 1st Anniv. — A250

**2006, Apr. 9     Litho.     Perf. 13¼**
1214 A250 £2 multi                5.75  5.75

---

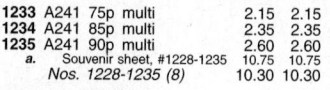

Queen Elizabeth II, 80th Birthday — A251

### Litho. & Embossed With Foil Application

**2006, Apr. 21          Perf. 13½**
1215 A251 £5 dk bl & multi       14.50 14.50
   a.  Prussian blue & multi     14.50 14.50
   b.  Souvenir sheet, #1215a,
        New Zealand #2068a        20.00 20.00

See New Zealand No. 2068. No. 1215b sold for £7.

### Souvenir Sheet

2006 World Cup Soccer Championships, Germany — A252

**2006, June 9     Litho.     Perf. 14¼**
1216 A252 £2 multi                6.00  6.00

Island Views — A253

**Serpentine Die Cut 11¼     Self-Adhesive**
### Coil Stamps
### Inscribed "2006"

**2006, July 11**
1217 A253 (37p) Greve de Lecq    1.50  1.50
   a.  Inscribed "2009"          1.75  1.75
1218 A253 (37p) La Rocque        1.50  1.50
   a.  Inscribed "2009"          1.75  1.75
1219 A253 (37p) Portelet         1.50  1.50
   a.  Inscribed "2009"          1.75  1.75
1220 A253 (37p) St. Brelade's
               Bay               1.50  1.50
   a.  Inscribed "2009"          1.75  1.75
   b.  Horiz. strip of 4, #1217-1220     6.00
   c.  Horiz. strip of 4, #1217a-1220a   7.50

Issued: Nos. 1217a-1220a, 1220c, 3/10/09.

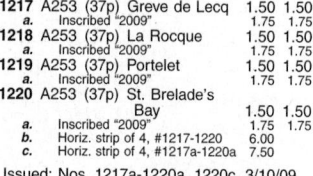

Butterflies & Moths — A254

Designs: 34p, Red underwing moth. 37p, Comma butterfly. 42p, Black arches moth. 51p, Small copper butterfly. 57p, Holly blue butterfly. 74p, Orange-tip butterfly.

**2006, Aug. 1          Perf. 14¾x14**
### Stamps With White Margin
1221 A254 34p multi           .95   .95
1222 A254 37p multi          1.05  1.05
1223 A254 42p multi          1.15  1.15
1224 A254 51p multi          1.40  1.40
1225 A254 57p multi          1.65  1.65
1226 A254 74p multi          2.10  2.10
     Nos. 1221-1226 (6)      8.30  8.30

### Souvenir Sheet
### Stamps Without White Margin
1227    Sheet of 3            5.75  5.75
   a.  A254 51p multi         2.00  1.10
   b.  A254 57p multi         1.75  1.20
   c.  A254 74p multi         2.25  1.60

### Flowers Type of 2005
Designs: 1p, Yellow bartsia. 3p, Wild angelica. 5p, Marsh St. John's wort. 15p, Bog pimpernel. 70p, Ragged robin. 75p, Brooklime. 85p, Cuckoo flower. 90p, Yellow iris.

**2006, Sept. 26     Litho.     Perf. 13¼**
1228 A241  1p multi           .25   .25
1229 A241  3p multi           .25   .25
1230 A241  5p multi           .25   .25
1231 A241 15p multi           .45   .45
1232 A241 70p multi          2.00  2.00

---

1233 A241 75p multi          2.15  2.15
1234 A241 85p multi          2.35  2.35
1235 A241 90p multi          2.60  2.60
   a.  Souvenir sheet, #1228-1235   10.75 10.75
     Nos. 1228-1235 (8)      10.30 10.30

Jersey Post Vehicles — A255

Designs: 34p, 2004 LDV Luton Van. 37p, 1999-2004 Renault Kangaroo. 42p, 1994-2004 LDV Pilot. 51p, 1988-96 Ford Transit Luton Body. 57p, Morris Marina 440/575, c. 1978. 74p, Morris Minor, c. 1969.

**2006, Oct. 31          Perf. 13x13¼**
1236 A255 34p multi          1.00   .75
1237 A255 37p multi          1.10   .80
1238 A255 42p multi          1.25   .90
1239 A255 51p multi          1.50  1.10
1240 A255 57p multi          1.75  1.20
1241 A255 74p multi          2.25  1.60
   a.  Booklet pane, #1236-1241      6.00   —
   b.  Booklet pane, #1239-1241 +
        binding stub               4.00   —
        Complete booklet, #1241b,
        3 #1241a                   22.50
   c.  Souvenir sheet, #1239-1241   5.75  5.75

No. 1241a has three different layouts of stamps on pane and three different margins. No. 1241c has a straight edge at left, while No. 1241b is separated from binding stub by a row of rouletting.

Minerals — A256

Designs: 34p, Molybdenite. 37p, Muscovite in pegmatite vein, feldspar and quartz. 42p, Orthoclase and plagioclase. 51p, Quartz coated with manganese oxide. 74p, Smoky quartz.

**2007, Jan. 23     Litho.     Perf. 13x13¼**
1242 A256 34p multi          1.00  1.00
1243 A256 37p multi          1.10  1.10
1244 A256 42p multi          1.25  1.25
1245 A256 51p multi          1.50  1.50
1246 A256 74p multi          2.25  2.25
     Nos. 1242-1246 (5)      7.10  7.10

### Souvenir Sheet

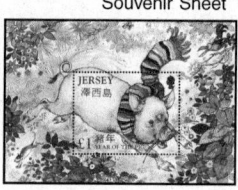

New Year 2007 (Year of the Pig) A257

**2007, Feb. 18          Perf. 14¼**
1247 A257 £1 multi                3.25  3.25

Scouting, Cent. — A258

Lord Robert Baden-Powell and Scouts: 34p, With kayak, sailboard and kite-propelled vehicle. 37p, With musical instruments and flags. 42p, In go-carts and wagons, scouts climbing. 74p, With uniform patches.

**2007, Mar. 6          Perf. 14**
1248 A258 34p multi          1.00  1.00
1249 A258 37p multi          1.10  1.10
1250 A258 42p multi          1.25  1.25
1251 A258 74p multi          2.25  2.25
     Nos. 1248-1251 (4)      5.60  5.60

Europa (37p, 42p).

Mammals A259

---

Designs: 34p, Long-tailed field mouse. 37p, Rabbits. 42p, Polecat. 51p, Common shrew. 57p, Stoat. 74p, Brown rat.

**2007, Apr. 10          Perf. 14¾x14**
### Stamps With White Frames
1252 A259 34p multi          1.00  1.00
1253 A259 37p multi          1.10  1.10
1254 A259 42p multi          1.25  1.25
1255 A259 51p multi          1.50  1.50
1256 A259 57p multi          1.75  1.75
1257 A259 74p multi          2.25  2.25
     Nos. 1252-1257 (6)      8.85  8.85

### Souvenir Sheet
### Stamps Without White Frames
1258    Sheet of 3            5.75  5.75
   a.  A259 51p multi         1.50  1.50
   b.  A259 57p multi         1.75  1.75
   c.  A259 74p multi         2.25  2.25

Birds — A260

Designs: 34p, House sparrow. 37p, Chaffinch. 42p, Blue tit. 51p, Blackbird. 57p, Magpie. 74p, Great tit.

**2007, June 19     Litho.     Perf. 13x13½**
### Stamps With White Frames
1259 A260 34p multi          1.00  1.00
1260 A260 37p multi          1.10  1.10
1261 A260 42p multi          1.25  1.25
1262 A260 51p multi          1.50  1.50
1263 A260 57p multi          1.75  1.75
1264 A260 74p multi          2.25  2.25
   a.  Miniature sheet, #1259-1264   9.25  9.25
     Nos. 1259-1264 (6)      8.85  8.85

### Souvenir Sheet
### Stamps Without White Frames
1265    Sheet of 3            5.75  5.75
   a.  A260 51p multi.        1.50  1.50
   b.  A260 57p multi         1.75  1.75
   c.  A260 74p multi         2.25  2.25

See Nos. 1342-1348, 1389-1395, 1429-1435.

### Souvenir Sheet

Gorey Regatta A261

**2007, June 22          Perf. 12¾x13½**
1266 A261 £2 multi                6.00  6.00

### Flowers Type of 2005
Designs: 10p, Black bryony. 25p, Horseshoe vetch. 35p, English stonecrop. 45p, Tutsan. 55p, Ox-eye daisy. 60p, Rock sea-spurrey. 80p, Mouse-ear hawkweed. £1.50, Devil's-bit scabious.

**2007, July 25          Perf. 13¼**
1267 A241  10p multi          .30   .30
1268 A241  25p multi          .75   .75
1269 A241  35p multi         1.00  1.00
1270 A241  45p multi         1.40  1.40
   a.  Dated "2011"          1.40  1.40
1271 A241  55p multi         1.75  1.60
1272 A241  60p multi         1.75  1.40
1273 A241  80p multi         2.40  2.25
1274 A241 £1.50 multi        4.50  4.50
   a.  Miniature sheet, #1267-1274   15.00 15.00
     Nos. 1267-1274 (8)      13.85 13.20

Issued: No. 1270a, 6/16/11.

Summer Flowers — A262

Designs: 34p, Clematis. 37p, Roses. 42p, Honeysuckles. 51p, Fuchsias. 57p, Sweet peas. 74p, Lilacs.

**2007, July 25          Perf. 13½**
1275 A262 34p multi          1.00  1.00
1276 A262 37p multi          1.10  1.10
1277 A262 42p multi          1.25  1.25
1278 A262 51p multi          1.60  1.50
1279 A262 57p multi          2.00  1.75
1280 A262 74p multi          2.25  2.25
     Nos. 1275-1280 (6)      9.20  8.85

Airplanes — A263

Designs: 34p, Dornier Do 24 ATT. 37p, Avro Vulcan B-2. 42p, Junkers Ju-52. 51p, Sukhoi Su-27 Flanker. 57p, Boeing B-52 Stratofortress. 74p, Concorde.
£2.50, Red Arrows in formation.

**2007, Sept. 13** — Perf. 13x13¼
| | | | | |
|---|---|---|---|---|
| 1281 | A263 | 34p multi | 1.00 | 1.00 |
| 1282 | A263 | 37p multi | 1.10 | 1.10 |
| 1283 | A263 | 42p multi | 1.25 | 1.25 |
| 1284 | A263 | 51p multi | 1.60 | 1.50 |
| 1285 | A263 | 57p multi | 2.00 | 1.75 |
| 1286 | A263 | 74p multi | 2.25 | 2.25 |
| a. | | Booklet pane, #1281-1286 | 8.00 | — |
| | | Complete booklet, #1287a, 3 #1286a | 25.00 | |
| | | *Nos. 1281-1286 (6)* | 9.20 | 8.85 |

**Souvenir Sheet** — Perf. 13¼x13
| | | | | |
|---|---|---|---|---|
| 1287 | A263 | £2.50 multi | 7.50 | 7.50 |
| a. | | Booklet pane, #1287 | 6.50 | |

No. 1287 contains one 60x40mm stamp. Size of No. 1287a: 150x100mm. The complete booklet contains three examples of No. 1286a, each of which has a different arrangement of the stamps.

Jersey Attractions — A264

Designs: 34p, Queen's Valley Reservoir. 37p, Mont Orgueil Castle. 42p, Bonne Nuit Harbor. 51, La Hogue Bie. 57p, Bouley Bay. 74p, Le Corbiere Lighthouse.

**2007, Oct. 1** — Perf. 14x13½
| | | | | |
|---|---|---|---|---|
| 1288 | A264 | 34p multi | 1.00 | 1.00 |
| 1289 | A264 | 37p multi | 1.10 | 1.10 |
| 1290 | A264 | 42p multi | 1.25 | 1.25 |
| 1291 | A264 | 51p multi | 1.60 | 1.50 |
| 1292 | A264 | 57p multi | 2.00 | 1.75 |
| 1293 | A264 | 74p multi | 2.25 | 2.25 |
| | | *Nos. 1288-1293 (6)* | 9.20 | 8.85 |

No. 1290 inscribed "sepac". See Nos. 1396-1401, 1541-1546.

Christmas Songs — A265

No. 1294: a, Minuit Chrétiens. b, While Shepherds Watched. c, O Come, All Ye Faithful. d, O Christmas Tree. e, Jingle Bells.
No. 1295: a, Hark! The Herald Angels Sing. b, We Three Kings. c, Ding Dong! Merrily On High. d, Holly and the Ivy. e, Good King Wenceslas.

*Serpentine Die Cut 11¼*
**2007, Nov. 7  Litho.  Self-Adhesive**
**Coil Stamps**
**Inscribed "2007"**
| | | | | |
|---|---|---|---|---|
| 1294 | | Horiz. strip of 5 | 5.25 | |
| a.-e. | A265 (35p) Any single | | 1.00 | 1.00 |
| g. | As #1294, inscribed "2008" | | 6.00 | |
| h.-l. | A265 (35p) As #1294a-1294e, any single, inscribed "2008" | | 1.10 | 1.10 |
| m. | As #1294, inscribed "2009" | | 6.00 | |
| n.-r. | A265 (35p) As #1294a-1294e, any single, inscribed "2009" | | 1.10 | 1.10 |
| 1295 | | Horiz. strip of 5 | 6.00 | |
| a.-e. | A265 (39p) Any single | | 1.20 | 1.20 |
| g. | As #1295, inscribed "2008" | | 7.00 | |
| h.-l. | A265 (39p) As #1295a-1295e, any single, inscribed "2008" | | 1.25 | 1.25 |
| m. | As #1295, inscribed "2009" | | 7.00 | |
| n.-r. | A265 (42p) As #1295a-1295e, any single, inscribed "2009" | | 1.25 | 1.25 |

Issued: Nos. 1294g, 1295g, 11/14/08; Nos. 1294m, 1295m, 11/10/09.

---

Wedding of Queen Elizabeth II and Prince Philip, 60th Anniv. A266

**2007, Nov. 20** — Perf. 13¼
| | | | | |
|---|---|---|---|---|
| 1296 | A266 | £3 multi | 9.00 | 9.00 |

Jersey Signal Station, 300th Anniv. — A267

Designs: 35p, Sun, sunshine recorder, clouds. 39p, Clouds, weather symbols for wind speed, weather vane. 43p, Clouds, raindrops, weather symbols and barometer. 58p, Sun, thermometer and weather station. 76p, Tide measuring device, French flag, Moon.

**2008, Jan. 15  Litho.** — Perf. 14
| | | | | |
|---|---|---|---|---|
| 1297 | A267 | 35p multi | .95 | .95 |
| 1298 | A267 | 39p multi | 1.10 | 1.10 |
| 1299 | A267 | 43p multi | 1.25 | 1.25 |
| 1300 | A267 | 58p multi | 1.55 | 1.55 |
| 1301 | A267 | 76p multi | 2.10 | 2.10 |
| | | *Nos. 1297-1301 (5)* | 6.95 | 6.95 |

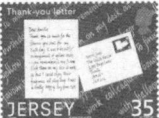

Letters — A268

Designs: 35p, Thank-you letter. 39p, Love letter. 43p, Letter to Santa Claus. 76p, Family letter.

**2008, Feb. 14** — Perf. 13½x14
| | | | | |
|---|---|---|---|---|
| 1302 | A268 | 35p multi | 1.00 | 1.00 |
| 1303 | A268 | 39p multi | 1.15 | 1.15 |
| 1304 | A268 | 43p multi | 1.30 | 1.30 |
| 1305 | A268 | 76p multi | 2.20 | 2.20 |
| | | *Nos. 1302-1305 (4)* | 5.65 | 5.65 |

Europa (39p, 43p).

Jersey Eisteddfod, Cent. — A269

Designs: 35p, Arts and crafts. 39p, Dance and drama. 43p, Speech. 58p, Films and photography. 76p, Music.

**2008, Mar. 3** — Perf. 14
| | | | | |
|---|---|---|---|---|
| 1306 | A269 | 35p multi | .95 | .95 |
| 1307 | A269 | 39p multi | 1.10 | 1.10 |
| 1308 | A269 | 43p multi | 1.20 | 1.20 |
| 1309 | A269 | 58p multi | 1.50 | 1.50 |
| 1310 | A269 | 76p multi | 2.10 | 2.10 |
| | | *Nos. 1306-1310 (5)* | 6.85 | 6.85 |

Buses — A270

Designs: 35p, Grey Bus Services Daimler CB bus. 39p, Safety Coach Service Ex LGOC K single decker bus. 43p, Jersey Motor Transport horse-drawn town bus. 52p, Jersey Motor Transport Leyland Lion Charcoal Burner bus. 58p, Jersey Bus Service Bedford WLB bus. 76p, Jersey Motor Transport Commer Commando bus.
£2.50, Jersey Motor Transport Ford Willowbrook bus.

**2008, Apr. 8** — Perf. 14¼x14
| | | | | |
|---|---|---|---|---|
| 1311 | A270 | 35p multi | 1.00 | 1.00 |
| 1312 | A270 | 39p multi | 1.10 | 1.10 |
| 1313 | A270 | 43p multi | 1.25 | 1.25 |
| 1314 | A270 | 52p multi | 1.40 | 1.40 |
| 1315 | A270 | 58p multi | 1.55 | 1.55 |
| 1316 | A270 | 76p multi | 2.15 | 2.15 |
| | | *Nos. 1311-1316 (6)* | 8.45 | 8.45 |

---

**Souvenir Sheet** — Perf. 13½x13¾
| | | | | |
|---|---|---|---|---|
| 1317 | A270 | £2.50 multi | 7.25 | 7.25 |
| a. | | As #1317, with WIPA 08 emblem in sheet margin | 7.25 | 7.25 |

No. 1317 contains one 75x30mm stamp. No. 1317a issued 9/18.

**Souvenir Sheet**

World Jersey Cattle Bureau Conference — A271

**2008, May 18** — Perf. 13
| | | | | |
|---|---|---|---|---|
| 1318 | A271 | £2 multi | 5.75 | 5.75 |

Orchids — A272

Designs: 35p, Cymbidium Avranches "Victoria Village." 39p, Miltonia "Tesson Mill." 43p, Anguloa Victoire "Trinity." 52p, Phragmipedium La Hougette. 58p, Phragmipedium Havre des Pas "Jersey." 76p, Paphiopedilum Rolfei "Trinity."
£2.50, Paphiopedilum Rocco Tower.

**2008, May 20** — Perf. 13x13¼
| | | | | |
|---|---|---|---|---|
| 1319 | A272 | 35p multi | 1.00 | 1.00 |
| 1320 | A272 | 39p multi | 1.10 | 1.10 |
| 1321 | A272 | 43p multi | 1.25 | 1.25 |
| 1322 | A272 | 52p multi | 1.40 | 1.40 |
| 1323 | A272 | 58p multi | 1.55 | 1.55 |
| 1324 | A272 | 76p multi | 2.15 | 2.15 |
| | | *Nos. 1319-1324 (6)* | 8.45 | 8.45 |

**Souvenir Sheet**
| | | | | |
|---|---|---|---|---|
| 1325 | A272 | £2.50 multi | 7.25 | 7.25 |

**Souvenir Sheet**

2008 World Cricket League Division 5 Tournament, Jersey — A273

**2008, May 23  Litho.** — Perf. 12¾x13¼
| | | | | |
|---|---|---|---|---|
| 1326 | A273 | £2 multi | 5.75 | 5.75 |

Royal Navy Vessels — A274

Designs: 35p, HMS Roebuck. 39p, HMS Monmouth. 43p, HMS Edinburgh. 52p, HMS Express. 58p, HMS Severn. 76p, HMS Cottesmore.
£2.50, HMY Britannia.

**2008, June 24  Litho.** — Perf. 13x13¼
| | | | | |
|---|---|---|---|---|
| 1327 | A274 | 35p multi | 1.00 | 1.00 |
| 1328 | A274 | 39p multi | 1.10 | 1.10 |
| 1329 | A274 | 43p multi | 1.25 | 1.25 |
| 1330 | A274 | 52p multi | 1.40 | 1.40 |
| 1331 | A274 | 58p multi | 1.55 | 1.55 |
| 1332 | A274 | 76p multi | 2.15 | 2.15 |
| a. | | Booklet pane, #1327-1332 | 9.50 | 9.50 |
| | | *Nos. 1327-1332 (6)* | 8.45 | 8.45 |

**Souvenir Sheet** — Perf. 13¼x13
| | | | | |
|---|---|---|---|---|
| 1333 | A274 | £2.50 multi | 7.00 | 7.00 |
| a. | | Booklet pane of 1 #1333 | 7.00 | 7.00 |
| | | Complete booklet, #1333a, 3 #1332a | 25.00 | |

No. 1333 contains one 60x40mm stamp. No. 1333a has a binding stub at left. Complete booklet contains 3 examples of No. 1332a, each with a different margin and different arrangement of the stamps.

---

**Souvenir Sheet**

Jersey Festival of Speed A275

**2008, Aug. 23  Litho.** — Perf. 13x13¼
| | | | | |
|---|---|---|---|---|
| 1334 | A275 | £2.50 multi | 7.00 | 7.00 |

Farm Animals and Their Young — A276

No. 1335: a, Rooster, hen and chicks. b, Sheep and lambs. c, Sow and piglets. d, Ducks and ducklings. e, Cows and calf.

*Serpentine Die Cut 11¼*
**2008, Aug. 26  Self-Adhesive**
**Coil Stamps**
| | | | | |
|---|---|---|---|---|
| 1335 | | Horiz. strip of 5 | 5.50 | |
| a.-e. | A276 (35p) Any single | | 1.10 | 1.10 |
| f. | Horiz. strip of 5, dated "2010" | | 5.00 | |
| g.-k. | (36p) As #1335a-1335e, dated "2010," any single | | .90 | .90 |

Issued: No. 1335f, 4/2/10.

Insects — A277

Designs: 35p, Carpenter bee. 39p, Buff-tailed bumblebee. 43p, Clown-faced bug. 52p, Large migrant hoverfly. 58p, Ruby-tailed wasp. 76p, 22-spot ladybug.

**2008, Sept. 8** — Perf. 13x13¼
| | | | | |
|---|---|---|---|---|
| 1336 | A277 | 35p multi | 1.00 | 1.00 |
| 1337 | A277 | 39p multi | 1.15 | 1.15 |
| 1338 | A277 | 43p multi | 1.40 | 1.25 |
| 1339 | A277 | 52p multi | 1.50 | 1.50 |
| 1340 | A277 | 58p multi | 1.65 | 1.65 |
| 1341 | A277 | 76p multi | 2.10 | 2.10 |
| | | *Nos. 1336-1341 (6)* | 8.80 | 8.65 |

**Birds Type of 2007**

Designs: 35p, Northern wheatear. 39p, Whinchat. 43p, Pied flycatcher. 52p, Yellow wagtail. 58p, Ring ouzel. 76p, Common redstart.

**2008, Oct. 21  Litho.**
**Stamps With White Frames**
| | | | | |
|---|---|---|---|---|
| 1342 | A260 | 35p multi | .85 | .85 |
| 1343 | A260 | 39p multi | .95 | .95 |
| 1344 | A260 | 43p multi | 1.10 | 1.10 |
| 1345 | A260 | 52p multi | 1.35 | 1.35 |
| 1346 | A260 | 58p multi | 1.45 | 1.45 |
| 1347 | A260 | 76p multi | 1.95 | 1.95 |
| a. | | Souvenir sheet, #1342-1347 | 9.00 | 9.00 |
| | | *Nos. 1342-1347 (6)* | 7.65 | 7.65 |

**Souvenir Sheet**
**Stamps Without White Frames**
| | | | | |
|---|---|---|---|---|
| 1348 | | Sheet of 3 | 5.50 | 5.50 |
| a. | A260 52p multi | | 1.35 | 1.35 |
| b. | A260 58p multi | | 1.50 | 1.50 |
| c. | A260 76p multi | | 1.95 | 1.95 |

Prince Charles, 60th Birthday — A278

**2008, Nov. 14** — Perf. 13¼
| | | | | |
|---|---|---|---|---|
| 1349 | A278 | £4 multi | 10.75 | 10.75 |
| a. | | Souvenir sheet of 1 | 10.75 | 10.75 |

Airplanes — A279

Designs: 35p, Douglas C-47 Dakota 3 Pion-air. 39p, Vickers Viscount 833. 43p, Handley Page HPR7 Dart-Herald. 52p, Bristol Super-freighter 32. 58p, Fokker F-27 Friendship. 76p, Bombardier Q400 Dash 8. £3, De Havilland D.H. 84 Dragon 2.

**2009, Jan. 13**     Litho.     Perf. 14

| | | | | |
|---|---|---|---|---|
| 1350 | A279 | 35p multi | .90 | .90 |
| 1351 | A279 | 39p multi | 1.00 | 1.00 |
| 1352 | A279 | 43p multi | 1.15 | 1.15 |
| 1353 | A279 | 52p multi | 1.35 | 1.35 |
| 1354 | A279 | 58p multi | 1.45 | 1.45 |
| 1355 | A279 | 76p multi | 1.90 | 1.90 |
| | | *Nos. 1350-1355 (6)* | 7.75 | 7.75 |

**Souvenir Sheet**

| | | | | |
|---|---|---|---|---|
| 1356 | A279 | £3 multi | 7.75 | 7.75 |

First flight from Jersey to Southampton, 75th anniv. (No. 1356).

Intl. Year of Astronomy
A280

Galileo Galilei, one quarter of Jupiter and: 35p, Jupiter's moon Io, Ursa Major and Cassi-opeia constellations. 39p, Jupiter's moon Europa, Boötes and Corona Borealis constel-lations. 43p, Jupiter's moon Ganymede, Cygnus and Pegasus constellations. 76p, Jupiter's moon Callisto, Perseus and Orion constellations.

**Litho. & Embossed With Foil Application**

**2009, Feb. 10**     Perf. 13x13¼

| | | | | |
|---|---|---|---|---|
| 1357 | A280 | 35p multi | .90 | .90 |
| 1358 | A280 | 39p multi | .95 | .95 |
| 1359 | A280 | 43p multi | 1.10 | 1.10 |
| 1360 | A280 | 76p multi | 2.00 | 2.00 |
| | | *Nos. 1357-1360 (4)* | 4.95 | 4.95 |

Europa (39p, 43p).

Endangered Species — A281

Designs: 35p, Blue iguana. 39p, Madagas-car giant jumping rat. 43p, Mountain chicken frog. 52p, Livingstone's fruit bat. 58p, Andean bear. 76p, Western lowland gorilla.

**2009, Mar. 10**     Litho.     Perf. 14¾x14

| | | | | |
|---|---|---|---|---|
| 1361 | A281 | 35p multi | .95 | .95 |
| 1362 | A281 | 39p multi | 1.10 | 1.10 |
| 1363 | A281 | 43p multi | 1.10 | 1.10 |
| 1364 | A281 | 52p multi | 1.40 | 1.40 |
| 1365 | A281 | 58p multi | 1.55 | 1.55 |
| 1366 | A281 | 76p multi | 2.00 | 2.00 |
| | | *Nos. 1361-1366 (6)* | 8.10 | 8.10 |

Durrell Wildlife Conservation Trust, 50th anniv.

Spring Flowers — A282

Designs: 35p, Crocus and grape hyacinth. 39p, Daffodils. 43p, Anemones de Caen. 52p, Tulips. 58p, Hyacinths. 76p, Polyanthus and primulas.

**2009, Apr. 1**     Perf. 13¼

| | | | | |
|---|---|---|---|---|
| 1367 | A282 | 35p multi | .95 | .95 |
| 1368 | A282 | 39p multi | 1.10 | 1.10 |
| 1369 | A282 | 43p multi | 1.10 | 1.10 |
| 1370 | A282 | 52p multi | 1.40 | 1.40 |
| 1371 | A282 | 58p multi | 1.55 | 1.55 |
| 1372 | A282 | 76p multi | 2.00 | 2.00 |
| | | *Nos. 1367-1372 (6)* | 8.10 | 8.10 |

Locomotives and Rail Cars — A283

Designs: 37p, 0-4-2T Mont Orgueil locomo-tive. 42p, 2-4-0T Corbière locomotive. 45p, 0-4-2T Carteret locomotive. 55p, Pioneer rail

car. 61p, 2-4-0T La Moye locomotive. 80p, 2-4-0T St. Brelades locomotive. £3, 2-4-0T Corbière locomotive, diff.

**2009, May 6**     Perf. 13x13¼

| | | | | |
|---|---|---|---|---|
| 1373 | A283 | 37p multi | 1.00 | 1.00 |
| 1374 | A283 | 42p multi | 1.15 | 1.15 |
| 1375 | A283 | 45p multi | 1.20 | 1.20 |
| 1376 | A283 | 55p multi | 1.40 | 1.40 |
| 1377 | A283 | 61p multi | 1.60 | 1.60 |
| 1378 | A283 | 80p multi | 2.10 | 2.10 |
| a. | | Booklet pane of 6, #1373-1378 | 6.25 | 6.25 |
| | | *Nos. 1373-1378 (6)* | 8.45 | 8.45 |

**Souvenir Sheet**
**Perf. 13¼x13**

| | | | | |
|---|---|---|---|---|
| 1379 | A283 | £3 multi | 8.50 | 8.50 |
| a. | | Booklet pane of 1 #1379 | 6.00 | 6.00 |
| | | Complete booklet, #1379a, 3 #1378a | 25.00 | |
| b. | | As #1379, with IBRA em-blem in sheet margin | 8.75 | 8.75 |

No. 1379 contains one 60x40mm stamp. No. 1379a has a binding stub at left. Complete booklet contains three examples of No. 1378a, each with a different margin and different arrangement of the stamps.

**Souvenir Sheet**

Surfing A284

**2009, June 2**     Perf. 13¼

| | | | | |
|---|---|---|---|---|
| 1380 | A284 | £3 multi | 8.00 | 8.00 |

Jersey Surfboard Club, 50th anniv.

**Souvenir Sheet**

St. Helier Broad Street Post Office, Cent. A285

**2009, June 21**     Perf. 14

| | | | | |
|---|---|---|---|---|
| 1381 | A285 | £3 multi | 8.25 | 8.25 |

**Souvenir Sheet**

Investiture of Prince Charles as Prince of Wales, 40th Anniv. — A286

**2009, July 1**     Perf. 13¼

| | | | | |
|---|---|---|---|---|
| 1382 | A286 | £3 multi | 8.25 | 8.25 |

Seaweed — A287

Designs: 37p, Egg wrack. 42p, Gutweed. 45p, Red rags. 55p, Sea lettuce. 61p, Lamina-ria hyperborea. 80p, Velvet horn.

**2009, July 7**     Perf. 13x13¼

| | | | | |
|---|---|---|---|---|
| 1383 | A287 | 37p multi | 1.05 | 1.05 |
| 1384 | A287 | 42p multi | 1.20 | 1.20 |
| 1385 | A287 | 45p multi | 1.25 | 1.25 |
| 1386 | A287 | 55p multi | 1.60 | 1.60 |
| 1387 | A287 | 61p multi | 1.70 | 1.70 |
| 1388 | A287 | 80p multi | 2.20 | 2.20 |
| | | *Nos. 1383-1388 (6)* | 9.00 | 9.00 |

**Birds Type of 2007**

Designs: 37p, Dunnock. 42p, Song thrush. 45p, Wren. 55p, Blackcap. 61p, Mistle thrush. 80p, Robin.

**2009, Aug. 4**     Litho.     Perf. 13x13¼
**Stamps With White Frames**

| | | | | |
|---|---|---|---|---|
| 1389 | A260 | 37p multi | 1.05 | 1.05 |
| 1390 | A260 | 42p multi | 1.15 | 1.15 |
| 1391 | A260 | 45p multi | 1.25 | 1.25 |
| 1392 | A260 | 55p multi | 1.60 | 1.60 |
| 1393 | A260 | 61p multi | 1.75 | 1.75 |
| 1394 | A260 | 80p multi | 2.30 | 2.30 |
| a. | | Souvenir sheet, #1389-1394 | 9.25 | 9.25 |
| | | *Nos. 1389-1394 (6)* | 9.10 | 9.10 |

**Souvenir Sheet**
**Stamps Without White Frames**

| | | | | |
|---|---|---|---|---|
| 1395 | | Sheet of 3 | 5.75 | 5.75 |
| a. | A260 | 55p multi | 1.60 | 1.60 |
| b. | A260 | 61p multi | 1.75 | 1.75 |
| c. | A260 | 80p multi | 2.25 | 2.25 |

**Jersey Attractions Type of 2007**

Designs: 37p, Green Island. 42p, Gorey Castle. 45p, St. Aubin's Harbor. 55p, St. Peter's Valley. 61p, La Rocque Harbor. 80p, Greve de Lecq.

**2009, Sept. 16**     Litho.     Perf. 14x13½

| | | | | |
|---|---|---|---|---|
| 1396 | A264 | 37p multi | 1.05 | 1.05 |
| 1397 | A264 | 42p multi | 1.20 | 1.20 |
| 1398 | A264 | 45p multi | 1.30 | 1.30 |
| 1399 | A264 | 55p multi | 1.50 | 1.50 |
| 1400 | A264 | 61p multi | 1.70 | 1.70 |
| 1401 | A264 | 80p multi | 2.20 | 2.20 |
| | | *Nos. 1396-1401 (6)* | 8.95 | 8.95 |

Mushrooms — A288

Designs: 37p, Parrot wax-cap. 42p, Russula sardonia. 45p, Velvet foot. 55p, Honey fungus. 61p, Orange peel fungus. 80p, Jewelled deathcap.

**2009, Oct. 15**     Litho.     Perf. 13¼x13

| | | | | |
|---|---|---|---|---|
| 1402 | A288 | 37p multi | 1.05 | 1.05 |
| 1403 | A288 | 42p multi | 1.20 | 1.20 |
| 1404 | A288 | 45p multi | 1.30 | 1.30 |
| 1405 | A288 | 55p multi | 1.60 | 1.60 |
| 1406 | A288 | 61p multi | 1.80 | 1.80 |
| 1407 | A288 | 80p multi | 2.35 | 2.35 |
| | | *Nos. 1402-1407 (6)* | 9.30 | 9.30 |

Ships on Which Sir George Carteret Sailed — A289

Designs: 37p, HMS Garland. 42p, HMS Eighth Lion's Whelp. 45p, HMS Unicorn. 55p, HMS Mary Rose. 61p, HMS Antelope. 80p, HMS Rainbow.

**2009, Oct. 15**     Litho.     Perf. 13¼x13

| | | | | |
|---|---|---|---|---|
| 1408 | A289 | 37p multi | 1.00 | 1.00 |
| 1409 | A289 | 42p multi | 1.15 | 1.15 |
| 1410 | A289 | 45p multi | 1.20 | 1.20 |
| 1411 | A289 | 55p multi | 1.55 | 1.55 |
| 1412 | A289 | 61p multi | 1.70 | 1.70 |
| 1413 | A289 | 80p multi | 2.25 | 2.25 |
| | | *Nos. 1408-1413 (6)* | 8.85 | 8.85 |

Girl Guides, Cent. — A290

Inscriptions: 37p, Healthy lifestyles. 42p, Global awareness. 45p, Skills & relationships. 61p, Celebrating diversity. 80p, Discovery.

**2010, Jan. 12**     Litho.     Perf. 14

| | | | | |
|---|---|---|---|---|
| 1414 | A290 | 37p multi | 1.05 | 1.05 |
| 1415 | A290 | 42p multi | 1.15 | 1.15 |
| 1416 | A290 | 45p multi | 1.25 | 1.25 |
| 1417 | A290 | 61p multi | 1.65 | 1.65 |
| 1418 | A290 | 80p multi | 2.15 | 2.15 |
| | | *Nos. 1414-1418 (5)* | 7.25 | 7.25 |

Maps of Jersey — A291

No. 1419 — Map: a, Circa 1685. b, Circa 1844. c, Circa 1980s. d, Circa 2000. e, Satel-lite view.

**Serpentine Die Cut 11¼**
**2010, Feb. 9**     Self-Adhesive
**Coil Stamps**

| | | | | |
|---|---|---|---|---|
| 1419 | | Horiz. strip of 5 | 7.00 | |
| a.-e. | A291 | (42p) Any single | 1.35 | 1.35 |

Children's Book Characters A292

Designs: 37p, Pushmi-pullyu from *Dr. Doo-little*, by Hugh Lofting. 42p, Elephant from *How the Elephant Got His Trunk*, by Rudyard Kipling. 45p, Mad Hatter from *Alice in Wonder-land*, by Lewis Carroll. 80p, *The Dong with a Luminous Nose*, by Edward Lear.

**2010, Feb. 9**     Perf. 13x13¼

| | | | | |
|---|---|---|---|---|
| 1420 | A292 | 37p multi | 1.00 | 1.00 |
| 1421 | A292 | 42p multi | 1.10 | 1.10 |
| 1422 | A292 | 45p multi | 1.25 | 1.25 |
| 1423 | A292 | 80p multi | 2.25 | 2.25 |
| | | *Nos. 1420-1423 (4)* | 5.60 | 5.60 |

Europa (42p, 45p).

Rocks — A293

Designs: 37p, Brecciated pegmatite, ortho-clase feldspar crystals re-cemented with chal-cedony. 42p, Diorite with incipient orbicular structure. 45p, Granite. 61p, Jasper in ande-site. 80p, Pebbles of granite, andesite and shale in Rozel conglomerate.

**2010, Mar. 9**     Perf. 13x13¼

| | | | | |
|---|---|---|---|---|
| 1424 | A293 | 37p multi | 1.00 | 1.00 |
| 1425 | A293 | 42p multi | 1.10 | 1.10 |
| 1426 | A293 | 45p multi | 1.25 | 1.25 |
| 1427 | A293 | 61p multi | 1.70 | 1.70 |
| 1428 | A293 | 80p multi | 2.25 | 2.25 |
| | | *Nos. 1424-1428 (5)* | 7.30 | 7.30 |

**Birds Type of 2007**

Designs: 37p, Jay. 42p, Great spotted woodpecker. 45p, Short-toed treecreeper. 55p, Chiffchaff. 61p, Long-tailed tit. 80p, Turtle dove.

**2010, Apr. 1**
**Stamps With White Frames**

| | | | | |
|---|---|---|---|---|
| 1429 | A260 | 37p multi | 1.00 | 1.00 |
| 1430 | A260 | 42p multi | 1.10 | 1.10 |
| 1431 | A260 | 45p multi | 1.25 | 1.25 |
| 1432 | A260 | 55p multi | 1.55 | 1.55 |
| 1433 | A260 | 61p multi | 1.70 | 1.70 |
| 1434 | A260 | 80p multi | 2.25 | 2.25 |
| a. | | Souvenir sheet, #1429-1434 | 8.75 | 8.75 |
| | | *Nos. 1429-1434 (6)* | 8.85 | 8.85 |

**Souvenir Sheet**
**Stamps Without White Frames**

| | | | | |
|---|---|---|---|---|
| 1435 | | Sheet of 3 | 5.50 | 5.50 |
| a. | A260 | 55p multi | 1.50 | 1.50 |
| b. | A260 | 61p multi | 1.65 | 1.65 |
| c. | A260 | 80p multi | 2.20 | 2.20 |

British Regional Stamps of 1958-69 — A294

Designs: 36p, Jersey #2. 39p, Jersey #1. 45p, Jersey #3. 55p, Jersey #4. 60p, Jersey #6. 72p, Jersey #5.

**2010, May 8**     Perf. 13x13¼

| | | | | |
|---|---|---|---|---|
| 1436 | A294 | 36p multi | 1.00 | 1.00 |
| 1437 | A294 | 39p multi | 1.00 | 1.00 |
| 1438 | A294 | 45p multi | 1.25 | 1.25 |
| 1439 | A294 | 55p multi | 1.45 | 1.45 |
| 1440 | A294 | 60p multi | 1.60 | 1.60 |
| 1441 | A294 | 72p multi | 1.90 | 1.90 |
| a. | | Souvenir sheet, #1436-1441 | 8.50 | 8.50 |
| | | *Nos. 1436-1441 (6)* | 8.20 | 8.20 |

Mail Ships — A295

Designs: 39p, Royal Charlotte. 45p, Dispatch. 55p, Diana. 60p, Reindeer. 72p, Caesarea (II). 80p, St. Patrick (III).
£3, Watersprite.

| 2010, May 8 | | | Perf. 13x13¼ | |
|---|---|---|---|---|
| 1442 | A295 | 39p multi | 1.00 | 1.00 |
| 1443 | A295 | 45p multi | 1.25 | 1.25 |
| 1444 | A295 | 55p multi | 1.45 | 1.45 |
| 1445 | A295 | 60p multi | 1.60 | 1.60 |
| 1446 | A295 | 72p multi | 1.90 | 1.90 |
| 1447 | A295 | 80p multi | 2.15 | 2.15 |
| a. | Booklet pane, #1442-1447 | | 7.00 | |
| b. | Souvenir sheet, #1442-1447 | | 9.75 | 9.75 |
| | Nos. 1442-1447 (6) | | 9.35 | 9.35 |

**Souvenir Sheet**
**Perf. 13¼x13**

| 1448 | A295 | £3 multi | 8.25 | 8.25 |
|---|---|---|---|---|
| a. | Booklet pane of 1 + binding stub | | 6.00 | — |
| | Complete booklet, #1448a, 3 #1447a | | 27.50 | |

No. 1448 contains one 60x40mm stamp. Complete booklet contains three examples of No. 1447a, each with a different margin and different arrangement of the stamps.

Roses — A296

Rose varieties: 36p, Nostalgia. 39p, Mountbatten. 45p, Royal William. 55p, Elina. 60p, New Dawn. 72p, Lovers Meeting.
£3, Pride of England.

| 2010, June 8 | | | Perf. 13x13¼ | |
|---|---|---|---|---|
| 1449 | A296 | 36p multi | 1.00 | 1.00 |
| 1450 | A296 | 39p multi | 1.00 | 1.00 |
| 1451 | A296 | 45p multi | 1.30 | 1.30 |
| 1452 | A296 | 55p multi | 1.45 | 1.45 |
| 1453 | A296 | 60p multi | 1.60 | 1.60 |
| 1454 | A296 | 72p multi | 1.95 | 1.95 |
| | Nos. 1449-1454 (6) | | 8.30 | 8.30 |

**Souvenir Sheet**

| 1455 | A296 | £3 multi | 8.25 | 8.25 |
|---|---|---|---|---|
| a. | As #1455, with Salon du Timbre emblem in sheet margin | | 8.75 | 8.75 |

Issued: No. 1455a, 6/12.

Sea Anemones A297

Designs: 36p, Strawberry anemone. 39p, Snakelock anemone. 45p, Jewel anemone. 55p, Parasitic anemone. 60p, Tube anemone. 72p, Beadlet anemone.
£3, Dahlia anemone.

| 2010, July 6 | | | Litho. | |
|---|---|---|---|---|
| 1456 | A297 | 36p multi | 1.00 | 1.00 |
| 1457 | A297 | 39p multi | 1.15 | 1.15 |
| 1458 | A297 | 45p multi | 1.30 | 1.30 |
| 1459 | A297 | 55p multi | 1.60 | 1.60 |
| 1460 | A297 | 60p multi | 1.75 | 1.75 |
| 1461 | A297 | 72p multi | 2.05 | 2.05 |
| | Nos. 1456-1461 (6) | | 8.85 | 8.85 |

**Souvenir Sheet**

| 1462 | A297 | £3 multi | 8.25 | 8.25 |
|---|---|---|---|---|

Automobiles A298

Designs: 39p, 1912 Rolls Royce Silver Ghost. 45p, 1926 Bugatti Type 37. 55p, 1933 Austin Seven. 60p, 1938 Citroen Light 15. 72p, 1946 Morris 10. 80p, 1949 Rover 75 Sports Saloon.

| 2010, Aug. 3 | | | Perf. 14¼x14 | |
|---|---|---|---|---|
| 1463 | A298 | 39p multi | 1.10 | 1.10 |
| 1464 | A298 | 45p multi | 1.35 | 1.35 |
| 1465 | A298 | 55p multi | 1.55 | 1.55 |
| 1466 | A298 | 60p multi | 1.70 | 1.70 |
| 1467 | A298 | 72p multi | 2.10 | 2.10 |
| 1468 | A298 | 80p multi | 2.30 | 2.30 |
| | Nos. 1463-1468 (6) | | 10.10 | 10.10 |

Fish — A299

Designs: 36p, Perch. 39p, Tench. 45p, Roach. 55p, Rudd. 60p, Mirror carp. 72p, Common bream.
£3, Brown trout.

| 2010, Sept. 7 | Litho. | | Perf. 14¾x14 | |
|---|---|---|---|---|
| 1469 | A299 | 36p multi | 1.00 | 1.00 |
| 1470 | A299 | 39p multi | 1.10 | 1.10 |
| 1471 | A299 | 45p multi | 1.25 | 1.25 |
| 1472 | A299 | 55p multi | 1.55 | 1.55 |
| 1473 | A299 | 60p multi | 1.70 | 1.70 |
| 1474 | A299 | 72p multi | 2.00 | 2.00 |
| | Nos. 1469-1474 (6) | | 9.65 | 9.65 |

**Souvenir Sheet**

| 1475 | A299 | £3 multi | 8.50 | 8.50 |
|---|---|---|---|---|

La Cotte de St. Brelade Archaeological Site — A300

Designs: 39p, Human teeth, models of head of Neanderthal man. 45p, Skull of Woolly rhinoceros. 55p, Tooth and tusks of Woolly mammoth. 60p, Flint tools and timeline. 80p, Antler of Giant deer.

| 2010, Oct. 12 | | | Perf. 14 | |
|---|---|---|---|---|
| 1476 | A300 | 39p multi | 1.05 | 1.05 |
| 1477 | A300 | 45p multi | 1.25 | 1.25 |
| 1478 | A300 | 55p multi | 1.60 | 1.60 |
| 1479 | A300 | 60p multi | 1.70 | 1.70 |
| 1480 | A300 | 80p multi | 2.20 | 2.20 |
| | Nos. 1476-1480 (5) | | 9.25 | 9.25 |

Map of Jersey and Heraldic Lions — A301

Inscriptions: (36p), Standard Letter. (39p), Priority Letter. (45p), UK Letter.

***Serpentine Die Cut 11½x11¼***

| 2010, Nov. 1 | | | Self-Adhesive | |
|---|---|---|---|---|

**Coil Stamps**
**Background Color**

| 1481 | A301 | (36p) dark red | 1.40 | 1.40 |
|---|---|---|---|---|
| 1482 | A301 | (39p) blue | 1.40 | 1.40 |
| 1483 | A301 | (45p) green | 1.65 | 1.65 |
| | Nos. 1481-1483 (3) | | 4.00 | 4.00 |

Buses — A302

Designs: 36p, Paragon C10 AEC B, c. 1926. 45p, Ramblers Tours Chevrolet, c. 1935. 55p, JMT Leyland Lioness, c. 1938. 60p, JMT Leyland PLSC1 Lion, c. 1939. 72p, Mascot Motors Morris C/F 13/5, c. 1948. 80p, Mascot Motors AEC Regal 4, c. 1961.

| 2011, Jan. 11 | Litho. | | Perf. 14 | |
|---|---|---|---|---|
| 1484 | A302 | 36p multi | 1.05 | 1.05 |
| 1485 | A302 | 45p multi | 1.25 | 1.25 |
| 1486 | A302 | 55p multi | 1.45 | 1.45 |
| 1487 | A302 | 60p multi | 1.60 | 1.60 |
| 1488 | A302 | 72p multi | 2.00 | 2.00 |
| 1489 | A302 | 80p multi | 2.20 | 2.20 |
| | Nos. 1484-1489 (6) | | 11.40 | 11.40 |

Intl. Year of Forests — A303

Tree branches: 39p, Silver birch. 45p, English oak. 55p, Beech. 80p, Linden (Lime).

| 2011, Feb. 8 | Litho. | | Perf. 13¼ | |
|---|---|---|---|---|
| 1490 | A303 | 39p multi | 1.25 | 1.25 |
| 1491 | A303 | 45p multi | 1.50 | 1.50 |
| 1492 | A303 | 55p multi | 1.75 | 1.75 |
| 1493 | A303 | 80p multi | 2.60 | 2.60 |
| | Nos. 1490-1493 (4) | | 7.10 | 7.10 |

Europa (45p, 55p).

Famous Women — A304

Designs: 36p, Dame Margot Fonteyn (1919-91), ballerina. 45p, Florence Nightingale (1820-1910), nurse. 60p, Marie Curie (1867-1934), chemist. 72p, Mother Teresa (1910-97), humanitarian.

| 2011, Mar. 8 | | | | |
|---|---|---|---|---|
| 1494 | A304 | 36p multi | 1.25 | 1.25 |
| 1495 | A304 | 45p multi | 1.50 | 1.50 |
| 1496 | A304 | 60p multi | 2.00 | 2.00 |
| 1497 | A304 | 72p multi | 2.40 | 2.40 |
| | Nos. 1494-1497 (4) | | 7.15 | 7.15 |

Marine Life — A305

Designs: (36p), Gooseberry sea squirt. (39p), Finger sponge. (45p), Purse sponge. 60p, Star squirt. 72p, Light bulb sea squirt. 80p, Red sea squirt.

| 2011, Apr. 7 | | | Perf. 14¾x14 | |
|---|---|---|---|---|

**Stamps With White Frames**

| 1498 | A305 | (36p) multi | 1.10 | 1.10 |
|---|---|---|---|---|
| 1499 | A305 | (39p) multi | 1.10 | 1.10 |
| 1500 | A305 | (45p) multi | 1.35 | 1.35 |
| 1501 | A305 | 60p multi | 1.80 | 1.80 |
| 1502 | A305 | 72p multi | 2.15 | 2.15 |
| 1503 | A305 | 80p multi | 2.30 | 2.30 |
| | Nos. 1498-1503 (6) | | 9.80 | 9.80 |

**Souvenir Sheet**
**Stamps Without White Frames**

| 1504 | | Sheet of 3 | 6.00 | 6.00 |
|---|---|---|---|---|
| a. | A305 60p multi | | 1.70 | 1.70 |
| b. | A305 72p multi | | 2.00 | 2.00 |
| c. | A305 80p multi | | 2.20 | 2.20 |

Queen Elizabeth II, 85th Birthday — A306

| 2011, Apr. 21 | | | Perf. 13¼x13½ | |
|---|---|---|---|---|
| 1505 | A306 | £3 multi | 8.00 | 8.00 |
| a. | Souvenir sheet of 1 | | 8.00 | 8.00 |

Wedding of Prince William and Catherine Middleton A307

| 2011, Apr. 29 | | | Perf. 13½x13¼ | |
|---|---|---|---|---|
| 1506 | A307 | £3.50 multi | 9.25 | 9.25 |

Printed in sheets of 4.

Orchids — A308

Designs: (36p), Paphiopedilum La Garenne "Saint John." (39p), Odontioda Les Brayes "Pontac." (45p), Phragmipedium Don Wimber. 55p, Kriegerara Kemp Tower "Trinity." 60p, Angulocaste Noirmont "Isle of Jersey." 72p, Calanthe Beresford "Victoria Village."
£3, Miltonia Poinde des Pas "Jersey."

| 2011, May 17 | | | Perf. 13¼x13¼ | |
|---|---|---|---|---|
| 1507 | A308 | (36p) multi | 1.00 | 1.00 |
| 1508 | A308 | (39p) multi | 1.00 | 1.00 |
| 1509 | A308 | (45p) multi | 1.20 | 1.20 |
| 1510 | A308 | 55p multi | 1.50 | 1.50 |

| 1511 | A308 | 60p multi | 1.60 | 1.60 |
|---|---|---|---|---|
| 1512 | A308 | 72p multi | 1.95 | 1.95 |
| | Nos. 1507-1512 (6) | | 8.25 | 8.25 |

**Souvenir Sheet**

| 1513 | A308 | £3 multi | 8.00 | 8.00 |
|---|---|---|---|---|

**Birds Type of 2007**

Designs: 42p, Barn swallow. 50p, Spotted flycatcher. 59p, Cuckoo. 64, Whitethroat. 79p, Linnet. 86p, Swift.

| 2011, June 16 | | | Litho. | |
|---|---|---|---|---|

**Stamps With White Frames**

| 1514 | A260 | 42p multi | 1.20 | 1.20 |
|---|---|---|---|---|
| 1515 | A260 | 50p multi | 1.35 | 1.35 |
| 1516 | A260 | 59p multi | 1.60 | 1.60 |
| 1517 | A260 | 64p multi | 1.80 | 1.80 |
| 1518 | A260 | 79p multi | 2.20 | 2.20 |
| 1519 | A260 | 86p multi | 2.35 | 2.35 |
| a. | Souvenir sheet of 6, #1514-1519 | | 10.00 | 10.00 |
| | Nos. 1514-1519 (6) | | 10.50 | 10.50 |

**Souvenir Sheet**
**Stamps Without White Frames**

| 1520 | | Sheet of 3 | 6.00 | 6.00 |
|---|---|---|---|---|
| a. | A260 64p multi | | 1.70 | 1.70 |
| b. | A260 79p multi | | 2.10 | 2.10 |
| c. | A260 86p multi | | 2.20 | 2.20 |

Shipwrecks A309

Designs: 37p, TSS Princess Ena, 1935. 49p, SS Caledonia, 1881. 59p, TSS Ibex, 1897. 64p, SS Schokland, 1943. 79p, PT509, 1944. 86p, PS Superb, 1950.
£3, TSS Roebuck, 1911

| 2011, July 12 | | | Perf. 13x13¼ | |
|---|---|---|---|---|
| 1521 | A309 | 37p multi | 1.05 | 1.05 |
| 1522 | A309 | 49p multi | 1.35 | 1.35 |
| 1523 | A309 | 59p multi | 1.70 | 1.70 |
| 1524 | A309 | 64p multi | 1.75 | 1.75 |
| 1525 | A309 | 79p multi | 2.20 | 2.20 |
| 1526 | A309 | 86p multi | 2.30 | 2.30 |
| a. | Booklet pane of 6, #1521-1526 | | 8.50 | — |
| | Nos. 1521-1526 (6) | | 10.35 | 10.35 |

**Souvenir Sheet**

| 1527 | A309 | £3 multi | 8.50 | 8.50 |
|---|---|---|---|---|
| a. | Booklet pane of 1 | | 7.00 | — |
| | Complete booklet, #1527a, 3 #1526a | | 32.50 | |

No. 1527 is 110x75mm; No. 1527a, 150x100mm. No. 1526a has three different layouts of stamps on pane and three different margins.

National Trust for Jersey, 75th Anniv. — A310

Designs: 42p, Marsh harrier, La Caumine à Marie Best, painted white. 50p, Swallowtail butterfly, Victoria Tower. 59p, Dartford warbler, La Cotte Battery. 64p, Red squirrel, Le Moulin de Quétivel. 75p, Marsh harrier, La Caumine à Marie Best, painted green. 79p, Puffins, North Coast sea cliffs.

| 2011, Aug. 3 | | | Perf. 14¾x14 | |
|---|---|---|---|---|
| 1528 | A310 | 42p multi | 1.20 | 1.20 |
| 1529 | A310 | 50p multi | 1.35 | 1.35 |
| 1530 | A310 | 59p multi | 1.70 | 1.70 |
| 1531 | A310 | 64p multi | 1.80 | 1.80 |
| 1532 | A310 | 75p multi | 2.10 | 2.10 |
| 1533 | A310 | 79p multi | 2.20 | 2.20 |
| | Nos. 1528-1533 (6) | | 10.35 | 10.35 |

Ancient Celtic Coins Found Buried on Jersey — A311

Obverse and reverse of: 37p, Billon stater of XN series. 49p, Durotriges base gold quarter stater. 59p, Baiocasses gold stater. 64p, Gold chute type stater. 79p, Southern British silver unit. 86p, Billon stater Coriosolite Tribe coin.

| 2011, Aug. 30 | | | | |
|---|---|---|---|---|
| 1534 | A311 | 37p multi | 1.05 | 1.05 |
| 1535 | A311 | 49p multi | 1.35 | 1.35 |
| 1536 | A311 | 59p multi | 1.65 | 1.65 |
| 1537 | A311 | 64p multi | 1.80 | 1.80 |

| | | | |
|---|---|---|---|
| **1538** | A311 | 79p multi | 2.15 2.15 |
| **1539** | A311 | 86p multi | 2.35 2.35 |
| | *Nos. 1534-1539 (6)* | | 10.35 10.35 |

### Souvenir Sheet

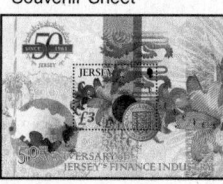

Jersey's Finance Industry, 50th Anniv. A312

### Litho. & Embossed

**2011, Sept. 12**     **Perf. 13x13¼**

| | | | |
|---|---|---|---|
| **1540** | A312 | £3 multi | 8.50 8.50 |

### Jersey Attractions Type of 2007

Designs: 42p, Beauport. 49p, St. Ouen's Bay. 50p, Ouaisné. 64p, St. Brelade's Bay. 79p, Mont Orgueil. 86p, Portelet Bay.

**2011, Sept. 28**   **Litho.**    **Perf. 13½**

| | | | |
|---|---|---|---|
| **1541** | A264 | 42p multi | 1.20 1.20 |
| **1542** | A264 | 49p multi | 1.40 1.40 |
| **1543** | A264 | 50p multi | 1.40 1.40 |
| **1544** | A264 | 64p multi | 1.70 1.70 |
| **1545** | A264 | 79p multi | 2.15 2.15 |
| **1546** | A264 | 86p multi | 2.35 2.35 |
| | *Nos. 1541-1546 (6)* | | 10.20 10.20 |

Mills — A313

Designs: 37p, Rozel Windmill. 42p, Tesson Mill. 49p, St. Peter's Windmill. 50p, Ponterrin Mill. 59p, Quétivel Mill. 79p, Greve de Lecq Mill.

**2011, Oct. 11**      **Perf. 14**

| | | | |
|---|---|---|---|
| **1547** | A313 | 37p multi | 1.10 1.10 |
| **1548** | A313 | 42p multi | 1.20 1.20 |
| **1549** | A313 | 49p multi | 1.40 1.40 |
| **1550** | A313 | 50p multi | 1.40 1.40 |
| **1551** | A313 | 59p multi | 1.65 1.65 |
| **1552** | A313 | 79p multi | 2.25 2.25 |
| | *Nos. 1547-1552 (6)* | | 9.00 9.00 |

Christmas A314

Various Christmas tree ornaments and decorations.

**2011, Nov. 8**     **Perf. 13x13¼**

| | | | |
|---|---|---|---|
| **1553** | A314 | 37p multi | 1.00 1.00 |
| **1554** | A314 | 42p multi | 1.15 1.15 |
| **1555** | A314 | 49p multi | 1.30 1.30 |
| **1556** | A314 | 50p multi | 1.30 1.30 |
| **1557** | A314 | 79p multi | 2.00 2.00 |
| **1558** | A314 | 86p multi | 2.20 2.20 |
| | *Nos. 1553-1558 (6)* | | 8.95 8.95 |

Jersey Symphony Orchestra, 25th Anniv. — A315

Various musical scores and: 37p, Violin. 50p, Trumpets. 59p, Harp. 64p, Timpani. 79p, Bassoons. 86p, French horn.

**2011, Nov. 15**      **Perf. 14**

| | | | |
|---|---|---|---|
| **1559** | A315 | 37p multi | 1.05 1.05 |
| **1560** | A315 | 50p multi | 1.35 1.35 |
| **1561** | A315 | 59p multi | 1.60 1.60 |
| **1562** | A315 | 64p multi | 1.70 1.70 |
| **1563** | A315 | 79p multi | 2.10 2.10 |
| **1564** | A315 | 86p multi | 2.30 2.30 |
| | *Nos. 1559-1564 (6)* | | 10.10 10.10 |

Tourism A316

---

Designs: 42p, Food and wine bottle. 49p, Surfer, sailboats, land yachts. 59p, Cyclist, people on pathways. 86p, Military reenactment.

**2012, Jan. 10**      **Perf. 13¼**

| | | | |
|---|---|---|---|
| **1565** | A316 | 42p multi | 1.15 1.15 |
| **1566** | A316 | 49p multi | 1.35 1.35 |
| **1567** | A316 | 59p multi | 1.60 1.60 |
| **1568** | A316 | 86p multi | 2.30 2.30 |
| | *Nos. 1565-1568 (4)* | | 6.40 6.40 |

Europa (49p, 59p).

Reign of Queen Elizabeth II, 60th Anniv. A317

Nos. 1569 and 1570: a, Queen Elizabeth II. b, King George VI.

**2012, Feb. 6**   **Litho.**    **Perf. 13½**

### Stamps With White Frames

| | | | |
|---|---|---|---|
| **1569** | A317 | Horiz. pair | 11.00 11.00 |
| ***a.-b.*** | | £2 Either single | 5.50 5.50 |

### Souvenir Sheet
### Stamps Without White Frames

| | | | |
|---|---|---|---|
| **1570** | A317 | Sheet of 2 | 11.00 11.00 |
| ***a.-b.*** | | £2 Either single | 5.50 5.50 |

A sheet similar to No. 1570 having a diamond attached to the crown in the sheet margin was produced in limited quantities and sold for £131.95.

Jersey Airport, 75th Anniv. — A318

Aircraft at Jersey Airport: 37p, DeHavilland DH86. 49p, Bristol 170 Wayfarer. 50p, Airspeed Ambassador. 64p, Hawker Siddeley Trident. 79p, Britten-Norman Trislander. 86p, Vickers VC10. £3, Fairchild Dornier 328-110.

**2012, Mar. 10**     **Perf. 13x13¼**

| | | | |
|---|---|---|---|
| **1571** | A318 | 37p multi | 1.10 1.10 |
| **1572** | A318 | 49p multi | 1.40 1.40 |
| **1573** | A318 | 50p multi | 1.40 1.40 |
| **1574** | A318 | 64p multi | 1.85 1.85 |
| **1575** | A318 | 79p multi | 2.20 2.20 |
| **1576** | A318 | 86p multi | 2.40 2.40 |
| ***a.*** | | Booklet pane of 6, #1571-1576 | 7.00 |
| | *Nos. 1571-1576 (6)* | | 10.35 10.35 |

### Souvenir Sheet
### Perf. 13¼x13

| | | | |
|---|---|---|---|
| **1577** | A318 | £3 multi | 7.00 7.00 |
| ***a.*** | | Booklet pane of 1, 163x100mm | 9.50 9.50 |
| | Complete booklet, #1577a, 3 #1576a | | 32.50 |

No. 1577 contains one 60x40mm stamp. Sheet size of No. 1577: 110x75mm. Complete booklet contains three examples of No. 1576a, each with different arrangements of the stamps.

### Souvenir Sheet

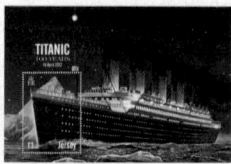

Sinking of the Titanic, Cent. A319

**2012, Apr. 14**      **Perf. 14¼**

| | | | |
|---|---|---|---|
| **1578** | A319 | £3 multi | 8.25 8.25 |

Butterflies and Moths — A320

Designs: (45p), Broad-bordered yellow underwing moth. (55p), Painted lady butterfly. (60p), Merveille du jour moth. (68p), Queen of Spain fritillary butterfly. (72p), Large emerald moth. (86p), Red admiral butterfly.

---

**2012, May 8**     **Perf. 13x13¼**

### Stamps With White Frames

| | | | |
|---|---|---|---|
| **1579** | A320 | (45p) multi | 1.25 1.25 |
| **1580** | A320 | (55p) multi | 1.55 1.55 |
| **1581** | A320 | (60p) multi | 1.70 1.70 |
| **1582** | A320 | (68p) multi | 1.90 1.90 |
| **1583** | A320 | (72p) multi | 2.00 2.00 |
| **1584** | A320 | (86p) multi | 2.45 2.45 |
| | *Nos. 1579-1584 (6)* | | 10.85 10.85 |

### Souvenir Sheet
### Stamps Without White Frame

| | | | |
|---|---|---|---|
| **1585** | | Sheet of 3 | 6.50 6.50 |
| ***a.*** | A320 | (68p) multi | 1.90 1.90 |
| ***b.*** | A320 | (72p) multi | 2.00 2.00 |
| ***c.*** | A320 | (86p) multi | 2.45 2.45 |

Inscriptions: No. 1579, "Local Letter." No. 1580, "UK Letter." No. 1581, "Europe." Nos. 1582, 1585a, "Local Large." Nos. 1583, 1585b, "UK Large." Nos. 1584, 1585c, "International."

Mont Orgueil Castle A321

Archirondel Tower A322

La Corbière Lighthouse A323

Clasped Hands Sculpture A324

### Serpentine Die Cut 13½

**2012, May 8**       **Litho.**

### Self-Adhesive

| | | | |
|---|---|---|---|
| **1586** | A321 | (45p) multi | 1.50 1.50 |
| ***a.*** | | Serpentine die cut 12½x12¾ | 1.50 1.50 |
| **1587** | A322 | (45p) multi | 1.50 1.50 |
| ***a.*** | | Booklet pane of 10 | 15.00 |
| ***b.*** | | Serpentine die cut 12½x12¾ | 1.50 1.50 |
| **1588** | A323 | (55p) multi | 1.90 1.90 |
| ***a.*** | | Serpentine die cut 12½x12¾ | 1.90 1.90 |
| **1589** | A324 | (55p) multi | 1.90 1.90 |
| ***a.*** | | Booklet pane of 10 | 19.00 |
| ***b.*** | | Serpentine die cut 12½x12¾ | 1.90 1.90 |
| ***c.*** | | Miniature sheet of 4, #1586a, 1587b, 1588a, 1589b | 7.00 |
| | *Nos. 1586-1589 (4)* | | 6.80 6.80 |

Reign of Queen Elizabeth II, 60th Anniv. — A325

### Litho. with Hologram Affixed

**2012, June 1**       **Perf. 13¼**

| | | | |
|---|---|---|---|
| **1590** | A325 | £10 blk & sil | 27.50 27.50 |

Duke of Cambridge, 30th Birthday — A326

Prince William wearing various military uniforms. 68p, 70p, horiz.

**2012, June 21**   **Litho.**    **Perf. 14**

| | | | |
|---|---|---|---|
| **1591** | A326 | 45p multi | 1.25 1.25 |
| **1592** | A326 | 68p multi | 1.85 1.85 |
| **1593** | A326 | 70p multi | 1.95 1.95 |
| **1594** | A326 | 88p multi | 2.40 2.40 |
| | *Nos. 1591-1594 (4)* | | 7.45 7.45 |

---

Trees — A327

Designs: 45p, Magnolia. 55p, Swamp cypress. 60p, Flowering cherry. 68p, Maidenhair. 70p, Hill cherry. 88p, London plane.

**2012, July 3**     **Perf. 13¼x14**

| | | | |
|---|---|---|---|
| **1595** | A327 | 45p multi | 1.25 1.25 |
| **1596** | A327 | 55p multi | 1.55 1.55 |
| **1597** | A327 | 60p multi | 1.65 1.65 |
| **1598** | A327 | 68p multi | 1.85 1.85 |
| **1599** | A327 | 70p multi | 2.00 2.00 |
| **1600** | A327 | 88p multi | 2.40 2.40 |
| | *Nos. 1595-1600 (6)* | | 10.70 10.70 |

Celebrations — A328

Designs: No. 1601, Champagne flutes. No. 1602, Flower. No. 1603, Curled ribbons. No. 1604, Teddy bear. No. 1605, Balloons. No. 1606, Birthday candles on cake. No. 1607, Ribbon bow. No. 1608, Ribbon in shape of heart.

### Serpentine Die Cut 12½x12

**2012, Aug. 2**     **Self-Adhesive**

### Inscribed "Local Letter"

| | | | |
|---|---|---|---|
| **1601** | A328 | (45p) multi | 1.35 1.35 |
| **1602** | A328 | (45p) multi | 1.35 1.35 |
| **1603** | A328 | (45p) multi | 1.35 1.35 |
| **1604** | A328 | (45p) multi | 1.35 1.35 |

### Inscribed "UK Letter"

| | | | |
|---|---|---|---|
| **1605** | A328 | (55p) multi | 1.60 1.60 |
| **1606** | A328 | (55p) multi | 1.60 1.60 |
| **1607** | A328 | (55p) multi | 1.60 1.60 |
| **1608** | A328 | (55p) multi | 1.60 1.60 |
| ***a.*** | | Miniature sheet of 8, #1601-1608 | 11.75 |
| | *Nos. 1601-1608 (8)* | | 11.80 11.80 |

Nos. 1601-1608 were each available in sheets of 20 stamps + 20 labels that could be personalized.

### Birds Type of 2007

Designs: 45p, Lesser spotted woodpecker. 55p, Stonechat. 60p, Yellowhammer. 68p, Serin. 70p, Bullfinch. 88p, Cirl bunting.

### Stamps With White Frames

**2012, Aug. 14**     **Perf. 13x13½**

| | | | |
|---|---|---|---|
| **1609** | A260 | 45p multi | 1.25 1.25 |
| **1610** | A260 | 55p multi | 1.45 1.45 |
| **1611** | A260 | 60p multi | 1.70 1.70 |
| **1612** | A260 | 68p multi | 1.90 1.90 |
| **1613** | A260 | 70p multi | 1.90 1.90 |
| **1614** | A260 | 88p multi | 2.50 2.50 |
| ***a.*** | | Souvenir sheet of 6, #1609-1614 | 10.75 10.75 |
| | *Nos. 1609-1614 (6)* | | 10.70 10.70 |

### Souvenir Sheet
### Stamps Without White Frames

| | | | |
|---|---|---|---|
| **1615** | | Sheet of 3 | 6.25 6.25 |
| ***a.*** | A260 | 68p multi | 1.85 1.85 |
| ***b.*** | A260 | 70p multi | 1.85 1.85 |
| ***c.*** | A260 | 88p multi | 2.50 2.50 |

Jambo the Gorilla (1972-92), First Male Gorilla Born in Captivity — A329

Jambo: 45p, With bushes in background. 60p, Amidst trees. 80p, With two other gorillas. 88p, Head. £1, Jambo facing right, vert.

**2012, Sept. 15**   **Litho.**   **Perf. 14¾x14**

| | | | |
|---|---|---|---|
| **1616** | A329 | 45p multi | 1.30 1.30 |
| **1617** | A329 | 60p multi | 1.70 1.70 |
| **1618** | A329 | 80p multi | 2.20 2.20 |
| **1619** | A329 | 88p multi | 2.55 2.55 |
| | *Nos. 1616-1619 (4)* | | 7.75 7.75 |

### Souvenir Sheet
### Perf. 14x14¾

| | | | |
|---|---|---|---|
| **1620** | A329 | £1 multi | 2.75 2.75 |

Towers — A330

Designs: 45p, Flicquet Tower. 55p, Portelet Tower. 60p, Ouaisné Tower. 68p, Lewis Tower. 70p, Noirmont Tower. 80p, St. Catherine's Tower.

**2012, Oct. 12**     **Perf. 14**
| | | | | |
|---|---|---|---|---|
| 1621 | A330 | 45p multi | 1.30 | 1.30 |
| 1622 | A330 | 55p multi | 1.50 | 1.50 |
| 1623 | A330 | 60p multi | 1.65 | 1.65 |
| 1624 | A330 | 68p multi | 1.95 | 1.95 |
| 1625 | A330 | 70p multi | 1.95 | 1.95 |
| 1626 | A330 | 80p multi | 2.25 | 2.25 |
| | | Nos. 1621-1626 (6) | 10.60 | 10.60 |

Dolmens — A331

Dolmens at: 45p, Mont Ubé. 55p, Le Couperon. 60p, Ville-és-Nouaux. 68p, Les Mont Grantez. 88p, La Pouquelaye de Faldouet.

**2012, Nov. 2**    **Litho.**    **Perf. 13**
| | | | | |
|---|---|---|---|---|
| 1627 | A331 | 45p multi | 1.30 | 1.30 |
| 1628 | A331 | 55p multi | 1.50 | 1.50 |
| 1629 | A331 | 60p multi | 1.65 | 1.65 |
| 1630 | A331 | 68p multi | 1.95 | 1.95 |
| 1631 | A331 | 88p multi | 2.55 | 2.55 |
| | | Nos. 1627-1631 (5) | 8.95 | 8.95 |

Christmas
A332

Scenes from *A Christmas Carol,* by Charles Dickens, with inscriptions of: 40p, A Merry Christmas one and all! 45p, Bah Humbug! 50p, The End of It. 55p, Scrooge with Marley's ghost. 60p, The Ghost of Christmas Past. 68p, The Ghost of Christmas Present. 80p, The Ghost of Christmas Future. 88p, Bob Cratchit and Tiny Tim.

**2012, Nov. 15**    **Litho.**    **Perf. 13x13½**
| | | | | |
|---|---|---|---|---|
| 1632 | A332 | 40p multi | 1.10 | 1.10 |
| 1633 | A332 | 45p multi | 1.30 | 1.30 |
| 1634 | A332 | 50p multi | 1.40 | 1.40 |
| 1635 | A332 | 55p multi | 1.50 | 1.50 |
| 1636 | A332 | 60p multi | 1.70 | 1.70 |
| 1637 | A332 | 68p multi | 1.95 | 1.95 |
| 1638 | A332 | 80p multi | 2.25 | 2.25 |
| 1639 | A332 | 88p multi | 2.60 | 2.60 |
| | | Nos. 1632-1639 (8) | 13.80 | 13.80 |

Flora — A333

Designs: 45p, Camellia sasonqua "Paradise Belinda." 55p, Butcher's broom. 60p, Snowdrop. 68p, Mistletoe. 80p, Bramble. 88p, Hawthorn.

**2013, Jan. 8**
| | | | | |
|---|---|---|---|---|
| 1640 | A333 | 45p multi | 1.25 | 1.25 |
| 1641 | A333 | 55p multi | 1.60 | 1.60 |
| 1642 | A333 | 60p multi | 1.65 | 1.65 |
| 1643 | A333 | 68p multi | 1.85 | 1.85 |
| 1644 | A333 | 80p multi | 2.15 | 2.15 |
| 1645 | A333 | 88p multi | 2.50 | 2.50 |
| | | Nos. 1640-1645 (6) | 11.00 | 11.00 |

Statues of King Edward VII — A334

Statue in: 45p, Liverpool. 55p, Aberdeen, Scotland. 60p, Birmingham. 68p, Reading. 80p, Bristol. 88p, London.
£2, Queen's Park, Toronto, Ontario, Canada.

**2013, Feb. 5**     **Perf. 13x13¼**
| | | | | |
|---|---|---|---|---|
| 1646 | A334 | 45p multi | 1.25 | 1.25 |
| 1647 | A334 | 55p multi | 1.55 | 1.55 |
| 1648 | A334 | 60p multi | 1.55 | 1.55 |
| 1649 | A334 | 68p multi | 1.85 | 1.85 |
| 1650 | A334 | 80p multi | 2.15 | 2.15 |
| 1651 | A334 | 88p multi | 2.30 | 2.30 |
| | | Nos. 1646-1651 (6) | 10.65 | 10.65 |

**Souvenir Sheet**
| | | | | |
|---|---|---|---|---|
| 1652 | A334 | £2 multi | 5.50 | 5.50 |

Kennel Club of Jersey, 125th Anniv. — A335

Dogs: 45p, Boxer. 55p, Lhasa Apso. 60p, Irish setter. 68p, Kerry blue terrier. 80p, Pomeranian. 88p, Afghan hound.

**2013, Mar. 8**     **Perf. 13¼**
| | | | | |
|---|---|---|---|---|
| 1653 | A335 | 45p multi | 1.25 | 1.25 |
| 1654 | A335 | 55p multi | 1.55 | 1.55 |
| 1655 | A335 | 60p multi | 1.55 | 1.55 |
| 1656 | A335 | 68p multi | 1.85 | 1.85 |
| 1657 | A335 | 80p multi | 2.10 | 2.10 |
| 1658 | A335 | 88p multi | 2.30 | 2.30 |
| | | Nos. 1653-1658 (6) | 10.60 | 10.60 |

Postal Vehicles A336

Designs: 45p, Bicycles and mail cart. 55p, Vans. 60p, Van, truck, ferry. 80p, Airplanes and cargo bins.

**2013, Mar. 19**     **Perf. 13¼x13**
| | | | | |
|---|---|---|---|---|
| 1659 | A336 | 45p multi | 1.25 | 1.25 |
| 1660 | A336 | 55p multi | 1.55 | 1.55 |
| 1661 | A336 | 60p multi | 1.65 | 1.65 |
| 1662 | A336 | 80p multi | 2.10 | 2.10 |
| | | Nos. 1659-1662 (4) | 6.55 | 6.55 |

Europa (#1660, 1662).

Jersey Motor Transport Buses — A337

Designs: 45p, Leyland bus, La Hogue Bie, c. 1948. 55p, Leyland bus, Mont Orgueil Castle, c. 1955. 60p, Karrier Bantam bus, West Park Pavilion, c. 1960. 68p, Leyland Tiger Cub bus, La Corbière Lighthouse, c. 1962. 80p, Leyland bus, Rozel Harbor, c. 1963. 88p, Leyland Triton bus, Odeon Cinema, St. Helier, c. 1963.

**2013, Apr. 2**     **Perf. 14¾x14**
| | | | | |
|---|---|---|---|---|
| 1663 | A337 | 45p multi | 1.20 | 1.20 |
| 1664 | A337 | 55p multi | 1.50 | 1.50 |
| 1665 | A337 | 60p multi | 1.65 | 1.65 |
| 1666 | A337 | 68p multi | 1.80 | 1.80 |
| 1667 | A337 | 80p multi | 2.05 | 2.05 |
| 1668 | A337 | 88p multi | 2.35 | 2.35 |
| | | Nos. 1663-1668 (6) | 10.55 | 10.55 |

Corbiere, Winner of 1983 Grand National Steeplechase A338

Designs: 55p, Horses at start. 60p, Horses running. 68p, Corbiere jumping over fence. 80p, Horses near rail.
£2, Corbiere, jockey, La Corbière Lighthouse.

**2013, Apr. 11**     **Perf. 14x13¼**
| | | | | |
|---|---|---|---|---|
| 1669 | A338 | 55p multi | 1.55 | 1.55 |
| 1670 | A338 | 60p multi | 1.65 | 1.65 |
| 1671 | A338 | 68p multi | 1.85 | 1.85 |
| 1672 | A338 | 80p multi | 2.20 | 2.20 |
| | | Nos. 1669-1672 (4) | 7.25 | 7.25 |

**Souvenir Sheet**
| | | | | |
|---|---|---|---|---|
| 1673 | A338 | £2 multi | 5.50 | 5.50 |

No. 1673 contains one 80x51mm stamp.

International Red Cross, 150th Anniv. — A339

Designs: (45p), Tracing and messaging (volunteer at reuniting of family members). (55p), Red Cross staff and volunteers (distribution of supplies from trucks). (60p), Water, shelter and food (volunteer near water source). (68p), First aid training. (80p), Emergency response (helicopter). (88p), Protecting people in armed conflict (Princess Diana visiting minefield).
£2, Red Cross ship SS Vega.

**2013, May 8**    **Litho.**    **Perf. 14**
**Inscription at Lower Left**
| | | | | |
|---|---|---|---|---|
| 1674 | A339 | (45p) Local Letter | 1.25 | 1.25 |
| 1675 | A339 | (55p) UK Letter | 1.55 | 1.55 |
| 1676 | A339 | (60p) Europe | 1.70 | 1.70 |
| 1677 | A339 | (68p) Local Large | 1.85 | 1.85 |
| 1678 | A339 | (80p) International | 2.20 | 2.20 |
| 1679 | A339 | (88p) UK Large | 2.45 | 2.45 |
| | | Nos. 1674-1679 (6) | 11.00 | 11.00 |

**Souvenir Sheet**
| | | | | |
|---|---|---|---|---|
| 1680 | A339 | £2 multi | 5.50 | 5.50 |

No. 1680 contains one 85x43mm stamp.

Coronation of Queen Elizabeth II, 60th Anniv. — A340

No. 1681: a, Queen Elizabeth II. b, Jersey #14.

**2013, June 2**     **Perf. 13½**
| | | | | |
|---|---|---|---|---|
| 1681 | A340 | Horiz. pair | 11.00 | 11.00 |
| a.-b. | | £2 Either single | 5.50 | 5.50 |
| c. | | Souvenir sheet of 2, #1681a-1681b | 11.00 | 11.00 |

A341

Scenes From Movie *Man of Steel* A342

Various images of Henry Cavill portraying Superman.

**Litho., Litho With Foil Application (60p), Litho. & Silk-Screened (80p, 88p)**

**2013, June 7**     **Perf. 12½**
| | | | | |
|---|---|---|---|---|
| 1682 | A341 | 45p multi | 1.25 | 1.25 |
| 1683 | A341 | 60p multi | 1.65 | 1.65 |
| 1684 | A341 | 68p multi | 1.85 | 1.85 |
| 1685 | A341 | 80p multi | 2.20 | 2.20 |
| 1686 | A341 | 88p multi | 2.40 | 2.40 |
| | | Nos. 1682-1686 (5) | 9.35 | 9.35 |

**Litho. With Three-Dimensional Plastic Affixed**
**Perf. 14¼**
**Souvenir Sheet**
| | | | | |
|---|---|---|---|---|
| 1687 | A342 | £3 multi | 8.25 | 8.25 |

**Litho. On Plastic Foil**
**Serpentine Die Cut 13**
**Self-Adhesive**
| | | | | |
|---|---|---|---|---|
| 1688 | A341 | 55p multi | 1.55 | 1.55 |

Portions of the design on No. 1684 are printed with thermochromic ink, which changes color when heated. Granite grit is embedded in the ink used on portions of the deagn on No. 1685. Portions of the design on No. 1686 are printed with glow-in-the-dark ink.

Dragonflies and Damselflies A343

Designs: 45p, Beautiful demoiselle. 55p, Golden-ringed dragonfly. 60p, Dainty damselfly. 68p, Large red damselfly. 80p, Willow emerald damselfly. 88p, Scarlet darter.

**2013, July 4**    **Litho.**    **Perf. 14x13½**
| | | | | |
|---|---|---|---|---|
| 1689 | A343 | 45p multi | 1.20 | 1.20 |
| 1690 | A343 | 55p multi | 1.50 | 1.50 |
| 1691 | A343 | 60p multi | 1.60 | 1.60 |
| 1692 | A343 | 68p multi | 1.75 | 1.75 |
| 1693 | A343 | 80p multi | 2.05 | 2.05 |
| 1694 | A343 | 88p multi | 2.30 | 2.30 |
| | | Nos. 1689-1694 (6) | 10.40 | 10.40 |

Tall Ships — A344

Designs: 45p, Stavros S. Niarchos. 55p, H.M. Bark Endeavour. 60p, STS Tenacious. 68p, Eye of the Wind. 80p, Prince William. 88p, Sk/S Christian Radich.

**2013, Aug. 8**    **Litho.**    **Perf. 13x13½**
| | | | | |
|---|---|---|---|---|
| 1695 | A344 | 45p multi | 1.25 | 1.25 |
| 1696 | A344 | 55p multi | 1.50 | 1.50 |
| 1697 | A344 | 60p multi | 1.60 | 1.60 |
| 1698 | A344 | 68p multi | 1.90 | 1.90 |
| 1699 | A344 | 80p multi | 2.20 | 2.20 |
| 1700 | A344 | 88p multi | 2.30 | 2.30 |
| a. | | Souvenir sheet of 6, #1695-1700 | 11.00 | 11.00 |
| | | Nos. 1695-1700 (6) | 10.75 | 10.75 |

Military Vehicles — A345

Designs: 45p, Stoewer R200. 55p, Kettenkrad NSU HK 101. 60p, HMMWV M998. 68p, Kubelwagen Type 82. 80p, Sd. Kfz 251 Ausf C Half Track. 88p, Ford Willys Jeep GPW.

**2013, Aug. 30**    **Litho.**    **Perf. 14x13½**
| | | | | |
|---|---|---|---|---|
| 1701 | A345 | 45p multi | 1.30 | 1.30 |
| 1702 | A345 | 55p multi | 1.50 | 1.50 |
| 1703 | A345 | 60p multi | 1.60 | 1.60 |
| 1704 | A345 | 68p multi | 1.90 | 1.90 |
| 1705 | A345 | 80p multi | 2.20 | 2.20 |
| 1706 | A345 | 88p multi | 2.35 | 2.35 |
| a. | | Booklet pane of 6, #1701-1706 | 9.00 | |
| | | Complete booklet, 4 #1706a | 37.50 | |
| | | Nos. 1701-1706 (6) | 10.85 | 10.85 |

Complete booklet contains four examples of No. 1706a, each with different arrangements of the stamps and different pane margins.

Paintings of Jersey Cows by Kathy Rondel — A346

Cows named: (45p), Clover. (55p), Daisy. (60p), Butterfly. (68p), Florence. (80p), Dolly Maud. (88p), Buttercup.

**Perf. 14¼x14¾**
**2013, Sept. 20**     **Litho.**
**Inscription at Lower Left**
| | | | | |
|---|---|---|---|---|
| 1707 | A346 | (45p) Local Letter | 1.30 | 1.30 |
| 1708 | A346 | (55p) UK Letter | 1.55 | 1.55 |
| 1709 | A346 | (60p) Europe | 1.65 | 1.65 |
| 1710 | A346 | (68p) Local Large | 1.95 | 1.95 |
| 1711 | A346 | (80p) International | 2.30 | 2.30 |
| 1712 | A346 | (88p) UK Large | 2.65 | 2.65 |
| | | Nos. 1707-1712 (6) | 11.40 | 11.40 |

Formula 1 Race Cars of Nigel Mansell A347

Designs: 45p, Lotus, 1984 US Grand Prix. 55p, Williams Honda, 1985 European Grand Prix. 60p, Ferrari, 1989 Brazilian Grand Prix. 68p, Williams Renault, 1992 Hungarian Grand Prix. 80p, Newman/Haas Lola Ford, 1993 Nazareth Speedway. 88p, Mansell with Ayrton Senna at Silverstone, 1991.

**2013, Oct. 15　Litho.　Perf. 13¼x13¾**

| 1713 | A347 | 45p | multi | 1.30 | 1.30 |
|---|---|---|---|---|---|
| 1714 | A347 | 55p | multi | 1.55 | 1.55 |
| 1715 | A347 | 60p | multi | 1.65 | 1.65 |
| 1716 | A347 | 68p | multi | 1.95 | 1.95 |
| 1717 | A347 | 80p | multi | 2.30 | 2.30 |
| 1718 | A347 | 88p | multi | 2.65 | 2.65 |
| a. | Souvenir sheet of 6, #1713-1718 | | | 11.50 | 11.50 |
| | Nos. 1713-1718 (6) | | | 11.40 | 11.40 |

Prince Charles, 65th Birthday — A348

**2013, Nov. 14　Litho.　Perf. 13¼**
**Stamp With White Frame**

| 1719 | A348 | £4 | multi | 11.00 | 11.00 |
|---|---|---|---|---|---|

**Souvenir Sheet**
**Stamp Without White Frame**

| 1720 | A348 | £4 | multi | 11.00 | 11.00 |
|---|---|---|---|---|---|

Souvenir Sheet

Jersey Royal Mace, 350th Anniv. A349

**2013, Nov. 14　Litho.　Perf. 13¾**

| 1721 | A349 | £1 | multi | 2.90 | 2.90 |
|---|---|---|---|---|---|

Christmas — A350

Traditional food and drink: 40p, Christmas pudding. 45p, Mulled wine. 50p, Gingerbread men and hearts. 55p, Christmas cake. 60p, Stollen. 68p, Mixed nuts. 88p, Gingerbread house. 95p, Chocolate Yule log.

**2013, Nov. 27　Litho.　Perf. 14x13¼**

| 1722 | A350 | 40p | multi | 1.20 | 1.20 |
|---|---|---|---|---|---|
| 1723 | A350 | 45p | multi | 1.30 | 1.30 |
| 1724 | A350 | 50p | multi | 1.40 | 1.40 |
| 1725 | A350 | 55p | multi | 1.50 | 1.50 |
| 1726 | A350 | 60p | multi | 1.75 | 1.75 |
| 1727 | A350 | 68p | multi | 1.95 | 1.95 |
| 1728 | A350 | 88p | multi | 2.60 | 2.60 |
| 1729 | A350 | 95p | multi | 2.80 | 2.80 |
| | Nos. 1722-1729 (8) | | | 14.50 | 14.50 |

Manor Houses — A351

Designs: 45p, Trinity Manor. 55p, Longueville Manor. 60p, Rosel Manor. 68p, St. John's Manor. 80p, St. Ouen's Manor. 88p, Millbrook Manor.

**2014, Jan. 7　Litho.　Perf. 13x13¼**

| 1730 | A351 | 45p | multi | 1.30 | 1.30 |
|---|---|---|---|---|---|
| 1731 | A351 | 55p | multi | 1.50 | 1.50 |
| 1732 | A351 | 60p | multi | 1.70 | 1.70 |
| 1733 | A351 | 68p | multi | 1.95 | 1.95 |
| 1734 | A351 | 80p | multi | 2.20 | 2.20 |
| 1735 | A351 | 88p | multi | 2.60 | 2.60 |
| | Nos. 1730-1735 (6) | | | 11.25 | 11.25 |

Musical Instruments — A352

Designs: 45p, Electric guitar. 55p, Piano. 60p, Saxophone. 80p, Banjo.

**2014, Mar. 25　Litho.　Perf. 14**

| 1736 | A352 | 45p | multi | 1.25 | 1.25 |
|---|---|---|---|---|---|
| 1737 | A352 | 55p | multi | 1.60 | 1.60 |
| 1738 | A352 | 60p | multi | 1.70 | 1.70 |
| 1739 | A352 | 80p | multi | 2.30 | 2.30 |
| | Nos. 1736-1739 (4) | | | 6.85 | 6.85 |
| | Europa (60p, 80p). | | | | |

William Shakespeare (1564-1616), Writer — A353

Designs: 46p, Heart and dagger (Romeo and Juliet). 56p, Skull with crown (Hamlet). 62p, King chess piece (Macbeth). 70p, Raised fist (Othello). 82p, Guitar (Twelfth Night). 91p, Butterfly (A Midsummer Night's Dream).
£3, Shakespeare, horiz.

**2014, Apr. 23　Litho.　Perf. 14x14¾**

| 1740 | A353 | 46p | multi | 1.35 | 1.35 |
|---|---|---|---|---|---|
| 1741 | A353 | 56p | multi | 1.60 | 1.60 |
| 1742 | A353 | 62p | multi | 1.75 | 1.75 |
| 1743 | A353 | 70p | multi | 2.00 | 2.00 |
| 1744 | A353 | 82p | multi | 2.30 | 2.30 |
| 1745 | A353 | 91p | multi | 2.75 | 2.75 |
| | Nos. 1740-1745 (6) | | | 11.75 | 11.75 |

**Souvenir Sheet**

| 1746 | A353 | £3 | multi | 8.50 | 8.50 |
|---|---|---|---|---|---|

No. 1746 contains one 48x32mm stamp.

World War I, Cent. — A354

Designs: 46p, Poppies and group of soldiers. 56p, Poppy and torch. 70p, Poppy and soldier with rifle. 82p, Poppy and military medal. 91p, Poppy and three soldiers.
£3, Poppies.

**2014, May 6　Litho.　Perf. 13¼**

| 1747 | A354 | 46p | multi | 1.35 | 1.35 |
|---|---|---|---|---|---|
| 1748 | A354 | 56p | multi | 1.60 | 1.60 |
| 1749 | A354 | 62p | multi | 1.75 | 1.75 |
| 1750 | A354 | 70p | multi | 2.05 | 2.05 |
| 1751 | A354 | 82p | multi | 2.30 | 2.30 |
| 1752 | A354 | 91p | multi | 2.55 | 2.55 |
| | Nos. 1747-1752 (6) | | | 11.60 | 11.60 |

**Souvenir Sheet**
**Perf. 13½**

| 1753 | A354 | £3 | multi | 8.50 | 8.50 |
|---|---|---|---|---|---|

Poppy seeds are found under a gummed circle of plastic affixed to Nos. 1747 and 1748. No. 1753 contains one 40x40mm stamp.

D-Day, 70th Anniv. — A355

Invasion forces: 46p, Mine clearers at Sword Beach. 56p, Paratroopers jumping over Sainte-Mère-Eglise. 62p, Minesweepers at Gold Beach. 70p, Soldiers at Pegasus Bridge. 82p, Soldiers approaching Carentan. 91p, Soldiers off Gold Beach.
£2, Piper Bill and troops at Pegasus Bridge.

**2014, June 6　Litho.　Perf. 13¼x13**

| 1754 | A355 | 46p | multi | 1.35 | 1.35 |
|---|---|---|---|---|---|
| 1755 | A355 | 56p | multi | 1.60 | 1.60 |
| 1756 | A355 | 62p | multi | 1.75 | 1.75 |
| 1757 | A355 | 70p | multi | 2.00 | 2.00 |
| 1758 | A355 | 82p | multi | 2.30 | 2.30 |
| 1759 | A355 | 91p | multi | 2.70 | 2.70 |
| | Nos. 1754-1759 (6) | | | 11.70 | 11.70 |

**Souvenir Sheet**

| 1760 | A355 | £2 | multi | 6.00 | 6.00 |
|---|---|---|---|---|---|

Jersey in Summer — A356

Photographs by Andy Le Gresley: 46p, Boat at Belcroute Bay. 56p, Seymour Tower at High Tide. 62p, Summer Calm at Beauport. 69p, Fisherman's Chapel, St. Brelade's Bay. 70p, The White House at Sunrise. 82p, South Coast Rocks. 91p, Reflections of Archirondel Tower. £1.20, A View Underwater at Les Ecréhous.

**2014, June 30　Litho.　Perf. 13¼x14**

| 1761 | A356 | 46p | multi | 1.35 | 1.35 |
|---|---|---|---|---|---|
| 1762 | A356 | 56p | multi | 1.60 | 1.60 |
| 1763 | A356 | 62p | multi | 1.75 | 1.75 |
| 1764 | A356 | 69p | multi | 2.00 | 2.00 |
| 1765 | A356 | 70p | multi | 2.00 | 2.00 |
| 1766 | A356 | 82p | multi | 2.30 | 2.30 |
| 1767 | A356 | 91p | multi | 2.70 | 2.70 |
| 1768 | A356 | £1.20 | multi | 3.50 | 3.50 |
| | Nos. 1761-1768 (8) | | | 17.20 | 17.20 |

Royal Air Force Red Arrows 50th Display Season A357

Designs: 46p, One airplane. 56p, Four airplanes. 62p, Seven airplanes. 70p, Seven airplanes, diff. 82p, One airplane, diff. 91p, Two airplanes.

**2014, July 11　Litho.　Perf. 13x13¼**

| 1769 | A357 | 46p | multi | 1.35 | 1.35 |
|---|---|---|---|---|---|
| 1770 | A357 | 56p | multi | 1.60 | 1.60 |
| 1771 | A357 | 62p | multi | 1.80 | 1.80 |
| 1772 | A357 | 70p | multi | 2.05 | 2.05 |
| 1773 | A357 | 82p | multi | 2.35 | 2.35 |
| 1774 | A357 | 91p | multi | 2.80 | 2.80 |
| a. | Souvenir sheet of 6, #1769-1774 | | | 12.00 | 12.00 |
| | Nos. 1769-1774 (6) | | | 11.95 | 11.95 |

World War I, Cent. — A358

Designs: 46p, Jersey militiaman. 56p, Volunteer Aid Detachment nurse. 62p, French reservist. 70p, Land worker. 82p, Flag seller. 91p, Royal Navy officer.
£1, Soldiers, cannon, nurse, Union Jack, horiz.

**2014, Aug. 4　Litho.　Perf. 13¼**

| 1775 | A358 | 46p | multi | 1.35 | 1.35 |
|---|---|---|---|---|---|
| 1776 | A358 | 56p | multi | 1.60 | 1.60 |
| 1777 | A358 | 62p | multi | 1.80 | 1.80 |
| 1778 | A358 | 70p | multi | 2.05 | 2.05 |
| 1779 | A358 | 82p | multi | 2.35 | 2.35 |
| 1780 | A358 | 91p | multi | 2.75 | 2.75 |
| a. | Souvenir sheet of 6, #1775-1780 | | | 12.00 | 12.00 |
| | Nos. 1775-1780 (6) | | | 11.90 | 11.90 |

**Souvenir Sheet**
**Perf. 13½x13¼**

| 1781 | A358 | £1 | multi | 3.00 | 3.00 |
|---|---|---|---|---|---|

No. 1781 contains one 50x36mm stamp.

Roman Connections of Jersey — A359

Various depictions of military and everyday life in Jersey under Roman rule and: 46p, Julius Caesar. 56p, Governor Gnaeus Julius Agricola. 62p, Emperor Hadrian. 70p, Emperor Constantine. 82p, Emperor Honorius. 91p, Emperor Nero.
£2, Elephant in battle.

**2014, Aug. 27　Litho.　Perf. 13¼x14**

| 1782 | A359 | 46p | multi | 1.35 | 1.35 |
|---|---|---|---|---|---|
| 1783 | A359 | 56p | multi | 1.60 | 1.60 |
| 1784 | A359 | 62p | multi | 1.80 | 1.80 |
| 1785 | A359 | 70p | multi | 2.05 | 2.05 |
| 1786 | A359 | 82p | multi | 2.35 | 2.35 |
| 1787 | A359 | 91p | multi | 2.55 | 2.55 |
| | Nos. 1782-1787 (6) | | | 11.70 | 11.70 |

**Souvenir Sheet**

| 1788 | A359 | £2 | multi | 5.75 | 5.75 |
|---|---|---|---|---|---|

New Jersey, 350th Anniv. — A360

Map and: 46p, Barnegat Lighthouse, New Jersey. 56p, Elizabeth Castle, Jersey. 62p, Corbière Lighthouse, Jersey. 70p, Seymour Tower, Jersey. 82p, Statue of Liberty, New Jersey. 91p, George Washington Bridge, New Jersey and New York.

**2014, Sept. 15　Litho.　Perf. 12½x13**

| 1789 | A360 | 46p | multi | 1.30 | 1.30 |
|---|---|---|---|---|---|
| 1790 | A360 | 56p | multi | 1.65 | 1.65 |
| 1791 | A360 | 62p | multi | 1.75 | 1.75 |
| 1792 | A360 | 70p | multi | 1.95 | 1.95 |
| 1793 | A360 | 82p | multi | 2.25 | 2.25 |
| 1794 | A360 | 91p | multi | 2.60 | 2.60 |
| a. | Souvenir sheet of 6, #1789-1794, perf. 12½ | | | 11.75 | 11.75 |
| | Nos. 1789-1794 (6) | | | 11.50 | 11.50 |

Oyster Fishing — A361

Designs: 46p, Ships, 19th cent. 56p, Women hauling oyster baskets off ship, 19th cent. 62p, Oystermen bringing up catch, 19th cent. 70p, Oystermen tending to farmed oysters, 20th-21st cent. 82p, Loading farmed oysters on trailer, 20th-21st cent. 91p, Oyster boat, 20th cent.
£2, Oysters and basket.

**2014, Oct. 9　Litho.　Perf. 13x13¼**

| 1795 | A361 | 46p | multi | 1.35 | 1.35 |
|---|---|---|---|---|---|
| 1796 | A361 | 56p | multi | 1.60 | 1.60 |
| 1797 | A361 | 62p | multi | 1.80 | 1.80 |
| 1798 | A361 | 70p | multi | 2.05 | 2.05 |
| 1799 | A361 | 82p | multi | 2.35 | 2.35 |
| 1800 | A361 | 91p | multi | 2.70 | 2.70 |
| a. | Booklet pane of 6, #1795-1800 | | | 9.50 | — |
| | Nos. 1795-1800 (6) | | | 11.85 | 11.85 |

**Souvenir Sheet**

| 1801 | A361 | £2 | multi | 5.25 | 5.25 |
|---|---|---|---|---|---|
| a. | Booklet pane of 1 | | | 4.50 | — |
| | Complete booklet, #1801, 3 #1800a | | | 32.50 | |

The three examples of No. 1800a in the complete booklet have different pane margins and orders of component stamps. No. 1801a has a vertical row or rouletting at the left.

Pirates and Privateering A362

Designs: 46p, The Vulture attacking French ship. 56p, Pirates on board a French ship. 69p, Crew of French ship escaping pirates in rowboat. £1.20, Ships Charming Nancy and Le Heron.

**2014, Oct. 30  Litho.  Perf. 13¼x13¾**
| | | | | |
|---|---|---|---|---|
| 1802 | A362 | 46p multi | 1.35 | 1.35 |
| 1803 | A362 | 56p multi | 1.60 | 1.60 |
| 1804 | A362 | 69p multi | 2.05 | 2.05 |
| 1805 | A362 | £1.20 multi | 3.60 | 3.60 |
| a. | | Souvenir sheet of 4, #1802-1805 | 8.50 | 8.50 |
| | | Nos. 1802-1805 (4) | 8.60 | 8.60 |

My Moments — A363

No. 1806: a, Teddy bear, blue background. b, Balloons. c, Hands making heart, island. d, Gift box. e, Arms of Jersey. f, Fireworks.
No. 1807: a, Teddy bear, red background. b, "Hello" written in beach sand. c, Heart-shaped rock with ribbon. d, Champagne flutes and bottle. e, Flag of Jersey. f, Map of Europe with lines coming from Jersey.

**Die Cut Perf. 14¼x14 Syncopated**
**2014, Nov. 12                           Litho.**

**Self-Adhesive**
**Inscribed "Local Letter"**
| | | | | |
|---|---|---|---|---|
| 1806 | | Horiz. strip of 6 | 8.00 | |
| a.-f. | A363 (46p) Any single | | 1.35 | 1.35 |

**Inscribed "UK Letter"**
| | | | | |
|---|---|---|---|---|
| 1807 | | Horiz. strip of 6 | 9.35 | |
| a.-f. | A363 (56p) Any single | | 1.50 | 1.50 |

Christmas — A364

Santa Claus: 41p, With girl sitting on lap. 46p, Walking in snow. 51p, Wrapping gifts. 56p, At chimney. 62p, Holding cookie and drink. 70p, Holding list. 91p, Standing in snow with girl. £1.10, Leaving gifts under Christmas tree.

**2014, Nov. 27  Litho.  Perf. 14x14¾**
| | | | | |
|---|---|---|---|---|
| 1808 | A364 | 41p multi | 1.10 | 1.10 |
| 1809 | A364 | 46p multi | 1.30 | 1.30 |
| 1810 | A364 | 51p multi | 1.40 | 1.40 |
| 1811 | A364 | 56p multi | 1.55 | 1.55 |
| 1812 | A364 | 62p multi | 1.75 | 1.75 |
| 1813 | A364 | 70p multi | 2.00 | 2.00 |
| 1814 | A364 | 91p multi | 2.65 | 2.65 |
| 1815 | A364 | £1.10 multi | 3.10 | 3.10 |
| | | Nos. 1808-1815 (8) | 14.85 | 14.85 |

Dragons — A365

Designs: 46p, Beowulf dragon. 56p, St. George and the dragon. 62p, Bakunawa. 70p, Colchian dragon. 82p, Chinese dragons. 91p, Welsh dragon.

**2015, Jan. 6  Litho.  Perf. 13x13¼**
| | | | | |
|---|---|---|---|---|
| 1816 | A365 | 46p multi | 1.25 | 1.25 |
| 1817 | A365 | 56p multi | 1.55 | 1.55 |
| 1818 | A365 | 62p multi | 1.70 | 1.70 |
| 1819 | A365 | 70p multi | 1.85 | 1.85 |
| 1820 | A365 | 82p multi | 2.25 | 2.25 |
| 1821 | A365 | 91p multi | 2.45 | 2.45 |
| a. | | Souvenir sheet of 6, #1816-1821 | 11.00 | 11.00 |
| | | Nos. 1816-1821 (6) | 11.05 | 11.05 |

Arms of Jersey — A366

**2015, Feb. 18  Litho.  Perf. 14x13¾**
**Denomination Color**
| | | | | |
|---|---|---|---|---|
| 1822 | A366 | 1p purple | .25 | .25 |
| 1823 | A366 | 2p bister | .25 | .25 |
| 1824 | A366 | 3p dark blue | .25 | .25 |
| 1825 | A366 | 4p dark green | .25 | .25 |
| 1826 | A366 | 5p brown lake | .25 | .25 |
| 1827 | A366 | 10p magenta | .25 | .25 |
| 1828 | A366 | 20p orange | .55 | .55 |
| 1829 | A366 | 40p turq blue | 1.15 | 1.15 |
| 1830 | A366 | 50p yellow green | 1.45 | 1.45 |
| 1831 | A366 | £1 scarlet | 2.70 | 2.70 |

**Litho. With Hologram Affixed**
**Perf. 13½**
**Size: 38x51mm**
| | | | | |
|---|---|---|---|---|
| 1832 | A366 | £5 silver | 14.00 | 14.00 |
| | | Nos. 1822-1832 (11) | 21.35 | 21.35 |

See Nos. 2017-2022.

Hornby Toy Trains — A367

Designs: 46p, British Pullman. 56p, GWR Passenger Freight train. 62p, Flying Scotsman. 70p, Cornishman. 82p, Mixed Freight train. 91p, Caledonian Belle.

**Perf. 13¼x13¾**
**2015, Mar. 24                           Litho.**
| | | | | |
|---|---|---|---|---|
| 1833 | A367 | 46p multi | 1.40 | 1.40 |
| 1834 | A367 | 56p multi | 1.75 | 1.75 |
| 1835 | A367 | 62p multi | 1.90 | 1.90 |
| 1836 | A367 | 70p multi | 2.10 | 2.10 |
| 1837 | A367 | 82p multi | 2.50 | 2.50 |
| 1838 | A367 | 91p multi | 2.75 | 2.75 |
| | | Nos. 1833-1838 (6) | 12.40 | 12.40 |

Europa (62p, 82p).

Hubble Space Telescope, 25th Anniv. — A368

Images from Hubble Space Telescope: 47p, Light echo of V838 Moncerotis. 57p, M74 (NGC 628) spiral galaxy. 64p, "Mystic Mountain" dust and gas clouds of Carina Nebula. 71p, New Red Spot on Jupiter. 73p, Cat's Eye Nebula (NGC 6543). 85p, Mars. 95p, Rose of Galaxies (Interacting galaxies UGC1810 and UGC1813). £1.25, Pistol Star.
£2, Hubble Space Telescope above Earth, vert.

**2015, Apr. 24  Litho.  Perf. 13¼**
| | | | | |
|---|---|---|---|---|
| 1839 | A368 | 47p multi | 1.40 | 1.40 |
| 1840 | A368 | 57p multi | 1.65 | 1.65 |
| 1841 | A368 | 64p multi | 1.85 | 1.85 |
| 1842 | A368 | 71p multi | 2.10 | 2.10 |
| 1843 | A368 | 73p multi | 2.10 | 2.10 |
| 1844 | A368 | 85p multi | 2.45 | 2.45 |
| 1845 | A368 | 95p multi | 2.80 | 2.80 |
| 1846 | A368 | £1.25 multi | 3.50 | 3.50 |
| | | Nos. 1839-1846 (8) | 17.85 | 17.85 |

**Souvenir Sheet**
**Perf. 13**
| | | | | |
|---|---|---|---|---|
| 1847 | A368 | £2 multi | 6.25 | 6.25 |

No. 1847 contains one 36x42mm stamp.

Victory in World War II, 70th Anniv. — A369

"V" and: 47p, Pennants, date of liberation. 57p, HMS Beagle, 64p, Arms and map of Jersey. 73p, International Red Cross ship SS Vega, map of Europe. 85p, Buildings and paving stones in Royal Square, St. Helier. 95p, Microphone.
£3, Sir Winston Churchill, vert.

**2015, May 9  Litho.  Perf. 13x13¼**
| | | | | |
|---|---|---|---|---|
| 1848 | A369 | 47p multi | 1.50 | 1.50 |
| 1849 | A369 | 57p multi | 1.75 | 1.75 |
| 1850 | A369 | 64p multi | 2.00 | 2.00 |
| 1851 | A369 | 73p multi | 2.25 | 2.25 |
| 1852 | A369 | 85p multi | 2.60 | 2.60 |
| 1853 | A369 | 95p multi | 3.00 | 3.00 |
| a. | | Souvenir sheet of 6, #1848-1853 | 12.50 | 12.50 |
| | | Nos. 1848-1853 (6) | 13.10 | 13.10 |

**Souvenir Sheet**
**Litho. & Engr.**
| | | | | |
|---|---|---|---|---|
| 1854 | A369 | £3 org & multi | 8.50 | 8.50 |

No. 1854 contains one 58x72mm stamp.

Magna Carta, 800th Anniv. — A370

Designs: 47p, Balance (Justice). 57p, Key (Freedom). 64p, Fist (Human rights). 73p, Dove (Liberty). 85p, Map of Jersey (Citizenship). 95p, Saltire (Democracy).
£1.50, Text.

**2015, June 15  Litho.  Perf. 13¼**
| | | | | |
|---|---|---|---|---|
| 1855 | A370 | 47p multi | 1.40 | 1.40 |
| 1856 | A370 | 57p multi | 1.65 | 1.65 |
| 1857 | A370 | 64p multi | 1.85 | 1.85 |
| 1858 | A370 | 73p multi | 2.10 | 2.10 |
| 1859 | A370 | 85p multi | 2.55 | 2.55 |
| 1860 | A370 | 95p multi | 2.80 | 2.80 |
| | | Nos. 1855-1860 (6) | 12.35 | 12.35 |

**Souvenir Sheet**
**Perf. 14¼**
| | | | | |
|---|---|---|---|---|
| 1861 | A370 | £1.50 multi | 4.50 | 4.50 |

No. 1861 contains one 43x43mm stamp.

16th Island Games — A371

**2015, June 27  Litho.  Perf. 13¼x14**
| | | | | |
|---|---|---|---|---|
| 1862 | A371 | (62p) Beach volleyball | 1.85 | 1.85 |
| a. | | Perf. 13¼ | 1.85 | 1.85 |
| 1863 | A371 | (62p) Basketball | 1.85 | 1.85 |
| a. | | Perf. 13¼ | 1.85 | 1.85 |
| 1864 | A371 | (62p) Soccer | 1.85 | 1.85 |
| a. | | Perf. 13¼ | 1.85 | 1.85 |
| b. | | Booklet pane of 6, 2 each #1862a, 1863a, 1864a | 11.00 | |
| 1865 | A371 | (62p) Sailing | 1.85 | 1.85 |
| a. | | Perf. 13¼ | 1.85 | 1.85 |
| 1866 | A371 | (62p) Swimming | 1.85 | 1.85 |
| a. | | Perf. 13¼ | 1.85 | 1.85 |
| 1867 | A371 | (62p) Triathlon | 1.85 | 1.85 |
| a. | | Perf. 13¼ | 1.85 | 1.85 |
| b. | | Booklet pane of 6, 2 each #1865a, 1866a, 1867a | 11.00 | — |
| 1868 | A371 | (62p) Badminton | 1.85 | 1.85 |
| a. | | Perf. 13¼ | 1.85 | 1.85 |
| 1869 | A371 | (62p) Table tennis | 1.85 | 1.85 |
| a. | | Perf. 13¼ | 1.85 | 1.85 |
| 1870 | A371 | (62p) Tennis | 1.85 | 1.85 |
| a. | | Perf. 13¼ | 1.85 | 1.85 |
| b. | | Booklet pane of 6, 2 each #1868a, 1869a, 1870a | 11.00 | — |
| 1871 | A371 | (62p) Cycling | 1.85 | 1.85 |
| a. | | Perf. 13¼ | 1.85 | 1.85 |
| 1872 | A371 | (62p) Track | 1.85 | 1.85 |
| a. | | Perf. 13¼ | 1.85 | 1.85 |
| 1873 | A371 | (62p) Golf | 1.85 | 1.85 |
| a. | | Perf. 13¼ | 1.85 | 1.85 |
| b. | | Booklet pane of 6, 2 each #1871a, 1872a, 1873a | 11.00 | — |
| 1874 | A371 | (62p) Shooting | 1.85 | 1.85 |
| a. | | Perf. 13¼ | 1.85 | 1.85 |
| 1875 | A371 | (62p) Archery | 1.85 | 1.85 |
| a. | | Perf. 13¼ | 1.85 | 1.85 |
| b. | | Booklet pane of 4, 2 each #1874a, 1875a | 7.50 | — |
| | | Complete booklet, #1864b, 1867b, 1870b, 1873b, 1875b | 47.50 | |
| | | Nos. 1862-1875 (14) | 25.90 | 25.90 |

Nos. 1862-1875 are each inscribed "Postcard."

Battle of Britain, 75th Anniv. — A372

Designs: 47p, Mk I Spitfire. 57p, Radar installation and airplanes. 64p, Royal Air Force emblem. 73p, Royal Air Force and Luftwaffe airplane insignia. 85p, Barrage balloons. 95p, Hawker Hurricanes, map of English Channel.
£3, Sir Winston Churchill.

**2015, July 10  Litho.  Perf. 13x13¼**
| | | | | |
|---|---|---|---|---|
| 1876 | A372 | 47p multi | 1.50 | 1.50 |
| 1877 | A372 | 57p multi | 1.75 | 1.75 |
| 1878 | A372 | 64p multi | 2.00 | 2.00 |
| 1879 | A372 | 73p multi | 2.25 | 2.25 |
| 1880 | A372 | 85p multi | 2.75 | 2.75 |
| 1881 | A372 | 95p multi | 3.00 | 3.00 |
| a. | | Souvenir sheet of 6, #1876-1881 | 13.50 | 13.50 |
| | | Nos. 1876-1881 (6) | 13.25 | 13.25 |

**Litho. & Engr.**
**Souvenir Sheet**
| | | | | |
|---|---|---|---|---|
| 1882 | A372 | £3 gray, blk lil & blk | 9.50 | 9.50 |

No. 1882 contains one 58x72mm stamp.

World War I, Cent. — A373

Inscriptions: 47p, Mechanization. 57p, Communication. 64p, Camouflage and deception. 73p, Uniforms. 85p, Observation. 95p, Tactics of war.
£1, Wight Seaplane of Flight Lieutenant Charles Stanley Mossop.

**2015, Aug. 4  Litho.  Perf. 13½x13¼**
| | | | | |
|---|---|---|---|---|
| 1883 | A373 | 47p multi | 1.50 | 1.50 |
| 1884 | A373 | 57p multi | 1.75 | 1.75 |
| 1885 | A373 | 64p multi | 2.00 | 2.00 |
| 1886 | A373 | 73p multi | 2.25 | 2.25 |
| 1887 | A373 | 85p multi | 2.60 | 2.60 |
| 1888 | A373 | 95p multi | 3.00 | 3.00 |
| a. | | Souvenir sheet of 6, #1883-1888 | 13.50 | 13.50 |
| | | Nos. 1883-1888 (6) | 13.10 | 13.10 |

**Souvenir Sheet**
| | | | | |
|---|---|---|---|---|
| 1889 | A373 | £1 multi | 3.25 | 3.25 |

**Souvenir Sheet**

Sark as a Fief to the Crown, 450th Anniv. — A374

**2015, Aug. 6  Litho.  Perf. 14x14¾**
| | | | | |
|---|---|---|---|---|
| 1890 | A374 | £1.50 multi | 4.75 | 4.75 |

Queen Elizabeth II, Longest-Reigning British Monarch — A375

Photographic portrait of Queen Elizabeth II for: 47p, 1953 Coronation, by Cecil Beaton. 57p, 1977 Silver Jubilee, by Peter Grugeon. 71p, 2002 Golden Jubilee, by John Swannell. £1.25, 2012 Diamond Jubilee, by Swannell.
£3, The Coronation Theater, Westminster Abbey: A Portrait of Her Majesty Queen Elizabeth II, painting by Ralph Heimans.

**2015, Sept. 9  Litho.  Perf. 13¼x13**
| | | | | |
|---|---|---|---|---|
| 1891 | A375 | 47p multi | 1.50 | 1.50 |
| 1892 | A375 | 57p multi | 1.75 | 1.75 |
| 1893 | A375 | 71p multi | 2.25 | 2.25 |
| 1894 | A375 | £1.25 multi | 3.75 | 3.75 |
| a. | | Souvenir sheet of 4, #1891-1894 | 9.25 | 9.25 |
| | | Nos. 1891-1894 (4) | 9.25 | 9.25 |

**Souvenir Sheet**
**Silk-Faced Paper**
**Perf. 13¾x13¼**
| | | | | |
|---|---|---|---|---|
| 1895 | A375 | £3 multi | 9.25 | 9.25 |

No. 1895 contains one 28x45mm stamp.

Flowers — A376

**2015, Sept. 22  Litho.  Perf. 13x13¼**
| | | | | |
|---|---|---|---|---|
| 1896 | A376 | 47p Magnolia | 1.50 | 1.50 |
| 1897 | A376 | 47p Camellia | 1.50 | 1.50 |
| 1898 | A376 | 47p Azalea | 1.50 | 1.50 |
| 1899 | A376 | 47p Hydrangea | 1.50 | 1.50 |
| 1900 | A376 | 47p Chrysanthemum | 1.50 | 1.50 |
| 1901 | A376 | 47p Peony | 1.50 | 1.50 |
| a. | | Souvenir sheet of 2, #1900-1901 | 3.00 | 3.00 |
| | | Nos. 1896-1901 (6) | 9.00 | 9.00 |

Jersey in Autumn — A377

Photographs by Andy Le Gresley: 47p, Country Lane Near St. John's Village. 57p, Sun Through the Clouds at Corbière. 64p, Autumn in the Sand Dunes. 71p, Stormy Day at Noirmont Point. 73p, High Tide Shore Break at St. Catherine's Bay. 85p, Sunset at the Radio Tower, St. Brelade. 95p, Woodland Path Through St. Peter's Valley. £1.25, Kempt Tower Through the Beach Grass, St. Ouen.

| 2015, Oct. 15 | Litho. | Perf. 13¼x13¾ | | |
|---|---|---|---|---|
| 1902 | A377 | 47p multi | 1.30 | 1.30 |
| 1903 | A377 | 57p multi | 1.55 | 1.55 |
| 1904 | A377 | 64p multi | 1.75 | 1.75 |
| 1905 | A377 | 71p multi | 2.00 | 2.00 |
| 1906 | A377 | 73p multi | 2.00 | 2.00 |
| 1907 | A377 | 85p multi | 2.30 | 2.30 |
| 1908 | A377 | 95p multi | 2.65 | 2.65 |
| 1909 | A377 | £1.25 multi | 3.50 | 3.50 |
| | Nos. 1902-1909 (8) | | 17.05 | 17.05 |

Winning Children's Art in Stamp Design Contest — A378

No. 1910: a, Cow and flowers, by Millie Foley. b, House and flowers, by Jennifer Crocker. c, Surfboard, sailboat and Sun, by Matthew Brown. d, Children at beach, by Leah O'Brien. e, Tower, by Anna Le Moine Gray.
No. 1911: a, Puffin, by Sophie Dixon. b, Jersey Royal Potatoes, by Ciaran Britton. c, Cow and calf at beach, by Allan Giles McCartney. d, Lighthouse, by Skye Leather. e, Jersey Arms, by Claudia Dixon.

### Serpentine Die Cut 12¼x13

| 2015, Nov. 9 | | | Litho. |
|---|---|---|---|
| **Self-Adhesive** | | | |
| **Inscribed "Local Letter"** | | | |
| 1910 | Horiz. strip of 5 | | 7.00 |
| a.-e. | A378 (47p) Any single | | 1.40 1.40 |
| **Inscribed "UK Priority Letter"** | | | |
| 1911 | Horiz. strip of 5 | | 8.75 |
| a.-e. | A378 (57p) Any single | | 1.75 1.75 |

Christmas — A379

Stained-glass windows by Henry Thomas Bosdet depicting: 42p, Virgin Mary looking right. 47p, Archangel Gabriel looking left. 52p, Gabriel looking right. 57p, Mary hands clasped. 64p, Gabriel both hands shown. 73p, Mary's hands unclasped. 95p, Gabriel left hand down, right hand up. £1.15, Mary, hand over heart.

### Perf. 13¾x13½

| 2015, Nov. 27 | | | Litho. |
|---|---|---|---|
| 1912 | A379 | 42p multi | 1.25 1.25 |
| 1913 | A379 | 47p multi | 1.40 1.40 |
| 1914 | A379 | 52p multi | 1.60 1.60 |
| 1915 | A379 | 57p multi | 1.75 1.75 |
| 1916 | A379 | 64p multi | 2.00 2.00 |
| 1917 | A379 | 73p multi | 2.25 2.25 |
| 1918 | A379 | 95p multi | 3.00 3.00 |
| 1919 | A379 | £1.15 multi | 3.50 3.50 |
| | Nos. 1912-1919 (8) | | 16.75 16.75 |

New Year 2016 (Year of the Monkey) — A380

Monkey facing: 47p, Left. £1, Right.

| 2016, Jan. 5 | Litho. | Perf. 13¼ | | |
|---|---|---|---|---|
| 1920 | A380 | 47p multi | 1.40 1.40 |
| **Souvenir Sheet** | | | | |
| 1921 | A380 | £1 multi | 3.00 3.00 |
| No. 1921 contains one 60x60mm stamp. | | | | |

Royal Air Force Search and Rescue Service, 75th Anniv. — A381

Designs: 47p, Lockheed Hudson search plane over man in life raft. 57p, Rescue boat. 71p, Supermarine Walrus seaplane approaching men in life raft. 73p, Westland Whirlwind helicopter winching sinking boat. 95p, Westland Whirlwind helicopter near oil rig. £1.25, Westland Sea King helicopter making mountain rescue.

| 2016, Feb. 6 | Litho. | Perf. 13x13¼ | | |
|---|---|---|---|---|
| 1922 | A381 | 47p multi | 1.40 | 1.40 |
| 1923 | A381 | 57p multi | 1.60 | 1.60 |
| 1924 | A381 | 71p multi | 2.00 | 2.00 |
| 1925 | A381 | 73p multi | 2.10 | 2.10 |
| 1926 | A381 | 95p multi | 2.75 | 2.75 |
| 1927 | A381 | £1.25 multi | 3.50 | 3.50 |
| a. | Souvenir sheet of 6, #1922-1927 | | 13.50 | 13.50 |
| | Nos. 1922-1927 (6) | | 13.35 | 13.35 |

King George V (1865-1936) — A382

King George V in: 47p, 1911. 57p, 1914. 64p, 1922. 73p, 1926. 85p, 1933. 95p, 1934. £2, King George V in 1934, horiz.

| 2016, Mar. 9 | Litho. | Perf. 13½x14 | | |
|---|---|---|---|---|
| 1928 | A382 | 47p multi | 1.40 | 1.40 |
| 1929 | A382 | 57p multi | 1.60 | 1.60 |
| 1930 | A382 | 64p multi | 1.90 | 1.90 |
| 1931 | A382 | 73p multi | 2.10 | 2.10 |
| 1932 | A382 | 85p multi | 2.40 | 2.40 |
| 1933 | A382 | 95p multi | 2.75 | 2.75 |
| | Nos. 1928-1933 (6) | | 12.15 | 12.15 |
| **Souvenir Sheet** | | | | |
| 1934 | A382 | £2 multi | 5.75 | 5.75 |
| No. 1934 contains one 54x40mm stamp. | | | | |

Queen Elizabeth II, 90th Birthday — A383

Designs: No. 1935, Princess Elizabeth, 1928. No. 1936, Princess' Elizabeth and Margaret with parents, 1931. No. 1937, Princess Elizabeth with her fiancée, Lt. Philip Mountbatten, 1947. No. 1938, Princess Elizabeth, Princes Philip and Charles, Princess Anne, 1951. 66p, Queen Elizabeth II and Princes Andrew and Edward, 1964. 74p, Queen Elizabeth II, Prince Philip, their children, and grandson, Peter Phillips, 1979. 76p, Queen Elizabeth II, her mother, and her sister, Princess Margaret, 1980. 88p, Queen Elizabeth II and her mother, 1997. £1, Queen Elizabeth II and Prince Philip, 2005. £1.29, Queen Elizabeth II, Duke and Duchess of Cambridge, Princes Harry and George, 2015.

| 2016, Apr. 21 | Litho. | Perf. 13¼ | | |
|---|---|---|---|---|
| 1935 | A383 | 48p multi | 1.40 | 1.40 |
| 1936 | A383 | 48p multi | 1.40 | 1.40 |
| 1937 | A383 | 60p multi | 1.75 | 1.75 |
| a. | Booklet pane of 6, 2 each #1935-1937 | | 9.25 | — |
| 1938 | A383 | 60p multi | 1.75 | 1.75 |
| 1939 | A383 | 66p multi | 2.00 | 2.00 |
| a. | Booklet pane of 4, 2 each #1938-1939 | | 7.50 | — |
| 1940 | A383 | 74p multi | 2.25 | 2.25 |
| 1941 | A383 | 76p multi | 2.25 | 2.25 |
| 1942 | A383 | 88p multi | 2.60 | 2.60 |
| a. | Booklet pane of 6, 2 each #1940-1942 | | 14.50 | — |
| 1943 | A383 | £1 multi | 3.00 | 3.00 |
| 1944 | A383 | £1.29 multi | 3.75 | 3.75 |
| a. | Booklet pane of 4, 2 each #1943-1944 | | 13.50 | — |
| | Complete booklet, #1937a, 1939a, 1942a, 1944a | | 45.00 | |
| | Nos. 1935-1944 (10) | | 22.15 | 22.15 |

Duke and Duchess of Cambridge, 5th Wedding Anniversay — A384

Duke and Duchess of Cambridge: 48p, On wedding day. 2011. 60p, Touring Tuvalu, 2012. 74p, With infant Prince George, 2013. £1, With Prince George on his first birthday, 2014. £1.29, With infant Princess Charlotte, 2015.
£2, Duke and Duchess of Cambridge, Prince George and Princess Charlotte.

| 2016, Apr. 29 | Litho. | Perf. 13x13¼ | | |
|---|---|---|---|---|
| 1945 | A384 | 48p multi | 1.75 | 1.75 |
| 1946 | A384 | 60p multi | 1.75 | 1.75 |
| 1947 | A384 | 74p multi | 2.25 | 2.25 |
| 1948 | A384 | £1 multi | 3.00 | 3.00 |
| 1949 | A384 | £1.29 multi | 3.75 | 3.75 |
| | Nos. 1945-1949 (5) | | 12.50 | 12.50 |
| **Souvenir Sheet** | | | | |
| **Perf. 13¼x13** | | | | |
| 1950 | A384 | £2 multi | 6.00 | 6.00 |
| No. 1950 contains one 52x40mm stamp. | | | | |

A385

"Think Green" — A386

Ecology-related words in: 74p, Head. 76p, Map of Jersey. £1, Globe.

| 2016, May 3 | Litho. | Perf. 13¼ | | |
|---|---|---|---|---|
| 1951 | A385 | 74p green | 2.10 | 2.10 |
| 1952 | A385 | 76p green | 2.25 | 2.25 |
| 1953 | A385 | £1 green | 3.00 | 3.00 |
| 1954 | A386 | £1.29 multi | 3.75 | 3.75 |
| | Nos. 1951-1954 (4) | | 11.10 | 11.10 |
| Europa (#1951, 1954). | | | | |

Publication of Albert Einstein's Theory of General Relativity, Cent. — A387

Einstein and: 48p, Gyroscope. 60p, Mercury and map of planetary orbits. 66p, Einstein field equations. 76p, Electromagnetic wave. 88p, Diagram of bending of light rays, space telescope. £1, Radio telescope.
£2, Einstein, Einstein field equation, diagram of space-time curvature.

| 2016, May 11 | Litho. | Perf. 13¼ | | |
|---|---|---|---|---|
| 1955 | A387 | 48p multi | 1.40 | 1.40 |
| 1956 | A387 | 60p multi | 1.75 | 1.75 |
| 1957 | A387 | 66p multi | 1.90 | 1.90 |
| 1958 | A387 | 76p multi | 2.25 | 2.25 |
| 1959 | A387 | 88p multi | 2.60 | 2.60 |
| 1960 | A387 | £1 multi | 3.00 | 3.00 |
| a. | Souvenir sheet of 6, #1955-1960 | | 13.00 | 13.00 |
| | Nos. 1955-1960 (6) | | 12.90 | 12.90 |
| **Souvenir Sheet** | | | | |
| 1961 | A387 | £2 multi | 5.75 | 5.75 |
| a. | As No. 1961, with World Stamp Show 2016, New York emblem in sheet margin | | 5.75 | 5.75 |
| No. 1961 contains one 72x72mm stamp. | | | | |

Jersey Old Motor Club, 50th Anniv. — A388

Designs: 48p, 1948 MG TC. 60p, 1928 Rolls-Royce 20. 66p, 1903 60hp Mercedes. 74p, 1934 Daimler 15. 76p, 1929 Morgan Aero Three Wheeler. 88p, 1934 3½ liter Bentley. £1, 1929 Austin 7 Chummy. £1.29, 1902 Gladiator Tonneau.
£2, 1912 Talbot.

| 2016, June 7 | Litho. | Perf. 14x13½ | | |
|---|---|---|---|---|
| 1962 | A388 | 48p multi | 1.25 | 1.25 |
| 1963 | A388 | 60p multi | 1.60 | 1.60 |
| 1964 | A388 | 66p multi | 1.75 | 1.75 |
| 1965 | A388 | 74p multi | 2.00 | 2.00 |
| 1966 | A388 | 76p multi | 2.10 | 2.10 |
| 1967 | A388 | 88p multi | 2.40 | 2.40 |
| 1968 | A388 | £1 multi | 2.75 | 2.75 |
| 1969 | A388 | £1.29 multi | 3.50 | 3.50 |
| | Nos. 1962-1969 (8) | | 17.35 | 17.35 |
| **Souvenir Sheet** | | | | |
| 1970 | A388 | £2 multi | 5.50 | 5.50 |
| No. 1970 contains one 42x34mm stamp. | | | | |

Popular Culture of the 1950's — A389

Designs: 48p, "Daddy-o." 68p, Dancers, records and juke box. 66p, Woman's full skirt. 76p, People watching coronation of Queen Elizabeth II on television 88p, Woman, child, molded gelatin. £1, Boy with model cars.
£2, Shops and restaurant.

| 2016, July 5 | Litho. | Perf. 13¼ | | |
|---|---|---|---|---|
| 1971 | A389 | 48p multi | 1.25 | 1.25 |
| 1972 | A389 | 60p multi | 1.60 | 1.60 |
| 1973 | A389 | 66p multi | 1.75 | 1.75 |
| 1974 | A389 | 76p multi | 2.00 | 2.00 |
| 1975 | A389 | 88p multi | 2.40 | 2.40 |
| 1976 | A389 | £1 multi | 2.75 | 2.75 |
| a. | Souvenir sheet of 6, #1971-1976 | | 12.00 | 12.00 |
| | Nos. 1971-1976 (6) | | 11.75 | 11.75 |
| **Souvenir Sheet** | | | | |
| 1977 | A389 | £2 multi | 5.25 | 5.25 |
| No. 1977 contains one 72x72mm stamp. | | | | |

World War I, Cent. — A390

Designs: 48p, First Battle of Ypres, 1914. 60p, Battle of Gallipoli, 1915-16. 66p, Battle of Jutland, 1916. 76p, Somme Offensive, 1916. 88p, Battle of Aqaba, 1917. £1, Battle of Passchendaele, 1917.
£2, Tank and soldiers at Battle of Cambrai, 1917.

| 2016, Aug. 4 | Litho. | Perf. 13½ | | |
|---|---|---|---|---|
| 1978 | A390 | 48p multi | 1.25 | 1.25 |
| 1979 | A390 | 60p multi | 1.60 | 1.60 |
| 1980 | A390 | 66p multi | 1.75 | 1.75 |
| 1981 | A390 | 76p multi | 2.00 | 2.00 |
| 1982 | A390 | 88p multi | 2.40 | 2.40 |
| 1983 | A390 | £1 multi | 2.75 | 2.75 |
| a. | Souvenir sheet of 6, #1978-1983 | | 12.00 | 12.00 |
| | Nos. 1978-1983 (6) | | 11.75 | 11.75 |
| **Souvenir Sheet** | | | | |
| 1984 | A390 | £2 multi | 5.50 | 5.50 |
| No. 1984 contains one 51x30mm stamp. | | | | |

Waterfowl — A391

Designs: No. 1985, Tufted duck. No. 1986, Mallard. No. 1987, Smew. No. 1988, Northern pintail. No. 1989, Common shelduck. No. 1990, Mandarins.

| 2016, Sept. 22 | Litho. | Perf. 13¼ | | |
|---|---|---|---|---|
| 1985 | A391 | 48p multi | 1.25 | 1.25 |
| 1986 | A391 | 48p multi | 1.25 | 1.25 |
| 1987 | A391 | 48p multi | 1.25 | 1.25 |
| 1988 | A391 | 48p multi | 1.25 | 1.25 |
| 1989 | A391 | 48p multi | 1.25 | 1.25 |
| 1990 | A391 | 48p multi | 1.25 | 1.25 |
| a. | Souvenir sheet of 2, #1989-1990 | | 2.50 | 2.50 |
| | Nos. 1985-1990 (6) | | 7.50 | 7.50 |

Myths and Legends — A392

Designs: 48p, Fairies of St. Brelade's Church. 60p, William and the Sea Sprite. 74p, Witches of Rocqueberg. 76p, Dragon of St. Lawrence. £1, Black Dog of Bouley Bay. £1.29, Ghostly Bride of Waterworks Valley.

## 2016, Oct. 6  Litho.  Perf. 13x13¼

| | | | | |
|---|---|---|---|---|
| 1991 | A392 | 48p multi | 1.25 | 1.25 |
| 1992 | A392 | 60p multi | 1.50 | 1.50 |
| 1993 | A392 | 74p multi | 1.90 | 1.90 |
| 1994 | A392 | 76p multi | 1.90 | 1.90 |
| 1995 | A392 | £1 multi | 2.50 | 2.50 |
| 1996 | A392 | £1.29 multi | 3.25 | 3.25 |
| a. | | Souvenir sheet of 6, #1991-1996 | 12.50 | 12.50 |
| | | Nos. 1991-1996 (6) | 12.30 | 12.30 |

Jersey in Winter — A393

Photographs by Andy Le Gresley: 48p, Corbière Lighthouse Surrounded by Stormy Winter Seas. 60p, A Winter Wonderland at St. Catherine's Woods. 66p, Cold Water at Noirmont Tower. 74p, Snow at Mont Orgueil Castle. 76p, Night Skies at Les Ecréhous. 88p, Hail Showers Passing by La Moye Golf Course. £1, Winter Woodland at Noirmont. £1.29, Gales Blow Into the Headland at Corbière.

## 2016, Nov. 4  Litho.  Perf. 13¼x14

| | | | | |
|---|---|---|---|---|
| 1997 | A393 | 48p multi | 1.25 | 1.25 |
| 1998 | A393 | 60p multi | 1.50 | 1.50 |
| 1999 | A393 | 66p multi | 1.75 | 1.75 |
| 2000 | A393 | 74p multi | 1.90 | 1.90 |
| 2001 | A393 | 76p multi | 2.00 | 2.00 |
| 2002 | A393 | 88p multi | 2.25 | 2.25 |
| 2003 | A393 | £1 multi | 2.60 | 2.60 |
| 2004 | A393 | £1.29 multi | 3.25 | 3.25 |
| | | Nos. 1997-2004 (8) | 16.50 | 16.50 |

Christmas — A394

Designs: 43p, Father Christmas, flying sleigh, Corbière Lighthouse. 48p, Father Christmas's sleigh beginning flight, St. Ouen's Manor. 55p, Father Christmas at open mailbox, Royal Square. 60p, Flying sleigh above Trinity Church. 66p, Flying sleigh near Elizabeth Castle. 76p, Father Christmas, reindeer at Jersey Post Headquarters. £1, Father Christmas at Samarès Farmhouse. £1.19, Father Christmas in chimney, St. Thomas' Church.

£2.92, Father Christmas in house.

## 2016, Nov. 21  Litho.  Perf. 13x13¼

| | | | | |
|---|---|---|---|---|
| 2005 | A394 | 43p multi | 1.10 | 1.10 |
| 2006 | A394 | 48p multi | 1.25 | 1.25 |
| 2007 | A394 | 55p multi | 1.40 | 1.40 |
| 2008 | A394 | 60p multi | 1.50 | 1.50 |
| 2009 | A394 | 66p multi | 1.75 | 1.75 |
| 2010 | A394 | 76p multi | 2.00 | 2.00 |
| 2011 | A394 | £1 multi | 2.60 | 2.60 |
| 2012 | A394 | £1.19 multi | 3.00 | 3.00 |
| | | Nos. 2005-2012 (8) | 14.60 | 14.60 |

### Souvenir Sheet
### Perf. 13¼

| | | | | |
|---|---|---|---|---|
| 2013 | A394 | £2.92 multi | 7.50 | 7.50 |

No. 2013 contains one 72x72mm stamp.

New Year 2017 (Year of the Rooster) — A395

Designs: 48p, Rooster. £1, Hen and chicks.

## 2017, Jan. 5  Litho.  Perf. 13¼

| | | | | |
|---|---|---|---|---|
| 2014 | A395 | 48p gold & multi | 1.25 | 1.25 |

### Souvenir Sheet

| | | | | |
|---|---|---|---|---|
| 2015 | A395 | £1 gold & multi | 2.60 | 2.60 |

No. 2015 contains one 60x60mm stamp.

---

### Souvenir Sheet

King Edward VIII (1894-1972) — A396

## 2017, Jan. 20  Litho.  Perf. 14¼x14

| | | | | |
|---|---|---|---|---|
| 2016 | A396 | £2 multi | 5.25 | 5.25 |

### Arms Type of 2015
## 2017, Feb. 2  Litho.  Perf. 14x13¾
### Denomination Color

| | | | | |
|---|---|---|---|---|
| 2017 | A366 | 48p rose | 1.25 | 1.25 |
| 2018 | A366 | 60p lavender | 1.50 | 1.50 |
| 2019 | A366 | 66p aquamarine | 1.75 | 1.75 |
| 2020 | A366 | 76p brt lilac | 1.90 | 1.90 |
| 2021 | A366 | 88p org yellow | 2.25 | 2.25 |
| 2022 | A366 | £1 dull claret | 2.50 | 2.50 |
| | | Nos. 2017-2022 (6) | 11.15 | 11.15 |

Castles — A397

Designs: 74p, Grosnez Castle. 76p, Elizabeth Castle. £1, St. Aubin's Fort. £1.29, Mont Orgueil Castle.

## 2017, Mar. 2  Litho.  Perf. 13¼

| | | | | |
|---|---|---|---|---|
| 2023 | A397 | 74p multi | 1.90 | 1.90 |
| 2024 | A397 | 76p multi | 1.90 | 1.90 |
| 2025 | A397 | £1 multi | 2.50 | 2.50 |
| 2026 | A397 | £1.29 multi | 3.25 | 3.25 |
| a. | | Souvenir sheet of 2, #2023, 2026 | 5.25 | 5.25 |
| | | Nos. 2023-2026 (4) | 9.55 | 9.55 |

Europa (Nos. 2023, 2026).

Archaeological Artifacts — A398

Designs: 49p, Golden torque, 1st cent. B.C. 63p, Rotary quern, 1st cent. B.C. 73p, St. Lawrence Parish Church pillar, 800 A.D. 79p, Bronze dagger, 1st cent. B.C. 90p, Flint arrowhead, 2850-2250 B.C. £1.07, Silver and gilt brooch, 14th cent. £1.32, Bronze statue, 2nd cent. B.C. £2.52, Bronze Age axe head, 1500-800 B.C.

## 2017, Apr. 11  Litho.  Perf. 13½

| | | | | |
|---|---|---|---|---|
| 2027 | A398 | 49p multi | 1.25 | 1.25 |
| 2028 | A398 | 63p multi | 1.60 | 1.60 |
| 2029 | A398 | 73p multi | 1.90 | 1.90 |
| 2030 | A398 | 79p multi | 2.10 | 2.10 |
| 2031 | A398 | 90p multi | 2.40 | 2.40 |
| 2032 | A398 | £1.07 multi | 2.75 | 2.75 |
| a. | | Booklet pane of 4, #2028, 2030-2032 | 9.00 | — |
| 2033 | A398 | £1.32 multi | 3.50 | 3.50 |
| 2034 | A398 | £2.52 multi | 6.50 | 6.50 |
| a. | | Booklet pane of 4, #2027, 2029, 2033-2034 | 13.50 | — |
| | | Complete booklet, 2 each #2032a, 2034a | 45.00 | |
| | | Nos. 2027-2034 (8) | 22.00 | 22.00 |

Complete booklet contains two examples of Nos. 2032a and 2034a, each with different pane margins.

King George VI (1895-1952) — A399

Photograph of King George VI taken in: 49p, 1937. 63p, 1938. 73p, 1941. 79p, 1943. 90p, 1944. £1.07, 1948.

£2, 1939, horiz.

---

## 2017, May 12  Litho.  Perf. 13½x14

| | | | | |
|---|---|---|---|---|
| 2035 | A399 | 49p multi | 1.25 | 1.25 |
| 2036 | A399 | 63p multi | 1.60 | 1.60 |
| 2037 | A399 | 73p multi | 1.90 | 1.90 |
| 2038 | A399 | 79p multi | 2.10 | 2.10 |
| 2039 | A399 | 90p multi | 2.40 | 2.40 |
| 2040 | A399 | £1.07 multi | 2.75 | 2.75 |
| | | Nos. 2035-2040 (6) | 12.00 | 12.00 |

### Souvenir Sheet
### Perf. 14¼

| | | | | |
|---|---|---|---|---|
| 2041 | A399 | £2 multi | 5.25 | 5.25 |

No. 2041 contains one 56x40mm stamp.

Lions Clubs International, Cent. — A400

Designs: 49p, Swimmers raising funds in Jersey Swimarathon. 63p, Treating eye disease and recycled glasses. 73p, Worldwide disaster relief. 79p, Tackling environmental issues. 90p, Hearing tests and recycled hearing aids. £1.07, Holidays for the disabled.

£2, Worldwide disaster relief, diff.

## 2017, June 7  Litho.  Perf. 13x13¼

| | | | | |
|---|---|---|---|---|
| 2042 | A400 | 49p multi | 1.25 | 1.25 |
| 2043 | A400 | 63p multi | 1.60 | 1.60 |
| 2044 | A400 | 73p multi | 1.90 | 1.90 |
| 2045 | A400 | 79p multi | 2.10 | 2.10 |
| 2046 | A400 | 90p multi | 2.40 | 2.40 |
| 2047 | A400 | £1.07 multi | 2.75 | 2.75 |
| | | Nos. 2042-2047 (6) | 12.00 | 12.00 |

### Souvenir Sheet

| | | | | |
|---|---|---|---|---|
| 2048 | A400 | £2 multi | 5.25 | 5.25 |

Fauna — A401

Charles Darwin (1809-82), Naturalist — A402

Designs: 49p, Mangrove finch. 63p, Livingstone's fruit bat. 73p, Telfair's skink. 79p, Mountain chicken. 90p, Hispaniolan solenodon. £1.07, Pygmy hog.

## 2017, June 14  Litho.  Perf. 13x13¼

| | | | | |
|---|---|---|---|---|
| 2049 | A401 | 49p multi | 1.25 | 1.25 |
| 2050 | A401 | 63p multi | 1.60 | 1.60 |
| 2051 | A401 | 73p multi | 1.90 | 1.90 |
| 2052 | A401 | 79p multi | 2.10 | 2.10 |
| 2053 | A401 | 90p multi | 2.40 | 2.40 |
| 2054 | A401 | £1.07 multi | 2.75 | 2.75 |
| | | Nos. 2049-2054 (6) | 12.00 | 12.00 |

### Souvenir Sheet
### On Sycamore Veneer
### Self-Adhesive
### Die Cut Perf. 7¼x6¾

| | | | | |
|---|---|---|---|---|
| 2055 | A402 | £3 multi | 7.75 | 7.75 |

Darwin Initiative, 25th anniv.

Kaleidoscope, 200th Anniv. — A403

Kaleidoscopic images of: 49p, Shells and anemones. 63p, Feathers and eggs. 73p, Flowers. 79p, Mammals and birds. 90p, Insects. £1.07, Fish and crabs.

## 2017, July 10  Litho.  Perf. 13¾x13½

| | | | | |
|---|---|---|---|---|
| 2056 | A403 | 49p multi | 1.40 | 1.40 |
| 2057 | A403 | 63p multi | 1.75 | 1.75 |
| 2058 | A403 | 73p multi | 2.00 | 2.00 |
| 2059 | A403 | 79p multi | 2.10 | 2.10 |
| 2060 | A403 | 90p multi | 2.40 | 2.40 |

---

| | | | | |
|---|---|---|---|---|
| 2061 | A403 | £1.07 multi | 3.00 | 3.00 |
| a. | | Souvenir sheet of 6, #2056-2061 | 13.00 | 13.00 |
| | | Nos. 2056-2061 (6) | 12.65 | 12.65 |

Airplanes of World War I — A404

Designs: 49p, Sopwith Camel. 63p, Airco DH.2 and Albatros D.II. 73p, Nieuport 16 and Fokker Eindecker. 79p, Fokker DR.I. 90p, Sopwith Triplane. £1.07, Nieuport 28.

£2, Airco DH.2.

## 2017, Aug. 4  Litho.  Perf. 13¼x13¾

| | | | | |
|---|---|---|---|---|
| 2062 | A404 | 49p multi | 1.25 | 1.25 |
| 2063 | A404 | 63p multi | 1.60 | 1.60 |
| 2064 | A404 | 73p multi | 1.90 | 1.90 |
| 2065 | A404 | 79p multi | 2.10 | 2.10 |
| 2066 | A404 | 90p multi | 2.40 | 2.40 |
| 2067 | A404 | £1.07 multi | 2.75 | 2.75 |
| a. | | Souvenir sheet of 6, #2062-2067 | 12.00 | 12.00 |
| | | Nos. 2062-2067 (6) | 12.00 | 12.00 |

### Souvenir Sheet
### Perf. 14

| | | | | |
|---|---|---|---|---|
| 2068 | A404 | £2 multi | 5.25 | 5.25 |

World War I, cent. No. 2068 contains one 70x42mm stamp.

Butterflies Found in Jersey and China — A405

Designs: No. 2069, Black-veined white butterfly. No. 2070, Small tortoiseshell butterfly. No. 2071, Swallowtail butterfly. No. 2072, Purple emperor butterfly. No. 2073, White admiral butterfly. No. 2074, Camberwell beauty butterfly.

## 2017, Sept. 1  Litho.  Perf. 13¼

| | | | | |
|---|---|---|---|---|
| 2069 | A405 | 49p multi | 1.25 | 1.25 |
| 2070 | A405 | 49p multi | 1.25 | 1.25 |
| 2071 | A405 | 49p multi | 1.25 | 1.25 |
| a. | | Souvenir sheet of 2, #2069, 2071 | 2.50 | 2.50 |
| 2072 | A405 | 49p multi | 1.25 | 1.25 |
| 2073 | A405 | 49p multi | 1.25 | 1.25 |
| 2074 | A405 | 49p multi | 1.25 | 1.25 |
| a. | | Souvenir sheet of 6, #2069-2074 | 7.50 | 7.50 |
| | | Nos. 2069-2074 (6) | 7.50 | 7.50 |

A406

Lillie Langtry (1853-1929), Actress — A407

Langtry as: No. 2075, Kate Hardcastle in She Stoops to Conquer. No. 2076, Blanche Hays in Ours. No. 2077, Rosalind in As You Like It. No. 2078, Hester Grazebrook in An Unequal Match. 73p, Mademoiselle Mars in Mademoiselle Mars. 79p, Lena Despard in As in a Looking Glass. 90p, Lady Macbeth in Macbeth. £1.07, Pauline in The Lady of Lyons.

£2, Langry as Cleopatra in Antony and Cleopatra.

## 2017, Sept. 22  Litho.  Perf. 13¼x13
### Frame Color

| | | | | |
|---|---|---|---|---|
| 2075 | A406 | 49p pink | 1.40 | 1.40 |
| 2076 | A406 | 49p lilac | 1.40 | 1.40 |
| 2077 | A406 | 63p pale grnsh yel | 1.75 | 1.75 |
| 2078 | A406 | 63p cinnamon | 1.75 | 1.75 |
| 2079 | A406 | 73p sage green | 2.00 | 2.00 |
| 2080 | A406 | 79p light blue | 2.10 | 2.10 |

| | | | | |
|---|---|---|---|---|
| 2081 | A406 | 90p lt tan | 2.40 | 2.40 |
| 2082 | A406 | £1.07 lt rose | 3.00 | 3.00 |
| | | Nos. 2075-2082 (8) | 15.80 | 15.80 |

### Souvenir Sheet
### Self-Adhesive
### Die Cut Perf. 7¾

| | | | | |
|---|---|---|---|---|
| 2083 | A407 | £2 shown | 5.50 | 5.50 |

### Jersey Beekeepers Association, Cent. — A408

Designs: 49p, Bee on flower. 63p, Bees on honeycomb. 73p, Apiarist with smoker near hives. 79p, Apiarist holding hive frame. 90p, Removing wax from frame. £1.07, Jar of honey and dipper.
£2, Bee on honeycomb.

**2017, Oct. 3    Litho.    Perf. 13x13¼**

| | | | | |
|---|---|---|---|---|
| 2084 | A408 | 49p multi | 1.40 | 1.40 |
| 2085 | A408 | 63p multi | 1.75 | 1.75 |
| 2086 | A408 | 73p multi | 2.00 | 2.00 |
| 2087 | A408 | 79p multi | 2.10 | 2.10 |
| 2088 | A408 | 90p multi | 2.40 | 2.40 |
| 2089 | A408 | £1.07 multi | 3.00 | 3.00 |
| | | Nos. 2084-2089 (6) | 12.65 | 12.65 |

### Souvenir Sheet
### Perf. 13

| | | | | |
|---|---|---|---|---|
| 2090 | A408 | £2 multi | 5.50 | 5.50 |

Nos. 2084-2090 are impregnated with a honey scent. No. 2090 contains one 40x35mm hexagonal stamp.

### 70th Wedding Anniversary of Queen Elizabeth II and Prince Philip — A409

Designs: 49p, Engagement photograph. 63p, Wedding day photograph. 73p, Honeymoon photograph 79p, Silver wedding anniversary photograph. 90p, Golden wedding anniversary photograph. £1.07, Diamond wedding anniversary photograph.
£2, 2016 photograph, horiz.

**2017, Nov. 3    Litho.    Perf. 13¼x13**

| | | | | |
|---|---|---|---|---|
| 2091 | A409 | 49p multi | 1.40 | 1.40 |
| 2092 | A409 | 63p multi | 1.75 | 1.75 |
| 2093 | A409 | 73p multi | 2.00 | 2.00 |
| 2094 | A409 | 79p multi | 2.10 | 2.10 |
| 2095 | A409 | 90p multi | 2.50 | 2.50 |
| 2096 | A409 | £1.07 multi | 3.00 | 3.00 |
| a. | | Souvenir sheet of 6, #2091-2096 | 13.00 | 13.00 |
| | | Nos. 2091-2096 (6) | 12.75 | 12.75 |

### Souvenir Sheet
### Perf. 13¼x14

| | | | | |
|---|---|---|---|---|
| 2097 | A409 | £2 multi | 5.50 | 5.50 |

No. 2097 contains one 51x40mm stamp.

### Christmas A410

Designs: 43p, Family looking for Christmas tree. 49p, Christmas tree decorating. 55p, Children hanging stockings on fireplace mantle. 63p, Singing Christmas carols. 73p, Making a Christmas cake. 79p, Building a snowman. 90p, Exchanging gifts. £1.07, Nativity play.

**2017, Nov. 20    Litho.    Perf. 13x13¼**

| | | | | |
|---|---|---|---|---|
| 2098 | A410 | 43p multi | 1.25 | 1.25 |
| 2099 | A410 | 49p multi | 1.40 | 1.40 |
| 2100 | A410 | 55p multi | 1.50 | 1.50 |
| 2101 | A410 | 63p multi | 1.75 | 1.75 |
| 2102 | A410 | 73p multi | 2.00 | 2.00 |
| 2103 | A410 | 79p multi | 2.10 | 2.10 |
| 2104 | A410 | 90p multi | 2.50 | 2.50 |
| 2105 | A410 | £1.07 multi | 3.00 | 3.00 |
| | | Nos. 2098-2105 (8) | 15.50 | 15.50 |

### New Year 2018 (Year of the Dog) — A411

Designs: 49p, Dog. £1, Dogs.

**2018, Jan. 5    Litho.    Perf. 13¼**

| | | | | |
|---|---|---|---|---|
| 2106 | A411 | 49p gold & multi | 1.40 | 1.40 |

### Souvenir Sheet

| | | | | |
|---|---|---|---|---|
| 2107 | A411 | £1 gold & multi | 3.00 | 3.00 |

No. 2107 contains one 60x60mm stamp.

### Popular Culture of the 1960s — A412

Designs: 49p, Flower Power. 63p, Rock guitarist. 73p, Women wearing miniskirts. 79p, Landing of men on the Moon. 90p, Cheese and pineapple sticks. £1.07, Girl and doll house.
£2, Shops in 1960s Jersey.

**2018, Jan. 26    Litho.    Perf. 13¼**

| | | | | |
|---|---|---|---|---|
| 2108 | A412 | 49p multi | 1.40 | 1.40 |
| 2109 | A412 | 63p multi | 1.75 | 1.75 |
| 2110 | A412 | 73p multi | 2.10 | 2.10 |
| 2111 | A412 | 79p multi | 2.25 | 2.25 |
| 2112 | A412 | 90p multi | 2.50 | 2.50 |
| 2113 | A412 | £1.07 multi | 3.00 | 3.00 |
| a. | | Souvenir sheet of 6, #2108-2113 | 13.00 | 13.00 |
| | | Nos. 2108-2113 (6) | 13.00 | 13.00 |

### Souvenir Sheet

| | | | | |
|---|---|---|---|---|
| 2114 | A412 | £2 multi | 5.75 | 5.75 |

No. 2114 contains one 72x72mm stamp. Examples of No. 2114 with a rouletted tab at right with a serial number and the Stampex 2018 emblem and dates were produced in limited quantities.

### Jersey in Spring — A413

Photographs by Andy Le Gresley: No. 2115, Sunset from the Walkway at Devil's Hole. No. 2116, Waves Breaking at Ouaisné. 63p, Daffodils in Rozel Woods. 73p, Calm Seas at Portelet Bay. 79p, Grosnez Castle at Dusk. 90p, A St. Lawrence Valley View in Springtime. £1.07, The Headland Overlooking St. Brelade's Bay. £1.32, Sun Shining Through the Trees at Grantez.

**Perf. 13¼x13½**

| | | | | |
|---|---|---|---|---|
| 2115 | A413 | 49p multi | 1.40 | 1.40 |
| 2116 | A413 | 49p multi | 1.40 | 1.40 |
| 2117 | A413 | 63p multi | 1.75 | 1.75 |
| 2118 | A413 | 73p multi | 2.00 | 2.00 |
| 2119 | A413 | 79p multi | 2.25 | 2.25 |
| 2120 | A413 | 90p multi | 2.50 | 2.50 |
| 2121 | A413 | £1.07 multi | 3.00 | 3.00 |
| 2122 | A413 | £1.32 multi | 3.75 | 3.75 |
| | | Nos. 2115-2122 (8) | 18.05 | 18.05 |

### Bridges and Causeways A414

Designs: 73p, Havre de Pas Bridge. 79p, La Corbiere Causeway. 90p, Queen's Valley Reservoir. £1.07, Elizabeth Castle Causeway.

**2018, Mar. 9    Litho.    Perf. 13½x13¼**

| | | | | |
|---|---|---|---|---|
| 2123 | A414 | 73p multi | 2.10 | 2.10 |
| 2124 | A414 | 79p multi | 2.25 | 2.25 |
| 2125 | A414 | 90p multi | 2.60 | 2.60 |
| a. | | Souvenir sheet of 2, #2123, 2125 | 4.75 | 4.75 |
| 2126 | A414 | £1.07 multi | 3.00 | 3.00 |
| | | Nos. 2123-2126 (4) | 9.95 | 9.95 |

Europa (73p, 90p).

### Royal Air Force, Cent. — A415

Designs: 50p, Royal Aircraft Factory SE5a. 65p, Hawker Fury Mk. I. 76p, Short Stirling B.III. 82p, Supermarine Spitfire PR.XIX. 94p, English Electric Lightning F.6. £1.12, Eurofighter Typhoon.

**Perf. 13¼x13½**

**2018, Mar. 31    Litho.**

| | | | | |
|---|---|---|---|---|
| 2127 | A415 | 50p multi | 1.40 | 1.40 |
| 2128 | A415 | 65p multi | 1.90 | 1.90 |
| 2129 | A415 | 76p multi | 2.10 | 2.10 |
| 2130 | A415 | 82p multi | 2.40 | 2.40 |
| a. | | Booklet pane of 3, #2127, 2129, 2130 | 6.00 | |
| 2131 | A415 | 94p multi | 2.75 | 2.75 |
| a. | | Souvenir sheet of 2, #2128, 2131 | 4.75 | 4.75 |
| b. | | Booklet pane of 4, #2127, 2128, 2129, 2131 | 8.25 | — |
| 2132 | A415 | £1.12 multi | 3.25 | 3.25 |
| a. | | Booklet pane of 3, #2127, 2130, 2132 | 7.25 | |
| b. | | Booklet pane of 4, #2128, 2129, 2131, 2132 | 10.00 | |
| c. | | Booklet pane of 4, #2128, 2130, 2131, 2132 | 10.50 | |
| | | Complete booklet, #2130a, 2131b, 2132a, 2132b, 2132c | 42.00 | |
| | | Nos. 2127-2132 (6) | 13.80 | 13.80 |

### Dam Busters Raid, 75th Anniv. — A416

Designs: 50p, Airmen and airplane in flight. 65p, Pilot, airplane, anti-aircraft fire. 76p, Bombardier, airplane over reservoir. 82p, Bomb hitting water. 94p, Airplane over bomb hitting dam, Operation Chastise leaders looking at map, £1.12, Sir Barnes Wallis (1887-1979), inventor of bouncing bomb.
£2, Wing Commander Guy Gibson (1918-44).

**2018, May 16    Litho.    Perf. 14x13¼**

| | | | | |
|---|---|---|---|---|
| 2133 | A416 | 50p multi | 1.40 | 1.40 |
| 2134 | A416 | 65p multi | 1.75 | 1.75 |
| 2135 | A416 | 76p multi | 2.00 | 2.00 |
| 2136 | A416 | 82p multi | 2.25 | 2.25 |
| 2137 | A416 | 94p multi | 2.50 | 2.50 |
| 2138 | A416 | £1.12 multi | 3.00 | 3.00 |
| | | Nos. 2133-2138 (6) | 12.90 | 12.90 |

### Souvenir Sheet
### Perf. 13½

| | | | | |
|---|---|---|---|---|
| 2139 | A416 | £2 multi | 5.50 | 5.50 |

No. 2139 contains one 44x44mm stamp.

### Jersey Society for Prevention of Cruelty to Animals, 150th Anniv. — A417

Designs: 50p, Puppy, JSPCA vehicle. 65p, Dog in hands of veterinarian. 76p, Snake. 82p, Sleeping cat. 94p, Dog in shelter. £1.12, Dog on leash. £1.38, Rabbit. £2.64, Owl.

**2018, May 25    Litho.    Perf. 14½**

| | | | | |
|---|---|---|---|---|
| 2140 | A417 | 50p multi | 1.40 | 1.40 |
| 2141 | A417 | 65p multi | 1.75 | 1.75 |
| 2142 | A417 | 76p multi | 2.00 | 2.00 |
| 2143 | A417 | 82p multi | 2.25 | 2.25 |
| 2144 | A417 | 94p multi | 2.50 | 2.50 |
| a. | | Souvenir sheet of 2, #2143, 2144 | 4.75 | 4.75 |
| 2145 | A417 | £1.12 multi | 3.00 | 3.00 |
| 2146 | A417 | £1.38 multi | 3.75 | 3.75 |
| 2147 | A417 | £2.64 multi | 7.00 | 7.00 |
| | | Nos. 2140-2147 (8) | 23.65 | 23.65 |

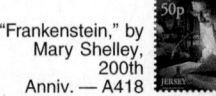

### "Frankenstein," by Mary Shelley, 200th Anniv. — A418

Quotations: 50p, "I began the creation of a human being." 65p, "I beheld the accomplishment of my toils." 76p, "His eyes, if eyes they may be called, were fixed on me." 82p, "I was a poor, helpless, miserable, wretch." 94p, "My heart yearned to be known and loved by these amiable creatures." £1.12, "Remember, that I

am thy creature." £1.38, "You are my creator, but I am your master; - obey!" £2.64, "Where can I find rest but in death?"
£3, "I beheld the wretch - the miserable monster whom I had created."

**2018, June 18    Litho.    Perf. 13x13¼**

| | | | | |
|---|---|---|---|---|
| 2148 | A418 | 50p sil & multi | 1.40 | 1.40 |
| 2149 | A418 | 65p sil & multi | 1.75 | 1.75 |
| 2150 | A418 | 76p sil & multi | 2.00 | 2.00 |
| 2151 | A418 | 82p sil & multi | 2.25 | 2.25 |
| 2152 | A418 | 94p sil & multi | 2.50 | 2.50 |
| 2153 | A418 | £1.12 sil & multi | 3.00 | 3.00 |
| 2154 | A418 | £1.38 sil & multi | 3.75 | 3.75 |
| 2155 | A418 | £2.64 sil & multi | 7.00 | 7.00 |
| a. | | Souvenir sheet of 8, #2148-2155 | 24.00 | 24.00 |
| | | Nos. 2148-2155 (8) | 23.65 | 23.65 |

### Souvenir Sheet
### Litho. With Lenticular Lens Affixed
### Perf. 14¼x14

| | | | | |
|---|---|---|---|---|
| 2156 | A418 | £3 multi | 8.00 | 8.00 |

### Jersey Overseas Aid, 50th Anniv. — A419

Projects: 50p, Jersey cow program, Rwanda. 65p, Famine relief, South Sudan. 76p, Tropical diseases, Uganda. 82p, Economic development, Nepal. 94p, Rural livelihoods, Madagascar. £1.12, Sand dam construction, Kenya.

**2018, July 12    Litho.    Perf. 13¼x13**

| | | | | |
|---|---|---|---|---|
| 2157 | A419 | 50p multi | 1.40 | 1.40 |
| 2158 | A419 | 65p multi | 1.75 | 1.75 |
| 2159 | A419 | 76p multi | 2.00 | 2.00 |
| 2160 | A419 | 82p multi | 2.25 | 2.25 |
| 2161 | A419 | 94p multi | 2.50 | 2.50 |
| 2162 | A419 | £1.12 multi | 3.00 | 3.00 |
| | | Nos. 2157-2162 (6) | 12.90 | 12.90 |

### End of World War I, Cent. — A420

Jersey residents taking part in World War I: 50p, Private Charles William Moody. 65p, Second Lieutenant Kenneth Strickland Dunlop. 76p, Petty Officer George Alfred Jeune. 82p, Private Clifford Helier Brée. 94p, Lieutenant William McCrae Bruce. £1.12, Nurse Madeleine Louise Norman.
£2, Corporal Robert Leonard Norman, horiz.

**2018, Aug. 4    Litho.    Perf. 13¼x14**

| | | | | |
|---|---|---|---|---|
| 2163 | A420 | 50p multi | 1.25 | 1.25 |
| 2164 | A420 | 65p multi | 1.75 | 1.75 |
| 2165 | A420 | 76p multi | 2.00 | 2.00 |
| 2166 | A420 | 82p multi | 2.10 | 2.10 |
| 2167 | A420 | 94p multi | 2.40 | 2.40 |
| 2168 | A420 | £1.12 multi | 3.00 | 3.00 |
| a. | | Souvenir sheet of 6, #2163-2168 | 12.50 | 12.50 |
| | | Nos. 2163-2168 (6) | 12.50 | 12.50 |

### Souvenir Sheet
### Perf. 13¾x13¼

| | | | | |
|---|---|---|---|---|
| 2169 | A420 | £2 multi | 5.25 | 5.25 |

No. 2169 contains one 55x42mm stamp.

### Birds — A421

Designs: No. 2170, Red-billed chough. No. 2171, Yellowhammer. No. 2172, Barn swallow. No. 2173, Stonechat. No. 2174, Goldfinch. No. 2175, Linnet.

**2018, Sept. 3    Litho.    Perf. 13¼**

| | | | | |
|---|---|---|---|---|
| 2170 | A421 | 50p multi | 1.25 | 1.25 |
| 2171 | A421 | 50p multi | 1.25 | 1.25 |
| 2172 | A421 | 50p multi | 1.25 | 1.25 |
| 2173 | A421 | 50p multi | 1.25 | 1.25 |
| a. | | Souvenir sheet of 2, #2170, 2173 | 2.50 | 2.50 |
| 2174 | A421 | 50p multi | 1.25 | 1.25 |
| 2175 | A421 | 50p multi | 1.25 | 1.25 |
| a. | | Souvenir sheet of 6, #2170-2175 | 7.50 | 7.50 |
| | | Nos. 2170-2175 (6) | 7.50 | 7.50 |

Woman Suffrage, Cent. — A422

Suffragette holding sign or banner inscribed: 50p, "National Union of Women's Suffrage Societies." 65p, "Deeds Not Words." 76p, "Women's War Work." 82p, "Votes for Women." 94p, "First Vote for Women in Jersey." £1.12, "First Female MP in Parliament." £2, "Votes for Women" sign.

**2018, Oct. 2          Litho.          Perf. 13**

| | | | |
|---|---|---|---|
| 2176 | A422 | 50p multi | 1.25 1.25 |
| 2177 | A422 | 65p multi | 1.75 1.75 |
| 2178 | A422 | 76p multi | 2.00 2.00 |
| 2179 | A422 | 82p multi | 2.10 2.10 |
| 2180 | A422 | 94p multi | 2.40 2.40 |
| 2181 | A422 | £1.12 multi | 3.00 3.00 |
| *a.* | | Souvenir sheet of 6, #2176-2181 | 12.50 12.50 |
| | | Nos. 2176-2181 (6) | 12.50 12.50 |

**Souvenir Sheet**
**Perf. 13¼x13¾**

| | | | |
|---|---|---|---|
| 2182 | A422 | £2 multi | 5.25 5.25 |

No. 2182 contains one 42x55mm stamp.

A423          A424

Prince Charles, 70th Birthday A425

Photograph of Prince Charles taken in: 50p, 1957. 65p, 1966. 76p, 1975. 82p, c. 1977. 94p, 1998. £1.12, 2012. £3, 2006. £2, 2017.

**Litho., Litho. With Foil Application (£3)**
**2018, Nov. 14          Perf. 13½x13¼**

| | | | |
|---|---|---|---|
| 2183 | A423 | 50p sil & multi | 1.25 1.25 |
| 2184 | A423 | 65p sil & multi | 1.75 1.75 |
| 2185 | A423 | 76p sil & multi | 2.00 2.00 |
| 2186 | A423 | 82p sil & multi | 2.10 2.10 |
| 2187 | A423 | 94p sil & multi | 2.40 2.40 |
| 2188 | A423 | £1.12 sil & multi | 3.00 3.00 |

**Perf. 13¼x13½**

| | | | |
|---|---|---|---|
| 2189 | A424 | £3 sil & multi | 7.75 7.75 |
| | | Nos. 2183-2189 (7) | 20.25 20.25 |

**Souvenir Sheet**
**Perf. 11¾**

| | | | |
|---|---|---|---|
| 2190 | A425 | £2 sil & multi | 5.25 5.25 |

Christmas — A426

Sweaters showing: 44p, Snowflakes. 50p, Angel playing horn. 57p, Santa Claus suit. 65p, Snowman. 76p, Christmas tree and gifts. 82p, Holly. 94p, Reindeer wearing snow cap. £1.12, Magi.

**Serpentine Die Cut 14 Syncopated**
**2018, Nov. 19          Litho.**
**Self-Adhesive**

| | | | |
|---|---|---|---|
| 2191 | A426 | 44p multi | 1.10 1.10 |
| 2192 | A426 | 50p multi | 1.25 1.25 |
| 2193 | A426 | 57p multi | 1.50 1.50 |
| 2194 | A426 | 65p multi | 1.75 1.75 |
| 2195 | A426 | 76p multi | 2.00 2.00 |
| 2196 | A426 | 82p multi | 2.10 2.10 |

| | | | |
|---|---|---|---|
| 2197 | A426 | 94p multi | 2.40 2.40 |
| 2198 | A426 | £1.12 multi | 3.00 3.00 |
| | | Nos. 2191-2198 (8) | 15.10 15.10 |

New Year 2019 (Year of the Pig) — A427

Designs: 50p, Pig, bird and flowers. £1, Pig, piglets, birds and flowers.

**2019, Jan. 4          Litho.          Perf. 13¼**

| | | | |
|---|---|---|---|
| 2199 | A427 | 50p gold & multi | 1.25 1.25 |

**Souvenir Sheet**

| | | | |
|---|---|---|---|
| 2200 | A427 | £1 gold & multi | 2.60 2.60 |

No. 2200 contains one 60x60mm stamp.

Popular Culture of the 1970s — A428

Designs: 50p, "Boogie." 65p, "Punk" and safety pin. 76p, Flared pants. 82p, Cassette for video cassette recorder. 94p, Man and woman eating fondue. £1.12, Roller skate. £2, Shops in 1970s Jersey.

**2019, Jan. 18          Litho.          Perf. 13¼**

| | | | |
|---|---|---|---|
| 2201 | A428 | 50p multi | 1.25 1.25 |
| 2202 | A428 | 65p multi | 1.75 1.75 |
| 2203 | A428 | 76p multi | 2.00 2.00 |
| 2204 | A428 | 82p multi | 2.10 2.10 |
| 2205 | A428 | 94p multi | 2.40 2.40 |
| 2206 | A428 | £1.12 multi | 3.00 3.00 |
| *a.* | | Souvenir sheet of 6, #2201-2206 | 12.50 12.50 |
| | | Nos. 2201-2206 (6) | 12.50 12.50 |

**Souvenir Sheet**

| | | | |
|---|---|---|---|
| 2207 | A428 | £2 multi | 5.25 5.25 |

No. 2207 contains one 72x72mm stamp. Examples of No. 2207 with a rouletted tab at right with a serial number and the Stampex 2019 emblem and dates were produced in limited quantities.

Sir Walter Raleigh (c. 1552-1618), Governor of Jersey and New World Expedition Leader — A429

Designs: 50p, Fort Isabella Bellissima (Elizabeth Castle). 65p, Hand holding quill pen, and text, "Soldier, Sailor, Author, Poet & Adventurer." 76p, Ship and text, " Whosoever commands the sea commands the trade." 82p, Ship, map, monument and text, "When we have wandered all our ways. . ." 94p, Castle and text, "Twere pity to cast it down." £1.12, Raleigh and text, "To my verie loving friends the bailiffe and Justices of Jersey." £2, Raleigh, ship and map.

**2019, Feb. 5          Litho.          Perf. 14x13¼**

| | | | |
|---|---|---|---|
| 2208 | A429 | 50p multi | 1.40 1.40 |
| 2209 | A429 | 65p multi | 1.75 1.75 |
| 2210 | A429 | 76p multi | 2.00 2.00 |
| 2211 | A429 | 82p multi | 2.10 2.10 |
| 2212 | A429 | 94p multi | 2.50 2.50 |
| 2213 | A429 | £1.12 multi | 3.00 3.00 |
| | | Nos. 2208-2213 (6) | 12.75 12.75 |

**Souvenir Sheet**
**Perf. 14¼x14**

| | | | |
|---|---|---|---|
| 2214 | A429 | £2 multi | 5.25 5.25 |

No. 2214 contains one 56x40mm stamp.

Birds — A430

Designs: 50p, Kestrel. 65p, Swallow. 76p, Swan. 82p, Peacock. 94p, Kingfisher. £1.12, Stork.

**Litho. With Foil Application**
**2019, Mar. 5          Perf. 13¾x14**

| | | | |
|---|---|---|---|
| 2215 | A430 | 50p multi | 1.40 1.40 |
| 2216 | A430 | 65p multi | 1.75 1.75 |
| 2217 | A430 | 76p multi | 2.00 2.00 |
| 2218 | A430 | 82p multi | 2.25 2.25 |
| 2219 | A430 | 94p multi | 2.50 2.50 |
| *a.* | | Souvenir sheet of 2, #2217, 2219 | 4.50 4.50 |
| 2220 | A430 | £1.12 multi | 3.00 3.00 |
| | | Nos. 2215-2220 (6) | 12.90 12.90 |

Europa (Nos. 2217, 2219).

Dame Margot Fonteyn (1919-91) Ballerina — A431

Fonteyn dancing in: 52p, Romeo and Juliet. 67p, The Sleeping Beauty. 80p, Amazon Forest. 85p, Amazon Forest, diff. 99p, Romeo and Juliet, diff. £1.15, The Sleeping Beauty, diff. £2, Swan Lake.

**2019, Apr. 2          Litho.          Perf. 13¾x13½**

| | | | |
|---|---|---|---|
| 2221 | A431 | 52p gold & multi | 1.40 1.40 |
| 2222 | A431 | 67p gold & multi | 1.75 1.75 |
| 2223 | A431 | 80p gold & multi | 2.10 2.10 |
| 2224 | A431 | 85p gold & multi | 2.25 2.25 |
| 2225 | A431 | 99p gold & multi | 2.60 2.60 |
| 2226 | A431 | £1.15 gold & multi | 3.00 3.00 |
| | | Nos. 2221-2226 (6) | 13.10 13.10 |

**Souvenir Sheet**

| | | | |
|---|---|---|---|
| 2227 | A431 | £2 gold & multi | 5.25 5.25 |

No. 2227 contains one 70x70mm stamp.

First Wedding Anniversary of the Duke and Duchess of Sussex — A432

Various photographs of the Duke and Duchess of Sussex.

**2019, May 2          Litho.          Perf. 13**

| | | | |
|---|---|---|---|
| 2228 | A432 | 52p multi | 1.40 1.40 |
| 2229 | A432 | 67p multi | 1.75 1.75 |
| 2230 | A432 | 80p multi | 2.00 2.00 |
| 2231 | A432 | 85p multi | 2.25 2.25 |
| 2232 | A432 | 99p multi | 2.50 2.50 |
| 2233 | A432 | £1.15 multi | 3.00 3.00 |
| *a.* | | Souvenir sheet of 6, #2228-2233 | 13.00 13.00 |
| | | Nos. 2228-2233 (6) | 12.90 12.90 |

**Souvenir Sheet**

| | | | |
|---|---|---|---|
| 2234 | A432 | £3 multi | 7.75 7.75 |

No. 2234 contains one 52x40mm stamp.

Queen Victoria (1819-1901) — A433

Images of Queen Victoria from around: 52p, 1837-39. 67p, 1838-40. 80p, 1843. 85p, 1844. 99p, 1856. £1.15, 1890. £2, Portrait by Franz Xaver Winterhalter.

**2019, May 24          Litho.          Perf. 14x13½**

| | | | |
|---|---|---|---|
| 2235 | A433 | 52p multi | 1.40 1.40 |
| 2236 | A433 | 67p multi | 1.75 1.75 |
| 2237 | A433 | 80p multi | 2.00 2.00 |
| 2238 | A433 | 85p multi | 2.25 2.25 |
| 2239 | A433 | 99p multi | 2.50 2.50 |
| 2240 | A433 | £1.15 multi | 3.00 3.00 |
| | | Nos. 2235-2240 (6) | 12.90 12.90 |

**Souvenir Sheet**

| | | | |
|---|---|---|---|
| 2241 | A433 | £2 multi | 5.25 5.25 |

No. 2241 contains one 45x33mm stamp.

Hamptonne Country Life Museum — A434

Designs: 52p, Exterior of Hamptonne House. 67p, Cider press. 80p, Exterior of Langlois House. 85p, Interior of Hamptonne House. 99p, Interior of Langlois House. £1.15, Hamptonne House fireplace.

**2019, June 11          Litho.          Perf. 13x13¼**

| | | | |
|---|---|---|---|
| 2242 | A434 | 52p multi | 1.40 1.40 |
| 2243 | A434 | 67p multi | 1.75 1.75 |
| 2244 | A434 | 80p multi | 2.00 2.00 |
| 2245 | A434 | 85p multi | 2.25 2.25 |
| 2246 | A434 | 99p multi | 2.50 2.50 |
| 2247 | A434 | £1.15 multi | 3.00 3.00 |
| | | Nos. 2242-2247 (6) | 12.90 12.90 |

Investiture of the Prince of Wales, 50th Anniv. — A435

Designs: 80p, Prince Charles saluting, Princess Anne. 85p, Queen Elizabeth II placing crown on head of Prince Charles, horiz. 99p, Queen Elizabeth II holding hand of Prince Charles, horiz. £1.15, Queen Elizabeth and Prince Charles, diff. £2, Prince Charles wearing crown.

**Perf. 14x13½, 13½x14**
**2019, July 1          Litho.**

| | | | |
|---|---|---|---|
| 2248 | A435 | 80p multi | 2.00 2.00 |
| 2249 | A435 | 85p multi | 2.25 2.25 |
| 2250 | A435 | 99p multi | 2.50 2.50 |
| 2251 | A435 | £1.15 multi | 3.00 3.00 |
| | | Nos. 2248-2251 (4) | 9.75 9.75 |

**Souvenir Sheet**

| | | | |
|---|---|---|---|
| 2252 | A435 | £2 multi | 5.25 5.25 |

No. 2252 contains one 36x50mm stamp.

First Man on the Moon, 50th Anniv. — A436

Designs: 52p, Liftoff of Apollo 11. 67p, Touchdown of Lunar Module on Moon. 80p, Command and Service Modules in lunar orbit. 85p, Astronaut on Moon. 99p, Lunar Module leaving Moon. £1.15, Splashdown of Apollo 11 capsule. £3, Televised image of astronauts on Moon, horiz.

**2019, July 20          Litho.          Perf. 14**

| | | | |
|---|---|---|---|
| 2253 | A436 | 52p multi | 1.25 1.25 |
| 2254 | A436 | 67p multi | 1.60 1.60 |
| 2255 | A436 | 80p multi | 2.00 2.00 |
| 2256 | A436 | 85p multi | 2.10 2.10 |
| 2257 | A436 | 99p multi | 2.40 2.40 |
| 2258 | A436 | £1.15 multi | 2.75 2.75 |
| *a.* | | Souvenir sheet of 6, #2253-2258 | 12.50 12.50 |
| | | Nos. 2253-2258 (6) | 12.10 12.10 |

**Souvenir Sheet**
**Perf. 14x13¼**

| | | | |
|---|---|---|---|
| 2259 | A436 | £3 multi | 7.25 7.25 |

No. 2259 contains one 70x51mm stamp.

Girl Guides in Jersey, Cent. — A437

Girl Guides: 52p, Tending flower garden. 67p, At transportation center. 80p, At campground. 85p, Surfing. 99p, Assisting Girl Guide in wheelchair. £1.15, Looking at globe.

**2019, Aug. 6          Litho.          Perf. 13¾x13¼**

| | | | |
|---|---|---|---|
| 2260 | A437 | 52p multi | 1.25 1.25 |
| 2261 | A437 | 67p multi | 1.60 1.60 |
| 2262 | A437 | 80p multi | 2.00 2.00 |
| 2263 | A437 | 85p multi | 2.10 2.10 |
| 2264 | A437 | 99p multi | 2.40 2.40 |
| 2265 | A437 | £1.15 multi | 2.75 2.75 |
| | | Nos. 2260-2265 (6) | 12.10 12.10 |

Mammals and
Birds — A438

Designs: No. 2266, Stoat. No. 2267, Barn
owl. No. 2268, Long-eared owl. No. 2269,
Long-tailed field mouse. No. 2270, Hawfinch.
No. 2271, Red squirrel.

| 2019, Sept. 2 | | Litho. | | Perf. 13¼ | |
|---|---|---|---|---|---|
| 2266 | A438 | 52p multi | | 1.25 | 1.25 |
| 2267 | A438 | 52p multi | | 1.25 | 1.25 |
| 2268 | A438 | 52p multi | | 1.25 | 1.25 |
| 2269 | A438 | 52p multi | | 1.25 | 1.25 |
| 2270 | A438 | 52p multi | | 1.25 | 1.25 |
| 2271 | A438 | 52p multi | | 1.25 | 1.25 |
| a. | | Souvenir sheet of 2, #2268, 2271 | | 2.50 | 2.50 |
| b. | | Souvenir sheet of 6, #2266-2271 | | 7.50 | 7.50 |
| | | Nos. 2266-2271 (6) | | 7.50 | 7.50 |

Postal Worker
and Old Mail
Van — A439

Modern Mail
Van — A440

Postal
Workers
Sorting Mail
A441

Postal Worker
and Electonic
Sorting
Equipment
A442

Customers at
Post Office
Counter
A443

Customer
Using
Computerized
Mailing
Station
A444

Postal Worker
and Bicycle
A445

Transportation
Of Mail by
Airplane
A446

**Litho. With Foil Application**

| 2019, Oct. 1 | | | | Perf. 13¾x13¼ | |
|---|---|---|---|---|---|
| 2272 | A439 | 52p multi | | 1.25 | 1.25 |
| 2273 | A440 | 52p multi | | 1.25 | 1.25 |
| a. | | Horiz. pair, #2272-2273 | | 2.50 | 2.50 |
| 2274 | A441 | 67p multi | | 1.75 | 1.75 |
| 2275 | A442 | 67p multi | | 1.75 | 1.75 |
| a. | | Horiz. pair, #2274-2275 | | 3.50 | 3.50 |
| b. | | Booklet pane of 4, #2272-2275 | | 6.00 | — |
| 2276 | A443 | 99p multi | | 2.50 | 2.50 |
| 2277 | A444 | 99p multi | | 2.50 | 2.50 |
| a. | | Horiz. pair, #2276-2277 | | 5.00 | 5.00 |
| b. | | Booklet pane of 4, #2274-2277 | | 8.50 | — |

| 2278 | A445 | £1.46 multi | | 3.75 | 3.75 |
|---|---|---|---|---|---|
| 2279 | A446 | £1.46 multi | | 3.75 | 3.75 |
| a. | | Horiz. pair, #2278-2279 | | 7.50 | 7.50 |
| b. | | Booklet pane of 4, #2272-2273, 2278-2279 | | 10.00 | — |
| c. | | Booklet pane of 4, #2276-2279 | | 12.50 | — |
| | | Complete booklet, #2275b, 2277b, 2279b, 2279c | | 37.00 | |
| | | Nos. 2272-2279 (8) | | 18.50 | 18.50 |

Postal independence of Jersey, 50th anniv.

A447

Inscription: 52p, "An island of orchards."
67p, "The grand old castle." 80p, "The first
lovely walk." 85p, "A peaceful, scarcely rippled
sea." 99p, "A delicious evening." £1.15, "A little
of Jersey human nature."

| 2019, Nov. 1 | | Litho. | | Perf. 13x13¼ | |
|---|---|---|---|---|---|
| 2280 | A447 | 52p multi | | 1.40 | 1.40 |
| 2281 | A447 | 67p multi | | 1.75 | 1.75 |
| 2282 | A447 | 80p multi | | 2.10 | 2.10 |
| 2283 | A447 | 85p multi | | 2.25 | 2.25 |
| 2284 | A447 | 99p multi | | 2.60 | 2.60 |
| 2285 | A447 | £1.15 multi | | 3.00 | 3.00 |
| | | Nos. 2280-2285 (6) | | 13.10 | 13.10 |

Scenes of 19th century Jersey and quotations from writings of George Eliot (1819-80).

Christmas — A448

Various children acting in Nativity play.

**Serpentine Die Cut 13¾**

| 2019, Nov. 20 | | | | Litho. | |
|---|---|---|---|---|---|
| **Self-Adhesive** | | | | | |
| 2286 | A448 | 45p multi | | 1.25 | 1.25 |
| 2287 | A448 | 52p multi | | 1.40 | 1.40 |
| 2288 | A448 | 59p multi | | 1.50 | 1.50 |
| 2289 | A448 | 67p multi | | 1.75 | 1.75 |
| 2290 | A448 | 80p multi | | 2.10 | 2.10 |
| 2291 | A448 | 85p multi | | 2.25 | 2.25 |
| 2292 | A448 | 99p multi | | 2.60 | 2.60 |
| 2293 | A448 | £1.15 multi | | 3.00 | 3.00 |
| | | Nos. 2286-2293 (8) | | 15.85 | 15.85 |

New Year 2020
(Year of the
Rat) — A449

Designs: 52p, Rats and bowl.
£1, Rat in palanquin.

| 2020, Jan. 3 | | Litho. | | Perf. 13¼ | |
|---|---|---|---|---|---|
| 2294 | A449 | 52p multi | | 1.40 | 1.40 |

**Souvenir Sheet**

| 2295 | A449 | £1 multi | | 2.60 | 2.60 |
|---|---|---|---|---|---|

No. 2295 contains one 60x60mm stamp.

Photographs by
Claude Cahun (1894-
1954) — A450

Various untitled photographs.

| | | **Perf. 13¼x13½** | | | |
|---|---|---|---|---|---|
| 2020, Feb. 12 | | | | | Litho. |
| 2296 | A450 | 52p sil & multi | | 1.40 | 1.40 |
| 2297 | A450 | 67p sil & multi | | 1.75 | 1.75 |
| 2298 | A450 | 80p sil & multi | | 2.10 | 2.10 |
| 2299 | A450 | 85p sil & multi | | 2.25 | 2.25 |
| 2300 | A450 | 99p sil & multi | | 2.60 | 2.60 |
| 2301 | A450 | £1.15 sil & multi | | 3.00 | 3.00 |
| 2302 | A450 | £1.46 sil & multi | | 3.75 | 3.75 |
| 2303 | A450 | £2.78 sil & multi | | 7.25 | 7.25 |
| | | Nos. 2296-2303 (8) | | 24.10 | 24.10 |

Ludwig van
Beethoven (1770-
1827), Composer
A451

Name of composition by Beethoven: 54p,
Piano Concerto No. 1, Op. 15. 70p, Romance
for Violin No. 2, Op. 50. 84p, Coriolan Overture, Op. 62. 88p, Egmont Overture, Op. 84.
£1.05, Symphony No. 7, Op. 92. £1.18, Symphony No. 9, Op. 125.
£2, Beethoven (Symphony No. 5 in C Minor,
Op. 67), vert.

| 2020, Mar. 26 | | Litho. | | Perf. 13 | |
|---|---|---|---|---|---|
| 2304 | A451 | 54p multi | | 1.40 | 1.40 |
| 2305 | A451 | 70p multi | | 1.75 | 1.75 |
| 2306 | A451 | 84p multi | | 2.10 | 2.10 |
| 2307 | A451 | 88p multi | | 2.25 | 2.25 |
| 2308 | A451 | £1.05 multi | | 2.60 | 2.60 |
| 2309 | A451 | £1.18 multi | | 3.00 | 3.00 |
| | | Nos. 2304-2309 (6) | | 13.10 | 13.10 |

**Souvenir Sheet**

**Perf. 14**

| 2310 | A451 | £2 multi | | 5.00 | 5.00 |
|---|---|---|---|---|---|

No. 2310 contains one 33x37mm stamp.

Mail
Ships — A452

Designs: 54p, Rover. 70p, Atalanta. 84p,
Cygnus. 88p, Lydia. £1.05, Isle of Jersey.
£1.18, Caesarea III.

| 2020, Apr. 7 | | Litho. | | Perf. 13¾x14 | |
|---|---|---|---|---|---|
| 2311 | A452 | 54p sil & multi | | 1.40 | 1.40 |
| 2312 | A452 | 70p sil & multi | | 1.75 | 1.75 |
| 2313 | A452 | 84p sil & multi | | 2.10 | 2.10 |
| 2314 | A452 | 88p sil & multi | | 2.25 | 2.25 |
| 2315 | A452 | £1.05 sil & multi | | 2.60 | 2.60 |
| a. | | Souvenir sheet of 2, #2313, 2315 | | 4.75 | 4.75 |
| 2316 | A452 | £1.18 sil & multi | | 3.00 | 3.00 |
| | | Nos. 2311-2316 (6) | | 13.10 | 13.10 |

Europa (Nos. 2313, 2315).

Liberation of
Jersey, 75th
Anniv. — A453

Designs: 54p, Servicemen and Union Jack.
70p, Soldier giving Union Jack to young girl.
84p, Servicemen and women in jeep. 88p,
Servicemen holding flags. £1.05, Three
women singing. £1.18, Man carrying mace.

| 2020, May 9 | | Litho. | | Perf. 13¼x13¼ | |
|---|---|---|---|---|---|
| 2317 | A453 | 54p multi | | 1.40 | 1.40 |
| 2318 | A453 | 70p multi | | 1.75 | 1.75 |
| 2319 | A453 | 84p multi | | 2.10 | 2.10 |
| 2320 | A453 | 88p multi | | 2.25 | 2.25 |
| 2321 | A453 | £1.05 multi | | 2.60 | 2.60 |
| 2322 | A453 | £1.18 multi | | 3.00 | 3.00 |
| a. | | Souvenir sheet of 6, #2317-2322 | | 13.50 | 13.50 |
| | | Nos. 2317-2322 (6) | | 13.10 | 13.10 |

Scenes From Stories
by Charles Dickens
(1812-70) — A454

Scene from: 54p, A Tale of Two Cities. 70p,
David Copperfield. 84p, The Old Curiosity
Shop. 88p, Bleak House. £1.05, Great Expec-
tations. £1.18, Nicholas Nickleby. £1.50, Oliver
Twist. £2.92, A Christmas Carol.

| 2020, June 9 | | Litho. | | Perf. 13¼x13 | |
|---|---|---|---|---|---|
| 2323 | A454 | 54p multi | | 1.40 | 1.40 |
| 2324 | A454 | 70p multi | | 1.75 | 1.75 |
| 2325 | A454 | 84p multi | | 2.10 | 2.10 |
| 2326 | A454 | 88p multi | | 2.25 | 2.25 |
| 2327 | A454 | £1.05 multi | | 2.60 | 2.60 |
| 2328 | A454 | £1.18 multi | | 3.00 | 3.00 |
| 2329 | A454 | £1.50 multi | | 3.75 | 3.75 |
| 2330 | A454 | £2.92 multi | | 7.25 | 7.25 |
| a. | | Souvenir sheet of 8, #2323-2330 | | 24.50 | 24.50 |
| | | Nos. 2323-2330 (8) | | 24.10 | 24.10 |

Harry Vardon
(1870-1937),
Professional
Golfer — A455

Various photographs of Vardon, flags of
Great Britain and United States, British Open
Claret Jug and U.S. Open Championship trophy: 54p, 70p, 84p, 88p, £1.05, £1.18.
£3, Vardon and Ted Ray (1877-1943), horiz.

| 2020, July 9 | | Litho. | | Perf. 13¼ | |
|---|---|---|---|---|---|
| 2331 | A455 | 54p sil & multi | | 1.40 | 1.40 |
| 2332 | A455 | 70p sil & multi | | 1.90 | 1.90 |
| 2333 | A455 | 84p sil & multi | | 2.25 | 2.25 |
| 2334 | A455 | 88p sil & multi | | 2.40 | 2.40 |
| 2335 | A455 | £1.05 sil & multi | | 2.75 | 2.75 |
| 2336 | A455 | £1.18 sil & multi | | 3.25 | 3.25 |
| | | Nos. 2331-2336 (6) | | 13.95 | 13.95 |

**Souvenir Sheet**

| 2337 | A455 | £3 sil & multi | | 7.75 | 7.75 |
|---|---|---|---|---|---|

No. 2337 contains one 72x36mm stamp.

Princess Anne, 70th
Birthday — A456

Various photographs of Princess Anne from:
54p, 1972. 70p, 2010. 84p, 2012. 88p, 1976.
£1.05, 1999. £1.18, 2019.
£3, 1975, horiz.

| 2020, Aug. 15 | | Litho. | | Perf. 13¼x13 | |
|---|---|---|---|---|---|
| 2338 | A456 | 54p multi | | 1.40 | 1.40 |
| 2339 | A456 | 70p multi | | 1.90 | 1.90 |
| 2340 | A456 | 84p multi | | 2.25 | 2.25 |
| 2341 | A456 | 88p multi | | 2.40 | 2.40 |
| 2342 | A456 | £1.05 multi | | 2.75 | 2.75 |
| 2343 | A456 | £1.18 multi | | 3.25 | 3.25 |
| | | Nos. 2338-2343 (6) | | 13.95 | 13.95 |

**Souvenir Sheet**

**Perf. 13¼**

| 2344 | A456 | £3 multi | | 8.00 | 8.00 |
|---|---|---|---|---|---|

No. 2344 contains one 60x60mm stamp.

Jersey Motorcycle &
Light Car Club,
Cent. — A457

Designs: 54p, Motorcycle. 70p, Race car.
84p, Motorcycle, diff. 88p, Race car, diff.
£1.05, Race car, diff. £1.18, Motorcycle, diff.
£1.50, Race car, diff. £2.92, Motorcycle, diff.
£3, Race car in Jersey's first international
road race, 1947, horiz.

| 2020, Sept. 8 | | Litho. | | Perf. 13¼ | |
|---|---|---|---|---|---|
| 2345 | A457 | 54p multi | | 1.40 | 1.40 |
| 2346 | A457 | 70p multi | | 1.90 | 1.90 |
| 2347 | A457 | 84p multi | | 2.25 | 2.25 |
| 2348 | A457 | 88p multi | | 2.25 | 2.25 |
| 2349 | A457 | £1.05 multi | | 2.75 | 2.75 |
| 2350 | A457 | £1.18 multi | | 3.25 | 3.25 |
| 2351 | A457 | £1.50 multi | | 4.00 | 4.00 |
| a. | | Booklet pane of 4, #2345, 2347, 2349, 2351 | | 10.50 | — |
| b. | | Booklet pane of 4, #2346, 2348, 2349, 2351 | | 11.00 | — |
| 2352 | A457 | £2.92 multi | | 7.50 | 7.50 |
| a. | | Souvenir sheet of 8, #2345-2352 | | 25.50 | 25.50 |
| b. | | Booklet pane of 4, #2346, 2348, 2350, 2352 | | 15.00 | — |
| c. | | Booklet pane of 4, #2345, 2347, 2350, 2352 | | 14.50 | — |
| | | Complete booklet, #2351a, 2351b, 2352b, 2352c | | 51.00 | |
| | | Nos. 2345-2352 (8) | | 25.30 | 25.30 |

**Souvenir Sheet**

**Perf. 13¾x14**

| 2353 | A457 | £3 multi | | 7.75 | 7.75 |
|---|---|---|---|---|---|

No. 2353 contains one 45x33mm stamp.

Popular Culture of
the 1980s — A458

Designs: 54p, "Rad!" 70p, Singer at microphone. 84p, Women wearing jacket with shoulder pads. 88p, Emblem for Live Aid concert. £1.05, Piña colada. £1.18, Boombox. £3, Shops and gymnasium in 1980s Jersey.

### 2020, Oct. 6    Litho.    Perf. 13¼

| | | | | |
|---|---|---|---|---|
| 2354 | A458 | 54p multi | 1.40 | 1.40 |
| 2355 | A458 | 70p multi | 1.75 | 1.75 |
| 2356 | A458 | 84p multi | 2.25 | 2.25 |
| 2357 | A458 | 88p multi | 2.25 | 2.25 |
| 2358 | A458 | £1.05 multi | 2.75 | 2.75 |
| 2359 | A458 | £1.18 multi | 3.00 | 3.00 |
| a. | | Souvenir sheet of 6, #2354-2359 | 13.50 | 13.50 |
| | | Nos. 2354-2359 (6) | 13.40 | 13.40 |

#### Souvenir Sheet

| | | | | |
|---|---|---|---|---|
| 2360 | A458 | £3 multi | 7.75 | 7.75 |

No. 2360 contains one 72x72mm stamp.

Myths and Legends — A459

Designs: 54p, The Bull Among the Rocks. 70p, Legend of the Plank. 84p, Jeffrey's Leap. 88p, Spanish Ship on the Rocks. £1.05, Lavoir des Dames. £1.18, The Martyrdom of St. Helier.

### 2020, Nov. 3    Litho.    Perf. 14

| | | | | |
|---|---|---|---|---|
| 2361 | A459 | 54p multi | 1.50 | 1.50 |
| 2362 | A459 | 70p multi | 1.90 | 1.90 |
| 2363 | A459 | 84p multi | 2.25 | 2.25 |
| 2364 | A459 | 88p multi | 2.40 | 2.40 |
| 2365 | A459 | £1.05 multi | 3.00 | 3.00 |
| 2366 | A459 | £1.18 multi | 3.25 | 3.25 |
| a. | | Souvenir sheet of 6, #2361-2366 | 14.50 | 14.50 |
| | | Nos. 2361-2366 (6) | 14.30 | 14.30 |

Christmas — A460

Paper cuttings of: 46p, Le Don Hilton guard house. 54p, Corbière Lighthouse and deer. 62p, Grouville Church. 70p, Mont Orgueil Castle. 84p, People in Liberation Square. 88p, L'ile au Guerdain and robin. £1.05, St. Brelade's Bay. £1.18, Jersey cows and Santa Claus in flying sleigh.

#### Serpentine Die Cut 13¾x14¼

### 2020, Nov. 23    Litho.

#### Self-Adhesive

| | | | | |
|---|---|---|---|---|
| 2367 | A460 | 46p multi | 1.25 | 1.25 |
| 2368 | A460 | 54p multi | 1.50 | 1.50 |
| 2369 | A460 | 62p multi | 1.75 | 1.75 |
| 2370 | A460 | 70p multi | 1.90 | 1.90 |
| 2371 | A460 | 84p multi | 2.25 | 2.25 |
| 2372 | A460 | 88p multi | 2.40 | 2.40 |
| 2373 | A460 | £1.05 multi | 2.75 | 2.75 |
| 2374 | A460 | £1.18 multi | 3.25 | 3.25 |
| | | Nos. 2367-2374 (8) | 17.05 | 17.05 |

New Year 2021 (Year of the Ox) — A461

Designs: 54p, Ox. £1, Two oxen, bird and flower.

### 2021, Jan. 5    Litho.    Perf. 13¼

| | | | | |
|---|---|---|---|---|
| 2375 | A461 | 54p multi | 1.50 | 1.50 |

#### Souvenir Sheet

| | | | | |
|---|---|---|---|---|
| 2376 | A461 | £1 multi | 2.75 | 2.75 |

No. 2376 contains one 60x60mm stamp.

Historic Maps of Jersey — A462

Map made by: 54p, John Norden, 1595. 70p, Jan Jannson, 1646. 84p, Nicholas Dobrée, 1746. 88p, Clement Lempriere, 1796. £1.05, Capt. Martin White, 1826. £1.18, Harry Clark, 1930.

### 2021, Feb. 17    Litho.    Perf. 12

| | | | | |
|---|---|---|---|---|
| 2377 | A462 | 54p multi | 1.50 | 1.50 |
| 2378 | A462 | 70p multi | 2.00 | 2.00 |
| 2379 | A462 | 84p multi | 2.40 | 2.40 |
| 2380 | A462 | 88p multi | 2.50 | 2.50 |
| 2381 | A462 | £1.05 multi | 3.00 | 3.00 |
| 2382 | A462 | £1.18 multi | 3.25 | 3.25 |
| | | Nos. 2377-2382 (6) | 14.65 | 14.65 |

Lockdown Birds — A463

Numbered paintings of various birds by Berni Martin created during 2020 COVID-19 lockdown: No. 2383, Bird #52. No. 2384, Bird #19, vert. No. 2385, Bird #12. No. 2386, Bird #22, vert. No. 2387, Bird #58. No. 2388, Bird #8, vert. No. 2389, Bird #28. No. 2390, Bird, #97, vert.

#### Serpentine Die Cut 13¾x14¼, 14¼x13¾

### 2021, Mar. 1    Litho.

#### Self-Adhesive

| | | | | |
|---|---|---|---|---|
| 2383 | A463 | 54p multi | 1.50 | 1.50 |
| 2384 | A463 | 54p multi | 1.50 | 1.50 |
| 2385 | A463 | 70p multi | 2.00 | 2.00 |
| 2386 | A463 | 70p multi | 2.00 | 2.00 |
| 2387 | A463 | 84p multi | 2.40 | 2.40 |
| 2388 | A463 | 84p multi | 2.40 | 2.40 |
| 2389 | A463 | 88p multi | 2.50 | 2.50 |
| 2390 | A463 | 88p multi | 2.50 | 2.50 |
| | | Nos. 2383-2390 (8) | 16.80 | 16.80 |

Endangered Wildlife — A464

Designs: 54p, Atlantic puffin. 70p, Loggerhead turtle. 84p, Orcas. 88p, Bottlenose dolphins. £1.05, Balearic shearwater. £1.18, Gray seal.

#### Perf. 13¾x13¼

### 2021, Mar. 11    Litho.

| | | | | |
|---|---|---|---|---|
| 2391 | A464 | 54p multi | 1.50 | 1.50 |
| 2392 | A464 | 70p multi | 2.00 | 2.00 |
| 2393 | A464 | 84p multi | 2.40 | 2.40 |
| 2394 | A464 | 88p multi | 2.50 | 2.50 |
| 2395 | A464 | £1.05 multi | 3.00 | 3.00 |
| a. | | Souvenir sheet of 2, #2391, 2395 | 4.50 | 4.50 |
| 2396 | A464 | £1.18 multi | 3.25 | 3.25 |
| | | Nos. 2391-2396 (6) | 14.65 | 14.65 |

Europa (Nos. 2391, 2395, 2395a).

Aerial Photographs of Jersey Landmarks — A465

Designs: 54p, La Hougue Bie. 74p, St. Catherine's Breakwater. 88p, Fields in sunlight, Trinity. £1, St. Helier at night. £1.25, Kayaks at Sorel Point. £1.30, Jersey cows. £1.75, Corbière Lighthouse. £3.50, Tractor and boat at St. Ouen's Bay.

### 2021, Apr. 1    Litho.    Perf. 13¼

| | | | | |
|---|---|---|---|---|
| 2397 | A465 | 54p multi | 1.50 | 1.50 |
| 2398 | A465 | 74p multi | 2.10 | 2.10 |
| 2399 | A465 | 88p multi | 2.50 | 2.50 |
| 2400 | A465 | £1 multi | 2.75 | 2.75 |
| 2401 | A465 | £1.25 multi | 3.50 | 3.50 |
| 2402 | A465 | £1.30 multi | 3.75 | 3.75 |
| 2403 | A465 | £1.75 multi | 5.00 | 5.00 |
| 2404 | A465 | £3.50 multi | 9.75 | 9.75 |
| a. | | Souvenir sheet of 8, #2397-2404 | 31.00 | 31.00 |

See Nos. 2561-2568.

Queen Elizabeth II, 95th Birthday — A466

Designs: 54p, Princess Elizabeth. 74p, Queen Elizabeth II at coronation. 88p, Queen

Elizabeth II and Prince Philip. £1, Queen Elizabeth II, diff. £1.25, Queen Elizabeth II, diff. £1.30, Queen Elizabeth II, diff.

### 2021, Apr. 21    Litho.    Perf. 13¼

| | | | | |
|---|---|---|---|---|
| 2405 | A466 | 54p multi | 1.50 | 1.50 |
| 2406 | A466 | 74p multi | 2.10 | 2.10 |
| 2407 | A466 | 88p multi | 2.50 | 2.50 |
| 2408 | A466 | £1 multi | 2.75 | 2.75 |
| 2409 | A466 | £1.25 multi | 3.50 | 3.50 |
| 2410 | A466 | £1.30 multi | 3.75 | 3.75 |
| | | Nos. 2405-2410 (6) | 16.10 | 16.10 |

See Isle of Man No. 2150a.

Surfing A467

Various photographs of surfers at St. Ouen's Bay.

### 2021, May 18    Litho.    Perf. 11¾x11½

| | | | | |
|---|---|---|---|---|
| 2411 | A467 | 54p multi | 1.60 | 1.60 |
| 2412 | A467 | 74p multi | 2.10 | 2.10 |
| 2413 | A467 | 88p multi | 2.50 | 2.50 |
| 2414 | A467 | £1 multi | 3.00 | 3.00 |
| 2415 | A467 | £1.25 multi | 3.50 | 3.50 |
| 2416 | A467 | £1.30 multi | 3.75 | 3.75 |
| | | Nos. 2411-2416 (6) | 16.45 | 16.45 |

#### Souvenir Sheet
#### Perf. 12½

| | | | | |
|---|---|---|---|---|
| 2417 | A467 | £3 multi | 8.50 | 8.50 |

No. 2417 contains one 80x48mm stamp.

Prince Philip (1921-2021) A468

Photographs of Prince Philip: 54p, Wearing bow tie. 74p, With horse. 88p, Wearing hard hat. £1, Wearing military cap. £1.25, Wearing bowler hat. £1.30, With Queen Elizabeth II.

### 2021, July 6    Litho.    Perf. 13¼

| | | | | |
|---|---|---|---|---|
| 2418 | A468 | 54p multi | 1.50 | 1.50 |
| 2419 | A468 | 74p multi | 2.10 | 2.10 |
| 2420 | A468 | 88p multi | 2.50 | 2.50 |
| 2421 | A468 | £1 multi | 2.75 | 2.75 |
| 2422 | A468 | £1.25 multi | 3.50 | 3.50 |
| 2423 | A468 | £1.30 multi | 3.75 | 3.75 |
| | | Nos. 2418-2423 (6) | 16.10 | 16.10 |

Popular Culture of the 1990s — A469

Designs: 54p, "Fresh" (graffiti art). 74p, Members of a boy band. 88p, Woman wearing crop top. £1, Personal computer. £1.25, Candies and bottles of soda. £1.30, Yo-yo. £3, Storefronts.

### 2021, July 14    Litho.    Perf. 13¼

| | | | | |
|---|---|---|---|---|
| 2424 | A469 | 54p multi | 1.50 | 1.50 |
| 2425 | A469 | 74p multi | 2.10 | 2.10 |
| 2426 | A469 | 88p multi | 2.50 | 2.50 |
| 2427 | A469 | £1 multi | 2.75 | 2.75 |
| 2428 | A469 | £1.25 multi | 3.50 | 3.50 |
| 2429 | A469 | £1.30 multi | 3.75 | 3.75 |
| a. | | Souvenir sheet of 6, #2424-2429 | 16.50 | 16.50 |
| | | Nos. 2424-2429 (6) | 16.10 | 16.10 |

#### Souvenir Sheet

| | | | | |
|---|---|---|---|---|
| 2430 | A469 | £3 multi | 8.50 | 8.50 |

No. 2430 contains one 72x72mm stamp.

Parishes of Jersey — A470

Parish: No. 2431, St. John. No. 2432, St. Helier. No. 2433, St. Martin. No. 2434, St. Ouen. No. 2435, St. Saviour. No. 2436, St. Peter. No. 2437, St. Mary. No. 2438, Trinity. No. 2439, St. Brelade. No. 2440, St. Lawrence. No. 2441, St. Clement. No. 2442, Grouville.

#### Serpentine Die Cut 12

### 2021, Aug. 17    Litho.

#### Booklet Stamps
#### Self-Adhesive
#### Inscribed "Local Letter"

| | | | | |
|---|---|---|---|---|
| 2431 | A470 | (54p) multi | 1.50 | 1.50 |
| 2432 | A470 | (54p) multi | 1.50 | 1.50 |
| 2433 | A470 | (54p) multi | 1.50 | 1.50 |
| 2434 | A470 | (54p) multi | 1.50 | 1.50 |
| 2435 | A470 | (54p) multi | 1.50 | 1.50 |
| 2436 | A470 | (54p) multi | 1.50 | 1.50 |
| a. | | Booklet pane of 30, 5 each #2431-2436 | 45.00 | |

#### Inscribed "UK Priority Letter"

| | | | | |
|---|---|---|---|---|
| 2437 | A470 | (74p) multi | 2.10 | 2.10 |
| 2438 | A470 | (74p) multi | 2.10 | 2.10 |
| 2439 | A470 | (74p) multi | 2.10 | 2.10 |
| 2440 | A470 | (74p) multi | 2.10 | 2.10 |
| 2441 | A470 | (74p) multi | 2.10 | 2.10 |
| 2442 | A470 | (74p) multi | 2.10 | 2.10 |
| a. | | ooklet pane of 30, 5 each #2437-2442 | 63.00 | |
| | | Nos. 2431-2442 (12) | 21.60 | 21.60 |

Race Cars of British Formula 1 World Champions A471

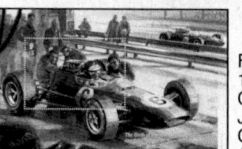

Formula 1 Race Car of James Hunt A472

Formula 1 Race Car of Jim Clark A473

Race car of: No. 2443, Mike Hawthorn, 1958 champion. No. 2444, Graham Hill, 1962, 1968 champion. No. 2445, Jim Clark, 1963, 1965 champion. No. 2446, John Surtees, 1964 champion. 88p, James Hunt, 1976 champion. £1, Jackie Stewart, 1969, 1971, 1973 champion. £1.25, Nigel Mansell, 1992 champion. £1.30, Damon Hill, 1996 champion. £1.75, Jenson Button, 2009 champion. £3.50, Lewis Hamilton, 2008, 2014, 2015, 2017, 2018, 2019, 2020 champion.

#### Litho. With Foil Application

### 2021, Sept. 1    Perf. 13¼x13½

| | | | | |
|---|---|---|---|---|
| 2443 | A471 | 54p multi | 1.50 | 1.50 |
| 2444 | A471 | 54p multi | 1.50 | 1.50 |
| 2445 | A471 | 74p multi | 2.10 | 2.10 |
| 2446 | A471 | 74p multi | 2.10 | 2.10 |
| 2447 | A471 | 88p multi | 2.10 | 2.10 |
| 2448 | A471 | £1 multi | 2.75 | 2.75 |
| 2449 | A471 | £1.25 multi | 3.50 | 3.50 |
| 2450 | A471 | £1.30 multi | 3.75 | 3.75 |
| 2451 | A471 | £1.75 multi | 4.75 | 4.75 |
| a. | | Souvenir sheet of 5, #2443, 2445, 2448, 2450, 2451 | 15.00 | 15.00 |
| 2452 | A471 | £3.50 multi | 9.75 | 9.75 |
| a. | | Souvenir sheet of 5, #2444, 2446, 2447, 2449, 2452 | 19.50 | 19.50 |
| | | Nos. 2443-2452 (10) | 33.80 | 33.80 |

#### Souvenir Sheets
#### Perf. 14

| | | | | |
|---|---|---|---|---|
| 2453 | A472 | £3 multi | 8.25 | 8.25 |
| 2454 | A473 | £3 multi | 8.25 | 8.25 |

Brewing in Jersey, 150th Anniv. — A474

Designs: 54p, Hops and grains for malting. 74p, Grains in mashing tun. 88p, Hands holding hops. £1, Brewer and fermentation vessels. £1.25, Worker racking keg. £1.30, Pint of beer, Mont Orgueil Castle. £3, 1920s beer keg delivery truck.

### 2021, Oct. 5    Litho.    Perf. 13¼

| | | | | |
|---|---|---|---|---|
| 2455 | A474 | 54p multi | 1.50 | 1.50 |
| 2456 | A474 | 74p multi | 2.10 | 2.10 |
| 2457 | A474 | 88p multi | 2.40 | 2.40 |
| 2458 | A474 | £1 multi | 2.75 | 2.75 |

| | | | | |
|---|---|---|---|---|
| 2459 | A474 | £1.25 multi | 3.50 | 3.50 |
| 2460 | A474 | £1.30 multi | 3.75 | 3.75 |
| | *Nos. 2455-2460 (6)* | | 16.00 | 16.00 |

**Souvenir Sheet**

| | | | | |
|---|---|---|---|---|
| 2461 | A474 | £3 multi | 8.25 | 8.25 |

No. 2461 contains one 70x40mm stamp.

*Bergerac Television Series, 40th Anniv. — A475*

Various characters.

**2021, Oct. 18   Litho.   Perf. 13x13¼**

| | | | | |
|---|---|---|---|---|
| 2462 | A475 | 54p multi | 1.50 | 1.50 |
| 2463 | A475 | 74p multi | 2.10 | 2.10 |
| 2464 | A475 | 88p multi | 2.40 | 2.40 |
| 2465 | A475 | £1 multi | 2.75 | 2.75 |
| 2466 | A475 | £1.25 multi | 3.50 | 3.50 |
| 2467 | A475 | £1.30 multi | 3.75 | 3.75 |
| 2468 | A475 | £1.75 multi | 4.75 | 4.75 |
| a. | Booklet pane of 4, #2462, 2464, 2466, 2468 | | 12.50 | — |
| b. | Booklet pane of 4, #2463, 2464, 2466, 2468 | | 13.00 | — |
| 2469 | A475 | £3.50 multi | 9.50 | 9.50 |
| a. | Booklet pane of 4, #2463, 2465, 2467, 2469 | | 18.50 | — |
| b. | Booklet pane of 4, #2462, 2465, 2467, 2469 | | 17.50 | — |
| | Complete booklet, #2468a, 2468b, 2469a, 2469b | | 61.50 | |
| | *Nos. 2462-2469 (8)* | | 30.25 | 30.25 |

A476

Christmas — A477

Designs: £3.50, Mother and child reading book about Santa Claus.

46p, Christmas tree and sleeping cat near fireplace. 54p, Boy watching sleigh of Santa Claus in flight. 66p, Sleigh of Santa Claus in flight. 74p, Sleigh of Santa Claus landing on roof of house. 88p, Santa Claus emerging from fireplace. £1, Boy watching Santa Claus from behind Christmas tree. £1.25, Santa Claus and Christmas tree. £1.30, Sleigh of Santa Claus leaving roof of house.

**2021, Nov. 22   Litho.   Perf. 14**

**Souvenir Sheet**

| | | | | |
|---|---|---|---|---|
| 2470 | A476 | £3.50 multi | 9.25 | 9.25 |

**Self-Adhesive**

**Serpentine Die Cut 13¾x14¼**

| | | | | |
|---|---|---|---|---|
| 2471 | A477 | 46p multi | 1.25 | 1.25 |
| 2472 | A477 | 54p multi | 1.50 | 1.50 |
| 2473 | A477 | 66p multi | 1.75 | 1.75 |
| 2474 | A477 | 74p multi | 2.00 | 2.00 |
| 2475 | A477 | 88p multi | 2.40 | 2.40 |
| 2476 | A477 | £1 multi | 2.75 | 2.75 |
| 2477 | A477 | £1.25 multi | 3.25 | 3.25 |
| 2478 | A477 | £1.30 multi | 3.50 | 3.50 |
| | *Nos. 2471-2478 (8)* | | 18.40 | 18.40 |

*New Year 2022 (Year of the Tiger) — A478*

Designs: 88p, Tiger. £3, Tigress and her cubs.

**2022, Jan. 4   Litho.   Perf. 13¼**

| | | | | |
|---|---|---|---|---|
| 2479 | A478 | 88p multi | 2.40 | 2.40 |

**Souvenir Sheet**

| | | | | |
|---|---|---|---|---|
| 2480 | A478 | £3 multi | 8.00 | 8.00 |

No. 2480 contains one 60x60mm stamp.

*Commercial Aircraft That Have Landed on Jersey — A479*

Designs: 54p, De Havilland DH.86 Express, c. 1936. 74p, Fokker Friendship F27-200, c. 1993. 88p, Scottish Aviation Twin Pioneer I, c. 1971. £1, BAC One-Eleven, c. 1989. £1.25, Britten-Norman BN 2A Mk III Trislander in flight, c. 1971-77. £1.30, Vickers Viscount 806, c. 1990.

£4, Britten-Norman BN 2A Mk III Trislander on ground c. 1983.

**2022, Jan. 20   Litho.   Perf. 12**

| | | | | |
|---|---|---|---|---|
| 2481 | A479 | 54p multi | 1.50 | 1.50 |
| 2482 | A479 | 74p multi | 2.00 | 2.00 |
| 2483 | A479 | 88p multi | 2.40 | 2.40 |
| 2484 | A479 | £1 multi | 2.75 | 2.75 |
| 2485 | A479 | £1.25 multi | 3.50 | 3.50 |
| 2486 | A479 | £1.30 multi | 3.50 | 3.50 |
| a. | Souvenir sheet of 6, #2481-2486 | | 16.00 | 16.00 |
| | *Nos. 2481-2486 (6)* | | 15.65 | 15.65 |

**Souvenir Sheet**

| | | | | |
|---|---|---|---|---|
| 2487 | A479 | £4 multi | 11.00 | 11.00 |

No. 2487 contains one 50x50mm stamp.

*Myths and Legends — A480*

Designs: 54p, The Vioge of Crack Ankle Lane. 74p, The Woman in Black. 88p, The Belenji. £1, The Bells of Les Minquiers. £1.25, The Bride and Groom of Gorey. £1.30, The Soldiers of Vinchelez Lane.

**2022, Mar. 16   Litho.   Perf. 14x13¼**

| | | | | |
|---|---|---|---|---|
| 2488 | A480 | 54p multi | 1.40 | 1.40 |
| 2489 | A480 | 74p multi | 2.00 | 2.00 |
| 2490 | A480 | 88p multi | 2.40 | 2.40 |
| 2491 | A480 | £1 multi | 2.60 | 2.60 |
| 2492 | A480 | £1.25 multi | 3.25 | 3.25 |
| a. | Souvenir sheet of 2, #2490, 2492 | | 5.75 | 5.75 |
| 2493 | A480 | £1.30 multi | 3.50 | 3.50 |
| | *Nos. 2488-2493 (6)* | | 15.15 | 15.15 |

Europa (Nos. 2490, 2492).

Tractors — A481

Designs: 56p, Ferguson TE20 plowing field. 82p, Renault 85-12TX towing boat. 91p, Massey Ferguson 6714s planting field. £1.20, John Deere 6310 cutting back vegetation. £1.37, Fordson Model F binding. £1.75, New Holland T6 baling hay. £2.10, John Deere 5115M farming oysters. £3.65, International W14 plowing field.

**2022, Apr. 1   Litho.   Perf. 12**

| | | | | |
|---|---|---|---|---|
| 2494 | A481 | 56p multi | 1.50 | 1.50 |
| 2495 | A481 | 82p multi | 2.25 | 2.25 |
| 2496 | A481 | 91p multi | 2.40 | 2.40 |
| 2497 | A481 | £1.20 multi | 3.25 | 3.25 |
| 2498 | A481 | £1.37 multi | 3.75 | 3.75 |
| 2499 | A481 | £1.75 multi | 4.75 | 4.75 |
| 2500 | A481 | £2.10 multi | 5.50 | 5.50 |
| 2501 | A481 | £3.65 multi | 9.50 | 9.50 |
| a. | Souvenir sheet of 8, #2494-2501 | | 33.00 | 33.00 |
| | *Nos. 2494-2501 (8)* | | 32.90 | 32.90 |

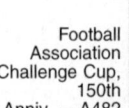

*Football Association Challenge Cup, 150th Anniv. — A482*

Score and scene from: 56p, Blackpool 4 vs. Bolton Wanderers 3, 1953 final. 82p, Coventry 3 vs. Spurs 2, 1987 final. 91p, Sunderland 1 vs. Leeds 0, 1973 final. £1.20, Wimbledon 1 vs. Liverpool 0, 1988 final. £1.37, Hereford 2 vs. Newcastle 1, 1972 third round replay. £1.75, Manchester City 3 vs. Birmingham City 1, 1956 final. £2.10, Liverpool 3 vs. West Ham 3, 2006 final. £3.65, Spurs 3 vs. Manchester City 2, 1981 final replay.

£4, Players from 1872 Wanderers 1 vs. Royal Engineers 0 final.

**2022, May 10   Litho.   Perf. 13¼x13½**

| | | | | |
|---|---|---|---|---|
| 2502 | A482 | 56p multi | 1.40 | 1.40 |
| 2503 | A482 | 82p multi | 2.10 | 2.10 |
| 2504 | A482 | 91p multi | 2.25 | 2.25 |
| 2505 | A482 | £1.20 multi | 3.00 | 3.00 |
| 2506 | A482 | £1.37 multi | 3.50 | 3.50 |
| a. | Souvenir sheet of 3, #2502, 2503, 2506 | | 7.00 | 7.00 |
| b. | Booklet pane of 3, #2504-2506 | | 8.75 | — |
| 2507 | A482 | £1.75 multi | 4.50 | 4.50 |
| a. | Booklet pane of 4, #2502, 2504, 2506, 2507 | | 12.00 | — |
| 2508 | A482 | £2.10 multi | 5.25 | 5.25 |
| a. | Booklet pane of 3, #2503, 2507, 2508 | | 12.00 | — |
| 2509 | A482 | £3.65 multi | 9.25 | 9.25 |
| a. | Souvenir sheet of 8, #2502-2509 | | 31.50 | 31.50 |
| b. | Booklet pane of 3, #2503, 2505, 2509 | | 14.50 | — |
| c. | Booklet pane of 3, #2502, 2508, 2509 | | 16.00 | — |
| | Complete booklet, #2506b, 2507a, 2508a, 2509b, 2509c | | 63.50 | |
| | *Nos. 2502-2509 (8)* | | 31.25 | 31.25 |

**Souvenir Sheet**

| | | | | |
|---|---|---|---|---|
| 2510 | A482 | £4 multi | 10.00 | 10.00 |

No. 2510 contains one 60x60mm stamp.

*Food and Drink — A483*

Designs: 56p, Jersey wonders. 82p, Jersey royals. 91p, Jersey cider. £1.20, Jersey milk and ice cream. £1.37, Jersey black butter. £1.75, Jersey bean crock and cabbage loaf.

**2022, May 24   Litho.   Perf. 12½**

| | | | | |
|---|---|---|---|---|
| 2511 | A483 | 56p multi | 1.40 | 1.40 |
| 2512 | A483 | 82p multi | 2.10 | 2.10 |
| 2513 | A483 | 91p multi | 2.25 | 2.25 |
| 2514 | A483 | £1.20 multi | 3.00 | 3.00 |
| 2515 | A483 | £1.37 multi | 3.50 | 3.50 |
| 2516 | A483 | £1.75 multi | 4.50 | 4.50 |
| | *Nos. 2511-2516 (6)* | | 16.75 | 16.75 |

*Reign of Queen Elizabeth II (1926-2022), 70th Anniv. — A484*

**Litho. With Foil Application**

**2022, June 1   Perf. 13¼**

| | | | | |
|---|---|---|---|---|
| 2517 | A484 | £10 sil & multi | 25.00 | 25.00 |

*Jersey Statues and Sculpture — A485*

Designs: 56p, La Travailleux d'Cauchie, St. Helier. 82p, King George II, St. Helier. 91p, Centaur with Cupid, St. Helier. £1.20, Saint-Malo Memorial, Saint Brelade. £1.37, Le Crapaud, St. Helier. £1.75, Swimmers II, St. Helier.

**2022, June 16   Litho.   Perf. 12**

| | | | | |
|---|---|---|---|---|
| 2518 | A485 | 56p multi | 1.40 | 1.40 |
| 2519 | A485 | 82p multi | 2.00 | 2.00 |
| 2520 | A485 | 91p multi | 2.25 | 2.25 |
| 2521 | A485 | £1.20 multi | 3.00 | 3.00 |
| 2522 | A485 | £1.37 multi | 3.50 | 3.50 |
| 2523 | A485 | £1.75 multi | 4.25 | 4.25 |
| | *Nos. 2518-2523 (6)* | | 16.40 | 16.40 |

*Jersey Island Cricket Club, Cent. — A486*

Designs: 56p, Fielders and running batsmen. 82p, Bowler and fielders. 91p, Batter swinging at ball. £1.20, Batsman, wicketkeeper and umpire. £1.37, Bowler and batsman. £1.75, Fielder attempting to catch batted ball.

No. 2530: a, Bowler and runner (60x50mm). b, Batsman and wicketkeeper (50x40mm).

**2022, July 7   Litho.   Perf. 12**

| | | | | |
|---|---|---|---|---|
| 2524 | A486 | 56p multi | 1.40 | 1.40 |
| 2525 | A486 | 82p multi | 2.00 | 2.00 |
| 2526 | A486 | 91p multi | 2.25 | 2.25 |
| 2527 | A486 | £1.20 multi | 3.00 | 3.00 |
| 2528 | A486 | £1.37 multi | 3.50 | 3.50 |
| 2529 | A486 | £1.75 multi | 4.25 | 4.25 |
| | *Nos. 2524-2529 (6)* | | 16.40 | 16.40 |

**Souvenir Sheet**

| | | | | |
|---|---|---|---|---|
| 2530 | | Sheet of 2 | 14.50 | 14.50 |
| a. | A486 | £2.10 multi | 5.25 | 5.25 |
| b. | A486 | £3.65 multi | 9.00 | 9.00 |

*Inventions and Inventors — A487*

Designs: 56p, Telephone, invented by Alexander Graham Bell (1847-1922). 82p, Electric light bulb, by Thomas Edison (1847-1931). 91p, Phonograph, by Edison. £1.20, Metal detector, by Bell. £1.37, Kinetograph (motion picture camera), by Edison. £1.75, Twisted-pair cabling, by Bell.

No. 2537, vert.: a, Bell. b, Edison.

**2022, Aug. 2   Litho.   Perf. 12½**

| | | | | |
|---|---|---|---|---|
| 2531 | A487 | 56p multi | 1.30 | 1.30 |
| 2532 | A487 | 82p multi | 1.90 | 1.90 |
| 2533 | A487 | 91p multi | 2.10 | 2.10 |
| 2534 | A487 | £1.20 multi | 2.75 | 2.75 |
| 2535 | A487 | £1.37 multi | 3.25 | 3.25 |
| 2536 | A487 | £1.75 multi | 4.00 | 4.00 |
| | *Nos. 2531-2536 (6)* | | 15.30 | 15.30 |

**Souvenir Sheet**

**Perf. 11½**

| | | | | |
|---|---|---|---|---|
| 2537 | | Sheet of 2 | 13.50 | 13.50 |
| a. | A487 | £2.10 multi | 5.00 | 5.00 |
| b. | A487 | £3.65 multi | 8.50 | 8.50 |

No. 2537 contains two 38x49mm stamps.

*Jèrriais Words and Phrases — A488*

Designs: 56p, Lé branchage. 82p, Lé côti. 91p, Lé vrai. £1.20, La rocaue. £1.37, La mielle. £1.75, La grève.

£4, La veue d'la Corbiethe.

**2022, Sept. 6   Litho.   Perf. 12**

| | | | | |
|---|---|---|---|---|
| 2538 | A488 | 56p sil & multi | 1.25 | 1.25 |
| 2539 | A488 | 82p sil & multi | 1.90 | 1.90 |
| 2540 | A488 | 91p sil & multi | 2.10 | 2.10 |
| 2541 | A488 | £1.20 sil & multi | 2.75 | 2.75 |
| 2542 | A488 | £1.37 sil & multi | 3.25 | 3.25 |
| 2543 | A488 | £1.75 sil & multi | 4.00 | 4.00 |
| a. | Souvenir sheet of 6, #2538-2543 | | 15.50 | 15.50 |
| | *Nos. 2538-2543 (6)* | | 15.25 | 15.25 |

**Souvenir Sheet**

| | | | | |
|---|---|---|---|---|
| 2544 | A488 | £4 sil & multi | 9.00 | 9.00 |

No. 2544 contains one 60x60mm stamp.

*Black History of Jersey — A489*

Designs: 56p, William Smith (1816-95), advocate for education of women. 82p, "Pompey," attributed as avenger of the death of Major Francis Peirson in 1781 Battle of Jersey, as seen in "The Death of Major Peirson," painting by John Singleton Copley. 91p, Adelaide Smith Casely-Hayford (1868-1960), student at Jersey Ladies' College who became activist for Creoles in Sierra Leone. £1.20, Hortense Watson, enslaved servant at Windsor Crescent, c. 1841. £1.37, John Jea (1773-c. 1817), preacher and author of autobiography about his life as a slave. £1.75, Regina Wilson, teacher in Sierra Leone, c. 1894.

**2022, Oct. 20   Litho.   Perf. 12**

| | | | | |
|---|---|---|---|---|
| 2545 | A489 | 56p multi | 1.30 | 1.30 |
| 2546 | A489 | 82p multi | 1.90 | 1.90 |
| 2547 | A489 | 91p multi | 2.10 | 2.10 |
| 2548 | A489 | £1.20 multi | 2.75 | 2.75 |
| 2549 | A489 | £1.37 multi | 3.25 | 3.25 |
| 2550 | A489 | £1.75 multi | 4.00 | 4.00 |
| a. | Souvenir sheet of 6, #2545-2550 | | 15.50 | 15.50 |
| | *Nos. 2545-2550 (6)* | | 15.30 | 15.30 |

Christmas — A490

**Symbols of Christmas:** 48p, Snowflake. 56p, Bells. 74p, Wreath. 82, Tree ornament. 91p, Robin. £1.20, Angel. £1.37, Star. £1.75, Christmas tree.

### Serpentine Die Cut 13½
**2022, Nov. 14        Litho.**
#### Self-Adhesive

| | | | | |
|---|---|---|---|---|
| 2551 | A490 | 48p multi | 1.25 | 1.25 |
| 2552 | A490 | 56p multi | 1.40 | 1.40 |
| 2553 | A490 | 74p multi | 1.75 | 1.75 |
| 2554 | A490 | 82p multi | 2.00 | 2.00 |
| 2555 | A490 | 91p multi | 2.25 | 2.25 |
| 2556 | A490 | £1.20 multi | 3.00 | 3.00 |
| 2557 | A490 | £1.37 multi | 3.25 | 3.25 |
| 2558 | A490 | £1.75 multi | 4.25 | 4.25 |
| | *Nos. 2551-2558 (8)* | | 19.15 | 19.15 |

New Year 2023 (Year of the Rabbit) — A491

**Designs:** 98p, Rabbit facing right. £3, Rabbit, vegetable and insect.

**2023, Jan. 5        Litho.        Perf. 13¼**

| | | | | |
|---|---|---|---|---|
| 2559 | A491 | 98p multi | 2.40 | 2.40 |

#### Souvenir Sheet
| | | | | |
|---|---|---|---|---|
| 2560 | A491 | £3 multi | 7.25 | 7.25 |

No. 2560 contains one 60x60mm stamp.

### Aerial Photographs of Jersey Landmarks Type of 2021

**Designs:** 60p, Bouley Bay Hill. No. 2562, Grosnez Castle. No. 2563, Faldouet Dolmen. £1.65, St. Aubin's Harbor. £1.85, Cliffs near Plémont. £2.55, Val de la Mare Reservoir. £3.25, Archirondel Tower. £4.20, Manor Farm, St. Ouen.

**2023, Jan. 28        Litho.        Perf. 13¼**

| | | | | |
|---|---|---|---|---|
| 2561 | A465 | 60p multi | 1.50 | 1.50 |
| 2562 | A465 | 98p multi | 2.50 | 2.50 |
| 2563 | A465 | 98p multi | 2.50 | 2.50 |
| 2564 | A465 | £1.65 multi | 4.25 | 4.25 |
| 2565 | A465 | £1.85 multi | 4.75 | 4.75 |
| 2566 | A465 | £2.55 multi | 6.50 | 6.50 |
| 2567 | A465 | £3.25 multi | 8.00 | 8.00 |
| 2568 | A465 | £4.20 multi | 10.50 | 10.50 |
| a. | Souvenir sheet of 8, #2561-2568 | | 40.50 | 40.50 |
| | *Nos. 2561-2568 (8)* | | 40.50 | 40.50 |

## POSTAGE DUE STAMPS

Numeral D1

Map of Jersey D2

**Unwmk.**
**1969, Oct. 1        Litho.        Perf. 14**

| | | | | |
|---|---|---|---|---|
| J1 | D1 | 1p violet blue | .80 | 1.10 |
| J2 | D1 | 2p sepia | 1.00 | 1.25 |
| J3 | D1 | 3p brt carmine | 1.10 | 1.25 |
| J4 | D2 | 1sh emerald | 6.30 | 6.30 |
| J5 | D2 | 2sh6p gray green | 14.25 | 14.00 |
| J6 | D2 | 5sh red orange | 16.50 | 13.50 |
| | *Nos. J1-J6 (6)* | | 39.95 | 37.40 |

### Type of 1969
#### Decimal Currency
**1971-75        Litho.        Perf. 14**

| | | | | |
|---|---|---|---|---|
| J7 | D2 | ½p black | .25 | .25 |
| J8 | D2 | 1p pale violet | .25 | .25 |
| J9 | D2 | 2p brown | .25 | .25 |
| J10 | D2 | 3p bright pink | .25 | .25 |
| J11 | D2 | 4p orange | .25 | .25 |
| J12 | D2 | 5p emerald | .25 | .25 |
| J13 | D2 | 6p orange ('74) | .25 | .25 |
| J14 | D2 | 7p brt yellow ('74) | .25 | .25 |
| J15 | D2 | 8p grnsh blue ('75) | .25 | .25 |
| J16 | D2 | 10p gray | .25 | .25 |
| J17 | D2 | 11p bister ('75) | .25 | .25 |
| J18 | D2 | 14p lilac | .30 | .30 |

| | | | | |
|---|---|---|---|---|
| J19 | D2 | 25p dull green ('74) | .45 | .45 |
| J20 | D2 | 50p plum ('75) | .90 | .90 |
| | *Nos. J7-J20 (14)* | | 4.40 | 4.40 |

St. Clement Arms, Dovecote, Samares — D3

**Arms and Scenes from Jersey Parishes:** 2p, St. Lawrence and Handois Reservoir. 3p, St. John and Sorel Point. 4p, St. Ouen and Pinnacle Rock. 5p, St. Peter and Quetivel Mill. 10p, St. Martin and St. Catherine's Breakwater. 12p, St. Helier and St. Helier Harbor. 14p, St. Saviour and Highlands College. 15p, St. Brelade and Beauport Bay. 20p, Grouville and La Hougue Bie. 50p, St. Mary and Perry Farm. £1, Trinity and Bouley Bay.

**1978, Jan. 17        Litho.        Perf. 14**

| | | | | |
|---|---|---|---|---|
| J21 | D3 | 1p brt green & blk | .25 | .25 |
| J22 | D3 | 2p orange & blk | .25 | .25 |
| J23 | D3 | 3p maroon & blk | .25 | .25 |
| J24 | D3 | 4p vermilion & blk | .25 | .25 |
| J25 | D3 | 5p dp ultra & blk | .25 | .25 |
| J26 | D3 | 10p olive & blk | .25 | .25 |
| J27 | D3 | 12p blue & blk | .25 | .25 |
| J28 | D3 | 14p red org & blk | .25 | .25 |
| J29 | D3 | 15p lilac rose & blk | .25 | .25 |
| J30 | D3 | 20p yel green & blk | .30 | .30 |
| J31 | D3 | 50p brown & blk | .70 | .70 |
| J32 | D3 | £1 violet & blk | 1.10 | 1.10 |
| | *Nos. J21-J32 (12)* | | 4.35 | 4.35 |

St. Brelade — D4

**1982, Sept. 4        Litho.        Perf. 13½x14**

| | | | | |
|---|---|---|---|---|
| J33 | D4 | 1p shown | .25 | .25 |
| J34 | D4 | 2p St. Aubin | .25 | .25 |
| J35 | D4 | 3p Rozel | .25 | .25 |
| J36 | D4 | 4p Greve de Lecq | .25 | .25 |
| J37 | D4 | 5p Bouley Bay | .25 | .25 |
| J38 | D4 | 6p St. Catherine | .25 | .25 |
| J39 | D4 | 7p Gorey | .25 | .25 |
| J40 | D4 | 8p Bonne Nuit | .25 | .25 |
| J41 | D4 | 9p La Rocque | .25 | .25 |
| J42 | D4 | 10p St. Helier | .25 | .25 |
| J43 | D4 | 20p Ronez | .30 | .30 |
| J44 | D4 | 30p La Collette | .35 | .35 |
| J45 | D4 | 40p Elizabeth Castle | .55 | .55 |
| J46 | D4 | £1 Upper Harbor Marina | 1.45 | 1.45 |
| | *Nos. J33-J46 (14)* | | 5.15 | 5.15 |

## OCCUPATION STAMPS

### Issued Under German Occupation

Catalogue values for unused stamps in this section are for hinged items.

OS1

**1941-42        Typo.        Unwmk.        Perf. 11**

| | | | | |
|---|---|---|---|---|
| N1 | OS1 | ½p bright green | 8.00 | 7.00 |
| N2 | OS1 | 1p vermilion | 8.00 | 6.90 |

Issue dates: No. N1, 1/29/42; No. N2, 4/1/41.

Jersey Views — OS2

**Designs:** ½p, Old Jersey farm; 1p, Portelet Bay; 1½p, Corbiere Lighthouse; 2p, Elizabeth Castle; 2½, Mont Orgueil Castle; 3p, Gathering seaweed.

**1943-44        Perf. 13½**

| | | | | |
|---|---|---|---|---|
| N3 | OS2 | ½p dark green | 8.25 | 13.75 |
| a. | On rough, gray paper | | 10.25 | 16.00 |
| N4 | OS2 | 1p scarlet | 2.00 | .60 |
| a. | On newsprint | | 2.40 | .85 |
| N5 | OS2 | 1½p brown | 8.25 | 6.50 |
| N6 | OS2 | 2p orange | 7.50 | 2.25 |

| | | | | |
|---|---|---|---|---|
| N7 | OS2 | 2½p blue | 2.25 | 1.15 |
| a. | On newsprint | | .85 | 2.00 |
| N8 | OS2 | 3p red violet | 2.25 | 3.15 |
| | *Nos. N3-N8 (6)* | | 30.50 | 27.40 |

Issued: ½p, 1p, 6/1/43; 1½p, 2p, 6/8/43; 2½p, 3p, 6/29/43; No. N4a, 2/28/44; No. N7a, 2/25/44.

Nos. N1-N8 remained valid until 4/13/46.

# ISLE OF MAN

ˈīˌel əv ˈman

**LOCATION** — In the Irish Sea, off Northwest coast of England
**GOVT.** — Semi-autonomous within the British Commonwealth
**AREA** — 221 sq. mi.
**POP.** — 75,686 (1999 est.)
**CAPITAL** — Douglas

Catalogue values for unused stamps in this section are for Never Hinged items, beginning with Scott 1 in the regular postage section and Scott J1 in the postage due section.

### British Regional Issues

A1

Manx Emblem — A2

#### Perf. 15x14
**1958-69        Photo.        Wmk. 322**

| | | | | |
|---|---|---|---|---|
| 1 | A1 | 2½p rose red ('64) | .90 | .90 |
| 2 | A2 | 3p purple | .60 | .60 |
| p. | Phosphor. ('68) | | .25 | .25 |
| 3 | A2 | 4p ultra ('66) | 1.00 | 1.00 |
| p. | Phosphor. ('67) | | .30 | .30 |

#### Unwmk.
| | | | | |
|---|---|---|---|---|
| 4 | A2 | 4p ultra ('68) | .25 | .25 |
| 5 | A2 | 4p olive brown ('68) | .25 | .25 |
| 6 | A2 | 4p bright red ('69) | .45 | .45 |
| 7 | A2 | 5p dark blue ('68) | .45 | .45 |
| | *Nos. 1-7 (7)* | | 3.90 | 3.90 |

Nos. 4-7 are phosphorescent.
A 1963 printing of No. 2 is on chalky paper.

Manx Emblem — A3

**1971, July 7        Photo.        Unwmk.**

| | | | | |
|---|---|---|---|---|
| 8 | A3 | 2½p magenta | .30 | .30 |
| 9 | A3 | 3p ultramarine | .30 | .30 |
| 10 | A3 | 5p bluish lilac | .70 | .70 |
| 11 | A3 | 7½p light red brown | .80 | .80 |
| | *Nos. 8-11 (4)* | | 2.10 | 2.10 |

Sold to the general public only at post offices within the Isle of Man, but valid for postage throughout Great Britain.

### Bailiwick Issues

Castletown and Manx Emblem — A4

Manx Cat — A5

1p, Port Erin. 1½p, Mt. Snaefell. 2p, Laxey Village. 2½p, Tynwald Hill. 3p, Douglas Promenade. 3½p, Port St. Mary. 4p, Fairy Bridge. 5p, Peel, Castle and shore. 6p, Cregneish Village. 7½p, Ramsey Bay. 9p, Douglas Bay. 20p, Manx ram. 50p, Manx shearwaters. £1, Viking longship.

#### Perf. 11½
**1973, July 5        Photo.        Unwmk.**

| | | | | |
|---|---|---|---|---|
| 12 | A4 | ½p shown | .25 | .25 |
| a. | Booklet pane of 2 | | 2.75 | |
| b. | Booklet pane of 4 ('74) | | .90 | |
| 13 | A4 | 1p multicolored | .25 | .25 |
| 14 | A4 | 1½p multicolored | .25 | .25 |
| 15 | A4 | 2p multicolored | .25 | .25 |
| a. | Booklet pane of 2 | | 2.75 | |
| 16 | A4 | 2½p multicolored | .25 | .25 |
| a. | Booklet pane of 2 | | .75 | |
| | Complete booklet, #12a, 15a, 16a | | 12.00 | |
| | Complete booklet, 5 #16a | | 3.75 | |
| 17 | A4 | 3p multicolored | .25 | .25 |
| a. | Booklet pane of 2 | | .70 | |
| | Complete booklet, 5 #17a | | 22.50 | |
| | Complete booklet, 4 #16a, 5 #17a | | 10.00 | |
| b. | Booklet pane of 4 ('74) | | .90 | |
| 18 | A4 | 3½p multicolored | .25 | .25 |
| a. | Booklet pane of 4 ('74) | | 5.00 | |
| | Complete booklet, 2 #12b, 1 each #17b, 18a | | 5.00 | |
| | Complete booklet, 2 #17b, 1 each #12b, 18a | | 5.00 | |
| | Complete booklet, 3 #17b, 1 #18a | | 5.00 | |
| 19 | A4 | 4p multicolored | .25 | .25 |
| 20 | A4 | 5p multicolored | .25 | .25 |
| 21 | A4 | 6p multicolored | .25 | .25 |
| 22 | A4 | 7½p multicolored | .25 | .25 |
| 23 | A4 | 9p multicolored | .30 | .30 |
| 24 | A5 | 10p shown | .40 | .30 |
| 25 | A5 | 20p multicolored | .60 | .60 |
| 26 | A5 | 50p multicolored | 1.50 | 1.60 |
| 27 | A5 | £1 multicolored | 3.25 | 3.25 |
| | *Nos. 12-27 (16)* | | 8.80 | 8.80 |

See Nos. 52-59.
No. 17 exists with an olive-bistre border. No. 18 exists with a gray-brown border.

Vikings Landing on Man, 938 — A6

**1973, July 5        Perf. 14**

| | | | | |
|---|---|---|---|---|
| 28 | A6 | 15p multicolored | .35 | .35 |

Inauguration of postal independence. Compare with No. 251. Inscription under "Isle of Man" reads "Post Office Decennium" on No. 251.

Engine No. 1, Sutherland, 1873 — A7

**1973, Aug. 4        Perf. 14½x14**

| | | | | |
|---|---|---|---|---|
| 29 | A7 | 2½p shown | .25 | .25 |
| 30 | A7 | 3p Caledonia, 1885 | .25 | .25 |
| 31 | A7 | 7½p Kissack, 1910 | .35 | .35 |
| 32 | A7 | 9p Pender, 1873 | .35 | .35 |
| | *Nos. 29-32 (4)* | | 1.20 | 1.20 |

Centenary of Manx steam railroad.

Leslie Randles, 1923 Winner — A8

3½p, Alan Holmes, 1957 double winner.

**1973, Sept. 4        Litho.        Perf. 14**

| | | | | |
|---|---|---|---|---|
| 33 | A8 | 3p multicolored | .25 | .25 |
| 34 | A8 | 3½p multicolored | .25 | .25 |

Manx Grand Prix Motorcycle Race, 50th anniversary.

Princess Anne and Mark Phillips A9

**Litho. & Engr.**
**1973 Nov. 14        Perf. 14x13½**

| | | | | |
|---|---|---|---|---|
| 35 | A9 | 25p lt blue & multi | .90 | .90 |

Wedding of Princess Anne and Capt. Mark Phillips, Nov. 14, 1973.

William Hillary,
R.N.L.I.
Badge — A10

Wreck of "St.
George" — A11

Designs: 8p, Tower of Refuge and lifeboat
"Manchester & Salford." 10p, "Osman Gabriel"
at Port Erin. 3½p and 8p are from paintings.

**1974, Mar. 4 Photo. Perf. 11½**
| | | | | |
|---|---|---|---|---|
| 36 | A10 | 3p black & multi | .25 | .25 |
| 37 | A11 | 3½ black & multi | .25 | .25 |
| 38 | A11 | 8p black & multi | .25 | .25 |
| 39 | A11 | 10p black & multi | .30 | .30 |
| | | Nos. 36-39 (4) | 1.05 | 1.05 |

Sesqui. of the founding of the Royal Natl.
Lifeboat Institution by Sir William Hillary.

Stanley Woods
on Moto Guzzi
Motorcycle
A12

Designs: 3½p, Freddie Frith on Norton. 8p,
Max Deubel on BMW with sidecar. 10p, Mike
Hailwood on Honda.

**1974, May 29 Litho. Perf. 13**
| | | | | |
|---|---|---|---|---|
| 40 | A12 | 3p yellow grn & multi | .25 | .25 |
| 41 | A12 | 3½p crimson & multi | .25 | .25 |
| a. | | Perf. 14 (#1425b) | .25 | .25 |
| 42 | A12 | 8p yellow & multi | .25 | .25 |
| 43 | A12 | 10p ultra & multi | .25 | .35 |
| | | Nos. 40-43 (4) | 1.00 | 1.10 |

Tourist Trophy Motorcycle Races on the Isle
of Man.
Issued: No. 41a, 2015.

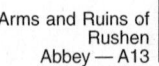

Arms and Ruins of
Rushen
Abbey — A13

Designs: 4½p, King Edgar of England visiting Chester in boat rowed by 8 kings including
King Magnus Haraldson. 8p, Fleet under King
Magnus' command and arms he gave to Isle
of Man. 10p, Bridge at Avignon, Bishop's mitre
and Three Legs of Man.

**1974, Sept. 18 Litho. Perf. 14**
| | | | | |
|---|---|---|---|---|
| 44 | A13 | 3½p multicolored | .25 | .25 |
| 45 | A13 | 4½p multicolored | .25 | .25 |
| 46 | A13 | 8p multicolored | .25 | .25 |
| 47 | A13 | 10p multicolored | .25 | .25 |
| | | Nos. 44-47 (4) | 1.00 | 1.00 |

1,000th death anniv. of Magnus Haraldson,
King of Many Islands (Nos. 45-46), and 600th
death anniv. of William Russell, Bishop of
Sodor and Mann (Nos. 44, 47).

Churchill and
"Bugler
Dunne at
Colenso,
1899" — A14

Sir Winston Churchill: 4½p, Government
Buildings, Douglas, and Warrant of Appoint-
ment. 8p, Manx A.A. Regiment in action. 20p,
Freedom of Douglas Scroll, and scroll casket.

**1974, Nov. 22 Photo. Perf. 11½**
| | | | | |
|---|---|---|---|---|
| 48 | A14 | 4½p multicolored | .25 | .25 |
| 49 | A14 | 4½p multicolored | .25 | .25 |
| 50 | A14 | 8p multicolored | .25 | .25 |
| 51 | A14 | 20p multicolored | .25 | .25 |
| a. | | Souvenir sheet of 4, #48-51 | 1.10 | 1.10 |
| | | Nos. 48-51 (4) | 1.00 | 1.00 |

**Type of 1973**
**1975 Unwmk. Perf. 11½**
| | | | | |
|---|---|---|---|---|
| 52 | A4 | 4½p Tynwald Hill | .25 | .25 |
| 53 | A4 | 5½p Douglas Promenade | .25 | .25 |
| 54 | A4 | 7p Laxey Village | .25 | .25 |
| 55 | A4 | 8p Ramsey Bay | .30 | .30 |

| | | | | |
|---|---|---|---|---|
| 58 | A4 | 11p Monk's Bridge | .40 | .35 |
| 59 | A4 | 13p Derbyhaven | .45 | .40 |
| | | Nos. 52-59 (6) | 1.90 | 1.80 |

Issued: Nos. 52, 55, 1/8; Nos. 53-54, 5/28;
Nos. 58-59, 10/29.

Log Cabin
School, Cleveland
Medal, Names of
Settlers — A15

Designs: 5½p, Terminal Tower Building,
Cleveland, John Gill and Robert Carran. 8p,
Clague House Museum, Margaret and Robert
Clague. 10p, Thomas Quayle and S. S. Wil-
liam T. Graves.

**1975, Mar. 14 Photo. Perf. 11½**
| | | | | |
|---|---|---|---|---|
| 62 | A15 | 4½p multicolored | .25 | .25 |
| 63 | A15 | 5½p multicolored | .25 | .25 |
| 64 | A15 | 8p multicolored | .25 | .25 |
| 65 | A15 | 10p multicolored | .25 | .35 |
| | | Nos. 62-65 (4) | 1.00 | 1.10 |

Sesquicentennial of arrival of Manx settlers
in Cleveland, Ohio area.

Tom Sheard
and "Douglas"
A16

Designs: 7p, Walter L. Handley and "Rex-
Acme." 10p, Geoffrey Duke and "Gilera." 12p,
Peter Williams and "Norton."

**1975, May 28 Litho. Perf. 13½**
| | | | | |
|---|---|---|---|---|
| 66 | A16 | 5½p bister & multi | .25 | .25 |
| 67 | A16 | 7p salmon & multi | .25 | .25 |
| 68 | A16 | 10p lt green & multi | .25 | .25 |
| 69 | A16 | 12p ultra & multi | .25 | .25 |
| a. | | Perf. 14 (#1425b) | .25 | .25 |
| | | Nos. 66-69 (4) | 1.00 | 1.00 |

Tourist Trophy Motorcycle races on Isle of
Man.
Issued: No. 69a, 2015.

Sir George Goldie
and his
Birthplace — A17

Designs (Sir George Goldie and): 7p, Map
of Africa with Niger River basin, vert. 10p, Goldie as president of Royal Geographical Society and Society emblem, vert. 12p, River
boats: trading hulk, native canoe,
sternwheeler.

**1975, Sept. 9 Photo. Perf. 11½**
| | | | | |
|---|---|---|---|---|
| 70 | A17 | 5½p multicolored | .25 | .25 |
| 71 | A17 | 7p multicolored | .25 | .25 |
| 72 | A17 | 10p multicolored | .25 | .25 |
| 73 | A17 | 12p multicolored | .25 | .25 |
| | | Nos. 70-73 (4) | 1.00 | 1.00 |

Sir George Dashwood Goldie-Taubman
(1846-1925), founder of Royal Niger
Company.

Manx Bible — A18

Bicentenary of Manx Bible and Christmas
1975: 7p, Rev. Philip Moore and Old Ballaugh
Church. 11p, Bishop Mark Hildesley and Bishops Court. 13p, Shipwreck off Cumberland
Coast with John Kelly holding manuscript
above water.

**1975, Oct. 29 Litho. Perf. 14**
| | | | | |
|---|---|---|---|---|
| 74 | A18 | 5½p multicolored | .25 | .25 |
| 75 | A18 | 7p multicolored | .25 | .25 |
| 76 | A18 | 11p multicolored | .25 | .25 |
| 77 | A18 | 13p multicolored | .25 | .25 |
| | | Nos. 74-77 (4) | 1.00 | 1.00 |

William Christian
Listening to Patrick
Henry — A19

Designs: 7p, Christian carrying Fincastle
Resolutions to Williamsburg. 13p, Col. Patrick
Henry and Lt. Col. William Christian of 1st Virginia Regiment. 20p, Christian as frontiersman
and Indians.

**1976, Mar. 12 Litho. Perf. 13½**
| | | | | |
|---|---|---|---|---|
| 78 | A19 | 5½p multicolored | .25 | .25 |
| 79 | A19 | 7p multicolored | .25 | .25 |
| 80 | A19 | 13p multicolored | .30 | .30 |
| 81 | A19 | 20p multicolored | .35 | .45 |
| a. | | Souv. sheet of 4, #78-81, perf. 14 | 1.40 | 1.40 |
| | | Nos. 78-81 (4) | 1.15 | 1.25 |

American Bicentennial. William Christian
(1743-1786), patriot, son of a Manx-man and
Patrick Henry's brother-in-law.

First Double-
decker Tram
Car — A20

Designs: 7p, Toast-rack tram, 1890. 11p,
Horse bus, 1895. 13p, Decorated tram with
Queen Elizabeth II and Prince Philip.

**1976, May 26 Photo. Perf. 11½**
| | | | | |
|---|---|---|---|---|
| 82 | A20 | 5½p multicolored | .25 | .25 |
| 83 | A20 | 7p multicolored | .25 | .25 |
| 84 | A20 | 11p multicolored | .30 | .30 |
| 85 | A20 | 13p multicolored | .30 | .30 |
| | | Nos. 82-85 (4) | 1.10 | 1.10 |

Douglas horse trams, centenary.

Barroose Beaker, Bronze
Age — A21

Europa (Manx Ceramic Art): No. 87, Souvenir teapot (3-legged man), 19th cent. No. 88,
Laxey jug, 1854. No. 89, Cronk Aust food vessel, early Bronze Age. No. 90, Sansbury bowl,
1851. No. 91, Knox urn, 20th cent. Nos. 89-91,
horiz.

**1976, July 28 Photo. Perf. 11½**
| | | | | |
|---|---|---|---|---|
| 86 | A21 | 5p multicolored | .25 | .25 |
| 87 | A21 | 5p multicolored | .25 | .25 |
| 88 | A21 | 5p multicolored | .25 | .25 |
| a. | | Strip of 3, #86-88 | .70 | .70 |
| 89 | A21 | 10p multicolored | .25 | .25 |
| 90 | A21 | 10p multicolored | .25 | .25 |
| 91 | A21 | 10p multicolored | .25 | .25 |
| a. | | Strip of 3, #89-91 | .70 | .70 |
| | | Nos. 86-91 (6) | 1.50 | 1.50 |

Printed in sheets of 9 (3x3).

Virgin and Child, on
Sodor and Man
Banner — A22

Virgin and Child on Embroidered Church
Banners: 7p, St. Peter's, Onchan, Mothers'
Union. 11p, Castletown. 13p, St. Olav's,
Ramsey.

**1976, Oct. 14 Litho. Perf. 14¾x14½**
| | | | | |
|---|---|---|---|---|
| 92 | A22 | 6p multicolored | .25 | .25 |
| 93 | A22 | 7p multicolored | .25 | .25 |
| 94 | A22 | 11p multicolored | .25 | .25 |
| 95 | A22 | 13p multicolored | .35 | .35 |
| | | Nos. 92-95 (4) | 1.10 | 1.10 |

Christmas 1976 & cent. of Mothers' Union.

Elizabeth II and
Arms of
Man — A23

Designs: 7p, Queen Elizabeth II and Prince
Philip, vert. 25p, Queen, 1976 portrait.

***Perf. 13½x14, 14x13½***
**1977, Mar. 1 Litho. & Engr.**
| | | | | |
|---|---|---|---|---|
| 96 | A23 | 6p multicolored | .25 | .25 |
| 97 | A23 | 7p multicolored | .25 | .25 |
| 98 | A23 | 25p multicolored | .50 | .50 |
| | | Nos. 96-98 (3) | 1.00 | 1.00 |

25th anniv. of the reign of Elizabeth II.

Carrick Bay from Tom-the-
Dipper's — A24

Europa: 10p, Looking south from Mooragh
Park, Ramsey.

**1977, May 25 Litho. Perf. 14**
| | | | | |
|---|---|---|---|---|
| 99 | A24 | 6p multicolored | .25 | .25 |
| 100 | A24 | 10p multicolored | .35 | .35 |

"Pa" Applebee
at Ballig Bridge,
1912 — A25

Designs: 7p, Hairpin curve at Governor's
Bridge and ambulance attendants. 11p, Boy
Scouts tending scoreboards. 13p, John Wil-
lams at Windy Corner on Snaefell Mountain,
winner of 1976 Open Classic Race.

**1977, May 25 Perf. 13½**
| | | | | |
|---|---|---|---|---|
| 101 | A25 | 6p multicolored | .25 | .25 |
| 102 | A25 | 7p multicolored | .25 | .25 |
| 103 | A25 | 11p multicolored | .25 | .25 |
| 104 | A25 | 13p multicolored | .25 | .25 |
| | | Nos. 101-104 (4) | 1.00 | 1.00 |

Tourist Trophy Motorcycle Races, and Boy
Scouts, 70th anniv.; St. John Ambulance
Assoc. cent. (in GB).

Meeting House, Mt.
Morrison — A26

Designs: 7p, John Wesley preaching at
Castletown, 1777. 11p, Wesley preaching
outside Braddan Church. 13p, Methodist
Church on Douglas Promenade, 1976.

**1977, Oct. 19 Photo. Perf. 11½**
**Size: 30x24mm**
| | | | | |
|---|---|---|---|---|
| 105 | A26 | 6p multicolored | .25 | .25 |

**Size: 37½x24mm**
| | | | | |
|---|---|---|---|---|
| 106 | A26 | 7p multicolored | .25 | .25 |
| 107 | A26 | 11p multicolored | .25 | .25 |

**Size: 30x24mm**
| | | | | |
|---|---|---|---|---|
| 108 | A26 | 13p multicolored | .25 | .25 |
| | | Nos. 105-108 (4) | 1.00 | 1.00 |

Bicentenary of John Wesley's first visit to
the Isle of Man.

Seaplane and
Carrier Ben
My
Chree — A27

Royal Air Force, 60th Anniv.: 7p, Bristol
Scout and carrier Vindex, 1915. 11p, Boulton
Paul Defiant over Douglas Bay, 1941. 13p,
RAF Jaguar over Ramsey, 1977.

**1978, Feb. 28 Litho. Perf. 13½x14**
| | | | | |
|---|---|---|---|---|
| 109 | A27 | 6p multicolored | .25 | .25 |
| 110 | A27 | 7p multicolored | .25 | .25 |
| 111 | A27 | 11p multicolored | .25 | .25 |
| 112 | A27 | 13p multicolored | .25 | .25 |
| | | Nos. 109-112 (4) | 1.00 | 1.00 |

Watch Tower, Langness A28

Jurby Church A29

Fuchsia — A30

Landmarks: 6p, Government buildings. 7p, Tynwald Hill. 8p, Milner's Tower. 9p, Laxey Wheel. 10p, Castle Rushen. 11p, St. Ninian's Church. 12p, Tower of Refuge. 13p, St. German's Cathedral. 14p, Point of Ayre Lighthouse. 15p, Corrin's Tower. 16p, Douglas Head Lighthouse. 25p, Manx cat. 50p, Chough (crows). £1, Viking warrior.

**1978** **Litho.** **Perf. 14**

| | | | | |
|---|---|---|---|---|
| 113 | A28 | ½p multicolored | .25 | .25 |
| 114 | A29 | 1p multicolored | .25 | .25 |
| 115 | A28 | 6p multicolored | .25 | .25 |
| 116 | A29 | 7p multicolored | .25 | .25 |
| 117 | A28 | 8p multicolored | .25 | .25 |
| 118 | A29 | 9p multicolored | .25 | .25 |
| 119 | A29 | 10p multicolored | .25 | .25 |
| 120 | A28 | 11p multicolored | .25 | .25 |
| 121 | A29 | 12p multicolored | .25 | .25 |
| 122 | A29 | 13p multicolored | .30 | .30 |
| 123 | A29 | 14p multicolored | .40 | .40 |
| 124 | A29 | 15p multicolored | .55 | .55 |
| 125 | A29 | 16p multicolored. | .45 | .45 |

**Photo.**
**Perf. 11½**

| | | | | |
|---|---|---|---|---|
| 126 | A30 | 20p multicolored | .60 | .60 |
| 127 | A30 | 25p multicolored | .60 | .60 |
| 128 | A30 | 50p multicolored | 1.10 | 1.10 |
| 129 | A30 | £1 multicolored | 2.00 | 2.00 |
| | | *Nos. 113-129 (17)* | 8.25 | 8.25 |

Issued: Nos. 113-125, 2/28; Nos. 126-129, 10/18.

**Perf. 14½**

| | | | | |
|---|---|---|---|---|
| 113a | A28 | ½p multicolored | .25 | .25 |
| 114a | A29 | 1p multicolored | .25 | .25 |
| 116a | A29 | 7p multicolored | 7.00 | 7.00 |
| 117a | A28 | 8p multicolored | .25 | .25 |
| 118a | A29 | 9p multicolored | .25 | .25 |
| 119a | A29 | 10p multicolored | .25 | .25 |
| 120a | A28 | 11p multicolored | .25 | .25 |
| 121a | A29 | 12p multicolored | .25 | .25 |
| 122a | A29 | 13p multicolored | .25 | .25 |
| 123a | A29 | 14p multicolored | .30 | .30 |
| 124a | A29 | 15p multicolored | .30 | .30 |
| 125a | A29 | 16p multicolored | 15.00 | 15.00 |
| | | *Nos. 113a-125a (12)* | 24.60 | 24.60 |

Elizabeth II — A31

**1978, May 24** **Litho.** **Perf. 14½x14¼**
130 A31 25p blue & multi .75 .75
25th anniv. of coronation of Elizabeth II.

Keeil Chiggyrt Stone — A32

Europa (Carved Gravestones): No. 132, Wheel-headed cross slab. No. 133, Celtic Wheel cross. No. 134, Thor cross. No. 135, Olaf Liotulfson cross. No. 136, Odd's and Thorleif's crosses.

**1978, May 24** **Perf. 11½**

| | | | | |
|---|---|---|---|---|
| 131 | A32 | 6p multicolored | .25 | .25 |
| 132 | A32 | 6p multicolored | .25 | .25 |
| 133 | A32 | 6p multicolored | .25 | .25 |
| a. | | Strip of 3, #131-133 | .30 | .30 |
| 134 | A32 | 11p multicolored | .30 | .30 |
| 135 | A32 | 11p multicolored | .30 | .30 |
| 136 | A32 | 11p multicolored | .30 | .30 |
| a. | | Strip of 3, #134-136 | .75 | .75 |
| | | *Nos. 131-136 (6)* | 1.65 | 1.65 |

Printed se-tenant in sheets of 9 (3x3).

J. K. Ward, Ward Library, Peel — A33

13p, Lumber camp at Three Rivers & J. K. Ward.

**1978, June 10** **Litho.** **Perf. 13½**
137 A33 6p multicolored .25 .25
138 A33 13p multicolored .25 .25

James K. Ward (1819-1910), Manx pioneer in Canada.

Athletes, Games' Emblem and Manx Arms — A34

Eagle, Manx Arms, Maple Leaf — A35

**1978, June 10**
139 A34 7p multicolored .25 .25
140 A35 11p multicolored .25 .25

11th Commonwealth Games, Edmonton, Aug. 3-12 (7p); North American Manx Soc., 50th anniv. (11p).

"Hunt the Wren" — A36

**1978, Oct. 18** **Litho.** **Perf. 13**
141 A36 5p multicolored .25 .25

Christmas 1978.

Philip M. C. Kermode and Nassa Kermodei — A37

7p, Peregrine falcons. 11p, Fulmars. 13p, Asilid fly.

**1979, Feb. 27** **Litho.** **Perf. 14**

| | | | | |
|---|---|---|---|---|
| 142 | A37 | 6p multicolored | .25 | .25 |
| 143 | A37 | 7p multicolored | .25 | .25 |
| 144 | A37 | 11p multicolored | .30 | .30 |
| 145 | A37 | 13p multicolored | .40 | .40 |
| | | *Nos. 142-145 (4)* | 1.20 | 1.20 |

Isle of Man Natural History and Antiquarian Society.

Viking Ship — A38

A39

Viking Raid at Garwick — A40

Designs (Tynwald Emblem and): 7p, 10th century meeting at Tynwald. 11p, Tynwald Hill and St. John's Church. 13p, Contemporary Tynwald Day parade.

**Perf. 14½x14 (#146-147), 13¼ (#148-151)**

**1979, May 16** **Litho.**
146 A38 3p *Insularem* .25 .25
a. Bklt. pane, 4 #146, 2 #147 .60
Complete booklet, #146a 1.00
Complete booklet, 2 #146a 1.50
Complete booklet, 3 #146a 2.00
b. *Insularum* (inscribed "1980") .25 .25
c. Bklt. pane, 4 #146a, 2 #147a 1.25

147 A39 4p multicolored .25 .25
a. Inscribed "1980" .25 .25
148 A40 6p multicolored .25 .25
149 A40 7p multicolored .25 .25
150 A40 11p multicolored .25 .25
151 A40 13p multicolored .25 .25
*Nos. 146-151 (6)* 1.50 1.50

Millennium of Tynwald, Legislative Council. Nos. 146-147 printed se-tenant in sheets of 80.
No. 146a comes in two arrangements.
The booklet panes were printed in strips of three panes: No. 146a (4p stamps in the middle); separated by a gutter from No. 146a (4p stamps on top); and separated by another gutter, from a pane of four 4p. The unsevered strips were available from the Philatelic Bureau.
See No. 190a.

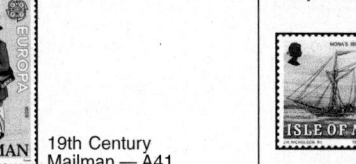

19th Century Mailman — A41

Europa: 11p, Contemporary mailman.

**1979, May 16** **Perf. 14½**
152 A41 6p multicolored .25 .25
153 A41 11p multicolored .35 .35

Ceremony on Tynwald Hill — A42

Design: 13p, Procession from St. John's Church to Tynwald Hill.

**1979, July 5** **Litho.** **Perf. 14½**
154 A42 7p multicolored .25 .25
155 A42 13p multicolored .40 .40

Visit of Queen Elizabeth II for the celebration of millennium of Tynwald.

Girl Holding Teddy Bear — A43

Christmas and IYC: 7p, Children with Santa.

**1979, Oct. 19** **Litho.** **Perf. 13¼x13½**
156 A43 5p multicolored .25 .25
157 A43 7p multicolored .25 .25

Capt. John Quilliam and Spencer — A44

Capt. Quilliam: 6p, Seized by press gang. 8p, Battle of Trafalgar. 15p, Castle Rushen.

**1979, Oct. 19** **Perf. 14**

| | | | | |
|---|---|---|---|---|
| 158 | A44 | 6p multicolored | .25 | .25 |
| 159 | A44 | 8p multicolored | .25 | .25 |
| 160 | A44 | 13p multicolored | .30 | .30 |
| 161 | A44 | 15p multicolored | .40 | .40 |
| | | *Nos. 158-161 (4)* | 1.20 | 1.20 |

Capt. John Quilliam (1771-1829), British naval hero and member of House of Keys.

"Odin's Raven" — A45

**1979, Oct. 19** **Perf. 14x14½**
162 A45 15p multicolored .60 .60

Voyage of replica Viking longboat across North Sea (Trondheim to Peel), May 27-July 4. See No. 176a.

Conglomerate Arch, Langness, and Emblem — A46

Royal Geographical Society Emblem and: 8p, Braaid Circle. 12p, Cashtal yn Ard (Neolithic burial ground). 13p, Volcanic rocks, Scarlett. 15p, Sugar-loaf Rock.

**1980, Feb. 5** **Litho.** **Perf. 14½**

| | | | | |
|---|---|---|---|---|
| 163 | A46 | 7p multicolored | .25 | .25 |
| 164 | A46 | 8p multicolored | .25 | .25 |
| 165 | A46 | 12p multicolored | .35 | .35 |
| 166 | A46 | 13p multicolored | .35 | .35 |
| 167 | A46 | 15p multicolored | .35 | .35 |
| | | *Nos. 163-167 (5)* | 1.55 | 1.55 |

Royal Geographical Society, 150th anniv.

"Mona's Isle I" — A47

8p, Douglas I. 11½p, Mona's Queen II, sinking U-boat. 12p, King Orry III. 13p, Ben-My-Chree IV. 15p, Lady of Mann II.

**1980, May 6** **Photo.** **Perf. 11½**
**Granite Paper**

| | | | | |
|---|---|---|---|---|
| 168 | A47 | 7p shown | .25 | .25 |
| 169 | A47 | 8p multicolored | .25 | .25 |
| 170 | A47 | 11½p multicolored | .25 | .25 |
| 171 | A47 | 12p multicolored | .25 | .25 |
| 172 | A47 | 13p multicolored | .30 | .30 |
| 173 | A47 | 15p multicolored | .35 | .35 |
| a. | | Souvenir sheet of 6, #168-173 | 2.00 | 2.00 |
| | | *Nos. 168-173 (6)* | 1.65 | 1.65 |

Isle of Man Steam Packet Co. sesqui.; London 80 Intl. Stamp Exhib., May 6-14.

Thomas Edward Brown and Characters from his Poems A48

Europa (Brown (1830-1897), Poet and Scholar): 13½p, Cricket game, Clifton College Bristol.

**1980, May 6**
174 A48 7p multicolored .25 .25
175 A48 13½p multicolored .35 .35

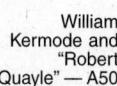

Visit of King Olav V of Norway — A49

**1980, June 13** **Litho.** **Perf. 14½**
176 A49 12p multicolored .50 .50
a. Souv. sheet of 2, #162, 176 1.00 1.00

Visit of King Olav V of Norway, Aug. 2-7, 1979, and NORWEX 80 stamp exhibition, Oslo, June 13-22.

William Kermode and "Robert Quayle" — A50

Kermode Family (First Manx Pioneers in Tasmania): 9p, First homestead, Mona Vale, Merino sheep, 1834. 13½p, Ross Bridge, W. Kermode. 15p, Mona Vale (Calendar House), 1868. 17½p, Parliament Buildings, Hobart, Robert Quayle Kermode.

**1980, Sept. 29** **Litho.**

| | | | | |
|---|---|---|---|---|
| 177 | A50 | 7p multicolored | .25 | .25 |
| 178 | A50 | 9p multicolored | .25 | .25 |
| 179 | A50 | 13½p multicolored | .35 | .35 |
| 180 | A50 | 15p multicolored | .40 | .40 |
| 181 | A50 | 17½p multicolored | .45 | .45 |
| | | *Nos. 177-181 (5)* | 1.70 | 1.70 |

Wren — A51

**1980, Sept. 29 Litho. Perf. 13½x14**
182 A51 6p shown .25 .25
183 A51 8p Robin .25 .25
Wildlife conservation and Christmas 1980.

Luggers, Red Pier, Douglas — A52

9p, Wanderer saving Lusitania Survivors. 18p, Nickey, Port St. Mary. 20p, Nobby, Ramsey Harbor. 22p, Sunbeam and Zebra, Port Erin.

**1981, Feb. 24 Litho. Perf. 14**
184 A52 8p shown .25 .25
185 A52 9p multicolored .25 .25
186 A52 18p multicolored .35 .35
187 A52 20p multicolored .45 .45
188 A52 22p multicolored .50 .50
Nos. 184-188 (5) 1.80 1.80
Royal National Mission to Deep Sea Fishermen centenary.

Peregrine Falcon — A53

**1980, Sept. 29 Litho. Perf. 14½x14**
**Booklet Stamps**
189 A53 1p shown .35 .35
190 A53 5p Loghtyn ram .35 .35
a. Bklt. pane, 2 each #147a, 189, 190 1.25
Complete booklet, #146c, 190a 2.50
Complete booklet, 2 each #146c, 190a 5.00

Crosh Cuirn (Cross of Mountain Ash Twigs, Harvest Charm) — A54

Europa: 18p, Bollan fish cross-bone (fishermen's charm).

**1981, May 22 Litho. Perf. 14½**
191 A54 8p multicolored .25 .25
192 A54 18p multicolored .50 .50

Col. Mark Wilks, Peel Castle — A55

20p, Wilks, Fort. St. George, Madras. 22p, Wilks, Napoleon. 25p, Wilks at Kirby estate.

**1981, May 22 Perf. 14**
193 A55 8p shown .25 .25
194 A55 20p multicolored .45 .45
195 A55 22p multicolored .50 .50
196 A55 25p multicolored .60 .60
Nos. 193-196 (4) 1.80 1.80
Wilks (d. 1831), governor of St. Helena.

Suffragettes Emmeline Goulden Pankhurst and Sophia Jane Goulden — A56

**1981, May 22 Perf. 14**
197 A56 9p multicolored .45 .45
Centenary of women's suffrage and of House of Keys Election Act (granting widows and unmarried women voting rights).

Prince Charles and Lady Diana — A57

**1981, July 29 Litho. Perf. 14**
198 A57 9p multicolored .25 .25
199 A57 25p multicolored .85 .85
a. Souv. sheet, 2 each #198-199 2.75 2.75
Royal Wedding.

Queen Elizabeth II — A58

**1981, Sept. 29 Photo. Perf. 11½**
**Granite paper**
200 A58 £2 multicolored 4.75 4.75

Douglas War Memorial, Poppies, Quote from Laurence Binyon's For the Fallen A59

10p, Maj. R.H. Cain, Battle of Arnhem, 1944. 18p, Festival of Remembrance. 20p, Tynwald and Spitfire, Dunkirk, 1940.

**1981, Sept. 29 Granite Paper**
201 A59 8p shown .25 .25
202 A59 10p multicolored .25 .25
203 A59 18p multicolored .45 .45
204 A59 20p multicolored .55 .55
Nos. 201-204 (4) 1.50 1.50
Royal British Legion, 60th anniv.

Nativity Stained-glass Window, 1865, St. George's Church, Douglas — A60

9p: Christmas pageant, Glencrutchery Special School, Douglas.

**1981, Sept. 29 Litho. Perf. 14½x14**
205 A60 7p multicolored .25 .25
**Size: 47x28mm**
206 A60 9p multicolored .30 .30
Christmas and St. George's Church bicen. (7p), IYD (9p).

Scouting Year — A61

Designs: 9p, Cunningham House (Man Scout Headquarters). 10p, Baden-Powell's visit, 1911. 19½p, Portrait (32x41mm., Perf. 14½). 24p, Baden-Powell with scouts, message. 29p, Sign, handshake, globe, emblem.

**1982, Feb. 23 Litho. Perf. 13½x14**
207 A61 9p multicolored .25 .25
208 A61 10p multicolored .25 .25
209 A61 19½p multicolored .40 .40
210 A61 24p multicolored .55 .55
211 A61 29p multicolored .65 .65
Nos. 207-211 (5) 2.10 2.10

Europa 1982 — A62

Designs: 9p, Bishop Thomas Wilson (1663-1755) and his "The Principles and Duties of Christianity," first book printed in Manx, 1707. 19½p, Visit of Thomas, 2nd Earl of Derby, 1507.

**1982, June 1 Photo. Perf. 12½**
**Granite Paper**
212 A62 9p multicolored .25 .25
213 A62 19½p multicolored .50 .50

75th Anniv. of Tourist Trophy Motorcycle Races — A63

Designs: Winners on their bikes: 9p, Charlie Collier, 431 Matchless, 1907. 10p, Freddie Dixon, Douglas, 1923. 24p, Jimmie Simpson, Norton, 1932. 26p, Mike Hailwood, Norton, 1961. 29p, Jock Taylor, 700 Fowler Yamaha, '80.

**1982, June 1 Litho. Perf. 14**
214 A63 9p multicolored .25 .25
215 A63 10p multicolored .25 .25
216 A63 24p multicolored .65 .65
217 A63 26p multicolored .65 .65
218 A63 29p multicolored .65 .65
Nos. 214-218 (5) 2.45 2.45

Isle of Man Steam Packet Co. Mail Contract Sesquicentennial — A64

**1982, Oct. 5 Litho. Perf. 13½x14**
219 A64 12p Mona I .40 .40
220 A64 19½p Manx Maid II .55 .55

Christmas 1982 — A65

8p, Three Kings. 11p, Robin, Christmas tree, vert.

**Perf. 13¼x13½, 13½x13¼**
**1982, Oct. 5**
221 A65 8p multicolored .25 .25
222 A65 11p multicolored .45 .45

**Souvenir Sheet**

Princess Diana and Prince William A66

**1982, Oct. 12 Perf. 14½x14¼**
223 A66 50p multicolored 2.25 2.25
Birth of Prince William of Wales (June 21) and 21st birthday of Princess Diana (July 1).

Marine Birds — A67

1p, Puffins, Cranstal. 2p, Gannets, Point of Ayre. 5p, Lesser black-backed gulls, Santon. 8p, Cormorants, Maughold Head. 10p, Kittiwakes, White Strand. 11p, Shags, Calf of Man. 12p, Herons, Douglas Foreshore. 13p, Herring gulls, Peel. 14p, Razorbills, Calf of Man. 15p,

Great black-backed gulls, Calf of Man. 16p, Shelducks, Poyll Vaaish. 18p, Oystercatchers, Langness.

**1983, Feb. 15 Litho. Perf. 14½**
224 A67 1p multicolored .25 .25
225 A67 2p multicolored .25 .25
226 A67 5p multicolored .25 .25
227 A67 8p multicolored .30 .30
228 A67 10p multicolored .40 .40
229 A67 11p multicolored .45 .45
230 A67 12p multicolored .50 .50
231 A67 13p multicolored .50 .50
232 A67 14p multicolored .50 .50
233 A67 15p multicolored .60 .60
234 A67 16p multicolored .65 .65
235 A67 18p multicolored .70 .70

**Size: 39x25mm**

**1983, Sept. 14 Perf. 14**
20p, Arctic terns, Blue Point. 25p, Guillemots, Calf of Man. 50p, Redshanks, Langness. £1, Mute swans, Port St. Mary Bay.
236 A67 20p multicolored .75 .75
237 A67 25p multicolored .95 .95
238 A67 50p multicolored 1.70 1.70
239 A67 £1 multicolored 3.50 3.50
Nos. 224-239 (16) 12.25 12.25

Centenary of Salvation Army in Isle of Man — A68

Designs: 10p, Citadel opening ceremony, 1932, T.H. Cannell. 12p, Founder William Booth, early meeting place (former Unitarian Church, Douglas). 19½p, Band, Bandmaster Gordon Cowley, 1981. 26p, Lt.-Col. Thomas Bridson, treating lepers in Dutch East Indies.

**1983, Feb. 15 Photo. Perf. 11½**
**Granite Paper**
240 A68 10p multicolored .25 .25
241 A68 12p multicolored .35 .35
242 A68 19½ multicolored .50 .50
243 A68 26p multicolored .65 .65
Nos. 240-243 (4) 1.75 1.75

Europa 1983 A69

10p, Laxey Wheel. 20½p, Designer Robert Casement.

**1983, May 18 Perf. 14**
244 A69 10p multicolored .35 .35
245 A69 20½p multicolored .55 .55

King William's College Sesquicentennial A70

Graduates: 10p, Nick Keig, Yachtsman. 12p, College, arms. 28p, William Bragg, 1915 Nobel Prize winner in physics, ionization spectrometer. 31p, Gen. George Stuart White, Defense of Ladysmith, Boer War.

**1983, May 18 Photo. Perf. 11½**
**Granite Paper**
246 A70 10p multicolored .25 .25
247 A70 12p multicolored .25 .25
248 A70 28p multicolored .75 .75
249 A70 31p multicolored .80 .80
Nos. 246-249 (4) 2.05 2.05

World Communications Year and 10th Anniv. of Post Office — A71

10p, New P.O. Headquarters. 15p, Viking landing, 938.

**1983, July 5 Litho. Perf. 15**
250 A71 10p multicolored .35 .35
251 A6 15p multicolored .60 .60
Compare No. 251 with No. 28.

Christmas 1983 — A72

**1983, Sept. 14   Litho.      Perf. 13x13½**
252  A72  9p Shepherds        .30  .30
253  A72  12p Three Kings     .40  .40

Karran Fleet — A73

Links with Falkland Islands A74

10p, Manx King, 1884. 13p, Hope, 1858. 20½p, Rio Grande, 1868. 28p, Lady Elizabeth, 1879. 31p, Sumatra, 1858.

**1984, Feb. 14   Litho.      Perf. 14**
254  A73  10p multicolored   .25  .25
255  A73  13p multicolored   .35  .35
256  A73  20½p multicolored  .55  .55
257  A73  28p multicolored   .90  .90
258  A73  31p multicolored   1.00 1.00
      Nos. 254-258 (5)        3.05 3.05

**1984, Feb. 14**
259  A74  Sheet of 2, #257, 259a  2.25 2.25
  a.   31p multicolored            1.50 1.50

Europa (1959-1984) A75

**1984, Apr. 27   Photo.      Perf. 11½**
260  A75  10p dk yel org, dk brn
                 & buff         .35  .35
261  A75  20½p blue, dk bl & lt bl  .65  .65

DH-48, Ronaldsway Airport — A76

13p, DH-86, Calf of Man. 26p, DC-3, Ronaldsway Airport. 28p, Vickers Viscount, Douglas. 31p, Islander, Ronaldsway Airport.

**1984, Apr. 27   Litho.      Perf. 14**
262  A76  11p shown          .35  .35
263  A76  13p multicolored   .40  .40
264  A76  26p multicolored   .75  .75
265  A76  28p multicolored   .75  .75
266  A76  31p multicolored   .75  .75
      Nos. 262-266 (5)        3.00 3.00

50th Anniv. of official airmail service and 40th anniv. of Intl. Civil Aviation Org.

William Cain as Mayor of Melbourne, 1886-87 — A77

11p, Ballasalla (birthplace). 22p, Voyage to Australia. 28p, Railway, Victoria. 33p, Royal Exhibition Buildings, Melbourne.

**1984, Sept. 21   Litho.      Perf. 14½**
267  A77  11p multicolored   .30  .30
268  A77  22p multicolored   .60  .60
269  A77  28p multicolored   .70  .70
270  A77  30p shown          .80  .80
271  A77  33p multicolored   .80  .80
      Nos. 267-271 (5)        3.20 3.20

William Cain (1831-1914), building contractor and public servant in Australia.

Queen Elizabeth II, CPA Emblem — A78

**1984, Sept. 21              Perf. 14**
272  A78  14p shown          .40  .40
273  A78  33p Arms, Elizabeth II  1.00 1.00

30th Conference of Commonwealth Parliamentary Assoc., Sept. 28-Oct. 5.

Christmas — A79

Stained-glass windows: 10p, Birds, Glen-crutchery House. 13p, Arms, Lonan Old Church.

**1984, Sept. 21**
274  A79  10p multicolored   .40  .40
275  A79  13p multicolored   .60  .60

75th Anniv. of Girl Guides — A80

Designs: 11p, Cunningham House (headquarters), Mrs. W. and J. Cunningham (early Island Commissioners). 14p, Princess Margaret (president), color guard. 29p, Lady Olave Baden-Powell, headquarters opening. 31p, Uniforms, 1910-85. 34p, Sign, handclasp, trefoil.

**1985, Jan. 31   Photo.      Perf. 12**
276  A80  11p multicolored   .35  .35
277  A80  14p multicolored   .45  .45
278  A80  29p multicolored   .80  .80
279  A80  31p multicolored   .85  .85
280  A80  34p multicolored   1.05 1.05
      Nos. 276-280 (5)        3.50 3.50

Elizabeth II — A81

**1985, Jan. 31   Litho.      Perf. 14**
281  A81  £5 multicolored    10.50 10.50

Europa 1985 A82

Manx composers: No. 282a, "O'Land of our Birth." No. 282b, William H. Gill (1839-1922). No. 283a, Hymn "Crofton;" No. 283b, Dr. John Clague (1842-1908).

**1985, Apr. 24   Photo.      Perf. 12**
282  A82  Pair              1.10 1.10
  a.-b.   12p any single     .55  .55
283  A82  Pair              1.30 1.30
  a.-b.   22p any single     .65  .65

Motoring A83

Motor races and winning vehicles: No. 284a, 1906 Tourist Trophy Race. No. 284b, 1922 Tourist Trophy Race. No. 285a, 1950 British Empire Trophy Race. No. 285b, 1934 Manin Moar Race. No. 286a, 1984 Tourist Trophy Motorcycle Race (official car). No. 286b, 1981 Rothmans Manx Intl. Rally.

**1985, May 25   Litho.      Perf. 14**
284  A83  Pair              .80  .80
  a.-b.   12p any single     .35  .35
285  A83  Pair              1.00 1.00
  a.-b.   14p any single     .45  .45

286  A83  Pair              2.00 2.00
  a.-b.   31p any single     .80  .80
      Nos. 284-286 (3)        3.80 3.80

H.R.H. Alexandra (1885-1925), Princess of Wales — A84

SSA presidents: 15p, Queen Mary (1925-1953). 29p, Earl Mountbatten of Burma (1953-1979). 34p, Prince Michael of Kent (1982- ).

**1985, Sept. 4   Litho.      Perf. 14**
287  A84  12p multicolored  .35  .35
288  A84  15p multicolored  .45  .45
289  A84  29p multicolored  .85  .85
290  A84  34p multicolored  1.05 1.05
      Nos. 287-290 (4)       2.70 2.70

Soldier's, Sailors' & Airmen's Families Assoc., cent.

Lt.-Gen. Sir Mark Cubbon, K.C.B. (1785-1861), Commissioner of Mysore — A85

12p, Kirk Maughold Parish Church, 14th century. 22p, Portrait, vert. 45p, Equestrian monument, 1866 Bangalore, India, vert.

**1985, Oct. 2   Litho.      Perf. 14**
291  A85  12p multicolored  .45  .45
292  A85  22p multicolored  .75  .75
293  A85  45p multicolored  1.50 1.50
      Nos. 291-293 (3)       2.70 2.70

Christmas 1985 — A86

11p, Onchan Parish Church, 1833. 14p, St. John's Church. 31p, Bride Parish Church, 1876.

**1985, Oct. 2   Litho.      Perf. 13½**
294  A86  11p multicolored  .35  .35
295  A86  14p multicolored  .60  .60
296  A86  31p multicolored  1.10 1.10
      Nos. 294-296 (3)       2.05 2.05

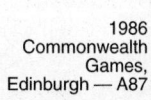

1986 Commonwealth Games, Edinburgh — A87

**1986, Feb. 5   Litho.      Perf. 14**
297  A87  12p Women's swimming  .35  .35
298  A87  15p Walking            .55  .55
299  A87  31p Rifle shooting     .85  .85
300  A87  34p Bicycling          1.10 1.10
      Nos. 297-300 (4)            2.85 2.85

Viking Necklace, Peel Castle — A88

Artifacts, architecture: 15p, Meayll Circle burial ground, Rushen. 22p, Prehistoric Cervus giganteus skeleton, Glose-y-Garey, vert. 26p, Norwegian viking longship, vert. 29p, Open-air Museum, Cregneash.

**1986, Feb. 5   Perf. 14½x14, 14x14½**
301  A88  12p multicolored  .35  .35
302  A88  15p multicolored  .45  .45
303  A88  22p multicolored  .65  .65
304  A88  26p multicolored  .70  .70
305  A88  29p multicolored  .90  .90
      Nos. 301-305 (5)       3.05 3.05

Centenaries of Manx Museum and Ancient Monuments Act.
Nos. 303 and 304 are vert.

Europa 1986, Manx National Trust A89

Designs: No. 306a, Bride hills and the Ayres. No. 306b, Calf of Man. No. 307a, Eary Cushlin. No. 307b, St. Michael's Isle.

**1986, Apr. 10   Litho.      Perf. 12**
306  A89  Pair              .90  .90
  a.-b.   12p any single     .45  .45
307  A89  Pair              1.60 1.60
  a.-b.   22p any single     .80  .80

Settling of Plymouth — A90

Designs: 12p, Ellanbane, Isle of Man, Myles Standish's home. 15p, The Mayflower. 31p, Pilgrims landing, 1620. 34p, Capt. Myles Standish (c. 1584-1656).

**1986, May 22              Perf. 13½**
308  A90  12p multicolored  .40  .40
309  A90  15p multicolored  .50  .50
310  A90  31p multicolored  1.05 1.05
311  A90  34p multicolored  1.35 1.35
  a.   Souvenir sheet of 2, #310-311,
         perf. 13x12½         2.75 2.75
      Nos. 308-311 (4)        3.30 3.30

AMERIPEX '86, Chicago, May 22-June 1.

Heritage Year — A91

2p, Viking longship bow. 10p, Celtic cross.

**Booklet Stamps**

**1986, Apr. 10   Litho.      Perf. 15x14**
312  A91  2p multicolored   .25  .25
  a.   Bklt. pane of 6, 2 #312, 4 #313  4.50
313  A91  10p multicolored  .90  .90
  a.   Bklt. pane of 3 + 3 labels  2.75
      Complete booklet, #190a, 313a  2.00
      Complete booklet, #146c, 190a,
        312a, 313a           4.00

Wedding of Prince Andrew and Sarah Ferguson — A92

**1986, July 23**
314  A92  15p Wedding date      .65  .65
315  A92  40p Engagement date   1.45 1.45

Royal Birthdays A93

No. 316: a, Prince Philip, 65. b, Elizabeth II, 60. No. 317 is the same size as No. 316.

**1986, Aug. 28              Perf. 11½**
316  A93  Pair              1.20 1.20
  a.-b.   15p any single     .60  .60
317  A93  34p Royal couple  1.20 1.20

STOCKHOLMIA '86, Swedish Post Office 350th anniv. Stamps issued in sheets of 6.

Intl. Peace Year — A94

11p, Robins, globe, Braille. 14p, Hands, dove. 31p, Hand-holding, sign language.

**1986, Sept. 25   Litho.      Perf. 14**
318  A94  11p multicolored  .40  .40
319  A94  14p multicolored  .45  .45
320  A94  31p multicolored  1.05 1.05
      Nos. 318-320 (3)       1.90 1.90

Accession of
Queen Victoria to
the British Throne,
150th
Anniv. — A95

Photographs of Victorian Douglas, by John
Miller Nicholson: 2p, North Quay. 3p, The Old
Fish Market. 10p, Breakwater. 15p, Jubilee
Clock. 31p, Loch Promenade. 34p, Beach.

**1987, Jan. 21    Litho.    Perf. 14½**
321 A95  2p multicolored          .25  .25
322 A95  3p multicolored          .25  .25
323 A95 10p multicolored          .35  .35
  a.  Bklt. pane of 8 (2 2p, 2 3p, 4
        10p) ('87)                 2.10
      Complete booklet, #323a      2.10
324 A95 15p multicolored          .50  .50
  a.  Bklt. pane of 8 (2 2p, 2 3p, 2
        10p, 2 15p) ('87)          1.75
      Complete booklet, #323a, #324a 8.50
325 A95 31p multicolored          .95  .95
326 A95 34p multicolored         1.00 1.00
      Nos. 321-326 (6)            3.30 3.30

No. 323a comes in two arrangements.

19th Century
Paintings by John
Miller Nicholson
(1840-1913)
A96

Harbor scenes: 12p, The Old Fish Market
and Harbor, Douglas. 26p, Red Sails at Douglas. 29p, The Double Corner. 34p, Peel
Harbor.

**1987, Feb. 18    Perf. 13½**
327 A96 12p multicolored          .35  .35
328 A96 26p multicolored          .70  .70
329 A96 29p multicolored          .80  .80
330 A96 34p multicolored         1.00 1.00
      Nos. 327-330 (4)            2.85 2.85

Promenade, Douglas — A97

No. 331, Sea Terminal, 1965. No. 332,
Tower of Refuge, 1832. No. 333, Gaiety Theater, c. 1900. No. 334, Villa Marina.

**1987, Apr. 29    Litho.    Perf. 13½**
331      12p multicolored         .45  .45
332      12p multicolored         .45  .45
  a.  A97 Pair, #331-332          .90  .90
333      22p multicolored         .75  .75
334      22p multicolored         .75  .75
  a.  A97 Pair, #333-334         1.50 1.50
      Nos. 331-334 (4)           2.40 2.40

Europa 1987.

Tourist Trophy
Motorcycle
Races, 80th
Anniv. — A98

12p, 1939 Supercharged BMW 500CC. 15p,
1953 Manx "Kneeler" Norton 350CC. 29p,
1956 MV Agusta 500CC 4. 31p, 1957 Guzzi
500CC V8. 34p, 1967 Honda 250CC 6.

**1987, May 27    Perf. 13½x13**
335 A98 12p multicolored          .40  .40
336 A98 15p multicolored          .50  .50
  a.  Perf. 14 (#1425b)           .45  .45
337 A98 29p multicolored          .90  .90
338 A98 31p multicolored         1.00 1.00
339 A98 34p multicolored         1.15 1.15
  a.  Souv. sheet of 5, #335-339 + 7
        labels, perf 14x13½       4.50 4.50
      Nos. 335-339 (5)            3.95 3.95

Issued: No. 336a, 2015.

Wildflowers — A99

16p, Fuchsia, wild roses. 29p, Field scabius,
ragwort. 31p, Wood anemone, celandine. 34p,
Violets, primroses.

---

**1987, Sept. 9    Litho.    Perf. 14½x13½**
340 A99 16p multicolored          .55  .55
341 A99 29p multicolored         1.00 1.00
342 A99 31p multicolored         1.10 1.10
343 A99 34p multicolored         1.35 1.35
      Nos. 340-343 (4)            4.00 4.00

Christmas — A100

Victorian family scenes based on drawings
by Alfred Hunt for The Illustrated London
News, c. 1870-1890: 12p, Stirring the pudding.
15p, Christmas tree selection. 31p, Decorating
tree.

**1987, Oct. 16    Perf. 14**
344 A100 12p multicolored         .40  .40
345 A100 15p multicolored         .50  .50
346 A100 31p multicolored        1.10 1.10
      Nos. 344-346 (3)            2.00 2.00

Railways &
Tramways — A101

Designs: 1p, Horse-drawn "Toast Rack"
tram, Douglas Bay, 1884. 2p, No. 5 electric
tram, Snaefell Mountain Railway, 1895. 3p,
No. 3 open-top double-deck electric tram,
Marine Drive-Port Soderick line, Douglas
Southern Electric Tramway, 1896. 5p, Tower of
Refuge and open tram, Douglas Head Incline
Railway. 10p, Electric tram at Maughold Head,
1893, Douglas and Laxey Coast Electric Tram-
way. 13p, Douglas Cable Car No. 72, 1896.
14p, Manx Northern Railway No. 4 Caledonia,
a Dubs 0-6-0T, 1885, at Gob-y-Deigan. 15p,
Great Laxey Mine Railway Lewin steam
engine Ant pulling coal cars. 16p, Henry B.
Loch, first locomotive on the island, Port Erin
Breakwater Railway, 1864. 17p, Locomotive
No. 1, Ramsey Harbor Tramway. 18p, Engine
No. 7 Tynwald, 1880, Foxdale Railway. 19p,
Douglas Corp. engine, Baldwin Reservoir
Railway. 20p, "Kissack" leaving St. John's for
Peel. 25p, "Hutchinson" leaving Douglas Sta-
tion. 50p, "Polar Bear" of Groudle Glen Rail-
way. £1, The Royal Train.

**Inscribed 1988**

**1988    Litho.    Perf. 13½**
347 A101  1p multicolored         .25  .25
348 A101  2p multicolored         .25  .25
349 A101  3p multicolored         .25  .25
  a.  Inscribed "1989"            .35  .35
350 A101  5p multicolored         .25  .25
351 A101 10p multicolored         .40  .40
352 A101 13p multicolored         .50  .50
353 A101 14p multicolored         .55  .55
  a.  Inscribed "1989"            .65  .65
354 A101 15p multicolored         .60  .60
  a.  Inscribed "1990"            .65  .65
355 A101 16p multicolored         .65  .65
  b.  Bklt. pane 2 #349, #352, 2
        #355                       2.25
      Complete booklet #355b       3.00
  c.  Bklt. pane, 4 #352, 6 #355   6.00
      Complete booklet #355b,
        355c                      11.50
356 A101 17p multicolored         .70  .70
  a.  Bklt. pane 2 #349a, 2 #353a,
        #356c                      2.25
      Complete booklet, #356a      3.00
  b.  Booklet pane, 4 #353a, 6
        #356c                      6.50
      Complete booklet, #356a,
        356b                       9.50
  c.  Inscribed "1989"            .80  .80
  d.  Inscribed "1991"           1.00 1.00
357 A101 18p multicolored         .70  .70
358 A101 19p multicolored         .75  .75
  e.  Inscribed "1990"            .80  .80
  f.  Bklt. pane, 4 #354a, 6 #358e 7.00
      Complete booklet, 4 #354a, 6
        #358e                      7.50
  g.  Bklt. pane, 1 #354a, 2 #358e 2.10
      Complete booklet, #354a,
        358e                       2.50

**Perf. 15**
358A A101 20p multicolored        .80  .80
358B A101 25p multicolored       1.00 1.00
358C A101 50p multicolored       2.00 2.00
  a.  Inscribed "1992"            8.75 8.75
358D A101 £1 multicolored        4.00 4.00
  a.  Inscribed "1992"          19.00 19.00
      Nos. 347-358D (16)         13.65 13.65

Nos. 356a and 356b also exist in special
booklet sheets of 50 stamps containing either
10 No. 356a or 5 No. 356b.
Issued: 1p-19p, 2/10; Nos. 355b-355c, 3/16;
20p-£1, 9/21; Nos. 356a, 356b, 10/16/89; No.
358f, 2/14/90.
See Nos. 448-459.

---

Car
Racing
A102

Winning automobiles, drivers: 13p, Vauxhall
Opel, Russell Brookes, 1985. 26p, Ford
Escort, Ari Vatanen of Finland, 1976. 31p,
Repco March 761, Terry Smith, 1980. 34p,
Williams/Honda Nigel Mansell, 1986-87.

**1988, Feb. 10    Perf. 13½x14½**
359 A102 13p multicolored         .55  .55
360 A102 26p multicolored        1.10 1.10
361 A102 31p multicolored        1.25 1.25
362 A102 34p multicolored        1.35 1.35
      Nos. 359-362 (4)            4.25 4.25

Europa 1988 — A103

Telecommunications: No. 363, IOM-UK optical fiber cable-laying plow. No. 364, Cable-
laying ship. No. 365, 1st IOM Earth station,
Braddan, established by Manx Telecom. No.
366, Intelsat V satellite.

**1988, Apr. 14    Litho.    Perf. 14x13½**
363      13p multicolored         .55  .55
364      13p multicolored         .55  .55
  a.  A103 Pair, #363-364         1.15 1.15
365      22p multicolored         .90  .90
366      22p multicolored         .90  .90
  a.  A103 Pair, #365-366         1.80 1.80
      Nos. 363-366 (4)            2.90 2.90

Submarine cable linking the Isle of Man and
Silecroft in Cumbria, 1987 (13p). Nos. 364a,
366a have continuous designs.

Historic Ships
Built on the
Isle — A104

Isle of Man flag, Australia bicen. emblem or
US flag and: 16p, Euterpe, 1863, built in Ramsey. 29p, Vixen leaving Peel for Australia,
1853. 31p, Ramsey, an immigrant ship in Bris-
bane, 1870. 34p, Star of India (renamed in
1906, was the Euterpe), restored 1960-1976,
Maritime Museum at San Diego.

**1988, May 11    Litho.    Perf. 14**
367 A104 16p multicolored         .55  .55
368 A104 29p multicolored        1.05 1.05
369 A104 31p multicolored        1.05 1.05
370 A104 34p multicolored        1.10 1.10
  a.  Souvenir sheet of 2 (16p, 34p) 2.50 2.50
      Nos. 367-370 (4)            3.75 3.75

Fuchsia
Blossoms — A105

**1988, Sept. 21    Litho.    Perf. 13½x14**
371 A105 13p Magellanica         .40  .30
372 A105 16p Pink cloud          .45  .35
373 A105 22p Leonora             .70  .65
374 A105 29p Satellite           .95  .95
375 A105 31p Preston Guild      1.05 1.05
376 A105 34p Thalia             1.20 1.20
      Nos. 371-376 (6)           4.75 4.50

British Fuchsia Society, 50th anniv.

Christmas
A106

**1988, Oct. 12    Perf. 14**
377 A106 12p Long-eared owl       .60  .60
378 A106 15p Robin                .75  .75
379 A106 31p Partridge           1.40 1.40
      Nos. 377-379 (3)            2.75 2.75

---

Manx
Cats — A107

Designs: 16p, Ginger. 27p, Black and white.
30p, Tortoiseshell and white. 40p,
Tortoiseshell.

**1989, Feb. 8**
380 A107 16p multicolored         .50  .50
381 A107 27p multicolored         .85  .85
382 A107 30p multicolored        1.20 1.20
383 A107 40p multicolored        1.25 1.25
      Nos. 380-383 (4)            3.80 3.80

Celtic Works of
Art by Archibald
Knox (1864-1933)
A108

Designs: 13p, Tudric pewter and enamel
clock, 1903, vert. 16p, Cross, a watercolor,
vert. 23p, Silver tankard, 1902, vert. 32p, Liberty silver and Cymric gold brooches. 35p, Silver jewel box with inlaid turquoise, mother-of-
pearl and enamel, 1900.

**1989, Feb. 8    Litho.    Perf. 13**
384 A108 13p multicolored         .40  .40
385 A108 16p multicolored         .50  .50
386 A108 23p multicolored         .70  .70
387 A108 32p multicolored         .90  .90
388 A108 35p multicolored        1.20 1.20
      Nos. 384-388 (5)            3.70 3.70

Mutiny on the
Bounty — A109

Designs: 13p, William Bligh, Old Onchan
Church. 16p, Bligh and crewmen cast adrift.
30p, Peter Heywood on Tahiti, 1770. 32p,
Bounty off Pitcairn. 35p, Fletcher Christian on
Pitcairn.

**1989, Apr. 28    Litho.    Perf. 14**
389 A109 13p multicolored         .35  .35
390 A109 16p multicolored         .50  .50
391 A109 30p multicolored         .80  .80
392 A109 32p multicolored         .90  .90
393 A109 35p multicolored        1.00 1.00
      Nos. 389-393 (5)            3.55 3.55

**Souvenir Sheet**
394      Sheet of 3 + label      4.00 4.00
  a.  A109 23p Pitcairn Isls. No. 321d  .65  .65
  b.  A109 27p Norfolk Is. No. 453  .75  .75
  c.  Booklet pane, #394           2.60
  d.  Booklet pane, 1 each #389-393,
        394a                       3.35
  e.  Bklt. pane of 6, #389-393, #394b 3.35
  f.  Booklet pane, 3 each #394a,
        #394b                      3.15
      Complete booklet #394c, 394d,
        394e, 394f                13.00

See Norfolk Is. Nos. 452-456 and Pitcairn
Isls. Nos. 320-322.
No. 394 contains Nos. 393, 394a-394b.
No. 394c is 145x101mm and is rouletted at
left.

Europa
1989 — A110

Children's games: No. 395, Jumping rope,
hopscotch, London Bridge is falling down. No.
396, Running, wheelbarrow race, leap frog,
piggyback ride. No. 397, Boy building fort, girl
blowing soap bubbles, puzzle. No. 398, Doll
house, blocks, girl playing with rag doll and
puzzle.

**1989, May 17    Perf. 13½**
395 A110 13p multicolored         .45  .45
396 A110 13p multicolored         .45  .45
  a.  Pair, #395-396              .90  .90
397 A110 23p multicolored         .95  .95
398 A110 23p multicolored         .95  .95
  a.  Pair, #397-398             1.90 1.90
      Nos. 395-398 (4)            2.80 2.80

Nos. 396a, 398a have continuous designs.

World Wildlife Fund — A111

**1989, Sept. 20        Litho.        Perf. 14**
| | | | | |
|---|---|---|---|---|
| 399 | A111 | 13p Puffin | .70 | .70 |
| 400 | A111 | 13p Black guillemot | .70 | .70 |
| 401 | A111 | 13p Cormorant | .70 | .70 |
| 402 | A111 | 13p Kittiwake | .70 | .70 |
| | *a.* | Block or strip of 4, #399-402 | 3.50 | 3.50 |
| | | *Nos. 399-402 (4)* | 2.80 | 2.80 |

Exists as sheetlet of 16 with "World Stamp Expo '89" printed in selvage.

Intl. Red Cross, 125th Anniv. — A112

14p, Training youths. 17p, Emblems. 23p, Signing 1st Geneva convention, 1864. 30p, Ambulance services. 35p, Henri Dunant, founder.

**1989, Oct. 16        Litho.        Perf. 14**
| | | | | |
|---|---|---|---|---|
| 403 | A112 | 14p multicolored | .40 | .40 |
| 404 | A112 | 17p multicolored | .45 | .45 |
| 405 | A112 | 23p multicolored | .65 | .65 |
| 406 | A112 | 30p multicolored | .90 | .90 |
| 407 | A112 | 35p multicolored | 1.00 | 1.00 |
| | | *Nos. 403-407 (5)* | 3.40 | 3.40 |

Noble's Hospital, Douglas, cent.

Christmas — A113

13p, Maternity home. 16p, Mother and child. 34p, Madonna and child, scripture. 37p, Church, baptismal ceremony.

**1989, Oct. 16        Perf. 14½x15**
| | | | | |
|---|---|---|---|---|
| 408 | A113 | 13p multicolored | .40 | .40 |
| 409 | A113 | 16p multicolored | .50 | .50 |
| 410 | A113 | 34p multicolored | 1.10 | 1.10 |
| 411 | A113 | 37p multicolored | 1.25 | 1.25 |
| | | *Nos. 408-411 (4)* | 3.25 | 3.25 |

Jane Crookall Maternity Home 50th anniv. (13p) and 75th anniv. of the consecration of St. Ninian's Church (37p).

Queen Elizabeth II, Lord of Man, Trooping the Colors — A114

**1990, Feb. 14        Litho.        Perf. 14½**
| | | | | |
|---|---|---|---|---|
| 412 | A114 | £2 multicolored | 5.50 | 5.50 |

Humorous Edwardian Postcards A115

15p, The Isle of Man Express Going Up a Gradient. 19p, A Way We Have in the Isle of Man. 32p, Douglas — Waiting for the Male Boat. 34p, The Last Toast Rack Home Douglas Parade. 37p, The Last Isle of Man Boat.

**1990, Feb. 14        Perf. 14**
| | | | | |
|---|---|---|---|---|
| 413 | A115 | 15p multicolored | .40 | .40 |
| 414 | A115 | 19p multicolored | .60 | .60 |
| 415 | A115 | 32p multicolored | .95 | .95 |
| 416 | A115 | 34p multicolored | 1.10 | 1.10 |
| 417 | A115 | 37p multicolored | 1.35 | 1.35 |
| | | *Nos. 413-417 (5)* | 4.40 | 4.40 |

Europa 1990 — A116

Mailmen and post offices: No. 418, Mailman, 1990. No. 419, Ramsey P.O., 1990. No. 420, Mailman, c. 1890. No. 421, Douglas P.O., c. 1890.

**1990, Apr. 18        Litho.        Perf. 13½**
**Size of Nos. 419, 421: 42x28mm**
| | | | |
|---|---|---|---|
| 418 | 15p multicolored | .50 | .50 |
| 419 | 15p multicolored | .50 | .50 |
| *a.* | A116 Pair, #418-419 | 1.00 | 1.00 |
| 420 | 24p multicolored | .85 | .85 |
| 421 | 24p multicolored | .85 | .85 |
| *a.* | A116 Pair, #420-421 | 1.70 | 1.70 |
| | *Nos. 418-421 (4)* | 2.70 | 2.70 |

Great Britain No. 1 — A117

Designs: 19p, Wyon Medal. 32p, William Wyon's essay. 34p, Perkins Bacon engine-turned essay of 1839. 37p, Great Britain No. 2.
No. 423 (various Penny Blacks and text): a.-e. Positions AA-AE. f.-j. Positions BA-BE. k.-n. Positions CA-CE. p.-t. Positions DA-DE. u.-y. Positions EA-EE.
**Note** that A-A top of square on No. 423a, centered on No. 422a.

**1990, May 3        Litho.        Perf. 14x13½**
| | | | |
|---|---|---|---|
| 422 | Pane of 5 | 4.00 | 4.00 |
| *a.* | A117 1p shown | .25 | .25 |
| *b.* | A117 19p multicolored | .60 | .60 |
| *c.* | A117 32p multicolored | 1.00 | 1.00 |
| *d.* | A117 34p multicolored | 1.10 | 1.10 |
| *e.* | A117 37p multicolored | 1.15 | 1.15 |
| *g.* | Bklt. pane, 2 each #422b-422e | 8.50 | |
| *h.* | No. 422 ovptd. "From STAMP WORLD LONDON '90 / To NEW ZEALAND '90" | 14.00 | 14.00 |

**Miniature Sheet**
| | | | |
|---|---|---|---|
| 423 | Sheet of 25 | 2.75 | 2.75 |
| *a.-y.* | A117 1p like #422a, any single | .25 | .25 |
| *z.* | Pane of 8, #a.-d., f.-i. | .50 | |

**Souvenir Sheet**
**Litho. & Engr.**
| | | | |
|---|---|---|---|
| 424 | A117 £1 4 Great Britain #1 | 4.25 | 4.25 |
| *a.* | Booklet pane of 1 | 4.25 | 4.25 |
| | Complete booklet, #422g, 423z, 424a | 8.00 | |

Left margin of Nos. 422g, 423z and 424a rouletted.

Queen Mother, 90th Birthday — A118

**1990, Aug. 4        Litho.        Perf. 13x13½**
| | | | | |
|---|---|---|---|---|
| 425 | A118 | 90p multicolored | 3.00 | 3.00 |

Sheets of 10 alternating with 10 labels.

Battle of Britain, 50th Anniv. — A119

No. 426, Home defense. No. 427, Air sea rescue. No. 428, Rearming fighters. No. 429, Height of battle. No. 430, Civil defense. No. 431, Anti-aircraft defense.

**1990, Sept. 5        Litho.        Perf. 14**
| | | | | |
|---|---|---|---|---|
| 426 | A119 | 15p multicolored | .55 | .55 |
| 427 | A119 | 15p multicolored | .55 | .55 |
| | *a.* | Pair, #426-427 | 1.10 | 1.10 |
| 428 | A119 | 24p multicolored | .80 | .80 |
| 429 | A119 | 24p multicolored | .80 | .80 |
| | *a.* | Pair, #428-429 | 1.60 | 1.60 |
| 430 | A119 | 29p multicolored | 1.00 | 1.00 |
| 431 | A119 | 29p multicolored | 1.00 | 1.00 |
| | *a.* | Pair, #430-431 | 2.00 | 2.00 |
| | | *Nos. 426-431 (6)* | 4.70 | 4.70 |

Sir Winston Churchill (1874-1965) A120

**1990, Sept. 5        Perf. 13½**
| | | | | |
|---|---|---|---|---|
| 432 | A120 | 19p multicolored | .50 | .50 |
| 433 | A120 | 32p multicolored | .85 | .85 |
| 434 | A120 | 34p multicolored | .90 | .90 |
| 435 | A120 | 37p multicolored | 1.00 | 1.00 |
| | | *Nos. 432-435 (4)* | 3.25 | 3.25 |

Christmas — A121

**1990, Oct. 10        Perf. 13x13½**
| | | | | |
|---|---|---|---|---|
| 436 | A121 | 14p Mailing letters | .45 | .45 |
| 437 | A121 | 18p Sledding, skating | .55 | .55 |
| 438 | A121 | 34p Snowman | 1.25 | 1.25 |
| 439 | A121 | 37p Throwing snowball | 1.40 | 1.40 |
| | *a.* | Souvenir sheet of 4, #436-439 | 3.65 | 3.65 |
| | | *Nos. 436-439 (4)* | 3.65 | 3.65 |

Denominations on stamps in No. 439a are black.

Manx Photographers A122

Designs: 17p, Henry Bloom Noble, by Marshall Wane. 21p, Douglas, by Frederic Frith & Co. 26p, Studio Portrait, by Hilda Newby. 31p, Cashtal yn Ard, by Christopher Killip. 40p, Peel, by Colleen Corlett.

**1991, Jan. 6        Litho.        Perf. 14x14½**
| | | | | |
|---|---|---|---|---|
| 440 | A122 | 17p black, gray | .50 | .50 |
| 441 | A122 | 21p brown | .60 | .60 |
| 442 | A122 | 26p sepia | .75 | .75 |
| 443 | A122 | 31p black, gray | 1.05 | 1.05 |
| 444 | A122 | 40p multicolored | 1.35 | 1.35 |
| | | *Nos. 440-444 (5)* | 4.25 | 4.25 |

**Railways and Tramways Type of 1988 with Queen's Head in White (#448, 458)**
Designs: 18p, TPO Special leaving Douglas Station, 1991. 23p, Double decker horse tram.

**1991-92        Litho.        Perf. 13½**
| | | | | |
|---|---|---|---|---|
| 448 | A101 | 4p like No. 352 | .25 | .25 |
| 456 | A101 | 18p multicolored | .70 | .70 |
| 458 | A101 | 21p like No. 353 | .85 | .85 |
| | *a.* | Souv. sheet, 2 each #448, #458 | 2.60 | 2.60 |
| | *b.* | Bklt. pane, #458, 3 #448, 4 #356d | 3.75 | |
| | | Complete booklet, #458b | 4.00 | |
| | *c.* | Bklt. pane, 3 #448, 1 each #356d, #458 | 1.90 | |
| | | Complete booklet, #458c | 2.00 | |
| 459 | A101 | 23p multicolored | .90 | .90 |
| | *a.* | Bklt. pane, 6 #456, 4 #459 | 9.00 | |
| | | Complete booklet, #459a | 2.00 | |
| | *b.* | Bklt. pane, 3 #456, 2 #459 | 5.00 | |
| | | Complete booklet, #459b | 2.00 | |
| | | *Nos. 448-459 (4)* | 2.70 | 2.70 |

No. 458a for Ninth Conf. of Commonwealth Postal Administrations, Douglas, Isle of Man. Issued: 4p, 21p, Nos. 458b, 458c, 1/9; No. 458a, 7/1; 18p, 23p, No. 459a, 1/8/92.
No. 458b exists in special booklet sheets containing 5 No. 458b and 5 each Nos. 448, 458.
No. 458b dated 1991.

Manx Lifeboats A123

17p, Sir William Hillary. 21p, Osman Gabriel. 26p, James & Ann Ritchie. 31p, The Gough Ritchie. 37p, John Batstone.

**1991, Feb. 13        Perf. 14**
| | | | | |
|---|---|---|---|---|
| 463 | A123 | 17p multicolored | .50 | .50 |
| 464 | A123 | 21p multicolored | .70 | .70 |
| 465 | A123 | 26p multicolored | .80 | .80 |
| 466 | A123 | 31p multicolored | 1.00 | 1.00 |
| 467 | A123 | 37p multicolored | 1.10 | 1.10 |
| | | *Nos. 463-467 (5)* | 4.10 | 4.10 |

Europa — A124

**1991, Apr. 24        Litho.        Perf. 14**
| | | | | |
|---|---|---|---|---|
| 468 | | 17p Satellites | .60 | .60 |
| 469 | | 17p Boats, Ariane rocket | .60 | .60 |
| | *a.* | A124 Vert. pair, #468-469 | 1.25 | 1.25 |
| 470 | | 26p Satellites, diff. | 1.00 | 1.00 |
| 471 | | 26p Space shuttle, jet | 1.00 | 1.00 |
| | *a.* | A124 Vert. pair, #470-471 | 2.00 | 2.00 |
| | | *Nos. 468-471 (4)* | 3.20 | 3.20 |

Tourist Trophy Mountain Course, 80th Anniv. — A125

Designs: 17p, Oliver Godfrey, Indian 500cc, Bray Hill, 1911. 21p, Freddie Dixon, Douglas banking sidecar, Ballacraine, 1923. 26p, Bill Ivy, Yamaha 125cc, Waterworks, 1968. 31p, Giacomo Agostini, MV Agusta 500cc, Cregny-Baa, 1972. 37p, Joey Dunlop, RVF Honda 750cc, Ballaugh Bridge, 1985.

**1991, May 30        Litho.        Perf. 14½x13**
| | | | | |
|---|---|---|---|---|
| 472 | A125 | 17p multicolored | .50 | .50 |
| 473 | A125 | 21p multicolored | .65 | .65 |
| 474 | A125 | 26p multicolored | .70 | .70 |
| 475 | A125 | 31p multicolored | .90 | .90 |
| 476 | A125 | 37p multicolored | 1.10 | 1.10 |
| | *a.* | Souv. sheet of 5, #472-476 + 7 labels | 4.75 | 4.75 |
| | *b.* | As "a," ovptd. in black & red in sheet margin | 15.00 | 15.00 |
| | | *Nos. 472-476 (5)* | 3.85 | 3.85 |

No. 476b overprint includes show emblem and "PHILA / NIPPON '91."
Issue date: No. 476b, Nov. 16.

Fire Engines — A126

Designs: 17p, Laxey hand cart. 21p, Douglas horse drawn steamer. 30p, Merryweather Hatfield pump. 33p, Dennis F8 pumping appliance. 37p, Volvo turntable ladder.

**1991, Sept. 18        Litho.        Perf. 14½**
| | | | | |
|---|---|---|---|---|
| 477 | A126 | 17p multicolored | .55 | .55 |
| 478 | A126 | 21p multicolored | .70 | .70 |
| 479 | A126 | 30p multicolored | .95 | .95 |
| 480 | A126 | 33p multicolored | 1.10 | 1.10 |
| 481 | A126 | 37p multicolored | 1.25 | 1.25 |
| | | *Nos. 477-481 (5)* | 4.55 | 4.55 |

Swans — A127

Designs: No. 482, Mute swans, Douglas Harbor. No. 483, Black swans, Curraghs Wildlife Park. No. 484, Whooper swans, Bishops Dub, Ballaugh. No. 485, Bewick's swans, Eairy Dam, Foxdale. No. 486, Coscaroba swans, Curraghs Wildlife Park. No. 487, Trumpeter swans, Curraghs Wildlife Park.

**1991, Sept. 18        Perf. 13**
| | | | | |
|---|---|---|---|---|
| 482 | | 17p multicolored | .55 | .55 |
| 483 | | 17p multicolored | .55 | .55 |
| | *a.* | A127 Pair, #482-483 | 1.10 | 1.10 |
| 484 | | 26p multicolored | .90 | .90 |
| 485 | | 26p multicolored | .90 | .90 |
| | *a.* | A127 Pair, #484-485 | 1.80 | 1.80 |
| 486 | | 37p multicolored | 1.15 | 1.15 |
| 487 | | 37p multicolored | 1.15 | 1.15 |
| | *a.* | A127 Pair, #486-487 | 2.30 | 2.30 |
| | | *Nos. 482-487 (6)* | 5.20 | 5.20 |

Pairs have continuous designs.

Christmas — A128

16p, Three kings. 20p, Jesus in manger, Mary. 26p, Shepherds. 37p, Angels.

| | | | | | |
|---|---|---|---|---|---|
| **1991, Oct. 14** | | | **Perf. 14x14½** | |
| 488 | A128 | 16p multicolored | .50 | .50 |
| 489 | A128 | 20p multicolored | .60 | .60 |
| 490 | A128 | 26p multicolored | .80 | .80 |
| 491 | A128 | 37p multicolored | 1.10 | 1.10 |
| | *Nos. 488-491 (4)* | | 3.00 | 3.00 |

**Litho.**
*Die Cut*
**Self-Adhesive Booklet Stamps**

| | | | | |
|---|---|---|---|---|
| 492 | A128 | 16p like #488 | .80 | .80 |
| 493 | A128 | 20p like #489 | 1.00 | 1.00 |
| a. | Bklt. pane, 8 #492, 4 #493 | | 7.25 | 7.25 |
| | Complete booklet, 2 #493a | | 14.50 | |

Queen Elizabeth II's Accession to the Throne, 40th Anniv. — A129

Various portraits of Queen Elizabeth II.

| | | | | |
|---|---|---|---|---|
| **1992, Feb. 6** | | **Litho.** | **Perf. 14** | |
| 494 | A129 | 18p multicolored | .50 | .50 |
| 495 | A129 | 20p multicolored | .65 | .65 |
| 496 | A129 | 28p multicolored | .80 | .80 |
| 497 | A129 | 33p multicolored | .90 | .90 |
| 498 | A129 | 39p multicolored | 1.20 | 1.20 |
| | *Nos. 494-498 (5)* | | 4.05 | 4.05 |

Parachute Regiment, 50th Anniv. — A130

Designs: No. 499, North Africa & Italy, 1942-43. No. 500, Operation Overlord, Normandy, 1944. No. 501, Operation Market Garden, Arnhem, 1944. No. 502, Operation Varsity, Rhine, 1945. No. 503, Near, Middle and Far East, 1945-68. No. 504, Operation Corporate, Falkland Islands, 1982, and Utrinque Paratus, 1992.

| | | | | |
|---|---|---|---|---|
| **1992, Feb. 6** | | | **Perf. 14** | |
| 499 | | 23p multicolored | .65 | .65 |
| 500 | | 23p multicolored | .65 | .65 |
| a. | A130 Pair, #499-500 | | 1.30 | 1.30 |
| 501 | | 28p multicolored | .80 | .80 |
| 502 | | 28p multicolored | .80 | .80 |
| a. | A130 Pair, #501-502 | | 1.60 | 1.60 |
| 503 | | 39p multicolored | 1.25 | 1.25 |
| 504 | | 39p multicolored | 1.25 | 1.25 |
| a. | A130 Pair, #503-504 | | 2.50 | 2.50 |
| | *Nos. 499-504 (6)* | | 5.40 | 5.40 |

Printed in sheets of 8.

Pilgrims' Voyage to America, 1620 — A131

Europa: No. 505, Pilgrims in longboats. No. 506, Speedwell, Delfshaven, Holland. No. 507, Mayflower. No. 508, Speedwell, Dartmouth, England.

| | | | | |
|---|---|---|---|---|
| **1992, Apr. 16** | | **Litho.** | **Perf. 14x13½** | |
| 505 | A131 | 18p multicolored | .45 | .45 |
| 506 | A131 | 18p multicolored | .45 | .45 |
| a. | Pair, #505-506 | | .90 | .90 |
| 507 | A131 | 28p multicolored | 1.00 | 1.00 |
| 508 | A131 | 28p multicolored | 1.00 | 1.00 |
| a. | Pair, #507-508 | | 2.00 | 2.00 |
| | *Nos. 505-508 (4)* | | 2.90 | 2.90 |

Nos. 506a, 508a have continuous design.

Port Erin Marine Laboratory, Cent. — A132

| | | | | |
|---|---|---|---|---|
| **1992, Apr. 16** | | | **Perf. 14½** | |
| 509 | A132 | 18p Brittle stars | .55 | .55 |
| 510 | A132 | 23p Phytoplankton | .75 | .75 |
| 511 | A132 | 28p Herring | .85 | .85 |
| 512 | A132 | 33p Great scallop | .95 | .95 |
| 513 | A132 | 39p Dahlia anemone, delesseria | 1.20 | 1.20 |
| | *Nos. 509-513 (5)* | | 4.30 | 4.30 |

Union Pacific, First Transcontinental Railroad — A133

No. 514, "Jupiter," 1869. No. 515, "#119," 1869. No. 516, "#844," 1992. No. 517, "#3985," 1992. £1.50, Golden Spike Ceremony, Union Pacific and Central Pacific Railroads, 1869.

| | | | | |
|---|---|---|---|---|
| **1992, May 22** | | **Litho.** | **Perf. 13½x14** | |
| 514 | | 33p multicolored | 1.00 | 1.00 |
| 515 | | 33p multicolored | 1.00 | 1.00 |
| a. | A133 Pair, #514-515 + label | | 2.10 | 2.10 |
| 516 | | 39p multicolored | 1.25 | 1.25 |
| 517 | | 39p multicolored | 1.25 | 1.25 |
| a. | A133 Pair, #516-517 + label | | 2.75 | 2.75 |
| b. | Bklt. pane, 1 ea #515a, 517a | | 4.75 | 4.75 |

**Souvenir Sheet**

| | | | | |
|---|---|---|---|---|
| 518 | A133 | £1.50 multicolored | 5.50 | 5.50 |
| a. | Booklet pane, #518 | | 4.75 | |
| b. | Bklt. pane, #518a, 2 #517b | | 12.75 | |
| | Complete booklet, #518b | | 12.75 | |

World Columbian Stamp Expo '92. No. 518 contains one 60x50mm stamp.
Nos. 514-515 and 516-517 issued in sheets of 10.
Nos. 515a, 517a have 3 different labels. No. 517b exists with two different pairs of labels. No. 518a has a rouletted white border at left and right.

Manx Harbors A134

No. 519, King Orry V, Douglas Harbor. 23p, Castletown Harbor. 37p, Port St. Mary Harbor. 40p, Ramsey Harbor. a, King Orry. b, St. Eloi.

| | | | | |
|---|---|---|---|---|
| **1992, Sept. 18** | | **Litho.** | **Perf. 14½x14** | |
| 519 | A134 | 18p multicolored | .55 | .55 |
| 520 | A134 | 23p multicolored | .70 | .70 |
| 521 | A134 | 37p multicolored | 1.25 | 1.25 |
| 522 | A134 | 40p multicolored | 1.50 | 1.50 |
| | *Nos. 519-522 (4)* | | 4.00 | 4.00 |

**Souvenir Sheet**

| | | | | |
|---|---|---|---|---|
| 523 | | Sheet of 2 | 4.00 | 4.00 |
| a. | A134 18p multicolored | | .65 | .65 |
| b. | A134 £1 multicolored | | 3.25 | 3.25 |

Genoa '92. No. 523 contains 30x24mm stamps.

Christmas — A135

Designs: 17p, Nativity window, St. German's Cathedral, Peel. 22p, Adoration of the Magi panel, St. Matthew's Church, Douglas. 28p, Nativity window, St. George's Church, Douglas. 37p, Reredos of The Annunciation, St. Mary of the Isle, Douglas. 40p, Good Shepherd window, Trinity Methodist Church, Douglas.

| | | | | |
|---|---|---|---|---|
| **1992, Oct. 13** | | **Litho.** | **Perf. 14½** | |
| 524 | A135 | 17p multicolored | .45 | .45 |
| 525 | A135 | 22p multicolored | .65 | .65 |
| 526 | A135 | 28p multicolored | .85 | .85 |
| 527 | A135 | 37p multicolored | .85 | .85 |
| 528 | A135 | 40p multicolored | 1.20 | 1.20 |
| | *Nos. 524-528 (5)* | | 4.00 | 4.00 |

Nigel Mansell, Formula I World Champion, 1992 — A136

Williams Renault FW 14B at: 20p, British Grand Prix, 1992. 24p, French Grand Prix, 1992.

| | | | | |
|---|---|---|---|---|
| **1992, Nov. 8** | | | **Perf. 13½** | |
| 529 | A136 | 20p multicolored | .75 | .75 |
| 530 | A136 | 24p multicolored | 1.00 | 1.00 |

Ships — A137

Royal Ensign of the Isle of Man — A137a

Queen Elizabeth II — A137b

1p, HMS Amazon. 2p, Fingal. 4p, Sir Winston Churchill. 5p, Dar Mlodziezy. 20p, Tynwald I. 21p, Ben Veg. 22p, Waverley. 23p, HMY Britannia. 24p, Francis Drake. 25p, Royal Viking Sky. 26p, Lord Nelson. 27p, Europa. 30p, Snaefell V. 35p, Sea Cat. 40p, Lady of Mann I. 50p, Mona's Queen II. £1, QE2, Mona's Queen V.

| | | | | |
|---|---|---|---|---|
| **1993-96** | | **Litho.** | **Perf. 13½** | |
| 531 | A137 | 1p multi | .25 | .25 |
| 532 | A137 | 2p multi | .25 | .25 |
| 533 | A137 | 4p multi | .25 | .25 |
| a. | Inscribed "1997" | | 1.25 | 1.25 |
| 534 | A137 | 5p multi | .25 | .25 |
| 543 | A137 | 20p multi | .45 | .45 |
| a. | Inscribed "1995" | | 1.20 | 1.20 |
| 544 | A137 | 21p multi | .55 | .55 |
| a. | Inscribed "1997" | | 1.15 | 1.15 |
| 545 | A137 | 22p multi | .55 | .55 |
| 546 | A137 | 23p multi | .60 | .60 |
| a. | Souv. sheet of 1, Perf. 13 | | 1.00 | 1.00 |
| 547 | A137 | 24p multi | .55 | .55 |
| a. | Bklt. pane, 4 #543, 6 #547 | | 5.50 | |
| | Complete booklet, #547a | | 5.50 | |
| b. | Bklt. pane, 2 #543, 3 #547 | | 2.75 | |
| | Complete booklet, #547b | | 2.75 | |
| c. | Inscribed "1995" | | 1.50 | 1.50 |
| 548 | A137 | 25p multi | .65 | .65 |
| a. | Booklet pane, 2 #533a, 2 #544a, 2 #548b | | 4.25 | |
| | Complete booklet, #548a | | 4.25 | |
| b. | Inscribed "1997" | | 1.40 | 1.40 |
| 549 | A137 | 26p multi | .70 | .70 |
| 550 | A137 | 27p multi | .70 | .70 |
| 551 | A137 | 30p multi | .80 | .80 |
| 551A | A137 | 35p multi | .95 | .95 |
| 552 | A137 | 40p multi | 1.10 | 1.10 |
| 553 | A137 | 50p multi | 1.40 | 1.40 |
| 553A | A137 | £1 multi | 3.50 | 3.50 |
| a. | Inscribed "1997" | | 7.50 | 7.50 |

**Perf. 14½**

| | | | | |
|---|---|---|---|---|
| 553B | A137a | £2 multi | 5.00 | 5.00 |
| 553C | A137b | £5 multi | 15.00 | 15.00 |
| | *Nos. 531-553C (19)* | | 33.50 | 33.50 |

No. 546a, for return of Hong Kong to China, is wmk. 373. Stamp in No. 546a is dated "1997".
No. 553C has a holographic image. Soaking in water may affect the hologram.
Issued: 1p-5p, 20p-27p, 1/4/93; 30p, 40p-£1, 9/15/93; £2, 1/24/94; £5, 7/5/94; 35p, 1/11/96; No. 546a, 7/1/97; No. 548a, 1997.
See Nos. 683-697.

Manx Electric Railway, Cent. A138

20p, #13 trailer, #1 motor car. 24p, #19 trailer, #9 tunnel car. 28p, #59 Royal trailer special saloon car, #19 motor car. 39p, #33 motor car, #45 trailer, #13 small van.

| | | | | |
|---|---|---|---|---|
| **1993, Feb. 3** | | | **Perf. 14** | |
| 554 | A138 | 20p multicolored | .65 | .65 |
| 555 | A138 | 24p multicolored | .75 | .75 |
| 556 | A138 | 28p multicolored | 1.00 | 1.00 |
| 557 | A138 | 39p multicolored | 1.10 | 1.10 |
| a. | Booklet pane of #554-557 | | 3.00 | 3.50 |
| | Complete booklet, 4 #557a | | 12.75 | |
| | *Nos. 554-557 (4)* | | 3.50 | 3.50 |

No. 557a exists with four different marginal inscriptions and in four different arrangements.

Contemporary Art by Bryan Kneale — A139

Europa: No. 558, Statue of Sir Hall Caine. No. 559, Painting, The Brass Bedstead. No. 560, Abstract bronze. No. 561, Drawing of polar bear skeleton.

| | | | | |
|---|---|---|---|---|
| **1993, Apr. 14** | | **Litho.** | **Perf. 14** | |
| 558 | A139 | 20p multicolored | .60 | .60 |
| 559 | A139 | 20p multicolored | .60 | .60 |
| a. | Pair, #558-559 | | 1.20 | 1.20 |
| 560 | A139 | 28p multicolored | .80 | .80 |
| 561 | A139 | 28p multicolored | .80 | .80 |
| a. | Pair, #560-561 | | 1.60 | 1.60 |
| | *Nos. 558-561 (4)* | | 2.80 | 2.80 |

Motorcycling Events A140

Riders and events: 20p, Gold Medalists Graham Oates, Bill Marshall, Intl. Six-Day Trial, 1933, Ariel Square Four. 24p, Geoff Duke, Team Sergeant, Royal Signals Display Team, 1947, Triumph Twin. 28p, Denis Parkinson, winner of Senior Manx Grand Prix, 1953, Manx Norton. 33p, Richard Swallow, winner of Junior Classic Manx Grand Prix, 1991, Aermacchi. 39p, Steve Colley, winner of Scottish Six-Day Trial, 1992, Beta Zero.

| | | | | |
|---|---|---|---|---|
| **1993, June 3** | | **Litho.** | **Perf. 13½x14** | |
| 562 | A140 | 20p multicolored | .60 | .60 |
| 563 | A140 | 24p multicolored | .65 | .65 |
| 564 | A140 | 28p multicolored | .75 | .75 |
| 565 | A140 | 33p multicolored | .90 | .90 |
| 566 | A140 | 39p multicolored | 1.05 | 1.05 |
| a. | Souv. sheet of 5, #562-566 + 4 labels | | 4.50 | 4.50 |
| | *Nos. 562-566 (5)* | | 3.95 | 3.95 |

Butterflies — A141

| | | | | |
|---|---|---|---|---|
| **1993, Sept. 15** | | **Litho.** | **Perf. 14½** | |
| 567 | A141 | 24p Dark green fritillary | .80 | .80 |
| 568 | A141 | 24p Painted lady | .80 | .80 |
| 569 | A141 | 24p Holly blue | .80 | .80 |
| 570 | A141 | 24p Red admiral | .80 | .80 |
| 571 | A141 | 24p Peacock | .80 | .80 |
| a. | Strip of 5, #567-571 | | 4.00 | 4.00 |

Christmas — A142

Designs: 19p, Children decorating Christmas tree. 23p, Snowman, girl. 28p, Boy unwrapping presents. 39p, Girl, teddy bear. 40p, Girl with holly basket, boy on sled.

| | | | | |
|---|---|---|---|---|
| **1993, Oct. 12** | | | **Perf. 14** | |
| 572 | A142 | 19p multicolored | .55 | .55 |
| | Complete booklet, 10 #572 | | 5.25 | |
| 573 | A142 | 23p multicolored | .60 | .60 |
| | Complete booklet, 10 #573 | | 6.00 | |
| 574 | A142 | 28p multicolored | .75 | .75 |
| 575 | A142 | 39p multicolored | 1.05 | 1.05 |
| 576 | A142 | 40p multicolored | 1.05 | 1.05 |
| | *Nos. 572-576 (5)* | | 4.00 | 4.00 |

Tourism — A143

No. 577, Gaiety Theatre, Douglas. No. 578, Field hockey, golf, soccer (#577). No. 579, Yacht racing, artist's hand painting picture of castle (#580). No. 580, TT Motorcycle Races, Red Arrows demonstration squadron. (#581). No. 581, Musical instruments. No. 582, Laxey Wheel, Manx cat. No. 583, Tower of Refuge, beach, sand bucket (#584). No. 584, Cyclist. No. 585, Tynwald Day, classic racing car (#579, 580, 584, 586). No. 586, Santa Claus riding Mince Pie Train, Groudle Glen.

**Booklet Stamps**

| | | | | |
|---|---|---|---|---|
| **1994, Feb. 18** | | **Litho.** | **Perf. 13½** | |
| 577 | A143 | 24p multicolored | .65 | .65 |
| 578 | A143 | 24p multicolored | .65 | .65 |
| 579 | A143 | 24p multicolored | .65 | .65 |

| | | | |
|---|---|---|---|
| 580 | A143 | 24p multicolored | .65 .65 |
| 581 | A143 | 24p multicolored | .65 .65 |
| 582 | A143 | 24p multicolored | .65 .65 |
| 583 | A143 | 24p multicolored | .65 .65 |
| 584 | A143 | 24p multicolored | .65 .65 |
| 585 | A143 | 24p multicolored | .65 .65 |
| 586 | A143 | 24p multicolored | .65 .65 |
| a. | | Booklet pane of 10, #577-586 | 6.75 |
| | | Complete booklet, #586a + pane of 12 labels | 6.75 |

Birds — A144

Magpie, Calf of Man Bird Observatory — A145

No. 587, White-throated robin. No. 588, Black-eared wheatear. No. 589, Goldcrest. No. 590, Northern oriole. No. 591, Kingfisher. No. 592, Hoopoe.

**1994, Feb. 18**       **Perf. 14**

| | | | |
|---|---|---|---|
| 587 | A144 | 20p multicolored | .50 .50 |
| 588 | A144 | 20p multicolored | .50 .50 |
| a. | | Pair, #587-588 | 1.05 1.05 |
| 589 | A144 | 24p multicolored | .80 .80 |
| 590 | A144 | 24p multicolored | .80 .80 |
| a. | | Pair, #589-590 | 1.60 1.60 |
| 591 | A144 | 30p multicolored | 1.10 1.10 |
| 592 | A144 | 30p multicolored | 1.10 1.10 |
| a. | | Pair, #591-592 | 2.20 2.20 |
| | | Nos. 587-592 (6) | 4.80 4.80 |

**Souvenir Sheet**
**Perf. 13½x13**

| | | | |
|---|---|---|---|
| 593 | A145 | £1 shown | 3.50 3.50 |

Hong Kong '94 (No. 593).

Europa — A146

Designs, Forbes and Discoveries: No. 594, Eubranchus tricolor. No. 595, Loligo forbesii. No. 596, Edward Forbes (1815-54), naturalist. No. 597, Solaster moretonis. No. 598, Adamsia carciniopados on hermit crab. No. 599, Solaster endeca.

**1994, May 5**    **Litho.**    **Perf. 13¼x14½**

| | | | |
|---|---|---|---|
| 594 | A146 | 20p multicolored | .50 .50 |
| 595 | A146 | 20p multicolored | .50 .50 |
| 596 | A146 | 20p multicolored | .50 .50 |
| a. | | Strip of 3, #594-596 | 1.60 1.60 |
| 597 | A146 | 30p multicolored | .80 .80 |
| 598 | A146 | 30p multicolored | .80 .80 |
| 599 | A146 | 30p multicolored | .80 .80 |
| a. | | Strip of 3, #597-599 | 2.50 2.50 |

D-Day, 50th Anniv. — A147

Designs: No. 600, Transport Ben-My-Chree IV, landing ships, US Maj. Gen. Walter Bedell Smith. No. 601, Transports Victoria, Lady of Mann I, Adm. Sir Bertram Ramsay, RN, Naval Commander. No. 602, Infantry, tanks on Gold, Juno, Sword Beaches, Gen. Montgomery, Commander, 21st Army Group. No. 603, Tanks, landing craft on Gold, Juno, Sword Beaches, Lt. Gen. Sir Miles C. Dempsey, Commander, British 2nd Army. No. 604, US 8th, 9th Air Forces, Air Chief Marshal Sir Trafford Leigh-Mallory, RAF, Air Force Commander. No. 605, Air Chief Marshal Sir Arthur Tedder, RAF, Deputy Supreme Allied Commander, RAF 2nd Tactical Air Force & Bomber Command. No. 606, Landing craft, Omaha, Utah Beaches, Lt. Gen. Omar N. Bradley, Commander, US 1st Army. No. 607, Infantry, tanks on Omaha, Utah Beaches, Gen. Eisenhower, Supreme Allied Commander.

**1994, June 6**    **Litho.**    **Perf. 14**

| | | | |
|---|---|---|---|
| 600 | A147 | 4p multicolored | .25 .25 |
| 601 | A147 | 4p multicolored | .25 .25 |
| a. | | Pair, #600-601 | .25 .25 |

| | | | |
|---|---|---|---|
| 602 | A147 | 20p multicolored | .50 .50 |
| a. | | Dated "2014" (#1658a) | .55 .55 |
| 603 | A147 | 20p multicolored | .50 .50 |
| a. | | Pair, #602-603 | 1.20 1.20 |
| b. | | Dated "2014" (#1658a) | .55 .55 |
| 604 | A147 | 30p multicolored | .80 .80 |
| 605 | A147 | 30p multicolored | .80 .80 |
| a. | | Pair, #604-605 | 1.90 1.90 |
| 606 | A147 | 41p multicolored | 1.10 1.10 |
| a. | | Dated "2014" (#1658a) | 1.10 1.10 |
| 607 | A147 | 41p multicolored | 1.10 1.10 |
| a. | | Pair, #606-607 | 2.50 2.50 |
| b. | | Dated "2014" (#1658a) | 1.10 1.10 |
| | | Nos. 600-607 (8) | 5.30 5.30 |

Nos. 601a, 603a, 605a, 607a are continuous designs.
Issued: Nos. 602a, 603b, 606a, 607b, 5/8/14.

Postman Pat — A148

Postman Pat at: 1p, Sea Terminal, Douglas. 20p, Laxey Wheel. 24p, Cregneash. 30p, Manx Electric Railway. 36p, Peel Harbor. 41p, Tourist office, Douglas Promenade. £1, Postman Pat.

**1994, Sept. 14**    **Litho.**    **Perf. 14½x14**

| | | | |
|---|---|---|---|
| 608 | A148 | 1p multicolored | .25 .25 |
| a. | | Booklet pane of 2 | .25 |
| 609 | A148 | 20p multicolored | .55 .55 |
| a. | | Booklet pane of 2 | .90 |
| 610 | A148 | 24p multicolored | .65 .65 |
| a. | | Booklet pane of 2 | 1.05 |
| 611 | A148 | 30p multicolored | .85 .85 |
| a. | | Booklet pane of 2 | 1.35 |
| 612 | A148 | 36p multicolored | 1.05 1.05 |
| a. | | Booklet pane of 2 | 1.60 |
| 613 | A148 | 41p multicolored | 1.15 1.15 |
| a. | | Booklet pane of 2 | 1.95 |
| | | Nos. 608-613 (6) | 4.50 4.50 |

**Souvenir Sheet**
**Perf. 13**

| | | | |
|---|---|---|---|
| 614 | A148 | £1 multicolored | 3.00 3.00 |
| a. | | Booklet pane of 1 | 2.00 2.00 |
| | | Complete booklet, #608a-614a | 10.25 |

No. 614a is rouletted 9 at left.

Intl. Olympic Committee, Cent. — A149

**1994, Oct. 11**       **Perf. 14**

| | | | |
|---|---|---|---|
| 615 | A149 | 10p Cycling | .30 .30 |
| 616 | A149 | 20p Alpine skiing | .65 .65 |
| 617 | A149 | 24p Swimming | .75 .75 |
| 618 | A149 | 35p Steeplechase | 1.15 1.15 |
| 619 | A149 | 48p Emblem | 1.30 1.30 |
| | | Nos. 615-619 (5) | 4.15 4.15 |

A150

Christmas: 19p, Santa, Mrs. Claus greeting children on Santa Train to Santon, horiz. 23p, Santa Claus on tractor, Postman Pat. 60p, Santa Claus arriving by boat, Port St. Mary, horiz.

**1994, Oct. 11**

| | | | |
|---|---|---|---|
| 620 | A150 | 19p multicolored | .65 .65 |
| 621 | A150 | 23p multicolored | .85 .85 |
| 622 | A150 | 60p multicolored | 1.75 1.75 |
| | | Nos. 620-622 (3) | 3.25 3.25 |

Snaefell Mountain Electric Railway, Cent. A151

Designs: 20p, Opening day, Car No. 2. 24p, Car 3 ascending Laxey Valley, Car 4 in green livery. 35p, Car 5, Car 6. 42p, Caledonia on construction duty, Goods Car 7. £1, Bungalow Hotel & Station, Snaefell.

**1995, Feb. 8**    **Litho.**    **Perf. 14**

| | | | |
|---|---|---|---|
| 623 | A151 | 20p multicolored | .60 .60 |
| 624 | A151 | 24p multicolored | .75 .75 |
| 625 | A151 | 35p multicolored | 1.10 1.10 |
| 626 | A151 | 42p multicolored | 1.25 1.25 |
| a. | | Bklt. pane of #623-626 | 3.25 |
| | | Nos. 623-626 (4) | 3.70 3.70 |

**Souvenir Sheet**
**Perf. 14x13½**

| | | | |
|---|---|---|---|
| 627 | A151 | £1 multicolored | 3.25 3.25 |
| a. | | Sheet from souvenir booklet | 2.50 2.50 |
| | | #627a | |
| | | Complete booklet, 3 #626a, #627a | 12.00 12.00 |

No. 627 contains one 61x38mm stamp.
No. 626a comes with three different arrangements of the stamps. Value the same for each.
No. 627a is rouletted in margin at left with additional vertical sheet margin inscriptions. At left is a description of the design. At right is "1895-Centenary Snaefell Mountain Railway-1995."

Steam-Powered Vehicles — A152

Designs: 20p, Foden Wagon, 5 ton. 24p, Clayton & Shuttleworth, 7hp, Fowler, 6hp. 30p, Wallis & Steevens, 6hp. 35p, Marshall, 6hp. 41p, Marshall Convertible, 5hp.

**1995, Feb. 8**       **Perf. 13½**

| | | | |
|---|---|---|---|
| 628 | A152 | 20p multicolored | .55 .55 |
| 629 | A152 | 24p multicolored | .70 .70 |
| 630 | A152 | 30p multicolored | .90 .90 |
| 631 | A152 | 35p multicolored | 1.10 1.10 |
| 632 | A152 | 41p multicolored | 1.20 1.20 |
| | | Nos. 628-632 (5) | 4.45 4.45 |

Peace & Freedom — A153

Europa: 20p, Flight of doves forming tidal wave, Tower of Refuge, Douglas Bay. 30p, Dove with olive branch breaking barbed wire.

**1995, Apr. 28**    **Litho.**    **Perf. 13½**

| | | | |
|---|---|---|---|
| 633 | A153 | 20p multicolored | .65 .65 |
| 634 | A153 | 30p multicolored | .85 .85 |

VE Day, 50th Anniv. — A154

Designs: No. 635, Spitfire, tank, 1939-45 Germany Star. No. 636, France and Germany Star, Italy Star, Hawker Typhoon, artillery. No. 637, Lancaster bomber, aircraft carrier, Air Crew Europe Star, Atlantic Star. No. 638, Pacific Star, Burma Star, Avenger torpedo bomber, soldiers. No. 639, Parliament, Manx flag. No. 640, British flag, crowd celebrating. No. 641, Children celebrating at street party, Manx flag. No. 642, British flag, visit of Queen Elizabeth, King George VI, 1945.

**1995, May 8**       **Perf. 14**

| | | | |
|---|---|---|---|
| 635 | A154 | 10p multicolored | .30 .30 |
| 636 | A154 | 10p multicolored | .30 .30 |
| a. | | Pair, #635-636 | .60 .60 |
| 637 | A154 | 20p multicolored | .60 .60 |
| 638 | A154 | 20p multicolored | .60 .60 |
| a. | | Pair, #637-638 | 1.25 1.25 |
| 639 | A154 | 24p multicolored | .65 .65 |
| 640 | A154 | 24p multicolored | .65 .65 |
| a. | | Pair, #639-640 | 1.35 1.35 |
| 641 | A154 | 40p multicolored | 1.10 1.10 |
| 642 | A154 | 40p multicolored | 1.10 1.10 |
| a. | | Pair, #641-642 | 2.25 2.25 |
| | | Nos. 635-642 (8) | 5.30 5.30 |

British Motor Car Racing, 90th Anniv. — A155

Tourist Trophy Race drivers, cars: 20p, R. Parnell, 1951 Maserati 4 CLT. 24p, S. Moss, 1951 Frazer Nash. 30p, R.J.B. Seaman, 1936 Delage. 36p, Prince Bira, 1937 ERA R2B

Romulus. 41p, K. Lee Guinness, 1914 Sunbeam 1. 42p, F. Dixon, 1934 Riley. £1, John S. Napier, 1905 Arrol Johnston.

**1995, May 8**

| | | | |
|---|---|---|---|
| 643 | A155 | 20p multicolored | .60 .60 |
| 644 | A155 | 24p multicolored | .70 .70 |
| 645 | A155 | 30p multicolored | .85 .85 |
| 646 | A155 | 36p multicolored | 1.05 1.05 |
| 647 | A155 | 41p multicolored | 1.15 1.15 |
| 648 | A155 | 42p multicolored | 1.20 1.20 |
| | | Nos. 643-648 (6) | 5.55 5.55 |

**Souvenir Sheet**

| | | | |
|---|---|---|---|
| 649 | A155 | £1 multicolored | 3.50 3.50 |

No. 649 contains one 47x58mm stamp.

Mushrooms — A156

Designs: 20p, Amanita muscaria. 24p, Boletus edulis. 30p, Coprinus disseminatus. 35p, Pleurotus ostreatus. 45p, Geastrum triplex. £1, Shaggy ink cap, bee orchid.

**1995, Sept. 1**    **Litho.**    **Perf. 13½x14**

| | | | |
|---|---|---|---|
| 650 | A156 | 20p multicolored | .60 .60 |
| 651 | A156 | 24p multicolored | .65 .65 |
| 652 | A156 | 30p multicolored | .90 .90 |
| 653 | A156 | 35p multicolored | 1.00 1.00 |
| 654 | A156 | 45p multicolored | 1.25 1.25 |
| | | Nos. 650-654 (5) | 4.40 4.40 |

**Souvenir Sheet**
**Perf. 14x13½**

| | | | |
|---|---|---|---|
| 655 | A156 | £1 multicolored | 3.25 3.25 |

No. 655 contains one 51x60mm stamp. Singapore '95 (No. 655).

Thomas the Tank Engine — A157

Designs: 20p, Bertie arrives on the quayside. 24p, Mail train and Thomas. 30p, Bertie and trains at Ballasalla. 36p, Viking and Thomas at Port Erin. 41p, The mail gets through. 45p, Race at Laxey Wheel.

**1995, Sept. 1**       **Perf. 14**

| | | | |
|---|---|---|---|
| 656 | A157 | 20p multicolored | .60 .60 |
| 657 | A157 | 24p multicolored | .70 .70 |
| a. | | Booklet pane of 2, #656-657 | 1.30 |
| 658 | A157 | 30p multicolored | .90 .90 |
| a. | | Booklet pane of 2, #657-658 | 1.60 |
| 659 | A157 | 36p multicolored | 1.10 1.10 |
| a. | | Booklet pane of 2, #658-659 | 2.00 |
| 660 | A157 | 41p multicolored | 1.30 1.30 |
| a. | | Booklet pane of 2, #659-660 | 2.40 |
| 661 | A157 | 45p multicolored | 1.30 1.30 |
| a. | | Booklet pane of 2, #656, 661 | 1.90 |
| b. | | Booklet pane of 2, #660-661 | 2.75 |
| | | Complete booklet, #657a, 658a, 659a, 660a, 661a-661b | 13.00 |
| | | Nos. 656-661 (6) | 5.90 5.90 |

Christmas — A158

Designs: 19p, Church, holly. 23p, Bird on holly branch. 42p, Snow crocuses, church. 50p, snowdrops, antique farming equipment in snow.

**1995, Oct. 10**    **Litho.**    **Perf. 14x14½**

| | | | |
|---|---|---|---|
| 662 | A158 | 19p multicolored | .60 .60 |
| 663 | A158 | 23p multicolored | .70 .70 |
| 664 | A158 | 42p multicolored | 1.30 1.30 |
| 665 | A158 | 50p multicolored | 1.50 1.50 |
| | | Nos. 662-665 (4) | 4.10 4.10 |

Lighthouses A159

Location, year opened: 20p, Langness, 1880, vert. 24p, Point of Ayre, 1818. 30p, Chicken Rock, 1873, vert. 36p, Calf of Man, 1818. 41p, Douglas Head, 1832, vert. 42p, Maughold Head, 1914.

## 1996, Feb. 27　Litho.　Perf. 14

| | | | | |
|---|---|---|---|---|
| 666 | A159 | 20p multicolored | .60 | .60 |
| a. | | Booklet pane of 4 + 4 labels | 2.60 | |
| 667 | A159 | 24p multicolored | .70 | .70 |
| a. | | Booklet pane of 4 | 3.00 | |
| 668 | A159 | 30p multicolored | .95 | .95 |
| 669 | A159 | 36p multicolored | 1.05 | 1.05 |
| 670 | A159 | 41p multicolored | 1.30 | 1.30 |
| a. | | Booklet pane, 2 each #668, 670 + 4 labels | 4.50 | |
| 671 | A159 | 42p multicolored | 1.30 | 1.30 |
| a. | | Bklt. pane, 2 ea #669, 671 | 4.75 | |
| | | Complete booklet, #666a, 667a, 670a, 671a | 15.00 | |
| | | Nos. 666-671 (6) | 5.90 | 5.90 |

Manx
Cats — A160

Various cats and: 20p, Arms of Man. 24p, British Union Flag as of ball yarn. 36p, Brandenburg Gate. 42p, US flag, Statue of Liberty. 48p, Australian flag, map.
£1.50, Gray adult cat, gray and yellow kittens.

## 1996, Mar. 14

| | | | | |
|---|---|---|---|---|
| 672 | A160 | 20p multicolored | .55 | .55 |
| 673 | A160 | 24p multicolored | .65 | .65 |
| 674 | A160 | 36p multicolored | 1.00 | 1.00 |
| 675 | A160 | 42p multicolored | 1.20 | 1.20 |
| 676 | A160 | 48p multicolored | 1.40 | 1.40 |
| | | Nos. 672-676 (5) | 4.80 | 4.80 |

### Souvenir Sheet

| | | | | |
|---|---|---|---|---|
| 677 | A160 | £1.50 multicolored | 4.25 | 4.25 |
| a. | | With additional inscription | 7.50 | 7.50 |

No. 677 contains one 51x60mm stamp. No. 677a contains CAPEX '96 exhibition emblem in sheet margin. Issued 6/8/96.

Douglas Borough,
Cent. — A161

### Die Cut Perf. 9x9½

## 1996, Mar. 14　　　　Litho.

### Self-Adhesive

| | | | | |
|---|---|---|---|---|
| 678 | A161 | (40p) multicolored | 1.20 | 1.20 |

The backing of No. 678 is rouletted 13.

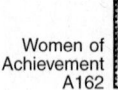

Women of
Achievement
A162

Europa: 24p, Princess Anne, children of different nations. 30p, Queen Elizabeth II, people of different nations.

## 1996　　　　　　　Perf. 14

| | | | | |
|---|---|---|---|---|
| 679 | A162 | 24p multicolored | .60 | .60 |
| 680 | A162 | 30p multicolored | .85 | .85 |

Queen Elizabeth II, 70th birthday (No. 680). See Guernsey Nos. 564-565.

### Ship Type of 1993

## 1996　　　　Litho.　Perf. 14

### Size: 21x19mm

| | | | | |
|---|---|---|---|---|
| 683 | A137 | 4p like #533 | .65 | .65 |
| 693 | A137 | 20p like #543 | .70 | .70 |
| 697 | A137 | 24p like #547 | .90 | .90 |
| | | Nos. 683-697 (3) | 2.25 | 2.25 |
| a. | | Bklt. pane, 2 ea 4p, 20p, 24p | 7.00 | |
| | | Complete booklet, No. 697a | 7.00 | |

Irish Winners of
Tourist Trophy
Motorcycle
Races — A163

20p, Alec Bennett. 24p, Stanley Woods. 45p, Artie Bell. 60p, Robert & Joey Dunlop.
£1, Demonstration squadron Hawks flying over motorcycles, vert.

## 1996, May 30　Litho.　Perf. 14

| | | | | |
|---|---|---|---|---|
| 701 | A163 | 20p multicolored | .65 | .65 |
| 702 | A163 | 24p multicolored | .70 | .70 |
| 703 | A163 | 45p multicolored | 1.35 | 1.35 |
| 704 | A163 | 60p multicolored | 1.75 | 1.75 |
| | | Nos. 701-704 (4) | 4.45 | 4.45 |

### Souvenir Sheet

| | | | | |
|---|---|---|---|---|
| 705 | A163 | £1 multicolored | 3.25 | 3.25 |

See Ireland Nos. 1010-1014.

Royal British Legion,
75th Anniv. — A164

Poppies and: 20p, National poppy appeal trophy. 24p, Manx war memorial. 42p, Poppy appeal. 75p, Crest.

## 1996, June 8

| | | | | |
|---|---|---|---|---|
| 706 | A164 | 20p multicolored | .55 | .55 |
| 707 | A164 | 24p multicolored | .65 | .65 |
| 708 | A164 | 42p multicolored | 1.20 | 1.20 |
| 709 | A164 | 75p multicolored | 2.10 | 2.10 |
| | | Nos. 706-709 (4) | 4.50 | 4.50 |

UNICEF, 50th
Anniv. — A165

Children receiving aid, map of country: No. 710, Mexico. No. 711, Sri Lanka. No. 712, Colombia. No. 713, Zambia. No. 714, Afghanistan. No. 715, Viet Nam.

## 1996, Sept. 18　Litho.　Perf. 13½x14

| | | | | |
|---|---|---|---|---|
| 710 | A165 | 24p multicolored | .65 | .65 |
| 711 | A165 | 24p multicolored | .65 | .65 |
| a. | | Pair, #710-711 | 1.30 | 1.30 |
| 712 | A165 | 30p multicolored | .85 | .85 |
| 713 | A165 | 30p multicolored | .85 | .85 |
| a. | | Pair, #712-713 | 1.75 | 1.75 |
| 714 | A165 | 42p multicolored | 1.25 | 1.25 |
| 715 | A165 | 42p multicolored | 1.25 | 1.25 |
| a. | | Pair, #714-715 | 2.50 | 2.50 |
| | | Nos. 710-715 (6) | 5.50 | 5.50 |

Dogs — A166

20p, Labrador. 24p, Border collie. 31p, Dalmatian. 38p, Mongrel. 43p, English setter. 63p, Alsatian.
£1.20, Border collie, labrador.

## 1996, Sept. 18　　　　Perf. 14½

| | | | | |
|---|---|---|---|---|
| 716 | A166 | 20p multi | .60 | .60 |
| a. | | Booklet pane of 4 | 2.05 | |
| 717 | A166 | 24p multi | .65 | .65 |
| a. | | Booklet pane of 4 | 2.20 | |
| 718 | A166 | 31p multi | .90 | .90 |
| 719 | A166 | 38p multi | 1.15 | 1.15 |
| 720 | A166 | 43p multi | 1.30 | 1.30 |
| 721 | A166 | 63p multi | 1.90 | 1.90 |
| a. | | Booklet pane, 1 each #718-721 | 4.50 | |
| | | Nos. 716-721 (6) | 6.50 | 6.50 |

### Souvenir Sheet
### Perf. 13½x14

| | | | | |
|---|---|---|---|---|
| 722 | A166 | £1.20 multi | 3.50 | 3.50 |
| a. | | Booklet pane of 1 | 3.50 | |
| | | Complete booklet, #716a, 717a, 721a, 722a | 12.75 | |

Nos. 716-721 are each printed with se-tenant label. No. 722 contains one 38x50mm stamp. No. 722a is rouletted around margin of sheet.

Christmas — A167

Children's drawings: 19p, Snowman. 23p, Santa, "Happy Christmas" in Manx. 50p, Family, Christmas tree, presents. 75p, Santa in sleigh flying over rooftops.

## 1996, Nov. 2　Litho.　Perf. 14x14½

| | | | | |
|---|---|---|---|---|
| 723 | A167 | 19p multicolored | .55 | .55 |
| 724 | A167 | 23p multicolored | .65 | .65 |
| 725 | A167 | 50p multicolored | 1.30 | 1.30 |
| 726 | A167 | 75p multicolored | 2.25 | 2.25 |
| | | Nos. 723-726 (4) | 4.75 | 4.75 |

Owls — A168

20p, Barn owl. 24p, Short-eared owl. 31p, Long-eared owl. 36p, Little owl. 43p, Snowy owl. 56p, Tawny owl.
£1.20, Long-eared owl.

## 1997, Feb. 12　Litho.　Perf. 14

| | | | | |
|---|---|---|---|---|
| 727 | A168 | 20p multicolored | .60 | .60 |
| a. | | Booklet pane of 4 | 2.00 | |
| 728 | A168 | 24p multicolored | .75 | .75 |
| a. | | Booklet pane of 4 | 2.50 | |
| 729 | A168 | 31p multicolored | 1.00 | 1.00 |
| 730 | A168 | 36p multicolored | 1.15 | 1.15 |
| 731 | A168 | 43p multicolored | 1.45 | 1.45 |
| 732 | A168 | 56p multicolored | 1.75 | 1.75 |
| a. | | Booklet pane of 4, #729-732 | 4.50 | |
| | | Nos. 727-732 (6) | 6.70 | 6.70 |

### Souvenir Sheet
### Perf. 13

| | | | | |
|---|---|---|---|---|
| 733 | A168 | £1.20 multi | 4.00 | 4.00 |
| a. | | Booklet pane of 1 | 3.50 | |
| | | Complete booklet, #727a, 728a, 732a, 733a | 12.50 | |

No. 733, 733a each contain one 56x60mm stamp. No. 733a is rouletted at left. Hong Kong '97 (Nos. 733, 733a).

Springtime — A169

## 1997, Feb. 12　　　　Perf. 14

| | | | | |
|---|---|---|---|---|
| 734 | A169 | 20p Spring flowers | .55 | .55 |
| 735 | A169 | 24p Sheep | .65 | .65 |
| 736 | A169 | 43p Waterfowl | 1.30 | 1.30 |
| 737 | A169 | 63p Frog, ducks | 1.90 | 1.90 |
| | | Nos. 734-737 (4) | 4.40 | 4.40 |

Stories and
Legends — A170

21p, Moddey Dhoo. 25p, The Trammen Tree. 31p, Fairy Bridge. 36p, Fin Macooil. 37p, The Buggane of St. Trinian's. 43p, Fynoderee.

## 1997, Apr. 24　Litho.　Perf. 13½x14

| | | | | |
|---|---|---|---|---|
| 738 | A170 | 21p multicolored | .60 | .60 |
| 739 | A170 | 25p multicolored | .75 | .75 |
| 740 | A170 | 31p multicolored | 1.00 | 1.00 |
| 741 | A170 | 36p multicolored | 1.10 | 1.10 |
| 742 | A170 | 37p multicolored | 1.10 | 1.10 |
| 743 | A170 | 43p multicolored | 1.45 | 1.45 |
| | | Nos. 738-743 (6) | 6.00 | 6.00 |

Europa (Nos. 739-740).

Aircraft — A171

Designs: No. 744, Sopwith Tabloid. No. 745, Grumman Tiger. No. 746, Manx Airlines BAe ATP. No. 747, Manx Airlines BAe 146-200. No. 748, Boeing 757-200. No. 749, Farman biplane. No. 750, Spitfire. No. 751, Hurricane.

## 1997, Apr. 24　　　　Perf. 14

| | | | | |
|---|---|---|---|---|
| 744 | A171 | 21p multicolored | .55 | .55 |
| 745 | A171 | 21p multicolored | .55 | .55 |
| a. | | Pair, #744-745 | 1.10 | 1.10 |
| 746 | A171 | 25p multicolored | .70 | .70 |
| 747 | A171 | 25p multicolored | .70 | .70 |
| a. | | Pair, #746-747 | 1.40 | 1.40 |
| 748 | A171 | 31p multicolored | .95 | .95 |
| 749 | A171 | 31p multicolored | .95 | .95 |
| a. | | Pair, #748-749 | 1.90 | 1.90 |
| 750 | A171 | 36p multicolored | 1.00 | 1.00 |
| 751 | A171 | 36p multicolored | 1.00 | 1.00 |
| a. | | Pair, #750-751 | 2.00 | 2.00 |
| | | Nos. 744-751 (8) | 6.40 | 6.40 |

See No. 1671.

Golf
Courses — A172

1997 Ryder Cup, Valderrama,
Spain — A173

21p, 14th Hole, Ramsey Golf Club. 25p, 15th Hole, King Edward Bay Golf and Country Club. 43p, 17th Hole, Rowany Golf Club. 50p, 8th Hole, Castletown Golf Links.

## 1997, May 29　Litho.　Perf. 14

| | | | | |
|---|---|---|---|---|
| 752 | A172 | 21p multicolored | .60 | .60 |
| a. | | Booklet pane of 3 | 1.80 | |
| 753 | A172 | 25p multicolored | .80 | .80 |
| a. | | Booklet pane of 3 | 2.40 | |
| 754 | A172 | 43p multicolored | 1.25 | 1.25 |
| 755 | A172 | 50p multicolored | 1.30 | 1.30 |
| a. | | Bklt. pane, 2 ea #754-755 | 5.00 | |
| | | Nos. 752-755 (4) | 3.95 | 3.95 |

### Souvenir Sheet

| | | | | |
|---|---|---|---|---|
| 756 | A173 | £1.30 multicolored | 4.00 | 4.00 |
| a. | | Booklet pane of 1 | 4.00 | |
| | | Complete booklet, #752a, 753a, 755a, 756a | 13.50 | |

PACIFIC 97 (No. 756). No. 756 contains one 40mm diameter stamp.
No. 756a has a large white border, is 155x96mm and is sewn into booklet.

Trial of Nations
Motorcycle
Competition
A174

Various motorcyclists: 21p, Steve Colley. 25p, Steve Saunders. 37p, Sammy Miller. 44p, Don Smith.

## 1997, Sept. 29　Litho.　Perf. 13½

| | | | | |
|---|---|---|---|---|
| 757 | A174 | 21p multicolored | .55 | .55 |
| 758 | A174 | 25p multi, vert. | .70 | .70 |
| 759 | A174 | 37p multi, vert. | 1.15 | 1.15 |
| 760 | A174 | 44p multicolored | 1.30 | 1.30 |
| | | Nos. 757-760 (4) | 3.70 | 3.70 |

Queen Elizabeth II and Prince Philip,
50th Wedding Anniv. — A175

Designs: a, Early drawing of couple. b, Wedding portrait. c, Drawing of Queen waving, Prince in top hat. d, Portrait, 1997.
£1, Queen, Prince touring Isle of Man, 1989.

## 1997, Nov. 3　Litho.　Perf. 14x14½

| | | | | |
|---|---|---|---|---|
| 761 | A175 | 50p Strip of 4, #a.-d. | 6.25 | 6.25 |

### Souvenir Sheet
### Perf. 14

| | | | | |
|---|---|---|---|---|
| 762 | A175 | £1 multicolored | 3.50 | 3.50 |

No. 761 was issued in sheets of 16 stamps. No. 762 contains one 48x58mm stamp.

Christmas — A176

20p, Angel, shepherd. 24p, Wise man, angel. 63p, Shepherd, Holy Family, two kings.

**1997, Nov. 3**     **Perf. 14**
763 A176 20p multicolored   .70   .70
764 A176 24p multicolored   .75   .75

**Size: 54x39mm**
765 A176 63p multicolored   2.10   2.10
    *Nos. 763-765 (3)*   3.55   3.55

Flowers — A177

4p, Shamrocks. 21p, Cushag. 25p, Princess of Wales Rose. 50p, Daffodil. £1, Spear thistle.

**1998, Feb. 12**   **Litho.**   **Perf. 13x13½**
766 A177 4p multi   .25   .25
   a.   Inscribed "1999"   2.00   2.00
767 A177 21p multi   .65   .65
768 A177 25p multi   .80   .80
   a.   Booklet pane, 2 ea #766-768   3.75
    Complete booklet, #768a   3.75
769 A177 50p multi   1.55   1.55
770 A177 £1 multi   3.15   3.15
    *Nos. 766-770 (5)*   6.40   6.40

Nos. 766-768 also exist in special booklet sheets containing 10 of each denomination. Booklet panes made from these sheets contain 2 each Nos. 766-768.
See Nos. 794-801.

A178

Viking Longships: 21p, Dragon's head figurehead. 25p, Ship under full sail. 31p, Ship with sail furled. 75p Ship's stern.
£1, Man on ship pointing, Peel Castle.

**1998, Feb. 14**     **Perf. 14**
771 A178 21p multicolored   .60   .60
772 A178 25p multicolored   .75   .75
773 A178 31p multicolored   .95   .95
774 A178 75p multicolored   2.20   2.20
    *Nos. 771-774 (4)*   4.50   4.50

**Souvenir Sheet**
775 A178 £1 multicolored   3.25   3.25

Marine Life — A179

Designs: 10p, Bottle-nosed dolphin. 21p, Basking shark swimming right. 25p, Basking shark swimming forward. 31p, Minke whale. 63p, Killer whale.

**1998, Mar. 14**   **Litho.**   **Perf. 14**
776 A179 10p multicolored   .30   .30
777 A179 21p multicolored   .60   .60
   a.   Booklet pane of 6, 3 each
    #776-777 + 3 labels   2.50
778 A179 25p multicolored   .80   .80
779 A179 31p multicolored   1.00   1.00
780 A179 63p multicolored   1.80   1.80
   a.   Bklt. pane of 8, #776-777, 2 ea
    #778-780 + label   7.00
    Souvenir booklet, #777a, 780a   9.50
    *Nos. 776-780 (5)*   4.50   4.50

Trains — A180

Designs: 21p, Hutchinson 2-4-0. 25p, G.H. Wood 2-4-0. 31p, Maitland 2-4-0. 63p, Loch 2-4-0.

**1998, May 2**   **Litho.**   **Perf. 14½x14**
781 A180 21p multicolored   .65   .65
782 A180 25p multicolored   .80   .80
783 A180 31p multicolored   1.00   1.00

---

784 A180 63p multicolored   2.00   2.00
   a.   Bklt. pane of 4, #781-784   3.80   3.80
    *Nos. 781-784 (4)*   4.45   4.45

**Souvenir Sheet**
785 A180   Sheet of 2   4.00   4.00
   a.   £1 Engine   3.25   3.25
   b.   25p Passenger cars   .50   .50
   c.   Booklet pane of 1   3.50   3.50
    Complete bklt., #785c, 2
    #784a   11.25
   d.   As #785, inscribed in sheet
    margin   8.00   8.00

No. 784a exists with two different backgrounds and stamps in different order. Complete booklets contain one of each pane.
No. 785d is inscribed in sheet margin with PhilexFrance '99, World Philatelic Exhibition emblem and was issued 7/2/99.

Europa — A181

National Days celebration: 25p, People under tent, seated in stand, watching ceremony. 30p, Women dancing in traditional costumes.

**1998, July 2**     **Perf. 13x13½**
786 A181 25p multicolored   .75   .75
787 A181 30p multicolored   .95   .95

1998 Tourist Trophy Motorcycle Races — A182

Designs: 21p, Eight-man pyramid. 25p, Joey Dunlop rounding curve. 31p, Dave Molyneux with side car. 43p, Naomi Taniguchi racing. 63p, Mike Hailwood racing.

**1998, June 1**   **Litho.**   **Perf. 14**
788 A182 21p multicolored   .60   .60
789 A182 25p multicolored   .75   .75
790 A182 31p multicolored   .95   .95
791 A182 43p multicolored   1.20   1.20
792 A182 63p multicolored   1.85   1.85
    *Nos. 788-792 (5)*   5.35   5.35

A183

Diana, Princess of Wales (1961-97): a, In black evening dress. b, Accepting flowers. c, Holding hand to face. d, In protective clothing.

**1998, June 19**     **Perf. 13**
793 A183 25p Strip of 4, #a.-d.   2.95   2.95
   e.   As "a," dated "2017," perf.
    13½x13   .65   .65
   f.   As "b," dated "2017," perf.
    13½x13   .65   .65
   g.   As "c," dated "2017," perf.
    13½x13   .65   .65
   h.   As "d," dated "2017," perf.
    13½x13   .65   .65
   i.   Horiz. strip of 4, #793e-793h   2.60   2.60
    Issued: Nos. 793e-793i, 9/6/17.

**Flower Type**
**Perf. 13, 13x13½ (5p, 22p, 26p)**
**1998-99**     **Litho.**

Flowers: 1p, Bearded iris. 2p, Daisy. 5p, Silver jubilee rose. 10p, Oriental poppy. 20p, Heath spotted orchid. 22p, Gorse. 26p, Dog rose. 30p, Fuchsia - lady thumb.

794 A177 1p multicolored   .25   .25
795 A177 2p multicolored   .25   .25
796 A177 5p multicolored   .25   .25
797 A177 10p multicolored   .35   .35
798 A177 20p multicolored   .70   .70
799 A177 22p multicolored   .70   .70
800 A177 26p multicolored   .85   .85
   a.   Bklt. pane, #800, 2 #766, 3 #799   4.00
    Complete booklet, #800a   4.00
801 A177 30p multicolored   1.05   1.05
    *Nos. 794-801 (8)*   4.40   4.40

Issued: 5p, 22p, 26p, 4/26/99; others, 7/2/98.

---

Queen Mother and Queen Elizabeth II
A185

**1998, July 2**   **Litho.**   **Perf. 13**
802 A185 £2.50 multicolored   7.25   7.25

Christmas A186

Santa Claus: 20p, Loading sleigh at North Pole. 24p, With list, reindeer standing in clouds, Isle of Man below. 30p, Going over Spring Valley Sorting Office. 43p, Passing through Baldrine. 63p, Leaving presents, children inside house.

**1998, Sept. 25**   **Litho.**   **Perf. 14½x14**
803 A186 20p multicolored   .55   .55
804 A186 24p multicolored   .65   .65
805 A186 30p multicolored   .95   .95
806 A186 43p multicolored   1.20   1.20
807 A186 63p multicolored   1.90   1.90
    *Nos. 803-807 (5)*   5.25   5.25

Manx Nature Reserve and Parks (Europa) — A187

Designs: 25p, Cottage, Ballaglass Glen. 30p, Glen Maye Waterfall.

**1999, Mar. 4**   **Litho.**   **Perf. 14**
808 A187 25p multicolored   1.00   1.00
809 A187 30p multicolored   1.25   1.25

Post Boxes — A188

10p, Oval box, Kirk Onchan Post Office. 20p, Wall box, Ballaterson, Ballaugh. 21p, Cylindrical box, Laxey Station. 25p, Wall box, Spaldrick, Port Erin. 44p, Oval box, Derby Road, Douglas. 63p, Wall box, Baldrine Station.

**1999, Mar. 4**
810 A188 10p multicolored   .30   .30
811 A188 20p multicolored   .65   .65
812 A188 21p multicolored   .65   .65
813 A188 25p multicolored   .70   .70
814 A188 44p multicolored   1.20   1.20
815 A188 63p multicolored   1.80   1.80
    *Nos. 810-815 (6)*   5.30   5.30

Royal Natl. Lifeboat Institution, 175th Anniv. — A189

21p, Ramsey lifeboat. 25p, Douglas lifeboat. 37p, Peel lifeboat. 43p, Port Erin lifeboat. 56p, Port St. Mary lifeboat. £1, William Hillary (1771-1847).

**1999, Mar. 4**
816 A189 21p multicolored   .55   .55
817 A189 25p multicolored   .70   .70
818 A189 37p multicolored   1.05   1.05
819 A189 43p multicolored   1.10   1.10

---

820 A189 56p multicolored   2.05   2.05
   a.   Bklt. pane, #816-820 + 4 labels   5.00
    *Nos. 816-820 (5)*   5.45   5.45

**Booklet Stamps**
821 A189 43p #38   5.00   5.00
822 A189 56p #464   5.00   5.00
   a.   Booklet pane, #816-818, #821-
    822 + 4 labels   11.00

**Souvenir Sheet**
823 A189 £1 multicolored   3.50   3.50
   a.   Booklet pane of 1   2.75
    Complete booklet, #820a,
    #822a, #823a   18.50

IBRA '99 (No. 822a), Australia '99, World Stamp Expo. (No. 823). No. 823 contains one 38x50mm stamp.
An unstitched booklet pane containing 1 each of Nos. 816-818, 821-822 exists, just as No. 822a, but without the stitching.

Celtic Jewelry Depicting Seasons — A190

**1999, May 11**     **Perf. 14½x14**
824 A190 22p Winter   .70   .70
825 A190 26p Spring   .80   .80
826 A190 50p Summer   1.50   1.50
827 A190 63p Autumn   2.00   2.00
    *Nos. 824-827 (4)*   5.00   5.00

Manx Gaelic Society, Centennial.

20th Century British Monarchs A191

Monarch and Lord of Man: a, Victoria. b, Edward VII. c, George V. d, Edward VIII. e, George VI. f, Elizabeth II.

**1999, June 2**   **Litho.**   **Perf. 14**
828 A191 26p Sheet of 6, #a.-f.   5.00   5.00

Manx Buses — A192

22p, 1922 Tilling Stevens 46 double-decker. 26p, 1928 Thornycroft BC 28-seat. 28p, 1927 ADC 416 28-seat. 37p, 1914 Staker Squire 25-seat. 38p, 1927 Thornycroft A2 20-seat. 40p, 1938 Leyland Lion LT9 34-seat.

**1999, June 18**
829 A192 22p multicolored   .65   .65
830 A192 26p multicolored   .75   .75
831 A192 28p multicolored   .85   .85
832 A192 37p multicolored   1.10   1.10
833 A192 38p multicolored   1.10   1.10
834 A192 40p multicolored   1.20   1.20
    *Nos. 829-834 (6)*   5.65   5.65

831a   Bklt. pane, #829-830, 2 #831   2.75
832a   Bklt. pane, #829-830, 2 #832   3.15
833a   Bklt. pane, #829-830, 2 #833   3.15
834a   Bklt. pane, #829-830, 2 #834   3.35
    Complete booklet, #831a-834a   12.50

Wedding of Prince Edward and Sophie Rhys-Jones A193

22p, Sophie, vert. 39p, Prince Edward, vert. 44p, Couple.

**1999, June 19**
835 A193 22p multicolored   .70   .70
836 A193 39p multicolored   1.20   1.20
837 A193 44p multicolored   1.35   1.35
    *Nos. 835-837 (3)*   3.25   3.25

**Royal Wedding Photos — A193a**

Designs: 26p, Couple standing. 53p, Couple seated in carriage, horiz.

**1999, Sept. 1　Litho.　Perf. 14¼**
| | | | |
|---|---|---|---|
| 837A | A193a | 26p multi | .85 | .85 |
| 837B | A193a | 53p multi | 1.75 | 1.75 |

**Churches — A194**

21p, St. Luke, Baldwin. 25p, St. Mark's, Malew. 30p, St. Germain Parish Church and Cathedral, Peel. 64p, Kirk Christ Church, Rushan.

**Perf. 13¼x13½**
**1999, Sept. 22　　　　Litho.**
| | | | | |
|---|---|---|---|---|
| 838 | A194 | 21p multicolored | .65 | .65 |
| 839 | A194 | 25p multicolored | .75 | .75 |
| 840 | A194 | 30p multicolored | .90 | .90 |
| 841 | A194 | 64p multicolored | 2.00 | 2.00 |
| | | Nos. 838-841 (4) | 4.30 | 4.30 |

**Bee Gees Songs — A195**

Designs: 22p, "Massachusetts." 26p, "Words." 29p, "I've Gotta Get a Message to You." 37p, "Ellan Vannin." 38p, "You Win Again." 66p, "Night Fever." 60p, "Immortality." 90p, "Stayin' Alive."

**1999, Oct. 12　Litho.　Perf. 13¼x13½**
| | | | | |
|---|---|---|---|---|
| 842 | A195 | 22p multicolored | .70 | .70 |
| 843 | A195 | 26p multicolored | .80 | .80 |
| 844 | A195 | 29p multicolored | .90 | .90 |
| 845 | A195 | 37p multicolored | 1.10 | 1.10 |
| 846 | A195 | 38p multicolored | 1.10 | 1.10 |
| 847 | A195 | 66p multicolored | 2.00 | 2.00 |
| | | Nos. 842-847 (6) | 6.60 | 6.60 |

**Souvenir Sheets**
| | | | | |
|---|---|---|---|---|
| 848 | A195 | 60p multicolored | 2.50 | 2.50 |
| 849 | A195 | 90p multicolored | 3.50 | 3.50 |

Nos. 848-849 each contain one 40mm diameter stamp. Nos. 842-847 each issued in sheets of 9 stamps and 3 labels.

**Souvenir Sheet**

**Millennium — A196**

Objects in the night sky: a, 50p, Mars, stars Deneb, Altair, Vega. b, £2, Constellations Lynx, Draco, Ursa Minor, Ursa Major. c, 50p, Mercury, Venus, Deneb, Vega, Altair, orbit of International Space Station (ISS).

**Perf. 14¼x14½**
**1999, Dec. 31　　　　　　Litho.**
| | | | | |
|---|---|---|---|---|
| 850 | A196 | Sheet of 3, #a.-c. | 9.50 | 9.50 |

**History of Time — A197**

Clock escapements of: 22p, 1735 by John Harrison. 26p, 2000 by George Daniels. 29p, 1767 by Harrison. 34p, 1769 by Thomas Mudge. 38p, 1779 by John Arnold. 44p, 1780 by Thomas Earnshaw.

---

**2000, Jan. 24　Litho.　Perf. 13x13½**
| | | | | |
|---|---|---|---|---|
| 851 | A197 | 22p multi | .65 | .65 |
| 852 | A197 | 26p multi | .75 | .75 |
| 853 | A197 | 29p multi | .80 | .80 |
| 854 | A197 | 34p multi | 1.00 | 1.00 |
| 855 | A197 | 38p multi | 1.15 | 1.15 |
| 856 | A197 | 44p multi | 1.30 | 1.30 |
| | | Nos. 851-856 (6) | 5.65 | 5.65 |

**Queen Mother (b. 1900) A198**

Pictures of Queen Mother from — No. 857: a, 1923. b, 1940. c, 1944.
No. 858: a, 1954. b, 1985. c, 1988.
No. 859, 1984.
£1, Queen Mother on Isle of Man.

**2000, Feb. 29　Litho.　Perf. 14**
| | | | | |
|---|---|---|---|---|
| 857 | | Strip of 3 | 2.50 | 2.50 |
| a. | A198 | 22p multi | .65 | .65 |
| b. | A198 | 26p multi | .85 | .85 |
| c. | A198 | 30p multi | .90 | .90 |
| 858 | | Strip of 3 | 5.00 | 5.00 |
| a. | A198 | 44p multi | 1.35 | 1.35 |
| b. | A198 | 52p multi | 1.60 | 1.60 |
| c. | A198 | 64p multi | 2.00 | 2.00 |

**Souvenir Sheet**
**Perf. 14¼**
| | | | | |
|---|---|---|---|---|
| 859 | A198 | £1 multi | 3.00 | 3.00 |
| a. | | With emblem of The Stamp Show 2000 in margin | 6.00 | 6.00 |

Size of Nos. 857a-857c, 858a-858c, 42x28mm.
Issued: No. 859a, 5/22/00.

**Song Birds — A199**

**2000, May 5　　　　Perf. 14½x14¼**
| | | | | |
|---|---|---|---|---|
| 860 | | Strip of 4 | 5.75 | 5.75 |
| a. | A199 | 22p Swallow | .70 | .70 |
| b. | A199 | 26p Spotted flycatcher | .75 | .75 |
| c. | A199 | 64p Skylark | 1.90 | 1.90 |
| d. | A199 | 77p Yellowhammer | 2.20 | 2.20 |

World Wildlife Fund.

**Military Leaders and Isle of Man Military Personnel A200**

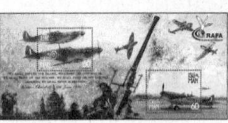

**Battle of Britain, 60th Anniv. A201**

No. 861: a, John Quilliam (1771-1829), Admiral Lord Nelson (1758-1805). b, Caesar Bacon (1791-1876), Duke of Wellington (1769-1852).
No. 862: a, Thomas Leigh Goldie (1807-54), Earl of Cardigan (1797-1868). b, John Dunne (1884-1950), Sir Robert Baden-Powell (1857-1941).
No. 863: a, George Kneale (1896-1917), Viscount Kitchener (1850-1916). b, Alan Watterson (1910-42), Sir Winston Churchill (1874-1965).
No. 864: a, 60p, Planes in air. b, 60p, Plane on ground.

**2000, May 22　Litho.　Perf. 13¼**
| | | | | |
|---|---|---|---|---|
| 861 | | Pair, #a-b, + central label | 1.60 | 1.60 |
| a. | A200 | 22p multi | .70 | .70 |
| b. | A200 | 26p multi | .85 | .85 |
| 862 | | Pair, #a-b, + central label | 2.75 | 2.75 |
| a. | A200 | 36p multi | 1.20 | 1.20 |
| b. | A200 | 48p multi | 1.50 | 1.50 |
| 863 | | Pair, #a-b, + central label | 4.00 | 4.00 |
| a. | A200 | 50p multi | 1.60 | 1.60 |
| b. | A200 | 77p multi | 2.40 | 2.40 |
| c. | | Booklet pane, #861a, 861b, 862a, 862b, 863a | 5.00 | |
| d. | | Booklet pane, #861a, 862b, 863a, 863b | 4.75 | |
| | | Nos. 861-863 (3) | 8.35 | 8.35 |

**Souvenir Sheet**
**Perf. 14¾x14¼**
| | | | | |
|---|---|---|---|---|
| 864 | A201 | Sheet of 2, #a-b | 4.00 | 4.00 |
| c. | | Booklet pane, #864 | 4.50 | |
| | | Booklet, #863c, 863d, 864c | 14.00 | |

No. 864c has stitched margin at left.

---

Souvenir Sheet

**Prince William, 18th Birthday — A202**

**2000, June 21　Litho.　Perf. 14**
| | | | | |
|---|---|---|---|---|
| 865 | A202 | Sheet of 5 | 5.75 | 5.75 |
| a. | | 22p As toddler | .70 | .70 |
| b. | | 26p With Queen Mother | .90 | .90 |
| c. | | 45p In checked shirt | 1.55 | 1.55 |
| d. | | 52p With Princes Charles, Harry | 1.70 | 1.70 |
| e. | | 56p In ski gear | 1.75 | 1.75 |

**Gaiety Theater, Cent. — A203**

**2000, July 16**
| | | | | |
|---|---|---|---|---|
| 866 | A203 | 22p Ballet | .65 | .65 |
| 867 | A203 | 26p Comedy | .75 | .75 |
| 868 | A203 | 36p Drama | 1.10 | 1.10 |
| 869 | A203 | 45p Pantomime | 1.35 | 1.35 |
| 870 | A203 | 52p Opera | 1.45 | 1.45 |
| 871 | A203 | 65p Musicals | 1.80 | 1.80 |
| | | Nos. 866-871 (6) | 7.10 | 7.10 |

**Global Challenge Yacht Race — A204**

Sail from yacht "Isle of Man," and ports of call: 22p, Southampton. 26p, Sydney. 36p, Wellington. 40p, Buenos Aires. 44p, Boston. 65p, Cape Town.

**Perf. 13¼x13¾**
**2000, Sept. 10　　　　　Litho.**
| | | | | |
|---|---|---|---|---|
| 872 | A204 | 22p multi | .60 | .60 |
| 873 | A204 | 26p multi | .80 | .80 |
| 874 | A204 | 36p multi | 1.15 | 1.15 |
| 875 | A204 | 40p multi | 1.15 | 1.15 |
| 876 | A204 | 44p multi | 1.25 | 1.25 |
| 877 | A204 | 65p multi | 1.90 | 1.90 |
| | | Nos. 872-877 (6) | 6.85 | 6.85 |

**Travel Poster Art of Isle of Man Steam Packet Co. — A205**

Designs: 22p, Three legs of Man, ship. 26p, Cliffs and sailboats. 36p, Woman and Isle of Man. 45p, Woman, ship, flag. 65p, Ship.

**2000, Oct. 6　　　　Perf. 13½x13¼**
| | | | | |
|---|---|---|---|---|
| 878 | A205 | 22p multi | .65 | .65 |
| 879 | A205 | 26p multi | .80 | .80 |
| 880 | A205 | 36p multi | 1.10 | 1.10 |
| 881 | A205 | 45p multi | 1.40 | 1.40 |
| 882 | A205 | 65p multi | 1.90 | 1.90 |
| | | Nos. 878-882 (5) | 5.85 | 5.85 |

**Europa, 2000**
**Common Design Type**

**2000, Nov. 7　　　　　　　Perf. 14**
| | | | | |
|---|---|---|---|---|
| 883 | CD17 | 36p multi | 1.75 | 1.75 |

**Christmas — A206**

**2000, Nov. 7**
| | | | | |
|---|---|---|---|---|
| 884 | A206 | 21p Peace | .75 | .75 |
| 885 | A206 | 25p Hope | .85 | .85 |
| 886 | A206 | 45p Love | 1.60 | 1.60 |
| 887 | A206 | 65p Faith | 2.25 | 2.25 |
| | | Nos. 884-887 (4) | 5.45 | 5.45 |

---

**Souvenir Sheet**

**New Year 2001 (Year of the Snake) A207**

**Litho. with Foil Application**
**2001, Jan. 2　　　　　Perf. 13¾**
| | | | | |
|---|---|---|---|---|
| 888 | A207 | £1 St. Patrick | 3.25 | 3.25 |

Hong Kong 2001 Stamp Exhibition.

**Queen Victoria (1819-1901) A208**

Designs: 22p, Wyon medal, Queen Victoria, Great Britain Type A1. 26p, Great Exhibition medal, Albert Tower. 34p, Coin, Steamship Great Britain. 39p, Coin, scene from Oliver Twist, St. Thomas' Church, Douglas. 40p, Coin, first train to arrive in Vancouver, Canada and Jubilee streetlamp standard. 52p, Coin, Foxdale Clock Tower, family of diamond magnate Joe Mylchreest.

**2001, Jan. 22　Litho.　Perf. 13½**
| | | | | |
|---|---|---|---|---|
| 889 | A208 | 22p multi | .70 | .70 |
| 890 | A208 | 26p multi | .80 | .80 |
| 891 | A208 | 34p multi | 1.10 | 1.10 |
| 892 | A208 | 39p multi | 1.20 | 1.20 |
| 893 | A208 | 40p multi | 1.30 | 1.30 |
| 894 | A208 | 52p multi | 1.60 | 1.60 |
| | | Nos. 889-894 (6) | 6.70 | 6.70 |

**Insects — A209**

Designs: 22p, White-tailed bumblebee. 26p, Seven-spot ladybug. 29p, Lesser mottled grasshopper. 58p, Manx robber fly. 66p, Elephant hawkmoth.

**2001, Feb. 1　　　　　Perf. 14½**
| | | | | |
|---|---|---|---|---|
| 895 | A209 | 22p multi | .65 | .65 |
| 896 | A209 | 26p multi | .80 | .80 |
| 897 | A209 | 29p multi | .90 | .90 |
| 898 | A209 | 58p multi | 1.80 | 1.80 |
| 899 | A209 | 66p multi | 2.00 | 2.00 |
| | | Nos. 895-899 (5) | 6.15 | 6.15 |

**Souvenir Sheet**

**Queen Elizabeth II, 75th Birthday A210**

Stamps: 29p, Great Britain #MH1. 34p, Great Britain #300. 37p, Isle of Man #8. 50p, Isle of Man #3.

**2001, Apr. 18　Litho.　Perf. 14**
| | | | | |
|---|---|---|---|---|
| 900 | A210 | Sheet of 4, #a-d | 4.75 | 4.75 |
| e. | | As #900, with Hafnia 01 emblem added in sheet margin | 6.50 | 6.50 |

No. 900e issued 10/29.

**Manx Postmen and Cancels — A211**

**2001, Apr. 18**
| | | | | |
|---|---|---|---|---|
| 901 | A211 | 22p 1805 | .65 | .65 |
| 902 | A211 | 26p 1859 | .80 | .80 |
| 903 | A211 | 36p 1910 | 1.10 | 1.10 |
| 904 | A211 | 39p 1933 | 1.20 | 1.20 |
| 905 | A211 | 40p 1983 | 1.25 | 1.25 |
| 906 | A211 | 66p 2001 | 1.95 | 1.95 |
| | | Nos. 901-906 (6) | 6.95 | 6.95 |

William Joseph Dunlop (1952-2000), Motorcycle Racer — A212

Various photographs.

**2001, May 17**
| | | | |
|---|---|---|---|
| 907 | A212 22p multi | .65 | .65 |
| 908 | A212 26p multi | .80 | .80 |
| 909 | A212 36p multi | 1.10 | 1.10 |
| 910 | A212 45p multi | 1.40 | 1.40 |
| 911 | A212 65p multi | 1.95 | 1.95 |
| 912 | A212 77p multi | 2.20 | 2.20 |
| a. | Sheet of 12, 6 each #911-912, + 6 labels | 27.00 | 27.00 |
| | Nos. 907-912 (6) | 8.10 | 8.10 |

Issued: No. 912a, 5/15/13. No. 912a sold for £9.97.

Horse Racing — A213

Designs: 22p, Manx Derby. 26p, Post Haste. 36p, Red Rum. 52p, Hyperion. 63p, Isle of Man.

**2001, May 18      Perf. 13¼x13½**
| | | | |
|---|---|---|---|
| 913 | A213 22p multi | .70 | .70 |
| 914 | A213 26p multi | .80 | .80 |
| 915 | A213 36p multi | 1.15 | 1.15 |
| 916 | A213 52p multi | 1.60 | 1.60 |
| 917 | A213 63p multi | 1.90 | 1.90 |
| | Nos. 913-917 (5) | 6.15 | 6.15 |

Gourmet Food — A214

**2001, Aug. 10    Litho.    Perf. 14¼**
| | | | |
|---|---|---|---|
| 918 | A214 22p Beef | .70 | .70 |
| 919 | A214 26p Queenies | .75 | .75 |
| a. | Sheet of 10 | 7.50 | |
| 920 | A214 36p Seafood | 1.05 | 1.05 |
| a. | Sheet of 10 | 10.50 | |
| 921 | A214 45p Lamb | 1.35 | 1.35 |
| 922 | A214 50p Kippers | 1.60 | 1.60 |
| 923 | A214 66p Lemon tart | 2.00 | 2.00 |
| | Nos. 918-923 (6) | 7.45 | 7.45 |

Europa (Nos. 919, 920).

Architecture of Mackay Hugh Baillie Scott — A215

Designs: 22p, Castletown Police Station, 1901. 26p, Leafield/Braeside, 1897. 37p, Red House, 1893. 40p, Ivydene, 1893. 80p, Onchan Village Hall, 1898.

**2001, Sept. 3      Perf. 13¼x13½**
| | | | |
|---|---|---|---|
| 924 | A215 22p multi | .70 | .70 |
| 925 | A215 26p multi | .75 | .75 |
| 926 | A215 37p multi | 1.10 | 1.10 |
| 927 | A215 40p multi | 1.20 | 1.20 |
| 928 | A215 80p multi | 2.35 | 2.35 |
| | Nos. 924-928 (5) | 6.10 | 6.10 |

Reign of Queen Elizabeth II, 50th Anniv. (in 2002) — A216

Drawings of Queen: 22p, At dining table. 26p, With crowd, holding flower bouquet. 39p, With dogs. 40p, With men wearing hats. 45p, With correspondence. 65p, Alone, holding flower bouquet.

**Litho. With Foil Application**
**2001-02      Perf. 14¼**
| | | | |
|---|---|---|---|
| 929 | A216 22p multi | .65 | .65 |
| 930 | A216 26p multi | .75 | .75 |
| 931 | A216 39p multi | 1.20 | 1.20 |
| a. | Booklet pane of 3, #929-931 | 3.00 | — |
| 932 | A216 40p multi | 1.20 | 1.20 |
| 933 | A216 45p multi | 1.30 | 1.30 |
| 934 | A216 65p multi | 1.85 | 1.85 |
| a. | Booklet pane of 3, #932-934 | 5.00 | — |
| | Nos. 929-934 (6) | 6.95 | 6.95 |

Issued: Nos. 929-934, 10/29/01. Nos. 931a, 934a, 2/6/02.

Christmas — A217

Floral arrangements: 21p, Holly on Christmas tree-shaped frame. 25p, Wreath. 37p, Table decoration with candles. 45p, Topiary tree. 65p, Wreath, diff.

**Stamp + Label**
**2001, Nov. 5    Litho.    Perf. 14x14½**
**Background Color**
| | | | |
|---|---|---|---|
| 935 | A217 21p green | .70 | .70 |
| 936 | A217 25p red | .85 | .85 |
| 937 | A217 37p gold | 1.20 | 1.20 |
| 938 | A217 45p silver | 1.50 | 1.50 |
| 939 | A217 65p violet | 2.00 | 2.00 |
| | Nos. 935-939 (5) | 6.25 | 6.25 |

Reign of Queen Elizabeth II, 50th Anniv. — A218

No. 940 — Paintings: a, The Coronation, by Terence Cuneo. b, Her Majesty the Queen as Colonel in Chief, Grenadier Guards on Imperial, by Cuneo (Queen on horse). c, Her Majesty in Evening Dress, by June Mendoza. d, Her Majesty the Queen, by Chen Yan Ning. e, The Royal Family, by John Wonnacott.

£1, Her Majesty Queen Elizabeth II Lord of Mann, sculpture by David Cregeen.

**Litho. with Foil Application**
**2002, Feb. 6      Perf. 14**
| | | | |
|---|---|---|---|
| 940 | Vert. strip of 5 | 7.50 | 7.50 |
| a.-e. | A218 50p Any single | 1.50 | 1.50 |
| f. | Booklet pane of 3, #940a-940c | 4.50 | — |
| g. | Booklet pane of 2, #940d-940e | 3.00 | — |

**Souvenir Sheet**
**Perf. 14½x14**
| | | | |
|---|---|---|---|
| 941 | A218 £1 multi | 3.25 | 3.25 |
| a. | Booklet pane of 1 with larger margin | 3.00 | — |
| | Complete booklet, #931a, 934a, 940f, 940g, 941a | 17.50 | |
| b. | As 941, inscribed in sheet margin in purple The Isle of Man Celebrates The Jubilee / 4th June 2002 | 4.75 | 4.75 |

No. 941 contains one 60x40mm stamp.

17th Commonwealth Games, Manchester, England — A219

Designs: 22p, Cycling. 26p, Running. 29p, Javelin, women's high jump. 34p, Swimming. 40p, Hurdles, pole vault. 45p, Wheelchair racing.

**2002, Mar. 11    Litho.    Perf. 14**
| | | | |
|---|---|---|---|
| 942 | A219 22p multi | .65 | .65 |
| 943 | A219 26p multi | .75 | .75 |
| 944 | A219 29p multi | .90 | .90 |
| 945 | A219 34p multi | 1.05 | 1.05 |
| 946 | A219 40p multi | 1.20 | 1.20 |
| 947 | A219 45p multi | 1.30 | 1.30 |
| | Nos. 942-947 (6) | 5.85 | 5.85 |

Queen Mother Elizabeth (1900-2002) — A220

**2002, Apr. 23      Perf. 13x13¼**
| | | | |
|---|---|---|---|
| 948 | A220 £3 multi | 9.25 | 9.25 |

Paintings by Toni Onley — A221

Designs: 22p, Monks' Bridge, Ballasalla. 26p, Laxey. 37p, Langness Lighthouse. 45p, King William's College. 65p, The Mull Circle & Bradda Head.

**2002, May 1      Perf. 13¼x13½**
| | | | |
|---|---|---|---|
| 949 | A221 22p multi | .70 | .70 |
| 950 | A221 26p multi | .80 | .80 |
| 951 | A221 37p multi | 1.20 | 1.20 |
| 952 | A221 45p multi | 1.40 | 1.40 |
| 953 | A221 65p multi | 1.95 | 1.95 |
| | Nos. 949-953 (5) | 6.05 | 6.05 |

2002 World Cup Soccer Championships, Japan and Korea — A222

Various players.

**2002, May 1      Perf. 13½**
| | | | |
|---|---|---|---|
| 954 | A222 22p multi | .70 | .70 |
| 955 | A222 26p multi | .75 | .75 |
| 956 | A222 39p multi | 1.20 | 1.20 |
| 957 | A222 40p multi | 1.20 | 1.20 |
| 958 | A222 66p multi | 1.90 | 1.90 |
| 959 | A222 68p multi | 2.15 | 2.15 |
| | Nos. 954-959 (6) | 7.90 | 7.90 |

Flower Sketches by Sir Paul McCartney — A223

Various sketches.

**2002, July 1    Litho.    Perf. 13¼x12¾**
| | | | |
|---|---|---|---|
| 960 | A223 22p multi | .65 | .65 |
| 961 | A223 26p multi | .75 | .75 |
| 962 | A223 29p multi | .85 | .85 |
| 963 | A223 52p multi | 1.50 | 1.50 |
| 964 | A223 63p multi | 1.90 | 1.90 |
| 965 | A223 77p multi | 2.35 | 2.35 |
| | Nos. 960-965 (6) | 8.00 | 8.00 |

Photographs of Local Scenes — A224

Nos. 966-967: a, Laxey Wheel, by Kathy Brown. b, Sheep at Druidale, by John Hall. c, Carousel at Silverdale, by Colin Edwards. d, Grandma, by Stephanie Corkill. e, Manx Rock, by Ruth Nicholls. f, TT Riders at Signpost, by Neil Brew. g, Groudle Railway, by Albert Lowe. h, Royal Cascade, by Brian Speedie. i, St. Johns, by John Hall. j, Niarbyl Cottages with Poppies, by Cathy Galbraith.

**2002    Litho.    Perf. 14**
| | | | |
|---|---|---|---|
| 966 | Block of 10 | 7.75 | 7.75 |
| a.-j. | A224 27p Any single | .75 | .75 |

**Self-Adhesive**
**Serpentine Die Cut 6¼**
| | | | |
|---|---|---|---|
| 967 | Booklet of 10 | 16.00 | |
| a.-j. | A224 27p Any single | 1.60 | 1.60 |

Designs: a, Manx Milestone, by Mrs. B. J. Trimble. b, Plow Horses, by Miss D. Flint. c, Manx Emblem, by Ruth Nicholls. d, Loaghtan Sheep, by Diana Buford. e, Fishing Fleet at Port St. Mary, by Phil Thomas. f, Peel, by Michael Thompson. g, Daffodils, by Michael

Thompson. h, Millennium Sword, by Mr. F. K. Smith. i, Peel Castle, by Kathy Brown. j, Snaefell Railway, by Joan Burgess.

**Litho.**
**Perf. 14**
| | | | |
|---|---|---|---|
| 968 | Block of 10 | 8.50 | 8.50 |
| a.-j. | A224 23p Any single | .85 | .85 |

**Self-Adhesive**
**Serpentine Die Cut 6¼**
| | | | |
|---|---|---|---|
| 969 | Booklet of 10 | 16.00 | |
| a.-j. | A224 23p Any single | 1.60 | 1.60 |

Issued: Nos. 966-967, 8/30; Nos. 968-969, 10/1.

Christmas and Europa — A225

Designs: 22p, Santa Claus. 26p, Madonna and Child. 37p, Clown. 47p, Cymbal player. 68p, Fairy. £1.30, "Christmas."

**2002, Nov. 5      Perf. 14x14½**
| | | | |
|---|---|---|---|
| 970 | A225 22p multi | .65 | .65 |
| 971 | A225 26p multi | .80 | .80 |
| 972 | A225 37p multi | 1.25 | 1.25 |
| a. | Sheet of 10 + 10 labels | 13.50 | 13.50 |
| 973 | A225 47p multi | 1.25 | 1.25 |
| 974 | A225 68p multi | 2.10 | 2.10 |
| | Nos. 970-974 (5) | 6.05 | 6.05 |

**Miniature Sheet**
**Perf. 14¾**
| | | | |
|---|---|---|---|
| 975 | A225 £1.30 multi | 4.00 | 4.00 |

Europa (No. 972). No. 975 contains one 99x38mm stamp.

Post Office Vehicles — A226

Designs: 23p, Handcart. 27p, Morris Z van. 37p, Morris LD van. 42p, DI BSA Bantam motorcycle. 89p, Ford Escort 55 delivery van.

**2003, Feb. 14      Perf. 14¼**
| | | | |
|---|---|---|---|
| 976 | A226 23p multi | .70 | .70 |
| 977 | A226 27p multi | .90 | .90 |
| 978 | A226 37p multi | 1.10 | 1.10 |
| 979 | A226 42p multi | 1.30 | 1.30 |
| 980 | A226 89p multi | 2.60 | 2.60 |
| | Nos. 976-980 (5) | 6.60 | 6.60 |

Space Exploration — A227

No. 981: a, Tromode Teleport. b, Satellite earth station.
No. 982: a, Pioneering the space frontier (denomination at left). b, Pioneering the space frontier (denomination at right).
No. 983: a, Sea Launch Odyssey launch platform. b, Sea Launch Commander.
No. 984: a, Loral Skynet Telstar 1. b, Loral Skynet Telstar 8.
No. 985: a, Space station, Phobos. b, Astronauts, Mars.

**2003, Feb. 14      Perf. 13¼x13½**
| | | | |
|---|---|---|---|
| 981 | A227 Horiz. pair | 1.35 | 1.35 |
| a.-b. | 23p Either single | .65 | .65 |
| 982 | A227 Horiz. pair | 1.70 | 1.70 |
| a.-b. | 27p Either single | .85 | .85 |
| 983 | A227 Horiz. pair | 2.35 | 2.35 |
| a.-b. | 37p Either single | 1.15 | 1.15 |
| 984 | A227 Horiz. pair | 2.50 | 2.50 |
| a.-b. | 42p Either single | 1.25 | 1.25 |
| | Nos. 981-984 (4) | 7.90 | 7.90 |

**Souvenir Sheet**
**Perf. 13¼x13**
| | | | |
|---|---|---|---|
| 985 | A227 Horiz. pair | 4.50 | 4.50 |
| a.-b. | 75p Either single | 2.25 | 2.25 |

No. 985 contains two 29x38mm stamps.

## Coronation of Queen Elizabeth II, 50th Anniv. — A228

No. 986: a, Queen wearing St. Edward's Crown (brown background, 29x59mm). b, Queen wearing Sovereign's ring and armills (29x29mm). c, Sovereign's orb (29x29mm). d, Scepter with Cross, Rod with Dove (29x29mm). e, Queen wearing Imperial State Crown (blue green background, 29x59mm) f, Queen in State Coach (89x29mm).

### Litho. With Foil Application

| | | | | |
|---|---|---|---|---|
| **2003, Apr. 12** | | | **Perf. 13¼** | |
| **986** | A228 | Block of 6 | 8.75 | 8.75 |
| *a.-f.* | | 50p Any single | 1.40 | 1.40 |

## Powered Flight, Cent. — A229

No. 987: a, DH 83 Fox Moth, Saro Cloud. b, DH 61 Giant Moth, DH Puss Moth. c, Avro Anson, B-17 Flying Fortress.
No. 988: a, Eurofighter Typhoon, Avro Vulcan. b, Handley Page Herald, Bristol Wayfarer. c, Concorde, A380 Airbus.

| | | | | |
|---|---|---|---|---|
| **2003, May 9** | | **Litho.** | **Perf. 13¼** | |
| **987** | | Strip of 3 | 2.50 | 2.50 |
| *a.* | A229 | 23p multi | .65 | .65 |
| *b.* | A229 | 27p multi | .80 | .80 |
| *c.* | A229 | 37p multi | 1.10 | 1.10 |
| **988** | | Strip of 3 | 6.00 | 6.00 |
| *a.* | A229 | 40p multi | 1.20 | 1.20 |
| *b.* | A229 | 67p multi | 2.00 | 2.00 |
| *c.* | A229 | 89p multi | 2.50 | 2.50 |

### Souvenir Sheet

## Dambuster's Raid, 60th Anniv. — A230

| | | | | |
|---|---|---|---|---|
| **2003** | | | | |
| **989** | A230 | £2 multi | 6.00 | 6.00 |
| *a.* | | With "Ticino 2003" emblem in margin | 7.00 | 7.00 |

Issued: No. 989, 5/9; No. 989a, 6/18.

## Prince William, 21st Birthday — A231

Various photographs.

| | | | | |
|---|---|---|---|---|
| **2003, June 9** | | | **Perf. 13¼x13½** | |
| **990** | A231 | 42p black | 1.20 | 1.20 |
| **991** | A231 | 47p black | 1.40 | 1.40 |
| **992** | A231 | 52p black | 1.40 | 1.40 |
| **993** | A231 | 68p black | 1.80 | 1.80 |
| | | *Nos. 990-993 (4)* | 5.80 | 5.80 |

## Literature With Manx Connections — A232

Designs: 23p, Manx Gold, by Agatha Christie. 27p, Quartermass and the Pit, by Nigel Kneale. 30p, Flashman at the Charge, by George MacDonald Fraser. 38p, The Eternal City, by Hall Caine. 40p, Islanders, by Mona Douglas. 53p, Emma's Secret, by Barbara Taylor Bradford.

| | | | | |
|---|---|---|---|---|
| **2003, July 9** | | | **Perf. 13¼** | |
| | | **Stamp + Label** | | |
| **994** | A232 | 23p multi | .60 | .60 |
| **995** | A232 | 27p multi | .80 | .80 |
| **996** | A232 | 30p multi | .85 | .85 |

| | | | | |
|---|---|---|---|---|
| **997** | A232 | 38p multi | 1.15 | 1.15 |
| *a.* | | Sheet of 10 + 10 labels | 12.50 | 12.50 |
| **998** | A232 | 40p multi | 1.15 | 1.15 |
| **999** | A232 | 53p multi | 1.35 | 1.35 |
| | | *Nos. 994-999 (6)* | 5.90 | 5.90 |
| | | Europa (No. 997). | | |

## End of Tudor Reign, 400th Anniv. — A233

Designs: 23p, Crowning of King Henry VII at Bosworth. 27p, King Henry VIII, Dissolution of the Monasteries. 38p, Queen Elizabeth I, Sir Francis Drake circumnavigates the globe. 40p, King Henry VIII, Hampton Court. 47p, Queen Mary I, Tudor rose. 67p, Queen Elizabeth I, Spanish Armada.

| | | | | |
|---|---|---|---|---|
| **2003, Sept. 15** | | | **Perf. 14** | |
| **1000** | A233 | 23p multi | .65 | .65 |
| **1001** | A233 | 27p multi | .80 | .80 |
| **1002** | A233 | 38p multi | 1.10 | 1.10 |
| **1003** | A233 | 40p multi | 1.15 | 1.15 |
| **1004** | A233 | 47p multi | 1.35 | 1.35 |
| **1005** | A233 | 67p multi | 1.80 | 1.80 |
| | | *Nos. 1000-1005 (6)* | 6.85 | 6.85 |

## Henry Bloom Noble Trust, Cent. — A234

No. 1006: a, Boys' Orphanage. b, Ramsey Cottage Hospital. c, Children's Home. d, Noble's Baths. e, Scout Headquarters.
No. 1007: a, Noble's Hospital. b, Villa Marina. c, Noble's Park. d, St. Ninian's Church. e, Noble's Library.

| | | | | |
|---|---|---|---|---|
| **2003, Oct. 1** | | | | |
| **1006** | | Horiz. strip of 5 | 3.35 | 3.35 |
| *a.-e.* | A234 | 23p Any single | .65 | .65 |
| **1007** | | Horiz. strip of 5 | 4.25 | 4.25 |
| *a.-e.* | A234 | 27p Any single | .85 | .85 |

### Booklet Stamps
### Self-Adhesive
### Serpentine Die Cut 6¼

| | | | | |
|---|---|---|---|---|
| **1007F** | A234 | 23p Like #1006a | 1.25 | 1.25 |
| **1007G** | A234 | 23p Like #1006b | 1.25 | 1.25 |
| **1007H** | A234 | 23p Like #1006c | 1.25 | 1.25 |
| **1007I** | A234 | 23p Like #1006d | 1.25 | 1.25 |
| **1007J** | A234 | 23p Like #1006e | 1.25 | 1.25 |
| *p.* | | Booklet pane, 2 each #1007F-1007J | 12.50 | 12.50 |
| **1007K** | A234 | 27p Like #1007a | 1.50 | 1.50 |
| **1007L** | A234 | 27p Like #1007b | 1.50 | 1.50 |
| **1007M** | A234 | 27p Like #1007c | 1.50 | 1.50 |
| **1007N** | A234 | 27p Like #1007d | 1.50 | 1.50 |
| **1007O** | A234 | 27p Like #1007e | 1.50 | 1.50 |
| *q.* | | Booklet pane, 2 each #1007K-1007O | 15.00 | |
| | | *Nos. 1007F-1007O (10)* | 13.75 | 13.75 |

Nos. 1007Jp and 1007Oq are complete booklets, the backing serving as the booklet covers.

## Christmas — A235

Various snowmen, based on Raymond Briggs' children's story The Snowman.

### Litho. With Foil Application

| | | | | |
|---|---|---|---|---|
| **2003, Nov. 5** | | | **Perf. 14¼** | |
| | | **Background Color** | | |
| **1008** | A235 | 22p red | .65 | .65 |
| **1009** | A235 | 26p deep blue | .70 | .70 |
| **1010** | A235 | 38p blue green | 1.10 | 1.10 |
| **1011** | A235 | 47p orange | 1.40 | 1.40 |
| **1012** | A235 | 68p yellow | 1.80 | 1.80 |
| | | *Nos. 1008-1012 (5)* | 5.65 | 5.65 |

## Debut of Movie The Lord of the Rings: The Return of the King — A236

Designs: 23p, Aragorn. 27p, Gimli. 30p, Gandalf the White. 38p, Legolas on horseback. 42p, Gollum. 47p, Frodo Baggins and Samwise Gamgee. 68p, Legolas with bow and arrow. 85p, Aragorn on horseback. £2, Ring.

| | | | | |
|---|---|---|---|---|
| **2003, Dec. 17** | | **Litho.** | **Perf. 13¼** | |
| **1013** | A236 | 23p multi | .65 | .65 |
| **1014** | A236 | 27p multi | .85 | .85 |
| **1015** | A236 | 30p multi | .95 | .95 |
| **1016** | A236 | 38p multi | 1.15 | 1.15 |
| **1017** | A236 | 42p multi | 1.20 | 1.20 |
| **1018** | A236 | 47p multi | 1.40 | 1.40 |
| **1019** | A236 | 68p multi | 2.10 | 2.10 |
| **1020** | A236 | 85p multi | 2.60 | 2.60 |
| | | *Nos. 1013-1020 (8)* | 10.90 | 10.90 |

### Souvenir Sheet
### Perf. 13½

| | | | | |
|---|---|---|---|---|
| **1021** | A236 | £2 multi | 6.00 | 6.00 |

No. 1021 contains one 44x39mm stamp. Nos. 1013-1020 were each printed in sheets of six.

## Steam Locomotives A237

Designs: 23p, Maitland. 27p, Evening Star. 40p, Penydarren Tramroad locomotive. 57p, Duchess of Hamilton. 61p, City of Truro. 90p, Mallard.

| | | | | |
|---|---|---|---|---|
| **2004, Feb. 21** | | **Litho.** | **Perf. 13x13½** | |
| **1022** | A237 | 23p multi | .70 | .70 |
| **1023** | A237 | 27p multi | .90 | .90 |
| **1024** | A237 | 40p multi | 1.25 | 1.25 |
| **1025** | A237 | 57p multi | 1.55 | 1.55 |
| **1026** | A237 | 61p multi | 1.85 | 1.85 |
| **1027** | A237 | 90p multi | 2.45 | 2.45 |
| | | *Nos. 1022-1027 (6)* | 8.70 | 8.70 |

## D-Day, 60th Anniv. A238

No. 1028: a, Two soldiers near walkways, tanks on beach. b, Soldiers in water, tanks on beach.
No. 1029: a, Soldiers in water between two boats. b, Soldiers in water, landing craft with gangway open.
No. 1030: a, Lady of Mann, two blimps. b, Ben-my-Chree, three landing craft, five blimps.
No. 1031: a, Two US B-24 Liberators, RAF Horsa glider. b, Three RAF Horsa gliders.
No. 1032: a, Sir Winston Churchill. b, Soldiers near airplane propeller. c, Military vehicles on street in residential area. d, Soldiers reading book.
Illustration reduced.

| | | | | |
|---|---|---|---|---|
| **2004, Apr. 6** | | | **Perf. 14** | |
| **1028** | A238 | Horiz. pair | 1.40 | 1.40 |
| *a.-b.* | | 23p Either single | .70 | .70 |
| *c.* | | As "a," dated "2014" (#1658a) | .70 | .70 |
| *d.* | | As "b," dated "2014" (#1658a) | .70 | .70 |
| **1029** | A238 | Horiz. pair | 1.65 | 1.65 |
| *a.-b.* | | 27p Either single | .80 | .80 |
| *c.* | | As "a," dated "2014" (#1658a) | .80 | .80 |
| *d.* | | As "b," dated "2014" (#1658a) | .80 | .80 |
| **1030** | A238 | Horiz. pair | 2.80 | 2.80 |
| *a.-b.* | | 47p Either single | 1.40 | 1.40 |
| *c.* | | As "a," dated "2014" (#1658a) | 1.35 | 1.35 |
| *d.* | | As "b," dated "2014" (#1658a) | 1.35 | 1.35 |
| **1031** | A238 | Horiz. pair | 3.90 | 3.90 |
| *a.-b.* | | 68p Either single | 1.95 | 1.95 |
| *c.* | | As "a," dated "2014" (#1658a) | 1.90 | 1.90 |
| *d.* | | As "b," dated "2014" (#1658a) | 1.90 | 1.90 |
| | | *Nos. 1028-1031 (4)* | 9.75 | 9.75 |

### Souvenir Sheet
### Perf. 13¼x13¾

| | | | | |
|---|---|---|---|---|
| **1032** | A238 | Sheet of 4 | 6.25 | 6.25 |
| *a.-d.* | | 50p Any single | 1.50 | 1.50 |
| *e.* | | As "a," perf. 14, dated "2014" (#1658a) | 1.75 | 1.75 |
| *f.* | | As "d," perf. 14, dated "2014" (#1658a) | 1.75 | 1.75 |

Issued: Nos. 1028c, 1028d, 1029c, 1029d, 1030c, 1030d, 1031c, 1031d, 1032e, 1032f, 5/8/14.

## Flowers — A239

Designs: 25p, Lesser celandine. 28p, Red campion. 37p, Devil's bit scabious. 40p, Northern harebell. 68p, Wood anemone. 85p, Common spotted orchid.

| | | | | |
|---|---|---|---|---|
| **2004, May 3** | | | **Perf. 13½** | |
| **1033** | A239 | 25p multi | .70 | .70 |
| **1034** | A239 | 28p multi | .80 | .80 |
| **1035** | A239 | 37p multi | 1.10 | 1.10 |
| **1036** | A239 | 40p multi | 1.10 | 1.10 |
| **1037** | A239 | 68p multi | 2.00 | 2.00 |
| **1038** | A239 | 85p multi | 2.50 | 2.50 |
| | | *Nos. 1033-1038 (6)* | 8.20 | 8.20 |

## George Formby (1904-61), Movie Actor — A240

Various scenes from film No Limit and text: 25p, No Limit. 28p, George. 40p, Speed Demon. 43p, Florence. 50p, Shuttleworth. 74p, Formby.

| | | | | |
|---|---|---|---|---|
| **2004, May 26** | | | **Perf. 13¼** | |
| **1039** | A240 | 25p multi | .70 | .70 |
| **1040** | A240 | 28p multi | .80 | .80 |
| **1041** | A240 | 40p multi | 1.15 | 1.15 |
| **1042** | A240 | 43p multi | 1.25 | 1.25 |
| **1043** | A240 | 50p multi | 1.45 | 1.45 |
| **1044** | A240 | 74p multi | 2.15 | 2.15 |
| | | *Nos. 1039-1044 (6)* | 7.50 | 7.50 |

## 2004 Summer Olympics, Athens — A241

Designs: 25p, Johnny Weismuller, Paris Olympics, 1924. 28p, Jesse Owens, runners, Berlin Olympics, 1936. 43p, John Mark, torch bearer, London Olympics, 1948. 55p, Fanny Blankers-Koen, runners, London Olympics, 1948. 91p, Sir Steve Redgrave, rowers, Sydney Olympics, 2000.

| | | | | |
|---|---|---|---|---|
| **2004, July 1** | | **Litho.** | **Perf. 14** | |
| **1045** | A241 | 25p multi | .70 | .70 |
| **1046** | A241 | 28p multi | .85 | .85 |
| **1047** | A241 | 43p multi | 1.25 | 1.25 |
| **1048** | A241 | 55p multi | 1.55 | 1.55 |
| **1049** | A241 | 91p multi | 2.65 | 2.65 |
| | | *Nos. 1045-1049 (5)* | 7.00 | 7.00 |

## Manx History — A242

Designs: Nos. 1050a, 1052, Celtic islander and Viking invaders. Nos. 1050b, 1053, Ships and the sea. Nos. 1050c, 1054, Laxey miners. Nos. 1050d, 1055, Kings and Lords of Mann. Nos. 1050e, 1056, Farmers and crofters. Nos. 1051a, 1057, Calf of Man. Nos. 1051b, 1058, Peel Castle. Nos. 1051c, 1059, Laxey Wheel. Nos. 1051d, 1060, Castle Rushen. Nos. 1051e, 1061, Cregneash.

| | | | | |
|---|---|---|---|---|
| **2004, Aug. 3** | | | **Perf. 14¼** | |
| **1050** | | Horiz. strip of 5 | 4.50 | 4.50 |
| *a.-e.* | A242 | (25p) Any single | .90 | .90 |
| **1051** | | Horiz. strip of 5 | 5.00 | 5.00 |
| *a.-e.* | A242 | (28p) Any single | 1.00 | 1.00 |

### Booklet Stamps
### Self-Adhesive
### Serpentine Die Cut 12½

| | | | | |
|---|---|---|---|---|
| **1052** | A242 | (25p) multi | .95 | .95 |
| **1053** | A242 | (25p) multi | .95 | .95 |
| **1054** | A242 | (25p) multi | .95 | .95 |
| **1055** | A242 | (25p) multi | .95 | .95 |
| **1056** | A242 | (25p) multi | .95 | .95 |
| *a.* | | Booklet pane, 2 each #1052-1056 | 9.50 | |
| **1057** | A242 | (28p) multi | 1.00 | 1.00 |
| **1058** | A242 | (28p) multi | 1.00 | 1.00 |
| **1059** | A242 | (28p) multi | 1.00 | 1.00 |
| **1060** | A242 | (28p) multi | 1.00 | 1.00 |

**1061** A242 (28p) multi 1.00 1.00
  a.  Booklet pane, 2 each 10.00
    #1057-1061
    *Nos. 1050-1061 (12)* 19.25 19.25

Nos. 1056a and 1061a are complete booklets, the backing serving as the booklet covers.

### Souvenir Sheet

Laxey Wheel, 150th Anniv. A243

**2004, Aug. 3**     *Perf. 14¼*
**1062** A243 £2 multi 6.00 6.00
  a.  With Sindelfingen 2004 emblem added in sheet margin 8.00 8.00

No. 1062a issued 10/29.

Watercolors by Alfred Heaton Cooper (1864-1929) A244

Designs: 25p, Maughold Church. 28p, Port St. Mary. 40p, Ballaugh Old Church. 41p, Douglas Bay (A Midsummer's Night). 43p, Point of Ayre. 74p, Peel Harbor and Castle.

**2004, Oct. 21 Litho.**   *Perf. 13¼x12¾*
**1063** A244 25p multi .75 .75
**1064** A244 28p multi .80 .80
  a.  Sheet of 10 + 10 labels 8.00 8.00
**1065** A244 40p multi 1.15 1.15
  a.  Sheet of 10 + 10 labels 11.75 11.75
**1066** A244 41p multi 1.15 1.15
**1067** A244 43p multi 1.25 1.25
**1068** A244 74p multi 2.20 2.20
    *Nos. 1063-1068 (6)* 7.30 7.30

Europa (Nos. 1064-1065).

Robins — A245

Robin on: 25p, Flowerpot. 28p, Rock. 40p, Branch. 47p, Window sill. 68p, Log.

**2004, Nov. 9**     *Perf. 12½x13*
**1069** A245 25p multi .70 .70
**1070** A245 28p multi .85 .85
**1071** A245 40p multi 1.25 1.25
**1072** A245 47p multi 1.35 1.35
**1073** A245 68p multi 1.95 1.95
  a.  Miniature sheet, 2 each 24.00 24.00
    #1069-1073
    *Nos. 1069-1073 (5)* 6.10 6.10

Scenes from *Harry Potter and the Prisoner of Azkaban* — A246

Designs: 25p, Harry Potter, Ron Weasley and Hermione Granger. 28p, Owl Post. 39p, Harry and Petronus. 40p, Hogwarts Express. 49p, Hagrid. 55p, Knight Bus. 57p, Harry and Dementor. 68p, Harry and Buckbeak.

**2004, Dec. 7**     *Perf. 13¼*
**1074** A246 25p multi .75 .75
**1075** A246 28p multi .90 .90
**1076** A246 39p multi 1.30 1.30
**1077** A246 40p multi 1.45 1.45
**1078** A246 49p multi 1.45 1.45
**1079** A246 55p multi 1.65 1.65
**1080** A246 57p multi 1.85 1.85
**1081** A246 68p multi 2.05 2.05
    *Nos. 1074-1081 (8)* 11.40 11.40

Each printed in sheets of 5.

Battle of Trafalgar, Bicent. A247

---

No. 1082: a, Nile Campaign. b, Battle of Copenhagen.
No. 1083: a, Emma Horatia Nelson. b, Band of brothers.
No. 1084: a, Prepare for battle. b, Victory in sight.
No. 1085: a, Fall of Nelson. b, Death of Nelson.
No. 1086: a, #861a. b, #159.

**2005, Jan. 9**     *Perf. 12½x13*
**1082** A247 Horiz. pair 1.50 1.50
  a.-b.  25p Either single .75 .75
**1083** A247 Horiz. pair 1.70 1.70
  a.-b.  28p Either single .85 .85
**1084** A247 Horiz. pair 2.80 2.80
  a.-b.  50p Either single 1.40 1.40
**1085** A247 Horiz. pair 3.60 3.60
  a.-b.  65p Either single 1.80 1.80
    *Nos. 1082-1085 (4)* 9.60 9.60

### Souvenir Sheet
*Perf. 13¼x13*
**1086** A247 Sheet of 2 6.50 6.50
  a.-b.  £1 Either single 3.25 3.25

Victory in World War II, 60th Anniv. A248

No. 1087: a, Women and sailors. b, Soldiers and women marching together.
No. 1088: a, Soldier trying on hat. b, Servicewomen.
No. 1089: a, Winston Churchill and Royal family waving. b, Royal family in carriage.
No. 1090: a, Servicemen without shirts. b, Cemetery.
No. 1091: a, Manx Regiment. b, Royal visit, 1945.

**2005, Apr. 15 Litho.**   *Perf. 13¼x13¾*
**1087** A248 Horiz. pair 1.50 1.50
  a.-b.  26p Either single .75 .75
**1088** A248 Horiz. pair 1.65 1.65
  a.-b.  29p Either single .80 .80
**1089** A248 Horiz. pair 3.35 3.35
  a.-b.  60p Either single 1.65 1.65
**1090** A248 Horiz. pair 3.95 3.95
  a.-b.  65p Either single 1.95 1.95
    *Nos. 1087-1090 (4)* 10.45 10.45

### Souvenir Sheet
**1091** A248 Sheet of 2 6.50 6.50
  a.-b.  £1 Either single 3.25 3.25

Paintings of Isle of Man Steam Packet Company Ships — A249

No. 1092: a, Mona's Isle, by Samuel Walters. b, Viking, by Norman Wilkinson.
No. 1093: a, King Orry, by Robert Lloyd. b, Mona's Queen, by Arthur Burgess.
No. 1094: a, Ben-my-Chree, by John Nicholson. b, King Orry, by Robert Lloyd, diff.
No. 1095: a, Ben-my-Chree, by Robert Lloyd. b, Lady of Mann, by Robert Lloyd.

**2005, May 6**     *Perf. 14*
**1092** A249 Horiz. pair 1.50 1.50
  a.-b.  26p Either single .75 .75
  c.  Booklet pane, #1092, 1093 2.75 —
**1093** A249 Horiz. pair 1.70 1.70
  a.-b.  29p Either single .85 .85
**1094** A249 Horiz. pair 2.35 2.35
  a.-b.  40p Either single 1.15 1.15
  c.  Booklet pane, #1092, 1094 3.25 —
**1095** A249 Horiz. pair 3.85 3.85
  a.-b.  66p Either single 1.90 1.90
  c.  Booklet pane, #1093, 1095 4.75 —
  d.  Booklet pane, #1094, 1095 5.25 —
  e.  Booklet pane, #1095 3.25 —
    Complete booklet, #1093c, 19.00
    1094c, 1095c, 1095d,
    1095e
    *Nos. 1092-1095 (4)* 9.40 9.40

Complete booklet sold for £7.80.

Motorcycle Racers — A250

Designs: 26p, Bill Ivy, Phil Read. 29p, Joey Dunlop, Ray McCullough. 40p, Steve Hislop. 42p, Carl Fogarty. 68p, David Jefferies. 78p, John McGuinness.

**2005, May 17**
**1096** A250 26p multi .75 .75
**1097** A250 29p multi .80 .80
**1098** A250 40p multi 1.15 1.15
**1099** A250 42p multi 1.30 1.30
**1100** A250 68p multi 2.05 2.05

---

**1101** A250 78p multi 2.25 2.25
  a.  Miniature sheet, 2 each 21.00 21.00
    #1096-1101
    *Nos. 1096-1101 (6)* 8.30 8.30

Yamaha motorcycles, 50th anniv.

Rotary International, Cent. — A251

Rotary International emblem, various photos and inscription: 26p, Paul Harris, The Man Behind The Movement. 29p, Rotary's Dreams For The Future. 40p, Polioplus: Rotary's Finest Hour. 42p, Youth Programme: Junior Masterchef. 64p, A Day In The Life of Rotary International. 68p, Serving The World Community.

     *Perf. 13¼x13½*
**2005, June 15**     *Litho.*
**1102** A251 26p multi .75 .75
**1103** A251 29p multi .85 .85
**1104** A251 40p multi 1.20 1.20
**1105** A251 40p multi 1.30 1.30
  a.  Sheet of 10 + 10 labels 11.75 11.75
**1106** A251 64p multi 1.85 1.85
**1107** A251 68p multi 2.10 2.10
    *Nos. 1102-1107 (6)* 8.05 8.05

No. 1105 is inscribed "Europa 2005."

Photographs of Everyday Life — A252

Inscriptions: Nos. 1108a, 1110, Guttin' Herrin'. Nos. 1108b, 1111, Pickin' Spuds. Nos. 1108c, 1112, Master Butcher. Nos. 1108d, 1113, Winckles: Foxdale. Nos. 1108e, 1114, Palace Ballroom. Nos. 1109a, 1115, Land Army. Nos. 1109c, 1117, Summer Season Stars. Nos. 1109d, 1118, Donkey Rides. Nos. 1109e, 1119, Give us a go Mister!

**2005, Aug. 12**     *Perf. 12½x13*
**1108** Horiz. strip of 5 4.00 4.00
  a.-e.  A252 26p Any single .80 .80
**1109** Horiz. strip of 5 4.25 4.25
  a.-e.  A252 29p Any single .85 .85

### Booklet Stamps
**Self-Adhesive**
*Serpentine Die Cut 10½x10¼*
**1110** A252 26p multi 1.00 1.00
  a.  Die cut perf 12½x13 1.25 1.25
**1111** A252 26p multi 1.00 1.00
  a.  Die cut perf 12½x13 1.25 1.25
**1112** A252 26p multi 1.00 1.00
  a.  Die cut perf 12½x13 1.25 1.25
**1113** A252 26p multi 1.00 1.00
  a.  Die cut perf 12½x13 1.25 1.25
**1114** A252 26p multi 1.00 1.00
  a.  Booklet pane, 2 each 10.00
    #1110-1114
    Complete booklet, #1114a 10.00
  b.  Die cut perf 12½x13 1.25 1.25
  c.  Strip of 5, #1110a-1113a, 6.25
    1114b
**1115** A252 29p multi 1.10 1.10
  a.  Die cut perf 12½x13 1.25 1.25
**1116** A252 29p multi 1.10 1.10
  a.  Die cut perf 12½x13 1.25 1.25
**1117** A252 29p multi 1.10 1.10
  a.  Die cut perf 12½x13 1.25 1.25
**1118** A252 29p multi 1.10 1.10
  a.  Die cut perf 12½x13 1.25 1.25
**1119** A252 29p multi 1.10 1.10
  a.  Booklet pane, 2 each 11.00
    #1115-1119
    Complete booklet, #1119a 11.00
  b.  Die cut perf 12½x13 1.25 1.25
  c.  Strip of 5, #1115a-1118a, 6.25
    1119b
    *Nos. 1110-1119 (10)* 10.50 10.50

Nos. 1114a and 1119a are complete booklets, the backing serving as booklet covers. The die-cut 12½x13 stamps are from sheets of 50.

### Souvenir Sheet

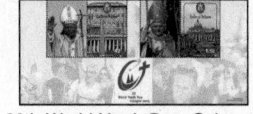

20th World Youth Day, Cologne, Germany A253

---

**2005, Aug. 15**
**1120** A253 Sheet of 2 + 2 labels 6.00 6.00
  a.  42p Apostolic Palace 1.25 1.25
  b.  £1.50 St. Peter's Basilica 4.50 4.50

Scenes From *Harry Potter and the Goblet of Fire* — A254

Designs: 26p, Harry Potter. 29p, Harry, Ron Weasley, Hermione Granger, Goblet of Fire. 33p, Triwizard Cup. 64p, Hungarian Horntail. 68p, Hogwarts coat of arms. 75p, Murcus.

**2005, Oct. 21**     *Perf. 13¼*
**1121** A254 26p multi .75 .75
**1122** A254 29p multi .80 .80
**1123** A254 33p multi 1.05 1.05
**1124** A254 64p multi 1.80 1.80
**1125** A254 68p multi 2.10 2.10
**1126** A254 75p multi 2.25 2.25
    *Nos. 1121-1126 (6)* 8.75 8.75

### Souvenir Sheet

Battle of Trafalgar, Bicent. A255

**2005, Oct. 21 Litho.**   *Perf. 13¼*
**1127** A255 Sheet, #1127a, Gibraltar #1028a 6.25 6.25
  a.  £1 Funeral of Admiral Nelson 3.00 3.00

See Gibraltar No. 1028. No. 1127 has an Isle of Man Post emblem in the margin.

Christmas — A256

Stained glass windows: 26p, Madonna and Child, St. German's Cathedral, Peel. 29p, Angel with Crown of Glory, St. German's Cathedral. 42p, Adoration of the Shepherds, St. German's Cathedral. 60p, Nativity, Kirk Church, Rushen. 68p, Adoration of the Magi, Kirk Church.

**2005, Nov. 7 Litho.**   *Perf. 13½x13*
**1128** A256 26p multi .75 .75
**1129** A256 29p multi .80 .80
**1130** A256 42p multi 1.30 1.30
**1131** A256 60p multi 1.70 1.70
**1132** A256 68p multi 2.05 2.05
    *Nos. 1128-1132 (5)* 6.60 6.60

Queen Elizabeth II, 80th Birthday — A257

No. 1133: a, At age 5 with family, 1931. b, In uniform, 1944. c, Wearing tiara, 1952. d, With husband and children, 1972.
No. 1134: a, With Prince Philip, 1972. b, Seated in Throne Room, 2001. c, With Prince William. d, With crowd, 2002.

**2006, Jan. 16**     *Perf. 13¾*
**1133** Horiz. strip of 4 2.35 2.35
  a.-d.  A257 20p Any single .55 .55
**1134** Horiz. strip of 4 9.75 9.75
  a.-d.  A257 80p Any single 2.40 2.40

Isle of Man Natural History and Antiquarian Society — A258

Designs: 26p, Jurby Church, chalice. 29p, Peel Castle, Viking pinhead. 64p, Meayll Hill, Neolithic potsherd. 68p, Cronk Sumark, Manx stoat. 78p, South Barrule Hill, hen harrier. 97p, Scarlett Point, ammonite fossil.

| **2006, Feb. 15** | | **Litho.** | **Perf. 14** | |
|---|---|---|---|---|
| **1135** | A258 | 26p multi | .75 | .75 |
| **1136** | A258 | 29p multi | .85 | .85 |
| **1137** | A258 | 64p multi | 1.85 | 1.85 |
| **1138** | A258 | 68p multi | 2.10 | 2.10 |
| **1139** | A258 | 78p multi | 2.25 | 2.25 |
| **1140** | A258 | 97p multi | 2.80 | 2.80 |
| | *Nos. 1135-1140 (6)* | | 10.60 | 10.60 |

Birds — A259

No. 1141: a, Peregrine falcon. b, Puffin. c, Manx shearwater. d, Chough. e, Guillemot.
No. 1142: a, Whinchat. b, Hen harrier. c, Goldcrest. d, Gray wagtail. e, Wren.
No. 1142G: i, Peregrine falcon. j, Puffin. k, Manx shearwater. l, Chough. m, Guillemot.
No. 1142H: n, Whinchat. o, Hen harrier. p, Goldcrest. q, Gray wagtail. r, Wren.

| **2006, Apr. 17** | | | **Perf. 12½** | |
|---|---|---|---|---|
| **1141** | | Horiz. strip of 5 | 4.00 | 4.00 |
| *a.-e.* | A259 | 28p multi | .80 | .80 |
| **1142** | | Horiz. strip of 5 | 4.60 | 4.60 |
| *a.-e.* | A259 | 31p multi | .90 | .90 |
| *f.* | | Miniature sheet, #1141a- | | |
| | | 1141e, 1142a-1142e | 40.00 | 40.00 |

**Self-Adhesive**
*Serpentine Die Cut 12½*

| **1142G** | | Horiz. strip of 5 | 18.00 | 18.00 |
|---|---|---|---|---|
| *i.-m.* | A259 | 28p Any single | 3.50 | 3.50 |
| **1142H** | | Horiz. strip of 5 | 19.50 | 19.50 |
| *n.-r.* | A259 | 31p Any single | 3.75 | 3.75 |

No. 1142f issued 10/11, for Belgica '06 Intl. Philatelic Exhibition.

**Souvenir Sheet**

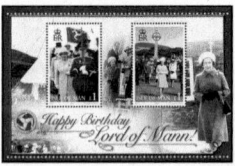

Queen Elizabeth II, 80th Birthday A260

No. 1143: a, Queen, swordbearer, Manx flag, 2003. b, Queen, crowd, cross, 1972.

| **2006, Apr. 21** | | | **Perf. 14** | |
|---|---|---|---|---|
| **1143** | A260 | Sheet of 2 | 6.00 | 6.00 |
| *a.-b.* | | £1 Either single | 3.00 | 3.00 |
| *c.* | | As #1143a, perf. 12¾, dated "2017" | 3.50 | 3.50 |
| *d.* | | As #1143b, perf. 12¾, dated "2017" | 3.50 | 3.50 |
| *e.* | | Vert. pair, #1143c-1143d | 7.00 | 7.00 |

Issued: Nos. 1143c, and 1143d, 7/5/17. Nos. 1143c and 1143d were printed together in sheets of 10 (5 of each stamp) that sold for £12.50.

**Souvenir Sheet**

 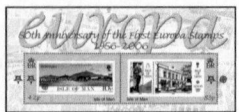

Europa Stamps, 50th Anniv. A261

No. 1144: a, #100. b, #419a.

| **2006, May 2** | | | **Perf. 13¼x13¾** | |
|---|---|---|---|---|
| **1144** | A261 | Sheet of 2 | 3.75 | 3.75 |
| *a.* | | 42p multi | 1.30 | 1.30 |
| *b.* | | 83p multi | 2.45 | 2.45 |

2006 World Cup Soccer Championships, Germany — A262

Various photographs of English team's 1966 World Cup championship match and celebrations.

| **2006, May 2** | | | **Perf. 12½** | |
|---|---|---|---|---|
| **1145** | A262 | 28p multi | .80 | .80 |
| **1146** | A262 | 31p multi | .95 | .95 |
| **1147** | A262 | 44p multi | 1.30 | 1.30 |
| **1148** | A262 | 72p multi | 2.05 | 2.05 |
| **1149** | A262 | 83p multi | 2.45 | 2.45 |
| **1150** | A262 | 94p multi | 2.85 | 2.85 |
| | *Nos. 1145-1150 (6)* | | 10.40 | 10.40 |

Manx Ties to Washington, D.C. — A263

Designs: 28p, Letitia Tyler, wife of Pres. John Tyler, White House. 31p, Speaker of the House Joseph G. Cannon, Cannon House Office Building. 45p, Matthew Quay, Medal of Honor recipient, battle scene. 50p, Mary Clemmer, journalist, inkwell and U.S. Constitution. 76p, Ewan Clague, economist, Castletown. 83p, Henry "Marse" Watterson, newspaper publisher, Pres. Theodore Roosevelt.

| **2006, May 23** | | | **Perf. 13¾** | |
|---|---|---|---|---|
| **1151** | A263 | 28p multi | .90 | .90 |
| **1152** | A263 | 31p multi | 1.00 | 1.00 |
| **1153** | A263 | 45p multi | 1.40 | 1.40 |
| **1154** | A263 | 50p multi | 1.60 | 1.60 |
| **1155** | A263 | 76p multi | 2.40 | 2.40 |
| **1156** | A263 | 83p multi | 2.60 | 2.60 |
| | *Nos. 1151-1156 (6)* | | 9.90 | 9.90 |

Peel Cars — A264

Designs: 28p, Peel P50. 31p, Trident. 38p, Viking Sport. 41p, BMC GRP Mini. 54p, Manxcar. 94p, P1000.

| **2006, July 23** | | | **Perf. 13¼** | |
|---|---|---|---|---|
| **1157** | A264 | 28p multi | .80 | .80 |
| **1158** | A264 | 31p multi | .90 | .90 |
| **1159** | A264 | 38p multi | 1.10 | 1.10 |
| **1160** | A264 | 41p multi | 1.15 | 1.15 |
| **1161** | A264 | 54p multi | 1.50 | 1.50 |
| **1162** | A264 | 94p multi | 2.80 | 2.80 |
| | *Nos. 1157-1162 (6)* | | 8.25 | 8.25 |

National Portrait Gallery, London, 150th Anniv. — A265

Portraits: 28p, Ewan Christian, by unknown artist. 31p, Dame Agatha Christie, by John Gay. 38p, Sir Hall Caine, by Harry Furniss. 41p, William Bligh, by John Condé. 44p, Lady Maria Callcott, by Sir Thomas Lawrence. 54p, John Martin, by Henry Warren. 64p, Sir John Betjeman, by Stephen Hyde. 96p, Sir Edward Elgar, by Herbert Lambert.

| **2006, Aug. 25** | | | **Litho.** | **Perf. 13½** |
|---|---|---|---|---|
| **1163** | A265 | 28p multi | .80 | .80 |
| **1164** | A265 | 31p multi | .95 | .95 |
| **1165** | A265 | 38p multi | 1.10 | 1.10 |
| **1166** | A265 | 41p multi | 1.15 | 1.15 |
| **1167** | A265 | 44p multi | 1.30 | 1.30 |
| **1168** | A265 | 54p multi | 1.55 | 1.55 |
| **1169** | A265 | 64p multi | 1.85 | 1.85 |
| **1170** | A265 | 96p multi | 2.90 | 2.90 |
| | *Nos. 1163-1170 (8)* | | 11.60 | 11.60 |

**Souvenir Sheet**

Tales of Beatrix Potter A266

No. 1171: a, Benjamin Bunny. b, Jemima Puddle-duck, horiz. c, Peter Rabbit, horiz. d, Jeremy Fisher.

| **2006, Oct. 11** | | | | **Perf. 13** |
|---|---|---|---|---|
| **1171** | A266 | Sheet of 4 | 7.25 | 7.25 |
| *a.* | | 28p multi | .90 | .90 |
| *b.* | | 50p multi | 1.60 | 1.60 |
| *c.* | | 72p multi | 2.25 | 2.25 |
| *d.* | | 75p multi | 2.50 | 2.50 |

Christmas — A267

Various Christmas trees with panel colors of: 28p, Red. 31p, Dark violet. 41p, Green. 44p, Light blue. 72p, Purple. 94p, Orange.

**Litho. with Foil Application**

| **2006, Oct. 11** | | | | **Perf. 14¼** |
|---|---|---|---|---|
| **1172** | A267 | 28p multi | .80 | .80 |
| **1173** | A267 | 31p multi | .95 | .95 |
| *a.* | | Sheet of 10 | 9.50 | 9.50 |
| **1174** | A267 | 41p multi | 1.10 | 1.10 |
| **1175** | A267 | 44p multi | 1.30 | 1.30 |
| *a.* | | Sheet of 10 | 13.00 | 13.00 |
| **1176** | A267 | 72p multi | 2.05 | 2.05 |
| **1177** | A267 | 94p multi | 2.85 | 2.85 |
| | *Nos. 1172-1177 (6)* | | 9.05 | 9.05 |

**Self-Adhesive**
**Booklet Stamps**
*Die Cut Perf. 9x9½*

| **1178** | A267 | 28p multi | .85 | .85 |
|---|---|---|---|---|
| *a.* | | Booklet pane of 10 | 8.50 | |
| **1179** | A267 | 31p multi | 1.15 | 1.15 |
| *a.* | | Booklet pane of 10 | 11.50 | |

Europa (31p, 44p).
Nos. 1178a and 1179a are complete booklets, the backing as the booklet covers.

TT Motorcycle Races, Cent. — A268

No. 1180 — Various racers with panel color of: a, Pink. b, Light blue. c, Purple. d, Indigo. e, Orange.
No. 1181: a, Red violet. b, Green. c, Gray blue. d, Red. e, Red brown.

| **2007, Jan. 1** | | | **Litho.** | **Perf. 14¼** |
|---|---|---|---|---|
| **1180** | | Horiz. strip of 5 | 5.00 | 5.00 |
| *a.-e.* | A268 | 28p UK Any single | 1.00 | 1.00 |
| *f.* | | As "e," perf. 14¾, dated "2014" (#1324b) | 1.40 | 1.40 |
| **1181** | | Horiz. strip of 5 | 7.00 | 7.00 |
| *a.-e.* | A268 | E Any single | 1.40 | 1.40 |
| *f.* | | Sheet of 10, #1180a-1180e, 1181a-1181e, + 10 labels | 35.00 | 35.00 |
| *g.* | | Sheet of 12 #1181b + 13 labels | 27.00 | 27.00 |

On day of issue Nos. 1180a-1180e each sold for 31p, Nos. 1181a-1181e each sold for 44p.
Issued: No. 1181f, 7/9. No. 1181g, 5/15/13. No. 11.81g sold for £8.52.
Issued: No. 1180f, 2014. No. 1180f sold for 42p on day of issue.

A269

Scouting, Cent. A270

Designs: 28p, Hiking expedition near South Barrule. 31p, Scout investiture on Douglas Beach. 44p, Backpacking below Cronk-ny-Arrey-Laa. 72p, Manx Scouts on parade at St. Johns. 83p, Sea kayaking off Laxey Beach. £1, Manx Scouts operating the TT scoreboard.
No. 1188: a, Scouts and table (43x29mm). b, Scouts, tent and campfire (43x57mm).

| **2007, Feb. 22** | | | **Litho.** | **Perf. 14** |
|---|---|---|---|---|
| **1182** | A269 | 28p multi | .85 | .85 |
| **1183** | A269 | 31p multi | .95 | .95 |
| *a.* | | Sheet of 10 | 9.50 | 9.50 |
| **1184** | A269 | 44p multi | 1.40 | 1.40 |
| *a.* | | Booklet pane, #1182-1184 | 2.75 | |
| *b.* | | Sheet of 10 | 14.00 | 14.00 |
| **1185** | A269 | 72p multi | 2.20 | 2.20 |
| **1186** | A269 | 83p multi | 2.60 | 2.60 |
| *a.* | | Booklet pane, #1182, 1184, 1186 | 4.25 | |
| **1187** | A269 | £1 multi | 3.05 | 3.05 |
| *a.* | | Booklet pane, #1185-1187 | 6.50 | 6.50 |
| *b.* | | Booklet pane, #1183, 1185, 1187 | 5.25 | 5.25 |
| | *Nos. 1182-1187 (6)* | | 11.05 | 11.05 |

**Souvenir Sheet**

| **1188** | A270 | Sheet of 2 | 6.00 | 6.00 |
|---|---|---|---|---|
| *a.* | | 50p multi | 1.50 | 1.50 |
| *b.* | | £1.50 multi | 4.50 | 4.50 |
| *c.* | | Booklet pane, #1188 (154x96mm) | 7.75 | — |
| | | Complete booklet, #1184a, 1186a, 1187a, 1187b, 1188c | 24.00 | |
| *d.* | | As No. 1188, with 2007 Intl. Scout Jamboree emblem in margin | 7.25 | 7.25 |

Europa (31p, 44p).
No. 1188d issued 7/26.

Wedding of Queen Elizabeth II and Prince Philip, 60th Anniv. — A271

Various photos of Queen and Prince with denomination colors of: a, Dark blue. b, Lilac. c, Rose pink. d, Light blue. e, Dark green. f, Yellow bister.

| **2007, Feb. 22** | | | **Perf. 14** | |
|---|---|---|---|---|
| **1189** | | Horiz. strip of 6 | 10.75 | 10.75 |
| *a.-f.* | A271 | 60p Any single | 1.75 | 1.75 |

Paintings by Norman Sayle — A272

Designs: Nos. 1190, 1198, Headland, Cornaa. Nos. 1191, 1199, Headland, Sound. Nos. 1192, 1200, St. Mark's Church. Nos. 1193, 1201, Castletown Harbour Moonlight. 42p, Bridge House, Castletown. 44p, Winter Sun. 65p, In Ancient Times. 75p, Bracken Mountain.

| **2007, Apr. 12** | | | **Perf. 12½x13** | |
|---|---|---|---|---|
| **1190** | A272 | 28p multi | .80 | .80 |
| **1191** | A272 | 28p multi | .80 | .80 |
| **1192** | A272 | 31p multi | .85 | .85 |
| **1193** | A272 | 31p multi | .85 | .85 |
| **1194** | A272 | 42p multi | 1.25 | 1.25 |
| **1195** | A272 | 44p multi | 1.25 | 1.25 |
| **1196** | A272 | 65p multi | 1.90 | 1.90 |
| **1197** | A272 | 75p multi | 2.20 | 2.20 |
| | *Nos. 1190-1197 (8)* | | 9.90 | 9.90 |

**Booklet Stamps**
**Self-Adhesive**
*Serpentine Die Cut 10x9½*

| **1198** | A272 | 28p multi | 1.10 | 1.10 |
|---|---|---|---|---|
| **1199** | A272 | 28p multi | 1.10 | 1.10 |
| *a.* | | Booklet pane, 5 each #1198-1199 | 11.00 | |
| **1200** | A272 | 31p multi | 1.25 | 1.25 |
| **1201** | A272 | 31p multi | 1.25 | 1.25 |
| *a.* | | Booklet pane, 5 each #1200-1201 | 12.50 | |
| | *Nos. 1198-1201 (4)* | | 4.70 | 4.70 |

Nos. 1199a and 1201a are complete booklets, the backing serving as the booklet covers.

Settlement of Jamestown, Virginia, 400th Anniv. — A273

Designs: 28p, Map. 31p, Capt. John Smith and ships. 44p, Aerial view of settlement. 54p, Indians and colonists. 78p, Settlement buildings. 90p, Indian village.

| **2007, Apr. 26** | | | **Perf. 13½** | |
|---|---|---|---|---|
| **1202** | A273 | 28p multi | .80 | .80 |
| **1203** | A273 | 31p multi | .85 | .85 |
| **1204** | A273 | 44p multi | 1.25 | 1.25 |
| **1205** | A273 | 54p multi | 1.55 | 1.55 |
| **1206** | A273 | 78p multi | 2.35 | 2.35 |
| **1207** | A273 | 90p multi | 2.75 | 2.75 |
| | *Nos. 1202-1207 (6)* | | 9.55 | 9.55 |

Royal Charter of Liverpool, 800th Anniv. — A274

Designs: 31p, King John and Royal Charter. 48p, The spiritual heart of Liverpool. 54p, Liverpool war heroes. 74p, Liverpool heritage (St. George's Hall). 80p, Port of Liverpool. £1, Wall of Fame.

No. 1214: a, James Brown, Manx election pioneer. b, Joseph Cunningham, philantropist. c, William Gill, ship captain. d, Dalrymple Maitland, industrialist.

| 2007, Apr. 26 | | | Perf. 14 | |
|---|---|---|---|---|
| 1208 | A274 | 31p multi | .85 | .85 |
| 1209 | A274 | 48p multi | 1.40 | 1.40 |
| 1210 | A274 | 54p multi | 1.60 | 1.60 |
| 1211 | A274 | 74p multi | 2.15 | 2.15 |
| 1212 | A274 | 80p multi | 2.35 | 2.35 |
| 1213 | A274 | £1 multi | 2.75 | 2.75 |
| | | Nos. 1208-1213 (6) | 11.10 | 11.10 |

| 2007, May 10 | | Souvenir Sheet | | |
|---|---|---|---|---|
| 1214 | | Sheet of 4 | 6.75 | 6.75 |
| a. | | A274 25p multi | .75 | .75 |
| b. | | A274 40p multi | 1.15 | 1.15 |
| c.-d. | | A274 80p Either single | 2.45 | 2.45 |

Historical Maps of Isle of Man — A275

Designs: 28p, Map by John Speed, 1605. 31p, Map by Capt. Greenville Collins, 1693. 44p, Map by John Drinkwater, 1826. 48p, Ordnance Survey County Series map, 1870. 75p, Six-inch Series map, 1975. 88p, 1:100,000 map by Isle of Man Government Mapping Office, 2006.

| 2007, Aug. 1 | Litho. | | Perf. 12½x13 | |
|---|---|---|---|---|
| 1215 | A275 | 28p multi | .80 | .80 |
| 1216 | A275 | 31p multi | .90 | .90 |
| 1217 | A275 | 44p multi | 1.30 | 1.30 |
| 1218 | A275 | 48p multi | 1.45 | 1.45 |
| 1219 | A275 | 75p multi | 2.25 | 2.25 |
| 1220 | A275 | 88p multi | 2.85 | 2.85 |
| | | Nos. 1215-1220 (6) | 9.55 | 9.55 |

Intl. Polar Year — A276

Designs: 28p, Capt. John Ross, ship Victory trapped in ice. 31p, Flares shot from Victory. 55p, Victory crewmen hunting with Inuit. 75p, Musk ox hunted by Victory crewmen. 90p, Victory crewmen pulling sled after abandoning ship. 117p, Whaler Isabella rescuing Victory crewmen.

| 2007, Aug. 20 | | | | |
|---|---|---|---|---|
| 1221 | A276 | 28p multi | .85 | .85 |
| 1222 | A276 | 31p multi | .95 | .95 |
| 1223 | A276 | 55p multi | 1.70 | 1.70 |
| 1224 | A276 | 75p multi | 2.30 | 2.30 |
| 1225 | A276 | 90p multi | 2.95 | 2.95 |
| 1226 | A276 | 117p multi | 3.60 | 3.60 |
| | | Nos. 1221-1226 (6) | 12.35 | 12.35 |

Souvenir Sheet

Manx Connections With Northern Canada — A277

No. 1227: a, Ben-My-Chree Cabin, British Columbia. b, Graham "Jimmy" Oates, first man to reach Hudson Bay on rubber-tired vehicle, vert. c, Kermode bear, vert. d, Hudson Bay Post Office and dog team.

| 2007, Aug. 20 | | | Perf. 13 | |
|---|---|---|---|---|
| 1227 | A277 | Sheet of 4 | 7.50 | 7.50 |
| a.-b. | | 50p Either single | 1.50 | 1.50 |
| c.-d. | | 75p Either single | 2.25 | 2.25 |

Intl. Polar Year.

Europen Vintage Plowing Championships A278

Designs: 28p, Manx-style plowing. 31p, Vintage plowing. 48p, Horse and digger plow. 71p, Swing plow. 90p, World-style plowing.

---

£1.27, Jean Burns, first woman to compete in Manx plowing contest, on tractor.

| 2007, Sept. 1 | | | Perf. 13¼ | |
|---|---|---|---|---|
| 1228 | A278 | 28p multi | .80 | .80 |
| 1229 | A278 | 31p multi | .85 | .85 |
| 1230 | A278 | 48p multi | 1.40 | 1.40 |
| 1231 | A278 | 71p multi | 2.15 | 2.15 |
| 1232 | A278 | 90p multi | 2.75 | 2.75 |
| 1233 | A278 | £1.27 multi | 3.75 | 3.75 |
| | | Nos. 1228-1233 (6) | 11.70 | 11.70 |

Christmas — A279

Various angels with panel color of: 28p, Blue. 31p, Pink. 69p, Orange. 78p, Green. £1.24, Dark blue.

Serpentine Die Cut 13x13¼

| 2007, Oct. 19 | | Self-Adhesive | | |
|---|---|---|---|---|
| 1234 | A279 | 28p multi | .80 | .80 |
| 1235 | A279 | 31p multi | .95 | .95 |
| 1236 | A279 | 69p multi | 2.05 | 2.05 |
| 1237 | A279 | 78p multi | 2.25 | 2.25 |
| 1238 | A279 | £1.24 multi | 3.50 | 3.50 |
| | | Nos. 1234-1238 (5) | 9.55 | 9.55 |

Souvenir Sheet

Cunard Ocean Liners A280

No. 1239: a, Queen Elizabeth 2. b, Queen Mary 2. c, Queen Victoria.

| 2008, Jan. 13 | Litho. | | Perf. 14x13¼ | |
|---|---|---|---|---|
| 1239 | A280 | Sheet of 3 | 8.75 | 8.75 |
| a.-c. | | £1 Any single | 2.75 | 2.75 |
| d. | | Sheet of 10 #1239a + 10 labels | 27.50 | — |
| e. | | Sheet of 10 #1239b + 10 labels | 27.50 | — |
| f. | | Sheet of 10 #1239c + 10 labels | 27.50 | — |

Royal Air Force, 90th Anniv. — A281

Aircraft: No. 1240, H.P. 0/400, Bristol F2B fighter. No. 1241, Avro 504N, Westland Wapiti. No. 1242, Hawker Hurricane, Short Sunderland. No. 1243, Gloster Meteor, Westland Whirlwind. No. 1244, Hawker Hunter, E.E. Canberra. No. 1245, BAE Harrier, Lockheed Hercules.

| 2008, Jan. 15 | | | Perf. 13¼ | |
|---|---|---|---|---|
| 1240 | A281 | 31p multi | .85 | .85 |
| 1241 | A281 | 31p multi | .85 | .85 |
| 1242 | A281 | 31p multi | .85 | .85 |
| a. | | Horiz. strip, #1240-1242 | 2.55 | 2.55 |
| 1243 | A281 | 90p multi | 2.55 | 2.55 |
| a. | | Booklet pane, #1240-1243 | 4.00 | — |
| 1244 | A281 | 90p multi | 2.55 | 2.55 |
| a. | | Booklet pane, #1240-1241, 1243-1244 | 5.50 | — |
| 1245 | A281 | 90p multi | 2.55 | 2.55 |
| a. | | Horiz. strip, #1243-1245 | 7.75 | 7.75 |
| b. | | Booklet pane, #1242-1245 | 6.75 | — |
| c. | | Booklet pane, #1240-1241, 1244-1245 | 5.50 | — |
| | | Complete booklet, #1243a, 1244a, 1245b, 1245c | 22.00 | |
| | | Nos. 1240-1245 (6) | 10.20 | 10.20 |

Vikings on Isle of Man — A282

Designs: 28p, Pagan Lady of Peel. 31p, Ship burial. 44p, Godred Crovan (King Orry). 54p, Gautr Bjornsson the Sculptor. 69p, Sigurd the Dragon Slayer. £1.24, Coming of Christianity.

---

| 2008, Feb. 18 | Litho. | | Perf. 13¼ | |
|---|---|---|---|---|
| 1246 | A282 | 28p multi | .75 | .75 |
| 1247 | A282 | 31p multi | .90 | .90 |
| 1248 | A282 | 44p multi | 1.20 | 1.20 |
| 1249 | A282 | 54p multi | 1.55 | 1.55 |
| 1250 | A282 | 69p multi | 1.90 | 1.90 |
| 1251 | A282 | £1.24 multi | 3.45 | 3.45 |
| | | Nos. 1246-1251 (6) | 9.75 | 9.75 |

Manx Bank Notes — A283

Designs: 30p, 1956 Isle of Man Bank one-pound note. 31p, 1972 Isle of Man Government ten-pound note. 44p, 1882 Manx Bank one-pound note. 56p, 1969 Isle of Man Government fifty-pence note. 85p, 1983 Isle of Man Government fifty-pound note. 114p, 1918 Parr's Bank one-pound note.

| 2008, Apr. 7 | | | Perf. 14 | |
|---|---|---|---|---|
| 1252 | A283 | 30p multi | .85 | .85 |
| 1253 | A283 | 31p multi | .85 | .85 |
| 1254 | A283 | 44p multi | 1.20 | 1.20 |
| 1255 | A283 | 56p multi | 1.50 | 1.50 |
| 1256 | A283 | 85p multi | 2.45 | 2.45 |
| 1257 | A283 | 114p multi | 3.00 | 3.00 |
| | | Nos. 1252-1257 (6) | 9.85 | 9.85 |

Booklet Stamp
Self-Adhesive
Die Cut Perf. 12x12¼

| 1258 | A283 | 30p multi | 1.15 | 1.15 |
|---|---|---|---|---|
| a. | | Booklet pane of 10 | 11.50 | |
| | | Complete booklet, #1258a | 11.50 | |

Miniature Sheet

2008 Summer Olympics, Beijing — A284

| 2008, Apr. 21 | | | Perf. 13¼ | |
|---|---|---|---|---|
| 1259 | A284 | Sheet of 4 | 2.75 | 2.75 |
| a. | | 1p Archery | .25 | .25 |
| b. | | 2p Equestrian | .25 | .25 |
| c. | | 3p Cycling | .25 | .25 |
| d. | | 94p Olympic torch | 2.50 | 2.50 |
| e. | | As No. 1259, with Olympex inscription in sheet margin | 3.50 | 3.50 |
| f. | | Souvenir sheet, #1259c, #1259d | 3.50 | 3.50 |

Issued: No. 1259e, 8/8; No. 1259f, 8/9.

Interceltic Music Festival, Lorient, France — A285

Flags of regions with Celtic language heritage: 20p, Cornwall. 30p, Isle of Man. 31p, Scotland. 48p, Brittany. 50p, Ireland. 56p, Asturias. 72p, Wales. £1.13, Galicia.

| 2008, May 12 | | | Perf. 13¼ | |
|---|---|---|---|---|
| 1260 | A285 | 20p multi | .55 | .55 |
| 1261 | A285 | 30p multi | .85 | .85 |
| 1262 | A285 | 31p multi | .85 | .85 |
| a. | | Sheet of 10 | 8.50 | 8.50 |
| 1263 | A285 | 48p multi | 1.30 | 1.30 |
| 1264 | A285 | 50p multi | 1.30 | 1.30 |
| a. | | Sheet of 10 | 13.00 | 13.00 |
| 1265 | A285 | 56p multi | 1.50 | 1.50 |
| 1266 | A285 | 72p multi | 2.05 | 2.05 |
| 1267 | A285 | £1.13 multi | 3.00 | 3.00 |
| a. | | Sheet of 8 #1260-1267 (Aug. 1) | 20.00 | |
| | | Nos. 1260-1267 (8) | 11.40 | 11.40 |

Europa (31p, 50p).

Famous Race Drivers and Their Cars — A286

Designs: 20p, Reg Parnell. 30p, Mike Hawthorn. 70p, Tony Brooks. 81p, Roy Salvadori. 94p, Stirling Moss. £1.22, Jim Clark.

| 2008, July 10 | Litho. | | Perf. 14 | |
|---|---|---|---|---|
| 1268 | A286 | 20p multi | .50 | .50 |
| 1269 | A286 | 30p multi | .85 | .85 |
| 1270 | A286 | 70p multi | 1.85 | 1.85 |

---

| 1271 | A286 | 81p multi | 2.25 | 2.25 |
|---|---|---|---|---|
| 1272 | A286 | 94p multi | 2.60 | 2.60 |
| 1273 | A286 | £1.22 multi | 3.35 | 3.35 |
| | | Nos. 1268-1273 (6) | 11.40 | 11.40 |

Miniature Sheet

Race Cars A287

No. 1274: a, 1961 Aston Martin DB4 GT Zagato. b, 1965 Ferrari 250 LM. c, 1962 Ferrari 250 GTO. d, 1965 Ford GT40. e, 1955 Mercedes-Benz 300 SLR. f, 1964 Shelby Cobra.

| 2008, July 10 | | | Perf. 14¾x14 | |
|---|---|---|---|---|
| 1274 | A287 | Sheet of 6 | 8.25 | 8.25 |
| a.-f. | | 50p Any single | 1.35 | 1.35 |

Famous People — A288

No. 1275: a, Mary Louisa Wood (1839-1925), founder of Isle of Man Fine Arts and Industrial Guild. b, Harry Kelly (1852-1935), last native Manx speaker. c, Sir Frank Gill (1866-1950), telephone and communications engineer. d, Ramsey Gelling Johnson (1889-1972), judge, president of Royal Manx Agricultural Society. e, John Nicholson (1911-88), stamp designer.

No. 1276: a, Dr. Dorothy Pantin (1896-1985), first female doctor. b, Richard Costain (1839-1902), construction business entrepreneur. c, Sir William Percy Cowley (1886-1958), judge. d, Rev. Fred Cubbon (1902-80), philantropist. e, William Henry Gill (1839-1922), author, musician.

| 2008, Aug. 1 | | | Perf. 13¼ | |
|---|---|---|---|---|
| 1275 | | Horiz. strip of 5 | 4.35 | 4.35 |
| a.-e. | | A288 31p Any single | .85 | .85 |
| 1276 | | Horiz. strip of 5 | 6.80 | 6.80 |
| a.-e. | | A288 50p Any single | 1.30 | 1.30 |

End of World War I, 90th Anniv. — A289

Poppy and letter from soldier: 30p, Second Lieutenant Roy F. Corlett. 31p, Second Lieutenant John W. Lewis. 44p, Private Joseph Killey. 56p, Lieutenant Colonel W. A. W. Crellin. 81p, Lance Corporal Tom Quilliam. 94p, Private Robert Oates. £2, National War Memorial, St. John's.

| 2008, Oct. 1 | Litho. | | Perf. 14 | |
|---|---|---|---|---|
| 1277 | A289 | 30p multi | .85 | .85 |
| 1278 | A289 | 31p multi | .85 | .85 |
| 1279 | A289 | 44p multi | 1.25 | 1.25 |
| 1280 | A289 | 56p multi | 1.55 | 1.55 |
| 1281 | A289 | 81p multi | 2.30 | 2.30 |
| 1282 | A289 | 94p multi | 2.50 | 2.50 |
| | | Nos. 1277-1282 (6) | 9.30 | 9.30 |

Souvenir Sheet

| 1283 | A289 | £2 multi | 5.50 | 5.50 |
|---|---|---|---|---|

Flora and Fauna of Ballaugh Curragh — A290

Designs: 30p, Orange-tip butterfly. 31p, Curlew. 50p, Birch bracket fungus. 70p, Large red damselfly. 82p, Marsh cinquefoil. £1.38, Royal fern.

| 2008, Oct. 1 | | | Perf. 13¼ | |
|---|---|---|---|---|
| 1284 | A290 | 30p multi | .85 | .85 |
| 1285 | A290 | 31p multi | .85 | .85 |
| 1286 | A290 | 50p multi | 1.35 | 1.35 |
| 1287 | A290 | 70p multi | 1.90 | 1.90 |
| 1288 | A290 | 82p multi | 2.30 | 2.30 |
| 1289 | A290 | £1.38 multi | 3.75 | 3.75 |
| | | Nos. 1284-1289 (6) | 11.00 | 11.00 |

Christmas
A291

Postman from *The Jolly Christmas Postman,* by Janet and Allen Ahlberg: 28p, On bicycle, letters. 31p, And mouse in cracker box. 48p, And bear family. 50p, And Toy Town. 56p, On bicycle, with truck and horsecart on winding road. £1.56, At home.

**2008, Oct. 20**     **Perf. 14x14¼**
| | | | |
|---|---|---|---|
| 1290 | A291 | 28p multi | .80 | .80 |
| 1291 | A291 | 31p multi | .85 | .85 |
| 1292 | A291 | 48p multi | 1.40 | 1.40 |
| 1293 | A291 | 50p multi | 1.40 | 1.40 |
| 1294 | A291 | 56p multi | 1.65 | 1.65 |
| 1295 | A291 | £1.56 multi | 3.90 | 3.90 |
| | Nos. 1290-1295 (6) | 10.00 | 10.00 |

Lewis Hamilton, Formula 1 Race Car Driver — A292

No. 1296: a, Hamilton driving race car. b, Hamilton celebrating victory with champagne spray.
No. 1297: a, Hamilton driving past finish line. b, Hamilton in race car cockpit.
No. 1298: a, Hamilton driving race car, diff. b, Hamilton in helmet with arms extended.

**2009, Jan. 15**   **Litho.**   **Perf. 14**
| | | | | |
|---|---|---|---|---|
| 1296 | | Horiz. pair | 1.55 | 1.55 |
| a. | A292 30p multi | | .75 | .75 |
| b. | A292 31p multi | | .80 | .80 |
| 1297 | | Horiz. pair | 3.55 | 3.55 |
| a. | A292 56p multi | | 1.40 | 1.40 |
| b. | A292 85p multi | | 2.15 | 2.15 |
| 1298 | | Horiz. pair | 6.00 | 6.00 |
| a. | A292 98p multi | | 2.45 | 2.45 |
| b. | A292 £1.42 multi | | 3.55 | 3.55 |
| | Nos. 1296-1298 (3) | 11.10 | 11.10 |

Naval Aviation, Cent. — A293

No. 1299: a, Fairey Barracuda II. b, Blackburn Buccaneer S.2. c, Fairey Flycatcher.
No. 1300: a, EH101 Merlin helicopter. b, BAe Sea Harrier FRS.1. c, Sea Scout SS.24 airship.

**2009, Jan. 15**
| | | | | |
|---|---|---|---|---|
| 1299 | | Horiz. strip of 3 | 3.35 | 3.35 |
| a. | A293 30p multi | | .75 | .75 |
| b. | A293 31p multi | | .80 | .80 |
| c. | A293 72p multi | | 1.80 | 1.80 |
| d. | Booklet pane of 4, 2 each #1299a, 1299b | | 2.75 | — |
| 1300 | | Horiz. strip of 3 | 8.00 | 8.00 |
| a. | A293 85p multi | | 2.15 | 2.15 |
| b. | A293 98p multi | | 2.45 | 2.45 |
| c. | A293 £1.36 multi | | 3.30 | 3.30 |
| d. | Booklet pane of 4, #1299a, 1299b, 1300a, 1300c | | 5.00 | — |
| e. | Booklet pane of 4, #1299a, 1300a, 1300b, 1300c | | 6.50 | — |
| f. | Booklet pane of 4, #1299c, 1300a, 1300b, 1300c | | 8.75 | — |
| | Complete booklet, #1299d, 1300d, 1300e, 1300f | | 23.00 | |

Accession to the Throne of Henry VIII, 500th Anniv. — A294

No. 1301: a, King Henry VIII. b, Catherine of Aragon (first wife). c, Anne Boleyn (second wife). d, Jane Seymour (third wife).
No. 1302: a, Anne of Cleves (fourth wife). b, Catherine Howard (fifth wife). c, Catherine Parr (sixth wife). d, Hampton Court.

**2009, Feb. 18**     **Perf. 13¼**
| | | | | |
|---|---|---|---|---|
| 1301 | | Horiz. strip of 4 | 5.00 | 5.00 |
| a.-d. | A294 50p Any single | | 1.25 | 1.25 |
| 1302 | | Horiz. strip of 4 | 5.00 | 5.00 |
| a.-d. | A294 50p Any single | | 1.25 | 1.25 |

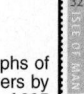

Photographs of Mills and Millers by Chris Killip — A295

No. 1303: a, Ballakilley Farm. b, Grenaby Farm.
No. 1304: a, Mr. Cubbon. b, Glenmoar Mill.
No. 1305: a, Golden Meadow Mill. b, Bernie Mylcraine.
No. 1306: a, Golden Meadow Mill, diff. b, Loughtan Farm.
No. 1307, Like #1303a. No. 1308, Like #1303b. No. 1309, Like #1304b. No. 1310, Like #1304a.

**2009, Apr. 1**     **Perf. 13¼**
| | | | |
|---|---|---|---|
| 1303 | | Pair | 1.55 | 1.55 |
| a.-b. | A295 32p Either single | .75 | .75 |
| 1304 | | Pair | 1.70 | 1.70 |
| a.-b. | A295 33p Either single | .85 | .85 |
| 1305 | | Pair | 2.45 | 2.45 |
| a.-b. | A295 50p Either single | 1.20 | 1.20 |
| 1306 | | Pair | 4.00 | 4.00 |
| a.-b. | A295 78p Either single | 2.00 | 2.00 |
| | Nos. 1303-1306 (4) | 9.70 | 9.70 |

**Booklet Stamps**
**Self-Adhesive**
*Serpentine Die Cut 12½*
| | | | | |
|---|---|---|---|---|
| 1307 | A295 | 32p black | .95 | .95 |
| 1308 | A295 | 32p black | .95 | .95 |
| a. | Booklet pane of 10, 5 each #1307-1308 | | 9.00 | |
| | Complete booklet, #1308a | | 9.00 | |
| 1309 | A295 | 33p black | 1.00 | 1.00 |
| 1310 | A295 | 33p black | 1.00 | 1.00 |
| a. | Booklet pane of 10, 5 each #1309-1310 | | 10.00 | |
| | Complete booklet, #1310a | | 10.00 | |
| | Nos. 1307-1310 (4) | 3.90 | 3.90 |

**Miniature Sheet**

Peonies
A296

No. 1311 — Denomination color: a, Yellow. b, Light green. c, Pink. d, Blue. e, Violet. f, Red. g, Blue green. h, Olive green.

**2009, Apr. 10**     **Perf. 13¼**
| | | | |
|---|---|---|---|
| 1311 | A296 | Sheet of 8 | 2.40 | 2.40 |
| a.-h. | 10p Any single | .30 | .30 |

First Man on the Moon, 40th Anniv. — A297

Paintings by Astronaut Alan Bean: 33p, First Boot Print, Sunrise Over Antares. 50p, Clan MacBean Arrives on the Moon, Documenting the Sample. 56p, Pete and Me. 81p, Headed for the Last Parking Lot. 105p, The Eagle is Headed Home, In the Beginning. 135p, Ceremony on the Plain at Hadley, The Hoer. £2.50, On the Rim, vert.

**2009, Apr. 12**     **Perf. 12½**
| | | | | |
|---|---|---|---|---|
| 1312 | A297 | 33p multi | .85 | .85 |
| a. | Sheet of 10 | | 8.50 | 8.50 |
| b. | Perf. 13, dated "2020" (2080n) | | — | — |
| 1313 | A297 | 50p multi | 1.30 | 1.30 |
| a. | Perf. 13, dated "2019" (2022e) | | 1.40 | 1.40 |
| 1314 | A297 | 56p multi | 1.50 | 1.50 |
| a. | Sheet of 10 | | 15.00 | 15.00 |
| b. | Perf. 13, dated "2019" (2022e) | | 1.50 | 1.50 |
| 1315 | A297 | 81p multi | 2.05 | 2.05 |
| a. | Perf. 13, dated "2020" (2080b) | | — | — |
| 1316 | A297 | 105p multi | 2.80 | 2.80 |
| a. | Perf. 13, dated "2019" (2022e) | | 2.75 | 2.75 |
| 1317 | A297 | 135p multi | 3.20 | 3.20 |
| a. | Perf. 13, dated "2020" (2080b) | | — | — |
| | Nos. 1312-1317 (6) | 11.70 | 11.70 |

**Souvenir Sheet**
| | | | | |
|---|---|---|---|---|
| 1318 | A297 | £2.50 multi | 6.50 | 6.50 |
| a. | As #1318, with 40th anniversary emblem in sheet margin, perf. 12 | | 7.25 | 7.25 |

Europa (33p, 56p).
Issued: No. 1318a, 7/20; Nos. 1313a, 1314b, 1316a, 2019; Nos. 1312b, 1315a, 1317a, 2/26/20.

Honda Racing Motorcycles A298

Motorcycle from the: 32p, 1950s. 33p, 1960s. 56p, 1970s. 62p, 1980s. 90p, 1990s. £1.77, 2000s.

**2009, May 11**     **Perf. 14**
| | | | | |
|---|---|---|---|---|
| 1319 | A298 | 32p multi | .75 | .75 |
| 1320 | A298 | 33p multi | .85 | .85 |
| 1321 | A298 | 56p multi | 1.40 | 1.40 |
| 1322 | A298 | 62p multi | 1.50 | 1.50 |
| 1323 | A298 | 90p multi | 2.35 | 2.35 |
| 1324 | A298 | £1.77 multi | 4.50 | 4.50 |
| a. | Dated "2014" | | 5.25 | 5.25 |
| b. | Souvenir sheet of 8, 3 #1180f, 5 #1324a, + 4 labels | | 30.00 | 30.00 |
| | Nos. 1319-1324 (6) | 11.35 | 11.35 |

Issued: Nos. 1324a, 1324b, 2014.

**Souvenir Sheet**

2009 England Vs. Australia The Ashes Cricket Test Match A299

No. 1325: a, W. G. Grace at Lord's Cricket Ground (42x28mm). b, Marylebone Cricket Club Ashes trophy and urn (30x40mm). c, England vs. Australia, Lord's Cricket Ground, 2005 (42x28mm).

**Perf. 14 (#1325a, 1325c), 14x14¾**
**2009, June 20**
| | | | | |
|---|---|---|---|---|
| 1325 | A299 | Sheet of 3 | 7.75 | 7.75 |
| a.-c. | £1 Any single | | 2.50 | 2.50 |

The Bee Gees, 50th Anniv. — A300

No. 1326: a, Barry, Robin and Maurice Gibb as children. b, "Children of the World" album cover. c, "Spirits Having Flown" album cover. d, "Still Waters" album cover.
No. 1327: a, "One Night Only" album cover. b, "This Is Where I Came In" album cover. c, "Number Ones" album cover. d, "The Studio Albums 1967-1968" album cover.

**2009, July 1**     **Perf. 13x12½**
| | | | | |
|---|---|---|---|---|
| 1326 | | Horiz. strip of 4 + central label | 4.25 | 4.25 |
| a. | A300 32p multi | | .75 | .75 |
| b. | A300 33p multi | | .85 | .85 |
| c. | A300 50p multi | | 1.20 | 1.20 |
| d. | A300 54p multi | | 1.30 | 1.30 |
| 1327 | | Horiz. strip of 4 + central label | 8.50 | 8.50 |
| a. | A300 56p multi | | 1.50 | 1.50 |
| b. | A300 62p multi | | 1.60 | 1.60 |
| c. | A300 78p multi | | 2.05 | 2.05 |
| d. | A300 £1.28 multi | | 3.20 | 3.20 |

Paintings of Wildlife by Jeremy Paul — A301

Paintings: 32p, Brown Hare. 33p, Hedgehogs. 54p, Pheasants. 90p, Barn Owl. 92p, Cockerel. £1.58, On the Hill.

**2009, Sept. 1**   **Litho.**   **Perf. 12½**
| | | | | |
|---|---|---|---|---|
| 1328 | A301 | 32p multi | .85 | .85 |
| 1329 | A301 | 33p multi | .85 | .85 |
| 1330 | A301 | 54p multi | 1.40 | 1.40 |
| 1331 | A301 | 90p multi | 2.35 | 2.35 |
| 1332 | A301 | 92p multi | 2.35 | 2.35 |
| 1333 | A301 | £1.58 multi | 4.10 | 4.10 |
| a. | Sheet of 6, #1328-1333 | | 12.00 | 12.00 |
| | Nos. 1328-1333 (6) | 11.90 | 11.90 |

Watercolors by Archibald Knox — A302

Watercolors: 32p, Bridge Possibly at Laxey. 33p, Willows and Blue Mountain Possibly Greeba. 56p, Kew. 62p, Eairy Beg Glen Helen. 81p, Leaning Trees. 182p, Old Laxey.

**2009, Sept. 16**     **Perf. 12½**
| | | | | |
|---|---|---|---|---|
| 1334 | A302 | 32p multi | .80 | .80 |
| 1335 | A302 | 33p multi | .90 | .90 |
| 1336 | A302 | 56p multi | 1.45 | 1.45 |
| 1337 | A302 | 62p multi | 1.55 | 1.55 |
| 1338 | A302 | 81p multi | 2.15 | 2.15 |
| 1339 | A302 | 182p multi | 4.70 | 4.70 |
| | Nos. 1334-1339 (6) | 11.55 | 11.55 |

**Souvenir Sheet**

Sinking of the Ellan Vannin, Cent. A303

No. 1340: a, Captain James Teare and Ellan Vannan at sea. b, Ellan Vannan in harbor.

**2009, Oct. 1**     **Perf. 14**
| | | | | |
|---|---|---|---|---|
| 1340 | A303 | Sheet of 2 | 7.75 | 7.75 |
| a.-b. | £1.50 Either single | | 3.85 | 3.85 |

Christmas — A304

Santa Claus: 30p, Filling stocking. 33p, Making a list. 56p, Holding bag of toys. 62p, Near chimney, holding gift. 81p, Holding staff and bag. 90p, Holding chalice.

**2009, Oct. 20**     **Perf. 14**
| | | | | |
|---|---|---|---|---|
| 1341 | A304 | 30p multi | .75 | .75 |
| 1342 | A304 | 33p multi | .85 | .85 |
| 1343 | A304 | 56p multi | 1.45 | 1.45 |
| 1344 | A304 | 62p multi | 1.60 | 1.60 |
| 1345 | A304 | 81p multi | 2.05 | 2.05 |
| 1346 | A304 | 90p multi | 2.30 | 2.30 |
| | Nos. 1341-1346 (6) | 9.00 | 9.00 |

**Size: 23x34mm**
**Self-Adhesive**
*Die Cut Perf. 13x13½*
| | | | | |
|---|---|---|---|---|
| 1347 | A304 | 30p multi | 1.25 | 1.25 |
| 1348 | A304 | 33p multi | 1.50 | 1.50 |

A305     A306

A307     A308

A309     A310

A311

A312

A313

Island Life — A314

**2010, Jan. 12**       **Perf. 12½**
| 1349 | Horiz. strip of 4 | 3.35 | 3.35 |
|---|---|---|---|
| a. | A305 (32p) multi | .85 | .85 |
| b. | A306 (32p) multi | .85 | .85 |
| c. | A307 (32p) multi | .85 | .85 |
| d. | A308 (32p) multi | .85 | .85 |
| 1350 | Horiz. strip of 4 | 3.50 | 3.50 |
| a. | A309 (33p) multi | .85 | .85 |
| b. | A310 (33p) multi | .85 | .85 |
| c. | A311 (33p) multi | .85 | .85 |
| d. | A312 (33p) multi | .85 | .85 |
| 1351 | A313 56p multi | 1.35 | 1.35 |
| 1352 | A314 90p multi | 2.35 | 2.35 |
| | Nos. 1349-1352 (4) | 10.55 | 10.55 |

### Booklet Stamps
### Self-Adhesive
*Serpentine Die Cut 13¾x13*
| 1353 | A305 (32p) multi | .95 | .95 |
|---|---|---|---|
| 1354 | A306 (32p) multi | .95 | .95 |
| 1355 | A307 (32p) multi | .95 | .95 |
| 1356 | A308 (32p) multi | .95 | .95 |
| a. | Booklet pane of 12, 3 each #1353-1356 | 11.25 | 11.25 |
| 1357 | A309 (33p) multi | 1.00 | 1.00 |
| 1358 | A310 (33p) multi | 1.00 | 1.00 |
| 1359 | A311 (33p) multi | 1.00 | 1.00 |
| 1360 | A312 (33p) multi | 1.00 | 1.00 |
| a. | Booklet pane of 12, 3 each #1357-1360 | 12.50 | |
| | Nos. 1353-1360 (8) | 7.80 | 7.80 |

Nos. 1356a and 1360a are complete booklets, the backing serving as the booklet covers.

Girl Guides, Cent. A315

No. 1361 — Rainbows with denomination in: a, Red. b, Blue.
No. 1362 — Brownies with denomination in: a, Red. b, Blue.
No. 1363 — Girl Guides with denomination in: a, Red. b, Blue.
No. 1364 — Senior Section members with denomination in: a, Red. b, Blue.
No. 1365 — Adult volunteers with denomination in: a, Red. b, Blue.

**2010**       **Perf. 14**
| 1361 | A315 | Horiz. pair | 1.45 | 1.45 |
|---|---|---|---|---|
| a.-b. | | 32p Either single | .70 | .70 |
| 1362 | A315 | Horiz. pair | 1.45 | 1.45 |
| a.-b. | | 33p Either single | .70 | .70 |
| c. | | Sheet of 10 #1362a | 7.00 | 7.00 |
| 1363 | A315 | Horiz. pair | 2.70 | 2.70 |
| a.-b. | | 56p Either single | 1.35 | 1.35 |
| c. | | Sheet of 10 #1363a | 13.50 | 13.50 |
| 1364 | A315 | Horiz. pair | 4.50 | 4.50 |
| a.-b. | | £1 Either single | 2.25 | 2.25 |
| | | Nos. 1361-1364 (4) | 10.10 | 10.10 |

### Souvenir Sheet
| 1365 | A315 | Sheet of 2 | 7.75 | 7.75 |
|---|---|---|---|---|
| a.-b. | | £1.50 Either single | 3.85 | 3.85 |
| c. | | As #1365, with Centenary Camp emblem added in sheet margin | 11.00 | 11.00 |

Issued: Nos. 1361-1365, 2/18; No. 1365c, 7/31. Europa (Nos. 1362a, 1363a).

Battle of Britain, 70th Anniv. A317

No. 1366: a, Messerschmitt BF110 and Hurricane. b, Blenheim I and Junkers 88. c, Heinkel III and Spitfire.

No. 1367: a, Messerschmitt BF109 and Defiant. b, Spitfire and Messerschmitt BF109. c, Junkers JU-87 and Hurricane.
No. 1368: a, Ben My Chree arriving at Folkstone with troops evacuated from Dunkirk, Isle of Man #204. b, Airmen running to planes, Isle of Man #429a.

**2010, Apr. 20**      **Perf. 13¼**
| 1366 | Horiz. strip of 3 | 5.60 | 5.60 |
|---|---|---|---|
| a.-c. | A316 70p Any single | 1.85 | 1.85 |
| d. | As "a," dated "2015" | 2.25 | 2.25 |
| e. | As "b," dated "2015" | 2.25 | 2.25 |
| f. | As "c," dated "2015" | 2.25 | 2.25 |
| 1367 | Horiz. strip of 3 | 5.60 | 5.60 |
| a.-c. | A316 70p Any single | 1.85 | 1.85 |
| d. | As "a," dated "2015" | 2.25 | 2.25 |
| e. | As "b," dated "2015" | 2.25 | 2.25 |
| f. | As "c," dated "2015" | 2.25 | 2.25 |
| g. | Sheet of 12, 2 each #1366d-1366f, 1367d-1367f, + 8 labels | 27.00 | 27.00 |

### Souvenir Sheet
### Perf. 13¾
| 1368 | A317 | Sheet of 2 | 8.25 | 8.25 |
|---|---|---|---|---|
| a.-b. | | £1.50 Either single | 4.00 | 4.00 |

Issued: Nos. 1366d-1366f, 1367d-1367f, 7/17/15.

Accession to Throne of King George V, Cent. — A318

Photographs of 1920 royal visit to Isle of Man and items from Royal Philatelic Collection: 55p, Royal party at Bishops Court, Ballaugh, cast of proposed 1913 stamp depicting King George V. 60p, King George V and Queen Mary on Tynwald Hill, two used pairs of Cape of Good Hope 1p triangle stamps. 67p, Queen's Pier, Ramsey, unissued 2p plum stamp of Great Britain. 96p, Visit to war disabled at Ramsey Cottage Hospital, Niger Coast Protectorates #35. 97p, Tree planting at Bishops Court, Great Britain #151. £1.10, Royal party at Castletown, Mauritius #2.

**2010, May 6**      **Perf. 14**
| 1369 | A318 | 55p multi | 1.40 | 1.40 |
|---|---|---|---|---|
| 1370 | A318 | 60p multi | 1.50 | 1.50 |
| 1371 | A318 | 67p multi | 1.65 | 1.65 |
| 1372 | A318 | 96p multi | 2.60 | 2.60 |
| 1373 | A318 | 97p multi | 2.60 | 2.60 |
| 1374 | A318 | £1.10 multi | 2.85 | 2.85 |
| | | Nos. 1369-1374 (6) | 12.60 | 12.60 |

Model T Fords — A319

Designs: 35p, 1915 Speedster. 36p, 1926 Coupe. 60p, 1923 Van. 74p, 1912 Town Car. 97p, 1922 Charabanc. 172p, 1912 Tourer.

**2010, May 7**      **Perf. 13¼**
| 1375 | A319 | 35p multi | .95 | .95 |
|---|---|---|---|---|
| 1376 | A319 | 36p multi | .95 | .95 |
| 1377 | A319 | 60p multi | 1.55 | 1.55 |
| 1378 | A319 | 74p multi | 1.90 | 1.90 |
| 1379 | A319 | 97p multi | 2.65 | 2.65 |
| 1380 | A319 | 172p multi | 4.50 | 4.50 |
| | | Nos. 1375-1380 (6) | 12.50 | 12.50 |

Railways A320

Designs: 35p, Caledonia at summit of Snaefell Mountain. 36p, Isle of Man Railways steam locomotive No. 1 and Manx Electric Railway car No. 1 at Laxey. 55p, Caledonia at Bulgham. 88p, Isle of Man Railways Loch locomotive at Skinscoe Curve. £1.32, Manx Electric Railway car No. 33 approaching Keristal. £1.46, Loch and Maitland locomotives near White Hoe.

**2010, June 24**      **Perf. 14**
| 1381 | A320 | 35p multi | 1.00 | 1.00 |
|---|---|---|---|---|
| 1382 | A320 | 36p multi | 1.00 | 1.00 |
| 1383 | A320 | 55p multi | 1.60 | 1.60 |
| 1384 | A320 | 88p multi | 2.50 | 2.50 |
| 1385 | A320 | £1.32 multi | 3.50 | 3.50 |
| 1386 | A320 | £1.46 multi | 4.00 | 4.00 |
| a. | | Sheet of 6, #1381-1386 + 3 labels | 17.50 | 17.50 |
| | | Nos. 1381-1386 (6) | 13.60 | 13.60 |

History of Manx Coinage — A321

Designs: 35p, 1709 Lord Derby halfpenny, Castle Rushen. 36p, 1798 Cartwheel penny, Soho Mint, Birmingham. 55p, 1839 Queen Victoria Farthing, Douglas. 60p, 1965 gold coin, Castle Rushen. 67p, 1971 Decimal currency 5p coin, Tower of Refuge. £1.87, 2010 £5 Laxey Wheel coin, Laxey Wheel.

**2010, June 24**      **Perf. 12¾**
| 1387 | A321 | 35p multi | .95 | .95 |
|---|---|---|---|---|
| 1388 | A321 | 36p multi | .95 | .95 |
| 1389 | A321 | 55p multi | 1.50 | 1.50 |
| 1390 | A321 | 60p multi | 1.65 | 1.65 |
| 1391 | A321 | 67p multi | 1.80 | 1.80 |
| 1392 | A321 | £1.87 multi | 5.00 | 5.00 |
| | | Nos. 1387-1392 (6) | 11.85 | 11.85 |

### Souvenir Sheet
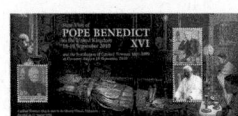
Beatification of Cardinal John Henry Newman (1801-90) — A322

No. 1393: a, Newman, table and book. b, Newman.

**2010, Aug. 11**      **Perf. 13¼**
| 1393 | A322 | Sheet of 2 + label | 8.00 | 8.00 |
|---|---|---|---|---|
| a.-b. | | £1.50 Either single | 4.00 | 4.00 |

State visit of Pope Benedict XVI.

Artwork by Internees in Isle of Man World War II Internment Camps — A323

Designs: 35p, Three-legged Postman, by Bertram. 36p, Peveril Camp, Peel, by Herbert Kaden. 55p, Life at Palace Camp, Douglas, by Imre Goth. 67p, Douglas, Isle of Man, by Hermann Fechenbach. 132p, Violinist at Onchan Camp, by Ernst Eisenmayer. 172p, Portrait of Klaus E. Hinrichsen, by Kurt Schwitters.

**2010, Sept. 24**      **Litho.**
| 1394 | A323 | 35p multi | .95 | .95 |
|---|---|---|---|---|
| 1395 | A323 | 36p multi | .95 | .95 |
| 1396 | A323 | 55p multi | 1.50 | 1.50 |
| 1397 | A323 | 67p multi | 1.75 | 1.75 |
| 1398 | A323 | 132p multi | 3.25 | 3.25 |
| 1399 | A323 | 172p multi | 4.45 | 4.45 |
| | | Nos. 1394-1399 (6) | 12.85 | 12.85 |

### Souvenir Sheet
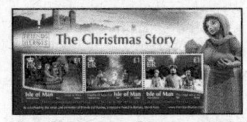
The Christmas Story — A324

No. 1400 — Characters from Friends and Heroes animated TV show depicting the Nativity: a, Jesus is born. b, Shepherds hear first. c, The Magi see a star.

**2010, Oct. 1**     **Litho.**    **Perf. 13¼x13¾**
| 1400 | A324 | Sheet of 3 | 8.00 | 8.00 |
|---|---|---|---|---|
| a.-c. | | £1 Any single | 2.65 | 2.65 |

Photographs of Snowfall of 2009-10 Winter — A325

Photographs of: 35p, Old Braddan Church, by Bill Dale. 36p, The Braaid, by Seamus Whelan. 60p, Dhoon Glen, by Simon Park. 88p, Dhoon Beach, by Park. 97p, Cronk ny Aree Laa, by Dale. £1.46, St. Patrick's Isle in Snow, by Victoria Harrop.

**2010, Oct. 20**      **Perf. 13x13¼**
| 1401 | A325 | 35p multi | .95 | .95 |
|---|---|---|---|---|
| 1402 | A325 | 36p multi | .95 | .95 |
| 1403 | A325 | 60p multi | 1.50 | 1.50 |
| 1404 | A325 | 88p multi | 2.35 | 2.35 |
| 1405 | A325 | 97p multi | 2.60 | 2.60 |
| 1406 | A325 | £1.46 multi | 3.65 | 3.65 |
| | | Nos. 1401-1406 (6) | 15.50 | 15.50 |

### Souvenir Sheet

Engagement of Prince William of Wales and Catherine Middleton — A326

No. 1407 — Prince William: a, Close-up, no shirt visible. b, Shirt visible.

**2010, Nov. 26**    **Litho.**    **Perf. 14¾x14**
| 1407 | A326 | Sheet of 2 | 8.00 | 8.00 |
|---|---|---|---|---|
| a.-b. | | £1.50 Either single | 4.00 | 4.00 |

Service of Queen Elizabeth II and Prince Philip A327

Designs: 35p, Queen Elizabeth II, 1953 coronation photograph. 36p, Queen and Prince Philip, 2007. 55p, Queen and Prince Philip as newlyweds. 60p, Queen and Prince Philip in uniforms, 1971. £1.14, Queen and Prince Philip, 2002. £1.46, Prince Philip at 1953 coronation.
£3, Queen and Prince Philip, 1970s.

**2011, Feb. 6**      **Perf. 13¼**
| 1408 | A327 | 35p multi | .90 | .90 |
|---|---|---|---|---|
| 1409 | A327 | 36p multi | .95 | .95 |
| 1410 | A327 | 55p multi | 1.40 | 1.40 |
| 1411 | A327 | 60p multi | 1.55 | 1.55 |
| 1412 | A327 | £1.14 multi | 3.10 | 3.10 |
| 1413 | A327 | £1.46 multi | 3.75 | 3.75 |
| a. | | Souvenir sheet of 6, #1408-1413, + 3 labels | 15.25 | 15.25 |
| | | Nos. 1408-1413 (6) | 14.50 | 14.50 |

### Souvenir Sheet
| 1414 | A327 | £3 multi | 7.75 | 7.75 |
|---|---|---|---|---|
| a. | | Sheet of 13, #1413, 1414, 3 #1411, 2 each #1408-1410, 1412, + 16 labels | 29.00 | 29.00 |

Issued: No. 1414a, 6/4/12.
Stamps in No. 1413a have dull purple borders, while Nos. 1408-1413 have darker black purple borders.

Genealogy — A328

Inscription in frame at UL: No. 1415, Baptisms. No. 1416, School Days. No. 1417, Working Life. No. 1418, Weddings. No. 1419, Family Album. No. 1420, Emigration. No. 1421, Memorials. No. 1422, Family Tree.

**2011, Feb. 18**    **Litho.**    **Perf. 13½**
### Frame Color
| 1415 | A328 | 35p org brown | .90 | .90 |
|---|---|---|---|---|
| 1416 | A328 | 35p deep claret | .90 | .90 |
| 1417 | A328 | 36p car rose | 1.00 | 1.00 |
| 1418 | A328 | 36p Prus blue | 1.00 | 1.00 |
| 1419 | A328 | 67p slate grn | 1.80 | 1.80 |
| 1420 | A328 | 67p emerald | 1.80 | 1.80 |
| 1421 | A328 | £1.10 ol green | 2.90 | 2.90 |
| 1422 | A328 | £1.10 brown | 2.90 | 2.90 |
| | | Nos. 1415-1422 (8) | 16.20 | 16.20 |

Greatest TT Motorcycle Races — A329

No. 1423: a, Stanley Woods v. Jimmy Guthrie, 1935 Senior race. b, Mike Hailwood v. Giacomo Agostini, 1967 Senior race. c, John Williams v. Tom Herron, 1976 Senior race. d, George O'Dell and Kenny Arthur v. Dick Greasley and Mick Skeels, 1977 Sidecar A race. e, Alex George v. Mike Hailwood, 1979 Classic race.

No. 1424: a, Steve Hislop v. Carl Fogarty, 1992 Senior race. b, Joey Dunlop v. David Jefferies, 2000 Formula 1 race. c, John McGuiness v. Cameron Donald, 2008 Senior race. d, Klaus Klaffenbock and Dan Sayle v. John Holden and Andy Winkle, 2010 Sidecar 2 race. e, Ian Hutchinson v. Ryan Farquhar, 2010 Superstock race.

£3, Hislop v. Fogarty, 1992 Senior race, horiz..

**2011, Apr. 1     Litho.     Perf. 14¼**

| | | | | |
|---|---|---|---|---|
| **1423** | | Horiz. strip of 5 | 4.75 | 4.75 |
| a.-e. | | A329 38p Any single | .95 | .95 |
| f. | | As "a," perf. 14¾ (#1425b) | 1.25 | 1.25 |
| **1424** | | Horiz. strip of 5 | 8.75 | 8.75 |
| a.-e. | | A329 68p Any single | 1.75 | 1.75 |
| f. | | As "a," perf. 14¾ (#1425b) | 2.25 | 2.25 |

**Souvenir Sheet**
**Perf. 14¼x15**

| | | | | |
|---|---|---|---|---|
| **1425** | A329 | £3 multi | 7.75 | 7.75 |
| a. | | Perf. 14 (#1425b) | 8.75 | 8.75 |
| b. | | Sheet of 8, #41a, 69a, 217, 336a, 703, 1423f, 1424f, 1425a, + 5 labels | 16.00 | 16.00 |

No. 1425 contains one 45x30mm stamp. Issued: Nos. 1423f, 1424f, 1425a, 2015. No. 1425b sold for £6.

Butterflies — A330

Designs: No. 1426, Wall butterfly. No. 1427, Dark green fritillary. No. 1428, Comma butterfly. No. 1429, Red admiral. Nos. 1430, 1434, Small tortoiseshell butterfly. No. 1431, Common blue butterfly. No. 1432, Green-veined white butterfly. No. 1433, Speckled wood butterfly.

**2011, Apr. 1       Perf. 13¼**
**With WWF Emblem at Lower Left**

| | | | | |
|---|---|---|---|---|
| **1426** | A330 | 37p multi | .95 | .95 |
| **1427** | A330 | 38p multi | .95 | .95 |
| **1428** | A330 | 58p multi | 1.50 | 1.50 |
| **1429** | A330 | 115p multi | 2.90 | 2.90 |
| a. | | Sheet of 16, 4 each #1426-1429 | 27.50 | 27.50 |

**Without WWF Emblem**

| | | | | |
|---|---|---|---|---|
| **1430** | A330 | 37p multi | .95 | .95 |
| **1431** | A330 | 38p multi | .95 | .95 |
| **1432** | A330 | 58p multi | 1.50 | 1.50 |
| **1433** | A330 | 115p multi | 2.90 | 2.90 |
| | | Nos. 1426-1433 (8) | 12.60 | 12.60 |

**Booklet Stamp**
**Self-Adhesive**
**Serpentine Die Cut 13¼**

| | | | | |
|---|---|---|---|---|
| **1434** | A330 | 37p multi | 1.15 | 1.15 |
| a. | | Booklet pane of 12 | 14.00 | 14.00 |

No. 1434a is a complete booklet, the backing serving as the booklet cover.

Souvenir Sheet

Wedding of Prince William and Catherine Middleton — A331

No. 1435: a, Middleton. b, Prince William.

**2011, Apr. 15      Perf. 14¾x14**

| | | | | |
|---|---|---|---|---|
| **1435** | A331 | Sheet of 2 | 5.25 | 5.25 |
| a.-b. | | £1 Either single, dated 2011 | 3.00 | 3.00 |
| c. | | Sheet of 10, 5 each #1435a-1435b, + 10 labels | 27.00 | 27.00 |
| d.-e. | | £1 Either single, dated 2013 | 3.00 | 3.00 |
| f. | | Sheet of 8, 4 each #1435d-1435e, + 4 labels | 24.00 | 24.00 |
| g.-h. | | £1 Either single, dated 2015 | 3.00 | 3.00 |
| i. | | Sheet of 8, 4 each #1435g-1435h, + 4 labels | 24.00 | 24.00 |
| j. | | £1 As #1435a, dated 2021, perf. 13x12¾ | 2.75 | 2.75 |
| k. | | £1 As #1435b, dated 2021, perf. 13x12¾ | 2.75 | 2.75 |
| l. | | Sheet of 8, 4 each #1435j-1435k, + 4 labels | 22.50 | 22.50 |

No. 1435f, was issued 7/31/13. Birth of Prince George of Cambridge (No. 1435f). No. 1435i, has different labels noting the birth of Princess Charlotte: issued 5/11/15. No. 1435l has different labels noting the couple's 10th wedding anniversary; issued 4/29/21.

Political Cartoons by Harold "Dusty" Miller (1898-1964) A332

Designs: 37p, The Southern Hundred. 38p, I'm Staking My Claim On the Sands at Douglas. 68p, Over the Water - I Must Get Me a Bigger Horse. 76p, Will Uncle Sam Provide the Third Leg? 110p, Bob a Job Week. 165p, Well, Councilor - Did You Vote For Evening Meetings?

**2011, May 10      Perf. 13¼**
**Color of Panel and Frame**

| | | | | |
|---|---|---|---|---|
| **1436** | A332 | 37p red | .90 | .90 |
| **1437** | A332 | 38p purple | .90 | .90 |
| **1438** | A332 | 68p green | 1.60 | 1.60 |
| **1439** | A332 | 76p red violet | 1.80 | 1.80 |
| **1440** | A332 | 110p Prussian blue | 2.70 | 2.70 |
| **1441** | A332 | 165p bister | 4.00 | 4.00 |
| | | Nos. 1436-1441 (6) | 11.90 | 11.90 |

Picture Post Cards Depicting Manx Cats — A333

Various post cards depicting cats and arms of Isle of Man.

**2011, June 23      Perf. 13¼x13½**
**Panel Color**

| | | | | |
|---|---|---|---|---|
| **1442** | A333 | 37p dark blue | 1.00 | 1.00 |
| **1443** | A333 | 38p bister | 1.00 | 1.00 |
| **1444** | A333 | 58p light blue | 1.50 | 1.50 |
| **1445** | A333 | 76p red violet | 2.00 | 2.00 |
| **1446** | A333 | 115p red | 3.00 | 3.00 |
| **1447** | A333 | 165p brown | 4.25 | 4.25 |
| | | Nos. 1442-1447 (6) | 12.75 | 12.75 |

Postal History of Knockaloe Internment Camp — A334

No. 1448: a, Post card depicting troops marching, half of 1908 Camp Knockaloe cancel. b, Address side of post card, Great Britain #143 with 1908 Camp Knockaloe cancel.

No. 1449: a, Post card depicting camp, part of 1914 Peel cancel. b, Address side of post card, pair of Great Britain #159 with 1914 Peel cancel.

No. 1450: a, Easter post card from 1915-19, half of registry label. b, Half of registry label, registered mail envelope with camp cancel.

No. 1451: a, Post card depicting camp, Knockaloe cancel. b, Internee-produced local stamp, local stamp on cover.

No. 1452: a, Post card depicting camp huts, Camp Knockaloe censor marking. b, Great Britain #160 with 1915 Camp Knockaloe cancel, prisoner-of-war cover. c, 1917 Easter post card, 1915 Camp Knockaloe cancel. d, Great Britain envelope stamp with 1915 Camp Knockaloe cancel, registered mail envelope.

**2011, Aug. 8      Perf. 13¼x13½**

| | | | | |
|---|---|---|---|---|
| **1448** | A334 | Horiz. pair | 2.45 | 2.45 |
| a.-b. | | 37p Either single | 1.20 | 1.20 |
| **1449** | A334 | Horiz. pair | 2.45 | 2.45 |
| a.-b. | | 38p Either single | 1.20 | 1.20 |
| **1450** | A334 | Horiz. pair | 3.80 | 3.80 |
| a.-b. | | 58p Either single | 1.90 | 1.90 |
| **1451** | A334 | Horiz. pair | 7.75 | 7.75 |
| a.-b. | | £1.15 Either single | 3.85 | 3.85 |
| | | Nos. 1448-1451 (4) | 16.45 | 16.45 |

**Souvenir Sheet**

| | | | | |
|---|---|---|---|---|
| **1452** | A334 | Sheet of 4 | 8.00 | 8.00 |
| a.-b. | | 50p Either single | 1.40 | 1.40 |
| c.-d. | | £1 Either single | 2.60 | 2.60 |

Miniature Sheet

Narcissi — A335

No. 1453: a, c, and e, Flowers, flower to right of "Man." b, d, and f, Flowers, diff, leaf to right of "Man."

**2011, Sept. 1   Litho.   Perf. 13¾x13½**

| | | | | |
|---|---|---|---|---|
| **1453** | A335 | Sheet of 6 | 2.75 | 2.75 |
| a.-b. | | 5p Either single | .25 | .25 |
| c.-d. | | 10p Either single | .25 | .25 |
| e.-f. | | 35p Either single | .95 | .95 |

Miniature Sheet

2011 Commonwealth Youth Games, Isle of Man — A336

No. 1454 — Mascot: a, Running (48x32mm). b, Playing badminton (24x26mm). c, Boxing (24x26mm). d, Playing rugby (24x26mm). e, Cycling (24x26mm). f, On gymnastics horse (24x26mm). g, Crossing finish line (24x26mm). h, Swimming (24x26mm).

**Perf. 14x14¾ on 3 or 4 Sides**
**2011, Sept. 1**

| | | | | |
|---|---|---|---|---|
| **1454** | A336 | Sheet of 8 | 8.00 | 8.00 |
| a.-h. | | 38p Any single | 1.00 | 1.00 |

Birds in Winter — A337

Designs: (37p), Robin. (38p), Redwing. 58p, Goldfinch. 68p, Siskin. 76p, Waxwing. £2, Long-tailed tit.

**2011, Sept. 28      Perf. 13¼x13**
**Panel Color**

| | | | | |
|---|---|---|---|---|
| **1455** | A337 | (37p) bright red | .90 | .90 |
| **1456** | A337 | (38p) olive brown | .90 | .90 |
| **1457** | A337 | 58p bluish black | 1.40 | 1.40 |
| **1458** | A337 | 68p dark green | 1.65 | 1.65 |
| a. | | Perf. 12½x12 | 1.65 | 1.65 |
| **1459** | A337 | 76p maroon | 1.85 | 1.85 |
| **1460** | A337 | £2 gray blue | 4.60 | 4.60 |
| | | Nos. 1455-1460 (6) | 11.30 | 11.30 |

**Self-Adhesive**
**Panel Color**
**Rouletted 14**

| | | | | |
|---|---|---|---|---|
| **1461** | A337 | (37p) bright red | .90 | .90 |
| **1462** | A337 | (38p) olive brown | .90 | .90 |

Europa (No. 1458). No. 1458a was printed in sheets of 10.

Transportation Created on Top Gear Television Show — A338

Designs: 37p, Triumph Herald Sailboat. 38p, Citroen Grand Design. 58p, Polar Hilux. 68p, Hammerhead Eagle I-thrust. £1.10, Robin Reliant Space Shuttle. £1.82, Caravan Airship.

**2011, Nov. 5   Litho.   Perf. 13**

| | | | | |
|---|---|---|---|---|
| **1463** | A338 | 37p multi + label | .95 | .95 |
| **1464** | A338 | 38p multi + label | .95 | .95 |
| **1465** | A338 | 58p multi + label | 1.45 | 1.45 |
| **1466** | A338 | 68p multi + label | 1.70 | 1.70 |

| | | | | |
|---|---|---|---|---|
| **1467** | A338 | £1.10 multi + label | 2.75 | 2.75 |
| **1468** | A338 | £1.82 multi + label | 4.75 | 4.75 |
| | | Nos. 1463-1468 (6) | 12.55 | 12.55 |

**Self-Adhesive**
**Die Cut**

| | | | | |
|---|---|---|---|---|
| **1469** | A338 | £1.10 multi + label | 3.25 | 3.25 |
| **1470** | A338 | £1.82 multi + label | 5.75 | 5.75 |

Nos. 1469 and 1470 each were printed in sheets of 5.

2012 Summer Olympics, London — A339

Designs: 37p, Sailing. 38p, Cycling. 58p, Swimming. 68p, Tennis. 76p, Rowing. £1, Track. £1.15, Archery.
£3, Cycling, diff.

**2012, Jan. 1      Perf. 13½**

| | | | | |
|---|---|---|---|---|
| **1471** | A339 | 37p multi | 1.05 | 1.05 |
| **1472** | A339 | 38p multi | 1.05 | 1.05 |
| **1473** | A339 | 58p multi | 1.60 | 1.60 |
| **1474** | A339 | 68p multi | 1.75 | 1.75 |
| **1475** | A339 | 76p multi | 2.10 | 2.10 |
| **1476** | A339 | £1 multi | 2.75 | 2.75 |
| **1477** | A339 | £1.15 multi | 3.25 | 3.25 |
| a. | | Souvenir sheet of 14, 2 each #1471-1477 | 30.00 | 30.00 |
| | | Nos. 1471-1477 (7) | 13.55 | 13.55 |

**Souvenir Sheet**
**Perf. 13**

| | | | | |
|---|---|---|---|---|
| **1478** | A339 | £3 multi | 8.25 | 8.25 |
| a. | | Sheet of 6, 3 each #1472, 1478, + 6 labels | 30.00 | 30.00 |

No. 1478 contains one 52x40mm stamp. No. 1478a sold for £10.

Reign of Queen Elizabeth II, 60th Anniv. A340

Photographs of Queen Elizabeth II: 37p, Wearing tiara, 1990. 38p, Trooping the colors, 1979. 58p, Wearing tiara, 1955. 68p, Wearing blue hat, 1982. £1.10, Without hat, 1968. £1.82, Wearing red hat, 2008.
£3, Queen Elizabeth II wearing crown, 2005.

**2012      Perf. 13¼**

| | | | | |
|---|---|---|---|---|
| **1479** | A340 | 37p multi | 1.05 | 1.05 |
| **1480** | A340 | 38p multi | 1.05 | 1.05 |
| **1481** | A340 | 58p multi | 1.60 | 1.60 |
| **1482** | A340 | 68p multi | 1.90 | 1.90 |
| **1483** | A340 | £1.10 multi | 3.00 | 3.00 |
| **1484** | A340 | £1.82 multi | 5.00 | 5.00 |
| a. | | Souvenir sheet of 6, #1478-1484, + 3 labels | 13.25 | 13.25 |
| | | Nos. 1479-1484 (6) | 13.60 | 13.60 |

**Souvenir Sheet**

| | | | | |
|---|---|---|---|---|
| **1485** | A340 | £3 multi | 8.25 | 8.25 |
| a. | | Sheet of 11, #1483-1485, 2 each #1479-1482, + 18 labels | 30.00 | 30.00 |

Issued: Nos. 1479-1484, 2/6; No. 1485, 4/21; No. 1484a, 2/6; No. 1485a, 6/5.

Frost Arbory, by William Hoggatt (1879-1961) A341

A Colby Mill, by Hoggatt — A342

Landing the Catch, Port St. Mary, by Hoggatt — A343

Early Spring, by Hoggatt — A344

Port Erin Bay, by Hoggatt — A345

**2012, Feb. 20**     **Perf. 14**
| | | | | |
|---|---|---|---|---|
| 1486 | A341 | 38p multi | 1.05 | 1.05 |
| 1487 | A342 | 38p multi | 1.05 | 1.05 |
| 1488 | A343 | 38p multi | 1.05 | 1.05 |
| 1489 | A344 | 38p multi | 1.05 | 1.05 |
| 1490 | A345 | 38p multi | 1.05 | 1.05 |
| a. | | Horiz. strip of 5, #1486-1490 | 5.25 | 5.25 |
| | | *Nos. 1486-1490 (5)* | 5.25 | 5.25 |

Sinking of the Titanic, Cent. — A346

No. 1491: a, Titanic at dock and at sea, breakfast menu. b, Male passenger, dining room. c, Capt. Edward J. Smith, White Star Line stationery, life preserver.
No. 1492: a, Titanic sinking, life preserver. b, Lifeboats, newspaper boy with newspaper announcing sinking. c, Newspaper, Titanic, passengers.

**2012, Apr. 2**     **Litho.**
| | | | | |
|---|---|---|---|---|
| 1491 | | Horiz. strip of 3 | 4.00 | 4.00 |
| a. | | A346 37p multi | 1.05 | 1.05 |
| b. | | A346 38p multi | 1.05 | 1.05 |
| c. | | A346 68p multi | 1.90 | 1.90 |
| 1492 | | Horiz. strip of 3 | 9.75 | 9.75 |
| a. | | A346 76p multi | 2.10 | 2.10 |
| b. | | A346 £1.15 multi | 3.25 | 3.25 |
| c. | | A346 £1.65 multi | 4.50 | 4.50 |
| d. | | Souvenir sheet of 9, #1491a-1491c, 2 each #1492a-1492c, + 9 labels | 26.50 | 26.50 |

Lighthouses A347

Designs: 1p, Castletown Harbor Lighthouse. 68p, Douglas Harbor Lighthouse. 75p, Peel Harbor Lighthouse. £1, Laxey Harbor Lighthouse. £1.30, Ramsey Harbor Lighthouse. £1.60, Port St. Mary Harbor Lighthouse.

**2012, Apr. 2**     **Perf. 13¾**
| | | | | |
|---|---|---|---|---|
| 1493 | A347 | 1p multi | .25 | .25 |
| 1494 | A347 | 68p multi | 1.80 | 1.80 |
| a. | | Sheet of 10 | 18.00 | 18.00 |
| 1495 | A347 | 75p multi | 2.00 | 2.00 |
| 1496 | A347 | £1 multi | 2.60 | 2.60 |
| 1497 | A347 | £1.30 multi | 3.55 | 3.55 |
| 1498 | A347 | £1.60 multi | 4.25 | 4.25 |
| | | *Nos. 1493-1498 (6)* | 14.45 | 14.45 |

Europa (No. 1494).

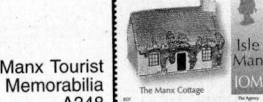

Manx Tourist Memorabilia A348

Designs: (38p), Goss China Manx cottage. (41p), Crown Devon Manx race car. 58p, Royal Doulton Postman at Maughold spittoon. 68p, Willow Art China Manx dog. £1.10, Kettlespring Kilns commemorative plate depicting Ginger the Manx cat. £1.82, Archibald Knox Jewel.

**2012, May 8**     **Perf. 14¾x14¼**
| | | | | |
|---|---|---|---|---|
| 1499 | A348 | (38p) multi | 1.05 | 1.05 |
| 1500 | A348 | (41p) multi | 1.05 | 1.05 |
| 1501 | A348 | 58p multi | 1.65 | 1.65 |
| 1502 | A348 | 68p multi | 1.80 | 1.80 |
| 1503 | A348 | £1.10 multi | 3.05 | 3.05 |
| 1504 | A348 | £1.82 multi | 4.90 | 4.90 |
| | | *Nos. 1499-1504 (6)* | 13.50 | 13.50 |

Inscriptions: No. 1499, "IOM." No. 1500, "UK."

---

Miniature Sheet

Thames Diamond Jubilee Pageant A349

No. 1505: a, Eighteen-oarsman barge Gloriana (42x28mm). b, Lady of Mann near London Eye (42x28mm). c, Viking longboat Vital Spark (42x28mm). d, Royal barge Spirit of Chartwell (85x28mm).

**2012, June 3**     **Perf. 14**
| | | | | |
|---|---|---|---|---|
| 1505 | A349 | Sheet of 4 | 8.25 | 8.25 |
| a.-c. | | 50p Any single | 1.35 | 1.35 |
| d. | | £1.50 multi | 4.10 | 4.10 |
| e. | | Souvenir sheet of 12, 3 each #1505a-1505d, + 9 labels | 26.00 | 26.00 |

Mark Cavendish, Cyclist — A350

Cavendish: 38p, Holding Manx flag after winning 2006 Commonwealth Games Scratch race. 41p, Cycling in 2007 Scheldeprijs Vlaanderen. 65p, Cycling in 2009 Milan-San Remo Classic. 71p, Cycling in 2011 Tour de France. 80p, Celebrating victory in 2011 World Road Race Championships. 105p, Wearing rainbow jersey and medal. 116p, Cycling with rainbow jersey.

**2012, June 19**     **Perf. 13**
| | | | | |
|---|---|---|---|---|
| 1506 | A350 | 38p multi | .95 | .95 |
| 1507 | A350 | 41p multi | .95 | .95 |
| 1508 | A350 | 65p multi | 1.60 | 1.60 |
| 1509 | A350 | 71p multi | 1.75 | 1.75 |
| 1510 | A350 | 80p multi | 1.90 | 1.90 |
| 1511 | A350 | 105p multi | 2.50 | 2.50 |
| 1512 | A350 | 116p multi | 3.00 | 3.00 |
| a. | | Sheet of 13, #1510, 2 each #1506-1509, 1511-1512, + 7 labels | 26.00 | 26.00 |
| | | *Nos. 1506-1512 (7)* | 12.65 | 12.65 |

Bees — A351

Designs: 38p, Colletes succinctus. 41p, Epeolus variegatus. £1, Osmia rufa. £1.05, Halictus rubicunctus. £1.30, Bombus monticola. £1.47, Apis mellifera.

**2012, Aug. 8**     **Perf. 13**
| | | | | |
|---|---|---|---|---|
| 1513 | A351 | 38p multi | 1.10 | 1.10 |
| 1514 | A351 | 41p multi | 1.10 | 1.10 |
| 1515 | A351 | £1 multi | 2.85 | 2.85 |
| 1516 | A351 | £1.05 multi | 2.85 | 2.85 |
| 1517 | A351 | £1.30 multi | 3.55 | 3.55 |
| 1518 | A351 | £1.47 multi | 4.00 | 4.00 |
| | | *Nos. 1513-1518 (6)* | 15.45 | 15.45 |

**Booklet Stamps**
**Self-Adhesive**
**Die Cut Perf. 13¼x12¾**
| | | | | |
|---|---|---|---|---|
| 1519 | A351 | 38p multi | 1.05 | 1.05 |
| a. | | Booklet pane of 10 | 10.75 | |
| 1520 | A351 | 41p multi | 1.05 | 1.05 |
| a. | | Booklet pane of 10 | 10.75 | |

Nos. 1513-1518 were impregnated with a honey scent.
Nos. 1519a and 1520a are complete booklets, the backing service as booklet covers.

Royal Flying Corps, Cent. — A352

Military aircraft: 38p, AW FK.8 B5773, 1918. 41p, MS Type L 3253, 1915. 65p, DH.2 5964, 1916. 80p, Sopwith Camel B5648, 1918. £1.37, RAF BE.2C, 4359, 1917. £1.91, Short S.32 402, 1912.

**2012, Sept. 20**     **Perf. 13¼x13½**
| | | | | |
|---|---|---|---|---|
| 1521 | A352 | 38p multi | 1.05 | 1.05 |
| 1522 | A352 | 41p multi | 1.20 | 1.20 |
| 1523 | A352 | 65p multi | 1.75 | 1.75 |
| 1524 | A352 | 80p multi | 2.25 | 2.25 |
| 1525 | A352 | £1.37 multi | 3.75 | 3.75 |
| 1526 | A352 | £1.91 multi | 5.25 | 5.25 |
| | | *Nos. 1521-1526 (6)* | 15.25 | 15.25 |

---

Souvenir Sheet

Antarctic Expedition of Robert Falcon Scott, Cent. — A353

No. 1527: a, Expedition ship, Dicovery, and ice. b, Memorial cairn.

**2012, Oct. 2**     **Perf. 13¼x13**
| | | | | |
|---|---|---|---|---|
| 1527 | A353 | Sheet of 2 | 8.25 | 8.25 |
| a.-b. | | £1.50 Either single | 4.00 | 4.00 |

Christmas — A354

Designs: 38p, Ramsey Christmas lights. 41p, Mail carrier delivering mail in Glen Auldyn. 71p, Castletown Police Station. £1.05, Sulby Glen. £1.16, Martin's Sweet Shop, Ramsey. £1.73, Lake Lane, Peel.

**2012, Oct. 20**     **Perf. 13**
| | | | | |
|---|---|---|---|---|
| 1528 | A354 | 38p multi | 1.05 | 1.05 |
| 1529 | A354 | 41p multi | 1.20 | 1.20 |
| 1530 | A354 | 71p multi | 1.90 | 1.90 |
| 1531 | A354 | £1.05 multi | 3.00 | 3.00 |
| 1532 | A354 | £1.16 multi | 3.25 | 3.25 |
| 1533 | A354 | £1.73 multi | 4.75 | 4.75 |
| | | *Nos. 1528-1533 (6)* | 15.15 | 15.15 |

**Self-Adhesive**
**Serpentine Die Cut 11¼**
| | | | | |
|---|---|---|---|---|
| 1534 | A354 | 38p multi | 1.25 | 1.25 |
| 1535 | A354 | 41p multi | 1.40 | 1.40 |

Chronicles of Man and Lewis Chessmen A355

Various chessmen and segments of text from Chronicles with panel color of: 38p, Gray. 41p, Red violet. 71p, Bister. 80p, Purple. 130p, Green. 191p, Brown.

**2013, Jan. 11**     **Perf. 13½**
| | | | | |
|---|---|---|---|---|
| 1536 | A355 | 38p multi | 1.00 | 1.00 |
| 1537 | A355 | 41p multi | 1.15 | 1.15 |
| 1538 | A355 | 71p multi | 2.00 | 2.00 |
| 1539 | A355 | 80p multi | 2.15 | 2.15 |
| 1540 | A355 | 130p multi | 3.55 | 3.55 |
| 1541 | A355 | 191p multi | 5.00 | 5.00 |
| | | *Nos. 1536-1541 (6)* | 14.85 | 14.85 |

Items Produced to Commemorate Coronations A356

Items depicting: 38p, Queen Victoria. 41p, King Edward VII. 65p, King George V. £1.05, King George VI. £1.37, Queen Elizabeth II. £1.73, Queen Elizabeth II, diff.

**2013, Feb. 6**     **Perf. 14**
| | | | | |
|---|---|---|---|---|
| 1542 | A356 | 38p multi | 1.05 | 1.05 |
| 1543 | A356 | 41p multi | 1.20 | 1.20 |
| 1544 | A356 | 65p multi | 1.75 | 1.75 |
| 1545 | A356 | £1.05 multi | 3.00 | 3.00 |
| 1546 | A356 | £1.37 multi | 3.75 | 3.75 |
| 1547 | A356 | £1.73 multi | 4.75 | 4.75 |
| a. | | Dated "2015" | 5.25 | 5.25 |
| b. | | Sheet of 26 | 57.50 | 57.50 |
| | | *Nos. 1542-1547 (6)* | 18.25 | 18.25 |

Issued: No. 1547a, 11/27/15. No. 1547a was issued in a sheet containing 26 stamps depicting Queen Elizabeth II from various countries. Twenty-four of the stamps in the sheet have the same designs as previously-issued stamps, though perforations may differ (Antigua No. 3182b, Ascension No. 1142, Bahamas No. 1438, Barbados No. 1198, British Antarctic Territory No. 486, Cook Islands No. 1542a, Falkland Islands No. 1147, Grenada No. 3912, Kenya No. 88, Nevis No. 1521a, New Zealand No. 2602. Niue No. 876, St. Kitts No. 696a, Samoa No. 1220c, Sierra Leone No. 2007, South Georgia and South Sandwich Islands No. 539, Tanzania No. 1595, Tokelau No. 404, Tonga No. 1282d, Tristan da Cunha No. 1047, Turks and Caicos Islands No. 1454b, Tuvalu No. 1234a, Uganda

---

No. 1493 and Zambia No. 685a). The sheet also contains a stamp that is an altered version of St. Vincent No. 3820 and a Papua New Guinea stamp that is unlike any previous Papua New Guinea issue. The foreign stamps on the sheet may be recognized as valid in those countries, but the entire sheet was sold only by Isle of Man postal authorities for £20.

Miniature Sheet

New Year 2013 (Year of the Snake) A357

No. 1548: a, Snake. b, Chinese character with fish, flowers and butterfly. c, Chinese character with cranes and peaches. d, Chinese character with deer. e, Chinese character with birds and flowers. f, Snake coiled in spiral.

**2013, Feb. 8**     **Perf. 12**
| | | | | |
|---|---|---|---|---|
| 1548 | A357 | Sheet of 6, #a-f | 8.50 | 8.50 |
| a. | | 5p multi | .25 | .25 |
| b.-e. | | 20p Any single | .50 | .50 |
| f. | | £2.15 multi | 5.75 | 5.75 |
| g. | | Sheet of 20, #1548b-1548e, 16 #1548a | 4.25 | 4.25 |

Also exists as perf. 15 with same values.

Isle of Man Constabulary, 150th Anniv. — A358

Designs: 38p, Uniforms. 41p, Vehicles. 71p, Dogs. 80p, Communications. £1.47, Community. £1.82, Stations.

**2013, Feb. 20**     **Perf. 14**
| | | | | |
|---|---|---|---|---|
| 1549 | A358 | 38p multi | 1.05 | 1.05 |
| 1550 | A358 | 41p multi | 1.05 | 1.05 |
| 1551 | A358 | 71p multi | 1.90 | 1.90 |
| 1552 | A358 | 80p multi | 2.10 | 2.10 |
| 1553 | A358 | £1.47 multi | 3.75 | 3.75 |
| 1554 | A358 | £1.82 multi | 4.75 | 4.75 |
| | | *Nos. 1549-1554 (6)* | 17.25 | 17.25 |

Souvenir Sheet

Isle of Man Fire and Rescue Services A359

**2013, Feb. 20**     **Perf. 13¾x14**
| | | | | |
|---|---|---|---|---|
| 1555 | A359 | £3 multi | 8.00 | 8.00 |

Manx Triskelion — A360

Various depictions of Manx triskelion (national symbol).

**2013, Apr. 13**     **Perf. 13¼**
| | | | | |
|---|---|---|---|---|
| 1556 | A360 | 5p multi | .25 | .25 |
| 1557 | A360 | 10p multi | .25 | .25 |
| 1558 | A360 | 40p multi | 1.05 | 1.05 |
| 1559 | A360 | 42p multi | 1.05 | 1.05 |
| 1560 | A360 | 69p multi | 1.75 | 1.75 |
| 1561 | A360 | 73p multi | 1.90 | 1.90 |
| 1562 | A360 | £1.19 multi | 3.25 | 3.25 |
| 1563 | A360 | £2 multi | 5.00 | 5.00 |
| | | *Nos. 1556-1563 (8)* | 14.50 | 14.50 |

**Booklet Stamps**
**Self-Adhesive**
**Die Cut Perf. 12¾x13¼**
| | | | | |
|---|---|---|---|---|
| 1564 | A360 | 40p Like #1558 | 1.10 | 1.10 |
| a. | | Booklet pane of 10 | 11.25 | |
| 1565 | A360 | 42p Like #1559 | 1.10 | 1.10 |
| a. | | Booklet pane of 10 | 11.25 | |

Nos. 1564a and 1565a are complete booklets, the backing serving as the booklet covers.

## Souvenir Sheet

Coronation of Queen Elizabeth II, 60th Anniv. — A361

**2013, Apr. 21**      **Perf. 14¾x14**
| | | | | |
|---|---|---|---|---|
| 1566 | A361 | £3 multi | 8.00 | 8.00 |

Robin Gibb (1949-2012), Singer — A362

Record covers: 2p, Robin's Reign, 1970. 40p, How Old Are You, 1983. 42p, Secret Agent, 1984. 50p, Walls Have Eyes, 1985. 69p, Magnet, 2003. 73p, Robin Gibb Live with the Neue Philharmonie Orchestra, 2005. 120p, The Titanic Requiem, 2012. 178p, 50 St. Catherine's Drive, 2013.

**2013, Apr. 24**      **Perf. 13¼**
| | | | | |
|---|---|---|---|---|
| 1567 | A362 | 2p multi | .25 | .25 |
| 1568 | A362 | 40p multi | 1.05 | 1.05 |
| 1569 | A362 | 42p multi | 1.20 | 1.20 |
| 1570 | A362 | 50p multi | 1.35 | 1.35 |
| 1571 | A362 | 69p multi | 1.90 | 1.90 |
| 1572 | A362 | 73p multi | 1.90 | 1.90 |
| 1573 | A362 | 120p multi | 3.25 | 3.25 |
| 1574 | A362 | 178p multi | 4.75 | 4.75 |
| *a.* | | Sheet of 12, #1567-1570, 2 each #1571-1574, + 3 labels | 32.00 | 32.00 |
| | | *Nos. 1567-1574 (8)* | 15.65 | 15.65 |

Railways — A363

Rolling stock, company emblems and slogan: 40p, The Best Way to the Beauty Spots. 42p, The Perfect Resort So Near to Home. 69p, Breezy and Invigorating. 119p, Isle of Man for Happy Holidays. 160p, Port Erin Southern Beauty Spot. 161p, The Finest Glens and Mountain Views.

**2013, May 17**   **Litho.**   **Perf. 14**
| | | | | |
|---|---|---|---|---|
| 1575 | A363 | 40p multi | 1.05 | 1.05 |
| 1576 | A363 | 42p multi | 1.20 | 1.20 |
| 1577 | A363 | 69p multi | 1.90 | 1.90 |
| 1578 | A363 | 119p multi | 3.25 | 3.25 |
| 1579 | A363 | 160p multi | 4.25 | 4.25 |
| 1580 | A363 | 161p multi | 4.25 | 4.25 |
| | | *Nos. 1575-1580 (6)* | 15.90 | 15.90 |

100th Tour de France Bicycle Race — A364

Cyclists: 1p, Eugène Christophe (1885-1970). 40p, Mark Cavendish. 42p, Brian Robinson. 69p, Miguel Indurain. 73p, Jacques Anquetil (1934-87). 108p, Eddy Merckx. 119p, Bernard Hinault. 120p, Bradley Wiggins.

**2013, June 19**      **Perf. 13¼**
| | | | | |
|---|---|---|---|---|
| 1581 | A364 | 1p multi | .25 | .25 |
| *a.* | | Dated "2014" | .25 | .25 |
| 1582 | A364 | 40p multi | 1.05 | 1.05 |
| *a.* | | Dated "2014" | 1.05 | |
| *b.* | | Souvenir sheet of 2 #1582a + 3 labels | 2.10 | 2.10 |
| 1583 | A364 | 42p multi | 1.05 | 1.05 |
| *a.* | | Dated "2014" | 1.20 | |
| *b.* | | Souvenir sheet of 2 #1583a + 3 labels | 2.25 | 2.25 |
| 1584 | A364 | 69p multi | 1.75 | 1.75 |
| *a.* | | Dated "2014" | 1.90 | 1.90 |
| 1585 | A364 | 73p multi | 1.90 | 1.90 |
| *a.* | | Dated "2014" | 2.00 | |
| *b.* | | Souvenir sheet of 2, #1584a, 1585a, + 3 labels | 4.00 | 4.00 |
| 1586 | A364 | 108p multi | 2.75 | 2.75 |
| *a.* | | Dated "2014" | 3.00 | |
| *b.* | | Souvenir sheet of 2 #1586a + 3 labels | 6.00 | 6.00 |

| | | | | |
|---|---|---|---|---|
| 1587 | A364 | 119p multi | 3.25 | 3.25 |
| *a.* | | Dated "2014" | 3.25 | 3.25 |
| *b.* | | Souvenir sheet of 2, #1581a, 1587a, + 3 labels | 3.50 | 3.50 |
| 1588 | A364 | 120p multi | 3.25 | 3.25 |
| *a.* | | Dated "2014" | 3.25 | 3.25 |
| *b.* | | Souvenir sheet of 2 #1588a + 3 labels | 6.50 | 6.50 |
| | | *Nos. 1581-1588 (8)* | 15.25 | 15.25 |

Issued: Nos. 1581a-1588a, 2014.

The Times Newspaper, 225th Anniv. — A365

News stories: 40p, Last flight of the Concorde, 2003. 42p, England wins the World Cup, 1966. 73p, Isle of Man postal independence, 1973. 108p, State visit of Queen Elizabeth II to the People's Republic of China, 1986. 141p, Assassination of Pres. John F. Kennedy in Dallas, 1963. 179p, Man lands on the Moon, 1969.

**2013, July 4**      **Perf. 14¾x14**
| | | | | |
|---|---|---|---|---|
| 1589 | A365 | 40p multi + label | 1.05 | 1.05 |
| 1590 | A365 | 42p multi + label | 1.05 | 1.05 |
| 1591 | A365 | 73p multi + label | 1.90 | 1.90 |
| *a.* | | Miniature sheet of 10 + 10 labels | 19.00 | 19.00 |
| 1592 | A365 | 108p multi + label | 2.75 | 2.75 |
| 1593 | A365 | 141p multi + label | 3.75 | 3.75 |
| 1594 | A365 | 179p multi + label | 4.75 | 4.75 |
| | | *Nos. 1589-1594 (6)* | 15.25 | 15.25 |

Europa (No. 1591).

## Souvenir Sheet

St. Thomas' Church Murals by John Miller Nicholson (1840-1913) — A366

No. 1595: a, Angels with banner. b, Saints.

**2013, Aug. 8**      **Perf. 13x13¼**
| | | | | |
|---|---|---|---|---|
| 1595 | A366 | Sheet of 2 | 8.00 | 8.00 |
| *a.* | | £1 multi | 2.75 | 2.75 |
| *b.* | | £2 multi | 5.25 | 5.25 |

A367

Paintings of Wildlife by Jeremy Paul A368

Designs: 40p, Lion. 42p, Snow leopard. 69p, Tiger. 120p, Cheetah. 160p, Leopard. 161p, Jaguar.
No. 1602: a, Baboon. b, Rhinoceros, horiz. c, Giraffes, horiz. d, Kudu.

**2013, Sept. 13**   **Litho.**   **Perf. 13¼**
| | | | | |
|---|---|---|---|---|
| 1596 | A367 | 40p multi | 1.05 | 1.05 |
| 1597 | A367 | 42p multi | 1.20 | 1.20 |
| 1598 | A367 | 69p multi | 1.90 | 1.90 |
| 1599 | A367 | 120p multi | 3.25 | 3.25 |
| 1600 | A367 | 160p multi | 4.25 | 4.25 |
| 1601 | A367 | 161p multi | 4.50 | 4.50 |
| | | *Nos. 1596-1601 (6)* | 16.15 | 16.15 |

### Souvenir Sheet
| | | | | |
|---|---|---|---|---|
| 1602 | A368 | Sheet of 4 | 8.25 | 8.25 |
| *a.-d.* | | 75p Any single | 2.00 | 2.00 |

Christmas — A369

Details of vignettes from past Isle of Man Christmas stamps: 40p, Mailing letters, 1990 (#436). 42p, Three Kings, 1991 (#488). 73p,

Angel with Crown of Glory, 2005 (#1129). 108p, Robin, 1988 (#378). 119p, Church and holly, 1995 (#662). 178p, Christmas tree, 2006 (#1172).

**2013, Oct. 17**   **Litho.**   **Perf. 13¼**
| | | | | |
|---|---|---|---|---|
| 1603 | A369 | 40p multi | 1.05 | 1.05 |
| 1604 | A369 | 42p multi | 1.20 | 1.20 |
| 1605 | A369 | 73p multi | 2.10 | 2.10 |
| 1606 | A369 | 108p multi | 3.00 | 3.00 |
| 1607 | A369 | 119p multi | 3.25 | 3.25 |
| 1608 | A369 | 178p multi | 5.00 | 5.00 |
| | | *Nos. 1603-1608 (6)* | 15.60 | 15.60 |

### Self-Adhesive
***Serpentine Die Cut 11x11¼***
| | | | | |
|---|---|---|---|---|
| 1609 | A369 | 40p multi | 1.10 | 1.10 |
| 1610 | A369 | 42p multi | 1.25 | 1.25 |

Isle of Man, Island of Culture — A370

Designs: No. 1611, Visual arts. No. 1612, Drama. No. 1613, Literaure. No. 1614, Film. No. 1615, Music. No. 1616, Craft. No. 1617, Dance. No. 1618, Design.

**2014, Jan. 6**   **Litho.**   **Perf. 13**
| | | | | |
|---|---|---|---|---|
| 1611 | A370 | IOM multi | 1.30 | 1.30 |
| 1612 | A370 | IOM multi | 1.30 | 1.30 |
| 1613 | A370 | UK multi | 1.30 | 1.30 |
| 1614 | A370 | UK multi | 1.30 | 1.30 |
| 1615 | A370 | EU multi | 2.30 | 2.30 |
| *a.* | | Miniature sheet of 10 | 23.00 | 23.00 |
| 1616 | A370 | RoW multi | 2.30 | 2.30 |
| 1617 | A370 | RoW multi | 3.80 | 3.80 |
| 1618 | A370 | RoW multi | 3.80 | 3.80 |
| | | *Nos. 1611-1618 (8)* | 17.40 | 17.40 |

Europa (No. 1615). On day of issue, Nos. 1611-1612 each sold for 40p, Nos. 1613-1614 each sold for 42p, Nos. 1615 sold for 73p, and Nos. 1616-1618 each sold for £1.19.

## Miniature Sheet

Winter Flora A371

No. 1619: a, Ivy berries (denomination at UR). b, Teasels (denomination at UL). c, Hellebore flowers (denomination at UR). d, Rose hips (denomination at UL).

**2014, Jan. 6**   **Litho.**   **Perf. 13**
| | | | | |
|---|---|---|---|---|
| 1619 | A371 | Sheet of 4, #a-d | 8.50 | 8.50 |
| *a.-d.* | | 75p Any single | 2.10 | 2.10 |

Compare No. 1619c with No. 1659.

World War I, Cent. — A372

Photographs of soldiers, memorial poppies, and inscription: 40p, Communications. 42p, Sappers. 69p, Trenches. £1.08, Horses. £1.41, Christmas truce. £1.60, Officers' dugout.

**2014, Feb. 19**   **Litho.**   **Perf. 14**
| | | | | |
|---|---|---|---|---|
| 1620 | A372 | 40p multi | 1.20 | 1.20 |
| 1621 | A372 | 42p multi | 1.20 | 1.20 |
| 1622 | A372 | 69p multi | 1.90 | 1.90 |
| 1623 | A372 | £1.08 multi | 3.00 | 3.00 |
| 1624 | A372 | £1.41 multi | 4.00 | 4.00 |
| 1625 | A372 | £1.60 multi | 4.50 | 4.50 |
| | | *Nos. 1620-1625 (6)* | 15.80 | 15.80 |

Examples of No. 1623 with a 2020 year date come from a sheet containing four of these stamps and 8 labels that sold for £20.
See Nos. 1698-1703.

## Souvenir Sheet

World War I Trench Art A373

**2014, Feb. 19**   **Litho.**   **Perf. 15x14¼**
| | | | | |
|---|---|---|---|---|
| 1626 | A373 | £3 multi | 8.25 | 8.25 |

Royal Air Force Red Arrows Aerobatic Team — A374

Various photographs of Red Arrows in flight.

**2014, Feb. 19**   **Litho.**   **Perf. 13¼**
| | | | | |
|---|---|---|---|---|
| 1627 | A374 | 40p multi | 1.20 | 1.20 |
| 1628 | A374 | 42p multi | 1.20 | 1.20 |
| 1629 | A374 | 69p multi | 1.90 | 1.90 |
| 1630 | A374 | 73p multi | 2.10 | 2.10 |
| 1631 | A374 | 108p multi | 3.00 | 3.00 |
| 1632 | A374 | 265p multi | 7.50 | 7.50 |
| | | *Nos. 1627-1632 (6)* | 16.90 | 16.90 |

### Red Arrows Type of 2014
Designs as before.

***Serpentine Die Cut 13¾***
| | | | | |
|---|---|---|---|---|
| **2014** | | **Self-Adhesive Booklet Stamps** | | **Litho.** |
| 1633 | A374 | 40p multi | 1.40 | 1.40 |
| 1634 | A374 | 42p multi | 1.40 | 1.40 |
| 1635 | A374 | 69p multi | 2.25 | 2.25 |
| *a.* | | Booklet pane of 3, #1633-1635 | 3.75 | |
| 1636 | A374 | 73p multi | 2.40 | 2.40 |
| 1637 | A374 | 108p multi | 3.50 | 3.50 |
| 1638 | A374 | 265p multi | 8.75 | 8.75 |
| *a.* | | Booklet pane of 3, #1636-1638 | 10.50 | |
| *b.* | | Booklet pane of 6, #1633-1638 | 14.00 | |
| | | Complete booklet, #1635a, 1638a, 1638b | 29.00 | |

No. 1638b was also sold separately from complete booklet.

Deer's Cry — A375

To the Virtue of His Crucifixion With — A376

In Splendor of Fire — A377

God's Wisdom to Guide Me — A378

In Compactness of Rock — A379

God's Shield to Protect Me — A380

His Ascension A381

In the Creator of the Universe A382

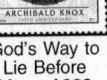

God's Way to
Lie Before
Me — A383

I Bind Myself
Today
To — A384

**2014, Apr. 4    Litho.    Perf. 13¼x12½**
| | | | |
|---|---|---|---|
| 1639 | | Horiz. strip of 5 | 5.60 | 5.60 |
| a. | A375 | 42p multi | 1.10 | 1.10 |
| b. | A376 | 42p multi | 1.10 | 1.10 |
| c. | A377 | 42p multi | 1.10 | 1.10 |
| d. | A378 | 42p multi | 1.10 | 1.10 |
| e. | A379 | 42p multi | 1.10 | 1.10 |
| 1640 | | Horiz. strip of 5 | 10.25 | 10.25 |
| a. | A380 | 75p multi | 2.05 | 2.05 |
| b. | A381 | 75p multi | 2.05 | 2.05 |
| c. | A382 | 75p multi | 2.05 | 2.05 |
| d. | A383 | 75p multi | 2.05 | 2.05 |
| e. | A384 | 75p multi | 2.05 | 2.05 |

**Booklet Stamps**
**Self-Adhesive**

**Serpentine Die Cut 13½**
| | | | |
|---|---|---|---|
| 1641 | A375 | 42p multi | 1.20 | 1.20 |
| 1642 | A376 | 42p multi | 1.20 | 1.20 |
| 1643 | A377 | 42p multi | 1.20 | 1.20 |
| 1644 | A378 | 42p multi | 1.20 | 1.20 |
| 1645 | A379 | 42p multi | 1.20 | 1.20 |
| a. | | Booklet pane of 12, 3 each | | |
| | | #1641, 1645, 2 each | | |
| | | #1642-1644 | 14.50 | |
| | | Nos. 1641-1645 (5) | 6.00 | 6.00 |

Manuscript illuminations by Archibald Knox (1864-1933).

Battle of Clontarf,
1000th Anniv. — A385

Designs: 2p, Brodir the Warrior. 42p, Battle of Clontarf. 90p, Eithne weaves the raven banner. £1, Clontarf warrior. £1.60, King Brian Boru. £2.30, Fight for the raven banner.

**2014, Apr. 15    Litho.    Perf. 14**
| | | | |
|---|---|---|---|
| 1646 | A385 | 2p multi | .25 | .25 |
| 1647 | A385 | 42p multi | 1.15 | 1.15 |
| 1648 | A385 | 90p multi | 2.40 | 2.40 |
| 1649 | A385 | £1 multi | 2.75 | 2.75 |
| 1650 | A385 | £1.60 multi | 4.50 | 4.50 |
| 1651 | A385 | £2.30 multi | 6.25 | 6.25 |
| | | Nos. 1646-1651 (6) | 17.30 | 17.30 |

**Miniature Sheet**

Rare
Farm
Animal
Breeds
A386

No. 1652: a, Manx Loaghtan ram. b, Northern dairy shorthorn cattle. c, Cotswold sheep. d, Exmoor ponies. e, Gloucester old spot pig. f, Irish moiled cattle.

**2014, Apr. 16    Litho.    Perf. 13¼x13½**
| | | | |
|---|---|---|---|
| 1652 | A386 | Sheet of 6 | 6.00 | 6.00 |
| a.-f. | | 38p Any single | 1.00 | 1.00 |

Southern District Agricultural Society, cent.; Rare Breeds Survival Trust, 40th anniv.

D-Day, 70th
Anniv. — A387

Various photographs of invading troops in action.

**2014, May 8    Litho.    Perf. 14**
| | | | |
|---|---|---|---|
| 1653 | A387 | 42p blk & red | 1.15 | 1.15 |
| 1654 | A387 | 75p blk & red | 2.00 | 2.00 |
| 1655 | A387 | 90p blk & red | 2.40 | 2.40 |
| 1656 | A387 | 110p multi | 3.00 | 3.00 |
| 1657 | A387 | 144p blk & red | 4.00 | 4.00 |
| 1658 | A387 | 182p blk & red | 4.75 | 4.75 |
| a. | | Sheet of 16, #602a, 603b, | | |
| | | 606a, 607b, 1028c, | | |
| | | 1028d, 1029c, 1029d, | | |
| | | 1030c, 1030d, 1031c, | | |
| | | 1031d, 1032e, 1032f, | | |
| | | 1657-1658 | 24.00 | 24.00 |
| | | Nos. 1653-1658 (6) | 17.30 | 17.30 |

Winter
Flowers — A388

**2014, July 16    Litho.    Perf. 12¾**
| | | | |
|---|---|---|---|
| 1659 | A388 | 75p multi | 2.10 | 2.10 |

Compare No. 1659 with No. 1619c.

Manx Playing
Cards — A389

Designs: 42p, Ace of clubs with Peel Castle and Douglas Lighthouse. 75p, Ace of diamonds with Douglas and Douglas Iron Pier. 90p, Ace of spades with Webb's Louvre. 110p, Ace of hearts with Bradda Head and Douglas Lighthouse. 121p, Ace of spades with Laxey Wheel and Fort Anne Hotel. 182p, Ace of diamonds with Groudle Wheel and Peel Castle.

**2014, Aug. 8    Litho.    Perf. 13x12½**
| | | | |
|---|---|---|---|
| 1660 | A389 | 42p multi | 1.20 | 1.20 |
| 1661 | A389 | 75p multi | 2.10 | 2.10 |
| 1662 | A389 | 90p multi | 2.50 | 2.50 |
| 1663 | A389 | 110p multi | 3.15 | 3.15 |
| 1664 | A389 | 121p multi | 3.40 | 3.40 |
| 1665 | A389 | 182p multi | 4.95 | 4.95 |
| | | Nos. 1660-1665 (6) | 17.30 | 17.30 |

**Souvenir Sheet**

MS
Queen
Elizabeth
and Map
of
Panama
A390

**2014, Aug. 8    Litho.    Perf. 14¼**
| | | | |
|---|---|---|---|
| 1666 | A390 | £3.50 multi | 10.00 | 10.00 |

Panama Canal, cent.

Constellations — A391

Designs: 42p, Orion. 164p, Leo. 182p, Cygnus. 230p, Andromeda.

**2014, Sept. 1    Litho.    Perf. 14¼**
| | | | |
|---|---|---|---|
| 1667 | A391 | 42p multi | 1.20 | 1.20 |
| 1668 | A391 | 164p multi | 4.65 | 4.65 |
| 1669 | A391 | 182p multi | 4.90 | 4.90 |
| 1670 | A391 | 230p multi | 6.45 | 6.45 |
| | | Nos. 1667-1670 (4) | 17.20 | 17.20 |

**Aircraft Type of 1997**

**2014    Litho.    Perf. 14**
| | | | |
|---|---|---|---|
| 1671 | A171 | 75p Sopwith Tabloid | 4.50 | 4.50 |

No. 1671 was printed in sheets of 5 + 4 labels. Imperforate sheets of 5 + 4 labels sold for £7.50.

Manx Radio, 50th
Anniv. — A392

Designs: No. 1672, Mannin Line. No. 1673, Countryside. No. 1674, Weather reports. No. 1675, Jackson's Jollybodys. No. 1676, Mandate. No. 1677, Jazz Hour. No. 1678, Radio TT. No. 1679, Outside broadcasts.

**2014, Oct. 1    Litho.    Perf. 13½**
| | | | |
|---|---|---|---|
| 1672 | A392 | 42p multi | 1.20 | 1.20 |
| 1673 | A392 | 42p multi | 1.20 | 1.20 |
| 1674 | A392 | 50p multi | 1.40 | 1.40 |
| 1675 | A392 | 50p multi | 1.40 | 1.40 |
| 1676 | A392 | 75p multi | 2.00 | 2.00 |
| 1677 | A392 | 75p multi | 2.00 | 2.00 |
| 1678 | A392 | £1.20 multi | 3.45 | 3.45 |
| 1679 | A392 | £1.20 multi | 3.45 | 3.45 |
| | | Nos. 1672-1679 (8) | 16.10 | 16.10 |

**Souvenir Sheet**

Celtic Kingdom Festival of Silk — A393

**2014, Oct. 23    Litho.    Perf. 13x12¾**
| | | | |
|---|---|---|---|
| 1680 | A393 | £3 multi | 7.75 | 7.75 |

Christmas — A394

Scenes from *The Snowman and the Snowdog*, by Raymond Briggs: Nos. 1681, 1687, Snowman, Snowdog and Billy flying. Nos. 1682, 1688, Snowman, Snowdog and Santa Claus. 75p, Snowman and Snowdog. 90p, Snowdog chasing ball. £1.21, Snowman skiing, Snowdog and Billy on toboggan. £2.21, Snowman, Snowdog and Billy.

**2014, Oct. 23    Litho.    Perf. 13**
| | | | |
|---|---|---|---|
| 1681 | A394 | 42p multi | 1.30 | 1.30 |
| 1682 | A394 | 42p multi | 1.30 | 1.30 |
| 1683 | A394 | 75p multi | 2.10 | 2.10 |
| 1684 | A394 | 90p multi | 2.70 | 2.70 |
| 1685 | A394 | £1.21 multi | 3.65 | 3.65 |
| 1686 | A394 | £2.21 multi | 6.40 | 6.40 |
| | | Nos. 1681-1686 (6) | 17.45 | 17.45 |

**Self-Adhesive**

**Serpentine Die Cut 11¼**
| | | | |
|---|---|---|---|
| 1687 | A394 | 42p multi | 1.30 | 1.30 |
| 1688 | A394 | 42p multi | 1.30 | 1.30 |

**Souvenir Sheet**

New Year 2015 (Year of the Sheep)
A395

**2015, Jan. 2    Litho.    Perf. 13¼**
| | | | |
|---|---|---|---|
| 1689 | A395 | Sheet of 2 | 7.75 | 7.75 |
| a. | | 10p Ram | .25 | .25 |
| b. | | £3 Ewe | 7.25 | 7.25 |
| c. | | Sheet of 16 #1689a + 4 labels | 4.00 | 4.00 |

Sir Winston Churchill
(1874-1965), Prime
Minister — A396

Churchill: No. 1690, As young man wearing military uniform. No. 1691, Wearing top hat. No. 1692, With hand on hip. No. 1693, Reading while smoking cigar. No. 1694, Giving victory salute. No. 1695, Behind microphones. No. 1696, Painting picture. No. 1697, Building brick wall.

**2015, Jan. 2    Litho.    Perf. 13¾x13¼**
| | | | |
|---|---|---|---|
| 1690 | A396 | 42p multi | 1.10 | 1.10 |
| 1691 | A396 | 42p multi | 1.10 | 1.10 |
| a. | | Vert. pair, #1690-1691 | 2.20 | 2.20 |
| 1692 | A396 | 75p multi | 2.00 | 2.00 |
| 1693 | A396 | 75p multi | 2.00 | 2.00 |
| a. | | Vert. pair, #1692-1693 | 4.00 | 4.00 |
| 1694 | A396 | 90p multi | 2.25 | 2.25 |
| 1695 | A396 | 90p multi | 2.25 | 2.25 |
| a. | | Vert. pair, #1694-1695 | 4.50 | 4.50 |
| 1696 | A396 | 110p multi | 2.75 | 2.75 |
| 1697 | A396 | 110p multi | 2.75 | 2.75 |
| a. | | Vert. pair, #1696-1697 | 5.50 | 5.50 |
| | | Nos. 1690-1697 (8) | 16.20 | 16.20 |

**World War I, Cent. Type of 2014**

Photographs, memorial poppies and inscription: No. 1698, Home Front. No. 1699, Palestine. 75p, Western Front. £1.10, Eastern Front. £1.44, Gallipoli. £1.64, Italy.

**2015, Feb. 17    Litho.    Perf. 14**
| | | | |
|---|---|---|---|
| 1698 | A372 | 42p multi | 1.10 | 1.10 |
| 1699 | A372 | 42p multi | 1.10 | 1.10 |
| 1700 | A372 | 75p multi | 1.90 | 1.90 |
| 1701 | A372 | £1.10 multi | 2.75 | 2.75 |
| 1702 | A372 | £1.44 multi | 3.75 | 3.75 |
| 1703 | A372 | £1.64 multi | 4.00 | 4.00 |
| | | Nos. 1698-1703 (6) | 14.60 | 14.60 |

Nos. 1698-1703 each were printed in sheets of 8 + central label.

Penny Black, 175th
Anniv. — A397

Designs: 1p, Great Britain #1. 42p, Great Britain #2. 90p, Great Britain #3. £1.20, Stanley Gibbons (1840-1913), stamp dealer, and *Gibbons Stamp Monthly*. £1.60, William Mulready (1786-1863), designer of stamped envelopes, Great Britain #U1. £2.30, Sir Rowland Hill (1795-1879), inventor of postage stamp, cover bearing Great Britain #3.

**2015, Feb. 17    Litho.    Perf. 13¾**
| | | | |
|---|---|---|---|
| 1704 | A397 | 1p multi | .25 | .25 |
| 1705 | A397 | 42p multi | 1.00 | 1.00 |
| 1706 | A397 | 90p multi | 2.25 | 2.25 |
| a. | | Sheet of 20, 16 #1704, 2 | | |
| | | each #1705-1706 | 7.00 | 7.00 |
| 1707 | A397 | £1.20 multi | 3.00 | 3.00 |
| 1708 | A397 | £1.60 multi | 4.00 | 4.00 |
| 1709 | A397 | £2.30 multi | 5.75 | 5.75 |
| | | Nos. 1704-1709 (6) | 16.25 | 16.25 |

Victory in World War II, 70th Anniv.
A398

No. 1710: a, Gurkha soldier. b, Soldier aiming rifle.
£1.50, Military medal, woman celebrating victory in Europe, newspaper.

**2015, Feb. 26    Litho.    Perf. 13¾**
| | | | |
|---|---|---|---|
| 1710 | A398 | Sheet of 2 | 5.25 | 5.25 |
| a.-b. | | £1 Either single | 2.60 | 2.60 |
| c. | | Sheet of 10 #1710a + 10 labels | 26.00 | 26.00 |

**Souvenir Sheet**
| | | | |
|---|---|---|---|
| 1711 | A398 | £1.50 multi | 4.00 | 4.00 |

A399

Design: Caesar Bacon (1791-1876) and Duke of Wellington (1769-1862).

**2015, Mar. 9    Litho.    Perf. 13¼**
| | | | |
|---|---|---|---|
| 1712 | A399 | £1 multi | 3.00 | 3.00 |

Napoleon's Hundred Days Campaign, 200th anniv.

Millennium of Tynwald
Tapestry — A400

Inscriptions: Nos. 1713a, 1715, The Viking Arrival. Nos. 1713b, 1716, Manx Bill of Rights. Nos. 1713c, 1717, Tourist Industry. Nos. 1713d, 1718, Spuds 'n' Herring. Nos. 1713e, 1719, Fishing Industry. No. 1714a, TT. No. 1714b, Transport. No. 1714c, Old House of Keys in Castletown. No. 1714d, Woman's Suffrage. No. 1714e, Tynwald Hill.

**2015, Apr. 10    Litho.    Perf. 14¼**
| | | | |
|---|---|---|---|
| 1713 | | Horiz. strip of 5 | 5.25 | 5.25 |
| a.-e. | | A400 1st Any single | 1.05 | 1.05 |
| 1714 | | Horiz. strip of 5 | 9.50 | 9.50 |
| a.-e. | | A400 EU Any single | 1.90 | 1.90 |
| f. | | As "b," Queen's head 5mm | | |
| | | tall | 1.90 | 1.90 |

**Booklet Stamps**
**Self-Adhesive**
**Die Cut Perf. 13¼**
| | | | |
|---|---|---|---|
| 1715 | A400 | 1st multi | 1.25 | 1.25 |
| 1716 | A400 | 1st multi | 1.25 | 1.25 |
| 1717 | A400 | 1st multi | 1.25 | 1.25 |
| 1718 | A400 | 1st multi | 1.25 | 1.25 |

**1719** A400 1st multi 1.25 1.25
  *a.* Booklet pane of 12, 3 each
    #1715, 1717, 2 each
    #1716, 1718, 1719 15.00
  *Nos. 1715-1719 (5)* 6.25 6.25

Europa (#1714b, 1714f). On day of issue, Nos. 1713a-1713e, 1715-1719 each sold for 42p, and Nos. 1714a-1714e each sold for 75p. Queen's head is 4½mm tall on No. 1714b. No. 1715f was printed in sheets of 10.

Women's Institute, Cent. — A401

Designs: No. 1720, Women with loudspeaker. No. 1721, Two women with signs supporting dairy farmers. No. 1722, Women protesting for equal pay. No. 1723, Women protesting for litter control. No. 1724, Group of women with signs supporting dairy farmers. No. 1725, Women with signs showing years and achievements.

**2015, Apr. 25** Litho. Perf. 13½
**1720** A401 1st multi 1.05 1.05
**1721** A401 1st multi 1.05 1.05
**1722** A401 £1 multi 2.75 2.75
**1723** A401 £1 multi 2.75 2.75
**1724** A401 £1.75 multi 4.75 4.75
**1725** A401 £1.75 multi 4.75 4.75
  *Nos. 1720-1725 (6)* 17.10 17.10

On day of issue, Nos. 1720-1721 each sold for 42p. Nos. 1720-1725 are impregnated with a rose scent.

**Miniature Sheet**

Paintings of Ships by John Halsall A402

No. 1726: a, Master Frank. b, HMS Ramsey. c, HMS Ben my Chree. d, Lusitania and Wanderer.

**2015, May 1** Litho. Perf. 13½x13¾
**1726** A402 Sheet of 4 9.00 9.00
  *a.-b.* 75p Either single 1.90 1.90
  *c.-d.* £1 Either single 2.60 2.60

A403

A404

A405

Battle of Waterloo, 200th Anniv. — A406

No. 1727: a, Duke of Wellington on horseback. b, Battle of Quatre-Bras.
No. 1728: a, Fighting at La Haye-Sainte. b, Napoleon in the Battle of Waterloo.
No. 1729: a, Defense of Château de Hougoumont. b, Wellington defeats Ney at Quatre-Bras.
No. 1730: a, Wellington and Blücher. b, General Hill and the Last Stand of the French Imperial Guard.

**2015, May 8** Litho. Perf. 12¾
**1727** A403 Horiz. pair 4.00 4.00
  *a.-b.* 75p Either single 2.00 2.00
**1728** A404 Horiz. pair 4.00 4.00
  *a.-b.* 75p Either single 2.00 2.00
**1729** A405 Horiz. pair 4.50 4.50
  *a.-b.* 90p Either single 2.25 2.25
**1730** A406 Horiz. pair 4.50 4.50
  *a.-b.* 90p Either single 2.25 2.25
  *Nos. 1727-1730 (4)* 17.00 17.00

Queen Elizabeth II — A407

Various photographs of Queen Elizabeth II with inscriptions of: Nos. 1731, 1739a, The Coronation. Nos. 1732, 1739b, The Investiture. Nos. 1733, 1739c, The Silver Jubilee. Nos. 1734, 1739d, Order of the Garter. Nos. 1735, 1739e, Trooping the Color. Nos. 1736, 1739f, The Golden Jubilee. Nos. 1737, 1739g, The Diamond Jubilee. Nos. 1738, 1739h, Opening of Parliament.

*Perf. 14¼x14¾*

**2015, June 18** Litho.
**1731** A407 44p multi 1.10 1.10
**1732** A407 44p multi 1.10 1.10
**1733** A407 77p multi 1.90 1.90
**1734** A407 77p multi 1.90 1.90
**1735** A407 93p multi 2.40 2.40
**1736** A407 93p multi 2.40 2.40
**1737** A407 £1.24 multi 3.25 3.25
**1738** A407 £1.24 multi 3.25 3.25
  *Nos. 1731-1738 (8)* 17.30 17.30

**Miniature Sheet**
**Self-Adhesive**
*Die Cut Perf. 11¾*

**1739** Sheet of 8 22.50
  *a.-b.* A407 44p Either single 1.40 1.40
  *c.-d.* A407 77p Either single 2.35 2.35
  *e.-f.* A407 93p Either single 3.10 3.10
  *g.-h.* A407 £1.24 Either single 4.10 4.10
  *i.* Booklet pane of 2, #1739a-
    1739b 2.40
  *j.* Booklet pane of 3, #1739c-
    1739e 6.60
  *k.* Booklet pane of 3, #1739f-
    1739h 9.60
  *l.* Booklet pane of 8, #1739a-
    1739h 18.60
  Complete booklet, #1739i-
    1739l 37.50

No. 1739l has staple holes and other half of the folio. No. 1739 can be cut from No. 1739l.

Curraghs Wildlife Park, 50th Anniv. — A408

Designs: No. 1740, Humboldt penguin. No. 1741, Red panda. 93p, Ruffed lemur. £1.13, Waldrapp ibis. £1.24, Fishing cat. £2.38, Rodrigues fruit bat.

**2015, July 3** Litho. Perf. 13¾x13¼
**1740** A408 44p multi 1.10 1.10
**1741** A408 44p multi 1.10 1.10
**1742** A408 93p multi 2.60 2.60
**1743** A408 £1.13 multi 3.00 3.00
**1744** A408 £1.24 multi 3.50 3.50
**1745** A408 £2.38 multi 6.50 6.50
  *Nos. 1740-1745 (6)* 17.80 17.80

Buses — A409

Designs: 44p, Douglas Corporation Transport Leyland Cub KPZ1. 60p, Isle of Man Road Services Leyland/MCW Olympic HR40. 77p, Isle of Man Road Services Leyland Tiger PS1. 93p, Douglas Corporation Transport Daimler CWA6. 147p, Isle of Man Road Services Leyland Titan PD1. 186p, Douglas Corporation Transport AEC Regent 1.

**2015, July 15** Litho. Perf. 13¼
**1746** A409 44p multi 1.10 1.10
**1747** A409 60p multi 1.60 1.60
**1748** A409 77p multi 2.00 2.00
**1749** A409 93p multi 2.60 2.60
**1750** A409 147p multi 4.00 4.00
**1751** A409 186p multi 5.00 5.00
  *Nos. 1746-1751 (6)* 16.30 16.30

1865 Companies Act, 150th Anniv. A410

Registration certificates and memorabilia of: 44p, Isle of Man Bank Limited. 77p, Isle of Man Steam Packet Company Limited. 93p, Finch Hill Pavilion and Bowling Club Limited. 113p, Heron and Brearley Limited. 154p, Farmers Combine Limited. 165p, Peel Golf Club Limited.

**2015, Sept. 28** Litho. Perf. 13¼
**1752** A410 44p multi 1.10 1.10
**1753** A410 77p multi 2.00 2.00
**1754** A410 93p multi 2.60 2.60
**1755** A410 113p multi 3.00 3.00
**1756** A410 154p multi 4.00 4.00
**1757** A410 165p multi 4.25 4.25
  *Nos. 1752-1757 (6)* 16.95 16.95

Art of Bryan Kneale — A411

No. 1758: a, Self-portrait, 1954. b, Pendulum, 1964. c, The Watcher, 1977. d, Three Legs of Man, 1979. e, Horse, 1985. f, The Deemster Fish, 1996. g, Captain Quilliam, 2005. h, Illiam Dhone, 2006. i, Triton III, 2009. j, Quince, 2015.

**2015, Oct. 1** Litho. Perf. 13¼x12½
**1758** Block of 10 12.00 12.00
  *a.-j.* A411 44p Any single 1.20 1.20

Christmas — A412

Manx words from Manx Christmas Prayer Book: 44p, Niart (strength). 77p, Grayse (grace). 93p, Shee (peace). 124p, Graih (love). 320p, Credjue (faith).

*Serpentine Die Cut 13½*

**2015, Oct. 23** Litho.
**Self-Adhesive**
**1759** A412 44p multi 1.10 1.10
  *a.* Booklet pane of 10 11.00
**1760** A412 77p multi 2.00 2.00
**1761** A412 93p multi 2.60 2.60
**1762** A412 124p multi 3.50 3.50
**1763** A412 320p multi 8.50 8.50
  *Nos. 1759-1763 (5)* 17.70 17.70

Manx Christmas Prayer Book, 250th anniv.

Royal Aeronautical Society, 150th Anniv. — A413

No. 1764: a, 1784 balloon ascent of Vincenzo Lunardi. b, Sir George Cayley (1773-1857), and flying machine designs. c, Wright A Flyer at Reims, France, 1909. d, Yuri Gagarin (1934-68), first man in space.
No. 1765: a, Hawker P1127. b, British Airways Concorde. c, Rolls-Royce Trent 900 jet engine. d, International Space Station.

**2016, Jan. 12** Litho. Perf. 13¼
**1764** Horiz. strip of 4 7.00 7.00
  *a.-b.* A413 1st Either single 1.25 1.25
  *c.-d.* A413 77p Either single 2.25 2.25
**1765** Horiz. strip of 4 13.00 13.00
  *a.-b.* A413 93p Either single 2.75 2.75
  *c.-d.* A413 124p Either single 3.75 3.75

Nos. 1764a-1764b each sold for 44p on day of issue.

New Year 2016 (Year of the Monkey) A414

No. 1766: a, One monkey. b, Two monkeys.

**2016, Jan. 20** Litho. Perf. 13¼
**1766** A414 Sheet of 2 6.00 6.00
  *a.* 10p multi .25 .25
  *b.* £2 multi 5.75 5.75
  *c.* Sheet of 20 #1766a 5.00 5.00

Queen Elizabeth II, 90th Birthday — A415

Queen Elizabeth II wearing: No. 1767, Purple coat and hat. No. 1768, Maroon coat, red and maroon hat. No. 1769, Bright green coat and hat. No. 1770, White dress and tiara. No. 1771, Royal blue and greenish blue coat and hat. No. 1772, Red dress. No. 1773, Pale blue coat and hat. No. 1774, Red coat and hat.

**2016** Litho. Perf. 13
**1767** A415 1st multi 1.25 1.25
**1768** A415 1st multi 1.25 1.25
**1769** A415 77p multi 2.25 2.25
**1770** A415 77p multi 2.25 2.25
**1771** A415 93p multi 2.60 2.60
**1772** A415 93p multi 2.60 2.60
  *a.* Souvenir sheet of 2, #1770,
    1772 5.00 5.00
**1773** A415 £1.24 multi 3.50 3.50
**1774** A415 £1.24 multi 3.50 3.50
  *a.* Souvenir sheet of 2, #1771,
    1774 6.25 6.25
  *Nos. 1767-1774 (8)* 19.20 19.20

Issued: Nos. 1767-1774, 2/6; Nos. 1772a, 1774a, 4/21. Nos. 1767-1768 each sold for 44p on day of issue.

Battle of the Somme, Cent. — A416

Poppies and: 1st, Soldiers near cannon. 77p, Aerial dogfight. 93p, Soldiers and cemetery. 124p, Tanks. 165p, Injured soldiers walking past dead soldiers. 186p, Memorial.

**2016** Litho. Perf. 14x14¼
**1775** A416 1st multi 1.25 1.25
**1776** A416 77p multi 2.25 2.25
**1777** A416 93p multi 2.60 2.60
**1778** A416 124p multi 3.50 3.50
**1779** A416 165p multi 4.75 4.75
**1780** A416 186p multi 5.25 5.25
  *a.* Souvenir sheet of 6, #1775-
    1780 18.50 18.50
  *Nos. 1775-1780 (6)* 19.60 19.60

Issued: Nos. 1775-1780, 2/17; No. 1780a, 7/1. On day of issue, No. 1775 sold for 44p.

**Souvenir Sheet**

Battle of Jutland, Cent. A417

No. 1781: a, British Admiral Sir John Jellicoe (1859-1935), German Admiral Reinhard Scheer (1863-1928), denomination at UL. b, British Vice Admiral Sir David Beatty (1871-1936), German Vice Admiral Franz Hipper (1863-1932), denomination at UR.

**2016, Feb. 17** Litho. Perf. 14x14¼
**1781** A417 Sheet of 2 10.00 10.00
  *a.-b.* 175p Either single 5.00 5.00

Birds — A418

Designs: Nos. 1782a, 1784, Manx shearwater. Nos. 1782b, 1785, Robin. Nos. 1782c, 1786, Pheasant. Nos. 1782d, 1787, Goldfinch. Nos. 1782e, 1788, Tawny owl. No. 1783a, Starling. No. 1783b, Blue tit. No. 1783c, Puffin. No. 1783d, Hobby. No. 1783e, Cormorant.

**2016, Mar. 24    Litho.    Perf. 12½**

| | | | | |
|---|---|---|---|---|
| 1782 | | Horiz. strip of 5 | 6.25 | 6.25 |
| a.-e. | | A418 1st Any single | 1.25 | 1.25 |
| 1783 | | Horiz. strip of 5 | 11.50 | 11.50 |
| a.-e. | | A418 EU Any single | 2.25 | 2.25 |
| f. | | Miniature sheet of 9, 3 each #1782a, 1783c, 1783e | 17.50 | 17.50 |

**Booklet Stamps**
**Self-Adhesive**

**Serpentine Die Cut 13**

| | | | | |
|---|---|---|---|---|
| 1784 | A418 | 1st multi | 1.25 | 1.25 |
| 1785 | A418 | 1st multi | 1.25 | 1.25 |
| 1786 | A418 | 1st multi | 1.25 | 1.25 |
| 1787 | A418 | 1st multi | 1.25 | 1.25 |
| 1788 | A418 | 1st multi | 1.25 | 1.25 |
| a. | | Booklet pane of 10, 2 each #1784-1788 | 12.50 | |
| | | Nos. 1784-1788 (5) | 6.25 | 6.25 |

On day of issue, Nos. 1782a-1782e, 1784-1788 each sold for 44p, and Nos. 1783a-1783e each sold for 77p.

Royal Artillery, 300th Anniv. — A419

Designs: 45p, Artilleryman, c. 1716. 50p, Royal Horse Artillery officer, c. 1800. 95p, Gunner of 4th Mountain Artillery Battery, 1890. £1.27, Major John Drinkwater of Royal Field Artillery in World War I uniform. £1.69, Officer from Royal Artillery Light Anti-Aircraft Regiment in World War II. £2.44, Major Kate Philp in Afghanistan, 2008.

**2016, May 9    Litho.    Perf. 13½**

| | | | | |
|---|---|---|---|---|
| 1789 | A419 | 45p multi | 1.40 | 1.40 |
| 1790 | A419 | 50p multi | 1.50 | 1.50 |
| 1791 | A419 | 95p multi | 2.75 | 2.75 |
| 1792 | A419 | £1.27 multi | 3.75 | 3.75 |
| 1793 | A419 | £1.69 multi | 5.00 | 5.00 |
| 1794 | A419 | £2.44 multi | 7.00 | 7.00 |
| | | Nos. 1789-1794 (6) | 21.40 | 21.40 |

**Booklet Stamps**
**Self-Adhesive**

**Die Cut Perf. 11¾**

| | | | | |
|---|---|---|---|---|
| 1795 | A419 | 45p multi | 1.40 | 1.40 |
| 1796 | A419 | 50p multi | 1.50 | 1.50 |
| 1797 | A419 | 95p multi | 2.75 | 2.75 |
| a. | | Booklet pane of 3, #1795-1797 | 5.75 | |
| 1798 | A419 | £1.27 multi | 3.75 | 3.75 |
| 1799 | A419 | £1.69 multi | 5.00 | 5.00 |
| a. | | Booklet pane of 2, #1798-1799 | 8.75 | |
| 1800 | A419 | £2.44 multi | 7.00 | 7.00 |
| a. | | Booklet pane of 1 | 7.00 | |
| b. | | Booklet pane of 6, #1795-1800 | 21.50 | |
| | | Complete booklet, #1797a, 1799a, 1800a, 1800b | 43.00 | |
| | | Nos. 1795-1800 (6) | 21.40 | 21.40 |

**Souvenir Sheet**

Antarctic Explorers — A420

No. 1801: a, Captain Frank Worsley of Endurance Expedition, 1914-17. b, Henry Worsley of Shackleton Solo Expedition, 2015-16.

**2016, May 10    Litho.    Perf. 13½x13**

| | | | | |
|---|---|---|---|---|
| 1801 | A420 | Sheet of 2 | 10.00 | 10.00 |
| a.-b. | | £1.75 Either single | 5.00 | 5.00 |

Imperial Trans-Antarctic Expedition, cent.

2016 Summer Olympics, Rio de Janeiro — A421

No. 1802: a, Cycling. b, Track and field. c, Gymnast putting chalk on hands. d, Swimming.

**2016    Litho.    Perf. 13¼**

| | | | | |
|---|---|---|---|---|
| 1802 | | Horiz. strip of 4 | 15.00 | 15.00 |
| a.-d. | | A421 £1.27 Any single | 3.75 | 3.75 |
| e. | | Souvenir sheet of 4, #a-d + 8 labels | 15.00 | 15.00 |
| f. | | Souvenir sheet of 4, #a-d + 4 labels | 12.50 | 12.50 |

Issued: Nos. 1802, 1802e, 5/23; No. 1802f, 10/21.

Churches on Manx Telecom Parish Walk Race Route — A422

No. 1803: a, St. Brendan's Church, Braddan. b, Marown Parish Church, Marown. c, St. Sanctain's Church, Santon. d, St. Lupus Church, Malew. e, Parish Church of St. Columba, Arbory. f, Holy Trinity Church, Rushen. g, Holy Trinity Church, Patrick. h, St. German's Cathedral, Peel. i, St. Michael's Church, Michael. j, St. Mary's Church, Ballaugh. k, St. Patrick's Church, Jurby. l, St. Bridget's Church, Bride. m, St. Andrew's Church, Andreas. n, Kirk Christ, Lezayre. o, Maughold Parish Church, Maughold. p, All Saints' Church, Lonan. q, St. Peter's Church, Onchan.

**2016, June 15    Litho.    Perf. 13¼**

| | | | | |
|---|---|---|---|---|
| 1803 | | Block of 17 + label | 21.50 | 21.50 |
| a.-q. | | A422 1st Any single | 1.25 | 1.25 |

On day of issue, Nos. 1803a-1803q each sold for 45p. Nos. 1803a-1803q were also printed in a sheet of 108 stamps, lacking labels, which contains 12 No. 1803a and 6 each of Nos. 1803b-1803q, arranged in blocks of 6 of the same stamp.

Physics — A423

Designs: 45p, Albert Einstein (1879-1955), mass-energy equivalence equation. 50p, Stephen Hawking, black hole entropy equation. 95p, Gravitational waves produced by two black holes. £1.27, Hawking radiation. £1.69, Two black holes colliding. £2.44, Black hole.

**Litho. With Foil Application**

**2016    Perf. 13½**

| | | | | |
|---|---|---|---|---|
| 1804 | A423 | 45p multi | 1.25 | 1.25 |
| 1805 | A423 | 50p multi | 1.40 | 1.40 |
| 1806 | A423 | 95p multi | 2.60 | 2.60 |
| 1807 | A423 | £1.27 multi | 3.50 | 3.50 |
| 1808 | A423 | £1.69 multi | 4.50 | 4.50 |
| 1809 | A423 | £2.44 multi | 6.50 | 6.50 |
| a. | | Souvenir sheet of 6, #1804-1809 | 20.00 | 20.00 |
| | | Nos. 1804-1809 (6) | 19.75 | 19.75 |

**Booklet Stamps**
**Self-Adhesive**

**Die Cut Perf. 15**

| | | | | |
|---|---|---|---|---|
| 1810 | A423 | 45p multi | 1.25 | 1.25 |
| a. | | Booklet pane of 1 | 1.25 | 1.25 |
| 1811 | A423 | 50p multi | 1.40 | 1.40 |
| a. | | Booklet pane of 1 | 1.40 | |
| 1812 | A423 | 95p multi | 2.60 | 2.60 |
| 1813 | A423 | £1.27 multi | 3.50 | 3.50 |
| 1814 | A423 | £1.69 multi | 4.50 | 4.50 |
| 1815 | A423 | £2.44 multi | 6.50 | 6.50 |
| a. | | Booklet pane of 4, #1812-1815 | 17.50 | |
| b. | | Booklet pane of 6, #1810-1815 | 20.00 | |
| | | Complete booklet, #1810a, 1811a, 1815a, 1815b | 41.00 | |

Einstein's General Theory of Relativity, cent. Issued: Nos. 1804-1809, 7/1; Nos. 1810-1815, 7/15.

Aardman Animation Characters A424

Inscriptions: No. 1816, Morph, Laxey tram. No. 1817, Wallace and Gromit, motorcycle and ladder. No. 1818, Shaun the Sheep, Bitzer the dog. No. 1819, Timmy Time. No. 1820, Shaun the Sheep jijack road line painting macine. No. 1821, Wallace and Gromit at the beach. No. 1822, Creature Comforts. No. 1823, Morph, Laxey wheel.

**2016, Aug. 12    Litho.    Perf. 15x14**

| | | | | |
|---|---|---|---|---|
| 1816 | A424 | 1st multi | 1.25 | 1.25 |
| 1817 | A424 | 1st multi | 1.25 | 1.25 |
| 1818 | A424 | 77p multi | 2.10 | 2.10 |
| 1819 | A424 | 77p multi | 2.10 | 2.10 |
| a. | | Souvenir sheet of 6 | 13.00 | 13.00 |
| 1820 | A424 | 95p multi | 2.60 | 2.60 |
| a. | | Souvenir sheet of 6, 3 each #1818, 1820 | 14.50 | 14.50 |
| 1821 | A424 | 95p multi | 2.60 | 2.60 |
| a. | | Souvenir sheet of 6, 3 each #1817, 1821 | 12.00 | 12.00 |
| 1822 | A424 | £1.24 multi | 3.25 | 3.25 |
| a. | | Souvenir sheet of 6 | 19.50 | 19.50 |
| 1823 | A424 | £1.24 multi | 3.25 | 3.25 |
| a. | | Souvenir sheet of 6, 3 each #1816, 1823 | 13.50 | 13.50 |
| | | Nos. 1816-1823 (8) | 18.40 | 18.40 |

On day of issue, Nos. 1816-1817 each sold for 45p.

Art of Roger Dean A425

Designs: 45p, Meeting Place. 77p, Blind Owl Late Landing. 95p, Pathways. £1.24, Green Parrot Island. £1.69, Tales From Topographic Oceans. £2.08, Sea of Light.

**2016, Aug. 19    Litho.    Perf. 13**

| | | | | |
|---|---|---|---|---|
| 1824 | A425 | 45p multi | 1.25 | 1.25 |
| 1825 | A425 | 77p multi | 2.10 | 2.10 |
| 1826 | A425 | 95p multi | 2.60 | 2.60 |
| 1827 | A425 | £1.24 multi | 3.25 | 3.25 |
| 1828 | A425 | £1.69 multi | 4.50 | 4.50 |
| 1829 | A425 | £2.08 multi | 5.50 | 5.50 |
| | | Nos. 1824-1829 (6) | 19.20 | 19.20 |

Islands and Bridges Exhibition of Art by Dean, Manx Museum, Douglas.

Sand Castle — A426

Europa — A427

Recycling Emblem, Richmond Hill Waste-to-Energy Plant — A428

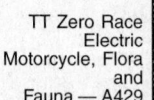

TT Zero Race Electric Motorcycle, Flora and Fauna — A429

Hydroelectic Power Emblem, Fish — A430

**2016, Oct. 7    Litho.    Perf. 13½**

| | | | | |
|---|---|---|---|---|
| 1830 | A426 | 45p multi | 1.10 | 1.10 |
| 1831 | A427 | 77p multi | 1.90 | 1.90 |
| a. | | Miniature sheet of 10 | 19.00 | 19.00 |
| 1832 | A428 | £1.13 multi | 2.75 | 2.75 |
| 1833 | A429 | £1.47 multi | 3.75 | 3.75 |
| 1834 | A430 | £2.33 multi | 5.75 | 5.75 |
| | | Nos. 1830-1834 (5) | 15.25 | 15.25 |

Think Green Issue, Europa (No. 1831).

**Souvenir Sheet**

Circumnavigation of Solar Impulse 2 Solar-Powered Airplane — A431

**2016, Oct. 14    Litho.    Perf. 14¼x14**

| | | | | |
|---|---|---|---|---|
| 1835 | A431 | £3 multi | 7.50 | 7.50 |

Christmas Pantomime Shows — A432

Props from: 45p, The Wizard of Oz. 77p, Peter Pan. 95p, Aladdin. 113p, Snow White and the Seven Dwarfs. 124p, Dick Whittington. 186p, Robin Hood.

**2016, Oct. 20    Litho.    Perf. 13**

| | | | | |
|---|---|---|---|---|
| 1836 | A432 | 45p multi | 1.10 | 1.10 |
| 1837 | A432 | 77p multi | 1.90 | 1.90 |
| 1838 | A432 | 95p multi | 2.40 | 2.40 |
| 1839 | A432 | 113p multi | 2.75 | 2.75 |
| 1840 | A432 | 124p multi | 3.00 | 3.00 |
| 1841 | A432 | 186p multi | 4.75 | 4.75 |
| | | Nos. 1836-1841 (6) | 15.90 | 15.90 |

**Self-Adhesive**

**Serpentine Die Cut 13½**

| | | | | |
|---|---|---|---|---|
| 1842 | A432 | 45p multi | 1.10 | 1.10 |

Tourism — A433

Tourism art by Adam Berry for: 1st, Peel. EU, Castletown. 95p, Onchan. £1.24, Ramsey. £1.27, Port St. Mary. £2.33, Port Erin.

**2017, Jan. 19    Litho.    Perf. 13½x13¼**

| | | | | |
|---|---|---|---|---|
| 1843 | A433 | 1st multi | 1.25 | 1.25 |
| a. | | Miniature sheet of 10 | 12.50 | 12.50 |
| 1844 | A433 | EU multi | 2.00 | 2.00 |
| a. | | Miniature sheet of 10 | 20.00 | 20.00 |
| 1845 | A433 | 95p multi | 2.40 | 2.40 |
| 1846 | A433 | £1.24 multi | 3.25 | 3.25 |
| 1847 | A433 | £1.27 multi | 3.25 | 3.25 |
| 1848 | A433 | £2.33 multi | 6.00 | 6.00 |
| | | Nos. 1843-1848 (6) | 18.15 | 18.15 |

On day of issue, No. 1843 sold for 45p; No. 1844, 77p.

Reign of Queen Elizabeth II, 65th Anniv. — A434

Photograph of Queen Elizabeth II taken in: 45p, Australia, 1954. 77p, China, 1986. 95p, India, 1983. £1.13, Isle of Man, 1979. £1.24, Canada, 2010. £2.37, Tuvalu, 1982. £3.75, Queen Elizabeth II receiving horse from Royal Canadian Mounted Police, 1969.

**2017, Feb. 6    Litho.    Perf. 13**

| | | | | |
|---|---|---|---|---|
| 1849 | A434 | 45p multi | 1.10 | 1.10 |
| 1850 | A434 | 77p multi | 1.90 | 1.90 |
| 1851 | A434 | 95p multi | 2.40 | 2.40 |
| 1852 | A434 | £1.13 multi | 2.75 | 2.75 |
| 1853 | A434 | £1.24 multi | 3.00 | 3.00 |
| 1854 | A434 | £2.37 multi | 6.00 | 6.00 |
| | | Nos. 1849-1854 (6) | 17.15 | 17.15 |

**Souvenir Sheet**

| | | | | |
|---|---|---|---|---|
| 1855 | A434 | £3.75 multi | 9.25 | 9.25 |
| a. | | Overprinted in red in sheet margin with Canada 150th anniv. emblem | 9.75 | 9.75 |

Issued: No. 1855a, 7/1.

### First General Election of the House of Keys, 150th Anniv. A435

Designs: 1st, Douglas Court House on Election Day, Register of Electors John Senhouse Goldie-Taubman, and poll book. £1, Castle Rushen, Proclamation for dissolving the House of Keys, and Lieutenant Governor Henry Loch. £1.50, Jail of Castle Rushen, *Isle of Man Times* newspaper and its owner, James Brown. £2, Journalist Robert Fargher, Castletown House of Keys, and Fargher's *Mona's Herald* newspaper.

| | | **2017, Feb. 13** | **Litho.** | **Perf. 13¼** |
|---|---|---|---|---|
| 1856 | A435 | 1st multi | 1.10 | 1.10 |
| 1857 | A435 | £1 multi | 2.50 | 2.50 |
| 1858 | A435 | £1.50 multi | 3.75 | 3.75 |
| 1859 | A435 | £2 multi | 5.00 | 5.00 |
| | | *Nos. 1856-1859 (4)* | 12.35 | 12.35 |

On day of issue, No. 1856 sold for 45p.

### Miniature Sheet

### Festivals A436

No. 1860: a, Conductor's hands (Mananan International Festival). b, Man reading book (Manx Litfest). c, Actress (Manx Music, Speech and Dance Festival). d, Dancer (Shennaghys Jiu). e, Accordion player (Celtfest).

| | | **2017, Apr. 6** | **Litho.** | **Perf. 13¼x13** |
|---|---|---|---|---|
| 1860 | A436 | Sheet of 5 | 10.00 | 10.00 |
| a.-e. | | 75p Any single | 2.00 | 2.00 |

### Food Production — A437

Inscription: Nos. 1861, 1867, Farm to Yarn. Nos. 1862, 1868, Fish to Dish. EU, Welly to Belly. 98p, Cow to Cup. RoW, Tree to Table. £2.52, Field to Fork.

| | | **2017** | **Litho.** | **Perf. 13¼x13** |
|---|---|---|---|---|
| 1861 | A437 | 1st multi | 1.25 | 1.25 |
| 1862 | A437 | 1st multi | 1.25 | 1.25 |
| 1863 | A437 | EU multi | 2.00 | 2.00 |
| 1864 | A437 | 98p multi | 2.50 | 2.50 |
| 1865 | A437 | RoW multi | 3.25 | 3.25 |
| 1866 | A437 | £2.52 multi | 6.50 | 6.50 |
| | | *Nos. 1861-1866 (6)* | 16.75 | 16.75 |

### Booklet Stamps
### Self-Adhesive
### Serpentine Die Cut 12½

| | | | | |
|---|---|---|---|---|
| 1867 | A437 | 1st multi | 1.90 | 1.90 |
| 1868 | A437 | 1st multi | 1.90 | 1.90 |
| a. | | Booklet pane of 10, 5 each #1867-1868 | 19.00 | |

Issued: Nos. 1861-1866, 5/3; Nos. 1867-1868, 5/15. On day of issue, Nos. 1861-1862 each sold for 45p; No. 1863, 77p; No. 1865, £1.24, Nos. 1867-1868, 47p.

### Symbols of Freemasonry A438

Designs: 20p, Jewel of the Steward. 1st, Jewel of the Inner Guard. 50p, Jewel of the Junior and Senior Deacon. £1.30, Jewel of the Junior Warden. £1.74, Jewel of the Senior Warden. £3.40, Jewel of the Worshipful Master.

### Litho. With Foil Application

| | | **2017, May 11** | | **Perf. 13½** |
|---|---|---|---|---|
| 1869 | A438 | 20p gold & multi | .55 | .55 |
| 1870 | A438 | 1st gold & multi | 1.25 | 1.25 |
| 1871 | A438 | 50p gold & multi | 1.40 | 1.40 |
| 1872 | A438 | £1.30 gold & multi | 3.50 | 3.50 |
| 1873 | A438 | £1.74 gold & multi | 4.50 | 4.50 |
| 1874 | A438 | £3.40 gold & multi | 8.75 | 8.75 |
| a. | | Souvenir sheet of 6, #1869-1874 | 20.00 | 20.00 |
| | | *Nos. 1869-1874 (6)* | 19.95 | 19.95 |

English Freemasonry, 300th anniv.

### TT Motorcycle Race Winners A439

Designs: 1st, Joey Dunlop, 1977. EU, Steve Hislop, 1987. RoW, Ian Simpson, 1997. £2.50, Ian Hutchinson, 2007.

| | | **2017, May 26** | **Litho.** | **Perf. 13** |
|---|---|---|---|---|
| 1875 | A439 | 1st multi | 1.25 | 1.25 |
| 1876 | A439 | EU multi | 2.10 | 2.10 |
| 1877 | A439 | RoW multi | 3.50 | 3.50 |
| 1878 | A439 | £2.50 multi | 6.50 | 6.50 |
| | | *Nos. 1875-1878 (4)* | 13.35 | 13.35 |

On day of issue, No. 1875 sold for 47p; No. 1876, 80p; No. 1877, £1.30.

### Prince Philip A440

Various photographs of Prince Philip.

| | | **2017, June 10** | **Litho.** | **Perf. 13** |
|---|---|---|---|---|
| 1879 | A440 | Block of 6 | 18.50 | 18.50 |
| a. | | 47p multi | 1.25 | 1.25 |
| b. | | 80p multi | 2.10 | 2.10 |
| c. | | 98p multi | 2.60 | 2.60 |
| d. | | £1.18 multi | 3.00 | 3.00 |
| e. | | £1.30 multi | 3.50 | 3.50 |
| f. | | £2.33 multi | 6.00 | 6.00 |
| g. | | Sheet of 6, #1879a-1879f, + 6 labels | 22.50 | 22.50 |

issued: No. 1879g, 3/31/21. No. 1879g sold for £8.

### Birds — A441

Designs: 47p, Oystercatchers. 80p, Eiders. 98p, Little tern. £1.18, Fulmars. £1.30, Black guillemots. £1.94, Razorbills.

| | | **2017, June 29** | **Litho.** | **Perf. 14** |
|---|---|---|---|---|
| 1880 | A441 | 47p multi | 1.25 | 1.25 |
| 1881 | A441 | 80p multi | 2.10 | 2.10 |
| 1882 | A441 | 98p multi | 2.60 | 2.60 |
| 1883 | A441 | £1.18 multi | 3.00 | 3.00 |
| 1884 | A441 | £1.30 multi | 3.50 | 3.50 |
| 1885 | A441 | £1.94 multi | 5.00 | 5.00 |
| | | *Nos. 1880-1885 (6)* | 17.45 | 17.45 |

### 70th Wedding Anniversary of Queen Elizabeth II and Prince Philip — A442

Flowers and various photographs of Queen Elizabeth II and Prince Philip from: 1st, 1947. 80p, 1957. 98p, 1987. £1.30, 1997. £1.86, 2007. £2.33, 2017.

| | | **2017, July 9** | **Litho.** | **Perf. 14** |
|---|---|---|---|---|
| 1886 | A442 | 1st multi | 1.25 | 1.25 |
| 1887 | A442 | 80p multi | 2.10 | 2.10 |
| 1888 | A442 | 98p multi | 2.60 | 2.60 |
| 1889 | A442 | £1.30 multi | 3.50 | 3.50 |
| 1890 | A442 | £1.86 multi | 5.00 | 5.00 |
| 1891 | A442 | £2.33 multi | 6.25 | 6.25 |
| | | *Nos. 1886-1891 (6)* | 20.70 | 20.70 |

On day of issue, No. 1886 sold for 47p.

### John C. Taylor, Inventor and Philanthropist A443

Designs: 47p, Chronophage. 80p, Taylor's clock collection. £1.30, Bimetal kettle switch. £1.47, Otter G switch. £1.68, Arragon Mooar. £1.86, Taylor Library and statue.

### Perf. 12x11¾ Syncopated

| | | **2017, Sept. 13** | | **Litho.** |
|---|---|---|---|---|
| 1892 | A443 | 47p sil & multi | 1.25 | 1.25 |
| 1893 | A443 | 80p sil & multi | 2.25 | 2.25 |
| 1894 | A443 | £1.30 sil & multi | 3.50 | 3.50 |
| 1895 | A443 | £1.47 sil & multi | 4.00 | 4.00 |
| 1896 | A443 | £1.68 sil & multi | 4.50 | 4.50 |
| 1897 | A443 | £1.86 sil & multi | 5.00 | 5.00 |
| | | *Nos. 1892-1897 (6)* | 20.50 | 20.50 |

### Self-Adhesive
### Die Cut Perf. 9½ Syncopated

| | | **1898** | | Sheet of 6 | 20.50 | |
|---|---|---|---|---|---|---|
| a. | | A443 47p sil & multi | | | 1.25 | 1.25 |
| b. | | A443 80p sil & multi | | | 2.25 | 2.25 |
| c. | | A443 £1.30 sil & multi | | | 3.50 | 3.50 |
| d. | | A443 £1.47 sil & multi | | | 4.00 | 4.00 |
| e. | | A443 £1.68 sil & multi | | | 4.50 | 4.50 |
| f. | | A443 £1.86 sil & multi | | | 5.00 | 5.00 |

### Souvenir Sheet

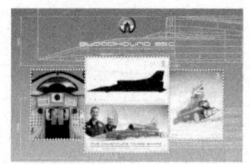

### Bloodhound SSC Supersonic Land Vehicle — A444

No. 1899: a, Blodhound SSC in motion (28x34mm). b, Silhouette of Bloodhound SSC (40x24mm)

### Perf. 13½x13¼ (#1899a), 13x13¼ (#1899b)
### Litho. & Silk-screened

| | | **2017, Sept. 22** | | |
|---|---|---|---|---|
| 1899 | A444 | Sheet of 2 + 2 labels | 12.00 | 12.00 |
| a. | | £2 sil & multi | 5.25 | 5.25 |
| b. | | £2.50 sil & multi | 6.75 | 6.75 |

### Paintings of Manx Cats by Lesley Anne Ivory — A445

Various cats with frame color of: 47p, Red. £1.30, Lilac. £1.57, Green. £3.68, Gray blue.

| | | **2017, Oct. 10** | **Litho.** | **Perf. 12¾** |
|---|---|---|---|---|
| 1900 | A445 | 47p multi | 1.25 | 1.25 |
| 1901 | A445 | £1.30 multi | 3.50 | 3.50 |
| 1902 | A445 | £1.57 multi | 4.25 | 4.25 |
| 1903 | A445 | £3.68 multi | 9.75 | 9.75 |
| | | *Nos. 1900-1903 (4)* | 18.75 | 18.75 |

### Christmas — A446

Nos. 1904 and 1905 — Items from Christmas song "The Twelve Days of Christmas": a, "1," partridge and pears. b, "2," turtle doves. c, "3," French hen. d, "4," calling birds. e, "5," golden rings. f, "6," goose and eggs. g, "7," swan. h, "8," cow and milkmaid with bucket. i, "9," ladies dancing. j, "10," leaping lord. k, "11," piper. l, "12," drum and sticks.

| | | **2017, Oct. 19** | **Litho.** | **Perf. 12½** |
|---|---|---|---|---|
| 1904 | A446 | Block of 12 | 15.00 | 15.00 |
| a.-l. | | 1st Any single | 1.25 | 1.25 |
| m. | | Sheet of 12, #a-l | 15.00 | 15.00 |

### Self-Adhesive
### Serpentine Die Cut 12¾

| | | **1905** | | Sheet of 12 | 15.00 | |
|---|---|---|---|---|---|---|
| a.-l. | | 1st Any single | | | 1.25 | 1.25 |

On day of issue, Nos. 1904a-1904l and 1905a-1905l each sold for 47p.

### Tholtans (Abandoned Structures) — A447

Tholtan: 20p, Ballagale, Surby. 1st, Pairk Mooar, Maughold. EU, Cronk Dhoo, Kirk Michael. RoW, North Laxey Mines. £1.74, Carnagrie, Slieau Whallian. £2.08, Kirk Michael Mines.

| | | **2018, Jan. 5** | **Litho.** | **Perf. 13** |
|---|---|---|---|---|
| 1906 | A447 | 20p multi | .60 | .60 |
| 1907 | A447 | 1st multi | 1.40 | 1.40 |
| 1908 | A447 | EU multi | 2.25 | 2.25 |
| 1909 | A447 | RoW multi | 3.75 | 3.75 |
| 1910 | A447 | £1.74 multi | 5.00 | 5.00 |
| 1911 | A447 | £2.08 multi | 6.00 | 6.00 |
| | | *Nos. 1906-1911 (6)* | 19.00 | 19.00 |

On day of issue, No. 1907 sold for 47p; No. 1908, for 80p; and No. 1909, for £1.30.

### Royal Air Force, Cent. — A448

Designs: Nos. 1912, 1920a, Sopwith Camel. Nos. 1913, 1920b, Supermarine Spitfire. Nos. 1914, 1920c, Avro Lancaster. Nos. 1915, 1920d, Avro Vulcan. Nos. 1916, 1920e, Boeing Chinook helicopter. Nos. 1917, 1920f, Hawker Siddeley Harrier. Nos. 1918, 1920g, Eurofighter Typhoon. Nos. 1919, 1920h, Lockheed-Martin Lightning II.

| | | **2018, Jan. 15** | **Litho.** | **Perf. 14x13½** |
|---|---|---|---|---|
| 1912 | A448 | 1st multi | 1.40 | 1.40 |
| 1913 | A448 | 1st multi | 1.40 | 1.40 |
| 1914 | A448 | EU multi | 2.25 | 2.25 |
| 1915 | A448 | EU multi | 2.25 | 2.25 |
| 1916 | A448 | £1 multi | 3.00 | 3.00 |
| 1917 | A448 | £1 multi | 3.00 | 3.00 |
| 1918 | A448 | RoW multi | 3.75 | 3.75 |
| 1919 | A448 | RoW multi | 3.75 | 3.75 |
| | | *Nos. 1912-1919 (8)* | 20.80 | 20.80 |

### Self-Adhesive
### Die Cut Perf. 13½x13¼

| | | **1920** | | Sheet of 8 | 21.00 | |
|---|---|---|---|---|---|---|
| a.-b. | | A448 1st Either single | | | 1.40 | 1.40 |
| c.-d. | | A448 EU Either single | | | 2.25 | 2.25 |
| e.-f. | | A448 £1 Either single | | | 3.00 | 3.00 |
| g.-h. | | A448 RoW Either single | | | 3.75 | 3.75 |

On day of issue, Nos. 1912-1913, 1920a-1920b each sold for 47p; Nos. 1914-1915, 1920c-1920d, for 80p; and Nos. 1918-1919, 1920g-1920h, for £1.30.

### Preen Line of Women's Clothing by Thornton and Bregazzi A449

Designs: 1st, Red Finella. EU, Citrus power dress. £1, Quilted floral dress. RoW, Pink velvet hitch dress. £1.57, Striped Flintoff dress. £1.86, Pink silk wrap dress.

| | | **2018, Feb. 1** | **Litho.** | **Perf. 13** |
|---|---|---|---|---|
| 1921 | A449 | 1st multi | 1.40 | 1.40 |
| 1922 | A449 | EU multi | 2.25 | 2.25 |
| 1923 | A449 | £1 multi | 3.00 | 3.00 |
| 1924 | A449 | RoW multi | 3.75 | 3.75 |
| 1925 | A449 | £1.57 multi | 4.50 | 4.50 |
| 1926 | A449 | £1.86 multi | 5.25 | 5.25 |
| | | *Nos. 1921-1926 (6)* | 20.15 | 20.15 |

On day of issue, No. 1921 sold for 47p; No. 1922, for 80p; and No. 1924, for £1.30

New Year
2018 (Year
of the Dog)
A450

Dog's head facing: £1.50, Right. £2, Left.

**2018, Feb. 8    Litho.    Perf. 13**
1927 A450  £1.50 multi  4.25 4.25
1928 A450  £2 multi  5.50 5.50

Actors and Actresses
Starring in Film
Adaptations by Sir
Thomas Hall Caine
(1853-1931) — A451

Designs: No. 1929, Pola Negri (1897-1987) in Barbed Wire. No. 1930, Anny Ondra (1902-87) in The Manxman. EU, Conrad Nagel (1897-1970) in Name the Man. 98p, Barbara La Marr (1896-1926) in The Eternal City. RoW, Richard Dix (1893-1949) in The Christian. £1.50, Norman Kerry (1894-1956) in The Bondman.

**2018, Feb. 14    Litho.    Perf. 13**
1929 A451  1st sil & multi  1.40 1.40
1930 A451  1st sil & multi  1.40 1.40
1931 A451  EU sil & multi  2.25 2.25
1932 A451  98p sil & multi  2.75 2.75
1933 A451  RoW sil & multi  3.75 3.75
1934 A451  £1.50 sil & multi  4.25 4.25
  Nos. 1929-1934 (6)  15.80 15.80

On day of issue, Nos. 1929-1930 each sold for 47p; No. 1931 sold for 80p; No. 1933, for £1.30.

Wedding of
Prince Harry and
Meghan
Markle — A452

Couple: £1.75, Legs visible. £2, Legs not visible.

**2018, Mar. 28    Litho.    Perf. 13x13¼**
1935 A452  £1.75 multi  5.00 5.00
1936 A452  £2 multi  5.75 5.75
  a. Souvenir sheet of 4, 2 each #1935-1936, + 2 central labels  21.50 21.50
  b. Souvenir sheet of 4, 2 each #1935-1936, labels at UL and LR  20.00 20.00

Issued: No. 1936b, 6/20.

Walkers Above
Fleshwick
A453

TT Fireworks
and Light
Show
A454

Sand Castle
with Manx
Flag, Port
Erin — A455

Manx Telecom
Parish
Walk — A456

Michael
Starkey
Painting
A457

Niarbyl Coast
A458

Skeddan Jiarg
Dance
Group — A459

Sunset at
Peel — A460

Lonan Cross
A461

Niarbyl Cottage
and Kayaks
A462

**2018, Apr. 10    Litho.    Perf. 12½**
1937  Horiz. strip of 5  7.00 7.00
  a. A453 1st multi  1.40 1.40
  b. A454 1st multi  1.40 1.40
  c. A455 1st multi  1.40 1.40
  d. A456 1st multi  1.40 1.40
  e. A457 1st multi  1.40 1.40
1938  Horiz. strip of 5  11.50 11.50
  a. A458 EU multi  2.25 2.25
  b. A459 EU multi  2.25 2.25
  c. A460 EU multi  2.25 2.25
  d. A461 EU multi  2.25 2.25
  e. A462 EU multi  2.25 2.25

**Miniature Sheet**
**Self-Adhesive**
**Serpentine Die Cut 13**
1939  Sheet of 5  7.00 7.00
  a. A453 1st multi  1.40 1.40
  b. A454 1st multi  1.40 1.40
  c. A455 1st multi  1.40 1.40
  d. A456 1st multi  1.40 1.40
  e. A457 1st multi  1.40 1.40

On day of issue, Nos. 1937a-1937e, 1939a-1939e each sold for 52p, and Nos. 1938a-1938e each sold for 83p.

Isle of Man
International
Motor Scooter
Rally, 60th
Anniv. — A463

Designs: No. 1940, Sand races. No. 1941, Ramsey Sprint. No. 1942, Ride Out. No. 1943, Concours d'Elegance. £1, Team time trials. No. 1945, Display team. No. 1946, Sidecar hill climb. No. 1947, Scooter Girl.

**2018, May 10    Litho.    Perf. 14**
1940 A463  1st multi  1.40 1.40
1941 A463  1st multi  1.40 1.40
1942 A463  EU multi  2.25 2.25
1943 A463  EU multi  2.25 2.25
1944 A463  £1 multi  2.75 2.75
1945 A463  RoW multi  3.75 3.75
1946 A463  RoW multi  3.75 3.75
1947 A463  RoW multi  3.75 3.75
  a. Sheet of 8, #1940-1947, + central label  21.00 21.00
  Nos. 1940-1947 (8)  21.30 21.30

On day of issue, Nos. 1940-1941 each sold for 52p; Nos. 1942-1943, for 83p; Nos. 1945-1947, for £1.40. No. 1947a sold for £7.90.

British Motorcycles — A464

No. 1948: a, 1920 Zenith JAP engine. b, Zenith racing. c, 1936 Excelsior Manxman engine. d, Excelsior Manxman in race. e, Douglas flat-twin in race. f, 1937 Douglas engine. g, AJS 500cc V-four in race. h, 1939 AJS engine. i, 1949 Vincent HRD chain drive. j, Vincent HRD 1000cc V-twin in race. k, 1961 Norton Manx engine. l, Norton Manx single in race.

**2018, May 17    Litho.    Perf. 12½**
1948 A464  Block of 12  17.00 17.00
  a.-l.  1st Any single  1.40 1.40

On day of issue, Nos. 1948a-1948l each sold for 52p.

Motion Picture 2001:
A Space Odyssey,
50th Anniv. of
Premiere — A465

Designs: 20p, Stanley Kubrick (1928-99), director, and actors. 30p, Arthur C. Clarke (1917-2008), screenplay writer, and props. 52p, Space Station V. 75p, Zero gravity. £1.40, Starchild. £1.93, Dr. David Bowman. £2.01, HAL 9000.

**2018, June 14    Litho.    Perf. 14x13½**
1949 A465  25p multi  .65 .65
1950 A465  30p multi  .80 .80
1951 A465  52p multi  1.40 1.40
1952 A465  75p multi  2.00 2.00
1953 A465  83p multi  2.25 2.25
1954 A465  £1.40 multi  3.75 3.75
1955 A465  £1.93 multi  5.00 5.00
1956 A465  £2.01 multi  5.25 5.25
  a. Sheet of 8, #1949-1956, + central label  21.50 21.50
  Nos. 1949-1956 (8)  21.10 21.10

Manx Electric
Railway, 125th
Anniv. — A466

Designs: 1st, Cars 6, 22 and 16 at Derby Castle Terminus. EU, Car 9 on Ballure Viaduct. £1.25, Car 1 near Laxey. RoW, Car 16 with mail car, near Onchan Head. £1.87, Cars 1 and 2 at Derby Castle Terminus. £1.93, Car 7 at Bulgham Rocks.

**2018, June 30    Litho.    Perf. 13**
1957 A466  1st multi  1.40 1.40
1958 A466  EU multi  2.25 2.25
1959 A466  £1.25 multi  3.25 3.25
1960 A466  RoW multi  3.75 3.75
1961 A466  £1.87 multi  5.00 5.00
1962 A466  £1.93 multi  5.00 5.00
  Nos. 1957-1962 (6)  20.65 20.65

**Self-Adhesive**
**Serpentine Die Cut 13x14**
1963  Sheet of 6  21.00
  a. A466 1st multi  1.40 1.40
  b. A466 EU multi  2.25 2.25
  c. A466 £1.25 multi  3.25 3.25
  d. A466 RoW multi  3.75 3.75
  e. A466 £1.87 multi  5.00 5.00
  f. A466 £1.93 multi  5.00 5.00
  g. Booklet pane of 2, #1963a-1963c  3.75
  h. Booklet pane of 2, #1963c-1963d  7.00
  i. Booklet pane of 2, #1963e-1963f  10.00
  j. Booklet pane of 6, #1963a-1963f  21.00
  Complete booklet, #1963g-1963j  42.00

Europa (#1958, 1963b). On day of issue, Nos. 1957 and 1963a each sold for 52p; Nos. 1958 and 1963b, for 83p; and Nos. 1960 and 1963d, for £1.40. The complete booklet consists of pages folded and stapled in the center, with Nos. 1963g-1963h and 1963i-1963j, being connected on opposite sides of the fold when exploded from the booklet. No. 1963 is merely a cut down version of No. 1963j that was sold separately from the complete booklet.

ANZAC
Memorials
Sculpted by
Rayner Hoff
(1894-1937)
A467

Soldier and details from memorials in Sydney and Adelaide: 52p, Pioneer sculpture, waratah flower. 83p, Sacrifice sculpture, kangaroo paw flower and Hoff. £1.25, Aviator sculpture, rosemary sprig. £1.40, Soldiers and horse bas-relief, blue gum branch. £1.75, Female angel sculpture, poppy. £2.05, Male angel sculpture, golden wattle flower.

**2018, Aug. 4    Litho.    Perf. 13**
1964 A467  52p multi  1.40 1.40
1965 A467  83p multi  2.25 2.25
1966 A467  £1.25 multi  3.25 3.25
1967 A467  £1.40 multi  3.75 3.75
1968 A467  £1.75 multi  4.50 4.50
1969 A467  £2.05 multi  5.25 5.25
  Nos. 1964-1969 (6)  20.40 20.40

Prince Charles,
70th
Birthday — A468

Paintings of Prince Charles by: 52p, Richard Stone. 83p, David Griffiths. £1.01, Stone, diff. £1.25, June Mendoza. £1.75, Mendoza, diff. £2.42, Michael Noakes.

**2018, Sept. 26    Litho.    Perf. 13**
1970 A468  52p multi  1.40 1.40
1971 A468  83p multi  2.25 2.25
1972 A468  £1.01 multi  2.75 2.75
1973 A468  £1.25 multi  3.25 3.25
1974 A468  £1.75 multi  4.75 4.75
1975 A468  £2.42 multi  6.50 6.50
  Nos. 1970-1975 (6)  20.90 20.90

Manx Folk
Traditions — A469

Designs: 1st, Yn Melliah. EU, Hop-tu-naa. £1.01, Hunt the wren. £1.40, New Year's Eve. £1.75, Quaaltagh. £2.15, Eve of Old Christmas Day.

**2018, Oct. 8    Litho.    Perf. 13**
1976 A469  1st brnz & multi  1.40 1.40
1977 A469  EU brnz & multi  2.25 2.25
1978 A469  £1.01 brnz & multi  2.60 2.60
1979 A469  £1.40 brnz & multi  3.75 3.75
1980 A469  £1.75 brnz & multi  4.50 4.50
1981 A469  £2.15 brnz & multi  6.50 6.50
  Nos. 1976-1981 (6)  20.00 20.00

On day of issue, No. 1976 sold for 52p and No. 1977 sold for 83p.

Lighthouses — A470

Designs: 52p, Point of Ayre Lighthouse and service buildings. £1.53, Winkie automatic light and Point of Ayre Lighthouse. £2.60, Upper and Lower Calf of Man Lighthouses. £3.10, Upper Calf of Man Lighthouse.

**2018, Oct. 18    Litho.    Perf. 13¼**
1982 A470  52p multi  1.40 1.40
1983 A470  £1.53 multi  4.00 4.00
1984 A470  £2.60 multi  6.75 6.75
1985 A470  £3.10 multi  8.00 8.00
  Nos. 1982-1985 (4)  20.15 20.15

Point of Ayre Lighthouse and Calf of Man Lighthouse, bicent.

Christmas — A471

Characters from The Beano comic magazine by Nigel Parkinson: Nos. 1986, 1994a, Dennis the Menace throwing pie at Santa Claus on steam locomotive. Nos. 1987, 1994b, Dennis and Gnasher at Castle Rushen. Nos. 1988, 1994c, Gnasher chsaing Manx cat at Douglas Sea Terminal. Nos. 1989, 1994d, Dennis on Laxey Wheel pelting Santa Claus with snow. Nos. 1990, 1994e, Dennis and Gnasher in cart with postman in mail sack. Nos. 1991, 1994f, Santa Claus in car chasing Dennis and Gnasher at Marine Drive Toll Gate. Nos. 1992, 1994g, Viking throwing snowball at Dennis and Gnasher building snow castle. Nos. 1993, 1994hDennis and Gnasher with Minx fairies applying stamps to letters.

**2018, Oct. 29    Litho.    Perf. 13¼**
1986 A471  1st multi  1.40 1.40
1987 A471  1st multi  1.40 1.40
  a. Vert. pair, #1986-1987  2.80 2.80

| 1988 | A471 | EU multi | 2.25 | 2.25 |
|---|---|---|---|---|
| 1989 | A471 | EU multi | 2.25 | 2.25 |
| a. | | Vert. pair, #1988-1989 | 4.50 | 4.50 |
| 1990 | A471 | £1.25 multi | 3.25 | 3.25 |
| 1991 | A471 | £1.25 multi | 3.25 | 3.25 |
| a. | | Vert. pair, #1990-1991 | 6.50 | 6.50 |
| 1992 | A471 | RoW multi | 3.75 | 3.75 |
| 1993 | A471 | RoW multi | 3.75 | 3.75 |
| a. | | Vert. pair, #1992-1993 | 7.50 | 7.50 |
| | | Nos. 1986-1993 (8) | 21.30 | 21.30 |

**Stamp Size: 32x32mm**

**Perf. 12½**

| 1994 | | Sheet of 8 | 21.50 | 21.50 |
|---|---|---|---|---|
| a.-b. | A471 | 1st Either single | 1.40 | 1.40 |
| c.-d. | A471 | EU Either single | 2.25 | 2.25 |
| e.-f. | A471 | £1.25 Either single | 3.25 | 3.25 |
| g.-h. | A471 | RoW Either single | 3.75 | 3.75 |

On day of issue, Nos. 1986-1987, 1994a-1994b, each sold for 52p; Nos. 1988-1989, 1994c-1994d, for 83p; Nos. 1992-1993,1994g-1994h, for £1.40.

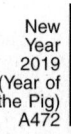

New Year 2019 (Year of the Pig) A472

Various drawings of pigs.

| **2019, Jan. 22** | | **Litho.** | **Perf. 13¼** | |
|---|---|---|---|---|
| 1995 | A472 | 52p multi | 1.40 | 1.40 |
| 1996 | A472 | £2.02 multi | 5.25 | 5.25 |
| 1997 | A472 | £2.42 multi | 6.50 | 6.50 |
| 1998 | A472 | £2.95 multi | 7.75 | 7.75 |
| | | Nos. 1995-1998 (4) | 20.90 | 20.90 |

Buses — A473

Designs: 1st, Leyland Titan PD2. EU, AEC Regent V. £1.25, AEC Reliance. RoW, Leyland Leopard. £1.87, Leyland National. £2.02, Bedford YRQ.

| **2019, Jan. 29** | | **Litho.** | **Perf. 13** | |
|---|---|---|---|---|
| 1999 | A473 | 1st multi | 1.40 | 1.40 |
| 2000 | A473 | EU multi | 2.25 | 2.25 |
| 2001 | A473 | £1.25 multi | 3.25 | 3.25 |
| 2002 | A473 | RoW multi | 3.75 | 3.75 |
| 2003 | A473 | £1.87 multi | 5.00 | 5.00 |
| 2004 | A473 | £2.02 multi | 5.25 | 5.25 |
| | | Nos. 1999-2004 (6) | 20.90 | 20.90 |

On day of issue, No. 1999 sold for 52p; No. 2000, 83p; No. 2002, £1.40.

Wildlife — A474

Designs: Nos. 2005a, 2006, Hares. Nos. 2005b, 2007, Common blue butterfly. Nos. 2005c, 2008, Gannet. Nos. 2005d, 2009, Kingfisher. Nos. 2005e, 2010, Common lizard. No. 2005f, Stonechat. No. 2005g, Wallaby. No. 2005h, Hedgehog. No. 2005i, Crimson and gold moth. No. 2005j, Field mouse.

| **2019, Feb. 12** | | **Litho.** | **Perf. 12½** | |
|---|---|---|---|---|
| 2005 | | Block of 10 | 22.50 | 22.50 |
| a.-e. | A474 | 1st Any single | 1.40 | 1.40 |
| f. | A474 | EU multi | 2.25 | 2.25 |
| g.-h. | A474 | Large Letter Either single | 2.75 | 2.75 |
| i.-j. | A474 | RoW Either single | 3.75 | 3.75 |

**Booklet Stamps**
**Self-Adhesive**

**Serpentine Die Cut 13**

| 2006 | A474 | 1st multi | 1.40 | 1.40 |
|---|---|---|---|---|
| 2007 | A474 | 1st multi | 1.40 | 1.40 |
| 2008 | A474 | 1st multi | 1.40 | 1.40 |
| 2009 | A474 | 1st multi | 1.40 | 1.40 |
| 2010 | A474 | 1st multi | 1.40 | 1.40 |
| a. | | Booklet pane of 10, 2 each #2006-2010 | 14.00 | |

Europa (No. 2005f). On day of issue, Nos. 2005a-2005e, 2006, 2010 each sold for 52p; No. 2005f, 83p; Nos. 2005g-2005h, £1.01; Nos. 2005i-2005j, £1.40.

D-Day, 75th Anniv. A475

---

No. 2011: a, Isle of Man #600. b, Isle of Man #601.

No. 2012: a, Isle of Man #602. b, Isle of Man #603.

No. 2013: a, Isle of Man #604. b, Isle of Man #605.

No. 2014: a, Isle of Man #606. b, Isle of Man #607.

| **2019, Apr. 22** | | **Litho.** | **Perf. 13** | |
|---|---|---|---|---|
| 2011 | A475 | Horiz. pair | 3.00 | 3.00 |
| a.-b. | | 1st Either single | 1.50 | 1.50 |
| 2012 | A475 | Horiz. pair | 4.80 | 4.80 |
| a.-b. | | EU Either single | 2.40 | 2.40 |
| 2013 | A475 | Horiz. pair | 6.00 | 6.00 |
| a.-b. | | Large Letter Either single | 3.00 | 3.00 |
| 2014 | A475 | Horiz. pair | 8.00 | 8.00 |
| c. | | RoW Either single | 4.00 | 4.00 |
| | | Souvenir sheet of 8, #2011a-2011b, 2012a-2012b, 2013a-2013b, 2014a-2014b | 22.00 | 22.00 |
| | | Nos. 2011-2014 (4) | 21.80 | 21.80 |

On day of issue, Nos. 2011a-2011b each sold for 57p; Nos. 2012a-2012b, 90p; Nos. 2013a-2013b, £1.10; Nos. 2014a-2014b, £1.50.

First Man on the Moon, 50th Anniv. — A476

Designs: No. 2015, Moon. No. 2016, Apollo Mission Control Room. No. 2017, View of Florida taken from Apollo 7. No. 2018, Photograph of Earthrise taken from Apollo 8. No. 2019, View of separated Lunar Module taken from Command Module of Apollo 9. No. 2020, View of Command Module taken from separated Lunar Module of Apollo 10. No. 2021, Footprint of Apollo 11 astronaut on Moon. No. 2022, Lunar Module of Apollo 12 and scientific equipment on Moon.

| **2019, Apr. 29** | | **Litho.** | **Perf. 13** | |
|---|---|---|---|---|
| 2015 | A476 | 1st multi | 1.50 | 1.50 |
| a. | | Perf. 13 (2022e) | 1.50 | 1.50 |
| 2016 | A476 | 1st multi | 1.50 | 1.50 |
| a. | | Horiz. pair, #2015-2016 | 3.00 | 3.00 |
| b. | | Booklet pane of 2, #2015-2016, + 2 labels | 3.00 | — |
| c. | | Perf. 13 (2022e) | 1.50 | 1.50 |
| 2017 | A476 | EU multi | 2.40 | 2.40 |
| a. | | Perf. 13 (2022e) | 2.40 | 2.40 |
| 2018 | A476 | EU multi | 2.40 | 2.40 |
| a. | | Horiz. pair, #2017-2018 | 4.80 | 4.80 |
| b. | | Perf. 13 (2022e) | 2.40 | 2.40 |
| 2019 | A476 | Large multi | 3.00 | 3.00 |
| a. | | Perf. 13 (2022e) | 3.00 | 3.00 |
| 2020 | A476 | Large multi | 3.00 | 3.00 |
| a. | | Horiz. pair, #2019-2020 | 6.00 | 6.00 |
| b. | | Booklet pane of 4, #2017-2020, + 4 labels | 11.00 | — |
| c. | | Perf. 13 (2022e) | 3.00 | 3.00 |
| 2021 | A476 | RoW multi | 4.00 | 4.00 |
| a. | | Perf. 13 (2022e) | 4.00 | 4.00 |
| 2022 | A476 | RoW multi | 4.00 | 4.00 |
| a. | | Horiz. pair, #2021-2022 | 8.00 | 8.00 |
| b. | | Booklet pane of 8, #2015-2022 | 22.00 | — |
| c. | | Booklet pane of 2, #2015-2016, + 2 labels | 8.00 | — |
| | | Complete booklet, #2016b, 2020b, 2022b, 2022c | 44.00 | |
| d. | | Perf. 13 (2022e) | 4.00 | 4.00 |
| e. | | Sheet of 11, #1313a, 1314b, 1316a, 2015a, 2016c, 2017a, 2018b, 2019a, 2020c, 2021a, 2022d | 27.50 | 27.50 |
| | | Nos. 2015-2022 (8) | 21.80 | 21.80 |

On day of issue, Nos. 2015-2016 each sold for 57p; Nos. 2017-2018, 90p; Nos. 2019-2020, £1.10; Nos. 2021-2022, £1.50. Nos. 2016b and 2020b are printed on one sheet of paper that is stapled in the middle along the fold of the booklet, as are Nos. 2022b and 2022c.

Paintings of Ships by John Halsall (1943-2017) A477

Designs: 1st, Star of India. EU, Lady Elizabeth. Large, White Heather. £1.35, Empress Queen. ROW, King Orry. £2.05, Lady of Mann.

| **2019, May 18** | | **Litho.** | **Perf. 13** | |
|---|---|---|---|---|
| 2023 | A477 | 1st multi | 1.50 | 1.50 |
| 2024 | A477 | EU multi | 2.25 | 2.25 |
| 2025 | A477 | Large multi | 2.75 | 2.75 |
| 2026 | A477 | £1.35 multi | 3.50 | 3.50 |
| 2027 | A477 | ROW multi | 3.75 | 3.75 |
| 2028 | A477 | £2.05 multi | 5.25 | 5.25 |
| | | Nos. 2023-2028 (6) | 19.00 | 19.00 |

On day of issue, No. 2023 sold for 57p; No. 2024, 90p; No. 2025, £1.10; No. 2027, £1.50.

---

Victorian Era Engineering A478

Designs: 57p, William Kennish (1799-1862), and his marine theodolite. 90p, John Jonathan Kermode (1859-1931), and his air and steam oil burners. £1.10, John Callow (1856-1929), and his dough dividing machine. £1.85, Benjamin Alfred Dobson (1847-98), and his carding engine. £2.05, The Jane, first bulk oil tanker, built by Thomas Cummings Gibson (1800-70). £2.50, Ball bearing cage, invented by Charles Greenway (1786-1871).

| **2019, May 24** | | **Litho.** | **Perf. 13** | |
|---|---|---|---|---|
| 2029 | A478 | 57p multi | 1.50 | 1.50 |
| 2030 | A478 | 90p multi | 2.25 | 2.25 |
| 2031 | A478 | £1.10 multi | 2.75 | 2.75 |
| 2032 | A478 | £1.85 multi | 4.75 | 4.75 |
| 2033 | A478 | £2.05 multi | 5.25 | 5.25 |
| 2034 | A478 | £2.50 multi | 5.50 | 5.50 |
| | | Nos. 2029-2034 (6) | 22.00 | 22.00 |

17th Century Age of Rebellion in Isle of Man A479

Inset image of: 57p, James Stanley, 7th Earl of Derby (1607-51), imprisoner of Edward Christian in Peel Castle. 90p, Countess Charlotte (1599-1664), wife of 7th Earl of Derby, and Royalist's Ball at Castle Rushen. £1.10, Illiam Dhone (1608-63), rebel leader, and meeting at his farm. £1.52, Dhone, and Colonel Robert Duckenfield's troops landing at Ramsey. £1.60, Oliver Cromwell (1599-1658), Lord Protector, and Dhone informing Countess Charlotte of death of her husband. £1.85, Chales Stanley, 8th Earl of Derby (1628-72), and trial of Dhone.

| **2019, July 1** | | **Litho.** | **Perf. 13** | |
|---|---|---|---|---|
| 2035 | A479 | 57p sil & multi | 1.50 | 1.50 |
| 2036 | A479 | 90p sil & multi | 2.25 | 2.25 |
| 2037 | A479 | £1.10 sil & multi | 2.75 | 2.75 |
| 2038 | A479 | £1.52 sil & multi | 4.00 | 4.00 |
| 2039 | A479 | £1.60 sil & multi | 4.00 | 4.00 |
| 2040 | A479 | £1.85 sil & multi | 4.75 | 4.75 |
| | | Nos. 2035-2040 (6) | 19.25 | 19.25 |

Manx Language Greetings — A480

Equivalent English and Manx phrases: 1st, Good morning, Moghrey mie. EU, How are you?, Kys t'ou? Large, Cheers, Slaynt vie. £1.30, Good afternoon, Fastyr mie. RoW, Goodbye, Slane lhiu. £2.05, Good night, Oie vie.

| **2019, July 4** | | **Litho.** | **Perf. 13x13¼** | |
|---|---|---|---|---|
| 2041 | A480 | 1st multi | 1.40 | 1.40 |
| 2042 | A480 | EU multi | 2.25 | 2.25 |
| 2043 | A480 | Large multi | 2.75 | 2.75 |
| 2044 | A480 | £1.30 multi | 3.25 | 3.25 |
| 2045 | A480 | RoW multi | 4.75 | 4.75 |
| 2046 | A480 | £2.05 multi | 5.00 | 5.00 |
| | | Nos. 2041-2046 (6) | 19.40 | 19.40 |

On day of issue, No. 2041 sold for 57p; No. 2042, 90p; No. 2043, £1.10; No. 2045, £1.50.

Characters from *Moby Dick,* by Herman Melville (1819-91) — A481

Designs: 1st, Captain Ahab. EU, Ishmael. Large, Starbuck. RoW, The Manxman. £1.52, Queequeg. £1.85, Stubb.

| **2019, July 22** | | **Litho.** | **Perf. 13¼** | |
|---|---|---|---|---|
| 2047 | A481 | 1st multi | 1.40 | 1.40 |
| 2048 | A481 | EU multi | 2.25 | 2.25 |
| 2049 | A481 | Large multi | 2.75 | 2.75 |
| 2050 | A481 | RoW multi | 3.75 | 3.75 |

---

| 2051 | A481 | £1.52 multi | 3.75 | 3.75 |
|---|---|---|---|---|
| 2052 | A481 | £1.85 multi | 4.50 | 4.50 |
| | | Nos. 2047-2052 (6) | 18.40 | 18.40 |

On day of issue, No. 2047 sold for 57p; No. 2048, 90p; No. 2049, £1.10, No. 2050, £1.50.

Transatlantic Flight, Cent. A482

Designs: 1st, Curtiss NC-4. EU, Ryan NYP. L, Vickers Vimy. RoW, R34 Dirigible. £1.52, English Electric Canberra B.2. £2.55, De Havilland DH.84 Dragon.

| **2019, Aug. 20** | | **Litho.** | **Perf. 13** | |
|---|---|---|---|---|
| 2053 | A482 | 1st multi | 1.40 | 1.40 |
| 2054 | A482 | EU multi | 2.25 | 2.25 |
| 2055 | A482 | L multi | 2.75 | 2.75 |
| 2056 | A482 | RoW multi | 3.50 | 3.50 |
| 2057 | A482 | £1.52 multi | 3.75 | 3.75 |
| 2058 | A482 | £2.55 multi | 6.25 | 6.25 |
| | | Nos. 2053-2058 (6) | 19.90 | 19.90 |

On day of issue, No. 2053 sold for 57p; No. 2054, 90p; No. 2055, £1.10; No. 2056, £1.50.

Birds — A483

No. 2059: a, House sparrow. b, Coal tit. c, Wheatear. d, Long-tailed tit.
No. 2060: a, Goldfinch. b, Stonechat. c, Chaffinch. d, Blackbird.

| **2019, Sept. 19** | | **Litho.** | **Perf. 13** | |
|---|---|---|---|---|
| 2059 | | Horiz. strip of 4 | 5.75 | 5.75 |
| a.-d. | A483 | 1st Any single | 1.40 | 1.40 |
| 2060 | | Horiz. strip of 4 | 15.00 | 15.00 |
| a.-d. | A483 | RoW Any single | 3.75 | 3.75 |

On day of issue Nos. 2059a-2059d each sold for 57p and Nos. 2060a-2060d each sold for £1.50.

Sir Frank Gill (1866-1950), Engineer — A484

Gill and: 57p, National Telephone Company emblem and Dublin Telephone Exchange Building, 1897. 90p, Telephone exchange apparatus room, 1909. £1.10, Emblems of British Broadcasting Company, General Electric, British Thomson-Houston, Metropolitan Vickers, Marconi, Radio Communication Company, Western Electric and Burndept Wireless Apparatus Company. £1.50, First transatlantic radio telephone call, 1923. £1.52, 1927 London Gazette article and Order of Isabel the Catholic awarded to Gill by King Alfonso XIII of Spain. £1.85, Medals from Great Britain awarded to Gill.

| **2019, Oct. 14** | | **Litho.** | **Perf. 13¼x13½** | |
|---|---|---|---|---|
| 2061 | A484 | 57p multi | 1.50 | 1.50 |
| 2062 | A484 | 90p multi | 2.40 | 2.40 |
| 2063 | A484 | £1.10 multi | 3.00 | 3.00 |
| 2064 | A484 | £1.50 multi | 4.00 | 4.00 |
| 2065 | A484 | £1.52 multi | 4.00 | 4.00 |
| 2066 | A484 | £1.85 multi | 4.75 | 4.75 |
| | | Nos. 2061-2066 (6) | 19.65 | 19.65 |

Santa Checking His List, Christmas Card by Jeannine Petty — A485

Postbox and Geese, Christmas Card by Marina Brook — A486

The Gardeners' Friend, Christmas Card by Cordelia Hutchinson A487

Christmas Tree, Christmas Card by Brook A488

The Nativity, Christmas Card by Hutchinson A489

Champagne Flutes, Christmas Card by Rachel Hare A490

Church in the Snow, Christmas Card by Gordon Barker A491

O Little Town Of Bethlehem, Christmas Card by Hutchinson A492

Tatty Teddy, Christmas Card by MetoYou.com A493

Holly Berries, Christmas Card by Charlotte Day A494

| 2019, Oct. 28 | Litho. | Perf. 12½ | |
|---|---|---|---|
| 2067 | Horiz. strip of 5 | 7.50 | 7.50 |
| a. | A485 (57p) multi | 1.50 | 1.50 |
| b. | A486 (57p) multi | 1.50 | 1.50 |
| c. | A487 (57p) multi | 1.50 | 1.50 |
| d. | A488 (57p) multi | 1.50 | 1.50 |
| e. | A489 (57p) multi | 1.50 | 1.50 |
| 2068 | Horiz. strip of 5 | 15.00 | 15.00 |
| a. | A490 (£1.10) multi | 3.00 | 3.00 |
| b. | A491 (£1.10) multi | 3.00 | 3.00 |
| c. | A492 (£1.10) multi | 3.00 | 3.00 |
| d. | A493 (£1.10) multi | 3.00 | 3.00 |
| e. | A494 (£1.10) multi | 3.00 | 3.00 |

New Year 2020 (Year of the Rat) A495

Rat and: 57p, Four flowers. £1.67, Holding flower with tail. £2.55, Bull made of flowersl. £2.85, Head of rat, flowers.

| 2020, Jan. 15 | Litho. | Perf. 13½ | |
|---|---|---|---|
| 2069 | A495 | 57p multi | 1.50 | 1.50 |
| 2070 | A495 | £1.67 multi | 4.50 | 4.50 |
| 2071 | A495 | £2.55 multi | 6.75 | 6.75 |
| 2072 | A495 | £2.85 multi | 7.50 | 7.50 |
| | Nos. 2069-2072 (4) | | 20.25 | 20.25 |

Space Exploration A496

Designs: No. 2073, Apollo 13 Mission Control Room. No. 2074, Apollo 14 astronaut Alan B. Shepard, Jr. on Moon. No. 2075, Apollo 15 astronaut James B. Irwin near Lunar Rover. No. 2076, Apollo 16 astronaut Charles M. Duke, Jr. near Lunar Rover. No. 2077, Apollo

17 astronaut Harrison Schmitt near boulder on Moon. No. 2078, Skylab. No. 2079, Space Shuttle Atlantis. No. 2080, International Space Station.

| 2020, Feb. 26 | Litho. | Perf. 13 | |
|---|---|---|---|
| 2073 | A496 | 1st multi | 1.50 | 1.50 |
| 2074 | A496 | 1st multi | 1.50 | 1.50 |
| a. | Horiz. pair, #2073-2074 | 3.00 | 3.00 |
| 2075 | A496 | EU multi | 2.25 | 2.25 |
| 2076 | A496 | EU multi | 2.25 | 2.25 |
| a. | Horiz. pair, #2075-2076 | 4.50 | 4.50 |
| 2077 | A496 | Large multi | 3.00 | 3.00 |
| 2078 | A496 | Large multi | 3.00 | 3.00 |
| a. | Horiz. pair, #2077-2078 | 6.00 | 6.00 |
| 2079 | A496 | RoW multi | 4.00 | 4.00 |
| 2080 | A496 | RoW multi | 4.00 | 4.00 |
| a. | Horiz. pair, #2079-2080 | 8.00 | 8.00 |
| b. | Sheet of 11, #1312b, 1315a, 1317a, 2073-2080 | — | — |
| | Nos. 2073-2080 (8) | | 21.50 | 21.50 |

On day of issue, Nos. 2073-2074 each sold for 57p; Nos. 2075-2076, 90p; Nos. 2077-2078, £1.10; Nos. 2079-2080, £1.50.
Issued: No. 2080b, 2/26/20.

Douglas School of Art — A497

Designs: Nos. 2081a, 2083a, St. Matthew's Church, by John Miller Nicholson (1840-1913). Nos. 2081b, 2083b, Harvest Time, by William James Merritt (1856-?). Nos. 2081c, 2083c, Port St. Mary, by David Robertson (1859-1909). Nos. 2081d, 2083d, Liberty Tudric Vase, by Archibald Knox (1864-1933). Nos. 2081e, 2083e, Peel Castle Against a Sunset, by Peter Chisholm (1875-1962). Nos. 2082a, 2083f, Alderman S. A. Quirk, sculpture by William Hargreaves Whitehead (1896-1971). Nos. 2082b, 2083g, Cregneash, by Eric G. Houlgrave (1917-2001). Nos. 2082c, 2083h, Douglas Promenade Railing, by Norman Sayle (1926-2007). Nos. 2082d, 2083i, The Old Chapel, by David Fletcher (1948-2008). Nos. 2082e, 2083j, The Old Art School, by Ian Coulson.

| 2020, Mar. 16 | Litho. | Perf. 13x12½ | |
|---|---|---|---|
| 2081 | Horiz. strip of 5 | 7.00 | 7.00 |
| a.-e. | A497 First Any single | 1.40 | 1.40 |
| 2082 | Horiz. strip of 5 | 14.00 | 14.00 |
| a.-e. | A497 Large Any single | 2.75 | 2.75 |

**Self-Adhesive**
**Serpentine Die Cut 12¾x13**

| 2083 | Booklet pane of 10 | 14.00 | |
|---|---|---|---|
| a.-j. | A497 First Any single | 1.40 | 1.40 |

On day of issue, Nos. 2081a-2081e, 2083a-2083j each sold for 57p; Nos. 2082a-2082e, £1.10.

William Wordsworth (1770-1850), Poet — A498

Designs: 1st, Wordsworth, Dove Cottage, line from I Wandered Lonely as a Cloud. EU, Peel Fishing Boats, by John Holland, line from At Sea Off the Isle of Man. L, Port e Chee, by Holland, line from Canto XIV from the Itinerary Poems of 1833. RoW, Douglas Bay, by unknown artist, line from On Entering Douglas Bay. £1.61, Monks Bridge, by unknown artist, line from At Bala-sala, Isle of Man. £1.92, The Tynwald Ceremony, St. Johns, by John Warwick Smith, line from Tynwald Hill.

| 2020, Apr. 7 | Litho. | Perf. 13 | |
|---|---|---|---|
| 2084 | A498 | 1st multi | 1.60 | 1.60 |
| 2085 | A498 | EU multi | 2.40 | 2.40 |
| 2086 | A498 | L multi | 3.00 | 3.00 |
| 2087 | A498 | RoW multi | 4.00 | 4.00 |
| 2088 | A498 | £1.61 multi | 4.00 | 4.00 |
| 2089 | A498 | £1.92 multi | 5.00 | 5.00 |
| | Nos. 2084-2089 (6) | | 20.00 | 20.00 |

On day of issue, No. 2084 sold for 62p; No. 2085, 94p; No. 2086, £1.17; No. 2087, £1.58.

Voyage of the Mayflower, 400th Anniv. — A499

Designs: 1st, Departure. EU, Landing at Plymouth Rock. Large, Signing of the Compact. RoW, Thanksgiving. £1.85, Myles Standish (c. 1584-1656), military adviser for Plymouth Colony. £2.50, First church in New England.

| 2020, Apr. 22 | Litho. | Perf. 13x13¼ | |
|---|---|---|---|
| 2090 | A499 | 1st multi | 1.60 | 1.60 |
| 2091 | A499 | EU multi | 2.40 | 2.40 |
| 2092 | A499 | Large multi | 3.00 | 3.00 |
| 2093 | A499 | RoW multi | 4.00 | 4.00 |
| 2094 | A499 | £1.85 multi | 4.75 | 4.75 |
| 2095 | A499 | £2.50 multi | 6.25 | 6.25 |
| | Nos. 2090-2095 (6) | | 22.00 | 22.00 |

On day of issue, No. 2090 sold for 62p; No. 2091, 94p; No. 2092, £1.17; No. 2093, £1.58.

Carry Us Through — A500

No. 2096 — Word at top: a, Love. b, Faith. c, Care. d, Compassion.
No. 2097 — Word at top: a, Work. b, Community. c, Words. d, Science.

| 2020, May 4 | Litho. | Perf. 13 | |
|---|---|---|---|
| 2096 | Vert. strip of 4 | 6.50 | 6.50 |
| a.-d. | A500 1st Any single | 1.60 | 1.60 |
| 2097 | Vert. strip of 4 | 14.00 | 14.00 |
| a.-b. | A500 Large Either single | 3.00 | 3.00 |
| c.-d. | A500 ROW Either single | 4.00 | 4.00 |

Promotion of togetherness during Coronavirus pandemic. On day of issue, Nos. 2096a-2096d each sold for 62p; Nos. 2097a-2097b, £1.17; Nos. 2097c-2097d, £1.58.

Year of the Nurse and Midwife — A501

Inscription: No. 2098, Midwifery. No. 2099, Health visiting & school nursing. No. 2100, Hospital nursing. No. 2101, Mental health nursing. No. 2102, Practice nursing. No. 2103, Community nursing. No. 2104, Advanced nurse practitioner nursing. No. 2105, Older people & end of life nursing.

| 2020, May 12 | Litho. | Perf. 13 | |
|---|---|---|---|
| 2098 | A501 | 1st multi | 1.60 | 1.60 |
| 2099 | A501 | 1st multi | 1.60 | 1.60 |
| 2100 | A501 | 1st multi | 1.60 | 1.60 |
| 2101 | A501 | 1st multi | 1.60 | 1.60 |
| 2102 | A501 | Large multi | 3.00 | 3.00 |
| 2103 | A501 | Large multi | 3.00 | 3.00 |
| 2104 | A501 | £1.82 multi | 4.50 | 4.50 |
| 2105 | A501 | £1.82 multi | 4.50 | 4.50 |
| | Nos. 2098-2105 (8) | | 21.40 | 21.40 |

On day of issue, Nos. 2098-2101 each sold for 62p and Nos. 2102-2013 each sold for £1.17.

Snaefell Mountain Railway, 125th Anniv. — A502

Designs: 1st, Opening day, 1895. EU, Tram 1 approaching The Bungalow Station. L, Tram 6 at Lhergy Veg. RoW, Tram 5 passing statue of Laxey Miner. £1.82, Evening service Tram 5 at summit. £1.92, Snaefell Summit Hotel, 1905.

| 2020, June 25 | Litho. | Perf. 13 | |
|---|---|---|---|
| 2106 | A502 | 1st multi | 1.60 | 1.60 |
| 2107 | A502 | EU multi | 2.40 | 2.40 |
| 2108 | A502 | L multi | 3.00 | 3.00 |
| 2109 | A502 | RoW multi | 4.00 | 4.00 |
| 2110 | A502 | £1.82 multi | 4.50 | 4.50 |
| 2111 | A502 | £1.92 multi | 4.75 | 4.75 |
| | Nos. 2106-2111 (6) | | 20.25 | 20.25 |

On day of issue, No. 2106 sold for 62p; No. 2107, 94p; No. 2108, £1.17; No. 2109, £1.58.

Winning Photographs in "O Land of Our Birth" Competition — A503

No. 2112: a, Port St. Mary, by John Jones. b, Fenella Beach, by Terrence Meadmore. c, Streets of Peel, by Sarah Elliot. d, Thousla Cross and sunset over Irish Sea, by Liz Lillis-Ingram. e, Herd of Loaghtan sheep, by Colin Gill. f, Peel Marina, by Sue Furner. g, Ballaglass Glen, by Marionette Espinosa. h, Show them the world and let them conquer it all (child on hill), by William Hale. i, Ye sons of the soil, in hardship and toil (farmer and horse), by Tim Norton. j, Douglas Quay monument, by Hilary Denison. k, Calm Arrival (large ship in harbor), by Craig Harriman. l, Glen Maye Beach, by Gareth Caley.

| 2020, July 29 | Litho. | Perf. 12½ | |
|---|---|---|---|
| 2112 | A503 | Block of 12 | 19.50 | 19.50 |
| a.-l. | 1st Any single | 1.60 | 1.60 |

On day of issue, Nos. 2112a-2112l each sold for 62p.

Watchmakers and Their Watches — A504

Designs: 62p, John Harwood (1893-1964) and Automatic 1929. 94p, George Daniels (1926-2011) and The Grand Complication. 117p, Daniels and Space Traveller. 140p, Daniels, Roger W. Smith and The Blue. 158p, Smith and face of The Great Britain. 237p, Smith and mechanism of The Great Britain.

| 2020, Aug. 11 | Litho. | Perf. 13 | |
|---|---|---|---|
| 2113 | A504 | 62p multi | 1.75 | 1.75 |
| 2114 | A504 | 94p multi | 2.60 | 2.60 |
| a. | Booklet pane of 2, #2113-2114, + 4 labels | 4.50 | |
| 2115 | A504 | 117p multi | 3.25 | 3.25 |
| 2116 | A504 | 140p multi | 3.75 | 3.75 |
| a. | Booklet pane of 2, #2115-2116, + 4 labels | 6.00 | |
| 2117 | A504 | 158p multi | 4.25 | 4.25 |
| 2118 | A504 | 237p multi | 6.50 | 6.50 |
| a. | Booklet pane of 6, #2113-2118 | 22.50 | |
| b. | Booklet pane of 2, #2117-2118, + 4 labels | 11.00 | |
| | Complete booklet, #2114a, 2116a, 2118a, 2118b | 44.00 | |
| | Nos. 2113-2118 (6) | | 22.10 | 22.10 |

Mitch Murray, Song Writer and Music Producer, 80th Birthday — A505

No. 2119: a, Sheet music cover for "I Like It," record and sheet music cover for "How Do You Do It." b, Sheet music covers for "I'm Telling You Now" and "You Were Made for Me." c, Murray and record of "Down Came the Rain." d, Sheet music cover for "The Ballad of Bonnie and Clyde," gold record and certificate of honor awarded to Murray. e, Murray, founder of the Society of Distinguished Songwriters, photograph of members, and medallion.
No. 2120: a, Photographs of Murray and songwriting partner Peter Callander, sheet music covers for "Hitchin' a Ride" and "Even the Bad Times Are Good." b, Sheet music covers for "I Did What I Did for Maria," "Las Vegas," and "Avenues and Alleyways." c, Murray's Ivor Novello Award, sheet music covers

for "The Black-eyed Boys," "The Night Chicago Died," and "Billy Don't Be a Hero." d, Murray and sheet music covers for "Goodbye Sam, Hello Samantha," and "Turn on the Sun." e, Fairy Bridge, Murray with his books.

**Perf. 13¼x12½**

| | | | | |
|---|---|---|---|---|
| **2020, Sept. 16** | | | | **Litho.** |
| 2119 | | Horiz. strip of 5 + 5 labels | 8.00 | 8.00 |
| *a.-e.* | A505 | 1st Any single + label | 1.60 | 1.60 |
| *f.* | | Booklet pane of 5, #2119a-2119e, perf. 12½ | 8.00 | — |
| 2120 | | Horiz. strip of 5 + 5 labels | 15.00 | 15.00 |
| *a.-e.* | A505 | Large Any single + label | 3.00 | 3.00 |
| *f.* | | Booklet pane of 10, #2119a-2119e, 2120a-2120f, perf. 12½ | 23.00 | |
| *g.* | | Booklet pane of 5, #2120a-2120e, perf. 12½ | 15.00 | |
| | | Complete booklet, #2119f, 2120f, 2120g | 46.00 | |

On day of issue, Nos. 2119a-2119e each sold for 62p, and Nos. 2120a-2120e, for £1.17.

37¾ Mile Isle of Man TT Course,
Cent.
A506

No. 2121 — Old and recent photographs of motorcycle racers at Signpost Corner with checkered flag at: a, LR. b, LL.
No. 2122 — Old and recent photographs of motorcycle racers at Governor's Bridge with checkered flag at: a, LR. b, LL.
No. 2123 — Old and recent photographs of motorcycle racers at Cronk-Ny-Mona with checkered flag at: a, LR. b, LL.
No. 2124 — Old and recent photographs of motorcycle racers at Grandstand with checkered flag at: a, LR. b, LL.

**Perf. 13¼x13½**

| | | | | |
|---|---|---|---|---|
| **2020, Sept. 30** | | | | **Litho.** |
| 2121 | A506 | Horiz. pair | 3.25 | 3.25 |
| *a.-b.* | | 1st Either single | 1.60 | 1.60 |
| 2122 | A506 | Horiz. pair | 5.00 | 5.00 |
| *a.-b.* | | EU Either single | 2.50 | 2.50 |
| 2123 | A506 | Horiz. pair | 6.50 | 6.50 |
| *a.-b.* | | £1.25 Either single | 3.25 | 3.25 |
| 2124 | A506 | Horiz. pair | 8.50 | 8.50 |
| *a.-b.* | | ROW Either single | 4.25 | 4.25 |
| | | Nos. 2121-2124 (4) | 23.25 | 23.25 |

On day of issue, Nos. 2121a-2121b each sold for 62p; Nos. 2122a-2122b, for 94p; and Nos. 2124a-2124b, for £1.58.

Charles Dickens (1812-70), Writer — A507

Designs: 62p, The Christmas Bowl, illustration from *A Christmas Carol.* 94p, Mr. Fezziwig's Ball, illustration from *A Christmas Carol.* £1.17, Scrooge's Third Visitor, illustration from *A Christmas Carol.* £1.58, Extinguishing the Spirits, illustration from *A Christmas Carol.* £1.82, Scrooge and Marley's Ghost, illustration from *A Christmas Carol.* £2.47, Portrait of Dickens, by Margaret Gillies (1803-87).

| | | | | |
|---|---|---|---|---|
| **2020, Oct. 14** | | **Litho.** | | **Perf. 13½x13¼** |
| 2125 | A507 | 62p multi | 1.60 | 1.60 |
| 2126 | A507 | 94p multi | 2.50 | 2.50 |
| 2127 | A507 | £1.17 multi | 3.00 | 3.00 |
| 2128 | A507 | £1.58 multi | 4.25 | 4.25 |
| 2129 | A507 | £1.82 multi | 4.75 | 4.75 |
| 2130 | A507 | £2.47 multi | 6.50 | 6.50 |
| *a.* | | Souvenir sheet of 6, #2125-2130 | 23.00 | 23.00 |
| | | Nos. 2125-2130 (6) | 22.60 | 22.60 |

Christmas — A508

Designs: 62p, An Angel Playing a Flageolet, by Edward Burne-Jones (1833-98). 94p, The Annunciation to the Shepherds, from the Classic Bible Art Collection. £1.17, Nativity, by Burne-Jones. £1.58, The Adoration of the Shepherds, by Guido Reni (1575-1642). £2.15, The Nativity, by unkown artist. £2.37, O Little Town of Bethlehem, from the Lifeway Collection.

| | | | | |
|---|---|---|---|---|
| **2020, Oct. 30** | | **Litho.** | | **Perf. 13** |
| 2131 | A508 | 62p multi | 1.60 | 1.60 |
| 2132 | A508 | 94p multi | 2.50 | 2.50 |
| 2133 | A508 | £1.17 multi | 3.00 | 3.00 |
| 2134 | A508 | £1.58 multi | 4.25 | 4.25 |
| 2135 | A508 | £2.15 multi | 5.50 | 5.50 |
| 2136 | A508 | £2.37 multi | 6.25 | 6.25 |
| | | Nos. 2131-2136 (6) | 23.10 | 23.10 |

New Year 2021 (Year of the Ox) A509

No. 2137: a, Ox and rooster. b, Ox and rat. c, Ox. d, Head of ox.

| | | | | |
|---|---|---|---|---|
| **2021, Jan. 7** | | **Litho.** | | **Perf. 13x12¾** |
| 2137 | | Horiz. strip of 4 | 22.00 | 22.00 |
| *a.* | A509 | 62p multi | 1.75 | 1.75 |
| *b.* | A509 | £1.58 multi | 4.50 | 4.50 |
| *c.* | A509 | £2.44 multi | 6.75 | 6.75 |
| *d.* | A509 | £3.22 multi | 9.00 | 9.00 |

No. 2137 exists imperforate.

Show Birds — A510

Designs: 1st, Fife canary. EU, Gouldian finch. L, Budgerigar. ROW, Redpoll-bullfinch hybrid. £1.82, Paradise tanager. USA, Diamond sparrow.

| | | | | |
|---|---|---|---|---|
| **2021, Feb. 9** | | **Litho.** | | **Perf. 13½** |
| 2138 | A510 | 1st multi | 1.75 | 1.75 |
| 2139 | A510 | EU multi | 2.60 | 2.60 |
| 2140 | A510 | L multi | 3.25 | 3.25 |
| 2141 | A510 | ROW multi | 4.50 | 4.50 |
| 2142 | A510 | £1.82 multi | 5.25 | 5.25 |
| 2143 | A510 | USA multi | 6.00 | 6.00 |
| | | Nos. 2138-2143 (6) | 23.35 | 23.35 |

On day of issue, No. 2138 sold for 62p; No. 2139, 94p; No. 2140, £1.17; No. 2141, £1.58; No. 2143, £2.15.

Calf of Man — A511

Designs: Nos. 2144a, 2146a, The Calf of Man Nature Reserve. Nos. 2144b, 2146b, Calf of Man Attending Boat. Nos. 2144c, 2146c, Calf of Man Crucifixion Stone. Nos. 2144d, 2146d, Gray seals at Calf of Man and Wart Bank Marine Nature Reserve. Nos. 2144e, 2146e, Jellyfish at Calf of Man and Wart Bank Marine Nature Reserve. Nos. 2145a, 2146f, Manx shearwater chick. Nos. 2145b, 2146g, Fence and lighthouse. Nos. 2145c, 2146h, Thrift flowers. Nos. 2145d, 2146i, Garden tiger moth. Nos. 2145e, 2146j, Common whitethroat and Calf of Man Bird Observatory.

| | | | | |
|---|---|---|---|---|
| **2021, Apr. 12** | | **Litho.** | | **Perf. 12** |
| 2144 | | Horiz. strip of 5 | 8.75 | 8.75 |
| *a.-e.* | A511 | 1st Any single | 1.75 | 1.75 |
| 2145 | | Horiz. strip of 5 | 13.00 | 13.00 |
| *a.-e.* | A511 | EU Any single | 2.60 | 2.60 |
| *f.* | | Sheet of 10 #2145a | 26.00 | 26.00 |

**Self-Adhesive**
***Serpentine Die Cut 12¾***

| | | | | |
|---|---|---|---|---|
| 2146 | | Booklet pane of 10 | 17.50 | |
| *a.-j.* | A511 | 1st Any single | 1.75 | 1.75 |

Europa (Nos. 2145a, 2145f, 2146f). On day of issue, Nos. 2144a-2144e, 2146a-2146j each sold for 62p, and Nos. 2145a-2145e each sold for 94p.

Queen Elizabeth II, 95th Birthday — A512

Designs: No. 2147, Princess Elizabeth as teenager. No. 2148, Queen Elizabeth II and Prince Philip at coronation, 1953. L, Queen Elizabeth II and Prince Philip in 1972. £1.82, Queen Elizabeth II holding camera. £2.17, Queen Elizabeth II wearing State Diadem tiara. £2.37, Queen Elizabeth II wearing bright purple hat.

| | | | | |
|---|---|---|---|---|
| **2021, Apr. 21** | | **Litho.** | | **Perf. 13¼** |
| 2147 | A512 | 62p multi | 1.75 | 1.75 |
| 2148 | A512 | 62p multi | 1.75 | 1.75 |
| 2149 | A512 | L multi | 3.25 | 3.25 |
| 2150 | A512 | £1.82 multi | 5.25 | 5.25 |
| *a.* | | Multi-country sheet of 11 + label (see footnote) | 42.00 | |
| 2151 | A512 | £2.17 multi | 6.00 | 6.00 |
| 2152 | A512 | £2.37 multi | 6.75 | 6.75 |
| | | Nos. 2147-2152 (6) | 24.75 | 24.75 |

No. 2149 sold for £1.17 on day of issue. Nos. 2147-2152 exist imperforate.

No. 2150a is a sheet of eleven stamps plus one label, containing Ascension No. 1235, Bahamas No. 1526, British Antarctic Territory No. 604, Falkland Islands No. 1295, Gibraltar No. 1792, Guernsey No. 1613, Jersey No. 2410, Isle of Man No. 2150, South Georgia and South Sandwich Islands No. 643, Tristan da Cunha No. 1213, and Virgin Islands No. 1208 sold for £15 by the philatelic bureaus of Guernsey, Jersey, and Isle of Man. The philatelic bureaus of the other areas whose stamps appear on the sheet did not offer the sheet for sale.

John Ruskin (1819-1900), Writer — A513

Ruskin, quotation and: 1st, Laxey Woollen Mill and its founder, Egbert Rydings (1832-1912), St. George slaying dragon. EU, Ruskin quote on poster, bay window. L, Drawing of crab by Ruskin. ROW, The Journey to Venice, painting by John Miller Nicholson (1840-1913). £1.82, Calais Pier, painting by Joseph Mallord William Turner (1775-1851). £2.17, Ruskin Land.

| | | | | |
|---|---|---|---|---|
| **2021, Apr. 27** | | **Litho.** | | **Perf. 13½** |
| 2153 | A513 | 1st multi | 1.75 | 1.75 |
| 2154 | A513 | EU multi | 2.60 | 2.60 |
| 2155 | A513 | L multi | 3.25 | 3.25 |
| 2156 | A513 | ROW multi | 4.50 | 4.50 |
| 2157 | A513 | £1.82 multi | 5.25 | 5.25 |
| 2158 | A513 | £2.17 multi | 6.00 | 6.00 |
| | | Nos. 2153-2158 (6) | 23.35 | 23.35 |

On day of issue, No. 2153 sold for 62p; No. 2154, 94p; No. 2155, £1.17; No. 2156, £1.58.

2020 European Soccer Championships A514

Stadia hosting matches for 2020 European Soccer Championships in: No. 2159, London, England. No. 2160, Glasgow, Scotland. No. 2161, Seville, Spain. No. 2162, Rome, Italy. No. 2163, Munich, Germany. No. 2164, Copenhagen, Denmark. No. 2165, St. Petersburg, Russia. No. 2166, Baku, Azerbaijan.

| | | | | |
|---|---|---|---|---|
| **2021, June 11** | | **Litho.** | | **Perf. 12** |
| 2159 | A514 | 1st multi | 1.75 | 1.75 |
| 2160 | A514 | 1st multi | 1.75 | 1.75 |
| 2161 | A514 | EU multi | 2.60 | 2.60 |
| 2162 | A514 | EU multi | 2.60 | 2.60 |
| 2163 | A514 | L multi | 3.25 | 3.25 |
| 2164 | A514 | L multi | 3.25 | 3.25 |
| 2165 | A514 | £1.92 multi | 5.25 | 5.25 |
| 2166 | A514 | £1.92 multi | 5.25 | 5.25 |
| | | Nos. 2159-2166 (8) | 25.70 | 25.70 |

The 2020 European Soccer Championships were postponed until 2021 because of the COVID-19 pandemic. On day of issue, Nos. 2159-2160 each sold for 62p; Nos. 2161-2162 each sold for 94p, and Nos. 2163-2164 each sold for £1.17.

Royal British Legion, Cent. — A515

Designs: No. 2167, Ship, female legionaire with box of poppies. No. 2168, Woman and cenotaph. No. 2169, Male, female soldiers, child. No. 2170, Soldier and helicopters. No. 2171, Veteran at Battle Back Center. No. 2172, Old and new volunteers. No. 2173, Woman and health care building. No. 2174, Elderly veteran wearing hat at cemetery.

| | | | | |
|---|---|---|---|---|
| **2021, June 26** | | **Litho.** | | **Perf. 13** |
| 2167 | A515 | 1st multi | 1.75 | 1.75 |
| 2168 | A515 | 1st multi | 1.75 | 1.75 |
| 2169 | A515 | EU multi | 2.50 | 2.50 |
| 2170 | A515 | EU multi | 2.50 | 2.50 |
| 2171 | A515 | L multi | 3.25 | 3.25 |
| 2172 | A515 | L multi | 3.25 | 3.25 |
| 2173 | A515 | RoW multi | 4.25 | 4.25 |
| 2174 | A515 | RoW multi | 4.25 | 4.25 |
| | | Nos. 2167-2174 (8) | 23.50 | 23.50 |

On day of issue, Nos. 2167-2168 each sold for 62p; Nos. 2169-2170, 94p; Nos. 2171-2172, £1.17; Nos. 2173-2174, £1.58.

Olympic Athletes From Great Britain — A516

No. 2175: a, Mark Cavendish, cyclist, 2012, 2016 Olympics. b, Tim Kneale, shooter, 2016 Olympics. c, Marie Purvis, cyclist, 1992, 1996 Olympics. d, Maurice Herriott, steeplechase runner, 1964, 1968 Olympics. e, Peter Kennaugh, cyclist, 2012 Olympics. f, Sidney Swann, rower, 1912, 1920 Olympics. g, Adam Peaty, swimmer, 2016 Olympics. h, Sir Andy Murray, tennis player, 2012, 2106 Olympics. i, Dame Kelly Holmes, runner, 1996, 2000, 2004 Olympics. j, Sir Mo Farah, runner, 2008, 2012, 2016 Olympics. k, Sir Steve Redgrave, rower, 1984, 1988, 1992, 1996, 2000 Olympics. l, Rebecca Addlington, swimmer, 2008, 2012 Olympics.

| | | | | |
|---|---|---|---|---|
| **2021, July 15** | | **Litho.** | | **Perf. 12½** |
| 2175 | | Block of 12 | 26.50 | 26.50 |
| *a.-f.* | A516 | 1st Any single | 1.75 | 1.75 |
| *g.-l.* | A516 | EU Any single | 2.60 | 2.60 |
| *m.* | | Booklet pane of 12, #2175a-2175l | 26.50 | — |
| *n.* | | Booklet pane of 6, #2175a-2175l + 6 labels | 10.50 | — |
| *o.* | | Booklet pane of 6, #2175g-2175l + 6 labels | 16.00 | — |
| | | Complete booklet, #2175m, 2175n, 2175o | 53.00 | |

On day of issue, Nos. 2175a-2175f each sold for 62p, and Nos. 2175g-2175l each sold for 94p.

Vehicles in Transportation Museums — A517

Designs: 1st, Manx Transport Heritage Museum Shuttleworth Snap TT Racer and 1962 Peel P50 microcar. EU, Jurby Transport Museum 1972 Morris Mini 1000, 1972 Bedford TK truck and Guy Otter bus. L, Murray's Motorcycle Museum Nortom Wideline Cafe Racer, 1981 Suzuki RG500 and 1957 Mondial Bialbero 250. No. 2179, A. R. E. Classic Motorcycle Collection 1927 Scott 2-Speed, Ariel 650cc Huntsmaster Twin with Gerrard sidecar and 1939 Matchless G2 Clubman Deluxe 245cc. No. 2180, Milntown Car and Motorcycle Collection 1900 New Orleans automobile, 1922 Vauxhall motorcycle and 1923 Douglas motorcycle and sidecar. USA, Isle of Man Motor Museum GM PD-4501 Scenicruiser bus, Fleetwood Miyagata Reikyusha hearse, Humber Super Snipe Royal Tourer automobile.

| | | | | |
|---|---|---|---|---|
| **2021, July 28** | | **Litho.** | | **Perf. 13** |
| 2176 | A517 | 1st multi | 1.75 | 1.75 |
| 2177 | A517 | EU multi | 2.60 | 2.60 |
| 2178 | A517 | L multi | 3.25 | 3.25 |
| 2179 | A517 | RoW multi | 4.50 | 4.50 |
| 2180 | A517 | RoW multi | 4.50 | 4.50 |
| 2181 | A517 | USA multi | 6.00 | 6.00 |
| | | Nos. 2176-2181 (6) | 22.60 | 22.60 |

On day of issue, No. 2176 sold for 62p; No. 2177, 94p; No. 2178, £1.17; Nos. 2179-2180, £1.58 each; No. 2181, £2.15.

Captain John Quilliam (1771-1829), Battle of Trafalgar Participant A518

Designs: 1st, Quilliam and his grave. EU, Quilliam before the Emperor of China and his assistants and Royal Navy sailors. L, Ships at the Battle of Camperdown, 1797. USA, Victory at the Battle of Trafalgar, 1805, stained-glass window depicting Quilliam. EU Large, Statue depicting Quilliam, House of Keys Building and emblem, Balcony House, Castletown.

**2021, Sept. 21    Litho.    Perf. 13x13¼**

| | | | | |
|---|---|---|---|---|
| 2182 | A518 | 1st multi | 1.75 | 1.75 |
| 2183 | A518 | EU multi | 2.60 | 2.60 |
| 2184 | A518 | L multi | 3.25 | 3.25 |
| 2185 | A518 | RoW multi | 4.25 | 4.25 |
| 2186 | A518 | USA multi | 6.00 | 6.00 |
| 2187 | A518 | EU Large multi | 6.75 | 6.75 |
| | | Nos. 2182-2187 (6) | 24.60 | 24.60 |

On day of issue, No. 2182 sold for 62p; No. 2183, 94p; No. 2184, £1.17; No. 2185, £1.58; No. 2186, £2.15; No. 2187, £2.44.

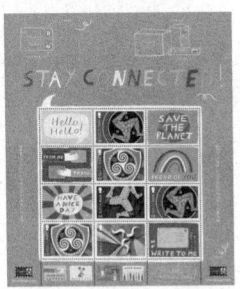

This sheet of six 1st stamps having a franking value of 62p each on the day of issue and six labels, released Sept. 20, 2021, was sold together with a sheet of five postcards for £8.

Mensa, 75th Anniv. A519

Designs: 1st, Addition logic puzzle. EU, Number logic puzzle. L, Puzzle of sixteen letters in grid. RoW, Letter puzzle. USA, Shapes in grid puzzle. £2.81, Word and number puzzle.

**2021, Oct. 1    Litho.    Perf. 13**

| | | | | |
|---|---|---|---|---|
| 2188 | A519 | 1st multi | 1.75 | 1.75 |
| a. | | Perf. 12 | 1.75 | 1.75 |
| 2189 | A519 | EU multi | 2.60 | 2.60 |
| a. | | Perf. 12 | 2.60 | 2.60 |
| b. | | Booklet pane of 2, #2188a, 2189a + 4 labels | 4.50 | |
| 2190 | A519 | L multi | 3.25 | 3.25 |
| a. | | Perf. 12 | 3.25 | 3.25 |
| 2191 | A519 | RoW multi | 4.25 | 4.25 |
| a. | | Perf. 12 | 4.25 | 4.25 |
| b. | | Booklet pane of 2, #2190a, 2191a + 4 labels | 7.50 | |
| 2192 | A519 | USA multi | 6.00 | 6.00 |
| a. | | Perf. 12 | 6.00 | 6.00 |
| 2193 | A519 | £2.81 multi | 7.75 | 7.75 |
| a. | | Perf. 12 | 7.75 | 7.75 |
| b. | | Booklet pane of 6 #2188a, 2189a, 2190a, 2191a, 2192a, 2193a | 26.00 | |
| c. | | Booklet pane of 2 #2192a, 2193a + 4 labels | 14.00 | |
| | | Complete booklet, #2189b, 2191b, 2193b, 2193c | 52.00 | |
| | | Nos. 2188-2193 (6) | 25.60 | 25.60 |

On day of issue, No. 2188 sold for 62p; No. 2189, 94p; No. 2190, £1.17; No. 2191, £1.58; No. 2192, £2.15.

Thomas the Tank Engine at Castletown A520

Toby on Snaefell Mountain A521

Duncan at Groudle Glen Railway A522

James at Ballasalla A523

Henry at Douglas A524

James and Gordon at Port Soderick A525

**2021, Oct. 27    Litho.    Perf. 12½**

| | | | | |
|---|---|---|---|---|
| 2194 | A520 | 1st multi | 1.90 | 1.90 |
| 2195 | A521 | EU multi | 2.75 | 2.75 |
| 2196 | A522 | L multi | 3.50 | 3.50 |
| 2197 | A523 | RoW multi | 4.75 | 4.75 |
| 2198 | A524 | USA multi | 6.50 | 6.50 |
| 2199 | A525 | EU Large multi | 7.25 | 7.25 |
| a. | | Souvenir sheet of 6, #2194-2199 | 27.00 | 27.00 |
| | | Nos. 2194-2199 (6) | 26.65 | 26.65 |

Christmas, Publicaton of *Thomas the Tank Engine* children's books by Reverend Wilbert Awdrey, 75th anniv.

On day of issue, No. 2194 sold for 67p; No. 2195, £1.02; No. 2196, £1.26; No. 2197, £1.71; No. 2198, £2.32; No. 2199, £2.64.

A526    A527

A528    A529

A530    A531

Sir Barry Gibb, Rock Musician — A532

**2021, Nov. 3    Litho.    Perf. 13¼**

| | | | | |
|---|---|---|---|---|
| 2200 | A526 | 1st multi | 1.75 | 1.75 |
| 2201 | A527 | 1st multi | 1.75 | 1.75 |
| 2202 | A528 | EU multi | 2.75 | 2.75 |
| 2203 | A529 | L multi | 3.50 | 3.50 |
| 2204 | A530 | RoW multi | 4.50 | 4.50 |
| 2205 | A531 | USA multi | 6.25 | 6.25 |
| 2206 | A532 | USA multi | 6.25 | 6.25 |
| | | Nos. 2200-2206 (7) | 26.75 | 26.75 |

On day of issue, Nos. 2200-2201 each sold for 67p; No. 2202, £1.02; No. 2203, £1.26; No. 2204, £1.71; Nos. 2205-2206, each, £2.32.

New Year 2022 (Year of the Tiger) — A533

Designs: 67p, Head of tiger on jug. £1.71, Two tigers. £2.32, Horse and tiger. £3.89, Tiger on pitcher.

**2022, Jan. 13    Litho.    Perf. 12½**

| | | | | |
|---|---|---|---|---|
| 2207 | A533 | 67p multi | 1.90 | 1.90 |
| 2208 | A533 | £1.71 multi | 4.75 | 4.75 |
| 2209 | A533 | £2.32 multi | 6.25 | 6.25 |
| 2210 | A533 | £3.89 multi | 10.50 | 10.50 |
| | | Nos. 2207-2210 (4) | 23.40 | 23.40 |

A534

A535

A536

Reign of Queen Elizabeth II (1926-2022), 70th Anniv. — A537

Various photographs of Queen Elizabeth II and inscription: No. 2211, God save our gracious Queen. No. 2212, Long live our noble Queen. No. 2213, God save the Queen. No. 2214, Send her victorious. No. 2215, Happy and glorioious. No. 2216, Long to reign over us. No. 2217, May she defend our laws. No. 2218, God save the Queen, diff.

No. 2219a — Reproduction of, or image used on Isle of Man stamp: b, #494. c, #929. d, #930. e, #496. f, #497. g, #498. h, #932. i, #933.

No. 2219j — Reproduction of, or image used on Isle of Man stamp: k, #96. l, #97. m, #98. n, #940d. o, #940e. p, #940a. q, #940b. r, #940c.

No. 2219s — Reproduction of, or image used on Isle of Man stamp: t, #1478. u, #1480. v, #1849. w, #1481. x, #1482. y, #1850. z, #1852. aa, #1853.

**2022, Feb. 6    Litho.    Perf. 12**

| | | | | |
|---|---|---|---|---|
| 2211 | A534 | 67p multi | 1.90 | 1.90 |
| 2212 | A534 | 67p multi | 1.90 | 1.90 |
| 2213 | A534 | £1.02 multi | 2.75 | 2.75 |
| 2214 | A534 | £1.02 multi | 2.75 | 2.75 |
| 2215 | A534 | £1.26 multi | 3.50 | 3.50 |
| 2216 | A534 | £1.26 multi | 3.50 | 3.50 |
| 2217 | A534 | £1.71 multi | 4.75 | 4.75 |
| 2218 | A534 | £1.71 multi | 4.75 | 4.75 |
| a. | | Booklet pane of 8, #2211-2218 | 26.00 | |
| | | Nos. 2211-2218 (8) | 25.80 | 25.80 |

**Souvenir Booklet**

| | | | | |
|---|---|---|---|---|
| 2219 | | Booklet of 4 panes, #2218a, 2219a, 2219j, 2219s | 57.00 | |
| a. | | A535 Booklet pane of 8, #2219b-2219i | 7.00 | |
| b. | | 18p multi | .50 | .50 |
| c. | | 22p multi | .60 | .60 |
| d. | | 26p multi | .70 | .70 |
| e. | | 28p multi | .75 | .75 |
| f. | | 33p multi | .90 | .90 |
| g. | | 39p multi | 1.10 | 1.10 |
| h. | | 40p multi | 1.10 | 1.10 |
| i. | | 45p multi | 1.25 | 1.25 |
| j. | | A536 Booklet pane of 8, #2219k-2219r | 8.25 | |
| k. | | 6p multi | .30 | .30 |
| l. | | 7p multi | .30 | .30 |
| m. | | 25p multi | .65 | .65 |
| n. | | 50p multi | 1.40 | 1.40 |
| o. | | 50p multi | 1.40 | 1.40 |
| p. | | 50p multi | 1.40 | 1.40 |
| q. | | 50p multi | 1.40 | 1.40 |
| r. | | 50p multi | 1.40 | 1.40 |
| s. | | A537 Booklet pane of 8, #2219t-2219aa | 15.50 | |
| t. | | 37p multi | 1.00 | 1.00 |
| u. | | 37p multi | 1.00 | 1.00 |
| v. | | 45p multi | 1.25 | 1.25 |
| w. | | 58p multi | 1.60 | 1.60 |
| x. | | 68p multi | 1.90 | 1.90 |
| y. | | 77p multi | 2.10 | 2.10 |
| z. | | £1.13 multi | 3.00 | 3.00 |
| aa. | | £1.24 multi | 3.50 | 3.50 |

Nos. 2218a and 2219s are connected in booklet with fold at center, as are Nos. 2219a and 2219j.

A538

A539

A540

Paintings by David Byrne and Nancy Corkish (1936-2021) — A541

No. 2220 — Painting by: a, Corkish. b, Byrne.
No. 2221 — Painting by: a, Byrne. b, Corkish.
No. 2222 — Painting by: a, Byrne. b, Corkish.
No. 2223 — Painting by: a, Corkish. b, Byrne.

**2022, Feb. 23    Litho.    Perf. 13¼**

Inscribed "First"

| | | | | |
|---|---|---|---|---|
| 2220 | A538 | Horiz. pair | 3.50 | 3.50 |
| a.-b. | | (62p) Either single | 1.75 | 1.75 |

Inscribed "Europe"

| | | | | |
|---|---|---|---|---|
| 2221 | A539 | Horiz. pair | 5.00 | 5.00 |
| a.-b. | | (94p) Either single | 2.50 | 2.50 |

Inscribed "Large"

| | | | | |
|---|---|---|---|---|
| 2222 | A540 | Horiz. pair | 6.50 | 6.50 |
| a.-b. | | (£1.17) Either single | 3.25 | 3.25 |

Inscribed "Rest of the World"

| | | | | |
|---|---|---|---|---|
| 2223 | A541 | Horiz. pair | 8.50 | 8.50 |
| a.-b. | | (£1.58) Either single | 4.25 | 4.25 |
| | | Nos. 2220-2223 (4) | 23.50 | 23.50 |

Sculptures by Michael Sandle A542

Designs: 1st, Memorial to the Lifeboat Men, Douglas. EU, Malta Siege Bell Memorial, Valletta, Malta. £1.26, St. George and the Dragon, London. £1.71, International Seafarers Memorial, London. £2.32, The Viking, Port Erin. £2.64, A Twentieth Century War Memorial, London.

**2022, Mar. 8    Litho.    Perf. 13**

| | | | | |
|---|---|---|---|---|
| 2224 | A542 | 1st multi | 1.75 | 1.75 |
| 2225 | A542 | EU multi | 2.50 | 2.50 |
| 2226 | A542 | £1.26 multi | 3.50 | 3.50 |
| 2227 | A542 | £1.71 multi | 4.50 | 4.50 |
| 2228 | A542 | £2.32 multi | 6.25 | 6.25 |
| 2229 | A542 | £2.64 multi | 7.00 | 7.00 |
| | | Nos. 2224-2229 (6) | 25.50 | 25.50 |

On day of issue, No. 2224 sold for 62p, and No. 2225 sold for 94p.

Paintings by Eileen Schaer — A543

Designs: 73p, Lady Dreaming of a Tiger. £1.38, Birdsong. £1.54, Moonlight. £1.75, Lady with Birds. £1.91, Just Friends. £2.12, Lady Kneeling.

**2022, Apr. 12　Litho.　Perf. 13¾x13½**

| | | | | |
|---|---|---|---|---|
| 2230 | A543 | 73p multi | 1.90 | 1.90 |
| 2231 | A543 | £1.38 multi | 3.50 | 3.50 |
| 2232 | A543 | £1.54 multi | 4.00 | 4.00 |
| 2233 | A543 | £1.75 multi | 4.50 | 4.50 |
| 2234 | A543 | £1.91 multi | 4.75 | 4.75 |
| 2235 | A543 | £2.12 multi | 5.50 | 5.50 |
| | | Nos. 2230-2235 (6) | 24.15 | 24.15 |

A544　　Manx Museum, Cent. — A545

Items in Manx Museum: Nos. 2236a, 2238a, 1911 Renault, oldest surviving Manx motor vehicle. Nos. 2236b, 2238b, Isle of Man #1. Nos. 2236c, 2238c, Head and Shoulders of a Child, sculpture by Frank Mowbray Taubman (1868-1946). Nos. 2236d, 2238d, On the Beach at Douglas, painting by William Hardie Hay (1859-1933). Nos. 2236e, 2238e, Pygmy shrew taxidermy. Nos. 2237a, 2238f, Elephant hawk-moth. Nos. 2237b, 2238g, Silver penny depicting King Sihtric, c. 1030. Nos. 2237c, 2238h, Rushen Abbey floor tile, c. 1400. Nos. 2237d, 2238i, 1886 photograph of laying of foundation stone for Isle of Man Hospital, Douglas. Nos. 2237e, 2238j, Sign for Sulby Glen Corn Flour, 19th cent.

**2022, Apr. 28　Litho.　Perf. 13¼x13**

| | | | | |
|---|---|---|---|---|
| 2236 | | Horiz. strip of 5 | 9.50 | 9.50 |
| a.-e. | A544 | 73p Any single | 1.90 | 1.90 |
| 2237 | | Horiz. strip of 5 | 13.00 | 13.00 |
| a.-e. | A544 | £1.04 Any single | 2.60 | 2.60 |

**Self-Adhesive**
*Serpentine Die Cut 17x16½*

| | | | |
|---|---|---|---|
| 2238 | | Booklet pane of 10 | 19.00 |
| a.-j. | A545 | 73p Any single | 1.90 | 1.90 |

Buses — A546

Designs: 73p, 1979-80 Leyland Leopard. £1.00, 1982 Leyland Atlantean. £1.38, 1988 Leyland Lynx. £1.83, 2001-05 DAF DB250. £1.91, 2009 Volvo B9TL. £2.16, 2020 Wrightbus StreetDeck.

**2022, May 5　Litho.　Perf. 12**

| | | | | |
|---|---|---|---|---|
| 2239 | A546 | 73p multi | 1.90 | 1.90 |
| 2240 | A546 | £1 multi | 2.50 | 2.50 |
| 2241 | A546 | £1.38 multi | 3.50 | 3.50 |
| 2242 | A546 | £1.83 multi | 4.50 | 4.50 |
| 2243 | A546 | £1.91 multi | 4.75 | 4.75 |
| 2244 | A546 | £2.16 multi | 5.50 | 5.50 |
| | | Nos. 2239-2244 (6) | 22.65 | 22.65 |

British Broadcasting Corporation, Cent. — A547

No. 2245: a, Tardis from *Doctor Who*, "Time and Relative Dimensions in Space." b, Mirrored ball trophy from *Strictly Come Dancing*, "Keep Dancing!" c, Badge from *Blue Peter*, "Here's one I made earlier." d, BBC News globe, "Here is the News from the BBC." e,

Soccer ball program identification from *Match of the Day*, "They think it is all over. . . it is now." f, Alpine parrot from BBC Natural History programming, "The future of life on earth depends on us now." g, Adder and ruff from *Blackadder*, "I have a cunning plan!" h, Bust of Queen Victoria from *EastEnders*, "Doof-Doof-Doof-Doof-Doof-Doof-Doof-Doof!" i, Violin and bow symbol from *BBC Proms*, "Welcome to the BBC Proms from the Royal Albert Hall." j, Record from *Desert Island Discs* radio show, "Eight tracks, a book and a luxury." k, Bitesize emblem, "Inform, educate, entertain!" l, Sir Patrick Moore, telescope and Moon from *Sky at Night*, "World's longest running TV show with the same presenter."

**2022, May 19　Litho.　Perf. 12½**

| | | | | |
|---|---|---|---|---|
| 2245 | A547 | Block of 12 | 23.00 | 23.00 |
| a.-l. | | 73p Any single | 1.90 | 1.90 |

Culture Vannin, 40th Anniv. — A548

No. 2246: a, People running with flags, person running while reading book. b, Arhaeologist with shovel in cart hooked to small vehicle, man pushing cart. c, Man holding large key, people carrying Culture Vannin display with flag.

No. 2247: a, Woman carrying large pencil, men carrying model of building with flag. b, Birds, rabbit, man on sheep holding fish. c, Women dancing, man carrying boat, man playing recorder.

**2022, July 4　Litho.　Perf. 13¼**

| | | | | |
|---|---|---|---|---|
| 2246 | | Horiz. strip of 3 | 8.00 | 8.00 |
| a. | A548 | 73p multi | 1.75 | 1.75 |
| b. | A548 | £1.04 multi | 2.60 | 2.60 |
| c. | A548 | £1.38 multi | 3.50 | 3.50 |
| 2247 | | Horiz. strip of 3 | 16.50 | 16.50 |
| a. | A548 | £1.91 multi | 4.75 | 4.75 |
| b. | A548 | £2.16 multi | 5.25 | 5.25 |
| c. | A548 | £2.57 multi | 6.25 | 6.25 |

Creative Network Artist Collective, 10th Anniv. — A549

No. 2248: a, Sugarloaf Rock, painting by Graham Rider. b, Three Boxes, wood-turned vessels by Graham Hall. c, Child's hand-sewn dress by Myra Gilbert. d, Wren, illustration on music score, by Dawn Kennaugh. e, Gateway at Ballagyr, painting by Sarah Devereau.

No. 2249: a, Black Rhino, ceramic stoneware by Erica Kermode. b, The Gift, digital illustration by Bruno Cavellec. c, Sea Kale, embroidery by Maureen Kennaugh. d, Leaf, kiln-formed glass by Debra Tracey-Carney. e, Bridge Street, Peel, photograph by Eric Glithero.

**2022, July 28　Litho.　Perf. 12½**

| | | | | |
|---|---|---|---|---|
| 2248 | | Horiz. strip of 5 | 8.75 | 8.75 |
| a.-e. | A549 | 73p Any single | 1.75 | 1.75 |
| 2249 | | Horiz. strip of 5 | 16.00 | 16.00 |
| a.-b. | A549 | £1.04 Either single | 2.60 | 2.60 |
| c.-e. | A549 | £1.38 Any single | 3.50 | 3.50 |

David Bowie (1947-2016), Rock Musician and Actor — A550

Various photographs of Bowie inscribed at bottom: No. 2250, Final portrait, 2016. No. 2251, Everybody Loves Sunshine, 1999. No. 2252, Labyrinth, 1986. No. 2253, Merry Christmas, Mr. Lawrence, 1983. No. 2254, Baal, 1982. No. 2255, The Elephant Man, 1980. No. 2256, Just a Gigolo, 1978. No. 2257, The Man Who Fell to Earth, 1976.

**2022, Sept. 12　Litho.　Perf. 12**

| | | | | |
|---|---|---|---|---|
| 2250 | A550 | 73p multi | 1.75 | 1.75 |
| 2251 | A550 | 73p multi | 1.75 | 1.75 |
| 2252 | A550 | 104p multi | 2.40 | 2.40 |
| 2253 | A550 | 104p multi | 2.40 | 2.40 |
| 2254 | A550 | 138p multi | 3.25 | 3.25 |
| 2255 | A550 | 138p multi | 3.25 | 3.25 |
| a. | | Booklet pane of 4, #2250, 2251, 2254, 2255, with #2255 at UL | 10.00 | — |
| b. | | As "a," with #2250 at UL | 10.00 | — |
| 2256 | A550 | 175p multi | 4.00 | 4.00 |
| 2257 | A550 | 175p multi | 4.00 | 4.00 |
| a. | | Booklet pane of 4, #2252, 2253, 2256, 2257, with #2252 at UL | 13.00 | — |
| b. | | As "a," with #2257 at UL | 13.00 | — |

| | | |
|---|---|---|
| Complete booklet, #2255a, 2255b, 2257a, 2257b | 46.00 | |
| Nos. 2250-2257 (8) | 22.80 | 22.80 |

Nos. 2255a and 2257b, and Nos. 2255b and 2257a, are printed on the same sheet of paper, which are folded in half and stapled in the booklet.

---

### POSTAGE DUE STAMPS

> **Catalogue values for unused stamps in this section are for Never Hinged items.**

D1

**Imprint: "1973 Questa"**

*Perf. 13½*

**1973, July 5　Litho.　Unwmk.**
**Inscriptions and Coat of Arms in Black and Red**

| | | | | |
|---|---|---|---|---|
| J1 | D1 | ½p yellow | .25 | .25 |
| J2 | D1 | 1p buff | .25 | .25 |
| J3 | D1 | 2p lt yellow grn | .90 | .90 |
| J4 | D1 | 3p gray | 1.60 | 1.60 |
| J5 | D1 | 4p dull rose | 2.50 | 2.50 |
| J6 | D1 | 5p light blue | 2.75 | 2.75 |
| J7 | D1 | 10p light violet | 6.25 | 6.25 |
| J8 | D1 | 20p lt grnsh blue | 15.00 | 15.00 |
| | | Nos. J1-J8 (8) | 29.50 | 29.50 |

**Inscribed: "1973 A Questa"**

**1973, Sept.**

| | | | | |
|---|---|---|---|---|
| J1a | D1 | ½p | 1.40 | 1.20 |
| J2a | D1 | 1p | .75 | .80 |
| J3a | D1 | 2p | .25 | .25 |
| J4a | D1 | 3p | .25 | .25 |
| J5a | D1 | 4p | .25 | .25 |
| J6a | D1 | 5p | .25 | .25 |
| J7a | D1 | 10p | .35 | .35 |
| J8a | D1 | 20p | .75 | .60 |
| | | Nos. J1a-J8a (8) | 4.25 | 3.95 |

D2

**1975, Jan. 8　Litho.　Perf. 14**
**Inscriptions and Coat of Arms in Black and Red**

| | | | | |
|---|---|---|---|---|
| J9 | D2 | ½p yellow | .25 | .25 |
| J10 | D2 | 1p buff | .25 | .25 |
| J11 | D2 | 4p lilac rose | .25 | .25 |
| J12 | D2 | 7p blue | .25 | .25 |
| J13 | D2 | 9p sepia | .25 | .25 |
| J14 | D2 | 10p lilac | .25 | .25 |
| J15 | D2 | 50p orange | .65 | .65 |
| J16 | D2 | £1 bright green | 1.25 | 1.25 |
| | | Nos. J9-J16 (8) | 3.40 | 3.40 |

D3

D4

**1982-92　Litho.　Perf. 15x14**

| | | | | |
|---|---|---|---|---|
| J17 | D3 | 1p light green | .25 | .25 |
| J18 | D3 | 2p bright pink | .25 | .25 |
| J19 | D3 | 5p grnsh blue | .25 | .25 |
| J20 | D3 | 10p bright lilac | .25 | .25 |
| J21 | D3 | 20p gray | .50 | .50 |
| J22 | D3 | 50p dull yellow | 1.35 | 1.35 |
| J23 | D3 | £1 brick red | 2.05 | 2.05 |
| J24 | D3 | £2 blue | 4.00 | 4.00 |

**Litho.**
*Perf. 13x13½*

| | | | | |
|---|---|---|---|---|
| J25 | D4 | £5 multicolored | 10.50 | 10.50 |
| | | Nos. J17-J25 (9) | 19.40 | 19.40 |

Issued: £5, 9/16/92; others, 10/5/82.

# Measure Up Your Collection

## Scott Multi-Gauge
Item No. LIN01

**$9.89** *AA\* price*
$10.99 Retail

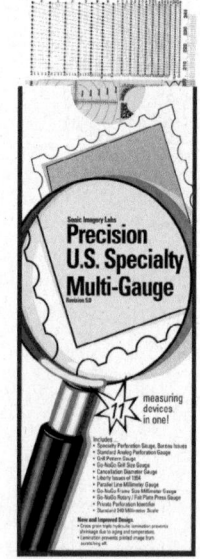

## U.S. Specialized Multi-Gauge
Item No. USSMG02

**$13.59** *AA\* price*
$15.99 Retail

AmosAdvantage.com
1-800-572-6885

**ORDERING INFORMATION:** \*AA prices apply to paid subscribers of Amos Media titles, or for orders placed online. Prices, terms and product availability subject to change.

# GREECE

'grēs

## (Hellas)

LOCATION — Southern part of the Balkan Peninsula in southeastern Europe, bordering on the Ionian, Aegean and Mediterranean Seas
GOVT. — Republic
AREA — 50,949 sq. mi.
POP. — 10,511,000 (1997 est.)
CAPITAL — Athens

In 1923 the reigning king was forced to abdicate and the following year Greece was declared a republic. In 1935, the king was recalled by a "plebiscite" of the people. Greece became a republic in June 1973. The country today includes the Aegean Islands of Chios, Mytilene (Lesbos), Samos, Icaria (Nicaria) and Lemnos, the Ionian Islands (Corfu, etc.) Crete, Macedonia, Western Thrace and part of Eastern Thrace, the Mount Athos District, Epirus and the Dodecanese Islands.

100 Lepta = 1 Drachma
100 Cents = 1 Euro (2002)

Catalogue values for unused stamps in this country are for Never Hinged items, beginning with Scott 472 in the regular postage section, Scott B1 in the semi-postal section, Scott C48 in the airpost section, Scott CB1 in the airpost semi-postal section, Scott RA69 in the postal tax section, and Scott N239 in the occupation and annexation section.

Values for unused stamps are for examples with original gum as defined in the catalogue introduction. Any exceptions will be noted.

Values for Large Hermes Head stamps with double control numbers on the back, Nos. 20e, 21c, 27a, et al, are for examples with two distinct and separate impressions, not for blurred or "slide doubles" caused by paper slippage on the press.

### Watermarks

Wmk. 129 — Crown and ET

Wmk. 252 — Crowns

### Paris Print

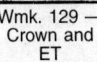

Hermes (Mercury) — A1

---

Paris Print, Fine Impression

The enlarged illustrations show the head in various states of the plates. The differences are best seen in the shading lines on the cheek and neck.

| 1861 | | Unwmk. | Typo. | *Imperf.* |
|---|---|---|---|---|
| **Without Figures on Back** | | | | |
| 1 | A1 | 1 l choc, *brnsh* | 600.00 | 550.00 |
| a. | | 1 l red brown, *brnish* | 725.00 | 600.00 |
| b. | | 1 l brown | 575.00 | 475.00 |
| 2 | A1 | 2 l ol bis, *straw* | 67.50 | 87.50 |
| a. | | 2 l brown buff, *buff* | 55.00 | 75.00 |
| b. | | 2 l yellowish bister | 55.00 | 75.00 |
| 3 | A1 | 5 l yel grn, *grnsh* | 700.00 | 150.00 |
| a. | | 5 l emerald green | 875.00 | 175.00 |
| 4 | A1 | 20 l bl, *bluish* | 1,150. | 95.00 |
| a. | | 20 l deep blue, *bluish* | 1,100. | 340.00 |
| b. | | On pelure paper | 1,350. | 275.00 |
| 5 | A1 | 40 l vio, *bl* | 325.00 | 130.00 |
| 6 | A1 | 80 l rose, *pink* | 250.00 | 120.00 |

### Large Figures, 8mm high, on Back

| 7 | A1 | 10 l red org, *bl* | 1,040. | 500.00 |
|---|---|---|---|---|
| a. | | "10" on back inverted | — | — |
| c. | | "0" of "10" invtd. on back | — | 1,850. |
| d. | | "1" of "10" invtd. on back | — | 2,750. |

No. 7 without "10" on back is a proof.
Trial impressions of Paris prints exist in many shades, some being close to those of the issued stamps. The gum used was thin and smooth instead of thick, brownish and crackly as on the issued stamps.
See Nos. 8-58. For surcharges see Nos. 130, 132-133, 137-139, 141-143, 147-149, 153-154, 157-158.

Faint quadrille, horizontal or vertical lines are visible in the background of some Athens print large Hermes head stamps.
Nos. 16, 16a, 16b are the only 1 l stamps that have these lines.

### Athens Prints

Athens Print, Typical Fine Impression

Athens Print, Typical Coarse Impression

---

### Figures on Back
5 l:

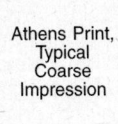

#11    #18-45

### Fine Printing (F)
Fine Printing (F, '62) see footnote
Coarse Printing (C)

| **1861-62** | | **Without Figures on Back** | | |
|---|---|---|---|---|
| 8 | A1 | 1 l choc, *brnsh* (F, '62) | 490.00 | 490.00 |
| | | No gum | 350.00 | |
| a. | | 1 l dk chocolate, *brnish* (F) | 1,300. | 1,325. |
| | | No gum | 700.00 | |
| b. | | 1 l chocolate, *brnish* (F) | 590.00 | 590.00 |
| | | No gum | 460.00 | |
| 9 | A1 | 2 l bis brn, *bister* (F) | 75.00 | 110.00 |
| | | No gum | 40.00 | |
| a. | | 2 l dark brown, *straw,* (C) | 6,750. | — |
| b. | | 2 l bister brown, *bister* (C) | 90.00 | 135.00 |
| c. | | 2 l bister brown, *bister* (F, '62) | 90.00 | 135.00 |
| 10 | A1 | 20 l dk bl, *bluish* (C) | 15,000. | |

### With Figures on Back

| 11 | A1 | 5 l grn, *grnsh* (F) | 300.00 | 135.00 |
|---|---|---|---|---|
| | | No gum | 175.00 | |
| a. | | 5 l green, *greenish* (C) | 375.00 | 190.00 |
| b. | | As "a," double "5" on back (F, C) | — | 2,850. |
| c. | | 5 l green, *greenish,* bl grn figures on back (F, '62) | 350.00 | 135.00 |
| 12 | A1 | 10 l org, *grnsh* (F, '62) | 600.00 | 90.00 |
| | | No gum | 325.00 | |
| a. | | 10 l orange, *greenish* (C) | 1,950. | 300.00 |
| c. | | 10 l orange, *greenish* (F) | 600.00 | 135.00 |
| 13 | A1 | 20 l blue, *bluish* (F, '62) | 475.00 | 57.50 |
| a. | | 20 l dull blue, *bluish* (F) | 6,750. | 245.00 |
| b. | | 20 l dark blue, *bluish,* (F) | 3,500. | 110.00 |
| 14 | A1 | 40 l red vio, *pale bl* (F, '62) | 5,250. | 475.00 |
| a. | | 40 l red violet, *blue* (F) | 10,000. | 600.00 |
| b. | | 40 l red violet, *blue,* (F) | 5,250. | 475.00 |
| 15 | A1 | 80 l car, *pink* (F, '62) | 1,200. | 165.00 |
| a. | | 80 l carmine, *pink* (F) | 1,200. | 165.00 |
| b. | | 80 l dl rose, *pink* (F) | 1,200. | 165.00 |

Nos. 8-15 are known as the "Athens Provisionals." The first printings were not very successful, producing the "coarse printings." Later printings used an altered printing method that gave better results (the "fine printings"). All these were issued in the normal manner by the Post Office.
Nos. 8, 9c, 11c, 12, 13, 14, 15 have uninterrupted and even shading lines that do not taper off at the ends. They were produced in May 1862 (F, '62). Other fine printing stamps were produced in Feb.-Apr. 1862 (F).
The numerals on the back are strongly shaded in the right lines with the corresponding left lines being quite thin. The colors of the numerals are generally strong and often show clumps of ink.
Nos. 15a and 15b have vermilion figures on the back, while those of all later printings are carmine.

---

Athens Print, Consecutive Print

### With Figures on Back
Except 1 l, 2 l

| **1862-67** | | | | |
|---|---|---|---|---|
| 16 | A1 | 1 l brn, *brnish* (poor print) | 60.00 | 60.00 |
| a. | | 1 l red brn, *brnish* (poor print) | 150.00 | 150.00 |
| b. | | 1 l choc, *brnish* | 67.50 | 67.50 |
| 17 | A1 | 2 l bister, *bister* | 55.00 | 60.00 |
| a. | | 2 l brnsh bis, *bister* | 13.00 | 24.00 |
| 18 | A1 | 5 l grn, *grnsh* | 250.00 | 24.00 |
| a. | | 5 l yellowish green, *grnsh* | 250.00 | 12.00 |
| 19 | A1 | 10 l org, *blue* ('64) | 400.00 | 47.50 |
| a. | | 10 l yel org, *bluish* | 650.00 | 60.00 |
| b. | | As "a," "10" inverted on front of stamp | | 23,500. |
| c. | | 10 l red org, *bl* (Dec. '65) | 650.00 | 27.50 |
| d. | | "01" on back | 9,000. | 175.00 |
| 20 | A1 | 20 l bl, *bluish* | 250.00 | 24.00 |
| a. | | 20 l lt bl, *bluish* (fine print) | 375.00 | 24.00 |
| b. | | 20 l dark blue, *bluish* | 2,000. | 67.50 |
| c. | | 20 l blue, *greenish* | 1,700. | 37.50 |
| d. | | "80" on back | | 2,450. |
| e. | | Double "20" on back | | 1,500. |
| f. | | Without "20" on back | | 5,500. |
| 21 | A1 | 40 l lilac, *bl* | 550.00 | 37.50 |
| a. | | 40 l grayish lilac, *blue* | 1,750. | 37.50 |
| b. | | 40 l lilac brown, *lil gray* | 1,500. | 47.50 |
| c. | | Double "40" on back | | 1,600. |
| 22 | A1 | 80 l car, *pale rose* | 80.00 | 24.00 |
| a. | | 80 l rose, *pale rose* | 80.00 | 24.00 |
| b. | | "8" on back inverted | — | 550.00 |
| c. | | "80" on back inverted | | |
| d. | | "8" only on back | | 700.00 |
| e. | | "0" only on back | | 700.00 |

Nos. 16-22 represent a series of printings for each value, from 1862 through 1867, until a major cleaning of the plates was done in 1868. Impressions range from very fine and clear to coarse and blotchy.
Some printings of Nos. 16, 16a, 16b show faint vertical, horizontal or quadrilled lines in the background. Later 1 l stamps do not show these lines.
Many stamps of this and succeeding issues which are normally imperforate are known privately rouletted, pin-perforated, percé en scie, etc.

### With Figures on Back, Except 1 l, 2 l

| **1868** | | **From Cleaned Plates** | | |
|---|---|---|---|---|
| 23 | A1 | 1 l gray brn, *brnish* | 67.50 | 75.00 |
| 24 | A1 | 2 l gray bis, *bister* | 32.50 | 47.50 |
| 25 | A1 | 5 l grn, *grnsh* | 6,500. | 150.00 |
| a. | | 5 l yellow green, *grnsh* | 6,500. | 50.00 |
| 26 | A1 | 10 l pale org, *bluish* | 1,650. | 40.00 |
| a. | | "01" on back | | |
| 27 | A1 | 20 l pale bl, *bluish* | 1,500. | 24.00 |
| a. | | Double "20" on back | | 1,450. |
| 28 | A1 | 40 l rose vio, *bl* | 325.00 | 37.50 |
| a. | | "20" on back, corrected to "40" | — | 2,750. |
| 29 | A1 | 80 l rose car, *pale rose* | 190.00 | 250.00 |

The "0" on the back of No. 29 is printed more heavily than the "8."

SARANTOPOULOS ★PHILATELICS★
GREEK STAMP STORE
Peter Sarantopoulos • P.O. Box 2410 • Des Plaines, IL 60017
Telephone: (847) 997-3140 (Please leave a message!) • E-mail: Peter@GreekStampStore.com

SPECIALIZING IN STAMPS AND POSTAL HISTORY OF GREECE AND TERRITORIES.

VISIT OUR WEBSITE!
WWW.GREEKSTAMPSTORE.COM

Member of the Hellenic Philatelic Society, American Philatelic Society, American Stamp Dealers Association and the National Stamp Dealers Association (U.S.)

## With Figures on Back, Except 1 l

**1870**

| | | | |
|---|---|---|---|
| 30 | A1 | 1 l dp reddish brn, *brnish* | 175.00 | 200.00 |
| a. | | 1 l redsh brn, *brnish* | 200.00 | 240.00 |
| 31 | A1 | 1 l lt bl, *bluish* | 1,900. | 24.00 |
| b. | | 20 l blue, *bluish* | 2,000. | 35.00 |
| b. | | "02" on back | | 1,225. |
| c. | | "20" on back inverted | | 675.00 |

Nos. 30 and 30a have short lines of shading on cheek. The spandrels of No. 31 are very pale with the lines often broken or missing.

This was an Athens Printing made under supervision of German workmen.

## Medium to Thin Paper
### With Figures on Back, Except 1 l, 2 l

**1870**     **Without Mesh**

| | | | | |
|---|---|---|---|---|
| 32 | A1 | 1 l brn, *brnish* | 325.00 | 325.00 |
| a. | | 1 l purple brown, *brnish* | 325.00 | 325.00 |
| 33 | A1 | 2 l sal bis, *bister* | 19.00 | 45.00 |
| 34 | A1 | 5 l grn, *grnsh* | 6,000. | 120.00 |
| 35 | A1 | 10 l lt red org, *grnsh* | — | 240.00 |
| a. | | "01" on back | | |
| b. | | "10" on back inverted | | |
| 36 | A1 | 20 l bl, *bluish* | 1,400. | 24.00 |
| a. | | "02" on back | — | 600.00 |
| b. | | Double "20" on back | | 1,375. |
| 37 | A1 | 40 l sal, *grnsh* | 825.00 | 82.50 |
| a. | | 40 l lilac, *greenish* | | 75,000. |

The stamps of this issue have rather coarse figures on back.

No. 37a is printed in the exact shade of the numerals on the back of No. 37.

## Thin Transparent Paper
### With Figures on Back, Except 1 l

**1872**     **Showing Mesh**

| | | | | |
|---|---|---|---|---|
| 38 | A1 | 1 l grayish brn, *straw* | 55.00 | 75.00 |
| a. | | 1 l red brn, *yelsh* | 82.50 | 115.00 |
| 39 | A1 | 5 l grn, *greenish* | 675.00 | 30.00 |
| a. | | 5 l dark green, *grnsh* | 725.00 | 40.00 |
| b. | | Double "5" on back | | 225.00 |
| 40 | A1 | 10 l red org, *grnsh* | 1,050. | 37.50 |
| a. | | 10 l red orange, *pale lilac* | 7,750. | 150.00 |
| b. | | As #40, "10" on back inverted | — | 90.00 |
| c. | | Double "10" on back | — | 1,125. |
| d. | | "0" on back | — | 525.00 |
| e. | | "01" on back | — | 2,100. |
| 41 | A1 | 20 l dp bl, *bluish* | 1,375. | 30.00 |
| a. | | 20 l blue, *bluish* | 1,375. | 32.50 |
| b. | | 20 l dark blue, *blue* | 2,500. | 35.00 |
| 42 | A1 | 40 l brn, *bl* | 45.00 | 67.50 |
| a. | | 40 l olive brown, *blue* | 45.00 | 70.00 |
| b. | | 40 l red violet, *blue* | 1,000. | 95.00 |
| c. | | 40 l gray violet, *blue* | 825.00 | 75.00 |
| d. | | Figures on back bister (#42b, 42c) | 1,100. | 95.00 |

The mesh is not apparent on Nos. 38, 38a.

## On Cream Paper Unless Otherwise Stated
### With Figures on Back, Except 1 l, 2 l

**1875**

| | | | | |
|---|---|---|---|---|
| 43 | A1 | 1 l gray brn | 15.00 | 12.00 |
| a. | | 1 l Deep red brown | 35.00 | 20.00 |
| b. | | 1 l black brown, *yellowish* | 175.00 | 160.00 |
| c. | | 1 l red brown | 45.00 | 60.00 |
| d. | | 1 l dark red brown | 75.00 | 87.50 |
| e. | | 1 l purple brown | 75.00 | 87.50 |
| 44 | A1 | 2 l bister | 30.00 | 32.50 |
| 45 | A1 | 5 l pale yel grn | 200.00 | 30.00 |
| a. | | 5 l dk yel grn | 275.00 | 40.00 |
| 46 | A1 | 10 l orange | 425.00 | 45.00 |
| a. | | 10 l orange, *yellow* | 240.00 | 25.00 |
| b. | | "00" on back | 925.00 | 200.00 |
| d. | | "1" on back | — | 260.00 |
| e. | | "0" on back | — | 225.00 |
| f. | | "01" on back | — | 535.00 |
| g. | | Double "10" on back | — | 800.00 |
| 47 | A1 | 20 l ultra | 160.00 | 24.00 |
| a. | | 20 l blue | 290.00 | 24.00 |
| b. | | 20 l deep Prussian blue | 1,600. | 60.00 |
| c. | | "02" on back | — | 475.00 |
| d. | | "20" on back inverted | — | 11,000. |
| e. | | "2" instead of "20," inverted | — | 3,000. |
| f. | | Double "20" on back | — | 1,350. |
| g. | | "20" inverted, on front of stamp | | 210,000. |
| 48 | A1 | 40 l salmon | 30.00 | 90.00 |

The back figures are found in many varieties, including "1" and "0" inverted in "10."

Value for No. 47e is for example with "2" of "02" broken (deformed). Also known with unbroken "2"; value used about $600.

## Paris Print, Clear Impression

**1876**     **Without Figures on Back**

| | | | | |
|---|---|---|---|---|
| 49 | A1 | 30 l ol brn, *yelsh* | 290.00 | 60.00 |
| a. | | 30 l brown, *yellowish* | 500.00 | 135.00 |
| 50 | A1 | 60 l grn | 40.00 | 115.00 |

### Athens Print, Coarse Impression, Yellowish Paper

**1876**

| | | | | |
|---|---|---|---|---|
| 51 | A1 | 30 l dark brown | 75.00 | 13.50 |
| a. | | 30 l black brown | 75.00 | 13.50 |
| 52 | A1 | 60 l green | 625.00 | 67.50 |

## Without Figures on Back

**1880-82**     **Cream Paper**

| | | | | |
|---|---|---|---|---|
| 53 | A1 | 5 l green | 30.00 | 9.50 |
| 54 | A1 | 10 l orange | 27.50 | 9.50 |
| a. | | 10 l yellow | 27.50 | 9.50 |
| b. | | 10 l red orange | 8,250. | 75.00 |
| 55 | A1 | 20 l ultra | 450.00 | 190.00 |
| 56 | A1 | 20 l pale rose (aniline ink) ('82) | 8.25 | 8.25 |
| a. | | 20 l rose (aniline ink) ('82) | 8.25 | 8.25 |
| b. | | 20 l deep carmine | 275.00 | 17.50 |
| 57 | A1 | 30 l ultra ('82) | 225.00 | 17.50 |
| a. | | 30 l slate blue | 230.00 | 17.50 |
| 58 | A1 | 40 l lilac | 67.50 | 15.00 |
| a. | | 40 l violet | 67.50 | 24.00 |

Stamps of type A1 were not regularly issued with perf. 11½ but were freely used on mail.

Hermes — A2

Lepta denominations have white numeral tablets.

### Belgian Print, Clear Impression

**1886-88**     ***Imperf.***

| | | | | |
|---|---|---|---|---|
| 64 | A2 | 1 l brown ('88) | 4.00 | 4.00 |
| 65 | A2 | 2 l bister ('88) | 9.50 | 225.00 |
| 66 | A2 | 5 l yel grn ('88) | 12.00 | 2.75 |
| 67 | A2 | 10 l yellow ('88) | 16.00 | 2.40 |
| 68 | A2 | 20 l car rose ('88) | 45.00 | 4.00 |
| 69 | A2 | 25 l blue | 160.00 | 2.75 |
| 70 | A2 | 40 l violet ('88) | 105.00 | 30.00 |
| 71 | A2 | 50 l gray grn | 8.25 | 2.75 |
| 72 | A2 | 1d gray | 120.00 | 4.00 |
| | | *Nos. 64-72 (9)* | 479.75 | 277.65 |

See Nos. 81-116. For surcharges see Nos. 129, 134, 140, 144, 150, 151-152, 155-156.

**1891**     ***Perf. 11½***

| | | | | |
|---|---|---|---|---|
| 81 | A2 | 1 l brown | 8.25 | 3.50 |
| 82 | A2 | 2 l bister | 13.50 | — |
| 83 | A2 | 5 l yel grn | 27.50 | 13.00 |
| 84 | A2 | 10 l yellow | 40.00 | 13.00 |
| 85 | A2 | 20 l car rose | 55.00 | 18.00 |
| 86 | A2 | 25 l blue | 275.00 | 25.00 |
| 87 | A2 | 40 l violet | 190.00 | 190.00 |
| 88 | A2 | 50 l gray grn | 22.50 | 6.50 |
| 89 | A2 | 1d gray | 200.00 | 8.25 |
| | | *Nos. 81-89 (9)* | 831.75 | 277.25 |

The Belgian Printings perf. 13½ and most of the values perf. 11½ (Nos. 82-86) were perforated on request of philatelists at the main post office in Athens. While not regularly issued they were freely used for postage.

### Athens Print, Poor Impression
### Wmk. Greek Words in Some Sheets

**1889-95**     ***Imperf.***

| | | | | |
|---|---|---|---|---|
| 90 | A2 | 1 l black brn | 6.75 | 2.75 |
| a. | | 1 l brown | 6.75 | 4.00 |
| 91 | A2 | 2 l pale bister | 1.75 | 1.60 |
| a. | | 2 l buff | 2.75 | 2.75 |
| 92 | A2 | 5 l green | 11.00 | 1.60 |
| a. | | Double impression | 200.00 | — |
| b. | | 5 l deep green | 40.00 | 9.50 |
| 93 | A2 | 10 l yellow | 125.00 | 5.50 |
| a. | | 10 l orange | 47.50 | 4.00 |
| b. | | 10 l dull yellow | 125.00 | 5.50 |
| 94 | A2 | 20 l carmine | 11.00 | 8.25 |
| a. | | 20 l rose | 75.00 | 40.00 |
| 95 | A2 | 25 l dull blue | 125.00 | 9.50 |
| a. | | 25 l indigo | 150.00 | 6.75 |
| b. | | 25 l ultra | 125.00 | 6.75 |
| c. | | 25 l brt blue | 135.00 | 9.50 |
| 96 | A2 | 25 l lilac | 13.50 | 2.75 |
| a. | | 25 l red vio ('93) | 20.00 | 4.00 |
| 97 | A2 | 40 l red vio ('91) | 125.00 | 27.50 |
| 98 | A2 | 40 l blue ('93) | 9.50 | 2.75 |
| 99 | A2 | 1d gray ('95) | 475.00 | 8.25 |

***Perf. 13½***

| | | | | |
|---|---|---|---|---|
| 100 | A2 | 1 l brown | 80.00 | — |
| 101 | A2 | 2 l buff | 2.00 | 1.60 |
| 104 | A2 | 20 l carmine | 67.50 | 5.25 |
| a. | | 20 l rose | 80.00 | 6.25 |
| 105 | A2 | 40 l red violet | 130.00 | 47.50 |

Other denominations of type A2 were not officially issued with perf. 13½.

***Perf. 11½***

| | | | | |
|---|---|---|---|---|
| 107 | A2 | 1 l brown | 3.00 | 1.60 |
| a. | | 1 l black brown | 7.25 | 5.75 |
| 108 | A2 | 2 l pale bister | 2.50 | 2.00 |
| a. | | 2 l buff | 2.75 | 2.75 |
| 109 | A2 | 5 l pale green | 13.50 | 2.00 |
| a. | | 5 l deep green | 55.00 | 3.00 |
| 110 | A2 | 10 l yellow | 95.00 | 1.25 |
| a. | | 10 l dull yellow | 165.00 | 2.50 |
| b. | | 10 l orange | 300.00 | 5.75 |
| 111 | A2 | 20 l carmine | 55.00 | .75 |
| a. | | 20 l rose | 160.00 | 1.60 |
| 112 | A2 | 25 l dull blue | 110.00 | 3.75 |
| a. | | 25 l indigo | 300.00 | 21.00 |
| b. | | 25 l ultra | 110.00 | 52.50 |
| c. | | 25 l bright blue | 160.00 | 9.00 |
| 113 | A2 | 25 l lilac | 6.75 | 1.60 |
| a. | | 25 l red violet | 20.00 | 2.75 |

| | | | | |
|---|---|---|---|---|
| 114 | A2 | 40 l red violet | 160.00 | 37.50 |
| 115 | A2 | 40 l blue | 16.50 | 2.75 |
| 116 | A2 | 1d gray | 600.00 | — |

Partly-perforated varieties sell for about twice as much as normal stamps.

The watermark on Nos. 90-116 consists of three Greek words meaning Paper for Public Service. It is in double-lined capitals, measures 270x35mm, and extends across three panes.

Boxers
A3

Discobolus by Myron
A4

Vase Depicting Pallas Athene (Minerva)
A5

Chariot Driving
A6

Stadium and Acropolis
A7

Statue of Hermes by Praxiteles
A8

Statue of Victory by Paeonius
A9

Acropolis and Parthenon
A10

***Perf. 14x13½, 13½x14***

**1896**     **Unwmk.**

| | | | | |
|---|---|---|---|---|
| 117 | A3 | 1 l ocher | 4.00 | 3.00 |
| 118 | A3 | 2 l rose | 3.00 | 3.00 |
| a. | | Without engraver's name | 30.00 | 21.00 |
| 119 | A4 | 5 l lilac | 12.50 | 5.25 |
| 120 | A4 | 10 l slate gray | 12.50 | 7.25 |
| 121 | A5 | 20 l red brn | 25.00 | 8.25 |
| 122 | A6 | 25 l red | 30.00 | 10.50 |
| 123 | A5 | 40 l violet | 14.50 | 9.50 |
| 124 | A6 | 60 l black | 42.50 | 21.00 |
| 125 | A7 | 1d blue | 115.00 | 26.00 |
| 126 | A8 | 2d bister | 325.00 | 105.00 |
| a. | | Horiz. pair, imperf. btwn. | | |
| 127 | A9 | 5d green | 575.00 | 500.00 |
| 128 | A10 | 10d brown | 625.00 | 550.00 |
| | | *Nos. 117-128 (12)* | 1,784. | 1,249. |

1st intl. Olympic Games of the modern era, held at Athens. Counterfeits of Nos. 123-124 and 126-128 exist.

For surcharges see Nos. 159-164.

## Preceding Issues Surcharged

**1900**     ***Imperf.***

| | | | | |
|---|---|---|---|---|
| 129 | A2 | 20 l on 25 l dl bl, #95c | 3.00 | 1.60 |
| a. | | 20 l on 25 l indigo, #95a | 67.50 | 47.50 |
| b. | | 20 l on 25 l ultra, #95b | 70.00 | 55.00 |
| c. | | Double surcharge | 57.50 | 57.50 |
| d. | | Triple surcharge | 85.00 | 85.00 |
| e. | | Inverted surcharge | 60.00 | 57.50 |
| f. | | "20" above word | 110.00 | 105.00 |
| g. | | Pair, one without surcharge | 250.00 | |
| h. | | "20" without word | 165.00 | 165.00 |

| | | | | |
|---|---|---|---|---|
| 130 | A1 | 30 l on 40 l vio, cr, #58a | 6.50 | 6.25 |
| a. | | 30 l on 40 l lilac, #58 | 15.50 | 15.50 |
| b. | | Broad "0" in "30" | 10.50 | 8.25 |
| c. | | First letter of word is "A" | 135.00 | 135.00 |
| d. | | Double surcharge | 625.00 | 625.00 |
| 132 | A1 | 40 l on 2 l bis, cr, #44 | 8.50 | 8.25 |
| a. | | Broad "0" in "40" | 12.50 | 12.50 |
| b. | | First letter of word is "A" | 165.00 | 165.00 |
| 133 | A1 | 50 l on 40 l sal, cr, #48 | 6.25 | 6.25 |
| a. | | Broad "0" in "50" | 10.00 | 8.25 |
| b. | | First letter of word is "A" | 135.00 | 135.00 |
| c. | | "50" without word | 200.00 | 175.00 |
| d. | | "50" above word | 200.00 | 175.00 |
| 134 | A2 | 1d on 40 l red vio (No. 97) | 15.50 | 6.25 |
| 137 | A1 | 3d on 10 l org, cr, #54 | 52.50 | 52.50 |
| a. | | 3d on 10 l yellow, #54a | 52.50 | 52.50 |
| 138 | A1 | 5d on 40 l red vio, bl, #21 | 150.00 | 150.00 |
| a. | | 5d on 40 l red vio, bl, #28 | 190.00 | 190.00 |
| b. | | "20" on back corrected to "40" | | 1,400. |
| 139 | A1 | 5d on 40 l red vio, bl, #42b | 575.00 | |

***Perf. 11½***

| | | | | |
|---|---|---|---|---|
| 140 | A2 | 20 l on 25 l dl bl, #112 | 3.25 | 3.25 |
| a. | | 20 l on 25 l indigo, #112a | 100.00 | 90.00 |
| b. | | 20 l on 25 l ultra, #112b | 80.00 | 77.50 |
| c. | | Double surcharge | 67.50 | 70.00 |
| d. | | Triple surcharge | 95.00 | 95.00 |
| e. | | Inverted surcharge | 67.50 | 67.50 |
| f. | | "20" above word | 150.00 | 150.00 |
| 141 | A1 | 30 l on 40 l vio, cr, #58a | 10.50 | 10.50 |
| a. | | 30 l on 40 l lilac, #58 | 17.50 | 17.50 |
| b. | | Broad "0" in "30" | 12.50 | 12.50 |
| c. | | First letter of word is "A" | 150.00 | 150.00 |
| d. | | Double surcharge | | |
| 142 | A1 | 40 l on 2 l bis, cr, #44 | 15.50 | 15.50 |
| a. | | Broad "0" in "40" | 15.50 | 15.50 |
| b. | | First letter of word is "A" | 165.00 | 165.00 |
| 143 | A1 | 50 l on 40 l sal, cr, #48 | 10.50 | 10.50 |
| a. | | Broad "0" in "50" | 12.50 | 12.50 |
| b. | | First letter of word is "A" | 135.00 | 135.00 |
| c. | | "50" without word | 200.00 | 175.00 |
| 144 | A2 | 1d on 40 l red vio, #114 | 145.00 | 160.00 |
| 147 | A1 | 3d on 10 l yel, cream, #54a | 57.50 | 57.50 |
| a. | | 3d on 10 l org, cr, #54 | 60.00 | 65.00 |
| 148 | A1 | 5d on 40 l red vio, bl, #21 | 150.00 | 175.00 |
| a. | | 5d on 40 l red vio, bl, #28 | 175.00 | 225.00 |
| 149 | A1 | 5d on 40 l red vio, bl, #42b | 625.00 | |

***Perf. 13½***

| | | | | |
|---|---|---|---|---|
| 150 | A2 | 2d on 40 l red vio, #105 | 12.00 | 12.50 |

The 1d on 40 l perf. 13½ and the 2d on 40 l, both imperf. and perf. 13½, were not officially issued.

## Surcharge Including "A M"

"A M" = "Axia Metalliki" or "Value in Metal (gold)."

**1900**     ***Imperf.***

| | | | | |
|---|---|---|---|---|
| 151 | A2 | 25 l on 40 l vio, #70 | 6.00 | 10.50 |
| 152 | A2 | 50 l on 25 l bl, #69 | 26.50 | 24.00 |
| 153 | A1 | 1d on 40 l brn, bl, #42b | 125.00 | 150.00 |
| 154 | A1 | 2d on 5 l grn, cr, #53 | 16.00 | 21.00 |

***Perf. 11½***

| | | | | |
|---|---|---|---|---|
| 155 | A2 | 25 l on 40 l vio, #87 | 12.00 | 15.50 |
| 156 | A2 | 50 l on 25 l bl, #86 | 52.50 | 62.50 |
| 157 | A1 | 1d on 40 l brn, bl, #42b | 160.00 | 160.00 |
| 158 | A1 | 2d on 5 l grn, cr, #53 | 20.00 | 26.00 |
| | | *Nos. 151-158 (8)* | 418.00 | 469.50 |

Partly-perforated varieties of Nos. 129-158 sell for about two to three times as much as normal stamps.

Surcharge in Red

**1900-01**     ***Perf. 14x13½***

| | | | | |
|---|---|---|---|---|
| 159 | A7 | 5 l on 1d blue | 15.00 | 9.50 |
| a. | | Wrong font "M" with serifs | 75.00 | 80.00 |
| b. | | Double surcharge | 225.00 | 200.00 |
| 160 | A5 | 25 l on 40 l vio | 70.00 | 67.50 |
| a. | | Double surcharge | 900.00 | |
| 161 | A8 | 50 l on 2d bister | 80.00 | 62.50 |
| a. | | Broad "0" in "50" | 80.00 | 62.50 |
| 162 | A9 | 1d on 5d grn ('01) | 250.00 | 200.00 |
| a. | | Greek "Δ" instead of "A" as 3rd letter | 650.00 | 700.00 |
| 163 | A10 | 2d on 10d brn ('01) | 70.00 | 100.00 |
| a. | | Greek "Δ" instead of "A" as 3rd letter | 275.00 | 250.00 |
| | | *Nos. 159-163 (5)* | 485.00 | 439.50 |

Black Surcharge on No. 160

**164** A5 50 l on 25 l on 40 l
vio (R + Bk)    500.00   475.00
  *a.*   Broad "0" in "50"    475.00   575.00

Nos. 151-164 and 179-183, gold currency stamps, were generally used for parcel post and foreign money orders. They were also available for use on letters, but cost about 20 per cent more than the regular stamps of the same denomination.

Counterfeit surcharges exist of Nos. 159-164.

Giovanni da Bologna's Hermes
A11    A12

A13

Type I     Type II

FIVE LEPTA.
Type I — Letters of "ΕΛΛΑΣ" not outlined at top and left. Only a few faint horizontal lines between the outer vertical lines at sides.
Type II — Letters of "ΕΛΛΑΣ" fully outlined. Heavy horizontal lines between the vertical frame lines.

**Perf. 11½, 12½, 13½**

| 1901 | | Engr. | Wmk. 129 | |
|---|---|---|---|---|
| **165** | A11 | 1 l yellow brn | .40 | .25 |
| **166** | A11 | 2 l gray | .60 | .25 |
| **167** | A11 | 3 l orange | .65 | .30 |
| **168** | A12 | 5 l grn, type I | .80 | .25 |
| *a.* | | 5 l yellow green, type I | .60 | .25 |
| *b.* | | 5 l yellow green, type II | .60 | .25 |
| **169** | A12 | 10 l rose | 3.25 | .25 |
| **170** | A11 | 20 l red lilac | 6.50 | .25 |
| **171** | A12 | 25 l ultra | 6.50 | .25 |
| **172** | A11 | 30 l dl vio | 12.00 | 2.00 |
| **173** | A11 | 40 l dk brn | 25.00 | 3.00 |
| **174** | A11 | 50 l brn lake | 20.00 | 1.50 |

**Perf. 12½, 14 and Compound**

| **175** | A13 | 1d black | 47.50 | 3.00 |
|---|---|---|---|---|
| *a.* | | Horiz. pair, imperf. btwn. | 325.00 | |
| *c.* | | Horiz. pair, imperf. vert. | 300.00 | |
| *d.* | | Vert. pair, imperf. horiz. | 300.00 | |

**Litho.**
**Perf. 12½**

| **176** | A13 | 2d bronze | 11.00 | 8.00 |
|---|---|---|---|---|
| **177** | A13 | 3d silver | 11.00 | 12.00 |
| **178** | A13 | 5d gold | 13.00 | 15.00 |
| | | *Nos. 165-178 (14)* | 158.20 | 46.30 |
| | | Set, never hinged | 325.00 | |

All values 1 l through 1d issued on both thick and thin paper. Nos. 173-174 are values for thin paper — values for thick paper are higher.
For overprints and surcharges see Nos. RA3-RA13, N16, N109.

**Imperf., Pairs**

| 165a | A11 | 1 l | | 12.00 |
|---|---|---|---|---|
| 166a | A11 | 2 l | | 15.00 |
| 167a | A11 | 3 l | | 15.00 |
| 168c | A12 | 5 l | | 12.00 |
| 169a | A12 | 10 l | | 19.00 |
| 170a | A11 | 20 l | | 15.00 |
| 171a | A12 | 25 l | | 15.00 |
| 172a | A11 | 30 l | | 250.00 |

---

| 173a | A11 | 40 l | | 300.00 |
|---|---|---|---|---|
| 174a | A11 | 50 l | | 70.00 |
| 175b | A13 | 1d | | 250.00 |

Nos. 165a-175a were issued on both thick and thin paper. Values are for the less expensive thin paper.

Hermes — A14

| 1902, Jan. 1 | | Engr. | Perf. 13½ | |
|---|---|---|---|---|
| **179** | A14 | 5 l deep orange | 2.00 | 1.10 |
| *a.* | | Imperf., pair | 82.50 | |
| **180** | A14 | 25 l emerald | 30.00 | 3.00 |
| **181** | A14 | 50 l ultra | 30.00 | 3.75 |
| *a.* | | Imperf., pair | 550.00 | |
| **182** | A14 | 1d rose red | 30.00 | 8.25 |
| **183** | A14 | 2d orange brn | 52.50 | 50.00 |
| | | *Nos. 179-183 (5)* | 144.50 | 66.10 |
| | | Set, never hinged | 375.00 | |

See note after No. 164. In 1913 remainders of Nos. 179-183 were used as postage dues.

Apollo Throwing Discus A15    Jumper, with Jumping Weights A16

Victory A17    Atlas and Hercules A18

Struggle of Hercules and Antaeus A19    Wrestlers A20

Daemon of the Games A21    Foot Race A22

Nike, Priest and Athletes in Pre-Games Offering to Zeus — A23

**Wmk. Crown and ET (129)**

| 1906, Mar. | | Engr. | Perf. 13½, 14 | |
|---|---|---|---|---|
| **184** | A15 | 1 l brown | .55 | .40 |
| *a.* | | Imperf., pair | 300.00 | |
| **185** | A15 | 2 l gray | .55 | .40 |
| *a.* | | Imperf., pair | 300.00 | |
| **186** | A16 | 3 l orange | .55 | .40 |
| *a.* | | Imperf., pair | 300.00 | |
| **187** | A16 | 5 l green | 1.25 | .40 |
| *a.* | | Imperf., pair | 110.00 | |
| **188** | A17 | 10 l rose red | 3.00 | .60 |
| *a.* | | Imperf., pair | 300.00 | |
| **189** | A18 | 20 l magenta | 5.00 | .60 |
| *a.* | | Imperf., pair | 575.00 | |
| **190** | A19 | 25 l ultra | 6.00 | .85 |
| *a.* | | Imperf., pair | 575.00 | |
| **191** | A20 | 30 l dl pur | 5.00 | 2.75 |
| *a.* | | Double impression | 1,100. | |
| **192** | A21 | 40 l dk brown | 5.00 | 2.75 |
| **193** | A18 | 50 l brn lake | 10.00 | 3.25 |
| **194** | A22 | 1d gray blk | 65.00 | 13.00 |
| *a.* | | Imperf., pair | 1,100. | |

---

| **195** | A22 | 2d rose | 100.00 | 35.00 |
|---|---|---|---|---|
| **196** | A22 | 3d olive yel | 155.00 | 125.00 |
| **197** | A23 | 5d dull blue | 160.00 | 140.00 |
| | | *Nos. 184-197 (14)* | 516.90 | 325.40 |
| | | Set, never hinged | 1,500. | |

Greek Special Olympic Games of 1906 at Athens, celebrating the 10th anniv. of the modern Olympic Games.
Surcharged stamps of this issue are revenues.

A24

Iris Holding Caduceus A25    Hermes Donning Sandals A26

 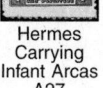

Hermes Carrying Infant Arcas A27    Hermes, from Old Cretan Coin A28

Designs A24 to A28 are from Cretan and Arcadian coins of the 4th Century, B.C.

**Serrate Roulette 13½**

| 1911-21 | | Engr. | Unwmk. | |
|---|---|---|---|---|
| **198** | A24 | 1 l green | .65 | .30 |
| **199** | A25 | 2 l car rose | .65 | .30 |
| **200** | A24 | 3 l vermilion | .95 | .30 |
| **201** | A26 | 5 l green | 2.00 | .30 |
| **202** | A24 | 10 l car rose | 9.50 | .30 |
| **203** | A25 | 20 l gray lilac | 3.00 | .80 |
| **204** | A25 | 25 l ultra | 15.00 | .80 |
| *a.* | | Rouletted in black | 190.00 | 140.00 |
| **205** | A26 | 30 l car rose | 4.50 | 1.60 |
| **206** | A25 | 40 l deep blue | 10.00 | 4.00 |
| **207** | A26 | 50 l dl vio | 15.00 | 3.00 |
| **208** | A27 | 1d ultra | 20.00 | .80 |
| **209** | A27 | 2d vermilion | 27.50 | .95 |
| **210** | A27 | 3d car rose | 27.50 | 1.40 |
| *a.* | | Size 20¼x25½mm ('21) | 100.00 | 50.00 |
| **211** | A27 | 5d ultra | 35.00 | 4.00 |
| *a.* | | Size 20¼x25½mm ('21) | 200.00 | 25.00 |
| **212** | A27 | 10d dp bl ('21) | 140.00 | 70.00 |
| *a.* | | Size 20x26½mm ('11) | 300.00 | 125.00 |
| **213** | A28 | 25d deep blue | 87.50 | 55.00 |
| | | *Nos. 198-213 (16)* | 398.75 | 143.85 |
| | | Set, never hinged | 750.00 | |

The 1921 reissues of the 3d, 5d and 10d measure 20¼x25½mm instead of 20x26½mm.
See Nos. 214-231. For overprints see Nos. 233-248B, N1, N10-N15, N17-N52A, N110-N148, Thrace 22-30, N26-N75.

---

**Imperf., Pairs**

| 198a | A24 | 1 l | | 90.00 | 90.00 |
|---|---|---|---|---|---|
| 200a | A24 | 3 l | | 240.00 | 240.00 |
| 201a | A26 | 5 l | | 30.00 | 30.00 |
| 202a | A24 | 10 l | | 52.50 | 52.50 |
| 203a | A25 | 20 l | | 225.00 | 225.00 |
| 204b | A25 | 25 l | | 300.00 | 300.00 |
| 206a | A25 | 40 l | | 350.00 | |
| 207a | A26 | 50 l | | 350.00 | |
| 208a | A27 | 1d | | 350.00 | |
| 209a | A27 | 2d | | 350.00 | |
| 210b | A27 | 3d | | 350.00 | |
| 211b | A27 | 5d | | 240.00 | |
| 212b | A27 | 10d As "a" | | 1,600. | |
| 213a | A28 | 25d | | 2,250. | |

**Serrate Roulette 10½x13½, 13½**

| 1913-23 | | | Litho. | |
|---|---|---|---|---|
| **214** | A24 | 1 l green | .25 | .25 |
| *a.* | | Without period after "ΕΛ–ΛΑΣ" | 77.50 | — |
| **215** | A25 | 2 l rose | .25 | .25 |
| **216** | A24 | 3 l vermilion | .25 | .25 |
| **217** | A26 | 5 l green | .25 | .25 |
| **218** | A24 | 10 l carmine | .25 | .25 |
| **219** | A25 | 15 l dl bl ('18) | .35 | .25 |
| **220** | A25 | 20 l slate | .35 | .25 |
| **221** | A25 | 25 l ultra | 4.00 | .50 |
| *a.* | | 25 l blue | .25 | .25 |
| *c.* | | Double impression | — | |
| **222** | A26 | 30 l rose ('14) | .95 | .40 |
| **223** | A25 | 40 l indigo ('14) | 2.10 | .70 |
| **224** | A26 | 50 l vio brn ('14) | 4.25 | .35 |
| **225** | A26 | 80 l vio brn ('23) | 5.25 | 1.40 |
| **226** | A27 | 1d ultra ('19) | 7.00 | .70 |
| **227** | A27 | 2d ver ('19) | 6.50 | .70 |
| **228** | A27 | 3d car rose ('20) | 8.50 | .80 |
| **229** | A27 | 5d ultra ('22) | 12.00 | 1.00 |
| **230** | A27 | 10d dp bl ('22) | 12.00 | 1.25 |
| **231** | A28 | 25d indigo ('22) | 16.00 | 4.75 |
| | | *Nos. 214-231 (18)* | 80.50 | 14.30 |
| | | Set, never hinged | 225.00 | |

Nos. 221, 223 and 226 were re-issued in 1926, printed in Vienna from new plates. There are slight differences in minor details.
The 10 lepta brown, on thick paper, type A28, is not a postage stamp. It was issued in 1922 to replace coins of this denomination during a shortage of copper.

**Imperf., Pairs**

| 214b | A24 | 1 l | | 65.00 | |
|---|---|---|---|---|---|
| 215a | A25 | 2 l | | 110.00 | |
| 216a | A24 | 3 l | | 175.00 | |
| 217a | A26 | 5 l | | 65.00 | |
| 218a | A24 | 10 l | | 82.50 | |
| 220a | A25 | 20 l | | 82.50 | |
| 221b | A25 | 25 l | | 175.00 | |
| 222a | A26 | 30 l | | 175.00 | |
| 223a | A25 | 40 l | | 175.00 | |
| 224a | A26 | 50 l | | 300.00 | |
| 225b | A26 | 80 l | | 92.50 | |
| 226a | A27 | 1d | | | 250.00 |
| 227a | A27 | 2d | | 100.00 | |
| 228b | A27 | 3d | | 300.00 | |
| 229a | A27 | 5d | | 360.00 | |

Search

PHILASEARCH
www.Philasearch.com

Raising Greek
Flag at Suda
Bay,
Crete — A29

**1913, Dec. 1**    **Engr.**    **Perf. 14½**
| | | | | |
|---|---|---|---|---|
| 232 | A29 | 25 l blue & black | 8.00 | 5.00 |
| a. | | Never hinged | 16.00 | |
| b. | | Imperf., pair | 1,400. | |

Union of Crete with Greece. Used only in Crete.

Stamps of 1911-14
Overprinted in Red or
Black

### Serrate Roulette 13½
**1916, Nov. 1**      **Litho.**
| | | | | |
|---|---|---|---|---|
| 233 | A24 | 1 l green (R) | .25 | .25 |
| 234 | A24 | 2 l rose | .25 | .25 |
| 235 | A24 | 3 l vermilion | .25 | .25 |
| 236 | A26 | 5 l green (R) | .50 | .40 |
| 237 | A24 | 10 l carmine | .75 | .40 |
| 238 | A25 | 20 l slate (R) | 1.50 | .40 |
| 239 | A25 | 25 l blue (R) | 1.50 | .40 |
| a. | | 25 l ultra | 140.00 | 26.00 |
| 240 | A26 | 30 l rose | 1.50 | .90 |
| a. | | Pair, one without ovpt. | | |
| 241 | A25 | 40 l indigo | 11.00 | 3.00 |
| 242 | A26 | 50 l vio brn (R) | 37.50 | 2.50 |

**Engr.**
| | | | | |
|---|---|---|---|---|
| 243 | A24 | 3 l vermilion | .50 | .50 |
| 244 | A26 | 30 l car rose | 1.25 | 1.25 |
| 245 | A27 | 1d ultra (R) | 40.00 | .80 |
| a. | | Rouletted in black | 325.00 | 225.00 |
| 246 | A27 | 2d vermilion | 24.00 | 3.50 |
| 247 | A27 | 3d car rose | 14.00 | 3.50 |
| 248 | A27 | 5d ultra (R) | 95.00 | 15.00 |
| 248B | A27 | 10d dp bl (R) | 24.00 | 22.50 |
| | | Nos. 233-248B (17) | 253.75 | 55.80 |
| | | Set, never hinged | 500.00 | |

Most of Nos. 233-248B exist with overprint double, inverted, etc. Minimum value of errors $18. Excellent counterfeits of the overprint varieties exist.

### Issued by the Venizelist Provisional Government

Iris — A32

**1917, Feb. 5**    **Litho.**    **Perf. 14**
| | | | | |
|---|---|---|---|---|
| 249 | A32 | 1 l dp green | .40 | .25 |
| 250 | A32 | 5 l yel grn | .40 | .25 |
| 251 | A32 | 10 l rose | .80 | .35 |
| 252 | A32 | 25 l lt blue | 1.10 | .35 |
| 253 | A32 | 50 l gray vio | 9.00 | 2.50 |
| 254 | A32 | 1d ultra | 2.25 | .75 |
| 255 | A32 | 2d lt red | 4.50 | 1.50 |
| 256 | A32 | 3d claret | 25.00 | 7.75 |
| 257 | A32 | 5d gray bl | 5.75 | 3.00 |
| 258 | A32 | 10d dk blue | 70.00 | 20.00 |
| 259 | A32 | 25d slate | 125.00 | 160.00 |
| | | Nos. 249-259 (11) | 244.20 | 196.70 |
| | | Set, never hinged | 400.00 | |

The 4d was used only as a revenue stamp.

**Imperf., Pairs**
| | | | |
|---|---|---|---|
| 249a | A32 | 1 l | 9.50 |
| 250a | A32 | 5 l | 9.50 |
| 251a | A32 | 10 l | 9.50 |
| 252a | A32 | 25 l | 17.50 |
| 253a | A32 | 50 l | 25.00 |
| 254a | A32 | 1d | 30.00 |
| 255a | A32 | 2d | 30.00 |
| 256a | A32 | 3d | 65.00 |
| 257a | A32 | 5d | 65.00 |
| 258a | A32 | 10d | 110.00 |
| 259a | A32 | 25d | 125.00 |

Stamps of 1917
Surcharged

**1923**
| | | | | |
|---|---|---|---|---|
| 260 | A32 | 5 l on 10 l rose | .25 | .25 |
| a. | | Inverted surcharge | 24.00 | 35.00 |
| 261 | A32 | 50 l on 50 l gray vio | .25 | .25 |
| 262 | A32 | 1d on 1d ultra | .25 | .25 |
| a. | | 1d on 1d gray | .25 | .25 |
| 263 | A32 | 2d on 2d lt red | .55 | .55 |
| 264 | A32 | 3d on 3d claret | 1.60 | 1.60 |

---

| | | | | |
|---|---|---|---|---|
| 265 | A32 | 5d on 5d dk bl | 2.00 | 2.00 |
| 266 | A32 | 25d on 25d slate | 27.50 | 27.50 |
| | | Nos. 260-266 (7) | 32.40 | 32.40 |
| | | Set, never hinged | 125.00 | |

### Same Surcharge on Occupation of Turkey Stamps, 1913
#### Perf. 13½
| | | | | |
|---|---|---|---|---|
| 267 | O2 | 5 l on 3 l org | .25 | .25 |
| a. | | Inverted surcharge | 19.00 | |
| 268 | O1 | 10 l on 20 l vio | 1.50 | 1.50 |
| a. | | Inverted surcharge | 82.50 | |
| 269 | O2 | 10 l on 25 l pale bl | .25 | .25 |
| a. | | Inverted surcharge | 60.00 | 35.00 |
| 270 | O1 | 10 l on 30 l gray grn | .25 | .25 |
| 271 | O2 | 10 l on 40 l ind | 1.25 | 1.25 |
| 272 | O1 | 50 l on 50 l dk bl | .25 | .25 |
| a. | | Inverted surcharge | 72.50 | 37.50 |
| 273 | O1 | 2d on 2d gray brn | 60.00 | 60.00 |
| 274 | O2 | 3d on 3d dl bl | 4.50 | 6.00 |
| a. | | Imperf., pair | 500.00 | |
| 275 | O1 | 5d on 5d gray | 4.00 | 7.00 |
| 276 | O2 | 10d on 1d vio brn | 15.00 | 22.50 |
| 276A | O2 | 10d on 10d car | 800.00 | |
| | | Nos. 267-276 (10) | 87.25 | 99.25 |
| | | Set, never hinged | 150.00 | |

Dangerous counterfeits of No. 276A exist.

### Same Surcharge on Stamps of Crete
#### On Crete Nos. 50, 52, 59
#### Perf. 14
| | | | | |
|---|---|---|---|---|
| 276B | A6 | 5 l on 1 l dk brn | 27.50 | 27.50 |
| 277 | A8 | 10 l on 10 l red | .25 | .25 |
| 277B | A8 | 10 l on 25 l bl | 110.00 | 110.00 |

#### On Crete Nos. 66-69, 71
| | | | | |
|---|---|---|---|---|
| 278 | A8 | 10 l on 25 l blue | .25 | .25 |
| 279 | A6 | 50 l on 50 l lilac | .45 | .70 |
| 279A | A6 | 50 l on 50 l ultra | 8.50 | 14.00 |
| 280 | A9 | 50 l on 1d gray vio | 3.00 | 4.00 |
| 280A | A11 | 50 l on 5d grn & blk | 27.50 | 27.50 |

#### On Crete Nos. 77-82
| | | | | |
|---|---|---|---|---|
| 281 | A15 | 10 l on 20 l bl grn | 125.00 | 125.00 |
| 282 | A16 | 10 l on 25 l ultra | .45 | .45 |
| a. | | Double surcharge | 50.00 | 50.00 |
| 283 | A17 | 50 l on 50 l yel brn | .25 | .35 |
| 284 | A18 | 50 l on 1d rose car & brn | 2.00 | 1.75 |
| a. | | Imperf., pair | 425.00 | |
| 285 | A19 | 3d on 3d org & blk | 14.00 | 14.00 |
| 286 | A20 | 5d on 5d ol grn & blk | 9.00 | 9.00 |

#### On Crete Nos. 83-84
| | | | | |
|---|---|---|---|---|
| 287 | A21 | 10 l on 25 l bl & blk | 3.25 | 1.75 |
| a. | | Imperf., pair | | |
| 287B | A22 | 50 l on 1d grn & blk | 8.00 | 4.50 |

Surcharged on Crete No. 96

| | | | | |
|---|---|---|---|---|
| 288 | A23 | 10 l on 10 l brn red | .25 | .25 |
| a. | | Inverted surcharge | 45.00 | 40.00 |

#### On Crete No. 91
| | | | | |
|---|---|---|---|---|
| 288B | A17 | 50 l on 50 l yel brn | 800.00 | |

Dangerous counterfeits of the overprint on No. 288B are plentiful.

#### On Crete No. 109
| | | | | |
|---|---|---|---|---|
| 289 | A19 | 3d on 3d org & blk | 17.50 | 17.50 |

#### On Crete Nos. 111, 113-120
| | | | | |
|---|---|---|---|---|
| 290 | A6 | 5 l on 1 l vio brn | .25 | .25 |
| a. | | Inverted surcharge | 25.00 | |
| 291 | A13 | 5 l on 5 l grn | .25 | .25 |
| a. | | Inverted surcharge | 47.50 | |
| 292 | A23 | 10 l on 10 l brn red | .25 | .25 |
| a. | | Inverted surcharge | 47.50 | |
| 293 | A15 | 10 l on 20 l bl grn | .30 | .30 |
| a. | | Inverted surcharge | 47.50 | |
| 294 | A16 | 10 l on 25 l ultra | .35 | .35 |
| a. | | Inverted surcharge | 47.50 | |
| 295 | A17 | 50 l on 50 l yel brn | .40 | .40 |
| 296 | A18 | 50 l on 1d rose car & brn | 5.25 | 5.25 |
| a. | | Inverted surcharge | | |
| b. | | Double surcharge | 225.00 | |
| c. | | Double surch., one invtd. | | |
| d. | | Imperf., pair | | |
| 297 | A19 | 3d on 3d org & blk | 16.00 | 16.00 |
| 298 | A20 | 5d on 5d ol grn & blk | 200.00 | 200.00 |

Dangerous counterfeits of No. 298 exist.

---

### Crete Nos. J2-J9
| | | | | |
|---|---|---|---|---|
| 299 | D1 | 5 l on 5 l red | .25 | .25 |
| a. | | Inverted surcharge | 45.00 | 6.75 |
| 300 | D1 | 10 l on 10 l red | .30 | .30 |
| 301 | D1 | 10 l on 20 l red | 12.00 | 12.00 |
| a. | | Inverted surcharge | | |
| 302 | D1 | 10 l on 40 l red | .30 | .30 |
| 303 | D1 | 50 l on 10 l red | .30 | .55 |
| 304 | D1 | 50 l on 1d red | .30 | .50 |
| a. | | Double surcharge | | |
| 305 | D1 | 50 l on 1d on 1d red | 9.50 | 9.50 |
| 306 | D1 | 2d on 2d red | 1.25 | 1.25 |

### On Crete Nos. J11-J13
| | | | | |
|---|---|---|---|---|
| 307 | D1 | 5 l on 5 l red | 6.00 | 6.00 |
| 308 | D1 | 5 l on 10 l red | 1.50 | 1.50 |
| a. | | "ΕΛΛΑΣ" inverted | 6.50 | |
| 309 | D1 | 50 l on 50 l red | 55.00 | 55.00 |

### On Crete Nos. J20-J22, J24-J26
| | | | | |
|---|---|---|---|---|
| 310 | D1 | 5 l on 5 l red | .25 | .25 |
| 311 | D1 | 5 l on 10 l red | .25 | .25 |
| a. | | Inverted surcharge | 12.00 | |
| 312 | D1 | 10 l on 20 l red | .25 | .25 |
| 313 | D1 | 50 l on 50 l red | .55 | .55 |
| 314 | D1 | 50 l on 1d red | 4.00 | 4.00 |
| 315 | D1 | 2d on 2d red | 7.00 | 7.00 |

These surcharged Postage Due stamps were intended for the payment of ordinary postage.

Nos. 260 to 315 were surcharged in commemoration of the revolution of 1922.

Nos. 59, 91, 109, 111, 113-120, J11-J13, J20-J22, J24-J26 are on stamps previously overprinted by Crete.

### Issues of the Republic

Lord Byron
A33

Byron at Missolonghi
A34

**1924, Apr. 16**   **Engr.**   **Perf. 12**
| | | | | |
|---|---|---|---|---|
| 316 | A33 | 80 l dark blue | .55 | .25 |
| 317 | A34 | 2d dk vio & blk | 1.25 | .65 |
| | | Set, never hinged | 3.25 | |

Death of Lord Byron (1788-1824) at Missolonghi.

Tomb of Markos
Botsaris — A35

### Serrate Roulette 13½
**1926, Apr. 24**      **Litho.**
| | | | | |
|---|---|---|---|---|
| 318 | A35 | 25 l lilac | .85 | .50 |
| | | Never hinged | 1.75 | |

Centenary of the defense of Missolonghi against the Turks.

Corinth
Canal
A36

Dodecanese
Costume
A37

Macedonian
Costume
A38

Monastery
of Simon
Peter on
Mt. Athos
A39

White
Tower of
Salonika
A40

Temple of
Hephaestus
A41

---

The
Acropolis
A42

Cruiser
"Georgios
Averoff"
A43

Academy of
Sciences,
Athens
A44

Temple of
Hephaestus
A45

Acropolis — A46

### Perf. 12½x13, 13, 13x12½, 13½, 13½x13
**1927, Apr. 1**      **Engr.**
| | | | | |
|---|---|---|---|---|
| 321 | A36 | 5 l dark green | .25 | .25 |
| a. | | Vert. pair, imperf. horiz. | 140.00 | 92.50 |
| 322 | A37 | 10 l orange red | .30 | .25 |
| a. | | Horiz. pair, imperf. between | 140.00 | 92.50 |
| c. | | Double impression | 77.50 | |
| 323 | A38 | 20 l violet | .30 | .25 |
| 324 | A39 | 25 l slate blue | .50 | .25 |
| a. | | Imperf., pair | 140.00 | 140.00 |
| b. | | Vert. pair, imperf. between | 150.00 | 110.00 |
| 325 | A40 | 40 l slate blue | .50 | .25 |
| 326 | A36 | 50 l violet | 1.10 | .25 |
| 327 | A36 | 80 l dk bl & blk | .95 | .25 |
| a. | | Imperf., pair | 825.00 | |
| 328 | A41 | 1d dk bl & bis brn (I) | 1.10 | .25 |
| a. | | Imperf., pair | 150.00 | 125.00 |
| b. | | Center inverted | | 6,500. |
| c. | | Double impression of center | 325.00 | 225.00 |
| d. | | Double impression of frame | 325.00 | 225.00 |
| 329 | A42 | 2d dk grn & blk | 6.50 | .30 |
| a. | | Imperf., pair | 600.00 | 800.00 |
| 330 | A43 | 3d dp vio & blk | 6.00 | .30 |
| a. | | Double impression of center | 225.00 | 275.00 |
| b. | | Center inverted | | 8,000. |
| 331 | A44 | 5d yel & blk | 15.00 | 2.00 |
| a. | | Imperf., pair | 925.00 | 925.00 |
| b. | | Center inverted | 10,000. | 4,500. |
| c. | | 5d yellow & green | 110.00 | 37.50 |
| 332 | A45 | 10d brn car & blk | 45.00 | 11.00 |
| 333 | A44 | 15d brt yel grn & blk | 57.50 | 16.00 |
| 334 | A46 | 25d green & blk | 110.00 | 18.00 |
| a. | | Double impression of center | | |
| | | Nos. 321-334 (14) | 245.00 | 49.60 |
| | | Set, never hinged | 700.00 | |

See Nos. 364-371 and notes preceding No. 364. For overprints see Nos. RA55, RA57, RA60, RA66, RA70-RA71.

This series as prepared, included a 1 lepton dark brown, type A37, but that value was never issued. Most stamps were burned. Value $300.

Gen. Charles N.
Fabvier and
Acropolis — A47

**1927, Aug. 1**      **Perf. 12**
| | | | | |
|---|---|---|---|---|
| 335 | A47 | 1d red | .30 | .25 |
| 336 | A47 | 3d dark blue | 2.00 | .60 |
| 337 | A47 | 6d green | 12.00 | 9.00 |
| | | Nos. 335-337 (3) | 14.30 | 9.85 |
| | | Set, never hinged | 42.50 | |

Cent. of the liberation of Athens from the Turks in 1826.
For surcharges see Nos. 376-377.

Bay of Navarino
and Pylos — A48

Battle of Navarino
A49

"Edward"
omitted
A50

"Edward"
added
A51

Admiral de
Rigny
A52

Admiral van der
Heyden — A53

Designs: Nos. 340-341, Sir Edward Codrington.

**Perf. 13½x12½, 12½x13½, 13x12½, 12½x13**

**1927-28**     Litho.

| | | | | |
|---|---|---|---|---|
| 338 | A48 | 1.50d gray green | 1.60 | .35 |
| a. | | Imperf., pair | 275.00 | |
| b. | | Horiz. pair, imperf. btwn. | 875.00 | |
| c. | | Horiz. pair, imperf. vert. | 250.00 | |
| 339 | A49 | 4d dk gray bl ('28) | 7.00 | 1.50 |
| 340 | A50 | 5d dk brn & gray | 5.50 | 4.75 |
| a. | | 5d blk brn & blk ('28) | 13.00 | 6.50 |
| 341 | A51 | 5d dk brn & blk ('28) | 35.00 | 12.00 |
| 342 | A52 | 5d vio bl & blk ('28) | 35.00 | 12.00 |
| 343 | A53 | 5d lake & blk ('28) | 20.00 | 9.50 |
| | | Nos. 338-343 (6) | 104.10 | 40.10 |
| | | Set, never hinged | 275.00 | |

Centenary of the naval battle of Navarino.
For surcharges see Nos. 372-375.

Admiral
Lascarina
Bouboulina
A54

Athanasios
Diakos
A55

Map of
Greece in
1830 and
1930
A56

Sortie from
Missolonghi
A58

Patriots
Declaring
Independence
A57

Portraits: 10 l, Constantine Rhigas Ferreos. 20 l, Gregorios V. 40 l, Prince Alexandros Ypsilantis. No. 345, Bouboulina. No. 355, Diakos. No. 346, Theodoros Kolokotronis. No. 356, Konstantinos Kanaris. No.347, Georgios Karaiskakis. No. 357, Markos Botsaris. 2d, Andreas Miaoulis. 3d, Lazaros Koundouriotis. 5d, Count John Capo d'Istria (Capodistria), statesman and doctor. 10d, Petros Mavromichalis. 15d, Dionysios Solomos. 20d, Adamantios Korais.

**Various Frames**

**1930, Apr. 1**   Engr.   **Perf. 13½, 14**
**Imprint of Perkins, Bacon & Co.**

| | | | | |
|---|---|---|---|---|
| 344 | A55 | 10 l brown | .25 | .25 |
| 345 | A54 | 50 l red | .25 | .25 |
| 346 | A54 | 1d car rose | .30 | .30 |
| 347 | A55 | 1.50d lt blue | .40 | .40 |
| 348 | A55 | 2d orange | .45 | .45 |
| 349 | A55 | 5d purple | 1.50 | 1.50 |
| 350 | A54 | 10d gray blk | 6.50 | 6.50 |
| 351 | A54 | 15d yellow grn | 12.00 | 12.00 |
| 352 | A55 | 20d blue blk | 17.50 | 17.50 |

**Imprint of Bradbury, Wilkinson & Co.**
**Perf. 12**

| | | | | |
|---|---|---|---|---|
| 353 | A55 | 20 l black | .25 | .25 |
| 354 | A55 | 40 l blue grn | .25 | .25 |
| 355 | A55 | 50 l brt blue | .25 | .25 |
| 356 | A55 | 1d brown org | .30 | .30 |
| 357 | A55 | 1.50d dk red | .40 | .40 |
| 358 | A55 | 3d dk brown | .65 | .65 |
| 359 | A54 | 4d dk blue | 3.00 | 3.00 |
| 360 | A57 | 25d black | 17.50 | 17.50 |
| 361 | A58 | 50d red brn | 45.00 | 45.00 |
| | | Nos. 344-361 (18) | 106.75 | 106.75 |
| | | Set, never hinged | 275.00 | |

Greek independence, cent. Some exist imperf.

Arcadi Monastery and Abbot Gabriel (Mt. Ida in Background)
A60

**1930, Nov. 8**     **Perf. 12**

| | | | | |
|---|---|---|---|---|
| 363 | A60 | 8d deep violet | 13.00 | 1.10 |
| | | Never hinged | 55.00 | |

**Issue of 1927 Re-engraved**

Type I

Type II

1d. Type I — Greek letters "Λ," "A," "Δ" have sharp pointed tops; numerals "1" are 1½mm wide at the foot, and have a straight slanting serif at top.
1d. Type II — Greek letters "Λ," "A," "Δ" have flat tops; numerals "1" are 2mm wide at foot and the serif at top is slightly curved. Perf. 14. There are many minor differences in the lines of the two designs.
1d. Type III — The "1" in lower left corner has no serif at left of foot. Lines of temple have been deepened, so details stand out more clearly.
2d. On 1927 stamp the Parthenon is indistinct and blurred. On 1933 stamp it is strongly outlined and clear. Between the two pillars at lower right are four blocks of marble. These blocks are clear and distinct on the 1933 stamp but run together on the 1927 issue.
3d. Design is clearer, especially vertical lines of shading in smoke stacks and reflections in the water. Two or more sides perf. 11½.
10d. Background and shading of entire stamp have been lightened. Detail of frame is clearer and more distinct.
15d. Many more lines of shading in sky and foreground. Engraving is sharp and clear, particularly in frame. Two or more sides perf. 11½.
25d. Background has been lightened and foreground reduced until base of larger upright column is removed and fallen column appears nearly submerged.
50 l, Design is clearer, especially "50" and the 10 letters.
Sizes in millimeters:
50 l, 1927, 18x24¾. 1933, 18½x24½.
1d, 1927, 24¾x17¾. 1931, 24¾x17¼. 1933, 24½x18¼.
2d, 1927, 24½x17¾. 1933, 24½x18½.

**Perf. 11½, 11½x12½, 12½x10, 13, 13x12½, 14**

**1931-35**

| | | | | |
|---|---|---|---|---|
| 364 | A36 | 50 l dk vio ('33) | 4.00 | 1.00 |
| 365 | A41 | 1d dk bl & org brn, type II | 10.00 | 1.00 |
| 366 | A41 | 1d dk bl & org brn, type III ('33) | 5.75 | .25 |
| 367 | A42 | 2d dk grn & blk ('33) | 2.75 | .50 |
| 368 | A43 | 3d red vio & blk ('34) | 3.25 | .25 |
| a. | | Imperf., pair | | |
| 369 | A45 | 10d brn car & blk ('35) | 47.50 | 1.50 |
| 370 | A44 | 15d pale yel grn & blk ('34) | 82.50 | 17.50 |
| a. | | Imperf., pair | 1,100. | |

| | | | | |
|---|---|---|---|---|
| 371 | A46 | 25d dk grn & blk ('35) | 25.00 | 17.00 |
| | | Nos. 364-371 (8) | 180.75 | 39.00 |
| | | Set, never hinged | 600.00 | |

Nos. 336-337, 340-343 Surcharged in Red

**1932**   **Perf. 12½x13½, 12½x13**

| | | | | |
|---|---|---|---|---|
| 372 | A52 | 1.50d on 5d | 2.00 | .25 |
| 373 | A53 | 1.50d on 5d | 2.00 | .25 |
| a. | | Double surcharge | 110.00 | |
| 374 | A50 | 2d on 5d | 5.00 | .25 |
| 375 | A51 | 2d on 5d | 9.00 | .25 |

**Perf. 12**

| | | | | |
|---|---|---|---|---|
| 376 | A47 | 2d on 3d | 2.25 | .25 |
| a. | | Double surcharge | 125.00 | |
| 377 | A47 | 4d on 6d | 2.50 | 1.10 |
| | | Nos. 372-377 (6) | 22.75 | 2.35 |
| | | Set, never hinged | 50.00 | |

Adm. Pavlos Koundouriotis and Cruiser "Averoff" — A61

Pallas Athene
A62

Youth of Marathon
A63

**1933**   **Perf. 13½x13, 13x13½**

| | | | | |
|---|---|---|---|---|
| 378 | A61 | 50d black & ind | 50.00 | 1.60 |
| a. | | Imperf., pair | 2,250. | |
| 379 | A62 | 75d blk & vio brn | 110.00 | 175.00 |
| a. | | Imperf., pair | 825.00 | |
| | | Never hinged | 1,700. | |
| 380 | A63 | 100d brn & dull grn | 625.00 | 29.00 |
| a. | | Imperf., pair | 2,750. | |
| | | Nos. 378-380 (3) | 785.00 | 205.60 |
| | | Set, never hinged | 1,800. | |

The imperf pairs are without gum.
For surcharges see Nos. 386-387.

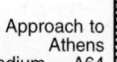
Approach to Athens Stadium — A64

**Perf. 11½, 11½x10, 13x11½**

**1934, Dec. 10**

| | | | | |
|---|---|---|---|---|
| 381 | A64 | 8d blue | 65.00 | 2.25 |
| | | Never hinged | 200.00 | |

Perforations on No. 381 range from 10½ to 13, including compounds.

Church of Pantanassa, Mistra — A65

**1935, Nov. 1**     **Perf. 13x12½**

| | | | | |
|---|---|---|---|---|
| 382 | A65 | 4d brown | 17.00 | 1.60 |
| | | Never hinged | 47.50 | |
| a. | | Horiz. pair, imperf. between | 725.00 | |
| b. | | Imperf., pair | 725.00 | |

**Issues of the Monarchy**
J71, J76, J82, 380, 379 Surcharged in Red or Blue

Nos. 383-385

Nos. 386-387

**Serrate Roulette 13½**

**1935, Nov. 24**     Litho.

| | | | | |
|---|---|---|---|---|
| 383 | D3 | 50 l on 40 l indigo (R) | .25 | .25 |
| a. | | Double surcharge | 27.50 | |

| | | | | |
|---|---|---|---|---|
| 384 | D3 | 3d on 3d car (Bl) | .55 | .40 |

**Perf. 13**

| | | | | |
|---|---|---|---|---|
| 385 | D3 | 3d on 3d rose red (Bl) | 2.75 | 2.00 |

**Perf. 13x13½**

| | | | | |
|---|---|---|---|---|
| 386 | A63 | 5d on 100d (R) | 2.25 | 2.00 |
| 387 | A62 | 15d on 75d (Bl) | 6.50 | 6.00 |
| | | Nos. 383-387 (5) | 12.30 | 10.65 |
| | | Set, never hinged | 30.00 | |

King Constantine — A66

**Center Engr., Frame Litho.**
**Perf. 12x13½**

**1936, Nov. 18**     **Wmk. 252**

| | | | | |
|---|---|---|---|---|
| 389 | A66 | 3d black & brown | .55 | .40 |
| a. | | Pair, printer's name in Greek | 22.50 | |
| b. | | Pair, printer's name in English | 22.50 | |
| 390 | A66 | 8d black & blue | 1.10 | .90 |
| a. | | Pair, printer's name in Greek | 22.50 | |
| b. | | Pair, printer's name in English | 22.50 | |
| | | Set, never hinged | 3.25 | |

Re-burial of the remains of King Constantine and Queen Sophia.
Two printings exist, the first containing varieties "a" and "b" with gray border; second with black border.

King George II — A67

**1937, Jan. 24**   Engr.   **Perf. 12½x12**

| | | | | |
|---|---|---|---|---|
| 391 | A67 | 1d green | .25 | .25 |
| 392 | A67 | 3d red brown | .25 | .25 |
| 393 | A67 | 8d dp blue | .90 | .40 |
| 394 | A67 | 100d carmine lake | 12.00 | 12.00 |
| | | Nos. 391-394 (4) | 13.40 | 12.90 |
| | | Set, never hinged | 30.00 | |

For surcharges see Nos. 484-487, 498-500, RA86-RA87, N241-N242.

Pallas Athene — A68

**1937, Apr. 17**   Unwmk.   **Perf. 11½**

| | | | | |
|---|---|---|---|---|
| 395 | A68 | 3d yellow brown | .55 | .25 |
| | | Never hinged | 1.10 | |

Centenary of the University of Athens.

Contest with Bull
A69

Lady of Tiryns
A70

Zeus of Dodona
A71

Coin of Amphictyonic League
A72

Diagoras of Rhodes, Victor at Olympics A73

Venus of Melos A74

Battle of Salamis — A75

Chariot of Panathenaic Festival — A76

Alexander the Great at Battle of Issos — A77

St. Paul Preaching to Athenians — A78

St. Demetrius' Church at Salonika — A79

Leo III Victory over Arabs — A80

Allegorical Figure of Glory — A81

**Perf. 13½x12, 12x13½**

| | | | | |
|---|---|---|---|---|
| **1937, Nov. 1** | | **Litho.** | **Wmk. 252** | |
| 396 | A69 | 5 l brn red & bl | .25 | .25 |
| a. | | Double impression of frame | 60.00 | |
| 397 | A70 | 10 l bl & brn red | .25 | .25 |
| a. | | Double impression of frame | 60.00 | |
| 398 | A71 | 20 l black & grn | .25 | .25 |
| 399 | A72 | 40 l green & blk | .25 | .25 |
| a. | | Green impression doubled | 60.00 | |
| 400 | A73 | 50 l brown & blk | .25 | .25 |
| 401 | A74 | 80 l ind & yel brn | .25 | .25 |

**Engr.**

| | | | | |
|---|---|---|---|---|
| 402 | A75 | 2d ultra | .25 | .25 |
| 403 | A76 | 5d red | .25 | .25 |
| a. | | Printer's name omitted | 5.50 | |
| 404 | A77 | 6d olive brn | .25 | .25 |
| 405 | A78 | 7d dk brown | .55 | .50 |
| 406 | A79 | 10d red brown | .25 | .25 |
| 407 | A80 | 15d green | .25 | .25 |
| 408 | A81 | 25d dk blue | .25 | .25 |
| | | Nos. 396-408 (13) | 3.55 | 3.50 |
| | | Set, never hinged | 4.00 | |

See Nos. 413, 459-466. For overprints and surcharges see Nos. 455-458, 476-477, RA75-RA78, RA83-RA85, N202-N217, N246-N247.

**Cerigo, Paxos, Lefkas**
Greek stamps with Italian overprints for the islands of Cerigo (Kithyra), Paxos and Lefkas (Santa Maura) are fraudulent.

**Royal Wedding Issue**

Princess Frederika-Louise and Crown Prince Paul — A82

| | | | | |
|---|---|---|---|---|
| **1938** | | **Wmk. 252** | **Perf. 13½x12** | |
| 409 | A82 | 1d green | .25 | .25 |
| 410 | A82 | 3d orange brn | .30 | .25 |
| 411 | A82 | 8d dark blue | .55 | .65 |
| | | Nos. 409-411 (3) | 1.10 | 1.15 |
| | | Set, never hinged | 2.75 | |

Arms of Greece, Romania, Yugoslavia and Turkey — A83

**Perf. 12x12½**

| | | | | |
|---|---|---|---|---|
| **1938, Feb. 8** | | **Litho.** | **Unwmk.** | |
| 412 | A83 | 6d blue | 5.50 | 1.75 |
| | | Never hinged | 14.00 | |

Balkan Entente.

**Tiryns Lady Type of 1937**
**Corrected Inscription**

| | | | | |
|---|---|---|---|---|
| **1938** | | **Wmk. 252** | **Perf. 12x13½** | |
| 413 | A70 | 10 l blue & brn red | .50 | .70 |
| | | Never hinged | .85 | |

The first four letters of the third word of the inscription read "TIPY" instead of "TYPI."

Statue of King Constantine — A84

**Perf. 12x13½**

| | | | | |
|---|---|---|---|---|
| **1938, Oct. 8** | | **Engr.** | **Unwmk.** | |
| 414 | A84 | 1.50d green | .45 | .25 |
| 415 | A84 | 30d orange brn | 2.25 | 3.25 |
| | | Set, never hinged | 5.50 | |

For overprint see No. N218.

Coats of Arms of Ionian Islands A85

Fort at Corfu A86

King George I of Greece and Queen Victoria of England — A87

**Perf. 12½x12, 13½x12**

| | | | | |
|---|---|---|---|---|
| **1939, May 21** | | **Engr.** | **Unwmk.** | |
| 416 | A85 | 1d dk blue | .85 | .25 |
| 417 | A86 | 4d green | 2.90 | 1.00 |
| 418 | A87 | 20d yellow org | 17.00 | 17.00 |
| 419 | A87 | 20d dull blue | 17.00 | 17.00 |
| 420 | A87 | 20d car lake | 17.00 | 17.00 |
| | | Nos. 416-420 (5) | 54.75 | 52.25 |
| | | Set, never hinged | 125.00 | |

75th anniv. of the union of the Ionian Islands with Greece.

Runner with Shield — A88

10th Pan-Balkan Games: 3d, Javelin thrower. 6d, Discus thrower. 8d, Jumper.

**Perf. 12x13½**

| | | | | |
|---|---|---|---|---|
| **1939, Oct. 1** | | **Litho.** | **Unwmk.** | |
| 421 | A88 | 50 l slate grn & grn | .25 | .25 |
| 422 | A88 | 3d hen brn & dl rose | 1.25 | .55 |
| 423 | A88 | 6d cop brn & dl org | 3.00 | 2.25 |
| 424 | A88 | 8d ultra & gray | 3.00 | 2.50 |
| | | Nos. 421-424 (4) | 7.50 | 5.55 |
| | | Set, never hinged | 18.00 | |

Arms of Greece, Romania, Turkey and Yugoslavia — A92

**Perf. 13x12½**

| | | | | |
|---|---|---|---|---|
| **1940, May 27** | | | **Wmk. 252** | |
| 425 | A92 | 6d blue | 10.00 | 2.25 |
| 426 | A92 | 8d blue gray | 7.00 | 2.25 |
| | | Set, never hinged | 45.00 | |

Balkan Entente.

Emblem of Youth Organization A93

Boy Member A94

Designs: 3d, 100d, Emblem of Greek Youth Organization. 10d, Girl member. 15d, Javelin Thrower. 20d, Column of members. 25d, Flag bearers and buglers. 30d, Three youths. 50d, Line formation. 75d, Coat of arms.

**Perf. 12½, 13½x12½**

| | | | | |
|---|---|---|---|---|
| **1940, Aug. 3** | | **Litho.** | **Wmk. 252** | |
| 427 | A93 | 3d sil, dp ultra & red | .85 | 1.25 |
| 428 | A94 | 5d dk bl & blk | 6.50 | 7.50 |
| 429 | A94 | 10d red org & blk | 7.50 | 10.00 |
| 430 | A94 | 15d dk grn & blk | 30.00 | 32.50 |
| 431 | A94 | 20d lake & blk | 25.00 | 25.00 |
| 432 | A94 | 25d dk bl & blk | 25.00 | 25.00 |
| 433 | A94 | 30d rose vio & blk | 25.00 | 25.00 |
| 434 | A94 | 50d lake & blk | 30.00 | 30.00 |
| 435 | A94 | 75d dk bl, brn & gold | 30.00 | 32.50 |
| 436 | A93 | 100d sil, dp ultra & red | 50.00 | 37.50 |
| | | Nos. 427-436,C38-C47 (20) | 535.20 | 529.00 |
| | | Set, never hinged | 1,000. | |

4th anniv. of the founding of the Greek Youth Organization. The stamps were good for postal duty Aug. 3-5, 1940, only. They remained on sale until Feb. 3, 1941.

For overprints see Nos. N219-N238.

Windmills on Mykonos A103

Bourtzi Fort A104

Aspropotamos River — A105

Candia Harbor, Crete — A106

Houses at Hydra A107

Meteora Monasteries A108

Edessa — A109

Pantokratoros Monastery and Port — A110

Bridge at Konitsa — A111

Ekatontapiliani Church, Paros — A112

Ponticonissi, Corfu (Mouse Island) — A113

**Perf. 12½, 13½x12½**

| | | | | |
|---|---|---|---|---|
| **1942-44** | | **Litho.** | **Wmk. 252** | |
| 437 | A103 | 2d red brown | .25 | .25 |
| 438 | A104 | 5d lt bl grn | .25 | .25 |
| a. | | "ΝΑΥΘΛΙΟΝ" instead of "ΝΑΥΠ–ΛΙΟΝ" | 8.25 | 8.25 |
| 439 | A105 | 10d lt blue | .25 | .25 |
| 440 | A106 | 15d red vio | .25 | .25 |
| 441 | A107 | 25d org red | .25 | .25 |
| 442 | A108 | 50d sapphire | .25 | .25 |
| 443 | A109 | 75d dp rose | .25 | .25 |
| 444 | A110 | 100d black | .25 | .25 |
| 445 | A110 | 200d ultra | .25 | .25 |
| a. | | Imprint omitted | 4.00 | 4.00 |
| 446 | A111 | 500d dk olive | .25 | .25 |
| 447 | A112 | 1000d org brn | .25 | .25 |
| 448 | A113 | 2000d dp blue | .25 | .25 |
| 449 | A111 | 5000d rose red | .25 | .25 |
| 450 | A112 | 15,000d rose lil | .25 | .25 |
| 451 | A113 | 25,000d green | .25 | .25 |
| 452 | A105 | 500,000d blue | .25 | .25 |
| 453 | A103 | 2,000,000d turq grn | .25 | .25 |
| 454 | A104 | 5,000,000d rose brn | .25 | .30 |
| | | Nos. 437-454 (18) | 4.50 | 4.55 |
| | | Set, never hinged | 4.50 | |

Double impressions exist of 10d, 25d, 50d, 100d, 200d, 1,000d and 2,000d. Value, each $30.

Issued: Nos. 439-442, 9/1; 200d, 12/1; Nos. 446-448, 3/15/44; Nos. 449-451, 7/1/44; Nos. 452-454, 9/15/44.

For surcharges and overprint see Nos. 472C, 473B-475, 478-481, 501-505, B1-B5, B11-B15, RA72-RA74, N239-N240, N243-N245, N248.

**Imperf., Pairs**

| | | | |
|---|---|---|---|
| 439a | A105 | 10d | 57.50 |
| 440a | A106 | 15d | 57.50 |
| 441a | A107 | 25d | 45.00 |
| 442a | A108 | 50d | 45.00 |
| 446a | A111 | 500d | 45.00 |
| 447a | A112 | 1000d | 45.00 |
| 448a | A113 | 2000d | 45.00 |
| 449a | A111 | 5000d | 45.00 |
| 450a | A112 | 15,000d | 45.00 |
| 451a | A113 | 25,000d | 45.00 |
| 452a | A105 | 500,000d | 45.00 |
| 454a | A104 | 5,000,000d | 45.00 |

Nos. 400, 402-404 Surcharged in Blue Black

| | | | | |
|---|---|---|---|---|
| **1944-45** | | | **Perf. 13½x12** | |
| 455 | A73 | 50 l brn & blk | .25 | .25 |
| a. | | Double surcharge | 40.00 | 40.00 |
| b. | | Pair, one without surcharge | 65.00 | |
| 456 | A75 | 2d ultra | .25 | .25 |
| a. | | Double surcharge | 40.00 | |
| b. | | Pair, one without surcharge | 65.00 | |
| 457 | A76 | 5d red | .25 | .25 |
| a. | | Inverted surcharge | 47.50 | |
| b. | | Double surcharge | 47.50 | |
| c. | | Printer's name omitted (403a) | 12.00 | 12.00 |
| d. | | Pair, one without surcharge | 20.00 | |
| 458 | A77 | 6d olive brn ('45) | .25 | .25 |
| a. | | Double surcharge | 55.00 | |
| | | Nos. 455-458 (4) | | 1.00 |
| | | Set, never hinged | .90 | |

**Glory Type of 1937**
**Perf. 12½x13½**

| | | | | |
|---|---|---|---|---|
| **1945** | | **Litho.** | **Wmk. 252** | |
| 459 | A81 | 1d dull rose vio | .40 | .25 |
| 460 | A81 | 3d rose brown | .40 | .25 |
| 461 | A81 | 5d ultra | .40 | .25 |
| 462 | A81 | 10d dull brown | .40 | .25 |
| 463 | A81 | 20d dull violet | .40 | .25 |
| 464 | A81 | 50d olive black | .40 | .25 |
| 465 | A81 | 100d pale blue | 6.00 | 6.00 |
| 466 | A81 | 200d slate | 5.25 | 4.75 |
| | | Nos. 459-466 (8) | 13.65 | 12.25 |
| | | Set, never hinged | 27.50 | |

**Imperf., Pairs**

| | | | |
|---|---|---|---|
| 459a | A81 | 1d | 145.00 |
| 460a | A81 | 3d | 145.00 |
| 461a | A81 | 5d | 145.00 |
| 462a | A81 | 10d | 145.00 |
| 463a | A81 | 20d | 145.00 |
| 464a | A81 | 50d | 145.00 |
| 465a | A81 | 100d | 160.00 |
| 466a | A81 | 200d | 175.00 |

Doric Column and Greek Flag — A114

| | | | | |
|---|---|---|---|---|
| **1945, Oct. 28** | | | **Unwmk.** | |
| 467 | A114 | 20d orange brown | .25 | .25 |
| a. | | Imperf., pair | 50.00 | |

| | | | | |
|---|---|---|---|---|
| **468** A114 | 40d blue | | .25 | .25 |
| a. | Double impression | | 30.00 | |
| b. | Imperf., pair | | 50.00 | |
| | Set, never hinged | | .75 | |

Vote of Oct. 28, 1940, refusing Italy's ultimatum. "OXI" means "No."
Exist imperf.

Franklin D.
Roosevelt — A115

**1945, Dec. 21** — **Unwmk.**

| | | | | |
|---|---|---|---|---|
| **469** A115 | 30d blk & red brn | | .30 | .25 |
| a. | Center double | | 27.00 | |
| c. | Inverted frame | | 72.50 | |
| d. | Imperf., pair | | 45.00 | |
| **470** A115 | 60d blk & sl gray | | .30 | .25 |
| b. | 60d black & blue gray | | 11.00 | 11.00 |
| c. | Imperf., pair | | 27.50 | |
| d. | Inverted frame | | 65.00 | |
| **471** A115 | 200d blk & vio brn | | .30 | .25 |
| a. | Center double | | 27.50 | 77.50 |
| b. | Imperf., pair | | 45.00 | |
| | *Nos. 469-471 (3)* | | .90 | .75 |
| | Set, never hinged | | 1.50 | |

Death of Pres. Franklin D. Roosevelt.

> **Catalogue values for unused stamps in this section, from this point to the end of the section, are for Never Hinged items.**

Nos. C61, C63, 447-451, 453, 398, 401, 454 and 452 Surcharged in Black or Carmine

**Perf. 12½, 12x13½, 13½x12½**

**1946** — **Wmk. 252**

| | | | | |
|---|---|---|---|---|
| **472** AP35 | 10d on 10d | | .40 | .25 |
| a. | Inverted surcharge | | 100.00 | — |
| b. | Double surcharge | | 22.50 | |
| **472C** A113 | 10d on 2000d | | .40 | .25 |
| | | (C) | | |
| **473** AP35 | 20d on 50d | | .40 | .25 |
| | | (C) | | |
| a. | Inverted surcharge | | 125.00 | |
| c. | Imperf., pair | | — | |
| **473B** A112 | 20d on 1000d | | .40 | .25 |
| a. | Double surcharge | | 125.00 | |
| **474** A113 | 50d on 25,000d | | .55 | .25 |
| | | (C) | | |
| a. | Double surcharge | | 120.00 | |
| **475** A103 | 100d on 2,000,000d | | .95 | .30 |
| | | (C) | | |
| **476** A71 | 130d on 20 l | | 1.00 | .25 |
| a. | Double surcharge | | 27.50 | |
| **476A** A71 | 250d on 20 l | | 1.25 | .25 |
| | | (C) | | |
| c. | Double surcharge | | 92.50 | |
| **477** A74 | 300d on 80 l | | 1.00 | .25 |
| a. | Purple brown surcharge | | 17.00 | 17.00 |
| b. | Double surcharge | | 90.00 | |
| c. | Pair, #477 and #477a | | 45.00 | |
| **478** A104 | 500d on 5,000,000d | | 4.00 | .80 |
| a. | Inverted surcharge | | 85.00 | |
| b. | Double surcharge | | 85.00 | |
| **479** A105 | 1000d on 500,000d | | 14.00 | 2.25 |
| | | (C) | | |
| a. | Double surcharge | | 250.00 | |
| **480** A111 | 2000d on 5000d | | 52.50 | 4.50 |
| a. | Double surcharge | | 250.00 | |
| **481** A112 | 5000d on 15,000d | | 160.00 | 35.00 |
| a. | Blue surcharge | | 160.00 | 140.00 |
| | *Nos. 472-481 (13)* | | 236.85 | 44.85 |

The surcharge exists in various shades on most denominations. A 150d on 20 l exists but was not officially issued. Value, unused $300. Examples are known used in Macedonia and Thrace; these are very scarce.

Eleutherios K.
Venizelos — A116

**Perf. 12x13½**

**1946, Mar. 25** — **Litho.** — **Wmk. 252**

| | | | | |
|---|---|---|---|---|
| **482** A116 | 130d brn ol & buff | | .40 | .25 |
| a. | Double impression of brn olive | | 7.25 | |
| b. | Imperf., pair | | 45.00 | |

| | | | | |
|---|---|---|---|---|
| **483** A116 | 300d red brn & pale brn | | .40 | .25 |
| a. | Double impression of red brown | | 14.00 | |
| b. | Imperf., pair | | 45.00 | |

Venizelos (1864-1936), statesman.

Nos. 391 to 394
Surcharged in Blue
Black

**1946, Sept. 28** — **Perf. 12½x12**

| | | | | |
|---|---|---|---|---|
| **484** A67 | 50d on 1d | | .70 | .25 |
| a. | Double surcharge | | 100.00 | |
| **485** A67 | 250d on 3d | | 1.60 | .25 |
| a. | Date omitted | | 32.50 | |
| b. | Inverted surcharge | | 32.50 | — |
| c. | Double surcharge | | 75.00 | |
| **486** A67 | 600d on 8d | | 11.00 | 1.25 |
| a. | Additional surcharge on back, inverted | | 72.50 | |
| b. | Carmine surcharge | | 150.00 | |
| **487** A67 | 3000d on 100d | | 27.50 | 2.00 |
| | *Nos. 484-487 (4)* | | 40.80 | 3.75 |

Plebiscite of Sept. 1, 1946, which resulted in the return of King George II to Greece.

Panaghiotis
Tsaldaris — A117

**Perf. 12½x13½**

**1946, Nov. 15** — **Litho.** — **Unwmk.**

| | | | | |
|---|---|---|---|---|
| **488** A117 | 250d red brn & buff | | 4.00 | 1.25 |
| a. | Imperf., pair | | 45.00 | |
| **489** A117 | 600d dp bl & pale bl | | 4.00 | 1.25 |
| a. | Double impression | | 22.50 | |
| b. | Imperf., pair | | 55.00 | |

Naval Convoy
A118

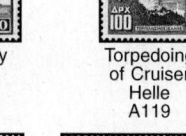

Torpedoing
of Cruiser
Helle
A119

Women Carrying
Ammunition in
Pindus
Mountains
A120

Troops in
Albania
A121

Campaign
of Greek
Troops in
Italy
A122

Allegory of Flight
A123

Greek Torpedo Boat
Towing Captive
Submarine — A124

Design: 5000d, Memorial Tomb, El Alamein.

**1946-47** — **Unwmk.** — **Engr.** — **Perf. 13**

| | | | | |
|---|---|---|---|---|
| **490** A118 | 50d dk bl grn | | .25 | .25 |
| **491** A119 | 100d dp ultra | | .65 | .25 |
| **492** A120 | 250d yel grn ('46) | | .65 | .25 |
| **493** A121 | 500d yel brn | | 1.05 | .25 |
| **494** A122 | 600d dk brown | | 1.40 | .85 |
| **495** A123 | 1000d dull lil | | 7.25 | .40 |
| **496** A124 | 2000d dp ultra | | 30.00 | 2.50 |

| | | | | |
|---|---|---|---|---|
| **497** A119 | 5000d dk car | | 40.00 | 2.50 |
| a. | Imperf., pair | | 1,500. | |
| | *Nos. 490-497 (8)* | | 81.25 | 7.25 |

1947 stamps issued May 1.

### King George II Memorial Issue

Nos. 391-393
Surcharged in Black

**Perf. 12½x12**

**1947, Apr. 15** — **Wmk. 252**

| | | | | |
|---|---|---|---|---|
| **498** A67 | 50d on 1d grn | | .60 | .25 |
| a. | Double surcharge | | 72.50 | |
| **499** A67 | 250d on 3d red brn | | 1.25 | .25 |
| a. | Double surcharge | | 72.50 | |
| b. | Pair, one without surcharge | | 72.50 | |
| **500** A67 | 600d on 8d dp bl | | 10.00 | .55 |
| a. | Double surcharge | | 72.50 | |
| | *Nos. 498-500 (3)* | | 11.85 | 1.05 |

Nos. 446, 438, 442,
439 and 443
Surcharged in
Carmine or Black

**1947** — **Perf. 12½**

| | | | | |
|---|---|---|---|---|
| **501** A111 | 20d on 500d | | .30 | .25 |
| a. | Double surcharge | | 27.50 | |
| **502** A104 | 30d on 5d | | .95 | .40 |
| a. | "NAYOΛION" instead of "NAYΠΛION" | | 35.00 | 45.00 |
| **503** A108 | 50d on 50d | | .45 | .25 |
| **504** A105 | 100d on 10d | | 1.60 | .25 |
| a. | Double surcharge | | 150.00 | |
| **505** A109 | 450d on 75d (Bk) | | 2.50 | .25 |
| | *Nos. 501-505 (5)* | | 5.80 | 1.40 |

Castellorizo
Castle
A126

Dodecanese
Vase
A127

Dodecanese
Costume
A128

Monastery where
St. John
Preached,
Patmos
A129

Emanuel
Xanthos
A130

Sailing
Vessel of
1824
A131

Revolutionary Stamp of
1912 — A132

Statue of
Hippocrates
A133

Colossus of
Rhodes
A134

**Perf. 12½x13½, 13½x12½**

**1947-48** — **Litho.** — **Wmk. 252**

| | | | | |
|---|---|---|---|---|
| **506** A126 | 20d ultra | | .30 | .25 |
| **507** A127 | 30d blk brn & buff | | .30 | .25 |
| **508** A128 | 50d chlky bl | | .50 | .25 |
| **509** A129 | 100d blk brn & pale grn | | .50 | .25 |
| **510** A130 | 250d gray grn & pale grn | | 1.00 | .25 |
| **511** A132 | 450d dp bl ('48) | | 2.25 | .25 |
| **512** A131 | 450d dp bl & pale bl ('48) | | 1.75 | .25 |
| **513** A132 | 500d red | | 1.40 | .25 |
| **514** A133 | 600d vio brn & pale pink | | 1.40 | .25 |
| **515** A134 | 1000d brn & cream | | 2.00 | .25 |
| | *Nos. 506-515 (10)* | | 11.40 | 2.50 |

Return of the Dodecanese to Greece. See Nos. 520-522, 525-534.

### Imperf., Pairs

| | | | |
|---|---|---|---|
| *506a* A126 | 20d | | 250.00 |
| *507a* A127 | 30d | | 250.00 |
| *508a* A128 | 50d | | 250.00 |
| *509a* A129 | 100d | | 260.00 |
| *510a* A130 | 250d | | 260.00 |
| *512a* A131 | 450d | | 275.00 |
| *514a* A133 | 600d | | 300.00 |
| *515a* A134 | 1000d | | 250.00 |

Battle of
Crete — A135

**1948, Sept. 15** — **Engr.** — **Perf. 13x13½**

| | | | | |
|---|---|---|---|---|
| **516** A135 | 1000d dark green | | 6.50 | .50 |

Battle of Crete, 7th anniversary.

Abduction of
Children — A136

Concentration
Camp
A137

Protective
Mother
A138

**Perf. 13½x12½, 12½x13½**

**1949, Feb. 1** — **Litho.** — **Wmk. 252**

| | | | | |
|---|---|---|---|---|
| **517** A136 | 450d dk & lt violet | | 3.75 | .65 |
| a. | Imperf., pair | | 360.00 | |
| **518** A137 | 1000d dk & lt brown | | 13.50 | 4.00 |
| **519** A138 | 1800d dk red & cream | | 17.50 | .40 |
| | *Nos. 517-519 (3)* | | 34.75 | 5.05 |

A variety of No. 519 exists in green and cream.

### Types of 1947

**1950, Apr. 5** — **Perf. 12½x13½**

| | | | | |
|---|---|---|---|---|
| **520** A127 | 2000d org brn & sal | | 50.00 | .55 |
| a. | Imperf., pair | | 140.00 | |
| **521** A133 | 5000d rose vio | | 55.00 | .55 |
| **522** A134 | 10,000d ultra | | 95.00 | 1.25 |
| | *Nos. 520-522 (3)* | | 200.00 | 2.35 |

Map of Crete
and
Flags — A139

**Perf. 13½x13**

**1950, Apr. 28** — **Engr.** — **Wmk. 252**

| | | | | |
|---|---|---|---|---|
| **523** A139 | 1000d deep blue | | 17.50 | .40 |
| a. | Imperf., pair | | 1,500. | |

Battle of Crete, 9th anniversary.

Youth of
Marathon — A140

## Engraved and Lithographed

**1950, May 21**     **Perf. 13x13½**

| | | | | |
|---|---|---|---|---|
| 524 | A140 | 1000d cream & dp grn | 2.00 | .60 |
| a. | | Without dates | 450.00 | |
| b. | | "1949" only | 450.00 | |
| c. | | Dates inverted | 450.00 | |
| d. | | Dates doubled | 450.00 | |

75th anniv. (in 1949) of the UPU.
No. 524 exists imperforate in used condition.

### Types of 1947-48
**Perf. 12½x13½, 13½x12½**

| **1950** | | **Litho.** | **Wmk. 252** | |
|---|---|---|---|---|
| 525 | A130 | 200d orange | .70 | .25 |
| 526 | A128 | 300d orange | .95 | .25 |
| a. | | Imperf., pair | 275.00 | |
| 527 | A129 | 400d blue | 1.75 | .25 |
| 528 | A133 | 700d lilac rose | 2.25 | .25 |
| 529 | A133 | 700d blue green | 27.50 | .25 |
| a. | | Imperf., pair | 290.00 | |
| 530 | A131 | 800d pur & pale grn | 2.75 | .25 |
| a. | | Imperf., pair | 275.00 | |
| 531 | A132 | 1300d carmine | 12.00 | .25 |
| 532 | A126 | 1500d brn org | 82.50 | 1.10 |
| 533 | A127 | 1600d ultra & bl gray | 8.50 | .25 |
| 534 | A134 | 2600d emer & pale grn | 11.50 | .85 |
| | | Nos. 525-534 (10) | 150.40 | 3.95 |

Altar and Sword — A141

St. Paul — A142

St. Paul by El Greco A143

Preaching to Athenians A144

**Perf. 13½x12, 12x13½**

| **1951, June 15** | | **Engr.** | **Unwmk.** | |
|---|---|---|---|---|
| 535 | A141 | 700d red vio | 3.50 | 1.00 |
| 536 | A142 | 1600d lt blue | 14.50 | 8.75 |
| 537 | A143 | 2600d dk ol bis | 25.00 | 9.00 |
| 538 | A144 | 10,000d red brn | 175.00 | 80.00 |
| | | Nos. 535-538 (4) | 218.00 | 98.75 |

1900th anniv. of St. Paul's visit to Athens.

Industrialization A145

Designs: 800d, Fishing. 1300d, Rebuilding. 1600d, Farming. 2600d, Home Industries. 5000d, Electrification and map of Greece.

**Perf. 12½x13½**

| **1951, Sept. 20** | | | **Wmk. 252** | |
|---|---|---|---|---|
| 539 | A145 | 700d red org | 5.00 | .30 |
| 540 | A145 | 800d aqua | 7.25 | .30 |
| 541 | A145 | 1300d grnsh bl | 10.00 | .30 |
| 542 | A145 | 1600d olive grn | 30.00 | .50 |
| 543 | A145 | 2600d vio gray | 75.00 | 2.25 |
| 544 | A145 | 5000d dp plum | 100.00 | 1.50 |
| | | Nos. 539-544 (6) | 227.25 | 4.15 |

Issued to publicize Greek recovery under the Marshall Plan.

King Paul I A146

Allegorical Figure and Medal A147

---

**1952, Dec. 14**   **Engr.**   **Perf. 12½x12**

| | | | | |
|---|---|---|---|---|
| 545 | A146 | 200d deep green | 2.00 | .25 |
| 546 | A146 | 1000d red | 6.00 | .35 |
| 547 | A147 | 1400d blue | 20.00 | 2.25 |
| 548 | A146 | 10,000d dk red lil | 60.00 | 14.00 |
| | | Nos. 545-548 (4) | 88.00 | 16.85 |

50th birthday of King Paul I.

Oranges A148     Tobacco A149

National Products: 1000d, Olive oil, Pallas Athene. 1300d, Wine. 2000d, Figs. 2600d, Grapes and bread. 5000d, Bacchus holding grapes.

**1953, July 1**    **Perf. 13½x13, 13x13½**

| | | | | |
|---|---|---|---|---|
| 549 | A148 | 500d dp car & org | 1.90 | .25 |
| 550 | A149 | 700d dk brn & org yel | 1.90 | .25 |
| a. | | Imperf., pair | 600.00 | |
| 551 | A148 | 1000d bl & lt ol grn | 4.00 | .25 |
| a. | | Imperf., pair | 450.00 | |
| 552 | A149 | 1300d dp plum & org brn | 5.50 | .25 |
| 553 | A149 | 2000d dk brn & lt grn | 13.50 | .40 |
| a. | | Imperf., pair | 600.00 | |
| 554 | A149 | 2600d vio & ol bis | 37.50 | 1.75 |
| 555 | A149 | 5000d dk brn & yel grn | 37.50 | .90 |
| | | Nos. 549-555 (7) | 101.80 | 4.05 |

Pericles A150

Homer A151

Hunting Wild Boar — A152

Shepherd Carrying Calf — A152a

Designs: 200d, Mycenaean oxhead vase. 500d, Zeus of Istiaea. 600d, Head of a youth. 1000d, Alexander the Great. 1200d, Charioteer of Delphi. 2000d, Vase of Dipylon. 4000d, Voyage of Dionysus. 20,000d, Pitcher bearers.

**Perf. 13½x13, 12½x12, 13x13½**

| **1954, Jan. 15** | | | **Litho.** | |
|---|---|---|---|---|
| 556 | A150 | 100d red brn | .50 | .25 |
| 557 | A150 | 200d black | .50 | .25 |
| 558 | A151 | 300d blue vio | 1.25 | .25 |
| 559 | A151 | 500d green | 2.00 | .25 |
| 560 | A151 | 600d rose pink | 2.00 | .25 |
| 561 | A151 | 1000d dl bl & blk | 2.50 | .25 |
| 562 | A150 | 1200d ol grn | 2.50 | .25 |
| 563 | A150 | 2000d red brn | 11.00 | .25 |
| 564 | A152 | 2400d grnsh bl | 11.00 | .40 |
| a. | | Double impression | 150.00 | |
| 565 | A152a | 2500d dk bl grn | 11.00 | .25 |
| 566 | A151 | 4000d dk car | 27.50 | .40 |
| 567 | A150 | 20,000d rose lilac | 225.00 | 1.25 |
| | | Nos. 556-567 (12) | 296.75 | 4.30 |

See Nos. 574-581, 632-638, and 689.

British Parliamentary Debate and Ink Blot — A153

**1954, Sept.**     **Perf. 12½**
**Center in Black**

| | | | | |
|---|---|---|---|---|
| 568 | A153 | 1.20d cream | 4.00 | .45 |
| 569 | A153 | 2d orange | 20.00 | 3.75 |
| 570 | A153 | 2d lt bl | 20.00 | 9.25 |
| 571 | A153 | 2.40d lilac | 20.00 | 2.50 |

---

| | | | | |
|---|---|---|---|---|
| 572 | A153 | 2.50d pink | 20.00 | 2.50 |
| 573 | A153 | 4d citron | 60.00 | 3.75 |
| | | Nos. 568-573 (6) | 144.00 | 22.20 |

Document in English on Nos. 569, 572, 573; in French on Nos. 570, 571 and in Greek on No. 568.

Issued to promote the proposed union between Cyprus and Greece.

### Types of 1954

Designs: 20 l, Mycenaean oxhead vase. 30 l, Pericles. 50 l, Zeus of Istiaea. 1d, Head of a youth. 2d, Alexander the Great. 3d, Hunting wild boar. 3.50d, Homer. 4d, Voyage of Dionysus.

**Perf. 13½x13, 12½x12, 13x13½**

| **1955** | | **Litho.** | **Wmk. 252** | |
|---|---|---|---|---|
| 574 | A150 | 20 l dk green | .40 | .25 |
| 575 | A150 | 30 l yellow brn | .60 | .25 |
| 576 | A151 | 50 l car lake | .90 | .25 |
| 577 | A151 | 1d blue grn | 2.25 | .25 |
| 578 | A151 | 2d brown & blk | 7.25 | .25 |
| 579 | A152 | 3d red org | 11.00 | .25 |
| 580 | A151 | 3.50d rose crim | 11.00 | .70 |
| 581 | A151 | 4d violet bl | 82.50 | .45 |
| | | Nos. 574-581 (8) | 115.90 | 2.65 |

Samos Coin Picturing Pythagoras A154

Pythagorean Theorem A155

Samos Mapped in Antique Style — A156

**1955, Aug. 20**     **Perf. 12x13½**

| | | | | |
|---|---|---|---|---|
| 582 | A154 | 2d green | 3.75 | .40 |
| 583 | A155 | 3.50d intense blk | 13.50 | 3.00 |
| 584 | A154 | 5d plum | 45.00 | 2.00 |
| 585 | A156 | 6d blue | 57.50 | 32.50 |
| | | Nos. 582-585 (4) | 119.75 | 37.90 |

2500th anniv. of the founding of the 1st School of Philosophy by Pythagoras on Samos.

Globe and Rotary Emblem — A157

**Perf. 12x13½**

| **1956, May 15** | | **Litho.** | **Wmk. 252** | |
|---|---|---|---|---|
| 586 | A157 | 2d ultra | 17.50 | .40 |

50th anniv. of Rotary Intl. (in 1955).

King Alexander A158

Crown Prince Constantine A159

Portraits: 30 l, George I. 50 l, Queen Olga. 70 l, King Otto. 1d, Queen Amalia. 1.50d, King Constantine. 2d, 7.50d, King Paul. 3d, George II. 3.50d, Queen Sophia. 4d, Queen Frederica. 5d, King Paul and Queen Frederica. 10d, King, Queen and Crown Prince.

**Perf. 13½x12, 12x13½**

| **1956, May 21** | | | | **Engr.** |
|---|---|---|---|---|
| 587 | A158 | 10 l blue vio | .25 | .25 |
| 588 | A159 | 20 l dull pur | .25 | .25 |
| 589 | A159 | 30 l sepia | .25 | .25 |
| 590 | A159 | 50 l red brn | .30 | .25 |
| 591 | A159 | 70 l lt ultra | .50 | .25 |
| 592 | A159 | 1d grnsh bl | .50 | .25 |
| 593 | A159 | 1.50d gray bl | 3.50 | .25 |
| 594 | A159 | 2d black | 4.75 | .25 |
| 595 | A159 | 3d brown | 3.50 | .25 |
| 596 | A159 | 3.50d copper brn | 11.50 | .25 |

---

| | | | | |
|---|---|---|---|---|
| 597 | A159 | 4d gray green | 11.50 | .25 |
| 598 | A158 | 5d rose car | 11.50 | .25 |
| 599 | A159 | 7.50d ultra | 11.50 | 2.00 |
| 600 | A158 | 10d dk blue | 60.00 | 1.10 |
| | | Nos. 587-600 (14) | 119.80 | 6.10 |

See Nos. 604-617.

Dionysios Solomos and Nicolaos Mantzaros A160

Dionysios Solomos A161

5d, View on Zante and bust of Solomos.

**Perf. 13½x12, 12x13½**

| **1957, Mar. 26** | | **Litho.** | **Wmk. 252** | |
|---|---|---|---|---|
| 601 | A160 | 2d red brn & ocher | 4.25 | .50 |
| 602 | A161 | 3.50d bl & gray | 6.75 | 3.25 |
| 603 | A160 | 5d dk grn & ol bis | 9.00 | 4.75 |
| | | Nos. 601-603 (3) | 20.00 | 8.50 |

Centenary of the death of Dionysios Solomos (1798-1857), nationalist poet best known for the poem *Hymn to Liberty*, the first two stanzas of which were adopted as the lyrics of the Greek national anthem.

### Types of 1956

Designs as before.

**Perf. 13½x12**

| **1957** | | **Wmk. 252** | | **Engr.** |
|---|---|---|---|---|
| 604 | A158 | 10 l rose lake | .50 | .25 |
| 605 | A159 | 20 l orange | .50 | .25 |
| 606 | A159 | 30 l gray blk | .50 | .25 |
| 607 | A159 | 50 l grnsh blk | .50 | .25 |
| 608 | A159 | 70 l rose lil | 1.50 | .65 |
| 609 | A159 | 1d rose red | 1.00 | .25 |
| 610 | A159 | 1.50d lt ol grn | 1.75 | .25 |
| 611 | A159 | 2d carmine | 3.25 | .25 |
| 612 | A159 | 3d dk blue | 4.00 | .25 |
| 613 | A159 | 3.50d blk vio | 10.00 | .25 |
| a. | | Imperf., pair | | |
| 614 | A159 | 4d red brn | 10.00 | .25 |
| 615 | A158 | 5d gray blue | 10.00 | .25 |
| 616 | A159 | 7.50d yel org | 3.00 | 1.25 |
| 617 | A158 | 10d green | 75.00 | .80 |
| | | Nos. 604-617 (14) | 121.50 | 5.45 |

Oil Tanker — A162

Ships: 1d, Ocean liner. 1.50d, Sailing ship, 1820. 2d, Byzantine vessel. 3.50d, Ship from 6th century B. C. 5d, "Argo."

| **1958, Jan. 30** | | **Litho.** | **Perf. 13½x12** | |
|---|---|---|---|---|
| 618 | A162 | 50 l multi | .50 | .25 |
| 619 | A162 | 1d ultra, blk & bis | .50 | .25 |
| 620 | A162 | 1.50d blk & car | 1.50 | .95 |
| a. | | Double impression of blk | 160.00 | |
| 621 | A162 | 2d vio bl, blk & red brn | .50 | .30 |
| 622 | A162 | 3.50d lt bl, blk & red | 2.00 | 1.25 |
| a. | | Double impression of blk | 160.00 | 125.00 |
| 623 | A162 | 5d bl grn, blk & car | 13.50 | 13.00 |
| | | Nos. 618-623 (6) | 18.50 | 13.00 |

Issued to honor the Greek merchant marine.

Narcissus — A163

Designs: 30 l, Daphne (laurel) and Apollo. 50 l, Adonis (hibiscus) and Aphrodite. 70 l, Pitys (pine) and Pan. 1d, Crocus. 2d, Iris. 3.50d, Tulips. 5d, Cyclamen.

**1958, Sept. 15**   **Wmk. 252**   **Perf. 13**
**Size: 22½x38mm**

| | | | | |
|---|---|---|---|---|
| 624 | A163 | 20 l multi | .25 | .25 |
| 625 | A163 | 30 l multi | .25 | .25 |
| 626 | A163 | 50 l multi | .25 | .25 |
| 627 | A163 | 70 l multi | .25 | .25 |

**Perf. 12½x12**
**Size: 21½x26mm**

| | | | | |
|---|---|---|---|---|
| 628 | A163 | 1d multi | .45 | .40 |

**Perf. 12x13½**
**Size: 22x32mm**

| | | | | |
|---|---|---|---|---|
| 629 | A163 | 2d multi | .25 | .25 |
| 630 | A163 | 3.50d multi | 1.75 | 1.75 |
| a. | | Imperf., pair | 325.00 | |
| 631 | A163 | 5d multi | 5.00 | 5.00 |
| | *Nos. 624-631 (8)* | | 8.45 | 8.40 |

International Congress for the Protection of Nature, held in Athens.

### Types of 1954

Designs: 10 l, Pericles. 20 l, Mycenaean oxhead vase. 50 l, Zeus of Istiaea. 70 l, Charioteer of Delphi. 1d, Head of a youth. 1.50d, Pitcher bearers. 2.50d, Alexander the Great.
Two types of 2.50d:
I — 9 dots in upper half of right border.
II — 10 dots.

**Perf. 13½x13, 12½x12**

| **1959** | | **Litho.** | | **Wmk. 252** |
|---|---|---|---|---|
| 632 | A150 | 10 l emerald | .50 | .25 |
| 633 | A150 | 20 l magenta | .80 | .25 |
| 634 | A151 | 50 l lt bl grn | 1.75 | .25 |
| a. | | Imperf., pair | 1,500. | |
| 635 | A150 | 70 l red org | .50 | .25 |
| 636 | A151 | 1d reddish brn | 4.50 | .25 |
| 637 | A150 | 1.50d brt bl | 25.00 | .25 |
| 638 | A151 | 2.50d mag & blk (II) | 17.50 | .30 |
| a. | | Type I | 60.00 | .55 |
| | *Nos. 632-638 (7)* | | 50.55 | 1.80 |

Zeus-Eagle Coin
A164

Helios-Rose Coin
A165

Ancient Greek Coins: 20 l, Athena & Owl. 50 l, Nymph Arethusa & Chariot. 70 l, Hercules & Zeus. 1.50d, Griffin & Square. 2.50d, Apollo & Lyre. 4.50d, Apollo & Labyrinth. 6d, Aphrodite & Apollo. 8.50d, Ram's Head & Incuse Squares.

**1959, Mar. 24   Wmk. 252   Perf. 14**
**Coins in Various Shades of Gray**

| | | | | |
|---|---|---|---|---|
| 639 | A164 | 10 l red brn & blk | .45 | .25 |
| 640 | A164 | 20 l dp bl & blk | .45 | .25 |
| 641 | A164 | 50 l plum & blk | .60 | .25 |
| 642 | A164 | 70 l ultra & blk | 1.10 | .30 |
| 643 | A165 | 1d dk car rose & blk | 1.50 | .25 |
| 644 | A164 | 1.50d ocher & blk | 1.75 | .25 |
| 645 | A164 | 2.50d dp mag & blk | 2.50 | .25 |
| 646 | A165 | 4.50d Prus grn & blk | 5.50 | .40 |
| 647 | A165 | 6d ol grn & blk | 25.00 | .25 |
| 648 | A165 | 8.50d dp car & blk | 10.00 | 1.75 |
| | *Nos. 639-648 (10)* | | 48.85 | 4.20 |

See Nos. 750-758.

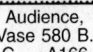

Audience, Vase 580 B. C. — A166

Theater, Delphi — A167

Designs: 50 l, Clay tragedy mask, 3rd cent. B.C. 1d, Flute, drum and lyre. 2.50d, Clay statue of an actor, 3rd cent. B.C. 4.50d, Andromeda, vase, 4th cent. B.C. 6d, Actors, bowl 410 B.C.

**Perf. 13½x13½, 13½x13**

| **1959, June 20** | | **Litho.** | | **Wmk. 252** |
|---|---|---|---|---|
| 649 | A166 | 20 l blk, fawn & gray | .30 | .25 |
| 650 | A166 | 50 l dk red brn & ol bis | .30 | .25 |
| 651 | A166 | 1d grn, brn & ocher | .30 | .25 |
| 652 | A166 | 2.50d brn & bl | .80 | .65 |
| 653 | A167 | 3.50d red brn, grn & sep | 15.00 | 10.50 |
| 654 | A167 | 4.50d blk & fawn | 1.50 | 1.25 |

| | | | | |
|---|---|---|---|---|
| 655 | A166 | 6d blk, fawn & gray | 1.75 | 1.50 |
| | *Nos. 649-655 (7)* | | 19.95 | 14.65 |

Ancient Greek theater.

"Victory" and Soldiers — A168

**Perf. 13x13½**

| **1959, Aug. 29** | | | | **Wmk. 252** |
|---|---|---|---|---|
| 656 | A168 | 2.50d red brn, ultra & blk | 5.00 | .50 |

10th anniversary of civil war.

St. Basil
A169

The Good Samaritan
A170

Designs: 20 l, Plane tree of Hippocrates. 50 l, Aesculapius. 2.50d, Achilles and Patroclus. 3d, Globe and Red Cross over people receiving help. 4.50d, Henri Dunant.

**Perf. 13½x12, 12x13½**

| **1959, Sept. 21** | | | | **Litho.** |
|---|---|---|---|---|
| 657 | A170 | 20 l multi | .25 | .25 |
| 658 | A169 | 50 l multi | .25 | .25 |
| 659 | A169 | 70 l multi | .25 | .25 |
| 660 | A169 | 2.50d multi | .60 | .50 |
| 661 | A169 | 3d multi | 10.00 | 10.00 |
| 662 | A169 | 4.50d multi | 1.60 | 1.60 |
| 663 | A170 | 6d multi | 1.50 | 1.50 |
| | *Nos. 657-663 (7)* | | 14.45 | 14.35 |

Cent. of the Red Cross idea. Sizes: Nos. 658-660, 662 24½x32mm, No. 661 32x47mm.

Imre Nagy — A171

**Perf. 13x13½**

| **1959, Dec. 8** | | | | **Wmk. 252** |
|---|---|---|---|---|
| 664 | A171 | 4.50d org brn & dk brn | 1.75 | 1.75 |
| 665 | A171 | 6d brt bl, bl & blk | 1.75 | 1.75 |

3rd anniv. of the crushing of the 1956 Hungarian Revolution, and to honor Premier Imre Nagy, its leader.

Costis Palamas — A172

**1960, Jan. 25   Perf. 12x13½**

| | | | | |
|---|---|---|---|---|
| 666 | A172 | 2.50d multi | 5.75 | .60 |

Centenary of the birth of Costis Palamas (1859-1943), poet.

Ship Battling Storm — A173

4.50d, Ship in calm sea and rainbow.

**Perf. 13½x13**

| **1960, Apr. 7** | | | | **Wmk. 252** |
|---|---|---|---|---|
| 667 | A173 | 2.50d multi | .40 | .35 |
| 668 | A173 | 4.50d multi | 1.60 | 1.15 |

Issued to publicize World Refugee Year, July 1, 1959-June 30, 1960.

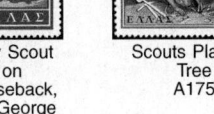

Boy Scout on Horseback, St. George and Dragon
A174

Scouts Planting Tree
A175

30 l, Scout taking oath & boy of ancient Athens. 40 l, Scouts helping in disaster. 70 l, Scouts reading map & tent. 1d, Boy Scout, Sea Scout & Air Scout. 2.50d, Crown Prince Constantine. 6d, Scout flag of Greece & Military Merit medal.

**Perf. 13x13½, 13½x13**

| **1960, Apr. 23** | | | | **Litho.** |
|---|---|---|---|---|
| 669 | A174 | 20 l multi | .25 | .25 |
| 670 | A174 | 30 l multi | .25 | .25 |
| 671 | A174 | 40 l multi | .25 | .25 |
| 672 | A175 | 70 l multi | .25 | .25 |
| 673 | A174 | 1d multi | .65 | .45 |
| 674 | A175 | 1d multi | .65 | .45 |
| 675 | A174 | 2.50d multi | 1.60 | 1.00 |
| 676 | A175 | 6d multi | 2.00 | 1.20 |
| | *Nos. 669-676 (8)* | | 5.50 | 3.80 |

Greek Boy Scout Organization, 50th anniv.

Greek Holding Sacred Disk Proclaiming Armistice During Games
A176

Lighting Olympic Flame
A177

Designs: 70 l, Youth taking oath. 80 l, Boy cutting olive branches for Olympic prizes. 1d, Judges entering stadium. 1.50d, Long jump. 2.50d, Discus thrower. 4.50d, Sprinters. 5d, Javelin thrower. 6d, Crowning the victors. 12.50d, Victor in chariot entering home town.

**Perf. 13x13½, 13½x13**

| **1960, Aug. 12** | | | | **Wmk. 252** |
|---|---|---|---|---|
| 677 | A176 | 20 l multi | .25 | .25 |
| 678 | A177 | 50 l multi | .25 | .25 |
| 679 | A176 | 70 l multi | .25 | .25 |
| 680 | A177 | 80 l multi | .25 | .25 |
| a. | | Imperf., pair | 475.00 | |
| 681 | A177 | 1d multi | .35 | .25 |
| 682 | A177 | 1.50d multi | .35 | .25 |
| 683 | A176 | 2.50d multi | .65 | .40 |
| 684 | A177 | 4.50d multi | .80 | .60 |
| a. | | Dbl. impression of black | 290.00 | 350.00 |
| 685 | A176 | 5d multi | 2.25 | 1.30 |
| 686 | A177 | 6d multi | 2.25 | 1.30 |
| 687 | A177 | 12.50d multi | 12.00 | 8.00 |
| | *Nos. 677-687 (11)* | | 19.65 | 13.10 |

17th Olympic Games, Rome, 8/25-9/11.

### Common Design Types
pictured following the introduction.

### Europa Issue, 1960
Common Design Type
**Perf. 13½x12**

| **1960, Sept. 19** | | **Litho.** | | **Wmk. 252** |
|---|---|---|---|---|
| | | **Size: 33x23mm** | | |
| 688 | CD3 | 4.50d ultra | 4.25 | 1.75 |
| a. | | Double impression | 325.00 | |

### Shepherd Type of 1954

| **1960, Sept. 1** | | **Wmk. 252** | | **Perf. 13** |
|---|---|---|---|---|
| 689 | A152a | 3d ultra | 1.90 | .35 |
| a. | | Imperf., pair | 1,100. | |

Crown Prince Constantine and Yacht — A178

**1961, Jan. 18   Perf. 13½x13**

| | | | | |
|---|---|---|---|---|
| 690 | A178 | 2.50d multi | .80 | .25 |

Victory of Crown Prince Constantine and his crew at the 17th Olympic Games, Rome (Gold medal, Yachting, Dragon class).

Castoria
A179

Delphi
A180

Landscapes and Ancient Monuments: 20 l, Meteora. 50 l, Hydra harbor. 70 l, Acropolis, Athens. 80 l, Mykonos. 1d, St. Catherine's Church, Salonika. 1.50d, Olympia. 2.50d, Knossos. 3.50d, Rhodes. 4d, Epidauros amphitheater. 4.50d, Temple of Poseidon, Sounion. 5d, Temple of Zeus, Athens. 7.50d, Aslan's mosque, Ioannina. 8d, Mount Athos. 8.50d, Santorini. 12.50d, Marble lions, Delos.

**Perf. 13½x12½, 12½x13½**

| **1961, Feb. 15** | | **Engr.** | | **Wmk. 252** |
|---|---|---|---|---|
| 691 | A179 | 10 l dk gray bl | .25 | .25 |
| 692 | A179 | 20 l dk purple | .25 | .25 |
| 693 | A179 | 50 l blue | .25 | .25 |
| 694 | A179 | 70 l dk purple | .25 | .25 |
| 695 | A179 | 80 l brt ultra | .35 | .25 |
| 696 | A179 | 1d red brn | .60 | .25 |
| 697 | A179 | 1.50d brt grn | .80 | .25 |
| 698 | A179 | 2.50d carmine | 3.00 | .25 |
| 699 | A179 | 3.50d purple | 1.15 | .25 |
| 700 | A179 | 4d sl grn | 9.00 | .25 |
| 701 | A179 | 4.50d dk blue | 1.00 | .25 |
| 702 | A179 | 5d claret | 9.00 | .25 |
| 703 | A180 | 6d slate grn | 2.00 | .25 |
| 704 | A179 | 7.50d black | .60 | .25 |
| 705 | A180 | 8d dk vio bl | 3.75 | .25 |
| 706 | A180 | 8.50d org ver | 5.75 | .55 |
| 707 | A179 | 12.50d dk brn | 2.25 | 1.20 |
| | *Nos. 691-707 (17)* | | 40.25 | 5.50 |

Issued for tourist publicity.

Lily Vase
A181

Partridge and Fig Pecker
A182

Minoan Art: 1d, Fruit dish. 1.50d, Rhyton bearer. 2.50d, Ladies of Knossos Palace. 4.50d, Sarcophagus of Hagia Trias. 6d, Dancer. 10d, Two vessels with spouts.

**Perf. 13x13½, 13½x13**

| **1961, June 30** | | | | **Litho.** |
|---|---|---|---|---|
| 708 | A181 | 20 l multi | .40 | .25 |
| 709 | A182 | 50 l multi | .40 | .25 |
| 710 | A182 | 1d multi | .40 | .25 |
| 711 | A181 | 1.50d multi | .80 | .25 |
| 712 | A182 | 2.50d multi | 5.75 | .25 |
| 713 | A182 | 4.50d multi | 2.40 | 1.60 |
| 714 | A182 | 6d multi | 11.00 | 1.30 |
| 715 | A182 | 10d multi | 12.00 | 6.50 |
| | *Nos. 708-715 (8)* | | 33.15 | 10.65 |

Democritus Nuclear Research Center — A183

Democritus
A184

## 1961, July 31 — Perf. 13½x13

| | | | | |
|---|---|---|---|---|
| 716 | A183 | 2.50d dp lil rose & rose lil | .40 | .25 |
| 717 | A184 | 4.50d vio bl & pale vio bl | .80 | .50 |

Inauguration of the Democritus Nuclear Research Center at Aghia Paraskevi.

### Europa Issue, 1961
### Common Design Type

## 1961, Sept. 18 — Perf. 13½x12
### Size: 32½x22mm

| | | | | |
|---|---|---|---|---|
| 718 | CD4 | 2.50d ver & pink | .40 | .25 |
| a. | | Pink omitted (inscriptions white) | 27.50 | 27.50 |
| 719 | CD4 | 4.50d ultra & lt ultra | .40 | .25 |

Nicephoros Phocas — A185

## 1961, Sept. 22 — Wmk. 252

| | | | | |
|---|---|---|---|---|
| 720 | A185 | 2.50d multi | .80 | .50 |

1000th anniv. of the liberation of Crete from the Saracens by the Byzantine general (later emperor) Phocas.

Hermes Head of 1861 — A186

Each denomination shows a different stamp of 1861 issue.

## 1961, Dec. 20 Litho. — Perf. 13x13½

| | | | | |
|---|---|---|---|---|
| 721 | A186 | 20 l brn, red brn & cream | .25 | .25 |
| 722 | A186 | 50 l brn, bis & straw | .25 | .25 |
| 723 | A186 | 1.50d emer & gray | .25 | .25 |
| 724 | A186 | 2.50d red org & ol bis | .25 | .25 |
| 725 | A186 | 4.50d dk bl, bl & gray | .40 | .25 |
| 726 | A186 | 6d rose lil, pale rose & bl | .60 | .40 |
| 727 | A186 | 10d car, rose & cr | 1.20 | 1.20 |
| | | Nos. 721-727 (7) | 3.20 | 2.85 |

Centenary of Greek postage stamps.

Tauropos Dam and Lake A187

Ptolemais Power Station A188

Designs: 50 l, Ladhon river hydroelectric plant. 1.50d, Louros river dam. 2.50d, Aliverion power plant. 4.50d, Salonika hydroelectric sub-station. 6d, Agra river hydroelectric station, interior.

### Perf. 13x13½, 13½x13

## 1962, Apr. 14 — Wmk. 252

| | | | | |
|---|---|---|---|---|
| 728 | A187 | 20 l multi | .25 | .25 |
| 729 | A187 | 50 l multi | .25 | .25 |
| 730 | A188 | 1d multi | .25 | .25 |
| 731 | A188 | 1.50d multi | .25 | .25 |
| 732 | A188 | 2.50d multi | 1.00 | .25 |
| 733 | A188 | 4.50d multi | .80 | .60 |
| 734 | A188 | 6d multi | 3.25 | 3.25 |
| | | Nos. 728-734 (7) | 6.05 | 5.10 |

National electrification project.

---

Youth with Shield and Helmet from Ancient Vase — A189

Designs: 2.50d, Zappion hall, horiz. 4.50d, Kneeling soldier from Temple of Aphaea, Aegina. 6d, Standing soldier from stele of Ariston.

### Perf. 13¼x14, 12x13½

## 1962, May 3 Litho. — Wmk. 252
### Sizes: 22x33mm, 33x22mm

| | | | | |
|---|---|---|---|---|
| 735 | A189 | 2.50d grn, bl, red & brn | .25 | .25 |
| 736 | A189 | 3d brn, buff & red brn | .25 | .25 |
| 737 | A189 | 4.50d bl & gray | .35 | .35 |

### Size: 21x37mm

| | | | | |
|---|---|---|---|---|
| 738 | A189 | 6d brn red & blk | .35 | .25 |
| | | Nos. 735-738 (4) | 1.20 | 1.30 |

Ministerial congress of NATO countries, Athens, May 3-5.

### Europa Issue, 1962
### Common Design Type

## 1962, Sept. 17 — Perf. 13½x12
### Size: 33x23mm

| | | | | |
|---|---|---|---|---|
| 739 | CD5 | 2.50d ver & blk | .70 | .40 |
| 740 | CD5 | 4.50d ultra & blk | 1.30 | .75 |

Hands and Grain — A190

## 1962, Oct. 30 — Perf. 13x13½

| | | | | |
|---|---|---|---|---|
| 741 | A190 | 1.50d dp car, blk & brn | .40 | .25 |
| 742 | A190 | 2.50d brt grn, blk & brn | .60 | .25 |

Agricultural Insurance Program.

Demeter — A191

Design: 4.50d, Wheat and globe.

### Perf. 12x13½

## 1963, Apr. 25 — Wmk. 252

| | | | | |
|---|---|---|---|---|
| 743 | A191 | 2.50d brn car, gray & blk, gold | .35 | .25 |
| 744 | A191 | 4.50d blue, gray, blk, tan | .70 | .30 |

FAO "Freedom from Hunger" campaign.

George I, Constantine XII, Alexander I, George II and Paul I — A192

### Perf. 13½x12½

## 1963, June 29 — Engr.

| | | | | |
|---|---|---|---|---|
| 745 | A192 | 50 l rose car | .25 | .25 |
| 746 | A192 | 1.50d green | .40 | .25 |
| 747 | A192 | 2.50d redsh brn | .80 | .25 |
| 748 | A192 | 4.50d dk blue | 1.30 | 1.00 |
| 749 | A192 | 6d violet | 3.00 | .50 |
| | | Nos. 745-749 (5) | 5.75 | 2.25 |

Centenary of the Greek dynasty.

### Coin Types of 1959

Ancient Greek Coins: 50 l, Nymph Arethusa & Chariot. 80 l, Hercules & Zeus. 1d, Helios & Rose. 1.50d, Griffin & Square. 3d, Zeus & Eagle. 3.50d, Athena & Owl. 4.50d, Apollo & Labyrinth. 6d, Aphrodite & Apollo. 8.50d, Ram's head & Incuse Squares.

---

### Perf. 13½x13, 13x13½

## 1963, July 5 Litho. — Wmk. 252
### Coins in Various Shades of Gray

| | | | | |
|---|---|---|---|---|
| 750 | A164 | 50 l violet bl | .25 | .25 |
| 751 | A164 | 80 l dp magenta | .25 | .25 |
| 752 | A165 | 1d emerald | .25 | .25 |
| 753 | A164 | 1.50d lilac rose | .70 | .25 |
| 754 | A164 | 3d olive | .50 | .25 |
| 755 | A164 | 3.50d vermilion | .60 | .25 |
| 756 | A165 | 4.50d redsh brn | .70 | .40 |
| 757 | A165 | 6d blue grn | .90 | .25 |
| 758 | A165 | 8.50d brt blue | 1.60 | .70 |
| | | Nos. 750-758 (9) | 5.75 | 2.85 |

"Acropolis at Dawn" by Lord Baden-Powell A193

Jamboree Badge (Boeotian Shield) A194

Designs: 2.50d, Crown Prince Constantine, Chief Scout. 3d, Athanassios Lefkadites (founder of Greek Scouts) and Lord Baden-Powell. 4.50d, Scout bugling with conch shell.

## 1963, Aug. 1

| | | | | |
|---|---|---|---|---|
| 759 | A193 | 1d bl, sal & ol | .25 | .25 |
| 760 | A194 | 1.50d dk bl, org brn & brn | .25 | .25 |
| 761 | A194 | 2.50d multi | 1.00 | .25 |
| 762 | A193 | 3d multi | .40 | .45 |
| 763 | A194 | 4.50d multi | 1.00 | .45 |
| | | Nos. 759-763 (5) | 2.90 | 1.65 |

11th Boy Scout Jamboree, Marathon, July 29-Aug. 16, 1963.

Athenian Treasury, Delphi — A195

2d, Centenary emblem. 2.50d, Queen Olga, founder of Greek Red Cross. 4.50d, Henri Dunant.

## 1963, Sept. 16 — Perf. 12x13½

| | | | | |
|---|---|---|---|---|
| 764 | A195 | 1d multi | .40 | .25 |
| 765 | A195 | 2d multi | .25 | .25 |
| 766 | A195 | 2.50d multi | .25 | .25 |
| 767 | A195 | 4.50d multi | .60 | .40 |
| | | Nos. 764-767 (4) | 1.50 | 1.15 |

International Red Cross Centenary.

### Europa Issue, 1963
### Common Design Type

## 1963, Sept. 16 — Perf. 13½x12
### Size: 33x23mm

| | | | | |
|---|---|---|---|---|
| 768 | CD6 | 2.50d green | 1.90 | .40 |
| 769 | CD6 | 4.50d brt magenta | 2.75 | 1.25 |

Vatopethion Monastery — A196

Designs: 80 l, St. Denys' Monastery. 1d, "Protaton" (Founder's) Church, horiz. 2d, Stavronikita Monastery. 2.50d, Jeweled cover of Nicephoros Phocas Gospel. 3.50d, Fresco of St. Athanassios, founder of community. 4.50d, Presentation of Christ, 11th century manuscript. 6d, Great Lavra Church, horiz.

### Perf. 13x13½, 13½x13

## 1963, Dec. 5 Litho. — Wmk. 252

| | | | | |
|---|---|---|---|---|
| 770 | A196 | 30 l multi | .25 | .25 |
| 771 | A196 | 80 l multi | .25 | .25 |
| 772 | A196 | 1d multi | .25 | .25 |
| 773 | A196 | 2d multi | .80 | .25 |
| 774 | A196 | 2.50d multi | 2.40 | .25 |
| 775 | A196 | 3.50d multi | .80 | .70 |

---

| | | | | |
|---|---|---|---|---|
| 776 | A196 | 4.50d multi | .80 | .45 |
| 777 | A196 | 6d multi | .90 | .45 |
| | | Nos. 770-777 (8) | 6.45 | 2.85 |

Millennium of the founding of the monastic community on Mt. Athos.

King Paul I (1901-1964) — A197

## 1964, May 6 — Perf. 12x13½

| | | | | |
|---|---|---|---|---|
| 778 | A197 | 30 l brown | .25 | .25 |
| 779 | A197 | 50 l purple | .25 | .25 |
| 780 | A197 | 1d green | .60 | .25 |
| 781 | A197 | 1.50d orange | .35 | .25 |
| 782 | A197 | 2d blue | .60 | .25 |
| 783 | A197 | 2.50d chocolate | .60 | .25 |
| 784 | A197 | 3.50d red brn | .60 | .25 |
| 785 | A197 | 4d ultra | 1.60 | .25 |
| 786 | A197 | 4.50d bluish blk | 1.60 | .65 |
| 787 | A197 | 6d rose pink | 2.40 | .25 |
| | | Nos. 778-787 (10) | 8.85 | 3.45 |

Archangel Michael — A198

Designs: 1d, Bulgaroctonus coin of Emperor Basil II. 1.50d, Two armed saints from ivory triptych by Harbaville, Louvre. 2.50d, Lady, fresco by Panselinos, Protaton Church, Mt. Athos. 4.50d, Angel, mosaic, Daphni Church, Athens.

## 1964, June 10 — Perf. 12x13½

| | | | | |
|---|---|---|---|---|
| 788 | A198 | 1d multi | .25 | .25 |
| 789 | A198 | 1.50d multi | .25 | .25 |
| 790 | A198 | 2d multi | .25 | .25 |
| 791 | A198 | 2.50d multi | .25 | .25 |
| 792 | A198 | 4.50d multi | .65 | .40 |
| | | Nos. 788-792 (5) | 1.65 | 1.40 |

Byzantine Art and for the Byzantine Art Exhibition, Athens, Apr.-June, 1964.
Exist imperf.

Birth of Aphrodite, Emblem of Kythera — A199

Designs (emblems of islands): 20 l, Trident, Paxos. 1d, Head of Ulysses, Ithaca. 2d, St. George slaying dragon, Lefkas. 2.50d, Zakyntnos, Zante. 4.50d, Cephalus, dog and spear, Cephalonia. 6d, Trireme, Corfu.

### Perf. 13½x12

## 1964, July 20 Litho. — Wmk. 252

| | | | | |
|---|---|---|---|---|
| 793 | A199 | 20 l multi | .25 | .25 |
| 794 | A199 | 30 l multi | .25 | .25 |
| 795 | A199 | 1d multi | .25 | .25 |
| 796 | A199 | 2d multi | .25 | .25 |
| 797 | A199 | 2.50d sl grn & dl grn | .40 | .25 |
| 798 | A199 | 4.50d multi | .80 | .60 |
| 799 | A199 | 6d multi | .80 | .35 |
| | | Nos. 793-799 (7) | 3.00 | 2.20 |

Centenary of the union of the Ionian Islands with Greece.

Child and Sun — A200

## 1964, Sept. 10 — Wmk. 252

| | | | | |
|---|---|---|---|---|
| 800 | A200 | 2.50d multi | .80 | .25 |

50th anniv. of the Natl. Institute of Social Welfare for the Protection of Children and Mothers (P.I.K.P.A.).

### Europa Issue, 1964
### Common Design Type

## 1964, Sept. 14 Litho. — Perf. 13x13½
### Size: 23x39mm

| | | | | |
|---|---|---|---|---|
| 801 | CD7 | 2.50d lt grn & dk red | 1.75 | .35 |
| 802 | CD7 | 4.50d gray & brn | 2.40 | 1.20 |

King Constantine II and
Queen Anne-
Marie — A201

**1964, Sept. 18   Engr.   Perf. 13½x14**
803  A201  1.50d green            .25   .25
804  A201  2.50d rose car         .25   .25
805  A201  4.50d brt ultra        .40   .25
     Nos. 803-805 (3)             .90   .75

Wedding of King Constantine II and Princess Anne-Marie of Denmark, Sept. 18, 1964.

Peleus and Atalante
Fighting, 6th Cent. B.C.
Vase — A202

Designs: 1d, Runners on amphora, horiz. 2d, Athlete on vase, horiz. 2.50d, Discus thrower and judge, pitcher. 4.50d, Charioteer, sculpture, horiz. 6d, Boxers, vase, horiz. 10d, Apollo, frieze from Zeus Temple at Olympia.

**Perf. 12x13½, 13½x12**
**1964, Oct. 24   Litho.   Wmk. 252**
806  A202   10 l  multi          .25   .25
807  A202    1d  multi           .25   .25
808  A202    2d  multi           .25   .25
809  A202  2.50d  multi          .25   .25
810  A202  4.50d  multi          .40   .30
811  A202    6d  multi           .25   .25
812  A202   10d  multi           .30   .25
     Nos. 806-812 (7)           1.95  1.80

18th Olympic Games, Tokyo, Oct. 10-25.

Detail from "Christ
Stripped of His
Garments" by El
Greco — A203

Paintings by El Greco: 1d, Concert of the Angels. 1.50d, El Greco's painted signature, horiz. 2.50d, Self-portrait. 4.50d, Storm-lashed Toledo.

**Perf. 12x13½, 13½x12**
**1965, Mar. 6   Litho.   Wmk. 252**
813  A203   50 l  sepia &
              multi              .25   .25
814  A203    1d  gray & multi    .25   .25
  a.   Double impression of black  115.00
815  A203  1.50d  multi          .25   .25
816  A203  2.50d  sl & multi     .25   .25
817  A203  4.50d  multi         1.25  1.25
     Nos. 813-817 (5)           1.25  1.25

350th anniv. of the death of Domenico Theotocopoulos, El Greco (1541-1614).

Aesculapius Theatre,
Epidauros — A204

Design: 4.50d, Herod Atticus Theatre, and Acropolis, Athens.

**1965, Apr. 30   Litho.   Perf. 12x13½**
818  A204  1.50d  multi          .25   .25
819  A204  4.50d  multi          .25   .25

Epidauros and Athens theatrical festivals.

ITU Emblem, Old
and New
Telecommunication
Equipment — A205

**1965, Apr. 30   Perf. 13½x12**
820  A205  2.50d  multi          .35   .25

Cent. of the ITU.

Swearing-in
Ceremony
A206

Flag of Philiki
Hetaeria, the
Friends' Society
A207

**Perf. 13½x12**
**1965, May 31   Litho.   Wmk. 252**
821  A206  1.50d  multi          .25   .25
822  A207  4.50d  gray & multi   .25   .25

150th anniv. of the Friends' Society, a secret organization for the liberation of Greece from Turkey.

Emblem of
A.H.E.P.A. — A208

**1965, June 30**
823  A208  6d  lt bl, blk & ol   .50   .25

Congress of the American Hellenic Educational Progressive Association, Athens.

Eleutherios Venizelos,
Therissos, 1905 — A209

Designs: 2d, Venizelos signing Treaty of Sevres, 1920. 2.50d, Venizelos portrait.

**1965, June 30   Engr.   Perf. 12½x13**
824  A209  1.50d  green          .25   .25
825  A209    2d  dark blue       .35   .25
826  A209  2.50d  brown          .25   .25
     Nos. 824-826 (3)            .85   .75

Cent. of the birth of Eleutherios Venizelos (1864-1936), statesman and prime minister.

Symbols of
Planets
A210

Astronaut in
Space
A211

Design: 6d, Two space ships over globe.

**Perf. 12½x13½**
**1965, Sept. 11   Litho.   Wmk. 252**
827  A210   50 l  multi          .25   .25
828  A211  2.50d  multi          .25   .25
829  A211    6d  multi           .25   .25
     Nos. 827-829 (3)            .75   .75

16th Astronautical Cong., Athens, 9/12-18.

Victory
Medal
A212

Stadium, Phaleron
A213

Design: 1d, Games' emblem and "JBA."

**Perf. 13½x13, 13x13½**
**1965, Sept. 11**
830  A213  1d  multicolored      .25   .25
831  A212  2d  multicolored      .25   .25
832  A213  6d  multicolored      .25   .25
     Nos. 830-832 (3)            .75   .75

24th Balkan Games, Sept. 1-10.

## Europa Issue, 1965
### Common Design Type

**1965, Oct. 21   Perf. 13½x12**
### Size: 33x23mm
833  CD8  2.50d  bl gray, blk & dk
              bl                  .75   .40
834  CD8  4.50d  olive, blk & grn  1.50  .75

Hipparchus and
Astrolabe — A214

**1965, Oct. 21   Litho.   Wmk. 252**
835  A214  2.50d  bl grn, blk & dk
              red                 .35   .25

Opening of the Evghenides Planetarium, Athens.

St. Andrew's
Church,
Patras
A215

St. Andrew
A216

**1965, Nov. 30   Perf. 12x13½**
836  A215  1d  multicolored      .25   .25
837  A216  5d  multicolored      .25   .25

Return of the head of St. Andrew from St. Peter's, Rome to St. Andrew's, Patras. The design of the 5d is from an 11th cent. mosaic at St. Luke's Monastery, Boeotia.

Ants and
Anthill
A217

Savings
Bank and
Book
A218

**1965, Nov. 30   Litho.   Wmk. 252**
838  A217   10 l  grn, blk & bis  .25   .25
839  A218  2.50d  multi          .25   .25

50th anniv. of the Post Office Savings Bank.

Theodore
Brysakes — A219

Greek Painters: 1d, Nikeforus Lytras. 2.50d, Constantin Volonakis. 4d, Nicolas Gyses. 5d, George Jacobides.

**Perf. 13x13½**
**1966, Feb. 28   Litho.   Wmk. 252**
840  A219   80 l  multi          .25   .25
841  A219    1d  multi           .25   .25
842  A219  2.50d  multi          .25   .25
843  A219    4d  multi           .25   .25
844  A219    5d  multi           .25   .25
     Nos. 840-844 (5)           1.25  1.25

Jean Gabriel
Eynard — A220

Banknote of
1867
A221

2.50d, Georgios Stavros.  4d, Bank's 1st headquarters, etching by Yannis Kefallinos.

**Perf. 12x13½**
**1966, Mar. 30   Engr.   Wmk. 252**
845  A220  1.50d  gray grn        .25   .25
846  A220  2.50d  brown          .25   .25
847  A221    4d  ultra           .25   .25
848  A221    6d  black           .25   .25
     Nos. 845-848 (4)           1.00  1.00

National Bank of Greece, 125th anniv.

Symbolic
Water Cycle
A222

UNESCO
Emblem
A223

WHO
Headquarters,
Geneva — A224

**Perf. 12x13½, 13½x12**
**1966, Apr. 18   Litho.**
849  A222  1d  multicolored      .25   .25
850  A223  3d  multicolored      .25   .25
851  A224  5d  multicolored      .25   .25
     Nos. 849-851 (3)            .75   .75

Hydrological Decade (UNESCO), 1965-74, (1d); 20th anniv. of UNESCO (3d); inauguration of the WHO Headquarters, Geneva (5d).

Geannares
Michael
(Hatzes)
A225

Explosion at
Arkadi Monastery
A226

Map of
Crete — A227

**1966, Apr. 18**
852  A225    2d  multi           .25   .25
853  A226  2.50d  multi          .25   .25
854  A227  4.50d  multi          .25   .25
     Nos. 852-854 (3)            .75   .75

Cent. of the Cretan revolt against the Turks. Geannares Michael (Hatzes), the leader of the revolt, was a member of Cretan government and a writer.

Copper
Mask, 4th
Century,
B.C.
A228

Dionysus on a
Thespian Ship-
Chariot
A229

Designs: 2.50d, Old Theater of Dionysus, Athens, 6th Century B.C. 4.50d, Dancing Dionysus, from vase by Kleophrades, c. 500 B.C.

**Perf. 12x13½, 13½x12**
**1966, May 26   Litho.   Wmk. 252**
855  A228    1d  multi           .25   .25
856  A229  1.50d  multi          .25   .25
857  A229  2.50d  multi          .25   .25
858  A228  4.50d  multi          .25   .25
     Nos. 855-858 (4)           1.00  1.00

2500th anniversary of Greek theater.

Boeing 707-320 over New York Buildings and Greek Column — A230

**1966, May 26**      *Perf. 13x12½*
859 A230 6d blue & dark blue    .35   .25

Inauguration of transatlantic flights of Olympic Airways.

Tobacco Worker — A231

Design: 5d, Woman sorting tobacco leaves.

*Perf. 12½x13½*
**1966, Sept. 19**   **Litho.**   **Wmk. 252**
860 A231 1d multicolored    .25   .25
861 A231 5d multicolored    .40   .25

Greek tobacco industry, and 4th Intl. Scientific Tobacco Congress, Athens, Sept. 19-26.

**Europa Issue, 1966**
Common Design Type

**1966, Sept. 19**   **Litho.**   **Wmk. 252**
**Size: 23x33mm**
862 CD9 1.50d olive    .70   .35
863 CD9 4.50d lt red brown    1.40   .70

Carved Cases for Knitting Needles A232

Bridegroom, Embroidery from Epirus A233

Designs (Popular Art): 50 l, Lyre, Crete. 1d, Massa (stringed instrument). 1.50d, Bas-relief (cross and angels). 2d, Icon (Sts. Constantine and Helena). 2.50d, Virgin (wood carving, Church of St. Nicholas, Galaxeidon). 3d, Embroidery (sailing ship from Skyros). 4d, Embroidery (wedding parade). 4.50d, Carved wooden distaff (Sts. George and Barbara). 5d, Silver and agate necklace and earrings. 20d, Handwoven cloth, Cyprus.

*Perf. 12x13½, 13½x12*
**1966, Nov. 21**   **Litho.**   **Wmk. 252**
864 A232 10 l multi    .25   .25
865 A233 30 l multi    .25   .25
866 A232 50 l multi    .25   .25
867 A232 1d multi    .25   .25
868 A232 1.50d multi    .25   .25
869 A232 2d multi    1.25   .25
870 A232 2.50d multi    .25   .25
871 A233 3d multi    .25   .25
872 A233 4d multi    .55   .25
873 A233 4.50d multi    .25   .25
874 A232 5d multi    .60   .25
875 A233 20d multi    1.20   .40
     *Nos. 864-875 (12)*    5.60 3.15

King Constantine II, Queen Anne-Marie and Princess Alexia — A234

Designs: 2d, Princess Alexia. 3.50d, Queen Anne-Marie and Princess Alexia.

*Perf. 13½x14*
**1966, Dec. 19**   **Engr.**   **Wmk. 252**
876 A234 2d green    .25   .25
877 A234 2.50d brown    .25   .25
878 A234 3.50d ultra    .25   .25
     *Nos. 876-878 (3)*    .75   .75

Princess Alexia, successor to the throne of Greece.

---

"Night" by John Cossos (1830-73) — A235

Sculptures: 50 l, Penelope by Leonides Drosses (1836-1882). 80 l, Shepherd by George Fytales. 2d, Woman's torso by Constantine Demetriades (1881-1943). 2.50d, "Colocotrones" (equestrian statue) by Lazarus Sochos (1862-1911). 3d, Sleeping Young Lady by John Halepas (1851-1938), horiz. 10d, Woodcutter by George Filippotes (1839-1919), horiz.

*Perf. 12x13½, 13½x12*
**1967, Feb. 28**   **Litho.**   **Wmk. 252**
879 A235 20 l Prus bl, gray & blk    .25   .25
880 A235 50 l brn, gray & blk    .25   .25
881 A235 80 l brn red, gray & blk    .25   .25
882 A235 2d vio bl, gray & blk    .25   .25
883 A235 2.50d ultra, blk & grn    .25   .25
884 A235 3d bl, lt bl, gray & blk    .35   .25
885 A235 10d bl & multi    .25   .25
     *Nos. 879-885 (7)*    1.85 1.75

Issued to honor modern Greek sculptors.

World Map and Olympic Rings A236

Discus Thrower by C. Demetriades A237

Designs: 1.50d, Runners on ancient clay vessel. 2.50d, Hurdler and map of Europe and Near East. 6d, Rising sun over Altis ruins at Olympia.

*Perf. 13½x12, 12x13½*
**1967, Apr. 6**   **Litho.**   **Wmk. 252**
886 A236 1d multi    .25   .25
887 A236 1.50d multi    .25   .25
888 A236 2.50d multi    .25   .25
889 A237 5d multi    .35   .25
890 A236 6d multi    .40   .25
     *Nos. 886-890 (5)*    1.50 1.25

Olympic Games Day, Apr. 6 (1d); Classic Marathon Race, Apr. 6 (1.5d); athletic qualifying rounds for the Cup of Europe, June 24-25 (2.50d); 9th contest for the European Athletic Championships, 1969 (5d); founding of the Intl. Academy at Olympia and the 7th meeting of the Academy, July 29-Aug. 14, 1967 (6d).

**Europa Issue, 1967**
Common Design Type

*Perf. 12x13½*
**1967, May 2**   **Litho.**   **Wmk. 252**
**Size: 23x33½mm**
891 CD10 2.50d buff, lt & dk brn    .80   .25
892 CD10 4.50d grn, lt & dk grn    *2.25*   *.60*

Chapel, Skopelos Island A238

Plaka District, Athens A239

Intl. Tourist Year: 4.50d, Doric Temple of Epicurean Apollo, by Itkinus, c. 430 B.C.

*Perf. 13½x12, 12x13½*
**1967, June 26**   **Litho.**   **Wmk. 252**
893 A238 2.50d multi    .25   .25
894 A238 4.50d multi    .40   .35
    a.   Double impression of black
895 A239 6d multi    .40   .30
     *Nos. 893-895 (3)*    1.05   .90

---

Destroyer and Sailor A240

Training Ship, Merchant Marine Academy A241

Maritime Week: 2.50d, Merchant Marine Academy, Aspropyrgos, Attica, and rowing crew. 3d, Cruiser Georgios Averoff and Naval School, Poros. 6d, Merchant ship and bearded figurehead.

**1967, June 26**
896 A240 20 l multi    .25   .25
897 A241 1d multi    .25   .25
898 A240 2.50d multi    .25   .25
899 A240 3d multi    .25   .25
900 A240 6d multi    .35   .25
     *Nos. 896-900 (5)*    1.35 1.25

Soldier and Rising Phoenix — A242

*Perf. 12x13½*
**1967, Aug. 30**   **Litho.**   **Wmk. 252**
901 A242 2.50d blue & multi    .25   .25
902 A242 3d orange & multi    .25   .25
903 A242 4.50d multi    .25   .25
     *Nos. 901-903 (3)*    .75   .75

Revolution of Apr. 21, 1967.

Blast Furnaces — A243

**1967, Nov. 29**      *Perf. 13x14*
904 A243 4.50d brt bl & dk vio bl    .35   .35

1st meeting of the UN Industrial Development Organization, Athens, Nov. 29-Dec. 20.

Sailboats — A244

Children's Drawings: 1.50d, Steamship and island. 3.50d, Farmhouse. 6d, Church on hill.

**1967, Dec. 20**      *Perf. 13½x12½*
905 A244 20 l multi    .25   .25
906 A244 1.50d grn, dk bl & blk    .25   .25
907 A244 3.50d multi    .35   .35
908 A244 6d multi    .35   .35
     *Nos. 905-908 (4)*    1.20 1.20

Javelin — A245

Apollo, Olympic Academy Seal — A246

Discus Thrower by Demetriades — A247

Designs: 1d, Jumping. 2.50d, Attic vase showing lighting of Olympic torch. 4d, Olympic

---

rings and world map, horiz. 6d, Long-distance runners, vert.

**Wmk. 252**
**1968, Feb. 28**   **Litho.**   *Perf. 12½*
909 A245 50 l ultra & bis    .25   .25
910 A245 1d grn, yel, blk & gray    .25   .25
911 A246 1.50d blk, bl & buff    .25   .25
912 A246 2.50d ol grn, blk & org brn    .25   .25
913 A246 4d gray & multi    .30   .25
914 A247 4.50d bl, grn, yel & blk    1.00   .30
915 A245 6d brn, red & bl    .25   .25
     *Nos. 909-915 (7)*    2.55 1.80

50 l, 1d, 6d, 27th Balkan Games, Athens, Aug. 29-Sept. 1; 1.50d, Meeting of the Intl. Olympic Academy; 2.50d, Lighting of the Olympic torch for 19th Olympic Games, Mexico City; 4d, Olympic Day, Apr. 6; 4.50d, 9th European Athletic Championships, 1969.

**Europa Issue, 1968**
Common Design Type

*Perf. 13½x12*
**1968, Mar. 29**   **Litho.**   **Wmk. 252**
**Size: 33x23mm**
916 CD11 2.50d cop red, bis & blk    *1.00*   *.35*
917 CD11 4.50d vio, bister & blk    *2.10 1.10*

Emblems of Greek and International Automobile Clubs — A248

**1968, Mar. 29**      *Perf. 13x14*
918 A248 5d ultra & org brn    .80   .35

General Assembly of the International Automobile Federation, Athens, Apr. 8-14.

Athena Defeating Alkyoneus, from Pergamos Altar, 180 B.C. — A249

Athena, 2nd Century, B.C. — A250

Winged Victory of Samothrace, c. 190 B.C. — A251

Designs: 50 l, Alexander the Great on horseback, from sarcophagus, c. 310 B.C. 1.50d, Emperors Constantine and Justinian bringing offerings to Virgin Mary, Byzantine mosaic. 2.50d, Emperor Constantine Paleologos, lithograph by D. Tsokos, 1859. 3d, Greece in Missolonghi, by Delacroix. 4.50d, Greek Soldier (evzone), by G. B. Scott.

*Perf. 13½x13, 13x13½, 13½x14 (A249)*
**1968, Apr. 27**
919 A249 10 l gray & multi    .25   .25
920 A250 20 l grn & multi    .25   .25
921 A250 50 l pur & multi    .25   .25
922 A249 1.50d gray & multi    .25   .25
923 A250 2.50d multi    .25   .25
924 A251 3d multi    .25   .25
925 A251 4.50d multi    .25   .25
926 A251 6d multi    .30   .25
     *Nos. 919-926 (8)*    2.05 2.00

"The Hellenic Fight for Civilization" exhibition

Monument to the Unknown Priest and Teacher, Rhodes A252

Map & Flag of Greece A253

**Perf. 14x13½, 13½x14**

**1968, July 11    Litho.    Wmk. 252**
927  A252  2d multicolored    .35    .25
928  A253  5d multicolored    .70    .70

20th anniv. of the union of the Dodecanese Islands with Greece.

Cross and Globe — A254

**1968, July 11    Perf. 13½x14**
929  A254  6d multicolored    .45    .35

19th Biennial Congress of the Greek Orthodox Archdiocese of North and South America.

Antique Lamp (GAPA Emblem) — A255

**1968, July 11    Perf. 14x13½**
930  A255  6d multicolored    .40    .25

Regional Congress of the Greek-American Progressive Association, G.A.P.A.

Fragment of Bas-relief, Temple of Aesculapius, Athens — A256

**Perf. 13½x14**

**1968, Sept. 8    Litho.    Wmk. 252**
931  A256  4.50d multicolored    1.20    .75

Issued to publicize the 5th European Cardiology Congress, Athens, Sept. 8-14.

View of Olympia, Site of Ancient Games — A257

Pindar and Olympic Ode — A258

Design: 2.50d, Panathenaic Stadium, site of 1896 Olympic Games.

**Perf. 14x13½, 13x13½**

**1968, Sept. 25    Litho.    Wmk. 252**
932  A257  2.50d multicolored    .25    .25
933  A257  5d green & multi    .50    .25
934  A258  10d bl, yel & brn    1.20    .65
    Nos. 932-934 (3)    1.95    1.15

19th Olympic Games, Mexico City, 10/12-27.
On 10d, hyphen is omitted at end of 5th line of ode on 5 of 50 stamps in each sheet.

Hygeia and WHO Emblem — A259

**1968, Nov. 8    Perf. 13½x14**
935  A259  5d gray & multi    .60    .35

20th anniv. of WHO.

Mediterranean, Breguet 19 and Flight Route, 1928 — A260

Farman, 1912, Plane and F-104G Jet — A261

Design: 2.50d, Greek air force pilot ramming enemy plane over Langada.

**1968, Nov. 8    Perf. 14x13½, 13½x14**
936  A260  2.50d ultra, blk & yel    .25    .25
937  A260  3.50d multicolored    .25    .25
938  A261    8d multicolored    1.00    .75
    Nos. 936-938 (3)    1.50    1.25

Exploits of Royal Hellenic Air Force.

St. Zeno, The Letter Bearer — A262

**Perf. 13½x14**
**1969, Feb. 10    Litho.    Wmk. 252**
939  A262  2.50d multicolored    .40    .25

Establishment of the feast day of St. Zeno as the day of Greek p.o. personnel.

Hephaestus and Cyclops, Bas-relief A263

Parade of Harvesters, Minoan Vase A264

**1969, Feb. 10    Perf. 13½x12½**
940  A263  1.50d multicolored    .30    .25
941  A264  10d multicolored    .75    .55

50th anniv. of the ILO.

Yachts in Vouliagmeni Harbor — A265

Athens Festival, Chorus of Elders — A266

View of Astypalaia A267

**Perf. 13½x12½, 12½x13½**

**1969, Mar. 3**
942  A265  1d multicolored    .25    .25
943  A266  5d multicolored    .65    .60
944  A267  6d multicolored    .35    .25
    Nos. 942-944 (3)    1.25    1.10

Issued for tourist publicity.

Attic Shield and Helmet on Greek Coin, 461-450 B.C. — A268

Hoplites and Flutist, from Proto-Corinthian Pitcher, 640-630 B.C. — A269

**Perf. 12½x13½, 13½x12½**
**1969, Apr. 4    Litho.    Wmk. 252**
945  A268  2.50d rose red, blk & sl    .30    .25
946  A269  4.50d multi    .80    .55

20th anniv. of NATO.

**Europa Issue, 1969**
**Common Design Type**
**1969, May 5    Perf. 13½x12½**
**Size: 33x23mm**
947  CD12  2.50d multi    1.40    .25
948  CD12  4.50d multi    2.60    1.00

Victory Medal A270

Pole Vault and Pentathlon (from Panathenaic Amphora) A271

5d, Relay race and runners from amphora, 525 B.C., horiz. 8d, Modern and ancient (Panathenaic amphora, c. 480 B.C.) discus throwers.

**Perf. 12½x13½, 13½x12½**
**1969, May 5**
949  A270  20 l  red & multi    .25    .25
950  A271  3d gray & multi    .25    .25
951  A271  5d multicolored    .25    .25
952  A271  8d multicolored    1.15    .60
    Nos. 949-952 (4)    1.90    1.35

Issued to publicize the 9th European Athletic Championships, Athens, Sept. 16-21.

**Greece and the Sea Issue**

Oil Tanker — A272

Merchant Vessels and Warships, 1821 — A273

Designs: 80 l, Brig and steamship, painting by Ioannis Poulakas, vert. 4.50d, Warships on maneuvers. 6d, Battle of Salamis, 480 B.C., painting by Constantine Volonakis.

**Perf. 12½x13½, 13½x12½, 13½x13**
**1969, June 28    Litho.    Wmk. 252**
953  A272    80 l  multicolored    .25    .25
954  A272    2d blk, bl & gray    .25    .25
955  A273  2.50d dk bl & multi    .25    .25
956  A272  4.50d brn, gray & bl    .50    .25
957  A273    6d multicolored    .75    .30
    Nos. 953-957 (5)    2.00    1.30

Raising Greek Flag — A274

**1969, Aug. 31    Perf. 13x13½**
958  A274  2.50d blue & multi    .60    .25

20th anniv. of the Grammos-Vitsi victory.

Athena Promachos and Map of Greece A275

"National Resistance" A276

Greek Participation in World War II — A277

**Perf. 13x13½, 13½x14**
**1969, Oct. 12    Litho.    Wmk. 252**
959  A275  4d multicolored    .25    .25
960  A276  5d multicolored    1.20    .60
961  A277  6d multicolored    .55    .25
    Nos. 959-961 (3)    2.00    1.10

25th anniv. of the liberation of Greece in WW II.
No. 960 exists imperf.

Demetrius Tsames Karatasios, by G. Demetriades A278

Pavlos Melas, by P. Mathiopoulos A279

2.50d, Emmanuel Pappas, statue by Nicholas Perantinos. 4.50d, Capetan Kotas.

**Perf. 12x13½**
**1969, Nov. 12    Litho.    Wmk. 252**
962  A278  1.50d multicolored    .25    .25
963  A278  2.50d blue & multi    .25    .25
964  A279  3.50d gray & multi    .25    .25
965  A279  4.50d multicolored    .75    .45
    Nos. 962-965 (4)    1.50    1.20

Issued to honor Greek heroes in Macedonia's struggle for liberation.

Angel of the Annunciation, Daphni Church, 11th Century A280

Dolphins, Delos, 110 B.C. A281

Christ's Descent into Hell, Nea Moni Church, 11th Cent. — A282

Greek Mosaics: 1.50d, The Holy Ghost (dove), Hosios Loukas Monastery, 11th cent. 2d, The Hunter, Pella, 4th cent. B.C. 5d, Bird, St. George's Church, Salonica, 5th cent.

**Perf. 12x13½, 13½x12 (1d), 13x13½ (6d)**

| 1970, Jan. 16 | Litho. | Wmk. 252 | |
|---|---|---|---|
| 966 A280 | 20 l multicolored | .25 | .25 |
| 967 A281 | 1d multicolored | .25 | .25 |
| 968 A280 | 1.50d blue & multi | .25 | .25 |
| 969 A280 | 2d gray & multi | .40 | .25 |
| 970 A280 | 5d bister & multi | .45 | .30 |
| 971 A282 | 6d multicolored | .60 | .60 |
| Nos. 966-971 (6) | | 2.20 | 1.90 |

Hercules and the Cretan Bull A283

Hercules and the Erymanthian Boar A284

Labors of Hercules: 30 l, Capture of Cerberus. 1d, Capture of the golden apples of the Hesperides. 1.50d, Lernean Hydra. 2d, Slaying of Geryon. 3d, Centaur Nessus. 4.50d, Fight with the river god Achelos. 5d, Nemean lion. 6d, Stymphalian birds. 20d, Giant Antaeus. Designs of 20 l and 1d are from Temple of Zeus, Olympia; others from various vessels; all from 7th-5th cent. B.C.

**Perf. 13½x12, 12x13½**

| 1970, Mar. 16 | Litho. | Wmk. 252 | |
|---|---|---|---|
| 972 A283 | 20 l gray, blk & yel | .25 | .25 |
| 973 A283 | 30 l ocher & multi | .25 | .25 |
| 974 A284 | 1d bl gray, blk & bl | .25 | .25 |
| 975 A283 | 1.50d dk brn, bis & sl grn | .25 | .25 |
| 976 A283 | 2d ocher & multi | 1.75 | .25 |
| 977 A284 | 2.50d ocher, dk brn & dl red | .25 | .25 |
| 978 A284 | 3d multicolored | 1.75 | .25 |
| 979 A283 | 4.50d dk bl & multi | .40 | .25 |
| 980 A283 | 5d multicolored | .40 | .25 |
| 981 A283 | 6d multicolored | .40 | .25 |
| 982 A283 | 20d black & multi | 1.40 | .70 |
| Nos. 972-982 (11) | | 7.35 | 3.20 |

Satellite, Earth Station and Hemispheres A285

| 1970, Apr. 21 | | Perf. 13½x12 | |
|---|---|---|---|
| 983 A285 | 2.50d bl, gray & yel | .40 | .25 |
| 984 A285 | 4.50d brn, ol & bl | 1.00 | .90 |

Opening of the Earth Satellite Telecommunications Station "Thermopylae," Apr. 21, 1970.

**Europa Issue, 1970**
Common Design Type and

Owl (Post Horns and CEPT) — A287

| 1970, Apr. 21 | Perf. 13½x12, 12x13½ | | |
|---|---|---|---|
| 985 CD13 | 2.50d rose red & org | 1.60 | .60 |
| 986 A287 | 3d brt bl, gray & vio bl | 1.60 | .60 |
| 987 CD13 | 4.50d ultra & org | 4.75 | 1.00 |
| Nos. 985-987 (3) | | 7.95 | 2.20 |
| Nos. 985,987 (2) | | 6.35 | 1.60 |

St. Demetrius with Cyril and Methodius as Children A288

Emperor Michael III with Sts. Cyril and Methodius A290

A289

2d, St. Cyril. 10d, St. Methodius.

**Perf. 13½x14 (50 l); 12x13½ (2d, 10d); 13x13½ (5d)**

| 1970, Apr. 17 | Litho. | Wmk. 252 | |
|---|---|---|---|
| 988 A288 | 50 l multi | .25 | .25 |
| 989 | 2d multi | .50 | .40 |
| 990 A290 | 5d multi | .40 | .25 |
| 991 | 10d multi | .60 | .40 |
| a. | A289 Pair, #989, 991 | 1.00 | 1.00 |
| Nos. 988-991 (4) | | 1.75 | 1.30 |

Sts. Cyril and Methodius who translated the Bible into Slavonic.

Greek Fir A292

Jankaea Heldreichii A293

6d, Rock partridge, horiz. 8d, Wild goat.

**Perf. 13x14, 14x13, 12x13½ (2.50d)**

| 1970, June 16 | Litho. | Wmk. 252 | |
|---|---|---|---|
| 992 A292 | 80 l multi | .30 | .30 |
| 993 A293 | 2.50d multi | 1.00 | .25 |
| 994 A292 | 6d multi | 1.90 | .45 |
| 995 A292 | 8d multi | 2.25 | 1.90 |
| Nos. 992-995 (4) | | 5.45 | 2.90 |

European Nature Conservation Year, 1970.

Map Showing Link Between AHEPA Members and Greece — A294

| 1970, Aug. 1 | | Perf. 13½x13 | |
|---|---|---|---|
| 996 A294 | 6d blue & multi | .80 | .35 |

48th annual AHEPA (American Hellenic Educational Progressive Assoc.) Cong., Athens, Aug. 1970.

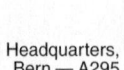
UPU Headquarters, Bern — A295

Education Year Emblem A296

Mahatma Gandhi A297

United Nations Emblem A298

Ludwig van Beethoven A299

**Perf. 13½x12, 13x14, 12x13½**

| 1970, Oct. 7 | Litho. | Wmk. 252 | |
|---|---|---|---|
| 997 A295 | 50 l bis & multi | .25 | .25 |
| 998 A296 | 2.50d bl & multi | .35 | .25 |
| 999 A297 | 3.50d multi | .25 | .25 |
| 1000 A298 | 4d bl & multi | .60 | .25 |
| 1001 A299 | 4.50d multi | 1.20 | .90 |
| Nos. 997-1001 (5) | | 2.65 | 1.90 |

Inauguration of the UPU Headquarters, Bern (50 l); Intl. Education Year (2.50d); cent. of the birth of Mohandas K. Gandhi (1869-1948), leader in India's struggle for independence (3.50d); 25th anniv. of the UN (4d); Ludwig van Beethoven (1770-1827), composer (4.50d).

The Shepherds (Mosaic) — A300

Christmas (from Mosaic in the Monastery of Hosios Loukas, Boetia, 11th cent.): 4.50d, The Three Kings and Angel. 6d, Nativity, horiz.

| 1970, Dec. 5 | Perf. 13x14, 14x13 | | |
|---|---|---|---|
| 1002 A300 | 2d bister & multi | .25 | .25 |
| 1003 A300 | 4.50d bister & multi | .35 | .25 |
| 1004 A300 | 6d bister & multi | .65 | .65 |
| Nos. 1002-1004 (3) | | 1.25 | 1.15 |

"Leonidas" A301

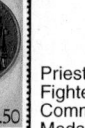
Priest Sworn in as Fighter, from Commemorative Medal — A302

Eugenius Voulgaris (1716-1806) A303

Battle of Corinth A304

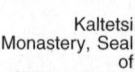
Kaltetsi Monastery, Seal of Peloponnesian Senate — A305

Death of Bishop Isaias, Battle of Alamana A306

Designs: No. 1009, Pericles. No. 1010, Sacrifice of Kapsalis. 1.50d, Terpsichore. No. 1012, Patriarch Grigorius IV. No. 1013, Suliot women in battle, horiz. No. 1015, Karteria. No.

1016, Adamantios Korais, M.D. No. 1017, Memorial column, provincial administrative seal of Epidaurus. 3d, Naval battle, Samos, horiz. 5d, Battle of Athens. 6d, Naval battle, Yeronda. 6.50d, Battle of Maniaki. 9d, Battle of Karpenisi, death of Marcos Botsaris. 10d, Bishop Germanos blessing flag. 15d, Secret School. 20d, John Capodistrias' signature and seal.

| 1971 | Litho. | Wmk. 252 | |
|---|---|---|---|
| 1005 A301 | 20 l multi | .25 | .25 |
| 1006 A302 | 50 l multi | .25 | .25 |
| 1007 A303 | 50 l multi | .25 | .25 |
| 1008 A304 | 50 l multi | .25 | .25 |
| 1009 A301 | 1d multi | .25 | .25 |
| 1010 A301 | 1d multi | .25 | .25 |
| 1011 A301 | 1.50d multi | .25 | .25 |
| 1012 A302 | 2d multi | .25 | .25 |
| 1013 A304 | 2d multi | .25 | .25 |
| 1014 A305 | 2d multi | .25 | .25 |
| 1015 A301 | 2.50d multi | .25 | .25 |
| 1016 A303 | 2.50d multi | .25 | .25 |
| 1017 A305 | 2.50d multi | .25 | .25 |
| 1018 A304 | 3d multi | .55 | .35 |
| 1019 A304 | 4d multi | .25 | .25 |
| 1020 A304 | 5d multi | .35 | .25 |
| 1021 A301 | 6d multi | 1.00 | .75 |
| 1022 A301 | 6.50d multi | .35 | .25 |
| 1023 A301 | 9d multi | .80 | .75 |
| 1024 A306 | 10d multi | .90 | .75 |
| 1025 A306 | 15d multi | 1.00 | .90 |
| 1026 A305 | 20d multi | 1.75 | 1.15 |
| Nos. 1005-1026 (22) | | 10.20 | 8.65 |

Sesquicentennial of Greece's uprising against the Turks. Emphasize role of Navy (Nos. 1005, 1009, 1011, 1015, 1018, 1021), issued 3/15; Church (Nos. 1006, 1012, 1019, 1024), 2/8; Instructors (Nos. 1007, 1016, 1025), 6/21; Land Forces (Nos. 1008, 1010, 1013, 1020, 1022-1023), 9/21; Provincial Administrations (Nos. 1014, 1017, 1026), 10/19.

Sizes: 37x24mm: Nos. 1005, 1009, 1011, 1015; 40x27½mm, No. 1021; 48x33mm, Nos. 1022, 1023.

Perfs.: 14x13, Nos. 1005, 1009, 1011, 1013, 1015, 1018; 13½x14, Nos. 1006, 1012; 12x13½, Nos. 1007, 1016, 1019, 1022-1025; 13x14, Nos. 1008, 1010, 1020; 13½x13, Nos. 1014, 1017, 1021, 1026.

Spyridon Louis, Winner of 1896 Marathon Race, Arriving at Stadium A307

Pierre de Coubertin and Memorial Column A308

**Perf. 13½x13, 13x13½**

| 1971, Apr. 10 | Litho. | Wmk. 252 | |
|---|---|---|---|
| 1027 A307 | 3d multi | .40 | .25 |
| 1028 A308 | 8d multi | 1.00 | .75 |

Olympic Games revival, 75th anniv.

**Europa Issue, 1971**
Common Design Type

| 1971, May 18 | Perf. 13½x12 | | |
|---|---|---|---|
| Size: 33x22½mm | | | |
| 1029 CD14 | 2.50d grn, yel & blk | 1.00 | .30 |
| 1030 CD14 | 5d org, yel & blk | 3.00 | 1.50 |

Hosios Lukas Monastery A309

Monasteries and Churches: 1d, Daphni Church. 2d, St. John the Divine, Patmos. 2.50d, Koumbelidiki Church, Kastoria. 4.50d, Chalkeon Church, Thessalonica. 6.50d, Paregoritissa Church, Arta. 8.50d, St. Paul's Monastery, Mt. Athos.

| 1972, Jan. 17 | Perf. 14x13 | | |
|---|---|---|---|
| 1031 A309 | 50 l multi | .25 | .25 |
| 1032 A309 | 1d multi | .25 | .25 |
| 1033 A309 | 2d multi | .25 | .25 |
| 1034 A309 | 2.50d multi | .25 | .25 |
| 1035 A309 | 4.50d multi | .25 | .25 |
| 1036 A309 | 6.50d multi | .25 | .25 |
| 1037 A309 | 8.50d multi | .80 | .80 |
| Nos. 1031-1037 (7) | | 2.30 | 2.30 |

Cretan Costume — A310

Greek regional costumes: 1d, Woman, Pindus. 2d, Man, Missolonghi. 2.50d, Woman, Sarakatsan, Attica. 3d, Woman, Island of Nisyros. 4.50d, Woman, Megara. 6.50d, Woman, Trikeri. 10d, Woman, Pylaia, Macedonia.

| | | | |
|---|---|---|---|
| **1972, Mar. 1** | | **Perf. 12½x13½** | |
| 1038 | A310 | 50 l shown | .25 .25 |
| 1039 | A310 | 1d multi | .25 .25 |
| 1040 | A310 | 2d multi | .25 .25 |
| 1041 | A310 | 2.50d multi | .25 .25 |
| *a.* | | "1972" omitted | 15.00 15.00 |
| 1042 | A310 | 3d multi | .25 .25 |
| 1043 | A310 | 4.50d multi | .25 .25 |
| 1044 | A310 | 6.50d multi | .25 .25 |
| 1045 | A310 | 10d multi | 2.40 .80 |
| | | Nos. 1038-1045 (8) | 4.15 2.55 |

See Nos. 1073-1089, 1121-1135.

Memorial Medal, Science and Industry A311

Flag and Map of Greece A312

Honeycomb, Transportation and Industry — A313

| | | | |
|---|---|---|---|
| | | **Perf. 13½x13, 13x13½** | **Wmk. 252** |
| **1972, Apr. 21** | | | |
| 1046 | A311 | 2.50d blue & multi | .25 .25 |
| 1047 | A312 | 4.50d ocher & multi | .25 .25 |
| 1048 | A313 | 5d multi | .35 .35 |
| | | Nos. 1046-1048 (3) | .85 .85 |

5th anniversary of the revolution.

### Europa Issue 1972
### Common Design Type

| | | | |
|---|---|---|---|
| **1972, May 2** | | **Perf. 12x13½** | |
| | | **Size: 23x33mm** | |
| 1049 | CD15 | 3d multi | .50 .30 |
| 1050 | CD15 | 4.50d blue & multi | 1.50 1.25 |

Acropolis and Car — A314

Route of Automobile Rally — A315

| | | | |
|---|---|---|---|
| **1972, May 26** | | **Perf. 13½x12** | |
| 1051 | A314 | 4.50d multi | .50 .50 |
| 1052 | A315 | 5d bl & multi | .50 .50 |

20th Acropolis Automobile Rally, May 26-29.

Gaia Handing Erecthonius to Athena, Cecrops — A316

Designs: 2d, Uranus, from altar of Zeus at Pergamum. 2.50d, Gods defeating the Giants, Treasury of Siphnos. 5d, Zeus of Dodona.

| | | | |
|---|---|---|---|
| **1972, June 26** | | **Litho.** | **Perf. 14x13½** |
| 1053 | A316 | 1.50d yel grn & blk | .25 .25 |
| 1054 | A316 | 2d dk bl & blk | .25 .25 |
| 1055 | A316 | 2.50d org brn & blk | .25 .25 |
| 1056 | A316 | 5d dk brn & blk | .40 .35 |
| *a.* | | Strip of 4, #1053-1056 | 1.60 1.60 |

Greek mythology. No. 1056 issued only setenant with Nos. 1053-1055 in sheets of 40 (4x10). Nos. 1053-1055 issued also in sheets of 50 each.

Olympic Rings, Wrestlers — A317

50 l, Young athlete, crowning himself, c. 480 B.C., vert. 3.50d, Spartan woman running, Archaic period, vert. 4.50d, Episkyros ball game, 6th century B.C. 10d, Running youths, from Panathenaic amphora.

| | | | |
|---|---|---|---|
| | | **Perf. 13½x14, 14x13½** | |
| **1972, July 28** | | **Litho.** | **Wmk. 252** |
| 1057 | A317 | 50 l mar, blk & gray | .25 .25 |
| 1058 | A317 | 1.50d brn, gray & blk | .25 .25 |
| 1059 | A317 | 3.50d ocher & multi | .40 .25 |
| 1060 | A317 | 4.50d grn, buff & blk | .25 .25 |
| 1061 | A317 | 10d blk & fawn | .80 .45 |
| | | Nos. 1057-1061 (5) | 1.95 1.45 |

20th Olympic Games, Munich, 8/26-9/11.

Young Stamp Collector — A318

| | | | |
|---|---|---|---|
| **1972, Nov. 15** | | **Perf. 13x14** | |
| 1062 | A318 | 2.50d multi | .25 .25 |

Stamp Day.

Three Kings and Angels — A319

| | | | |
|---|---|---|---|
| **1972, Nov. 15** | | | |
| 1063 | A319 | 2.50d shown | .25 .25 |
| 1064 | A319 | 4.50d Nativity | .25 .25 |
| *a.* | | Pair, #1063-1064 | .35 .35 |

Christmas 1972.

Technical University, 1885, by Luigi Lanza — A320

| | | | |
|---|---|---|---|
| **1973, Mar. 30** | | **Perf. 13½x13** | |
| 1065 | A320 | 2.50d multi | .35 .35 |

Centenary of the Metsovion National Technical University.

"Spring," Fresco — A321

Breast-form Jug — A322

"Wooing and Twittering Swallows" Fresco — A323

Designs: 30 l, "Blue Apes" fresco. 1.50d, Jug decorated with birds. 5d, "Wild Goats" fresco. 6.50d, Wrestlers, fresco.

| | | | |
|---|---|---|---|
| **1973, Mar. 30** | | **Perf. 13x13½, 13½x13** | |
| 1066 | A321 | 10 l multi | .25 .25 |
| 1067 | A322 | 20 l multi | .25 .25 |
| 1068 | A323 | 30 l multi | .25 .25 |
| 1069 | A322 | 1.50d grn & multi | .25 .25 |
| 1070 | A323 | 2.50d multi | .25 .25 |
| 1071 | A323 | 5d multi | .25 .25 |
| 1072 | A323 | 6.50d multi | .50 .50 |
| | | Nos. 1066-1072 (7) | 2.00 2.00 |

Archaeological treasures from Santorini Island (Thera).

### Costume Type of 1972

Women's costumes except 10 l, 20 l, 50 l, 5d, 15d.

| | | | |
|---|---|---|---|
| **1973, Apr. 18** | | **Perf. 12½x13½** | |
| 1073 | A310 | 10 l Peloponnesus | .25 .25 |
| 1074 | A310 | 20 l Sterea Hellas | .25 .25 |
| 1075 | A310 | 30 l Locris | .25 .25 |
| 1076 | A310 | 50 l Skyros | .25 .25 |
| 1077 | A310 | 1d Spetsai | .25 .25 |
| 1078 | A310 | 1.50d Almyros | .25 .25 |
| 1079 | A310 | 2.50d Macedonia | .25 .25 |
| 1080 | A310 | 3.50d Salamis | .25 .25 |
| 1081 | A310 | 4.50d Epirus | .25 .25 |
| 1082 | A310 | 5d Lefkas | .25 .25 |
| 1083 | A310 | 6.50d Skyros | .25 .25 |
| 1084 | A310 | 8.50d Corinth | .35 .25 |
| 1085 | A310 | 10d Corfu | .35 .25 |
| 1086 | A310 | 15d Epirus | .35 .25 |
| 1087 | A310 | 20d Thessaly | 1.00 .25 |
| 1088 | A310 | 30d Macedonia | 1.30 .30 |
| 1089 | A310 | 50d Thrace | 2.60 1.30 |
| | | Nos. 1073-1089 (17) | 8.70 5.35 |

### Europa Issue 1973
### Common Design Type

| | | | |
|---|---|---|---|
| **1973, May 2** | | **Perf. 13½x12½** | |
| | | **Size: 35x22mm** | |
| 1090 | CD16 | 2.50d dp bl & lt bl | .30 .25 |
| 1091 | CD16 | 3d dp car & dp org | .30 .30 |
| 1092 | CD16 | 4.50d ol grn & yel | 1.50 .85 |
| | | Nos. 1090-1092 (3) | 2.10 1.40 |

Zeus Battling Typhoeus, from Amphora — A324

1d, Mount Olympus, after photograph. 2.50d, Zeus battling Giants, from Pergamum Altar. 4.50d, Punishment of Atlas and Prometheus, from vase.

| | | | |
|---|---|---|---|
| | | **Perf. 14x13½** | |
| **1973, June 25** | | **Wmk. 252** | |
| 1093 | A324 | 1d gray & blk | .25 .25 |
| 1094 | A324 | 2d multi | .25 .25 |
| 1095 | A324 | 2.50d gray, blk & buff | .25 .25 |
| 1096 | A324 | 4.50d ocher & multi | .40 .40 |
| *a.* | | Strip of 4, #1093-1096 | 1.40 1.40 |

Greek mythology.

Dr. George Papanicolaou — A325

| | | | |
|---|---|---|---|
| | | **Perf. 13x13½** | |
| **1973, Aug. 10** | | **Litho.** | **Wmk. 252** |
| 1097 | A325 | 2.50d multi | .25 .25 |
| 1098 | A325 | 6.50d multi | .25 .25 |

Dr. George Papanicolaou (1883-1962), cytologist and cancer researcher.

Icon, The Annunciation — A326

| | | | |
|---|---|---|---|
| **1973, Aug. 10** | | | |
| 1099 | A326 | 2.50d multi | .35 .25 |

Miraculous icon of Our Lady of the Annunciation found on Tinos, 1823.

A327

Triptolemus holding wheat on chariot.

| | | | |
|---|---|---|---|
| | | **Perf. 13x14** | |
| **1973, Oct. 22** | | **Litho.** | **Wmk. 252** |
| 1100 | A327 | 4.50d buff, dk brn & red | .25 .25 |

5th Symposium of the European Conf. of Transport Ministers, Athens, Oct. 22-25.

A328

National Benefactors: 1d, Georgios Averoff. 2d, Apostolos Arsakis. 2.50d, Constantine Zappas. 4d, Andrea Sygros. 6.50d, John Varvakis.

| | | | |
|---|---|---|---|
| **1973, Nov. 15** | | | **Engr.** |
| 1101 | A328 | 1.50d dk red brn | .25 .25 |
| 1102 | A328 | 2d car rose | .25 .25 |
| 1103 | A328 | 2.50d slate green | .25 .25 |
| 1104 | A328 | 4d purple | .25 .25 |
| 1105 | A328 | 6.50d black | .25 .25 |
| | | Nos. 1101-1105 (5) | 1.25 1.25 |

Child Examining Stamp — A329

| | | | |
|---|---|---|---|
| **1973, Nov. 15** | | **Litho.** | **Perf. 14x13** |
| 1106 | A329 | 2.50d multi | .25 .25 |

Stamp Day.

Lord Byron in Souliot Costume A330

Byron Taking Oath at Grave of Botsaris A331

| | | | |
|---|---|---|---|
| | | **Perf. 13x14** | |
| **1974, Apr. 4** | | **Wmk. 252** | **Litho.** |
| 1107 | A330 | 2.50d multi | .25 .25 |
| 1108 | A331 | 4.50d multi | .25 .25 |

George Gordon, Lord Byron (1788-1824), English poet involved in Greek struggle for independence.

Harpist of Keros, c. 2800-2200 B.C. — A332

Europa: 4.50d, Statue of Young Women, c. 510 B.C. 6.50d, Charioteer of Delphi, c. 480-450 B.C.

| | | | |
|---|---|---|---|
| **1974, May 10** | | **Perf. 13x14** | |
| 1109 | A332 | 3d dp bl & multi | .40 .25 |
| 1110 | A332 | 4.50d dl red & multi | .60 .25 |
| 1111 | A332 | 6.50d yel & multi | 1.50 .65 |
| | | Nos. 1109-1111 (3) | 2.50 1.15 |

Zeus and Hera Enthroned, and Iris — A333

Greek mythology (from Vases, 5th Cent. B.C.): 2d, Birth of Athena, horiz. 2.50d, Artemis, Apollo, Leto, horiz. 10d, Hermes, the messenger.

**1974, June 24          Perf. 13x14, 14x13**

| 1112 | A333 | 1.50d ocher, blk & brn | | |
|---|---|---|---|---|
| | | | .25 | .25 |
| 1113 | A333 | 2d blk, ocher & brn | | |
| | | | .25 | .25 |
| 1114 | A333 | 2.50d blk, ocher & brn | | |
| | | | .25 | .25 |
| 1115 | A333 | 10d blk, ocher & brn | | |
| | | | .25 | .25 |
| | | Nos. 1112-1115 (4) | 1.00 | 1.00 |

Design from Mycenean Vase and UPU Emblem — A334

UPU cent.: 4.50d, Hermes on the Move, horiz. 6.50d, Woman reading letter.

**1974, Sept. 14          Perf. 12½x13½**

| 1116 | A334 | 2d vio & blk | .25 | .25 |
|---|---|---|---|---|
| 1117 | A334 | 4.50d vio & blk | .25 | .25 |
| 1118 | A334 | 6.50d vio & blk | .25 | .25 |
| | | Nos. 1116-1118 (3) | .75 | .75 |

Crete No. 80 — A335

**1974, Nov. 15     Litho.     Perf. 13½x13**

| 1119 | A335 | 2.50d multi | .25 | .25 |
|---|---|---|---|---|

Stamp Day.

Flight into Egypt A336

**1974, Nov. 15          Perf. 13½x14**

| 1120 | A336 | Strip of 3 | .80 | 1.00 |
|---|---|---|---|---|
| a. | | 2d ocher & multi | .25 | .25 |
| b. | | 4.50d ocher & multi | .25 | .25 |
| c. | | 8.50d ocher & multi | .25 | .25 |

Christmas 1974. Design is from 11th cent. Codex of Dionysos Monastery on Mount Athos.

**Costume Type of 1972**

Designs: Women's costumes, except 1.50d.

**1974, Dec. 5          Perf. 12½x13½**

| 1121 | A310 | 20 l | Megara | .25 | .25 |
|---|---|---|---|---|---|
| 1122 | A310 | 30 l | Salamis | .25 | .25 |
| 1123 | A310 | 50 l | Edipsos | .25 | .25 |
| 1124 | A310 | 1d | Kyme | .25 | .25 |
| 1125 | A310 | 1.50d | Sterea Hellas | .25 | .25 |
| 1126 | A310 | 2d | Desfina | .25 | .25 |
| 1127 | A310 | 3d | Epirus | .25 | .25 |
| 1128 | A310 | 3.50d | Naousa | .25 | .25 |
| 1129 | A310 | 4d | Hasia | .25 | .25 |
| 1130 | A310 | 4.50d | Thasos | .25 | .25 |
| 1131 | A310 | 5d | Skopelos | .25 | .25 |
| 1132 | A310 | 6.50d | Epirus | .25 | .25 |
| 1133 | A310 | 10d | Pelion | .25 | .25 |
| 1134 | A310 | 25d | Kerkyra | .60 | .25 |
| 1135 | A310 | 30d | Boeotia | 1.50 | .50 |
| | | Nos. 1121-1135 (15) | | 5.35 | 4.00 |

Secret Vostitsa Assembly, 1821 A337

Grigorios Dikeos-Papaflessas A338

Aghioi Apostoli Church, Kalamata — A339

**Perf. 13½x12½, 12½x13½**

**1975, Mar. 24**

| 1136 | A337 | 4d multi | .25 | .25 |
|---|---|---|---|---|
| 1137 | A338 | 7d multi | .25 | .25 |
| 1138 | A339 | 11d multi | .25 | .25 |
| | | Nos. 1136-1138 (3) | .75 | .75 |

Grigorios Dikeos-Papaflessas (1788-1825), priest and leader in Greece's uprising against the Turks, sesquicentennial of death.

Vase with Flowers A340

Erotokritos and Aretussa A341

Europa: 11d, Girl with Hat. All designs are after paintings by Theophilos Hatzimichael (d. 1934).

**Perf. 12½x13½**

**1975, May 10     Litho.     Wmk. 252**

| 1139 | A340 | 4d multi | .50 | .45 |
|---|---|---|---|---|
| 1140 | A341 | 7d multi | .75 | .65 |
| 1141 | A340 | 11d multi | 2.00 | 1.25 |
| | | Nos. 1139-1141 (3) | 3.25 | 2.35 |

House, Kastoria A342

Greek Houses, 18th Cent.: 40 l, Arnea, Halkidiki. 4d, Veria. 6d, Siatista. 11d, Ambelakia, Thessaly.

**1975, June 26          Perf. 13½x12½**

| 1142 | A342 | 10 l | brt bl & blk | .25 | .25 |
|---|---|---|---|---|---|
| 1143 | A342 | 40 l | red org & blk | .25 | .25 |
| 1144 | A342 | 4d | bister & blk | .25 | .25 |
| 1145 | A342 | 6d | ultra & multi | .25 | .25 |
| 1146 | A342 | 11d | org & blk | .25 | .25 |
| | | Nos. 1142-1146 (5) | | 1.25 | 1.25 |

IWY Emblem, Neolithic Goddess A343

"Looking to the Future" A344

8.50d, Confrontation between Antigone & Creon.

**Perf. 12½x13½**

**1975, Sept. 29     Litho.     Wmk. 252**

| 1147 | A343 | 1.50d lilac & dk brn | .25 | .25 |
|---|---|---|---|---|
| 1148 | A343 | 8.50d bis, blk & brn | .25 | .25 |
| 1149 | A344 | 11d bl & blk | .25 | .25 |
| | | Nos. 1147-1149 (3) | .75 | .75 |

International Women's Year 1975.

Papanastasiou and University Buildings — A345

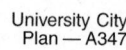

First University Building — A346

University City Plan — A347

**1975, Sept. 29          Perf. 14x13½**

| 1150 | A345 | 1.50d tan & sepia | .25 | .25 |
|---|---|---|---|---|
| 1151 | A346 | 4d multi | .25 | .25 |
| 1152 | A347 | 11d multi | .25 | .25 |
| | | Nos. 1150-1152 (3) | .75 | .75 |

Thessaloniki University, 50th anniversary. Alexandros Papanastasiou (1876-1936), founded University while Prime Minister.

Evangelos Zappas and Zappeion Building — A348

National Benefactors: 4d, Georgios Rizaris and Rizarios Ecclesiastical School. 6d, Michael Tositsas and Metsovion Technical University. 11d, Nicolaos Zosimas and Zosimea Academy.

**Perf. 14x13**

**1975, Nov. 15     Litho.     Wmk. 252**

| 1153 | A348 | 1d blk & grn | .25 | .25 |
|---|---|---|---|---|
| 1154 | A348 | 4d blk & brn | .25 | .25 |
| 1155 | A348 | 6d blk & org | .25 | .25 |
| 1156 | A348 | 11d blk & brick red | .25 | .25 |
| | | Nos. 1153-1156 (4) | 1.00 | 1.00 |

Greece No. 380 — A349

**1975, Nov. 15          Perf. 13x14**

| 1157 | A349 | 11d dull grn & brn | .35 | .30 |
|---|---|---|---|---|

Stamp Day 1975.

Pontos Lyre A350

Musicians, Byzantine Mural A351

Designs: 1d, Cretan lyre. 1.50d, Tambourine. 4d, Guitarist, from amphora, horiz. 6d, Bagpipes. 7d, Lute. 10d, Barrel organ. 11d, Pipes and zournadas. 20d, Musicians and singers praising God, Byzantine mural, horiz. 25d, Drums. 30d, Kanonaki, horiz.

**Perf. 12½x13½, 13½x12½**

**1975, Dec. 15     Litho.     Wmk. 252**

| 1158 | A350 | 10 l | multi | .25 | .25 |
|---|---|---|---|---|---|
| 1159 | A350 | 20 l | multi | .25 | .25 |
| 1160 | A350 | 1d | ultra & multi | .25 | .25 |
| 1161 | A350 | 1.50d | multi | .25 | .25 |
| 1162 | A351 | 4d | multi | .25 | .25 |
| 1163 | A350 | 6d | multi | .25 | .25 |
| 1164 | A350 | 7d | multi | .25 | .25 |
| 1165 | A350 | 10d | multi | .25 | .25 |
| 1166 | A351 | 11d | red & multi | .25 | .25 |
| 1167 | A351 | 20d | multi | .25 | .25 |
| 1168 | A350 | 25d | multi | .25 | .25 |
| 1169 | A350 | 30d | multi | .75 | .75 |
| | | Nos. 1158-1169 (12) | | 3.50 | 3.50 |

Popular musical instruments.

Early Telephone, Globe, Waves — A352

11d, Globe, waves, telephone 1976.

**Perf. 13½x12½**

**1976, Mar. 23     Litho.     Wmk. 252**

| 1170 | | 7d blk & multi | .25 | .25 |
|---|---|---|---|---|
| 1171 | | 11d blk & multi | .25 | .25 |
| a. | A352 | Pair, Nos. 1170-1171 | .40 | .40 |

1st telephone call by Alexander Graham Bell, Mar. 10, 1876.

Sortie of Missolonghi A353

**1976, Mar. 23          Perf. 13½x13**

| 1172 | A353 | 4d multi | .25 | .25 |
|---|---|---|---|---|

Sortie of the garrison of Missolonghi, sesquicentennial.

Florina Jugn A354

Avramidis Plate A355

Europa: 11d, Egina pitcher with Greek flags.

**Perf. 13x14, 12½x12 (A355)**

**1976, May 10     Litho.     Wmk. 252**

| 1173 | A354 | 7d buff & multi | .40 | .30 |
|---|---|---|---|---|
| 1174 | A355 | 8.50d blk & multi | .50 | .30 |
| 1175 | A354 | 11d gray & multi | 1.40 | .85 |
| | | Nos. 1173-1175 (3) | 2.30 | 1.45 |

Lion Attacking Bull A356

Head of Silenus A357

Designs: 4.50d, Flying aquatic birds. 7d, Wounded bull. 11d, Cow feeding calf, horiz. Designs from Creto-Mycenaean engraved seals, c. 1400 B.C.

**Perf. 13x12½, 13½x14, 14x13½**

**1976, May 10**

| 1176 | A356 | 2d bis & multi | .25 | .25 |
|---|---|---|---|---|
| 1177 | A356 | 4.50d multi | .25 | .25 |
| 1178 | A356 | 7d multi | .25 | .25 |
| 1179 | A357 | 8.50d pur & multi | .25 | .25 |
| 1180 | A357 | 11d brn & multi | .25 | .25 |
| | | Nos. 1176-1180 (5) | 1.25 | 1.25 |

Long Jump — A358

Montreal and Athens Stadiums A359

Designs (Classical and Modern Events): 2d, Basketball. 3.50d, Wrestling. 4d, Swimming. 25d, Lighting Olympic flame and Montreal Olympic Games torch.

**Perf. 14x13½, 12½x13½ (A359)**
**1976, June 25    Litho.    Wmk. 252**
| | | | | |
|---|---|---|---|---|
| 1181 | A358 | 50 l org & multi | .25 | .25 |
| 1182 | A358 | 2d org & multi | .25 | .25 |
| 1183 | A358 | 3.50d org & multi | .25 | .25 |
| 1184 | A358 | 4d bl & multi | .25 | .25 |
| 1185 | A359 | 11d multi | .25 | .25 |
| 1186 | A358 | 25d org & multi | .60 | .60 |
| | | Nos. 1181-1186 (6) | 1.85 | 1.85 |

21st Olympic Games, Montreal, Canada, July 17-Aug. 1.

Lesbos, View and Map — A360

**Perf. 13½x14, 14x13½**
**1976, July 26    Litho.    Wmk. 252**
| | | | | |
|---|---|---|---|---|
| 1187 | A360 | 30d Lemnos, vert. | .40 | .25 |
| 1188 | A360 | 50d shown | .60 | .25 |
| 1189 | A360 | 75d Chios | .75 | .25 |
| 1190 | A360 | 100d Samos | 1.75 | 1.40 |
| | | Nos. 1187-1190 (4) | 3.50 | 2.15 |

Greek Aegean Islands.

Three Kings Speaking to the Jews — A361

Christmas: 7d, Nativity. Designs from manuscripts in Esfigmenou Monastery, Mount Athos.

**1976, Dec. 8    Perf. 13½x14**
| | | | | |
|---|---|---|---|---|
| 1191 | A361 | 4d yellow & multi | .25 | .25 |
| 1192 | A361 | 7d yellow & multi | .25 | .25 |

Greek Grammar of 1478 — A362

**1976, Dec. 8    Perf. 14x13**
| | | | | |
|---|---|---|---|---|
| 1193 | A362 | 4d multi | .25 | .25 |

500th anniversary of printing of first Greek book by Constantin Lascaris, Milan.

Heinrich Schliemann A363

Brooch with Figure of Goddess A364

Designs: 4d, Gold bracelet, horiz. 7d, Gold diadem, horiz. 11d, Gold mask (Agamemnon). Treasures from Mycenaean tombs.

**1976, Dec. 8    Perf. 13x14, 14x13**
| | | | | |
|---|---|---|---|---|
| 1194 | A363 | 2d multi | .25 | .25 |
| 1195 | A364 | 4d multi | .25 | .25 |
| 1196 | A364 | 5d grn & multi | .25 | .25 |
| 1197 | A364 | 7d multi | .25 | .25 |
| 1198 | A364 | 11d multi | .40 | .40 |
| | | Nos. 1194-1198 (5) | 1.40 | 1.40 |

Cent. of the discovery of the Mycenaean royal shaft graves by Heinrich Schliemann.

Aesculapius with Patients A365

Patient in Clinic A366

Designs: 1.50d, Aesculapius curing young man. 2d, Young Hercules with old nurse. 20d, Old man with votive offering of large leg.

**Perf. 12½x13½ (A365); 13x12 (A366)**
**1977, Mar. 15    Litho.    Wmk. 252**
| | | | | |
|---|---|---|---|---|
| 1199 | A365 | 50 l multi | .25 | .25 |
| 1200 | A366 | 1d multi | .25 | .25 |
| 1201 | A366 | 1.50d multi | .25 | .25 |
| 1202 | A366 | 2d multi | .25 | .25 |
| 1203 | A365 | 20d multi | .25 | .25 |
| | | Nos. 1199-1203 (5) | 1.25 | 1.25 |

International Rheumatism Year.

Winged Wheel, Modern Transportation A367

**1977, May 16    Litho.    Perf. 14x13½**
| | | | | |
|---|---|---|---|---|
| 1204 | A367 | 7d multi | .25 | .25 |

European Conference of Ministers of Transport (E.C.M.T.), Athens, June 1-3.

Mani Castle, Vathia — A368

Europa: 7d, Santorini, vert. 15d, Windmills on Lasithi plateau.

**Perf. 14x13½, 13½x14**
**1977, May 16    Litho.    Wmk. 252**
| | | | | |
|---|---|---|---|---|
| 1205 | A368 | 5d multicolored | .45 | .25 |
| 1206 | A368 | 7d multicolored | .45 | .35 |
| 1207 | A368 | 15d multicolored | 1.50 | .50 |
| | | Nos. 1205-1207 (3) | 2.40 | 1.10 |

Alexandria Lighthouse, from Roman Coin — A369

Designs: 1d, Alexander places Homer's works into Achilles' tomb, fresco by Raphael. 1.50d, Alexander descends to the bottom of the sea, Flemish miniature. 3d, Alexander searching for water of life, Hindu plate. 7d, Alexander on horseback, Coptic carpet. 11d, Alexander hearing oracle that his days are numbered, Byzantine manuscript. 30d, Death of Alexander, Persian miniature. All designs include gold coin of Lysimachus with Alexander's head.

**1977, July 23    Perf. 14x13**
| | | | | |
|---|---|---|---|---|
| 1208 | A369 | 50 l silver & multi | .25 | .25 |
| 1209 | A369 | 1d silver & multi | .25 | .25 |
| 1210 | A369 | 1.50d silver & multi | .25 | .25 |
| 1211 | A369 | 3d silver & multi | .25 | .25 |
| 1212 | A369 | 7d silver & multi | .25 | .25 |
| 1213 | A369 | 11d silver & multi | .25 | .25 |
| 1214 | A369 | 30d silver & multi | .30 | .30 |
| | | Nos. 1208-1214 (7) | 1.80 | 1.80 |

Cultural influence of Alexander the Great (356-323 B.C.), King of Macedonia.

"Greece Rising Again" A370

People in Front of University A371

Greek Flags, Laurel, University — A372

**Perf. 13½x12½, 12x12½, 12½x12**
**1977, July 23    Unwmk.**
| | | | | |
|---|---|---|---|---|
| 1215 | A370 | 4d multi | .25 | .25 |
| 1216 | A371 | 7d multi | .25 | .25 |
| 1217 | A372 | 20d multi | .25 | .25 |
| | | Nos. 1215-1217 (3) | .75 | .75 |

Restoration of Democracy in Greece.

Archbishop Makarios, Map of Cyprus — A373

Design: 4d, Archbishop Makarios, vert.

**Perf. 13x13½, 13½x13**
**1977, Sept. 10    Unwmk.**
| | | | | |
|---|---|---|---|---|
| 1218 | A373 | 4d sepia & blk | .25 | .25 |
| 1219 | A373 | 7d buff, brn & blk | .25 | .25 |

Archbishop Makarios (1913-1977), President of Cyprus.

Old Athens Post Office — A374

Neo-Hellenic architecture: 1d, Institution for the Blind, Salonika. 1.50d, Townhall, Syros. 2d, National Bank of Greece, Piraeus. 5d, Byzantine Museum, Athens. 50d, Municipal Theater, Patras.

**1977, Sept. 22    Perf. 13½x13**
| | | | | |
|---|---|---|---|---|
| 1220 | A374 | 50 l multi | .25 | .25 |
| 1221 | A374 | 1d multi | .25 | .25 |
| 1222 | A374 | 1.50d multi | .25 | .25 |
| 1223 | A374 | 2d multi | .25 | .25 |
| 1224 | A374 | 5d multi | .25 | .25 |
| 1225 | A374 | 50d multi | 1.50 | 1.50 |
| | | Nos. 1220-1225 (6) | 1.50 | 1.50 |

Battle of Navarino, Lithograph A375

Adm. Van Heyden, Sir Edward Codrington, Count de Rigny — A376

**1977, Oct. 20    Perf. 13½x13**
| | | | | |
|---|---|---|---|---|
| 1226 | A375 | 4d brn, buff & blk | .25 | .25 |
| 1227 | A376 | 7d multi | .25 | .25 |

150th anniversary of Battle of Navarino.

Parthenon and Refinery A377

Caryatid and Factories A379

Fish and Birds Suffering from Pollution — A378

Design: 7d, Birds and trees in polluted air.

Greek Flags — A377 (continued)

**1977, Oct. 20    Perf. 13½x14, 14x13½**
| | | | | |
|---|---|---|---|---|
| 1228 | A377 | 3d org & blk | .25 | .25 |
| 1229 | A378 | 4d multi | .25 | .25 |
| 1230 | A378 | 7d multi | .25 | .25 |
| 1231 | A379 | 30d blk, gray & slate | .35 | .35 |
| | | Nos. 1228-1231 (4) | 1.10 | 1.10 |

Protection of the environment.

Map of Greece and Ships — A380

Globe and Swallows — A381

Letter with Flags, Swallow — A382

5d, Globe with Greek flag. 13d, World map showing dispersion of Greeks abroad.

**1977, Dec. 15    Perf. 13½x12½**
| | | | | |
|---|---|---|---|---|
| 1232 | A380 | 4d multi | .25 | .25 |
| 1233 | A380 | 5d multi | .25 | .25 |
| 1234 | A381 | 7d multi | .25 | .25 |
| 1235 | A382 | 11d multi | .25 | .25 |
| 1236 | A380 | 13d multi | .25 | .25 |
| | | Nos. 1232-1236 (5) | 1.25 | 1.25 |

Greeks living abroad.

Kalamata Harbor, by Constantine Parthenis A383

Greek Paintings: 2.50d, Boats, Arsanas, by Spyros Papaloucas, vert. 4d, Santorini, by Constantine Maleas. 7d, The Engagement, by Nicolaus Gyzis. 11d, Woman with Straw Hat, by Nicolaus Lytras, vert. 15d, "Spring" (nude), by Georgio Iacovidis.

**1977, Dec. 15    Perf. 13½x13, 13x13½**
| | | | | |
|---|---|---|---|---|
| 1237 | A383 | 1.50d yel & multi | .25 | .25 |
| 1238 | A383 | 2.50d yel & multi | .25 | .25 |
| 1239 | A383 | 4d yel & multi | .25 | .25 |
| 1240 | A383 | 7d yel & multi | .25 | .25 |
| 1241 | A383 | 11d yel & multi | .25 | .25 |
| 1242 | A383 | 15d yel & multi | .25 | .25 |
| | | Nos. 1237-1242 (6) | 1.50 | 1.50 |

Ebenus Cretica — A384

Greek Flora: 2.50d, Dwarf lily. 3d, Campanula oreadum. 4d, Tiger lily. 7d, Viola delphinantha. 25d, Paeonia rhodia.

**1978, Mar. 30    Litho.    Perf. 13x13½**
| | | | | |
|---|---|---|---|---|
| 1243 | A384 | 1.50d multi | .25 | .25 |
| 1244 | A384 | 2.50d multi | .25 | .25 |
| 1245 | A384 | 3d multi | .25 | .25 |
| 1246 | A384 | 4d multi | .25 | .25 |
| 1247 | A384 | 7d multi | .25 | .25 |
| 1248 | A384 | 25d multi | .25 | .25 |
| | | Nos. 1243-1248 (6) | 1.50 | 1.50 |

Postrider, Cancellation A385

5d, S.S. Maximilianos & Hermes Head. 7d, 19th cent. mail train & #122. 30d, Mailmen on motorcycles & #1062.

**1978, May 15    Perf. 13½x12½**
| | | | | |
|---|---|---|---|---|
| 1249 | A385 | 4d buff & multi | .25 | .25 |
| 1250 | A385 | 5d buff & multi | .25 | .25 |
| 1251 | A385 | 7d buff & multi | .25 | .25 |
| 1252 | A385 | 30d buff & multi | .25 | .25 |
| a. | | Souvenir sheet of 4 | 1.00 | 1.00 |
| | | Nos. 1249-1252 (4) | 1.00 | 1.00 |

150th anniv. of Greek postal service.

No. 1252a issued Sept. 25, contains Nos. 1249-1252 in slightly changed colors. Sold for 60d.

Lighting Olympic Flame, Olympia A386

Start of 100-meter Race A387

**1978, May 15**     **Perf. 13x14**
| | | | | |
|---|---|---|---|---|
| 1253 | A386 | 7d multi | .35 | .25 |
| 1254 | A387 | 13d multi | .75 | .35 |

80th session of International Olympic Committee, Athens, May 10-21.

### Europa Issue

St. Sophia, Salonica A388

Lysicrates Monument, Athens A389

**1978, May 15**     **Perf. 13x14, 14x13**
| | | | | |
|---|---|---|---|---|
| 1255 | A388 | 4d multi | .75 | .30 |
| 1256 | A389 | 7d multi | 1.50 | .70 |

Aristotle, Roman Bust A390

School of Athens, by Raphael A391

Map of Chalcidice, Base of Statue from Attalus Arcade A392

Aristotle the Wise, Byzantine Fresco, St. George's Church, Ioannina A393

**Perf. 13x13½, 13½x14 (20d)**
**1978, July 10**     **Litho.**
| | | | | |
|---|---|---|---|---|
| 1257 | A390 | 2d multi | .25 | .25 |
| 1258 | A391 | 4d multi | .25 | .25 |
| 1259 | A392 | 7d multi | .25 | .25 |
| 1260 | A393 | 20d multi | .25 | .25 |
| | | Nos. 1257-1260 (4) | 1.00 | 1.00 |

Aristotle (384-322 B.C.), systematic philosopher.

Rotary Emblem A394

Surgeons Operating A395

Ugo Foscolo, View of Zante — A396

Hellenistic Bronze Head — A397

Charioteer's Hand, Delphi A398

Wright Brothers' Plane, Daedalus and Icarus A399

**1978, Sept. 21**     **Litho.**     **Perf. 12½**
| | | | | |
|---|---|---|---|---|
| 1261 | A394 | 1d multi | .25 | .25 |
| 1262 | A395 | 1.50d multi | .25 | .25 |
| 1263 | A396 | 2.50d multi | .25 | .25 |
| 1264 | A397 | 5d multi | .25 | .25 |
| 1265 | A398 | 7d multi | .35 | .25 |
| 1266 | A399 | 13d multi | .35 | .35 |
| | | Nos. 1261-1266 (6) | 1.70 | 1.60 |

Rotary in Greece, 50th anniv. (1d); 11th Greek Surgery Cong., Salonica (1.50d); Ugo Foscolo (1778-1827), Italian writer (2.50d); European Convention on Human Rights, 25th anniv. (5d); 2nd Conf. of Ministers of Culture of the Council of Europe member countries, Athens, Oct. 23-27 (7d); 75th anniv. of 1st powered flight (13d).

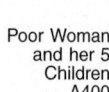

Poor Woman and her 5 Children A400

Scenes from Fairy Tale "The 12 Months": 3d, The poor woman and the 12 months. 4d, The poor woman and the gold coins. 20d, Punishment of the greedy woman.

**1978, Nov. 6**     **Litho.**     **Perf. 13½x13**
| | | | | |
|---|---|---|---|---|
| 1267 | A400 | 2d multi | .25 | .25 |
| 1268 | A400 | 3d multi | .25 | .25 |
| 1269 | A400 | 4d multi | .25 | .25 |
| 1270 | A400 | 20d multi | .25 | .25 |
| | | Nos. 1267-1270 (4) | 1.00 | 1.00 |

"Transplants" A401

The Miracle of St. Anarghiri A402

**1978, Nov. 6**     **Perf. 12½x13½**
| | | | | |
|---|---|---|---|---|
| 1271 | A401 | 4d multi | .25 | .25 |
| 1272 | A402 | 10d multi | .25 | .25 |

Advancements in organ transplants.

Cruiser — A403

New and Old Greek Naval Ships: 1d, Torpedo boats. 2.50d, Submarine Papanicolis. 4d, Battleship Psara. 5d, Sailing ship "Madonna of Hydra." 7d, Byzantine corvette. 50d, Archaic trireme.

**1978, Dec. 15**     **Litho.**     **Perf. 13½x12**
| | | | | |
|---|---|---|---|---|
| 1273 | A403 | 50 l multi | .25 | .25 |
| 1274 | A403 | 1d multi | .25 | .25 |
| 1275 | A403 | 2.50d multi | .25 | .25 |
| 1276 | A403 | 4d multi | .25 | .25 |
| 1277 | A403 | 5d multi | .25 | .25 |
| 1278 | A403 | 7d multi | .25 | .25 |
| 1279 | A403 | 50d multi | .40 | .40 |
| | | Nos. 1273-1279 (7) | 1.90 | 1.90 |

Cadet Officer, Military School, Nauplia A404

Cadet Officers' School Emblem A405

Design: 10d, Cadet Officers Military School, Athens, Cadet's uniform, 1978.

**1978, Dec. 15**     **Perf. 13½x12, 12x13½**
| | | | | |
|---|---|---|---|---|
| 1280 | A404 | 1.50d multi | .25 | .25 |
| 1281 | A405 | 2d multi | .25 | .25 |
| 1282 | A404 | 10d multi | .25 | .25 |
| | | Nos. 1280-1282 (3) | .75 | .75 |

Cadet Officers Military School, 150th anniv.

Virgin and Child A406

Baptism of Christ A407

Designs from 16th century icon stands in Stavronikita Monastery.

**1978, Dec. 15**     **Perf. 13x13½**
| | | | | |
|---|---|---|---|---|
| 1283 | A406 | 4d multi | .25 | .25 |
| 1284 | A407 | 7d multi | .25 | .25 |

Christmas 1978.

Map of Greece — A408

**1978, Dec. 28**     **Perf. 14x13**
| | | | | |
|---|---|---|---|---|
| 1285 | A408 | 7d multi | .25 | .25 |
| 1286 | A408 | 11d multi | .25 | .25 |
| 1287 | A408 | 13d multi | .25 | .25 |
| | | Nos. 1285-1287 (3) | .75 | .75 |

Kitsos Tzavellas A409

Souli Castle A410

10d, Fighting Souliots. 20d, Fight of Zalongo.

**Perf. 12½x13½, 13½x12½**
**1979, Mar. 12**     **Litho.**
| | | | | |
|---|---|---|---|---|
| 1288 | A409 | 1.50d buff, blk & brn | .25 | .25 |
| 1289 | A410 | 3d multi | .25 | .25 |
| 1290 | A410 | 10d multi | .25 | .25 |
| 1291 | A409 | 20d buff, blk & brn | .25 | .25 |
| | | Nos. 1288-1291 (4) | 1.00 | 1.00 |

Struggle of the Souliots, 18th century fighters for freedom from Turkey.

Cycladic Figure from Amorgos — A411

**1979, Apr. 26**     **Litho.**     **Perf. 12x13½**
| | | | | |
|---|---|---|---|---|
| 1292 | A411 | 20d multi | .30 | .30 |

Aegean art.

Mailmen from Crete — A412

Europa: 7d, Rural mailman on horseback, Crete.

**1979, May 11**     **Perf. 13½x14**
| | | | | |
|---|---|---|---|---|
| 1293 | A412 | 4d multi | .80 | .25 |
| 1294 | A412 | 7d multi | .80 | .45 |
| a. | | Pair, #1293-1294 | 1.75 | 1.75 |

Nicolas Scoufas A413

Basketball A415

Locomotives A414

Mene Psarianosi Symeonidis Fossil A416

Temple of Hephaestus and Byzantine Church A417

Victory of Paeonius Statue, Flags of Balkan Countries — A418

**1979, May 12**     **Perf. 13x14, 14x13**
| | | | | |
|---|---|---|---|---|
| 1295 | A413 | 1.50d multi | .25 | .25 |
| 1296 | A414 | 2d multi | .25 | .25 |
| 1297 | A415 | 3d multi | .25 | .25 |
| 1298 | A416 | 4d multi | .25 | .25 |
| 1299 | A417 | 10d multi | .25 | .25 |
| 1300 | A418 | 20d multi | .30 | .30 |
| | | Nos. 1295-1300 (6) | 1.55 | 1.55 |

Nicolas Scoufas (1779-1818), founder of (patriotic) Friendly Society; Piraeus-Athens-to-the-frontier railroad, 75th anniv.; European Basketball Championship; 7th Intl. Cong. for the Study of the Neocene Period in the Mediterranean; Balkan Tourist Year 1979; 50 years of track and field competitions in Balkan countries.

Wheat with Members' Flags, Greek Coins — A419

European Parliament, Strasbourg — A420

**Perf. 13x14, 14x13**
**1979, May 28**     **Litho.**
| | | | | |
|---|---|---|---|---|
| 1301 | A419 | 7d multi | .25 | .25 |
| 1302 | A420 | 30d multi | .30 | .30 |

Greece's entry into European Economic Community and Parliament.

Statue of a Girl, IYC Emblem — A421

Intl. Year of the Child: 8d, Girl & pigeons. 20d, Mother & Children, painting by Iacovides.

**1979, June 27    Litho.    Perf. 13x14**
1303  A421  5d multi          .25  .25
1304  A421  8d multi          .25  .25
1305  A421  20d multi         .25  .25
     Nos. 1303-1305 (3)       .75  .75

Philip II, Bust — A422

Designs: 8d, Golden wreath. 10d, Copper vessel. 14d, Golden casket, horiz. 18d, Silver ewer. 20d, Golden quiver (detail). 30d, Gold and iron cuirass.

**Perf. 13½x14, 14x13½**
**1979, Sept. 15                Litho.**
1306  A422  6d multi          .25  .25
1307  A422  8d multi          .25  .25
1308  A422  10d multi         .25  .25
1309  A422  14d multi         .25  .25
1310  A422  18d multi         .25  .25
1311  A422  20d multi         .25  .25
1312  A422  30d multi         .35  .35
     Nos. 1306-1312 (7)       1.85  1.85

Archaeological finds from Vergina, Macedonia.

Purple Heron — A423

Protected Birds: 8d, Gull. 10d, Falcon, horiz. 14d, Kingfisher, horiz. 20d, Pelican. 25d, White-tailed sea eagle.

**1979, Oct. 15**
1313  A423  6d multi          .25  .25
1314  A423  8d multi          .25  .25
1315  A423  10d multi         .25  .25
1316  A423  14d multi         .25  .25
1317  A423  20d multi         .25  .25
1318  A423  25d multi         .60  .50
     Nos. 1313-1318 (6)       1.85  1.75

Council of Europe wildlife and natural habitat protection campaign.

Agricultural Bank A424

St. Cosmas A425

Basil the Great A426

Balkan Countries, Magnifier A427

Aristotelis Valaoritis A428

Golfer A429

Hippocrates A430

Parliament in Session A431

**Perf. 14x13½, 13½x14**
**1979, Nov. 24                Litho.**
1319  A424  3d multi          .25  .25
1320  A425  4d multi          .25  .25
1321  A426  6d multi          .25  .25
1322  A427  8d multi          .25  .25
1323  A427  10d multi, horiz. .25  .25
1324  A428  12d multi         .25  .25
1325  A429  14d multi         .25  .25
1326  A430  18d multi         .25  .25
1327  A431  25d multi         .35  .35
     Nos. 1319-1327 (9)       2.35  2.35

Agricultural Bank of Greece, 50th anniv.; Cosmas the Aetolian (1714-79), Greek missionary and martyr; Basil the Great (330-379), Archbishop of Caesarea; Balkanfila, Balkan Stamp Exhibition, Athens, Nov. 24-Dec. 2; Aristotelis Valaoritis (1824-79), Greek poet; 27th World Golf Championship, Nov. 8-11; Intl. Hippocratic Foundation of Cos; Greek Parliament, 104th anniv.

Parnassus A432

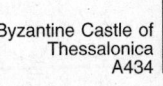

Tempe Valley A433

2d, Melos. 4d, Vikos Gorge. 5d, Missolonghi Salt Lake. 6d, Louros Aqueduct. 7d, Samothrace. 8d, Sithonia-Halkidiki. 10d, Samarias Gorge, vert. 12d, Siphnos. 14d, Kyme. 18d, Ios. 20d, Thasos. 30d, Paros. 50d, Cephalonia.

**Perf. 12½x13½, 13½x12½**
**1979, Dec. 15                Litho.**
1328  A432  50 l shown        .25  .25
1329  A433  1d shown          .25  .25
1330  A432  2d multicolored   .25  .25
1331  A432  4d multicolored   .25  .25
1332  A433  5d multicolored   .25  .25
1333  A432  6d multicolored   .25  .25
1334  A432  7d multicolored   .25  .25
1335  A433  8d multicolored   .25  .25
1336  A433  10d multicolored  .25  .25
1337  A432  12d multicolored  .25  .25
1338  A433  14d multicolored  .25  .25
1339  A432  18d multicolored  .25  .25
1340  A432  20d multicolored  .25  .25
1341  A433  30d multicolored  .25  .25
1342  A432  50d multicolored  .40  .35
     Nos. 1328-1342 (15)      3.90  3.85

Byzantine Castle of Thessalonica A434

4d, Aegosthena Castle, vert. 8d, Cave of Perama Ioannina, vert. 10d, Cave of Dyros, Mani, vert. 14d, Arta Bridge. 20d, Kalogiros Bridge, Epirus.

**Perf. 12½x14, 14x12½**
**1980, Mar. 15                Litho.**
1343  A434  4d multi          .25  .25
1344  A434  6d multi          .25  .25
1345  A434  8d multi          .25  .25
1346  A434  10d multi         .25  .25
1347  A434  14d multi         .25  .25
1348  A434  20d multi         .25  .25
     Nos. 1343-1348 (6)       1.50  1.50

Gate of Galerius — A435

**1980, Mar. 15**
1349  A435  8d multi          .25  .25
1st Hellenic Congress of Nephrology, Thessalonica, Mar. 20-22.

Solar System — A436

Design: 10d, Temple of Hera, Aristarchus' theory and diagram.

**1980, May 5    Litho.    Perf. 13½x12½**
1350  A436  10d multi         .25  .25
1351  A436  20d multi         .35  .30

Aristarchus of Samos, first astronomer to discover heliocentric theory of universe, 2300th birth anniv.; Intl. Scientific Congress on Aristarchus, Samos, June 17-19.

Maria Callas (1923-1977), Opera Singer — A437

Europa: 8d, Georges Seferis (1900-1971), writer and diplomat.

**1980, May 5**
1352  A437  8d multi          .35  .35
1353  A437  14d multi         1.30  1.00

Energy Conservation Manual — A438

20d, Candle in bulb, vert.

**Perf. 13½x12½, 12½x13½**
**1980, May 5**
1354  A438  8d shown          .25  .25
1355  A438  20d multicolored  .25  .25

Firemen A439

St. Demetrius, Angel, Fresco A440

Ancient Vase, Olives A442

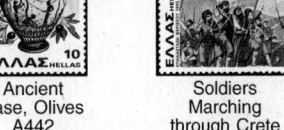

Soldiers Marching through Crete A441

Federation Emblem, Newspaper A443

Constantinos Ikonomos A444

**1980, July 14    Litho.    Perf. 12½**
1356  A439  4d multi          .25  .25
1357  A440  6d multi          .25  .25
1358  A441  8d multi          .25  .25
1359  A442  10d multi         .25  .25

1360  A443  14d multi         .25  .25
1361  A444  20d multi         .35  .35
     Nos. 1356-1361 (6)       1.60  1.60

Fire Brigade, 50th anniv.; St. Demetrius, 1700th birth anniv.; Therissos Revolution, 75th anniv.; 2nd Intl. Olive Oil Year; Intl. Federation of Journalists, 15th Cong., Athens, May 12-16; Constantinos Ikonomos (1780-1857), writer and revolutionary.

Olympic Stadium, Temple Coin, Olympia — A445

Olympic Rings and: 14d, Stadium and coin of Delphi 18d, Epidaurus theater, coin of Olympia 20d, Rhodes Stadium, Cos coin. 50d, Panathenean Stadium; 1st Olympic Games medal.

**1980, Aug. 11    Litho.    Perf. 13½x13**
1362  A445  8d multi          .25  .25
1363  A445  14d multi         .30  .25
1364  A445  18d multi         .25  .25
1365  A445  20d multi         .25  .25
1366  A445  50d multi         .55  .45
     Nos. 1362-1366 (5)       1.60  1.45

22nd Summer Olympic Games, Moscow, July 19-Aug. 3.

Asbestos — A446

**Perf. 13½x12½**
**1980, Sept. 22                Litho.**
1367  A446  6d shown          .25  .25
1368  A446  8d Gypsum, vert.  .25  .25
1369  A446  10d Copper ore    .25  .25
1370  A446  14d Barite, vert. .30  .30
1371  A446  18d Chromite      .25  .25
1372  A446  20d Mixed sulphides,
            vert.             .25  .25
1373  A446  30d Bauxite, vert. .30  .30
     Nos. 1367-1373 (7)       1.85  1.85

Tow Truck — A447

Air Force Jet — A448

Airplane and Hangar — A449

Ships in Port — A450

Students' Association Headquarters — A451

**1980, Oct. 31    Litho.    Perf. 12½**
1374  A447  6d multi          .25  .25
1375  A448  8d multi          .25  .25
1376  A449  12d multi         .25  .25
1377  A450  20d multi         .30  .25
1378  A451  25d multi         .35  .35
     Nos. 1374-1378 (5)       1.40  1.35

Road Assistance Service of Automobile and Touring Club of Greece, 20th anniv.; Air Force, 50th anniv.; Flyers' Club of Thessaloniki, 50th anniv.; Piraeus Port Organization, 50th anniv.; Association for Macedonian Studies, 40th anniv.

Madonna and Child, by Theodore
Poulakis — A452

Christmas 1980: He is Happy Thanks to
You, by Theodore Poulakis. No. 1381a has
continuous design.

| 1980, Dec. 10 | | Perf. 13½ | |
|---|---|---|---|
| 1379 | 6d multi | .25 | .25 |
| 1380 | 14d multi | .25 | .25 |
| 1381 | 20d multi | .25 | .25 |
| a. | A452 Strip of 3, #1379-1381 | .60 | .60 |

Vegetables for
Export — A453

| 1981, Mar. 16 | Litho. | Perf. 12½ | |
|---|---|---|---|
| 1382 | A453 9d shown | .25 | .25 |
| 1383 | A453 17d Fruits | .25 | .25 |
| 1384 | A453 20d Cotton | .25 | .25 |
| 1385 | A453 25d Marble | .25 | .25 |
| | Nos. 1382-1385 (4) | 1.00 | 1.00 |

**Europa Issue**

Kira Maria Folk
Dance,
Alexandria
A454

17d, Cretan Sousta (dance).

| 1981, May 4 | Litho. | Perf. 14x13 | |
|---|---|---|---|
| 1386 | A454 12d shown | .40 | .25 |
| 1387 | A454 17d multicolored | .80 | .60 |

Runner, Olympic
Stadium,
Kalogreza
A455

| 1981, May 4 | | | |
|---|---|---|---|
| 1388 | A455 12d shown | .25 | .25 |
| 1389 | A455 17d Runners, Europe | .35 | .35 |

13th European Athletic Championship, Athens, 1982.

Torso
Showing
Kidneys
A456

Sky Diver
and
Airplanes
A457

Oil Rig and
Map of
Thassos
Island
A460

Views of
Thessaly
and Epirus
A458

Vase with Painted
Eyes — A459

Globes and
Ancient Coin
A461

Heart and
Vessels
A462

**Perf. 13½x14, 14x13½**

| 1981, May 22 | | Litho. | |
|---|---|---|---|
| 1390 | A456 2d multi | .25 | .25 |
| 1391 | A457 3d multi | .25 | .25 |
| 1392 | A458 9d multi | .25 | .25 |
| 1393 | A459 9d multi | .25 | .25 |
| 1394 | A460 12d multi | .25 | .25 |
| 1395 | A461 21d multi | .40 | .40 |
| 1396 | A462 40d multi | .60 | .60 |
| | Nos. 1390-1396 (7) | 2.25 | 2.25 |

8th Intl. Nephrology Conf., Athens, June 7-
12; Greek National Air Club, 50th anniv.; Intl.
Historical Symposium, Volos, Sept. 27-30;
Greek Ophthalmological Society, 50th anniv.;
inauguration of oil production at Thassos
Island; World Assoc. for Intl. Relations, Athens, 2nd anniv.; 15th Intl. Cardiovascular Surgery Conference, Athens, Sept. 6-10.

Cockles — A463

| 1981, June 30 | Litho. | Perf. 14x13½ | |
|---|---|---|---|
| 1397 | A463 4d shown | .25 | .25 |
| 1398 | A463 5d Parrot fish | .25 | .25 |
| 1399 | A463 12d Painted comber | .25 | .25 |
| 1400 | A463 15d Common dentex | .25 | .25 |
| 1401 | A463 17d Parnassius apollo | .40 | .25 |
| 1402 | A463 50d Colias hyale | .90 | .75 |
| | Nos. 1397-1402 (6) | 2.30 | 2.00 |

Bell Tower,
Epirus
A464

Altar Gate,
St.
Paraskevi's
Church
A465

Bell Towers and Wood Altar Gates (Iconos-
tases): 9d, Pelion, horiz. 12d, Church of Sts.
Constantine and Helen, Epirus. 17d, St. Nicolas Church, Velvendos, horiz. 30d, St. Jacob
icon, Church Museum, Alexandroupolis. 40d,
St. Nicholas Church, Makrinitsa.

| 1981, Sept. 30 | | Litho. | |
|---|---|---|---|
| 1403 | A464 4d multi | .25 | .25 |
| 1404 | A465 6d multi | .25 | .25 |
| 1405 | A465 9d multi | .25 | .25 |
| 1406 | A464 12d multi | .25 | .25 |
| 1407 | A465 17d multi | .25 | .25 |
| 1408 | A465 30d multi | .30 | .30 |
| 1409 | A465 40d multi | .50 | .50 |
| | Nos. 1403-1409 (7) | 2.05 | 2.05 |

European Urban
Renaissance Year
A466

St. Simeon,
Archbishop
of
Thessalonica
A467

Promotion of
Breastfeeding
A468

Gina
Bachauer,
Pianist, 5th
Death Anniv.
A469

Constantine
Broumidis,
Artist, Death
Centenary
A470

Sesquicentennial of
Greek Banknotes
A471

**Perf. 14x13½, 13½x14**

| 1981, Nov. 20 | | Litho. | |
|---|---|---|---|
| 1410 | A466 3d multi | .25 | .25 |
| 1411 | A467 9d multi | .25 | .25 |
| 1412 | A468 12d multi | .25 | .25 |
| 1413 | A469 17d multi | .35 | .25 |
| 1414 | A470 21d multi | .40 | .25 |
| 1415 | A471 50d multi | .60 | .50 |
| | Nos. 1410-1415 (6) | 2.10 | 1.75 |

Old Parliament
Building, Athens
A472

Angelos
Sikelianos
(1884-
1951), Poet
A473

Harilaos
Tricoupis,
Politician,
Birth
Sesquicentennial
A474

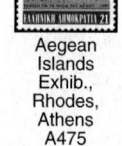

Aegean
Islands
Exhib.,
Rhodes,
Athens
A475

Olympic Airlines,
25th Anniv.
A476

Petralona
Cave and
Skull
A477

**Perf. 13½x12½, 12½x13½**

| 1982, Mar. 15 | | Litho. | |
|---|---|---|---|
| 1416 | A472 2d multi | .25 | .25 |
| 1417 | A473 9d multi | .25 | .25 |
| 1418 | A474 15d multi | .25 | .25 |
| 1419 | A475 21d multi | .35 | .35 |
| 1420 | A476 30d multi | .55 | .45 |
| 1421 | A477 50d multi | .90 | .80 |
| | Nos. 1416-1421 (6) | 2.55 | 2.35 |

Historical and Ethnological Society centennial (2d); 3rd European Anthropology Congress, Halkidiki, Sept. (50d).

Europa 1982 — A478

21d, Battle of Marathon, 490 BC. 30d, 1826
Revolution.

| 1982, May 10 | Litho. | Perf. 13½x14 | |
|---|---|---|---|
| 1422 | A478 21d multicolored | 1.60 | .80 |
| 1423 | A478 30d multicolored | 3.25 | 1.60 |

13th European Athletic
Championships,
Athens — A479

21d, Pole vaulting, horiz. 25d, Running. 40d,
Sports, horiz.

| 1982, May 10 | Perf. 14x13½, 13½x14 | | |
|---|---|---|---|
| 1424 | A479 21d multicolored | .25 | .25 |
| 1425 | A479 25d multicolored | .35 | .25 |
| 1426 | A479 40d multicolored | .65 | .55 |
| | Nos. 1424-1426 (3) | 1.25 | 1.05 |

Byzantine Book
Illustrations — A480

4d, Gospel book heading. 6d, Illuminated
"E," vert. 12d, Illuminated "T," vert. 15d, Gospel reading canon table, vert. 80d, Zoology
book heading.

**Perf. 13½x12½, 12½x13½**

| 1982, June 26 | | Litho. | |
|---|---|---|---|
| 1427 | A480 4d multicolored | .25 | .25 |
| 1428 | A480 6d multicolored | .25 | .25 |
| 1429 | A480 12d multicolored | .25 | .25 |
| 1430 | A480 15d multicolored | .25 | .25 |
| 1431 | A480 80d multicolored | 1.00 | 1.00 |
| | Nos. 1427-1431 (5) | 2.00 | 2.00 |

Georgios Karaiskakis
(1782-1827),
Liberation
Hero — A481

Designs: 12d, Camp in Piraeus, by von
Krazeisen. 50d, Meditating.

| 1982, Sept. 20 | Litho. | Perf. 13x13½ | |
|---|---|---|---|
| 1432 | A481 12d multicolored | .35 | .25 |
| 1433 | A481 50d multicolored | .65 | .40 |

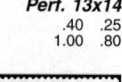

Amnesty Intl. — A482

| 1982, Sept. 20 | | Perf. 13x14 | |
|---|---|---|---|
| 1434 | A482 15d Vigil | .40 | .25 |
| 1435 | A482 75d Prisoners | 1.00 | .80 |

Natl. Resistance
Movement, 1941-
44 — A483

Designs: 1d, Demonstration of Mar. 24,
1942. 2d, Sacrifice of Inhabitants of Kalavrita,
by S. Vasiliou. 5d, Resistance Fighters in
Thrace, by A. Tassos. 9d, The Start of Resistance in Crete, by P. Gravalos. 12d, Partisan
Men and Women, by P. Gravalos. 21d, Blowing Up a Bridge, by A. Tassos. 30d, Fighters at
a Barricade, by G. Sikeliotis. 50d, The Fight in

segment removed

GREECE

545

Northern Greece, by B. Katraki, 5d, 9d, 12d, 21d vert.

| 1982, Nov. 8 | Litho. | Perf. 12½ | |
|---|---|---|---|
| 1436 | A483 | 1d multi | .25 .25 |
| 1437 | A483 | 2d multi | .25 .25 |
| 1438 | A483 | 5d multi | .25 .25 |
| 1439 | A483 | 9d multi | .25 .25 |
| 1440 | A483 | 12d multi | .25 .25 |
| 1441 | A483 | 21d multi | .25 .25 |
| a. | | Souv. sheet, 5d, 9d, 12d, 21d | 1.40 1.40 |
| 1442 | A483 | 30d multi | .40 .30 |
| 1443 | A483 | 50d multi | 1.00 .45 |
| a. | | Souv. sheet, 1d, 2d, 30d, 50d | 1.60 1.60 |
| | | Nos. 1436-1443 (8) | 2.90 2.25 |

Christmas 1982 — A484

Designs: Various Byzantine Nativity bas-reliefs, Byzantine Museum.

| 1982, Dec. 6 | Litho. | Perf. 13½x12½ | |
|---|---|---|---|
| 1444 | A484 | 1d multi | .25 .25 |
| 1445 | A484 | 21d multi | .25 .25 |
| a. | | Pair, #1444-1445 | .55 .55 |

25th Anniv. of Intl. Maritime Org. — A485

Ship Figureheads: 11d, Ares, Tsamados. 15d, Ares, Miaoulis, vert. 18d, Female figure, vert. 25d, Spetses, Bouboulina, vert. 40d, Epameinondas, K. Babas, vert. 50d, Carteria.

| 1983, Mar. 14 | Perf. 14x13½, 13½x14 | | |
|---|---|---|---|
| 1446 | A485 | 11d multicolored | .25 .25 |
| 1447 | A485 | 15d multicolored | .25 .25 |
| 1448 | A485 | 18d multicolored | .25 .25 |
| 1449 | A485 | 25d multicolored | .35 .25 |
| 1450 | A485 | 40d multicolored | .50 .30 |
| 1451 | A485 | 50d multicolored | 1.00 .80 |
| | | Nos. 1446-1451 (6) | 2.60 2.10 |

Postal Code Inauguration A486

| 1983, Mar. 14 | Litho. | Perf. 12½ | |
|---|---|---|---|
| 1452 | A486 | 15d Cover, map | .25 .25 |
| 1453 | A486 | 25d Hermes, post horn, vert. | .40 .35 |

Rowing — A487

18d, Water skiing, vert. 27d, Wind surfing, vert. 50d, Skiiers on chairlift, vert. 80d, Skiing.

| 1983, Apr. 28 | Perf. 14x13, 13x14 | | |
|---|---|---|---|
| 1454 | A487 | 15d shown | .25 .25 |
| 1455 | A487 | 18d multicolored | .25 .25 |
| 1456 | A487 | 27d multicolored | .50 .50 |
| 1457 | A487 | 50d multicolored | .50 .50 |
| 1458 | A487 | 80d multicolored | 1.50 1.40 |
| | | Nos. 1454-1458 (5) | 3.00 2.90 |

### Europa Issue

Acropolis A488

Archimedes and His Hydrostatic Principle — A489

| Perf. 12½x13½, 13x13½ | | | |
|---|---|---|---|
| 1983, Apr. 28 | | | Litho. |
| 1459 | A488 | 25d multi | 2.00 1.00 |
| 1460 | A489 | 80d multi | 4.00 3.00 |

Marinos Antypas (1873-1907), Farmers' Movement Leader — A490

Designs: 9d, Nicholas Plastiras (1883-1953), prime minister. 15d, George Papandreou (1888-1968), statesman. 20d, Constantine Cavafy (1863-1933), poet. 27d, Nikos Kazantzakis (1883-1957), writer. 32d, Manolis Calomiris (1883-1962), composer. 40d, George Papanicolaou (1883-1962), medical researcher. 50d, Despina Achladioti (1890-1982), nationalist.

| 1983, July 11 | Litho. | Perf. 13½x14 | |
|---|---|---|---|
| 1461 | A490 | 6d multi | .25 .25 |
| 1462 | A490 | 9d multi | .25 .25 |
| 1463 | A490 | 15d multi | .25 .25 |
| 1464 | A490 | 20d multi | .25 .25 |
| 1465 | A490 | 27d multi | .30 .25 |
| 1466 | A490 | 32d multi | .50 .25 |
| 1467 | A490 | 40d multi | .60 .25 |
| 1468 | A490 | 50d multi | .70 .50 |
| | | Nos. 1461-1468 (8) | 3.10 2.25 |

Portrait Bust — A491

| 1983, Sept. 26 | Litho. | Perf. 13½x13 | |
|---|---|---|---|
| 1469 | A491 | 50d multi | 2.00 1.00 |

1st Intl. Conf. on the Works of Democritus (Philosopher, 460-370 BC), Xanthe, Oct.

A492

| 1983, Nov. 17 | Litho. | Perf. 13 | |
|---|---|---|---|
| 1470 | A492 | 15d Poster | .25 .25 |
| 1471 | A492 | 30d Flight from school | .40 .30 |

Polytechnic School Uprising, 1st anniv.

The Deification of Homer — A493

Homer Inspired Artworks: 3d, The Abduction of Helen by Paris, horiz. 4d, The Wooden Horse, horiz. 6d, Achilles. 10d, Hector Receiving His Arms from His Parents. 14d, Single-handed Battle Between Ajax and Hector, horiz. 15d, Priam Requesting the Body of Hector, horiz. 20d, The Blinding of Polyphemus. 27d, Ulysses Escaping from Polyphemus' Cave, horiz. 30d, Ulysses Meeting with Nausica. 32d, Ulysses on the Island of the Sirens, horiz. 50d, Ulysses Slaying the Suitors, horiz. 75d, The Heroes of the Iliad, horiz. 100d, Homer.

| 1983, Dec. 19 | Litho. | Perf. 13 | |
|---|---|---|---|
| 1472 | A493 | 2d multi | .25 .25 |
| 1473 | A493 | 3d multi | .25 .25 |
| 1474 | A493 | 4d multi | .25 .25 |
| 1475 | A493 | 5d multi | .25 .25 |
| 1476 | A493 | 6d multi | .25 .25 |
| 1477 | A493 | 10d multi | .25 .25 |
| 1478 | A493 | 14d multi | .25 .25 |
| 1479 | A493 | 15d multi | .25 .25 |
| 1480 | A493 | 20d multi | .25 .25 |
| 1481 | A493 | 27d multi | .25 .25 |
| 1482 | A493 | 30d multi | .35 .25 |
| 1483 | A493 | 32d multi | .40 .25 |
| 1484 | A493 | 50d multi | .50 .25 |
| 1485 | A493 | 75d multi | 1.00 .50 |
| 1486 | A493 | 100d multi | 1.50 .65 |
| | | Nos. 1472-1486 (15) | 6.25 4.40 |

Horse's Head from Chariot of Seline — A494

Dionysus — A494a

Hestia, Dione, Aphrodite — A494b

Lapith, Centaur — A494c

Horsemen and Heroes — A495

Design: No. 1490, Ilissus.
Nos. 1492a-1492b, Equestrian scene. Nos. 1492c-1492d, Athenian Elders.

| 1984, Mar. 15 | Litho. | Perf. 14½x14 | |
|---|---|---|---|
| 1487 | A494 | 14d shown | .25 .25 |
| 1488 | A494a | 15d multi | .30 .25 |
| 1489 | A494b | 20d multi | .55 .25 |
| 1490 | A494b | 27d multi | .70 .25 |
| 1491 | A494c | 32d multi | 1.20 .60 |
| | | Nos. 1487-1491 (5) | 3.00 1.60 |

**Souvenir Sheet**
Perf. 13x13½

| 1492 | A495 | Sheet of 4 | 4.25 4.25 |
|---|---|---|---|
| a. | | 15d multi | .70 .70 |
| b. | | 21d multi | .80 .80 |
| c. | | 27d multi | .90 .90 |
| d. | | 32d multi | 1.10 1.10 |

Marble from the Parthenon. No. 1492 sold for 107d.
Nos. 1492a-1492b and 1492c-1492d have continuous designs.

Europa (1959-84) — A496

| 1984, Apr. 30 | Litho. | Perf. 14x13½ | |
|---|---|---|---|
| 1493 | A496 | 15d multi | .60 .35 |
| 1494 | A496 | 27d multi | 1.40 .80 |
| a. | | Pair, #1493-1494 | 2.60 2.60 |

1984 Summer Olympics — A497

Designs: 14d, Ancient Olympic stadium crypt. 15d, Athletes training. 20d, Broad jump, discus thrower. 32d, Athletes, diff. 80d, Stadium, Demetrius Bikelos, poet, organizer of 1896 Athens games.

| 1984, Apr. 30 | | Perf. 13½x14 | |
|---|---|---|---|
| 1495 | A497 | 14d multi | .25 .25 |
| 1496 | A497 | 15d multi | .35 .30 |
| 1497 | A497 | 20d multi | .40 .40 |
| 1498 | A497 | 32d multi | .60 .55 |
| 1499 | A497 | 80d multi | 1.40 1.15 |
| a. | | Strip of 5, #1495-1499 | 3.75 3.75 |

Also issued in booklets.

Turkish Invasion of Cyprus, 10th Anniv. — A498

| 1984, July 10 | Litho. | Perf. 13 | |
|---|---|---|---|
| 1500 | A498 | 20d Tank, map, vert. | .35 .25 |
| 1501 | A498 | 32d Map, barbed wire | .50 .40 |

Also issued in booklets.

Greek Railway Centenary A499

15d, Pelion. 20d, Papadia Bridge, vert. 30d, Piraeus-Peloponnese. 50d, Cogwheel Calavryta, vert.

| Perf. 13x13½, 13½x13 | | | |
|---|---|---|---|
| 1984, July 20 | | | Litho. |
| 1502 | A499 | 15d multicolored | .50 .25 |
| 1503 | A499 | 20d multicolored | 1.50 1.10 |
| 1504 | A499 | 30d multicolored | .50 .25 |
| 1505 | A499 | 50d multicolored | 1.50 1.10 |
| | | Nos. 1502-1505 (4) | 4.00 2.70 |

Sesquicentenary of Athens as Capital City — A500

15d, 4d silver coin, 5th cent. BC, city plan, vert. 100d, Views of ancient & modern Athens.

| Perf. 13½x13, 13x13½ | | | |
|---|---|---|---|
| 1984, Oct. 12 | | | Litho. |
| 1506 | A500 | 15d multi | .35 .25 |
| 1507 | A500 | 100d multi | 1.30 .80 |

10th Anniv. of Democratic Govt. — A501

| 1984, Oct. 12 | Litho. | Perf. 13x13½ | |
|---|---|---|---|
| 1508 | A501 | 95d "10" on flag | 1.40 .60 |

Christmas 1984 — A502

Scenes from 18th cent. icon by Athanasios Tountas: 14d, Annunciation. 20d, Nativity. 25d, Presentation in the Temple. 32d, Baptism of Christ.

| 1984, Dec. 6 | Litho. | Perf. 13½x13 | |
|---|---|---|---|
| 1509 | A502 | 14d multicolored | .40 .25 |
| 1510 | A502 | 20d multicolored | .40 .25 |
| 1511 | A502 | 25d multicolored | .40 .35 |
| 1512 | A502 | 32d multicolored | .40 .40 |
| a. | | Block of 4, #1509-1512 | 2.00 2.00 |

Also issued in booklets.

Runner — A503

Palais des Sports — A504

| Perf. 13, 13x13½ (#1515) | | | |
|---|---|---|---|
| 1985, Mar. 1 | | | Litho. |
| 1513 | A503 | 12d shown | .25 .25 |
| 1514 | A503 | 15d Shot put | .30 .25 |
| 1515 | A504 | 20d shown | .30 .25 |
| 1516 | A503 | 25d Hurdles | .60 .25 |
| 1517 | A503 | 80d Women's high jump | 1.15 .65 |
| | | Nos. 1513-1517 (5) | 2.60 1.65 |

European Indoor Athletics Championships, Palais des Sports, New Phaleron.

Europa 1985 A505

CEPT emblem and: 27d, Musical contest between Marsyas and Apollo. 80d, Dimitris Mitropoulos (1896-1960) and Nikos Skalkottas (1904-1949), composers.

**1985, Apr. 29**     *Perf. 14x14½*
**1518** A505 27d multi    .75   .50
**1519** A505 80d multi    1.50   1.00

Exist se-tenant as strip of 3, 27d+80d+27d in booklets.

Melos Catacombs, A.D. 2nd Cent., Trypete — A506

15d, Niche. 20d, Altar, Central Gallery. 100d, Catacombs.

**1985, Apr. 29**     *Perf. 14½x14*
**1520** A506 15d multicolored    .25   .25
**1521** A506 20d multicolored    .40   .25
**1522** A506 100d multicolored    1.30   .90
   Nos. 1520-1522 (3)    1.95   1.40

Republic of Cyprus, 25th Anniv. — A507

**1985, June 24**     *Perf. 13x13½*
**1523** A507 32d Map of Cyprus, urn    .80   .40

Coin of King Cassander (315 B.C.), Personification of Salonika, Galerius Era Bas-relief — A508

Sts. Demetrius and Methodius, Mosaics A509

Designs: 15d, Emperor sacrificing at Altar, Arch of Galerius, Roman era. 20d, Eastern walls of Salonika, Byzantine era. 32d, Houses in the Upper City. 50d, Liberation of Salonika by the Greek Army, 1912. 80d, German occupation, 1941-44, the Old Mosque. 95d, View of city, Trade Fair grounds, Aristotelian University tower.

*Perf. 14½x14 (A508), 14x14½ (A509)*
**1985, June 24**
**1524** A508 1d multi    .25   .25
**1525** A509 5d multi    .30   .25
**1526** A508 15d multi    .35   .25
**1527** A508 20d multi    .35   .25
**1528** A508 32d multi    .40   .25
**1529** A508 50d multi    .50   .25
**1530** A508 80d multi    1.00   .40
**1531** A509 95d multi    1.40   1.20
   Nos. 1524-1531 (8)    4.55   3.10

Salonika City, 2300th anniv. Aristotelian University, Trade Fair, 60th annivs.

Athenian Cultural Heritage — A510

Ancient art and architecture: 15d, Democracy Crowning the City, bas-relief from a column, Ancient Agora of Athens, vert. 20d, Mosaic pavement of tritons, nereids, dolphins, etc., Roman baths at Hieratus, Isthmia, A.D. 2nd cent. 32d, Angel, fresco, Grotto of Pentheli, A.D. 13th cent., vert. 80d, Capodistrian University, Athens.

**1985, Oct. 7**     *Perf. 13½x13, 13x13½*
**1532** A510 15d multi    .25   .25
**1533** A510 20d multi    .25   .25
**1534** A510 32d multi    .55   .25
**1535** A510 80d multi    1.15   .90
   Nos. 1532-1535 (4)    2.20   1.65

Intl. Youth Year A511

UN 40th Anniv. A512

15d, Children, olive wreath. 25d, Children, doves. 27d, UN General Assembly, dove. No. 1539, 100d, UN building, emblem.
No. 1540, Girl crowned with flowers, Stadium of Peace and Friendship, Athens.

**1985, Oct. 7**     *Perf. 14x14½*
**1536** A511 15d multicolored    .25   .25
**1537** A511 25d multicolored    .40   .25
**1538** A512 27d multicolored    .45   .25
**1539** A512 100d multicolored    1.30   1.20
   Nos. 1536-1539 (4)    2.40   1.95

**Souvenir Sheet**

**1985, Nov. 22**     *Perf. 14x13*
**1540** A511 100d multicolored    1.75   1.75

No. 1540 contains one 43x47mm stamp.

Pontic Hellenism Cultural Reformation A513

12d, Folk dance. 15d, Our Lady Soumela Monastery. 27d, Folk costumes, vert. 32d, Trapezus High School. 80d, Sinope Castle.

*Perf. 14x12½, 12½x14*
**1985, Dec. 9**     *Litho.*
**1541** A513 12d multicolored    .25   .25
**1542** A513 15d multicolored    .25   .25
**1543** A513 27d multicolored    .40   .25
**1544** A513 32d multicolored    .40   .25
**1545** A513 80d multicolored    .90   .80
   Nos. 1541-1545 (5)    2.20   1.80

Greek Gods — A514

**1986, Feb. 17**     *Litho.*    *Perf. 13*
**1546** A514 5d Hestia    .25   .25
**1547** A514 18d Hermes    .25   .25
**1548** A514 27d Aphrodite    .25   .25
**1549** A514 32d Ares    .40   .30
**1550** A514 35d Athena    .50   .30
**1551** A514 40d Hephaestus    .60   .25
**1552** A514 50d Artemis    .80   .30
**1553** A514 110d Apollo    .90   .30
**1554** A514 150d Demeter    1.40   .30
**1555** A514 200d Poseidon    2.00   .40
**1556** A514 300d Hera    3.50   .80
**1557** A514 500d Zeus    7.75   3.75
   Nos. 1546-1557 (12)    18.60   7.45

**Booklet Stamps**
*Perf. 13 Horiz.*
**1546A** A514 5d Hestia    .25   .25
**1547A** A514 18d Hermes    .25   .25
**1548A** A514 27d Aphrodite    .35   .25
**1549A** A514 32d Ares    .35   .25
**1550A** A514 35d Athena    .35   .25
**1551A** A514 40d Hephaestus    .35   .25
**1552A** A514 50d Artemis    .45   .25
**1553A** A514 110d Apollo    .80   .25
**1554A** A514 150d Demeter    2.60   .25
**1555A** A514 200d Poseidon    2.60   .25
**1556A** A514 300d Hera    4.00   .25
**1557A** A514 500d Zeus    9.75   .25
   Nos. 1546A-1557A (12)    22.10   3.00

Nos. 1546A-1557A were each sold in booklets containing 20 panes of 5 stamps.

Youth of Antikythera A515

Soccer Players A517

Diadoumenos, by Polycleitus A516

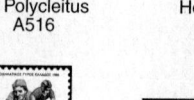

Wrestlers, Hellenic Era Statue A518

Cyclists A520

Volleyball Players A519

Commemorative Design for 1st Modern Olympic Games — A521

**1986, Mar. 3**     *Perf. 12*
**1558** A515 18d multi    .35   .25
**1559** A516 27d multi    1.15   .35
**1560** A517 32d multi    2.25   .75
**1561** A518 35d multi    1.15   1.00
**1562** A519 40d multi    1.15   .40
**1563** A520 50d multi    1.15   .40
**1564** A521 110d multi    3.75   1.30
   Nos. 1558-1564 (7)    10.95   4.45

First World Junior Athletic Championships. Pan-European Junior Soccer Championships. Pan-European Free-style and Greco-Roman Wrestling Championships. Men's World Volleyball Championships. Sixth International Round-Europe Cycling Meet. Modern Olympic Games, 90th anniv.

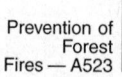

European Traffic Safety Year — A522

**1986, Mar. 3**     *Perf. 12½x14*
**1565** A522 18d Seat belts    .25   .25
**1566** A522 27d Motorcycle    .80   .80
**1567** A522 110d Speed limits    1.20   .40
   Nos. 1565-1567 (3)    2.25   1.45

Prevention of Forest Fires — A523

**1986, Apr. 23**    *Litho.*    *Perf. 14x13½*
**1568** A523 35d shown    3.75   1.60
**1569** A523 110d Prespa Lakes wetlands    4.00   3.25
   *a.*   Pair, 35d, 110d    7.25   7.25

**Booklet Stamps**
*Perf. 13½ Vert.*
**1568A** A523 35d shown    4.50   4.50
**1569B** A523 110d Prespa Lakes wetlands    4.50   4.50
   *c.*   Pair, #1568A, 1569B    10.00   10.00
   *d.*   Bklt. pane, 2 each #1568A, 1569B    20.00

Europa.

New Postal Services — A524

18d, Intelpost. 110d, Express mail, horiz.

**1986, Apr. 23**     *Perf. 13½x14, 14x13½*
**1570** A524 18d multicolored    .35   .25
**1571** A524 110d multicolored    1.30   .65

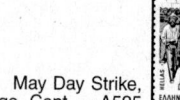

May Day Strike, Chicago, Cent. — A525

40d, Strikers, monument.

**1986, Apr. 23**     *Perf. 12½*
**1572** A525 40d multicolored    .55   .40

Eleutherios K. Venizelos (1864-1936), Premier — A526

18d, Venizelos, Ministers taking oath of office, 1917. 110d, Old Hania Harbor, Crete.

**1986, June 30**    *Litho.*    *Perf. 14x12½*
**1573** A526 18d multi    .25   .25
**1574** A526 110d multi    1.40   .60

6th Intl. Cretological Conference, Crete.

Intl. Peace Year — A527

18d, Dove, sun, vert. 35d, Flags, dove, vert. 110d, World cage, dove.

**1986, Oct. 6**    *Litho.*    *Perf. 12½*
**1575** A527 18d multicolored    .25   .25
**1576** A527 35d multicolored    .55   .35
**1577** A527 110d multicolored    1.40   .60
   Nos. 1575-1577 (3)    2.20   1.20

Christmas — A528

Religious art in the Benaki Museum: 22d, Madonna and Child Enthroned, triptych center panel, 15th cent. 46d, Adoration of the Magi, 15th cent. 130d, Christ Enthroned with St. John the Evangelist, triptych panel.

**1986, Dec. 1**    *Litho.*    *Perf. 13½x14*
**1578** A528 22d multi    .25   .25
**1579** A528 46d multi    .55   .40
**1580** A528 130d multi    1.40   1.00
   Nos. 1578-1580 (3)    2.20   1.00

Size of No. 1579: 27x35mm.

Aesop's Fables — A529

2d, Fox and the Grapes. 5d, North Wind and the Sun. 10d, Stag and the Lion. 22d, Zeus and the Snake. 32d, Crow and the Fox. 40d, Woodcutter and Hermes. 46d, Ass in a Lion's Skin. 130d, Tortoise and the Hare.

**1987, Mar. 5**    *Litho.*    *Perf. 12½*
**1581** A529 2d multicolored    .25   .25
**1582** A529 5d multicolored    .25   .25
**1583** A529 10d multicolored    .25   .25
**1584** A529 22d multicolored    .50   .25
**1585** A529 32d multicolored    .90   .25
**1586** A529 40d multicolored    1.00   .35
**1587** A529 46d multicolored    1.75   .55
**1588** A529 130d multicolored    3.75   1.30
   Nos. 1581-1588 (8)    8.65   3.45

**Booklet Stamps**
*Perf. 13½ Horiz.*
**1581A** A529 2d multicolored    .25   .25
**1582A** A529 5d multicolored    .25   .25
**1583A** A529 10d multicolored    .35   .25
**1584A** A529 22d multicolored    .65   .25
**1585A** A529 32d multicolored    1.30   .25
**1586A** A529 40d multicolored    1.60   .25
**1587A** A529 46d multicolored    3.25   .25
**1588A** A529 130d multicolored    16.00   .65
   Nos. 1581A-1588A (8)    23.65   2.40

Nos. 1581A-1588A were each sold in booklets containing 20 panes of 5 stamps.

Europa
1987 — A530

Modern art: 40d, Composition, by Achilleas Apergis. 130d, Delphic Light, by Gerassimos Sklavos.

| | | | Perf. 12½ | |
|---|---|---|---|---|
| **1987, May 4** | | **Litho.** | | |
| 1589 | A530 | 40d multi | 2.40 | 1.60 |
| 1590 | A530 | 130d multi | 3.25 | 2.40 |
| a. | | Pair, #1589-1590 | 6.00 | 6.00 |

**Booklet Stamps**
*Perf. 12½ Vert.*

| | | | | |
|---|---|---|---|---|
| 1589A | A530 | 40d multi | 2.25 | 1.30 |
| 1590B | A530 | 130d multi | 2.25 | 1.30 |
| c. | | Pair, #1589A, 1590B | 8.00 | 8.00 |
| d. | | Bklt. pane, 2 each #1589A,1590B | 17.00 | |

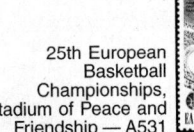

25th European Basketball Championships, Stadium of Peace and Friendship — A531

A532

22d, Jump shot, stadium, vert. 25d, Emblem, spectators. 130d, Two players, vert.

| | | | Perf. 13½x14, 12½ | |
|---|---|---|---|---|
| **1987, May 4** | | | | |
| 1591 | A531 | 22d multicolored | .50 | .50 |
| 1592 | A532 | 25d multicolored | .35 | .25 |
| 1593 | A531 | 130d multicolored | 1.50 | .90 |
| | | Nos. 1591-1593 (3) | 2.35 | 1.65 |

Higher Education Sesquicentenary
A533

3d, Students, tapestry. 23d, Owl, medallion. 40d, Institute, symbols of science. 60d, Institute, students.

| | | Perf. 14x13½, 13½x14 | | |
|---|---|---|---|---|
| **1987, May 4** | | **Litho.** | | |
| 1594 | A533 | 3d multicolored | .25 | .25 |
| 1595 | A533 | 23d multicolored | .35 | .25 |
| 1596 | A533 | 40d multicolored | .60 | .35 |
| 1597 | A533 | 60d multicolored | .80 | .60 |
| | | Nos. 1594-1597 (4) | 2.00 | 1.45 |

Capodistrias University of Athens (Nos. 1594-1595); The Natl. Metsovio Polytechnic Institute (Nos. 1596-1597). Nos. 1596-1597 vert.

**Souvenir Sheet**

25th European Men's Basketball Championships — A534

| | | | Perf. 13x14 | |
|---|---|---|---|---|
| **1987, June 3** | | **Litho.** | | |
| 1598 | A534 | Sheet of 3 | 5.00 | 5.00 |
| a. | | 40d Jump ball | .75 | .75 |
| b. | | 60d Layup | 1.00 | 1.00 |
| c. | | 100d Dunk shot | 1.75 | 1.75 |

Architecture
A535

Designs: 2d, Ionic and Corinthian capitals, Archaic Era. 26d, Doric capital, the Parthenon (detail). 40d, Ionic capital and the Erechteum. 60d, Corinthian capital and the Tholos in Epidaurus.

| | | | Perf. 13½x12½ | |
|---|---|---|---|---|
| **1987, July 1** | | **Litho.** | | |
| 1599 | A535 | 2d multi | .25 | .25 |
| 1600 | A535 | 26d multi | .30 | .25 |
| 1601 | A535 | 40d multi | .45 | .30 |
| 1602 | A535 | 60d multi | .90 | .80 |
| | | Nos. 1599-1602 (4) | 1.90 | 1.60 |

Engraving by Yiannis Kephalinos
A536

Panteios School
A537

| | | Perf. 12½x14, 14x12½ | | |
|---|---|---|---|---|
| **1987, Oct. 1** | | **Litho.** | | |
| 1603 | A536 | 26d multi | .30 | .25 |
| 1604 | A537 | 60d multi | .70 | .60 |

School of Fine Arts, 150th anniv. (26d), and Panteios School of Political Science, 60th anniv. (60d).

Greek Natl. Team, Winner, 25th European Men's Basketball Championship
A538

| | | Perf. 13x14 | | |
|---|---|---|---|---|
| **1987, Oct. 1** | | | | |
| 1605 | A538 | 40d multi | .75 | .75 |

Traditional and Modern Greek Theater — A539

Designs: 2d, Eleni Papadaki in Hecuba, by Euripides, and outdoor theater, Philippi. 4d, Christopher Nezer in The Wasps, by Aristophane, and outdoor theater, Dodona. 7d, Emilios Veakis in Oedipus Rex and theater, Delphi. 26d, Marika Cotopouli in The Shepherdess's Love, by Dimitris Koromilas. 40d, Katina Paxinou in Abraham's Sacrifice, by Vitzentzos Cornaros. 50d, Kyveli in Countess Valeraina's Secret, by Gregory Xenopoulos. 60d, Director Carolos Koun, stage setting. 100d, Dimitris Rontiris teaching ancient dance, Greek National Theater.

| | | | Perf. 14x13½ | |
|---|---|---|---|---|
| **1987, Dec. 2** | | **Litho.** | | |
| 1606 | A539 | 2d multi | .25 | .25 |
| 1607 | A539 | 4d multi | .25 | .25 |
| 1608 | A539 | 7d multi | .25 | .25 |
| 1609 | A539 | 26d multi | .35 | .25 |
| 1610 | A539 | 40d multi | .50 | .25 |
| 1611 | A539 | 50d multi | .60 | .25 |
| 1612 | A539 | 60d multi | .85 | .85 |
| 1613 | A539 | 100d multi | 1.60 | .35 |
| | | Nos. 1606-1613 (8) | 4.65 | 2.70 |

Christmas
A540

| | | | Perf. 13x12½ | |
|---|---|---|---|---|
| **1987, Dec. 2** | | | | |
| 1614 | | 26d Angel facing right | .50 | .25 |
| 1615 | | 26d Angel facing left | .50 | .25 |
| a. | | Bklt. pane, 5 each #1614-1615 | 7.00 | |
| b. | | A540 Pair, #1614-1615 | 1.00 | 1.00 |

Marine Life — A541

30d, Codonellina. 40d, Diaperoecia major. 50d, Artemia. 60d, Posidonia oceanica. 100d, Padina pavonica.

| | | | Perf. 14x12½ | |
|---|---|---|---|---|
| **1988, Mar. 2** | | | | |
| 1616 | A541 | 30d multicolored | .65 | .35 |
| 1617 | A541 | 40d multicolored | 1.00 | .50 |
| 1618 | A541 | 50d multicolored | 1.40 | .75 |
| 1619 | A541 | 60d multicolored | 3.25 | 1.60 |
| 1620 | A541 | 100d multicolored | 3.25 | 1.60 |
| | | Nos. 1616-1620 (5) | 9.55 | 4.80 |

**Booklet Stamps**
*Perf. 12½ Vert.*

| | | | | |
|---|---|---|---|---|
| 1616A | A541 | 30d multicolored | 3.50 | .40 |
| 1617A | A541 | 40d multicolored | 2.00 | .40 |
| 1618A | A541 | 50d multicolored | 6.25 | .40 |
| 1619A | A541 | 60d multicolored | 7.00 | .40 |
| 1620A | A541 | 100d multicolored | 10.50 | .40 |
| | | Nos. 1616A-1620A (5) | 29.25 | 2.00 |

Nos. 1616A-1620A were each sold in booklets containing 20 panes of 5 stamps.

Europa
1988
A542

Communication and transport: 60d, Telecommunications satellite, telephone and facsimile machine. 150d, Passenger trains.

| | | | Perf. 12½ | |
|---|---|---|---|---|
| **1988, May 6** | | **Litho.** | | |
| 1621 | | 60d multi | 4.00 | 2.40 |
| 1622 | | 150d multi | 4.50 | 3.25 |
| a. | | A542 Pair, 60d, 150d | 9.25 | 9.25 |

**Booklet Stamps**
*Perf. 14 Vert.*

| | | | | |
|---|---|---|---|---|
| 1621A | | 60d multi | 3.25 | 2.25 |
| 1622B | | 150d multi | 3.25 | 2.25 |
| c. | | A542 Pair, #1621A, 1622B | 9.75 | 9.75 |
| d. | | Bklt. pane of 4, 2 each #1621A, 1622B | 21.00 | |

1988
Olympics — A543

Designs: 4d, Ancient Olympia and Temple of Zeus. 20d, Javelin thrower and and ancient Olympians in open-air gymnasium. 30d, Centenary emblem of the modern Games (cent. in 1996). 60d, Wrestlers, runners and other ancient athletes in training. 170d, Modern torch-bearer.

| | | | Perf. 14x12 | |
|---|---|---|---|---|
| **1988, May 6** | | | | |
| 1623 | A543 | 4d multi | .40 | .30 |
| 1624 | A543 | 20d multi | .90 | .50 |
| 1625 | A543 | 30d multi | 1.60 | .75 |
| 1626 | A543 | 60d multi | 3.00 | 2.25 |
| 1627 | A543 | 170d multi | 4.25 | 2.60 |
| a. | | Strip of 5, #1623-1627 | 11.50 | 11.50 |

**Booklet Stamps**
*Perf. 14 Vert.*

| | | | | |
|---|---|---|---|---|
| 1623A | A543 | 4d multi | .35 | .25 |
| 1624A | A543 | 20d multi | .35 | .35 |
| 1625A | A543 | 30d multi | 1.90 | 1.30 |
| 1626A | A543 | 60d multi | 3.25 | 2.60 |
| 1627B | A543 | 170d multi | 6.00 | 3.75 |
| c. | | Bklt. pane of 5, #1623A-1626A, 1627B | 15.50 | 15.50 |

Nos. 1623A-1626A, 1627B were sold in bklts. containing 20 panes of 5 stamps. See Korea No. B53.

A544

Waterfalls: 10d, Cataractis village falls at the foot of the Tzoumerca Mountain Range. 60d, Edessa Waterfalls. 100d, Edessaios River cascades.

| | | | Perf. 12½x14 | |
|---|---|---|---|---|
| **1988, July 4** | | **Litho.** | | |
| 1628 | A544 | 10d multi | 1.60 | .35 |
| 1629 | A544 | 60d multi | 5.75 | 1.75 |
| 1630 | A544 | 100d multi | 8.00 | 1.75 |
| | | Nos. 1628-1630 (3) | 15.35 | 3.85 |

**Booklet Stamps**
*Perf. 14 Vert.*

| | | | | |
|---|---|---|---|---|
| 1628A | A544 | 10d multi | 4.00 | 1.25 |
| 1629A | A544 | 60d multi | 9.50 | 1.25 |
| 1630A | A544 | 100d multi | 14.50 | 5.50 |
| | | Nos. (3) | 28.00 | 8.00 |

Nos. 1628A-1630A were sold in booklets containing 20 panes of 5 stamps.

A545

| | | | Perf. 13x12½ | |
|---|---|---|---|---|
| **1988, July 4** | | | | |
| 1631 | A545 | 60d multi | 6.50 | 2.00 |

**Booklet Stamp**
*Perf. 14 Vert.*

| | | | | |
|---|---|---|---|---|
| 1631A | A545 | 60d multi | 15.00 | 1.50 |

20th Pan-European Postal Trade Unions Congress. No. 1631A was sold in booklets containing 20 panes of 5 stamps.

A546

Designs: 30d, Premier Eleutherios Venizelos (1864-1936), natl. flag and map. 70d, Lady liberty, flag and map.

| | | | Perf. 12½x13 | |
|---|---|---|---|---|
| **1988, Oct. 7** | | **Litho.** | | |
| 1632 | A546 | 30d shown | .70 | .25 |
| 1633 | A546 | 70d multi | 1.15 | .60 |

**Booklet Stamps**
*Perf. 14 Horiz.*

| | | | | |
|---|---|---|---|---|
| 1632A | A546 | 30d shown | 3.25 | .40 |
| 1633A | A546 | 70d multi | 4.75 | 1.20 |

Union of Crete with Greece and liberation of Epirus and Macedonia from Turkish rule, 75th annivs.

Nos. 1632A-1633A were sold in booklets containing 20 panes of 5 stamps.

A547

Departmental Seats: 2d, Mytilene-Lesbos Harbor, painting by Theophilos. 3d, Alexandroupolis lighthouse. 4d, St. Nicholas bell tower, Kozane. 5d, Labor Center, Hermoupolis. 7d, Sparta Town Hall. 8d, Pegasus of Leukas. 10d, Castle of the Knights, Rhodes. 20d, The Acropolis, Athens. 25d, Kavalla aqueduct. 30d, Statue of Athanasios Diakos and castle, Lamia. 50d, Preveza cathedral bell tower and Venetian clock. 60d, Corfu promenade. 70d, Harbor view of Hagios Nicolaos. 100d, Poligiros public fountains. 200d, Church of the Apostle Paul, Corinth.

| | | | Perf. 13 | |
|---|---|---|---|---|
| **1988, Oct. 7** | | | | |
| 1634 | A547 | 2d multi | .25 | .25 |
| 1635 | A547 | 3d multi | .25 | .25 |
| 1636 | A547 | 4d multi | .25 | .25 |
| 1637 | A547 | 5d multi | .25 | .25 |
| 1638 | A547 | 7d multi | .25 | .25 |
| 1639 | A547 | 8d multi | .25 | .25 |
| 1640 | A547 | 10d multi | .25 | .25 |
| 1641 | A547 | 20d multi | .25 | .25 |
| 1642 | A547 | 25d multi | .30 | .25 |
| 1643 | A547 | 30d multi | .35 | .25 |
| 1644 | A547 | 50d multi | .50 | .25 |
| 1645 | A547 | 60d multi | 1.00 | .50 |
| 1646 | A547 | 70d multi | 1.00 | .50 |
| 1647 | A547 | 100d multi | 1.60 | .35 |
| 1648 | A547 | 200d multi | 3.25 | .60 |
| | | Nos. 1634-1648 (15) | 10.00 | 4.70 |

**Booklet Stamps**
*Perf. 13 Horiz. or Vert.*

| | | | | |
|---|---|---|---|---|
| 1634A | A547 | 2d multi | .25 | .25 |
| 1635A | A547 | 3d multi | .25 | .25 |
| b. | | Perf. 13 on 3 sides | .25 | .25 |
| 1636A | A547 | 4d multi | .25 | .25 |
| 1637A | A547 | 5d multi | .25 | .25 |
| b. | | Perf. 13 on 3 sides | .25 | .25 |
| 1638A | A547 | 7d multi | .25 | .25 |
| 1639A | A547 | 8d multi | .25 | .25 |
| 1640A | A547 | 10d multi | .25 | .25 |
| b. | | Perf. 13 on 3 sides | .25 | .25 |
| 1641A | A547 | 20d multi | .25 | .25 |
| b. | | Perf. 13 on 3 sides | .25 | .25 |
| c. | | Bklt. pane, 4 each #1635Ab, 1637Ab, 1640Ab, 1641Ab | 5.00 | |
| | | Complete booklet, #1641Ac | 5.00 | |
| 1642A | A547 | 25d multi | .25 | .25 |
| 1643A | A547 | 30d multi | .25 | .25 |
| 1644A | A547 | 50d multi | .80 | .25 |
| 1645A | A547 | 60d multi | 1.25 | .60 |
| 1646A | A547 | 70d multi | 1.25 | .60 |
| 1647A | A547 | 100d multi | 2.40 | .40 |
| 1648A | A547 | 200d multi | 4.00 | .80 |
| | | Nos. 1634A-1648A (15) | 12.20 | 5.15 |

Nos. 1634A-1648A, were each sold in booklets containing 20 panes of 5 stamps. Nos. 1634A, 1638A-1639A, 1642A, and 1645A-1648A are perforated horizontally. Nos.

1635A-1637A, 1640A-1641A, and 1643A-1644A are perforated vertically.

Council of Europe, Rhodes, Dec. 2-3 — A548

Designs: 60d, Map and Castle of the Knights, Rhodes. 100d, Head of Helios, Rhodian 2nd-3rd cent. B.C. coin, and flags.

**1988, Dec. 2    Litho.    Perf. 12½**
| | | | | |
|---|---|---|---|---|
| 1649 | A548 | 60d multi | 1.60 | 1.40 |
| 1650 | A548 | 100d multi | 2.40 | 1.00 |

**Booklet Stamps**
**Perf. 14 Horiz.**
| | | | | |
|---|---|---|---|---|
| 1649A | A548 | 60d multi | 4.00 | 2.00 |
| 1650A | A548 | 100d multi | 6.00 | 3.00 |

Nos. 1649A-1650A were sold in booklets containing 20 panes of 5.

Christmas — A549

Paintings: 30d, Adoration of the Magi, by El Greco. 70d, The Annunciation, by Costas Parthenis, horiz.

**1988, Dec. 2    Perf. 12½**
| | | | | |
|---|---|---|---|---|
| 1651 | A549 | 30d multi | .65 | .35 |
| a. | | Bklt. pane of 10 | 23.00 | |

Stamps in No. 1651a are perf 12½ on three sides.

| | | | | |
|---|---|---|---|---|
| 1652 | A549 | 70d multi | 1.40 | .70 |

**Booklet Stamp**
**Perf. 14 Vert.**
| | | | | |
|---|---|---|---|---|
| 1652A | A549 | 70d multi | 10.00 | 5.00 |

No. 1652A was sold in booklets containing 20 panes of 5 stamps.

A550

Athens '96 emblem and: 30d, High jumper and ancient Olympia. 60d, Wrestlers and view of Delphi. 70d, Swimmers and The Acropolis, Athens. 170d, Sports complex.

**1989, Mar. 17    Litho.    Perf. 13¼x14**
| | | | | |
|---|---|---|---|---|
| 1653 | A550 | 30d multi | .40 | .25 |
| 1654 | A550 | 60d multi | .80 | .75 |
| 1655 | A550 | 70d multi | 1.20 | 1.15 |
| 1656 | A550 | 170d multi | 2.40 | 1.60 |
| a. | | Strip of 4, Nos. 1653-1656 | 5.75 | 5.75 |

**Booklet Stamps**
**Perf. 13¼ Vert.**
| | | | | |
|---|---|---|---|---|
| 1653A | A550 | 30d multi | .65 | .35 |
| 1654A | A550 | 60d multi | 1.00 | .80 |
| 1655A | A550 | 70d multi | 1.30 | 1.00 |
| 1656B | A550 | 170d multi | 2.25 | .85 |
| c. | | Bklt. pane of 4, #1653A-1655A, 1656B | 7.00 | |

A551

Europa: Children's toys.

**1989, May 22    Litho.    Perf. 12½x14**
| | | | | |
|---|---|---|---|---|
| 1657 | A551 | 60d Whistling bird | 3.75 | 2.00 |
| 1658 | A551 | 170d Butterfly | 4.00 | 2.00 |
| a. | | Pair, #1657-1658 | 8.00 | 8.00 |

Printed se-tenant in sheets of 16.

**Booklet Stamps**
**Perf. 13¾ Vert.**
| | | | | |
|---|---|---|---|---|
| 1657A | A551 | 60d Whistling bird | 3.25 | 2.00 |
| 1658B | A551 | 170d Butterfly | 3.25 | 2.00 |
| c. | | Pair, #1657A, 1658B | 7.50 | 3.25 |
| d. | | Bklt. pane, 2 each #1657A/1658B | 15.00 | — |

**Perf. 13¼ Vert.**
| | | | | |
|---|---|---|---|---|
| 1657B | A551 | 60d Whistling bird | 2.00 | 1.20 |
| 1658E | A551 | 170d Butterfly | 2.00 | 1.20 |

Sold in booklets containing 20 panes of 5 stamps.

Anniversaries A552

**1989, May 22    Perf. 14x13¼**
| | | | | |
|---|---|---|---|---|
| 1659 | A552 | 30d Flags | .60 | .35 |
| 1660 | A552 | 50d Flag, La Liberte | .60 | .35 |
| 1661 | A552 | 60d Flag, ballot box | 1.40 | .90 |
| 1662 | A552 | 70d Coin, emblem | 1.40 | .90 |
| 1663 | A552 | 200d Flag, "40" | 3.25 | 1.20 |
| | | Nos. 1659-1663 (5) | 7.25 | 3.70 |

**Booklet Stamps**
**Perf. 13 Horiz.**
| | | | | |
|---|---|---|---|---|
| 1659A | A552 | 30d Flags | 1.00 | .50 |
| 1660A | A552 | 50d Flag, La Liberte | 10.00 | 3.50 |
| 1661A | A552 | 60d Flag, ballot box | 10.00 | 3.50 |
| 1662A | A552 | 70d Coin, emblem | 10.00 | 3.50 |
| 1663A | A552 | 200d Flag, "40" | 10.00 | 3.50 |
| | | Nos. 1659A-1663A (5) | 41.00 | 14.50 |

Six-nation Initiative for Peace and Disarmament, 5th anniv. (30d); French revolution, bicent. (50d); European Parliament Elections in Greece, 10th anniv. (60d); Interparliamentary Union, cent. (70d); and Council of Europe, 40th anniv. (200d).

Nos. 1659A-1663A were each issued in booklets containing 20 panes of 5 stamps.

A553

BALKANFILA XII, Sept. 30-Oct. 8, Salonica — A554

**1989, Sept. 25    Litho.    Perf. 14x12½**
| | | | | |
|---|---|---|---|---|
| 1664 | A553 | 60d shown | .70 | .40 |
| 1665 | A553 | 70d Eye, magnifying glass | .70 | .60 |

**Souvenir Sheet**
**Perf. 14x13**
| | | | | |
|---|---|---|---|---|
| 1666 | A554 | 200d shown | 3.00 | 3.00 |

Wildflowers — A555

**1989, Dec. 8    Litho.    Perf. 14x12½**
| | | | | |
|---|---|---|---|---|
| 1667 | A555 | 8d Wild rose | .25 | .25 |
| 1668 | A555 | 10d Common myrtle | .25 | .25 |
| 1669 | A555 | 20d Field poppy | .25 | .25 |
| 1670 | A555 | 30d Anemone | .35 | .25 |
| 1671 | A555 | 60d Dandelion, chicory | .65 | .35 |
| 1672 | A555 | 70d Mallow | .75 | .40 |
| 1673 | A555 | 200d Thistle | 2.00 | 1.50 |
| | | Nos. 1667-1673 (7) | 4.50 | 3.25 |

Ursus arctos — A556

Rare and endangered species: 70d, Caretta caretta. 90d, Monachus monachus. 100d, Lynx lynx.

**1990, Mar. 16    Litho.    Perf. 14x12½**
| | | | | |
|---|---|---|---|---|
| 1674 | A556 | 40d shown | .35 | .25 |
| 1675 | A556 | 70d multicolored | 1.25 | .35 |
| 1676 | A556 | 90d multicolored | 1.50 | .35 |
| 1677 | A556 | 100d multicolored | 1.75 | .75 |
| | | Nos. 1674-1677 (4) | 4.85 | 1.70 |

Europa 1990 — A557

Post offices: 70d, Old Central P.O. interior. 210d, Contemporary p.o. exterior.

**1990, May 11    Litho.    Perf. 13¼x12¼**
| | | | | |
|---|---|---|---|---|
| 1678 | A557 | 70d multicolored | 2.60 | 2.25 |
| 1679 | A557 | 210d multicolored | 4.75 | 4.00 |
| a. | | Pair, #1678-1679 | 7.75 | 7.75 |

Nos. 1678-1679 were printed se-tenant in sheets of 16.

**Booklet Stamps**
**Perf. 12¼ Vert.**
| | | | | |
|---|---|---|---|---|
| 1678A | A557 | 70d multicolored | 2.60 | 2.25 |
| 1679B | A557 | 210d multicolored | 4.75 | 4.00 |
| c. | | Pair, #1678A, 1679B | 8.00 | 8.00 |
| d. | | Bklt. pane, 2 each #1678A, 1679B | 16.00 | |

Natl. Reconcilation — A558

**1990, May 11    Perf. 12½x13½**
| | | | | |
|---|---|---|---|---|
| 1680 | A558 | 40d Flag, handshake | .40 | .25 |
| 1681 | A558 | 70d Dove, ribbon | .75 | .35 |
| 1682 | A558 | 100d Map, gift of flowers | 1.10 | 1.10 |
| | | Nos. 1680-1682 (3) | 2.25 | 1.70 |

Political Reformers — A559

No. 1683, Gregoris Lambrakis (1912-63). No. 1684, Pavlos Bakoyiannis (1935-89).

**1990, May 11**
| | | | | |
|---|---|---|---|---|
| 1683 | A559 | 40d multicolored | .55 | .35 |
| 1684 | A559 | 40d multicolored | .55 | .35 |

A560

Department Seats: 2d, Karditsa, the commercial-animal fair. 5d, Trikkala fort and clock tower. 8d, Veroia, street with traditional architecture. 10d, Mesolongion, Central Monument of Fallen Heroes in the Exodus. 15d, Chios, view. 20d, Tripolis, street with neoclassical architecture. 25d, Volos, view with town hall, woodcut by A. Tassou. 40d, Kalamata, neoclassical town hall. 50d, Pyrgos, central marketplace. 70d, Ioannina, view of lake and island. 80d, Rethymnon, sculpture at the port. 90d, Argostolion, view before earthquake. 100d, Nauplia, Bourtzi with Palamidi in the background. 200d, Patras, central lighthouse. 250d, Florina, street with neoclassical architecture. Nos. 1685, 1687, 1695, 1698 vert.

**Perf. 12¾x12¼, 12¼x12¾**
**1990, June 20                  Litho.**
| | | | | |
|---|---|---|---|---|
| 1685 | A560 | 2d multicolored | .25 | .25 |
| 1686 | A560 | 5d multicolored | .25 | .25 |
| 1687 | A560 | 8d multicolored | .25 | |
| 1688 | A560 | 10d multicolored | .25 | .25 |
| 1689 | A560 | 15d multicolored | .25 | .25 |
| 1690 | A560 | 20d multicolored | .25 | .25 |
| 1691 | A560 | 25d multicolored | .35 | .25 |
| 1692 | A560 | 40d multicolored | .50 | .25 |
| 1693 | A560 | 50d multicolored | .60 | .25 |
| 1694 | A560 | 70d multicolored | .80 | .35 |
| 1695 | A560 | 80d multicolored | .90 | .40 |
| 1696 | A560 | 90d multicolored | 1.15 | .40 |
| 1697 | A560 | 100d multicolored | 1.75 | .50 |

| | | | | |
|---|---|---|---|---|
| 1698 | A560 | 200d multicolored | 3.75 | .90 |
| 1699 | A560 | 250d multicolored | 5.00 | 1.20 |
| | | Nos. 1685-1699 (15) | 16.30 | 5.75 |

**Booklet Stamps**
**Perf. 13½ Vert. or Horiz.**
| | | | | |
|---|---|---|---|---|
| 1685A | A560 | 2d multicolored | .25 | .25 |
| 1686A | A560 | 5d multicolored | .25 | .25 |
| 1687A | A560 | 8d multicolored | .25 | .25 |
| 1688A | A560 | 10d multicolored | .25 | .25 |
| 1689A | A560 | 15d multicolored | .25 | .25 |
| 1690A | A560 | 20d multicolored | .25 | .25 |
| 1691A | A560 | 25d multicolored | .50 | .50 |
| 1692A | A560 | 40d multicolored | .50 | .50 |
| 1693A | A560 | 50d multicolored | .50 | .50 |
| 1694A | A560 | 70d multicolored | .50 | .50 |
| 1695A | A560 | 80d multicolored | 1.00 | 1.00 |
| 1696A | A560 | 90d multicolored | 1.00 | 1.00 |
| 1697A | A560 | 100d multicolored | 1.00 | 1.00 |
| 1698A | A560 | 200d multicolored | 3.25 | 3.25 |
| 1699A | A560 | 250d multicolored | 4.25 | 4.25 |
| | | Nos. 1685A-1699A (15) | 14.00 | 14.00 |

Nos. 1685A-1699A were each sold in booklets containing 20 panes of 5 stamps. Nos. 1685A, 1687A, 1695A, and 1698A are perforated vertically. Nos. 1686A, 1688A-1694A, 1696A-1697A, and 1699A are perforated horizontally.

See Nos. 1749-1760, 1792-1801.

1996 Summer Olympics — A561

**1990, July 13    Perf. 12½x13½**
| | | | | |
|---|---|---|---|---|
| 1700 | A561 | 20d Sailing | .25 | .25 |
| 1701 | A561 | 50d Wrestling | .50 | .25 |
| 1702 | A561 | 80d Sprinting | .75 | .75 |
| 1703 | A561 | 100d Basketball | 1.00 | .75 |
| 1704 | A561 | 250d Soccer | 2.40 | 1.20 |
| a. | | Strip of 5, #1700-1704 | 5.75 | 5.75 |

Athens, proposed site for centennial Summer Olympic Games. Exists perf. 13½ vert.

Heinrich Schliemann (1822-1890), Archaeologist A562

**1990, Oct. 11    Litho.    Perf. 14x13½**
| | | | | |
|---|---|---|---|---|
| 1705 | A562 | 80d multicolored | 4.50 | 2.75 |

See Germany No. 1615.

Greco-Italian War, 50th Anniv. — A563

50d, Woman knitting. 80d, Virgin Mary, soldier. 100d, Women volunteers.

**1990, Oct. 11    Perf. 12½**
| | | | | |
|---|---|---|---|---|
| 1706 | A563 | 50d multicolored | .50 | .25 |
| 1707 | A563 | 80d multicolored | .80 | .65 |
| 1708 | A563 | 100d multicolored | 1.15 | .65 |
| | | Nos. 1706-1708 (3) | 2.45 | 1.55 |

**Souvenir Sheet**

Stamp Day — A564

**1990, Dec. 14    Litho.    Perf. 14x13**
| | | | | |
|---|---|---|---|---|
| 1709 | A564 | 300d multicolored | 8.00 | 8.00 |

The Muses — A565

Designs: 50d, Calliope, Euterpe, Erato. 80d, Terpsichore, Polyhymnia, Melpomene. 250d, Thalia, Clio, Urania.

## 1991, Mar. 11    Litho.    Perf. 12½

| 1710 | A565 | 50d multicolored | .50 | .25 |
|---|---|---|---|---|
| 1711 | A565 | 80d multicolored | .80 | .35 |
| 1712 | A565 | 250d multicolored | 2.25 | 1.00 |
| | | Nos. 1710-1712 (3) | 3.55 | 1.60 |

Battle of Crete by Ioannis Anousakis A566

300d, Map, flags of participating allied armies.

## 1991, May 20    Litho.    Perf. 12½x13½

| 1713 | A566 | 60d multicolored | 1.30 | .35 |
|---|---|---|---|---|

### Size: 32x24mm
### Perf. 12½

| 1714 | A566 | 300d multicolored | 2.60 | 1.20 |
|---|---|---|---|---|

Battle of Crete, 50th anniv.

Europa — A567

Designs: 80d, Icarus pushing modern satellite. 300d, Chariot of the Sun.

## 1991, May 20    Perf. 12½

| 1715 | A567 | 80d multicolored | 3.25 | 2.40 |
|---|---|---|---|---|
| 1716 | A567 | 300d multicolored | 4.50 | 3.75 |
| a. | | Pair, #1715-1716 | 8.00 | 8.00 |

No. 1716a printed in continuous design in sheets of 16.

### Booklet Stamps
### Perf. 12½ Vert.

| 1715A | A567 | 80d multicolored | 3.25 | 2.60 |
|---|---|---|---|---|
| 1716B | A567 | 300d multicolored | 3.25 | 2.60 |
| c. | | Pair, #1715A, 1716B | 9.00 | 9.00 |
| d. | | Bklt. pane, 2 ea. #1715A, 1716B | 18.00 | 18.00 |

A568

## 1991, June 25    Litho.    Perf. 13½x14

| 1717 | A568 | 10d Swimming | .25 | .25 |
|---|---|---|---|---|
| 1718 | A568 | 60d Basketball | .40 | .25 |
| 1719 | A568 | 90d Gymnastics | .75 | .25 |
| 1720 | A568 | 130d Weight lifting | 1.00 | .40 |
| 1721 | A568 | 300d Hammer throw | 3.00 | 1.60 |
| | | Nos. 1717-1721 (5) | 5.40 | 2.75 |

1991 Mediterranean Games, Athens.

A569

## 1991, Sept. 20    Litho.    Perf. 13½x14

| 1722 | A569 | 100d multicolored | 1.10 | .60 |
|---|---|---|---|---|

Athenian Democracy, 2500th anniv.

### Europa Souvenir Sheet

Greek Presidency of CEPT — A570

---

Europe with Zeus metmorphosed into a bull, from Attic vase, c. 500 B.C.

## 1991, Sept. 20    Perf. 14x13

| 1723 | A570 | 300d multicolored | 16.00 | 16.00 |
|---|---|---|---|---|

A571

Greek Membership in EEC, 10th anniv.: 50d, Pres. Konstantin Karamanlis signing Treaty of Greek entrance into EEC. 80d, Map showing EEC members, Pres. Karamanlis.

## 1991, Dec. 9    Litho.    Perf. 13x14

| 1724 | A571 | 50d multicolored | .50 | .25 |
|---|---|---|---|---|
| 1725 | A571 | 80d multicolored | .80 | .40 |

A572

## 1991, Dec. 9    Perf. 12½x13½

| 1726 | A572 | 80d Speed skaters | .75 | .65 |
|---|---|---|---|---|
| 1727 | A572 | 300d Slalom skier | 2.60 | .90 |
| a. | | Pair, #1726-1727 | 3.50 | 3.50 |

16th Winter Olympics, Albertville.

A573                 1992 Summer Olympics, Barcelona — A574

### Perf. 12½, 14x13½ (90d, 340d)

## 1992, Apr. 3    Litho.

| 1728 | A573 | 10d Javelin | .25 | .25 |
|---|---|---|---|---|
| 1729 | A573 | 60d Equestrian | .75 | .25 |
| 1730 | A574 | 90d Runner | 1.15 | .60 |
| 1731 | A573 | 120d Gymnastics | 2.25 | .65 |
| 1732 | A574 | 340d Runners | 3.75 | 1.75 |
| | | Nos. 1728-1732 (5) | 8.15 | 3.50 |

Health — A575

Designs: 60d, Protection against AIDS. 80d, Diseases of digestive system. 90d, Dying flower symbolizing cancer. 120d, Hephaestus at his forge, 6th century BC. 280d, Alexandros S. Onassis Cardiosurgical Center.

## 1992, May 22    Litho.    Perf. 12½

| 1733 | A575 | 60d multicolored | .50 | .25 |
|---|---|---|---|---|
| 1734 | A575 | 80d multicolored | .70 | .35 |
| 1735 | A575 | 90d multicolored | .75 | .40 |
| 1736 | A575 | 120d multicolored | 1.20 | .55 |
| 1737 | A575 | 280d multicolored | 2.60 | 1.40 |
| | | Nos. 1733-1737 (5) | 5.75 | 2.95 |

No. 1734, 1st United European Gastroenterology Week. No. 1736, European Year of Social Security, Hygiene and Health in the Workplace.

Discovery of America, 500th Anniv. — A576

Europa: 340d, Map of 15th century Chios, Columbus.

---

## 1992, May 22    Perf. 13¹³⁄₁₆x12¼

| 1738 | A576 | 90d shown | 2.25 | 1.60 |
|---|---|---|---|---|
| 1739 | A576 | 340d multicolored | 5.25 | 4.00 |
| a. | | Pair, #1738-1739 | 8.00 | 8.00 |

No. 1739a was printed in continuous design in sheets of 16.

### Booklet Stamps
### Perf. 12½ Vert.

| 1738A | A576 | 90d shown | 2.40 | 1.75 |
|---|---|---|---|---|
| 1739B | A576 | 340d multicolored | 5.50 | 4.50 |
| c. | | Bklt. pane, 2 each #1738A, 1739B | 16.00 | 16.00 |
| d. | | Pair, #1738A, 1739B | 8.00 | 8.00 |

### Souvenir Sheet

European Conference on Transportation — A577

## 1992, June 8    Perf. 14x13

| 1740 | A577 | 300d multicolored | 7.00 | 7.00 |
|---|---|---|---|---|

Macedonian Treasures — A578

Designs: 10d, Head of Hercules wearing lion skin, Vergina treasures. 20d, Bust of Aristotle, map of Macedonia, horiz. 60d, Alexander the Great at Battle of Issus, horiz. 80d, Archaeologist Manolis Andronikos, tomb of King Philip II. 90d, Deer hunt mosaic, Pella. 120d, Macedonian tetradrachm. 340d, St. Paul, 4th century church near Philippi.

## 1992, July 17    Litho.    Perf. 12½

| 1741 | A578 | 10d multicolored | .40 | .25 |
|---|---|---|---|---|
| 1742 | A578 | 20d multicolored | .40 | .25 |
| 1743 | A578 | 60d multicolored | .50 | .25 |
| 1744 | A578 | 80d multicolored | 1.30 | .45 |
| 1745 | A578 | 90d multicolored | 1.50 | .25 |
| 1746 | A578 | 120d multicolored | 1.90 | .80 |
| 1747 | A578 | 340d multicolored | 7.00 | 2.00 |
| | | Nos. 1741-1747 (7) | 13.00 | 4.05 |

European Unification A579

## 1992, Oct. 12    Litho.    Perf. 14x13

| 1748 | A579 | 90d multicolored | .90 | .90 |
|---|---|---|---|---|

### Departmental Seat Type of 1990

Designs: 10d, Piraeus, the old clock. 20d, Amphissa, view of city with citadel. 30d, Samos (Vathy), the Heraion. 40d, Canea, city in 1800s. 50d, Zakinthos (Zante), view in 1800s. 60d, Karpenision, Velouchi and city. 70d, Kilkis, the cave, vert. 80d, Xanthe, door of Town Hall, vert. 90d, Salonika, Macedonian Struggle Museum. 120d, Komotine, Tsanakleous School. 340d, Drama, spring. 400d, Larissa, Pinios bridge.

## 1992, Oct. 12    Perf. 12¾

| 1749 | A560 | 10d multicolored | .25 | .25 |
|---|---|---|---|---|
| 1750 | A560 | 20d multicolored | .25 | .25 |
| 1751 | A560 | 30d multicolored | .25 | .25 |
| 1752 | A560 | 40d multicolored | .30 | .25 |
| 1753 | A560 | 50d multicolored | .35 | .25 |
| 1754 | A560 | 60d multicolored | .40 | .25 |
| 1755 | A560 | 70d multicolored | .50 | .30 |
| 1756 | A560 | 80d multicolored | .50 | .30 |
| 1757 | A560 | 90d multicolored | 1.00 | .35 |
| 1758 | A560 | 120d multicolored | 2.00 | .55 |
| 1759 | A560 | 340d multicolored | 3.25 | 1.30 |
| 1760 | A560 | 400d multicolored | 4.50 | 1.75 |
| | | Nos. 1749-1760 (12) | 13.55 | 6.05 |

### Booklet Stamps
### Perf. 10½ Horiz. or Vert.

| 1749A | A560 | 10d multicolored | .25 | .25 |
|---|---|---|---|---|
| 1750A | A560 | 20d multicolored | .25 | .25 |
| 1751A | A560 | 30d multicolored | .25 | .25 |
| 1752A | A560 | 40d multicolored | .25 | .25 |
| 1753A | A560 | 50d multicolored | .25 | .25 |
| 1754A | A560 | 60d multicolored | .35 | .25 |
| 1755A | A560 | 70d multicolored | .35 | .25 |
| 1756A | A560 | 80d multicolored | 1.30 | .25 |
| 1757A | A560 | 90d multicolored | 1.30 | .25 |
| 1758A | A560 | 120d multicolored | 1.90 | .35 |

---

| 1759A | A560 | 340d multicolored | 3.25 | .80 |
|---|---|---|---|---|
| 1760A | A560 | 400d multicolored | 4.25 | 1.30 |
| | | Nos. 1749A-1760A (12) | 13.95 | 4.70 |

Nos. 1749A-1760A were each sold in booklets containing 20 panes of 5 stamps. Nos. 1749A-1754A, and 1757A-1760A are perforated horizontally. Nos. 1755A-1756A are perforated vertically.

City of Rhodes, 2400th Anniv. — A580

Designs: 60d, Headstone, 4th cent. B.C. 90d, Bathing Aphrodite, 1st cent. B.C. 120d, St. Irene, Church of St. Catherine, 14th cent. 250d, St. Paul's Gate, 15th cent.

## 1993, Feb. 26    Litho.    Perf. 13x14

| 1761 | A580 | 60d multicolored | .65 | .35 |
|---|---|---|---|---|
| 1762 | A580 | 90d multicolored | 1.00 | .65 |
| 1763 | A580 | 120d multicolored | 1.10 | .65 |
| 1764 | A580 | 250d multicolored | 3.75 | 1.60 |
| | | Nos. 1761-1764 (4) | 6.50 | 3.25 |

Remembrances of Greek Wars — A581

Designs: 10d, Death of Georgakis Olympios, 1821. 30d, Theodore Kolokotronis in battle, 1821. 60d, Pavlos Melas. 90d, Glory lays wreath over graves of dead from Balkan Wars. 120d, Greek soldiers at Battle of El Alamein, 1942, horiz. 150d, Greek troops in Aegean Islands, 1943-45, horiz. 200d, Kalavryta Massacre Memorial.

### Perf. 13x14, 14x13

## 1993, May 25    Litho.

| 1765 | A581 | 10d multicolored | .25 | .25 |
|---|---|---|---|---|
| 1766 | A581 | 30d multicolored | .35 | .25 |
| 1767 | A581 | 60d multicolored | .50 | .30 |
| 1768 | A581 | 90d multicolored | .90 | .35 |
| 1769 | A581 | 120d multicolored | 2.00 | .90 |
| 1770 | A581 | 150d multicolored | 2.00 | 1.40 |
| 1771 | A581 | 200d multicolored | 4.25 | 2.00 |
| | | Nos. 1765-1771 (7) | 10.25 | 5.45 |

The Benefits of Transportation, by K. Parthenis — A582

Europa: 90d, Tree, three people, ships. 350d, Woman and children, town.

## 1993, May 25    Perf. 13x13¾

| 1772 | | 90d multicolored | 1.20 | 1.00 |
|---|---|---|---|---|
| 1773 | | 350d multicolored | 5.50 | 4.50 |
| a. | | A582 Pair, #1772-1773 | 7.25 | 7.25 |

No. 1773a was printed in continuous design in sheets of 16.

### Booklet Stamps
### Perf. 13¼ Vert.

| 1772A | | 90d multicolored | 1.20 | 1.00 |
|---|---|---|---|---|
| 1773B | | 350d multicolored | 5.50 | 4.50 |
| c. | | Bklt. pane, 2 each #1772A, 1773B | 14.50 | 14.50 |
| d. | | Pair, #1772A, 1773B | 7.25 | 7.25 |

Buildings in Athens — A583

Designs: 30d, Concert Hall. 60d, Numismatic Museum (Iliou Melathron). 90d, Natl. Library of Greece. 200d, Opthalmology Hospital.

**1993, Oct. 4 Litho. Perf. 14**

| 1774 | A583 | 30d multicolored | .70 | .25 |
|---|---|---|---|---|
| 1775 | A583 | 60d multicolored | .70 | .25 |
| 1776 | A583 | 90d multicolored | .80 | .65 |
| 1777 | A583 | 200d multicolored | 4.00 | 1.60 |
| | | Nos. 1774-1777 (4) | 6.20 | 2.75 |

Souvenir Sheet

Greek Presidency of the European Community Council of Ministers — A584

**1993, Dec. 20 Litho. Perf. 14**

| 1778 | A584 | 400d multicolored | 4.75 | 4.75 |
|---|---|---|---|---|

Chariot of Selene Driven by Hermes — A585

**1994, Mar. 7 Litho. Perf. 13x13½**

| 1779 | A585 | 200d multicolored | 1.90 | 1.25 |
|---|---|---|---|---|

2nd Pan-European Transportation Conference.

Passion of Christ — A586

Designs: 30d, Last Supper, 16th cent. icon, St. Catherine's Church, Crete, vert. 60d, Crucifixion, detail from 1552 wall drawing, Great Meteoron, vert. 90d, Burial, 1620-45 icon, Church of the Presentation of the Lord, Patmos. 150d, Resurrection, illustrated manuscript of Mt. Athos, 11th cent.

**1994, Apr. 8 Litho. Perf. 14**

| 1780 | A586 | 30d multicolored | .35 | .25 |
|---|---|---|---|---|
| 1781 | A586 | 60d multicolored | .45 | .25 |
| 1782 | A586 | 90d multicolored | .65 | .40 |
| 1783 | A586 | 150d multicolored | 1.40 | .80 |
| | | Nos. 1780-1783 (4) | 2.85 | 1.70 |

European Inventors, Discoverers — A587

Europa: 90d, Thales of Miletus (625?-547? B.C.), philosopher, mathematician. 350d, Konstantinos Karatheodoris (1873-1950).

**1994, May 9 Litho. Perf. 14x13½**

| 1784 | A587 | 90d multicolored | 1.40 | 1.20 |
|---|---|---|---|---|
| 1785 | A587 | 350d multicolored | 3.00 | 2.60 |
| a. | | Pair, #1784-1785 | 5.00 | 5.00 |

Nos. 1784-1785 was issued in sheets of 16.

**Booklet Stamps**
**Perf. 13¾ Vert.**

| 1784A | A587 | 90d multicolored | 1.60 | 1.40 |
|---|---|---|---|---|
| 1785B | A587 | 350d multicolored | 3.25 | 3.00 |
| c. | | Bkt. pane, 2 each #1784A-1785B | 10.50 | 10.50 |
| d. | | Pair, #1784A, 1785B | 5.25 | 5.25 |

Athletic Events, Anniversaries A588

Designs: 60d, Demetrios Vikelas (1835-1908), first president Intl. Olympic Committee, vert. 90, Modern, ancient soccer players. 120d, Volleyball, net, vert. 400d, Statue of Liberty, modern, ancient soccer players.

**1994, June 6 Litho. Perf. 14**

| 1786 | A588 | 60d multicolored | .60 | .25 |
|---|---|---|---|---|
| 1787 | A588 | 90d multicolored | .70 | .50 |
| 1788 | A588 | 120d multicolored | 1.40 | .75 |
| | | Nos. 1786-1788 (3) | 2.70 | 1.50 |

**Souvenir Sheet**
**Perf. 14x13½**

| 1789 | A588 | 400d multicolored | 6.25 | 6.25 |
|---|---|---|---|---|

Intl. Olympic Committee, cent. (No. 1786). 1994 World Cup Soccer Championships, US (Nos. 1787, 1789). World Volleyball Championships, Piraeus & Salonika (No. 1788). No. 1789 contains one 42x52mm stamp.

Greek Presidency of European Community Council of Ministers — A589

Designs: 90d, Winged chariot driven by Greece. 120d, Doric columns, European Community flag.

**1994, June 21 Perf. 13**

| 1790 | A589 | 90d multicolored | .95 | .75 |
|---|---|---|---|---|
| 1791 | A589 | 120d multicolored | 1.15 | .75 |

**Departmental Seat Type of 1990**

Designs: 10d, Katerine, Tsalopoulou mansion house, vert. 20d, Arta, Byzantine Church Parigoritissas. 30d, Lebadea, medieval bridge, tower of catalanian castle, Krias springs vert. 40d, Kastoria, Church of Panagia Koumbelidkis. 50d, Grevena, outdoor theatre. 60d, Edessa, waterfall. 80d, Chalcis, red house. 90d, Serrai, government house, Merarchias road, Acropolis of Koulas. 120d, Candia (Herakleion), town hall. 150d, Egoumenitsa, Church of Evangelistria, vert.

**1994, Oct. 5 Litho. Perf. 12¾**

| 1792 | A560 | 10d multicolored | .25 | .25 |
|---|---|---|---|---|
| 1793 | A560 | 20d multicolored | .25 | .25 |
| 1794 | A560 | 30d multicolored | .25 | .25 |
| 1795 | A560 | 40d multicolored | .35 | .25 |
| 1796 | A560 | 50d multicolored | .40 | .25 |
| 1797 | A560 | 60d multicolored | .55 | .25 |
| 1798 | A560 | 80d multicolored | .60 | .25 |
| 1799 | A560 | 90d multicolored | .65 | .25 |
| 1800 | A560 | 120d multicolored | .80 | .35 |
| 1801 | A560 | 150d multicolored | 1.00 | .40 |
| | | Nos. 1792-1801 (10) | 5.10 | 2.75 |

**Booklet Stamps**
**Perf. 10½ Vert. or Horiz.**

| 1792A | A560 | 10d multicolored | .25 | .25 |
|---|---|---|---|---|
| b. | | Perf. 13¼ vert. | | |
| 1793A | A560 | 20d multicolored | .25 | .25 |
| 1794A | A560 | 30d multicolored | .25 | .25 |
| 1795A | A560 | 40d multicolored | .35 | .25 |
| 1796A | A560 | 50d multicolored | .40 | .25 |
| 1797A | A560 | 60d multicolored | .55 | .25 |
| 1798A | A560 | 80d multicolored | .60 | .25 |
| 1799A | A560 | 90d multicolored | 1.60 | .25 |
| 1800A | A560 | 120d multicolored | 1.60 | .25 |
| 1801A | A560 | 150d multicolored | 1.90 | .65 |
| | | Nos. 1792A-1801A (10) | 7.75 | 2.90 |

Nos. 1792A-1801A were each sold in booklets containing 20 panes of 5 stamps. Nos. 1792A, 1794A, and 1801A are perforated vertically. Nos. 1793A, and 1795A-1800A ar perforated horizontally.

Constitution, 150th Anniv. — A590

Designs: 60d, People, army demonstrating, by Carl Howpt, vert. 150d, Portraits of Ioannis Makriyannis, Andreas Metaxas, Demetrios Kallergis. 200d, Painting of night of Sept. 3, 1843. 340d, Article 107, seal of Greek Parliament, signature of President.

**1994, Nov. 21 Litho. Perf. 14x13**

| 1802 | A590 | 60d multicolored | .55 | .35 |
|---|---|---|---|---|
| 1803 | A590 | 150d multicolored | .90 | .55 |
| 1804 | A590 | 200d multicolored | 1.75 | .80 |
| 1805 | A590 | 340d multicolored | 3.50 | 1.60 |
| | | Nos. 1802-1805 (4) | 6.70 | 3.30 |

Melina Mercouri (1925-94), Actress, Politician A591

90d, Portrait, Parthenon. 100d, Portraits as actress. 340d, Portrait, vert.

**1995, Mar. 7 Litho. Perf. 14x13**

| 1806 | A591 | 60d shown | .55 | .25 |
|---|---|---|---|---|
| 1807 | A591 | 90d multicolored | .65 | .35 |
| 1808 | A591 | 100d multicolored | 2.40 | .80 |
| 1809 | A591 | 340d multicolored | 5.50 | 1.75 |
| | | Nos. 1806-1809 (4) | 9.10 | 3.15 |

Liberation of Concentration Camps, 50th Anniv. — A592

Europa: 90d, Prisoners. 340d, Peace doves, broken barbed wire fence.

**1995, May 3 Litho. Perf. 14**

| 1810 | A592 | 90d multicolored | 1.60 | |
|---|---|---|---|---|
| 1811 | A592 | 340d multicolored | 3.25 | 3.25 |
| a. | | Pair, #1810-1811 | 5.25 | 5.25 |

**Booklet Stamps**
**Perf. 13½ Vert.**

| 1810A | A592 | 90d multicolored | 1.60 | 1.60 |
|---|---|---|---|---|
| 1811B | A592 | 340d multicolored | 3.25 | 3.25 |
| c. | | Bkt. pane, 2 each #1810A, 1811B | 10.50 | 10.50 |
| | | Complete booklet, #1811c | 10.50 | |
| d. | | Pair, #1810A, 1811B | 5.25 | 5.25 |

Anniversaries & Events — A593

Designs: 10d, Stylized emblem, basketball, vert. 70d, University building. 90d, Architectural ruins, vert. 100d, Flag, soldier, vert. 120d, Statue of Peace, by Kifissodotos, vert. 150d, Dolphins. 200d, Early telephone, push buttons, vert. 300d, Owl, basketball, vert.

**Perf. 13½x13, 13x13½**
**1995, June 21 Litho.**

| 1812 | A593 | 10d multicolored | .25 | .25 |
|---|---|---|---|---|
| 1813 | A593 | 70d multicolored | .80 | .25 |
| 1814 | A593 | 90d multicolored | 1.00 | .35 |
| 1815 | A593 | 100d multicolored | 1.25 | .40 |
| 1816 | A593 | 120d multicolored | 1.40 | .45 |
| 1817 | A593 | 150d multicolored | 1.60 | .60 |
| 1818 | A593 | 200d multicolored | 2.25 | .80 |
| 1819 | A593 | 300d multicolored | 3.75 | 1.00 |
| | | Nos. 1812-1819 (8) | 12.30 | 4.10 |

5th World Junior Basketball Championships (No. 1812). Agricultural University of Athens, 75th anniv. (No. 1813). UN, 50th anniv. (Nos. 1814, 1816). End of World War II, 50th anniv. (No. 1815). European Nature Conservation Year (No. 1817). Telephone in Greece, cent. (No. 1818). 29th European Basketball Championships (No. 1819).

Book of Revelation, 1900th Anniv. A594

Visions of the Apocalypse: 80d, First vision, Angels of the Seven Churches of Asia Minor, icon by Thomas Bathas, vert. 110d, Apostle John at Cave of the Apocalypse dictating to Prochoros, miniature from manuscript of Four Gospels, vert. 300d, First Angel with trumpet from silver gilded Gospel cover.

**1995, Sept. 18 Litho. Perf. 14**

| 1820 | A594 | 80d multicolored | 1.60 | .30 |
|---|---|---|---|---|
| 1821 | A594 | 110d multicolored | 2.25 | .75 |
| 1822 | A594 | 300d multicolored | 3.00 | 1.60 |
| | | Nos. 1820-1822 (3) | 6.85 | 2.65 |

Jason & the Argonauts — A595

Designs: 80d, Argonauts, the Argus, goddess Athena setting out for Colchis. 120d, Phineas, Hermes, one of the Voreadae, Harpy. 150d, Jason taming the bull, Medea and Nike. 200d, Jason takes Golden Fleece, kills serpent with Medea's help. 300d, Medea watches, Jason, crowned by Nike, giving Golden Fleece to Pelias.

**1995, Nov. 6 Litho. Perf. 13x13½**

| 1823 | A595 | 80d multicolored | .85 | .40 |
|---|---|---|---|---|
| 1824 | A595 | 120d multicolored | .85 | .70 |
| 1825 | A595 | 150d multicolored | 1.00 | .60 |

| 1826 | A595 | 200d multicolored | 1.40 | .70 |
|---|---|---|---|---|
| 1827 | A595 | 300d multicolored | 4.00 | 1.40 |
| | | Nos. 1823-1827 (5) | 8.10 | 3.80 |

Lighthouses — A596

**1995, Dec. 18 Litho. Perf. 14**

| 1828 | A596 | 80d Psyttaleia | .90 | .40 |
|---|---|---|---|---|
| 1829 | A596 | 120d Sapienza | 1.35 | .55 |
| 1830 | A596 | 150d Kastri (Othonoi) | 1.75 | 1.00 |
| 1831 | A596 | 500d Zourva (Hydra) | 6.75 | 2.10 |
| | | Nos. 1828-1831 (4) | 10.75 | 4.05 |

Souvenir Sheets

Modern Olympic Games, Cent. A597

**Perf. 13½x13, 13x13½**
**1996, Mar. 25 Litho.**

| 1832 | A597 | Sheet of 4 | 13.50 | 13.50 |
|---|---|---|---|---|
| a. | | 80d like #117, vert. | 2.75 | 2.75 |
| b. | | 120d like #118, vert. | 2.75 | 2.75 |
| c. | | 150d like #119, vert. | 2.75 | 2.75 |
| d. | | 650d like #120, vert. | 2.75 | 2.75 |
| 1833 | A597 | Sheet of 4 | 13.50 | 13.50 |
| a. | | 80d like #122 | 2.75 | 2.75 |
| b. | | 120d like #124 | 2.75 | 2.75 |
| c. | | 150d like #125 | 2.75 | 2.75 |
| d. | | 650d like #128 | 2.75 | 2.75 |
| 1834 | A597 | Sheet of 4 | 13.50 | 13.50 |
| a. | | 80d like #121, vert. | 2.75 | 2.75 |
| b. | | 120d like #123, vert. | 2.75 | 2.75 |
| c. | | 150d like #126, vert. | 2.75 | 2.75 |
| d. | | 650d like #127, vert. | 2.75 | 2.75 |

Famous Women A598

Europa: 120d, Sappho (c.610-580BC), lyric poet. 430d, Amalia Fleming.

**1996, Apr. 22 Litho. Perf. 14x14½**

| 1835 | A598 | 120d multicolored | 1.35 | 1.35 |
|---|---|---|---|---|
| 1836 | A598 | 430d multicolored | 4.25 | 4.25 |
| a. | A598 | Pair, #1835-1836 | 5.75 | 5.75 |

**Booklet Stamps**
**Perf. 14½ Vert.**

| 1835A | A598 | 120d multicolored | 1.35 | 1.35 |
|---|---|---|---|---|
| 1836B | A598 | 430d multicolored | 4.25 | 4.25 |
| c. | | Booklet pane, 2 each #1835A, 1836B | 11.50 | 11.50 |
| | | Complete booklet, #1836c | 11.50 | |
| d. | | Pair, #1835A, 1836B | 5.75 | 5.75 |

Modern Olympic Games, Cent. — A599

Stylized designs: 10d, Greek runners, vert. 80d, Discus thrower, vert. 120d, Weight lifter, vert. 200d, Wrestlers.

**Perf. 13½x14, 14x13½**
**1996, June 4 Litho.**

| 1837 | A599 | 10d multicolored | .45 | .25 |
|---|---|---|---|---|
| 1838 | A599 | 80d multicolored | 1.45 | .45 |
| 1839 | A599 | 120d multicolored | 2.75 | .70 |
| 1840 | A599 | 200d multicolored | 4.50 | 1.75 |
| | | Nos. 1837-1840 (4) | 9.15 | 3.15 |

First Intl. Medical Olympiad — A600

**1996, July 8**    **Litho.**    **Perf. 13½**
1841 A600 80d Hippocrates   1.50 .60
1842 A600 120d Galen   2.00 1.00

Castles — A601

**1996, Oct. 7**    **Litho.**    **Perf. 13¼**
1843 A601 10d Mytilene   .25 .25
1844 A601 20d Lindos   .25 .25
1845 A601 30d Rethymnon   .30 .25
1846 A601 70d Assos
    Cephalonia   .65 .25
1847 A601 80d Serbs   .75 .55
1848 A601 120d Monemvasia   .95 .60
1849 A601 200d Didimotihon   1.60 .90
1850 A601 430d Vonitsas   4.00 2.75
1851 A601 1000d Nikopolis   9.50 6.00
   Nos. 1843-1851 (9)   18.25 11.90

**Booklet Stamps**
**Perf. 13¼ Vert.**

1843A A601 10d Mytilene   .25 .25
1844A A601 20d Lindos   .25 .25
1845A A601 30d Rethymnon   .30 .25
1846A A601 70d Assos
    Cephalonia   .65 .25
1847A A601 80d Serbs   .75 .30
1848A A601 120d Monemva-
    sia   .95 .30
1849A A601 200d Didimo-
    tihon   1.60 .45
1850A A601 430d Vonitsas   4.00 1.35
1851A A601 1000d Nikopolis   9.50 3.00
   Nos. 1843A-1851A (9)   18.25 6.40

Nos. 1843A-1851A were each sold in booklets containing 20 panes of 5 stamps.

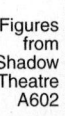

Figures from Shadow Theatre A602

100d, Four characters, diff. 120d, Three characters. 200d, Two characters, dragon.

**1996, Nov. 15**    **Litho.**    **Perf. 14**
1852 A602 80d multicolored   .80 .40
1853 A602 100d multicolored   .80 .45
1854 A602 120d multicolored   1.60 .60
1855 A602 200d multicolored   2.40 .90
   Nos. 1852-1855 (4)   5.60 2.35

Hellenic Language — A603

Designs: 80d, Oldest Hellenic inscription, wine pitcher, 720BC. 120d, Verse IX, 436-445 from Homer's Iliad, 1st-2nd cent. AD. 150d, Psalm of the Holy Apostles, 6th cent. AD. 350d, Reference to Hellenic language, Dionysios Solomos, 1824.

**1996, Dec. 18**    **Litho.**    **Perf. 13x13½**
1856 A603 80d multicolored   .85 .50
1857 A603 120d multicolored   1.10 .75
1858 A603 150d multicolored   1.75 1.25
1859 A603 350d multicolored   4.25 1.75
   Nos. 1856-1859 (4)   7.95 4.25

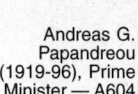

Andreas G. Papandreou (1919-96), Prime Minister — A604

Papandreou at various ages and: 80d, Graduation cap, books, diploma. 120d, Leaving airplane. 150d, Building. 500d, Greek flag, dove.

**1997, Feb. 12**    **Litho.**    **Perf. 13**
1860 A604 80d multicolored   1.00 .30
1861 A604 120d multicolored   1.00 .45
1862 A604 150d multicolored   1.60 .80
1863 A604 500d multicolored   3.75 2.45
   Nos. 1860-1863 (4)   7.35 2.45

Thessaloniki, European Cultural Capital — A605

Designs: 80d, Frescoe of St. Dimitrios, patron saint of Thessaloniki, Church of Aghios Nikolaos Orphanos, vert. 100d, Hippocratic Hospital. 120d, Marble pedestal with inscription, medallion with woman's head, vert. 150d, Detail of mosaic from Rotunda cupola, vert. 300d, "Iaspis" chalice, 14th cent., Mt. Athos.

**1997, Mar. 26**     **Perf. 13½**
1864 A605 80d multicolored   .75 .40
1865 A605 100d multicolored   1.10 .50
1866 A605 120d multicolored   1.25 .60
1867 A605 150d multicolored   1.40 .80
1868 A605 300d multicolored   3.50 1.60
   Nos. 1864-1868 (5)   8.00 3.90

Bridges of Macedonia — A606

80d, Village of Trikomo. 120d, Portitsa. 150d, Village of Ziakas. 350d, Village of Kastro.

**1997, Apr. 24**    **Litho.**    **Perf. 14**
1869 A606 80d multicolored   .60 .35
1870 A606 120d multicolored   .90 .50
1871 A606 150d multicolored   1.60 .70
1872 A606 350d multicolored   4.25 1.50
   Nos. 1869-1872 (4)   7.35 3.05

Stories and Legends — A607

Europa: 120d, Prometheus, the giver of fire. 430d, Digenis Akritas, Greek swordsmen on horseback.

**1997, May 19**    **Litho.**    **Perf. 14**
1873 A607 120d multicolored   1.60 1.35
1874 A607 430d multicolored   3.75 3.25
   a.   Pair, #1873-1874   5.25 5.25

**Booklet Stamps**
**Perf. 13½ Vert.**

1873A A607 120d multicolored   1.40 1.25
1874B A607 430d multicolored   3.25 2.75
   c.   Booklet pane, 2 each
     #1873A, 1874B   10.50 10.50
     Complete booklet, #1874c   10.50
   d.   Pair, #1873A, 1874B   5.25 5.25

6th IAAF World Track & Field Championships, Athens — A608

Official IAAF emblem, Greek flag and: 20d, Runners. 100d, Nike. 140d, High jump. 170d, Hurdles. 500d, Olympic Stadium, Athens.

**1997, July 11**    **Litho.**    **Perf. 13x13½**
1875 A608 20d multicolored   .25 .25
1876 A608 100d multicolored   .70 .35
1877 A608 140d multicolored   1.00 .65
1878 A608 170d multicolored   1.25 .80
1879 A608 500d multicolored   4.25 2.00
   Nos. 1875-1879 (5)   7.45 4.05

Famous People — A609

Designs: 20d, Alexandros Panagoulis (1939-76), resistance leader, vert. 30d, Grigorios Xenopoulos (1867-1951), novelist, vert. 40d, Odysseus Elytis (1911-96), poet. 50d, Panayiotis Kanellopoulos (1902-86), prime minister, vert. 100d, Harilaos Trikoupis (1832-96), politician. 170d, Maria Callas (1923-77), opera singer. 200d, Rigas Vélestinlis-Feraios (1757-98), revolutionary, vert.

**Perf. 13½x13, 13x13½**

**1997, Oct. 31**        **Litho.**
1880 A609 20d multicolored   .25 .25
1881 A609 30d multicolored   .45 .25
1882 A609 40d multicolored   .55 .25
1883 A609 50d multicolored   .85 .25

1884 A609 100d multicolored   1.35 .70
1885 A609 170d multicolored   2.75 1.30
1886 A609 200d multicolored   3.25 1.45
   Nos. 1880-1886 (7)   9.45 4.45

Film Comedians — A610

Designs: 20d, Vassilis Avlonitis. 30d, Vassilis Argyropoulos. 50d, Georgia Vassileiadou. 70d, Lambros Constantaras. 100d, Vassilis Logothetidis. 140d, Dionysis Papagiannopoulos. 170d, Nikos Stavrides. 200d, Mimis Fotopoulos.

**1997, Dec. 17**    **Litho.**    **Perf. 13x13½**
1887 A610 20d multicolored   .25 .25
1888 A610 30d multicolored   .35 .25
1889 A610 50d multicolored   .50 .35
1890 A610 70d multicolored   .70 .55
1891 A610 100d multicolored   .90 .70
1892 A610 140d multicolored   1.25 1.25
1893 A610 170d multicolored   1.90 1.25
1894 A610 200d multicolored   4.00 1.25
   Nos. 1887-1894 (8)   9.85 5.85

Incorporation of the Dodecanese Islands into Greece, 50th Anniv. — A611

100d, German commander signing treaty turning islands over to English and Greek military, Symi (Simi), May 8, 1945. 140d, Greece and Colossus of Rhodes, Greek flag. 170d, English general turns islands over to Greek military command, Rhodes, 3/31/47. 500d, Greek flag raised over Dodencanese, Kasos (Caso), 3/7/47.

**1998, Feb. 27**    **Litho.**    **Perf. 13½x13**
1895 A611 100d multicolored   .80 .50
1896 A611 140d multicolored   1.10 1.10
1897 A611 170d multicolored   1.60 1.40
1898 A611 500d multicolored   4.50 1.00
   Nos. 1895-1898 (4)   8.00 4.00

Hagia Sophia General Children's Hospital, Cent. A612

Holy Monastery of Xenon, 1000th Anniv. A613

4th World Congress of Thracians, Nea Orestiada A614

16th World Congress of Cardiology Research, Athens A615

European Movement, 50th Anniv. — A616

**Perf. 13x13½, 13½x13**

**1998, Apr. 30**        **Litho.**
1899 A612 20d multicolored   .25 .25
1900 A613 100d multicolored   .75 .40
1901 A614 140d multicolored   1.00 1.00
1902 A615 150d Building, heart,
    horiz.   1.00 1.00
1903 A615 170d multicolored   1.60 1.25
1904 A616 500d multicolored   5.25 1.50
   Nos. 1899-1904 (6)   9.85 5.40

**Souvenir Sheet**

1998 FIBA World Basketball Championships, Greece — A617

**1998, June 15**    **Litho.**    **Perf. 14**
1905 A617 300d multicolored   4.00 4.00

Natl. Festivals — A618

Europa: 140d, Culture Festival, Grecian Theatre, Epidaurus. 500d, Culture Festival, Herod Atticus Theatre, Athens.

**1998, May 29**    **Litho.**    **Perf. 14x13½**
1906 A618 140d multicolored   1.35 1.35
1907 A618 500d multicolored   4.00 4.00
   a.   Pair, #1906-1907   6.00 6.00

**Booklet Stamps**
**Perf. 13 Vert.**

1906A A618 140d multicolored   1.60 1.60
1907B A618 500d multicolored   4.50 4.50
   c.   Bklt. pane, 2 ea. #1906A,
     1907B   13.50 13.50
     Complete booklet, #1907c   13.50
   d.   Pair, #1906A, 1907B   6.75 6.75

Castle Ruins in Greece — A619

30d, Hierapetra. 50d, Korfu. 70d, Limnos. 100d, Argolis. 150d, Iraklion. 170d, Navpaktos, vert. 200d, Ioannina, vert. 400d, Plataea. 550d, Karitainas, vert. 600d, Fragkokastello, Crete.

**1998, July 15**    **Litho.**    **Perf. 13¼**
1908 A619 30d multicolored   .25 .25
1909 A619 50d multicolored   .30 .25
1910 A619 70d multicolored   .45 .25
1911 A619 100d multicolored   .60 .30
1912 A619 150d multicolored   .60 .50
1913 A619 170d multicolored   1.00 .75
1914 A619 200d multicolored   1.60 .80
1915 A619 400d multicolored   3.50 1.25
1916 A619 550d multicolored   5.00 1.75
1917 A619 600d multicolored   5.25 2.25
   Nos. 1908-1917 (10)   18.55 8.35

**Booklet Stamps**
**Perf. 13¼ Vert. or Horiz.**

1908A A619 30d multicolored   .25 .25
1909A A619 50d multicolored   .40 .25
1910A A619 70d multicolored   .50 .30
1911A A619 100d multicolored   .70 .40
1912A A619 150d multicolored   .70 .60
1913A A619 170d multicolored   1.15 .85
1914A A619 200d multicolored   1.75 .90
1915A A619 400d multicolored   4.25 1.35
1916A A619 550d multicolored   5.75 2.00
1917A A619 600d multicolored   6.00 2.50
   Nos. 1908A-1917A (10)   21.45 9.40

Nos. 1908A-1917A were each sold in booklets containing 20 panes of 5 stamps. Nos.1908A-1912A, 1915A, and 1917A are perforated horizontally. Nos. 1913A-1914A, and 1916A are perforated vertically.

Greek Orthodox Community of Venice, 500th Anniv. A620

Designs: 30d, Cathedral. 40d, Icon, vert. 140d, Illuminated manuscript, vert. 230d, Icon of Madonna and Child surrounded by saints.

**1998, Oct. 26　Litho.　Perf. 14**
| | | | | |
|---|---|---|---|---|
| 1918 | A620 | 30d multicolored | .30 | .25 |
| 1919 | A620 | 40d multicolored | .50 | .35 |
| 1920 | A620 | 140d multicolored | 1.35 | .80 |
| 1921 | A620 | 230d multicolored | 3.25 | 1.75 |
| | *Nos. 1918-1921 (4)* | | 5.40 | 3.15 |

Greek Writers of
Antiquity — A621

**1998　Litho.　Perf. 13½x13**
| | | | | |
|---|---|---|---|---|
| 1922 | A621 | 20d Homer | .25 | .25 |
| 1923 | A621 | 100d Sophocles | 1.25 | 1.25 |
| 1924 | A621 | 140d Thucydides | 1.50 | 1.50 |
| 1925 | A621 | 200d Plato | 1.90 | 1.90 |
| 1926 | A621 | 250d Demosthenes | 3.00 | 3.00 |
| | *Nos. 1922-1926 (5)* | | 7.90 | 7.90 |

Intl. Year of the
Ocean — A622

Designs: 40d, Ancient ship, map of Mediterranean Sea. 100d, Sailing ship, Neptune. 200d, Modern ship. 500d, Silver tetradrachm of Antigonos Doson, 229-221 B.C.

**1999, Feb. 19　Litho.　Perf. 13x13½**
| | | | | |
|---|---|---|---|---|
| 1927 | A622 | 40d multicolored | .30 | .25 |
| 1928 | A622 | 100d multicolored | .80 | .40 |
| 1929 | A622 | 200d multicolored | 1.40 | .90 |
| 1930 | A622 | 500d multicolored | 2.75 | 1.25 |
| | *Nos. 1927-1930 (4)* | | 5.25 | 2.80 |

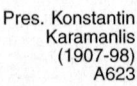

Pres. Konstantin
Karamanlis
(1907-98)
A623

Various portraits of Karamanlis and: 100d, Representations of economic development, 1955-63. 170d, People celebrating. 200d, Emblem of European Union. 500d, National flag, vert.

**1999, Apr. 19　Litho.　Perf. 14**
| | | | | |
|---|---|---|---|---|
| 1931 | A623 | 100d multicolored | .55 | .30 |
| 1932 | A623 | 170d multicolored | 1.00 | .60 |
| 1933 | A623 | 200d multicolored | 1.25 | .70 |
| 1934 | A623 | 500d multicolored | 2.50 | 1.60 |
| | *Nos. 1931-1934 (4)* | | 5.30 | 3.20 |

Europa — A624

Various views Mytikas peak (Mt. Olympus) and wildflowers.

**1999, May 24　Litho.　Perf. 14**
| | | | | |
|---|---|---|---|---|
| 1935 | A624 | 170d multicolored | *1.50* | *1.50* |
| 1936 | A624 | 550d multicolored | *4.00* | *3.50* |
| a. | Pair, #1935-1936 | | *6.00* | *6.00* |

**Booklet Stamps**
**Perf. 13¼ Vert.**
| | | | | |
|---|---|---|---|---|
| 1935A | A624 | 170d multicolored | 1.60 | 1.50 |
| 1936B | A624 | 550d multicolored | 4.25 | 3.50 |
| c. | Booklet pane, 2 each #1935A, 1936B | | 12.00 | 12.00 |
| | Complete booklet, #1936c | | 12.00 | |
| d. | Pair, #1935A, 1936B | | 6.25 | 6.25 |

Greece-Japan
Diplomatic
Relations,
Cent. — A625

**1999, June 28　Litho.　Perf. 13¾x14**
| | | | | |
|---|---|---|---|---|
| 1937 | A625 | 120d multicolored | .75 | .75 |

4000 Years
of
Hellenism
A626

Designs: a, Sanctuary of Apollo Hylates, Kourion. b, Mycenaean "Krater of the Warriors," Athens. c, Mycenaean amphoral krater, Cyprus Museum. d, Sanctuary of Apollo Epikourios, Delphi.

**1999, June 28　Litho.　Perf. 13½x13**
| | | | | |
|---|---|---|---|---|
| 1938 | A626 | 120d Block of 4, #a.-d. | 3.25 | 3.25 |

See Cyprus No. 936.

Community
Support
Framework, 5th
Anniv. — A627

Designs: 20d, Modernization of Greek Railway Organization. 120d, Rio-Antirrio Bridge. 140d, Modernization of Greek Post Office. 250d, Athens Metro train. 500d, Eleftherios Venizelos Airport, Athens.

**1999, Nov. 8　Litho.　Perf. 13x13¼**
| | | | | |
|---|---|---|---|---|
| 1939 | A627 | 20d multi | .25 | .25 |
| 1940 | A627 | 120d multi | .65 | .65 |
| 1941 | A627 | 140d multi | .75 | .75 |
| 1942 | A627 | 250d multi | 1.25 | 1.25 |
| 1943 | A627 | 500d multi | 2.50 | 2.50 |
| | *Nos. 1939-1943 (5)* | | 5.40 | 5.40 |

Armed
Forces — A628

20d, Exercise with helicopters, rafts. 30d, Patrol boat. 40d, F-16s in flight. 50d, CL-215 dousing forest fire. 70d, Destroyers. 120d, Distribution of goods in Bosnia. 170d, Mirage 2000 in flight. 250d, Exercise with helicopters, tanks. 600d, Submarine Okeanos.

**Perf. 13¾x13½**
| | | | | |
|---|---|---|---|---|
| | | | | *Litho.* |
| 1944 | A628 | 20d multi | .25 | .25 |
| 1945 | A628 | 30d multi | .25 | .25 |
| 1946 | A628 | 40d multi | .25 | .25 |
| 1947 | A628 | 50d multi | .30 | .30 |
| 1948 | A628 | 70d multi | .40 | .40 |
| 1949 | A628 | 120d multi | .65 | .45 |
| 1950 | A628 | 170d multi | 1.15 | 1.00 |
| 1951 | A628 | 250d multi | 1.60 | 1.35 |
| 1952 | A628 | 600d multi | 3.50 | 3.25 |
| | *Nos. 1944-1952 (9)* | | 8.35 | 7.50 |

Christianity, 2000th
Anniv. — A629

Designs: 20d, Birth of Christ, vert. 50d, Inter-religious dialogue, vert. 120d, Angels with instruments, vert. 170d, Dove. 200d, Communion. 500d, Providence, vert.

**2000, Jan. 1　Perf. 14¼x14**
| | | | | |
|---|---|---|---|---|
| 1953 | A629 | 20d multi | .25 | .25 |
| 1954 | A629 | 50d multi | .30 | .30 |
| 1955 | A629 | 120d multi | .65 | .65 |

**Perf. 14x14¼**
| | | | | |
|---|---|---|---|---|
| 1956 | A629 | 170d multi | .90 | .90 |

**Size: 35x35mm**
**Perf. 13¾**
| | | | | |
|---|---|---|---|---|
| 1957 | A629 | 200d multi | 1.15 | 1.15 |

**Size: 27x57mm**
**Perf. 13½x14**
| | | | | |
|---|---|---|---|---|
| 1958 | A629 | 500d multi | 2.75 | 2.75 |
| | *Nos. 1953-1958 (6)* | | 6.00 | 6.00 |

**Europa, 2000**
**Common Design Type**
**2000, May 9　Litho.　Perf. 13¼x13**
| | | | | |
|---|---|---|---|---|
| 1959 | CD17 | 170d multi | 2.75 | 2.75 |

**Booklet Stamps**
**Perf. 13 Vert.**
| | | | | |
|---|---|---|---|---|
| 1959A | CD17 | 170d multi | 2.75 | 2.75 |
| b. | Booklet pane, 4 #1959A | | 12.00 | 12.00 |
| | Complete booklet, #1959b | | 12.00 | |

Ships — A630

Designs: 10d, Steamship Ilissos. 120d, Destroyer Adrias. 170d, Steamship Ia II. 400d, Destroyer Vas. Olga.

**Perf. 14¼x13¾**
| | | | | |
|---|---|---|---|---|
| 2000, June 26 | | | | *Litho.* |
| 1960 | A630 | 10d multi | .25 | .25 |
| 1961 | A630 | 120d multi | .80 | .50 |
| 1962 | A630 | 170d multi | 1.50 | .90 |
| 1963 | A630 | 400d multi | 3.75 | 2.25 |
| | *Nos. 1960-1963 (4)* | | 6.30 | 3.90 |

Stampin' the
Future Children's
Stamp Design
Contest
Winners — A631

Art by: 130d, Spyros Dalakos (rainbow). 180d, Ornella Moshovaki-Chaiger (robots). 200d, Zisis Zariotis (building, tree, vehicles). 620d, Athina Limoudi (rocket).

**2000, June 26**
| | | | | |
|---|---|---|---|---|
| 1964 | A631 | 130d multi | .55 | .55 |
| 1965 | A631 | 180d multi | .90 | .90 |
| 1966 | A631 | 200d multi | 1.40 | 1.40 |
| 1967 | A631 | 620d multi | 3.50 | 3.50 |
| | *Nos. 1964-1967 (4)* | | 6.35 | 6.35 |

Sydney and
Athens — A632

Olympic torch, flag and: 200d, Parthenon. 650d, Sydney Opera House.

**2000, Sept. 15　Litho.**
| | | | | |
|---|---|---|---|---|
| 1968-1969 | A632 | Set of 2 | 4.50 | 4.50 |

See Australia Nos. 1873-1874.

Emblem of 2004 Athens
Olympic Games — A633

Various backgrounds. Denominations: 10d, 50d, 130d, 180d, 200d, 650d.

**2000, Nov. 7　Perf. 14x14¼**
| | | | | |
|---|---|---|---|---|
| 1970-1975 | A633 | Set of 6 | 7.25 | 7.25 |

**Souvenir Sheet**

Stamps of the Cretan Government,
Cent. — A634

No. 1976: a, 200d, Crete #69. b, 650d, Crete #71.

**2000, Dec. 18　Litho.　Perf. 14x14¼**
| | | | | |
|---|---|---|---|---|
| 1976 | A634 | Sheet of 2, #a-b | 12.00 | 12.00 |

Christianity, 2000th
Anniv. — A635

Designs: 20d, Sculpture of Christ as Orpheus, vert. 30d, Sculpture of The Good Shepherd, vert. 40d, Mosaic of Christ, vert. 100d, Mural of Christ. 130d, Icon of Christ (green frame), vert. 150d, Icon of Christ with open Bible, vert. 180d, Icon of Christ with closed Bible (dark blue frame), vert. 1000d, Byzantine coin depicting Christ.

**2000, Dec. 18　Perf. 14x14¼, 14¼x14**
| | | | | |
|---|---|---|---|---|
| 1977-1984 | A635 | Set of 8 | 9.00 | 9.00 |

Post Office
Savings Bank,
Cent. — A636

Designs: 20d, Mother and child, vert. 130d, Emblem and 2-euro coin.

**Perf. 13¼x13¾, 13¾x13¼**
| | | | | |
|---|---|---|---|---|
| 2001, May 15 | | | | *Litho.* |
| 1985-1986 | A636 | Set of 2 | 1.00 | 1.00 |

UN High
Commissioner for
Refugees, 50th
Anniv. — A637

**2001, May 15　Perf. 13¾x13¼**
| | | | | |
|---|---|---|---|---|
| 1987 | A637 | 140d multi | 1.15 | 1.15 |

Thessaloniki Intl.
Trade Fair, 75th
Anniv. — A638

**2001, May 15　Perf. 13¼x13¾**
| | | | | |
|---|---|---|---|---|
| 1988 | A638 | 180d multi | 1.15 | 1.15 |

Aristotle
University,
Thessaloniki, 75th
Anniv. — A639

**2001, May 15　Perf. 13¾x13¼**
| | | | | |
|---|---|---|---|---|
| 1989 | A639 | 200d multi | 1.35 | 1.35 |

Academy of
Athens, 75th
Anniv. — A640

**2001, May 15**
| | | | | |
|---|---|---|---|---|
| 1990 | A640 | 500d multi | 3.50 | 3.50 |

Ioannis Zigdis (1913-
97), Politician — A641

**2001, May 15　Perf. 13¼x13¾**
| | | | | |
|---|---|---|---|---|
| 1991 | A641 | 700d multi | 4.50 | 4.50 |

Europa
A642

Designs: Nos. 1992a, 1992c, Dry leaf, parched earth. Nos. 1992b, 1992d, Water, fresh leaves.

| 2001, May 15 | | Perf. 14¼x13¾ | |
|---|---|---|---|
| 1992 A642 | Horiz. pair | 6.75 | 6.75 |
| a. | 180d multi | 1.40 | 1.40 |
| b. | 650d multi | 5.25 | 5.25 |

**Booklet Stamps**
*Perf. 13¼ Vert.*

| 1992C A642 | Horiz. pair | 7.00 | 7.00 |
|---|---|---|---|
| d. | 180d multi | 1.50 | 1.50 |
| e. | 650d multi | 5.50 | 5.50 |
| f. | Booklet pane, 2 # 1992C | 14.00 | |
| | Booklet, #1992f | 14.00 | |

Birds and
Flowers — A643

Designs: 20d, Little egret. 50d, White stork. 100d, Bearded vulture. 140d, Orchid, vert. 150d, Dalmatian pelican, vert. 200d, Lily, Plastira Lake. 700d, Egyptian vulture. 850d, Black vulture.

*Perf. 13¾x13¼, 13¼x13¾*

| 2001, June 27 | | | |
|---|---|---|---|
| 1993-2000 A643 | Set of 8 | 14.00 | 14.00 |

Symbol of Hellenic Post
A644

| 2001, Sept. 8 | Litho. | Perf. 13x12¾ | |
|---|---|---|---|
| 2001 A644 | Pair + 2 labels | 2.25 | 2.25 |
| a. | 140d blue & yellow | 1.00 | 1.00 |
| b. | 200d blue | 1.50 | 1.50 |

Wording on label varies. No. 2001 could be personalized by adding photos to the labels.

Souvenir Sheet

Christianity in Armenia, 1700th
Anniv. — A645

| 2001, Dec. 5 | | Perf. 13 | |
|---|---|---|---|
| 2002 A645 | 850d multi | 7.75 | 7.75 |

Souvenir Sheet

2004 Summer Olympics,
Athens — A646

| 2001, Dec. 5 | | Perf. 13¾ | |
|---|---|---|---|
| 2003 A646 | 1200d multi | 7.75 | 7.75 |

**100 Cents = 1 Euro (€)**

Dances — A647

Designs: 2c, Kamakaki. 3c, Bride's dowry. 5c, Zagorissios, vert. 10c, Balos. 15c, Synkathistos. 20c, Tsakonikos, vert. 30c, Pyrrichios. 35c, Fourles, vert. 40c, Apokriatikos. 45c, Kotsari. 50c, Pentozalis, vert. 55c, Karagouna. 60c, Hassapiko. 65c, Zalistos. 85c, Pogonissios. €1, Kalamatianos. €2, Maleviziotis. €2.15, Tsamikos. €2.60, Zeibekikos, vert. €3, Nyfiatikos. €4, Paschaliatikos.

*Perf. 13x13¼, 13¼x13*

| 2002, Jan. 2 | | Litho. | |
|---|---|---|---|
| 2004 A647 | 2c multi | .25 | .25 |
| 2005 A647 | 3c multi | .25 | .25 |
| 2006 A647 | 5c multi | .25 | .25 |
| 2007 A647 | 10c multi | .25 | .25 |
| 2008 A647 | 15c multi | .35 | .35 |
| 2009 A647 | 20c multi | .50 | .50 |
| 2010 A647 | 30c multi | .70 | .70 |
| 2011 A647 | 35c multi | .80 | .80 |
| 2012 A647 | 40c multi | 1.00 | 1.00 |
| 2013 A647 | 45c multi | 1.10 | 1.10 |
| 2014 A647 | 50c multi | 1.20 | 1.20 |
| 2015 A647 | 55c multi | 1.25 | 1.25 |
| 2016 A647 | 60c multi | 1.40 | 1.40 |
| 2017 A647 | 65c multi | 1.50 | 1.50 |
| 2018 A647 | 85c multi | 2.00 | 2.00 |
| 2019 A647 | €1 multi | 2.40 | 2.40 |
| 2020 A647 | €2 multi | 4.75 | 4.75 |
| 2021 A647 | €2.15 multi | 5.00 | 5.00 |
| 2022 A647 | €2.60 multi | 6.00 | 6.00 |
| 2023 A647 | €3 multi | 7.00 | 7.00 |
| 2024 A647 | €4 multi | 9.50 | 9.50 |
| *Nos. 2004-2024 (21)* | | 47.45 | 47.45 |

**Booklet Stamps**
*Perf. 13¼ Vert. or Horiz.*

| 2004A A647 | 2c multi | .25 | .25 |
|---|---|---|---|
| 2005A A647 | 3c multi | .25 | .25 |
| 2006A A647 | 5c multi | .25 | .25 |
| 2007A A647 | 10c multi | .25 | .25 |
| 2008A A647 | 15c multi | .35 | .35 |
| 2009A A647 | 20c multi | .50 | .50 |
| 2010A A647 | 30c multi | .70 | .70 |
| 2011A A647 | 35c multi | .80 | .80 |
| 2012A A647 | 40c multi | 1.00 | 1.00 |
| 2013A A647 | 45c multi | 1.10 | 1.10 |
| 2014A A647 | 50c multi | 1.20 | 1.20 |
| 2015A A647 | 55c multi | 1.25 | 1.25 |
| 2016A A647 | 60c multi | 1.40 | 1.40 |
| 2017A A647 | 65c multi | 1.50 | 1.50 |
| 2018A A647 | 85c multi | 2.00 | 2.00 |
| 2019A A647 | €1 multi | 2.40 | 2.40 |
| 2020A A647 | €2 multi | 4.75 | 4.75 |
| 2021A A647 | €2.15 multi | 5.00 | 5.00 |
| 2022A A647 | €2.60 multi | 6.00 | 6.00 |
| 2023A A647 | €3 multi | 7.00 | 7.00 |
| 2024A A647 | €4 multi | 9.50 | 9.50 |
| *Nos. 2004A-2024A (21)* | | 47.45 | 47.45 |

Nos. 2004A-2024A were each sold in booklets containing 20 panes of 5 stamps.

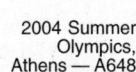

2004 Summer
Olympics,
Athens — A648

Ancient Olympics: 41c, Runners. 59c, Sculpture of charioteer, vert. 80c, Javelin thrower. €2.05, Doryphoros of Polycleitos, vert. €2.35, Weight lifter. €5, Stadium archway.

*Perf. 13¾x13¼, 13¼x13¾*

| 2002, Mar. 15 | | Litho. | |
|---|---|---|---|
| 2025-2029 A648 | Set of 5 | 15.00 | 15.00 |

**Souvenir Sheet**
*Perf. 12¾*

| 2030 A648 | €5 multi | 13.00 | 13.00 |
|---|---|---|---|

No. 2030 contains one 49x28mm stamp.

Europa
A649

| 2002, May 9 | | Perf. 13¼x13¾ | |
|---|---|---|---|
| 2031 A649 | Horiz. pair, #a-b | 7.00 | 7.00 |
| a. | 60c Elephant | 1.40 | 1.40 |
| b. | €2.60 Equestrian act | 5.50 | 5.50 |

**Booklet Stamp**
*Perf. 13¼ Vert.*

| 2031C A649 | Horiz. pair, #d-e | 7.00 | 7.00 |
|---|---|---|---|
| d. | 60c Elephant | 1.40 | 1.40 |
| e. | €2.60 Equestrian act | 5.50 | 5.50 |
| f. | Booklet pane, 2, #2031C | 14.00 | |
| | Booklet, #2031f | 14.00 | |

Scouting — A650

Designs: 45c, Navy Scout, sailboats. 60c, Scout, emblem of World Conference. 70c, Scouts planting tree. €2.15, Scouts, map and mountain.

| 2002, June 26 | Litho. | Perf. 13x13½ | |
|---|---|---|---|
| 2032-2035 A650 | Set of 4 | 9.25 | 9.25 |
| 2035a | Miniature sheet, 2 each #2032-2035 + 4 labels | 21.00 | 21.00 |

Greek
Language — A651

Designs: 45c, Hieros Nomos, Athens Acropolis, 5th cent. B.C. 60c, Linear B script, 13th cent. B.C., vert. 90c, The Memoirs of General Makriyiannis. €2.15, Byzantine script, 11th cent., vert.

*Perf. 13¾x13¼, 13¼x13¾*

| 2002, Sept. 23 | | | |
|---|---|---|---|
| 2036-2039 A651 | Set of 4 | 8.50 | 7.50 |

Ancient Olympic
Winners With Laurel
Wreaths — A652

Head color: 45c, Green. 60c, Dark blue. €2.15, Pink. €2.60, Light blue.

| 2002, Oct. 30 | Litho. | Perf. 13¼x13¾ | |
|---|---|---|---|
| 2040-2043 A652 | Set of 4 | 14.00 | 14.00 |
| 2043a | Miniature sheet, 2 each #2040-2043 | 29.00 | 29.00 |

Souvenir Sheet

Stadia of
First
Olympics
A653

| 2002, Oct. 30 | | Perf. 12¾ | |
|---|---|---|---|
| 2044 A653 | €6 multi | 18.00 | 18.00 |

Archbishops of
Athens — A654

Archbishop and years of reign: 10c, Chrystostomos I (1923-38). 45c, Chrysanthos (1938-41). €2.15, Damaskinos (1941-49). €2.60, Serapheim (1974-98).

| 2002, Dec. 10 | | Perf. 13x13½ | |
|---|---|---|---|
| 2045-2048 A654 | Set of 4 | 13.00 | 13.00 |

Olympic Sports
Equipment — A655

Designs: 2c, Discus. 5c, Hammer. 47c, Javelin. 65c, Pole vault pole and bar. €2.17, Hurdles. €2.85, Weights.

| 2003, Feb. 11 | | Perf. 13¾x14¼ | |
|---|---|---|---|
| 2049-2054 A655 | Set of 6 | 17.00 | 8.50 |
| 2054a | Sheet, #2049-2054 | 20.00 | 20.00 |

2004 Summer Olympics, Athens.

Souvenir Sheet

Mascots for 2004 Summer Olympics,
Athens — A656

No. 2055: a, €2.50, Mascot with red shirt. b, €2.85, Mascot with blue shirt.

| 2003, Feb. 11 | | Perf. 13¼ | |
|---|---|---|---|
| 2055 A656 | Sheet of 2, #a-b | 13.00 | 13.00 |

Greetings — A657

No. 2056: a, Globe. b, Athens 2004 Olympic Games emblem and Olympic rings. c, Ancient Greek athlete with laurel wreath. d, Roses and wedding headband. e, Spheres and grid. f, Child's drawing of train. g, Man and woman holding flowers. h, Stone carving of face. i, Acropolis.

| 2003, Mar. 18 | Litho. | Perf. 14x13¾ | |
|---|---|---|---|
| 2056 A657 | Sheet of 9 | 14.00 | 14.00 |
| a.-g. | 47c Any single | 1.40 | 1.40 |
| h.-i. | 65c Either single | 2.00 | 2.00 |
| q. | No. 2056h + label | 4.00 | 4.00 |
| r. | #2056a + label | 4.00 | 4.00 |
| s. | #2056b + label | 4.00 | 4.00 |
| t. | #2056c + label | 4.00 | 4.00 |
| u. | #2056d + label | 4.00 | 4.00 |
| v. | #2056e + label | 4.00 | 4.00 |
| w. | #2056f + label | 4.00 | 4.00 |
| x. | #2056g + label | 4.00 | 4.00 |
| y. | #2056i + label | 4.00 | 4.00 |

Nos. 2056q and 2056y were issued in sheets of 15 stamps and 15 labels that sold for €19.50. Labels could be personalized. No. 2056q exists dated "2004." Stamps dated "2004" were issued in sheets of 5 stamps + 5 preprinted labels that sold for €4 per sheet. Nos. 2056r-2056x were printed in sheets of 15 + 15 labels that sold for €14.10. Labels could be personalized.

Dove and
Stars
A658

White Tower
of
Thessaloniki
in Letters
A659

Fresco
of
Birds
A660

Jigsaw Puzzle
Pieces
A661

| 2003, Apr. 16 | | Perf. 14x13¾ | |
|---|---|---|---|
| 2057 A658 | 47c multi | 1.10 | 1.10 |
| 2058 A659 | 65c multi | 1.60 | 1.60 |
| 2059 A660 | €2.17 multi | 5.25 | 5.25 |
| 2060 A661 | €2.85 multi | 7.00 | 7.00 |
| 2060a | Sheet, 2 each #2057-2060 | 30.00 | 30.00 |
| *Nos. 2057-2060 (4)* | | 14.95 | 14.95 |

Greek Presidency of European Union.

Europa
A662

Poster art: a, 65c, Abstract. b, €2.85, Tourist poster.

**2003, May 9    Litho.    Perf. 13¼x13¾**

| 2061 | A662 | Horiz. pair | 10.50 | 10.50 |
|---|---|---|---|---|
| a. | | 65c multi | 2.00 | 2.00 |
| b. | | €2.85 multi | 8.50 | 8.50 |

**Booklet Stamps**
**Perf. 13¼ Vert.**

| 2061C | A662 | Horiz. pair | 10.50 | 10.50 |
|---|---|---|---|---|
| d. | | 65c multi | 2.00 | 2.00 |
| e. | | €2.85 multi | 8.50 | 8.50 |
| f. | | Booklet pane, 2 #2061C | 21.00 | |
| | | Complete booklet, #2061f | 21.00 | |

A663

No. 2062: a, Water polo. b, Diving. c, Swimming.
No. 2063, vert.: a, Table tennis. b, Basketball. c, Soccer. d, Handball.
No. 2064: a, Kayak slalom. b, Windsurfing.
No. 2065, vert.: a, Rhythmic gymnastics. b, Judo. c, Archery. d, Trampoline.
No. 2066: a, Kayak (flatwater). b, Rowing (coxswain). c, Rowing (rower).
No. 2067, vert.: a, Badminton. b, Fencing. c, Tennis. d, Taekwondo.
No. 2068: a, Cycling. b, Triathlon.
No. 2069, vert.: a, Baseball. b, Beach volleyball. c, Field hockey. d, Boxing.
No. 2070, vert.: a, Weight lifting (figure in red) b), Weight lifting (figure in blue).

**2003, May 9    Litho.    Perf. 13¼**

| 2062 | A663 | Booklet pane of 3 + label | 4.75 | |
|---|---|---|---|---|
| a.-c. | | 47c Any single | 1.50 | 1.40 |
| 2063 | A663 | Booklet pane of 4 | 6.00 | — |
| a.-d. | | 47c Any single | 1.50 | 1.40 |
| 2064 | A663 | Booklet pane of 2 | 3.50 | — |
| a.-b. | | 47c Either single | 1.75 | 1.40 |
| 2065 | A663 | Booklet pane of 4 | 6.00 | — |
| a. | | 30c multi | 1.25 | 1.00 |
| b.-d. | | 47c Any single | 1.50 | 1.40 |
| 2066 | A663 | Booklet pane of 3 + label | 4.75 | — |
| a.-c. | | 47c Any single | 1.50 | 1.40 |
| 2067 | A663 | Booklet pane of 4 | 6.00 | — |
| a. | | 30c multi | 1.25 | 1.00 |
| b.-d. | | 47c Any single | 1.50 | 1.40 |
| 2068 | A663 | Booklet pane of 2 | 3.50 | — |
| a.-b. | | 47c Either single | 1.75 | 1.40 |
| 2069 | A663 | Booklet pane of 4 | 6.00 | — |
| a. | | 35c multi | 1.25 | 1.10 |
| b.-d. | | 47c Any single | 1.50 | 1.40 |
| 2070 | A663 | Booklet pane of 2 | 3.50 | — |
| a.-b. | | 47c Either single | 1.75 | 1.40 |
| | | Complete booklet, #2062-2070 | 50.00 | |

Booklet containing Nos. 2062-2070 sold for €14.99.

Environmental Protection — A664

Designs: 15c, Apple falling from tree. 47c, Apple in water. 65c, Laurel wreath over seacoast. €2.85, Moon over tree.

**2003, June 5    Perf. 13¼x13¾**

| 2071-2074 | A664 | Set of 4 | 10.00 | 10.00 |
|---|---|---|---|---|

Olympic Sports — A665

Designs: 5c, High jump. 47c, Wrestling. 65c, Running. 80c, Cycling, vert. €4, Windsurfing, vert.

**Perf. 13¾x13¼, 13¼x13¾**
**2003, Sept. 9**

| 2075-2079 | A665 | Set of 5 | 18.00 | 18.00 |
|---|---|---|---|---|
| 2079a | | Miniature sheet, #2075-2079 | 18.00 | 18.00 |

---

**Souvenir Sheet**

Mascots for 2004 Summer Olympics, Athens — A666

No. 2080: a, Figure in red. b, Figure in blue.

**2003, Sept. 9    Perf. 13¼**

| 2080 | A666 | Sheet of 2 | 13.00 | 13.00 |
|---|---|---|---|---|
| a. | | €2.50 multi | 6.00 | 6.00 |
| b. | | €2.85 multi | 7.00 | 7.00 |

Trades of the Past — A667

Designs: 3c, Stair carving. 10c, Shoemaking. 50c, Blacksmithing. €1, Typesetting by hand. €1.40, Sponge fishing. €4, Weaving.

**2003, Oct. 17    Perf. 13¾x13¼**

| 2081-2086 | A667 | Set of 6 | 17.00 | 17.00 |
|---|---|---|---|---|
| 2086a | | Miniature sheet, #2081-2086 | 21.00 | 21.00 |

Olympic Athletes — A668

Various athletes: 20c, 30c, 40c, 47c, €2, €2.85.

**Perf. 13¼x13¾**

**2003, Nov. 28    Litho.**

| 2087-2092 | A668 | Set of 6 | 16.00 | 16.00 |
|---|---|---|---|---|
| 2092a | | Miniature sheet, #2087-2092 | 20.00 | 20.00 |

Greek Olympians A669

Athletes: 3c, Spyridon Louis, marathon, 1896 gold medalist. 10c, Aristides Konstantinides, cycling road race, 1896 gold medalist. €2, Ioannis Fokianos, gymnastics coach. €2.17, Ioannis Mitropoulos, rings, 1896 gold medalist. €3.60, Konstantinos Tsiklitiras, standing long jump, 1912 gold medalist.

**Litho. with Foil Application**
**2004, Jan. 15    Perf. 13x13½**

| 2093-2097 | A669 | Set of 5 | 19.50 | 19.50 |
|---|---|---|---|---|

Cities Hosting Events at 2004 Olympics — A670

Designs: 1c, Volos. 2c, Patra. 5c, Iraklion. 47c, Athens. €1.40, Thessaloniki. €4, Athens, diff.

**2004, Jan. 15    Litho.**

| 2098-2103 | A670 | Set of 6 | 15.00 | 15.00 |
|---|---|---|---|---|
| 2103a | | Miniature sheet, #2098-2103 | 20.00 | 20.00 |

Olympic Sports — A671

Designs: 5c, Swimmer. 10c, Gymnast chalking hands. 20c, Kayak. 47c, Relay race. €2, Rhythmic gymnastics, vert. €5, Men's rings, vert.

**2004, Mar. 24    Litho.    Perf. 13¼**

| 2104-2109 | A671 | Set of 6 | 19.50 | 19.50 |
|---|---|---|---|---|
| 2109a | | Miniature sheet, #2104-2109 | 21.00 | 21.00 |

---

Europa A672

**2004, May 4    Perf. 13¼x13¾**

| 2110 | A672 | Horiz. pair | 10.50 | 10.50 |
|---|---|---|---|---|
| a. | | 65c Sailboat | 2.00 | 2.00 |
| b. | | €2.85 Balloon | 8.50 | 8.50 |

**Booklet Stamps**
**Perf. 13¼ Vert.**

| 2110C | A672 | Horiz. pair | 8.50 | 8.50 |
|---|---|---|---|---|
| d. | | 65c Sailboat | 1.60 | 1.60 |
| e. | | €2.85 Balloon | 6.75 | 6.75 |
| f. | | Booklet pane, 2 #2110C | 17.00 | |
| | | Complete booklet, #2110f | 17.00 | |

**Souvenir Sheets**

Olympic Flame A673

Olympic Dove A674

**2004, May 4    Perf. 13¾x14**

| 2111 | A673 | Sheet of 2 | 9.00 | 9.00 |
|---|---|---|---|---|
| a. | | 47c Torch bearer | 1.40 | 1.40 |
| b. | | €2.50 Torch bearer, city | 7.50 | 7.50 |
| c. | | #2111a + label, perf. 14x13¾ | 2.40 | 2.40 |

**Perf. 13¼**

| 2112 | A674 | Sheet of 2 | 9.00 | 9.00 |
|---|---|---|---|---|
| a. | | 47c Dove, Olympic rings | 1.40 | 1.40 |
| b. | | €2.50 Dove, people | 7.50 | 7.50 |

No. 2111c was printed in sheets of 15 + 15 labels that sold for €15. Labels could be personalized.

Olympic Coins — A675

Obverse and reverse of: 47c, Silver three-drachma of Cos, 480-450 BC. 65c, Gold stater of Philip II of Macedonia. €2, Silver two-drachma of Elis, 460 BC. €2.17, Silver four-drachma of Philip II of Macedonia.

**2004, June 15    Perf. 13¼**

| 2113-2116 | A675 | Set of 4 | 13.00 | 13.00 |
|---|---|---|---|---|
| 2116a | | Miniature sheet, #2113-2116 | 27.00 | 27.00 |

**Souvenir Sheets**

Modern Art and the Olympics A676

**2004, July 23    Perf. 13x13¼**

| 2117 | A676 | Sheet of 2 | 8.50 | 8.50 |
|---|---|---|---|---|
| a. | | 50c Wavy lines | 1.25 | 1.25 |
| b. | | €2.50 Stripes of color | 7.00 | 7.00 |

**Perf. 13¼x13**

| 2118 | A676 | Sheet of 2 | 9.00 | 9.00 |
|---|---|---|---|---|
| a. | | €1 Paint brush, vert. | 3.00 | 3.00 |
| b. | | €2 Paint roller, vert. | 6.00 | 6.00 |
| c. | | Miniature sheet, #2117a-2117b, 2118a-2118b | 20.00 | 20.00 |

Greece, 2004 European Soccer Champions A677

---

Designs: 47c, Greek flag, trophy. 65c, Greek players celebrating. €1, Greek players holding trophy. €2.88, Greek players, trophy.

**2004, July 16    Litho.    Perf. 13x13¼**

| 2119-2122 | A677 | Set of 4 | 12.00 | 12.00 |
|---|---|---|---|---|
| a. | | Souvenir sheet, #2119-2122 | 15.00 | 15.00 |

Greek Flag and Trophy A678

**2004, July    Litho.    Perf. 14x13¾**

| 2123 | A678 | 47c multi + label | 5.00 | 5.00 |
|---|---|---|---|---|
| a. | | Sheet of 5 + 5 labels | 25.00 | |
| b. | | Sheet of 10 + 10 labels | 60.00 | |

No. 2123 was printed in sheets of 15 + 15 labels that could be personalized. The sheet sold for €15. Nos. 2123a and 2123b have labels that depict soccer players or emblems, which cannot be personalized. Nos. 2123a and 2123b exist with two different sets of labels, and the set of 4 sheets sold for €20.

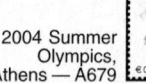

2004 Summer Olympics, Athens — A679

Designs: 50c, Hall of Good Harvest, Temple of Heaven, Beijing. 65c, Parthenon, Athens.

**2004, Aug. 9    Litho.    Perf. 14**

| 2124-2125 | A679 | Set of 2 | 4.00 | 4.00 |
|---|---|---|---|---|
| 2125a | | Souvenir sheet, #2124-2125 | 4.00 | 4.00 |
| 2125b | | #2125 + label | 6.00 | 6.00 |

No. 2125b was issued in sheets of 15 + 15 labels that sold for €19.50. Labels could be personalized. See People's Republic of China Nos. 3376-3377.

**Souvenir Sheet**

Olymphilex 2004 Philatelic Exhibition — A680

**2004, Aug. 13    Perf. 13½x13¼**

| 2126 | A680 | €6 multi | 15.00 | 15.00 |
|---|---|---|---|---|

Nikos Syranidis and Thomas Bimis, Synchronized Diving Gold Medalists A681

Leonidas Sampanis, Disqualified Bronze Medalist in 62 Kilogram Weight Lifting A682

Ilias Iliadis, Judo Gold Medalist A683

Sofia Bekatorou and Emilia Tsoulfa, Women's 470 Sailing Gold Medalists A684

Pyrros Dimas, 85 Kilogram Weight Lifting Bronze Medalist — A685

Dimosthenis Tampakos, Rings Gold Medalist — A686

Anastasia Kelesidou, Women's Discus Silver Medalist A687

Vasilis Polymeros and Nikos Skiathitis, Lightweight Double Sculls Bronze Medalists A688

Athanasia Tzoumeleka, Women's 20 Kilometer Walk Gold Medalist — A689

Chrysopigi Devezi, Women's Triple Jump Silver Medalist — A690

Fani Chalkia, Women's 400-Meter Hurdles Gold Medalist — A691

Nikos Kaklamanakis, Men's Mistral Sailing Silver Medalist — A692

Artiom Kiouregian, 55 Kilogram Greco-Roman Wrestling Bronze Medalist — A693

Women's Water Polo Team, Silver Medalist — A694

Mirela Maniani, Women's Javelin Bronze Medalist — A695

Elisavet Mystakidou, Women's 67 Kilogram Taekwondo Silver Medalist — A696

Alexandros Nikolaidis, Men's 80 Kilogram Taekwondo Silver Medalist — A697

### Digitally Printed
**2004, Aug.** — Perf. 13¼

| | | | | |
|---|---|---|---|---|
| 2127 | A681 | 65c multi | 1.90 | 1.90 |
| 2128 | A682 | 65c multi | 15.50 | 15.50 |
| 2129 | A683 | 65c multi | 1.90 | 1.90 |

| | | | | |
|---|---|---|---|---|
| 2130 | A684 | 65c multi | 1.90 | 1.90 |
| 2131 | A685 | 65c multi | 1.90 | 1.90 |
| 2132 | A686 | 65c multi | 1.90 | 1.90 |
| 2133 | A687 | 65c multi | 1.60 | 1.60 |
| 2134 | A688 | 65c multi | 1.90 | 1.90 |
| 2135 | A689 | 65c multi | 1.90 | 1.90 |
| 2136 | A690 | 65c multi | 1.90 | 1.90 |
| 2137 | A691 | 65c multi | 1.90 | 1.90 |
| 2138 | A692 | 65c multi | 1.90 | 1.90 |
| 2139 | A693 | 65c multi | 1.90 | 1.90 |
| 2140 | A694 | 65c multi | 1.90 | 1.90 |
| 2141 | A695 | 65c multi | 1.90 | 1.90 |
| 2142 | A696 | 65c multi | 1.90 | 1.90 |
| 2143 | A697 | 65c multi | 1.90 | 1.90 |
| | *Nos. 2127-2143 (17)* | | 45.90 | 45.90 |

**Litho.**

| | | | | |
|---|---|---|---|---|
| 2144 | A681 | 65c multi | 1.90 | 1.90 |
| 2145 | A682 | 65c multi | 12.00 | 12.00 |
| 2146 | A683 | 65c multi | 1.90 | 1.90 |
| 2147 | A684 | 65c multi | 1.90 | 1.90 |
| 2148 | A685 | 65c multi | 1.90 | 1.90 |
| 2149 | A686 | 65c multi | 1.90 | 1.90 |
| 2150 | A687 | 65c multi | 1.90 | 1.90 |
| 2151 | A688 | 65c multi | 1.90 | 1.90 |
| 2152 | A689 | 65c multi | 1.90 | 1.90 |
| 2153 | A690 | 65c multi | 1.90 | 1.90 |
| 2154 | A691 | 65c multi | 1.90 | 1.90 |
| 2155 | A692 | 65c multi | 1.90 | 1.90 |
| 2156 | A693 | 65c multi | 1.90 | 1.90 |
| 2157 | A694 | 65c multi | 1.90 | 1.90 |
| 2158 | A695 | 65c multi | 1.90 | 1.90 |
| 2159 | A696 | 65c multi | 1.90 | 1.90 |
| 2160 | A697 | 65c multi | 1.90 | 1.90 |
| a. | Souvenir sheet, #2144, 2146-2160 | | 32.50 | 32.50 |
| | *Nos. 2144-2160 (17)* | | 42.40 | 42.40 |

Issued: Nos. 2127-2128, 8/17; No. 2129, 8/18; Nos. 2130-2131, 8/22; Nos. 2132-2134, 8/23, Nos. 2135-2136, 8/24, Nos. 2137-2139, 8/26, No. 2140, 8/27; No. 2141, 8/28; No. 2142, 8/29; No. 2143, 8/30. Nos. 2144-2160 were to have been issued within days of the digitally printed stamps with the same design. The digitally printed stamps have almost illegible lettering above the Olympic rings at upper right, and fuzzy, indistinct details in the emblem above this lettering. These details are clearer and more readable on the lithographed stamps.

Nos. 2128 and 2145 were withdrawn from circulation after the athlete shown was stripped of his medal after failing a drug test.

2004 Paralympics, Athens — A698

Designs: 20c, Horses and riders. 49c, Handicapped runner. €2, Wheelchair basketball. €2.24, Archer in wheelchair.

**Perf. 13¼x13¾**
**2004, Sept. 22** — Litho.
2161-2164 A698 Set of 4 — 10.00 10.00

Island Views A699

**2004, Dec. 27** — Perf. 14x13¾

| | | | | |
|---|---|---|---|---|
| 2165 | A699 | 2c Santorini | .25 | .25 |
| 2166 | A699 | 3c Karpathos | .25 | .25 |
| 2167 | A699 | 5c Crete-Vai | .25 | .25 |
| 2168 | A699 | 10c Mykonos | .25 | .25 |
| 2169 | A699 | 49c Canea | 1.25 | 1.25 |
| 2170 | A699 | 50c Castellorizo | 1.25 | 1.25 |
| 2171 | A699 | €1 Astipalaia | 2.40 | 2.40 |
| 2172 | A699 | €2 Serifos | 5.00 | 5.00 |
| 2173 | A699 | €2.24 Melos | 5.50 | 5.50 |
| 2174 | A699 | €4 Skiathos | 9.75 | 9.75 |
| | *Nos. 2165-2174 (10)* | | 26.15 | 26.15 |

**Booklet Stamps**
**Perf. 13¼ Horiz.**

| | | | | |
|---|---|---|---|---|
| 2165A | A699 | 2c Santorini | .25 | .25 |
| 2166A | A699 | 3c Karpathos | .25 | .25 |
| 2167A | A699 | 5c Crete-Vai | .25 | .25 |
| 2168A | A699 | 10c Mykonos | .25 | .25 |
| 2169A | A699 | 49c Canea | 1.25 | 1.25 |
| 2170A | A699 | 50c Castellorizo | 1.25 | 1.25 |
| 2171A | A699 | €1 Astipalaia | 2.40 | 2.40 |
| 2172A | A699 | €2 Serifos | 5.00 | 5.00 |
| 2173A | A699 | €2.24 Melos | 5.50 | 5.50 |
| 2174A | A699 | €4 Skiathos | 9.75 | 9.75 |
| | *Nos. 2165A-2174A (10)* | | 26.15 | 26.15 |

Jewelry — A700

Designs: 1c, Necklace, 730 B.C. 15c, Snake-shaped bracelet, 2nd-3rd cent. B.C., vert. 30c, Necklace, 5th cent. 49c, Crown, 2nd cent. €4, Earring, 8th cent. B.C., vert.

**Perf. 13¾x13¼, 13¼x13¾**
**2005, Feb. 25**
2175-2179 A700 Set of 5 — 12.00 12.00

State Laboratory, 75th Anniv. A701

European Diabetes Association, 41st Meeting A702

European Society for Cardiovascular Surgery, 54th Congress A703

I. Kondilakis, First President of Athens Journalists Union A704

Year of Economic Competitiveness A705

**2005, Apr. 5** — Perf. 13¼x13, 13x13¼

| | | | | |
|---|---|---|---|---|
| 2180 | A701 | 1c multi | .25 | .25 |
| 2181 | A702 | 4c multi | .25 | .25 |
| 2182 | A703 | 5c multi | .25 | .25 |
| 2183 | A704 | 40c multi | 1.00 | 1.00 |
| 2184 | A705 | 49c multi | 1.25 | 1.25 |
| 2185 | A706 | €1.40 multi | 3.50 | 3.50 |
| 2186 | A707 | €3.50 multi | 8.50 | 8.50 |
| | *Nos. 2180-2186 (7)* | | 15.00 | 15.00 |

Greek Mastological Society, 25th Anniv. A706

Angel, by Alekos Kontopoulos A707

Flowers — A708

Designs: 20c, Gladiolus illyricus. 40c, Crocus sieberi. 49c, Narcissus tazetta. €1.40, Rhododendron luteum. €3, Tulipa boeotica.

**2005, Apr. 5** — Perf. 13¼x13¾
2187-2191 A708 Set of 5 — 13.00 13.00

Europa A709

**2005, May 19** — Perf. 14¼x13¾

| | | | | |
|---|---|---|---|---|
| 2192 | A709 | Horiz. pair | 7.50 | 7.50 |
| a. | | 65c Finished dish | 1.60 | 1.60 |
| b. | | €2.35 Ingredients | 5.75 | 5.75 |

**Booklet Stamps**
**Perf. 13¼ Vert.**

| | | | | |
|---|---|---|---|---|
| 2192C | A709 | Horiz. pair | 9.00 | 9.00 |
| e. | | 65c Finished dish | 2.00 | 2.00 |
| e. | | €2.35 Ingredients | 7.00 | 7.00 |
| f. | | Booklet pane, 2 #2192C | 18.00 | |
| | | Complete booklet, #2192f | 18.00 | — |

Wine Grapes — A710

Designs: 20c, Agiorgitiko grapes and grape pickers, Peloponnisos. 49c, Assyrtiko grapes, Santorini. 65c, Xinomavro grapes and coin, Macedonia. €2.24, Robolla grapes, Cephalonia. €2.40, Moschofilero, Peloponnisos.

**2005, May 19** — Perf. 13¾x14
2193-2197 A710 Set of 5 — 15.00 15.00

Blackboard A711

Girl Reading A712

Envelope A713

Stylized People A714

Grid — A715

Globe and Stylized Stamp — A716

Flowers A717

Church A718

**2005, July 15** — Perf. 14x13¾

| | | | | |
|---|---|---|---|---|
| 2198 | A711 | 49c multi | 1.25 | 1.25 |
| a. | | #2198 + label | 5.00 | 5.00 |
| 2199 | A712 | 49c multi | 1.25 | 1.25 |
| a. | | #2199 + label | 5.00 | 5.00 |
| 2200 | A713 | 49c multi | 1.25 | 1.25 |
| a. | | #2200 + label | 5.00 | 5.00 |
| 2201 | A714 | 49c multi | 1.25 | 1.25 |
| a. | | #2201 + label | 5.00 | 5.00 |
| 2202 | A715 | 49c multi | 1.25 | 1.25 |
| a. | | #2202 + label | 5.00 | 5.00 |
| 2203 | A716 | 49c multi | 1.25 | 1.25 |
| a. | | #2203 + label | 5.00 | 5.00 |
| 2204 | A717 | 49c multi | 1.25 | 1.25 |
| a. | | #2204 + label | 5.00 | 5.00 |
| 2205 | A718 | 65c multi | 1.25 | 1.25 |
| a. | | #2205 + label | 5.00 | 5.00 |
| | *Nos. 2198-2205 (8)* | | 10.00 | 10.00 |

Nos. 2198a, 2199a and 2200a were printed in sheets of 10 + 10 labels that sold for €10. Nos. 2201a, 2202a, 2203a and 2204a were printed in sheets of 15 + 15 labels that sold for €15. No. 2205a was printed in sheets of 10 + 10 labels that sold for €13. Labels could be personalized.

Drawing by Fokion Dimitriadis A719

Drawing by Archelaos A720

Drawing by Themos Anninos A721

Drawing by Dimitris Galanis A722

Drawing by Kostas Mitropoulos A723

Unattributed Odyssey Scene A724

**2005, Sept. 16**   **Perf. 13¼x13¾**

| | | | | |
|---|---|---|---|---|
| 2206 | A719 | 15c multi | .35 | .35 |
| 2207 | A720 | 20c multi | .50 | .50 |
| 2208 | A721 | 30c multi | .75 | .75 |
| 2209 | A722 | 50c multi | 1.25 | 1.25 |
| 2210 | A723 | 65c multi | 1.50 | 1.50 |
| 2211 | A724 | €4 multi | 9.75 | 9.75 |
| Nos. 2206-2211 (6) | | | 14.10 | 14.10 |

**Booklet Panes of 1**
**Self-Adhesive**

| | | | | |
|---|---|---|---|---|
| 2212 | A719 | 15c multi | .45 | .45 |
| 2213 | A720 | 20c multi | .60 | .60 |
| 2214 | A721 | 30c multi | .90 | .90 |
| 2215 | A722 | 50c multi | 1.50 | 1.50 |
| 2216 | A723 | 65c multi | 1.90 | 1.90 |
| 2217 | A724 | €4 multi | 12.00 | 12.00 |
| | Complete booklet, #2212-2217 | | 17.50 | |
| Nos. 2212-2217 (6) | | | 17.35 | 17.35 |

Greece, 2005 European Basketball Champions A725

Basketball, net and: 30c, Players in game. 50c, Championship bowl. 65c, Fans. €3.55, Players celebrating.

**2005, Oct. 7**   **Litho.**   **Perf. 13x13¼**

| | | | | |
|---|---|---|---|---|
| 2218-2221 | A725 | Set of 4 | 15.00 | 15.00 |
| 2221a | | Souvenir sheet, #2218-2221 | 15.00 | 15.00 |

Greece, 2005 European Basketball Champions — A725a

**2005, Oct. 7**   **Litho.**   **Perf. 14x13¾**

| | | | | |
|---|---|---|---|---|
| 2221B | A725a | 50c multi + label | 5.00 | 5.00 |

No. 2221B was printed in sheets of 10 + 10 labels that sold for €10. Labels could be personalized.

Automobiles A726

Designs: 1c, Mini Cooper. 30c, Fiat 500. 50c, Citroen 2CV. €2.25, Volkswagen Beetle. €2.85, Ford Model T.

**2005, Nov. 4**   **Perf. 13x13¼**

| | | | | |
|---|---|---|---|---|
| 2222-2226 | A726 | Set of 5 | 14.00 | 14.00 |
| 2226a | | As #2226, without inscription "Ford Model T" | 15.00 | 15.00 |
| 2226b | | Booklet pane, #2222-2225, 2226a | 20.00 | — |
| | | Complete booklet, #2226b | 20.00 | |

Panathinaikos Soccer Team Emblem A727

Panionios Soccer Team Emblem A728

Iraklis Soccer Team Emblem A729

PAOK Soccer Team Emblem A730

Panellinios Sports Club Emblem — A731

Designs: 30c, Ethnikos Sports Club emblem. €4, Omilos Ereton emblem.

**2005, Nov. 30**   **Litho.**   **Perf. 14x13¾**

| | | | | |
|---|---|---|---|---|
| 2227 | A727 | 30c multi | .75 | .75 |
| 2228 | A727 | 50c multi | 1.25 | 1.25 |
| a. | | #2228 + label | 5.00 | 5.00 |
| 2229 | A728 | 50c multi | 1.25 | 1.25 |
| a. | | #2229 + label | 5.00 | 5.00 |
| 2230 | A729 | 50c multi | 1.25 | 1.25 |
| a. | | #2230 + label | 5.00 | 5.00 |
| 2231 | A730 | 65c multi | 1.50 | 1.50 |
| a. | | #2231 + label | 5.00 | 5.00 |
| 2232 | A731 | 65c multi | 1.50 | 1.50 |
| a. | | #2232 + label | 5.00 | 5.00 |
| 2233 | A727 | €4 multi | 9.75 | 9.75 |
| Nos. 2227-2233 (7) | | | 17.25 | 17.25 |

Nos. 2228a, 2229a and 2230a were printed in sheets of 10 + 10 labels that sold for €10. Nos. 2231a and 2232a were printed in sheets of 10 + 10 labels that sold for €13. Labels could be personalized.

Christmas — A732

Icons: 1c, Hodeghetria Virgin. 20c, Kardiotissa Virgin. 70c, Glykophiloussa Virgin. €3.20, Virgin with Symbols of the Passion.

**Litho. With Foil Application**
**2005, Dec. 20**   **Perf. 13¾**

| | | | | |
|---|---|---|---|---|
| 2234-2237 | A732 | Set of 4 | 10.00 | 10.00 |

**Souvenir Sheet**

Europa Stamps, 50th Anniv. A733

**2006, Jan. 10**   **Litho.**   **Perf. 13x13¼**

| | | | | |
|---|---|---|---|---|
| 2238 | A733 | Sheet of 2 | 12.00 | 12.00 |
| a. | | €1.50 Greece #1255 | 4.50 | 4.50 |
| b. | | €2.50 Greece #1459 | 7.50 | 7.50 |

Patras, 2006 European Cultural Capital — A734

Designs: 1c, Drama masks. 15c, Buildings, sailboat, lighthouse. 20c, Child. 50c, Carnival dragon and clown. 65c, Emblem, vert. €2.25, Jars, containers and boxes. €2.30, Icon, vert.

**2006, Feb. 28**   **Perf. 13x13¼, 13¼x13**

| | | | | |
|---|---|---|---|---|
| 2239-2245 | A734 | Set of 7 | 15.00 | 15.00 |

Carnival Dragon and Clown — A734a

Emblem — A734b

**2006, Feb. 28**   **Litho.**   **Perf. 14x13¾**

| | | | | |
|---|---|---|---|---|
| 2245A | A734a | 50c multi + label | 5.00 | 5.00 |
| 2245B | A734b | 65c multi + label | 5.00 | 5.00 |

Patras, 2006 European Cultural Capital. Nos. 2245A and 2245B were issued in sheets of 10 stamps and 10 labels that could be personalized. Sheets of No. 2245A sold for €10; No. 2245B for €13.

Items in Greek Museums — A735

Designs: 5c, Kouros of Anavissos, sculpture, 530 B.C., Natl. Archaeological Museum. 20c, Seated figure, 2800-2300 B.C., Museum of Cycladic Art. 50c, Spiral (28x28mm). 65c, Pediment from Parthenon, Acropolis Museum, horiz. €1.40, Greco-Roman portrait of an Egyptian, 4th cent. €2.25, Concert of the Angels, by El Greco, Natl. Art Gallery, horiz.

**Litho with Foil Application, Litho. (50c)**
**2006, Apr. 7**   **Perf. 14x13¾, 13¾x14**

| | | | | |
|---|---|---|---|---|
| 2246-2251 | A735 | Set of 6 | 12.00 | 12.00 |
| 2248a | | #2248 + label | 5.00 | 5.00 |

No. 2248a was printed in sheets of 10 + 10 labels that sold for €10. Labels could be personalized.

Pediment From Parthenon — A735a

**2006, Apr. 7**   **Litho.**   **Perf. 14x13¾**

| | | | | |
|---|---|---|---|---|
| 2251A | A735a | 65c multi + label | 5.00 | 5.00 |

No. 2251A was printed in sheets of 10 + 10 labels that sold for €13. Labels could be personalized.

**Souvenir Sheets**

Stamps Issued for 1906 Interim Olympic Games A736

No. 2252: a, 20c, #187. b, 30c, #191. c, 50c, #188. d, €2, #192.
No. 2253: a, 50c, #189. b, 65c, #194. c, 85c, #197. d, €1, #190.

**2006, Apr. 7**   **Litho.**   **Perf. 13x13¼**
**Sheets of 4, #a-d**

| | | | | |
|---|---|---|---|---|
| 2252-2253 | A736 | Set of 2 | 18.00 | 18.00 |

Europa A737

**2006, May 15**   **Perf. 13¾x14¼**

| | | | | |
|---|---|---|---|---|
| 2254 | A737 | Horiz. pair | 9.00 | 9.00 |
| a. | | 65c Rope and moon | 1.50 | 1.50 |
| b. | | €3 Rope and sun | 7.25 | 7.25 |

**Booklet Stamps**
**Perf. 13¼ Vert.**

| | | | | |
|---|---|---|---|---|
| 2254C | A737 | Horiz. pair | 11.00 | 11.00 |
| d. | | 65c Rope and moon | 1.90 | 1.90 |
| e. | | €3 Rope and sun | 9.00 | 9.00 |
| f. | | Booklet pane, 2 #2254C | 22.50 | |
| | | Complete booklet, #2254f | 22.50 | |

State General Archives A738

Admission to European Union, 25th Anniv. A739

2006 Eurovision Song Contest, Athens A740

Olive and Olive Oil Year A741

Tinia, Etruscan Sky God A742

Greek Participation in 2005-06 UN Security Council A743

**2006, May 15**   **Perf. 14x13¾**

| | | | | |
|---|---|---|---|---|
| 2255 | A738 | 15c multi | .35 | .35 |
| 2256 | A739 | 20c multi | .50 | .50 |
| 2257 | A740 | 50c multi | 1.25 | 1.25 |
| a. | | #2257 + label | 5.00 | 5.00 |
| 2258 | A741 | 65c multi | 1.50 | 1.50 |
| a. | | #2258 + label | 5.00 | 5.00 |
| 2259 | A742 | €1.40 multi | 3.50 | 3.50 |
| 2260 | A743 | €3 multi | 7.25 | 7.25 |
| Nos. 2255-2260 (6) | | | 14.35 | 14.35 |

No. 2257a was printed in sheets of 10 + 10 labels that sold for €10. No. 2258a was printed in sheets of 10 + 10 labels that sold for €13. Labels could be personalized.

Island Views — A744

**2006, June 16**   **Litho.**   **Perf. 14¼x14**

| | | | | |
|---|---|---|---|---|
| 2261 | A744 | 1c Lesbos | .25 | .25 |
| 2262 | A744 | 3c Hydra | .25 | .25 |
| 2263 | A744 | 10c Sifnos | .25 | .25 |
| 2264 | A744 | 20c Levkas | .50 | .50 |
| 2265 | A744 | 40c Samothrace | 1.00 | 1.00 |
| 2266 | A744 | 50c Syros | 1.25 | 1.25 |
| 2267 | A744 | 65c Rhodes | 1.50 | 1.50 |
| 2268 | A744 | 85c Cephalonia | 2.00 | 2.00 |
| 2269 | A744 | €2.25 Corfu | 5.50 | 5.50 |
| 2270 | A744 | €5 Naxos | 12.00 | 12.00 |
| Nos. 2261-2270 (10) | | | 24.50 | 24.50 |

**Booklet Stamps**
**Perf. 13¼ Vert.**

| | | | | |
|---|---|---|---|---|
| 2261A | A744 | 1c Lesbos | .25 | .25 |
| 2262A | A744 | 3c Hydra | .25 | .25 |
| 2263A | A744 | 10c Sifnos | .25 | .25 |
| 2264A | A744 | 20c Levkas | .50 | .50 |
| 2265A | A744 | 40c Samothrace | 1.00 | 1.00 |
| 2266A | A744 | 50c Syros | 1.25 | 1.25 |
| 2267A | A744 | 65c Rhodes | 1.50 | 1.50 |
| 2268A | A744 | 85c Cephalonia | 2.00 | 2.00 |

| | | | |
|---|---|---|---|
| 2269A | A744 | €2.25 Corfu | 5.50 5.50 |
| 2270A | A744 | €5 Naxos | 12.00 12.00 |
| | *Nos. 2261A-2270A (10)* | | 24.50 24.50 |

Syros — A744a

Rhodes — A744b

**2006, June 16   Litho.   Perf. 14x13¾**

| | | | |
|---|---|---|---|
| 2270B | A744a | 50c multi + label | 4.00 4.00 |
| 2270C | A744b | 65c multi + label | 5.00 5.00 |

No. 2270B was printed in sheets of 10 + 10 labels that sold for €10. No. 2270C was printed in sheets of 10 + 10 labels that sold for €13. Labels could be personalized.

Ancient Greek Technology A745

Designs: 3c, Trireme "Olympias." 5c, Odometer, by Hero of Alexandria. 50c, Piston water pump, vert. 65c, Antikythera Mechanism, vert. €3.80, Automatic temple gates, by Hero of Alexandria, vert.

**Litho. With Foil Application**
**Perf. 13¾x13¼, 13¼x13¾**
**2006, Sept. 14**

| | | | |
|---|---|---|---|
| 2271-2275 | A745 | Set of 5 | 12.00 12.00 |

**Souvenir Sheet**

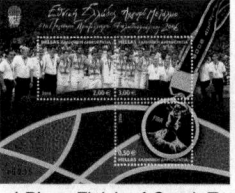

Second Place Finish of Greek Team at 2006 World Basketball Championships — A746

**Litho. With Foil Application**
**2006, Oct. 16                Perf. 13¼**

| | | | |
|---|---|---|---|
| 2276 | A746 | Sheet of 3 | 14.00 14.00 |
| a. | | 50c Silver medal | 1.25 1.25 |
| b. | | €2 Team | 4.75 4.75 |
| c. | | €3 Team, medal ribbon | 7.25 7.25 |

Silver Medal of 2006 Greek Team at World Basketball Championships — A746a

**2006, Oct. 16   Litho.   Perf. 14x13¾**

| | | | |
|---|---|---|---|
| 2276D | A746a | 50c multi + label | 5.00 5.00 |

No. 2276D was printed in sheets of 5 + 5 labels that could not be personalized.

Soccer Team Emblems — A747

Designs: 2c, Apollon Kalamaria. 3c, Atromitos Athinon. 52c, Aris Thessaloniki. €2.27, Ethnikos Piraeus. €3.20, Apollon Smyrnis.

**2006, Nov. 29   Litho.   Perf. 14x13¾**

| | | | |
|---|---|---|---|
| 2277-2281 | A747 | Set of 5 | 15.00 15.00 |
| 2279a | | #2279 + label | 4.00 4.00 |

No. 2279a was printed in sheets of 10 + 10 labels that sold for €10. Labels could be personalized.

Items in Toys, Games and Childhood Section of Benaki Museum — A748

Designs: 5c, Doll, chest and clothing from France, c. 1905. 15c, Wooden airplanes, c. 1940. 30c, Dolls made by Skonouchi Karopoulos, c. 1925. 40c, Horses on wheels made by Anestis Romeopoulos, c. 1920. 52c, Dominos, toy cat, duck on wheels. 72c, Parachutist, c. 1950, vert. €2.27, Airplane carousel, 1950s, vert. €4, Puppet theater of the Resistance, 1941-45, vert.

**Perf. 13¾x13¼, 13¼x13¾**
**2006, Dec. 22**

| | | | |
|---|---|---|---|
| 2282-2289 | A748 | Set of 8 | 20.00 20.00 |

Faces — A749

Globe — A750

Crescents A751

Artemis A752

Ring Around Earth A753

Parthenon A754

Phrasikleia Kore — A755

**2007, Mar. 12   Litho.   Perf. 14x13¾**

| | | | |
|---|---|---|---|
| 2290 | A749 | 52c multi | 1.15 1.15 |
| a. | | #2290 + label | 4.00 4.00 |
| 2291 | A750 | 52c multi | 1.10 1.15 |
| a. | | #2291 + label | 4.00 4.00 |
| 2292 | A751 | 52c multi | 1.10 1.15 |
| a. | | #2292 + label | 4.00 4.00 |
| 2293 | A752 | 52c multi | 1.10 1.15 |
| a. | | #2293 + label | 4.00 4.00 |
| 2294 | A753 | 52c multi | 1.10 1.15 |
| a. | | #2294 + label | 4.00 4.00 |
| 2295 | A754 | 65c multi | 1.40 1.40 |
| a. | | #2295 + label | 5.00 5.00 |
| 2296 | A755 | 65c multi | 1.40 1.40 |
| a. | | Miniature sheet, #2290-2296 | 8.50 8.50 |
| b. | | #2296 + label | 5.00 5.00 |
| | *Nos. 2290-2296 (7)* | | 8.35 8.55 |

Nos. 2290a, 2292a amd 2293a were printed in sheets of 10 + 10 labels that sold for €10. Nos. 2291a and 2294a were printed in sheets of 15 + 15 labels that sold for €15. Nos. 2295a and 2296b were printed in sheets of 10 + 10 labels that sold for € 13. Labels could be personalized.

Kostis Palamas (1859-1943), Poet — A756

Greek Cultural Year in China — A757

Symposium of Seven Cardiovascular Surgeons, Athens and Delphi A758

2nd Union Network International World Postal Conference A759

Treaty of Rome, 50th Anniv. A760

Georgios Kotzias (1918-77) A761

Rigas Velestinlis (1757-98), Poet A762

Year of Innovation A763

State Legal Council, 125th Anniv. — A764

**Perf. 13¼x13¾, 13¾x13¼**
**2007, Apr. 25**

| | | | |
|---|---|---|---|
| 2297 | A756 | 2c multi | .25 .25 |
| 2298 | A757 | 10c multi | .25 .25 |
| 2299 | A758 | 20c multi | .45 .45 |
| 2300 | A759 | 52c multi | 1.10 1.10 |
| 2301 | A760 | 65c multi | 1.40 1.40 |
| 2302 | A761 | 85c multi | 1.90 1.90 |
| 2303 | A762 | €1 multi | 2.25 2.25 |
| 2304 | A763 | €2.27 multi | 5.00 5.00 |
| 2305 | A764 | €3 multi | 6.75 6.75 |
| | *Nos. 2297-2305 (9)* | | 19.35 19.35 |

Europa A765

No. 2306: a, Scouting fleur-de-lis, dove's tail. b, Scouts, dove's head.

**2007, May 25                Perf. 14¼x14**

| | | | |
|---|---|---|---|
| 2306 | A765 | Horiz. pair | 8.75 8.75 |
| a. | | 65c multi | 1.40 1.40 |
| b. | | €3.15 multi | 7.00 7.00 |

**Booklet Stamps**
**Perf. 13¾ Vert.**

| | | | |
|---|---|---|---|
| 2306C | A765 | Horiz. pair | 8.75 8.75 |
| d. | | 65c multi | 1.40 1.40 |
| e. | | €3.15 multi | 7.00 7.00 |
| f. | | Booklet pane, 2 #2306C | 18.00 — |
| | | Complete booklet, #2306f | 18.00 |

Scouting, cent.

Signs of the Zodiac — A766

**Litho. With Foil Application**
**Perf. 13¾x13¼, 13¼x13¾**
**2007, May 25**

| | | | |
|---|---|---|---|
| 2307 | A766 | 2c Scorpio | .25 .25 |
| 2308 | A766 | 3c Cancer | .25 .25 |
| 2309 | A766 | 5c Capricorn | .25 .25 |
| 2310 | A766 | 10c Taurus | .30 .30 |

| | | | |
|---|---|---|---|
| 2311 | A766 | 20c Sagittarius, vert. | .55 .55 |
| 2312 | A766 | 40c Leo, vert. | 1.10 1.10 |
| 2313 | A766 | 52c Virgo, vert. | 1.40 1.40 |
| 2314 | A766 | 65c Aries | 1.75 1.75 |
| 2315 | A766 | 85c Aquarius | 2.40 2.40 |
| 2316 | A766 | €1 Libra | 2.75 2.75 |
| 2317 | A766 | €2.27 Pisces | 6.25 6.25 |
| 2318 | A766 | €2.80 Gemini | 7.50 7.50 |
| | *Nos. 2307-2318 (12)* | | 24.75 24.75 |

**Souvenir Sheet**

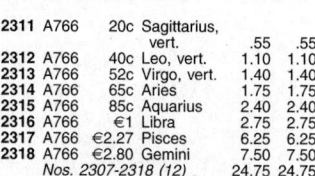

Statues of Asclepius, Greek God of Medicine — A767

No. 2319: a, Statue from Museum of Ampurias, Spain. b, Statue from National Archaeological Museum, Athens.

**2007, June 28   Litho.   Perf. 13¾**

| | | | |
|---|---|---|---|
| 2319 | A767 | Sheet of 2 | 13.00 13.00 |
| a.-b. | | €2.50 Either single | 6.50 6.50 |

See Spain No. 3521.

Discovery of the Tomb of St. Cyril, 150th Anniv. — A768

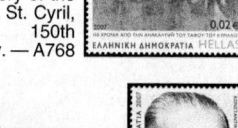

University of Macedonia, 50th Anniv. A769

Konstantinos Tsatsos (1899-1987), Politician A770

**Litho. With Foil Application**
**2007, Sept. 28              Perf. 13¾x14**

| | | | |
|---|---|---|---|
| 2320 | A768 | 2c multi | .25 .25 |

**Litho.**

| | | | |
|---|---|---|---|
| 2321 | A769 | 3c multi | .25 .25 |

**Perf. 14x13¾**

| | | | |
|---|---|---|---|
| 2322 | A770 | €4 multi | 9.25 9.25 |
| | *Nos. 2320-2322 (3)* | | 9.75 9.75 |

Sports Team Emblems — A771

Designs: 2c, Ergotelis Sports Club. 4c, OFI. 54c, Olympiacos C.F.P. €2.29, Doxa Dramas Sports Club. €5, Nautical Club of Mytilini.

**2007, Nov. 2   Litho.   Perf. 14x13¾**

| | | | |
|---|---|---|---|
| 2323-2327 | A771 | Set of 5 | 18.50 18.50 |
| 2325a | | #2325 + label | 5.00 5.00 |

No. 2325a was printed in sheets of 10 + 10 labels that sold for €10. Labels could be personalized.

Busts of Goddesses — A772

Designs: 54c, Bust of Aphrodite. €2.40, Bust of Goddess Anahit, Armenia.

**2007, Dec. 14                Perf. 14x14¼**

| | | | |
|---|---|---|---|
| 2328-2329 | A772 | Set of 2 | 7.25 7.25 |

See Armenia Nos. 774-775.

Islands — A773

**2008, Feb. 27  Litho.  Perf. 14¼x14**

| | | | | |
|---|---|---|---|---|
| 2330 | A773 | 2c Chios | .25 | .25 |
| 2331 | A773 | 5c Amorgos | .25 | .25 |
| 2332 | A773 | 10c Nísiros | .25 | .25 |
| 2333 | A773 | 20c Paxos | .50 | .50 |
| 2334 | A773 | 40c Leros | 1.00 | 1.00 |
| 2335 | A773 | 54c Kalymnos | 1.40 | 1.40 |
| 2336 | A773 | 67c Kos | 1.75 | 1.75 |
| 2337 | A773 | €1 Simi | 2.40 | 2.40 |
| 2338 | A773 | €2.29 Zákinthos | 5.75 | 5.75 |
| 2339 | A773 | €4 Inousses | 10.00 | 10.00 |
| | | Nos. 2330-2339 (10) | 23.55 | 23.55 |

**Booklet Stamps**
**Perf. 13¼ Vert.**

| | | | | |
|---|---|---|---|---|
| 2330A | A773 | 2c Chios | .25 | .25 |
| 2331A | A773 | 5c Amorgos | .25 | .25 |
| 2332A | A773 | 10c Nísiros | .25 | .25 |
| 2333A | A773 | 20c Paxos | .50 | .50 |
| 2334A | A773 | 40c Leros | 1.00 | 1.00 |
| 2335A | A773 | 54c Kalymnos | 1.40 | 1.40 |
| 2336A | A773 | 67c Kos | 1.75 | 1.75 |
| 2337A | A773 | €1 Simi | 2.40 | 2.40 |
| 2338A | A773 | €2.29 Zákinthos | 5.75 | 5.75 |
| 2339A | A773 | €4 Inousses | 10.00 | 10.00 |
| | | Nos. 2330A-2339A (10) | 23.55 | 23.55 |

2008 Summer Olympics, Beijing — A774

Designs: 3c, Discus thrower. 35c, Lighting of Olympic flame. No. 2342, 67c, Torch bearer. No. 2343, 67c, Three cyclists, horiz.

**2008, Mar. 14  Perf. 13½x13, 13x13½**

| | | | | |
|---|---|---|---|---|
| 2340-2343 | A774 | Set of 4 | 4.50 | 4.50 |

Letter A775

Numbers A776

Heart — A777

Kites — A778

Pillar — A779

Greek Flag — A780

**2008, Apr. 21  Litho.  Perf. 14x13¾**

| | | | | |
|---|---|---|---|---|
| 2344 | A775 | 54c multi | 1.75 | 1.75 |
| a. | | #2344 + label | 4.75 | 4.75 |
| 2345 | A776 | 54c multi | 1.75 | 1.75 |
| a. | | #2345 + label | 4.75 | 4.75 |
| 2346 | A777 | 54c multi | 1.75 | 1.75 |
| a. | | #2346 + label | 4.75 | 4.75 |
| 2347 | A778 | 54c multi | 1.75 | 1.75 |
| a. | | #2347 + label | 4.75 | 4.75 |
| 2348 | A779 | 67c multi | 2.10 | 2.10 |
| a. | | #2348 + label | 5.75 | 5.75 |
| 2349 | A780 | 67c multi | 2.10 | 2.10 |
| a. | | Miniature sheet, #2344-2349 | 11.50 | 11.50 |
| b. | | #2349 + label | 5.75 | 5.75 |
| | | Nos. 2344-2349 (6) | 11.20 | 11.20 |

Nos. 2344a, 2345a, 2346a and 2347a each were printed in sheets of 10 + 15 labels that sold for €10. Nos. 2348a and 2348b each were printed in sheets of 10 + 15 labels that sold for €13. Labels could be personalized.

Europa A781

No. 2350: a, Inkwell, pen and papers. b, Fountain pen and papers.

**2008, May 26  Perf. 14¼x14**

| | | | | |
|---|---|---|---|---|
| 2350 | A781 | Horiz. pair | 10.00 | 10.00 |
| a. | | 67c multi | 1.90 | 1.90 |
| b. | | €3.17 multi | 8.00 | 8.00 |

**Booklet Stamps**
**Perf. 13¾ Vert.**

| | | | | |
|---|---|---|---|---|
| 2350C | A781 | Horiz. pair | 10.00 | 10.00 |
| d. | | 67c multi | 1.90 | 1.90 |
| e. | | €3.17 multi | 8.00 | 8.00 |
| f. | | Booklet pane, 2 #2350C | 20.00 | |
| | | Complete booklet, #2350f | 20.00 | |

Anniversaries — A782

Curved lines and: 3c, Emblem of Hellenic Post. 5c, Posthorn, Greek men. 10c, Ioannis Kapodistrias (1776-1831), provisional president of Greece. 57c, M. Karagatsis (1908-60), writer. 70c, Fish. €1.85, Emblem of National Hellenic Research Foundation. €3, Emblem of National Council of Women.

**2008, June 20  Perf. 13¼x13¾**

| | | | | |
|---|---|---|---|---|
| 2351-2357 | A782 | Set of 7 | 17.00 | 17.00 |

Hellenic Post, 180th anniv. (Nos. 2351-2352); Inauguration of Kapodistrias, 180th anniv. (No. 2353); Intl. Year of Planet Earth (No. 2355); National Hellenic Research Foundation, 50th anniv. (No. 2356), National Council of Women, cent. (No. 2357).

Greek Products — A783

Designs: 3c, Feta cheese and tomatoes. 5c, Mastic. 20c, Olive, bottle of olive oil, horiz. 57c, Bottle of ouzo, marine life and boat. €1, Pistachio nuts. €4, Bees, rose, jar of honey.

**Perf. 13¼x13¾, 13¾x13¼**
**2008, Sept. 19**

| | | | | |
|---|---|---|---|---|
| 2358-2363 | A783 | Set of 6 | 14.00 | 14.00 |

Sports Team Emblems — A784

Designs: 40c, Diagoras Rhodos Sports Club. 57c, A.E.K. soccer team. 70c, Asteras Tripolis soccer team. €2, Panserraoikos soccer team. €3, Kerkiraikos Sports Club.

**2008, Oct. 20  Perf. 14x13¾**

| | | | | |
|---|---|---|---|---|
| 2364-2368 | A784 | Set of 5 | 15.00 | 15.00 |
| 2365a | | #2365 + label | 5.00 | 5.00 |
| 2366a | | #2366 + label | 5.00 | 5.00 |

Nos. 2365a and 2366a each were printed in sheets of 10 + 10 labels that sold for €13. Labels could be personalized.

Fairy Tales, Fables and Children's Literature A785

Designs: 10c, The Mermaid and Alexander the Great. 57c, Little Red Riding Hood. €1, The Fairies. €1.85, The Little Match Girl. €3, Arion and the Lyre.

**2008, Dec. 16  Perf. 13¾x14**

| | | | | |
|---|---|---|---|---|
| 2369-2373 | A785 | Set of 5 | 18.00 | 18.00 |

Actors and Actresses — A786

Designs: 1c, Manos Katrakis (1908-84). 20c, Dinos Iliopoulos (1915-2001). 35c, Elli Lambeti (1926-83). 40c, Alekos Alexandrakis (1928-2005). 50c, Aliki Vougioklaki (1934-96). 57c, Jenny Karezi (1932-92). €1, Dimitris Horn (1921-98). €2.42, Nikos Kourkoulos (1934-2007). €3.50, Thanos Kotsopoulos (1911-94).

**2009, Feb. 9  Litho.  Perf. 13¾x13¼**

| | | | | |
|---|---|---|---|---|
| 2374-2382 | A786 | Set of 9 | 23.00 | 23.00 |
| 2382a | | Miniature sheet of 9, #2374-2382 | 23.00 | 23.00 |

Compare with type A828.

Souvenir Sheet

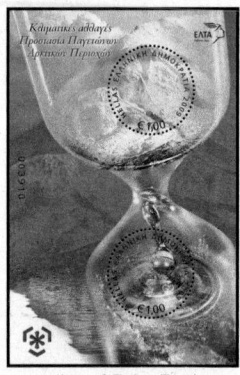

Preservation of Polar Regions and Glaciers — A787

No. 2383: a, Snow-covered mountain. b, Droplet of water.

**2009, Mar. 3  Perf.**

| | | | | |
|---|---|---|---|---|
| 2383 | A787 | €1 Sheet of 2, #a-b | 5.75 | 5.75 |

No. 2383 contains two 30mm diameter stamps.

Sivitanidios School, 80th Anniv. A788

University of Piraeus, 70th Anniv. A789

Natl. Archaeological Museum, 180th Anniv. — A790

Greek Presidency of UPU Postal Operations Council — A791

 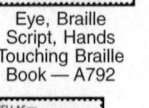

Eye, Braille Script, Hands Touching Braille Book — A792

Introduction of Euro, 10th Anniv. — A793

Lord Byron (1788-1824), Poet — A794

Natl. Real Estate Registry — A795

**Litho., Litho. With Foil Application (10c, 50c), Litho. & Embossed (57c)**
**Perf. 13¾x13¼, 13¼x13¾**
**2009, Mar. 30**

| | | | | |
|---|---|---|---|---|
| 2384 | A788 | 5c multi | .25 | .25 |
| 2385 | A789 | 10c multi | .30 | .30 |
| 2386 | A790 | 20c multi | .60 | .60 |
| 2387 | A791 | 50c multi | 1.50 | 1.50 |
| 2388 | A792 | 57c multi | 1.75 | 1.75 |
| 2389 | A793 | 70c multi | 2.10 | 2.10 |
| 2390 | A794 | €2.42 multi | 7.25 | 7.25 |
| 2391 | A795 | €3 multi | 9.00 | 9.00 |
| | | Nos. 2384-2391 (8) | 22.75 | 22.75 |

Louis Braille (1809-52), educator of the blind (No. 2388), Hellenophile and Intl. Solidarity Day (No. 2390).

Europa A796

No. 2392: a, Pulsar diagram. b, Aristarchos Telescope.

**2009, May 11  Litho.  Perf. 14¾x14**

| | | | | |
|---|---|---|---|---|
| 2392 | A796 | Horiz. pair | 11.00 | 11.00 |
| a. | | 70c multi | 2.00 | 2.00 |
| b. | | €3.20 multi | 9.00 | 9.00 |

**Booklet Stamps**
**Perf. 13¾ Vert.**

| | | | | |
|---|---|---|---|---|
| 2392C | A796 | Horiz. pair | 11.00 | 11.00 |
| d. | | 70c multi | 2.00 | 2.00 |
| e. | | €3.20 multi | 9.00 | 9.00 |
| f. | | Booklet pane, 2 #2392C | 22.00 | |
| | | Complete booklet, #2392f | 22.00 | |

Intl. Year of Astronomy.

UNESCO World Heritage Sites — A797

Designs: No. 2393, 57c, Acropolis (denomination at LL). No. 2394, 57c, Meteora (denomination at UR). No. 2395, 70c, Delphi (denomination at UR). No. 2396, 70c, Mycenae (denomination at LL). €2, Mystras. €3, Delos.

**Litho. With Foil Application**
**2009, June 20  Perf. 13¾x14**

| | | | | |
|---|---|---|---|---|
| 2393-2398 | A797 | Set of 6 | 21.00 | 21.00 |
| 2398a | | Miniature sheet of 6, #2393-2398 | 21.00 | 21.00 |

Acropolis A797a

Meteora A797b

Delphi — A797c

Mycenae — A797d

**2009, June 20  Litho.  Perf. 14x13¾**

| | | | | |
|---|---|---|---|---|
| 2398B | A797a | 57c multi + label | 5.00 | 5.00 |
| 2398C | A797b | 57c multi + label | 5.00 | 5.00 |
| 2398D | A797c | 70c multi + label | 5.50 | 5.50 |
| 2398E | A797d | 70c multi + label | 5.50 | 5.50 |
| | | Nos. 2398B-2398E (4) | 21.00 | 21.00 |

Nos. 2398B and 2398C each were printed in sheets of 10 + 10 labels that sold for €10. Nos, 2398D and 2398E each were printed in sheets of 10 + 10 labels that sold for €13. Labels could be personalized.

Lighthouses — A798

Designs: 1c, Didimi Islet Lighthouse. 57c, Tourlitis Lighthouse. 70c, Chania Lighthouse. €1, Korakas Paros Lighthouse, horiz. €4.20, Strongyli Lighthouse, horiz.

**Litho. With Foil Application**
*Perf. 13¼x13¾, 13¾x13¼*
**2009, Aug. 21**
2399-2403  A798  Set of 5  19.00 19.00
2403a  Souvenir sheet, #2399-2403  19.00 19.00

Greek Mythology A799

Designs: 1c, Theseus against the Minotaur. 5c, Heracles and Triton. 57c, Odysseus and the Sirens, vert. 70c, Talos and the Dioskuroi. €5, Vellerofontis riding Pegasus, vert.

*Perf. 13¾x14, 14x13¾*
**2009, Oct. 20**  Litho.
2404-2408  A799  Set of 5  19.00 19.00

Convention on Rights of the Child, 20th Anniv. — A800

Designs: 20c, Hands of adult and child. 58c, Child standing against wall, horiz. 72c, Clasped hands of children, horiz. €1, Child looking through barred window. €4, Child in darkness.

*Perf. 13¼x13, 13x13¼*
**2009, Dec. 7**  Litho.
2409-2413  A800  Set of 5  19.00 19.00

**Souvenir Sheets**

Medals For Greek National Basketball Teams — A801

Designs: No. 2414, €2, Gold medal for men's under-20 team at 2009 European Basketball Championships. No. 2415, €2, Silver medal for men's under-19 team at 2009 World Basketball Championships. No. 2416, €2, Bronze medal for men's team at 2009 European Basketball Championships.

**Litho. & Embossed With Foil Application**
**2009, Dec. 15**  *Perf. 13x13¼*
2414-2416  A801  Set of 3  17.50 17.50

20th Century Paintings by Greeks — A802

Designs: 1c, Stuffed Head, by Giannis Gaitis. 5c, Orpheus, Hermes and Eurydice, by Nikos Engonopoulos. 50c, Erotic, by Yannis Moralis. 58c, Sailor Sitting at the Table, Pink Background, by Yannis Tsarouchis. €2.43, Wattle Fences, by Nikos Hadjikyriakos-Ghika. €3, The Drawing, by Diamantis Diamantopoulos.

**2010, Feb. 11**  Litho.  *Perf. 14x13¾*
2417-2422  A802  Set of 6  18.00 18.00
2422a  Sheet of 6, #2417-2422  18.00 18.00

Renewable Energy Development — A803

Designs: 1c, Solar energy. 40c, Water energy. 58c, Wind energy, horiz. 72c, Self-contained man. €2.43, Wave energy. €2.50, Bioenergy.

*Perf. 13¼x13¾, 13¾x13¼*
**2010, Apr. 26**
2423-2428  A803  Set of 6  18.00 18.00

Europa A804

No. 2429: a, Boy in balloon, Puss in Boots. b, Girl on books.

**2008, May 26**  Litho.  *Perf. 14¼x14*
2429  A804  Horiz. pair  9.50 9.50
a.  72c multi  1.75 1.75
b.  €3.22 multi  7.75 7.75

**Booklet Stamps**
*Perf. 13¾ Vert.*
2429C  A804  Horiz. pair  9.50 9.50
d.  72c multi  1.75 1.75
e.  €3.22 multi  7.75 7.75
f.  Booklet pane, 2 #2429C  19.00 —
Complete booklet, #2429f  19.00

New Acropolis Museum — A805

Designs: 5c, Peplos kore. 58c, Parthenon gallery, horiz. 72c, Fragment of Parthenon frieze, horiz. €1, Entrance to new museum, horiz. €4, Marble sculpture of dog, horiz.

*Perf. 13¼x13¾, 13¾x13¼*
**2010, June 21**  Litho.
2430-2434  A805  Set of 5  16.00 16.00
2434a  Souvenir sheet, #2430-2434  16.00 16.00

Parthenon Gallery — A805a

Fragment of Parthenon Frieze — A805b

**2010, June 21  Litho.**  *Perf. 14x13¾*
2435  A805a  58c multi + label  5.00 5.00
2436  A805b  72c multi + label  5.00 5.00

Nos. 2435-2436 each were printed in sheets of 10 stamps + 10 labels that could be personalized. The sheet containing No. 2435 sold for €10, and that of No. 2436 sold for €13.

Battle of Marathon, 2500th Anniv. — A806

Designs: 50c, Athenian and Persian fighting. 58c, Phalanx marching into battle. 72c, Battle scene. €3, Bronze Corinthian helmet.

**Litho. With Foil Application**
**2010, June 23**  *Perf. 13¾x14*
2437-2440  A806  Set of 4  12.50 12.50

Popular Musicians — A807

Designs: 10c, Vasilis Tsitsanis (1915-84). 20c, Giorgos Zampetas (1925-92). 58c, Stelios Kazantzidis (1931-2001). 72c, Grigoris Bithikotsis (1922-2005). €1, Vicky Moscholiou (1945-2005). €4.80, Sotiria Bellou (1921-97).

*Perf. 13¾x13¼*
**2010, Sept. 16**  Litho.
2441-2446  A807  Set of 6  21.00 21.00
2446a  Souvenir sheet, #2441-2446  21.00 21.00

Paper Boat A808

Spiral Staircase A809

**2010, Oct. 14**  *Perf. 14x13¾*
2447  A808  (58c) multi  1.75 1.75
2448  A809  (72c) multi  2.10 2.10

**Booklet Stamps**
*Perf. 12¾ Vert.*
2447A  A808  (58c) multi  1.75 1.75
2448A  A809  (72c) multi  2.10 2.10

Islands — A810

**2010, Oct. 14**  *Perf. 14¼x14*
2449  A810  2c Limnos  .25 .25
2450  A810  5c Paros  .25 .25
2451  A810  20c Ithaki  .60 .60
2452  A810  40c Tinos  1.25 1.25
2453  A810  50c Skyros  1.40 1.40
2454  A810  €1 Evia-Chalkida  3.00 3.00
2455  A810  €2 Samos  5.75 5.75
2456  A810  €4 Kassos  11.50 11.50
Nos. 2449-2456 (8)  23.90 23.90

**Booklet Stamps**
*Perf. 12¾ Vert.*
2449A  A810  2c Limnos  .25 .25
2450A  A810  5c Paros  .25 .25
2451A  A810  20c Ithaki  .60 .60
2452A  A810  40c Tinos  1.25 1.25
2453A  A810  50c Skyros  1.40 1.40
2454A  A810  €1 Evia-Chalkida  3.00 3.00
2455A  A810  €2 Samos  5.75 5.75
2456A  A810  €4 Kassos  11.50 11.50
Nos. 2449A-2456A (8)  24.00 24.00

Buildings A811

Designs: 20c, Municipal Theater of Piraeus. 58c, Benaki Museum. €2.43, National Theater. €2.50, National Gallery of Nafplio.

**Litho. With Foil Application**
**2010, Nov. 16**  *Perf. 13¾x14*
2457-2460  A811  Set of 4  15.50 15.50

Christmas A812

Designs: 50c, Doves, holly leaves, stars. 58c, Angel with horn. €1, Ship with Christmas decorations. €3.50, Christmas tree, birds, holly leaves.

**2010, Dec. 10**  Litho.  *Perf. 13¾x14*
2461-2464  A812  Set of 4  15.00 15.00

**Self-Adhesive**
**Miniature Sheet**
*Die Cut Perf. 13¼*
2465  Sheet of 4  15.00
a.  A812 50c multi  1.40 1.40
b.  A812 58c multi  1.60 1.60
c.  A812 €1 multi  2.75 2.75
d.  A812 €3.50 multi  9.25 9.25

20th Century Greek Engraving and Wood-Cut Prints — A813

Designs: 3c, Aigaion V, by Kostas Grammatopoulos (1916-2003). 30c, To Pagoni, by Giannis Kefallinos (1894-1957), horiz. 60c, Maria, by A. Tassos (1914-85). €1, Plastikes Rimes, by Dimitris Galanis (1879-1966), horiz. €4, Mikros Kavalaris, by Vasso Katraki (1914-88).

**Litho. with Foil Application**
**2011, Jan. 20**  *Perf. 14x13¾, 13¾x14*
2466-2470  A813  Set of 5  16.50 16.50

European Year of Volunteers — A814

Academy of Athens, 85th Anniv. — A815

Alexandros Papadiamantis (1851-1911), Writer — A816

Battle of Crete, 70th Anniv. — A817

Organization for Economic Cooperation and Development, 50th Anniv. A818

Spyros Samaras (1861-1917), Composer A819

*Perf. 13¾x14, 14x13¾*
**2011, Feb. 23**  Litho.
2471  A814  3c multi  .25 .25
2472  A815  10c multi  .30 .30
2473  A816  20c multi  .55 .55
2474  A817  60c multi  1.75 1.75
2475  A818  €1.50 multi  4.25 4.25
2476  A819  €3 multi  8.50 8.50
Nos. 2471-2476 (6)  15.60 15.60

A820

## 2011 Special Olympics, Athens — A821

Special Olympics emblem and: 2c, Heart, stylized people, emblem of 2011 Athens Special Olympics. 4c, Stylized person, buildings, emblem of 2011 Athens Special Olympics. No. 2479, 60c, Emblem of 2011 Athens Special Olympics, vert. 75c, Sun, emblem of 2011 Athens Special Olympics, vert. €4.20, Emblem of 2011 Athens Special Olympics.
No. 2482, Emblems of Special Olympics and 2011 Athens Special Olympics.

**2011, Mar. 18** *Perf. 13¾x14, 14x13¾*
| | | |
|---|---|---|
| 2477-2481 A820 | Set of 5 | 16.50 16.50 |

**Booklet Stamp**
*Perf. 14x13¾*
| | | |
|---|---|---|
| 2482 A821 60c multi + label | | 2.00 2.00 |
| a. | Booklet pane of 1 + label | 2.00 — |
| | Complete booklet, 24 #2484a | 52.50 |

Complete booklet sold for €18. Each booklet pane in booklet has a label with a different image.

## Ancient Greek Ships — A822

Designs: 1c, Ship from a Thera wall painting, 1500 B.C. 20c, Polyreme, 4th-2nd cent. B.C., horiz. 60c, Triaconter, 15th-4th cent. B.C., horiz. 75c, Hellenic trireme, 7th-4th cent. B.C., horiz. €2.47, Macedonian hexareme, 4th-3rd cent. B.C., horiz. €2.50, Byzantine dromond, 5th-11th cent. A.D.

**Litho. With Foil Application**
**2011, Apr. 18** *Perf. 13¾*
| | | |
|---|---|---|
| 2483-2488 A822 | Set of 6 | 19.00 19.00 |
| 2488a | Souvenir sheet of 6, #2483-2488 | 19.00 19.00 |

## Europa A823

No. 2489 — Leaves and: a, Wildlife. b, Trees.

**2011, May 17** *Perf. 13¼x13½*
| | | |
|---|---|---|
| 2489 A823 | Horiz. pair | 12.00 12.00 |
| a. | 75c multi | 2.25 2.25 |
| b. | €3.25 multi | 9.50 9.50 |

**Booklet Stamps**
*Perf. 12¾ Vert.*
| | | |
|---|---|---|
| 2489C A823 | Horiz. pair | 12.00 12.00 |
| d. | 75c multi | 2.25 2.25 |
| e. | €3.25 multi | 9.50 9.50 |
| f. | Booklet pane, 2 #2489C | 24.00 |
| | Complete booklet, #2489f | 24.00 |

Intl. Year of Forests.

## Tourism A824

Text "www.visitgreece.gr" and: 1c, Stylized waves. 3c, Drama mask. 60c, Paper boat. 75c, Columns. €4, Town on cliff.

**2011, June 22** *Litho.* *Perf. 13¾*
| | | |
|---|---|---|
| 2490-2494 A824 | Set of 5 | 15.50 15.50 |

**Booklet Stamp**
**Self-Adhesive**
*Die Cut Perf. 12x11¼*
| | | |
|---|---|---|
| 2495 A824 75c multi | | 2.10 2.10 |
| a. | Booklet pane of 10 | 21.00 |

## Primary School Book Cover Art — A825

Book cover art from: 2c, 1954 third grade reading book. 20c, *Little Children*, 1939 first grade reading book. 60c, *Alphavitario*, 1955 first grade reading book. 75c, 1955 second grade reading book. €1, *Krinoloulouda*, 1939 second grade reading book. €3.50, 1955 fifth grade reading book.

**2011, Sept. 5** *Litho.* *Perf. 14x14¼*
| | | |
|---|---|---|
| 2496-2501 A825 | Set of 6 | 17.00 17.00 |
| 2501a | Souvenir sheet of 6, #2496-2501 | 17.00 17.00 |

**Booklet Stamp**
**Self-Adhesive**
*Die Cut Perf. 13¼*
| | | |
|---|---|---|
| 2502 A825 60c Like #2498 | | 1.75 1.75 |
| a. | Booklet pane of 10 | 17.50 |

## Alphavitario, 1955 First Grade Reading Book — A825a

**2011, Sept. 5** *Litho.* *Perf. 14x13¾*
| | | |
|---|---|---|
| 2503 A825a 60c multi + label | | 4.00 4.00 |

No. 2503 was printed in sheets of 10 + 10 labels that sold for €10. Labels could be personalized.

## First Greek Postage Stamps, 150th Anniv. — A827

Type A1 stamp with original denominations removed in: 15c, Chocolate. 50c, Bister. 60c, Green. 75c, Orange. €1, Blue. €2, Violet. €5, Red.

**Perf. 13¼x13¾**
**2011, Oct. 1** *Litho. & Engr.*
| | | |
|---|---|---|
| 2504-2510 A827 | Set of 7 | 27.50 27.50 |
| 2510a | Souvenir sheet of 1, #2510 | 14.00 14.00 |

## Actors and Actresses — A828

Designs: 1c, Vassilis Diamantopoulos (1920-99). 5c, Rena Vlachopoulou (1923-2004). 50c, Orestis Makris (1898-1975). 60c, Thanasis Veggos (1927-2011). €2.47, Mary Aroni (1916-92). €2.50, Sapfo Notara (c. 1907-85).

**Perf. 13¾x13½**
**2011, Nov. 22** *Litho.*
| | | |
|---|---|---|
| 2511-2516 A828 | Set of 6 | 16.50 16.50 |
| 2516a | Souvenir sheet of 6, #2511-2516 | 16.50 16.50 |

Compare with type A786.

### Souvenir Sheets

## Gold Medalists at 2011 FINA World Championships — A829

Designs: No. 2517, €3, Greek flag and medal for Greek women's water polo team.

No. 2518, €3, Spyros Gianniotis, swimmer, and gold medal.

**2011, Dec. 15**
| | | |
|---|---|---|
| 2517-2518 A829 | Set of 2 | 16.00 16.00 |

## A830

## A831

## Marine Life — A832

Designs: 2c, Palinurus elephas. 3c, Octopus vulgaris. 5c, Anemonia viridis. 20c, Caretta caretta. 35c, Epinephelus marginatus. 50c, Dentex dentex. (60c), Hippocampus guttulatus. €1, Aurelia aurita. (€2.47), Dasyatis pastinaca. €3, Charcharius taurus.

**2012, Feb. 21** *Perf. 14¼x14*
| | | | |
|---|---|---|---|
| 2519 A830 | 2c multi | .25 | .25 |
| 2520 A830 | 3c multi | .25 | .25 |
| 2521 A830 | 5c multi | .25 | .25 |
| 2522 A830 | 20c multi | .55 | .55 |
| 2523 A830 | 35c multi | .95 | .95 |
| 2524 A830 | 50c multi | 1.40 | 1.40 |
| 2525 A831 | (60c) multi | 1.60 | 1.60 |
| 2526 A830 | €1 multi | 2.60 | 2.60 |
| 2527 A832 | (€2.47) multi | 6.50 | 6.50 |
| 2528 A830 | €3 multi | 8.00 | 8.00 |
| Nos. 2519-2528 (10) | | 22.35 | 22.35 |

**Booklet Stamps**
*Perf. 12¾ Vert.*
| | | | |
|---|---|---|---|
| 2519A A830 | 2c multi | .25 | .25 |
| 2520A A830 | 3c multi | .25 | .25 |
| 2521A A830 | 5c multi | .25 | .25 |
| 2522A A830 | 20c multi | .55 | .55 |
| 2523A A830 | 35c multi | .95 | .95 |
| 2524A A830 | 50c multi | 1.40 | 1.40 |
| 2525A A831 | (60c) multi | 1.60 | 1.60 |
| 2526A A830 | €1 multi | 2.60 | 2.60 |
| 2527A A832 | (€2.47) multi | 6.50 | 6.50 |
| 2528A A830 | €3 multi | 8.00 | 8.00 |
| Nos. 2519A-2528A (10) | | 22.35 | 22.35 |

## A834

## Children's Games — A835

Children and: 2c. Soccer ball. 10c, Scooter, vert. 35c, Jump rope. (60c), Marbles. €2, Tops. €3, Hopscotch.

**Perf. 14¼x14, 14x14¼**
**2012, Apr. 18** *Litho.*
| | | | |
|---|---|---|---|
| 2530 A834 | 2c multi | .25 | .25 |
| 2531 A834 | 10c multi | .30 | .30 |
| 2532 A834 | 35c multi | .95 | .95 |
| 2533 A835 | (60c) multi | 1.60 | 1.60 |
| 2534 A834 | €2 multi | 5.25 | 5.25 |
| 2535 A834 | €3 multi | 8.00 | 8.00 |
| Nos. 2530-2535 (6) | | 16.35 | 16.35 |

**Booklet Stamp**
**Self-Adhesive**
*Die Cut Perf. 13¼*
| | | | |
|---|---|---|---|
| 2536 A835 | (60c) multi | 1.60 | 1.60 |
| a. | Booklet pane of 10 | 16.00 | |

## Europa A836

No. 2537 — Background color: a, Beige. b, White.

**Litho. With Foil Application**
**2012, May 10** *Perf. 13½x13¼*
| | | |
|---|---|---|
| 2537 A836 | Horiz. pair | 10.00 10.00 |
| a. | 75c multi | 1.90 1.90 |
| b. | €3.25 multi | 8.00 8.00 |

**Booklet Stamps**
*Perf. 12¾ Vert.*
| | | |
|---|---|---|
| 2537C A836 | Horiz. pair | 10.00 10.00 |
| d. | 75c multi | 1.90 1.90 |
| e. | €3.25 multi | 8.00 8.00 |
| f. | Booklet pane, 2 #2537C | 20.00 |
| | Complete booklet, #2537f | 20.00 |

## Nature Tourism A837

Designs: 1c, Tzoumerka Mountains, Epirus, rock climber. 10c, Rope bridge over Evinos River, backpacker. 62c, Samaria Gorge, Crete, hikers. 78c, Acheron River, Epirus, kayaker. €2, Rhodope Mountain stream, backpacker. €2.50, Field near Xanthi, backpacker.

**2012, June 25** *Litho.* *Perf. 13¾*
| | | |
|---|---|---|
| 2538-2543 A837 | Set of 6 | 15.00 15.00 |

**Booklet Stamps**
**Self-Adhesive**
*Die Cut Perf. 12x11½*
| | | |
|---|---|---|
| 2543A A837 | 62c multi | 1.60 1.60 |
| c. | Booklet pane of 10 | 16.00 |
| 2543B A837 | 78c multi | 1.90 1.90 |
| d. | Booklet pane of 10 | 19.00 |

## 2012 Summer Olympics, London — A838

Emblem of 2012 Summer Olympics and: 78c, London landmarks and years London hosted previous Olympic Games. €1.70, Athletes and sporting equipment.

**2012, July 2**
| | | |
|---|---|---|
| 2544-2545 A838 | Set of 2 | 6.25 6.25 |

### Souvenir Sheets

## Dimitris Chondrokoukis, 2012 Intl. High Jump Champion — A839

## Vlassis Maras, 2001-02 Intl. Horizontal Bar Champion — A840

**2012, July 16** *Perf. 13¾x13¼*
| | | |
|---|---|---|
| 2546 A839 | €2.50 multi | 6.25 6.25 |
| 2547 A840 | €2.50 multi | 6.25 6.25 |

## Greek Ships — A841

Designs: 1c, Paron, 1821. 15c, Mistiko, 17th cent. 62c, Corvette, 18th cent. 78c, Ionian-Cretan galley, 16th cent. €2, Sakoleva, 19th cent. €2.40, latinadiko in shipyard, 18th cent.

**Litho. With Foil Application**
**2012, Sept. 12**
2548-2553 A841 Set of 6 15.50 15.50

Liberation of
Thessalonica,
Cent. — A842

Designs: 40c, Battle of Deskati. 62c, Greek Army entering Thessalonica (47x25mm). 85c, Cruiser G. Averof at sea. €2.50, Battle of Sarantaporo.

*Perf. 13¾, 13½x13¼ (62c)*
**2012, Oct. 26**
2554-2557 A842 Set of 4 11.50 11.50
See Nos. 2595-2597.

Christmas — A843

Triangle, beater and Christmas ornament in shape of: 10c, Sphere. 62c, Christmas tree. 78c, Stocking. €3, Gift.

**2012, Dec. 12** *Perf. 14x14¼*
2558-2561 A843 Set of 4 12.00 12.00
**Booklet Stamps**
**Self-Adhesive**
*Die Cut Perf. 13¼*
2562 A843 62c multi 1.75 1.75
  *a.* Booklet pane of 8 14.00
2563 A843 78c multi 2.10 2.10
  *a.* Booklet pane of 8 17.00

No. 2562a sold for €4.90 and No. 2563a sold for €6.20.

Liberation of
Ioannina,
Cent. — A844

Paintings by Kenan Messare: 3c, Women of Hepirus in Struggle. 55c, Campaign. 62c, Shell Blast.

**Litho. With Foil Application**
**2013, Feb. 21** *Perf. 13¾*
2564-2566 A844 Set of 3 3.25 3.25

**Souvenir Sheet**

Plato's Academy, 2400th
Anniv. — A845

No. 2567: a, Circles and triangles. b, "N" and checkerboard pattern.

*Perf. 13¼x13¾*
**2013, Mar. 28** Litho.
2567 A845 Sheet of 2 7.75 7.75
  *a.* €1 multi 2.50 2.50
  *b.* €2 multi 5.25 5.25

Greek Films — A846

Designs: 20c, Voyage to Cythera, 1984. 30c, Electra, 1962. 62c, The Travelling Players, 1975. €2.80, The Ogre of Athens, 1956.

**Litho. With Foil Application**
**2013, Apr. 22** *Perf. 13¾*
2568-2571 A846 Set of 4 10.50 10.50

Europa
A847

No. 2572: a, Postal van. b, Postal bicycle.

**2013, May 9** Litho. *Perf. 13¾*
2572 A847 Horiz. pair 11.00 11.00
  *a.* 78c multi 2.10 2.10
  *b.* €3.28 multi 8.75 8.75
**Booklet Stamps**
*Perf. 13¾ Vert.*
2572C A847 Horiz. pair 11.00 11.00
  *d.* 78c multi 2.10 2.10
  *e.* €3.28 multi 8.75 8.75
  *f.* Booklet pane, 2 #2572C 22.00
    Complete booklet, #2572f 22.00

Complete booklet sold for €8.10.

A848

A849

Sailboats — A850

Various sailboats.

**2013, June 4** *Perf. 13½x13*
2573 A848 5c multi .25 .25
2574 A848 30c multi .80 .80
2575 A848 47c multi 1.25 1.25
  *a.* Souvenir sheet of 3, #2573-
    2575 2.40 2.40
2576 A849 (62c) multi 1.75 1.75
2577 A850 (78c) multi 2.10 2.10
2578 A848 €3 multi 8.00 8.00
  *a.* Souvenir sheet of 3, #2576-
    2578 12.00 12.00
  *Nos. 2573-2578 (6)* 14.15 14.15
**Booklet Stamps**
**Self-Adhesive**
*Die Cut Perf. 13*
2579 A849 (62c) multi 1.75 1.75
  *a.* Booklet pane of 10 17.50
2580 A850 (78c) multi 2.10 2.10
  *a.* Booklet pane of 10 21.00

First Ascent of
Mt. Olympus,
Cent. — A851

Centenary emblem and various photographs of Mt. Olympus: 5c, 10c, (78c), €3.50.

**Litho. With Foil Application**
**2013, July 19** *Perf. 13¼*
2581-2584 A851 Set of 4 12.00 12.00

Famous Men With
Greek
Heritage — A852

Designs: 5c, Andrew N. Liveris, President of Dow Chemical Company. 10c, Dr. Aristides A. N. Patrinos, head of U.S. National Human Genome Research Institute. 20c, James N. Gianopulos, chariman of Fox Entertainment Group. 72c, Stavros Niarchos (1909-96), shipping tycoon and philanthropist, horiz. 80c, Vangelis, composer. €3, Nikos A. Aliagas, French television host.

*Perf. 14x14¼, 14¼x14*
**2013, Sept. 16** Litho.
2585-2590 A852 Set of 6 13.50 13.50

Classic
Elements — A853

Designs: 5c, Earth. 47c, Water. €1, Air. €2.50, Fire.

**2013, Oct. 3** Litho. *Perf. 13¼*
2591-2594 A853 Set of 4 11.00 11.00
2594a Souvenir sheet of 4,
    #2591-2594 11.00 11.00

**Liberation of Ioannia Type of 2013**

Designs: 72c, Greek flag over Port of Chania in Crete. €1, Map of Crete from 1676, by Philippus Cluverius. €2.40, Surrender of Mount Athos to Greek Navy.

**Litho. With Foil Application**
**2013** *Perf. 13¾*
2595-2597 A844 Set of 3 11.50 11.50

Issued: 72c, €1, 12/2; €2.40, 10/3. International recognition of union of Greece and Crete, cent. (72c, €1); Surrender of Mount Athos, cent. (€2.40).

Evolution of
Postal
Services — A854

Designs: 1c, Computer and cable, bar code. 10c, Computer cable, flash drive, fingerprint. 72c, Quick response code. €2.62, Key, wavy lines, stripes from airmail envelope.

**2013, Dec. 2** Litho. *Perf. 13¼x13¾*
2598-2601 A854 Set of 4 9.50 9.50
**Booklet Stamp**
**Self-Adhesive**
*Serpentine Die Cut 12¼x13¼*
2602 A854 72c multi 2.00 2.00
  *a.* Booklet pane of 10 20.00

A855

A856

A857

Greek Presidency
of the European
Union — A858

**2014, Jan. 15** Litho. *Perf. 14x13¼*
2603 A855 3c multi .25 .25
2604 A856 72c multi 2.00 2.00
2605 A857 €2 multi 5.50 5.50
  *a.* Souvenir sheet of 2, #2604-
    2605 7.50 7.50
2606 A858 €2.15 multi 5.75 5.75
  *a.* Souvenir sheet of 2, #2603,
    2606 6.00 6.00
  *Nos. 2603-2606 (4)* 13.50 13.50

Corinth Canal,
120th Anniv.
A859

Filiki Eteria
(Society of
Friends)
Independence
Movement,
200th Anniv.
A860

Ionian Islands
as Greek
Territory,
150th Anniv.
A861

Thessaloniki,
2014
European
Youth Capital
A862

University of
Ioannina, 50th
Anniv. — A863

St. Cosmas of
Aetolia (c. 1714-
79) — A864

*Perf. 13¼x13¾, 13¾x13¼*
**2014, Feb. 17** Litho.
2607 A859 5c multi .25 .25
2608 A860 38c blk & red 1.10 1.10
2609 A861 72c multi 2.00 2.00
2610 A862 90c multi 2.50 2.50
2611 A863 €1.50 multi 4.25 4.25
2612 A864 €1.95 multi 5.50 5.50
  *Nos. 2607-2612 (6)* 15.60 15.60
**Booklet Stamp**
**Self-Adhesive**
*Die Cut Perf. 13¾x13¼*
2613 A862 90c multi 2.50 2.50
  *a.* Booklet pane of 10 25.00

Songbirds — A865

Designs: Nos. 2614, 2619, Luscinia megarhynchos. Nos. 2615, 2620, Carduelis chloris. €1, Carduelis cannabina. €1.62, Carduelis spinus. €2.62, Carduelis carduelis.

### Perf. 13¾x13¼
**2014, Mar. 20**     **Litho.**

| | | | | |
|---|---|---|---|---|
| 2614 | A865 | 72c multi | 2.00 | 2.00 |
| a. | | Booklet pane of 1 | 3.50 | — |
| 2615 | A865 | 72c multi | 2.00 | 2.00 |
| a. | | Booklet pane of 1 | 3.50 | — |
| 2616 | A865 | €1 multi | 2.75 | 2.75 |
| a. | | Booklet pane of 1 | 5.00 | — |
| 2617 | A865 | €1.62 multi | 4.50 | 4.50 |
| a. | | Booklet pane of 1 | 8.00 | — |
| 2618 | A865 | €2.62 multi | 7.25 | 7.25 |
| a. | | Booklet pane of 1 | 13.00 | — |
| | | Complete booklet, #2614a, 2615a, 2616a, 2617a, 2618a | 33.00 | |
| | | Nos. 2614-2618 (5) | 18.50 | 18.50 |

### Booklet Stamps
### Self-Adhesive
### Die Cut Perf. 13¾

| | | | | |
|---|---|---|---|---|
| 2619 | A865 | 72c multi | 2.00 | 2.00 |
| a. | | Booklet pane of 10 | 20.00 | |
| 2620 | A865 | 72c multi | 2.00 | 2.00 |
| a. | | Booklet pane of 10 | 20.00 | |

Complete booklet sold for €12.

April — A866

July — A867

December A868

January A869

March — A870

August — A871

June — A872

November A873

September A874

May — A875

February A876

October A877

### Perf. 13¼x13¾, 13¾x13¼
**2014, Apr. 24**     **Litho.**

| | | | | |
|---|---|---|---|---|
| 2621 | A866 | 2c multi | .25 | .25 |
| 2622 | A867 | 20c multi | .55 | .55 |
| 2623 | A868 | 40c multi | 1.10 | 1.10 |
| 2624 | A869 | 50c multi | 1.40 | 1.40 |
| 2625 | A870 | 72c multi | 2.00 | 2.00 |
| 2626 | A871 | 80c multi | 2.25 | 2.25 |
| 2627 | A872 | 85c multi | 2.40 | 2.40 |
| 2628 | A873 | 90c multi | 2.50 | 2.50 |
| 2629 | A874 | €1 multi | 2.75 | 2.75 |
| 2630 | A875 | €2.62 multi | 7.25 | 7.25 |
| 2631 | A876 | €3 multi | 8.25 | 8.25 |
| 2632 | A877 | €3.10 multi | 8.75 | 8.75 |
| | | Nos. 2621-2632 (12) | 39.45 | 39.45 |

### Booklet Stamps
### Perf. 13¾ Vert.

| | | | | |
|---|---|---|---|---|
| 2621A | A866 | 2c multi | .25 | .25 |
| 2622A | A867 | 20c multi | .55 | .55 |
| 2623A | A868 | 40c multi | 1.10 | 1.10 |
| 2624A | A869 | 50c multi | 1.40 | 1.40 |
| 2625A | A870 | 72c multi | 2.00 | 2.00 |
| 2626A | A871 | 80c multi | 2.25 | 2.25 |
| 2627A | A872 | 85c multi | 2.40 | |
| 2628A | A873 | 90c multi | 2.50 | 2.50 |
| 2629A | A874 | €1 multi | 2.75 | 2.75 |
| 2630A | A875 | €2.62 multi | 7.25 | 7.25 |
| 2631A | A876 | €3 multi | 8.25 | 8.25 |
| 2632A | A877 | €3.10 multi | 8.75 | 8.75 |
| | | Nos. 2621A-2632A (12) | 37.05 | 39.45 |

### Booklet Stamps
### Self-Adhesive
### Die Cut Perf. 12x11½

| | | | | |
|---|---|---|---|---|
| 2633 | A870 | 72c multi | 2.00 | 2.00 |
| a. | | Booklet pane of 10 | 20.00 | |
| 2634 | A871 | 80c multi | 2.25 | 2.25 |
| a. | | Booklet pane of 10 | 22.50 | |

Folk art depicting the months of the year.

Europa A878

No. 2635: a, Musician bowing a stringed instrument. b, Lyrist.

**2014, May 19**   **Litho.**   **Perf. 13¼x13¾**

| | | | | |
|---|---|---|---|---|
| 2635 | A878 | Horiz. pair | 12.00 | 12.00 |
| a. | | 90c multi | 2.50 | 2.50 |
| b. | | €3.40 multi | 9.25 | 9.25 |

### Booklet Stamps
### Perf. 13¾ Vert.

| | | | | |
|---|---|---|---|---|
| 2635C | A878 | Horiz. pair | 12.00 | 12.00 |
| d. | | 90c multi | 2.50 | 2.50 |
| e. | | €3.40 multi | 9.25 | 9.25 |
| f. | | Booklet pane, 2 #2635C | 24.00 | — |
| | | Complete booklet, #2635f | 24.00 | |

Bicycles — A879

Designs: No. 2636, Bicycle with training wheels, children at play. Nos. 2637, 2640,

Green and red adult men's bicycle. 80c, White women's bicycle. €2, Red and green child's bicycle.

### Perf. 13¾x13¼
**2014, June 12**     **Litho.**

| | | | | |
|---|---|---|---|---|
| 2636 | A879 | 72c multi | 2.00 | 2.00 |
| a. | | Souvenir sheet of 1 | 2.00 | 2.00 |
| 2637 | A879 | 72c multi | 2.00 | 2.00 |
| a. | | Souvenir sheet of 1 | 2.00 | 2.00 |
| 2638 | A879 | 80c multi | 2.25 | 2.25 |
| a. | | Souvenir sheet of 1 | 2.25 | 2.25 |
| 2639 | A879 | €2 multi | 5.50 | 5.50 |
| a. | | Souvenir sheet of 1 | 5.50 | 5.50 |
| | | Nos. 2636-2639 (4) | 11.75 | 11.75 |

### Booklet Stamps
### Self-Adhesive
### Die Cut Perf. 13¾

| | | | | |
|---|---|---|---|---|
| 2640 | A879 | 72c multi | 2.00 | 2.00 |
| a. | | Booklet pane of 10 | 20.00 | |
| 2641 | A879 | 80c multi | 2.25 | 2.25 |
| a. | | Booklet pane of 10 | 22.50 | |

A booklet with panes containing one perf. 13¼x13¾ example each of Nos. 2636-2639 sold for €12.

2014 World Cup Soccer Championships, Brazil — A880

No. 2642: a, Mascot holding soccer ball. b, Silhouette of soccer player.

**2014, June 12**   **Litho.**   **Perf. 13¼x14**

| | | | | |
|---|---|---|---|---|
| 2642 | A880 | Pair | 6.00 | 6.00 |
| a. | | 90c multi | 2.50 | 2.50 |
| b. | | €1.30 multi | 3.50 | 3.50 |
| c. | | Souvenir sheet of 1 #2642a | 2.50 | 2.50 |
| d. | | Souvenir sheet of 1 #2642b | 3.50 | 3.50 |

Euromed Postal Emblem and Mediterranean Sea — A881

**2014, July 9**   **Litho.**   **Perf. 13¼x13¾**

| | | | | |
|---|---|---|---|---|
| 2643 | A881 | €3 multi | 8.00 | 8.00 |
| a. | | Perf. 13¾ vert. | 8.00 | 8.00 |
| b. | | Booklet pane of 2 #2643a | 16.00 | — |
| | | Complete booklet, #2643b | 16.00 | |

Fishing Boat — A882

Rhodes — A883

Santorini — A884

### Die Cut Perf. 13
**2014, Aug. 8**     **Litho.**
### Booklet Stamps
### Self-Adhesive

| | | | | |
|---|---|---|---|---|
| 2647 | A882 | (80c) multi | 2.25 | 2.25 |
| a. | | Booklet pane of 10 | 22.50 | |
| 2648 | A883 | (80c) multi | 2.25 | 2.25 |
| a. | | Booklet pane of 10 | 22.50 | |
| 2649 | A884 | (80c) multi | 2.25 | 2.25 |
| a. | | Booklet pane of 10 | 22.50 | |
| | | Nos. 2647-2649 (3) | 6.75 | 6.75 |

### Souvenir Sheet

The Entombment of Christ, by El Greco (1541-1614) — A885

No. 2650 — Painting details: a, Grieving women, b, Jesus.

### Litho. With Foil Application
**2014, Sept. 10**     **Perf. 13½x13**

| | | | | |
|---|---|---|---|---|
| 2650 | A885 | Sheet of 2 | 6.25 | 6.25 |
| a. | | €1 multi | 2.50 | 2.50 |
| b. | | €1.50 multi | 3.75 | 3.75 |

Writers — A886

Designs: 10c, Kostas Varnalis (1884-1974). 40c, Dido Sotiriou (1909-2004). €2, Antonis Samarakis (1919-2003). €2.10, Stratis Tsirkas (1911-80).

**2014, Oct. 23**   **Litho.**   **Perf. 13½x13¾**

| | | | | |
|---|---|---|---|---|
| 2651-2654 | A886 | Set of 4 | 11.50 | 11.50 |

A887

Christmas A888

Designs: No. 2655, Christmas tree and elves. No. 2656, Elf and toys. No. 2657, Reindeer and snowman. No. 2658, Toys in bag.

### Die Cut Perf. 13 ½ (A887), 12½ (A888)
**2014, Dec. 12**     **Litho.**
### Booklet Stamps
### Self-Adhesive
### Color of QR Code

| | | | | |
|---|---|---|---|---|
| 2655 | A887 | 72c red | 1.75 | 1.75 |
| 2656 | A888 | 72c purple | 1.75 | 1.75 |
| a. | | Booklet pane of 10, 5 each #2655-2656 | 17.50 | |
| 2657 | A887 | 90c blue | 2.25 | 2.25 |
| 2658 | A888 | 90c green | 2.25 | 2.25 |
| a. | | Booklet pane of 10, 5 each #2657-2658 | 22.50 | |
| | | Nos. 2655-2658 (4) | 8.00 | 8.00 |

Advertisement for Misko Pasta — A889

Advertisement for Papadopoulos "Petit-Beurre" Biscuits — A890

**2014, Dec. 18 Litho. Perf. 14x13¼**
| | | | | |
|---|---|---|---|---|
| 2659 | A889 | 72c multi | 1.75 | 1.75 |
| 2660 | A890 | 72c multi | 1.75 | 1.75 |

**Booklet Stamps**
**Self-Adhesive**
*Die Cut Perf. 11½x12*
| | | | | |
|---|---|---|---|---|
| 2661 | A889 | 72c multi | 1.75 | 1.75 |
| a. | | Booklet pane of 10 | 17.50 | |
| 2662 | A890 | 72c multi | 1.75 | 1.75 |
| a. | | Booklet pane of 10 | 17.50 | |

Journalists' Union of Athens Daily Newspapers — A891

Designs: 1c, Paulos Palaiologos, Dimitris Psathas. 20c, Ioannis Iakovos Mager, Vlasis Gavriilidis. 50c, Maria Rezan, Nikos Karantinos. 72c, Aimilios Chourmouzios, Marios Ploritis. €2.62, Union emblem, quotation by Mager.

**2015, Jan. 21 Litho. Perf. 13¼x13¾**
| | | | | |
|---|---|---|---|---|
| 2663-2667 | A891 | Set of 5 | 9.25 | 9.25 |

Thermal Springs A892

Designs: 5c, Methana. 10c, Loutraki Perachora. 23c, Lefkada Ikaria. 72c, Edipsos. 90c, Loutraki Aridaia (Pozar). €2, Vouliagmeni Lake.

**2015, Feb. 26 Litho. Perf. 14x13¼**
| | | | | |
|---|---|---|---|---|
| 2668-2673 | A892 | Set of 6 | 9.00 | 9.00 |

Locomotives of Greek Railways A893

Designs: 20c, German 40-45, 1951. 72c, Austrian La901-940, 1925-27. 80c, American G401-420, 1915. €2.50, French Z501-517, 1890-1901.

**2015, Mar. 30 Litho. Perf. 14x13¼**
| | | | | |
|---|---|---|---|---|
| 2674 | A893 | 20c multi | .45 | .45 |
| a. | | Souvenir sheet of 1 | .45 | .45 |
| 2675 | A893 | 72c multi | 1.60 | 1.60 |
| a. | | Souvenir sheet of 1 | 1.60 | 1.60 |
| 2676 | A893 | 80c multi | 1.75 | 1.75 |
| a. | | Souvenir sheet of 1 | 1.75 | 1.75 |
| 2677 | A893 | €2.50 multi | 5.50 | 5.50 |
| a. | | Souvenir sheet of 1 | 5.50 | 5.50 |
| | | Nos. 2674-2677 (4) | 9.30 | 9.30 |

**Booklet Stamps**
**Self-Adhesive**
*Die Cut Perf. 13¼x12¾*
| | | | | |
|---|---|---|---|---|
| 2678 | A893 | 72c multi | 1.60 | 1.60 |
| a. | | Booklet pane of 10 | 16.00 | |
| 2679 | A893 | 80c multi | 1.75 | 1.75 |
| a. | | Booklet pane of 10 | 17.50 | |

Sakis Karayorgas and Kostas Yorgakis A894

Nikiforos Mandilaras and Panayotis Elis — A895

Dimitris Opropoulos and Spyros Moustaklis A896

Design: 90c, Yorgos Tsarouhas and Yannis Halkidis.

**Litho. With Foil Application**
**2015, Apr. 21 Perf. 13¼x13¾**
| | | | | |
|---|---|---|---|---|
| 2680 | A894 | 72c multi | 1.60 | 1.60 |
| 2681 | A895 | 72c multi | 1.60 | 1.60 |
| 2682 | A896 | 72c multi | 1.60 | 1.60 |
| 2683 | A896 | 90c multi | 2.10 | 2.10 |
| | | Nos. 2680-2683 (4) | 6.90 | 6.90 |

Fighters against the 1967 junta.

Europa A897

No. 2684 — Marbles and: a, Top, toy airplane. b, Toy car, slingshots.

**2015, May 11 Litho. Perf. 13¾**
| | | | | |
|---|---|---|---|---|
| 2684 | A897 | Horiz. pair | 9.50 | 9.50 |
| a. | | 90c multi | 2.00 | 2.00 |
| b. | | €3.40 multi | 7.50 | 7.50 |

**Booklet Stamps**
*Perf. 13¾ Vert.*
| | | | | |
|---|---|---|---|---|
| 2684C | A897 | Horiz. pair | 9.50 | 9.50 |
| d. | | 90c multi | 2.00 | 2.00 |
| e. | | €3.40 multi | 7.50 | 7.50 |
| f. | | Booklet pane, 2 #2684C | 19.00 | |
| | | Complete booklet, #2684C | 19.00 | |

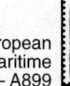

2015 European Sea Ports Organization Conference, Athens — A898

European Maritime Day — A899

Designs: 72c, Emblem and ships. No. 2686, Emblem, ship, rope and mooring bollard. No. 2687, Map of Piraeus harbor.

**2015, May 20 Litho. Perf. 13¼x13¾**
| | | | | |
|---|---|---|---|---|
| 2685 | A898 | 72c multi | 1.60 | 1.60 |
| 2686 | A898 | 80c multi | 1.75 | 1.75 |
| 2687 | A899 | 80c multi | 1.75 | 1.75 |
| | | Nos. 2685-2687 (3) | 5.10 | 5.10 |

**Miniature Sheets**

A901

A902

A903

No. 2689: a, Owls and books. b, Sun, flowers, birds with letters. c, Cogwheels, handshake. d, Letters, airplane, cogwheels, Sydney Opera House, Big Ben, Roman Colosseum, Eiffel Tower.
No. 2690: a, Birds on baby carriage. b, Birds and heart. c, Balloons and baby. d, Woman and man on penny-farthing bicycles, flowers.
No. 2691: a, Unofficial flag of Greece. b, Column and capital. c, Birds and flowers. d, Ancient art.

**2015, June 11 Litho. Perf. 14x13½**
| | | | | |
|---|---|---|---|---|
| 2689 | A901 | Sheet of 4 | 7.00 | 7.00 |
| a.-c. | | 72c Any single | 1.60 | 1.60 |
| d. | | 90c multi | 2.00 | 2.00 |
| 2690 | A902 | Sheet of 4 | 7.00 | 7.00 |
| a.-c. | | 72c Any single | 1.60 | 1.60 |
| d. | | 90c multi | 2.00 | 2.00 |
| 2691 | A903 | Sheet of 4 | 7.25 | 7.25 |
| a.-b. | | 72c Either single | 1.60 | 1.60 |
| c.-d. | | 90c Either single | 2.00 | 2.00 |
| | | Nos. 2689-2691 (3) | 21.25 | 21.25 |

Fishing Boat — A904

**2015, July 9 Litho. Perf. 13¼x13¾**
| | | | | |
|---|---|---|---|---|
| 2692 | A904 | €3 multi | 6.75 | 6.75 |
| a. | | Perf. 13¾ vert. | 6.75 | 6.75 |
| b. | | Booklet pane of 2 #2692a | 13.50 | — |
| | | Complete booklet, #2692a | 13.50 | |

Diving — A905

Diver and: 10c, Shipwreck. 50c, Ancient jar. Nos. 2695, 2699, 80c, Fish and sponges. Nos. 2696, 2700, 80c, Byzantine shipwreck. €1.62, Shipwreck, diff. €2, Yellow gorgonians.

**2015, July 20 Litho. Perf. 13¼x13¾**
| | | | | |
|---|---|---|---|---|
| 2693-2698 | A905 | Set of 6 | 13.00 | 13.00 |

**Booklet Stamps**
**Self-Adhesive**
*Die Cut Perf. 13¾x14*
| | | | | |
|---|---|---|---|---|
| 2699 | A905 | 80c multi | 1.75 | 1.75 |
| 2700 | A905 | 80c multi | 1.75 | 1.75 |
| a. | | Booklet pane of 10, 5 each #2699-2700 | 17.50 | |

Volcanoes A906

Designs: 1c, Milos Volcano. 20c, Nisyros Volcano. €1, Santorini Volcano. €2, Nisyros Volcano, diff.

**2015, Sept. 8 Litho. Perf. 13¼x13¾**
| | | | | |
|---|---|---|---|---|
| 2701-2704 | A906 | Set of 4 | 7.25 | 7.25 |

Flanghinis College, 350th Anniv. — A907

Designs: 3c, Tomasso Flangini (1578-1648), school founder. 72c, Our Lady of the Flanghinis College. €1.50, Flanghinis College building, Venice. €2, Emblem of Hellenic Institute of Byzantine and Post-Byzantine Studies of Venice.

**Litho. With Foil Application**
**2015, Oct. 9 Perf. 13¾x13¼**
| | | | | |
|---|---|---|---|---|
| 2705-2708 | A907 | Set of 4 | 9.50 | 9.50 |

**Souvenir Sheet**

Greek Postal Savings Bank, 115th Anniv. A908

**Litho. With Foil Application**
**2015, Oct. 30 Perf. 13¾**
| | | | | |
|---|---|---|---|---|
| 2709 | A908 | €1 multi | 2.25 | 2.25 |

Notos 2015 International Philatelic Exhibition, Athens — A909

Designs: 72c, Exhibition emblem. 90c, Exhibition emblem, map and origami bird.

**2015, Nov. 4 Litho. Perf. 13¾**
| | | | | |
|---|---|---|---|---|
| 2710-2711 | A909 | Set of 2 | 3.50 | 3.50 |
| 2711a | | Souvenir sheet of 2, #2710-2711 | 3.50 | 3.50 |

United Nations. 70th Anniv. — A910

**2015, Nov. 4 Litho. Perf. 13¾**
| | | | | |
|---|---|---|---|---|
| 2712 | A910 | €1 multi | 2.25 | 2.25 |

**Souvenir Sheet**

Maritime Cooperation Between Greece and People's Republic of China — A911

**2015, Nov. 4 Litho. Perf. 13¾**
| | | | | |
|---|---|---|---|---|
| 2713 | A911 | €3 multi | 6.50 | 6.50 |

Advertisement for Loumidis-Papagalos Coffee — A912

Advertisement for Sun Spices — A913

Advertisement for Attiki Honey — A914

Advertisement for Pitsos Home Appliances A915

Advertisement for Hatzopoulos Flexible Packaging A916

**Litho. With Foil Application**

**2015, Dec. 14**     **Perf. 13¾**
2714 A912 72c multi    1.60 1.60

**Litho.**

| 2715 | A913 | 72c multi | 1.60 | 1.60 |
|---|---|---|---|---|
| 2716 | A914 | 72c multi | 1.60 | 1.60 |
| 2717 | A915 | 72c multi | 1.60 | 1.60 |
| 2718 | A916 | 90c multi | 2.00 | 2.00 |
| | | *Nos. 2714-2718 (5)* | 8.40 | 8.40 |

Diplomatic Relations Between Greece and Israel, 25th Anniv. — A917

**2016, Feb. 9**    **Litho.**    **Perf. 14**
2719 A917 90c multi    2.00 2.00

See Israel No. 2091.

National Liberation Front, 75th Anniv. — A918

Members of National Liberation Front (World War II resistance fighters): 20c, Kostas Maragkoudakis. 50c, Apostolos (Lakis) Santas (1920-2011). €1, Manolis Glezos. €2, Vardis Vardinogiannis. €2.10, Stelios Zamanos.

**2016, Feb. 23**   **Litho.**   **Perf. 14¼x14**
2720-2724 A918   Set of 5    12.50 12.50

National Bank of Greece, 175th Anniv. — A919

Designs: 5c, Drawing of Central Bank Office, by Eugène Troump, 1900. 10c, Ludwig Square, 1847, painting by Johannes Rabe. 50c, Design for 60th anniversary medal, by George Lakovidis, 1902. €2.62, Karatzas Building, 2002.

**Litho. With Foil Application**

**2016, Mar. 30**     **Perf. 13¾**
| 2725 | A919 | 5c multi | .25 | .25 |
|---|---|---|---|---|
| *a.* | | Souvenir sheet of 1 | .25 | .25 |
| 2726 | A919 | 10c multi | .25 | .25 |
| *a.* | | Souvenir sheet of 1 | .25 | .25 |
| 2727 | A919 | 50c multi | 1.25 | 1.25 |
| *a.* | | Souvenir sheet of 1 | 1.25 | 1.25 |
| 2728 | A919 | €2.62 multi | 6.00 | 6.00 |
| *a.* | | Souvenir sheet of 1 | 6.00 | 6.00 |
| | | *Nos. 2725-2728 (4)* | 7.75 | 7.75 |

A920

A921

A922

Year of Greece in Russia — A923

**2016, Apr. 18**   **Litho.**   **Perf. 13¾**
| 2729 | A920 | 80c multi | 1.90 | 1.90 |
|---|---|---|---|---|
| 2730 | A921 | 80c multi | 1.90 | 1.90 |
| 2731 | A922 | 80c multi | 1.90 | 1.90 |
| 2732 | A923 | 90c multi | 2.10 | 2.10 |
| *a.* | | Souvenir sheet of 4, #2729-2732 | 8.00 | 8.00 |
| | | *Nos. 2729-2732 (4)* | 7.80 | 7.80 |

**Booklet Stamp**
**Self-Adhesive**
**Die Cut Perf. 11½x12**
2733 A922 80c multi    1.90 1.90
*a.*   Booklet pane of 10    19.00

Labor Leaders A924

Designs: 5c, Napoleon Soukatzidis (1909-44), executed trade union leader. 50c, Tasos Toussis (1911-36), murdered striker. €1, Kostas Theos (1896-1958), exiled labor leader. €2, Sotiris Paraskevaidis, Communist activist killed at 1924 rally, denomination at LL.

**2016, Apr. 21**   **Litho.**   **Perf. 13¾**
2734-2737 A924   Set of 4    8.25 8.25

A925

Europa — A926

**2016, May 11**   **Litho.**   **Perf. 14¼x14**
| 2738 | A925 | 90c multi | 2.00 | 2.00 |
|---|---|---|---|---|
| 2739 | A926 | €3.40 multi | 7.75 | 7.75 |
| *b.* | | Horiz. pair, #2738-2739 | 9.75 | 9.75 |

**Booklet Stamps**
**Perf. 14 Vert.**
| 2738A | A925 | 90c multi | 2.00 | 2.00 |
|---|---|---|---|---|
| 2739A | A926 | €3.40 multi | 7.75 | 7.75 |
| *c.* | | Horiz. pair, #2738A-2739A | 9.75 | 9.75 |
| *d.* | | Booklet pane of 4, 2 each #2738A-2739A | 19.50 | 19.50 |
| | | Complete booklet, #2739d | 19.50 | |

Think Green Issue.

Aristotle (384-322 B.C.), Philosopher — A927

Designs: 72c, Aristotle. 80c, Aristotle and his student, Alexander the Great. €1, Aristotle and his teacher, Plato.

**2016, May 23**   **Litho.**   **Perf. 13¾**
| 2740 | A927 | 72c multi | 1.60 | 1.60 |
|---|---|---|---|---|
| *a.* | | Souvenir sheet of 1 | 1.60 | 1.60 |
| 2741 | A927 | 80c multi | 1.75 | 1.75 |
| *a.* | | Souvenir sheet of 1 | 1.75 | 1.75 |
| 2742 | A927 | €1 multi | 2.25 | 2.25 |
| *a.* | | Souvenir sheet of 1 | 2.25 | 2.25 |
| | | *Nos. 2740-2742 (3)* | 5.60 | 5.60 |

**Booklet Stamps**
**Self-Adhesive**
**Die Cut Perf. 11½x12**
| 2743 | A927 | 72c multi | 1.60 | 1.60 |
|---|---|---|---|---|
| *a.* | | Booklet pane of 10 | 16.00 | |
| 2744 | A927 | 80c multi | 1.75 | 1.75 |
| *a.* | | Booklet pane of 10 | 17.50 | |

Personalized Stamps — A927a

Designs: 72c, Aristotle. 80c, Aristotle and his student, Alexander the Great.

**2016, May 23**   **Litho.**   **Perf. 14**
| 2744B | A927a | 72c multi + label | 2.50 | 2.50 |
|---|---|---|---|---|
| 2744C | A927a | 80c multi + label | 2.75 | 2.75 |

Nos. 2744B and 2744C were each printed in sheets of 5 + 5 labels that could be personalized. The generic label is shown.

**Souvenir Sheet**

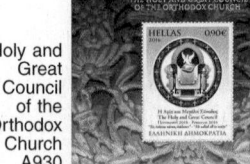

Patriarch Bartholomew of Constantinople, 25th Anniv. of Installation — A928

No. 2745: a, Patriarch Bartholomew. b, Emblem of Patriarchate.

**Litho., Sheet Margin Litho. With Foil Application**
**2016, June 10**     **Perf. 13¾**
| 2745 | A928 | Sheet of 2 | 4.25 | 4.25 |
|---|---|---|---|---|
| *a.* | | 90c multi | 2.00 | 2.00 |
| *b.* | | €1 multi | 2.25 | 2.25 |

A929

Holy and Great Council of the Orthodox Church A930

**2016, June 16**   **Litho.**   **Perf. 14**
2746 A929 90c multi + label    3.75 3.75

**Souvenir Sheet**
**Litho., Sheet Margin Litho. With Foil Application**
**Perf. 13¾**
2747 A930 90c multi    2.00 2.00

No. 2746 was printed in sheets of 5 + 5 labels that sold for €8. Labels could be personalized. The generic label is shown.

A930a

Personalized Stamps — A930b

**2016, June 15**   **Litho.**   **Perf. 14**
| 2747A | A930a | 80c multi + label | 2.75 | 2.75 |
|---|---|---|---|---|
| 2747B | A930b | 80c multi + label | 2.75 | 2.75 |

Nos. 2747A and 2747B were each printed in sheets of 5 + 5 labels that could be personalized. The generic labels are shown.

Fish of the Mediterranean Sea — A931

**2016, July 8**   **Litho.**   **Perf. 13¾**
2748 A931 €3 multi    6.75 6.75

**Booklet Stamps**
**Perf. 12¾ Vert.**
| 2748A | A931 | €3 multi | 6.75 | 6.75 |
|---|---|---|---|---|
| *b.* | | Booklet pane of 2 #2748A | 13.50 | |
| | | Complete booklet, #2748b | 13.50 | |

2016 Summer Olympics, Rio de Janeiro — A932

Silhouette of Rio de Janeiro skyline, Christ the Redeemer statue, Greek Olympic Committee emblem, ancient Greek statues and: 80c, Gymnast on rings. 90c, Runner crossing finish line.

**2016, July 8**   **Litho.**   **Perf. 13¾**
2749-2750 A932   Set of 2    3.75 3.75

Lambrakis Youth Movement A933

Designs: 20c, Sotiris Petroulas (1942-65), student killed in protest. 72c, Andreas Lentakis (1935-97), politician. 80c, Mikis Theodorakis, composer and first president of Lambrakis Democratic Youth. €2, Christos Rekleitis (1937-2014), anti-junta protestor tortured by military, denomination at LR.

**2016, July 8**   **Litho.**   **Perf. 13¾**
2751-2754 A933   Set of 4    8.50 8.50

2016 International Foundation for Greece Award Recipients — A934

Emblem and: 72c, Rita Wilson, actress. 80c, Costa-Gavras, film director. 90c, John A. Catsimatidis, businessman. €1, George Stephanopoulos, television journalist. €1.20, Dr. Peter Diamandis, engineer and chairman of X PRIZE Foundation.

**2016, Sept. 1**   **Litho.**   **Perf. 14x14¼**
2755-2759 A934   Set of 5    10.50 10.50

Siege of Corfu, 300th Anniv. — A935

**Litho. With Foil Application**
**2016, Oct. 20**     **Perf. 13¼x13**
2760 A935 €2 multi    4.50 4.50

## Souvenir Sheet

Marathon Race of Modern Olympics, 120th Anniv. — A936

No. 2761: a, Ancient naked marathon runner. b, Modern runner wearing cap.

### Litho., Sheet Margin Litho. With Foil Application

**2016, Nov. 10**      **Perf. 13¾**
| | | | |
|---|---|---|---|
| 2761 | A936 | Sheet of 2 | 6.50 6.50 |
| a. | | 90c multi | 2.00 2.00 |
| b. | | €2.10 multi | 4.50 4.50 |

Personalized Stamp — A936a

**2016, Nov. 10**    **Litho.**    **Perf. 14**
| | | | |
|---|---|---|---|
| 2761C | A936a | 90c multi + label | 3.50 3.50 |

No. 2761C was printed in sheets of 5 + 5 labels that could be personalized. The sheet sold for €8. The generic label is shown.

Television Broadcasting in Greece, 50th Anniv. — A937

**2016, Nov. 24**    **Litho.**    **Perf. 13¾**
| | | | |
|---|---|---|---|
| 2762 | A937 | €1.50 multi | 3.25 3.25 |

Herbs — A938

Designs: 20c, Cistus creticus. 40c, Origanum dictamus. 50c, Hypericum empetrifolium. 72c, Sideritis clandestina. €1, Origanum vulgare. €2.62, Salvia fruticosa.

**2016, Dec. 15**    **Litho.**    **Perf. 14x14¼**
| | | | |
|---|---|---|---|
| 2763-2768 | A938 | Set of 6 | 11.50 11.50 |

No. 2768 is impregnated with a Greek oregano scent.

National Archaeological Museum, 150th Anniv. (in 2016) — A939

Designs: 10c, The Kiss. 50c, Odysseus of Antikythera statue, vert. 72c, Diadoumenos sculpture, vert. 90c, Poseidon of Livadostra statue, vert. €1.50, Athenian Youth, vert. €2, Mycenaean Lady.

### Litho. With Foil Application

**2017, Mar. 15**      **Perf. 13¾**
| | | | |
|---|---|---|---|
| 2769-2774 | A939 | Set of 6 | 12.50 12.50 |
| 2769a | | Souvenir sheet of 1 | .25 .25 |
| 2770a | | Souvenir sheet of 1 | 1.10 1.10 |
| 2771a | | Souvenir sheet of 1 | 1.60 1.60 |
| 2772a | | Souvenir sheet of 1 | 2.00 2.00 |
| 2773a | | Souvenir sheet of 1 | 3.25 3.25 |
| 2774a | | Souvenir sheet of 1 | 4.25 4.25 |

### Booklet Stamp
### Self-Adhesive
### Litho.
#### Die Cut Perf. 11½x12

| | | | |
|---|---|---|---|
| 2775 | A939 | 72c multi | 1.60 1.60 |
| a. | | Booklet pane of 10 | 16.00 |

 Sports — A940

 Arts — A941

 Literature — A942

 Music — A943

 Tourism — A944

 Wine — A945

**2017, Apr. 7**    **Litho.**    **Perf. 13¾**
| | | | |
|---|---|---|---|
| 2776 | A940 | 72c multi | 1.60 1.60 |
| 2777 | A941 | 72c multi | 1.60 1.60 |
| 2778 | A942 | 72c multi | 1.60 1.60 |
| 2779 | A943 | 72c multi | 1.60 1.60 |
| 2780 | A944 | 80c multi | 1.75 1.75 |
| 2781 | A945 | 90c multi | 2.00 2.00 |
| | | Nos. 2776-2781 (6) | 10.15 10.15 |

### Booklet Stamp
### Self-Adhesive
#### Die Cut Perf. 13¾

| | | | |
|---|---|---|---|
| 2782 | A944 | 80c multi | 1.75 1.75 |
| a. | | Booklet pane of 10 | 17.50 |

#### Size: 30x30mm
#### Water-Activated Gum
#### Perf. 13¼

| | | | |
|---|---|---|---|
| 2783 | A940 | 72c multi + label | 2.75 2.75 |
| 2784 | A941 | 72c multi + label | 2.75 2.75 |
| 2785 | A942 | 72c multi + label | 2.75 2.75 |
| 2786 | A943 | 72c multi + label | 2.75 2.75 |
| 2787 | A944 | 80c multi + label | 3.50 3.50 |
| 2788 | A945 | 90c multi + label | 3.50 3.50 |
| | | Nos. 2783-2788 (6) | 18.00 18.00 |

Nos. 2783-2788 were each printed in sheets of 5 + 5 labels that could be personalized. Sheets of Nos. 2783-2786 each sold for €6; Nos. 2787-2788, for €8.

## Souvenir Sheet

Ancient Civilizations Forum, Athens — A946

**2017, Apr. 24**    **Litho.**    **Perf. 12¾**
| | | | |
|---|---|---|---|
| 2789 | A946 | €2 multi | 4.50 4.50 |

Cross and Initials of Apostoliki Diakonia A947

St. Helen A948

**2017, May 11**    **Litho.**    **Perf. 13¾**
| | | | |
|---|---|---|---|
| 2790 | A947 | 72c multi | 1.60 1.60 |

### Souvenir Sheet
### Litho. Margin Litho. With Foil Application

| | | | |
|---|---|---|---|
| 2791 | A948 | €2 multi | 4.50 4.50 |

Apostoliki Diakonia of the Church of Greece, 80th anniv.

Europa A949

No. 2792: a, Palamidi Castle, Nafplio. b, Methoni Castle.

**2017, May 18**    **Litho.**    **Perf. 14¼x14**
| | | | |
|---|---|---|---|
| 2792 | A949 | Horiz. pair | 9.75 9.75 |
| a. | | 90c multi | 2.00 2.00 |
| b. | | €3.40 multi | 7.75 7.75 |
| c. | | Horiz. pair, perf. 14 vert. | 9.75 9.75 |
| d. | | As "a," perf. 14 vert. | 2.00 2.00 |
| e. | | As "b," perf. 14 vert. | 7.75 7.75 |
| f. | | Booklet pane, 2 #2792c | 19.50 — |
| | | Complete booklet, #2792f | 19.50 |

Mastic Trees — A950

**2017, June 27**    **Litho.**    **Perf. 13¾**
| | | | |
|---|---|---|---|
| 2793 | A950 | €2.62 multi | 6.00 6.00 |
| a. | | Souvenir sheet of 1 | 6.00 6.00 |
| b. | | Perf. 13¾ horiz. | 6.00 6.00 |
| c. | | Booklet pane of 2 #2793b | 12.00 |
| | | Complete booklet, #2793c | 12.00 |

Seven Wise Men of Antiquity — A951

Designs: 5c, Chilon of Sparta. 10c, Cleobulus of Lindos. 20c, Periander of Corinth. 50c, Pittacus of Mytilene. 80c, Solon of Athens. €1, Thales of Miletus. €2, Bias of Priene.

**2017, July 27**    **Litho.**    **Perf. 14x14¼**
| | | | |
|---|---|---|---|
| 2794-2800 | A951 | Set of 7 | 11.00 11.00 |

Compare with types A997-A998.

Greek Theater Costume — A952

Bamboo Shoot and Olive Branch — A953

Chinese Theater Costume — A954

**2017, Sept. 8**    **Litho.**    **Perf. 13¾**
| | | | |
|---|---|---|---|
| 2801 | A952 | 50c multi | 1.25 1.25 |
| 2802 | A953 | 90c multi | 2.10 2.10 |
| c. | | Souvenir sheet of 1 | 2.10 2.10 |

| | | | |
|---|---|---|---|
| 2803 | A954 | €2 multi | 4.75 4.75 |
| a. | | Souvenir sheet of 2, #2801, 2803 | 6.00 6.00 |
| | | Nos. 2801-2803 (3) | 8.10 8.10 |

Year of Cultural Exchanges and Cooperation of Creative Industries of Greece and China.

Monument to Fighters in 1944 Battle of the Keratsini Power Station — A955

Battle of the Keratsini Power Station — A956

**2017, Oct. 11**    **Litho.**    **Perf. 13¾**
| | | | |
|---|---|---|---|
| 2804 | A955 | 50c multi | 1.25 1.25 |
| a. | | Souvenir sheet of 1 | 1.25 1.25 |
| 2805 | A956 | €1 blk & car | 2.40 2.40 |
| a. | | Souvenir sheet of 1 | 2.40 2.40 |

Greek Philatelists — A957

Designs: 5c, Alexander Argyropoulos (1883-1962). 20c, Charilis Binos (1909-78). 72c, Moses Konstantinis (1932-2018). 90c, Georgios Papastephanou (1890-1978). €1.50, Stephanos Makrymichalos (1902-83). €2, Nikolaus Atzaritis (1900-76).

### Litho. With Gold Foil Application

**2017, Nov. 16**      **Perf. 13¾**
| | | | |
|---|---|---|---|
| 2806-2811 | A957 | Set of 6 | 14.00 14.00 |

Discovery of Temple of Artemis Amarynthia — A958

### Litho. With Foil Application

**2017, Nov. 24**      **Perf. 13¾**
| | | | |
|---|---|---|---|
| 2812 | A958 | €1 multi | 2.40 2.40 |
| a. | | Souvenir sheet of 1 | 2.40 2.40 |

Christmas — A959

Children and: No. 2813, 72c, Penguin. No. 2814, 72c, Squirrel. No. 2815, 2817, 72c, Reindeer. Nos. 2816, 2818, 90c, Bear.

**2017, Dec. 5**    **Litho.**    **Perf. 13¾**
| | | | |
|---|---|---|---|
| 2813-2816 | A959 | Set of 4 | 7.50 7.50 |

### Booklet Stamps
### Self-Adhesive
#### Die Cut Perf. 11½x12

| | | | |
|---|---|---|---|
| 2817 | A959 | 72c multi | 1.75 1.75 |
| a. | | Booklet pane of 10 | 17.50 |
| 2818 | A959 | 90c multi | 2.25 2.25 |
| a. | | Booklet pane of 10 | 22.50 |

Civil Servants Joint Stock Fund Building, Athens — A960

Dimitrios N. Levidis (1806-93), Founder of Civil Servants Joint Stock Fund — A961

Civil Servants Joint Stock Fund Building, Athens
A962

**Litho. With Foil Application**
**2017, Dec. 8**      **Perf. 13¾**
2819 A960   72c gold & multi   1.75 1.75
2820 A961 €2.50 gold & multi   6.00 6.00
**Litho.**
**Perf. 14**
2821 A962   72c gold & multi + label   2.40 2.40

Civil Servants Joint Stock Fund, 150th anniv. No. 2821 was printed in sheets of 10 + 10 labels that could be personalized. Sheets sold for €10.

Souvenir Sheet

Reconstructed Appearance of "Myrtis," Girl Who Died in 430 B.C. Typhoid Epidemic in Athens — A963

**Litho., Sheet Margin Litho. With Foil Application**
**2018, Feb. 15**     **Perf. 13¾**
2822 A963 €1.50 sil & multi   3.75 3.75

A964

International Women's Day — A965

**2018, Mar. 8**   **Litho.**   **Perf. 14¼x14**
2823 A964 72c multi   1.75 1.75
**Litho. With Foil Application**
**Perf. 14x14¼**
2824 A965 90c multi   2.25 2.25

Art in Microscope Photography
A966

Artistic shapes found in microscope photography by Maria Lambropoulou: 10c, Flowers.

---

20c, Butterfly. 72c, Heart. €1, Wreath. €2, Deer.

**2018, Mar. 19**   **Litho.**   **Perf. 13¼**
2825-2829 A966   Set of 5   10.00 10.00

A.E.K. Basketball Club Emblem, Basketball Player, Backboard, and European Basketball Winner's Cup — A967

Panathenaic Stadium
A968

**2018, Mar. 30**   **Litho.**   **Perf. 13¾**
2830 A967 72c multi   1.75 1.75
   *a.*   Souvenir sheet of 1   1.75 1.75
2831 A968 90c multi   2.25 2.25
   *a.*   Souvenir sheet of 1   2.25 2.25

Victory of A.E.K. Basketball Club in European Championships, 50th anniv.

Souvenir Sheet

Juan de Fuca (1536-1602), Explorer — A969

**Litho., Sheet Margin Litho. With Foil Application**
**2018, Apr. 24**      **Perf. 13¾**
2832 A969 €2.50 multi   6.00 6.00

Juan de Fuca was born as Ioannis Phokas in Greece.

A.E.K. Basketball Club Emblem, Basketball Player, Backboard, and European Basketball Winner's Cup — A970

**2018, Apr. 26**   **Litho.**   **Perf. 13¼**
2833 A970 72c multi + label   3.00 3.00

No. 2833 was printed in sheets of 5 + 5 labels that could be personalized. Sheets sold for €6.

Souvenir Sheets

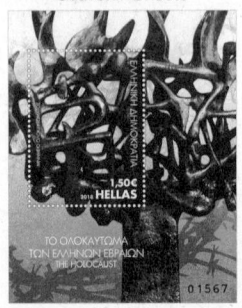

Greek Holocaust Monument — A971

---

Monastir Synagogue — A972

Holocaust Memorial Museum of Greece — A973

**2018, May 16**     **Litho.**    **Perf. 13¾**
2834 A971 €1.50 multi   3.50 3.50
2835 A972 €1.50 multi   3.50 3.50
2836 A973 €1.50 multi   3.50 3.50
   *Nos. 2834-2836 (3)*   10.50 10.50

World Bee Day — A974

Apis mellifera and: 50c, Lilac flower. 72c, Honeycomb. 80c, Plant. €2, Pink flower.

**2018, May 20**   **Litho.**   **Perf. 13¾x13½**
2837 A974 50c multi   1.25 1.25
   *a.*   Souvenir sheet of 1   1.25 1.25
2838 A974 72c multi   1.75 1.75
   *a.*   Souvenir sheet of 1   1.75 1.75
2839 A974 80c multi   1.90 1.90
   *a.*   Souvenir sheet of 1   1.90 1.90
2840 A974 €2 multi   4.75 4.75
   *a.*   Souvenir sheet of 1   4.75 4.75
   *Nos. 2837-2840 (4)*   9.65 9.65

Sheet margins on Nos. 2837a-3840a are litho. with foil application.

Souvenir Sheet

General Confederation of Greek Workers, Cent. — A975

No. 2841: a, Centenary emblem. b, Centenary emblem, workers and flag.

**2018, May 21**   **Litho.**   **Perf. 13¾**
2841 A975 €1 Sheet of 2, #a-b   4.75 4.75

Europa
A976

No. 2842: a, Rio-Antirrio Bridge. b, Plaka Bridge.

**2018, May 24**   **Litho.**   **Perf. 14¼x13¾**
2842 A976    Horiz. pair   10.00 10.00
   *a.*   90c multi   2.00 2.00
   *b.*   €3.40 multi   8.00 8.00
   *c.*   Horiz. pair, perf. 13¾ vert.   10.00 10.00
   *d.*   As "a," perf. 13¾ vert.   2.00 2.00
   *e.*   As "b," perf. 13¾ vert.   7.75 7.75
   *f.*   Booklet pane, 2 #2842c   20.00 —
     Complete booklet, #2842f   20.00

---

Hellenic Army Academy, 190th Anniv. — A977

Designs: 72c, Academy emblem. 80c, Governor of Greece Ioannis Kapodistrias awarding decroation to cadet. €1, Soldiers at flag lowering ceremony at academy, horiz. €2.62, Cadet and new academy building.

**Litho. With Gold Foil Application**
**2018, June 15**   Set of 4   **Perf. 13¾**
2843-2846 A977   Set of 4   12.00 12.00

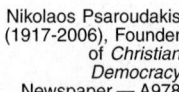

Nikolaos Psaroudakis (1917-2006), Founder of *Christian Democracy* Newspaper — A978

**2018, June 19**   **Litho.**   **Perf. 14**
2847 A978 72c multi   1.75 1.75

Hellenic Mathematical Society, Cent. — A979

**2018, June 19**   **Litho.**   **Perf. 14**
2848 A979 80c multi   1.90 1.90

Inter-Parliamentary Assembly on Orthodoxy, 25th Anniv. — A980

**Litho. With Foil Application**
**2018, June 19**      **Perf. 13¾**
2849 A980 90c multi   2.10 2.10

Tower in Mani — A981

Mansion in Pelion — A982

Cycladic House
A983

Houses in Dodecanese
A984

**2018, July 20**   **Litho.**   **Perf. 13¼x13½**
2850 A981 72c multi   1.75 1.75
   *a.*   Souvenir sheet of 1   1.75 1.75
   *b.*   Perf. 13¾ vert.   1.75 1.75
2851 A982 72c multi   1.75 1.75
   *a.*   Souvenir sheet of 1   1.75 1.75
   *b.*   Perf. 13¾ vert.   1.75 1.75
2852 A983 80c multi   1.90 1.90
   *a.*   Souvenir sheet of 1   1.90 1.90
   *b.*   Perf. 13¾ vert.   1.90 1.90
2853 A984 90c multi   2.10 2.10
   *a.*   Souvenir sheet of 1   2.10 2.10
   *b.*   Perf. 13¾ vert.   2.10 2.10
   *c.*   Booklet pane of 4, #2850b, 2851b, 2852b, 2853b   7.50 —
     Complete booklet, #2853c   7.50
   *Nos. 2850-2853 (4)*   7.50 7.50

## Souvenir Sheets

Alexander the Great, Painting by Theophilos Hatzimihail (1873-1934) — A985

Erotokritos and Aretousa, Painting by Hatzimihail — A986

**Litho., Sheet Margin Litho. With Foil Application**

| 2018, July 25 | | | Perf. 13¾ | |
|---|---|---|---|---|
| 2854 | A985 | €1 copper & multi | 2.40 | 2.40 |
| 2855 | A986 | €1 copper & multi | 2.40 | 2.40 |

Museum of Modern Greek Culture, Athens, cent.

Corinth Canal, 125th Anniv. — A987

**Litho. With Hologram Affixed**

| 2018, Aug. 25 | | Die Cut Perf. 11½x12 | | |
|---|---|---|---|---|
| | | Booklet Stamp | | |
| | | Self-Adhesive | | |
| 2856 | A987 | (72c) multi | 1.75 | 1.75 |
| a. | | Booklet pane of 10 | 17.50 | |

No. 2856 was printed with a hologram and a frame that is found on numerous subsequent self-adhesive booklet pane stamps. The subsequent issues having this frame and hologram were called "personalized stamps" by postal officials, though no purchaser could personalize these stamps with their own pictures. No. 2856 was not called a "personalized stamp" by Greek postal officials, however, and many of the subsequent booklets containing stamps with this frame and hologram were produced in limited quantities. Each booklet produced contains ten stamps. Some booklets contain stamps that show the same vignette, while other booklets contain stamps with as many as ten different vignettes. The color of the country name "Hellas" has appeared in a variety of colors. A variety of different denominations or postal rate inscriptions written in Greek or English are known to exist.

Special Disaster Response Unit, 30th Anniv. — A988

| 2018, Sept. 5 | | Litho. | Perf. 13¾x14¼ | |
|---|---|---|---|---|
| 2857 | A988 | 72c multi | 1.75 | 1.75 |

Orthodox Academy of Crete, 50th Anniv. — A989

| 2018, Sept. 5 | | Litho. | Perf. 14¼x13¾ | |
|---|---|---|---|---|
| 2858 | A989 | €1 multi | 2.40 | 2.40 |

A990

83rd Thessaloniki International Trade Fair — A991

| 2018, Sept. 5 | | Litho. | Perf. 14¼x13¾ | |
|---|---|---|---|---|
| 2859 | A990 | 80c multi | 1.90 | 1.90 |
| | | | Perf. 13½ | |
| 2860 | A991 | 80c multi + label | 3.75 | 3.75 |

No. 2860 was printed in sheets of 5 + 5 labels that could be personalized. The sheet sold for €8. The generic label is shown.

Greek Mail Boxes — A992

Designs: 10c, Yellow mailbox. 50c, Black mailbox. 72c, Orange mailbox. €2.62, Greenish yellow mailbox.

**Litho. With Foil Application**

| 2018, Oct. 9 | | | Perf. 13¾ | |
|---|---|---|---|---|
| 2861-2864 | A992 | Set of 4 | 9.00 | 9.00 |

Greek Postal Service, 190th anniv.

A993

Christmas — A994

Designs: Nos. 2865, 2869, 2870, 72c, Santa Claus and reindeer. No. 2866, 72c, Child writing Christmas list. No. 2867, 2871, 80c, Children placing letter in mailbox. No. 2868, 90c, Child opening Christmas present.

| 2018, Nov. 23 | | Litho. | Perf. 13¾ | |
|---|---|---|---|---|
| 2865-2868 | A993 | Set of 4 | 7.25 | 7.25 |
| | | | Perf. 13¼ | |
| 2869 | A994 | 72c multi + label | 2.75 | 2.75 |

**Booklet Stamps**
**Self-Adhesive**
**Die Cut Perf. 11½x12**

| 2870 | A993 | 72c multi | 1.75 | 1.75 |
|---|---|---|---|---|
| a. | | Booklet pane of 10 | 17.50 | |
| 2871 | A993 | 80c multi | 1.90 | 1.90 |
| a. | | Booklet pane of 10 | 19.00 | |

No. 2869 was printed in sheets of 5 + 5 labels that could be personalized. The generic label is shown. Sheets sold for €6.

## Souvenir Sheet

Hellenic Space Agency Satellite A995

| 2018, Nov. 30 | | Litho. | Perf. 13¾ | |
|---|---|---|---|---|
| 2872 | A995 | €2.50 multi | 5.75 | 5.75 |

Presidential Guard, 150th Anniv. — A996

Designs: 5c, Three guardsmen. 10c, Two guardsmen at Monument of the Unknown Soldier, horiz. 20c, Guardsmen at the Acropolis, horiz. €1, Guardsman in winter uniform at Monument of the Unknown Soldier. €2, Guardsman raising flag at Acropolis.

**Litho. With Foil Application**

| 2018, Dec. 12 | | Perf. 14x14¼, 14¼x14 | | |
|---|---|---|---|---|
| 2873-2877 | A996 | Set of 5 | 7.75 | 7.75 |

A997

Famous Ancient Greek Men — A998

Designs: 5c, Epicurus (341-270 B.C.), philosopher. 20c, Xenophon (c. 451-354 B.C.), philosopher. 50c, Socrates (c. 470-399 B.C.), philosopher. €1, Herodotus (c. 484-c. 425 B.C.), historian. (€2.62), Euripides (c. 480- c. 406 B.C.), playwright.

| | | | Perf. 13¾x14¼ | |
|---|---|---|---|---|
| 2019, Mar. 15 | | | Litho. | |
| 2878 | A997 | 5c multi | .25 | .25 |
| a. | | Perf. 14¼ vert. | .25 | .25 |
| 2879 | A997 | 20c multi | .45 | .45 |
| a. | | Perf. 14¼ vert. | .45 | .45 |
| 2880 | A997 | 50c multi | 1.10 | 1.10 |
| a. | | Perf. 14¼ vert. | 1.10 | 1.10 |
| 2881 | A997 | €1 multi | 2.25 | 2.25 |
| a. | | Perf. 14¼ vert. | 2.25 | 2.25 |
| 2882 | A998 | (€2.62) multi | 5.75 | 5.75 |
| a. | | Perf. 14¼ vert. | 5.75 | 5.75 |
| b. | | Souvenir sheet of 5, #2878-2882 | 10.00 | 10.00 |
| | | Nos. 2878-2882 (5) | 9.80 | 9.80 |

Compare with type A951.

A999

A1000

A1001

Winning Art in Children's Art Contest A1002

| 2019, Apr. 9 | | Litho. | Perf. 13¾ | |
|---|---|---|---|---|
| 2883 | A999 | 72c multi | 1.60 | 1.60 |
| 2884 | A1000 | 72c multi | 1.60 | 1.60 |
| 2885 | A1001 | 90c multi | 2.10 | 2.10 |
| 2886 | A1002 | €2.50 multi | 5.75 | 5.75 |
| | | Nos. 2883-2886 (4) | 11.05 | 11.05 |

Europa A1003

No. 2887: a, Sitta neumayer. b, Flaco eleonorae.

| 2019, May 9 | | Litho. | Perf. 13¾ | |
|---|---|---|---|---|
| 2887 | A1003 | Horiz. pair | 9.75 | 9.75 |
| a. | | 90c multi | 2.00 | 2.00 |
| b. | | €3.40 multi | 7.75 | 7.75 |
| c. | | Horiz. pair, perf. 13¾ vert. | 9.75 | 9.75 |
| d. | | As "a," perf. 13¾ vert. | 2.00 | 2.00 |
| e. | | As "b," perf. 13¾ vert. | 7.75 | 7.75 |
| f. | | Booklet pane, 2 #2887c | 19.50 | — |
| | | Complete booklet, #2887f | 19.50 | |

Bridal Costume, Lefkada, 19th-20th Cent. A1004

Bridal Costume, Castellorizo, 19th Cent. A1005

Bridal Costume, Crete, 20th Cent. A1006

Refugee's Costume, Xanthi, 19th Cent. A1007

| 2019, July 15 | | Litho. | Perf. 14x14¼ | |
|---|---|---|---|---|
| 2888 | A1004 | (72c) multi | 1.60 | 1.60 |
| a. | | Perf. 14¼ vert. | 1.60 | 1.60 |
| 2889 | A1005 | (80c) multi | 1.75 | 1.75 |
| a. | | Perf. 14¼ vert. | 1.75 | 1.75 |
| 2890 | A1006 | (80c) multi | 1.75 | 1.75 |
| a. | | Perf. 14¼ vert. | 1.75 | 1.75 |
| 2891 | A1007 | (€2.62) multi | 5.75 | 5.75 |
| a. | | Perf. 14¼ vert. | 5.75 | 5.75 |
| b. | | Booklet pane of 4, #2888a-2891a | 11.00 | |
| | | Complete booklet, #2891b | 11.00 | |
| c. | | Souvenir sheet of 4, #2888-2891 | 11.00 | 11.00 |
| | | Nos. 2888-2891 (4) | 10.85 | 10.85 |

Ship and Helicopter A1008

Emblem — A1009

Centenary Emblem A1010

Patrol Boat — A1011

**Litho., Litho. With Foil Application (#2893)**

**2019, Sept. 16** **Perf. 13¾**

| | | | | |
|---|---|---|---|---|
| 2892 | A1008 | 20c multi | .45 | .45 |
| 2893 | A1009 | (72c) multi | 1.60 | 1.60 |
| 2894 | A1010 | 90c multi | 2.00 | 2.00 |
| 2895 | A1011 | (€3.40) multi | 7.50 | 7.50 |
| | Nos. 2892-2895 (4) | | 11.55 | 11.55 |

Greek Coast Guard, cent.

2019 International Foundation for Greece Award Recipients — A1012

Emblem and: 5c, C. Dean Metropoulos, businessman. 10c, Korina Mentzelopoulou, vintner. (72c), Dimitrios Nanopoulos, physicist. €1.50, Alexandre Desplat, composer. €2, George D. Behrakis, philanthropist.

**2019, Oct. 7** **Litho.** **Perf. 14x14½**

| | | | | |
|---|---|---|---|---|
| 2896-2900 | A1012 | Set of 5 | 9.75 | 9.75 |

Holy Monastery of Saint Xenophon, Mount Athos, 200th Anniv. — A1013

**Litho. With Foil Application**

**2019, Oct. 20** **Perf. 13¾**

| | | | | |
|---|---|---|---|---|
| 2901 | A1013 | €2.50 multi | 5.75 | 5.75 |
| a. | Souvenir sheet of 1 | | 5.75 | 5.75 |

Flamingo A1014

Sloth A1015

Unicorn A1016

Llama A1017

**2019, Nov. 25** **Litho.** **Perf. 13¾**

| | | | | |
|---|---|---|---|---|
| 2902 | A1014 | (72c) multi | 1.60 | 1.60 |
| 2903 | A1015 | (72c) multi | 1.60 | 1.60 |

**Litho. With Foil Application**

| | | | | |
|---|---|---|---|---|
| 2904 | A1016 | (72c) multi | 1.60 | 1.60 |
| 2905 | A1017 | (90c) multi | 2.00 | 2.00 |
| a. | Souvenir sheet of 4, #2902-2905 | | 7.00 | 7.00 |
| | Nos. 2902-2905 (4) | | 6.80 | 6.80 |

**Booklet Stamps**
**Self-Adhesive**
**Litho.**

*Die Cut Perf. 11½x12*

| | | | | |
|---|---|---|---|---|
| 2906 | A1016 | (72c) multi | 1.60 | 1.60 |
| a. | Booklet pane of 10 | | 16.00 | |
| 2907 | A1017 | (90c) multi | 2.00 | 2.00 |
| a. | Booklet pane of 10 | | 20.00 | |

Christmas.

---

Ancient Greek Theaters A1018

Theater at: 10c, Gitanae. 50c, Cassope. €1, Dodona. €2, Nicopolis. €2.50, Ambracia.

**2020, Apr. 8** **Litho.** **Perf. 13¾**

| | | | | |
|---|---|---|---|---|
| 2908-2912 | A1018 | Set of 5 | 13.50 | 13.50 |

Europa A1019

No. 2913 — Ships: a, Prince Maximilian. b, Archduke Ludovico.

**2020, May 8** **Litho.** **Perf. 14¼x14**

| | | | | |
|---|---|---|---|---|
| 2913 | A1019 | Horiz. pair | 14.50 | 14.50 |
| a. | €2 multi | | 4.50 | 4.50 |
| b. | €4.50 multi | | 10.00 | 10.00 |
| c. | Horiz. pair, perf. 14 vert. | | 14.50 | 14.50 |
| d. | As "a," perf. 14 vert. | | 4.50 | 4.50 |
| e. | As "b," perf. 14 vert. | | 10.00 | 10.00 |
| f. | Booklet pane, 2 #2913c | | 29.00 | |
| | Complete booklet, #2913f | | 29.00 | |

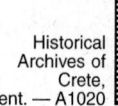

Historical Archives of Crete, Cent. — A1020

Agricultural University of Athens, Cent. A1021

Athens University of Economics and Business, Cent. A1022

Military Academy of Combat Support Officers, 50th Anniv. — A1023

**Perf. 14¼x14, 14x14¼**

**2020, May 21** **Litho.**

| | | | | |
|---|---|---|---|---|
| 2914 | A1020 | 10c multi | .25 | .25 |
| 2915 | A1021 | 90c multi | 2.00 | 2.00 |
| 2916 | A1022 | €1 multi | 2.25 | 2.25 |
| 2917 | A1023 | €2 multi | 4.50 | 4.50 |
| | Nos. 2914-2917 (4) | | 9.00 | 9.00 |

Greek Cuisine — A1024

Designs: 10c, Green pie. 50c, Octopus. €2.50, Lamb. €3, Moussaka.

**2020, July 20** **Litho.** **Perf. 14¼x14**

| | | | | |
|---|---|---|---|---|
| 2918 | A1024 | 10c multi | .25 | .25 |
| a. | Perf. 14 vert. | | .25 | .25 |
| 2919 | A1024 | 50c multi | 1.25 | 1.25 |
| a. | Perf. 14 vert. | | 1.25 | 1.25 |
| 2920 | A1024 | €2.50 multi | 6.00 | 6.00 |
| a. | Perf. 14 vert. | | 6.00 | 6.00 |
| 2921 | A1024 | €3 multi | 7.00 | 7.00 |
| a. | Perf. 14 vert. | | 7.00 | 7.00 |
| b. | Booklet pane of 4, #2918a, 2919a, 2920a, 2921a | | 14.50 | — |
| | Complete booklet, #2921b | | 14.50 | |
| | Nos. 2918-2921 (4) | | 14.50 | 14.50 |

Ion Dragoumis (1878-1920), Diplomat and Politician — A1025

---

**Litho. With Foil Application**

**2020, July 31** **Perf. 14x14¼**

| | | | | |
|---|---|---|---|---|
| 2922 | A1025 | €2 gold & multi | 4.75 | 4.75 |
| a. | Souvenir sheet of 1 | | 4.75 | 4.75 |

Aerial View of Trireme A1026

Side View of Trireme A1027

Themistocles (c. 524-459 B.C.), Naval Commander and Politician A1028

Ships Ramming Each Other — A1029

**Litho. With Foil Application**

**2020, Sept. 22** **Perf. 13¾**

| | | | | |
|---|---|---|---|---|
| 2923 | A1026 | 90c gold & multi | 2.10 | 2.10 |
| 2924 | A1027 | €1 gold & multi | 2.40 | 2.40 |
| 2925 | A1028 | €1 gold & multi | 2.40 | 2.40 |
| a. | Souvenir sheet of 2, #2924-2925 | | 4.80 | 4.80 |
| 2926 | A1029 | €2 gold & multi | 4.75 | 4.75 |
| a. | Souvenir sheet of 2, #2923, 2926 | | 7.00 | 7.00 |
| | Nos. 2923-2926 (4) | | 11.65 | 11.65 |

Battle of Salamis, 2500th anniv.

Detail of Sculpture of Fighters at Battle of Thermopylae, by Vasos Falireas (1905-79) A1030

Detail of Sculpture by Falireas, and Quotation A1031

Statue of Leonidas, by Falireas A1032

Detail of Sculpture of Fighters at Battle of Thermopylae, by Falireas A1033

**Litho. With Foil Application**

**2020, Nov. 3** **Perf. 13¾**

| | | | | |
|---|---|---|---|---|
| 2927 | A1030 | 50c gold & multi | 1.25 | 1.25 |
| 2928 | A1031 | 90c gold & multi | 2.25 | 2.25 |
| 2929 | A1032 | €1 gold & multi | 2.40 | 2.40 |
| a. | Souvenir sheet of 2, #2928-2929 | | 4.75 | 4.75 |

---

| | | | | |
|---|---|---|---|---|
| 2930 | A1033 | €2.50 gold & multi | 6.00 | 6.00 |
| a. | Souvenir sheet of 2, #2927, 2930 | | 7.25 | 7.25 |
| | Nos. 2927-2930 (4) | | 11.90 | 11.90 |

Battle of Thermopylae, 2500th anniv.

A1034

Christmas — A1035

**2020, Nov. 23** **Litho.** **Perf. 13¾**

| | | | | |
|---|---|---|---|---|
| 2931 | A1034 | 90c multi | 2.25 | 2.25 |
| 2932 | A1035 | €1 multi | 2.40 | 2.40 |
| a. | Souvenir sheet of 2, #2931-2932 | | 4.75 | 4.75 |

**Booklet Stamp**
**Self-Adhesive**
*Die Cut Perf. 11½x12*

| | | | | |
|---|---|---|---|---|
| 2933 | A1034 | 90c multi | 2.25 | 2.25 |
| a. | Booklet pane of 10 | | 22.50 | |
| 2934 | A1035 | €1 multi | 2.40 | 2.40 |
| a. | Booklet pane of 10 | | 24.00 | |

A1036

A1037

A1038

Campaign to Stop Bullying — A1039

**2020, Dec. 2** **Litho.** **Perf. 13¾**

| | | | | |
|---|---|---|---|---|
| 2935 | A1036 | 10c multi | .25 | .25 |
| 2936 | A1037 | 90c multi | 2.25 | 2.25 |
| 2937 | A1038 | €1 multi | 2.50 | 2.50 |
| 2938 | A1039 | €2 multi | 5.00 | 5.00 |
| | Nos. 2935-2938 (4) | | 10.00 | 10.00 |

Greek Revolution, 200th Anniv. — A1040

Background color: 90c, Blue. €1, Tan.

**Litho. With Foil Application**

**2021, Jan. 28** **Perf. 13¾**

| | | | | |
|---|---|---|---|---|
| 2939-2940 | A1040 | Set of 2 | 4.75 | 4.75 |
| 2940a | | Souvenir sheet of 2, #2939-2940 | 4.75 | 4.75 |

Patriotic Lithographs and Paintings A1041

Designs: 20c, The Patriotic Oath of the Greeks, by Alphonese-Marie-Adolphe dee Neuville ((1835-85). €1, The Heroism of the Women of Souli, by de Neuville. €3, The Death of Markos Botsaris, by Jean Charles Langlois (1789-1870). €4, The Oath, painting by Dionysios Tsokos (c. 1814-62).

**Litho. With Foil Application**
| 2021, Mar. 25 | | Perf. 13¾ | |
|---|---|---|---|
| 2941-2944 | A1041 | Set of 4 | 19.50 19.50 |
| 2944a | | Booklet pane of 4, | |
| | | #2941-2944 | 28.50 — |
| | | Complete booklet, #2944a | 28.50 |

Complete booklet sold for €12.

Endangered Animals — A1042

No. 2945: a, Cervus elaphus. b, Delphinus delphis.

**Litho. With Foil Application**
| 2021, May 6 | | Perf. 13¾ | |
|---|---|---|---|
| 2945 | A1042 | Horiz. pair | 16.00 16.00 |
| a. | | €2 gold & multi | 5.00 5.00 |
| b. | | €4.50 gold & multi | 11.00 11.00 |
| c. | | Horiz. pair, perf. 13¾ vert. | 16.00 16.00 |
| d. | | As "a," perf. 13¾ vert. | 5.00 5.00 |
| e. | | As "b," perf. 13¾ vert. | 11.00 11.00 |
| f. | | Booklet pane, 2 #2945c | 32.00 — |
| | | Complete booklet, #2945f | 32.00 |

Europa.

Souvenir Sheets

Buildings in Tokyo A1043

Hanetsuki Court and Shuttlecock — A1044

**Litho., Sheet Margin Litho. With Foil Application**
| 2021, June 3 | | Perf. 13¾ | |
|---|---|---|---|
| 2946 | A1043 | €2.40 multi | 5.75 5.75 |
| 2947 | A1044 | €2.40 multi | 5.75 5.75 |

2020 Summer Olympics, Tokyo. The 2020 Summer Olympics were postponed until 2021 because of the COVID-19 pandemic.

Jewelry — A1045

Designs: 90c, Gold earrings, 2nd cent. B.C. €1, Gold buckle, 6th-7th cent. €1.90, Silver gilt necklace with silver pendants, coral and colored stones, 17th-18th cent. €2, Bridal jewelry, 19thcent.

**Litho. With Foil Application**
| 2021, July 13 | | Perf. 14¼x14 | |
|---|---|---|---|
| 2948-2951 | A1045 | Set of 4 | 14.00 14.00 |
| 2948a | | Perf. 14 vert. | 2.25 2.25 |
| 2949a | | Perf. 14 vert. | 2.40 2.40 |
| 2950a | | Perf. 14 vert. | 4.50 4.50 |
| 2951a | | Souvenir sheet of 4, | |
| | | #2948-2951 | 14.00 14.00 |
| 2951b | | Perf. 14 vert. | 4.75 4.75 |
| 2951c | | Booklet pane of 4, | |
| | | #2948a, 2949a, 2950a, | |
| | | 2951b | 14.00 — |
| | | Complete booklet, #2951c | 14.00 |

Alexander Pushkin (1799-1837), Writer A1046

Eugène Delacroix (1798-1863), Painter A1047

Percy Bysshe Shelley (1792-1822), Poet A1048

Samuel Howe (1801-76), Physician A1049

Karl Krazelsen (1794-1878), Soldier and Artist — A1050

| 2021, Sept. 23 | Litho. | Perf. 14x14¼ | |
|---|---|---|---|
| 2952 | | Horiz. strip of 5 | 12.00 12.00 |
| a. | A1046 | €1 multi | 2.40 2.40 |
| b. | A1047 | €1 multi | 2.40 2.40 |
| c. | A1048 | €1 multi | 2.40 2.40 |
| d. | A1049 | €1 multi | 2.40 2.40 |
| e. | A1050 | €1 multi | 2.40 2.40 |

19th century philhellenists.

A1051

A1052

A1053

Winning Children's Drawings in Greek Revolution Bicentenary Stamp Design Contest A1054

| 2021, Oct. 7 | | Litho. | Perf. 13¾ | |
|---|---|---|---|---|
| 2953 | A1051 | €1 multi | 2.40 2.40 |
| 2954 | A1052 | €1 multi | 2.40 2.40 |
| 2955 | A1053 | €1 multi | 2.40 2.40 |
| 2956 | A1054 | €1 multi | 2.40 2.40 |
| | | Nos. 2953-2956 (4) | 9.60 9.60 |

Christmas — A1056

A1055

| 2021, Nov. 4 | | Litho. | Perf. 13¾ | |
|---|---|---|---|---|
| 2957 | A1055 | 90c multi | 2.10 2.10 |
| 2958 | A1056 | €1 multi | 2.25 2.25 |
| a. | | Souvenir sheet of 4, 2 each | |
| | | #2957-2958 | 8.75 8.75 |

**Booklet Stamps**
**Self-Adhesive**
*Die Cut Perf. 11½x12*
| 2959 | A1055 | 90c multi | 2.10 2.10 |
|---|---|---|---|
| a. | | Booklet pane of 10 | 21.00 |
| 2960 | A1056 | €1 multi | 2.25 2.25 |
| a. | | Booklet pane of 10 | 22.50 |

Souvenir Sheet

Notos 2021 European Philatelic Exhibition, Athens — A1057

No. 2961 — Hermes facing: a, Right. b, Left.

**Litho. With Foil Application**
| 2021, Nov. 19 | | | Perf. 13¾ | |
|---|---|---|---|---|
| 2961 | A1057 | Sheet of 2 | 11.00 11.00 |
| a.-b. | | €2.40 Either single | 5.50 5.50 |

Two Warriors, by Theodoros Vryzakis (1819-78) A1058

Georgios Karaiskakis Riding on Horseback to the Acropolis, by Georgios Margaritis (1814-84) A1059

Karaiskakis' Camp, by Vryzakis A1060

War Scene, by Vryzakis A1061

Grateful Hellas, by Vryzakis A1062

**Litho. With Foil Application**
| 2021, Dec.16 | | | Perf. 14x14¾ | |
|---|---|---|---|---|
| 2962 | A1058 | 90c gold & multi | 2.10 2.10 |
| 2963 | A1059 | 90c gold & multi | 2.10 2.10 |
| 2964 | A1060 | €1 gold & multi | 2.25 2.25 |
| 2965 | A1061 | €1 gold & multi | 2.25 2.25 |
| | | Nos. 2962-2965 (4) | 8.70 8.70 |

**Souvenir Sheet**
*Perf. 13¼x13½*
| 2966 | A1062 | €4 multi | 9.00 9.00 |
|---|---|---|---|

Greek Revolution, 200th anniv.

Geneleos Group of Statues, Heraion of Samos UNESCO World Heritage Site — A1063

Mosaic of Archangel Michael, Nea Moni of Chios UNESCO World Heritage Site — A1064

Tiryns Archaeological Site UNESCO World Heritage Site — A1065

Mural Depicting Hades Abducting Persephone, Aigai Archaeological Site UNESCO World Heritage Site — A1066

**Litho. With Foil Application**
| 2022, Feb. 3 | | | Perf. 13¾ | |
|---|---|---|---|---|
| 2967 | A1063 | 40c gold & multi | .90 .90 |
| 2968 | A1064 | 50c gold & multi | 1.10 1.10 |
| 2969 | A1065 | €1.90 gold & multi | 4.25 4.25 |
| 2970 | A1066 | €3.40 gold & multi | 7.75 7.75 |
| | | Nos. 2967-2970 (4) | 14.00 14.00 |

Traffic Safety — A1067

Designs: 10c, Traffic light with face and hands, cars and crosswalk. 50c, Red light, children crossing at crosswalk, crossing guard. €2, Green light, bicyclists in traffic. €2.50, Yellow light, children wearing seat belts.

**Litho. With Foil Application**
| 2022, Mar. 24 | | Perf. 13¼ | |
|---|---|---|---|
| 2971-2974 | A1067 | Set of 4 | 11.50 11.50 |

A1068

A1069

A1070

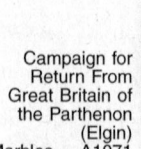

Campaign for
Return From
Great Britain of
the Parthenon
(Elgin)
Marbles — A1071

**Litho. With Foil Application**
**2022, May 19**

| | | | | |
|---|---|---|---|---|
| 2975 | A1068 | €1 multi + label | 2.25 | 2.25 |
| 2976 | A1069 | €1 multi + label | 2.25 | 2.25 |
| 2977 | A1070 | €1 multi + label | 2.25 | 2.25 |
| 2978 | A1071 | €1 multi + label | 2.25 | 2.25 |
| | | Nos. 2975-2978 (4) | 9.00 | 9.00 |

Murder
of
Orpheus
by the
Maenads
A1072

No. 2979: a, Maenads. b, Orpheus fending
off attack.

**2022, May 26      Litho.      Perf. 13¾**

| | | | | |
|---|---|---|---|---|
| 2979 | A1072 | Horiz. pair | 14.00 | 14.00 |
| a. | | €2 multi | 4.25 | 4.25 |
| b. | | €4.50 multi | 9.75 | 9.75 |
| c. | | Horiz. pair, perf. 13¾ vert. | 14.00 | 14.00 |
| d. | | As "a," perf. 13¾ vert. | 4.25 | 4.25 |
| e. | | As "b," perf. 13¾ vert. | 9.75 | 9.75 |
| f. | | Booklet pane, 2 #2979c | 28.00 | — |
| | | Complete booklet, #2979f | 28.00 | |

Europa.

Vikos-Aoos
Geopark
A1073

Lesvos Geopark
A1074

Psiloritis
Geopark
A1075

Helmos-Vouraikos Geopark — A1076

Sitia Geopark
A1077

**2022, June 5      Litho.      Perf. 13¾**

| | | | | |
|---|---|---|---|---|
| 2980 | A1073 | €1 multi | 2.10 | 2.10 |
| 2981 | A1074 | €1 multi | 2.10 | 2.10 |
| 2982 | A1075 | €1.50 multi | 3.25 | 3.25 |
| 2983 | A1076 | €2 multi | 4.25 | 4.25 |
| 2984 | A1077 | €2.50 multi | 5.25 | 5.25 |
| | | Nos. 2980-2984 (5) | 16.95 | 16.95 |

Maritime Archaeology — A1078

No. 2985 — Items from Peristeras shipwreck: a, One amphora in foreground. b,
Amphoras.

**2022, July 11      Litho.      Perf. 14¼x14**

| | | | | |
|---|---|---|---|---|
| 2985 | A1078 | Horiz. pair | 14.50 | 14.50 |
| a. | | €3 multi | 6.25 | 6.25 |
| b. | | €4 multi | 8.25 | 8.25 |
| c. | | Souvenir sheet of 4, 2 each #2985a-2985b | 29.00 | 29.00 |
| d. | | Horiz. pair, perf. 14 vert. | 14.50 | 14.50 |
| e. | | As "a," perf. 14 vert. | 6.25 | 6.25 |
| f. | | As "b," perf. 14 vert. | 8.25 | 8.25 |
| g. | | Booklet pane, 2 #2985d | 29.00 | |
| | | Complete booklet, #2985g | 29.00 | |

Souvenir Sheet

American Hellenic Educational
Progressive Association,
Cent. — A1079

**2022, July 26      Litho.      Perf. 13¾**

| | | | | |
|---|---|---|---|---|
| 2986 | A1079 | €4 multi | 8.25 | 8.25 |

Establishment
of Urban
Refugee
Settlements
After Greco-
Turkish War,
Cent. — A1080

Settlement at: 90c, Caesariani. €1.50, Kok-
kinia. €2.50, Byrona. €3.40, Nea Ionia.

**2022, Sept. 14      Litho.      Perf. 13¾**

| | | | | |
|---|---|---|---|---|
| 2987-2990 | A1080 | Set of 4 | 16.50 | 16.50 |

Christmas — A1085

Designs: Nos. 2995, 2999, 90c, Drummer
nutcracker. Nos. 2996, 3000, 90c, Jack-in-the-
box. Nos. 2997, 3001, €1, Ballerina with triangle. Nos. 2998, 3002, €1, Rocking horse.

**2022, Nov. 10      Litho.      Perf. 13¾**

| | | | | |
|---|---|---|---|---|
| 2995-2998 | A1085 | Set of 4 | 8.00 | 8.00 |
| 2998a | | Souvenir sheet of 4, #2995-2998 | 8.00 | 8.00 |

**Booklet Stamps**
**Self-Adhesive**
*Die Cut Perf. 11½x12*

| | | | | |
|---|---|---|---|---|
| 2999-3002 | A1085 | Set of 4 | 8.00 | 8.00 |
| 3000a | | Booklet pane of 10, 5 each #2999-3000 | 19.00 | |
| 3002a | | Booklet pane of 10, 5 each #3001-3002 | 21.00 | |

---

## SEMI-POSTAL STAMPS

> **Catalogue values for unused
> stamps in this section are for
> Never Hinged items.**

Nos. 440-444
Surcharged in Blue

**1944      Wmk. 252      Perf. 12½**

| | | | | |
|---|---|---|---|---|
| B1 | A106 | 100,000d on 15d | 1.25 | 1.50 |
| B2 | A107 | 100,000d on 25d | 1.25 | 1.50 |
| a. | | Inverted surcharge | 50.00 | |
| b. | | Double impression | 150.00 | |
| B3 | A108 | 100,000d on 50d | 1.25 | 1.50 |
| a. | | Double impression | 150.00 | |
| B4 | A109 | 100,000d on 75d | 1.25 | 1.50 |
| B5 | A110 | 100,000d on 100d | 1.25 | 1.50 |
| a. | | Inverted surcharge | 50.00 | |
| b. | | Double impression | 75.00 | |
| | | Nos. B1-B5,CB1-CB5 (10) | 12.50 | 16.05 |

The proceeds aided victims of the Piraeus
bombing, Jan. 11, 1944. The exceptionally
high face value discouraged the use of these
stamps.

Nos. 437-441
Surcharged in Blue

**1944, July 20      50,000d + 450,000d**

| | | | | |
|---|---|---|---|---|
| B11 | A103 | on 2d | .75 | 1.00 |
| B12 | A104 | on 5d | .75 | 1.00 |
| a. | | "NAYOLION" instead of "NAYPLION" | 55.00 | 60.00 |
| B13 | A105 | on 10d | .75 | 1.00 |
| B14 | A106 | on 15d | .75 | 1.00 |
| a. | | Pair, one without surcharge | 80.00 | |
| b. | | Inverted surcharge | 35.00 | |
| B15 | A107 | on 25d | .75 | 1.00 |
| | | Nos. B11-B15,CB6-CB10 (10) | 10.00 | 10.00 |

The surtax aided children's camps.

---

## AIR POST STAMPS

**Italy-Greece-Turkey-Rhodes Service**

Flying Boat off
Phaleron
Bay — AP1

Flying Boat
over Acropolis
AP2

Flying Boat
over Map of
Southern
Europe — AP3

Flying Boat
Seen through
Colonnade
AP4

**Perf. 11½**

**1926, Oct. 20      Unwmk.      Litho.**

| | | | | |
|---|---|---|---|---|
| C1 | AP1 | 2d multicolored | 1.60 | 1.25 |
| a. | | Horiz. pair, imperf. vert. | 725.00 | |
| C2 | AP2 | 3d multicolored | 12.00 | 11.00 |
| C3 | AP3 | 5d multicolored | 1.60 | 1.25 |
| C4 | AP4 | 10d multicolored | 12.00 | 12.00 |
| | | Nos. C1-C4 (4) | 27.20 | 25.50 |
| | | Set, never hinged | 80.00 | |

**Graf Zeppelin Issue**

Zeppelin over
Acropolis — AP5

**1933, May 2      Perf. 13½x12½**

| | | | | |
|---|---|---|---|---|
| C5 | AP5 | 30d rose red | 13.00 | 13.00 |
| C6 | AP5 | 100d deep blue | 52.50 | 52.50 |
| C7 | AP5 | 120d dark brown | 52.50 | 52.50 |
| | | Nos. C5-C7 (3) | 118.00 | 118.00 |
| | | Set, never hinged | 325.00 | |

Propeller and
Pilot's
Head — AP6

Temple of Apollo,
Corinth — AP7

Plane over
Hermoupolis,
Syros — AP8

Allegory of Flight
AP9      AP12

Map of Italy-Greece-Turkey-Rhodes
Airmail Route — AP10

Head of Hermes and
Airplane — AP11

**1933, Oct. 10      Engr.      Perf. 12**

| | | | | |
|---|---|---|---|---|
| C8 | AP6 | 50 l green & org | .25 | .25 |
| C9 | AP7 | 1d bl & brn org | .30 | .25 |
| C10 | AP8 | 3d dk vio & org | .50 | .50 |
| C11 | AP9 | 5d brn org & dk bl | 7.25 | 4.50 |
| C12 | AP10 | 10d dp red & blk | 1.50 | 1.40 |
| C13 | AP11 | 20d black & grn | 7.25 | 4.00 |
| C14 | AP12 | 50d dp brn & dp bl | 50.00 | 55.00 |
| | | Nos. C8-C14 (7) | 67.05 | 65.90 |
| | | Set, never hinged | 200.00 | |

By error the 1d stamp is inscribed in the
plural "ΔΡΑΧΜΑΙ" instead of the singular
"ΔΡΑΧΜΗ." This stamp exists bisected, used
as a 50 lepta denomination.

All values of this set exist imperforate but
were not regularly issued.

## For General Air Post Service

Airplane over Map of Greece AP13

Airplane over Map of Icarian Sea AP14

Airplane over Acropolis — AP15

### Perf. 13x13½, 13x12½, 13½x13, 12½x13

**1933, Nov. 2**

| | | | | |
|---|---|---|---|---|
| C15 | AP13 | 50 l green | .25 | .25 |
| C16 | AP13 | 1d red brown | .30 | .55 |
| C17 | AP14 | 2d lt violet | .60 | .85 |
| C18 | AP15 | 5d ultra | 3.50 | 3.50 |
| a. | | Imperf., pair | 650.00 | 550.00 |
| b. | | Horiz. pair, imperf. vert. | 650.00 | |
| C19 | AP14 | 10d car rose | 6.50 | 7.75 |
| C20 | AP13 | 25d dark blue | 30.00 | 20.00 |
| C21 | AP15 | 50d dark brown | 30.00 | 42.50 |
| a. | | Imperf., pair | 775.00 | 650.00 |
| | | Nos. C15-C21 (7) | 71.15 | 75.40 |
| | | Set, never hinged | 225.00 | |

Helios Driving the Sun Chariot — AP16

Iris — AP17

Daedalus Preparing Icarus for Flying AP18

Pallas Athene Holding Pegasus AP19

Hermes AP20

Zeus Carrying off Ganymede AP21

Triptolemos, King of Eleusis AP22

Bellerophon and Pegasus AP23

Phrixos and Helle on the Ram Flying over the Hellespont — AP24

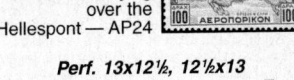

### Perf. 13x12½, 12½x13

**1935, Nov. 10**     Engr.

### Grayish Paper

Size: 34x23½mm, 23½x34mm

| | | | | |
|---|---|---|---|---|
| C22 | AP16 | 1d deep red | 1.50 | 1.50 |
| C23 | AP17 | 2d dull blue | 1.50 | 1.50 |
| C24 | AP18 | 5d dk violet | 17.50 | 4.00 |
| C25 | AP19 | 7d blue violet | 25.00 | 7.25 |
| C26 | AP20 | 10d bister brown | 5.00 | 5.00 |

| | | | | |
|---|---|---|---|---|
| C27 | AP21 | 25d rose | 6.00 | 5.75 |
| C28 | AP22 | 30d dark green | 2.00 | 2.00 |
| C29 | AP23 | 50d violet | 8.00 | 6.00 |
| C30 | AP24 | 100d brown | 2.50 | 2.25 |
| | | Nos. C22-C30 (9) | 69.00 | 35.25 |
| | | Set, never hinged | 150.00 | |

### Re-engraved

Size: 34¼x24mm, 24x34¼mm

**1937-39**     White Paper

| | | | | |
|---|---|---|---|---|
| C31 | AP16 | 1d red | .30 | .25 |
| C32 | AP17 | 2d gray blue | .30 | .25 |
| C33 | AP18 | 5d violet | .30 | .25 |
| C34 | AP19 | 7d dp ultra | .30 | .25 |
| C35 | AP20 | 10d brn org | 2.40 | 3.50 |
| | | Nos. C31-C35 (5) | 3.60 | 4.50 |
| | | Set, never hinged | 7.00 | |

Issued: #C35, 3/1/39; others 8/3/37.

Postage Due Stamp, 1913, Overprinted in Red

### Serrate Roulette 13½

**1938, Aug. 8**    Litho.    Unwmk.

| | | | | |
|---|---|---|---|---|
| C36 | D3 | 50 l violet brown | .25 | .25 |
| | | Never hinged | .25 | |
| a. | | "O" for "P" in word at foot | 30.00 | 30.00 |

Same Overprint on No. J79 in Red

**1939, June 26**    Perf. 13½x12½

| | | | | |
|---|---|---|---|---|
| C37 | D3 | 50 l dark brown | .25 | .25 |
| | | Never hinged | .25 | |

Meteora Monasteries, near Trikkala — AP25

Designs: 4d, Simon Peter Monastery. 6d, View of Santorin. 8d, Church of Pantanassa. 16d, Santorin view. 32d, Ponticonissi, Corfu. 45d, Acropolis, Athens. 55d, Erechtheum. 65d, Temple of Nike Apteros. 100d, Temple of the Olympian Zeus, Athens.

### Wmk. Crowns (252)

**1940, Aug. 3**    Litho.    Perf. 12½

| | | | | |
|---|---|---|---|---|
| C38 | AP25 | 2d red org & blk | .85 | 1.25 |
| C39 | AP25 | 4d dk grn & blk | 3.50 | 3.50 |
| C40 | AP25 | 6d lake & blk | 6.50 | 6.50 |
| C41 | AP25 | 8d dk bl & blk | 17.00 | 16.50 |
| C42 | AP25 | 16d rose vio & blk | 27.50 | 25.00 |
| C43 | AP25 | 32d red org & blk | 47.50 | 47.50 |
| C44 | AP25 | 45d dk grn & blk | 47.50 | 47.50 |
| C45 | AP25 | 55d lake & blk | 47.50 | 47.50 |
| C46 | AP25 | 65d dk bl & blk | 47.50 | 47.50 |
| C47 | AP25 | 100d rose vio & blk | 60.00 | 60.00 |
| | | Nos. C38-C47 (10) | 305.35 | 302.75 |
| | | Set, never hinged | 550.00 | |

4th anniv. of the founding of the Greek Youth Organization. The stamps were good for postal duty on Aug. 3-5, 1940, only. They remained on sale until Feb. 3, 1941.
For overprints see Nos. N229-N238.

Catalogue values for unused stamps in this section, from this point to the end of the section, are for Never Hinged items.

Postage Due Stamps Nos. J81 and J75 Surcharged in Red

**1941-42**    Unwmk.    Perf. 13x12½

| | | | | |
|---|---|---|---|---|
| C48 | D3 | 1d on 2d lt red | .25 | .25 |
| a. | | Inverted surcharge | 45.00 | |

### Serrate Roulette 13½

| | | | | |
|---|---|---|---|---|
| C49 | D3 | 1d on 2d ver ('42) | .25 | .25 |
| a. | | Inverted surcharge | 32.50 | |
| b. | | Double surcharge | 22.50 | |

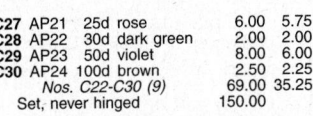

Nos. J83, J84, J86, J87 Overprinted in Red

**1941-42**    Perf. 13, 12½x13

| | | | | |
|---|---|---|---|---|
| C50 | D3 | 5d gray bl ('42) | .25 | .25 |
| a. | | Inverted overprint | 45.00 | |
| b. | | Double overprint | 32.50 | |
| c. | | Pair, one without ovpt. | 22.50 | |
| d. | | Surcharge on back | 22.50 | |
| e. | | On No. J78 ('42) | 140.00 | 160.00 |
| C51 | D3 | 10d gray grn | .30 | .30 |
| a. | | Inverted overprint | 16.00 | |
| b. | | Vert. pair, imperf. btwn. | 325.00 | |
| C52 | D3 | 25d lt red | .85 | .85 |
| a. | | Inverted overprint | 110.00 | |
| C53 | D3 | 50d orange | 1.50 | 1.50 |
| | | Nos. C50-C53 (4) | 2.90 | 2.90 |

Boreas, North Wind — AP35

Winds: 5d, Notus, South. 10d, Apeliotes, East. 20d, Lips, Southwest. 25d, Zephyrus, West. 50d, Kaikias, Northeast.

### Wmk. 252

**1942, Aug. 15**   Litho.   Perf. 12½

| | | | | |
|---|---|---|---|---|
| C55 | AP35 | 2d emerald | .25 | .25 |
| C56 | AP35 | 5d red org | .25 | .25 |
| a. | | Imperf., pair | 325.00 | |
| b. | | Double impression | 55.00 | — |
| C57 | AP35 | 10d red brown | .45 | .45 |
| C58 | AP35 | 20d brt blue | .50 | .50 |
| C59 | AP35 | 25d dk red org | .50 | .50 |
| C60 | AP35 | 50d gray blk | 2.00 | 2.00 |
| a. | | Double impression | 110.00 | |
| | | Nos. C55-C60 (6) | 3.95 | 3.95 |

**1943, Sept. 15**

Winds: 10d, Apeliotes, East. 25d, Zephyrus, West. 50d, Kaikias, Northeast. 100d, Boreas, North. 200d, Eurus, Southeast. 400d, Skiron, Northwest.

| | | | | |
|---|---|---|---|---|
| C61 | AP35 | 10d rose red | .25 | .25 |
| C62 | AP35 | 25d Prus green | .25 | .25 |
| C63 | AP35 | 50d violet blue | .25 | .25 |
| C64 | AP35 | 100d slate black | .25 | .25 |
| C65 | AP35 | 200d claret | .25 | .25 |
| C66 | AP35 | 400d steel blue | .25 | .25 |
| | | Nos. C61-C66 (6) | 1.50 | 1.50 |

Double impressions exist of 10d and 400d. Value, each $30.
For surcharges see #472, 473, CB1-CB10.

### Imperf., Pairs

| | | | |
|---|---|---|---|
| C61a | AP35 | 10d | 110.00 |
| C62a | AP35 | 25d | 110.00 |
| C63a | AP35 | 50d | 110.00 |
| C64a | AP35 | 100d | 110.00 |
| C65a | AP35 | 200d | 110.00 |
| C66a | AP35 | 400d | 110.00 |

Priest Blessing Troops on Summit of Mt. Grammos — AP36

Designs: 1700d, Victory above Mt. Vitsi. 2700d, Battle Scene. 7000d, Victory leading infantry.

**1952, Aug. 29**   Engr.   Perf. 12x13½

| | | | | |
|---|---|---|---|---|
| C67 | AP36 | 1000d deep blue | 1.50 | .30 |
| C68 | AP36 | 1700d dp blue grn | 5.00 | 2.00 |
| C69 | AP36 | 2700d brown | 15.00 | 6.00 |
| C70 | AP36 | 7000d olive green | 45.00 | 15.00 |
| | | Nos. C67-C70 (4) | 66.50 | 23.30 |

Greek army's struggle against communism.

Torchbearer — AP37

Designs: 2400dr, Coin of Amphictyonic League. 4000dr, Pallas Athene.

**1954, May 15**     Perf. 13

| | | | | |
|---|---|---|---|---|
| C71 | AP37 | 1200d dp orange | 7.50 | .35 |
| C72 | AP37 | 2400d dk green | 37.50 | .50 |
| C73 | AP37 | 4000d dp ultra | 65.00 | 3.50 |
| | | Nos. C71-C73 (3) | 110.00 | 6.35 |

5th anniv. of the signing of the North Atlantic Treaty.

Piraeus — AP38

Harbors: 15d, Salonika. 20d, Patras. 25d, Hermoupolis (Syra). 30d, Volos. 50d, Cavalla. 100d, Herakleion (Candia).

### Perf. 13½x13

**1958, July 1**   Wmk. 252   Litho.

| | | | | |
|---|---|---|---|---|
| C74 | AP38 | 10d multicolored | 12.50 | .25 |
| C75 | AP38 | 15d multicolored | 1.75 | .40 |
| C76 | AP38 | 20d multicolored | 12.50 | .25 |
| C77 | AP38 | 25d multicolored | 2.00 | .80 |
| C78 | AP38 | 30d multicolored | 2.25 | .80 |
| C79 | AP38 | 50d multicolored | 8.00 | .80 |
| C80 | AP38 | 100d multicolored | 40.00 | 4.00 |
| | | Nos. C74-C80 (7) | 79.00 | 7.30 |

## AIR POST SEMI-POSTAL STAMPS

Catalogue values for unused stamps in this section are for Never Hinged items.

### Nos. C61-C65 Surcharged in Blue like Nos. B1-B5

**1944, June**   Wmk. 252   Perf. 12½

| | | | | |
|---|---|---|---|---|
| CB1 | AP35 | 100,000d on 10d | 1.25 | 1.75 |
| CB2 | AP35 | 100,000d on 25d | 1.25 | 1.75 |
| CB3 | AP35 | 100,000d on 50d | 1.25 | 1.75 |
| a. | | Inverted overprint | 55.00 | |
| CB4 | AP35 | 100,000d on 100d | 1.25 | 1.65 |
| a. | | Double surcharge | 55.00 | |
| CB5 | AP35 | 100,000d on 200d | 1.25 | 1.65 |
| | | Nos. CB1-CB5 (5) | 6.25 | 8.55 |

The exceptionally high face value discouraged the use of these stamps.
The proceeds aided victims of the Piraeus bombing, January 11, 1944.
No. CB2 exists with double impression of No. C62.

### Nos. C61-C65 Surcharged in Blue like Nos. B11-B15

**1944, July**    50,000d + 450,000d

| | | | | |
|---|---|---|---|---|
| CB6 | AP35 | on 10d | 1.25 | 1.00 |
| a. | | Inverted surcharge | 135.00 | |
| b. | | Double surcharge | 55.00 | |
| CB7 | AP35 | on 25d | 1.25 | 1.00 |
| a. | | Inverted surcharge | 70.00 | |
| b. | | Double surcharge | 55.00 | |
| CB8 | AP35 | on 50d | 1.25 | 1.00 |
| a. | | Inverted surcharge | 55.00 | |
| b. | | Double surcharge | 55.00 | |
| CB9 | AP35 | on 100d | 1.25 | 1.00 |
| a. | | Inverted surcharge | 55.00 | |
| b. | | Double surcharge | 55.00 | |
| CB10 | AP35 | on 200d | 1.25 | 1.00 |
| a. | | Inverted surcharge | 55.00 | |
| b. | | Double surcharge | 55.00 | |
| | | Nos. CB6-CB10 (5) | 6.25 | 5.00 |

The surtax aided children's camps.

## POSTAGE DUE STAMPS

D1

### Perf. 9, 9½, and 10, 10½ and Compound

**1875**    Litho.    Unwmk.

| | | | | |
|---|---|---|---|---|
| J1 | D1 | 1 l green & black | 1.50 | 1.50 |
| J2 | D1 | 2 l green & black | 1.50 | 1.50 |
| J3 | D1 | 5 l green & black | 1.75 | 1.25 |
| J4 | D1 | 10 l green & black | 1.75 | 1.25 |
| J5 | D1 | 20 l green & black | 42.50 | 30.00 |
| J6 | D1 | 40 l green & black | 8.25 | 5.95 |
| J7 | D1 | 60 l green & black | 42.50 | 30.00 |
| J8 | D1 | 70 l green & black | 8.25 | 5.95 |
| J9 | D1 | 80 l green & black | 17.50 | 14.50 |
| J10 | D1 | 90 l green & black | 11.00 | 11.00 |

| J11 | D1 | 1d green & black | 12.00 | 11.00 |
|---|---|---|---|---|
| J12 | D1 | 2d green & black | 13.00 | 11.00 |
| | | Nos. J1-J12 (12) | 161.50 | 124.00 |

Imperforate and part perforated, double and inverted center varieties of Nos. J1-J12 are believed to be printers' waste.

### Perf. 12, 13 and 10½x13

| J13 | D1 | 1 l green & black | 1.60 | 1.60 |
|---|---|---|---|---|
| J14 | D1 | 2 l green & black | 22.50 | 22.50 |
| J15 | D1 | 5 l green & black | 2.75 | 2.75 |
| J16 | D1 | 10 l green & black | 3.25 | 3.25 |
| J17 | D1 | 20 l green & black | 40.00 | 27.50 |
| J18 | D1 | 40 l green & black | 10.00 | 7.75 |
| J19 | D1 | 60 l green & black | 42.50 | 27.50 |
| J20 | D1 | 70 l green & black | 7.75 | 7.75 |
| J21 | D1 | 80 l green & black | 12.00 | 12.00 |
| J22 | D1 | 90 l green & black | 17.50 | 12.00 |
| J23 | D1 | 1d green & black | 27.50 | 17.50 |
| J24 | D1 | 2d green & black | 22.50 | 17.50 |
| | | Nos. J13-J24 (12) | 209.85 | 159.60 |

D2

### Redrawn
### "Lepton" or "Lepta" in Larger Greek Letters
**1876    Perf. 9, 9½, and 10, 10½**

| J25 | D2 | 1 l green & black | 4.50 | 4.50 |
|---|---|---|---|---|
| J26 | D2 | 2 l dk grn & blk | 6.00 | 5.75 |
| J27 | D2 | 5 l dk grn & blk | 360.00 | 275.00 |
| J28 | D2 | 10 l green & black | 3.00 | 2.10 |
| J29 | D2 | 20 l green & black | 4.00 | 3.00 |
| J30 | D2 | 40 l green & black | 32.50 | 25.00 |
| J31 | D2 | 60 l green & black | 27.50 | 15.00 |
| J32 | D2 | 70 l green & black | 22.50 | 25.00 |
| J33 | D2 | 80 l green & black | 17.50 | 15.00 |
| J34 | D2 | 90 l green & black | 17.50 | 16.00 |
| J35 | D2 | 100 l green & black | 22.50 | 15.00 |
| J36 | D2 | 200 l green & black | 22.50 | 15.00 |
| | | Nos. J25-J36 (12) | 540.00 | 416.35 |

**Perf. 11½ to 13**

| J37 | D2 | 1 l yel grn & blk | 1.75 | .95 |
|---|---|---|---|---|
| J38 | D2 | 2 l yel grn & blk | 1.75 | .95 |
| J39 | D2 | 5 l yel grn & blk | 4.75 | 1.25 |
| J40 | D2 | 10 l yel grn & blk | 2.75 | 2.00 |
| a. | | Perf. 10-10½x11½-13 | 4.00 | |
| J41 | D2 | 20 l yel grn & blk | 2.75 | 2.00 |
| J42 | D2 | 40 l yel grn & blk | 15.00 | 11.00 |
| J43 | D2 | 60 l yel grn & blk | 9.50 | 9.50 |
| J47 | D2 | 100 l yel grn & blk | 12.00 | 12.00 |
| J48 | D2 | 200 l yel grn & blk | 13.50 | 11.00 |
| | | Nos. J37-J48 (9) | 63.75 | 50.65 |

Footnote below No. J12 applies also to Nos. J25-J48.

D3

**1902    Engr.    Wmk. 129    Perf. 13½**

| J49 | D3 | 1 l chocolate | .30 | .25 |
|---|---|---|---|---|
| J50 | D3 | 2 l gray | .30 | .25 |
| J51 | D3 | 3 l orange | .30 | .25 |
| J52 | D3 | 5 l yel grn | .30 | .25 |
| J53 | D3 | 10 l scarlet | .30 | .25 |
| J54 | D3 | 20 l lilac | .45 | .25 |
| J55 | D3 | 25 l ultra | 8.00 | 4.00 |
| J56 | D3 | 30 l dp vio | .50 | .30 |
| J57 | D3 | 40 l dk brn | .60 | .50 |
| J58 | D3 | 50 l red brn | .60 | .40 |
| J59 | D3 | 1d black | 1.50 | .90 |

**Litho.**

| J60 | D3 | 2d bronze | 2.00 | 1.25 |
|---|---|---|---|---|
| J61 | D3 | 3d silver | 3.00 | 3.00 |
| J62 | D3 | 5d gold | 6.50 | 9.00 |
| | | Nos. J63-J62 (14) | 24.85 | 20.85 |

See Nos. J63-J88, J90-J93. For overprints and surcharges see Nos. 383-385, J89, RA56, RA58-RA59, NJ1-NJ31.

**Imperf., Pairs**

| J50a | D3 | 2 l | | 90.00 |
|---|---|---|---|---|
| J51a | D3 | 3 l | | 90.00 |
| J52a | D3 | 5 l | | 90.00 |
| J55a | D3 | 25 l | | 150.00 |
| J56a | D3 | 30 l | | 150.00 |
| J58a | D3 | 50 l | | 150.00 |
| J59a | D3 | 1d | | 150.00 |

**Serrate Roulette 13½**
**1913-26    Unwmk.**

| J63 | D3 | 1 l green | .25 | .25 |
|---|---|---|---|---|
| J64 | D3 | 2 l carmine | .25 | .25 |
| J65 | D3 | 3 l vermilion | .25 | .25 |
| J66 | D3 | 5 l green | .25 | .25 |
| a. | | Imperf., pair | 150.00 | |
| b. | | Double impression | 60.00 | |
| c. | | "o" for "p" in lowest word | 5.00 | 5.00 |
| J67 | D3 | 10 l carmine | .25 | .25 |
| J68 | D3 | 20 l slate | .25 | .25 |
| J69 | D3 | 25 l ultra | .25 | .25 |

| J70 | D3 | 30 l carmine | .25 | .25 |
|---|---|---|---|---|
| J71 | D3 | 40 l indigo | .25 | .25 |
| J72 | D3 | 50 l vio brn | .30 | .25 |
| a. | | "o" for "p" in lowest word | 25.00 | 20.00 |
| J73 | D3 | 80 l lil brn ('24) | .40 | .25 |
| J74 | D3 | 1d blue | 8.00 | 1.25 |
| a. | | 1d ultramarine | 12.00 | 5.00 |
| J75 | D3 | 2d vermilion | 8.00 | 1.50 |
| J76 | D3 | 3d carmine | 8.00 | 1.50 |
| J77 | D3 | 5d ultra | 30.00 | 12.00 |
| J78 | D3 | 5d gray bl ('26) | 8.00 | 4.00 |
| | | Nos. J63-J78 (16) | 64.95 | 23.00 |

In 1922-23 and 1941-42 some postage due stamps were used for ordinary postage.

In 1916 Nos. J52, and J63 to J75 were surcharged for the Mount Athos District (see note after No. N166) but were never issued there. By error some of them were put in use as ordinary postage due stamps in Dec., 1924. In 1932 the balance of them was burned.

### Type of 1902 Issue
**Perf. 13, 13½x12½, 13½x13**
**1930    Litho.**

| J79 | D3 | 50 l dk brown | .30 | .30 |
|---|---|---|---|---|
| J80 | D3 | 1d lt blue | .30 | .30 |
| J81 | D3 | 2d lt red | .30 | .30 |
| J82 | D3 | 3d rose red | 27.50 | 25.00 |
| J83 | D3 | 5d gray blue | .30 | .30 |
| J84 | D3 | 10d gray green | .30 | .30 |
| J85 | D3 | 15d red brown | .30 | .30 |
| J86 | D3 | 25d light red | .70 | .65 |
| | | Nos. J79-J86 (8) | 30.00 | 27.45 |

See Nos. J63-J88, J90-J93. For overprints and surcharges see Nos. 383-385, J89, RA56, RA58-RA59, NJ1-NJ31.

### Type of 1902 Issue
**1935    Engr.    Perf. 12½x13**

| J87 | D3 | 50d orange | .30 | .30 |
|---|---|---|---|---|
| J88 | D3 | 100d slate green | .30 | .30 |

### No. J70 Surcharged with New Value in Black
**1942**

| J89 | D3 | 50 (l) on 30 l carmine | 1.50 | 1.50 |
|---|---|---|---|---|

### Type of 1902 Issue
**1943    Wmk. 252    Litho.    Perf. 12½**

| J90 | D3 | 10d red orange | .25 | .25 |
|---|---|---|---|---|
| J91 | D3 | 25d ultramarine | .25 | .25 |
| J92 | D3 | 100d black brown | .25 | .25 |
| J93 | D3 | 200d violet | .25 | .25 |
| | | Nos. J90-J93 (4) | 1.00 | 1.00 |

### POSTAL TAX STAMPS

"The Tragedy of War" — PT1

**Serrate Roulette 13½**
**1914    Litho.    Unwmk.**

| RA1 | PT1 | 2 l red ('18) | .30 | .25 |
|---|---|---|---|---|
| a. | | 2 l carmine | .45 | .25 |
| b. | | Imperf., pair | 265.00 | |
| RA2 | PT1 | 5 l blue | .50 | .50 |
| a. | | Imperf., pair | 375.00 | |

Red Cross, Nurses, Wounded and Bearers — PT1a

**1915    Serrate Roulette 13**

| RA2B | PT1a | (5 l) dk bl & red | 12.00 | 2.00 |
|---|---|---|---|---|

The tax was for the Red Cross.

Women's Patriotic League Badge PT1b

**1915, Nov.    Perf. 11½**

| RA2C | PT1b | (5 l) dk bl & car | 1.25 | 1.25 |
|---|---|---|---|---|
| d. | | Horiz. pair, imperf. btwn. | 55.00 | |
| e. | | Imperf., pair | 55.00 | |

The tax was for the Greek Women's Patriotic League.

### Nos. 165, 167, 170, 172-175
### Surcharged in Black or Brown

a    b

In type "b" the letters, especially those in the first line, are thinner than in type "a," making them appear taller.

**Perf. 11½, 12½, 13½ and Compound**
**1917    Engr.    Wmk. 129**

| RA3 | A11(a) | 1 l on 1 l | 1.50 | 1.50 |
|---|---|---|---|---|
| a. | | Double surcharge | 8.50 | |
| b. | | Inverted surcharge | 10.00 | |
| c. | | Dbl. surch., one invtd. | 10.00 | |
| RA4 | A11(a) | 1 l on 1 l (Br) | 24.00 | 30.00 |
| RA5 | A11(a) | 1 l on 3 l | .30 | .30 |
| RA6 | A11(b) | 1 l on 3 l | .30 | .30 |
| a. | | Triple surcharge | 12.00 | |
| b. | | Dbl. surch., one invtd. | 6.00 | |
| c. | | "K.M." for "K.Π." | 20.00 | |
| d. | | Inverted surcharge | 7.00 | |
| e. | | Double surcharge | 7.00 | |
| RA7 | A11(a) | 5 l on 1 l | 2.00 | 2.00 |
| a. | | Double surcharge | 12.00 | |
| b. | | Dbl. surch., one invtd. | 12.00 | |
| c. | | Inverted surcharge | 13.50 | |
| RA8 | A11(a) | 5 l on 20 l | .65 | .65 |
| a. | | Double surcharge | 13.50 | |
| b. | | Dbl. surch., one invtd. | 13.50 | |
| c. | | Inverted surcharge | 15.00 | |
| RA9 | A11(b) | 5 l on 40 l | .65 | .65 |
| a. | | Imperf. | 200.00 | 250.00 |
| b. | | Double surcharge | 13.50 | |
| c. | | Dbl. surch., one invtd. | 13.50 | |
| d. | | Triple surcharge | 47.50 | |
| RA10 | A11(b) | 5 l on 50 l | .65 | .65 |
| a. | | Double surcharge | 25.00 | |
| b. | | Dbl. surch., one invtd. | 25.00 | |
| c. | | Inverted surcharge | 15.00 | |
| d. | | Triple surcharge | 24.00 | |
| e. | | Triple surch., two invtd. | 30.00 | |
| f. | | Pair, imperf. | 225.00 | 185.00 |
| RA11 | A13(b) | 5 l on 1d | 2.25 | 2.25 |
| a. | | Imperf. | 200.00 | |
| b. | | Inverted surcharge | 55.00 | |
| c. | | Double surcharge | 35.00 | |
| d. | | Dbl. surch., one invtd. | 55.00 | |
| e. | | Triple surcharge | 55.00 | |
| f. | | Horiz. pair, imperf. vert. | — | |
| g. | | Vert. pair, imperf. horiz. | — | |
| RA12 | A11(a) | 10 l on 30 l | .80 | .80 |
| a. | | Imperf. | | |
| b. | | Double surcharge | 18.00 | |
| c. | | Dbl. surch., one invtd. | 18.00 | |
| d. | | Inverted surcharge | 35.00 | |
| RA13 | A11(a) | 30 l on 30 l | .90 | .90 |
| a. | | Double surcharge | 20.00 | |
| b. | | Dbl. surch., one invtd. | 24.00 | |
| c. | | Triple surch., one invtd. | 24.00 | |
| d. | | Inverted surcharge | 17.00 | |
| | | Nos. RA3-RA13 (11) | 34.00 | 40.00 |

### Same Surcharge On Occupation Stamps of 1912
**Serrate Roulette 13½**
**1917    Litho.    Unwmk.**

| RA14 | O2 (b) | 5 l on 25 l pale bl | .45 | .45 |
|---|---|---|---|---|
| a. | | Triple surch., one invtd. | 15.00 | |
| b. | | Double surcharge | 12.00 | |
| c. | | Dbl. surch., one invtd. | 13.50 | |
| d. | | Dbl. surch., both invtd. | 13.50 | |
| e. | | Inverted surcharge | 15.50 | |
| RA15 | O2 (b) | 5 l on 40 l indigo | .35 | .35 |
| a. | | Dbl. surch., one invtd. | 10.00 | |
| b. | | Double surcharge | 10.00 | |
| c. | | Dbl. surch., both invtd. | 13.50 | |
| d. | | Inverted surcharge | 13.50 | |
| e. | | Triple surcharge | 13.50 | |
| f. | | Triple surch., one invtd. | 20.00 | |
| RA16 | O1 (b) | 5 l on 50 l dk bl | .25 | .25 |
| a. | | Double surcharge | 12.00 | |
| b. | | Inverted surcharge | 12.00 | |
| c. | | Dbl. surch., one invtd. | 13.50 | |
| d. | | Triple surcharge | 27.00 | |
| e. | | Triple surch., two invtd. | 27.00 | |
| | | Nos. RA14-RA16 (3) | 1.05 | 1.05 |

There are many wrong font, omitted and misplaced letters and punctuation marks and similar varieties in the surcharges on Nos. RA3 to RA16.

### Revenue Stamps Surcharged in Brown

"Victory"

**1917**

| RA17 | R1 | 1 l on 10 l blue | .70 | 1.00 |
|---|---|---|---|---|
| RA18 | R1 | 1 l on 80 l blue | .70 | 1.00 |
| RA19 | R1 | 5 l on 50 l blue | 18.00 | 27.50 |
| RA20 | R1 | 5 l on 60 l blue | 6.00 | 7.25 |
| a. | | Perf. vert. through middle | 9.50 | 15.00 |

| b. | | As "a," inverted surcharge | | |
|---|---|---|---|---|
| RA21 | R1 | 5 l on 80 l blue | 3.25 | 4.50 |
| a. | | Perf. vert. through middle | 9.50 | 15.00 |
| b. | | Inverted surcharge | | |
| RA22 | R1 | 10 l on 70 l blue | 18.00 | 25.00 |
| a. | | Perf. vert. through middle | 7.25 | 10.00 |
| RA23 | R1 | 10 l on 90 l blue | 13.50 | 37.50 |
| a. | | Perf. vert. through middle | 22.50 | 45.00 |
| RA24 | R1 | 20 l on 30 l blue | 6,500. | 3,600. |
| RA25 | R1 | 20 l on 30 l blue | 12.00 | 9.50 |
| RA26 | R1 | 20 l on 40 l blue | 14.50 | 21.00 |
| RA27 | R1 | 20 l on 60 l blue | 12.00 | 12.00 |
| RA28 | R1 | 20 l on 60 l blue | 500.00 | 375.00 |
| RA29 | R1 | 20 l on 80 l blue | 60.00 | 72.50 |
| RA30 | R1 | 20 l on 90 l blue | 5.00 | 9.75 |
| a. | | Inverted surcharge | 100.00 | |
| b. | | Double surcharge | | |
| | | Nos. RA17-RA30 (14) | 7,164. | 4,204. |

No. RA19 is known only with vertical perforation through the middle.

Counterfeits exist of Nos. RA17-RA43, used.

### Surcharged in Brown or Black

| RA31 | R1 | 1 l on 50 l vio (Bk) | .85 | 1.40 |
|---|---|---|---|---|
| RA32 | R1 | 5 l on 10 l bl (Br) | .85 | 1.40 |
| a. | | Inverted surcharge | 85.00 | |
| b. | | Left "5" invert. | 97.50 | |
| RA33 | R1 | 10 l on 50 l vio (Br) | .85 | 1.40 |
| RA34 | R1 | 10 l on 50 l vio (Br) | 6.00 | 12.00 |
| RA35 | R1 | 10 l on 50 l vio (Bk) | 25.00 | 32.50 |
| a. | | Double surcharge | 85.00 | |
| RA36 | R1 | 20 l on 2d bl (Bk) | 9.75 | 9.75 |
| a. | | Surcharged "20 lept. 30" | 80.00 | 120.00 |
| b. | | Horiz. pair, imperf. btwn. | | |
| | | Nos. RA31-RA36 (6) | 43.30 | 58.45 |

The "T," fourth Greek letter of the denomination in the surcharge ("ΛΕΠΤ."), is normally omitted on Nos. RA31, RA34-RA36.

### Corfu Issue

### Surcharged in Black
**1917**

| RA37 | R1 | 1 l on 10 l blue | 2.50 | 2.50 |
|---|---|---|---|---|
| RA38 | R1 | 5 l on 50 l blue | 60.00 | 80.00 |
| RA39 | R1 | 10 l on 50 l blue | 725.00 | 725.00 |
| RA40 | R1 | 20 l on 50 l blue | 2,850. | 1,075. |

### Surcharged in Black

| RA41 | R1 | 10 l on 50 l blue | 13.50 | 14.50 |
|---|---|---|---|---|
| RA42 | R1 | 20 l on 50 l blue | 30.00 | 30.00 |
| RA43 | R1 | 30 l on 50 l blue | 18.00 | 18.00 |

### Surcharged in Black

Without serifs    With serifs

| RA44 | R1 | 5 l on 10 l vio & red | 9.75 | 13.50 |
|---|---|---|---|---|
| a. | | "K" with serifs | 13.50 | 25.00 |

Counterfeits exist of Nos. RA17-RA44. Similar stamps with denominations higher than 30 lepta were for revenue use.

Wounded
Soldier — PT2

**1918** *Serrate Roulette 13½, 11½*
RA45 PT2 5 l bl, yel & red          8.50 2.00

Overprinted

RA46 PT2 5 l blue, yel & red       11.00 2.00
  *e.*   Double overprint               290.00

The letters are the initials of Greek words equivalent to "Patriotic Relief Institution." The proceeds were given to the Patriotic League, for the aid of disabled soldiers.
Counterfeits exist of Nos. RA45-RA46.

PT3

**Surcharge in Red**

**1922**    *Litho.*    *Perf. 11½*
**Dark Blue & Red**
RA46A PT3 5 l on 10 l      325.00 16.00
  *f.*   Double surcharge     410.00 410.00
RA46B PT3 5 l on 20 l       97.50 57.50
RA46C PT3 5 l on 50 l      325.00 275.00
RA46D PT3 5 l on 1d         12.00 60.00

Counterfeit surcharges exist. Examples of Nos. RA46A-RA46C without surcharge, each 50 cents.
Value for No. RA46Af unused is for example without gum.

Red Cross Help to
Soldier and
Family — PT3a

**1924**      *Perf. 13½ x 12½*
RA47 PT3a 10 l blue, buff & red    .85 .25

Proceeds were given to the Red Cross.

**1926**        *Perf. 11½*
RA47C PT3a 10 l blue, buff & red
                    .30 .25
  *a.*   Imperf., pair               40.00
  *b.*   Horiz. pair, imperf. btwn.    40.00
  *c.*   Horiz. pair, imperf. vert.    45.00
  *e.*   Vert. pair, imperf. horiz.    50.00

St. Demetrius — PT4

**1934**        *Perf. 11½*
RA48 PT4 20 l brown            .35 .25
  *a.*   Horizontal pair, imperf. be-
      tween                     10.00
  *b.*   Vertical pair, imperf. between  16.00
  *c.*   Imperf., pair                 18.00
  *d.*   Horiz. pair, imperf. vert.     16.00
  *e.*   Vert. pair, imperf. horiz.     16.00
  *f.*   Double impression             60.00

No. RA48 was obligatory as a tax on all interior mail, including air post, mailed from Salonika.
For surcharge see No. RA69.

"Health" — PT5

**1934, Dec. 28**   *Perf. 13, 13x13½*
RA49 PT5 10 l bl grn, org & buff   .25 .25
  *a.*   Pair, one imperf. horiz.
RA50 PT5 20 l ultra, org & buff    .25 .25
RA51 PT5 50 l grn, org & buff     2.00 .70
    *Nos. RA49-RA51 (3)*         2.50 1.20

For surcharge see No. RA67.

"Health" — PT6

**1935**
RA52 PT6 10 l yel grn, org & buff   .25 .25
RA53 PT6 20 l ultra, org & buff     .30 .25
RA54 PT6 50 l grn, org & buff       .70 .70
    *Nos. RA52-RA54 (3)*          1.25 1.20

The use of #RA49-RA54 was obligatory on all mail during 4 weeks each year including Christmas, the New Year and Easter, and on parcel post packages at all times. For the benefit of the tubercular clerks and officials of the Post, Telephone and Telegraph Service.
See No. RA64. For surcharge see No. RA68.

No. 364 Overprinted in
Red

**1937, Jan. 20**   *Engr.*   *Perf. 13x12½*
RA55 A36 50 l violet           1.40 .25
  *a.*   Inverted overprint          .75 .25

No. RA55a first appeared as an error, then was issued deliberately in quantity to avoid speculation.

**Same Overprint in Blue on No. J67**
**Litho.**
       *Serrate Roulette 13½*
RA56 D3 10 l carmine           .80 .25
  *a.*   Inverted overprint         50.00
  *b.*   Without accent mark on "O"   .90 .50

No. RA56 has accent mark on "O." No. RA56 with blue overprint double exists only with additional black overprint of Ionian Islands No. NRA1a.

**Same Overprint in Green on No. 364**
**1937**     *Engr.*     *Perf. 13x12½*
RA57 A36 50 l violet           .30 .25

Nos. J66, J68 and 323
Surcharged in Blue or
Black

       *Serrate Roulette 13½*
**1938**    *Litho.*       *Unwmk.*
RA58 D3 50 l on 5 l grn        1.50 .80
  *a.*   Accent mark on "O"          7.50 1.00
  *b.*   "O" for "P" in lowest word  30.00 25.00
  *c.*   As No. RA58, vert. pair, im-
      perf. horiz.               65.00 120.00
RA59 D3 50 l on 20 l slate     1.50 .80
  *a.*   Accent mark on "O"         240.00 47.50

Nos. RA58 and RA59 have no accent mark on "O."

       *Engr.*      *Perf. 13x12½*
RA60 A38 50 l on 20 l vio (Bk)   .40 .25
    *Nos. RA58-RA60 (3)*          3.40 1.85

Surcharge on No. RA60 is 14½x16½mm.

Queens Olga and
Sophia — PT7

**1939, Feb. 1**   *Litho.*   *Perf. 13½x12*
RA61 PT7 10 l brt rose, *pale*
          *rose*                 .25 .25
RA62 PT7 50 l gray grn, *pale*
          *grn*                  .25 .25
  *a.*   Double impression                120.00
  *b.*   Imperf., pair
RA63 PT7 1 d dl bl, *lt bl*      .25 .25
    *Nos. RA61-RA63 (3)*           .75 .75

For overprints and surcharges see Nos. RA65, RA79-RA81A, NRA1-NRA3.

**"Health" Type of 1935**
**1939**              *Perf. 12½*
RA64 PT6 50 l brn & buff       .40 .30

No. RA62
Overprinted in Red

**1940**            *Perf. 13½x12*
RA65 PT7 50 l gray grn, *pale*
          *grn*                  .25 .25
  *a.*   Inverted overprint          27.50
  *b.*   Pair, one without overprint  80.00
  *c.*   Double impression                120.00

Proceeds of Nos. RA64-RA65 were used for the benefit of the tubercular clerks and officials of the Post, Telephone and Telegraph Service. No. RA65 was used in Albania during the Greek occupation, 1940-41 without additional overprint.

No. 321 Surcharged in
Carmine

**1941**   *Unwmk.*   *Engr.*   *Perf. 13½x13*
RA66 A36 50 l on 5 l dk grn    .25 .25
  *a.*   Inverted surcharge          18.00

**No. RA49 and Type of 1935**
**Surcharged with New Value in Black**
    *Perf. 12½x13, 13x13½*
            Litho.
RA67 PT5 50 l on 10 l           .75 5.00
  *a.*   Inverted surcharge          47.50
RA68 PT6 50 l on 10 l dp bl
       grn, dl org &
       buff                       .25 .25
  *a.*   Inverted surcharge          40.00
  *b.*   Double surcharge            40.00

> Catalogue values for unused stamps in this section, from this point to the end of the section, are for Never Hinged items.

No. RA48 Surcharged in
Green

**1942**             *Perf. 11½*
RA69 PT4 1 d on 20 l brn        .30 .25
  *a.*   Pair, one without surcharge  37.50
  *b.*   Imperf., pair
  *c.*   Double surcharge            25.00 25.00
  *d.*   Horiz. pair, imperf. vert.   37.50

Nos. 321, 324 Surcharged
In Red or Carmine

**1942-43**   *Engr.*   *Perf. 13½x13*
RA70 A36 10 d on 5 l ('43)      .25 .25
  *a.*   Double surcharge            25.00
  *b.*   Inverted surcharge          45.00
  *c.*   Imperf., pair              300.00
  *d.*   Horiz. pair, imperf. vert.  200.00
RA71 A39 10 d on 25 l (C)       .25 .25
  *a.*   Inverted surcharge          45.00
  *b.*   Double surcharge            25.00
  *c.*   Imperf., pair              300.00
  *d.*   Horiz. pair, imperf. vert.  200.00

No. 444 Overprinted
in Red

**1944**   *Wmk. 252*   *Litho.*   *Perf. 12½*
RA72 A110 100d black           .25 .25
  *a.*   Double overprint            12.00
  *b.*   Inverted overprint          10.00

No. 443 Surcharged
in Blue

RA73 A109 5000d on 75d         .25 .25
  *a.*   Double surcharge            27.50
  *b.*   Inverted surcharge          30.00

No. 437 Surcharged
in Blue

RA74 A103 25000d on 2d         .25 .25
  *a.*   Double surcharge            30.00
  *b.*   Additional surcharge on
      back                      120.00
  *c.*   Inverted surcharge
  *d.*   Inv. surch. on back only    135.00

No. 399
Surcharged in Blue
or Carmine

**1945**             *Perf. 13½x12*
RA75 A72 1 d on 40 l           .25 .25
  *a.*   Double surcharge            20.00
  *b.*   Triple surcharge            50.00
RA76 A72 2 d on 40 l (C)       .25 .25
  *a.*   Vert. pair, one without surch.  30.00
  *b.*   Surcharged on back
  *c.*   Inverted surcharge          30.00
  *d.*   Double surcharge            30.00

Tax on Nos. RA67, RA68-RA70 to RA76 aided the postal clerks' tuberculosis fund.

Nos. 396 and 399
Surcharged in
Carmine

**1946**
RA77 A72 20 d on 40 l          .30 .25
  *a.*   Pair, one without surcharge
  *b.*   Inverted surcharge          40.00
  *c.*   Double surcharge            40.00
  *d.*   Violet surcharge            18.00
RA78 A69 20 d on 5 l           .75 .30

**Same Surcharge in Carmine on**
**Nos. RA62 and RA63**
**1946-47**   *Unwmk.*   *Perf. 13½x12*
RA79 PT7 50 d on 50 l ('47)     .50 .25
  *a.*   Inverted surcharge          30.00
  *b.*   Pair, one without
      surcharge                 120.00
  *c.*   Double surcharge            20.00
  *d.*   Imperf., pair              180.00
RA80 PT7 50 d on 1 d            .30 .25
  *a.*   Red violet surcharge         8.00 3.00
  *b.*   Brown violet surcharge      16.00 20.00
  *c.*   Additional surcharge on
      back

The tax on Nos. RA77 to RA80 was for the Postal Clerks' Welfare Fund.

Nos. RA65 and
RA62 Surcharged
in Carmine

**1947**
RA81 50d on 50 l (RA65)        2.00 .25
  *b.*   Double surcharge           130.00
RA81A 50d on 50 l (RA62)      40.00 45.00

Tax for the postal clerks' tuberculosis fund.

St. Demetrius — PT8

**1948**    **Litho.**    **Perf. 12x13½**
RA82 PT8 50d yellow brown    .25   .25
  *a.*   Imperf., pair    40.00

Obligatory on all domestic mail. The tax was for restoration of historical monuments and churches destroyed during World War II.

Nos. 397 and 413
Surcharged in Blue

**1950**          **Wmk. 252**
RA83 A70 50d on 10 l (#397)   1.25   .30
  *a.*   Stamp with double frame   165.00
  *b.*   Surcharge reading down   25.00   25.00
  *c.*   Double surcharge   30.00
RA84 A70 50d on 10 l (#413)   1.00   .25
  *a.*   Surcharge reading down   25.00   25.00
  *b.*   Double surcharge   30.00
  *c.*   Stamp with double frame   165.00

Tax for the Postal Clerks' Welfare Fund.

No. 396
Surcharged in
Carmine

**1951**          **Perf. 13½x12**
RA85 A69 50d on 5 l    2.00   .25
  *a.*   Double surcharge

Tax for the Postal Employees' Welfare Fund.

No. 392 Surcharged in
Black

**1951**   **Wmk. 252**   **Perf. 12½x12**
RA86 A67 50d on 3d red brn   1.25   .25
  *a.*   Pair, one without surcharge   100.00
  *b.*   "50" omitted   75.00
  *c.*   Inverted surcharge   47.50
  *d.*   Cross of Lorraine omitted

Tax for the postal clerks' tuberculosis fund.

No. 393 Surcharged in
Carmine

**1952**
RA87 A67 100d on 8d deep
     blue    1.00   .25
  *a.*   Double surcharge   45.00
  *b.*   Add'l surch. on back (inverted)   120.00

The tax was for the State Welfare Fund.

Ruins of Church of
Phaneromeni,
Zante — PT9

500d, Map & scene of destruction, Argostoli.

**1953**   **Wmk. 252**   **Litho.**   **Perf. 12½**
RA88 PT9 300d indigo & pale
     grn    1.25   .25
RA89 PT9 500d dk brn & buff   3.75   .70

The tax was for the reconstruction of Cephalonia, Ithaca, and Zante, Ionian Islands destroyed by earthquake.

Zeus on Macedonian
Coin of Philip II — PT10

Design: 1d, Aristotle.

**1956**          **Perf. 13½**
RA90 PT10 50 l dk car rose   1.25   .25
  *a.*   Imperf., pair   275.00
RA91 PT10 1d brt blue   4.50   1.25

Tax for archaeological research in Macedonia. The coin on No. RA90 portrays Zeus despite inscription of Philip's name.

**1958**          **Perf. 12½x13½**
RA90B PT10 50 l dk car rose   20.00   .50
RA91A PT10 1d brt blue   55.00   4.50

### POSTAL TAX SEMI-POSTAL STAMPS

Child
PTSP1

Mother and
Child
PTSP2

Virgin and Christ
Child — PTSP3

       **Perf. 12x13½**
**1943**    **Wmk. 252**    **Litho.**
RAB1 PTSP1   25d + 25d bl
         grn    .25   .50
  *a.*   Imperf., pair   65.00
RAB2 PTSP2   100d + 50d rose
         vio    .25   .50
  *a.*   Imperf., pair   65.00
RAB3 PTSP3   200d + 100d red
         brn    .25   .50
  *a.*   Imperf., pair   65.00
    Nos. RAB1-RAB3 (3)    .75   1.50

Surtax aided needy children. These stamps were compulsory on domestic mail in Oct. 1943.

### OCCUPATION AND ANNEXATION STAMPS

During the Balkan wars, 1912-13, Greece occupied certain of the Aegean Islands and part of Western Turkey. She subsequently acquired these territories and they were known as the New Greece.

Most of the special issues for the Aegean Islands were made by order of the military commanders.

**For Use in the Aegean Islands Occupied by Greece**

### CHIOS

Greece No. 221
Overprinted in Red

**1913**     **Serrate Roulette 13½**
        **Litho.**    **Unwmk.**
N1 A25 25 l ultramarine   60.00   85.00
  *a.*   Inverted overprint   200.00   225.00
  *b.*   "Λ" for "Δ" in overprint   225.00   250.00
  *c.*   As "b," overprint inverted   475.00   525.00

### ICARIA (NICARIA)

Penelope — I1

**1912**   **Unwmk.**   **Litho.**   **Perf. 11½**
N2 I1   2 l orange   1.25   2.50
N3 I1   5 l blue green   1.25   2.50
N4 I1   10 l rose   1.25   2.50
N5 I1   25 l ultra   1.25   2.50
  *a.*   Pair, imperf. between   80.00   80.00
N6 I1   50 l gray lilac   1.50   3.50
  *a.*   Pair, imperf. between   80.00   80.00
N7 I1   1d dark brown   2.50   9.00
N8 I1   2d claret   3.50   15.00
N9 I1   5d slate   5.00   22.50
    Nos. N2-N9 (8)    17.50   60.00

Counterfeits of Nos. N1-N15 are plentiful.

Stamps of Greece, 1911-23, Overprinted Reading Up

**1913**    **On Issue of 1911-21**   **Engr.**
N10 A25   2 l car rose   40.00   30.00
N11 A24   3 l vermilion   40.00   30.00
         **Litho.**
   **On Issue of 1912-23**
N12 A24   1 l green   40.00   30.00
N12A A25   2 l car rose   40.00   30.00
N13 A24   3 l vermilion   40.00   30.00
N14 A26   5 l green   40.00   30.00
N15 A24 10 l carmine   40.00   30.00
    Nos. N10-N15, N12A (7)   280.00   210.00

### LEMNOS

Regular Issues of Greece
Overprinted in Black

     **On Issue of 1901**
**1912**   **Wmk. 129**   **Engr.**   **Perf. 13½**
N16 A11   20 l red lilac   2.00   2.00
  *a.*   Inverted overprint   22.50
  *b.*   Double overprint   22.50
     **On Issue of 1911-21**
         **Unwmk.**
     **Serrate Roulette 13½**
N17 A24   1 l green   .60   .60
  *a.*   Inverted overprint   15.00
  *b.*   Double overprint   15.00
  *c.*   Double ovpt., one inverted   30.00
N18 A25   2 l carmine rose   .70   .70
  *a.*   Inverted overprint   15.00
  *b.*   Double overprint   15.00
N19 A24   3 l vermilion   .70   .70
  *a.*   Inverted overprint   15.00
  *b.*   Double overprint   15.00
  *c.*   Double ovpt., one inverted   20.00
  *d.*   Triple overprint   72.50
  *e.*   Triple ovpt., one inverted   72.50
  *f.*   Inverted ovpt. on face, upright ovpt. on reverse   120.00
N20 A26   5 l green   .70   .70
  *a.*   Inverted overprint   15.00
  *b.*   Double overprint   15.00
N21 A24   10 l car rose   1.00   1.00
  *a.*   Inverted overprint   15.00
  *b.*   Double overprint   15.00
  *c.*   Double ovpt., one inverted   30.00
N22 A25   20 l gray lilac   1.50   1.75
  *a.*   Inverted overprint   15.00
  *b.*   Double overprint   27.00
N23 A25   25 l ultra   1.50   1.75
  *a.*   Inverted overprint   22.50
  *b.*   Double overprint   22.50
N24 A26   30 l car rose   3.00   3.00
  *a.*   Inverted overprint   50.00
  *b.*   Double overprint   50.00
N25 A24   40 l deep blue   4.75   5.50
  *a.*   Inverted overprint   55.00
N26 A26   50 l dl violet   5.00   5.50
N27 A27   1d ultra   6.00   6.00
  *b.*   Double overprint   60.00
N28 A27   2d vermilion   20.00   20.00
N29 A27   3d car rose   22.50   22.50
N30 A27   5d ultra   26.00   26.00
N31 A27   10d deep blue   80.00   97.50
N32 A28   25d deep blue   150.00   150.00
    Nos. N17-N32 (16)   323.95   343.20
     **On Issue of 1912-23**
         **Litho.**
N33 A24   1 l green   .60   .60
  *a.*   Inverted overprint   15.00
  *b.*   Double overprint   15.00
  *c.*   Double overprint, one inverted   22.50
  *d.*   Double overprint, both inverted   22.50
  *e.*   Inverted overprint on face, upright overprint on reverse   40.00
  *g.*   Triple ovpt, one inverted   40.00
N34 A26   5 l green   .70   .70
  *a.*   Inverted overprint   12.00
  *b.*   Double overprint   12.00   120.00
N35 A24 10 l carmine   .70   .70
  *a.*   Inverted overprint   12.00
  *b.*   Double overprint   13.50

N36 A25 25 l ultra   3.00   3.00
  *a.*   Inverted overprint   22.50
  *b.*   Double overprint   15.00
    Nos. N33-N36 (4)    5.00   5.00

     **Red Overprint**
   **On Issue of 1911-23**
         **Engr.**
N37 A25 40 l deep blue   2.00   2.00
N38 A26 50 l dull violet   2.00   2.00
N39 A27   1d vermilion   3.00   3.00
N40 A27   3d car rose   15.00   15.00
N41 A27   5d gray blue   400.00   300.00
N42 A27 10d deep blue   120.00   120.00
N43 A28 25d deep blue   150.00   150.00
         **Litho.**
N44 A24   5 l green   .60   .60
  *a.*   Inverted overprint   —
  *b.*   Double overprint   —
N45 A25 25 l ultramarine   2.00   2.00
    Nos. N37-N45 (9)   694.60   594.60

    **Carmine Overprint**
         **Engr.**
N46 A25   2 l carmine   3.00   3.00
  *a.*   Double overprint   30.00
  *b.*   Triple overprint   60.00
N47 A24   3 l vermilion   3.00   3.00
N48 A25 20 l gray blue   12.00   12.00
N49 A26 30 l carmine rose   6.00   6.00
  *a.*   Inverted overprint   30.00
  *b.*   Double overprint   30.00
N50 A27   2d vermilion   360.00   300.00
  *a.*   Inverted overprint   —
  *b.*   Double overprint   —
  *c.*   Double ovpt., both inverted   —
N51 A27   3d car rose   120.00   90.00
N51A A27   5d ultramarine   60.00   60.00
  *b.*   Double overprint   120.00
N51B A28 25d deep blue   1,200.   475.00
N51C A24   1 l green   2.00   2.00
  *a.*   Without period after "ΕΛ–ΛΑΣ" (on #214a)   175.00   185.00
  *b.*   As "a.," double overprint   —
  *e.*   As N51C, double ovpt.   15.00
N52 A24 10 l carmine   4.00   4.00
  *g.*   Double overprint   24.00
    Nos. N46-N52 (10)   1,770.   955.00

   **No. N33 with Added "Greek Administration" Overprint, as on Nos. N109-N148, in Black**
**1913**
N52A A24   1 l green   25.00   25.00
  *b.*   Period omitted after "ΕΛ–ΛΑΣ" (on #N33f)   360.00
  *c.*   Inverted "ΛΗΜΝΟΣ" overprint (on No. N33a)   90.00
  *d.*   Double"ΛΗΜΝΟΣ" overprint (on No. N33a)   90.00
  *e.*   As "b," double"ΛΗΜΝΟΣ" overprint (on No. N33f)   —
  *f.*   As "b," inverted"ΛΗΜΝΟΣ" overprint (on No. N33f)

Counterfeits of Nos. N16-N52A are plentiful.

### MYTILENE (LESBOS)

Turkey Nos. 162, 158
Overprinted in Blue

   **Perf. 12, 13½ and Compound**
**1912**    **Typo.**    **Unwmk.**
N53 A21 20pa rose   22.50   22.50
N54 A21 10pi dull red   125.00   *135.00*
   **On Turkey Nos. P68, 151-155, 137, 157-158 in Black**
N55 A21   2pa olive green   2.00   2.00
N56 A21   5pa ocher   2.00   2.00
N57 A21 10pa blue green   2.00   2.00
N58 A21 20pa rose   2.00   2.00
N59 A21   1pi ultra   4.00   4.00
N60 A21   2pi blue black   25.00   25.00
N61 A19   2½pi dk brown   12.00   12.00
N62 A21   5pi dk violet   26.00   26.00
N63 A21 10pi dull red   125.00   *135.00*
    Nos. N55-N63 (9)   200.00   210.00
   **On Turkey Nos. 161-163, 145 in Black**
N64 A21 10pa blue green   7.25   7.25
  *a.*   Double overprint   47.50   47.50
N65 A21 20pa rose   7.25   7.25
  *a.*   Blue overprint   40.00   40.00
N66 A21   1pi ultra   7.25   7.25
N67 A19   2pi blue black   65.00   65.00
   **Nos. N55, N58, N65, N59 Surcharged in Blue or Black**
N68 A21 25 l on 2pa   12.00   12.00
  *a.*   New value inverted   45.00   *50.00*
N68C A21 25 l on 20pa   30.00   30.00
N68D A21 50 l on 2pa   30.00   30.00
N69 A21 50 l on 20pa   12.00   12.00
  *b.*   New value inverted   50.00   *50.00*

| | | | | | |
|---|---|---|---|---|---|
| N70 | A21 | 1d on 20pa | (N65) (Bk) | 40.00 | 40.00 |
| a. | | New value inverted | | 72.50 | 72.50 |
| c. | | Blue surcharge | | 37.50 | 40.00 |
| d. | | As "c," new value inverted | | 120.00 | 120.00 |
| N71 | A21 | 2d on 1pi (Bk) | | 24.00 | 27.50 |
| a. | | New value inverted | | | |

### Same Overprint on Turkey No. J49

| | | | | | |
|---|---|---|---|---|---|
| N72 | A19 | 1pi blk, dp rose | | 60.00 | 72.50 |

The overprint is found on all values reading up or down with inverted "i" in the first word and inverted "e" in the third word.
No. N72 was only used for postage.
Counterfeits of Nos. N53-N72 are plentiful.

---

## SAMOS

### Issues of the Provisional Government

Map of Samos — OS1

| 1912 | | Unwmk. | Typo. | Imperf. |
|---|---|---|---|---|
| N73 | OS1 | 5 l gray green | 24.00 | 10.00 |
| N74 | OS1 | 10 l red | 20.00 | 10.00 |
| a. | | 10 l pale green (error) | 240.00 | — |
| N75 | OS1 | 25 l blue | 55.00 | 20.00 |
| a. | | 25 l pale green (error) | 500.00 | 600.00 |
| b. | | 25 l red (error) | 500.00 | — |
| | | Nos. N73-N75 (3) | 99.00 | 40.00 |

Only one example of No. N75c is known.
Counterfeits exist of Nos. N73 to N75.

Hermes — OS2

| 1912 | | Litho. | Perf. 11½ | |
|---|---|---|---|---|
| | | **Without Overprint** | | |
| N76 | OS2 | 1 l gray | 2.00 | 1.50 |
| N77 | OS2 | 5 l lt green | 2.00 | 1.50 |
| N78 | OS2 | 10 l rose | 3.50 | 1.80 |
| b. | | Half used as 5 l on cover | | 240.00 |
| N79 | OS2 | 25 l lt blue | 8.50 | 2.25 |
| N80 | OS2 | 50 l violet brn | 15.00 | 6.00 |
| | | **With Overprint** | | |
| N81 | OS2 | 1 l gray | 1.00 | 1.20 |
| b. | | Pair, imperf. between | 120.00 | |
| N82 | OS2 | 5 l blue grn | 1.00 | 1.20 |
| b. | | Pair, imperf. between | 120.00 | |
| N83 | OS2 | 10 l rose | 1.00 | 1.20 |
| b. | | Half used as 5 l on cover | | 240.00 |
| N84 | OS2 | 25 l blue | 2.00 | 1.50 |
| N85 | OS2 | 50 l violet brn | 1.00 | 7.25 |
| N86 | OS2 | 1d orange | 15.00 | 13.50 |
| | | Nos. N76-N86 (11) | 63.00 | 38.90 |

For overprints and surcharge see Nos. N92-N103.

### Imperf., Pairs
#### Without Overprint

| | | | | |
|---|---|---|---|---|
| N76a | OS2 | 1 l | 37.50 | 30.00 |
| N77a | OS2 | 5 l | 37.50 | 30.00 |
| N78a | OS2 | 10 l | 37.50 | 30.00 |
| N79a | OS2 | 25 l | 37.50 | 30.00 |
| N80a | OS2 | 50 l | 37.50 | 30.00 |

#### With Overprint

| | | | | |
|---|---|---|---|---|
| N81a | OS2 | 1 l | 85.00 | 40.00 |
| N82a | OS2 | 5 l | 85.00 | 40.00 |
| N83a | OS2 | 10 l | 85.00 | 40.00 |
| N85a | OS2 | 50 l | 85.00 | 40.00 |

Church in Savior's Name and Fort Ruins — OS3

### Manuscript Initials in Red or Black

| 1913 | | | | |
|---|---|---|---|---|
| N87 | OS3 | 1d brown (R) | 18.00 | 15.00 |
| a. | | Without initials | 23.00 | 42.50 |
| N88 | OS3 | 2d deep blue (R) | 18.00 | 15.00 |
| a. | | Without initials | 23.00 | 42.50 |
| N89 | OS3 | 5d gray grn (R) | 37.50 | 30.00 |
| a. | | Without initials | 80.00 | 120.00 |
| N90 | OS3 | 10d yellow grn (R) | 100.00 | 95.00 |
| a. | | Without initials | 180.00 | 250.00 |

| | | | | |
|---|---|---|---|---|
| N91 | OS3 | 25d red (Bk) | 100.00 | 85.00 |
| a. | | Without initials | 180.00 | 225.00 |
| c. | | Horiz. pair, imperf. vert. | 800.00 | |
| d. | | Initials in red | | |
| | | Nos. N87-N91 (5) | 273.50 | 240.00 |

Victory of the Greek fleet in 1824 and the union with Greece of Samos in 1912. The manuscript initials are those of Pres. Themistokles Sofulis.
Exist imperf. Counterfeits of Nos. N87-N91 are plentiful.
For overprints see Nos. N104-N108.

### Imperf., Pairs
#### Without Initials

| | | | |
|---|---|---|---|
| N87b | OS3 | 1 d | 150.00 |
| N88b | OS3 | 5 d | 150.00 |
| N89b | OS3 | 5 d | 200.00 |
| N90b | OS3 | 10 d | 800.00 |
| N91b | OS3 | 25 d | 800.00 |

Nos. N76 to N80 Overprinted

ΕΛΛΑΣ

| 1914 | | | | |
|---|---|---|---|---|
| N92 | OS2 | 1 l gray | 7.25 | 6.00 |
| a. | | Inverted overprint | 200.00 | 160.00 |
| b. | | Imperf., pair | 90.00 | |
| N93 | OS2 | 5 l lt green | 7.25 | 6.00 |
| a. | | Inverted overprint | 200.00 | 160.00 |
| b. | | Imperf., pair | 90.00 | |
| N94 | OS2 | 10 l rose | 7.25 | 6.00 |
| a. | | Double overprint | 60.00 | |
| b. | | Inverted overprint | 230.00 | 175.00 |
| c. | | Imperf., pair | 90.00 | |
| N95 | OS2 | 25 l lt blue | 12.00 | 12.00 |
| b. | | Inverted overprint | 230.00 | 175.00 |
| c. | | Imperf., pair | 90.00 | |
| N96 | OS2 | 50 l violet brn | 9.00 | 9.00 |
| a. | | Double overprint | 90.00 | 100.00 |
| b. | | Inverted overprint | 170.00 | 135.00 |
| c. | | Imperf., pair | 90.00 | |
| | | Nos. N92-N96 (5) | 42.75 | 39.00 |

### Charity Issues of Greek Administration

Nos. N81 to N86 Overprinted in Red or Black

| 1915 | | | | |
|---|---|---|---|---|
| N97 | OS2 | 1 l gray (R) | 18.00 | 22.00 |
| a. | | Black overprint | 145.00 | 160.00 |
| b. | | As N97, double overprint | 180.00 | |
| N98 | OS2 | 5 l blue grn (Bk) | 1.50 | 2.00 |
| a. | | Red overprint | 135.00 | 150.00 |
| b. | | As N98, double overprint | 145.00 | 220.00 |
| N99 | OS2 | 10 l rose (Bk) | 1.50 | 2.00 |
| a. | | Red overprint | 135.00 | 160.00 |
| b. | | As N99, inverted overprint | 125.00 | 150.00 |
| N100 | OS2 | 25 l blue (Bk) | 1.50 | 2.00 |
| a. | | Red overprint | 135.00 | 160.00 |
| N101 | OS2 | 50 l violet brn (Bk) | 1.50 | 2.00 |
| a. | | Red overprint | 135.00 | 160.00 |
| N102 | OS2 | 1d orange (R) | 3.50 | 4.00 |
| a. | | Inverted overprint | 135.00 | 220.00 |
| b. | | Black overprint | 120.00 | 190.00 |
| c. | | As "b," double overprint | 160.00 | 220.00 |

No. N102 With Additional Surcharge in Black

ΕΛΛΑΣ
ΛΕΠΤΟΝ

| | | | | |
|---|---|---|---|---|
| N103 | OS2 | 1 l on 1d orange | 20.00 | 20.00 |
| a. | | Black surcharge double | 180.00 | 325.00 |
| b. | | Black surcharge inverted | 180.00 | |
| | | Nos. N97-N103 (7) | 47.50 | 54.00 |

### Issue of 1913 Overprinted in Red or Black

### Without Sofulis' Initials Above Overprint

| 1915 | | | | |
|---|---|---|---|---|
| N104 | OS3 | 1d brown (R) | 28.00 | 17.00 |
| a. | | With initials | 40.00 | 25.00 |
| N105 | OS3 | 2d dp blue (R) | 28.00 | 23.00 |
| a. | | With initials | 47.50 | 37.50 |
| b. | | As "a," double overprint | | |

| | | | | |
|---|---|---|---|---|
| N106 | OS3 | 5d gray grn (R) | 45.00 | 28.00 |
| a. | | As "a," black overprint | 40.00 | 25.00 |
| | | | 1,500. | |
| N107 | OS3 | 10d yellow grn (Bk) | 85.00 | 72.50 |
| a. | | Inverted overprint | 1,600. | |
| N108 | OS3 | 25d red (Bk) | 600.00 | 650.00 |
| a. | | With initials | 750.00 | 750.00 |
| | | Nos. N104-N108 (5) | 786.00 | 790.50 |

Nos. N97 to N108 inclusive have an embossed control mark, consisting of a cross encircled by a Greek inscription.
Counterfeits of Nos. N104-N108 are plentiful.

---

### FOR USE IN PARTS OF TURKEY OCCUPIED BY GREECE (NEW GREECE)

Regular Issues of Greece Overprinted

#### Black Overprint Meaning "Greek Administration"
#### On Issue of 1901

| 1912 | | Wmk. 129 | Engr. | Perf. 13½ | |
|---|---|---|---|---|---|
| N109 | A11 | 20 l red lilac | | 3.25 | 2.75 |
| a. | | Double overprint | | 45.00 | 45.00 |

#### On Issue of 1911-21
#### Unwmk.
#### Serrate Roulette 13½

| | | | | |
|---|---|---|---|---|
| N110 | A24 | 1 l green | 1.00 | 1.00 |
| N111 | A25 | 2 l car rose | 1.00 | 1.00 |
| a. | | Double overprint | 22.50 | 22.00 |
| b. | | Double ovpt., one inverted | 6.75 | 8.00 |
| | | | 70.00 | |
| N112 | A24 | 3 l vermilion | 1.00 | 1.00 |
| a. | | Double overprint | 6.75 | 8.00 |
| N113 | A26 | 5 l green | 1.00 | 1.00 |
| a. | | Double overprint | 10.00 | 10.00 |
| N114 | A24 | 10 l car rose | 1.50 | 2.00 |
| a. | | Double overprint | 10.00 | 10.00 |
| N115 | A25 | 20 l gray lilac | 2.75 | 2.75 |
| a. | | Double overprint | 22.50 | 22.50 |
| g. | | Imperf., pair | 1,200. | |
| N116 | A25 | 25 l ultra | 2.75 | 2.75 |
| a. | | Double overprint | 22.50 | 18.50 |
| N117 | A26 | 30 l car rose | 2.75 | 3.00 |
| a. | | Double overprint | 25.00 | 25.00 |
| N118 | A25 | 40 l deep blue | 3.75 | 4.50 |
| a. | | Double overprint | 27.50 | 24.00 |
| N119 | A26 | 50 l dl violet | 4.50 | 5.00 |
| a. | | Double overprint | 30.00 | 30.00 |
| N120 | A27 | 1d ultra | 11.00 | 3.50 |
| a. | | Double overprint | 90.00 | 90.00 |
| N121 | A27 | 2d vermilion | 55.00 | 25.00 |
| a. | | Double overprint | 120.00 | 120.00 |
| N122 | A27 | 3d car rose | 55.00 | 32.50 |
| N123 | A27 | 5d ultra | 25.00 | 45.00 |
| N124 | A27 | 10d deep blue | 265.00 | 265.00 |
| N125 | A28 | 25d dp bl, ovpt. horiz. | 325.00 | 325.00 |

#### On Issue of 1913-23
#### Litho.

| | | | | |
|---|---|---|---|---|
| N126 | A24 | 1 l green | 1.00 | 1.00 |
| a. | | Double overprint | 5.50 | 7.00 |
| b. | | Double ovpt., one inverted | 55.00 | 55.00 |
| c. | | Period omitted after "ΕΛΛΑΣ" (on #214a) | 145.00 | 75.00 |
| f. | | As "c," double overprint | | |
| g. | | As "c," double ovpt., one inverted | | |
| N127 | A26 | 5 l green | 1.00 | 1.00 |
| a. | | Double overprint | 7.00 | 8.00 |
| b. | | Imperf., pair | | |
| N128 | A24 | 10 l carmine | 4.00 | 3.00 |
| a. | | Double overprint | 7.00 | 8.00 |
| b. | | Double overprint, one inverted | 140.00 | 140.00 |
| N129 | A25 | 25 l blue | 6.00 | 6.00 |
| a. | | Double overprint | 22.50 | 22.50 |
| b. | | Triple overprint | 225.00 | |
| | | Nos. N109-N129 (21) | 773.25 | 721.25 |

#### Red Overprint, Reading Up
#### On Issues of 1911-21
#### Engr.

| | | | | |
|---|---|---|---|---|
| N130 | A24 | 1 l green | 1.00 | 1.00 |
| N131 | A26 | 5 l green | 1.00 | 1.00 |
| N132 | A25 | 20 l gray lilac | 5.50 | 5.00 |
| a. | | Inverted overprint (reading down) | 3,000. | 1,800. |
| N133 | A25 | 40 l deep blue | 2.75 | 2.75 |
| a. | | Double overprint | 275.00 | 275.00 |
| N134 | A26 | 50 l dull violet | 3.25 | 3.25 |
| N135 | A27 | 1d ultramarine | 20.00 | 15.00 |
| N136 | A27 | 2d vermilion | 90.00 | 100.00 |
| N137 | A27 | 3d carmine rose | 32.50 | 45.00 |
| N138 | A27 | 5d ultramarine | 550.00 | 400.00 |
| N139 | A27 | 10d deep blue | 40.00 | 55.00 |
| a. | | Double overprint | 725.00 | |
| N140 | A28 | 25d dp bl, ovpt. horiz. | 75.00 | 100.00 |
| a. | | Double overprint | 1,800. | |
| b. | | Inverted overprint (reading down) | 550.00 | 550.00 |

| | | | | |
|---|---|---|---|---|
| c. | | Inverted overprint (reading up) | 650.00 | 650.00 |
| | | **Litho.** | | |
| N141 | A26 | 5 l green | 1.60 | 1.75 |
| N142 | A25 | 25 l ultra, ovpt. vert. (reading up) | 2.75 | 1.75 |
| | | Nos. N130-N142 (13) | 825.35 | 731.50 |

Nos. N140b and N140c were the only horizontal or vertical overprints placed into normal circulation.

#### Engr.
#### Carmine Overprint, Reading Up

| | | | | |
|---|---|---|---|---|
| N143 | A25 | 2 l carmine rose | 12.00 | 13.00 |
| a. | | Double overprint | 40.00 | |
| N144 | A24 | 3 l vermilion | 12.00 | 13.00 |
| N145 | A25 | 20 l gray lilac | 50.00 | 80.00 |
| a. | | Double overprint | 75.00 | |
| N146 | A25 | 25 l ultramarine | 90.00 | 90.00 |
| N147 | A26 | 30 l carmine rose | 110.00 | 110.00 |
| a. | | Double overprint | 290.00 | |
| N148 | A27 | 2d vermilion | 200.00 | 165.00 |
| N149 | A27 | 5d ultramarine | 550.00 | 400.00 |
| a. | | Double overprint | 625.00 | |

#### Litho.

| | | | | |
|---|---|---|---|---|
| N150 | A24 | 1 l green | 11.00 | 12.50 |
| b. | | Period omitted after "ΕΛΛΑΣ" (on #214a) | 450.00 | |
| e. | | Ovpt. reading down | 1,575. | |
| f. | | As "e," period omitted after "ΕΛΛΑΣ" (on #214a) | | |
| N151 | A24 | 10 l carmine rose | 65.00 | 65.00 |
| | | Nos. N143-N151 (9) | 1,100. | 948.50 |

There are numerous broken, missing and wrong font letters with a Greek "Λ" instead of "Δ" as the first letter of the second word.
Counterfeits exist of Nos. N109-N151.

Cross of Constantine O1   Eagle of Zeus O2

| 1912 | | | Litho. | |
|---|---|---|---|---|
| N150A | O1 | 1 l brn, grayish | .30 | .30 |
| c. | | 1 l brown, yellowish | 5.50 | 5.50 |
| N152 | O2 | 2 l red, yelwsh | .30 | .30 |
| N153 | O2 | 3 l org, grayish | .30 | .30 |
| a. | | 3 l orange, yellowish | 5.50 | 5.50 |
| N154 | O1 | 5 l grn, grayish | .30 | .30 |
| a. | | 5 l green, yellowish | 6.50 | 6.50 |
| N155 | O1 | 10 l rose red, grayish | .30 | .30 |
| a. | | 10 l rose red, yellowish | 11.00 | 3.25 |
| N156 | O1 | 20 l vio, grayish | 22.50 | 4.00 |
| N157 | O2 | 25 l pale bl, yellowish | 3.00 | 1.00 |
| N158 | O1 | 30 l gray grn, yellowish | 70.00 | 3.00 |
| N159 | O2 | 40 l indigo, grayish | 11.00 | 5.00 |
| a. | | 40 l indigo, yellowish | 17.50 | 8.50 |
| c. | | Double impression | — | |
| N160 | O1 | 50 l dk bl, yellowish | 5.00 | 3.00 |
| N161 | O1 | 1d vio brn, grayish | 15.00 | 4.50 |
| a. | | 1d violet brn, yellowish | | |
| N162 | O1 | 2d gray brn, grayish | 55.00 | 9.00 |
| a. | | 2d violet brn | | |
| N163 | O2 | 3d dl bl, yelwsh | 225.00 | 32.50 |
| a. | | 3d dull blue, grayish | 700.00 | 110.00 |
| N164 | O1 | 5d gray, grayish | 200.00 | 32.50 |
| N165 | O2 | 10d car, grayish | 225.00 | 325.00 |
| N166 | O1 | 25d gray blk, yelwsh | 225.00 | 350.00 |
| | | Nos. N150A-N166 (16) | 1,058. | 771.00 |

There are numerous broken, missing and wrong font letters with a Greek "Λ" instead of "A" as the first letter of the second word. Occupation of Macedonia, Epirus and some of the Aegean Islands.
Sold only in New Greece.
Dangerous forgeries of Nos. N165-N166 exist.
In 1916 some stamps of this issue were overprinted in Greek: "I (era) Koinotis Ag (iou) Orous" for the Mount Athos Monastery District. They were never placed in use and most of them were destroyed.
For surcharges and overprints see Nos. 267-276A, RA14-RA16, Thrace 31-33.

#### Imperf., Pairs
#### Without Overprint

| | | | | |
|---|---|---|---|---|
| N150d | O1 | 1 l (as #N150Ac) | 500.00 | |
| N151b | O2 | 2 l | 500.00 | |
| N152b | O2 | | 500.00 | |
| N153b | O1 | 3 l (as #153a) | 450.00 | |
| N154b | O1 | 5 l (as #154a) | 200.00 | |
| N155b | O1 | 10 l (as #155a) | 200.00 | |
| N156b | O1 | 20 l | 1,800. | |
| N157b | O2 | 25 l | 1,800. | |
| N158b | O1 | 30 l | 1,800. | |
| N159b | O2 | 40 l | 1,800. | |
| N160b | O1 | 50 l | 2,000. | |
| N161b | O2 | 1d | 2,000. | |

| | | | | |
|---|---|---|---|---|
| N163b | O2 | 3d | | 2,800. |
| N163c | O2 | 3d | (As #N163a) | 2,800. |
| N164a | O1 | 5d | | 2,800. |
| N165a | O2 | 10d | | 2,800. |

## CAVALLA

Bulgaria Nos. 89-97
Surcharged in Red

### 1913 Unwmk. Engr. Perf. 12

| | | | | |
|---|---|---|---|---|
| N167 | A20 | 5 l on 1s myr grn | 30.00 | 30.00 |
| N168 | A25 | 10 l on 10s red & blk | 550.00 | 450.00 |
| | | Never hinged | 850.00 | |
| N169 | A25 | 10 l on 15s brn bis | 70.00 | 70.00 |
| N170 | A26 | 10 l on 25s ultra & blk | 35.00 | 35.00 |
| N171 | A21 | 15 l on 2s car & blk | 70.00 | 70.00 |
| N172 | A22 | 20 l on 3s lake & blk | 70.00 | 70.00 |
| N173 | A23 | 25 l on 5s grn & blk | 25.00 | 15.00 |
| N174 | A24 | 50 l on 10s red & blk | 45.00 | 35.00 |
| N175 | A25 | 1d on 15s brn bis | 300.00 | 250.00 |
| N176 | A27 | 1d on 30s bl & blk | 120.00 | 120.00 |
| N177 | A28 | 1d on 50s ocher & blk | 165.00 | 165.00 |

### Blue Surcharge

| | | | | |
|---|---|---|---|---|
| N178 | A24 | 50 l on 10s red & blk | 25.00 | 25.00 |
| | | Nos. N167-N178 (12) | 1,505. | 1,335. |

The counterfeits and reprints of Nos. N167-N178 are difficult to distinguish from originals. Many overprint varieties exist.

Some specialists question the status of Nos. N167-N178.

## DEDEAGATCH

### (Alexandroupolis)

D1-(10 lepta)

### Control Mark in Red

### 1913 Unwmk. Typeset Perf. 11½

| | | | | |
|---|---|---|---|---|
| N179 | D1 | 5 l black | 40.00 | 30.00 |
| N180 | D1 | 10 l black | 5.50 | 4.00 |
| N181 | D1 | 25 l black | 6.50 | 5.00 |
| | | Sheet of 8 | 135.00 | 110.00 |
| | | Nos. N179-N181 (3) | 52.00 | 39.00 |

Nos. N179-N181 issued without gum in sheets of 8, consisting of one 5 l, three 10 l normal, one 10 l inverted, three 25 l and one blank. The sheet yields se-tenant pairs of 5 l & 10 l, 10 l & 25 l; tete beche pairs of 5 l & 10 l, 10 l & 25 l and 10 l & 10 l.

Also issued imperf., value $200 unused, $160 canceled.

The 5 l reads "PENTE LEPTA" in Greek letters; the 10 l is illustrated; the 25 l carries the numeral "25."

Bulgaria Nos. 89-90, 92-93, 95 Surcharged

### 1913 Red Surcharge Perf. 12

| | | | | |
|---|---|---|---|---|
| N182 | A20 | 5 l on 1s myr grn | 65.00 | 45.00 |
| a. | | "ΔΕΛΕΑΓΤΕ" instead of "ΔΕΔΕΑΓΤΕ" | 150.00 | 110.00 |
| N183 | A26 | 1d on 25s ultra & blk | 100.00 | 60.00 |
| a. | | "ΔΕΛΕΑΓΤΕ" instead of "ΔΕΔΕΑΓΤΕ" | 180.00 | 125.00 |

### Blue Surcharge

| | | | | |
|---|---|---|---|---|
| N184 | A24 | 10 l on 10s red & blk | 32.50 | 25.00 |
| N185 | A23 | 25 l on 5s grn & blk | 35.00 | 27.50 |

| | | | | |
|---|---|---|---|---|
| N187 | A21 | 50 l on 2s car & blk | 65.00 | 45.00 |
| | | Nos. N182-N185,N187 (5) | 297.50 | 202.50 |

The surcharges on Nos. N182 to N187 are printed from a setting of eight, which was used for all, with the necessary changes of value. No. 6 in the setting has a Greek "L" instead of "D" for the third letter of the third word of the surcharge.

The 25 l surcharge also exists on 8 examples of the 25s, Bulgaria No. 95.

D2

### 1913, Sept. 15 Typeset Perf. 11½
### Control Mark in Blue

| | | | | |
|---|---|---|---|---|
| N188 | D2 | 1 l blue | 200.00 | 65.00 |
| N189 | D2 | 2 l blue | 200.00 | 65.00 |
| N190 | D2 | 3 l blue | 200.00 | 65.00 |
| N191 | D2 | 5 l blue | 200.00 | 65.00 |
| N192 | D2 | 10 l blue | 200.00 | 65.00 |
| N193 | D2 | 25 l blue | 200.00 | 65.00 |
| N194 | D2 | 40 l blue | 200.00 | 65.00 |
| N195 | D2 | 50 l blue | 200.00 | 65.00 |
| a. | | Sheet of 8 | 2,200. | 1,000. |
| | | Nos. N188-N195 (8) | 1,600. | 520.00 |

Issued without gum in sheets of 8 containing all values.
Counterfeits of Nos. N188-N195 exist.

D3

### 1913, Sept. 25 Typeset
### Control Mark in Blue

| | | | | |
|---|---|---|---|---|
| N196 | D3 | 1 l blue, gray blue | 175.00 | 55.00 |
| N197 | D3 | 5 l blue, gray blue | 175.00 | 55.00 |
| N198 | D3 | 10 l blue, gray blue | 175.00 | 55.00 |
| N199 | D3 | 25 l blue, gray blue | 175.00 | 55.00 |
| N200 | D3 | 30 l blue, gray blue | 175.00 | 55.00 |
| N201 | D3 | 50 l blue, gray blue | 175.00 | 55.00 |
| a. | | Sheet of 6 | 1,350. | 500.00 |
| | | Nos. N196-N201 (6) | 1,050. | 330.00 |

Nos. N196 to N201 were issued without gum in sheets of six containing all values.

Counterfeits of Nos. N182-N201 are plentiful.

## FOR USE IN NORTH EPIRUS (ALBANIA)

Greek Stamps of 1937-38 Overprinted in Black

### Perf. 13½x12, 12x13½
### 1940 Litho. Wmk. 252

| | | | | |
|---|---|---|---|---|
| N202 | A69 | 5 l brn red & bl | .25 | .30 |
| a. | | Inverted overprint | 55.00 | |
| b. | | Double impression of frame | | |
| N203 | A70 | 10 l bl & brn red (No. 413) | .25 | .30 |
| a. | | Double impression of frame | 150.00 | |
| b. | | Double impression | | |
| N204 | A71 | 20 l blk & grn | .25 | .30 |
| a. | | Inverted overprint | 55.00 | |
| b. | | Double impression of grn | | |
| N205 | A72 | 40 l grn & blk | .25 | .30 |
| a. | | Inverted overprint | 55.00 | |
| b. | | Double impression of grn | | |
| N206 | A73 | 50 l brn & blk | .25 | .30 |
| N207 | A74 | 80 l ind & yel brn | .35 | .35 |
| a. | | Double impression of frame | 55.00 | |
| N208 | A67 | 1d green | .35 | .35 |
| a. | | Inverted overprint | 90.00 | |
| b. | | "ΔΙΟΙΚΗΕΙΕ" instead of "ΔΙΟΙΚΗΕΙΕ" | 24.00 | |
| c. | | Double overprint | 200.00 | |
| N209 | A75 | 2d ultra | .35 | .40 |
| N210 | A67 | 3d red brn | .75 | .80 |
| a. | | "ΔΙΟΙΚΗΕΙΕ" instead of "ΔΙΟΙΚΗΕΙΕ" | 24.00 | |
| N211 | A76 | 5d red | .75 | .80 |
| N212 | A77 | 6d dk brn | .85 | .95 |
| N213 | A78 | 7d dk brn | .95 | 1.00 |
| N214 | A67 | 8d deep blue | .95 | 1.00 |
| a. | | "ΔΙΟΙΚΗΕΙΕ" instead of "ΔΙΟΙΚΗΕΙΕ" | 24.00 | |
| N215 | A79 | 10d red brn | 2.00 | 2.00 |
| N216 | A80 | 15d green | 2.00 | 2.00 |

| | | | | |
|---|---|---|---|---|
| N217 | A81 | 25d dark blue | 5.00 | 6.25 |
| a. | | Inverted overprint | 100.00 | |

### Engr.
### Unwmk.

| | | | | |
|---|---|---|---|---|
| N218 | A84 | 30d org brn | 8.00 | 15.00 |
| a. | | Double overprint | 23.55 | 32.40 |
| | | Nos. N202-N218 (17) | | |

### Same Overprinted in Carmine on National Youth Issue

### 1941 Litho. Perf. 12½, 13½x12½

| | | | | |
|---|---|---|---|---|
| N219 | A93 | 3d sil, dp ultra & red | 1.00 | 1.00 |
| N220 | A94 | 5d dk bl & blk | 3.00 | 4.50 |
| N221 | A94 | 10d red org & blk | 4.50 | 6.75 |
| N222 | A94 | 15d dk grn & blk | 18.50 | 20.00 |
| N223 | A94 | 20d lake & blk | 13.50 | 15.00 |
| N224 | A94 | 25d dk bl & blk | 13.50 | 15.00 |
| N225 | A94 | 30d rose vio & blk | 13.50 | 15.00 |
| N226 | A94 | 50d lake & blk | 13.50 | 15.00 |
| N227 | A94 | 75d dk bl, brn & gold | 15.00 | 15.00 |
| N228 | A93 | 100d sil, dp ultra & red | 22.50 | 20.00 |
| a. | | Inverted overprint | 475.00 | |
| | | Nos. N219-N228 (10) | 118.50 | 127.25 |

### Same Overprint in Carmine on National Youth Air Post Stamps

| | | | | |
|---|---|---|---|---|
| N229 | AP25 | 2d red org & blk | 1.00 | 1.00 |
| a. | | Inverted overprint | 165.00 | |
| N230 | AP25 | 4d dk grn & blk | 3.50 | 4.50 |
| a. | | Inverted overprint | 165.00 | |
| N231 | AP25 | 6d lake & blk | 6.50 | 7.00 |
| a. | | Inverted overprint | 165.00 | |
| N232 | AP25 | 8d dk bl & blk | 6.50 | 7.00 |
| N233 | AP25 | 16d rose vio & blk | 11.00 | 9.00 |
| N234 | AP25 | 32d red org & blk | 15.00 | 15.00 |
| N235 | AP25 | 45d dk grn & blk | 16.00 | 14.00 |
| N236 | AP25 | 55d lake & blk | 16.00 | 14.00 |
| N237 | AP25 | 65d dk bl & blk | 16.00 | 14.00 |
| N238 | AP25 | 100d rose vio & blk | 25.00 | 30.00 |
| | | Nos. N229-N238 (10) | 116.50 | 115.50 |

Some specialists have questioned the status of Nos. N230a and N231a.

For other stamps issued by Greece for use in occupied parts of Epirus and Thrace, see the catalogue listings of those countries.

> **Catalogue values for unused stamps in this section, from this point to the end of the section, are for Never Hinged items.**

## FOR USE IN THE DODECANESE ISLANDS

Greece, No. 472C, with Additional Overprint in Carmine or Silver

### 1947 Wmk. 252 Litho. Perf. 12½

| | | | | |
|---|---|---|---|---|
| N239 | A113 | 10d on 2,000d (C) | 2.25 | 2.40 |
| a. | | Double overprint | 70.00 | |
| N240 | A113 | 10d on 2,000d (S) | 2.25 | 2.40 |
| a. | | Inverted overprint | 55.00 | |
| b. | | Dbl. ovpt., one car. one sil. | 145.00 | |

These stamps sold for 5 lire (100 drachmas) and paid postage for that amount.

### King George II Memorial Issue

Greece, Nos. 484 and 485, With Additional Overprint in Black

### 1947 Engr. Perf. 12½x12

| | | | | |
|---|---|---|---|---|
| N241 | A67 | 50d on 1d green | 1.40 | 1.50 |
| a. | | Inverted overprint | 110.00 | |
| N242 | A67 | 250d on 3d red brn | 1.40 | 1.50 |
| a. | | Inverted overprint | 145.00 | |

The letters are initials of the Greek words for "Military Administration of the Dodecanese."

Greece, Nos. 501 and 502 Overprinted in Carmine

### 1947 Wmk. 252 Litho. Perf. 12½

| | | | | |
|---|---|---|---|---|
| N243 | A111 | 20d on 500d dk ol | 2.00 | 2.25 |
| N244 | A104 | 30d on 5d lt bl grn | 2.00 | 2.25 |
| a. | | "ΝΑΥΟΛΙΟΝ" instead of "ΝΑΥΠΛΙΟΝ" | 32.50 | 35.00 |

Greece, Nos. 437, 406, 407 and 445, Surcharged in Black or Carmine

### 1947 Perf. 12½, 13½x12

| | | | | |
|---|---|---|---|---|
| N245 | A103 | 50d on 2d | 2.25 | 2.25 |

### Engr.

| | | | | |
|---|---|---|---|---|
| N246 | A79 | 250d on 10d | 6.00 | 6.75 |
| a. | | Double overprint | | |
| N247 | A80 | 400d on 15d (C) | 7.75 | 8.75 |
| a. | | Inverted surcharge | 145.00 | |
| b. | | Double overprint | 175.00 | |
| c. | | Surch. and ovpt. inverted | 225.00 | |

### Litho.

| | | | | |
|---|---|---|---|---|
| N248 | A110 | 1000d on 200 (C) | 4.50 | 5.50 |
| a. | | Imprint omitted | 32.50 | 32.50 |
| | | Nos. N245-N248 (4) | 23.90 | 23.90 |

## POSTAGE DUE STAMPS

### FOR USE IN PARTS OF TURKEY OCCUPIED BY GREECE (NEW GREECE)

1902 Postage Due Stamps of Greece Overprinted

### 1912 Wmk. 129 Engr. Perf. 13½
### Black Overprint, Reading Up

| | | | | |
|---|---|---|---|---|
| NJ1 | D3 | 1 l chocolate | .55 | .65 |
| a. | | Double overprint | 22.00 | |
| NJ2 | D3 | 2 l gray | .55 | .65 |
| a. | | Double overprint | 15.50 | |
| NJ3 | D3 | 3 l orange | .55 | .65 |
| a. | | Double overprint | 15.50 | 20.00 |
| NJ4 | D3 | 5 l yel grn | .95 | 1.10 |
| a. | | Double overprint | 20.00 | |
| NJ5 | D3 | 10 l scarlet | 1.45 | 1.60 |
| a. | | Double overprint | 20.00 | |
| NJ6 | D3 | 20 l lilac | 1.45 | 1.60 |
| NJ7 | D3 | 30 l dp vio | 3.00 | 3.50 |
| a. | | Double overprint | 75.00 | |
| NJ8 | D3 | 40 l dk brn | 6.50 | 7.00 |
| a. | | Double overprint | 122.50 | |
| NJ9 | D3 | 50 l red brn | 9.50 | 10.00 |
| NJ10 | D3 | 1d black | 45.00 | 47.50 |
| NJ11 | D3 | 2d bronze (overprint reading down) | 72.50 | 82.50 |
| NJ12 | D3 | 3d silver (overprint reading down) | 142.50 | 120.00 |
| NJ13 | D3 | 5d gold (overprint reading down) | 225.00 | 250.00 |
| | | Nos. NJ1-NJ13 (13) | 509.50 | 526.75 |

### Red Overprint, Reading Up

| | | | | |
|---|---|---|---|---|
| NJ14 | D3 | 1 l chocolate | 1.00 | 1.00 |
| NJ15 | D3 | 2 l gray | 1.00 | 1.00 |
| a. | | Double overprint | 80.00 | |
| NJ16 | D3 | 5 l yellow green | 1.00 | 1.00 |
| NJ17 | D3 | 20 l lilac | 1.00 | 1.00 |
| NJ18 | D3 | 30 l deep violet | 5.00 | 5.00 |
| NJ19 | D3 | 40 l dark brown | 1.45 | 1.60 |
| NJ20 | D3 | 50 l red brown | 1.45 | 1.60 |
| NJ21 | D3 | 1d black | 10.00 | 10.50 |
| NJ22 | D3 | 2d bronze | 20.00 | 21.00 |
| NJ23 | D3 | 3d silver | 24.50 | 27.00 |
| NJ24 | D3 | 5d gold | 60.00 | 62.50 |
| | | Nos. NJ14-NJ24 (11) | 126.40 | 133.20 |

### Carmine Overprint, Reading Up

| | | | | |
|---|---|---|---|---|
| NJ25 | D3 | 2 l gray | 10.00 | 11.00 |
| NJ26 | D3 | 3 l orange | 147.50 | 170.00 |
| NJ27 | D3 | 1d black | 82.50 | 110.00 |
| a. | | Double overprint, one inverted | 245.00 | |
| NJ28 | D3 | 2d bronze | 500.00 | |
| NJ29 | D3 | 3d silver | | 2,000. |
| | | Nos. NJ25-NJ29 (5) | 740.00 | 2,291. |

### Carmine Overprint, Reading Down

| | | | | |
|---|---|---|---|---|
| NJ30 | D3 | 2 l gray | 4.00 | 4.00 |
| NJ31 | D3 | 3 l orange | 10.00 | 11.00 |
| NJ32 | D3 | 5 l yellow green | 9.00 | 9.00 |
| NJ33 | D3 | 10 l scarlet | 15.00 | 15.00 |
| a. | | Double overprint | 275.00 | |
| NJ34 | D3 | 1d black | 55.00 | 55.00 |
| NJ35 | D3 | 2d bronze | 85.00 | 90.00 |
| NJ36 | D3 | 3d silver | 385.00 | 400.00 |
| NJ37 | D3 | 5d gold | 750.00 | 775.00 |
| | | Nos. NJ30-NJ37 (8) | 1,313. | 1,359. |

Some of the varieties of lettering that occur on the postage stamps are also found on the postage due stamps.

## FOR USE IN NORTH EPIRUS (ALBANIA)

Postage Due Stamps of Greece, 1930, Surcharged or Overprinted in Black

a     b

### Perf. 13, 13x12½

| 1940 | | Litho. | Unwmk. |
|---|---|---|---|
| NJ38 | D3(a) | 50 l on 25d lt red | .45 | .90 |
| NJ39 | D3(b) | 2d light red | 1.10 | 1.75 |
| a. | | Inverted overprint | 67.50 | |
| NJ40 | D3(b) | 5d blue gray | .55 | 1.45 |
| NJ41 | D3(b) | 10d green | 1.10 | 1.90 |
| NJ42 | D3(b) | 15d red brown | 1.10 | 1.90 |
| | | Nos. NJ38-NJ42 (5) | 4.30 | 7.90 |

## POSTAL TAX STAMPS

### FOR USE IN NORTH EPIRUS (ALBANIA)

Greece Nos. RA61-RA63 Overprinted Type "b" in Black

| 1940 | Unwmk. | Litho. | Perf. 13½x12 |
|---|---|---|---|
| NRA1 | PT7 | 10 l | .25 | .35 |
| NRA2 | PT7 | 50 l | .35 | .55 |
| a. | | Inverted overprint | 65.00 | |
| NRA3 | PT7 | 1d | .95 | 1.75 |
| | | Nos. NRA1-NRA3 (3) | 1.55 | 2.65 |

## MOUNT ATHOS

Catalogue values for unused stamps in this section are for Never Hinged items.

All stamps also are available for postage in Greece.

Nikiforos Fokas — A1

Ioannis Tsimiskis — A2

Map of Mount Athos — A3

Church of the Protaton — A4

Staff of Protepistates A5

### Litho. With Foil Application
### Perf. 13¼x13

| 2008, May 16 | | | Unwmk. | |
|---|---|---|---|---|
| 1 | A1 | 40c multi + label | 1.25 | 1.25 |
| 2 | A2 | 60c multi + label | 1.90 | 1.90 |
| 3 | A3 | 70c multi + label | 2.25 | 2.25 |
| 4 | A4 | €2 multi + label | 6.50 | 6.50 |
| 5 | A5 | €4 multi + label | 13.00 | 13.00 |
| | | Nos. 1-5 (5) | 24.90 | 24.90 |

Megisti Lavra Monastery — A6

Vatopedi Monastery — A7

Koutloumousiou Monastery — A8

Iveron Monastery — A9

Helandariou Monastery — A10

| 2008, June 13 | | | | |
|---|---|---|---|---|
| 6 | A6 | 57c multi + label | 1.75 | 1.75 |
| 7 | A7 | 70c multi + label | 2.25 | 2.25 |
| 8 | A8 | €1 multi + label | 3.25 | 3.25 |
| 9 | A9 | €1.85 multi + label | 5.75 | 5.75 |
| 10 | A10 | €3 multi + label | 9.25 | 9.25 |
| | | Nos. 6-10 (5) | 22.25 | 22.25 |

Pantokratoros Monastery — A11

Xeropotamou Monastery — A12

Karakalou Monastery — A13

Zografou Monastery — A14

Docheiariou Monastery — A15

| 2008, July 4 | | | | |
|---|---|---|---|---|
| 11 | A11 | 57c multi + label | 1.90 | 1.90 |
| 12 | A12 | 70c multi + label | 2.25 | 2.25 |
| 13 | A13 | 80c multi + label | 2.50 | 2.50 |
| 14 | A14 | €1.50 multi + label | 4.75 | 4.75 |
| 15 | A15 | €3.50 multi + label | 11.00 | 11.00 |
| | | Nos. 11-15 (5) | 22.40 | 22.40 |

Agiou Pavlou Monastery — A16

Dionysiou Monastery — A17

Stavronikita Monastery — A18

Simonos Petras Monastery — A19

Filotheou Monastery — A20

| 2008, Aug. 22 | | | | |
|---|---|---|---|---|
| 16 | A16 | 57c multi + label | 1.75 | 1.75 |
| 17 | A17 | 70c multi + label | 2.10 | 2.10 |
| 18 | A18 | €1.20 multi + label | 3.50 | 3.50 |
| 19 | A19 | €1.80 multi + label | 5.25 | 5.25 |
| 20 | A20 | €3 multi + label | 9.00 | 9.00 |
| | | Nos. 16-20 (5) | 21.60 | 21.60 |

Xenophontos Monastery — A21

Osiou Grigoriou Monastery — A22

Esphigmenou Monastery — A23

Konstamonitou Monastery — A24

Agiou Panteleimon Monastery — A25

| 2008, Nov. 7 | | | | |
|---|---|---|---|---|
| 21 | A21 | 57c multi + label | 1.50 | 1.50 |
| 22 | A22 | 70c multi + label | 1.90 | 1.90 |
| 23 | A23 | 85c multi + label | 2.25 | 2.25 |
| 24 | A24 | €2.42 multi + label | 6.25 | 6.25 |
| 25 | A25 | €3 multi + label | 7.75 | 7.75 |
| | | Nos. 21-25 (5) | 19.65 | 19.65 |

Monk Ringing Talanton — A26

Monk in Library — A27

Protepistate Konstantinos Prigoumenos Vatopaidinos A28

Monk Sculpting Wood — A29

Monk Packing Mule — A30

| 2009, May 11 | | | | |
|---|---|---|---|---|
| 26 | A26 | 57c multi + label | 1.60 | 1.60 |
| 27 | A27 | 70c multi + label | 2.00 | 2.00 |
| 28 | A28 | 85c multi + label | 2.40 | 2.40 |

| 29 | A29 | €2.42 multi + label | 6.75 | 6.75 |
|----|-----|---------------------|------|------|
| 30 | A30 | €3 multi + label | 8.50 | 8.50 |
| | | Nos. 26-30 (5) | 21.25 | 21.25 |

Monk Sewing Clothes — A31

Monk Binding Book — A32

Monk Cooking — A33

Monk Watering Flowers — A34

Monk Hiking — A35

**2009, June 12**

| 31 | A31 | 57c multi + label | 1.60 | 1.60 |
|----|-----|-------------------|------|------|
| 32 | A32 | 70c multi + label | 2.00 | 2.00 |
| 33 | A33 | €1 multi + label | 2.75 | 2.75 |
| 34 | A34 | €1.85 multi + label | 5.25 | 5.25 |
| 35 | A35 | €3.30 multi + label | 9.25 | 9.25 |
| | | Nos. 31-35 (5) | 20.85 | 20.85 |

Olive Collecting, by Polykleitos Rengos — A36

Old Apostolos with His Lines, by Fotis Kontoglou — A37

Shipwright, by Kontoglou — A38

Icon Painter on Mount Athos, by Theodoros Rallis — A39

Monk at Study, by Dimitris Gioldasis — A40

**2009, Sept. 18**

| 36 | A36 | 57c multi + label | 1.75 | 1.75 |
|----|-----|-------------------|------|------|
| 37 | A37 | 70c multi + label | 2.10 | 2.10 |
| 38 | A38 | 80c multi + label | 2.40 | 2.40 |
| 39 | A39 | €1 multi + label | 3.00 | 3.00 |
| 40 | A40 | €4.50 multi + label | 13.50 | 13.50 |
| | | Nos. 36-40 (5) | 22.75 | 22.75 |

Holy Epistiasia of the Holy Community of Mount Athos, 1938 — A41

Athonias School, 1936 — A42

Archimandrite Gabriel Celebrating Feast of the Holy Monastery of Xenophontos, 1967 — A43

Holy Community of Mount Athos, 1951 — A44

Archimandrite Vyssarion, 1998 — A45

**2009, Nov. 17**    *Perf. 13½*

| 41 | A41 | 58c multi + label | 1.75 | 1.75 |
|----|-----|-------------------|------|------|
| 42 | A42 | 70c multi + label | 2.10 | 2.10 |
| 43 | A43 | €1.20 multi + label | 3.75 | 3.75 |
| 44 | A44 | €1.85 multi + label | 5.50 | 5.50 |
| 45 | A45 | €3 multi + label | 9.00 | 9.00 |
| | | Nos. 41-45 (5) | 22.10 | 22.10 |

Flora and Fauna — A46

Designs: No. 46, 58c, Pansy. No. 47, 72c, Judas tree. No. 48, €1, Arbutus. No. 49, €2.43, European tree frog. No. 50, €3, Heath.

### Litho. With Foil Application
**2010, May 11**    *Perf. 13½x13*
**Stamps + Label**

| 46-50 | A46 | Set of 5 | 18.50 | 18.50 |
|-------|-----|----------|-------|-------|

**2010, June 21**    **Stamps + Label**

Designs: No. 51, 50c, Silene orphanidis. No. 52, 58c, Nightingale. No. 53, 72c, European roe deer. No. 54, €2, Laurel. No. 55, €3.50, European sand lizard.

| 51-55 | A46 | Set of 5 | 18.50 | 18.50 |
|-------|-----|----------|-------|-------|

### Flora and Fauna Type of 2010

Designs: No. 56, 58c, Two-tailed pasha butterfly. No. 57, 72c, Golden eagle. No. 58, €1, Mountain tea (white flowers and mountain). No. 59, €2.43, Amaranth (plant). No. 60, €3, Mediterranean monk seal.

**Stamps + Label**

### Litho. With Foil Application
**2010, Sept. 16**    *Perf. 13½x13*

| 56-60 | A46 | Set of 5 | 21.50 | 21.50 |
|-------|-----|----------|-------|-------|

**2010, Nov. 16**    **Stamps + Label**

Designs: No. 61, 50c, Chestnut. No. 62, 58c, Fir tree. No. 63, 72c, Sage. No. 64, €2, Wild boar. No. 65, €3.50, Spiny puffball mushroom.

| 61-65 | A46 | Set of 5 | 19.50 | 19.50 |
|-------|-----|----------|-------|-------|

A47

A48

A49

A50

A51

Illuminated Greek Letters — A52

### Litho. With Foil Application
**2011, Mar. 18**    *Perf. 13½x13*

| 66 | A47 | 50c multi + label | 1.50 | 1.50 |
|----|-----|-------------------|------|------|
| 67 | A48 | 60c multi + label | 1.75 | 1.75 |
| 68 | A49 | 75c multi + label | 2.25 | 2.25 |
| 69 | A50 | €1 multi + label | 3.00 | 3.00 |
| 70 | A51 | €1.50 multi + label | 4.50 | 4.50 |
| 71 | A52 | €2.15 multi + label | 6.25 | 6.25 |
| | | Nos. 66-71 (6) | 19.25 | 19.25 |

A55

A56

A57

Illuminated Greek Letters — A58

**2011, May 17**

| 72 | A53 | 50c multi + label | 1.50 | 1.50 |
|----|-----|-------------------|------|------|
| 73 | A54 | 60c multi + label | 1.75 | 1.75 |
| 74 | A55 | 75c multi + label | 2.25 | 2.25 |
| 75 | A56 | €1 multi + label | 3.00 | 3.00 |
| 76 | A57 | €1.47 multi + label | 4.25 | 4.25 |
| 77 | A58 | €2 multi + label | 5.75 | 5.75 |
| | | Nos. 72-77 (6) | 18.50 | 18.50 |

A59

A60

A61

A62

A63

Illuminated Greek
Letters — A64

**2011, July 18**

| | | | | |
|---|---|---|---|---|
| 78 | A59 | 50c multi + label | 1.50 | 1.50 |
| 79 | A60 | 60c multi + label | 1.75 | 1.75 |
| 80 | A61 | 75c multi + label | 2.25 | 2.25 |
| 81 | A62 | 85c multi + label | 2.50 | 2.50 |
| 82 | A63 | €1.47 multi + label | 4.25 | 4.25 |
| 83 | A64 | €2 multi + label | 5.75 | 5.75 |
| | | Nos. 78-83 (6) | 18.00 | 18.00 |

A65

A66

A67

A68

A69

Illuminated Greek
Letters — A70

**2011, Dec. 15**

| | | | | |
|---|---|---|---|---|
| 84 | A65 | 50c multi + label | 1.40 | 1.40 |
| 85 | A66 | 60c multi + label | 1.60 | 1.60 |
| 86 | A67 | 85c multi + label | 2.25 | 2.25 |
| 87 | A68 | €1 multi + label | 2.60 | 2.60 |
| 88 | A69 | €1.47 multi + label | 4.00 | 4.00 |
| 89 | A70 | €2 multi + label | 5.25 | 5.25 |
| | | Nos. 84-89 (6) | 17.10 | 17.10 |

Megisti Lavra
Monastery
Katholikon — A71

Helandariou
Monastery
Katholikon — A72

Iveron Monastery
Katholikon — A73

Dionysiou
Monastery
Katholikon — A74

Vatopedi
Monastery
Katholikon — A75

Protaton
Katholikon — A76

**2012, Jan. 26**      **Perf. 13½x13**

| | | | | |
|---|---|---|---|---|
| 90 | A71 | 50c multi + label | 1.40 | 1.40 |
| 91 | A72 | 60c multi + label | 1.60 | 1.60 |
| 92 | A73 | 75c multi + label | 2.00 | 2.00 |
| 93 | A74 | 85c multi + label | 2.25 | 2.25 |
| 94 | A75 | €1 multi + label | 2.60 | 2.60 |
| 95 | A76 | €2.20 multi + label | 5.75 | 5.75 |
| | | Nos. 90-95 (6) | 15.60 | 15.60 |

Koutloumousiou
Monastery
Katholikon — A77

Pantokratoros
Monastery
Katholikon — A78

Xeropotamou
Monastery
Katholikon — A79

Zografou
Monastery
Katholikon — A80

Docheiariou
Monastery
Katholikon — A81

**2012, Mar. 20**

| | | | | |
|---|---|---|---|---|
| 96 | A77 | 50c multi + label | 1.40 | 1.40 |
| 97 | A78 | 60c multi + label | 1.60 | 1.60 |
| 98 | A79 | €1 multi + label | 2.60 | 2.60 |
| 99 | A80 | €1.50 multi + label | 4.00 | 4.00 |
| 100 | A81 | €2 multi + label | 5.25 | 5.25 |
| | | Nos. 96-100 (5) | 14.85 | 14.85 |

Karakalou
Monastery
Katholikon — A82

Filotheou
Monastery
Katholikon — A83

Simonos Petras
Monastery
Katholikon — A84

Agiou Pavlou
Monastery
Katholikon — A85

Stavronikita
Monastery
Katholikon — A86

**2012, Sept. 12**

| | | | | |
|---|---|---|---|---|
| 101 | A82 | 62c multi + label | 1.60 | 1.60 |
| 102 | A83 | 78c multi + label | 2.00 | 2.00 |
| 103 | A84 | 85c multi + label | 2.25 | 2.25 |
| 104 | A85 | €1 multi + label | 2.60 | 2.60 |
| 105 | A86 | €2.10 multi + label | 5.50 | 5.50 |
| | | Nos. 101-105 (5) | 13.95 | 13.95 |

Xenophontos
Monastery
Katholikon — A87

Osiou Grigoriou
Monastery
Katholikon — A88

Esphigmenou
Monastery
Katholikon — A89

Agiou
Panteleimon
Monastery
Katholikon — A90

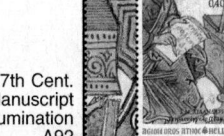

Konstamonitou
Monastery
Katholikon — A91

**2012, Nov. 20**

| | | | | |
|---|---|---|---|---|
| 106 | A87 | 50c multi + label | 1.40 | 1.40 |
| 107 | A88 | 62c multi + label | 1.60 | 1.60 |
| 108 | A89 | €1 multi + label | 2.60 | 2.60 |
| 109 | A90 | €1.50 multi + label | 4.00 | 4.00 |
| 110 | A91 | €2.10 multi + label | 5.50 | 5.50 |
| | | Nos. 106-110 (5) | 15.10 | 15.10 |

17th Cent.
Manuscript
Illumination
A92

13th Cent.
Manuscript
Illumination
A93

17th Cent.
Manuscript
Illumination
A94

13th Cent.
Manuscript
Illumination
A95

14th Cent.
Manuscript
Illumination
A96

10th Cent.
Manuscript
Illumination
A97

**2013, Apr. 22**

| | | | | |
|---|---|---|---|---|
| 111 | A92 | 40c multi + label | 1.10 | 1.10 |
| 112 | A93 | 50c multi + label | 1.40 | 1.40 |
| 113 | A94 | 62c multi + label | 1.60 | 1.60 |
| 114 | A95 | 78c multi + label | 2.10 | 2.10 |

| | | | | |
|---|---|---|---|---|
| **115** | A96 | 85c multi + label | 2.25 | 2.25 |
| **116** | A97 | €2 multi + label | 5.25 | 5.25 |
| | | *Nos. 111-116 (6)* | 13.70 | 13.70 |

13th Cent. Manuscript Illumination A98

9th Cent. Manuscript Illumination A99

17th Cent. Manuscript Illumination A100

16th Cent. Manuscript Illumination A101

17th Cent. Manuscript Illumination A102

**2013, May 9**

| | | | | |
|---|---|---|---|---|
| **117** | A98 | 50c multi + label | 1.40 | 1.40 |
| **118** | A99 | 62c multi + label | 1.75 | 1.75 |
| **119** | A100 | 78c multi + label | 2.10 | 2.10 |
| **120** | A101 | €1 multi + label | 2.75 | 2.75 |
| **121** | A102 | €2.20 multi + label | 6.00 | 6.00 |
| | | *Nos. 117-121 (5)* | 14.00 | 14.00 |

18th Cent. Manuscript Illumination A103

12th Cent. Manuscript Illumination A104

17th Cent. Manuscript Illumination A105

14th Cent. Manuscript Illumination A106

16th Cent. Manuscript Illumination A107

### Litho. With Foil Application
**2013, Sept. 9**    *Perf. 13½x13*

| | | | | |
|---|---|---|---|---|
| **122** | A103 | 40c multi + label | 1.10 | 1.10 |
| **123** | A104 | 62c multi + label | 1.75 | 1.75 |
| **124** | A105 | 78c multi + label | 2.10 | 2.10 |
| **125** | A106 | €1 multi + label | 2.75 | 2.75 |
| **126** | A107 | €2.50 multi + label | 6.75 | 6.75 |
| | | *Nos. 122-126 (5)* | 14.45 | 14.45 |

17th Cent. Manuscript Illumination A108

17th Cent. Manuscript Illumination A109

11th Cent. Manuscript Illumination A110

12th Cent. Manuscript Illumination A111

17th Cent. Manuscript Illumination A112

### Litho. With Foil Application
**2013, Nov. 5**    *Perf. 13½x13*

| | | | | |
|---|---|---|---|---|
| **127** | A108 | 62c multi + label | 1.75 | 1.75 |
| **128** | A109 | 72c multi + label | 2.00 | 2.00 |
| **129** | A110 | 80c multi + label | 2.25 | 2.25 |
| **130** | A111 | 90c multi + label | 2.40 | 2.40 |
| **131** | A112 | €2.10 multi + label | 5.75 | 5.75 |
| | | *Nos. 127-131 (5)* | 14.15 | 14.15 |

Gold Embroidered Priest's Stole, 16th-17th Cent. — A113

Parament, 17th Cent. — A114

Liturgical Vestments, 20th Cent. — A115

Liturgical Vestments, 20th Cent. — A116

Priest's Stole, 17th Cent. — A117

Priest's Stole, 1813 — A118

### Litho. With Foil Application
**2014, July 9**    *Perf. 13½x13¾*

| | | | | |
|---|---|---|---|---|
| **132** | A113 | 40c multi + label | 1.10 | 1.10 |
| **133** | A114 | 50c multi + label | 1.40 | 1.40 |
| **134** | A115 | 72c multi + label | 2.00 | 2.00 |
| **135** | A116 | 90c multi + label | 2.40 | 2.40 |
| **136** | A117 | €1 multi + label | 2.75 | 2.75 |
| **137** | A118 | €1.50 multi + label | 4.00 | 4.00 |
| | | *Nos. 132-137 (6)* | 13.65 | 13.65 |

Icon Case Parament, 16th Cent. — A119

Parament, 18th Cent. — A120

Embroidered Item, 20th Cent. — A121

Parament, 18th Cent. — A122

Icon Case Parament, 17th Cent. — A123

### Litho. With Foil Application
**2014, July 9**    *Perf. 13½x13¾*

| | | | | |
|---|---|---|---|---|
| **138** | A119 | 50c multi + label | 1.40 | 1.40 |
| **139** | A120 | 72c multi + label | 2.00 | 2.00 |
| **140** | A121 | 80c multi + label | 2.10 | 2.10 |
| **141** | A122 | 85c multi + label | 2.25 | 2.25 |
| **142** | A123 | €1.62 multi + label | 4.50 | 4.50 |
| | | *Nos. 138-142 (5)* | 12.25 | 12.25 |

Priest's Vestment, 18th Cent. — A124

Liturgical Stole, 16th Cent. — A125

Parament, 1627 — A126

Liturgical Cuffs, 18th Cent. — A127

Liturgical Fan, 17th Cent. — A128

### Litho. With Foil Application
**2014, Sept. 10**    *Perf. 13½x13¾*

| | | | | |
|---|---|---|---|---|
| **143** | A124 | 30c multi + label | .75 | .75 |
| **144** | A125 | 40c multi + label | 1.00 | 1.00 |
| **145** | A126 | 72c multi + label | 1.90 | 1.90 |
| **146** | A127 | €1 multi + label | 2.50 | 2.50 |
| **147** | A128 | €1.50 multi + label | 3.75 | 3.75 |
| | | *Nos. 143-147 (5)* | 9.90 | 9.90 |

Cloth Cover, 20th Cent. — A129

Liturgical Vestments A130

Napoleon's Battle Tent — A131

Liturgical Fan, 19th Cent. — A132

Portable Icon, 19th Cent. — A133

**Litho. With Foil Application**

**2014, Nov. 19**      *Perf. 13½x13¾*

| | | | | |
|---|---|---|---|---|
| 148 | A129 | 50c multi + label | 1.25 | 1.25 |
| 149 | A130 | 72c multi + label | 1.75 | 1.75 |
| 150 | A131 | 85c multi + label | 2.10 | 2.10 |
| 151 | A132 | 90c multi + label | 2.25 | 2.25 |
| 152 | A133 | €1.20 multi + label | 3.00 | 3.00 |
| | | *Nos. 148-152 (5)* | 10.35 | 10.35 |

16th Cent. Wood Carving, Protaton Church — A134

15th Cent. Wood Carving, Vatopedi Monastery A135

18th Cent. Wood Carving, Helandariou Monastery A136

18th Cent. Wood Carving, Iveron Monastery A137

Wood Carving, Dionysiou Monastery, c. 1615 — A138

**Litho. With Foil Application**

**2015, May 20**      *Perf. 13½x13¾*

| | | | | |
|---|---|---|---|---|
| 153 | A134 | 50c multi + label | 1.10 | 1.10 |
| 154 | A135 | 72c multi + label | 1.60 | 1.60 |
| 155 | A136 | 90c multi + label | 2.00 | 2.00 |
| 156 | A137 | €1 multi + label | 2.25 | 2.25 |
| 157 | A138 | €1.50 multi + label | 3.50 | 3.50 |
| | | *Nos. 153-157 (5)* | 10.45 | 10.45 |

19th Cent. Wood Carving, Pantokratoros Monastery A139

18th Cent. Wood Carving, Zografou Monastery A140

18th Cent. Wood Carving, Xeropotamou Monastery A141

18th Cent. Wood Carving, Docheiariou Monastery A142

18th Cent. Wood Carving, Koutloumousiou Monastery A143

**Litho. With Foil Application**

**2015, July 9**      *Perf. 13½x13¾*

| | | | | |
|---|---|---|---|---|
| 158 | A139 | 40c multi + label | .90 | .90 |
| 159 | A140 | 72c multi + label | 1.60 | 1.60 |
| 160 | A141 | 80c multi + label | 1.75 | 1.75 |
| 161 | A142 | 85c multi + label | 1.90 | 1.90 |
| 162 | A143 | €1.50 multi + label | 3.25 | 3.25 |
| | | *Nos. 158-162 (5)* | 9.40 | 9.40 |

Wood Carving, Simonos Petras Monastery A144

14th Cent. Wood Carving, Filotheou Monastery A145

18th Cent. Wood Carving, Agiou Pavlou Monastery A146

16th Cent. Wood Carving, Stavronikita Monastery A147

18th Cent. Wood Carving, Karakalou Monastery A148

**Litho. With Foil Application**

**2015, Sept. 8**      *Perf. 13½x13¾*

| | | | | |
|---|---|---|---|---|
| 163 | A144 | 30c multi + label | .70 | .70 |
| 164 | A145 | 50c multi + label | 1.10 | 1.10 |
| 165 | A146 | 72c multi + label | 1.60 | 1.60 |

| | | | | |
|---|---|---|---|---|
| 166 | A147 | €1 multi + label | 2.25 | 2.25 |
| 167 | A148 | €1.62 multi + label | 3.75 | 3.75 |
| | | *Nos. 163-167 (5)* | 9.40 | 9.40 |

Wood Carving, Osiou Grigoriou Monastery A149

Wood Carving, Xenophontos Monastery A150

18th Cent. Wood Carving, Agiou Panteleimon Monastery A151

Wood Carving, Konstamonitou Monastery, c. 1870-1900 A152

16th Cent. Wood Carving, Esphigmenou Monastery A153

**Litho. With Foil Application**

**2015, Nov. 5**      *Perf. 13½x13¾*

| | | | | |
|---|---|---|---|---|
| 168 | A149 | 20c multi + label | .45 | .45 |
| 169 | A150 | 50c multi + label | 1.10 | 1.10 |
| 170 | A151 | 85c multi + label | 1.90 | 1.90 |
| 171 | A152 | 90c multi + label | 1.90 | 1.90 |
| 172 | A153 | €1.20 multi + label | 2.60 | 2.60 |
| | | *Nos. 168-172 (5)* | 7.95 | 7.95 |

Stone Relief, Protaton — A154

Stone Relief, Megisti Lavra Monastery A155

Stone Relief, Vatopedi Monastery A156

Stone Relief, Iveron Monastery A157

Stone Relief, Helandariou Monastery A158

Stone Relief, Dionysiou Monastery A159

**Litho. With Foil Application**

**2016, Jan. 26**      *Perf. 13½x13*

| | | | | |
|---|---|---|---|---|
| 173 | A154 | 20c multi + label | .45 | .45 |
| 174 | A155 | 72c multi + label | 1.60 | 1.60 |
| 175 | A156 | 80c multi + label | 1.75 | 1.75 |
| 176 | A157 | 90c multi + label | 2.00 | 2.00 |
| 177 | A158 | €1 multi + label | 2.25 | 2.25 |
| 178 | A159 | €1.20 multi + label | 2.60 | 2.60 |
| | | *Nos. 173-178 (6)* | 10.65 | 10.65 |

Stone Relief, Pantokratoros Monastery A160

Stone Relief, Xeropotamou Monastery A161

Stone Relief, Zografou Monastery A162

Stone Relief, Koutloumousiou Monastery A163

Stone Relief, Docheiariou Monastery A164

**Litho. With Foil Application**

**2016, Mar. 30**      *Perf. 13½x13*

| | | | | |
|---|---|---|---|---|
| 179 | A160 | 50c multi + label | 1.25 | 1.25 |
| 180 | A161 | 72c multi + label | 1.75 | 1.75 |
| 181 | A162 | 80c multi + label | 1.90 | 1.90 |
| 182 | A163 | 85c multi + label | 2.00 | 2.00 |
| 183 | A164 | €1.20 multi + label | 2.75 | 2.75 |
| | | *Nos. 179-183 (5)* | 9.65 | 9.65 |

Stone Relief, Stavronikita Monastery A165

Stone Relief,
Karakalou
Monastery
A166

Stone Relief,
Filotheou
Monastery
A167

Stone Relief,
Agiou Pavlou
Monastery
A168

Stone Relief,
Simonos Petras
Monastery
A169

**Litho. With Foil Application**
**2016, Oct. 6**          *Perf. 13½x13*

| | | | | |
|---|---|---|---|---|
| 184 | A165 | 30c multi + label | .70 | .70 |
| 185 | A166 | 50c multi + label | 1.10 | 1.10 |
| 186 | A167 | 72c multi + label | 1.60 | 1.60 |
| 187 | A168 | €1 multi + label | 2.25 | 2.25 |
| 188 | A169 | €1.62 multi + label | 3.75 | 3.75 |
| | | *Nos. 184-188 (5)* | 9.40 | 9.40 |

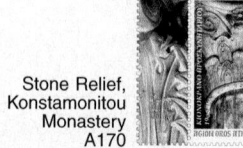

Stone Relief,
Konstamonitou
Monastery
A170

Stone Relief,
Agiou
Panteleimon
Monastery
A171

Stone Relief,
Xenophontos
Monastery
A172

Stone Relief,
Esphigmenou
Monastery
A173

Stone Relief,
Osiou Gregoriou
Monastery
A174

**Litho. With Foil Application**
**2016, Nov. 10**          *Perf. 13½x13*

| | | | | |
|---|---|---|---|---|
| 189 | A170 | 20c multi + label | .45 | .45 |
| 190 | A171 | 50c multi + label | 1.10 | 1.10 |
| 191 | A172 | 85c multi + label | 1.90 | 1.90 |

| | | | | |
|---|---|---|---|---|
| 192 | A173 | 90c multi + label | 2.00 | 2.00 |
| 193 | A174 | €1.20 multi + label | 2.60 | 2.60 |
| | | *Nos. 189-193 (5)* | 8.05 | 8.05 |

Xeropotamou
Monastery
A175

Zografou
Monastery
A176

Filotheou
Monastery
A177

Xenophontos
Monastery
A178

Konstamonitou
Monastery
A179

Esphigmenou
Monastery
A180

Osiou Grigoriou
Monastery
A181

**Litho. With Foil Application**
**2017, July 27**          *Perf. 13½x13*

| | | | | |
|---|---|---|---|---|
| 194 | A175 | 20c blk & gold + label | .50 | .50 |
| 195 | A176 | 50c blk & gold + label | 1.25 | 1.25 |
| 196 | A177 | 72c blk & gold + label | 1.75 | 1.75 |
| 197 | A178 | 80c blk & gold + label | 1.90 | 1.90 |
| 198 | A179 | 80c blk & gold + label | 1.90 | 1.90 |
| 199 | A180 | €1 blk & gold + label | 2.40 | 2.40 |
| 200 | A181 | €1.62 blk & gold + label | 4.00 | 4.00 |
| | | *Nos. 194-200 (7)* | 13.70 | 13.70 |

Engravings by Vassileios Grigorovic Barskij (c. 1701-47).

Megisti Lavra
Monastery
A182

Vatopedi
Monastery
A183

Iveron Monastery
A184

Docheiariou
Monastery
A185

Agiou Pavlou
Monastery
A186

Agiou
Panteleimon
Monastery
A187

**Litho. With Gold Foil Application**
**2017, Sept. 25**          *Perf. 13½x13*

| | | | | |
|---|---|---|---|---|
| 201 | A182 | 72c multi + label | 1.75 | 1.75 |
| 202 | A183 | 80c multi + label | 1.90 | 1.90 |
| 203 | A184 | 90c multi + label | 2.10 | 2.10 |
| 204 | A185 | €1 multi + label | 2.40 | 2.40 |
| 205 | A186 | €1.50 multi + label | 3.50 | 3.50 |
| 206 | A187 | €2.62 multi + label | 6.25 | 6.25 |
| | | *Nos. 201-206 (6)* | 17.90 | 17.90 |

Paintings by Vladimir Davydov (1871-1906).

Karyes — A188

Chilandariou
Monastery
A189

Dionysiou
Monastery
A190

Pantokratoros
Monastery
A191

Koutloumousiou
Monastery
A192

Stavronikita
Monastery
A193

Karakalou
Monastery
A194

Simonos Petras
Monastery
A195

**Litho. With Gold Foil Application**
**2017, Nov. 8**          *Perf. 13½x13*

| | | | | |
|---|---|---|---|---|
| 207 | A188 | 20c multi + label | .50 | .50 |
| 208 | A189 | 72c multi + label | 1.75 | 1.75 |
| 209 | A190 | 80c multi + label | 1.90 | 1.90 |
| 210 | A191 | 85c multi + label | 2.00 | 2.00 |
| 211 | A192 | 90c multi + label | 2.25 | 2.25 |
| 212 | A193 | €1 multi + label | 2.40 | 2.40 |
| 213 | A194 | €1.50 multi + label | 3.75 | 3.75 |
| 214 | A195 | €1.62 multi + label | 4.00 | 4.00 |
| | | *Nos. 207-214 (8)* | 18.55 | 18.55 |

Paintings by Spyros Papaloukas (1892-1957).

# GREENLAND

'grēn-lənd

LOCATION — North Atlantic Ocean
GOVT. — Danish
AREA — 840,000 sq. mi.
POP. — 56,076 (1998)
CAPITAL — Nuuk (Godthaab)

In 1953 the colony of Greenland became an integral part of Denmark.

100 Ore = 1 Krone

> **Catalogue values for unused stamps in this country are for Never Hinged items, beginning with Scott 28 in the regular postage section, Scott B1 in the semipostal section.**

Christian X — A1

Polar Bear — A2

### Perf. 13x12½

**1938-46**    **Unwmk.**    **Engr.**

| | | | | |
|---|---|---|---|---|
| 1 | A1 | 1o olive black | 2.00 | .30 |
| 2 | A1 | 5o rose lake | 2.10 | 1.25 |
| 3 | A1 | 7o yellow green | 2.25 | 3.75 |
| 4 | A1 | 10o dk violet | .85 | .75 |
| 5 | A1 | 15o red | .85 | .75 |
| 6 | A1 | 20o red ('46) | .95 | 1.25 |
| 7 | A2 | 30o blue | 4.00 | 7.25 |
| 8 | A2 | 40o blue ('46) | 18.00 | 8.50 |
| 9 | A2 | 1k light brown | 5.00 | 8.50 |
| | | Nos. 1-9 (9) | 36.00 | 32.30 |
| | | Set, never hinged | 90.00 | |

Issued: Nov. 1, 1938; Aug. 1, 1946.
For surcharges see Nos. 39-40.

Harp Seal — A3

Christian X — A4

Dog Team — A5

Designs: 1k, Polar bear. 2k, Eskimo in kayak. 5k, Eider duck.

**1945, Feb. 1**    **Perf. 12**

| | | | | |
|---|---|---|---|---|
| 10 | A3 | 1o ol blk & vio | 18.50 | 40.00 |
| 11 | A3 | 5o rose lake & ol bister | 18.50 | 40.00 |
| 12 | A3 | 7o green & blk | 18.50 | 40.00 |
| 13 | A4 | 10o purple & olive | 18.50 | 40.00 |
| 14 | A4 | 15o red & brt ultra | 18.50 | 40.00 |
| 15 | A5 | 30o dk blue & red brn | 18.50 | 40.00 |
| 16 | A5 | 1k brown & gray blk | 18.50 | 40.00 |
| 17 | A5 | 2k sepia & dp grn | 18.50 | 40.00 |
| 18 | A5 | 5k dk pur & dl brn | 18.50 | 40.00 |
| | | Nos. 10-18 (9) | 166.50 | 360.00 |
| | | Set, never hinged | 325.00 | |

### Nos. 10-18 Overprinted in Carmine or Blue

**1945**

| | | | | |
|---|---|---|---|---|
| 19 | A3 | 1o (C) | 75.00 | 75.00 |
| 20 | A3 | 5o (BI) | 75.00 | 75.00 |
| 21 | A3 | 7o (C) | 75.00 | 75.00 |
| 22 | A4 | 10o (BI) | 95.00 | 110.00 |
| a. | | Overprint in carmine | 375.00 | 700.00 |
| 23 | A4 | 15o (C) | 95.00 | 110.00 |
| a. | | Overprint in blue | 200.00 | 240.00 |
| 24 | A5 | 30o (BI) | 95.00 | 110.00 |
| a. | | Overprint in carmine | 200.00 | 240.00 |
| 25 | A5 | 1k (C) | 95.00 | 110.00 |
| a. | | Overprint in blue | 200.00 | 240.00 |
| 26 | A5 | 2k (C) | 95.00 | 110.00 |
| a. | | Overprint in blue | 200.00 | 240.00 |

| | | | | |
|---|---|---|---|---|
| 27 | A5 | 5k (BI) | 95.00 | 110.00 |
| a. | | Overprint in carmine | 200.00 | 240.00 |
| | | Nos. 19-27 (9) | 795.00 | 885.00 |
| | | Set, never hinged | 1,350. | |
| | | Nos. 22a-27a (6) | 1,375. | 1,900. |
| | | Set, never hinged | 2,900. | |

Liberation of Denmark from the Germans.
Overprint illustrated as on Nos. 19-21. Larger type and different settings used for Types A4 and A5. Overprint sizes: A3, 11.5 mm; A4, 13 mm; A5, 14.5 mm. A variety of No. 23 exists with overprint measuring 11.5 mm. Value: $3,300. Overprint often smudged.

Nos. 19-27 exist with overprint inverted. Values: 1k and 30o, each $1,200; others, each $1,000.

> **Catalogue values for unused stamps in this section, from this point to the end of the section, are for Never Hinged items.**

Frederik IX — A6

Polar Ship "Gustav Holm" — A7

**1950-60**    **Unwmk.**    **Engr.**    **Perf. 13**

| | | | | |
|---|---|---|---|---|
| 28 | A6 | 1o dark olive green | .35 | .30 |
| 29 | A6 | 5o deep carmine | .30 | .30 |
| 30 | A6 | 10o green | .35 | .35 |
| 31 | A6 | 15o purple | .60 | .40 |
| a. | | 15o dull purple | 4.25 | 1.50 |
| 32 | A6 | 25o vermilion | 2.60 | 1.00 |
| 33 | A6 | 30o dark blue | 40.00 | 2.25 |
| 34 | A6 | 30o vermilion | .70 | .35 |
| 35 | A7 | 50o deep blue | 52.50 | 11.00 |
| 36 | A7 | 1k brown | 16.00 | 3.25 |
| 37 | A7 | 1k dull red | 8.75 | 3.25 |
| 38 | A7 | 5k gray | 2.75 | 2.00 |
| | | Nos. 28-38 (11) | 124.90 | 24.45 |

Issued: Nos. 28-30, 31a, 32, 35-37, 8/15/50; No. 33, 12/1/53; No. 38, 8/14/58; No. 34, 10/29/59; No. 31, 10/60.
For surcharges see Nos. B1-B2.

Nos. 8 and 9 Surcharged

**1956, Mar. 8**

| | | | | |
|---|---|---|---|---|
| 39 | A2 | 60o on 40o blue | 8.50 | 1.60 |
| 40 | A2 | 60o on 1k lt brown | 67.50 | 9.00 |

Drum Dancer — A8

Designs: 50o, The Boy and the Fox. 60o, The Mother of the Sea. 80o, The Girl and the Eagle. 90o, The Great Northern Diver and the Raven.

**1957-69**    **Engr.**    **Perf. 13**

| | | | | |
|---|---|---|---|---|
| 41 | A8 | 35o gray olive | 1.10 | 1.00 |
| 42 | A8 | 50o brown red | 1.10 | 1.25 |
| 43 | A8 | 60o blue | 4.00 | 1.25 |
| 44 | A8 | 80o light brown | 1.25 | 1.25 |
| 45 | A8 | 90o dark blue | 3.50 | 3.50 |
| | | Nos. 41-45 (5) | 10.95 | 8.25 |

Issued: 35o, 3/16/61; 50o, 9/22/66; 60o, 5/2/57; 80o, 9/18/69; 90o, 11/23/67.

Hans Egede — A9

**1958, Nov. 5**

| | | | | |
|---|---|---|---|---|
| 46 | A9 | 30o henna brown | 9.00 | 1.50 |

200th anniv. of death of Hans Egede, missionary to Eskimos in Greenland.

Knud Rasmussen — A10

**1960, Nov. 24**    **Perf. 13**

| | | | | |
|---|---|---|---|---|
| 47 | A10 | 30o dull red | 1.60 | 1.00 |

50th anniv. of establishment by Rasmussen of the mission and trading station at Thule (Dundas).

Northern Lights and Crossed Anchors — A11

Frederik IX A12

Polar Bear A13

**1963-68**    **Engr.**

| | | | | |
|---|---|---|---|---|
| 48 | A11 | 1o gray | .30 | .35 |
| 49 | A11 | 5o rose claret | .30 | .35 |
| 50 | A11 | 10o green | .40 | .50 |
| 51 | A11 | 12o yellow grn | .40 | .40 |
| 52 | A11 | 15o rose vio | .90 | 1.25 |
| 53 | A12 | 20o ultra | 4.25 | 3.50 |
| 54 | A12 | 25o lt brown | .75 | .75 |
| 55 | A12 | 30o green | .30 | .50 |
| 56 | A12 | 35o dull red | .30 | .30 |
| 57 | A12 | 40o gray | .35 | .55 |
| 58 | A12 | 50o grnsh blue | 9.00 | 10.00 |
| 59 | A12 | 50o dark red | .35 | .45 |
| 60 | A12 | 60o rose claret | .40 | .45 |
| 61 | A12 | 80o orange | .80 | .85 |
| 62 | A13 | 1k brown | .65 | .35 |
| 63 | A13 | 2k dull red | 3.25 | 1.10 |
| 64 | A13 | 5k dark blue | 2.75 | 2.25 |
| 65 | A13 | 10k dull slate grn | 5.00 | 1.10 |
| | | Nos. 48-65 (18) | 30.45 | 25.00 |

Issued: Nos. 48-52, 3/7/63; No. 53, 61, 7/25/63; Nos. 62-65, 9/17/63; Nos. 54, 56-58, 3/11/64; No. 59, 9/9/65; No. 60, 2/29/68; No. 55, 11/21/68.

Niels Bohr (1885-1962) and Atom Diagram — A14

**1963, Nov. 21**    **Unwmk.**

| | | | | |
|---|---|---|---|---|
| 66 | A14 | 35o red brown | .40 | .55 |
| 67 | A14 | 60o dark blue | 4.75 | 4.75 |

50th anniv. of atom theory of Prof. Bohr. See Denmark Nos. 409-410.

A15

**1964, Nov. 26**

| | | | | |
|---|---|---|---|---|
| 68 | A15 | 35o brown red | .65 | .65 |

Samuel Kleinschmidt (1814-1886), philologist.

A16

**1967, June 10**

| | | | | |
|---|---|---|---|---|
| 69 | A16 | 50o dull red | 3.50 | 3.50 |

Wedding of Crown Princess Margrethe and Prince Henri de Monpezat.

Frederik IX and Map of Greenland — A17

**1969, Mar. 11**    **Engr.**    **Perf. 13**

| | | | | |
|---|---|---|---|---|
| 70 | A17 | 60o dull red | 1.40 | 1.40 |

70th birthday of King Frederik IX.

Musk Ox — A18

Designs: 1k, Right whale diving off Disko Island. 2k, Narwhal. 5k, Polar bear. 10k, Walruses.

**1969-76**    **Engr.**    **Perf. 13**

| | | | | |
|---|---|---|---|---|
| 71 | A18 | 1k dark blue | .40 | .40 |
| 72 | A18 | 2k gray green | .90 | .60 |
| 73 | A18 | 5k blue | 2.00 | .75 |
| 74 | A18 | 10k sepia | 4.00 | 1.90 |
| 75 | A18 | 25k greenish gray | 9.00 | 3.75 |
| | | Nos. 71-75 (5) | 16.30 | 7.40 |

Issued: 1k, 3/5/70; 2k, 2/20/75; 5k, 2/19/76; 10k, 2/15/73; 25k, 11/27/69.

**Greenland** and Scandinavia

• Free Catalog • Stamps
• Postal History • Literature
• Want Lists Filled • Albums

www.JaySmith.com

**Jay Smith**
P.O. Box 650-X982
Snow Camp, NC 27349
email:info-x982@JaySmith.com

**CALL TOLL FREE**
**1-800-447-8267**
**(U.S. and CANADA)**
**or 336-376-9991**

• The Scandinavia Specialist Since 1973 •

Liberation Celebration at Jakobshaven — A19

**1970, May 4**
76 A19 60o red brown 2.25 2.25

Hans Egede and Gertrude Rask on the Haabet — A20

**1971, May 6 Engr. Perf. 13**
77 A20 60o brown red 1.60 1.60

250th anniv. of arrival of Hans Egede in Greenland and the beginning of its colonization.

Mail-carrying Kayaks — A21

Designs: 70o, Umiak (women's rowboat). 80o, Catalina seaplane dropping mail by parachute. 90o, Dog sled. 1k, Coaster Kununguak and pilot boat. 1.30k, Schooner Sokongen. 1.50k, Longboat off Greenland coast. 2k, Helicopter over mountains.

**1971-77 Engr. Perf. 13**
78 A21 50o blue grn .30 .25
79 A21 70o dull red ('72) .35 .25
80 A21 80o black ('76) .40 .40
81 A21 90o blue ('72) .35 .25
82 A21 1k red ('76) .40 .40
83 A21 1.30k dl blue ('75) .85 .65
84 A21 1.50k gray grn ('74) .80 .55
85 A21 2k blue ('77) 1.00 .85
   Nos. 78-85 (8) 4.45 3.60

Issued: No. 78, 11/4; No. 81, 2/29; No. 79, 9/21; No. 84, 2/21; No. 83, 4/17; No. 80, 10/11; No. 85, 2/24.

Queen Margrethe — A22

**1973-79 Engr. Perf. 13**
86 A22 5o car rose ('78) .30 .25
87 A22 10o gray green .30 .25
a. 10o emerald ('89) 5.00 5.00
88 A22 60o sepia .60 .45
89 A22 80o sepia ('79) .30 .30
90 A22 90o red brown ('74) .65 .55
91 A22 1k dark red ('77) .30 .30
a. Bklt. pane, 4 #87a, 6 #91b 32.50
b. 1k carmine ('89) 5.00 5.00
92 A22 1.20k dk blue ('74) .65 1.00
93 A22 1.20k maroon ('78) .75 .50
94 A22 1.30k dk blue ('77) .55 .60
95 A22 1.30k red ('79) .55 .50
96 A22 1.60k blue ('79) .65 .70
97 A22 1.80k dl green ('78) .85 .70
   Nos. 86-97 (12) 6.45 6.10

Nos. 86, 89, 93, 95-97 inscribed "Kalaallit Nunaat."
The background lines on Nos. 87, 91 are sharp and complete. On No. 87a, 91b they are irregular and broken.
Issued: Nos. 87-88, 4/16. Nos. 90, 92, 10/24. Nos. 91, 94, 5/26. Nos. 86, 93, 97, 4/17. Nos. 89, 95-96, 3/29.

Trawler and Kayaks — A23

2k, Old Trade Buildings, Copenhagen, vert.

**1974, May 16 Engr. Perf. 13**
98 A23 1k lt red brown .55 .90
99 A23 2k sepia .65 .60

Royal Greenland Trade Dept. Bicentennial.

Falcon and Radar — A24

**1975, Sept. 4 Engr. Perf. 13**
100 A24 90o red .60 .60

50th anniversary of Greenland's telecommunications system.

Sirius Sled Patrol — A25

**1975, Oct. 16 Engr. Perf. 13**
101 A25 1.20k sepia .40 .40

Sirius sled patrol in northeast Greenland, 25th anniversary.

Inuit Cult Mask — A26

Designs: 6k, Tupilac, a magical creature, carved whalebone. 7k, Soapstone sculpture. 8k, Eskimo with Family, driftwood sculpture, by Johannes Kreutzmann (1862-1940).

**1977-80**
102 A26 6k deep rose lilac 2.25 1.90
103 A26 7k gray olive 2.50 2.25
104 A26 8k dark blue 3.00 2.50
105 A26 9k black 3.25 3.00
   Nos. 102-105 (4) 11.00 9.65

Issue dates: 6k, Oct. 5, 1978. 7k, Sept. 6, 1979. 8k, Feb. 29, 1980. 9k, Sept. 6, 1977. The 6k, 7k, 8k are inscribed "Kalaallit Nunaat."

Jorgen Bronlund, Jakobshavn, Disko Bay — A27

**1977, Oct. 20**
106 A27 1k red brown .40 .25

Jorgen Bronlund, arctic explorer, birth centenary.

Meteorite — A28

**1978, Jan. 20 Engr. Perf. 13**
107 A28 1.20k dull red .55 .45

Scientific Research Commission, centenary.

Sun Rising over Mountains — A29

**1978, June 5 Engr. Perf. 13**
108 A29 1.50k dark blue .55 .55

25th anniversary of Constitution.

Hans Egede, Settlers, Troops and Drummer — A30

**1978, Aug. 29 Engr. Perf. 13**
109 A30 2.50k red brown .95 .65

Founding of Godthaab, 250th anniversary.

Navigator — A31

**1979, May 1 Engr.**
110 A31 1.10k brown .40 .40

Establishment of home rule, May 1, 1979.

A32

Eskimo Boy, aurora borealis, IYC emblem.

**1979, Oct. 18 Engr. Perf. 13**
111 A32 2k olive green .80 .80

International Year of the Child.

The Legend of the Reindeer and the Larva, by Jens Kreutzmann, 1860 — A33

Designs: 2.70k, Harpooning a Walrus, Jakob Danielsen. No. 114, Life in Thule, c. 1900, by Aninaaq. No. 115, Landscape, Ammassalik Fjord, Eastern Greenland, Peter Rosing (1892-1965). 3k, Footrace, woodcut by Aron from Kagec (1822-1869). 3.70k, Polar Bear Killing Seal Hunter, K. Andreassen (1890-1934). 9k, Hares Hunting, Gerhard Kleist (1855-1931).

**1980-87 Engr. Perf. 13**
112 A33 1.60k red .65 .65
113 A33 2.70k deep violet 1.10 1.00
114 A33 2.80k lake 1.10 .95
115 A33 2.80k lake 1.40 1.00
116 A33 3k black 1.25 1.10
117 A33 3.70k blue black 1.75 1.50
118 A33 9k dark green 4.00 2.75
   Nos. 112-118 (7) 11.25 8.95

Issued: 1.60k, 3/26/81; 2.70k, 6/24/82; No. 114, 9/4/86; No. 115, 4/9/87; 3k, 9/4/80; 3.70k, 2/9/84; 9k, 9/5/85.

Queen Margrethe, Map of Greenland — A34

**1980-89 Engr. Perf. 13**
120 A34 50o purple ('81) .30 .30
a. 50o dull purple ('89) 5.75 5.75
121 A34 80o sepia .40 .40
122 A34 1.30k red .60 .60
123 A34 1.50k royal blue ('82) .70 .70
124 A34 1.60k ultra .90 .90
125 A34 1.80k dull red ('82) .90 .70
126 A34 2.30k dk grn ('81) .90 .75
127 A34 2.50k red ('83) 1.10 .75
128 A34 2.80k copper red ('85) 1.75 .80
129 A34 3k fawn ('88) 2.00 2.00
130 A34 3.20k rose ('89) 2.00 2.00
a. Bklt. pane of 10 (4 #120a, 6 #130) 32.50
131 A34 3.80k slate blue ('85) 1.75 1.75
132 A34 4.10k brt blue ('88) 2.25 2.25
133 A34 4.40k ultra ('89) 2.25 2.25
   Nos. 120-133 (14) 18.80 16.65

Issued: Nos. 121-122, 124, 4/16; Nos. 120, 126, 1/29; Nos. 123, 125, 5/13; No. 127, 3/30; Nos. 128, 131, 2/7; Nos. 129, 132, 2/4; Nos. 130, 133, 1/30.

Rasmus Berthelsen (Teacher, Hymnist), in Training College Library, 1830 — A35

**1980, May 29 Engr. Perf. 13**
134 A35 2k brown, cream .70 .70

Greenland Public Library Service, 150th anniv.

Ejnar Mikkelsen on board Gustav Holm, 1934 — A36

**1980, Oct. 16 Engr. Perf. 13**
135 A36 4k slate green 1.40 1.40

Ejnar Mikkelsen, inspector of East Greenland, birth centenary.

Pandalus Borealis — A37

Designs: No. 137, Anarhicas minor. No. 138, Reinhardtius Hippoglossoides. No. 139, Mallotus villosus. 25k, Codfish. 50k, Salmo salar.

**1981-86 Engr. Perf. 13**
136 A37 10k multicolored 3.50 2.00
137 A37 10k dk bl & blk 5.50 4.00
138 A37 10k multicolored 4.00 4.00
139 A37 10k grnsh blk & blk 4.25 4.75
140 A37 25k multicolored 8.75 4.25
141 A37 50k multicolored 18.00 10.00
   Nos. 136-141 (6) 44.00 29.00

Issued: 25k, 5/21; No. 136, 4/1/82; 50k, 1/27/83; No. 137, 10/11/84; No. 138, 10/10/85; No. 139, 10/16/86.

Saqqaq Eskimo in Kayak, Reindeer — A38

5k, Tunit-Dorset hunters hauling seal.

**1981, Oct. 15 Engr. Perf. 12½**
146 A38 3.50k dark blue 1.00 1.00
147 A38 5k brown 1.50 1.50

Thule District Eskimos Catching Whale, 1000AD — A39

Greenland history: No. 149, Bishop Joen Smyrill's house and staff, 12th cent. No. 150, Wooden dolls, 13th cent. No. 151, Eskimo mummy, sacrificial stones, 14th cent. No. 152, Hans Pothorst, explorer, 15th cent. No. 153, Glass pearls, 16th cent. No. 154, Apostle spoons, 17th cent. No. 155, Key, trading station, 18th cent. No. 156, Trade Ship Hvalfisken, masthead, 19th cent. No. 157, Communications satellite, Earth, 20th cent.

**1982, Sept. 30**
148 A39 2k brown red .75 .75
149 A39 2.70k dark blue 1.05 1.05
**1983, Sept. 15**
150 A39 2.50k red .85 .85
151 A39 3.50k brown 1.30 1.30
152 A39 4.50k blue 1.50 1.50
**1984, Mar. 29**
153 A39 2.70k red brown 1.50 1.50
154 A39 3.70k dark blue 1.50 1.50
155 A39 5.50k brown 1.90 1.90
**1985, Mar. 21**
156 A39 2.80k violet 1.50 1.50
157 A39 6k blue black 2.40 2.40
   Nos. 148-157,B10 (11) 15.50 15.50

250th Anniv. of Settlement of New Herrnhut — A40

**1983, Nov. 2 Engr.**
158 A40 2.50k carmine lake .90 .90

Henrik Lund, Natl. Anthem Score, Lichtenau Fjord — A41

**1984, Sept. 6 Engr.**
159 A41 5k black 2.75 2.75

Henrik Lund (1875-1948), natl. anthem composer, artist, only Greenlander to win Ingenio et Arti medal.

**A42**

**1984, June 6      Engr.      Perf. 13**
160  A42  2.70k dull red          1.75  1.75
Prince Henrik, 50th birthday.
See Denmark No. 757.

Danish Grenadier,
1734 — A43

**1984, July 25      Engr.      Perf. 13**
161  A43  3.70k vio brn          1.40  1.40
Town of Christianshab, 250th anniv.

Ingrid, Queen Mother
of Denmark,
Chrysanthemums
A44

**1985, May 21        Litho. & Engr.**
162  A44  2.80k multicolored     1.10  1.10
Arrival in Denmark of Princess Ingrid, 50th
anniv. See Denmark No. 775.

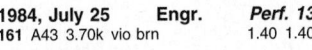

Intl. Youth Year — A45

3.80k, Emblem, birds nesting, fiord.

**1985, June 27                   Litho.**
163  A45  3.80k multicolored     1.25  1.25

Greenland Port Post
Office, Flags — A46

**1986, Mar. 6      Engr.      Perf. 13**
164  A46  2.80k dark red          1.05  1.05
Transfer of postal control under Greenland
Home Rule, Jan. 1, 1986.

Artifacts — A47

2.80k, Sewing needles, case. 3k, Buckets,
bowl, scoop. No. 166, 3.80k, Ulos. No. 167,
3.80k, Masks. 5k, Harpoon points. 6.50k, Lard
lamps. 10k, Carved faces.

**1986-88          Engr.      Perf. 13**
165   A47   2.80k multicolored   1.25    .95
165A  A47   3k multicolored      1.10    .90
166   A47   3.80k multicolored   1.25   1.25
167   A47   3.80k multicolored   1.60   1.60
168   A47   5k multicolored      1.75   1.50
169   A47   6.50k multicolored   2.50   2.50
172   A47   10k multicolored     4.00   3.25
        Nos. 165-172 (7)        13.45  11.95
Issued: No. 166, 6.50k, 5/22. 2.80k, 3.80k,
6/11, 1987. 3k, 5k, 10k, 10/27/88.

Souvenir Sheet

HAFNIA
'87
A48

**1987, Jan. 23      Litho.      Perf. 13**
175  A48    Sheet of 3          8.00   8.00
 a.   2.80k Gull in flight      2.25   2.25
 b.   3.80k Mountain            2.75   2.75
 c.   6.50k Gulls in water      2.75   2.75
No. 175 sold for 19.50k. See No. 199.

Year of the Fishing,
Sealing and Whaling
Industries — A49

**1987, Apr. 9      Litho.      Perf. 13**
176  A49  3.80k multi            1.50  1.50

Lagopus                  Birds of
Mutus                    Prey
A50                      A51

3k, Falco rusticolus. 3.20k, Clangula
hyemalis. 4k, Anser caerulescens. 4.10k, Corvus corax. 4.40k, Plectrophenax nivalis. No.
183, 5.50k, Haliaeetus albicilla. No. 184,
5.50k, Cepphus grylle. 6.50k, Uria lomvia. 7k,
Gavia immer. 7.50k, Stercorarius longicaudus.
10k, Nyctea scandiaca.

**1987-90          Litho.      Perf. 13**
177  A51   3k shown             1.50   1.50
178  A51   3.20k multicolored   2.10   1.25
179  A51   4k multicolored      1.50   1.25
180  A51   4.10k multicolored   1.90   1.90
181  A51   4.40k multicolored   2.10   2.10
182  A50   5k shown             2.60   2.40
183  A51   5.50k multicolored   3.25   3.00
184  A51   5.50k multicolored   2.60   2.25
185  A51   6.50k multicolored   3.50   2.60
186  A51   7k multicolored      3.25   3.50
187  A51   7.50k multicolored   3.00   3.00
188  A50   10k multicolored     3.75   3.75
        Nos. 177-188 (12)      31.05  28.50
Issued: 5k, 10k, 9/3; 3k, 4.10k, No. 183, 7k,
4/14/88; 3.20k, 4.40k, No. 184, 6.50k, 3/16/89;
4k, 7.50k, 1/15/90.

Plants — A52

No. 189, 4k, Campanula gieseckiana. No.
190, 4k, Pedicularis hirsuta. 5k, Eriophorum
scheuchzeri. 5.50k, Ledum groenlandicum.
6.50k, Cassiope tetragona. 7.25k, Saxifraga
oppositifolia. 10k, Papaver radicatum, vert.

**1989-92          Litho.      Perf. 13**
189  A52   4k multicolored      1.60   1.50
190  A52   4k multicolored      1.90   1.50
191  A52   5k multicolored       .225  2.10
192  A52   5.50k multicolored   2.00   2.25
193  A52   6.50k multicolored   2.60   2.75
194  A52   7.25k multicolored   3.00   3.00
196  A52   10k multicolored     4.25   4.00
        Nos. 189-196 (7)       15.58  17.10
Issued: 5k, 10k, 10/12/89; No. 189, 5.50k,
6.50k, 6/7/90; No. 190, 7.25k, 3/26/92. Nos.
189-190 vert.

**HAFNIA type of 1987**
Souvenir Sheet
Uummannaq Mountain in winter, horiz.

**1987, Oct. 16   Litho.   Perf. 13x12½**
199  A48  2.80k slate blue & lake  2.75  3.75
No. 199 sold for 4k.

Greenland Home Rule,
10th Anniv.
A53            A54

**1989, May 1      Litho.      Perf. 13**
200  A53  3.20k Flag, landscape   1.25  1.25
201  A54  4.40k Coat of arms      2.25  1.75

Queen Margrethe — A55

and

Nos. 214, 217
Surcharged in Red or
Blue

**1990-96          Engr.      Perf. 13**
214  A55   25o green            .30    .30
217  A55   1k brown             .55    .45
 a.   Bklt. pane, 4 #214, 6 #217   35.00
 b.   Bklt. pane, 4 each #214,
      217                        16.00
224  A55   4k carmine rose      1.50   1.25
      Complete booklet, 217a, 10
      #224                       35.00
225  A55  4.25k red             2.60   2.60
226  A55  4.25k on 25o #214
                    (R)         5.00   5.00
 a.   Inverted surcharge      1,100.
227  A55  4.50k on 1k #217
                    (Bl)        5.00   5.00
228  A55  6.50k blue            2.75   2.75
229  A55  7k violet             3.50   3.50
        Nos. 214-229 (8)       21.20  20.85
Value for No. 225 is for stamp with yellow
fluorescence. Value for stamp with white fluorescence, $5.50.
Issued: No. 217a, 5/3/90; No. 217b, 9/9/93;
7k, 2/10/94; No. 225, 1996; Nos. 226-227,
12/31/95; others, 4/5/90.
First-day covers of Nos. 226-227 are dated
1/2/96.

Frederik Lynge (1889-
1957),
Politician — A56

25k, Augo Lynge (1899-1959), politician

**1990, Oct. 18   Engr.   Perf. 13x12½**
231  A56  10k rose brn & dk bl    5.00  3.00
232  A56  25k vio & dk bl        11.50  7.00
          See Nos. 242-243, 249.

Phoca
Hispida — A57

Walrus and Seals: No. 234, Pagophilus
groenlandicus. No. 235, Cystophora cristata.
No. 236, Odobenus rosmarus. No. 237,
Erignatus barbatus. No. 238, Phoca vitulina.

**Litho. & Engr.                 Perf. 13**
233  A57   4k shown             1.50   1.50
234  A57   4k multicolored      1.50   1.50
235  A57  7.25k multicolored    3.00   3.00
236  A57  7.25k multicolored    3.00   3.00
237  A57  8.50k multicolored    3.25   3.25
238  A57  8.50k multicolored    3.25   3.25
 a.   Miniature sheet of 6, #233-238  17.00  17.00
        Nos. 233-238 (6)       15.50  15.50

Village of Ilulissat,
250th Anniv. — A58

**1991, May 15   Litho.   Perf. 13**
239  A58  4k multicolored        1.60  1.60

Tourism
A59

**1991, May 15        Perf. 12½x13**
240  A59   4k Iceberg            1.50   1.50
241  A59  8.50k Skiers, sled dogs  3.50  3.50
          See Nos. 259-260, 289-290.

**Famous Men Type of 1990**
10k, Jonathan Petersen (1881-1961), musician. 50k, Hans Lynge (1906-88), artist &

writer. 100k, Lars Moller (1842-1926), newspaper editor.

**1991-92          Engr.   Perf. 13x12½**
242  A56  10k black & dk blue    4.75   3.00
243  A56  50k red brn & blue    20.00  15.00
249  A56  100k claret & slate   35.00  30.00
        Nos. 242-249 (3)        59.75  48.00
Issued: 10k, 50k, 9/5; 100k, 9/15/92.

Settlement of
Paamiut, 250th
Anniv. — A60

**1992, May 14      Engr.      Perf. 13**
252  A60  7.25k dk bl & ol brn   3.25  3.00

Denmark's
Queen
Margrethe
and Prince
Henrik,
Silver
Wedding
Anniv.
A61

**1992, June 10   Litho.   Perf. 12½x13**
253  A61  4k multicolored        2.40  2.40
          See Denmark No. 946.

A62

**1992, Nov. 12    Litho.      Perf. 13**
254  A62  4k Christmas           2.50  1.90

A63

**1993, Feb. 4      Litho.      Perf. 13**
255  A63  4k multicolored        2.25  1.50
          Intl. Year of Indigenous Peoples.

Crabs — A64

4k, Neolithodes grimaldii. 7.25k, Chionoecetes oiliqo. 8.50k, Hyas coarctatus, Hyas
araneus.

**Litho. & Engr.**
**1993, Mar. 25                  Perf. 13**
256  A64   4k multicolored      1.25   1.25
257  A64  7.25k multicolored    4.00   4.00
 a.   Chionoecetes opilio      10.00  10.00
 b.   Booklet pane, 4 each #256,
      257a                      45.00
258  A64  8.50k multicolored    5.00   5.00
        Nos. 256-258 (3)       10.25  10.25
Issue date: No. 257b, Sept. 9.

**Tourism Type of 1991**
**1993, May 6   Litho.   Perf. 12½x13**
259  A59   4k Village in winter  2.00  2.00
260  A59  8.50k Ruins, coastline  3.50  3.50

AIDS
Research — A66

**1993, Sept. 9     Litho.      Perf. 13**
261  A66  4k multicolored        2.25  2.25

Native
Animals — A67

5k, Canis lupus. 8.50k, Alopex lagopus. 10k,
Rangifer tarandus.

### Litho. & Engr.
| | | | **Perf. 13** |
|---|---|---|---|
| **1993, Oct. 14** | | | |
| 262 | A67 | 5k multicolored | 2.50 2.50 |
| 263 | A67 | 8.50k multicolored | 4.00 4.00 |
| 264 | A67 | 10k multicolored | 4.50 4.50 |
| | | Nos. 262-264 (3) | 11.00 11.00 |

See Nos. 270-272, 296-298.

Christmas — A68

| **1993, Nov. 11** | Litho. | **Perf. 13** |
|---|---|---|
| 265 A68 4k multicolored | | 2.00 2.00 |

Buksefjord
Electrical
Project — A69

### Litho. & Engr.
| **1994, Mar. 24** | | **Perf. 13** |
|---|---|---|
| 266 A69 4k multicolored | | 1.50 1.50 |

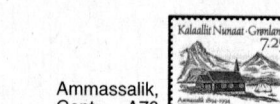

Ammassalik,
Cent. — A70

| **1994, Mar. 24** | | |
|---|---|---|
| 267 A70 7.25k multicolored | | 3.00 3.00 |

Expedition to
North East
Greenland, 1906-
08 — A71

Europa: 4k, Icebound Danmark. 7.25k,
Danmark, expedition car, dogs.

| **1994, May 5** | Litho. | **Perf. 13** |
|---|---|---|
| 268 | A71 | 4k multicolored | 1.50 1.50 |
| 269 | A71 | 7.25k multicolored | 3.25 3.25 |

### Native Animal Type of 1993
Designs: 5.50k, Mustela erminea. 7.25k,
Dicrostonyx torquatus. 9k, Lepus arcticus.

### Litho. & Engr.
| | | | **Perf. 13** |
|---|---|---|---|
| **1994, Sept. 8** | | | |
| 270 | A67 | 5.50k multicolored | 2.50 2.50 |
| 271 | A67 | 7.25k multicolored | 4.00 4.00 |
| 272 | A67 | 9k multicolored | 4.50 4.50 |
| | | Nos. 270-272 (3) | 11.00 11.00 |

Ship's
Figureheads
A72

### Litho. & Engr.
| **1994, Oct. 13** | | **Perf. 13** |
|---|---|---|
| 273 | A72 | 4k Ceres | 1.50 1.50 |
| 274 | A72 | 8.50k Nordlyset | 3.50 3.50 |

See Nos. 299-300, 309-310.

Christmas
Paintings, by
Julia
Pars — A73

| **1994, Nov. 10** | Litho. | **Perf. 12½x13** |
|---|---|---|
| 275 A73 4k shown | | 2.00 2.00 |
| 276 A73 5k Santa, dogs, igloo | | 3.00 3.00 |

Orchids — A74

4k, Listera cordata. 4.25k, Corallorhiza
trifida. 4.50k, Amerorchis rotundifolia. 7.25k,
Leucorchis albida. 7.50k, Plantanthera
hyperborea.

### Litho. & Engr.
| **1995-96** | | **Perf. 13x12½** |
|---|---|---|
| 279 | A74 | 4k multicolored | 2.00 2.00 |
| 280 | A74 | 4.25k multicolored | 1.75 1.75 |
| 281 | A74 | 4.50k multicolored | 1.90 1.90 |
| 282 | A74 | 7.25k multicolored | 3.00 3.00 |
| 283 | A74 | 7.50k multicolored | 3.25 3.25 |
| a. | | Booklet pane, #281, 283, 2 ea | |
| | | #225, 280 + 4 labels | 12.50 |
| | | Complete booklet, 2 #283a | 25.00 |
| | | Nos. 279-283 (5) | 11.90 11.90 |

No. 283a exists with different labels and
stamps in different order. Complete booklet
contains one of each type of No. 283a.
Issued: 4k, 7.25k, 2/9/95.

Ilinniarfissuaq Seminarium, Nuuk (The
Greenland Training College), 150th
Anniv. — A75

### Litho. & Engr.
| **1995, Mar. 23** | | **Perf. 13** |
|---|---|---|
| 287 A75 4k multicolored | | 1.75 1.75 |

United Nations, 50th
Anniv. — A76

**1995, Mar. 23**
| 288 A76 7.25k multicolored | | 3.75 3.75 |
|---|---|---|

### Tourism Type of 1991
| **1995, Apr. 20** | Litho. | **Perf. 12½x13** |
|---|---|---|
| 289 | A59 | 4k Iceberg, inlet | 2.10 2.10 |
| 290 | A59 | 8.50k Mountains | 4.25 4.25 |

Peace &
Liberty — A77

Europa: 4k, Envelope, simulated stamp.
8.50k, Doves flying over Greenland.

| **1995, May 5** | | **Perf. 12½x13** |
|---|---|---|
| 291 | A77 | 4k multicolored | 1.75 1.75 |
| 292 | A77 | 8.50k multicolored | 4.00 4.00 |

### Souvenir Sheets
### Types A3-A5 Surcharged

America Series — A78

Designs: No. 295a, Dog team. b, Polar bear.
c, Eskimo in kayak. d, Eider duck.

| **1995, May 5** | | Litho. | **Perf. 13** |
|---|---|---|---|
| 293 | A78 | Sheet of 2 + 4 labels | 6.50 6.50 |
| a. | | 5k on 10o pur & ol (Type A4) | 3.00 3.00 |
| b. | | 5k on 15o red & vio (Type A4) | 3.00 3.00 |
| 294 | A78 | Sheet of 3 | 7.75 7.75 |
| a. | | 1k on 1o dk ol & vio bl (Type A3) | .60 .60 |
| b. | | 5k on 5o rose lake & brn (Type A3) | |
| c. | | 7k on 7o dk grn & blk (Type A3) | 4.25 4.25 |
| 295 | A78 | Sheet of 4 | 10.00 10.00 |
| a. | | 4k on 30o dk bl & red brn (Type A5) | 2.40 2.40 |
| b. | | 4k on 1k brn & gray blk (Type A5) | 2.40 2.40 |

| c. | 4k on 2k sep & dp grn (Type A5) | 2.40 2.40 |
|---|---|---|
| d. | 4k on 5k dp pur & dl brn (Type A5) | 2.40 2.40 |

### Native Animal Type of 1993
### Litho. & Engr.
| | | | **Perf. 13** |
|---|---|---|---|
| **1995, Sept. 7** | | | |
| 296 | A67 | Ursus maritimus | 2.00 2.00 |
| 297 | A67 | 7.25k Gulo gulo | 3.25 3.25 |
| 298 | A67 | 7.50k Ovibus moschatus | 3.25 3.25 |
| | | Nos. 296-298 (3) | 8.50 8.50 |

### Ship's Figureheads Type of 1994
### Litho. & Engr.
| **1995, Oct. 12** | | **Perf. 13** |
|---|---|---|
| 299 | A72 | 4k Hvalfisken, vert. | 1.60 1.60 |
| 300 | A72 | 8.50k Tjalfe | 3.75 3.75 |

Christmas — A79

| **1995, Nov. 9** | Litho. | **Perf. 13** |
|---|---|---|
| 301 | A79 | 4k Boy running in snow | 1.50 1.50 |
| 302 | A79 | 5k Girl running in snow | 2.00 2.00 |

Whales — A80

Designs: 25o, Orcinus orca. 50o, Megaptera
novaeangliae. 1k, Delphinapterus leucas.
4.50k, Physeter catodon. 6.50k, Balaena mysticetus. 9.50k, Balaenoptera acutorostrata.

| **1996, Apr. 25** | | Litho. | **Perf. 13** |
|---|---|---|---|
| 303 | A80 | 25o blue, blk & red | .25 .25 |
| 304 | A80 | 50o blue, blk & red | .25 .25 |
| 305 | A80 | 1k blue, blk & red | .65 .65 |
| 306 | A80 | 4.50k blue, blk & red | 2.00 2.00 |
| a. | | Bkt. pane, #304, 2 ea #303, 306 | 5.00 |
| | | Complete booklet, 2 #306a | 10.00 |
| 307 | A80 | 6.50k blue, blk & red | 3.25 3.25 |
| 308 | A80 | 9.50k blue, blk & red | 4.50 4.50 |
| a. | | Souvenir sheet, Nos. 303-308 | 11.50 11.50 |
| | | Nos. 303-308 (6) | 10.90 10.90 |

No. 306a exists with stamps in different
order. Issued: No. 306a, 1/14/97.
See Nos. 319-322, 329-334.

### Ship's Figureheads Type of 1994
### Litho. & Engr.
| **1996, Sept. 5** | | **Perf. 13** |
|---|---|---|
| 309 | A72 | 15k Blaahejren, vert. | 5.50 5.50 |
| 310 | A72 | 20k Gertrud Rask | 7.50 7.50 |

Arnarulunnguaq
(1896-1933),
Member of Thule
Expedition — A81

| **1996, Sept. 5** | | Engr. |
|---|---|---|
| 311 A81 4.50k dark blue | | 1.75 1.75 |

Europa.

Christmas — A82

Designs: 4.25k, Girl looking through frozen
window pane, angels scratched in ice. 4.50k,
Paper star, children singing.

| **1996, Nov. 7** | | Litho. | **Perf. 13** |
|---|---|---|---|
| 312 | A82 | 4.25k multicolored | 2.00 2.00 |
| 313 | A82 | 4.50k multicolored | 2.50 2.50 |
| a. | | Booklet pane, 3 each #312-313 | 13.00 |
| | | Complete booklet, 2 #313a | 26.00 |

No. 313a was issued in two formats, one
with No. 312 at the UL, the other with No. 313
at the UL. The complete booklet contains one
of each format.

A83

### Litho. & Engr.
| **1997, Jan. 14** | | **Perf. 13** |
|---|---|---|
| 314 A83 4.50k multicolored | | 2.25 2.25 |

Coronation of Queen Margrethe II, 25th
anniv.

A84

Butterflies: 2k, Clossiana chariclea. 3k,
Colias hecla. 4.75k, Plebejus franklinii. 8k,
Lycaena phlaeas.

| **1997, Jan. 14** | | | |
|---|---|---|---|
| 315 | A84 | 2k multicolored | 1.10 1.10 |
| 316 | A84 | 3k multicolored | 1.75 1.75 |
| 317 | A84 | 4.75k multicolored | 1.75 1.75 |
| 318 | A84 | 8k multicolored | 3.50 3.50 |
| a. | | Booklet pane of 6, 2 #314, 1 ea #315-318 + 2 labels | 13.00 |
| | | Complete booklet, 2 #318a | 26.00 |
| | | Nos. 315-318 (4) | 8.10 8.10 |

Issued: No. 318a, 5/5.
No. 318a exists with stamps in two different
orders and with two different backgrounds,
one of green plants, the other of red flowers.
The complete booklet contains one of each
type of pane.

### Whale Type of 1996
Designs: 5k, Balaenoptera musculus. 5.75k,
Balaenoptera physalus. 6k, Balaenoptera
borealis. 8k, Monodon monoceros.

| **1997, May 5** | | Litho. | **Perf. 13** |
|---|---|---|---|
| 319 | A80 | 5k blue, blk & red | 1.90 1.90 |
| 320 | A80 | 5.75k blue, blk & red | 2.25 2.25 |
| 321 | A80 | 6k blue, blk & red | 2.25 2.25 |
| 322 | A80 | 8k blue, blk & red | 3.25 3.25 |
| a. | | Souvenir sheet of 4, #319-322 | 10.00 10.00 |
| | | Nos. 319-322 (4) | 9.65 9.65 |

Story of the "Bear of
the Sea" — A85

| **1997, May 5** | Litho. & Engr. | **Perf. 13** |
|---|---|---|
| 323 A85 4.75k dark blue | | 2.50 2.50 |

Europa.

Town of
Nanortalik,
Bicent. — A86

### Litho. & Engr.
| **1997, Aug. 15** | | **Perf. 13** |
|---|---|---|
| 324 A86 4.50k multicolored | | 1.75 1.75 |

Paintings by
Aage Gitz-
Johansen
(1897-1977)
A87

Designs: 10k, Native dancer, Thule. 16k,
Nude woman, Ammassalik.

| **1997, Aug. 15** | Litho. | **Perf. 13x12½** |
|---|---|---|
| 325 A87 10k multicolored | | 3.75 3.75 |
| 326 A87 16k multicolored | | 5.75 5.75 |

Christmas — A88

Designs: 4.50k, Child with dogs in snow. 4.75k, Family in sled with Christmas presents, tree, father preparing harness.

**1997, Nov. 6    Litho.    Perf. 13x12½**
| 327 | A88 | 4.50k multicolored | 2.00 | 2.00 |
|-----|-----|--------------------|------|------|
| 328 | A88 | 4.75k multicolored | 2.00 | 2.00 |
| a. | | Booklet pane, 3 each #327-328 | 14.00 | |
| | | Complete booklet, 2 #328a | 28.00 | |

No. 328a comes in two configurations. One has No. 327 at UL, the second has No. 328 at UL. Complete booklet has one of each pane.

**Whale Type of 1996**

Designs: 2k, Phocoena phocoena. 3k, Lagenorhynchus albirostris. No. 331, Globicephala melaena. No. 332, Hyperoodon ampullatus. No. 333, Lagenorhynchus acutus. No. 334, Eubalaena glacialis.

**1998, Feb. 5    Litho.    Perf. 13**
| 329 | A80 | 2k multicolored | .65 | .65 |
|-----|-----|-----------------|-----|-----|
| 330 | A80 | 3k multicolored | 1.25 | 1.25 |
| 331 | A80 | 4.50k multicolored | 2.00 | 2.00 |
| 332 | A80 | 4.50k multicolored | 2.00 | 2.00 |
| 333 | A80 | 4.75k multicolored | 2.00 | 2.00 |
| 334 | A80 | 4.75k multicolored | 2.00 | 2.00 |
| a. | | Souvenir sheet of 6, #329-334 | 10.00 | 10.00 |
| | | Nos. 329-334 (6) | 9.90 | 9.90 |

Intl. Year of the Ocean.

New Order of 1950 — A89

Design: Augo Lynge, Frederik Lynge, first Greenland politicians in Danish Parliament.

**1998, Feb. 5    Engr.    Perf. 13**
| 335 | A89 | 4.50k multicolored | 1.75 | 1.75 |
|-----|-----|--------------------|------|------|

Europa — A90

Children's drawings of "Children's Day in Greenland:" 4.75k, Happy faces beside lake. 10k, People celebrating across Greenland.

**1998, May 29    Litho.    Perf. 13**
| 336 | A90 | 4.75k multicolored | 1.50 | 1.50 |
|-----|-----|--------------------|------|------|
| 337 | A90 | 10k multicolored | 4.00 | 4.00 |

Ships — A91

**Litho. & Engr.**

**1998, Aug. 20    Perf. 13**
| 338 | A91 | 4.50k Gertrud Rask | 2.00 | 2.00 |
|-----|-----|--------------------|------|------|
| a. | | Booklet pane of 6 | 12.00 | |
| 339 | A91 | 4.75k Hans Egede | 2.00 | 2.00 |
| a. | | Booklet pane of 6 | 12.00 | |
| | | Complete booklet, #338a, 339a | 24.00 | |

Paintings by Hans Lynge (1906-88) A92

Designs: 11k, "Brother Gets Breast-fed." 25k, "Refuelling" (men in boat).

**1998, Aug. 20    Litho.    Perf. 13**
| 340 | A92 | 11k multicolored | 3.75 | 3.75 |
|-----|-----|------------------|------|------|
| 341 | A92 | 25k multicolored | 8.75 | 8.75 |

Christmas — A93

**1998, Nov. 5    Litho.    Perf. 13**
| 342 | A93 | 4.50k Dickey, kamikker | 2.00 | 2.00 |
|-----|-----|------------------------|------|------|
| a. | | Booklet pane of 6 | 15.00 | |
| 343 | A93 | 4.75k Kamikker, hat | 2.50 | 2.50 |
| a. | | Booklet pane of 6 | 15.00 | |
| | | Complete booklet, #342a, 343a | 30.00 | |

World Wildlife Fund — A94

Nyctea scandiaca (snowy owl): 1k, Nesting with young. 4.75k, In flight. 5.50k, Two adults. 5.75k, Perched on rock.

**Litho. & Engr.**

**1999, Feb. 8    Perf. 13**
| 344 | A94 | 1k multicolored | .60 | .60 |
|-----|-----|-----------------|-----|-----|
| 345 | A94 | 4.75k multicolored | 2.00 | 2.00 |
| a. | | Booklet pane, 3 each #344-345 | 8.50 | |
| 346 | A94 | 5.50k multicolored | 2.25 | 2.25 |
| 347 | A94 | 5.75k multicolored | 2.50 | 2.50 |
| a. | | Booklet pane, 3 each #346-347 | 14.50 | |
| | | Complete booklet, #345a, 347a | 25.00 | |
| | | Nos. 344-347 (4) | 7.35 | 7.35 |

Europa — A95

**1999, May 7    Litho. & Engr.    Perf. 13**
| 348 | A95 | 6k Polar bear | 2.50 | 2.50 |
|-----|-----|---------------|------|------|

Paintings, by Peter Rosing (1892-1965) A96

Designs: 7k, The Man from Aluk, 1944. 20k, Homecoming, 1956.

**1999, May 7    Litho.    Perf. 12½x13**
| 349 | A96 | 7k multicolored | 2.00 | 2.00 |
|-----|-----|-----------------|------|------|
| 350 | A96 | 20k multicolored | 7.00 | 7.00 |

Arctic Vikings — A97

4.50k, Viking ship. 4.75k, Man on driftwood. 5.75k, Arrowhead, coins. 8k, Tjodhilde's church.

**1999, Aug. 13    Engr.    Perf. 13x13¼**
| 351 | A97 | 4.50k multicolored | 1.75 | 1.75 |
|-----|-----|--------------------|------|------|
| 352 | A97 | 4.75k multicolored | 1.75 | 1.75 |
| 353 | A97 | 5.75k multicolored | 2.25 | 2.25 |
| 354 | A97 | 8k multicolored | 3.00 | 3.00 |
| a. | | Souvenir sheet, #351-354 | 9.00 | 9.00 |
| | | Nos. 351-354 (4) | 8.75 | 8.75 |

See Nos. 358-361, 380-383.

Christmas — A98

**1999, Nov. 11    Litho.    Perf. 13x13¼**
| 355 | A98 | 4.50k Writing letter | 1.50 | 1.50 |
|-----|-----|----------------------|------|------|
| a. | | Booklet pane of 6 | 9.00 | |
| 356 | A98 | 4.75k Handshake | 1.75 | 1.75 |
| a. | | Booklet pane of 6 | 10.50 | |
| | | Complete booklet, #355a, 356a | 20.00 | |

Millennium — A99

**1999, Nov. 11    Litho.    Perf. 13x13¼**
| 357 | A99 | 5.75k multicolored | 2.00 | 2.00 |
|-----|-----|--------------------|------|------|

**Arctic Vikings Type of 1999**

Designs: 25o, Hunter, four walruses. 3k, Storyteller. 5.50k, Dog chasing reindeer. 21k, Man, gyrfalcon, polar bear, narwhal tusk, items made from animals.

**2000, Feb. 21    Engr.    Perf. 13x13¼**
| 358 | A97 | 25o bl gray & brn | .25 | .25 |
|-----|-----|-------------------|-----|-----|
| 359 | A97 | 3k bl gray & brn | 1.40 | 1.40 |
| 360 | A97 | 5.50k bl gray | 2.25 | 2.25 |
| 361 | A97 | 21k bl gray | 9.00 | 9.00 |
| a. | | Souvenir sheet, #358-361 | 13.00 | 13.00 |
| | | Nos. 358-361 (4) | 12.90 | 12.90 |

Navy Dog Sled Patrol — A100

**Litho. & Engr.**

**2000, Feb. 21    Perf. 12¾**
| 362 | A100 | 10k multi | 3.25 | 3.25 |
|-----|------|-----------|------|------|

**Europa, 2000**
**Common Design Type**

**2000, May 9    Litho.    Perf. 13¼x13**
| 363 | CD17 | 4.75k multi | 1.90 | 1.90 |
|-----|------|-------------|------|------|

Queen Margrethe — A101

**2000-02    Engr.    Perf. 13x13¼**
| 364 | A101 | 25o blk & bl gray | .30 | .25 |
|-----|------|-------------------|-----|-----|
| 365 | A101 | 50o red brn & bl gray | .25 | .25 |
| 367 | A101 | 4.50k red & bl gray | 1.60 | 1.60 |
| 368 | A101 | 4.75k bl & bl gray | 1.75 | 1.75 |
| | | Complete booklet, 4 each #364, #368 | 8.00 | |
| 372 | A101 | 8k yel grn & bl gray | 3.00 | 3.00 |
| 374 | A101 | 10k grn & bl gray | 3.50 | 3.50 |
| 375 | A101 | 12k pur & bl gray | 4.25 | 4.25 |
| | | Nos. 364-375 (7) | 14.65 | 14.60 |

Issued: 4.50k, 4.75k, 8k, 10k, 5/9/00. 25o, 12k, 5/9/01. 50o, 10/21/02.

Cultural Heritage — A102

**2000, Aug. 18    Litho.    Perf. 13¼x13**
| 376 | A102 | 4.50k Wooden map | 1.50 | 1.50 |
|-----|------|------------------|------|------|
| a. | | Booklet pane of 6 | 9.00 | |
| 377 | A102 | 4.75k Sealskin | 1.75 | 1.75 |
| a. | | Booklet pane of 6 + 2 labels | 10.50 | |
| | | Booklet, #376a, 377a | 20.00 | |

See Nos. 384-385, 392-393, 414-415

Christmas A103

**2000, Nov. 9    Litho.    Perf. 13x13¼**
| 378 | A103 | 4.50k Stars, candles | 1.75 | 1.75 |
|-----|------|----------------------|------|------|
| a. | | Booklet pane of 6 | 10.50 | |
| 379 | A103 | 4.75k Star | 1.90 | 1.90 |
| a. | | Booklet pane of 6 | 11.50 | |
| | | Booklet, #378a, 379a | 22.50 | |

**Arctic Vikings Type of 1999**

Designs: 1k, Hunter, dead seals. 4.50k, Mice eating food. 5k, Man and pack animals leaving. 10k, Birds on ruins.

**2001, Feb. 5    Engr.    Perf. 13x13¼**
| 380 | A97 | 1k indigo & red | 1.00 | 1.00 |
|-----|-----|-----------------|------|------|
| 381 | A97 | 4.50k indigo & blue | 1.15 | 1.15 |
| 382 | A97 | 5k indigo & blue | 2.10 | 2.10 |

| 383 | A97 | 10k indigo & red | 4.25 | 4.25 |
|-----|-----|------------------|------|------|
| a. | | Souvenir sheet, #380-383 | 8.00 | 8.00 |
| | | Nos. 380-383 (4) | 8.50 | 8.50 |

**Cultural Heritage Type of 2000**

Designs: 4.50k, Smoked fish. 4.75k, Fishing spear.

**2001, May 9    Litho.    Perf. 13¼x13**
| 384 | A102 | 4.50k multi | 1.50 | 1.50 |
|-----|------|-------------|------|------|
| a. | | Booklet pane of 6 + 2 labels | 10.00 | |
| 385 | A102 | 4.75k multi | 2.00 | 2.00 |
| a. | | Booklet pane of 6 + 2 labels | 10.00 | |
| | | Complete booklet, #384a, 385a | 20.00 | |

Europa — A104

**2001, May 9    Litho. & Engr.    Perf. 13**
| 386 | A104 | 15k Krill | 4.75 | 4.75 |
|-----|------|-----------|------|------|

Unissued Stamps from the 1930s — A105

Designs: 5.75k, 5o Northern lights. 8k, 10o Seal. 21k, 15o Polar bear.

**Litho. & Engr.**

**2001, Oct. 16    Perf. 12¾**
| 387 | A105 | 5.75k blk & brn | 2.25 | 2.25 |
|-----|------|-----------------|------|------|
| 388 | A105 | 8k blk & brn | 3.25 | 3.25 |
| 389 | A105 | 21k blk & brn | 8.25 | 8.25 |
| a. | | Souvenir sheet, #387-389 + 3 labels | 14.00 | 14.00 |

Christmas — A106

Grouse and: 4.50k, Berries. 4.75k, Mountain.

**2001, Oct. 16    Litho.    Perf. 13x13¼**
| 390 | A106 | 4.50k multi | 1.50 | 1.50 |
|-----|------|-------------|------|------|
| a. | | Booklet pane of 6 | 9.00 | |
| 391 | A106 | 4.75k multi | 1.75 | 1.75 |
| a. | | Booklet pane of 6 | 10.50 | |
| | | Complete booklet, #390a, 391a | 20.00 | |

**Cultural Heritage Type of 2000**

Designs: 4.50k, Thule drum. 4.75k, Mask.

**2002, Mar. 5    Litho.    Perf. 13x13¼**
| 392 | A102 | 4.50k multi | 1.75 | 1.75 |
|-----|------|-------------|------|------|
| a. | | Miniature sheet of 8 + label | 14.00 | |
| 393 | A102 | 4.75k multi | 1.90 | 1.90 |
| a. | | Miniature sheet of 8 + label | 15.00 | |

Sculptures — A107

Designs: 1k, Stone and Man, by various sculptors. 31k, Nuuk Snow Festival snow sculpture.

**2002, Mar. 5    Perf. 12¾**
| 394 | A107 | 1k multi | .40 | .40 |
|-----|------|----------|-----|-----|
| 395 | A107 | 31k multi | 12.00 | 12.00 |

Europa — A108

**2002, June 24    Litho.    Perf. 12¾**
| 396 | A108 | 11k multi | 4.00 | 4.00 |
|-----|------|-----------|------|------|

Ships — A109

**2002, June 24    Engr.    Perf. 13x13¼**

| | | | | |
|---|---|---|---|---|
| 397 | A109 | 2k Nordlyset | .80 | .80 |
| 398 | A109 | 4k Hvidbjornen | 1.60 | 1.60 |
| 399 | A109 | 6k Staerkodder | 2.40 | 2.40 |
| *a.* | | Booklet pane of 4, 2 each #398-399 | 8.00 | — |
| 400 | A109 | 16k Haabet | 6.25 | 6.25 |
| *a.* | | Booklet pane of 4, 2 each #397, 400 | 14.00 | — |
| | | Complete booklet, #399a, 400a | 22.50 | |
| | | Nos. 397-400 (4) | 11.05 | 11.05 |

See Nos. 416-419, 434-437, 452-455.

Intl. Council for Exploration of the Seas, Cent. — A110

Designs: 7k, Somniosus microcephalus and iceberg. 19k, Sebastes mentella and exploration ship Paamiut.

**Litho. & Engr.**

**2002, Oct. 21    Perf. 13¼x13**

| | | | | |
|---|---|---|---|---|
| 401 | A110 | 7k multi | 2.25 | 2.25 |
| 402 | A110 | 19k multi | 6.25 | 6.25 |
| *a.* | | Souvenir sheet, #401-402 | 8.50 | 8.50 |

See Denmark Nos. 1237-1238, Faroe Islands No. 426.

Christmas — A111

Designs: 4.50k, Man with gifts, children on sled with tree. 4.75k, Family with gifts near fire.

**2002, Oct. 21    Litho.    Perf. 12¾**

| | | | | |
|---|---|---|---|---|
| 403 | A111 | 4.50k multi | 2.00 | 2.00 |
| 404 | A111 | 4.75k multi | 2.00 | 2.00 |

**Booklet Stamps**
**Self-Adhesive**
*Serpentine Die Cut 14*

| | | | | |
|---|---|---|---|---|
| 405 | A111 | 4.50k multi | 2.00 | 2.00 |
| 406 | A111 | 4.75k multi | 2.25 | 2.25 |
| *a.* | | Horiz. pair, #405-406 | 4.50 | |
| *b.* | | Booklet, 6 each #405-406 | 27.00 | |

Danish Literary Greenland Expedition, Cent. — A112

Designs: 15k, Campsite. 21k, Knud Rasmussen.

**2003, Mar. 12    Engr.    Perf. 12¾**

| | | | | |
|---|---|---|---|---|
| 407 | A112 | 15k multi | 6.00 | 6.00 |

**Size: 28x21mm**

| | | | | |
|---|---|---|---|---|
| 408 | A112 | 21k blue gray | 8.00 | 8.00 |
| *a.* | | Souvenir sheet, #407-408 + label | 14.00 | 14.00 |

Sled Dogs — A113

Designs: 4.50k, Puppies playing. 4.75k, Close-up of dog. 6k, Dog in harness.

**2003, Mar. 12    Perf. 13x13¼**

| | | | | |
|---|---|---|---|---|
| 409 | A113 | 4.50k blue gray | 1.90 | 1.90 |
| *a.* | | Sheet of 8 + central label | 15.00 | 15.00 |
| 410 | A113 | 4.75k blue gray | 2.00 | 2.00 |
| *a.* | | Sheet of 8 + central label | 16.00 | 16.00 |
| 411 | A113 | 6k blue gray | 2.60 | 2.60 |
| *a.* | | Booklet pane, 2 each #409-411, with #411 at UL | 15.00 | — |
| *b.* | | Booklet pane, 2 each #409-411, with #409 at UL | 15.00 | — |
| | | Complete booklet, #411a, 411b | 30.00 | |
| | | Nos. 409-411 (3) | 6.50 | 6.50 |

Europa — A114

**2003, June 16    Litho.    Perf. 13¼x13**

| | | | | |
|---|---|---|---|---|
| 412 | A114 | 5.50k multi | | 2.60 2.60 |

Town of Qaanaaq, 50th Anniv. — A115

**2003, June 16    Perf. 12¾**

| | | | | |
|---|---|---|---|---|
| 413 | A115 | 15k multi | 6.00 | 6.00 |

**Cultural Heritage Type of 2000**

Designs: 25o, Comb. 1k, Ice bucket.

**2003, June 16    Perf. 13¼x13**

| | | | | |
|---|---|---|---|---|
| 414 | A102 | 25o multi | .25 | .25 |
| 415 | A102 | 1k multi | .55 | .55 |

**Ship Type of 2002**
**Litho. & Engr.**

**2003, Oct. 20    Perf. 13x13¼**

| | | | | |
|---|---|---|---|---|
| 416 | A109 | 6.75k Emma | 2.75 | 2.75 |
| 417 | A109 | 7.75k Gamle Fox | 3.00 | 3.00 |
| 418 | A109 | 8.75k Godthaab | 3.50 | 3.50 |
| 419 | A109 | 26k Sonja | 10.00 | 10.00 |
| | | Nos. 416-419 (4) | 19.25 | 19.25 |

Christmas — A116

Designs: Nos. 420, 422, Christmas tree. Nos. 421, 423, Church.

**2003, Oct. 20    Litho.    Perf. 12¾**

| | | | | |
|---|---|---|---|---|
| 420 | A116 | 5k multi | 2.00 | 2.00 |
| 421 | A116 | 5.50k multi | 2.25 | 2.25 |

**Booklet Stamps**
**Self-Adhesive**
*Serpentine Die Cut 12¼x12¾*

| | | | | |
|---|---|---|---|---|
| 422 | A116 | 5k multi | 2.50 | 2.50 |
| 423 | A116 | 5.50k multi | 2.50 | 2.50 |
| *b.* | | Booklet pane of 12, 6 each #422-423 | 30.00 | |
| | | Nos. 420-423 (4) | 9.25 | 9.25 |

Polar Air Route, 50th Anniv. — A117

**2004, Mar. 26    Litho.    Perf. 13¼x13**

| | | | | |
|---|---|---|---|---|
| 424 | A117 | 8.75k multi | | 3.25 3.25 |

Home Rule, 25th Anniv. — A118

**2004, Mar. 26    Perf. 12¾x12½**

| | | | | |
|---|---|---|---|---|
| 425 | A118 | 11k multi | | 4.00 4.00 |

Landing Boat From Expedition of Arctic Explorer Otto Sverdrup (1854-1930) — A119

**Litho. & Engr.**

**2004, Mar. 26    Perf. 13¼x13**

| | | | | |
|---|---|---|---|---|
| 426 | A119 | 17.50k multi | 7.50 | 7.50 |
| *a.* | | Souvenir sheet of 1 + 2 labels | 7.50 | 7.50 |

See Canada Nos. 2026-2027, Norway Nos. 1398-1399.

Norse Mythology — A120

Designs: 5.50k, Moon Man. 6.50k, Northern Lights.

**2004, Mar. 26    Litho.    Perf. 12¾**

| | | | | |
|---|---|---|---|---|
| 427 | A120 | 5.50k multi | 2.75 | 2.75 |
| 428 | A120 | 6.50k multi | 3.00 | 3.00 |
| *a.* | | Souvenir sheet, #427-428 | 5.75 | 5.75 |

Wedding of Crown Prince Frederik and Mary Donaldson — A121

Designs: 5k, Couple facing right. 5.50k, Couple facing left.

**2004, May 14    Perf. 13¼**

| | | | | |
|---|---|---|---|---|
| 429 | A121 | 5k multi | 2.00 | 2.00 |
| 430 | A121 | 5.50k multi | 2.25 | 2.25 |
| *a.* | | Souvenir sheet, #429-430 + central label | 4.25 | 4.25 |
| *b.* | | Booklet pane, 3 each #429-430, with #429 at top | 13.00 | |
| *c.* | | As "b," with #430 at top | 13.00 | |
| | | Complete booklet, #430b-430c | 26.00 | |

See Denmark No. 1275 and Faroe Islands No. 444.

Edible Plants — A122

Designs: 5k, Angelica archangelica. 5.50k, Thymus praecox. 17k, Empetrum hermaphroditum.

**2004, May 14    Perf. 13x13¼**

| | | | | |
|---|---|---|---|---|
| 431 | A122 | 5k multi | 2.00 | 2.00 |
| *a.* | | Sheet of 8 + central label | 16.00 | 16.00 |
| 432 | A122 | 5.50k multi | 2.25 | 2.25 |
| *a.* | | Sheet of 8 + central label | 18.00 | 18.00 |
| 433 | A122 | 17k multi | 6.75 | 6.75 |
| | | Nos. 431-433 (3) | 11.00 | 11.00 |

See Nos. 459-461

**Ships Type of 2002**

6.50k, Constance. 8.75k, Disko. 14k, Julius Thomsen. 21.75k, Misigssut.

**Litho. & Engr.**

**2004, Oct. 18    Perf. 13x13¼**

| | | | | |
|---|---|---|---|---|
| 434 | A109 | 6.50k multicolored | 2.25 | 2.25 |
| 435 | A109 | 8.75k multicolored | 3.25 | 3.25 |
| 436 | A109 | 14k multicolored | 5.00 | 5.00 |
| 437 | A109 | 21.75k multi | 8.00 | 8.00 |
| | | Nos. 434-437 (4) | 18.50 | 18.50 |

Europa — A123

**2004, Oct. 18    Litho.    Perf. 13¼x13**

| | | | | |
|---|---|---|---|---|
| 438 | A123 | 6.50k multi | | 2.75 2.75 |

Christmas — A124

Designs: 5k, Family, Christmas tree. 5.50k, Carolers with lanterns.

**2004, Oct. 18    Perf. 12¾**

| | | | | |
|---|---|---|---|---|
| 439 | A124 | 5k multi | 2.00 | 2.00 |
| 440 | A124 | 5.50k multi | 2.00 | 2.00 |

**Booklet Stamps**
**Self-Adhesive**
*Serpentine Die Cut 12¼x12¾*

| | | | | |
|---|---|---|---|---|
| 441 | A124 | 5k multi | 2.00 | 2.00 |
| 442 | A124 | 5.50k multi | 2.00 | 2.00 |
| *a.* | | Horiz. pair, #441-442 | 4.00 | 4.00 |
| *b.* | | Complete booklet, 6 #442a | 24.00 | |
| | | Nos. 439-442 (4) | 8.00 | 8.00 |

Ilulissat Ice Fjord, UNESCO World Heritage Site — A125

**2005, Jan. 17    Litho.    Perf. 12¾**

| | | | | |
|---|---|---|---|---|
| 443 | A125 | 6k multi | | 2.40 2.40 |

Church and School Systems Law, Cent. — A126

**2005, Jan. 17    Perf. 12¾**

| | | | | |
|---|---|---|---|---|
| 444 | A126 | 9.25k multi | | 3.50 3.50 |

Europa — A127

**2005, Jan. 17    Perf. 13¼x13**

| | | | | |
|---|---|---|---|---|
| 445 | A127 | 11.75k multi | | 4.50 4.50 |

Mushrooms A128

Designs: 5.25k, Leccinum sp. 6k, Russula subrubens. 7k, Amanita groenlandica.

**2005, Jan. 17    Perf. 13x13¼**

| | | | | |
|---|---|---|---|---|
| 446 | A128 | 5.25k multi | 2.10 | 2.10 |
| *a.* | | Sheet of 8 + central label | 17.00 | |
| 447 | A128 | 6k multi | 2.40 | 2.40 |
| *a.* | | Sheet of 8 + central label | 19.00 | |
| 448 | A128 | 7k multi | 2.75 | 2.75 |
| | | Nos. 446-448 (3) | 7.25 | 7.25 |

**Booklet Stamps**
**Self-Adhesive**
*Serpentine Die Cut 9¾x10¼*

| | | | | |
|---|---|---|---|---|
| 449 | A128 | 5.25k multi | 2.10 | 2.10 |
| 450 | A128 | 6k multi | 2.40 | 2.40 |
| 451 | A128 | 7k multi | 2.75 | 2.75 |
| *a.* | | Booklet pane, 2 each #449-451 | 14.50 | |
| | | Complete booklet, 2 #451a | 29.00 | |
| | | Nos. 449-451 (3) | 7.25 | 7.25 |

No. 451a has two different marginal designs. See Nos. 476-480.

**Ships Type of 2002**
**Litho. & Engr.**

**2005, June 20    Perf. 13x13¼**

| | | | | |
|---|---|---|---|---|
| 452 | A109 | 5.25k Dannebrog | 2.10 | 2.10 |
| 453 | A109 | 6k Kista Arctica | 2.40 | 2.40 |
| 454 | A109 | 18.50k Sarpik Ittuk | 7.25 | 7.25 |
| 455 | A109 | 23k Triton | 9.25 | 9.25 |
| | | Nos. 452-455 (4) | 21.00 | 21.00 |

Science In Greenland — A129

Designs: 7.25k, Geological map. 9.25k, Diver at limestone columns in Ikka Fjord, horiz. 10k, Limnognathia maerski, horiz.

**Perf. 13¼x13, 13x13¼**

**2005, June 20**

| | | | | |
|---|---|---|---|---|
| 456 | A129 | 7.25k multi | 2.75 | 2.75 |
| 457 | A129 | 9.25k multi | 3.50 | 3.50 |
| 458 | A129 | 10k multi | 3.75 | 3.75 |
| | | Nos. 456-458 (3) | 10.00 | 10.00 |

**Edible Plants Type of 2004**

Designs: 75o, Ligusticum scoticum. 6.50k, Rhodiola rosea. 8.25k, Oxyria digyna.

## 2005, Oct. 31 Litho. Perf. 13x13¼

| | | | | |
|---|---|---|---|---|
| **459** | A122 | 75o multi | .30 | .30 |
| **460** | A122 | 6.50k multi | 2.25 | 2.25 |
| **461** | A122 | 8.25k multi | 3.00 | 3.00 |
| | | Nos. 459-461 (3) | 5.55 | 5.55 |

Admiral Robert E. Peary (1856-1920), Explorer — A130

## Litho. & Engr.
### 2005, Oct. 31 Perf. 13

| | | | | |
|---|---|---|---|---|
| **462** | A130 | 27.50k multi | 10.00 | 10.00 |
| *a.* | | Souvenir sheet of 1 | 10.00 | 10.00 |

Parcel Post Stamps, Cent. A131

### 2005-07 Litho. Perf. 14x13½

| | | | | |
|---|---|---|---|---|
| **463** | A131 | 25k #Q3 | 10.00 | 10.00 |

### Perf. 12¾x13

| | | | | |
|---|---|---|---|---|
| **464** | A131 | 50k #Q4 | 20.00 | 20.00 |
| *a.* | | Perf. 14x13½, dated "2007" | 18.00 | 18.00 |

Issued: 25k, 1/16/06; No. 464, 10/3; No. 464a, 2007.

No. 464a is found only in No. 497a, along with an example of No. 463 dated "2007." Issued: No. 464a, 5/21/07.

See No. 497.

Christmas — A132

Designs: 5.25k, Boy at left. 6k, Girl at right.

### 2006, Oct. 31 Perf. 12¾

| | | | | |
|---|---|---|---|---|
| **465** | A132 | 5.25k multi | 2.00 | 2.00 |
| **466** | A132 | 6k multi | 2.00 | 2.00 |

### Booklet Stamps
### Self-Adhesive
### Serpentine Die Cut 12¾x13

| | | | | |
|---|---|---|---|---|
| **467** | A132 | 5.25k multi | 2.00 | 2.00 |
| **468** | A132 | 6k multi | 2.00 | 2.00 |
| *b.* | | Booklet pane, 6 each #467-468 | 24.00 | |

Whale Jaw Gate and Blue Church, Sisimiut — A138

### 2006, Jan. 16 Perf. 13¾x13¼

| | | | | |
|---|---|---|---|---|
| **469** | A138 | 9.75k multi | 3.50 | 3.50 |

Sisimiut, 250th anniv.

Nordic Union "Norden" Stamps, 50th Anniv. — A139

### 2006, Jan. 16

| | | | | |
|---|---|---|---|---|
| **470** | A139 | 19.50k multi | 7.00 | 7.00 |

European Philatelic Cooperation, 50th Anniv. — A140

### 2006, Jan. 16 Perf. 14x13¼

| | | | | |
|---|---|---|---|---|
| **471** | A140 | 26.50k #438 and stars | 10.00 | 10.00 |

Europa stamps, 50th anniv.

Norse Mythology — A141

Designs: 7.50k, The Mother of the Sea. 13.50k, Asiaq, Mistress of the Weather.

### Perf. 13¾x13½
### 2006, Mar. 29 Litho.

| | | | | |
|---|---|---|---|---|
| **472** | A141 | 7.50k multi | 2.75 | 2.75 |
| **473** | A141 | 13.50k multi | 4.75 | 4.75 |
| *a.* | | Souvenir sheet, #472-473 | 7.50 | 7.50 |

Sheep Farming in Greenland, Cent. — A142

### 2006, May 22

| | | | | |
|---|---|---|---|---|
| **474** | A142 | 7.50k multi | 3.00 | 3.00 |

Alfred Wegener (1880-1930), Geophysicist — A143

### 2006, May 22 Engr. Perf. 13x13¼

| | | | | |
|---|---|---|---|---|
| **475** | A143 | 20.75k red & blue | 8.00 | 8.00 |
| *a.* | | Souvenir sheet of 1 | 8.00 | 8.00 |

### Mushrooms Type of 2005

Designs: 5.50k, Rozites caperatus. 7k, Lactarius dryadophilus. 10k, Calvatia cretacea.

### 2006, May 22 Litho. Perf. 14x13¼

| | | | | |
|---|---|---|---|---|
| **476** | A128 | 5.50k multi | 2.25 | 2.25 |
| *a.* | | Sheet of 8 + central label | 18.00 | 18.00 |
| **477** | A128 | 7k multi | 2.75 | 2.75 |
| *a.* | | Sheet of 8 + central label | 22.00 | 22.00 |
| **478** | A128 | 10k multi | 4.00 | 4.00 |
| | | Nos. 476-478 (3) | 9.00 | 9.00 |

### Self-Adhesive
### Booklet Stamps
### Serpentine Die Cut 12¼x12

| | | | | |
|---|---|---|---|---|
| **479** | A128 | 5.50k multi | 2.25 | 2.25 |
| **480** | A128 | 7k multi | 2.75 | 2.75 |
| *a.* | | Booklet pane, 3 each #479-480 | 15.00 | |
| | | Complete booklet, 2 #480a | 30.00 | |

No. 480a has two different marginal designs.

Galathea 3 Research Expedition — A144

### 2006, Sept. 9 Litho. Perf. 13½x14

| | | | | |
|---|---|---|---|---|
| **481** | A144 | 9.75k multi | 3.75 | 3.75 |

Science — A145

Designs: 50o, Larch tree preserved in Kap Kobenhavn Formation. 8k, Geologist obtaining rock sample from mountains at Isua. 15.50k, Qeqertarsuaq Arctic Station, cent.

### Litho. & Engr.
### 2006, Nov. 6 Perf. 13¼x13

| | | | | |
|---|---|---|---|---|
| **482** | A145 | 50o multi | .25 | .25 |
| **483** | A145 | 8k multi | 3.00 | 3.00 |
| **484** | A145 | 15.50k multi | 5.75 | 5.75 |
| | | Nos. 482-484 (3) | 9.00 | 9.00 |

See Nos. 502-504, 524-526, 552-554.

Christmas — A146

Music for hymn and: 5.50k, Angel. 7k, Candle.

### 2006, Nov. 6 Litho. Perf. 13¾x13½

| | | | | |
|---|---|---|---|---|
| **485** | A146 | 5.50k multi | 2.10 | 2.10 |

| | | | | |
|---|---|---|---|---|
| **486** | A146 | 7k multi | 2.50 | 2.50 |

### Booklet Stamps
### Self-Adhesive
### Serpentine Die Cut 12¼x12

| | | | | |
|---|---|---|---|---|
| **487** | A146 | 5.50k multi | 2.00 | 2.00 |
| **488** | A146 | 7k multi | 2.50 | 2.50 |
| *a.* | | Booklet pane, 3 each #487-488 | 13.50 | |
| | | Complete booklet, 2 #488a | 27.00 | |

Hydroelectric Power — A147

### 2007, Jan. 15 Litho. Perf. 13¾x13½

| | | | | |
|---|---|---|---|---|
| **489** | A147 | 5k multi | 1.75 | 1.75 |

West Nordic Council, 10th anniv.

Crown Prince Frederik, Crown Princess Mary and Prince Christian — A148

### 2007, Jan. 15 Perf. 13¼x14

| | | | | |
|---|---|---|---|---|
| **490** | A148 | 14.25k multi | 5.00 | 5.00 |

Intl. Polar Year — A149

Designs: 7.50k, Scientists drilling ice cores. 8k, Urbanization.

### Litho. & Engr.
### 2007, Jan. 15 Perf. 13x13¼

| | | | | |
|---|---|---|---|---|
| **491** | A149 | 7.50k multi | 2.75 | 2.75 |
| **492** | A149 | 8k multi | 3.00 | 3.00 |
| *a.* | | Souvenir sheet, #491-492 | 5.75 | 5.75 |

Europa — A150

Scouts: 5.75k, And rock pile. 7.50k, At campsite.

### 2007, Jan. 15 Litho. Perf. 13¾x13¼

| | | | | |
|---|---|---|---|---|
| **493** | A150 | 5.75k multi | 2.25 | 2.25 |
| *a.* | | Sheet of 8 + central label | 18.00 | 18.00 |
| **494** | A150 | 7.50k multi | 2.75 | 2.75 |
| *a.* | | Sheet of 8 + central label | 22.00 | 22.00 |

### Booklet Stamps
### Self-Adhesive
### Serpentine Die Cut 12¼x12

| | | | | |
|---|---|---|---|---|
| **495** | A150 | 5.75k multi | 2.25 | 2.25 |
| **496** | A150 | 7.50k multi | 2.75 | 2.75 |
| *a.* | | Booklet pane, 3 each #495-496 | 15.00 | |
| | | Complete booklet, 2 #496a | 30.00 | |

### Parcel Post Stamp Centenary Type of 2005-06

### 2007, May 21 Perf. 14x13½

| | | | | |
|---|---|---|---|---|
| **497** | A131 | 100k #Q6 | 37.50 | 37.50 |
| *a.* | | Souvenir sheet, #463, 464a, 497 | 65.00 | 65.00 |

Examples of Nos. 463 and 464a in No. 497a are dated "2007."

A151

Contemporary Art — A152

Unnamed paintings by: 3k, Jens Rosing. 8.50k, Anne-Birthe Hove. 10.50k, Linda Riber Sorensen.

### 2007, May 21

| | | | | |
|---|---|---|---|---|
| **498** | A151 | 3k multi | 1.25 | 1.25 |
| **499** | A152 | 8.50k multi | 3.50 | 3.50 |
| **500** | A152 | 10.50k multi | 4.00 | 4.00 |
| | | Nos. 498-500 (3) | 8.75 | 8.75 |

Greenlandic Landscape A153

### 2007, Oct. 1

| | | | | |
|---|---|---|---|---|
| **501** | A153 | 6.50k multi | 2.75 | 2.75 |

### Science Type of 2006

Designs: 75o, Planting of Greenlandic flag on Tubbiap Queqertaa. 2k, Soapstone bowl and quarry. 10.25k, Cyanobacteria.

### Litho. & Engr.
### 2007, Oct. 1 Perf. 13¼x13

| | | | | |
|---|---|---|---|---|
| **502** | A145 | 75o multi | .35 | .35 |
| **503** | A145 | 2k multi | .85 | .85 |
| **504** | A145 | 10.25k multi | 4.25 | 4.25 |
| | | Nos. 502-504 (3) | 5.45 | 5.45 |

Ship Pourquois-Pas? — A154

Paul-Emile Victor (1907-95), Arctic Explorer — A155

### 2007, Nov. 8 Engr. Perf. 13½

| | | | | |
|---|---|---|---|---|
| **505** | A154 | 5.75k multi | 2.50 | 2.50 |
| **506** | A155 | 7.50k multi | 3.25 | 3.25 |
| *a.* | | Souvenir sheet, #505-506, + label | 5.75 | 5.75 |

See France No. 3369.

Christmas — A156

Snowflakes and: 5.75k, Angel. 7.50k, Star.

### 2007, Nov. 8 Litho. Perf. 13½x13¾

| | | | | |
|---|---|---|---|---|
| **507** | A156 | 5.75k multi | 2.25 | 2.25 |
| **508** | A156 | 7.50k multi | 3.00 | 3.00 |

### Self-Adhesive
### Booklet Stamps
### Serpentine Die Cut 12x12¼

| | | | | |
|---|---|---|---|---|
| **509** | A156 | 5.75k multi | 2.25 | 2.25 |
| **510** | A156 | 7.50k multi | 3.00 | 3.00 |
| *b.* | | Booklet pane of 12, 6 each #509-510 | 31.50 | |

Europa — A157

Envelope half and: 5.75k, Man. 7.50k, Woman.

### 2008, Jan. 31 Litho. Perf. 13¾x13½

| | | | | |
|---|---|---|---|---|
| **511** | A157 | 5.75k multi | 2.40 | 2.40 |
| *a.* | | Sheet of 8 + central label | 19.50 | 19.50 |
| **512** | A157 | 7.50k multi | 3.00 | 3.00 |
| *a.* | | Sheet of 8 + central label | 24.00 | 24.00 |

### Booklet Stamps
### Self-Adhesive
### Serpentine Die Cut 12¼x12

| | | | | |
|---|---|---|---|---|
| **513** | A157 | 5.75k multi | 2.40 | 2.40 |
| **514** | A157 | 7.50k multi | 3.00 | 3.00 |
| *a.* | | Booklet pane, 6 each #513-514 | 32.50 | |

Contemporary Art — A158

Unnamed paintings by: 5.50k, Ina Rosing. 14.25k, Buuti Pedersen. 30.50k, Aka Hoegh.

**2008, Jan. 31**      *Perf. 14x13½*
| | | | | |
|---|---|---|---|---|
| 515 | A158 | 5.50k multi | 2.25 | 2.25 |
| 516 | A158 | 14.25k multi | 5.75 | 5.75 |
| 517 | A158 | 30.50k multi | 12.50 | 12.50 |
| | | *Nos. 515-517 (3)* | 20.50 | 20.50 |

Mythical Places — A159

Myths of: 7k, Kayaker and river rocks. 8k, Bear of the Lake.

*Perf. 13¾x13½*
**2008, Mar. 27**      *Litho.*
| | | | | |
|---|---|---|---|---|
| 518 | A159 | 7k multi | 3.25 | 3.25 |
| 519 | A159 | 8k multi | 3.50 | 3.50 |
| a. | Souvenir sheet, #518-519 | | 6.75 | 6.75 |

Wedding of Prince Joachim and Marie Cavallier — A160

**2008, May 24**    *Litho.*    *Perf. 13½x14*
| | | | | |
|---|---|---|---|---|
| 520 | A160 | 10.25k multi | 4.75 | 4.75 |

Fossils — A161

Designs: 1k, Halkieria evangelista. 20.50k, Ichthyostega stensioei. 25k, Eudimorphodon cromptonellus.

**Litho. & Engr.**
**2008, May 24**      *Perf. 13x13¼*
| | | | | |
|---|---|---|---|---|
| 521 | A161 | 1k multi | .45 | .45 |
| 522 | A161 | 20.50k multi | 8.75 | 8.75 |
| 523 | A161 | 25k multi | 10.50 | 10.50 |
| | | *Nos. 521-523 (3)* | 19.70 | 19.70 |

See Nos. 553-555.

**Science Type of 2006**

Designs: 6.50k, Scientist, equipment hauler, satellite above Greenland. 10.50k, French station at Scoresbysund. 28k, Danish Arctic station at Nuuk.

**Litho. & Engr.**
**2008, Oct. 20**      *Perf. 13¼x13*
| | | | | |
|---|---|---|---|---|
| 524 | A145 | 6.50k multi | 2.50 | 2.50 |
| 525 | A145 | 10.50k multi | 4.00 | 4.00 |
| 526 | A145 | 28k multi | 10.50 | 10.50 |
| a. | Souvenir sheet, #524-526 | | 17.00 | 17.00 |
| | | *Nos. 524-526 (3)* | 17.00 | 17.00 |

International Geophysical Year, 50th anniv. (No. 524); French station at Scoresbysund, 75th anniv. (No. 525); Danish Arctic station at Nuuk, 125th anniv. (No. 526).

Expedition Ship Sofia — A162

---

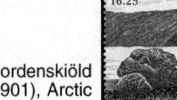

Adolf Erik Nordenskiöld (1832-1901), Arctic Explorer — A163

**2008, Oct. 20**      *Perf. 13¼x13*
| | | | | |
|---|---|---|---|---|
| 527 | A162 | 8.50k multi | 3.00 | 3.00 |
| 528 | A163 | 16.25k multi | 5.75 | 5.75 |
| a. | Souvenir sheet, #527-528, + label | | 8.75 | 8.75 |

See Finland No. 1321.

Christmas — A164

Designs: 5.75k, Reindeer and house. 7.50k, Christmas tree and houses.

**2008, Oct. 20**    *Litho.*    *Perf. 13¾x13¼*
| | | | | |
|---|---|---|---|---|
| 529 | A164 | 5.75k multi | 2.25 | 2.25 |
| 530 | A164 | 7.50k multi | 2.75 | 2.75 |

**Booklet Stamps**
**Self-Adhesive**
*Serpentine Die Cut 12¼x12*
| | | | | |
|---|---|---|---|---|
| 531 | A164 | 5.75k multi | 2.25 | 2.25 |
| 532 | A164 | 7.50k multi | 2.75 | 2.75 |
| b. | Booklet pane of 12, 6 each #531-532 | | 30.00 | |

**Fossils Type of 2008**

Designs: 2k, Schizoneura carcinoides. 11.50k, Scaphites rosenkrantzi. 22k, Mallotus villosus.

**Litho. & Engr.**
**2009, Jan. 19**      *Perf. 13x13¼*
| | | | | |
|---|---|---|---|---|
| 533 | A161 | 2k multi | .70 | .70 |
| 534 | A161 | 11.50k multi | 4.00 | 4.00 |
| 535 | A161 | 22k multi | 7.75 | 7.75 |
| | | *Nos. 533-535 (3)* | 12.45 | 12.45 |

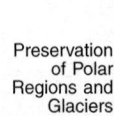

Preservation of Polar Regions and Glaciers A165

**2009, Jan. 19**    *Litho.*    *Perf. 14x13¼*
| | | | | |
|---|---|---|---|---|
| 536 | A165 | 5k multi | 2.00 | 2.00 |

Europa — A166

Designs: 6.25k, Ursa Major constellation. 8k, Ursa Major constellation and outline of bear.

**2009, Jan. 19**      *Perf. 13¼x13¾*
| | | | | |
|---|---|---|---|---|
| 537 | A166 | 6.25k multi | 2.25 | 2.25 |
| a. | Sheet of 8 + central label | | 18.00 | 18.00 |
| 538 | A166 | 8k multi | 2.75 | 2.75 |
| | Sheet of 8 + central label | | 22.00 | 22.00 |

**Booklet Stamps**
**Self-Adhesive**
*Serpentine Die Cut 12x12¼*
| | | | | |
|---|---|---|---|---|
| 539 | A166 | 6.25k multi | 2.25 | 2.25 |
| 540 | A166 | 8k multi | 2.75 | 2.75 |
| a. | Booklet pane of 12, 6 each #539-540 | | 30.00 | |

Intl. Year of Astronomy.

Prince Henrik, 75th Birthday — A167

**2009, June 11**    *Litho.*    *Perf. 13¼x14*
| | | | | |
|---|---|---|---|---|
| 541 | A167 | 8k multi | 3.25 | 3.25 |

---

Self-Governance — A168

**2009, June 21**      *Perf. 14x13¼*
| | | | | |
|---|---|---|---|---|
| 542 | A168 | 6.25k multi | 2.60 | 2.60 |

Matthew Henson (1866-1955), Polar Explorer A169

**2009, June 21**      *Perf. 13¼x13¾*
| | | | | |
|---|---|---|---|---|
| 543 | A169 | 9k multi | 3.50 | 3.50 |

First Steps, Comic Strip by Nuka K. Godtfredsen A170

**2009, June 21**      *Perf. 14x13¼*
| | | | | |
|---|---|---|---|---|
| 544 | A170 | 15.50k multi | 6.00 | 6.00 |
| a. | Souvenir sheet of 1 | | 6.00 | 6.00 |

Contemporary Art — A171

Designs: 6k, Two Polar Bears From Above, by Ivalo Abelsen. 18k, Window to the World, by Camilla Nielsen. 33k, Gletscher, by Naja Abelsen.

**2009, June 21**
| | | | | |
|---|---|---|---|---|
| 545 | A171 | 6k multi | 2.25 | 2.25 |
| 546 | A171 | 18k multi | 6.75 | 6.75 |
| 547 | A171 | 33k multi | 12.50 | 12.50 |
| | | *Nos. 545-547 (3)* | 21.50 | 21.50 |

Greenlandic Landscape A172

**2009, Sept. 16**    *Litho.*    *Perf. 14x13¼*
| | | | | |
|---|---|---|---|---|
| 548 | A172 | 7k multi | 2.75 | 2.75 |

North Star Mission Station, Thule, Cent. — A173

**2009, Oct. 19**    *Engr.*    *Perf. 13¼x13*
| | | | | |
|---|---|---|---|---|
| 549 | A173 | 15.25k blk & blue | 6.25 | 6.25 |

Otto Nordenskjold (1869-1928), Arctic Explorer — A174

**Litho. & Engr.**
**2009, Oct. 19**      *Perf. 13¼x13*
**Sans-Serif Inscriptions**
| | | | | |
|---|---|---|---|---|
| 550 | A174 | 30k multi | 12.00 | 12.00 |

---

**Souvenir Sheet**
**Serifed Inscriptions**
| | | | | |
|---|---|---|---|---|
| 551 | A174 | 30k multi + label | 12.00 | 12.00 |

**Science Type of 2006**

Designs: 1k, Cryolite mine, Ivittuut. 15.50k, Himantolophus groenlandicus. 23.50k, Gold mine, Nalunaq.

**2009, Oct. 19**      *Perf. 13¼x14*
| | | | | |
|---|---|---|---|---|
| 552 | A145 | 1k multi | .40 | .40 |
| 553 | A145 | 15.50k multi | 6.25 | 6.25 |
| 554 | A145 | 23.50k multi | 9.50 | 9.50 |
| a. | Souvenir sheet, #552-554 | | 16.50 | 16.50 |
| | | *Nos. 552-554 (3)* | 16.15 | 16.15 |

Christmas — A175

Star and: 6.25k, Family. 8k, Baby.

**2009, Oct. 19**   *Litho.*   *Perf. 13¾x13¼*
| | | | | |
|---|---|---|---|---|
| 555 | A175 | 6.25k multi | 2.50 | 2.50 |
| 556 | A175 | 8k multi | 3.25 | 3.25 |

**Booklet Stamps**
**Self-Adhesive**
*Serpentine Die Cut 12¼x12*
| | | | | |
|---|---|---|---|---|
| 557 | A175 | 6.25k multi | 2.50 | 2.50 |
| 558 | A175 | 8k multi | 3.25 | 3.25 |
| b. | Booklet pane, 6 each #557-558 | | 35.00 | |

Air Greenland, 50th Anniv. — A176

**2010, Jan. 18**    *Litho.*    *Perf. 12½x12¾*
| | | | | |
|---|---|---|---|---|
| 559 | A176 | 16.50k multi | 6.25 | 6.25 |

Contemporary Art — A177

Designs: 6.50k, Polar Bear, by Maria Panínguak Kjaerulff. 7.50k, Sun, by Miki Jacobsen, vert. 50k, Greenland Razorbills, by Bolatta Silis-Hoegh.

**2010, Jan. 18**    *Perf. 14x13¼, 13¼x14*
| | | | | |
|---|---|---|---|---|
| 560 | A177 | 6.50k multi | 2.50 | 2.50 |
| 561 | A177 | 7.50k multi | 2.75 | 2.75 |
| 562 | A177 | 50k multi | 19.00 | 19.00 |
| | | *Nos. 560-562 (3)* | 24.25 | 24.25 |

Europa — A178

Designs: 8.50k, Boy reading book. 9.50k, Children reading book.

**2010, Jan. 18**      *Perf. 13¾x13¼*
| | | | | |
|---|---|---|---|---|
| 563 | A178 | 8.50k multi | 3.25 | 3.25 |
| a. | Sheet of 8 + central label | | 26.00 | 26.00 |
| 564 | A178 | 9.50k multi | 3.50 | 3.50 |
| a. | Sheet of 8 + central label | | 28.00 | 28.00 |

**Booklet Stamps**
**Self-Adhesive**
*Serpentine Die Cut 12¼x12*
| | | | | |
|---|---|---|---|---|
| 565 | A178 | 8.50k multi | 3.25 | 3.25 |
| 566 | A178 | 9.50k multi | 3.50 | 3.50 |
| a. | Booklet pane of 12, 6 each #565-566 | | 41.00 | |

Intl. Women's Day, Cent. — A179

**2010, Mar. 8** **Litho.** **Perf. 13¼x14**
567 A179 12.50k multi 4.50 4.50

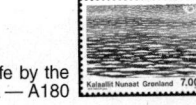

Life by the Sea — A180

Designs: 7k, Sea ice. 8.50k, Port and sea ice.

**2010, Mar. 24** **Perf. 13¾x13¼**
568 A180 7k multi 2.75 2.75
569 A180 8.50k multi 3.50 3.50
  a. Souvenir sheet, #568-569 6.25 6.25

Queen Margrethe II, 70th Birthday A181

**2010, Apr. 16** **Perf. 13¼x14**
570 A181 35k multi 12.00 12.00

Flag of Greenland, 25th Anniv. — A182

**2010, May 1**
571 A182 7k multi 2.50 2.50

Buuarsikkut, Comic Strip by Robert Holmene A183

**2010, May 1** **Perf. 14x13¼**
572 A183 23.50k multi 8.25 8.25
  a. Souvenir sheet of 1 8.25 8.25

Thule Trading Station, Cent. — A184

**2010, Oct. 18** **Engr.** **Perf. 12¼x12½**
573 A184 25k blk & blue 9.50 9.50

Hans Sakaeus (c. 1797-1819), Interpreter for Explorer John Ross — A185

Ross Expedition Ships Isabella and Alexander — A186

**2010, Oct. 18** **Perf. 12½x12**
574 A185 25o pur & bl blk .25 .25
575 A186 32k pur & bl blk 12.00 12.00
  a. Souvenir sheet, #574-575, + label 12.50 12.50

Mining in Greenland — A187

Designs: 50o, King Frederik VII's copper mine. 26.50k, Ivituut cryolite mine.

**Die Cut Perf. 13x13¼**
**2010, Oct. 18** **Litho.**
**Self-Adhesive**
576 A187 50o multi .25 .25
577 A187 26.50k multi 10.00 10.00

See Nos. 601-602, 616-617, 634-635, 661-662, 688-689.

Christmas — A188

Santa Claus and: 7k, Two children. 8.50k, One child.

**2010, Oct. 18** **Perf. 13¾x13¼**
578 A188 7k multi 2.75 2.75
579 A188 8.50k multi 3.25 3.25

**Booklet Stamps**
**Self-Adhesive**
**Serpentine Die Cut 12¼x12**
580 A188 7k multi 2.75 2.75
581 A188 8.50k multi 3.25 3.25
  b. Booklet pane of 12, 6 each #580-581 36.00

Herbs — A189

Designs: 13.50k, Sorbus groenlandica. 25k, Vaccinium vitis-idaea.

**2011, Jan. 17** **Perf. 13**
582 A189 13.50k multi 5.00 5.00
583 A189 25k multi 9.25 9.25

See Nos. 608-609.

Mail Delivery Man in Kamik — A190

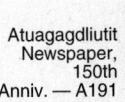

Atuagagdliutit Newspaper, 150th Anniv. — A191

Greenland Connect Submarine Cable, 2nd Anniv. — A192

**2011, Jan. 17** **Perf. 13**
584 A190 2k multi .75 .75
  a. Perf. 12¾x12½ .75 .75
585 A191 7.50k multi 2.75 2.75
  a. Perf. 12½x12½ 2.75 2.75
586 A192 46.50k multi 17.00 17.00
  a. Perf. 12¾x12½ 17.00 17.00
  b. Souvenir sheet of 3, #584a, 585a, 586a 20.50 20.50
  Nos. 584-586 (3) 20.50 20.50

Communications in Greenland.

Europa — A193

Trees in: 9k, Winter. 10k, Summer.

**2011, Jan. 17** **Perf. 12¾x13**
587 A193 9k multi 3.25 3.25
  a. Sheet of 8 + central label 26.00 26.00
588 A193 10k multi 3.75 3.75
  a. Sheet of 8 + central label 30.00 30.00

**Booklet Stamps**
**Self-Adhesive**
**Serpentine Die Cut 13x13¼**
589 A193 9k multi 3.25 3.25
590 A193 10k multi 3.75 3.75
  b. Booklet pane of 12, 6 each #589-590 42.00

Intl. Year of Forests.

Civil Aircraft A194

Designs: 8k, Consolidated PBY-5A Catalina. 17.50k, De Havilland DHC-3 Otter.

**2011, May 9** **Engr.** **Perf. 12½x12**
591 A194 8k multi 3.00 3.00
592 A194 17.50k multi 6.75 6.75

See Nos. 624-626, 653-654, 678, 695-697, 727-728.

Queen Margrethe II — A195

**2011, May 9** **Engr.** **Perf. 13**
593 A195 50o claret 1.75 1.75
594 A195 1k blue green 3.75 3.75

Kaassassuk, Comic Strip by Christian Fleischer Rex — A196

**2011, May 9** **Litho.** **Perf. 12¾x12½**
595 A196 20k multi 8.00 8.00
  a. Souvenir sheet of 1 8.00 8.00

Commonwealth of the Realm Pause, by Julie Edel Hardenberg — A197

Painting by Naja Rosing-Asvid A198

Painting by Anne-Lise Lovstrom A199

**2011, May 9**
596 A197 3k multi 1.25 1.25
597 A198 7k multi 2.75 2.75
598 A199 34k multi 13.00 13.00
  Nos. 596-598 (3) 17.00 17.00

Naomi Uemura (1941-84), Adventurer — A200

**2011, July 28** **Engr.** **Perf. 12½x12**
599 A200 36.50k multi 15.00 15.00
  a. Souvenir sheet of 1, perf. 12¾x12½ 15.00 15.00

Uemura was, in 1978, the first man to cross Greenland from north to south.

Dogsleds Near Iceberg — A201

**2011, Sept. 28** **Litho.** **Perf. 12¾**
600 A201 8k multi 3.00 3.00

**Mining Type of 2010**

Designs: 75o, Shaft tower, Josva's copper mine. 28k, Miners and equipment, Qaarsuarsuk coal mine.

**2011, Oct. 17** **Die Cut Perf. 13x13¼**
**Self-Adhesive**
601 A187 75o multi .30 .30
602 A187 28k multi 10.50 10.50

Christmas — A202

Girls: 7.50k, Looking at Christmas star through window. 9k, With dogsled carrying gifts, horiz.

**2011, Oct. 17** **Perf. 12½x13**
603 A202 7.50k multi 2.75 2.75

**Perf. 13x12½**
604 A202 9k multi 3.50 3.50

**Booklet Stamps**
**Self-Adhesive**
**Serpentine Die Cut 13x13¼**
605 A202 7.50k multi 2.75 2.75

**Serpentine Die Cut 13¼x13**
606 A202 9k multi 3.50 3.50
  a. Booklet pane of 12, 6 each #605-606 37.50

Reign of Queen Margrethe II, 40th Anniv. — A203

**Litho. & Engr.** **Perf. 13¼**
**2012, Jan. 4**
607 A203 26.50k multi 9.50 9.50
  a. Souvenir sheet of 1 9.50 9.50

**Herbs Type of 2011**

Designs: 14.50k, Vaccinium uliginosum. 18.50k, Ledum groenlandicum.

**2012, Jan. 16    Litho.    Perf. 14x13¼**
| | | | | |
|---|---|---|---|---|
| 608 | A189 | 14.50k multi | 5.25 | 5.25 |
| 609 | A189 | 18.50k multi | 6.50 | 6.50 |

Knud Rasmussen
Folk High School,
Sisimiut, 50th
Anniv. — A204

**2012, Jan. 16**
| | | | | |
|---|---|---|---|---|
| 610 | A204 | 21k multi | 7.50 | 7.50 |

Painting by
Jessie
Kleemann
A205

Iceberg by
Frederik
"Kunngi"
Kristensen
A206

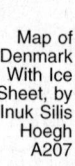

Map of
Denmark
With Ice
Sheet, by
Inuk Silis
Hoegh
A207

**2012, Jan. 16**
| | | | | |
|---|---|---|---|---|
| 611 | A205 | 8.50k multi | 3.00 | 3.00 |
| 612 | A206 | 9.50k multi | 3.50 | 3.50 |
| 613 | A207 | 38.50k multi | 14.00 | 14.00 |
| a. | | Souvenir sheet of 1 | 14.00 | 14.00 |
| | | Nos. 611-613 (3) | 20.50 | 20.50 |

Marine Life — A208

Iceberg and: 8k, Seal. 9.50k, Whale.

**2012, Mar. 21    Perf. 13¾x13¼**
| | | | | |
|---|---|---|---|---|
| 614 | A208 | 8k multi | 3.00 | 3.00 |
| 615 | A208 | 9.50k multi | 3.50 | 3.50 |
| a. | | Souvenir sheet of 2, #614-615 | 6.50 | 6.50 |

**Mining Type of 2010**

Designs: 25o, Eqalussuit graphite mine. 14.50k, Amitsoq graphite mine.

**2012, May 7    Die Cut Perf. 13x13¼**
**Self-Adhesive**
| | | | | |
|---|---|---|---|---|
| 616 | A187 | 25o multi | .25 | .25 |
| 617 | A187 | 14.50k multi | 5.00 | 5.00 |

Agriculture — A209

Designs: 75o, Field of vegetables. 49k, Cattle.

**2012, May 7    Perf. 12¾x12½**
| | | | | |
|---|---|---|---|---|
| 618 | A209 | 75o multi | .25 | .25 |
| 619 | A209 | 49k multi | 17.50 | 17.50 |

Europa — A210

Designs: 9.50k, Aurora Borealis. 10.50k, Ship and sea ice.

**2012, May 7    Perf. 14x13½**
| | | | | |
|---|---|---|---|---|
| 620 | A210 | 9.50k multi | 3.25 | 3.25 |
| a. | | Sheet of 8 + central label | 26.00 | 26.00 |
| 621 | A210 | 10.50k multi | 3.50 | 3.50 |
| a. | | Sheet of 8 + central label | 28.00 | 28.00 |

**Booklet Stamps**
**Self-Adhesive**
**Serpentine Die Cut 13x12¾**
| | | | | |
|---|---|---|---|---|
| 622 | A210 | 9.50k multi | 3.25 | 3.25 |
| 623 | A210 | 10.50k multi | 3.50 | 3.50 |
| a. | | Booklet pane of 12, 6 each #622-623 | 41.00 | |

**Civil Aircraft Type of 2011**

Designs: 7.50k, Douglas DC-4. 28k, Sikorsky S61N helicopter. 36k, Bell 206 Jet Ranger helicopter.

**Litho. & Engr.**
**2012, Oct. 22    Perf. 13**
| | | | | |
|---|---|---|---|---|
| 624 | A194 | 7.50k multi | 2.60 | 2.60 |
| 625 | A194 | 28k multi | 9.75 | 9.75 |
| 626 | A194 | 36k multi | 12.50 | 12.50 |
| | | Nos. 624-626 (3) | 24.85 | 24.85 |

Queen Margrethe
II — A211

**Litho. & Engr.**
**2012, Oct. 22    Perf. 13¼x13**
| | | | | |
|---|---|---|---|---|
| 627 | A211 | 50o red & blue | .25 | .25 |
| 628 | A211 | 1k green & blue | .35 | .35 |

See Nos. 655, 698-699, 729-730, 809, 875.

Hans Hendrik
(Suersaq) (1834-89),
Polar Explorer — A212

**2012, Oct. 22    Perf. 13**
| | | | | |
|---|---|---|---|---|
| 629 | A212 | 29.50k mar & blk | 10.00 | 10.00 |
| a. | | Souvenir sheet of 1 | 10.00 | 10.00 |

Christmas — A213

Heads of Inuit girls: 8k, On Christmas trees. 9.50k, In circles, evergreen branches, flags of Greenland, horiz.

**2012, Oct. 22    Litho.    Perf. 13¼x13¾**
| | | | | |
|---|---|---|---|---|
| 630 | A213 | 8k multi | 2.75 | 2.75 |

**Perf. 13¾x13¼**
| | | | | |
|---|---|---|---|---|
| 631 | A213 | 9.50k multi | 3.25 | 3.25 |

**Booklet Stamps**
**Self-Adhesive**
**Serpentine Die Cut 13x12½**
| | | | | |
|---|---|---|---|---|
| 632 | A213 | 8k multi | 2.75 | 2.75 |

**Serpentine Die Cut 12½x13**
| | | | | |
|---|---|---|---|---|
| 633 | A213 | 9.50k multi | 3.25 | 3.25 |
| a. | | Booklet pane of 12, 6 each #632-633 | 36.00 | |

**Mining Type of 2010**

Designs: 38k, Coal mine, Qullissat. 49k, Marble quarry, Maarmorilik.

**Die Cut Perf. 13¼x13½**
**2013, Jan. 14**
**Self-Adhesive**
| | | | | |
|---|---|---|---|---|
| 634 | A187 | 38k multi | 14.00 | 14.00 |
| 635 | A187 | 49k multi | 18.00 | 18.00 |

Contemporary
Art — A214

Designs: 50o, Sculpture by Isle Hessner. 2k, Painting of iceberg by Niels "Mo" Motzfeldt. 40.50k, Painting by Kristian Olsen aaju.

**2013, Jan. 14    Perf. 13¼**
| | | | | |
|---|---|---|---|---|
| 636 | A214 | 50o multi | .25 | .25 |
| 637 | A214 | 2k multi | .75 | .75 |
| 638 | A214 | 40.50k multi | 15.00 | 15.00 |
| | | Nos. 636-638 (3) | 16.00 | 16.00 |

Europa — A215

Postal conveyance: 10.50k, Dog sled. 11.50k, Truck, van and scooter.

**2013, Jan. 14    Perf. 12½**
| | | | | |
|---|---|---|---|---|
| 639 | A215 | 10.50k multi | 4.00 | 4.00 |
| a. | | Miniature sheet of 9 | 36.00 | 36.00 |
| 640 | A215 | 11.50k multi | 4.25 | 4.25 |
| a. | | Miniature sheet of 9 | 39.00 | 39.00 |

**Booklet Stamps**
**Self-Adhesive**
**Serpentine Die Cut 13¼x13½**
| | | | | |
|---|---|---|---|---|
| 641 | A215 | 10.50k multi | 4.00 | 4.00 |
| 642 | A215 | 11.50k multi | 4.25 | 4.25 |
| a. | | Booklet pane of 12, 6 each #641-642 | 50.00 | |

Uummannaq,
250th Anniv.
A216

**2013, June 11    Perf. 13¼x13**
| | | | | |
|---|---|---|---|---|
| 643 | A216 | 9k multi | 3.25 | 3.25 |

Musk
Ox — A217

**2013, June 11**
| | | | | |
|---|---|---|---|---|
| 644 | A217 | 11.50k multi | 4.25 | 4.25 |

Whale — A218

**2013, June 11    Perf. 12½**
| | | | | |
|---|---|---|---|---|
| 645 | A218 | 16k multi | 5.75 | 5.75 |

Aasiaat, 250th anniv.

Polar
Bear — A219

**2013, June 11    Perf. 13¼**
| | | | | |
|---|---|---|---|---|
| 646 | A219 | 19.50k multi | 7.00 | 7.00 |
| a. | | Souvenir sheet of 1 | 7.00 | 7.00 |

See Israel No. 1987.

Herbs — A220

Designs: 8.50k, Fucus vesiculosus. 28k, Juniperus communis var. saxatalis, horiz.

**2013, June 11    Perf. 12½**
| | | | | |
|---|---|---|---|---|
| 647 | A220 | 8.50k multi | 3.00 | 3.00 |
| 648 | A220 | 28k multi | 10.00 | 10.00 |

Agriculture — A221

Designs: 20k, Sheep in meadow. 29.50k, Farm machinery in field.

**2013, June 11    Perf. 13x12½**
| | | | | |
|---|---|---|---|---|
| 649 | A221 | 20k multi | 7.25 | 7.25 |
| 650 | A221 | 29.50k multi | 11.00 | 11.00 |

Greenland
Post Office,
75th Anniv.
A222

**Litho. & Engr.**
**2013, Sept. 17    Perf. 14x13½**
| | | | | |
|---|---|---|---|---|
| 651 | A222 | 20k red & blk | 7.25 | 7.25 |
| a. | | Souvenir sheet of 1 | 7.25 | 7.25 |

Sheet margin of No. 651a contains imperforate reproduction of Greenland No. 5 that is is invalid for postage.

Limited quantities of imperforate examples of No. 651a were sold at a stamp show and later given as gifts to standing order customers. Value, $32.50

Fishermen on
Dock at Nordafar
Fishery,
Foroyinghavn,
Greenland
A223

**Perf. 13½x13¾**
**2013, Sept. 23    Litho. & Engr.**
| | | | | |
|---|---|---|---|---|
| 652 | A223 | 22.50k multi | 8.25 | 8.25 |
| a. | | Souvenir sheet of 1 + 2 labels | 8.25 | 8.25 |

See Faroe Islands No. 609.

**Civil Aircraft Type of 2011**

Designs: 1k, Sikorsky S58ET helicopter. 28k, De Havilland Canada DHC-6 Twin Otter.

**Perf. 14¼x13¾**
**2013, Oct. 21    Litho. & Engr.**
| | | | | |
|---|---|---|---|---|
| 653 | A194 | 1k multi | .35 | .35 |
| 654 | A194 | 28k multi | 10.00 | 10.00 |

**Queen Margrethe II Type of 2012**
**Litho. & Engr.**
**2013, Oct. 21    Perf. 13¼x13**
**Size: 26x36mm**
| | | | | |
|---|---|---|---|---|
| 655 | A211 | 10k dk bl & blue | 3.75 | 3.75 |

Carl
Petersen
(1813-80),
Polar
Explorer
A224

**Perf. 14¼x13¾**
**2013, Oct. 21    Litho. & Engr.**
| | | | | |
|---|---|---|---|---|
| 656 | A224 | 31.50k multi | 11.50 | 11.50 |
| a. | | Souvenir sheet of 1 | 11.50 | 11.50 |

Christmas — A225

Christmas decorations with polar bear and: 9k, Candle. 10.50k, Lace, folded-paper stars.

**2013, Oct. 21    Litho.    Perf. 13x12½**
| | | | | |
|---|---|---|---|---|
| 657 | A225 | 9k multi | 3.25 | 3.25 |
| 658 | A225 | 10.50k multi | 3.75 | 3.75 |

**Booklet Stamps**
**Self-Adhesive**
**Serpentine Die Cut 13½x13¾**
| | | | | |
|---|---|---|---|---|
| 659 | A225 | 9k multi | 3.25 | 3.25 |
| 660 | A225 | 10.50k multi | 3.75 | 3.75 |
| a. | | Booklet pane of 12, 6 each #659-660 | 42.00 | |

## Mining Type of 2010

Designs: 10k, Mine cars at lead mine, Mesters Vig. 56k, Cableway at Black Angel lead and zinc mine, Maarmorilik.

**Die Cut Perf. 13¼x13½**
**2014, Jan. 20**    **Litho.**
**Self-Adhesive**
661 A187 10k multi    3.75 3.75
662 A187 56k multi    20.50 20.50

Rhodiola Flowers — A226

**2014, Jan. 20**    **Litho.**    **Perf. 12½**
663 A226 13k multi    4.75 4.75

A227

Illustrations of Song Lyrics by Camilla Nielsen — A228

**2014, Jan. 20**    **Litho.**    **Perf. 12½**
664 A227 5k multi    1.90 1.90
665 A228 12.50k multi    4.50 4.50

Europa — A229

Designs; 11.50k, Man with drum. 13k, Musicians with violin and accordion, horiz.

**2014, Jan. 20**    **Litho.**    **Perf. 12½**
666 A229 11.50k multi    4.25 4.25
   a.   Miniature sheet of 9    39.00 39.00
667 A229 13k multi    4.75 4.75
   a.   Miniature sheet of 9    43.00 43.00

**Booklet Stamps**
**Self-Adhesive**
**Serpentine Die Cut 13¾**
668 A229 11.50k multi    4.25 4.25
669 A229 13k multi    4.75 4.75
   a.   Booklet pane of 12, 6 each #668-669    54.00

Maritime Heritage — A230

Designs: 10k, People looking at boats at sea. 11.50k, Ship at night.

**2014, Mar. 17**    **Litho.**    **Perf. 12½**
670 A230 10k multi    3.75 3.75
671 A230 11.50k multi    4.25 4.25
   a.   Souvenir sheet of 2, #670-671    8.00 8.00

Prince Henrik, 80th Birthday — A231

**Perf. 13½x13¼**
**2014, June 11**    **Litho.**
672 A231 17.50k multi    6.50 6.50
   a.   Souvenir sheet of 1    6.50 6.50

Sheep Farming — A232

Designs: 21.50k, Feeding of sheep in barn. 31.50k, Sheep mustering.

**2014, June 11**    **Litho.**    **Perf. 12½**
673 A232 21.50k multi    8.00 8.00
674 A232 31.50k multi    11.50 11.50

Contemporary Art — A233

Designs: 3k, Painting of face by Sissi Moller. 24k, Painting of snow hut by Lisa Kreutzmann, horiz. 30.50k, Painting by Isak Brandt, horiz.

**2014, June 11**    **Litho.**    **Perf. 13¼**
675 A233 3k multi    1.10 1.10
676 A233 24k multi    8.75 8.75
677 A233 30.50k multi    11.50 11.50
   Nos. 675-677 (3)    21.35 21.35

## Civil Aviation Type of 2011
**Litho. & Engr.**
**2014, Oct. 20**    **Perf. 13¼**
678 A194 41k Bell 212 helicopter    14.00 14.00

Polar Bear and Map of Greenland — A234

**2014, Oct. 20**    **Litho.**    **Perf. 14½**
679 A234 21.50k multi    7.25 7.25
   a.   Souvenir sheet of 1 + label    7.25 7.25

Value for No. 679 is for stamp with surrounding selvage. See New Zealand Ross Dependency No. L138a.

Hunter's Life — A235

Hunters and prey from: 50ö, Northern Greenland. 45k, Southern Greenland.

**2014, Oct. 20**    **Litho.**    **Perf. 12½**
680 A235 50ö multi    .25 .25
681 A235 45k multi    15.00 15.00

Denmark Expedition of Greenland of 1906-08 — A236

Designs: 9k, Jorgen Bronlund (1877-1907), Niels Peter Hoeg Hagen (1877-1907), explorers, and dog team. 30.50k, Ludvig Mylius-Erichsen (1872-1907), expedition leader, and ship.

**Litho. & Engr.**
**2014, Oct. 20**    **Perf. 13¼**
682 A236 9k multi    3.00 3.00
683 A236 30.50k multi    10.50 10.50
   a.   Souvenir sheet of 2, #682-683    13.50 13.50

Christmas — A237

Christmas tree and: 10k, Musicians playing instruments. 11.50k, Choir.

**2014, Oct. 20**    **Litho.**    **Perf. 12½**
684 A237 10k multi    3.50 3.50
685 A237 11.50k multi    4.00 4.00

**Booklet Stamps**
**Self-Adhesive**
**Serpentine Die Cut 13½x13¼**
686 A237 10k multi    3.50 3.50
687 A237 11.50k multi    4.00 4.00
   a.   Booklet pane of 12, 6 each    45.00

## Mining Type of 2010

Designs: 3k, Nalunaq Gold Mine, Nanortalik. 18.50k, Seqi Olivine Mine, Fiskefjord.

**Die Cut Perf. 13¼x13½**
**2015, Jan. 19**    **Litho.**
**Self-Adhesive**
688 A187 3k multi    .95 .95
689 A187 18.50k multi    5.75 5.75

Hunter's Life — A238

Various hunters and prey.

**2015, Jan. 19**    **Litho.**    **Perf. 12½**
690 A238 11k multi    3.50 3.50
691 A238 19k multi    5.75 5.75

A239

Illustrations of Song Lyrics by Camilla Nielsen — A240

**2015, Jan. 19**    **Litho.**    **Perf. 12½**
692 A239 50ö multi    .25 .25
693 A240 49k multi    15.00 15.00

Queen Margrethe II, 75th Birthday — A241

**2015, Apr. 16**    **Litho.**    **Perf. 12½**
694 A241 23.50k multi    7.25 7.25

## Civil Aircraft Type of 2011

Designs: 1k, DeHavilland Canada DHC7. 34.50k, Boeing B767-383ER. 45k, Boeing B727-100.

**Litho. & Engr.**
**2015, May 13**    **Perf. 13¼**
695 A194 1k multi    .30 .30
696 A194 34.50k multi    10.50 10.50
697 A194 45k multi    13.50 13.50
   Nos. 695-697 (3)    24.30 24.30

## Queen Margrethe II Type of 2012
**Litho. & Engr.**
**2015, May 13**    **Perf. 13¼x13**
**Size: 26x36mm**
698 A211 5k purple & blue    1.50 1.50
699 A211 20k brown & blue    6.00 6.00

Nuuk Gay Pride — A242

**2015, May 13**    **Litho.**    **Perf. 12½**
700 A242 11k multi    3.50 3.50

Europa — A243

Toys: 12.50k, String puzzle. 14k, Wooden dolls.

**2015, May 13**    **Litho.**    **Perf. 12½**
701 A243 12.50k multi    3.25 3.25
   a.   Miniature sheet of 9    29.50 29.50
702 A243 14k multi    3.75 3.75
   a.   Miniature sheet of 9    34.00 34.00

**Booklet Stamps**
**Self-Adhesive**
**Serpentine Die Cut 13¼x13½**
703 A243 12.50k multi    3.75 3.75
704 A243 14k multi    4.25 4.25
   a.   Booklet pane of 12, 6 each #703-704    48.00

Renewable Energy — A244

Designs: 13.50k, Sun and solar panel. 37.50k, Water turbine and high-tension wires.

**2015, Oct. 19**    **Litho.**    **Perf. 12½**
705 A244 13.50k multi    4.00 4.00
706 A244 37.50k multi    11.00 11.00
   a.   Souvenir sheet of 2, #705-706    15.00 15.00

Architecture — A245

Designs: 2k, Winter house. 10k, Modern buildings in Nuuk and Sisimiut. 26k, High-rise apartment buildings, older apartment buildings, houses. 33.50k, Summer tent.

**2015, Oct. 19**    **Litho.**    **Perf. 13¼**
707 A245 2k multi    .60 .60
708 A245 10k multi    3.00 3.00
709 A245 26k multi    7.75 7.75
   a.   Souvenir sheet of 2, #708-709    11.00 11.00
710 A245 33.50k multi    10.00 10.00
   a.   Souvenir sheet of 2, #707, 710    11.00 11.00
   Nos. 707-710 (4)    21.35 21.35

Christmas — A246

Designs: 11k, Polar bear and cubs. 12.50k, Greenlandic family.

**2015, Oct. 19**    **Litho.**    **Perf. 12½**
711 A246 11k multi    3.25 3.25
712 A246 12.50k multi    3.75 3.75

**Booklet Stamps**
**Self-Adhesive**
**Serpentine Die Cut 13½x13¾**
713 A246 11k multi    3.25 3.25
714 A246 12.50k multi    3.75 3.75
   a.   Booklet pane of 12, 6 each #713-714    42.00

Dog Sled in Winter — A247

Hikers in Summer — A248

**2016, Jan. 18    Litho.    Perf. 12½**
| | | | |
|---|---|---|---|
| 715 | A247 | 13k multi | 3.00 | 3.00 |
| 716 | A248 | 27k multi | 6.50 | 6.50 |

Traditional Women's Clothing — A249

Woman from: 10.50k, Northern Greenland. 12k, Western Greenland. 13.50k, Eastern Greenland. 48.50k, Southern Greenland.

**2016, Jan. 18    Litho.    Perf. 12½**
| | | | | |
|---|---|---|---|---|
| 717 | A249 | 10.50k multi | 2.50 | 2.50 |
| 718 | A249 | 12k multi | 2.75 | 2.75 |
| 719 | A249 | 13.50k multi | 3.25 | 3.25 |
| 720 | A249 | 48.50k multi | 11.50 | 11.50 |
| | | Nos. 717-720 (4) | 20.00 | 20.00 |

**Booklet Stamps**
**Self-Adhesive**
**Serpentine Die Cut 13¾x13¼**
| | | | | |
|---|---|---|---|---|
| 721 | A249 | 10.50k multi | 2.50 | 2.50 |
| 722 | A249 | 12k multi | 2.75 | 2.75 |
| 723 | A249 | 13.50k multi | 3.25 | 3.25 |
| 724 | A249 | 48.50k multi | 11.50 | 11.50 |
| a. | | Booklet pane of 8, 2 each #721-724 | 40.00 | |
| | | Nos. 721-724 (4) | 20.00 | 20.00 |

Greenlandic Foods — A250

Designs: 12k, Capelin. 13.50k, Whale skin.

**2016, Mar. 21    Litho.    Perf. 12½**
| | | | | |
|---|---|---|---|---|
| 725 | A250 | 12k multi | 3.00 | 3.00 |
| a. | | Perf. 13x13¼ | 3.00 | 3.00 |
| 726 | A250 | 13.50k multi | 3.50 | 3.50 |
| a. | | Perf. 13x13¼ | 3.50 | 3.50 |
| b. | | Souvenir sheet of 2, #725a, 726a, + label | 6.50 | 6.50 |

**Civil Aircraft Type of 2011**

Designs: 15k, Airbus 330-200. 24.50k, De Havilland DHC8-200 (Dash-8).

**Litho. & Engr.**
**2016, May 12    Perf. 13¼**
| | | | | |
|---|---|---|---|---|
| 727 | A194 | 15k multi | 4.00 | 4.00 |
| 728 | A194 | 24.50k multi | 7.00 | 7.00 |

**Queen Margrethe II Type of 2012**
**Litho. & Engr.**
**2016, May 12    Perf. 13¼x13**
**Size: 26x36mm**
| | | | | |
|---|---|---|---|---|
| 729 | A211 | 2k blue | .60 | .60 |
| 730 | A211 | 50k pur & bl | 13.50 | 13.50 |

Sports — A251

Designs: 75o, Arctic Circle Race. 25.50k, Alpine skier. 39k, Kayak race.

**2016, May 12    Litho.    Perf. 12½**
| | | | | |
|---|---|---|---|---|
| 731 | A251 | 75o multi | .25 | .25 |
| a. | | Perf. 13x13¼ | .25 | .25 |
| 732 | A251 | 25.50k multi | 6.25 | 6.25 |
| a. | | Perf. 13x13¼ | 6.25 | 6.25 |
| 733 | A251 | 39k multi | 9.50 | 9.50 |
| a. | | Perf. 13x13¼ | 9.50 | 9.50 |
| b. | | Souvenir sheet of 3, #731a, 732a, 733a | 16.00 | 16.00 |
| | | Nos. 731-733 (3) | 16.00 | 16.00 |

See Nos. 746-748, 772-774.

Crown Prince Frederik and His Family — A252

**2016, Oct. 17    Litho.    Perf. 13**
| | | | | |
|---|---|---|---|---|
| 734 | A252 | 20.50k multi | 6.25 | 6.25 |
| a. | | Souvenir sheet of 1 | 6.25 | 6.25 |

Greenland in World War II — A253

Designs: 25o, National Assembly members. 36k, Family seated around table. 36.50k, Children holding fruit, ship, people carrying sacks.

**Litho. & Engr.**
**2016, Oct. 17    Perf. 13¼**
| | | | | |
|---|---|---|---|---|
| 735 | A253 | 25o multi | .25 | .25 |
| 736 | A253 | 36k multi | 11.00 | 11.00 |
| 737 | A253 | 36.50k multi | 11.00 | 11.00 |
| | | Nos. 735-737 (3) | 22.25 | 22.25 |

See Nos. 749, 792-793, 802-803, 840-841.

Zackenberg Research Station — A254

Designs: 11.50k, Greenlandic wildlife. 14k, Scientists and research equipment.

**2016, Oct. 17    Litho.    Perf. 12½**
| | | | | |
|---|---|---|---|---|
| 738 | A254 | 11.50k multi | 3.50 | 3.50 |
| a. | | Miniature sheet of 9 | 32.00 | 32.00 |
| 739 | A254 | 14k multi | 4.25 | 4.25 |
| a. | | Miniature sheet of 9 | 39.00 | 39.00 |

**Self-Adhesive**
**Die Cut Perf. 13½x13¼**
| | | | | |
|---|---|---|---|---|
| 740 | A254 | 11.50k multi | 3.50 | 3.50 |
| 741 | A254 | 14k multi | 4.25 | 4.25 |

Christmas — A255

Designs: 12k, Candles and iceberg. 13.50k, Christmas tree, star and sofa.

**2016, Oct. 17    Litho.    Perf. 12½x13**
| | | | | |
|---|---|---|---|---|
| 742 | A255 | 12k multi | 3.75 | 3.75 |
| 743 | A255 | 13.50k multi | 4.00 | 4.00 |

**Booklet Stamps**
**Self-Adhesive**
**Serpentine Die Cut 13¾x13½**
| | | | | |
|---|---|---|---|---|
| 744 | A255 | 12k multi | 3.75 | 3.75 |
| 745 | A255 | 13.50k multi | 4.00 | 4.00 |
| a. | | Booklet pane of 12, 6 each #744-745 | 46.50 | |

**Sports Type of 2016**

Designs: 16k, National Dogsled Championships. 19.50k, Kang-Nu Race. 22k, Town relay race.

**2017, Jan. 23    Litho.    Perf. 12½**
| | | | | |
|---|---|---|---|---|
| 746 | A251 | 16k multi | 4.75 | 4.75 |
| a. | | Perf. 13x13¼ | 4.75 | 4.75 |
| 747 | A251 | 19.50k multi | 5.75 | 5.75 |
| a. | | Perf. 13x13¼ | 5.75 | 5.75 |
| 748 | A251 | 22k multi | 6.50 | 6.50 |
| a. | | Perf. 13x13¼ | 6.50 | 6.50 |
| b. | | Souvenir sheet of 3, #746a-748a | 17.00 | 17.00 |
| | | Nos. 746-748 (3) | 17.00 | 17.00 |

**Greenland in World War II Type of 2016**

Design: 36.50k, Cryolite in train cars awaiting shipping

**Litho. & Engr.**
**2017, Jan. 23    Perf. 13¼**
| | | | | |
|---|---|---|---|---|
| 749 | A253 | 36.50k multi | 10.50 | 10.50 |

Music — A256

Designs: 1k, Drum singing. 24.50k, Choral singing. 27k, Accordion player.

**2017, Jan. 23    Litho.    Perf. 13x13¼**
| | | | | |
|---|---|---|---|---|
| 750 | A256 | 1k multi | .30 | .30 |
| 751 | A256 | 24.50k multi | 7.25 | 7.25 |
| 752 | A256 | 27k multi | 7.75 | 7.75 |
| | | Nos. 750-752 (3) | 15.30 | 15.30 |

Sealskin Coat — A257

**2017, May 15    Litho.    Perf. 12½**
| | | | | |
|---|---|---|---|---|
| 753 | A257 | 15k multi | 4.50 | 4.50 |

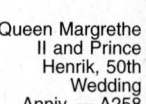

Queen Margrethe II and Prince Henrik, 50th Wedding Anniv. — A258

**2017, May 15    Litho.    Perf. 13½**
| | | | | |
|---|---|---|---|---|
| 754 | A258 | 50k multi | 15.00 | 15.00 |
| a. | | Souvenir sheet of 1 | 15.00 | 15.00 |

See Denmark No. 1777, Faroe Islands No. 686.

Flags at Abandoned Gronnedal Naval Base — A259

Barrels at Abandoned Ikateq Air Base — A260

**2017, May 15    Litho.    Perf. 12½**
| | | | | |
|---|---|---|---|---|
| 755 | A259 | 5k multi | 1.50 | 1.50 |
| 756 | A260 | 14k multi | 4.25 | 4.25 |

Illustrations from Greenlandic Banknotes A261

Designs: No. 757, Birds from 1911 25-ore banknote. No. 758, Seal from 1911 50-ore banknote (53x35mm).
No. 758A, As #757, but with partial letters from banknote above and below circle. No. 758B, As #758, but with partial letters from banknote above and below crest.

**Litho. & Engr.**
**2017, May 17    Perf. 13**
| | | | | |
|---|---|---|---|---|
| 757 | A261 | 20k multi | 6.00 | 6.00 |
| 758 | A261 | 39k multi | 12.00 | 12.00 |

**Souvenir Sheets**
| | | | | |
|---|---|---|---|---|
| 758A | A261 | 20k multi | 6.00 | 6.00 |
| 758B | A261 | 39k multi | 12.00 | 12.00 |

See Nos. 784-787, 810-813, 831-832, 860-861.

Europa — A262

Various paintings of icebergs by Buuti Pedersen.

**2017, May 15    Litho.    Perf. 12½**
| | | | | |
|---|---|---|---|---|
| 759 | A262 | 15k multi | 4.50 | 4.50 |
| a. | | Miniature sheet of 9 | 41.00 | 41.00 |
| 760 | A262 | 16k multi | 5.00 | 5.00 |
| a. | | Miniature sheet of 9 | 45.00 | 45.00 |

**Booklet Stamps**
**Self-Adhesive**
**Serpentine Die Cut 13¼x13¾**
| | | | | |
|---|---|---|---|---|
| 761 | A262 | 15k multi | 4.50 | 4.50 |
| 762 | A262 | 16k multi | 5.00 | 5.00 |
| a. | | Booklet pane of 12, 6 each #761-762 | 57.00 | |

Birds of the Antarctic and Arctic — A263

Designs: 10.50k, Sterna paradisaea. 27k, Haliaeetus albicilla.

**Litho. & Engr.**
**2017, Oct. 27    Perf. 13**
**Stamps With White Frames**
| | | | | |
|---|---|---|---|---|
| 763 | A263 | 10.50k multi | 3.50 | 3.50 |
| 764 | A263 | 27k multi | 8.50 | 8.50 |

**Souvenir Sheet**
**Stamps Without White Frames**
| | | | | |
|---|---|---|---|---|
| 765 | | Sheet of 2 + label | 12.00 | 12.00 |
| a. | A263 | 10.50k multi | 3.50 | 3.50 |
| b. | A263 | 27k multi | 8.50 | 8.50 |

Diplomatic relations between Greenland and French Southern and Antarctic Territories. See French Southern and Antarctic Territories Nos. 571-573.

Weather Balloon A264

Laundry on Clothesline A265

**Die Cut Perf. 13½**
**2017, Oct. 27    Litho.**
**Self-Adhesive**
| | | | | |
|---|---|---|---|---|
| 766 | A264 | 2k multi | .65 | .65 |
| 767 | A265 | 11.50k multi | 3.75 | 3.75 |

A266

Christmas — A267

**2017, Oct. 27    Litho.    Perf. 13¼x12½**
| | | | | |
|---|---|---|---|---|
| 768 | A266 | 13k multi | 4.25 | 4.25 |
| 769 | A267 | 15k multi | 4.75 | 4.75 |

**Booklet Stamps**
**Self-Adhesive**
**Serpentine Die Cut 13½x13¾**
| | | | | |
|---|---|---|---|---|
| 770 | A266 | 13k multi | 4.25 | 4.25 |
| 771 | A267 | 15k multi | 4.75 | 4.75 |
| a. | | Booklet pane of 12, 6 each #770-771 | 54.00 | |

**Sports Type of 2016**

Inuit and Dene games: 50o, Arm pull. 14.50k, Two foot high kick. 28.50k, Pole push.

**2018, Jan. 22    Litho.    Perf. 12½**
| | | | | |
|---|---|---|---|---|
| 772 | A251 | 50o multi | .25 | .25 |
| a. | | Perf. 13x13¼ | .25 | .25 |
| 773 | A251 | 14.50k multi | 5.00 | 5.00 |
| a. | | Perf. 13x13¼ | 5.00 | 5.00 |

| | | | |
|---|---|---|---|
| 774 | A251 | 28.50k multi | 9.50 9.50 |
| a. | | Perf. 13x13¼ | 9.50 9.50 |
| b. | | Souvenir sheet of 3, #772a, 773a, 774a | 15.00 15.00 |
| | | *Nos. 772-774 (3)* | 14.75 14.75 |

**United Nations Wor...
Oceans Day — A31...**

**2021, June 8 Litho...**
867 A316 26.50k multi

Designs: 17k, Anser...
19k, Phoca vitulina.

**2021, June 8 Lith...**
868 A317 17k multi
869 A317 19k multi

**Booklet
Self-Ad...**

*Serpentine Die...*
870 A317 17k multi
871 A317 19k multi
a. Booklet pane of 12... #870-871

Eur...

Kalaallit Nur...

Hans Egede (1686...
Preaching in G...

Kalaallit Nu...

Arrival of Egede i...

**2021, June 8**
872 A318 5k multi...

Pe...

873 A319 41k multi
a. Perf. 13¼
b. Souvenir sheet... 873a

Reintroduction of...
by Egede, 300th ann...

Souv...

Czeslaw Slania...
of Postage...

**2021, Aug. 12**
874 A320 33.50k...

See Denmark N...
788.

**Queen Margr...
Lith...**

**2021, Sept. 17
Size...**
875 A211 28k oli...

**Posters for...
Ty...**

Poster for: 3k, T...
Light, 1998.

## Column 2 (A268–A273 overlay)

**Abandoned Camp
Century — A268**

**Abandoned
Narsaq Point
Weather
Station — A269**

**2018, Jan. 22 Litho. Perf. 12½**
775 A268 11k multi 3.75 3.75
776 A269 40.50k multi 13.50 13.50

**Polar
Bear — A270**

Ice — A271

***Die Cut Perf. 13½x13¼***
**2018, Jan. 22 Litho.**
**Self-Adhesive**
777 A270 20k multi 6.75 6.75
778 A271 23.50k multi 8.00 8.00

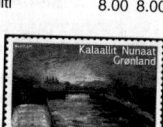

Europa — A272

Designs: 16k, Bridge in Qaqortok. 17k, Ice bridge.

**2018, Jan. 22 Litho. Perf. 12½**
779 A272 16k multi 5.50 5.50
a. Miniature sheet of 9 50.00 50.00
780 A272 17k multi 5.75 5.75
a. Miniature sheet of 9 52.00 52.00

**Booklet Stamps
Self-Adhesive**
*Serpentine Die Cut 13¼x13½*
781 A272 16k multi 5.50 5.50
782 A272 17k multi 5.75 5.75
a. Booklet pane of 12, 6 each #781-782 67.50

Mountains — A273

**2018, May 25 Litho. Perf. 12½**
783 A273 16k multi 5.00 5.00

SEPAC.

### Illustrations From Greenlandic Banknotes Type of 2017

Designs: No. 784, Caribou from 1911 1-krone banknote (53x35mm). No. 785, Polar bear from 1911 5-krone banknote (45x35mm). No. 786, As #784, but with partial letters from banknote at UL and UR. No. 787, As #785, but with partial lettering from banknote around circle.

***Perf. 13¾ (38k), 13½x13¼ (40k)***
**2018, May 25 Litho. & Engr.**
784 A261 38k multi 12.00 12.00
785 A261 40k multi 12.50 12.50

**Souvenir Sheets**
786 A261 38k multi 12.00 12.00
787 A261 40k multi 12.50 12.50

Fish — A274

Designs: 12k, Two mackerel. 16k, Three herring.

**2018, May 25 Litho. Perf. 12½
Stamps With Pale Buff Background**
788 A274 12k multi 3.75 3.75
789 A274 16k multi 5.00 5.00

**Souvenir Sheet
Stamps with Pale Blue Background**
***Perf. 12½x13***
790 Sheet of 2 8.75 8.75
a. A274 12k multi 3.75 3.75
b. A274 16k multi 5.00 5.00

**Crown Prince
Frederik, 50th
Birthday — A275**

**2018, May 26 Litho. Perf. 12½**
791 A275 50k multi 16.00 16.00
a. Souvenir sheet of 1, perf. 13x13¼ 16.00 16.00

Sheet margin on No. 791a is embossed.

### Greenland In World War II Type of 2016

Designs: 5k, Military airplanes over airport. 20.50k, Men and women dancing, phonograph and record, advertisements from Sears Mail Order Catalog.

***Perf. 14¼x13¾***
**2018, Oct. 22 Litho. & Engr.**
792 A253 5k multi 1.60 1.60
793 A253 20.50k multi 6.25 6.25

Kujataa
UNESCO
World
Heritage
Site
A276

**2018, Oct. 22 Litho. Perf. 13x13¼**
794 A276 17k multi 5.25 5.25

Laarseeraw
Svendsen
(1926-75),
Singer — A277

Jens
Hendriksen
(1928-2001),
Musician
A278

First Record
Album by
Greenlanic
Performers
A279

**2018, Oct. 22 Litho. Perf. 13¼**
795 A277 3k multi .95 .95
796 A278 10k multi 3.00 3.00
797 A279 25.50k multi 7.75 7.75
*Nos. 795-797 (3)* 11.70 11.70

A280

Christmas — A281

**2018, Oct. 22 Litho. Perf. 12½**
798 A280 14k multi 4.25 4.25
799 A281 16k multi 5.00 5.00

**Booklet Stamps
Self-Adhesive**
*Serpentine Die Cut 13¼x13½*
800 A280 14k multi 4.25 4.25
801 A281 16k multi 5.00 5.00
a. Booklet pane of 12, 6 each #800-801 56.00

No. 798 is impregnated with a cinnamon scent. No. 799 is impregnated with a pine scent.

### Greenland in World War II Type of 2016

Designs: 25k, Newspapers and Greenlanders listening to radio. 41k, Weather station.

***Perf. 14¼x13¾***
**2019, Jan. 21 Litho. & Engr.**
802 A253 25k multi 7.75 7.75
803 A253 41k multi 13.00 13.00

Arctic Desert
Near
Uummannaq
A282

**2019, Jan. 21 Litho. Perf. 12½**
804 A282 15k multi 4.75 4.75

Fish — A283

Designs: 2k, Micromesistius poutassou. 30k, Hippoglossoides platessoides.

**2019, Jan. 21 Litho. Perf. 12½**
805 A283 2k multi .65 .65
a. Perf. 12½x13 .65 .65
806 A283 30k multi 9.25 9.25
a. Perf. 12½x13 9.25 9.25
b. Sheet of 2, #805a, 806a 10.00 10.00

**Abandoned DYE-2
Radar Station
A284**

Abandoned
Angissoq
Long Range
Navigation
Station
A285

**2019, Jan. 21 Litho. Perf. 12½**
807 A284 11k multi 3.50 3.50
808 A285 42k multi 13.00 13.00

### Queen Margrethe II Type of 2012

**Litho. & Engr.**
**2019, June 21 Perf. 13¼x14**
**Size: 26x36mm**
809 A211 15k red violet & blue 4.50 4.50

### Illustrations From Greenlandic Banknotes Type of 2017

Designs: 26k, Polar bear from 1953 5-krone banknote. 56k, Whale from 1953 10-krone banknote.

**Litho. & Engr.**
**2019, June 21 Perf. 13¾**
**Size: 53x46mm**
**Stamps Without Ornamentation
Outside of Circle**
810 A261 26k multi 8.00 8.00
811 A261 56k multi 17.00 17.00

**Souvenir Sheet
Stamps With Ornamentation
Outside Circle**
812 A261 26k multi 8.00 8.00
813 A261 56k multi 17.00 17.00

**Self-government in Greenland, 10th
Anniv. — A286**

**2019, June 21 Litho. Perf. 13**
814 A286 11k multi 3.50 3.50

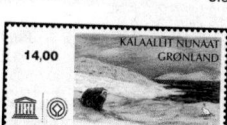

**Aasivissuit-Nipisat Inuit Hunting Area
UNESCO World Heritage Site — A287**

**2019, June 21 Litho. Perf. 13**
815 A287 14k multi 4.25 4.25

House of Poul
Egede Built in
1751,
Ilimanaq — A288

**2019, June 21 Litho. Perf. 12½**
816 A288 17k multi 5.25 5.25

Europa — A289

Birds: 15k, Lagopus mutus and Anas platyrhynchos. 17k, Plectrophenax nivalis and Corvus corax.

**2019, June 21 Litho. Perf. 12½**
817 A289 15k multi 4.50 4.50
818 A289 17k multi 5.25 5.25

**Booklet Stamps
Self-Adhesive**
*Serpentine Die Cut 13½x13¼*
819 A289 15k multi 4.50 4.50
820 A289 17k multi 5.25 5.25
a. Booklet pane of 12, 6 each #819-820 58.50

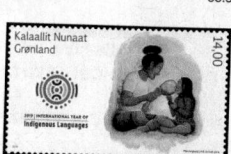

**International Year of Indigenous
Languages — A290**

**2019, Aug. 9 Litho. Perf. 13**
821 A290 14k multi 4.25 4.25

World
Anniv

**2019, Oct. 9** Lit...
822 A291 17k multi

Coal Bag Tag and Women Carrying Coal Bags — A292

**2019, Oct. 21** L...
823 A292 11k multi
824 A293 30k multi

Birds Eating Plastic Trash A294

***Die Cut Pe...***
**2019, Oct. 21 Self-A...**
825 A294 25k multi
***Die Cut Pe...***
826 A295 26k multi

A296

Ch...

**Litho. With ... App...**
**2019, Oct. 21**
827 A296 15k mult
828 A297 17k mult

**Book...**
**Self-...**
***Serpentine ...***
829 A296 15k mult
***Serpentine ...***
830 A297 17k mult
a. Booklet pane ... #829-830

**Illustrations Banknote...**
Designs: No. 831... banknote. No. 832,... tation from note ou...

**Lith...**
**2020, Feb. 28 Size...**
831 A261 26.50k
**Souv...**
832 A261 26.50k

---

Arferup Pania (The Whale's Daughter), Street Art by Hollie Kielsen A343

Inuussut (Livelihood), Street Art by Naja-Theresia Hoegh A344

A345

***Die Cut Perf. 13½x13¼***
**2022, Nov. 11** **Litho.**
**Self-Adhesive**
910 A342 10k multi   2.75 2.75
911 A343 25k multi   7.00 7.00
***Die Cut Perf. 13¼x13½***
912 A344 27k multi   7.50 7.50
   Nos. 910-912 (3)   17.25 17.25

Christmas — A346

**2022, Nov. 11** **Litho.** ***Perf. 13x13½***
913 A345 18k multi   5.00 5.00
***Perf. 13½x13***
914 A346 20k multi   5.75 5.75

**Booklet Stamps**
**Self-Adhesive**
***Serpentine Die Cut 13½***
915 A345 18k multi   5.00 5.00
916 A346 20k multi   5.75 5.75
a.   Booklet pane of 12, 6 each #915-916   64.50

## SEMI-POSTAL STAMPS

> Catalogue values for unused stamps in this section are for Never Hinged items.

No. 35 Surcharged in Red

**1958, May 22** **Engr.** ***Perf. 13***
B1 A7 30o + 10o on 50o   4.50 1.90
The surtax was for the campaign against tuberculosis in Greenland.

No. 32 Surcharged

**1959, Feb. 23** **Unwmk.**
B2 A6 30o + 10o on 25o   4.75 4.75
The surtax was for the benefit of the Greenland Fund.

Two Greenland Boys in Round Tower — SP1

**1968, Sept. 12** **Engr.** ***Perf. 13***
B3 SP1 60o + 10o dark red   1.00 *1.50*
Surtax for child welfare work in Greenland.

Hans Egede Explaining Bible to Natives — SP2

**1971, July 3** **Engr.** ***Perf. 13***
B4 SP2 60o + 10o red brown   2.75 2.75
See footnote after No. 77.

Frederik IX, "Dannebrog" off Umanak — SP3

**1972, Apr. 20**
B5 SP3 60o + 10o dull red   1.50 1.50
King Frederik IX (1899-1972). The surtax was for humanitarian and charitable purposes.

Heimaey Town and Volcano — SP4

**1973, Oct. 18** **Engr.** ***Perf. 13***
B6 SP4 70o + 20o blue & red   1.75 1.75
The surtax was for the victims of the eruption of Heimaey Volcano.

Arm Pulling, by Hans Egede — SP5

**1976, Apr. 8** **Engr.** ***Perf. 12½***
B7 SP5 100o + 20o grn, dk lil brn   .60 .60
Surtax for the Greenland Athletic Union.

Rasmussen and Eskimos — SP6

**1979, June 7** **Engr.** ***Perf. 13***
B8 SP6 1.30k + 20o brown red   .75 .75
Knud Rasmussen (1879-1933), arctic explorer and ethnologist.

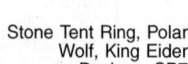

Stone Tent Ring, Polar Wolf, King Eider Ducks — SP7

**1981, Sept. 3** **Engr.** ***Perf. 13***
B9 SP7 1.60k + 20o lt red brn   1.10 1.10
Surtax was for Peary Land Expeditions.

**History Type of 1982**
Design: Eric the Red sailing for Greenland.

**1982, Aug. 2** **Engr.** ***Perf. 12½***
B10 A39 2k + 40o dk red brn   1.25 1.25
Surtax was for Cultural House, Julianehab.

Blind Man — SP8

**1983, May 19** **Engr.**
B11 SP8 2.50k + 40o multi   1.50 1.50
Surtax was for the handicapped.

Greenland Sports Union — SP9

No. B12, Water game.
**1986, Apr. 17** **Litho.**
B12 SP9 2.80k + 50o multi   2.00 2.00
Surtax for the Sports Union.

Greenland PO, 50th Anniv. SP10

**1988, Sept. 16** **Litho.** ***Perf. 12½x13***
B13 SP10 300o +50o multi   2.75 2.75
Surtax for the purchase of postal artifacts.

Sled Dog, Common Eider — SP11

**Litho. & Engr.**
**1990, Sept. 6** ***Perf. 13***
B14 SP11 400o + 50o multi   3.75 3.75
Surtax for the Greenland Environmental Foundation.

SP12

**1991, Sept. 5** **Litho.** ***Perf. 13***
B15 SP12 4k +50o multi   15.00 15.00
Blue Cross of Greenland, 75th Anniv. Surtax benefits Blue Cross of Greenland.

Cancer Research in Greenland — SP13

**1992, Oct. 8** **Litho.** ***Perf. 13***
B16 SP13 4k +50o multi   3.75 *4.50*

Red Cross — SP14

Boy Scouts in Greenland, 50th Anniv. — SP15

**1993, June 17** **Litho.** ***Perf. 13***
B17 SP14 4k +50o red & blue   2.50 2.50
B18 SP15 4k +50o multi   2.50 2.50
a.   Souv. sheet, 2 ea #B17-B18   22.50 22.50

1994 Winter Olympics, Lillehammer — SP16

**1994, Feb. 10** **Litho.** ***Perf. 13***
B19 SP16 4k +50o Skiers   3.00 3.00
a.   Souvenir sheet of 4   12.00 12.00
Surtax to support Greenlandic athletes.

Natl. Flag, 10th Anniv. — SP17

**1995, June 21** **Litho.** ***Perf. 13***
B20 SP17 4k +50o multi   2.75 2.75
a.   Souvenir sheet of 4   11.00 11.00
Surtax for benefit of Greenland Flag Society.

Handicapped and Disabled in Greenland — SP18

**1996, Sept. 5** **Litho.** ***Perf. 13***
B21 SP18 4.25k +50o multi   2.50 2.50
a.   Souvenir sheet of 4   10.00 10.00

Katuaq Cultural Center, Nuuk — SP19

**Litho. & Engr.**
**1997, Jan. 14** ***Perf. 13***
B22 SP19 4.50k +50o multi   2.50 2.50
a.   Souvenir sheet of 4   10.00 10.00

SP20

Women's Society of Greenland: Kathrine Chemnitz (1894-1978), first Gen. Secretary.

**1998, May 29** **Litho.** ***Perf. 13***
B23 SP20 4.50k +50o multi   2.50 2.50
a.   Souvenir sheet of 4   10.00 10.00

Pincushion, Natl. Museum — SP21

**1999, May 7** **Engr.** ***Perf. 13***
B24 SP21 4.50k +50o multi   1.60 1.60
a.   Souvenir sheet of 4   7.00 7.00
Surtax for the benefit of Greenland National Museum & Archives.

Drum Dance — SP22

**Litho. & Engr.**
**2000, Aug. 18** ***Perf. 13¼x13***
B25 SP22 4.50k + 1k multi   1.75 1.75
a.   Souvenir sheet of 4   7.00 7.00
Surtax to benefit the Hafnia 01 Philatelic Exhibition, Copenhagen.

2002 Arctic Winter Games — SP23

**2001, Feb. 5** **Litho.** ***Perf. 13¼x13***
B26 SP23 4.50k +50o multi   1.75 1.75
a.   Souvenir sheet of 4   7.00 7.00

SP24

**2002, Mar. 5**      *Perf. 12¾*
B27 SP24 4.50k +50o multi    2.00 2.00
   a.   Souvenir sheet of 4    8.00 8.00
Surtax for "Children Are People, Too" Project of Paarisa.

Ornament With Santa Claus, Map of Greenland, House — SP25

**2003, Oct. 20**      *Perf. 13¼*
B28 SP25 5k +50o multi    2.25 2.25
   a.   Souvenir sheet of 4    9.00 9.00

Society of Greenlandic Children, 80th Anniv. — SP26

**2004, May 14**      *Perf. 13x13¼*
B29 SP26 5k +50o multi    2.25 2.25
   a.   Souvenir sheet of 4    9.00 9.00
Surtax for Society of Greenlandic Children.

Child — SP27

**2005, Jan. 17**      *Perf. 12¾*
B30 SP27 5.25k +50o multi    2.10 2.10
   a.   Souvenir sheet of 4    8.50 8.50
Surtax for Save the Children Fund.

Crown Prince Frederik and Crown Princess Mary — SP28

**2006, Mar. 29**      *Perf. 13¼x13¾*
B31 SP28 5.50k +50o multi    2.10 2.10
   a.   Souvenir sheet of 4    8.50 8.50
Surtax for children's charities.

Amnesty Greenland — SP29

**2007, Jan. 15**      *Perf. 13¾x13¼*
B32 SP29 575o +50o multi    2.25 2.25
   a.   Souvenir sheet of 4    9.00 9.00

Fight Against Tuberculosis — SP30

**2008, May 24**      *Perf. 13¾x13½*
B33 SP30 575o +50o multi    2.75 2.75
   a.   Souvenir sheet of 4    11.00 11.00

Fight Against Cancer — SP31

**2009, Jan. 19**      *Perf. 13¼x14*
B34 SP31 6.25k +50o blk & red    2.50 2.50
   a.   Souvenir sheet of 4    10.00 10.00
Surtax for Greenlandic Cancer Society.

Performer SP32

**2010, Jan. 18**      *Perf. 14x13¼*
B35 SP32 7k +50o multi    3.00 3.00
   a.   Souvenir sheet of 4    12.00 12.00
Surtax for Silamiut Theater Group.

SP33

**2011, Jan. 17**    Litho.    *Perf. 13*
B36 SP33 7.50k+50o multi    3.00 3.00
   a.   Souvenir sheet of 4    12.00 12.00
Surtax for KIMIK (Association of Artists in Greenland).

Family — SP34

**2012, Jan. 16**    Litho.    *Perf. 12½x12¾*
B37 SP34 800o+50o multi    3.00 3.00
   a.   Souvenir sheet of 4    12.00 12.00
Surtax for NAKUUSA, a collaborative children's rights project of Naalakersuisut and UNICEF.

Children and Boat — SP35

**2013, Jan. 14**      *Perf. 12½*
B38 SP35 9k+50o multi    3.50 3.50
   a.   Souvenir sheet of 4    14.00 14.00
Surtax for Better Childlife Organization.

Homeless Person — SP36

**2014, Jan. 20**    Litho.    *Perf. 12½*
B39 SP36 10k+1k multi    4.00 4.00
   a.   Souvenir sheet of 4    16.00 16.00
Surtax for facilities for the homeless.

2016 Arctic Winter Games, Nuuk — SP37

**2015, Jan. 19**    Litho.    *Perf. 12½x13¼*
B40 SP37 11k+1k multi    3.75 3.75
   a.   Perf. 12½    3.75 3.75
No. B40a was printed in sheets of 4.

Child's Face and Emblem of MIO — SP38

**2016, Jan. 18**    Litho.    *Perf. 12½*
B41 SP38 12k+1k multi    3.75 3.75
   a.   Perf. 13¼x13    3.75 3.75
Surtax for MIO, Greenland's Children's Rights Institution. No. B41a was printed in sheets of 4.

Kofoed's School, Nuuk — SP39

**2017, Oct. 18**    Litho.    *Perf. 12½*
B42 SP39 13k+1k multi    4.50 4.50
   a.   Perf. 13x13¼    4.50 4.50
Surtax for Kofoed's School. No. B42a was printed in sheets of 4.

SP40

SP41

SP42

SP43

SP44

SP45

Watercolor Landscapes Painted by Queen Margrethe II — SP46

**2018, Apr. 16**    Litho.    *Perf. 13x13¼*
B43 SP40 14k+1k multi    5.00 5.00
   a.   Perf. 13¼ (B44)    5.00 5.00

**Miniature Sheet**
*Perf. 13¼*
B44    Sheet of 7, #B43a, B44a-B44f, + 2 labels    17.00 17.00
   a.   SP41 2k multi    .70 .70
   b.   SP42 2k multi    .70 .70
   c.   SP43 5k multi    1.75 1.75
   d.   SP44 5k multi    1.75 1.75
   e.   SP45 10k multi    3.50 3.50
   f.   SP46 10k multi    3.50 3.50
No. B44 sold for 52k. Surtax for Association for Greenlandic Children. Labels on No. B44 are embossed.

Greenlanders and Salvation Army Emblem — SP47

**2019, Jan. 21**    Litho.    *Perf. 12½*
B45 SP47 15k+1k multi    5.00 5.00
   a.   Perf. 13x13¼    5.00 5.00
Surtax for relief efforts of the Salvation Army. No. B45a was printed in sheets of 4.

Campaign Against COVID-19 SP48

**2020, Aug. 10**    Litho.    *Perf. 13x13¼*
B46 SP48 16k+1k multi    5.50 5.50
   a.   Souvenir sheet of 4    22.00 22.00
Surtax for organizations fighting COVID-19 pandemic.

Greenlandic Centers in Denmark — SP49

**2021, Feb. 22**    Litho.    *Perf. 13x13¼*
B47 SP49 17k +1k multi    6.00 6.00
   a.   Souvenir sheet of 4    24.00 24.00
Surtax for the Greenlandic Centers in Denmark.

50th Birthday of Crown Princess Mary — SP50

**2022, Feb. 5**    Litho.    *Perf. 13*
B48 SP50 18k+1k multi    5.75 5.75
   a.   Souvenir sheet of 4    23.00 23.00
Surtax for the Maelkebotte Center, Nuuk.

## PARCEL POST STAMPS

Arms of Greenland — PP1

*Perf. 10¾, 11½*

| 1905-37 | | Unwmk. | Typo. |
|---|---|---|---|
| Q1 | PP1 1o ol grn ('15-'26) | 45.00 | 50.00 |
|    a. | Perf. 12½ ('05) | 600.00 | 650.00 |
| Q2 | PP1 2o yel ('15-'24) | 300.00 | 110.00 |
| Q3 | PP1 5o brn ('18-'28) | 120.00 | 120.00 |
|    a. | Perf. 12½ ('05) | 600.00 | 650.00 |
| Q4 | PP1 10o blue ('37) | 30.00 | 60.00 |
|    a. | Perf. 12½ ('05) | 750.00 | 550.00 |
|    b. | Perf. 11½ ('18) | 45.00 | 55.00 |
| Q5 | PP1 15o vio ('15-'28) | 225.00 | 225.00 |
| Q6 | PP1 20o red ('15-'33) | 10.00 | 12.00 |
|    a. | Perf. 11 ('37) | 42.50 | 50.00 |
| Q7 | PP1 70o violet ('37) | 25.00 | 140.00 |
|    a. | Perf. 11½ ('30) | 225.00 | 200.00 |
| Q8 | PP1 1k yellow ('37) | 32.50 | 100.00 |
|    a. | Perf. 11½ ('30) | 40.00 | 55.00 |
| Q9 | PP1 3k brown ('30) | 110.00 | 160.00 |
| | Nos. Q1-Q9 (9) | 897.50 | 977.00 |
| | Nos. Q1-Q9, never hinged | 3,000. | |

## 1937 Litho. Perf. 11

| | | | |
|---|---|---|---|
| Q10 | PP1 | 70o pale violet | 27.50 140.00 |
| Q11 | PP1 | 1k yellow | 30.00 90.00 |
| | Nos. Q10-Q11, never hinged | | 135.00 |

On lithographed stamps, PAKKE-PORTO is slightly larger, hyphen has rounded ends and lines in shield are fine, straight and evenly spaced.

On typographed stamps, hyphen has squared ends and shield lines are coarse, uneven and inclined to be slightly wavy.

Used values are for stamps postally used from Denmark. Numeral cancels indicate use as postal savings stamps and are usually worth as much or more than postally used examples. Greenland village cancels on Nos. Q6, Q6a and Q8a often reflect postal savings use. These are often worth as much or more than postally used examples. Parcel post stamps not regularly used for postal savings that have village cancellations are often worth much more.

Sheets of 25. Certain printings of Nos. Q1-Q2, Q3a, Q4a and Q5-Q6 were issued without sheet margins. Stamps from the outer rows are straight edged. Some of these sheets had the outer straight edges officially perforated in 1918. Stamps with falsified reperforations exist.

# GRENADA

grə-'nā-də

LOCATION — Windward Islands, West Indies
GOVT. — Independent nation in the British Commonwealth
AREA — 133 sq. mi.
POP. — 98,600 (1998 est.)
CAPITAL — St. George's

Grenada consists of Grenada Island and the southern Grenadines, including Carriacou. This colony was granted associated statehood with Great Britain in 1967 and became an independent state Feb. 7, 1974.

12 Pence = 1 Shilling
100 Cents = 1 Dollar (1949)

Catalogue values for unused stamps in this country are for Never Hinged items, beginning with Scott 143 in the regular postage section, Scott B1 in the semi-postal section, Scott C1 in the air post section, Scott J15 in the postage due section, and Scott O1 in the official section.

### Watermarks

Wmk. 5 — Small Star

Wmk. 6 — Large Star

Wmk. 7 — Large Star with Broad Points

Values for unused stamps are for examples with original gum as defined in the catalogue introduction. Very fine examples of Nos. 1-19, 27-29, and 31-38 will have perforations touching the design on at least one side due to the narrow spacing of the stamps on the plates. Stamps with perfs clear of the design on all four sides are scarce and will command higher prices.

Queen Victoria — A1

### Rough Perf. 14 to 16

**1861 Engr. Unwmk.**

| | | | | |
|---|---|---|---|---|
| 1 | A1 | 1p green | 57.50 | 55.00 |
| a. | | 1p blue green | 5,250. | 350.00 |
| b. | | As No. 1, horiz. pair, imperf. btwn. | | |
| 2 | A1 | 6p rose | 1,050. | 110.00 |
| b. | | 6p lake red, perf. 11-12½ | 1,000. | |

No. 2b was not issued. No. 2 imperf is a proof.

**1863-71 Wmk. 5**

| | | | | |
|---|---|---|---|---|
| 3 | A1 | 1p green ('64) | 120.00 | 17.50 |
| a. | | 1p yellow green | 145.00 | 30.00 |
| 4 | A1 | 6p rose | 775.00 | 20.00 |
| 5 | A1 | 6p vermilion ('71) | 875.00 | 20.00 |
| a. | | 6p dull red | 4,000. | 275.00 |
| g. | | Double impression | | 2,350. |
| i. | | 6p orange red ('66) | 750.00 | 14.00 |

No. 5a always has sideways watermark. Other colors sometimes have sideways watermark.

**1873-78 Clean-Cut Perf. about 15**

| | | | | |
|---|---|---|---|---|
| 5B | A1 | 1p deep green | 140.00 | 55.00 |
| j. | | Pair, imperf between | | 14,000. |
| c. | | 1p blue green ('78) | 275.00 | 45.00 |
| h. | | Half used as ½p on cover | | 11,000. |
| 5D | A1 | 6p vermilion ('75) | 925.00 | 55.00 |
| e. | | 6p dull red | 950.00 | 40.00 |
| f. | | Double impression | | 2,350. |

**1873 Wmk. 6**

| | | | | |
|---|---|---|---|---|
| 6 | A1 | 1p blue green | 110.00 | 28.00 |
| a. | | Diagonal half used as ½p on cover | | 11,000. |
| 7 | A1 | 6p vermilion | 775.00 | 35.00 |

**1875 Perf. 14**

| | | | | |
|---|---|---|---|---|
| 7A | A1 | 1p yellow green | 95.00 | 9.00 |
| b. | | Half used as ½p on cover | | 16,000. |
| c. | | Perf. 15 | 10,000. | 2,600. |

A2

A2a

### Revenue Designs Surcharged in Black
Perf. 14, 14½

**1875-81**

| | | | | |
|---|---|---|---|---|
| 8 | A2 | ½p purple ('81) | 17.50 | 7.50 |
| a. | | "OSTAGE" | 225.00 | 150.00 |
| b. | | Imperf., pair | 350.00 | |
| c. | | "ALF" | 4,000. | |
| e. | | No hyphen between "HALF" and "PENNY" | 225.00 | 150.00 |
| f. | | Double surcharge | 350.00 | 350.00 |
| 9 | A2a | 2½p lake ('81) | 75.00 | 10.00 |
| a. | | Imperf., pair | 650.00 | |
| b. | | Imperf. vertically, pair | 6,500. | |
| c. | | "PENCF" | 525.00 | 225.00 |
| d. | | No period after "PENNY" | 290.00 | 90.00 |
| 10 | A2 | 4p blue ('81) | 150.00 | 10.00 |

### Revenue Designs Surcharged in Dark Blue

| | | | | |
|---|---|---|---|---|
| 11 | A2 | 1sh purple | 775.00 | 20.00 |
| a. | | "ONE SHLLIING" | 6,500. | 800.00 |
| b. | | "NE SHILLING" | | 3,250. |
| c. | | "OSTAGE" | 7,250. | 3,000. |
| d. | | Invtd. "S" in "POSTAGE" | 4,500. | 750.00 |

See Nos. 27-35.

**1881 Wmk. 7**

| | | | | |
|---|---|---|---|---|
| 12 | A2 | 2½p lake | 200.00 | 57.50 |
| a. | | 2½p claret | 550.00 | 200.00 |
| b. | | As No. 12, "PENCF" | 875.00 | 325.00 |
| c. | | As No. 12, No period after "PENNY" | 650.00 | 230.00 |
| d. | | As "a," "PENCF" | 1,850. | 825.00 |
| e. | | As "a," no period after "PENNY" | 1,275. | 575.00 |
| 13 | A2 | 4p blue | 350.00 | 210.00 |

### Revenue Stamp Overprinted "POSTAGE" in Black

A3

A4

A5

### Revenue Stamp Handstamped "POSTAGE" in Manuscript

A6

**1883 Wmk. 5**
**Denomination & Crown in 2nd Color**

| | | | | |
|---|---|---|---|---|
| 14 | A3 | ½p orange & grn | 900.00 | 275.00 |
| a. | | Unsevered pair | 5,000. | 1,500. |
| b. | | "POSTAGE" inverted | | 1,500. |
| 15 | A4 | ½p orange & grn | 325.00 | 150.00 |
| a. | | Unsevered pair | 2,000. | 525.00 |
| 16 | A5 | 1p orange & grn | 400.00 | 65.00 |
| a. | | Inverted overprint | 3,500. | 2,600. |
| b. | | Double overprint | 1,625. | 1,275. |
| c. | | Inverted "S" in "Postage" | 1,150. | 700.00 |
| d. | | Diagonal half used as ½p on cover | | 3,500. |

### "Postage" in Manuscript, Red or Black

| | | | | |
|---|---|---|---|---|
| 18 | A6 | 1p org & grn (R) | | 21,000. |
| 19 | A6 | 1p org & grn | — | 15,000. |

On Nos. 14-19 the words "ONE PENNY" measure from 10-11¼mm in length.
On No. 15, the lower "POSTAGE" is always inverted.
It has been claimed that although Nos. 18 and 19 were used, they were not officially authorized by Grenada's postmaster.

A8

**1883 Wmk. 2 Perf. 14**

| | | | | |
|---|---|---|---|---|
| 20 | A8 | ½p green | 2.75 | 1.25 |
| a. | | Tete beche pair | 5.50 | 21.00 |
| 21 | A8 | 1p rose | 90.00 | 4.00 |
| a. | | Tete beche pair | 325.00 | 375.00 |
| 22 | A8 | 2½p ultra | 14.00 | 1.25 |
| a. | | Tete beche pair | 35.00 | 60.00 |
| 23 | A8 | 4p slate | 15.00 | 2.25 |
| a. | | Tete beche pair | 37.50 | 65.00 |
| 24 | A8 | 6p red lilac | 6.00 | 6.50 |
| a. | | Tete beche pair | 21.00 | 65.00 |
| 25 | A8 | 8p bister | 10.50 | 14.00 |
| a. | | Tete beche pair | 40.00 | 90.00 |
| 26 | A8 | 1sh violet | 160.00 | 65.00 |
| a. | | Tete beche pair | 2,000. | 2,250. |
| | | Nos. 20-26 (7) | 298.25 | 94.25 |

Stamps of types A8, A10 and D2 were printed with alternate horizontal rows inverted. For surcharges see Nos. 36-38, J4-J7.

### Revenue Stamps Surcharged

**1886 Wmk. 6**

| | | | | |
|---|---|---|---|---|
| 27 | A2 | 1p on 1½ org & grn | 60.00 | 50.00 |
| a. | | Inverted surcharge | 475.00 | 350.00 |
| b. | | Diagonal half used as ½ on cover | | 2,250. |
| c. | | Double surcharge | 775.00 | 350.00 |
| d. | | "HALH" instead of "HALF" | 300.00 | 275.00 |
| e. | | "F" for first "E" in "THREE" | 300.00 | 225.00 |
| f. | | "PFNCE" for "PENCE" | 300.00 | 225.00 |
| 28 | A2 | 1p on 1sh org & grn | 50.00 | 45.00 |
| a. | | "SHILLNG" instead of "SHILLING" | 525.00 | 450.00 |
| b. | | No period after "POSTAGE" | 500.00 | |
| c. | | Half used as ½p on cover | | 2,350. |

**Wmk. 5**

| | | | | |
|---|---|---|---|---|
| 29 | A2 | 1p on 4p org & grn | 190.00 | 110.00 |

A10

**1887 Wmk. 2**

| | | | | |
|---|---|---|---|---|
| 30 | A10 | 1p rose | 5.00 | 1.75 |
| a. | | Tete beche pair | 11.00 | 30.00 |

### Revenue Stamps Surcharged

h

i

j

k

l

**1888-91 Wmk. 5 Perf. 14½**

| | | | | |
|---|---|---|---|---|
| 31 | A2 (h) | ½p on 2sh org & grn ('89) | 17.50 | 32.50 |
| a. | | Double surcharge | 350.00 | 375.00 |
| b. | | First "S" in "SHILLINGS" inverted | 325.00 | 350.00 |
| 32 | A2 (i) | 4p on 2sh org & grn | 50.00 | 22.50 |
| a. | | "4d" and "POSTAGE" 5mm apart | 80.00 | 37.50 |
| b. | | "S" inverted, as in #31b | 550.00 | 400.00 |
| c. | | As "a," inverted "S," as in #31b | 750.00 | 650.00 |
| 33 | A2 (j) | 4p on 2sh org & grn | 875.00 | 475.00 |
| 34 | A2 (k) | 1p on 2sh org & grn ('90) | 92.50 | 87.50 |
| a. | | Inverted surcharge | 875.00 | — |
| b. | | "S" inverted | 825.00 | 750.00 |
| 35 | A2 (l) | 1p on 2sh org & grn ('91) | 75.00 | 70.00 |
| b. | | No period after "d" | 450.00 | — |
| c. | | "S" inverted | 575.00 | 575.00 |

### No. 25 Surcharged in Black

**Wmk. 2**

| | | | | |
|---|---|---|---|---|
| 36 | A8 | 1p on 8p bister | 12.00 | 20.00 |
| a. | | Tete beche pair | 50.00 | 70.00 |
| b. | | Inverted surcharge | 375.00 | 325.00 |
| c. | | No period after "d" | 300.00 | 300.00 |

### "2" of "½" Upright

| | | | | |
|---|---|---|---|---|
| 37 | A8 | 2½p on 8p bister | 11.00 | 14.00 |
| a. | | Tete beche pair | 50.00 | 70.00 |
| c. | | Double surcharge | 1,000. | 925.00 |
| d. | | Triple surcharge | | 1,100. |
| e. | | Double surcharge, one inverted | 650.00 | 575.00 |

### "2" of "½" Italic

| | | | | |
|---|---|---|---|---|
| 38 | A8 | 2½p on 8p bister | 22.00 | 13.00 |
| a. | | Tete beche pair | 50.00 | 70.00 |
| b. | | Tete beche pair, #37, 38 | 125.00 | |
| c. | | Inverted surcharge | | |
| d. | | Double surcharge | 875.00 | 925.00 |
| e. | | Triple surcharge | | 1,050. |
| f. | | Triple surch., two inverted | | 1,000. |
| g. | | Double surcharge, one inverted | 625.00 | 575.00 |

Queen Victoria — A17

**1895-99 Wmk. 2 Typo. Perf. 14**

| | | | | |
|---|---|---|---|---|
| 39 | A17 | ½p lilac & green | 4.75 | 2.00 |
| 40 | A17 | 1p lil & car rose | 6.75 | .90 |
| 41 | A17 | 2p lilac & brown | 47.50 | 37.50 |
| 42 | A17 | 2½p lilac & ultra | 12.50 | 1.75 |
| 43 | A17 | 3p lilac & orange | 8.00 | 18.00 |
| 44 | A17 | 6p lilac & green | 23.00 | 65.00 |
| 45 | A17 | 8p lilac & black | 15.00 | 52.50 |
| 46 | A17 | 1sh green & org | 22.50 | 65.00 |
| | | Nos. 39-46 (8) | 140.00 | 242.65 |

Numerals of ½p, 3p, 8p and 1sh of type A17 are in color on colorless tablet.
Issue dates: 1p, May, 1896; ½p, 2p, Sept. 1899; others, Sept. 5, 1895.

Columbus' Flagship, La Concepcion — A18

**1898, Aug. 15 — Engr. — Wmk. 1**

| | | | | |
|---|---|---|---|---|
| 47 | A18 | 2½p ultra | 22.50 | 8.00 |
| a. | | Bluish paper | 40.00 | 47.50 |

Discovery of the island by Columbus, Aug. 15th, 1498.

King Edward VII — A19

**1902 — Wmk. 2 — Typo.**

| | | | | |
|---|---|---|---|---|
| 48 | A19 | ½p violet & grn | 4.50 | 1.50 |
| 49 | A19 | 1p vio & car rose | 10.00 | .35 |
| 50 | A19 | 2p vio & brown | 6.50 | 11.50 |
| 51 | A19 | 2½p vio & ultra | 7.00 | 3.25 |
| 52 | A19 | 3p vio & org | 7.00 | 10.50 |
| 53 | A19 | 6p vio & green | 9.00 | 20.00 |
| 54 | A19 | 1sh green & org | 13.00 | 40.00 |
| 55 | A19 | 2sh grn & ultra | 40.00 | 65.00 |
| 56 | A19 | 5sh grn & car rose | 47.50 | 85.00 |
| 57 | A19 | 10sh green & vio | 160.00 | 300.00 |
| | | Nos. 48-57 (10) | 304.50 | 537.10 |

Numerals of ½p, 3p, 1sh, 2sh and 10sh of type A19 are in color on colorless tablet.

**1904-06 — Wmk. 3 — Perf. 14**
Ordinary Paper

| | | | | |
|---|---|---|---|---|
| 58 | A19 | ½p vio & green | 22.50 | 47.50 |
| 59 | A19 | 1p vio & car rose | 24.00 | 3.00 |
| 60 | A19 | 2p vio & brown | 65.00 | 130.00 |
| 61 | A19 | 2½p vio & ultra | 65.00 | 75.00 |
| 62 | A19 | 3p vio & org | 6.50 | 15.00 |
| a. | | Chalky paper | 7.50 | 9.00 |
| 63 | A19 | 6p vio & green | 17.00 | 30.00 |
| a. | | Chalky paper | 18.00 | 40.00 |
| 64 | A19 | 1sh green & org | 7.25 | 40.00 |
| 65 | A19 | 2sh grn & ultra | 60.00 | 85.00 |
| a. | | Chalky paper | 50.00 | 80.00 |
| 66 | A19 | 5sh grn & car rose | 80.00 | 120.00 |
| 67 | A19 | 10sh green & vio | 190.00 | 300.00 |
| | | Nos. 58-67 (10) | 537.25 | 845.50 |

Issued: Nos. 58, 60-62, 64, 1905; Nos. 63, 65-67, 1906.

Seal of Colony — A20

**1906-11 — Engr.**

| | | | | |
|---|---|---|---|---|
| 68 | A20 | ½p green | 5.25 | .35 |
| 69 | A20 | 1p carmine | 10.00 | .25 |
| 70 | A20 | 2p yellow | 5.25 | 3.50 |
| 71 | A20 | 2½p blue | 7.00 | 2.00 |
| a. | | 2½p ultramarine | 11.00 | 3.75 |

**Typo.**
Chalky Paper
Numerals white on dark ground

| | | | | |
|---|---|---|---|---|
| 72 | A20 | 3p vio, yel ('08) | 8.25 | 1.90 |
| 73 | A20 | 6p violet ('08) | 22.50 | 10.00 |
| 74 | A20 | 1sh blk, grn ('11) | 8.00 | 5.00 |
| 75 | A20 | 2sh vio & blue, blue ('08) | 40.00 | 14.00 |
| 76 | A20 | 5sh red & grn, yel ('08) | 80.00 | 95.00 |
| | | Nos. 68-76 (9) | 186.25 | 132.00 |

**1908 — Wmk. 2**

| | | | | |
|---|---|---|---|---|
| 77 | A20 | 1sh black, green | 50.00 | 80.00 |
| 78 | A20 | 10sh red & grn, grn | 160.00 | 300.00 |

King George V — A21

**1913 — Ordinary Paper — Wmk. 3**

| | | | | |
|---|---|---|---|---|
| 79 | A21 | ½p green | 1.25 | 1.60 |
| 80 | A21 | 1p carmine | 2.50 | .35 |
| a. | | 1p scarlet ('16) | 14.00 | 2.00 |
| 81 | A21 | 2p orange | 1.90 | .35 |
| 82 | A21 | 2½p ultra | 2.00 | 2.00 |

**Chalky Paper**

| | | | | |
|---|---|---|---|---|
| 83 | A21 | 3p violet, yel | .75 | 1.00 |
| 84 | A21 | 6p dl vio & red vio | 1.75 | 10.00 |
| 85 | A21 | 1sh black, green | 1.10 | 11.50 |
| a. | | 1sh black, emerald | 1.75 | 20.00 |
| b. | | 1sh blk, bl grn, olive back | 52.50 | 90.00 |
| c. | | As "a," olive back | 1.75 | 15.00 |
| 86 | A21 | 2sh vio & ultra, bl | 7.25 | 14.00 |
| 87 | A21 | 5sh grn & red, yel | 20.00 | 67.50 |

| | | | | |
|---|---|---|---|---|
| 88 | A21 | 10sh grn & red, grn | 70.00 | 130.00 |
| a. | | 10sh grn & red, emer | 70.00 | 190.00 |
| | | Nos. 79-88 (10) | 108.50 | 238.30 |

**1914 — Surface-colored Paper**

| | | | | |
|---|---|---|---|---|
| 89 | A21 | 3p violet, yel | .70 | 1.60 |
| 90 | A21 | 1sh black, green | 1.40 | 8.50 |

**1921-29 — Ordinary Paper — Wmk. 4**

| | | | | |
|---|---|---|---|---|
| 91 | A21 | ½p green | 1.40 | .35 |
| 92 | A21 | 1p rose red | .90 | .85 |
| 93 | A21 | 1p brown ('23) | 1.75 | .35 |
| 94 | A21 | 1½p rose red ('22) | 1.75 | 1.75 |
| 95 | A21 | 2p orange | 1.40 | .35 |
| 96 | A21 | 2p gray ('26) | 2.75 | 3.00 |
| 97 | A21 | 2½p ultramarine | 8.50 | 10.00 |
| 98 | A21 | 2½p gray ('22) | 1.10 | 10.00 |
| 99 | A21 | 3p ultra ('22) | 1.75 | 12.50 |

**Chalky Paper**

| | | | | |
|---|---|---|---|---|
| 100 | A21 | 3p vio, yel ('26) | 3.50 | 5.75 |
| 101 | A21 | 4p blk & red, yel ('26) | 1.10 | 4.25 |
| 102 | A21 | 5p gray vio & ol grn ('22) | 1.75 | 4.75 |
| 103 | A21 | 6p dl vio & red vio | 1.50 | 29.00 |
| 104 | A21 | 6p blk & red ('26) | 2.50 | 2.75 |
| 105 | A21 | 9p gray vio & blk ('22) | 2.50 | 11.00 |
| 106 | A21 | 1sh blk, emer ('23) | 3.00 | 60.00 |
| 107 | A21 | 1sh org brn ('26) | 4.50 | 11.00 |
| 108 | A21 | 2sh vio & ultra, bl ('22) | 7.00 | 19.00 |
| 109 | A21 | 2sh6p blk & red, bl ('29) | 15.00 | 24.00 |
| 110 | A21 | 3sh grn & vio ('22) | 12.00 | 30.00 |
| 111 | A21 | 5sh grn & red, yel ('23) | 14.00 | 40.00 |
| 112 | A21 | 10sh grn & red, emer ('23) | 57.50 | 150.00 |
| | | Nos. 91-112 (22) | 147.15 | 430.65 |

Grand Anse Beach A22
Seal of the Colony A23

View of Grand Etang A24
View of St. George's A25

**1934, Oct. 23 — Engr. — Perf. 12½**

| | | | | |
|---|---|---|---|---|
| 114 | A22 | ½p green | .25 | 1.25 |
| a. | | Perf. 12½x13 ('36) | 11.00 | 70.00 |

**Perf. 13½x12½**

| | | | | |
|---|---|---|---|---|
| 115 | A23 | 1p blk brn & blk | .65 | .35 |
| a. | | Perf 12½ | 2.00 | 4.00 |

**Perf. 12½x13½**

| | | | | |
|---|---|---|---|---|
| 116 | A24 | 1½p car & black | 1.25 | .45 |
| a. | | Perf 12½ ('36) | 10.00 | 7.50 |

**Perf. 12½**

| | | | | |
|---|---|---|---|---|
| 117 | A23 | 2p org & black | 1.10 | .80 |
| 118 | A25 | 2½p deep blue | .55 | .55 |
| 119 | A23 | 3p ol grn & blk | 1.10 | 3.25 |
| 120 | A23 | 6p claret & blk | 3.75 | 2.00 |
| 121 | A23 | 1sh brown & blk | 4.50 | 4.50 |
| 122 | A23 | 2sh6p ultra & blk | 9.00 | 30.00 |
| 123 | A23 | 5sh vio & black | 50.00 | 55.00 |
| | | Nos. 114-123 (10) | 72.15 | 98.15 |
| | | Set, never hinged | 130.00 | |

Common Design Types pictured following the introduction.

**Silver Jubilee Issue**
Common Design Type

**1935, May 6 — Perf. 11x12**

| | | | | |
|---|---|---|---|---|
| 124 | CD301 | ½p green & blk | 1.00 | 1.35 |
| 125 | CD301 | 1p black & ultra | 1.10 | 2.00 |
| 126 | CD301 | 1½p car & blue | 1.10 | 3.25 |
| 127 | CD301 | 1sh brn vio & ind | 13.50 | 34.00 |
| | | Nos. 124-127 (4) | 16.70 | 40.60 |
| | | Set, never hinged | 29.00 | |

**Coronation Issue**
Common Design Type

**1937, May 12 — Wmk. 4 — Perf. 11x11½**

| | | | | |
|---|---|---|---|---|
| 128 | CD302 | 1p dark purple | .25 | .25 |
| 129 | CD302 | 1½p dark carmine | .25 | .25 |
| 130 | CD302 | 2½p deep ultra | .50 | .35 |
| | | Nos. 128-130 (3) | 1.00 | .85 |
| | | Set, never hinged | 1.60 | |

George VI — A26

**Chalky Paper**

**1937, July 12 — Photo. — Perf. 14½x14**

| | | | | |
|---|---|---|---|---|
| 131 | A26 | ¼p chestnut | 3.25 | .25 |
| a. | | Ordinary paper ('42) | .65 | 3.00 |

Grand Anse Beach A27
Seal of the Colony A28

View of Grand Etang A29
View of St. George's A30

Seal of the Colony — A31

**1938, Mar. 16 — Engr. — Perf. 12½**

| | | | | |
|---|---|---|---|---|
| 132 | A27 | 1p green | .70 | 1.40 |
| 133 | A28 | 1p blk brn & blk | .50 | .55 |
| 134 | A29 | 1½p scarlet & blk | .25 | .95 |
| 135 | A28 | 2p orange & blk | .25 | .55 |
| 136 | A30 | 2½p ultramarine | .25 | .35 |
| 137 | A28 | 3p ol grn & blk | .25 | 2.10 |
| 138 | A28 | 6p red vio & blk | 2.10 | .45 |
| 139 | A28 | 1sh org brn & blk | 3.00 | .45 |
| 140 | A28 | 2sh ultra & black | 21.00 | 2.00 |
| 141 | A28 | 5sh purple & blk | 4.25 | 2.75 |

**Perf. 14**

| | | | | |
|---|---|---|---|---|
| 142 | A31 | 10sh rose car & gray blue | 19.00 | 13.00 |
| a. | | 10sh deep car & gray blue, perf. 12 ('43) | 500.00 | 1,900. |
| b. | | Perf. 12x13 | 36.00 | 12.00 |
| | | Nos. 131-142 (12) | 54.80 | 24.80 |
| | | Set, never hinged | 72.50 | |

**1938-42 — Perf. 12½x13½, 13½x12½**

| | | | | |
|---|---|---|---|---|
| 132a | A27 | ½p | 3.00 | .90 |
| 133a | A28 | 1p | .30 | .25 |
| 134a | A29 | 1½p car & blk | 1.10 | .40 |
| 135a | A28 | 2p | 1.25 | .75 |
| 136a | A30 | 2½p | 7,500. | 200.00 |
| 137a | A28 | 3p | 2.10 | 1.00 |
| 138a | A28 | 6p ('42) | 1.10 | .35 |
| 139a | A28 | 1sh ('42) | 2.50 | 2.50 |
| 140a | A28 | 2sh ('41) | 21.00 | 2.00 |
| 141a | A28 | 5sh ('47) | 3.50 | 4.50 |

> **Catalogue values for unused stamps in this section, from this point to the end of the section, are for Never Hinged items.**

**Peace Issue**
Common Design Type

**1946, Sept. 25 — Perf. 13½x14**

| | | | | |
|---|---|---|---|---|
| 143 | CD303 | 1½p carmine | .25 | .25 |
| 144 | CD303 | 3½p deep blue | .25 | .70 |

**Silver Wedding Issue**
Common Design Types

**1948, Oct. 27 — Photo. — Perf. 14½x14**

| | | | | |
|---|---|---|---|---|
| 145 | CD304 | 1½p scarlet | .25 | .25 |

**Engr.; Name Typo.**
**Perf. 11½x11**

| | | | | |
|---|---|---|---|---|
| 146 | CD305 | 10sh gray green | 21.50 | 21.50 |

**UPU Issue**
Common Design Types
Engr.; Name Typo. on 6c, 12c
**Perf. 13½, 11x11½**

**1949, Oct. 10 — Wmk. 4**

| | | | | |
|---|---|---|---|---|
| 147 | CD306 | 5c ultra | .25 | .25 |
| 148 | CD307 | 6c deep olive | 1.35 | 2.25 |
| 149 | CD308 | 12c red lilac | .30 | .50 |
| 150 | CD309 | 24c red brown | .25 | .55 |
| | | Nos. 147-150 (4) | 2.15 | 3.55 |

A32
A33

A34

**1951, Jan. 8 — Engr. — Perf. 11½**
Center in Black

| | | | | |
|---|---|---|---|---|
| 151 | A32 | ½c chestnut | .25 | 1.30 |
| 152 | A32 | 1c blue green | .25 | .55 |
| 153 | A32 | 2c dark brown | .25 | .25 |
| 154 | A32 | 3c carmine | .25 | .25 |
| 155 | A32 | 4c deep orange | .40 | .25 |
| 156 | A32 | 5c purple | .50 | .30 |
| 157 | A32 | 6c olive | .50 | .60 |
| 158 | A32 | 7c blue | 2.00 | .25 |
| 159 | A32 | 12c red violet | 2.25 | .70 |

**Perf. 11½x12½**

| | | | | |
|---|---|---|---|---|
| 160 | A33 | 25c dark brown | 2.50 | .85 |
| 161 | A33 | 50c ultra | 6.50 | .55 |
| 162 | A33 | $1.50 orange | 8.25 | 8.00 |

**Perf. 11½x13**
Center in Gray Blue

| | | | | |
|---|---|---|---|---|
| 163 | A34 | $2.50 deep carmine | 9.50 | 5.50 |
| | | Nos. 151-163 (13) | 33.40 | 19.40 |

See Nos. 180-183, 202. For overprints see Nos. 166-169.

**University Issue**
Common Design Types

**1951, Feb. 16 — Perf. 14x14½**

| | | | | |
|---|---|---|---|---|
| 164 | CD310 | 3c dp car & gray blk | .55 | 1.00 |
| 165 | CD311 | 6c olive & black | .65 | .60 |

Nos. 154-156 and 159 Overprinted in Black or Carmine

**1951, Sept. 21 — Perf. 11½**

| | | | | |
|---|---|---|---|---|
| 166 | A32 | 3c carmine & black | .25 | .40 |
| 167 | A32 | 4c dp orange & black | .25 | .40 |
| 168 | A32 | 5c purple & black (C) | .30 | .65 |
| 169 | A32 | 12c red violet & black | .30 | .90 |
| | | Nos. 166-169 (4) | 1.10 | 2.35 |

Adoption of a new constitution for the Windward Islands.

**Coronation Issue**
Common Design Type

**1953, June 3 — Perf. 13½x13**

| | | | | |
|---|---|---|---|---|
| 170 | CD312 | 3c carmine & black | .30 | .25 |

**Types of 1951 Inscribed "E II R" and**

Queen Elizabeth II — A35

**1953-59 — Engr. — Perf. 11½**
Center in Black

| | | | | |
|---|---|---|---|---|
| 171 | A35 | ½c chestnut ('54) | .25 | .25 |
| 172 | A35 | 1c blue green | .25 | .25 |
| 173 | A35 | 2c dark brown | .30 | .25 |
| 174 | A35 | 3c carmine ('54) | .25 | .25 |
| 175 | A35 | 4c dp orange ('54) | .25 | .25 |
| 176 | A35 | 5c purple ('54) | .25 | .25 |
| 177 | A35 | 6c olive | 2.00 | 1.25 |
| 178 | A35 | 7c blue ('55) | 2.50 | .25 |
| 179 | A35 | 12c red violet | .30 | .25 |

**Perf. 11½x12½**

| | | | | |
|---|---|---|---|---|
| 180 | A33 | 25c dk brn ('55) | 1.40 | .30 |
| 181 | A33 | 50c ultra ('55) | 6.00 | .80 |

**182** A33 $1.50 orange ('55)   12.50   11.50

### Perf. 11½x13
#### Center in Gray Blue
**183** A34 $2.50 deep car ('59)   25.00   9.00
*Nos. 171-183 (13)*   51.25   24.85

See Nos. 195-202.

No. 182 was locally surcharged "2" and two black horizontal lines and issued Dec. 23, 1965, for revenue use. It was used postally, though not authorized for postal use. The "2" is found in two type faces.

### West Indies Federation
#### Common Design Type
### Perf. 11½x11

**1958, Apr. 22**      **Wmk. 314**
**184** CD313 3c green   .35   .25
**185** CD313 6c blue   .55   .70
**186** CD313 12c carmine rose   .60   .25
*Nos. 184-186 (3)*   1.50   1.20

Victoria and Elizabeth II and Mail Truck — A36

Queens and: 8c, "La Concepcion" and Dakota plane. 25c, Steam Packet "Solent" and B.O.A.C. plane.

**1961, June 1**   **Photo.**   **Perf. 14½x14**
**187** A36 3c gray & deep car   .25   .25
**188** A36 8c orange & ultra   .50   .25
**189** A36 25c blue & maroon   .55   .25
*Nos. 187-189 (3)*   1.30   .75

Centenary of first Grenada postage stamps.

### Freedom from Hunger Issue
#### Common Design Type
**1963, June 4**      **Perf. 14x14½**
**190** CD314 8c green   .30   .25

### Red Cross Centenary Issue
#### Common Design Type
**1963, Sept. 2**   **Litho.**   **Perf. 13**
**191** CD315 3c black & red   .25   .25
**192** CD315 25c ultra & red   .55   .25

### Types of 1953-55
#### Wmk. 314
**1963-64**   **Engr.**   **Perf. 11½**
#### Center in Black
**195** A35 2c dark brown   .25   .25
**196** A35 3c carmine   .25   .25
**197** A35 4c dp orange   .25   .80
**198** A35 5c purple   .25   .25
**199** A35 6c olive   180.00   95.00
**201** A35 12c red violet   .30   .25
#### Perf. 11½x12½
**202** A33 25c dark brown   2.50   1.00
*Nos. 195-198,201-202 (6)*   3.80   2.80

Issued: 6c, 1963; others, May 12, 1964.

### ITU Issue
#### Common Design Type
**1965, May 17**   **Litho.**   **Perf. 11x11½**
**205** CD317 2c vermilion & olive   .25   .25
**206** CD317 50c yellow & ver   .25   .25

### Intl. Cooperation Year Issue
#### Common Design Type
**1965, Oct. 25**   **Litho.**   **Perf. 14½**
**207** CD318 1c blue grn & claret   .25   .25
**208** CD318 25c lt violet & green   .25   .25

### Churchill Memorial Issue
#### Common Design Type
**1966, Jan. 24**   **Photo.**   **Perf. 14**
#### Design in Black, Gold and Carmine Rose
**209** CD319 1c bright blue   .25   .25
**210** CD319 3c green   .25   .25
**211** CD319 25c brown   .25   .25
**212** CD319 35c violet   .35   .35
*Nos. 209-212 (4)*   1.10   1.10

### Royal Visit Issue
#### Common Design Type
**1966, Feb. 4**   **Litho.**   **Perf. 11x12**
**213** CD320 3c violet blue   .25   .25
**214** CD320 35c dark car rose   .55   .25

---

Careenage, St. George's A37

Queen Elizabeth II A38

Designs: 1c, Hillsborough, Carriacou. 2c, Bougainvillea. 3c, Flamboyant plant. 5c, Levera Beach. 8c, Annandale Falls. 10c, Cacao pods. 12c, Inner Harbor. 15c, Nutmeg. 25c, St. George's. 35c, Grand Anse Beach. 50c, Bananas. $1, Seal of Colony. $3, Map of Grenada.

### Perf. 14½x13½, 14½ (A38)
**1966, Apr. 1**   **Photo.**   **Wmk. 314**
**215** A37 1c blue, grn & yel   .25   .80
**216** A37 2c dk grn & dp car rose   .25   .25
**217** A37 3c multicolored   .90   .90
**218** A37 5c multicolored   1.10   .25
**219** A37 6c ultra, grn & car rose   .95   .25
**220** A37 8c dp grn, ind & yel   .95   .25
**221** A37 10c yel grn, brn & dk car   .50   .25
**222** A37 12c multicolored   .30   .90
**223** A37 15c multicolored   .30   .90
**224** A37 25c dk bl, grn & car rose   .30   .25
**225** A37 35c multicolored   .40   .25
**226** A37 50c violet & green   1.10   2.00
**227** A38 $1 brn, ultra & dull grn   7.25   3.50
**228** A38 $2 multicolored   4.50   9.00
**229** A38 $3 brt grnsh bl, dk bl & dl yel   4.00   15.00
*Nos. 215-229 (15)*   23.05   34.75

For overprints and surcharges see Nos. 237-261, B1A-B1D.

### World Cup Soccer Issue
#### Common Design Type
**1966, July 1**   **Litho.**   **Perf. 14**
**230** CD321 5c multicolored   .25   .25
**231** CD321 50c multicolored   .40   .70

### WHO Headquarters Issue
#### Common Design Type
**1966, Sept. 20**   **Litho.**   **Perf. 14**
**232** CD322 8c multicolored   .25   .25
**233** CD322 25c multicolored   .55   .25

### UNESCO Anniversary Issue
#### Common Design Type
**1966, Dec. 1**   **Litho.**   **Perf. 14**
**234** CD323 2c "Education"   .25   .25
**235** CD323 15c "Science"   .25   .25
**236** CD323 50c "Culture"   .60   .70
*Nos. 234-236 (3)*   1.10   1.20

### Nos. 216-217, 220 and 224 Overprinted "ASSOCIATED STATEHOOD 1967" in Silver
### Perf. 14½x13½
**1967, Mar. 3**   **Photo.**   **Wmk. 314**
**237** A37 2c dk grn & dp car rose   .25   .25
**238** A37 3c multicolored   .25   .25
**239** A37 8c dp grn, ind & yel   .25   .25
**240** A37 25c dk bl, grn & car rose   .25   .25
*Nos. 237-240 (4)*   1.00   1.00

Nos. 216, 221, 223 and 227-228 Surcharged

### Perf. 14½x13½, 14½ (A38)
**1967, July 1**   **Photo.**   **Wmk. 314**
**241** A37 1c on 15c multi   .25   .25
**242** A37 2c dk grn & dp car rose   .25   .25
**243** A37 3c on 10c multi   .25   .25
**244** A38 $1 multicolored   .25   .25
**245** A38 $2 multicolored   .35   .35
*Nos. 241-245 (5)*   1.35   1.35

EXPO '67 Intl. Exhib., Montreal, Apr. 28-Oct. 27.

---

Nos. 215-229 Ovptd. in Black

**1967-68**     **Photo.**   **Wmk. 314**
**246** A37 1c multicolored   .25   .25
**247** A37 2c multicolored   .25   .25
**248** A37 3c multicolored   .25   .25
**249** A37 5c multicolored   .25   .25
**250** A37 6c multicolored   .25   .25
**251** A37 8c multicolored   .25   .25
**252** A37 10c multicolored   .25   .25
**253** A37 12c multicolored   .25   .25
**254** A37 15c multicolored   .25   .25
**255** A37 25c multicolored   .25   .25
**256** A37 35c multicolored   .50   .25
**257** A37 50c multicolored   .80   .30
**258** A38 $1 multicolored   1.10   .60
**259** A38 $2 multicolored   1.00   2.40
**260** A38 $3 multicolored   2.00   4.00

#### Overprinted and Surcharged
**261** A38 $5 on $2 multi   1.40   3.75
*Nos. 246-261 (16)*   9.30   13.80

Issued: $5, 5/18/68; others, 10/19/67.
For surcharges, see Nos. B1A-B1D.

Pres. John F. Kennedy A39

Pres. Kennedy and: 25c, 50c, Bird-of-paradise flower. 35c, $1, Roses.

### Perf. 14½x14
**1968, Jan. 13**      **Unwmk.**
**262** A39 1c lt blue & multi   .25   .25
**263** A39 15c orange & multi   .25   .25
**264** A39 25c violet & multi   .25   .25
**265** A39 35c multicolored   .25   .25
**266** A39 50c blue & multi   .30   .25
**267** A39 $1 multicolored   .40   .70
*Nos. 262-267 (6)*   1.70   1.95

50th anniv. of the birth of Pres. John F. Kennedy (1917-1963).

Bugler and Jamboree Emblem — A40

Jamboree Emblem and: 2c, 50c, Boy Scouts sitting in tent. 3c, $1, Lord Baden-Powell.

**1968, Feb. 1**   **Photo.**   **Perf. 13x14**
**268** A40 1c orange & multi   .25   .25
**269** A40 2c emer & multi   .25   .25
**270** A40 3c yellow & multi   .25   .25
**271** A40 35c multicolored   .30   .25
**272** A40 50c blue & multi   .40   .40
**273** A40 $1 multicolored   .55   .70
*Nos. 268-273 (6)*   2.00   2.10

12th Boy Scout Jamboree, Farragut State Park, Idaho, Aug. 1-9, 1967.

Seascape, by Winston Churchill A41

Paintings: 12c, Pine at the shore. 15c, 35c, Houses at the shore. 50c, Churchill painting a seascape.

### Perf. 14x14½
**1968, Mar. 23**      **Unwmk.**
**274** A41 10c multicolored   .25   .25
**275** A41 12c multicolored   .25   .25
**276** A41 15c multicolored   .25   .25
**277** A41 25c multicolored   .25   .25
**278** A41 35c multicolored   .25   .25
**279** A41 50c multicolored   .40   .25
*Nos. 274-279 (6)*   1.65   1.50

Winston Churchill as a painter.

---

Edith McGuire, US, 200m. Dash, 1964 — A42

Gold Medal Winners: 2c, 50c, Arthur Wint, Jamaica, 400m run, 1948. 3c, 60c, Adhemar Ferreira da Silva, Brazil, hop, step and jump, 1952 & 1956. 10c, Like 1c.

**1968, Sept. 24**   **Photo.**   **Perf. 12½**
**280** A42 1c ultra & multi   .25   .30
**281** A42 2c lilac & multi   .25   .30
**282** A42 3c green & multi   .25   .30
**283** A42 10c red org & multi   .25   .30
**284** A42 50c Prus blue & multi   .35   .75
**285** A42 60c orange & multi   .40   .85
*Nos. 280-285 (6)*   1.75   2.80

19th Olympic Games, Mexico City, Oct. 12-27. Nos. 280-282 and 283-285 are printed in sheets of 9 (3 of each denomination).
For surcharges see Nos. 310-315.

Transplant Operations — A43

### Perf. 13x13½
**1968, Nov. 25**   **Photo.**   **Unwmk.**
**286** A43 5c Kidney   .25   .25
**287** A43 25c Heart   .30   .25
**288** A43 35c Lung   .40   .25
**289** A43 50c Cornea   .45   .60
*Nos. 286-289 (4)*   1.40   1.35

20th anniv. of WHO.

Adoration of the Magi, by Veronese — A44

Paintings: 15c, Madonna and Child with St. John and St. Catherine, by Titian. 35c, Adoration of the Magi, by Botticelli. $1, "A Knight Adoring the Infant Christ" by Vincenzo di Biagio Catena.

**1968, Dec. 3**      **Perf. 12½**
**290** A44 5c vio blue & multi   .25   .25
**291** A44 15c crimson & multi   .25   .25
**292** A44 35c dk green & multi   .25   .25
**293** A44 $1 dk blue & multi   .25   .25
*Nos. 290-293 (4)*   1.00   1.00

Christmas. For overprints see Nos. 341-344.

Hibiscus and "La Concepcion" — A45

Yacht in St. George's Harbour — A45a

Designs: 2c, Bird-of-paradise flower. 3c, Bougainvillea. 5c, Rock hind (fish; horiz.). 6c, Sailfish. 8c, Red snapper, horiz. 10c, Giant toad, horiz. 12c, Yellowfoot tortoise. No. 302, Tree boa, horiz. No. 302A, Thunbergia. 25c, Mouse opossum. 35c Armadillo, horiz. 50c, Mona monkey. $1, Bananaquit (bird). $2, Brown pelican. $3, Magnificent frigate bird. $5, Bare-eyed thrush.

### Perf. 14x14½, 14½x14; 14x13½ (#302A); 13½x14 (#305A)
### Photo.; Litho. (#302A, 305A)
**1968-71**      **Unwmk.**
**294** A45 1c dl yel & multi   .25   .25
**295** A45 2c brt pink & multi   .25   .25
**296** A45 3c blue & multi   .25   .25
**297** A45 5c violet & multi   .25   .25

| | | | | |
|---|---|---|---|---|
| 298 | A45 | 6c emer & multi | .25 | .25 |
| 299 | A45 | 8c multicolored | .25 | .25 |
| 300 | A45 | 10c multicolored | .25 | .25 |
| 301 | A45 | 12c ver & multi | .25 | .25 |
| 302 | A45 | 15c emer & multi | .90 | .85 |
| 302A | A45 | 15c gray & multi | 5.00 | 3.25 |
| 303 | A45 | 25c multicolored | .30 | .25 |
| 304 | A45 | 35c multicolored | .35 | .25 |
| 305 | A45 | 50c ultra & multi | .45 | .25 |
| 305A | A45 | 75c blue & multi | 10.00 | 8.00 |
| 306 | A45 | $1 multicolored | 3.00 | 2.40 |
| 307 | A45 | $2 multicolored | 4.25 | 10.00 |
| 308 | A45 | $3 yel & multi | 4.25 | 5.00 |
| 309 | A45 | $5 multicolored | 6.00 | 19.00 |
| | | Nos. 294-309 (18) | 36.50 | 51.25 |

Nos. 294-309 vary in size from 25x44mm to 29x46mm.

The overprint "VOTE/FEB. 28 1972" was applied to the 2c, 3c, 6c and 25c in Feb., 1972.

Issued: 5c, 10c, 25c, $2, 2/4/69; 3c, 8c, 35c, $5, 7/1/69; No. 302A, 1970; 75c, 10/9/71; others, 10/68.

For surcharges see Nos. 462-464. For overprints see Nos. 528-541, C3-C19.

### Nos. 280-285 Surcharged in Carmine

Gov. Hilda Bynoe and View of St. George's — A46

**1969, Feb.**     **Perf. 12½**

| | | | | |
|---|---|---|---|---|
| 310 | A42 | 5c on 1c multi | .25 | .25 |
| 311 | A42 | 8c on 2c multi | .25 | .25 |
| 312 | A42 | 25c on 3c multi | .25 | .25 |
| 313 | A42 | 35c on 10c multi | .25 | .25 |
| 314 | A42 | $1 on 50c multi | .25 | .25 |
| 315 | A42 | $2 on 60c multi | .40 | .60 |
| | | Nos. 310-315 (6) | 1.65 | 1.85 |

Gov. Hilda Bynoe and View of St. George's — A46

Designs: 15c, Premier Eric M. Gairy, fruits and St. George's. 60c, Emblems of Brussels, New York and Montreal World's Fairs.

**1969, May 1**   **Litho.**   **Perf. 13x13½**

| | | | | |
|---|---|---|---|---|
| 316 | A46 | 5c multicolored | .25 | .25 |
| 317 | A46 | 15c multicolored | .25 | .25 |
| 318 | A46 | 50c multicolored | .25 | .25 |
| 319 | A46 | 60c multicolored | .25 | .30 |
| | | Nos. 316-319 (4) | 1.00 | 1.05 |

Nos. 310-319 issued to publicize CARIFTA (Caribbean Free Trade Area) Exposition, St. George's, May 5-30.

Gov. Hilda Bynoe — A47

Designs: 25c, Dr. Martin Luther King, Jr. $1, Belshazzar's Feast, by Rembrandt, horiz.

    **Perf. 13x12½, 12½x13**

**1969, June 8**   **Photo.**   **Unwmk.**

| | | | | |
|---|---|---|---|---|
| 320 | A47 | 5c multicolored | .25 | .25 |
| 321 | A47 | 25c multicolored | .25 | .25 |
| 322 | A47 | 35c multicolored | .25 | .25 |
| 323 | A47 | $1 multicolored | .30 | .40 |
| | | Nos. 320-323 (4) | 1.05 | 1.15 |

International Human Rights Year.

Batsman Playing Off-drive A48

Cricket: 10c, Batsman playing defensive stroke. 25c, Batsman sweeping ball. 35c, Batsman playing on-drive.

---

**1969, Aug. 1**     **Perf. 14x14½**

| | | | | |
|---|---|---|---|---|
| 324 | A48 | 3c dk blue & multi | .25 | .95 |
| 325 | A48 | 10c fawn & multi | .25 | .40 |
| 326 | A48 | 25c dp green & multi | .45 | .80 |
| 327 | A48 | 35c brt purple & multi | .60 | .85 |
| | | Nos. 324-327 (4) | 1.55 | 3.00 |

Astronaut Collecting Moon Rocks, Landing Module and Earth — A49

Designs: ½c, like $1. 1c, Apollo 11, moon and earth. 2c, Landing module "Eagle." 3c, Memorial tablet left on moon. 8c, Separation of rocket and spaceship. 25c, Take off from Cape Kennedy, vert. 35c, Apollo 11 circling the moon, vert. 50c, Splashdown, vert. ½c, 2c, 25c, 50c, $1 inscribed: "We came in peace for all mankind." 1c, 3c, 8c, 35c inscribed: "Like the moon it shall be established forever" Psalms 89:37.

   **Perf. 13x13½ (½c), 12½**

**1969, Sept. 24**   **Litho.**   **Unwmk.**

      **Size: 56x35mm**

| | | | | |
|---|---|---|---|---|
| 328 | A49 | ½c multicolored | .25 | .25 |

   **Size: 44½x28mm, 28x44½mm**

| | | | | |
|---|---|---|---|---|
| 329 | A49 | 1c multicolored | .25 | .25 |
| 330 | A49 | 2c multicolored | .25 | .25 |
| 331 | A49 | 3c multicolored | .25 | .25 |
| 332 | A49 | 8c multicolored | .25 | .25 |
| 333 | A49 | 25c multicolored | .25 | .25 |
| 334 | A49 | 35c multicolored | .25 | .25 |
| 335 | A49 | 50c multicolored | .25 | .25 |
| 336 | A49 | $1 multicolored | .40 | .60 |
| a. | | Souvenir sheet of 2 | 2.00 | 2.00 |
| | | Nos. 328-336 (9) | 2.40 | 2.60 |

Man's first moonlanding (Apollo 11), July 20, 1969.

No. 336a contains stamps similar to Nos. 331 and 336 with simulated perforations.

For surcharge and overprints see Nos. 349, 379-382.

Mahatma Gandhi A50

Gandhi in various positions. 15c, 25c are vert.

**1969, Oct. 8**   **Perf. 11½x12, 12x11½**
     **Queen's Head in Gold**

| | | | | |
|---|---|---|---|---|
| 337 | A50 | 6c multicolored | .25 | .25 |
| 338 | A50 | 15c multicolored | .25 | .25 |
| 339 | A50 | 25c multicolored | .55 | .25 |
| 340 | A50 | $1 multicolored | .85 | 1.10 |
| a. | | Souvenir sheet of 4 | 5.00 | 5.00 |
| | | Nos. 337-340 (4) | 1.90 | 1.85 |

Mohandas K. Gandhi (1869-1948), leader in India's fight for independence.

No. 340a contains stamps similar to Nos. 337-340 with simulated perforation.

Nos. 290-293 Overprinted in Black or Silver

**1969, Dec. 23**   **Photo.**   **Perf. 12½**

| | | | | |
|---|---|---|---|---|
| 341 | A44 | 2c on 15c multi | .25 | .75 |
| 342 | A44 | 5c multi (S) | .25 | .25 |
| 343 | A44 | 35c multi (S) | .25 | .25 |
| 344 | A44 | $1 multi (S) | .65 | 1.75 |
| | | Nos. 341-344 (4) | 1.40 | 3.00 |

Christmas.

Edward Teach (Blackbeard) — A51

---

Pirates: 25c, Anne Bonney and sailboats. 50c, Jean Lafitte and sailboats. $1, Mary Read, ships and fighting pirates.

**1970, Feb. 1**   **Engr.**   **Perf. 13x13½**

| | | | | |
|---|---|---|---|---|
| 345 | A51 | 15c black | .60 | .25 |
| 346 | A51 | 25c emerald | 1.00 | .25 |
| 347 | A51 | 50c purple | 1.90 | .25 |
| 348 | A51 | $1 carmine | 3.00 | .95 |
| | | Nos. 345-348 (4) | 6.50 | 1.70 |

### No. 328 Surcharged

Type I

Type II

**1970, Mar. 18**   **Litho.**   **Perf. 13x13½**

| | | | | |
|---|---|---|---|---|
| 349 | A49 | 5c on ½c multi (I) | .40 | .40 |
| a. | | Type II | 1.25 | 1.50 |

Christ, from "The Last Supper," by Andrea del Sarto A52

Paintings: No. 351 (5c), St. John, from Last Supper by Andrea del Sarto. Nos. 352-353 (15c), Christ Crowned with Thorns, by Anthony Van Dyck. Nos. 354-355 (25c), Passion of Christ, by Hans Memling. Nos. 356-357 (60c), Christ in the Tomb, by Peter Paul Rubens. Nos. 350, 352, 354 and 356 have denomination in lower right corner; others in lower left corner. The stamps of the same denomination are printed se-tenant without separating margin, reproducing continuous picture.

**1970, Apr. 13**   **Litho.**   **Perf. 11½x11**

| | | | | |
|---|---|---|---|---|
| 350 | | 5c rose car & multi | .25 | .25 |
| 351 | | 5c rose car & multi | .25 | .25 |
| a. | | A52 Pair, #350-351 | .40 | .40 |
| 352 | | 15c ultra & multi | .25 | .25 |
| 353 | | 15c ultra & multi | .25 | .25 |
| a. | | A52 Pair, #352-353 | .40 | .50 |
| 354 | | 25c brt vio & multi | .25 | .25 |
| 355 | | 25c brt vio & multi | .25 | .25 |
| a. | | A52 Pair, #354-355 | .40 | .50 |
| 356 | | 60c dull org & multi | .25 | .55 |
| 357 | | 60c dull org & multi | .25 | .55 |
| a. | | A52 Pair, #356-357 | .40 | 1.10 |
| b. | | Souvenir sheet of 4, #354-357 | 1.25 | 1.25 |
| | | Nos. 350-357 (8) | 2.00 | 2.60 |

Easter.

Girl Pushing Carriage with Kittens A53

Designs: 15c, Girl playing with puppy and kitten. 30c, Boy fishing and cat. 60c, Children with pets.

**1970, May 27**   **Litho.**   **Perf. 11**

| | | | | |
|---|---|---|---|---|
| 358 | A53 | 5c multicolored | .25 | .25 |
| 359 | A53 | 15c multicolored | .25 | .25 |
| 360 | A53 | 30c multicolored | .35 | .35 |
| a. | | Souvenir sheet of 2 | 2.00 | 2.00 |
| 361 | A53 | 60c multicolored | .75 | 1.00 |
| a. | | Souvenir sheet of 2 | 2.00 | 2.00 |
| | | Nos. 358-361 (4) | 1.60 | 1.85 |

William Wordsworth (1770-1850). English poet. No. 360a contains stamps similar to Nos. 358 and 360; No. 361a contains stamps similar to Nos. 359 and 361. Sheets have simulated perforations.

---

Indian Parliament A54

Commonwealth Parliamentary Association Emblem and: 25c, British Parliament. 50c, Canadian Parliament. 60c, Grenadian Parliament.

**1970, June 15**     **Perf. 14½x14**

| | | | | |
|---|---|---|---|---|
| 362 | A54 | 5c multicolored | .25 | .25 |
| 363 | A54 | 25c multicolored | .25 | .25 |
| 364 | A54 | 50c multicolored | .25 | .25 |
| 365 | A54 | 60c multicolored | .25 | .25 |
| a. | | Souvenir sheet of 4, #362-365 | 1.00 | 1.00 |
| | | Nos. 362-365 (4) | 1.00 | 1.00 |

7th Caribbean Regional Conf. of the Commonwealth Parliamentary Assoc., St. George's. June 13-20.

Sun Tower and EXPO Emblem — A55

EXPO Emblem and: 2c, Livelihood Industry pavilion, horiz. 3c, Ikenobo, Japanese floral art, vert. 10c, Adam and Eve, by Tintoretto and Italian pavilion, horiz. 25c, UN pavilion and flags reflected in pool. 50c, Peace statue of St. Francis, San Francisco pavilion, cable car and Golden Gate Bridge, $1, Toshiba-Ihi pavilion, horiz.

**1970, Aug. 8**   **Litho.**   **Perf. 13½**

| | | | | |
|---|---|---|---|---|
| 366 | A55 | 1c brt blue & multi | .25 | .25 |
| 367 | A55 | 2c multicolored | .25 | .25 |
| 368 | A55 | 3c buff & multi | .25 | .25 |
| 369 | A55 | 10c multicolored | .25 | .25 |
| 370 | A55 | 25c gray & multi | .25 | .25 |
| 371 | A55 | 50c gray & multi | .25 | 1.00 |
| | | Nos. 366-371 (6) | 1.50 | 2.25 |

### Souvenir Sheet

| | | | | |
|---|---|---|---|---|
| 372 | A55 | $1 gold & multi | 1.00 | 1.75 |

EXPO '70 Intl. Exhib., Osaka, Japan, Mar. 15-Sept. 13.

Pres. Roosevelt and Flag-Raising on Iwo Jima — A56

Designs: 5c, Marshal Georgi K. Zhukov and fall of Berlin. 15c, Winston Churchill and evacuation of Dunkirk. 25c, Charles de Gaulle and liberation of Paris. 50c, General Dwight D. Eisenhower and D-Day landing. 60c, Field Marshal Bernard Montgomery and Battle of Alamein.

**1970, Sept. 3**     **Perf. 11**

| | | | | |
|---|---|---|---|---|
| 373 | A56 | ½c multicolored | .25 | .60 |
| 374 | A56 | 5c multicolored | 1.00 | .35 |
| 375 | A56 | 15c multicolored | 1.50 | 1.00 |
| 376 | A56 | 25c multicolored | 1.75 | .55 |
| 377 | A56 | 50c multicolored | 2.00 | 1.60 |
| 378 | A56 | 60c multicolored | 2.25 | 3.00 |
| a. | | Souv. sheet of 4 #373, 375, 377-378 | 5.75 | 5.75 |
| | | Nos. 373-378 (6) | 8.75 | 6.65 |

End of World War II, 25th anniversary.

### Nos. 333-336 Overprinted in Black or Silver: "PHILYMPIA / LONDON 1970"

**1970, Sept. 18**     **Perf. 12½**

| | | | | |
|---|---|---|---|---|
| 379 | A49 | 25c multicolored | .25 | .25 |
| 380 | A49 | 35c multicolored | .25 | .25 |
| 381 | A49 | 50c multicolored | .25 | .25 |
| 382 | A49 | $1 multi (S) | .40 | .40 |
| | | Nos. 379-382 (4) | 1.15 | 1.25 |

Philympia 1970, London philatelic exhibition, Sept. 18-26. The overprint on No. 382 is vertical, reading up.

This overprint was applied in silver to No. 336a. Value $45.

UPU Headquarters, Emblem and Old Transportation — A57

UPU Headquarters, emblem and: 25c, Jet plane, ship and diesel train. 50c, Rowland Hill, vert. $1, Abraham Lincoln, vert.

**1970, Oct. 17    Litho.    Perf. 14½**
| | | | | |
|---|---|---|---|---|
| 383 | A57 | 15c orange & multi | .65 | .25 |
| 384 | A57 | 25c blue & multi | .65 | .25 |
| 385 | A57 | 50c multicolored | .40 | .40 |
| 386 | A57 | $1 rose & multi | .60 | 2.00 |
| a. | | Souvenir sheet of 2 | 1.90 | 3.00 |
| | | Nos. 383-386 (4) | 2.30 | 2.90 |

Opening of the new UPU Headquarters in Bern. No. 386a contains stamps similar to Nos. 385-386.

Madonna of the Goldfinch, by Tiepolo — A58

Christmas (Paintings): No. 388, 35c, Virgin and Child with Sts. Peter and Paul, by Dirk Bouts. No. 389, $1, Virgin and Child, by Bellini. 3c, Like No. 387. 2c, 50c, Madonna of the Basket, by Correggio.

**1970, Dec. 5    Perf. 14x13½**
| | | | | |
|---|---|---|---|---|
| 387 | A58 | ½c yel grn & multi | .25 | .25 |
| 388 | A58 | ½c pink & multi | .25 | .25 |
| 389 | A58 | ½c yellow & multi | .25 | .25 |
| 390 | A58 | 2c lt blue & multi | .25 | .25 |
| 391 | A58 | 3c dp rose & multi | .25 | .25 |
| 392 | A58 | 35c dk green & multi | .25 | .40 |
| 393 | A58 | 50c brown & multi | .35 | .50 |
| 394 | A58 | $1 purple & multi | .50 | 1.10 |
| a. | | Souvenir sheet of 2, #393-394 | 2.25 | 3.00 |
| | | Nos. 387-394 (8) | 2.35 | 3.25 |

Nursing in 19th Century — A59

Designs: 15c, Horse-drawn ambulance, Northern France, 1918. 25c, First aid station, 1941. 60c, Red Cross truck loaded on plane, 1970 emergency aid.

**1970, Dec. 12    Litho.    Perf. 14½x14**
| | | | | |
|---|---|---|---|---|
| 395 | A59 | 5c red & multi | .25 | .25 |
| 396 | A59 | 15c red & multi | .30 | .25 |
| 397 | A59 | 25c red & multi | .50 | .35 |
| 398 | A59 | 60c red & multi | 1.00 | 1.25 |
| a. | | Souvenir sheet of 4, #395-398 | 2.50 | 2.25 |
| | | Nos. 395-398 (4) | 2.05 | 2.10 |

Centenary of the British Red Cross Society.

John Dewey, Children Learning to Paint — A60

Designs: 10c, Jean-Jacques Rousseau and students. 50c, Moses Maimonides and biology student. $1, Bertrand Russell and boys.

**1971, May 8    Litho.    Perf. 13½**
| | | | | |
|---|---|---|---|---|
| 399 | A60 | 5c multicolored | .25 | .25 |
| 400 | A60 | 10c multicolored | .25 | .25 |
| 401 | A60 | 50c multicolored | .50 | .50 |
| 402 | A60 | $1 multicolored | 1.10 | .75 |
| a. | | Souvenir sheet of 2, #401-402 | 2.00 | 2.25 |
| | | Nos. 399-402 (4) | 2.10 | 1.75 |

International Education Year.

Jennifer Hosten and Map of Grenada — A61

**1971, June 1    Litho.    Perf. 13½**
| | | | | |
|---|---|---|---|---|
| 403 | A61 | 5c vio blue & multi | .25 | .25 |
| 404 | A61 | 10c red lilac & multi | .25 | .25 |
| 405 | A61 | 15c brt rose & multi | .25 | .25 |
| 406 | A61 | 25c violet & multi | .25 | .25 |
| 407 | A61 | 35c blue & multi | .30 | .45 |
| 408 | A61 | 50c red & multi | .65 | .65 |
| a. | | Souvenir sheet of 1 | 1.90 | 2.00 |
| | | Nos. 403-408 (6) | 1.95 | 2.10 |

Honoring Miss Jennifer Hosten of Grenada, Miss World, 1971. No. 408a, printed on silk, contains imperf. stamp similar to No. 408.

Nos. 403-408 and 408a were overprinted "INTERPEX/1972" in Mar. 1972. Value $9.50.

For surcharge and overprints Nos. 465, C23-C26.

Canadian and French Boy Scouts A62

Boy Scouts from: 35c, West Germany and US. 50c, Australia and Japan. 75c, Grenada and Great Britain.

**1971, Aug.    Litho.    Perf. 11**
| | | | | |
|---|---|---|---|---|
| 409 | A62 | 5c multicolored | .25 | .25 |
| 410 | A62 | 35c multicolored | .40 | .40 |
| 411 | A62 | 50c multicolored | .50 | .60 |
| 412 | A62 | 75c multicolored | .65 | .90 |
| a. | | Souvenir sheet of 2, #411-412 | 2.00 | 2.75 |
| | | Nos. 409-412 (4) | 1.80 | 2.15 |

13th Boy Scout World Jamboree, Asagiri Plain, Japan, Aug. 2-10.

Napoleon, by Edouard Détaille — A63

Paintings of Napoleon: 15c, Outside Madrid, by Carle Vernet. 35c, Crossing the Alps, by Jacques Louis David. $2, Portrait, by David.

**1971, Sept.    Perf. 13x13½**
| | | | | |
|---|---|---|---|---|
| 413 | A63 | 5c multicolored | .25 | .25 |
| 414 | A63 | 15c multicolored | .25 | .25 |
| 415 | A63 | 35c multicolored | .40 | .40 |
| a. | | Souvenir sheet of 1 | 2.50 | 3.25 |
| 416 | A63 | $2 multicolored | 1.25 | 1.60 |
| | | Nos. 413-416 (4) | 2.15 | 2.50 |

Sesquicentennial of the death of Napoleon Bonaparte (1769-1821).

No. 415a contains stamp similar to No. 415 with simulated perforations.

Grenada No. 1 — A64

15c, Grenada #2 & Queen Elizabeth II. 35c, Grenada #1, 2. 50c, Grenada #1 & scroll.

**1971, Nov. 6    Litho.    Perf. 11**
| | | | | |
|---|---|---|---|---|
| 417 | A64 | 5c dk red & multi | .25 | .25 |
| 418 | A64 | 15c multicolored | .35 | .25 |
| 419 | A64 | 35c dull org & multi | .55 | .25 |
| 420 | A64 | 50c dk green & multi | .75 | 1.75 |
| a. | | Souvenir sheet of 2, #419-420 | 1.75 | 1.75 |
| | | Nos. 417-420 (4) | 1.90 | 2.50 |

110th anniversary of postal service.

Splashdown, Apollo 13 — A65

Designs: 2c, Capsule and rafts in ocean, Apollo 13. 3c, Separation of landing module from rocket, Apollo 14. 10c, Astronauts collecting moon rocks, Apollo 14. 25c, Astronauts in moon rover, Apollo 15. 50c, $1, Rocket blast-off, Apollo 15, vert.

**1971, Nov.**
| | | | | |
|---|---|---|---|---|
| 421 | A65 | 1c multicolored | .25 | .30 |
| 422 | A65 | 2c multicolored | .25 | .30 |
| 423 | A65 | 3c black & multi | .25 | .30 |
| 424 | A65 | 10c black & multi | .35 | .25 |
| 425 | A65 | 25c multicolored | 1.10 | .35 |
| 426 | A65 | $1 multicolored | 2.25 | 3.50 |
| | | Nos. 421-426 (6) | 4.45 | 5.00 |

**Souvenir Sheet**
| | | | | |
|---|---|---|---|---|
| 427 | A65 | 50c multicolored | 2.50 | 2.50 |

US moon missions of Apollo 13, 14 and 15.

67th Regiment of Foot, 1787 — A66

Designs: 1c, 45th Regiment of Foot, 1792. 2c, 29th Regiment of Foot, 1794. 10c, 9th Regiment of Foot, 1801. 25c, 2nd Regiment of Foot, 1815. $1, 70th Regiment of Foot, 1764.

**1971, Dec.    Perf. 13½x14**
| | | | | |
|---|---|---|---|---|
| 428 | A66 | ½c red & multi | .25 | .25 |
| 429 | A66 | 1c red & multi | .25 | .25 |
| 430 | A66 | 2c red & multi | .25 | .25 |
| 431 | A66 | 10c red & multi | .50 | .25 |
| 432 | A66 | 25c red & multi | .90 | .30 |
| 433 | A66 | $1 red & multi | 2.75 | 2.75 |
| a. | | Souv. sheet of 2, #432-433, perf. 15 | 4.00 | 4.00 |
| | | Nos. 428-433 (6) | 4.90 | 4.05 |

Uniforms of British units stationed in Grenada.

For surcharges see Nos. 439, C1-C2.

Adoration of the Kings, by Memling — A67

Christmas: 25c, Madonna and Child, sculpture by Michelangelo. 35c, Madonna and Child, by Murillo. 50c, Madonna with the Apple, by Memling. $1, Adoration of the Kings, by Jan Mostaert.

**1971, Dec.    Perf. 14x13½**
| | | | | |
|---|---|---|---|---|
| 434 | A67 | 15c gold & multi | .25 | .25 |
| 435 | A67 | 25c gold & multi | .25 | .25 |
| 436 | A67 | 35c gold & multi | .30 | .25 |
| 437 | A67 | 50c gold & multi | .40 | .75 |
| | | Nos. 434-437 (4) | 1.20 | 1.50 |

**Souvenir Sheet**
| | | | | |
|---|---|---|---|---|
| 438 | A67 | $1 gold & multi | 1.00 | 1.00 |

No. 430 Surcharged

**1972, Feb. 3    Perf. 13½x14**
| | | | | |
|---|---|---|---|---|
| 439 | A66 | $2 on 2c red & multi | 1.25 | 1.25 |
| a. | | Souvenir sheet of 2 | 2.00 | 2.00 |

11th Winter Olympic Games, Sapporo, Japan, Feb. 3-13. See Nos. C1-C2.

No. 439a is overprinted in red on No. 433a (no surcharge); margin inscribed in red: "SAPPORO 1972."

King Arthur, UNICEF Emblem — A68

UNICEF Emblem and: 1c, 50c, Robin Hood. 2c, 75c, Robinson Crusoe, vert. 25c, like ½c. $1, Mary and her Little Lamb, vert.

**1972, Mar. 4    Perf. 14½x14, 14x14½**
| | | | | |
|---|---|---|---|---|
| 450 | A68 | ½c dp blue & multi | .25 | .25 |
| 451 | A68 | 1c yellow & multi | .25 | .25 |
| 452 | A68 | 2c dp yel & multi | .25 | .25 |
| 453 | A68 | 25c salmon & multi | .25 | .25 |
| 454 | A68 | 50c multicolored | .25 | .35 |
| 455 | A68 | 75c blue & multi | .30 | .60 |
| 456 | A68 | $1 multicolored | .40 | .85 |
| a. | | Souvenir sheet of 1 | 1.00 | 1.00 |
| | | Nos. 450-456 (7) | 1.95 | 2.80 |

25th anniv. (in 1971) of UNICEF.

Yachting — A69

1c, 50c, Equestrian. 2c, 35c, Running, vert.

**1972, Sept. 8    Litho.    Perf. 14**
| | | | | |
|---|---|---|---|---|
| 457 | A69 | ½c multicolored | .25 | .25 |
| 458 | A69 | 1c lt blue & multi | .25 | .25 |
| 459 | A69 | 2c orange & multi | .25 | .25 |
| 460 | A69 | 35c yellow & multi | .40 | .80 |
| 461 | A69 | 50c yel grn & multi | .60 | 1.00 |
| | | Nos. 457-461,C20-C21 (7) | 3.15 | 3.70 |

20th Olympic Games, Munich, Aug. 26-Sept. 11. See No. C22.

Nos. 294-296, 403 Surcharged

**Perf. 14x14½, 13½**
**1972, Oct.    Photo.**
| | | | | |
|---|---|---|---|---|
| 462 | A45 | 12c on 1c multi | .50 | .55 |
| 463 | A45 | 12c on 2c multi | .50 | .55 |
| 464 | A45 | 12c on 3c multi | .50 | .55 |
| 465 | A61 | 12c on 5c multi | .50 | .55 |
| | | Nos. 462-465 (4) | 2.00 | 2.20 |

**Silver Wedding Issue, 1972**
Common Design Type

Design: Queen Elizabeth II, Prince Philip, seal of Grenada and myristica fragrans.

**Perf. 14x14½**
**1972, Nov. 20    Wmk. 314**
| | | | | |
|---|---|---|---|---|
| 466 | CD324 | 8c olive & multi | .25 | .25 |
| 467 | CD324 | $1 multicolored | .45 | .45 |

Boy Scout Saluting — A70

Designs: 1c, Two Scouts knotting ropes. 2c, 70c, 75c, Scouts from different nations. 3c, 60c, $1, Lord Baden-Powell.

**Unwmk.**
**1972, Dec. 2    Litho.    Perf. 14**
| | | | | |
|---|---|---|---|---|
| 468 | A70 | ½c yellow & multi | .25 | .25 |
| 469 | A70 | 1c red & multi | .25 | .25 |
| 470 | A70 | 2c yellow & multi | .25 | .25 |
| 471 | A70 | 3c brt lilac & multi | .25 | .25 |
| 472 | A70 | 75c lt blue & multi | .80 | .80 |
| 473 | A70 | $1 multicolored | 1.25 | 1.25 |
| | | Nos. 468-473,C27-C28 (8) | 4.05 | 3.95 |

**Souvenir Sheet**
| | | | | |
|---|---|---|---|---|
| 474 | | Sheet of 2 | 2.75 | 2.75 |
| a. | | A70 60c ocher & multi | 1.25 | 1.25 |
| b. | | A70 70c pale lilac & multi | 1.50 | 1.50 |

Boy Scouts, 65th anniversary.

Virgin and Child, Crosier — A71

Christmas: 3c, 35c, 70c, The Three Kings. 5c, $1, Holy Family. 25c, 60c, Like 1c.

**1972, Dec. 9   Litho.   Perf. 14x13½**
| | | | | |
|---|---|---|---|---|
|475|A71|1c blue & multi|.25|.25|
|476|A71|3c gray & multi|.25|.25|
|477|A71|5c multicolored|.25|.25|
|478|A71|25c multicolored|.25|.25|
|479|A71|35c lt blue & multi|.25|.25|
|480|A71|$1 ocher & multi|.60|.60|
| |Nos. 475-480 (6)|1.85|1.85|

**Souvenir Sheet**
**Perf. 15**
|481| |Sheet of 2|1.10|1.10|
|a.|A71 60c blue & multi|.45|.45|
|b.|A71 70c bright pink & multi|.60|.60|

Flamingos A72

**1973, Jan. 5   Litho.   Perf. 14**
|482|A72|25c shown|1.00|.25|
|483|A72|35c Tapir|.80|.25|
|484|A72|60c Macaws|1.75|1.75|
|485|A72|70c Ocelot|1.60|2.25|
| |Nos. 482-485 (4)|5.15|4.50|

National Zoo of Grenada.

Class II Ocean Racing Yacht — A73

35c, Boats in St. George's Harbour. 60c, Yacht "Bloodhound". 70c, St. George's Harbour.

**1973, Jan. 26   Litho.   Perf. 13½x14**
|486|A73|25c shown|.40|.35|
|487|A73|35c multicolored|.55|.50|
|488|A73|60c multicolored|.90|.85|
|489|A73|70c multicolored|.95|1.10|
| |Nos. 486-489 (4)|2.80|2.80|

Yachting off Grenada.

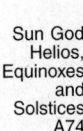 Sun God Helios, Equinoxes and Solstices A74

WMO Emblem and: 1c, Poseidon and Nomad automatic storm detector. 2c, Zeus and radarscope. 3c, Goddess Iris, rainbow, weather balloon. 35c, Hermes, ATS 3 satellite. 50c, Zephyr and circulation of atmosphere. 75c, Demeter, space photograph of storm. $1, Selene, globe showing world rainfall. $2, Computer weather map (42x31mm).

**1973, July 6   Litho.   Perf. 13½**
|490|A74|½c multicolored|.25|.25|
|491|A74|1c multicolored|.25|.25|
|492|A74|2c multicolored|.25|.25|
|493|A74|3c multicolored|.25|.25|
|494|A74|35c multicolored|.30|.25|
|495|A74|50c multicolored|.45|.25|
|496|A74|75c multicolored|.55|.45|
|497|A74|$1 multicolored|.55|.55|
| |Nos. 490-497 (8)|2.85|2.50|

**Souvenir Sheet**
|498|A74|$2 multicolored|1.75|1.75|

Intl. meteorological cooperation, cent.

 Racing Class Yachts — A75

1c, Cruising class. 2c, Open-decked sloops. 35c, Sloop Mermaid. 50c, St. George's Harbour. 75c, Map of Carriacou. $1, Boat building. $2, End of race.

**1973, Aug. 3   Litho.   Perf. 13½**
|499|A75|½c shown|.25|.25|
|500|A75|1c multicolored|.25|.25|
|501|A75|2c multicolored|.25|.25|
|502|A75|35c multicolored|.35|.25|
|503|A75|50c multicolored|.45|.25|
|504|A75|75c multicolored|.65|.65|
|505|A75|$1 multicolored|.80|.80|
| |Nos. 499-505 (7)|3.00|2.70|

**Souvenir Sheet**
|506|A75|$2 multicolored|1.50|1.75|

Carriacou Regatta, August 1973.

 Ignaz Philipp Semmelweiss — A76

Designs: Physicians and scientists.

**1973, Sept. 17   Litho.   Perf. 14½**
|507|A76|½c shown|.25|.25|
|508|A76|1c Louis Pasteur|.25|.25|
|509|A76|2c Edward Jenner|.25|.25|
|510|A76|3c Sigmund Freud|.25|.25|
|511|A76|25c Emil von Behring|.45|.45|
|512|A76|35c Carl Jung|.60|.60|
|513|A76|50c Charles Calmette|.90|.90|
|514|A76|$1 William Harvey|1.75|1.75|
| |Nos. 507-514 (8)|4.70|4.70|

**Souvenir Sheet**
|515|A76|$2 Marie Curie|3.50|3.50|

WHO, 25th anniv.

 Princess Anne and Mark Phillips — A77

**1973, Nov. 14   Wmk. 314   Perf. 13½**
|516|A77|25c dp orange & multi|.30|.80|
|517|A77|$2 green & multi|.30|.80|
|a.|Souv. sheet of 2 (75c, $1)|.60|.60|

Wedding of Princess Anne and Capt. Mark Phillips.
Nos. 516-517 were issued only in sheets of 5 plus label. Colors of 75c and $1 are as those of 25c and $2.

 Virgin and Child, by Carlo Maratti — A78

Christmas (Paintings): 1c, Virgin and Child, by Carlo Crivelli. 2c, Virgin and Child, by Verrocchio. 3c, Adoration of the Shepherds, by Roberti. 25c, Holy Family, by Federigo Baroccio. 35c, Holy Family, by Bronzino. 75c, Mystic Nativity, by Botticelli. $1, Adoration of the Kings, by Geertgen tot Sint Jans. $2, Adoration of the Kings, by Jan Mostaert (30x45mm).

**1973, Nov.   Unwmk.   Perf. 14½**
|519|A78|½c lt brown & multi|.25|.25|
|520|A78|1c citron & multi|.25|.25|
|521|A78|2c blue & multi|.25|.25|
|522|A78|3c green & multi|.25|.25|
|523|A78|25c multicolored|.25|.25|
|524|A78|35c multicolored|.25|.25|
|525|A78|75c vio blue & multi|.25|.80|
|526|A78|$1 multicolored|.30|1.00|
| |Nos. 519-526 (8)|2.05|3.30|

**Souvenir Sheet**
**Perf. 13½x14**
|527|A78|$2 red & multi|2.00|2.00|

**Nos. 294-297, 299-301, 303-304, 305A-309 Overprinted**

**Perf. 14x14½, 14½x14**
**1974, Feb. 7   Photo.**
|528|A45|1c multicolored|.25|.25|
|529|A45|2c multicolored|.25|.25|
|530|A45|3c multicolored|.25|.25|
|531|A45|5c multicolored|.25|.25|
|532|A45|8c multicolored|.25|.25|
|533|A45|10c multicolored|.25|.25|
|534|A45|12c multicolored|.25|.25|
|535|A45|25c multicolored|.40|.40|
|536|A45|35c multicolored|.60|.60|

**Litho.**
**Perf. 13½x14**
|537|A45a|75c multicolored|2.10|1.50|

**Photo.**
**Perf. 14x14½**
|538|A45|$1 multicolored|3.75|1.75|
|539|A45|$2 multicolored|5.75|6.50|
|540|A45|$3 multicolored|7.25|8.25|
|541|A45|$5 multicolored|11.50|18.50|
| |Nos. 528-541 (14)|33.10|39.25|

Grenada's independence, Feb. 7, 1974. Size of overprint on vertical stamps 16x5mm; on horizontal stamps 20x6mm.

 Creative Arts Theater, Jamaica Campus A79

Designs: 25c, Marryshow House, University Center. 50c, Chapel, vert. $1, $2, University coat of arms, vert.

**1974, Apr. 10   Litho.   Perf. 13½**
|542|A79|10c multicolored|.25|.25|
|543|A79|25c multicolored|.25|.25|
|544|A79|50c multicolored|.25|.25|
|545|A79|$1 multicolored|.30|.30|
| |Nos. 542-545 (4)|1.05|1.05|

**Souvenir Sheet**
|546|A79|$2 multicolored|.90|.90|

25th anniv. of the University of the West Indies.

 Prime Minister Eric M. Gairy — A80

3c, Nutmeg and mace. 8c, Map of Grenada. 35c, Anse Beach and Flag. $1, Coat of arms. $2, Coat of arms.

**1974, Aug. 19   Litho.   Perf. 13½**
|547|A80|3c multicolored|.25|.25|
|548|A80|8c multicolored|.25|.25|
|549|A80|25c shown|.30|.30|
|550|A80|35c multicolored|.35|.35|
|551|A80|$1 multicolored|.85|.85|
| |Nos. 547-551 (5)|2.00|2.00|

**Souvenir Sheet**
|552|A80|$2 multicolored|1.10|1.10|

Grenada's independence.

 Soccer, Flags of West Germany and Chile — A81

Soccer Games and Flags: 1c, East Germany and Australia. 2c, Yugoslavia and Brazil. 10c, Scotland and Zaire. 25c, Netherlands and Uruguay. 50c, Sweden and Bulgaria. 75c, Italy

and Haiti. $1, Poland and Argentina. $2, Flags of participating nations, horiz.

**1974, Sept. 3   Litho.   Perf. 14½**
|553|A81|½c multicolored|.25|.25|
|554|A81|1c multicolored|.25|.25|
|555|A81|2c multicolored|.25|.25|
|556|A81|10c multicolored|.25|.25|
|557|A81|25c multicolored|.25|.25|
|558|A81|50c multicolored|.25|.25|
|559|A81|75c multicolored|.30|.30|
|560|A81|$1 multicolored|.45|.45|
| |Nos. 553-560 (8)|2.25|2.25|

**Souvenir Sheet**
**Perf. 13**
|561|A81|$2 multicolored|1.60|1.60|

World Cup Soccer Championship, Munich, June 13-July 7.

 19th Century US Mail Train, Concorde and UPU Emblem A82

UPU Emblem and: 1c, Sailing ship "Caesar," 1839, and helicopter. 2c, Zeppelin, jet and early planes. 8c, Pigeon post, 1480, telephone dial. 15c, Bellman, 18th cent. and radar. 25c, German Imperial messenger, 1450, satellite. 35c, French pillar box and ocean liner. $1, German mailman, 18th cent., and futuristic mail train. $2, St. Gotthard mail coach, 1735, vert.

**1974, Oct. 8   Litho.   Perf. 14½**
|562|A82|½c rose & multi|.25|.25|
|563|A82|1c gray & multi|.25|.25|
|564|A82|2c dull pink & multi|.25|.25|
|565|A82|8c yellow & multi|.25|.25|
|566|A82|15c yel grn & multi|.40|.25|
|567|A82|25c dull yel & multi|.45|.25|
|568|A82|35c lilac & multi|.70|.25|
|569|A82|$1 lt blue & multi|1.75|1.60|
| |Nos. 562-569 (8)|4.30|3.35|

**Souvenir Sheet**
**Perf. 13**
|570|A82|$2 multicolored|1.75|2.25|

UPU, cent.

 Sir Winston Churchill A83

Design: $2, Churchill, different portrait.

**1974, Oct. 28   Litho.   Perf. 13½**
|571|A83|35c multicolored|.25|.25|
|572|A83|$2 multicolored|.65|.65|

**Souvenir Sheet**
|573| |Sheet of 2|1.10|1.10|
|a.|A83 75c like 35c|.45|.45|
|b.|A83 $1 like $2|.65|.65|

Winston Churchill (1874-1965).

 Virgin and Child, by Botticelli — A84

Christmas: Paintings of the Virgin and Child.

**1974, Nov. 18   Perf. 14½**
|574|A84|½ shown|.25|.25|
|575|A84|1c Niccolo di Pietro|.25|.25|
|576|A84|2c Van der Weyden|.25|.25|
|577|A84|3c Bastiani|.25|.25|
|578|A84|10c Giovanni|.25|.25|
|579|A84|25c Van der Weyden|.25|.25|
|580|A84|50c Botticelli|.25|.25|
|581|A84|$1 Mantegna|.40|.40|
| |Nos. 574-581 (8)|2.15|2.15|

**Souvenir Sheet**
**Perf. 13½**
|582|A84|$2 Niccolo di Pietro|1.40|1.40|

Yachts and Point Saline — A85

1c, Grenada Yacht Club race, St. George's. 2c, Carenage taxi (boat). 3c, Large working boats. 5c, Deep Water Dock, St. George's. 6c, Cacao beans in drying trays. 8c, Nutmeg branch. 10c, River Antoine Estate rum distillery, c. 1785. 12c, Cacao branch. 15c, Fishermen landing catch at Fontenoy. 20c, Parliament Building, St. George's. 25c, Fort George cannons. 35c, Pearls Airport. 50c, General Post Office. 75c, Carib Leap, Sauteurs Bay. $1, Careenage, St. George's. $2, St. George's harbor at night. $3, Grand Anse Beach. $5, Canoe Bay and Black Bay from Point Saline Lighthouse. $10, Sugar-loaf Island from Levera Beach.

| | | | |
|---|---|---|---|
| **1975** | | **Litho.** | **Perf. 14½** |
| | | **Size: 38x25mm** | |
| 583 | A85 | ½c multicolored | .25 .55 |
| 584 | A85 | 1c multicolored | .25 .25 |
| 585 | A85 | 2c multicolored | .25 .25 |
| 586 | A85 | 3c multicolored | .25 .25 |
| 587 | A85 | 5c multicolored | .25 .25 |
| 588 | A85 | 6c multicolored | .25 .25 |
| 589 | A85 | 8c multicolored | 1.00 .25 |
| 590 | A85 | 10c multicolored | .25 .25 |
| 591 | A85 | 12c multicolored | .35 .25 |
| 592 | A85 | 15c multicolored | .25 .25 |
| 593 | A85 | 20c multicolored | .25 .25 |
| 594 | A85 | 25c multicolored | .25 .25 |
| 595 | A85 | 35c multicolored | .25 .25 |
| 596 | A85 | 50c multicolored | .25 .25 |
| | | **Perf. 13½x14** | |
| | | **Size: 45x28mm** | |
| 597 | A85 | 75c multicolored | .50 .40 |
| 598 | A85 | $1 multicolored | .55 .60 |
| 599 | A85 | $2 multicolored | .55 1.25 |
| 600 | A85 | $3 multicolored | .60 1.75 |
| 601 | A85 | $5 multicolored | .70 2.50 |
| 602 | A85 | $10 multicolored | 2.00 5.50 |
| | | Nos. 583-602 (20) | 9.25 15.80 |

Issue dates: Nos. 583-596, Jan. 13; Nos. 597-601, Jan. 22; No. 602, Mar. 26. For overprints, see Nos. 965-979.

| | | | |
|---|---|---|---|
| **1978** | | | **Perf. 13** |
| 584a | A85 | 1c | .25 .25 |
| 585a | A85 | 2c | .25 .25 |
| 586a | A85 | 3c | .25 .25 |
| 587a | A85 | 5c | .25 .25 |
| 588a | A85 | 6c | .25 .25 |
| 589a | A85 | 10c | .25 .25 |
| 592a | A85 | 15c | .25 .30 |
| 593a | A85 | 20c | .25 .40 |
| 594a | A85 | 25c | .25 .50 |
| 596a | A85 | 50c | .40 .55 |
| | | Nos. 584a-596a (10) | 2.65 3.25 |

Sailfish — A86

Designs: Big game fish.

| | | | |
|---|---|---|---|
| **1975, Feb. 3** | | | **Perf. 14½** |
| 603 | A86 | ½c shown | .25 .25 |
| 604 | A86 | 1c Blue marlin | .25 .25 |
| 605 | A86 | 2c White marlin | .25 .25 |
| 606 | A86 | 10c Yellowfin tuna | .25 .25 |
| 607 | A86 | 25c Wahoo | .35 .30 |
| 608 | A86 | 50c Dolphin | .55 .40 |
| 609 | A86 | 70c Grouper | .75 .40 |
| 610 | A86 | $1 Great barracuda | .90 .50 |
| | | Nos. 603-610 (8) | 3.55 2.60 |
| | | **Souvenir Sheet** | |
| | | **Perf. 13** | |
| 611 | A86 | $2 Mako shark | 2.40 2.40 |

Passiflora Quadrangularis A87

Flowers of Grenada: 1c, Bleeding heart. 2c, Poinsettia. 3c, Obroma cacao. 10c, Gladioli. 25c, Red head-yellow head. 50c, Plumbago. $1, Orange blossoms. $2, Barbados gooseberry.

| | | | |
|---|---|---|---|
| **1975, Feb. 26** | | **Litho.** | **Perf. 14½** |
| 612 | A87 | ½c shown | .25 .25 |
| 613 | A87 | 1c multicolored | .25 .25 |
| 614 | A87 | 2c multicolored | .25 .25 |
| 615 | A87 | 3c multicolored | .25 .25 |
| 616 | A87 | 10c multicolored | .25 .25 |
| 617 | A87 | 25c multicolored | .45 .25 |

| | | | |
|---|---|---|---|
| 618 | A87 | 50c multicolored | .65 .25 |
| 619 | A87 | $1 multicolored | .95 .45 |
| | | Nos. 612-619 (8) | 3.30 2.20 |
| | | **Souvenir Sheet** | |
| | | **Perf. 13½** | |
| 620 | A87 | $2 multicolored | 1.75 1.75 |

Grenada Flag and UN Emblem — A88

Designs: 1c, UN and Grenada flags. 2c, $1, UN emblem and Grenada coat of arms. 35c, UN emblem over map of Grenada. 50c, Grenada flag in front of UN Headquarters. 75c, like ½c. $2, UN emblem and scroll.

| | | | |
|---|---|---|---|
| **1975, Mar. 19** | | | **Perf. 14½** |
| 621 | A88 | ½c multicolored | .25 .25 |
| 622 | A88 | 1c multicolored | .25 .25 |
| 623 | A88 | 2c multicolored | .25 .25 |
| 624 | A88 | 35c multicolored | .25 .25 |
| 625 | A88 | 50c multicolored | .25 .25 |
| 626 | A88 | $2 multicolored | .50 .50 |
| | | Nos. 621-626 (6) | 1.75 1.75 |
| | | **Souvenir Sheet** | |
| | | **Perf. 13½** | |
| 627 | | Sheet of 2 | 1.40 1.40 |
| a. | | A88 75c multicolored | .55 .55 |
| b. | | A88 $1 multicolored | .90 .90 |

Grenada's admission to the United Nations, Sept. 17, 1974.

> Remainders of Grenada stamps between Scott Nos. 630 and 872, except Nos. 747-748 and 802-804, were later canceled to order and sold at a fraction of their face value. Used values for these stamps are for c-t-o examples. Postally used stamps are worth the same as unused, never hinged examples.

Midnight Ride of Paul Revere — A89

1c, Crispus Attucks at Boston Massacre. 2c, Patrick Henry. 3c, Franklin visiting Washington at the front. 5c, Lexington-Concord. 10c, John Paul Jones. No. 634, Arms of Grenada & US. No. 635, Flags of Grenada & US.

| | | | |
|---|---|---|---|
| **1975, May 6** | | **Litho.** | **Perf. 14½, 13** |
| 628 | A89 | ½c Prus blue & multi | .25 .25 |
| 629 | A89 | 1c buff & multi | .25 .25 |
| 630 | A89 | 2c dp org & multi | .25 .25 |
| 631 | A89 | 3c orange & multi | .25 .25 |
| 632 | A89 | 5c Prus blue & multi | .25 .25 |
| 633 | A89 | 10c ultra & multi | .25 .25 |
| | | Nos. 628-633,C29-C32 (10) | 3.40 2.50 |
| | | **Souvenir Sheets** | |
| | | **Perf. 13½** | |
| 634 | A89 | $2 tan & multi | 1.00 .45 |
| 635 | A89 | $2 gray & multi | 1.00 .45 |

American Revolution Bicentennial. Size of stamps on Nos. 634-635: 47x34mm. Nos. 628-633 issued in sheets of 40. Each denomination was also printed in sheets of 5 plus label, perf. 13.

Angel Collecting Jesus' Blood in Grail, by Bellini — A90

Easter (Paintings): 1c, Pieta, by Bellini. 2c, The Deposition, by Rogier van der Weyden. 3c, Pieta, by Bellini. 35c, Descent from the Cross, by Bellini. 75c, Jesus Rising from the Tomb, by Bellini. $1, Descent from the Cross, by Procaccini. $2, Pieta, by Botticelli.

| | | | |
|---|---|---|---|
| **1975, May 21** | | | |
| 636 | A90 | ½c multicolored | .25 .25 |
| 637 | A90 | 1c multicolored | .25 .25 |
| 638 | A90 | 2c multicolored | .25 .25 |

| | | | |
|---|---|---|---|
| 639 | A90 | 3c multicolored | .25 .25 |
| 640 | A90 | 35c multicolored | .30 .25 |
| 641 | A90 | 50c multicolored | .35 .25 |
| 642 | A90 | $1 multicolored | .45 .25 |
| | | Nos. 636-642 (7) | 2.10 1.75 |
| | | **Souvenir Sheet** | |
| | | **Perf. 13½** | |
| 643 | A90 | $2 multicolored | 1.40 .65 |

Scouts Studying Wildlife, Nordjamb 75 Emblem — A91

Nordjamb 75 Emblem and: 1c, Seamanship; Scouts in sailboat. 2c, Survival; Scouts reading map. 35c, First aid. 40c, Physical fitness; gymnastics. 75c, Mountaineering. $1, Emergency boat building. $2, Scouts singing.

| | | | |
|---|---|---|---|
| **1975, July 2** | | **Litho.** | **Perf. 14** |
| 644 | A91 | ½c blue & multi | .25 .25 |
| 645 | A91 | 1c blue & multi | .25 .25 |
| 646 | A91 | 2c blue & multi | .25 .25 |
| 647 | A91 | 35c blue & multi | .45 .25 |
| 648 | A91 | 40c blue & multi | .50 .25 |
| 649 | A91 | 75c blue & multi | .60 .25 |
| 650 | A91 | $2 blue & multi | 1.25 .35 |
| | | Nos. 644-650 (7) | 3.55 1.85 |
| | | **Souvenir Sheet** | |
| 651 | A91 | $1 blue & multi | 1.60 .35 |

Nordjamb 75, 14th Boy Scout World Jamboree, Lillehammer, Norway, July 29-Aug. 7.

Leafy Jewel Box — A92

Sea shells — 1c, Emerald nerite. 2c, Yellow cockle. 25c, Purple sea snail. 50c, Turkey wing. 75c, West Indian fighting conch. $1, Noble wentletrap. $2, Music volute.

| | | | |
|---|---|---|---|
| **1975, Aug. 1** | | **Litho.** | **Perf. 14** |
| 652 | A92 | ½c shown | .25 .25 |
| 653 | A92 | 1c multicolored | .25 .25 |
| 654 | A92 | 2c multicolored | .25 .25 |
| 655 | A92 | 25c multicolored | 1.00 .25 |
| 656 | A92 | 50c multicolored | 2.00 .40 |
| 657 | A92 | 75c multicolored | 2.75 .50 |
| 658 | A92 | $1 multicolored | 2.75 .50 |
| | | Nos. 652-658 (7) | 9.25 2.40 |
| | | **Souvenir Sheet** | |
| 659 | A92 | $2 multicolored | 4.50 .90 |

Butterflies — A93

½c, Large tiger. 1c, Five continents. 2c, Large striped blue. 35c, Gonatryx. 45c, Spear-winged cattle heart. 75c, Risty nymula. $2, Blue night. $1, Lycrophon.

| | | | |
|---|---|---|---|
| **1975, Sept. 22** | | **Litho.** | **Perf. 14** |
| 660 | A93 | ½c multicolored | .25 .25 |
| 661 | A93 | 1c multicolored | .25 .25 |
| 662 | A93 | 2c multicolored | .25 .25 |
| 663 | A93 | 35c multicolored | .85 .25 |
| 664 | A93 | 45c multicolored | 1.00 .30 |
| 665 | A93 | 75c multicolored | 1.50 .40 |
| 666 | A93 | $2 multicolored | 3.75 .75 |
| | | Nos. 660-666 (7) | 7.85 2.45 |
| | | **Souvenir Sheet** | |
| 667 | A93 | $1 multicolored | 3.00 1.00 |

Crew Race — A94

1c, Women's swimming. 2c, Steeplechase. 35c, Gymnastics. 45c, Soccer. 75c, Boxing. $2, Bicycling. $1, Sailing.

| | | | |
|---|---|---|---|
| **1975, Oct. 13** | | **Litho.** | **Perf. 14** |
| 668 | A94 | ½c multicolored | .25 .25 |
| 669 | A94 | 1c multicolored | .25 .25 |
| 670 | A94 | 2c multicolored | .25 .25 |
| 671 | A94 | 35c multicolored | .25 .25 |
| 672 | A94 | 45c multicolored | .25 .25 |
| 673 | A94 | 75c multicolored | .30 .25 |
| 674 | A94 | $2 multicolored | 1.10 .40 |
| | | Nos. 668-674 (7) | 2.65 1.90 |
| | | **Souvenir Sheet** | |
| 675 | A94 | $1 multicolored | 2.00 .45 |

7th Pan-American Games, Mexico City, Oct. 13-26.

Young Man, by Michelangelo — A95

Works by Michelangelo (except 50c): ½c, David. 2c, Moses. 40c, Zachariah. 50c, St. John the Baptist (sculpture). 75c, Judith and Holofernes (detail). $1, Madonna (head from Pietà). $2, Doni Madonna (detail from Holy Family).

| | | | |
|---|---|---|---|
| **1975, Nov. 3** | | | |
| 676 | A95 | ½c black & multi | .25 .25 |
| 677 | A95 | 1c black & multi | .25 .25 |
| 678 | A95 | 2c black & multi | .25 .25 |
| 679 | A95 | 40c black & multi | .40 .25 |
| 680 | A95 | 50c black & multi | .50 .25 |
| 681 | A95 | 75c black & multi | .75 .25 |
| 682 | A95 | $2 black & multi | 1.25 .45 |
| | | Nos. 676-682 (7) | 3.65 1.95 |
| | | **Souvenir Sheet** | |
| 683 | A95 | $1 black & multi | 2.25 .40 |

Michelangelo Buonarroti (1475-1564), Italian painter, sculptor and architect.

Virgin and Child Paintings — A96

½c, Filippino Lippi. 1c, Mantegna. 2c, Luis de Morales. 35c, G. M. Morandi. 50c, Antonello da Messina. 75c, Durer. $1, Velazquez. $2, Bellini.

| | | | |
|---|---|---|---|
| **1975, Dec. 8** | | | |
| 684 | A96 | ½c multicolored | .25 .25 |
| 685 | A96 | 1c multicolored | .25 .25 |
| 686 | A96 | 2c multicolored | .25 .25 |
| 687 | A96 | 35c multicolored | .25 .25 |
| 688 | A96 | 50c multicolored | .25 .25 |
| 689 | A96 | 75c multicolored | .30 .25 |
| 690 | A96 | $1 multicolored | .35 .25 |
| | | Nos. 684-690 (7) | 1.90 1.75 |
| | | **Souvenir Sheet** | |
| 691 | A96 | $2 multicolored | 1.60 .45 |

Christmas.

Bananaquit — A97

Designs: 1c, Orange-rumped agouti. 2c, Hawksbill turtle, horiz. 5c, Dwarf poinciana. 35c, Albacores, horiz. 40c, Cardinal's guard flower. $1, Belted kingfisher. $2, Antillean armadillo, horiz.

| | | | |
|---|---|---|---|
| **1976, Jan. 20** | | **Litho.** | **Perf. 14** |
| 692 | A97 | ½c multicolored | .25 .25 |
| 693 | A97 | 1c multicolored | .25 .25 |
| 694 | A97 | 2c multicolored | .25 .25 |
| 695 | A97 | 5c multicolored | .25 .25 |
| 696 | A97 | 35c multicolored | 1.10 .25 |

| | | | | |
|---|---|---|---|---|
| 697 | A97 | 40c multicolored | 1.25 | .25 |
| 698 | A97 | $2 multicolored | 3.00 | .75 |
| | | Nos. 692-698 (7) | 6.35 | 2.25 |

**Souvenir Sheet**

| | | | | |
|---|---|---|---|---|
| 699 | A97 | $1 multicolored | 7.25 | 1.00 |

Carnival Dancers — A98

Designs: 1c, Scuba diving. 2c, Cruise ship in St. George's Harbor. 35c, Game fishing. 50c, St. George's Golf Course. 75c, Tennis. $1, Mount Rich rock carvings. $2, Sailboats.

**1976, Feb. 25    Litho.    Perf. 14**

| | | | | |
|---|---|---|---|---|
| 700 | A98 | ½c multicolored | .25 | .25 |
| 701 | A98 | 1c multicolored | .25 | .25 |
| 702 | A98 | 2c multicolored | .25 | .25 |
| 703 | A98 | 35c multicolored | .90 | .25 |
| 704 | A98 | 50c multicolored | 3.00 | .25 |
| 705 | A98 | 75c multicolored | 3.25 | .35 |
| 706 | A98 | $1 multicolored | 3.50 | .35 |
| | | Nos. 700-706 (7) | 11.40 | 1.95 |

**Souvenir Sheet**

| | | | | |
|---|---|---|---|---|
| 707 | A98 | $2 multicolored | 2.75 | .75 |

Tourist publicity.

Descent from the Cross, by Master of Okolicsno — A99

Easter (Paintings): 1c, Pieta, by Correggio. 2c, Crucifixion, by van der Weyden. 3c, Burial of Christ, by Dürer. 35c, God the Father Holding Crucified Christ, by unknown master (Florence). 75c, Ascension, by Raphael. $1, Burial of Christ, by Raphael. $2, Pieta, by Crespi.

**1976, Mar. 29**

| | | | | |
|---|---|---|---|---|
| 708 | A99 | ½c multicolored | .25 | .25 |
| 709 | A99 | 1c multicolored | .25 | .25 |
| 710 | A99 | 2c multicolored | .25 | .25 |
| 711 | A99 | 3c multicolored | .25 | .25 |
| 712 | A99 | 35c multicolored | .25 | .25 |
| 713 | A99 | 75c multicolored | .30 | .25 |
| 714 | A99 | $1 multicolored | .40 | .25 |
| | | Nos. 708-714 (7) | 1.95 | 1.75 |

**Souvenir Sheet**

| | | | | |
|---|---|---|---|---|
| 715 | A99 | $2 multicolored | 1.25 | 1.25 |

Sharpshooters, 1780 — A100

First Stars and Stripes and: 1c, Defense of Liberty Pole. 2c, Men loading muskets. 35c, 75c, Fight for Liberty. 50c, $2, Peace Treaty, 1783. $1, Drumming march on Breed's Hill. $3, Gunboat, c. 1776.

**1976, Apr. 15    Litho.    Perf. 14**

| | | | | |
|---|---|---|---|---|
| 716 | A100 | ½c multicolored | .25 | .25 |
| 717 | A100 | 1c multicolored | .25 | .25 |
| 718 | A100 | 2c multicolored | .25 | .25 |
| 719 | A100 | 35c multicolored | .45 | .25 |
| 720 | A100 | 50c multicolored | .55 | .25 |
| 721 | A100 | $1 multicolored | .90 | .25 |
| 722 | A100 | $3 multicolored | 2.25 | .25 |
| | | Nos. 716-722 (7) | 4.90 | 1.75 |

**Souvenir Sheet**

| | | | | |
|---|---|---|---|---|
| 723 | | Sheet of 2 | 2.00 | 1.40 |
| a. | A100 | 75c multicolored | .65 | .55 |
| b. | A100 | $2 multicolored | 1.40 | .25 |

American Bicentennial.

Girl Guide Emblems, Nature Study — A101

Various Girl Guide Emblems and: 1c, Cooking. 2c, $2, First aid, diff. 50c, Tenting. 75c, Home economics. $1, Drawing.

**1976, June 1    Litho.    Perf. 14**

| | | | | |
|---|---|---|---|---|
| 724 | A101 | ½c multicolored | .25 | .25 |
| 725 | A101 | 1c multicolored | .25 | .25 |
| 726 | A101 | 2c multicolored | .25 | .25 |
| 727 | A101 | 50c multicolored | .50 | .25 |
| 728 | A101 | 75c multicolored | .75 | .25 |
| 729 | A101 | $2 multicolored | 1.75 | .45 |
| | | Nos. 724-729 (6) | 3.75 | 1.70 |

**Souvenir Sheet**

| | | | | |
|---|---|---|---|---|
| 730 | A101 | $1 multicolored | 1.75 | .80 |

Girl Guides of Grenada, 50th anniv.

Volleyball — A102

Olympic Rings and: 1c, Bicycling. 2c, Rowing. 35c, Judo. 45c, Hockey. 75c, Women's gymnastics. $1, High jump. $3, Equestrian.

**1976, June 21    Litho.    Perf. 14**

| | | | | |
|---|---|---|---|---|
| 731 | A102 | ½c multicolored | .25 | .25 |
| 732 | A102 | 1c multicolored | .25 | .25 |
| 733 | A102 | 2c multicolored | .25 | .25 |
| 734 | A102 | 35c multicolored | .30 | .25 |
| 735 | A102 | 45c multicolored | .55 | .25 |
| 736 | A102 | 75c multicolored | .60 | .40 |
| 737 | A102 | $1 multicolored | .70 | .40 |
| | | Nos. 731-737 (7) | 2.90 | 2.05 |

**Souvenir Sheet**

| | | | | |
|---|---|---|---|---|
| 738 | A102 | $3 multicolored | 1.75 | 1.25 |

21st Olympic Games, Montreal, Canada, July 17-Aug. 1.

Moulin Rouge, by Toulouse-Lautrec A103

Paintings by Toulouse-Lautrec: 1c, Start of the Quadrille. 2c, Woman's Head. 3c, Hall at the Moulin Rouge. 40c, Man Delivering Laundry. 50c, Dancing the Bolero. $1, Lady with Boa. $2, Signor Boileau at the Cafe.

**1976, July 20    Litho.    Perf. 14**

| | | | | |
|---|---|---|---|---|
| 739 | A103 | ½c multicolored | .25 | .25 |
| 740 | A103 | 1c multicolored | .25 | .25 |
| 741 | A103 | 2c multicolored | .25 | .25 |
| 742 | A103 | 3c multicolored | .25 | .25 |
| 743 | A103 | 40c multicolored | .75 | .25 |
| 744 | A103 | 50c multicolored | .95 | .25 |
| 745 | A103 | $2 multicolored | 2.50 | .50 |
| | | Nos. 739-745 (7) | 5.20 | 2.00 |

**Souvenir Sheet**

| | | | | |
|---|---|---|---|---|
| 746 | A103 | $1 multicolored | 4.50 | 1.25 |

Henri de Toulouse-Lautrec (1864-1901), painter, 75th death anniv.

Map of West Indies, Bats, Wicket and Ball — A103a

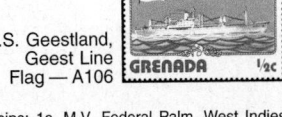

Prudential Cup — A103b

**1976, July 26**

| | | | | |
|---|---|---|---|---|
| 747 | A103a | 35c lt blue & multi | .60 | .60 |
| 748 | A103b | $1 lilac rose & blk | 1.50 | 1.50 |

World Cricket Cup, won by West Indies Team, 1975.

Piper Apache — A104

Airplanes: 1c, Beech Twin Bonanza. 2c, D.H. Twin Otter. 40c, Britten Norman Islander. 50c, D.H. Heron. $2, Hawker Siddeley Avro 748. $3, B.A.C. One-Eleven.

**1976, Aug. 18**

| | | | | |
|---|---|---|---|---|
| 749 | A104 | ½c multicolored | .25 | .25 |
| 750 | A104 | 1c multicolored | .25 | .25 |
| 751 | A104 | 2c multicolored | .25 | .25 |
| 752 | A104 | 40c multicolored | .75 | .25 |
| 753 | A104 | 50c multicolored | .80 | .25 |
| 754 | A104 | $2 multicolored | 2.50 | .75 |
| | | Nos. 749-754 (6) | 4.80 | 2.00 |

**Souvenir Sheet**

| | | | | |
|---|---|---|---|---|
| 755 | A104 | $3 multicolored | 3.00 | 1.10 |

Helios Mission, Assembly — A105

Designs: 1c, Helios spacecraft in space. 2c, Helios assembled. 15c, Helios, system test and checkout. 45c, Viking nearing Mars, horiz. 75c, Viking on Mars. $2, Viking spacecraft assembled. $3, Helios orbiter and Viking lander.

**1976, Sept. 1    Litho.    Perf. 14**

| | | | | |
|---|---|---|---|---|
| 756 | A105 | ½c multicolored | .25 | .25 |
| 757 | A105 | 1c multicolored | .25 | .25 |
| 758 | A105 | 2c multicolored | .25 | .25 |
| 759 | A105 | 15c multicolored | .25 | .25 |
| 760 | A105 | 45c multicolored | .25 | .25 |
| 761 | A105 | 75c multicolored | .35 | .25 |
| 762 | A105 | $2 multicolored | .65 | .35 |
| | | Nos. 756-762 (7) | 2.25 | 1.85 |

**Souvenir Sheet**

| | | | | |
|---|---|---|---|---|
| 763 | A105 | $3 multicolored | 1.75 | 1.00 |

Helios (solar probe) mission and Viking Mars missions.

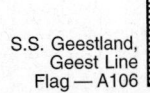

S.S. Geestland, Geest Line Flag — A106

Ships: 1c, M.V. Federal Palm, West Indies Shipping Service. 2c, H.M.S. Blake and ship's crest. 25c, M.V. Vistafjord and Norwegian-American Line flag. 75c, S.S. Canberra and P. & O. Line flag. $1, S.S. Regina and Chandris Line flag. $2, Santa Maria and Spanish flag, 1492. $5, S.S. Arandora and Blue Star Line flag.

**1976, Nov. 3    Litho.    Perf. 14½**

| | | | | |
|---|---|---|---|---|
| 764 | A106 | ½c blue & multi | .25 | .25 |
| 765 | A106 | 1c blue & multi | .25 | .25 |
| 766 | A106 | 2c blue & multi | .55 | .25 |
| 767 | A106 | 25c blue & multi | .55 | .25 |
| 768 | A106 | 75c blue & multi | 1.00 | .25 |
| 769 | A106 | $1 blue & multi | 1.25 | .30 |
| 770 | A106 | $5 blue & multi | 2.50 | .65 |
| | | Nos. 764-770 (7) | 6.05 | 2.20 |

**Souvenir Sheet**

| | | | | |
|---|---|---|---|---|
| 771 | A106 | $2 multicolored | 2.50 | 2.50 |

Ships connected with Grenada's development.

Altarpiece of San Barnaba, by Botticelli — A107

Christmas (Paintings): 1c, Annunciation, by Botticelli. 2c, Madonna with Chancellor Rolin, by Jan van Eyck. 35c, Annunciation, by Fra Filippo Lippi. 50c, Madonna of the Magnificat, by Botticelli. 75c, Madonna of the Pomegranate, by Botticelli. $2, Gipsy Madonna, by Titian. $3, Madonna with St. Cosmas and Saints, by Botticelli.

**1976, Dec. 8    Litho.    Perf. 14**

| | | | | |
|---|---|---|---|---|
| 772 | A107 | ½c multicolored | .25 | .25 |
| 773 | A107 | 1c multicolored | .25 | .25 |
| 774 | A107 | 2c multicolored | .25 | .25 |
| 775 | A107 | 35c multicolored | .25 | .25 |
| 776 | A107 | 50c multicolored | .25 | .25 |
| 777 | A107 | 75c multicolored | .35 | .25 |
| 778 | A107 | $3 multicolored | .75 | .40 |
| | | Nos. 772-778 (7) | 2.35 | 1.90 |

**Souvenir Sheet**

| | | | | |
|---|---|---|---|---|
| 779 | A107 | $2 multicolored | 1.60 | .75 |

Globe and Telephone Users — A108

Designs: ½c, A. G. Bell, 1876 and modern telephones. 2c, Satellites around globe, world map. 18c, Videophone. 40c, Satellite and ground stations. $1, Satellite and telephone communication with ships. $2, British "Trimphone" and radar station. $5, Flags of the world surrounding globe, and telephone.

**1976, Dec. 17    Litho.    Perf. 14**

| | | | | |
|---|---|---|---|---|
| 780 | A108 | ½c multicolored | .25 | .25 |
| 781 | A108 | 1c multicolored | .25 | .25 |
| 782 | A108 | 2c multicolored | .25 | .25 |
| 783 | A108 | 18c multicolored | .25 | .25 |
| 784 | A108 | 40c multicolored | .30 | .25 |
| 785 | A108 | $1 multicolored | .40 | .25 |
| 786 | A108 | $2 multicolored | .65 | .45 |
| | | Nos. 780-786 (7) | 2.35 | 1.95 |

**Souvenir Sheet**

| | | | | |
|---|---|---|---|---|
| 787 | A108 | $5 multicolored | 2.25 | .90 |

Centenary of first telephone conversation by Alexander Graham Bell, Mar. 10, 1876.

Coronation of Elizabeth II — A109

Designs: ½c, Coronation. 1c, Orb and scepter. 35c, $1, Trooping of the Guards. 50c, $2, Spoon and ampulla. 35c, (bklt.), $2.50, Elizabeth II and Prince Philip. $5, Royal visit to Grenada.

**1977, Feb. 8    Litho.    Perf. 14, 12**

| | | | | |
|---|---|---|---|---|
| 788 | A109 | ½c multicolored | .25 | .25 |
| 789 | A109 | 1c multicolored | .25 | .25 |
| 790 | A109 | 35c multicolored | .25 | .25 |
| 791 | A109 | $2 multicolored | .30 | .30 |
| 792 | A109 | $2.50 multicolored | .35 | .30 |
| a. | | Booklet pane of 6 (35c) | .95 | |
| b. | | Booklet pane of 3 (50c, $1, $3) | 3.25 | |
| | | Nos. 788-792 (5) | 1.40 | 1.35 |

**Souvenir Sheet**

| | | | | |
|---|---|---|---|---|
| 793 | A109 | $5 multicolored | 1.10 | 1.10 |

Reign of Queen Elizabeth II, 25th anniv.
Nos. 792a-792b are self-adhesive, roulette x imperf. Marginal inscriptions.
Nos. 788-792 were printed in sheets of 40 (10x4), perf. 14, and sheets of 5 plus label, perf. 12, in changed colors.
For overprints see Nos. 821-826.

Water Skiing, One-ski Slalom — A110

Designs: 1c, Speedboat racing around Grand Anse. 2c, Crew racing, St. George's. 22c, Swimming, Grand Anse. 35c, Local work boat races. 75c, Water polo, careenage, St. George's. $2, Game fishing. $3, South Coast yacht race.

**1977, Apr. 13    Litho.    Perf. 14**

| | | | | |
|---|---|---|---|---|
| 794 | A110 | ½c multicolored | .25 | .25 |
| 795 | A110 | 1c multicolored | .25 | .25 |
| 796 | A110 | 2c multicolored | .25 | .25 |
| 797 | A110 | 22c multicolored | .25 | .25 |
| 798 | A110 | 35c multicolored | .35 | .25 |
| 799 | A110 | 75c multicolored | .55 | .25 |
| 800 | A110 | $2 multicolored | 1.10 | .35 |
| | | Nos. 794-800 (7) | 3.00 | 1.85 |

**Souvenir Sheet**

| | | | | |
|---|---|---|---|---|
| 801 | A110 | $3 multicolored | 1.75 | 1.25 |

1977 Easter Water Parade.

Tent, OAS Emblem — A111

## 1977, June 14 — Litho. — Perf. 14

| | | | |
|---|---|---|---|
| 802 | A111 | 35c multicolored | .25 .25 |
| 803 | A111 | $1 multicolored | .35 .35 |
| 804 | A111 | $2 multicolored | .60 .60 |
| | | Nos. 802-804 (3) | 1.20 1.20 |

7th Regular Session, General Assembly of Organization of American States.

Scouts on Raft — A112

Designs: 1c, Tug-of-war. 2c, Boy Scout regatta. 18c, Scouts around camp fire. 40c, Field kitchen. $1, Boy Scouts and Sea Scouts. $2, Hiking and map reading. $3, Semaphore.

## 1977, Sept. 6 — Litho. — Perf. 14

| | | | |
|---|---|---|---|
| 805 | A112 | ½c multicolored | .25 .25 |
| 806 | A112 | 1c multicolored | .25 .25 |
| 807 | A112 | 2c multicolored | .25 .25 |
| 808 | A112 | 18c multicolored | .30 .25 |
| 809 | A112 | 40c multicolored | .45 .25 |
| 810 | A112 | $1 multicolored | 1.10 .35 |
| 811 | A112 | $2 multicolored | 2.00 .55 |
| | | Nos. 805-811 (7) | 4.60 2.15 |

### Souvenir Sheet

| | | | |
|---|---|---|---|
| 812 | A112 | $3 multicolored | 2.75 1.25 |

6th Caribbean Jamboree, Kingston, Jamaica, Aug. 5-14.

Annunciation to the Shepherds A113

Ceiling Paintings, St. Martin's Church, Zillis, Switzerland, 12th Century: 1c, Joseph on his way. 2c, Virgin and Child, Flight into Egypt. 22c, Angel leading the way. 35c, King on way to Herod. 75c, Three horses. $2, Virgin and Child. $3, Adoration of the Kings.

## 1977, Nov. 3 — Litho. — Perf. 14

| | | | |
|---|---|---|---|
| 813 | A113 | ½c multicolored | .25 .25 |
| 814 | A113 | 1c multicolored | .25 .25 |
| 815 | A113 | 2c multicolored | .25 .25 |
| 816 | A113 | 22c multicolored | .25 .25 |
| 817 | A113 | 35c multicolored | .25 .25 |
| 818 | A113 | 75c multicolored | .25 .25 |
| 819 | A113 | $3 multicolored | .35 .25 |
| | | Nos. 813-819 (7) | 1.85 1.75 |

### Souvenir Sheet

| | | | |
|---|---|---|---|
| 820 | A113 | $3 multicolored | 1.50 1.00 |

Christmas.

Nos. 788-793 Overprinted

## 1977, Nov. 10 — Perf. 12, 14

| | | | |
|---|---|---|---|
| 821 | A109 | ½c multicolored | .25 .25 |
| 822 | A109 | 1c multicolored | .25 .25 |
| 823 | A109 | 35c multicolored | .25 .25 |
| 824 | A109 | $2 multicolored | .25 .35 |
| 825 | A109 | $2.50 multicolored | .25 .45 |
| | | Nos. 821-825 (5) | 1.25 1.55 |

### Souvenir Sheet
### Perf. 14

| | | | |
|---|---|---|---|
| 826 | A109 | $5 multicolored | .75 1.40 |

Caribbean visit of Queen Elizabeth II. Nos. 821-822 are perf. 12, others perf. 12 and 14.

Christjaan Eijkman — A114

Portraits: 1c, Winston Churchill, Literature, 1953. 2c, Woodrow Wilson, Peace, 1919. 35c, Frederic Passy, Peace 1901. $1, Albert Einstein, Physics, 1921. $2, Alfred Nobel, founder. $3, Carl Bosch, Chemistry, 1931.

## 1978, Jan. 25 — Litho. — Perf. 14

| | | | |
|---|---|---|---|
| 827 | A114 | ½c multicolored | .25 .25 |
| 828 | A114 | 1c multicolored | .25 .25 |
| 829 | A114 | 2c multicolored | .25 .25 |
| 830 | A114 | 35c multicolored | .30 .25 |
| 831 | A114 | $1 multicolored | .85 .30 |
| 832 | A114 | $3 multicolored | 2.25 .55 |
| | | Nos. 827-832 (6) | 4.15 1.85 |

### Souvenir Sheet

| | | | |
|---|---|---|---|
| 833 | A114 | $2 multicolored | 2.00 1.00 |

Nobel Prize winners.

Early Zeppelin and Count Zeppelin — A115

Designs: 1c, Lindbergh and Spirit of St. Louis. 2c, "Deutschland" airship. 22c, Lindbergh landing in Paris. 35c, Lindbergh in cockpit. 75c, Lindbergh and Spirit of St. Louis in flight. $1, Zeppelin over Alps. $2, Count Zeppelin and early airship. $3, Zeppelin over Capitol.

## 1978, Feb. 13 — Litho. — Perf. 14

| | | | |
|---|---|---|---|
| 834 | A115 | ½c multicolored | .25 .25 |
| 835 | A115 | 1c multicolored | .25 .25 |
| 836 | A115 | 2c multicolored | .25 .25 |
| 837 | A115 | 22c multicolored | .40 .25 |
| 838 | A115 | 75c multicolored | .75 .25 |
| 839 | A115 | $1 multicolored | .90 .25 |
| 840 | A115 | $3 multicolored | 2.00 .50 |
| | | Nos. 834-840 (7) | 4.80 2.00 |

### Souvenir Sheet

| | | | |
|---|---|---|---|
| 841 | | Sheet of 2 | 3.25 1.00 |
| a. | | A115 35c multicolored | .75 |
| b. | | A115 $2 multicolored | 2.50 |

Aviation history.

Launching of Space Shuttle — A116

Space Shuttle: 1c, Booster separation. 2c, External tank separation. 18c, In orbit. 75c, Satellite placement. $2, Landing approach. $3, On landing pad.

## 1978, Feb. 28

| | | | |
|---|---|---|---|
| 842 | A116 | ½c multicolored | .25 .25 |
| 843 | A116 | 1c multicolored | .25 .25 |
| 844 | A116 | 2c multicolored | .25 .25 |
| 845 | A116 | 18c multicolored | .40 .25 |
| 846 | A116 | 75c multicolored | .90 .25 |
| 847 | A116 | $2 multicolored | 1.75 .40 |
| | | Nos. 842-847 (6) | 3.80 1.65 |

### Souvenir Sheet

| | | | |
|---|---|---|---|
| 848 | A116 | $3 multicolored | 2.10 1.00 |

US space shuttle.

Black-headed Gulls — A117

Wild Birds of Grenada and Wildlife Fund Emblem: 1c, Wilson's petrels. 2c, Killdeers. 50c, White-necked jacobin and hibiscus. 75c, Blue-faced booby. $1, Broad-winged hawk. $2, Scaley-necked pigeon. $3, Scarlet ibis.

## 1978, Mar. 8 — Litho. — Perf. 14

| | | | |
|---|---|---|---|
| 849 | A117 | ½c multicolored | .30 .25 |
| 850 | A117 | 1c multicolored | .30 .25 |
| 851 | A117 | 2c multicolored | .30 .25 |
| 852 | A117 | 50c multicolored | 2.50 .40 |
| 853 | A117 | 75c multicolored | 3.00 .60 |
| 854 | A117 | $1 multicolored | 4.00 .80 |
| 855 | A117 | $2 multicolored | 6.50 1.50 |
| | | Nos. 849-855 (7) | 16.90 4.05 |

### Souvenir Sheet

| | | | |
|---|---|---|---|
| 856 | A117 | $3 multicolored | 11.00 2.00 |

Marquise de Spinola, by Rubens — A118

Paintings by Peter Paul Rubens (1577-1640): 5c, Reception of Marie de Medicis. 15c, Rubens and Helena Fourment. 25c, Ludovicus Nonnius. 45c, Helena Fourment with her Children. 75c, Child's head. $3, Suzanne Fourment in Velvet Hat.

## 1978, Mar. 30 — Litho. — Perf. 13½x14

| | | | |
|---|---|---|---|
| 857 | A118 | 5c lt blue & multi | .30 .25 |
| 858 | A118 | 15c lt blue & multi | .30 .25 |
| 859 | A118 | 18c lt blue & multi | .30 .25 |
| 860 | A118 | 25c lt blue & multi | .30 .25 |
| 861 | A118 | 45c lt blue & multi | .55 .25 |
| 862 | A118 | 75c lt blue & multi | .80 .25 |
| 863 | A118 | $3 lt blue & multi | 1.75 .55 |
| | | Nos. 857-863 (7) | 4.30 2.05 |

### Souvenir Sheet

| | | | |
|---|---|---|---|
| 864 | A118 | $5 lt blue & multi | 3.75 1.00 |

Ludwig van Beethoven — A119

Designs: 15c, Woman violinist playing concerto. 18c, Various musical instruments. 22c, Piano. 50c, Two violins. 75c, Beethoven's piano and score. $2, Beethoven and score. $3, Beethoven and his house. 15c, 18c, 22c, 75c, $2, $3, horiz.

## 1978, Apr. 24 — Perf. 14

| | | | |
|---|---|---|---|
| 865 | A119 | 5c multicolored | .25 .25 |
| 866 | A119 | 15c multicolored | .25 .25 |
| 867 | A119 | 18c multicolored | .50 .25 |
| 868 | A119 | 22c multicolored | .50 .25 |
| 869 | A119 | 50c multicolored | .85 .35 |
| 870 | A119 | 75c multicolored | 1.60 .50 |
| 871 | A119 | $3 multicolored | 2.75 .65 |
| | | Nos. 865-871 (7) | 6.70 2.50 |

### Souvenir Sheet

| | | | |
|---|---|---|---|
| 872 | A119 | $2 multicolored | 3.25 1.25 |

Ludwig van Beethoven (1770-1827), composer, death sesquicentennial.

Elizabeth II with Crown, Scepter and Orb A120

Trooping of the Colors A121

Designs: 35c, Coronation. $2.50, St. Edward's crown. $5, Elizabeth II and Prince Philip.

## 1978, June 2 — Litho. — Perf. 14

| | | | |
|---|---|---|---|
| 873 | A120 | 35c multicolored | .25 .25 |
| 874 | A120 | $2 multicolored | .45 .45 |
| 875 | A120 | $2.50 multicolored | .45 .45 |
| | | Nos. 873-875 (3) | 1.15 1.15 |

### Souvenir Sheet

| | | | |
|---|---|---|---|
| 876 | A120 | $5 multicolored | .85 .85 |

### Imperf
### Self-adhesive

35c, Elizabeth II at Maundy Money distribution ceremony. $5, Elizabeth II and Prince Philip.

| | | | |
|---|---|---|---|
| 877 | | Souvenir booklet | 3.25 |
| a. | | A121 Bklt. pane, 3 each 25c, 35c | 1.00 |
| b. | | A121 Booklet pane of 1, $5 | 2.50 |

Coronation of Queen Elizabeth II, 25th anniv. Nos. 873-875 were printed in sheets of 40 (10x4), perf. 14, and sheets of 3 plus label, perf. 12, in changed colors. Labels show royal insignia.

No. 877 contains 2 booklet panes printed on peelable paper backing showing coins.

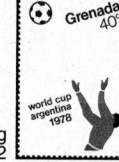

Goalkeeper Reaching for Ball — A122

Designs: Goalkeeper reaching for ball, various stages of motion.

## 1978, Aug. 1 — Litho. — Perf. 15

| | | | |
|---|---|---|---|
| 878 | A122 | 40c multicolored | .25 .25 |
| 879 | A122 | 60c multicolored | .25 .25 |
| 880 | A122 | 90c multicolored | .35 .35 |
| 881 | A122 | $2 multicolored | .85 .85 |
| | | Nos. 878-881 (4) | 1.70 1.70 |

### Souvenir Sheet

| | | | |
|---|---|---|---|
| 882 | A122 | $2.50 multicolored | 1.75 1.75 |

11th World Cup Soccer Championship, Argentina, June 1-25.

Flying Objects, 16th Century Drawing and Flying Saucer, 1962 — A123

Designs: 35c, Radar probing skies, and Mars surface. $2, Prime Minister Eric Gairy and UN General Assembly Building. $3, Flying saucer with downwards beam, and UFO photograph.

## 1978, Aug. 17

| | | | |
|---|---|---|---|
| 883 | A123 | 5c multicolored | .30 .30 |
| 884 | A123 | 35c multicolored | .55 .40 |
| 885 | A123 | $3 multicolored | 3.50 3.25 |
| | | Nos. 883-885 (3) | 4.35 3.95 |

### Souvenir Sheet

| | | | |
|---|---|---|---|
| 886 | A123 | $2 multicolored | 3.50 3.50 |

Proposal by Prime Minister Eric Gairy of Grenada to the UN General Assembly to study unidentified flying objects, Oct. 7, 1977.

Wright Glider and Allegory of Flight — A124

15c, Flyer I, 1903, & eagle. 18c, Flyer III & allegory of flight. 22c, Flyer III & eagle. 50c, Orville Wright, Flyer & allegory of flight. 75c, Flyer, 1908, & eagle. $2, Flyer & allegory of flight. $3, Wilbur Wright, Flyer & allegory of flight.

## 1978, Aug. 24 — Perf. 14

| | | | |
|---|---|---|---|
| 887 | A124 | 5c multicolored | .25 .25 |
| 888 | A124 | 15c multicolored | .25 .25 |
| 889 | A124 | 18c multicolored | .25 .25 |
| 890 | A124 | 22c multicolored | .25 .25 |
| 891 | A124 | 50c multicolored | .45 .35 |
| 892 | A124 | 75c multicolored | .55 .45 |
| 893 | A124 | $3 multicolored | 1.35 1.35 |
| | | Nos. 887-893 (7) | 3.35 3.15 |

### Souvenir Sheet

| | | | |
|---|---|---|---|
| 894 | A124 | $2 multicolored | 3.75 3.75 |

75th anniversary of first powered flight by Wright brothers, Dec. 17, 1903.

Hawaiian Feast in Capt. Cook's Honor — A125

Capt. Cook and: 35c, Hawaiian warriors' dance. 75c, Honolulu harbor. $3, "Resolution." $4, Death scene.

## 1978, Dec. 5 — Litho. — Perf. 14

| | | | |
|---|---|---|---|
| 895 | A125 | 18c multicolored | .90 .50 |
| 896 | A125 | 35c multicolored | 1.10 .60 |
| 897 | A125 | 75c multicolored | 2.00 1.90 |
| 898 | A125 | $3 multicolored | 2.75 4.50 |
| | | Nos. 895-898 (4) | 6.75 7.50 |

### Souvenir Sheet

| | | | |
|---|---|---|---|
| 899 | A125 | $4 multicolored | 5.00 5.00 |

Bicentenary of Capt. Cook's arrival in Hawaii and 250th anniversary of his birth.

Detail from
Paumgartner Altar, by
Dürer — A126

Dürer Paintings: 60c, The Three Kings. 90c, Virgin and Child. $2, Head of the Virgin. $4, Virgin and Child.

**1978, Dec. 20    Litho.    Perf. 14**
| | | | | |
|---|---|---|---|---|
| 900 | A126 | 40c multicolored | .25 | .25 |
| 901 | A126 | 60c multicolored | .35 | .35 |
| 902 | A126 | 90c multicolored | .40 | .40 |
| 903 | A126 | $2 multicolored | .75 | .75 |
| | | Nos. 900-903 (4) | 1.75 | 1.75 |

**Souvenir Sheet**
| | | | | |
|---|---|---|---|---|
| 904 | A126 | $4 multicolored | 2.00 | 2.00 |

Christmas and 450th death anniv. of Albrecht Dürer (1471-1528), German painter.

Convention and
Cultural Center — A127

18c, Geodesic Dome. 22c, Rowboat race, Easter parade, St. George's. 35c, Prime Minister Eric M. Gairy. $3, Cross at Fort Frederick at night.

**1979, Feb. 8    Litho.    Perf. 14**
| | | | | |
|---|---|---|---|---|
| 905 | A127 | 5c multicolored | .25 | .25 |
| 906 | A127 | 18c multicolored | .25 | .25 |
| 907 | A127 | 22c multicolored | .25 | .25 |
| 908 | A127 | 35c multicolored | .40 | .40 |
| 909 | A127 | $3 multicolored | .40 | .40 |
| | | Nos. 905-909 (5) | 1.40 | 1.40 |

5th anniversary of independence.

Chenille Plant — A128

Native Flowers: 50c, Red hibiscus. $1, Skyflower. $2, Pink pride of India. $3, Rosebay.

**1979, Feb. 26**
| | | | | |
|---|---|---|---|---|
| 910 | A128 | 18c multicolored | .25 | .25 |
| 911 | A128 | 50c multicolored | .30 | .30 |
| 912 | A128 | $1 multicolored | .50 | .45 |
| 913 | A128 | $3 multicolored | 1.25 | 1.10 |
| | | Nos. 910-913 (4) | 2.30 | 2.05 |

**Souvenir Sheet**
| | | | | |
|---|---|---|---|---|
| 914 | A128 | $2 multicolored | 1.60 | 1.60 |

Birds in Flight — A129

$2, Bird in flight & Human Rights emblem.

**1979, Mar. 15**
| | | | | |
|---|---|---|---|---|
| 915 | A129 | 15c multicolored | .25 | .25 |
| 916 | A129 | $2 multicolored | .75 | .75 |

Universal Declaration of Human Rights, 30th anniversary.

Children Playing
Cricket — A130

IYC Emblem and: 22c, Boys playing baseball. $4, Children with model spaceship. $5, Three children.

**1979, Apr. 23    Litho.    Perf. 14**
| | | | | |
|---|---|---|---|---|
| 917 | A130 | 18c multicolored | 1.00 | .50 |
| 918 | A130 | 22c multicolored | .50 | .30 |
| 919 | A130 | $5 multicolored | 4.50 | 6.00 |
| | | Nos. 917-919 (3) | 6.00 | 6.80 |

**Souvenir Sheet**
| | | | | |
|---|---|---|---|---|
| 920 | A130 | $4 multicolored | 2.25 | 2.25 |

Intl. Year of the Child.

Balloon and
Space
Shuttle — A131

Designs: 35c, Octopus holding sailors, nuclear submarine. 75c, Rocket and moon. $3, Imaginary plane and space ship. $4, Multi-propelled ship and US space shuttle.

**1979, May 4**
| | | | | |
|---|---|---|---|---|
| 921 | A131 | 18c multicolored | .40 | .25 |
| 922 | A131 | 35c multicolored | .70 | .25 |
| 923 | A131 | 75c multicolored | .90 | .65 |
| 924 | A131 | $4 multicolored | 2.40 | 3.00 |
| | | Nos. 921-924 (4) | 4.40 | 4.15 |

**Souvenir Sheet**
| | | | | |
|---|---|---|---|---|
| 925 | A131 | $4 multicolored | 2.25 | 2.25 |

Jules Verne (1828-1905), science fiction writer.

African Mail
Runner — A132

Sir Rowland Hill (1795-1879), originator of penny postage, and: 40c, American Pony Express. $1, Oriental pigeon post. $3, European mail coach. $5, Tete-beche stamps with revenue surcharge, 1883.

**1979, July 23    Litho.    Perf. 14**
| | | | | |
|---|---|---|---|---|
| 926 | A132 | 20c multicolored | .25 | .25 |
| 927 | A132 | 40c multicolored | .25 | .25 |
| 928 | A132 | $1 multicolored | .25 | .25 |
| 929 | A132 | $3 multicolored | .40 | .40 |
| | | Nos. 926-929 (4) | 1.15 | 1.15 |

**Souvenir Sheet**
| | | | | |
|---|---|---|---|---|
| 930 | A132 | $5 multicolored | 1.00 | 1.00 |

Nos. 926-929 were printed in sheets of 40, perf. 14, and in sheets of 5 plus label, perf. 12, in changed colors.
For overprints see Nos. 989A-989D.

Boys, Map of Grenada,
Vaccination
Gun — A133

**1979, Aug. 2    Litho.    Perf. 14**
| | | | | |
|---|---|---|---|---|
| 931 | A133 | 5c multicolored | .25 | .25 |
| 932 | A133 | $1 multicolored | .90 | .90 |

Intl. Year of the Child, immunization of children.

Reef
Shark — A134

Designs: 45c, Spotted eagle ray. 50c, Many-tooth conger. 60c, Golden olive shells. 70c, West Indian murex. 75c, Giant tuns. 90c, Brown boobies. $1, Magnificent frigate bird. $2.50, Sooty tern.

**1979, Aug. 22    Litho.    Perf. 14**
| | | | | |
|---|---|---|---|---|
| 933 | A134 | 40c multicolored | .40 | .35 |
| 934 | A134 | 45c multicolored | .40 | .35 |
| 935 | A134 | 50c multicolored | .45 | .40 |
| 936 | A134 | 60c multicolored | .75 | .60 |
| 937 | A134 | 70c multicolored | .90 | .70 |
| 938 | A134 | 75c multicolored | 1.10 | 1.10 |
| 939 | A134 | 90c multicolored | 1.75 | 2.25 |
| 940 | A134 | $1 multicolored | 1.75 | 2.25 |
| | | Nos. 933-940 (8) | 7.50 | 8.00 |

**Souvenir Sheet**
| | | | | |
|---|---|---|---|---|
| 941 | A134 | $2.50 multicolored | 3.25 | 3.25 |

Flight into Egypt,
Tapestry — A135

Tapestries: 25c, Virgin and Child. 30c, Angel, vert. 40c, Infant Jesus, by Doge Marino Grimani, vert. 90c, Shepherds, vert. $1, Flight into Egypt, vert. $2, Virgin in Glory, vert. $4, Virgin and Child, by Grimani, vert.

**1979, Oct. 16    Litho.    Perf. 14**
| | | | | |
|---|---|---|---|---|
| 942 | A135 | 6c multicolored | .25 | .25 |
| 943 | A135 | 25c multicolored | .25 | .25 |
| 944 | A135 | 30c multicolored | .25 | .25 |
| 945 | A135 | 40c multicolored | .25 | .25 |
| 946 | A135 | 90c multicolored | .25 | .25 |
| 947 | A135 | $1 multicolored | .25 | .25 |
| 948 | A135 | $2 multicolored | .30 | .30 |
| | | Nos. 942-948 (7) | 1.80 | 1.80 |

**Souvenir Sheet**
| | | | | |
|---|---|---|---|---|
| 949 | A135 | $4 multicolored | 1.25 | 1.25 |

Christmas.

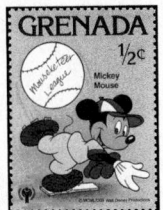

Disney Characters
and IYC
Emblem — A135a

Sport scenes: ½c, Mickey Mouse, baseball. 1c, Donald, high jump. 2c, Goofy, basketball. 3c, Goofy, hurdles. 4c, Donald Duck, golf. 5c, Mickey, cricket. 10c, Mickey, soccer. $2, Mickey, tennis. $2.50, Minnie, equestrian. $3, Goofy in riding habit.

**1979, Nov. 2    Litho.    Perf. 11**
| | | | | |
|---|---|---|---|---|
| 950 | A135a | ½c multi | .25 | .25 |
| 951 | A135a | 1c multi | .25 | .25 |
| 952 | A135a | 2c multi | .25 | .25 |
| 953 | A135a | 3c multi | .25 | .25 |
| 954 | A135a | 4c multi | .25 | .25 |
| 955 | A135a | 5c multi | .25 | .25 |
| 956 | A135a | 10c multi | .25 | .25 |
| 957 | A135a | $2 multi | 3.00 | 3.50 |
| 958 | A135a | $2.50 multi | 3.00 | 3.50 |
| | | Nos. 950-958 (9) | 7.75 | 8.75 |

**Souvenir Sheet**
**Perf. 13½**
| | | | | |
|---|---|---|---|---|
| 959 | CD329 | $3 multi | 2.50 | 2.50 |

See Nos. 1031-1032.

Hands, Paul P. Harris,
Rotary
Emblem — A136

Rotary Emblem and Hands Holding: 30c, Caduceus. 90c, Wheat. $2, Family. $4, Emblem.

**1980, Feb. 25    Litho.    Perf. 14**
| | | | | |
|---|---|---|---|---|
| 960 | A136 | 6c multicolored | .25 | .25 |
| 961 | A136 | 30c multicolored | .25 | .25 |
| 962 | A136 | 90c multicolored | .25 | .25 |
| 963 | A136 | $2 multicolored | .60 | .60 |
| | | Nos. 960-963 (4) | 1.35 | 1.35 |

**Souvenir Sheet**
| | | | | |
|---|---|---|---|---|
| 964 | A136 | $4 multicolored | 1.60 | 1.60 |

Rotary International, 75th anniversary.

**Nos. 585-586, 588-591, 593-594, 596-602 Overprinted in Black**

**1980    Perf. 15, 13½**
| | | | | |
|---|---|---|---|---|
| 965 | A85 | 2c multicolored | .25 | .25 |
| 966 | A85 | 3c multicolored | .25 | .25 |
| 967 | A85 | 6c multicolored | .25 | .25 |
| 968 | A85 | 8c multicolored | .25 | .25 |
| 969 | A85 | 10c multicolored | .25 | .25 |
| 970 | A85 | 12c multicolored | .25 | .25 |
| 971 | A85 | 20c multicolored | .25 | .25 |
| 972 | A85 | 25c multicolored | .40 | .60 |
| 973 | A85 | 50c multicolored | .40 | .60 |
| 974 | A85 | 75c multicolored | .65 | .95 |
| 975 | A85 | $1 multicolored | 1.00 | 1.25 |
| 976 | A85 | $2 multicolored | 1.75 | 2.40 |
| 977 | A85 | $3 multicolored | 2.25 | 3.25 |
| 978 | A85 | $5 multicolored | 3.00 | 5.50 |
| 979 | A85 | $10 multicolored | 4.25 | 8.00 |
| | | Nos. 965-979 (15) | 15.45 | 24.30 |

Issue dates: 25c, Apr. 7; others, Feb. 28.

Boxing, Kremlin,
Olympic
Rings — A137

**1980, Mar. 24    Perf. 14**
| | | | | |
|---|---|---|---|---|
| 980 | A137 | 25c shown | .25 | .25 |
| 981 | A137 | 40c Bicycling | .25 | .25 |
| 982 | A137 | 90c Equestrian | .25 | .25 |
| 983 | A137 | $2 Running | .60 | .60 |
| | | Nos. 980-983 (4) | 1.35 | 1.35 |

**Souvenir Sheet**
| | | | | |
|---|---|---|---|---|
| 984 | A137 | $4 Yachting | 1.25 | 1.25 |

22nd Summer Olympic Games, Moscow, July 19-Aug. 3.

Tropical
Kingbirds — A138

40c, Rufous-breasted hermits. $1, Troupials. $2, Ruddy quail doves. $3, Prairie warblers.

**1980, Apr. 8**
| | | | | |
|---|---|---|---|---|
| 985 | A138 | 20c shown | 1.00 | .80 |
| 986 | A138 | 40c multicolored | 1.40 | 1.10 |
| 987 | A138 | $1 multicolored | 1.90 | 1.60 |
| 988 | A138 | $2 multicolored | 2.25 | 4.00 |
| | | Nos. 985-988 (4) | 6.55 | 7.50 |

**Souvenir Sheet**
| | | | | |
|---|---|---|---|---|
| 989 | A138 | $3 multicolored | 5.00 | 5.00 |

**Nos. 926-929 Overprinted:
"LONDON 1980"**

**1980, May 6    Litho.    Perf. 12**
| | | | | |
|---|---|---|---|---|
| 989A | A132 | 20c multicolored | .25 | .25 |
| 989B | A132 | 40c multicolored | .30 | .30 |
| 989C | A132 | $1 multicolored | .50 | .50 |
| 989D | A132 | $3 multicolored | 1.40 | 1.40 |
| | | Nos. 989A-989D (4) | 2.45 | 2.45 |

London '80 Intl. Stamp Exhib., May 6-14.

Free School Hot
Lunches — A139

**1980, May 19    Litho.    Perf. 14**
| | | | | |
|---|---|---|---|---|
| 990 | A139 | 10c shown | .25 | .25 |
| 991 | A139 | 40c Food canning | .25 | .25 |
| 992 | A139 | $1 Health care | .40 | .40 |
| 993 | A139 | $2 Housing projects | .65 | .65 |
| | | Nos. 990-993 (4) | 1.55 | 1.55 |

**Souvenir Sheet**
| | | | | |
|---|---|---|---|---|
| 994 | A139 | $5 Prime Minister Bishop, vert. | 1.50 | 1.50 |

People's Revolution, 1st anniv.

Jamb
Statues,
West Portal,
Chartres
Cathedral
A140

Masterpieces: 10c, Les Desmoiselles d'Avignon, by Picasso. 40c, Winged Victory of

Samothrace. 50c, The Night Watch, by Rembrandt. $1, Edward VI as a Child, by Holbein, the Younger. $3, Queen Nefertiti. $4, Weier Haws, by Dürer, vert.

**1980, June    Litho.    Perf. 14**

| | | | | |
|---|---|---|---|---|
| 995 | A140 | 8c multicolored | .25 | .25 |
| 996 | A140 | 10c multicolored | .25 | .25 |
| 997 | A140 | 40c multicolored | .25 | .25 |
| 998 | A140 | 50c multicolored | .25 | .25 |
| 999 | A140 | $1 multicolored | .35 | .35 |
| 1000 | A140 | $3 multicolored | .90 | .90 |

*Nos. 995-1000 (6)    2.25 2.25*

**Souvenir Sheet**

| | | | | |
|---|---|---|---|---|
| 1001 | A140 | $4 multicolored | 1.50 | 1.50 |

Carib Canoes — A141

Designs: 1c, Boat building. 2c, Small workboat. 4c, "Santa Maria." 5c, West India man barque, 1840. 6c, "Orinoco," 1851. 10c, Schooner. 12c, Trimaran. 15c, "Petite Amie," Spice Island cruising yacht. 20c, Fishing pirogue. 25c, Harbor police launch. 30c, Grand Anse speedboat. 40c, "Seimstrand." 50c, "Ariadne," 3-masted schooner. 90c, "Geestide," banana boat. $1, "Cunard Countess," cruise ship. $3, Rumrunner. $5, "Statendam." $10, Coast Guard patrol boat.

**1980, Sept. 9    Litho.    Perf. 14**

| | | | | |
|---|---|---|---|---|
| 1002 | A141 | ½c multicolored | .25 | .25 |
| 1003 | A141 | 1c multicolored | .25 | .25 |
| 1004 | A141 | 2c multicolored | .25 | .25 |
| 1005 | A141 | 4c multicolored | .40 | .55 |
| 1006 | A141 | 5c multicolored | .40 | .55 |
| 1007 | A141 | 6c multicolored | .40 | .55 |
| 1008 | A141 | 10c multicolored | .45 | .25 |
| 1009 | A141 | 12c multicolored | .90 | .70 |
| 1010 | A141 | 15c multicolored | .50 | .25 |
| 1011 | A141 | 20c multicolored | .90 | .25 |
| 1012 | A141 | 25c multicolored | 1.75 | .45 |
| 1013 | A141 | 30c multicolored | 1.25 | .25 |
| 1014 | A141 | 40c multicolored | 2.00 | .55 |
| 1015 | A141 | 50c multicolored | .60 | .70 |
| 1016 | A141 | 90c multicolored | 1.75 | .70 |
| 1017 | A141 | $1 multicolored | 3.00 | 1.25 |
| 1018 | A141 | $3 multicolored | 2.50 | 4.50 |
| 1019 | A141 | $5 multicolored | 3.50 | 7.25 |
| 1020 | A141 | $10 multicolored | 4.25 | 9.50 |

*Nos. 1002-1020 (19)    25.30 29.20*

No. 1017 reprinted inscribed 1982, No. 1015, 1984.

For overprints see Nos. O1-O10, O12-O13, O15, O17.

**1982-84    Perf. 12½x12**

| | | | | |
|---|---|---|---|---|
| 1002a | A141 | ½c | .45 | .45 |
| 1006a | A141 | 5c | 1.05 | 1.05 |
| 1008a | A141 | 10c | 1.15 | 1.15 |
| 1011a | A141 | 20c | 1.75 | 1.75 |
| 1012a | A141 | 25c | 3.50 | 3.50 |
| 1013a | A141 | 30c | 2.75 | 2.75 |
| 1014a | A141 | 40c | 3.50 | 3.50 |
| 1015a | A141 | 50c ('84) | 1.45 | 1.45 |
| 1018a | A141 | $3 | 5.25 | 5.25 |
| 1019a | A141 | $5 | 7.50 | 7.50 |
| 1020a | A141 | $10 ('84) | 17.00 | 17.00 |

*Nos. 1002a-1020a (11)    45.35 45.35*

Snow White at Well — A142

Christmas: Various scenes from Walt Disney's Snow White and the Seven Dwarfs.

**1980, Sept. 25    Litho.    Perf. 11**

| | | | | |
|---|---|---|---|---|
| 1021 | A142 | ½c multicolored | .25 | .25 |
| 1022 | A142 | 1c multicolored | .25 | .25 |
| 1023 | A142 | 2c multicolored | .25 | .25 |
| 1024 | A142 | 3c multicolored | .25 | .25 |
| 1025 | A142 | 4c multicolored | .25 | .25 |
| 1026 | A142 | 5c multicolored | .25 | .25 |
| 1027 | A142 | 10c multicolored | .25 | .25 |
| 1028 | A142 | $2.50 multicolored | 2.75 | 2.75 |
| 1029 | A142 | $3 multicolored | 3.25 | 3.25 |

*Nos. 1021-1029 (9)    7.75 7.75*

**Souvenir Sheet**

| | | | | |
|---|---|---|---|---|
| 1030 | A142 | $4 multicolored | 5.25 | 5.25 |

No. 1030 contains a vertical stamp.

**Disney Type of 1980**

50th anniversary of Pluto character: $2, Pluto and birthday cake. $4, Pluto.

**1981, Jan. 19    Litho.    Perf. 14**

| | | | | |
|---|---|---|---|---|
| 1031 | A135a | $2 multicolored | 2.50 | 2.50 |

**Souvenir Sheet**

| | | | | |
|---|---|---|---|---|
| 1032 | A135a | $4 multicolored | 3.50 | 3.50 |

No. 1031 issued in sheets of 8.

Adult Education — A143

5c, Flags of the Revolution and Grenada. 15c, Food processing plant. 25c, Agriculture. 40c, Fishing boat, crawfish. 90c, Ships. $1, Palm trees. $3, Map.

**1981, Mar. 13    Litho.    Perf. 12½**

| | | | | |
|---|---|---|---|---|
| 1033 | A143 | 5c multicolored | .25 | .25 |
| 1034 | A143 | 10c shown | .25 | .25 |
| 1035 | A143 | 15c multicolored | .25 | .25 |
| 1036 | A143 | 25c multicolored | .25 | .25 |
| 1037 | A143 | 40c multicolored | .25 | .25 |
| 1038 | A143 | 90c multicolored | .65 | .65 |
| 1039 | A143 | $1 multicolored | .70 | .70 |
| 1040 | A143 | $3 multicolored | 2.10 | 2.10 |

*Nos. 1033-1040 (8)    4.70 4.70*

2nd Festival of the Revolution.

Mickey Mouse and Goofy with Easter Basket — A144

Easter: Various Disney characters with Easter baskets.

**1981, Apr. 7    Perf. 11**

| | | | | |
|---|---|---|---|---|
| 1041 | A144 | 35c multi | .30 | .30 |
| 1042 | A144 | 40c multi | .30 | .30 |
| 1043 | A144 | $2 multi | 1.60 | 1.60 |
| 1044 | A144 | $2.50 multi | 2.10 | 2.10 |

*Nos. 1041-1044 (4)    4.30 4.30*

**Souvenir Sheet**

| | | | | |
|---|---|---|---|---|
| 1045 | A144 | $4 multi | 3.25 | 3.25 |

Large Heads, by Picasso — A145

Paintings by Pablo Picasso (1881-1973): 25c, Woman-Flower. 30c, Portrait of Madame. 90c, Cavalier with Pipe. $5, Woman on the Bank of the Seine.

**1981, Apr. 28    Perf. 14**

| | | | | |
|---|---|---|---|---|
| 1046 | A145 | 25c multicolored | .25 | .25 |
| 1047 | A145 | 30c multicolored | .25 | .25 |
| 1048 | A145 | 90c multicolored | .45 | .45 |
| 1049 | A145 | $4 multicolored | 2.25 | 2.25 |

*Nos. 1046-1049 (4)    3.20 3.20*

**Souvenir Sheet**

| | | | | |
|---|---|---|---|---|
| 1050 | A145 | $5 multicolored | 4.75 | 4.75 |

**Royal Wedding Issue**
**Common Design Type**

**1981, June 16    Litho.    Perf. 15**

| | | | | |
|---|---|---|---|---|
| 1051 | CD331a | 50c Couple | .25 | .25 |
| 1052 | CD331a | $2 Holyrood House | .30 | .30 |
| 1053 | CD331a | $4 Charles | .40 | .40 |

*Nos. 1051-1053 (3)    .95 .95*

**Souvenir Sheet**

| | | | | |
|---|---|---|---|---|
| 1054 | CD331 | $5 Glass coach | .90 | .90 |

**Souvenir Booklet**

| | | | |
|---|---|---|---|
| 1055 | CD331 | multi | 8.00 |
| a. | | Pane of 6 (3x$1, Lady Diana, 3x$2, Charles) | 5.50 |
| b. | | Pane of 1, $5, Couple | 2.50 |

No. 1055 contains imperf., self-adhesive stamps.

Sheets of 5 plus label contain 30c, 40c or $4 in changed colors, perf. 14x14½.

For overprints see Nos. O11, O14, O16,

The Bath, by Mary Cassatt (1845-1926) — A146

Decade for Women (Paintings by Women): 40c, Mademoiselle Charlotte du Val d'Ognes, by Constance Marie Charpentier. 60c, Self-portrait, by Mary Beale. $3, Woman in White Stockings, by Suzanne Valadon. $5, The Artist Hesitating between the Arts of Music and Painting, horiz.

**1981, Oct. 13    Litho.    Perf. 14**

| | | | | |
|---|---|---|---|---|
| 1058 | A146 | 15c multicolored | .25 | .25 |
| 1059 | A146 | 40c multicolored | .30 | .30 |
| 1060 | A146 | 60c multicolored | .45 | .45 |
| 1061 | A146 | $3 multicolored | 2.00 | 2.00 |

*Nos. 1058-1061 (4)    3.00 3.00*

**Souvenir Sheet**

| | | | | |
|---|---|---|---|---|
| 1062 | A146 | $5 multicolored | 3.00 | 3.00 |

Cinderella and Prince Charming Dancing at the Ball — A147

Christmas: Scenes from Walt Disney's Cinderella.

**1981, Nov. 2    Litho.    Perf. 14x13½**

| | | | | |
|---|---|---|---|---|
| 1063 | A147 | ½c multi | .25 | .25 |
| 1064 | A147 | 1c multi | .25 | .25 |
| 1065 | A147 | 2c multi | .25 | .25 |
| 1066 | A147 | 3c multi | .25 | .25 |
| 1067 | A147 | 4c multi | .25 | .25 |
| 1068 | A147 | 5c multi | .25 | .25 |
| 1069 | A147 | 10c multi | .25 | .25 |
| 1070 | A147 | $2.50 multi | 3.00 | 3.00 |
| 1071 | A147 | $3 multi | 3.50 | 3.50 |

*Nos. 1063-1071 (9)    8.25 8.25*

**Souvenir Sheet**

| | | | | |
|---|---|---|---|---|
| 1072 | A147 | $5 multi | 6.75 | 6.75 |

Columbia Space Shuttle — A148

Views of the Columbia space shuttle.

**1981, Nov. 12**

| | | | | |
|---|---|---|---|---|
| 1073 | A148 | 30c multicolored | .25 | .25 |
| 1074 | A148 | 60c multicolored | .40 | .40 |
| 1075 | A148 | 70c multicolored | .50 | .50 |
| 1076 | A148 | $3 multicolored | 2.00 | 2.00 |

*Nos. 1073-1076 (4)    3.15 3.15*

**Souvenir Sheet**

| | | | | |
|---|---|---|---|---|
| 1077 | A148 | $5 multicolored | 3.25 | 3.25 |

UPU Membership Centenary A149

**1981, Dec. 10    Litho.    Perf. 15**

| | | | | |
|---|---|---|---|---|
| 1078 | A149 | 25c St. George's P.O. | .25 | .25 |
| 1079 | A149 | 30c No. 1 | .25 | .25 |
| 1080 | A149 | 90c No. 384 | .50 | .50 |
| 1081 | A149 | $4 No. 189 | 2.25 | 2.25 |

*Nos. 1078-1081 (4)    3.25 3.25*

**Souvenir Sheet**

| | | | | |
|---|---|---|---|---|
| 1082 | A149 | $5 No. 562 | 4.00 | 4.00 |

Intl. Year of the Disabled (1981) — A150

30c, Artist. 40c, Computer operator. 70c, Teaching Braille. $3, Drummer. $4, Auto mechanic.

**1982, Feb. 4    Perf. 14**

| | | | | |
|---|---|---|---|---|
| 1083 | A150 | 30c multicolored | .25 | .25 |
| 1084 | A150 | 40c multicolored | .30 | .30 |
| 1085 | A150 | 70c multicolored | .50 | .50 |
| 1086 | A150 | $3 multicolored | 2.00 | 2.00 |

*Nos. 1083-1086 (4)    3.05 3.05*

**Souvenir Sheet**

| | | | | |
|---|---|---|---|---|
| 1087 | A150 | $4 multicolored | 3.50 | 3.50 |

Scouting Year — A151

**1982, Feb. 19    Perf. 15**

| | | | | |
|---|---|---|---|---|
| 1088 | A151 | 70c Gardening | .60 | .60 |
| 1089 | A151 | 90c Map reading | .75 | .75 |
| 1090 | A151 | $1 Bee keeping | .85 | .80 |
| 1091 | A151 | $4 Hospital reading | 2.75 | 2.75 |

*Nos. 1088-1091 (4)    4.95 4.90*

**Souvenir Sheet**

| | | | | |
|---|---|---|---|---|
| 1092 | A151 | $5 Trophy presentation | 3.50 | 3.50 |

Flambeaux — A152

60c, Large orange sulphurs. $1, Red anartias. $3, Polydamas swallowtails. $5, Caribbean buckeyes.

**1982, Mar. 24    Litho.    Perf. 14**

| | | | | |
|---|---|---|---|---|
| 1093 | A152 | 10c shown | .70 | .25 |
| 1094 | A152 | 60c multicolored | 2.50 | 1.25 |
| 1095 | A152 | $1 multicolored | 3.00 | 2.10 |
| 1096 | A152 | $3 multicolored | 8.00 | 7.25 |

*Nos. 1093-1096 (4)    14.20 10.85*

**Souvenir Sheet**

| | | | | |
|---|---|---|---|---|
| 1097 | A152 | $5 multicolored | 8.75 | 8.75 |

Norman Rockwell — A153

**1982, Apr. 12    Litho.    Perf. 14x13½**

| | | | | |
|---|---|---|---|---|
| 1098 | A153 | 15c shown | .40 | .25 |
| 1099 | A153 | 30c Card Tricks | .65 | .25 |
| 1100 | A153 | 60c Pharmacist | 1.10 | 1.00 |
| 1101 | A153 | 70c Pals | 1.40 | 1.25 |

*Nos. 1098-1101 (4)    3.55 2.75*

**Princess Diana Issue**
**Common Design Type**

50c, Kensington Palace. $1, Couple in field. $3, Diana in green dress. $5, Diana, diff.

**1982, July 1    Litho.    Perf. 14½x14**

| | | | | |
|---|---|---|---|---|
| 1101A | CD332 | 50c multicolored | .55 | .75 |
| 1102 | CD332 | 60c like 50c | .60 | .50 |
| 1102A | CD332 | $1 multi | .90 | .80 |
| 1103 | CD332 | $2 like $1 | 2.25 | 1.75 |
| 1103A | CD332 | $3 multi | 2.50 | 2.50 |
| 1104 | CD332 | $4 like $3 | 3.25 | 3.25 |

*Nos. 1101A-1104 (6)    10.05 9.55*

**Souvenir Sheet**

| | | | | |
|---|---|---|---|---|
| 1105 | CD332 | $5 multi | 6.00 | 6.00 |

For overprints see Nos. 1115A-1119.

Franklin Roosevelt Birth Centenary A154

Designs: 10c, Mary McLeod Bethune, director of Negro Affairs, 1942. 60c, Leadbelly (Huddie Ledbetter, Works Progress Administration). $1.10, Signing Fair Employment Act, 1941. $3, Farm Security Administration.

**1982, July 27**    Litho.    *Perf. 14*

| | | | | |
|---|---|---|---|---|
| 1106 | A154 | 10c multi | .25 | .25 |
| 1107 | A154 | 60c multi | .30 | .30 |
| 1108 | A154 | $1.10 multi | .50 | .50 |
| 1109 | A154 | $3 multi | 1.40 | 1.40 |

*Nos. 1106-1109 (4)*    2.45   2.45

**Souvenir Sheet**

| | | | | |
|---|---|---|---|---|
| 1110 | A154 | $5 multi | 2.50 | 2.50 |

Easter — A155

Details from Raphael's "On the Way to Calvary." 70c, $1.10, $4, $5, vert.

**1982, Sept. 2**    *Perf. 14½*

| | | | | |
|---|---|---|---|---|
| 1111 | A155 | 40c multi | .25 | .25 |
| 1112 | A155 | 70c multi | .30 | .30 |
| 1113 | A155 | $1.10 multi | .55 | .55 |
| 1114 | A155 | $4 multi | 1.75 | 1.75 |

*Nos. 1111-1114 (4)*    2.85   2.85

**Souvenir Sheet**

| | | | | |
|---|---|---|---|---|
| 1115 | A155 | $5 multi | 3.00 | 3.00 |

Nos. 1101A-1105
Overprinted in Black

**1982, Sept. 27**    Litho.    *Perf. 14½x14*

| | | | | |
|---|---|---|---|---|
| 1115A | CD332 | 50c multi | .35 | .35 |
| 1116 | CD332 | 60c multi | .40 | .40 |
| 1116A | CD332 | $1 multi | .65 | .65 |
| 1117 | CD332 | $2 multi | 1.25 | 1.25 |
| 1117A | CD332 | $3 multi | 2.00 | 2.00 |
| 1118 | CD332 | $4 multi | 2.50 | 2.50 |

*Nos. 1115A-1118 (6)*    7.15   7.15

**Souvenir Sheet**

| | | | | |
|---|---|---|---|---|
| 1119 | CD332 | $5 multi | 4.50 | 4.50 |

Birth of Prince William of Wales, June 21.

Orient
Express — A156

60c, Trans-Siberian Express. 70c, Fleche D'or. 90c, Flying Scotsman. $1, German Federal Railways. $3, German Natl. Railways. $5, 20th Century Limited, US.

**1982, Oct. 4**

| | | | | |
|---|---|---|---|---|
| 1120 | A156 | 30c shown | .35 | .40 |
| 1121 | A156 | 60c multicolored | .65 | .65 |
| 1122 | A156 | 70c multicolored | .75 | .75 |
| 1123 | A156 | 90c multicolored | .95 | .95 |
| 1124 | A156 | $1 multicolored | 1.25 | 1.25 |
| 1125 | A156 | $3 multicolored | 3.00 | 4.00 |

*Nos. 1120-1125 (6)*    6.95   8.00

**Souvenir Sheet**

| | | | | |
|---|---|---|---|---|
| 1126 | A156 | $5 multicolored | 3.75 | 3.75 |

Christmas
A157

Scenes from Walt Disney's Robin Hood.

**1982, Dec. 7**    Litho.    *Perf. 14*

| | | | | |
|---|---|---|---|---|
| 1127 | A157 | ½c multi | .25 | .25 |
| 1128 | A157 | 1c multi | .25 | .25 |
| 1129 | A157 | 2c multi | .25 | .25 |
| 1130 | A157 | 3c multi | .25 | .25 |
| 1131 | A157 | 4c multi | .25 | .25 |
| 1132 | A157 | 5c multi | .25 | .25 |
| 1133 | A157 | 10c multi | .25 | .25 |
| 1134 | A157 | $2.50 multi | 2.75 | 2.75 |
| 1135 | A157 | $3 multi | 3.00 | 3.00 |

*Nos. 1127-1135 (9)*    7.50   7.50

**Souvenir Sheet**

| | | | | |
|---|---|---|---|---|
| 1136 | A157 | $5 multi | 7.25 | 7.25 |

Italy's Victory
in 1982 World
Cup — A158

60c, Stolen ball. $4, Captain holding trophy. $5, Flags.

**1982, Dec. 2**    *Perf. 14x13½*

| | | | | |
|---|---|---|---|---|
| 1137 | A158 | 60c multicolored | .50 | .50 |
| 1138 | A158 | $4 multicolored | 3.25 | 3.25 |

**Souvenir Sheet**

| | | | | |
|---|---|---|---|---|
| 1139 | A158 | $5 multicolored | 3.75 | 3.75 |

Killer Whale — A159

40c, Sperm whale. 70c, Blue whale. $3, Common dolphins.
$5, Humpback whale.

**1982, Dec. 15**    *Perf. 14*

| | | | | |
|---|---|---|---|---|
| 1140 | A159 | 15c shown | 1.50 | .50 |
| 1141 | A159 | 40c multicolored | 2.50 | .75 |
| 1142 | A159 | 70c multicolored | 3.50 | 2.75 |
| 1143 | A159 | $3 multicolored | 6.00 | 6.00 |

*Nos. 1140-1143 (4)*    13.50   10.00

**Souvenir Sheet**

| | | | | |
|---|---|---|---|---|
| 1144 | A159 | $5 multicolored | 11.00 | 11.00 |

500th Birth
Anniv. of
Raphael
A160

25c, Construction of the Ark. 30c, Jacob's Vision. 90c, Joseph Interprets the Dreams. $4, Joseph Interprets Pharaoh's Dream. $5, Creation of the Animals.

**1983, Feb. 15**    Litho.    *Perf. 14*

| | | | | |
|---|---|---|---|---|
| 1145 | A160 | 25c multicolored | .25 | .25 |
| 1146 | A160 | 30c multicolored | .25 | .25 |
| 1147 | A160 | 90c multicolored | .55 | .55 |
| 1148 | A160 | $4 multicolored | 1.75 | 1.75 |

*Nos. 1145-1148 (4)*    2.80   2.80

**Souvenir Sheet**

| | | | | |
|---|---|---|---|---|
| 1149 | A160 | $5 multicolored | 2.75 | 2.75 |

A161

10c, Dental care. 70c, Airport runway construction. $1.10, Beach. $3, Boat building.

**1983, Mar. 14**

| | | | | |
|---|---|---|---|---|
| 1150 | A161 | 10c multicolored | .25 | .25 |
| 1151 | A161 | 70c multicolored | .40 | .40 |
| 1152 | A161 | $1.10 multicolored | .65 | .65 |
| 1153 | A161 | $3 multicolored | 1.25 | 1.75 |

*Nos. 1150-1153 (4)*    2.55   3.05

Commonwealth Day.

World
Communication
Year — A162

30c, Ship-satellite communication. 40c, Rural telephone installation. $2.50, Weather map. $3, Airport control tower.
$5, Satellite.

**1983, Nov.**    *Perf. 11*

| | | | | |
|---|---|---|---|---|
| 1175 | A165 | ½c multicolored | .25 | .25 |
| 1176 | A165 | 1c multicolored | .25 | .25 |
| 1177 | A165 | 2c multicolored | .25 | .25 |
| 1178 | A165 | 3c multicolored | .25 | .25 |
| 1179 | A165 | 4c multicolored | .25 | .25 |
| 1180 | A165 | 5c multicolored | .30 | .25 |
| 1181 | A165 | 10c multicolored | .30 | .25 |
| 1182 | A165 | $2.50 multicolored | 2.75 | 2.75 |
| 1183 | A165 | $3 multicolored | 2.75 | 2.75 |

*Nos. 1175-1183 (9)*    7.35   7.25

**Souvenir Sheet**

| | | | | |
|---|---|---|---|---|
| 1184 | A165 | $5 multicolored | 7.50 | 7.50 |

1984
Olympics
A166

**1983, Apr. 18**

| | | | | |
|---|---|---|---|---|
| 1154 | A162 | 30c multicolored | .25 | .25 |
| 1155 | A162 | 40c multicolored | 1.25 | 1.25 |
| 1156 | A162 | $2.50 multicolored | 1.50 | 1.50 |
| 1157 | A162 | $3 multicolored | 3.25 | 3.25 |

*Nos. 1154-1157 (4)*    3.25   3.25

**Souvenir Sheet**

| | | | | |
|---|---|---|---|---|
| 1158 | A162 | $5 multicolored | 2.75 | 2.75 |

For overprints see Nos. 1248-1250.

Franklin Sport
Sedan,
1928 — A163

10c, Delage D8, 1933. 40c, Alvis, 1938. 60c, Invicta S-type Tourer, 1931. 70c, Alfa-Romeo 1750 Gran Sport, 1930. 90c, Isotta Fraschini, 1930. $1, Bugatti Royal Type 41, 1941. $2, BMV 328, 1938. $3, Marmon V-16, 1931. $4, Lincoln KB Saloon, 1932. $5, Cougar XR-7, 1972.

**1983, May 4**    Litho.    *Perf. 15*

| | | | | |
|---|---|---|---|---|
| 1159 | A163 | 6c shown | .25 | .25 |
| 1160 | A163 | 10c multicolored | .25 | .25 |
| 1161 | A163 | 40c multicolored | .25 | .25 |
| 1162 | A163 | 60c multicolored | .40 | .40 |
| 1163 | A163 | 70c multicolored | .45 | .45 |
| 1164 | A163 | 90c multicolored | .65 | .60 |
| 1165 | A163 | $1 multicolored | .70 | .70 |
| 1166 | A163 | $2 multicolored | 1.25 | 1.25 |
| 1167 | A163 | $3 multicolored | 1.75 | 1.75 |
| 1168 | A163 | $4 multicolored | 2.50 | 2.50 |

*Nos. 1159-1168 (10)*    8.45   8.40

**Souvenir Sheet**

| | | | | |
|---|---|---|---|---|
| 1169 | A163 | $5 multicolored | 3.25 | 3.25 |

Manned Flight
Bicentenary
A164

30c, Norge blimp. 60c, Gloster-VI sea plane. $1.10, Curtiss NC-4. $4, Dornier Do-18. $5, Hot air ballooning, vert.

**1983, July 18**    Litho.    *Perf. 14*

| | | | | |
|---|---|---|---|---|
| 1170 | A164 | 30c multicolored | .60 | .60 |
| 1171 | A164 | 60c multicolored | 1.00 | 1.00 |
| 1172 | A164 | $1.10 multicolored | 1.75 | 1.75 |
| 1173 | A164 | $4 multicolored | 4.25 | 4.25 |

*Nos. 1170-1173 (4)*    7.60   7.60

**Souvenir Sheet**

| | | | | |
|---|---|---|---|---|
| 1174 | A164 | $5 multicolored | 4.25 | 4.25 |

Christmas — A165

Walt Disney's It's Beginning to look a lot like Christmas: ½c, Morty and Patches. 1c, Ludwig von Drake. 2c, Gyro Gearloose. 3c, Pluto and Figaro. 4c, Morty and Ferdy. 5c, Mickey Mouse and Goofy. 10c, Chip'n'Dale. $2.50, Mickey and Minnie. $3, Donald and Grandma Duck.
$5, Goofy.

Designs: Various Disney characters.

**1983, Dec. 19**    Litho.    *Perf. 13½*

| | | | | |
|---|---|---|---|---|
| 1185 | A166 | ½c Pommel Horse | .25 | .25 |
| 1186 | A166 | 1c Boxing | .25 | .25 |
| 1187 | A166 | 2c Archery | .25 | .25 |
| 1188 | A166 | 3c Uneven bars | .25 | .25 |
| 1189 | A166 | 4c Hurdles | .25 | .25 |
| 1190 | A166 | 5c Weightlifting | .25 | .25 |
| 1191 | A166 | $1 Kayak | 1.75 | 1.75 |
| 1192 | A166 | $2 Marathon | 2.50 | 2.50 |
| 1193 | A166 | $3 Pole Vault | 3.00 | 3.50 |

*Nos. 1185-1193 (9)*    8.75   9.25

**Souvenir Sheet**

| | | | | |
|---|---|---|---|---|
| 1194 | A166 | $5 Medley Relay, vert. | 8.00 | 8.00 |

**Inscribed with Olympic Rings Emblem**

**1984**    *Perf. 12½x12*

| | | | | |
|---|---|---|---|---|
| 1185a | A166 | ½c | .25 | .25 |
| 1186a | A166 | 1c | .25 | .25 |
| 1187a | A166 | 2c | .25 | .25 |
| 1188a | A166 | 3c | .25 | .25 |
| 1189a | A166 | 4c | .25 | .25 |
| 1190a | A166 | 5c | .25 | .25 |
| 1191a | A166 | $1 | 1.75 | 1.75 |
| 1192a | A166 | $2 | 2.50 | 2.50 |
| 1193a | A166 | $3 | 3.00 | 3.50 |

*Nos. 1185a-1193a (9)*    8.75   9.25

**Souvenir Sheet**

| | | | | |
|---|---|---|---|---|
| 1194a | A166 | $5 Olympic rings emblem inscribed | 8.00 | 8.00 |

Nos. 1185a-1193a printed in sheets of 5.

Banana
Boat — A167

70c, Queen Elizabeth 2. 90c, Working sailboats. $4, Amerikanis.
$5, Spanish galleon, flotilla.

**1984, July 16**    Litho.    *Perf. 15*

| | | | | |
|---|---|---|---|---|
| 1195 | A167 | 40c shown | 1.00 | .60 |
| 1196 | A167 | 70c multicolored | 1.50 | 1.00 |
| 1197 | A167 | 90c multicolored | 1.60 | 2.00 |
| 1198 | A167 | $4 multicolored | 6.00 | 8.00 |

*Nos. 1195-1198 (4)*    10.10   11.60

**Souvenir Sheet**

| | | | | |
|---|---|---|---|---|
| 1199 | A167 | $5 multicolored | 6.75 | 6.75 |

King William I, 1066-
87 — A168

British Kings or Queens and Years of their reigns: No. 1200b, William II, 1087-1100. c, Henry I, 1100-35. d, Stephen, 1135-54. e, Henry II, 1154-89. f, Richard I, 1189-99. g, John, 1199-1216.

No. 1201a, Henry III, 1216-72. b, Edward I, 1272-1307. c, Edward II, 1307-27. d, Edward III, 1327-77. e, Richard II, 1377-99. f, Henry IV, 1399-1413. g, Henry V, 1413-22.

No. 1202a, Henry VI, 1422-61. b, Edward IV, 1461-83. c, Edward V, 1483. d, Richard III, 1483-85. e, Henry VII, 1485-1509. f, Henry VIII, 1509-47. g, Edward VI, 1547-53.

No. 1203a, Jane Grey, 1553. b, Mary I, 1553-58. c, Elizabeth I, 1558-1603. d, James I, 1603-25. e, Charles I, 1625-49. f, Charles II, 1660-85. g, James II, 1685-88.

No. 1204a, William III, 1688-1702. b, Mary II, 1688-94. c, Anne, 1702-14. d, George I, 1714-27. e, George II, 1727-60. f, George III, 1760-1820. g, George IV, 1820-30.

No. 1205a, William IV, 1830-37. b, Victoria, 1837-1901. c, Edward VII, 1901-10. d, George V, 1910-36. e, Edward VIII, 1936. f, George VI, 1936-52. g, Elizabeth II, since 1952. Size: 141x128mm.

**1984, Jan. 25**    Litho.    *Perf. 14*

| | | | | |
|---|---|---|---|---|
| 1200 | | Sheet of 7 + label | 19.00 | 19.00 |
| a.-g. | A168 | $4, any single | 2.75 | 2.75 |
| 1201 | | Sheet of 7 + label | 19.00 | 19.00 |
| a.-g. | A168 | $4, any single | 2.75 | 2.75 |
| 1202 | | Sheet of 7 + label | 19.00 | 19.00 |
| a.-g. | A168 | $4, any single | 2.75 | 2.75 |
| 1203 | | Sheet of 7 + label | 19.00 | 19.00 |
| a.-g. | A168 | $4, any single | 2.75 | 2.75 |
| 1204 | | Sheet of 7 + label | 19.00 | 19.00 |
| a.-g. | A168 | $4, any single | 2.75 | 2.75 |
| 1205 | | Sheet of 7 + label | 19.00 | 19.00 |
| a.-g. | A168 | $4, any single | 2.75 | 2.75 |

Local Flowers — A169

**1984, May** — **Perf. 15**

| 1206 | A169 | 25c Lantana | .25 | .25 |
|---|---|---|---|---|
| 1207 | A169 | 30c Plumbago | .30 | .25 |
| 1208 | A169 | 90c Spider lily | .70 | .60 |
| 1209 | A169 | $4 Giant alocasia | 2.75 | 2.75 |
| | | Nos. 1206-1209 (4) | 4.00 | 3.85 |

**Souvenir Sheet**

| 1210 | A169 | $5 Orange trumpet vine | 3.25 | 3.25 |
|---|---|---|---|---|

For overprints see Nos. 1216-1218.

Coral Reef Fish, World Wildlife Fund Emblem — A170

10c, Blue parrot fish. 30c, Flame-back cherub fish. 70c, Painted wrasse. 90c, Straight-tailed razorfish. $5, Spanish hogfish.

**1984, May** — **Litho.** — **Perf. 14**

| 1211 | A170 | 10c multicolored | 3.25 | .95 |
|---|---|---|---|---|
| 1212 | A170 | 30c multicolored | 5.25 | 1.60 |
| 1213 | A170 | 70c multicolored | 9.00 | 4.00 |
| 1214 | A170 | 90c multicolored | 12.00 | 5.25 |
| | | Nos. 1211-1214 (4) | 29.50 | 11.80 |

**Souvenir Sheet**

| 1215 | A170 | $5 multicolored | 10.00 | 10.00 |
|---|---|---|---|---|

**Nos. 1208-1210 Overprinted in Black**

**1984** — **Litho.** — **Perf. 15**

| 1216 | A169 | 90c multi | .70 | .70 |
|---|---|---|---|---|
| 1217 | A169 | $4 multi | 3.00 | 3.00 |

**Souvenir Sheet**

| 1218 | A169 | $5 multi | 3.50 | 3.50 |
|---|---|---|---|---|

AUSIPEX '84 — A171

**1984, Sept. 21** — **Perf. 14**

| 1219 | A171 | $1.10 Puffing Billy | 1.10 | 1.10 |
|---|---|---|---|---|
| 1220 | A171 | $4 Australia II | 5.25 | 5.25 |

**Souvenir Sheet**

| 1221 | A171 | $5 Melbourne tram | 6.75 | 6.75 |
|---|---|---|---|---|

Correggio & Degas — A171a

Paintings by Correggio: 10c, The Night (detail). 30c, Virgin Adoring the Child. 90c, Mystical Marriage of St. Catherine with St. Sebastian. $4, Madonna and the Fruit Basket. No. 1230, Madonna at the Spring.

Paintings by Degas: 25c, L'Absinthe. 70c, Pouting, horiz. $1.10, The Millinery Shop. $3, The Bellelli Family, horiz. No. 1231, The Cotton Market.

**1984, Aug.** — **Litho.** — **Perf. 14**

| 1222 | A171a | 10c multi | .45 | .25 |
|---|---|---|---|---|
| 1223 | A171a | 25c multi | .60 | .30 |
| 1224 | A171a | 30c multi | .80 | .40 |
| 1225 | A171a | 70c multi | 1.25 | 1.00 |
| 1226 | A171a | 90c multi | 1.50 | 1.00 |
| 1227 | A171a | $1.10 multi | 1.75 | 1.75 |
| 1228 | A171a | $3 multi | 3.00 | 4.00 |
| 1229 | A171a | $4 multi | 4.00 | 5.00 |
| | | Nos. 1222-1229 (8) | 13.35 | 13.70 |

**Souvenir Sheets**

| 1230 | A171a | $5 multi | 6.25 | 6.25 |
|---|---|---|---|---|
| 1231 | A171a | $5 multi | 6.25 | 6.25 |

450th Anniversary of the Death of Correggio (Painter), 1494-1534 and 150th Anniversary of the Birth of Edgar Degas (Painter), 1834-1917.

19th Cent. Locomotives A172

30c, Locomotion, 1825. 40c, Novelty, 1829. 60c, Washington Farmer, 1836. 70c, French Crampton, 1859. 90c, Dutch State, 1873. $1.10, Champion, 1882. $2, Webb Compound, 1893. $4, Berlin 74, 1900.

No. 1240, Crampton Phoenix, 1863. No. 1241, 2-8-2 Mikado, 1897.

**1984, Oct.** — **Perf. 14½**

| 1232 | A172 | 30c multicolored | .80 | .35 |
|---|---|---|---|---|
| 1233 | A172 | 40c multicolored | .90 | .45 |
| 1234 | A172 | 60c multicolored | 1.00 | .70 |
| 1235 | A172 | 70c multicolored | 1.00 | 1.00 |
| 1236 | A172 | 90c multicolored | 1.25 | 1.00 |
| 1237 | A172 | $1.10 multicolored | 1.50 | 2.00 |
| 1238 | A172 | $2 multicolored | 2.40 | 3.00 |
| 1239 | A172 | $4 multicolored | 4.75 | 5.00 |
| | | Nos. 1232-1239 (8) | 13.60 | 13.50 |

**Souvenir Sheets**

| 1240 | A172 | $5 multicolored | 4.25 | 4.25 |
|---|---|---|---|---|
| 1241 | A172 | $5 multicolored | 4.25 | 4.25 |

Christmas and 50th Anniv. of Donald Duck — A173

Scenes from various Donald Duck movies.

**Perf. 13½x14, 12 ($2)**

**1984, Nov.** — **Litho.**

| 1242 | A173 | 45c multicolored | 1.00 | .65 |
|---|---|---|---|---|
| 1243 | A173 | 60c multicolored | 1.25 | .95 |
| 1244 | A173 | 90c multicolored | 2.00 | 1.50 |
| 1245 | A173 | $2 multicolored | 3.25 | 3.25 |
| 1246 | A173 | $4 multicolored | 6.50 | 6.50 |
| | | Nos. 1242-1246 (5) | 14.00 | 12.85 |

**Souvenir Sheet**

| 1247 | A173 | $5 multicolored | 8.50 | 8.50 |
|---|---|---|---|---|

**Nos. 1155. 1157, and 1158 Overprinted**

**1984, Oct. 28** — **Litho.** — **Perf. 14½x14**

| 1248 | A162 | 40c on #1155 | .50 | .50 |
|---|---|---|---|---|
| 1249 | A162 | $3 on #1157 | 3.00 | 3.00 |

**Souvenir Sheet**

**Same Overprint in Margin in 2 Lines**

| 1250 | A162 | $5 on #1158 | 4.50 | 4.50 |
|---|---|---|---|---|

Audubon Birth Bicentenary — A174

50c, Clapper Rail. 70c, Hooded Warbler. 90c, Flicker. $4, Bohemian Waxwing. $5, Pigeon Hawk, horiz.

**1985, Feb.** — **Litho.** — **Perf. 14**

| 1251 | A174 | 50c multi | 2.00 | .75 |
|---|---|---|---|---|
| 1252 | A174 | 70c multi | 2.50 | 1.50 |
| 1253 | A174 | 90c multi | 3.00 | 1.75 |
| 1254 | A174 | $4 multi | 6.50 | 7.50 |
| | | Nos. 1251-1254 (4) | 14.00 | 11.50 |

**Souvenir Sheet**

| 1255 | A174 | $5 multi | 11.00 | 11.00 |
|---|---|---|---|---|

See Nos. 1352-1356.

Motorcycle Centenary A175

25c, Honda XL500R. 50c, Suzuki GS1100ES. 90c, Kawasaki KZ700. $4, BMW K100.

$5, Yamaha 500CC.

**1985, Mar. 11** — **Litho.** — **Perf. 14**

| 1256 | A175 | 25c multicolored | 1.50 | .75 |
|---|---|---|---|---|
| 1257 | A175 | 50c multicolored | 1.75 | 1.50 |
| 1258 | A175 | 90c multicolored | 2.50 | 1.60 |
| 1259 | A175 | $4 multicolored | 5.75 | 7.50 |
| | | Nos. 1256-1259 (4) | 11.50 | 11.35 |

**Souvenir Sheet**

| 1260 | A175 | $5 multicolored | 9.00 | 9.00 |
|---|---|---|---|---|

Girl Guides, 75th Anniv. — A176

25c, Nature hike. 60c, Cookout. 90c, Singing around campfire. $3, Public service. $5, Flags.

**1985, Apr. 15**

| 1261 | A176 | 25c multicolored | .65 | .40 |
|---|---|---|---|---|
| 1262 | A176 | 60c multicolored | 1.00 | .90 |
| 1263 | A176 | 90c multicolored | 1.50 | 1.25 |
| 1264 | A176 | $3 multicolored | 4.50 | 4.50 |
| | | Nos. 1261-1264 (4) | 7.65 | 7.05 |

**Souvenir Sheet**

| 1265 | A176 | $5 multicolored | 4.75 | 4.75 |
|---|---|---|---|---|

Opening of Point Saline Intl. Airport, Oct. 28, 1984 — A177

Inaugural flights.

**1985, Apr. 30**

| 1266 | A177 | 70c From Barbados | 2.50 | 1.40 |
|---|---|---|---|---|
| 1267 | A177 | $1 From New York | 3.50 | 2.00 |
| 1268 | A177 | $4 To Miami | 7.50 | 8.50 |
| | | Nos. 1266-1268 (3) | 13.50 | 11.90 |

**Souvenir Sheet**

| 1269 | A177 | $5 Point Saline Intl. Airport | 7.75 | 7.75 |
|---|---|---|---|---|

Intl. Civil Aviation Org., 40th Anniv. — A178

10c, McDonnell Douglas DC-8. 50c, Super Constellation. 60c, Vickers Vanguard. $4, DeHavilland Twin Otter.

$5, Avro 748 Turboprop.

**1985, May 15**

| 1270 | A178 | 10c multicolored | .40 | .25 |
|---|---|---|---|---|
| 1271 | A178 | 50c multicolored | 1.00 | .65 |
| 1272 | A178 | 60c multicolored | 1.50 | .80 |
| 1273 | A178 | $4 multicolored | 5.00 | 6.50 |
| | | Nos. 1270-1273 (4) | 7.90 | 8.20 |

**Souvenir Sheet**

| 1274 | A178 | $5 multicolored | 5.00 | 5.00 |
|---|---|---|---|---|

Water Sports — A179

10c, Model boat racing. 50c, Snorkeling, Sandy Island carriacou. $1.10, Sailing, Grand Anse Beach. $4, Windsurfing. $5, Snorkelers, surfers, sailboats.

**1985, June 15** — **Perf. 15**

| 1275 | A179 | 10c multicolored | .25 | .25 |
|---|---|---|---|---|
| 1276 | A179 | 50c multicolored | .40 | .40 |
| 1277 | A179 | $1.10 multicolored | .90 | .90 |
| 1278 | A179 | $4 multicolored | 2.75 | 2.75 |
| | | Nos. 1275-1278 (4) | 4.30 | 4.30 |

**Miniature Sheet**

| 1279 | A179 | $5 multicolored | 4.75 | 4.75 |
|---|---|---|---|---|

Island Flowers — A180

½c, Strelitzia reginae. 1c, Passiflora coccinea. 2c, Nerium oleander. 4c, Ananas comosus. 5c, Anthurium andraeanum. 6c, Bougainvillea glabra. 10c, Hibiscus rosa-sinensis. 15c, Alpinia purpurata. 25c, Euphorbia pulcherrima. 30c, Antigonon leptopus. 40c, Datura candida. 50c, Hippeastrum puniceum. 60c, Opuntia megacantha. 70c, Acalypha hispida. 75c, Cordia sebestina. $1, Catharan-thus roseus. $1.10, Ixora macrothyrsa. $3, Justicia brandegeeana. $5, Plumbago capensis. $10, Lantana camara. $20, Jatropha integerrima.

**1985-88** — **Perf. 14**

| 1280 | A180 | ½c multi | .25 | .25 |
|---|---|---|---|---|
| 1281 | A180 | 1c multi | .25 | .25 |
| 1282 | A180 | 2c multi | .25 | .25 |
| 1283 | A180 | 4c multi | .25 | .25 |
| 1284 | A180 | 5c multi | .25 | .25 |
| 1285 | A180 | 6c multi | .25 | .25 |
| 1286 | A180 | 10c multi | .25 | .25 |
| 1287 | A180 | 15c multi | .25 | .25 |
| 1288 | A180 | 25c multi | .25 | .25 |
| 1289 | A180 | 30c multi | .25 | .25 |
| 1290 | A180 | 40c multi | .50 | .50 |
| 1291 | A180 | 50c multi | .60 | .60 |
| 1292 | A180 | 60c multi | .70 | .70 |
| 1293 | A180 | 70c multi | .75 | .75 |
| 1293B | A180 | 75c multi | 1.00 | 1.00 |
| 1294 | A180 | $1 multi | 1.20 | 1.20 |
| 1295 | A180 | $1.10 multi | 1.30 | 1.30 |
| 1296 | A180 | $3 multi | 3.25 | 3.25 |
| 1297 | A180 | $5 multi | 5.25 | 5.25 |
| 1297A | A180 | $10 multi | 11.00 | 11.00 |
| 1297B | A180 | $20 multi | 21.50 | 21.50 |
| | | Nos. 1280-1297B (21) | 49.55 | 49.55 |

Issued: Nos. 1280-1293, 1294-1297, 7/1; $10, 11/11; $20, 8/1/86; 75c, 1/12/88.

For overprints see Nos. 1357-1358, 1558-1560.

**1986** — **Perf. 12x12½**

**No date inscription**

| 1280a | A180 | ½c | .25 | .25 |
|---|---|---|---|---|
| 1281a | A180 | 1c | .25 | .25 |
| 1282a | A180 | 2c | .25 | .25 |
| 1283a | A180 | 4c | .25 | .25 |
| 1284a | A180 | 5c | .25 | .25 |
| 1285a | A180 | 6c | .25 | .25 |
| 1286a | A180 | 10c | .25 | .25 |
| | | b. Inscribed "1988" | 2.75 | 2.75 |
| 1287a | A180 | 15c | .25 | .25 |
| 1288a | A180 | 25c | .25 | .25 |
| 1289a | A180 | 30c | .25 | .25 |
| 1290a | A180 | 40c | .25 | .25 |
| 1291a | A180 | 50c | .30 | .30 |
| 1292a | A180 | 60c | .35 | .35 |
| 1293a | A180 | 70c | .40 | .40 |
| 1294a | A180 | $1 | .60 | .60 |
| 1295a | A180 | $1.10 | .65 | .65 |
| 1296a | A180 | $3 | 2.75 | 2.75 |
| 1297c | A180 | $5 | 3.75 | 3.75 |
| 1297d | A180 | $10 | 6.75 | 6.75 |
| | | Nos. 1280a-1297d (19) | 18.30 | 18.30 |

Issued: Nos. 1280a-1285a, 1287a-1292a, 1294a-1296a, Mar.; 10c, 70c, $5, July; $10, Dec.

**1987** — **Inscribed "1987"**

| 1289b | A180 | 30c | .95 | .65 |
|---|---|---|---|---|
| 1291b | A180 | 50c | 1.25 | .80 |
| 1292b | A180 | 60c | 1.60 | 1.25 |
| 1294b | A180 | $1 | 2.25 | 1.25 |
| | | Nos. 1289b-1294b (4) | 6.05 | 3.95 |

Queen Mother, 85th Birthday — A181

Photographs: $1, At the Royal Opera, vert. $1.50, Playing pool, London Press Club. $2.50, At Epsom for the Oaks Day races, vert. $5, In open carriage with Prince Charles, Thanksgiving Day, 1980, vert.

## 1985, July 5
| | | | | |
|---|---|---|---|---|
| 1298 | A181 | $1 multicolored | .60 | .60 |
| 1299 | A181 | $1.50 multicolored | .90 | .90 |
| 1300 | A181 | $2.50 multicolored | 1.40 | 1.40 |
| | | Nos. 1298-1300 (3) | 2.90 | 2.90 |
| | | **Souvenir Sheet** | | |
| 1301 | A181 | $5 multicolored | 3.50 | 3.50 |

## 1986, Jan. 20    Litho.    Perf. 12x12½
| | | | | |
|---|---|---|---|---|
| 1301A | A181 | 90c like #1298 | .55 | .55 |
| 1301B | A181 | $1 like #1299 | .65 | .65 |
| 1301C | A181 | $3 like #1300 | 1.90 | 1.90 |
| | | Nos. 1301A-1301C (3) | 3.10 | 3.10 |

Nos. 1301A-1301C issued in sheets of 5 + label.

Intl. Youth Year — A182

## 1985, Aug. 21                        Perf. 15
| | | | | |
|---|---|---|---|---|
| 1302 | A182 | 25c Gardening | .40 | .25 |
| 1303 | A182 | 50c At the beach | .50 | .40 |
| 1304 | A182 | $1 Education | 1.00 | 1.00 |
| 1305 | A182 | $3 Health care | 2.10 | 2.10 |
| | | Nos. 1302-1305 (4) | 4.00 | 3.75 |
| | | **Souvenir Sheet** | | |
| 1306 | A182 | $5 Harmonizing | 4.00 | 4.00 |

4th Caribbean Cuboree, Aug. 17-23 — A183

## 1985, Sept. 5                         Perf. 14
| | | | | |
|---|---|---|---|---|
| 1307 | A183 | 10c Pitching tents | .40 | .25 |
| 1308 | A183 | 50c Swimming | .80 | .65 |
| 1309 | A183 | $1 Stamp collecting | 1.90 | 1.40 |
| 1310 | A183 | $4 Bird watching | 5.25 | 5.25 |
| | | Nos. 1307-1310 (4) | 8.35 | 7.55 |
| | | **Souvenir Sheet** | | |
| 1311 | A183 | $5 Grand Circle ritual | 5.75 | 5.75 |

Johann Sebastian Bach — A184

Portrait, signature, music from Ciaccona and: 25c, Crumhorn. 70c, Oboe d'amore. $1, Violin. $3, Harpsichord. $5, Portrait.

## 1985, Sept. 19
| | | | | |
|---|---|---|---|---|
| 1312 | A184 | 25c multicolored | .75 | .25 |
| 1313 | A184 | 70c multicolored | 1.40 | .85 |
| 1314 | A184 | $1 multicolored | 1.75 | 1.25 |
| 1315 | A184 | $3 multicolored | 3.50 | 3.50 |
| | | Nos. 1312-1315 (4) | 7.40 | 5.85 |
| | | **Souvenir Sheet** | | |
| 1316 | A184 | $5 multicolored | 5.75 | 5.75 |

The Prince & the Pauper A185

Walt Disney characters: 25c, Prince & Pauper meet. 50c, Exchange clothes. $1.10, Prince as the Pauper. $1.50, Prince rescued. $2, Pauper as the Prince. $5, Prince & Pauper celebrate.

## 1985, Oct. 30
| | | | | |
|---|---|---|---|---|
| 1317 | A185 | 25c multicolored | 1.25 | .40 |
| 1318 | A185 | 50c multicolored | 1.50 | .80 |
| 1319 | A185 | $1.10 multicolored | 2.00 | 1.75 |
| 1320 | A185 | $1.50 multicolored | 2.75 | 2.50 |
| 1321 | A185 | $2 multicolored | 4.00 | 4.00 |
| | | Nos. 1317-1321 (5) | 11.50 | 9.45 |
| | | **Souvenir Sheet** | | |
| 1322 | A185 | $5 multicolored | 9.50 | 9.50 |

IYY, Mark Twain (1835-1910), author.

---

Elizabeth II, Royal Visit to Spice Island — A186

50c, Flags of Grenada, U.K. $1, Elizabeth II, vert. $4, HMS Britannia. $5, Map.

## 1985, Oct. 31                        Perf. 14½
| | | | | |
|---|---|---|---|---|
| 1323 | A186 | 50c multicolored | 1.00 | .50 |
| 1324 | A186 | $1 multicolored | 1.00 | 1.25 |
| 1325 | A186 | $4 multicolored | 3.50 | 3.50 |
| | | Nos. 1323-1325 (3) | 5.50 | 5.25 |
| | | **Souvenir Sheet** | | |
| 1326 | A186 | $5 multicolored | 3.75 | 3.75 |

The Brothers Grimm A187

Disney characters in The Fisherman and His Wife.

## 1985, Nov. 4    Litho.    Perf. 14
| | | | | |
|---|---|---|---|---|
| 1327 | A187 | 30c multicolored | 1.00 | .50 |
| 1328 | A187 | 60c multicolored | 1.50 | 1.00 |
| 1329 | A187 | 70c multicolored | 2.00 | 1.10 |
| 1330 | A187 | $1 multicolored | 3.00 | 1.60 |
| 1331 | A187 | $3 multicolored | 5.00 | 5.00 |
| | | Nos. 1327-1331 (5) | 12.50 | 9.20 |
| | | **Souvenir Sheet** | | |
| 1332 | A187 | $5 multicolored | 9.50 | 9.50 |

Indigenous Fish and Coral — A188

25c, Red-spotted hawkfish. 50c, Spotfin butterflyfish. $1.10, Fire coral, orange sponge. $3, Pillar coral. $5, Bigeye.

## 1985, Nov. 15
| | | | | |
|---|---|---|---|---|
| 1333 | A188 | 25c multicolored | 1.75 | .80 |
| 1334 | A188 | 50c multicolored | 2.75 | 1.25 |
| 1335 | A188 | $1.10 multicolored | 5.00 | 3.25 |
| 1336 | A188 | $3 multicolored | 8.75 | 8.75 |
| | | Nos. 1333-1336 (4) | 18.25 | 14.05 |
| | | **Souvenir Sheet** | | |
| 1337 | A188 | $5 multicolored | 7.00 | 7.00 |

UN, 40th Anniv. — A189

UN stamps and famous people: 50c, No. 258, Mary McLeod Bethune (1875-1955), American educator. $2, No. 156, Maimonides (1135-1204), Judaic scholar. $2.50, No. 41, Alexander Graham Bell (1847-1922), inventor of the telephone. $5, Dag Hammarskjold (1905-1961), 2nd UN secretary general.

## 1985, Nov. 22                        Perf. 14½
| | | | | |
|---|---|---|---|---|
| 1338 | A189 | 50c multicolored | .75 | .65 |
| 1339 | A189 | $2 multicolored | 3.25 | 3.25 |
| 1340 | A189 | $2.50 multicolored | 3.25 | 3.75 |
| | | Nos. 1338-1340 (3) | 7.25 | 7.65 |
| | | **Souvenir Sheet** | | |
| 1341 | A189 | $5 multicolored | 4.25 | 4.25 |

Christmas A190

Religious paintings: 25c, Adoration of the Shepherds, by Andre Mantegna (1431-1506). 60c, Journey of the Magi, by Sassetta (d. 1450). 90c, Madonna and Child Enthroned with Saints, by Raphael (1483-1520). $4, Nativity, by Monaco. $5, Madonna and Child Enthroned with Saints, by Agnolo Gaddi (c. 1350-1396).

---

## 1985, Dec. 23                        Perf. 15
| | | | | |
|---|---|---|---|---|
| 1342 | A190 | 25c multicolored | .25 | .25 |
| 1343 | A190 | 60c multicolored | .35 | .35 |
| 1344 | A190 | 90c multicolored | .55 | .55 |
| 1345 | A190 | $4 multicolored | 2.50 | 2.50 |
| | | Nos. 1342-1345 (4) | 3.65 | 3.65 |
| | | **Souvenir Sheet** | | |
| 1346 | A190 | $5 multicolored | 3.25 | 3.25 |

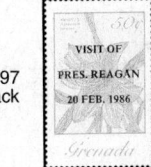

Statue of Liberty, Cent. — A191

Views of New York City: 5c, Columbus Circle, 1893. 25c, Circle, 1986. 40c, Central Park Mounted Police, 1895. $4, Mounted Police, 1986. $5, Statue of Liberty.

## 1986, Jan. 6
| | | | | |
|---|---|---|---|---|
| 1347 | A191 | 5c multicolored | .50 | .25 |
| 1348 | A191 | 25c multicolored | 1.00 | .45 |
| 1349 | A191 | 40c multicolored | 1.75 | 1.25 |
| 1350 | A191 | $4 multicolored | 6.50 | 8.00 |
| | | Nos. 1347-1350 (4) | 9.75 | 9.95 |
| | | **Souvenir Sheet** | | |
| 1351 | A191 | $5 multicolored | 5.50 | 5.50 |

Nos. 1347-1348, 1351 vert.

### Audubon Type of 1985

50c, Snowy egret. 90c, Red flamingo. $1.10, Barnacle goose. $3, Smew. $5, Brant Goose, horiz.

## 1986, Jan. 20            Perf. 12x12½
| | | | | |
|---|---|---|---|---|
| 1352 | A174 | 50c multi | 2.00 | 1.00 |
| 1353 | A174 | 90c multi | 2.75 | 1.60 |
| 1354 | A174 | $1.10 multi | 3.00 | 2.50 |
| 1355 | A174 | $3 multi | 5.50 | 5.50 |
| | | Nos. 1352-1355 (4) | 13.25 | 10.60 |
| | | **Souvenir Sheet** | | |
| | | **Perf. 14** | | |
| 1356 | A174 | $5 multi | 16.00 | 16.00 |

Nos. 1291 and 1297 Overprinted in Black

## 1986, Feb. 20                        Perf. 14
| | | | | |
|---|---|---|---|---|
| 1357 | A180 | 50c multicolored | .45 | .45 |
| 1358 | A180 | $5 multicolored | 4.50 | 4.50 |

St. George Methodist Church, Bicent. — A192

## 1986, Feb. 24                        Perf. 15
| | | | | |
|---|---|---|---|---|
| 1359 | A192 | 60c multicolored | .80 | .80 |
| | | **Souvenir Sheet** | | |
| 1360 | A192 | $5 multicolored | 3.50 | 3.50 |

Heritage Year.

1986 World Cup Soccer Championships, Mexico — A193

Various soccer plays.

## 1986, Mar. 6                         Perf. 14
| | | | | |
|---|---|---|---|---|
| 1361 | A193 | 50c multicolored | .80 | .70 |
| 1362 | A193 | 70c multicolored | 1.00 | 1.00 |
| 1363 | A193 | 90c multicolored | 1.50 | 1.50 |
| 1364 | A193 | $4 multicolored | 5.25 | 5.25 |
| | | Nos. 1361-1364 (4) | 8.55 | 8.45 |
| | | **Souvenir Sheet** | | |
| 1365 | A193 | $5 multicolored | 6.00 | 6.00 |

For overprints see Nos. 1399-1403.

---

Halley's Comet — A194

5c, Clyde Tombaugh, discovered Pluto, 1930, & Dudley Observatory. 20c, US X-24B space shuttle prototype, 1973. 40c, Medallic art, Catholic Church, 1618. $4, Lot & his daughters fleeing Sodom & Gomorrah, 1949 B.C. $5, Comet over Grand Anse Beach.

## 1986, Mar. 20
| | | | | |
|---|---|---|---|---|
| 1366 | A194 | 5c multicolored | .50 | .50 |
| 1367 | A194 | 20c multicolored | .75 | .25 |
| 1368 | A194 | 40c multicolored | 1.00 | .40 |
| 1369 | A194 | $4 multicolored | 4.25 | 4.25 |
| | | Nos. 1366-1369 (4) | 6.50 | 5.40 |
| | | **Souvenir Sheet** | | |
| 1370 | A194 | $5 multicolored | 7.75 | 7.75 |

For overprints see Nos. 1416-1420.

### Queen Elizabeth II, 60th Birthday
### Common Design Type

2c, Signing the log, 1951. $1.50, Presenting polo trophy, Windsor, 1965. $4, Derby Day, 1977. $5, Royal family portrait, 1939.

## 1986, Apr. 21                        Perf. 14
| | | | | |
|---|---|---|---|---|
| 1371 | CD339 | 2c yel & blk | .25 | .25 |
| 1372 | CD339 | $1.50 pale grn & multi | .90 | .90 |
| 1373 | CD339 | $4 dl lil & multi | 2.40 | 2.40 |
| | | Nos. 1371-1373 (3) | 3.55 | 3.55 |
| | | **Souvenir Sheet** | | |
| 1374 | CD339 | $5 tan & blk | 3.25 | 3.25 |

AMERIPEX '86 — A195

Walt Disney characters playing baseball.

## 1986, May 22    Litho.    Perf. 11
| | | | | |
|---|---|---|---|---|
| 1375 | A195 | 1c Pitcher | .25 | .25 |
| 1376 | A195 | 2c Catcher | .25 | .25 |
| 1377 | A195 | 3c Strike | .25 | .25 |
| 1378 | A195 | 4c Force out | .25 | .25 |
| 1379 | A195 | 5c Fly ball | .25 | .25 |
| 1380 | A195 | 6c Third base | .25 | .25 |
| 1381 | A195 | $2 Manager | 2.10 | 1.90 |
| 1382 | A195 | $3 Error | 3.00 | 3.00 |
| | | Nos. 1375-1382 (8) | 6.60 | 6.40 |
| | | **Souvenir Sheets** | | |
| | | **Perf. 14** | | |
| 1383 | A195 | $5 Batter | 6.50 | 6.50 |
| 1384 | A195 | $5 Grand slam | 6.50 | 6.50 |

### Royal Wedding Issue, 1986
### Common Design Type

Designs: 2c, Prince Andrew and Sarah Ferguson. $1.10, Andrew. $4, Andrew in flight suit, helicopter. $5, Couple, diff.

## 1986, July 23                        Perf. 14
| | | | | |
|---|---|---|---|---|
| 1385 | CD340 | 2c multicolored | .25 | .25 |
| 1386 | CD340 | $1.10 multicolored | .80 | .80 |
| 1387 | CD340 | $4 multicolored | 3.00 | 3.00 |
| | | Nos. 1385-1387 (3) | 4.05 | 4.05 |
| | | **Souvenir Sheet** | | |
| 1388 | CD340 | $5 multicolored | 4.25 | 4.25 |

Seashells A196

Designs: 25c, Gmelin brown-lined latirus. 60c, Lamarck lamellose wentletrap. 70c, Swainson turkey wing. $4, Linne rooster-tail conch. $5, Linne angular triton.

## 1986, July 15    Litho.    Perf. 15
| | | | | |
|---|---|---|---|---|
| 1389 | A196 | 25c multicolored | .50 | .25 |
| 1390 | A196 | 60c multicolored | .75 | .55 |
| 1391 | A196 | 70c multicolored | .90 | .90 |
| 1392 | A196 | $4 multicolored | 3.50 | 3.50 |
| | | Nos. 1389-1392 (4) | 5.65 | 5.20 |
| | | **Souvenir Sheet** | | |
| 1393 | A196 | $5 multicolored | 3.50 | 3.50 |

Mushrooms — A197

10c, Lepiota roselamellata. 60c, Lentinus bertieri. $1, Lentinus retinervis. $4, Eccilia cystiophorus. $5, Cystolepiota eriophora.

**1986, Aug. 1** — **Perf. 15**
| | | | | |
|---|---|---|---|---|
| 1394 | A197 | 10c multicolored | .65 | .40 |
| 1395 | A197 | 60c multicolored | 1.25 | 1.00 |
| 1396 | A197 | $1 multicolored | 2.75 | 2.00 |
| 1397 | A197 | $4 multicolored | 6.50 | 6.50 |
| | | Nos. 1394-1397 (4) | 11.15 | 9.90 |

**Souvenir Sheet**
| 1398 | A197 | $5 multicolored | 13.50 | 13.50 |
|---|---|---|---|---|

Nos. 1361-1365 Ovptd. in Gold

**1986, Sept. 15** — **Litho.** — **Perf. 14**
| 1399 | A193 | 50c multicolored | .95 | .95 |
|---|---|---|---|---|
| 1400 | A193 | 70c multicolored | 1.25 | 1.25 |
| 1401 | A193 | 90c multicolored | 1.50 | 1.50 |
| 1402 | A193 | $4 multicolored | 5.50 | 5.50 |
| | | Nos. 1399-1402 (4) | 9.20 | 9.20 |

**Souvenir Sheet**
| 1403 | A193 | $5 multicolored | 5.75 | 5.75 |
|---|---|---|---|---|

Disarmament Week and Intl. Peace Year — A198

60c, Mahatma Gandhi, rifles, dove. $4, Martin Luther King, Jr., hands, olive branch.

**1986, Sept. 15** — **Perf. 15**
| 1404 | A198 | 60c multi, vert. | .40 | .40 |
|---|---|---|---|---|
| 1405 | A198 | $4 multi | 2.75 | 2.75 |

Christmas A199

Disney characters: 30c, Mickey, hearth. 45c, Mickey, Santa. 60c, Donald, Mickey Mouse phone. 70c, Goofy, toy band. $1.10, Daisy, dolls. $2, Goofy as Santa. $2.50, Goofy playing piano. $3, Train ride. No. 1414, Donald, Goofy, Mickey. No. 1415, Dewey. Nos. 1406-1407, 1411-1412 vert.

**1986, Nov. 3** — **Perf. 11**
| 1406 | A199 | 30c multi | .50 | .30 |
|---|---|---|---|---|
| 1407 | A199 | 45c multi | .75 | .45 |
| 1408 | A199 | 60c multi | .90 | .60 |
| 1409 | A199 | 70c multi | 1.10 | .70 |
| 1410 | A199 | $1.10 multi | 1.25 | 1.10 |
| 1411 | A199 | $2 multi | 1.90 | 1.90 |
| 1412 | A199 | $2.50 multi | 2.10 | 2.10 |
| 1413 | A199 | $3 multi | 2.50 | 2.50 |
| | | Nos. 1406-1413 (8) | 11.00 | 9.65 |

**Souvenir Sheets**
| 1414 | A199 | $5 multi | 6.75 | 6.75 |
|---|---|---|---|---|
| 1415 | A199 | $5 multi | 6.75 | 6.75 |

Nos. 1366-1370 Ovptd. with Halley's Comet Emblem

**1986, Oct. 15** — **Litho.** — **Perf. 14**
| 1416 | A194 | 5c multicolored | .60 | .60 |
|---|---|---|---|---|
| 1417 | A194 | 20c multicolored | .80 | .60 |
| 1418 | A194 | 40c multicolored | 1.10 | .70 |
| 1419 | A194 | $4 multicolored | 7.00 | 7.00 |
| | | Nos. 1416-1419 (4) | 9.50 | 8.90 |

**Souvenir Sheet**
| 1420 | A194 | $5 multicolored | 5.00 | 5.00 |
|---|---|---|---|---|

Fauna and Flora — A200

10c, Chicken, rooster. 30c, Fish-eating bat. 60c, Goat. 70c, Cow. $1, Anthurium. $1.10, Royal poinciana. $2, Frangipani. $4, Orchid. No. 1429, Horse. No. 1430, Trees.

**1986, Nov. 17** — **Perf. 14**
| 1421 | A200 | 10c multicolored | .25 | .25 |
|---|---|---|---|---|
| 1422 | A200 | 30c multicolored | .40 | .40 |
| 1423 | A200 | 60c multicolored | .85 | .75 |
| 1424 | A200 | 70c multicolored | 1.00 | .90 |
| 1425 | A200 | $1 multicolored | 1.50 | 1.10 |
| 1426 | A200 | $1.10 multicolored | 1.50 | 1.25 |
| 1427 | A200 | $2 multicolored | 2.50 | 2.50 |
| 1428 | A200 | $4 multicolored | 5.00 | 6.50 |
| | | Nos. 1421-1428 (8) | 13.00 | 13.50 |

**Souvenir Sheets**
| 1429 | A200 | $5 multicolored | 4.75 | 4.75 |
|---|---|---|---|---|
| 1430 | A200 | $5 multicolored | 4.75 | 4.75 |

Automobile, Cent. — A202

1886 Daimler and modern automobiles: 10c, 1984 Maserati Biturbo. 30c, 1960 AC Cobra. 60c, 1963 Corvette. 70c, 1932 Duesenberg SJ7. 90c, 1957 Porsche. $1.10, 1930 Stoewer. $2, 1957 VW Beetle. $3, 1963 Mercedes 600 Limo. No. 1439, 1914 Stutz. No. 1440, 1941 Packard.

**1986, Nov. 20** — **Perf. 15**
| 1431 | A202 | 10c multicolored | .25 | .25 |
|---|---|---|---|---|
| 1432 | A202 | 30c multicolored | .35 | .35 |
| 1433 | A202 | 60c multicolored | .55 | .55 |
| 1434 | A202 | 70c multicolored | .65 | .65 |
| 1435 | A202 | 90c multicolored | .75 | .75 |
| 1436 | A202 | $1.10 multicolored | 1.00 | 1.00 |
| 1437 | A202 | $2 multicolored | 1.60 | 1.60 |
| 1438 | A202 | $3 multicolored | 2.40 | 2.75 |
| | | Nos. 1431-1438 (8) | 7.55 | 7.90 |

**Souvenir Sheets**
| 1439 | A202 | $5 multicolored | 3.75 | 3.75 |
|---|---|---|---|---|
| 1440 | A202 | $5 multicolored | 3.75 | 3.75 |

Song of Songs, by Marc Chagall (1887-1984) A203

Paintings: No. 1441, The Rooster. No. 1442, Lovers in the Moonlight. No. 1443, Woman and Haystack. No. 1444, Snow-Covered Church. No. 1445, Peasant Life. No. 1446, Moses Receiving the Tablets. No. 1447, Vitebsk: From Mt. Zadunuv. No. 1449, Song of Songs, diff. No. 1450, The Creation of Man. No. 1451, Spring. No. 1452, Jacob's Struggle with the Angel. No. 1453, Song of Songs (wedding detail). No. 1454, The Painter to the Moon, 1917. No. 1455, Moses Striking the Rock. No. 1456, To My Betrothed, 1911. No. 1457, Sacrifice of Isaac. No. 1458, Monkey Acting as Judge Over Dispute Between Wolf and Fox, 1925. No. 1459, Song of Songs (bride riding Pegasus). No. 1460, Lovers in the Lilac, 1930. No. 1461, Song of Songs (sun, spirits). No. 1462, Jacob's Dream (figures with ladder). No. 1463, Purim, 1916. No. 1464, Fantastic Horsecart. No. 1465, Listening to the Cock, 1944. No. 1466, Self-portrait, 1914. No. 1467, The Juggler, 1943. No. 1468, Noah and the Rainbow, 1945. No. 1469, Moses Before the Burning Bush. No. 1470, Around Her, 1945. No. 1471, The Trough, 1925. No. 1472, The Poet of Half-Past-Three. No. 1473, The Tree of Life, 1948. No. 1474, Bride with the Blue Face, 1932. No. 1475, Chrysanthemums, 1926. No. 1476, Spoonful of Milk, 1912. No. 1477, The Soldier Drinks, 1911. No. 1478, Noah's Ark. No. 1479, Flowers and Fruit. No. 1480, Adam and Eve Expelled fron Paradise. No. 1481, Return from Synagogue. No. 1482, Aleko: A Fantasy of St. Petersburg. No. 1483, The

Orchard. No. 1484, Solitude. No. 1485, Paris Through the Window, 1913. No. 1486, The Wedding (bridal couple, musicians), 1910. No. 1487, Paradise. No. 1488, The Dream, 1939. No. 1489, Abraham and the Three Angels. No. 1490, Water Carrier Under the Moon, 1914.

**1986-87**
| 1441-1480 | A203 | $1 Set of 40 | 40.00 | 40.00 |
|---|---|---|---|---|

**Size: 110x95mm**

***Imperf***
| 1481-1490 | A203 | $5 Set of 10 | 40.00 | 40.00 |
|---|---|---|---|---|

Nos. 1441-1446, 1450-1452 1455-1458, 1464-1467 and 1470-1479 vert. Issued: Nos. 1441-1452, 1481-1483, 1986; Nos. 1453-1480, 1484-1490, 1987.

A204

America's Cup — A205

**1987, Feb. 5** — **Litho.** — **Perf. 15**
| 1491 | A204 | 10c Columbia, 1958 | .25 | .25 |
|---|---|---|---|---|
| 1492 | A204 | 60c Resolute, 1920 | .45 | .45 |
| 1493 | A204 | $1.10 Endeavor, 1934 | .80 | .80 |
| 1494 | A204 | $4 Rainbow, 1934 | 3.00 | 3.00 |
| | | Nos. 1491-1494 (4) | 4.50 | 4.50 |

**Souvenir Sheet**
| 1495 | A205 | $5 Weatherly, 1962 | 3.75 | 3.75 |
|---|---|---|---|---|

Virgin Mary — A206

Map of Voyage, Columbus' Signature — A207

30c, Nina, Pinta, Santa Maria. 50c, Columbus, map. 60c, Columbus. 90c, Isabella, Ferdinand. $1.10, Discovering the Antilles. $2, Carib Indians. $3, American Indians, 1493. No. 1505, Columbus, Christ child.

**1987, Apr. 27** — **Perf. 15**
| 1496 | A206 | 10c shown | .30 | .25 |
|---|---|---|---|---|
| 1497 | A206 | 30c multicolored | .55 | .25 |
| 1498 | A206 | 50c multicolored | .65 | .40 |
| 1499 | A206 | 60c multicolored | .75 | .45 |
| 1500 | A206 | 90c multicolored | .85 | .70 |
| 1501 | A206 | $1.10 multicolored | .90 | .80 |
| 1502 | A206 | $2 multicolored | 1.50 | 1.50 |
| a. | | Souv. sheet of 3, 30c, 90c, $2 | 2.40 | 2.40 |
| 1503 | A206 | $3 multicolored | 2.25 | 2.25 |
| a. | | Souv. sheet of 5 + label, 10c, 50c, 60c, $1.10, $3 | 4.00 | 4.00 |
| | | Nos. 1496-1503 (8) | 7.75 | 6.60 |

**Souvenir Sheets**
| 1504 | A207 | $5 shown | 3.75 | 3.75 |
|---|---|---|---|---|
| 1505 | A207 | $5 multicolored | 3.75 | 3.75 |

Discovery of America 500th anniv. (in 1992). Nos. 1497, 1500 and 1502 horiz.

CAPEX '87 — A208

Fish: 10c, Black grouper, vert. 30c, Blue marlin. 60c, White marlin, vert. 70c, Big-eye thresher shark. $1, Bonefish. $1.10, Wahoo. $2, Sailfish. $4, Albacore. No. 1514, Barracuda. No. 1515, Yellowfin tuna, vert.

**1987, June 15**
| 1506 | A208 | 10c multicolored | .40 | .25 |
|---|---|---|---|---|
| 1507 | A208 | 30c multicolored | .60 | .25 |
| 1508 | A208 | 60c multicolored | .75 | .50 |
| 1509 | A208 | 70c multicolored | .85 | .65 |
| 1510 | A208 | $1 multicolored | 1.25 | 1.00 |
| 1511 | A208 | $1.10 multicolored | 1.50 | 1.25 |
| 1512 | A208 | $2 multicolored | 2.25 | 2.00 |
| 1513 | A208 | $4 multicolored | 3.50 | 3.50 |
| | | Nos. 1506-1513 (8) | 11.10 | 9.35 |

**Souvenir Sheets**
| 1514 | A208 | $5 multicolored | 4.50 | 4.50 |
|---|---|---|---|---|
| 1515 | A208 | $5 multicolored | 4.50 | 4.50 |

Transportation Innovations A209

10c, Cornu's Helicopter, 1907. 15c, The Monitor and Merrimack, 1862. 30c, LZ1 Zeppelin, c. 1900. 50c, S.S. Sirius, 1838. 60c, Trans-Siberian Railway. 70c, USS Enterprise, 1960. 90c, Blanchard's Balloon, 1785. $1.50, USS Holland 1, 1900. $2, S.S. Oceanic, 1871. $3, 1984 Lamborghini Countach.

**1987, May 18** — **Perf. 14**
| 1516 | A209 | 10c multicolored | .80 | .60 |
|---|---|---|---|---|
| 1517 | A209 | 15c multicolored | .80 | .60 |
| 1518 | A209 | 30c multicolored | 1.00 | .80 |
| 1519 | A209 | 50c multicolored | 1.10 | .85 |
| 1520 | A209 | 60c multicolored | 1.25 | 1.00 |
| 1521 | A209 | 70c multicolored | 1.40 | 1.10 |
| 1522 | A209 | 90c multicolored | 1.50 | 1.40 |
| 1523 | A209 | $1.50 multicolored | 2.25 | 2.25 |
| 1524 | A209 | $2 multicolored | 3.00 | 3.00 |
| 1525 | A209 | $4 multicolored | 4.50 | 4.50 |
| | | Nos. 1516-1525 (10) | 17.60 | 16.10 |

For overprints see Nos. 1599-1602.

Statue of Liberty, Cent. — A210

10c, Computer structural diagrams. 25c, Fireworks around statue. 50c, Fireworks in front of statue. 60c, Statue, boats. 70c, Structural diagram, close-up. $1, Rear of statue, close-up. $1.10, Liberty and Manhattan Islands. $2, Statue, boats, diff. $4, Ocean liner, New York Harbor.

**1987, Aug. 5**
| 1526 | A210 | 10c multicolored | .25 | .25 |
|---|---|---|---|---|
| 1527 | A210 | 25c multicolored | .25 | .25 |
| 1528 | A210 | 50c multicolored | .50 | .50 |
| 1529 | A210 | 60c multicolored | .65 | .60 |
| 1530 | A210 | 70c multicolored | .90 | .65 |
| 1531 | A210 | $1 multicolored | 1.00 | .95 |
| 1532 | A210 | $1.10 multicolored | 1.10 | 1.25 |
| 1533 | A210 | $2 multicolored | 2.00 | 2.25 |
| 1534 | A210 | $4 multicolored | 3.25 | 4.50 |
| | | Nos. 1526-1534 (9) | 9.90 | 11.20 |

Nos. 1529, 1531-1534 vert.

Inventors and Innovators A211

Designs: 50c, Sir Isaac Newton (1642-1727), law of gravity. $1.10, Jons Jakob Berzelius (1779-1848), symbols of chemical elements. $2, Robert Boyle (1627-1691), and Boyle's Law of pressure and volume. $3, James Watt (1736-1819), and diagram of steam engine. $5, Wright Flyer, Voyager.

**1987, Sept. 9**
| 1535 | A211 | 50c multicolored | .90 | .90 |
|---|---|---|---|---|
| 1536 | A211 | $1.10 multicolored | 2.00 | 2.00 |
| 1537 | A211 | $2 multicolored | 2.75 | 2.75 |
| 1538 | A211 | $3 multicolored | 5.00 | 5.00 |
| | | Nos. 1535-1538 (4) | 10.65 | 10.65 |

**Souvenir Sheet**
| 1539 | A211 | $5 multicolored | 5.25 | 5.25 |
|---|---|---|---|---|

No. 1536 inscribed with incorrect spelling of inventors name, "John Jacob Berzelius." No. 1538 inscribed with incorrect caption; James Watt and Watt engine are pictured, not Rudolf Diesel and the Diesel engine.

## Miniature Sheets

**Fairy Tales — A212**

Snow White (50th Anniv.): No. 1540a, Snow White scrubs stairs. b, Wicked Queen, looking glass. c, Snow White fleeing. d, Dwarfs, mine. e, Snow White at cottage. f, Snow White, dwarfs. g, Snow White dancing with dwarfs. h, Eating poison apple. i, Prince kissing Snow White.

Sleeping Beauty: No. 1541a, Royal family. b, Maleficent cursing infant (Aurora). c, Merryweather altering curse. d, Three good fairies. e, Briar Rose (Aurora), forest animals. f, Aurora, spinning wheel. g, Sleeping Beauty (Aurora). h, Prince Phillip battling dragon (Maleficent). i, Sleeping Beauty awakes.

Cinderella: No. 1542a, Ella (Cinderella) and father. b, Cinderella sweeping. c, Cinderella, animals in barn. d, Cinderella, stepmother, stepsisters. e, Mice. f, Fairy Godmother. g, Cinderella transformed, coach. h, i, Duke puts glass slipper on Cinderella's foot.

Pinocchio: No. 1543a, Geppetto and puppet. b, Jiminy Cricket. c, Pinocchio, J. Worthington Foulfellow and Gideon. d, Pinocchio, Master Stromboli. e, Blue Fairy rescues Pinocchio. f, Pinocchio, donkeys. g, Pinocchio riding fish. h, Pinocchio and Geppetto at sea. i, Pinocchio transformed into a boy.

Alice in Wonderland: No. 1544a, Alice, rabbit hole. b, Alice in bottle. c, Walrus and Carpenter. d, White Rabbit in pink house. e, Alice, pink butterfly. f, March Hare, Mad Hatter. g, Alice in garden. h, Queen of Hearts. i, Alice on trial.

Peter Pan: No. 1545a, Nana. b, Peter Pan. c, Peter Pan, Tinker Bell, Wendy, John and Michael Darling flying. d, In NeverNever Land. e, Peter Pan and Tiger Lily. f, Captain Hook and First Mate Smee. g, Pater Pan dueling with Captain Hook. h, Tinker Bell, pirate ship. i, Captain Hook, crocodile.

No. 1546, Snow White and Prince riding off into sunset. No. 1547, Aurora and Prince Phillip dancing. No. 1548, Cinderella and Prince Charming marry. No. 1549, Pinocchio, Jiminy Cricket and Gepetto. No. 1550, Alice, cat, mother. No. 1551, Darling children waving goodbye to Peter Pan.

| **1987, Sept. 9** | | | **Perf. 14x13½** | |
|---|---|---|---|---|
| **1540** | A212 | Sheet of 9 | 4.25 | 4.25 |
| **a.-i.** | | 30c any single | .45 | .45 |
| **1541** | A212 | Sheet of 9 | 4.25 | 4.25 |
| **a.-i.** | | 30c any single | .45 | .45 |
| **1542** | A212 | Sheet of 9 | 4.25 | 4.25 |
| **a.-i.** | | 30c any single | .45 | .45 |
| **1543** | A212 | Sheet of 9 | 4.25 | 4.25 |
| **a.-i.** | | 30c any single | .45 | .45 |
| **1544** | A212 | Sheet of 9 | 4.25 | 4.25 |
| **a.-i.** | | 30c any single | .45 | .45 |
| **1545** | A212 | Sheet of 9 | 4.25 | 4.25 |
| **a.-i.** | | 30c any single | .45 | .45 |
| | | Nos. 1540-1545 (6) | 25.50 | 25.50 |

### Souvenir Sheets

| **1546-1551** | A212 | $5 each | 6.75 | 6.75 |
|---|---|---|---|---|

### Souvenir Sheet

Baseball All-Star Game, Oakland, July 14 A213

Athletes, team emblems: a, Wade Boggs, Boston Red Sox. b, Eric Davis, Cincinnati Reds.

| **1987, Nov. 2** | | **Litho.** | **Perf. 14** | |
|---|---|---|---|---|
| **1552** | A213 | Sheet of 2 | 2.00 | 2.00 |
| **a.-b.** | | $1 any single | .95 | .95 |

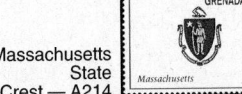

Massachusetts State Crest — A214

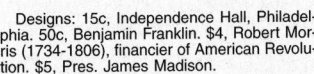

Designs: 15c, Independence Hall, Philadelphia. 50c, Benjamin Franklin. $4, Robert Morris (1734-1806), financier of American Revolution. $5, Pres. James Madison.

| **1987, Nov. 2** | | | | |
|---|---|---|---|---|
| **1553** | A214 | 15c multi, vert. | .25 | .25 |
| **1554** | A214 | 50c multi, vert. | .30 | .30 |
| **1555** | A214 | 60c shown | .40 | .40 |
| **1556** | A214 | $4 multi, vert. | 2.50 | 2.50 |
| | | Nos. 1553-1556 (4) | 3.45 | 3.45 |

### Souvenir Sheet

| **1557** | A214 | $5 multi, vert. | 3.25 | 3.25 |
|---|---|---|---|---|

US Constitution bicent.

Nos. 1286, 1291 and 1296 Overprinted

| **1987, Nov. 2** | | | | |
|---|---|---|---|---|
| **1558** | A180 | 10c multicolored | .25 | .25 |
| **1559** | A180 | 50c multicolored | .35 | .35 |
| **1560** | A180 | $3 multicolored | 2.00 | 2.00 |
| | | Nos. 1558-1560 (3) | 2.60 | 2.60 |

HAFNIA '87 — A215

Disney animated characters in adaptation of fairy tales by Hans Christian Andersen: 25c, The Shadow. 30c, The Storks. 50c, The Emperor's New Clothes. 60c, The Tinderbox. 70c, The Shepherdess and the Chimney Sweep. $1.50, The Little Mermaid. $3, The Princess and the Pea. $4, The Marsh King's Daughter.

No. 1569, The Flying Trunk, horiz. No. 1570, The Sandman, horiz.

| **1987, Nov. 16** | | **Litho.** | **Perf. 14** | |
|---|---|---|---|---|
| **1561** | A215 | 25c multicolored | .50 | .30 |
| **1562** | A215 | 30c multicolored | .50 | .35 |
| **1563** | A215 | 50c multicolored | .75 | .60 |
| **1564** | A215 | 60c multicolored | 1.00 | .65 |
| **1565** | A215 | 70c multicolored | 1.25 | .80 |
| **1566** | A215 | $1.50 multicolored | 2.25 | 1.75 |
| **1567** | A215 | $3 multicolored | 3.25 | 3.25 |
| **1568** | A215 | $4 multicolored | 4.25 | 4.25 |
| | | Nos. 1561-1568 (8) | 13.75 | 11.95 |

### Souvenir Sheets

| **1569** | A215 | $5 multicolored | 7.50 | 7.50 |
|---|---|---|---|---|
| **1570** | A215 | $5 multicolored | 7.50 | 7.50 |

Christmas — A216

Religious paintings: 15c, The Annunciation, by Fra Angelico. 30c, The Annunciation, attributed to Hubert van Eyck (c. 1370-1426). 60c, Adoration of the Magi, by Januarius Zick (1730-1797). $4, The Flight Into Egypt, by David. $5, The Circumcision, produced by artists of the Giovanni Bellini Studio, 14th cent.

| **1987, Dec. 15** | | | | |
|---|---|---|---|---|
| **1571** | A216 | 15c multicolored | .55 | .45 |
| **1572** | A216 | 30c multicolored | 1.00 | .50 |
| **1573** | A216 | 60c multicolored | 1.75 | 1.40 |
| **1574** | A216 | $4 multicolored | 6.75 | 6.75 |
| | | Nos. 1571-1574 (4) | 10.05 | 9.10 |

### Souvenir Sheet

| **1575** | A216 | $5 multicolored | 8.00 | 8.00 |
|---|---|---|---|---|

T. Albert Marryshow (b. 1887) — A217

| **1988, Jan. 22** | | **Litho.** | **Perf. 14** | |
|---|---|---|---|---|
| **1576** | A217 | 25c scarlet, red brn & brn blk | .30 | .30 |

40th Wedding Anniv. of Queen Elizabeth II and Prince Philip — A218

15c, Wedding portrait, 1947. 50c, Elizabeth, Charles, Anne. $1, Elizabeth, Anne. $4, Elizabeth, c. 1980.
$5, Elizabeth, 1947.

| **1988, Feb. 15** | | | | |
|---|---|---|---|---|
| **1577** | A218 | 15c multicolored | .30 | .25 |
| **1578** | A218 | 50c multicolored | .60 | .45 |
| **1579** | A218 | $1 multicolored | 1.00 | 1.00 |
| **1580** | A218 | $4 multicolored | 3.00 | 3.00 |
| | | Nos. 1577-1580 (4) | 4.90 | 4.70 |

### Souvenir Sheet

| **1581** | A218 | $5 multicolored | 3.75 | 3.75 |
|---|---|---|---|---|

Disney Animated Characters and 1988 Summer Olympics, Seoul — A219

1c, Lighting torch, Olympia. 2c, Torch bearers. 3c, Flag bearers. 4c, Releasing doves. 5c, Opening ceremony. 10c, Olympic motto. $6, Tiger character trademark. $7, Oldest Korean p.o.

No. 1590, Sportsmanship oath. No. 1591, Closing ceremony.

| **1988, Apr. 13** | | **Litho.** | **Perf. 13½x14** | |
|---|---|---|---|---|
| **1582** | A219 | 1c multicolored | .25 | .25 |
| **1583** | A219 | 2c multicolored | .25 | .25 |
| **1584** | A219 | 3c multicolored | .25 | .25 |
| **1585** | A219 | 4c multicolored | .25 | .25 |
| **1586** | A219 | 5c multicolored | .25 | .25 |
| **1587** | A219 | 10c multicolored | .25 | .25 |
| **1588** | A219 | $6 multicolored | 5.50 | 5.50 |
| **1589** | A219 | $7 multicolored | 6.00 | 5.50 |
| | | Nos. 1582-1589 (8) | 13.00 | 12.50 |

### Souvenir Sheets

| **1590** | A219 | $5 multicolored | 5.50 | 5.50 |
|---|---|---|---|---|
| **1591** | A219 | $5 multicolored | 5.50 | 5.50 |

Boy Scouts — A220

| **1988, May 3** | | **Litho.** | **Perf. 14** | |
|---|---|---|---|---|
| **1592** | A220 | 20c Fishing, vert. | .40 | .25 |
| **1593** | A220 | 70c Hiking | 1.25 | 1.00 |
| **1594** | A220 | 90c First-aid | 1.75 | 1.40 |
| **1595** | A220 | $3 Canoeing, vert. | 4.00 | 4.00 |
| | | Nos. 1592-1595 (4) | 7.40 | 6.65 |

### Souvenir Sheet

| **1596** | A220 | $5 Scout holding koala, vert. | 3.75 | 3.75 |
|---|---|---|---|---|

Rotary Conference, District 405, St. George, May 5-7 — A221

Rotary Intl. emblem and: $2, Map of District 405 island nations (Grenada, Guyana, Surinam and French Guiana), 15th cent. Spanish galleon Santa Maria, vert. $10, Motto "Service Above Self."

| **1988, May 5** | | | **Perf. 13½x14** | |
|---|---|---|---|---|
| **1597** | A221 | $2 multicolored | 1.50 | 1.50 |

### Souvenir Sheet
**Perf. 14x13½**

| **1598** | A221 | $10 shown | 7.25 | 7.25 |
|---|---|---|---|---|

## Nos. 1522-1525 Overprinted for Philatelic Exhibitions

a

b

c

d

| **1988, Apr. 19** | | **Litho.** | **Perf. 14** | |
|---|---|---|---|---|
| **1599** | A209 (a) | 90c multi | 1.25 | .85 |
| **1600** | A209 (b) | $1.50 multi | 1.75 | 1.50 |
| **1601** | A209 (c) | $2 multi | 2.25 | 2.25 |
| **1602** | A209 (d) | $3 multi | 2.75 | 2.75 |
| | | Nos. 1599-1602 (4) | 8.00 | 7.35 |

Birds — A222

10c, Roseate tern. 25c, Laughing gull. 50c, Osprey. 60c, Rose-breasted grosbeak. 90c, Purple gallinule. $1.10, White-tailed tropicbird. $3, Blue-faced booby. $4, Northern shoveler.

No. 1611, Belted kingfisher. No. 1612, Rusty-tailed flycatcher.

| **1988, May 31** | | | | |
|---|---|---|---|---|
| **1603** | A222 | 10c multicolored | .80 | .30 |
| **1604** | A222 | 25c multicolored | 1.00 | .30 |
| **1605** | A222 | 50c multicolored | 1.25 | .60 |
| **1606** | A222 | 60c multicolored | 1.25 | .60 |
| **1607** | A222 | 90c multicolored | 1.25 | .95 |
| **1608** | A222 | $1.10 multicolored | 1.25 | 1.10 |
| **1609** | A222 | $3 multicolored | 3.00 | 3.00 |
| **1610** | A222 | $4 multicolored | 4.25 | 4.25 |
| | | Nos. 1603-1610 (8) | 14.05 | 11.10 |

### Souvenir Sheet

| **1611** | A222 | $5 multicolored | 5.00 | 5.00 |
|---|---|---|---|---|
| **1612** | A222 | $5 multicolored | 5.00 | 5.00 |

### Miniature Sheets

Classic Automobiles — A223

Cars (U.S. unless otherwise stated): No. 1613a, 1934 Tatra Type 77, Czechoslovakia. b, 1938 Rolls-Royce Phantom III, Britain. c, 1947 Studebaker Champion Starlight. d, 1948 Porsche Gmund, Germany. e, 1948 Tucker. f, 1931 Peerless V-16. g, 1931 Minerva AL, Belgium. h, 1933 REO Royale. i, 1933 Pierce-Arrow Silver Arrow. j, 1934 Hupmobile Aerodynamic.

No. 1614a, 1925 Vauxhall Type OE30/98, Britain. b, 1926 Wills Sainte Claire. c, 1928 Bucciali, France. d, 1929 Irving Napier Golden Arrow, Britain. e, 1930 Studebaker President. f, 1907 Thomas Flyer. g, 1908 Isotta-Fraschini Tipo J, Italy. h, 1910 Fiat 10/14HP, Italy. i, 1911 Mercer Type 35 Raceabout. j, 1917 Marmon Model 34 Cloverleaf.

No. 1615a, 1965 Peugeot 404, France. b, 1969 Ford Capri, Britain. c, 1975 Ferrari 312T, Italy. d, 1978 Lotus T-79, Britain. e, 1979 Williams-Cosworth FW07, Britain. f, 1948 H.R.G. 1500 Sports, Britain. g, 1949 Crosley Hotshot. h, 1955 Volvo PV444, Sweden. i, 1960 Maserati Tipo 61, Italy. j, 1963 Saab 96, Sweden.

## 1988, June 1 — Perf. 13x13½

| | | | | |
|---|---|---|---|---|
| 1613 | A223 | Sheet of 10 | 13.00 | 13.00 |
| a.-j. | | $2 any single | 1.25 | 1.25 |
| 1614 | A223 | Sheet of 10 | 13.00 | 13.00 |
| a.-j. | | $2 any single | 1.25 | 1.25 |
| 1615 | A223 | Sheet of 10 | 13.00 | 13.00 |
| a.-j. | | $2 any single | 1.25 | 1.25 |

Paintings by Titian
(c. 1488-1576)
A224

Paintings by Titian: 10c, Lavinia Vecellio, c. 1546. 20c, Portrait of a Man, c. 1510. 25c, Andrea De Franceschi, 1532. 90c, Head of a Soldier, 1511. $1, Man With a Flute. $2, Lucrezia and Tarquinius, c. 1515. $3, Duke of Mantua with Dog, 1525. $4, La Bella Di Tiziano, 1536. No. 1624, Allegory of Alfonso D'Avalos. No. 1625, Fall of Man, 1570, horiz.

## 1988, June 15 — Perf. 13½x14

| | | | | |
|---|---|---|---|---|
| 1616 | A224 | 10c multicolored | .25 | .25 |
| 1617 | A224 | 20c multicolored | .25 | .25 |
| 1618 | A224 | 25c multicolored | .25 | .25 |
| 1619 | A224 | 90c multicolored | .60 | .60 |
| 1620 | A224 | $1 multicolored | .65 | .65 |
| 1621 | A224 | $2 multicolored | 1.40 | 1.40 |
| 1622 | A224 | $3 multicolored | 2.10 | 2.10 |
| 1623 | A224 | $4 multicolored | 2.50 | 2.50 |
| | | Nos. 1616-1623 (8) | 8.00 | 8.00 |

### Souvenir Sheets

| | | | | |
|---|---|---|---|---|
| 1624 | A224 | $5 multicolored | 3.75 | 3.75 |

#### Perf. 14x13½

| | | | | |
|---|---|---|---|---|
| 1625 | A224 | $5 multicolored | 3.75 | 3.75 |

Zeppelins
A225

Designs: 10c, Graf Zeppelin over the Federal Building, Chicago, 1933 World's Fair, vert. 15c, LZ-1 over Lake Constance, 1900. 25c, Washington aerial balloon lifting off the aircraft carrier USS George Washington Parke Custis off Port Royal, South Carolina, 1862, vert. 45c, Hindenburg over a Maybach Zeppelin automobile, Friedrichshaven, 1936. 50c, Goodyear Blimp over the Statue of Liberty, 1986, vert. 60c, Hindenburg passing over the Statue of Liberty during its final flight, 1937. 90c, Experimental docking of aircraft (piloted by Ernst Udet) with the Hindenburg, 1936. $2, Hindenburg over the Olympic stadium, Berlin, 1936, vert. $3, Hindenburg over Christ the Redeemer statue, Rio de Janeiro, 1937, vert. $4, Hindenburg over mail plane catapult ship Bremen, 1936. No. 1636, Zepplin over DLH base, Bathurst, Gambia, 1935. No. 1637, Graf Zeppelin over St. Basil's Cathedral, Moscow, 1930.

## 1988, July 1 — Perf. 14

| | | | | |
|---|---|---|---|---|
| 1626 | A225 | 10c multicolored | .50 | .25 |
| 1627 | A225 | 15c multicolored | .60 | .25 |
| 1628 | A225 | 25c multicolored | .70 | .35 |
| 1629 | A225 | 45c multicolored | .75 | .40 |
| 1630 | A225 | 50c multicolored | .80 | .45 |
| 1631 | A225 | 60c multicolored | .85 | .50 |
| 1632 | A225 | 90c multicolored | 1.00 | .80 |
| 1633 | A225 | $2 multicolored | 1.75 | 1.75 |
| 1634 | A225 | $3 multicolored | 2.50 | 2.50 |
| 1635 | A225 | $4 multicolored | 3.50 | 3.50 |
| | | Nos. 1626-1635 (10) | 12.95 | 10.75 |

### Souvenir Sheets

| | | | | |
|---|---|---|---|---|
| 1636 | A225 | $5 multicolored | 3.75 | 3.75 |
| 1637 | A225 | $5 multicolored | 3.75 | 3.75 |

The ship name on No. 1628 is incorrect.

SYDPEX '88, Sydney, Australia
A226

Walt Disney characters in Australian settings: 1c, Camping in the Outback, a howling Tasmanian wolf. 2c, Offering peanuts to wallabies. 3c, With a kangaroo and joey against Ayers Rock. 4c, Riding emus, emu-wrens. 5c, Camp and wombat. 10c, Duck-billed platypuses. No. 1644, Photographing a kookaburra. $6, Koala and Mickey waving flags of

---

Grenada, Australia and the United States, map. No. 1646, Flags and candles atop Cake in the shape of Australia. No. 1647, Mickey, Minnie Pluto and Goofy taking a break during a walkabout.

## 1988, Aug. 1 — Litho. — Perf. 14x13½

| | | | | |
|---|---|---|---|---|
| 1638 | A226 | 1c multicolored | .25 | .25 |
| 1639 | A226 | 2c multicolored | .25 | .25 |
| 1640 | A226 | 3c multicolored | .25 | .25 |
| 1641 | A226 | 4c multicolored | .25 | .25 |
| 1642 | A226 | 5c multicolored | .25 | .25 |
| 1643 | A226 | 10c multicolored | .25 | .25 |
| 1644 | A226 | $5 multicolored | 5.50 | 5.50 |
| 1645 | A226 | $6 multicolored | 6.50 | 6.50 |
| | | Nos. 1638-1645 (8) | 13.50 | 13.50 |

### Souvenir Sheet

| | | | | |
|---|---|---|---|---|
| 1646 | A226 | $5 multicolored | 6.50 | 6.50 |
| 1647 | A226 | $5 multicolored | 6.50 | 6.50 |

Mickey Mouse, 60th anniversary.

Intl. Fund for Agricultural Development, 10th Anniv. — A227

## 1988, Aug. 11 — Litho. — Perf. 14

| | | | | |
|---|---|---|---|---|
| 1648 | A227 | 25c Pineapple, vert. | .40 | .40 |
| 1649 | A227 | 75c Banana, vert. | .80 | .80 |
| 1650 | A227 | $3 Mace, nutmeg | 2.50 | 2.25 |
| | | Nos. 1648-1650 (3) | 3.70 | 3.45 |

Flowering Trees and Shrubs of the Caribbean
A228

15c, Lignum vitae. 25c, Saman. 35c, Red frangipani. 45c, Flowering maple. 60c Yellow poui. $1, Wild chestnut. $3, Mountain immortelle. $4, Queen of flowers.
No. 1659, Flamboyant. No. 1660, Orchid tree.

## 1988, Sept. 30 — Litho.

| | | | | |
|---|---|---|---|---|
| 1651 | A228 | 15c multicolored | .25 | .25 |
| 1652 | A228 | 25c multicolored | .25 | .25 |
| 1653 | A228 | 35c multicolored | .25 | .25 |
| 1654 | A228 | 45c multicolored | .35 | .35 |
| 1655 | A228 | 60c multicolored | .45 | .45 |
| 1656 | A228 | $1 multicolored | .75 | .75 |
| 1657 | A228 | $3 multicolored | 2.25 | 2.25 |
| 1658 | A228 | $4 multicolored | 3.00 | 3.00 |
| | | Nos. 1651-1658 (8) | 7.55 | 7.55 |

### Souvenir Sheets

| | | | | |
|---|---|---|---|---|
| 1659 | A228 | $5 multicolored | 3.75 | 3.75 |
| 1660 | A228 | $5 multicolored | 3.75 | 3.75 |

### Miniature Sheet

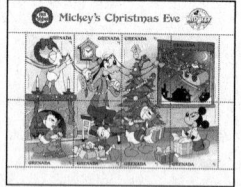

Christmas, Mickey Mouse 60th Anniv. — A229

Designs: a, Huey draping garland. b, Goofy stringing popcorn. c, Chip'n'Dale decorating tree. d, Santa Claus in his sleigh. e, Dewey hanging stockings. f, Louie unpacking decorations. g, Donald Duck. h, Mickey Mouse. No. 1662, Morty and Ferdie leaving milk and cookies for Santa, horiz. No. 1663, Morty and Ferdie dreaming of presents, horiz.

#### Perf. 13½x14, 14x13½

## 1988, Dec. 1 — Litho.

| | | | | |
|---|---|---|---|---|
| 1661 | A229 | Sheet of 8 | 7.50 | 7.50 |
| a.-h. | | $1 any single | .90 | .90 |

### Souvenir Sheets

| | | | | |
|---|---|---|---|---|
| 1662 | A229 | $5 multicolored | 5.00 | 5.00 |
| 1663 | A229 | $5 multicolored | 5.00 | 5.00 |

---

### Miniature Sheets

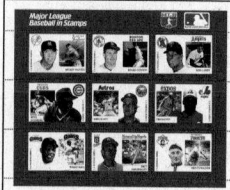

Major League Baseball Players — A230

No. 1664: a, Mickey Mantle. b, Roger Clemens. c, Rod Carew. d, Ryne Sandberg. e, Mike Scott. f, Tim Raines. g, Willie Mays. h, Bret Saberhagen. i, Honus Wagner.
No. 1665: a, Roberto Clemente. b, Cal Ripken, Jr. c, Bob Feller. d, George Bell. e, Mark McGwire. f, Alvin Davis. g, Pete Rose. h, Dan Quisenberry. i, Babe Ruth.
No. 1666: a, Jackie Robinson. b, Dwight Gooden. c, Brooks Robinson, Jr. d, Nolan Ryan. e, Mike Schmidt. f, Gary Gaetti. g, Nellie Fox. h, Tony Gwynn. i, Dizzy Dean.
No. 1667: a, Ernie Banks. b, National League emblem. c, Julio Franco. d, Jack Morris. e, Fernando Valenzuela. f, Lefty Grove. g, Ted Williams. h, Darryl Strawberry. i, Dale Murphy.
No. 1668: a, Johnny Bench. b, Dave Stieb. c, Reggie Jackson. d, Harold Baines. e, Wade Boggs. f, Pete O'Brien. g, Stan Musial. h, Wally Joyner. i, Grover Cleveland Alexander.
No. 1669: a, Jose Cruz. b, American League emblem. c, Al Kaline. d, Chuck Klein. e, Don Mattingly. f, Mike Witt. g, Mark Langston. h, Hubie Brooks. i, Harmon Killebrew.
No. 1670: a, George Brett. b, Joe Carter. c, Frank Robinson. d, Mel Ott. e, Benito Santiago. f, Teddy Higuera. g, Lloyd Moseby. h, Bobby Bonilla. i, Warren Spahn.
No. 1671: a, Gary Carter. b, Hank Aaron. c, Gaylord Perry. d, Ty Cobb. e, Andre Dawson. f, Charlie Hough. g, Kirby Puckett. h, Robin Yount. i, Don Drysdale.
No. 1672: a, Luis Aparicio. b, Paul Molitor. c, Lou Gehrig. d, Jeffrey Leonard. e, Eric Davis. f, Pete Incaviglia. g, Steve Rogers. h, Ozzie Smith. i, Randy Jones.

## 1988, Nov. 28 — Litho. — Perf. 14

| | | | | |
|---|---|---|---|---|
| 1664 | A230 | Sheet of 9 | 1.75 | 1.75 |
| a.-i. | | 30c any single | .25 | .25 |
| 1665 | A230 | Sheet of 9 | 1.75 | 1.75 |
| a.-i. | | 30c any single | .25 | .25 |
| 1666 | A230 | Sheet of 9 | 1.75 | 1.75 |
| a.-i. | | 30c any single | .25 | .25 |
| 1667 | A230 | Sheet of 9 | 1.75 | 1.75 |
| a.-i. | | 30c any single | .25 | .25 |
| 1668 | A230 | Sheet of 9 | 1.75 | 1.75 |
| a.-i. | | 30c any single | .25 | .25 |
| 1669 | A230 | Sheet of 9 | 1.75 | 1.75 |
| a.-i. | | 30c any single | .25 | .25 |
| 1670 | A230 | Sheet of 9 | 1.75 | 1.75 |
| a.-i. | | 30c any single | .25 | .25 |
| 1671 | A230 | Sheet of 9 | 1.75 | 1.75 |
| a.-i. | | 30c any single | .25 | .25 |
| 1672 | A230 | Sheet of 9 | 1.75 | 1.75 |
| a.-i. | | 30c any single | .25 | .25 |
| | | Nos. 1664-1672 (9) | 15.75 | 15.75 |

No. 1665 was reprinted with No. 1665g replaced by a label inscribed "U.S. Baseball Series."

Singers — A231

10c, Tina Turner. 25c, Lionel Ritchie. 45c, Whitney Houston. 60c, Joan Armatrading. 75c, Madonna. $1, Elton John. $3, Bruce Springsteen. $4, Bob Marley.
No. 1681: a, Yoko Minamino. b, Yoko Minamino, diff.

## 1988, Dec. 5 — Litho. — Perf. 14

| | | | | |
|---|---|---|---|---|
| 1673 | A231 | 10c multicolored | .30 | .25 |
| 1674 | A231 | 25c multicolored | .30 | .25 |
| 1675 | A231 | 45c multicolored | .45 | .40 |
| 1676 | A231 | 60c multicolored | .60 | .50 |
| 1677 | A231 | 75c multicolored | 1.00 | .65 |
| 1678 | A231 | $1 multicolored | 1.25 | .85 |
| 1679 | A231 | $3 multicolored | 2.25 | 2.25 |
| 1680 | A231 | $4 multicolored | 3.00 | 3.00 |
| | | Nos. 1673-1680 (8) | 9.15 | 8.15 |

### Souvenir Sheet

| | | | | |
|---|---|---|---|---|
| 1681 | | Sheet of 4 (2 55c, 2 $1) | 3.50 | 3.50 |
| a. | A231 | 55c multicolored | .75 | .75 |
| b. | A231 | $1 multicolored | 2.50 | 2.50 |

Armatrading is misspelled "Ammertrading."

---

## Car Type of 1988
### Miniature Sheets

Locomotives.
No. 1682: a, 1889 Canada Atlantic Railway No. 2 0-6-0, Canada. b, 1875 Virginia & Truckee Railroad J.W. Bowker 2-4-0, US. c, 1872 Philadelphia & Reading Railway Ariel 2-2-2, US. d, 1867 Chicago & Rock Is. Railroad America 4-4-0, US. e, 1866 Lehigh Valley Railroad Consolidation No. 63 2-8-0, US. f, 1860 Great Western Railway Scotia 0-6-0, Canada. g, 1854 Grand Trunk Railway Birkenhead Class 4-4-0, Canada. h, 1837 Camden & Amboy Railroad Monster 0-8-0, US. i, 1834 B&O Railroad Grasshopper Class 0-4-0, US. j, 1829 B&O Railroad Tom Thumb 0-2-2, US.
No. 1683: a, 1925 United Railways of Yucatan Yucatan 4-4-0, Mexico. b, 1924 Canadian Natl. Railways Class T2 2-10-2, Canada. c, 1919 St. Louis-San Francisco Railroad USRA Light Mikado 2-8-2, US. d, 1919 Atlantic Coast Line Railroad USRA Light Pacific 4-6-2, US. e, 1913 Edaville Railroad (Bridgton & Saco River Railroad) No. 7 2-4-4-T, US. f, 1903 Denver & Rio Grande Western Railroad Mudhens Class K27 2-8-2, US. g, 1902 PRR Class E-2 No. 7002 4-4-2, US. h, 1899 PRR Class H6 2-8-0, US. i, 1893 Mohawk & Hudson Railroad De Witt Clinton 0-4-0, US. j, 1891 St. Clair Tunnel Company No. 598 0-10-0, Canada.
No. 1684: a, 1947 Chesapeake & Ohio Railroad M-1 Class No. 500 steam turbine electric, US. b, 1946 Rutland Railroad No. 93 4-8-2, US. c, 1942 PRR Class T1 4-4-4-4, US. d, 1942 Chesapeake & Ohio Railroad Class H-8 2-6-6-6, US. e, 1941 Atchison, Topeka & Santa Fe Railway EMD Model FT Bo-Bo, US. f, 1940 Gulf, Mobile & Ohio Railroad ALCO Models S-1 & S-2 Bo-Bo, US. g, 1937 New York, New Haven & Hartford Railroad Class 15 4-6-4, US. h, 1936 Seaboard Air Line Railroad Class R 2-6-6-4, US. i, 1930 Newfoundland Railway Class R-2 2-8-2, Canada. j, 1928 Canadian Natl. Railway No. 9000 2-Do-1 + 1-Do-2, Canada.

## 1989, Jan. 23 — Litho. — Perf. 13x13½

| | | | | |
|---|---|---|---|---|
| 1682 | A223 | Sheet of 10 | 14.00 | 14.00 |
| a.-j. | | $2 any single | 1.40 | 1.40 |
| 1683 | A223 | Sheet of 10 | 14.00 | 14.00 |
| a.-j. | | $2 any single | 1.40 | 1.40 |
| 1684 | A223 | Sheet of 10 | 14.00 | 14.00 |
| a.-j. | | $2 any single | 1.40 | 1.40 |

Medalists of the 1988 Summer Olympics, Seoul — A232

Designs: 10c, Jackie Joyner-Kersee, US, long jump. 25c, Steffi Graf, Federal Republic of Germany, women's singles tennis. 45c, Peter Rono, Kenya, 1500m run. 75c, Greg Barton, US, kayak singles. $1, Italy, women's team foil. $2, Kristin Otto, German Democratic Republic, women's 100m freestyle swimming. $3, Holger Behrendt, German Democratic Republic, still rings. $4, Japan, duet synchronized swimming. No. 1693, Yukio Iketani, Japan, men's floor exercise. No. 1694, West Germany, 400m relay, and (Olympic) flame over track.

## 1989, Apr. 6 — Litho. — Perf. 14

| | | | | |
|---|---|---|---|---|
| 1685 | A232 | 10c multicolored | .30 | .30 |
| 1686 | A232 | 25c multicolored | .70 | .40 |
| 1687 | A232 | 45c multicolored | .80 | .40 |
| 1688 | A232 | 75c multicolored | .90 | .60 |
| 1689 | A232 | $1 multicolored | 1.00 | .75 |
| 1690 | A232 | $2 multicolored | 1.50 | 1.50 |
| 1691 | A232 | $3 multicolored | 2.25 | 2.25 |
| 1692 | A232 | $4 multicolored | 2.75 | 2.75 |
| | | Nos. 1685-1692 (8) | 10.20 | 8.90 |

### Souvenir Sheets

| | | | | |
|---|---|---|---|---|
| 1693 | A232 | $6 multicolored | 4.75 | 4.75 |
| 1694 | A232 | $6 multicolored | 4.75 | 4.75 |

"The Fifty-three Stations on the Tokaido"
A233

Prints by Hiroshige (1797-1858): 10c, Shinagawa on Edo Bay. 25c, Pine Trees on the Road to Totsuka. 60c, Kanagawa on Edo Bay. 75c, Crossing Banyu River to Hiratsuka. $1, Windy Shore at Odawara. $2, Snow-covered Post Station of Mishima. $3, Full Moon at Fuchu. $4, Crossing the Stream at Okitsu. No. 1703, Mt. Uzu at Okabe. No. 1704, Mountain Pass at Nissaka.

## 1989, May 15    Litho.    Perf. 14x13½

| | | | | |
|---|---|---|---|---|
| 1695 | A233 | 10c multicolored | .25 | .25 |
| 1696 | A233 | 25c multicolored | .25 | .25 |
| 1697 | A233 | 60c multicolored | .45 | .45 |
| 1698 | A233 | 75c multicolored | .65 | .65 |
| 1699 | A233 | $1 multicolored | 1.00 | .75 |
| 1700 | A233 | $2 multicolored | 1.50 | 1.50 |
| 1701 | A233 | $3 multicolored | 2.25 | 2.25 |
| 1702 | A233 | $4 multicolored | 3.00 | 3.00 |
| | | Nos. 1695-1702 (8) | 9.35 | 9.10 |

### Souvenir Sheets

| | | | | |
|---|---|---|---|---|
| 1703 | A233 | $5 multicolored | 3.75 | 3.75 |
| 1704 | A233 | $5 multicolored | 3.75 | 3.75 |

Hirohito (1901-1989) and enthronement of Akihito as emperor of Japan.

Indigenous Birds — A234

5c, Great blue heron. 10c, Green heron. 15c, Ruddy turnstone. 25c, Blue-winged teal. 35c, Ring-necked plover. 45c, Emerald-throated hummingbird. 50c, Hairy hermit. 60c, Lesser Antillean bullfinch. 75c, Brown pelican. $1, Black-crowned night heron. $3, Sparrow hawk. $5, Barn swallow. $10, Red-billed tropicbird. $20, Barn owl.

## 1989, June 6    Litho.    Perf. 14

| | | | | |
|---|---|---|---|---|
| 1705 | A234 | 5c multicolored | .75 | 1.00 |
| 1706 | A234 | 10c multicolored | .75 | .60 |
| 1707 | A234 | 15c multicolored | .80 | .60 |
| 1708 | A234 | 25c multicolored | .90 | .30 |
| 1709 | A234 | 35c multicolored | 1.10 | .30 |
| 1710 | A234 | 45c multicolored | 1.10 | .40 |
| 1711 | A234 | 50c multicolored | 1.25 | .45 |
| 1712 | A234 | 60c multicolored | 1.40 | .55 |
| 1713 | A234 | 75c multicolored | 1.50 | .55 |
| 1714 | A234 | $1 multicolored | 1.60 | 1.00 |
| 1715 | A234 | $3 multicolored | 2.40 | 2.40 |
| 1716 | A234 | $5 multicolored | 4.00 | 4.00 |
| 1717 | A234 | $10 multicolored | 8.00 | 8.00 |
| 1718 | A234 | $20 multicolored | 21.50 | 21.50 |
| | | Nos. 1705-1718 (14) | 47.05 | 41.75 |

Nos. 1709-1718 vert.

## 1990-93    Litho.    Perf. 11½x13

| | | | | |
|---|---|---|---|---|
| 1705a | A234 | 5c | .70 | .70 |
| 1706a | A234 | 10c | .70 | .60 |
| 1707a | A234 | 15c | .75 | .60 |
| 1708a | A234 | 25c | .85 | .30 |

### Perf. 13x11½

| | | | | |
|---|---|---|---|---|
| 1709a | A234 | 35c | 1.00 | .30 |
| 1710a | A234 | 45c | 1.00 | .35 |
| 1711a | A234 | 50c | 1.10 | .45 |
| 1712a | A234 | 60c | 1.25 | .50 |
| 1713a | A234 | 75c | 1.40 | .55 |
| 1714a | A234 | $1 | 1.50 | .90 |
| 1715a | A234 | $3 | 2.40 | 2.40 |
| 1716a | A234 | $5 | 4.00 | 4.00 |
| 1717a | A234 | $10 | 8.00 | 8.00 |
| 1718a | A234 | $20 | 21.50 | 21.50 |
| | | Nos. 1705a-1718a (14) | 46.15 | 41.15 |

Issued: No. 1718a, 1/22/90.

1990 World Cup Soccer Championships, Italy — A235

10c, Scotland. 25c, England vs. Brazil. 60c, Paolo Rossi, Italy. 75c, Jairzinho of Brazil. $1, Swedish Striker. $2, Pele, Brazil. $3, Mario Kempes, Argentina. $4, Pat Jennings.
No. 1727, Argentina vs. Holland. No. 1728, Goalie.

## 1989, June 12    Perf. 14

| | | | | |
|---|---|---|---|---|
| 1719 | A235 | 10c multicolored | .50 | .30 |
| 1720 | A235 | 25c multicolored | .60 | .50 |
| 1721 | A235 | 60c multicolored | .80 | .70 |
| 1722 | A235 | 75c multicolored | 1.00 | .80 |
| 1723 | A235 | $1 multicolored | 1.25 | 1.00 |
| 1724 | A235 | $2 multicolored | 2.50 | 2.00 |
| 1725 | A235 | $3 multicolored | 2.75 | 2.75 |
| 1726 | A235 | $4 multicolored | 3.75 | 3.75 |
| | | Nos. 1719-1726 (8) | 13.15 | 11.80 |

### Souvenir Sheets

| | | | | |
|---|---|---|---|---|
| 1727 | A235 | $6 multicolored | 5.50 | 5.50 |
| a. | | $6 1990 score ovptd. in margin | 7.50 | 7.50 |
| 1728 | A235 | $6 multicolored | 5.50 | 5.50 |

Issue date: No. 1727a, Nov. 30, 1990.

---

PHILEXFRANCE '89 — A236

19th Cent. ships and cargo: 25c, Chebeck, sugarcane. 75c, Lugger, cotton. $1, Merchantman, cocoa. $4, Ketch, coffee. $6, Vue du Fort et Ville de St. George dans l'Isle de la Grenade et du Morne, 1779.

## 1989, July 7    Perf. 14

| | | | | |
|---|---|---|---|---|
| 1729 | A236 | 25c multicolored | .90 | .30 |
| 1730 | A236 | 75c multicolored | 1.10 | .85 |
| 1731 | A236 | $1 multicolored | 1.40 | 1.10 |
| 1732 | A236 | $4 multicolored | 5.50 | 5.50 |

### Size: 114x71mm
### Imperf

| | | | | |
|---|---|---|---|---|
| 1733 | A236 | $6 multicolored | 6.00 | 6.00 |
| | | Nos. 1729-1733 (5) | 14.90 | 13.75 |

First Moon Landing, 20th Anniv. — A237

Space achievements: 15c, Alan Shepard, 1st American in space, 1961. 35c, Friendship 7, piloted by John Glenn, 1st manned orbit of the Earth, 1962. 45c, Apollo 8 mission, 1st manned orbit of the Moon, 1968. 70c, Lunar rover on Moon, 1972. $1, Apollo 11 mission emblem and Eagle lunar module on the Moon, 1969. $2, Gemini 8-Agena, 1st space docking, 1969. $3, Edward White, 1st American to walk in space, 1965. $4, Apollo 7 mission emblem. No. 1742, Simple flight plan for the Apollo 11 mission. No. 1743, Raising of the American flag on the Moon.

## 1989, July 20    Perf. 14

| | | | | |
|---|---|---|---|---|
| 1734 | A237 | 25c multicolored | .50 | .40 |
| 1735 | A237 | 35c multicolored | .60 | .45 |
| 1736 | A237 | 45c multicolored | .80 | .60 |
| 1737 | A237 | 70c multicolored | 1.00 | .70 |
| 1738 | A237 | $1 multicolored | 1.50 | 1.10 |
| 1739 | A237 | $2 multicolored | 2.50 | 2.10 |
| 1740 | A237 | $3 multicolored | 3.00 | 3.00 |
| 1741 | A237 | $4 multicolored | 4.00 | 4.00 |
| | | Nos. 1734-1741 (8) | 13.90 | 12.35 |

### Souvenir Sheets

| | | | | |
|---|---|---|---|---|
| 1742 | A237 | $5 multicolored | 5.50 | 5.50 |
| 1743 | A237 | $5 multicolored | 5.50 | 5.50 |

Mushrooms — A238

15c, Hygrocybe occidentalis scarletina. 40c, Marasmius haematocephalus. 50c, Hygrocybe hypohaemacta. 70c, Lepiota pseudoignicolor. 90c, Cookeina tricholoma. $1.10, Leucopaxillus gracillimus. $2.25, Hygrocybe nigrescens. $4, Clathrus crispus.
No. 1752, Mycena holoporphyra. No. 1753, Xeromphalina tenuipes.

## 1989, Aug. 17    Litho.    Perf. 14

| | | | | |
|---|---|---|---|---|
| 1744-1751 | A238 | Set of 8 | 15.00 | 15.00 |

### Souvenir Sheets

| | | | | |
|---|---|---|---|---|
| 1752-1753 | A238 | $6 Set of 2 | 15.00 | 15.00 |

YWCA, Cent. — A239

## 1989, Sept. 11    Perf. 14

| | | | | |
|---|---|---|---|---|
| 1754 | A239 | 50c shown | .70 | .70 |
| 1755 | A239 | 75c Emblem, horiz. | .90 | .90 |

Butterflies A240

---

6c, Orion. 30c, Southern daggertail. 40c, Soldier. 60c, Silver spot. $1.10, Gulf fritillary. $1.25, Monarch. $4, Polydamas swallowtail. $5, Flambeau.
No. 1764, St. Christopher hairstreak. No. 1765, White peacock.

## 1989, Oct. 2    Perf. 14

| | | | | |
|---|---|---|---|---|
| 1756 | A240 | 6c multicolored | .35 | .35 |
| 1757 | A240 | 30c multicolored | .50 | .50 |
| 1758 | A240 | 40c multicolored | .65 | .65 |
| 1759 | A240 | 60c multicolored | 1.00 | 1.00 |
| 1760 | A240 | $1.10 multicolored | 1.60 | 1.60 |
| 1761 | A240 | $1.25 multicolored | 1.90 | 1.90 |
| 1762 | A240 | $4 multicolored | 4.00 | 4.00 |
| 1763 | A240 | $5 multicolored | 4.75 | 4.75 |
| | | Nos. 1756-1763 (8) | 14.75 | 14.75 |

### Souvenir Sheets

| | | | | |
|---|---|---|---|---|
| 1764 | A240 | $6 multicolored | 6.00 | 6.00 |
| 1765 | A240 | $6 multicolored | 6.00 | 6.00 |

Discovery of America, 500th Anniv. (in 1992) — A241

Anniv. and UPAE emblems and various pre-Columbian petroglyphs.

## 1989, Oct. 16    Litho.    Perf. 14

| | | | | |
|---|---|---|---|---|
| 1766 | A241 | 45c multicolored | .90 | .90 |
| 1767 | A241 | 60c multi, diff. | 1.10 | 1.10 |
| 1768 | A241 | $1 multi, diff. | 1.25 | 1.25 |
| 1769 | A241 | $4 multi, diff. | 4.75 | 4.75 |
| | | Nos. 1766-1769 (4) | 8.00 | 8.00 |

### Souvenir Sheet

| | | | | |
|---|---|---|---|---|
| 1770 | A241 | $6 multi, diff. | 5.50 | 5.50 |

World Stamp Expo '89, Scenes from *Ben and Me* — A242

Walt Disney characters, story of the American Revolution: 1c, Amos leaves home. 2c, Amos meets young Benjamin Franklin. 3c, Invention of the Franklin stove. 4c, Invention of bifocals. 5c, *Pennsylvania Gazette.* 6c, Franklin at printing press. 10c, Experimenting with electricity. $5, As an American diplomat in England. No. 1779, Amos's "Document of Agreement." No. 1780, Franklin presiding over meeting of the Ben Franklin Stamp Club. No. 1781, 2nd Continental Congress, Philadelphia, 1775.

### Perf. 14x13½, 13½x14

## 1989, Nov. 17    Litho.

| | | | | |
|---|---|---|---|---|
| 1771 | A242 | 1c multi | .25 | .25 |
| 1772 | A242 | 2c multi | .25 | .25 |
| 1773 | A242 | 3c multi | .25 | .25 |
| 1774 | A242 | 4c multi | .25 | .25 |
| 1775 | A242 | 5c multi | .25 | .25 |
| 1776 | A242 | 6c multi | .25 | .25 |
| 1777 | A242 | 10c multi | .25 | .25 |
| 1778 | A242 | $5 multi | 5.50 | 5.50 |
| 1779 | A242 | $6 multi | 5.75 | 6.00 |
| | | Nos. 1771-1779 (9) | 13.00 | 13.25 |

### Souvenir Sheets

| | | | | |
|---|---|---|---|---|
| 1780 | A242 | $6 multi, vert. | 5.50 | 5.50 |
| 1781 | A242 | $6 multi | 5.50 | 5.50 |

Christmas — A243

Paintings by Rubens: 20c, *Christ in the House of Mary and Martha.* 35c, *The Circumcision.* 60c, *Trinity Adored by Duke of Mantua and Family.* $2, *Holy Family with St. Francis.* $3, *The Ildefonso Altarpiece.* $4, *Madonna and Child with Garland and Putti,* by Rubens and Jan Brueghel. No. 1788, *Adoration of the Magi.* No. 1789, *Virgin and Child Adored by Angels.*

## 1990, Jan. 4    Litho.    Perf. 14

| | | | | |
|---|---|---|---|---|
| 1782 | A243 | 20c multicolored | .50 | .25 |
| 1783 | A243 | 35c multicolored | .65 | .45 |
| 1784 | A243 | 60c multicolored | 1.00 | .65 |
| 1785 | A243 | $2 multicolored | 2.00 | 2.00 |

---

| | | | | |
|---|---|---|---|---|
| 1786 | A243 | $3 multicolored | 2.50 | 2.50 |
| 1787 | A243 | $4 multicolored | 3.50 | 3.50 |
| | | Nos. 1782-1787 (6) | 10.15 | 9.35 |

### Souvenir Sheets

| | | | | |
|---|---|---|---|---|
| 1788 | A243 | $5 multicolored | 4.50 | 4.50 |
| 1789 | A243 | $5 multicolored | 4.50 | 4.50 |

Anniversaries and Events (in 1989) — A244

Designs: 10c, Alexander Graham Bell, early telephone, telephone lines. 25c, George Washington, the Capitol Building. 35c, William Shakespeare, birthplace, Stratford-on-Avon. 75c, Jawaharlal Nehru, Mahatma Gandhi. $1, Hugo Eckener, Ferdinand von Zeppelin, zeppelin *Delag.* $2, Charlie Chaplin. $3, Ship in port. $4, Pres. Friedrich Ebert, Heidelberg Gate. No. 1798, Concorde jet. No. 1799, Ship, 13th century, vert.

## 1990, Feb. 12    Litho.    Perf. 14

| | | | | |
|---|---|---|---|---|
| 1790 | A244 | 10c multicolored | .35 | .25 |
| 1791 | A244 | 25c multicolored | .35 | .25 |
| 1792 | A244 | 35c multicolored | 1.10 | .55 |
| 1793 | A244 | 75c multicolored | 2.00 | 1.60 |
| 1794 | A244 | $1 multicolored | 1.40 | 1.40 |
| 1795 | A244 | $2 multicolored | 2.75 | 2.75 |
| 1796 | A244 | $3 multicolored | 3.00 | 3.00 |
| 1797 | A244 | $4 multicolored | 4.25 | 4.25 |
| | | Nos. 1790-1797 (8) | 15.20 | 14.05 |

### Souvenir Sheets

| | | | | |
|---|---|---|---|---|
| 1798 | A244 | $6 multicolored | 6.00 | 6.00 |
| 1799 | A244 | $6 multicolored | 6.00 | 6.00 |

Invention of the telephone, 1876 (10c); American presidency, 200th anniv. (25c); 425th birth anniv. of Shakespeare (35c); birth cent. of Nehru (75c); 1st passenger zeppelin, 80th anniv. ($1); birth cent. of Charlie Chaplin ($2); Hamburg, 800th anniv. ($3, No. 1799); Federal Republic of Germany, 40th anniv. ($4); and test flight of the Concorde supersonic jet, 20th anniv. (No. 1798).

Orchids — A245

1c, Odontoglossum triumphans. 25c, Oncidium splendidum. 60c, Laelia anceps. 75c, Cattleya trianaei. $1, Odontoglossum rossii. $2, Brassia gireoudiana. $3, Cattleya dowiana. $4, Sobralia macrantha.
No. 1808, Laelia rubescens. No. 1809, Oncidium lanceanum.

## 1990, Mar. 6    Litho.    Perf. 14

| | | | | |
|---|---|---|---|---|
| 1800 | A245 | 1c multicolored | .25 | .25 |
| 1801 | A245 | 25c multicolored | .30 | .30 |
| 1802 | A245 | 60c multicolored | .65 | .65 |
| 1803 | A245 | 75c multicolored | .80 | .80 |
| 1804 | A245 | $1 multicolored | 1.25 | 1.25 |
| 1805 | A245 | $2 multicolored | 1.75 | 1.75 |
| 1806 | A245 | $3 multicolored | 2.50 | 2.50 |
| 1807 | A245 | $4 multicolored | 3.25 | 3.25 |
| | | Nos. 1800-1807 (8) | 10.75 | 10.75 |

### Souvenir Sheets

| | | | | |
|---|---|---|---|---|
| 1808 | A245 | $6 multicolored | 5.50 | 5.50 |
| 1809 | A245 | $6 multicolored | 5.50 | 5.50 |

EXPO '90 Intl. Garden and Greenery Exposition, Japan.

America Issue — A246

Butterflies, UPAE and discovery of America 500th anniv. emblems: 15c, Southern daggertail. 25c, Caribbean buckeye. 75c, Malachite. 90c, Orion. $1, St. Lucia mestra. $2, Red rim. $3, Flambeau. $4, Red anartia. No. 1818, Giant hairstreak. No. 1819, Orange-barred sulphur.

## 1990, Mar. 16    Litho.    Perf. 14

| | | | | |
|---|---|---|---|---|
| 1810 | A246 | 15c multicolored | .65 | .25 |
| 1811 | A246 | 25c multicolored | .80 | .25 |
| 1812 | A246 | 75c multicolored | 1.25 | .80 |
| 1813 | A246 | 90c multicolored | 1.40 | .95 |

| | | | | | |
|---|---|---|---|---|---|
| 1814 | A246 | $1 multicolored | | 1.50 | 1.00 |
| 1815 | A246 | $2 multicolored | | 2.00 | 2.00 |
| 1816 | A246 | $3 multicolored | | 3.00 | 3.00 |
| 1817 | A246 | $4 multicolored | | 4.00 | 4.00 |

*Nos. 1810-1817 (8)*     14.60   12.25

**Souvenir Sheets**

| 1818 | A246 | $6 multicolored | 7.00 | 7.00 |
|---|---|---|---|---|
| 1819 | A246 | $6 multicolored | 7.00 | 7.00 |

Wildlife — A247

10c, Caribbean monk seal. 15c, Little brown bat. 45c, Norway rat. 60c, Old-world rabbit. $1, Water opossum. $2, White-nosed ichneumon. $3, Little big-eared bat. $4, Mouse opossums. No. 1828, Old-world rabbit. diff. No. 1829, Water opossum.

**1990, Apr. 3    Litho.    Perf. 14**

| 1820 | A247 | 10c multicolored | .50 | .30 |
|---|---|---|---|---|
| 1821 | A247 | 15c multicolored | .55 | .30 |
| 1822 | A247 | 45c multicolored | .65 | .50 |
| 1823 | A247 | 60c multicolored | .75 | .60 |
| 1824 | A247 | $1 multicolored | 1.00 | .90 |
| 1825 | A247 | $2 multicolored | 1.60 | 1.60 |
| 1826 | A247 | $3 multicolored | 2.40 | 2.40 |
| 1827 | A247 | $4 multicolored | 3.25 | 3.25 |

*Nos. 1820-1827 (8)*    10.70   9.85

**Souvenir Sheets**

| 1828 | A247 | $6 multicolored | 5.50 | 5.50 |
|---|---|---|---|---|
| 1829 | A247 | $6 multicolored | 5.50 | 5.50 |

No. 1826 is vert. Nos. 1828-1829 have multicolored decorative margins continiuning the designs and picturing little brown bat, prehensile-tailed porcupine and mouse opossum (No. 1828) or four-eyed opossum, West Indies manatee and Norway rat (No. 1829).

World War II — A248

Designs: 25c, Operation Battleaxe, June 15, 1941. 35c, Allied landing in southern France, Aug. 15, 1944. 45c, US invasion of Guadalcanal, Aug. 7, 1942. 50c, Allied defeat of Japanese army in New Guinea, Jan. 22, 1943. 60c, US forces secure Leyte, Dec. 11, 1944. 75c, US forces enter Cologne, Mar. 5, 1945. $1, Allied offensive to break out of Anzio, May 23, 1944. $2, Battle of the Bismarck Sea, Mar. 3, 1943. $3, US fleet under Adm. Nimitz, Dec. 17, 1941. $4, Allied landing at Salerno, Sept. 9, 1943. $6, German U-boat.

**1990, Apr. 30   Litho.   Perf. 14x13½**

| 1830 | A248 | 25c multicolored | .40 | .40 |
|---|---|---|---|---|
| 1831 | A248 | 35c multicolored | .50 | .50 |
| 1832 | A248 | 45c multicolored | .60 | .60 |
| 1833 | A248 | 50c multicolored | .70 | .70 |
| 1834 | A248 | 60c multicolored | .80 | .80 |
| 1835 | A248 | 75c multicolored | 1.00 | 1.00 |
| 1836 | A248 | $1 multicolored | 1.50 | 1.50 |
| 1837 | A248 | $2 multicolored | 1.75 | 1.75 |
| 1838 | A248 | $3 multicolored | 2.50 | 2.50 |
| 1839 | A248 | $4 multicolored | 3.50 | 3.50 |

*Nos. 1830-1839 (10)*    13.25   13.25

**Souvenir Sheet**

| 1840 | A248 | $6 multicolored | 7.00 | 7.00 |
|---|---|---|---|---|

**Souvenir Sheet**

Penny Black, 150th Anniv. A249

**1990, May 3    Litho.    Perf. 14**

| 1841 | A249 | $6 violet | 5.50 | 5.50 |
|---|---|---|---|---|

Stamp World London '90.

Stamp World London '90 — A250

---

Walt Disney characters and British trains: 5c, 1925 King Arthur Class. 10c, 1813 Puffing Billy. 20c, 1765 Colliery Tram-wagon. 45c, 1935 No. 2509 Silver Link. $1, 1948 No. 60149 Amadis. $2, 1830 Liverpool. $4, 1870 Flying Scotsman. $5, 1972 Advanced Passenger Train.

No. 1852, Stockton & Darlington Railway Opening, 1825, vert. No. 1853, 1809 *Catch-Me-Who-Can.*

**1990, June 21    Perf. 14**

| 1844 | A250 | 5c multicolored | .45 | .25 |
|---|---|---|---|---|
| 1845 | A250 | 10c multicolored | .45 | .25 |
| 1846 | A250 | 20c multicolored | .60 | .25 |
| 1847 | A250 | 45c multicolored | 1.00 | .55 |
| 1848 | A250 | $1 multicolored | 1.50 | 1.50 |
| 1849 | A250 | $2 multicolored | 2.25 | 2.10 |
| 1850 | A250 | $4 multicolored | 4.00 | 4.00 |
| 1851 | A250 | $5 multicolored | 4.75 | 4.50 |

*Nos. 1844-1851 (8)*    15.00   13.00

**Souvenir Sheets**

| 1852 | A250 | $6 multicolored | 6.50 | 6.50 |
|---|---|---|---|---|
| 1853 | A250 | $6 multicolored | 6.50 | 6.50 |

Queen Mother, 90th Birthday — A251

**1990, July 5    Litho.    Perf. 14**

| 1854 | A251 | $2 Wearing black hat | 2.10 | 2.10 |
|---|---|---|---|---|
| 1855 | A251 | $2 shown | 2.10 | 2.10 |
| 1856 | A251 | $2 Wearing crown | 2.10 | 2.10 |

*Nos. 1854-1856 (3)*    6.30   6.30

**Souvenir Sheet**

| 1857 | A251 | $6 Like No. 1855 | 5.00 | 5.00 |
|---|---|---|---|---|

1992 Summer Olympics, Barcelona — A252

Character trademark and: 10c, Men's steeplechase. 15c, Equestrian. 45c, Men's 200 meter butterfly. 50c, Field hockey. 65c, Balance beam. 75c, Flying Dutchman Class yachting. $2, Freestyle wrestling. $3, Men's diving. $4, Women's cycling. $5, Men's basketball. No. 1863, Three-day equestrian event. No. 1863A, Men's 10,000 M race.

**1990, July 9**

| 1858 | A252 | 10c multicolored | .35 | .30 |
|---|---|---|---|---|
| 1858A | A252 | 15c multicolored | .45 | .35 |
| 1859 | A252 | 45c multicolored | .55 | .40 |
| 1859A | A252 | 50c multicolored | .80 | .60 |
| 1860 | A252 | 65c multicolored | .80 | .60 |
| 1860A | A252 | 75c multicolored | 1.00 | .80 |
| 1861 | A252 | $2 multicolored | 1.75 | 1.75 |
| 1861A | A252 | $3 multicolored | 2.50 | 2.50 |
| 1862 | A252 | $4 multicolored | 3.75 | 3.75 |
| 1862A | A252 | $5 multicolored | 4.00 | 4.00 |

*Nos. 1858-1862A (10)*    15.95   15.05

**Souvenir Sheet**

| 1863 | A252 | $8 multicolored | 6.00 | 6.00 |
|---|---|---|---|---|
| 1863A | A252 | $8 multicolored | 6.00 | 6.00 |

Nos. 1858A, 1859A, 1860A, 1861A, 1862A, 1863A were not available until 1991.

US Airborne, 50th Anniv. — A253

75c, Mass jump. $2.50, Paratrooper landing. $6, Paratroopers 1940, 1990.

**1990, July 3**

| 1864 | A253 | 75c multicolored | 2.50 | 2.50 |
|---|---|---|---|---|

**Souvenir Sheets**

| 1865 | A253 | $2.50 multicolored | 2.50 | 2.50 |
|---|---|---|---|---|
| 1866 | A253 | $6 multicolored | 5.50 | 5.50 |

Yellow Goatfish — A254

---

25c, Black margate. 65c, Bluehead wrasse. 75c, Puddingwife. $1, Foureye butterflyfish. $2, Honey damselfish. $3, Queen angelfish. $5, Cherubfish.
No. 1875, Smooth trunkfish. No. 1876, Sergeant major.

**1990, Aug. 8**

| 1867 | A254 | 10c shown | .40 | .40 |
|---|---|---|---|---|
| 1868 | A254 | 25c multicolored | .60 | .60 |
| 1869 | A254 | 65c multicolored | 1.00 | 1.00 |
| 1870 | A254 | 75c multicolored | 1.25 | 1.25 |
| 1871 | A254 | $1 multicolored | 1.50 | 1.50 |
| 1872 | A254 | $2 multicolored | 1.90 | 1.90 |
| 1873 | A254 | $3 multicolored | 2.50 | 2.50 |
| 1874 | A254 | $5 multicolored | 4.50 | 4.50 |

*Nos. 1867-1874 (8)*    13.65   13.65

**Souvenir Sheets**

| 1875 | A254 | $6 multicolored | 6.50 | 6.50 |
|---|---|---|---|---|
| 1876 | A254 | $6 multicolored | 6.50 | 6.50 |

Birds — A255

15c, Tropical mockingbird. 25c, Gray kingbird. 65c, Bare-eyed thrush. 75c, Antillean crested hummingbird. $1, House wren. $2, Purple martin. $4, Hooded tanager. $5, Common ground dove.
No. 1885, Fork-tailed flycatcher. No. 1886, Smooth-billed ani.

**1990, Sept. 10    Litho.    Perf. 14**

| 1877 | A255 | 15c multicolored | .45 | .45 |
|---|---|---|---|---|
| 1878 | A255 | 25c multicolored | .50 | .50 |
| 1879 | A255 | 65c multicolored | .80 | .80 |
| 1880 | A255 | 75c multicolored | 1.00 | 1.00 |
| 1881 | A255 | $1 multicolored | 1.50 | 1.50 |
| 1882 | A255 | $2 multicolored | 1.90 | 1.90 |
| 1883 | A255 | $4 multicolored | 3.50 | 3.50 |
| 1884 | A255 | $5 multicolored | 4.25 | 4.25 |

*Nos. 1877-1884 (8)*    13.90   13.90

**Souvenir Sheets**

| 1885 | A255 | $6 multicolored | 7.50 | 7.50 |
|---|---|---|---|---|
| 1886 | A255 | $6 multicolored | 7.50 | 7.50 |

Crustaceans A256

5c, Coral crab. 10c, Smoothtail spiny lobster. 15c, Flamestreaked swimming crab. 25c, Spotted swimming crab. 75c, Sally lightfoot rock crab. $1, Spotted spiny lobster. $3, Longarm spiny lobster. $20, Caribbean spiny lobster.
No. 1895, Spanish lobster. No. 1896, Caribbean furry lobster.

**1990, Sept. 17**

| 1887 | A256 | 5c multicolored | .25 | .25 |
|---|---|---|---|---|
| 1888 | A256 | 10c multicolored | .25 | .25 |
| 1889 | A256 | 15c multicolored | .25 | .25 |
| 1890 | A256 | 25c multicolored | .25 | .25 |
| 1891 | A256 | 75c multicolored | .70 | .70 |
| 1892 | A256 | $1 multicolored | .90 | .90 |
| 1893 | A256 | $3 multicolored | 2.60 | 2.60 |
| 1894 | A256 | $20 multicolored | 16.50 | 16.50 |

*Nos. 1887-1894 (8)*    21.70   21.70

**Souvenir Sheets**

| 1895 | A256 | $6 multicolored | 6.75 | 6.75 |
|---|---|---|---|---|
| 1896 | A256 | $6 multicolored | 6.75 | 6.75 |

World Cup Soccer Championships, Italy — A257

Players from participating countries.

**1990, Sept. 24**

| 1897 | A257 | 10c Cameroun | .25 | .25 |
|---|---|---|---|---|
| 1898 | A257 | 25c Spain | .25 | .25 |
| 1899 | A257 | $1 West Germany | .80 | .80 |
| 1900 | A257 | $5 Scotland | 3.75 | 3.75 |

*Nos. 1897-1900 (4)*    5.05   5.05

**Souvenir Sheets**

| 1901 | A257 | $6 Uruguay | 6.00 | 6.00 |
|---|---|---|---|---|
| 1902 | A257 | $6 Italy | 6.00 | 6.00 |

---

Christmas — A258

Paintings by Raphael: 10c, The Ansidei Madonna. 15c, The Sistine Madonna. $1, Madonna of the Baldacchino. $2, The Large Holy Family. $5, Madonna in the Meadow. No. 1908, Madonna of the Veil. No. 1909, Madonna of the Diadem.

**1990, Dec. 31    Litho.    Perf. 14**

| 1903 | A258 | 10c multicolored | .30 | .25 |
|---|---|---|---|---|
| 1904 | A258 | 15c multicolored | .30 | .25 |
| 1905 | A258 | $1 multicolored | 1.50 | 1.00 |
| 1906 | A258 | $2 multicolored | 2.40 | 2.40 |
| 1907 | A258 | $5 multicolored | 5.00 | 5.00 |

*Nos. 1903-1907 (5)*    9.50   8.90

**Souvenir Sheets**

| 1908 | A258 | $6 multicolored | 6.75 | 6.75 |
|---|---|---|---|---|
| 1909 | A258 | $6 multicolored | 6.75 | 6.75 |

Peter Paul Rubens (1577-1640), Painter A259

Entire paintings or different details from: 5c, $1, $4, The Brazen Serpent. 10c, Garden of Love. 25c, Head of Cyrus. 75c, Tournament in Front of a Castle. $2, Judgement of Paris. $5, The Kermesse. No. 1918, The Prodigal Son. No. 1919, Anger of Neptune.

**1991, Jan. 31    Litho.    Perf. 14**

| 1910 | A259 | 5c multicolored | .35 | .25 |
|---|---|---|---|---|
| 1911 | A259 | 10c multicolored | .35 | .25 |
| 1912 | A259 | 25c multicolored | .60 | .25 |
| 1913 | A259 | 75c multicolored | .80 | .60 |
| 1914 | A259 | $1 multicolored | 1.00 | .80 |
| 1915 | A259 | $2 multicolored | 1.60 | 1.60 |
| 1916 | A259 | $4 multicolored | 3.00 | 3.00 |
| 1917 | A259 | $5 multicolored | 4.00 | 4.00 |

*Nos. 1910-1917 (8)*    11.70   10.75

**Souvenir Sheets**

| 1918 | A259 | $6 multicolored | 6.50 | 6.50 |
|---|---|---|---|---|
| 1919 | A259 | $6 multicolored | 6.50 | 6.50 |

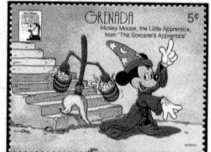

Disney Film *Fantasia,* 50th Anniv. A260

5c, Mickey as Sorcerer's apprentice, walking broom. 10c, Mushroom Dance Ensemble from The Nutcracker Suite. 20c, Pterodactyls from The Rite of Spring. 45c, Centaurs from The Pastoral Symphony. $1, Bacchus & Jacchus from The Pastoral Symphony. $2, Ostrich ballerina in Dance of the Hours. $4, Elephant dance from Dance of the Hours. $5, Diana, Goddess of the Moon from Dance of the Hours. No. 1928, Mickey as Sorcerer's apprentice. No. 1929, Mickey, Leopold Stokowski. $12, Mickey as Sorcerer's Apprentice, vert.

**1991, Feb. 4    Litho.    Perf. 14**

| 1920 | A260 | 5c multicolored | .75 | .25 |
|---|---|---|---|---|
| 1921 | A260 | 10c multicolored | .75 | .25 |
| 1922 | A260 | 20c multicolored | 1.10 | .25 |
| 1923 | A260 | 45c multicolored | 1.25 | .55 |
| 1924 | A260 | $1 multicolored | 1.75 | 1.75 |
| 1925 | A260 | $2 multicolored | 2.75 | 2.75 |
| 1926 | A260 | $4 multicolored | 5.00 | 5.00 |
| 1927 | A260 | $5 multicolored | 6.50 | 6.50 |

*Nos. 1920-1927 (8)*    19.85   17.30

**Souvenir Sheets**

| 1928 | A260 | $6 multicolored | 8.50 | 8.50 |
|---|---|---|---|---|
| 1929 | A260 | $6 multicolored | 8.50 | 8.50 |
| 1930 | A260 | $12 multicolored | 16.50 | 16.50 |

Butterflies A261

5c, Adelphia iphicla. 10c, Nymphalidae claudina. 15c, Brassolidae polyxena. 20c, Zebra longwing. 25c, Marpesia corinna. 30c, Morpho hecuba. 45c, Morpho rhetenor. 50c, Dismorphia spio. 60c, Prepona omphale. 70c, Morpho anaxibia. 75c, Marpesia iole. $1, Metalmark. $2, Morpho cisseis. $3, Danaidae plexippus. $4, Morpho achilleana. $5, Calliona argenissa. No. 1947, Anteos clorinde. No. 1948, Haetera piera. No. 1949, Papilio cresphontes. No. 1950, Prepona pheridames.

**1991, Apr. 8    Litho.    Perf. 14**

| | | | | |
|---|---|---|---|---|
| **1931** | A261 | 5c multicolored | .55 | .45 |
| **1932** | A261 | 10c multicolored | .60 | .45 |
| **1933** | A261 | 15c multicolored | .65 | .45 |
| **1934** | A261 | 20c multicolored | .70 | .35 |
| **1935** | A261 | 25c multicolored | .75 | .35 |
| **1936** | A261 | 30c multicolored | .85 | .35 |
| **1937** | A261 | 45c multicolored | .95 | .60 |
| **1938** | A261 | 50c multicolored | 1.00 | .65 |
| **1939** | A261 | 60c multicolored | 1.20 | .75 |
| **1940** | A261 | 70c multicolored | 1.30 | .95 |
| **1941** | A261 | 75c multicolored | 1.75 | 1.75 |
| **1942** | A261 | $1 multicolored | 1.90 | 1.90 |
| **1943** | A261 | $2 multicolored | 2.60 | 2.60 |
| **1944** | A261 | $3 multicolored | 4.00 | 4.00 |
| **1945** | A261 | $4 multicolored | 5.50 | 5.50 |
| **1946** | A261 | $5 multicolored | 7.00 | 7.00 |
| | | *Nos. 1931-1946 (16)* | 31.30 | 28.10 |

**Souvenir Sheets**

| | | | | |
|---|---|---|---|---|
| **1947** | A261 | $6 multicolored | 8.50 | 8.50 |
| **1948** | A261 | $6 multicolored | 8.50 | 8.50 |
| **1949** | A261 | $6 multicolored | 8.50 | 8.50 |
| **1950** | A261 | $6 multicolored | 8.50 | 8.50 |

Voyages of
Discovery
A262

Explorer's ships: 5c, Vitus Bering, 1728-1729. 10c, Louis de Bougainville, 1766-1769. 25c, Polynesians. 50c, Álvaro de Mendana, 1567-1569. $1, Charles Darwin, 1831-1835. $2, Capt. James Cook, 1768-1771. $4, Capt. Willem Schouten, 1615-1617. $5, Abel Tasman, 1642-1644. No. 1959, Columbus' ship Santa Maria. No. 1960, Loss of Santa Maria.

**1991, Apr. 29**

| | | | | |
|---|---|---|---|---|
| **1951** | A262 | 5c multicolored | .50 | .40 |
| **1952** | A262 | 10c multicolored | .50 | .40 |
| **1953** | A262 | 25c multicolored | .50 | .30 |
| **1954** | A262 | 50c multicolored | .90 | .50 |
| **1955** | A262 | $1 multicolored | 1.50 | 1.25 |
| **1956** | A262 | $2 multicolored | 2.75 | 2.50 |
| **1957** | A262 | $4 multicolored | 3.75 | 3.75 |
| **1958** | A262 | $5 multicolored | 4.75 | 4.75 |
| | | *Nos. 1951-1958 (8)* | 15.15 | 13.85 |

**Souvenir Sheets**

| | | | | |
|---|---|---|---|---|
| **1959** | A262 | $6 multicolored | 6.50 | 6.50 |
| **1960** | A262 | $6 multicolored | 6.50 | 6.50 |

Discovery of America, 500th anniv. (in 1992).

PHILANIPPON '91 — A263

Walt Disney characters celebrating festivals of Japan: 5c, Daisy Duck and Minnie Mouse, Peach Fete, Festival of the Dolls. 10c, Morty and Ferdie, Tango Festival, Boys' Day Festival. 20c, Mickey, Minnie Mouse, Hoshi-Matsuri, Star Festival. 45c, Minnie, Daisy folk dancing at Bon-Odori Summer Festival. $1, Huey, Dewey and Louie wearing Eboshi headdresses at Yari-Matsuri, Spear Festival of Ohji. $2, Mickey, Goofy pulling Daisy, Minnie in Yamaboko, Gion Festival of Kyoto. $3, Minnie, Daisy preparing rice broth for Nanakusa, Festival of the Seven Plants. $5, Huey, Dewey floating straw boat at O-Bon, Festival of Lanterns. No. 1969, Goofy, Tori-No-Hichi or Rake Festival, vert. No. 1970, Minnie Mouse, Japanese New Year, vert. No. 1971, Mickey, Snow Festival, vert.

**1991, May 6    Litho.    Perf. 13½x14**

| | | | | |
|---|---|---|---|---|
| **1961** | A263 | 5c multicolored | .45 | .25 |
| **1962** | A263 | 10c multicolored | .45 | .25 |
| **1963** | A263 | 20c multicolored | .95 | .25 |
| **1964** | A263 | 45c multicolored | 1.25 | .80 |
| **1965** | A263 | $1 multicolored | 2.25 | 1.25 |
| **1966** | A263 | $2 multicolored | 3.00 | 3.00 |
| **1967** | A263 | $4 multicolored | 4.25 | 4.25 |
| **1968** | A263 | $5 multicolored | 5.00 | 5.00 |
| | | *Nos. 1961-1968 (8)* | 17.60 | 15.05 |

**Souvenir Sheets**

| | | | | |
|---|---|---|---|---|
| **1969** | A263 | $6 multicolored | 5.75 | 5.75 |
| **1970** | A263 | $6 multicolored | 5.75 | 5.75 |
| **1971** | A263 | $6 multicolored | 5.75 | 5.75 |

Paintings by Vincent Van Gogh
A264

Designs: 20c, Blossoming Almond Branch in a Glass, vert. 25c, La Mousme, Sitting, vert. 30c, Still Life with Red Cabbages and Onions. 40c, Japonaiserie: Flowering Plum Tree, vert. 45c, Japonaiserie: Bridge in Rain, vert. 60c, Still Life with Basket of Apples. 75c, Italian Woman (Agostina Segatori), vert. $1, The Painter on His Way to Work, vert. $2, Portrait of Pere Tanguy, vert. $3, Still Life with Plaster Statuette, a Rose and Two Novels, vert. $4, Still Life: Bottle, Lemons and Oranges. $5, Orchard with Blossoming Apricot Trees. No. 1984, Farmhouse in a Wheatfield. No. 1985, The "Roubine du Roi" Canal with Washerwoman, vert. No. 1986, Japonaiserie: Oiran, vert. No. 1987, The Gleize Bridge over the Viguerat Canal. No. 1988, Rocks with Oak Wood.

**1991, May 13    Litho.    Perf. 13½**

| | | | | |
|---|---|---|---|---|
| **1972** | A264 | 20c multicolored | .50 | .25 |
| **1973** | A264 | 25c multicolored | .50 | .25 |
| **1974** | A264 | 30c multicolored | .55 | .30 |
| **1975** | A264 | 40c multicolored | .75 | .40 |
| **1976** | A264 | 45c multicolored | .75 | .50 |
| **1977** | A264 | 60c multicolored | 1.00 | .70 |
| **1978** | A264 | 75c multicolored | 1.10 | 1.00 |
| **1979** | A264 | $1 multicolored | 1.25 | 1.25 |
| **1980** | A264 | $2 multicolored | 1.60 | 1.60 |
| **1981** | A264 | $3 multicolored | 2.40 | 2.40 |
| **1982** | A264 | $4 multicolored | 3.25 | 3.25 |
| **1983** | A264 | $5 multicolored | 4.00 | 4.00 |
| | | *Nos. 1972-1983 (12)* | 17.65 | 15.90 |

**Size: 100x75mm, 75x100mm**

*Imperf*

| | | | | |
|---|---|---|---|---|
| **1984-1988** | A264 | $6 each | 5.00 | 5.00 |

Mushrooms — A265

Designs: 15c, Psilocybe cubensis. 25c, Leptonia caeruleocapitata. 65c, Cystolepiota eriophora. 75c, Chlorophyllum molybdites. $1, Xerocomus hypoxanthus. $2, Volvariella cubensis. $4, Xerocomus coccolobae. $5, Pluteus chrysophlebius. No. 1997, Hygrocybe miniata. No. 1998, Psathyrella tuberculata.

**1991, June 1    Perf. 14**

| | | | | |
|---|---|---|---|---|
| **1989** | A265 | 15c multicolored | .70 | .30 |
| **1990** | A265 | 25c multicolored | .85 | .30 |
| **1991** | A265 | 65c multicolored | 1.25 | .75 |
| **1992** | A265 | 75c multicolored | 1.50 | 1.00 |
| **1993** | A265 | $1 multicolored | 1.75 | 1.00 |
| **1994** | A265 | $2 multicolored | 2.00 | 2.00 |
| **1995** | A265 | $4 multicolored | 4.25 | 4.25 |
| **1996** | A265 | $5 multicolored | 4.75 | 4.75 |
| | | *Nos. 1989-1996 (8)* | 17.05 | 14.35 |

**Souvenir Sheet**

| | | | | |
|---|---|---|---|---|
| **1997** | A265 | $6 multicolored | 8.25 | 8.25 |
| **1998** | A265 | $6 multicolored | 8.25 | 8.25 |

**Miniature Sheets**

Exploration of Mars — A266

Designs (all different): No. 1999: a, Johannes Kepler, 1571-1630. b, Galileo Galilei, 1564-1642. c, Martian canals drawn by Giovanni Schiaparelli, 1886. d, Sir William Herschel, 1738-1842. e, Mars, planets. f, Percival Lowell at telescope. g, Mariner 4. h, Mars 2. i, Mars 3.
No. 2000: a, e, Profiles of Mars. b, Olympus Mons. c, Dusty face of Mars. d, Martian moon Phobos. f, Martian moon Deimos. g, Nix Olympica. h, Terrain feature resembling human face. i, South Polar Cap.

No. 2001: a, Mars from Phobus. b, Martian dusk. c, "Voyager descent." d, Viking 2 lander on Mars. e, f, Martian landscape. g, h, i, Panorama view from Viking 2 lander.
No. 2002: a, b, Mariner 9. c, Mars. d, Polar cycle. e, Plain of Sinai. f, South pole. g, Nix Olympica. h, Martian surface. i, Outflow channel.
No. 2003, Phobos spacecraft over Mars. No. 2004, Future spacecraft. No. 2005, Future spacecraft, Mars.

**1991, June 21    Perf. 14x13½**

**Sheets of 9**

| | | | | |
|---|---|---|---|---|
| **1999** | A266 | 75c #a.-i. | 4.25 | 4.25 |
| **2000** | A266 | $1.25 #a.-i. | 6.75 | 6.75 |
| **2001** | A266 | $2 #a.-i. | 11.00 | 11.00 |
| **2002** | A266 | $7 #a.-i. | 37.50 | 37.50 |

**Souvenir Sheets**

| | | | | |
|---|---|---|---|---|
| **2003** | A266 | $6 multicolored | 5.00 | 5.00 |
| **2004** | A266 | $6 multicolored | 5.00 | 5.00 |
| **2005** | A266 | $6 multicolored | 5.00 | 5.00 |

**Royal Family Birthday, Anniversary**
Common Design Type

**1991, July 5    Litho.    Perf. 14**

| | | | | |
|---|---|---|---|---|
| **2006** | CD347 | 10c multicolored | .50 | .25 |
| **2007** | CD347 | 15c multicolored | .50 | .25 |
| **2008** | CD347 | 40c multicolored | .95 | .35 |
| **2009** | CD347 | 50c multicolored | 1.50 | .70 |
| **2010** | CD347 | $1 multicolored | 1.75 | 1.50 |
| **2011** | CD347 | $2 multicolored | 2.75 | 1.75 |
| **2012** | CD347 | $4 multicolored | 3.25 | 3.25 |
| **2013** | CD347 | $5 multicolored | 3.75 | 3.75 |
| | | *Nos. 2006-2013 (8)* | 14.95 | 11.60 |

**Souvenir Sheet**

| | | | | |
|---|---|---|---|---|
| **2014** | CD347 | $5 Philip, Elizabeth | 5.25 | 5.25 |
| **2015** | CD347 | $5 Diana, sons, Charles | 5.25 | 5.25 |

10c, 50c, $1, Nos. 2013, 2015, Charles and Diana, 10th Wedding anniversary. Others, Queen Elizabeth II, 65th birthday.

University of West Indies, 40th Anniv. — A266a

Designs: 45c, Marryshow House, Grenada. 50c, Administrative Building, Barbados.

**1991, July 19**

| | | | | |
|---|---|---|---|---|
| **2016** | A266a | 45c multicolored | .85 | .50 |
| **2017** | A266a | 50c multicolored | .90 | .90 |

Anglican High School, 75th Anniv. — A267

**1991, July 29**

| | | | | |
|---|---|---|---|---|
| **2018** | A267 | 10c Existing school | .35 | .25 |
| **2019** | A267 | 25c New school design | .60 | .25 |

Railways of the World
A269

Railways of Great Britain: No. 2020a, Stephenson's first engine, 1814. b, George Stephenson (1781-1848). c, Stephenson's Killingworth engine, 1816. d, Locomotion No. 1, 1825. e, Locomotion in Darlington, 1825. f, Opening of Stockton & Darlington Railway, 1825. g, Royal George No. 5, 1827. h, Northumbrian Rocket, 1829. i, Planet Class engine, 1830.
No. 2021a, Old Ironsides, US, 1832. b, Wilberforce, Stockton & Darlington Railway, Great Britain, 1832. c, Stephenson's Der Adler, Germany, 1835. d, Stephenson's North Star, Great Britain, 1837. e, London & Birmingham No. 1, Great Britain, 1838. f, Stephenson's 1st Austrian locomotive, 1838. g, Mud Digger, US, 1840. h, Standard Norris, US, 1840. i, Fire Fly Class, Great Britain, 1840.
No. 2022a, Lion, Liverpool and Manchester, Great Britain, 1841. b, Beuth 2-2-2, Berlin-Anhalt Railway, Germany, 1843. c, Derwent dusk. c, "Stockton & Darlington" North Star, Great Britain, 1845. d, MKpV, WCB, Vienna, 1846. e, First railway in Hungary, Budapest to Vac,

1846. f, Stockton & Darlington, 1846. g, Stephenson's long boiler type, Paris, 1847. h, Baldwin 4-4-0, US, 1850. i, 2-4-0, Germany, 1850. No. 2023, Boiler of Locomotion No. 1. No. 2024, Liverpool & Manchester Railway, Great Britain, 1833.

**1991-92    Litho.    Perf. 14**

**Sheets of 9**

| | | | | |
|---|---|---|---|---|
| **2020** | A269 | 75c #a.-i. | 6.50 | 6.50 |
| **2021** | A269 | $1 #a.-i. | 9.00 | 9.00 |
| **2022** | A269 | $2 #a.-i. | 17.00 | 17.00 |

**Souvenir Sheet**

| | | | | |
|---|---|---|---|---|
| **2023** | A269 | $6 multicolored | 7.50 | 7.50 |
| **2024** | A269 | $6 multicolored | 7.50 | 7.50 |

Issued: 75c, No. 2023, 12/2; others, 5/7/92.

**Miniature Sheet**

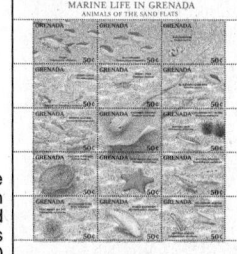

Marine Life in the Sand Flats
A270

Designs: No. 2025a, Barbu. b, Beaugregory. c, Porcupinefish. d, Conchfish, queen conch. e, Hermit crab. f, Bluestripe lizardfish. g, Spotfin mojarra. h, Southern stingray. i, Slippery dick, long-spined sea urchin. j, Peacock flounder. k, West Indian sea star. l, Spotted goatfish. m, West Indian sea egg, reticulated olive. n, Pearly razorfish. o, Mottled and yellowhead jawfish. $6, Shortnose batfish.

**1991, Dec. 5    Litho.    Perf. 14**

| | | | | |
|---|---|---|---|---|
| **2025** | A270 | 50c Sheet of 15, #a.-o. | 12.00 | 12.00 |

**Souvenir Sheet**

| | | | | |
|---|---|---|---|---|
| **2026** | A270 | $6 multicolored | 11.00 | 11.00 |

Christmas — A271

Details from paintings by Albrecht Durer: 10c, Adoration of the Magi. 35c, The Madonna with the Siskin. 50c, The Feast of the Rose Garlands. 75c, Madonna and Child (Virgin with the Pear). $1, The Virgin in Half-Length. $2, Madonna and Child. $4, Virgin and Child with St. Anne. $5, Virgin and Child, diff. No. 2035, Virgin with a Multitude of Animals. No. 2036, The Nativity.

**1991, Dec. 9    Perf. 12**

| | | | | |
|---|---|---|---|---|
| **2027** | A271 | 10c multicolored | .40 | .25 |
| **2028** | A271 | 35c multicolored | .60 | .35 |
| **2029** | A271 | 50c multicolored | .65 | .45 |
| **2030** | A271 | 75c multicolored | 1.00 | .70 |
| **2031** | A271 | $1 multicolored | 1.10 | .90 |
| **2032** | A271 | $2 multicolored | 1.75 | 1.75 |
| **2033** | A271 | $4 multicolored | 4.00 | 4.00 |
| **2034** | A271 | $5 multicolored | 4.50 | 4.50 |
| | | *Nos. 2027-2034 (8)* | 14.00 | 12.90 |

**Souvenir Sheets**

**Perf. 14½**

| | | | | |
|---|---|---|---|---|
| **2035** | A271 | $6 multicolored | 7.00 | 7.00 |
| **2036** | A271 | $6 multicolored | 7.00 | 7.00 |

Thrill Sports
A272

Walt Disney characters enjoying thrill sports: 5c, Windsurfing. 10c, Skateboarding. 20c, Gliding. 45c, Stunt kite flying. $1, Mountain biking. $2, Parachuting. $4, Go-carting. $5, Water skiing.
No. 2045, Roller blade hockey. No. 2046, Bungee jumping. No. 2046A, Hang gliding. No. 2046B, River rafting.

**1992, Feb. 11    Litho.    Perf. 14x13½**

| | | | | |
|---|---|---|---|---|
| 2037 | A272 | 5c multicolored | .45 | .35 |
| 2038 | A272 | 10c multicolored | .55 | .35 |
| 2039 | A272 | 20c multicolored | .80 | .35 |
| 2040 | A272 | 45c multicolored | 1.25 | .35 |
| 2041 | A272 | $1 multicolored | 1.50 | 1.00 |
| 2042 | A272 | $2 multicolored | 2.25 | 2.25 |
| 2043 | A272 | $4 multicolored | 4.50 | 4.50 |
| 2044 | A272 | $5 multicolored | 5.00 | 5.00 |
| | | Nos. 2037-2044 (8) | 16.30 | 14.15 |

**Souvenir Sheets**

| | | | | |
|---|---|---|---|---|
| 2045 | A272 | $6 multicolored | 6.00 | 6.00 |
| 2046 | A272 | $6 multicolored | 6.00 | 6.00 |
| 2046A | A272 | $6 multicolored | 6.00 | 6.00 |
| 2046B | A272 | $6 multicolored | 6.00 | 6.00 |

**Queen Elizabeth II's Accession to the Throne, 40th Anniv.**

Common Design Type

**1992, Feb. 6    Perf. 14**

| | | | | |
|---|---|---|---|---|
| 2047 | CD348 | 10c multicolored | .25 | .25 |
| 2048 | CD348 | 50c multicolored | .40 | .40 |
| 2049 | CD348 | $1 multicolored | .80 | .80 |
| 2050 | CD348 | $5 multicolored | 3.50 | 3.50 |
| | | Nos. 2047-2050 (4) | 4.95 | 4.95 |

**Souvenir Sheets**

| | | | | |
|---|---|---|---|---|
| 2051 | CD348 | $6 Queen at left | 5.50 | 5.50 |
| 2052 | CD348 | $6 Queen at right | 5.50 | 5.50 |

Spanish Art — A273

Paintings: 10c, The Corpus Christi Procession in Seville, by Manuel Cabral y Aguado, horiz. 35c, The Mancorbo Channel, by Carlos de Haes. 50c, Countess of Vilches, by Federico de Madrazo y Kuntz. 75c, Countess of Santovenia, by Eduardo Rosales Gallina. $1, Queen Maria Isabel de Braganza, by Bernardo Lopez Piquer. $2, $4, The Presentation of Don John of Austria to Charles V (different details), by Gallina. $5, The Testament of Isabella the Catholic, by Eduardo Rosales Gallina, horiz. No. 2061, Meeting of Poets in Antonio Maria Esquivel's Studio, by Antonio Maria Esquivel y Suarez de Urbina. No. 2062, The Horse Corral in the Old Madrid Bullring, by Manuel Castellano, horiz.

**1992, Apr. 30    Litho.    Perf. 13**

| | | | | |
|---|---|---|---|---|
| 2053 | A273 | 10c multicolored | .35 | .25 |
| 2054 | A273 | 35c multicolored | .45 | .35 |
| 2055 | A273 | 50c multicolored | .55 | .45 |
| 2056 | A273 | 75c multicolored | .80 | .65 |
| 2057 | A273 | $1 multicolored | 1.25 | .85 |
| 2058 | A273 | $2 multicolored | 1.75 | 1.75 |
| 2059 | A273 | $4 multicolored | 3.25 | 3.25 |
| 2060 | A273 | $5 multicolored | 4.00 | 4.00 |

**Size: 120x95mm**

*Imperf*

| | | | | |
|---|---|---|---|---|
| 2061 | A273 | $6 multicolored | 5.50 | 5.50 |
| 2062 | A273 | $6 multicolored | 5.50 | 5.50 |
| | | Nos. 2053-2062 (10) | 23.40 | 22.55 |

Granada '92.

A274

10c, Green-winged parrot. 25c, Santa Maria. 35c, Columbus. 50c, Hourglass. 75c, Queen Isabella. $4, Cantino map, 1502.

No. 2069, Map, ship, fish. No. 2070, Map, arms, Genoa.

**1992, May 7    Litho.    Perf. 14**

| | | | | |
|---|---|---|---|---|
| 2063 | A274 | 10c multicolored | .50 | .25 |
| 2064 | A274 | 25c multicolored | .50 | .25 |
| 2065 | A274 | 35c multicolored | .50 | .45 |
| 2066 | A274 | 50c multicolored | .70 | .60 |
| 2067 | A274 | 75c multicolored | 1.25 | 1.00 |
| 2068 | A274 | $4 multicolored | 4.50 | 4.50 |
| | | Nos. 2063-2068 (6) | 7.95 | 7.05 |

**Souvenir Sheets**

| | | | | |
|---|---|---|---|---|
| 2069 | A274 | $6 multicolored | 6.75 | 6.75 |
| 2070 | A274 | $6 multicolored | 6.75 | 6.75 |

World Columbian Stamp Expo '92, Chicago.

Discovery of America, 500th Anniv. — A275

**1992    Perf. 14½**

| | | | | |
|---|---|---|---|---|
| 2071 | A275 | $1 Coming ashore | 1.40 | 1.40 |
| 2072 | A275 | $2 Native, ships | 2.50 | 2.50 |

Organization of East Caribbean States.

Hummingbirds — A276

10c, Ruby-throated. 25c, Vervain. 35c, Blue-headed. 50c, Cuban Emerald. 75c, Antillean Mango. $2, Purple-throated carib. $4, Puerto Rican emerald. $5, Green-throated carib.

No. 2081, Rufous-breasted hermit. No. 2082, Antillean crested.

**1992, May 28**

| | | | | |
|---|---|---|---|---|
| 2073 | A276 | 10c multicolored | .75 | .30 |
| 2074 | A276 | 25c multicolored | .90 | .30 |
| 2075 | A276 | 35c multicolored | .95 | .35 |
| 2076 | A276 | 50c multicolored | 1.25 | .50 |
| 2077 | A276 | 75c multicolored | 1.50 | .75 |
| 2078 | A276 | $2 multicolored | 1.60 | 1.60 |
| 2079 | A276 | $4 multicolored | 3.25 | 3.25 |
| 2080 | A276 | $5 multicolored | 4.00 | 4.00 |
| | | Nos. 2073-2080 (8) | 14.20 | 11.05 |

**Souvenir Sheets**

| | | | | |
|---|---|---|---|---|
| 2081 | A276 | $6 multicolored | 8.00 | 8.00 |
| 2082 | A276 | $6 multicolored | 8.00 | 8.00 |

Genoa '92.

USO, 50th Anniv. — A277

15c, Gracie Fields. 25c, Jack Benny. 35c, Jinx Falkenburg. 50c, Frances Langford. 75c, Joe E. Brown. $1, Phil Silvers. $2, Danny Kaye. $5, Frank Sinatra.

No. 2091, Anna May Wong. No. 2092, Bob Hope.

**1992, June 1    Perf. 14**

| | | | | |
|---|---|---|---|---|
| 2083 | A277 | 15c multicolored | .35 | .25 |
| 2084 | A277 | 25c multicolored | .45 | .25 |
| 2085 | A277 | 35c multicolored | .50 | .40 |
| 2086 | A277 | 50c multicolored | .65 | .50 |
| 2087 | A277 | 75c multicolored | 1.00 | 1.00 |
| 2088 | A277 | $1 multicolored | 1.25 | 1.25 |
| 2089 | A277 | $2 multicolored | 2.50 | 2.50 |
| 2090 | A277 | $5 multicolored | 5.75 | 5.75 |
| | | Nos. 2083-2090 (8) | 12.45 | 11.90 |

**Souvenir Sheets**

| | | | | |
|---|---|---|---|---|
| 2091 | A277 | $6 multicolored | 6.50 | 6.50 |
| 2092 | A277 | $6 multicolored | 6.50 | 6.50 |

1992 Summer Olympics, Barcelona — A278

10c, Badminton. 25c, Women's long jump. 35c, Women's 100-meter dash. 50c, Cycling. 75c, Decathlon (pole vault), horiz. $4, Women's gymnastics. $5, Javelin.

No. 2101, Men's floor exercise. No. 2102, Men's vault.

**1992**

| | | | | |
|---|---|---|---|---|
| 2093 | A278 | 10c multicolored | .50 | .30 |
| 2094 | A278 | 25c multicolored | .50 | .25 |
| 2095 | A278 | 35c multicolored | .50 | .30 |
| 2096 | A278 | 50c multicolored | 1.00 | .50 |
| 2097 | A278 | 75c multicolored | 1.00 | .70 |
| 2098 | A278 | $2 multicolored | 1.60 | 1.60 |

| | | | | |
|---|---|---|---|---|
| 2099 | A278 | $4 multicolored | 3.25 | 3.25 |
| 2100 | A278 | $5 multicolored | 4.00 | 4.00 |
| | | Nos. 2093-2100 (8) | 12.35 | 10.90 |

**Souvenir Sheets**

| | | | | |
|---|---|---|---|---|
| 2101 | A278 | $6 multicolored | 5.50 | 5.50 |
| 2102 | A278 | $6 multicolored | 5.50 | 5.50 |

Model Trains — A279

Designs: 10c, The Blue Comet, standard gauge, US, 1933. 35c, Switching locomotive, 2-inch gauge, 1906. 40c, B & O Tunnel locomotive, 2-inch gauge, 1905. 75c, Grand Canyon, standard gauge, US, 1931. $1, Lithographed tin streamliner, O gauge, 1930's. $2, Switching locomotive #237, No. 1 gauge, US, 1911. $4, Parlor car, standard gauge, US, 1928. $5, Locomotive #4687 of Improved President's Special, standard gauge, 1927. No. 2111, Engine #3239, No. 1 gauge, US, 1912. No. 2112, Ives engine #1132, 1921.

**1992, Oct. 22    Litho.    Perf. 14**

| | | | | |
|---|---|---|---|---|
| 2103 | A279 | 10c multicolored | .45 | .25 |
| 2104 | A279 | 35c multicolored | .50 | .30 |
| 2105 | A279 | 40c multicolored | .50 | .35 |
| 2106 | A279 | 75c multicolored | .90 | .50 |
| 2107 | A279 | $1 multicolored | 1.25 | 1.00 |
| 2108 | A279 | $2 multicolored | 1.50 | 1.50 |
| 2109 | A279 | $4 multicolored | 3.00 | 3.00 |
| 2110 | A279 | $5 multicolored | 3.75 | 3.75 |
| | | Nos. 2103-2110 (8) | 11.85 | 10.65 |

**Souvenir Sheet**

**Perf. 13**

| | | | | |
|---|---|---|---|---|
| 2111 | A279 | $6 multicolored | 6.00 | 6.00 |
| 2112 | A279 | $6 multicolored | 6.00 | 6.00 |

Nos. 2111-2112 contains one 51x40mm stamp.

**Souvenir Sheet**

Guggenheim Museum, NYC — A280

**1992, Oct. 28    Perf. 14**

| | | | | |
|---|---|---|---|---|
| 2113 | A280 | $6 multicolored | 5.00 | 5.00 |

Postage Stamp Mega Event '92, NYC.

Christmas — A281

Details or entire paintings: 10c, The Adoration of the Magi, by Fra Filippo Lippi. 15c, Madonna Adoring Child in a Wood, by Fra Filippo Lippi. 25c, Adoration of the Magi, by Botticelli. 35c, The Epiphany-Adoration of the Magi, by Hieronymus Bosch. 50c, Adoration of the Magi, by Giovanni de Paolo. 75c, The Adoration of the Magi, by Gentile da Fabriano. 90c, Adoration of the Magi, by Juan Batista Maino. $1, The Adoration of the Child, by Master of Liesborn. $2, The Adoration of the Kings, by Master of Liesborn. $3, The Adoration of the Three Wise Men, by Pedro Berruguete. $4, The Adoration of the Child, by Filippo Lippi. $5, Adoration of the Child, by Correggio. No. 2126, Adoration of the Magi, by Hans Memling. No. 2127, Adoration of the Magi, by Andrea Mantegna. No. 2128, Adoration of the Shepherds, by De La Tour.

**1992, Nov. 16    Litho.    Perf. 13½x14**

| | | | | |
|---|---|---|---|---|
| 2114 | A281 | 10c multicolored | .45 | .25 |
| 2115 | A281 | 15c multicolored | .50 | .25 |
| 2116 | A281 | 25c multicolored | .55 | .25 |
| 2117 | A281 | 35c multicolored | .75 | .40 |
| 2118 | A281 | 50c multicolored | .90 | .50 |
| 2119 | A281 | 75c multicolored | 1.10 | .80 |
| 2120 | A281 | 90c multicolored | 1.25 | .90 |
| 2121 | A281 | $1 multicolored | 1.50 | 1.00 |
| 2122 | A281 | $2 multicolored | 1.75 | 1.75 |
| 2123 | A281 | $3 multicolored | 2.75 | 2.75 |

| | | | | |
|---|---|---|---|---|
| 2124 | A281 | $4 multicolored | 3.75 | 3.75 |
| 2125 | A281 | $5 multicolored | 4.75 | 4.75 |
| | | Nos. 2114-2125 (12) | 20.00 | 17.35 |

**Souvenir Sheet**

| | | | | |
|---|---|---|---|---|
| 2126 | A281 | $6 multicolored | 6.00 | 6.00 |
| 2127 | A281 | $6 multicolored | 6.00 | 6.00 |
| 2128 | A281 | $6 multicolored | 6.00 | 6.00 |

Regattas of the World — A282

Yachts, races: 15c, Matador, Newport News Regatta. 25c, Awesome, Antigua Regatta. 35c, Mistress Quickly, Bermuda Regatta. 50c, Emeraude, St. Tropez Regatta. $1, Diva G, German Admirals Cup. $2, Lady Be, French Admirals Cup. $4, Midnight Sun, Admirals Cup Regatta. $5, Carat, Sardinia Cup Regatta. No. 2137, 1979 Fastnet Race, horiz. No. 2138, Grenada Regatta, horiz.

**1992, Oct.    Litho.    Perf. 14**

| | | | | |
|---|---|---|---|---|
| 2129 | A282 | 15c multicolored | .25 | .25 |
| 2130 | A282 | 25c multicolored | .25 | .25 |
| 2131 | A282 | 35c multicolored | .30 | .25 |
| 2132 | A282 | 50c multicolored | .75 | .40 |
| 2133 | A282 | $1 multicolored | 1.00 | .75 |
| 2134 | A282 | $2 multicolored | 1.40 | 1.40 |
| 2135 | A282 | $4 multicolored | 3.00 | 3.00 |
| 2136 | A282 | $5 multicolored | 3.75 | 3.75 |
| | | Nos. 2129-2136 (8) | 10.70 | 10.10 |

**Souvenir Sheets**

| | | | | |
|---|---|---|---|---|
| 2137 | A282 | $6 multicolored | 7.00 | 7.00 |
| 2138 | A282 | $6 multicolored | 7.00 | 7.00 |

A283

Anniversaries and Events — A284

Designs: 25c, LZ1 on maiden flight, 1900. 50c, Endosat, proposed robot plane. 75c, Konrad Adenauer, factory. $1.50, Golden lion tamarin. No. 2143 Mountain gorilla. No. 2144, WHO emblem and "Heartbeat-the Rhythm of Health." $3, Wolfgang Amadeus Mozart. No. 2146, German flag, map, Adenauer. No. 2147, Voyager 2, Neptune. $5, Count Zeppelin, Graf Zeppelin. $6, Lion's Club emblem, Admiral Richard E. Byrd. No. 2150, Scene from "The Magic Flute." No. 2151, Konrad Adenauer. No. 2152, Earth Summit emblem, northern spotted owl. No. 2153, Count Zeppelin. No. 2154, Satellite rescue, vert.

**1992    Litho.    Perf. 14**

| | | | | |
|---|---|---|---|---|
| 2139 | A283 | 25c multicolored | 1.50 | 1.50 |
| 2140 | A283 | 50c multicolored | 1.50 | 1.50 |
| 2141 | A283 | 75c multicolored | 1.50 | 1.50 |
| 2142 | A283 | $1.50 multicolored | 3.50 | 3.50 |
| 2143 | A283 | $2 multicolored | 4.00 | 4.00 |
| 2144 | A283 | $2 multicolored | 4.75 | 4.75 |
| 2145 | A284 | $3 multicolored | 5.75 | 5.75 |
| 2146 | A283 | $4 multicolored | 4.00 | 4.00 |
| 2147 | A283 | $4 multicolored | 5.50 | 5.50 |
| 2148 | A283 | $5 multicolored | 8.00 | 8.00 |
| 2149 | A283 | $6 multicolored | 5.50 | 5.50 |
| | | Nos. 2139-2149 (11) | 45.50 | 45.50 |

**Souvenir Sheets**

| | | | | |
|---|---|---|---|---|
| 2150 | A284 | $6 multicolored | 6.25 | 6.25 |
| 2151 | A283 | $6 multicolored | 5.75 | 5.75 |
| 2152 | A283 | $6 multicolored | 5.50 | 5.50 |
| 2153 | A283 | $6 multicolored | 5.75 | 5.75 |
| 2154 | A284 | $6 multicolored | 5.50 | 5.50 |

Count Ferdinand von Zeppelin, 75th anniv. of death (Nos. 2139, 2148, 2153). Intl. Space Year (Nos. 2140, 2147, 2154). Konrad Adenauer, 25th anniv. of death (Nos. 2141, 2146, 2151). Earth Summit, Rio de Janeiro (Nos. 2142-2143, 2152). Mozart, bicent. of death (in 1991) (Nos. 2145, 2150). Lions Intl., 75th anniv. (No. 2149).

Issue dates: Nos. 2145, 2150, Oct. Nos. 2140-2141, 2144, 2146-2147, 2149, 2151, 2154, Nov. Nos. 2139, 2142-2143, 2148, 2152-2153, Dec.

Grenada Dove — A285

**1992**

2155 A285 10c multicolored 2.00 2.00

Entertainers — A286

Gold record award winners: No. 2156a, Cher. b, Michael Jackson. c, Elvis Presley. d, Dolly Parton. e, Johnny Mathis. f, Madonna. g, Nat King Cole. h, Janis Joplin.
No. 2157a, Frank Sinatra. b, Perry Como.
No. 2158a, Chuck Berry. b, James Brown.

**1992, Nov. 19 Litho. Perf. 14**
**Miniature Sheet**
2156 A286 90c Sheet of 8,
#a.-h. 11.50 11.50
**Souvenir Sheets**
2157 A286 $3 Sheet of 2,
#a.-b. 7.50 7.50
2158 A286 $3 Sheet of 2,
#a.-b. 7.50 7.50

Care Bears
Promote
Conservation
A287

75c, Bear on uncontaminated beachfront. $2, Bear with parasol, butterfly on flower, vert.

**1992, Dec. 15 Litho. Perf. 14**
2159 A287 75c multicolored 1.00 1.00
**Souvenir Sheet**
2160 A287 $2 multicolored 4.00 4.00

Dogs — A288

Designs: 10c, Samoyed, St. Basil's Cathedral, Moscow. 15c, Chow chow, Ling Yin Monastery, China. 25c, Boxer, Traitor's Gate, United Kingdom. 90c, Basenji, Yamma Mosque, Niger. $1, Golden Labrador Retriever, Parliament, Ottawa, Canada. $3, Saint Bernard, Parsenn, Switzerland. $4, Rhodesian ridgeback, Melrose House, South Africa. $5, Afghan, Mazar-i-Sharif, Afghanistan. No. 2169, Alaskan malamute, Alaska. No. 2170, Australian cattle dog, Australia.

**1993, Jan. 20 Litho. Perf. 14**
2161 A288 10c multicolored .70 .40
2162 A288 15c multicolored .85 .40
2163 A288 25c multicolored .90 .40
2164 A288 90c multicolored 1.25 .75
2165 A288 $1 multicolored 1.50 1.00
2166 A288 $3 multicolored 2.25 2.25
2167 A288 $4 multicolored 3.00 3.00
2168 A288 $5 multicolored 3.75 3.75
Nos. 2161-2168 (8) 14.20 11.95
**Souvenir Sheet**
2169 A288 $6 multicolored 5.75 5.75
2170 A288 $6 multicolored 5.75 5.75

**Miniature Sheet**

Louvre
Museum,
Bicent.
A289

Paintings by Jean-Antoine Watteau (1684-1721): a, The Faux-Pas. b, A Gentleman. c, Young Lady with Archlute. d, Young Man Dancing. e, Autumn. f, The Judgement of Paris. g-h, Pierrot (diff. details).
No. 2172, The Embarkation for Cythera, horiz.

**1993, Mar. 8 Litho. Perf. 12**
2171 A289 $1 Sheet of 8, #a.-h. + label 9.50 9.50
**Souvenir Sheet**
**Perf. 14½**
2172 A289 $6 multicolored 7.25 7.25
No. 2172 contains one 88x55mm stamp.

Moths — A290

10c, Magnificent. 35c, Metzl's io. 45c, Owl. 75c, Pink-spotted hawk. $1, Faithful beauty. $2, Green geometrid. $4, Gaudy sphinx. $5, Black witch.
No. 2181, Titan hawk, vert. No. 2182, Avocado, vert.

**1993, Apr. 13 Litho. Perf. 14**
2173 A290 10c multicolored .35 .25
2174 A290 35c multicolored .50 .35
2175 A290 45c multicolored .60 .40
2176 A290 75c multicolored 1.00 .60
2177 A290 $1 multicolored 1.25 .75
2178 A290 $2 multicolored 2.50 1.50
2179 A290 $4 multicolored 2.75 2.75
2180 A290 $5 multicolored 3.50 3.50
Nos. 2173-2180 (8) 12.45 10.10
**Souvenir Sheets**
2181 A290 $6 multicolored 5.25 5.25
2182 A290 $6 multicolored 5.25 5.25

Flowers — A291

10c, Heliconia. 35c, Pansy. 45c, Water lily. 75c, Bougainvillea. $1, Calla lily. $2, California poppy. $4, Red ginger. $5, Anthurium.
No. 2191, Christmas rose, horiz. No. 2192, Moth orchids, horiz.

**1993, May 17 Litho. Perf. 14**
2183 A291 10c multicolored .35 .25
2184 A291 35c multicolored .50 .35
2185 A291 45c multicolored .60 .40
2186 A291 75c multicolored .85 .60
2187 A291 $1 multicolored 1.00 .75
2188 A291 $2 multicolored 1.50 1.50
2189 A291 $4 multicolored 3.00 3.00
2190 A291 $5 multicolored 3.75 3.75
Nos. 2183-2190 (8) 11.55 10.60
**Souvenir Sheet**
2191 A291 $6 multicolored 5.75 5.75
2192 A291 $6 multicolored 5.75 5.75

Baha'i Shrine, Haifa,
Israel — A292

**1993, May Litho. Perf. 13½x14**
2193 A292 75c multicolored 1.90 1.90
Baha'i faith in Grenada, cent.

**Miniature Sheet**

Coronation of Queen Elizabeth II, 40th
Anniv. — A293

Designs: a, 35c, Official coronation photograph. b, 70c, Queen Consort's Ivory Rod, Queen Consort's Scepter. c, $1, Elizabeth accepting scepter during ceremony. $5, Queen, family, 1960s.
$6, Portrait, by Peter George Greenham, 1965.

**1993, June 2 Perf. 13½x14**
2194 A293 Sheet, 2 each #a.-d. 12.00 12.00
**Souvenir Sheet**
**Perf. 14**
2195 A293 $6 multicolored 6.25 6.25
No. 2195 contains one 28x42mm stamp.

A294 Anniversaries and
Events — A295

Designs: 35c, Telescope. 50c, Willy Brandt, Sen. Edward Kennedy, Mrs. Robert Kennedy, 1973. $4, Astronaut standing on moon. No. 2199, Willy Brandt, Kurt Waldheim. No. 2200, Copernicus. $6, Newspaper headline announcing Brandt's resignation.

**1993, July 1 Litho. Perf. 14**
2196 A294 35c multicolored .50 .50
2197 A295 50c black & brown .75 .75
2198 A294 $4 multicolored 4.50 4.50
2199 A295 $5 black & brown 4.25 4.25
Nos. 2196-2199 (4) 10.00 10.00
**Souvenir Sheets**
2200 A294 $5 multicolored 5.50 5.50
2201 A295 $6 brown & black 5.75 5.75

Nicolaus Copernicus, 450th anniv. of death (Nos. 2196, 2198, 2200). Willy Brandt, 1st anniv. of death (Nos. 2197, 2199, 2201).

Grenada
Carnival,
1992 — A296

35c, Public Library, vert. 75c, Dancers.

**1993, July 1**
2202 A296 35c multicolored .50 .50
2203 A296 75c multicolored .95 .95
Public Library, cent. (in 1992) (No. 2202).

**Miniature Sheet**

Songbirds — A297

Designs: No. 2204a, 15c, Red-eyed vireo. b, 25c, Scissor-tailed flycatcher (g). c, 35c, Palmchat. d, 35c, Chaffinch. e, 45c, Yellow wagtail. f, 45c, Painted bunting. g, 50c, Short-tailed pygmy flycatcher. h, 65c, Rainbow bunting. i, 75c, Red crossbill. j, 75c, Kauai akialoa. k, $1, Yellow-throated wagtail. l, $4, Barn swallow.
No. 2205, Song thrush. No. 2206, White-crested laughing thrush.

**1993, July 13**
2204 A297 Sheet of 12,
#a.-l. 13.00 13.00
**Souvenir Sheets**
2205 A297 $6 multicolored 5.25 5.25
2206 A297 $6 multicolored 5.25 5.25

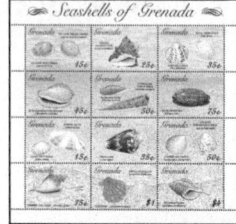

**Miniature Sheet**

Seashells — A298

Designs: No. 2207a, 15c, Atlantic gray cowrie, Atlantic yellow cowrie. b, 15c, Candy stick tellin, sunrise tellin. c, 25c, Common Atlantic vase. d, 35c, Lightning venus, royal comb venus. e, 35c, Crown cone. f, 45c, Reticulated cowrie-helmet. g, 50c, Barbados miter, variegated turret shell. h, 50c, Common egg cockle, Atlantic strawberry cockle. i, 75c, Measled cowrie. j, 75c, Rooster tail conch. k, $1, Lion's paw, Antillean scallop. l, $4, Dog-head triton.
No. 2208, Dyson's keyhole limpet. No. 2209, Virgin nerite, emerald nerite.

**1993, July 19 Litho. Perf. 14**
2207 A298 Sheet of 12,
#a.-l. 14.00 14.00
**Souvenir Sheets**
2208 A298 $6 multicolored 7.00 7.00
2209 A298 $6 multicolored 7.00 7.00

A299

Picasso (1881-1973): 25c, Woman with Loaves, 1906. 90c, Weeping Woman, 1937. $4, Woman Seated in Armchair, 1947. $6, Three Women at the Spring, 1921.

**1993, July 1 Litho. Perf. 14**
2210 A299 25c multicolored .35 .35
2211 A299 90c multicolored 1.25 1.00
2212 A299 $4 multicolored 4.00 4.00
Nos. 2210-2212 (3) 5.60 5.35
**Souvenir Sheet**
2213 A299 $6 multicolored 4.75 4.75

A300

1994 Winter Olympics, Lillehammer, Norway: 35c, Gaeten Boucher, speedskating gold medalist, 1984. $5, Norbert Schramm, figure skater. $6, Michela Figini, Sigrid Wolf, Karen Percy, Super G medalists, 1988, horiz.

**1993, July 1**
2214 A300 35c multicolored .50 .30
2215 A300 $5 multicolored 4.50 4.50
**Souvenir Sheet**
2216 A300 $6 multicolored 5.75 5.75

Polska '93 — A301

Paintings: $1, Portrait of Marii Prohaska, by Tytus Czyzewski, 1923. $3, Marysia et Burek a Geylan, by S.I. Wirkiewicz, 1920-21. $6, Parting, by Witold Wojtkiewicz, 1908.

**1993, July 1     Litho.     Perf. 14**
| | | | |
|---|---|---|---|
| 2217 | A301 | $1 multicolored | 1.25 | 1.25 |
| 2218 | A301 | $3 multicolored | 3.75 | 3.75 |

**Souvenir Sheet**
| | | | |
|---|---|---|---|
| 2219 | A301 | $6 multicolored | 6.25 | 6.25 |

Taipei '93 — A302

Designs: 35c, Fire-breathing dragon, New Year's Fair, Chongqing. 45c, Stone elephant, Spirit Way to Ming Tomb, Nanjing. $2, Marble peifang, Ming Tombs, Beijing. $4, Stone pillar, Nanjing.
Paintings by Han Meilin: No. 2224a, Ornamental cock. b, Tiger cub. c, Owl. d, Cat. e, Gorillas. f, Leopard.
No. 2225, Orangutan.

**1993, Aug. 13     Litho.     Perf. 14**
| | | | |
|---|---|---|---|
| 2220 | A302 | 35c multicolored | .25 | .25 |
| 2221 | A302 | 45c multicolored | .75 | .75 |
| 2222 | A302 | $2 multicolored | 3.25 | 3.25 |
| 2223 | A302 | $4 multicolored | 6.25 | 6.25 |
| | | Nos. 2220-2223 (4) | 10.50 | 10.50 |

**Miniature Sheet**
| | | | |
|---|---|---|---|
| 2224 | A302 | $1.50 Sheet of 6, #a.-f. | 6.75 | 6.75 |

**Souvenir Sheet**
| | | | |
|---|---|---|---|
| 2225 | A302 | $6 multicolored | 5.50 | 5.50 |

**With Bangkok '93 Emblem**
Designs: 35c, Nora Nair, Prasad Phra Thepidon, Wat Phra Kaew. 45c, Stucco deities, Library, Wat Phra Singh. $2, Naga snake, Chiang Mai's Temple. $4, Stucco elephants, Wat Chang Lom.
Thai sculpture: No. 2230a, Horses. b, Wheel of the Law, 7th-8th cent. c, Lanna bronze elephant, 1575. d, Kendi in form of elephant. e, Bronze duck, 14th-15th cent. f, Horseman, 14th-15th cent.
No. 2231, Elephants, horiz.

**1993, Aug. 13**
| | | | |
|---|---|---|---|
| 2226 | A302 | 35c multicolored | .25 | .25 |
| 2227 | A302 | 45c multicolored | .35 | .35 |
| 2228 | A302 | $2 multicolored | 1.50 | 1.50 |
| 2229 | A302 | $4 multicolored | 3.00 | 3.00 |
| | | Nos. 2226-2229 (4) | 5.10 | 5.10 |

**Miniature Sheet**
| | | | |
|---|---|---|---|
| 2230 | A302 | $1.50 Sheet of 6, #a.-f. | 6.75 | 6.75 |

**Souvenir Sheet**
| | | | |
|---|---|---|---|
| 2231 | A302 | $6 multicolored | 4.50 | 4.50 |

**With Indopex '93 Emblem**
35c, Megalithic carving, Sumba Island, Indonesia. 45c, Entrance to Gao Gaja (Elephant Cave), Bali. $2, Loving Mother Bridge, Taroko Gorge Natl. Park. $4, Kala head gateway to Balinese Temple, Northern Bali.
Indonesian sculpture - No. 2236: a, Kris holder and Kris, 19th cent. b, Hanuman protecting Sita, I. Dojotan of Mas. c, Sendi of Visnu mounted on Garuda, 19th cent. d, Wahana (mini vehicle for votive fig.), 20th cent. e, Mercurial monkey warrior Hanuman, Rodja of Mas. f, Singa (polychrome lion).
No. 2237, Loris.

**1993, Aug. 13     Perf. 13½x14**
| | | | |
|---|---|---|---|
| 2232 | A302 | 35c multicolored | .25 | .25 |
| 2233 | A302 | 45c multicolored | .35 | .35 |
| 2234 | A302 | $2 multicolored | 1.50 | 1.50 |
| 2235 | A302 | $4 multicolored | 3.00 | 3.00 |
| | | Nos. 2232-2235 (4) | 5.10 | 5.10 |

---

**Miniature Sheet**
| | | | |
|---|---|---|---|
| 2236 | A302 | $1.50 Sheet of 6, #a.-f. | 11.00 | 11.00 |

**Souvenir Sheet**
| | | | |
|---|---|---|---|
| 2237 | A302 | $6 multicolored | 5.50 | 5.50 |

Miniature Sheet

Italian Soccer Assoc. and Genoa Soccer Club, Cent. A303

Players for Genoa Soccer Club, each $3: No. 2238a, Vittorio Sardelli. b, Juan Carlos Verdeal. c, Fosco Becattini. d, Julio Cesar Abadie. e, Luigi Meroni. f, Roberto Pruzzo.
No. 2239a, each $3: James K. Spensley. b, Renzo de Vecchi. c, Giovanni de Pra. d, Luigi Burlando. e, Felice Levratto. f, Guglielmo Stabile.
Each $15: No. 2240, 1991 Genoa team photo, horiz. No. 2241, Genoa team emblem.

**1993, Sept. 7     Litho.     Perf. 14**
**Sheets of 6, #a-f**
| | | | |
|---|---|---|---|
| 2238-2239 | A303 | Set of 2 | 40.00 | 40.00 |

**Souvenir Sheets**
| | | | |
|---|---|---|---|
| 2240-2241 | A303 | Set of 2 | 37.00 | 37.00 |

No. 2240 contains one 48x35mm stamp. No. 2241 contains one 29x45mm stamp.

1994 World Cup Soccer Championships, US — A304

Designs: 10c, Nikolai Larionov, Russia. 25c, Andrea Carnevale, Italy. 35c, Enzo Scifo, Belgium, Soon-Ho Choi, South Korea. 45c, Gary Lineker, England. $1, Diego Maradona, Argentina. $2, Lothar Matthaeus, Germany. $4, Jan Karas, Poland, Julio Cesar Silva, Brazil. $5, Claudio Caniggia, Argentina.
Each $6: No. 2250, Wlodzimierz, Poland. No. 2251, Jose Basualdo, Argentina.

**1993, Sept. 7     Litho.     Perf. 14**
| | | | |
|---|---|---|---|
| 2242-2249 | A304 | Set of 8 | 12.00 | 12.00 |

**Souvenir Sheets**
| | | | |
|---|---|---|---|
| 2250-2251 | A304 | Set of 2 | 11.00 | 11.00 |

Mickey Mouse, 65th Birthday A305

Movie clips: 25c, The Band Concert, 1935. 35c, Mickey's Circus, 1936. 50c, Magician Mickey, 1937. 75c, Moose Hunters, 1937. $1, Mickey's Amateurs, 1937. $2, Tugboat Mickey, 1940. $4, Orphan's Benefit, 1941. $5, Mickey's Christmas, 1983.
Each $6: No. 2260, Mickey's Birthday Party, 1942. No. 2261, Mickey's Trailer, 1938.

**1993, Nov. 11     Litho.     Perf. 14x13½**
| | | | |
|---|---|---|---|
| 2252-2259 | A305 | Set of 8 | 12.50 | 12.50 |

**Souvenir Sheets**
| | | | |
|---|---|---|---|
| 2260-2261 | A305 | Set of 2 | 13.00 | 13.00 |

Christmas — A306

---

Woodcuts by Durer: 10c, The Nativity. 25c, "The Annunciation." $1, "Adoration of the Magi." $5, "The Virgin Mary in the Sun."
Paintings by Leonardo Da Vinci: 35c, The Litta Madonna. 60c, Madonna and Child with St. Anne and the Infant St. John. 90c, Madonna with the Carnation. $4, The Benois Madonna.
Each $6: No. 2270, The Holy Family with Three Hares, by Durer. No. 2271, Adoration of the Magi, by Da Vinci.
The 25c actually shows the Adoration of the Magi. The $1 actually shows The Virgin Mary in the Sun. The $5 actually shows The Annunciation.

**1993, Nov. 22     Litho.     Perf. 13½x14**
| | | | |
|---|---|---|---|
| 2262-2269 | A306 | Set of 8 | 10.50 | 10.50 |

**Souvenir Sheets**
| | | | |
|---|---|---|---|
| 2270-2271 | A306 | Set of 2 | 10.50 | 10.50 |

Hugo Eckener (1868-1954) A307

Graf Zeppelin over: 35c, Vienna. 75c, Pyramids at Giza. $5, Rio de Janeiro. No. 2275, Flensburg.

**1993, Dec. 21     Perf. 14**
| | | | |
|---|---|---|---|
| 2272-2274 | A307 | Set of 3 | 5.50 | 5.50 |

**Souvenir Sheet**
| | | | |
|---|---|---|---|
| 2275 | A307 | $6 multicolored | 5.50 | 5.50 |

Royal Air Force, 75th Anniv. — A308

**1993, Dec. 21**
| | | | |
|---|---|---|---|
| 2276 | A308 | 50c Lysander | 1.00 | 1.00 |
| 2277 | A308 | $3 Hawker Typhoon | 4.25 | 4.25 |

**Souvenir Sheet**
| | | | |
|---|---|---|---|
| 2278 | A308 | $6 Hawker Hurricane | 5.50 | 5.50 |

Automotive Anniversaries A309

35c, 1932 Mercedes Benz 370 S Cabriolet. 45c, 1966 Ford Mustang. $3, 1930 Model A Ford Phaeton. $4, Mercedes Benz 300 SL Gullwing.
Each $6: No. 2283, 1903 Ford Model A. No. 2284, 1934 Mercedes Benz 290.

**1993, Dec. 21     Litho.     Perf. 14**
| | | | |
|---|---|---|---|
| 2279-2282 | A309 | Set of 4 | 10.00 | 10.00 |

**Souvenir Sheets**
| | | | |
|---|---|---|---|
| 2283-2284 | A309 | Set of 2 | 10.50 | 10.50 |

1st Benz 4-wheel car, cent. 1st Ford engine, cent.

First Gas Balloon Flight in America, Bicent. — A310

Designs: 45c, Lift-off from Philadelphia. $2, Balloon in flight, vert. $6, Blanchard's balloon in flight, diff., vert.

**1993, Dec. 21     Litho.     Perf. 14**
| | | | |
|---|---|---|---|
| 2285-2286 | A310 | Set of 2 | 3.00 | 3.00 |

**Souvenir Sheet**
| | | | |
|---|---|---|---|
| 2287 | A310 | $6 multicolored | 6.50 | 6.50 |

Fine Art — A311

---

Self-portraits, by Matisse: 15c, 1900. 45c, 1918. $2, 1906. $4, 1900, diff.
Self-portraits, by Rembrandt: 35c, 1629. 50c, 1640. 75c, 1652. $5, 1625-31.
No. 2296, The Painter in His Studio, by Matisse. No. 2297, The Sampling Officials of the Draper's Guild, by Rembrandt, horiz.

**1993, Dec. 31     Litho.     Perf. 13½x14**
| | | | |
|---|---|---|---|
| 2288 | A311 | 15c multicolored | .40 | .25 |
| 2289 | A311 | 35c multicolored | .50 | .25 |
| 2290 | A311 | 45c multicolored | .55 | .40 |
| 2291 | A311 | 50c multicolored | .65 | .45 |
| 2292 | A311 | 75c multicolored | 1.00 | .60 |
| 2293 | A311 | $2 multicolored | 1.75 | 1.60 |
| 2294 | A311 | $4 multicolored | 3.25 | 3.25 |
| 2295 | A311 | $5 multicolored | 4.00 | 4.00 |
| | | Nos. 2288-2295 (8) | 12.10 | 10.80 |

**Souvenir Sheets**
| | | | |
|---|---|---|---|
| 2296 | A311 | $6 multicolored | 5.25 | 5.25 |

**Perf. 14x13½**
| | | | |
|---|---|---|---|
| 2297 | A311 | $6 multicolored | 5.25 | 5.25 |

Spice Islands Billfish Tournament, 25th Anniv. — A312

15c, Blue marlin. 25c, Sailfish with angler. 35c, Yellowfin tuna with angler. 50c, White marlin with angler. 75c, Catching a sailfish.

**1993, Dec.     Litho.     Perf. 14**
| | | | |
|---|---|---|---|
| 2302-2306 | A312 | Set of 5 | 4.00 | 4.00 |

A313

Hong Kong '94 A314

Stamps, painting, Hong Kong Post Office-1846, by M. Bruce: No. 2307, Hong Kong #263, left detail. No. 2308, Right detail, #1597.
Porcelain ware, Qing Dynasty: No. 2309a, Vase with dragon decor. b, Hat stand. c, Gourd-shaped vase. d, Rotating vase with openwork. e, Candlestick with dogs. f, Hat stand, diff.

**1994, Feb. 18     Litho.     Perf. 14**
| | | | |
|---|---|---|---|
| 2307 | | 40c multicolored | .65 | .65 |
| 2308 | | 40c multicolored | .65 | .65 |
| a. | A313 | Pair, #2307-2308 | 1.40 | 1.40 |

**Miniature Sheet**
| | | | |
|---|---|---|---|
| 2309 | A314 | 45c Sheet of 6, #a.-f. | 3.75 | 3.75 |

Nos. 2307-2308 issued in sheets of 5 pairs. No. 2308a is a continuous design.
New Year 1994 (Year of the Dog) (No. 2309e).

Independence, 20th Anniv. — A315

**1994, Feb. 8     Litho.     Perf. 14**
| | | | |
|---|---|---|---|
| 2310 | A315 | 35c Natl. flag, boat | .80 | .80 |

**Souvenir Sheet**
| | | | |
|---|---|---|---|
| 2311 | A315 | $6 Map of Granada | 6.25 | 6.25 |

## Miniature Sheets

### Dinosaurs — A316

Jurassic: No. 2312a, Germanodactylus. b, Dimorphodon. c, Ramphorhynchus. d, Apatosaurus (h). e, Pterodactylus. f, Stegosaurus. g, Brachiosaurus. h, Allosaurus (l). i, Plesiosaurus. j, Ceratosaurus. k, Compsognathus. l, Elaphosaurus.

Cretaceous: No. 2313a, Quetzalcoatlus. b, Pteranodon ingens (c). c, Tropeognathus. d, Phobetor. e, Alamosaurus (i). f, Triceratops (e). g, Tyrannosaurus rex (h). h, Tyrannosaurus rex (up close) (l). i, Lambeosaurus. j, Spinosaurus. k, Parasaurolophus (l). l, Hadrosaurus.

No. 2314, Plateosaurus, vert. No. 2315, Pteranodon ingens.

**1994, Apr. 13**      **Sheets of 12**
| | | | | |
|---|---|---|---|---|
| 2312 | A316 | 75c #a.-l. | 8.00 | 8.00 |
| 2313 | A316 | 75c #a.-l. | 8.00 | 8.00 |

**Souvenir Sheets**
| | | | | |
|---|---|---|---|---|
| 2314 | A316 | $6 multicolored | 5.25 | 5.25 |
| 2315 | A316 | $6 multicolored | 5.25 | 5.25 |

### Mushrooms — A317

Designs: 35c, Hygrocybe acutoconica. 45c, Leucopaxillus gracillimus. 50c, Leptonia caeruleocapitata. 75c, Leucoprinus birnbaumii. $1, Marasmius atrorubens. $2, Boletellus cubensis. $4, Chlorophyllum molybdites. $5, Psilocybe cubensis.

No. 2324, Mycena pura. No. 2325, Pyrrhoglossum lilaceipes.

**1994, Apr. 6**
| | | | | |
|---|---|---|---|---|
| 2316 | A317 | 35c multicolored | .50 | .25 |
| 2317 | A317 | 45c multicolored | .60 | .35 |
| 2318 | A317 | 50c multicolored | .70 | .40 |
| 2319 | A317 | 75c multicolored | .90 | .50 |
| 2320 | A317 | $1 multicolored | 1.25 | .75 |
| 2321 | A317 | $2 multicolored | 1.60 | 1.25 |
| 2322 | A317 | $4 multicolored | 3.25 | 3.25 |
| 2323 | A317 | $5 multicolored | 3.75 | 3.75 |
| | | Nos. 2316-2323 (8) | 12.55 | 10.50 |

**Souvenir Sheets**
| | | | | |
|---|---|---|---|---|
| 2324 | A317 | $6 multicolored | 6.00 | 6.00 |
| 2325 | A317 | $6 multicolored | 6.00 | 6.00 |

### D-Day, 50th Anniv. — A318

Designs: 40c, Sherman Dual-Drive swimming tanks. $2, Churchill "Ark" in operation. $3, Churchill "Bobbin" lays path over soft ground.

$6, Churchill "Avre."

**1994, Aug. 4**    **Litho.**    **Perf. 14**
| | | | | |
|---|---|---|---|---|
| 2326-2328 | A318 | Set of 3 | 6.50 | 6.50 |

**Souvenir Sheet**
| | | | | |
|---|---|---|---|---|
| 2329 | A318 | $6 multicolored | 6.25 | 6.25 |

## Miniature Sheet

### First Manned Moon Landing, 25th Anniv. A319

Tribute to crew of space shuttle Challenger: No. 2330a, Flame erupting before explosion. b, Judith A. Resnick. c, Aircraft flyover in "Missing Man" formation. d, Dick Scobee. e, Challenger 51-L patch. f, Michael J. Smith.

$6, Crew of mission 51-L.

**1994, Aug. 4**
| | | | | |
|---|---|---|---|---|
| 2330 | A319 | $2 Sheet of 6, #a.-f. | 8.50 | 8.50 |

**Souvenir Sheet**
| | | | | |
|---|---|---|---|---|
| 2331 | A319 | $6 multicolored | 5.25 | 5.25 |

A320

### PHILAKOREA '94 — A321

Designs: 40c, Wonson Park & Garden. $1, Port of Pusan. $4, National Theatre, Seoul.

Paintings by Sin Yunbok, Late Choson Dynasty: No. 2335a-2335b, Lady in a Hooded Cloak. c-d, Kiaseng House. e-f, Amorous Youth on a Picnic. g-h, Chasing a Cat.

$6, Roof Tiling, by Kim Hongdo, vert.

**1994, Aug. 4**    *Perf. 14, 13½ (#2335)*
| | | | | |
|---|---|---|---|---|
| 2332-2334 | A320 | Set of 3 | 4.00 | 4.00 |

**Miniature Sheet**
| | | | | |
|---|---|---|---|---|
| 2335 | A321 | $1 Sheet of 8, #a.-h. | 6.00 | 6.00 |

**Souvenir Sheet**
| | | | | |
|---|---|---|---|---|
| 2336 | A320 | $6 multicolored | 4.50 | 4.50 |

A322

Orchids: 15c, Brassavola cuculatta. 25c, Comparettia falcata. 45c, Epidendrum ciliare. 75c, Epidendrum cochleatum. $1, Ionopsis utriculariodes. $2, Oncidium ceboletta. $4, Oncidium luridium. $5, Rodriquezia secunda.

Each $6: No. 2345, Ionopis utriculariodes, diff. No. 2346, Onicium luridum, diff.

**1994, Aug. 7**       **Perf. 14**
| | | | | |
|---|---|---|---|---|
| 2337-2344 | A322 | Set of 8 | 11.50 | 11.50 |

**Souvenir Sheets**
| | | | | |
|---|---|---|---|---|
| 2345-2346 | A322 | Set of 2 | 12.00 | 12.00 |

A323

1994 World Cup Soccer Championships, US: No. 2347a, Tony Meola, US. b, Steve Mark, Grenada. c, Gianluigi Lentini, Italy. d, Belloumi, Algeria. e, Nunoz, Spain. f, Lothar Matthaus, Germany.

Each $6: No. 2348, Steve Mark, diff. No. 2349, Poster from 1st World Cup Championships, Uruguay, 1930.

**1994, Aug. 11**       **Perf. 14**
**Miniature Sheet**
| | | | | |
|---|---|---|---|---|
| 2347 | A323 | 75c Sheet of 6, #a.-f. | 5.50 | 5.50 |

**Souvenir Sheet**
| | | | | |
|---|---|---|---|---|
| 2348-2349 | A323 | Set of 2 | 10.00 | 10.00 |

### Fish — A324

Designs: 15c, Yellowtail snapper. 20c, Blue tang. 25c, Porkfish, vert. 75c, Foureye butterlyfish. $1, Longsnout seahorse, vert. $2, Spotted moray eel, vert. $4, Fairy basslet. $5, Queen triggerfish, vert.

Each $6: No. 2358, Queen angelfish. No. 2359, Squirrelfish.

**1994, Sept. 1**
| | | | | |
|---|---|---|---|---|
| 2350-2357 | A324 | Set of 8 | 9.25 | 9.25 |

**Souvenir Sheets**
| | | | | |
|---|---|---|---|---|
| 2358-2359 | A324 | Set of 2 | 11.00 | 11.00 |

A325

### Intl. Olympic Committee, Cent. — A326

Designs: 50c, Heike Dreschler, Germany, long jump, 1992. $1.50, Nadia Comaneci, Romania, Gymnastics, 1976, 1980.

$6, Dan Jansen, US, 1000-meters long track speed skating, 1994.

**1994, Aug. 4**
| | | | | |
|---|---|---|---|---|
| 2360 | A325 | 50c multicolored | 1.00 | 1.00 |
| 2361 | A325 | $1.50 multicolored | 2.25 | 2.25 |

**Souvenir Sheet**
| | | | | |
|---|---|---|---|---|
| 2362 | A326 | $6 multicolored | 5.00 | 5.00 |

### 1994, Year of the Dog — A327

Scenes from Disney's Society Dog Show: 2c, Mickey bathing Pluto. 3c, Using atomizer. 4c, Putting on mascara. 5c, Having tail "set." 10c, Having nails done. 15c, Mickey using flea powder on Pluto. 20c, On judge's stand. $4, Judge looking at Pluto. $5, Pluto in chair with first prize.

No. 2372, Pluto wearing "13," first prize ribbon. No. 2373, Little dog beside judge. No. 2374, Pluto with first prize ribbon.

**1994, Sept. 22**  **Litho.**  *Perf. 14x13½*
| | | | | |
|---|---|---|---|---|
| 2363-2371 | A327 | Set of 9 | 10.00 | 10.00 |

**Souvenir Sheets**
| | | | | |
|---|---|---|---|---|
| 2372-2374 | A327 | $6 each | 4.75 | 4.75 |

### Butterflies — A328

10c, Red anartia. 15c, Ruddy daggerwing. 25c, Fiery skipper. 35c, Caribbean buckeye. 45c, Giant hairstreak. 50c, Zebra longwing. 75c, Diadem. $1, Blue night. $2, Orion. $3, Orange-barred sulphur. $4, Long-tail skipper. $5, Polydamas swallowtail. $10, Bamboo page. $20, Queen cracker.

**1994, Sept. 28**       **Perf. 14**
| | | | | |
|---|---|---|---|---|
| 2375 | A328 | 10c multicolored | .35 | .25 |
| 2376 | A328 | 15c multicolored | .35 | .25 |
| 2377 | A328 | 25c multicolored | .40 | .25 |
| a. | | Inscribed "1996" | .40 | .25 |
| 2378 | A328 | 35c multicolored | .45 | .40 |
| a. | | Inscribed "1996" | .45 | .25 |
| 2379 | A328 | 45c multicolored | .50 | .40 |
| 2380 | A328 | 50c multicolored | .60 | .50 |
| 2381 | A328 | 75c multicolored | .70 | .70 |
| 2382 | A328 | $1 multicolored | 1.25 | 1.25 |
| 2383 | A328 | $2 multicolored | 2.25 | 2.25 |
| 2384 | A328 | $3 multicolored | 3.50 | 3.50 |
| 2385 | A328 | $4 multicolored | 4.50 | 4.50 |
| 2386 | A328 | $5 multicolored | 5.25 | 5.25 |
| 2386A | A328 | $10 multicolored | 10.00 | 10.00 |
| 2386B | A328 | $20 multicolored | 16.50 | 16.50 |
| | | Nos. 2375-2386B (14) | 46.60 | 46.00 |

See Nos. 2585-2586.

### Intl. Year of the Family — A329

**1994, Aug. 4**
| | | | | |
|---|---|---|---|---|
| 2387 | A329 | $1 multicolored | .90 | .90 |

### Order of the Caribbean Community A330

First award recipients: 15c, Sir Shridath Ramphal, statesman, Guyana. 65c, William Demas, economist, Trinidad & Tobago. $2, Derek Walcott, writer, St. Lucia.

**1994, Sept. 1**
| | | | | |
|---|---|---|---|---|
| 2388-2390 | A330 | Set of 3 | 3.00 | 3.00 |

### Christmas — A331

Paintings, by Zurbaran: 10c, The Virgin and Child with St. John. 15c, The Circumcision. 25c, Adoration of St. Joseph. 35c, Adoration of the Magi. 75c, The Portiuncula. $1, The Virgin and Child with St. John, 1662. $2, The Virgin and Child with St. John, 1658-64. $4, The Flight into Egypt.

Each $6: No. 2399, Adoration of the Shepherds, horiz. No. 2400, Our Lady of Ransom and Two Mercedarians.

**1994, Dec. 5**  **Litho.**  *Perf. 13½x14*
| | | | | |
|---|---|---|---|---|
| 2391-2398 | A331 | Set of 8 | 7.25 | 7.25 |

**Souvenir Sheets**
| | | | | |
|---|---|---|---|---|
| 2399-2400 | A331 | Set of 2 | 10.00 | 10.00 |

A332

Birds: 25c, Grenada dove, horiz. 35c, Grenada doves, horiz. 45c, Cuban tody. No. 2404, 75c, Grenada dove, diff. No. 2405, 75c, Painted bunting, horiz. No. 2406, $1, Grenada dove, in flight. No. 2407, $1, Red-legged honeycreeper, horiz. $5, Green jay, horiz.

Each $6: No. 2409, Chestnut-sided shrike-vireo, horiz. No. 2410, Chaffinch, horiz.

**1995, Jan. 10**  **Litho.**   **Perf. 14**
| | | | | |
|---|---|---|---|---|
| 2401-2408 | A332 | Set of 8 | 15.00 | 15.00 |

**Souvenir Sheet**
| | | | | |
|---|---|---|---|---|
| 2409-2410 | A332 | Set of 2 | 11.50 | 11.50 |

World Wildlife Fund (Nos. 2401-2402, 2404, 2406).

A333

Designs: 25c, Junior Murray, Grenada/W. Indies. 35c, R.B. Richardson, Leeward Isl./W. Indies. $2, A.J. Steward, England, horiz. No. 2414, West Indies team, horiz.

**1995, Jan. 12**
2411-2413  A333  Set of 3    3.00 3.00
**Souvenir Sheet**
2414  A333  $3 multicolored    4.00 4.00

English Touring Cricket, cent.

Water Birds — A334

25c, Hooded merganser. 35c, Teal. $1, Harlequin duck. $3, European wigeon.
No. 2419a, King eider. b, Shoveler. c, Long-tailed duck. d, Chiloe wigeon. e, Red-breasted merganser. f, Falcated teal. g, Vericolor teal. h, Smew. i, Red-crested pochard. j, Northern pintail. k, Barrow's goldeneye. l, Stellar's eider.
No. 2420, European wigeon, diff. No. 2421, Egyptian goose.

**1995, Mar. 27    Litho.    Perf. 14**
2415-2418  A334  Set of 4    5.00 5.00
**Miniature Sheet**
2419  A334  75c Sheet of 12, #a.-l.    9.00 9.00
**Souvenir Sheets**
2420  A334  $5 multicolored    4.00 4.00
2421  A334  $6 multicolored    4.50 4.50

New Year 1995 (Year of the Boar) A335

a, 50c, Pig priest, China. b, 75c, Porcelain pig, Scotland. c, $1, Porcelain pig, Italy. $2, Jade pig, China.

**1995, Apr. 21    Litho.    Perf. 14**
2422  A335  Strip of 3, #a.-c.    3.00 3.00
**Souvenir Sheet**
2423  A335  $2 multicolored    3.25 3.25

No. 2422 was issued in miniature sheets containing 3 No. 2422.

Miniature Sheets of 6 and 8

End of World War II, 50th Anniv. — A336

No. 2423A: b, Great Marianas Turkey Shoot. c, Battle of Midway. d, Battle of the Bismarck Sea. e, Musashi sinks at Leyte Gulf. f, Henderson Field. g, Battle of Guadalcanal.
Fighter planes: No. 2424a, Lavochkin LA7, Soviet Air Force. b, Hawker Hurricane, Royal Air Force (RAF). c, North American P-51D, US Army Air Force (USAAF). d, Messerschmitt ME 109F, Luftwaffe. e, Bristol Beaufighter, RAF. f, Messerschmitt ME 262, Luftwaffe. g, Republic P-47D, USAAF. h, Hawker Tempest V, RAF.
No. 2425, Nose of P-47D. No. 2425A, B-29 bomber.

**1995, May 8**
2423A  A336  $2 #b.-g. + label    12.00 12.00
2424  A336  $2 #a.-h. + label    15.00 15.00
**Souvenir Sheets**
2425  A336  $6 multicolored    7.00 7.00
2425A  A336  $6 multicolored    6.50 6.50

18th World Scout Jamboree, Holland — A337

Designs: a, 75c, Palm trees, scout. b, $1, Mountain climbing. c, $2, Scout salute, flag. $6, Canoeing.

**1995, May 8**
2426  A337  Strip of 3, #a.-c.    3.25 3.25
**Souvenir Sheet**
2427  A337  $6 multicolored    5.25 5.25

No. 2426 issued in sheets of 9 stamps.

UN, 50th Anniv. — A338

Designs: a, 75c, Man bending sword into plowshare. b, $1, Earth, dove. c, $2, UN Headquarters. $6, Emblem.

**1995, May 8**
2428  A338  Strip of 3, #a.-c.    3.25 3.25
**Souvenir Sheet**
2429  A338  $6 multicolored    5.00 5.00

No. 2428 is a continuous design and was issued in sheets of 9 stamps.

Grenada-Republic of China Friendship — A339

Designs: 75c, Flags of Grenada, Republic of China. $1, Prime Minister Nicholas Brathwaite, Grenada, Pres. Lee Teng-hui, Republic of China.

**1995, Apr. 27    Litho.    Perf. 14**
2430  A339  75c multicolored    1.25 1.25
2431  A339  $1 multicolored    1.50 1.50
  a.    Souvenir sheet, #2430-2431    2.75 2.75

Domesticated Animals — A340

Designs: 10c, Cocker spaniel. 15c, Pinto. 25c, Rottweiler. 35c, German shepherd. 45c, Persian. 50c, Snowshoe. 75c, Percheron. $1, Scottish fold. $2, Arabian. $3, Andalusian. $4, C.P. shorthair. $5, Chihuahua.
No. 2444, $5, Manx. No. 2445, $5, Donkey. No. 2446, $6, Shar pei.

**1995, May 3**
2432-2443  A340  Set of 12    16.00 16.00
**Souvenir Sheets**
2444-2445  A340  Set of 2    8.00 8.00
2446  A340  multi    5.25 5.25

Miniature Sheet

Sierra Club, Cent. — A341

No. 2447, vert., each $1: a, Margay, mouth open. b, Margay seated. c, Margay up close. d, Condor facing left. e, Condor facing right. f, Condor looking back. g, White-faced saki on tree limb. h, White-faced saki, face in light. i, Patagonia Region, South America.
No. 2448, each $1: a, Darwin's rhea, two facing right. b, Darwin's rhea, two facing left. c, One Darwin's rhea. d, Snow covered mountains, Patagonia Region. e, Mountain peaks, Patagonia Region. f, White-faced saki. g, Crested caracara facing right. h, Two crested caracara. i, Crested caracara facing left.

**1995, May 5    Sheets of 9, #a.-i.**
2447-2448  A341  Set of 2    22.00 22.00

FAO, 50th Anniv. A342

No. 2449: a, 75c, Woman with baskets. b, $1, Boy with basket. c, $2, Men working in field.
$6, FAO emblem.

**1995, May 8**
2449  A342  Strip of 3, #a.-c.    3.25 3.25
**Souvenir Sheet**
2450  A342  $6 multicolored    5.00 5.00

No. 2449 was issued in sheets of 9 stamps.

Rotary Intl., 90th Anniv. — A343

$6, Paul Harris, emblem.

**1995, May 8**
2451  A343  $5 shown    4.25 4.25
**Souvenir Sheet**
2452  A343  $6 multicolored    5.00 5.00

Queen Mother, 95th Birthday A344

No. 2453: a, Drawing. b, Holding flower. c, Formal portrait. d, Blue hat, white coat.
$6, As younger woman.

**1995, May 8    Perf. 13½x14**
2453  A344  $1.50 Strip or block of 4, #a.-d.    6.75 6.75
**Souvenir Sheet**
2454  A344  $6 multicolored    6.25 6.25

No. 2453 was issued in sheets of 8 stamps. Sheets of Nos. 2453 and 2454 exist with black border and text "In Memoriam 1900-2002" overprinted in sheet margins.

1996 Summer Olympics, Atlanta — A345

No. 2455: a, Tian Bingyi, China, badminton. b, Waldemar Leigien, Poland, Frank Wieneke, Germany, judo. c, Nelli Kim, USSR, women's gymnastics. d, Allessandro Andri, Italy, shot put.
No. 2456: a, Jackie Joyner, US, heptathlon. b, Mitsuo Tsukahara, Japan, gymnastics. c, Flo Hyman, US, Zhang Rung Fang, China, volleyball. d, Steffi Graf, Germany, tennis.
Each $6: No. 2457, Sailing. No. 2458, Wilma Rudolph, US, track.

**1995, June 23**
2455  A345  75c Strip of 4, #a.-d.    3.00 3.00
2456  A345  $2 Strip of 4, #a.-d.    7.75 7.75
**Souvenir Sheets**
2457-2458  A345  Set of 2    10.00 10.00

Anniversaries & Events — A346

25c, Junior Murray, cricket player. 75c, Spices. No. 2461, $1, Sendall Tunnel, cent. No. 2462, $1, Caribbean Development Bank, 25th anniv.

**1995, Aug. 18    Litho.    Perf. 14**
2459-2462  A346  Set of 4    3.50 3.50

Miniature Sheet

Trains of the World — A347

No. 2463: a, ETR 450, Italy. b, Isparta to Bozanonu, Turkey. c, TGV, France. d, ICE Inter-City Express, Germany. e, Nishi Nippon Rail, Japan. f, Bullet Train, Japan. g, Standard 4-4-0, Central Pacific RR, US. h, Amatrak 900 Bo-Bo Electric, US. i, Sir Nigel Gresley LNER, Great Britain.
No. 2464: a, Bi Level Vista Dome, Kinki Nippon Rail, Japan. b, Rolios Rail, South Africa. c, Class 460 Bo-Bo, Switzerland. d, The Central, Peru. e, X2000 Tilt Body Train, Sweden. f, Toronto-Vancouver, Canada. g, Talisman 125 Class 31, Great Britain. h, Flying Scotsman, Great Britain. i, Indian Pacific, Australia.
$5, Diesel Hydraulic, Korea. $6, Trans-Mongolian Beijing to Ulan Bator.

**1995, Sept. 5    Sheet of 9, #a.-i.**
2463-2464  A347  $1 Set of 2    17.50 17.50
**Souvenir Sheets**
2465  A347  $5 multicolored    4.25 4.25
2466  A347  $6 multicolored    5.00 5.00

Singapore '95 (No. 2463).

Miniature Sheet

Elvis Presley (1935-77) — A348

Various portraits.

**1995, Sept. 5    Perf. 13½x14**
2467  A348  $1 Sheet of 9, #a.-i.    7.50 7.50

A349

Motion Picture, Cent. — A350

No. 2470: a, Film reel, Oscar statuette. b, "HOLLYWOOD" sign. c, Charlie Chaplin. d, Shirley Temple. e, Spencer Tracy, Katherine Hepburn. f, Marilyn Monroe. g, John Wayne. h, Marlon Brando. i, Tom Cruise.
$5, Orson Welles as Citizen Kane, horiz.

**1995, Sept. 5**      **Perf. 14**
2468 A349 75c Marilyn Monroe   1.00 1.00
2469 A349 75c Elvis Presley   1.00 1.00

**Miniature Sheet**
**Perf. 13½x14**
2470 A350 $1 Sheet of 9, #a.-i.   8.00 8.00

**Souvenir Sheet**
**Perf. 14x13½**
2471 A350 $5 multicolored   8.75 8.75

Nos. 2468-2469 were each issued in miniature sheets of 16. No. 2470 is a continuous design.

Local Entertainers — A351

Designs: No. 2472, 35c, Ajamu, white outfit. No. 2473, 35c, Mighty Sparrow, blue suit. 50c, Mighty Sparrow, black tuxedo. 75c, Ajamu, checkered shirt, sailor hat.

**1995, Sept. 5**   **Litho.**   **Perf. 14**
2472-2475 A351 Set of 4   2.75 2.75

**Miniature Sheets**

Marine Life — A352

No. 2476: a, Yellowtail damselfish. b, Bluehead wrasse. c, Balloonfish. d, Shy hamlet. e, Orange tube coral. f, Rock beauty.
No. 2477: a, Creole wrasse. b, Queen angelfish. c, Trumpetfish (e, f). d, Barred hamlet. e, Tube sponge (b, f, h, i). f, Porcupine fish. g, Fire coral (d, e, h). h, Fairy basslet. i, Anemone.
Each $6: No. 2478, Elkhorn coral. No. 2479, Common seahorse, gulfweed.

**1995, Apr. 24**
2476 A352 $1 Sheet of 6, #a.-f.   5.25 5.25
2477 A352 $1 Sheet of 9, #a.-i.   7.25 7.25

**Souvenir Sheets**
2478-2479 A352 Set of 2   9.00 9.00

Issued: No. 2477, 2478, 4/24/95; Nos. 2476, 2479, 9/19/95.

Mickey's High Sea Adventure — A353

Designs: 15c, Mickey sword fighting with pirate. 25c, Mickey with treasure chest. 35c, Minnie trying on jewelry from chest. 75c, Pluto with telescope, Mickey over barrel. $3, Pirate. $5, Mickey holding scarf with Minnie's name.
Each $6: No. 2486, Pirate fox fighting on ratlines. No. 2487, Minnie lowered from pirate ship to Mickey.

**1995, Oct. 2**    **Perf. 13½x14**
2480-2485 A353 Set of 6   8.50 8.50

**Souvenir Sheets**
2486-2487 A353 Set of 2   10.00 10.00

Miniature Sheets

Nobel Prize Fund Established, Cent. — A354

Recipients: No. 2488a, Albert A. Michelson, physics, 1907. b, Ralph Bunche, peace, 1950. c, Edwin Neher, physiology or medicine, 1991. d, Klaus von Klitzing, physics, 1985. e, Johann Deisenhofer, chemistry, 1988. f, Max Delbrück, physiology or medicine, 1969. g, J. Georg Bednorz, physics, 1987. h, Feodor Lynen, physiology or medicine, 1964. i, Walther Bothe, physics, 1954.
No. 2489: a, Hans G. Dehmelt, physics, 1989. b, Heinrich Böll, literature, 1972. c, Georges Köhler, physiology or medicine, 1984. d, Wolfgang Pauli, physics, 1945. e, Sir Bernard Katz, physiology or medicine, 1970. f, Ernest Ruska, physics, 1986. g, William Golding, literature, 1983. h, Hartmut Michel, chemistry, 1988. i, Hans A. Bethe, physics, 1967.
No. 2490: a, James Franck, physics, 1925. b, Gustav Hertz, physics, 1925. c, Friedrich Bergius, chemistry, 1931. d, Otto Loewi, physiology or medicine, 1936. e, Fritz Lipmann, physiology or medicine, 1953. f, Otto Meyerhof, physiology or medicine, 1922. g, Paul Heyse, literature, 1910. h, Jane Addams, peace, 1931. i, Carl F. Braun, physics, 1909.
Each $6: No. 2491, Winston Churchill, literature, 1953. No. 2492, Woodrow Wilson, peace, 1919. No. 2493, Theodore Roosevelt, peace, 1906.

**1995, Oct. 18**   **Litho.**   **Perf. 14**
**Sheets of 9, #a.-i.**
2488-2490 A354 $1 Set of 3   25.00 25.00

**Souvenir Sheets**
2491-2493 A354 Set of 3   14.50 14.50

Teresa Teng, Chinese Entertainer A355

Nos. 2495-2496: Various portraits.

**1995, Sept. 29**
2494 A355 75c shown   1.00 1.00

**Miniature Sheets**
2495 A355 35c Sheet of 16, #a.-p.   5.50 5.50
2496 A355 75c Sheet of 9, #a.-i.   7.00 7.00

Nos. 2495a-2495p are 24x38mm.

Christmas — A356

Details or entire paintings: 15c, The Madonna, by Montagna. 25c, Sacred Conversation Piece, by dei Pitati. 35c, Nativity, by Van Loo. 75c, The Virgin of the Fountain, Van Eyck. $2, Apparition of the Virgin, by Tiepolo. $5, The Holy Family, by Ribera.
Each $6: No. 1503, Madonna with the Christ Child, by Van Dyck. No. 1504, Vision of St. Anthony, by Van Dyck.

**1995, Nov. 28**   **Litho.**   **Perf. 13½x14**
2497-2502 A356 Set of 6   6.50 6.50

**Souvenir Sheets**
2503-2504 A356 Set of 2   10.50 10.50

Liberation of Grenada, 12th Anniv. — A357

US Pres. Ronald Reagan and: No. 2505: a, Fort George. b, US, Grenada flags. c, St. George. No. 2506, Island scene, map. No. 2507, Waterfall.

**1995, Dec. 8**    **Perf. 14**
2505 A357 75c Strip of 3, #a.-c.   2.50 2.50

**Souvenir Sheets**
2506 A357 $5 multicolored   5.25 5.25
2507 A357 $6 multicolored   6.00 6.00

No. 2505 was issued in sheets of 9 stamps.

Pope John Paul II, 1995 Visit to New York City — A358

A358a

Pope John Paul II and: No. 2508, Statue of Liberty. No. 2509, St. Patrick's Cathedral. No. 2510, New York skyline.

**1995, Dec. 13**
2508 A358 $1 multicolored   1.00 1.00
2509 A358 $1 multicolored   1.00 1.00

**Souvenir Sheet**
2510 A358 $6 multicolored   5.25 5.25

**Litho. & Embossed**
**Perf. 9**
2510A A358a $30 gold & multi   32.50

Nos. 2508-2509 were each issued in sheets of 9.

New Year 1996 (Year of the Rat) A359

Stylized rats: a, green & multi. b, red & multi. c, orange brown & multi.
$1, Two rats, horiz.

**1996, Jan. 2**   **Litho.**   **Perf. 14**
2511 A359 75c Strip of 3, #a.-c.   2.50 2.50

**Miniature Sheet**
2512 A359 75c Sheet of 1 #2511   2.50 2.50

**Souvenir Sheet**
2513 A359 $1 multicolored   1.75 1.75

No. 2511 was issued in sheets of 9 stamps.

Woodcuts by Dürer and Paintings by Rubens — A360

Details or entire works: 15c, Young Woman, by Dürer. 25c, Four Horsemen from Apocalypse, by Dürer. 35c, Assumption and Coronation of Virgin, by Rubens. $1, Anthony Van Dyck Aged 15, by Rubens. $2, Head of a Young Monk, by Rubens. $3, A Scholar Inspired by Nature, by Rubens. $5, Hanns Dürer, by Dürer.
$5, Martrydom of St. Ursula, by Rubens. $6, The Death and Life of a Virgin, by Dürer.

**1996, Jan. 29**   **Litho.**   **Perf. 13½x14**
2514-2521 A360 Set of 8   10.50 10.50

**Souvenir Sheets**
2522 A360 $5 multicolored   5.00 5.00
2523 A360 $6 multicolored   5.50 5.50

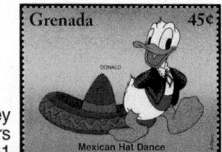

Disney Dancers A361

Character, dance: 35c, Goofy, tap dance, vert. 45c, Donald, Mexican hat dance. 75c, Daisy, hula, vert. 90c, Mickey, Minnie, tango. $1, Daisy, Donald, jitterbug, vert. $2, Mickey, Minnie, Ukrainian folk dance. $3, Goofy, Pluto, ballet. $4, Minnie, Mickey, line dancing.
$5, Minnie, the can-can. $6, Scrooge McDuck, Scottish sword dance.

**Perf. 13½x14, 14x 13½**
**1996, Feb. 26**    **Litho.**
2524-2531 A361 Set of 8   11.50 11.50

**Souvenir Sheets**
2532 A361 $5 multicolored   5.00 5.00
2533 A361 $6 multicolored   6.00 6.00

Queen Elizabeth II, 70th Birthday — A362

Designs: No. 2534a, 35c, In blue dress. b, 75c, In white hat. c, $4, In black hat. $6, Younger picture with Prince Phillip.

**1996, May 8**   **Litho.**   **Perf. 13½x14**
2534 A362 Strip of 3, #a.-c.   4.50 4.50

**Souvenir Sheet**
2535 A362 $6 multicolored   5.25 5.25

No. 2534 was issued in sheets of 9 stamps.

Ferrari Race Cars A363

Designs: a, 125-F1. b, Tipo 625. c, P4. d, 312P. e, 312, Formula 1. f, 312B. $6, F333 SP.

**1996, May 8**     *Perf. 14*
2536 A363 $1.50 Sheet of 6,
     #a.-f.      10.00 10.00
**Souvenir Sheet**
2537 A363   $6 multicolored   5.75 5.75
China '96, 9th Asian Intl. Philatelic Exhibition (No. 2536). No. 2537 contains one 85x28mm stamp.

Modern Olympic
Games,
Cent. — A364

Designs: 35c, 1896 Olympic Gold Medal, vert. 75c, Olympic Stadium, Athens, 1896. $2, Ancient Greek Olympic runners. $3, Spiridon Louis, 1896 marathon winner.

**1996, May 8**    *Litho.*    *Perf. 14*
2538-2541 A364 Set of 4    5.00 5.00
See Nos. 2599-2602.

Jerusalem, 3000th
Anniv. — A365

Various city gates: 75c, $2, $3. $5, Buildings inside city, horiz.

**1996, June 26**
2542-2544 A365 Set of 3    4.75 4.75
**Souvenir Sheet**
2545 A365   $5 multicolored   4.75 4.75

UNICEF, 50th
Anniv. — A366

Designs: 35c, Child writing in book. $2, Child planting seedling. $3, Faces of boy, girl. $5, Boy, vert.

**1996, June 26**
2546-2548 A366 Set of 3    4.25 4.25
**Souvenir Sheet**
2549 A366   $5 multicolored   4.00 4.00

Radio,
Cent. — A367

Entertainers: 35c, Jack Benny. 75c, Gertrude Berg. $1, Eddie Cantor. $2, Groucho Marx.
$6, George Burns, Gracie Allen, horiz.

*Perf. 13½x14, 14x13½*
**1996, June 26**
2550-2553 A367 Set of 4    4.25 4.25
**Souvenir Sheet**
2554 A367   $6 multicolored   5.25 5.25

Classic
Cars — A368

No. 2555: a, 1939 Type 57C Atalante. b, 1900 Cannstatt-Daimler. c, 1925 Delage. d, 1899 Coventry Daimler. e, 1900 Vauxhall. f, 1912 T-15 Hispano-Suza.
No. 2556: a, 35c, 1929 Mercedes-Benz. b, 1935 J. Duesenberg. c, 1914 Mercer. d, 1927 Bugatti Type 35. e, 1929 Alfa Romeo. f, 1910 Rolls Royce.
Each $6: No. 2557, 1915 L-Head Mercer. No. 2558, 1937 Mercedes.

---

**1996, July 25**    *Litho.*    *Perf. 14*
2555 A368 $1 Sheet of 6, #a.-
     f.      5.00 5.00
2556 A368    Sheet of 6, #a.-
     f.      6.25 6.25
**Souvenir Sheets**
2557-2558 A368 Set of 2    10.50 10.50
Nos. 2557-2558 each contain one 57x43mm stamp.

Ships — A369

War ships, No. 2559, each $1: a, Bounty, Britain, 1788. b, Bismark, Germany, 1941. c, Chuii Apoo, China, 1849. d, F224 Lubeck, Germany, 1970. e, Barbary Corsair, France, 1655. f, Augsburg, Germany, 1970. g, Henri Grace A Dieu, 1514, France. h, Prince of Wales, Britain, 1941. i, Santa Anna, Spain, 1512.
Sailing ships, each $1: No. 2560a, Gorch Fock, Germany, 1916. b, Henry B. Hyde, US, 1886. c, Resolution, Britain, 1652. d, USS Constitution, 1797. e, Nippon Maru, Japan, 1930. f, Preussen, Germany, 1902. g, Taeping, Britain, 1852. h, Chariot of Fame, US, 1853. i, Star of India, US, 1861.
$5, Victory, Britain, 1805. $6, Cutty Sark, Britain, 1869.

**1996, Aug. 14**    **Sheets of 9, #a-i**
2559-2560 A369 Set of 2    16.00 16.00
**Souvenir Sheets**
2561 A369   $5 multicolored   4.50 4.50
2562 A369   $6 multicolored   5.25 5.25

Trains — A370

Designs: 35c, C51 Imperial Train, Japan. 75c, Reingold, Germany. $2, Pioneer, US. $3, LA France, France.
Trains of the Orient, each $1: No. 2567: a, C62 4-6-4, Japanese Natl. Railways. b, 4-6-0, Shantung Railways, China. c, C57 Light 4-6-2, Japanese Natl. Railways. d, Diesel Express, Japanese Natl. Railways. e, 4-6-2, Shanghai-Nanking Railway, China. f, 051 2-8-2, Japanese Natl. Railways.
Trains of the world, each $1: No. 2568a, Atlantic Coast Line. b, #1619, Pioneer Smith Compound, England. c, 4-8-4 Trans-Siberian Railway. d, "Atlantic type," Palatinate Railway, Germany. e, 4-6-0 Paris, Lyons and Mediterranean Railway, France. f, 0341 Diesel Electric, Italian State Railways.
$5, Baden State Railways, Germany. $6, C11 2-6-4, Japanese National Railways.

**1996, Aug. 28**
2563-2566 A370 Set of 4    4.50 4.50
**Sheets of 6, #a-f**
2567-2568 A370 Set of 2    9.00 9.00
**Souvenir Sheets**
2569 A370   $5 multicolored   4.25 4.25
2570 A370   $6 multicolored   5.00 5.00

Flowers — A371

No. 2571, each $1: a, Winter jasmine. b, Chrysanthemum. c, Lilac. d, Japanese iris. e, Hibiscus. f, Sacred lotus. g, Apple blossom. h, Gladiolus. i, Japanese quince.
No. 2572, vert, each $1: a, Canterbury bell. b, Rose. c, Nasturtium. d, Daffodil. e, Tulip. f, Snapdragon. g, Zinnia. h, Sweetpea. i, Pansy.
$5, Aster. $6, Peony, vert.

**1996, Sept. 9**    *Litho.*    *Perf. 14*
**Sheets of 9, #a-i**
2571-2572 A371 Set of 2    15.00 15.00
**Souvenir Sheets**
2573 A371   $5 multicolored   5.00 5.00
2574 A371   $6 multicolored   5.50 5.50

---

Zeppelins
A372

No. 2575: a, 30c, L31, Germany. b, 30c, L35, Germany. c, 50c, L30, Germany. d, 75c, LZ10, Germany. e, $3, L3, Germany. f, $3, Beardmore No. 24, British.
No. 2576: a, Zeppelin L21, Germany. b, Zodiac Type 13 Spiess, France. c, NI "Norge." d, D-LZ 127 "Graf Zeppelin," Germany. e, D-LZ 129 "Hindenburg," Germany. f, Zeppelin NT, Germany, 1996.
Each $5: No. 2577, L13, Germany. No. 2578, Zeppelin ZT, Germany.

**1996, Sept. 9**    **Sheets of 6**
2575 A372   #a.-f.   7.50 7.50
2576 A372 $1.50 #a.-f.   8.00 8.00
**Souvenir Sheets**
2577-2578 A372 Set of 2    10.00 10.00

Birds — A373

No. 2579: a, Horned guan. b, St. Lucia parrot. c, Black penelopina. d, Grenada dove. e, St. Vincent parrot. f, White-breasted thrasher. $5, Barbados yellow warbler. $6, Semper's warbler.

**1996**
2579 A373 $1.50 Sheet of 6, #a.-
     f.      8.75 8.75
**Souvenir Sheets**
2580 A373   $5 multicolored   4.50 4.50
2581 A373   $6 multicolored   5.25 5.25

Endangered
Species — A374

Designs: a, Blue whale. b, Humpback whale. c, Right whale. d, Hawksbill turtle. e, Leatherback turtle. f, Green turtle.

**1996, Sept. 18**    *Litho.*    *Perf. 14*
2582 A374 $1.50 Sheet of 6,
     #a.-f.      11.50 11.50

Jacqueline Kennedy
Onassis (1929-
94) — A375

Various portraits.

**1996, Aug. 26**
2583 A375 $1 Sheet of 9, #a.-i.   8.75 8.75
**Souvenir Sheet**
2584 A375   $6 multicolored   5.25 5.25

**Butterfly Type of 1994**
90c, Tropical chequered skipper. $1.50, Godman's hairstreak.

**1996, Nov. 7**    *Litho.*    *Perf. 12*
2585 A328   90c multicolored   .80 .80
2586 A328 $1.50 multicolored   1.25 1.25

A376

Sea Creatures: No. 2587, each $1: a, Killer whale. b, Dolphin. c, Dolphins. d, Sea lion, royal angelfish. e, Dolphins, hawksbill turtle. f, Hawksbill turtles (e). g, Royal angelfish. h, Pennant butterflyfish. i, Sea lion, squirrel fish.

---

No. 2588, each $1: a, Brown pelican. b, Killer whale. c, Whale (c). d, Dolphins, sea lion. e, Shortfin pilot whale, blue ringed octopus, sea lion (d, f, h). f, Hammerhead sharks, sea lion. g, Blue striped grunts. h, Stingray, Van Gogh fusiliers (i). i, Van Gogh fusiliers, golden coney, ribbon moray eel (h).
Each $6: No. 2589, Sea lions, horiz. No. 2590, Dolphins, horiz.

**1996, Nov. 7**     *Perf. 14*
**Sheets of 9, #a-i**
2587-2588 A376 Set of 2   16.00 16.00
**Souvenir Sheets**
2589-2590 A376 Set of 2   10.00 10.00

Christmas — A377

Details or entire paintings: 25c, The Visitation, by Tintoretto. 35c, Virgin with the Child, by Palma Vecchio. 50c, The Adoration of the Magi, by Botticeli. 75c, The Annunciation, by Titian. $1, The Flight into Egypt, by Tintoretto. $3, The Holy Family with the Infant Saint John, by Andrea Del Sarto.
Each $6: No. 2597, Adoration of the Magi, by Paolo Schiavo. No. 2598, Madonna and Child with Saints, by Vincenzo Foppa.

**1996, Nov. 18**    *Perf. 13½x14*
2591-2596 A377 Set of 6    5.50 5.50
**Souvenir Sheets**
2597-2598 A377 Set of 2    10.50 10.50

**Modern Olympic Games Type of 1996**
Marathon medalists: No. 2599: a, Boughera El Quafi, 1928. b, Gustav Jansson, 1952. c, Spiridon Louis, 1896. d, Basil Heatley, 1964. e, Emil Zatopek, 1952. f, Frank Shorter, 1972. g, Alain Mimoun, 1956. h, Kokichi Tsuburaya, 1964. i, Delfo Cabrera, 1948.
Weight lifting medalists: No. 2600: a, Harald Sakata, 1948. b, Tom Kono, 1952. c, Naim Suleymanoglu, 1988. d, Lee Hyung Kun, 1988. e, Vassily Alexeyev, 1972. f, Chen Weiqiang, 1984. g, Ye Huanming, 1988. h, Manfred Nerlinger, 1984. i, Joseph Depietro, 1948.
$5, Manfred Nerlinger, vert. $6, Thomas Hicks, 1904, vert.

**1996, July 8**    *Litho.*    *Perf. 14*
**Sheets of 9**
2599-2600 A364 $1 #a.-i., each   7.75 7.75
**Souvenir Sheets**
2601 A364   $5 multicolored   4.25 4.25
2602 A364   $6 multicolored   5.00 5.00

US Pres. Ronald
Reagan — A378

Various portraits.

**1996, Aug. 26**    *Perf. 13½*
2603 A378 $1 Sheet of 9, #a.-i.   7.25 7.25

Sylvester Stallone in
Movie,
"Rocky" — A379

**1996, Nov. 21**    *Litho.*    *Perf. 14*
2604 A379 $2 Sheet of 3    5.25 5.25

New Year 1997 (Year of the Ox) A380

Oxen: Nos. 2605a, 2606a, Horns pointed down. Nos. 2605b, 2606b, Horns pointed up. Nos. 2605c, 2606c, Shown.

**Self-Adhesive**

*Serpentine Die Cut 11*

**1997, Jan. 2    Litho.    Sheets of 3**
2605  A380  $2 #a.-c., gold & multi  4.50  4.50
2606  A380  $2 #a.-c., sil & multi  4.50  4.50

Mickey Visits Hong Kong A381

No. 2607: a, Pet birds. b, Kung-fu tea. c, Chinese Wet Market. d, Handmade grasshopper. e, Mid-Autumn Festival. f, Tai-chi.

No. 2608: a, 35c, Tram. b, 50c, Victoria Harbor. c, 75c, Buddha. d, 90c, Bank of China. e, $2, Bottle gas. f, $3, Seafood restaurant.

No. 2609, Mickey at The Peak, vert. $4, Minnie, Mickey, Hong Kong mail, vert. $5, Mickey pulling rickshaw, vert. $6, Mickey at Peking Noodle Show, vert.

**1997, Feb. 12    Litho.    Perf. 14x13½**
2607  A381  $1 Sheet of 6, #a.-f.  7.00  7.00
2608  A381   Sheet of 6, #a.-f.  8.75  8.75
**Souvenir Sheets**
*Perf. 13½x14*
2609  A381  $3 multicolored  3.50  3.50
2610  A381  $4 multicolored  4.25  4.25
2611  A381  $5 multicolored  5.25  5.25
2612  A381  $6 multicolored  6.00  6.00

Hong Kong '97.

UNESCO, 50th Anniv. A382

Designs: 35c, Kyoto, Japan. 75c, Quedlinburg, Germany. 90c, Dubrovnik, Croatia. $1, Ruins, Delphi, Greece. $2, Tomar, Portugal. $3, Palace of Chaillot, Paris, France.

No. 2619, Chinese sites, vert., each $1: a, Entrance to caves, Desert of Taklamakan. b, House, Taklamakan. c, Monument, Taklamakan. d, Palace of Cielos Purpuras, Wudang. e, House, Wudang. f, Stone Guard, Great Wall. g, Ming Dynasty, Wudang. h, Section, Great Wall.

No. 2620, vert, each $1: a, Bryggen Wharf, Bergen, Norway. b, Old City of Bern, Switzerland. c, Warsaw, Poland. d, Fortress Walls, Luxembourg. e, Palace of Drottningholm, Sweden. f, Petäjävesi Old Church, Finland. g, Vilnius, Lithuania. h, Church of Jelling, Denmark.

No. 2621: a, Cathedral, Segovia, Spain. b, Würzburg, Germany. c, Lakes of Plitvice, Croatia. d, Monastery of Batalha, Portugal. e, River Seine, Paris, France.

Each $6: No. 2622, Monastery of Popocatepetl, Mexico. No. 2623, Shirakami-Sanchi, Japan. No. 2624, Monastery of the Hieronymites and Tower of Belem, Portugal.

**1997, Apr. 3    Litho.    Perf. 14**
2613-2618  A382  Set of 6  7.50  7.50
**Sheets of 8 or 5 + Label**
2619-2620  A382  Set of 2  15.00  15.00
2621  A382  $1.50 #a.-e.  7.00  7.00
**Souvenir Sheets**
2622-2624  A382  Set of 3  11.00  11.00

Cats — A383

Cats: 35c, Devon rex. 90c, Japanese bobtail. $2, Cornish rex.

No. 2628: a, Turkish van. b, Ragdoll. c, Siberian. d, Egyptian mau. e, American shorthair. f, Bengal. g, Asian longhair. h, Somali. i, Turkish angora.

**1997, Apr. 10**
2625-2627  A383  Set of 3  3.50  3.50
**Sheet of 9**
2628  A383  $1 #a.-i.  8.50  8.50
**Souvenir Sheet**
2629  A383  $6 Singapura  5.75  5.75

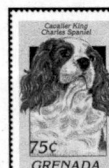

Dogs — A384

Dogs: 75c, Cavalier King Charles spaniel. $1, Afghan hound. $3, Pekingese.

No. 2633: a, Lhasa apso. b, Rough collie. c, Norwich terrier. d, America cocker spaniel. e, Chinese crested dog. f, Old English sheepdog. g, Standard poodle. h, German shepherd. i, German shorthaired pointer.

No. 2634, Bernese mountain dog.

**1997, Apr. 10**
2630-2632  A384  Set of 3  4.00  4.00
**Sheet of 9**
2633  A384  $1 #a.-i.  8.50  8.50
**Souvenir Sheet**
2634  A384  $6 multicolored  5.75  5.75

Prehistoric Animals — A385

Designs: 35c, Dunkleosteus. 75c, Tyrannosaurus rex. $2, Askeptosaurus, vert. $3, Triceratops, vert.

No. 2639: a, Sordes. b, Dimorphodon. c, Diplodocus. d, Allosaurus. e, Pentaceratops. f, Protoceratops.

Each $6: No. 2640, Maiasaura, vert. No. 2641, Tristychius, Cladoselache, vert.

**1997, Apr. 15**
2635-2638  A385  Set of 4  6.50  6.50
2639  A385  $1.50 Sheet of 6, #a.-f.  8.25  8.25
**Souvenir Sheets**
2640-2641  A385  Set of 2  12.50  12.50

Marine Life — A386

Designs: 45c, Porcelain crab. 75c, Humpback whale. 90c, Hermit crab. $1, Great white shark. $3, Green sea turtle. $4, Whale shark.

No. 2648, vert: a, Octopus. b, Lei triggerfish. c, Lionfish. d, Harlequin wrasse. e, Clown fish. f, Moray eel.

Each $6: No. 2649, Pacific barracudas. No. 2650, Scalloped hammerhead shark.

**1997, May 2**
2642-2647  A386  Set of 6  9.00  9.00
2648  A386  $1.50 Sheet of 6, #a.-f.  8.50  8.50
**Souvenir Sheets**
2649-2650  A386  Set of 2  11.50  11.50

Queen Elizabeth II, Prince Philip, 50th Wedding Anniv. — A386a

No. 2651: a, Queen, Prince waving. b, Royal Arms. c, Formal portrait in royal attire. d, Formal portrait in street clothes. e, Windsor Castle. f, Prince Philip.

$6, Formal portrait in royal attire, diff.

**1997, May 28    Litho.    Perf. 14**
2651  A386a  $1 Sheet of 6, #a.-f.  6.00  6.00
**Souvenir Sheet**
2652  A386a  $6 multicolored  6.00  6.00

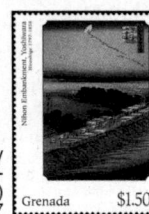

Paintings by Hiroshige (1797-1858) A387

No. 2653: a, Nihon Embankment, Yoshiwara. b, Asakusa Ricefields and Torinomachi Festival. c, Senju Great Bridge. d, Dawn Inside the Yoshiwara. e, Tile Kilns and Hasiba Ferry, Sumida River. f, View from Massaki of Suijin Shrine, Uchigawa Inlet and Sekiya.

Each $6: No. 2654, Kinryuzan Temple, Asakusa. No. 2655, Night View of Saruwakamachi.

**1997, May 28    Perf. 13½x14**
2653  A387  $1.50 Sheet of 6, #a.-f.  9.50  9.50
**Souvenir Sheets**
2654-2655  A387  Set of 2  11.50  11.50

Heinrich von Stephan (1831-97), Founder of UPU — A388

No. 2656: a, Postal delivery on motorcycle. b, UPU emblem. c, Postal delivery on skis and snowshoes, Rockies, 1900. $6, Chinese long distance carrier.

**1997, May 28    Litho.    Perf. 14**
2656  A388  $2 Sheet of 3, #a.-c.  6.00  6.00
**Souvenir Sheet**
2657  A388  $6 multicolored  6.00  6.00

PACIFIC 97.

Paul P. Harris (1868-1947), Founder of Rotary, Intl. — A389

Designs: $3, Rotary emblem, vocational training service program, The Philippines, portrait of Harris.

$6, Doves, hands holding globe inscribed "Act with Integrity, Serve with love, Work for Peace".

**1997, May 28**
2658  A389  $3 multicolored  2.75  2.75
**Souvenir Sheet**
2659  A389  $6 multicolored  5.25  5.25

Chernobyl Disaster, 10th Anniv. — A390

Designs: No. 2660, Chabad's Children of Chernobyl. No. 2661, UNESCO.

**1997, May 28    Perf. 13½x14**
2660  A390  $2 multicolored  2.00  2.00
2661  A390  $2 multicolored  2.00  2.00

Grimm's Fairy Tales — A391

Mother Goose A392

Scenes from "Snow White and the Seven Dwarfs:" No. 2662: a, Witch as woman looking into mirror. b, Dwarfs looking at Snow White as she sleeps. c, Snow White awakening, Prince. $6, Witch holding out apple for Snow White.

$5, "Little Johnny" walking in rain with umbrella.

**1997, May 28    Perf. 13½x14**
2662  A391  $2 Sheet of 3, #a.-c.  6.25  6.25
**Souvenir Sheets**
*Perf. 14, 13½x14*
2663  A392  $5 multicolored  4.00  4.00
2664  A391  $6 multicolored  5.00  5.00

1998 Winter Olympics Games, Nagano — A393

Designs: 45c, Luge. 75c, Speed skater in red. $2, Male figure skater. $3, Slalom skier.

No. 2669: a, Luge, diff. b, Ski jumper. c, Downhill skier. d, Speed skater in blue. e, Two-man bobsled. f, Female figure skater. g, Biathlon. h, Hockey. i, Freestyle skier upside down.

Each $6: No. 2670, Downhill skier in air, vert. No. 2671, 4-Man bobsled.

**1997, June 26    Perf. 14**
2665-2668  A393  Set of 4  6.50  6.50
2669  A393  $1 Sheet of 9, #a.-i.  9.00  9.00
**Souvenir Sheets**
2670-2671  A393  Set of 2  11.50  11.50

Return of Hong Kong to China — A394

Views of city, Chinese flag as Chinese inscription: 90c, Bank of China, night scene. $1, Skyscrapers. $1.75, "Hong Kong," city in lights, horiz. $2, Deng Xiaoping (1904-97), Hong Kong, horiz.

**1997, July 1**
2672-2675  A394  Set of 4  7.00  7.00

Nos. 2672-2673 were issued in sheets of 4. Nos. 2674-2675 are 59x28mm and were issued in sheets of 3.

Disney's
Hercules — A395

No. 2676: a, Hercules. b, Pegasus. c, Megara. d, Philoctetes. e, Nessus. f, Hydra. g, Pain and Panic. h, Hades.

Each $6: No. 2677, Young Hercules. No. 2678, Calliope surrounded by Terpsichore, Melpomene, Clio, Thalia.

**1997, Aug. 7**    **Litho.**    **Perf. 13½x14**
2676 A395 $1 Sheet of 8, #a.-
    h.            7.75   7.75
       **Souvenir Sheets**
2677-2678 A396 Set of 2     13.00   13.00

Butterflies
A396

Designs: 45c, Peacock. 75c, Orange flambeau. 90c, Eastern tailed blue. $2, Black and red. $3, Large white. $4, Oriental swallowtail.

No. 2685: a, Brimstone. b, Mocker swallowtail. c, American painted lady. d, Tiger swallowtail. e, Long wing. f, Sunset moth. g, Australian blue mountain swallowtail. h, Bird wing.

Each $5: No. 2686, Monarch. No. 2687, Blue morpho.

**1997, Aug. 12**        **Perf. 14**
2679-2684 A396 Set of 6    10.00   10.00
2685 A396 $1 Sheet of 8, #a.-
    h.            7.50   7.50
       **Souvenir Sheets**
2686-2687 A396 Set of 2     10.50   10.50

1998 World Cup Soccer
Championships, France — A397

Various actions scenes from Italy v. West Germany, 1982. 15c, 75c, 90c, $2, $3, $4, vert.

Winning teams: No. 2694, each $1: a, Uruguay. b, Brazil, 1958. c, Germany. d, Argentina. e, Italy. f, West Germany. g, Italy. h, Brazil, 1970.

Soccer players: No. 2695, each $1: a, Seaman, England. b, Klinsmann, Germany. c, Berger, Czech Rep. d, McCoist, Scotland. e, Gascoigne, England. f, Djorkaeff, France. g, Sammer, Germany. h, Futre, Portugal.

Each $6: No. 2696, Beckenbauer, Germany, vert. No. 2697, Moore, England.

**1997**              **Perf. 13½x14**
2688-2693 A397 Set of 6    10.00   10.00
       **Sheets of 8, #a-h**
          **Perf. 14x13½**
2694-2695 A397 Set of 2    14.50   14.50
       **Souvenir Sheets**
2696-2697 A397 Set of 2    12.00   12.00

Minnie
Mouse in
Hawaiian
Holiday
A398

Stamps in flip book sequence showing Minnie doing Hula dance: No. 2698: a, 1. b, 2. c, 3. d, 4. e, 5. f, 6. g, 7. h, 8.

No. 2699: a, 9. b, 10. c, 11. d, 12. e, 13. f, 14. g, 15. h, 16. i, 17.

$6, 18.

**1997, Aug. 7**    **Litho.**    **Perf. 14x13½**
       **Sheets of 8 or 9**
2698 A398 50c #a.-h. + label    5.50   5.50

2699 A398 50c #a.-i.          6.00   6.00
       **Souvenir Sheet**
2700 A398 $6 multicolored    8.50   8.50
          PACIFIC 97.

Mushrooms
A399

Designs: 35c, Boletus erythropus. 75c, Armillariella mellea. 90c, Amanita flavorubens. $1, Indigo milky. $2, Tylopilus balloui. $4, Boletus parasiticus.

No. 2707, each $1.50: a, Boletus parasiticus, diff. b, Frostis bolete. c, Amanita myscara flavilolvata. d, Volvariella volvacea. e, Stuntz's blue legs. f, Orange-latex milky.

No. 2708, each $1.50: a, Agaricus solidipes. b, Salmon waxy cap. c, Fused marasmius. d, Shellfish-scented russula. e, Red-capped scaber stalk. f, Calocybe tricholoma gambosum.

Each $6: No. 2709, Omphalotus illudens. No. 2710, Agaricus agrenteus.

**1997, Sept. 4**         **Perf. 14**
2701-2706 A399 Set of 6    8.75   8.75
       **Sheets of 6, #a-f**
2707-2708 A399 Set of 2    16.50   16.50
       **Souvenir Sheets**
2709-2710 A399 Set of 2    11.50   11.50

Orchids — A400

Designs: 20c, Paphiopedilum urbanianum. 35c, Trichoceros parviflorus. 45c, Euanthe sanderiana, vert. 75c, Oncidium macranthum, vert. 90c, Psychopsis kramerianum, vert. $1, Oncidium hastatum, vert. $3, Masdevallia saltatrix, vert. $4, Cattleya luteola.

No. 2719, vert, each $2: a, Odontoglossum crispum. b, Cattleya brabantiae, c, Cattleya bicolor. d, Trichopilia suavia. e, Encyclia mariae. f, Angraecum leonis.

No. 2720, vert, each $2: a, Broughtonia sanguinea. b, Anguloa virginalis. c, Dendrobium Bigibbum. d, T. forcia, L. lucasiana. e, Cymbidium. f, Cymbidium, diff.

Each $6: No. 2721, Oncidium onustum. No. 2722, Laelia milleri.

**1997, Sept. 4**
2711-2718 A400 Set of 8    13.00   13.00
       **Sheets of 6, #a-f**
2719-2720 A400 Set of 2    26.00   26.00
       **Souvenir Sheets**
2721-2722 A400 Set of 2    15.00   15.00

Diana, Princess of Wales (1961-
97) — A401

Various portraits.

**1997, Oct. 15**    **Litho.**    **Perf. 14½**
2723 A401 $1.50 Sheet of 6, #a.-
    f.            7.75   7.75
       **Souvenir Sheet**
2724 A401 $5 multicolored    4.75   4.75

Christmas — A402

Works of art, entire paintings, or details: 35c, Angel, by Matthias Grunewald. 50c, Saint Demetrius (icon). 75c, Reliquary in the Form

of a Triptych. $1, Angel of the Annunciation, by Jan van Eyck. $3, The Annunciation, by Simone Martini. $4, Saint Michael (mosaic).

Each $6: No. 2731, The Annunciation, by Titian, horiz. No. 2732, The Coronation of the Virgin, by Fra Angelico.

**1997, Dec. 5**    **Litho.**    **Perf. 14**
2725-2730 A402 Set of 6    8.75   8.75
       **Souvenir Sheets**
2731-2732 A402 Set of 2    12.50   12.50

New
Year
1998
(Year of
the
Tiger)
A403

Designs: a, shown. b, With mouth open. c, With ears rolled back.

**1998, Jan. 5**    **Litho.**    **Die Cut Perf. 9**
         **Self-Adhesive**
       **Sheets of 3, #a.-c.**
2733 A403 $1.50 gold & multi     30.00
2734 A403 $1.50 sil & multi      30.00

Nos. 2733b, 2734b have point of triangle down.

Fish — A404

65c, Black-tailed humbug. 90c, Yellow sweetlips. $1, Common squrrelfish. $2, Powder blue surgeon.

No. 2739, each $1.50: a, Blue tang. b, Porkfish. c, Banded butterflyfish. d, Threadfin butterflyfish. e, Red-headed. f, Emperor angelfish.

No. 2740, each $1.50: a, Scribbled angelfish. b, Lemonpeel angelfish. c, Bandit angelfish. d, Bicolor cherub. e, Regal tang. f, Yellow tang.

Each $6: No. 2741, Two-banded anemonefish. No. 2742, Long-nosed butterflyfish.

**1998, Feb. 10**    **Litho.**    **Perf. 14**
2735-2738 A404 Set of 4    6.00   6.00
       **Sheets of 6, #a.-f.**
2739-2740 A404 Set of 2    18.50   18.50
       **Souvenir Sheets**
2741-2742 A404 Set of 2    15.00   15.00

Orchids — A405

No. 2743, each $1.50: a, Arachnis clarkei. b, Cymbidium eburneum. c, Dendrobium chrysotoxum. d, Paphiopedilum insigne. e, Paphiopedilum venustum. f, Renanthera imschootiana.

No. 2744, each $1.50: a, Sophronitis grandiflora. b, Phalaenopsis amboinensis. c, Zygopetalum intermedium. d, Paphiopedilum purpuratum. e, Miltonia regnellii. f, Dendrobium parishii.

Each $6: No. 2745, Lycaste aromatica. No. 2746, Pleione maculata.

**1998, Apr. 21**    **Litho.**    **Perf. 14**
       **Sheets of 6, #a.-f.**
2743-2744 A405 Set of 2    21.00   21.00
       **Souvenir Sheets**
2745-2746 A405 Set of 2    14.00   14.00

Ships — A406

No. 2747, each $1: a, Brig. b, Clipper. c, Caique. d, Mississippi Riverboat. e, Luxury liner. f, The Mayflower. g, Frigate. h, Janggolan. i, Junk.

No. 2748, each $1: a, Dhow. b, Galleon. c, Felucca. d, Schooner. e, Aircraft carrier. f, Knau. g, Destroyer. h, Longship. i, Queen Elizabeth 2.

Each $6: No. 2749, The Lusitania. No. 2750, Submarine.

**1998, Apr. 26**    **Litho.**    **Perf. 14**
       **Sheets of 9, #a-i**
2747-2748 A406 Set of 2    19.00   19.00
       **Souvenir Sheets**
2749-2750 A406 Set of 2    12.50   12.50

No. 2749 contains one 85x28mm stamp; No. 2750 one 56x42mm stamp.

Disney's
Hercules — A407

Hercules grows up — No. 2751: a, Hercules, Zeus. b, Hercules and Pegasus walking past creature. c, Phil, Hercules. d, Hercules swinging through air. e, Centaur carrying captured Meg. f, Hercules attacking centaur. g, Hercules fighting lion. h, Hercules, Pegasus looking at prints.

Birth and childhood of Hercules — No. 2752, each $1: a, Zeus and Hera with newborn Hercules. b, Hades finds baby. c, Hades in the night. d, Baby sleeping. e, Baby swept away by Pain and Panic. f, Old couple with Baby Hercules. g, Hercules pulling cart. h, Hercules looking into mirror.

Hercules triumphant — No. 2753, each $1: a, Hercules carrying Meg. b, Meg, Hades. c, Hercules being trained by Phil. d, Hercules meeting Hades. e, Monster coming through city. f, Zeus. g, Hercules lifting column off Meg. h, Hercules diving into water.

Each $6: No. 2754, Hercules with sword, fighting Hydra. No. 2755, Hades on fire. No. 2756, Hercules, Meg on Pegasus, horiz. No. 2757, Zeus, Hercules, horiz. No. 2758, Hades. No. 2759, Zeus with baby Pegasus.

**1998, June 16**    **Litho.**    **Perf. 13½x14**
       **Sheets of 8**
2751 A407 10c #a.-h.      3.75   3.75
2752-2753 A407 Set of 2    19.00   19.00
       **Souvenir Sheets**
2754-2759 A407 Set of 6    40.00   40.00

Sea Birds — A408

Designs: 90c, Arctic skua. $1.10, Humboldt penguin. $2, Herring gull. $3, Red knot.

No. 2764, horiz.: a, Northern fulmar. b, Black-legged kittiwake. c, Cape petrel. d, Mediterranean gull. e, Brandt's cormorant (h). f, Greater shearwater. g, Black-footed albatross. h, Red-necked phalarope. i, Black skimmer (f).

Each $5: No. 2765, Black-browed albatross. No. 2766, King penguin.

**1998, June 30**    **Litho.**    **Perf. 14**
2760-2763 A408 Set of 4    6.00   6.00
2764 A408 $1 Sheet of 9, #a.-
    i.            10.00   10.00
       **Souvenir Sheets**
2765-2766 A408 Set of 2    11.50   11.50

Diana, Princess of Wales (1961-
97) — A409

Portrait of Diana with rose: No. 2767, Wearing hat. No. 2768, Without hat.

       **Litho. & Embossed**
**1998, July 14**        **Die Cut 7½**
2767 A409 $20 gold & multi
2768 A409 $20 gold & multi

**Supermarine Spitfires — A410**

No. 2769, each $1.50: a, MK IX. b, MK XIV. c, MK XII. d, MK XI. e, H.F. MK VIII. f, MK VB.
No. 2770, each $1.50: a, MK I. b, MK VIII. c, MK III. d, MK XVI. e, MK V. f, MK XIX.
Each $6: No. 2771, MK IX. No. 2772, MK IA.

**1998, July 20    Litho.    Perf. 14**
**Sheets of 6, #a.-f.**
2769-2770  A410  Set of 2    15.00 15.00
**Souvenir Sheets**
2771-2772  A410  Set of 2    12.00 12.00
Nos. 2771-2772 each contain one 57x43mm stamp.

**Intl. Year of the Ocean — A411**

No. 2773: a, Walrus. b, African black footed penguins. c, African black-footed penguin. d, California sea lion. e, Green turtle. f, Redfin anthias. g, Sperm whale. h, French angelfish, Australian sea lion. i, Jellyfish. j, Sawfish. k, Male and female cuckoo wrasse. l, Garibaldi. m, Spinecheek anemonefish. n, Leafy seadragon. o, Blue-spotted goatfish. p, Two-spot gobies.
No. 2774, Atlantic spotted dolphins. No. 2775, Octopus.

**1998, Aug. 19**
2773  A411  75c Sheet of 16, #a.-p.    13.50 13.50
**Souvenir Sheets**
2774  A411  $5 multicolored    5.00 5.00
2775  A411  $6 multicolored    6.25 6.25

**CARICOM, 25th Anniv. — A412**

**1998, Sept. 15    Litho.    Perf. 13½**
2776  A412  $1 multicolored    1.10 1.10

**Mahatma Gandhi (1869-1948) — A413**

Design: $6, Portrait, head down.

**1998, Sept. 13    Perf. 14**
2777  A413  $1 multicolored    1.50 1.50
**Souvenir Sheet**
2778  A413  $6 multicolored    6.50 6.50
No. 2777 was issued in sheets of 4.

**Paintings by Pablo Picasso (1881-1973) — A414**

45c, The Bathers, 1918, vert. $2, Luncheon on the Grass, 1960. $3, The Swimmer, 1929. $5, Woman Reading, 1944, vert.

**Perf. 14½x14, 14x14½**
**1998, Sept. 15**
2779-2781  A414  Set of 3    5.25 5.25
**Souvenir Sheet**
2782  A414  $5 multicolored    5.25 5.25

**Paintings by Eugéne Delacroix (1798-1863) — A415**

No. 2783: a, Horsemen Fighting in the Plain. b, The Assassination of the Bishop of Liege. c, Still-life with Lobsters. d, The Battle of Nancy. e, The Shipwreck of Don Juan. f, The Death of Ophelia. g, Attila and the Barbarians. h, Entertaining the Arabians.
$5, Entry of the Crusaders into Constantinople.

**1998, Sept. 15    Perf. 14**
**Sheet of 8**
2783  A415  $1 #a.-h.    7.75 7.75
**Souvenir Sheet**
2784  A415  $5 multicolored    5.25 5.25

**Organization of American States, 50th Anniv. — A416**

**1998, Sept. 15    Litho.    Perf. 14**
2785  A416  $1 multicolored    1.10 1.10

**Diana, Princess of Wales (1961-97) — A417**

No. 2786: a, Inscription panel at left. b, Panel at right.

**1998    Perf. 14½**
2786  A417  $1 Horiz. pair, #a-b  2.50 2.50
**Self-Adhesive**
**Serpentine Die Cut Perf. 11½**
**Sheet of 1**
**Size: 52x65mm**
2786A A417  $6 Diana, buildings    6.00
No. 2786 was issued in sheets of 6. Soaking in water may affect the multi-layer image of No. 2786A.
Issued: $1, 9/15; $6, 11/5/98.

**Enzo Ferrari (1898-1988), Automobile Manufacturer — A418**

No. 2787: a, 250 GT Berlinetta Lusso. b, 250 GTO. c, 250 GT Boano/Ellena cabriolet.
$5, Dino 246 GTS.

**1998, Sept. 15    Perf. 14**
2787  A418  $2 Sheet of 3, #a.-c.  6.00 6.00
**Souvenir Sheet**
2788  A418  $5 multicolored    6.00 6.00
No. 2786 was issued in sheets of 6. No. 2788 contains one 91x35mm stamp.

**1998 World Scouting Jamboree, Chile — A419**

Designs: $2, Scout salute. $3, World Scout flag. $4, Scout first aid. $6, World Scout flag.

**1998, Sept. 15**
2789-2791  A419  Set of 3    8.75 8.75
**Souvenir Sheet**
2792  A419  $6 multi, horiz.    7.00 7.00

**Royal Air Force, 80th Anniv. — A420**

No. 2793, each $2: a, Vickers Supermarine Spitfire HF Mk1XB flying right. c, Vickers Supermarine Spitfire HF Mk1Xb flying left. d, Hawker Hurricane 11C.
No. 2794, each $2: a, EF-2000 Eurofighter prototype. b, Nimrod MR2P. c, Eurofighter 2000, diff. d, C-47 Dakota.
Each $6: No. 2795, Eurofighter 2000, VC10. No. 2796, Biplane, hawk's head. No. 2797, Biplane, hawk. No. 2798, Eurofighter 2000, Jet Provost.

**1998, Sept. 15    Sheets of 4, #a-d**
2793-2794  A420  Set of 2    16.00 16.00
**Souvenir Sheets**
2795-2798  A420  Set of 4    25.00 25.00

**Tennis Stars — A421**

45c, Arthur Ashe. 75c, Martina Hingis. 90c, Chris Evert. $1, Steffi Graf. $1.50, Arantxa Sanchez Vicario. $2, Martina Navratilova. $2, Monica Seles. $6, Martina Hingis, diff.

**1998, Oct. 28**
2799-2805  A421  Set of 7    8.75 8.75
**Souvenir Sheet**
2806  A421  $6 multicolored    7.00 7.00

**Peacekeepers, Beirut, Lebanon, 1982-84 — A422**

**1998, Nov. 30    Litho.    Perf. 14**
2807  A422  $1 multicolored    1.25 1.25

**Christmas — A423**

Birds: 45c, Blue-hooded Euphonia. 75c, Black-bellied whistling duck. 90c, Purple martin. $1, Imperial parrot. $2, Adelaide's warbler. $3, Roseate flamingo.
$5, Green-throated carib. $6, Purple-throated carib, Canada #85.

**1998, Dec. 1**
2808-2813  A423  Set of 6    7.75 7.75
**Souvenir Sheet**
2814  A423  $5 multicolored    5.25 5.25
2815  A423  $6 multicolored    8.00 8.00
No. 2815 contains one 38x61mm stamp.

**Christmas — A424**

Works of art: 35c, Painting, The Angel's Parting from Tobias, by Jean Bilevelt. 45c, Painting, Allegory of Faith, by Moretto da Brescia. 90c, Painting, Cross, with Depiction of the Crucifixion, by Ugolino di Tedice. $1, The Triumphal Entry into Jerusalem, Master of the Thuison Altarpiece.

**1998, Dec. 1**
2816-2819  A424  Set of 4    2.75 2.75

**New Year 1999 (Year of the Rabbit) — A425**

Various rabbits, color of country name: a, green. b, orange. c, red.

**1999, Jan. 4    Litho.    Die Cut Perf. 9**
**Self-Adhesive**
**Sheet of 3**
2820  A425  $1 sil & multi, #a.-c.    4.00 4.00
No. 2820b has point of triangle down.

**A426**

Famous People: No. 2821: a, Martin Luther King, Jr. (1929-68). b, Socrates (470-399BC). c, Thomas Moore (1478-1535). d, Chaim Weizmann (1874-1952). e, Alexander Solzhenitsyn (1918-2008). f, Galileo Galilei (1564-1642). g, Michael Servetus (1511-53). h, Salman Rushdie (b. 1947).
$6, Mother Teresa (1910-97).

**1999, Mar. 1    Litho.    Perf. 14**
2821  A426  $1 Sheet of 8, #a.-h.    10.00 10.00
**Souvenir Sheet**
2822  A426  $6 multicolored    7.00 7.00
Nos. 2821b-2821c, 2821e-2821f are 53x38mm.

**A427**

Space Exploration — No. 2823, each $1.50: a, Robert H. Goddard. b, Werner von Braun. c, Yuri Gagarin. d, Freedom 7 rocket. e, Aleksei Leonov. f, Apollo 11 astronauts on moon.
No. 2824, each $1.50: a, Mariner 9. b, Voyager 1. c, Bruce McCandless. d, Giotto probe. e, Space Shuttle. f, Magellan probe.
Each $6: No. 2825, John H. Glenn, Jr. No. 2826, Neil A. Armstrong.

**1999, Mar. 5    Sheets of 6, #a-f**
2823-2824  A427  Set of 2    16.00 16.00
**Souvenir Sheets**
2825-2826  A427  Set of 2    12.00 12.00

**Mickey's Dream Wedding — A428**

No. 2827: a, Goofy. b, Mickey. c, Minnie. d, Daisy Duck. e, Donald Duck. f, Pluto. g, Huey, Dewey & Louie. h, Dog.
Each $6: No. 2828, Mickey eating cake. No. 2829, Mickey, Minnie in back of carriage, horiz.

**1999, Mar. 12    Perf. 13½x14, 14x13½**
2827  A428  $1 Sheet of 8, #a.-h.    8.00 8.00
**Souvenir Sheets**
2828-2829  A428  Set of 2    14.50 14.50
Mickey Mouse, 70th anniv.

Trains — A429

Designs: 25c, Grand Trunk Western. 35c, Louisville & Nashville. 45c, Gulf, Mobile & Ohio. 75c, Missouri Pacific. 90c, RTG, French Natl. Railway. $1, Florida East Coast. $3, Kansas City Southern. $4, New Haven.

No. 2838, each $1.50: a, Western Pacific. b, Union Pacific. c, Chesapeake & Ohio. d, Southern Pacific. e, Baltimore & Ohio. f, Wabash.

No. 2839, each $1.50: a, Burlington Route. b, Texas Special, Missouri, Kansas & Texas. c, City of Los Angeles. d, Northwestern. e, Canadian National. f, Rock Island.

No. 2840, each $1.50: a, Rio Grande. b, Erie Lackawanna. c, New York Central. d, Pennsylvania. e, Milwaukee Road. f, Illinois Central.

No. 2841, each $1.50: a, TGV, French National Railways. b, HST, British Railways. c, TEE, Trans Europe Express. d, Ancona Express Itay. e, XPT, Australia. f, APT-P, British Railways.

Each $6: No. 2842, Bullet Train, Japan. No. 2843, Inter City Express, Germany. No. 2844, Santa Fe. No. 2845, ELD 4, Netherlands.

| 1999, Mar. 15 | | | Perf. 14 | |
|---|---|---|---|---|
| 2830-2837 | A429 | Set of 8 | 9.00 | 9.00 |
| **Sheets of 6, #a-f** | | | | |
| 2838-2841 | A429 | Set of 4 | 34.00 | 34.00 |
| **Souvenir Sheets** | | | | |
| 2842-2845 | A429 | Set of 4 | 24.00 | 24.00 |

Australia '99, World Stamp Expo — A430

Flora and fauna: $1, Orangutan. $2, Dourocouli. $3, Black caiman. $4, Black leopard, vert.

No. 2850, vert, each 75c: a, African binturong. b, Two elephants. c, One elephant. d, Garkulax mitratus. e, Vanda hookeriana (a, f). f, Heron. g, Fur seal (f). h, Pied shag (g). i, Round batfish (e). j, Loggerhead turtle (f, k). k, Three harlequin sweet lips (l). l, Two harlequin sweet lips (k).

No. 2851, each 75c: a, Papilio blumei (d). b, Egret (e). c, Kumarahou (b, f). d, Javan rhinoceros (g). e, Silver eye. f, Kiore (i). g, Cyclorana novaehollandiae. h, Caterpillar. i, Grey duck (h). j, Honey blue-eye. k, Krefft's tortoise. l, Archer fish.

Each $6: No. 2852, Impalas. No. 2853, Ring-tailed lemurs.

| 1999, Apr. 12 | | | Litho. | | Perf. 14 | |
|---|---|---|---|---|---|
| 2846-2849 | A430 | Set of 4 | 9.50 | 9.50 |
| **Sheets of 12, #a-l** | | | | |
| 2850-2851 | A430 | Set of 2 | 17.50 | 17.50 |
| **Souvenir Sheets** | | | | |
| 2852-2853 | A430 | Set of 2 | 12.50 | 12.50 |

Paintings by Hokusai (1760-1849) A431

Entire paintings or details — No. 2854, each $1.50: a, The Actor Ichikawa Danjuro as Tomoe Gozen. b, E-Tehon drawings (washing clothes). c, The Prostitute of Eguchi. d, Sudden Shower from a Fine Sky. e, E-tehon drawings (hanging clothes up to dry). f, Shimada.

No. 2855, each $1.50: a, Head of Old Man. b, Horse Drawings (with head down). c, Girl Making Cord for Binding Hats. d, Li Po Admiring the Waterfall of Lo-Shan. e, Horse drawings (with head up). f, Potted Dwarf Pine with Basin.

Each $6: No. 2856, Women on the Beach at Enoshima. No. 2857, The Guardian God Fudo Myoo and His Two Young Attendants.

| 1999, May 24 | | | Litho. | | Perf. 13½x14 | |
|---|---|---|---|---|---|
| **Sheets of 6, #a-f** | | | | |
| 2854-2855 | A431 | Set of 2 | 17.00 | 17.00 |
| **Souvenir Sheets** | | | | |
| 2856-2857 | A431 | Set of 2 | 12.50 | 12.50 |

Johann Wolfgang von Goethe (1749-1832), Poet — A432

No. 2858: a, Faust contempates the moon in his story. b, Portrait of Goethe and Freidrich von Schiller (1759-1805). c, Faust converses with Wagner outside the town gate.

No. 2860, Margaret Muses in "Faust."

| 1999, May 24 | | | | Perf. 14 | |
|---|---|---|---|---|---|
| 2858 | A432 | $3 Sheet of 3, #a.-c. | 8.75 | 8.75 |
| **Souvenir Sheet** | | | | |
| 2860 | A432 | $6 multi | 6.75 | 6.75 |

IBRA '99, World Philatelic Exhibition, Nuremberg — A433

IBRA'99 emblem, 1893 4-4-0 locomotive and: No. 2862, 75c, Prussia #2. No. 2864, $1, Saxony #1.

Emblem, Humboldt sailing ship and: No. 2863, 90c, Mecklenburg-Schwerin #1. No. 2865, $2, Mecklenburg-Strelitz #1.

$6, Saxony #1.

| 1999, May 24 | | | Litho. | | Perf. 14 | |
|---|---|---|---|---|---|
| 2862-2865 | A433 | Set of 4 | 5.25 | 5.25 |
| **Souvenir Sheet** | | | | |
| 2866 | A433 | $6 multicolored | 7.75 | 7.75 |

Apollo 11 Moon Landing, 30th Anniv. — A434

No. 2867, each $1.50: a, Footprint on moon. b, V2 Rocket. c, Command module, Columbia. d, Lunar rover. e, Lunar lander, Eagle. f, Command module during re-entry.

No. 2868, each $1.50: a, Moon. b, Edward H. White during first spacewalk. c, Edwin "Buzz" Aldrin. d, Earth. e, Michael Collins. f, Neal A. Armstrong, first man to walk on moon.

Each $6: No. 2869, Launch of Apollo 11, vert. No. 2870, US flag, Armstrong on Moon.

| 1999, May 24 | | | Sheets of 6, #a-f | |
|---|---|---|---|---|
| 2867-2868 | A434 | Set of 2 | 19.00 | 19.00 |
| **Souvenir Sheets** | | | | |
| 2869-2870 | A434 | Set of 2 | 12.50 | 12.50 |

**Souvenir Sheets**

PhilexFrance '99, World Philatelic Exhibition — A435

Designs, each $6: No. 2871, 2-8-0 Heavy freight locomotive, French State Railways. No. 2872, 4 Cylinder Compound Pacific, Paris-Lyons and Mediterranean Railway.

| 1999, May 24 | | | | Perf. 13¾ | |
|---|---|---|---|---|---|
| 2871-2872 | A435 | Set of 2 | 12.50 | 12.50 |

A436

Wedding of Prince Edward and Sophie Rhys-Jones — No. 2873: a, Edward. b, Sophie and Edward. c, Sophie.

$6, Couple, horiz.

| 1999, June 18 | | | Litho. | | Perf. 13½ | |
|---|---|---|---|---|---|
| 2873 | A436 | $3 Sheet of 3, #a.-c. | 8.75 | 8.75 |
| **Souvenir Sheet** | | | | |
| 2874 | A436 | $6 multicolored | 7.00 | 7.00 |

A437

Children: a, Two with fur hats. b, One with pink hat. c, Boy without shirt, girl with shawl.

$6, Wearing white shirt.

| 1999, May 24 | | | Litho. | | Perf. 14 | |
|---|---|---|---|---|---|
| 2875 | A437 | $3 Sheet of 3, #a.-c. | 8.75 | 8.75 |
| **Souvenir Sheet** | | | | |
| 2876 | A437 | $6 multicolored | 7.00 | 7.00 |

UN Rights of the Child, 10th anniv.

British Comedy "Carry On" — A438

a, Dick. b, Doctor. c, England. d, Matron. e, Round the Bend. f, Up the Jungle. g, Loving. h, Up the Khyber.

$6, Various characters.

| 1999, May 24 | | | | Perf. 13½x14 | |
|---|---|---|---|---|---|
| 2877 | A438 | $1 Sheet of 8, #a.-h. | 8.75 | 8.75 |
| | | | Perf. 13¾ | | |
| 2877I | A438 | $6 multicolored | 6.75 | 6.75 |

Variety Club of Great Britain, 50th anniv.

UPU, 125th Anniv. — A439

Mail from space: a, Cosmonaut with letter from home. b, Supply and mail ship, "Progress." c, Postmark of space station Mir. d, Buran shuttle, Mir in space.

$6, Space station Mir.

| 1999, May 24 | | | | Perf. 14 | |
|---|---|---|---|---|---|
| 2878 | A439 | $2 Sheet of 4, #a.-d. | 8.75 | 8.75 |
| **Souvenir Sheet** | | | | |
| 2879 | A439 | $6 multicolored | 7.00 | 7.00 |

Queen Mother, 100th Birthday (in 2000) — A440

A440a

No. 2880: a, Queen Mother, Prince Charles, 1948. b, Queen Mother, 1970. c, Queen Mother in Australia, 1958. d, Queen Mother, 1953.

$6, Queen Mother, 1953.

| 1999, Aug. 16 | | | | Gold Frames | |
|---|---|---|---|---|---|
| **Sheet of 4** | | | | |
| 2880 | A440 | $2 #a.-d. + label | 8.75 | 8.75 |
| **Souvenir Sheet** | | | | |
| 2881 | A440 | $6 multicolored | 7.00 | 7.00 |
| **Litho. & Embossed** | | | | |
| *Die Cut Perf. 8¾* | | | | |
| **Without Gum** | | | | |
| 2881A | A440a | $20 gold & multi | *20.00* | |

No. 2881 contains one 38x50mm stamp. Margins of sheet are embossed. See Nos. 3212-3213.

Birth of the Silver Screen — A441

Musicians — No. 2882, each $1: a, George Gershwin, 1929. b, Florence Mills, 1928. c, Sam Beckett, 1925. d, Bessie Smith, 1923. e, Billie Holiday, 1933. f, Bert Williams, 1914. g, Cole Porter, 1934. h, Sophie Tucker, 1915.

Actors — No. 2883, each $1: a, Lon Chaney, 1930. b, Buster Keaton, 1930. c, Norma Shearer, 1934. d, James Cagney, 1930. e, Hedda Hopper, 1933. f, Jean Harlow, 1931. g, Marlene Dietrich, 1930. h, Ramon Novarro, 1928.

Each $6: No. 2884, Louis Armstrong. No. 2885, Clark Gable, 1932,

| 1999, Aug. 18 | | | Sheets of 8, #a-h | |
|---|---|---|---|---|
| 2882-2883 | A441 | Set of 2 | 16.00 | 16.00 |
| **Souvenir Sheets** | | | | |
| 2884-2885 | A441 | Set of 2 | 14.00 | 14.00 |

Star Trek — A442

Various starships.

| 1999, July 20 | | | Litho. | | Perf. 13¼ | |
|---|---|---|---|---|---|
| 2886 | A442 | $1.50 Sheet of 9, #a.-i. | 14.50 | 14.50 |

Dinosaurs A443

35c, Ouranosaurus. 45c, Struthiomimus, vert. 75c, Parasaurolophus, vert. $2, Triceratops. $3, Stegoceras. $4, Stegosaurus.

No. 2893, each $1: a, Agathaumus. b, Camarosaurus. c, Quetzalcoatlus. d, Alioramus. e, Camptosaurus. f, Albertosaurus. g, Anatosaurus. h, Spinosaurus. i, Centrosaurus.

No. 2894, each $1: a, Archaeopteryx. b, Brachiosaurus. c, Dilophosaurus. d, Dimetrodon. e, Psittacosaurus. f, Acrocanthosaurus. g, Stenonychosaurus. h, Dryosaurus. i, Compsognathus.
Each $6: No. 2895, Velociraptor, vert. No. 2896, Tyrannosaurus, vert.

**1999, Sept. 1     Litho.     Perf. 14**
2887-2892 A443 Set of 6           10.00 10.00
**Sheets of 9, #a-i**
2893-2894 A443 Set of 2           18.00 18.00
**Souvenir Sheets**
2895-2896 A443 Set of 2           12.50 12.50

Christmas — A444

Candle and: 20c, Rose. 75c, Tulip. 90c, Pear. $1, Hibiscus. $4, Lily.
$6, The Nativity, by Sandro Botticelli.

**1999, Dec. 7     Litho.     Perf. 14**
2897-2901 A444 Set of 5            6.75 6.75
**Souvenir Sheet**
2902 A444 $6 multi                 7.00 7.00

Flowers — A445

Various flowers making up a photomosaic of Princess Diana.

**1999, Dec. 31     Litho.     Perf. 13¾**
2903 A445 $1 Sheet of 8, #a.-h.    9.50 9.50
See No. 3055.

New Year 2000 (Year of the Dragon) A446

Inscription color: a, Blue green. b, Red. c, Violet.

**2000, Feb. 5     Perf. 12½x12¾**
2904 A446 $2 Sheet of 3, #a.-c.    8.00 8.00
No. 2904b has point of triangle down.

Birds — A447

Designs: 75c, Roseate spoonbill. 90c, Scarlet ibis. $1.50, Sparkling violet-ear. $2, Northern jacana.
No. 2909, each $1: a, Blue-headed euphonia. b, Troupial. c, Caribbean parakeet. d, Forest thrush. e, Hooded tanager. f, Striped-headed tanager. g, Ringed kingfisher. h, Zenaida dove.
No. 2910, each $1: a, Adelaide's warbler. b, Hispaniolan trogon. c, Sun parakeet. d, Black-necked stilt. e, Sora rail. f, Fulvous tree duck. g, Blue-headed parrot. h, Tropical mockingbird.
Each $6: No. 2911, Antillean siskin. No. 2912, Cedar waxwing, vert.

**2000, Mar. 1     Litho.     Perf. 14**
2905-2908 A447 Set of 4            5.00 5.00
**Sheets of 8, #a-h**
2909-2910 A447 Set of 2           14.00 14.00
**Souvenir Sheets**
2911-2912 A447 Set of 2           11.00 11.00
No. 2911 contains one 50x37mm stamp. No. 2912 contains one 37x50mm stamp.

Mushrooms — A448

Designs: 35c, Clitocybe geotropa. 45c, Psalliota augusta. $1, Amanita rubescens. $4, Boletus satanas.
No. 2917, each $1.50: a, Ungulina marginata. b, Pleurotus ostreatus. c, Flammula penetrans. d, Morchella crassipes. e, Lepiota procera. f, Tricholoma aurantium.
No. 2918, each $1.50: a, Pholiota spectabilis. b, Mycena polygramma. c, Collybia iocephala. d, Corinus cornatus. e, Amanita muscaria. f, Boletus aereus.
Each $6: No. 2919, Lepiota acutesquamosa. No. 2920, Daedala quercina.

**2000, May 1     Perf. 14**
2913-2916 A448 Set of 4            6.25 6.25
**Sheets of 6, #a-f**
2917-2918 A448 Set of 2           17.00 17.00
**Souvenir Sheets**
2919-2920 A448 Set of 2           12.00 12.00

Paintings of Anthony Van Dyck — A449

No. 2921, each $1: a, Young Woman Resting Her Head on Her Hand. b, Self-portrait. c, Woman Looking Upwards. d, Head of an Old Man, c. 1621. e, Head of a Boy. f, Head of an Old Man, 1616-18.
No. 2922, each $1: a, Charles I on Horseback with Seigneur de St. Antoine. b, St. Martin Dividing His Cloak. c, Giovanni Paolo Balbi on Horseback. d, Marchese Anton Giulio Brignole-Sale on Horseback. e, Study of a Horse. f, An Oriental on Horseback.
No. 2923, each $1.50: a, Portrait of a Man. b, Portrait of a Man Aged Seventy. c, Portrait of a Woman. d, An Elderly Man. e, Portrait of a Young Man. f, Man with a Glove.
No. 2924, each $1.50: a, St. John the Baptist. b, St. Anthony of Padua and the Ass of Rimini. c, The Stoning of St. Stephen. d, The Martyrdom of St. Sebastian. e, St. Sebastian Bound for Martyrdom. f, St. Jerome.
No. 2925, each $1.50: a, Inscribed "Portrait of Anthony Van Dyck," actually a self-portrait of Rubens. b, Inscribed "Self-portrait (after Peter Paul Rubens)." c, Isabella Brant, Wife of Peter Paul Rubens. d, The Penitent Apostle Peter. e, Head of a Robber. f, The Heads of the Apostles, by Rubens.
Each $5: No. 2926, Prince Thomas-Francis of Savoy-Carignan on Horseback. No. 2927, Charles I on Horseback. No. 2928, The Emperor Theodosius Refused Entry in Milan Cathedral, horiz.
Each $6: No. 2929, St. Jerome (in the Wilderness). No. 2930, St. Martin Dividing His Cloak, horiz. No. 2931, Portrait of a Man and His Wife.

**2000, May 1     Perf. 13¾**
2921-2922 A449 Set of 2           10.50 10.50
**Sheets of 6, #a.-f.**
2923-2925 A449 Set of 3           22.50 22.50
**Souvenir Sheets**
2926-2928 A449 Set of 3           13.00 13.00
2929-2931 A449 Set of 3           14.50 14.50

Millennium — A450

Highlights of 1650-1700: a, Painter Jan Vermeer dies. b, Birth of microbiology. c, Salem Witch Trials. d, Sir Isaac Newton builds first reflecting telescope. e, Voltaire born. f, Ivan V and Peter become joint rulers of Russia. g, First Qing Dynasty Emperor, Shun Zhi, dies. h, Christiaan Huygens discovers rings of Saturn. i, Robert Hooke identifies cells. j, Wang Shih-min paints "Verdant Peaks." k, René Descartes dies. l, Canal du Midi completed. m, Glorious Revolution. n, King William's War ends. o, Gian Domenico Cassini observes polar caps on Mars. p, Newton formulates law of gravitation (60x40mm). q, Ole Roemer discovers that light moves at a finite speed.

**2000, May 1     Perf. 12½**
2932 A450 50c Sheet of 17, #a.-
      q., + label                  8.75 8.75

Orchids — A451

Designs: 75c, Brassolaeliocattleya. 90c, Maxilbera. $1, Isochilius. $2, Oncidium.
No. 2937, each $1.50: a, Laeliocattleya. b, Sophrocattleya (red). c, Epidendrum. d, Cattleya. e, Ionopsis. f, Brassoepidendrum.
No. 2938, each $1.50: a, Lycaste. b, Cochleanthes. c, Brassocattleya. d, Brassolaeliacattleya, diff. e, Iwanagaara. f, Sophrocattleya (orange).
Each $6: No. 2939, Vanilla. No. 2940, Brassocattleya, diff.

**2000, May 15     Litho.     Perf. 14**
2933-2936 A451 Set of 4            5.00 5.00
**Sheets of 6, #a.-f.**
2937-2938 A451 Set of 2           19.00 19.00
**Souvenir Sheets**
2939-2940 A451 Set of 2           12.50 12.50

100th Test Match at Lord's Ground — A452

90c, Junior Murray. $5, Rawl Lewis. $6, Lord's Ground, horiz.

**2000, May 15     Litho.     Perf. 14**
2941-2942 A452 Set of 2            4.75 4.75
**Souvenir Sheet**
2943 A452 $6 multi                 5.25 5.25

Prince William, 18th Birthday A453

No. 2944: a, In suit. b, In suit, with person in tan suit. c, In suit, waving. d, In ski jacket. $6, In suit, diff.

**2000, May 15     Perf. 14**
2944 A453 $1.50 Sheet of 4,
      #a-d                          4.50 4.50
**Souvenir Sheet**
**Perf. 13¾**
2945 A453 $6 multi                 4.50 4.50
No. 2944 contains four 28x42mm stamps.

First Zeppelin Flight, Cent. A454

No. 2946 — Ferdinand von Zeppelin and: a, LZ-130. b, LZ-2. c, LZ-127. $6, LZ-129.

**2000, May 15     Perf. 14**
2946 A454 $3 Sheet of 3, #a-c      8.00 8.00
**Souvenir Sheet**
2947 A454 $6 multi                 5.25 5.25
No. 2946 contains three 42x28mm stamps.

Berlin Film Festival, 50th Anniv. A455

No. 2948: a, Alphaville. b, Rod Steiger. c, Os Fuzis. d, Jean-Pierre Leaud. e, Cul-de-sac. f, Ikiru.
$6, Hsi Yen.

**2000, May 15**
2948 A455 $1.50 Sheet of 6, #a-f   6.75 6.75
**Souvenir Sheet**
2949 A455 $6 multi                 4.50 4.50

Apollo-Soyuz Mission, 25th Anniv. — A456

No. 2950, vert.: a, Soyuz launch vehicle. b, Soyuz 19. c, Apollo 18 and Soyuz 19 docked. $6, Valeri Kubasov and Thomas Stafford.

**2000, May 15**
2950 A456 $3 Sheet of 3, #a-c      7.75 7.75
**Souvenir Sheet**
2951 A456 $6 multi                 5.75 5.75

**Souvenir Sheets**

2000 Summer Olympics, Sydney — A457

No. 2952: a, Archibald Hahn. b, Show jumping. c, Sports Palace, Rome, and Italian flag. d, Ancient Greek chariot racing.

**2000, May 15**
2952 A457 $2 Sheet of 4, #a-d    7.00 7.00

Public Railways, 175th Anniv. — A458

No. 2953: a, Locomotion No. 1, George Stephenson. b, John Bull.

**2000, May 15**
2953 A458 $3 Sheet of 2, #a-b    5.75 5.75

Johann Sebastian Bach (1685-1750) — A459

**2000, May 15**
2954 A459 $6 multi    4.50 4.50

Souvenir Sheet

Albert Einstein (1879-1955) — A460

**2000, May 15    Litho.    Perf. 14¼**
2955 A460 $6 multi    4.50 4.50

Space A461

No. 2956: a, Luna 4. b, Clementine. c, Luna 12. d, Luna 16. e, Apollo 11 Lunar module. f, Ranger 7.
$6, Apollo command and service modules.

**2000, May 15    Litho.    Perf. 14**
2956 A461 $1.50 Sheet of 6, #a-f 7.75 7.75

Souvenir Sheet
2957 A461    $6 multi    5.25 5.25

World Stamp Expo 2000, Anaheim

Marine Life — A462

Designs: 45c, Porkfish. 75c, Short bigeye. 90c, Red snapper. $1, Creole wrasse. $2, Indigo hamlet. $3, Blue tang.
No. 2964: a, Juvenile French angelfish. b, Beaugregory. c, Queen angelfish. d, Sergeant major. e, Bank butterflyfish. f, Spanish hogfish. g, Porkfish. h, Banded butterflyfish. i, Longsnout seahorse.
No. 2965: a, Hawksbill turtle. b, Foureye butterflyfish. c, Porcupinefish. d, Yellowtail damselfish. e, Adult French angelfish. f, Yellow goatfish. g, Blue-striped grunt. h, Spanish grunt. i, Queen triggerfish.
No. 2966, Queen angelfish. No. 2967, Blue tang.

**2000, Aug. 8**
2958-2963 A462    Set of 5    7.00 7.00

Sheets of 9, #a-i
2964-2965 A462 $1 Set of 2    14.50 14.50

Souvenir Sheets
2966-2967 A462 $6 Set of 2    9.00 9.00

Grenada National Stadium — A463

Designs: $2, Aerial view.
No. 2969: a, Cricket team photo. b, Cricketers playing.

**2000, Aug. 8**
2968 A463 $2 multi    1.50 1.50

Souvenir Sheet
2969 A463 $1 Sheet of 2, #a-b    1.50 1.50

European Soccer Championships — A464

No. 2970, horiz. — Belgium: a, Vanderhaege. b, Belgian team. c, Ronny Gaspercic. d, Lorenzo Staelens. e, Stadium Koning Boudewijn. f, Strupar and Mpenza.
No. 2971, horiz. — Spain: a, Sergi Barjuan. b, Spanish team. c, Luis Enrique. d, Hierro. e, De Kuip Stadium. f, Raul Gonzales.
No. 2972, horiz. — Yugoslavia: a, Dejan Savicevic. b, Yugoslavian team. c, Predrag Migatovic. d, Savo Milosevic. e, Jan Breydel Stadium. f, Darko Kovacevic.
No. 2973, Belgian coach Robert Waseige. No. 2974, Spanish coach José Antonio Camacho. No. 2975, Yugoslavian coach Vujadin Boskov.
Illustration reduced.

**2000, Aug. 8    Perf. 13¾**
Sheets of 6, #a-f
2970-2972 A464 $1.50 Set of
3    20.00 20.00

Souvenir Sheets
2973-2975 A464 $6 Set of 3    13.50 13.50

Ferrari Automobiles A465

20c, 1953 500 Mondial. 45c, 1948 166 Inter. 75c, 1953 340 MM. 90c, 1964 500 Superfast. $1, 1948 166 MM. $1.50, 1952 250 S. $2, 1957 250 California. $3, 1966 365 California.

**2000, Sept. 5    Perf. 14**
2976-2983 A465    Set of 8    8.00 8.00

Antique Automobiles A466

45c, 1921 Marmon Model 34. 75c, 1917 Buick D44. 90c, 1918 Hudson Runabout Landau. $1, 1915 Chevrolet Royal Mail. $2, 1925 Kissel Speedster. $3, 1915 Ford Model T.
No. 2990: a, 1925 Cadillac V63. b, 1939 Plymouth. c, 1934 Franklin Club Sedan. d,

1933 Fiat Ardita. e, 1929 Essex Speedabout. f, 1932 Stutz Bearcat.
No. 2991: a, 1929 Rolls Royce. b, 1932 Graham Convertible. c, 1937 Mercedes-Benz 540K. d, 1948 Jaguar MkV. e, 1939 Lagonda Drophead Coupe. f, 1930 Alfa Romeo Gran Sport.
No. 2992, 1915 Dodge Tourer. No. 2993, 1924 Chrysler.

**2000, Sept. 5**
2984-2989 A466    Set of 6    6.00 6.00

Sheets of 6, #a-f
2990-2991 A466 $1.50 Set of
2    13.50 13.50

Souvenir Sheets
2992-2993 A466 $6 Set of 2    9.00 9.00

Popes A467

No. 2994: a, Stephen VIII, 939-42. b, Theodore I, 642-49. c, Theodore II, 897. d, Valentine, 827. e, Vitalian, 657-72. f, Zacharias, 741-52.
$6, Sylvester II, 999-1003.

**2000, Sept. 5    Perf. 13¾**
2994 A467 $1.50 Sheet of 6, #a-f 6.75 6.75

Souvenir Sheet
2995 A467    $6 multi    4.50 4.50

Monarchs — A468

No. 2996: a, George III of Great Britain, 1760-1820. b, George IV of Great Britain, 1820-30. c, Duchess Charlotte of Luxembourg, 1964-present. d, Grand Duke Jean of Luxembourg, 1964-present.
$6, Charles VIII of France, 1483-98.

**2000, Sept. 5    Perf. 13¾**
2996 A468 $1.50 Sheet of 4,
#a-d    4.50 4.50

Souvenir Sheet
2997 A468    $6 multi    4.50 4.50

Shirley Temple in "Heidi" A469

No. 2998, horiz.: a, With woman holding candle. b, With girl in green dress c, On stairs. d, With Christmas gift.
No. 2999, horiz.: a, Walking with woman. b, Touching bearded man. c, Holding goat. d, With doves. e, With bearded man. f, Seated with woman.

**2000, Oct. 6    Litho.    Perf. 13¾**
2998 A469 $1.50 Sheet of 4,
#a-d    4.50 4.50
2999 A469 $1.50 Sheet of 6,
#a-f    6.75 6.75

Souvenir Sheet
3000 A469    $6 Seated near
tree    4.50 4.50

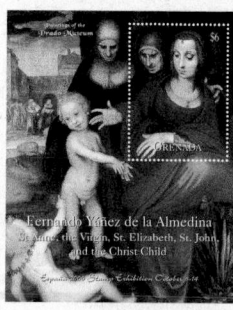

Paintings from the Prado A470

No. 3001: a, Monk and king from The Virgin of the Catholic Monarchs, by an Anonymous Castilian. b, Madonna and child from The Virgin of the Catholic Monarchs. c, Monk and queen from The Virgin of the Catholic Monarchs. d, The Flagellation, by Alexo Fernandez. e, The Virgin and Souls in Purgatory, by Pedro Machuca. f, The Holy Trinity, by El Greco.
No. 3002: a, Playing at Giants, by El Greco. b, The Holy Family Under the Oak Tree, by Raphael. c, Don Gaspar Melchior de Jovellanos, by Francisco de Goya. d, Man with arm on hip from Joseph in the Pharaoh's Palace, by Jacopo Amiconi. e, Man and woman from Joseph in the Pharaoh's Palace. f, Man on bended knee from Joseph in the Pharaoh's Palace.
No. 3003: a, The Savior Blessing, by Francisco de Zurbarán. b, St. John the Baptist, by Francisco Solimena. c, Noli Me Tangere, by Correggio. d, St. Casilda, by Zurbarán. e, Nicolás Omazur by Bartolomé Esteban Murillo. f, Juan Martínez Montañés, by Diego Velázquez.
No. 3004, St. Anne, the Virgin, St. Elizabeth, St. John and the Christ child, by Fernando Yáñez de la Almedina. No. 3005, The Virgin of the Catholic Monarchs. No. 3006, Joseph in the Pharaoh's Palace, horiz.
Illustration reduced.

**2000, Oct. 19    Perf. 12x12¼, 12¼x12**
Sheets of 6, #a-f
3001-3003 A470 $1.50 Set of
3    20.00 20.00

Souvenir Sheets
3004-3006 A470 $6 Set of 3    13.50 13.50

Espana 2000 Intl. Philatelic Exhibition.

Battle of Britain, 60th Anniv. A471

No. 3007: a, Messerschmitt BF 109E and bomb blast. b, Supermarine Spitfire MK XI. c, V1 flying bomb. d, U-boat. e, Ack-ack gun unit. f, Bedford field ambulance.
No. 3008: a, Messerschmitt BF 109E. b, German paratrooper. c, Hawker Hurricane HK 1. d, RAF airfield. e, Heinkel HE 111 H. f, Nose of Supermarine Spitfire MK XI.
No. 3009, Line of Hawker Hurricanes. No. 3010, Supermarine Spitfire MK XI.

**2000, Oct. 30    Perf. 14**
Sheets of 6, #a-f
3007-3008 A471 $1.50 Set of
2    16.00 16.00

Souvenir Sheets
3009-3010 A471 $6 Set of 2    12.00 12.00

A472

Birds: 25c, Purple gallinule. 40c, Limpkin. 50c, Black-necked stilt. 60c, Painted bunting. 75c, Yellow-breasted warbler. $1, Blackburnian warbler. $1.25, Blue grosbeak. $1.50, Black-and-white warbler. $1.60, Blue whistling thrush. $3, Common yellowthroat. $4, Indigo bunting. $5, Gray catbird. $10, Bananaquit. $20, Blue-gray gnatcatcher.

**2000, Oct. 30    Perf. 14¾x14**
3011-3024 A472    Set of 14    37.50 37.50

See No. 3540.

A473

Dogs: $2, Shetland sheepdog. $3, Central Asian sheepdog.
No. 3027, horiz.: a, Labrador retriever. b, Standard poodle. c, Boxer. d, Rough-coated Jack Russell terrier. e, Tibetan terrier. f, Welsh corgi.
$6, Irish red and white setter, horiz.

| 2000, June 23 | | Litho. | Perf. 14 | |
|---|---|---|---|---|
| 3025-3026 | A473 | Set of 2 | 3.75 | 3.75 |
| 3027 | A473 | $1.50 Sheet of 6, #a-f | 6.75 | 6.75 |

**Souvenir Sheet**

| 3028 | A473 | $6 multi | 4.50 | 4.50 |
|---|---|---|---|---|

Butterflies
A474

45c, Marpesia eleuchea bahamaensis. 75c, Pterourus palamedes. 90c, Dryas julia framptoni. $1, Hypna clytemnestra iphegenia.
No. 3033, $1.50: a, Danaus plexippus. b, Anartia amathea. c, Colobura dirce. d, Parides gundiachianus. e, Spiroeta stelenes. f, Hammadryas feronia.
No. 3034, $1.50: a, Merchantis isthmia. b, Colias eurytheme. c, Papilio troilus d, Junonia coenia. e, Doxocopa laure. f, Pierella hyalinus.
No. 3035, $6, Agraulis vanilae insularis. No. 3036, $6, Danaus gilippus.

**2000, June 26**

| 3029-3032 | A474 | Set of 4 | 3.00 | 3.00 |
|---|---|---|---|---|

**Sheets of 6, #a-f**

| 3033-3034 | A474 | Set of 2 | 17.00 | 17.00 |
|---|---|---|---|---|

**Souvenir Sheets**

| 3035-3036 | A474 | Set of 2 | 10.00 | 10.00 |
|---|---|---|---|---|

A475

Trains
A476

No. 3037, $1.50: a, Diesel-electric locomotive, Royal State Railway of Thailand. b, Diesel-electric locomotive, Danish Railways. c, French-built Turbo train. d, Diesel, Spanish Railways. e, Virgen del Rosario, Spanish Railways. f, 22 Class Co-Co Diesel-electric locomotive, Malayan Railways.
No. 3038, $1.50: a, Class 87 electric locomotive, British Railways. b, Electric-Diesel locomotive, Iraqi Railway. c, Electric locomotive, Austrian Railways. d, 1.4 meter gauge locomotive, South Australia Railways. e, Automated electric locomotive, Black Mesa & Lake Powell Railroad. f, Diesel-electric, Yugoslav Railways.
No. 3039, $1.50: a, Class 10 4-6-2, German Federal Railway. b, Class E.10 Bo-Bo Electric locomotive, German Federal Railways. c, Class 23 2-6-2, German Federal Railway. d, 2-8-4 locomotive, German Federal Railway. e, Rebuilt 01 Class Pacific, East German State Railway. f, High speed Diesel railcar, Deutschen Reichsbahn.
No. 3040, $1.50: a, Borsig Standard 2-2-2. b, Austerity 2-10-0 Series 52, German Federal Railway. c, Adler, facing right, Nuremburg-Furth Railway. d, Bardenia, Baden State Railways. e, Drache. f, Adler, facing left.
No. 3041, $6, Diesel T.E.E. Parsifal. No. 3042, $6, High speed electric, Netherlands Railway. No. 3043, $6, Electric train, Swiss

Railways. No. 3044, $6, Silver Fern, New Zealand Railways. No. 3045, $6, Borsig locomotive, Berlin and Anhalt Railway. No. 3046, $6, Krauss-Maffei V.200 Diesel-hydraulic locomotive, German Federal Railway.
Illustrations reduced.

**2000, Sept. 5          Sheets of 6, #a-f**

| 3037-3038 | A475 | Set of 2 | 15.00 | 15.00 |
|---|---|---|---|---|
| 3039-3040 | A476 | Set of 2 | 15.00 | 15.00 |

**Souvenir Sheets**

| 3041-3044 | A475 | Set of 4 | 21.00 | 21.00 |
|---|---|---|---|---|
| 3045-3046 | A476 | Set of 2 | 11.00 | 11.00 |

Descriptions of trains are in margins on Nos. 3039-3940, 3045-3046.

Nursery Rhymes
A477

No. 3047, Little Bo Peep, $1.50, vert.: a, Crook, tree, dove. b, Little Bo Peep. c, Sheep. d, Geese. e, Goose, Little Bo Peep's leg. f, Dog.
No. 3048, The Old Woman Who Lived in a Shoe, $1.50, vert.: a, Child, roof. b, Child with hat, rainbow. c, Cow, sun, rainbow. d, Child at door. e, Old woman, child. f, Child on shoe.
No. 3049, Little Boy Blue, $1.50, vert.: a, Sheep, house. b, Sun. c, Cow. d, Geese, path. e, Dog, Little Boy Blue's leg. f, Little Boy Blue.
No. 3050, The Cat and the Fiddle, $1.50, vert. a, Bird, house. b, Cow jumping over moon. c, Spoon. d, Dog, house. e, Cat and fiddle. f, Dish.
No. 3051, $6, Little Bo Peep. No. 3052, $6, The Old Woman Who Lived in a Shoe. No. 3053, $6, Little Boy Blue. No. 3054, Cow jumping over the moon.
Illustration reduced.

**2000, Sept. 9          Perf. 13¾x13¼**
**Sheets of 6, #a-f**

| 3047-3050 | A477 | Set of 4 | 27.50 | 27.50 |
|---|---|---|---|---|

**Souvenir Sheets**
**Perf. 13¼x13¾**

| 3051-3054 | A477 | Set of 4 | 18.00 | 18.00 |
|---|---|---|---|---|

**Flower Photomosaic Type of 1999**
**Queen Mother**

Various flowers making up photomosaic.

**2000, Nov. 20          Perf. 13¾**

| 3055 | A445 | $1 Sheet of 8, #a-h | 6.00 | 6.00 |
|---|---|---|---|---|

Cats — A478

75c, Maine Coon cat. 90c, Selkirk Rex.
No. 3058, horiz.: a, Spotted tabby British shorthair. b, Burmilla. c, British blue shorthair. d, Siamese. e, Japanese bobtail. f, Oriental shorthair.

| 2000, June 23 | | Litho. | Perf. 14 | |
|---|---|---|---|---|
| 3056-3057 | A478 | Set of 2 | 1.75 | 1.75 |
| 3058 | A478 | $1.50 Sheet of 6, #a-f | 8.00 | 8.00 |

**Souvenir Sheet**

| 3059 | A478 | $6 Scottish Fold | 5.75 | 5.75 |
|---|---|---|---|---|

Queen Mother, 100th Birthday — A479

**2000, Nov. 20**

| 3060 | A479 | $1.50 multi | 1.10 | 1.10 |
|---|---|---|---|---|

Printed in sheets of 6.

Christmas — A480

Designs: 15c, 50c, No. 3065b, Angel looking left. 25c, $5, No. 3065a, Angel looking right.

**2000, Dec. 4**

| 3061-3064 | A480 | Set of 4 | 4.50 | 4.50 |
|---|---|---|---|---|
| 3065 | A480 | $2 Sheet, 2 ea #a-b | 6.00 | 6.00 |

**Souvenir Sheet**

| 3066 | A480 | $6 Baby Jesus | 4.50 | 4.50 |
|---|---|---|---|---|

Souvenir Sheets

Betty Boop
A481

Designs: No. 3067, $6, Wearing lei. No. 3068, $6, Holding fishing pole and fish. No. 3069, $6, Wearing polka dot hat. No. 3070, $6, Holding castanets. No. 3071, $6, At Japanese tea ceremony. No. 3072, $6, Wearing pink hat. No. 3073, $6, In mountains, wearing flowered hat. No. 3074, $6, Wearing beret. No. 3075, $6, As Statue of Liberty. No. 3076, $6, In Hollywood. No. 3077, $6, On horse. No. 3078, $6, On camel's back.

| 2000, Oct. 11 | | Litho. | Perf. 13¾ | |
|---|---|---|---|---|
| 3067-3078 | A481 | Set of 12 | 60.00 | 60.00 |

Souvenir Sheet

New Year 2001 (Year of the Snake)
A482

No. 3079: a, Blue green denomination. b, Red denomination. c, Purple denomination.

| 2001, Jan. 2 | | | Perf. 12½x13 | |
|---|---|---|---|---|
| 3079 | A482 | $2 Sheet of 3, #a-c | 4.50 | 4.50 |

Rijksmuseum, Amsterdam, Bicent. — A483

No. 3080, $1.50: a, William I, Prince of Orange, by Adriaen Thomasz Key. b, Rutger Jan Schimmelpennick and Family, by Pierre Paul Prud'hon. c, Johan Rudolf Thorbecke, by Johan Heinrich Neuman. d, St. Sebastian, by Joachim Wtewael. e, St. Sebastian, by Hendrick ter Brugghen. f, Portrait of a Man With a Ring, by Werner Van Den Valckert.
No. 3081, $1.50: a, The Syndics of the Amsterdam Goldsmith's Guild, by Thomas de Keyser. b, Portrait of a Gentleman, by de Keyser. c, Portrait of Eva Wtewael, by Wtewael. d, The Cattle Ferry, by Esaias van de Velde. e, Landscape With the Parable of the Tares Among the Wheat, by Abraham

Bloemaert. f, Princess Henrietta Marie Stuart, by Bartholomeus van der Helst.
No. 3082, $1.50: a, The Merry Fiddler, by Gerard van Honthorst. b, The Merry Drinker, by Frans Hals. c, Granida and Daifilo, by van Honthorst. d, Vertumnus and Pomona, by Paulus Moreelse. e, Flutist from The Concert, by ter Brugghen. f, A Young Student at His Desk: Melancholy, by Pieter Codde.
No. 3083, $1.50: a, The Haarlem Painter Abraham Casteleyn and His Wife Margarieta van Bancken, by Jan de Bray. b, Two figures from The Concert. c, The Procuress, by Dirck van Baburen. d, Woman Seated at a Virginal, by Johannes Vermeer. e, Dignified Couples Courting, by Willem Buytewech. f, The Young Flute Player, by Judith Leyster.
No. 3084, $6, Interior of the Portuguese Synagogue in Amsterdam, by Emanuel de Witte. No. 3085, $6, The Denial of St. Peter, by Rembrandt, horiz. No. 3086, $6, Winter Landscape With Skaters, by Hendrick Avercamp, horiz. No. 3087, $6, The Raampoortje, by Wouter Johannes van Troostwijk, horiz.

**2001, Jan. 15          Perf. 13¾**
**Sheets of 6, #a-f**

| 3080-3083 | A483 | Set of 4 | 27.50 | 27.50 |
|---|---|---|---|---|

**Souvenir Sheets**

| 3084-3087 | A483 | Set of 4 | 18.00 | 18.00 |
|---|---|---|---|---|

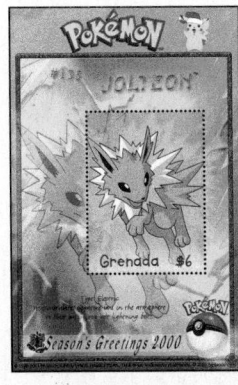

Pokémon
A484

No. 3088: a, Rattata. b, Sandshrew. c, Wartortle. d, Primeape. e, Golduck. f, Persian.

**2001, Feb. 1**

| 3088 | A484 | $1.50 Sheet of 6, #a-f | 6.75 | 6.75 |
|---|---|---|---|---|

**Souvenir Sheet**

| 3089 | A484 | $6 Jolteon | 4.50 | 4.50 |
|---|---|---|---|---|

Waterfowl — A485

No. 3090, $1.25: a, African pygmy goose. b, Silver teal. c, Marbled teal. d, Garganey. e, Wandering whistling duck. f, Northern shoveler.
No. 3091, $1.25: a, Female flightless steamer duck. b, Radjah. c, Cape teal. d, Hartlaub's duck. e, Ruddy shelduck. f, White-cheeked pintail.
No. 3092, $1.25, vert.: a, Fulvous whistling duck. b, African black duck. c, Madagascar white-eye. d, Female pygmy goose. e, Female wood duck. f, Male wood duck.
No. 3093, $6, Flightless steamer duck. No. 3094, $6, Flying steamer duck. No. 3095, $6, Australian shelduck, vert.

**Perf. 13¼x13¾, 13¾x13¼**
**2001, Mar. 5          Litho.**
**Sheets of 6, #a-f**

| 3090-3092 | A485 | Set of 3 | 17.00 | 17.00 |
|---|---|---|---|---|

**Souvenir Sheets**

| 3093-3095 | A485 | Set of 3 | 13.50 | 13.50 |
|---|---|---|---|---|

Hong Kong 2001 Stamp Exhibition.

Cricket
Players — A486

No. 3096: Various photos of Sir Donald Bradman swinging bat.
No. 3097, Various photos of Shane Warne bowling.
No. 3098, Various photos of Sir Jack Hobbs.
No. 3099, Various photos of Sir Vivian Richards.
No. 3100, Various photos of Sir Garfield Sobers.
No. 3101, oval vignettes: a, Bradman. b, Sobers. c, Hobbs. d, Warne. e, Richards.

| | | **2001, May 15** | | **Perf. 14** | |
|---|---|---|---|---|---|
| 3096 | | Sheet of 8, #a-h | | 6.00 | 6.00 |
| | a.-h. | A486 $1 Any single | | .75 | .75 |
| 3097 | | Sheet of 8, #a-h | | 6.00 | 6.00 |
| | a.-h. | A486 $1 Any single | | .75 | .75 |
| 3098 | | Sheet of 4, #a-d | | 6.00 | 6.00 |
| | a.-d. | A486 $2 Any single | | 1.50 | 1.50 |
| 3099 | | Sheet of 4, #a-d | | 6.00 | 6.00 |
| | a.-d. | A486 $2 Any single | | 1.50 | 1.50 |
| 3100 | | Sheet of 4, #a-d | | 6.00 | 6.00 |
| | a.-d. | A486 $2 Any single | | 1.50 | 1.50 |
| 3101 | | Sheet of 5, #a-e | | 7.50 | 7.50 |
| | a.-e. | A486 $2 Any single | | 1.50 | 1.50 |
| | | Nos. 3096-3101 (6) | | 37.50 | 37.50 |

A487

Phila
Nippon
'01,
Japan
A488

Art: 75c, Scenes of Daily Life in Edo, by Miyagawa Choshun. 90c, Twelve Famous Places in Japan, by Kano Isenin Naganobu. $1, After the Rain, by Kawai Gyokudo. $1.25, Ryogoku Bridge Crowded With People, by Kano Kyuei. No. 3106, $2, A Courtesan of Fukagawa, by Katsukawa Shunei. $3, Rite of Bear Killing, by unknown artist.
No. 3108 — Details from the Lotus Sutra, $2, vert.: a, Figure in white at left. b, Figure with flag at lower right. c, Water in center. d, White pagoda at top right.
No. 3109 — Details from the Tale of Genji, $2 (size: 84x28mm): a, Yugao Chapter. b, Suetsumuhana Chapter. c, Wakamurasaki Chapter. d, Momiji-no-ga Chapter.
No. 3110, $6, Pomegranates and a Small Bird, by Onishi Keisai. No. 3111, $6, Bodhisattva from the Lotus Sutra, vert.

| | | **2001, May 1** | **Litho.** | **Perf. 14** | |
|---|---|---|---|---|---|
| 3102-3107 | A487 | Set of 6 | | 6.75 | 6.75 |
| | | **Sheets of 4, #a-d** | | | |
| 3108-3109 | A488 | Set of 2 | | 12.00 | 12.00 |
| | | **Souvenir Sheets** | | | |
| 3110-3111 | A488 | Set of 2 | | 9.00 | 9.00 |

Marlene
Dietrich
A489

No. 3112: a, With cigarette. b, Behind microphone. c, Seated, showing legs. d, Seated.

| | | **2001, May 15** | | **Perf. 13¾** | |
|---|---|---|---|---|---|
| 3112 | A489 | $2 Sheet of 4, #a-d | | 6.00 | 6.00 |

Queen Victoria (1819-1901) — A490

No. 3113: a, In white, as young girl. b, Wearing crown as young woman. c, Wearing crown as old woman.
$6, On throne.

| | | **2001, May 15** | | **Perf. 14** | |
|---|---|---|---|---|---|
| 3113 | A490 | $3 Sheet of 3, #a-c | | 6.75 | 6.75 |
| | | **Souvenir Sheet** | | | |
| 3114 | A490 | $6 multi | | 4.50 | 4.50 |

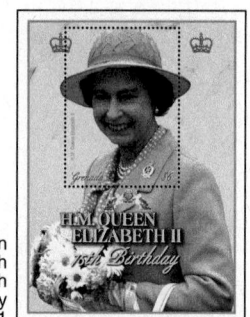

Queen
Elizabeth
II, 75th
Birthday
A491

No. 3115: a, Straw hat. b, Red hat. c, Flowered hat. d, Blue hat.
$6, Blue hat with brim.

| | | **2001, May 15** | | **Perf. 14** | |
|---|---|---|---|---|---|
| 3115 | A491 | $2 Sheet of 4, #a-d | | 6.00 | 6.00 |
| | | **Souvenir Sheet** | | | |
| | | **Perf. 13¾** | | | |
| 3116 | A491 | $6 multi | | 4.50 | 4.50 |

No. 3116 contains one 38x51mm stamp.

UN Women's Human
Rights
Campaign — A492

Designs: 90c, Woman, bird, torch. $1, Woman.

| | | **2001, May 15** | **Litho.** | **Perf. 14** | |
|---|---|---|---|---|---|
| 3117-3118 | A492 | Set of 2 | | 1.40 | 1.40 |

Mao Zedong (1893-1976) — A493

No. 3119 — background colors: a, Deep purple. b, Pinkish gray. c, Mottled red violet.
$6, Mao with cap.

| | | **2001, May 15** | | **Perf. 13¾** | |
|---|---|---|---|---|---|
| 3119 | A493 | $2 Sheet of 3, #a-c | | 4.50 | 4.50 |
| | | **Souvenir Sheet** | | | |
| 3120 | A493 | $3 multi | | 2.25 | 2.25 |

Giuseppe Verdi (1813-1910), Opera
Composer — A494

No. 3121: a, Actor with crown. b, Score from Ernani. c, Verdi. d, La Scala Theater, Milan. $6, Verdi with hat.

| | | **2001, May 15** | | **Perf. 14** | |
|---|---|---|---|---|---|
| 3121 | A494 | $2 Sheet of 4, #a-d | | 6.00 | 6.00 |
| | | **Souvenir Sheet** | | | |
| 3122 | A494 | $6 multi | | 4.50 | 4.50 |

Toulouse-Lautrec Paintings — A495

No. 3123: a, Alone. b, Two Half-naked Women. c, The Toilette. d, Justine Dieuhl. $6, Mademoiselle Dihau at the Piano.

| | | **2001, May 15** | | **Perf. 13¾** | |
|---|---|---|---|---|---|
| 3123 | A495 | $2 Sheet of 4, #a-d | | 6.00 | 6.00 |
| | | **Souvenir Sheet** | | | |
| 3124 | A495 | $6 multi | | 4.50 | 4.50 |

A496

Ships
A497

Designs: 45c, Phoenician trading ship. 75c, Portuguese caravel. 90c, Marblehead schooner. No. 3128, $1, Mala pansi. $1.50, US corvette. $2, Racing schooner.
No. 3131, $1: a, English carrack. b, Mediterranean carrack. c, Spanish galleon. d, Elizabeth Grumster. e, British East Indiaman. f, Clipper ship. g, British gunship. h, British flagship. i, English hoy.
No. 3132, $1: a, English cog. b, Roman merchantman. c, Greek war galley. d, Greek merchantman. e, Norse Oseberg ship. f, Egyptian sailboat. g, Egyptian oared ship. h, 16th cent. galleass. i, Norman sailing ship.
No. 3133, $1: a, Gloucester fishing schooner. b, Racing sloop. c, Chinese junk. d, Sambuk. e, Baltimore clipper schooner. f, Schooner yacht. g, US Clipper ship. h, US frigate. i Steam naval packet.
No. 3134, $6, Gulf Streamer. No. 3135, $6, Suhaili.

| | | **2001, June 18** | | **Perf. 14** | |
|---|---|---|---|---|---|
| 3125-3130 | A496 | Set of 6 | | 5.00 | 5.00 |
| | | **Sheets of 9, #a-i** | | | |
| 3131-3133 | A496 | Set of 3 | | 21.00 | 21.00 |
| | | **Miniature Sheets** | | | |
| 3134-3135 | A497 | Set of 2 | | 9.00 | 9.00 |

Belgica 2001 Intl. Stamp Exhibition, Brussels (Nos. 3131-3133).

A498

Flowers — A499

Designs: 25c, Brassavola nodosa. No. 3137, $1, Allamanda cathartica. No. 3138, $2, Aspasia epidendroides. $3, Oncidium splendidum.
35c, Flor de San Miguel. 75c, Red frangipani. No. 3142, $1, Paper flower. No. 3143, $2, Flor de muerto.
No. 3144, $1.50: a, Candlebush. b, Flamingo flower. c, Bush morning glory. d, Laelia anceps. e, Galeandra baueri. f, Chinese hibiscus.
No. 3145, $1.50: a, Red ginger. b, Bird of paradise. c, Psychlis atropurpurea. d, Cattleya velutina. e, Caularthron bicornutum. f, Cattleya warneri.
No. 3146, $1.50, vert.: a, Mandeville. b, Tithonia rotundifolia. c, June rose. d, Columnea argentea. e, Chameleon plant. f, Protlandia albiflora.
No. 3147, $1.50, vert.: a, Wild chestnut. b, Jatropha integerrima. c, Fern tree. d, Geiger tree. e, Golden trumpet. f, Saman.
No. 3148, $6, Ipomoea learii, horiz. No. 3149, $6, Anthurium scherzerianum, horiz.
No. 3150, $6, Ladies eardrops. No. 3151, $6, Heliconia psittacorum, vert.

| | | **2001** | | | |
|---|---|---|---|---|---|
| 3136-3139 | A498 | Set of 4 | | 6.25 | 6.25 |
| 3140-3143 | A499 | Set of 4 | | 4.75 | 4.75 |
| | | **Sheets of 6, #a-f** | | | |
| 3144-3145 | A498 | Set of 2 | | 15.00 | 15.00 |
| 3146-3147 | A499 | Set of 2 | | 15.00 | 15.00 |
| | | **Souvenir Sheets** | | | |
| 3148-3149 | A498 | Set of 2 | | 11.00 | 11.00 |
| 3150-3151 | A499 | Set of 2 | | 11.00 | 11.00 |

Kane
A500

No. 3152 — Kane: a, In air, above ring ropes. b, On one knee. c, In air. d, With red background. e, With gradiated gray and yellow background. f, Holding up opponent with both hands. g, With spotlight background. h, Holding up shirtless opponent. i, Holding up opponent with one hand.
No. 3153, $5, With red background, diff. No. 3154, $5, With opponent.

| | | **2001** | | **Perf. 13¾** | |
|---|---|---|---|---|---|
| 3152 | A500 | $1 Sheet of 9, #a-i | | 6.75 | 6.75 |
| | | **Souvenir Sheets** | | | |
| 3153-3154 | A500 | Set of 2 | | 7.50 | 7.50 |

The Three Stooges A501

No. 3155, $1: a, Larry, Moe, two cowboys. b, Moe and Shemp with hats, Larry. c, Shemp and Larry in drag, Moe with mustache. d, Moe with gun, Larry, Shemp, woman. e, Larry, Moe, Shemp with certificate. f, Shemp, Moe. g, Larry, picture. h, Moe, picture. i, Shemp.
No. 3156, $1: a, Larry, Curly, Moe with tool. b, Joe DeRita eating hay, horse, Larry, Moe. c, Shemp, Larry with flowers, Moe. d, Moe, Shemp, Larry, reading paper. e, Larry, Moe, Shemp with pots. f, Moe, Shemp, Larry with money. g, Shemp with knight. h, Joe DeRita, horse, Larry, Moe. i, Larry with knight.
No. 3157, $5, Larry, Moe, Shemp, woman from movie poster. No. 3158, $5, Shemp pulling Moe's arm. No. 3159, $5, Joe DeRita and Larry. No. 3160, $5, Larry and Joe DeRita, jet engine. No. 3161, $5, Moe, Larry holding woman's hand. No. 3162, $5, Larry, Moe listening to jet engine, horiz. No. 3163, $5, Larry, Moe, Shemp and cowboy, horiz. No. 3164, $5, Shemp behind bar, cowboys fighting Larry and Moe, horiz. No. 3165, $5, Curly, Moe, Larry and propeller, horiz. No. 3166, $5, Moe, Larry, woman with drink, horiz. No. 3167, $6, Moe, Larry with knight, horiz. No. 3168, $6, Curly in wringer, Moe, horiz.

| 2001 | | Sheets of 9, #a-i | | |
|---|---|---|---|---|
| 3155-3156 | A501 | Set of 2 | 13.50 | 13.50 |
| **Souvenir Sheets** | | | | |
| 3157-3168 | A501 | Set of 12 | 47.50 | 47.50 |

Lighthouses — A502

Designs: 25c, Montauk Point, NY. 50c, Alcatraz, CA. $1, Barnegat, NJ. $2, St. Augustine, FL.
No. 3173, $1.50: a, Admiralty Head, WA. b, Hooper's Strait, MD. c, Hunting Island, SC. d, Key West Lighthouse Museum, FL. e, Old Point Loma, CA. f, Old Mackinac Point, MI.
No. 3174, $1.50: a, Point Amour, Canada. b, Inubo-Saki, Japan. c, Belle-Ile. France. d, Faerder, Norway. e, Cape Agulhas, South Africa. f, Minicoy, India.
No. 3175, $1.50: a, Keri, Estonia. b, Anholt, Denmark. c, Porer, Croatia. d, Laotieshan, China. e, Sapientza Methoni, Greece. f, Arkona, Germany.
No. 3176, $6, Boston, MA. No. 3177, $6, Pellworm, Germany. No. 3178, $6, Kvitsoy, Norway. No. 3179, Mahota Pagoda, China.

| 2001, Aug. 27 | | Litho. | Perf. 14 | |
|---|---|---|---|---|
| 3169-3172 | A502 | Set of 4 | 2.75 | 2.75 |
| **Sheets of 6, #a-f** | | | | |
| 3173-3175 | A502 | Set of 3 | 20.00 | 20.00 |
| **Souvenir Sheets** | | | | |
| 3176-3179 | A502 | Set of 4 | 18.00 | 18.00 |

Marine Mammals A503

Designs: 25c, Commerson's dolphin. 50c, Pacific white-sided dolphin. $2, Northern bottlenosed whale. $3, Baird's beaked whale.
No. 3184, $1.50: a, Risso's dolphin. b, Fraser's dolphin. c, Dall's porpoise. d, Right whale. e, Gray whale. f, Minke whale.
No. 3185, $1.50: a, Common dolphin. b, Antillean beaked whale. c, Killer whale. d, Bryde's whale. e, Cuvier's beaked whale. f, Sei whale.

No. 3186, $1.50: a, Harbor porpoise. b, Beluga. c, White-beaked dolphin. d, Narwhal. e, Bowhead whale. f, Fin whale.
No. 3187, $6, Sperm whale. No. 3188, $6, Blue whale. No. 3189, $6, Southern right whale. No. 3190, $6, Humpback whale.

| 2001, Sept. 10 | | | | |
|---|---|---|---|---|
| 3180-3183 | A503 | Set of 4 | 4.25 | 4.25 |
| **Sheets of 6, #a-f** | | | | |
| 3184-3186 | A503 | Set of 3 | 20.00 | 20.00 |
| **Souvenir Sheets** | | | | |
| 3187-3190 | A503 | Set of 4 | 18.00 | 18.00 |

Monet Paintings A504

No. 3191, horiz.: a, Boats in Winter Quarters, Etretat. b, Regatta at Sainte Adresse. c, The Bridge at Bougival. d, The Beach at Sainte Adresse.
$6, Monet's Garden at Vétheuil.

| 2001, May 15 | | Litho. | Perf. 13¾ | |
|---|---|---|---|---|
| 3191 | A504 | $2 Sheet of 4, #a-d | 6.00 | 6.00 |
| **Souvenir Sheet** | | | | |
| 3192 | A504 | $6 multi | 4.50 | 4.50 |

2002 World Cup Soccer Championships, Japan and Korea — A505

No. 3193, $1.50: a, Poster, 1950. b, West German championship team, 1954. c, Just Fontaine, 1958. d, Garrincha, Brazil, 1962. e, Bobby Moore, England, 1966. f, Pelé, Brazil, 1970.
No. 3194, $1.50: a, Osvaldo Ardiles, Argentina, 1978. b, Lakhdar Belloumi, Algeria, 1982. c, Diego Maradona, Argentina, 1986. d, Matthaüs and Völler, West Germany, 1990. e, Seo Jung Won, South Korea, 1994. f, Ronaldo, Brazil, 1998.
No. 3195, $6, Face from Jules Rimet trophy. No. 3196, $6, Face and globe from World Cup trophy.

| 2001, Nov. 29 | | Perf. 13¾x14¼ | | |
|---|---|---|---|---|
| **Sheets of 6, #a-f** | | | | |
| 3193-3194 | A505 | Set of 2 | 13.50 | 13.50 |
| **Souvenir Sheet** | | | | |
| 3195-3196 | A505 | Set of 2 | 9.00 | 9.00 |

Christmas A506

Santa Claus and: 15c, House, Christmas tree. 50c, Trees, snowman. $1, Tree, ice skates. $4, Children.
$6, Santa eating cookie.

| 2001, Dec. 3 | | | Perf. 14 | |
|---|---|---|---|---|
| 3197-3200 | A506 | Set of 4 | 4.25 | 4.25 |
| **Souvneir Sheet** | | | | |
| 3201 | A506 | $6 multi | 4.50 | 4.50 |

A507

Nobel Prizes, Cent. A508

1901 Laureates: 75c, Emil A. von Behring, Medicine. 90c, Wilhelm C. Röntgen, Physics. $1, Jacobus H. van't Hoff, Chemistry. No. 3205, $1.50, Frederic Passy, Peace. $2, Jean-Henri Dunant, Peace. $3, René Sully-Prudhomme, Literature.
No. 3208, horiz.—Albert Einstein, 1921 Physics laureate, with: a, Dark hair, black suit. b, Pipe. c, Gray suit. d, Pink sweater. e, Gray hair, black suit. f, Blue sweater.
$6, Einstein wearing hat.

| 2001, Dec. 13 | | | | |
|---|---|---|---|---|
| 3202-3207 | A507 | Set of 6 | 7.00 | 7.00 |
| 3208 | A508 | $1.50 Sheet of 6, #a-f | 6.75 | 6.75 |
| **Souvenir Sheet** | | | | |
| 3209 | A508 | $6 multi | 4.50 | 4.50 |

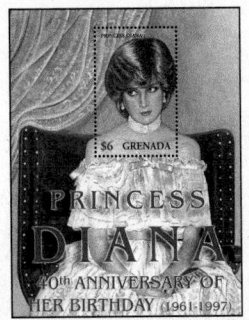

Princess Diana (1961-97) — A509

No. 3210: a, Blue gown. b, White gown. c, Red gown.
$6, With pink curtain.

| 2001, Dec. 13 | | | | |
|---|---|---|---|---|
| 3210 | A509 | $1.50 Sheet, 2 each #a-c | 6.75 | 6.75 |
| **Souvenir Sheet** | | | | |
| 3211 | A509 | $6 multi | 4.50 | 4.50 |

**Queen Mother Type of 1999**

No. 3212: a, Queen Mother, Prince Charles, 1948. b, Queen Mother, 1970. c, Queen Mother in Australia, 1958. d, Queen Mother. $6, Queen Mother, 1953.

| 2001, Dec. 13 | | | Perf. 14 | |
|---|---|---|---|---|
| **Yellow Orange Frames** | | | | |
| 3212 | A440 | $2 Sheet of 4, #a-d, + label | 6.00 | 6.00 |
| **Souvenir Sheet** | | | | |
| | | **Perf. 13¾** | | |
| 3213 | A440 | $6 multi | 4.50 | 4.50 |

Queen Mother's 101st birthday. No. 3213 contains one 38x50mm stamp with a redder backdrop than that found on No. 2881. Sheet margins of Nos. 3212-3213 lack embossing and gold arms found on Nos. 2880-2881.

New Year 2002 (Year of the Horse) A510

Ceramic horses of T'ang dynasty — No. 3214: a, Brown horse with long, tan mane. b, Blue horse with pink hooves. c, Black horse with gray mane. d, Tan horse with round ornaments.
$4, Brown horse with gray and green saddle.

| 2001, Dec. 17 | | | Perf. 13¾ | |
|---|---|---|---|---|
| 3214 | A510 | $1.50 Sheet of 4, #a-d | 4.50 | 4.50 |
| **Souvenir Sheet** | | | | |
| 3215 | A510 | $4 multi | 4.00 | 4.00 |

A511

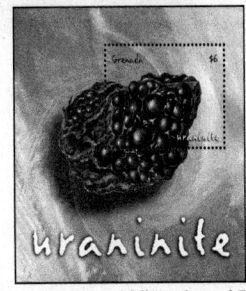

Gemstones and Minerals — A512

Monthly gemstones — No. 3216, $1.50: a, Garnet (January). b, Amethyst (February). c, Aquamarine (March). d, Diamond (April). e, Emerald (May). f, Pearl (June).
No. 3217, $1.50: a, Ruby (July). b, Sardonyx (August). c, Sapphire (September). d, Opal (October). e, Topaz (November). f, Turquoise (December).
Gemstones in mineral form — No. 3218: a, Ruby. b, Diamond. c, Sapphire. d, Opal. e, Turquoise. f, Jade.
No. 3219, $6, Uraninite. No. 3220, $6, Calcite. No. 3221, $6, Quartz, vert.

| 2001, Dec. 31 | | | Perf. 14 | |
|---|---|---|---|---|
| **Sheets of 6, #a-f** | | | | |
| 3216-3217 | A511 | Set of 2 | 14.50 | 14.50 |
| 3218 | A512 | $1.50 Sheet of 6, #a-f | 7.50 | 7.50 |
| **Souvenir Sheets** | | | | |
| 3219-3221 | A512 | Set of 3 | 14.50 | 14.50 |

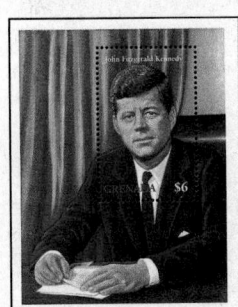

US Presidents — A513

No. 3222, $1.50 — John F. Kennedy and: a, Field. b, Flag, building, microphone. c, Airplane.
No. 3223, $1.50 — Ronald Reagan: a, In uniform with binoculars. b, With red tie. c, With flag.
No. 3224, $6, Kennedy. No. 3225, $6, Reagan.

| 2001, Dec. 31 | | Sheets, 2 each #a-c | | |
|---|---|---|---|---|
| 3222-3223 | A513 | Set of 2 | 13.50 | 13.50 |
| **Souvenir Sheets** | | | | |
| 3224-3225 | A513 | Set of 2 | 9.00 | 9.00 |

## Souvenir Sheets

I Love Lucy
A514

Designs: No. 3226, $6, Ethel watching Lucy and Ricky dance. No. 3227, $6, Desi, Lucy, Fred and Ethel near door. No. 3228, $6, Desi holding Lucy. No. 3229, $6, Lucy in plaid shirt.

**2001**      **Perf. 13¾**
3226-3229 A514   Set of 4    18.00 18.00

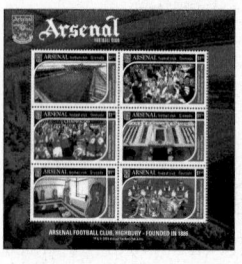

English Soccer Teams A515

No. 3230, $1.50 — Arsenal: a, Inside of Highbury Stadium. b, Players celebrate 1994 European Cup and Winner's Cup. c, Players celebrate 1998 premiership. d, East stands, Highbury Stadium. e, Locker rooms. f, Four players with trophies, 1998.

No. 3231, $1.50 — Aston Villa: a, Sign on Villa Park. b, Fans watching night game. c, Empty stadium, field at right. d, Empty stadium, field at left. e, Holte End of stadium. f, Fans in stands.

No. 3232, $1.50 — Bolton Wanderers: a, Empty Reebok Stadium. b, Players celebrating 2001 Division 1 playoff win. c, Promotion to Premier League. d, Fans celebrate. e, Players, coaches with trophy. f, Game played in Reebok Stadium.

No. 3233, $1.50 — Everton: a, 2001-02 team. b, Re-signing of Duncan Ferguson. c, Statue of Wiliam Ralph "Dixie" Dean. d, Fans. e, Goodison Park. f, 1969-70 league championship team.

No. 3234, $1.50 — Ipswich Town: a, Players holding banner and trophy after 2000 Division 1 playoff final. b, 2001-02 team. c, Manager George Burley and Chairman David Sheepshanks. d, Pablo Counago fights for ball. e, Captain Matt Holland. f, George Burley receives Manager of the Year award.

No. 3235, $1.50 — Liverpool: a, Anfield. b, 2000-01 Worthington Cup winners. c, 2000-01 FA Cup winners. d, Fans. e, 2000-01 UEFA Cup winners. f, Treble Cup parade.

No. 3236, $1.50 — Manchester United: a, Legends Meredith, Law and Charlton. b, Three 1998-99 trophies. c, Views of Old Trafford, 1948, 1956. d, Recent views of Old Trafford. e, Third premiership in three years, 2000-01. f, Heroes, Best, Robson and Beckham.

No. 3237, $1.50 — Rangers: a, View of Ibrox Stadium from street. b, 1972 European Cup and Winner's Cup team. c, Scottish FA Cup, Scottish Premier League Trophy. d, Aerial view of Ibrox Stadium. e, Fans in stadium. f, Nine consecutive Scottish League wins.

**2001, Sept. 12**   **Litho.**   **Perf. 13¼**
**Sheets of 6, #a-f**
3230-3237 A515   Set of 8    55.00 55.00
See Nos. 3286-3294.

---

Reign of Queen Elizabeth II, 50th Anniv. A516

GOLDEN JUBILEE - 6th February, 2002
50th Anniversary of Her Majesty Queen Elizabeth II's Accession

No. 3238: a, With Prince Philip. b, Wearing flowered hat. c, Wearing tiara. d, Wearing gray coat with white collar.
$6, Wearing uniform.

**2002, Feb. 6**      **Perf. 14½**
3238 A516 $2 Sheet of 4, #a-d   6.00 6.00
**Souvenir Sheet**
3239 A516 $6 multi      4.50 4.50

United We Stand — A517

**2002, Feb.**    **Perf. 13¾x13½**
3240 A517 $2 multi      1.50 1.50
Issued in sheets of 4.

Dale Earnhardt, Race Car Driver — A518

Years of Winston Cup Championships: No. 3241, $2, 1980. No. 3242, $2, 1986. No. 3243, $2, 1987. No. 3244, $2, 1990. No. 3245, $2, 1991. No. 3246, $2, 1993. No. 3247, $2, 1994.

**2002, Mar. 4**   **Litho.**   **Perf. 14x13¾**
3241-3247 A518   Set of 7    12.00 12.00

Mickey Mouse — A519

No. 3249 — Scenes from: a, The Nifty Nineties, 1941. b, Magician Mickey, 1937. c, Steamboat Willie, 1928. d, Fantasia, 1940. e, Mickey Mouse Club, 1955. f, Cactus Kid, 1930. g, The Prince and the Pauper, 1990. h, Brave Little Tailor, 1938. i, Canine Caddy, 1941.

**2002, Apr. 24**      **Perf. 13¾**
3248 A519 $1 shown      .90 .90
3249 A519 $1 Sheet of 9, #a-i   8.75 8.75
No. 3248 was printed in sheets of nine.

---

American Civil War Naval History — A520

No. 3250, $1: a, CSS Teaser. b, US gunboats on the James River. c, USS Tyler. d, USS Maratanza. e, USS Metacomet. f, USS Rattler.

No. 3251, $1.25: a, CSS Tennessee. b, USS Hartford. c, USS Chickasaw. d, USS Ossipee. e, Battle of Mobile Bay. f, USS Chickasaw at Mobile Bay.

No. 3252, $1.50: a, CSS H.L. Hunley. b, USS Cumberland. c, CSS Old Dominion. d, USS Housatonic. e, USS Hartford. f, USS Essex.

No. 3253, $1.50: a, CSS Alabama. b, USS Kearsarge and CSS Alabama. c, USS Hatteras. d, CSS Alabama and decoy. e, CSS Sumter. f, USS Kearsarge.

No. 3254, $6, USS Monitor. No. 3255, $6, CSS Florida. No. 3256, $6, CSS Tennessee. No. 3257, $6, Capt. Raphael Semmes aboard CSS Alabama.

**2002, Apr. 8**   **Litho.**   **Perf. 13¼x13½**
**Sheets of 6, #a-f**
3250-3253 A520   Set of 4    28.00 28.00
**Souvenir Sheets**
3254-3257 A520   Set of 4    22.00 22.00

Chiune Sugihara, Japanese Diplomat Who Saved Jews in World War II — A521

**2002, July 1**    **Perf. 13½x13¾**
3258 A521 $2 multi      1.50 1.50
Printed in sheets of 4.

2002 Winter Olympics, Salt Lake City — A522

Skier with: No. 3259, $2, Red skis. No. 3260, $2, Yellow skis.

**2002, July 1**    **Perf. 13¼x13½**
3259-3260 A522   Set of 2    3.00 3.00
   a. Souvenir sheet, #3259-3260   3.00 3.00

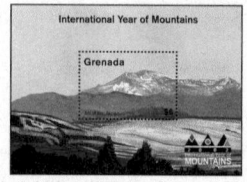

Intl. Year of Mountains — A523

No. 3261: a, Mt. Mawensi, Kenya. b, Mt. Stanley, Uganda. c, Mt. Taweche, Nepal. d, Mt. San Exupery, Argentina.
$6, Mt. Aso, Japan.

**2002, July 1**
3261 A523 $2 Sheet of 4, #a-d   6.00 6.00
**Souvenir Sheet**
3262 A523 $6 multi      4.50 4.50

---

Intl. Year of Ecotourism — A524

No. 3263, horiz.: a, Tower and pennants. b, Bird. c, Flower, vacationer on chair. d, Diver, fish. e, Fish. f, Sailboats.
$6, Map of Grenada, bird.

**2002, July 1**    **Perf. 13¼x13½**
3263 A524 $1 Sheet of 6, #a-f   4.50 4.50
**Souvenir Sheet**
**Perf. 13½x13¼**
3264 A524 $6 multi      4.50 4.50
No. 3263 was overprinted in sheet margin "Hurricane Relief 2004" in 2005.

20th World Scout Jamboree, Thailand — A525

No. 3265, horiz.: a, Scout in canoe with oar out of water. b, Scout in canoe with oar in water. c, Bugler. d, Scout making Scout sign.
$6, Scout saluting.

**2002, July 1**    **Perf. 13¼x13½**
3265 A525 $2 Sheet of 4, #a-d   7.50 7.50
**Souvenir Sheet**
**Perf. 13½x13¼**
3266 A525 $6 multi      5.00 5.00

Model Heidi Klum A526

No. 3267: a, Arms up. b, Arms down. c, No arms shown.

**2002, Aug. 16**      **Perf. 14**
3267 A526 $1.50 Horiz. strip of 3, #a-c    3.50 3.50
Printed in sheets containing two strips.

Elvis Presley (1935-77) — A527

**2002, Aug. 26**    **Perf. 13½x13¾**
3268 A527 $1 multi      .75 .75
Printed in sheets of 9.

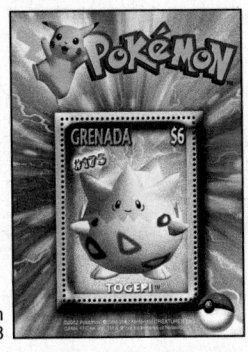

Pokémon
A528

No. 3269: a, Mareep. b, Sunkern. c, Teddi-ursa. d, Swinub. e, Murkrow. f, Snubbull.
$6, Togepi.

**2002, Aug. 26**     **Perf. 13¾**
3269 A528 $1.50 Sheet of 6, #a-f 6.75 6.75

**Souvenir Sheet**

3270 A528   $6 multi     4.50 4.50

A529

A530

Teddy
Bears,
Cent.
A531

No. 3271: a, 25c, Bear with red hat, lace collar, cheese wheels. b, $1.25, Bear with black cap. c, $3, Bear with wooden shoes. d, $5, Bear with red hat and ribbon.
No. 3272: a, Army bear. b, Navy bear. c, Air Force bear. d, Marines bear.
No. 3273: a, Basketball bear. b, Martial arts bear. c, Golf bear. d, Baseball bear.

**2002, Aug. 26**     **Perf. 14**
3271 A529   Sheet of 4, #a-d   7.25 7.25

**Perf. 14¼**
3272 A530 $2 Sheet of 4, #a-d   6.00 6.00
3273 A531 $2 Sheet of 4, #a-d   6.00 6.00

Dutch
Nobel
Prize
Winners
A532

Dutch Lighthouses — A533

Traditional Dutch Women's
Costumes — A534

No. 3274: a, Jacobus H. van't Hoff, Chemistry, 1901. b, Nobel Peace medal. c, Pieter Zeeman, Physics, 1902. d, Johannes D. van der Waals, Physics, 1910. e, Tobias M. C. Asser, Peace, 1911. f, Heike Kammerlingh-Onnes, Physics, 1913.
No. 3275: a, Schiermonnikoog. b, Texel. c, Egmond. d, Scheveningen. e, Schouwen. f, Hellevoetsluis.
No. 3276: a, Zeeland (woman with red necklace, patterned dress). b, Noord-Brabant (woman with black shawl). c, Noord-Holland (woman with flowered neckpiece).

**2002, Aug. 29**     **Perf. 13½x13¼**
3274 A532 $1.50 Sheet of 6, #a-f   6.75 6.75
3275 A533 $1.50 Sheet of 6, #a-f   6.75 6.75

**Perf. 13¼**
3276 A534   $3 Sheet of 3, #a-c   6.75 6.75

Amphilex 2002 Intl. Stamp Exhibition, Amsterdam.

Shirley
Temple
A535

Scenes from "Our Little Girl" — No. 3277, horiz.: a, With man. b, With man and woman. c, With dog and man. d, With woman and two men. e, On seesaw with dog. f, With dog.
No. 3278: a, With woman. b, With man and clown. c, Kneeling beside chair. d, With man and woman.
$6, In pink dress.

**2002, Sept. 3**     **Perf. 14¼**
3277 A535 $1.50 Sheet of 6, #a-f   6.75 6.75
3278 A535   $2 Sheet of 4, #a-d   6.00 6.00

**Souvenir Sheet**

3279 A535   $6 multi     4.50 4.50

Souvenir Sheet

Terrorist
Attack
on World
Trade
Center,
1st
Anniv.
A536

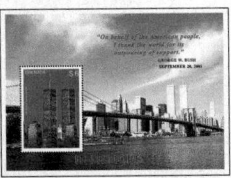

**2002, Sept. 11**     **Perf. 13¾**
3280 A536 $6 multi     4.50 4.50

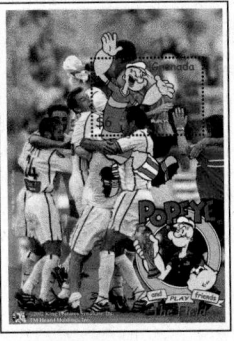

Popeye
A537

No. 3281, vert.: a, Popeye in Florence, Italy. b, Popeye and Brutus in Paris, France. c, Popeye in Athens, Greece. d, Popeye and Olive Oyl in Venice, Italy. e, Popeye in London, England. f, Popeye in Norway.
No. 3282, vert. — At soccer match: a, Swee'Pea. b, Jeep. c, Popeye. d, Brutus.
No. 3283, $6, Popeye playing soccer. No. 3284, $6, Brutus playing soccer. No. 3285, $6, Popeye at Leaning Tower of Pisa, vert.

**Perf. 14¼ (#3281, 3285), 14**
**2002, Sept. 23**
3281 A537 $1.50 Sheet of 6, #a-f   6.75 6.75
3282 A537   $2 Sheet of 4, #a-d   6.00 6.00

**Souvenir Sheets**

3283-3285 A537   Set of 3   13.50 13.50

No. 3218 contains six 38x50mm stamps; No. 3285 contains one 50x75mm stamp.

**English Soccer Teams Type of 2001**

No. 3286, $1.50 — Tottenham Hotspur: a, Fans watching match in White Hart Lane Stadium. b, Sheringham and Anderton in action against Fulham. c, Poyet scoring against Liverpool. d, Tottenham Hotspur wins UEFA Cup, 1972. e, Celebrations after win against Chelsea. f, Fans in stadium, team insignia.
No. 3287, $1.50 — Manchester City: a, Maine Road Stadium from stands. b, Fans celebrate becoming Division One champions. c, Manager Kevin Keegan and trophy. d, Team with trophy. e, Players wearing medals, with trophy. f, Field level view of Maine Road Stadium.
No. 3288, $1.50 — Norwich City: a, Match at the Nest. b, Promotion to the Top Flight, 1971-72. c, Milk Cup win, 1985. d, Carrow Road Stadium. e, Win against Bayern Munich, 1993. f, Action from 1958-59 Cup run.
No. 3289, $1.50 — Arsenal, Double Winners: a, Tony Adams and Patrick Vieira hold FA Cup. b, Team wearing tan shirts, holding championship banners. c, Team without banners, at Premiership trophy presentation. d, Photo of 2001-02 Premiership team, standing and wearing red shirts. e, Four players celebrate winning goal against Chelsea. f, Manager Arsene Wenger and Tony Adams at Double Winners Parade.
No. 3290, $1.50 — Arsenal, Premiership Winners: a, Inside of Highbury Stadium, team emblem and name in red panels. b, Celebrations after Gilberto scores winning goal. c, Team with FA Community Shield sign. d, Team photo, empty stands. e, Gilberto with FA Community Shield. f, Highbury Stadium with fans, team emblem.
No. 3291, $1.50 — Manchester United: a, David Beckham after free kick. b, Team photo, empty stands. c, Aerial view of Old Trafford Stadium. d, Celebration after Ole Gunnar Solskjaer's 100th goal for Manchester United. e, Fans at Old Trafford Stadium. f, North stand of Old Trafford Stadium.
No. 3292, $1.50 — Liverpool: a, Anfield's Centenary stand, as seen from Main stand. b, 2002-03 team photo. c, Gerard Houllier and Phil Thompson. d, Milan Baros celebrates goal. e, Vladimir Smicer congratulating Danny Murphy. f, The Kop, as seen from Anfield Road end.
No. 3293, $1.50 — Celtic: a, Interior of Celtic Park. b, Martin O'Neill with SPL Trophy.

c, Henrik Larsson celebrating goal. d, 2002-03 team photo. e, Players celebrating a goal. f, Exterior of Celtic Park.
No. 3294, $1.50 — Chelsea: a, Night match at Stamford Bridge Stadium. b, Team with 1998 Cup Winners' Cup Final trophy. c, Fans in stadium. d, Sign for the Shed End. e, Field level view of Stamford Bridge Stadium. f, Players celebrating 2000 FA Cup victory.

**2002**     **Perf. 14x13¾**
**Sheets of 6, #a-f**
3286-3294 A515   Set of 9   60.00 60.00

Issued: Nos. 3286-3289, 9/23; Nos. 3290-3294, 11/14.

Butterflies, Insects, Mushrooms and
Whales — A538

No. 3295, $1.50 — Butterflies: a, Common morpho. b, Blue night. c, Small flambeau. d, Grecian shoemaker. e, Orange-barred sulphur. f, Cramer's mesene.
No. 3296, $1.50 — Insects: a, Honeybees. b, Dragonfly. c, Milkweed bug. d, Bumblebee. e, Migratory grasshopper. f, Monarch caterpillar.
No. 3297, $1.50 — Mushrooms: a, Boletus crocipodius. b, King bolete. c, Velvet shank. d, Death cap. e, Golden cavalier. f, Fly agaric.
No. 3298, $1.50 — Whales: a, Blue. b, Pygmy sperm. c, Humpback. d, Killer. e, Bowhead. f, Gray.
No. 3299, $6, Figure-of-eight butterfly. No. 3300, $6, Hercules beetle. No. 3301, $6, Sharp-scaled parasol mushroom. No. 3302, $6, Blue whale, horiz.

**2002, Oct. 21**     **Perf. 14**
**Sheets of 6, #a-f**
3295-3298 A538   Set of 4   27.50 27.50

**Souvenir Sheets**

3299-3302 A538   Set of 4   18.00 18.00

Sir Norman Wisdom,
British
Comedian — A539

**2002, Nov. 3**     **Perf. 13¾**
3303 A539 $1.50 multi     1.10 1.10

Printed in sheets of 6.

Amerigo Vespucci (1454-1512),
Explorer — A540

No. 3304, $3: a, Map of South America, ship. b, Compass rose, ship. c, Map of Europe and Africa.
No. 3305, $3, horiz.: a, Sextant, map of northern South America. b, Vespucci, map of central South America. c, Ship, map of southern South America.
No. 3306, $6, Compass rose. No. 3307, $6, Globe.

**2002, Nov. 4**     **Perf. 13¾**
**Sheets of 3, #a-c**
3304-3305 A540   Set of 2   13.50 13.50

## Souvenir Sheets
### Perf. 14

3306-3307  A540  Set of 2  9.00  9.00

No. 3304 contains three 38x50mm stamps; No. 3305 contains three 50x38mm stamps.

Christmas
A541

Cimabue paintings: 15c, Madonna and Child, Four Angels and St. Francis, entire. 25c, Madonna and Child and Two Angels, vert. 50c, Madonna Enthroned, detail, vert. $1, Madonna Enthroned, entire, vert. $4, Madonna and Child, Four Angels and St. Francis, detail, vert. $6, Nativity by Perugino, vert.

**2002, Nov. 4**     **Perf. 14**
3308-3312  A541  Set of 5  4.50  4.50
### Souvenir Sheet
3313  A541  $6 multi  4.50  4.50

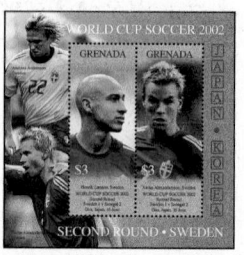

Second Round Matches of 2002 World Cup Soccer Championships, Japan and Korea — A542

No. 3314, $1.50 — Sweden vs. Senegal: a, Johan Mjalby. b, Magnus Hedman. c, Fredrik Ljungberg. d, Khalilou Fadiga. e, El Hadji Diouf. f, Papa Bouba Diop.
No. 3315, $1.50 — Brazil vs. Belgium: a, Roberto Carlos. b, Juninho Paulista. c, Ronaldinho. d, Johan Walem. e, Marc Wilmots. f, Bart Goor.
No. 3316, $3 — Swedish players: a, Henrik Larsson. b, Niclas Alexandersson.
No. 3317, $3 — Senegal players: a, Fadiga. b, Coach Bruno Metsu.
No. 3318, $3 — Brazil players: a, Coach Luiz Felipe Scolari. b, Ronaldo.
No. 3319, $3 — Belgium players: a, Wesley Sonck. b, Coach Robert Waseige.

**2002, Nov. 18**     **Perf. 13¼**
### Sheets of 6, #a-f
3314-3315  A542  Set of 2  13.50  13.50
### Souvenir Sheets of 2, #a-b
3316-3319  A542  Set of 4  18.00  18.00

### Souvenir Sheet

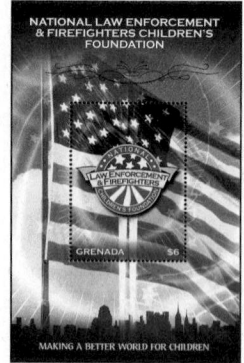

United States Natl. Law Enforcement and Firefighters Children's Foundation — A543

**2002, Nov. 28**     **Perf. 14¼**
3320  A543  $6 multi  4.50  4.50

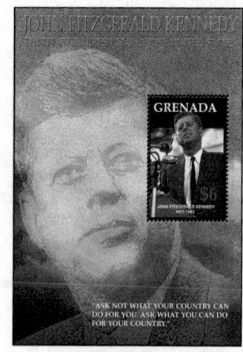

Pres. John F. Kennedy (1917-63) — A544

No. 3321, horiz.: a, Meeting with Cabinet. b, Signing bill into law. c, Meeting civil rights leaders. d, With Astronaut John Glenn. e, On campaign trail. f, Arrival in Dallas, Nov. 22, 1963.
$6, At microphone.

**2002, Dec. 4**     **Perf. 14**
3321  A544  $1.50 Sheet of 6, #a-f  6.75  6.75
### Souvenir Sheet
3322  A544  $6 multi  4.50  4.50

Intl. Federation of Stamp Dealers Associations, 50th Anniv. — A545

**2002, Dec. 16**     **Litho.**
3323  A545  $2 multi  1.50  1.50

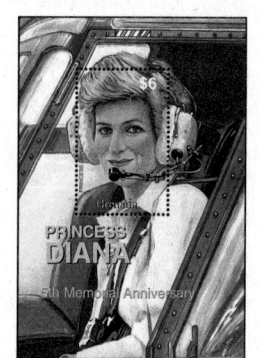

Princess Diana (1961-97) — A546

No. 3324: a, Wearing bow tie. b, Wearing blue dress. c, Wearing red and white hat. d, Holding flowers.
$6, Wearing earphones and microphone.

**2002**     **Perf. 14**
3324  A546  $2 Sheet of 4, #a-d  6.00  6.00
### Souvenir Sheet
3325  A546  $6 multi  4.50  4.50

### I Love Lucy Type of 2001
#### Souvenir Sheets

No. 3326, $6, Lucy standing near fireplace. No. 3327, $6, Lucy and Ethel at desk. No. 3328, $6, Fred and Desi standing. No. 3329, $6, Fred and Desi at desk, horiz.

**2002**     **Perf. 13¾**
3326-3329  A514  Set of 4  18.00  18.00

New Year 2003 (Year of the Ram) — A547

**2003, Jan. 27**     **Perf. 13¾**
3330  A547  $1.25 multi  .95  .95

Printed in sheets of 4.

M-Gears
A548

No. 3331: a, Airplane. b, Vehicle. c, Monster. d, Race car.

**2003, Feb. 16**     **Litho.**     **Perf. 14¼**
3331  A548  $2 Sheet of 4, #a-d  6.00  6.00

Astronauts Killed in Space Shuttle Columbia Accident — A549

No. 3332: a, Mission Specialist 1 David M. Brown. b, Commander Rick D. Husband. c, Mission Specialist 4 Laurel Blair Salton Clark. d, Mission Specialist 4 Kalpana Chawla. e, Payload Commander Michael P. Anderson. f, Pilot William C. McCool. g, Payload Specialist 4 Ilan Ramon.

**2003, Apr. 7**     **Perf. 13¼**
3332  A549  $1 Sheet of 7, #a-g  6.00  6.00

Paintings of Gustav Klimt (1862-1918) A550

Designs: 15c, Jardin aux Tournesols. 25c, L'allée aux Poulets. 75c, Allée dans le Parc du Schloss Kammer. $1, Portrait of Johanna Staude. $1.25, Portrait of Friederike Maria Beer. $3, Portrait of Mäda Primavesi.
No. 3339: a, La Jeune Fille. b, Les Amies. c, Le Berceau. d, La Vie et la Mort.
$6, Portrait of Margaret Stonborough-Wittgenstein.

**2003, Apr. 28**     **Perf. 14¼**
3333-3338  A550  Set of 6  5.00  5.00
3339  A550  $2 Sheet of 4, #a-d  6.00  6.00
### Size: 82x103mm
#### Imperf
3340  A550  $6 multi  4.50  4.50

Art of Yoshitoshi Taiso (1839-92) — A551

Designs: 75c, A Harlot in Repose. $1, A "Shakuni," or Geisha, Who Serves Wine or Sake. $1.25, A "Joro," or Low Ranking Prostitute, Having a Snack. $3, A Geisha Known as a "Geiko," or Entertainer Relaxing.
No. 3345: a, Enjoying a Cool Evening Breeze in a Pleasure Boat. b, A Fukagawa Waitress Carrying a Wooden Table Laden With Food. c, A Spoiled Unmarried Woman Pretending to Be Displeased With an Admirer. d, A Coy Young Girl, Biting Her Sleeve Pretending to Be Embarrassed.
$6, A Geisha About to Board a Party Boat.

**2003, Apr. 28**     **Perf. 14¼**
3341-3344  A551  Set of 4  4.50  4.50
3345  A551  $2 Sheet of 4, #a-d  6.00  6.00
### Souvenir Sheet
3346  A551  $6 multi  4.50  4.50

Paintings by Lucas Cranach the Elder (1472-1553) A552

Details from St. Catherine Altarpiece: 50c, Sts. Dorothy, Agnes and Cunigonde. 75c, St. Margaret, vert. $1.25, St. Barbara, vert. $3, Detail from left wing, vert.
No. 3351 — Painting details: a, Lot and His Daughters. b, David and Bathsheba. c, The Agony in the Garden. d, The Adoration of the Magi.
$6, Detail of Samson and Delilah, vert.

**2003, Apr. 28**
3347-3350  A552  Set of 4  4.25  4.25
3351  A552  $2 Sheet of 4, #a-d  6.00  6.00
### Souvenir Sheet
3352  A552  $6 multi  4.50  4.50

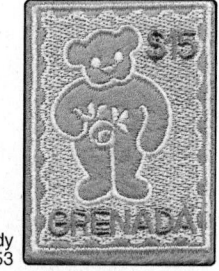

Teddy Bear — A553

**2003, Apr. 29 Embroidered**    *Imperf.*
### Self-Adhesive
3353  A553  $15 multi  11.50  11.50

Issued in sheets of 4.

Reading Rods A554

No. 3354 — Children and: a, Bulletin board. b, Blackboard. c, Globe. d, Teacher.

**2003, May 5**    **Litho.**    **Perf. 13¾**
3354  A554  $2 Sheet of 4, #a-d  6.00  6.00

Tour de France Bicycle Race, Cent. A555

No. 3355, $2: a, Sylvére Maes, 1939. b, Jean Lazaridés, 1946. c, Jean Robic, 1947. d, Gino Bartali, 1948.
No. 3356, $2: a, Fausto Coppi, 1949. b, Ferdinand Kubler, 1950. c, Hugo Koblet, 1951. d, Coppi, 1952.
No. 3357, $2: a, Roger Walkowiak, 1956. b, Jacques Anquetil, 1957. c, Charly Gaul, 1958. d, Federico Bahamontes, 1959.
No. 3358, $6, Coppi, 1949, diff. No. 3359, $6, Kubler, 1950, diff. No. 3360, $6, Anquetil, 1964.

**2003, June 17**     **Perf. 13¼**
### Sheets of 4, #a-d
3355-3357  A555  Set of 3  18.00  18.00
### Souvenir Sheets
3358-3360  A555  Set of 3  13.50  13.50

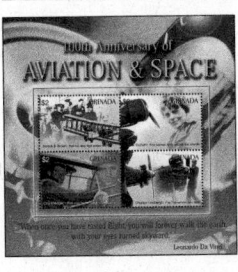

Powered Flight, Cent. A556

No. 3361, $2: a: First non-stop transatlantic flight by Alcock & Brown. b, Amelia Earhart, first woman to fly across Atlantic. c, Chuck Yeager, first man to break sound barrier. d, Charles Lindbergh, first solo transatlantic flight.

No. 3362, $2: a, Louis Bleriot, first flight across English Channel. b, Johnnie Johnson, ace pilot in World War II. c, Wright Brothers, first powered flight. d, Jacqueline Cochran, first woman to break sound barrier.

**2003, June 24**    *Perf. 13¼x13½*
**Sheets of 4, #a-d**
3361-3362 A556   Set of 2    12.00 12.00

Coronation of Queen Elizabeth II, 50th Anniv. A557

Designs: No. 3363, $2, Enthroning of the Queen. No. 3364, $2, Duke pays homage to the Queen. No. 3365, $2, Celebration of Holy Communion. No. 3366, $2, Floodlit mall. No. 3367, $2, Queen on balcony. No. 3368, $2, St. Edward's Chair. No. 3369, $2, Official coronation portrait. No. 3370, $2, Queen leaves Abbey.
$6, Queen in coach.

**2003, June 30**    *Perf. 13½x14*
3363-3370 A557   Set of 8    12.00 12.00
**Souvenir Sheet**
3371 A557 $6 multi    4.50 4.50
No. 3371 contains one 38x51mm stamp.

CARICOM, 30th Anniv. — A558

**2003, July 4**    *Perf. 14*
3372 A558 $1 multi    .75 .75

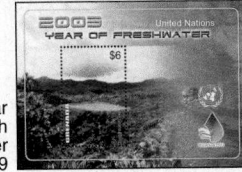

Intl. Year of Fresh Water A559

No. 3373: a, Levera Pond. b, Concord Falls. c, Lake Antoine.
$6, Lake Grand Etang.

**2003, July 4**    *Perf. 13½x13¼*
3373 A559 $2 Sheet of 3, #a-c   4.50 4.50
**Souvenir Sheet**
3374 A559 $6 multi    4.50 4.50

Circus Performers — A560

No. 3375, $2: a, Clive Andrews. b, Bell Bozo. c, Bumpsy. d, Annie Frattellini.
No. 3376, $2: a, Stag. b, Olga and Regina Kolpensky. c, Brad Byers. d, Tiger.

**2003, July 14**    *Perf. 14*
**Sheets of 4, #a-d**
3375-3376 A560   Set of 2    12.00 12.00

St. George's University School of Medicine — A561

Designs: 75c, Aerial view of campus. $1, Campus buildings.

**2003, July 23**
3377-3378 A561   Set of 2    1.40 1.40

Prince William, 21st Birthday A562

No. 3379, vert.: a, With bouquet of flowers. b, Wearing blue shirt. c, Wearing blue shirt, close-up.
$6, Wearing plaid shirt.

**2003, Aug. 25**
3379 A562 $3 Sheet of 3, #a-c   6.75 6.75
**Souvenir Sheet**
3380 A562 $6 multi    4.50 4.50

Operation Iraqi Freedom — A563

No. 3381, $1: a, Gazelle helicopter. b, Hovercraft. c, Jaguar. d, HMS Liverpool. e, Harrier GR7. f, Challenger 2 tank. g, Chinook helicopters. h, Tornado F3.
No. 3382, $1: a, Gen. Sir Mike Jackson. b, Air Vice-marshal Glenn Torpy. c, Air Marshal Brian Burridge. d, Maj. Gen. Tony Milton. e, Maj. Gen. Peter Wall. f, Maj. Gen. Barney White-Spunner. g, Adm. Sir Alan West. h, Air Chief Marshal Sir Peter Squire.

**2003, Aug. 29**    **Sheets of 8, #a-h**
3381-3382 A563   Set of 2    12.00 12.00

Pres. Ronald Reagan A564

No. 3383: a, On Korean demilitarized zone, 1983. b, With British Prime Minister Margaret Thatcher. c, Speaking at the Berlin Wall, 1987. d, Signing IMF treaty with Soviet Secretary General Mikhail Gorbachev. e, With Egyptian President Anwar Sadat, 1981. f, At home with his horse.
$6, Addressing the nation.

**2003**
3383 A564 $1.50 Sheet of 6, #a-f 6.75 6.75
**Souvenir Sheet**
3384 A564   $6 multi    4.50 4.50

Souvenir Sheet

Anatoly Karpov, Chess Champion — A565

**2003**    *Perf. 13¼*
3385 A565 $20 multi    15.00 15.00

Prehistoric Animals — A566

No. 3386, $2, horiz.: a, Spinosaurus. b, Herrerasaurus. c, Protarchaeopteryx. d, Sinosauropteryx.
No. 3387, $2, horiz.: a, Allosaurus. b, Crylophosaurus. c, Eoraptor. d, Caudipteryx.
No. 3388, $6, Archaeopteryx. No. 3389, $6, Triceratops.

**2003, Oct. 23 Litho.**   *Perf. 13¼x13½*
**Sheets of 4, #a-d**
3386-3387 A566   Set of 2    14.00 14.00
**Souvenir Sheets**
   *Perf. 13½x13¼*
3388-3389 A566   Set of 2    10.00 10.00

Flowers — A567

Designs: 25c, Yellow allamanda. 50c, Queen of the night. 75c, Anthurium. $3, Oleander.
No. 3394: a, Blue passion flower. b, Chinese hibiscus. c, Poinsettia. d, Bird of paradise.
$6, Shrimp flower.

**2003, Oct. 23**    *Perf. 14*
3390-3393 A567   Set of 4    3.50 3.50
3394 A567 $2 Sheet of 4, #a-d   6.00 6.00
**Souvenir Sheet**
3395 A567 $6 multi    4.50 4.50

Fish — A568

Designs: No. 3396, $1, Gold coney. No. 3397, $1, Spotfin butterflyfish. No. 3398, $1, Smallmouth grunt. $3, Night sergeant.
No. 3400: a, Cuban hogfish. b, Bluehead wrasse. c, Black cap gramma. d, Cherubfish.
$6, Banded butterflyfish.

**2003, Oct. 23**
3396-3399 A568   Set of 4    4.50 4.50
3400 A568 $2 Sheet of 4, #a-d   6.00 6.00
**Souvenir Sheet**
3401 A568 $6 multi    4.50 4.50

Birds — A569

Designs: No. 3402, $1.25, Osprey. No. 3403, $1.25, Northern oriole. No. 3404, $1.25, Red-eyed vireo. $3, Bahama pintail.
No. 3406: a, Slaty-capped shrike vireor. b, Northern flicker. c, Blackburnian warbler. d, Common tody-flycatcher.
$6, Blue grosbeak, vert.

**2003, Oct. 23**
3402-3405 A569   Set of 4    5.00 5.00
3406 A569 $2 Sheet of 4, #a-d   6.00 6.00
**Souvenir Sheet**
3407 A569 $6 multi    4.50 4.50

Christmas — A570

Paintings by Giotto: 35c, Madonna and Child, from the Church of the Ognissanti. 75c, Ognissanti Madonna. $1, Madonna of the Angels. $4, Madonna and Child, from the Florentine Church of San Giorgio alla Costa.
$6, Holy Family with John the Baptist and St. Elizabeth, horiz.

**2003, Nov. 17**    *Perf. 14¼*
3408-3411 A570   Set of 4    4.75 4.75
**Souvenir Sheet**
3412 A570 $6 multi    4.50 4.50
St. Petersburg, Russia, 300th anniv. (No. 3412).

Paintings by Norman Rockwell (1894-1978) — A571

No. 3413, vert.: a, The Spring Tonic. b, The Facts of Life. c, The Proper Gratuity. d, The Runaway.
$6, Boy with Carriage.

**2003, Dec. 8**    *Perf. 13¼*
3413 A571 $2 Sheet of 4, #a-d   6.00 6.00
**Souvenir Sheet**
3414 A571 $6 multi    4.50 4.50

Paintings in the Hermitage, St. Petersburg, Russia A572

Designs: 45c, At the Palmist's, by Jean-Baptiste Le Prince, vert. $1, A Visit to Grandmother, by Louis Le Nain. $1.50, Musicale, by Dirck Hals. $3, A Young Woman in the Morning, by Frans van Mieris the Elder, vert.
No. 3419, vert.: a, Louis, Grand Dauphin de France, by Louis Tocqué. b, Count P. A. Stroganov as a Child, by Jean-Baptiste Greuze. c, A Boy with a Book, by Jean-Baptiste Perronneau. d, A Girl with a Doll, by Greuze.
No. 3420, The Lute Player, by Caravaggio.
No. 3421, The Spoiled Child, by Greuze, vert.

**2003, Dec. 8**      **Perf. 13¼**
3415-3418 A572   Set of 4    4.50 4.50
3419 A572 $2 Sheet of 4, #a-d   6.00 6.00
*Imperf*
**Size: 78x65mm**
3420 A572 $6 multi       4.50 4.50
**Size: 67x78mm**
3421 A572 $6 multi       4.50 4.50

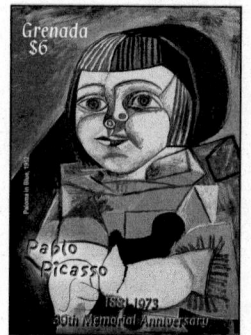

Paintings by Pablo Picasso (1881-1973) — A573

No. 3422: a, Claude Drawing. b, Claude and Paloma at Play. c, Paloma at Three Years Old. d, Paloma with an Orange.
$6, Paloma in Blue.

**2003, Dec. 8**   **Litho.**   **Perf. 13¼**
3422 A573 $2 Sheet of 4, #a-d   6.00 6.00
*Imperf*
3423 A573 $6 multi       4.50 4.50
No. 3422 contains four 37x50mm stamps.

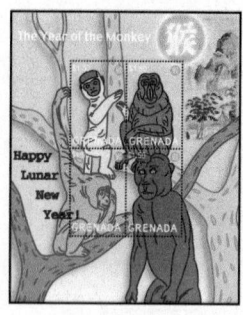

New Year 2004 (Year of the Monkey) A574

No. 3424: a, Buff monkey with brown features. b, Brown monkey. c, Tan monkey. d, Gray monkey.

**2004, Jan. 4**       **Perf. 14**
3424 A574 $1.50 Sheet of 4, #a-d   4.50 4.50

---

Souvenir Sheet

Training Ship "Lissy" A575

**2004, Jan. 16**   **Litho.**   **Perf. 14¼**
3425 A575 $6 multi       4.50 4.50
Opening of Weser Tunnel, Dedesdorf, Germany.

Paintings by Pu Hsin-yu (1896-1963) — A576

No. 3426: a, Woman. b, Monkeys in tree. c, Landscape. d, Bird in tree. e, Man seated. f, Man standing.
No. 3427: a, Branch. b, Man.

**2004, Jan. 29**      **Perf. 13½x13¼**
3426 A576 $1.50 Sheet of 6, #a-f   6.75 6.75
3427 A576 $3 Sheet of 2, #a-b   4.50 4.50
2004 Hong Kong Stamp Expo.

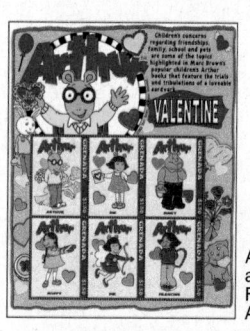

Arthur and Friends A577

No. 3428, $1.50: a, Arthur. b, D. W. with Valentine's Day card. c, Binky. d, Muffy. e, D. W. as Cupid. f, Francine.
No. 3429, $1.50: a, Muffy giving speech about butterflies. b, Francine giving presentation about butterflies. c, Brain with plants. d, D. W. in space. e, Sue Ellen with insects. f, Arthur with model of solar system.
No. 3430, $2: a, Robinson Crusoe. b, Treasure Island. c, Tom Sawyer. d, Jungle Book.
No. 3431, $2: a, Robin Hood. b, Rumplestiltskin. c, How Arthur Drew Forth His Sword. d, King Arthur.

**2004, Jan. 29**       **Perf. 13¼**
**Sheets of 6, #a-f**
3428-3429 A577   Set of 2   13.50 13.50
**Sheets of 4, #a-d**
3430-3431 A577   Set of 2   12.00 12.00

---

Cessation of Conorde Flights (in 2003) — A578

No. 3432, $3 — Concorde 210 G-BOAD, British and Singapore flags and: a, Roof line of buildings at UR. b, Curved and jagged lines at UR. c, Dark gray background at UR.
No. 3433, $3 — Concorde 001 F-WTSS, French flag and: a, Concorde above runway. b, Spectators near airport fence. c, Cockpit control panel.
No. 3434, $3 — Concorde 203 F-BVFA and: a, Top of US Capitol. b, Middle part of Capitol dome, head of statue. c, Base of Capitol and statue.

**2004, Feb. 16**     **Perf. 13¼x13½**
**Sheets of 3, #a-c**
3432-3434 A578   Set of 3   21.00 21.00

2004 Summer Olympics, Athens — A579

Designs: 75c, Lord Killanin, Intl. Olympic Committee President, 1972-80. $1, 10,000 meter run, 1928 Olympics, horiz. $1.25, Commemorative plaque from 1900 Paris Olympics. $3, Presentation of olive wreath.

**2004, Apr. 8**       **Perf. 13¼**
3435-3438 A579   Set of 4   4.50 4.50

American Indian Chiefs — A580

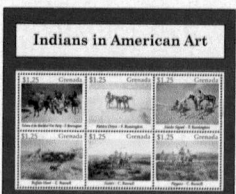

Paintings of American Indians — A581

No. 3439: a, American Horse. b, Blue Bird. c, Crow King. d, Crow Man. e, Gall. f, Good Horse. g, Goose. h, John Grass. i, Rain-in-the-Face. j, Red Cloud. k, Sitting Bull. l, Wild Horse.
No. 3440: a, Return of the Blackfoot War Party, by Frederic Remington. b, Ridden Down, by Remington. c, Smoke Signal, by Remington. d, Buffalo Hunt, by Charles Russell. e, Scouts, by Russell. f, Piegans, by Russell.

**2004, Apr. 19**       **Perf. 13¾**
3439 A580 75c Sheet of 12, #a-l   6.75 6.75
3440 A581 $1.25 Sheet of 6, #a-f   5.75 5.75

---

Souvenir Sheet

Deng Xiaoping (1904-97), Chinese Communist Party Leader — A582

**2004, May 3**       **Perf. 13½x13½**
3441 A582 $6 multi       4.50 4.50

Election of Pope John Paul II, 25th Anniv. A583

No. 3442: a, Kissing baby. b, With Mikhail Gorbachev. c, Waving to crowd. d, Meeting with Polish deportees. e, Visit to Russia.

**2004, May 3**     **Perf. 13¼x13½**
3442 A583 $2 Sheet of 5, #a-e   7.50 7.50

Marilyn Monroe (1926-62) — A584

No. 3444: a, Wearing red dress with strap over shoulder, mouth wide open. b, Wearing orange red dress, mouth closed. c, Wearing white dress. d, Wearing red dress, mouth partially open.

**2004, May 3**       **Perf. 14**
3443 A584 50c shown     .60 .60
      **Perf. 13½x13¼**
3444 A584 $2 Sheet of 4, #a-d   7.50 7.50
No. 3443 printed in sheets of 16.

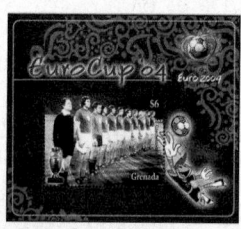

European Soccer Championships, Portugal — A585

No. 3445, vert.: a, Jan Svehlik. b, Franz Beckenbauer. c, Karol Dobias. d, Crvena Zvezda Stadium, Belgrade.
$6, 1976 Czechoslovakian team.

**2004, May 3**      **Perf. 13½x13¼**
3445 A585 $2 Sheet of 4, #a-d   6.00 6.00
**Souvenir Sheet**
**Perf. 13¼**
3446 A585 $6 multi       4.50 4.50
No. 3445 contains four 28x42mm stamps.

D-Day, 60th Anniv. — A586

Designs: 45c, Don Sheppard, Royal Engineers. $1, Air Chief Marshall Sir Arthur Tedder. $1.50, Douglas Kay, 13th/18th Royal Hussars. $3, Gen. Bernard Montgomery.

No. 3451: a, Germans detect Allied invasion. b, Germans prepare to engage Allied invasion fleet. c, Soldier, Merville Battery. d, Paratroopers capture Merville Battery.

No. 3452, $2: a, HMS Belfast fires on German shore batteries. b, Allies pound German coastal defenses. c, Air strikes over Utah Beach. d, Allied troops head towards Omaha Beach.

No. 3453, $6, Fake landing craft. No. 3454, $6, Pipeline under the ocean.

**2004, May 3**     *Perf. 14*
**Stamps + Labels (#3447-3450)**

3447-3450 A586 Set of 4    4.50 4.50
**Sheets of 4, #a-d**
3451-3452 A586 Set of 2    12.00 12.00
**Souvenir Sheets**
3453-3454 A586 Set of 2    9.00 9.00

Locomotives and Famous Men — A587

No. 3455, $1: a, Sir Lord Nelson 4-6-0. b, South African 16CR Class Pacific. c, Florisdorf 0-6-0 Fireless, Austria. d, GWR 57XX Class 0-6-0. e, GWR Castle Class 4-6-0. f, GWR Saint Class 4-6-0. g, GWR Star Class 4-6-0. h, GWR 28XX Class 2-8-0. i, GWR 51XX Class 2-6-2T.

No. 3456, $1, vert.: a, GN Stirling Single 4-2-2. b, Beyer Peacock Mogul 2-6-0. c, Prussian G8 0-8-0. d, George Stephenson. e, James Nasmyth. f, Nasmyth's steam hammer. g, Raven Z Class 4-4-2. h, Sir Vincent Raven. i, Thomas Cook.

No. 3457, $1, vert.: a, SR Schools Class 4-4-0. b, Indian Railways SGS Class 0-6-0. c, Borsig 0-4-0 Tram, Paraguay. d, Richard Trevithick. e, Herbert Garratt. f, Isambard Kingdom Brunel. g, Replica of Trevithick's Coalbrookdale Engine. h, Rhodesian 20th Class Garratt. i, Train on Brunel's Royal Saltash Bridge.

No. 3458, $6, California Zephyr. No. 3459, $6, Indian Pacific. No. 3460, $6, Cumbres and Toltec.

**2004, July 19**     *Litho.*
**Sheets of 9, #a-i**
3455-3457 A587 Set of 3    21.00 21.00
**Souvenir Sheets**
3458-3460 A587 Set of 3    13.50 13.50

Elvis Presley (1935-77) — A588

No. 3461: a, Holding guitar (brown). b, Playing guitar (green). c, Playing guitar, diff. (red violet). d, Portrait (brown). e, Like #3461b, (blue).

**2004, Aug. 3**     *Perf. 14*
3461 A588 $1.50 Sheet, #a-d,   2 #e    7.25 7.25

Operation Iraqi Freedom — A589

No. 3462: a, Pres. George W. Bush. b. Paul Bremer. c, Col. James Hickey, US Special Forces. d, A friendly welcome.

**2004, Aug. 25**     *Perf. 13¼x13½*
3462 A589 $2 Sheet of 4, #a-d    6.00 6.00

Queen Juliana of the Netherlands (1909-2004) A590

**2004, Aug. 25**    *Litho.*    *Perf. 13¼*
3463 A590 $2 multi    1.50 1.50
Printed in sheets of 6.

**Miniature Sheet**

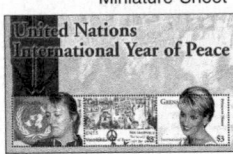

Intl. Year of Peace A591

No. 3464: a, Jody Williams, 1997 Nobel Peace laureate. b, Protesters against landmines. c, Princess Diana.

**2004, Sept. 7**     *Perf. 14*
3464 A591 $3 Sheet of 3, #a-c   6.75 6.75

**Miniature Sheet**

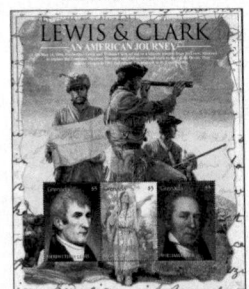

Lewis and Clark Expedition, Bicent. — A592

No. 3465: a, Meriwether Lewis. b, Sacajawea. c, William Clark.

**2004, Sept. 7**     *Perf. 14¼*
3465 A592 $3 Sheet of 3, #a-c   6.75 6.75

**Miniature Sheet**

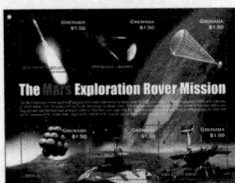

Mars Rover Mission A593

No. 3466: a, Delta II rocket blasts off. b, Entering Mars atmosphere. c, Parachute descent. d, Landing on the surface. e, Rover leaving lander. f, Rover on Mars surface.

**2004, Sept. 7**
3466 A593 $1.50 Sheet of 6, #a-f 6.75 6.75

Ocean Liners A594

No. 3467, $2: a, RMS Titanic. b, TSS Normandie. c, Mauritania. d, Lusitania.
No. 3468, $2: a, Queen Mary 2. b, Queen Elizabeth II. c, Queen Mary. d, Queen Elizabeth.
$6, Queen Mary 2, diff.

**2004, Sept. 7**     *Perf. 13¼x13*
**Sheets of 4, #a-d**
3467-3468 A594 Set of 2    12.00 12.00
**Souvenir Sheet**
3469 A594 $6 multi    4.50 4.50

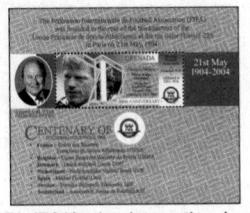

FIFA (Fédération Internationale de Football Association), Cent. — A595

No. 3470: a, Gabriel Batistuta. b, Cafu. c, Michel Platini. d, Gianluca Vialli. $6, Oliver Kahn.

**2004, Nov. 1**     *Perf. 12¾x12½*
3470 A595 $2 Sheet of 4, #a-d   6.00 6.00
**Souvenir Sheet**
3471 A595 $6 multi    4.50 4.50

National Basketball Association Players — A596

Designs: No. 3472, 75c, Pau Gasol, Memphis Grizzlies. No. 3473, 75c, Allen Iverson, Philadelphia 76ers. No. 3474, 75c, Stephon Marbury, New York Knicks.

**2004**     *Perf. 14*
3472-3474 A596 Set of 3    1.75 1.75
Issued: No. 3472, 11/3; No. 3473, 11/5; No. 3474, 11/6. Each printed in sheets of 12. See Nos. 3485-3487.

**Miniature Sheet**

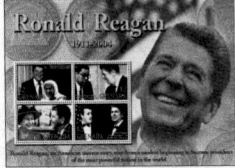

Pres. Ronald Reagan (1911-2004) — A597

No. 3475: a, With Mother Teresa. b, With Colin Powell. c, With Queen Elizabeth II. d, With Brian Mulroney.

**2004**     *Perf. 13½*
3475 A597 $2 Sheet of 4, #a-d   6.00 6.00

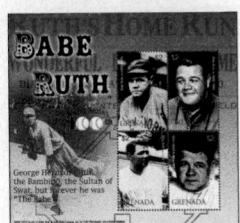

George Herman "Babe" Ruth (1895-1948), Baseball Player — A599

Various portraits.

**2004**     *Perf. 14*
3476 A598 $2 Sheet of 4, #a-d   6.00 6.00
           *Perf. 13¾x13¼*
3477 A599 $2 Sheet of 4, #a-d   6.00 6.00

Christmas — A600

Paintings by Norman Rockwell: 35c, Merry Christmas. 75c, Yuletide Merriment. $1, Dressing Up. $4, Christmas. $6, The London Coach.

**2004, Dec. 9**     *Perf. 12*
3478-3481 A600 Set of 4    4.75 4.75
**Souvenir Sheet**
3482 A600 $6 multi    4.50 4.50

New Year 2005 (Year of the Rooster) — A601

Paintings by Qi Baishi: $1, Chrysanthemums, Cocks and Hens. $4, Taro Leaves and Double Hens.

**2005, Jan. 17**   *Litho.*   *Perf. 11¾x12¼*
3483 A601 $1 multi    1.25 1.25
**Souvenir Sheet**
         *Perf. 12¾x13*
3484 A601 $4 multi    5.00 5.00
No. 3483 printed in sheets of 4. No. 3484 contains one 22x76mm stamp.

**Basketball Players Type of 2004**

Designs: No. 3485, 75c, Zydrunas Ilgauskas, Cleveland Cavaliers. No. 3486, 75c, Dwayne Wade, Miami Heat. $3, Tracy McGrady, Orlando Magic.

**2005, Feb. 10**     *Perf. 14*
3485-3487 A596 Set of 3    3.50 3.50

**Souvenir Sheet**

Intl. Year of Rice A602

No. 3488: a, Detail from Deities Overseeing the Transplanting of Rice, by unknown artist. b, Detail from the Taoist God Overseeing the Rice Planting, by unknown artist. c, Women Transplanting Rice in Late Spring Rain, by Hiroshige.

**2005, Feb. 10**
3488 A602 $3 Sheet of 3, #a-c   6.75 6.75

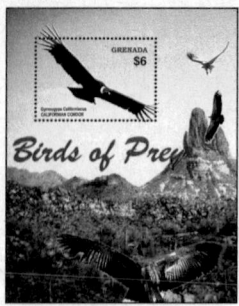

Birds, Wild Cats and Butterflies — A603

No. 3489, $1.50, vert. — Birds: a, Turkey vulture. b, Bald eagle. c, Peregrine falcon. d, Prairie falcon. e, Northern goshawk. f, Cooper's hawk.

No. 3490, $1.50, vert. — Wild cats: a, Cheetah. b, Lion. c, White tiger. d, Leopard. e, Bobcat. f, Bengal tiger.

No. 3491, $1.50 — Butterflies: a, Machaonides's swallowtail. b, Viceroy. c, Glasswing satyr. d, Birdwing. e, Ornithoptera goliath procus. f, Ornithoptera priamus alberio.

No. 3492, $6, California condor. No. 3493, $6, Jaguar, vert. No. 3494, $6, Lime butterfly.

**2005, Feb. 10**           **Litho.**
Sheets of 6, #a-f
3489-3491 A603   Set of 3    21.00 21.00
**Souvenir Sheets**
3492-3494 A603   Set of 3    13.50 13.50

A604

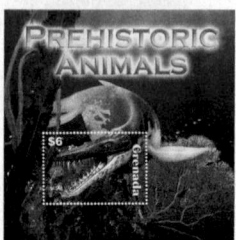

Prehistoric Animals — A605

No. 3495: a, Majungatholus. b, Diplodocus. c, Willo. d, Velociraptor.

No. 3496, $2: a, Archelon. b, Ammonite. c, Plesiosaur. d, Xiphactinus.

No. 3497, $2: a, Pteranodon. b, Dimorphodon. c, Pterodactylus. d, Rhamphorhynchus.

No. 3498, Spinosaurus.

No. 3499, $6, Pliosaur. No. 3500, $6, Tapejara imperator.

**2005, Feb. 10**
3495 A604 $2 Sheet of 4, #a-d   6.00   6.00
Sheets of 4, #a-d
3496-3497 A605   Set of 2    12.00 12.00
**Souvenir Sheets**
3498 A604 $6 multi         4.50   4.50
3499-3500 A605   Set of 2     9.00   9.00

Souvenir Sheet

Buildings Damaged in Hurricane Ivan — A606

No. 3501: a, Cathedral of Immaculate Conception. b, Anglican Church. c, York House. d, Springs Sub-office.

**2005, Mar. 8**        **Perf. 12¾**
3501 A606 $2 Sheet of 4, #a-d   6.00 6.00

Elvis Presley (1935-77) — A607

No. 3502, $1.50: a, Singing, 1955. b, Holding microphone, 1957. c, Playing guitar, 1959. d, Singing, 1961. e, Singing, 1968. f, With guitar, 1970.

No. 3503, $1.50: a, Dancing, 1957. b, Playing guitar, 1964. c, On saddle, 1965. d, Playing guitar, 1968. e, Playing piano, 1969. f, Singing, 1970.

**2005, Apr. 4**        **Perf. 13¾**
Sheets of 6, #a-f
3502-3503 A607   Set of 2    13.50 13.50

Yasujiro Ozu (1903-63), Film Director — A608

No. 3504: a, Tenement Gentleman, 1947. b, Tokyo Story, 1953. c, A Hen in the Wind, 1948. d, Floating Weeds, 1959.

**2005, Apr. 8**        **Perf. 14¼**
3504 A608 $2 Sheet of 4, #a-d   6.00 6.00

Dutch Royalty A609

No. 3505: a, King William I. b, King William II. c, King William III. d, Queen Wilhelmina. e, Queen Juliana. f, Queen Beatrix. g, Prince Willem-Alexander. h, Princess Catharina-Amalia.

**2005, Apr. 14**   **Litho.**   **Perf. 12**
3505 A609 $2 Sheet of 8, #a-h 12.00 12.00

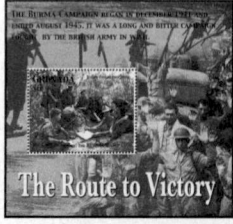

End of World War II, 60th Anniv. A610

No. 3506, $2 — Burma Campaign: a, "21 Curves" Road. b, British advance through the

jungle of Burma. c, Troops at Magwe airstrip. d, Allied troops escorting prisoners.

No. 3507, $2 — Operation Market Garden: a, Allied troops landing behind enemy lines. b, Allied troops fire on German defenders. c, German troops move up to counterattack. d, Bridges still remain in German hands.

No. 3508, $6, Troops discuss next move.

No. 3509, $6, Allied troops meet stiff resistance.

**2005, May 10**        **Perf. 13¼**
Sheets of 4, #a-d
3506-3507 A610   Set of 2    12.00 12.00
**Souvenir Sheets**
3508-3509 A610   Set of 2    9.00   9.00

V-E Day, 60th Anniv. A611

No. 3510: a, D-Day. b, Allied troops break through enemy lines. c, German troops begin to surrender. d, The war in Europe is over.

$6, Berlin falls to the armies of the Soviet Union.

**2005, May 10**        **Perf. 14**
3510 A611 $2 Sheet of 4, #a-d   6.00 6.00
**Souvenir Sheet**
3511 A611 $6 multi        4.50 4.50

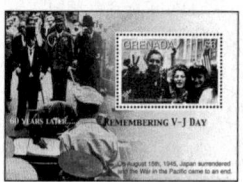

V-J Day, 60th Anniv. A612

No. 3512: a, Airplanes over islands of the Pacific. b, Allied forces storm the beaches of Japanese-held islands. c, Gen. Douglas MacArthur returns to the Philippines. d, The Japanese armies surrender.

$6, Allies enjoy victory celebration.

**2005, May 10**
3512 A612 $2 Sheet of 4, #a-d   6.00 6.00
**Souvenir Sheet**
3513 A612 $6 multi        4.50 4.50

Rotary International, Cent. — A613

No. 3514: a, Child receiving polio vaccination. b, District 7030 Governor David Edwards and wife, Donna. c, Paul P. Harris, Rotary International founder.

$6, 2001-02 Rotary President Richard D. King, children.

**2005, May 10**        **Perf. 14**
3514 A613 $3 Sheet of 3, #a-c   6.75 6.75
**Souvenir Sheet**
3515 A613 $6 multi        4.50 4.50

Miniature Sheet

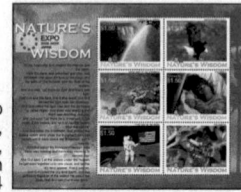

Expo 2005, Aichi, Japan A614

No. 3516: a, Victoria Falls. b, Bald eagle. c, Caribbean coral reef. d, Childbirth. e, First man on the moon. f, Pollination.

**2005, June 27**        **Perf. 12**
3516 A614 $1.50 Sheet of 6, #a-f 6.75 6.75

Albert Einstein (1879-1955), Physicist — A615

No. 3517 — Einstein and country name in: a, Blue. b, Black. c, White. d, Red
$6, Einstein with pipe.

**2005, June 27**        **Perf. 12¾**
3517 A615 $2 Sheet of 4, #a-d   6.00 6.00
**Souvenir Sheet**
3518 A615 $6 multi        4.50 4.50

Souvenir Sheet

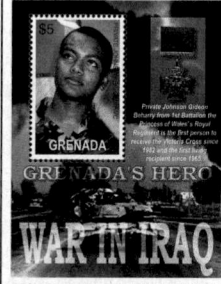

Private Johnson Beharry, Victoria Cross Recipient in Iraq War A616

**2005, July 11**        **Litho.**
3519 A616 $5 multi        3.75 3.75

Hans Christian Andersen (1805-75), Author — A617

No. 3520: a, Andersen, with hands shown. b, Photograph of Andersen. c, Andersen, with white tie.

$6, Andersen's tombstone, Copenhagen.

**2005, July 11**
3520 A617 $3 Sheet of 3, #a-c   6.75 6.75
**Souvenir Sheet**
3521 A617 $6 multi        4.50 4.50

Friedrich von Schiller (1759-1805), Writer — A618

No. 3522, vert.: a, William Tell Memorial, Altdorf, Switzerland. b, Animated movie of William Tell. c, Stage production of William Tell.
$6, Scene from William Tell story.

**2005, July 11**        **Perf. 14**
3522 A618 $3 Sheet of 3, #a-c   6.75 6.75
**Souvenir Sheet**
3523 A618 $6 multi        4.50 4.50

Jules Verne (1828-1905),
Writer — A619

No. 3524: a, Photograph of Verne. b, Photograph of Verne in oval. c, Drawing of Verne.
$6, From the Earth to the Moon.

**2005, July 11**     *Perf. 12¾*
3524 A619 $3 Sheet of 3, #a-c    6.75 6.75
    **Souvenir Sheet**
3525 A619 $6 multi     4.50 4.50

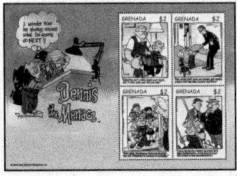

Battle of
Trafalgar,
Bicent.
A620

No. 3526, vert.: a, Admiral Horatio Nelson.
b, Napoleon Bonaparte. c, HMS Victory. d,
The Nelson Touch.
$6, Sailors on ship.

**2005, July 11**     *Perf. 12¾*
3526 A620 $2 Sheet of 4, #a-d    6.00 6.00
    **Souvenir Sheet**
3527 A620 $6 multi     4.50 4.50

    **Miniature Sheets**

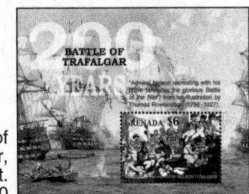

Dennis
The
Menace,
Comic
Strip by
Hank
Ketcham
A621

No. 3528, $2: a, "Grandpa got a new knee. . ." b, "Joey an' me don't have any money. . ." c, "Good news, Mrs. Wilson! . ." d, "I think the boy's. . ."
No. 3529, $2: a, "How 'bout a trade. . ." b, "It's not a good idea. . ." c, "I'll bet you were the top . ." d, "Boy, I'm glad I don't have to. . ."

**2005, July 11**     *Perf. 14¼*
    **Sheets of 4, #a-d**
3528-3529 A621   Set of 2    12.00 12.00

    Souvenir Sheet

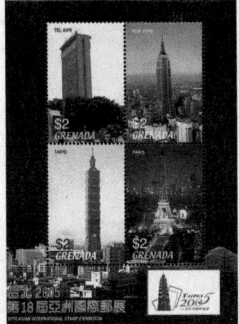

Taipei 2005 Intl. Stamp
Exhibition — A622

No. 3530: a, Shalom Meir Tower, Tel Aviv. b, Empire State Building, New York. c, Taipei 101 Building, Taipei. d, Eiffel Tower, Paris.

**2005, Aug. 19**     *Perf. 14*
3530 A622 $2 Sheet of 4, #a-d    6.00 6.00

Pope John Paul II
(1920-2005) and Lech
Walesa — A623

**2005, Aug. 22**     *Perf. 12¾*
3531 A623 $4 multi     3.00 3.00
    Printed in sheets of 4.

Wedding of Prince
Charles and Camilla
Parker Bowles — A624

Various pictures of couple with oval in: No. 3532, $2, Lemon. No. 3533, $2, Light blue. No. 3534, $2, Pink, horiz.

**2005, Sept. 7**     *Perf. 13½*
3532-3534 A624   Set of 3    4.50 4.50
    Each stamp printed in sheets of 4.

Christmas — A625

Designs: 25c, The Nativity, by Correggio. 75c, Virgin and Child, by Lorenzo Lotto. $1, The Holy Family, by Lotto. $5, Madonna and Child with the Saints, by Lotto.
$6, Allegory of Music, by Fra Filippo Lippi.

**2005, Nov. 15**     *Perf. 12¾*
3535-3538 A625   Set of 4    5.25 5.25
    **Souvenir Sheet**
3539 A625 $6 multi     4.50 4.50

    **Bird Type of 2000**
**2005**    **Litho.**    *Perf. 12x11¾*
    **Size:22x26mm**
3540 A472 10c Purple-throated
     Carib     .25 .25

    **Miniature Sheets**

Chelsea
Soccer
Team,
Cent.
A626

Liverpool
Soccer
Team
A627

No. 3541: a, Stadium and field. b, Stadium, field, team emblem and years. c, Players holding English League Championship award. d, Players in bus with cup and flag. e, Fans with flag. f, Aerial view of bus carrying players. g, Players. h, Coach. i, Stadium, field, team emblem. j, Team with award.
No. 3542: a, Crowd watching bus carrying players near stadium. b, Player and coach holding UEFA Cup. c, Gate. d, Aerial view of stadium. e, Banner. f, Players waving. g, Fans. h, Soccer match. i, Players celebrating. j, Crowd cheering players in bus.

The Two Hounds,
by Hui-Tsung
A628

**2005, Dec. 28**    **Litho.**    *Perf. 13¼*
3541 A626 $1.50 Sheet of 10,
     #a-j     11.50 11.50
3542 A627 $1.50 Sheet of 10,
     #a-j     11.50 11.50

**2006, Jan. 3**
3543 A628 $1 shown     .75 .75
    **Souvenir Sheet**
3544 A628 $4 Entire painting   3.00 3.00
    No. 3544 contains one 50x37mm stamp.

Pope Benedict
XVI — A629

**2006, Jan. 10**
3545 A629 $2 multi     1.50 1.50
    Printed in sheets of 4.

A630

Elvis Presley (1935-77) — A631

No. 3546 — Movie posters: a, Girls! Girls! Girls! b, Jailhouse Rock. c, Paradise - Hawaiian Style. d, It Happened at the World's Fair.

**2006**    **Litho.**    *Perf. 13¼*
3546 A630 $3 Sheet of 4, #a-
     d     9.00 9.00
    **Litho. & Embossed**
    *Die Cut Perf. 7¾*
    **Without Gum**
3547 A631 $20 shown    15.00 15.00
    Issued: No. 3546, 7/11, No. 3547, 2/21.

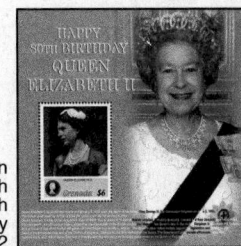

Queen
Elizabeth
II, 80th
Birthday
A632

No. 3548: a, Wearing necklace, no earrings. b, Wearing blue jacket. c, Portrait. d, Wearing jacket and earrings.
$6, Wearing hat.

**2006, Feb. 21**    **Litho.**    *Perf. 13¼*
3548 A632 $3 Sheet of 4, #a-d   9.00 9.00
    **Souvenir Sheet**
    *Perf. 12¼x12*
3549 A632 $6 multi     4.50 4.50

Teams Competing in 2006 World Cup
Soccer Championships,
Germany — A633

Designs: No. 3550, $1.50, Angola. No. 3551, $1.50, Argentina. No. 3552, $1.50, Australia. No. 3553, $1.50, Brazil. No. 3554, $1.50, Costa Rica. No. 3555, $1.50, Croatia. No. 3556, $1.50, Czech Republic. No. 3557, $1.50, Ecuador. No. 3558, $1.50, England. No. 3559, $1.50, France. No. 3560, $1.50, Germany. No. 3561, $1.50, Ghana. No. 3562, $1.50, Iran. No. 3563, $1.50, Italy. No. 3564, $1.50, Ivory Coast. No. 3565, $1.50, Japan. No. 3566, $1.50, Mexico. No. 3567, $1.50, Netherlands. No. 3568, $1.50, Paraguay. No. 3569, $1.50, Poland. No. 3570, $1.50, Portugal. No. 3571, $1.50, Saudi Arabia. No. 3572, $1.50, Serbia and Montenegro. No. 3573, $1.50, South Korea. No. 3574, $1.50, Spain. No. 3575, $1.50, Sweden. No. 3576, $1.50, Switzerland. No. 3577, $1.50, Togo. No. 3578, $1.50, Trinidad and Tobago. No. 3579, $1.50, Tunisia. No. 3580, $1.50, Ukraine. No. 3581, $1.50, United States.

**2006, Mar. 29**     *Perf. 12¼x12*
3550-3581 A633   Set of 32   36.00 36.00
    Nos. 3550-3581 each printed in sheets of 6. Stamps other than Nos. 3550, 3553, 3554, 3560, 3561, 3566, 3575, 3579 and 3581, which have solid color backgrounds, have multicolored backgrounds that vary within the sheet.

Marilyn Monroe (1926-62), Actress — A634

**2006, Mar. 30**     *Perf. 13¼*
3582 A634 $3 multi     2.25 2.25
    Printed in sheets of 4.

2006 Winter
Olympics,
Turin — A635

Designs: No. 3583, Poster for 1980 Lake Placid Winter Olympics. No. 3583A, Poster for 2006 Turin Winter Olympics. No. 3584, Switzerland #B173. No. 3584A, Italy #2722. $2, Poster for 1948 St. Moritz Winter Olympics. $3, Switzerland #B172.

**2006, May 10**     *Perf. 14¼*
3583 A635 75c multicolored   .55 .55
3583A A635 75c multicolored   .55 .55
3584 A635 90c multicolored   .70 .70
3584A A635 90c multicolored   .70 .70
3585 A635 $2 multicolored   1.50 1.50
3586 A635 $3 multicolored   2.25 2.25
    *Nos. 3583-3586 (6)*   6.25 6.25

Rosa Parks (1913-2005), American Civil
Rights Activist — A636

**2006, May 27**     *Perf. 11½x12*
3587 A636 $3 multi     2.25 2.25
    Printed in sheets of 3.

Flags and Uniforms of World Cup Soccer Champions A637

Designs: 75c, Brazil, 2002. 90c, Germany, 1990. $3, France, 1998.

**2006, June 9**     **Perf. 13¼**
3588-3590 A637   Set of 3     3.50 3.50

World Cup Trophy — A638

**2006, June 9**     **Die Cut**
**Self-Adhesive**
3591 A638 $6 multi     4.50 4.50

Rembrandt (1606-69), Painter — A639

Designs: 50c, The Little Jewish Bride. $1, Young Man in Velvet Cap. $1.50, Old Woman Sleeping. No. 3595, $3, Woman Reading. No. 3596, $6, Portrait of a Seated Man (70x100mm). No. 3597, $6, Portrait of a Scholar (70x100mm).

No. 3598, $3: a, Young Woman with Flowers in Her Hair. b, Portrait of a Seated Woman. c, Alijdt Adriaensor. d, Amalia van Solms.

*Perf. 12, 12½x12¼ (#3596, 3597)*
**2006, June 16**
3592-3597 A639   Set of 6    13.50 13.50
3597a    Imperf.        4.50 4.50

**Miniature Sheet**
**Perf. 13x13¼**
3598 A639 $3 Sheet of 4, #a-d   9.00 9.00

Souvenir Sheet

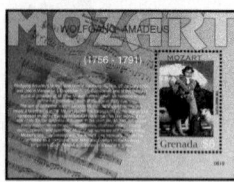

Wolfgang Amadeus Mozart (1756-91), Composer — A640

**2006, June 22**     **Perf. 12¾**
3599 A640 $6 multi     4.50 4.50

Souvenir Sheet

Ludwig Durr (1878-1956), Engineer, and Zeppelins — A641

No. 3600 — Durr and: a, Graf Zeppelin D-LZ-127. b, Graf Zeppelin LT. c, Graf Zeppelin L-26.

**2006, June 22**
3600 A641 $4 Sheet of 3, #a-c   9.00 9.00

---

Space A642

No. 3601, $2 — Sputnik 1: a, Sergei Korolev. b, Sputnik 1 in space. c, Inside Sputnik 1. d, Sputnik 1 capsule.

No. 3602, $2, vert. — Apollo-Soyuz: a, Apollo rocket. b, Apollo command module and adapter. c, Soyuz rocket on launchpad. d, Soyuz.

No. 3603 — Giotto Comet Probe: a, Halley's Comet, round head in yellow at right. b, Tip of Giotto Probe launcher Ariane V14. c, Halley's Comet, head at left, thin tail. d, Halley's Comet, head in white at right. e, Bottom of Giotto Probe launcher Ariane V14. f, Halley's Comet, head at left, wide tail.

No. 3604, $6, Stardust Comet Probe. No. 3605, $6, Comet Tempel 1 Deep Impact Mission. No. 3606, $6, Space Shuttle Discovery's return to space.

**2006, Sept. 14**   **Litho.**   **Perf. 12¾**
**Sheets of 4, #a-d**
3601-3602 A642   Set of 2    12.00 12.00
3603 A642 $2 Sheet of 6, #a-f   9.00 9.00

**Souvenir Sheets**
3604-3606 A642   Set of 3    13.50 13.50

Christopher Columbus (1451-1506), Explorer — A643

Designs: $1.50, Sinking of the Santa Maria. $2, Santa Maria, vert. $3, Columbus, sailor and ship, vert. $4, Columbus and ships, vert. $6, Fleet of ships, 1493.

**2006, Oct. 26**     **Perf. 12¾**
3607-3610 A643   Set of 4    8.00 8.00

**Souvenir Sheet**
3611 A643 $6 multi     4.50 4.50

Butterflies A644

Designs: 10c, Mourning cloak butterfly. 25c, Snout butterfly. $1, Tithorea pinthias. $2, Diadem butterfly. $4, Red satyr butterfly. $5, Taygetis chrysogone. $10, Pierella hortona. $20, Morpho aega.

**2006, Dec. 1**   **Litho.**   **Perf. 12½**
3612 A644 10c multi      .25 .25
3613 A644 25c multi      .25 .25
3614 A644 $1 multi      .75 .75
3615 A644 $2 multi     1.50 1.50
3616 A644 $4 multi     3.00 3.00
3617 A644 $5 multi     3.75 3.75
3618 A644 $10 multi    7.50 7.50
3619 A644 $20 multi   15.00 15.00
   Nos. 3612-3619 (8)   32.00 32.00

Princess Maxima of the Netherlands — A645

No. 3620: a, Head of Princess Maxima. b, Princess Maxima holding purse.

**2006, Dec. 7**     **Perf. 13½**
3620 A645 $1.50 Pair, #a-b   2.25 2.25
  Printed in sheets containing 3 of each stamp.

---

Christmas — A646

Details of The Adoration of the Shepherds, by Peter Paul Rubens: 25c, Man with hat. 50c, Mary. 75c, Shepherd. $1, Baby Jesus.

No. 3625: a, Like 25c. b, Like 50c. c, Like 75c. d, Like $1.

**2006, Dec. 21**     **Perf. 14**
3621-3624 A646   Set of 4    1.90 1.90
**Souvenir Sheet**
3625 A646 $2 Sheet of 4, #a-d   6.00 6.00

Betty Boop A647

No. 3626 — Betty Boop: a, Sitting on "E." b, With hands on thighs, between "Y" and "B." c, With one leg elevated. d, With hands clasped, Standing behind "E." e, With arms at side, standing in front of "Y." f, With arms raised upwards.

No. 3627: a, With hands clasped, blue circles. b, With arms at side, red and blue circles. c, With arms raised upwards, pink and blue circles. d, At microphone, blue circles.

No. 3628, $3: a, Holding mirror. b, Wearing fruited hat.

No. 3629, $3, horiz.: a, Head and upper torso. b, Lower torso.

**2006, Dec. 22**     **Perf. 14**
3626 A647 $1.50 Sheet of 6, #a-f 6.75 6.75
3627 A647   $2 Sheet of 4, #a-d                6.00 6.00
**Souvenir Sheets of 2, #a-b**
3628-3629 A647   Set of 2    9.00 9.00

Arsenal Soccer Team A648

No. 3630: a, $1, Players and crowd. b, $1, Soccer field at night. c, $1, Fans in seats at end of stadium. d, $1, Emirates Stadium exterior. e, $1, Players. f, $2, Players. g, $2, Aerial view of stadium exterior. h, $2, Fans. i, $2, Soccer field and fans. j, $2, Stadium exterior at night.

**2007, Jan. 16**
3630 A648   Sheet of 10, #a-j   11.50 11.50

Concorde Test Pilots and Flags — A649

No. 3631: a, Amore Turcat, French flag. b, Brian Trubshaw, British flag.

**2007, Feb. 15**
3631 A649 $2 Pair, #a-b   3.00 3.00
  Printed in sheets containing three of each stamp.

---

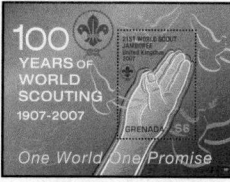

Scouting, Cent. A650

No. 3632 — Scout sign and denomination in: a, Blue. b, Orange. c, Red violet. d, Green $6, Orange.

**2007, Feb. 15**
3632 A650 $3 Sheet of 4, #a-d   9.00 9.00
**Souvenir Sheet**
3633 A650 $6 multi     4.50 4.50

Pres. John F. Kennedy (1917-63) — A651

No. 3634, $2 — First meeting with Soviet Premier Nikita Khrushchev: a, Khrushchev at the Simferopol Space Control Center. b, Kennedy greeting Khrushchev. c, Kennedy and Khrushchev on sofa. d, Kennedy and Khrushchev at residence of US Ambassador in Vienna.

No. 3635, $2 — Cuban Missile Crisis: a, Khrushchev and Fidel Castro. b, Kennedy addressing nation. c, Completed SA-2 missile site. d, Kennedy and Khrushchev shaking hands in Vienna.

**2007, Feb. 15**     **Sheets of 4, #a-d**
3634-3635 A651   Set of 2    12.00 12.00

Souvenir Sheet

New Year 2007 (Year of the Pig) A652

No. 3636 — Text "Traditional Chinese New Year Paper Cutting" in: a, $1, Black. b, $1, White. c, $2, Beige. d, $2, Yellow.

**2007, Feb. 18**     **Perf. 14**
3636 A652   Sheet of 4, #a-d   4.50 4.50

Pope Benedict XVI — A653

**2007, June 4**   **Litho.**   **Perf. 13¼**
3637 A653 $1 multi     .75 .75
  Printed in sheets of 8.

2007 Cricket World Cup, West Indies — A654

Designs: $1, Cricket World Cup emblem, flag and map of Grenada. $2, Rawl Lewis. $3, Queen's Park, horiz.
$6, Cricket World Cup emblem.

**2007, June 18**
3638-3640 A654 Set of 3    4.50 4.50

**Souvenir Sheet**
3641 A654 $6 multi    4.50 4.50

Wedding of Queen Elizabeth II and Prince Philip, 60th Anniv. A655

No. 3642: a, Queen and Prince, orange panel. b, Queen, orange panel. c, Queen, light blue panel. d, Queen and Prince, light blue panel. e, Queen and Prince, lilac panel. f, Queen, lilac panel.
$6, Queen and Prince, diff.

**2007, June 25**
3642 A655 $2 Sheet of 6, #a-f    9.00 9.00

**Souvenir Sheet**
3643 A655 $6 multi    4.50 4.50

Princess Diana (1961-97) — A656

No. 3644 — Diana with: a, Red dress. b, Light blue and white dress. c, White gown. d, Green and white dress.
No. 3645, $6, Scarf on head. No. 3646, $6, Red dress, horiz.

**2007, June 25**
3644 A656 $2 Sheet of 4, #a-d    6.00 6.00

**Souvenir Sheets**
3645-3646 A656 Set of 2    9.00 9.00

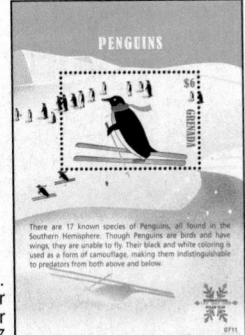

Intl. Polar Year A657

No. 3647, vert.: a, Adult penguin with head raised. b, Three penguins in distance. c, Adult penguin with head lowered. d, Juvenile penguin, ball. e, Juvenile penguin with wings extended. f, Juvenile penguin with head raised.
$6, Penguin on skis.

**2007, June 25**
3647 A657 $2 Sheet of 6, #a-f    9.00 9.00

**Souvenir Sheet**
3648 A657 $6 multi    4.50 4.50

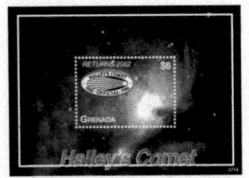

1986 Halley's Comet Merchandising Emblem — A658

No. 3649: a, Orange brown frame. b, Dark blue frame. c, Purple frame. d, Red frame.
$6, Emblem, night sky.

**2007, July 11**
3649 A658 $2 Sheet of 4, #a-d    6.00 6.00

**Souvenir Sheet**
3650 A658 $6 multi    4.50 4.50

U.S. Presidents — A659

No. 3651: a, 1c, George Washington. b, 2c, John Adams. c, 3c, Thomas Jefferson. d, 4c, James Madison. e, 5c, James Monroe. f, 6c, John Quincy Adams. g, 7c, Andrew Jackson. h, 8c, Martin Van Buren. i, 9c, William Henry Harrison. j, 10c, John Tyler. k, 11c, James Knox Polk. l, 12c, Zachary Taylor. m, 13c, Millard Fillmore. n, 14c, Franklin Pierce. o, $4, Presidential seal.
No. 3652: a, 15c, James Buchanan. b, 16c, Abraham Lincoln. c, 17c, Andrew Johnson. d, 18c, Ulysses S. Grant. e, 19c, Rutherford B. Hayes. f, 20c, James A. Garfield. g, 21c, Chester A. Arthur. h, 22c, Grover Cleveland. i, 23c, Benjamin Harrison. j, 24c, Grover Cleveland. k, 25c, William McKinley. l, 26c, Theodore Roosevelt. m, 27c, William Howard Taft. n, 28c, Woodrow Wilson. o, $2, Capitol Dome.
No. 3653: a, 29c, Warren G. Harding. b, 30c, Calvin Coolidge. c, 31c, Herbert Hoover. d, 32c, Franklin D. Roosevelt. e, 33c, Harry S Truman. f, 34c, Dwight D. Eisenhower. g, 35c, John F. Kennedy. h, 36c, Lyndon B. Johnson. i, 37c, Richard M. Nixon. j, 38c, Gerald R. Ford. k, 39c, Jimmy Carter. l, 40c, Ronald Reagan. m, 41c, George H. W. Bush. n, 42c, William J. Clinton. o, 43c, George W. Bush.

**2007, July 16**    *Perf. 12*
3651 A659 Sheet of 15, #a-o    3.75 3.75
3652 A659 Sheet of 15, #a-o    3.75 3.75
3653 A659 Sheet of 15, #a-o    4.00 4.00
   *Nos. 3651-3653 (3)*    11.50 11.50

Worldwide Fund for Nature (WWF) — A660

No. 3654 — Clymene dolphins with denomination in: a, Orange. b, Bluish green. c, Yellow. d, Aquamarine.

**2007, July 23**    *Perf. 13¼*
3654    Strip of 4    3.75 3.75
   a.-d.   A660 $1.20 Any single    .90 .90
   e.   Miniature sheet, 2 each #3654a-3654d    7.50 7.50

**Souvenir Sheet**

St. George's University, 30th Anniv. — A661

**2007, Oct. 26**    *Perf. 12¾*
3655 A661 $6 multi    4.50 4.50

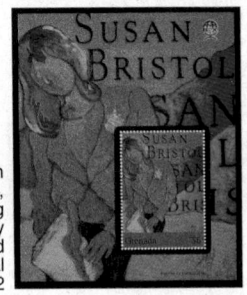

Susan Bristol, Painting by Bernard Vidal A662

**2007, Oct. 26**    *Perf. 13¼*
3656 A662 $6 multi    4.50 4.50

Victoria Cross, 150th Anniv. A663

No. 3657, vert.: a, Corporal Bryan Budd. b, Brigadier General James Forbes-Robertson. c, Private Johnson Beharry. d, Sergeant William J. Gordon. e, Private Henry Tandey. f, Private Jorgen Christian Jensen.
$6, Seaman Jack Mantel.

**2007, Oct. 26**    Litho.
3657 A663 $1.50 Sheet of 6, #a-f 6.75 6.75

**Souvenir Sheet**
3658 A663   $6 multi    4.50 4.50

First Helicopter Flight, Cent. — A664

No. 3659, horiz.: a, S-65/RH-53D. b, Autogyro and bird. c, BK 117. d, AS-64.
$6, AH-64 Apache.

**2007, Oct. 26**
3659 A664 $2 Sheet of 4, #a-d    6.00 6.00

**Souvenir Sheet**
3660 A664 $6 multi    4.50 4.50

**Miniature Sheets**

Intl. Holocaust Remembrance Day — A665

No. 3661 $1.40 — United Nations diplomats and delegates: a, Srgian Kerim, President of 62nd General Assembly. b, Andrei Dapkiunas, Belarus. c, Jean-Marie Ehouzou, Benin. d, Milos Prica, Bosnia & Herzegovina. e, Samuel O. Outlule, Botswana. f, Francis K. Butagira, Uganda. g, Valeriy P. Kuchinsky, Ukraine. h, Jean Ping, President of 59th General Assembly.
No. 3662, $1.40: a, Erasmo Lara-Peña, Dominican Republic. b, Diego Cordovez, Ecuador. c, Carmen M. Gallardo-Hernandez, El Salvador. d, Lino Sima Ekua Avomo, Equatorial Guinea. e, Tina Intelmann, Estonia. f, Dawit Yohannes, Ethiopia. g, Isikia Rabici Savua, Fiji. h, Lars Wide, Chef de Cabinet of 60th General Assembly.
No. 3663, $1.40: a, Angus Friday, Grenada. b, Alfredo Lopes Cabral, Guinea-Bissau. c, Samuel Rudolph Insanally, Guyana. d, Lèo Mérorès, Haiti. e, Ivan Romero-Martinez, Honduras. f, Gabor Brodi, Hungary. g, Hjalmar W. Hannesson, Iceland. h, Dan Gillerman, Israel.
No. 3664, $1.40: a, Colin Beck, Solomon Islands. b, Dumisani S. Kumalo, South Africa. c, Juan Antonio Yáñez-Barnueva, Spain. d,

Anders Liden, Sweden. e, Peter Maurer, Switzerland. f, K. Laxanachantorn Laohaphan, Thailand. g, José Luis Guterres, East Timor. h, Fekitamoeloa 'Utoikamanu, Tonga.

**2007, Oct. 26**    Litho.
**Sheets of 8, #a-h**
3661-3664 A665 Set of 4    35.00 35.00

Christmas A666

Various details from Nativity with the Annunciation to the Shepherds, by Follower of Jan Joest: 25c, 50c, 75c, $1.

**2007, Nov. 1**    *Perf. 14¾x14*
3665-3668 A666 Set of 4    1.90 1.90

New Year 2008 (Year of the Rat) — A667

**2007, Dec. 3**   Litho.   *Perf. 13x13¼*
3669 A667 $2 multi    1.50 1.50
   Printed in sheets of 4.

**Souvenir Sheet**

Breast Cancer Prevention — A668

**2007, Dec. 11**    *Perf. 14*
3670 A668 $6 multi    4.50 4.50

Princess Diana (1961-97) — A669

*Serpentine Die Cut 7¾*
**2007, Dec. 11**    Litho. & Embossed
**Without Gum**
3671 A669 $20 gold & multi    15.00 15.00

**Miniature Sheets**

A670

Elvis Presley (1935-77) — A671

No. 3672 — Presley: a, Holding guitar at neck. b, Singing, not touching microphone. c, Wearing green shirt. d, Facing right, playing guitar. e, Singing, holding microphone. f, Facing right, playing guitar.
No. 3673 — Presley: a, Holding microphone. b, Wearing necktie. c, Holding guitar over shoulder. d, And guitar head.

**2008** Litho. **Perf. 13¼**
3672 A670 $1.50 Sheet of 6, #a-f 6.75 6.75
3673 A671 $2 Sheet of 4, #a-
d 6.00 6.00
Issued: No. 3672, 1/14; No. 3673, 6/13.

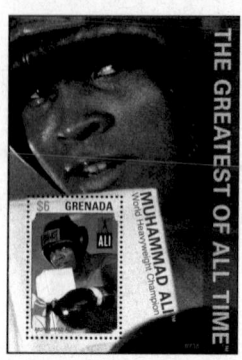

Muhammad Ali, Boxer — A672

No. 3674, $2 — Ali: a, With towel on head, bank of microphones at left. b, With towel on head, bank of microphone at right. c, With fist raised. d, With towel off head, bank of microphones at right.
No. 3675, $2, horiz. — Ali: a, With arms raised. b, Wearing robe. c, At punching bag. d, Boxing.
No. 3676, $6, Ali wearing protective headgear. No. 3677, $2, Ali with fan's hand on shoulder.

**Perf. 12x11½, 11½ (#3675)**
**2008, Jan. 14**
**Sheets of 4, #a-d**
3674-3675 A672 Set of 2 12.00 12.00
**Souvenir Sheets**
**Perf. 13¼**
3676-3677 A672 Set of 2 9.00 9.00

Paintings by Qi Baishi (1864-1957) — A673

No. 3678: a, Magnolias and Bees. b, Mother Hen, Chicks and Banana Leaves. c, Fish, Crabs and Watergrass. d, Crows Returning to Wintry Trees.
$4, Morning Glories.

**2008, Feb. 6** **Perf. 12½**
3678 A673 $1 Sheet of 4, #a-d 3.00 3.00
**Souvenir Sheet**
**Perf. 11¼x11½**
3679 A673 $4 multi 3.00 3.00

Miniature Sheet

2008 Summer Olympics, Beijing — A674

No. 3680: a, Greece #123. b, Poster for 1896 Olympic Games, Athens. c, Germany #B88. d, Poster for 1936 Olympic Games, Berlin.

**2008, Feb. 6** **Perf. 14¼**
3680 A674 $3 Sheet of 4, #a-d 9.00 9.00

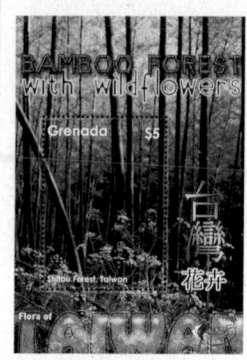

Flora of Taiwan A675

No. 3681, horiz.: a, Oolong tea. b, Pink lotus. c, Japanese maple. d, Bitter melon. e, Rice field. f, Lychees.
$5, Shitou Forest.

**2008, May 8** **Perf. 11½**
3681 A675 $1 Sheet of 6, #a-f 4.50 4.50
**Souvenir Sheet**
**Perf. 13½**
3682 A675 $5 multi 3.75 3.75
No. 3681 contains six 40x30mm stamps. 2008 Taipei Intl. Stamp Exhibition.

2008 World Stamp Championship, Israel — A676

**2008, May 14** **Imperf.**
3683 A676 $6 multi 4.50 4.50

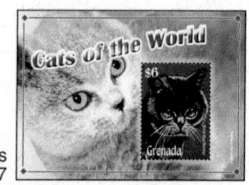

Cats A677

No. 3684: a, Tortoiseshell. b, Korat. c, Turkish Van. d, Manx.
$6, British blue shorthair.

**2008, June 18** **Perf. 11½**
3684 A677 $1.40 Sheet of 4, #a-
d 4.25 4.25
**Souvenir Sheet**
3685 A677 $6 multi 4.50 4.50

Miniature Sheet

Players on 2008 Los Angeles Lakers Basketball Team — A678

No. 3686: a, Trevor Ariza. b, Jordan Farmar. c, Derek Fisher. d, Pau Gasol. e, Kobe Bryant. f, Lamar Odom. g, Vladimir Radmanovic. h, Sasha Vujacic. i, Luke Walton.

**2008, June 17** Litho. **Perf. 13½**
3686 A678 $1 Sheet of 9, #a-i 6.75 6.75

Miniature Sheet

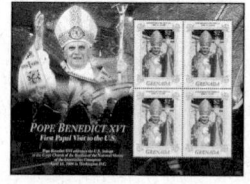

Visit of Pope Benedict XVI to United States A679

No. 3687 — Pope Benedict XVI and faded background showing: a, Bishop's red zucchetto under LL flourish. b, White ceiling tiles at top. c, Bishop's ear at UL. d, Bishop's hands at R.

**2008, June 18** **Perf. 13½**
3687 A679 $2 Sheet of 4, #a-d 6.00 6.00

Miniature Sheet

Pres. John F. Kennedy (1917-63) — A680

No. 3688 — Kennedy and background designs of: a, Flag's white stripe and blue field. b, Flag's white and red stripes. c, Necktie. d, Flag's red and white stripes, with blue in UL corner.

**2008, Oct. 10** **Perf. 11½x11¼**
3688 A680 $1.50 Sheet of 4, #a-
d 4.50 4.50

Miniature Sheets

A681

A682

A683

A684

A685

Shane Warne, Cricket Player A686

No. 3689 — Warne: a, Holding ball, tan frame. b, Waving to crowd, tan frame. c, Close-up, tan frame. d, Wearing white shirt, green frame. e, As "b," green frame. f, As "c," green frame.
No. 3690 — Warne: a, Bowling in Australia uniform, tan frame. b, Holding trophy, tan frame. c, Celebrating, tan frame. d, As "a," green frame. e, As "b," green frame. f, As "c," green frame.
No. 3691 — Drawings of Warne by Phillip Howe: a, The Mastery (tan frame). b, The Revolutionary (tan frame). c, The Appeal (tan frame). d, The Natural (tan frame). e, As "a," green frame. f, As "b," green frame. g, As "c,"

green frame. h, As "d," green frame. Titles are in sheet margin.

No. 3692 — Warne bowling: a, Left arm horizontal, tan frame. b, Leg lifted, hands even, tan frame. c, Leg lifted, right hand higher than left hand, tan frame. d, Arm above head, tan frame. e, As "a," green frame. f, As "b," green frame. g, As "c," green frame. h, As "d," green frame.

No. 3693 — Warne: a, Celebrating and making fist, tan frame. b, With ball near ear, tan frame. c, After releasing ball, tan frame. d, With arm above head, umpire in background, tan frame. e, As "a," green frame. f, As "b," green frame. g, As "c," green frame. h, As "d," green frame.

No. 3694 — Match scenes: a, Warne bowling against Mike Gatting, tan frame, horiz. b, Warne taking 600th test wicket, tan frame. c, Warne capturing 533rd wicket. d, Warne taking 356th test wicket. e, As "a," green frame. f, As "b," green frame. g, As "c," green frame. h, As "d," green frame. Match descriptions are in sheet margin.

**2008, Dec. 3    Perf. 14x14½, 14½x14**
| | | | | |
|---|---|---|---|---|
| 3689 | A681 | $2 Sheet of 6, #a-f | 9.25 | 9.25 |
| 3690 | A682 | $2 Sheet of 6, #a-f | 9.25 | 9.25 |
| 3691 | A683 | $2 Sheet of 8, #a-h | 12.50 | 12.50 |
| 3692 | A684 | $2 Sheet of 8, #a-h | 12.50 | 12.50 |
| 3693 | A685 | $2 Sheet of 8, #a-h | 12.50 | 12.50 |
| 3694 | A686 | $2 Sheet of 8, #a-h | 12.50 | 12.50 |
| | | Nos. 3689-3694 (6) | 68.50 | 68.50 |

### Miniature Sheet

Pope John Paul II (1920-2005) — A687

No. 3695 — Pope John Paul II: a, As child. b, At coronation. c, Holding books. d, With hands raised. e, Wearing biretta, hand on chin. f, Wearing zucchetto, hand touching face.

**2008, Dec. 8    Perf. 13½**
| | | | | |
|---|---|---|---|---|
| 3695 | A687 | $2 Sheet of 6, #a-f | 9.25 | 9.25 |

Coat of Arms A688

**2008, June 18    Litho.    Perf. 14x15**
| | | | | |
|---|---|---|---|---|
| 3696 | A688 | 250c multi + label | 1.90 | 1.90 |

Printed in sheets of 8 + 8 labels.

Inauguration of US Pres. Barack Obama — A689

**2009, Jan. 20    Perf. 12¼x11¾**
| | | | | |
|---|---|---|---|---|
| 3697 | A689 | $2.75 multi | 2.10 | 2.10 |

Printed in sheets of 4.

### Miniature Sheets

Space Exploration, 50th Anniv. (in 2007) — A690

No. 3698, $2: a, Ultraviolet photograph of Sun. b, Buzz Aldrin on Moon. c, Crane lifting Space Shuttle Atlantis at Kennedy Vehicle Assembly Building. d, Mars Orbiter looking at Victoria Crater. e, Cassini Mission to Saturn. f,

Engines being installed on Space Shuttle Atlantis.

No. 3699, $2: a, International Space Station. b, Concept for new lunar truck. c, Milky Way over Ontario. d, M16 and the Eagle Nebula. e, Astronaut in space on Expedition 16. f, Dextre robot working on the Space Station.

No. 3700, $2.50, vert.: a, Canadarm 2 (robotic arm on Space Station). b, Space Shuttle Atlantis on launch pad in daylight. c, Cat's Eye Nebula. d, Orion crew capsule.

No. 3701, $2.50, vert.: a, Space Shuttle Atlantis at Kennedy Space Center at night. b, International Space Station as seen from Space Shuttle Discovery. c, Aurora over Saturn. d, Kibo pressurized and logistic modules.

**2009, Jan. 22    Perf. 12**
**Sheets of 6, #a-f**
| | | | | |
|---|---|---|---|---|
| 3698-3699 | A690 | Set of 2 | 18.50 | 18.50 |

**Sheets of 4, #a-d**
**Perf. 12½**
| | | | | |
|---|---|---|---|---|
| 3700-3701 | A690 | Set of 2 | 15.50 | 15.50 |

A691

Birds A693

Designs: $1, White-crowned pigeon. $2, Blue-winged warbler. $4, Bananaquit. $5, Monk parakeet.

No. 3706: a, Yellow-crowned amazon. b, Yellow-bellied sapsucker. c, Jamaican mango.

No. 3707: a, Tree swallow. b, Ringed kingfisher. c, Black-and-white warbler.

**2009, Jan. 22    Perf. 12½**
| | | | | |
|---|---|---|---|---|
| 3702-3705 | A691 | Set of 4 | 9.25 | 9.25 |
| 3706 | A692 | $3 Sheet of 3, #a-c | 7.00 | 7.00 |

**Perf. 12¾x13**
| | | | | |
|---|---|---|---|---|
| 3707 | A693 | $3 Sheet of 3, #a-c | 7.00 | 7.00 |

New Year 2009 (Year of the Ox) — A694

**2009, Jan. 26    Perf. 12**
| | | | | |
|---|---|---|---|---|
| 3708 | A694 | $2.50 multi | 2.25 | 2.25 |

Printed in sheets of 4.

A695

Mushrooms — A696

Designs: 25c, Panaeolus papilionaceus. 50c, Panaeolus cyanescens. 75c, Panaeolus sphintrinus. 90c, Panaeolus fimicola. $1, Copelandia cyanescens. $4, Psilocybe cubensis.

No. 3715: a, Panaleus subbalteatus. b, Alboleptonia earlei. c, Porphyrellus portoricensis. d, Psilocybe caerulescens.

**2009, Feb. 9    Perf. 11½**
| | | | | |
|---|---|---|---|---|
| 3709-3714 | A695 | Set of 6 | 5.75 | 5.75 |
| 3715 | A696 | $2.50 Sheet of 4, #a-d | 7.75 | 7.75 |

### Miniature Sheet

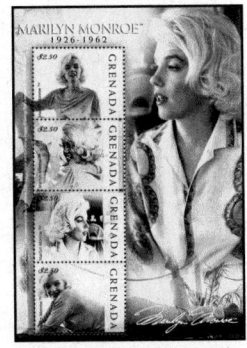

Marilyn Monroe (1926-62), Actress — A697

No. 3716 — Monroe: a, With arm extended. b, Touching wall. c, With chair in background. d, Resting on arms.

**2009, Feb. 9**
| | | | | |
|---|---|---|---|---|
| 3716 | A697 | $2.50 Sheet of 4, #a-d | 7.75 | 7.75 |

Flag of Grenada, and Designer Anthony C. George A698

Frame color: 10c, Blue green. 25c, Blue. 50c, Red. 75c, Yellow.
$6, Flag and George, vert.

**2009, Feb. 25    Perf. 13¼**
| | | | | |
|---|---|---|---|---|
| 3717-3720 | A698 | Set of 4 | 1.25 | 1.25 |

**Souvenir Sheet**
**Perf. 12**
| | | | | |
|---|---|---|---|---|
| 3721 | A698 | $6 multi | 4.75 | 4.75 |

No. 3721 contains one 30x40mm stamp.

Peony on Vase — A699

**2009, Apr. 10    Perf. 13¼**
| | | | | |
|---|---|---|---|---|
| 3722 | A699 | 75c multi | .55 | .55 |

**Souvenir Sheet**
| | | | | |
|---|---|---|---|---|
| 3723 | A699 | $5 Peony, diff. | 3.75 | 3.75 |

No. 3723 contains one 44x44mm stamp.
No. 3722 was printed in sheets of 12.

### Miniature Sheet

Olympic Track and Field Events A700

No. 3724: a, Pole vault. b, Hurdles. c, Relay race. d, High jump.

**2009, Apr. 29    Perf. 12**
| | | | | |
|---|---|---|---|---|
| 3724 | A700 | $1.40 Sheet of 4, #a-d | 4.25 | 4.25 |

China 2009 World Stamp Exhibition, Luoyang.

### Miniature Sheet

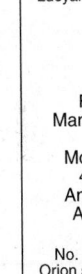

First Man on the Moon, 40th Anniv. A701

No. 3725: a, Proposed upper stages of Orion spacecraft, Wernher von Braun. b, Crew of Apollo 11. c, Lunar Orbiter. d, Ranger 7. e, Lunar Module, Pres. John F. Kennedy. f, Proposed Orion lunar module.

**2009, Apr. 29    Perf. 11½**
| | | | | |
|---|---|---|---|---|
| 3725 | A701 | $2 Sheet of 6, #a-f | 9.00 | 9.00 |

### Miniature Sheet

Joseph Haydn (1732-1809), Composer — A702

No. 3726: a, Haydn's birthplace, Rohrau, Austria. b, Johann Peter Salomon, impresario. c, Austro-Hungarian Haydn Orchestra. d, Wolfgang Amadeus Mozart, composer. e, Haydn's house, Vienna. f, Ludwig van Beethoven, composer and student of Haydn.

**2009, Apr. 29**
| | | | | |
|---|---|---|---|---|
| 3726 | A702 | $2.25 Sheet of 6, #a-f | 10.00 | 10.00 |

### Miniature Sheet

Elvis Presley (1935-77) — A703

No. 3727 — Presley: a, With guitar strap on both sides. b, Facing left. c, With hand raised. d, With guitar strap at right.

**2009, Apr. 29    Perf. 13¼**
| | | | | |
|---|---|---|---|---|
| 3727 | A703 | $2.50 Sheet of 4, #a-d | 7.50 | 7.50 |

## Miniature Sheets

Dogs
A704

No. 3728, $2.30 — Golden retriever: a, On outdoor chair. b, On lawn, with pumpkin and gourds. c, On sofa. d, Two dogs in basket.
No. 3729, $2.50 — Beagle: a, On desktop. b, Face. c, On lawn. d, Near stone wall.

**2009, Apr. 29**     **Perf. 11½**
**Sheets of 4, #a-d**
3728-3729 A704   Set of 2    14.50 14.50
American Kennel Club, 125th anniv.

## Miniature Sheet

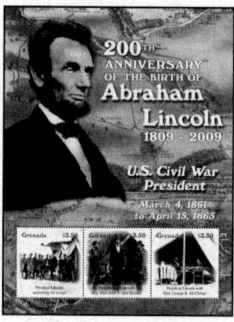

Pres. Abraham Lincoln (1809-65) — A705

No. 3730 — Lincoln: a, Addressing Union troops. b, With Major General John A. McClernand. c, With General George B. McClellan.

**2009, July 21**   **Litho.**   **Perf. 13½**
3730 A705 $3.50 Sheet of 3, #a-
c       8.00 8.00

## Miniature Sheet

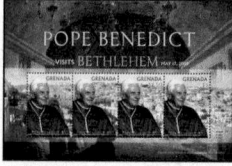

Visit of Pope Benedict XVI to Bethlehem — A706

No. 3731 — Pope Benedict and buildings in Bethlehem: a, $1.50. b, $2. c, $2.50. d, $3.

**2009, July 21**     **Perf. 11½**
3731 A706   Sheet of 4, #a-d
      6.75 6.75

## Miniature Sheet

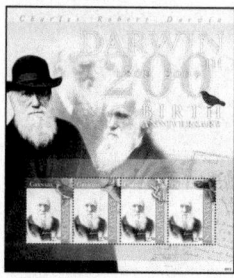

Charles Darwin (1809-82), Naturalist — A707

No. 3732 — Darwin and: a, Bird. b, Wolf. c, Fossil. d, Tortoise.

**2009, July 21**
3732 A707 $2.50 Sheet of 4, #a-
d       7.50 7.50

---

Chinese Aviation, Cent. A708

No. 3733: a, J-5. b, J-6. c, J-7G. d, J-7. $6, JF-17.

**2009, Nov. 13**   **Litho.**   **Perf. 14**
3733 A708 $2 Sheet of 4, #a-d   6.50 6.50
**Souvenir Sheet**
**Perf. 14¼**
3734 A708 $6 multi      4.75 4.75
2009 Aeropex, Beijing. No. 3733 contains four 42x28mm stamps.

## Miniature Sheet

Chinese Zodiac Animals A709

No. 3735: a, Rat. b, Ox. c, Tiger. d, Rabbit. e, Dragon. f, Snake. g, Horse. h, Ram. i, Monkey. j, Cock. k, Dog. l, Pig.

**2010, Jan. 4**     **Perf. 12**
3735 A709 60c Sheet of 12, #a-l   5.50 5.50

## Miniature Sheet

Elvis Presley (1935-77) — A710

Various views of Presley's face.

**2010, Jan. 7**     **Perf. 13¼**
3736 A710 $2.75 Sheet of 4,
   #a-d      8.50 8.50

Christmas 2009 — A711

Designs: $1, Fish wearing stocking caps. $2, Christmas tree, lights, fruit. $4, Bells. $5, Map of Grenada, stars, Christmas ornaments.

**2010, Jan. 13**     **Perf. 12½**
3737-3740 A711   Set of 4    9.25 9.25

Orchids — A712

Designs: $1.20, Brassia caudata. $1.80, Epidendrum imatophyllum. No. 3743, $3, Ionopsis utriculoides. $5, Habenaria bractescens.
No. 3745, horiz.: a, Vanilla pompona. b, Caularthron bicornutum. c, Epidendrum nocturnum. d, Aspasia variegata.
No. 3746, $3, horiz.: a, Epidendrum hartii. b, Brassavola cucullata.

**2010, Jan. 13**     **Perf. 13¼x13**
3741-3744 A712   Set of 4    8.50 8.50
**Perf. 13x13¼**
3745 A712 $2.75 Sheet of 4,
   #a-d      8.50 8.50

---

**Souvenir Sheet**
3746 A712   $3 Sheet of 2,
   #a-b      4.75 4.75

Ferrari Automobiles and Their Parts — A713

No. 3747, $1.25: a, Engine of 1989 F1-89. b, 1989 F1-89.
No. 3748, $1.25: a, Engine of 1994 F355 Berlinetta. b, 1994 F355 Berlinetta.
No. 3749, $1.25: a, Wires and parts to 1997 355 F1 Berlinetta. b, 1997 355 F1 Berlinetta.
No. 3750, $1.25: a, Steering wheel of 1997 F310 B. b, 1997 F310 B.

**2010, Mar. 1**     **Perf. 12**
**Vert. Pairs, #a-b**
3747-3750 A713   Set of 4    7.75 7.75

## Miniature Sheet

Pres. John F. Kennedy (1917-63), 50th Anniv. of Election — A714

No. 3751: a, Facing left, black and white photograph. b, Standing, black and white photograph. c, Color photograph. d, With flag in background, black and white photograph.

**2010, Apr. 9**     **Perf. 12x11½**
3751 A714 $2.75 Sheet of 4,
   #a-d      8.25 8.25

## Miniature Sheets

A715

Princess Diana (1961-97) — A716

No. 3752: a, Wearing black hat, gray and white along left margin of stamp. b, Wearing blue hat, with black frame at LL over gray area. c, As "b," with black frame at LL over white area. d, As "a," with hand of Princess Diana (from central illustration) touching black frame at left.
No. 3753: a, Wearing white hat, gray and white along left margin. b, Wearing no hat, with black frame at LL over red area. c, As "b," with LL corner over gray area. d, As "a," with entire left margin over red area (Diana's jacket from central illustration).

**2010, Apr. 9**
3752 A715 $2.75 Sheet of 4,
   #a-d      8.25 8.25
3753 A716 $2.75 Sheet of 4,
   #a-d      8.25 8.25

---

Girl Guides, Cent. A717

No. 3754, horiz. — Girl Guides: a, Looking at image taken by camera. b, With cameras. c, With movie clapboard. d, Looking at image take by camera with telephoto lens.
$6, Girl Guide with camera.

**2010, June 11**     **Perf. 13x13¼**
3754 A717 $2.75 Sheet of 4,
      #a-d      8.25 8.25
**Souvenir Sheet**
**Perf. 13¼x13**
3755 A717 $6 multi      4.50 4.50

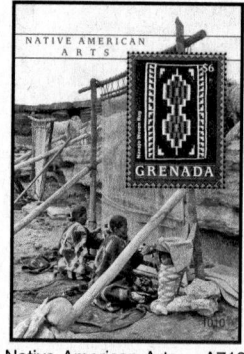

Native American Arts — A718

No. 3756: a, Apache woven basket. b, Sioux beaded moccasins. c, Iroquois cornhusk mask. d, Tlingit totem pole. e, Inuit hunter doll. f, Hopi pottery.
$6, Navajo woven rug.

**2010, June 11**     **Perf. 13¼x13**
3756 A718 $2 Sheet of 6, #a-f   9.00 9.00
**Souvenir Sheet**
3757 A718 $6 multi      4.50 4.50

**Souvenir Sheet**

New Year 2010 (Year of the Tiger) A719

No. 3758 — Half of tiger's head with denomination at: a, UL. b, UR.

**2010, Jan. 4**   **Litho.**   **Perf. 12**
3758 A719 $5 Sheet of 2, #a-b   7.75 7.75

2010 World Cup Soccer Championships, South Africa — A720

No. 3759, $1.50 — Group A first-round matches: a, South Africa vs. Mexico. b, Uruguay vs. France. c, Uruguay vs. South Africa.

d, France vs. Mexico. e, Mexico vs. Uruguay. f, France vs. South Africa.

No. 3760, $1.50 — Group B first-round matches: a, South Korea vs. Greece. b, Argentina vs. Nigeria. c, South Korea vs. Argentina. d, Nigeria vs. Greece. e, Nigeria vs. South Korea. f, Greece vs. Argentina.

No. 3761, $1.50 — Group C first-round matches: a, England vs. United States. b, Algeria vs. Slovenia. c, United States vs. Slovenia. d, England vs. Algeria. e, Slovenia vs. England. f, Algeria vs. United States.

No. 3762, $1.50 — Group D first-round matches: a, Serbia vs. Ghana. b, Germany vs. Australia. c, Germany vs. Serbia. d, Ghana vs. Australia. e, Ghana vs. Germany. f, Australia vs. Serbia.

No. 3763, $3.50: a, Nelson Mandela Bay Stadium, Port Elizabeth. b, Cape Town Stadium, Cape Town.

No. 3764, $3.50: a, Soccer City Stadium, Johannesburg. b, Moses Mabhida Stadium, Durban.

**2010, June 11**      **Perf. 13¼**
**Sheets of 6, #a-f**
3759-3762 A720   Set of 4    27.00 27.00
**Sheets of 2, #a-b**
3763-3764 A720   Set of 2    10.50 10.50

Miniature Sheet

Carl Edwards, NASCAR Driver A721

No. 3765 — Edwards: a, Wearing baseball cap, arms not visible. b, Without hat, arms raised. c, Wearing racing helmet. d, Wearing baseball cap, arms visible.

**2010, July 26**      **Perf. 12**
3765 A721 $2.75 Sheet of 4, #a-d    8.25 8.25

Frédéric Chopin (1810-49), Composer — A722

No. 3766: a, Sketch of Chopin facing left. b, George Sand, writer. c, Chopin, with arms folded. d, Chopin's birthplace.
$6, Chopin and musical notes.

**2010, Sept. 1**
3766 A722 $2.50 Sheet of 4, #a-d    7.50 7.50
**Souvenir Sheet**
3767 A722   $6 multi    4.50 4.50

Henri Dunant (1828-1910), Founder of the Red Cross — A723

No. 3768 — Dunant and members of Red Cross "Committee of Five" founding members: a, Louis Appia. b, Gustave Moynier. c, Théodore Maunoir. d, Henri Dufour.
$6, Dunant and the First Geneva Convention, 1894.

---

**2010, Sept. 1**
3768 A723 $2.50 Sheet of 4, #a-b    7.50 7.50
**Souvenir Sheet**
3769 A723   $6 multi    4.50 4.50

Miniature Sheet

Pope John Paul II (1920-2005) — A724

No. 3770 — Pope John Paul II: a, With crucifix. b, Without crucifix.

**2010, Nov. 4**
3770 A724 $2.75 Sheet of 4, #3770a, 3 #3770b    8.25 8.25

Boy Scouts of America, Cent. A725

No. 3771, $2.75: a, Scout saluting. b, Scout rescuing child.
No. 3772, $2.75: a, Scout assisting woman with groceries. b, Scout reading from book.

**2010, Nov. 4**      **Perf. 12½**
**Pairs, #a-b**
3771-3772 A725   Set of 2    8.25 8.25
Nos. 3771-3772 each were printed in sheets containing two pairs.

A726

Pres. Abraham Lincoln (1809-65) — A727

No. 3773 — Lincoln: a, With mouth to right of "resting." b, With mouth to right of "endure." c, Seated.
No. 3774 — Lincoln: a, Standing. b, With son, Tad. c, Seated.

**2010, Nov. 4**
3773 A726 $2 Horiz. strip of 3, #a-c    4.50 4.50
3774 A727 $2 Horiz. strip of 3, #a-c    4.50 4.50
Nos. 3773-3774 each were printed in sheets containing two strips.

Miniature Sheets

Pres. Barack Obama at Nuclear Security Summit A728

---

Pres. Obama and Mexican President Felipe Calderón — A729

No. 3775 — Pres. Obama: a, Facing right. b, With Vice-President Joseph Biden. c, Facing left. d, Greeting person.
No. 3776: a, Obama and Calderón shaking hands. b, Calderón. c, Obama. d, Calderón and Obama standing together.

**2010, Nov. 4**      **Perf. 12**
3775 A728 $2.75 Sheet of 4, #a-d    8.25 8.25
3776 A729 $2.75 Sheet of 4, #a-d    8.25 8.25

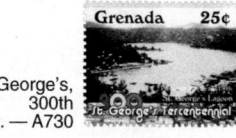

St. George's, 300th Anniv. — A730

Photographs from the mid-1900s: 25c, St. George's Lagoon. 50c, Church Street, St. George's, Grenada #91, vert. $1, Market Day, St. George's.

**2010, Dec. 9**   **Litho.**    **Perf. 12**
3777-3779 A730   Set of 3    1.40 1.40
Nos. 3777-3779 each were printed in sheets of 4.

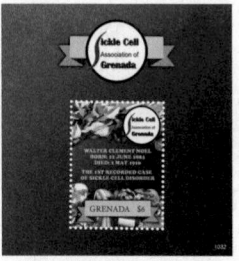

Sickle Cell Association of Grenada — A731

No. 3780 — Flowers, text, orange ribbon: a, 25c. b, 50c. c, $1. d, $2. $6, Flowers, text, blue ribbon.

**2010, Dec. 9**
3780 A731   Sheet of 4, #a-d    3.00 3.00
**Souvenir Sheet**
3781 A731   $6 multi    4.50 4.50

Souvenir Sheets

A732

A733

---

A734

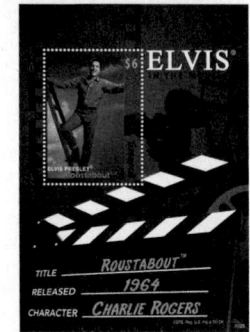

Elvis Presley (1935-77) — A735

**2010, Dec. 9**      **Perf. 12½**
3782 A732 $6 multi    4.50 4.50
3783 A733 $6 multi    4.50 4.50
3784 A734 $6 multi    4.50 4.50
3785 A735 $6 multi    4.50 4.50
Nos. 3782-3785 (4)    18.00 18.00

Christmas — A736

Designs: 25c, Three Wise Men. 50c, Adoration of the Shepherds, by Guido Reni. $1, Anbetung der Hirten, by Jusepe de Ribera. $2, Star of Bethlehem.
$6, Geburt Christi, by Max Bentele, horiz.

**2010, Dec. 9**      **Perf. 12**
3786-3789 A736   Set of 4    3.00 3.00
**Souvenir Sheet**
     **Perf. 12½**
3790 A736   $6 multi    4.50 4.50
Nos. 3786-3789 each were printed in sheets of 4. No. 3790 contains one 50x38mm stamp.

Souvenir Sheet

New Year 2011 (Year of the Rabbit) A737

No. 3791 — Background above rabbit's ears in: a, Tan. b, Green.

**2011, Feb. 1**      **Perf. 12**
3791 A737 $2.50 Sheet of 2, #a-b    3.75 3.75

Fish — A738

Designs: 25c, Rock beauty. $1.25, Graysby. $1.50, Beaugregory damselfish. $2, Juvenile Pomacanthus paru.
$100, Longsnout butterflyfish.

**2011, Feb. 1**     **Litho.**     *Perf. 13¼*
3792-3795 A738 Set of 4    3.75   3.75

**Souvenir Sheet**
*Perf. 14¾x14*

3796 A738 $100 multi    75.00 75.00

No. 3796 contains one 40x30mm stamp.

Forbidden City, Beijing — A739

No. 3797: a, Aerial view. b, Ancient sundial. c, Temple roof. d, Canal. $5, Golden lion, vert.

**2011, Feb. 1**     *Perf. 12*
3797 A739 $2 Sheet of 4, #a-d    6.00 6.00

**Souvenir Sheet**
*Perf. 12½*

3798 A739 $5 multi    3.75 3.75

2010 Beijing Intl. Stamp and Coin Exhibition. No. 3798 contains one 38x51mm stamp.

Engagement of Prince William and Catherine Middleton — A740

Designs: No. 3799, Couple.
No. 3800: a, Prince William. b, Catherine Middleton.

**2011, Feb. 18**    *Perf. 13 Syncopated*
3799 A740 $2.50 multi     1.90 1.90
3800 A740 $2.50 Horiz. pair, #a-b     3.75 3.75

No. 3799 was printed in sheets of 4; No. 3800, in sheets containing 2 pairs.

**Miniature Sheet**

Chinese Zodiac Animals A741

No. 3801: a, Rat. b, Ox. c, Tiger. d, Snake. e, Dragon. f, Rabbit. g, Horse. h, Ram. i, Monkey. j, Pig. k, Dog. l, Rooster.

**2011, Apr. 1**     *Perf. 12*
3801 A741 $1 Sheet of 12, #a-l    9.00 9.00

**Miniature Sheets**

A742

Elvis Presley (1935-77) — A743

No. 3802 — Signature in lilac with Presley: a, Wearing checked jacket, head tilted. b, Playing guitar. c, At dressing room table. d, Wearing checked jacket, head straight.
No. 3803 — Signature in blue with Presley: a, Wearing white jacket. b, Holding microphone, no guitar visible. c, Holding microphone, guitar visible. d, Playing guitar.

**2011, Apr. 6**
3802 A742 $2.75 Sheet of 4, #a-d    8.25 8.25

*Perf. 13 Syncopated*
3803 A743 $2.75 Sheet of 4, #a-d    8.25 8.25

**Miniature Sheets**

A744

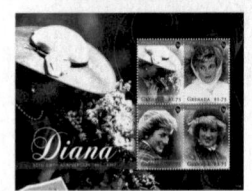

Princess Diana (1961-97) — A745

No. 3804 — Princess Diana wearing: a, Black hat and black jacket. b, White and pink hat with veil. c, Gray striped jacket. d, Black hat and white scarf.
No. 3805 — Princess Diana: a, Sniffing flowers. b, Wearing white veil around head. c, Wearing plaid jacket. d, Wearing black hat and black dress with white ruffled collar.

*Perf. 13 Syncopated*
**2011, Apr. 15**     **Litho.**
3804 A744 $2.75 Sheet of 4, #a-d    8.25 8.25

*Perf. 12*
3805 A745 $2.75 Sheet of 4, #a-d    8.25 8.25

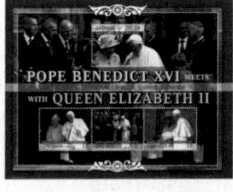

Meeting of Pope Benedict XVI and Queen Elizabeth II A746

No. 3806: a, Pope Benedict XVI, Queen Elizabeth II and girl. b, Pope and Queen looking at book. c, Pope and Queen with children and dignitaries. d, Pope and Queen, Pope pointing.
No. 3807, vert.: a, Queen. b, Pope.

**2011, Apr. 15**     *Perf. 11½x12*
3806 A746 $3 Sheet of 4, #a-d    9.00 9.00

**Souvenir Sheet**
*Perf. 11½*

3807 A746 $3.50 Sheet of 2, #a-b    5.25 5.25

First Man in Space, 50th Anniv. A747

No. 3808, $2.75: a, Bust of Yuri Gagarin. b, Aluminum medal depicting Gagarin. c, Vostok rocket. d, U.S. astronaut L. Gordon Cooper.
No. 3809, $2.75: a, Monument to the Conquerors of Space, Moscow. b, U.S. astronaut Walter Schirra. c, Gagarin wearing decorations. d, Vostok spaceship.
No. 3810, $6, Gagarin wearing military uniform and decorations, diff. No. 3811, $6, Vostok spaceship, horiz.

**2011, Apr. 15**     *Perf. 12x12½*
**Sheets of 4, #a-d**
3808-3809 A747 Set of 2    16.50 16.50

**Souvenir Sheets**
*Perf. 11¼x11½, 11½x11¼*
3810-3811 A747 Set of 2    9.00 9.00

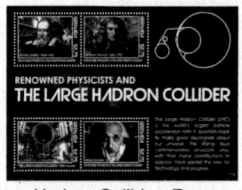

Large Hadron Collider, France and Switzerland — A748

No. 3812: a, Galileo Galilei. b, Sir Isaac Newton. c, Large Hadron Collider. d, Albert Einstein. $6, Collider, diff.

**2011, July 22**     *Perf. 12*
3812 A748 $2.75 Sheet of 4, #a-d    8.25 8.25

**Souvenir Sheet**
*Perf. 12½*

3813 A748 $6 multi    4.50 4.50

No. 3813 contains one 51x38mm stamp.

**Souvenir Sheets**

Chinese Civil Engineering Projects — A749

No. 3814, $6, Qingdao Cross-Sea Bridge. No. 3815, $6, Diagram of Qingdao Haozhouwan Tunnel.

**2011, July 22**     *Perf. 12*
3814-3815 A749 Set of 2    9.00 9.00

Parrots A750

No. 3816 — Map of Caribbean islands and: a, Scarlet macaw. b, Hyacinth macaw. c, Slender-billed parakeet. d, Blue-and-yellow macaw. e, Olive-throated parakeet. f, Burrowing parrot.
$6, Red-and-green macaw.

**2011, Sept. 15**    **Litho.**    *Perf. 12*
3816 A750 $2 Sheet of 6, #a-f    9.00 9.00

**Souvenir Sheet**

3817 A750 $6 multi    4.50 4.50

**Miniature Sheets**

Mother Teresa (1910-97), Humanitarian — A751

No. 3818, $2.50: a, Mother Teresa, curved frame at LR. b, Mother Teresa and Pope John Paul II. c, Mother Teresa and Princess Diana. d, Mother Teresa, curved frame at UL.
No. 3819, $2.50: a, Mother Teresa and Prince Charles. b, Mother Teresa, curved frame at LL. c, Motehr Teresa, curved frame at UR. d, Mother Teresa and Senator Edward M. Kennedy.

**Sheets of 4, #a-d**
**2011, Sept. 15**     *Perf. 12*
3818-3819 A751 Set of 2    15.00 15.00

**Miniature Sheets**

Pres. Abraham Lincoln (1809-65) — A752

No. 3820, $2.75 — Photograph of Lincoln with background color of: a, Green. b, Blue black. c, Gray black. d, Red brown.
No. 3820, $2.75, horiz. — Photograph of Lincoln with background color of: a, Black. b, Dark red. c, Brown. d, Purple.

**2011, Sept. 15**    *Perf. 13 Syncopated*
**Sheets of 4, #a-d**
3820-3821 A752 Set of 2    14.50 14.50

Chocolate Candy — A753

Chocolate Frosting — A754

No. 3822 — Candy with: a, Country name in gray, denomination in pink. b, Country name and denomination in pink. c, "GRE" in pink, "NADA" and denomination in gray.
No. 3823 — Teardrop-shaped swirl in frosting at: a, Left of "NA" in panel at right, above "ho" in "Chocolate," curved frame at UL. b, Left of "A $" in panel at right, above "Ch" in "Chocolate." c, Left of "EN" in panel at right, above "oc" in "Chocolate." d, Left of "RE" in panel at right, above "ho" in "Chocolate." e, Left of "GR" in panel at right, above "e" in "Chocolate." f, Left of "GR" in panel at right, above "oc" in "Chocolate." g, Left of "G" in panel at right (touching edge of stamp), above "ho" in "Chocolate," curved frame at LL. h, Left of "G" in panel at right (touching edge of stamp), above "e" in "Chocolate." i, Left of "G" in panel at right (touching edge of stamp), above "oc" in "Chocolate."

**2011, Oct. 26**    Litho.
3822   Horiz. strip of 3   5.25   5.25
a.-c.   A753 $2.25 Any single   1.75   1.75
3823   A754 $2.25 Sheet of 9,
   #a-i   15.00   15.00

No. 3822 is printed in sheets containing 3 strips. Nos. 3822-3823 are impregnated with a chocolate aroma.

British Monarchs — A755

Designs: No. 3824, $2, King William II (c. 1056-1100). No. 3825, $2, King Richard I (1157-99). No. 3826, $2, King Edward III (1312-77). No. 3827, $2, King Edward IV (1442-83). No. 3828, $2, King Henry VIII (1491-1547). No. 3829, $2, King Charles I (1600-49). No. 3830, $2, King George I (1660-1727). No. 3831, $2, King George V (1865-1936).

**2011, Oct. 26**    Perf. 14
3824-3831 A755   Set of 8   12.00   12.00

Nos. 3824-3831 each were printed in sheets of 8 + central label.

Sept. 11, 2011 Terrorist Attacks, 10th Anniv. A756

No. 3832: a, Tribute in light at World Trade Center site. b, Pentagon Memorial. c, September 11 Memorial, New York. d, September 11 Memorial, New Jersey.
$6, World Trade Center towers, vert.

**2011, Oct. 26**    Perf. 12
3832 A756 $2.75 Sheet of 4, #a-d   8.25   8.25

**Souvenir Sheet**
3833 A756   $6 multi   4.50   4.50

Mao Zedong (1893-1976), Chinese Leader — A757

**2011, Nov. 8**    Litho.
3834 A757 $3 shown   2.25   2.25

**Souvenir Sheet**
3835 A757 $6 Portrait, diff.   4.50   4.50

China 2011 Intl. Philatelic Exhibition, Wuxi (No. 3835). No. 3834 was printed in sheets of 3.

### Miniature Sheets

Visit of Pope Benedict XVI to Germany A758

No. 3836: a, Pope Benedict XVI wearing miter, facing left, building. b, Red City Hall, Berlin. c, Madonna in the Rose Bower, by Stefan Lochner. d, Pope Benedict XVI with arms extended, building.
No. 3837 — Various buildings and Pope Benedict XVI: a, Praying. b, Holding crucifix in his left hand, waving. c, Holding crucifix in his right hand.

**2011, Nov. 8**    Perf. 13¼x13
3836 A758 $2.75 Sheet of 4, #a-d   8.25   8.25
3837 A758 $3 Sheet of 3, #a-c   6.75   6.75

Chinese Zodiac Animals A759

New Year 2012 (Year fo the Dragon) A760

No. 3838: a, Rat. b, Ox. c, Tiger. d, Rabbit. e, Dragon. f, Snake. g, Horse. h, Sheep. i, Monkey. j, Rooster. k, Dog. l, Boar.
$8, Dragon.

**Litho. With Foil Application**
**2011**    Perf. 13 Syncopated
3838 A759 65c Sheet of 12, #a-l   5.75   5.75

**Souvenir Sheet**
**Litho.**
**Perf. 12**
3839 A760 $8 multi   6.00   6.00

Issued: No. 3838, 11/8; No. 3839, 10/26.

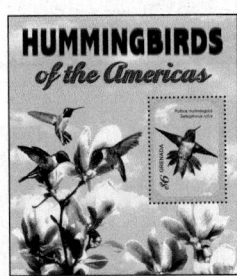

Hummingbirds — A761

No. 3840, horiz.: a, Calliope hummingbird. b, Anna's hummingbird. c, Black-chinned hummingbird. d, Ruby-throated hummingbird. e, Costa's hummingbird. f, Broad-billed hummingbird.
$6, Rufous hummingbird.

**2011, Dec. 16**    Litho.    Perf. 12
3840 A761 $2 Sheet of 6, #a-f   9.00   9.00

**Souvenir Sheet**
3841 A761 $6 multi   4.50   4.50

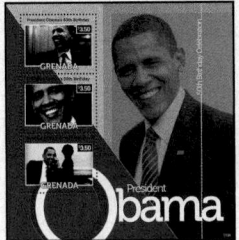

Pres. Barack Obama, 50th Birthday A762

No. 3842 — Pres. Obama: a, Looking left. b, Close-up. c, Holding hand to face.
$6, Pres. Obama, diff.

**2011, Dec. 16**    Perf. 12
3842 A762 $3.50 Sheet of 3, #a-c   7.75   7.75

**Souvenir Sheet**
**Perf. 12¾**
3843 A762 $6 multi   4.50   4.50

No. 3843 contains one 51x38mm stamp.

### Souvenir Sheets

Pres. John F. Kennedy (1917-63) — A763

No. 3844, $3 — Pres. Kennedy: a, Sitting in rocking chair. b, Standing behind microphone. c, Signing document.
No. 3855, $3 — Pres. Kennedy: a, Close-up photograph of head. b, On campaign posters at convention. c, Standing.

**2011, Dec. 16**    Perf. 13 Syncopated
**Sheets of 3, #a-c**
3844-3845 A763   Set of 2   13.50   13.50

Sinking of the Titanic, Cent. A764

No. 3846: a, Family waits for survivors. b, Survivors arrive at the docks. c, Captain Edward J. Smith. d, Titanic sinks into the sea.
$9, Titanic at sea.

**2012, Feb. 8**    Perf.
3846 A764 $3.50 Sheet of 4, #a-d   10.50   10.50

**Souvenir Sheet**
3847 A764 $9 multi   6.75   6.75

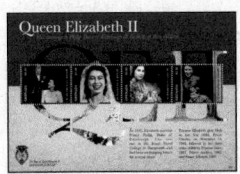

Reign of Queen Elizabeth II, 60th Anniv. A765

No. 3848 — Queen Elizabeth II: a, With Prince Philip. b, In wedding dress. c, Holding infant Prince Charles. d, With young Prince Andrew.
$9, With two children, vert.

**2012, Feb. 8**    Perf. 12
3848 A765 $3.50 Sheet of 4, #a-d   10.50   10.50

**Souvenir Sheet**
3849 A765 $9 multi   6.75   6.75

Mother Teresa (1910-97), Humanitarian — A766

No. 3850, $4 — Various photos of Mother Teresa with: a, Black denomination, white at UL corner of frame. b, Brown denomination. c, Black denomination, purple at UL corner of frame.
No. 3851, $4, Mother Teresa in truck.

**2012, Apr. 5**    Perf. 13 Syncopated
3850 A766 $4 Sheet of 3, #a-c   9.00   9.00

**Souvenir Sheet**
3851 A766 $4 multi   3.00   3.00

### Souvenir Sheets

A768

A769

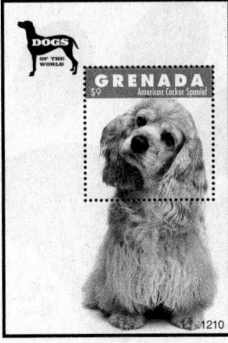

Elvis Presley (1935-77) — A770

**2012, Apr. 5**    Perf. 12¾
3852 A767 $9 multi   6.75   6.75
3853 A768 $9 multi   6.75   6.75
3854 A769 $9 multi   6.75   6.75
3855 A770 $9 multi   6.75   6.75
   Nos. 3852-3855 (4)   27.00   27.00

Dogs A771

No. 3856, vert.: a, Labrador retriever. b, Bernese mountain dog. c, Bordeaux mastiff. No. 3857: a, Great Dane. b, Chocolate Labrador retriever. c, Chihuahua. d, Miniature pinscher. No. 3858, $9, American cocker spaniel. No. 3859, $9, Shih tzu.

**2012, Apr. 24**    Perf. 13½x13¼
3856 A771 $3.50 Sheet of 3, #a-c   7.75   7.75

**Perf. 12¾**

3857 A771 $3.50 Sheet of 4, #a-d    10.50 10.50

**Souvenir Sheets**
**Perf. 12**

3858-3859 A771 Set of 2    13.50 13.50

No. 3856 contains three 30x50mm stamps. No. 3857 contains four 25x25mm stamps.

Emblem of the 2012 Summer Olympics, London — A772

No. 3860 — Emblem color: a, Pink. b, Orange. c, Blue. d, Green.

**2012, July 27**    **Perf. 13¼**
3860   Horiz. strip of 4    4.50 4.50
  a.-d. A772 $1.50 Any single    1.10 1.10

No. 3860 was printed in sheets containing three strips.

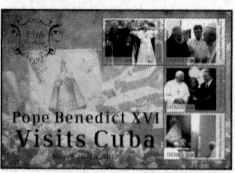

Visit of Pope Benedict XVI to Cuba A773

No. 3861: a, Pope with arms extended, with other clerics. b, Pope meeting with Fidel Castro. c, Pope meeting with Cuban Pres. Raul Castro and woman. d, Pope kneeling at altar. $9, Pope carrying crucifix before crowd.

**2012, Nov. 28**    **Perf. 14**
3861 A773 $3.50 Sheet of 4, #a-d    10.50 10.50

**Souvenir Sheet**
**Perf. 12**
3862 A773 $9 multi    6.75 6.75

Chinese Zodiac Animals — A774

Designs: No. 3863, 55c, Ram. No. 3864, 55c, Horse.

**2012, Nov. 28 Litho. Perf. 13¼x13**
3863-3864 A774 Set of 2    .85 .85

Christmas 2012 — A775

Paintings by Fra Angelico: No. 3865, $1, Annunciation. No. 3866, $1, Archangel Gabriel Annunciate. No. 3867, $2, Virgin Mary Annunciate. No. 3868, $2, The Virgin of the Annunciation. No. 3869, $5, Virgin and Child. No. 3870, $5, Adoration of the Magi.

**2013, Jan. 3**    **Perf. 12¾**
3865-3870 A775 Set of 6    12.00 12.00

A776

Seashells — A777

No. 3871: a, Short abbreviate coral shell (30x40mm). b, Winged surfclam (30x40mm). c, Brown-line niso (60x40mm).
No. 3872: a, Spotted Brazilian top shell. b, Accuminate phos. c, Florida fighting conch. d, Jasper cone.
No. 3873: a, Pointed nut clam. b, White pitar.
$9, Boring turret snail, horiz.

**2013, Jan. 3**    **Perf. 12**
3871 A776 $3.50 Sheet of 3, #a-c    7.75 7.75
3872 A776 $3.50 Sheet of 4, #a-d    10.50 10.50

**Souvenir Sheets**
3873 A777 $4.50 Sheet of 2, #a-b    6.75 6.75
3874 A777 $9 multi    6.75 6.75

No. 3874 contains one 80x30mm stamp.

Michelangelo's Completion of the Painting of the Sistine Chapel Ceiling, 500th Anniv. — A778

No. 3875: a, The Creation of Adam (detail of Adam). b, The Creation of Adam (detail of God). c, Deluge. d, The Downfall of Adam and Eve and Their Expulsion from the Garden of Eden.
$8, The Sacrifice of Noah, vert.

**2013, Jan. 3**    **Perf. 12¾**
3875 A778 $3.25 Sheet of 4, #a-d    9.75 9.75

**Souvenir Sheet**
3876 A778 $8 multi    6.00 6.00

Amelia Earhart (1897-1937), Aviator — A779

No. 3877 — Earhart in: a, 1921. b, 1928. c, 1930. d, 1932. e, 1935. f, 1937.
$9, Earhart and airplane.

**2013, Jan. 3**
3877 A779 $2.25 Sheet of 6, #a-f    10.00 10.00

**Souvenir Sheet**
3878 A779 $9 multi    6.75 6.75

**Miniature Sheets**

Princess Diana (1961-97) — A780

No. 3879, $3.50 — Black-and-white photographs of Princess Diana: a, Looking left. b, Wearing hat with veil. c, Looking up. d, Wearing pearl necklace.
No. 3880, $3.50 — Color photographs of Princess Diana wearing: a, Dark blue hat and

jacket. b, Red and white hat and dress. c, Black hooded raincoat. d, Red dress, no hat.

**2013, Jan. 3**    **Perf. 13 Syncopated**
  **Sheets of 4, #a-d**
3879-3880 A780 Set of 2    21.00 21.00

Butterflies — A781

No. 3881: a, Heliconius mimicry. b, Junonia evarete. c, Heliconius erato petiveranus. d, Agraulis vanillae.
$9, Anartia jatrophae, vert.

**2013, Jan. 3**    **Perf. 13¾**
3881 A781 $3.50 Sheet of 4, #a-d    10.50 10.50

**Souvenir Sheet**
**Perf. 12½**
3882 A781 $9 multi    6.75 6.75

No. 3882 contains one 38x51mm stamp.

**Souvenir Sheets**

Elvis Presley (1935-77) — A782

Frame color: No. 3883, $9, Red. No. 3884, $9, Gray. No. 3885, $9, Red (Presley holding microphone). No. 3886, $9, Purple. No. 3887, $9, Black.

**2013, Mar. 11**    **Perf. 12½**
3883-3887 A782 Set of 5    34.00 34.00

**Souvenir Sheet**

Elvis Presley (1935-77) — A783

**Litho., Margin Embossed**
2013    **Imperf.**
  **Without Gum**
3888 A783 $25 multi    18.50 18.50

**Souvenir Sheets**

History of Art A784

No. 3889, $3.75 — The Birth of Venus, by Sandro Botticelli (details): a, Man and woman. b, Venus. c, Woman facing left.
No. 3890, $3.75, vert. — Paintings by Fra Angelico: a, Noli Me Tangere. b, Lamentation Over the Dead Christ. c, Presentation in the Temple.
No. 3891, $3.75, vert. — Details of paintings of the Early Renaissance period: a, The Annunciation with St. Emidius, by Carlo Crivelli. b, The Crucified Christ, by Fra Angelico. c, The Baptism of Chirst, by Andrea del Verrocchio.

**2013, Apr. 4 Litho. Perf. 12¾**
  **Sheets of 3, #a-c**
3889-3891 A784 Set of 3    25.00 25.00

Ancient Roman Structures — A785

No. 3892: a, Colosseum. b, Roman Forum. c, Ostia Antica. d, Trajan's Market. e, Baths of Caracalla. f, Pantheon.
$9, View of Roman Forum from Palatine Hill, horiz.

**2013, Apr. 29 Litho. Perf. 13¾**
3892 A785 $2.50 Sheet of 6, #a-f    11.50 11.50

**Souvenir Sheet**
**Perf. 12¾**
3893 A785 $9 multi    6.75 6.75

No. 3893 contains one 51x38mm stamp.

Pope Benedict XVI A786

No. 3894, $3.25 — 2008 World Youth Day celebration photographs of Pope Benedict XVI with: a, Australian Prime Minister Kevin Rudd and his wife, Thérèse Rein. b, Youths, waving. c, Cross. d, Two priests celebrating Mass.
No. 3895, $3.25 — Photographs of Pope Benedict XVI at Lourdes, France: a, With French President Nicolas Sarkozy. b, Waving, wearing white vestments. c, With priests celebrating Mass. d, Waving, wearing red vestments.
No. 3896, $3.25, Pope Benedict XVI walking in front of cardinal at World Youth Day celebration. No. 3897, $9, Pope Benedict XVI praying at Lourdes.

**Perf. 13 Syncopated**
**2013, Apr. 29**    **Litho.**
  **Sheets of 4, #a-d**
3894-3895 A786 Set of 2    19.50 19.50

**Souvenir Sheets**
3896-3897 A786 Set of 2    9.25 9.25

A787

Election of Pope Francis A788

No. 3898 — Pope Francis: a, Waving to crowd. b, Delivering first Urbi et Orbi blessing at Easter Mass. c, Preparing to celebrate Mass. d, Delivering weekly address.

| | | | | |
|---|---|---|---|---|
| **2013, June 3** | | **Litho.** | | **Perf. 12** |
| 3898 | A787 | $3.25 Sheet of 4, #a-d | 9.75 | 9.75 |

**Litho., Margin Embossed**
**Souvenir Sheet**
**Without Gum**
*Imperf*

| | | | | |
|---|---|---|---|---|
| 3899 | A788 | $20 multi | 15.00 | 15.00 |

Birth of Prince George of Cambridge — A789

No. 3900 — Crown and: a, Prince George, Duke and Duchess of Cambridge. b, Prince George and Duchess of Cambridge. c, Baby carriage. d, Prince George and Duke of Cambridge.
$9, Prince George, Duke and Duchess of Cambridge, diff.

| | | | | |
|---|---|---|---|---|
| **2013, Sept. 27** | | **Litho.** | | **Perf. 12** |
| 3900 | A789 | $3.25 Sheet of 4, #a-d | 9.75 | 9.75 |

**Souvenir Sheet**

| | | | | |
|---|---|---|---|---|
| 3901 | A789 | $9 multi | 6.75 | 6.75 |

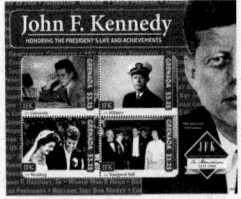

Pres. John F. Kennedy (1917-63) — A790

No. 3902 — John F. Kennedy: a, At desk as university student. b, In Navy uniform. c, With wife, Jacqueline, at wedding. d, With wife at inaugural ball.
No. 3903, vert.: a, Pres. Kennedy. b, Jacqueline Kennedy.

| | | | | |
|---|---|---|---|---|
| **2013, Oct. 10** | | **Litho.** | | **Perf. 12¾** |
| 3902 | A790 | $3.25 Sheet of 4, #a-d | 9.75 | 9.75 |

**Souvenir Sheet**
**Perf. 14**

| | | | | |
|---|---|---|---|---|
| 3903 | A790 | $4.75 Sheet of 2, #a-b | 7.00 | 7.00 |

No. 3903 contains two 30x40mm stamps.

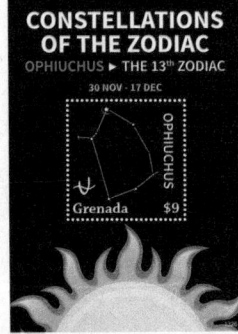

Constellations — A791

No. 3904, $3.75: a, Aries. b, Taurus. c, Gemini.
No. 3905, $3.75: a, Cancer. b, Virgo. c, Leo.
No. 3906, $3.75: a, Sagittarius. b, Scorpio. c, Libra.
No. 3907, $3.75: a, Aquarius. b, Pisces. c, Capricorn.
$9, Ophiuchus.

| | | | | |
|---|---|---|---|---|
| **2013, Oct. 10** | | **Litho.** | | **Perf. 13¾** |
| **Sheets of 3, #a-c** | | | | |
| 3904-3907 | A791 | Set of 4 | 33.50 | 33.50 |
| **Souvenir Sheet** | | | | |
| 3908 | A791 | $9 multi | 6.75 | 6.75 |

A792

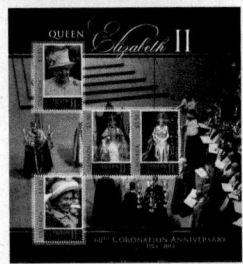

Coronation of Queen Elizabeth II, 60th Anniv. — A793

No. 3909 — Blue panels at bottom with photographs of Queen Elizabeth II: a, Wearing blue hat. b, At coronation. c, Wearing tiara, black-and-white photograph. d, Wearing tiara, color photograph.
No. 3910 — Maroon panels at bottom with photographs of Queen Elizabeth II: a, Wearing pink and white hat and white jacket. b, At coronation, holding scepter. c, At coronation, seated on throne. d, Wearing pinkish orange and white hat and pinkish orange jacket.
No. 3911, $9, Queen Elizabeth II wearing white hat. No. 3912, $9, Queen Elizabeth II wearing tiara, horiz.

| | | | | |
|---|---|---|---|---|
| **2013, Oct. 10** | | **Litho.** | | **Perf. 14** |
| 3909 | A792 | $3.50 Sheet of 4, #a-d | 10.50 | 10.50 |
| 3910 | A793 | $3.50 Sheet of 4, #a-d | 10.50 | 10.50 |
| **Souvenir Sheets** | | | | |
| **Perf. 12** | | | | |
| 3911-3912 | A793 | Set of 2 | 13.50 | 13.50 |

Lady Margaret Thatcher (1925-2013), British Prime Minister — A794

No. 3913 — Thatcher: a, On telephone. b, Wearing blue jacket and pearl necklace. c, Laughing. d, Wearing scarf around neck.
$9, Like No. 3913a.

| | | | | |
|---|---|---|---|---|
| **2013, Oct. 10** | | **Litho.** | | **Perf. 13¾** |
| 3913 | A794 | $3.25 Sheet of 4, #a-d | 9.75 | 9.75 |
| **Souvenir Sheet** | | | | |
| 3914 | A794 | $9 multi | 6.75 | 6.75 |

Shells A795

No. 3915: a, Brassica phyllonotus. b, Lyropecten subnodosus. c, Lobatus gigas. d, Cymatium lotorium.
$9, Charonia variegata.

| | | | | |
|---|---|---|---|---|
| **2013, Oct. 16** | | **Litho.** | | **Perf. 14** |
| 3915 | A795 | $3.25 Sheet of 4, #a-d | 9.75 | 9.75 |
| **Souvenir Sheet** | | | | |
| **Perf. 12** | | | | |
| 3916 | A795 | $9 multi | 6.75 | 6.75 |

Cats A796

No. 3917, $3.25 — Wild cats: a, Puma. b, Snow leopard. c, Jaguar. d, Fishing cat.
No. 3918, $3.25 — Domestic cat breeds: a, Bengal. b, Maine Coon. c, Russian Blue. d, Egyptian Mau.
No. 3919, $9, Lioness. No. 3920, $9, Persian cat.

| | | | | |
|---|---|---|---|---|
| **2013, Oct. 16** | | **Litho.** | | **Perf. 13¾** |
| **Sheets of 4, #a-d** | | | | |
| 3917-3918 | A796 | Set of 2 | 19.50 | 19.50 |
| **Souvenir Sheets** | | | | |
| 3919-3920 | A796 | Set of 2 | 13.50 | 13.50 |

Minerals A797

No. 3921: a, Azurite. b, Rhodonite. c, Baryte. d, Ruby in matrix. e, Chalcedony. f, Sodalite.
No. 3922, $4.50: a, Jade. b, Jasper.
No. 3923, $4.50: a, Hornblende. b, Turquenite.

| | | | | |
|---|---|---|---|---|
| **2013, Oct. 16** | | **Litho.** | | **Perf. 13¾** |
| 3921 | A797 | $2.50 Sheet of 6, #a-f | 11.50 | 11.50 |
| **Sheets of 2, #a-b** | | | | |
| 3922-3923 | A797 | Set of 2 | 13.50 | 13.50 |

A798

Mao Zedong (1893-1976), Chinese Communist Leader — A799

No. 3924 — Mao Zedong: a, Walking with Liu Shaoqi. b, Looking at document with Zhou Enlai. c, Standing with Zhu De in winter military uniforms.
No. 3925: a, Mao Zedong. b, Chinese text, people and flags. c, Chinese text, people seated and standing. d, Chinese text, three Chinese people. e, Chinese text, flag, group of people with horn player. f, Great Wall of China.

| | | | | |
|---|---|---|---|---|
| **2013, Oct. 18** | | **Litho.** | | **Perf. 14** |
| 3924 | A798 | 55c Horiz. strip of 3, #a-c | 1.25 | 1.25 |
| 3925 | A799 | 55c Sheet of 6, #a-f | 2.50 | 2.50 |

No. 3924 was printed in sheets containing 2 of each stamp.

Parrots — A800

Designs: 25c, Blue-and-yellow macaw. 35c, Blue-cheeked amazon. 40c, Scarlet macaw. 50c, Gold-capped conure. 75c, Blue-fronted amazon. $1, Blue-winged macaw. $1.25, Festive amazon. $1.50, Gold-capped conure. $2, Hyacinth macaw. $4, Military macaw. $5, White-eared conure. $10, Yellow-headed amazon. $50, Hispaniolan parakeet. $100, Mealy amazon.

| | | | | |
|---|---|---|---|---|
| **2013, Oct. 21** | | **Litho.** | | **Perf. 13¾** |
| 3926 | A800 | 25c multi | .25 | .25 |
| 3927 | A800 | 35c multi | .25 | .25 |
| 3928 | A800 | 40c multi | .30 | .30 |
| 3928A | A800 | 50c multi | .40 | .40 |
| | | ('19) | | |
| 3929 | A800 | 75c multi | .55 | .55 |
| 3930 | A800 | $1 multi | .75 | .75 |
| 3931 | A800 | $1.25 multi | .95 | .95 |
| 3932 | A800 | $1.50 multi | 1.10 | 1.10 |
| 3933 | A800 | $2 multi | 1.50 | 1.50 |
| 3934 | A800 | $4 multi | 3.00 | 3.00 |
| 3935 | A800 | $5 multi | 3.75 | 3.75 |
| 3936 | A800 | $10 multi | 7.50 | 7.50 |
| 3937 | A800 | $50 multi | 37.00 | 37.00 |
| 3937A | A800 | $100 multi | 75.00 | 75.00 |
| *Nos. 3926-3937A (14)* | | | 132.30 | 132.30 |

Issued: 50c, 2/1/19.

World Radio Day A801

No. 3938 — Scientists and flags: a, Heinrich Hertz (1857-94), flag of Germany. b, Jagadish Bose (1858-1937), flag of India. c, Alexander Popov (1859-1906), flag of Russia. d, Reginald Fessenden (1866-1932), flag of Canada.
$9, Guglielmo Marconi (1874-1937), flag of Italy.

| | | | | |
|---|---|---|---|---|
| **2013, Oct. 10** | | **Litho.** | | **Perf. 12½** |
| 3938 | A801 | $3.50 Sheet of 4, #a-d | 10.50 | 10.50 |
| **Souvenir Sheet** | | | | |
| **Perf.** | | | | |
| 3939 | A801 | $9 multi | 6.75 | 6.75 |

No. 3939 contains one 38mm diameter stamp.

Coronation of Queen Elizabeth II, 60th Anniv. A802

| | | | | |
|---|---|---|---|---|
| **2013, Oct. 10** | | **Embroidered** | | ***Imperf.*** |
| **Self-Adhesive** | | | | |
| 3940 | A802 | $20 multi | 15.00 | 15.00 |

Christmas — A803

Paintings: $1.10, The Annunciation, by Bernardo Daddi. $2.25, The Annunciation, by Jan de Beer. $2.50, Coronation of the Virgin, by Giovanni da Milano. $2.75, Madonna and Child, by Masolino da Panicale. $9, The Baptism of Christ, by Joachim Patinir.

| 2013, Dec. 25 | Litho. | Perf. 12½ |
|---|---|---|
| 3941-3944 A803 | Set of 4 | 6.50 6.50 |
| **Souvenir Sheet** | | |
| 3945 A803 | $9 multi | 6.75 6.75 |

New Year 2014 (Year of the Horse) — A804

| 2014 | Litho. | Perf. 13¾ |
|---|---|---|
| 3946 A804 | $1.50 multi | 1.10 1.10 |
| **Embroidered** | | |
| **Size: 50x50mm** | | |
| **Self-Adhesive** | | |
| 3947 A804 | $22 pink & red | 16.50 16.50 |

Issued: $1.50, 1/14; $22, 1/20. No. 3946 was printed in sheets of 9.

Animals of China A805

No. 3948: a, Red panda. b, Crested ibis. c, Golden pheasant. d, South China tiger. $9, Giant panda.

| 2014, Jan. 20 | Litho. | Perf. 14 |
|---|---|---|
| 3948 A805 | $3.25 Sheet of 4, #a-d | 9.75 9.75 |
| **Souvenir Sheet** | | |
| **Perf. 12** | | |
| 3949 A805 | $9 multi | 6.75 6.75 |

Turtles A806

No. 3950: a, Chelus fimbriata. b, Trachemys terrapen. c, Dermochelys coriacea. d, Lepidochelys kempii. $9, Eretmochelys imbricata.

| 2014, Jan. 20 | Litho. | Perf. 14 |
|---|---|---|
| 3950 A806 | $3.25 Sheet of 4, #a-d | 9.75 9.75 |
| **Souvenir Sheet** | | |
| **Perf. 12** | | |
| 3951 A806 | $9 multi | 6.75 6.75 |

Last Flight of the Concorde — A807

No. 3952: a, Concorde returns to Filton Airfield. b, Concorde at Manchester Airport. c, G-

BOAC Concorde on display. d, Front end of the Concorde. $9, Alpha-Foxtrot final flight over Bristol.

| 2014, Jan. 20 | Litho. | Perf. 12 |
|---|---|---|
| 3952 A807 | $3.25 Sheet of 4, #a-d | 9.75 9.75 |
| **Souvenir Sheet** | | |
| 3953 A807 | $9 multi | 6.75 6.75 |

Flowers A808

No. 3954: a, Lilium lancifolium. b, Brassica napus. c, Magnolia virginiana. d, Chamelaucium uncinatum. e, Cleistes divaricata. f, Striga densiflora. g, Lilium philadelphicum. h, Nerium oleander. i, Platanthera cristata. $9, Calopogon pulchellus.

| 2014, Jan. 20 | Litho. | Perf. 13¾ |
|---|---|---|
| 3954 A808 | $1 Sheet of 9, #a-i | 6.75 6.75 |
| **Souvenir Sheet** | | |
| 3955 A808 | $9 multi | 6.75 6.75 |

Sir Eric Gairy (1922-97), First Prime Minister of Grenada — A809

Frame color: 40c, Green. 75c, Yellow. $1, Red. $1.25, Blue. $10, Gairy, no frame.

| 2014, Feb. 7 | Litho. | Perf. 14 |
|---|---|---|
| 3956-3959 A809 | Set of 4 | 2.50 2.50 |
| **Souvenir Sheet** | | |
| **Perf. 12** | | |
| 3960 A809 | $10 multi | 7.50 7.50 |

Characters From *Downton Abbey* Television Series — A810

No. 3961: a, Earl of Grantham. b, Dowager Countess of Grantham. c, Lady Rosamund Painswick. d, Isobel Crawley. $9, Earl and Countess of Grantham, horiz.

| 2014, Apr. 7 | Litho. | Perf. 14 |
|---|---|---|
| 3961 A810 | $3.25 Sheet of 4, #a-d | 9.75 9.75 |
| **Souvenir Sheet** | | |
| 3962 A810 | $9 multi | 6.75 6.75 |

A811

Pope Francis A812

No. 3963 — Pope Francis: a, Wearing zucchetto and glasses. b, Wearing zucchetto, waving, archway in background. c, Wearing miter with gold trim. d, Wearing zucchetto, man in background.

No. 3964 — Pope Francis: a, Wearing zucchetto, waving, crowd in background. b, Wearing miter with black and gold trim, holding crucifix. c, Wearing zucchetto, leaving building. d, Wearing zucchetto, waving, building in background.

No. 3965, $5, horiz.: a, Pope Francis and King Letsie III of Lesotho. b, Pope Francis and party balloons.

No. 3966, $5, horiz.: a, Pope Francis with Congo President Denis Sassou Nguesso. b, Pope Francis wearing flower necklace.

| 2014, Apr. 7 | Litho. | Perf. 13¾ |
|---|---|---|
| 3963 A811 | $3.25 Sheet of 4, #a-d | 9.75 9.75 |
| 3964 A812 | $3.25 Sheet of 4, #a-d | 9.75 9.75 |
| **Souvenir Sheets of 2, #a-b** | | |
| **Perf. 14** | | |
| 3965-3966 A812 | Set of 2 | 15.00 15.00 |

Nos. 3965-3966 both contain two 40x30mm stamps.

A813

Nelson Mandela (1918-2013), President of South Africa — A814

No. 3967: a, Mandela wearing blue shirt with fist raised. b, Mandela wearing gray shirt, smiling.

No. 3968: a, Mandela with Queen Elizabeth II. b, Mandela wearing black and tan checked shirt. c, Mandela wearing sweater, with fist raised. d, Mandela wearing blue and white shirt, standing in front of wall. e, Mandela wearing black and gray patterned shirt. f, Mandela wearing suit and tie.

No. 3969, $9, Mandela wearing red shirt, with arm raised, vert. No. 3970, $9, Black-and-white photograph of Mandela as young man in suit and tie, vert.

| 2014, Apr. 17 | Litho. | Perf. 13¾ |
|---|---|---|
| 3967 A813 | $2.50 Pair, #a-b | 3.75 3.75 |
| 3968 A814 | $2.50 Sheet of 6, #a-f | 11.50 11.50 |
| **Souvenir Sheets** | | |
| **Perf. 12½** | | |
| 3969-3970 A814 | Set of 2 | 13.50 13.50 |

Nos. 3969-3970 both contain one 38x51mm stamp. No. 3967 was printed in sheets of 6 containing three each of Nos. 3967a and 3967b.

Pres. Barack Obama and Wife, Michelle — A815

Designs: No. 3972, $9, Pres. Obama and Vice-President Joe Biden. No. 3973, $9, Pres. Obama holding football, horiz.

| 2014, Apr. 23 | Litho. | Perf. 14 |
|---|---|---|
| 3971 A815 | $3.25 multi | 2.40 2.40 |
| **Souvenir Sheets** | | |
| **Perf. 12½** | | |
| 3972-3973 A815 | Set of 2 | 13.50 13.50 |

No. 3971 was printed in sheets of 4. No. 3972 contains one 38x51mm stamp. No. 3973 contains one 51x38mm stamp.

A816

Flowers A817

No. 3974, $4.75: a, Magnolias. b, Lilies. c, Calla lilies. d, Geraniums.

No. 3975, $4.75: a, Roses. b, Hydrangeas. c, Peonies. d, Oriental poppies.

No. 3976, $9.50: a, Magnolias, pink petal at UR corner. b, Magnolias, green leaf at UR corner.

No. 3977, $9.50: a, Hydrangeas, diff. b, Violets.

| 2014, Apr. 23 | Litho. | Perf. 13¾ |
|---|---|---|
| **Sheets of 4, #a-d** | | |
| 3974-3975 A816 | Set of 2 | 28.50 28.50 |
| **Souvenir Sheets of 2, #a-b** | | |
| **Perf. 12½** | | |
| 3976-3977 A817 | Set of 2 | 28.50 28.50 |

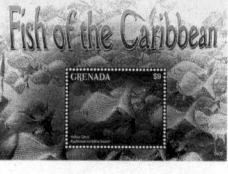

Fish A818

No. 3978, $3.25: a, Yellowhead wrasses. b, Píntanos. c, Queen angelfish. d, Stoplight parrotfish.

No. 3979, $3.25: a, Four-eyed butterflyfish. b, French angelfish. c, Juvenile French angelfish. d, Great barracudas.

No. 3980, $9, Yellow chubs. No. 3981, $9, Banded butterflyfish.

| **Perf. 14, 12 (#3981)** | | |
|---|---|---|
| 2014, Apr. 23 | | Litho. |
| **Sheets of 4, #a-d** | | |
| 3978-3979 A818 | Set of 2 | 19.50 19.50 |
| **Souvenir Sheets** | | |
| 3980-3981 A818 | Set of 2 | 13.50 13.50 |

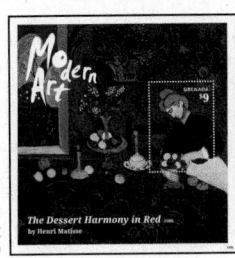

Modern Art
A819

No. 3982, $3.50 — Paintings by Henri Matisse (1869-1954): a, A Glimpse of Notre-Dame in the Late Afternoon. b, Dishes and Fruit. c, Fruit and Coffeepot.
No. 3983, $3.50 — Paintings by Adolf Dehn (1895-1968): a, Central Park. b, Landscape. c, Into the Rigging.
No. 3984, $9, The Dessert: Harmony in Red, by Matisse. No. 3985, $9, Cosmic Synchromy, by Morgan Russell (1886-1953).

**2014, Apr. 23    Litho.    Perf. 12½**
**Sheets of 3, #a-c**
3982-3983  A819    Set of 2         15.00 15.50
**Souvenir Sheets**
3984-3985  A819    Set of 2         13.50 13.50

Industry of South Korea
A820

No. 3986: a, Mobile devices. b, Transport vehicles. c, Automobiles. d, Circuitry. e, Petroleum. f, Construction. g, Mining. h, Textiles. $10, Tourism.

**2014, May 29    Litho.    Perf. 12**
3986  A820    $2.50 Sheet of 8, #a-h        15.00 15.00
**Imperf**
**Size: 70x70mm**
3987  A820    $10 multi                 7.50  7.50

A821

Canonization of Pope John Paul II — A822

No. 3988 — Pope John Paul II: a, Waving. b, Wearing miter, holding crucifix. c, Standing in Popemobile, holding post. d, Touching hands of people in crowd.
No. 3989 — Pope John Paul II: a, Standing in Popemobile, wearing miter. b, With arm raised. c, Touching wall. d, Standing in Popemobile, with arm extended, without miter.
No. 3990, $10, Pope John Paul II with arm raised, horiz. No. 3991, $10, Face of Pope John Paul II, horiz.

**2014, May 29    Litho.    Perf. 12**
3988  A821    $3.25 Sheet of 4, #a-d        9.75  9.75
3989  A822    $3.25 Sheet of 4, #a-d        9.75  9.75

---

**Souvenir Sheets**
**Perf. 12¾**
3990-3991  A822    Set of 2         15.00 15.00
Nos. 3990-3991 each contain one 51x38mm stamp.

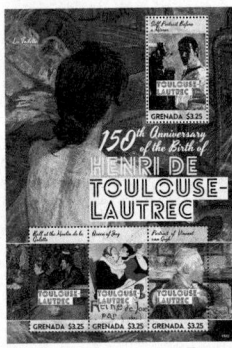

Paintings by Henri de Toulouse-Lautrec (1864-1901) — A823

No. 3992, $3.25: a, Self-portrait Before a Mirror. b, Ball at the Moulin de la Galette. c, Queen of Joy. d, Portrait of Vincent van Gogh.
No. 3993, $3.25: a, Self-portrait caricature. b, Au Moulin Rouge. c, La Revue Blanche. d, Hangover.
No. 3994, $5 — Details from At the Moulin Rouge: a, Dancing woman. b, Woman wearing hat.
No. 3995, $5 — Women from Salon at the Rue des Moulins with panel color of: a, Yellow brown. b, Gray.

**2014, May 29    Litho.    Perf. 12**
**Sheets of 4, #a-d**
3992-3993  A823    Set of 2         19.50 19.50
**Souvenir Sheets of 2, #a-b**
3994-3995  A823    Set of 2         15.00 15.00

Early Steam Locomotives — A824

No. 3996: a, Stephenson's Rocket, 1829. b, Vauxhall locomotive, 1831. c, Stephenson locomotive, 1833. d, Planet locomotive and tender, 1830.
No. 3997: a, Blenkinsop's rack locomotive, 1812. b, North Star locomotive, 1837.

**2014, June 23    Litho.    Perf. 14**
3996  A824    $3.25 Sheet of 4, #a-d        9.75  9.75
**Souvenir Sheet**
3997  A824    $5 Sheet of 2, #a-b          7.50  7.50

Moths A825

No. 3998: a, Common silver line moth. b, Cream-spotted tiger moth. c, Great tiger moth. d, Hebe moth. e, Magpie moth. f, Margate beauty moth. g, Pink under-wing moth. h, Small tiger moth. i, Argent and sable moth.
No. 3999, $5, horiz.: a, Clear-winged humming sphinx. b, Drury's sphinx.
No. 4000, $5, horiz.: a, Elephant sphinx. b, Spurge sphinx.

---

**2014, June 23    Litho.    Perf. 13¾**
3998  A825    $2 Sheet of 9, #a-i   13.50 13.50
**Souvenir Sheets of 2, #a-b**
**Perf. 12¾**
3999-4000  A825    Set of 2         15.00 15.00
Nos. 3999-4000 each contain two 51x38mm stamps.

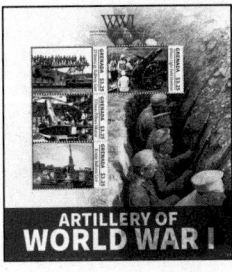

World War I, Cent.
A826

No. 4001, $3.25 — Artillery: a, 274mm/45 railway gun. b, 105mm light field howitzer. c, 370mm Filloux mortar. d, Krupp balloon gun.
No. 4002, $3.25, vert. — World leaders: a, Woodrow Wilson, flag of United States. b, King Albert I, flag of Belgium. c, Emperor Taisho, flag of Japan. d, King Victor Emmanuel III, flag of Italy.
No. 4003, $5 — Artillery: a, 2-inch mortar bombs. b, 6-inch mortar bombs.
No. 4004, $5 — World leaders: a, Tsar Nicholas II, flag of Russia. b, King George V, flag of Great Britain.

**2014, June 23    Litho.    Perf. 12**
**Sheets of 4, #a-d**
4001-4002  A826    Set of 2         19.50 19.50
**Souvenir Sheets of 2, #a-b**
4003-4004  A826    Set of 2         15.00 15.00

Paintings A827

No. 4005, $3.50: a, Meekness, by Eustache Le Sueur. b, Midsummer Eve, by Edward Robert Hughes. c, The Lion Polyptych, by Lorenzo Veneziano.
No. 4006, $3.50: a, Lady with a Unicorn, by Raphael. b, Portrait of a Woman, by Paolo Uccello. c, Flowers in a Brown Vase, by Odilon Redon.
No. 4007, $10, Portrait of a Man in Front of a Rose Hedge, by Hans Baldung. No. 4008, $10, Les Muses, by Maurice Denis.

**2014, June 23    Litho.    Perf. 12¾**
**Sheets of 3, #a-c**
4005-4006  A827    Set of 2         15.50 15.50
**Size: 100x100mm**
**Imperf**
4007-4008  A827    Set of 2         15.00 15.00

**Souvenir Sheets**

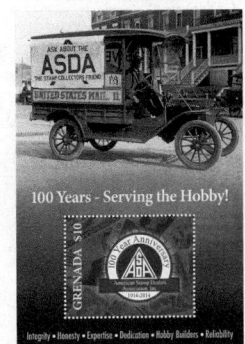

American Stamp Dealers' Association, Cent. — A828

---

Centennial emblem and background of: No. 4009, $10, Postage stamps. No. 4010, $10, Post office boxes, vert.

**2014, Oct. 24    Litho.    Perf. 12¾**
4009-4010  A828    Set of 2         15.00 15.00

Gulls A829

No. 4011, $3.25: a, Gray-headed gull. b, Hartlaub's gull. c, Red-billed gull. d, Silver gull.
No. 4012, $3.25: a, Black-billed gull. b, Andean gull. c, Brown-headed gull. d, Bonaparte's gull.
No. 4013, $5, horiz.: a, Black-headed gull, diff. b, Slender-billed gull.
No. 4014, $5, horiz.: a, Brown-hooded gull. b, Andean gull, diff.

**2014, Nov. 3    Litho.    Perf. 14**
**Sheets of 4, #a-d**
4011-4012  A829    Set of 2         19.50 19.50
**Souvenir Sheets of 2, #a-b**
4013-4014  A829    Set of 2         15.00 15.00

A830

A831

A832

Monarch Butterflies — A833

Various butterflies, as depicted.

**2014, Nov. 3    Litho.    Perf. 13¾**
4015  A830    $3.50 Sheet of 3, #a-c        7.75  7.75
4016  A831    $3.50 Sheet of 3, #a-c        7.75  7.75
**Souvenir Sheets**
4017  A832    $5 Sheet of 2, #a-b          7.50  7.50
4018  A833    $5 Sheet of 2, #a-b          7.50  7.50

Deng Xiaoping (1904-97), Chinese Leader — A834

No. 4019 — Flags, buildings and symbols of People's Republic of China and Macao with various images of Deng Xiaoping, numbered: a, (110-1). b, (110-2). c, (110-3). d, (110-4). e, (110-5). f, (110-6). g, (110-7). h, (110-8). i, (110-9). j, (110-10). k, (110-11). l, (110-12). m, (110-13). n, (110-14). o, (110-15). p, (110-16). q, (110-17). r, (110-18). s, (110-19). t, (110-20). u, (110-21). v, (110-22). w, (110-23). x, (110-24). y, (110-25). z, (110-26). aa, (110-27). ab, (110-28). ac, (110-29). ad, (110-30). ae, (110-31). af, (110-32). ag, (110-33). ah, (110-34). ai, (110-35). aj, (110-36). ak, (110-37). al, (110-38). am, (110-39). an, (110-40). ao, (110-41). ap, (110-42). aq, (110-43). ar, (110-44). as, (110-45). at, (110-46). au, (110-47). av, (110-48). aw, (110-49). ax, (110-50). ay, (110-51). az, (110-52). ba, (110-53). bb, (110-54). bc, (110-55). bd, (110-56). be, (110-57). bf, (110-58). bg, (110-59). bh, (110-60). bi, (110-61). bj, (110-62). bk, (110-63). bl, (110-64). bm, (110-65). bn, (110-66). bo, (110-67). bp, (110-68). bq, (110-69). br, (110-70). bs, (110-71). bt, (110-72). bu, (110-73). bv, (110-74). bw, (110-75). bx, (110-76). by, (110-77). bz, (110-78). ca, (110-79). cb, (110-80). cc, (110-81). cd, (110-82). ce, (110-83). cf, (110-84). cg, (110-85). ch, (110-86). ci, (110-87). cj, (110-88). ck, (110-89). cl, (110-90). cm, (110-91). cn, (110-92). co, (110-93). cp, (110-94). cq, (110-95). cr, (110-96). cs, (110-97). ct, (110-98). cu, (110-99). cv, (110-100). cw, (110-101). cx, (110-102). cy, (110-103). cz, (110-104). da, (110-105). db, (110-106). dc, (110-107). dd, (110-108). de, (110-109). df, (110-110).

**2014, Dec. 8    Litho.    Perf. 14¼x14¾**
4019    Sheet of 110    97.50 97.50
  *a.-df.* A834 $1.20 Any single    .85  .85

Worldwide Fund for Nature (WWF) — A835

Nos. 4020 and 4021: a, Oceanic whitetip shark and fish. b, Oceanic whitetip shark and ocean ripples. c, Two Oceanic whitetip sharks. d, Head of Oceanic whitetip shark.

**2014, Dec. 8    Litho.    Perf. 14¾x14**
4020  A835  $1.25  Block or vert.
            strip of 4, #a-d  3.75  3.75
4021  A835  $2.75  Block or vert.
            strip of 4, #a-d  8.25  8.25

Modernist Paintings — A836

No. 4022, vert.: a, Red Madras Headdress, by Henri Matisse. b, The Studio Boat, by Claude Monet. c, Mr. Loulou (Louis Le Ray), by Paul Gauguin. d, The Smoker, by Vincent van Gogh. e, Woman with Pigeons, by Gustave Courbet. f, Mussel Fishers at Berneval, by Pierre-Auguste Renoir. g, Woman Walking in an Exotic Forest, by Henri Rousseau. h, Peasant Standing with Arms Crossed, by Paul Cézanne.
$10, Blue Still Life, by Matisse.

**2015, May 18    Litho.    Perf. 12½**
4022  A836  $3.15  Sheet of 8,
            #a-h  14.00 14.00
        **Souvenir Sheet**
4023  A836  $10 multi  7.50  7.50

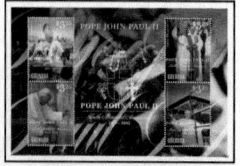

St. John Paul II (1920-2005) — A837

No. 4024 — Pope John Paul II: a, Waving to crowd, wearing miter. b, Waving, black-and-

---

white photograph. c, At Western Wall, Jerusalem. d, In Popemobile.
$10, Pope John Paul II, horiz.

**2015, May 18    Litho.    Perf. 14**
4024  A837  $3.25  Sheet of 4, #a-
            d  9.75  9.75
        **Souvenir Sheet**
        **Perf. 12½**
4025  A837  $10 multi  7.50  7.50
No. 4025 contains one 51x38mm stamp.

Large Cruise Ships A838

No. 4026: a, Oasis of the Seas. b, Allure of the Seas. c, Independence of the Seas.
$10, Allure of the Seas, diff.

**2015, May 18    Litho.    Perf. 12**
4026  A838  $3.50  Sheet of 3, #a-
            c  7.75  7.75
        **Souvenir Sheet**
        **Perf. 14**
4027  A838  $10 multi  7.50  7.50
No. 4026 contains three 50x30mm stamps.

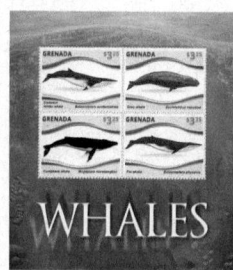

Whales A839

No. 4028, $3.25: a, Common minke whale. b, Gray whale. c, Humpback whale. d, Fin whale.
No. 4029, $3.25: a, Bowhead whale. b, Narwhal. c, Beluga whale. d, Pilot whale.
No. 4030, $10, Sperm whales. No. 4031, $10, Killer whale.

**2015, May 18    Litho.    Perf. 14**
        **Sheets of 4, #a-d**
4028-4029 A839  Set of 2  19.50 19.50
        **Souvenir Sheets**
        **Perf. 13¾**
4030-4031 A839  Set of 2  15.00 15.00
Nos. 4030-4031 each contain one 35x35mm stamp.

Horses in Art A840

No. 4032, $3.25 — Details from *The Horse Fair*, by Rosa Bonheur: a, Man holding bit of horse. b, Black horse rearing. c, Man standing, two riders on horses. d, Heads of two white horses.
No. 4033, $3.25, horiz.: a, *Before the Race*, by Eugène Delacroix. b, *Horses*, by Francis Picabia. c, *Horse Frightened by Lightning*, by Delacroix. d, *The Red Horses*, by Franz Marc.
No. 4034, $10, *Whistlejacket*, by George Stubbs. No. 4035, $10, *The Three Horses*, by Xu Beihong, horiz.

**2015, May 18    Litho.    Perf. 14**
        **Sheets of 4, #a-d**
4032-4033 A840  Set of 2  19.50 19.50
        **Souvenir Sheets**
        **Perf. 12½**
4034-4035 A840  Set of 2  15.00 15.00
No. 4034 contains one 38x51mm stamp.
No. 4035 contains one 51x38mm stamp.

---

Flag of People's Republic of China and Battle Scene — A841

Flag of People's Republic of China and Monuments A842

Flag of People's Republic of China and Japanese World War II Surrender A843

Flag of People's Republic of China and Islands — A844

**2015, May 28    Litho.    Perf. 14¾x14**
4036  A841  $1.20  multi  .90  .90
4037  A842  $1.20  multi  .90  .90
4038  A843  $1.20  multi  .90  .90
4039  A844  $1.20  multi  .90  .90
    *Nos. 4036-4039 (4)*  3.60  3.60

Pres. Abraham Lincoln (1809-65) — A845

No. 4040 — Lincoln and: a, Sculpture of soldiers riding horses into battle. b, Fence. c, Soldiers and cannon. d, Corner of Lincoln Memorial. e, Lincoln's home, Springfield, Illinois. f, Lincoln Memorial and steps.
$10, Lincoln and cannon.

**2015, May 28    Litho.    Perf. 14**
4040  A845  $3.15  Sheet of 6,
            #a-f  14.00 14.00
        **Souvenir Sheet**
        **Perf. 12½**
4041  A845  $10 multi  7.50  7.50
No. 4041 contains one 51x38mm stamp.

Paintings by Vincent van Gogh A846

No. 4042: a, The Church in Auvers-sur-Oise, View from the Chevet, 1890. b, Self-portrait, 1887. c, Café Terrace at Night, 1888. d, Three Sunflowers in a Vase, 1888. e, Portrait of Dr. Gachet, 1890. f, Still Life with Decanter and Lemons on a Plate, 1887.
$10, The Starry Night, 1889, horiz.

**2015, May 28    Litho.    Perf. 14**
4042  A846  $3.15  Sheet of 6,
            #a-f  14.00 14.00
        **Souvenir Sheet**
        **Perf. 12**
4043  A846  $10 multi  7.50  7.50
No. 4043 contains one 60x40mm stamp.

---

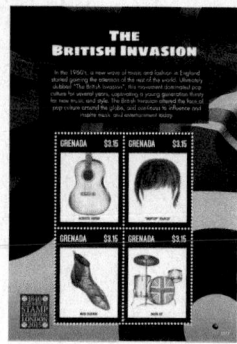

The 1960's British "Invasion" — A847

No. 4044: a, Acoustic guitar. b, Moptop haircut. c, Mod fashion. d, Drum kit.
$10, Electric guitar.

**2015, May 28    Litho.    Perf. 14**
4044  A847  $3.15  Sheet of 4, #a-
            d  9.50  9.50
        **Souvenir Sheet**
        **Perf. 12**
4045  A847  $10 multi  7.50  7.50
Europhilex 2015 Stamp Exhibition, London.

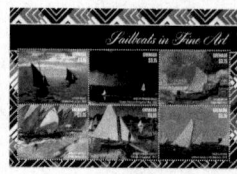

Sailboats in Art A848

No. 4046: a, Fishing Boats at Sea, by Claude Monet. b, Thunder Storm on Narragansett Bay, by Martin Johnson Heade. c, Yellow Boat, by Odilon Redon. d, Fishing Boats, by Joaquín Sorolla. e, Sailboats at Argenteuil, by Pierre-Auguste Renoir. f, Sailboats Racing on the Delaware, by Thomas Eakins.
$10, Fishing Boats on the Beach at Saintes-Maries-de-la-Mer, by Vincent van Gogh.

**2015, May 28    Litho.    Perf. 12¾**
4046  A848  $3.15  Sheet of 6,
            #a-f  14.00 14.00
        **Souvenir Sheet**
4047  A848  $10 multi  7.50  7.50

World Leaders — A849

Designs: No. 4048, $4.50, Chinese leader Mao Zedong (1893-1976 and flag of People's Republic of China (5-1). No. 4049, $4.50, Soviet leader Joseph Stalin (1879-1953) and Russian flag (5-2). No. 4050, $4.50, Pres. Franklin D. Roosevelt (1882-1945) and flag of United States (5-3). No. 4051, $4.50, British Prime Minister Sir Winston Churchill (1874-1965) and British flag (5-4). No. 4052, $4.50, French Pres. Charles de Gaulle (1890-1970) and French flag (5-5).

**2015, Aug. 3    Litho.    Perf. 14**
4048-4052 A849  Set of 5  17.00 17.00

People's Republic of China, 66th Anniv. — A850

Flag of People's Republic of China, various scenes from Chinese military parade, and stamp number at bottom: No. 4053, $4.50, (15-1). No. 4054, $4.50, (15-2). No. 4055, $4.50, (15-3). No. 4056, $4.50, (15-4). No. 4057, $4.50, (15-5). No. 4058, $4.50, (15-6). No. 4059, $4.50, (15-7). No. 4060, $4.50, (15-8). No. 4061, $4.50, (15-9). No. 4062, $4.50, (15-10). No. 4063, $4.50, (15-11). No. 4064, $4.50, (15-12). No. 4065, $4.50, (15-13). No.

4066, $4.50, (15-14). No. 4067, $4.50, (15-15).

**2015, Aug. 3**    Litho.    *Perf. 14*
4053-4067 A850   Set of 15   50.00 50.00

### Miniature Sheets

A851

A852

Popes
A853

No. 4068: a, Pope John Paul II wearing miter, waving. b, Pope Benedict XVI wearing miter. c, Pope Benedict XVI wearing zucchetto, praying. d, Pope John Paul II wearing zucchetto, in crowd.
No. 4069 — Pope Benedict XVI wearing: a, Black cassock. b, Miter and red vestments. c, Zucchetto and green vestments. d, Red cassock.
No. 4070 — Pope Benedict XVI wearing: a, Miter and white vestments. b, Stole, waving with both hands. c, Purple vestments. d, White cassock.

**2015, Aug. 26**    Litho.    *Perf. 14*
4068 A851 $3.25 Sheet of 4, #a-d   9.75 9.75
4069 A852 $3.25 Sheet of 4, #a-d   9.75 9.75
4070 A853 $3.25 Sheet of 4, #a-d   9.75 9.75
   Nos. 4068-4070 (3)   29.25 29.25

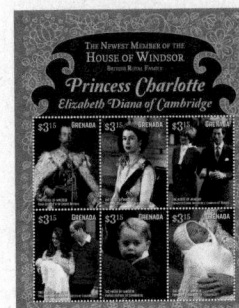

Birth of Princess Charlotte of Cambridge — A854

No. 4071: a, King George V. b, Queen Elizabeth II. c, Princess Diana and Prince Charles. d, Duke and Duchess of Cambridge with Princess Charlotte. e, Prince George of Cambridge. f, Duchess of Cambridge holding Princess Charlotte.
$10, King George V, Queen Elizabeth II, Princess Diana, Prince Charles, Duke and Duchess of Cambridge with Princess Charlotte, horiz.

**2015, Aug. 26**    Litho.    *Perf. 14*
4071 A854 $3.15 Sheet of 6, #a-f   14.00 14.00
   **Souvenir Sheet**
   *Perf. 13¾*
4072 A854   $10 multi   7.50 7.50
No. 4072 contains one 70x35mm stamp.

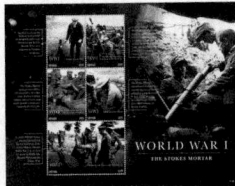

World War I, Cent. A855

No. 4073: a, Sir Wilfred Stokes and mortar (30x40mm). b, British troops firing a Stokes mortar (30x40mm). c, Members of King's Own Yorkshire Light Infantry fusing Stokes shells (30x40mm). d, Soldier loading a Stokes mortar (30x40mm). e, King George V inspecting Stokes mortar (60x40mm).
$10, Soldier loading Stokes mortar, diff., vert.

**2015, Aug. 26**    Litho.    *Perf. 14*
4073 A855 $3.25 Sheet of 5, #a-e   12.00 12.00
   **Souvenir Sheet**
   *Perf. 12½*
4074 A855   $10 multi   7.50 7.50
No. 4074 contains one 38x51mm stamp.

Queen Elizabeth II, Longest-Reigning British Monarch — A856

No. 4075: Various depictions of Queen Elizabeth II.
No. 4076, $10, Queen Elizabeth II, in coach. No. 4077, $10, Queen Elizabeth II and Prince Philip, horiz.

*Perf. 14, 12 (#4077)*
**2015, Nov. 1**         Litho.
4075 A856 $3.15 Horiz. strip of 3, #a-c   7.00 7.00
   **Souvenir Sheets**
4076-4077 A856   Set of 2   15.00 15.00
No. 4075 was printed in sheets containing two each Nos. 4075a-4075c.

Visit of Pope Francis to New York City A857

No. 4078: Various photographs of Pope Francis and Central Park, as shown.
$10, Pope Francis, diff.

**2015, Nov. 1**    Litho.    *Perf. 14*
4078 A857 $3.15 Sheet of 6, #a-f   14.00 14.00
   **Souvenir Sheet**
   *Perf. 12*
4079 A857   $10 multi   7.50 7.50

A858

A859

New Year 2016 (Year of the Monkey) — A860

Various depictions of monkeys.

**2015, Nov. 2**    Litho.    *Perf. 14*
4080 A858 $1.40 multi   1.00 1.00
4081 A859 $1.50 multi   1.10 1.10
4082 A860 $1.50 multi   1.10 1.10
4083 A859 $2 multi   1.50 1.50
4084 A860 $2 multi   1.50 1.50
4085 A860 $2.40 multi   1.75 1.75
4086 A860 $2.50 multi   1.90 1.90
4087 A858 $3 multi   2.25 2.25
4088 A859 $3.50 multi   2.60 2.60
4089 A859 $3.50 green & multi   2.60 2.60
4090 A859 $3.50 multi (white background)   2.60 2.60
4091 A860 $3.50 multi   2.60 2.60
   Nos. 4080-4091 (12)   22.50 22.50

### Miniature Sheet

New Year 2016 (Year of the Monkey) A861

No. 4092 — Monkey on: a, Horse, turquoise green background. b, Horse, rose background. c, Elephant, yellow background. d, Elephant, dull green background.

**2015, Nov. 2**    Litho.    *Perf. 13¾*
4092 A861 $3.25 Sheet of 4, #a-d   9.75 9.75

Christmas — A862

Paintings by Sandro Botticelli. 90c, Madonna of the Sea. $2.25, The Virgin Adoring the Child. $3.50, The Virgin and Child with Two Angels and the Young St. John the Baptist. $5, Mystic Nativity.

**2015, Nov. 2**    Litho.    *Perf. 12½*
4093-4096 A862   Set of 4   8.75 8.75

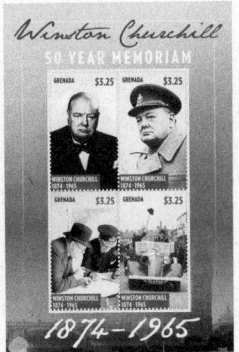

Sir Winston Churchill (1874-1965), British Prime Minister — A863

No. 4097 — Churchill: a, Wearing bowtie. b, Wearing military cap. c, Wearing hat, with military officer. d, In automobile.
$10, Churchill wearing hat.

**2015, Dec. 21**    Litho.    *Perf. 12*
4097 A863 $3.25 Sheet of 4, #a-d   9.75 9.75
   **Souvenir Sheet**
4098 A863   $10 multi   7.50 7.50

*Star Trek* Television Series, 50th Anniv. — A864

No. 4099 — Scene from episode: a, Dagger of the Mind. b, Spectre of the Gun. c, The City on the Edge of Forever. d, Mirror, Mirror. e, Spock's Brain. f, The Trouble with Tribbles.
$10, Amok Time.

**2015, Dec. 21**    Litho.    *Perf. 12*
4099 A864 $3.15 Sheet of 6, #a-f   14.00 14.00
   **Souvenir Sheet**
   *Perf. 12½*
4100 A864   $10 multi   7.50 7.50
No. 4100 contains one 38x51mm stamp.

Manatees — A865

No. 4101: a, Florida manatee swimming forward, entire manatee shown. b, Florida manatee swimming upside down, denomination on manatee. c, Two Caribbean manatees. d, Florida manatee swimming forward, tips of tail and flippers not on stamp. e, Head of Florida manatee, denomination near nose. f, Profile view of caribbean manatee.
$10, Caribbean manatee, diff.

**2015, Dec. 21**    Litho.    *Perf. 12*
4101 A865 $3.15 Sheet of 6, #a-f   14.00 14.00
   **Souvenir Sheet**
4102 A865   $10 multi   7.50 7.50

International Year of Light — A866

No. 4103 — a, Solar panel with single post, Sun at top center. b, Solar panel with single post at left, Sun at UR. c, Double array of solar panels with support and single post. d, Solar panel with single post at right, Sun at left.
$10, Solar panels, diff.

**2015, Dec. 21**    Litho.    *Perf. 14*
4103 A866 $3.25 Sheet of 4, #a-d   9.75 9.75
   **Souvenir Sheet**
   *Perf. 12*
4104 A866   $10 multi   7.50 7.50
No. 4104 contains one 50x30mm stamp.

Airplanes of World War I — A867

No. 4105 — Bombers: a, One Caproni Ca 33 450hp biplane. b, Two Ansaldo SVA5

biplanes. c, Two Caproni Ca 33 450hp biplanes. d, One Ansaldo SVA5 biplane.
$10, Two Caproni Ca 33 450 hp biplanes, diff.

**2015, Dec. 21    Litho.    Perf. 13¾**
4105  A867  $3.25 Sheet of 4, #a-
d                          9.75  9.75

**Souvenir Sheet**
**Perf. 12½**
4106  A867  $10 multi          7.50  7.50
No. 4106 contains one 51x38mm stamp.

Birds
A868

No. 4107: a, Egyptian goose. b, Woodpecker. c, Cedar waxwing. d, American avocet.
$10, Western tanager.

**2015, Dec. 21    Litho.    Perf. 14**
4107  A868  $3.25 Sheet of 4, #a-
d                          9.75  9.75

**Souvenir Sheet**
4108  A868  $10 multi          7.50  7.50

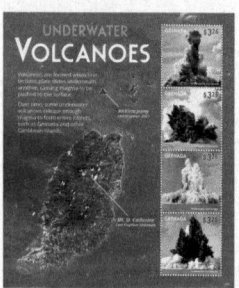
Underwater Volcanoes — A869

Volcanoes as shown.

**2015, Dec. 21    Litho.    Perf. 13¾**
4109  A869  $3.25 Sheet of 4, #a-
d                          9.75  9.75

**Souvenir Sheet**
**Perf. 12**
4110  A869  $10 multi          7.50  7.50
No. 4110 contains one 40x30mm stamp.

Fish
A870

No. 4111, $3.25: a, Queen angelfish. b, Foureye butterflyfish. c, Gray angelfish. d, Yellowtail snapper.
No. 4112, $3.25: a, Bar jack. b, Spotted trunkfish. c, Sergeant major. d, Rock beauty.
No. 4113, $10, Great barracuda. No. 4114, $10, Yellowtail damsel.

**2015, Dec. 21    Litho.    Perf. 14**
**Sheets of 4, #a-d**
4111-4112  A870  Set of 2   19.50  19.50

**Souvenir Sheets**
4113-4114  A870  Set of 2   15.00  15.00

A871

A872

Nos. 4115-4116: Various starfish, as shown.
No. 4117, $10, White starfish, vert. No. 4118, $10, Orange starfish, vert.

**2015, Dec. 21    Litho.    Perf. 14**
4115  A871  $3.25 Sheet of 4,
#a-d                       9.75  9.75
4116  A872  $3.25 Sheet of 4,
#a-d                       9.75  9.75

**Souvenir Sheets**
4117-4118  A872  Set of 2   15.00  15.00

Owls
A873

No. 4119, $3.25: a, Long-eared owl. b, Barn owl. c, Great gray owl. d, Burrowing owl.
No. 4120, $3.25: a, Eurasian eagle owl. b, Spotted owl. c, Short-eared owl. d, Spectacled owl.
No. 4121, $10, Northern hawk owl. No. 4122, $10, Barred owl, horiz.

**Perf. 12, 14 (#4120)**
**2015, Dec. 21    Litho.**
**Sheets of 4, #a-d**
4119-4120  A873  Set of 2   19.50  19.50

**Souvenir Sheets**
**Perf. 12½**
4121-4122  A873  Set of 2   15.00  15.00
No. 4121 contains one 38x51mm stamp.
No. 4122 contains one 51x38mm stamp.

A874

Chinese Art
A875

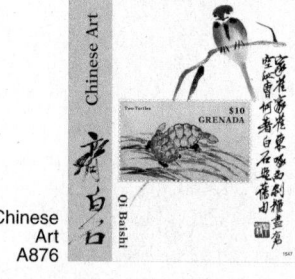
Chinese
Art
A876

Nos. 4123-4124: Various paintings by Chang Dai Chien, as shown.
No. 4125, $10, Two Turtles, by Qi Baishi, horiz. No. 4126, $10, Wisteria and Goldfish, by Qi Baishi, horiz.

**2015, Dec. 21    Litho.    Perf. 12½**
4123  A874  $3.25 Sheet of 4,
#a-d                       9.75  9.75
4124  A875  $3.25 Sheet of 4,
#a-d                       9.75  9.75

**Souvenir Sheets**
**Perf. 12**
4125-4126  A876  Set of 2   15.00  15.00

**Miniature Sheets**

Stamps of United Nations
Countries — A877

No. 4127, $3.15: a, Afghanistan #1. b, Albania #1. c, Algeria #1. d, Andorra (Spanish Administration) #1, Andorra (French Administration) #1. e, Angola #1. f, Antigua #1.
No. 4128, $3.15: a, Argentina #1. b, Armenia #1. c, Australia #1. d, Austria #1. e, Azerbaijan #1. f, Bahamas #5.
No. 4129, $3.15: a, Bahrain #1. b, Bangladesh #1. c, Barbados #1. d, Belarus #1. e, Belgium #1. f, Belize #312.
No. 4130, $3.15: a, Benin #1. b, Bhutan #1. c, Bolivia #1. d, Bosnia and Herzegovina #1. e, Botswana #1. f, Brazil #1.
No. 4131, $3.15: a, Honduras #1. b, Hungary #1. c, Iceland #1. d, India #1. e, Indonesia #1. f, Iran #1.
No. 4132, $3.15: a, Iraq #9. b, Ireland #1. c, Israel #1. d, Italy #17. e, Ivory Coast #1. f, Jamaica #1.
No. 4133, $3.15: a, Japan #1. b, Jordan #1. c, Kazakhstan #1. d, Kenya #1. e, Kiribati #325. f, Korean Republic #1.
No. 4134, $3.15: a, Democratic People's Republic of Korea #1. b, Kuwait #1. c, Kyrgyzstan #1. d, Laos #1. e, Latvia #1. f, Lebanon #1.

**2015, Dec. 21    Litho.    Perf. 12½**
**Sheets of 6, #a-f**
4127-4134  A877  Set of 8   115.00  115.00

Extraordinary Jubilee of Mercy — A878

No. 4135: a, Pope Benedict XVI. b, Popes Francis and Benedict XVI. c, Pope Francis. d, Pope Benedict XVI and attendants.
$10, Popes Francis and Benedict XVI.

**2016, Jan. 31    Litho.    Perf. 12**
4135  A878  $3.25 Sheet of 4, #a-
d                          9.75  9.75

**Souvenir Sheet**
4136  A878  $10 multi          7.50  7.50

Chinese Battle
Scene — A879

**2016, Feb. 2    Litho.    Perf. 14**
4137  A879  $2.50 multi        1.90  1.90

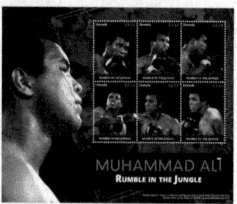
Muhammad Ali (1942-2016),
Boxer — A880

No. 4138 — Various photographs of Ali, as shown.
$10, Ali jumping rope.

**Perf. 13¼x12½**
**2016, Feb. 20    Litho.**
4138  A880  $3.15 Sheet of 6,
#a-f                       14.00  14.00

**Souvenir Sheet**
**Perf. 11¼x11¾**
4139  A880  $10 multi          7.50  7.50
No. 4139 contains one 30x50mm stamp.

Jimi Hendrix (1942-70), Rock
Guitarist — A881

No. 4140 — Paintings depicting Hendrix with panel color of: a, Purple. b, Blue. c, Pink. d, Orange brown.
$10, Hendrix, vert.

**2016, Mar. 8    Litho.    Perf. 13¾**
4140  A881  $3.25 Sheet of 4, #a-
d                          9.75  9.75

**Souvenir Sheet**
**Perf. 12½**
4141  A881  $10 multi          7.50  7.50
No. 4141 contains one 38x51mm stamp.

## Souvenir Sheets

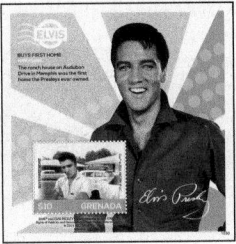

Elvis Presley (1935-77) — A882

Designs: No. 4142, $10, Presley buying first home. No. 4143, $10, Grammy Lifetime Achievement Award. No. 4144, $10, Presley's first public performance. No. 4145, $10, Presley wearing lei in Hawaii.

**2016, Mar. 8**   **Litho.**   **Perf. 12½x13¼**
4142-4145 A882   Set of 4    30.00   30.00

Queen Elizabeth II, 90th Birthday A883

No. 4146 — Queen Elizabeth wearing: a, Purple hat and coat. b, Purple dress, denomination at UR. c, Purple dress, denomination at UL. d, Purple kerchief and coat.
$13, Queen Elizabeth II holding flowers, vert.

**2016, May 16**   **Litho.**   **Perf. 13¾**
4146 A883 $3.25 Sheet of 4, #a-d    9.75   9.75

**Souvenir Sheet**
**Perf. 12½**
4147 A883   $13 multi    9.75   9.75
No. 4147 contains one 38x51mm stamp.

World Stamp Show 2016, New York A884

No. 4148 — World Stamp Show 2016 and New York landmarks: a, Bethesda Fountain, Central Park. b, Statue of Liberty. c, Grand Central Terminal. d, Williamsburg Bridge.
$8, New Yourk City skyline, horiz.

**2016, May 16**   **Litho.**   **Perf. 12**
4148 A884 $4 Sheet of 4, #a-d   12.00   12.00

**Souvenir Sheet**
**Perf. 14**
4149 A884   $8 multi    6.00   6.00
No. 4149 contains one 90x80mm stamp.

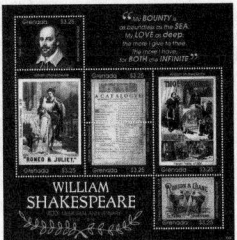

William Shakespeare (1564-1616), Writer — A885

No. 4150: a, Shakespeare (40x30mm). b, 1879 poster for Romeo and Juliet (40x60mm). c, Top of front page of Shakespeare's First Folio (40x30mm). d, Bottom of front page of Shakespeare's First Folio (40x30mm). e,

Poster for Hamlet, c. 1884 (40x60mm). f, Poster for The Comedy of Errors, c. 1879 (40x30mm).
No. 4151 — Shakespeare and line from: a, Othello. b, King Lear. c, Measure for Measure. d, Twelfth Night.
$14, Shakespeare and line from Richard III.

**2016, May 30**   **Litho.**   **Perf. 14**
4150 A885 $3.25 Sheet of 6, #a-f   14.50   14.50

**Perf. 12**
4151 A885 $3.50 Sheet of 4, #a-d   10.50   10.50

**Souvenir Sheet**
4152 A885   $14 multi    10.50   10.50
No. 4151 contains four 30x50mm stamps. No. 4152 contains one 30x50mm stamp.

A886

A887

A888

A889

A890

A891

A892

A893

A894

A895

A896

A897

A898

Chinese Paintings — A899

---

**2016, June 20**   **Litho.**   **Perf. 14**

| | | | | |
|---|---|---|---|---|
| 4153 | A886 | $1.20 multi | .90 | .90 |
| 4154 | A887 | $1.20 multi | .90 | .90 |
| 4155 | A888 | $1.20 multi | .90 | .90 |
| 4156 | A889 | $1.20 multi | .90 | .90 |
| 4157 | A890 | $1.20 multi | .90 | .90 |
| 4158 | A891 | $1.20 multi | .90 | .90 |
| 4159 | A892 | $1.20 multi | .90 | .90 |
| 4160 | A893 | $1.20 multi | .90 | .90 |
| 4161 | A894 | $1.20 multi | .90 | .90 |
| 4162 | A895 | $1.20 multi | .90 | .90 |
| 4163 | A896 | $1.20 multi | .90 | .90 |
| 4164 | A897 | $1.20 multi | .90 | .90 |
| 4165 | A898 | $1.20 multi | .90 | .90 |
| 4166 | A899 | $1.20 multi | .90 | .90 |
| | *Nos. 4153-4166 (14)* | | 12.60 | 12.60 |

Nos. 4155-4160 were printed in sheets of 24 containing six of each stamp. Nos. 4161-4166 were printed in sheets of 24 containing six of each stamp.

Sept. 11, 2001 Terrorist Attacks in New York, 15th Anniv. A900

No. 4167: a, World Trade Center in daylight. b, World Trade Center in daylight as seen from base. c, World Trade Center with lights on at dusk. d, World Trade Center with lights on at night. e, Tribute in Light. f, World Trade Center with lights on as seen from base.
No. 4168, vert. — World Trade Center: a, Orange sky. b, At night.
$14, Tribute in Light, vert.

**2016, June 30**   **Litho.**   **Perf. 14**
4167 A900 $3.25 Sheet of 6, #a-f   14.50   14.50

**Souvenir Sheets**
**Perf. 12**
4168 A900   $7 Sheet of 2, #a-b   10.50   10.50

**Perf. 12½**
4169 A900   $14 multi   10.50   10.50
No. 4169 contains one 38x51mm stamp.

Chinese Aerospace Day — A901

No. 4170 — Various satellites over Earth with denomination at: a, LL. b, LR.

**2016, July 29**   **Litho.**   **Perf. 14**
4170 A901 $5 Horiz. pair, #a-b   7.50   7.50

A902

A903

A904

A905

A906

---

A907

A908

Gates of the Great Wall of China A909

**2016, Aug. 15**   **Litho.**   **Perf. 12**

| | | | | |
|---|---|---|---|---|
| 4171 | A902 | $1.20 multi | .90 | .90 |
| 4172 | A903 | $1.20 multi | .90 | .90 |
| 4173 | A904 | $1.20 multi | .90 | .90 |
| 4174 | A905 | $1.20 multi | .90 | .90 |
| a. | | Block of 4, #4171-4174 | 3.60 | 3.60 |
| 4175 | A906 | $1.20 multi | .90 | .90 |
| 4176 | A907 | $1.20 multi | .90 | .90 |
| 4177 | A908 | $1.20 multi | .90 | .90 |
| 4178 | A909 | $1.20 multi | .90 | .90 |
| a. | | Block of 4, #4175-4178 | 3.60 | 3.60 |
| | *Nos. 4171-4178 (8)* | | 7.20 | 7.20 |

Nos. 4174-4174 and Nos. 4175-4178 were printed together in sheets of 16, with one block of four containing all four stamps at the center of the sheet.

A910

A911

A912

A913

A914

A915

A916

Chinese Long March — A917

**2016, Sept. 6**   **Litho.**   **Perf. 14¾x14¼**

| | | | | |
|---|---|---|---|---|
| 4179 | A910 | $1.20 multi (8-1) | .90 | .90 |
| 4180 | A911 | $1.20 multi (8-2) | .90 | .90 |
| 4181 | A912 | $1.20 multi (8-3) | .90 | .90 |

| 4182 | A913 | $1.20 multi (8-4) | .90 | .90 |
|------|------|-------------------|-----|-----|
| 4183 | A914 | $1.20 multi (8-5) | .90 | .90 |
| 4184 | A915 | $1.20 multi (8-6) | .90 | .90 |
| 4185 | A916 | $1.20 multi (8-7) | .90 | .90 |
| 4186 | A917 | $1.20 multi (8-8) | .90 | .90 |
| | Nos. 4179-4186 (8) | | 7.20 | 7.20 |

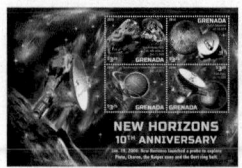

Launch of New Horizons Space Probe, 10th Anniv. — A918

No. 4187 — New Horizons probe and: a, APL asteroid. b, Charon. c, Neptune. d, Pluto. $10, Launch, vert.

**2016, Sept. 9      Litho.      Perf. 14**
| 4187 | A918 | $3.25 Sheet of 4, #a-d | 9.75 | 9.75 |
|------|------|------------------------|------|------|

**Souvenir Sheet**
**Perf. 12**
| 4188 | A918 | $10 multi | 7.50 | 7.50 |
|------|------|-----------|------|------|

Sea Birds — A919

No. 4189: a, Royal tern. b, Red-billed tropicbird. c, Magnificent frigatebird. d, Brown noddy.
No. 4190, vert.: a, Masked booby. b, Red-footed booby.

**2016, Sept. 16      Litho.      Perf. 14**
| 4189 | A919 | $4 Sheet of 4, #a-d | 12.00 | 12.00 |
|------|------|---------------------|-------|-------|

**Souvenir Sheet**
**Perf. 12**
| 4190 | A919 | $7 Sheet of 2, #a-b | 10.50 | 10.50 |
|------|------|---------------------|-------|-------|

A920

A921

A922

Worldwide Fund for Nature (WWF) A923

**2016, Nov. 3      Litho.      Perf. 12**
| 4191 | | Strip of 4 | 17.00 | 17.00 |
|------|--|------------|-------|-------|
| a. | A920 $5.50 multi | | 4.25 | 4.25 |
| b. | A921 $5.50 multi | | 4.25 | 4.25 |
| c. | A922 $5.50 multi | | 4.25 | 4.25 |
| d. | A923 $5.50 multi | | 4.25 | 4.25 |
| e. | Miniature sheet of 8, 2 each #4191a-4191d | | 34.00 | 34.00 |

Paintings by Hieronymus Bosch (c. 1450-1516) — A924

No. 4192: a, Ecce Homo. b, St. John the Baptist in the Wilderness. c, Christ Carrying the Cross. d, St. John, the Evangelist, on Patmos.
No. 4193: a, Crucifixion with a Donor. b, Christ Crowned with Thorns.

**2016, Nov. 14      Litho.      Perf. 14**
| 4192 | A924 | $5.50 Sheet of 4, #a-d | 16.50 | 16.50 |
|------|------|------------------------|-------|-------|

**Souvenir Sheet**
**Perf. 12½**
| 4193 | A924 | $7.50 Sheet of 2, #a-b | 11.50 | 11.50 |
|------|------|------------------------|-------|-------|

No. 4193 contains two 38x51mm stamps.

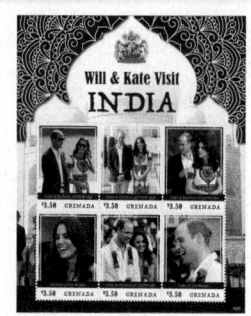

Duke and Duchess of Cambridge in India — A925

No. 4194: a, Duke and Duchess, Duchess touching ear. b, Duke and Duchess in front of building. c, Duke and Duchess, Duke's hand behind shoulder of Duchess. d, Duchess. e, Duke and Duchess standing in front of crowd. f, Duke.
No. 4195: a, Princess Diana seated on bench. b, Duke and Duchess seated on bench.

**2016, Nov. 25      Litho.      Perf. 14**
| 4194 | A925 | $3.50 Sheet of 6, #a-f | 15.50 | 15.50 |
|------|------|------------------------|-------|-------|

**Souvenir Sheet**
**Perf. 12**
| 4195 | A925 | $7.50 Sheet of 2, #a-b | 11.50 | 11.50 |
|------|------|------------------------|-------|-------|

Christmas — A926

Christmas tree-shaped items: No. 4196, $5.50, Ornament. No. 4197, $5.50, Decorated cookie. No. 4198, $10, Ornament, diff. No. 4199, $10, Cookie, diff.

**2016, Dec. 1      Litho.      Perf. 12½**
| 4196-4199 | A926 | Set of 4 | 23.00 | 23.00 |
|-----------|------|----------|-------|-------|

Monkey King A927

No. 4200: a, Monkey King looking towards LR. b, Cloud, orange stairway in background. c, Monkey King looking towards LL. d, Cloud, orange background. e, Monkey King with grass in mouth. f, Cloud, over temple. g, Monkey King over temple, rod pointing to LR. h, Cloud over temple, Monkey King in background. i, Monkey King over temple, looking left.
No. 4201 — Monkey King wearing: a, Carrying rod, b, Juggling fruit.

**2016, Dec. 1      Litho.      Perf. 13¾**
| 4200 | A927 | $1.50 Sheet of 9, #a-i | 10.00 | 10.00 |
|------|------|------------------------|-------|-------|

**Souvenir Sheet**
**Perf. 12**
| 4201 | A927 | $7.50 Sheet of 2, #a-b | 11.50 | 11.50 |
|------|------|------------------------|-------|-------|

No. 4201 contains two 30x40mm stamps.

A928

New Year 2017 (Year of the Rooster) A929

No. 4202: a, Flower over rooster, denomination at UR. b, Centipede over rooster, denomination at UL. c, Centipede over rooster, denomination at UR. d, Flower over rooster, denomination at UL.
No. 4203 — Rooster with: a, Blue neck facing right. b, Green neck facing right. c, Green neck facing left. d, Blue neck facing left.

**2016, Dec. 5      Litho.      Perf. 13¾**
| 4202 | A928 | $5.50 Sheet of 4, #a-d | 16.50 | 16.50 |
|------|------|------------------------|-------|-------|

**Perf.**
| 4203 | A929 | $5.50 Sheet of 4, #a-d | 16.50 | 16.50 |
|------|------|------------------------|-------|-------|

Attack on Pearl Harbor, 75th Anniv. A930

No. 4204: a, USS Arizona. b, USS Utah. c, USS Oklahoma. d, USS Nevada.
No. 4205, vert.: a, Pres. Franklin D. Roosevelt. b, Pres. Harry S. Truman.

**2016, Dec. 13      Litho.      Perf. 14**
| 4204 | A930 | $3.50 Sheet of 4, #a-d | 10.50 | 10.50 |
|------|------|------------------------|-------|-------|

**Souvenir Sheet**
**Perf. 12½**
| 4205 | A930 | $4 Sheet of 2, #a-b | 6.00 | 6.00 |
|------|------|---------------------|------|------|

No. 4205 contains two 38x51mm stamps.

A931

A932

A933

A934

A935

New Year 2017 (Year of the Rooster) — A936

**2016, Dec. 21      Litho.      Perf. 13¾**
| 4206 | A931 | $1.20 multi | .90 | .90 |
|------|------|-------------|-----|-----|
| 4207 | A932 | $1.20 multi | .90 | .90 |
| 4208 | A933 | $1.50 multi | 1.10 | 1.10 |
| 4209 | A934 | $1.50 multi | 1.10 | 1.10 |

| 4210 | A935 | $1.60 multi | 1.25 | 1.25 |
|------|------|-------------|------|------|
| 4211 | A936 | $1.60 multi | 1.25 | 1.25 |
| | Nos. 4206-4211 (6) | | 6.50 | 6.50 |

Swarovski Crystal Rooster — A937

**2016, Dec. 1      Litho.      Perf. 14**
| 4212 | A937 | $3.50 multi | 2.60 | 2.60 |
|------|------|-------------|------|------|

**Miniature Sheets**

A938

Pres. John F. Kennedy (1917-63) — A939

No. 4213 — Pres. Kennedy: a, At inauguration, mouth open. b, On telephone. c, At inauguration, mouth closed. d, With wife, Jacqueline (wearing lt blue dress and hat). e, With wife, Jacqueline (black-and-white photograph). f, With wife, Jacqueline (with crowd in background).
No. 4214 — Presidential seal and: a, Pres. Kennedy with wife, Jacqueline. b, Pres. Kennedy, red frame. c, Pres. Kennedy, flag at right. d, Pres. Kennedy, flag at left.

**2017, Feb. 7      Litho.      Perf. 14**
| 4213 | A938 | $4 Sheet of 6, #a-f | 18.00 | 18.00 |
|------|------|---------------------|-------|-------|
| 4214 | A939 | $5 Sheet of 4, #a-d | 15.00 | 15.00 |

**Miniature Sheets**

A940

Ranger 7, 50th Anniv. (in 2014) A941

No. 4215: a, Launch, text in black at right. b, Ranger 3 above Moon, text in white at right. c, Measurement gauge and Ranger 7 photograph of Moon before impact, text on one line at left. d, Ranger 7 above Moon, text in white at right.
No. 4216: a, Launch, text in white at left. b, Ranger 7 photograph of Moon before impact, text on two lines at left. c, Ranger 3 above Moon, text in white at left. d, Ranger 7 above Moon, text in white at left.

**2017, Feb. 28      Litho.      Perf. 14**
| 4215 | A940 | $3.25 Sheet of 4, #a-d | 9.75 | 9.75 |
|------|------|------------------------|------|------|
| 4216 | A941 | $3.25 Sheet of 4, #a-d | 9.75 | 9.75 |

Bats
A942

No. 4217: a, Great fruit-eating bat. b, Pallas's mastiff bat. c, Seba's short-tailed bat. d, Little yellow-shouldered bat. e, Mexican fruit bat. f, Greater bulldog bat.

No. 4218: a, Tree bat. b, Long-tailed skipper butterfly.

**2017, Feb. 28    Litho.    Perf. 13¾**
4217  A942  $3.50  Sheet of 6, #a-f                    15.50  15.50

**Souvenir Sheet**
**Perf.**
4218  A942  $7.50  Sheet of 2, #a-b                    11.00  11.00

No. 4218 contains two 38mm diameter stamps.

A943

A944

A945

A946

A947

A948

A949

A950

A951

Return of Hong Kong to People's Republic of China, 20th Anniv. — A952

**2017    Litho.    Perf. 13½x13¼**
4219  A943  $1.20  multi                    .90    .90
4220  A944  $1.20  multi                    .90    .90
**Perf. 14**
4221  A945  $1.20  multi                    .90    .90
4222  A946  $1.20  multi                    .90    .90
4223  A947  $1.20  multi                    .90    .90
4224  A948  $1.20  multi                    .90    .90
4225  A949  $1.50  multi                   1.10   1.10
4226  A950  $1.50  multi                   1.10   1.10
4227  A951  $1.50  multi                   1.10   1.10
4228  A952  $1.50  multi                   1.10   1.10
    Nos. 4219-4228 (10)                    9.80   9.80

Issued: Nos. 4219-4220, 3/21; Nos. 4221-4228, 5/9.

Beaches
A953

No. 4229: a, Whitehaven Beach, Australia. b, Grand Anse Beach, Grenada. c, Railay West Beach, Thailand. d, Hanalei Bay, Hawaii. e, Boulders Beach, South Africa. f, Cinque Terre, Italy.
$10, Navagio Beach, Greece.

**2017, Mar. 30    Litho.    Perf. 13½**
4229  A953  $3.50  Sheet of 6, #a-f                    15.50  15.50

**Souvenir Sheet**
**Perf. 12½x13¼**
4230  A953  $10  multi                    7.50   7.50

No. 4230 contains one 80x30mm stamp.

Miniature Sheets

Royal Air Force, Cent.
A954

No. 4231, $4: a, Red Arrow Hawk T1 in flight. b, Nine Red Arrow planes in diamond formation. c, Five Red Arrow planes flying to right. d, Nine Red Arrow planes flying forward. e, Ten Red Arrow planes in arc. f, Five Red Arrow planes flying to left.

No. 4232: a, $3, Westland Sea King helicopter. b, $3, Duke of Cambridge in helicopter. c, $3, Prince George of Cambridge wearing ear protection. d, $5, Emblem of Search and Rescue Force. e, $5, Princes William and Harry. f, $5, Queen Elizabeth II.

**2017, Apr. 1    Litho.    Perf. 14**
**Sheets of 6, #a-f**
4231-4232  A954  Set of 2                    36.00  36.00

Animals
A955

No. 4233: a, Caspian pond turtle. b, Pallid bat. c, Purple-banded sunbird. d, Bactrian camel.
$9, Dwarf rabbit, vert.

**2017, Apr. 3    Litho.    Perf. 12½**
4233  A955  $6  Sheet of 4, #a-d    18.00  18.00
**Souvenir Sheet**
4234  A955  $9  multi                    6.75   6.75

A956

Princess Diana (1961-97) — A957

No. 4235 — Princess Diana wearing: a, Lilac suit, hands not visible (30x40mm). b, Strapless gown (30x40mm). c, White shirt with ruffles, hands visible (30x40mm). d, Lilac dress (30x40mm). e, Green dress with white stripes and dots, white hat (30x40mm). f, Dark purple dress and lilac hat, (30x80mm).

No. 4236 — Princess Diana: a, Wearing dull rose blouse (30x40mm). b, Holding purse, wearing white dress (30x80mm). c, Wearing gown and jacket (30x80mm).

**2017, Apr. 14    Litho.    Perf. 14**
4235  A956  $3.50  Sheet of 6, #a-f                    15.50  15.50

**Souvenir Sheet**
4236  A957  $5  Sheet of 3, #a-c                    11.00  11.00

Miniature Sheets

A958

A959

Inauguration of Pres. Donald Trump — A960

No. 4237 — Inaugural Ball photographs of: a, Pres. Trump and wife, Melania, black background. b, Ivanka Trump and Jared Kushner. c, Vice-President Mike Pence and wife, Karen. d, Pres. Trump and wife, colored background.

No. 4238 — Barron Trump with: a, Father, 2007. b, Father, 2014. c, Father, 2017. d, Mother, 2007. e, Mother, 2010. f, Mother, 2017.

No. 4239: a, Melania Trump in black dress. b, Melania Trump in white dress. c, Ivanka Trump in pink dress. d, Ivanka Trump in black dress. e, Pres. Trump, flag in background. f, Pres. Trump, door in background.

**2017, June 26    Litho.    Perf. 14**
4237  A958  $4.50  Sheet of 4, #a-d          13.50  13.50
4238  A959  $4.50  Sheet of 6, #a-f          20.00  20.00
4239  A960  $4.50  Sheet of 6, #a-f          20.00  20.00

New Year 2018 (Year of the Dog) — A961

Chinese Zodiac Animals
A962

No. 4240 — Dog facing: a, Left. b, Right.
No. 4241: a, Rat. b, Ox. c, Tiger. d, Rabbit. e, Dragon. f, Snake. g, Horse. h, Goat. i, Monkey. j, Rooster. k, Dog. l, Pig.

**2017, Aug. 8    Litho.    Perf. 14**
4240  A961  $5.50  Vert. pair, #a-b                    8.25   8.25

**Miniature Sheet**
4241  A962  $1.80  Sheet of 12, #a-l                  16.00  16.00

No. 4240 was printed in sheets containing two pairs.

Dogs and Cats
A963

No. 4242, $7: a, Dog and squirrel in tree. b, Dog, sitting. c, Dog and ball.
No. 4243, $7: a, Cat and bird in cage. b, Cat, sitting. c, Cat and fish in tank.
No. 4244, $12, Dog with tongue out. No. 4245, $12, Cat and ball of yarn.

**2017, Aug. 9    Litho.    Perf. 14**
**Sheets of 3, #a-c**
4242-4243  A963  Set of 2                    31.00  31.00

**Souvenir Sheets**
**Perf. 12½**
4244-4245  A963  Set of 2                    18.00  18.00

Nos. 4244-4245 each contain one 38x51mm stamp.

Starfish
A964

No. 4246: a, Common starfish. b, Common sunstar. c, Brittle star. d, West Indian seastar.
$12, Starfish and coral, horiz.

**2017, Aug. 9    Litho.    Perf. 13¾**
4246  A964  $7  Sheet of 4, #a-                    21.00  21.00

**Souvenir Sheet**
**Perf. 14**
4247  A964  $12  multi                    9.00   9.00

No. 4247 contains one 80x30mm stamp.

## Souvenir Sheets

A965

Coral Reefs A966

No. 4248: a, Corals (40x360mm). b, Coral, fish and sea horse (80x30mm).
No. 4249: a, Shell. b, Octopus.

**2017, Aug. 9    Litho.    Perf. 12½x13¼**
4248  A965  $7.50 Sheet of 2, #a-b    11.00 11.00
    **Perf. 13¾**
4249  A966  $7.50 Sheet of 2, #a-b    11.00 11.00

70th Wedding Anniversary of Queen Elizabeth II and Prince Philip — A967

No. 4250 — Photographs of couple on wedding day: a, Princess Elizabeth waving. b, In wedding procession. c, Passing soldiers. d, Standing in front of curtain.
$18, Couple and attendants, vert.

**2017, Aug. 11    Litho.    Perf. 14**
4250  A967  $6 Sheet of 4, #a-d    18.00 18.00
    **Souvenir Sheet**
    **Perf. 12½**
4251  A967  $18 multi    13.50 13.50
No. 4251 contains one 38x51mm stamp.

Tropical Fish A968

No. 4252: a, Kole tang. b, Spotbase burrfish. c, Coral trout. d, Yellow tang.
No. 4253: a, Discus. b, Palette surgeonfish. c, Copperband butterflyfish.

    **Perf. 12½x13¼**
**2017, Aug. 16    Litho.**
4252  A968  $7 Sheet of 4, #a-d    21.00 21.00
    **Souvenir Sheet**
4253  A968  $7 Sheet of 3, #a-c    15.50 15.50

## Miniature Sheets

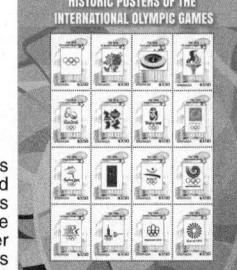

Emblems and Posters of the Summer Olympics A969

No. 4254, $3.50: a, Olympic rings, 2016. b, Mascots, 2016. c, Stadium, 2016. d, Olympic torch, 2016. e, 2016 emblem. f, 2012 emblem. g, 2008 emblem. h, 2004 emblem. i, 2000 emblem. j, 1996 emblem. k, 1992 emblem. l, 1988 emblem. m, 1984 emblem. n, 1980 emblem. o, 1976 emblem. p, 1972 emblem.
No. 4255, $3.50: a, 1968 emblem. b, 1964 emblem. c, 1960 emblem. d, 1956 emblem. e, 1952 emblem. f, 1948 emblem. g, 1936 emblem. h, 1932 emblem. i, 1928 poster. j, 1924 poster. k, 1920 poster. l, 1912 poster. m, 1908 poster. n, 1904 poster. o, 1900 poster. p, 1896 poster (erroneously inscribed "1986").

**2017, Sept. 14    Litho.    Perf. 14**
    **Sheets of 16, #a-p**
4254-4255  A969  Set of 2    85.00 85.00

Study of Two Characters from Los Borrachos, by Diego Velázquez — A970

**2017, Oct. 6    Litho.    Perf. 12½**
4256  A970  $50 multi    37.50 37.50

## Souvenir Sheets

Elvis Presley (1935-77) — A971

Inscriptions: No. 4257, $12, Receives draft notice. No. 4258, $12, Elvis dances despite the "wiggle ban." No. 4259, $12, Shower of Stars Benefit.

**2017, Oct. 26    Litho.    Perf. 12½**
4257-4259  A971  Set of 3    27.00 27.00

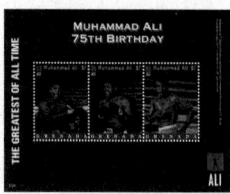

Muhammad Ali (1942-2016), Boxer — A972

No. 4260 — Various photographs of Ali, as shown.
$12, Ali looking right, fists ungloved.

**2017, Oct. 26    Litho.    Perf. 12**
4260  A972  $7 Sheet of 3, #a-c    15.50 15.50
    **Souvenir Sheet**
    **Perf. 12½**
4261  A972  $12 multi    9.00 9.00
No. 4261 contains one 38x51mm stamp.

## Miniature Sheet

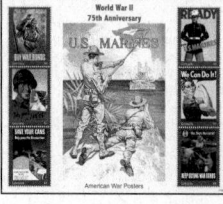

World War II, 75th Anniv. A973

No. 4262: a, Buy War Bonds poster. b, U.S. Marines recruitment poster. c, Woman Ordnance Worker poster. d, We Can Do It! poster.

e, Save Your Cans poster. f, Keep Buying War Bonds poster.

**2017, Dec. 4    Litho.    Perf. 14**
4262  A973  $4 Sheet of 6, #a-f    18.00 18.00

Christmas A974

Religious paintings: $1, The Adoration of the Shepherds, by Philippe de Champaigne. $2, The Adoration of the Kings, by Peter Paul Rubens. $5, The Adoration of the Kings, by Giuseppe Chiara. $10, Adoration of the Kings, by Abraham Bloemaert.

**2017, Dec. 17    Litho.    Perf. 12½**
4263-4266  A974  Set of 4    13.50 13.50

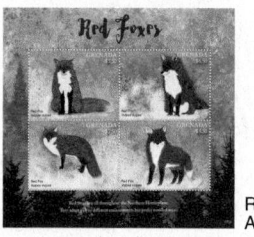

Red Fox A975

No. 4267 — Various depictions of red fox with denominations of: a, $5.50. b, $6.50. c, $7.50. d, 8.50.
No. 4268, $12, One red fox. No. 4269, $12, Two red foxes.

    **Perf. 12½, 13¾ (#4269)**
**2017, Dec. 18    Litho.**
4267  A975    Sheet of 4, #a-d    21.00 21.00
    **Souvenir Sheets**
4268-4269  A975  Set of 2    18.00 18.00
No. 4269 contains one 35x35mm stamp.

## Miniature Sheet

Chinese Paintings A976

Various Chinese paintings depicting dogs (Nos. 4270a-4270j) or flowers (Nos. 4270k-4270t) numbered: a, 2018-1. b, 2018-2. c, 2018-3. d, 2018-4. e, 2018-5. f, 2018-6. g, 2018-7. h, 2018-8. i, 2018-9. j, 2018-10. k, 2018-11. l, 2018-12. m, 2018-13. n, 2018-14. o, 2018-15. p, 2018-16. q, 2018-17. r, 2018-18. s, 2018-19. t, 2018-20.

**2018, Jan. 1    Litho.    Perf. 14**
4270  A976  $1.20 Sheet of 20, #a-t    18.00 18.00

Visit to People's Republic of China of Pres. Donald Trump A977

No. 4271: a, Melania Trump. b, Pres. Donald Trump. c, Chinese Pres. Xi Jinping. d, Peng Liyuan.
$12, Pres. Xi Jinping and the Trumps, horiz.

**2018, Jan. 24    Litho.    Perf. 12**
4271  A977  $8 Sheet of 4, #a-d    24.00 24.00
    **Souvenir Sheet**
    **Perf. 12½**
4272  A977  $12 multi    9.00 9.00
No. 4272 contains one 51x38mm stamp.

## Miniature Sheet

Engagement of Prince Harry and Meghan Markle — A978

No. 4273: a, Prince William. b, Catherine, Duchess of Cambridge. c, Prince Harry. d, Markle.

**2018, Mar. 5    Litho.    Perf. 14**
4273  A978  $7 Sheet of 4, #a-d  21.00 21.00

## Miniature Sheet

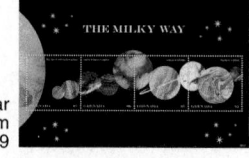

Solar System A979

No. 4274: a, $4, Neptune, Pluto. b, $5, Saturn, Uranus. c, $6, Earth, Mars, Jupiter. d, $7, Sun, Mercury, Venus.

**2018, May 22    Litho.    Perf. 13¾**
4274  A979    Sheet of 4, #a-d    16.50 16.50

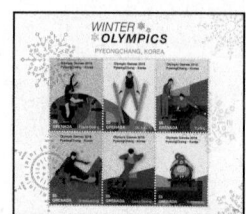

2018 Winter Olympics, Pyeongchang, South Korea — A980

No. 4275: a, Figure skating. b, Ski jumping. c, Curling. d, Snowboarding. e, Speed skating. f, Bobsledding.
No. 4276: a, Ice hockey. b, Freestyle skiing.

**2018, May 22    Litho.    Perf. 14**
4275  A980  $5 Sheet of 6, #a-f  22.50 22.50
    **Souvenir Sheet**
    **Perf. 12½**
4276  A980  $8 Sheet of 2, #a-b  12.00 12.00
No. 4276 contains two 38x51mm stamps.

## Souvenir Sheets

Coronation of Queen Elizabeth Ii, 65th Anniv. — A981

No. 4277 — Queen Elizabeth II: a, Standing. b, Seated in coach.
$10, Queen Elizabeth II waving.

**2018, May 22    Litho.    Perf. 14**
4277  A981  $8 Sheet of 2, #a-b    12.00 12.00
    **Perf. 12**
4278  A981  $10 multi    7.50 7.50

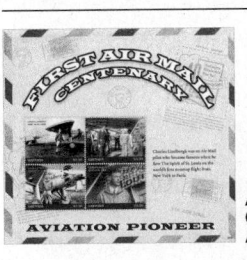

Airmail, Cent. A982

No. 4279 — Charles Lindbergh and the Spirit of St. Louis: a, Lindbergh standing under wing. b, Lindbergh with other people near airplane. c, Lindbergh standing behind wheel. d, Close-up of Lindbergh and name of airplane.
$10, U.S. #C10.

**2018, May 22    Litho.    Perf. 14**
4279 A982 $5.50 Sheet of 4, #a-d    16.50 16.50
**Souvenir Sheet**
**Perf. 12½**
4280 A982 $10 multi    7.50 7.50
No. 4280 contains one 51x38mm stamp.

Theobroma Cacao — A983

No. 4281: a, $3, Branch with brown pods. b, $4, Branch with yellow pod.
$10, Branch with pod, diff.

**2018, June 18    Litho.    Perf. 14**
4281 A983    Pair, #a-b    5.25 5.25
**Souvenir Sheet**
**Perf. 12½**
4282 A983 $10 multi    7.50 7.50
No. 4281 was printed in sheets containing three pairs. No. 4282 contains one 38x51mm stamp.

Nutmeg A984

No. 4283: a, $4, Ground nutmeg and nutmeg seeds. b, $5, Ground nutmeg. c, $6, Nutmeg seeds. d, $7, Mace aril surrounding nutmeg kernel.
$10, Nutmeg tree branch and seeds.

**2018, June 18    Litho.    Perf. 14**
4283 A984    Sheet of 4, #a-d    16.50 16.50
**Souvenir Sheet**
**Perf. 12½**
4284 A984 $10 multi    7.50 7.50
No. 4284 contains one 51x38mm stamp.

Wedding of Prince Harry and Meghan Markle A985

No. 4285: a, Prince Charles escorting bride. b, Bride and groom in church. c, Bride and groom holding hands. d, Bride and groom waving in car.
$10, Bride holding flower bouquet.

---

**2018, July 27    Litho.    Perf. 12**
4285 A985 $5 Sheet of 4, #a-d    15.00 15.00
**Souvenir Sheet**
**Perf. 12½**
4286 A985 $10 multi    7.50 7.50
No. 4286 contains one 51x38mm stamp.

Flora and Fauna — A986

Designs: $5, Cacao tree. $10, West Indian manatee. $20, Nine-banded armadillo. $40, Bougainvillea. $60, Nutmeg. $80, Grenada dove.

**2018, Aug. 3    Litho.    Perf. 14**
4287 A986 $5 multi    3.75 3.75
4288 A986 $10 multi    7.50 7.50
4289 A986 $20 multi    15.00 15.00
4290 A986 $40 multi    30.00 30.00
4291 A986 $60 multi    45.00 45.00
4292 A986 $80 multi    60.00 60.00
Nos. 4287-4292 (6)    161.25 161.25

**Souvenir Sheets**

Elvis Presley (1935-77) — A987

Inscriptions: No. 4293, $10, "Are You Lonesome Tonight?" No. 4294, $10, Elvis's first army leave. No. 4295, $10, Elvis trading cards, vert. No. 4296, $10, Memphis Music Hall of Fame.

**2018, Aug. 3    Litho.    Perf. 14**
4293-4296 A987    Set of 4    30.00 30.00

**Miniature Sheet**

Equids A988

No. 4297: a, $5, Donkeys. b, $6, Mules. c, $7, Horses.

**2018, Oct. 10    Litho.    Perf. 12**
4297 A988    Sheet of 3, #a-c    13.50 13.50

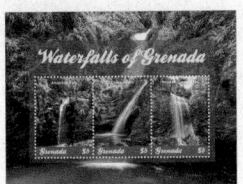

Grenada Waterfalls — A989

No. 4298: a, Annandale Falls. b, Concord Falls. c, Royal Mt. Carmel Falls.
$10, Seven Sisters Falls.

**2018, Oct. 10    Litho.    Perf. 12**
4298 A989 $5 Sheet of 3, #a-c    11.00 11.00
**Souvenir Sheet**
4299 A989 $10 multi    7.50 7.50
No. 4299 contains one 30x50mm stamp.

---

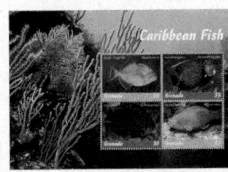

Fish A990

No. 4300: a, $4, Queen triggerfish. b, $5, French angelfish. c, $6, Cherubfish. d, $7, Queen parrotfish.
$10, Queen angelfish.

**2018, Oct. 10    Litho.    Perf. 14**
4300 A990    Sheet of 4, #a-d    16.50 16.50
**Souvenir Sheet**
**Perf. 12½**
4301 A990 $10 multi    7.50 7.50
No. 4301 contains one 51x38mm stamp.

Tropical Fruit A991

No. 4302: a, $5, Tamarinds. b, $5, Passion fruits. c, $6, Mangos. d, $6, Starfruits.
No. 4303: a, Guavas. b, Soursops.

**2018, Oct. 10    Litho.    Perf. 14**
4302 A991    Sheet of 4, #a-d    16.50 16.50
**Souvenir Sheet**
**Perf. 12**
4303 A991 $8 Sheet of 2, #a-b    12.00 12.00

**Miniature Sheet**

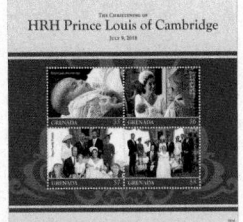

Christening of Prince Louis of Cambridge — A992

No. 4304: a, $5, Prince Louis. b, $6, Prince Louis in arms of Duchess of Cambridge, clergyman. c, $7, Princes William, Charles, and Harry with wives and children. d, $8, Princes William, Charles and Harry with wives, children and other family members.

**2018, Oct. 17    Litho.    Perf. 14**
4304 A992    Sheet of 4, #a-d    19.50 19.50

Flight of Apollo 11, 50th Anniv. (in 2019) A993

No. 4305: a, Launch. b, Lunar Module and astronaut on Moon. c, Astronaut on moon. d, Earth. e, Earth and Moon. f, Moon.
$11, Lunar Module above Moon, mission patch, horiz.

**2018, Oct. 17    Litho.    Perf. 12**
4305 A993 $5 Sheet of 6, #a-f    22.50 22.50
**Souvenir Sheet**
**Perf. 12½**
4306 A993 $11 multi    8.25 8.25
No. 4306 contains one 51x38mm stamp.

---

New Year 2019 (Year of the Pig) A994

No. 4307 — Pig facing: a, $5, Right, dark red flower on hindquarters. b, $5, Right, orange red flower on hindquarters. c, $6, Left, orange red flower on hindquarters. d, $6, Left, dark red flower on hindquarters.
$8, Pig, diff.

**2018, Oct. 17    Litho.    Perf. 14**
4307 A994    Sheet of 4, #a-d    16.50 16.50
**Souvenir Sheet**
**Perf. 12**
4308 A994 $8 multi    6.00 6.00
No. 4308 contains one 50x30mm stamp.

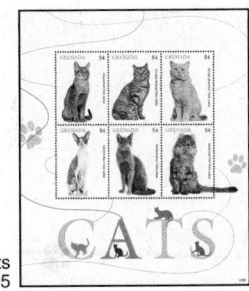

Cats A995

No. 4309: a, Abyssinian. b, Kurilian Bobtail. c, British Shorthair. d, Cornish Rex. e, Russian Blue. f, American Curl.
$10, Balinese, horiz.

**2018, Nov. 9    Litho.    Perf. 14**
4309 A995 $4 Sheet of 6, #a-f    18.00 18.00
**Souvenir Sheet**
**Perf. 12**
4310 A995 $10 multi    7.50 7.50

A996

2018 World Cup Soccer Championships, Russia — A997

**2018, Jan. 1    Litho.    Perf. 14**
4311 A996 $2.80 multi    2.10 2.10
4312 A997 $2.80 multi, peach background    2.10 2.10
a.    Gradiated background with white at top    2.10 2.10
b.    Sheet of 8, 4 each #4311, 4312a    17.00 17.00

**Miniature Sheet**

Butterflies — A998

No. 4313: a. $4, Napeocles jucunda. b, $5, Castina papilionaris. c, $6, Morpho patroclus. d, $7, Urania leilus.

**2018, Dec. 5    Litho.    Perf. 13½**
4313 A998    Sheet of 4, #a-d    16.50 16.50

Christmas — A999

Designs: $1, Wreath. $2, Bell. $5, Christmas ornament. $10, Santa Claus.

**2018, Dec. 5    Litho.    Perf. 13½**
4314-4317 A999    Set of 4    13.50 13.50

Miniature Sheet

Spice Island Billfish
Tournament — A1000

No. 4318: a, $2, Bait fish on hook. b, $3, Fishing boats. c, $4, Harbor. d, $5, Harbor, diff. e, $6, Fisherman with catch. f, $7, Swordfish on hook.

**2019, Jan. 11    Litho.    Perf. 13½**
4318 A1000    Sheet o 6, #a-f    20.00 20.00

Souvenir Sheet

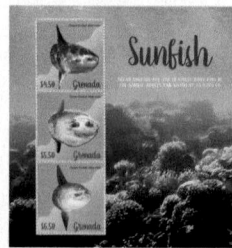

Ocean
Sunfish
A1001

No. 4319 — Various depictions of Ocean sunfish: a, $4.50. b, $5.50. c, $6.50.

**2019, Feb. 6    Litho.    Perf. 13½**
4319 A1001    Sheet of 3, #a-c    12.50 12.50

Souvenir Sheet

Pres. Donald Trump Visting Suresnes
American Cemetery, France — A1002

No. 4320: a, $4, Pres. Trump holding umbrella. b, $5, Tombstones and poppies. c, $6, Pres. Trump and tombstones.

**2019, Feb. 6    Litho.    Perf. 14**
4320 A1002    Sheet of 3, #a-c    11.00 11.00

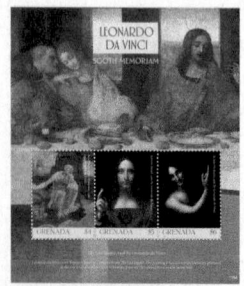

Paintings by Leonardo da Vinci (1452-
1519) — A1003

No. 4321: a, $4, Saint Jerome in the Wilderness. b, $5, Salvator Mundi. c, $6, St. John the Baptist.
$10, The Last Supper.

**2019, Feb. 18    Litho.    Perf. 12**
4321 A1003    Sheet of 3,
#a-c    11.00 11.00

**Size: 131x80mm**

*Imperf*

4322 A1003 $10 multi    7.50 7.50

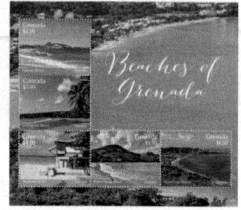

Beaches
of
Grenada
A1004

No. 4323: a, $2.50, Bathway Beach. b, $3.50, La Sagesse Beach. c, $4.50, Magazine Beach. d, $5.50, Morne Rouge Beach. e, $6.50, Grand Anse Beach.
$14, Levera Beach.

**2019, Mar. 12    Litho.    Perf. 14**
4323 A1004    Sheet of 5,
#a-e    17.00 17.00

**Souvenir Sheet**

*Perf. 12*

4324 A1004 $14 multi    10.50 10.50

No. 4324 contains one 50x30mm stamp.

Miniature Sheet

Pantropical Spotted Dolphins — A1005

No. 4325: a, One dolphin facing left. b, Two dolphins. c, Head of dolphin. d, One dolphin facing right.

**2019, Mar. 27    Litho.    Perf. 14**
4325 A1005 $5 Sheet of 4, #a-
d    15.00 15.00

Green
Iguanas
A1006

No. 4326 — Various depictions of green iguana: a, $4. b, $5. c, $6. d, $7.
$14, Green iguana, diff.

**2019, Mar. 27    Litho.    Perf. 12**
4326 A1006    Sheet of 4, #a-d    16.50 16.50

**Souvenir Sheet**

*Perf. 12½*

4327 A1006 $14 multi    10.50 10.50

No. 4327 contains one 51x38mm stamp.

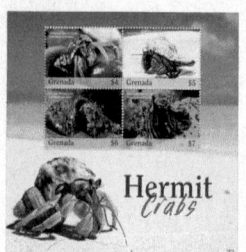

Hermit
Crabs
A1007

No. 4328: a, $4, Caribbean hermit crab. b, $5, Giant hermit crab. c, $6, Stareye hermit crab. d, $7, Red reef hermit crab.
No. 4329: a, Caribbean hermit crab facing right. b, Caribbean hermit crab facing forward.

**2019, Apr. 18    Litho.    Perf. 14**
4328 A1007    Sheet of 4, #a-d    16.50 16.50

**Souvenir Sheet**

*Perf. 13¾*

4329 A1007 $8 multi    12.00 12.00

No. 4329 contains two 35x35mm stamps.

Miniature Sheets

Statues Depicting Queen Victoria
(1819-1901) — A1008

No. 4330 — Statue at: a, $4, Victoria Park, St. Helier, Jersey. b, $4, Victoria Memorial Hall, Kolkata, India. c, $7, Republic Square, Valletta, Malta. d, Victoria, British Columbia, Canada.
No. 4331 — Statue at: a, $5, Queen's Park, Bangalore Cantonment, India. b, $5, Queen Victoria Gardens, Melbourne, Australia. c, $6, City of Westminster, London. d, $6, McGill University, Montreal, Quebec, Canada.

**2019, Apr. 18    Litho.    Perf. 14**
**Sheets of 4, #a-d**
4330-4331 A1008    Set of 2    32.50 32.50

Miniature Sheet

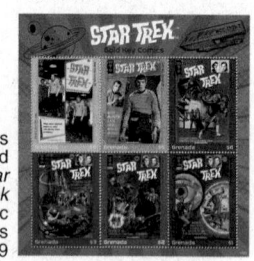

Covers
of Gold
Key *Star
Trek*
Comic
Books
A1009

No. 4332 — Cover of Gold Key Comic Book: a, $1, No. 25. b, $2, No. 18. c, $3, No. 15. d, $4, No. 11. e, $5, No. 9. f, $6, No. 8.

**2019, Apr. 29    Litho.    Perf. 12½**
4332 A1009    Sheet of 6, #a-f    15.50 15.50

Miniature Sheet

Birth of Prince Louis of
Cambridge — A1010

No. 4333: a, Prince Charles, Princess Diana, and infant Prince William. b, Princess Diana and Prince William. c, Duke and Duchess of Cambridge with Prince Louis. d, Duke and Duchess of Cambridge with Prince Louis, Duke waving.

**2019, May 17    Litho.    Perf. 13¾**
4333 A1010 $6 Sheet of 4, #a-
d    18.00 18.00

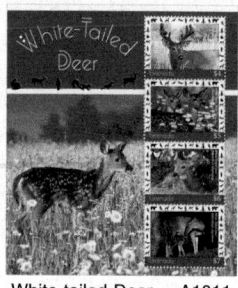

White-tailed Deer — A1011

No. 4334: a, $4, Buck. b, $5, Two does. c, $6, Fawn. d, $7, Doe and fawn.
$14, Fawn, vert.

**2019, May 24    Litho.    Perf. 12**
4334 A1011    Sheet of 4, #a-d    16.50 16.50

**Souvenir Sheet**

*Perf. 12½*

4335 A1011 $14 multi    10.50 10.50

No. 4335 contains one 38x51mm stamp.

Miniature Sheet

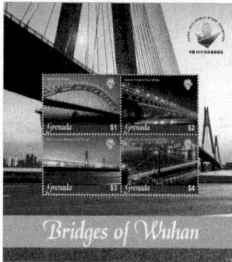

Bridges
of
Wuhan,
People's
Republic
of China
A1012

No. 4336: a, $1, Qingchuan Bridge. b, $2, Wuhan Yangtze River Bridge. c, $3, Tianxingzhou Yangtze River Bridge. d, $4, Yingwuzhou Yangtze River Bridge.

**2019, June 10    Litho.    Perf. 14**
4336 A1012    Sheet of 4, #a-d    7.50 7.50

China 2019 World Stamp Exhibition, Wuhan.

Miniature Sheet

Birth of Archie Mountbatten-
Windsor — A1013

No. 4337: a, $4, Duke and Duchess of Sussex with infant, Archie. b, $5, Princess Diana holding Prince Harry. c, $6, Duchess of Sussex holding Archie. d, $7, Prince Charles, Princess Diana and Prince Harry.

**2019, Aug. 30    Litho.    Perf. 14**
4337 A1013    Sheet of 4, #a-d    16.50 16.50

First
Man on
the
Moon,
50th
Anniv.
A1014

No. 4338: a, $4, Astronaut picking up Moon rocks. b, $5, Rocket launch. c, $6, Lunar Module leaving Moon. d, $7, Plaque left on Moon.

No. 4339, vert.: a, $4, Rocket launch. b, $5, Lunar, Command and Service Modules. c, $6, Command Module with parachutes deployed. $14, Astronaut picking up Moon rocks, diff.

**2019, Aug. 30**    **Litho.**    **Perf. 14**
4338 A1014 Sheet of 4, #a-d    16.50 16.50
4339 A1014 Sheet of 3, #a-c    11.00 11.00

**Souvenir Sheet**
**Perf. 12**
4340 A1014 $14 multi    10.50 10.50

Dorje Chang Buddha III, Buddhist Religious Leader — A1015

**2019, Sept. 3**   **Litho.**   **Perf. 13½x12½**
4341 A1015 $5 multi    3.75 3.75
No. 4341 was printed in sheets of 4.

Nine-banded Armadillo — A1016

No. 4342 — Armadillo facing: a, $4, Left. b, $5, Forward. c, $6, Right. $14, Armadillo on hind legs, vert.

**2019, Sept. 3**    **Litho.**    **Perf. 14**
4342 A1016 Sheet of 3, #a-c    11.00 11.00
**Souvenir Sheet**
**Perf. 12½**
4343 A1016 $14 multi    10.50 10.50
No. 4343 contains one 38x51mm stamp.

Roseate Spoonbills — A1017

No. 4344 — Various depictions of Roseate spoonbill: a, $4. b, $5. c, $6. d, $7.
No. 4344, vert. — Roseate spoonbill facing: a, Right. b, Left.

**2019, Sept. 8**    **Litho.**    **Perf. 12**
4344 A1017 Sheet of 4, #a-d    16.50 16.50
**Souvenir Sheet**
**Perf. 14**
4345 A1017 $4 Sheet of 2, #a-b    6.00 6.00

Rabbits A1018

No. 4346: a, Jackrabbit facing forward. b, Jackrabbit facing left. c, Cottontail rabbit facing forward. d, Cottontail rabbit facing right. e, Angora rabbit on ground. f, Angora rabbit and pail handle. $14, Cottontail rabbit facing left, vert.

**2019, Dec. 24**    **Litho.**    **Perf. 13¾**
4346 A1018 $4 Sheet of 6, #a-f    18.00 18.00

**Souvenir Sheet**
**Perf. 12**
4347 A1018 $14 multi    10.50 10.50
No. 4347 contains one 30x40mm stamp.

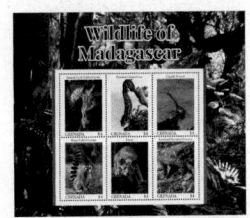

Wildlife of Madagascar — A1019

No. 4348: a, Satanic leaf-tailed gecko. b, Panther chameleon. c, Giraffe weevil. d, Ring-tailed lemur. e, Fossa. f, Lowland streaked tenrec. $14, Coquerel's sifaka.

**2020, Jan. 29**    **Litho.**    **Perf. 14**
4348 A1019 $4 Sheet of 6, #a-f    18.00 18.00
**Souvenir Sheet**
**Perf. 12**
4349 A1019 $14 multi    10.50 10.50

**Miniature Sheets**

A1020

Swiss Stamps, 175th Anniv. A1021

No. 4350: a, Switzerland #1L1. b, Switzerland #1L2. c, Left half of Switzerland #2L1. d, Right half of Switzerland #2L1. e, Switzerland #2L2. f, Switzerland #2L3. g, Switzerland #2L4 (like "f," with stamp background in darker green). h, View of Swiss city, boats in foreground. i, View of Swiss city, mountains in background. j, View of Swiss city, tree in foreground, bridge spanning river. k, View of Swiss city, horse and rider in foreground at LL. l, Switzerland #2L5. m, Switzerland #2L6. n, Switzerland #2L7. o, Switzerland #1L5. p, Switzerland #3L1.
No. 4351: a, Swiss mailbox. b, Melchior Berri (1801-54), architect.

**2020, Aug. 1**    **Litho.**    **Perf. 14**
4350 A1020 $1.75 Sheet of 18,
    #4350a-
    4350o, 3
    #4350p    23.50 23.50
4351 A1021 $1.75 Sheet of 4,
    #4351a-
    4351b, 2
    #4350p    5.25 5.25
For overprints, see Nos. 4359-4362.

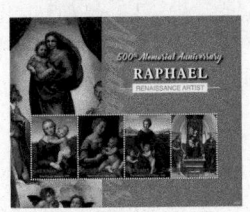

Paintings by Raphael (1483-1520) — A1022

No. 4352: a, Small Cowper Madonna. b, Madonna of the Pinks. c, The Madonna of the Meadow. d, The Ansidei Madonna.
No. 4353 — Details from the Sistine Madonna, horiz.: a, Madonna and Child. b, Putti.

**2020, Aug. 11**    **Litho.**    **Perf. 14**
4352 A1022 $5.50 Sheet of 4, #a-d    16.50 16.50
**Souvenir Sheet**
4353 A1022 $5 Sheet of 2, #a-b    7.50 7.50

**Miniature Sheet**

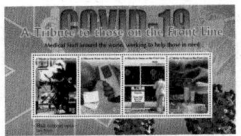

Tribute to Workers Combatting COVID-19 Pandemic — A1023

No. 4354: a, Rescue workers, ambulance and patient on gurney. b, Medical worker taking temperature of patient. c, Entrance to medical facility. d, Medical worker holding capped tubes.

**2020, Aug. 14**    **Litho.**    **Perf. 14**
4354 A1023 $5 Sheet of 4, #a-d    15.00 15.00

**Souvenir Sheets**

Elvis Presley (1935-77) — A1024

Inscriptions: No. 4355, $10, "My manager told me they was hollerin' because I was wigglin' my legs. The more I wiggled the louder they screamed." No. 4356, $10, "I wish." No. 4357, $10, "The life I lead moves very fast." No. 4358, $10, "My thanks to you."

**2020, Aug. 14**    **Litho.**    **Perf. 14**
4355-4358 A1024   Set of 4    30.00 30.00

Nos. 4350-4351 With Each Stamp Overprinted in Silver or Gold

**Methods and Perfs. As Before**
**2020, Aug. 1**
4359 A1020 $1.75 On #4350,
    sheet of 18,
    #4359a-
    4359o, 3
    #4359p (S)   23.50 23.50
4360 A1020 $1.75 On #4350,
    sheet of 18,
    #4360a-
    4360o, 3
    #4360p (G)   23.50 23.50
4361 A1021 $1.75 On #4351,
    sheet of 4,
    #4361a-
    4361b, 2
    #4359p (S)   5.25 5.25
4362 A1021 $1.75 On #4351,
    sheet of 4,
    #4362a-
    4362b, 2
    #4360p (G)   5.25 5.25
Nos. 4359-4362 (4)    57.50 57.50

A1025

Tet Offensive A1026

No. 4363: a, Rangers on alert, Saigon, Jan. 1968. b, Searching Bien Hoa, Feb. 1968. c, Fighting in Quang Tri, March 1968. d, Defending Tan Son Nhut, May 1968. 10, Marine Grenadier ready to fire.

**2020, Sept. 11**    **Litho.**    **Perf. 12½**
4363 A1025 $5 Sheet of 4, #a-d    15.00 15.00
**Souvenir Sheet**
4364 A1026 $10 multi    7.50 7.50

**Miniature Sheet**

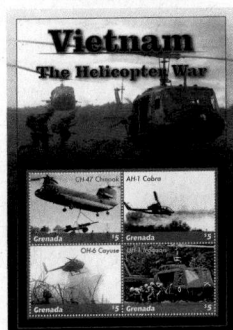

Helicopters of the Vietnam War — A1027

No. 4365: a, CH-47 Chinook. b, AH-1 Cobra. c, OH-6 Cayuse. d, UH-1 Iroquois.

**2020, Sept. 11**    **Litho.**    **Perf. 12½**
4365 A1027 $5 Sheet of 4, #a-d    15.00 15.00

**Souvenir Sheet**

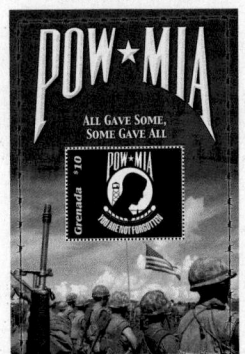

Prisoner of War-Missing in Action Flag — A1028

**2020, Sept. 11**    **Litho.**    **Perf. 12½**
4366 A1028 $10 multi    7.50 7.50

## Miniature Sheet

World War II Victory in Europe (V-E
Day). 75th Anniv.
A1029

No. 4367: a, Gen. Dwight D. Eisenhower
(1890-1969), Supreme Allied Commander in
Europe. b, Franklin D. Roosevelt (1882-1945),
32nd President of the United States. c, Gen.
Charles de Gaulle (1890-1970), leader of Free
France. d, Winston Churchill (1874-1965), Brit-
ish Prime Minister. e, Alfred Jodl (1890-1946),
German general.

**2020, Sept. 30**    **Litho.**    ***Perf. 12***
4367 A1029 $4.50 Sheet of 5,
      #a-e         17.00 17.00

A1030

Flamingos — A1031

No. 4368: a, Flamingo, black background,
neck at left. b, Flamingo on beach. c, Flamingo, foliage in background. d, Flock of flamingos. e, Flamingo, dark green background,
neck at right.
   $14, Flamingos in flight.

**2020, Sept. 30**    **Litho.**    ***Perf. 13¾***
4368 A1030 $4.50 Sheet of 5,
      #a-e         17.00 17.00
**Souvenir Sheet**
***Perf. 12***
4369 A1031   $14 multi     10.50 10.50

A1032

Seabirds
A1033

No. 4370: a, Blue-footed booby. b, Puffin. c,
Albatross. d, Gannets.
   $14, Frigatebird.

**2020, Sept. 30**    **Litho.**    ***Perf. 13¾***
4370 A1032 $5.50 Sheet of 4,
      #a-d         16.50 16.50
**Souvenir Sheet**
4371 A1033   $14 multi     10.50 10.50

A1034

---

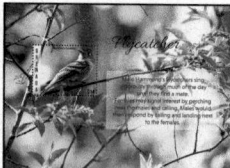

Flycatchers — A1035

No. 4372: a, Pied flycatcher (30x40mm). b,
Great crested flycatcher (30x40mm). c,
Forked-tailed flycatcher (30x80mm).
   $14, Hammond's flycatcher.

**2020, Sept. 30**    **Litho.**    ***Perf. 14***
4372 A1034   $6 Sheet of 3,
      #a-c         13.50 13.50
**Souvenir Sheet**
***Perf. 12***
4373 A1035   $14 multi     10.50 10.50

A1036

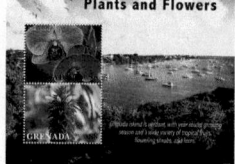

Plants
and
Flowers
A1037

No. 4374: a, Heliconia. b, Antherium. c,
Grand etang fern. d, Bougainvilleas.
No. 4375: a, Pink orchid. b, Spiral ginger.

**2020, Sept. 30**    **Litho.**    ***Perf. 14***
4374 A1036 $5.50 Sheet of 4,
      #a-d         16.50 16.50
**Souvenir Sheet**
4375 A1037   $8 Sheet of 2
      #a-b         12.00 12.00

Ludwig van Beethoven (1770-1827),
Composer — A1038

No. 4376 — Beethoven: a, Sculpture, deep
reddish purple panel. b, Drawing, brown red
panel. c, Drawing, orange brown panel. d,
Sculpture, turq green panel. e, Sculpture, gray
black panel.
No. 4377: a, Rose and cover of sonata. b,
Keyboard.

**2020, Sept. 30**    **Litho.**    ***Perf. 14***
4376 A1038 $4.50 Sheet of 5,
      #a-e         17.00 17.00
**Souvenir Sheet**
4377 A1038   $8 Sheet of 2
      #a-b         12.00 12.00

A1039

---

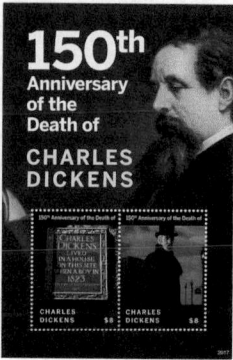

Charles Dickens (1812-70),
Writer — A1040

No. 4378: Images of Dickens, as shown.
No. 4379: a, Plaque on boyhood home of
Dickens. b, Dickens wearing hat.

**2020, Sept. 30**    **Litho.**    ***Perf. 14***
4378 A1039 $4.50 Sheet of 5,
      #a-e         17.00 17.00
**Souvenir Sheet**
4379 A1040   $8 Sheet of 2,
      #a-b         12.00 12.00
   Nos. 4379a-4379b are not inscribed with the
country name.

Fish and
Cetaceans — A1041

   Designs: 40c, Longsnout seahorse. $1,
Queen angelfish. $1.50, Sperm whale. $2,
Bottlenose dolphin. $5, Yellowtail snapper.

**2020, Dec. 7**    **Litho.**    ***Perf. 12½***
4380 A1041   40c multi     .30 .30
4381 A1041   $1 multi     .75 .75
4382 A1041 $1.50 multi     1.10 1.10
4383 A1041   $2 multi     1.50 1.50
4384 A1041   $5 multi     3.75 3.75
    Nos. 4380-4384 (5)     7.40 7.40

## Miniature Sheet

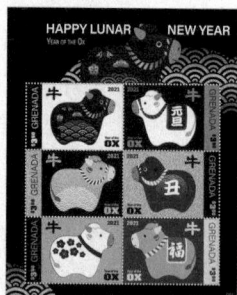

New
Year
2021
(Year of
the Ox)
A1042

No. 4385 — Ox, with background color of: a,
White. b, Red brown. c, Black. d, Olive bister.
e, Pink. f, Red.

       ***Perf. 13¼x12½***
**2020, Dec. 28**           **Litho.**
4385 A1042 $3.50 Sheet of 6,
      #a-f         15.50 15.50

A1043

---

Ruth Bader Ginsburg (1933-2020),
Associate Justice of United States
Supreme Court — A1044

No. 4386 — Justice Ginsburg with: a, Pres.
Jimmy Carter. b, Pres. Barack Obama and
other politicians. c, Pres. Bill Clinton at swearing-in ceremony. d, Justices Sonia Sotomayor
and Elena Kagan.
   $14, Justice Ginsburg, vert.

**2020**      **Litho.**    ***Perf. 14***
4386 A1043 $5.50 Sheet of 4,
      #a-d         16.50 16.50
**Souvenir Sheet**
***Perf. 12***
4387 A1044   $14 multi     10.50 10.50

   The date of issue for Nos. 4386-4387 is
unknown, though it was alleged to be September 18, which is the day on which Justice Ginsburg died.

A1045

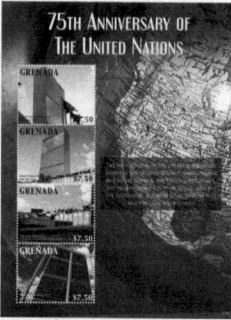

Joseph R. Biden, Jr., 46th President of
the United States — A1046

No. 4388 — Pres. Biden: a, Wearing blue
and white striped tie. b, With flags in background. c, Standing behind microphones. d,
Taking oath of office.
   $14, Pres. Biden behind microphones, diff.

**2021, Jan. 21**    **Litho.**    ***Perf. 13½x13¼***
4388 A1045 $4.60 Sheet of 4,
      #a-d         14.00 14.00
**Souvenir Sheet**
***Perf. 14¼x14***
4389 A1046 $14.60 multi     11.00 11.00

## Miniature Sheet

United
Nations,
75th
Anniv.
(in 2020)
A1047

No. 4390: a, Secretariat Building, flags at
LR. b, Secretariat Building, flags at bottom. c,
Dag Hammarskjold Library, flags and bushes.
d, Flagpoles in front of Secretariat Building.

**2021, Jan. 28**    **Litho.**    ***Perf. 14***
4390 A1047 $7.50 Sheet of 4,
      #a-d         22.50 22.50

## Miniature Sheet

Arrival of the Mayflower in North America, 400th Anniv. (in 2020) — A1048

No. 4391: a, Pilgrims at work at their settlement. b, Model of the Mayflower. c, Mayflower II, Plymouth, Massachusetts. d, Miles Standish (c. 1584-1656), military advisor for the Plymouth Colony.

**2021, Jan. 28    Litho.    Perf. 14**
4391 A1048  $5.50 Sheet of 4,
              #a-d              16.50 16.50

## Miniature Sheet

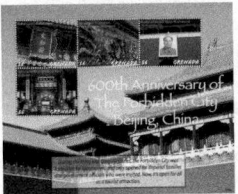

Forbidden City, Beijing, 600th Anniv. (in 2020) — A1049

No. 4392: a, Sign on Hall of Supreme Harmony. b, Nine Dragons Screen, Palace of Tranquil Longevity. c, Portrait of Mao Zedong (1893-1976), Gate of Heavenly Peace. d, Throne, Palace of Heavenly Purity.

**2021, Jan. 28    Litho.    Perf. 14**
4392 A1049  $6 Sheet of 4, #a-
              d                 18.00 18.00

A1050

Range Rovers, 50th Anniv. (in 2020) A1051

No. 4393: a, 2014 Range Rover. b, Queen Elizabeth II, Princes Philip and Andrew in Range Rover Evoque. c, Drawing of 2014 Range Rover Evoque convertible facing right. d, Drawing of 2014 Range Rover Evoque facing left.
$14, 2013 Land Range Rover.

**2021, Jan. 28    Litho.    Perf. 14**
4393 A1050  $5.50 Sheet of 4,
              #a-d              16.50 16.50
**Souvenir Sheet**
**Perf. 12½**
4394 A1051  $14 multi          10.50 10.50

Empire State Building, New York City, 90th Anniv. A1052

No. 4395: a, Aerial view in color. b, Construction worker bolting beams. c, Aluminum relief of Empire State Building in Fifth Avenue Lobby. d, 1932 black-and-white photograph of Empire State Building without antenna. e, Top of Empire State Building with antenna.

$14.90, Empire State Building at night.

**2021, Mar. 15    Litho.    Perf. 14**
4395 A1052  $5.90 Sheet of 5,
              #a-e              22.00 22.00
**Souvenir Sheet**
**Perf. 12**
4396 A1052  $14.90 multi        11.00 11.00
No. 4396 contains one 30x80mm stamp.

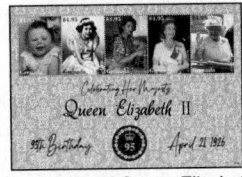

95th Birthday of Queen Elizabeth II (1926-2022) — A1053

No. 4397 — Queen Elizabeth II: a, As baby. b, As child. c, As young woman. d, Wearing tiara. e, Wearing hat.
$14.95, Queen Elizabeth II wearing hat, diff.

**2021, Mar. 15    Litho.    Perf. 14**
4397 A1053  $4.95 Sheet of 5,
              #a-e              18.50 18.50
**Souvenir Sheet**
**Perf. 12½**
4398 A1053  $14.95 multi        11.00 11.00
No. 4398 contains one 38x51mm stamp.

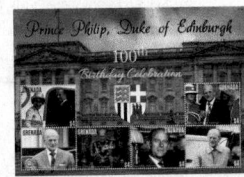

Prince Philip (1921-2021) — A1054

No. 4399 — Prince Philip: a, With Queen Elizabeth II in front of airplane's door. b, With soldiers. c, Wearing gray suit. d, Wearing military uniform and medals. e, Wearing blue suit and white shirt. f, Wearing overcoat.
$14, Black-and-white photograph of Prince Philip wearing military uniform.

**2021, Mar. 15    Litho.    Perf. 14**
4399 A1054  $4 Sheet of 6,
              #a-f              18.00 18.00
**Souvenir Sheet**
**Perf. 12½**
4400 A1054  $14 multi           10.50 10.50
No. 4400 contains one 51x38mm stamp. Prince Philip died April 9, after the issuance of Nos. 4399-4400, but before his 100th birthday.

Metropolitan Museum of Art, New York City, 150th Anniv. (in 2020) — A1055

No. 4401: a, Museum's original façade. b, Museum display of arms and armor. c, Washington Crossing the Delaware, painting by Emanuel Leutze. d, "William," blue faience statuette of hippopotamus. e, Great Hall. f, Greek and Roman sculptures.
$14, Museum entrance, vert.

**2021, Mar. 15    Litho.    Perf. 14**
4401 A1055  $3.50 Sheet of 6,
              #a-f              15.50 15.50
**Souvenir Sheet**
**Perf. 12**
4402 A1055  $10 multi            7.50 7.50
No. 4402 contains one 30x50mm stamp.

Duke and Duchess of Sussex, 3rd Wedding Anniversary — A1056

No. 4403 — Duke and Duchess: a, With Duke wearing blue suit, both hands visible. b, On wedding day, couple waving. c, With Duke wearing blue suit, one hand visible. d, On wedding day, couple holding hands.
$14, Duke and Duchess, horiz.

**2021, Apr. 30    Litho.    Perf. 14**
4403 A1056  $5.50 Sheet of 4,
              #a-d              16.50 16.50
**Souvenir Sheet**
**Perf. 12½**
4404 A1056  $14 multi           10.50 10.50
No. 4404 contains one 51x38mm stamp.

Dorje Chang Buddha III, Religious Leader — A1057

**2021, May 26    Litho.    Perf. 12x11½**
4405 A1057  $4 multi             3.00 3.00
No. 4405 was printed in sheets of 6.

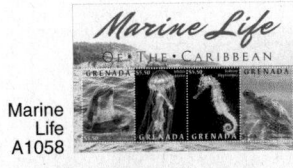

Marine Life A1058

No. 4406: a, Dolphin. b, Jellyfish. c, Seahorse. d, Green sea turtle.
$14, Mobula birostris, horiz.

**2021, June 17    Litho.    Perf. 14**
4406 A1058  $5.50 Sheet of 4,
              #a-d              16.50 16.50
**Souvenir Sheet**
**Perf. 12**
4407 A1058  $14 multi           10.50 10.50
No. 4407 contains one 50x30mm stamp.

Insects A1059

No. 4408: a, $4, Wasp. b, $4.50, Butterfly. c, $4.50, Ladybug. d, $4.50, Dragonfly. e, $5, Grasshopper.
$14, Fire ant.

**2021, June 17    Litho.    Perf. 14**
4408 A1059  Sheet of 5, #a-e    17.00 17.00
**Souvenir Sheet**
**Perf. 12**
4409 A1059  $14 multi           10.50 10.50

Meerkats A1060

No. 4410 — Meerkat: a, Emerging from hole. b, On rock, foliage in background. c, With open mouth. d, On rock, tan background.
No. 4411 — Meerkat with denomination at: a, LL. b, UR.

**2021, June 17    Litho.    Perf. 14**
4410 A1060  $5.50 Sheet of 4,
              #a-d              16.50 16.50
**Souvenir Sheet**
4411 A1060  $8 Sheet of 2,
              #a-b              12.00 12.00

Elvis Presley (1935-77) — A1061

No. 4412 — Presley: a, Holding microphone. b, Wearing suit and tie. c, Wearing military uniform. d, With brick wall in background.

**2021, July 5    Litho.    Perf. 14**
4412 A1061  $5.50 Sheet of 4,
              #a-d              16.50 16.50

Duke and Duchess of Cambridge, 10th Wedding Anniversary — A1062

No. 4413: a, Engagement ring. b, Duke and Duchess at Gandhi Smriti Museum, India. c, Duke and Duchess hiking to Tiger's Nest Monastery, Bhutan. d, Duke and Duchess at the Taj Mahal, India. e, Duke and Duchess at Trooping the Color Ceremony. f, Duke and Duchess of Cambridge with Duke and Duchess of Sussex.
$14, Duke and Duchess of Cambridge wearing red scarves.

**2021, July 5    Litho.    Perf. 14**
4413 A1062  $4 Sheet of 6,
              #a-f              18.00 18.00
**Souvenir Sheet**
**Perf. 12**
4414 A1062  $14 multi           10.50 10.50
No. 4414 contains one 50x30mm stamp.

Balls for Sports of the 2020 Summer Olympics, Tokyo — A1063

No. 4415: a, Baseball. b, Volleyball. c, Soccer ball. d, Basketball.

**2021, Aug. 16    Litho.    Perf. 13¾**
4415 A1063  $4.50 Sheet of 4,
              #a-d              13.50 13.50
The 2020 Summer Olympics was postponed until 2021 because of the COVID-19 pandemic.

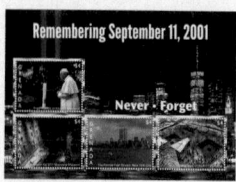

September 11, 2001 Terrorist Attacks,
20th Anniv. — A1064

No. 4416: a, Pope Francis at September 11
Memorial. b, Interior of September 11 Memorial Museum. c, Twin Towers of the World
Trade Center. d, Aerial view of September 11
Memorial.
$14, Reflecting pool.

**2021, Sept. 11    Litho.        Perf. 14**
4416 A1064  $4 Sheet of 4,
#a-d                        12.00 12.00
**Souvenir Sheet**
**Perf. 12**
4417 A1064 $14 multi              10.50 10.50
No. 4417 contains one 50x30mm stamp.

A1065

A1066

A1067

Apollo
13
Mission
A1068

No. 4418: a, Apollo 13 capsule being lowered onto deck of USS Iwo Jima. b, Apollo 13
capsule being lifted from Pacific Ocean. c,
Black-and-white photograph of Apollo 13 capsule, raft and small boat in Pacific Ocean. d,
Recovery crew in raft next to Apollo 13 capsule in Pacific Ocean.
No. 4419: a, Apollo 13 on launchpad. b,
Control panel. c, Vest worn by Flight Director
Gene Kranz during Apollo 13's return to Earth.
d, Mission Control. e, Diagram of fuel cells and
oxygen and hydrogen tanks. f, Apollo 13 lift-off.
No. 4420: a, Apollo 13 Lunar Module before
docking with Command Module. b, Damaged
Apollo 13 Service Module. c, Apollo 13 Lunar
Module after being jettisoned.
$14.50, Rocket on launch pad at night.

**2021, Oct. 1    Litho.        Perf. 12¾**
4418 A1065 $4 Sheet of 4, #a-
d                            12.00 12.00
4419 A1066 $4 Sheet of 6, #a-
f                            18.00 18.00
4420 A1067 $6 Sheet of 3, #a-
c                            13.50 13.50
Nos. 4418-4420 (3)            43.50 43.50
**Souvenir Sheet**
**Perf. 13x13¼**
4421 A1068 $14.50 multi       11.00 11.00

Dasypus Novemcinctus — A1069

No. 4422 — Various photographs of Nine-banded armadillo with denomination at: a, $3,
LR. b, $3, UR. c, $4, LR. d, $4, UR. e, $5, LR.
f, $5, UR.
$14, Nine-banded armadillo, vert.

**2021, Dec. 1    Litho.        Perf. 14**
4422 A1069    Sheet of 6, #a-f 18.00 18.00
**Souvenir Sheet**
**Perf. 12½**
4423 A1069 $14 multi          10.50 10.50
No. 4423 contains one 38x51mm stamp.

Red-Footed Tortoise — A1070

No. 4424: a, Tortoise facing forward, animal
name at left. b, Tortoise facing right, foliage
above head, animal name at left. c, Tortoise
facing right, animal name at right. d, Tortoise
facing right, animal name at left. e, Head of
tortoise facing left.
$14, Tortoise, diff.

**2021, Dec. 1    Litho.        Perf. 14**
4424 A1070  $5 Sheet of 5,
#a-e                        18.50 18.50
**Souvenir Sheet**
**Perf. 12½**
4425 A1070 $14 multi          10.50 10.50
No. 4425 contains one 51x38mm stamp.

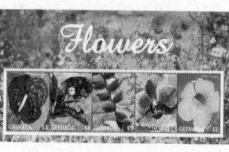

Flowers
A1071

No. 4426: a, $3, Flamingo flower. b, $4,
Bougainvilleas. c, $5, Heliconia. d, $6, Pink
orchid. e, $7, Golden trumpet.
$14, Striped Barbados lily.

**2021, Dec. 1    Litho.        Perf. 14**
4426 A1071    Sheet of 5, #a-e 18.50 18.50
**Souvenir Sheet**
**Perf. 12½**
4427 A1071 $14 multi          10.50 10.50
No. 4427 contains one 38x51mm stamp.

Dolphins
A1072

No. 4428: a, $2, Striped dolphin. b, $3,
Common bottlenose dolphin. c, $4, Short-beaked common dolphins. d, $5, Fraser's dolphins. e, $6, Spinner dolphins.
$14, Pantropical spotted dolphin.

**2021, Dec. 23    Litho.        Perf. 14**
4428 A1072    Sheet of 5, #a-e 15.00 15.00
**Souvenir Sheet**
**Perf. 12½**
4429 A1072 $14 multi          10.50 10.50
No. 4429 contains one 51x38mm stamp.

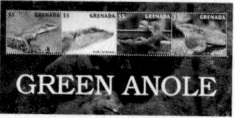

Anolis Carolinensis — A1073

No. 4430 — Drawing of Green anole: a, On
branch. b, Head, facing right. c, Two on
branch. d, Facing left.
No. 4431 — Drawing of Green anole facing:
a, Right. b, Left.

**2021, Dec. 23    Litho.        Perf. 14**
4430 A1073 $5 Sheet of 4, #a-
d                            15.00 15.00
**Souvenir Sheet**
**Perf. 12**
4431 A1073 $5 Sheet of 2, #a-
b                            7.50  7.50
No. 4431 contains two 50x30mm stamps.

Tourist Attractions of the United Arab
Emirates — A1074

No. 4432: a, $1, Al Fahidi Historical District,
Dubai. b, $1, Emirates Palace, Abu Dhabi. c,
$2, Dubai Frame, Dubai. d, $2, Big Red
Dunes, Dubai. e, $3, Jumeirah Mosque,
Dubai. f, $3, Burj Khalifa, Dubai.

**2022, Jan. 19    Litho.        Perf. 14**
4432 A1074    Sheet of 6, #a-f 9.00 9.00

New
Year
2022
(Year of
the
Tiger)
A1075

No. 4433 — Tiger: a, $5, Facing left. b, $5,
Facing right. c, $6, Facing left, diff. d, $6, Facing forward.

**2022, Feb. 1    Litho.        Perf. 14**
4433 A1075    Sheet of 4, #a-d 16.50 16.50

Reign of Queen Elizabeth II (1926-
2022), 70th Anniv. — A1076

No. 4434 — Queen Elizabeth II: a, As young
woman. b, Wearing crown. c, At Silver Jubilee
ceremony. d, Wearing blue dress.
$13.70, Queen Elizabeth II wearing crown
and waving.

**2022, Feb. 6    Litho.        Perf. 13¾**
4434 A1076  $3.70 Sheet of 4,
#a-d                        11.00 11.00
**Souvenir Sheet**
**Perf. 12¾x12½**
4435 A1076 $13.70 multi + label              10.50 10.50
No. 4435 contains one 38x51mm stamp.

Miniature Sheet

Dr. Jennifer Edwards Nixon,
Nutritionist — A1077

No. 4436 — Dr. Nixon: a, Wearing pearl
necklace. b, Wearing black, yellow and white
dress. c, With stethoscope. d, Wearing pilot's
cap. e, With cap on shoulder. f, Standing
beside vehicle's door.

**2022, Feb. 21    Litho.        Perf. 12x11½**
4436 A1077 $5 Sheet of 6, #a-
f                            22.50 22.50

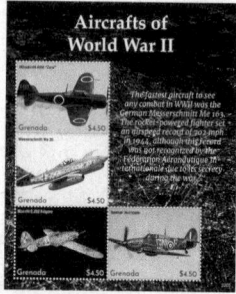

World
War II
Aircraft
A1078

No. 4437: a, Mitsubishi A6M Zero. b, Messerschmitt Me 26. c, Macchi C.202 Folgore. d,
Hawker Hurricane.
$14, Grumman F6F Hellcat.

**2022, Mar. 14    Litho.        Perf. 14**
4437 A1078  $4.50 Sheet of 4,
#a-d                        13.50 13.50
**Souvenir Sheet**
**Perf. 12¾x12½**
4438 A1078  $14 multi         10.50 10.50
No. 4438 contains one 51x38mm stamp.

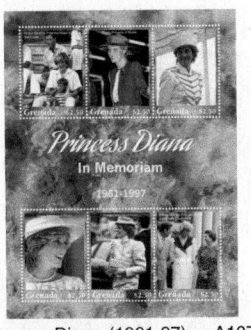

Princess Diana (1961-97) — A1079

No. 4439 — Princess Diana: a, With Princes Charles, William and Harry. b, Wearing red dress. c, Wearing white jacket with gold trim. d, Wearing white hat and pearl necklace. e, Holding purse. f, With Prince Charles and Queen Elizabeth II.
$12.50, Princess Diana with hand near ear.

| | | | | |
|---|---|---|---|---|
| **2022, Mar. 14** | | **Litho.** | | **Perf. 14** |
| 4439 | A1079 | $2.50 Sheet of 6, | | |
| | | #a-f | 11.00 | 11.00 |

**Souvenir Sheet**
**Perf. 12¾x12½**

| | | | | |
|---|---|---|---|---|
| 4440 | A1079 | $12.50 multi | 9.25 | 9.25 |

No. 4440 contains one 51x38mm stamp.

**Miniature Sheet**

Gold Medalists at the 2022 Winter Olympics, Beijing — A1080

No. 4441: a, Eileen Gu, freestyle skiing, flag of People's Republic of China. b, Clément Noel, skiing, flag of France. c, Christopher Grotheer, skeleton, flag of Germany. d, Irene Schouten, figure skating, flag of Netherlands.

| | | | | |
|---|---|---|---|---|
| **2022, Mar. 25** | | **Litho.** | | **Perf. 12½** |
| 4441 | A1080 | $5.50 Sheet of 4, | | |
| | | #a-d | 16.50 | 16.50 |

40th Birthday of Prince William A1081

No. 4442 — Prince William: a, As child, with mother, Princess Diana. b, Wearing medals at ceremony. c, Looking right. d, With wife, Catherine, Duchess of Cambridge.
$14, Prince William in military uniform, with his grandmother, Queen Elizabeth II.

| | | | | |
|---|---|---|---|---|
| **2022, July 11** | | **Litho.** | | **Perf. 14** |
| 4442 | A1081 | $5 Sheet of 4, | | |
| | | #a-d | 15.00 | 15.00 |

**Souvenir Sheet**
**Perf. 12¾x12½**

| | | | | |
|---|---|---|---|---|
| 4443 | A1081 | $14 multi | 10.50 | 10.50 |

No. 4443 contains one 51x38mm stamp.

## SEMI-POSTAL STAMPS

Catalogue values for unused stamps in this section are for Never Hinged items.

### Nos. 227-229 Overprinted

Type I                 Type II

| | | | | |
|---|---|---|---|---|
| **1968** | | | | **Type I** |
| B1A | A38 | 2c + 3c on $2 | | |
| | | #228 | .25 | .25 |
| B1B | A38 | 3c + 3c on $3 | | |
| | | #229 | .25 | .25 |
| | | **Type II** | | |
| B1C | A38 | 1c + 3c on $1 | | |
| | | #227 | .25 | .25 |
| B1D | A38 | 2c + 3c on $2 | | |
| | | #228 | 26.00 | 55.00 |
| | | Nos. B1A-B1D (4) | 26.75 | 55.75 |

Issued: B1A-B1B, 7/22; B1C-B1D, 8/19.

ESPANA '82
World Cup
Soccer — SP1

Players and Flags of Winning Countries — No. B1, West Germany, 1974. No. B2, Argentina, 1978. No. B3, Brazil, 1970. No. B4, Grt. Britain, 1966. No. B5, World Cup, ESPANA '82.

**Unwmk.**

| | | | | |
|---|---|---|---|---|
| **1981, Nov. 30** | | **Litho.** | | **Perf. 14** |
| B1 | SP1 | 25c + 10c multi | .50 | .50 |
| B2 | SP1 | 40c + 20c multi | .70 | .70 |
| B3 | SP1 | 50c + 25c multi | 1.00 | 1.00 |
| B4 | SP1 | $1 + 50c multi | 1.75 | 1.75 |
| | | Nos. B1-B4 (4) | 3.95 | 3.95 |

**Souvenir Sheet**

| | | | | |
|---|---|---|---|---|
| B5 | SP1 | $5 + 50c multi | 4.00 | 4.00 |

Nos. B1-B4 each issued in sheets of 12 with sheet background showing soccer ball.

1988 Seoul
Olympics — SP2

No. B6, Pole vault. No. B7, Balance beam. No. B8, Shot put. No. B9, High jump. No. B10, Swimming.

| | | | | |
|---|---|---|---|---|
| **1986, Dec. 1** | | **Litho.** | | **Perf. 15** |
| B6 | SP2 | 10c + 5c multi | .25 | .30 |
| B7 | SP2 | 50c + 20c multi | .55 | .65 |
| B8 | SP2 | 70c + 30c multi | .85 | .85 |
| B9 | SP2 | $2 + $1 multi | 1.75 | 2.50 |
| | | Nos. B6-B9 (4) | 3.40 | 4.30 |

**Souvenir Sheet**

| | | | | |
|---|---|---|---|---|
| B10 | SP2 | $3 + $1 multi | 3.50 | 3.50 |

Surtax for natl. Olympic team.

World Philatelic
Programs — SP3

Halley's Comet or Stamp Collecting emblem and: No. B11, Halley's initial work on nebulae, 1676. No. B12, Experiments at sea (tall ship, manned capsule). No. B13, Halley observes complete lunar cycle, 1720-1738. No. B14, Halley publishes Newton's Principia, 1687. No. B15, Halley charts the southern skies, 1676.

| | | | | |
|---|---|---|---|---|
| **1989, Apr. 25** | | **Litho.** | | **Perf. 14** |
| B11 | SP3 | 25c +5c multi | .85 | .85 |
| B12 | SP3 | 75c +5c multi | 1.45 | 1.45 |
| B13 | SP3 | 90c +5c multi | 1.75 | 1.75 |
| B14 | SP3 | $2 +5c multi | 2.25 | 2.25 |

**Size: 111x78mm**
*Imperf*

| | | | | |
|---|---|---|---|---|
| B15 | SP3 | $5 +5c multi | 5.00 | 5.00 |
| | | Nos. B11-B15 (5) | 11.30 | 11.30 |

## AIR POST STAMPS

Catalogue values for unused stamps in this section are for Never Hinged items.

### Nos. 428-429 Surcharged with New Value, Olympic Rings, "Air Mail" and: "WINTER OLYMPICS / FEB. 3-13, 1972 / SAPPORO, JAPAN"
**Perf. 13½x14**

| | | | | |
|---|---|---|---|---|
| **1972, Feb. 3** | | **Litho.** | | **Unwmk.** |
| C1 | A66 | 35c on ½c multi | .40 | .40 |
| C2 | A66 | 50c on 1c multi | .60 | .60 |

11th Winter Olympic Games, Sapporo, Japan, Feb. 3-13.

### Nos. 294-300, 302A, 303-309 Surcharged Type "a" or Overprinted Type "b"

a                          b

**Perfs. as Before**

| | | | | |
|---|---|---|---|---|
| **1972, May 2** | | | | **Photo.; Litho.** |
| C3 | A45 | 5c violet & multi | .25 | .25 |
| C4 | A45 | 8c multicolored | .25 | .25 |
| C5 | A45 | 10c orange & multi | .25 | .25 |
| C6 | A45 | 15c gray & multi | .25 | .25 |
| C7 | A45 | 25c multicolored | .40 | .30 |
| C8 | A45 | 30c on 1c multi | .50 | .35 |
| C9 | A45 | 35c multicolored | .55 | .40 |
| C10 | A45 | 40c on 2c multi | .60 | .45 |
| C11 | A45 | 45c on 3c multi | .65 | .50 |
| C12 | A45 | 50c multicolored | .70 | .55 |
| C13 | A45 | 60c on 5c multi | .80 | .70 |
| C14 | A45 | 70c on 6c multi | .95 | .90 |
| C15 | A45 | $1 multicolored | 6.50 | 1.25 |
| C16 | A45 | $1.35 on 8c multi | 3.25 | 3.00 |
| C17 | A45 | $2 multicolored | 8.00 | 7.00 |
| C18 | A45 | $3 multicolored | 10.00 | 9.00 |
| C19 | A45 | $5 multicolored | 13.00 | 16.00 |
| | | Nos. C3-C19 (17) | 46.90 | 41.40 |

"AIR MAIL" reading down on 5c, 15c, 25c, 35c, 60c and $5.

**Olympic Type of Regular Issue**

Olympic Rings and: 25c, 60c, $1, Boxing. 70c, Equestrian (not inscribed air mail).

| | | | | |
|---|---|---|---|---|
| **1972, Sept. 8** | | **Litho.** | | **Perf. 14** |
| C20 | A69 | 25c blue & multi | .50 | .30 |
| C21 | A69 | $1 green & multi | .90 | .75 |

**Souvenir Sheet**

| | | | | |
|---|---|---|---|---|
| C22 | | Sheet of 2 | 1.50 | 1.50 |
| a. | | A69 60c blue & multi | .50 | .50 |
| b. | | A69 70c deep yellow & multi | 1.00 | 1.00 |

### Nos. 409-412 Overprinted Vertically, Reading Up "AIR MAIL"

| | | | | |
|---|---|---|---|---|
| **1972, Oct.** | | **Litho.** | | **Perf. 11** |
| C23 | A62 | 5c multicolored | .60 | .25 |
| C24 | A62 | 35c multicolored | 1.50 | .60 |
| C25 | A62 | 50c multicolored | 1.75 | 1.00 |
| C26 | A62 | 75c multicolored | 2.50 | 2.00 |
| | | Nos. C23-C26 (4) | 6.35 | 3.85 |

**Boy Scout Type of Regular Issue**

Designs: 25c, Scout saluting. 35c, Two Scouts knotting ropes.

| | | | | |
|---|---|---|---|---|
| **1972, Nov.** | | | | **Perf. 14** |
| C27 | A70 | 25c dp blue & multi | .40 | .35 |
| C28 | A70 | 35c brn org & multi | .60 | .55 |

John Hancock — AP1

Designs: 50c, Benjamin Franklin. 75c, John Adams. $1, Marquis de Lafayette.

| | | | | |
|---|---|---|---|---|
| **1975, May 6** | | **Litho.** | **Perf. 14½, 13** | |
| C29 | AP1 | 40c multicolored | .25 | .25 |
| C30 | AP1 | 50c multicolored | .45 | .25 |
| C31 | AP1 | 75c multicolored | .55 | .25 |
| C32 | AP1 | $1 multicolored | .65 | .25 |
| | | Nos. C29-C32 (4) | 1.90 | 1.00 |

American Revolution Bicentennial.
Nos. C29-C32 issued in sheets of 40. Each denomination was also printed in sheets of 5 plus label, perf. 13.

## POSTAGE DUE STAMPS

D1

| | | | | |
|---|---|---|---|---|
| **1892** | | **Typo.** | **Wmk. 2** | **Perf. 14** |
| J1 | D1 | 1p black | 30.00 | 2.75 |
| J2 | D1 | 2p black | 225.00 | 3.25 |
| J3 | D1 | 3p black | 200.00 | 4.00 |
| | | Nos. J1-J3 (3) | 455.00 | 10.00 |

**Nos. 24 & 25 Surcharged in Black**

| | | | | |
|---|---|---|---|---|
| J4 | A8 | 1p on 6p red lilac | 110.00 | 2.25 |
| a. | | Tete beche pair | 2,750. | 1,800. |
| b. | | Double surcharge | | 225.00 |
| c. | | Same as "b," tete beche pair | | |
| J5 | A8 | 1p on 8p bister | 1,600. | 6.00 |
| a. | | Tete beche pair | 8,500. | 2,500. |
| J6 | A8 | 2p on 6p red lilac | 190.00 | 4.50 |
| a. | | Tete beche pair | 3,500. | 1,800. |
| J7 | A8 | 2p on 8p bister | 3,200. | 12.00 |
| a. | | Tete beche pair | 7,500. | 5,000. |
| | | Nos. J4-J7 (4) | 5,100. | 24.75 |

Nos. J4-J7 were printed with alternate horizontal rows inverted.

| | | | | |
|---|---|---|---|---|
| **1906-11** | | | | **Wmk. 3** |
| J8 | D1 | 1p black ('11) | 3.75 | 7.50 |
| J9 | D1 | 2p black | 12.50 | 3.75 |
| J10 | D1 | 3p black | 15.00 | 6.50 |
| | | Nos. J8-J10 (3) | 31.25 | 17.75 |

D3

| | | | | |
|---|---|---|---|---|
| **1921-22** | | | | **Wmk. 4** |
| J11 | D3 | 1p black | 2.00 | 1.40 |
| J12 | D3 | 1½p black | 10.00 | 25.00 |
| J13 | D3 | 2p black | 3.00 | 4.50 |
| J14 | D3 | 3p black | 3.00 | 4.75 |
| | | Nos. J11-J14 (4) | 18.00 | 35.65 |

Issued: 1½p, Dec. 15, 1922, others, Dec. 1921.

Catalogue values for unused stamps in this section, from this point to the end of the section, are for Never Hinged items.

| | | | | |
|---|---|---|---|---|
| **1952, Mar. 1** | | | | |
| J15 | D3 | 2c black | .50 | 9.00 |
| a. | | Wmk. 4a (error) | 55.00 | |
| J16 | D3 | 4c black | .50 | 17.00 |
| a. | | Wmk. 4a (error) | 60.00 | |
| J17 | D3 | 6c black | .65 | 13.00 |
| a. | | Wmk. 4a (error) | 100.00 | |
| J18 | D3 | 8c black | .75 | 14.00 |
| a. | | Wmk. 4a (error) | 200.00 | |
| | | Nos. J15-J18 (4) | 2.40 | 53.00 |

## WAR TAX STAMPS

Nos. 80a, 80 Overprinted

| | | | | |
|---|---|---|---|---|
| **1916** | | **Wmk. 3** | | **Perf. 14** |
| MR1 | A21 | 1p carmine | 2.50 | 2.00 |
| a. | | 1p scarlet | 3.00 | 3.00 |
| b. | | Double overprint | 325.00 | |
| c. | | Inverted overprint | 325.00 | |

No. 80 Overprinted

| | | | | |
|---|---|---|---|---|
| MR2 | A21 | 1p scarlet | .30 | .25 |

### OFFICIAL STAMPS

Catalogue values for unused stamps in this section are for Never Hinged items.

**Nos. 1006-1018, 1020, 1051-1053 Overprinted: "P.R.G."**

**1982, July 15    Litho.    Perf. 14, 15**

| | | | | |
|---|---|---|---|---|
| O1 | A141 | 5c multicolored | .25 | .25 |
| O2 | A141 | 6c multicolored | .25 | .25 |
| O3 | A141 | 10c multicolored | .25 | .25 |
| O4 | A141 | 12c multicolored | .25 | .25 |
| O5 | A141 | 15c multicolored | .25 | .25 |
| O6 | A141 | 20c multicolored | .25 | .25 |
| O7 | A141 | 25c multicolored | .25 | .25 |
| O8 | A141 | 30c multicolored | .25 | .25 |
| O9 | A141 | 40c multicolored | .30 | .30 |
| O10 | A141 | 50c multicolored | .40 | .40 |
| O11 | CD331 | 50c multicolored | .40 | .40 |
| O12 | A141 | 90c multicolored | .75 | .75 |
| O13 | A141 | $1 multicolored | .80 | .80 |
| O14 | CD331 | $2 multicolored | 1.75 | 1.75 |
| O15 | A141 | $3 multicolored | 2.25 | 2.25 |
| O16 | CD331 | $4 multicolored | 4.00 | 4.00 |
| O17 | A141 | $10 multicolored | 7.00 | 7.00 |
| | | Nos. O1-O17 (17) | 19.65 | 19.65 |

PRG stands for People's Revolutionary Government.

# Trust Scott to protect your collection
## with our full line of Scott Binders and Album Accessories

### 3-RING BINDER & SLIPCASE

With this three ring binder, pages lay flat while the locking mechanism ensures that the rings won't pop open, even when the binder is full.

| Item | | Retail | AA |
|---|---|---|---|
| ACBR01D | Small Metal-Hinged Binder | $46.99 | $37.59 |
| ACBR01SET | 3-Ring Binder and Slipcase – small | $85.49 | $70.32 |
| ACSR01 | Small Slipcase | $38.50 | $32.73 |
| ACBR03D | Large Metal-Hinged Binder | $46.99 | $37.59 |
| ACBR03SET | 3-Ring Binder and Slipcase | $85.49 | $70.32 |
| ACSR03 | Large Slipcase | $38.50 | $32.73 |

### 2-POST BINDER & SLIPCASE

For the traditional Scott collector, the standard hinge post binder is the perfect fit. Scott album pages are punched with rectangular holes that fit on rectangular posts. The posts and pages are held by a rod that slides down from the top. With the post binder pages do not lie flat.

| Item | | Retail | AA |
|---|---|---|---|
| ACBS03 | Large 2-Post Binder | $59.99 | $47.99 |
| ACBS03SET | 2-Square Post Binder and Slipcase | $98.49 | $80.72 |
| ACSS03 | Large 2-Post Slipcase | $38.50 | $32.73 |
| ACBU | Universal 2-Post Binder | $42.99 | $36.54 |
| ACBUSET | Universal Binder and Slipcase | $81.49 | $69.27 |
| ACSU | Universal 2-Post Slipcase | $38.50 | $32.73 |

### BINDER LABELS

Labels are available for just about every National and Specialty Album produced by Amos Media Co. These elegantly styled, self-adhesive labels add just the right touch to your album. For a complete listing of the labels available visit our web site or call our toll free number.

| Item | Retail | AA |
|---|---|---|
| National or Specialty Series Labels | $5.99 | $4.99 |
| Custom Labels | $16.99 | $10.99 |

### SPECIALTY BINDER ACCESSORIES

Protect your investment with these great flysheets and glassine interleaving. The first and last pages in your album will stay free from wrinkles and tears.

| Item | | Retail | AA |
|---|---|---|---|
| ACC101 | Green Protector Fly Sheets for 2-Post Binders (2 Pack) | $6.99 | $5.82 |
| ACC102 | Black Protector Fly Sheets for 3-Ring Binders (2 Pack) | $6.99 | $5.82 |
| ACC107 | Glassine Interleaving 100 Sheets per pack | $14.99 | $12.85 |
| ACC145 | Page Dividers for 3-Ring & 2-Post Binders (10 Pack) | $6.99 | $5.82 |

### PAGE PROTECTORS

Protect your stamps and album pages with a clear archival quality plastic sleeve. Sleeves fit over the entire page and protects pages from creases, fingerprints and tears. Sold in packages of 25.

| Item | | Retail | AA |
|---|---|---|---|
| ACC166 | Fits National/Specialty Series Pages (2-Post & 3-Ring) | $14.99 | $12.59 |

### SCOTT FILLER STRIPS

Use strips every 15 to 20 pages in 2-post albums to balance overstuffed binders.

| Item | | Retail | AA |
|---|---|---|---|
| ACC105 | 24 Strips Included | $13.99 | $10.76 |

## FREE SHIPPING!
### on orders $75+

Prices are subject to change. See AmosAdvantage.com for current pricing.

# AmosAdvantage.com
## 1-800-572-6885

**ORDERING INFORMATION:** *AA prices apply to paid subscribers of Amos Media titles, or for orders placed online. Prices, terms and product availability subject to change. **SHIPPING & HANDLING:** U.S.: Orders total $0-$10.00 charged $4.99 shipping. U.S. Order total $10.01-$74.99 charged $9.99 shipping. Orders totaling $75+ will ship FREE! Taxes will apply in CA, OH, & IL. Canada: 20% of order total. Minimum charge $19.99 Maximum charge $200.00. Foreign orders are shipped via FedEx Intl. or USPS and billed actual freight.

# GRENADA GRENADINES

grə-ˈnä-də ˌgre-nə-ˈdēnz

LOCATION — North of Grenada
GOVT. — Part of Grenada
CAPITAL — None

Main islands are Carriacou and Ronde.

> Catalogue values for all unused stamps in this country are for Never Hinged items.

All stamps are a type of Grenada unless otherwise noted or illustrated. Nos. 15-58 have the additional inscription Grenadines.

## Grenada Nos. 516-517a Overprinted

### Perf. 13½x14

| | | | Wmk. 314 | |
|---|---|---|---|---|
| **1973, Dec. 23** | | **Litho.** | | |
| 1 | A77 | 25c dp orange & multi | .25 | .25 |
| 2 | A77 | $2 green & multi | .50 | .50 |
| a. | | Souvenir sheet of 2 (75c, $1) | .75 | .50 |

Grenada Nos. 294-297, 299-301, 303, 306-309 Overprinted

### Perf. 14x14½, 14½x14

| | | | Unwmk. | |
|---|---|---|---|---|
| **1974, May 29** | | **Photo.** | | |
| | | **Size: 25x44mm** | | |
| 3 | A45 | 1c multicolored | .25 | .25 |
| 4 | A45 | 2c multicolored | .25 | .25 |
| 5 | A45 | 3c multicolored | .25 | .25 |
| 6 | A45 | 5c multicolored | .25 | .25 |
| 7 | A45 | 8c multicolored | .25 | .25 |
| 8 | A45 | 10c multicolored | .25 | .25 |
| 9 | A45 | 12c multicolored | .25 | .25 |
| 10 | A45 | 25c multicolored | .30 | .30 |
| | | **Size: 25x47mm** | | |
| 11 | A45 | $1 multicolored | 2.50 | 1.40 |
| 12 | A45 | $2 multicolored | 3.75 | 2.00 |
| 13 | A45 | $3 multicolored | 3.75 | 2.00 |
| 14 | A45 | $5 multicolored | 4.50 | 3.50 |
| | | Nos. 3-14 (12) | 16.55 | 11.85 |

### World Cup Soccer Type

Designs: Soccer matches and flags. ½c, West Germany-Chile. 1c, East Germany-Australia. 2c, Yugoslavia-Brazil. 10c, Scotland-Zaire. 25c, Netherlands-Uruguay. 50c, Sweden-Bulgaria. 75c, Italy-Haiti. $1, Poland-Argentina. $2, Flags of participating nations.

| | | | **Perf. 14½** | |
|---|---|---|---|---|
| **1974, Sept. 17** | | **Litho.** | | |
| 15 | A81 | ½c multicolored | .25 | .25 |
| 16 | A81 | 1c multicolored | .25 | .25 |
| 17 | A81 | 2c multicolored | .25 | .25 |
| 18 | A81 | 10c multicolored | .25 | .25 |
| 19 | A81 | 25c multicolored | .25 | .25 |
| 20 | A81 | 50c multicolored | .35 | .25 |
| 21 | A81 | 75c multicolored | .35 | .25 |
| 22 | A81 | $1 multicolored | .40 | .30 |
| | | Nos. 15-22 (8) | 2.35 | 2.05 |

#### Souvenir Sheet

| 23 | A81 | $2 multicolored | 2.00 | 2.00 |
|---|---|---|---|---|

### UPU Centenary Type

UPU Emblem and: 8c, Mailboat *Caesar*, 1839, helicopter. 25c, German messenger, 1540, satellite. 35c, Biplanes, zeppelin, jet. No. 27, US Mail train, 19th cent., Concorde. No. 28a, Bellman, 18th cent., radar. $2, German postman, 18th cent., mail train, 1980's.

| | | | **Perf. 14½** | |
|---|---|---|---|---|
| **1974, Oct. 8** | | | | |
| 24 | A82 | 8c multicolored | .25 | .25 |
| 25 | A82 | 25c multicolored | .25 | .25 |
| 26 | A82 | 35c multicolored | .25 | .25 |
| 27 | A82 | $1 multicolored | .95 | .50 |
| | | Nos. 24-27 (4) | 1.70 | 1.25 |

#### Souvenir Sheet
#### Perf. 13

| 28 | | Sheet of 2 | 1.75 | 1.75 |
|---|---|---|---|---|
| a. | A82 | $1 multicolored | .50 | .50 |
| b. | A82 | $2 multicolored | 1.25 | 1.25 |

### Churchill Type

Design: $2, Churchill, different portrait.

| | | | **Perf. 13½** | |
|---|---|---|---|---|
| **1974, Nov. 11** | | | | |
| 29 | A83 | 35c multicolored | .25 | .25 |
| 30 | A83 | $2 multicolored | .35 | .35 |

#### Souvenir Sheet

| 31 | | Sheet of 2 | .80 | .80 |
|---|---|---|---|---|
| a. | A82 | 75c like 35c | .30 | .30 |
| b. | A82 | $1 like $2 | .35 | .35 |

### Christmas Type

Paintings of the Virgin and Child: ½c, Botticelli. 1c, Niccolo di Pietro. 2c, Van der Weyden. 3c, Bastiani. 10c, Giovanni. 25c, Van der Weyden, diff. 50c, Botticelli. $1, Mantegna. $2, Niccolo di Pietro.

| | | | **Perf. 14½** | |
|---|---|---|---|---|
| **1974, Nov. 27** | | | | |
| 32 | A84 | ½c multicolored | .25 | .25 |
| 33 | A84 | 1c multicolored | .25 | .25 |
| 34 | A84 | 2c multicolored | .25 | .25 |
| 35 | A84 | 3c multicolored | .25 | .25 |
| 36 | A84 | 10c multicolored | .25 | .25 |
| 37 | A84 | 25c multicolored | .25 | .25 |
| 38 | A84 | 50c multicolored | .25 | .25 |
| 39 | A84 | $1 multicolored | .30 | .25 |
| | | Nos. 32-39 (8) | 2.05 | 2.00 |

#### Souvenir Sheet
#### Perf. 13½

| 40 | A84 | $2 multicolored | 1.00 | 1.00 |
|---|---|---|---|---|

### Big Game Fish Type

½c, Sailfish. 1c, Blue marlin. 2c, White marlin. 10c, Yellowfin tuna. 25c, Wahoo. 50c, Dolphin. 70c, Grouper. $1, Great barracuda. $2, Mako shark.

| | | | **Perf. 14½** | |
|---|---|---|---|---|
| **1975, Feb. 17** | | | | |
| 41 | A86 | ½c multicolored | .25 | .25 |
| 42 | A86 | 1c multicolored | .25 | .25 |
| 43 | A86 | 2c multicolored | .25 | .25 |
| 44 | A86 | 10c multicolored | .25 | .25 |
| 45 | A86 | 25c multicolored | .25 | .25 |
| 46 | A86 | 50c multicolored | .25 | .25 |
| 47 | A86 | 70c multicolored | .40 | .30 |
| 48 | A86 | $1 multicolored | .60 | .50 |
| | | Nos. 41-48 (8) | 2.50 | 2.30 |

#### Souvenir Sheet
#### Perf. 13

| 49 | A86 | $2 multicolored | 2.50 | 2.50 |
|---|---|---|---|---|

### Flowers of Grenada Type

½c, Grandilla barbadine. 1c, Bleeding heart. 2c, Poinsettia. 3c, Cocoa. 10c, Gladioli. 25c, Red head-yellow head. 50c, Plumbago. $1, Orange blossoms. $2, Barbados gooseberry.

| | | | **Perf. 14½** | |
|---|---|---|---|---|
| **1975, Mar. 11** | | | | |
| 50 | A87 | ½c multicolored | .25 | .25 |
| 51 | A87 | 1c multicolored | .25 | .25 |
| 52 | A87 | 2c multicolored | .25 | .25 |
| 53 | A87 | 3c multicolored | .25 | .25 |
| 54 | A87 | 10c multicolored | .25 | .25 |
| 55 | A87 | 25c multicolored | .25 | .25 |
| 56 | A87 | 50c multicolored | .35 | .35 |
| 57 | A87 | $1 multicolored | .60 | .55 |
| | | Nos. 50-57 (8) | 2.45 | 2.40 |

#### Souvenir Sheet
#### Perf. 13½

| 58 | A87 | $2 multicolored | 1.50 | 1.50 |
|---|---|---|---|---|

> Remainders of Grenada Grenadines stamps between Scott Nos. 59 and 269, except Nos. 109-128, 217-220, 237-240 and some souvenir sheets, were later canceled to order and sold at a fraction of their face value. Our used values for these stamps are for c-t-o examples. Postally used stamps are worth the same as unused, never hinged examples.

Christ Crowned with Thorns, by Titian — G1

Easter paintings of the Crucifixion by various artists: 1c, Giotto. 2c, Tintoretto. 3c, Cranach. 35c, Caravaggio. 75c, Tiepolo. $2, Velasquez.

---

$1, Titian, diff.

| | | | **Perf. 14½** | |
|---|---|---|---|---|
| **1975, June 24** | | | | |
| 59 | G1 | ½c shown | .25 | .25 |
| 60 | G1 | 1c multicolored | .25 | .25 |
| 61 | G1 | 2c multicolored | .25 | .25 |
| 62 | G1 | 3c multicolored | .25 | .25 |
| 63 | G1 | 35c multicolored | .25 | .25 |
| 64 | G1 | 75c multicolored | .25 | .25 |
| 65 | G1 | $2 multicolored | .30 | .25 |
| | | Nos. 59-65 (7) | 1.80 | 1.75 |

#### Souvenir Sheet
#### Perf. 13½

| 66 | G1 | $1 multicolored | 1.10 | 1.10 |
|---|---|---|---|---|

Works by Michelangelo (1475-1564) — G2

Designs: ½c, Dawn (sculpture, detail from Medici tomb). 1c, Delphic Sibyl. 2c, Giuliano de Medici (sculpture). 40c, The Creation. 50c, Lorenzo de Medici (sculpture). 75c, Persian Sibyl. $1, The Prophet Jeremiah. $2, Head of Christ (sculpture).

| | | | **Perf. 14½** | |
|---|---|---|---|---|
| **1975, July 16** | | | | |
| 67 | G2 | ½c violet & multi | .25 | .25 |
| 68 | G2 | 1c multicolored | .25 | .25 |
| 69 | G2 | 2c green & multi | .25 | .25 |
| 70 | G2 | 40c multicolored | .25 | .25 |
| 71 | G2 | 50c brt red & multi | .30 | .25 |
| 72 | G2 | 75c multicolored | .45 | .25 |
| 73 | G2 | $2 brt blue & multi | .75 | .25 |
| | | Nos. 67-73 (7) | 2.50 | 1.75 |

#### Souvenir Sheet
#### Perf. 13½

| 74 | G2 | $1 multicolored | 1.25 | .75 |
|---|---|---|---|---|

Butterflies — G3

½c, Emperor. 1c, Queen. 2c, Tiger pierid. 35c, Cracker. 45c, Scarlet bamboo page. 75c, Apricot. $2, Purple king shoemaker. $1, Bamboo page.

| | | | **Perf. 15** | |
|---|---|---|---|---|
| **1975, Aug. 12** | | | | |
| 75 | G3 | ½c multicolored | .25 | .25 |
| 76 | G3 | 1c multicolored | .25 | .25 |
| 77 | G3 | 2c multicolored | .25 | .25 |
| 78 | G3 | 35c multicolored | .55 | .25 |
| 79 | G3 | 45c multicolored | .70 | .25 |
| 80 | G3 | 75c multicolored | 1.25 | .25 |
| 81 | G3 | $2 multicolored | 3.25 | .25 |
| | | Nos. 75-81 (7) | 6.50 | 1.75 |

#### Souvenir Sheet
#### Perf. 13½

| 82 | G3 | $1 multicolored | 6.00 | 6.00 |
|---|---|---|---|---|

Jamboree Scenes and Badges — G4

Nordjamb 75 Emblem and: ½c, Progress badge. 1c, Boating badge. 2c, Coxswain badge. 35c, Interpreter badge. 45c, Ambulance badge. 75c, Chief scout's award. $1, Venture award. $2, Queen's scout award.

| | | | **Perf. 15** | |
|---|---|---|---|---|
| **1975, Aug. 22** | | | | |
| 83 | G4 | ½c lemon yel & multi | .25 | .25 |
| 84 | G4 | 1c vio blue & multi | .25 | .25 |
| 85 | G4 | 2c green & multi | .25 | .25 |
| 86 | G4 | 35c dull vio & multi | .25 | .25 |
| 87 | G4 | 45c org brown & multi | .25 | .25 |
| 88 | G4 | 75c brown & multi | .25 | .25 |
| 89 | G4 | $2 green & multi | .60 | .25 |
| | | Nos. 83-89 (7) | 2.10 | 1.75 |

#### Souvenir Sheet
#### Perf. 13½

| 90 | G4 | $1 dull vio & multi | 1.00 | .40 |
|---|---|---|---|---|

Nordjamb 75, 14th Boy Scout World Jamboree, Lillehammer, Norway, July 29-Aug. 7.

---

Surrender of Lord Cornwallis — G5

Designs: 1c, Minuteman. 2c, Paul Revere's Ride. 3c, Battle of Bunker Hill. 5c, *Spirit of '76.* 45c, Backwoodsman. 75c, Boston Tea Party. No. 98, Naval engagement. No. 99, George Washington. No. 100, White House, flags.

| | | | **Perf. 14** | |
|---|---|---|---|---|
| **1975, Sept. 30** | | | | |
| | | **Size: 39x25mm** | | |
| 91 | G5 | ½c multicolored | .25 | .25 |
| 92 | G5 | 1c multicolored | .25 | .25 |
| 93 | G5 | 2c multicolored | .25 | .25 |
| 94 | G5 | 3c multicolored | .25 | .25 |
| 95 | G5 | 5c multicolored | .25 | .25 |
| 96 | G5 | 45c multicolored | .25 | .25 |
| 97 | G5 | 75c multicolored | .25 | .25 |
| 98 | G5 | $2 multicolored | .45 | .45 |
| | | **Size: 59x39mm** | | |
| | | **Perf. 11** | | |
| 99 | G5 | $2 multicolored, vert. | .45 | .45 |
| a. | | Souvenir sheet of 1, imperf. | 1.00 | 1.00 |
| 100 | G4 | $2 multicolored | .45 | .45 |
| a. | | Souvenir sheet of 1, imperf. | 1.00 | 1.00 |
| | | Nos. 91-100 (10) | 3.10 | 3.10 |

American Revolution Bicentennial. Nos. 99a, 100a have simulated perfs.

Fencing — G6

| | | | **Perf. 15** | |
|---|---|---|---|---|
| **1975, Oct. 27** | | | | |
| 101 | G6 | ½c shown | .25 | .25 |
| 102 | G6 | 1c Hurdling | .25 | .25 |
| 103 | G6 | 2c Pole vault | .25 | .25 |
| 104 | G6 | 35c Weightlifting | .25 | .25 |
| 105 | G6 | 45c Javelin | .25 | .25 |
| 106 | G6 | 75c Discus | .25 | .25 |
| 107 | G6 | $2 Diving | .35 | .25 |
| | | Nos. 101-107 (7) | 1.85 | 1.75 |

#### Souvenir Sheet

| 108 | G6 | $1 Sprinter | .80 | .80 |
|---|---|---|---|---|

Pan American Games, Mexico City, Oct. 12-26, 1975.

### Type of 1975

Designs: ½c, Cruising Yachts, Point Saline. 1c, Yacht Club race, St. George's. 2c, Careenage Taxi. 3c, Working boats. 5c, Deep water dock, St. George's. 6c, Cocoa beans drying. 8c, Nutmegs. 10c, Rum distillery, River Antoine Estate. 12c, Cocoa tree. 15c, Landing catch at Fontenoy. 20c, Parliament building, St. George's. 25c, Fort George cannons. 35c, Pearls airport. 50c, General Post Office. 75c, Caribs Leap, Sauteurs Bay. $1, Careenage, St. George's. $2, St. George's harbor at night. $3, Grand Anse beach. $5, Canoe and Black Bays from Point Saline lighthouse. $10, Sugar Loaf Island from Levera beach.

| **1975-76** | | **Size: 38x25mm** | **Perf. 14½** | |
|---|---|---|---|---|
| 109 | A85 | ½c multicolored | .25 | .35 |
| 110 | A85 | 1c multicolored | .25 | .25 |
| 111 | A85 | 2c multicolored | .25 | .25 |
| 112 | A85 | 3c multicolored | .25 | .25 |
| 113 | A85 | 5c multicolored | .25 | .25 |
| 114 | A85 | 6c multicolored | .25 | .25 |
| 115 | A85 | 8c multicolored | .25 | .25 |
| 116 | A85 | 10c multicolored | .25 | .25 |
| 117 | A85 | 12c multicolored | .25 | .25 |
| 118 | A85 | 15c multicolored | .25 | .25 |
| 119 | A85 | 20c multicolored | .25 | .65 |
| 120 | A85 | 25c multicolored | .25 | .25 |
| 121 | A85 | 35c multicolored | 1.00 | .25 |
| 122 | A85 | 50c multicolored | .25 | 1.00 |
| | | **Perf. 13½x14** | | |
| | | **Size: 45x28mm** | | |
| 123 | A85 | 75c multicolored | .55 | .65 |
| 124 | A85 | $1 multicolored | .85 | .95 |
| 125 | A85 | $2 multicolored | 1.25 | 2.25 |
| 126 | A85 | $3 multicolored | 1.50 | 2.75 |
| 127 | A85 | $5 multicolored | 1.75 | 5.50 |
| 128 | A85 | $10 multicolored | 3.00 | 6.00 |
| | | Nos. 109-128 (20) | 13.15 | 22.85 |

Issued: Nos. 109-127, 11/5/75; No. 128, 1/1/76.

For overprints see Nos. 360-372.

Madonna and Child by Durer — G8

Christmas: Paintings showing Madonna and Child by various artists — 1c, Durer, diff. 2c, Correggio. 40c, Botticelli. 50c, Niccolo da Cremona. 75c, Correggio, diff. $2, Correggio, diff. $1, Bellini.

**1975, Dec. 17**     *Perf. 14*

| | | | | |
|---|---|---|---|---|
| 129 | G8 | ½c shown | .25 | .25 |
| 130 | G8 | 1c multicolored | .25 | .25 |
| 131 | G8 | 2c multicolored | .25 | .25 |
| 132 | G8 | 40c multicolored | .25 | .25 |
| 133 | G8 | 50c multicolored | .25 | .25 |
| 134 | G8 | 75c multicolored | .25 | .25 |
| 135 | G8 | $2 multicolored | .35 | .25 |
| | | Nos. 129-135 (7) | 1.85 | 1.75 |

**Souvenir Sheet**

| | | | | |
|---|---|---|---|---|
| 136 | G8 | $1 multicolored | .80 | .60 |

Sea Shells — G9

**1976, Jan. 13**

| | | | | |
|---|---|---|---|---|
| 137 | G9 | ½c Bleeding Tooth | .25 | .25 |
| 138 | G9 | 1c Wedge clam | .25 | .25 |
| 139 | G9 | 2c Hawk wing conch | .25 | .25 |
| 140 | G9 | 3c Distorsio clathrata | .25 | .25 |
| 141 | G9 | 25c Scotch bonnet | .45 | .25 |
| 142 | G9 | 50c King helmet | .90 | .25 |
| 143 | G9 | 75c Queen conch | 1.50 | .25 |
| | | Nos. 137-143 (7) | 3.85 | 1.75 |

**Souvenir Sheet**

| | | | | |
|---|---|---|---|---|
| 144 | G9 | $2 Atlantic triton | 2.75 | 1.00 |

Lignum Vitae — G10

Designs: 1c, Cocoa thrush. 2c, Tarantula. 35c, Hooded tanager. 50c, Nyctaginaceae. 75c, Grenada dove. $1, Marine toad. $2, Blue-hooded euphonia.

**1976, Feb. 4**

| | | | | |
|---|---|---|---|---|
| 145 | G10 | ½c multicolored | .25 | .25 |
| 146 | G10 | 1c multicolored | .25 | .25 |
| 147 | G10 | 2c multicolored | .25 | .25 |
| 148 | G10 | 35c multicolored | 1.25 | .25 |
| 149 | G10 | 50c multicolored | 1.25 | .25 |
| 150 | G10 | 75c multicolored | 2.50 | .30 |
| 151 | G10 | $1 multicolored | 2.50 | .30 |
| | | Nos. 145-151 (7) | 8.25 | 1.85 |

**Souvenir Sheet**

| | | | | |
|---|---|---|---|---|
| 152 | G10 | $2 multicolored | 5.75 | 1.25 |

Hooked Sailfish — G11

Designs: 1c, Careened schooner, Carriacou. 2c, Annual regatta. 18c, Boat building. 22c, Workboat race. 75c, Cruising off Petit Martinique. $1, Water skiing. $2, Yacht racing.

**1976, Feb. 17**

| | | | | |
|---|---|---|---|---|
| 153 | G11 | ½c multicolored | .25 | .25 |
| 154 | G11 | 1c multicolored | .25 | .25 |
| 155 | G11 | 2c multicolored | .25 | .25 |
| 156 | G11 | 18c multicolored | .25 | .25 |
| 157 | G11 | 22c multicolored | .25 | .25 |
| 158 | G11 | 75c multicolored | .40 | .25 |
| 159 | G11 | $1 multicolored | .55 | .25 |
| | | Nos. 153-159 (7) | 2.20 | 1.75 |

**Souvenir Sheet**

| | | | | |
|---|---|---|---|---|
| 160 | G11 | $2 multicolored | .90 | .90 |

Making a Camp Fire — G12

50th anniv. of Girl Guides of Grenada: 1c, First aid. 2c, Nature study. 50c, Cooking. $1, Drawing. $2, Playing guitar.

**1976, Mar. 17**

| | | | | |
|---|---|---|---|---|
| 161 | G12 | ½c multicolored | .25 | .25 |
| 162 | G12 | 1c multicolored | .25 | .25 |
| 163 | G12 | 2c multicolored | .25 | .25 |
| 164 | G12 | 50c multicolored | .45 | .25 |
| 165 | G12 | $1 multicolored | 1.00 | .30 |
| | | Nos. 161-165 (5) | 2.20 | 1.30 |

**Souvenir Sheet**

| | | | | |
|---|---|---|---|---|
| 166 | G12 | $2 multicolored | 1.40 | 1.00 |

Christ Mocked, by Bosch — G13

Easter Paintings: 1c, Christ Crucified by Messina. 2c, Adoration by Durer. 3c, Lamentation of Christ by Durer. 35c, The Entombment by Van Der Weyden. $2, Blood of the Redeemer by Bellini. $3, The Deposition by Raphael.

**1976, Apr. 28**

| | | | | |
|---|---|---|---|---|
| 167 | G13 | ½c multicolored | .25 | .25 |
| 168 | G13 | 1c multicolored | .25 | .25 |
| 169 | G13 | 2c multicolored | .25 | .25 |
| 170 | G13 | 3c multicolored | .25 | .25 |
| 171 | G13 | 35c multicolored | .25 | .25 |
| 172 | G13 | $3 multicolored | .30 | .30 |
| | | Nos. 167-172 (6) | 1.55 | 1.55 |

**Souvenir Sheet**

| | | | | |
|---|---|---|---|---|
| 173 | G13 | $2 multicolored | .80 | .80 |

Frigate South Carolina — G14

1c, Schooner Lee. 2c, HMS Roebuck. 35c, Andrew Doria. 50c, Sloop Providence. $1, Flagship Alfred. $2, Frigate Confederacy. $3, Cutter Revenge.

**1976, May 18**

| | | | | |
|---|---|---|---|---|
| 174 | G14 | ½c multicolored | .25 | .25 |
| 175 | G14 | 1c multicolored | .25 | .25 |
| 176 | G14 | 2c multicolored | .25 | .25 |
| 177 | G14 | 35c multicolored | .55 | .25 |
| 178 | G14 | 50c multicolored | .70 | .25 |
| 179 | G14 | $1 multicolored | 1.25 | .25 |
| 180 | G14 | $2 multicolored | 1.75 | .40 |
| | | Nos. 174-180 (7) | 5.00 | 1.90 |

**Souvenir Sheet**

| | | | | |
|---|---|---|---|---|
| 181 | G14 | $3 multicolored | 2.25 | 1.25 |

American Revolution Bicentennial.

Piper Apache — G15

Designs: 1c, Beech Twin Bonanza. 2c, de Havilland Twin Otter. 40c, Britten Norman Islander. 50c, de Havilland Heron. $2, Hawker Siddeley Avro 748. $3, BAC 1-11.

**1976, June 10**

| | | | | |
|---|---|---|---|---|
| 182 | G15 | ½c multicolored | .25 | .25 |
| 183 | G15 | 1c multicolored | .25 | .25 |
| 184 | G15 | 2c multicolored | .25 | .25 |
| 185 | G15 | 40c multicolored | .40 | .25 |
| 186 | G15 | 50c multicolored | .55 | .25 |
| 187 | G15 | $2 multicolored | 1.25 | .30 |
| | | Nos. 182-187 (6) | 2.95 | 1.55 |

**Souvenir Sheet**

| | | | | |
|---|---|---|---|---|
| 188 | G15 | $3 multicolored | 2.25 | 1.50 |

Olympic Games, Montreal — G16

**1976, July 1**

| | | | | |
|---|---|---|---|---|
| 189 | G16 | ½c Cycling | .25 | .25 |
| 190 | G16 | 1c Gymnastics | .25 | .25 |
| 191 | G16 | 2c Hurdling | .25 | .25 |
| 192 | G16 | 45c Shot put | .25 | .25 |
| 193 | G16 | 45c Diving | .25 | .25 |
| 194 | G16 | 75c Sprinting | .25 | .25 |
| 195 | G16 | $2 Rowing | .65 | .30 |
| | | Nos. 189-195 (7) | 2.15 | 1.80 |

**Souvenir Sheet**

| | | | | |
|---|---|---|---|---|
| 196 | G16 | $3 Sailing | 1.25 | 1.00 |

Virgin and Child by Cima — G17

Christmas: 1c, 2c, The Nativity by Romanino. 35c, Adoration of the Kings by Brueghel. 50c, Madonna and Child by Girolamo. 75c, Adoration of the Magi by Giorgione, horiz. $2, The Adoration of the Kings by Angelico, horiz. $3, The Holy Family by Garofalo.

**1976, Oct. 19**

| | | | | |
|---|---|---|---|---|
| 197 | G17 | ½c multicolored | .25 | .25 |
| 198 | G17 | 1c multicolored | .25 | .25 |
| 199 | G17 | 2c multicolored | .25 | .25 |
| 200 | G17 | 35c multicolored | .25 | .25 |
| 201 | G17 | 50c multicolored | .25 | .25 |
| 202 | G17 | 75c multicolored | .25 | .25 |
| 203 | G17 | $2 multicolored | .75 | .35 |
| | | Nos. 197-203 (7) | 2.25 | 1.85 |

**Souvenir Sheet**

| | | | | |
|---|---|---|---|---|
| 204 | G17 | $3 multicolored | 1.60 | 1.60 |

Alexander Graham Bell, First Telephone G18

Portraits of Bell and Telephone from: 1c, 1895. 2c, 1900. 35c, 1915. 75c, 1920. $1, 1929. $2, 1963. $3, 1976.

**1977, Jan. 28**

| | | | | |
|---|---|---|---|---|
| 205 | G18 | ½c multicolored | .25 | .25 |
| 206 | G18 | 1c multicolored | .25 | .25 |
| 207 | G18 | 2c multicolored | .25 | .25 |
| 208 | G18 | 35c multicolored | .25 | .25 |
| 209 | G18 | 75c multicolored | .25 | .25 |
| 210 | G18 | $1 multicolored | .30 | .25 |
| 211 | G18 | $2 multicolored | .55 | .25 |
| | | Nos. 205-211 (7) | 2.10 | 1.75 |

**Souvenir Sheet**

| | | | | |
|---|---|---|---|---|
| 212 | G18 | $3 multicolored | 1.75 | 1.00 |

Centenary of 1st telephone conversation, Mar. 10, 1876.

Coronation Coach — G19

Royal Visit — G20

Designs: 50c, Crown of St. Edward. No. 214, Queen entering Abbey. No. 219, Queen and Prince Charles. $4, Queen is crowned. No. 216, Mall on Coronation Night. No. 220, Queen's Flag.

**Litho. and Embossed**

**1977, Feb. 7**     *Perf. 13½*

| | | | | |
|---|---|---|---|---|
| 213 | G19 | 35c multicolored | .25 | .25 |
| 214 | G19 | $2 multicolored | .25 | .25 |
| 215 | G19 | $4 multicolored | .35 | .25 |
| | | Nos. 213-215 (3) | .85 | .75 |

**Souvenir Sheet**

*Perf. 14*

| | | | | |
|---|---|---|---|---|
| 216 | G19 | $5 multicolored | .90 | .90 |

**Booklet Stamps**

*Roulette x imperf.*

**Self-adhesive**

| | | | | |
|---|---|---|---|---|
| 217 | G20 | 35c multicolored | .25 | .25 |
| a. | | Booklet pane of 6 | | .75 |

| | | | | |
|---|---|---|---|---|
| 218 | G20 | 50c multicolored | .35 | .35 |
| 219 | G20 | $2 multicolored | .55 | .55 |
| 220 | G20 | $5 multicolored | .65 | .65 |
| a. | | Bkt. pane of 3, #218, #219, #220 | 1.25 | |

Reign of Queen Elizabeth II, 25th anniv. Nos. 213-215, perf. 11, have different background colors and come from sheetlets of 3 stamps plus label.
For overprints see Nos. 237-240.

Easter — G21

Paintings of the Crucifixion by various artists: ½c, Fra Angelico. 1c, Fra Angelico, diff. 2c, El Greco. 18c, El Greco, diff. 35c, Fra Angelico, diff. 50c, Giottino. $2, da Messina. $3, Fra Angelico, diff.

**1977, July 5**     **Litho.**     *Perf. 14*

| | | | | |
|---|---|---|---|---|
| 221 | G21 | ½c multicolored | .25 | .25 |
| 222 | G21 | 1c multicolored | .25 | .25 |
| 223 | G21 | 2c multicolored | .25 | .25 |
| 224 | G21 | 18c multicolored | .25 | .25 |
| 225 | G21 | 35c multicolored | .25 | .25 |
| 226 | G21 | 50c multicolored | .25 | .25 |
| 227 | G21 | $2 multicolored | .25 | .25 |
| | | Nos. 221-227 (7) | 1.75 | 1.75 |

**Souvenir Sheet**

| | | | | |
|---|---|---|---|---|
| 228 | G21 | $3 multicolored | 1.10 | .80 |

Adoration of Jesus by Correggio — G22

Christmas: Paintings of the Madonna and Child by various artists.

**1977, Nov. 17**     *Perf. 14*

| | | | | |
|---|---|---|---|---|
| 229 | G22 | ½c shown | .25 | .25 |
| 230 | G22 | 1c Giorgione | .25 | .25 |
| 231 | G22 | 2c Morales | .25 | .25 |
| 232 | G22 | 18c Raphael | .25 | .25 |
| 233 | G22 | 35c Van Dyck | .25 | .25 |
| 234 | G22 | 50c Filippo Lippi | .25 | .25 |
| 235 | G22 | $2 Filippo Lippi, diff. | .25 | .25 |
| | | Nos. 229-235 (7) | 1.75 | 1.75 |

**Souvenir Sheet**

| | | | | |
|---|---|---|---|---|
| 236 | G22 | $3 Ghirlandaio | 1.10 | .80 |

**Nos. 213-216 Overprinted**

**1977, Nov. 23**     *Perf. 13½*

| | | | | |
|---|---|---|---|---|
| 237 | G19 | 35c multicolored | .25 | .25 |
| 238 | G19 | $2 multicolored | .25 | .25 |
| 239 | G19 | $4 multicolored | .55 | .55 |
| | | Nos. 237-239 (3) | 1.05 | 1.05 |

**Souvenir Sheet**

| | | | | |
|---|---|---|---|---|
| 240 | G19 | $5 multicolored | .80 | .80 |

Caribbean visit of Queen Elizabeth II. Nos. 237-239 exist perf. 11.

Swimming and Life Saving — G23

6th Caribbean Jamboree, Kingston, Jamaica, Aug. 5-14: 1c, Hiking. 2c, Ropes and Knots. 22c, Erecting Tent. 35c, Limbo dance. 75c, Cooking. $2, Pioneer bridge building. $3, Sea Scouts' race.

**1977, Dec. 7**     *Perf. 14*

| | | | | |
|---|---|---|---|---|
| 241 | G23 | ½c multicolored | .25 | .25 |
| 242 | G23 | 1c multicolored | .25 | .25 |
| 243 | G23 | 2c multicolored | .25 | .25 |
| 244 | G23 | 22c multicolored | .25 | .25 |
| 245 | G23 | 35c multicolored | .25 | .25 |

246 G23 75c multicolored .60 .25
247 G23 $3 multicolored 1.10 .40
Nos. 241-247 (7) 2.95 1.90

**Souvenir Sheet**

248 G23 $2 multicolored 1.75 1.25

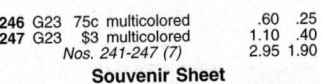

Space Shuttle
Blast-off — G24

Designs: 1c, Booster separation. 2c, External tank separation. 22c, Working in orbit. 50c, Re-entry. $2, Towing in. $3, Landing.

**1978, Feb. 3**

249 G24 ½c multicolored .25 .25
250 G24 1c multicolored .25 .25
251 G24 2c multicolored .25 .25
252 G24 22c multicolored .25 .25
253 G24 50c multicolored .25 .25
254 G24 $3 multicolored 1.25 .50
Nos. 249-254 (6) 2.50 1.75

**Souvenir Sheet**

255 G24 $2 multicolored 1.00 1.00

US Space Shuttle.

Alfred Nobel,
Medicine
Medal — G25

Alfred Nobel and: 1c, Physics, Chemistry Medal. 2c, Peace Medal. 22c, Nobel Institute, Oslo. 75c, Peace Prize committee. $2, Peace Medal, Nobel's will. $3, Literature Medal.

**1978, Feb. 22**

256 G25 ½c multicolored .25 .25
257 G25 1c multicolored .25 .25
258 G25 2c multicolored .25 .25
259 G25 22c multicolored .30 .25
260 G25 75c multicolored .70 .25
261 G25 $3 multicolored 2.25 .40
Nos. 256-261 (6) 4.00 1.65

**Souvenir Sheet**

262 G25 $2 multicolored 2.50 .90

Nobel Prize awards.

Germany No.
C37 — G26

15c, France #C43. 25c, Liechtenstein #C8 specimen. 35c, Panama #257. 50c, Russia #C15. 75c, US #C10. $2, Germany #C57. $3, Spain #C56.

**1978, Mar. 15**

263 G26 5c multicolored .25 .25
264 G26 15c multicolored .65 .25
265 G26 25c multicolored .25 .25
266 G26 35c multicolored .40 .25
267 G26 50c multicolored .75 .25
268 G26 $3 multicolored 1.90 .40
Nos. 263-268 (6) 4.20 1.65

**Souvenir Sheet**

269 Sheet of 2 2.50 1.25
a. G26 75c multicolored .50 .30
b. G26 $2 multicolored 1.50 .80

50th anniv. of Lindbergh's solo trans-Atlantic flight. 75th anniv. of 1st Zeppelin flight.

Coronation
Ring — G27

Designs: $2, Queen's Orb. $2.50, Imperial State Crown. $5, Queen Elizabeth II.

**1978, Apr. 12** Perf. 14

270 G27 50c multicolored .25 .25
271 G27 $2 multicolored .25 .25
272 G27 $2.50 multicolored .35 .35
Nos. 270-272 (3) .85 .85

**Souvenir Sheet**

273 G27 $5 multicolored .80 .80

Nos. 270-272, perf 12, printed in sheets of 3 + label, have different background colors. Issue date; June 2, 1978.

G28

Designs: 18c, Drummer, Royal Regiment of Fusiliers. 50c, Drummer, Royal Anglian Regiment. $5, Drum Major, Queen's Regiment.

**1978, Apr. 12** Roulette x imperf.

**Booklet Stamps**

**Self-Adhesive**

274 Souvenir booklet 2.50 3.00
a. G28 Pane of 6 (3 ea 18c, 50c) .75 .75
b. G28 Pane of 1 ($5) 1.50 1.50

G29

Paintings by Rubens: 5c, Le Chapeau de Paille. 15c, Hector Killed by Achilles. 18c, Helene Fourment and Her Children. 22c, Rubens and Isabella Brandt. 35c, Ildefonso Altarpiece. $2, Self-portrait. $3, Four Negro Heads.

**1978, May 18** Perf. 14

275 G29 5c multicolored .25 .25
276 G29 15c multicolored .25 .25
277 G29 18c multicolored .25 .25
278 G29 22c multicolored .30 .25
279 G29 35c multicolored .30 .25
280 G29 $3 multicolored 2.40 1.50
Nos. 275-280 (6) 3.75 2.75

**Souvenir Sheet**

281 G29 $2 multicolored 1.40 1.40

400th birth anniv. of Rubens.

Wright
Flyer — G30

Designs: 15c, Orville Wright, vert. 18c, Wilbur Wright, vert. 25c, 35c, 75c, $2, $3, various Wright airplanes.

**1978, Aug. 10**

282 G30 5c multicolored .25 .25
283 G30 15c multicolored .25 .25
284 G30 18c multicolored .25 .25
285 G30 22c multicolored .25 .25
286 G30 35c multicolored .25 .25
287 G30 75c multicolored .25 .25
288 G30 $3 multicolored 1.00 1.00
Nos. 282-288 (7) 2.50 2.50

**Souvenir Sheet**

289 G30 $2 multicolored 1.75 1.75

75th anniv. of first powered flight by the Wright brothers, Dec. 17, 1903.

Audubon's
Shearwater — G31

10c, Northern ring-necked plover. 18c, Garnet-throated hummingbird. 22c, Black-bellied tree duck. 40c, Purple martin. $1, Yellow-bellied tropic bird. $2, Long-billed curlew. $5, Snowy egret.

**1978, Sept. 28**

290 G31 5c multi 1.00 .25
291 G31 10c multi 1.25 .25
292 G31 18c multi, horiz. 1.50 .30
293 G31 22c multi, horiz. 2.00 .30
294 G31 40c multi, horiz. 3.00 .50
295 G31 $1 multi 4.25 .60
296 G31 $2 multi 5.75 1.10
Nos. 290-296 (7) 18.75 3.30

**Souvenir Sheet**

297 G31 $5 multicolored 17.00 17.00

Players, Soccer
Ball — G32

Soccer players in action.

**1978, Nov. 2**

298 G32 15c multicolored .25 .25
299 G32 35c multicolored .25 .25
300 G32 50c multicolored .25 .25
301 G32 $3 multicolored .65 .65
Nos. 298-301 (4) 1.40 1.40

**Souvenir Sheet**

302 G32 $2 multicolored 1.50 1.50

World Cup Soccer Championships, Argentina, June 1-25.

Captain Cook,
Kalaniopu (King
of Hawaii),
1778 — G33

22c, Cook, Hawaiian native. 50c, Cook, death scene, 2/14/79. $3, Cook and offering ceremony. $4, Cook, HMS Resolution.

**1978, Dec. 13**

303 G33 18c multicolored .50 .25
304 G33 22c multicolored .65 .25
305 G33 50c multicolored 1.10 .50
306 G33 $3 multicolored 2.75 2.00
Nos. 303-306 (4) 5.00 3.00

**Souvenir Sheet**

307 G33 $4 multicolored 3.00 3.00

250th birth anniv. of Captain James Cook and Bicentennial of his discovery of the Hawaiian Islands.

Durer Paintings — G34

Christmas: 40c, The Virgin at Prayer. 60c, Dresden Alterpiece. 90c, Madonna and Child. $2, Madonna and Child. $4, Salvator Mundi.

**1978, Dec 20**

308 G34 40c multicolored .25 .25
309 G34 60c multicolored .25 .25
310 G34 90c multicolored .25 .25
311 G34 $2 multicolored .70 .70
Nos. 308-311 (4) 1.45 1.45

**Souvenir Sheet**

312 G34 $4 multicolored 1.40 1.40

Strelitzia
Reginae — G35

40c, Euphorbia pulcherrima. $1, Heliconia humilis. $3, Thunbergia alata. $2, Bougainvillea glabra.

**1979, Feb. 15**

313 G35 22c shown .25 .25
314 G35 40c multicolored .40 .40
315 G35 $1 multicolored .80 .45
316 G35 $3 multicolored 1.40 .80
Nos. 313-316 (4) 2.85 1.90

**Souvenir Sheet**

317 G35 $2 multicolored 2.10 2.10

Children with
Pig — G36

International Year of the Child: 50c, Children with donkey. $1, Children with goats. $3, Children fishing. $4, Child with coconuts.

**1979, Mar. 22**

318 G36 18c multicolored .25 .25
319 G36 50c multicolored .25 .25
320 G36 $1 multicolored .40 .40
321 G36 $3 multicolored .60 .60
Nos. 318-321 (4) 1.50 1.50

**Souvenir Sheet**

322 G36 $4 multicolored 1.00 1.00

150th Birth
Anniv. of Jules
Verne — G37

Designs: 18c, 20,000 Leagues Under the Sea. 38c, From the Earth to the Moon. 75c, From the Earth to the Moon, diff. $3, Five Weeks in a Balloon. $4, Around the World in 80 Days.

**1979, Apr. 20**

323 G37 18c multicolored .65 .25
324 G37 38c multicolored .75 .25
325 G37 75c multicolored .90 .45
326 G37 $3 multicolored 1.75 1.75
Nos. 323-326 (4) 4.05 2.65

**Souvenir Sheet**

327 G37 $4 multicolored 3.00 3.00

Sir Rowland Hill,
Mail
Truck — G38

Designs: $1, Ocean liner. $2, Mail train. $3, Concorde. $4, Sir Rowland Hill.

**1979, July 30** Perf. 14

328 G38 15c multicolored .25 .25
329 G38 $1 multicolored .25 .25
330 G38 $2 multicolored .55 .55
331 G38 $3 multicolored .70 .70
Nos. 328-331 (4) 1.75 1.75

**Souvenir Sheet**

332 G38 $4 multicolored 1.25 1.25

Death centenary of Sir Rowland Hill. Nos. 328-331, perf. 12, printed in sheets of 5 + label, have different colored backgrounds.

Virgin and Child
Enthroned (Byzantine
Era, 11th Cent.) — G39

Christmas sculptures: 25c, Presentation in the Temple by Beauneveu c. 1390. 30c, Flight to Egypt (Utrecht, c. 1510). 40c, Madonna and Child by della Quercia, 1047-48. 90c, Madonna della Mela by della Robbia, c. 1455. $1, Madonna and Child by Rossellino, 1461-66. $2, Madonna (Antwerp, 1700). $4, Virgin (Krumau, c. 1390).

**1979, Oct. 23** Perf. 14

333 G39 6c multicolored .25 .25
334 G39 25c multicolored .25 .25
335 G39 30c multicolored .25 .25
336 G39 40c multicolored .25 .25
337 G39 90c multicolored .25 .25

| | | | | |
|---|---|---|---|---|
| 338 | G39 | $1 multicolored | .25 | .25 |
| 339 | G39 | $2 multicolored | .25 | .25 |
| | | Nos. 333-339 (7) | 1.75 | 1.75 |

**Souvenir Sheet**

| | | | | |
|---|---|---|---|---|
| 340 | G39 | $4 multicolored | 1.00 | 1.00 |

Great Hammerhead Shark — G40

Designs: 45c, Banded butterflyfish. 50c, Permit. 60c, Threaded turban. 70c, Milk conch. 75c, Great blue heron. 90c, Colored Atlantic natica. $1, Red footed booby. $2.50, Collared plover.

**1979, Nov. 9**

| | | | | |
|---|---|---|---|---|
| 341 | G40 | 40c multicolored | .50 | .50 |
| 342 | G40 | 45c multicolored | .55 | .55 |
| 343 | G40 | 50c multicolored | .65 | .65 |
| 344 | G40 | 60c multicolored | .75 | .75 |
| 345 | G40 | 70c multicolored | .90 | .90 |
| 346 | G40 | 75c multicolored | 1.50 | 1.00 |
| 347 | G40 | 90c multicolored | 1.30 | 1.30 |
| 348 | G40 | $1 multicolored | 1.90 | 1.90 |
| | | Nos. 341-348 (8) | 8.05 | 7.55 |

**Souvenir Sheet**

| | | | | |
|---|---|---|---|---|
| 349 | G40 | $2.50 multicolored | 2.50 | 2.50 |

Doctor Goofy — G41

International Year of the Child: 1c, Admiral Mickey Mouse. 2c, Fireman Goofy. 3c, Nurse Minnie Mouse. 4c, Drum Major Mickey Mouse. 5c, Policeman Donald Duck. 10c, Pilot Donald Duck. $2, Mailman Goofy, horiz. $2.50 Engineer Donald Duck, horiz. $3, Fireman Mickey Mouse.

**1979, Dec. 12**     **Perf. 11**

| | | | | |
|---|---|---|---|---|
| 350 | G41 | ½c multicolored | .25 | .25 |
| 351 | G41 | 1c multicolored | .25 | .25 |
| 352 | G41 | 2c multicolored | .25 | .25 |
| 353 | G41 | 3c multicolored | .25 | .25 |
| 354 | G41 | 4c multicolored | .25 | .25 |
| 355 | G41 | 5c multicolored | .25 | .25 |
| 356 | G41 | 10c multicolored | .25 | .25 |
| 357 | G41 | $2 multicolored | 2.50 | 2.50 |
| 358 | G41 | $2.50 multicolored | 2.75 | 2.75 |
| | | Nos. 350-358 (9) | 7.00 | 7.00 |

**Souvenir Sheet**
**Perf. 13½**

| | | | | |
|---|---|---|---|---|
| 359 | G41 | $3 multicolored | 3.50 | 3.50 |

**Nos. 114, 117-128 Overprinted**

**1980, Mar. 10**     **Perf. 15**

| | | | | |
|---|---|---|---|---|
| 360 | A85 | 6c multicolored | .25 | .25 |
| 361 | A85 | 12c multicolored | .25 | .25 |
| 362 | A85 | 15c multicolored | .25 | .25 |
| 363 | A85 | 20c multicolored | .25 | .25 |
| 364 | A85 | 25c multicolored | .25 | .25 |
| 365 | A85 | 35c multicolored | .25 | .25 |
| 366 | A85 | 50c multicolored | .30 | .35 |

**Perf. 13½x14**

| | | | | |
|---|---|---|---|---|
| 367 | A85 | 75c multicolored | .35 | .40 |
| 368 | A85 | $1 multicolored | .45 | .60 |
| 369 | A85 | $2 multicolored | .70 | .90 |
| 370 | A85 | $3 multicolored | 1.25 | 1.60 |
| 371 | A85 | $5 multicolored | 1.75 | 2.40 |
| 372 | A85 | $10 multicolored | 3.00 | 3.75 |
| | | Nos. 360-372 (13) | 9.30 | 11.50 |

Classroom G42

Rotary Intl., 75th anniv.: 30c, Rotary emblem, people. 60c, Rotary executive making contribution to physician. $3, Young

patients, nurses. $4, Paul P. Harris, founder of Rotary.

**1980, Mar. 12**     **Perf. 14**

| | | | | |
|---|---|---|---|---|
| 373 | G42 | 6c multicolored | .25 | .25 |
| 374 | G42 | 30c multicolored | .25 | .25 |
| 375 | G42 | 60c multicolored | .45 | .45 |
| 376 | G42 | $3 multicolored | 1.90 | 1.60 |
| | | Nos. 373-376 (4) | 2.85 | 2.55 |

**Souvenir Sheet**

| | | | | |
|---|---|---|---|---|
| 377 | G42 | $4 multicolored | 1.25 | 1.25 |

Yellow-bellied Seedeater — G43

40c, Blue-hooded euphonia. 90c, Yellow warbler. $2, Tropical mockingbird. $3, Barn owl.

**1980, Apr. 14**

| | | | | |
|---|---|---|---|---|
| 378 | G43 | 25c multicolored | .65 | .25 |
| 379 | G43 | 40c multicolored | .70 | .25 |
| 380 | G43 | 90c multicolored | 1.50 | .85 |
| 381 | G43 | $2 multicolored | 2.00 | 1.60 |
| | | Nos. 378-381 (4) | 4.85 | 2.95 |

**Souvenir Sheet**

| | | | | |
|---|---|---|---|---|
| 382 | G43 | $3 multicolored | 5.50 | 5.50 |

Running — G44

Designs: 40c, Soccer. 90c, Boxing. $2, Wrestling. $4, Runners in silhouette.

**1980, Apr. 21**

| | | | | |
|---|---|---|---|---|
| 383 | G44 | 30c multicolored | .25 | .25 |
| 384 | G44 | 40c multicolored | .25 | .25 |
| 385 | G44 | 90c multicolored | .40 | .40 |
| 386 | G44 | $2 multicolored | .85 | .85 |
| | | Nos. 383-386 (4) | 1.75 | 1.75 |

**Souvenir Sheet**

| | | | | |
|---|---|---|---|---|
| 387 | G44 | $4 multicolored | .90 | .90 |

22nd Summer Olympic Games, Moscow, July 19-Aug. 3.

**Nos. 328-331 Overprinted**

**1980, May 6**     **Perf. 12**

| | | | | |
|---|---|---|---|---|
| 388 | G38 | 15c multicolored | .25 | .25 |
| 389 | G38 | $1 multicolored | 1.10 | .50 |
| 390 | G38 | $2 multicolored | 2.25 | 1.75 |
| 391 | G38 | $3 multicolored | 3.75 | 3.00 |
| | | Nos. 388-391 (4) | 7.35 | 5.50 |

Issued in sheets of 5 + label.

Longspine Squirrelfish G45

Designs: 1c, Blue chromis. 2c, Foureye butterflyfish. 4c, Sergeant major. 5c, Yellowtail snapper. 6c, Mutton snapper. 10c, Cocoa damselfish. 12c, Royal gramma. 15c, Cherubfish. 20c, Blackbar soldierfish. 25c, Comb grouper. 30c, Longsnout butterflyfish. 40c, Pudding wife. 50c, Midnight parrotfish. 90c, Redspotted hawkfish. $1, Hogfish. $3, Beau gregory. $5, Rock beauty. $10, Barred hamlet.

**1980, Aug. 6**     **Perf. 14**
**No imprint date below design**

| | | | | |
|---|---|---|---|---|
| 392 | G45 | ½c multicolored | .25 | .25 |
| a. | | Perf. 12, inscribed 1982 | 10.00 | 10.00 |
| 393 | G45 | 1c multicolored | .25 | .25 |
| 394 | G45 | 2c multicolored | .25 | .25 |
| 395 | G45 | 4c multicolored | .25 | .25 |
| 396 | G45 | 5c multicolored | .25 | .25 |
| 397 | G45 | 6c multicolored | .25 | .25 |
| 398 | G45 | 10c multicolored | .25 | .25 |
| a. | | Inscribed "1984" | .50 | .50 |

| | | | | |
|---|---|---|---|---|
| 399 | G45 | 12c multicolored | .25 | .25 |
| 400 | G45 | 15c multicolored | .25 | .25 |
| 401 | G45 | 20c multicolored | .25 | .25 |
| a. | | Inscribed "1987" | 3.25 | 3.25 |
| 402 | G45 | 25c multicolored | .25 | .25 |
| 403 | G45 | 30c multicolored | .25 | .25 |
| 404 | G45 | 40c multicolored | .25 | .25 |
| 405 | G45 | 50c multicolored | .30 | .35 |
| 406 | G45 | 90c multicolored | .45 | .50 |
| 407 | G45 | $1 multicolored | .55 | .60 |
| 408 | G45 | $3 multicolored | 1.40 | 1.75 |
| 409 | G45 | $5 multicolored | 1.75 | 2.25 |
| 410 | G45 | $10 multicolored | 3.00 | 3.75 |
| | | Nos. 392-410 (19) | 10.70 | 12.45 |

Bambi with Mother G46

Various scenes from Walt Disney's Bambi.

**1980, Oct. 7**     **Perf. 11**

| | | | | |
|---|---|---|---|---|
| 411 | G46 | ½c multicolored | .25 | .25 |
| 412 | G46 | 1c multicolored | .25 | .25 |
| 413 | G46 | 2c multicolored | .25 | .25 |
| 414 | G46 | 3c multicolored | .25 | .25 |
| 415 | G46 | 4c multicolored | .25 | .25 |
| 416 | G46 | 5c multicolored | .25 | .25 |
| 417 | G46 | 10c multicolored | .25 | .25 |
| 418 | G46 | $2.50 multicolored | 1.50 | 1.50 |
| 419 | G46 | $3 multicolored | 1.50 | 1.50 |
| | | Nos. 411-419 (9) | 4.75 | 4.75 |

**Souvenir Sheet**

| | | | | |
|---|---|---|---|---|
| 420 | G46 | $4 multicolored | 3.00 | 3.00 |

Christmas.

The Unicorn in Captivity by Unknown 15th Cent. Artist — G47

Designs: 10c, The Fighting Temeraire by J.M.W. Turner. 25c, Sunday Afternoon on the Ile De La Grande-Jatte by Seurat. 90c, Max Schmitt in a Single Scull by Eakins. $2, The Burial of the Count of Orgaz by El Greco. $3, George Washington by Stuart. $5, Kaiser Karl the Great by Durer. Nos. 425-427 are vert.

**1981, Jan. 25**     **Perf. 14**

| | | | | |
|---|---|---|---|---|
| 421 | G47 | 6c multicolored | .25 | .25 |
| 422 | G47 | 10c multicolored | .25 | .25 |
| 423 | G47 | 25c multicolored | .25 | .25 |
| 424 | G47 | 90c multicolored | .50 | .50 |
| 425 | G47 | $2 multicolored | .90 | .90 |
| 426 | G47 | $3 multicolored | 1.25 | 1.25 |
| | | Nos. 421-426 (6) | 3.40 | 3.40 |

**Souvenir Sheet**

| | | | | |
|---|---|---|---|---|
| 427 | G47 | $5 multicolored | 2.75 | 2.75 |

**Disney Type of 1979**

50th anniv. of Pluto character: $2, Mickey Mouse, Pluto and birthday cake. $4, Pluto.

**1981, Jan. 26**

| | | | | |
|---|---|---|---|---|
| 428 | A135a | $2 multicolored | 1.10 | 1.10 |

**Souvenir Sheet**

| | | | | |
|---|---|---|---|---|
| 429 | A135a | $4 multicolored | 2.50 | 2.50 |

No. 428 issued in sheets of 8.

Chip Coloring Easter Eggs — G48

Easter: Various Disney characters coloring Easter eggs.

**1981, Apr. 14**     **Perf. 11**

| | | | | |
|---|---|---|---|---|
| 430 | G48 | 35c multicolored | .25 | .25 |
| 431 | G48 | 40c multicolored | .25 | .25 |
| 432 | G48 | $2 multicolored | .90 | .90 |
| 433 | G48 | $2.50 multicolored | 1.40 | 1.40 |
| | | Nos. 430-433 (4) | 2.80 | 2.80 |

**Souvenir Sheet**
**Perf. 14**

| | | | | |
|---|---|---|---|---|
| 434 | G48 | $4 multicolored | 2.75 | 2.75 |

Bust of a Woman — G49

Paintings by Pablo Picasso (1881-1973): 40c, Woman (Study for Les Demoiselles d'Avignon). 90c, Nude with Raised Arms (The Dancer of Avignon). $4, The Dryad. $5, Les Demoiselles d'Avignon.

**1981, May 5**     **Perf. 14**

| | | | | |
|---|---|---|---|---|
| 435 | G49 | 6c multicolored | .30 | .30 |
| 436 | G49 | 40c multicolored | .30 | .30 |
| 437 | G49 | 90c multicolored | .45 | .45 |
| 438 | G49 | $4 multicolored | 2.25 | 2.25 |

**Size: 103x128mm**
**Imperf**

| | | | | |
|---|---|---|---|---|
| 439 | G49 | $5 multicolored | 3.00 | 3.00 |
| | | Nos. 435-439 (5) | 6.30 | 6.30 |

Common Design Types pictured following the introduction.

**Royal Wedding Issue**
Common Design Type

**1981, June 16**     **Perf. 15**

| | | | | |
|---|---|---|---|---|
| 440 | CD331a | 40c Couple | .25 | .25 |
| 441 | CD331a | $2 Balmoral Castle | .25 | .25 |
| 442 | CD331a | $4 Charles | .45 | .45 |
| | | Nos. 440-442 (3) | .95 | .95 |

**Souvenir Sheet**

| | | | | |
|---|---|---|---|---|
| 443 | CD331a | $5 Royal Coach | 1.40 | 1.40 |

Sheets of 5 plus label contain 30c (like No. 440), 40c (like No. 441), or $4 in changed colors, perf 15x14½.

Diana — G50

$1, Diana. $2, Charles. $5, Diana and Charles.

**Booklet Stamps**

*Roulette x imperf. (#444a), Imperf. (#444b)*

**1981, June 16**     **Self-Adhesive**

| | | | | |
|---|---|---|---|---|
| 444 | G50 | Souvenir Booklet | 4.00 | |
| a. | | Pane of 6 (3 each $1, $2) | 2.25 | |
| b. | | Pane of 1, $5 | 1.75 | |

Royal wedding.

Amy Johnson, Pilot of 1st Britain-Australia Solo Flight by a Woman, May 1930 — G51

Decade for Women: 70c, Mme. la Baronne de Laroche, 1st qualified aviatrix, May 1910. $1.10, Ruth Nichols. $3, Amelia Earhart, 1st Atlantic solo flight by woman, May 1932. $5, Valentina Tereshkova, 1st woman in space, June 1963.

**1981, Oct. 13**     **Perf. 14**

| | | | | |
|---|---|---|---|---|
| 445 | G51 | 30c multicolored | .45 | .45 |
| 446 | G51 | 70c multicolored | .70 | .70 |
| 447 | G51 | $1.10 multicolored | .85 | .85 |
| 448 | G51 | $3 multicolored | 1.75 | 1.75 |
| | | Nos. 445-448 (4) | 3.75 | 3.75 |

**Souvenir Sheet**

| | | | | |
|---|---|---|---|---|
| 449 | G51 | $5 multicolored | 2.00 | 2.00 |

Lady and the Tramp G52

Christmas. Various scenes from Walt Disney's film Lady and the Tramp.

**1981, Nov. 2**
| | | | | |
|---|---|---|---|---|
| 450 | G52 | ½c multicolored | .25 | .25 |
| 451 | G52 | 1c multicolored | .25 | .25 |
| 452 | G52 | 2c multicolored | .25 | .25 |
| 453 | G52 | 3c multicolored | .25 | .25 |
| 454 | G52 | 4c multicolored | .25 | .25 |
| 455 | G52 | 5c multicolored | .25 | .25 |
| 456 | G52 | 10c multicolored | .25 | .25 |
| 457 | G52 | $2.50 multicolored | 3.50 | 1.75 |
| 458 | G52 | $3 multicolored | 3.50 | 2.25 |
| | | Nos. 450-458 (9) | 8.75 | 5.75 |

**Souvenir Sheet**
| | | | | |
|---|---|---|---|---|
| 459 | G52 | $5 multicolored | 7.00 | 6.00 |

747 Carrying Space Shuttle — G53

Designs: 40c, Re-entry. $1.10, External tank separation. $3, Touchdown. $5, Lift-off.

**1981, Nov. 2** — *Perf. 14½*
| | | | | |
|---|---|---|---|---|
| 460 | G53 | 10c multicolored | .40 | .25 |
| 461 | G53 | 40c multicolored | .75 | .30 |
| 462 | G53 | $1.10 multicolored | 1.40 | .80 |
| 463 | G53 | $3 multicolored | 2.25 | 1.50 |
| | | Nos. 460-463 (4) | 4.80 | 2.85 |

**Souvenir Sheet**
| | | | | |
|---|---|---|---|---|
| 464 | G53 | $5 multicolored | 5.00 | 4.00 |

Soccer Player — G54

World Cup Soccer Championships, Spain, 1982: Soccer players in various positions.

**1981, Nov. 30** — *Perf. 14*
| | | | | |
|---|---|---|---|---|
| 465 | G54 | 20c multicolored | .25 | .25 |
| 466 | G54 | 40c multicolored | .25 | .25 |
| 467 | G54 | $1 multicolored | .45 | .30 |
| 468 | G54 | $2 multicolored | .90 | .60 |
| | | Nos. 465-468 (4) | 1.85 | 1.40 |

**Souvenir Sheet**
| | | | | |
|---|---|---|---|---|
| 469 | G54 | $4 multicolored | 1.75 | 1.50 |

Stagecoach, Mail Truck — G55

UPU Membership Cent.: 40c, UPU Emblem. $2.50, Sailing ship, ocean liner. $4, Biplane, Concorde. $5, Steam train, high-speed trains.

**1982, Jan. 13** — *Perf. 15*
| | | | | |
|---|---|---|---|---|
| 470 | G55 | 30c multicolored | .40 | .25 |
| 471 | G55 | 40c multicolored | .40 | .25 |
| 472 | G55 | $2.50 multicolored | 1.75 | 1.00 |
| 473 | G55 | $4 multicolored | 3.00 | 2.00 |
| | | Nos. 470-473 (4) | 5.55 | 3.50 |

**Souvenir Sheet**
| | | | | |
|---|---|---|---|---|
| 474 | G55 | $5 multicolored | 4.75 | 4.25 |

Sprinting — G56

90c, Sea scouts sailing. $1.10, Hand crafts. $3, Animal husbandry. $5, Music around campfire.

**1982, Feb. 19**
| | | | | |
|---|---|---|---|---|
| 475 | G56 | 6c multicolored | .25 | .25 |
| 476 | G56 | 90c multicolored | .70 | .60 |
| 477 | G56 | $1.10 multicolored | .90 | .70 |
| 478 | G56 | $3 multicolored | 1.90 | 1.90 |
| | | Nos. 475-478 (4) | 3.75 | 3.45 |

**Souvenir Sheet**
| | | | | |
|---|---|---|---|---|
| 479 | G56 | $5 multicolored | 3.00 | 3.00 |

Boy Scouts, 75th anniv. Lord Baden-Powell, 125th birth anniv.

White Peacock — G57

Designs: 40c, St. Vincent long-tail skipper. $1.10, Painted lady. $3, Orion. $5, Silver spot.

**1982, Mar. 24** — *Perf. 14*
| | | | | |
|---|---|---|---|---|
| 480 | G57 | 30c multicolored | 1.25 | .60 |
| 481 | G57 | 40c multicolored | 1.25 | .85 |
| 482 | G57 | $1.10 multicolored | 3.00 | 2.50 |
| 483 | G57 | $3 multicolored | 5.25 | 5.25 |
| | | Nos. 480-483 (4) | 10.75 | 8.95 |

**Souvenir Sheet**
| | | | | |
|---|---|---|---|---|
| 484 | G57 | $5 multicolored | 6.50 | 6.50 |

**Princess Diana Issue**
Common Design Type

**1982, July 1** — *Perf. 14½x14*
| | | | | |
|---|---|---|---|---|
| 485 | CD332 | 50c Blenheim Palace | 1.25 | 1.25 |
| 486 | CD332 | 60c Like 50c | .75 | .75 |
| 487 | CD332 | $1 Couple in field | 1.75 | 1.75 |
| 488 | CD332 | $2 Like $1 | 1.90 | 1.90 |
| 489 | CD332 | $3 Diana | 2.50 | 2.50 |
| 490 | CD332 | $4 Like $3 | 2.50 | 2.50 |
| | | Nos. 485-490 (6) | 10.65 | 10.65 |

**Souvenir Sheet**
| | | | | |
|---|---|---|---|---|
| 491 | CD332 | $5 Diana, diff. | 7.00 | 7.00 |

50c, $1, $3 issued in sheets of 5 plus label.

Overprinted

**1982, Aug. 30**
| | | | | |
|---|---|---|---|---|
| 492 | CD332 | 50c multicolored | .75 | .75 |
| 493 | CD332 | 60c multicolored | .80 | .80 |
| 494 | CD332 | $1 multicolored | 1.00 | 1.00 |
| 495 | CD332 | $2 multicolored | 1.50 | 1.50 |
| 496 | CD332 | $3 multicolored | 1.90 | 1.90 |
| 497 | CD332 | $4 multicolored | 2.25 | 2.25 |
| | | Nos. 492-497 (6) | 8.20 | 8.20 |

**Souvenir Sheet**
| | | | | |
|---|---|---|---|---|
| 498 | CD332 | $5 multicolored | 5.25 | 5.25 |

Birth of Prince William of Wales, June 21.

**Roosevelt Type of 1982**

Designs: 30c, New Deal soil conservation. 40c, Roosevelt, George Washington Carver. 70c, Civilian Conservation Corps. $3, Roosevelt, Liberian Pres. Edwin Barclay. $5, Roosevelt addressing Howard University.

**1982, July 27** — *Perf. 14*
| | | | | |
|---|---|---|---|---|
| 499 | A154 | 30c multicolored | .50 | .25 |
| 500 | A154 | 40c multicolored | .50 | .25 |
| 501 | A154 | 70c multicolored | .60 | .30 |
| 502 | A154 | $3 multicolored | 1.40 | 1.40 |
| | | Nos. 499-502 (4) | 3.00 | 2.20 |

**Souvenir Sheet**
| | | | | |
|---|---|---|---|---|
| 503 | A154 | $5 multicolored | 3.25 | 3.25 |

Presentation of Christ in the Temple — G58

Easter Paintings by Rembrandt: 60c, Descent from the Cross. $2, Raising of the Cross. $4, Resurrection of Christ. $5, The Risen Christ.

**1982, Sept. 2** — *Perf. 14½*
| | | | | |
|---|---|---|---|---|
| 504 | G58 | 30c multicolored | .50 | .25 |
| 505 | G58 | 60c multicolored | .60 | .25 |
| 506 | G58 | $2 multicolored | .80 | .80 |
| 507 | G58 | $4 multicolored | 1.50 | 1.50 |
| | | Nos. 504-507 (4) | 3.40 | 2.80 |

**Souvenir Sheet**
| | | | | |
|---|---|---|---|---|
| 508 | G58 | $5 multicolored | 3.50 | 3.50 |

G59

**1982, Oct. 4** — *Perf. 15*
| | | | | |
|---|---|---|---|---|
| 509 | G59 | 10c Santa Fe | .65 | .75 |
| 510 | G59 | 40c Mistral | .90 | .30 |
| 511 | G59 | 70c Rheingold | 1.00 | .65 |
| 512 | G59 | $1 ET 403 | 1.25 | .70 |
| 513 | G59 | $1.10 Mallard | 1.50 | .75 |
| 514 | G59 | $2 Tokaido | 1.75 | 1.25 |
| | | Nos. 509-514 (6) | 7.05 | 3.90 |

**Souvenir Sheet**
| | | | | |
|---|---|---|---|---|
| 515 | G59 | $5 Settebello | 3.25 | 3.25 |

Soccer Players — G60

Italy, World Cup Soccer Champions: $4, Soccer players, diff. $5, Map of Italy.

**1982, Dec. 2** — *Perf. 14*
| | | | | |
|---|---|---|---|---|
| 516 | G60 | 60c multicolored | 1.00 | .45 |
| 517 | G60 | $4 multicolored | 2.75 | 2.75 |

**Souvenir Sheet**
| | | | | |
|---|---|---|---|---|
| 518 | G60 | $5 multicolored | 2.50 | 2.50 |

**Christmas Type of 1982**

Scenes from Walt Disney's film The Rescuers.

**1982, Dec. 14** — *Perf. 13½*
| | | | | |
|---|---|---|---|---|
| 519 | A157 | ½c multicolored | .25 | .25 |
| 520 | A157 | 1c multicolored | .25 | .25 |
| 521 | A157 | 2c multicolored | .25 | .25 |
| 522 | A157 | 3c multicolored | .25 | .25 |
| 523 | A157 | 4c multicolored | .25 | .25 |
| 524 | A157 | 5c multicolored | .25 | .25 |
| 525 | A157 | 10c multicolored | .25 | .25 |
| 526 | A157 | $2.50 multicolored | 3.00 | 3.25 |
| 527 | A157 | $3 multicolored | 3.00 | 3.25 |
| | | Nos. 519-527 (9) | 7.75 | 8.25 |

**Souvenir Sheet**
| | | | | |
|---|---|---|---|---|
| 528 | A157 | $5 multicolored | 6.75 | 6.75 |

**Whales Type of 1982**

Designs: 10c, Pilot whale. 60c, Dall porpoise. $1.10, Humpback whale. $3, Bowfin whale. $5, Spotted dolphin.

**1983, Jan. 10** — *Perf. 14*
| | | | | |
|---|---|---|---|---|
| 529 | A159 | 10c multicolored | 1.25 | 1.10 |
| 530 | A159 | 60c multicolored | 3.00 | 2.75 |
| 531 | A159 | $1.10 multicolored | 5.25 | 4.50 |
| 532 | A159 | $3 multicolored | 8.50 | 7.00 |
| | | Nos. 529-532 (4) | 18.00 | 15.35 |

**Souvenir Sheet**
| | | | | |
|---|---|---|---|---|
| 533 | A159 | $5 multicolored | 9.00 | 7.50 |

**Raphael Paintings Type**

Designs: 25c, David and Goliath. 30c, David Sees Bathsheba. 90c, Triumph of David. $4, Anointing of Solomon. $5, Anointing of David.

**1983, Feb. 15** — *Perf. 14*
| | | | | |
|---|---|---|---|---|
| 534 | A160 | 25c multicolored | .25 | .25 |
| 535 | A160 | 30c multicolored | .25 | .25 |
| 536 | A160 | 90c multicolored | .35 | .35 |
| 537 | A160 | $4 multicolored | .80 | .80 |
| | | Nos. 534-537 (4) | 1.65 | 1.65 |

**Souvenir Sheet**
| | | | | |
|---|---|---|---|---|
| 538 | A160 | $5 multicolored | 1.25 | 1.25 |

Audio and Video Communication G61

World Communications Year: 60c, Ambulance. $1.10, Helicopters. $3, Satellite. $5, Diver, bottle-nose porpoise.

**1983, Apr. 7** — *Perf. 14*
| | | | | |
|---|---|---|---|---|
| 539 | G61 | 30c multicolored | .25 | .25 |
| 540 | G61 | 60c multicolored | .45 | .45 |
| 541 | G61 | $1.10 multicolored | .80 | .80 |
| 542 | G61 | $3 blk, red & blue | 1.50 | 1.50 |
| | | Nos. 539-542 (4) | 3.00 | 3.00 |

**Souvenir Sheet**
| | | | | |
|---|---|---|---|---|
| 543 | G61 | $5 multicolored | 3.50 | 3.00 |

For overprints see Nos. 629-630A.

**Car Type of 1983**

Designs: 10c, 1931 Chrysler Imperial Roadster. 30c, 1925 Doble Steam Car. 40c, 1965 Ford Mustang. 60c, 1930 Packard Tourer. 70c, 1913 Mercer Raceabout. 90c, 1963 Corvette Stingray. $1.10, 1935 Auburn 851 Supercharger Speedster. $2.50, 1933 Pierce Arrow Silver Arrow. $3, 1929 Duesenberg Dual Cowl Phaeton. $4, 1928 Mercedes-Benz SSK. $5, 1923 McFarlan Knickerbocker Cabriolet.

**1983, May 4** — *Perf. 14½*
| | | | | |
|---|---|---|---|---|
| 544 | A163 | 10c multicolored | .25 | .25 |
| 545 | A163 | 30c multicolored | .35 | .35 |
| 546 | A163 | 40c multicolored | .35 | .35 |
| 547 | A163 | 60c multicolored | .50 | .50 |
| 548 | A163 | 70c multicolored | .50 | .50 |
| 549 | A163 | 90c multicolored | .50 | .50 |
| 550 | A163 | $1.10 multicolored | .50 | .50 |
| 551 | A163 | $2.50 multicolored | .80 | .80 |
| 552 | A163 | $3 multicolored | .90 | .90 |
| 553 | A163 | $4 multicolored | .90 | .90 |
| | | Nos. 544-553 (10) | 5.55 | 5.55 |

**Souvenir Sheet**
| | | | | |
|---|---|---|---|---|
| 554 | A163 | $5 multicolored | 3.25 | 3.25 |

**Anniversary of Manned Flight Type**

Designs: 40c, Short Solent flying boat. 70c, Curtiss R3C-2 seaplane. 90c, Hawker Nimrod biplane. $4, Montgolfier balloon. $5, Victoria Luise airship.

**1983, July 18** — *Perf. 14*
| | | | | |
|---|---|---|---|---|
| 555 | A164 | 40c multicolored | 1.00 | .25 |
| 556 | A164 | 70c multicolored | 1.25 | .50 |
| 557 | A164 | 90c multicolored | 1.50 | 1.50 |
| 558 | A164 | $4 multicolored | 3.75 | 3.25 |
| | | Nos. 555-558 (4) | 7.50 | 5.50 |

**Souvenir Sheet**
| | | | | |
|---|---|---|---|---|
| 559 | A164 | $5 multicolored | 3.50 | 3.50 |

Christmas — G62

Walt Disney characters in scenes from "Jingle Bells."

**1983, Nov. 7** — *Perf. 11*
| | | | | |
|---|---|---|---|---|
| 560 | G62 | ½c multicolored | .25 | .25 |
| 561 | G62 | 1c multicolored | .25 | .25 |
| 562 | G62 | 2c multicolored | .25 | .25 |
| 563 | G62 | 3c multicolored | .25 | .25 |
| 564 | G62 | 4c multicolored | .25 | .25 |
| 565 | G62 | 5c multicolored | .25 | .25 |
| 566 | G62 | 10c multicolored | .25 | .25 |
| 567 | G62 | $2.50 multicolored | 5.25 | 5.25 |
| 568 | G62 | $3 multicolored | 5.75 | 5.75 |
| | | Nos. 560-568 (9) | 12.75 | 12.75 |

**Souvenir Sheet**
*Perf. 13½*
| | | | | |
|---|---|---|---|---|
| 569 | G62 | $5 multicolored | 11.00 | 11.00 |

G63

**1984, Jan. 9** — *Perf. 14*
| | | | | |
|---|---|---|---|---|
| 570 | G63 | 30c Weightlifting | .25 | .25 |
| 571 | G63 | 60c Gymnastics | .55 | .50 |
| 572 | G63 | 70c Archery | .75 | .60 |
| 573 | G63 | $4 Sailing | 2.25 | 2.25 |
| | | Nos. 570-573 (4) | 3.80 | 3.60 |

**Souvenir Sheet**
| | | | | |
|---|---|---|---|---|
| 574 | G63 | $5 Basketball | 3.50 | 3.50 |

Olympic Games, Los Angeles.

G64

Designs: 15c, Frangipani. 40c, Dwarf poinciana. 70c, Walking iris. $4, Lady's slipper. $5, Brazilian glory vine.

| 1984, Apr. 9 | | | Perf. 15 | |
|---|---|---|---|---|
| 575 | G64 | 15c multicolored | .25 | .25 |
| 576 | G64 | 40c multicolored | .30 | .30 |
| 577 | G64 | 70c multicolored | .75 | .55 |
| 578 | G64 | $4 multicolored | 2.75 | 2.75 |
| | | Nos. 575-578 (4) | 4.05 | 3.85 |

**Souvenir Sheet**

| 579 | G64 | $5 multicolored | 3.75 | 3.75 |
|---|---|---|---|---|

For overprints see Nos. 598-600.

Easter — G65

Walt Disney characters with Easter hats.

| 1984, May 1 | | | Perf. 11 | |
|---|---|---|---|---|
| 580 | G65 | ½c multicolored | .25 | .25 |
| 581 | G65 | 1c multicolored | .25 | .25 |
| 582 | G65 | 2c multicolored | .25 | .25 |
| 583 | G65 | 3c multicolored | .25 | .25 |
| 584 | G65 | 4c multicolored | .25 | .25 |
| 585 | G65 | 5c multicolored | .25 | .25 |
| 586 | G65 | 10c multicolored | .25 | .25 |
| 587 | G65 | $2 multicolored | 1.90 | 1.90 |
| 588 | G65 | $4 multicolored | 2.75 | 2.75 |
| | | Nos. 580-588 (9) | 6.40 | 6.40 |

**Souvenir Sheet**

| 589 | G65 | $5 multicolored | 5.25 | 5.25 |
|---|---|---|---|---|

Bobolink — G66

Birds: 50c, Eastern kingbird. 60c, Barn swallow. 70c, Yellow warbler. $1, Rose-breasted grosbeak. $1.10, Yellowthroat. $2, Catbird. $5, Fork-tailed flycatcher.

| 1984, May 21 | | | Perf. 14 | |
|---|---|---|---|---|
| 590 | G66 | 40c multicolored | 2.50 | 2.00 |
| 591 | G66 | 50c multicolored | 2.90 | 2.25 |
| 592 | G66 | 60c multicolored | 3.25 | 2.90 |
| 593 | G66 | 70c multicolored | 3.25 | 2.90 |
| 594 | G66 | $1 multicolored | 3.50 | 3.50 |
| 595 | G66 | $1.10 multicolored | 4.00 | 4.00 |
| 596 | G66 | $2 multicolored | 5.00 | 4.00 |
| | | Nos. 590-596 (7) | 24.40 | 22.55 |

**Souvenir Sheet**

| 597 | G66 | $5 multicolored | 11.00 | 11.00 |
|---|---|---|---|---|

Nos. 577-579
Overprinted

| 1984, June 19 | | | Perf. 15 | |
|---|---|---|---|---|
| 598 | G64 | 70c multicolored | 1.10 | 1.10 |
| 599 | G64 | $4 multicolored | 5.00 | 5.00 |

**Souvenir Sheet**

| 600 | G64 | $5 multicolored | 4.50 | 4.50 |
|---|---|---|---|---|

Geeststar — G67

60c, Daphne. $1.10, Schooner Southwind. $4, Oceanic.

---

$5, Privateer.

| 1984, July 16 | | | Perf. 15 | |
|---|---|---|---|---|
| 601 | G67 | 30c shown | .85 | .85 |
| 602 | G67 | 60c multicolored | 1.10 | 1.10 |
| 603 | G67 | $1.10 multicolored | 1.40 | 1.40 |
| 604 | G67 | $4 multicolored | 2.40 | 2.40 |
| | | Nos. 601-604 (4) | 5.75 | 5.75 |

**Souvenir Sheet**

| 605 | G67 | $5 multicolored | 5.25 | 5.25 |
|---|---|---|---|---|

**Correggio Paintings Type**

Designs: 10c, The Hunt — Blowing the Horn. 30c, St. John the Evangelist, horiz. 90c, The Hunt — The Deer's Head. $4, The Virgin Crowned by Christ, horiz. $5, Martyrdom of the Four Saints.

| 1984, Aug. 22 | | | Perf. 14 | |
|---|---|---|---|---|
| 606 | A171a | 10c multicolored | .25 | .25 |
| 607 | A171a | 30c multicolored | .25 | .25 |
| 608 | A171a | 90c multicolored | .70 | .70 |
| 609 | A171a | $4 multicolored | 2.50 | 2.50 |
| | | Nos. 606-609 (4) | 3.70 | 3.70 |

**Souvenir Sheet**

| 610 | A171a | $5 multicolored | 3.50 | 3.50 |
|---|---|---|---|---|

The Song of the
Dog — G68

Paintings by Edgar Degas: 70c, Cafe-Concert. $1.10, The Orchestra of the Opera. $3, The Dance Lesson. $5, Madame Camus at the Piano.

| 1984, Aug. 22 | | | | |
|---|---|---|---|---|
| 611 | G68 | 25c multicolored | .45 | .25 |
| 612 | G68 | 70c multicolored | .75 | .60 |
| 613 | G68 | $1.10 multicolored | 1.60 | 1.60 |
| 614 | G68 | $3 multicolored | 3.00 | 3.00 |
| | | Nos. 611-614 (4) | 5.80 | 5.45 |

**Souvenir Sheet**

| 615 | G68 | $5 multicolored | 4.00 | 4.00 |
|---|---|---|---|---|

150th birth anniv. of Degas.

Queen Victoria
Gardens — G69

$4, Ayers Rock. $5, Yarra River, Melbourne.

| 1984, Sept. 21 | | | | |
|---|---|---|---|---|
| 616 | G69 | $1.10 multicolored | .85 | .85 |
| 617 | G69 | $4 multicolored | 3.25 | 3.25 |

**Souvenir Sheet**

| 618 | G69 | $5 multicolored | 4.00 | 4.00 |
|---|---|---|---|---|

AUSIPEX International Stamp Exhibition, Melbourne, Australia.

Colonel Steven's
Model,
"1825" — G70

Locomotives: 50c, Royal George, 1827. 60c, Stourbridge Lion, 1829. 70c, Liverpool, 1830. 90c, South Carolina, 1832. $1.10, Monster, 1836. $2, Lafayette, 1837. $4, Lion, 1838. No. 627, Sequin's Engine, 1829. No. 628, Der Adler, 1835.

| 1984, Oct. 3 | | | Perf. 15 | |
|---|---|---|---|---|
| 619 | G70 | 20c multicolored | .80 | .30 |
| 620 | G70 | 50c multicolored | 1.00 | .60 |
| 621 | G70 | 60c multicolored | 1.10 | .75 |
| 622 | G70 | 70c multicolored | 1.25 | 1.25 |
| 623 | G70 | 90c multicolored | 1.40 | 1.40 |
| 624 | G70 | $1.10 multicolored | 1.40 | 1.40 |
| 625 | G70 | $2 multicolored | 1.75 | 1.75 |
| 626 | G70 | $4 multicolored | 2.25 | 2.25 |
| | | Nos. 619-626 (8) | 10.95 | 9.70 |

**Souvenir Sheets**

| 627 | G70 | $5 multicolored | 4.00 | 4.00 |
|---|---|---|---|---|
| 628 | G70 | $5 multicolored | 4.00 | 4.00 |

---

**Nos. 539, 541, 543 Overprinted**

| 1984, Oct. 28 | | | Perf. 14 | |
|---|---|---|---|---|
| 629 | G61 | 30c multicolored | .35 | .25 |
| 630 | G61 | $1.10 multicolored | 1.25 | .95 |

**Souvenir Sheet**

| 630A | G61 | $5 multicolored | 6.25 | 5.25 |
|---|---|---|---|---|

Opening of the Point Saline International Airport. No. 630A is overprinted in the margin.

**Christmas Type of 1984**

Scenes from various Donald Duck movies.

| 1984, Nov. 26 | | | Perf. 13½x14 | |
|---|---|---|---|---|
| 631 | A173 | 45c multicolored | .95 | .55 |
| 632 | A173 | 60c multicolored | 1.10 | .75 |
| 633 | A173 | 90c multicolored | 1.50 | 1.25 |
| 634 | A173 | $2 multi, perf. 12 | 2.25 | 2.25 |
| 635 | A173 | $4 multicolored | 4.50 | 4.50 |
| | | Nos. 631-635 (5) | 10.30 | 9.30 |

**Souvenir Sheet**

| 636 | A173 | $5 multicolored | 6.50 | 6.00 |
|---|---|---|---|---|

No. 634 issued in sheets of 8.

**Audubon Type of 1985**

Designs: 50c, Blue-winged teal. 90c, White ibis. $1.10, Swallow-tailed kite. $3, Common Gallinule. $5, Mangrove cuckoo.

| 1985, Feb. 11 | | | Perf. 14 | |
|---|---|---|---|---|
| 637 | A174 | 50c multicolored | 2.25 | .90 |
| 638 | A174 | 90c multicolored | 2.75 | 1.60 |
| 639 | A174 | $1.10 multicolored | 3.50 | 2.10 |
| 640 | A174 | $3 multicolored | 4.50 | 4.50 |
| | | Nos. 637-640 (4) | 13.00 | 9.10 |

**Souvenir Sheet**

| 641 | A174 | $5 multicolored | 6.00 | 6.00 |
|---|---|---|---|---|

See Nos. 732-736.

Motorcycle
Centenary — G71

Anniv. emblem and: 30c, Kawasaki 750, 1972. 60c, Honda Goldwing GL1000, 1974, horiz. 70c, Kawasaki Z650, 1976, horiz. $4, Honda CBX, 1977. $5, BMW R100RS, 1978.

| 1985, Mar. 11 | | | | |
|---|---|---|---|---|
| 642 | G71 | 30c multicolored | .75 | .50 |
| 643 | G71 | 60c multicolored | 1.00 | 1.00 |
| 644 | G71 | 70c multicolored | 1.25 | 1.25 |
| 645 | G71 | $4 multicolored | 4.50 | 4.50 |
| | | Nos. 642-645 (4) | 7.50 | 7.25 |

**Souvenir Sheet**

| 646 | G71 | $5 multicolored | 5.75 | 5.75 |
|---|---|---|---|---|

Intl. Youth
Year — G72

Designs: 50c, Folding bandages (health). 70c, Diver, turtle (environment). $1.10, Sailing (leisure). $3, Boys playing chess (education). $5, Hands touching globe.

| 1985, Apr. 15 | | | | |
|---|---|---|---|---|
| 647 | G72 | 50c multicolored | .65 | .45 |
| 648 | G72 | 70c multicolored | 1.00 | .85 |
| 649 | G72 | $1.10 multicolored | 1.50 | 1.40 |
| 650 | G72 | $3 multicolored | 7.50 | 7.50 |
| | | Nos. 647-650 (4) | 10.65 | 10.20 |

**Souvenir Sheet**

| 651 | G72 | $5 multicolored | 4.75 | 4.75 |
|---|---|---|---|---|

Intl. Civil Aviation
Org., 40th
Anniv. — G73

---

Designs: 5c, Lockheed Lodestar. 70c, Avro 748 Turboprop. $1.10, Boeing 727. $4, Boeing 707. $5, Pilatus Britten-Norman Islander.

| 1985, Apr. 30 | | | | |
|---|---|---|---|---|
| 652 | G73 | 5c multicolored | .50 | .25 |
| 653 | G73 | 70c multicolored | 2.10 | .70 |
| 654 | G73 | $1.10 multicolored | 2.50 | 1.10 |
| 655 | G73 | $4 multicolored | 4.25 | 3.25 |
| | | Nos. 652-655 (4) | 9.35 | 5.30 |

**Souvenir Sheet**

| 656 | G73 | $5 multicolored | 5.50 | 5.00 |
|---|---|---|---|---|

**Girl Guides Type**

Designs: 30c, Lady Baden-Powell, Guide leaders. 50c, Botany field trip. 70c, Making camp, vert. $4, Sailing, vert. $5, Lord and Lady Baden-Powell, vert.

| 1985, May 30 | | | | |
|---|---|---|---|---|
| 657 | A176 | 30c multicolored | .50 | .25 |
| 658 | A176 | 50c multicolored | 1.25 | .35 |
| 659 | A176 | 70c multicolored | 1.25 | .55 |
| 660 | A176 | $4 multicolored | 5.00 | 2.75 |
| | | Nos. 657-660 (4) | 8.00 | 3.90 |

**Souvenir Sheet**

| 661 | A176 | $5 multicolored | 5.50 | 5.50 |
|---|---|---|---|---|

Grenadine
Grizzled
Skipper — G74

Butterflies: 1c, Red anartia. 2c, Lesser Antillean giant hairstreak. 4c, Santa Domingo longtail skipper. 5c, Spotted Manuel's skipper. 6c, Grenada's polydamus swallowtail. 10c, Palmira sulphur. 12c, Pupillated orange sulphur. 15c, Migrant sulphur. 20c, St. Christopher's hairstreak. 25c, St. Lucia mestra. 30c, Insular gulf fritillary. 40c, Michael's Caribbean buckeye. 60c, Frampton's flambeau. 70c, Bamboo page. $1.10, Antillean cracker. $2.50, Red crescent hairstreak. $5, Single colored Antillean white. $10, Lesser whirlabout. $20, Blue night.

| 1985-86 | | | Perf. 14 | |
|---|---|---|---|---|
| 662 | G74 | ½c multicolored | .25 | .25 |
| 663 | G74 | 1c multicolored | .25 | .25 |
| 664 | G74 | 2c multicolored | .25 | .25 |
| 665 | G74 | 4c multicolored | .25 | .25 |
| 666 | G74 | 5c multicolored | .25 | .25 |
| 667 | G74 | 6c multicolored | .25 | .25 |
| 668 | G74 | 10c multicolored | .40 | .25 |
| 669 | G74 | 12c multicolored | .60 | .25 |
| 670 | G74 | 15c multicolored | .60 | .25 |
| 671 | G74 | 20c multicolored | .80 | .25 |
| 672 | G74 | 25c multicolored | .80 | .25 |
| 673 | G74 | 30c multicolored | .80 | .30 |
| 674 | G74 | 40c multicolored | 1.00 | .60 |
| 675 | G74 | 60c multicolored | 1.40 | .95 |
| 676 | G74 | 70c multicolored | 1.60 | 1.00 |
| 677 | G74 | $1.10 multicolored | 2.50 | 1.90 |
| 678 | G74 | $2.50 multicolored | 4.50 | 3.75 |
| 679 | G74 | $5 multicolored | 6.75 | 6.25 |
| 680 | G74 | $10 multicolored | 11.00 | 11.00 |
| 681 | G74 | $20 multicolored | 15.50 | 15.50 |
| | | Nos. 662-681 (20) | 49.75 | 44.00 |

Issued: Nos. 662-679, 6/17; No. 680, 11/11; No. 681, 1/8/86.
For overprints see Nos. 737-738.

| 1986 | | | Perf. 12½x12 | |
|---|---|---|---|---|
| 662a | G74 | ½c multicolored | .40 | .40 |
| 663a | G74 | 1c multicolored | .40 | .40 |
| 664a | G74 | 2c multicolored | .40 | .40 |
| 665a | G74 | 4c multicolored | .40 | .40 |
| 666a | G74 | 5c multicolored | .40 | .40 |
| 667a | G74 | 6c multicolored | .40 | .40 |
| 668a | G74 | 10c multicolored | .40 | .40 |
| 669a | G74 | 12c multicolored | .40 | .40 |
| 670a | G74 | 15c multicolored | .40 | .40 |
| 671a | G74 | 20c multicolored | .40 | .40 |
| 672a | G74 | 25c multicolored | .40 | .40 |
| 673a | G74 | 30c multicolored | .60 | .60 |
| 674a | G74 | 40c multicolored | .70 | .70 |
| 675a | G74 | 60c multicolored | 1.25 | 1.25 |
| 676a | G74 | 70c multicolored | 1.25 | 1.25 |
| 677a | G74 | $1.10 multicolored | 2.00 | 2.00 |
| 678a | G74 | $2.50 multicolored | 7.00 | 7.00 |
| 679a | G74 | $5 multicolored | 12.00 | 12.00 |
| 680a | G74 | $10 multicolored | 20.00 | 20.00 |
| 681a | G74 | $20 multicolored | 26.00 | 26.00 |
| | | Nos. 662a-681a (20) | 75.20 | 75.20 |

Issued: Nos. 662a-677a, 679a, 1986; Nos. 678a, 680a, 9/1986; No. 681a, 5/1989.

**Queen Mother Birthday Type**

$1, Portrait. $1.50, At Ascot, horiz. $2.50, Queen Mother, Prince Charles. $5, Portrait, diff.

| 1985, July 3 | | | Perf. 14 | |
|---|---|---|---|---|
| 682 | A181 | $1 multicolored | .65 | .65 |
| 683 | A181 | $1.50 multicolored | 1.10 | 1.10 |
| 684 | A181 | $2.50 multicolored | 1.75 | 1.75 |
| | | Nos. 682-684 (3) | 3.50 | 3.50 |

**Souvenir Sheet**

| 685 | A181 | $5 multicolored | 3.75 | 3.75 |
|---|---|---|---|---|

| 1986, Jan. 28 | | Perf. 12x12½ | | |
|---|---|---|---|---|
| 686 | A181 | 70c like #682 | .60 | .60 |
| 687 | A181 | $1.10 like #683 | .75 | .75 |
| 688 | A181 | $3 like #684 | 2.50 | 2.50 |
| | | Nos. 686-688 (3) | 3.85 | 3.85 |

Issued in sheets of 5 plus label.

### Water Sports Type

Designs: 15c, Scuba diving. 70c, Playing in waterfall. 90c, Water skiing. $4, Swimming. $5, Skin diver, sailboat.

| 1985, July 15 | | | Perf. 15 | |
|---|---|---|---|---|
| 689 | A179 | 15c multicolored | .25 | .25 |
| 690 | A179 | 70c multicolored | .55 | .55 |
| 691 | A179 | 90c multicolored | 1.00 | 1.00 |
| 692 | A179 | $4 multicolored | 3.50 | 3.50 |
| | | Nos. 689-692 (4) | 5.30 | 5.30 |

**Souvenir Sheet**

| 693 | A179 | $5 multicolored | 4.50 | 4.50 |
|---|---|---|---|---|

Queen Conch — G75

Marine Life: 90c, Porcupine fish, fire coral. $1.10, Ghost crab. $4, West Indies spiny lobster. $5, Long-spined urchin.

| 1985, Aug. 1 | | | Perf. 14 | |
|---|---|---|---|---|
| 694 | G75 | 60c multicolored | .85 | .70 |
| 695 | G75 | 90c multicolored | 1.50 | 1.00 |
| 696 | G75 | $1.10 multicolored | 1.75 | 1.25 |
| 697 | G75 | $4 multicolored | 4.25 | 4.25 |
| | | Nos. 694-697 (4) | 8.35 | 7.20 |

**Souvenir Sheet**

| 698 | G75 | $5 multicolored | 8.50 | 8.50 |
|---|---|---|---|---|

### Bach Anniversary Type

Portrait, signature, music from Invention No. 9 and: 15c, Natural trumpet. 60c, Bass viol. $1.10, Flute. $3, Double flageolet. $5, Portrait.

| 1985, Sept. 3 | | | Perf. 14 | |
|---|---|---|---|---|
| 699 | A184 | 15c multicolored | .65 | .25 |
| 700 | A184 | 60c multicolored | 1.10 | .60 |
| 701 | A184 | $1.10 multicolored | 2.00 | 1.00 |
| 702 | A184 | $3 multicolored | 3.00 | 2.50 |
| | | Nos. 699-702 (4) | 6.75 | 4.35 |

**Souvenir Sheet**

| 703 | A184 | $5 multicolored | 4.50 | 4.50 |
|---|---|---|---|---|

### Royal Visit Type

10c, Arms of Great Britain, Grenada. $1, Queen Elizabeth II. $4, HMY Britannia. $5, Map.

| 1985, Nov. 4 | | | Perf. 14½ | |
|---|---|---|---|---|
| 704 | A186 | 10c multicolored | .25 | .25 |
| 705 | A186 | $1 multi, vert. | 1.50 | 1.50 |
| 706 | A186 | $4 multicolored | 4.50 | 4.50 |
| | | Nos. 704-706 (3) | 6.25 | 6.25 |

**Souvenir Sheet**

| 707 | A186 | $5 multicolored | 5.25 | 5.25 |
|---|---|---|---|---|

### UN Anniversary Type

UN stamps and famous people: $1, #373, Neil Armstrong. $2, #221, Mahatma Gandhi. $2.50, #43, Maimonides. $5, Ralph Bunche.

| 1985, Nov. 22 | | | | |
|---|---|---|---|---|
| 708 | A189 | $1 multicolored | 1.50 | 1.25 |
| 709 | A189 | $2 multicolored | 4.00 | 4.00 |
| 710 | A189 | $2.50 multicolored | 4.75 | 4.75 |
| | | Nos. 708-710 (3) | 10.25 | 10.00 |

**Souvenir Sheet**

| 711 | A189 | $5 multicolored | 5.00 | 5.00 |
|---|---|---|---|---|

### Twain & Disney Type

Walt Disney characters in scenes from "Letters From Hawaii": 25c, Mickey, Minnie on beach. 50c, Donald Duck surfing. $1.50, Donald roasting marshmallow. $3, Mickey canoeing. $5, Mickey, cat.

| 1985, Nov. 27 | | | Perf. 14x13½ | |
|---|---|---|---|---|
| 712 | A185 | 25c multicolored | .85 | .40 |
| 713 | A185 | 50c multicolored | 1.25 | .90 |
| 714 | A185 | $1.50 multicolored | 3.25 | 3.25 |
| 715 | A185 | $3 multicolored | 5.00 | 5.00 |
| | | Nos. 712-715 (4) | 10.35 | 9.55 |

**Souvenir Sheet**

| 716 | A185 | $5 multicolored | 7.00 | 7.00 |
|---|---|---|---|---|

### Brothers Grimm & Disney Type

Walt Disney characters in scenes from "The Elves and the Shoemaker": 30c, Mickey as shoemaker. 60c, Elves helping. 70c, Mickey, new shoes. $4, Minnie at sewing machine. $5, Minnie & Mickey.

| 1985, Nov. 27 | | | Perf. 13½x14 | |
|---|---|---|---|---|
| 717 | A187 | 30c multicolored | .85 | .45 |
| 718 | A187 | 60c multicolored | 1.25 | 1.00 |
| 719 | A187 | 70c multicolored | 1.60 | 1.25 |
| 720 | A187 | $4 multicolored | 4.75 | 4.75 |
| | | Nos. 717-720 (4) | 8.45 | 7.45 |

**Souvenir Sheet**

| 721 | A187 | $5 multicolored | 7.00 | 7.00 |
|---|---|---|---|---|

Madonna and Child by Titian — G76

Christmas paintings: 70c, Madonna and Child with St. Mary and John the Baptist by Bugiardini. $1.10, Adoration of the Magi by Di Fredi. $3, Madonna and Child with Young St. John the Baptist by Bartolomeo. $5, The Annunciation by Botticelli.

| 1985, Dec. 23 | | | Perf. 15 | |
|---|---|---|---|---|
| 722 | G76 | 50c multicolored | .60 | .45 |
| 723 | G76 | 70c multicolored | .70 | .55 |
| 724 | G76 | $1.10 multicolored | 1.10 | .90 |
| 725 | G76 | $3 multicolored | 2.10 | 2.10 |
| | | Nos. 722-725 (4) | 4.50 | 4.00 |

**Souvenir Sheet**

| 726 | G76 | $5 multicolored | 3.50 | 3.50 |
|---|---|---|---|---|

### Statue of Liberty Type of 1985

Designs: 5c, Croton Reservoir, 1875. 10c, NY Public Library, 1986. 70c, Old Boathouse, Central Park, 1894. $4, Boating, Central Park, 1986. $5, Statue of Liberty, vert.

| 1986, Jan. 6 | | | Perf. 15 | |
|---|---|---|---|---|
| 727 | A191 | 5c multicolored | .25 | .25 |
| 728 | A191 | 10c multicolored | .25 | .25 |
| 729 | A191 | 70c multicolored | .40 | .40 |
| 730 | A191 | $4 multicolored | 2.40 | 2.40 |
| | | Nos. 727-730 (4) | 3.30 | 3.30 |

**Souvenir Sheet**

| 731 | A191 | $5 multicolored | 5.00 | 5.00 |
|---|---|---|---|---|

### Audubon Type of 1985

Designs: 50c, Louisiana heron. 70c, Black-crowned night heron. 90c, Bittern. $4, Glossy ibis. $5, King eider.

| 1986, Jan. 28 | | | Perf. 12½x12 | |
|---|---|---|---|---|
| 732 | A174 | 50c multicolored | 2.25 | 1.10 |
| 733 | A174 | 70c multicolored | 2.75 | 1.60 |
| 734 | A174 | 90c multicolored | 3.00 | 2.40 |
| 735 | A174 | $4 multicolored | 5.50 | 5.50 |
| | | Nos. 732-735 (4) | 13.50 | 10.60 |

**Souvenir Sheet**

**Perf. 14**

| 736 | A174 | $5 multicolored | 8.00 | 8.00 |
|---|---|---|---|---|

Nos. 732-735 issued in sheets of 5 plus label.

### Nos. 676, 679 Overprinted

| 1986, Feb. 20 | | | Perf. 14 | |
|---|---|---|---|---|
| 737 | G74 | 70c multicolored | 1.50 | 1.50 |
| 738 | G75 | $5 multicolored | 6.50 | 6.50 |

World Cup Soccer Championships, Mexico — G77

Various soccer plays.

| 1986, Mar. 18 | | | | |
|---|---|---|---|---|
| 739 | G77 | 10c multicolored | .65 | .40 |
| 740 | G77 | 70c multicolored | 1.75 | 1.40 |
| 741 | G77 | $1 multicolored | 2.10 | 1.90 |
| 742 | G77 | $4 multicolored | 5.00 | 5.00 |
| | | Nos. 739-742 (4) | 9.50 | 8.70 |

**Souvenir Sheet**

| 743 | G77 | $5 multicolored | 6.00 | 6.00 |
|---|---|---|---|---|

For overprints see Nos. 772-776.

### Halley's Comet Type

Designs: 5c, Nicolaus Copernicus, Earl of Rossi's six foot reflector. 20c, Sputnik. 40c, Tycho Brahe's notes, sketch of comet of 1577. $4, Edmond Halley, comet of 1682. $5, Halley's comet. Captions on 40c and $4 are reversed.

| 1986, Mar. 26 | | | | |
|---|---|---|---|---|
| 744 | A194 | 5c multicolored | .55 | .50 |
| 745 | A194 | 20c multicolored | .90 | .50 |
| 746 | A194 | 40c multicolored | 1.10 | .75 |
| 747 | A194 | $4 multicolored | 5.25 | 5.25 |
| | | Nos. 744-747 (4) | 7.80 | 7.00 |

**Souvenir Sheet**

| 748 | A194 | $5 multicolored | 4.50 | 4.50 |
|---|---|---|---|---|

"Tycho," on 40c, and "Nicolaus" on 5c misspelled.
For overprints see Nos. 787-791. Compare No. 748 with No. 913.

### Queen Elizabeth II, 60th Birthday
#### Common Design Type

Designs: 2c, At Windsor Park, 1933. $1.50, Queen Elizabeth II. $4, In Sydney, Australia, 1970. $5, Family portrait, Coronation Day, 1937.

| 1986, Apr. 21 | | | | |
|---|---|---|---|---|
| 749 | CD339 | 2c yel & blk | .25 | .25 |
| 750 | CD339 | $1.50 pale grn & multi | .85 | .85 |
| 751 | CD339 | $4 dl lil & multi | 2.40 | 2.40 |
| | | Nos. 749-751 (3) | 3.50 | 3.50 |

**Souvenir Sheet**

| 752 | CD339 | $5 tan & blk | 3.25 | 3.25 |
|---|---|---|---|---|

### AMERIPEX '86 Type

Walt Disney characters visiting: 30c, Grand Canyon. 60c, Golden Gate Bridge. $1, Chicago Watertower. $3, The White House. $5, NY Harbor, Statue of Liberty.

| 1986, May 22 | | | Perf. 11 | |
|---|---|---|---|---|
| 753 | A195 | 30c multicolored | .80 | .50 |
| 754 | A195 | 60c multicolored | 1.20 | 1.20 |
| 755 | A195 | $1 multicolored | 2.00 | 2.00 |
| 756 | A195 | $3 multicolored | 4.00 | 4.00 |
| | | Nos. 753-756 (4) | 8.00 | 7.70 |

**Souvenir Sheet**
**Perf. 14**

| 757 | A195 | $5 multicolored | 6.00 | 6.00 |
|---|---|---|---|---|

### Royal Wedding Issue, 1986
#### Common Design Type

Designs: 60c, Prince Andrew and Sarah Ferguson. 70c, Andrew. $4, Andrew in dress uniform, helicopter. $5, Couple, diff.

| 1986, July 1 | | | Perf. 14 | |
|---|---|---|---|---|
| 758 | CD340 | 60c multicolored | .45 | .45 |
| 759 | CD340 | 70c multicolored | .55 | .55 |
| 760 | CD340 | $4 multicolored | 3.00 | 3.00 |
| | | Nos. 758-760 (3) | 4.00 | 4.00 |

**Souvenir Sheet**

| 761 | CD340 | $5 multicolored | 5.00 | 5.00 |
|---|---|---|---|---|

Mushrooms — G78

Designs: 15c, Hygrocybe firma. 50c, Xerocomus coccolobae. $2, Volvariella cubensis. $3, Lactarius putidus. $5, Leponia caeruleocapitata.

| 1986, July 15 | | | Perf. 15 | |
|---|---|---|---|---|
| 762 | G78 | 15c multicolored | 1.25 | .80 |
| 763 | G78 | 50c multicolored | 2.60 | 2.40 |
| 764 | G78 | $2 multicolored | 5.00 | 5.00 |
| 765 | G78 | $3 multicolored | 6.25 | 6.25 |
| | | Nos. 762-765 (4) | 15.10 | 14.45 |

**Souvenir Sheet**

| 766 | G78 | $5 multicolored | 13.00 | 13.00 |
|---|---|---|---|---|

Seashells — G79

Designs: 15c, Giant Atlantic pyram. 50c, Beau's murex. $1.10, West Indian fighting

conch. $4, Alphabet coral. $5, Brown-lined paper bubble.

| 1986, Aug. 1 | | | | |
|---|---|---|---|---|
| 767 | G79 | 15c multicolored | 1.25 | .60 |
| 768 | G79 | 50c multicolored | 3.00 | 1.75 |
| 769 | G79 | $1.10 multicolored | 3.25 | 3.25 |
| 770 | G79 | $4 multicolored | 5.75 | 5.75 |
| | | Nos. 767-770 (4) | 13.25 | 11.35 |

**Souvenir Sheet**

| 771 | G79 | $5 multicolored | 11.50 | 11.50 |
|---|---|---|---|---|

Nos. 739-743 Overprinted in Gold

| 1986, Sept. 15 | | | Perf. 14 | |
|---|---|---|---|---|
| 772 | G77 | 10c multicolored | .75 | .45 |
| 773 | G77 | 70c multicolored | 1.25 | 1.25 |
| 774 | G77 | $1 multicolored | 1.75 | 1.50 |
| 775 | G77 | $4 multicolored | 4.25 | 4.25 |
| | | Nos. 772-775 (4) | 8.00 | 7.45 |

**Souvenir Sheet**

| 776 | G77 | $5 multicolored | 7.50 | 7.50 |
|---|---|---|---|---|

Manicou — G80

Wildlife: 30c, Giant toad. 60c, Land tortoise. 70c, Murine opossum. 90c, Burmese mongoose. $1.10, Antillean armadillo. $2, Agouti. $3, Humpback whale.
No. 785, Mona monkey. No. 786, Iguana.

| 1986, Sept. 15 | | | Perf. 15 | |
|---|---|---|---|---|
| 777 | G80 | 10c shown | .25 | .25 |
| 778 | G80 | 30c multicolored | .50 | .50 |
| 779 | G80 | 60c multicolored | 1.00 | 1.00 |
| 780 | G80 | 70c multicolored | 1.10 | 1.10 |
| 781 | G80 | 90c multicolored | 1.25 | 1.25 |
| 782 | G80 | $1.10 multicolored | 1.60 | 1.60 |
| 783 | G80 | $2 multicolored | 2.50 | 2.50 |
| 784 | G80 | $3 multicolored | 5.75 | 5.75 |
| | | Nos. 777-784 (8) | 13.95 | 13.95 |

**Souvenir Sheets**

| 785 | G80 | $5 multicolored | 6.50 | 6.50 |
|---|---|---|---|---|
| 786 | G80 | $5 multicolored | 6.50 | 6.50 |

### Nos. 744-748 Overprinted in Silver or Black

| 1986, Oct. 15 | | | Perf. 14 | |
|---|---|---|---|---|
| 787 | A194 | 5c multi (Bk) | .90 | .75 |
| 788 | A194 | 20c multicolored | 1.10 | .65 |
| 789 | A194 | 40c multi (Bk) | 1.25 | .75 |
| 790 | A194 | $4 multicolored | 6.50 | 6.50 |
| | | Nos. 787-790 (4) | 9.75 | 8.65 |

**Souvenir Sheet**

| 791 | A194 | $5 multicolored | 8.50 | 8.50 |
|---|---|---|---|---|

### Christmas Type of 1986

25c, Chip 'n' Dale. 30c, Mickey Mouse. 50c, Piglet, Pooh, Jose Carioca. 60c, Daisy. 70c, A kiss under the mistletoe. $1.50, Huey, Dewey, and Louie. $3, Mickey Mouse, Morty. $4, Kittens on the keys.
No. 800, Mickey Mouse. No. 801, Bambi.

| 1986 Nov. 3 | | | Perf. 11 | |
|---|---|---|---|---|
| 792 | A199 | 25c multicolored | .55 | .25 |
| 793 | A199 | 30c multicolored | .55 | .30 |
| 794 | A199 | 50c multicolored | .70 | .40 |
| 795 | A199 | 60c multicolored | .80 | .50 |
| 796 | A199 | 70c multicolored | .95 | .60 |
| 797 | A199 | $1.50 multicolored | 1.75 | 1.75 |
| 798 | A199 | $3 multicolored | 2.00 | 2.00 |
| 799 | A199 | $4 multicolored | 3.50 | 3.50 |
| | | Nos. 792-799 (8) | 10.80 | 9.30 |

**Souvenir Sheets**

| 800 | A199 | 25c multicolored | 5.00 | 5.00 |
|---|---|---|---|---|
| 801 | A199 | $5 multicolored | 5.00 | 5.00 |

Nos. 793, 795-796, 799 vert.

## Automobile Centenary Type

Designs: 10c, 1984 Aston-Martin Volante. 30c, 1948 Jaguar Mk V. 60c, 1956 Nash Ambassador. 70c, 1984 Toyota Supra. 90c, 1985 Ferrari Testarossa. $1, 1955 BMW 501B. $2, 1968 Mercedes-Benz 280SL. $3, 1932 Austro-Daimler ADR8.

No. 810, 1977 Morgan +8. No. 811, Checker Taxi.

### 1986, Nov. 20 — Perf. 15

| | | | | |
|---|---|---|---|---|
| 802 | A202 | 10c multicolored | .30 | .30 |
| 803 | A202 | 30c multicolored | .55 | .55 |
| 804 | A202 | 60c multicolored | .75 | .75 |
| 805 | A202 | 70c multicolored | .75 | .75 |
| 806 | A202 | 90c multicolored | .90 | .90 |
| 807 | A202 | $1 multicolored | .90 | .90 |
| 808 | A202 | $2 multicolored | 1.25 | 1.25 |
| 809 | A202 | $3 multicolored | 1.60 | 1.60 |
| | | Nos. 802-809 (8) | 7.00 | 7.00 |

### Souvenir Sheets

| | | | | |
|---|---|---|---|---|
| 810 | A202 | $5 multicolored | 4.25 | 4.25 |
| 811 | A202 | $5 multicolored | 4.25 | 4.25 |

## Chagall Type

Paintings.: $1.10 — No. 812, The Mirror. No. 813, Dancer with a Fan. No. 814, The Acrobat. No. 815, Abraham's Sacrifice. No. 816, The Fruit Seller. No. 817, The Rooster, 1947. No. 818, The Wedding. No. 819, Horsewoman. No. 820, The Aged Lion from Fables of La Fontaine. No. 821, The Fruit Basket. No. 822, The Satyr and the Wayfarer. No. 823, Self-portrait with Seven Fingers. No. 824, Fruit and Flowers. No. 825, Lovers and Flowers. No. 826, The Wedded with an Angel. No. 827, In the Cafe, 1936. No. 828, The Equestrian. No. 829, Blue Violinist, 1947. No. 830, Zemphira costume design from Aleko scene I (dancer with red dress). No. 831, Portrait of Vava, 1955. No. 832, I and the Village, 1911. No. 833, The Accordion Player. No. 834, The Violinist, 1913. No. 835, Mother and Child, 1968. No. 836. Sunday, 1953. No. 837, Red and Black World, 1951. No. 838, Double Portrait with Wineglass, 1917. No. 839, Unknown (blonde woman in a blue dress). No. 840, Time is a River without Banks, 1930. No. 841, Homage to Apollinaire. No. 842, Unknown (rooster behind Eiffel tower). No. 843, The Blue Home, 1926. No. 844, Still-life, 1912, horiz. No. 845, Autumn Village. No. 846, Bonjour Paris. No. 847, The Jew in Pink, 1914. No. 848, Unknown (clown with violin). No. 849, War, 1943. No. 850, The Artist Angel. No. 851, Unknown (vase of flowers, woman at window).

$5 — No. 852, Birthday, 1915. No. 853, Wheatfield on a Summer Afternoon, 1942. No. 854, The Nude Above Vitebsk. No. 855, Aleko and Zemphira by Moonlight. No. 856, The Family Dinner. No. 857, Life (couple with baby, sun, celebrants). No. 858, The Flying Carriage, 1913. No. 859, The Studio. No. 860, Birth. No. 861, Rain.

### 1986-87 — Perf. 14x13½

| | | | | |
|---|---|---|---|---|
| 812-851 | A203 | Set of 40 | 55.00 | 55.00 |

### Size: 110x95mm
#### Imperf

| | | | | |
|---|---|---|---|---|
| 852-861 | A203 | Set of 10 | 42.50 | 42.50 |

Issued: Nos. 824-851, 855-861, 1987.

## America's Cup Type

25c, Defender, 1895. 45c, Caleta, 1886. 70c, Azzurra, 1981. $4, Australia II, 1983. $5, Columbia, Shamrock, 1899.

### 1987, Feb. 5 — Perf. 15

| | | | | |
|---|---|---|---|---|
| 862 | A204 | 25c multicolored | .85 | .55 |
| 863 | A204 | 45c multicolored | 1.10 | .85 |
| 864 | A204 | 70c multicolored | 1.40 | 1.40 |
| 865 | A204 | $4 multicolored | 2.75 | 2.75 |
| | | Nos. 862-865 (4) | 6.10 | 5.55 |

### Souvenir Sheet

| | | | | |
|---|---|---|---|---|
| 866 | A204 | $5 multicolored | 6.50 | 6.50 |

## Discovery of America Type

15c, Columbus. 30c, Queen Isabella. 50c, Santa Maria. 60c, Landing in New World. 90c, Lesser Antilles. $1, King Ferdinand. $2, Fort of La Navidad. $3, Galley off Hispaniola.

No. 875, Native Canoe. No. 876, Santa Maria at anchor.

### 1987, Apr. 27

| | | | | |
|---|---|---|---|---|
| 867 | A206 | 15c multicolored | .25 | .25 |
| 868 | A206 | 30c multicolored | .25 | .25 |
| 869 | A206 | 50c multicolored | .40 | .40 |
| 870 | A206 | 60c multicolored | .45 | .45 |
| 871 | A206 | 90c multicolored | .75 | .75 |
| 872 | A206 | $1 multicolored | .80 | .80 |
| 873 | A206 | $2 multicolored | 1.75 | 1.75 |
| 874 | A206 | $3 multicolored | 2.50 | 2.50 |
| a. | | Sheet of 8 | 12.00 | 12.00 |
| | | Nos. 867-874 (8) | 7.15 | 7.15 |

### Souvenir Sheets

| | | | | |
|---|---|---|---|---|
| 875 | A207 | $5 multicolored | 6.00 | 6.00 |
| 876 | A207 | $5 multicolored | 6.00 | 6.00 |

## Transportation Innovations Type

Designs: 10c, Saunders Roe SR-N1 Hovercraft, 1959. 15c, Bugatti Royale, 1931. 30c, Aleksei Leonov, 1st space walk, 1965. 50c, CSS Hunley, submarine, 1864. 60c, Rolls Royce Flying Bedstead, VTOL aircraft, 1954. 70c, Jenny Lind, locomotive, 1854. 90c, Duryea, 1893. $1.50, Steam locomotive, London subway, 1863. $2, SS Great Britain, screw-driven steamship, 1843. $3, Budweiser rocket, 1979.

### 1987, May 18 — Perf. 14

| | | | | |
|---|---|---|---|---|
| 877 | A209 | 10c multicolored | .55 | .30 |
| 878 | A209 | 15c multicolored | .60 | .40 |
| 879 | A209 | 30c multicolored | .80 | .50 |
| 880 | A209 | 50c multicolored | 1.10 | .75 |
| 881 | A209 | 60c multicolored | 1.25 | .90 |
| 882 | A209 | 70c multicolored | 1.40 | 1.25 |
| 883 | A209 | 90c multicolored | 1.50 | 1.25 |
| 884 | A209 | $1.50 multicolored | 2.25 | 2.25 |
| 885 | A209 | $2 multicolored | 2.75 | 2.75 |
| 886 | A209 | $3 multicolored | 3.00 | 3.00 |
| | | Nos. 877-886 (10) | 15.20 | 13.35 |

## Capex '87 Type

Fish.

### 1987, June 15

| | | | | |
|---|---|---|---|---|
| 887 | A208 | 6c Yellow chub | .25 | .25 |
| 888 | A208 | 30c Kingfish | .55 | .40 |
| 889 | A208 | 50c Mako shark | .75 | .65 |
| 890 | A208 | 60c Dolphinfish | .85 | .85 |
| 891 | A208 | 90c Bonito | 1.10 | 1.10 |
| 892 | A208 | $1.10 Cobia | 1.40 | 1.40 |
| 893 | A208 | $3 Great tarpon | 3.25 | 3.25 |
| 894 | A208 | $4 Swordfish | 3.50 | 3.50 |
| | | Nos. 887-894 (8) | 11.65 | 11.40 |

### Souvenir Sheets

| | | | | |
|---|---|---|---|---|
| 895 | A208 | $5 Jewfish | 5.00 | 5.00 |
| 896 | A208 | $5 Amberjack | 5.00 | 5.00 |

## Statue of Liberty Type

10c, Washing statue's face. 15c, Commemorative medals. 25c, Band facing right. 30c, Band facing forward. 45c, Liberty's face. 50c, Washing statue's hair, horiz. 60c, Commemorative statuettes, horiz. 70c, Boats in NY Harbor, horiz. $1, Re-opening. $1.10, Blimps, Liberty & Manhattan Islands. $2, Warship. $3, Commemorative flags.

### 1987, Aug. 5

| | | | | |
|---|---|---|---|---|
| 897 | A210 | 10c multicolored | .25 | .25 |
| 898 | A210 | 15c multicolored | .30 | .30 |
| 899 | A210 | 25c multicolored | .45 | .45 |
| 900 | A210 | 30c multicolored | .50 | .50 |
| 901 | A210 | 45c multicolored | .55 | .55 |
| 902 | A210 | 50c multicolored | .60 | .60 |
| 903 | A210 | 60c multicolored | .70 | .70 |
| 904 | A210 | 70c multicolored | .80 | .80 |
| 905 | A210 | $1 multicolored | .95 | .95 |
| 906 | A210 | $1.10 multicolored | 1.00 | 1.00 |
| 907 | A210 | $2 multicolored | 1.90 | 1.90 |
| 908 | A210 | $3 multicolored | 2.10 | 2.10 |
| | | Nos. 897-908 (12) | 10.10 | 10.10 |

## Inventors Type

Designs: 60c, Isaac Newton, Newton Medal. $1, Louis Daguerre, inventor of Daguerreotype. $2, Antoine Lavoisier, French chemist, apparatus. $3, Rudolf Diesel, German engineer, Diesel engine. $5, Halley's comet.

### 1987, Sept. 9

| | | | | |
|---|---|---|---|---|
| 909 | A211 | 60c multicolored | 1.00 | .80 |
| 910 | A211 | $1 multicolored | 1.25 | 1.25 |
| 911 | A211 | $2 multicolored | 2.60 | 2.60 |
| 912 | A211 | $3 multicolored | 6.00 | 6.00 |
| | | Nos. 909-912 (4) | 10.85 | 10.65 |

### Souvenir Sheet

| | | | | |
|---|---|---|---|---|
| 913 | A211 | $5 multicolored | 8.00 | 8.00 |

No. 913 inscribed "Great Scientific Discoveries" in margin.

No. 912 incorrectly inscribed "James Watt, Steam Engine." See Grenada No. 1538.

## US Constitution Bicentennial Type

10c, Constitutional Convention, Philadelphia. 50c, Georgia state flag. 60c, Capitol, vert. $4, Thomas Jefferson, vert. $5, Alexander Hamilton, vert.

### 1987, Nov. 1

| | | | | |
|---|---|---|---|---|
| 914 | A214 | 10c multicolored | .25 | .25 |
| 915 | A214 | 50c multicolored | .85 | .75 |
| 916 | A214 | 60c multicolored | .85 | .80 |
| 917 | A214 | $4 multicolored | 4.50 | 4.50 |
| | | Nos. 914-917 (4) | 6.45 | 6.30 |

### Souvenir Sheet

| | | | | |
|---|---|---|---|---|
| 918 | A214 | $5 multicolored | 4.00 | 4.00 |

## Hafnia '87 Type

Walt Disney characters in adaptations of Hans Christian Andersen Fairy Tales: 25c, The Swineherd. 30c, What the Good Man Does is Always Right. 50c, Little Tuk. 60c, The World's Fairest Rose. $1.50, The Naughty Boy. $3, What the Moon Saw. $4, Thumbelina. No. 927, Hans Clodhopper. No. 928, Elder Tree Mother.

### 1987, Nov. 16

| | | | | |
|---|---|---|---|---|
| 919 | A215 | 25c multicolored | .55 | .30 |
| 920 | A215 | 30c multicolored | .60 | .40 |
| 921 | A215 | 50c multicolored | .80 | .80 |
| 922 | A215 | 60c multicolored | .80 | .80 |
| 923 | A215 | 70c multicolored | .85 | .85 |
| 924 | A215 | $1.50 multicolored | 2.25 | 2.25 |
| 925 | A215 | $3 multicolored | 3.00 | 3.00 |
| 926 | A215 | $3 multicolored | 3.50 | 3.50 |
| | | Nos. 919-926 (8) | 12.35 | 11.90 |

### Souvenir Sheets

| | | | | |
|---|---|---|---|---|
| 927 | A215 | $5 multicolored | 6.25 | 6.25 |
| 928 | A215 | $5 multicolored | 6.25 | 6.25 |

Christmas — G81

Paintings by El Greco: 10c, Virgin and Child with Saints Martin and Agnes. 50c, Detail from Virgin and Child with Saints Martin and Agnes. 60c, The Annunciation. $4, Holy Family with St. Anne. $5, Adoration of the Shepherds.

### 1987, Dec. 15

| | | | | |
|---|---|---|---|---|
| 929 | G81 | 10c multicolored | .45 | .25 |
| 930 | G81 | 50c multicolored | 1.40 | .95 |
| 931 | G81 | 60c multicolored | 1.40 | 1.10 |
| 932 | G81 | $4 multicolored | 5.50 | 5.50 |
| | | Nos. 929-932 (4) | 8.75 | 7.80 |

### Souvenir Sheet

| | | | | |
|---|---|---|---|---|
| 933 | G81 | $5 multicolored | 9.25 | 9.25 |

## Wedding Anniv. Type

20c, Elizabeth, Anne. 30c, Wedding portrait. $2, Elizabeth, Charles, Anne. $3, Elizabeth wearing tiara.

$5, Elizabeth in wedding gown.

### 1988, Feb. 15

| | | | | |
|---|---|---|---|---|
| 934 | A218 | 20c multicolored | .25 | .25 |
| 935 | A218 | 30c multicolored | .25 | .25 |
| 936 | A218 | $2 multicolored | 1.40 | 1.40 |
| 937 | A218 | $3 multicolored | 2.00 | 2.00 |
| | | Nos. 934-937 (4) | 3.90 | 3.90 |

### Souvenir Sheet

| | | | | |
|---|---|---|---|---|
| 938 | A218 | $5 multicolored | 4.00 | 4.00 |

## 1988 Summer Olympics Type

Walt Disney characters in modern and ancient events: 1c, Rhythmic gymnastics. 2c, Pankration. 3c, Synchronized swimming. 4c, Hoplite race. 5c, Baseball. 10c, Horse race. $6, Windsurfing. $7, Chariot race.

No. 947, Tennis. No. 948, Pentathlon.

### 1988, Apr. 13 — Perf. 13½x14, 14x13½

| | | | | |
|---|---|---|---|---|
| 939 | A219 | 1c multicolored | .25 | .25 |
| 940 | A219 | 2c multicolored | .25 | .25 |
| 941 | A219 | 3c multicolored | .25 | .25 |
| 942 | A219 | 4c multicolored | .25 | .25 |
| 943 | A219 | 5c multicolored | .25 | .25 |
| 944 | A219 | 10c multicolored | .25 | .25 |
| 945 | A219 | $6 multicolored | 5.00 | 5.00 |
| 946 | A219 | $7 multicolored | 5.75 | 5.75 |
| | | Nos. 939-946 (8) | 12.25 | 12.25 |

### Souvenir Sheet

| | | | | |
|---|---|---|---|---|
| 947 | A219 | $5 multicolored | 5.00 | 5.00 |
| 948 | A219 | $5 multicolored | 5.00 | 5.00 |

## Boy Scout Type

50c, Semaphore, vert. 70c, Canoeing, vert. $1, Cook-out. $3, Campfire. $5, Pitching tent.

### 1988, May 3 — Perf. 14

| | | | | |
|---|---|---|---|---|
| 949 | A220 | 50c multicolored | .50 | .50 |
| 950 | A220 | 70c multicolored | .60 | .60 |
| 951 | A220 | $1 multicolored | .90 | .90 |
| 952 | A220 | $3 multicolored | 2.50 | 2.50 |
| | | Nos. 949-952 (4) | 4.50 | 4.50 |

### Souvenir Sheet

| | | | | |
|---|---|---|---|---|
| 953 | A220 | $5 multicolored | 4.50 | 4.50 |

## Bird Type

20c, Yellow-crowned night heron. 25c, Brown pelican. 45c, Audubon's shearwater. 60c, Red-footed booby. 70c, Bridled tern. 90c, Red-billed tropicbird. $3, Blue-winged teal. $4, Sora.

No. 962, Little blue heron. No. 963, Purple-throated carib.

### 1988, May 31

| | | | | |
|---|---|---|---|---|
| 954 | A222 | 20c multicolored | .30 | .30 |
| 955 | A222 | 25c multicolored | .30 | .30 |
| 956 | A222 | 45c multicolored | .45 | .40 |
| 957 | A222 | 60c multicolored | .65 | .45 |
| 958 | A222 | 70c multicolored | .65 | .60 |
| 959 | A222 | 90c multicolored | .90 | .90 |
| 960 | A222 | $3 multicolored | 2.50 | 2.50 |
| 961 | A222 | $4 multicolored | 3.50 | 3.50 |
| | | Nos. 954-961 (8) | 9.25 | 8.95 |

### Souvenir Sheets

| | | | | |
|---|---|---|---|---|
| 962 | A222 | $5 multicolored | 5.00 | 5.00 |
| 963 | A222 | $5 multicolored | 5.00 | 5.00 |

## Titian Type

Paintings by Titian: 15c, Man with Blue Eyes, 1545. 30c, The Three Ages of Man, 1512. 60c, Don Diego Mendoza, 1545. 75c, Emperor Charles V Seated, 1548. $1, A Young Man in a Fur, 1515. $2, Tobias and the Angel, 1543. $3, Pietro Bembo, 1540. $4, Pier Luigi Farnese, 1546. No. 972, Sacred and Profane Love. No. 973, Venus and Adonis.

### 1988, June 15 — Perf. 13½x14

| | | | | |
|---|---|---|---|---|
| 964 | A224 | 15c multicolored | .25 | .25 |
| 965 | A224 | 30c multicolored | .25 | .25 |
| 966 | A224 | 60c multicolored | .40 | .40 |
| 967 | A224 | 75c multicolored | .55 | .55 |
| 968 | A224 | $1 multicolored | .75 | .75 |
| 969 | A224 | $2 multicolored | 1.40 | 1.40 |
| 970 | A224 | $3 multicolored | 2.00 | 2.00 |
| 971 | A224 | $4 multicolored | 2.75 | 2.75 |
| | | Nos. 964-971 (8) | 8.35 | 8.35 |

### Souvenir Sheet

| | | | | |
|---|---|---|---|---|
| 972 | A224 | $5 multicolored | 5.00 | 5.00 |
| 973 | A224 | $5 multicolored | 5.00 | 5.00 |

## Airship Type

Historic flights: 10c, Hindenburg over Rio de Janeiro, 1937. 20c, Hindenburg over NYC, 1937. 30c, US Navy airships, WWII convoy to Europe, 1944. 40c, Hindenburg docking at Lakehurst, NJ, 1937, vert. 60c, Joint flight, Hindenburg and Graf Zeppelin, 1936, vert. 70c, DC-3, Hindenburg, Los Angeles at Lakehurst, 1936. $1, Graf Zeppelin II over England, 1939, vert. $2, Deutschland, 1st passenger flight, 1912. $3, Graf Zeppelin over Dome of the Rock, Jerusalem, 1931. $4, Hindenburg Olympic flight, 1936. No. 984, Graf Zeppelin over Vatican City, 1933, vert. No. 985, Graf Zeppelin Polar flight, 1931.

### 1988, July 1 — Perf. 14

| | | | | |
|---|---|---|---|---|
| 974 | A225 | 10c multicolored | .25 | .25 |
| 975 | A225 | 20c multicolored | .25 | .25 |
| 976 | A225 | 30c multicolored | .25 | .25 |
| 977 | A225 | 40c multicolored | .35 | .35 |
| 978 | A225 | 60c multicolored | .80 | .60 |
| 979 | A225 | 70c multicolored | 1.10 | .80 |
| 980 | A225 | $1 multicolored | 1.10 | .90 |
| 981 | A225 | $2 multicolored | 1.75 | 1.75 |
| 982 | A225 | $3 multicolored | 2.50 | 2.50 |
| 983 | A225 | $4 multicolored | 3.25 | 3.25 |
| | | Nos. 974-983 (10) | 11.60 | 10.90 |

### Souvenir Sheets

| | | | | |
|---|---|---|---|---|
| 984 | A225 | $5 multicolored | 6.00 | 6.00 |
| 985 | A225 | $5 multicolored | 6.00 | 6.00 |

## Fairy Tales Type
### Miniature Sheets

*Bambi*: No. 986a, Newborn Bambi, mother and forest animals. b, Bambi, Flower and Thumper. c, Bambi and opossum family hanging from tree. d, Bambi, his mother, and Faline, a female fawn. e, Foraging in a snow storm. f, Meeting his father, the Great Stag. g, Competing for Faline's attention. h, The Great Stag leading animals to safety during forest fire. i, Bambi, grown, becomes the Great Stag.

*The Fox and the Hound*: No. 987a, Big Mama, consoling the orphaned baby fox, Tod. b, Widow Tweed feeding Tod. c, Tod playing with Copper, the hound. d, Copper leashed. e, Copper and Chief. f, Chief barking at Tod, Copper shocked. g, Porcupine. h, Vixey, a female fox. i, Bear attacking Copper.

*101 Dalmatians*: No. 988a, Pongo, Perdita and their masters. b, Pongo and Perdita, courting. c, Three puppies. d, Cruella de Ville and henchmen. e, Captain the Horse, Colonel the Sheepdog and Tibbs the Cat. f, Dalmatians following Tibbs to freedom. g, Cruella racing car in pursuit. h, Dalmatians disguised in soot. i, Nanny dusting off the soot.

*Dumbo*: No. 989a, Stork delivering Dumbo. b, Elephant making fun of Dumbo's large ears. c, Dumbo, Mrs. Jumbo performing. d, Timothy the Mouse. e, Timothy and Dumbo. f, Crows pushing Dumbo off a cliff. g, Dumbo flying away from burning building. h, Dumbo flying with the crows. i, Dumbo and Mrs. Jumbo on train.

*Lady and the Tramp*: No. 990a, Darling holding Lady. b, Lady meets the Tramp. c, Lady looking in bassinet. d, Siamese cats, Lady. e, Lady, Tramp, crocodiles. f, Tramp kisses Lady. g, Lady in dog catcher's carriage. h, Lady and Tramp attacking rat. i, Trusty and Jock overturning dog catcher's carriage where Tramp is imprisoned.

*The Aristocats*: No. 991a, Edgar driving Madame Mornfamille's carriage. b, Dutchess and kittens. c, Edgar feeding the cats cream spiked with sleeping pills. d, Edgar transporting cats on motorcycle. e, Walter O'Malley discovers the abandoned cats. f, Three geese. g,

Scat Cat and friends holding a jam session. h, Edgar attacks O'Malley with a pitch fork. i, Frau-Frau kicking Edgar.

No. 992, Faline and newborn twin fawns. No. 993, Tod and Vixey. No. 994, Pongo, Perdita and puppies. No. 995, Dumbo flying with Timothy the Mouse. No. 996, Lady and Tramp's puppies. No. 997, Walter O'Malley, Dutchess and kittens.

**1988, July 25** — **Perf. 14x13½**

| | | | | |
|---|---|---|---|---|
| 986 | | Sheet of 9 | 4.00 | 4.00 |
| a.-i. | A212 | 30c any single | .40 | .40 |
| 987 | | Sheet of 9 | 4.00 | 4.00 |
| a.-i. | A212 | 30c any single | .40 | .40 |
| 988 | | Sheet of 9 | 4.00 | 4.00 |
| a.-i. | A212 | 30c any single | .40 | .40 |
| 989 | | Sheet of 9 | 4.00 | 4.00 |
| a.-i. | A212 | 30c any single | .40 | .40 |
| 990 | | Sheet of 9 | 4.00 | 4.00 |
| a.-i. | A212 | 30c any single | .40 | .40 |
| 991 | | Sheet of 9 | 4.00 | 4.00 |
| a.-i. | A212 | 30c any single | .40 | .40 |
| | | Nos. 986-991 (6) | 24.00 | 24.00 |

**Souvenir Sheets**

| | | | | |
|---|---|---|---|---|
| 992-997 | A212 | $5 each | 6.25 | 6.25 |

### SYDPEX '88 Type

Walt Disney characters: 1c, Conducting at Sydney Opera House. 2c, Climbing Ayers Rock. 3c, Working at a sheep station. 4c, Visiting Lone Pine Koala Sanctuary. 5c, Playing Australian football. 10c, Racing camels. No. 1004, Lawn bowling. $6, America's Cup trophy and Australia II. No. 1006, The Great Barrier Reef. No. 1007, Beach party.

**1988, Aug. 1** — **Perf. 14x13½**

| | | | | |
|---|---|---|---|---|
| 998 | A226 | 1c multicolored | .25 | .25 |
| 999 | A226 | 2c multicolored | .25 | .25 |
| 1000 | A226 | 3c multicolored | .25 | .25 |
| 1001 | A226 | 4c multicolored | .25 | .25 |
| 1002 | A226 | 5c multicolored | .25 | .25 |
| 1003 | A226 | 10c multicolored | .25 | .25 |
| 1004 | A226 | $5 multicolored | 5.50 | 5.50 |
| 1005 | A226 | $6 multicolored | 6.50 | 6.50 |
| | | Nos. 998-1005 (8) | 13.50 | 13.50 |

**Souvenir Sheets**

| | | | | |
|---|---|---|---|---|
| 1006 | A226 | $5 multicolored | 5.00 | 5.00 |
| 1007 | A226 | $5 multicolored | 5.00 | 5.00 |

### Flowering Trees Type

10c, Potato tree, vert. 20c, Wild cotton. 30c, Shower of gold, vert. 60c, Napoleon's button, vert. 90c, Geiger tree. $1, Fern tree. $2, French cashew. $4, Amherstia, vert.

No. 1016, African tulip tree, vert. No. 1017, Swamp immortelle.

**1988, Sept. 30** — **Perf. 14**

| | | | | |
|---|---|---|---|---|
| 1008 | A228 | 10c multicolored | .25 | .25 |
| 1009 | A228 | 20c multicolored | .25 | .25 |
| 1010 | A228 | 30c multicolored | .25 | .25 |
| 1011 | A228 | 60c multicolored | .50 | .45 |
| 1012 | A228 | 90c multicolored | .75 | .65 |
| 1013 | A228 | $1 multicolored | .85 | .85 |
| 1014 | A228 | $2 multicolored | 1.75 | 1.75 |
| 1015 | A228 | $4 multicolored | 3.00 | 3.00 |
| | | Nos. 1008-1015 (8) | 7.60 | 7.45 |

**Souvenir Sheets**

| | | | | |
|---|---|---|---|---|
| 1016 | A228 | $5 multicolored | 3.75 | 3.75 |
| 1017 | A228 | $5 multicolored | 3.75 | 3.75 |

### Car Type
#### Miniature Sheets

Designs: No. 1018a, 1925 Doble Series E, US. b, 1926 Alvis 12/50, United Kingdom. c, 1927 Sunbeam 3-liter, UK. d, 1928 Franklin Airman, US. e, 1929 Delage D8S, France. f, 1897 Mors, France. g, 1904 Peerless Green Dragon, US. h, 1909 Pope-Hartford, US. i, 1920 Daniels Submarine Speedster, US. j, 1922 McFarlan 9.3 liter, US.

No. 1019a, 1949 Frazer Nash Lemans Replica, UK. b, 1953 Pegaso Z102, Spain. No. 1019c, 1953 Siata Spyder V-8, Italy. d, 1953 Kurtis-Offenhauser, US. No. 1019e, 1954 Kaiser-Darrin, US. f, 1930 Tracta, France. g, 1932 Maybach Zeppelin, Germany. h, 1934 Railton Light Sports, UK. i, 1936 Hotchkiss, France. j, 1939 Mercedes-Benz W163, Germany.

No. 1020a, 1982 Aston Martin Vantage V8, UK. b, 1982 Porsche 956, Germany. No. 1020c, 1983 Lotus Esprit Turbo, UK. d, 1984 McLaren MP4/2, UK. e, 1985 Mercedes-Benz 190E 2-3-16, Germany. f, 1963 Ferrari 250 GT Lusso, Italy. g, 1964 Porsche 904, Germany. h, 1967 Volvo P1800, Sweden. i, 1970 McLaren-Chevrolet M8D, US. j, 1981 Jaguar XJ6, UK.

**1988, Oct. 7** — **Perf. 13x13½**

| | | | | |
|---|---|---|---|---|
| 1018 | | Sheet of 10 | 15.00 | 15.00 |
| a.-j. | A223 | $2 any single | 1.50 | 1.50 |
| 1019 | | Sheet of 10 | 15.00 | 15.00 |
| a.-j. | A223 | $2 any single | 1.50 | 1.50 |
| 1020 | | Sheet of 10 | 15.00 | 15.00 |
| a.-j. | A223 | $2 any single | 1.50 | 1.50 |

### Christmas and Mickey Mouse 60th Anniv. Type
#### Miniature Sheet

"Mickey's Christmas Parade": No. 1021a, Dumbo. b, Goofy. c, Minnie Mouse. d, Morty, Ferdy and Clarabelle Cow. e, Huey, Dewey and Louie. f, Donald Duck. g, Wooden soldiers marching. h, Mickey Mouse leading parade. No. 1022, Capt. Hook on float. No. 1023, Mickey and Donald on float.

**1988, Dec. 1** — **Perf. 13½x14**

| | | | | |
|---|---|---|---|---|
| 1021 | | Sheet of 8 | 6.00 | 6.00 |
| a.-h. | A229 | $1 any single | .75 | .75 |

**Souvenir Sheets**
**Perf. 14x13**

| | | | | |
|---|---|---|---|---|
| 1022 | A229 | $7 multicolored | 6.50 | 6.50 |
| 1023 | A229 | $7 multicolored | 6.50 | 6.50 |

### Japanese Painting Type

"The Fifty-three Stations on the Tokaido" by Hiroshige (1979-1858): 15c, Crossing the Oi at Shimada by Ferry. 20c, Daimyo and Entourage at Arai. 45c, Cargo Portage through Goyu. 75c, Snowfall at Fujigawa. $1, Horses for the Emperor at Chiryu. $2, Rainfall at Tsuchiyama. $3, At Inn of Ishibe. $4, On the Shore of Lake Biwa at Otsu. No. 1032, Pilgrimage to Atsuta Shrine at Miya. No. 1033, Fishing Village of Yokkaichi on the Mie.

**1989, May 15** — **Perf. 14x13½**

| | | | | |
|---|---|---|---|---|
| 1024 | A233 | 15c multicolored | .30 | .30 |
| 1025 | A233 | 20c multicolored | .35 | .35 |
| 1026 | A233 | 45c multicolored | .60 | .60 |
| 1027 | A233 | 75c multicolored | 1.00 | 1.00 |
| 1028 | A233 | $1 multicolored | 1.00 | 1.00 |
| 1029 | A233 | $2 multicolored | 1.75 | 1.75 |
| 1030 | A233 | $3 multicolored | 2.75 | 2.75 |
| 1031 | A233 | $4 multicolored | 3.75 | 3.75 |
| | | Nos. 1024-1031 (8) | 11.50 | 11.50 |

**Souvenir Sheets**

| | | | | |
|---|---|---|---|---|
| 1032 | A233 | $5 multicolored | 4.50 | 4.50 |
| 1033 | A233 | $5 multicolored | 4.50 | 4.50 |

### 1988 Olympic Medalists Type

Designs: 15c, Henry Maske, East Germany, boxing (165 lbs.). 50c, Andreas Schroeder, East Germany, freestyle wrestling (286 lbs.). 60c, East German team, women's gymnastics. 75c, Greg Louganis, US, men's springboard and platform diving. $1, Mitsuru Sato, Japan, freestyle wrestling (115 lbs.). $2, West German team, 4x200m freestyle relay. $3, Dieter Baumann, West Germany, 5000m race. $4, Jackie Joyner-Kersee, US, heptathlon. No. 1042, Joachim Kunz, East Germany, weight lifting (149 lbs.). No. 1043, West German equestrian team, 3-day event.

**1989, Apr. 13** — **Perf. 14**

| | | | | |
|---|---|---|---|---|
| 1034 | A232 | 15c multicolored | .30 | .25 |
| 1035 | A232 | 50c multicolored | .40 | .35 |
| 1036 | A232 | 60c multicolored | .50 | .40 |
| 1037 | A232 | 75c multicolored | .70 | .55 |
| 1038 | A232 | $1 multicolored | .85 | .75 |
| 1039 | A232 | $2 multicolored | 1.50 | 1.50 |
| 1040 | A232 | $3 multicolored | 2.25 | 2.25 |
| 1041 | A232 | $4 multicolored | 3.00 | 3.00 |
| | | Nos. 1034-1041 (8) | 9.50 | 9.05 |

**Souvenir Sheets**

| | | | | |
|---|---|---|---|---|
| 1042 | A232 | $6 multicolored | 4.75 | 4.75 |
| 1043 | A232 | $6 multicolored | 4.75 | 4.75 |

World Cup Soccer Championships, Italy — G82

Designs: 15c, World Cup, vert. 45c, Kaiser Franz, West Germany, vert. 75c, Like 20c, flag of Italy, 1982 champions. $1, Pele, Brazil, vert. $2, Like 20c, flag of West Germany, 1974 champions. $3, Like 20c, flag of Brazil, 1970 champions. $4, Jules Rimet Cup, vert. No. 1052, Pele, Jules Rimet Cup. No. 1053, Goalie.

**1989, June 12**

| | | | | |
|---|---|---|---|---|
| 1044 | G82 | 15c multicolored | .25 | .25 |
| 1045 | G82 | 20c multicolored | .25 | .25 |
| 1046 | G82 | 45c multicolored | .30 | .30 |
| 1047 | G82 | 75c multicolored | .55 | .55 |
| 1048 | G82 | $1 multicolored | 1.40 | 1.40 |
| 1049 | G82 | $2 multicolored | 2.60 | 2.60 |
| 1050 | G82 | $3 multicolored | 2.10 | 2.10 |
| 1051 | G82 | $4 multicolored | 2.60 | 2.60 |
| | | Nos. 1044-1051 (8) | 10.05 | 10.05 |

**Souvenir Sheets**

| | | | | |
|---|---|---|---|---|
| 1052 | G82 | $6 multicolored | 4.50 | 4.50 |
| 1053 | G82 | $6 multicolored | 4.50 | 4.50 |

### Car Type of 1988
#### Miniature Sheets

North American locomotives: No. 1054a, Morris & Essex, Dover, 1841. No. 1054b, B&O, Memmon No. 57, 1848. No. 1054c, Camden & Amboy, John Stevens, 1849. No. 1054d, Lawrence Machine Shop, Lawrence, 1853. No. 1054e, South Carolina, James S. Corry, 1859. No. 1054f, Mine Hill & Schuylkill Haven, Flexible Beam No. 3, 1860. No. 1054g, DL&W, Montrose, 1861. No. 1054h, Central Pacific, Pequop No. 68, 1868. No. 1054i, Boston & Providence, Daniel Nason, 1863. No. 1054j, Morris & Essex, Joe Scranton, 1870.

No. 1055a, Central Railroad of New Jersey, No. 124, 1871. No. 1055b, Baldwin Steam Motor for Street Railways, 1876. No. 1055c, Lackawanna & Bloomsburg, Luzerne, 1878. No. 1055d, Central Mexicano, No. 150, 1892. No. 1055e, Denver, South Park & Pacific, Breckenridge No. 15, 1879. No. 1055f, Miles Planting & Manufacturing Co., "Daisy" Plantation locomotive, 1894. No. 1055g, Central of Georgia, Baldwin 854 No. 1136, 1895. No. 1055h, Savannah, Florida & Western, No. 111, 1900. No. 1055i, Douglas, Gilmore, & Co. No. 3, 1902. No. 1055j, Lehigh Valley Coal Co., Compressed Air locomotive No. 900, 1903.

No. 1056a, Morgan's Louisiana & Texas, McKeen Motorcar, 1908. No. 1056b, Clear Lake Lumber Co., Type B Climax, 1910. No. 1056c, Blue Jay Lumber Co., Heisler No. 10, 1912. No. 1056d, Stewartstown, Gasoline Engine No. 6, 1920's. No. 1056e, Bangor & Aroostook, Class G No. 186, 1921. No. 1056f, Hammond Lumber Co., No. 6, 1923. No. 1056g, Central Railroad of New Jersey, No. 1000, 1925. No. 1056h, Atchison, Topeka & Santa Fe, Super Chief No. 1-1A, 1935. No. 1056i, Norfolk & Western, Class Y-6, 1948. No. 1056i, Boston & Maine, Budd Railcar, 1949.

**1989, June 28** — **Perf. 13x13½**

| | | | | |
|---|---|---|---|---|
| 1054 | | Sheet of 10 | 19.00 | 19.00 |
| a.-j. | A223 | $2 any single | 1.60 | 1.60 |
| 1055 | | Sheet of 10 | 19.00 | 19.00 |
| a.-j. | A223 | $2 any single | 1.60 | 1.60 |
| 1056 | | Sheet of 10 | 19.00 | 19.00 |
| a.-j. | A223 | $2 any single | 1.60 | 1.60 |

PHILEXFRANCE '89 — G83

Walt Disney characters in Paris: 1c, Military school. 2c, Conciergerie. 3c, Hotel de Ville, vert. 4c, Genie of the Bastille, vert. 5c, The Opera. 10c, Gardens of Luxembourg. $5, Arche de la Defense, vert. No. 1064, $6, Place Vendome, vert.

No. 1065, $6, Riding moped. No. 1066, $6, Hot air ballooning.

**1989, July 7** — **Perf. 14x13½, 13½x14**

| | | | | |
|---|---|---|---|---|
| 1057 | G83 | 1c multicolored | .25 | .25 |
| 1058 | G83 | 2c multicolored | .25 | .25 |
| 1059 | G83 | 3c multicolored | .25 | .25 |
| 1060 | G83 | 4c multicolored | .25 | .25 |
| 1061 | G83 | 5c multicolored | .25 | .25 |
| 1062 | G83 | 10c multicolored | .25 | .25 |
| 1063 | G83 | $5 multicolored | 7.00 | 7.00 |
| 1064 | G83 | $6 multicolored | 7.00 | 7.00 |
| | | Nos. 1057-1064 (8) | 15.50 | 15.50 |

**Souvenir Sheets**

| | | | | |
|---|---|---|---|---|
| 1065 | G83 | $6 multicolored | 7.00 | 7.00 |
| 1066 | G83 | $6 multicolored | 7.00 | 7.00 |

### Moon Landing Anniv. Type

Apollo 11 mission, 1969: 25c, Liftoff, vert. 50c, Splashdown. 60c, Spacecraft approaching moon, vert. 75c, Buzz Aldrin conducting experiment on lunar surface. $1, Leaving Earth orbit. $2, Transport of launch vehicle to pad, vert. $3, Lunar module liftoff. $4, Eagle lands on moon, vert. No. 1075, Footprint on moon. No. 1076, Armstrong stepping onto the moon, vert.

**1989, July 20** — **Perf. 14**

| | | | | |
|---|---|---|---|---|
| 1067 | A237 | 25c multicolored | .30 | .30 |
| 1068 | A237 | 50c multicolored | .50 | .50 |
| 1069 | A237 | 60c multicolored | .60 | .60 |
| 1070 | A237 | 75c multicolored | .75 | .75 |
| 1071 | A237 | $1 multicolored | .90 | .90 |
| 1072 | A237 | $2 multicolored | 2.00 | 2.00 |
| 1073 | A237 | $3 multicolored | 2.50 | 2.50 |
| 1074 | A237 | $4 multicolored | 3.50 | 3.50 |
| | | Nos. 1067-1074 (8) | 11.05 | 11.05 |

**Souvenir Sheets**

| | | | | |
|---|---|---|---|---|
| 1075 | A237 | $5 multicolored | 4.50 | 4.50 |
| 1076 | A237 | $5 multicolored | 4.50 | 4.50 |

### Mushroom Type

6c, Collybia aurea. 10c, Podaxis pistillaris. 20c, Hygrocybe firma. 30c, Agaricus rufoauranticaus. 75c, Leptonia howellii. $2, Marasmiellus purpureus. $3, Marasmius trinitatis. $4, Hygrocybe martinicensis.

No. 1086, Lentinus crinitus. No. 1087, Agaricus purpurellus.

**1989, Aug. 17**

| | | | | |
|---|---|---|---|---|
| 1078 | A238 | 6c multicolored | .40 | .25 |
| 1079 | A238 | 10c multicolored | .40 | .25 |
| 1080 | A238 | 20c multicolored | .65 | .50 |
| 1081 | A238 | 30c multicolored | .75 | .65 |
| 1082 | A238 | 75c multicolored | 1.60 | 1.60 |
| 1083 | A238 | $2 multicolored | 3.00 | 3.00 |
| 1084 | A238 | $3 multicolored | 3.50 | 3.50 |
| 1085 | A238 | $4 multicolored | 4.00 | 4.00 |
| | | Nos. 1078-1085 (8) | 14.30 | 13.75 |

**Souvenir Sheets**

| | | | | |
|---|---|---|---|---|
| 1086 | A238 | $6 multicolored | 8.00 | 8.00 |
| 1087 | A238 | $6 multicolored | 8.00 | 8.00 |

### Butterflies Type

25c, Androgeus swallowtail. 35c, Cloudless sulpher. 45c, Cracker. 50c, Painted lady. 75c, Great southern white. 90c, Little sulpher. $2, Migrant sulpher. $3, Mimic.

No. 1096, Giant hairstreak. No. 1097, Red anartia.

**1989, Oct. 2** — **Perf. 14**

| | | | | |
|---|---|---|---|---|
| 1088 | A239 | 25c multicolored | .85 | .85 |
| 1089 | A239 | 35c multicolored | 1.00 | 1.00 |
| 1090 | A239 | 45c multicolored | 1.10 | 1.10 |
| 1091 | A239 | 50c multicolored | 1.10 | 1.10 |
| 1092 | A239 | 75c multicolored | 1.75 | 1.75 |
| 1093 | A239 | 90c multicolored | 1.90 | 1.90 |
| 1094 | A239 | $2 multicolored | 4.25 | 4.25 |
| 1095 | A239 | $3 multicolored | 5.00 | 5.00 |
| | | Nos. 1088-1095 (8) | 16.95 | 16.95 |

**Souvenir Sheets**

| | | | | |
|---|---|---|---|---|
| 1096 | A239 | $6 multicolored | 8.50 | 8.50 |
| 1097 | A239 | $6 multicolored | 8.50 | 8.50 |

### World Stamp Expo Type

Scenes from Walt Disney animated films and quotes from Poor Richard's Almanack by Benjamin Franklin: 1c, "Beware of little expenses, a small leak will sink a great ship." 2c, "Trust thyself and another shall not betray thee." 3c, "A spoonful of honey will catch more flies than a gallon of vinegar." 4c, "No gain without pain." 5c, "A true friend is the best possession." 6c, "Haste makes waste." 8c, "A quiet conscience sleeps in thunder, but rest and guilt live far asunder." 10c, "The muses love the morning." $5, "An egg today is better than a hen tomorrow." No. 1107, "He that riseth late, must trot all day." No. 1108, "If you'd be belov'd, make yourself amiable." No. 1109, "In Christmas feasting pray take care; let not your table be a snare; but with the poor God's bounty share. Adieu my friends! Till the next year," vert.

**1989, Nov.** — **Litho.** — **Perf. 14x13½**

| | | | | |
|---|---|---|---|---|
| 1098 | A242 | 1c multicolored | .25 | .25 |
| 1099 | A242 | 2c multicolored | .25 | .25 |
| 1100 | A242 | 3c multicolored | .25 | .25 |
| 1101 | A242 | 4c multicolored | .25 | .25 |
| 1102 | A242 | 6c multicolored | .25 | .25 |
| 1103 | A242 | 6c multicolored | .25 | .25 |
| 1104 | A242 | 8c multicolored | .25 | .25 |
| 1105 | A242 | 10c multicolored | .25 | .25 |
| 1106 | A242 | $5 multicolored | 4.50 | 4.50 |
| 1107 | A242 | $6 multicolored | 5.50 | 5.50 |
| | | Nos. 1098-1107 (10) | 12.00 | 12.00 |

**Souvenir Sheet**

| | | | | |
|---|---|---|---|---|
| 1108 | A242 | $6 multicolored | 7.50 | 7.50 |
| 1109 | A242 | $6 multicolored | 7.50 | 7.50 |

World Stamp Expo '89, Washington, D.C.

Shakespearean Actors and Theater Masks — G84

15c, Ethel Barrymore (1879-1959). $1.10, Richard Burton (1925-1984). $2, John Barrymore (1882-1942). $3, Paul Robeson (1898-1976). $6, Bando Tamasaburo & Nakamura Kanzaburo.

**1989, Oct. 9** — **Litho.** — **Perf. 14**

| | | | | |
|---|---|---|---|---|
| 1110 | G84 | 15c multicolored | .40 | .30 |
| 1111 | G84 | $1.10 multicolored | 1.75 | 1.50 |
| 1112 | G84 | $2 multicolored | 2.50 | 2.50 |
| 1113 | G84 | $3 multicolored | 2.75 | 2.75 |
| | | Nos. 1110-1113 (4) | 7.40 | 7.05 |

**Souvenir Sheet**

| | | | | |
|---|---|---|---|---|
| 1114 | G84 | $6 multicolored | 6.50 | 6.50 |

## 20th Century Musicians — G85

### 1989, Oct. 9
| | | | | |
|---|---|---|---|---|
| 1115 | G85 | 10c Buddy Holly | .40 | .30 |
| 1116 | G85 | 25c Jimi Hendrix | .65 | .50 |
| 1117 | G85 | 75c Mighty Sparrow | .95 | .95 |
| 1118 | G85 | $4 Katsutoji Kineya | 4.25 | 4.25 |

*Nos. 1115-1118 (4)*   6.25   6.00

### Souvenir Sheet
| | | | | |
|---|---|---|---|---|
| 1119 | G85 | $6 Lotte Lenya, Kurt Weill | 6.25 | 6.25 |

Jimi is spelled incorrectly as "Jimmy."

### Discovery of America Type
#### 1989, Oct. 16
| | | | | |
|---|---|---|---|---|
| 1120 | A241 | 15c Canoeing | .40 | .30 |
| 1121 | A241 | 75c Cooking | 1.75 | 1.75 |
| 1122 | A241 | 90c Using stone tools | 1.75 | 1.75 |
| 1123 | A241 | $3 Eating | 4.50 | 4.50 |

*Nos. 1120-1123 (4)*   7.90   7.80

### Souvenir Sheet
| | | | | |
|---|---|---|---|---|
| 1124 | A241 | $6 Building fire | 6.25 | 6.25 |

### Christmas Type
Religious paintings by Rubens: 10c, The Annunciation. 15c, The Flight of the Holy Family into Egypt. 25c, The Presentation in the Temple. 45c, The Holy Family Under the Apple Tree. $4, Madonna and Child with Saints. No. 1132, The Holy Family. No. 1132, Adoration of the Magi. No. 1133, Adoration of the Magi, diff.

#### 1990, Jan. 4     *Perf. 14*
| | | | | |
|---|---|---|---|---|
| 1125 | A243 | 10c multicolored | .40 | .25 |
| 1126 | A243 | 15c multicolored | .45 | .25 |
| 1127 | A243 | 25c multicolored | .65 | .25 |
| 1128 | A243 | 45c multicolored | .85 | .40 |
| 1129 | A243 | $2 multicolored | 2.40 | 2.40 |
| 1130 | A243 | $4 multicolored | 3.50 | 3.50 |
| 1131 | A243 | $5 multicolored | 3.50 | 3.50 |

*Nos. 1125-1131 (7)*   11.75   10.55

### Souvenir Sheets
| | | | | |
|---|---|---|---|---|
| 1132 | A243 | $5 multicolored | 7.00 | 7.00 |
| 1133 | A243 | $5 multicolored | 7.00 | 7.00 |

## America Issue (Insects) — G86

35c, Hercules beetle. 40c, Click beetle. 50c, Harlequin beetle. 60c, Gold rim butterfly. $1, Red skimmer dragonfly. $2, Buprestid beetle. $3, Mimic butterfly. $4, Scarab beetle.
No. 1142, Canna skipper butterfly. No. 1143, Monarch butterfly.

### 1990, Mar. 16     *Perf. 14*
| | | | | |
|---|---|---|---|---|
| 1134 | G86 | 35c multicolored | .45 | .45 |
| 1135 | G86 | 40c multicolored | .45 | .45 |
| 1136 | G86 | 50c multicolored | .60 | .60 |
| 1137 | G86 | 60c multicolored | 1.10 | 1.10 |
| 1138 | G86 | $1 multicolored | 1.25 | 1.25 |
| 1139 | G86 | $2 multicolored | 2.40 | 2.40 |
| 1140 | G86 | $3 multicolored | 3.50 | 3.50 |
| 1141 | G86 | $4 multicolored | 3.50 | 3.50 |

*Nos. 1134-1141 (8)*   13.25   13.25

### Souvenir Sheets
| | | | | |
|---|---|---|---|---|
| 1142 | G86 | $6 multicolored | 6.50 | 6.50 |
| 1143 | G86 | $6 multicolored | 6.50 | 6.50 |

## Orchids — G87

15c, Brassocattleya thalie. 20c, Odontocidium tigersun. 50c, Odontioda hambuhren. 75c, Paphiopedium delrosi. $1, Vuylstekeara yokara. $2, Paphiopedium geelong. $3, Wilsonara tigerwood. $4, Cymbidium ormoulu.
No. 1152, Odontonia sappho. No. 1153, Cymbidium vieux rose.

### 1990, Mar. 6     *Litho.*     *Perf. 14*
| | | | | |
|---|---|---|---|---|
| 1144 | G87 | 15c multicolored | .35 | .35 |
| 1145 | G87 | 20c multicolored | .35 | .35 |
| 1146 | G87 | 50c multicolored | .55 | .55 |
| 1147 | G87 | 75c multicolored | .65 | .65 |
| 1148 | G87 | $1 multicolored | 1.10 | 1.10 |
| 1149 | G87 | $2 multicolored | 2.10 | 2.10 |
| 1150 | G87 | $3 multicolored | 2.75 | 2.75 |
| 1151 | G87 | $4 multicolored | 3.50 | 3.50 |

*Nos. 1144-1151 (8)*   11.35   11.35

### Souvenir Sheets
| | | | | |
|---|---|---|---|---|
| 1152 | G87 | $6 multicolored | 7.00 | 7.00 |
| 1153 | G87 | $6 multicolored | 7.00 | 7.00 |

EXPO '90 Intl. Garden and Greenery Exposition, Osaka, Japan.

### Wildlife Type
5c, West Indies giant rice rat. 25c, Agouti. 30c, Humpback whale. 40c, Pilot whale. $1, Spotted dolphin. $2, Mongoose. $3, Prehensile-tailed porcupine. $4, West Indies manatee.
No. 1162, Caribbean monk seal. No. 1163, Egyptian mongoose.

#### 1990, Apr. 3
| | | | | |
|---|---|---|---|---|
| 1154 | A247 | 5c multicolored | .30 | .30 |
| 1155 | A247 | 25c multicolored | .45 | .45 |
| 1156 | A247 | 30c multicolored | 1.00 | 1.00 |
| 1157 | A247 | 40c multicolored | 1.00 | 1.00 |
| 1158 | A247 | $1 multicolored | 1.25 | 1.25 |
| 1159 | A247 | $2 multicolored | 2.40 | 2.40 |
| 1160 | A247 | $3 multicolored | 3.25 | 3.25 |
| 1161 | A247 | $4 multicolored | 3.75 | 3.75 |

*Nos. 1154-1161 (8)*   13.40   13.40

### Souvenir Sheets
| | | | | |
|---|---|---|---|---|
| 1162 | A247 | $6 multicolored | 7.00 | 7.00 |
| 1163 | A247 | $6 multicolored | 7.00 | 7.00 |

### World War II Type
Designs: 6c, First British troops arrive in France, Sept. 6, 1939. 10c, British launch "Operation Crusader", Nov. 18, 1941. 20c, Rommel begins retreat from El Alamein, Nov. 4, 1942. 45c, US forces land on Aleutian Islands, May 11, 1943. 50c, US Marines land on Tarawa, Nov. 20, 1943. 60c, US 5th Army enters Rome, June 4, 1944. 75c, US troops reach River Seine, Aug. 19, 1944. $1, Battle of the Bulge, Dec. 16, 1944. $5, Allies launch final phase of Italian Campaign, Apr. 9, 1945. No. 1173, Atom bomb dropped on Hiroshima, Aug. 6, 1945. No. 1174, St. Paul's Catherdral during London blitz, Battle of Britain, 1940.

#### 1990, Apr. 30
| | | | | |
|---|---|---|---|---|
| 1164 | A248 | 6c multicolored | .40 | .40 |
| 1165 | A248 | 10c multicolored | .40 | .40 |
| 1166 | A248 | 20c multicolored | .65 | .65 |
| 1167 | A248 | 45c multicolored | .70 | .70 |
| 1168 | A248 | 50c multicolored | .80 | .80 |
| 1169 | A248 | 60c multicolored | .85 | .85 |
| 1170 | A248 | 75c multicolored | .95 | .95 |
| 1171 | A248 | $1 multicolored | 1.25 | 1.25 |
| 1172 | A248 | $5 multicolored | 4.00 | 4.00 |
| 1173 | A248 | $6 multicolored | 5.00 | 5.00 |

*Nos. 1164-1173 (10)*   15.00   15.00

### Souvenir Sheet
| | | | | |
|---|---|---|---|---|
| 1174 | A248 | $6 multicolored | 7.50 | 7.50 |

### Disney Type
Disney characters portraying Shakespearian characters: 15c, Daisy Duck at Ann Hathaway's Cottage, Shottery. 30c, Minnie Mouse and a young Shakespeare walking in Stratford birthplace, vert. 50c, Minnie as Mary Arden, Shakespeare's mother in Wilmcote, vert. 60c, Mickey in front of New Place, Stratford. $1, Mickey walking in Great Garden of New Place. $2, Mickey at Guild Chapel, Scholars Lane, vert. $4, Mickey at the Royal Shakespeare Theater, Stratford, vert. $5, Ludwig von Drake instructing Shakespeare. No. 1183, Mickey at Edge Hill, Stratford, vert. No. 1184, Mickey and Minnie rowing past Holy Trinity Church, Stratford-Upon-Avon.

#### 1990, May     *Perf. 14x13½*
| | | | | |
|---|---|---|---|---|
| 1175 | A250 | 15c multicolored | .50 | .25 |
| 1176 | A250 | 30c multicolored | .65 | .45 |
| 1177 | A250 | 50c multicolored | .95 | .85 |
| 1178 | A250 | 60c multicolored | 1.10 | 1.10 |
| 1179 | A250 | $1 multicolored | 1.50 | 1.50 |
| 1180 | A250 | $2 multicolored | 2.75 | 2.75 |
| 1181 | A250 | $4 multicolored | 4.00 | 4.00 |
| 1182 | A250 | $4 multicolored | 4.00 | 4.00 |

*Nos. 1175-1182 (8)*   15.45   14.90

### Souvenir Sheets
#### *Perf. 14*
| | | | | |
|---|---|---|---|---|
| 1183 | A250 | $6 multicolored | 7.50 | 7.50 |
| 1184 | A250 | $6 multicolored | 7.50 | 7.50 |

### Penny Black Type
Souvenir Sheet

#### 1990, May 3     *Litho.*     *Perf. 14*
| | | | | |
|---|---|---|---|---|
| 1185 | A249 | $6 Globe with South America | 8.00 | 8.00 |

Stamp World London '90.

### Queen Mother, 90th Birthday Type
#### 1990, July 5
| | | | | |
|---|---|---|---|---|
| 1186 | A251 | $2 Pink hat | 1.40 | 1.40 |
| 1187 | A251 | $2 With Charles | 1.40 | 1.40 |
| 1188 | A251 | $2 Blue outfit | 1.40 | 1.40 |

*Nos. 1186-1188 (3)*   4.20   4.20

### Souvenir Sheet
| | | | | |
|---|---|---|---|---|
| 1189 | A251 | $6 like #1187 | 4.25 | 4.25 |

### Bird Type
25c, Yellow-bellied seedeater. 45c, Carib grackle. 50c, Black-whiskered vireo. 75c, Bananaquit. $1, Collared swift. $2, Yellow-bellied elaenia. $3, Blue-hooded euphonia. $5, Eared dove.
No. 1198, Mangrove cuckoo. No. 1199, Scaly-breasted thrasher.

#### 1990, Sept. 10     *Litho.*     *Perf. 14*
| | | | | |
|---|---|---|---|---|
| 1190 | A255 | 25c multicolored | .45 | .45 |
| 1191 | A255 | 45c multicolored | .65 | .65 |
| 1192 | A255 | 50c multicolored | .75 | .75 |
| 1193 | A255 | 75c multicolored | .85 | .85 |
| 1194 | A255 | $1 multicolored | 1.25 | 1.25 |
| 1195 | A255 | $2 multicolored | 1.90 | 1.90 |
| 1196 | A255 | $3 multicolored | 2.50 | 2.50 |
| 1197 | A255 | $5 multicolored | 4.50 | 4.50 |

*Nos. 1190-1197 (8)*   12.85   12.85

### Souvenir Sheets
| | | | | |
|---|---|---|---|---|
| 1198 | A255 | $6 multicolored | 5.75 | 5.75 |
| 1199 | A255 | $6 multicolored | 5.75 | 5.75 |

### Crustaceans Type of 1990
10c, Slipper lobster. 25c, Green reef crab. 65c, Caribbean lobsterette. 75c, Blind deep sea lobster. $1, Flattened crab. $2, Ridged slipper lobster. $3, Land crab. $4, Mountain crab.
No. 1208, Caribbean king crab. No. 1209, Purse crab.

#### 1990, Sept. 17
| | | | | |
|---|---|---|---|---|
| 1200 | A256 | 10c multicolored | .25 | .25 |
| 1201 | A256 | 25c multicolored | .35 | .35 |
| 1202 | A256 | 65c multicolored | .70 | .70 |
| 1203 | A256 | 75c multicolored | .80 | .80 |
| 1204 | A256 | $1 multicolored | 1.10 | 1.10 |
| 1205 | A256 | $2 multicolored | 2.00 | 2.00 |
| 1206 | A256 | $3 multicolored | 2.25 | 2.25 |
| 1207 | A256 | $4 multicolored | 2.75 | 2.75 |

*Nos. 1200-1207 (8)*   10.20   10.20

### Souvenir Sheets
| | | | | |
|---|---|---|---|---|
| 1208 | A256 | $6 multicolored | 5.00 | 5.00 |
| 1209 | A256 | $6 multicolored | 5.00 | 5.00 |

G88

Players from participating countries.

#### 1990, Sept. 24
| | | | | |
|---|---|---|---|---|
| 1210 | G88 | 15c England | .25 | .25 |
| 1211 | G88 | 45c Argentina | .50 | .50 |
| 1212 | G88 | $2 Sweden | 1.75 | 1.75 |
| 1213 | G88 | $4 South Korea | 3.00 | 3.00 |

*Nos. 1210-1213 (4)*   5.50   5.50

### Souvenir Sheets
| | | | | |
|---|---|---|---|---|
| 1214 | G88 | $6 Yugoslavia | 4.50 | 4.50 |
| 1215 | G88 | $6 United States | 4.50 | 4.50 |

World Cup Soccer Championships, Italy.

G89

10c, Boxing. 25c, Olympic flame. 50c, Soccer. 75c, Discus. $1, Pole vault. $2, Equestrian 3-day event. $4, Women's basketball. $5, Men's gymnastics.
No. 1224, Sailboarding. No. 1225, Decathlon.

#### 1990, Nov. 11     *Litho.*     *Perf. 14*
| | | | | |
|---|---|---|---|---|
| 1216 | G89 | 10c multicolored | .25 | .25 |
| 1217 | G89 | 25c multicolored | .25 | .25 |
| 1218 | G89 | 50c multicolored | .50 | .50 |
| 1219 | G89 | 75c multicolored | .65 | .65 |
| 1220 | G89 | $1 multicolored | .90 | .90 |
| 1221 | G89 | $2 multicolored | 2.00 | 2.00 |
| 1222 | G89 | $4 multicolored | 4.00 | 4.00 |
| 1223 | G89 | $5 multicolored | 3.50 | 3.50 |

*Nos. 1216-1223 (8)*   12.05   12.05

### Souvenir Sheets
| | | | | |
|---|---|---|---|---|
| 1224 | G89 | $6 multicolored | 6.00 | 6.00 |
| 1225 | G89 | $6 multicolored | 6.00 | 6.00 |

1992 Summer Olympics, Barcelona.

### Rubens Type
Entire paintings or different details from: 5c, 25c, Adam and Eve. 15c, Esther before Ahasuerus. 50c, Expulsion from Eden. $1, Cain Slaying Abel, vert. $2, Lot's Flight. $4, Samson and Delilah. $5, Abraham and Melchizedek. No. 1234, The Meeting of David and Abigail. No. 1235, Daniel in the Lions Den.

#### 1991, Jan. 31     *Litho.*     *Perf. 14*
| | | | | |
|---|---|---|---|---|
| 1226 | A259 | 5c multicolored | .25 | .25 |
| 1227 | A259 | 15c multicolored | .40 | .25 |
| 1228 | A259 | 25c multicolored | .50 | .25 |
| 1229 | A259 | 50c multicolored | .85 | .65 |
| 1230 | A259 | $1 multicolored | 1.50 | 1.25 |
| 1231 | A259 | $2 multicolored | 2.00 | 2.00 |
| 1232 | A259 | $4 multicolored | 3.00 | 3.00 |
| 1233 | A259 | $5 multicolored | 3.50 | 3.50 |

*Nos. 1226-1233 (8)*   12.00   11.15

### Souvenir Sheets
| | | | | |
|---|---|---|---|---|
| 1234 | A259 | $6 multicolored | 6.00 | 6.00 |
| 1235 | A259 | $6 multicolored | 6.00 | 6.00 |

### Fish Type of 1990
15c, Barred hamlet. 35c, Squirrelfish. 45c, Red-spotted hawkfish. 75c, Bigeye. $1, Spiny puffer. $2, Smallmouth grunt. $3, Harlequin bass. $4, Creole fish.
No. 1244, Fairy basslet. No. 1245, Copper sweeper.

#### 1991, Feb. 5
| | | | | |
|---|---|---|---|---|
| 1236 | A254 | 15c multicolored | .55 | .30 |
| 1237 | A254 | 35c multicolored | .90 | .60 |
| 1238 | A254 | 45c multicolored | 1.00 | .70 |
| 1239 | A254 | 75c multicolored | 1.60 | 1.25 |
| 1240 | A254 | $1 multicolored | 1.90 | 1.50 |
| 1241 | A254 | $2 multicolored | 2.75 | 2.75 |
| 1242 | A254 | $3 multicolored | 3.50 | 3.50 |
| 1243 | A254 | $4 multicolored | 3.75 | 3.75 |

*Nos. 1236-1243 (8)*   15.95   14.35

### Souvenir Sheets
| | | | | |
|---|---|---|---|---|
| 1244 | A254 | $6 multicolored | 6.50 | 6.50 |
| 1245 | A254 | $6 multicolored | 6.50 | 6.50 |

## Hummel Figurines — G90

10c, Angel, star. 15c, Angel, guitar, Christ Child. 25c, Shepherd. 50c, Angel, lantern, horn. $1, Angel, children, Christ Child. $2, Angel, candle, Christ Child. $4, Angel with baskets. $5, Angels singing.

### 1991, Mar. 1     *Litho.*     *Perf. 14*
| | | | | |
|---|---|---|---|---|
| 1246 | G90 | 10c multicolored | .25 | .25 |
| 1247 | G90 | 15c multicolored | .35 | .25 |
| 1248 | G90 | 25c multicolored | .50 | .25 |
| 1249 | G90 | 50c multicolored | 1.00 | .55 |
| 1250 | G90 | $1 multicolored | 1.25 | 1.00 |
| 1251 | G90 | $2 multicolored | 2.25 | 2.25 |
| 1252 | G90 | $4 multicolored | 3.25 | 3.25 |
| 1253 | G90 | $5 multicolored | 3.50 | 3.50 |

*Nos. 1246-1253 (8)*   12.35   11.30

### Souvenir Sheets
| | | | | |
|---|---|---|---|---|
| 1254 | | Sheet of 4 | 5.00 | 5.00 |
| a. | G90 | 5c like No. 1247 | .25 | .25 |
| b. | G90 | 40c like No. 1249 | .30 | .30 |
| c. | G90 | 60c like No. 1250 | .50 | .50 |
| d. | G90 | $3 like No. 1253 | 2.75 | 2.75 |
| 1255 | | Sheet of 4 | 7.00 | 7.00 |
| a. | G90 | 20c like No. 1246 | .25 | .25 |
| b. | G90 | 30c like No. 1248 | .25 | .25 |
| c. | G90 | 75c like No. 1251 | .70 | .70 |
| d. | G90 | $6 like No. 1252 | 4.50 | 4.50 |

Christmas 1990.

## Orchids — G91

Designs: 5c, Brassia maculata. 10c, Oncidium lanceanum. 15c, Broughtonia sanguinea. 25c, Diacrium bicornutum. 35c, Cattleya labiata. 45c, Epidendrum fragrans. 50c, Oncidium papilio. 75c, Neocogniauxia monophylla. $1, Epidendrum polybulbon. $2, Spiranthes speciosa. $4, Epidendrum ciliare.

$5, Phais tankervilliae. $10, Brassia caudata. $20, Brassavola cordata.

## 1991-92 Litho. Perf. 14

| | | | | |
|---|---|---|---|---|
| 1256 | G91 | 5c multicolored | .70 | .70 |
| 1257 | G91 | 10c multicolored | .70 | .70 |
| 1258 | G91 | 15c multicolored | .75 | .30 |
| 1259 | G91 | 25c multicolored | .90 | .30 |
| 1260 | G91 | 35c multicolored | .90 | .30 |
| 1261 | G91 | 45c multicolored | 1.25 | .45 |
| 1262 | G91 | 50c multicolored | 1.25 | .50 |
| 1263 | G91 | 75c multicolored | 1.50 | .80 |
| 1264 | G91 | $1 multicolored | 2.00 | 1.25 |
| 1265 | G91 | $2 multicolored | 3.25 | 3.25 |
| 1266 | G91 | $4 multicolored | 5.25 | 5.25 |
| 1267 | G91 | $5 multicolored | 5.50 | 5.50 |
| 1268 | G91 | $10 multicolored | 10.50 | 10.50 |
| 1269 | G91 | $20 multicolored | 21.00 | 21.00 |
| | | Nos. 1256-1269 (14) | 55.45 | 50.80 |

Issued: $20, 6/92; others, 4/1/91.

### Butterfly Type

Designs: 5c, Crimson-patched longwing. 10c, Morpho helena. 15c, Morpho sulkowskyi. 20c, Dynastor napoleon. 25c, Pieridae callinira. 30c, Anartia amathea. 35c, Heliconiidae dido. 45c, Papilionidae columbus. 50c, Nymphalidae praeneste. 60c, Panacea prola. 75c, Julia. $1, Papilionidae orthosilaus. $2, Pyrrhopyge cometes. $3, Papilionidae paeon. $4, Morpho cypris. $5, Choringa. No. 1286, Caligo idomenides. No. 1287, Monarch. No. 1287A, Nymphalidae amydon. No. 1287B, Papilio childrenae.

## 1991, Apr. 8 Litho. Perf. 14

| | | | | |
|---|---|---|---|---|
| 1270 | A261 | 5c multicolored | .60 | .45 |
| 1271 | A261 | 10c multicolored | .60 | .45 |
| 1272 | A261 | 15c multicolored | .85 | .50 |
| 1273 | A261 | 20c multicolored | .95 | .55 |
| 1274 | A261 | 25c multicolored | .95 | .60 |
| 1275 | A261 | 30c multicolored | 1.10 | .70 |
| 1276 | A261 | 35c multicolored | 1.10 | .70 |
| 1277 | A261 | 45c multicolored | 1.25 | .95 |
| 1278 | A261 | 50c multicolored | 1.40 | 1.00 |
| 1279 | A261 | 60c multicolored | 1.60 | 1.10 |
| 1280 | A261 | 75c multicolored | 1.60 | 1.25 |
| 1281 | A261 | $1 multicolored | 2.00 | 1.60 |
| 1282 | A261 | $2 multicolored | 2.75 | 2.75 |
| 1283 | A261 | $3 multicolored | 3.50 | 3.50 |
| 1284 | A261 | $4 multicolored | 4.00 | 4.00 |
| 1285 | A261 | $5 multicolored | 5.00 | 5.00 |
| | | Nos. 1270-1285 (16) | 29.25 | 25.10 |

### Souvenir Sheets

| | | | | |
|---|---|---|---|---|
| 1286 | A261 | $6 multicolored | 6.50 | 6.50 |
| 1287 | A261 | $6 multicolored | 6.50 | 6.50 |
| 1287A | A261 | $6 multicolored | 6.50 | 6.50 |
| 1287B | A261 | $6 multicolored | 6.50 | 6.50 |

Save Our Planet G100

Walt Disney characters and ecology themes: 10c, Daisy and Donald, alternate forms of transportation. 15c, Goofy saving water. 25c, Donald, Daisy camping simply. 45c, Donald protecting birds. $1, Donald holding ascending balloons. $2, Minnie, Daisy using natural coolers. $4, Mickey, nephews cleaning beaches. $5, Scrooge McDuck using pedal power. No. 1296, Little Hiawatha and Iron Eyes Cody viewing destroyed forest. No. 1297, Donald, recycling. No. 1298, Minnie, Mickey planting trees.

## 1991, Apr. 22 Litho. Perf. 14

| | | | | |
|---|---|---|---|---|
| 1288 | G100 | 10c multicolored | .65 | .25 |
| 1289 | G100 | 15c multicolored | .75 | .25 |
| 1290 | G100 | 25c multicolored | 1.00 | .40 |
| 1291 | G100 | 45c multicolored | 1.40 | .60 |
| 1292 | G100 | $1 multicolored | 2.25 | 1.40 |
| 1293 | G100 | $2 multicolored | 3.25 | 3.00 |
| 1294 | G100 | $4 multicolored | 4.00 | 4.00 |
| 1295 | G100 | $5 multicolored | 4.00 | 4.00 |
| | | Nos. 1288-1295 (8) | 17.30 | 13.90 |

### Souvenir Sheets

| | | | | |
|---|---|---|---|---|
| 1296 | G100 | $6 multicolored | 6.50 | 6.50 |
| 1297 | G100 | $6 multicolored | 6.50 | 6.50 |
| 1298 | G100 | $6 multicolored | 6.50 | 6.50 |

### Voyages of Discovery Type

Discovery of America, 500th anniv. (in 1992).: 15c, Ferdinand Magellan, 1519-1521. 20c, Sir Francis Drake, 1577-1580. 50c, Capt. James Cook, 1768-1771. 60c, Douglas World Cruiser, 1924. $1, Sputnik, 1957. $2, Yuri Gagarin, 1961. $4, John Glenn, 1962. $5, Space Shuttle, 1981. No. 1307, Columbus' fleet. No. 1308, The Pinta, vert.

## 1991, Apr. 29 Litho. Perf. 14

| | | | | |
|---|---|---|---|---|
| 1299 | A262 | 15c multicolored | .40 | .30 |
| 1300 | A262 | 20c multicolored | .30 | .30 |
| 1301 | A262 | 50c multicolored | .60 | .60 |
| 1302 | A262 | 60c multicolored | .70 | .70 |

---

| | | | | |
|---|---|---|---|---|
| 1303 | A262 | $1 multicolored | 1.10 | 1.10 |
| 1304 | A262 | $2 multicolored | 2.25 | 2.25 |
| 1305 | A262 | $4 multicolored | 4.25 | 4.25 |
| 1306 | A262 | $5 multicolored | 5.25 | 5.25 |
| | | Nos. 1299-1306 (8) | 14.85 | 14.75 |

### Souvenir Sheets

| | | | | |
|---|---|---|---|---|
| 1307 | A262 | $6 multicolored | 6.00 | 6.00 |
| 1308 | A262 | $6 multicolored | 6.00 | 6.00 |

### Disney Phila Nippon '91 Type

Walt Disney characters demonstrating arts, crafts and industries of Japan: 15c, Minnie, silkworms. 30c, Mickey, Minnie, Morty and Ferdie photographing the Torii. 50c, Donald, Mickey, origami. 60c, Mickey, Minnie diving for pearls. $1, Minnie modeling kimono. $2, Mickey making masks. $4, Donald, Mickey making paper. $5, Minnie, Pluto, pottery. No. 317, Mickey making prints, vert. No. 1318, Mickey arranging flowers, vert. No. 1319, Mickey, tea ceremony, vert. No. 1320, Mickey carving ivory and wood into netsukes, vert.

## 1991, May 6

| | | | | |
|---|---|---|---|---|
| 1309 | A263 | 15c multi | .50 | .25 |
| 1310 | A263 | 30c multi | .85 | .35 |
| 1311 | A263 | 50c multi | 1.00 | .55 |
| 1312 | A263 | 60c multi | 1.10 | .60 |
| 1313 | A263 | $1 multi | 2.00 | 1.00 |
| 1314 | A263 | $2 multi | 2.75 | 2.50 |
| 1315 | A263 | $3 multi | 3.75 | 3.75 |
| 1316 | A263 | $5 multi | 4.50 | 4.50 |
| | | Nos. 1309-1316 (8) | 16.45 | 13.50 |

### Souvenir Sheets

| | | | | |
|---|---|---|---|---|
| 1317 | A263 | $6 multi | 5.00 | 5.00 |
| 1318 | A263 | $6 multi | 5.00 | 5.00 |
| 1319 | A263 | $6 multi | 5.00 | 5.00 |
| 1320 | A263 | $6 multi | 5.00 | 5.00 |

### Mushrooms Type

5c, Pyrrhoglossum pyrrhum. 45c, Agaricus purpurellus. 50c, Amanita craseoderma. 90c, Hygrocybe acutoconica. $1, Limacella guttata. $2, Lactarius hygrophoroides. $4, Boletellus cubensis. $5, Psilocybe caerulescens. No. 1329, Marasmius haemato-cephalus. No. 1330, Lepiota spiculata.

## 1991, June 1 Litho. Perf. 14

| | | | | |
|---|---|---|---|---|
| 1321 | A265 | 5c multicolored | .40 | .25 |
| 1322 | A265 | 45c multicolored | 1.00 | .55 |
| 1323 | A265 | 50c multicolored | 1.00 | .60 |
| 1324 | A265 | 90c multicolored | 1.75 | 1.25 |
| 1325 | A265 | $1 multicolored | 1.75 | 1.25 |
| 1326 | A265 | $2 multicolored | 2.50 | 2.50 |
| 1327 | A265 | $4 multicolored | 4.00 | 4.00 |
| 1328 | A265 | $5 multicolored | 4.00 | 4.00 |
| | | Nos. 1321-1328 (8) | 16.40 | 14.40 |

### Souvenir Sheets

| | | | | |
|---|---|---|---|---|
| 1329 | A265 | $6 multicolored | 7.50 | 7.50 |
| 1330 | A265 | $6 multicolored | 7.50 | 7.50 |

### Royal Family Birthday, Anniversary
#### Common Design Type

No. 1339, Elizabeth, Philip. No. 1340, Diana, Charles, with sons.

## 1991, July 5 Litho. Perf. 14

| | | | | |
|---|---|---|---|---|
| 1331 | CD347 | 5c multi | .50 | .30 |
| 1332 | CD347 | 20c multi | .30 | .30 |
| 1333 | CD347 | 25c multi | .30 | .25 |
| 1334 | CD347 | 60c multi | 1.00 | .75 |
| 1335 | CD347 | $1 multi | 1.00 | 1.00 |
| 1336 | CD347 | $2 multi | 1.75 | 1.75 |
| 1337 | CD347 | $3 multi | 3.00 | 3.00 |
| 1338 | CD347 | $5 multi | 4.50 | 4.50 |
| | | Nos. 1331-1338 (8) | 12.35 | 11.85 |

### Souvenir Sheet

| | | | | |
|---|---|---|---|---|
| 1339 | CD347 | $5 multi | 5.75 | 5.75 |
| 1340 | CD347 | $5 multi | 5.75 | 5.75 |

5c, 60c, $1, Nos. 1338, 1340, Charles and Diana, 10th wedding anniversary. Others, Queen Elizabeth II, 65th birthday.

### Van Gogh Painting Type

Designs: 5c, Two Thistles, vert. 10c, The Baby Marcelle Roulin, vert. 15c, Still Life: Basket with Six Oranges. 25c, Orchard in Blossom, vert. 45c, Portrait of Armand Roulin, vert. 50c, Wood Gatherers in the Snow (detail). 60c, Almond Tree in Blossom, vert. $1, Portrait of an Old Man, vert. $2, The Seine Bridge at Asnieres. $3, Vase with Lilacs, Daisies & Anemones, vert. $4, Self-portrait, vert. $5, Portrait of Patience Escalier, vert. No. 1353, Les Alyscamps, vert. No. 1354, Quay with Men Unloading Sand Barges. No. 1355, Sunset: Wheat Fields Near Arles.

### Perf. 13½x14, 14x13½

## 1991, Nov. 18 Litho.

| | | | | |
|---|---|---|---|---|
| 1341 | A264 | 5c multicolored | .40 | .25 |
| 1342 | A264 | 10c multicolored | .40 | .25 |
| 1343 | A264 | 15c multicolored | .40 | .25 |
| 1344 | A264 | 25c multicolored | .40 | .25 |
| 1345 | A264 | 45c multicolored | .50 | .40 |
| 1346 | A264 | 50c multicolored | .65 | .50 |
| 1347 | A264 | 60c multicolored | .70 | .60 |
| 1348 | A264 | $1 multicolored | 1.25 | 1.00 |
| 1349 | A264 | $2 multicolored | 2.25 | 2.25 |

---

| | | | | |
|---|---|---|---|---|
| 1350 | A264 | $3 multicolored | 3.00 | 3.00 |
| 1351 | A264 | $4 multicolored | 4.25 | 4.25 |
| 1352 | A264 | $5 multicolored | 4.75 | 4.75 |
| | | Nos. 1341-1352 (12) | 18.95 | 17.75 |

### Size: 102x127mm, 127x102mm
#### Imperf

| | | | | |
|---|---|---|---|---|
| 1353 | A264 | $6 multicolored | 5.00 | 5.00 |
| 1354 | A264 | $6 multicolored | 5.00 | 5.00 |
| 1355 | A264 | $6 multicolored | 5.00 | 5.00 |

### Marine Life Type
#### Miniature Sheet

Marine life of the deeper reef: No. 1356a, Sargassum triggerfish. b, Tobaccofish. c, Longsnout butterflyfish. d, Cherubfish. e, Black jack head. f, Black jack tail, masked goby. g, Spotfin hogfish. h, Fairy basslet. i, Orangeback bass. j, Candy basslet. k, Blackcap basslet. l, Longspine squirrelfish. m, Jackknife fish. n, Bigeye. o, Short Bigeye. $6, Caribbean flashlight fish.

## 1991, Dec. 5 Litho. Perf. 14

| | | | | |
|---|---|---|---|---|
| 1356 | A270 | 50c Sheet of 15, | | |
| | | #a.-o. | 20.00 | 20.00 |

### Souvenir Sheet

| | | | | |
|---|---|---|---|---|
| 1357 | A270 | $6 multicolored | 14.00 | 14.00 |

### Christmas Art Type

Details, entire paintings or engravings by Martin Schongauer: 10c, Angel of the Annunciation. 35c, Madonna of the Rose Hedge. 50c, Madonna of the Rose Hedge, diff. 75c, Nativity. $1, Adoration of the Shepherds. $2, Nativity, diff. $4, Nativity, diff. $5, Symbol of St. Matthew. No. 1366, Nativity, diff. No. 1367, Adoration of the Shepherds.

## 1991, Dec. 9 Perf. 12

| | | | | |
|---|---|---|---|---|
| 1358 | A271 | 10c multicolored | .45 | .25 |
| 1359 | A271 | 35c multicolored | .80 | .25 |
| 1360 | A271 | 50c multicolored | 1.10 | .45 |
| 1361 | 4E271 | 75c multicolored | 1.40 | .75 |
| 1362 | A271 | $1 multicolored | 1.50 | 1.00 |
| 1363 | A271 | $2 multicolored | 2.25 | 2.25 |
| 1364 | A271 | $4 multicolored | 2.75 | 2.75 |
| 1365 | A271 | $5 multicolored | 2.75 | 2.75 |
| | | Nos. 1358-1365 (8) | 13.00 | 10.70 |

### Souvenir Sheets
#### Perf. 14½

| | | | | |
|---|---|---|---|---|
| 1366 | A271 | $6 multicolored | 6.25 | 6.25 |
| 1367 | A271 | $6 multicolored | 6.25 | 6.25 |

### Queen Elizabeth II's Accession to the Throne, 40th Anniv.
#### Common Design Type

## 1992, Feb. 6 Litho. Perf. 14

| | | | | |
|---|---|---|---|---|
| 1368 | CD348 | 60c multicolored | .90 | .35 |
| 1369 | CD348 | 75c multicolored | 1.00 | .40 |
| 1370 | CD348 | $2 multicolored | 2.10 | 1.60 |
| 1371 | CD348 | $4 multicolored | 3.00 | 3.00 |
| | | Nos. 1368-1371 (4) | 7.00 | 5.35 |

### Souvenir Sheets

| | | | | |
|---|---|---|---|---|
| 1372 | CD348 | $6 Queen, rural scene | 5.00 | 5.00 |
| 1373 | CD348 | $6 Queen, harbor | 5.00 | 5.00 |

### Railways of the World Type

Steam locomotives: No. 1379a, Medoc Class, Switzerland, 1857. b, Sterling, Great Britain, 1870. c, No. 90, France, 1877. d, Standard, US, 1880. e, Vittorio Emanuel II, Italy, 1884. f, Johnson Single, Great Britain, 1887. g, No. 999, US, 1893. h, Q1 Class, Great Britain, 1896. i, Claud Hamilton, Great Britain, 1900.

No. 1380a, Class P8, Germany, 1906. b, Class P, Denmark, 1935. c, Class Ps, US, 1926. d, Class 4-4-0, Ireland, 1932. e, Class GS, US, 1937. f, Class 12, Belgium, 1938. g, Class J, US, 1941. h, PA series, US, 1946. i, Class 4E1, South Africa, 1954.

No. 1381a, Tee 4-car train, Europe, 1957. b, FL9B, US, 1960. c, Shin-Kansen 16-car train, Japan, 1964. d, Class 103.1, Germany 1970. e, RTG 4-car train set, France, 1972. f, ETR 401 Pendolino 4-car train, Italy, 1976. g, Class 370, Great Britain, 1981. h, LRC, Canada, 1982. i, Mav BZMOT 601 1B1, Hungary, 1983.

No. 1382, ETR 401 four-car train, Italy, 1976. No. 1382A, Werner von Siemens' first electric locomotive, Germany, 1879.

## 1992, Feb. 13 Litho. Perf. 14
### Sheets of 9

| | | | | |
|---|---|---|---|---|
| 1379 | A269 | 75c #a.-i. | 6.00 | 6.00 |
| 1380 | A269 | $1 #a.-i. | 8.00 | 8.00 |
| 1381 | A269 | $2 #a.-i. | 16.00 | 16.00 |
| | | Nos. 1379-1381 (3) | 30.00 | 30.00 |

### Souvenir Sheets

| | | | | |
|---|---|---|---|---|
| 1382 | A269 | $6 multicolored | 5.50 | 5.50 |
| 1382A | A269 | $6 multicolored | 5.50 | 5.50 |

---

1992 Summer Olympics, Barcelona — G101

Designs: 10c, Women's 100-meter backstroke. 15c, Women's handball. 25c, 4x100-meter relay. 35c, Hammer throw. 50c, 110-meter hurdles. 75c, Pole vault. $1, Volleyball. $2, Weight lifting. $5, Stationary rings. $6, Soccer. No. 1393, Baseball. No. 1394, Finn class single-handed dinghy.

## 1992, Mar. 23 Litho. Perf. 14

| | | | | |
|---|---|---|---|---|
| 1383 | G101 | 10c multicolored | .65 | .30 |
| 1384 | G101 | 15c multicolored | .70 | .30 |
| 1385 | G101 | 25c multicolored | .80 | .30 |
| 1386 | G101 | 35c multicolored | .85 | .35 |
| 1387 | G101 | 50c multicolored | 1.00 | .65 |
| 1388 | G101 | 75c multicolored | 1.40 | .85 |
| 1389 | G101 | $1 multicolored | 1.50 | 1.10 |
| 1390 | G101 | $2 multicolored | 2.50 | 2.50 |
| 1391 | G101 | $5 multicolored | 3.50 | 3.50 |
| 1392 | G101 | $6 multicolored | 3.75 | 3.75 |
| | | Nos. 1383-1392 (10) | 16.65 | 13.60 |

### Souvenir Sheets

| | | | | |
|---|---|---|---|---|
| 1393 | G101 | $15 multicolored | 10.50 | 10.50 |
| 1394 | G101 | $15 multicolored | 10.50 | 10.50 |

### Spanish Art Type

Paintings: 10c, The Surrender of Seville, by Francisco de Zurbaran. 35c, The Liberation of Saint Peter by an Angel, by Antonio de Pereda. 50c, Joseph Explains the Dreams of the Pharaoh, by Antonio del Castillo Saavedra, horiz. 75c, The Flower Vase, by Juan de Arellano. $1, The Duke of Pastrana, by Juan Carreno de Miranda. $2, $4, The Annunciation (diff. details), by Francisco Rizi. $5, Old Woman Seated, attributed to Antonio Puga. No. 1403, The Triumph of Saint Hermenegildo, by Francisco de Herrera, the Younger, vert. No. 1404, Relief of Genoa by the Second Marquis of Santa Cruz, by de Pereda, horiz.

## 1992, Apr. 30 Perf. 13

| | | | | |
|---|---|---|---|---|
| 1395 | A273 | 10c multicolored | .30 | .25 |
| 1396 | A273 | 35c multicolored | .50 | .35 |
| 1397 | A273 | 50c multicolored | .75 | .60 |
| 1398 | A273 | 75c multicolored | 1.00 | .75 |
| 1399 | A273 | $1 multicolored | 1.10 | .90 |
| 1400 | A273 | $2 multicolored | 1.75 | 1.75 |
| 1401 | A273 | $4 multicolored | 2.75 | 2.75 |
| 1402 | A273 | $5 multicolored | 2.75 | 2.75 |
| | | Nos. 1395-1402 (8) | 10.90 | 10.10 |

### Size: 95x110mm
#### Imperf

| | | | | |
|---|---|---|---|---|
| 1403 | A273 | $6 multicolored | 10.00 | 10.00 |
| 1404 | A273 | $6 multicolored | 10.00 | 10.00 |

Granada '92.

Discovery of America, 500th Anniv. — G102

Designs: 10c, Don Isaac Abarbanel (1437-1508), Spanish Minister of Finance. 25c, Columbus. 35c, Crewman sighting land. 50c, King Ferdinand and Queen Isabella. 60c, Columbus and Queen Isabella. $5, Santa Maria and map. No. 1411, Portrait of Columbus. No. 1412, Columbus at first landfall.

## 1992, May 7 Litho. Perf. 14

| | | | | |
|---|---|---|---|---|
| 1405 | G102 | 10c multicolored | .25 | .25 |
| 1406 | G102 | 25c multicolored | .35 | .30 |
| 1407 | G102 | 35c multicolored | .55 | .45 |
| 1408 | G102 | 50c multicolored | .85 | .85 |
| 1409 | G102 | 60c multicolored | 1.00 | 1.00 |
| 1410 | G102 | $5 multicolored | 7.00 | 7.00 |
| | | Nos. 1405-1410 (6) | 10.00 | 9.85 |

### Souvenir Sheets

| | | | | |
|---|---|---|---|---|
| 1411 | G102 | $6 multicolored | 5.25 | 5.25 |
| 1412 | G102 | $6 multicolored | 5.25 | 5.25 |

World Columbian Expo '92, Chicago.

### USO Anniv. Type of 1992

10c, James Cagney. 15c, Ann Sheridan. 35c, Jerry Colonna. 50c, Spike Jones. 75c, Edgar Bergen, Charlie McCarthy. $1, Andrews Sisters. $2, Dinah Shore. $5, Bing Crosby. No. 1421, Marlene Dietrich. No. 1422, Fred Astaire.

## 1992, May 7

| | | | | |
|---|---|---|---|---|
| 1413 | A277 | 10c multicolored | .55 | .25 |
| 1414 | A277 | 15c multicolored | .55 | .25 |
| 1415 | A277 | 35c multicolored | .55 | .25 |
| 1416 | A277 | 50c multicolored | .65 | .25 |

| | | | | |
|---|---|---|---|---|
| 1417 | A277 | 75c multicolored | .80 | .50 |
| 1418 | A277 | $1 multicolored | 1.25 | .75 |
| 1419 | A277 | $2 multicolored | 1.90 | 1.90 |
| 1420 | A277 | $5 multicolored | 4.25 | 4.25 |
| | | Nos. 1413-1420 (8) | 10.50 | 8.50 |

**Souvenir Sheets**

| | | | | |
|---|---|---|---|---|
| 1421 | A277 | $6 multicolored | 5.25 | 5.25 |
| 1422 | A277 | $6 multicolored | 5.25 | 5.25 |

### Hummingbird Type of 1992

Designs: 5c, Blue-headed male. 10c, Rufous-breasted hermit female. 20c, Blue-headed female. 45c, Green-throated carib male. 90c, Antillean crested male. $2, Purple-throated carib male. $4, Purple-throated carib female. $5, Antillean crested female. No. 1431, Rufous-breated hermit female. No. 1432, Green-throated carib female.

**1992, May 7**

| | | | | |
|---|---|---|---|---|
| 1423 | A276 | 5c multicolored | .25 | .25 |
| 1424 | A276 | 10c multicolored | .25 | .25 |
| 1425 | A276 | 20c multicolored | .25 | .25 |
| 1426 | A276 | 45c multicolored | .40 | .40 |
| 1427 | A276 | 90c multicolored | .85 | .85 |
| 1428 | A276 | $2 multicolored | 2.00 | 2.00 |
| 1429 | A276 | $4 multicolored | 4.00 | 4.00 |
| 1430 | A276 | $5 multicolored | 5.00 | 5.00 |
| | | Nos. 1423-1430 (8) | 13.00 | 13.00 |

**Souvenir Sheets**

| | | | | |
|---|---|---|---|---|
| 1431 | A276 | $6 multicolored | 6.00 | 6.00 |
| 1432 | A276 | $6 multicolored | 6.00 | 6.00 |

Genoa '92.

### Discovery of America Type

**1992**   *Perf. 14½*

| | | | | |
|---|---|---|---|---|
| 1433 | A275 | $1 Coming ashore | 1.25 | 1.25 |
| 1434 | A275 | $2 Natives, ships | 2.75 | 2.75 |

Walt Disney's Goofy, 60th Anniv. G103

Scenes from Disney cartoon films: 5c, Father's Day Off, 1953. 10c, Cold War, 1951. 15c, Home Made Home, 1951. 25c, Get Rich Quick, 1951. 50c, Man's Best Friend, 1952. 75c, Aquamania, 1961. 90c, Tomorrow We Diet, 1951. $1, Teachers Are People, 1952. $2, The Goofy Success Story, 1955. $3, Double Dribble, 1946. $4, Hello Aloha, 1952. $5, Father's Lion, 1952. No. 1447, Father's Weekend, 1953, vert. No. 1448, Motor Mania, 1950. No. 1449, Hold That Pose, 1950, vert.

**1992, Nov. 24**   Litho.   *Perf. 14x13½*

| | | | | |
|---|---|---|---|---|
| 1435 | G103 | 5c multicolored | .25 | .25 |
| 1436 | G103 | 10c multicolored | .25 | .25 |
| 1437 | G103 | 15c multicolored | .25 | .25 |
| 1438 | G103 | 25c multicolored | .25 | .25 |
| 1439 | G103 | 50c multicolored | .40 | .40 |
| 1440 | G103 | 75c multicolored | .60 | .60 |
| 1441 | G103 | 90c multicolored | .70 | .70 |
| 1442 | G103 | $1 multicolored | .75 | .75 |
| 1443 | G103 | $2 multicolored | 1.50 | 1.50 |
| 1444 | G103 | $3 multicolored | 2.25 | 2.25 |
| 1445 | G103 | $4 multicolored | 2.75 | 2.75 |
| 1446 | G103 | $5 multicolored | 3.50 | 3.50 |
| | | Nos. 1435-1446 (12) | 13.45 | 13.45 |

**Souvenir Sheets**
*Perf. 13½x14*

| | | | | |
|---|---|---|---|---|
| 1447 | G103 | $6 multicolored | 4.25 | 4.25 |
| 1448 | G103 | $6 multicolored | 4.25 | 4.25 |
| 1449 | G103 | $6 multicolored | 4.25 | 4.25 |

### Model Trains Type of 1992

Designs: 15c, #2220 Switcher locomotive, 2-inch gauge, US, 1910. 25c, 0-4-0 Engine, Bridge Port Line, O gauge, US, 1907. 50c, First Ives Co. electric toy locomotive, O gauge, US, 1910. 75c, J. C. Penney Special, standard gauge, US, 1920. $1, Cast metal locomotive, O gauge, US, 1916. $2, Copper-plated cast iron locomotive & tender pull toy, US, 1900. $4, Chromium plated locomotive #4689, standard gauge, US, 1928. $5, Ives long cab locomotive of the Olympian set, standard gauge, US, 1929. No. 1458, Clockwork model, O gauge, US, 1910. No. 1459, American Flyer Statesman passenger train.

**1992, Oct. 22**   Litho.   *Perf. 14*

| | | | | |
|---|---|---|---|---|
| 1450 | A279 | 15c multicolored | .25 | .25 |
| 1451 | A279 | 25c multicolored | .40 | .25 |
| 1452 | A279 | 50c multicolored | .70 | .45 |
| 1453 | A279 | 75c multicolored | .90 | .65 |
| 1454 | A279 | $1 multicolored | 1.00 | .90 |
| 1455 | A279 | $2 multicolored | 1.75 | 1.75 |
| 1456 | A279 | $4 multicolored | 3.25 | 3.25 |
| 1457 | A279 | $5 multicolored | 3.25 | 3.25 |
| | | Nos. 1450-1457 (8) | 11.50 | 10.75 |

**Souvenir Sheet**
*Perf. 13*

| | | | | |
|---|---|---|---|---|
| 1458 | A279 | $6 multicolored | 5.00 | 5.00 |
| 1459 | A279 | $6 multicolored | 5.00 | 5.00 |

Nos. 1458-1459 contain one 51x40mm stamp.

### New York City Type
Souvenir Sheet

**1992, Oct. 28**   *Perf. 14*

| | | | | |
|---|---|---|---|---|
| 1460 | A280 | $6 Brooklyn Bridge | 5.50 | 5.50 |

Postage Stamp Mega Event '92, New York City.

### Christmas Type of 1992

Details or entire paintings of The Annunciation by: 5c, Robert Campin. 25c, Melchior Broederlam. 25c, The Annunciation (2 panels), by Fra Filippo Lippi. 35c, Simone Martini. 50c, Fra Filippo Lippi, detail of angel. 75c, The Annunciation (Mary), by Fra Filippo Lippi. 90c, Albert Bouts. $1, D. Di Michelino. $2, Van der Weyden. $3, Sandro Botticelli, detail of angel. $4, Botticelli, detail of Mary. $5, Bernardo Daddi, horiz. No. 1472, Rogier Van der Weyden, vert. No. 1473, Hubert Van Eyck. No. 1474, Botticelli.

*Perf. 13½x14, 14x13½*
**1992, Nov. 16**

| | | | | |
|---|---|---|---|---|
| 1461 | A281 | 5c multicolored | .25 | .25 |
| 1462 | A281 | 15c multicolored | .30 | .25 |
| 1463 | A281 | 25c multicolored | .35 | .25 |
| 1464 | A281 | 35c multicolored | .45 | .30 |
| 1464A | A281 | 50c multicolored | .65 | .50 |
| 1465 | A281 | 75c multicolored | .85 | .70 |
| 1466 | A281 | 90c multicolored | .90 | .90 |
| 1467 | A281 | $1 multicolored | .90 | .90 |
| 1468 | A281 | $2 multicolored | 1.90 | 1.90 |
| 1469 | A281 | $3 multicolored | 2.50 | 2.50 |
| 1470 | A281 | $4 multicolored | 3.00 | 3.00 |
| 1471 | A281 | $5 multicolored | 3.25 | 3.25 |
| | | Nos. 1461-1471 (12) | 15.30 | 14.70 |

**Souvenir Sheets**

| | | | | |
|---|---|---|---|---|
| 1472 | A281 | $6 multicolored | 4.75 | 4.75 |
| 1473 | A281 | $6 multicolored | 4.75 | 4.75 |
| 1474 | A281 | $6 multicolored | 4.75 | 4.75 |

America's Cup Yacht Race — G104

Designs: 15c, Atalanta, Mischief, 1881. 25c, Valkyrie III, Defender. 35c, Shamrock IV, Resolute. 75c, Endeavour II, Ranger, 1937. $1, Sceptre, Columbia, 1958. $2, Australia II, Liberty. $4, Stars and Stripes, Kookaburra III. $5, New Zealand, Stars and Stripes, 1988. No. 1483, America, Aurora, 1851. No. 1484, Emblems of 1992 participants.

**1992, Oct.**   *Perf. 14*

| | | | | |
|---|---|---|---|---|
| 1475 | G104 | 15c multicolored | .55 | .25 |
| 1476 | G104 | 25c multicolored | .70 | .25 |
| 1477 | G104 | 35c multicolored | .85 | .40 |
| 1478 | G104 | 75c multicolored | 1.10 | .70 |
| 1479 | G104 | $1 multicolored | 1.25 | .90 |
| 1480 | G104 | $2 multicolored | 1.75 | 1.75 |
| 1481 | G104 | $4 multicolored | 2.75 | 2.75 |
| 1482 | G104 | $5 multicolored | 3.00 | 3.00 |
| | | Nos. 1475-1482 (8) | 11.95 | 10.00 |

**Souvenir Sheets**

| | | | | |
|---|---|---|---|---|
| 1483 | G104 | $6 multicolored | 5.50 | 5.50 |
| 1484 | G104 | $6 multicolored | 5.50 | 5.50 |

Nos. 1483-1484 contains one 58x43mm stamp.

G105

Anniversaries and Events — G106

Designs: 25c, Zeppelin Viktoria Luise over Kiel Harbor. 50c, Space Shuttle Columbia. 75c, Flag, arms of Germany, Konrad

Adenauer. $1.50, Giant anteater. No. 1489, Scarlet macaw, vert. No. 1490, Emblem of Intl. Conf. on Nutrition. $3, Wolfgang Amadeus Mozart. No. 1492, Berlin airlift. No. 1493, Space Shuttle Endeavour crew repairing Intelsat VI. $5, Hindenburg disaster. No. 1495, Adm. Richard E. Byrd's Ford Trimotor flying over North Pole, 1926. No. 1496, Map of Federal Republic of Germany, vert. No. 1497, Zeppelin Z.4 above clouds. No. 1498, First flight of space shuttle Endeavour. No. 1499, Scene from "The Marriage of Figaro." No. 1500, Jaguar.

**1992**   Litho.   *Perf. 14*

| | | | | |
|---|---|---|---|---|
| 1485 | G105 | 25c multicolored | .65 | .25 |
| 1486 | G105 | 50c multicolored | .75 | .35 |
| 1487 | G105 | 75c multicolored | .75 | .60 |
| 1488 | G105 | $1.50 multicolored | 1.10 | 1.10 |
| 1489 | G105 | $2 multicolored | 2.50 | 2.00 |
| 1490 | G105 | $2 multicolored | 1.50 | 1.50 |
| 1491 | G106 | $3 multicolored | 2.25 | 2.25 |
| 1492 | G105 | $4 multicolored | 3.00 | 3.00 |
| 1493 | G105 | $4 multicolored | 3.00 | 3.00 |
| 1494 | G105 | $5 multicolored | 3.75 | 3.75 |
| 1495 | G105 | $5 multicolored | 3.75 | 3.75 |
| | | Nos. 1485-1495 (11) | 23.00 | 21.55 |

**Souvenir Sheets**
*Perf. 13½*

| | | | | |
|---|---|---|---|---|
| 1496 | G105 | $6 multicolored | 4.75 | 4.75 |
| 1497 | G105 | $6 multicolored | 4.75 | 4.75 |
| 1498 | G105 | $6 multicolored | 4.75 | 4.75 |

*Perf. 14*

| | | | | |
|---|---|---|---|---|
| 1499 | G106 | $6 multicolored | 4.75 | 4.75 |
| 1500 | G105 | $6 multicolored | 4.75 | 4.75 |

Count Zeppelin, 75th anniv. of death (Nos. 1485, 1494, 1497). Intl. Space Year (Nos. 1486, 1493). Konrad Adenauer, 25th anniv. of death (Nos. 1487, 1492, 1496). Earth Summit, Rio de Janeiro (Nos. 1488-1489, 1500). Intl. Conf. on Nutrition, Rome (No. 1490). Wolfgang Amadeus Mozart, bicent. of death (in 1991) (Nos. 1491, 1499). Intl. Lions Intl., 75th anniv. (No. 1495). Space Year (No. 1498).

Issue dates: Nos. 1491, 1499, Oct. Nos. 1485-1486, 1490, 1493-1495, 1497, Nov. Nos. 1487-1489, 1492, 1496, 1500, Dec.

No. 1496 contains one 39x50mm stamp, Nos. 1497-1498 one 50x39mm stamp, No. 1500 one 52x40mm stamp.

### Entertainers Type of 1992
Miniature Sheet

Grammy award winners: No. 1501a, Leonard Bernstein. b, Ray Charles. c, Bob Dylan. d, Barbra Streisand. e, Frank Sinatra. f, Harry Belafonte. g, Aretha Franklin. h, Garth Brooks. No. 1502a, Johnny Cash. b, Willie Nelson. No. 1503a, Charlie Parker. b, Miles Davis.

**1992, Nov. 19**   *Perf. 14*

| | | | | |
|---|---|---|---|---|
| 1501 | A286 | 90c Sheet of 8, #a.-h. | 17.50 | 17.50 |

**Souvenir Sheets**

| | | | | |
|---|---|---|---|---|
| 1502 | A286 | $3 Sheet of 2, #a.-b. | 6.50 | 6.50 |
| 1503 | A286 | $3 Sheet of 2, #a.-b. | 6.50 | 6.50 |

Dogs — G107

Designs: 35c, Irish Setter, Glendalough, Ireland. 50c, Boston terrier, State House, Boston, US. 75c, Beagle, Temple to Athena, Greece. $1, Weimaraner, Nesselwang, Germany. $3, Norwegian elkhound, Urnes Stave Church, Norway. $4, Mastiff, Great Sphinx, Egypt. No. 1510, Akita, Kyoto torii, Japan. No. 1511, Saluki, Rub'al Khali, Saudi Arabia. No. 1512, Shar pei, China. No. 1513, Bulldog, United Kingdom.

**1993, Jan. 20**   Litho.   *Perf. 14*

| | | | | |
|---|---|---|---|---|
| 1504 | G107 | 35c multicolored | .65 | .35 |
| 1505 | G107 | 50c multicolored | .90 | .65 |
| 1506 | G107 | 75c multicolored | 1.25 | .75 |
| 1507 | G107 | $1 multicolored | 1.60 | 1.10 |
| 1508 | G107 | $3 multicolored | 3.25 | 3.25 |
| 1509 | G107 | $4 multicolored | 3.50 | 3.50 |
| 1510 | G107 | $5 multicolored | 3.50 | 3.50 |
| 1511 | G107 | $5 multicolored | 3.50 | 3.50 |
| | | Nos. 1504-1511 (8) | 18.15 | 16.60 |

**Souvenir Sheets**

| | | | | |
|---|---|---|---|---|
| 1512 | G107 | $6 multicolored | 4.75 | 4.75 |
| 1513 | G107 | $6 multicolored | 4.75 | 4.75 |

### Louvre Painting Type
Miniature Sheet

Details or entire paintings: No. 1514a, The Virgin and Child with Young St. John the Baptist, by Botticelli. b, The Buffet, by Chardin. c, The Provider, by Chardin. d, Erasmus, by Durer. e, Self-Portrait, by Durer. f, Jeanne of Aragon, by Raphael. g-h, La Belle Jardiniere (diff. details), by Raphael.

$6, Charles I, King of England, Hunting, by Van Dyck.

**1993, Mar. 8**   Litho.   *Perf. 12*

| | | | | |
|---|---|---|---|---|
| 1514 | A289 | $1 Sheet of 8, #a.-h. + label | 12.00 | 12.00 |

**Souvenir Sheet**
*Perf. 14½*

| | | | | |
|---|---|---|---|---|
| 1515 | A289 | $6 multicolored | 7.75 | 7.75 |

No. 1515 contains one 55x88mm stamp.

Butterflies — G108

15c, Polydamas swallowtail. 35c, Guaraguao skipper. 45c, Giant hairstreak. 75c, Malachite. $1, Cloudless sulphur. $2, Silver spot. $4, St. Christopher's hairstreak. $5, Common long-tail skipper.

No. 1524, Orion. No. 1525, Zebra.

**1993, Apr. 13**   Litho.   *Perf. 14*

| | | | | |
|---|---|---|---|---|
| 1516 | G108 | 15c multicolored | .35 | .35 |
| 1517 | G108 | 35c multicolored | .50 | .50 |
| 1518 | G108 | 45c multicolored | .55 | .55 |
| 1519 | G108 | 75c multicolored | 1.00 | 1.00 |
| 1520 | G108 | $1 multicolored | 1.25 | 1.25 |
| 1521 | G108 | $2 multicolored | 2.50 | 2.50 |
| 1522 | G108 | $4 multicolored | 5.00 | 5.00 |
| 1523 | G108 | $5 multicolored | 6.50 | 6.50 |
| | | Nos. 1516-1523 (8) | 17.65 | 17.65 |

**Souvenir Sheets**

| | | | | |
|---|---|---|---|---|
| 1524 | G108 | $6 multicolored | 8.00 | 8.00 |
| 1525 | G108 | $6 multicolored | 8.00 | 8.00 |

### Flowers Type of 1993

No. 1526, Hibiscus. No. 1527, Columbine. No. 1528, Red ginger. No. 1529, Bougainvillea. No. 1530, Crown imperial. No. 1531, Fairy orchid. No. 1532, Heliconia. No. 1533, Tulip. No. 1534, Balloonflower, horiz. No. 1535, Blackberry lily, horiz.

**1993, May**

| | | | | |
|---|---|---|---|---|
| 1526 | A291 | 35c multicolored | .65 | .30 |
| 1527 | A291 | 35c multicolored | .65 | .30 |
| 1528 | A291 | 45c multicolored | .65 | .35 |
| 1529 | A291 | 75c multicolored | .90 | .60 |
| 1530 | A291 | $1 multicolored | 1.00 | .75 |
| 1531 | A291 | $2 multicolored | 1.60 | 1.60 |
| 1532 | A291 | $4 multicolored | 2.75 | 2.75 |
| 1533 | A291 | $5 multicolored | 3.00 | 3.00 |
| | | Nos. 1526-1533 (8) | 11.20 | 9.65 |

**Souvenir Sheets**

| | | | | |
|---|---|---|---|---|
| 1534 | A291 | $6 multicolored | 4.50 | 4.50 |
| 1535 | A291 | $6 multicolored | 4.50 | 4.50 |

No. 1536 will not be assigned.

### Coronation of Queen Elizabeth II Type of 1993
Miniature Sheet

Designs: a, 35c, Official coronation photograph. b, 50c, Ampulla, spoon. c, $2, Queen, following coronation. d, $4, Queen, Prince Charles and his family, c. 1984.

$6, Portrait, by Pietro Annigoni, 1954.

**1993, June 2**   Litho.   *Perf. 13½x14*

| | | | | |
|---|---|---|---|---|
| 1537 | A293 | Sheet, 2 each #a.-d. | 10.50 | 10.50 |

**Souvenir Sheet**
*Perf. 14*

| | | | | |
|---|---|---|---|---|
| 1538 | A293 | $6 multicolored | 5.50 | 5.50 |

No. 1538 contains one 28x42mm stamp.

### Anniversaries and Events Types of 1993

Designs: 50c, Telescope. 75c, Willy Brandt, Lyndon Johnson, 1961. $4, Radio telescope. $5, Willy Brandt, Eleanor Hulles, 1957. No. 1543, Copernicus. No. 1544, Willy, Rut Brandt.

| 1993, July 1 | Litho. | | Perf. 14 |
|---|---|---|---|
| 1539 A294 50c multicolored | | 1.40 | .50 |
| 1540 A295 75c multicolored | | 1.60 | 1.60 |
| 1541 A294 $4 multicolored | | 4.00 | 4.00 |
| 1542 A295 $5 multicolored | | 4.00 | 4.00 |
| Nos. 1539-1542 (4) | | 11.00 | 10.10 |

**Souvenir Sheets**

| 1543 A294 $6 multicolored | 5.50 | 5.50 |
|---|---|---|
| 1544 A295 $6 multicolored | 5.50 | 5.50 |

Copernicus, 450th death anniv. (Nos. 1539, 1541, 1543). Willy Brandt, 1st death anniv. (Nos. 1540, 1542, 1544).

### Songbird Type of 1993
### Miniature Sheet

Designs: No. 1545a, 15c, Painted bunting. b, 15c, White-throated sparrow. c, 25c, Common grackle. d, 25c, Royal flycatcher. e, 35c, Swallow tanager. f, 35c, Vermilion flycatcher. g, 45c, Black headed bunting. h, 50c, Rosebreasted grosbeak. i, 75c, Corn bunting. j, 75c, Rosebreasted thrush tanager. k, $1, Buff-throated saltator. l, $4, Plush-capped finch.
No. 1546, Bohemian waxwing. No. 1547, Pine grosbeak.

| 1993, July 13 | | |
|---|---|---|
| 1545 A297 Sheet of 12, #a.-l. | 14.00 | 14.00 |

**Souvenir Sheets**

| 1546 A297 $6 multicolored | 7.25 | 7.25 |
|---|---|---|
| 1547 A297 $6 multicolored | 7.25 | 7.25 |

### Seashell Type of 1993
### Miniature Sheet

Designs: No. 1548a, 15c, Hawk wing conch. b, 15c, Music volute. c, 25c, Globe vase, deltoid rock shell. d, 35c, Spiny vase. e, 35c, Common sundial, common purple snail. f, 45c, Caribbean donax, gaudy asaphis. g, 45c, Mouse cone. h, 50c, Gold-mouthed triton. i, 75c, Tulip mussel, trigonal tivela. j, 75c, Common dove shell, chestnut latirus. k, $1, Widemouthed purpura. l, $4, Atlantic thorny oyster, Atlantic wing oyster.
No. 1549, Turkey wing. No. 1550, Zebra periwinkle.

| 1993, July 19 | Litho. | | Perf. 14 |
|---|---|---|---|
| 1548 A298 Sheet of 12, #a.-l. | | 13.00 | 13.00 |

**Souvenir Sheet**

| 1549 A298 $6 multicolored | 6.50 | 6.50 |
|---|---|---|
| 1550 A298 $6 multicolored | 6.50 | 6.50 |

### Picasso Type of 1993

Paintings: 15c, Painter and Model, 1928. $1, The Artist and His Model, 1963. $4, The Drawing Lession, 1925. $6, Picasso seated in front of canvas, 1956.

| 1993, July 1 | Litho. | | Perf. 14 |
|---|---|---|---|
| 1551 A299 15c multi, horiz. | | .60 | .35 |
| 1552 A299 $1 multi, horiz. | | 1.50 | 1.50 |
| 1553 A299 $4 multi, horiz. | | 3.75 | 3.75 |
| Nos. 1551-1553 (3) | | 5.85 | 5.60 |

**Souvenir Sheet**

| 1554 A299 $6 multi, horiz. | 5.00 | 5.00 |
|---|---|---|

### Olympics Type of 1993

Design: $6, Emil Zografski, ski jump.

| 1993, July 1 | | |
|---|---|---|
| 1554A A300 35c multi | .30 | .30 |
| 1554B A300 $5 multi | 3.75 | 3.75 |
| 1555 A300 $6 multicolored | 5.00 | 5.00 |
| Nos. 1554A-1555 (3) | 9.05 | 9.05 |

### Polska '93 Type of 1993

Paintings: 75c, Gra w Gudziki, by Ludomir Slendzinski, 1928. $2, Pocalunek Mongoskiego Ksiecia, by S.I. Witkiewicz, 1915. $6, Allegory, by Jan Wydra, 1929.

| 1993, July 1 | | |
|---|---|---|
| 1556 A301 75c multi, horiz. | 1.25 | 1.25 |
| 1557 A301 $2 multi, horiz. | 3.50 | 3.50 |

**Souvenir Sheet**

| 1558 A301 $6 multicolored | 5.25 | 5.25 |
|---|---|---|

### Taipei '93 Type

Designs: 35c, Macao Palace, Hong Kong. 45c, Stone pixie, Ming Tomb, Nanjing. $1, Stone camels, Ming Tomb, Nanjing. $5, Stone lion and elephant, Ming Tomb, Nanjing.
Sculpture: No. 1563a, Nesting quail incense burner. b, Standing quail incense burner. c, Seated qilin incense burner. d, Pottery horse, Han Dynasty. e, Seated caparisoned elephant. f, Cow (imitation delft).
No. 1564, Sumatran tiger.

| 1993 | Litho. | | Perf. 14x13½ |
|---|---|---|---|
| 1559 A302 35c multi, horiz. | | .25 | .25 |
| 1560 A302 45c multi, horiz. | | .35 | .35 |
| 1561 A302 $1 multi, horiz. | | .75 | .75 |
| 1562 A302 $5 multi, horiz. | | 3.75 | 3.75 |
| Nos. 1559-1562 (4) | | 5.10 | 5.10 |

### Miniature Sheet

| 1563 A302 $1.50 Sheet of 6, #a.-f. | 11.00 | 11.00 |
|---|---|---|

**Souvenir Sheet**
**Perf. 13½x14**

| 1564 A302 $6 multicolored | 7.50 | 7.50 |
|---|---|---|

Nos. 1563a-1563f are horiz.

### With Bangkok '93 Emblem

Designs: 35c, Naga snakes, Chiang Mai's Temple, Thailand. 45c, Sri Mariamman Temple, Singapore. $1, Topiary, Hua Hin Resort, Thailand. $5, Pak Tai Temple, Cheung Chau Island.
Thai paintings: No. 1569a, Buddha's victory over Mara. b, Mythological elephant. c, Battle with Mara. d, Untitled work, by Panya Wijinthanasarn, 1984. e, Temple mural. f, Elephants in Pahcekha Buddha's Heaven.
No. 1570, Monkey.

| 1993 | | Perf. 14x13½ |
|---|---|---|
| 1565 A302 35c multi, horiz. | .25 | .25 |
| 1566 A302 45c multi, horiz. | .35 | .35 |
| 1567 A302 $1 multi, horiz. | .75 | .75 |
| 1568 A302 $5 multi, horiz. | 3.75 | 3.75 |
| Nos. 1565-1568 (4) | 5.10 | 5.10 |

### Miniature Sheet

| 1569 A302 $1.50 Sheet of 6, #a.-f. | 11.00 | 11.00 |
|---|---|---|

**Souvenir Sheet**
**Perf. 13½x14**

| 1570 A302 $6 multicolored | 6.50 | 6.50 |
|---|---|---|

Nos. 1569a-1569f are horiz.

### Indopex '93 Type

Designs: 35c, Natl. Museum, Central Jakarta, Indonesia. 45c, Sacred Wheel & Deer, Monastery. $1, Ramayana relief, Panataran Temple. $5, Candi Tikus, Trawulan, East Java.
Paintings: No. 1575a, Bullock Carts, bu Batara Lubis, 1951. b, Surat Irsa II, by A.D. Pirous, 1983. c, Self-portrait with Goat, by Kartika, 1987. d, The Cow-est Cow, by Ivan Sagito, 1987. e, Rain Storm, by Sudjana Kerton, 1984. f, Story of Pucuk Flower, by Effendi, 1972.
No. 1576, Banteng cattle.

| 1993, Aug. 13 | Litho. | | Perf. 14x13½ |
|---|---|---|---|
| 1571 A302 35c multicolored | | .25 | .25 |
| 1572 A302 45c multicolored | | .35 | .35 |
| 1573 A302 $1 multicolored | | .75 | .75 |
| 1574 A302 $5 multicolored | | 3.75 | 3.75 |
| Nos. 1571-1574 (4) | | 5.10 | 5.10 |

### Miniature Sheet

| 1575 A302 $1.50 Sheet of 6, #a.-f. | 11.00 | 11.00 |
|---|---|---|

**Souvenir Sheet**

| 1576 A302 $6 multicolored | 5.25 | 5.25 |
|---|---|---|

Nos. 1571-1576 are horiz.

1994 World Cup Soccer Championships, US — G109

Designs: 15c, Stuart McCall, Carlos Verri. 25c, Carlos Verri, Diego Maradona. 35c, S. Schillaci, J.P. Saldana. 45c, Ruud Gullit, Mark Wright. $1, Carlos Verri, Diego Maradona. $2, Zubizarreta, Fernandez, Albert. $4, Gheorghe Hagi, Paul McGrath. $5, Alberto Gorriz, Enzo Scifo. No. 1585, Schaefer Stadium, Foxboro, MA. No. 1586, Rudi Voeller, vert.

| 1993, Sept. 7 | Litho. | | Perf. 14 |
|---|---|---|---|
| 1577 G109 15c multicolored | | .45 | .25 |
| 1578 G109 25c multicolored | | .45 | .25 |
| 1579 G109 35c multicolored | | .45 | .25 |
| 1580 G109 45c multicolored | | .45 | .40 |
| 1581 G109 $1 multicolored | | .75 | .75 |
| 1582 G109 $2 multicolored | | 1.50 | 1.50 |
| 1583 G109 $4 multicolored | | 3.00 | 3.00 |
| 1584 G109 $5 multicolored | | 3.75 | 3.75 |
| Nos. 1577-1584 (8) | | 10.80 | 10.15 |

**Souvenir Sheets**

| 1585 G109 $6 multicolored | 5.00 | 5.00 |
|---|---|---|
| 1586 G109 $6 multicolored | 5.00 | 5.00 |

### Mickey Mouse, 65th Anniv. Type

Movie clips: 15c, The Worm Turns, 1937. 35c, Mickey's Rival, 1936. 50c, The Pointer, 1939. 75c, Society Dog Show, 1939. $1, A Gentleman's Gentleman, 1941. $2, The Little Whirlwind, 1941. $4, Mickey Down Under, 1948. $5, R'coon Dawg, 1951.
No. 1595, Mickey's Garden, 1935, vert. No. 1596, Lonesome Ghosts, 1937.

| | Perf. 13½x14, 14x13½ |
|---|---|
| 1993, Nov. 11 | Litho. |
| 1587 A305 15c multicolored | .60 .25 |
| 1588 A305 35c multicolored | .80 .35 |
| 1589 A305 50c multicolored | 1.00 .60 |
| 1590 A305 75c multicolored | 1.40 1.00 |
| 1591 A305 $1 multicolored | 1.60 1.10 |
| 1592 A305 $2 multicolored | 2.25 2.25 |
| 1593 A305 $4 multicolored | 3.25 3.25 |
| 1594 A305 $5 multicolored | 3.25 3.25 |
| Nos. 1587-1594 (8) | 14.15 12.05 |

**Souvenir Sheets**

| 1595 A305 $6 multicolored | 5.50 | 5.50 |
|---|---|---|
| 1596 A305 $6 multicolored | 5.50 | 5.50 |

### Christmas Type of 1993

Various details from Adoration of the Shepherds by Durer: 10c, 75c, $1, $4. No. 1605, $6, horiz.
Various details from Oddi Altarpiece by Raphael: 25c, 35c, 50c, $5. No. 1606, $6.

| | Perf. 13½x14, 14x13½ (#1605) |
|---|---|
| 1993, Nov. 22 | Litho. |
| 1597-1604 A306 Set of 8 | 11.00 11.00 |

**Souvenir Sheets**

| 1605-1606 A306 Set of 2 | 11.00 11.00 |
|---|---|

### Eckener Type of 1993

Designs: 50c, Graf Zeppelin over Rio De Janeiro. 75c, Dr. Hugo Eckener. $5, Eckener commanding Graf Zeppelin. $6, Eckener, Pres. Herbert Hoover.

| 1993, Dec. 21 | Litho. | Perf. 14 |
|---|---|---|
| 1607-1609 A307 Set of 3 | | 5.25 5.25 |

**Souvenir Sheet**

| 1610 A307 $6 multicolored | 5.00 5.00 |
|---|---|

### Royal Air Force Anniv. Type of 1993

Designs: 15c, Avro Lancaster. $5, Short Sunderland. $6, Supermarine Spitfire.

| 1993, Dec. 21 | | |
|---|---|---|
| 1611 A308 15c multicolored | .35 | .25 |
| 1612 A308 $5 multicolored | 6.50 | 6.50 |

**Souvenir Sheet**

| 1613 A308 $6 multicolored | 7.00 7.00 |
|---|---|

### Automobile Anniv. Type

Designs: 25c, 1955 Mercedes Benz 300SLR. 45c, 1957 Ford Thunderbird. $4, 1929 Ford 150A Station Wagon. $5, Mercedes Benz 540K.
Each $6: No. 1618, 1929 Mercedes Benz SSK. No. 1619, 1924 Ford Model T.

| 1993, Dec. 21 | Litho. | Perf. 14 |
|---|---|---|
| 1614-1617 A309 Set of 4 | | 10.00 10.00 |

**Souvenir Sheets**

| 1618-1619 A309 Set of 2 | 11.00 11.00 |
|---|---|

1st Benz 4-wheel car, 1st Ford engine, cent.

### First Gas Balloon Flight in America Type

Designs: 35c, Blanchard's balloon crossing Delaware River. $3, Blanchard delivering Washington's passport of introduction. $6, Balloon in flight, vert.

| 1993, Dec. 21 | Litho. | Perf. 14 |
|---|---|---|
| 1620-1621 A310 Set of 2 | | 3.50 3.50 |

**Souvenir Sheet**

| 1622 A310 $6 multicolored | 5.00 5.00 |
|---|---|

### Fine Art Type

Details or entire paintings by Rembrandt: 15c, Hendrickje Stoffels as Flora. 35c, Lady & Gentlemen in Black. 50c, Mary Magdalene with Bust of Homer. $5, Christ & the Woman of Samaria.
Details or entire paintings by Matisse: 75c, Interior: Flowers and Parakeets. $1, Goldfish. $2, The Girl with Green Eyes. $3, Still Life with a Plaster Figure.
Each $6: No. 1631, Anna Accused of Stealing the Kid, by Rembrandt. No. 1632, Tea in the Garden by Matisse, horiz.

| | Perf. 13½x14, 14x13½ |
|---|---|
| 1993, Dec. 31 | Litho. |
| 1623-1630 A311 Set of 8 | 11.00 11.00 |

**Souvenir Sheets**

| 1631-1632 A311 Set of 2 | 11.00 11.00 |
|---|---|

### Hong Kong '94 Type

Designs: No. 1633, Hong Kong #426, jet at Kai Tak Airport. No. 1634, Junk, Kwaloon Bay, #975.
Chinese jade: No. 1635a, White jade brush washer. b, Archaic jade brush washer. c, Dark green jade brush washer. d, Green jade alms bowl. e, Archaic jade dog. f, Yellow jade brush washer.

| 1994, Feb. 18 | Litho. | Perf. 14 |
|---|---|---|
| 1633 A313 40c multicolored | | .90 .90 |
| 1634 A313 40c multicolored | | .90 .90 |
| a. Pair, #1633-1634 | | 2.40 2.40 |

### Miniature Sheet

| 1635 A314 45c Sheet of 6, #a.-f. | 7.50 7.50 |
|---|---|

Nos. 1633-1634 issued in sheets of of 5 pairs. No. 1634a is a continuous design. Nos. 1635a-1635f are horiz.
New Year 1994 (Year of the Dog) (No. 1635e).

Dinosaurs
G110

15c, Spinosaurus. 35c, Apatosaurus. 45c, Tyrannosaurus rex. 55c, Triceratops. $1, Pachycephalosaurus. $2, Pteranodon. $4, Parasaurolophus. $5, Brachiosaurus.
Each $6: No. 1644, Brachiosaurus, vert. No. 1645, Tyrannosaurus, spinosaurus, vert.

| 1994 | Litho. | Perf. 14 |
|---|---|---|
| 1636-1643 G110 Set of 8 | | 12.50 12.50 |

**Souvenir Sheets**

| 1644-1645 G110 Set of 2 | 11.00 11.00 |
|---|---|

Mushrooms — G111

Designs: 35c, Hygrocybe hypohaemacta. 45c, Cantherellus cinnabarinus. 50c, Marasmius haematocephalus. 75c, Mycena pura. $1, Gymnopilus russipes. $2, Galocybe cyanocephala. $4, Pleuteus chrysophlebius. $5, Chlorophyllum molybdites.
Each $6: No. 1654, Collybia fibrosipes. No. 1655, Xeromphalina tenuipes.

| 1994 | | |
|---|---|---|
| 1646-1653 G111 Set of 8 | 10.00 | 10.00 |

**Souvenir Sheets**

| 1654-1655 G111 Set of 2 | 9.50 9.50 |
|---|---|

### D-Day Type of 1994

40c, Churchill bridgelayer in action. $2, Sherman "Firefly" attacks beach. $3, Churchill Crocodile flame thrower. $6, Sherman "Crab" flail tank.

| 1994, Aug. 4 | Litho. | Perf. 14 |
|---|---|---|
| 1656-1658 A318 Set of 3 | | 5.00 5.00 |

**Souvenir Sheet**

| 1659 A318 $6 multicolored | 5.25 5.25 |
|---|---|

### First Manned Moon Landing, 25th Anniv. Type of 1994
### Miniature Sheet of 6

Tribute to Challenger crew: No. 1660a, Slidewire escape training. b, Christa A. McAuliffe. c, Challenger 51-L on pad LC39B. d, Gregory B. Jarvis. e, Ellison S. Onizuka. f, Ronald E. McNair.
$6, Judith A. Resnick, vert.

| 1994, Aug. 4 | | |
|---|---|---|
| 1660 A319 $1.10 #a.-f. | 7.50 | 7.50 |

**Souvenir Sheet**

| 1661 A319 $6 multicolored | 6.50 6.50 |
|---|---|

### PHILAKOREA '94 Type

Designs: 40c, Onung Tomb, Korea. $1, Stone pagoda, Mt. Nansan, Kyongju. $4, Pusan Port.
Paintings, by Sin Yunbok, late Choson Dynasty, 1758: No. 1665a-1665b, Admiring spring in the Country. c-d, Women on Dano Day. e-f, Enjoying Lotuses While Listening to Music. g-h, Women by a Crystal Stream.
$6, Blacksmith's Shop, by Kim Duksin (1754-1822).

| 1994, Aug. 4 | | Perf. 14, 13½ (#1665) |
|---|---|---|
| 1662-1664 A320 Set of 3 | 4.25 | 4.25 |

### Miniature Sheet of 8

| 1665 A321 $1 #a.-h. | 9.50 9.50 |
|---|---|

**Souvenir Sheet**

| 1666 A320 $6 multicolored | 5.00 5.00 |
|---|---|

## Orchid Type of 1994

15c, Cattleya aurantiaca. 25c, Blettia patula. 45c, Sobralia macrantha. 75c, Encyclia belizensis. $1, Sophrolaeliocattleya. $2, Encyclia frangrans. $4, Schombocattleya. $5, Brassolaeliocattleya.

Each $6: No. 1675, Brassavola nodosa. No. 1676, Ornithidium coccineum.

| 1994, Aug. 7 | | | Perf. 14 | |
|---|---|---|---|---|
| 1667-1674 | A322 | Set of 8 | 11.00 | 11.00 |
| **Souvenir Sheets** | | | | |
| 1675-1676 | A322 | Set of 2 | 10.00 | 10.00 |

## 1994 World Cup Soccer Type
### Miniature Sheet of 6

Designs: No. 1677a, Steve Mark, Grenada. b, Jurgen Kohler, Germany. c, Almir, Brazil. d, Michael Windischmann, US. e, Guiseppe Giannini, Italy. f, Rashidi Yekini, Nigeria.

Each $6: No. 1678, Kemari. No. 1679, The World Cup.

| 1994, Aug. 11 | | | Perf. 14 | |
|---|---|---|---|---|
| 1677 | A323 | 75c #a.-f. | 5.25 | 5.25 |
| **Souvenir Sheets** | | | | |
| 1678-1679 | A323 | Set of 2 | 9.50 | 9.50 |

Disney's PHILAKOREA '94 — G112

15c, Mickey, Unjin Miruk, Kwanch Ok Temple. 35c, Goofy, statue of Admiral Yi, Chonju. 50c, Cousin Gus, Donald. 75c, Mickey playing flute. $1, Goofy, Tolharubang Grandfather statue. $2, Mickey, Minnie, Hyang-Wonjong. $4, Mickey, Unsan Pyolshin Festival. $5, Minnie, ceremonial fan.

Each $6: No. 1688, Minnie, Buk drum, vert. No. 1689, Mickey, Pugok Hawaii, vert.

| 1994, Aug. 16 | Litho. | | Perf. 14x13½ | |
|---|---|---|---|---|
| 1680-1687 | G112 | Set of 8 | 15.00 | 15.00 |
| **Souvenir Sheets** | | | | |
| | | *Perf. 13½x14* | | |
| 1688-1689 | G112 | Set of 2 | 12.00 | 12.00 |

This set exists with very low face values.

## Fish Type of 1994

Designs, each 75c: No. 1690a, Yellowtail snapper (b, e). b, Caribbean reef shark (a). c, Great barracuda. d, Redtail parrotfish. e, Blue tang. f, Queen angelfish. g, Red hind (h). h, Rock beauty. i, Queen parrotfish. j, Spanish hogfish. k, Spotted moray. l, Queen triggerfish (i).

Each 75c: No. 1691a, Pork fish (b). b, Blue chromis (a). c, Caribbean reef shark. d, Long-spine squirrelfish. e, Foureye butterflyfish. f, Blue head. g, Royal gramma. h, Sharpnose puffer. i, Longsnout seahorse. j, Blackbar soldierfish (g, k). k, Redlip blenny. l, Rainbow wrasse.

Each $6: No. 1692, Rainbow wrasse, diff. No. 1693, Queen angelfish, diff.

| 1994, Sept. 1 | | | Perf. 14 | |
|---|---|---|---|---|
| **Miniature Sheets of 12** | | | | |
| 1690-1691 | A324 | Set of 2 | 24.00 | 24.00 |
| **Souvenir Sheets** | | | | |
| 1692-1693 | A324 | Set of 2 | 12.00 | 12.00 |

## Intl. Olympic Committee Type of 1994

Designs: 50c, Silke Renk, Germany, javelin, 1992. $1.50, Mark Spitz, US, swimming, 1972. $6, Team Japan, Nordic combined, 1994.

| 1994 | | | Perf. 14 | |
|---|---|---|---|---|
| 1694 | A325 | 50c multi, horiz. | .40 | .40 |
| 1695 | A325 | $1.50 multi, horiz. | 1.10 | 1.10 |
| **Souvenir Sheet** | | | | |
| 1696 | A326 | $6 multicolored | 5.00 | 5.00 |

## Intl. Year of the Family Type of 1994
### 1994

| 1697 | A329 | $1 Family of 5 | .80 | .80 |
|---|---|---|---|---|

## Order of the Caribbean Community Type

Designs: 25c, Sir Shridath Ramphal, statesman, Guyana. 50c, William Demas, economist, Trinidad & Tobago. $2, Derek Walcott, writer, St. Lucia.

| 1994, Sept. 1 | | | | |
|---|---|---|---|---|
| 1698-1700 | A330 | Set of 3 | 3.00 | 3.00 |

## Christmas Type of 1994

Paintings, by Bartolome Murillo: 15c, The Annunciation. 35c, The Adoration of the Shepherds. No. 1703, 50c, Flight into Egypt. No. 1704, 50c, Virgin and Child with St. Rose. 75c, Virgin and Child. $1, Virgin of the Rosary. $4, The Holy Family.

Each $6: No. 1708, Adoration of the Shepherds. No. 1709, The Holy Family with a Little Bird.

| 1994, Dec. 5 | Litho. | | Perf. 13½x14 | |
|---|---|---|---|---|
| 1701-1707 | A331 | Set of 7 | 7.50 | 7.50 |
| **Souvenir Sheets** | | | | |
| 1708-1709 | A331 | Set of 2 | 10.00 | 10.00 |

## Bird Type of 1995

25c, Ground dove. 50c, White-winged dove, horiz. $2, Inca dove. $4, Mourning dove, horiz.

| 1995, Jan. 10 | | | Perf. 14 | |
|---|---|---|---|---|
| 1710-1713 | A332 | Set of 4 | 9.50 | 9.50 |

## English Touring Cricket, Cent. Type

Designs: 50c, M.A. Atherton, England, horiz. 75c, C.E.L. Ambrose, Leeward Isl./W. Indies. $1, B.C. Lara, Trinidad/W. Indies. $3, West Indies Team, horiz.

| 1995, Jan. 12 | | | | |
|---|---|---|---|---|
| 1715-1717 | A333 | Set of 3 | 4.00 | 4.00 |
| **Souvenir Sheet** | | | | |
| 1718 | A333 | $3 multicolored | 4.00 | 4.00 |

### Miniature Sheet

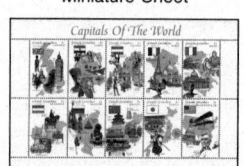

Capitals of the World — G113

Designs: a, London. b, Cairo. c, Vienna. d, Paris. e, Rome. f, Budapest. g, Moscow. h, Beijing. i, Tokyo. j, Wasington.

| 1995, Mar. 10 | Litho. | | Perf. 14 | |
|---|---|---|---|---|
| 1719 | G113 | $1 #a.-j. | 10.00 | 10.00 |

New Year 1995 (Year of the Boar) — G114

Various stylized boars with different Chinese inscriptions: a, Smiling, purple legs. b, Smiling, red legs. c, Brown legs. d, Red legs.

$2, Two boars, horiz.

| 1995, Apr. 21 | Litho. | | Perf. 14½ | |
|---|---|---|---|---|
| 1720 | G114 | 75c Block or horiz. | | |
| | | strip of 4, #a.-d. | 2.25 | 2.25 |
| e. | Souvenir sheet of 4, #1720a-1720d | | 3.00 | 3.00 |
| **Souvenir Sheet** | | | | |
| 1721 | G114 | $2 multicolored | 2.25 | 2.25 |

No. 1720 was issued in miniature sheets of 16 stamps.

## VE Day Type of 1995

No. 1721A: b, Mitsubishi G4M1 "Betty." c, Aircraft carrying submarine I-14. d, Mitsubishi G3M1. e, Destroyer Akizuki. f, Battleship Kirishima. g, Cruiser Asigari.

Bombers: No. 1722: a, Avro Lancaster, Tallboy bomb. b, Junkers JU-88. c, B-25 Mitchell. d, B-17 Flying Fortress. e, Petlyakov Pe-2. f, Martin B-26 Marauder. g, Henkel He-111. h, Consolidated B-24 Liberator.

No. 1723, Pres. Truman displaying newspaper headline. No. 1723A, Aichi D3A1 "Val" dive bomber.

| 1995, May 8 | | | Perf. 14 | |
|---|---|---|---|---|
| **Miniature Sheets of 6 and 8** | | | | |
| 1721A | A336 | $2 #b.-g. + label | 9.50 | 9.50 |
| 1722 | A336 | $2 #a.-h. + label | 13.00 | 13.00 |

### Souvenir Sheets

| 1723 | A336 | $6 multicolored | 5.25 | 5.25 |
|---|---|---|---|---|
| 1723A | A336 | $6 multicolored | 6.00 | 6.00 |

Inscription in central label of No. 1721A misidentifies a Yokosuka MXY-7 Okha kamikaze plane.

No. 1723 contains one 57x42mm stamp.

## Scout Jamboree Type of 1995

a, 75c, Beach scene, scout. b, $1, Mountains, sea, scout with pole. c, $2, Flag, scout salute.

$6, Snorkeling, fish.

| 1995, May 8 | | | | |
|---|---|---|---|---|
| 1724 | A337 | Strip of 3, #a.-c. | 3.00 | 3.00 |
| **Souvenir Sheet** | | | | |
| 1725 | A337 | $6 multicolored | 5.50 | 5.50 |

No. 1724 was issued in sheets of 9 stamps.

## UN, 50th Anniv. Type of 1995

Designs: a, 75c, Building, UN flag. b, $1, Trygve Lie (1896-1968), Norway, 1st Secretary General. c, $2, Flag, member of UN peacekeeping force.

$6, Dove, emblem.

| 1995, May 8 | | | | |
|---|---|---|---|---|
| 1726 | A338 | Strip of 3, #a.-c. | 3.00 | 3.00 |
| **Souvenir Sheet** | | | | |
| 1727 | A338 | $6 multicolored | 4.75 | 4.75 |

No. 1726 is a continuous design and was issued in sheets of 9 stamps.

Marine Life of the Caribbean
G115

No. 1728, each $1: a, Dolphins. b, Scorpion fish. c, Sea turtle, rock beauty. d, Butterflyfish, nurse shark. e, Angel fish. f, Grouper coney. g, Rainbow eel, moray eel. h, Sun flower-star, coral crab. i, Octopus.

No. 1729, each $1: a, Bull shark. b, Big white shark. c, Octopus. d, Barracuda (e). e, Moray eel (f, h, i). f, Spotted eagle ray. g, Goldspotted snake. h, Stingray. i, Grouper.

$5, French angelfish. $6, Hammerhead shark.

| 1995, May 3 | Litho. | | Perf. 14 | |
|---|---|---|---|---|
| **Miniature Sheets of 9, #a-i** | | | | |
| 1728-1729 | G115 | Set of 2 | 18.00 | 18.00 |
| **Souvenir Sheets** | | | | |
| 1730 | G115 | $5 multicolored | 4.25 | 4.25 |
| 1731 | G115 | $6 multicolored | 5.00 | 5.00 |

Domesticated Animals — G116

Horses: 15c, Suffolk punch. 25c, Shetland pony. $1, Arab. $3, Shire horse.

Dogs, each 75c: No. 1736a, Shetland sheepdog. b, Bull terrier. c, Afghan. d, Scottish terrier. e, Labrador retriever. f, English springer spaniel. g, Samoyed. h, Irish setter. i, Border collie. j, Pekingese. k, Dachshund. l, Weimaraner.

Cats, each 75c: No. 1737a, Blue persian. b, Sorrel abyssinian. c, White angora. d, Brown burmese. e, Red tabby exotic shorthair. f, Seal-point birman. g, Korat. h, Norwegian forest cat. i, Lilac-point Balinese. j, British shorthair. k, Red self longhair. l, Calico manx.

Each $6: No. 1738, English setter. No. 1739, Seal-point colorpoint.

| 1995, May 3 | | | | |
|---|---|---|---|---|
| 1732-1735 | G116 | Set of 4 | 3.50 | 3.50 |
| **Miniature Sheets of 12, #a-l** | | | | |
| 1736-1737 | G116 | Set of 2 | 14.00 | 14.00 |
| **Souvenir Sheets** | | | | |
| 1738-1739 | G116 | Set of 2 | 11.00 | 11.00 |

Sierra Club, Cent. — G117

No. 1740, each $1: a, Brown pelican. b, Northern spotted owl. c, Northern spotted owl in winter. d, Jaguarundi. e, Central American spider monkeys facing forward. f, Two Central American spider monkeys. g, Central American spider monkey. h, Wood stork. i, Maned wolves.

No. 1741, each $1, vert: a, Northern spotted owl. b, Brown pelican. c, Brown pelican up close. d, Jaguarundi up close. e, Jaguarundi. f, Maned wolf. g, Wood stork facing right. h, Wood stork facing left. i, Maned wolf up close.

| 1995, May 5 | | | | |
|---|---|---|---|---|
| **Miniature Sheets of 9, #a-i** | | | | |
| 1740-1741 | G117 | Set of 2 | 25.00 | 25.00 |

FAO, 50th Anniv. G118

No. 1742: a, 75c, Man working in field. b, $1, Woman working in field. c, $2, Two workers in field.

$6, Child with chopsticks.

| 1995, May 8 | | | | |
|---|---|---|---|---|
| 1742 | G118 | Strip of 3, #a.-c. | 3.00 | 3.00 |
| **Souvenir Sheet** | | | | |
| 1743 | G118 | $6 multicolored | 4.50 | 4.50 |

No. 1742 was issued in sheets of 9 stamps.

Rotary Intl., 90th Anniv. — G119

| 1995, May 8 | | | | |
|---|---|---|---|---|
| 1744 | G119 | $5 Paul Harris, emblem | 3.75 | 3.75 |
| **Souvenir Sheet** | | | | |
| 1745 | G119 | $6 Old, new emblems | 4.50 | 4.50 |

## Queen Mother, 95th Anniv. Type of 1995

No. 1746: a, Drawing. b, In black outfit. c, Formal portrait. d, In green outfit.

No. 1747, Speaking at Blitz Memorial.

| 1995, May 8 | | | | |
|---|---|---|---|---|
| 1746 | A344 | $1.50 Strip or block of 4, #a.-d. | 5.50 | 5.50 |
| **Souvenir Sheet** | | | | |
| 1747 | A344 | $6 multicolored | 5.50 | 5.50 |

No. 1746 was issued in sheets of 8 stamps.
Sheets of Nos. 1746-1747 exist with black border and text "In Memoriam - 1900-2002" in sheet margins.

## 1996 Summer Olympics Type

No. 1748, horiz: a, Rosemary Ackerman, East Germany, high jump. b, Li Ning, China, gymnastics. c, Denise Parker, US, archery.

No. 1749, horiz: a, Terry Carlisle, US, skeet shooting. b, Kathleen Nord, East Germany, 200-meter butterfly. c, Brigit Schmidt, East Germany, kayaking.

Each $6: No. 1750, George Foreman, US, boxing. No. 1751, Dan Gable US, Kikuo Wada, Japan, wrestling.

| 1995, June 23 | | | | |
|---|---|---|---|---|
| 1748 | A345 | 15c Strip of 3, #a.-c. | .60 | .60 |
| 1749 | A345 | $3 Strip of 3, #a.-c. | 9.50 | 9.50 |
| **Souvenir Sheets** | | | | |
| 1750-1751 | A345 | Set of 2 | 11.00 | 11.00 |

G120

Designs: 10c, Brown pelican. 15c, Common stilt. 25c, Cuban trogan. 35c, Flamingo. 75c, Parrot. $1, Pintail duck. $2, Ringed kingfisher. $3, Strip-headed tanager.

No. 1760: a, Great blue heron. b, Jamaican tody. c, Laughing gull. d, Purple-throated carib. e, Red-legged thrush. f, Ruddy duck. g, Shoveler duck. h, West Indian red-bellied woodpecker.

Each $5: No. 1761, Blue-hooded Euphonia. No. 1762, Village weaver.

**1995, Sept. 5**    **Litho.**    **Perf. 14**
1752-1759 G120 Set of 8    8.00   8.00

**Miniature Sheet of 8**
1760 G120 $1 #a.-h.    8.00   8.00

**Souvenir Sheets**
1761-1762 G120 Set of 2    10.50 10.50

Singapore '95 (Nos. 1760-1762). No. 1760d is misspelled.

Mickey's High Sea Adventure G121

10c, Goofy carrying treasure chests, Donald. 35c, Mickey, Minnie at helm. 75c, Mickey, Donald, Goofy opening treasure chest. $1, Pirates confronting Mickey. $2, Mickey, Goofy, Donald in life boat. $5, Goofy using mop to fight enemy.

Each $6: No. 1769, Cannonballs being shot at Goofy, vert. No. 1770, Mickey on island, monkey pinching his nose, vert.

**1995, Oct. 2**    **Litho.**    **Perf. 14x13½**
1763-1768 G121 Set of 6    7.00   7.00

**Souvenir Sheets**
**Perf. 13½x14**
1769-1770 G121 Set of 2    10.00 10.00

**Nobel Prize Recipients Type of 1995**

No. 1770A, Derek Walcott, literature, 1992. No. 1770B, W. Arthur Lewis, economics, 1979.

No. 1771, each $1: a, Heike Kamerlingh Onnes, physics, 1913. b, Fridtjof Nansen, 1922. c, Sir Ronald Ross, physiology or medicine, 1902. d, Paul Müller, physiology or medicine, 1948. e, Allvar Gullstrand, physiology or medicine, 1911. f, Gerhart Hauptmann, literature, 1912. g, Hans Spemann, physiology or medicine, 1935. h, Cecil F. Powell, physics, 1950. i, Walther Bothe, physics, 1954.

No. 1772, each $1: a, Jules Bordet, physiology or medicine, 1919. b, René Cassin, peace, 1968. c, Verner von Heidenstam, literature, 1916. d, Jose Echegaray, literature, 1904. e, Otto Wallach, chemistry, 1910. f, Corneille Heymans, physiology or medicine, 1938. g, Ivar Giaever, physics, 1973. h, Sir William Cremer, peace, 1903. i, John W. Strutt, physics, 1904.

No. 1773, each $1: a, James Franck, physics, 1925. b, Tobias M.C. Asser, peace, 1911. c, Carl F.G. Spitteler, literature, 1919. d, Christiaan Eijkman, physiology or medicine, 1929. e, Ragnar Granit, physiology or medicine, 1967. f, Frederic Passy, peace, 1901. g, Louis Neel, physics, 1970. h, Sir William Ramsay, chemistry, 1904. i, Philip Noel-Baker, peace, 1959.

Each $6: No. 1774, Albert Schweitzer, peace, 1952. No. 1775, Willy Brandt, peace, 1971. No. 1776, Winston Churchill, literature, 1953.

**1995, Oct. 18**    **Litho.**    **Perf. 14**
1770A A354 75c multicolored    .55   .55
1770B A354 75c multicolored    .55   .55

**Miniature Sheets of 9, #a-i**
1771-1773 A354 Set of 3    20.00 20.00

**Souvenir Sheets**
1774-1776 A354 Set of 3    18.00 18.00

**Miniature Sheets**

Motion Pictures, Cent. — G122

Actresses, each $1: No. 1777a, Marion Davies. b, Marlene Dietrich. c, Lillian Gish. d, Bette Davis. e, Elizabeth Taylor. f, Veronica Lake. g, Ava Gardner. h, Grace Kelly. i, Kim Novak.

Romantic couples, each $1: No. 1778a, Nita Naldi, Rudolph Valentino. b, Ramon Novarro,

Alice Terry. c, Frederic March, Joan Crawford. d, Clark Gable, Vivien Leigh. e, Barbara Stanwyck, Burt Lancaster. f, Warren Beatty, Natalie Wood. g, Spencer Tracy, Katharine Hepburn. h, Humphrey Bogart, Lauren Bacall. i, Omar Sharif, Julie Christie.

Each $6: No. 1779, Sophia Loren. No. 1780, Greta Garbo, John Gilbert, horiz.

**1995, Nov. 3**    **Perf. 13½x14**
**Sheets of 9, #a-i**
1777-1778 G122 Set of 2    15.00 15.00

**Souvenir Sheets**
**Perf. 13½x14, 14x13½**
1779-1780 G122 Set of 2    10.00 10.00

Classic Racing Cars — G123

Designs: 10c, 1990's Williams-Renault Formula 1. 25c, 1980's Le Mans Porsche 956. 35c, 1970's Lotus "John Player Special." 75c, 1960's Ford GT 40. $2, 1950's Mercedes Benz W196. $3, 1920's Mercedes SSK.
$6, 1971 Tyrrell-Ford Fourmula 1.

**1995, Nov. 7**    **Perf. 14**
1781-1786 G123 Set of 6    6.75   6.75

**Souvenir Sheet**
1787 G123 $6 multicolored    6.00   6.00

Local Transportation G124

**1995, Nov. 7**
1788 G124 35c Donkey    .60   .30
1789 G124 75c Bus    1.50   1.00

**Miniature Sheet**

Sailing Ships — G125

Designs: No. 1790a, Preussen. b, Japanese junk. c, Pirate ship. d, Mayflower. e, Chinese junk. f, Santa Maria.
$5, Spanish galleon.

**1995, Nov. 7**
1790 G125 $1 Sheet of 6, #a.-f.    6.00   6.00

**Souvenir Sheet**
1791 G125 $5 multicolored    5.00   5.00

No. 1791 contains one 57x42mm stamp.

**Christmas Type of 1995**

Details or entire paintings: 10c, Immaculate Conception, by De Cosimo. 15c, St. Michel Dedicating Arms to the Madonna, by Le Nain. 35c, Annunciation, by de Credi. 50c, The Holy Family, by Jordaens. $3, Madonna and Child, by Lippi. $5, Madonna and Child with Ten Saints, by Fiorentino.
Each $6: No. 1798, Adoration of the Shepherds, by Van Oost. No. 1799, Holy Family, by Del Sart.

**1995, Nov. 28**    **Perf. 13½x14**
1792-1797 A356 Set of 6    8.00   8.00

**Souvenir Sheets**
1798-1799 A356 Set of 2    11.00 11.00

New Year 1996 (Year of the Rat) G126

Stylized rats: No. 1800: a, blue & multi. b, violet & multi. c, red & multi. d, green & multi. $2, Two rats, horiz.

**1996, Jan. 2**    **Litho.**    **Perf. 14½**
1800 G126 75c Block of 4, #a.-d.    2.25   2.25

**Miniature Sheet**
1801 G126 75c Sheet of 1 #1800    2.25   2.25

**Souvenir Sheet**
1802 G126 $2 multicolored    1.75   1.75

No. 1800 was issued in sheets of 16 stamps.

**Works by Dürer and Rubens Type of 1996**

Details or entire work: 15c, The Centaur Family, by Dürer. 35c, Oriental Ruler Seated, by Dürer. 50c, The Entombment, by Dürer. 75c, Man in Armor, by Rubens. $1, Peace Embracing Plenty, by Rubens. $2, Departure of Lot, by Rubens. $3, The Four Evangelists, by Rubens. No. 1810, $5, Knight, Death and Devil, by Dürer.
No. 1811, The Father of the Church, by Rubens. $6, St. Jerome, 1514 engraving, by Dürer.

**1996, Jan. 29**    **Litho.**    **Perf. 14**
1803-1810 A360 Set of 8    10.00 10.00

**Souvenir Sheets**
1811 A360 $5 multicolored    4.50   4.50
1812 A360 $6 multicolored    4.50   4.50

Disney Holidays G127

Disney characters celebrating: 25c, New Year's Day, "Hopping John" Feast. 50c, May Day. 75c, Independence Day. 90c, Halloween. $3, Thanksgiving. $4, Hanukkah.
Each $6: No. 1819, Caribbean Carnival. No. 1820, St. Patrick's Day Parade, vert.

**1996, Apr. 17**    **Litho.**    **Perf. 14x13½**
1813-1818 G127 Set of 6    10.00 10.00

**Souvenir Sheets**
**Perf. 14x13½, 13½x14**
1819-1820 G127 Set of 2    13.00 13.00

Sites in China G128

No. 1821, each $1: a, Entryway to hall, Imperial Palace. b, Great Wall's eastern end, Shanhaiguan. c, Fortress in Great Wall, Shanhaiguan. d, Gate of Heavenly Peace, Tiananmen, main entrance to Imperial City.
No. 1822, each $1: a, Mausoleum of Dr. Sun Yat-Sen, Nanjing. b, Summer Palace, Beijing. c, Temple of Heaven, Beijing. d, Hall of Supreme Harmony, Forbidden City, Beijing.
Each $6: No. 1823, Great Wall of China. No. 1824, Marble boat, Summer Palace, Beijing. Illustration reduced.

**1996, May 8**    **Perf. 13**
**Sheets of 4, #a-d**
1821-1822 G128 Set of 2    13.00 13.00

**Souvenir Sheets**
1823-1824 G128 Set of 2    10.50 10.50

China '96, 9th Asian Intl. Philatelic Exhibition (Nos. 1821-1822).
No. 1823 contains one 40x51mm stamp, No. 1824 one 51x40mm stamp.
See No. 1881.

**Queen Elizabeth II, 70th Birthday Type of 1996**

Designs: a, 35c, Portrait in blue dress. b, $2, Wearing crown. c, $4, Windsor Castle.
$6, Standing in front of palace.

**1996, May 8**    **Litho.**    **Perf. 13½x14**
1825 A362 Strip of 3, #a.-c.    4.75   4.75

**Souvenir Sheet**
1826 A362 $6 multicolored    4.50   4.50

No. 1825 was issued in sheets of 9 stamps with each strip in a different order.

Flowers — G129

35c, Camellia "Apple Blossom." 90c, Camellia japonica "Extravaganza." $1, Chrysanthemum "Primrose Dorothy Else." $2, Dahlia "Brandaris."
No. 1831: a, Odontoglossum. b, Cattleya. c, Paphiopedilum "Venus's Slipper." d, Laeliocattleya "Marysville."
No. 1832: a, Fushcia "Citation." b, Fuchsia "Amy Lye." c, Clysonimus butterfly. d, Digitalis purpurea "Foxglove" (h). e, Lilium martagon "Martagon Lily." f, Tulip "Couleur Cardinal." g, Galanthus nivalis "Snowdrop." h, Rose "Superstar." i, Crocus "Dutch Yellow Mammouth." j, Lilium speciosum Japanese lily. k, Lilium "Joan Evans." l, Rose "Rosemary Harkness."
$5, Narcissus "Rembrandt." $6, Gladiollus "Flowersong."

**1996, June 12**    **Litho.**    **Perf. 14**
1827-1830 G129 Set of 4    4.50   4.50
1831 G129 75c Strip of 4, #a.-d.    3.50   3.50
1832 G129 75c Sheet of 12, #a.-l.    9.00   9.00

**Souvenir Sheets**
1833 G129 $5 multicolored    4.50   4.50
1834 G129 $6 multicolored    5.00   5.00

No. 1831 issued in sheets of 12 stamps.

UNICEF, 50th Anniv. — G130

Letters spelling UNICEF and: 75c, Child smiling. $2, Child eating. $3, Child reading.
$6, Child on mother's back.

**1996, June 26**
1836-1838 G130 Set of 3    4.50   4.50

**Souvenir Sheet**
1839 G130 $6 multicolored    4.50   4.50

Jerusalem, 3000th Anniv. — G131

Flowers and: a, $1, Pool of Bethesda. b, $2, Damascus Gate. c, $3, Church of All Nations, Gethsemane.
$6, Church of the Holy Sepulchre.

**1996, June 26**
1840 G131 Sheet of 3, #a.-c.    4.50   4.50
**Souvenir Sheet**
1841 G131 $6 multicolored    4.50   4.50

**Radio, Cent. Type of 1996**

Entertainers: 35c, Ed Wynn. 75c, Red Skelton. $1, Joe Penner. $3, Jerry Colonna.
$6, Bob Elliott, Ray Goulding, horiz.

**1996, June 26**    **Perf. 13½x14**
1842-1845 A367 Set of 4    3.75   3.75

**Souvenir Sheet**
**Perf. 14x13½**
1846 A367 $6 multicolored    4.50   4.50

**Olympics Type of 1996**

35c, Memorial Coliseum, Los Angeles, 1994. 75c, Connie Carpenter-Phinney, US. $2, Mohamed Bouchighe, Algeria, vert. $3, Jackie Joyner-Kersee, US.
No. 1851, Gymnasts, vert, each $1: a, Julianne McNamara, US. b, Takuti Hayata,

Japan. c, Nikolai Andrianov, Russia. d, Mitch Gaylord, US. e, Ludmilla Touricheva, Russia. f, Karin Janz, Germany. g, Peter Kormann, US. h, Sawao Kato, Japan. i, Nadia Comaneci, Romania.

No. 1852, Equestrian participants, vert, each $1: a, Josef Neckermann, Germany. b, Harry Boldt, Germany. c, Elena Petouchkova, Russia. d, Alwin Schockemoehle, Germany. e, Hans Winkler, Germany. f, Joe Fargis, US. g, David Broome, Great Britain. h, Reiner Klimke, Germany. i, Richard Meade, Great Britain.

No. 1853, Young Japanese girl, vert. No. 1854, William Steinkraus, US.

**1996, July 15**      **Perf. 14**
1847-1850 A364   Set of 4    4.50   4.50

**Sheets of 9, #a-i**
1851-1852 A364   Set of 2    13.50 13.50

**Souvenir Sheets**
1853 A364 $5 multicolored    3.75   3.75
1854 A364 $6 multicolored    4.50   4.50

Classic Cars — G132

No. 1855: a, Delaunay-Belleville HB6, France. b, Bugatti Type-15, Italy. c, Mazda Type 800, Japan. d, Mercedes 24/100/140 Sport, Germany. e, MG K3 Rover, England. f, Plymouth Fury, US.

No. 1856: a, 35c, Chevrolet Belair Convertible, US. b, 75c, Rolls Royce Torpedo, England. c, $1, Nissan Type "Cepric," Japan. d, 50c, VIP car. e, $2, Mercedes Benz 500k, Germany. f, $3, Bugatti Type-13, Italy.

$5, Bugatti "Roadster" Type-55. $6, Lincoln Type-L, US.

**1996, July 25**   **Litho.**    **Perf. 14**
1855 G132    Sheet of 6, #a.-f.   4.50 4.50
1856 G132    Sheet of 6, #a.-f.   5.75 5.75

**Souvenir Sheets**
1857 G132 $5 multicolored    3.75 3.75
1858 G132 $6 multicolored    4.50 4.50

Nos. 1857-1858 each contain one 51x39mm stamp.

Ships — G133

Traditional Grenada schooners: 35c, Red and white. 75c, Blue and white.

No. 1861, Ancient ships, each $1: a, Athenian war triremes, 1000BC. b, Egyptian Nile trader, 30BC. c, Bangladesh dinghi, 3100BC. d, Queen Hatshepsut warship, 1476BC. e, Chinese junk, 200BC. f, Polynesian voyager, 600BC.

No. 1862, Ocean liners, each $1: a, Europa, Germany, 1957. b, Lusitania, England, 1906. c, Queen Mary, England, 1936. d, Bianca C, Italy. e, SS France, 1932. f, Orion, England, 1915.

$5, Queen Elizabeth 2, England, 1969. $6, Viking ship, 610BC.

**1996, Aug. 14**
1859 G133 35c multicolored    .25   .25
1860 G133 75c multicolored    .55   .55

**Sheets of 6, #a-f**
1861-1862 G133   Set of 2    9.00 9.00

**Souvenir Sheets**
1863 G133 $5 multicolored    3.75 3.75
1864 G133 $6 multicolored    4.50 4.50

No. 1863 contains one 51x42mm stamp, No. 1864 one 42x51mm stamp.

Famous Composers — G134

Composer, work illustrated: No. 1865, each $1: a, Bèla Bartòk, "Mikrokosmos," b, Giacomo Puccini, "Madame Butterfly," 1904. c, George Gershwin, "Rhapsody in Blue," 1923. d, Leonard Bernstein, "West Side Story", 1957. e, Kurt Weill, "Three Penny

Opera," 1928. f, John Cage, "Music of Changes," 1951. g, Aaron Copland, "El Salón Mexico," 1936. h, Sergei Prokofiev, "Peter and the Wolf," 1936. i, Igor Stravinsky, "Rite of Spring," 1913.

No. 1866, each $1: a, Felix Mendelssohn, overture to "Midsummer Night's Dream," 1826. b, Franz Schubert, "Die Forelle" (The Trout) D.550, 1817. c, Franz Joseph Haydn, "String Quartet in D Major," (Op. 1 (Lark), 1790. d, Robert Schumann, "Spring," Symphony No. 1, Op. 38, 1841. e, Ludwig Van Beethoven, "Moonlight" sonata Op. 27, No. 2. f, Gioacchino Rossini, "William Tell," 1829. g, George Frederick Handel, "Royal Fireworks Music," 1749. h, Peter Ilyich Tchaikovsky, "Swan Lake," Op.20, 1876. i, Frederic Chopin, "Fantasia," in F minor, Op. 49, 1840-41.

$5, Richard Strauss. $6, Mozart, "Jupiter" symphony in C major.

**1996, Aug. 26**    **Sheets of 9, #a-i**
1865-1866 G134   Set of 2    14.00 14.00

**Souvenir Sheets**
1867 G134 $5 multicolored    3.75 3.75
1868 G134 $6 multicolored    4.50 4.50

Trains — G135

No. 1869, each $1.50: a, Pacific Blue Peter, British Eastern. b, Class P36 4-8-4, Russia. c, Class OJ 2-10-2, China. d, Class 12 4-4-2, Belgium. e, Challenger Class 4-6-6-4, US. f, Class 25 4-8-4 Condenser, South Africa.

No. 1870, each $1.50: a, Federal Railways Class 38 4-6-0, Germany. b, Duchess of Hamilton Class 4-6-2, London & Glasgow. c, Class WP 4-6-2, Indian State Railways. d, Class 141R "L'Americane" 282, France (American-built). e, Class A4 4-6-2 Mallard, England. f, Deutche Reichsbahn Class 18 4-6-2, Germany.

$5, Cornish Rivera Express, King Class 4-6-2, Britain. $6, Caledonian "Royal Scot Class," 4-6-0, Britain.

**1996, Aug. 28**    **Sheets of 6, #a-f**
1869-1870 G135   Set of 2    13.50 13.50

**Souvenir Sheets**
1871 G135 $5 multicolored    3.75 3.75
1872 G135 $6 multicolored    4.50 4.50

### Christmas Type of 1996

Details of painting, Suffer Little Children to Come Unto Me, by Van Dyck: 15c, Child with beads over shoulder. 25c, Christ anointing head of child. $1, Mother holding infant, father, children. $1.50, Christ, disciples. $2, Father, infant. $4, Christ, children, family.

Each $6: No. 1879, Entire painting, horiz. No. 1880, Adoration of the Shepherds, by Bernaldo Strozzi, horiz.

**1996, Nov. 18**   **Litho.**   **Perf. 13½x14**
1873-1878 A377   Set of 6    7.00 7.00

**Souvenir Sheets**
1879-1880 A377   Set of 2    9.00 9.00

**Souvenir Sheet**

China '96 G136

Painting depicting scene from "Hong Lou Meng."

**1996, May 8**   **Litho.**   **Perf. 13x13½**
1881 G136 $2 multicolored    4.00 4.00

No. 1881 was not available until March 1997.

Hong Kong Past and Present — G137

No. 1882, Man Ho Temple, each $3: a, 1841. b, 1983.
No. 1883, City of Victoria with view of St. John's Cathedral, each $3: a, 1886. b, 1983.
No. 1884, Victoria Harbor, Hong Kong, each $3: a, 1858. b, 1983.

No. 1885, each $3: a, Treaty of Nanking, 1842. b, Margaret Thatcher signing Joint Declaration, 1984.
No. 1886, Victoria Harbor, each $3: a, Older black & white photograph. b, Modern photograph.

**1997, Feb. 12**   **Litho.**   **Perf. 14**
   **Sheets of 2, #a-b**
1882-1886 G137   Set of 5    25.00 25.00

Hong Kong '97.

### UNESCO Type of 1997

Designs: 15c, Kyoto, Japan. 25c, Roman ruins at Trier, Germany. $1, Mount Taishan, China. $1.50, Scandola Nature Reserve, France. $2, Fortress Wall, Dubrovnik, Croatia. $4, Angra Do Heroismo, Portugal.

No. 1893, vert, each $1: a, Sanctuary of Congonhas, Brazil. b, Cartagena, Colombia. c, City of Puebla, Mexico. d, Mayan Ruins, Copan, Honduras. e, Monastery of Popocate-petl, Mexico. f, Galapagos Islands, Ecuador. g, Waterfall, La Amisted Natl. Park, Costa Rica. h, Glaciares Natl. Park, Argentina.

No. 1894, vert, each $1: a, b, c, Kyoto, Japan. d, Ayutthaya, Thailand. e, Temple of Borobudur, Indonesia. f, Monuments, Pattadakal, India. g, Polonnaruwa, Sri Lanka. h, Sagarmatha Natl. Park, Nepal.

No. 1895, each $1.50: a, Cathedral of Notre Dame, France. b, Timbered house, Maulbronn, Germany. c, Himeji-Jo, Japan. d, Ruins, Delphi, Greece. e, Palace of Fontainebleau, France.

Each $6: No. 1896, Temple, Chengde, China. No. 1897, Pre-hispanic city of Teotihuacan, Mexico. No. 1898, Mont St. Michel, France.

**1997, Apr. 3**   **Litho.**   **Perf. 14**
1887-1892 A382   Set of 6    6.75 6.75

**Sheets of 8**
1893-1894 A382   Set of 2    12.00 12.00

**Sheet of 5 + Label**
1895 A382   #a.-e.    5.75 5.75

**Souvenir Sheets**
1896-1898 A382   Set of 3    15.00 15.00

Dogs and Cats — G138

Dogs: 35c, Springer spaniel. 75c, Doberman pinscher. $1, Italian spinone, vert. $2, Cocker spaniel, vert.
No. 1903: a, Leonberger. b, Newfoundland. c, Boxer. d, St. Bernard. e, Silky terrier. f, Miniature schnauzer.
No. 1904, Golden retriever puppy.

**1997, Apr. 10**
1899-1902 G138   Set of 4    3.00 3.00
   **Sheet of 6**
1903 G138 $1.50 #a.-f.    6.75 6.75

**Souvenir Sheet**
1904 G138   $6 multicolored    6.75 6.75

**1997, Apr. 10**

Cats: 45c, Abyssinian blue. 50c, Bermese cream, vert. 90c, Persian tortoiseshell and white. $3, Oriental shorthair red Agouti tabby, vert.
No. 1909: a, Siamese chocolate point. b, Oriental shorthair white. c, Burmese sable. d, Abysinian tabby. e, Persian shaded silver. f, Tonkinese natural mink.

1905-1908 G138   Set of 4    3.75 3.75
   **Sheet of 6**
1909 G138 $1.50 #a.-f.    6.75 6.75

**Souvenir Sheet**
1910 G138   $6 Sphinx, vert.    6.75 6.75

### Prehistoric Animal Type of 1997

Designs: 45c, Stegosaurus. 90c, Diplodocus. $1, Pteranodon, vert. $2, Deinonychus, ankylasaurus, vert.
No. 1915: a, Rhamphorhynchus, brachiosaurus (c, d, e,). b, Archaeopteryx. c, Anurognathus. d, Albertosaurus (f). e, Herrerasaurus. f, Platyhystrix.
Each $6: No. 1916, Hypacrosaurus. No. 1917, Apatosaurus, allosaurus, vert.

**1997, Apr. 15**   **Litho.**   **Perf. 14**
1911-1914 A385   Set of 4    3.00 3.00
1915 A385 $1.50 Sheet of 6, #a.-f.    6.75 6.75

**Souvenir Sheets**
1916-1917 A385   Set of 2    9.00 9.00

### Queen Elizabeth II, Prince Philip, 50th Wedding Anniv. Type of 1997

No. 1918: a, Colored portrait. b, Royal Arms. c, Black and white portrait. d, Black and white portrait in royal attire. e, Sandringham House. f, Queen in blue dress, Prince in uniform.
$6, Wedding portrait.

**1997, May 28**   **Litho.**   **Perf. 14**
1918 A386a $1 Sheet of 6, #a.-f.   4.75 4.75

**Souvenir Sheet**
1919 A386a $6 multicolored    4.75 4.75

### Paintings by Hiroshige Type of 1997

No. 1920: a, Koume Embankment. b, Azuma Shrine and the Entwined Camphor. c, Yanagishima. d, Inside Akiba Shrine, Ukeji. e, Distant View of Kinryuzan Temple and Azuma Bridge. f, Night View of Matsuchiyama and the San'ya Canal.
Each $6: No. 1921, Five Pines, Onagi Canal. No. 1922, Spiral Hall, Five Hundred Rakan Temple.

**1997, May 28**    **Perf. 13½x14**
1920 A387 $1.50 Sheet of 6, #a.-f.    8.50 8.50

**Souvenir Sheets**
1921-1922 A387   Set of 2    11.00 11.00

### Heinrich von Stephan Type of 1997

**1997, May 28**   **Litho.**   **Perf. 14**

Portrait of Von Stephan and: No. 1923: a, The Pony Express, 1860-61. b, UPU emblem. c, Steam locomotive postal delivery, 1800's. $6, Camel courier, Baghdad.

1923 A388 $1.50 Sheet of 3, #a.-c.    2.75 2.75

**Souvenir Sheet**
1924 A388   $6 multicolored    4.50 4.50

PACIFIC 97.

### Paul P. Harris Type of 1997

Designs: $3, Women in Burkina Faso pumping well water, portrait of Harris.
$6, Early Rotary parade float.

**1997, May 28**
1925 A389 $3 multicolored    2.25 2.25

**Souvenir Sheet**
1926 A389 $6 multicolored    4.50 4.50

### Grimm's Fairy Tale and Mother Goose Types of 1997

Scenes from "The Fox and the Geese:" No. 1927: a, Fox, geese. b, Geese singing as fox waves knife, fork. c, Fox asleep, geese celebrating. No. 1928, Fox lurking in forest, horiz. No. 1929, Girl with black sheep.

**1997, May 28**    **Perf. 13½x14**
1927 A391 $2 Sheet of 3, #a.-c.   4.50 4.50

**Souvenir Sheets**
   **Perf. 14x13½, 14**
1928 A391 $6 multicolored    4.50 4.50
1929 A392 $6 multicolored    4.50 4.50

1998 Winter Olympic Games, Nagano — G139

Designs: 90c, Downhill skier. $2, Luge. $3, Male figure skater. $5, Speed skater in blue hat.
No. 1934: a, Downhill skier in air. b, Freestyle skier. c, Curling. d, Ski jumper. e, Bobsled. f, Biathlon. g, Speed skater in yellow and red hat. h, Hockey. i, Cross-country skier.
Each $6: No. 1935, Luge, diff., vert. No. 1936, Female figure skater.

**1997, June 26**    **Perf. 14**
1930-1933 G139   Set of 4    8.25 8.25
1934 G139 $1 Sheet of 9, #a.-i.   6.75 6.75

**Souvenir Sheets**
1935-1936 G139   Set of 2    9.50 9.50

### Return of Hong Kong to China Type

Chinese flag in foreground, "Hong Kong" in English and Chinese with city scene showing through words: $1, Night scene. $1.25, Daytime view of skyscrapers. $1.50, Skyline at night, horiz. $2, View of harbor, horiz.

**1997, July 1**
**1937-1940** A394    Set of 4    4.50 4.50

Nos. 1937-1938 were issued in sheets of 4. Nos. 1939-1940 are 59x28mm and were issued in sheets of 3.

Fish — G140

Designs: 10c, Wimplefish. 15c, Clown trigerfish. 25c, Ringed emperor angelfish. 35c, Hooded butterfly fish. 45c, Semicircle angelfish. 75c, Scribbled angelfish. 90c, Threadfin butterfly fish. $1, Clown surgeonfish.

**1997, July 22**    **Litho.**    **Perf. 14**
| | | | | |
|---|---|---|---|---|
| **1941** | G140 | 10c multicolored | .30 | .30 |
| **1942** | G140 | 15c multicolored | .30 | .30 |
| **1943** | G140 | 25c multicolored | .30 | .30 |
| **1944** | G140 | 35c multicolored | .30 | .30 |
| **1945** | G140 | 45c multicolored | .45 | .45 |
| **1946** | G140 | 75c multicolored | .70 | .70 |
| **1947** | G140 | 90c multicolored | .90 | .90 |
| **1948** | G140 | $1 multicolored | .95 | .95 |
| | | *Nos. 1941-1948 (8)* | 4.20 | 4.20 |

Winnie the Pooh — G141

No. 1949: a, Winnie the Pooh. b, Kanga & Roo. c, Eeyore. d, Tigger. e, Piglet & Gopher. f, Rabbit.
$6, Christopher Robin.

**1997, Aug. 7**    **Litho.**    **Perf. 13½x14**
**1949** G141    $1 Sheet of 6, #a.-f.    6.00 6.00
**Souvenir Sheet**
**1950** G141    $6 multicolored    6.00 6.00

**1998 World Cup Soccer Type of 1997**

Team pictures: 10c, Italy, 1934. 20c, Angola. 45c, Brazil, 1958. $1, Uruguay, 1950. $1.50, West Germany, 1974. $5, Italy, 1938.
World Cup winners: No. 1951, $1: a, England. b, W. Germany, 1954. c, Uruguay. d, West Germany, 1990. e, Argentina, 1986. f, Brazil. g, Argentina, 1978. h, W. Germany 1974.
Tournament stars, vert.: No. 1952, $1: a, Ademir, Brazil. b, Kocsis, Hungary. c, Leonidas, Brazil. d, Nejedly, Czechoslovakia. e, Schiavio, Italy. f, Stabile, Uruguay. g, Pele, Brazil. h, Walter, W. Germany.
Each $6: No. 1953, Shearer, England, vert. No. 1954, Paulao, Angola.

**1997, Aug. 11**
**1950A-1950F** A397    Set of 6    6.25 6.25
**Sheets of 8, #a-h**
**1951-1952** A397    Set of 2    12.50 12.50
**Souvenir Sheets**
**1953-1954** A397    Set of 2    9.50 9.50

**Fish Type of 1997**

$2, Tursiops truncatus. $5, Balistes vetula. $10, Pterois volitans. $20, Equetus lanceolatus.

**1997, July 22**    **Litho.**    **Perf. 14**
| | | | | |
|---|---|---|---|---|
| **1955** | G140 | $2 multicolored | 1.50 | 1.50 |
| **1956** | G140 | $5 multicolored | 3.75 | 3.75 |
| **1957** | G140 | $10 multicolored | 7.50 | 7.50 |
| **1958** | G140 | $20 multicolored | 15.00 | 15.00 |
| | | *Nos. 1955-1958 (4)* | 27.75 | 27.75 |

Sealed with a Kiss — G142

Characters from Disney's classic animated films: No. 1959: a, Snow White, 1937. b,

Pinocchio, 1940. c, Peter Pan, 1953. d, Cinderella, 1950. e, The Little Mermaid, 1989. f, Beauty and the Beast, 1991. g, Aladdin, 1992. h, Pocahontas, 1995. i, Hunchback of Notre Dame, 1996.
$5, The Aristocats, 1970, vert.

**1997, Aug. 7**    **Litho.**    **Perf. 14x13½**
**1959** G142    $1 Sheet of 9, #a.-i.    7.00 7.00
**Souvenir Sheet**
**Perf. 13½x14**
**1960** G142    $5 multicolored    4.00 4.00

Butterflies of the World — G143

75c, Polyura dehaani. 90c, Polyura dolon. $1, Charaxes candiope. $1.50, Pantaporia punctata. $2, Charaxes etesippe. $3, Charaxes castor.
No. 1967, Euphaedra, each $1.50: a, Francina. b, Eleus. c, Harpalyce. d, Cyparissa. e, Gausape. f, Imperialis.
No. 1968, each $1.50: a, Euthalia confucius. b, Euthalia kardama. c, Limenitis albomaculata. d, Hestina assimilis. e, Kalima inachus. f, Euthalia teutoides.
Each $6: No. 1969, Charaxes numenes, vert. No. 1970, Charaxes nobilis, vert.

**1997, Aug. 12**    **Perf. 14**
**1961-1966** G143    Set of 6    7.25 7.25
**Sheets of 6, #a-f**
**1967-1968** G143    Set of 2    16.00 16.00
**Souvenir Sheets**
**1969-1970** G143    Set of 2    10.00 10.00

James Dean (1931-55), Actor — G144

Various portraits.

**1997, Aug. 22**    **Perf. 14x13½**
**1971** G144    $1 Sheet of 9, #a.-i.    7.25 7.25

Mushrooms G145

Designs: 75c, Clitocybe metachroa. 90c, Clavulinopsis helvola. $1, Lycoperdon pyriforme. $1.50, Auricularia auricula-judae. $2, Clathrus archeri. $3, Lactarius trivialis.
No. 1978: a, Entoloma incanum. b, Coprinus atramentarius. c, Mycena polygramma. d, Lepista nuda. e, Pleurotis cornucopiae. f, Laccaria amethystina.
Each $6: No. 1979, Amanita muscaria. No. 1980, Morchella esculenta.

**1997, Sept. 4**    **Perf. 14**
**1972-1977** G145    Set of 6    7.00 7.00
**1978** G145    $1.50 Sheet of 6, #a.-f.    7.00 7.00
**Souvenir Sheets**
**1979-1980** G145    Set of 2    10.00 10.00

G146

Orchids — G147

Designs: 35c, Symphyglossum sanguineum. 45c, Doritaenopsis "Mythic Beauty." 75c, Odontoglossum cervantesii. 90c, Cattleya "Pumpernickel." $1, Vanda "Patricia Law." $1.50, Odontonia "Debutante." $2, Laeliocattleya "Mini Purple." $3, Phragmipedium "Dominiarium."
No. 1989, each $1: a, Cymbidium "Showgirl." b, Disa "Blackii." c, Phalaenopsis aphrodite. d, Iwanagaara "Apple Blossum." e, Masdevallia "Copper Angel." f, Paphiopedilum micranthum. g, Paphiopedilum "Claire de Lune." h, Cattleya forbesii. i, Dendrobium "Dawn Maree."
No. 1990, each $1: a, Lycaste "Aquila." b, Brassolaeliocattleya "Dorothy Bertsch." c, Phalaenopsis "Zuma Urchin." d, Promenaea xanthina. e, Amesiella philippinensis. f, Brassocattleya "Angel Lace." g, Brassoepidsendrum "Peggy Ann." h, Miltonia seine. i, Sophralaeliocattleya "Precious Stones."
No. 1991, each $1.50: a, Miltoniosis "Jean Sabourin." b, Cymbididium "Red Beauty." c, Brassocattleya "Green Dragon." d, Phalaenopsis hybrid. e, Laelio cattleya "Mary Ellen Carter." f, Disa hybrid.
No. 1992, each $1.50: a, Lycaste macrobulbon. b, Cochleanthes discolor. c, Cymbidium "Nang Carpenter." d, Paphiopedilum "Clair de Lune." e, Masdevallia caudata. f, Cymbidum "Showgirl."
$5, Phalenopsis "Medford Star." $6, Brassolaeliocattleya "Mem. Dorothy Bertsch."

**1997, Sept. 4**
**1981-1988** G146    Set of 8    7.50 7.50
**Sheets of 9, #a-i**
**1989-1990** G147    Set of 2    13.50 13.50
**Sheets of 6, #a-f**
**1991-1992** G146    Set of 2    13.50 13.50
**Souvenir Sheets**
**1993** G146    $5 multicolored    3.75 3.75
**1994** G146    $6 multicolored    4.50 4.50

Famous Composers, Musicians — G148

No. 1995, each $1: a, Beethoven. b, Tchaikovsky. c, J.S. Bach. d, Chopin. e, Stravinsky. f, Haydn. g, Mahler. h, Rossini.
Each $6: No. 1996, Mozart. No. 1997, Schubert.

**1997, Oct. 10**    **Litho.**    **Perf. 14½x14**
**Sheet of 8**
**1995** G148    #a.-h. + label    6.50 6.50
**Souvenir Sheets**
**1996-1997** G148    Set of 2    10.00 10.00

Diana, Princess of Wales (1961-97) G149

Various portraits of Diana wearing various hats, scenes following her death: No. 1998: a, Buckingham Palace. b, Island, Spencer Estate, Althorp. c, Westminster Abbey. d, Gate, Spencer Estate. e, Gate, Kensington Palace. g, Spencer Estate, Althorp.
$6, Diana smelling flowers in front of Kensington Palace.

**1997, Nov. 10**    **Perf. 14**
**1998** G149    $1.50 Sheet of 6, #a.-f.    6.75 6.75
**Souvenir Sheet**
**1999** G149    $6 multicolored    4.75 4.75
No. 1999 contains one 60x40mm stamp.

**Christmas Art Type of 1997**

Entire paintings, details, or sculptures: 20c, Choir of Angels, by Simon Marmion. 75c, The Annunciation, by Giotto. 90c, Festival of the Rose Garlands, by Albrecht Durer. $1.50, Madonna with Two Angels, by Hans Memling.

$2, The Ognissanti Madonna, by Giotto. $3, Angel with Candlestick, by Michelangelo.
Each $6: No. 2006, Cupid Commemorating a Marriage by Incising on a Table, by Jean-Baptiste Huet, horiz. No. 2007, The Rising of the Sun, by Francois Boucher, horiz.

**1997, Dec. 5**    **Litho.**    **Perf. 14**
**2000-2005** A402    Set of 6    12.50 12.50
**Souvenir Sheets**
**2006-2007** A402    Set of 2    9.00 9.00

**Marine Life Type of 1997**

No. 2008, each $1: a, Holocanthus ciliaris. b, Ballstoides conspicillum. c, Chaetodon quadrimaculatus. d, Microspathodon chrysurus. e, Halichoeres garnoti. f, Gramma loreto. g, Liopropoma carmabi. h, Lactophrys triqueter. i, Cephalopolis miniatus.
Each $6: No. 2009, Carcharhinus melanopterus. No. 2010, Obistognathus aurifrons, vert.

**1997, Dec. 12**    **Litho.**    **Perf. 14**
**2008** A386    Sheet of 9, #a.-i.    7.50 7.50
**Souvenir Sheets**
**2009-2010** A386    Set of 2    9.00 9.00

New Year 1998 (Year of the Tiger) — G150

**Die Cut Perf. 11**
**1998, Feb. 10**    **Litho.**
**Self-Adhesive**
**2011** G150    $1.50 Hologram    3.25
**Souvenir Sheet**
**2012** G150    $3 like #2011    5.50
No. 2011 was issued in sheets of 4. No. 2012 contains one 52x65mm stamp.

Great Ships, Shipwrecks G151

Ships — No. 2013: a, CSS Alabama. b, Persia. c, Ariel. d, CSS Florida. e, Great Eastern. f, Jacob Bell. g, Star of India. h, Robert E. Lee. i, US Monitor Passaic. j, Madagascar. k, HMS Devastation. l, General Grant.
"Gone with the Wind," vert. — No. 2014: a, Clark Gable. b, Blockade runner wrecked on Sullivan's Island, North Carolina, 1863. c, Margaret Mitchell. d, George Alfred Trenholm, model for character Rhett Butler. e, Dock Street Theater, confiscated from Trenholm after Civil War. f, Howlet sinks off Charleston, South Carolina, 1865. g, USS Tecumseh sunk by Confederate gunboats, 1864. h, City jail, where Trenholm was imprisioned, 1865.
Each $6: No. 2015, Nashville sinks the Union clipper, Harvey Birch, vert. No. 2016, Dr. Lee Spence, expert on shipwrecks and sunken treasures, Alabama sinking Hatteras off Texas coast.

**1998, May 7**    **Litho.**    **Perf. 14**
**2013** G151    75c Sheet of 12, #a.-l.    7.25 7.25
**2014** G151    $1 Sheet of 8, #a.-h.    6.50 6.50
**Souvenir Sheets**
**2015-2016** G151    Set of 2    9.50 9.50
Nos. 2015-2016 each contain one 57x43mm stamp.

Modern, Future Aircraft — G152

70c, Concept strike fighter. 90c, Concept space shuttle. $2, Concept air & space jet. $3, V Jet II.
No. 2021: a, Velocity 173 RG Elite. b, Davis DA 9. c, Concorde. d, Voyager. e, Factimobile. f, RAF 2000. g, Boomerang. h, N1M Flying Wing.
Each $6: No. 2022, Gee-Bee replica. No. 2023, Concept Aeropod.

**1998, May 13**
**2017-2020** G152    Set of 4    5.50 5.50

2021 G152 $1 Sheet of 8, #a.-h.   6.50 6.50

**Souvenir Sheets**

2022-2023 G152 Set of 2   9.00 9.00

No. 2022 is inscribed "Delmar."

Orchids — G153

Designs: $1, Laclia tenebrosa. $1.50, Phragmipedium besseae. $2, Pschopsis papilio. $3, Masdevallia coccinea.

No. 2028, each $1: a, Lycaste deppei. b, Dendrobium victoriae. c, Dendrobium nobile. d, Cymbidium danyanum. e, Cymbidium starbright. f, Cymbidium giganteum. g, Chysis aurea. h, Broughtonia sanguinea. i, Cattleya guttata.

No. 2029, each $1: a, Calanthe vestita. b, Cattleya bicolor. c, Laelia anceps. d, Epidendrum prismatocarpum. e, Coelogyne ochcracea. f, Doritaenopsis eclantant. g, Laelia gouldiana. h, Encyclia vitellina. i, Maxillaria praestans.

Each $6: No. 2030, Masdevallia ignea. No. 2031, Encyclia brassavolae.

**1998, May 19**

2024-2027 G153   Set of 4   6.25 6.25

**Sheets of 9, #a-i**

2028-2029 G153   Set of 2   14.00 14.00

**Souvenir Sheets**

2030-2031 G153   Set of 2   9.50 9.50

**Sea Birds Type of 1998**

75c, Bonaparte's gull. 90c, Western sandpiper. $2, Great black-backed gull. $3, Dotterell.

No. 2036, each $1.50: a, Terns. b, Brown pelican. c, Black-legged kittiwake. d, Herring gull. e, Lesser noddy. f, Kittiwake.

No. 2037, each $1.50: a, Whimbrels. b, Golden white-tailed tropic bird. c, Arctic tern. d, Ruddy turnstones. e, Imperial shag. f, Magellan gull.

Each $5: No. 2038, Yellow-nosed albatross, vert. No. 2039, Broad-billed prion.

**1998, June 30   Litho.   Perf. 14**

2032-2035 A408   Set of 4   6.00 6.00

**Sheets of 6, #a-f**

2036-2037 A408   Set of 2   15.00 15.00

**Souvenir Sheets**

2038-2039 A408   Set of 2   9.00 9.00

Diana, Princess of Wales (1961-97) — G155

Diana in front of Kensington Palace: No. 2040, Wearing tiara, ruffled dress. No. 2041, Wearing white dress, pearls.

**Litho. & Embossed**

**1998, July 14   Die Cut 7½**

2040 G155 $20 gold

2041 G155 $20 gold & multi

**Intl. Year of the Ocean Type**

No. 2042: a, Great black-backed gull. b, Common dolphin. c, Seal. d, Amazonian catfish. e, Shark. f, Goldfish. g, Cyathopharynx. h, Whale. i, Telmatochromis. j, Crab. k, Octopus. l, Turtle.

No. 2043: a, Dolphins. b, Seal. c, Turtle. d, Leopard shark. e, Flame angelfish. f, Syndontis. g, Lamprologus. h, Kryptopterus bicirrhus. i, Pterophyllum scalare. j, Swimming pancake. k, Cowfish. l, Sea horse.

---

Each $6: No. 2044, Tetraodon mbu. No. 2045, Goldfish.

**1998, Aug. 19   Litho.   Perf. 14**

**Sheets of 12**

2042 A411   75c #a.-l.   7.25 7.25

2043 A411   90c #a.-l.   8.50 8.50

**Souvenir Sheets**

2044-2045 A411   Set of 2   9.50 9.50

**Gandhi Type of 1998**

Portraits of Gandhi.

**1998, Sept. 15   Litho.   Perf. 14**

2046 A413 $1 multicolored   .75 .75

**Souvenir Sheet**

2047 A413 $6 multicolored   4.75 4.75

No. 2046 was issued in sheets of 4.

**Picasso Type of 1998**

Paintings: 45c, Bust of a Woman, 1943, vert. $2, Three Musicians, 1921. $3, Studio at La Californie, 1956.

$5, Woman with a Blue Hat, 1901.

**Perf. 14½x14, 14x14½**

**1998, Sept. 15**

2048-2050 A414   Set of 3   4.25 4.25

**Souvenir Sheet**

2051 A414 $5 multicolored   3.75 3.75

**Delacroix Type of 1998**

Paintings — No. 2052: a, The Natchez. b, Christ and His Disciples Crossing the Sea of Galilee. c, Sunset. d, Moroccans Outside the Walls of Tangier. e, The Fireplace. f, Forest View with a Oak Tree. g, View of the Harbor at Dieppe. h, Arabs Skirmishing in the Mountains.

$5, Orphan Girl in a Cemetary, vert.

**1998, Sept. 15   Litho.   Perf. 14**

2052 A415 $1 Sheet of 8, #a.-h.   6.50 6.50

**Souvenir Sheet**

2053 A415 $5 multicolored   4.75 4.75

**Organization of American States Type**

**1998, Sept. 15**

2054 A416 $1 multicolored   .90 .90

**Diana Type of 1998**

**1998   Perf. 14½**

2055   A417 $1.50 multicolored   1.25 1.25

**Self-Adhesive**

**Serpentine Die Cut Perf. 11½**

**Sheet of 1**

**Size: 53x65mm**

2055A A417   $8 Diana, buildings

No. 2055 was issued in sheets of 6. Soaking in water may affect the multi-layer image of No. 2055A.

Issued: $1.50, 9/15; $8, 11/5/98.

**Ferrari Type of 1998**

No. 2056: a, 275 GTB. b, 340 MM. c, 250 GT SWB Berlinetta SEFAC "Hot Rod."

$5, First Ferrari Cabriolet (011-S).

**1998, Sept. 15   Perf. 14**

2056 A418 $2 Sheet of 3, #a.-c.   4.75 4.75

**Souvenir Sheet**

2057 A418 $5 multicolored   4.75 4.75

No. 2057 contains one 91x35mm stamp.

**Scout Jamboree Type of 1998**

Designs: 90c, Scout sign. $1.50, Lord Baden-Powell. $5, Scout salute.

$6, Lord Baden-Powell, diff., vert.

**1998, Sept. 15**

2058-2060 A419   Set of 3   5.75 5.75

**Souvenir Sheet**

2061 A419 $6 multicolored   4.75 4.75

**Royal Air Force Type of 1998**

No. 2062, each $2: a, Chinook. b, BAe Harrier GR5. c, Panavia Tornado F3 ADV. d, Chinook HC2 carrying 105mm light gun.

No. 2063, each $2: a, Tornado GR1. b, BAe Hawk TIA. c, Sepecat Jaguar GRI. d, Harrier GR7.

Each $6: No. 2064, Eurofighter 2000, Hunter. No. 2065, Biplane, hawk in flight. No. 2066, Head of hawk, biplane. No. 2067, Eurofighter 2000, Tornado.

---

Disney Christmas Trains — G156

Silly Symphony Railroad — No. 2068, each $1: a, Santa in locomotive, rabbit. b, Giraffe, elephant, tiger. c, Wolf, Three Little Pigs. d, Robin Hood blowing horn, Jiminy Cricket, penguins, children. e, Geese, Indian boy, turtle in caboose.

Mickey's Toontown Christmas Train — No. 2069, each $1: a, Mickey in locomotive. b, Pluto, chipmunks in coal car. c, Donald, Daisy Duck in passenger car. d, Goofy leading Huey, Dewey, & Louie in caroling. e, Minnie in caboose.

Pooh's Railroad — No. 2070, each $1: a, Piglet as engineer. b, Winnie the Pooh shoveling honey. c, Rabbit, Owl. d, Kanga, Roo, Christopher Robin. e, Eeyore, Tigger.

Each $6: No. 2071, Santa setting up toy train under Christmas tree. No. 2072, Mickey as engineer. No. 2073, Winnie the Pooh reading paper, Rabbit, Piglet.

**1998, Oct. 15   Perf. 14x13½**

**Sheets of 5, #a-e**

2068-2070 G156   Set of 3   11.00 11.00

**Souvenir Sheets**

2071-2073 G156   Set of 3   13.00 13.00

**New Year 1999 (Year of the Rabbit) Type**

Various rabbits, color of country name: a, green. b, orange. c, red.

**Sheet of 3**

**Self-Adhesive**

**1999, Jan. 4   Litho.   Die Cut Perf. 9**

2074 A425 $1.50 gold & multi, #a.-c.   3.50 3.50

No. 2074b has point of triangle down.

Queen Elizabeth II and Prince Philip, 50th Wedding Anniv. G157

**Litho. & Embossed**

**1999, Jan. 8   Die Cut Perf. 7**

**Without Gum**

2075 G157 $20 gold & multi

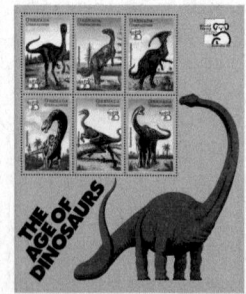

Australia '99, World Stamp Expo G158

Dinosaurs — No. 2076: a, Troodon. b, Camptosaurus. c, Parasaurolophus. d, Dryosaurus. e, Gallimimus. f, Camarasaurus (all vert.).

No. 2077: a, Duckbill. b, Lambeosaurus. c, Iguanodon. d, Euoplocephalus. e, Triceratops. f, Brachiosaurus. g, Ponoptosaurus. h, Stegosaurus.

---

Each $6: No. 2078, Edmontosaurus. No. 2079, Tyrannosaurus, vert. No. 2080, Halticosaurus, vert.

**1999, Mar. 1   Litho.   Perf. 14**

2076 G158   $1 Sheet of 6, #a.-f.   4.50 4.50

2077 G158   $1.50 Sheet of 8, #a.-h.   9.25 9.25

**Souvenir Sheets**

2078-2080 G158   Set of 3   13.50 13.50

Trains — G159

Designs: 15c, India, 4-4-0 express passenger and mail engine. 75c, Ireland, 4-4-0. 90c, Canada, 4-6-0. $1.50, India, 4-4-0 express. $2, Australia, 4-6-2. $3, Great Britain, Stirling 0-4-2.

No. 2087, each $2: a, Belgium, type 4-4-0. b, Sweden, class "Cc" type 4-4-0. c, Chile, 0-6-4. d, Bolivia, Fairlie-type double engine.

No. 2088, each $2: a, Belgium, 4-cylinder 4-6-0. b, England, 4-cylinder 4-6-0. c, Northern Ireland, 2-cylinder compound 4-4-0. d, Holland, 4-4-0.

No. 2089, each $2: a, Switzerland, 0-8-0. b, Ireland, 0-6-0. c, US 4-6-0. d, Great Britain, Prince of Wales class 4-2-2.

No. 2090, each $2: a, Ireland, narrow gauge 2-4-2. b, Russia, 0-8-0. c, England, Ivatt large-boilered Atlantic. d, Germany, Atlantic type express.

No. 2091, each $2: a, France, 4-6-0. b, New Zealand, 2-6-4. c, Burma, 4-4-4. d, Malaya, 4-6-0.

Each $6: No. 2092, France, 4-4-0. No. 2093, Italy, 0-6-4.

**1999, Apr. 12   Litho.   Perf. 14**

2081-2086 G159   Set of 6   6.25 6.25

**Sheets of 4, #a-d**

2087-2091 G159   Set of 5   30.00 30.00

**Souvenir Sheets**

2092-2093 G159   Set of 2   9.00 9.00

**Flora and Fauna Type of 1999**

Designs: 75c, Porkfish. 90c, Leatherback turtle. $1.50, Ruby-throated hummingbird. $2, Theope eudocia.

No. 2098, vert, each $1: a, White-tailed tropicbird. b, Laughing gull. c, Palm tree. d, Humpback whale. e, Painted bunting. f, Common grackle. g, Green anole. h, Morpho peleides. i, Prepoua meandor.

No. 2099, vert, each $1: a, Common dolphin. b, Catonephele numiti. c, Sooty tern. d, Vermilion flycatcher. e, Blue grosbeak. f, Great egret. g, Actinote pellenea. h, Anteos clorinade. i, Common iguana.

Each $6: No. 2100, Bannaquit. No. 2101, Beay gregory.

**1999, Apr. 26**

2094-2097 A430   Set of 4   4.00 4.00

**Sheets of 9, #a-i**

2098-2099 A430   Set of 2   14.00 14.00

**Souvenir Sheets**

2100-2101 A430   Set of 2   9.25 9.25

**Hokusai Type of 1999**

Entire paintings or details, horiz. — No. 2102, each $1.50: a, A Breeze on a Fine Day. b, Ejiri. c, Horse drawings (kicking up hind legs). d, Horse drawings (with head down). e, View Along the Bank of the Sumida River. f, Thunderstorm Below the Mountain.

No. 2103. each $1.50: a, Fuchû. b, Doll Fair at Fikkendana. c, Sumo Wrestlers (with arms locked). d, Sumo Wrestlers (one head butting). e, Sôjô Henjô. f, Twin Gardens Gateway of the Asakusa Kannon Temple.

Each $6: No. 2104, Kôbô Daishi Exorcising Demon that Causes Sickness. No. 2105, Stretching Cloth.

**1999, May 24   Litho.   Perf. 14x13½**

**Sheets of 6, #a-f**

2102-2103 A431   Set of 2   13.50 13.50

**Souvenir Sheet**

2104-2105 A431   Set of 2   9.00 9.00

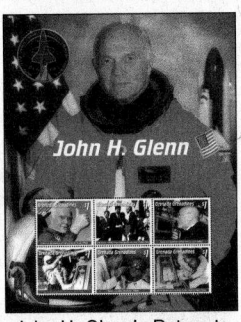

John H. Glenn's Return to Space — G160

Portraits — No. 2106: a, Thumbs up, 1998 flight. b, Receiving NASA Service Award from Pres. Kennedy, 1962. c, Talking to Ground Control from Discovery, 1998. d, Climbing out of Friendship 7, 1962. e, Being checked for balance, 1998. f, Climbing into Friendship 7, 1962.

No. 2107, vert.: a, Portrait as Ohio Senator, 1974. b, Official portrait, 1962. c, Suit-up test, 1998. d, Suiting up for Discovery, 1998. e, Meeting press after Discovery flight, 1998. f, Smiling aboard Discovery, 1998. g, Medical research, 1998. h, Official portrait, 1998.

**1999, May 24**      **Perf. 14x14½**
**Sheets of 6 and 8**
2106 G160 $1 #a.-f.      5.00 5.00
2107 G160 $1 #a.-h.      6.50 6.50

**Goethe Type of 1999**

No. 2108: a, Peasants dancing under the linden tree. b, Faust dreams of soaring above the mortal.
No. 2109, Portrait of Goethe.

**1999, May 24**      **Perf. 14**
2108 A432 $3 Sheet of 3, #a.-b., Grenada #2858b   6.75 6.75
**Souvenir Sheet**
2109 A432 $6 multi      4.50 4.50

**IBRA '99 World Stamp Expo Type of 1999**

IBRA '99 emblem, Luckenbach sailing ship and: No. 2110, 35c, Thurn and Taxis #1. No. 2113, $3, North German Confederation #1.
Emblem, Leipzig-Dresden Railway and: No. 2111, 45c, Schleswig-Holstein #1. No. 2112, $1.50, Oldenburg #4.
$6, Cover showing pair of Thurn & Taxis #1.

**1999, May 24**    **Litho.**    **Perf. 14**
2110-2113 A433   Set of 4    4.00 4.00
**Souvenir Sheet**
2114 A433 $6 multicolored    4.75 4.75

**Philexfrance '99 Type**
**Souvenir Sheets**

Designs, each $6: No. 2115, Co-co 7000 class high speed electric locomotive. No. 2116, Cha Pelon 4-8-0.

**1999, May 24**    **Litho.**    **Perf. 14**
2115-2116 A435   Set of 2    7.00 7.00

Beginning with Nos. 2117-2118, stamps from Grenada Grenadines will be inscribed GRENADA / Carriacou & Petite Martinique.

**Wedding of Prince Edward and Sophie Rhys-Jones Type**

No. 2117: a, Edward. b, Sophie, Edward. c, Sophie.
$6, Couple.

**1999, June 18**    **Litho.**    **Perf. 13½**
2117 A436 $3 Sheet of 3, #a.-c.   6.75 6.75
**Souvenir Sheet**
2118 A436 $6 multicolored    4.50 4.50

**UN Rights of the Child Type of 1999**

No. 2119: a, Boy. b, Liv Ullman, UNICEF's first woman ambassador. c, Woman.
$6, Maurice Pate, founding director of UNICEF.

**1999, May 24**    **Litho.**    **Perf. 14**
2119 A437 $3 Sheet of 3, #a.-c.   6.75 6.75
**Souvenir Sheet**
2120 A437 $6 multicolored    4.50 4.50

---

**Queen Mother Type of 1999**

No. 2121: a, Lady Elizabeth Bowles-Lyon. b, Queen Elizabeth in Rhodesia, 1957. c, Queen Elizabeth, Princess Elizabeth, and Princess Anne, 1950. d, Queen Mother, 1988.
$6, Queen Mother, Berlin.

**Gold frames**

**1999, Aug. 16**      **Sheet of 4**
2121 A440 $2 #a.-d. + label    6.00 6.00
**Souvenir Sheet**
2122 A440 $6 multicolored    4.50 4.50

No. 2122 contains one 38x50mm stamp. Margins of sheets are embossed.
See Nos. 2369-2370.

**Litho. & Embossed**
*Die Cut Perf. 8¾*
**Without Gum**
2122A A440a $20 gold & multi

**Famous People Type of 1999**

Actors — No. 2123: a, George Raft (1895-1980). b, Raft in movie scene. c, Fatty Arbuckle (1887-1933) in movie scene. d, Portrait of Arbuckle. e, Buster Keaton (1895-1966). f, Keaton in movie scene. g, Harold Lloyd (1893-1971) in movie scene. h, Portrait of Lloyd.
No. 2124: a, James Cagney (1899-1986). b, Cagney in movie scene. c, Edward G. Robinson (1893-1973). d, Robinson in movie scene.
$6, Charlie Chaplin (1889-1977).

**1999, Aug. 20**    **Litho.**    **Perf. 14**
2123 A426 $1 Sheet of 8, #a.-h.   6.00 6.00
2124 A426 $2 Sheet of 4, #a.-d.   6.00 6.00
**Souvenir Sheet**
2125 A426 $6 multicolored    4.50 4.50

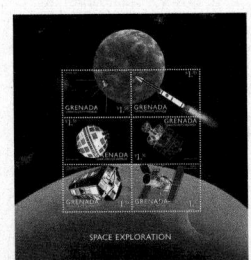

Space Exploration — G161

No. 2126, each $1.50: a, Sputnik I. b, Explorer I. c, Telstar I. d, Marisat I. e, Long Duration Exposure Facility. f, Hubble Space Telescope.
No. 2127, vert., each $1.50: a, X-15. b, Mercury Redstone 3 rocket, Freedom 7. c, Mercury Atlas 6 rocket, Friendship 7. d, Gemini 4, Edward H. White II. e, Saturn V rocket, Edwin Aldrin. f, Lunar rover.
Each $6: No. 2128, Space Shuttle Columbia. No. 2129, Mars Pathfinder.

**1999, Oct. 8**    **Litho.**    **Perf. 14**
**Sheets of 6, #a.-f.**
2126-2127 G161   Set of 2    13.50 13.50
**Souvenir Sheets**
2128-2129 G161   Set of 2    9.00 9.00

**Christmas Type of 1999**

Christmas plants: 15c, Poinsettia. 35c, Holly. 75c, Fir tree. $1.50, Ivy. $3, Geranium. $6, The Adoration of the Magi.

**1999, Nov. 23**    **Litho.**    **Perf. 13¾**
2130-2134 A444   Set of 5    4.25 4.25
**Souvenir Sheet**
2135 A444 $6 multicolored    4.50 4.50

Kirk Douglas (b. 1916), Actor — G162

Douglas in various poses.

**1999**    **Litho.**    **Perf. 13¾**
2136 G162 $1.50 Sheet of 6, #a.-f.   6.75 6.75
**Souvenir Sheet**
2137 G162   $6 multi    4.50 4.50

---

Elvis Presley — G163

Presley in various poses.

**1999**      **Sheet of 6**
2138 G163 $1.50 #a.-f.    6.75 6.75

**Millennium Type of 2000**

Highlights of 1970s — No. 2139: a, Salvador Allende elected Pres. of Chile. b, Earth Day. c, CAT scan introduced. d, Pres. Nixon goes to China. e, Massacre at Olympics. f, Gas shortages. g, Sydney Opera House opens. h, Pres. Nixon resigns. i, New theory of black holes. j, US bicentennial. k, 1st "Test tube" baby. l, Pope John Paul II visits Poland. m, Iran's Islamic Revolution. n, Concorde makes 1st flight. o, Charles de Gaulle dies. p, Camp David agreements (60x40mm). q, Mother Teresa wins Nobel Peace Prize.

Highlights of 1300-1350 — No. 2140: a, Robert the Bruce crowned King of Scotland. b, Giotto paints frescoes. c, Mansa Musa rules Mali. d, Dante completes "The Divine Comedy." e, Noh theater developed in Japan. f, Tenochtitlan founded by Aztecs. g, Ibn Battutah journeys to Africa and Asia. h, Munich fire. i, Ivan I of Russia increases Moscow's importance. j, Hundred Years' War begins. k, First use of cannons in Europe. l, Black Death devastates Europe. m, Boccaccio begins writing "Decameron." n, Eyeglasses developed in Italy. o, Plate armor replaces chain mail. p, Grand Canal of China completed. (60x40mm). q, Migration of Maoris to New Zealand.

Sea Exploration — No. 2141: a, Ferdinand Magellan. b, Restless seas. c, Queen Elizabeth I. d, Albatrosses. e, Penguins. f, Tahiti. g, Breadfruit. h, Easter Island. i, Maori carving. j, Lobster. k, Orchid. l, Walrus. m, Kangaroo. n, The Beagle. o, Frigatebird. p, Strait of Magellan (60x40mm). q, Capt. James Cook.

**2000**    **Litho.**    **Perf. 12¾x12½**
**Sheets of 17**
2139 A450 20c #a.-q., + label   2.50 2.50
2140 A450 50c #a.-q., + label   6.25 6.25
2141 A450 50c #a.-q., + label   6.25 6.25

Issued: Nos. 2139, 3/28; Nos. 2140-2141, 2/1.

**Souvenir Sheet**

New Year 2000 (Year of the Dragon) — G164

**2000, Feb. 5**      **Perf. 13¾**
2142 G164 $4 multi    3.00 3.00

G165

Birds G166

Parrots and Parakeets

---

Designs: 75c, Barn swallow. 90c, Caribbean coot. $2, Common moorhen. $3, Orange-winged parrot.

No. 2147, each $1: a, Red-collared lorikeet. b, Citron-crested cockatoo. c, Stella's lorikeet. d, Leadbeater's cockatoo. e, Golden conure. f, Red-spotted parakeet. g, Nobel macaw. h, Goffins cockatoo. i, Sun conure.

No. 2148, each $1: a, Turquoise parakeet. b, Scarlet-chested parakeet. c, Red-capped parakeet. d, Eastern rosella. e, Budgerigar. f, Orange-flanked parakeet. g, Mallee ringneck. h, Red-rumped parakeet. i, Yellow-fronted parakeet.

No. 2149, each $1.50: a, Puerto Rican emerald. b, Green mango. c, Red-legged thrush. d, Red-crowned parrot. e, Hispaniolan parrot. f, Yellow-crowned parrot.

No. 2150, each $1.50: a, Yellow-shouldered blackbird. b, Troupial. c, Green-throated Carib. d, Black-hooded parakeet. e, Scarlet tanager. f, Yellow-crowned bishop.

Each $6: No. 2151, Puerto Rican lizard-cuckoo. No. 2152, Pin-tailed whydah, vert. No. 2153, Pennant's parakeet. No. 2154, Scarlet macaw, vert.

**2000, Mar. 1**    **Litho.**    **Perf. 14**
2143-2146 G165 Set of 4    6.00 6.00
**Sheets of 9, #a.-i.**
2147-2148 G166 Set of 2    16.00 16.00
**Sheets of 6, #a.-f.**
2149-2150 G165 Set of 2    16.00 16.00
**Souvenir Sheets**
*Perf. 13¾*
2151-2152 G165 Set of 2    11.00 11.00
*Perf. 14*
2153-2154 G166 Set of 2    11.00 11.00

No. 2151 contains one 48x32mm stamp; No. 2152 contains one 32x48mm stamp.

Tropical Fish — G167

35c, Slender mbuna. 45c, Pygoplite diacanthus. 75c, Siamese fighting fish. No. 2158, 75c, Pomacanthus semicirclatus. 90c, Zanclus canescens. #No. 160, $1, Dwarf pencilfish. No. 2161, $1, Xiphophorus maculatus. No. 2162, $2, Wimplefish. No. 2163, $2, Gramma loreto. $3, Zebrasoma xanthurum.

No. 2165, each $1: a, Emperor angelfish. b, Strawberryfish. c, Jackknife fish. d, Flame angelfish. e, Clarke's anemonefish. f, Flashback dottyback. g, Coral trout. h, Foxface.

No. 2166, each $1: a, Bumblebee goby. b, Black-headed blenny. c, Boarfish. d, Achilles tang. e, Swordtail. f, Moorish idol. g, Banded pipefish. h, Striped sea catfish.

No. 2167, each $1.65: a, Bodianus rufus. b, Coris aygula. c, Centropyge bicolor. d, Balistoides conspicillum. e, Poecilia reticulata. f, Heniochus acuminatus.

No. 2168, each $1.65: a, Plectorhynchus chaetodonoids. b, Bodianus puchellus. c, Acanthurus leucosternon. d, Chromileptis altivelis. e, Pterophyllum scalare f, Premnas biaculeatus.

Each $6: No. 2169, Equetus punctatus. No. 2170, Harlequin tuskfish. No. 2171, Purple-queen. No. 2172, Pomacanthius imperator, vert.

**2000, Mar. 28**      **Perf. 14**
2155-2164 G167 Set of 10    10.00 10.00
**Sheets of 8, #a.-h.**
2165-2166 G167 Set of 2    13.00 13.00
**Sheets of 6, #a.-f.**
2167-2168 G167 Set of 2    16.00 16.00
**Souvenir Sheets**
2169-2172 G167 Set of 4    19.00 19.00

**Van Dyck Painting Type of 2000**

No. 2173, $1.50: a, Cardinal Bentivoglio. b, Cardinal Infante Ferdinand. c, Cesare Alessandro Scaglia. d, A Roman Clergyman. e, Jean-Charles della Faille. f, Cardinal Domenico Rivarola.

No. 2174, $1.50: a, Portrait of an Elderly Woman. b, Head of a Young Woman. c, Portrait of a Man. d, Jan van der Wouwer. e, Portrait of a Young Man. f, Portrait of Everhard Jabach.

No. 2175, $1.50: a, A Man in Armor. b, Portrait of a Young General. c, Emanuele Filiberto, Prince of Savoy. d, Donna Polixena Spinola Guzman de Leganes. e, Luigia Cattaneo Gentile. f, Portrait of Giovanni Battista Cattaneo.

No. 2176, $1.50: a, Marchesa Paolina Adorno Brignole-Sale, 1623-25. b, Marchesa Geronima Spinola. c, Marchesa Paolina Adorno Broignole-Sale, 1627. d, Marcello Durazzo. e, Marchesa Grimaldi Cattaneo with a Black Page. f, Young Man of the House of Spinola.

No. 2177, $5, Portrait of Jacques le Roy. No. 2178, $5, Hendrik van der Bergh.

No. 2179, $6, Frederik Hendrik, Prince of Orange. No. 2180, $6, Justus van Meerstraeten. No. 2181, $6, The Abbot Scaglia Adoring the Virgin and Child, horiz. No. 2182, $6, Maria Louisa de Tassis, horiz.

**2000, May 1**       **Perf. 13¾**

**Sheets of 6, #a.-f.**

| | | | | |
|---|---|---|---|---|
| 2173-2176 | A449 | Set of 4 | 27.00 | 27.00 |

**Souvenir Sheets**

| | | | | |
|---|---|---|---|---|
| 2177-2178 | A449 | Set of 2 | 7.50 | 7.50 |
| 2179-2182 | A449 | Set of 4 | 18.00 | 18.00 |

**Prince William Type of 2000**

No. 2183: a, Wearing scarf. b, Wearing suit with vest. c, Wearing casual shirt. d, Wearing gray suit.

$6, Wearing sweater.

**2000, May 15**    **Litho.**    **Perf. 14**

| | | | | |
|---|---|---|---|---|
| 2183 | A453 | $1.50 Sheet of 4, #a-d | 4.50 | 4.50 |

**Souvenir Sheet**

**Perf. 13¾**

| | | | | |
|---|---|---|---|---|
| 2184 | A453 | $6 multi | 4.50 | 4.50 |

No. 2183 contains four 28x42mm stamps.

**Zeppelin Type of 2000**

No. 2185 — Ferdinand von Zeppelin and: a, LZ-3. b, LZ-56. c, LZ-88.

$6, LZ-1.

**2000, May 15**       **Perf. 14**

| | | | | |
|---|---|---|---|---|
| 2185 | A454 | $3 Sheet of 3, #a-c | 6.75 | 6.75 |

**Souvenir Sheet**

| | | | | |
|---|---|---|---|---|
| 2186 | A454 | $6 multi | 4.50 | 4.50 |

No. 2185 contains three 42x28mm stamps.

**Berlin Film Festival Type of 2000**

No. 2187: a, James Stewart. b, Sachiko Hidari. c, Juliette Mayniel. d, Le Bonheur. e, La Notte. f, Lee Marvin.

$6, The Thin Red Line.

**2000, May 15**

| | | | | |
|---|---|---|---|---|
| 2187 | A455 | $1.50 Sheet of 6, #a-f | 6.75 | 6.75 |

**Souvenir Sheet**

| | | | | |
|---|---|---|---|---|
| 2188 | A455 | $6 multi | 4.50 | 4.50 |

**Olympics Type of 2000**

**Souvenir Sheets**

No. 2189: a, Frantz Reichel. b, Discus throw. c, Seoul Sports Complex and Korean flag. d, Ancient Greek wrestlers.

**2000, May 15**

| | | | | |
|---|---|---|---|---|
| 2189 | A457 | $2 Sheet of 4, #a-d | 6.00 | 6.00 |

**Public Railways Type of 2000**

No. 2190: a, Locomotion No. 1 and George Stephenson. b, Rocket.

**2000, May 15**

| | | | | |
|---|---|---|---|---|
| 2190 | A458 | $3 Sheet of 2, #a-b | 4.50 | 4.50 |

**Bach Type of 2000**

**2000, May 15**

| | | | | |
|---|---|---|---|---|
| 2191 | A459 | $6 Statue of Bach | 4.50 | 4.50 |

G168

---

Butterflies and Moths — G169

No. 2192, each $1.50: a, Clara satin moth. b, Spanish festoon. c, Giant silkmoth. d, Oak eggar. e, Common wall. f, Large oak blue.

No. 2193, each $1.50: a, Jersey tiger. b, Boisduval's autumnal moth. c, Orange swallow-tailed moth. d, Regent skipper. e, Hoop pine moth. f, Coppery oysphania.

No. 2194, each $1.50: a, Grecian shoemaker. b, 88. c, Cramer's mesene. d, Salt marsh moth. e, Ruddy dagger wing. f, Blue night.

No. 2195, each $1.50: a, Heliconius charitonius. b, Tiger pierid. c, Hewiton's blue hairstreak. d, Esmeralda. e, California dogface. f, Orange theope.

No. 2196, each $2: a, Hummingbird gleariwing. b, Gold-drop helicopis. c, Great tiger moth. d, Staudinger's longtail.

No. 2197, each $2: a, Common map. b, Papilio machaon. c, Purple emperor. d, Red-lined geometrid.

Each $6: No. 2198, Peacock royal. No. 2199, Queen Alexandra's birdwing. No. 2200, Giant leopard moth. No. 2201, Robin moth, vert.

**2000, May 29**       **Perf. 14**

**Sheets of 6, #a-f**

| | | | | |
|---|---|---|---|---|
| 2192-2193 | G168 | Set of 2 | 13.50 | 13.50 |
| 2194-2195 | G169 | Set of 2 | 13.50 | 13.50 |

**Sheets of 4, #a-d**

| | | | | |
|---|---|---|---|---|
| 2196-2197 | G168 | Set of 2 | 12.00 | 12.00 |

**Souvenir Sheets**

| | | | | |
|---|---|---|---|---|
| 2198-2199 | G168 | Set of 2 | 9.00 | 9.00 |
| 2200-2201 | G169 | Set of 2 | 9.00 | 9.00 |

**Apollo-Soyuz Type**

No. 2202, vert.: a, Thomas P. Stafford. b, Mission badge. c, Donald K. Slayton.

$6, Alexei Leonov, vert.

**2000, May 15**    **Litho.**    **Perf. 14**

| | | | | |
|---|---|---|---|---|
| 2202 | A456 | $3 Sheet of 3, #a-c | 6.75 | 6.75 |

**Souvenir Sheet**

| | | | | |
|---|---|---|---|---|
| 2203 | A456 | $6 Alexei Leonov | 4.50 | 4.50 |

**Einstein Type**

**Souvenir Sheet**

**2000, May 15**       **Perf. 14¼**

| | | | | |
|---|---|---|---|---|
| 2204 | A460 | $6 multi | 4.50 | 4.50 |

**Space Type**

Nos. 2205, each $1.50: a, Foton (green and orange background). b, Sub-satellite and comet tail. c, NEAR Eros (green background). d, Explorer 16 and sun. e, Astro Challenger (green and orange background). f, Giotto (green background).

No. 2206, each $1.50: a, Foton and asteroid. b, Sub-satellite and asteroid. c, NEAR Eros and asteroid. d, Explorer 16 and planet surface. e, Space Shuttle. f, Giotto (blue background).

Each $6: No. 2207, Lunar Prospector. No. 2208, Pegasus Saturn.

**2000, May 15**       **Perf. 14**

**Sheets of 6, #a-f**

| | | | | |
|---|---|---|---|---|
| 2205-2206 | A461 | Set of 2 | 13.50 | 13.50 |

**Souvenir Sheets**

| | | | | |
|---|---|---|---|---|
| 2207-2208 | A461 | Set of 2 | 9.00 | 9.00 |

Nos. 2205-2206 depict different satellites, but have the same inscriptions. World Stamp Expo 2000, Anaheim.

Trains — G170

Designs: 90c, Golsdorf 2-6-2, Vienna Metropolitan Railways. $1, Forrester 2-2-0, Dublin & Kingstown Railway. $2, Metro-Cammell Co-Co, Nigerian Railways. $3, TGV 001, French Natl. Railways.

No. 2213, each $1.50: a, Braithwait 0-4-0, Eastern Counties Railway. b, The Philadelphia, Austria. c, Stephenson 2-2-2, Russia. d, L'aigle, Western Railway of France. e, Borsig Standard 2-2-2, Germany. f, The Ajax, Great Western Railway.

---

No. 2214, each $1.50: a, Co-Co locomotive, Norwegian State Railways. b, Diesel-electric locomotive, Jamaica Railway. c, Diesel-electric locomotive, Railway of the People's Republic of China. d, Electric locomotive, Portuguese Railways. e, Re 6/6, Swiss Federal Railways. f, Dual-purpose Electric locomotive, Turkish State Railways.

No. 2215, each $1.50: a, 4-4-0 engine, Perak Government Railway. b, 2-4-2 tank engine, Rhondda & Swansea Railway. c, 2-4-2 tank engine, Lancashire & Yorkshire Railway. d, 2-8-2 tank engine, Northwestern Railway of India. e, 4-2-2 Imperial Yellow Mail engine, Shanghai-Nanking Railway. f, 2-4-2 engine, Danish State Railway.

No. 2216, each $1.50: a, Electric railcar, South Jersey Transit. b, Metroliner, US. c, HSST Mag-lev train. d, E60C, Amtrak. e, TEE Express "Parsifal." f, 2-Co-Co-2 electric, Amtrak.

No. 2217, $6, The Experiment, US. No. 2218, 2-8-2 locomotive, Central South African Railway. No. 2219, $6, The Prospector, Western Australian Government Railways. No. 2220, Diesel-electric locomotive, South African Railways.

**2000, June 13**

**Set of 4**

| | | | | |
|---|---|---|---|---|
| 2209-2212 | G170 | Set of 4 | 5.25 | 5.25 |

**Sheets of 6, #a-f**

| | | | | |
|---|---|---|---|---|
| 2213-2216 | G170 | Set of 4 | 26.00 | 26.00 |

**Souvenir Sheets**

| | | | | |
|---|---|---|---|---|
| 2217-2220 | G170 | Set of 4 | 18.00 | 18.00 |

**European Soccer Championships Type**

No. 2221, horiz., each $1.50 — Denmark: a, Tofting. b, Team photo. c, Michael Laudrup. d, Jorgensen. e, Philips Stadium, Eindhoven. f, Moller.

No. 2222, horiz., each $1.50 — France: a, Thuram. b, Team photo. c, Barthez. d, Zidane. e, Jan Breydel Stadium, Brugge. f, Michel Platini.

No. 2223, horiz., each $1.50 — Netherlands: a, Giovanni Van Bronckhorst. b, Team photo. c, Patrick Kluivert. d, Johan Cruyff. e, Amsterdam Arena Stadium. f, Zenden.

Each $6: No. 2224, Denmark coach Bo Johansson. No. 2225, France coach Roger Lemerre. No. 2226, Netherlands coach Frank Rijkaard.

**2000, Aug. 8**       **Perf. 13¾**

**Sheets of 6, #a-f**

| | | | | |
|---|---|---|---|---|
| 2221-2223 | A464 | Set of 3 | 20.00 | 20.00 |

**Souvenir Sheets**

| | | | | |
|---|---|---|---|---|
| 2224-2226 | A464 | Set of 3 | 13.50 | 13.50 |

**Popes Type**

No. 2227, each $1.50: a, Adrian VI, 1522-23. b, Paul II, 1464-71. c, Calixtus III, 1455-58. d, Eugenius IV, 1431-47.

**2000, Aug. 22**

| | | | | |
|---|---|---|---|---|
| 2227 | A467 | Sheet of 4, #a-d | 4.50 | 4.50 |

**Souvenir Sheet**

| | | | | |
|---|---|---|---|---|
| 2228 | A467 | $6 Gregory IX, 1370-78 | 4.50 | 4.50 |

**Monarchs Type**

No. 2229, each $1.50: a, Louis XVI of France, 1774-92. b, Louis XVIII of France, 1814-24. c, Queen of Kublai Khan, China. d, Mary Tudor of England, 1553-58. e, Mohammed Ali of Iran, 1907-09. f, Ch'ien-lung (Qian-long, Hung-li) of China, 1735-96.

$6, Vladimir I, Grand Prince of Kiev, 980-1015.

**2000, Aug. 22**

| | | | | |
|---|---|---|---|---|
| 2229 | A468 | Sheet of 6, #a-f | 6.75 | 6.75 |

**Souvenir Sheet**

| | | | | |
|---|---|---|---|---|
| 2230 | A468 | $6 Vladimir I | 4.50 | 4.50 |

Fauna — G171

Designs: 75c, St. Lucia Amazon. 90c, Three-toed sloth. $1, Hispaniolan solenodon. $2, Thick-billed parrot.

No. 2235, each $1.50: a, Jaguarundi. b, Andean condor. c, Darwin's rhea. d, Central American tapir. e, Jaguar. f, Jamaican hutia.

No. 2236, each $1.50: a, Red vakari. b, San Andreas vireo. c, Golden lion tamarin. d, American crocodile. e, Spectacled caiman. f, Rhinoceros iguana.

Each $6: No. 2237, Pronghorn. No. 2238, Kemp Ridley sea turtle.

**2000, Sept. 5**       **Perf. 14**

| | | | | |
|---|---|---|---|---|
| 2231-2234 | G171 | Set of 4 | 4.25 | 4.25 |

---

**Sheets of 6, #a-f**

| | | | | |
|---|---|---|---|---|
| 2235-2236 | G171 | Set of 2 | 17.00 | 17.00 |

**Souvenir Sheets**

| | | | | |
|---|---|---|---|---|
| 2237-2238 | G171 | Set of 2 | 12.00 | 12.00 |

The Stamp Show 2000, London (Nos. 2235-2238).

**Souvenir Sheet**

David Copperfield, Magician — G172

No. 2239, each $1.50: a, Copperfield's face at L, legs at R. b, Upper torso at L, face at R. c, Legs at L, face at R. d, Face at L, upper torso at R.

**2000, Sept. 14**

| | | | | |
|---|---|---|---|---|
| 2239 | G172 | Sheet of 4, #a-d | 4.50 | 4.50 |

**Prado Paintings Type**

No. 2240, each $1.50: a, St. John the Baptist and the Franciscan Maestro Henricus Werl, by Robert Campin. b, Justice and Peace, by Corrado Giaquinto. c, St. Barbara, by Campin. d, John Fane, 10th Count of Westmoreland, by Thomas Lawrence. e, The Marchioness of Manzanedo, by Jean-Louis-Ernest Meissonier. f, Mr. Storer, by Martin Archer Shee.

No. 2241, each $1.50: a, Isabella Carla Eugenia, by Alonso Sánchez Coello. b, Portrait of a Nobleman with His Hand on His Chest, by El Greco. c, Philip III, by Juan Pantoja de la Cruz. d, Madonna & child from The Holy Family with Saints Ildefons & John the Evangelist, & the Master Alonso de Villegas, by Blas del Prado. e, The Last Supper, by Bartolomé Carducci. f, Man with goblet from The Holy Family with Saints Ildefons & John the Evangelist, & the Master Alonso de Villegas.

No. 2242, each $1.50: a, Dominic of Silos, by Bartolomé Bermejo. b, Head of a Prophet, by Jaime Huguet. c, Christ Giving His Blessing, by Fernando Gallego. d, The Mystic Marriage of St. Catherine, by Alonso Sánchez Coello. e, St. Catherine of Alexandria, by Fernando Yáñez de la Almedina. f, Virgin and Child, by Luis de Morales.

Each $6: No. 2243, The Holy Family with Saints Ildefons & John the Evangelist, & the Master Alonso de Villegas. No. 2244, The Last Supper, horiz. No. 2245, The Coronation of the Virgin, by El Greco, horiz.

**2000, Oct. 19**    **Perf. 12x12¼, 12¼x12**

**Sheets of 6, #a-f**

| | | | | |
|---|---|---|---|---|
| 2240-2242 | A470 | Set of 3 | 20.00 | 20.00 |

**Souvenir Sheets**

| | | | | |
|---|---|---|---|---|
| 2243-2245 | A470 | Set of 3 | 13.50 | 13.50 |

Espana 2000, Intl. Philatelic Exhibition.

**Mushroom Type of 2000**

No. 2246, $2: a, Cinnabar chanterelle. b, Blackening wax cap. c, Edible cort. d, Orange scaber-stalk bolete.

No. 2247, $2: a, Crab russula. b, Steel blue entoloma. c, Tiger lentinus. d, Yellow-white mycena.

No. 2248, $2, horiz.: a, Le Gal's bolete. b, Emetic russula. c, Silvery violet cort. d, Tree volvariella.

No. 2249, $6, Scaly vase chanterelle, horiz. No. 2250, $6, Common collybia, horiz.

**2000, Mar. 3**    **Litho.**    **Perf. 14**

**Sheets of 4, #a-d**

| | | | | |
|---|---|---|---|---|
| 2246-2248 | A448 | Set of 3 | 18.00 | 18.00 |

**Souvenir Sheets**

| | | | | |
|---|---|---|---|---|
| 2249-2250 | A448 | Set of 2 | 9.00 | 9.00 |

**Dog Type of 2000**

Designs: 45c, Irish setter. 90c, Dalmatian. $2, German shepherd.

No. 2254, $1.50: a, Alaskan malamute. b, Golden retriever. c, Afghan hound. d, Long-haired dachshund. e, Irish terrier. f, Miniature poodle.

No. 2255, $1.50: a, Great Dane. b, Newfoundland. c, Rottweiler. d, Bulldog. e, Japanese spitz. f, Bull terrier.

No. 2256, $6, Labrador retriever. No. 2257, $6, Basset hound, horiz.

## 2000, June 23

| | | | | |
|---|---|---|---|---|
| 2251-2253 | A473 | Set of 3 | 2.50 | 2.50 |

**Sheets of 6, #a-f**

| | | | | |
|---|---|---|---|---|
| 2254-2255 | A473 | Set of 2 | 13.50 | 13.50 |

**Souvenir Sheets**

| | | | | |
|---|---|---|---|---|
| 2256-2257 | A473 | Set of 2 | 9.00 | 9.00 |

### Cat Type of 2000

Designs: 75c, Blue point snowshoe. $3, Black and white Maine coon cat. $4, Brown tabby British shorthair.

No. 2261, $1.50: a, California spangled cat. b, Russian blue. c, Seal point Siamese. d, Black Devon rex. e, Silver tabby British shorthair. f, Tricolor Japanese bobtail.

No. 2262, $1.50: a, British white shorthair. b, Blue cream American shorthair. c, Bombay. d, Red Burmese. e, Sorrel Abyssinian. f, Ocicat.

$5, Silver classic tabby Persian, horiz. No. 2263A, $5, Red-white bicolored British shorthair.

## 2000, June 23

| | | | | |
|---|---|---|---|---|
| 2258-2260 | A478 | Set of 3 | 5.75 | 5.75 |

**Sheets of 6, #a-f**

| | | | | |
|---|---|---|---|---|
| 2261-2262 | A478 | Set of 2 | 13.50 | 13.50 |

**Souvenir Sheet**

| | | | | |
|---|---|---|---|---|
| 2263 | A478 | $5 multi | 3.75 | 3.75 |
| 2263A | A478 | $5 multi | 3.75 | 3.75 |

### Battle of Britain Type of 2000

No. 2264, each $1: a, Women fire fighters, London. b, Family leaving after the Blitz. c, Searchlights, London. d, Winston Churchill in Coventry after German raid. e, Rescue after German bombing. f, Rescue after London bombing. g, Terror hits Buckingham Gate. h, After a German raid on Coventry.

No. 2265, each $1: a, Pilots scramble to their planes. b, Balloons to catch low-flying planes. c, Spitfire B. d, Speech by Princess Elizabeth. e, Fire Watchers, auxiliary fire service. f, Painting stripes to see at night. g, Bombed buildings in Britain. h, Air raid wardens, auxiliary police force.

Each $6: No. 2266, Hawker Hurricane. No. 2267, British family survives German bombing, vert.

## 2000, Oct. 30    Sheets of 8, #a-h

| | | | | |
|---|---|---|---|---|
| 2264-2265 | A471 | Set of 2 | 12.00 | 12.00 |

**Souvenir Sheets**

| | | | | |
|---|---|---|---|---|
| 2266-2267 | A471 | Set of 2 | 9.00 | 9.00 |

### Queen Mother Type of 2000

## 2000, Oct. 30

| | | | | |
|---|---|---|---|---|
| 2268 | A479 | $1.50 multi | 1.10 | 1.10 |

Printed in sheets of 6.

### Photomosaic Type of 1999

No. 2269, $1: Various flowers making up a photomosaic of the Queen Mother.

No. 2270, $1: Various photographs with religious theme making up a photomosaic of Pope John Paul II.

## 2000, Oct. 30    Perf. 13¾

| | | | | |
|---|---|---|---|---|
| 2269-2270 | A445 | Set of 2 | 12.00 | 12.00 |

Harry Houdini, Magician — G173

## 2000    Litho.    Perf. 14

| | | | | |
|---|---|---|---|---|
| 2271 | G173 | $1.50 multi | 1.10 | 1.10 |

Issued in sheets of 4.

**Souvenir Sheet**

Barbara Taylor Bradford, Author G174

## 2000    Litho.    Perf. 12¼

| | | | | |
|---|---|---|---|---|
| 2272 | G174 | $6 multi | 4.50 | 4.50 |

---

**Souvenir Sheet**

Hong Kong Comic Strip "The Storm Riders" G175

No. 2273: a, Character with arms folded. b, Character with sword. c, Character in brown cape. d, Character in green.

## 2000    Perf. 13½

| | | | | |
|---|---|---|---|---|
| 2273 | G175 | $4 Sheet of 4, #a-d | 9.00 | 9.00 |

New Year 2001 (Year of the Snake) G176

No. 2274: a, Rat snake. b, Mangrove snake. c, Boomslang. d, Emerald tree boa. e, African egg-eating snake. f, Chinese green tree viper.

## 2001, Jan. 2    Perf. 14

| | | | | |
|---|---|---|---|---|
| 2274 | G176 | 90c Sheet of 6, #a-f | 4.00 | 4.00 |

**Souvenir Sheet**

| | | | | |
|---|---|---|---|---|
| 2275 | G176 | $4 King cobra | 3.00 | 3.00 |

### Rijksmuseum Type of 2001

No. 2276, $1.50: a, Person with red shirt from Dune Landcape, by Jan van Goyen. b, The Raampoortje, by Wouter Johannes van Troostwijk. c, House and horse from The Cattle Ferry, by Esaias van de Velde. d, The Departure of a Senior Functionary from Middleburg, by Adriaen van de Venne. e, Steeple and ferry from The Cattle Ferry. f, Four people near rock from Dune Landscape.

No. 2277, $1.50: a, Building, statue and dog from Garden Party, by Dirck Hals. b, Still Life with Gilt Cup, by Willem Claesz Heda. c, Cloud of smoke from Orestes and Pylades Disputing at the Altar, by Pieter Lastman. d, Buildings from Orestes and Pylades Disputing at the Altar. e, Self-portrait in a Yellow Robe, by Jan Lievens. f, Birds in sky from Garden Party.

No. 2278, $1.50: a, Beatrix from Marriage Portrait of Isaac Massa and Beatrix van der Laen, by Frans Hals. b, Winter Landscape With Ice Skaters, by Hendrick Avercamp. c, Man and woman from The Spendthrift, by Cornelis Troost. d, Men in brown from The Spendthrift. e, Men and woman from The Art Gallery of Jan Gildermeester Jansz, by Adriaan de Lelie. f, Three men from The Art Gallery of Jan Gildermeester Jansz.

No. 2279, $1.50: a, Man from A Music Party, by Rembrandt. b, Woman from A Music Party. c, Girl and boy from Rutger Jan Schimmelpennick With His Wife and Children, by Pierre-Paul Prud'hon. d, Girl from Rutger Jan Schimmelpennick With His Wife and Children. e, Two men from The Syndics, by Thomas de Keyser. f, Isaac and Beatrix from Marriage Portrait of Isaac Massa and Beatrix van der Laen.

No. 2280, $6, A Music Party. No. 2281, $6, Anna Accused by Tobit of Stealing a Kid, by Rembrandt. No. 2282, $6, Cleopatra's Banquet, by Gerard Lairesse, horiz. No. 2283, $6, View of Tivoli, by Isaac de Moucheron.

## 2001, Jan. 15    Perf. 13¾

**Sheets of 6, #a-f**

| | | | | |
|---|---|---|---|---|
| 2276-2279 | A483 | Set of 4 | 27.50 | 27.50 |

**Souvenir Sheets**

| | | | | |
|---|---|---|---|---|
| 2280-2283 | A483 | Set of 4 | 18.00 | 18.00 |

### Pokémon Type of 2001

No. 2284, each $1.50: a, Bellsprout. b, Vulpix. c, Dewgong. d, Oddish. e, Dratini. f, Jigglypuff.

## 2001, Feb. 1

| | | | | |
|---|---|---|---|---|
| 2284 | A484 | Sheet of 6, #a-f | 6.75 | 6.75 |

**Souvenir Sheet**

| | | | | |
|---|---|---|---|---|
| 2285 | A484 | $6 Pikachu | 4.50 | 4.50 |

---

Animals of the Tropics — G177

Designs: 75c, Greater flamingo, vert. 90c, Cuban crocodile. $1, Jaguarundi, vert. $2, Wedge-capped capuchin monkey.

No. 2290, $1.50, vert.: a, Cuban pygmy owl. b, Woody spider monkey. c, Bee hummingbirds. d, Dragonfly, poison dart frog. e, Red brocket deer. f, Cuban stream anole.

No. 2291, $1.50, vert.: a, Red-breasted toucan. b, Mexican black howler monkey. c, Fleck's pygmy boa. d, Red-eyed tree frog. e, Caiman. f, Jaguar.

No. 2292, $6, Ocelot, vert. No. 2293, $6, Western knight anole, vert.

## 2001, Feb. 1    Perf. 14

| | | | | |
|---|---|---|---|---|
| 2286-2289 | G177 | Set of 4 | 4.25 | 4.25 |

**Sheets of 6, #a-f**

| | | | | |
|---|---|---|---|---|
| 2290-2291 | G177 | Set of 2 | 17.00 | 17.00 |

**Souvenir Sheets**

| | | | | |
|---|---|---|---|---|
| 2292-2293 | G177 | Set of 2 | 13.00 | 13.00 |

Hong Kong 2001 Stamp Exhibition.

### Fish Type of 2000 with Added WWF Emblem

No. 2294: a, Sparisoma rubripinne. b, Scarus vetula. c, Scarus taeniopterus. d, Sparisoma viride.

## 2001, Mar. 28    Litho.    Perf. 14

| | | | | |
|---|---|---|---|---|
| 2294 | G167 | 75c Strip of 4, #a-d | 4.25 | 4.25 |

Waterfowl — G178

No. 2295, horiz., each $1.50: a, Falklands streamer duck. b, Black-crowned night heron. c, Muscovy duck. d, Ruddy duck. e, Black-necked screamer. f, White-faced whistling duck.

## 2001, Mar. 28

| | | | | |
|---|---|---|---|---|
| 2295 | G178 | Sheet of 6, #a-f | 7.00 | 7.00 |

**Souvenir Sheet**

| | | | | |
|---|---|---|---|---|
| 2296 | G178 | $6 Great egret | 5.00 | 5.00 |

Scenes From "The Littlest Rebel," Starring Shirley Temple G179

Temple with — No. 2297, horiz.: a, Pointing soldier. b, Black woman. c, Soldier in carriage. d, Pres. Lincoln.

No. 2298: a, Spoon. b, Woman near tree. c, Soldier with hat. d, Woman. e, Black man and soldier. f, Man.

$6, Black man.

## 2001, Apr. 25    Perf. 13¾

| | | | | |
|---|---|---|---|---|
| 2297 | G179 | $2 Sheet of 4, #a-d | 6.00 | 6.00 |
| 2298 | G179 | $2 Sheet of 6, #a-f | 9.00 | 9.00 |

**Souvenir Sheet**

| | | | | |
|---|---|---|---|---|
| 2299 | G179 | $6 multi | 4.50 | 4.50 |

---

Clark Gable (1901-60) — G180

No. 2300, $1.50 — Color of photo: a, Purple. b, Sepia (wearing suit and tie). c, Yellow. d, Sepia (wearing sweater). e, Blue. f, Sepia (wearing bow tie).

No. 2301, $1.50 — Signature of Gable and Gable with: a, Cigar. b, Vest. c, Chair. d, Pen. e, Suit and tie. f, Pinstriped suit.

No. 2302, $6, Blue background. No. 2303, $6, Gable in uniform.

## 2001, Apr. 25    Perf. 14

**Sheets of 6, #a-f**

| | | | | |
|---|---|---|---|---|
| 2300-2301 | G180 | Set of 2 | 13.50 | 13.50 |

**Souvenir Sheets**

| | | | | |
|---|---|---|---|---|
| 2302-2303 | G180 | Set of 2 | 9.00 | 9.00 |

### Betty Boop Type of 2000

No. 2304 — Boop: a, With comb. b, With veil. c, With lei. d, At carnival. e, With flower in hair. f, With cowboy hat. g, With beret. h, In automobile. i, As Statue of Liberty.

No. 2305, $6, In sari. No. 2306, $6, In gondola.

## 2001, Apr. 25    Perf. 13¾

| | | | | |
|---|---|---|---|---|
| 2304 | A481 | $1 Sheet of 9, #a-i | 6.75 | 6.75 |

**Souvenir Sheets**

| | | | | |
|---|---|---|---|---|
| 2305-2306 | A481 | Set of 2 | 9.00 | 9.00 |

### Phila Nippon Type of 2001

Designs: 75c, Scenes of Daily Life in Edo, by Choshun Miyagawa. 90c, Twelve Famous Places in Japan, by Eisenin Naganobu Kano. $1, Scenery Along the Length of the Sumida River, by Kyuei Kano. $1.25, Cranes, by Eisenin Michinobu Kano. No. 2311, $2, A Courtesan of Yoshiwara, by Shunei Katsukawa. $3, Rite of Bear Killing: Praying to the Bear's Spirit, by unknown artist.

No. 2313, $2, vert. — Bodhisattva Samantabhadra from the Lotus Sutra with: a, Surrounding rings, yellow elephant. b, White elephant. c, Temple at left. d, Surrounding rings with rays.

No. 2314, $2 (85x28mm) — Chapter illustrations from Genji Monogatari Emaki, by Ryusetsu Hidenobu Kano: a, Kiritsubo. b, Akashi. c, Hatsune. d, E-Awase.

No. 2315, $6, A Sage Pointing at the Moon, by Ranseki Katagiri. No. 2316, $6, Frontispiece for Devadatta, Lotus Sutra, vert.

## 2001, May 1    Perf. 14

| | | | | |
|---|---|---|---|---|
| 2307-2312 | A487 | Set of 6 | 6.75 | 6.75 |

**Sheets of 4, #a-d**

| | | | | |
|---|---|---|---|---|
| 2313-2314 | A488 | Set of 2 | 12.00 | 12.00 |

**Souvenir Sheets**

| | | | | |
|---|---|---|---|---|
| 2315-2316 | A488 | Set of 2 | 9.00 | 9.00 |

### Marlene Dietrich Type of 2001

Dietrich with: a, Microphone. b, Robe. c, Flowered dress. d, Hat.

## 2001, May 15    Perf. 13¾

| | | | | |
|---|---|---|---|---|
| 2317 | A489 | $2 Sheet of 4, #a-d | 6.00 | 6.00 |

### Queen Victoria Type of 2001

No. 2318 — Queen Victoria with: a, Scepter. b, Flower. c, Sash.
$6, Sash, diff.

## 2001, May 15    Perf. 14

| | | | | |
|---|---|---|---|---|
| 2318 | A490 | $3 Sheet of 3, #a-c | 6.75 | 6.75 |

**Souvenir Sheet**

| | | | | |
|---|---|---|---|---|
| 2319 | A490 | $6 multi | 4.50 | 4.50 |

### Queen Elizabeth II Type of 2001

No. 2320, each $1.25 — Predominant background colors: a, Brown and yellow. b, Green. c, Blue. d, Black. e, Red and violet. f, Red and light blue.

No. 2320G, each $2: h, Green background. i, Purple background. j, Brown background.
$6, Tan.

**2001, May 15**     *Perf. 14*
2320 A491 Sheet of 6, #a-f    5.75 5.75
2320G A491 Sheet of 3, #h-j    4.50 4.50
**Souvenir Sheet**
*Perf. 13¾*
2321 A491 $6 multi     3.75 3.75
   No. 2321 contains one 38x51mm stamp.

**Ship Type of 2001**

Designs: 90c, Creole. $1, Britannia. $2, Ariel. $3, Sindia.
No. 2326, $1.25: a, William Fawcett. b, Sirius. c, S.S. Great Britain. d, Oriental. e, Lightning. f, Great Eastern.
No. 2327, $1.25: a, Santa Maria and Christopher Columbus. b, Sao Gabriel and Vasco da Gama. c, Victoria and Ferdinand Magellan. d, Golden Hind and Sir Francis Drake. e, Endeavour and Capt. James Cook. f, HMS Erebus and John Franklin.
No. 2328, $1.25, vert.: a, Mayflower. b, Gabriel. c, Beagle. d, Challenger. e, Vega. f, Fram.
No. 2329, $6, Challenge. No. 2330, $6, Cutty Sark.

**2001, June 18**     *Perf. 14*
2322-2325 Set of 4    5.25 5.25
**Sheets of 6, #a-f**
2326-2328 Set of 3    17.00 17.00
**Miniature Sheets**
2329-2330 Set of 2    9.00 9.00

**Magician Type of Grenada Grenadines of 2000**

Designs: No. 2331, $1.50, Howard Thurston. No. 2332, $1.50, Harry Kellar.

**2001**
2331-2332 G173 Set of 2    2.25 2.25
   Issued in sheets of 4.

**Mao Zedong Type of 2001**

No. 2333, horiz.: a, Mao on stairs. b, Mao at right, with soldiers. c, Mao at left, with peasants. d, Mao seated, with officers.
$3, Portrait.

**2001, May 15**   Litho.   *Perf. 14*
2333 A493 $1.50 Sheet of 4,
    #a-d    4.50 4.50
**Souvenir Sheet**
2334 A493 $3 multi    2.25 2.25

**Verdi Type of 2001**

No. 2335 — Verdi and score: a, 25c. b, 75c. c, $2. d, $3.
$6, Portrait.

**2001, May 15**     *Perf. 14*
2335 A494 Sheet of 4, #a-d    4.50 4.50
**Souvenir Sheet**
2336 A494 $6 multi    4.50 4.50

**Toulouse-Lautrec Type of 2001**

No. 2337, horiz.: a, Helene V. b, The Clownesse. c, Madame Berthe Bady. d, The Woman With The Black Boa.
$6, Loie Fuller at the Folies Bergére.

**2001, May 15**     *Perf. 13¾*
2337 A495 $1 Sheet of 4, #a-d    3.00 3.00
**Souvenir Sheet**
2338 A495 $6 multi    4.50 4.50

**Monet Type of 2001**

No. 2339, horiz.: a, The Magpie. b, La Pointe de la Hève at Low Tide. c, Boats: Regatta at Argenteuil. d, La Grenouillère.
$6, Portrait of J. F. Jaquemart with Parasol.

**2001, May 15**
2339 A504 $1 Sheet of 4, #a-d    3.00 3.00
**Souvenir Sheet**
2340 A504 $6 multi    4.50 4.50

Orchids — G181

Designs: 25c, Vanda Singapore. 50c, Vanda Joan Warne. 75c, Vanda lamellata. $2, Vanda merrillii.
No. 2345, $1.50: a, Papilionanthe teres. b, Vanda flabellata. c, Vanda tessellata (name at LL). d, Vanda pumila. e, Rhynchostylis gigantea. f, Vandopsis gigantea.
No. 2346, $1.50: a, Vanda tessellata (name at center left). b, Vanda helvola. c, Vanda

brunnea. d, Vanda stangeana. e, Vanda limbata. f, Vandopsis tricolor.
No. 2347, $6, Vanda insignis. No. 2348, $6, Vandopsis lissochiloides.

**2001, Oct. 15**     *Perf. 14*
2341-2344 G181 Set of 4    2.60 2.60
**Sheets of 6, #a-f**
2345-2346 G181 Set of 2    13.50 13.50
**Souvenir Sheets**
2347-2348 G181 Set of 2    9.00 9.00

Souvenir Sheets

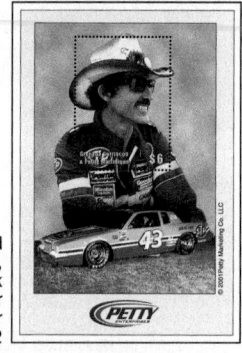
Richard Petty, Stock Car Racer G182

Designs: No. 2349, $6, shown. No. 2350, $6, Petty speaking into microphone.

**2001, Oct. 15**     *Perf. 13¾*
2349-2350 G182 Set of 2    9.00 9.00

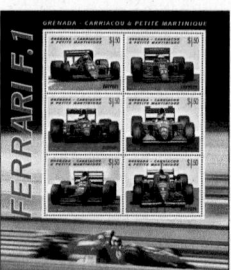
Ferrari Formula 1 Racing Cars G183

No. 2351: a, 1986 F1 86. b, 1989 F1 89. c, 1992 F92A. d, 1993 F1 93. e, 1994 412T1. f, 1996 F310.

**2001, Nov. 19**     *Perf. 13¾*
2351 G183 $1.50 Sheet of 6,
    #a-f    6.75 6.75

**World Cup Soccer Championships Type of 2001**

No. 2352, $1.50 — World Cup posters and badges from: a, 1950. b, 1954. c, 1958. d, 1962. e, 1966. f, 1970.
No. 2353, $1.50 — World Cup posters and badges from: a, 1978. b, 1982. c, 1986. d, 1990. e, 1994. f, 1998.
No. 2354, $6, World Cup poster and badge, 1930. No. 2355, $6, Head and globe from World Cup trophy.

**2001, Nov. 29**     *Perf. 13¾x14¼*
**Sheets of 6, #a-f**
2352-2353 A505 Set of 2    13.50 13.50
**Souvenir Sheets**
2354-2355 A505 Set of 2    9.00 9.00

Christmas — G184

Designs: 25c, Coronation of the Virgin, by Filippo Lippi. 75c, Virgin and Child, by Mantegna. $1.50, Madonna and Child, by Masaccio. $3, Madonna and Child, by Raphael.
$6, Virgin and child Enthroned with Angels, by Mantegna.

**2001, Dec. 3**     *Perf. 14*
2356-2359 G184 Set of 4    4.25 4.25
**Souvenir Sheet**
2360 G184 $6 multi    4.50 4.50

Royal Navy Ships — G185

Designs: 75c, HMS Renown in Portsmouth Harbor, 1922. 90c, Battle of the Saintes, 1782. $2, Battle of Trafalgar, 1805. $3, Embarkation at Dover, 1520.
No. 2365, $1.50, horiz.: a, Battle of Solebay, 1672. b, HMS Royal Prince, 1679. c, Battle of Texel, 1673. d, Battle of Scheveningen, 1653. e, Barbary Pirates, 1600s. f, Royal Charles, 1667.
No. 2366, $1.50, horiz.: a, Skirmishing preceding the Battle of the First of June. b, Moonlight Battle, 1780. c, Great ships of the Jacobean Navy, 1623. d, Battle of the Gulf of Genoa, 1795. e, Battle of the Nile, 1798. f, St. Lucia, 1778.
No. 2367, $6, Battle of Navarino, 1827, horiz. No. 2368, $6, HMS Repulse, 1924, horiz.

**2001, Dec. 10**     Litho.
2361-2364 G185 Set of 4    5.00 5.00
**Sheets of 6, #a-f**
2365-2366 G185 Set of 2    13.50 13.50
**Souvenir Sheets**
2367-2368 G185 Set of 2    9.00 9.00

**Queen Mother Type of 1999 Redrawn**

No. 2369: a, Lady Elizabeth Bowles-Lyon. b, In Rhodesia, 1957. c, With Princesses Elizabeth and Anne, 1950. d, In 1988.
$6, In Berlin.

**2001, Dec. 13**     *Perf. 14*
**Yellow Orange Frames**
2369 A440 $2 Sheet of 4, #a-d, +
    label    6.00 6.00
**Souvenir Sheet**
*Perf. 13¾*
2370 A440 $6 multi    4.50 4.50
   Queen Mother's 101st birthday. No. 2370 contains one 38x50mm stamp with a slightly darker appearance than that found on No. 2122. Sheet margins of Nos. 2369-2370 lack embossing and gold arms and frames found on Nos. 2121-2122.

**Princess Diana Type of 2001**
Souvenir Sheet

Diana in: a, Yellow dress. b, Red jacket. c, White pinstriped suit.

**2001, Feb. 15**     *Perf. 14*
2371 A509 $1.50 Sheet of 2 each
    #a-c    6.75 6.75

Pres. John F. Kennedy G187

No. 2372, vert. — Pres. Kennedy: a, In boat. b, In chair. c, Profile. d, Close-up, smiling. e, Close-up. f, Looking down.
$6, With Nikita Khrushchev.

**2001, Dec. 15**     *Perf. 13¾*
2372 G187 $1.50 Sheet of 6,
    #a-f    6.75 6.75
**Souvenir Sheet**
2373 G187 $6 multi    4.50 4.50

Jacqueline Kennedy Onassis (1929-94) — G188

No. 2374: a, Blue jacket, blue blouse. b, Red jacket, blue blouse. c, Green dress. d, Blue cape. e Pink and blue jacket. f, Blue jacket, yellow blouse.
No. 2375, $6, Mountain in background. No. 2376, $6, Beige background.

**2001, Dec. 15**     *Perf. 14*
2374 G188 $1.50 Sheet of 6,
    #a-f    6.75 6.75
**Souvenir Sheets**
2375-2376 G188 Set of 2    9.00 9.00

US Generals and Admirals G190

G189

No. 2377: a, Gen. Omar N. Bradley. b, Gen. George C. Marshall. c, Gen. Douglas MacArthur. d, Adm. William F. Halsey. e, Gen. Dwight D. Eisenhower. f, Adm. Chester Nimitz. g, Adm. William D. Leahy. h, Gen. Henry H. Arnold. i, Adm. Ernest J. King. j, Gen. George Washington. k, Gen. John J. Pershing.
No. 2378: a, Gen. George S. Patton, Jr. b, Gen. Joseph W. Stilwell. c, Adm. Thomas C. Kinkaid. d, Gen. Jonathan Wainwright. e, Lt. Gen. James H. Doolittle. f, Gen. Matthew B. Ridgway. g, Gen. Maxwell D. Taylor. h, Adm. Richmond Kelly Turner. i, Gen. Curtis E. LeMay. j, Gen. Hoyt S. Vandenberg. k, Gen. Carl Spaatz. l, Adm. Raymond Spruance.
No. 2379, $6, Eisenhower. No. 2380, $6, Douglas MacArthur.

**2001, Dec. 15**     *Perf. 14*
2377 G189 75c Sheet of 11, #a-
    k, + label    6.25 6.25
2378 G189 75c Sheet of 12, #a-l    6.75 6.75
**Souvenir Sheets**
*Perf. 13¾*
2379-2380 G190 Set of 2    9.00 9.00

Moths — G191

Designs: 75c, Pine emperor. 90c, Inquisitive monkey. $2, Oak eggar. $3, Madagascan sunset moth.
No. 2385, $1.50: a, Spanish moon moth. b, Coppery dysphania. c, Io moth. d, Large agarista. e, Millar's tiger. f, Tropical fruitpiercer.
No. 2386, $1.50: a, Indian moon moth. b, Beautiful tiger. c, Regal moth. d, Great tiger moth. e, Venus moth. f, Zodiac moth.
No. 2387, $6, Diva moth, vert. No. 2388, $6, African moon moth, vert.

**2001, Dec. 17**    *Perf. 14*
2381-2384 G191   Set of 4   5.00   5.00
**Sheets of 6, #a-f**
2385-2386 G191    13.50   13.50
**Souvenir Sheets**
2387-2388 G191   Set of 2   9.00   9.00
Vegaspex (No. 2386).

**Reign of Queen Elizabeth II, 50th Anniv. Type of 2002**

No. 2389: a, White hat. b, Red hat. c, Tiara. d, Hatless.
$6, With Princes Philip, Charles, Princess Anne.

**2002, Feb. 6**    *Perf. 14¼*
2389 A516 $2 Sheet of 4, #a-d   6.00   6.00
**Souvenir Sheet**
2390 A516 $6 multi   4.50   4.50

New Year 2002 (Year of the Horse) G192

Various horses with background colors of —
No. 2391: a, 75c, Light brown and light orange. b, $1.25, Light blue and olive green. c, $2, Tan and bister.
$6, Light orange and orange.

**2002, Mar. 4**   Litho.   *Perf. 13¾*
2391 G192   Sheet of 3, #a-c   3.00   3.00
**Souvenir Sheet**
2392 G192 $6 multi   4.50   4.50

United We Stand — G193

**2002, May 21**    *Perf. 14*
2393 G193 80c multi   .60   .60
Printed in sheets of 4.

**Chiune Sugihara Type of 2002**
**Souvenir Sheets**

Sugihara and: No. 2394, $6, Map of Asia. No. 2395, $6, Pink background.

**2002, July 1**    *Perf. 13½x13¼*
2394-2395 A521   Set of 2   9.00   9.00

**Winter Olympics Type of 2002**

Montages of: No. 2396, $3, Skier in air, course flag, vert. No. 2397, $3, Skier, no flag, vert.

**2002, July 1**    *Perf. 13½x13¼*
2396-2397 A522   Set of 2   4.50   4.50
2397a   Souvenir sheet, #2396-2397   4.50   4.50

**Intl. Year of Mountains Type of 2002**

No. 2398: a, Mt. Kilimanjaro, Tanzania. b, Mt. Kenya, Kenya. c, Mauna Kea, Hawaii. d, Mt. Fuji, Japan.
$6, Koolau Mountains, Hawaii.

**2002, July 1**    *Perf. 13¼x13½*
2398 A523 $2 Sheet of 4, #a-d   6.00   6.00
**Souvenir Sheet**
2399 A523 $6 multi   4.50   4.50

**Intl. Year of Ecotourism Type of 2002**

No. 2400, horiz.: a, Tourists at waterfall. b, Bird. c, Butterfly. d, Fish. e, Cactus. f, Orchid.
$6, Birds, horiz.

---

**2002, July 1**    *Perf. 13¼x13½*
2400 A524 $1.50 Sheet of 6, #a-f   6.75   6.75
**Souvenir Sheet**
2401 A524 $6 multi   4.50   4.50
Nos. 2400-2401 were each overprinted in sheet margins "Hurricane Relief 2004" in 2005.

**Scout Jamboree Type of 2002**

No. 2402, horiz.: a, Campfire, Scout emblem. b, Scout with walking stick and backpack. c, Scout feeding calf. d, Girl giving Scout sign.
No. 2403, $6, Scout with hat.

**2002, July 1**    *Perf. 13¼x13½*
2402 A525 $2 Sheet of 4, #a-d   6.00   6.00
**Souvenir Sheet**
*Perf. 13½x13¼*
2403 A525 $2 multi   1.50   1.50

Amerigo Vespucci (1454-1512), Explorer — G194

Various portraits with background colors of: $1, Purple. $2, Orange brown. $3, Green. $6, Vespucci and map.

**2002, July 1**    *Perf. 13½x13¼*
2404-2406 G194   Set of 3   4.50   4.50
**Souvenir Sheet**
2407 G194 $6 multi   4.50   4.50

**Butterflies, Insects, Mushrooms and Whales Type of 2002**

No. 2408, $1 — Whales: a, Sperm. b, Bottlenose. c, Sei. d, Killer. e, Humpback. f, Pygmy sperm.
No. 2409, $1 — Insects: a, Bumblebee. b, Dragonfly. c, Hercules beetle. d, Ladybug. e, Figure-of-eight butterfly. f, Praying mantis.
No. 2410, $2 — Butterflies: a, White peacock. b, Orange-barred sulphur. c, Blue night. d, Banded king shoemaker. e, Cramer's mesene. f, Common morpho.
No. 2411, $2 — Mushrooms: a, Shaggy mane. b, Shaggy parasol. c, Purple coincap. d, Sharp-scaled parasol. e, Thick-footed morel. f, Rosy-gill fairy helmet.
No. 2412, $6, Blue whale, horiz. No. 2413, $6, Dragonfly, horiz. No. 2414, $6, Blue night butterfly, horiz. No. 2415, $6, Death cap mushroom.

**2002, Aug. 12**    *Perf. 14*
**Sheets of 6, #a-f**
2408-2411 A538   Set of 4   27.50   27.50
**Souvenir Sheets**
2412-2415 A538   Set of 4   18.00   18.00

**Elvis Presley Type of 2002 and**

Elvis Presley G195

No. 2416, Color portrait.
No. 2417: a, Wearing light plaid shirt. b, Holding microphone. c, Wearing dark shirt. d, Holding guitar with neck up. e, Wearing suit, holding guitar. f, Wearing short-sleeve shirt, holding guitar. g, Wearing shirt with flowers on shoulders. h, Wearing wrist watch and short-sleeve shirt. i, Wearing dark plaid shirt, holding guitar.

**2002, Aug. 26**    *Perf. 13¾*
2416 A527 $1 multi   .75   .75
2417 G195 $1 Sheet of 9, #a-i   6.75   6.75
No. 2416 printed in sheets of 9.

---

**Dutch Nobel Prize Winners, Lighthouses and Women's Costumes Types of 2002**

No. 2418 — Nobel Prize winners: a, Paul Crutzen, Chemistry, 1995. b, Nobel Medal for Physics, Chemistry, Physiology or Medicine, and Literature. c, Martinus J. G. Veltman, Physics, 1999. d, Hendrik A. Lorentz, Physics, 1902. e, Christiaan Eijkman, Physiology or Medicine, 1929. f, Gerardus 't Hooft, Physics, 1999.
No. 2419 — Lighthouses: a, Ameland. b, Vlieland. c, Julianadorp. d, Noordwijk. e, Hoek van Holland. f, Goeree.
No. 2420 — Women's costumes: a, Noord-Holland (woman with child). b, Overijssel (woman with blue dress and plaid neckerchief). c, Zeeland (woman with necklace).

**2002, Aug. 29**    *Perf. 13½x13¼*
2418 A532 $1.50 Sheet of 6, #a-f   6.75   6.75
2419 A533 $1.50 Sheet of 6, #a-f   6.75   6.75
*Perf. 13¼*
2420 A534 $3 Sheet of 3, #a-c   6.75   6.75
Amphilex 2002 Intl. Stamp Exhibition, Amsterdam.

**Teddy Bear Centenary Types of 2002**

No. 2421 — Bear with: a, 15c, Tasseled helmet. b, $2, Black hat with red bullseye. c, $3, Hat and neck ruffle. d, $4, Gray hat.
No. 2422 — Bear with: a, 50c, Happy birthday heart. b, $1, Flower, vest, hat, and violin case. c, $2, Hat and trench coat. d, $5, Shorts.

**2002, Sept. 23**    *Perf. 14*
2421 A529   Sheet of 4, #a-d   7.00   7.00
2422 A530   Sheet of 4, #a-d   6.50   6.50

**Christmas Type of 2002**

Carpaccio paintings: 15c, The Redeemer and the Four Apostles. 25c, The Miracle of the Relic of the Cross, vert. 50c, The Presentation in the Temple. $2, The Visitation. $3, The Birth of the Virgin.
$6, Madonna and Child and Two Angels, by Cimabue, vert.

**2002, Nov. 4**    *Perf. 14*
2423-2427 A541   Set of 5   4.50   4.50
**Souvenir Sheet**
2428 A541 $6 multi   4.50   4.50

**World Cup Soccer Matches Type of 2002**

No. 2429, $1.50: a, Oliver Neuville, Eddie Pope. b, Claudio Reyna, Miroslav Klose. c, Christian Ziege, Frankie Hejduk. d, Nadal, Jung Hwan Ahn. e, Luis Enrique, Chong Gug Song. f, Park Ji Sung, Mendieta Gaizka.
No. 2430, $1.50: a, Danny Mills, Ronaldo. b, Roque Junior, Emile Heskey. c, Sol Campbell, Rivaldo. d, Lamine Diatta, Hakan Sukur. e, Umit Davala, Khalilou Fadiga. f, El Hadji Diouf, Tugay Kerimoglu.
No. 2431, $3: a, Oliver Kahn. b, Brad Friedel.
No. 2432, $3: a, Chun Soo Lee. b, Juan Carlos Valeron.
No. 2433, $3: a, David Beckham, Roberto Carlos. b, Ronaldinho, Nicky Butt.
No. 2434, $3: a, Alpay Ozalan. b, Fadiga.

**2002, Nov. 18**    *Perf. 13¼*
**Sheets of 6, #a-f**
2429-2430 A542   Set of 2   13.50   13.50
**Souvenir Sheets of 2, #a-b**
2431-2434 A542   Set of 4   18.00   18.00

**Dale Earnhardt Type of 2002**

No. 2435: a, $2, 1980 photo. b, $2, 1986 photo. c, $2, 1987 photo. d, $2, 1990 photo. e, $2, 1991 photo. f, $2, 1993 photo. g, $2, 1994 photo. h, $4, Two cars (75x50mm).

**2002**    *Perf. 13½x13¾*
2435 A518   Sheet of 8, #a-h   13.50   13.50

---

New Year 2003 (Year of the Ram) — G196

**2003, Jan. 27**    *Perf. 14*
2436 G196 $1.25 multi   1.25   1.25
Printed in sheets of 4.

G197

Coronation of Queen Elizabeth II, 50th Anniv. — G198

No. 2437: a, As child. b, In blue dress. c, On horse.
$6, Wearing sash and tiara.
$20, Wearing tiara.

**2003**    Litho.    *Perf. 14*
2437 G197 $3 Sheet of 3, #a-c   6.75   6.75
**Souvenir Sheet**
2438 G197 $6 multi   4.50   4.50
**Miniature Sheet**
**Litho. & Embossed**
*Perf. 13¼x13*
2439 G198 $20 gold & multi   15.00   15.00
Issued: Nos. 2437-2438, 8/25; No. 2439, 2/24.

**Space Shuttle Columbia Type of 2003**

No. 2440: a, Mission Specialist 1 David M. Brown. b, Commander Rick D. Husband. c, Mission Specialist 4 Laurel Blair Salton Clark. d, Mission Specialist 4 Kalpana Chawla. e, Payload Commander Michael P. Anderson. f, Pilot William C. McCool. g, Payload Specialist 4 Ilan Ramon.

**2003, Apr. 7**   Litho.   *Perf. 13¼*
2440 A549 $1 Sheet of 7, #a-g   5.25   5.25

**Klimt Paintings Type of 2003**

Designs: 15c, Le Chapeau de Plumes Noires. 25c, Le Schloss Kammer am Attersee. 50c, Malcesine sue le Lac de Garde. 75c, Ferme en Haute Autriche. $1.25, Portrait d'une Dame. $4, La Frise Beethoven.
No. 2447: a, Portrait de la Baronne Elisabeth Bachofen-Echt. b, Portrait d'une Dame, diff. c, Portrait d'Emilie Floge. d, Portrait d'Adele Bloch-Bauer.
$6, Le Baiser.

**2003, Apr. 28**      *Perf. 14¼*
2441-2446 A550    Set of 6      5.25 5.25

*Perf. 13¼*
2447 A550 $2 Sheet of 4, #a-d    6.00 6.00

**Size: 83x103mm**

*Imperf*
2448 A550 $6 multi      4.50 4.50

### Japanese Art Type of 2003

Paintings by Kunichika Toyohara: 50c, The Actor Danjuro Ichikawa IX as the Beggar Kagekiyo Akushichibyoe. 75c, The Actor Danjuro Ichikawa IX as the Female Demon Uwanari. $1.25, The Actor Tossho Sawamura II as Sutewakamaru. $3, The Actor Hikosaburo Bando V as Danjo Nikki.

No. 2453: a, The Actor Shikan Nakamura IV as Rokusuke Keyamura. b, The Actor Hikosaburo Bando V as Ichimisair No Musume Osono. c, The Actor Sadanji Ichikawa I as Wada No Shimobe Busuke. d, The Actor Sandanji Ichikawa I as Kiyomizu no Yoshitaka.

$6, The Actor Kikugoro Onoe V as Tsuneemon Torii Retruning to Mikawa, horiz.

**2003, Apr. 28**      *Perf. 14¼*
2449-2452 A551    Set of 4      4.25 4.25
2453 A551 $2 Sheet of 4, #a-d    6.00 6.00

**Souvenir Sheet**
2454 A551 $6 multi      4.50 4.50

### Cranach Paintings Type of 2003

Details from paintings by Lucas Cranach the Elder: 25c, The St. Mary Altarpiece, vert. $1, The St. Mary Altarpiece, diff., vert. $1.25, Duke John with St. James the Greater, from Altarpiece of the Princes, vert. $3, Frederick the Wise with St. Bartholomew, vert.

No. 2459: a, Judith at the Table of Holofernes. b, Central panel of St. Catherine Altarpeice. c, Judith Killing Holofernes. d, The Martyrdom of St. Catherine.

$6, Cardinal Albrecht of Brandenbourg as St. Jerome in the Wilderness, vert.

**2003, Apr. 28**
2455-2458 A552    Set of 4      4.25 4.25
2459 A552 $2 Sheet of 4, #a-d    6.00 6.00

**Souvenir Sheet**
2460 A552 $6 multi      4.50 4.50

### Teddy Bear Type of 2003

**2003, Apr. 29 Embroidered** *Imperf.*
**Self-Adhesive**
2461 A553 $15 multi      11.50 11.50

Issued in sheets of 4.

### Tour de France Type of 2003

No. 2462, $2: a, Ferdinand Kubler, 1950. b, Hugo Koblet, 1951. c, Fausto Coppi, 1952. d, Louison Bobet, 1953.

No. 2463, $2: a, Bobet, 1954. b, Bobet, 1955. c, Roger Walkowiak, 1956. d, Jacques Anquetil, 1957.

No. 2464, $2: a, Gastone Nencini, 1960. b, Anquetil, 1961. c, Anquetil, 1962. d, Anquetil, 1963.

No. 2465, $6, Bobet, 1953-55. No. 2466, $6, Anquetil, 1957, diff. No. 2467, $6, Eddy Merckx, 1969.

**2003, June 17**      *Perf. 13¼*
**Sheets of 4, #a-d**
2462-2464 A555    Set of 3      18.00 18.00

**Souvenir Sheets**
2465-2467 A555    Set of 3      13.50 13.50

### John F. Kennedy Type of 2002

No. 2468, $2: a, As Choate graduate, 1935. b, As congressman, 1946. c, With wife, Jacqueline, on tennis court. d, With son, John, Jr.

No. 2469, $2: a, With wife, Jacqueline. b, Announcing Cuban blockade, 1962. c, Seated in White House, 1962. d, Wife and children at funeral, 1963.

**2003, July 1**      *Perf. 14*
**Sheets of 4, #a-d**
2468-2469 A544    Set of 2      12.00 12.00

### Intl. Year of Fresh Water Type of 2003

No. 2470 — Flag and: a, La Sagesse. b, Annadale Falls. c, Grand Etang.

$6, Flag and St. George, horiz.

**2003, July 4**      *Perf. 13½x13¼*
2470 A559 $2 Sheet of 3, #a-c    4.50 4.50

**Souvenir Sheet**
*Perf. 13¼x13½*
2471 A559 $6 multi      4.50 4.50

---

### Circus Performers Type of 2003

No. 2472, $2 — Clowns: a, Anton Pilossian. b, Victor Vashnikov. c, Dan Rice. d, Tom Comet.

No. 2473, $2: a, Dog. b, Macaw. c, Monique. d, Vassily Trofimov.

**2003, July 14**      *Perf. 14*
**Sheets of 4, #a-d**
2472-2473 A560    Set of 2      12.00 12.00

### Powered Flight Type of 2003

No. 2474, $2: a, Wright Brothers Flyer. b, NC-4. c, Douglas World Cruiser. d, Fokker Eindecker.

No. 2475, $2: a, Hawker Hart. b, Martin B-10. c, Armstrong Whitworth Siskin IIIA. d, Loening OL-8.

No. 2476, $2: a, Hansa-Brandenberg D.1. b, B.E. 2e. c, Handley Page 0/400. d, Avro 504.

No. 2477, $6, Wright Brothers No. 3 glider. No. 2478, $6, Wright Brothers Flyer No. 2. No. 2479, $6, Gloster Gamecock.

**2003, July 14**    Sheets of 4, #a-d
2474-2476 A556    Set of 3      18.00 18.00

**Souvenir Sheets**
2477-2479 A556    Set of 3      13.50 13.50

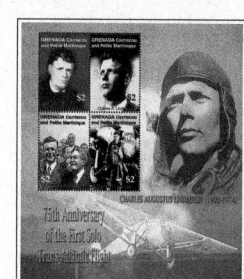

First Nonstop Solo Transatlantic Flight, 75th Anniv. — G199

No. 2480, $2: a, Charles Lindbergh (white denomination, blue background). b, Lindbergh (blue denomination, brown background. c, Lindbergh's arrival in Paris, 1927. d, Lindbergh and Spirit of St. Louis (white denomination, country name in blue)

No. 2481, $2: a, Lindbergh (blue denomination and background). b, Lindbergh and Spirit of St. Louis, blue denomination, red violet background). c, Lindbergh and Spirit of St. Louis (white denomination and country name). d, Lindbergh (white denomination, blue country name).

**2003, July 14**    Sheets of 4, #a-d
2480-2481 G199    Set of 2      12.00 12.00

### Prince William Type of 2003

No. 2482, vert.: a, Looking right. b, Looking forward. c, Looking left.

$6, In ski jacket, vert.

**2003, Sept. 22**
2482 A562 $3 Sheet of 3, #a-c    6.75 6.75

**Souvenir Sheet**
2483 A562 $6 multi      4.50 4.50

### Flowers Type of 2003

Designs: 75c, Wild rhododendron, vert. $1, Peony, vert. $1.25, Camellia, vert. No. 2487, $2, Laurel, vert.

No. 2488, $2, vert.: a, Apple blossom. b, Mock orange. c, Wild rose. d, Hibiscus.

$6, Violets, vert.

**2003, Oct. 23**      *Perf. 13½*
2484-2487 A567    Set of 4      3.75 3.75
2488 A567 $2 Sheet of 4, #a-d    6.00 6.00

**Souvenir Sheet**
2489 A567 $6 multi      4.50 4.50

ASDA Postage Stamp Mega-event (No. 2489).

### Fish Type of 2003

Designs: 25c, Domino damsel. 75c, Porcupine fish. $1.25, Damselfish. No. 2493, $2, Clownfish.

No. 2494, $2: a, Triggerfish. b, Half-and-half wrasse. c, Long-fin bannerfish. d, Butterflyfish.

$6, Blue-girdled angelfish.

**2003, Oct. 23**
2490-2493 A568    Set of 4      3.25 3.25
2494 A568 $2 Sheet of 4, #a-d    6.00 6.00

**Souvenir Sheet**
2495 A568 $6 multi      4.50 4.50

---

### Birds Type of 2003

Designs: 25c, Rose-breasted grosbeak. No. 2497, 50c, Gray catbird. No. 2498, 50c, Bullock's oriole. $1, Blue grosbeak.

No. 2500, $2, vert.: a, Lazuli bunting. b, Indigo bunting. c, Broad-tailed hummingbird. d, Scarlet tanager.

$6, Barn swallow.

**2003, Oct. 23**
2496-2499 A569    Set of 4      2.25 2.25
2500 A569 $2 Sheet of 4, #a-d    6.00 6.00

**Souvenir Sheet**
2501 A569 $6 multi      4.50 4.50

### Christmas Type of 2003

Designs: 35c, Madonna and Child, from Carnesecchi Tabernacle, by Domenico Veneziano. 75c, Madonna and Child, from Magnoli altarpiece, by Veneziano. 90c, Crevole Madonna, by Duccio di Buoninsegna. $3, Madonna and Child, by Veneziano.

$6, Madonna and Child by the Fireplace, by Robert Campin.

**2003, Nov. 17**      *Perf. 14¼*
2502-2505 A570    Set of 4      3.75 3.75

**Souvenir Sheet**
2506 A570 $6 multi      4.50 4.50

### Hermitage Paintings Type of 2003

Designs: 75c, Abraham and Isaac, by Rembrandt, vert. $1, David and Jonathan, by Rembrandt, vert. $1.25, St. Onuphrius, by Jusepe de Ribera, vert. No. 2510, $2, Pope Paul III, by Titian, vert.

No. 2511, $2: a, Rest on the Flight into Egypt, by Bartolomé Estéban Murillo. b, Esther Before Ahasuerus, by Nicolas Poussin. c, Abraham's Servant and Rebecca, by Jacob Hogers. d, The Prophet Elisha and Naaman, by Lambert Jacobsz.

No. 2512, Hagar Flees Abram's House, by Peter Paul Rubens. No. 2513, The Building of Noah's Ark, by Guido Reni, vert.

**2003, Dec. 8**      *Perf. 13½*
2507-2510 A572    Set of 4      3.75 3.75
2511 A572 $2 Sheet of 4, #a-d    6.00 6.00

*Imperf*
**Size: 78x65mm**
2512 A572 $6 multi      4.50 4.50

**Size: 67x78mm**
2513 A572 $6 multi      4.50 4.50

### Norman Rockwell Type of 2003

No. 2514, vert.: a, The Trumpeter. b, Waiting for the Vet. c, The Diving Board. d, The Discovery.

$6, Day in a Boy's Life.

**2003, Dec. 8 Litho.**    *Perf. 13¼*
2514 A571 $2 Sheet of 4, #a-d    6.00 6.00

**Souvenir Sheet**
2515 A571 $6 multi      4.50 4.50

### Pablo Picasso Type of 2003

No. 2516: a, Jacqueline Sitting. b, Jacqueline with Flower. c, Seated Nude. d, Woman in Armchair.

$6, Head of a Woman.

**2003, Dec. 8**      *Perf. 13¼*
2516 A573 $2 Sheet of 4, #a-d    6.00 6.00

*Imperf*
2517 A573 $6 multi      4.50 4.50

No. 2516 contains four 37x50mm stamps.

### New Year (Year of the Monkey) Type of 2004

No. 2518: a, White, blue and orange monkey. b, Blue monkey. c, Brown monkey. d, Monkey with orange face.

**2004, Jan. 4**      *Perf. 14*
2518 A574 $1.50 Sheet of 4,
     #a-d      4.50 4.50

Zhoa Mengfu (1254-1322), Artist — G200

---

No. 2519: a, The Mind Landscape of Xie Youyu. b, Scroll with green backround and large mountains at left and right. c, Twin Pines. d, Scroll with brown background and large mountain at left.

$6, Autumn.

**2004, Jan. 29 Litho.**    *Perf. 13½x13¼*
2519 G200 $2 Sheet of 4, #a-d    6.00 4.50

**Souvenir Sheet**
2520 G200 $6 multi      4.50 4.50

### Arthur and Friends Type of 2004

No. 2521: a, Brain. b, Binky. c, Francine. d, Prunella. e, Arthur. f, Muffy.

No. 2522, $2: a, Francine, diff. b, Buster. c, Muffy, diff. d, Sue Ellen.

No. 2523, $2: a, Francine and butterfly. b, Binky and map. c, Brain and blackboard. d, Arthur and model of solar system.

**2004, Jan. 29**      *Perf. 13¼*
2521 A577 $1.50 Sheet of 6,
     #a-f      6.75 6.75

**Sheets of 4, #a-d**
2522-2523 A577    Set of 2      12.00 12.00

### Olympics Type of 2004

Designs: 25c, Long jumper, 1924 Paris Olympics. 50c, Avery Brundage, Intl. Olympic Committee President, 1952-72. $1, Commemorative medal for 1972 Munich Olympics. $4, Paidotribai.

**2004, Apr. 8**      *Litho.*
2524-2527 A579    Set of 4      4.50 4.50

### Deng Xiaoping Type of 2004
**Souvenir Sheet**

**2004, May 3**      *Perf. 13½x13¼*
2528 A582 $6 Wearing cap    4.50 4.50

### Pope John Paul II Type of 2004

No. 2529: a, With Lech Walesa. b, With Meir Lau, Chief Rabbi of Israel. c, Blessing children. d, At computer. e, Wearing miter.

**2004, May 3**      *Perf. 13½*
2529 A583 $2 Sheet of 5, #a-e    7.50 7.50

### Marilyn Monroe Type of 2004

Designs: 50c, Portrait, diff.

No. 2531 — Various portraits with color and location of denomination of: a, Black, UL. b, Black, UR. c, White, UR. d, White, UL.

**2004, May 3**      *Perf. 13½x13¼*
2530 A584 50c multi      .40 .40
2531 A584 $2 Sheet of 4, #a-d    6.00 6.00

No. 2530 was printed in sheets of 16.

### D-Day Type of 2004

Designs: 25c, Admiral Sir Bertram Ramsay. 50c, Lt. Gen. Miles Dempsey. 75c, Bob Shrimpton, Submarine Detector on HMS Belfast. $4, Denis Edwards, 6th Airborne Division.

No. 2536, $2: a, Sir Winston Churchill without hat. b, Churchill with hat. c, British link up with Airborne troops. d, Link up at Orne River.

No. 2537, $2: a, US troops move inland. b, Troops move inland from Omaha Beach. c, Heavy fighting on Sword Beach. d, German generals meet.

No. 2538, $6, Assault landing craft head for invasion beaches. No. 2539, $6, Gunner in a British bomber.

**2004, July 19**      *Perf. 14*
**Stamps + Labels (#2532-2535)**
2532-2535 A586    Set of 4      4.25 4.25

**Sheets of 4, #a-d**
2536-2537 A586    Set of 2      12.00 12.00

**Souvenir Sheets**
2538-2539 A586    Set of 2      9.00 9.00

### Locomotives Type of 2004

No. 2540, $1: a, Liner V2 Class 2-6-2. b, Sudan Railways 2-8-2. c, China Railways DF4 Co-Co. d, LMS 2F 0-6-0 with Black 5 4-6-0. e, LMS Lickey Banker 0-10-0. f, LMS Princess Royal Pacific. g, LMS Reboilered Claughton Class 4-6-0. h, LMS Stanier 8F 2-8-0. i, Midland Railway Compound 4-4-0.

No. 2541, $1: a, Britannia Class 4-6-2. b, Indian Railways XD Class 2-8-2. c, China Railways KD6 2-8-0 (USATC S160). d, SE+CR 01 Class 0-6-0. e, Battle of Britain Light Pacific. f, SR King Arthur Class 4-6-0. g, SR Marsh 13 Class 4-4-2T. h, SR N Class 2-6-0. i, SR School Class 4-4-0.

No. 2542, $1: a, SR Merchant Navy Pacific 4-6-2. b, Gazira Cotton Railway, Sudan. c, Spanish Railways 4-8-4. d, LNER 04-1 Class 2-8-0. e, LNER A1 4-6-2 Pacific. f, LNER A3 Class 4-6-2. g, LNER A4 Class 4-6-2 Pacific. h, LNER B1 Class 4-6-0. i, LNER Ivatt Large Atlantic 4-4-2 A4 Pacific 4-6-2.

No. 2543, $6, Aberdeen to Penzance train. No. 2544, $6, London to Holyhead train. No. 2545, $6, Dublin to Tralee train.

**2004, July 19**     **Perf. 14**
**Sheets of 9, #a-i**
2540-2542 A587   Set of 3    21.00 21.00
**Souvenir Sheets**
2543-2545 A587   Set of 3    13.50 13.50

**Queen Juliana Type of 2004**
**2004, Aug. 25**   **Litho.**   **Perf. 13¼**
2546 A590 $2 1937 portrait    1.50 1.50
Printed in sheets of 6.

Carriacou Regatta Festival, 40th Anniv. — G201

Designs: 75c, Parade. 90c, People, boats in water. $1, Sailboats, vert.

**2004, Oct. 11**     **Perf. 14**
2547-2549 G201   Set of 3    2.00 2.00

**FIFA Type of 2004**
No. 2550: a, David Beckham. b, Marcel Desailly. c, Guido Buchwald. d, Alfonso. $6, Bobby Charlton.

**2004, Nov. 1**     **Perf. 12¾x12½**
2550 A595 $2 Sheet of 4, #a-d    6.00 6.00
**Souvenir Sheet**
2551 A595 $6 multi      4.50 4.50

Ocean Liners G202

Designs: 25c, Titanic. 75c, Michelangelo. $1, America. $1.25, Vaterland. $2, Deutschland. $3, Mauritania. $6, Ile de France.

**2004, Nov. 29**     **Perf. 14¼**
2552-2557 G202   Set of 6    6.25 6.25
**Souvenir Sheet**
2558 G202 $6 multi      4.50 4.50

**Elvis Presley Type of 2004**
No. 2559, $2: a, Wearing purple shirt. b, Playing guitar, wearing polka dot shirt, "Elvis Presley" at right. c, With guitar hanging from neck, "Elvis Presley" at right. d, Wearing patterned shirt.
No. 2560, $2: a, Wearing brown shirt. b, Playing guitar, wearing polka dot shirt, "Elvis Presley" at left. c, With guitar hanging from neck, "Elvis Presley" at left. d, Wearing gray suit and black shirt, playing guitar.

**2004, Nov. 29**     **Perf. 13¼**
**Sheets of 4, #a-d**
2559-2560 A588   Set of 2    12.00 12.00

**Christmas Type of 2004**
Paintings by Norman Rockwell. 35c, Follow Me in Merry Measure. 75c, The Merrie Old Coach Driver. 90c, Joy to the World. $3, Santa Reading His Mail.
$6, Wartime Santa.

**2004, Dec. 9**     **Perf. 12**
2561-2564 A600   Set of 4    3.75 3.75
**Size: 63x81mm**
*Imperf*
2565 A600 $6 multi      4.50 4.50

**Babe Ruth Type of 2004**
No. 2566: a, Blue background. b, White background.
No. 2567: a, Swinging bat. b, Looking forward. c, Looking to right. d, With glove.

**2004, Jan. 29**   **Litho.**   **Perf. 14**
2566 A598 50c Pair, #a-b    .75 .75
2567 A598 $2 Sheet of 4, #a-d   6.00 6.00

---

Moths — G202a

Designs: 75c, Scarlet-bodied wasp moth. 90c, Bella moth. $1, Sphinx moth. $3, Faithful beauty moth.
$6, Empyreuma affinis.

**2004, Nov. 17**     **Perf. 12¾**
2568-2571 G202a Set of 4    4.25 4.25
**Souvenir Sheet**
2572 G202a $6 multi      4.50 4.50

**Ronald Reagan Type of 2004**
No. 2573: a, With Press Secretary James Brady. b, With German Chancellor Helmut Kohl. c, With family. d, With Princess Diana.

**2004, Nov. 29**     **Perf. 13¼x13½**
2573 A597 $2 Sheet of 4, #a-d   6.00 6.00

**Year of the Rooster Type of 2005**
Paintings by Ren Yi: 75c, Double Chickens and Peony. $3, A Rooster, horiz.

**2005, Jan. 17**     **Perf. 12¾x13**
2574 A601 75c multi      .60 .60
**Souvenir Sheet**
2575 A601 $3 multi      2.25 2.25
No. 2574 printed in sheets of 4. No. 2575 contains one 56x35mm stamp.

**Intl. Year of Rice Type of 2005 and**

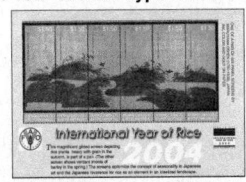

Screen Panels by Oshen Maruyama — G203

No. 2576 — Various panels depicting rice plants and birds.
$6, Rice Farming in Bali, by unknown artist, horiz.

**2005, Feb. 10**     **Perf. 14**
2576 G203 $1.50 Sheet of 6, #a-f 6.75 6.75
**Souvenir Sheet**
2577 A602   $6 multi    4.50 4.50

**Prehistoric Animals Type of 2005**
No. 2578: a, Psittacosaurus. b, Deinonychus. c, Suchomimus. d, Smilodon.
$6, Tenotosaurus.

**2005, Feb. 10**     **Perf. 13¼x13½**
2578 A604 $2 Sheet of 4, #a-d   6.00 6.00
**Souvenir Sheet**
2579 A604 $6 multi      4.50 4.50
See Nos. 2598-2601.

Reptiles and Amphibians — G204

No. 2580: a, Poison dart frog. b, Western Antillean anole. c, Black iguana. d, American crocodile.
$6, Anolis lizard.

**2005, Feb. 10**     **Perf. 12¾**
2580 G204 $2 Sheet of 4, #a-d   8.75 8.75
**Souvenir Sheet**
2581 G204 $6 multi      6.50 6.50

---

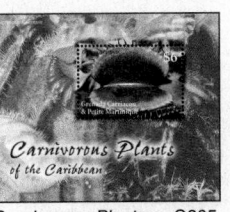

Carnivorous Plants — G205

No. 2582: a, Heliamphora tatei. b, Sarracenia flava, Genlisea pygmaea. c, Nepenthes bicalcarata. d, Utricularia intermedia.
$6, Dionaea muscipula.

**2005, Feb. 10**
2582 G205 $2 Sheet of 4, #a-d   6.00 6.00
**Souvenir Sheet**
2583 G205 $6 multi      4.50 4.50

**Elvis Presley Type of 2005**
No. 2584, $1.50: a, With guitar, 1955. b, Singing, 1956. c, With hand on chin, 1958. d, In suit, 1962. e, With guitar, 1968. f, Singing, 1972.
No. 2585, $1.50: a, In Army uniform, 1958. b, Wearing Hawaiian shirt, 1961. c, Wearing cap, 1963. d, Wearing turban, 1965. e, Sitting on sports car, 1966. f, With stethoscope, 1969.

**2005, Apr. 4**     **Perf. 13½**
**Sheets of 6, #a-f**
2584-2585 A607   Set of 2    13.50 13.50

Battle of Trafalgar, Bicent. — G206

Designs: 75c, Swiftsure. $1, British sail near Cape Trafalgar, horiz. $2, Capt. Alexander Ball. $3, Vice-Admiral Francedillaois Brueys d'Aigalliers.
$6, Admiral Aristide du Petit-Thouars.

**2005, Apr. 4**     **Perf. 14**
2586-2589 G206   Set of 4    5.25 5.25
**Souvenir Sheet**
2590 G206 $6 multi      4.50 4.50

**Yasujiro Ozu Type of 2005**
No. 2591: a, A Mother Should Be Loved, 1934. b, An Inn in Tokyo, 1935. c, Dragnet Girl, 1933. d, There Was a Father, 1942.

**2005, Apr. 8**     **Perf. 14¼**
2591 A608 $2 Sheet of 4, #a-d   6.00 6.00

**Basketball Players Type of 2004**
Designs: No. 2592, 75c, Steve Francis, Orlando Magic. No. 2593, 75c, Allan Houston, New York Knicks. No. 2594, 75c, Tracy McGrady, Houston Rockets. No. 2595, 75c, Steve Nash, Phoenix Suns. No. 2596, 75c, Shaquille O'Neal, Miami Heat. No. 2597, 75c, Chris Webber, Sacramento Kings.

**2005, Mar. 8**   **Litho.**   **Perf. 14**
2592-2597 A596   Set of 6    3.50 3.50
Each stamp printed in sheets of 12.

**Prehistoric Animals Type of 2005**
No. 2598, $2: a, Eurypholis. b, Ichthyosaurus. c, Plesiosaur. d, Varnerxiphactinus.
No. 2599, $2: a, Pterosaurus. b, Archaeopteryx. c, Pterosaurian. d, Microraptor.
No. 2600, $6, Uintatherium. No. 2601, $6, Mammoth, vert.

**Perf. 13¼x13¾, 13¾x13¼**
**2005, Apr. 15**   **Sheets of 4, #a-d**
2598-2599 A604   Set of 2    12.00 12.00
**Souvenir Sheets**
2600-2601 A604   Set of 2    9.00 9.00

**End of World War II Type of 2005**
No. 2602, $2 — Battle of El Alamein: a, Field Marshal Bernard Montgomery directs troops forward. b, Field Marshal Erwin Rommel ready for battle. c, Troops move forward into battle. d, Line of German prisoners after battle.
No. 2603, $2 — Fall of Berlin: a, Russians at the gates of Berlin. b, German soldiers surrender. c, Berlin in ruins. d, Picking up the pieces.

---

No. 2604, $6, Troops attacking. No. 2605, $6, Sign with quote by Adolf Hitler, vert.

**2005, May 10**     **Perf. 13¼**
**Sheets of 4, #a-d**
2602-2603 A610   Set of 2    12.00 12.00
**Souvenir Sheets**
2604-2605 A610   Set of 2    9.00 9.00

**Albert Einstein Type of 2005**
No. 2606, vert.: a, Einstein, planet, diagram of Earth and Moon. b, Einstein. c, Israeli Prime Minister David Ben Gurion.

**2005, June 27**     **Perf. 13¼**
2606 A615 $3 Sheet of 3, #a-c   6.75 6.75
No. 2606 contains three 38x50mm stamps.

**V-J Day Type of 2005**
No. 2607, $2: a, P-38J Lightning. b, P-51D Mustang. c, F-4 fighter plane. d, Douglas C-47 Skytrain.
No. 2608, $2: a, Officer reads V-J Day message to his troops. b, Chaplain's prayer. c, Rejoicing the victory. d, USS Missouri in Tokyo Bay.

**2005, July 11**     **Perf. 12¾**
**Sheets of 4, #a-d**
2607-2608 A612   Set of 2    12.00 12.00

**Rotary International Type of 2005**
No. 2609, horiz.: a, People in front of National Polio Laboratory. b, People in National Polio Laboratory. c, Rotary International emblem.

**2005, July 11**     **Perf. 14**
2609 A613 $3 Sheet of 3, #a-c   6.75 6.75

Pope John Paul II (1920-2005) G207

**2005, Sept. 22**     **Perf. 13¼x13½**
2610 G207 $3 multi    2.25 2.25
Printed in sheets of 6.

Maimonides (1135-1204), Philosopher G208

**2005**     **Perf. 12**
2611 G208 $2 multi      1.50 1.50

**Christmas Type of 2005**
Designs: 35c, Madonna and Child, by Andrea del Sarto. 75c, Madonna Pesaro, by Titian. 90c, Madonna and Child, by Titian. $3, Madonna and Child, by Peter Paul Rubens.
$6, Madonna and Child, by Domenico Veneziano.

**2005**     **Perf. 12¾**
2612-2615 A625   Set of 4    3.75 3.75
**Souvenir Sheet**
2616 A625 $6 multi      4.50 4.50

Dog, by Chang Dai-Chien G209

**2006, Jan. 3**   **Litho.**   **Perf. 11½x11¼**
2617 G209 $1 multi      .75 .75
New Year 2006 (Year of the Dog). Printed in sheets of 4.

**Pope Benedict XVI Type of 2006**
**2006, Jan. 10**     **Perf. 13¼**
2618 A629 $2 Pope, diff.    1.50 1.50
Printed in sheets of 4.

## Elvis Presley Type of 2006

*Variable Die Cut Perf.*

**2006, Feb. 21      Litho. & Embossed**
**Without Gum**
2619 A631 $20 multi                    15.00 15.00

## Queen Elizabeth II, 80th Birthday Type of 2006

No. 2620: a, Queen wearing hat, sepia photograph. b, Queen wearing tiara. c, Queen with Princess Anne. d, Queen wearing hat, color photograph.

$6, Portrait of Queen in robe.

**2006, Feb. 21      Litho.      Perf. 13¼**
2620 A632 $3 Sheet of 4, #a-d        9.00 9.00
**Souvenir Sheet**
**Perf. 12**
2621 A632 $6 multi                    4.50 4.50

## Marilyn Monroe Type of 2006

**2006, Mar. 30               Perf. 13½**
2622 A634 $3 Monroe, diff.           2.25 2.25

Printed in sheets of 4.

## Rembrandt Type of 2006

Designs: 75c, The Strolling Musicians. 90c, The Great Jewish Bride. $1, Old Haaringh. $4, Beggars Receiving Alms at the Door of a House. 2627, $6, Young Woman in a Pearl-trimmed Beret (70x100mm). No. 2628, $6, Portrait of a Boy (70x100mm).

No. 2629: a, Man from Lady and Gentleman in Black. b, Woman from Lady and Gentleman in Black. c, Man from The Shipbuilder and His Wife. d, Woman from The Shipbuilder and His Wife.

**Perf. 12, 12½x12¼ (#2627-2628)**
**2006, June 16**
2623-2628 A639    Set of 6     14.00 14.00
**Miniature Sheet**
2629 A639 $3 Sheet of 4, #a-d        9.00 9.00

## Mozart Type of 2006

**2006, June 22    Litho.    Perf. 12¾**
2630 A640 $6 Don Giovanni            4.50 4.50

## Space Type of 2006

No. 2631 — First Flight of Space Shuttle Columbia: a, Columbia on launchpad. b, Astronauts John W. Young and Robert L. Crippen. c, Liftoff of Columbia. d, Columbia in space. e, Crew in cabin. f, Columbia landing.

No. 2632, $3 — Apollo-Soyuz: a, Liftoff of Soyuz 19. b, Apollo-Soyuz crew. c, Crew in cabin. d, Soyuz 19.

No. 2633, $3 — Space Shuttle Discovery's return to space: a, Discovery on launchpad. b, Crew of Mission STS-114. c, Discovery and International Space Station. d, STS-114 space walk.

No. 2634, $6, Luna 9. No. 2635, $6, Venus Express. No. 2636, $6, Mars Reconnaissance Orbiter.

**2006, Sept. 14**
2631 A642 $2 Sheet of 6, #a-f        9.00 9.00
**Sheets of 4, #a-d**
2632-2633 A642    Set of 2     18.00 18.00
**Souvenir Sheets**
2634-2636 A642    Set of 3     13.50 13.50

## Columbus Type of 2006

Designs: 75c, Pinta, vert. $1.50, Nina, Pinta and Santa Maria set sail. $2, Ship and map. $3, Columbus discovers San Salvador.

$6, Columbus.

**2006, Oct. 26**
2637-2640 A643    Set of 4      5.50 5.50
**Souvenir Sheet**
2641 A643 $6 multi                    4.50 4.50

## Christmas Type of 2006

Details of St. Willibrod in Adoration Before Mary, Mother of God, by Peter Paul Rubens: 25c, Man. 50c, Angels. 75c, Mary and Jesus. $1, St. Willibrod.

No. 2646: a, Like 25c. b, Like 50c. c, Like 75c. d, Like $1.

**2006, Dec. 21               Perf. 14**
2642-2645 A646    Set of 4      1.90 1.90
**Souvenir Sheet**
2646 A646 $2 Sheet of 4, #a-d        6.00 6.00

---

Souvenir Sheet

Airships G210

No. 2647: a, LZ-127. b, Dining room of the Hindenburg. c, Marine airship L53.

**2007, Jan. 16               Perf. 13¼**
2647 G210 $3 Sheet of 3, #a-c        6.75 6.75

Souvenir Sheet

Elvis Presley (1935-77) — G211

No. 2648 — Various portraits with: a, Black denomination. b, Red denomination, playing guitar. c, White denomination. d, Red denomination, hands off guitar.

**2007, Jan. 16               Perf. 14¼**
2648 G211 $3 Sheet of 4, #a-d        9.00 9.00

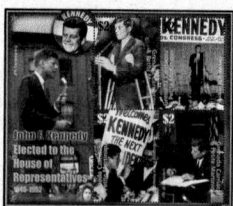

Pres. John F. Kennedy (1917-63) — G212

No. 2649, $2: a, On crutches, running for Congress. b, Campaigning for Congress. c, Campaigning in New Hampshire. d, As president.

No. 2650, $2.50: a, Naru Island. b, As Navy lieutenant on Solomon Islands, wearing cap. c, As lieutenant on Solomon Islands, without cap. d, SOS coconut carved by Kennedy.

**2007, Jan. 16               Perf. 13½**
**Sheets of 4, #a-d**
2649-2650 G212    Set of 2     13.50 13.50

## Scouting Type of 2007

Scout fleur-de-lis, "100," years "1907 / 2007," and background colors of: $2, Blue and green, horiz. $6, Orange and green, horiz.

**2007, Jan. 16**
2651 A650 $2 multi                    1.50 1.50
**Souvenir Sheet**
2652 A650 $6 multi                    4.50 4.50

No. 2651 printed in sheets of 4.

## Year of the Pig Type of 2007

**Miniature Sheet**

No. 2653 — Wild Boar, by Liu Jiyou and painting name in: a, $1, Black. b, $1, Brown. c, $2, Black. d, $2, Red.

**2007, Feb. 15    Litho.    Perf. 14**
2653 A652    Sheet of 4, #a-d        4.50 4.50

G213

---

G214

Mushrooms — G215

Designs: 75c, Morchella semilibera. No. 2655, $1, Ganoderma resinaceum. No. 2656, $1, Helvella crispa. $4, Ganoderma sp.

No. 2658, $2: a, Russula sardonia. b, Amanita cruzii. c, Macrocybe titans. d, Amanita microspora.

No. 2659, $2: a, Aleuria aurantia. b, Boletus sp. c, Boletellus russellii. d, Otidea onotica.

No. 2660, $5, Amanita polypyramis. No. 2661, $5, Boletellus ananas. No. 2662, $5, Cantharellus cibarius.

**2007, May 16    Litho.    Perf. 14**
2654-2657 G213    Set of 4      5.25 5.25
**Sheets of 4, #a-d**
2658-2659 G214    Set of 2     12.00 12.00
**Souvenir Sheets**
2660 G214 $5 multi                    3.75 3.75
2661-2662 G215    Set of 2      7.50 7.50

Birds — G216

Designs: 75c, Pied-billed grebe. No. 2664, $1, Black-crowned night heron. No. 2665, $1, Turkey vulture. $4, Green honeycreeper.

No. 2667, $2, horiz.: a, Caspian tern. b, Scarlet tanager. c, Common nighthawk. d, Osprey.

No. 2668, $2, horiz.: a, Hooded warbler. b, Northern flicker. c, Mockingbird. d, Blue tit. No. 2669, $5, White-winged parakeet. No. 2670, $5, Blackpoll warbler, horiz. No. 2671, $5, Yellow-green vireo, horiz.

**2007, May 16**
2663-2666 G216    Set of 4      5.75 5.75
**Sheets of 4, #a-d**
2667-2668 G216    Set of 2     12.00 12.00
**Souvenir Sheets**
2669-2671 G216    Set of 3     13.00 13.00

Orchids — G217

Designs: 75c, Goodyera tesselata. $1.50, Oncidium floridanum. No. 2674, $2, Hexalectris spicata. $3, Pogonia ophioglossoides.

No. 2676, $2: a, Platanthera blephariglottis. b, Epipactis helleborine. c, Cypripedium alaskanum. d, Zeuxine strateumatica.

No. 2677, $2: a, Platanthera grandiflora. b, Platanthera peramoena. c, Cyrtopodium punctatum. d, Spiranthes odorata.

No. 2678, $6, Platanthera chapmanii. No. 2679, $6, Bletilla striata, horiz. No. 2680, $6, Macradenia lutescens, horiz.

**2007, May 16               Perf. 12¾**
2672-2675 G217    Set of 4      5.50 5.50
**Sheets of 4, #a-d**
2676-2677 G217    Set of 2     12.00 12.00
**Souvenir Sheets**
2678-2680 G217    Set of 3     13.50 13.50

---

Betty Boop in "Snow White" G218

No. 2681, horiz.: a, Queen looking at ring in snow. b, Green witch looking at mirror, dog and clown. c, Dancing ghost. d, Betty Boop asleep, frozen skull.

No. 2682, horiz.: a, $1, Queen looking in mirror. b, $1, Angry queen. c, $1, Knights and tree stump. d, $2, Betty Boop with alarm clock. e, $2, Betty Boop with mirror, dog, clown. f, $2, Betty Boop in snow.

$6, Betty Boop running.

**2007, June 4               Perf. 13½**
2681 G218 $2 Sheet of 4, #a-d        6.00 6.00
2682 G218 $2 Sheet of 6, #a-f        6.75 6.75
**Souvenir Sheet**
2683 G218 $6 multi                    4.50 4.50

## Intl. Polar Year Type of 2007

No. 2684, vert. — Royal penguins with: a, Country name at UR, denomination at LR. b, Country name at top, denomination at LR. c, Country name at LR, denomination at UL. d, Country name at bottom, denomination at UL. e, Country name at bottom, denomination at UR. f, Country name at UL, denomination at LR.

$6, African penguin, vert.

**2007, June 25               Perf. 13½**
2684 A657 $2 Sheet of 6, #a-f        9.00 9.00
**Souvenir Sheet**
2685 A657 $6 multi                    4.50 4.50

## First Helicopter Flight, Cent. Type of 2007

No. 2686, horiz.: a, BK 117. b, UH-1 Iroquois. c, S-65/RH-53D. d, UH-1B/C Iroquois. e, Autogyro. f, BO 105.

$6, AH-64 Apache, horiz.

**2007, June 25**
2686 A664 $1.50 Sheet of 6, #a-f 6.75 6.75
**Souvenir Sheet**
2687 A664    $6 multi                4.50 4.50

## Pope Benedict XVI Type of 2007

**2007, July 11**
2688 A653 $1 Pope, diff.              .75 .75

Printed in sheets of 8.

Christmas — G219

Paintings: 25c, Virgin and Child with Saints Jerome and Bartholomew, by Alessandro Bonvicino. 50c, Virgin and Child Between Saints Thomas and Jerome, by Guido Reni. 75c, Virgin and Child, by Giovanni Batista Salvi. $1, Madonna of Decemviri, by Pietro Perugino.

**2007, Oct. 26           Perf. 14¼x14¾**
2689-2692 G219    Set of 4      1.90 1.90

## Wedding of Queen Elizabeth II and Prince Philip, 60th Anniv. Type of 2007

**Miniature Sheet**

No. 2693 — Couple, denomination at left, dull maroon panel. b, Queen, denomination at right, dull maroon panel. c, Queen, denomination at left, maroon panel. d, Couple, denomination at right, maroon panel. e, Couple, denomination at left, maroon panel. f, Queen, denomination at right, maroon panel.

**2007, June 25    Litho.    Perf. 13¼**
2693 A655 $1.50 Sheet of 6, #a-f 6.75 6.75

## Year of the Rat Type of 2007

**2007, Dec. 3               Perf. 13x13¼**
2694 A667 $1 multi                    .75 .75

Printed in sheets of 4.

## Princess Diana Type of 2007

No. 2695 — Diana wearing: a, Plaid jacket. b, Purple feathered hat. c, Green dress. d, Plaid jacket, close-up in frame. e, Purple feathered hat, close-up in frame. f, Green dress, close-up in frame.

$6, Princess Diana, Prince Charles and infant, horiz.

**2008, Jan. 14**      *Perf. 13¼*
2695 A656 $1.50 Sheet of 6, #a-f 6.75 6.75

### Souvenir Sheet
2696 A656   $6 multi     4.50 4.50

## Elvis Presley Type of 2008

No. 2697 — Presley: a, Silhouette, holding microphone, gray background. b, Wearing green shirt. c, Silhouette, holding microphone, olive green background. d, Playing guitar. e, Silhouette, playing guitar. f, Wearing orange shirt.

**2008, Jan. 14**      *Perf. 13¼*
2697 A671 $1.50 Sheet of 6, #a-f 6.75 6.75

## World Stamp Championship Type of 2008

Design: Aerial view of Jerusalem, horiz. (149x125mm).

**2008, May 14**      *Imperf.*
2698 A676 $6 multi     4.50 4.50

## Basketball Type of 2008
### Miniature Sheet

No. 2699 — Members of 2008 Boston Celtics basketball team: a, Ray Allen. b, Rajon Rondo. c, Paul Pierce. d, Kendrick Perkins. e, Kevin Garnett. f, Leon Powe. g, James Posey. h, Sam Cassell. i, P. J. Brown.

**2008, June 17**   Litho.   *Perf. 13½*
2699 A678 $1 Sheet of 9, #a-i   6.75 6.75

## Cats Type of 2008

No. 2700: a, Havana. b, Scottish Fold. c, American Curl. d, American Bobtail. e, Balinese. f, Singapura.

$6, Burmese, horiz.

**2008, June 18**      *Perf. 11½*
2700 A677 $1 Sheet of 6, #a-f   4.50 4.50

### Souvenir Sheet
2701 A677 $6 multi     4.50 4.50

## Elvis Presley Type of 2008
### Miniature Sheet

No. 2702 — Presley: a, Wearing lei, holding microphone in right hand. b, Playing guitar, red striped background. c, Wearing lei, holding microphone in left hand, right arm extended with hand in fist. d, Playing guitar, olive green and black background. e, Wearing lei, holding microphone in left hand, right hand at side. f, Wearing red shirt.

**2008, Oct. 10**      *Perf. 13¼*
2702 A670 $1.50 Sheet of 6, #a-f 6.75 6.75

Christmas
G220

Designs: 25c, Christmas ornament washing up on beach. 50c, Gift boxes hanging ornaments and electric Christmas lights. 75c, "Merry Christmas" written on beach. $1, Starfish and shells hanging ornaments, vert.

*Perf. 14¾x14¼, 14¼x14¾*
**2008, Dec. 3**      Litho.
2703-2706 G220   Set of 4    1.90 1.90

## Space Exploration Type of 2009
### Miniature Sheets

No. 2707, $2: a, Venus and Mercury. b, Jupiter. c, Earth and Mars. d, Saturn. e, Neptune. f, Uranus.

No. 2708, $2, vert. — Mariner 9: a, And the Valles Marineris on Mars. b, And technicians. c, And the Olympus Mons on Mars. d, Photograph of Valles Marineris. e, Lifting off on Atlas-Centaur rocket. f, And Phobos.

No. 2709, $2.50, vert. — Mariner 10: a, And Mars at UR. b, Lifting off on Atlas-Centaur rocket. c, And technicians. d, And Moon at UL.

No. 2710, $2.50, vert.: a, Pillars of Creation in Eagle Nebula. b, Orion Nebula. c, Crab Nebula. d, Horsehead Nebula.

---

**2008, Dec. 24**      *Perf. 14*
    **Sheets of 6, #a-f**
2707-2708 A690   Set of 2   18.00 18.00
    **Sheets of 4, #a-d**
2709-2710 A690   Set of 2   15.00 15.00

Fish — G221

Designs: $1, Blue chromis. No. 2712, $2, Clown wrasse. No. 2713, $4, Orange-spotted filefish. $5, Palometa.

No. 2715, $2: a, Tiger grouper. b, Bluehead wrasse. c, Squirrel fish. d, Queen parrotfish. e, Yellowtail snapper. f, Barred hamlet.

**2009, Jan. 9**      *Perf. 12½*
2711-2714 G221   Set of 4   9.00 9.00
     *Perf. 12*
2715 G221 $2 Sheet of 6, #a-f   9.00 9.00

G222

Shells
G223

Designs: 25c, True tulip. 50c Twisted plait olive. 75c, Junonia. $1, Royal comb venus.

No. 2720: a, Lion's paw. b, Banded tulip. c, Flame auger. d, Miniature melo, e, West Indian worm shell. f, Mouse cowry.

**2009, Jan. 9**      *Perf. 12½*
2716-2719 G222   Set of 4   2.25 2.25
     *Perf. 12*
2720 G223 $2 Sheet of 6, #a-f   9.00 9.00

## Obama Type of 2009

No. 2721 — Pres. Barack Obama: a, Pointing. b, Wearing blue tie, hands not shown. c, Touching thumb to index finger. d, Wearing red tie, hands not shown.

$10, Pres. Obama and US Capitol.

**2009, Jan. 20**      *Perf. 11½*
2721 A689 $2.75 Sheet of 4, #a-d   8.50 8.50

### Souvenir Sheet
     *Perf. 13¼*
2722 A689   $10 multi    7.75 7.75

No. 2722 contains one 38x51mm stamp.

New Year 2009 (Year
of the Ox) — G224

**2009, Jan. 26**      *Perf. 11½*
2723 G224 $2.50 multi   1.90 1.90

## Olympic Sports Type of 2009
### Miniature Sheet

No. 2724, vert.: a, Archery. b, Track cycling. c, Wrestling. d, Boxing.

**2009, Apr. 26**      *Perf. 12*
2724 A700 $1.40 Sheet of 4, #a-d   4.25 4.25

China 2009 World Stamp Exhibition, Luoyang.

---

### Miniature Sheet

Qianglong (1711-99), Chinese
Emperor — G225

No. 2725: a, Qianglong as young man, with chop at UR. b, Qianglong, women, table and tree. c, Qianglong at desk. d, Qianglong as older man.

**2009, Apr. 29**      *Perf. 12*
2725 G225 $1.40 Sheet of 4, #a-d   4.25 4.25

China 2009 World Stamp Exhibition, Luoyang.

## Elvis Presley Type of 2009
### Miniature Sheet

No. 2726, horiz. — Presley: a, Singing, with hand raised near mouth, denimination in yellow brown. b, Holding microphone, denomination in purple. c, Holding microphone, denomination in red violet. d, Singing and holding microphone, denomination in Prussian blue.

**2009, Apr. 29**      *Perf. 13½*
2726 A703 $2.50 Sheet of 4, #a-d   7.50 7.50

Worldwide Fund
for Nature
(WWF) — G226

No. 2727 — Various depictions of Caribbean spiny lobster with denomination in: a, Orange. b, Green. c, Pink. d, Yellow.

**2009, June 23**      *Perf. 13½*
2727    Strip of 4     9.00 9.00
  a.-d.   G226 $3 Any single   2.25 2.25
  e.   Sheet of 8 2 each #2727a-2727d   18.00 18.00

G227

G228

Mushrooms — G229

Designs: 25c, Psilocybe mexicana. $1, Crinipellis piceae. $2, Psilocybe subcubensis. $5, Psilocybe cubensis.

No. 2732: a, Panacolus fimicola. b, Psilocybe yungensis. c, Panacolus subbalteatus. d, Russula cremeolilacina.

No. 2736: a, Psilocybe guilartensis. b, Psilocybe aztecorum.

**2009, July 2**      *Perf. 14x14¾*
2728-2731 G227   Set of 4   6.25 6.25
     *Perf. 14¼x14¾*
2732 G228 $2.50 Sheet of 4, #a-d   7.50 7.50

---

### Souvenir Sheet
     *Perf. 14x14¾*
2733 G229   $3 Sheet of 2, #a-b   4.50 4.50

### Miniature Sheet

Pres. Abraham Lincoln (1809-
65) — G230

No. 2734 — Photograph of Lincoln: a, Without beard, ear showing at right. b, Without beard, ear showing at left. c, With beard, wearing vest. d, With beard, without vest.

**2009, July 21**   Litho.   *Perf. 13¼*
2734 G230 $2.50 Sheet of 4, #a-d   7.50 7.50

### Miniature Sheet

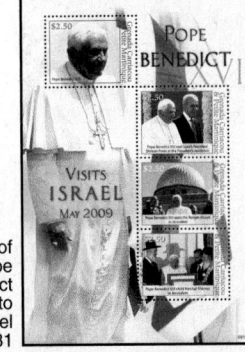

Visit of
Pope
Benedict
XVI to
Israel
G231

No. 2735: a, Pope Benedict XVI. b, Pope and Israeli President Shimon Peres. c, Pope at Temple Mount, Jerusalem. d, Pope and Heichal Shlomo.

**2009, Sept. 15**      *Perf. 11½x12*
2735 G231 $2.50 Sheet of 4, #a-d   7.50 7.50

### Miniature Sheet

Teenage
Mutant
Ninja
Turtles,
25th
Anniv.
G232

No. 2736: a, Donatello. b, Leonardo. c, Raphael. d, Michelangelo.

**2009, Sept. 15**      *Perf. 12x11½*
2736 G232 $2.50 Sheet of 4, #a-d   7.50 7.50

### Miniature Sheet

John F. Kennedy, Jr. (1960-99),
Magazine Publisher — G233

No. 2737: a, As child, with father Pres. John F. Kennedy. b, With mother, Jacqueline. c, Alone. d, As child with mother, father and sister Caroline.

**2009, Dec. 7** **Litho.** *Perf. 11¼x11½*
2737 G233 $2.50 Sheet of 4,
#a-d        7.75  7.75

**First Man on the Moon, 40th Anniv.
Type of 2009**

No. 2738, vert.: a, Saturn, Titan and Voyager I. b, Apollo 11 Lunar Module. c, Voyager I, Europa, Jupiter, Io, Callisto and Ganymede. $6, Apollo 11 Lunar Module, diff., vert.

**2009, Dec. 7** *Perf. 13¼*
2738 A701 $2 Horiz. strip of 3,
#a-c        4.75  4.75

**Souvenir Sheet**
2739 A701 $6 multi        4.75  4.75

No. 2738 was printed in sheets containing 2 strips of three stamps.

G234

G235

G236

G237

Elvis Presley (1935-77) — G238

No. 2740 — Presley: a, Facing crowd, with guitar at right. b, Facing crowd, with guitar in front of him. c, Close-up with crowd in background. d, Holding microphone, no crowd.

**2010, Jan. 7**
2740 G234 $2.75 Sheet of 4,
#a-d        8.50  8.50

**Souvenir Sheets**
2741 G235  $6 multi        4.75  4.75
2742 G236  $6 multi        4.75  4.75
2743 G237  $6 multi        4.75  4.75
2744 G238  $6 multi        4.75  4.75
Nos. 2741-2744 (4)        19.00 19.00

Miniature Sheet

Awarding of 2009 Nobel Peace Prize to Pres. Barack Obama G239

No. 2745 — Various photographs of Pres. Obama and gray map in background showing: a, Alaska, Western and Central United States. b, Greenland, Northeastern United States, Great Lakes. c, Southwestern United States, Mexico. d, Southeastern United States, Northern South America.

**2010, Mar. 4** *Perf. 12x11½*
2745 G239 $2.50 Sheet of 4,
#a-d        7.75  7.75

Orchids — G240

Designs: $1.20, Dendrophylax lindenii. $1.80, Scaphyglottis imbricata. No. 2748, $3, Encyclia ceratistes. $5, Scaphyglottis stellata. No. 2750: a, Oncidium excavatum. b, Brassavola nodosa. c, Cattleya gaskelliana. d, Phalaenopsis cultivars. No. 2751, $3: a, Lepanthopsis floripecten. b, Equitant oncidium.

*Perf. 11½x11¼, 11½x12 (#2750)*
**2010, Mar. 4**
2746-2749 G240  Set of 4        8.50  8.50
2750 G240 $2.50 Sheet of 4,
#a-d        7.75  7.75

**Souvenir Sheet**
2751 G240  $3 Sheet of 2,
#a-b        4.75  4.75

Miniature Sheets

G241

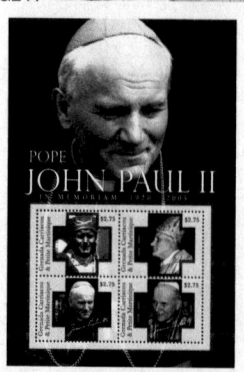

Pope John Paul II (1920-2005) — G242

No. 2752: a, Pope wearing zucchetto, country name over colored area. b, Pope wearing

miter, white area under and below denomination. c, As "b," with colored area under and below denomination. d, As "a," country name over white area.
No. 2753: a, Pope wearing miter, looking forward. b, Pope wearing miter, looking left. c, Pope wearing zucchetto, looking right. d, Pope wearing zucchetto, looking left.

**2010, Apr. 9** *Perf. 11½x12*
2752 G241 $2.75 Sheet of 4,
#a-d        8.25  8.25
2753 G242 $2.75 Sheet of 4,
#a-d        8.25  8.25

**Girl Guides Type of 2010**

No. 2754, horiz. — Girl Guides: a, And adult leader. b, In tent. c, Sitting in field of flowers. d, looking at young Girl Guide pointing. $6, Girl Guides wearing hooded sweatshirts.

**2010, June 11** *Perf. 13x13¼*
2754 A717 $2.75 Sheet of 4, #a-d        8.25  8.25

**Souvenir Sheet**
*Perf. 13¼x13*
2755 A717  $6 multi        4.50  4.50

**World Cup Type of 2010**

No. 2756, $1.50 — Group E first-round matches: a, Netherlands vs. Denmark. b, Japan vs. Cameroun. c, Netherlands vs. Japan. d, Denmark vs. Cameroun. e, Japan vs. Denmark. f, Cameroun vs. Netherlands.
No. 2757, $1.50 — Group F first-round matches: a, Italy vs. Paraguay. b, New Zealand vs. Slovakia. c, Slovakia vs. Paraguay. d, New Zealand vs. Italy. e, Slovakia vs. Italy. f, Paraguay vs. New Zealand.
No. 2758, $1.50 — Group G first-round matches: a, Ivory Coast vs. Portugal. b, Brazil vs. North Korea. c, Brazil vs. Ivory Coast. d, Portugal vs. North Korea. e, North Korea vs. Ivory Coast. f, Portugal vs. Brazil.
No. 2759, $1.50 — Group H first-round matches: a, Honduras vs. Chile. b, Spain vs. Switzerland. c, Chile vs. Switzerland. d, Honduras vs. Spain. e, Spain vs. Chile. f, Switzerland vs. Honduras.
No. 2760, $3.50 — a, Ellis Park Stadium, Johannesburg. b, Mbombela Stadium, Nelspruit.
No. 2761, $3.50 — a, Loftus Versfeld Stadium, Pretoria. b, Free State Stadium, Bloemfontein.
No. 2762, $3.50 — a, Peter Mokaba Stadium, Polokwane. b, Royal Bafokeng Stadium, Rustenburg.

**2010, June 11** **Litho.** *Perf. 13¼*
**Sheets of 6, #a-f**
2756-2759 A720  Set of 4        27.00 27.00
**Sheets of 2, #a-b**
2760-2762 A720  Set of 3        16.00 16.00

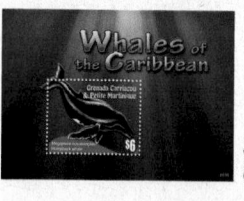

Whales G243

No. 2763: a, Gervais's beaked whale. b, Cuvier's beaked whale. c, Pygmy sperm whale. d, Melon-headed whale. e, Bryde's whale. f, Sperm whale. $6, Humpback whale.

**2010, Sept. 1** *Perf. 12*
2763 G243 $2 Sheet of 6, #a-f        9.00  9.00

**Souvenir Sheet**
2764 G243  $6 multi        4.50  4.50

Leonardo da Vinci (1452-1519), Artist — G244

No. 2765, vert.: a, Reputed self-portrait. b, Statue of da Vinci outside of Uffizi Gallery, Florence. c, Vitruvian Man. d, La Scapigliata. e, Mona Lisa. f, Study of Horses. $6, The Last Supper.

**2010, Nov. 4**
2765 G244 $2 Sheet of 6, #a-f        9.00  9.00
**Souvenir Sheet**
2766 G244 $6 multi        4.50  4.50

Miniature Sheets

G245

Elvis Presley (1935-77) — G246

No. 2767 — Presley: a, Standing behind microphone. b, With guitar, no microphone visible. c, Holding microphone, no guitar visible. d, With guitar, holding microphone.
No. 2768 — Presley: a, With guitar neck by face. b, Without microphone. c, Holding microphone. d, Playing guitar.

**2010, Nov. 4**
2767 G245 $2.75 Sheet of 4, #a-d        8.25  8.25
2768 G246 $2.75 Sheet of 4, #a-d        8.25  8.25

Engagement of Prince William and Catherine Middleton — G247

Engagement ring emblem and: No. 2769, Couple.
No. 2770: a, Middleton wearing fur hat. b, Prince William wearing military uniform and beret. c, Middleton without hat. d, Prince William in suit.
No. 2771: a, Middleton wearing beret. b, Prince William.
No. 2772, horiz.: a, Middleton wearing hat. b, Prince William, diff.

**2011, Feb. 18** **Litho.** *Perf. 12*
2769 G247 $2.50 multi        1.90  1.90
2770 G247 $2.50 Sheet of 4, #a-d        7.50  7.50

**Souvenir Sheets**
*Perf. 12¾x13 Syncopated*
2771 G247  $3 Sheet of 2, #a-b        4.50  4.50
*Perf. 13x12¾ Syncopated*
2772 G247  $3 Sheet of 2, #a-b        4.50  4.50

No. 2769 was printed in sheets of 4.

Miniature Sheet

Pres. Barack Obama in India G248

No. 2773: a, Obama holding microphone. b, Indian Prime Minister Manmohan Singh, Obama, woman. c, Obama and Singh. d, Obama at lectern.

*Perf. 12¾x13 Syncopated*
**2011, Mar. 30**
2773 G248 $2.75 Sheet of 4, #a-d        8.25  8.25

Indipex 2011, New Delhi.

## Miniature Sheet

Mother Teresa (1910-97),
Humanitarian — G249

No. 2774: a, Mother Teresa with hands together in prayer. b, Nobel Prize medal. c, Photographs of Mother Teresa. d, Bharat Ratna award.

**2011, Mar. 30**      **Perf. 12**
2774 G249 $2.75 Sheet of 4, #a-d      8.25 8.25

Indipex 2011, New Delhi.

## Miniature Sheets

G250

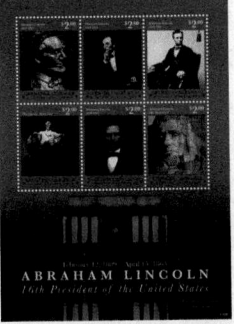

Pres. Abraham Lincoln (1809-65) — G251

No. 2775 — Photographs of Lincoln: a, With beard, both ears visible. b, Reading to son, Tad. c, Sitting in chair. d, Without beard, facing right. e, Without beard, facing forward. f, With beard, one ear visible.
No. 2776: a, Bust of Lincoln. b, Painting of Lincoln with hand at chin. c, Photograph of Lincoln sitting in chair. d, Statue in Lincoln Memorial. e, Painting of Lincoln, hands not visible. f, Mt. Rushmore sculpture of Lincoln.

**2011, Apr. 1**      **Perf. 12**
2775 G250 $2 Sheet of 6, #a-f      9.00 9.00
2776 G251 $2 Sheet of 6, #a-f      9.00 9.00

G252

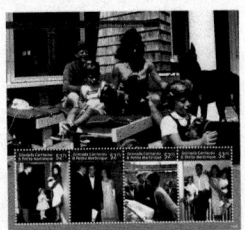

Pres. John F. Kennedy (1917-63) — G253

Designs: No. 2777, Kennedy at desk in Oval Office.
No. 2778: a, Kennedy and family in hallway. b, Kennedy and wife, Jacqueline, in formal wear. c, Kennedy and wife at stadium. d, Kennedy and family on porch.
No. 2779, Kennedy, window at side. No. 2780, Kennedy walking and reviewing papers with aides.

**2011, Apr. 1**      **Perf. 12**
2777 G252 $2.75 multi      2.10 2.10
2778 G253 $2.75 Sheet of 4, #a-d      8.25 8.25

### Souvenir Sheets
**Perf. 12¾x13 Syncopated**
2779 G252 $6 multi      4.50 4.50
2780 G253 $6 multi      4.50 4.50

No. 2777 was printed in sheets of 4.

### Miniature Sheets

Dogs
G254

No. 2781, $2.50: a, King Charles spaniel. b, Labador retriever. c, German shepherd. d, Weimaraner.
No. 2782, $2.50: a, Border collie. b, Briard. c, Great Dane. d, Afghan hound.

**2011, Apr. 15**   **Litho.**   **Perf. 12x12½**
Sheets of 4, #a-d
2781-2782 G254   Set of 2      15.00 15.00

### Miniature Sheets

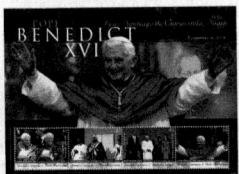

Visit to Spain of Pope Benedict XVI
G255

No. 2783, $3 — Visit to Santiago de Compostela: a, Pope Benedict XVI and Archbishop Julian Barrio. b, Pope holding crucifix. c, Pope with Prince and Princess of Asturias. d, Pope extending arms.
No. 2784, $3 — Visit to Barcelona: a, Pope holding Bible. b, Pope and priest in procession. c, Pope with King Juan Carlos and Queen Sofia. d, Pope at pulpit reading.

***Perf. 11½x12, 11½x11¼ (#2784)***
**2011, Apr. 15**
Sheets of 4, #a-d
2783-2784 G255   Set of 2      18.00 18.00

Beatification of Pope John Paul II — G256

No. 2785 — Pope John Paul II: a, Wearing miter. b, Kneeling in prayer. c, With arm extended.
$6, Pope with arms clasped.

**2011, Apr. 15**   **Perf. 13 Syncopated**
2785 G256 $3.30 Sheet of 3, #a-c      7.50 7.50

### Souvenir Sheet
**Perf. 12**
2786 G256 $6 multi      4.50 4.50

### Princess Diana Type of 2011

No. 2787 — Princess Diana: a, Wearing hat. b, With children. c, As young girl. d, Walking with Prince Charles. $6, Princess Diana wearing red hat.

**2011, Apr. 15**      **Perf. 12**
2787 A744 $2.75 Sheet of 4, #a-d      8.25 8.25

### Souvenir Sheet
**Perf. 13 Syncopated**
2788 A744 $6 multi      4.50 4.50

Wedding of Prince William and Catherine Middleton — G257

No. 2789, $2.75: a, Couple in coach waving. b, Bride facing left. c, Groom wearing hat. d, Couple holding hands.
No. 2790, $2.75: a, Groom without hat. b, Bride, diff. c, Soldiers on horseback. d, Couple waving.
No. 2791, vert.: a, Bride, diff. b, Groom, diff.

**2011, Sept. 15**   **Perf. 13 Syncopated**
Sheets of 4, #a-d
2789-2790 G257   Set of 2      16.50 16.50

### Souvenir Sheet
2791 G257 $3 Sheet of 2, #a-b      4.50 4.50

Birds
G258

No. 2792, $2.50: a, Troupial. b, Green-throated carib. c, Osprey. d, Green heron.
No. 2793, $2.50: a, Village weaver. b, Belted kingfisher. c, Scarlet tanager. d, Semi-palmated plover.
No. 2794, $6, Rose-breasted grosbeak. No. 2795, $6, Merlin.

**2011, Oct. 26**   **Perf. 13 Syncopated**
Sheets of 4, #a-d
2792-2793 G258   Set of 2      15.00 15.00

### Souvenir Sheets
**Perf. 12**
2794-2795 G258   Set of 2      9.00 9.00

Chinese Musical Instruments — G259

No. 2796: a, Pipa. b, Guqin. c, Dizi. d, Yangqin. e, Dagu.
$6, Erhu, vert.

**2011, Nov. 8**      **Perf. 13¼**
2796 G259 $2 Sheet of 5, #a-e      7.50 7.50

### Souvenir Sheet
**Perf. 13¼x13**
2797 G259 $6 multi      4.50 4.50

China 2011 Intl. Philatelic Exhibition, Wuxi. No. 2797 contains one 30x80mm stamp.

Christmas — G260

Paintings: 25c, Annunciation, by Niccolò di Pietro Gerini. 50c, The Annunciation, by Melchior Broederlam. $1, Coronation of the Virgin, by Giovanni da Milano. $2, Madonna, by André Beauneveu.

**2011, Nov. 1**      **Perf. 12**
2798-2801 G260   Set of 4      2.75 2.75

Chinese Zodiac Animals
G261

New Year 2012 (Year of the Dragon)
G262

No. 2802: a, Rat. b, Ox. c, Tiger. d, Rabbit. e, Dragon. f, Snake. g, Horse. h, Sheep. i, Monkey. j, Rooster. k, Dog. l, Boar.
$8, Dragon.

**Litho. With Foil Application**
**2011**      **Perf. 13 Syncopated**
2802 G261 65c Sheet of 12, #a-l    5.75 5.75

### Souvenir Sheet
**Litho.**
**Perf. 13¼**
2803 G262 $8 multi      6.00 6.00

Issued: No. 2802, 11/8; No. 2803, 10/26.

G263

Mushrooms — G264

No. 2804: a, Coltriciella navispora. b, Tylopilus rufonigricans. c, Chroogomphus rutilus. d, Entoloma rugostriatum. e, Xerocomus amazonicus. f, Coltricia oblectabilis.
No. 2805: a, Tylopilus exiguus. b, Mycena acicula. c, Panaeolus papilionaceus. d, Chroomogomphus ochraceus.
No. 2806, Amanita calochroa. No. 2807, Psilocybe cubensis.

**2011, Dec. 16**   **Perf. 13 Syncopated**
2804 G263 $2 Sheet of 6, #a-f 9.00 9.00
2805 G264 $2.50 Sheet of 4, #a-d      7.50 7.50

### Souvenir Sheets
2806 G263 $6 multi      4.50 4.50
2807 G264 $6 multi      4.50 4.50

Reptiles
G265

No. 2808, $3.50: a, Puerto Rican crested anole. b, Tropical house gecko. c, Dominican ground lizard. d, Eyed anole.
No. 2809, $3.50: a, Giant ditch frog. b, Coqui antillano. c, Gounouj. d, Tink frog.

No. 2810, $9, Lesser Antillean iguana. No. 2811, $9, Red-footed tortoise.

**2012, Feb. 8**    **Perf. 13 Syncopated**
**Sheets of 4, #a-d**
2808-2809 G265   Set of 2    21.00 21.00
**Souvenir Sheets**
2810-2811 G265   Set of 2    13.50 13.50

Miniature Sheet

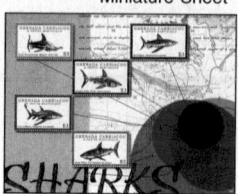

Sharks
G266

No. 2812: a, Great hammerhead shark. b, Reef shark. c, Longfin mako shark. d, Lemon shark. e, Great white shark.

**2012, Apr. 5**      **Perf. 12**
2812 G266 $3 Sheet of 5, #a-e 11.00 11.00

Space Exploration — G267

No. 2813: a, Pres. John F. Kennedy. b, Pres. Kennedy looking into space capsule. c, Emblem for NASA's Apollo program. d, Buzz Aldrin on the Moon.
$9, Pres. Kennedy greeting men under rocket.

**2012, Apr. 5**      **Perf. 14**
2813 G267 $3.50 Sheet of 4,
    #a-d     10.50 10.50
**Souvenir Sheet**
**Perf. 12**
2814 G267   $9 multi    6.75 6.75
No. 2814 contains one 30x50mm stamp.

Pope Benedict XVI, 85th Birthday G269

No. 2815 — Pope Benedict XVI: a, Waving. b, With hands together. c, At Vatican City. d, With crucifix.
No. 2816 — Pope Benedict XVI: a, Waving. b, Facing right. c, In front of microphone. d, Facing forward.
$9, Pope facing right wearing red vestments.

***Perf. 13 Syncopated (G268), 13¾***
**2012, Nov. 28**
2815 G268   $3 Sheet of 4,
    #a-d      9.00 9.00
2816 G269 $3.50 Sheet of 4,
    #a-d     10.50 10.50
**Souvenir Sheet**
2817 G268   $9 multi    6.75 6.75

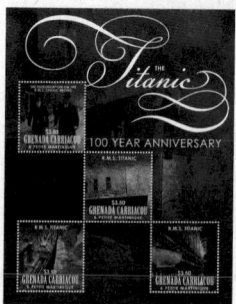

Sinking of the Titanic, Cent. (in 2012) G270

No. 2818 — Inscriptions: a, The investigation on the R.M.S. Titanic begins. b, R.M.S. Titanic (at sea, viewed from side). c, R.M.S. Titanic (viewed from above). d, R.M.S. Titanic (with lowered lifeboat).
$9, Newsboy with newspapers with headline about sinking.

**2013, Jan. 3**      **Perf. 13¾**
2818 G270 $3.50 Sheet of 4,
    #a-d     10.50 10.50
**Souvenir Sheet**
**Perf. 12**
2819 G270   $9 multi    6.75 6.75
No. 2819 contains one 30x50mm stamp.

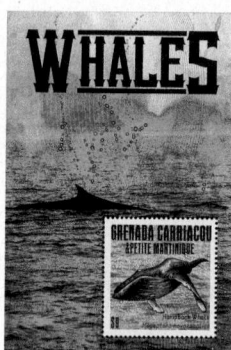

Whales
G271

No. 2820: a, Pygmy right whale. b, Gray whale. c, Pygmy killer whale. d, Bowhead whale.
$9, Humpback whale.

**2013, Jan. 3**      **Perf. 13¾**
2820 G271 $3.50 Sheet of 4,
    #a-d     10.50 10.50
**Souvenir Sheet**
2821 G271   $9 multi    6.75 6.75

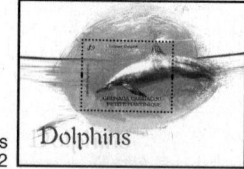

Dolphins G272

No. 2822: a, Dusky dolphin. b, Indo-Pacific humpback dolphin. c, Commerson's dolphin. d, Hector's dolphin. e, Atlantic spotted dolphin. f, Striped dolphin.
$9, Spinner dolphin.

**2013, Jan. 3**   **Perf. 13 Syncopated**
2822 G272 $2.75 Sheet of 6,
    #a-f     12.50 12.50
**Souvenir Sheet**
2823 G272   $9 multi    6.75 6.75

Princess Diana (1961-97) — G273

No. 2824 — Princess Diana wearing: a, Pink hat. b, Tiara. c, Checked dress. d, Lilac jacket.
$9, Princess Diana wearing pink hat, diff.

**2013, Jan. 3**      **Perf. 14**
2824 G273 $3.50 Sheet of 4,
    #a-d     10.50 10.50
**Souvenir Sheet**
**Perf. 12**
2825 G273   $9 multi    6.75 6.75

**Elvis Presley Type of 2013**
**Souvenir Sheets**

Frame color: No. 2826, $9, Gray. No. 2827, $9, Black. No. 2828, $9, Purple. No. 2829, $9, Red (Presley without guitar). No. 2830, $9, Red (Presley with guitar).

**2013, Jan. 3**      **Perf. 12¾**
2826-2830 A782   Set of 5    34.00 34.00

History of Art G274

No. 2831 — Holy Allegory, by Giovanni Bellini (details): a, Buildings in distance. b, Virgin Mary, two women and man. c, Old man, child shaking tree. d, Job and St. Sebastian.
No. 2832, vert.: a, The Annunciation, by Matthias Grünewald. b, St. Jerome in the Desert, by Bellini. c, Lady with an Ermine, by Leonardo da Vinci.
$9, Mona Lisa, by Leonardo, vert.

**2013, Apr. 4**      **Litho.**
2831 G274 $3.25 Sheet of 4, #a-
    d      9.75 9.75
2832 G274 $3.75 Sheet of 3, #a-
    c      8.50 8.50
**Souvenir Sheet**
2833 G274   $9 multi    6.75 6.75

G275

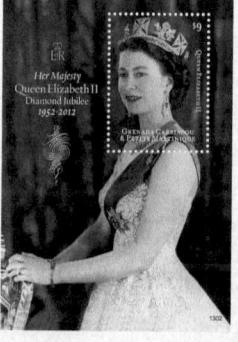

Reign of Queen Elizabeth II, 60th Anniv. (in 2012) G276

No. 2834 — Various images of Queen Elizabeth II with name at: a, Left in blue. b, Left in

white. c, Right in blue (black-and-white photograph). d, Right in blue (color photograph).

**2013, Apr. 25**      **Perf. 14**
2834 G275 $3.25 Sheet of 4, #a-d
       9.75 9.75
**Souvenir Sheet**
**Perf. 12**
2835 G276   $9 black    6.75 6.75

Election of Pope Francis G277

No. 2836 — Pope Francis: a, Facing right, assistant holding crucifix. b, With arms raised. c, Waving. d, Blessing crowd, assistant holding book.
$9, Pope Francis on balcony with cardinals.

**2013, June 3**      **Perf. 12**
2836 G277 $3.25 Sheet of 4, #a-d
       9.75 9.75
**Souvenir Sheet**
**Perf. 12½**
2837 G277   $9 multi    6.75 6.75
No. 2837 contains one 38x51mm stamp.

Pres. John F. Kennedy (1917-63) — G278

No. 2838 — Photographs of Pres. Kennedy: a, Touching lapel pocket of his jacket. b, Standing between two women. c, Sitting and pointing. d, Standing behind microphones, men and women in background. e, Sitting with legs crossed. f, Standing behind lectern with Presidential seal.
$9, Drawing of Pres. Kennedy, vert.

***Perf. 13 Syncopated***
**2013, Jan. 1**      **Litho.**
2838 G278 $2.50 Sheet of 6,
    #a-f     11.50 11.50
**Souvenir Sheet**
2839 G278   $9 multi    6.75 6.75

Birth of Prince George of Cambridge — G279

No. 2840: a, Duchess of Cambridge holding Prince George. b, Duke of Cambridge holding Prince George. c, Prince Charles and Princess Diana holding infant Prince William. d, Prince Gerorge, Duke and Duchess of Cambridge.
$9, Prince George, Duke and Duchess of Cambridge, diff.

**2013, Sept. 27**   **Litho.**   **Perf. 14**
2840 G279 $3.25 Sheet of 4, #a-
    d      9.75 9.75
**Souvenir Sheet**
2841 G279   $9 multi    6.75 6.75

SHIPS

War Ships G280

No. 2842: a, USS Arizona. b, Japanese battleship Yamato. c, USS Enterprise. d, German battleship Bismarck.
$9, HMS Victory, vert.

| 2013, Oct. 10 | Litho. | Perf. 12 |
|---|---|---|
| 2842 G280 $3.25 Sheet of 4, #a-d | | 9.75 9.75 |

**Souvenir Sheet**
**Perf. 12½**

| 2843 G280 | $9 multi | 6.75 6.75 |
|---|---|---|

No. 2843 contains one 38x51mm stamp.

MARINE LIFE

Marine Life G281

No. 2844: a, Blacktip sharks. b, Flying fish. c, Spotted eagle ray. d, Hammerhead sharks.
$9, Humpback whale, vert.

| 2013, Oct. 16 | Litho. | Perf. 13¾ |
|---|---|---|
| 2844 G281 $3.50 Sheet of 4, #a-d | | 10.50 10.50 |

**Souvenir Sheet**
**Perf. 12½**

| 2845 G281 | $9 multi | 6.75 6.75 |
|---|---|---|

No. 2845 contains one 38x51mm stamp.

Birds of the Caribbean

Birds G282

No. 2846, $3.75: a, American white ibis. b, Swallow-tailed kite. c, Sora.
No. 2847, $3.75: a, Red-billed tropicbird. b, Scarlet ibis. c, Stilt sandpiper.
No. 2848, $9, Tree swallow, horiz. No. 2849, $9, Purple gallinule, horiz.

| 2013, Oct. 16 | Litho. | Perf. 12½ |
|---|---|---|
| **Sheets of 3, #a-c** | | |
| 2846-2847 G282 | Set of 2 | 17.00 17.00 |

**Souvenir Sheets**

| 2848-2849 G282 | Set of 2 | 13.50 13.50 |
|---|---|---|

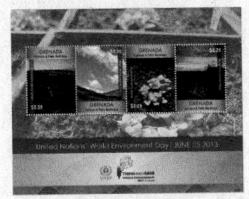

United Nations' World Environment Day · JUNE 05 2013

World Environment Day — G283

No. 2850: a, Rocks, denomination at LL. b, Mountains and clouds, denomination at UR. c, Plant, denomination at LL. d, Rocks, plants and clouds, denomination at UR.
$9, Fruits and vegetables, horiz.

| 2013, Oct. 10 | Litho. | Perf. 14 |
|---|---|---|
| 2850 G283 $3.25 Sheet of 4, #a-d | | 9.75 9.75 |

**Souvenir Sheet**
**Perf. 12**

| 2851 G283 | $9 multi | 6.75 6.75 |
|---|---|---|

THE AMAZING BAT
A CURIOUS FLYING MAMMAL

Bats G284

No. 2852: a, Chilonycteris gymnonotus (30x40mm). b, Vespertilio murinus (30x40mm). c, Rhinolophus clivosus (60x40mm). d, Vespertilio sinensis (30x40mm).
$9, Leptonycteris yerbabuenae.

| 2013, Oct. 16 | Litho. | Perf. 14 |
|---|---|---|
| 2852 G284 $3.50 Sheet of 4, #a-d | | 10.50 10.50 |

**Souvenir Sheet**
**Perf. 12**

| 2853 G284 | $9 multi | 6.75 6.75 |
|---|---|---|

No. 2853 contains one 30x50mm stamp.

### Christmas Type of 2013

Paintings: $2, The Annunciation, by Paolo Uccello. $2.25, Center panel of Triptych with the Birth of Christ, by Rogier van der Weyden. $2.50, The Flight into Egypt, by Annibale Carracci. $2.75, Madonna and Child with Angels, by Giottino.

| 2013, Dec. 25 | Litho. | Perf. 12¾ |
|---|---|---|
| 2854-2857 A803 | Set of 4 | 7.00 7.00 |

QUEEN ELIZABETH II
60th Coronation Anniversary · 1953-2013

Coronation of Queen Elizabeth II, 60th Anniv. (in 2013) — G285

No. 2858 — Color of coat worn by Queen Elizabeth II: a, Dark Blue. b, Lilac. c, Pink. d, Light blue.
$9, Queen Elizabeth II wearing tiara.

| 2014, Jan. 14 | Litho. | Perf. 14 |
|---|---|---|
| 2858 G285 $3.25 Sheet of 4, #a-d | | 9.75 9.75 |

**Souvenir Sheet**

| 2859 G285 | $9 multi | 6.75 6.75 |
|---|---|---|

100TH TOUR DE FRANCE

100th Tour de France Bicycle Race (in 2013) G286

No. 2860: a, Map of 2013 race. b, Cyclist facing left. c, Cyclists in peloton in Paris, van and building in background. d, Cyclists in peloton in Paris, buildings in background.
$9, Cyclist facing right, map, Eiffel Tower, airplane.

| 2014, Jan. 14 | Litho. | Perf. 13¾ |
|---|---|---|
| 2860 G286 $3.25 Sheet of 4, #a-d | | 9.75 9.75 |

**Souvenir Sheet**

| 2861 G286 | $9 multi | 6.75 6.75 |
|---|---|---|

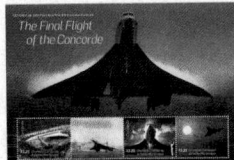

The Final Flight of the Concorde

Final New York to London Flight of the Concorde — G287

No. 2862: a, Concorde, stairs and crowd. b, Concorde taking off. c, Concorde, member of ground crew. d, Concorde in flight.
$9, Nose of Concorde.

| 2014, Jan. 20 | Litho. | Perf. 14 |
|---|---|---|
| 2862 G287 $3.25 Sheet of 4, #a-d | | 9.75 9.75 |

**Souvenir Sheet**
**Perf. 12**

| 2863 G287 | $9 multi | 6.75 6.75 |
|---|---|---|

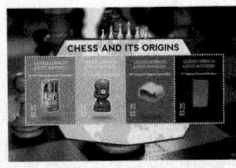

CHINESE FOLK ART

Chinese Folk Art G288

No. 2864: a, The Seven Fairy Maidens. b, Fairy Maiden. c, Lady of Heaven. d, Chang'e.
$9, Magu.

| 2014, Jan. 20 | Litho. | Perf. 12½ |
|---|---|---|
| 2864 G288 $2.50 Sheet of 4, #a-d | | 7.50 7.50 |

**Souvenir Sheet**

| 2865 G288 | $9 multi | 6.75 6.75 |
|---|---|---|

Nos. 2864-2685 exist with overprint "CHINA INTERNATIONAL COLLECTION EXPO" under the expo logo.

CHESS AND ITS ORIGINS

Chess and its Origins G289

No. 2866: a, European chess piece, 12th-16th cent. b, Russian chess piece, 18th cent. c, Egyptian senet piece, 30th cent. B.C. d, Chinese liubo piece, 2nd cent.
$9, Modern queen chess piece.

| 2014, Jan. 20 | Litho. | Perf. 14 |
|---|---|---|
| 2866 G289 $3.25 Sheet of 4, #a-d | | 9.75 9.75 |

**Souvenir Sheet**
**Perf. 12**

| 2867 G289 | $9 multi | 6.75 6.75 |
|---|---|---|

MICHELANGELO

Details From Ceiling of Sistine Chapel Painted by Michelangelo — G290

No. 2868: a, The Expulsion from Paradise (tree at right). b, The Expulsion from Paradise (tree at left). c, Sacrifice of Noah. d, Deluge.
$9, The Entombment, vert.

| 2014, Jan. 20 | Litho. | Perf. 12½ |
|---|---|---|
| 2868 G290 $3.25 Sheet of 4, #a-d | | 9.75 9.75 |

**Souvenir Sheet**

| 2869 G290 | $9 multi | 6.75 6.75 |
|---|---|---|

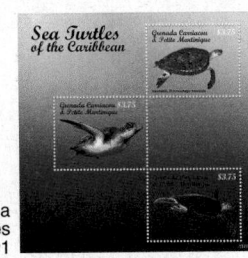

Sea Turtles of the Caribbean

Sea Turtles G291

No. 2870: a, Hawksbill turtle. b, Loggerhead turtle. c, Green turtle.
$9, Olive ridley turtle.

| 2014, Jan. 20 | Litho. | Perf. 14 |
|---|---|---|
| 2870 G291 $3.75 Sheet of 3, #a-c | | 8.50 8.50 |

**Souvenir Sheet**
**Perf. 12**

| 2871 G291 | $9 multi | 6.75 6.75 |
|---|---|---|

Exotic Purebred Cats

Purebred Cat Breeds G292

No. 2872, $3.25: a, Bengal. b, Egyptian Mau. c, Somali. d, Burmese.
No. 2873, $3.25: a, Savannah. b, Scottish Fold. c, British Shorthair. d, Bombay.
No. 2874, $9, Sphynx. No. 2875, $9, Siamese.

| 2014, Jan. 20 | Litho. | Perf. 14 |
|---|---|---|
| **Sheets of 4, #a-d** | | |
| 2872-2873 G292 | Set of 2 | 19.50 19.50 |

**Souvenir Sheets**

| 2874-2875 G292 | Set of 2 | 13.50 13.50 |
|---|---|---|

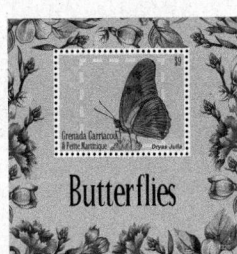

Butterflies — G293

No. 2876, $3.25: a, Astraptes anaphus. b, Danaus plexippus. c, Agraulis vanillae. d, Hypolimnas misippus.
No. 2877, $3.25: a, Urbanus proteus. b, Pyrgus oileus. c, Leptotes cassius. d, Hylephila phyleus.
No. 2878, $9, Dryas julia. No. 2879, $9, Heliconius charithonia.

| 2014, Jan. 20 | Litho. | Perf. 14 |
|---|---|---|
| **Sheets of 4, #a-d** | | |
| 2876-2877 G293 | Set of 2 | 19.50 19.50 |

**Souvenir Sheets**
**Perf. 12**

| 2878-2879 G293 | Set of 2 | 13.50 13.50 |
|---|---|---|

DOG BREEDS

CHOCOLATE LABRADOR

Chocolate Labrador Retrievers — G294

No. 2880: Various photograps of chocolate Labrador retrievers.
$9, Dog running.

**2014, Apr. 7**    Litho.    *Perf. 14*
2880 G294 $3.25 Sheet of 4, #a-d    9.75 9.75

**Souvenir Sheet**
*Perf. 12½*

2881 G294    $9 multi    6.75 6.75

No. 2881 contains one 51x38mm stamp.

Dalmatians — G295

No. 2882: Various photograps of Dalmatians.
$9, Dalmatian, diff.

**2014, Apr. 7**    Litho.    *Perf. 14*
2882 G295 $3.25 Sheet of 4, #a-d    9.75 9.75

**Souvenir Sheet**
*Perf. 12½*

2883 G295    $9 multi    6.75 6.75

No. 2883 contains one 51x38mm stamp.

Rocks and Minerals G296

No. 2884, $3.25: a, Wulfenite, mimetite. b, Calcite, Mercenaria permagna fossil. c, Hubnerite, cookeite, quartz. d, Heulandite, rose mordenite.
No. 2885, $3.25: a, Fluorapophyllite, stilbite. b, Garnet, epidote. c, Tourmaline. d, Uncut ruby crystal.
No. 2886, $9, Malachite, goethite. No. 2887, $9, Pyromorphite, baryte.

**2014, Apr. 7**    Litho.    *Perf. 14*
**Sheets of 4, #a-d**
2884-2885 G296   Set of 2    19.50 19.50

**Souvenir Sheets**
*Perf. 12*

2886-2887 G296   Set of 2    13.50 13.50

**Downton Abbey Characters Type of 2014**

No. 2888, $4.75: a, Lady Mary Crawley. b, Sarah O'Brien. c, Alfred Nugent. d, Lady Rosamund Painswick.
No. 2889, $4.75: a, Lady Edith Crawley. b, Daisy. c, Isobel Crawley. d, Earl of Grantham.

**2014, May 26**    Litho.    *Perf. 14*
**Sheets of 4, #a-d**
2888-2889 A810   Set of 2    28.50 28.50

Early Locomotives — G297

No. 2890: a, Four-wheel locomotive. c, 1878. b, 1880 Forney locomotive. c, 1885 passenger locomotive. d, 1890 Uncle Dick locomotive.
No. 2891: a, 1878 Forney locomotive. b, 1881 Fontaine locomotive.

**2014, June 23**    Litho.    *Perf. 14*
2890 G297 $3.25 Sheet of 4, #a-d    9.75 9.75

**Souvenir Sheet**

2891 G297    $5 Sheet of 2, #a-b    7.50 7.50

World War I, Cent. G298

No. 2892, $3.25 — Ships and submarines: a, U-14, Germany. b, U-9, Germany. c, RMS Lusitania, United Kingdom. d, HMS Aboukir, United Kingdom.
No. 2893, $3.25 — Airplanes: a, Albatros D.III, Germany. b, SPAD S.XIII, France. c, LFG Roland C.II, Germany. d, Nieuport 27, France.
No. 2894, $5 — Ships: a, USS New York, U.S. b, HMS Monarch, United Kingdom.
No. 2895, $5 — Airplanes: a, Siemens-Schuckert D.III, Germany. b, Sopwith 1½ Strutter, United Kingdom.

**2014, June 23**    Litho.    *Perf. 14*
**Sheets of 4, #a-d**
2892-2893 G298   Set of 2    19.50 19.50

**Souvenir Sheets of 2, #a-b**
2894-2895 G298   Set of 2    15.00 15.00

G299

G300

G301

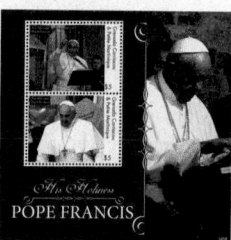

Pope Francis G302

No. 2896 — Pope Francis: a, Wearing zucchetto and glasses. b, Meeting with Palestinian Authority President Mahmoud Abbas. c, Meeing Trinidad and Tobago President Anthony Carmona. d, Kneeling at altar.
No. 2897 — Pope Francis: a, Wearing zucchetto, with arm raised. b, With arm raised, flag of Brazil in background. c, Holding railing in Popemobile. d, At microphone.
No. 2898 — Pope Francis: a, With spotlight behind head. b, With arm raised.
No. 2899 — Pope Francis: a, At microphone, with hand raised. b, With arms at side.

**2014, June 23**    Litho.    *Perf. 14*
2896 G299 $3.25 Sheet of 4, #a-d    9.75 9.75
2897 G300 $3.25 Sheet of 4, #a-d    9.75 9.75

**Souvenir Sheets**
2898 G301    $5 Sheet of 2, #a-b    7.50 7.50
2899 G302    $5 Sheet of 2, #a-b    7.50 7.50

Paintings G303

No. 2900, $3.50 — Paintings by Vincent van Gogh: a, Still Life with Decanter and Lemons on a Plate. b, Self-portrait, 1887. c, Skull.
No. 2901, $3.50: a, Ballerina and Lady with a Fan, by Edgar Degas. b, Strawberries in a Wan-li Bowl, by Adriaen Coorte. c, The Inspiration of Saint Matthew, by Caravaggio.
No. 2902, $10, Portrait of Dr. Gachet, by van Gogh. No. 2903, $10, Cardsharps, by Caravaggio.

**2014, June 23**    Litho.    *Perf. 12½*
**Sheets of 3, #a-c**
2900-2901 G303   Set of 2    15.50 15.50

**Size: 100x100mm**
*Imperf*
2902-2903 G303   Set of 2    15.00 15.00

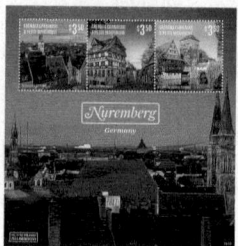

Nuremberg, Germany — G304

No. 2904: a, Skyline of Nuremberg. b, Albrecht Dürer House. c, Buildings in Old Town.
$10, Skyline of Nuremberg, horiz.

**2014, Oct. 24**    Litho.    *Perf. 13¾*
2904 G304 $3.50 Sheet of 3, #a-c    7.75 7.75

**Souvenir Sheet**
*Perf. 14*

2905 G304    $10 multi    7.50 7.50

Fall of the Berlin Wall, 25th anniv. No. 2905 contains one 80x30mm stamp.

Cattleya Mossiae G305

No. 2906, $3.25: a, Purple flower, green leaves at LL. b, Pink flower, green leaves at center and LL. c, Pink flower, green leaf under denomination. d, White flower, stem at LL.
No. 2907, $3.25, vert.: a, White flower, green leaf at center, gray background. b, White flower, no leaf, gray background. c, Lilac flower, leaf behind denomination. d, Lilac flower, green leaves at LR.
No. 2908, $5, vert.: a, Pink flower, green leaf at top. b, Pink flower, green leaf at bottom.
No. 2909, $5: a, White flower with yellow accents, green leaf at top center and LR. b, White flower with pink accents, green leaf at center.

*Perf. 14, 12 (#2909)*

**2014, Oct. 24**      Litho.
**Sheets of 4, #a-d**
2906-2907 G305   Set of 2    19.50 19.50

**Souvenir Sheets of 2, #a-b**
2908-2909 G305   Set of 2    15.00 15.00

**Miniature Sheets**

G306

New Year 2015 (Year of the Ram) G307

No. 2910: a, Ram's head. b, Chinese character for "ram." c, Chinese lantern with Chinese characters. d, Ram facing left. e, "2015 Year of the Ram" f, Ram facing right.
No. 2911 — Ram's head in; a, Green. b, Dark red. c, Purple and blue. d, Orange red and pale yellow.

**2014, Oct. 24**    Litho.    *Perf. 14*
2910 G306 $3.15 Sheet of 6, #a-f, + label 14.00 14.00
2911 G307 $3.25 Sheet of 4, #a-d    9.75 9.75

Nos. 2910-2911 are dated 2015.

Fruits and Vegetables — G308

No. 2912, $3.25: a, European pears. b, Peaches. c, Bananas. d, Apricot. e, Apples.
No. 2913, $3.25: a, Eggplant. b, Garlic. c, Bell pepper. d, Avocado. e, Tomato.
No. 2914, $10, Strawberries. No. 2915, $10, Mango and slice.

**2014, Nov. 3**    Litho.    *Perf. 12½*
**Sheets of 5, #a-e**
2912-2913 G308   Set of 2    24.00 24.00

**Souvenir Sheets**
2914-2915 G308   Set of 2    15.00 15.00

G309

Art of Qi Baishi (1864-1957) — G310

No. 2916: a, Frog. b, Peaches. c, Seated man. d, Fish. e, Leaves and twigs. f, Rooster. No. 2917: a, Crabs. b, Frogs. c, Shrimp. d, Insect on leaf. No. 2918, $10, Frog and tadpoles. No. 2929, $10, Chicks.

**Perf. 14, 12 (#2917)**

| | | | | |
|---|---|---|---|---|
| **2015, May 18** | | | **Litho.** | |
| 2916 | G309 | $3.15 Sheet of 6, | | |
| | | #a-f | 14.00 | 14.00 |
| 2917 | G310 | $3.25 Sheet of 4, | | |
| | | #a-d | 9.75 | 9.75 |

**Souvenir Sheets**

| | | | | |
|---|---|---|---|---|
| 2918-2919 | G310 | Set of 2 | 15.00 | 15.00 |

International Year of Light — G311

Various depictions of the Aurora Borealis.

| | | | | |
|---|---|---|---|---|
| **2015, May 28** | | **Litho.** | **Perf. 14** | |
| 2920 | G311 | $3.25 Sheet of 5, | | |
| | | #a-e | 12.00 | 12.00 |

**Souvenir Sheet**
**Perf. 12**

| | | | | |
|---|---|---|---|---|
| 2921 | G311 | $10 multi | 7.50 | 7.50 |

Paintings of Vincent van Gogh (1853-90) — G312

No. 2922: a, Two Women in the Moor. b, The Cottage. c, Weaver Near an Open Window. d, Still Life with Three Birds Nests. e, Cart with Red and White Ox. $10, The Potato Eaters.

| | | | | |
|---|---|---|---|---|
| **2015, Aug. 26** | | **Litho.** | **Perf. 14** | |
| 2922 | G312 | $3.15 Sheet of 5, | | |
| | | #a-e | 12.00 | 12.00 |

**Souvenir Sheet**
**Perf. 12**

| | | | | |
|---|---|---|---|---|
| 2923 | G312 | $10 multi | 7.50 | 7.50 |

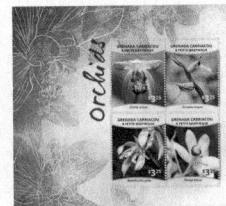

Orchids
G313

No. 2924: a, Bletilla striata. b, Serapias lingua. c, Brasiliorchis picta. d, Phaius flavus. $10, Aerangis luteoalba var. rhodosticta.

| | | | | |
|---|---|---|---|---|
| **2015, Aug. 26** | | **Litho.** | **Perf. 14** | |
| 2924 | G313 | $3.25 Sheet of 4, #a-d | 9.75 | 9.75 |

**Souvenir Sheet**
**Perf. 12**

| | | | | |
|---|---|---|---|---|
| 2925 | G313 | $10 multi | 7.50 | 7.50 |

**Miniature Sheets**

G314

G315

Pope Benedict XVI
G316

No. 2926 — Pope Benedict XVI: a, Wearing green vestments and miter. b, Without head covering, wearing white alb, waving. c, With mountain in background. d, With candle.
No. 2927 — Pope Benedict XVI at inauguration: a, Wearing miter, waving. b, Wearing miter, holding crucifix, waving. c, Flowers in background, without head covering, waving, d, Holding crucifix, attendant in background.
No. 2928: a, Pope John Paul II holding crucifix. b, Pope Benedict XVI wearing red vestments and zucchetto. c, Pope Benedict XVI wearing black vestments. d, Pope John Paul II and attendants.

| | | | | |
|---|---|---|---|---|
| **2015, Aug. 26** | | **Litho.** | **Perf. 14** | |
| 2926 | G314 | $3.25 Sheet of 4, #a-d | 9.75 | 9.75 |
| 2927 | G315 | $3.25 Sheet of 4, #a-d | 9.75 | 9.75 |
| 2928 | G316 | $3.25 Sheet of 4, #a-d | 9.75 | 9.75 |
| | | Nos. 2926-2928 (3) | 29.25 | 29.25 |

Queen Elizabeth II, Longest-Reigning British Monarch — G317

No. 2929 — Various photographs of Queen Elizabeth II, as shown.
$10, Queen Elizabeth II and Prince Philip, horiz.

| | | | | |
|---|---|---|---|---|
| **2015, Nov. 1** | | **Litho.** | **Perf. 14** | |
| 2929 | G317 | $3.15 Sheet of 6, | | |
| | | #a-f | 14.00 | 14.00 |

**Souvenir Sheet**
**Perf. 12**

| | | | | |
|---|---|---|---|---|
| 2930 | G317 | $10 multi | 7.50 | 7.50 |

Paintings by El Greco (1541-1614) — G318

No. 2931, $3.50: a, Portrait of Fray Hortensio Felix Paravicino. b, Madonna of Charity. c, St. Martin and the Beggar.
No. 2932, $3.50: a, Portrait of Diego de Covarrubias. b, Christ in the Olive Garden. c, St. Ildefonso.
No. 2933, $10, Mount Sinai. No. 2934, $10, Deposition in the Tomb.

**Perf. 12, 14 (#2932)**

| | | | | |
|---|---|---|---|---|
| **2015, Dec. 1** | | | **Litho.** | |
| **Sheets of 3, #a-c** | | | | |
| 2931-2932 | G318 | Set of 2 | 15.50 | 15.50 |
| **Size: 81x120mm** | | | | |
| **Imperf** | | | | |
| 2933-2934 | G318 | Set of 2 | 15.00 | 15.00 |

World War I Era Illustrations by Gerolamo Bartoletti — G319

No. 2935: a, Italian poster (40x60mm). b, House and graves (40x30mm). c, Gun battery (40x30mm). d, Damaged building (40x30mm). e, Soldiers in battle (40x30mm). $10, Cover of collection of illustrations, horiz.

| | | | | |
|---|---|---|---|---|
| **2015, Dec. 21** | | **Litho.** | **Perf. 14** | |
| 2935 | G319 | $3.25 Sheet of 5, | | |
| | | #a-e | 12.00 | 12.00 |

**Souvenir Sheet**
**Perf. 12**

| | | | | |
|---|---|---|---|---|
| 2936 | G319 | $10 multi | 7.50 | 7.50 |

No. 2936 contains one 60x40mm stamp.

Birds
G320

No. 2937: a, Purple-throated Carib. b, Lesser Antillean tanager. c, Grenada flycatcher. d, Bananaquit.
$10, Grenada dove, vert.

| | | | | |
|---|---|---|---|---|
| **2015, Dec. 21** | | **Litho.** | **Perf. 14** | |
| 2937 | G320 | $3.25 Sheet of 4, #a-d | 9.75 | 9.75 |

**Souvenir Sheet**
**Perf. 12**

| | | | | |
|---|---|---|---|---|
| 2938 | G320 | $10 multi | 7.50 | 7.50 |

No. 2938 contains one 30x50mm stamp.

Characters from *Star Trek: The Next Generation* Television Series — G321

No. 2939: a, Deanna Troi. b, Jean-Luc Picard. c, William Riker. d, Geordi La Forge. e, Worf. f, Beverly Crusher. g, Data. $10, Picard, horiz.

| | | | | |
|---|---|---|---|---|
| **2015, Dec. 21** | | **Litho.** | **Perf. 12** | |
| 2939 | G321 | $3.15 Sheet of 7, | | |
| | | #a-g | 16.50 | 16.50 |

**Souvenir Sheet**

| | | | | |
|---|---|---|---|---|
| 2940 | G321 | $10 multi | 7.50 | 7.50 |

No. 2940 contains one 40x30mm.

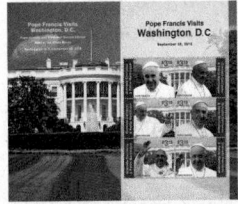

Visit of Pope Francis to Washington, D.C. — G322

No. 2941 — Various photographs of Pope Francis and White House, as shown.
$10, Pope Francis, Pres. Barack Obama and wife, Michelle.

| | | | | |
|---|---|---|---|---|
| **2016, Jan. 31** | | **Litho.** | **Perf. 14** | |
| 2941 | G322 | $3.15 Sheet of 6, | | |
| | | #a-f | 14.00 | 14.00 |

**Souvenir Sheet**

| | | | | |
|---|---|---|---|---|
| 2942 | G322 | $10 multi | 7.50 | 7.50 |

No. 2942 contains one 80x30mm stamp.

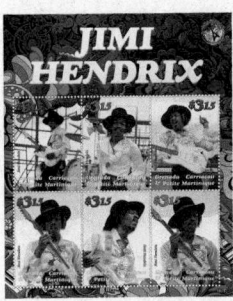

Jimi Hendrix (1942-70), Rock Guitarist — G323

No. 2943 — Hendrix: a, Picking guitar strings. b, Without guitar. c, With hand raised. d, With hand on guitar neck, "Jimi Hendrix" at left, orange red denomination. e, With hand on guitar neck, "Jimi Hendrix" at right, scarlet denomination. f, With hand on guitar neck, "Jimi Hendrix" at left, blue denomination. $10, Hendrix and microphone.

| | | | | |
|---|---|---|---|---|
| **2016, Mar. 8** | | **Litho.** | **Perf. 14** | |
| 2943 | G323 | $3.15 Sheet of 6, | | |
| | | #a-f | 14.00 | 14.00 |

**Souvenir Sheet**
**Perf. 12½**

| | | | | |
|---|---|---|---|---|
| 2944 | G323 | $10 multi | 7.50 | 7.50 |

No. 2944 contains one 38x51mm stamp.

**Elvis Presley Type of 2016**
**Souvenir Sheets**

Designs: No. 2945, $10, Presley buys motorcycle. No. 2946, $10, Presley kissing woman. No. 2947, $10, Presley appearing on *The Steve Allen Show*. No. 2948, $14, Presley rents out Memphis amusement park. No. 2949, $14, Presley begins tour with Andy Griffith, vert. No. 2950, $14, Presley meets future wife at party, vert. No. 2951, $14, Presley's first press interview, vert.

**Perf. 14, 13x13¼ (#2948), 13¼x13 (#2949-2951)**

**2016**     Litho.
2945-2951 A882   Set of 7   65.00 65.00
   Issued: Nos. 2945-2947, 3/8; Nos. 2948-2951, 6/30.

Queen Elizabeth II, 90th Birthday G324

No. 2952 — Photograph of Queen Elizabeth II from: a, 1972. b, 1946. c, 1943. d, 1965.
No. 2953, vert. — Photograph of Queen Elizabeth II from: a, 1971. b, 2015.

**2016, Apr. 1**    Litho.    **Perf. 12**
2952 G324 $3.25 Sheet of 4,
     #a-d     9.75   9.75
**Souvenir Sheet**
2953 G324   $7 Sheet of 2,
     #a-b     10.50 10.50

Space Flight of Valentina Tereshkova, 50th Anniv. (in 2013) — G325

No. 2954: a, Launch. b, Tereshkova wearing space helmet. c, Wedding of Tereshkova, 1963. d, Space capsule after re-entry.
$12, Tereshkova, vert.

**2016, May 2**    Litho.    **Perf. 12**
2954 G325 $3.25 Sheet of 4, #a-
     d     9.75   9.75
**Souvenir Sheet**
2955 G325   $12 multi     9.00   9.00

World Stamp Show 2016, New York G326

No. 2956 — World Stamp Show emblem and New York City landmarks: a, New York Stock Exchange. b, New York Public Library. c, St. Patrick's Cathedral. d, Bethesda Terrace. $14, Empire State Building and other buildings, vert.

**2016, May 2**    Litho.    **Perf. 12½**
2956 G326   $4 Sheet of 4, #a-
     d     12.00 12.00
**Souvenir Sheet**
**Perf. 12**
2957 G326 $14 multi     10.50 10.50
   No. 2957 contains one 60x80mm stamp.

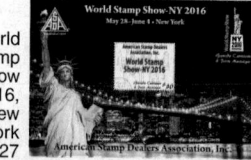

World Stamp Show 2016, New York G327

**2016, May 30**    Litho.    **Perf. 12½x12**
2958 G327 $30 multi     22.50 22.50

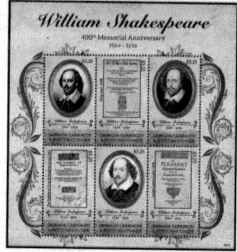

William Shakespeare (1564-1616), Writer — G328

No. 2959: a, Shakespeare, 6mm collar strings. b, Front page of *King Lear*. c, Shakespeare, 3mm collar strings. d, Front page of *King Richard III*. e, Shakespeare, 5mm collar strings. f, Front page of *Love's Labour's Lost*.
No. 2960: a, Shakespeare, collar with strings. b, Front page of *Hamlet*. c, Shakespeare, collar without strings. d, Front page of *Othello*.
$14, Shakespeare, diff.

**2016, May 30**    Litho.    **Perf. 12**
2959 G328 $3.25 Sheet of 6,
     #a-f     14.50 14.50
2960 G328 $3.50 Sheet of 4,
     #a-d     10.50 10.50
**Souvenir Sheet**
**Perf. 12½**
2961 G328 $14 multi     10.50 10.50
   No. 2961 contains one 38x51mm stamp.

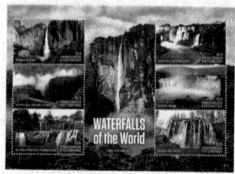

Waterfalls — G329

No. 2962: a, Yosemite Falls, U.S. b, Iguazu Falls, Argentina and Brazil. c, Victoria Falls, Zimbabwe and Zambia. d, Godhafoss, Iceland. e, Ban Gioc-Detian Falls, Viet Nam and People's Republic of China. f, Galovac Falls, Croatia.
$13, Niagara Falls, U.S. and Canada.

**2016, June 21**    Litho.    **Perf. 12**
2962 G329 $3.15 Sheet of 6,
     #a-f     14.00 14.00
**Souvenir Sheet**
2963 G329   $13 multi     9.75   9.75
   No. 2963 contains one 80x30mm stamp.

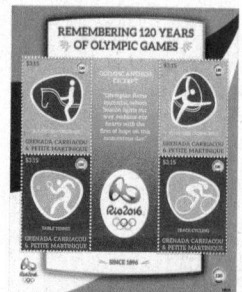

2016 Summer Olympics, Rio de Janeiro — G330

No. 2964: a, Equestrian dressage. b, Rhythmic gymnastics. c, Table tennis. d, Track cycling.
No. 2965: a, Fencing. b, Helene Mayer, Olympic fencer.

**2016, July 7**    Litho.    **Perf. 14**
2964 G330 $3.15 Sheet of 4,
     #a-d     9.50   9.50
**Souvenir Sheet**
**Perf. 12½**
2965 G330   $12 Sheet of 2,
     #a-b     18.00 18.00
   No. 2965 contains two 38x51mm stamps.

Crabs and Birds G331

No. 2966: a, Glossy ibis. b, Zombie crab. c, Yellow-crowned night heron. d, Blue land crab. e, Great blue heron. f, Red land crab.
No. 2967: a, Coral crab. b, Batwing coral crab.

**2016, Sept. 9**    Litho.    **Perf. 14**
2966 G331 $3.25 Sheet of 6,
     #a-f     14.50 14.50
**Souvenir Sheet**
**Perf. 12**
2967 G331   $7 Sheet of 2,
     #a-b     10.50 10.50

G332

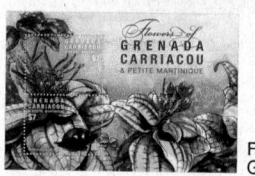

Flowers G333

No. 2968: a, Royal poinciana. b, Golden trumpet. c, Painted brasiliorchis. d, Flamingo flower. e, Barbados lily. f, Great bougainvillea.
No. 2969: a, Charianthus grenadensis. b, Bulimulus wiebesi snail.

**2016, Sept. 9**    Litho.    **Perf. 14**
2968 G332 $3.25 Sheet of 6,
     #a-f     14.50 14.50
**Souvenir Sheet**
**Perf. 12**
2969 G333   $7 Sheet of 2,
     #a-b     10.50 10.50

Christmas — G334

Designs: No. 2970, $5.50, Conifer branch and cones, Christmas ornaments. No. 2971, $5.50, Snowflake ornament. No. 2972, $10, Christmas tree, gift box. No. 2973, $10, Christmas ornaments.

**2016, Dec. 1**    Litho.    **Perf. 12½**
2970-2973 G334   Set of 4   23.00 23.00

G335

G336

New Year 2017 (Year of the Rooster) G337

No. 2974: a, Bird wing at top center. b, Butterflies at top center.

**2016, Dec. 5**    Litho.    **Perf. 12**
2974 G335 $5.50 Pair, #a-b   8.25   8.25
**Souvenir Sheets**
**Perf.**
2975 G336   $10 multi     7.50   7.50
2976 G337   $10 multi     7.50   7.50
   No. 2974 was printed in sheets containing two each Nos. 2974a-2974b.

G338

G339

Pres. John F. Kennedy (1917-63) and His Family — G340

No. 2977: a, Pres. Kennedy with wife, Jacqueline, and children, Caroline and John, Jr. (70x35mm). b, Pres. Kennedy with father, Joseph, and brother, Joe (70x35mm). c, Pres. Kennedy and wife at their wedding (35x35mm). d, Pres. Kennedy with wife and children (35x35mm). e, Jacqueline Kennedy (35x35mm). f, Pres. Kennedy and wife in limousine (35x35mm).
No. 2978: a, Pres. Kennedy and son. b, Jacqueline Kennedy and daughter. c, Pres. Kennedy with his children and horse. d, Caroline Kennedy and doll.
No. 2979: a, Pres. Kennedy and son under desk. b, Pres. Kennedy and daughter. c, Pres. Kennedy with wife and daughter.

**2017, Feb. 28**    **Litho.**    **Perf. 13¾**
2977 G338   $3 Sheet of 6,
    #a-f          13.50 13.50
2978 G339 $5.50 Sheet of 4,
    #a-d         16.50 16.50

**Souvenir Sheet**
**Perf. 12½**
2979 G340   $5 Sheet of 3,
    #a-c          11.00 11.00

**Miniature Sheets**

G341

G342

Princess Diana (1961-97) — G343

Various photographs of Princess Diana, as shown.

**2017, May 15**    **Litho.**    **Perf. 14**
2980 G341 $5.50 Sheet of 4,
    #a-d         16.50 16.50
2981 G342 $5.50 Sheet of 4,
    #a-d         16.50 16.50
2982 G343 $5.50 Sheet of 4,
    #a-d         16.50 16.50
   Nos. 2980-2982 (3)    49.50 49.50

Bats
G344

No. 2983: a, Mexican long-tongued bat. b, Hairy big-eyed bat. c, Little yellow-shouldered bat. d, Greater bulldog bat.
$12, Velvety free-tailed bat, horiz.

---

**2017, July 24**    **Litho.**    **Perf. 14**
2983 G344   $7 Sheet of 4, #a-
    d           21.00 21.00

**Souvenir Sheet**
**Perf. 12½**
2984 G344 $12 multi      9.00 9.00

No. 2984 contains one 51x38mm stamp.

New Year 2018 (Year of the Dog) — G345

Chinese Zodiac Animals G346

No. 2986: a, Rat. b, Ox. c, Tiger. d, Rabbit. e, Dragon. f, Snake. g, Horse. h, Ram. i, Monkey. j, Rooster. k, Dog. l, Pig.

**2017, Aug. 8**    **Litho.**    **Perf. 12**
2985 G345   $8 multi      6.00 6.00

**Miniature Sheet**
**Perf. 14**
2986 G346 $1.80 Sheet of 12,
    #a-l         16.00 16.00

No. 2985 was printed in sheets of 4.

Paintings by Gustav Klimt (1862-1918) — G347

No. 2987: a, Adele Bloch-Bauer I. b, Portrait of Fritza Riedler. c, Eugenia Primavesi. d, Mäda Gertrude Primavesi.
$15, The Kiss.

**2017, Aug. 11**    **Litho.**    **Perf. 14**
2987 G347   $7 Sheet of 4, #a-
    d           21.00 21.00

**Souvenir Sheet**
2988 G347 $15 multi     11.00 11.00

No. 2988 contains one 30x80mm stamp.

**Elvis Presley Type of 2017**
**Souvenir Sheets**

Inscriptions: No. 2989, $12, Last pre-Army concert. No. 2990, $12, Transatlantic interview. No. 2991, $12, Getting Army haircut. No. 2992, $12, First rock'n'roll gold record.

**2017, Oct. 26**    **Litho.**    **Perf. 12½**
2989-2992 A971   Set of 4    36.00 36.00

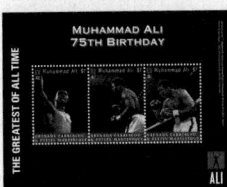

Muhammad Ali (1942-2016), Boxer — G348

No. 2993 — Ali: a, With arm raised. b, Fighting, lights in background. c, Leaning over boxing ring rope, no robe.
$12, Ali leaning on boxing ring rope, with robe.

---

**2017, Oct. 26**    **Litho.**    **Perf. 12**
2993 G348   $7 Sheet of 3, #a-
    c           15.50 15.50

**Souvenir Sheet**
**Perf. 12½**
2994 G348 $12 multi      9.00 9.00

No. 2994 contains one 38x51mm stamp.

**Miniature Sheet**

World War I, Cent. G349

No. 2995 — Poster: a, U.S. Official War Pictures. b, Men Wanted for the Army. c, For Liberty's Sake. d, Hello! This is Liberty Speaking. e, Adventure and Action. f, First in France U.S. Marines.

**2017, Nov. 14**    **Litho.**    **Perf. 12x11½**
2995 G349   $4 Sheet of 6, #a-f   18.00 18.00

**Miniature Sheets**

Ospreys G350

Broad-winged Hawks — G351

Barn Owls G352

No. 2996 — Various photographs of ospreys: a, $3. b, $5. c, $7. d, 9.
No. 2997 — Various photographs of broad-winged hawks: a, $5.50. b, $6.50. c, $7.50. d, $8.50.
No. 2998, $7, Various photographs of barn owls, as shown.

**2017, Dec. 31**    **Litho.**    **Perf. 14**
2996 G350   Sheet of 4, #a-d   18.00 18.00
2997 G351   Sheet of 4, #a-d   21.00 21.00
2998 G352   Sheet of 4, #a-d   21.00 21.00
   Nos. 2996-2998 (3)    60.00 60.00

**Miniature Sheets**

Jellyfish G353

No. 2999: a, $5, Cannonball jellyfish. b, $6, Comb jellyfish. c, $7, Moon jellyfish. d, $8, Mangrove upside-down jellyfish.

---

No. 3000: a, $6, Mauve jellyfish. b, $7, Box jellyfish. c, $8, Atlantic sea nettle. d, $9, Portuguese man-of-war.

**2018, Mar. 7**    **Litho.**    **Perf. 12**
2999 G353   Sheet of 4, #a-d   19.50 19.50
3000 G353   Sheet of 4, #a-d   22.50 22.50

Mammals — G354

No. 3001: a, $3, Central American agouti. b, $4, Small Asian mongoose. c, $5. Wild boar. d, $6, Common opossum. e, $7, Geoffroy's tailless bat.
$14, Mona monkey, vert.

**2018, Mar. 7**    **Litho.**    **Perf. 14**
3001 G354   Sheet of 5, #a-e   18.50 18.50

**Souvenir Sheet**
**Perf. 12½**
3002 G354 $14 multi     10.50 10.50

No. 3002 contains one 38x51mm stamp.

Mao Zedong (1893-1976), Chairman of Communist Party of China — G355

No. 3003 — Various depictions of Mao: a, $6. b, $7. c, $8.
$11, Mao, diff.

**2018, Mar. 7**    **Litho.**    **Perf. 12**
3003 G355   Sheet of 3, #a-c   15.50 15.50

**Souvenir Sheet**
3004 G355 $11 multi      8.25 8.25

Gemstones — G356

Diamonds — G357

No. 3005: a, $2, Tiger's eye. b, $3, Amethyst. c, $4, Zincite. d, $5, Lapis lazuli. e, $6, Turquoise. f, $7, Ruby.
No. 3006: a, Colored diamond at left, below colorless diamond. b, Colored diamond at right. c, Colored diamond at left, above colorless diamond.

**2018, Mar. 21    Litho.    Perf. 14**
3005 G356    Sheet of 6, #a-f   20.00  20.00
**Souvenir Sheet**
3006 G357 $7 Sheet of 3, #a-c  15.50  15.50

**Miniature Sheet**

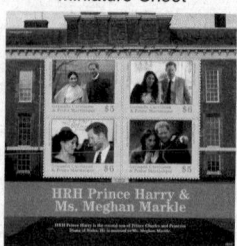

Engagement of Prince Harry and
Meghan Markle — G358

No. 3007 — Couple: a, $5, Tree in background. b, $5, Prince Harry pointing. c, $6, Markle with hand raised near head. d, $6, Sign in background.

**2018, July 27    Litho.    Perf. 14**
3007 G358    Sheet of 4, #a-d  16.50  16.50

Prince George of Cambridge, 5th
Birthday — G359

No. 3008 — Prince George: a, $5, Wearing shirt with buttons. b, $5, Wearing shirt without buttons. c, $5, With great-grandmother, Queen Elizabeth II. d, $6, As infant, with parents, Duke and Duchess of Cambridge.
$11, Prince George, with father, Prince William.

**2018, July 27    Litho.    Perf. 14**
3008 G359    Sheet of 4, #a-d  15.50  15.50
**Souvenir Sheet**
**Perf. 12½**
3009 G359 $11 multi           8.25  8.25
No. 3009 contains one 38x51mm stamp.

Elvis Presley (1935-
77) — G360

**2018, Aug. 3    Litho.    Perf. 12**
3010 G360 $5.50 multi          4.25  4.25
No. 3010 was printed in sheets of 3.

G361

New
Year
2019
(Year of
the Pig)
G362

**2018, Oct. 17    Litho.    Perf. 12**
3011 G361 $8 multi            6.00  6.00
**Souvenir Sheet**
**Perf. 13¾**
3012 G362 $6 multi            4.50  4.50

G363

Wedding
of Prince
Harry
and
Meghan
Markle
G364

No. 3013: a, $3, Prince Harry removing veil from face of wife. b, $3, Couple in car. c, $4, Couple holding hands. d, $5, Prince Harry. e, $5, Markle.
$10, Couple, vert.

**2018, Nov. 9    Litho.    Perf. 13¾**
3013 G363    Sheet of 5, #a-e  15.00  15.00
**Souvenir Sheet**
**Perf. 12**
3014 G364 $10 multi           7.50  7.50

**Miniature Sheet**

Butterflies — G365

No. 3015: a, $5, Uncertain owlet. b, $5, Montezuma's cattleheart. c, $6, Cotytto clearwing. d, $6, Spatiosa skipper.

**2018, Dec. 5    Litho.    Perf. 14**
3015 G365    Sheet of 4, #a-d  16.50  16.50

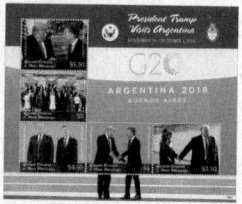

Visit to Argentina of Pres. Donald
Trump — G366

No. 3016 — Pres. Trump with: a, $3.50, Wife, Melania. b, $4, Argentinian Pres. Mauricio Macri, standing with hands extended. c, $4.50, Macri, standing. d, $5, World leaders. e, $5.50, Macri, shaking hands.

**2019, Feb. 6    Litho.    Perf. 14**
3016 G366    Sheet of 5, #a-e  20.00  20.00

Sea
Turtles
G367

No. 3017: a, $4, Leatherback sea turtle. b, $5, Green sea turtle. c, $6, Loggerhead sea turtle. d, $7, Olive ridley sea turtle.
$14, Leatherback sea turtle, diff.

**2019, Feb. 18    Litho.    Perf. 13¾**
3017 G367    Sheet of 4, #a-
d                              16.50  16.50
**Souvenir Sheet**
**Perf. 12½**
3018 G367 $14 multi          10.50  10.50
No. 3018 contains one 51x38mm stamp.

**Miniature Sheet**

Cacti
G368

No. 3019: a, $2, Turk's cap (flower in bloom). b, $2, Turk's cap (stem and cephalium). c, $4, Strawberry pear (flower in bloom). d, $4, Strawberry pear (stem with flowers). e, $6, Prickly pear (flower in bloom). f, $6, Prickly pear (stem and fruit).

**2019, Mar. 4    Litho.    Perf. 12**
3019 G368    Sheet of 6, #a-f  18.00  18.00

Sharks
G369

No. 3020: a, $4, Common remora. b, $5, Whitetip reef shark. c, $6, Scalloped hammerhead shark. d, $7, Lemon shark.
$14, Tiger shark. $15, Bull shark.

**2019, Mar. 4    Litho.    Perf. 12**
3020 G369    Sheet of 4, #a-
d                              16.50  16.50
**Souvenir Sheets**
**Perf. 12½**
3021 G369 $14 multi          10.50  10.50
3022 G369 $15 multi          11.00  11.50
Nos. 3021 and 3022 each contain one 51x38mm stamp.

**Miniature Sheet**

Wood
Stork
G370

No. 3023 — Various photographs of Wood stork: a, $1. b, $2. c, $3. d, $4. e, $5. f, $6.

**2019, Mar. 12    Litho.    Perf. 12**
3023 G370    Sheet of 6, #a-f  15.50  15.50

**Miniature Sheet**

Visit of
Pres.
Donald
Trump To
Germany
G371

No. 3024 — Pres. Trump and: a, $4, Wife, Melania. b, $5, German Chancellor Angela Merkel. c, $6, Merkel, diff. d, $7, Merkel, diff.

**2019, May 17    Litho.    Perf. 14**
3024 G371    Sheet of 4, #a-d  16.50  16.50

Birds
G372

No. 3025: a, $3, Ringed kingfisher. b, $3, Pearly-eyed thrasher. c, $4, Bananaquit. d, $4, Shiny cowbird. e, $5, Tropical mockingbird. f, $5, Lesser Antillean bullfinch.
$14, Purple gallinule, vert.

**2019, May 24    Litho.    Perf. 14**
3025 G372    Sheet of 6, #a-f  18.00  18.00
**Souvenir Sheet**
**Perf. 12½**
3026 G372 $14 multi          10.50  10.50
No. 3026 contains one 38x51mm stamp.

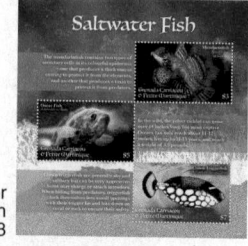

Saltwater
Fish
G373

No. 3027: a, $3, Mandarinfish. b, $5, Oscar. c, $7, Clown triggerfish.
No. 3028, $3, Lionfish.

**2019, Dec. 24    Litho.    Perf. 12**
3027 G373    Sheet of 3, #a-c  11.00  11.00
**Souvenir Sheet**
**Perf. 13¾**
3028 G373 $3 multi            2.25  2.25
No. 3028 contains one 35x35mm stamp.

# LIZARDS

Lizards G374

No. 3029: a, $2, Gold dust day gecko. b, $3, Rock iguana. c, $4, Gold dust day gecko, diff. d, $5, Rock iguana, diff.
$14, Desert spiny lizard.

**2019, Dec. 24    Litho.    Perf. 14**
3029 G374    Sheet of 4, #a-d    10.50 10.50
**Souvenir Sheet**
3030 G374    $14 multi    10.50 10.50
No. 3030 contains one 80x30mm stamp.

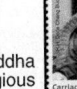

Dorje Chang Buddha III, Religious Leader — G375

**2020, Aug. 28    Litho.    Perf. 12½**
3031 G375    $5 multi    3.75 3.75
No. 3031 was printed in sheets of 4.

**Miniature Sheet**

Tribute to Workers Combating COVID-19 Pandemic — G376

No. 3032: a, Health care worker wearing protective face shield, mask and gloves holding large COVID-19 virus. b, Policeman and man wearing protective face masks. c, Health care worker with multichannel pipette. d, Health care worker holding drawing of heart.

**2020, Sept. 14    Litho.    Perf. 14**
3032 G376    $5 Sheet of 4, #a-d    15.00 15.00

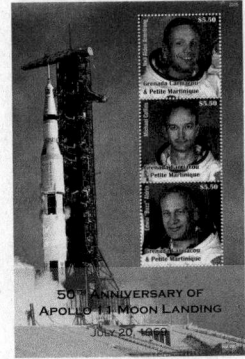

Spaceflight of Apollo 11, 50th Anniv. (in 2019) — G377

No. 3033 — Crew of Apollo 11: a, Neil Armstrong. b, Michael Collins. c, Edwin "Buzz" Aldrin, Jr.
No. 3034, vert.: a, Armstrong holding his space helmet. b, Footprint on Moon.

**2020, Sept. 30    Litho.    Perf. 13¾**
3033 G377    $5.50 Sheet of 3, #a-c    12.50 12.50
**Souvenir Sheet**
**Perf. 14**
3034 G377    $5 Sheet of 2, #a-b    7.50 7.50
No. 3034 contains two 30x40mm stamps.

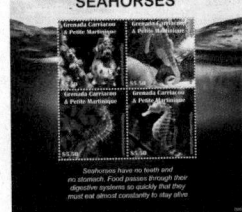

# SEAHORSES

Seahorses — G378

No. 3035: a, Hippocampus bargibanti with red features. b, Hippocampus kuda. c, Hippocampus bargibanti facing left, tip of nose under second "e" of "Petite." d, Hippocampus bargibanti facing left, tip of nose under first "e" of "Petite."
$14, Hippocampus, horiz.

**2020, Sept. 30    Litho.    Perf. 13¾**
3035 G378    $5.50 Sheet of 4, #a-d    16.50 16.50
**Souvenir Sheet**
**Perf. 12**
3036 G378    $14 multi    10.50 10.50
No. 3036 contains one 40x30mm stamp.

G379

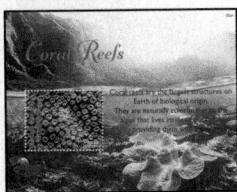

Corals G380

No. 3037: a, Brain coral. b, Pillar coral. c, Octocoral. d, Staghorn coral. e, Branch coral.
$14, Star coral.

**2020, Sept. 30    Litho.    Perf. 13¾**
3037 G379    $4.50 Sheet of 5, #a-e    17.00 17.00
**Souvenir Sheet**
**Perf. 12**
3038 G380    $14 multi    10.50 10.50

SEASHELLS

G381

Seashells — G382

No. 3039: a, Scallop shell. b, Angelwing shell. c, Coffee bean shell. d, Conch shell. e, Cerith mollusk shell.
$14, Spiral shell.

**2020, Sept. 30    Litho.    Perf. 13¾**
3039 G381    $4.50 Sheet of 5, #a-e    17.00 17.00
**Souvenir Sheet**
**Perf. 12**
3040 G382    $14 multi    10.50 10.50

Forbidden City, Beijing, 600th Anniv. — G383

No. 3041: a, Wall details depicting dragon. b, Emperor Seat, Union and Peace Hall. c, Guardian roof figures.
$25, Palace Museum.

**2020, Nov. 23    Litho.    Perf. 12**
3041 G383    $5 Sheet of 3, #a-c    11.00 11.00
**Souvenir Sheet**
3042 G383    $25 multi    18.50 18.50
No. 3042 contains one 80x30mm stamp.

**Miniature Sheet**

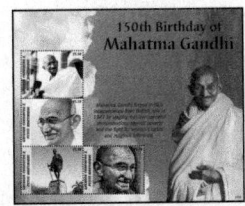

Mohandas K. Gandhi (1869-1948), Indian Nationalist Leader — G384

No. 3043: a, Black-and-white photograph. b, Color drawing. c, Sculpture. d, Deep claret drawing.

**2021, Jan. 28    Litho.    Perf. 14**
3043 G384    $5.50 Sheet of 4, #a-d    16.50 16.50

**Miniature Sheet**

Metropolitan Museum of Art, New York City, 150th Anniv. (in 2020) — G385

No. 3044: a, 1914 photograph of museum. b, Great Hall. c, Leaf from the Koran. d, Museum display of arms and armor.

**2021, Jan. 28    Litho.    Perf. 14**
3044 G385    $5.50 Sheet of 4, #a-d    16.50 16.50

**Miniature Sheet**

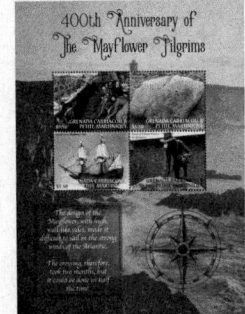

Arrival of the Mayflower in North America, 400th Anniv. (in 2020) — G386

No. 3045: a, Washing the Skins and Grading the Wool, painting by Isaac Claesz. van Swanenburg (1537-1614). b, Plymouth Rock. c, Model of the Mayflower. d, Droitwich, England Statue of Edward Winslow (1595-1655), Governor of Plymouth Colony.

**2021, Jan. 28    Litho.    Perf. 14**
3045 G386    $5.50 Sheet of 4, #a-d    16.50 16.50

**Miniature Sheet**

95th Birthday of Queen Elizabeth II (1926-2022) — G387

No. 3046 — Photograph of Queen Elizabeth II from: a, 2007. b, 1970. c, 2020. d, 2016.

**2021, Jan. 28    Litho.    Perf. 14**
3046 G387    $5.50 Sheet of 4, #a-d    16.50 16.50

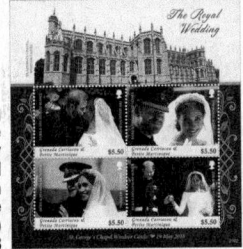

Wedding of Prince Harry and Meghan Markle (in 2018) G388

No. 3047 — Couple: a, Kissing. b, Smiling. c, Smiling, facing left. d, Holding hands.
$14, Couple holding hands, diff.

**2021, Jan. 28    Litho.    Perf. 14**
3047 G388    $5.50 Sheet of 4, #a-d    16.50 16.50
**Souvenir Sheet**
**Perf. 12½**
3048 G388    $14 multi    10.50 10.50
No. 3048 contains one 51x38mm stamp.

Range Rovers, 50th Anniv. (in 2020) G389

No. 3049: a, Brown 2014 Land Range Rover Evoque. b, 1996 Land Range Rover. c, 2014 Land Range Rover. d, Red 2014 Land Range Rover Evoque.
$14, Queen Elizabeth II, Prince Philip and Prince Andrew in Range Rover Evoque, horiz.

**2021, Jan. 28    Litho.    Perf. 13¾**
3049 G389    $5.50 Sheet of 4, #a-d    16.50 16.50
**Souvenir Sheet**
**Perf. 12½**
3050 G389    $14 multi    10.50 10.50
No. 3050 contains one 51x38mm stamp.

Joseph R. Biden, Jr., 46th President of the United States — G390

No. 3051 — Pres. Biden: a, Wearing blue and white striped tie. b, Standing behind microphones. c, With flag in background. d, Writing.
$14, Pres. Biden, vert.

**2021, Mar. 15    Litho.    Perf. 14½x14**
3051 G390 $5.50 Sheet of 4,
#a-d                    16.50 16.50
**Souvenir Sheet**
**Perf. 14x14½**
3052 G390    $14 multi        10.50 10.50

Dorje Chang Buddha III, Religious Leader — G391

**2021, May 17    Litho.    Perf. 13¼x12½**
3053 G391 $3 multi            2.25 2.25
No. 3053 was printed in sheets of 8.

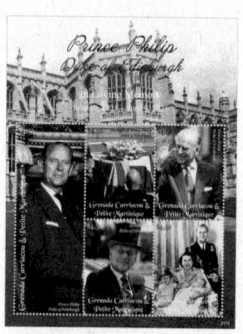

Prince Philip (1921-2021) — G392

No. 3054: a, Prince Philip (30x80mm). b, Coffin of Prince Philip and members of honor guard (30x40mm). c, Prince Philip waving (30x40mm). d, Prince Philip wearing top hat (30x40mm). e, Prince Philip, Queen Elizabeth II, and their children, Prince Charles and Princess Anne (30x40mm).
$14, Pallbearaers carrying coffin of Prince Philip.

**2021, June 14    Litho.    Perf. 14**
3054 G392 $4.50 Sheet of 5,
#a-e                    17.00 17.00
**Souvenir Sheet**
3055 G392    $14 multi        10.50 10.50
No. 3055 contains one 30x40mm stamp.

Discovery of Tomb of King Tutankhamun, Cent. — G393

No. 3056: a, Coffin of King Tutankhamun. b, Gold fan. c, Scarab beetle brooch. d, Removal of sarcophagus, 2007. e, King Tutankhamun and Queen Ankhesenamun. f, Valley of the Kings, Egypt.
$14, Gold funerary mask of King Tutankhamun.

**2021, Aug. 16    Litho.    Perf. 14**
3056 G393 $4 Sheet of 6, #a-
f                    18.00 18.00

**Souvenir Sheet**
**Perf. 12½**
3057 G393 $14 multi        10.50 10.50
No. 3057 contains one 51x38mm stamp.

**Souvenir Sheet**

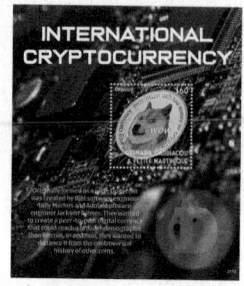

Dogecoin — G394

**2021, Oct. 1    Litho.    Perf. 13¾**
3058 G394 $60 multi        45.00 45.00

Flamingos — G395

No. 3059 — Various flamingos with country name in: a, Yellow orange (at left). b, Dark blue. c, Bright blue. d, Yellow orange (at top). e, Red. f, White.
No. 3060 — Flamingo facing: a, Right. b, Left.

**2021, Oct. 11    Litho.    Perf. 14**
3059 G395 $3.50 Sheet of 6,
#a-f                    15.50 15.50
**Souvenir Sheet**
3060 G395    $8 Sheet of 2,
#a-b                    12.00 12.00

Butterflies — G396

No. 3061: a, Red admiral butterfly. b, Little yellow butterfly. c, Tailed cecropian butterfly. d, Mimosa yellow butterfly. e, Tropical queen butterfly. f, Tropical white butterfly. g, Brush-footed butterfly. h, Hall's sulphur butterfly.
No. 3062: a, Cassius blue butterfly. b, Hanno blue butterfly.

**2021, Oct. 11    Litho.    Perf. 14**
3061 G396 $3.50 Sheet of 8,
#a-h                    21.00 21.00
**Souvenir Sheet**
3062 G396    $8 Sheet of 2,
#a-b                    12.00 12.00

Mushrooms — G397

No. 3063: a, Penny bun. b, Matsutake. c, Death cap. d, Shaggy mane. e, Horn of plenty. f, King trumpet. g, Parasol. h, Honey fungus. i, Saffron milk cap. j, Wood blewit. k, Slippery Jack. l, Inky cap.
No. 3064: a, Fly agaric. b, Destroying angel.

**2021, Oct. 11    Litho.    Perf. 14**
3063 G397 $2 Sheet of 12, #a-
l                    18.00 18.00
**Souvenir Sheet**
3064 G397 $8 Sheet of 2, #a-b 12.00 12.00

Iguanas
G398

No. 3065 — Various iguanas with denomination of: a, $4. b, $5. c, $6. d, $7.
$14, Iguana, diff.

**2021, Nov. 29    Litho.    Perf. 14**
3065 G398    Sheet of 4, #a-d 16.50 16.50
**Souvenir Sheet**
**Perf. 13¾**
3066 G398 $14 multi        10.50 10.50
No. 3066 contains one 35x35mm stamp.

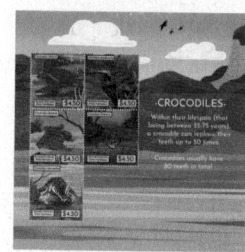

Crocodiles — G399

No. 3067: a, Crocodylus niloticus. b, Mecistops cataphractus. c, Crocodylus johnstoni. d, Crocodylus palustris. e, Crocodylus intermedius.
No. 3068: a, Crocodylus acutus. b, Crocodylus suchus.

**2021, Nov. 29    Litho.    Perf. 13¾**
3067 G399 $4.50 Sheet of 5,
#a-e                    17.00 17.00
**Souvenir Sheet**
3068 G399    $8 Sheet of 2,
#a-b                    12.00 12.00

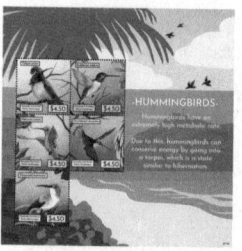

Hummingbirds — G400

No. 3069: a, Calypte costae. b, Archilochus colubris. c, Chlorestes notata. d, Chrysolampis mosquitus. e, Chrysuronia brevirostris.
No. 3070: a, Anthracothorax nigricollis. b, Eulampis jugularis.

**2021, Dec. 23    Litho.    Perf. 13¾**
3069 G400 $4.50 Sheet of 5,
#a-e                    17.00 17.00
**Souvenir Sheet**
3070 G400    $8 Sheet of 2,
#a-b                    12.00 12.00

Trichechus Manatus — G401

No. 3071 — Various photographs of West Indian manatee with denomination of: a, $4. b, $5. c, $6. d, $7.
$14, West Indian manatee, diff.

**2022, Apr. 18    Litho.    Perf. 14**
3071 G401    Sheet of 4, #a-d 16.50 16.50
**Souvenir Sheet**
**Perf. 12¾x12½**
3072 G401 $14 multi        10.50 10.50
No. 3072 contains one 51x38mm stamp.

**Souvenir Sheet**

Peace Dove, Parliament of Ukraine, Kyiv, and Kremlin, Moscow — G402

**2022, May 30    Litho.    Perf. 12**
3073 G402 $13 multi         9.75 9.75

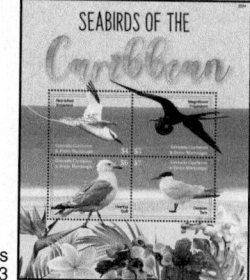

Seabirds
G403

No. 3074: a, $4, Red-billed tropicbird. b, $5, Magnificent frigatebird. c, $6, Herring gull. d, $7, Caspian tern.
No. 3075, vert.: a, Brown pelican. b, Red-footed booby.

**2022, June 1    Litho.    Perf. 14**
3074 G403    Sheet of 4, #a-d 16.50 16.50
**Souvenir Sheet**
**Perf. 12½x12¾**
3075 G403 $8 Sheet of 2, #a-b 12.00 12.00
No. 3075 contains two 38x51mm stamps.

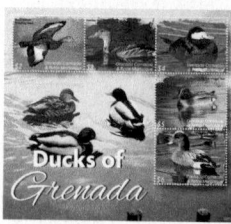

Ducks
G404

No. 3076: a, $2, Black-bellied whistling duck. b, $3, Fulvous whistling duck. c, $4, Ruddy duck. d, $5, Green-winged teal. e, $6, American wigeon.
$14, White-cheeked pintail.

**2022, June 1    Litho.    Perf. 14**
3076 G404    Sheet of 5, #a-e 15.00 15.00
**Souvenir Sheet**
**Perf. 12¾x12½**
3077 G404 $14 multi        10.50 10.50
No. 3077 contains one 51x38mm stamp.

## SEMI-POSTAL STAMPS

### 1988 Seoul Olympics Type

No. B1, Cycling. No. B2, Sailing. No. B3, Uneven Parallel Bars. No. B4, Dressage. No. B5, Marathon.

**1986, Dec. 1**    **Perf. 15**

| | | | | |
|---|---|---|---|---|
| B1 | SP2 | 10c +5c multi | .90 | .45 |
| B2 | SP2 | 50c +20c multi | .90 | .90 |
| B3 | SP2 | 70c +30c multi | .90 | .90 |
| B4 | SP2 | $2 +$1 multi | 2.40 | 2.40 |
| | | Nos. B1-B4 (4) | 5.10 | 4.65 |

**Souvenir Sheet**

| | | | | |
|---|---|---|---|---|
| B5 | SP2 | $3 +$1 multi | 4.00 | 4.00 |

## OFFICIAL STAMPS

Grenada Grenadines Nos. 396-408, 410, 440-442, 465-468 Overprinted "P.R.G."

**1982, June**    **Perf. 14, 15**

| | | | | |
|---|---|---|---|---|
| O1 | G45 | 5c multicolored | .25 | .25 |
| O2 | G45 | 6c multicolored | .25 | .25 |
| O3 | G45 | 10c multicolored | .25 | .25 |
| O4 | G45 | 12c multicolored | .25 | .25 |
| O5 | G45 | 15c multicolored | .25 | .25 |
| O6 | G45 | 20c multicolored | .25 | .25 |
| O7 | G54 | 20c multicolored | .25 | .25 |
| O8 | G45 | 25c multicolored | .25 | .25 |
| O9 | G45 | 30c multicolored | .25 | .25 |
| O10 | G45 | 40c multicolored | .25 | .25 |
| O11 | CD331 | 40c multicolored | .25 | .25 |
| O12 | G54 | 40c multicolored | .25 | .25 |
| O13 | G45 | 50c multicolored | .30 | .30 |
| O14 | G45 | 90c multicolored | .55 | .55 |
| O15 | G54 | $1 multicolored | .60 | .60 |
| O16 | G54 | $1 multicolored | .60 | .60 |
| O17 | CD331 | $2 multicolored | 1.10 | 1.10 |
| O18 | G54 | $2 multicolored | 1.10 | 1.10 |
| O19 | G45 | $3 multicolored | 1.60 | 1.60 |
| O20 | CD331 | $4 multicolored | 2.10 | 2.10 |
| O21 | G45 | $10 multicolored | 5.75 | 5.75 |
| | | Nos. O1-O21 (21) | 16.70 | 16.70 |

Royal Wedding stamps in changed colors, perf 15x14½ were also overprinted.

# GRIQUALAND WEST

'gri-kwə-,land 'west

LOCATION — In South Africa west of the Orange Free State and north of the Orange River
GOVT. — British Crown Colony
AREA — 15,197 sq. mi.
POP. — 83,375 (1891)
CAPITAL — Kimberley

Originally a territorial division of the Cape of Good Hope Colony, Griqualand West was declared a British Crown Colony in 1873 and together with Griqualand East was annexed to the Cape Colony in 1880.

12 Pence = 1 Shilling

Beware of forgeries.

Stamps of Cape of Good Hope 1864-65 (Type I, 4p, 6p, 1sh) and 1871-76 (Type II, ½p, 1p, 4p, 5sh) Surcharged or Overprinted

Type I — With frame line around stamp.
Type II — Without frame line.

**Manuscript Surcharge in Dark Red**

**1874**    **Wmk. 1**    **Perf. 14**

| | | | | |
|---|---|---|---|---|
| 1 | A3 | 1p on 4p blue (type I) | 1,900. | 2,600. |

Overprinted

**1877**    **Black Overprint**

| | | | |
|---|---|---|---|
| 2 | 1p rose | 800.00 | 115.00 |
| a. | Double overprint | | 3,250. |

**Red Overprint**

| | | | |
|---|---|---|---|
| 3 | 4p blue (type II) | 425.00 | 85.00 |

Overprinted In Black on the One Penny, in Red on the Other Values

Cape of Good Hope No. 17 Surcharged

| | | | | |
|---|---|---|---|---|
| 4 | (a) | ½p gray black | 45.00 | 47.50 |
| 5 | (a) | 1p rose | 45.00 | 30.00 |
| 6 | (a) | 4p blue (type I) | 475.00 | 75.00 |
| 7 | (a) | 4p blue (type II) | 425.00 | 50.00 |
| 8 | (a) | 6p dull violet | 325.00 | 57.50 |
| 9 | (a) | 1sh green | 375.00 | 47.50 |
| a. | | Inverted overprint | | 1,000. |
| 10 | (a) | 5sh orange | 1,150. | 57.50 |
| 11 | (b) | ½p gray black | 105.00 | 125.00 |
| 12 | (b) | 1p rose | 115.00 | 67.50 |
| 13 | (b) | 4p blue (type I) | 1,150. | 190.00 |
| 14 | (b) | 4p blue (type II) | 900.00 | 145.00 |
| 15 | (b) | 6p dull violet | 625.00 | 155.00 |
| 16 | (b) | 1sh green | 800.00 | 115.00 |
| 17 | (b) | 5sh orange | 1,900. | 135.00 |
| 18 | (c) | ½p gray black | 800.00 | 850.00 |
| 19 | (c) | 1p rose | 115.00 | 52.50 |
| 20 | (c) | 4p blue (type I) | 3,750. | 1,000. |
| 21 | (c) | 4p blue (type II) | 3,400. | 800.00 |
| 22 | (c) | 6p dull violet | 3,250. | 950.00 |
| 23 | (c) | 1sh green | 4,250. | 950.00 |
| 24 | (c) | 5sh orange | 4,750. | 1,050. |
| 25 | (d) | ½p gray black | 62.50 | 75.00 |
| 26 | (d) | 1p rose | 62.50 | 42.50 |
| 27 | (d) | 4p blue (type I) | 800.00 | 105.00 |
| 28 | (d) | 4p blue (type II) | 575.00 | 75.00 |
| 29 | (d) | 6p dull violet | 425.00 | 80.00 |
| 30 | (d) | 1sh green | 575.00 | 62.50 |
| 31 | (d) | 5sh orange | 1,575. | 80.00 |
| 32 | (e) | ½p gray black | 105.00 | 125.00 |
| 33 | (e) | 1p rose | 115.00 | 67.50 |
| 34 | (e) | 4p blue (type I) | 1,150. | 190.00 |
| 35 | (e) | 4p blue (type II) | 900.00 | 145.00 |
| 36 | (e) | 6p dull violet | 625.00 | 155.00 |
| 37 | (e) | 1sh green | 800.00 | 115.00 |
| a. | | Inverted overprint | | 1,600. |
| 38 | (e) | 5sh orange | 1,900. | 135.00 |
| 39 | (f) | ½p gray black | 115.00 | 135.00 |
| 40 | (f) | 1p rose | 125.00 | 85.00 |
| 41 | (f) | 4p blue (type I) | 1,250. | 235.00 |
| 42 | (f) | 4p blue (type II) | 950.00 | 165.00 |
| 43 | (f) | 6p dull violet | 750.00 | 175.00 |
| 44 | (f) | 1sh green | 900.00 | 145.00 |
| 45 | (f) | 5sh orange | 2,900. | 165.00 |
| 46 | (g) | ½p gray black | 57.50 | 67.50 |
| 47 | (g) | 1p rose | 45.00 | 30.00 |
| 48 | (g) | 4p blue (type I) | 575.00 | 95.00 |
| 49 | (g) | 4p blue (type II) | 525.00 | 62.50 |
| 50 | (g) | 6p dull violet | 400.00 | 77.50 |
| 51 | (g) | 1sh green | 525.00 | 57.50 |
| a. | | Inverted overprint | | 1,150. |
| 52 | (g) | 5sh orange | 1,475. | 67.50 |

There are minor varieties of types e and f.

Overprinted in Black

**1878**

| | | | | |
|---|---|---|---|---|
| 54 | (g) | 4p blue (type II) | 625.00 | 100.00 |
| 55 | (g) | 6p dull violet | 900.00 | 145.00 |
| 56 | (i) | 1p rose | 57.50 | 35.00 |
| 57 | (i) | 4p blue (type II) | 325.00 | 47.50 |
| 58 | (i) | 6p dull violet | 525.00 | 95.00 |
| a. | | Double overprint | | 1,600. |
| 59 | (k) | 1p rose | 115.00 | 52.50 |
| 60 | (k) | 4p blue (type II) | 575.00 | 90.00 |
| 61 | (k) | 6p dull violet | 850.00 | 135.00 |
| 62 | (l) | 1p rose | 50.00 | 32.50 |
| 63 | (l) | 4p blue (type II) | 290.00 | 47.50 |
| 64 | (l) | 6p dull violet | 475.00 | 85.00 |
| a. | | Double overprint | | 1,100. |
| 65 | (m) | 1p rose | 80.00 | 70.00 |
| 66 | (m) | 4p blue (type II) | 400.00 | 82.50 |
| 67 | (m) | 6p dull violet | 550.00 | 150.00 |
| 68 | (n) | 1p rose | 145.00 | 95.00 |
| 69 | (n) | 4p blue (type II) | 750.00 | 125.00 |
| 70 | (n) | 6p dull violet | 1,000. | 190.00 |
| a. | | Double overprint | | 1,750. |
| 71 | (o) | 1p rose | 125.00 | 75.00 |
| 72 | (o) | 4p blue (type II) | 625.00 | 105.00 |
| 73 | (o) | 6p dull violet | 900.00 | 175.00 |
| 74 | (p) | 1p rose | 200.00 | 135.00 |
| 75 | (p) | 4p blue (type II) | 1,000. | 190.00 |
| 76 | (p) | 6p dull violet | 1,375. | 300.00 |
| 77 | (q) | 1p rose | 125.00 | 85.00 |
| 78 | (q) | 4p blue (type II) | 625.00 | 105.00 |

| | | | | |
|---|---|---|---|---|
| 79 | (q) | 6p dull violet | 900.00 | 175.00 |
| 80 | (r) | 1p rose | 625.00 | 425.00 |
| 81 | (r) | 4p blue (type II) | 3,000. | 625.00 |
| 82 | (r) | 6p dull violet | 3,750. | 950.00 |

There are two minor varieties of type i and one of type p.

**1878**    **Overprinted in Red**

| | | | | |
|---|---|---|---|---|
| 83 | (s) | ½p gray black | 28.00 | 30.00 |
| a. | | Double overprint | 85.00 | 100.00 |
| b. | | Inverted overprint | 30.00 | 30.00 |
| c. | | Double overprint, inverted | 165.00 | 190.00 |
| 84 | (s) | 4p blue (type II) | 625.00 | 165.00 |
| a. | | Inverted overprint | 700.00 | 135.00 |
| 85 | (t) | ½p gray black | 30.00 | 30.00 |
| a. | | Double overprint | 135.00 | 135.00 |
| b. | | Inverted overprint | 30.00 | 30.00 |
| 86 | (t) | 4p blue (type II) | | 150.00 |
| a. | | Inverted overprint | 625.00 | 150.00 |

**Black Overprint**

| | | | | |
|---|---|---|---|---|
| 87 | (s) | ½p gray black | 375.00 | 190.00 |
| a. | | Inverted overprint | 400.00 | 400.00 |
| b. | | With 2nd ovpt. (s) in red, invtd | | 625.00 |
| c. | | With 2nd ovpt. (t) in red, invtd | | 350.00 |
| 88 | (s) | 1p rose | 30.00 | 20.00 |
| a. | | Double overprint | 375.00 | 90.00 |
| b. | | Inverted overprint | 30.00 | 30.00 |
| c. | | Double overprint, both inverted | 375.00 | 115.00 |
| d. | | With second overprint (s) in red, both inverted | 70.00 | 70.00 |
| 89 | (s) | 4p blue (type I) | | 300.00 |
| 90 | (s) | 4p blue (type II) | 265.00 | 50.00 |
| a. | | Double overprint | | 400.00 |
| b. | | Inverted overprint | 425.00 | 150.00 |
| c. | | Double overprint, both inverted | | 475.00 |
| 91 | (s) | 6p dull violet | 290.00 | 50.00 |
| 92 | (t) | ½p gray black | 85.00 | 85.00 |
| a. | | Inverted overprint | 180.00 | 125.00 |
| b. | | With 2nd ovpt. inverted | | 350.00 |
| 93 | (t) | 1p rose | 30.00 | 22.50 |
| a. | | Double overprint | | 160.00 |
| b. | | Inverted overprint | 145.00 | 50.00 |
| c. | | Double overprint, both inverted | | 190.00 |
| d. | | With 2nd ovpt. (t) in red, both invtd | 150.00 | 150.00 |
| 94 | (t) | 4p blue (type I) | | 300.00 |
| 95 | (t) | 4p blue (type II) | 300.00 | 27.50 |
| a. | | Double overprint | | 375.00 |
| b. | | Inverted overprint | 450.00 | 50.00 |
| c. | | Double overprint, both inverted | | 200.00 |
| 96 | (t) | 6p dull violet | | 50.00 |

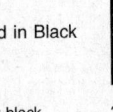

Overprinted in Black

| | | | |
|---|---|---|---|
| 97 | ½p gray black | 35.00 | 12.00 |
| a. | Double overprint | 550.00 | 350.00 |
| 98 | 1p rose | 37.50 | 9.00 |
| a. | Double overprint | | 175.00 |
| b. | Triple overprint | | 325.00 |
| c. | Inverted overprint | | 115.00 |
| 99 | 4p blue (type II) | 70.00 | 9.00 |
| a. | Double overprint | | 150.00 |
| 100 | 6p brt violet | 300.00 | 15.00 |
| a. | Double overprint | 1,150. | 210.00 |
| b. | Inverted overprint | | 150.00 |
| 101 | 1sh green | 275.00 | 10.00 |
| a. | Double overprint | 650.00 | 140.00 |
| 102 | 5sh orange | 850.00 | 27.50 |
| a. | Double overprint | 1,050. | 140.00 |
| b. | Inverted overprint | | 140.00 |

These stamps were declared obsolete in 1880 and the remainders were used in Cape of Good Hope offices as ordinary stamps. Prices for used stamps are for examples with such cancels.

# GUADELOUPE

'gwä-dəl-,üp

LOCATION — In the West Indies lying between Montserrat and Dominica
GOVT. — French colony
AREA — 688 sq. mi.
POP. — 271,262 (1946)
CAPITAL — Basse-Terre

Guadeloupe consists of two large islands, Guadeloupe proper and Grande-Terre, together with five smaller dependencies. Guadeloupe became an integral part of the Republic, acquiring the same status as the departments in metropolitan France, under a law effective Jan. 1, 1947.

100 Centimes = 1 Franc

Catalogue values for unused stamps in this country are for Never Hinged items, beginning with Scott 168 in the regular postage section, Scott B12 in the semipostal section, Scott C1 in the airpost section, and Scott J38 in the postage due section.

See France Nos. 850, 909, 1280, 1913 for French stamps inscribed "Guadeloupe."

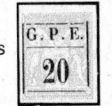

Stamps of French Colonies Surcharged

**1884**    **Unwmk.**    **Imperf.**

| | | | | |
|---|---|---|---|---|
| 1 | A8 | 20c on 30c brn, *bis* | 70.00 | 55.00 |
| a. | | Large "2" | 325.00 | 260.00 |
| 2 | A8 | 25c on 35c blk, *org* | 57.50 | 55.00 |
| a. | | Large "2" | 325.00 | 260.00 |
| b. | | Large "5" | 160.00 | 125.00 |

The 5c on 4c (French Colonies No. 40) was not regularly issued. Three examples exist. Value $42,500.

The 5c on 4c also exists as an essay, surcharge similar to the issued values. Value $1,000.

c    d

**1889**    **Perf. 14x13½**

**Surcharged Type c**

| | | | | |
|---|---|---|---|---|
| 3 | A9 | 3c on 20c red, *grn* | 5.25 | 5.25 |
| 4 | A9 | 15c on 20c red, *grn* | 32.50 | 27.50 |
| 5 | A9 | 25c on 20c red, *grn* | 32.50 | 27.50 |
| | | Nos. 3-5 (3) | 70.25 | 60.25 |

**Surcharged Type d**

| | | | | |
|---|---|---|---|---|
| 6 | A9 | 5c on 1c blk, *lil bl* | 14.50 | 13.50 |
| a. | | Inverted surcharge | | 1,400. |
| 7 | A9 | 10c on 40c red, *straw* | 40.00 | 35.00 |
| a. | | Double surcharge | 475.00 | 475.00 |
| 8 | A9 | 15c on 20c red, *grn* | 32.50 | 30.00 |
| a. | | Double surcharge | 475.00 | 475.00 |
| 9 | A9 | 25c on 30c brn, *bis* | 52.50 | 40.00 |
| a. | | Double surcharge | 475.00 | 475.00 |
| | | Nos. 6-9 (4) | 139.50 | 118.50 |

The word "centimes" in surcharges "b" and "c" varies from 10 to 12½mm.
Issue dates: No. 6, June 25; others, Mar. 22.

Stamps of French Colonies Surcharged

**1891**

| | | | | |
|---|---|---|---|---|
| 10 | A9 | 5c on 10c blk, *lav* | 15.00 | 12.00 |
| 11 | A9 | 5c on 1fr brnz grn, *straw* | 16.00 | 11.00 |

Stamps of French Colonies Overprinted in Black

**1891**    **Imperf.**

| | | | | |
|---|---|---|---|---|
| 12 | A7 | 30c brn, *yelsh* | 350.00 | 375.00 |
| a. | | Double overprint | 725.00 | 725.00 |
| 13 | A7 | 80c car, *pnksh* | 1,100. | 1,300. |

**Perf. 14x13½**

| | | | | |
|---|---|---|---|---|
| 14 | A9 | 1c blk, *lil bl* | 1.75 | 1.60 |
| a. | | Double overprint | 40.00 | 40.00 |
| b. | | Inverted overprint | 150.00 | 150.00 |
| 15 | A9 | 2c brn, *buff* | 2.60 | 2.00 |
| a. | | Double overprint | 45.00 | 40.00 |

| | | | | |
|---|---|---|---|---|
| 16 | A9 | 4c claret, *lav* | 6.00 | 5.25 |
| 17 | A9 | 5c grn, *grnsh* | 8.75 | 7.25 |
| a. | | Double overprint | 45.00 | 40.00 |
| b. | | Inverted overprint | 160.00 | 160.00 |
| 18 | A9 | 10c blk, *lavender* | 17.00 | 13.50 |
| 19 | A9 | 15c blue | 52.50 | 6.00 |
| a. | | Double overprint | | 110.00 |
| 20 | A9 | 20c red, *grn* | 45.00 | 30.00 |
| a. | | Double overprint | 240.00 | 240.00 |
| 21 | A9 | 25c blk, *rose* | 47.50 | 5.25 |
| a. | | Double overprint | 240.00 | 240.00 |
| b. | | Inverted overprint | 225.00 | 225.00 |
| 22 | A9 | 30c brn, *bister* | 45.00 | 30.00 |
| a. | | Double overprint | 240.00 | 240.00 |
| 23 | A9 | 35c dp vio, *org* | 87.50 | 72.50 |
| a. | | Double overprint | 675.00 | 675.00 |
| 24 | A9 | 40c red, *straw* | 65.00 | 52.50 |
| a. | | Double overprint | 675.00 | 675.00 |
| 25 | A9 | 75c car, *rose* | 130.00 | 125.00 |
| 26 | A9 | 1fr brnz grn, *straw* | 92.50 | 72.50 |
| | | *Nos. 14-26 (13)* | 601.10 | 423.35 |

Navigation and Commerce — A7

### Perf. 14x13½

**1892-1901 Typo. Unwmk.**
**Colony Name in Blue or Carmine**

| | | | | |
|---|---|---|---|---|
| 27 | A7 | 1c blk, *lil bl* | 1.40 | 1.40 |
| 28 | A7 | 2c brn, *buff* | 1.50 | 1.40 |
| 29 | A7 | 4c claret, *lav* | 1.75 | 1.50 |
| 30 | A7 | 5c grn, *grnsh* | 3.50 | 1.50 |
| 31 | A7 | 5c yel grn ('01) | 6.00 | 1.60 |
| 32 | A7 | 10c blk, *lavender* | 10.00 | 3.25 |
| 33 | A7 | 10c red ('00) | 8.75 | 2.40 |
| a. | | Imperf. | 120.00 | |
| b. | | As "a," country name omitted | | 150.00 |
| 34 | A7 | 15c blue, quadrille paper | 18.00 | 1.75 |
| 35 | A7 | 15c gray, *lt gray* ('00) | 13.00 | 1.60 |
| 36 | A7 | 20c red, *grn* | 11.00 | 6.50 |
| 37 | A7 | 25c blk, *rose* | 11.00 | 3.00 |
| 38 | A7 | 25c blue ('00) | 100.00 | 100.00 |
| 39 | A7 | 30c brn, *bister* | 24.00 | 15.00 |
| 40 | A7 | 40c red, *straw* | 24.00 | 15.00 |
| 41 | A7 | 50c car, *rose* | 30.00 | 16.00 |
| 42 | A7 | 50c brn, *az* ('00) | 45.00 | 42.50 |
| 43 | A7 | 75c dp vio, *org* | 32.50 | 22.50 |
| 44 | A7 | 1fr brnz grn, *straw* | 32.50 | 30.00 |
| | | *Nos. 27-44 (18)* | 373.90 | 266.90 |

Perf. 13½x14 stamps are counterfeits.
For surcharges see Nos. 45-53, 83-85.

### Nos. 39-41, 43-44 Surcharged in Black

**1903**

| | | | | |
|---|---|---|---|---|
| 45 | A7 (f) | 5c on 30c | 4.00 | 4.00 |
| a. | | "C" instead of "G" | 32.50 | 32.50 |
| b. | | Inverted surcharge | 45.00 | 45.00 |
| c. | | Double surcharge | 140.00 | 140.00 |
| d. | | Double surch., inverted | 160.00 | |
| 46 | A7 (g) | 10c on 40c | 9.50 | 9.50 |
| a. | | "C" instead of "G" | 40.00 | 40.00 |
| b. | | "1" inverted | 60.00 | 60.00 |
| c. | | Inverted surcharge | 55.00 | 55.00 |
| d. | | Double surcharge | 200.00 | 200.00 |
| 47 | A7 (f) | 15c on 50c | 13.00 | 13.00 |
| a. | | "C" instead of "G" | 40.00 | 40.00 |
| b. | | Inverted surcharge | 110.00 | 110.00 |
| c. | | "15" inverted | 375.00 | 375.00 |
| e. | | Double surcharge | 200.00 | 200.00 |
| 48 | A7 (g) | 40c on 1fr | 13.00 | 13.00 |
| a. | | "C" instead of "G" | 52.50 | 52.50 |
| b. | | "4" inverted | 120.00 | 120.00 |
| c. | | Inverted surcharge | 110.00 | 110.00 |
| d. | | Double surcharge | 240.00 | 240.00 |
| e. | | Triple surcharge | 500.00 | 500.00 |
| 49 | A7 (h) | 1fr on 75c | 42.50 | 42.50 |
| a. | | "C" instead of "G" | 160.00 | 160.00 |
| b. | | "1" inverted | 160.00 | 160.00 |
| c. | | Value above "G & D" | 300.00 | 300.00 |
| d. | | Inverted surcharge | 125.00 | 125.00 |
| | | *Nos. 45-49 (5)* | 82.00 | 82.00 |

Letters and figures from several fonts were used for these surcharges, resulting in numerous minor varieties.

### Nos. 48-49 With Additional Overprint "1903" in a Frame

---

**1904, Mar. Red Overprint**

| | | | | |
|---|---|---|---|---|
| 50 | A7 (g) | 40c on 1fr | 75.00 | 85.00 |
| b. | | Inverted surcharge | 600.00 | 650.00 |
| c. | | Double surcharge | 1,250. | 1,250. |
| 51 | A7 (h) | 1fr on 75c | 92.50 | 100.00 |
| a. | | Double surcharge | 950.00 | 950.00 |

**Overprinted in Blue**

| | | | | |
|---|---|---|---|---|
| 52 | A7 (g) | 40c on 1fr | 60.00 | 65.00 |
| 53 | A7 (h) | 1fr on 75c | 87.50 | 95.00 |
| | | *Nos. 50-53 (4)* | 315.00 | 345.00 |

The date "1903" may be found in 19 different positions and type faces within the frame. These stamps may also be found with the minor varieties of Nos. 48-49.

The 40c exists with black overprint. Value, $500 unused or used.

Harbor at Basse-Terre — A8

View of La Soufrière — A9

Pointe-à-Pitre, Grand-Terre — A10

**1905-27 Typo. Perf. 14x13½**

| | | | | |
|---|---|---|---|---|
| 54 | A8 | 1c blk, *bluish* | .30 | .30 |
| 55 | A8 | 2c vio brn, *straw* | .30 | .30 |
| 56 | A8 | 4c bis brn, *az* | .30 | .30 |
| 57 | A8 | 5c green | 2.40 | .65 |
| 58 | A8 | 5c dp blue ('22) | .25 | .25 |
| 59 | A8 | 10c rose | 2.25 | .65 |
| 60 | A8 | 10c green ('22) | 1.40 | 1.25 |
| 61 | A8 | 10c red, *bluish* ('25) | .25 | .25 |
| 62 | A8 | 15c violet | .55 | .50 |
| 63 | A9 | 20c red, *grn* | .55 | .40 |
| 64 | A9 | 20c bl grn ('25) | .65 | .65 |
| 65 | A9 | 25c blue | .95 | .55 |
| 66 | A9 | 25c ol grn ('22) | .65 | .65 |
| 67 | A9 | 30c black | 5.00 | 3.25 |
| 68 | A9 | 30c rose ('22) | .70 | .70 |
| 69 | A9 | 30c brn ol, *lav* ('25) | .55 | .55 |
| 70 | A9 | 35c blk, *yel* ('06) | .80 | .80 |
| 71 | A9 | 40c red, *straw* | .80 | .80 |
| 72 | A9 | 45c ol gray, *lil* ('07) | 1.40 | .85 |
| 73 | A9 | 45c rose ('25) | .80 | .80 |
| 74 | A9 | 50c grn, *straw* | 5.50 | 4.00 |
| 75 | A9 | 50c dp bl ('22) | 1.25 | 1.10 |
| 76 | A9 | 50c violet ('25) | .70 | .70 |
| 77 | A9 | 65c blue ('27) | .70 | .70 |
| 78 | A9 | 75c car, *bl* | .90 | .80 |
| 79 | A10 | 1fr blk, *green* | 1.75 | 1.50 |
| 80 | A10 | 1fr lt bl ('25) | 1.00 | .95 |
| 81 | A10 | 2fr car, *grnsh* | 2.25 | 2.00 |
| 82 | A10 | 5fr dp bl, *org* | 7.50 | 7.50 |
| | | *Nos. 54-82 (29)* | 42.40 | 33.65 |

Nos. 57, 59 and 82 exist imperf. Value, Nos. 57 and 59 each $60, No. 82 $140.
For surcharges see #86-95, 167, B1-B2.

### Nos. 29, 39 and 40 Surcharged in Carmine or Black

**1912, Nov.**

| | | | | |
|---|---|---|---|---|
| 83 | A7 | 5c on 4c claret, *lav* (C) | 1.50 | 1.50 |
| 84 | A7 | 5c on 30c brn, *bis* (C) | 2.00 | 2.00 |
| 85 | A7 | 10c on 40c red, *straw* | 2.25 | 2.25 |
| | | *Nos. 83-85 (3)* | 5.75 | 5.75 |

Two spacings between the surcharaged numerals are found on Nos. 83 to 85. For detailed listings, see the *Scott Classic Specialized Catalogue of Stamps and Covers.*

### Stamps & Types of 1905-27 Surcharged

No. 89

---

No. 94

**1924-27**

| | | | | |
|---|---|---|---|---|
| 86 | A10 | 25c on 5fr dp bl, *org* | .75 | .70 |
| 87 | A10 | 65c on 1fr gray grn | 1.40 | 1.25 |
| 88 | A10 | 85c on 1fr gray grn | 1.50 | 1.40 |
| 89 | A9 | 90c on 75c dl red | 1.40 | 1.25 |
| 90 | A10 | 1.05fr on 2fr ver (Bl) | 1.00 | .85 |
| 91 | A10 | 1.25fr on 1fr lt bl (R) | .65 | .65 |
| 92 | A10 | 1.50fr on 1fr dk bl | .65 | .65 |
| 93 | A10 | 3fr on 5fr org brn | 1.50 | 1.50 |
| 94 | A10 | 10fr on 5fr vio rose, *org* | 11.00 | 11.00 |
| 95 | A10 | 20fr on 5fr rose lil, *pnksh* | 14.00 | 13.00 |
| | | *Nos. 86-95 (10)* | 34.45 | 32.85 |

Years issued: Nos. 87-88, 1925. Nos. 90-91, 1926. Nos. 89, 92-95, 1927.

Sugar Mill — A11

Saints Roadstead — A12

Harbor Scene — A13

### Perf. 14x13½

**1928-40 Unwmk. Typo.**

| | | | | |
|---|---|---|---|---|
| 96 | A11 | 1c yel & vio | .25 | .25 |
| 97 | A11 | 2c blk & lt red | .25 | .25 |
| 98 | A11 | 3c yel & red vio ('40) | .30 | .30 |
| 99 | A11 | 4c yel grn & org brn | .25 | .25 |
| 100 | A11 | 5c ver & grn | .25 | .25 |
| 101 | A11 | 10c bis brn & dp bl | .25 | .25 |
| 102 | A11 | 15c brn red & blk | .30 | .30 |
| 103 | A11 | 20c lil & ol brn | .50 | .50 |
| 104 | A12 | 25c grnsh bl & olvn | .55 | .55 |
| 105 | A12 | 30c gray grn & yel grn | .40 | .40 |
| 106 | A12 | 35c bl grn ('38) | .40 | .40 |
| 107 | A12 | 40c yel & vio | .40 | .40 |
| 108 | A12 | 45c vio brn & slate | .95 | .80 |
| 109 | A12 | 45c bl grn & dl grn ('40) | 1.10 | 1.00 |
| 110 | A12 | 50c bl grn & org | .30 | .30 |
| 111 | A12 | 55c ultra & car ('38) | 1.40 | 1.25 |
| 112 | A12 | 60c ultra & car ('40) | .65 | .65 |
| 113 | A12 | 65c gray blk & ver | .55 | .55 |
| 114 | A12 | 70c gray blk & ver ('40) | .70 | .70 |
| 115 | A12 | 75c dl red & bl grn | .70 | .70 |
| 116 | A12 | 80c car & brn ('38) | .85 | .85 |
| 117 | A12 | 90c dl red & dl rose | 2.00 | 1.75 |
| 118 | A12 | 90c rose red & bl ('39) | 1.25 | 1.10 |
| 119 | A13 | 1fr lt rose & lt bl | 5.25 | 3.75 |
| 120 | A13 | 1fr rose red & org ('38) | 1.75 | 1.50 |
| 121 | A13 | 1fr bl gray & blk brn ('40) | .70 | .70 |
| 122 | A13 | 1.05fr lt bl & rose | 1.25 | 1.10 |
| 123 | A13 | 1.10fr lt red & grn | 4.00 | 2.75 |
| 124 | A13 | 1.25fr bl gray & blk brn ('33) | .65 | .65 |
| 125 | A13 | 1.25fr brt rose & red org ('39) | .95 | .95 |
| 126 | A13 | 1.40fr lt bl & lil rose ('40) | .70 | .70 |
| 127 | A13 | 1.50fr dl bl & bl | .40 | .40 |
| 128 | A13 | 1.60fr lil rose & yel brn ('40) | .70 | .70 |
| 129 | A13 | 1.75fr lil rose & yel brn ('33) | 5.75 | 3.25 |
| 130 | A13 | 1.75fr vio bl ('38) | 6.00 | 4.00 |
| 131 | A13 | 2fr bl grn & dk brn | .40 | .40 |
| 132 | A13 | 2.25fr vio bl ('39) | 1.25 | 1.25 |
| 133 | A13 | 2.50fr pale org & grn ('40) | 1.25 | 1.25 |
| 134 | A13 | 3fr org brn & sl | .65 | .65 |
| 135 | A13 | 5fr dl bl & org | 1.25 | 1.00 |
| 136 | A13 | 10fr vio & ol brn | 1.25 | 1.00 |
| 137 | A13 | 20fr green & mag | 1.50 | 1.40 |
| | | *Nos. 96-137 (42)* | 50.20 | 40.95 |

Nos. 96-103, 110, 119, 123, 134, 137 exist imperf. Values each $30-$60.
For surcharges see Nos. 161-166.
For 10c, type A11, without "RF," see No. 163A.

---

Common Design Types pictured following the introduction.

**Colonial Exposition Issue**
Common Design Types

**1931, Apr. 13 Engr. Perf. 12½**
**Name of Country in Black**

| | | | | |
|---|---|---|---|---|
| 138 | CD70 | 40c deep green | 4.75 | 4.75 |
| 139 | CD71 | 50c violet | 4.75 | 4.75 |
| 140 | CD72 | 90c red orange | 4.75 | 4.75 |
| 141 | CD73 | 1.50fr dull blue | 4.75 | 4.75 |
| | | *Nos. 138-141 (4)* | 19.00 | 19.00 |

Cardinal Richelieu Establishing French Antilles Co., 1635
A14

Victor Hugues and his Corsairs
A15

**1935 Perf. 13**

| | | | | |
|---|---|---|---|---|
| 142 | A14 | 40c gray brown | 10.00 | 10.00 |
| 143 | A14 | 50c dull red | 10.00 | 10.00 |
| 144 | A14 | 1.50fr dull blue | 10.00 | 10.00 |
| 145 | A15 | 1.75fr lilac rose | 10.00 | 10.00 |
| 146 | A15 | 5fr dark brown | 10.00 | 10.00 |
| 147 | A15 | 10fr blue green | 10.00 | 10.00 |
| | | *Nos. 142-147 (6)* | 60.00 | 60.00 |

Tercentenary of the establishment of the French colonies in the West Indies.

**Paris International Exposition Issue**
Common Design Types

**1937 Perf. 13**

| | | | | |
|---|---|---|---|---|
| 148 | CD74 | 20c deep violet | 1.90 | 1.90 |
| 149 | CD75 | 30c dark green | 1.75 | 1.75 |
| 150 | CD76 | 40c car rose | 1.50 | 1.50 |
| 151 | CD77 | 50c dk brn & blk | 1.50 | 1.50 |
| 152 | CD78 | 90c red | 1.50 | 1.50 |
| 153 | CD79 | 1.50fr ultra | 1.90 | 1.90 |
| | | *Nos. 148-153 (6)* | 10.05 | 10.05 |

**Colonial Arts Exhibition Issue**
Souvenir Sheet
Common Design Type

**1937 Imperf.**

| | | | | |
|---|---|---|---|---|
| 154 | CD75 | 3fr dark blue | 9.50 | 11.00 |

**New York World's Fair Issue**
Common Design Type

**1939 Engr. Perf. 12½x12**

| | | | | |
|---|---|---|---|---|
| 155 | CD82 | 1.25fr car lake | 1.25 | 1.25 |
| 156 | CD82 | 2.25fr ultra | 1.25 | 1.25 |

For surcharges see Nos. 159-160.

La Soufrière View and Marshal Pétain — A16

**1941 Engr. Perf. 12½x12**

| | | | | |
|---|---|---|---|---|
| 157 | A16 | 1fr lilac | | .80 |
| 158 | A16 | 2.50fr blue | | .80 |

Nos. 157-158 were issued by the Vichy government in France, but were not placed on sale in Guadeloupe.
For surcharges, see Nos. B11A-B11B.

### Nos. 155, 156, 113, 117 and 118 Surcharged in Black

**1943 Perf. 14x13½, 12½x12**

| | | | | |
|---|---|---|---|---|
| 159 | CD82 | 40c on 1.25fr | .80 | .80 |
| 160 | CD82 | 40c on 2.25fr | 1.60 | 1.60 |
| 161 | A12 | 50c on 65c | 1.00 | 1.00 |
| 162 | A12 | 1fr on 90c (#117) | 1.40 | 1.40 |
| 163 | A12 | 1fr on 90c (#118) | 1.25 | 1.25 |
| | | *Nos. 159-163 (5)* | 6.05 | 6.05 |

## Type of 1928 Without "RF"

**1943**      *Perf. 14x13½*
163A A11 10c bis brn & dp blue   .65

No. 163A was issued by the Vichy government in France, and was not placed on sale in Guadeloupe.

No. 106 Surcharged

No. 104 Surcharged

No. 113 Surcharged

No. 90 Surcharged

**1944**      *Perf. 14x13½*
| | | | | |
|---|---|---|---|---|
| 164 | A12 | 40c on 35c | 1.10 | 1.10 |
| 165 | A12 | 50c on 25c | .30 | .30 |
| 166 | A12 | 1fr on 65c | 1.25 | 1.25 |
| a. | | Double surcharge | 200.00 | 150.00 |
| 167 | A10 | 4fr on 1.05fr on 2fr | 1.75 | 1.75 |
| | | *Nos. 164-167 (4)* | 4.40 | 4.40 |

**Catalogue values for unused stamps in this section, from this point to the end of the section, are for Never Hinged items.**

Dolphins — A17

**1945**   Unwmk.   Photo.   *Perf. 11½*
| | | | | |
|---|---|---|---|---|
| 168 | A17 | 10c chlky bl & red org | .30 | .25 |
| 169 | A17 | 30c lt yel grn & red | .30 | .25 |
| 170 | A17 | 40c lt bl & car | .85 | .65 |
| 171 | A17 | 50c red org & yel grn | .40 | .30 |
| 172 | A17 | 60c ol bis & lt bl | .40 | .30 |
| 173 | A17 | 70c lt gray & yel grn | .85 | .65 |
| 174 | A17 | 80c lt bl grn & yel | .85 | .65 |
| 175 | A17 | 1fr brn vio & grn | .40 | .30 |
| 176 | A17 | 1.20fr brt red vio & yel grn | .40 | .30 |
| 177 | A17 | 1.50fr dl brn & car | .90 | .55 |
| 178 | A17 | 2fr cer & bl | .90 | .55 |
| 179 | A17 | 2.40fr sal & yel grn | 1.50 | .95 |
| 180 | A17 | 3fr gray brn & bl vio | .85 | .55 |
| 181 | A17 | 4fr ultra & buff | .70 | .30 |
| 182 | A17 | 4.50fr brn org & grn | .90 | .55 |
| 183 | A17 | 5fr dk vio & grn | 1.10 | .65 |
| 184 | A17 | 10fr gray grn & red vio | 1.10 | .65 |
| 185 | A17 | 15fr sl gray & org | 1.50 | .85 |
| 186 | A17 | 20fr pale gray & dl org | 2.50 | 1.00 |
| | | *Nos. 168-186 (19)* | 16.70 | 10.25 |

### Eboue Issue
Common Design Type

**1945**   Engr.   *Perf. 13*
| | | | | |
|---|---|---|---|---|
| 187 | CD91 | 2fr black | .65 | .50 |
| 188 | CD91 | 25fr Prussian green | 1.40 | 1.10 |

Basse-Terre Harbor and Woman — A18

Cutting Sugar Cane — A19

---

Pineapple Bearer A20

Guadeloupe Woman A21

Gathering Coffee A22

Guadeloupe Woman A23

**1947**   Unwmk.   Engr.   *Perf. 13*
| | | | | |
|---|---|---|---|---|
| 189 | A18 | 10c red brown | .30 | .25 |
| 190 | A18 | 30c sepia | .30 | .25 |
| 191 | A18 | 50c blue grn | .40 | .30 |
| 192 | A19 | 60c black brn | .75 | .50 |
| 193 | A19 | 1fr dp carmine | 1.00 | .65 |
| 194 | A19 | 1.50fr dk gray bl | 1.50 | .85 |
| 195 | A20 | 2fr blue grn | 1.50 | .85 |
| 196 | A20 | 2.50fr dp car | 1.40 | .95 |
| 197 | A20 | 3fr deep blue | 1.50 | .95 |
| 198 | A21 | 4fr violet | 1.40 | .95 |
| 199 | A21 | 5fr blue grn | 1.40 | .95 |
| 200 | A21 | 6fr red | 1.40 | .95 |
| 201 | A22 | 10fr deep blue | 1.50 | 1.00 |
| 202 | A22 | 15fr dk vio brn | 2.50 | 1.25 |
| 203 | A22 | 20fr rose red | 2.75 | 1.50 |
| 204 | A23 | 25fr blue green | 7.00 | 3.00 |
| 205 | A23 | 40fr red | 8.00 | 4.00 |
| | | *Nos. 189-205 (17)* | 34.60 | 19.15 |

### SEMI-POSTAL STAMPS

Nos. 59 and 62 Surcharged in Red

**1915-17**   Unwmk.   *Perf. 14 x 13½*
| | | | | |
|---|---|---|---|---|
| B1 | A8 | 10c + 5c rose | 5.25 | 3.50 |
| B2 | A8 | 15c + 5c violet | 5.25 | 3.50 |
| a. | | Double surcharge | 225.00 | 225.00 |
| b. | | Triple surcharge | 240.00 | 240.00 |
| c. | | Inverted surcharge | 240.00 | 240.00 |
| d. | | In pair with unovptd. stamp | 275.00 | |

### Curie Issue
Common Design Type

**1938, Oct. 24**     *Perf. 13*
B3 CD80 1.75fr + 50c brt ultra   11.00   10.50

### French Revolution Issue
Common Design Type
Name and Value Typo. in Black

**1939, July 5**   Photo.   *Perf. 13*
| | | | | |
|---|---|---|---|---|
| B4 | CD83 | 45c + 25c green | 10.00 | 10.00 |
| B5 | CD83 | 70c + 30c brown | 10.00 | 10.00 |
| B6 | CD83 | 90c + 35c red org | 10.00 | 10.00 |
| B7 | CD83 | 1.25fr + 1fr rose pink | 10.00 | 10.00 |
| B8 | CD83 | 2.25fr + 2fr blue | 50.00 | 50.00 |
| | | *Nos. B4-B8 (5)* | | |

### Common Design Type and

Colonial Artillery SP1

Colonial Infantry SP2

**1941**   Photo.   *Perf. 13½*
| | | | |
|---|---|---|---|
| B9 | SP1 | 1fr + 1fr red | 1.00 |
| B10 | CD86 | 1.50fr + 3fr maroon | 1.00 |
| B11 | SP2 | 2.50fr + 1fr blue | 1.50 |
| | | *Nos. B9-B11 (3)* | 3.50 |

Nos. B9-B11 were issued by the Vichy government in France, but were not placed on sale in Guadeloupe.

---

Nos. 157-158 Surcharged in Black or Red

**1944**   Engr.   *Perf. 12½x12*
| | | | |
|---|---|---|---|
| B11A | | 50c + 1.50fr on 2.50fr blue (R) | .80 |
| B11B | | 2 + 2.50fr on 1fr lilac | .80 |

Colonial Development Fund.
Nos. B11A-B11B were issued by the Vichy government in France, but were not placed on sale in Guadeloupe.

**Catalogue values for unused stamps in this section, from this point to the end of the section, are for Never Hinged items.**

### Red Cross Issue
Common Design Type

**1944**     *Perf. 14½x14*
B12 CD90 5fr + 20fr ultra   1.40   1.00

The surtax was for the French Red Cross and national relief.

---

### AIR POST STAMPS

**Catalogue values for unused stamps in this section are for Never Hinged items.**

Common Design Type

**1945**   Unwmk.   Photo.   *Perf. 14½x14*
| | | | | |
|---|---|---|---|---|
| C1 | CD87 | 50fr green | 1.50 | 1.00 |
| C2 | CD87 | 100fr deep plum | 2.25 | 1.50 |

### Victory Issue
Common Design Type

**1946, May 8**   Engr.   *Perf. 12½*
C3 CD92 8fr redsh brn   1.25   1.00

### Chad to Rhine Issue
Common Design Types

**1946, June 6**
| | | | | |
|---|---|---|---|---|
| C4 | CD93 | 5fr dk slate grn | 2.00 | 1.60 |
| C5 | CD94 | 10fr deep blue | 2.00 | 1.60 |
| C6 | CD95 | 15fr brt violet | 2.00 | 1.60 |
| C7 | CD96 | 20fr brown car | 2.00 | 1.60 |
| C8 | CD97 | 25fr black | 2.00 | 1.60 |
| C9 | CD98 | 50fr red brown | 2.00 | 1.60 |
| | | *Nos. C4-C9 (6)* | 12.00 | 9.60 |

Gathering Bananas AP1

Seaplane at Roadstead AP2

Pointe-a-Pitre Harbor and Guadeloupe Woman — AP3

**1947**   Unwmk.    *Perf. 13*
| | | | | |
|---|---|---|---|---|
| C10 | AP1 | 50fr dk brown violet | 6.00 | 2.75 |
| C11 | AP2 | 100fr deep blue | 8.75 | 5.25 |
| C12 | AP3 | 200fr red | 11.50 | 5.50 |
| | | *Nos. C10-C12 (3)* | 26.25 | 13.50 |

---

### AIR POST SEMI-POSTAL STAMPS

Mother & Nurse with Children SPAP1

**1942, June 22**   Engr.   *Perf. 13*
| | | | |
|---|---|---|---|
| CB1 | SPAP1 | 1.50fr + 3.50fr green | 1.00 |
| CB2 | SPAP1 | 2fr + 6fr brn & red | 1.00 |

Native children's welfare fund.
Nos. CB1-CB2 were issued by the Vichy government in France, but were not on sale in Guadeloupe.

### Colonial Education Fund
Common Design Type

**1942, June 22**
CB3 CD86a 1.20fr + 1.80fr blue & red   1.10

No. CB3 was issued by the Vichy government in France, but was not placed on sale in Guadeloupe.

---

### POSTAGE DUE STAMPS

D1      D2      D3

**1876**   Unwmk.   Typeset   *Imperf.*
| | | | | |
|---|---|---|---|---|
| J1 | D1 | 25c black | 1,350. | 925. |
| J2 | D2 | 40c black, *blue* | | 37,500. |
| J3 | D3 | 40c black | 1,500. | 1,200. |

Twenty varieties of each.
*Nos. J1 and J3 have been reprinted on thinner and whiter paper than the originals.*

D4

**1879**
| | | | | |
|---|---|---|---|---|
| J4 | D4 | 15c black, *blue* | 55.00 | 52.50 |
| a. | | Period after "c" omitted | 175.00 | 175.00 |
| J5 | D4 | 30c black | 110.00 | 87.50 |
| a. | | Period after "c" omitted | 240.00 | 225.00 |

Twenty varieties of each.

D5

**1884**
| | | | | |
|---|---|---|---|---|
| J6 | D5 | 5c black | 35.00 | 35.00 |
| a. | | Double impression | 100.00 | 100.00 |
| J7 | D5 | 10c black, *blue* | 75.00 | 65.00 |
| a. | | Double impression | 150.00 | 150.00 |
| J8 | D5 | 15c black, *violet* | 110.00 | 87.50 |
| a. | | Double impression | 225.00 | 225.00 |
| J9 | D5 | 20c black, *rose* | 160.00 | 100.00 |
| a. | | Italic "2" in "20" | 1,000. | 950.00 |
| J10 | D5 | 30c black, *yellow* | 160.00 | 160.00 |
| a. | | Double impression | 450.00 | 450.00 |
| J11 | D5 | 35c black, *gray* | 60.00 | 52.50 |
| a. | | Double impression | 225.00 | 225.00 |
| J12 | D5 | 50c black, *green* | 32.50 | 27.50 |
| a. | | Double impression | 200.00 | 200.00 |
| | | *Nos. J6-J12 (7)* | 632.50 | 527.50 |

There are ten varieties of the 35c, and fifteen of each of the other values, also numerous wrong font and missing letters.

Postage Due Stamps of French Colonies Surcharged in Black

Two surcharge types: I, wide font, "3" with rounded top; II, narrow font, "3" with flat top.

**1903**       **Type I**
| | | | | |
|---|---|---|---|---|
| J13 | D1 | 30c on 60c brn, cr | 325.00 | 325.00 |
| a. | | Inverted surcharge | 1,100. | 1,100. |
| b. | | Bee corner ornament turned | 1,150. | 1,150. |

## Guadeloupe (continued)

| | | | |
|---|---|---|---|
| c. | As "b," inverted surcharge | 1,700. | |
| d. | "G" omitted | 800.00 | 800.00 |
| e. | As "d," inverted surcharge | 1,250. | |
| f. | Corrected surcharge, "30" over "33" | 10,500. | 10,500. |
| J14 | D1 30c on 1fr rose, cr | 400.00 | 400.00 |
| a. | Inverted surcharge | 1,150. | 1,150. |
| b. | "30" sideways | 10,000. | 10,000. |
| c. | As "b," inverted surcharge | 10,000. | 10,000. |

**Type II**

| | | | |
|---|---|---|---|
| J13A | D1 30c on 60c brn, cr | 1,000. | 1,000. |
| a. | Inverted surcharge | 1,900. | 1,900. |
| b. | Bee corner ornament turned | 1,600. | 1,600. |
| c. | As "b," inverted surcharge | 2,200. | |
| d. | "G" omitted | 1,000. | 1,000. |
| e. | As "d," inverted surcharge | 1,500. | |
| f. | Corrected surcharge, "30" over "33" | 10,500. | 10,500. |
| J14A | D1 30c on 1fr rose, cr | 400.00 | 400.00 |
| a. | Inverted surcharge | 1,200. | 1,200. |
| b. | "30" sideways | 10,500. | 10,500. |
| c. | As "b," inverted surcharge | 10,500. | 10,500. |

Gustavia Bay — D6

**1905-06  Typo.  Perf. 14x13½**

| | | | |
|---|---|---|---|
| J15 | D6 5c blue | .55 | .55 |
| J16 | D6 10c brown | .55 | .55 |
| J17 | D6 15c green | 1.00 | 1.00 |
| J18 | D6 20c black, yel ('06) | 1.00 | 1.00 |
| J19 | D6 30c rose | 1.25 | 1.25 |
| J20 | D6 50c black | 3.25 | 3.25 |
| J21 | D6 60c brown orange | 1.75 | 1.75 |
| J22 | D6 1fr violet | 3.25 | 3.25 |
| | Nos. J15-J22 (8) | 12.60 | 12.60 |

**Type of 1905-06 Issue Surcharged**

**1926-27**

| | | | |
|---|---|---|---|
| J23 | D6 2fr on 1fr gray | 2.00 | 2.00 |
| J24 | D6 3fr on 1fr ultra ('27) | 2.75 | 2.75 |

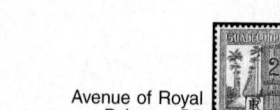

Avenue of Royal Palms — D7

**1928, June 18**

| | | | |
|---|---|---|---|
| J25 | D7 2c olive brn & lil | .25 | .25 |
| J26 | D7 4c bl & org brn | .25 | .25 |
| J27 | D7 5c gray grn & dk brn | .25 | .25 |
| J28 | D7 10c dl vio & yel | .30 | .30 |
| J29 | D7 15c rose & olive grn | .30 | .30 |
| J30 | D7 20c brn org & ol grn | .50 | .50 |
| J31 | D7 25c brn red & bl grn | .50 | .50 |
| J32 | D7 30c slate & olivine | .80 | .80 |
| J33 | D7 50c ol brn & lt red | .80 | .80 |
| J34 | D7 60c dp bl & blk | .80 | .80 |
| J35 | D7 1fr green & orange | 3.00 | 2.60 |
| J36 | D7 2fr bis brn & lt red | 2.25 | 1.90 |
| J37 | D7 3fr vio & bl blk | 1.25 | 1.10 |
| | Nos. J25-J37 (13) | 11.25 | 10.35 |

**Type of 1928 Without "RF"**

**1944**

| | | | |
|---|---|---|---|
| J37A | D7 60c dp bl & blk | .30 | |
| J37B | D7 1fr green & orange | .65 | |
| J37C | D7 2fr bis brn & lt red | .65 | |
| | Nos. J37A-J37C (3) | 1.60 | |

Nos. J37A-J37C were issued by the Vichy government in France, but were not placed on sale in Guadeloupe.

Catalogue values for unused stamps in this section, from this point to the end of the section, are for Never Hinged items.

D8

**Perf. 14x13**

**1947, June 2  Unwmk.  Engr.**

| | | | |
|---|---|---|---|
| J38 | D8 10c black | .30 | .25 |
| J39 | D8 30c dull blue green | .40 | .30 |
| J40 | D8 50c bright ultra | .40 | .30 |
| J41 | D8 1fr dark green | .65 | .50 |
| J42 | D8 2fr dark blue | .85 | .70 |
| J43 | D8 3fr black brown | 1.25 | 1.00 |
| J44 | D8 4fr lilac rose | 1.40 | 1.25 |
| J45 | D8 5fr purple | 1.90 | 1.60 |
| J46 | D8 10fr red | 2.60 | 2.10 |
| J47 | D8 20fr dark violet | 3.00 | 2.25 |
| | Nos. J38-J47 (10) | 12.75 | 10.25 |

# GUATEMALA

ˌgwä-lə-ˈmä-lə

LOCATION — Central America, bordering on Atlantic and Pacific Oceans
GOVT. — Republic
AREA — 42,042 sq. mi.
POP. — 12,335,580 (1999 est.)
CAPITAL — Guatemala City

100 Centavos = 8 Reales = 1 Peso
100 Centavos de Quetzal = 1 Quetzal (1927)

Catalogue values for unused stamps in this country are for Never Hinged items, beginning with Scott 316 in the regular postage section, Scott B5 in the semipostal section, Scott C137 in the air post section, Scott CB5 in the air post semi-postal section and Scott E2 in the special delivery section.

Coat of Arms — A1

Two types of 10c:
Type I — Both zeros in "10" are wide.
Type II — Left zero narrow.

**Perf. 14x13½**

**1871, Mar. 1  Typo.  Unwmk.**

| | | | |
|---|---|---|---|
| 1 | A1 1c ocher | 2.00 | 50.00 |
| a. | Imperf., pair | 10.00 | |
| b. | Printed on both sides, imperf. | 135.00 | |
| 2 | A1 5c lt bister brn | 9.00 | 22.50 |
| a. | Imperf., pair | 50.00 | |
| b. | Tête bêche pair | 350.00 | |
| c. | Tête bêche pair, imperf. | 3,500. | |
| 3 | A1 10c blue (I) | 11.00 | 25.00 |
| a. | Imperf., pair (I) | 75.00 | |
| b. | Type II | 25.00 | 50.00 |
| c. | Imperf. pair (II) | 110.00 | |
| 4 | A1 20c rose | 9.00 | 24.00 |
| a. | Imperf., pair | 75.00 | |
| b. | 20c blue (error) | 350.00 | 125.00 |
| c. | As "b," imperf. | 1,750. | |
| | Nos. 1-4 (4) | 31.00 | 121.50 |

Forgeries exist. Forged cancellations abound. See No. C458.

Coat of Arms — A2

**1873  Litho.  Perf. 12**

| | | | |
|---|---|---|---|
| 5 | A2 4r dull red vio | 675.00 | 175.00 |
| 6 | A2 1p dull yellow | 350.00 | 215.00 |

Forgeries exist. Only one pair of No. 5 is known on cover.

Liberty
A3    A4

A5    A6

**1875, Apr. 15  Engr.**

| | | | |
|---|---|---|---|
| 7 | A3 ¼r black | 42.50 | 22.00 |
| 8 | A4 ½r blue green | 42.50 | 14.00 |
| 9 | A5 1r blue | 42.50 | 14.00 |
| 10 | A6 2r dull red | 42.50 | 14.00 |
| | Nos. 7-10 (4) | 170.00 | 64.00 |

Nos. 7-10 normally lack gum.
Forgeries and forged cancellations exist.

Indian Woman — A7

**Typographed on Tinted Paper**

**1878, Jan. 10  Perf. 13**

| | | | |
|---|---|---|---|
| 11 | A7 ½r yellow grn | 2.75 | 6.75 |
| 12 | A7 2r carmine rose | 4.25 | 13.00 |
| 13 | A7 4r violet | 4.25 | 14.50 |
| 14 | A7 1p yellow | 5.00 | 35.00 |
| | Nos. 11-14 (4) | 16.25 | 69.25 |

Some sheets of Nos. 11-14 have papermaker's watermark, "LACROIX FRERES," in double-lined capitals appearing on six stamps.
Part perforate pairs of Nos. 11, 12 and 14 exist. Value for each, about $100.
Forgeries of Nos. 11-14 are plentiful. Forged cancellations exist.
For surcharges see Nos. 18, 20.
One pair of No. 14 is known to exist on cover.

**Imperf., Pairs**

| | | |
|---|---|---|
| 11a | A7 ½r yellow green | 215.00 |
| 12a | A7 2r carmine rose | 215.00 |
| 13a | A7 4r violet | 215.00 |
| 14a | A7 1p yellow | 250.00 |

Quetzal — A8

**1879  Engr.  Perf. 12**

| | | | |
|---|---|---|---|
| 15 | A8 ¼r brown & green | 16.00 | 20.00 |
| 16 | A8 1r black & green | 24.00 | 30.00 |

For similar types see A11, A72, A103, A121, A146. For surcharges see Nos. 17, 19.

Nos. 11, 12, 15, 16 Surcharged in Black

**1881  Perf. 12 and 13**

| | | | |
|---|---|---|---|
| 17 | A8 1c on ¼r brn & grn | 25.00 | 35.00 |
| a. | "ecntavo" | 87.50 | 100.00 |
| b. | Pair, one without surcharge | 425.00 | |
| c. | Period omitted | 87.50 | 100.00 |
| 18 | A7 5c on ½r yel grn | 19.00 | 30.00 |
| a. | "ecntavos," | 80.00 | 110.00 |
| b. | "5" omitted | 215.00 | |
| c. | Double surcharge | 200.00 | 260.00 |
| 19 | A8 10c on 1r blk & grn | 40.00 | 50.00 |
| a. | "s" of "centavos" missing | 115.00 | 135.00 |
| b. | "ecntavos" | 145.00 | 190.00 |
| 20 | A7 20c on 2r car rose | 100.00 | 145.00 |
| a. | Horiz. pair, imperf. between | 750.00 | |
| b. | Period omitted | 125.00 | 175.00 |
| c. | Comma for period | 200.00 | 260.00 |
| | Nos. 17-20 (4) | 184.00 | 260.00 |

The 5c had three settings.
Surcharge varieties found on Nos. 17-20 include: Period omitted; comma instead of period; "ecntavo." or "ecntavos."; "s" omitted; spaced "centavos."; wider "0" in "20."
Counterfeits of Nos. 17-20 are plentiful.

Quetzal — A11

**1881, Nov. 7  Engr.  Perf. 12**

| | | | |
|---|---|---|---|
| 21 | A11 1c black & grn | 6.00 | 4.25 |
| 22 | A11 2c brown & grn | 6.00 | 4.50 |
| a. | Center inverted | 725.00 | 550.00 |
| 23 | A11 5c red & grn | 13.00 | 5.50 |
| a. | Center inverted | 7,000. | 2,500. |
| 24 | A11 10c gray vio & grn | 6.00 | 4.50 |
| 25 | A11 20c yellow & grn | 6.00 | 5.25 |
| a. | Center inverted | 825.00 | 575.00 |
| | Nos. 21-25 (5) | 37.00 | 24.00 |

**Surcharged in Black**

Gen. Justo Rufino Barrios — A12

A12a    A12b

**1886, Mar. 6**

| | | | |
|---|---|---|---|
| 26 | A12 25c on 1p ver | 1.00 | 1.00 |
| a. | "centovos" | 20.00 | 20.00 |
| b. | "centanos" | 20.00 | 20.00 |
| c. | "255" instead of "25" | 150.00 | 225.00 |
| d. | Inverted "S" in "Nacionales" | 20.00 | 22.50 |
| f. | "cen avos" | 40.00 | |
| h. | "Corre cionales" | 25.00 | |
| i. | Inverted surcharge | 100.00 | |
| 27 | A12 50c on 1p ver | 1.00 | 1.00 |
| a. | "centovos" | 10.00 | 10.00 |
| b. | "centanos" | 10.00 | 10.00 |
| c. | "Carreos" | 10.00 | 10.00 |
| d. | Inverted surcharge | 100.00 | 100.00 |
| e. | Double surcharge | 110.00 | |
| f. | Inverted "S" in "Nacionales" | 110.00 | |
| g. | "centavo" | 22.50 | |
| h. | "cen avos" | 40.00 | |
| 28 | A12 75c on 1p ver | 1.00 | 1.00 |
| a. | "centovos" | 10.00 | 10.00 |
| b. | "centanos" | 10.00 | 10.00 |
| c. | "Carreos" | 10.00 | 10.00 |
| d. | "50" for "75" at upper right | 10.00 | 10.00 |
| e. | Inverted "S" in "Nacionales" | 10.00 | 10.00 |
| f. | Double surcharge | 100.00 | |
| g. | "ales" inverted | 100.00 | |
| 29 | A12a 100c on 1p ver | 2.00 | 3.00 |
| a. | "110" at upper left and "á" at lower left, instead of "100" | 17.50 | 25.00 |
| b. | Inverted surcharge | 100.00 | 100.00 |
| c. | "Guatemala" bolder; 23mm instead of 18½mm wide | 9.00 | 10.00 |
| d. | Double surcharge, one diagonal | 100.00 | |
| 30 | A12b 150c on 1p ver | 2.00 | 3.50 |
| a. | Inverted "G" | 7.50 | 7.50 |
| b. | "Guetemala" and italic "5" in upper 4 numerals | 10.00 | 10.00 |
| d. | Inverted surcharge | 125.00 | |
| e. | Pair, one without surcharge | 150.00 | |
| f. | Double surcharge | 130.00 | |
| | Nos. 26-30 (5) | 7.00 | 9.50 |

There are many other minor varieties, such as wrong font letters, etc.
Used values of Nos. 26-30 are for canceled to order stamps. Postally used sell for much more.

National Emblem — A13

**1886, July 1  Litho.  Perf. 12**

| | | | |
|---|---|---|---|
| 31 | A13 1c dull blue | 7.50 | 3.00 |
| 32 | A13 2c yel brn | 8.50 | 4.50 |
| 33 | A13 5c purple | 55.00 | 1.50 |
| 34 | A13 10c red | 25.00 | 1.50 |
| 35 | A13 20c emerald | 25.00 | 2.00 |
| 36 | A13 25c orange | 27.50 | 2.00 |
| 37 | A13 50c olive green | 15.00 | 4.50 |
| 38 | A13 75c carmine rose | 17.50 | 4.50 |
| 39 | A13 100c red brown | 17.50 | 10.00 |
| 40 | A13 150c dark blue | 20.00 | 12.50 |
| 41 | A13 200c orange yellow | 25.00 | 12.50 |
| | Nos. 31-41 (11) | 243.50 | 58.50 |

Used values of Nos. 38-41 are for canceled to order stamps. Postally used sell for much more.
See Nos. 43-50, 99-107. For surcharges see Nos. 42, 51-59, 75-85, 97-98, 108-110, 124-130.

No. 32 Surcharged in Black

Two settings:
I — "1886" (no period).

II — "1886." (period).

**1886, Nov. 12**

| | | | | |
|---|---|---|---|---|
| 42 | A13 1c on 2c brown, I | | 5.50 | 10.00 |
| a. | Date inverted, I | | 125.00 | |
| b. | Date double, I | | 125.00 | |
| c. | Date omitted, I | | 125.00 | |
| d. | Date double, one invtd., I | | 135.00 | |
| e. | Date triple, one inverted, I | | 135.00 | |
| f. | Setting II | | 3.50 | 2.00 |
| g. | Inverted surcharge, II | | 10.00 | |
| h. | Double surcharge, II | | 125.00 | |

Forgeries exist.

Type I          Type II

Two types of 5c:
I — Thin "5"
II — Larger, thick "5"

**1886-95**              **Engr.**       **Perf. 12**

| | | | |
|---|---|---|---|
| 43 | A13 1c blue | 1.50 | .50 |
| 44 | A13 2c yellow brn | 3.50 | .50 |
| a. | Half used as 1c on cover | | 125.00 |
| 45 | A13 5c purple (I) | 200.00 | 5.00 |
| 46 | A13 5c vio (II) ('88) | 4.50 | .75 |
| 47 | A13 6c lilac ('95) | 4.50 | .50 |
| 48 | A13 10c red ('90) | 4.50 | .50 |
| 49 | A13 20c green ('93) | 7.50 | 1.00 |
| 50 | A13 25c red ('93) | 12.50 | 2.00 |
| | Nos. 43-44,46-50 (7) | 38.50 | 5.75 |

The impression of the engraved stamps is sharper than that of the lithographed. On the engraved stamps the top four lines at left are heavier than those below them. (This is also true of the 1c litho., which is distinguished from the engraved only by a slight color difference and the impression.)

The "2" and "5" (I) are more open than the litho. numerals. The "10" of the engraved is wider. The 20c and 25c of the engraved have a vertical line at right end of the "centavos" ribbon.

No. 38 Surcharged in
Blue Black

**"1894" 14½mm wide**

**1894, Apr. 25**

| | | | |
|---|---|---|---|
| 51 | A13 10c on 75c car rose | 9.00 | 7.50 |
| a. | Double surcharge | 175.00 | |
| b. | Inverted surcharge | 90.00 | |

### Same on Nos. 38-41 in Blue or Red "1894" 14mm wide

**1894, June 13**

| | | | |
|---|---|---|---|
| 52 | A13 2c on 100c | 7.50 | 6.00 |
| 53 | A13 6c on 150c (R) | 7.50 | 6.00 |
| 54 | A13 10c on 75c | 1,000. | 900.00 |
| a. | Thick "1" in "10" | 1,100. | 1,100. |
| 55 | A13 10c on 200c | 10.00 | 5.00 |
| c. | Inverted surcharge | 125.00 | |
| d. | "207" (position 29) | 50.00 | |
| e. | Thick "1" in "10" | 12.50 | 7.50 |

Nos. 54-55 exist with thick or thin "1" in new value.

### Same on Nos. 39-41 in Black or Red "1894" 12mm wide

**1894, July 14**

| | | | |
|---|---|---|---|
| 52a | A13 2c on 100c red brn (Bk) | 12.50 | 6.50 |
| b. | Vert. pair, one without surcharge | 250.00 | |
| 53a | A13 6c on 150c dk bl (R) | 12.50 | 6.50 |
| 55a | A13 10c on 200c org yel (Bk) | 12.50 | 6.50 |
| d. | Inverted surcharge | 110.00 | |
| e. | Vert. pair, one without surcharge | 160.00 | |
| f. | "207" (position 29) | 250.00 | |

### Nos. 44 and 46 Surcharged in Black, Blue Black, or Red

b          c

d          e

**1894-96**

| | | | |
|---|---|---|---|
| 56 | A13 (b) 1c on 2c (Bk) | .75 | .30 |
| a. | "Centav" | 5.00 | 5.00 |
| b. | Double surcharge | 75.00 | |
| c. | As "a," dbl. surcharge | 150.00 | |
| d. | Blue black surcharge | 20.00 | 20.00 |
| e. | Dbl. surch., one inverted | 150.00 | |
| 57 | A13 (c) 1c on 5c (R) ('95) | .50 | .25 |
| a. | Inverted surcharge | 3.00 | 3.00 |
| b. | "1894" instead of "1895" | 3.50 | 3.00 |
| c. | Double surcharge | 50.00 | |
| 58 | A13 (d) 1c on 5c (R) ('95) | .75 | .25 |
| a. | Inverted surcharge | 50.00 | 50.00 |
| b. | Double surcharge | 50.00 | 50.00 |
| 59 | A13 (e) 1c on 5c (R) ('96) | 1.25 | .40 |
| a. | Inverted surcharge | 50.00 | 50.00 |
| b. | Double surcharge | 50.00 | 50.00 |
| | Nos. 56-59 (4) | 3.25 | 1.20 |

Nos. 56-58 may be found with thick or thin "1" in the new value.

National Arms and
President J. M.
Reyna
Barrios — A21

**1897, Jan. 1     Engr.     Unwmk.**

| | | | |
|---|---|---|---|
| 60 | A21 1c blk, *gray* | .55 | .55 |
| 61 | A21 2c blk, *grnsh gray* | .55 | .55 |
| 62 | A21 6c blk, *brn org* | .55 | .55 |
| 63 | A21 10c blk, *dl bl* | .55 | .55 |
| 64 | A21 12c blk, *rose red* | .55 | .55 |
| 65 | A21 18c blk, *grysh white* | 9.50 | 9.50 |
| 66 | A21 20c blk, *scarlet* | 1.00 | 1.00 |
| 67 | A21 25c blk, *bis brn* | 1.60 | 1.00 |
| 68 | A21 50c blk, *redsh brn* | 1.00 | 1.00 |
| 69 | A21 75c blk, *gray* | 52.50 | 52.50 |
| 70 | A21 100c blk, *bl grn* | 1.00 | 1.00 |
| 71 | A21 150c blk, *dl rose* | 105.00 | 135.00 |
| 72 | A21 200c blk, *magenta* | 1.00 | 1.00 |
| 73 | A21 500c blk, *yel grn* | 1.00 | 1.00 |
| | Nos. 60-73 (14) | 176.35 | 205.75 |

Issued for Central American Exposition.
Stamps often sold as Nos. 65, 69 and 71 are examples with telegraph overprint removed.

Used values for Nos. 60-73 are for canceled-to-order stamps. Postally used examples are worth more.

The paper of Nos. 64 and 66 was originally colored on one side only, but has "bled through" on some examples.

No. 64 Surcharged
in Violet

**1897, Nov.**

| | | | |
|---|---|---|---|
| 74 | A21 1c on 12c *rose red* | 1.00 | 1.00 |
| a. | Inverted surcharge | 30.00 | 30.00 |
| b. | Pair, one without surcharge | 75.00 | |
| c. | Dbl. surch., one invtd. | 100.00 | |

### Stamps of 1886-93 Surcharged in Red

f          g

**1898**

| | | | |
|---|---|---|---|
| 75 | (f) 1c on 5c violet | 1.00 | 1.00 |
| a. | Inverted surcharge | 75.00 | |
| 76 | (f) 1c on 50c ol grn | 1.50 | 1.25 |
| a. | Inverted surcharge | 100.00 | 100.00 |
| 77 | (f) 6c on 5c violet | 4.50 | 1.00 |
| 78 | (f) 6c on 150c dk bl | 4.50 | 3.25 |
| 79 | (g) 10c on 20c emerald | 5.00 | 4.00 |
| a. | Double surch., one inverted | 125.00 | 125.00 |
| | Nos. 75-79 (5) | 16.50 | 11.00 |

### Black Surcharge

| | | | |
|---|---|---|---|
| 80 | (f) 1c on 25c red org | 2.00 | 2.00 |
| 81 | (f) 1c on 75c car rose | 1.50 | 1.50 |
| a. | Double surcharge | 100.00 | |
| 82 | (f) 6c on 10c red | 10.00 | 9.00 |
| 83 | (f) 6c on 20c emer | 5.00 | 4.00 |
| 84 | (f) 6c on 100c red brn | 5.00 | 4.00 |
| 85 | (f) 6c on 200c org yel | 5.00 | 4.00 |
| a. | Inverted surcharge | 50.00 | 50.00 |
| | Nos. 80-85 (6) | 28.50 | 24.50 |

Information indicates that No. 77 inverted and double surcharges are counterfeits.

National
Emblem — A24

### Revenue Stamp Overprinted or Surcharged in Carmine

**Perf. 12, 12x14, 14x12**

**1898, Oct. 8     Litho.**

| | | | |
|---|---|---|---|
| 86 | A24 1c dark blue | 1.40 | 1.40 |
| a. | Inverted overprint | 12.50 | 12.50 |
| 87 | A24 2c on 1c dk bl | 2.25 | 2.25 |
| a. | Inverted surcharge | 12.50 | 12.50 |

Counterfeits exist.
See type A26.

National Emblem — A25

### Revenue Stamps Surcharged in Carmine

**1898     Engr.     Perf. 12½ to 16**

| | | | |
|---|---|---|---|
| 88 | A25 1c on 10c bl gray | .75 | .75 |
| a. | "ENTAVO" | 5.00 | 5.00 |
| 89 | A25 2c on 5c pur | 1.25 | 1.00 |
| 90 | A25 2c on 10c bl gray | 6.50 | 7.00 |
| a. | Double surch., car & blk | 100.00 | 75.00 |
| 91 | A25 2c on 50c dp bl | 9.25 | 9.25 |
| a. | Double surch., car & blk | 100.00 | 100.00 |
| | Nos. 88-91 (4) | 17.75 | 18.00 |

### Black Surcharge

| | | | |
|---|---|---|---|
| 92 | A25 2c on 1c lil rose | 3.50 | 2.00 |
| 93 | A25 2c on 25c red | 7.50 | 8.00 |
| 94 | A25 6c on 1p purple | 4.00 | 4.50 |
| 95 | A25 6c on 5p gray vio | 7.50 | 7.50 |
| 96 | A25 6c on 10p emer | 7.50 | 7.50 |
| | Nos. 92-96 (5) | 30.00 | 29.50 |

Nos. 88 and 90 are found in shades ranging from Prussian blue to slate blue.
Varieties other than those listed are bogus.
Counterfeits exist of No. 92.
Soaking in water causes marked fading.
See type A27.

No. 46 Surcharged in
Red

**1899, Sept.     Perf. 12**

| | | | |
|---|---|---|---|
| 97 | A13 1c on 5c violet | .40 | .30 |
| a. | Inverted surcharge | 7.50 | 7.50 |
| b. | Double surcharge | 15.00 | 15.00 |
| c. | Double surcharge, one inverted | 15.00 | 15.00 |

No. 48 Surcharged in
Black

**1900, Jan.**

| | | | |
|---|---|---|---|
| 98 | A13 1c on 10c red | .65 | .50 |
| a. | Inverted surcharge | 10.00 | 10.00 |
| b. | Double surcharge | 75.00 | 75.00 |

### Quetzal Type of 1886

**1900-02     Engr.**

| | | | |
|---|---|---|---|
| 99 | A13 1c dark green | .60 | .25 |
| 100 | A13 2c carmine | .60 | .25 |
| 101 | A13 5c blue (II) | 2.25 | 1.25 |
| 102 | A13 6c lt green | .75 | .25 |
| 103 | A13 10c bister brown | 7.50 | 1.00 |
| 104 | A13 20c purple | 7.50 | 7.50 |
| 105 | A13 20c bister brn ('02) | 7.50 | 7.50 |
| 106 | A13 25c yellow | 7.50 | 7.50 |
| 107 | A13 25c blue green ('02) | 7.50 | 7.50 |
| | Nos. 99-107 (9) | 41.70 | 33.00 |

No. 49 Surcharged in
Black

**1901, May**

| | | | |
|---|---|---|---|
| 108 | A13 1c on 20c green | .50 | .50 |
| a. | Inverted surcharge | 22.50 | 22.50 |
| b. | Double surch., one diagonal | 50.00 | |
| 109 | A13 2c on 20c green | 1.50 | 1.50 |

No. 50 Surcharged in
Black

**1901, Apr.**

| | | | |
|---|---|---|---|
| 110 | A13 1c on 25c red org | .60 | .60 |
| a. | Inverted surcharge | 25.00 | 25.00 |
| b. | Double surcharge | 50.00 | 50.00 |

Search

PHILASEARCH

www.PhilaSearch.com

| A26 | A27 |

### Revenue Stamps Surcharged in Carmine or Black

**1902, July**　　**Perf. 12, 14x12, 12x14**

| | | | |
|---|---|---|---|
| 111 | A26 1c on 1c dk blue | 1.10 | 1.10 |
| a. | Double surcharge | 20.00 | |
| b. | Inverted surcharge | 20.00 | |
| 112 | A26 2c on 1c dk blue | 1.10 | 1.10 |
| a. | Double surcharge | 90.00 | |
| b. | Inverted surcharge | 25.00 | |

**Perf. 14, 15**

| | | | |
|---|---|---|---|
| 113 | A27 6c on 25c red (Bk) | 2.50 | 2.50 |
| a. | Double surch., one invtd. | 75.00 | 75.00 |
| | Nos. 111-113 (3) | 4.70 | 4.70 |

National Emblem A28 　　Statue of Justo Rufino Barrios A29

"La Reforma" Palace A30 　　Temple of Minerva A31

Lake Amatitlán A32 　　Cathedral in Guatemala A33

Columbus Theater A34 　　Artillery Barracks A35

Monument to Columbus A36 　　School for Indians A37

**1902**　　**Engr.**　　**Perf. 12 to 16**

| | | | |
|---|---|---|---|
| 114 | A28 1c grn & claret | .30 | .25 |
| a. | Horiz. pair, imperf. vert. | 100.00 | |
| 115 | A29 2c lake & blk | .30 | .25 |
| a. | Horiz. or vert. pair, imperf. btwn. | 150.00 | |
| 116 | A30 5c blue & blk | .30 | .25 |
| a. | 5c ultra & blk | .75 | .40 |
| b. | Imperf., pair | 100.00 | 100.00 |
| c. | Horiz. pair, imperf. vert. | 100.00 | |
| 117 | A31 6c bister & grn | .30 | .25 |
| a. | Horiz. pair, imperf. btwn. | 150.00 | |
| 118 | A32 10c orange & bl | .40 | .40 |
| a. | Horiz. pair, imperf. vert. | 100.00 | |
| 119 | A33 20c rose lil & blk | .60 | .40 |
| a. | Horiz. pair, imperf. vert. | 100.00 | |
| 120 | A34 50c red brn & bl | .45 | .40 |
| a. | Vert. pair, imperf. btwn. | 350.00 | |
| 121 | A35 75c gray lil & blk | .55 | .40 |
| a. | Horiz. pair, imperf. btwn. | 150.00 | |
| b. | Horiz. pair, imperf. vert. | 100.00 | |
| 122 | A36 1p brown & blk | .85 | .40 |
| a. | Horiz. pair, imperf. btwn. | 150.00 | |
| 123 | A37 2p ver & blk | 1.00 | .85 |
| | Nos. 114-123 (10) | 5.05 | 3.85 |

See Nos. 210, 212-214, 219, 223, 239-241, 243. For overprints and surcharges see Nos. 133, 135-139, 144-157, 168, 170-171, 178, 192-194, 298-299, 301, C19, C27, C123.

---

Issues of 1886-1900 Surcharged in Black or Carmine

**1903, Apr. 18**　　**Perf. 12**

| | | | |
|---|---|---|---|
| 124 | A13 25c on 1c dk grn | 1.25 | .55 |
| a. | Inverted surcharge | 50.00 | 50.00 |
| 125 | A13 25c on 2c carmine | 1.50 | .55 |
| 126 | A13 25c on 6c lt grn | 2.50 | 1.75 |
| a. | Inverted surcharge | 40.00 | 40.00 |
| 127 | A13 25c on 10c bis brn | 7.50 | 7.00 |
| 128 | A13 25c on 75c rose | 10.00 | 10.00 |
| 129 | A13 25c on 150c dk bl (C) | 9.00 | 9.00 |
| 130 | A13 25c on 200c yellow | 10.00 | 10.00 |
| | Nos. 124-130 (7) | 41.75 | 38.85 |

Forgeries and bogus varieties exist.

Declaration of Independence — A38

**1907, Jan. 1**　　**Perf. 13½ to 15**

| | | | |
|---|---|---|---|
| 132 | A38 12½c ultra & blk | .45 | .45 |
| a. | Horiz. pair, imperf. btwn. | 150.00 | |

For surcharge see No. 134.

### Nos. 118, 119 and 132 Surcharged in Black or Red

**1908, May**

| | | | |
|---|---|---|---|
| 133 | A32 1c on 10c org & bl | .30 | .30 |
| a. | Double surcharge | 25.00 | |
| b. | Inverted surcharge | 15.00 | 15.00 |
| c. | Pair, one without surcharge | 50.00 | |
| 134 | A38 2c on 12½c ultra & blk (R) | .25 | .30 |
| a. | Horiz. or vert. pair, imperf. btwn. | 100.00 | |
| b. | Inverted surcharge | 15.00 | 10.00 |
| c. | Double surcharge | 30.00 | |
| 135 | A33 6c on 20c rose lil & blk | .45 | .30 |
| a. | Inverted surcharge | 20.00 | 20.00 |
| | Nos. 133-135 (3) | 1.00 | .90 |

### Similar Surcharge, Dated 1909, in Red or Black on Nos. 121 and 120

**1909, Apr.**

| | | | |
|---|---|---|---|
| 136 | A35 2c on 75c (R) | .55 | .55 |
| 137 | A34 6c on 50c (R) | 62.50 | 62.50 |
| a. | Double surcharge | 125.00 | 125.00 |
| 138 | A34 6c on 50c (Bk) | .30 | .30 |
| | Nos. 136-138 (3) | 63.35 | 63.35 |

Counterfeits exist of Nos. 137, 137a.

### No. 123 Surcharged in Black

| | | | |
|---|---|---|---|
| 139 | A37 12½c on 2p ver & blk | .30 | .30 |
| a. | Inverted surcharge | 25.00 | 25.00 |
| b. | Period omitted after "1909" | 15.00 | 15.00 |

Counterfeits exist.

Gen. Miguel García Granados, Birth Cent. (in 1909) — A39

**1910, Feb. 11**　　**Perf. 14**

| | | | |
|---|---|---|---|
| 140 | A39 6c bis & indigo | .55 | .40 |
| a. | Imperf., pair | 55.00 | |

Some sheets used for this issue contained a two-line watermark, "SPECIAL POSTAGE PAPER / LONDON." For surcharge see No. 143.

General Post Office A40 　　Pres. Manuel Estrada Cabrera A41

---

**1911, June**　　**Perf. 12**

| | | | |
|---|---|---|---|
| 141 | A40 25c bl & blk | .55 | .25 |
| a. | Center inverted | 1,750. | 900.00 |
| 142 | A41 5p red & blk | .65 | .65 |
| a. | Center inverted | 30.00 | 27.50 |

### Nos. 116, 118 and 140 Surcharged in Black or Red

h 　　i

j

**1911**　　**Perf. 14**

| | | | |
|---|---|---|---|
| 143 | A39 (h) 1c on 6c | 25.00 | 9.75 |
| a. | Double surcharge | 75.00 | 75.00 |
| 144 | A30 (i) 2c on 5c (R) | 1.60 | .85 |
| 145 | A32 (j) 6c on 10c | 1.25 | 1.25 |
| a. | Double surcharge | 50.00 | |
| | Nos. 143-145 (3) | 27.85 | 11.85 |

See watermark note after No. 140. Forgeries exist.

### Nos. 119-121 Surcharged in Black

k

l

m

**1912, Sept.**

| | | | |
|---|---|---|---|
| 147 | A33 (k) 1c on 20c | .40 | .40 |
| a. | Inverted surcharge | 12.50 | 12.50 |
| b. | Double surcharge | 15.00 | 15.00 |
| 148 | A34 (l) 2c on 50c | .40 | .40 |
| a. | Inverted surcharge | 12.50 | 12.50 |
| b. | Double surcharge | 12.50 | |
| c. | Double inverted surcharge | 25.00 | |
| 149 | A35 (m) 5c on 75c | .80 | .80 |
| a. | "191" for "1912" | 7.50 | 7.50 |
| b. | Double surcharge | 15.00 | 15.00 |
| c. | Inverted surcharge | 10.00 | |
| | Nos. 147-149 (3) | 1.60 | 1.60 |

Forgeries exist.

### Nos. 120, 122 and 123 Surcharged in Blue, Green or Black

n 　　o

p

**1913, July**

| | | | |
|---|---|---|---|
| 151 | A34 (n) 1c on 50c (Bl) | .30 | .30 |
| a. | Inverted surcharge | 10.00 | |
| b. | Double surcharge | 17.50 | |
| c. | Horiz. pair, imperf. btwn. | 100.00 | |
| 152 | A36 (o) 6c on 1p (G) | .30 | .30 |
| 153 | A37 (p) 12½c on 2p (Bk) | .30 | .30 |
| a. | Inverted surcharge | 15.00 | 15.00 |
| b. | Double surcharge | 40.00 | |
| c. | Horiz. pair, imperf. btwn. | 100.00 | |
| | Nos. 151-153 (3) | .90 | .90 |

Forgeries exist.

---

### Nos. 114 and 115 Surcharged in Black

q 　　r

s 　　t

**1916-17**

| | | | |
|---|---|---|---|
| 154 | A28 (q) 2c on 1c ('17) | .30 | .30 |
| 155 | A28 (r) 6c on 1c | .30 | .30 |
| 156 | A28 (s) 12½c on 1c | .30 | .30 |
| 157 | A29 (t) 25c on 2c | .30 | .30 |
| | Nos. 154-157 (4) | 1.20 | 1.20 |

Numerous errors of value and color, inverted and double surcharges and similar varieties are in the market. They were not regularly issued, but were surreptitiously made and sold.

Counterfeit surcharges abound.

"Liberty" and President Estrada Cabrera — A51

**1917, Mar. 15**　　**Perf. 14, 15**

| | | | |
|---|---|---|---|
| 158 | A51 25c dp blue & brown | .30 | .30 |

Re-election of President Estrada Cabrera.

Estrada Cabrera and Quetzal — A52

**1918**　　**Perf. 12**

| | | | |
|---|---|---|---|
| 161 | A52 1.50p dark blue | .30 | .30 |

Radio Station A54 　　"Joaquina" Maternity Hospital A55

"Estrada Cabrera" Vocational School A56 　　National Emblem A57

**1919, May 3**　　**Perf. 14, 15**

| | | | |
|---|---|---|---|
| 162 | A54 30c red & blk | 3.75 | .75 |
| 163 | A55 60c ol grn & blk | 1.10 | .75 |
| 164 | A56 90c red brn & blk | 1.10 | .75 |
| 165 | A57 3p dp grn & blk | 2.50 | .50 |
| | Nos. 162-165 (4) | 8.45 | 2.50 |

See Nos. 215, 227. For surcharges see Nos. 166-167, 179-185, 188, 195-198, 245-246, C8-C11, C21-C22.

No. 162 Ovptd. in Blue & Srchd. in Black

**1920, Jan.**　　**Unwmk.**

| | | | |
|---|---|---|---|
| 166 | A54 2c on 30c red & blk | .30 | .30 |
| a. | Inverted surcharge | 12.50 | 12.50 |
| b. | "1920" double | 10.00 | 10.00 |
| c. | "1920" omitted | 15.00 | 15.00 |
| d. | "2 centavos" omitted | 20.00 | |
| e. | Imperf, pair | 100.00 | |
| f. | Pair, imperf. btwn. | 100.00 | |

## Nos. 123 and 163 Surcharged

u      v

**1920**
| | | | | |
|---|---|---|---|---|
| 167 | A55 | 2c on 60c (Bk & R) | .30 | .30 |
| a. | | Inverted surcharge | 10.00 | 10.00 |
| b. | | "1920" inverted | 7.50 | 7.50 |
| c. | | "1920" omitted | 10.00 | 10.00 |
| d. | | "1920" only | 10.00 | |
| e. | | Double surcharge | 25.00 | |
| 168 | A37 | 25c on 2p (Bk) | .30 | .30 |
| a. | | "35" for "25" | 10.00 | 10.00 |
| b. | | Large "5" in "25" | 10.00 | 10.00 |
| c. | | Inverted surcharge | 15.00 | 15.00 |
| d. | | Double surcharge | 25.00 | |

A61

**1920**
| | | | | |
|---|---|---|---|---|
| 169 | A61 | 25c green | .30 | .30 |
| a. | | Double overprint | | 50.00 |
| b. | | Double overprint, inverted | 75.00 | |

See types A65-A66.

## No. 119 Surcharged

**1921, Apr.**
| | | | | |
|---|---|---|---|---|
| 170 | A33 | 12½c on 20c | .30 | .30 |
| a. | | Double surcharge | 15.00 | |
| b. | | Inverted surcharge | 15.00 | |

## No. 121 Surcharged

**1921, Apr.**
| | | | | |
|---|---|---|---|---|
| 171 | A35 | 50c on 75c lil & blk | .50 | .30 |
| a. | | Double surcharge | 22.50 | |
| b. | | Inverted surcharge | 25.00 | 25.00 |

Mayan Stele at Quiriguá A62    Monument to President Granados A63

"La Penitenciaria" Bridge — A64

**1921, Sept. 1**     **Perf. 13½, 14, 15**
| | | | | |
|---|---|---|---|---|
| 172 | A62 | 1.50p blue & org | .85 | .25 |
| 173 | A63 | 5p brown & grn | 2.75 | 1.25 |
| 174 | A64 | 15p black & red org | 22.50 | 12.50 |
| | | Nos. 172-174 (3) | 26.10 | 14.00 |

See Nos. 216, 228, 229. For surcharges see Nos. 186-187, 189-191, 199-201, 207, 231, 247-251, C1-C5, C12, C23-C24.

## Telegraph Stamps Overprinted or Surcharged in Black or Red

A65      A66

**1921**        **Perf. 14**
| | | | | |
|---|---|---|---|---|
| 175 | A65 | 25c green | .50 | .25 |
| 176 | A66 | 12½c on 25c grn (R) | .50 | .25 |
| 177 | A66 | 12½c on 25c grn | 30.00 | 15.00 |
| | | Nos. 175-177 (3) | 31.00 | 15.50 |

## Nos. 119, 163 and 164 Surcharged in Black or Red

w

x

**1922, Mar.**
| | | | | |
|---|---|---|---|---|
| 178 | A33(w) | 12½c on 20c | .25 | .25 |
| a. | | Inverted surcharge | 10.00 | 10.00 |
| 179 | A55(w) | 12½c on 60c (R) | .50 | .50 |
| a. | | Inverted surcharge | 25.00 | |
| 180 | A56(w) | 12½c on 90c (R) | .50 | .50 |
| a. | | Inverted surcharge | 25.00 | |
| 181 | A55(x) | 25c on 60c | 1.00 | 1.00 |
| a. | | Inverted surcharge | 20.00 | 20.00 |
| 182 | A55(x) | 25c on 60c (R) | 125.00 | 125.00 |
| 183 | A56(x) | 25c on 90c | 1.00 | 1.00 |
| a. | | Inverted surcharge | 25.00 | |
| 184 | A56(x) | 25c on 90c (R) | 4.00 | 4.00 |
| | | Nos. 178-181,183-184 (6) | 7.25 | 7.25 |

Counterfeits exist.

## Nos. 165, 173-174 Surcharged in Red or Dark Blue

**1922, May**
| | | | | |
|---|---|---|---|---|
| 185 | A57 | 12½c on 3p grn & blk (R) | .25 | .25 |
| 186 | A63 | 12½c on 5p brn & grn | .50 | .45 |
| 187 | A64 | 12½c on 15p blk & ver | .50 | .45 |
| | | Nos. 185-187 (3) | 1.25 | 1.15 |

## Nos. 165, 173-174 Surcharged in Red or Black

Type I      Type II

Type III      Type IV

**1922**
| | | | | |
|---|---|---|---|---|
| 188 | A57 | 25c on 3p (I) (R) | .30 | .30 |
| a. | | Type II | .60 | .60 |
| b. | | Type III | .60 | .60 |
| c. | | Type IV | .30 | .30 |
| d. | | Inverted surcharge | 40.00 | 40.00 |
| e. | | Horiz. or vert. pair, imperf. btwn. (I) | 125.00 | |
| 189 | A63 | 25c on 5p (I) | 1.00 | 2.00 |
| a. | | Type II | 2.00 | 3.00 |
| b. | | Type III | 2.00 | 3.00 |
| c. | | Type IV | 1.00 | 2.00 |
| 190 | A64 | 25c on 15p (I) | 1.00 | 1.50 |
| a. | | Type II | 2.00 | 3.00 |
| b. | | Type III | 2.00 | 3.00 |
| c. | | Type IV | 1.00 | 1.50 |
| 191 | A64 | 25c on 15p (I) (R) | 50.00 | 30.00 |
| a. | | Type II | 40.00 | 45.00 |
| b. | | Type III | 45.00 | 45.00 |
| c. | | Type IV | 30.00 | 35.00 |
| | | Nos. 188-191 (4) | 52.30 | 33.80 |

## Stamps of 1902-21 Surcharged in Dark Blue or Red

Type V      Type VI

Type VII      Type VIII

Type IX

**1922, Aug.**     On Nos. 121-123
| | | | | |
|---|---|---|---|---|
| 192 | A35 | 25c on 75c (V) | .40 | .40 |
| a. | | Type VI | 1.75 | 1.75 |
| b. | | Type VII | 5.50 | 4.75 |
| c. | | Type VIII | 6.50 | 6.00 |
| 193 | A36 | 25c on 1p (V) | .30 | .30 |
| a. | | Type VI | .30 | .30 |
| b. | | Type VII | 1.25 | 1.25 |
| c. | | Type VIII | 2.50 | 2.50 |
| d. | | Type IX | 4.00 | 3.50 |
| e. | | Inverted surcharge | 40.00 | |
| 194 | A37 | 25c on 2p (V) | .45 | .45 |
| a. | | Type VI | .45 | .45 |
| b. | | Type VII | 1.25 | 1.25 |
| c. | | Type VIII | 4.00 | 4.00 |
| d. | | Type IX | 6.50 | 6.50 |

**On Nos. 162-165**
| | | | | |
|---|---|---|---|---|
| 195 | A54 | 25c on 30c (V) | .45 | .45 |
| a. | | Type VI | .45 | .45 |
| b. | | Type VII | 1.25 | 1.25 |
| c. | | Type VIII | 5.50 | 5.50 |
| d. | | Type IX | 6.50 | 6.50 |
| 196 | A55 | 25c on 60c (V) | 1.00 | 1.50 |
| a. | | Type VI | 1.25 | 1.50 |
| b. | | Type VII | 6.25 | 7.75 |
| c. | | Type VIII | 8.50 | 9.50 |
| d. | | Type IX | 10.00 | 11.00 |
| 197 | A56 | 25c on 90c (V) | 1.00 | 1.50 |
| a. | | Type VI | 1.50 | 2.00 |
| b. | | Type VII | 6.00 | 6.75 |
| c. | | Type VIII | 8.50 | 9.50 |
| d. | | Type IX | 10.00 | 11.00 |
| 198 | A57 | 25c on 3p (R) (V) | .40 | .40 |
| a. | | Type VI | .40 | .40 |
| b. | | Type VII | 5.00 | 5.00 |
| c. | | Type VIII | 6.00 | 4.50 |
| d. | | Type IX | 6.50 | 6.00 |
| e. | | Inverted surcharge | 50.00 | |

**On Nos. 172-174**
| | | | | |
|---|---|---|---|---|
| 199 | A62 | 25c on 1.50p (V) | .30 | .30 |
| a. | | Type VI | .30 | .30 |
| b. | | Type VII | 1.25 | 1.00 |
| c. | | Type VIII | 5.00 | 3.00 |
| d. | | Type IX | 4.50 | 4.50 |
| e. | | Inverted surcharge | 40.00 | |
| 200 | A63 | 25c on 5p (V) | .75 | .90 |
| a. | | Type VI | .80 | 1.00 |
| b. | | Type VII | 3.00 | 3.50 |
| c. | | Type VIII | 5.50 | 6.00 |
| d. | | Type IX | 8.00 | 8.50 |
| 201 | A64 | 25c on 15p (V) | .85 | .90 |
| a. | | Type VI | 1.50 | 1.50 |
| b. | | Type VII | 5.00 | 5.50 |
| c. | | Type VIII | 6.50 | 6.50 |
| d. | | Type IX | 12.00 | 12.00 |
| | | Nos. 192-201 (10) | 5.90 | 7.10 |

Centenary Palace A69    National Palace at Antigua A70

### Printed by Waterlow & Sons

**1922**        **Perf. 14, 14½**
| | | | | |
|---|---|---|---|---|
| 202 | A69 | 12½c green | .30 | .30 |
| a. | | Horiz. or vert. pair, imperf. btwn. | 100.00 | |
| 203 | A70 | 25c brown | .30 | .30 |

See Nos. 211, 221, 234.

Columbus Theater A71    Quetzal A72

Granados Monument — A73

### Litho. by Castillo Bros.

**1924, Feb.**      **Perf. 12**
| | | | | |
|---|---|---|---|---|
| 204 | A71 | 50c rose | .60 | .25 |
| a. | | Imperf., pair | 7.50 | |
| b. | | Horiz. or vert. pair, imperf. btwn. | 25.00 | |
| 205 | A72 | 1p dark green | 2.75 | .25 |
| a. | | Imperf. vertically | 15.00 | |
| b. | | Vert. pair, imperf. btwn. | 20.00 | |
| c. | | Imperf., pair | 7.50 | |
| 206 | A73 | 5p orange | 1.60 | .90 |
| a. | | Imperf., pair | 8.50 | |
| b. | | Horiz. pair, imperf. btwn. | 20.00 | |
| | | Nos. 204-206 (3) | 4.95 | 1.00 |

For surcharges see Nos. 208-209.

## Nos. 172 and 206 Surcharged

**1924, July**
| | | | | |
|---|---|---|---|---|
| 207 | A62 | 1p on 1.50p bl & org | .30 | .25 |
| 208 | A73 | 1.25p on 5p orange | .50 | .50 |
| a. | | "UN PESO 25 Cents." omitted | 40.00 | |
| b. | | Horiz. pair, imperf. btwn. | 25.00 | |

## No. 208 Overprinted

No. 208 Overprinted

**1924**
| | | | | |
|---|---|---|---|---|
| 209 | A73 | 1p on 5p orange | .50 | .50 |

### Types of 1902-22 Issues
### Engr. by Perkins Bacon & Co.

**1924, Aug.**    **Re-engraved**    **Perf. 14**
| | | | | |
|---|---|---|---|---|
| 210 | A31 | 6c bister | .30 | .25 |
| 211 | A70 | 25c brown | .30 | .25 |
| 212 | A34 | 50c red | .30 | .25 |
| 213 | A36 | 1p orange brn | .30 | .25 |
| 214 | A37 | 2p orange | .50 | .25 |
| 215 | A57 | 3p deep green | 2.75 | .50 |
| 216 | A64 | 15p black | 6.75 | 2.75 |
| | | Nos. 210-216 (7) | 11.20 | 4.50 |

The designs of the stamps of 1924 differ from those of the 1902-22 issues in many details which are too minute to illustrate. The re-engraved issue may be readily distinguished by the imprint "Perkins Bacon & Co. Ld. Londres."

Pres. Justo Rufino Barrios A74    Lorenzo Montúfar A75

**1924, Aug.**
| | | | | |
|---|---|---|---|---|
| 217 | A74 | 1.25p ultra | .30 | .30 |
| 218 | A75 | 2.50p dk violet | 1.20 | .30 |

See Nos. 224, 226. For surcharges see Nos. 232, C6, C20.

Aurora Park — A76    National Post Office — A77

National Observatory — A78

### Types of 1921-24 Re-engraved and New Designs Dated 1926
### Engraved by Waterlow & Sons, Ltd.

**1926, July-Aug.**     **Perf. 12½**
| | | | | |
|---|---|---|---|---|
| 219 | A31 | 6c ocher | .25 | .25 |
| 220 | A76 | 12½c green | .25 | .25 |
| 221 | A70 | 25c brown | .25 | .25 |
| 222 | A77 | 50c red | .25 | .25 |
| 223 | A36 | 1p orange brn | .25 | .25 |
| 224 | A74 | 1.50p dk blue | .25 | .25 |
| 225 | A78 | 2p orange | 1.25 | 1.00 |
| 226 | A75 | 2.50p dk violet | 1.50 | 1.25 |
| 227 | A57 | 3p dark green | .45 | .25 |
| 228 | A63 | 5p brown vio | 1.00 | .40 |
| 229 | A64 | 15p black | 6.00 | 2.75 |
| | | Nos. 219-229 (11) | 11.70 | 7.15 |

These stamps may be distinguished from those of the same designs in preceding issues by the imprint "Waterlow & Sons, Limited, Londres," the date, "1926," and the perforation. See Nos. 233, 242. For surcharge see No. 230.

Nos. 225-226, 228 Surcharged in Various Colors

## 1928

| | | | | |
|---|---|---|---|---|
| 230 | A78 | ½c on 2p (Bl) | .65 | .50 |
| a. | | Inverted surcharge | 13.50 | |
| 231 | A63 | ½c on 5p (Bk) | .35 | .25 |
| a. | | Inverted surcharge | 10.00 | 10.00 |
| b. | | Double surcharge | 50.00 | |
| c. | | Blue surcharge | 45.00 | 45.00 |
| d. | | Blue and black surcharge | 50.00 | 50.00 |
| 232 | A75 | 1c on 2.50p (R) | .35 | .25 |
| b. | | Double surcharge | 50.00 | |
| | | Nos. 230-232 (3) | 1.35 | 1.00 |

Barrios A79

Montúfar A80

Granados A81

General Orellana A82

Coat of Arms of Guatemala City — A83

### Engraved by T. De la Rue & Co.

**1929, Jan.**     **Perf. 14**

| | | | | |
|---|---|---|---|---|
| 233 | A78 | ½c yellow grn | .75 | .25 |
| 234 | A70 | 1c dark brown | .25 | .25 |
| 235 | A79 | 2c deep blue | .25 | .25 |
| 236 | A80 | 3c dark violet | .25 | .25 |
| 237 | A81 | 4c orange | .25 | .25 |
| 238 | A82 | 5c dk carmine | .50 | .25 |
| 239 | A31 | 10c brown | .40 | .25 |
| 240 | A36 | 15c ultra | .50 | .25 |
| 241 | A29 | 25c brown org | 1.00 | .25 |
| 242 | A76 | 30c green | .90 | .30 |
| 243 | A32 | 50c pale rose | 2.00 | .60 |
| 244 | A83 | 1q black | 3.00 | .40 |
| | | Nos. 233-244 (12) | 10.05 | 3.55 |

Nos. 233, 234 and 239 to 243 differ from the illustrations in many minor details, particularly in the borders.

See No. 300 for bisect of No. 235. For overprints and surcharges see Nos. 297, C13, C17-C18, C25-C26, C28, E1, RA17-RA18.

No. 227 Surcharged in Black or Red

**1929, Dec. 28**     **Perf. 12½, 13**

| | | | | |
|---|---|---|---|---|
| 245 | A57 | 3c on 3p dk grn (Blk) | 1.50 | 1.90 |
| a. | | Inverted surcharge | 15.00 | 15.00 |
| 246 | A57 | 5c on 3p dk grn (R) | 1.50 | 1.90 |
| a. | | Inverted surcharge | 15.00 | 15.00 |

Inauguration of the Eastern Railroad connecting Guatemala and El Salvador.

No. 229 Surcharged in Red

**1930, Mar. 30**     **Unwmk.**

| | | | | |
|---|---|---|---|---|
| 247 | A64 | 1c on 15p black | 1.25 | 1.40 |
| 248 | A64 | 2c on 15p black | 1.25 | 1.40 |
| 249 | A64 | 3c on 15p black | 1.25 | 1.40 |
| 250 | A64 | 5c on 15p black | 1.25 | 1.40 |
| 251 | A64 | 15c on 15p black | 1.25 | 1.40 |
| | | Nos. 247-251 (5) | 6.25 | 7.00 |

Opening of Los Altos electric railway.

Hydroelectric Dam — A85

Los Altos Railway — A86

Railroad Station — A87

**1930, Mar. 30**     **Typo.**     **Perf. 12**

| | | | | |
|---|---|---|---|---|
| 252 | A85 | 2c brn vio & blk | 1.50 | 1.90 |
| a. | | Horiz. pair, imperf. btwn. | 125.00 | |
| 253 | A86 | 3c dp red & blk | 3.00 | 2.75 |
| a. | | Vert. pair, imperf. btwn. | 125.00 | |
| 254 | A87 | 5c buff & dk blk | 3.00 | 2.75 |
| | | Nos. 252-254 (3) | 7.50 | 7.40 |

Opening of Los Altos electric railway. Exist imperf.

Mayan Stele at Quiriguá — A91

**1932, Apr. 8**     **Engr.**

| | | | | |
|---|---|---|---|---|
| 258 | A91 | 3c carmine rose | 5.00 | .40 |

See Nos. 302-303.

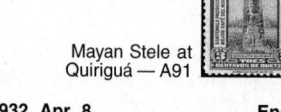

Flag of the Race, Columbus and Tecum Uman — A92

**1933, Aug. 3**     **Litho.**     **Perf. 12½**

| | | | | |
|---|---|---|---|---|
| 259 | A92 | ½c dark green | .75 | .75 |
| 260 | A92 | 1c dull brown | 1.25 | 1.25 |
| 261 | A92 | 2c deep blue | 1.25 | 1.25 |
| 262 | A92 | 3c dull violet | 1.25 | 1.25 |
| 263 | A92 | 5c rose | 1.25 | 1.25 |
| | | Nos. 259-263 (5) | 5.75 | 5.75 |

Day of the Race and 441st anniv. of the sailing of Columbus from Palos, Spain, Aug. 3, 1492, on his 1st voyage to the New World. The 3c and 5c exist imperf.

Birthplace of Barrios — A93

View of San Lorenzo — A94

Justo Rufino Barrios — A95

National Emblem and Locomotive — A96

General Post Office A97

Telegraph Building and Barrios A98

Military Academy A99

National Police Headquarters A100

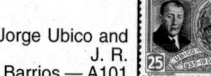

Jorge Ubico and J. R. Barrios — A101

**1935, July 19**     **Photo.**

| | | | | |
|---|---|---|---|---|
| 264 | A93 | ½c yel grn & mag | .50 | .45 |
| 265 | A94 | 1c org red & pck bl | .50 | .45 |
| 266 | A95 | 2c orange & blk | .50 | .55 |
| 267 | A96 | 3c car rose & pck bl | 4.50 | 2.25 |
| 268 | A97 | 4c pck bl & org red | 4.50 | 10.00 |
| 269 | A98 | 5c bl grn & brn | 3.50 | 4.25 |
| 270 | A99 | 10c slate grn & rose lake | 4.50 | 5.50 |
| 271 | A100 | 15c ol grn & org brn | 4.50 | 4.75 |
| 272 | A101 | 25c scarlet & bl | 4.50 | 4.75 |
| | | Nos. 264-272 (9) | 27.50 | 32.95 |

General Barrios. See Nos. C29-C31.

Lake Atitlán A102

Quetzal A103

Legislative Building — A104

**1935, Oct. 10**

| | | | | |
|---|---|---|---|---|
| 273 | A102 | 1c brown & crim | .25 | .30 |
| 274 | A103 | 3c rose car & pck grn | .70 | .30 |
| 275 | A103 | 3c red org & pck grn | .70 | .30 |
| 276 | A104 | 4c brt bl & dp rose | .35 | .30 |
| | | Nos. 273-276 (4) | 2.00 | 1.20 |

See No. 277. For surcharges see Nos. B1-B3.

**No. 273 perforated diagonally through the center**

**1936, June**     **Perf. 12½x12**

| | | | | |
|---|---|---|---|---|
| 277 | A102 | (½c) brown & crimson | .30 | .30 |
| a. | | Unsevered pair | .60 | .60 |

Bureau of Printing A105

Map of Guatemala A106

**1936, Sept. 24**     **Perf. 12½**

| | | | | |
|---|---|---|---|---|
| 278 | A105 | ½c green & pur | .25 | .30 |
| 279 | A106 | 5c blue & dk brn | .90 | .30 |

For surcharge see No. B4.

Quetzal A107

Union Park, Quezaltenango A108

Gen. Jorge Ubico on Horseback — A109

1c, Tower of the Reformer. 3c, National Post Office. 4c, Government Building, Retalhuleu. 5c, Legislative Palace entrance. 10c, Custom House. 15c, Aurora Airport Custom House. 25c, National Fair. 50c, Residence of Presidential Guard. 1.50q, General Ubico, portrait standing, no cap.

**1937, May 20**

| | | | | |
|---|---|---|---|---|
| 280 | A107 | ½c pck bl & car rose | .85 | .45 |
| 281 | A107 | 1c ol gray & red brn | .85 | .35 |
| 282 | A108 | 2c vio & car rose | .70 | .35 |
| 283 | A108 | 3c brn vio & brt bl | .70 | .25 |
| 284 | A108 | 4c yel & dl ol grn | 3.25 | 3.00 |
| 285 | A107 | 5c crim & brt vio | 3.25 | 3.00 |
| 286 | A107 | 10c mag & brn blk | 4.75 | 4.00 |
| 287 | A108 | 15c ultra & cop red | 3.25 | 3.00 |
| 288 | A108 | 25c red org & vio | 4.75 | 4.00 |
| 289 | A108 | 50c dk grn & org red | 7.25 | 6.00 |
| 290 | A109 | 1q mag & blk | 60.00 | 50.00 |
| 291 | A109 | 1.50q red brn & blk | 60.00 | 50.00 |
| | | Nos. 280-291 (12) | 149.60 | 124.40 |

Second term of President Ubico.

Mayan Calendar A119

Natl. Flower (White Nun Orchid) A120

Quetzal A121

Map of Guatemala A122

**1939, Sept. 7**     **Perf. 13x12, 12½**

| | | | | |
|---|---|---|---|---|
| 292 | A119 | ½c grn & red brn | .85 | .25 |
| 293 | A120 | 2c bl & gray blk | 5.00 | 1.00 |
| 294 | A121 | 3c red org & turq grn | 6.50 | 1.75 |
| 295 | A121 | 3c ol bis & turq grn | 6.50 | 1.75 |
| 296 | A122 | 5c blue & red | 5.75 | 5.75 |
| | | Nos. 292-296 (5) | 24.60 | 10.50 |

For overprints see Nos. 324, C157.

No. 235 Surcharged in Red

**1939, Sept.**     **Perf. 14**

| | | | | |
|---|---|---|---|---|
| 297 | A79 | 1c on 2c deep blue | .30 | .30 |

### Stamps of 1929 Surcharged in Blue

y

z

**1940, June**

| | | | | |
|---|---|---|---|---|
| 298 | A29 | (y) 1c on 25c brn org | .30 | .30 |
| 299 | A32 | (z) 5c on 50c pale rose (bar 10x¾mm) | .30 | .30 |
| a. | | Bar 12½x2mm | .30 | .30 |
| b. | | Bar 12½x1mm | 50.00 | 5.00 |

**No. 235 perforated diagonally through the center**

**1941, Aug. 16**     **Perf. 14x11½**

| | | | | |
|---|---|---|---|---|
| 300 | A79 | (1c) deep blue | .30 | .30 |
| a. | | Unsevered pair | .80 | .80 |

No. 241 Surcharged in Black

**1941, Dec. 24**     **Perf. 14**

| | | | | |
|---|---|---|---|---|
| 301 | A29 | ½c on 25c brn org | .30 | .30 |

## Type of 1932 Inscribed "1942"

**1942**   **Engr.**   **Perf. 12**
302 A91 3c green ... .95 .30
303 A91 3c deep blue ... .95 .30

Issued to publicize the coffee of Guatemala.

Vase of Guastatoya A123

Home for the Aged A124

**1942, July 13**   **Unwmk.**
304 A123 ½c red brown ... .35 .30
305 A124 1c carmine rose ... .35 .30

National Printing Works — A125

**1943, Jan. 25**   **Engr.**   **Perf. 11, 12**
307 A125 2c scarlet ... .30 .30
a. Vert. pair, imperf. horiz. ... 35.00

Rafael Maria Landivar — A126

**1943, Aug.**   **Perf. 11**
308 A126 5c brt ultra ... .30 .30

Death of Rafael Landivar, poet, 150th anniv.

National Palace — A127

**1944, June 30**   **Perf. 11**
309 A127 3c dk blue green ... .30 .30

Inauguration of the Natl. Palace, Nov. 10, 1943.
See Nos. C137A-C139. For overprints see Nos. 311-311A, C133.

Ruins of Zakuleu — A128

**1945, Jan. 6**
310 A128 ½c black brown ... .30 .30

## Type of 1944 Overprinted in Blue

**1945, Jan. 15**
311 A127 3c deep blue ... .30 .30
**Overprint Bar 1mm Thick**
311A A127 3c deep blue ... 1.00 .70

Allegory of the Revolution — A129

**1945, Feb. 20**
312 A129 3c grayish blue ... .30 .25
Nos. 312,C128-C131 (5) ... 2.50 1.45
Revolution of 10/20/44.

---

Torch — A130

**1945, Oct. 20**
313 A130 3c deep blue ... .25 .30

1st anniv. of the Revolution of Oct. 20, 1944.
See No. C135-C136, C147-C150.

José Milla y Vidaurre A131

Payo Enriquez de Rivera A132

**1945**   **Perf. 11, 12½**
314 A131 1c deep green ... .25 .25
315 A132 2c dull lilac ... .25 .25
Nos. 314-315,C134-C134A (4) ... 2.20 1.80

See Nos. 343-346, 379, C137, C269, C311-C315.

> **Catalogue values for unused stamps in this section, from this point to the end of the section, are for Never Hinged items.**

José Batres y Montufar — A133

**1946**   **Unwmk.**
316 A133 ½c sepia ... .55 .30
317 A133 3c deep blue ... .55 .30
See Nos. 319, C142.

UPU Monument Bern, Switzerland — A134

**1946, Aug. 5**   **Photo.**   **Perf. 14x13**
318 A134 1c vio & gray brn ... .50 .30
Nos. 318,C140-C141 (3) ... 2.20 .90
Centenary of the first postage stamp.

### Batres Type of 1946

**1947, Nov. 11**   **Engr.**   **Perf. 11, 12½**
319 A133 3c dull green ... .55 .30

Symbolical of Labor — A135

**1948, May 14**   **Unwmk.**   **Perf. 11**
320 A135 1c deep green ... .75 .30
a. Perf. 12½ ... 6.00 5.00
321 A135 2c sepia ... .75 .30
a. Perf. 12½ ... 6.00 5.00
322 A135 3c deep ultra ... .75 .30
a. Perf. 12½ ... 6.00 5.00
323 A135 5c rose carmine ... .75 .30
a. Perf. 12½ ... 6.00 5.00
Nos. 320-323 (4) ... 3.00 1.20

Labor Day, May 1, 1948. Other perfs. and compound perfs. exist.

---

### No. 296 Overprinted in Carmine at Lower Right

**1948, May 14**   **Perf. 12½**
324 A122 5c blue & red ... .65 .30

Bartolomé de las Casas and Indian — A136

**1949, Oct. 8**   **Engr.**   **Perf. 12½, 13½**
325 A136 ½c red ... .55 .30
326 A136 1c black brown ... .55 .30
327 A136 2c dk blue grn ... .55 .30
a. 2c green, perf. 11, 11½ ('60) ... .55 .30
328 A136 3c rose pink ... .55 .30
a. 3c car, perf. 11, 12½, 13½ ('64) ... .55 .30
329 A136 4c ultra ... .55 .30
Nos. 325-329 (5) ... 2.75 1.50

See Nos. 384-386.

Gathering Coffee — A137

1c, Poptun Agricultural Colony. 2c, Banana trees. 3c, Sugar cane field. 6c, Intl. Bridge.

**1950, Feb.**   **Photo.**   **Perf. 14**
330 A137 ½c vio bl, pink & ol gray ... .55 .30
331 A137 1c red brn, yel & grnsh gray ... .55 .30
332 A137 2c ol grn, pink & bl gray ... .55 .30
333 A137 3c pur, bl & org brn ... .55 .30
334 A137 6c dp org, aqua & vio ... 1.00 .30
Nos. 330-334 (5) ... 3.20 1.50

See Nos. 347-349.

Badge of Public and Social Assistance Ministry A138

Nurse A139

Map Showing Hospitals — A140

**1950-51**   **Litho.**   **Perf. 12, 12½x12**
335 A138 1c car rose & bl ... .40 .30
336 A139 3c dl grn & rose red ... .60 .30
**Perf. 12**
337 A140 5c dk bl & choc ('51) ... .85 .30
a. Souvenir sheet, #335-337 ... 8.50 8.50
Nos. 335-337 (3) ... 1.85 .90

Issued to publicize the National Hospitals Fund.
No. 337a exists perf. and imperf., same values.
A perforated souvenir sheet is known which is similar to No. 337a, but with the 5c stamp like the basic stamp of No. C232 (with "BRITISH HONDURAS" inscription).
See Nos. C177-C180a. For overprint see No. C232.

---

Motorcycle Messenger A141

**1951, May 22**   **Perf. 14x12½**
337B A141 4c bl grn & gray blk ... 1.25 .60

Issued for regular postage, although inscribed "Expreso." See No. E2.

### Souvenir Sheet

A142

### Typographed and Engraved
**1951, Oct. 22**   **Imperf.**
338 A142 Sheet of 2 ... 5.25 5.25
a. 1c rose carmine ... 2.00 1.50
b. 10c deep ultramarine ... 2.00 1.50

75th anniv. (in 1949) of the UPU.
For overprint see No. 419.

A143

Modern Model Schools — A144

**1951, Oct. 22**   **Photo.**   **Perf. 13½x14**
339 A143 ½c brn car & dl grn ... .60 .30
340 A144 1c brn car & dl grn ... .60 .30
341 A143 2c grnsh bl & red brn ... .60 .30
342 A144 4c blk brn & rose vio ... .60 .30
Nos. 339-342 (4) ... 2.40 1.20

### Enriquez de Rivera Type of 1945 Re-engraved

**1952, June 4**   **Perf. 12½**
343 A132 ½c violet ... .45 .30
344 A132 1c rose carmine ... .45 .30
345 A132 2c green ... .45 .30
346 A132 4c orange ... .85 .30
Nos. 343-346 (4) ... 2.20 1.20

A panel containing the dates "1660-1951" has been added below the portrait.

### Produce Type of 1950

Designs: ½c, Sugar cane field. 1c, Banana trees. 2c, Poptun Agricultural Colony.

**1953, Feb. 11**   **Photo.**   **Perf. 13½**
347 A137 ½c dk brn & dp bl ... .95 .30
348 A137 1c red org & ol grn ... .95 .30
349 A137 2c dk car & gray blk ... .95 .30
Nos. 347-349 (3) ... 2.85 .90

Issued to publicize farming.

Rafael Alvarez Ovalle and José Joaquin Palma — A145

**1953, May 13**
350 A145 ½c purple & blk ... .80 .40
351 A145 1c dk grn & org brn ... .80 .40
352 A145 2c org brn & ol grn ... .80 .40
353 A145 3c dk bl & ol grn ... .80 .40
Nos. 350-353 (4) ... 3.20 1.60

Authors of Guatemala's national anthem.
For overprints see Nos. 374-378.

Quetzal — A146

**1954, Sept. 27**   **Engr.**   **Perf. 12½, 11**
354 A146 1c dp violet blue ... 2.00 .30

See Nos. 367-373, 380-382A, 434-444. For overprint see No. 395.

Mario Camposeco — A147

10c, Carlos Aguirre Matheu. 15c, Goalkeeper.

**1955-56      Unwmk.      Perf. 12½**
355  A147  4c violet              1.10   .25
356  A147  4c carmine ('56)       1.10   .25
357  A147  4c blue grn ('56)      1.10   .25
358  A147  10c bluish grn         3.75   .75
359  A147  15c dark blue          3.75  2.00
      Nos. 355-359 (5)           10.80  3.50

50 years of Soccer in Guatemala.

Globe and Red
Cross — A148

Designs: 3c, Red Cross, Telephone and "5110." 4c, Nurse, patient and Red Cross flag.

**1956, May 23      Perf. 13x12½**
360  A148  1c brown & car         .60   .30
361  A148  3c dk green & red      .60   .30
362  A148  4c dk sl grn & red     .65   .30
      Nos. 360-362 (3)           1.85   .90

Red Cross. See Nos. B5-B7, CB5-CB7. For surcharges see Nos. CB8-CB10.

Dagger-Cross of the
Liberation — A149

1c, Map showing 2,000 km. (1,243 miles) of new roads. 3c, Oil production.

**1956      Engr.      Perf. 12½**
363  A149  ½c violet              .55   .30
364  A149  1c dk blue grn         .55   .30
      **Perf. 11**
365  A149  3c sepia               .55   .30
      Nos. 363-365 (3)           1.65   .90

Liberation of 1954-55. Issue dates: ½c, 1c, July 27; 3c, Oct. 31. See Nos. C210-C218.

**Quetzal Type of 1954**
**1957-58      Perf. 11, 12½**
367  A146  2c violet            1.00   .30
368  A146  3c carmine rose       1.20   .30
369  A146  3c ultra             1.20   .30
  a.  3c dark blue, perf. 11½ ('72)    —    —
370  A146  4c orange            1.50   .30
371  A146  5c brown             2.10   .30
372  A146  5c org ver ('58)     2.10   .30
373  A146  6c yellow grn        2.75   .30
      Nos. 367-373 (7)         11.85  2.10

No. 368 is only perf. 12½. The 2c, 4c and No. 369 are found in perf. 11 and 12½. Other values only perf. 11.

**No. 350 Ovptd. in Blue, Black, Carmine, Red Orange or Green**

**1958, Nov.-Dec.      Photo.      Perf. 13½**
374  A145  ½c purple & blk (Bl)   .90   .65
375  A145  ½c purple & blk (Bk)   .90   .65
376  A145  ½c purple & blk (C)    .90   .65
377  A145  ½c purple & blk (RO)   .90   .65
378  A145  ½c purple & blk (G)    .90   .65
      Nos. 374-378 (5)          4.50  3.25

Cent. of the birth of Rafael Alvarez Ovalle, composer of Guatemala's national anthem.

**Re-engraved Rivera Type of 1945**
**1959, Sept. 12  Engr.  Perf. 11, 12½**
379  A132  4c gray blue          .55   .30

See note after No. 346.

**Quetzal Type of 1954**
**1960-63      Unwmk.      Perf. 11**
380  A146  2c brown ('61)       1.10   .35
381  A146  4c lt violet         1.75   .35
382  A146  5c blue green        2.10   .35
      **Perf. 12½**
382A A146  5c slate gray ('63)  3.25   .55
      Nos. 380-382A (4)         8.20  1.60

Romulus and Remus
Statue, Rome — A150

**1961      Photo.      Perf. 14**
383  A150  3c blue                    .90   .30

Inauguration of the Plaza Italia.

**Las Casas Type of 1949**
**Perf. 11, 11½, 12½, 13½**
**1962-64      Engr.**
384  A136  ½c blue               .55   .30
385  A136  1c brt violet ('64)   .55   .30
386  A136  4c brown ('64)        .55   .30
      Nos. 384-386 (3)          1.65   .90

1871 Stamp — A151

**1963-66      Unwmk.      Perf. 11**
387  A151  10c carmine           .60   .30
388  A151  10c slate ('64)       .60   .30
      **Perf. 11½**
389  A151  10c olive brn ('66)   .60   .30
390  A151  20c dp purple ('64)   .95   .30
391  A151  20c dk blue ('65)     .95   .30
      Nos. 387-391 (5)          3.70  1.50

For souvenir sheet, see No. C310.

Pedro Bethancourt
Comforting Sick
Man — A152

**1964, Jan. 6      Engr.      Perf. 11**
394  A152  2½c olive bister      .70   .30

Beatification (1962-63) of Pedro Bethancourt (1626-67). See Nos. C319-C322. For overprints see Nos. C381-C382.

**Quetzal Type of 1957-58
Overprinted in Blue**

**1964, Dec. 29      Engr.      Perf. 12½**
395  A146  4c orange             .75   .30

15th anniv. (in 1963) of the Intl. Soc. of Guatemala Collectors.

Map of Guatemala
and British
Honduras — A153

**1967, Apr. 28  Litho.  Perf. 14x13½**
396  A153  4c ol, vio bl & dp rose   .80   .30
397  A153  5c ocher, vio bl & dp
                        org         .70   .30
398  A153  6c dp org, vio bl & gray  .70   .30
      Nos. 396-398 (3)           2.20   .90

Issued to state Guatemala's claim to British Honduras.
For overprints see Nos. C411-C413.

Quetzal, Mayan Ball
Game Goal — A154

**Lithographed and Engraved**
**1968, Oct. 15      Perf. 11½**
399  A154  1c blk, lt grn & red     1.20   .30
400  A154  5c yel, lt grn & red     1.60   .30
401  A154  8c org, lt grn & red     2.00   .30
402  A154  15c bl, lt grn & red     3.25   .30
403  A154  30c lt vio, lt grn & red 6.00  1.10
      Nos. 399-403 (5)            14.05  2.30

19th Olympic Games, Mexico City, 10/12-27. The 1c, 5c, 8c, 15c also exist perf 12½, 1c, 8c, perf 13½.
See Nos. 412-415. For overprints see Nos. 408-411, C431-C435.

Child and
Poinsettia — A155

**1968-70      Typo.      Perf. 13½**
404  A155  2½c grn, dp bis & car    .45   .25
405  A155  2½c grn, org & car
                           ('70)    .65   .55
406  A155  5c green, gray & car     .65   .25
407  A155  21c green, lil & car    1.50   .85
      Nos. 404-407 (4)            3.25  1.90

Issued to help abandoned children.

**Type of 1968 Overprinted in Black or Red**

**1970, Mar. 19      Litho.      Perf. 13½**
408  A154  8c org, lt grn & red     .70  1.25
409  A154  8c org, lt grn & red
                           (R)      .70  1.25
      **Perf. 12½**
410  A154  15c bl, lt grn & red    1.00  1.25
411  A154  15c bl, lt grn & red (R) 1.00  1.25
      Nos. 408-411 (4)            3.40  5.00

50th anniv. of ILO. Gold overprint believed to be a trial color.

**Type of 1968**
**1971      Typo. & Engr.      Perf. 11½**
412  A154  1c gray, yel grn & red   .60   .25
      **Typo.**
413  A154  5c brt pink, yel grn &
                           red     1.10   .25
414  A154  5c brown, grn & red     1.10   .25
415  A154  5c dk bl, grn & red     1.10   .55
      Nos. 412-415 (4)            3.90  1.30

Mayas and CARE
Package — A156

**1971-72      Typo.      Perf. 13½**
416  A156  1c black & multi        .55   .30
      **Perf. 11½**
417  A156  1c violet & multi ('72) .55   .30
418  A156  1c brown & multi ('72)  .55   .30
      Nos. 416-418 (3)            1.65   .90

10th anniv. of CARE in Guatemala, a US-Canadian Cooperative for American Relief Everywhere. Exist imperf. See No. C459.

**No. 338 (trimmed) Overprinted in Orange**
**Souvenir Sheet**

**Typo. & Engr.**
**1972, Oct. 23      Imperf.**
419  A142  Sheet of 2            1.75  1.75
  a.  1c rose carmine ("Munich")  .40   .40
  b.  10c deep ultra ("1972")     .50   .50

20th Olympic Games, Munich, Aug. 26-Sept. 11. Commemorative inscriptions on No. 338 at left, top and right have been trimmed off. Size: 61x45mm (approximately). Many varieties exist. Gold overprints probably are proofs.

Pres. Carlos
Arana
Osorio — A157

Designs: 3c, 5c, President Osorio seated, vert. 8c, Pres. Osorio standing, vert.

**1973-74      Typo.      Perf. 12½**
420  A157  2c blue & blk          .95   .30
421  A157  3c orange & brn       1.20   .30
422  A157  5c rose car & blk     1.50   .30
423  A157  8c black & brt grn    1.80   .30
  a.  Lithographed ('74)         1.20   .30
      Nos. 420-423 (4)            5.45  1.20

8th population and 3rd dwellings census, Mar. 26-Apr. 7, 1973.

Francisco
Ximenez — A158

**Typographed, Lithographed (#426)**
**1973-77      Perf. 11½, 13½ (#426)**
424  A158  2c black & emer        .50   .30
425  A158  3c dk brn & org        .50   .30
426  A158  3c black & yellow     1.00   .30
427  A158  6c black & brt bl     1.00   .30
      Nos. 424-427 (4)            3.00  1.20

Brother Francisco Ximenez, discoverer and translator of National Book of Guatemala. No. 427 issued for Intl. Book Year 1972.
Issued: 6c, 8/2; 2c, 1/14/75; No. 425, 3/5/75; No. 426, 9/26/77.

Sculpture of
Christ, by
Pedro de
Mendoza,
1643 — A159

8c, Sculpture by Lanuza Brothers, 18th century.

**1977, Apr. 4      Litho.      Perf. 11**
428  A159  6c purple & multi      .65   .35
429  A159  8c purple & multi      .65   .35
      Nos. 428-429,C614-C619 (8)  6.30  3.55

Holy Week 1977.

INTERFER 77
Emblem — A160

**1977, Oct. 31**    **Litho.**    **Perf. 11½**
430 A160 7c black & multi    .70   .30
INTERFER 77, 4th International Fair, Guatemala, Oct. 31-Nov. 13.

Rotary Intl., 75th Anniv. — A161

6c, Diamond and Quetzal. 10c, Paul P. Harris.

**1980, July 31**    **Litho.**    **Perf. 11½**
431 A161 4c shown    1.00   .25
432 A161 6c multicolored    1.00   .25
433 A161 10c multicolored    1.60   .60
    Nos. 431-433 (3)    3.60   1.10

**Quetzal Type of 1954**

**1984-87**    **Engr.**    **Perf. 12½**
434 A146 1c deep green    3.00   .90
435 A146 2c deep blue    3.00   .90
436 A146 3c olive green    3.00   2.75
437 A146 3c sepia    3.00   .90
438 A146 3c blue    3.00   .90
439 A146 3c red    3.00   2.75
440 A146 3c orange    3.00   2.75
441 A146 3c vermilion    3.00   2.75
442 A146 4c lt red brn    3.00   .90
443 A146 5c magenta    3.00   .90
444 A146 6c deep blue    3.00   2.75
    Nos. 434-444 (11)    33.00   19.15

Issued: Nos. 436-439, 2/20; No. 441, 6c, 4/25/86; 1c, 4c, 5c, 2/16/87; 2c, 3/25/87.

Miguel Angel Asturias
Cultural Center — A162

**Perf. 12½, 11½ (5c, 9c), 12½x11½ (4c), 13x12½ (6c)**

**1987-96**        **Litho.**
445 A162 1c light blue    .75   .30
446 A162 2c bister brown    .75   .30
447 A162 3c ultra    .75   .30
448 A162 4c bright pink    .75   .30
449 A162 5c orange    .75   .30
450 A162 6c pale green    .75   .30
451 A162 7c vermilion    .75   .30
452 A162 8c brt pink    .75   .30
453 A162 9c black    .75   .30
454 A162 10c pale green    .75   .30
    Nos. 445-454 (10)    7.50   3.00

Miguel Angel Asturias (1899-1974), 1967 Nobel laureate in literature.
Issued: 3c, 11/24; 7c, 11/17; 8c, 11/27; 10c, 12/8; 2c, 3/2/88; 5c, 3/23/90; 9c, 10/1/91; 4c, 6c, 3/16/93; 1c, 7/9/96.
For surcharge see No. 573.

Central American and Caribbean University Games — A163

Toucan as a participant in various events.

**1990**    **Litho.**    **Perf. 12½**
455 A163 15c shown    .35   .30
456 A163 20c Torch bearer, vert.    .50   .30
457 A163 25c Volleyball    .70   .30
458 A163 30c Soccer    .80   .30
459 A163 45c Karate    1.20   .30
460 A163 1q Baseball    2.75   .70
461 A163 2q Basketball    5.00   1.50
462 A163 3q Hurdles    8.25   2.50
    Nos. 455-462 (8)    19.55   6.20

Issued: 20c, 8/22; 30c, 3q, 7/10; others, 4/25.

A164

Oct. 20 Revolution, 50th Anniv. — A165

A166

Designs: 1q, Student holding book, rifle. 2q, Constitution, city buildings, San Carlos University, social security building.

**1994, Nov. 8**    **Litho.**    **Perf. 11½**
463 A164 40c multicolored    .35   .30
464 A165 60c multicolored    .60   .35
465 A164 1q multicolored    1.20   .65
466 A166 2q multicolored    1.90   1.25
467 A166 3q multicolored    3.25   1.75
    Nos. 463-467 (5)    7.30   4.30

UNICEF, 50th Anniv. — A167

Designs: 10c, Soldier hugging child, vert. 20c, Children flying on doves.

**1997, May 21**    **Litho.**    **Perf. 12½**
468 A167 10c multicolored    .55   .30
**Perf. 11½x12½**
469 A167 20c multicolored    .55   .30

Landmark Buildings — A168

Designs: 50c, Paraninfo University. 1q, Central American Brewery Building, vert.

**1997, Mar. 6**      **Perf. 12½**
470 A168 50c multicolored    .80   .30
471 A168 1q multicolored    1.30   .65

Famous Guatemalans With 1999 Birth Anniversaries — A169

Designs: 3q, Francisco Marroquin (b. 1499), first Guatemalan bishop. 4q, Jacinto Rodriguez Diaz (b. 1899), aviator. 8.75q, Miguel Angel Asturias (1899-1974), 1967 Nobel Laureate for Literature. 10q, Cesar Brañas (b. 1899), writer.

**2001, Oct. 9**    **Litho.**    **Perf. 12½x11½**
472-475 A169    Set of 4    29.50   10.00

A170        A170a

A170b

Designs: Nos. 476, 483a, Saint and churches. Nos. 477, 483b, Saint and bell. Nos. 478, 483c, Pope, Saint and church. Nos. 479, 483d, Saint, painting of nativity, and bell. Nos. 480, 483e, Pope and Guatemala Archbishop Quezada Toruño. Nos. 481, 483f, Pope, fountain and church decoration. Nos. 482, 483g, Pope and churches.

**2002, July 16**    **Litho.**    **Perf. 12½**
476 A170 20c multicolored    .25   .25
477 A170 25c multicolored    .30   .25
478 A170a 50c multicolored    .55   .25
479 A170 1q multicolored    1.05   .40
480 A170b 2q multicolored    2.10   .85
481 A170a 5q multicolored    5.25   2.25
482 A170a 8.75q multicolored    9.00   3.75
    Nos. 476-482 (7)    18.50   8.00

**Souvenir Sheet**
**Rouletted 8½**
483 A170   Sheet of 7, #a-g    20.00   20.00

Visit of Pope John Paul II and Canonization of St. Peter of San José Betancur (1626-67).

Universal Postal Union, 125th Anniv. (in 1999) — A171

Designs: 20c, Quetzal, air mail envelopes, globe, flags. 2q, UPU emblem, quetzal, envelopes. 3q, Globe, quetzal, UPU emblem. 5q, Map of Guatemala, globe, envelopes and flags.

**2002, Oct. 31**    **Litho.**    **Perf. 12½**
484-487 A171   Set of 4    8.50   4.25

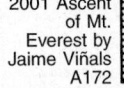

2001 Ascent of Mt. Everest by Jaime Viñals
A172

**2002, Nov. 22**
488 A172 3q multi    2.50   1.25

Pan-American Health Organization, Cent. — A173

**2002, Dec. 18**
489 A173 4q multi    3.25   1.60

St. Josemaría Escrivá de Balaguer (1902-75) — A174

Balaguer and: 20c, Farmer. 50c, Fisherman with boatful of fish. 3q, Fisherman, mountain. 10q, Church.

**2003**        **Litho.**    **Perf. 12¼**
490-493 A174   Set of 4    11.50   5.75

Masks for Dances — A175

Mask for: 20c, Dance of the Conquest. 2q, Dance of the Moors and Christians. 3q, Dance of the Deer. 4q, Dance of the Jaguar. 5q, Dance of Paabanc.

**2003, July 9**    **Litho.**    **Perf. 12½**
494-497 A175   Set of 4    11.00   8.00
**Souvenir Sheet**
**Rouletted 8½**
498 A175 5q multi    5.50   5.50

No. 498 was issued in sheets of 18 and has perf. 12½ margins.

Regional Sanitary Agricultural Organization, 50th Anniv. — A176

Designs: 20c, Banana picker. 1q, Hands in corn. 2q, Cow. 4q, Cultivated field. 5q, Sliced meat. 10q, Eye, map, ear of corn. 3q, Basket of vegetables.

**2003, Dec. 8**    **Litho.**    **Perf. 12½**
499-504 A176   Set of 6    16.00   8.00
**Souvenir Sheet**
**Rouletted 8¼**
505 A176 3q multi    3.00   3.00

Tourist Attractions of Izabal Department A177

Designs: 20c, Punta de Manabique. 50c, Siete Altares. 1q, Las Escobas. 1.50q, View between Barrios and Pichilingo. 2q, Acropolis, Quiriguá. 3q, Livingston on the Río Dulce. No. 512, 4q, Castle of San Felipe. 5q, El Estor. 8.75q, Agua Caliente. 10q, Río Polochic. No. 516, Quiriguá.

**2004, Jan. 30**        **Perf. 12½**
506-515 A177   Set of 10    26.50   13.50
**Souvenir Sheet**
**Rouletted 6½**
516 A177 4q multi    4.25   4.25

Elevation to Cardinal of Archbishop Rodolfo Quezada Toruño — A178

Designs: 20c, Cardinal, cathedral. 25c, Cardinal holding crucifix, cathedral. 50c, Cardinal wearing biretta kneeling before Pope. 1q, Cardinal wearing zucchetto kneeling before Pope. 2q, Cardinal holding biretta, wearing zucchetto. No. 522, 3q, Cardinal wearing zucchetto. 4q, Cardinal wearing miter. 5q, Cardinal kissing hand of Pope. 8.75q, Cardinal and bishops. 10q, Coat of arms No. 527, 3q, Statue of Virgin Mary.

**2004, Nov. 5**    **Litho.**    **Perf. 12½**
517-526 A178   Set of 10    25.00   12.50
**Souvenir Sheet**
**Rouletted 6½**
527 A178 3q multi    4.25   4.25

America Issue, Flora and Fauna — A179

Designs: 50c, Sarcoranphus papa. 3q, Heliconia collinsiana, vert. 5q, Felis concolor. 10q, Heliconius petiveranus. 12q, Tapirus vairdii.

**2005, Apr. 29**    **Litho.**    **Perf. 12½**
528 A179 50c multi    .80   .80
529 A179 3q multi    6.00   6.00
530 A179 5q multi    10.00   10.00
531 A179 10q multi    20.00   20.00
    Nos. 528-531 (4)    36.80   36.80

## Souvenir Sheet
### Rouletted 6½
532 A179 12q multi　　21.00 21.00

Diplomatic Relations Between Guatemala and Japan — A180

Flags of Guatemala and Japan and: 1q, Child, flowing well pipe, San Pedro La Laguna. 8q, Child, hospital, Puerto Barrios. 14q, Mt. Fuji.

**2005, July 29　Litho.　Perf. 12½**
533-534 A180　Set of 2　　5.75 5.75
### Souvenir Sheet
### Rouletted 8½
535 A180 14q multi　　8.50 8.50

Majolica — A181

Designs: 1q, Incense burner. 2q, Jars. 6.50q, Bowls. 8q, Lantern. 12q, Covered jar and sugar bowls.

**2005, Oct. 4　　Perf. 12½**
536-539 A181　Set of 4　　11.00 11.00
### Souvenir Sheet
### Rouletted 8½
540 A181 12q multi　　7.75 7.75

Rotary International, Cent. — A182

Designs: 2q, Emblem, handshake, Western Hemisphere. 6.50q, Emblem, Polio Plus emblem. 8q, Emblem.

**2005, Nov. 15　　Perf. 12½**
541-542 A182　Set of 2　　5.25 5.25
### Souvenir Sheet
### Rouletted 8½
543 A182 8q multi　　5.00 5.00

America Issue, Fight Against Poverty A183

No. 544, 50c: a, Open hands. b, Two children
No. 545, 5q: a, Clasped hands. b, Two children, diff.

**2006, Feb. 22　　Perf. 12½**
**Horiz. Pairs, #a-b**
544-545 A183　Set of 2　　7.25 7.25

Prof. José Joaquín Pardo, Historian, Cent. of Birth — A184

**2006, Feb. 28**
546 A184 3q multi　　2.00 2.00

Churches — A185

Designs: 50c, Santa Cruz Hermitage, Antigua Guatemala. 1q, San Jacinto Church, Salcajá. 2q, San Andres Xecul Church, Totonicapan, vert. 3q, El Calvario Church, Chichicastenango, vert. 4q, San Cristobal

Acasaguastlán, El Progreso, vert. 5q, Antigua Cathedral, Antigua Guatemala. 8q, San Pedro Church and Hospital, Antigua Guatemala. 10q, San Pedro Las Huertas Church, Antigua Guatemala. 14q, Metropolitan Cathedral, Guatemala City.

**2006, Mar. 15　　Perf. 12½**
547-554 A185　Set of 8　　21.00 21.00
### Souvenir Sheet
### Rouletted 8½
555 A185 14q multi　　11.00 11.00

Christmas — A186

Various ceramic creche figurines: 20c, 6.50q.

**2006, Nov. 27　Litho.　Perf. 12½**
556-557 A186　Set of 2　　4.50 4.50

Coffee Growing Regions — A187

Designs: 50c, Acatenango. 1q, Antigua. 2q, Atitlán. 6.50q, Cobán. 8q, Fraijanes. 10q, Huehue.
No. 564: a, 5q, Oriente. b, 20q, San Marcos.

**2006, Nov. 29　　Perf. 12½**
558-563 A187　Set of 6　　18.00 18.00
### Souvenir Sheet
### Rouletted 6½
564 A187　Sheet of 2, #a-b　　15.00 15.00

America Issue, Energy Conservation A188

Designs: 3q, Oil wells, gasoline pump nozzle. 10q, Light switch, solar panels.

**2006, Dec. 7　　Perf. 12½**
565-566 A188　Set of 2　　8.25 8.25

Diplomatic Relations Between Guatemala and Brazil, Cent. — A189

No. 567: a, Baile de la Conquista dancers. b, Maracatu dancers.

**2006, Dec. 12**
567 A189 4q Horiz. pair, #a-b　15.00 15.00

## Nos. 453, C850-C852, C863, C865, C870-C871 Surcharged

### Methods and Perfs As Before
**2007, Jan. 23**
| | | | | |
|---|---|---|---|---|
| 568 | AP186 | 50c on 40c #C850 | .35 | .35 |
| 569 | AP188 | 50c on 40c #C863 | .35 | .35 |
| 570 | AP186 | 1q on 60c #C851 | .60 | .60 |
| 571 | AP191 | 1q on 80c #C871 | 1.35 | 1.35 |
| 572 | AP188 | 3q on 60c #C865 | 2.10 | 2.10 |
| 573 | A162 | 5q on 9c #453 | 4.25 | 4.25 |
| 574 | AP186 | 8q on 80c #C852 | 5.75 | 5.75 |
| 575 | AP191 | 10q on 60c #C870 | 6.75 | 6.75 |
| | | *Nos. 568-575 (8)* | 21.50 | 21.50 |

"Aereo" on Nos. 568-572, 574-575 is not obliterated.

Year of Transparency (in 2006) — A190

Designs: 20c, Hand holding ball with map of Guatemala. 6.50q, Magnifying glass, fingerprint (45x25mm).

**2007, Jan. 23　Litho.　Perf. 12½**
576-577 A190　Set of 2　　5.50 5.50
　　Dated 2006.

Guatemala Philatelic Association, 75th Anniv. — A191

Designs: 1q, Guatemala #21. 3q, Guatemala #22. 6.50q, Guatemala #23. 8q, Guatemala #24. 25q, Guatemala #25.

**2007, July 19　Litho.　Perf. 12½**
578-581 A191　Set of 4　　10.00 9.50
### Souvenir Sheet
582 A191 25q multi　　18.00 18.00

Diplomatic Relations Between Guatemala and Uruguay, Cent. — A192

No. 583: a, Santa Catarina Arch, Antigua, Guatemala. b, City gate, Colonia del Sacramento, Uruguay.

**2007, Sept. 7**
583 A192 4q Horiz. pair, #a-b　　6.50 6.50
　　See Uruguay No. 2205.

America Issue, Education For All — A193

No. 584 — Stick figure children and: a, Blue panel. b, Red panel. c, Yellow orange panel. d, Green panel.

**2007, Oct. 25**
584 A193 4q Block of 4, #a-d　　9.00 9.00

Christmas — A194

Creche figures: 20c, Holy Family. 6.50q, Magi, horiz. (36x31mm).

**2007, Dec. 4**
585-586 A194　Set of 2　　3.75 3.75

Scouting, Cent. — A195

**2007, Dec. 5**
587 A195 20c multi　　.65 .40

Institute For Municipal Development, 50th Anniv. (in 2007) — A196

**2008, Jan. 30**
588 A196 3q multi　　1.75 1.75
　　Dated 2007.

Monsignor Juan Gerardi Conedera (1922-98) — A197

**2008, Apr. 25　Litho.　Perf. 12½**
589 A197 8q multi　　3.50 3.50

19th Cent. Defensive Bulwarks of Guatemala City — A198

No. 590: a, San Rafael de Matamoros. b, San José de Buena Vista.

**2008, June 27**
590 A198 1q Horiz. pair, #a-b　1.40 1.00

2008 Summer Olympics, Beijing — A199

**2008, Oct. 17　Litho.　Perf. 12½**
591 A199 6.50q multi　　2.50 2.50

Birds — A200

Designs: 50c, Trogon violaceus braccatus. 1q, Amarilia beryllina viola. 2q, Turdus rufitorques. 4q, Glaucidium brasilianum ridgwayi. 20q, Brotogeris jugularis.

**2008, Nov. 14**
592-595 A200　Set of 4　　4.25 4.25
### Souvenir Sheet
596 A200 20q multi　　9.50 9.50

Christmas — A201

Needlepoint: 20c, Flower. 8q, Christmas tree.

**2008, Dec. 2　　　Litho.**
597-598 A201　Set of 2　　3.75 3.75

Franciscan Order, 800th Anniv. (in 2009) — A202

**2008, Dec. 16**
599 A202 3q multi　　1.50 1.40

Consecration of Basilica of Esquipulus, 250th Anniv. — A203

**2009, Jan. 3**
**600** A203 50c multi .75 .50

Natl. Marine Defense, 50th Anniv. — A204

**2009, Jan. 12**
**601** A204 1q multi 2.25 2.00

America Issue, National Festivals — A205

Designs: 50c, Dancers, Comalapa. 2q, All Saints Day Festival, Santiago Sacatepequez. 3q, Dancers and marimba players. 5q, Dancers.
8q, Cofrades y Capitanas.

**2009, Feb. 6**
**602-605** A205 Set of 4 5.00 5.00
**Souvenir Sheet**
**606** A205 8q multi 3.50 3.50

Native Costumes — A206

Designs: 50c, San Juan Atitán man. 1q, San Juan Sacatepéquez woman. 2q, Tamahú woman. 3q, San Rafael Petzal woman. 4q, Totonicapán man. 5q, Patzicia woman. 8q, San Pedro San Marcos woman.
10q, San Juan Cotzal man and woman.

**2009, Apr. 14 Litho. Perf. 12½**
**607-613** A206 Set of 7 22.00 22.00
**Souvenir Sheet**
**614** A206 10q multi 31.00 31.00
See Nos. 645-648.

Marimbas A207

Designs: 3q, Gourd marimba. 4q, 18th cent. marimba. 5q, Double marimba. 8q, Concert marimba. 10q, Man playing marimba.

**2009, Oct. 30**
**615-619** A207 Set of 5 12.00 12.00

Louis Braille (1809-52), Educator of the Blind — A208

**2009, Nov. 13 Litho. & Embossed**
**620** A208 1q multi 1.00 .75

Christmas A209

Beaded ornaments: 20c, Spheres. 50c, Reindeer. 1q, Angels. 6.50q, Star.

**2009, Dec. 4 Litho.**
**621-624** A209 Set of 4 4.00 4.00

Battle of La Arada, 150th Anniv. (in 2011) A210

No. 625: a, Sword and arms. b, Pres. Rafael Carrera.
10q, Carrera, vert.

**2010, Feb. 12 Perf. 12½**
**625** A210 5q Horiz. pair, #a-b 4.00 4.00
**Souvenir Sheet**
**626** A210 10q multi 3.75 3.75

America Issue — A211

Traditional toys and games: 50c, Capitucho. 1q, Barillete (kite). 6.50q, Yo-yo. 8q, Trompo (top).

**2010, Mar. 17**
**627-630** A211 Set of 4 6.50 6.50
Dated 2009.

José Ernesto Monzón (1917-2003), Musician — A212

**2010, Aug. 6 Litho. Perf. 12½**
**631** A212 2q multi 1.00 .75

Tourist Sites in Chiquimula Department A213

No. 632: a, Ipala Volcano. b, Ipala Lake.

**2010, Sept. 11**
**632** A213 8q Vert. pair, #a-b 6.00 6.00

Christmas — A214

No. 633: a, Joseph. b, Infant Jesus and Star of Bethlehem. c, Mary.

**2010, Dec. 2**
**633** A214 3q Horiz. strip of 3, #a-c 3.75 3.75

Textile Art by Priscilla Bianchi — A215

Various designs.

**2010, Dec. 15 Perf. 12½**
**634** A215 20c multi .30 .30
   *a.* Dated "2016" .30 .30

| | | | | |
|---|---|---|---|---|
| **635** | A215 | 50c multi | .30 | .30 |
| *a.* | Dated "2016" | | .30 | .30 |
| **636** | A215 | 1q multi | .30 | .30 |
| *a.* | Dated "2016" | | .30 | .30 |
| **637** | A215 | 2q multi | .75 | .75 |
| *a.* | Dated "2016" | | .55 | .55 |
| **638** | A215 | 3q multi | 1.10 | 1.10 |
| **639** | A215 | 4q multi | 1.30 | 1.30 |
| **640** | A215 | 5q multi | 1.50 | 1.50 |
| *a.* | Dated "2016" | | 1.40 | 1.40 |
| **641** | A215 | 6.50q multi | 2.50 | 2.50 |
| **642** | A215 | 8q multi | 2.75 | 2.75 |
| *a.* | Dated "2016" | | 2.10 | 2.10 |
| **643** | A215 | 10q multi | 3.50 | 3.50 |
| *a.* | Dated "2016" | | 2.75 | 2.75 |
| | *Nos. 634-643 (10)* | | 14.30 | 14.30 |

See Nos. 709-711.

Postal Union of the Americas, Spain and Portugal (UPAEP), Cent. — A216

**2011, Mar. 23 Litho. Perf. 12½**
**644** A216 2q multi 1.25 .75

**Native Costumes Type of 2009**

Designs: 50c, San Mateo Ixtatán woman. 5q, Almolonga man. 6.50q, Tecpán woman. 10q, Palín man and women.

**2011, May 17**
**645-647** A206 Set of 3 5.25 5.25
**Souvenir Sheet**
**648** A206 10q multi 4.00 4.00

National Journalism Library, 50th Anniv. — A217

**2011, May 17 Litho. Perf. 12½**
**649** A217 5q multi 2.10 2.10

Phragmipedium Humboltii A218

**2011, June 29**
**650** A218 5q multi 2.10 2.10
Alexander von Humboldt (1769-1859), naturalist.

America Issue, National Symbols — A219

Designs: 20c, Ceiba tree. 10q, White nun orchids.

**2011, Sept. 14 Litho. Perf. 12½**
**651-652** A219 Set of 2 4.25 4.25

Republic of China, Cent. A220

**2011, Oct. 3**
**653** A220 2q multi 1.25 .75

Civil Aviation in Guatemala, Cent. — A221

**2011, Dec. 8**
**654** A221 8q multi 3.25 3.25

Christmas — A222

Creche scenes from: 4q, Señora de las Misericordias Church. 10q, Merced Parish Church.

**2011, Dec. 9**
**655-656** A222 Set of 2 5.50 5.50

José Joaquín Palma (1844-1911), Poet — A223

**2011, Dec. 23**
**657** A223 1q multi .75 .35

Mailbox — A224

**2012, Oct. 22**
**658** A224 5q multi 2.00 2.00
America issue.

Museums in a Changing World — A225

No. 659: a, Pre-Columbian figurines (goat at right). b, Modern figurines (goat at left).

**2012, Dec. 11**
**659** A225 4q Horiz. pair, #a-b 3.25 3.25

Max Tott Half Marathon, Guatemala City, 75th Anniv. — A226

**2012, Dec. 12**
**660** A226 8q multi 3.00 3.00

Daughters of Charity of St. Vincent de Paul, 150th Anniv. in Guatemala — A227

**2012, Dec. 13**
**661** A227 6.50q multi 2.50 2.50

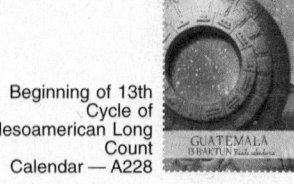

Beginning of 13th
Cycle of
Mesoamerican Long
Count
Calendar — A228

Designs: 1q, Calendar wheel. 2q, Leiden Plate. 3q, Zoomorph P, Quiriguá. 4q, Pelota player holding calendar wheel. No. 666, Stela D, Quiriguá. No. 667, Pelota player holding ball. 8q, Stela C, Quiriguá. No. 669, Mayan Ab' calendar. No. 670, Mixco Viejo Archaeological Site.

| 2012, Dec. 17 | Litho. | Perf. 12½ | |
|---|---|---|---|
| 662 A228 | 1q multi | .40 | .40 |
| 663 A228 | 2q multi | .85 | .85 |
| 664 A228 | 3q multi | 1.20 | 1.20 |
| 665 A228 | 4q multi | 1.60 | 1.60 |
| a. | Booklet pane of 3, #662, 663, 665 | 4.50 | — |
| 666 A228 | 5q multi | 2.10 | 2.10 |
| 667 A228 | 6q multi | 2.10 | 2.10 |
| 668 A228 | 8q multi | 3.00 | 3.00 |
| 669 A228 | 10q multi | 4.00 | 4.00 |
| a. | Booklet pane of 3, #666, 668, 669 | 11.00 | — |
| 670 A228 | 10q multi | 4.00 | 4.00 |
| a. | Booklet pane of 3, #664, 667, 670 | 9.50 | — |
| | Complete booklet, #665a, 669a, 670a | 27.50 | |
| | Nos. 662-670 (9) | 19.25 | 19.25 |

A229

Emblem and motorcyclists with: No. 671, Pale orange color at lower corners. No. 672, Gray color at lower corners.

| 2013, Feb. 2 | Litho. | Perf. 12½ | |
|---|---|---|---|
| 671 A229 | 10q multi | 3.75 | 3.50 |

**Souvenir Sheet**

| 672 A229 | 10q multi | 3.75 | 3.50 |

Caravana del Zorro motorcycle ride from Guatemala City to Esquipulas, 50th anniv.

Rodolfo Galeotti Torres (1912-88), and His Sculpture "La Puerta del Saber" — A230

| 2013, Sept. 27 | Litho. | Perf. 12½ | |
|---|---|---|---|
| 673 A230 | 50c multi | 1.25 | .35 |

America
Issue — A231

Myths and legends: 1q, El Sombrerón. 5q, La Tatuana. 8q, La Llorona. 10q, Xocomil.

| 2013, Oct. 11 | Litho. | Perf. 12½ | |
|---|---|---|---|
| 674-677 A231 | Set of 4 | 9.00 | 9.00 |

Christmas
A232

Designs: 2q, Angels. 3q, Nativity scene.

| 2013, Nov. 14 | Litho. | Perf. 12½ | |
|---|---|---|---|
| 678-679 A232 | Set of 2 | 2.75 | 2.00 |

Villa Nueva,
250th Anniv.
A233

| 2013, Dec. 13 | Litho. | Perf. 12½ | |
|---|---|---|---|
| 680 A233 | 6.50q multi | 3.25 | 2.50 |

Abies Guatemalensis — A234

No. 681: a, Grove of trees (48x30mm). b, Cones on tree (28x30mm).

| 2014, Jan. 13 | Litho. | Perf. 12½ | |
|---|---|---|---|
| 681 A234 | 5q Horiz. pair, #a-b | 4.00 | 3.00 |

Jesus Nazareno de
Candelaria Statue,
450th Anniv. — A235

| 2014, Feb. 5 | Litho. | Perf. 12½ | |
|---|---|---|---|
| 682 A235 | 20c multi | .75 | .35 |

Native
Cuisine — A236

Designs: 2q, Plátanos en mole (plantains in mole sauce). 5q, Kaq Ik (turkey in tomato sauce). 6q, Pepián (chicken in vegetable sauce). 10q, Jocón (chicken in tomatillo and cilantro sauce).

| 2014, Mar. 4 | Litho. | Perf. 12½ | |
|---|---|---|---|
| 683-686 A236 | Set of 4 | 9.50 | 8.00 |

Numismatic
Museum of
Guatemala
A237

| 2014, Mar. 28 | Litho. | Perf. 12½ | |
|---|---|---|---|
| 687 A237 | 50c multi | .65 | .40 |

Items
Made of
Jade
A238

No. 688: a, Bracelet with jaguar heads, sculpture of God of Corn, three carved jaguars. b, Carved jaguar, Tikal funerary mask, nahuales. c, Ring, nahuales, sculpture of King of Corn,

| 2014, Apr. 3 | Litho. | Perf. 12½ | |
|---|---|---|---|
| 688 A238 | 50c Horiz. strip of 3, #a-c | 1.60 | .80 |

Lizards — A239

Designs: 1q, Abronia vasconcelosi. 5q, Abronia fimbriata. 6.50q, Abronia meledona. 10q, Abronia frosti.

| 2014, July 4 | Litho. | Perf. 12½ | |
|---|---|---|---|
| 689-692 A239 | Set of 4 | 9.25 | 7.00 |

Campaign
Against
Discrimination
A240

| 2014, Aug. 6 | Litho. | Perf. 12½ | |
|---|---|---|---|
| 693 A240 | 1q multi | 2.25 | .35 |

America issue.

Landscapes
A241

Designs: 1q, Volcán de Fuego and Acatenango. 3q, El Pino Lake. 6.50q, Magdalena Lake. 8q, Lake Chicabal.

| 2014, Aug. 12 | Litho. | Perf. 12½ | |
|---|---|---|---|
| 694-697 A241 | Set of 4 | 7.75 | 6.50 |

**Souvenir Sheet**

Virgen del Carmen Chapel, Guatemala
City, 400th Anniv. — A242

| 2014, Nov. 21 | Litho. | Perf. 12½ | |
|---|---|---|---|
| 698 A242 | 10q multi | 4.00 | 3.00 |

Christmas
A243

Religious paintings from Our Lady of Peace Church and text: 6.50q, Feliz Navidad. 8q, Bendicianes.

| 2014, Nov. 25 | Litho. | Perf. 12½ | |
|---|---|---|---|
| 699-700 A243 | Set of 2 | 6.00 | 5.00 |

America
Issue — A244

Designs: 20c, Juan José Arévalo (1904-90), first democratically elected president of Guatemala. 10q, Juan Matalbatz, K'iche' chief converted to Christianity, Spanish provincial governor.

| 2014, Dec. 10 | Litho. | Perf. 12½ | |
|---|---|---|---|
| 701-702 A244 | Set of 2 | 4.50 | 3.50 |

Guatemala, 2015
Iberoamerican Capital of
Culture — A245

Designs: 2q, Parrot holding torch. 8q, Stylized birds in flight (46x31mm).

| 2015, Feb. 26 | Litho. | Perf. 12½ | |
|---|---|---|---|
| 703-704 A245 | Set of 2 | 3.25 | 3.00 |
| 704a | Booklet pane of 8, 4 each #703-704 | 19.50 | |
| | Complete booklet, #704a | 19.50 | |

Complete booklet sold for 50q.

Metropolitan
Cathedral,
Guatemala
City, Bicent.
A246

Designs: 50c, Dome. 5q, Interior. 6.50q, Clock tower.

| 2015, Apr. 24 | Litho. | Perf. 12½ | |
|---|---|---|---|
| 705-707 A246 | Set of 3 | 5.50 | 4.50 |

A booklet containing panes of one of each stamp sold for 40q. Value, $16.

Postal Headquarters — A247

No. 708 — Postal Headquarters in: a, Guatemala (denomination at left). b, Paraguay (denomination at right).

| 2015, Aug. 13 | Litho. | Perf. 12½ | |
|---|---|---|---|
| 708 A247 | 4q Horiz. pair, #a-b | 3.25 | 2.50 |

See Paraguay No. 3030.

**Textile Art Type of 2010**

Various designs.

| 2015, Feb. 15 | Litho. | Perf. 12½ | |
|---|---|---|---|
| 709 A215 | 25q multi | 8.75 | 8.75 |
| a. | Dated "2016" | 8.75 | 8.75 |
| 710 A215 | 50q multi | 17.50 | 17.50 |
| a. | Dated "2016" | 17.50 | 17.50 |
| 711 A215 | 100q multi | 34.00 | 34.00 |
| a. | Dated "2016" | 34.00 | 34.00 |

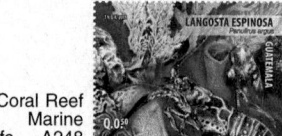

Coral Reef
Marine
Life — A248

Designs: 50c, Panulirus argus. 5q, Pomacanthus paru. 6.50q, Sparisoma viride. 10q, Chelonia mydas.

| 2015, Sept. 25 | Litho. | Perf. 12½ | |
|---|---|---|---|
| 712-715 A248 | Set of 4 | 8.25 | 6.50 |
| 715a | Souvenir sheet of 4, #712-715 | 20.50 | 20.50 |

Guatemala No.
C260 — A249

| 2015, Nov. 6 | Litho. | Perf. 12½ | |
|---|---|---|---|
| 716 A249 | 6.50q multi | 2.75 | 1.00 |

Discovery of onchocerciasis in Central America by Dr. Rodolfo Robles, cent.

Campaign to End
Violence Against
Women — A250

| 2015, Nov. 25 | Litho. | Perf. 12½ | |
|---|---|---|---|
| 717 A250 | 8q multi | 3.50 | 1.75 |

See Dominican Republic No. 1583, Ecuador No. 2173, El Salvador No. 1747, Venezuela No. 1731.

Christmas — A251

Designs: 50c, Wreath and toy horse. 5q, Christmas tree decorated with ornaments (30x56mm).

| 2015, Dec. 1 | Litho. | Perf. 12½ |
|---|---|---|
| 718-719 A251 | Set of 2 | 2.75 1.50 |

Guatemala Military Engineers, 125th Anniv. — A252

No. 720: a, Military engineers and building (45x30mm). b, Surveyors and vehicles (25x30mm). c, Vehicles and bridge (45x30mm).

| 2015, Dec. 3 | Litho. | Perf. 12½ |
|---|---|---|
| 720 A252 1q Horiz. strip of 3, #a-c | | 2.00 1.25 |

Campaign Against Human Trafficking — A253

No. 721: a, Black hand, broken chain. b, Orange hand, Sun.

| 2015, Dec. 11 | Litho. | Perf. 12½ |
|---|---|---|
| 721 A253 4q Horiz. pair, #a-b | | 3.75 1.90 |

America Issue.

Orchids — A254

Designs: 1q, Pleurothallis orchilarum. 2q, Lycaste dowiana var. isabelli. 3q, Brassia brunnea. 4q, Selbyana oscarrodrogoii. 5q, Lycaste guatemelensis.
10q, Lycaste virginalis forme alba.

| 2020, Oct. 9 | Litho. | Perf. 10½ |
|---|---|---|
| 722-726 A254 | Set of 5 | 6.25 3.00 |
| **Souvenir Sheet** | | |
| 727 A254 10q multi | | 3.50 1.75 |

Christmas — A255

| 2020, Dec. 11 | Litho. | Perf. 12½ |
|---|---|---|
| 728 A255 6q multi | | 2.25 1.10 |

A256

America Issue A257

Designs: 1q, Children's drawing by Sofía Luttmann.
No. 730: a, Guatemala Olympic Committee emblem. b, Dog. c, Salad and toppings. d, Atitlán Volcano and Lake Atitlán.

| 2020, Dec. 16 | Litho. | Perf. 12½ |
|---|---|---|
| 729 A256 1q multi | | .65 .35 |
| **Miniature Sheet** | | |
| 730 A257 5q Sheet of 4, #a-d | | 5.25 2.60 |

Ludwig van Beethoven (1770-1827), Composer — A258

| 2021, Apr. 29 | Litho. | Perf. 10½ |
|---|---|---|
| 731 A258 7q multi | | 2.75 1.40 |

Independence of Guatemala, 200th Anniv. — A259

Designs: 5q, Conspiracy of Belen, 1813. No. 733, 10q, Atanasio Tzul (1760-1830), leader of Totonicapán Indigenous Uprising of 1820 declared later as king. No. 734, 10q, Dolores Bedoya (1783-1853), organizer of women in independence movement. 20q, September 15, 1821 proclamation of independence. 25q, Establishment of the United Provinces of Central America, 1823.

**Litho. With Foil Application**

| 2021, June 1 | | Perf. 10½ |
|---|---|---|
| 732-736 A259 | Set of 5 | 24.00 20.00 |

Souvenir Sheet

Establishment of City of Chiquimula, 200th Anniv. — A260

No. 737: a, Clock tower. b, Priest and steam locomotive.

| 2021, June 29 | Litho. | Perf. 10½ |
|---|---|---|
| 737 A260 25q Sheet of 2, #a-b | | 16.50 13.00 |

Arms of the Republic of Guatemala and QR Code — A261

**Litho. With Foil Application**

| 2021, Sept. 6 | | Perf. 10½ |
|---|---|---|
| 738 A261 25q gold & multi | | 13.00 6.50 |

Independence of Guatemala, 200th anniv.

Independence of Guatemala, 200th Anniv. — A262

Designs: 4q, 1871 flag and coat of arms of Guatemala. 6q, Introduction of railroads to Guatemala, 1884. 7q, Second Totoposte War, 1903. 8q, Allegory of the Union of the Pacific and Atlantic, 1908. 10q, Centenary of Guatemalan Independence, 1921. 15q, 1-quetzal coin, 1924.

**Litho. With Foil Application**

| 2021, Sept. 8 | | Perf. 10½ |
|---|---|---|
| 739-744 A262 | Set of 6 | 26.00 13.00 |

Independence of Guatemala, 200th Anniv. — A263

Designs: 1q, Guatemala Social Security Institute labor code, 1947. 4q, Development of the arts. 25q, Jurun Marinala Hydroelectric Project.

**Litho. With Foil Application**

| 2021, Sept. 13 | | Perf. 10½ |
|---|---|---|
| 745-747 A263 | Set of 3 | 15.00 7.75 |

Independence of Guatemala, 200th Anniv. — A264

Designs: 10q, Political Constitution of 1985. 15q, Signing of the 1996 peace accords.

**Litho. With Foil Application**

| 2021, Sept. 14 | | Perf. 10½ |
|---|---|---|
| 748-749 A264 | Set of 2 | 17.00 6.50 |

Souvenir Sheet

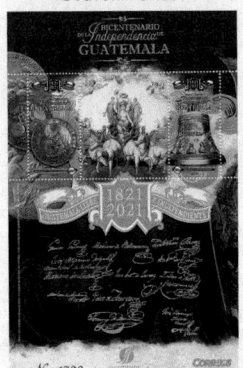

Independence of Guatemala, 200th Anniv. — A265

No. 750: a, Independence medal, 1821. b, Voices of Freedom Bell.

**Litho., Sheet Margin Litho. With Foil Application**

| 2021, Sept. 14 | | Perf. 10½ |
|---|---|---|
| 750 A265 50q Sheet of 2, #a-b | | 32.50 30.00 |

Guatemalan Air Force, Cent. A266

Various airplanes and air force members in: No. 751, 10q, Black-and-white photographs. No. 752, 10q, Color photographs.

| 2021, Nov. 5 | Litho. | Perf. 10½ |
|---|---|---|
| 751-752 A266 | Set of 2 | 5.25 5.25 |
| 752a | Souvenir sheet of 2, #751-752 | 5.25 5.25 |

First Guatemalan Postage Stamps, 150th Anniv. — A267

Designs: 5q, Guatemala #1. 10q, Guatemala #2. 15q, Guatemala #3. 20q, Guatemala #4.

| 2021, Dec. 10 | Litho. | Perf. 10½ |
|---|---|---|
| 753-756 A267 | Set of 4 | 12.50 12.50 |

A booklet pane containing four lithographed and engraved stamps similar to Nos. 753-756 sold for 150q.

Attractions at IRTRA Amusement Park — A268

No. 757 — Various park attractions with inscription: a, Fantasía. b, Descanso. c, Adrenalina. d, Aventura. e, Felicidad.

| 2022, Aug. 17 | | Perf. 10½ |
|---|---|---|
| 757 | Booklet pane of 5 + 6 labels | 12.00 |
| a. | A268 1q multi + label | .30 .30 |
| b. | A268 4q multi + label | 1.00 1.00 |
| c. | A268 10q multi + label | 2.60 2.60 |
| c. | A268 10q Either single + label | 4.00 4.00 |
| | Complete booklet, #757 | 12.00 |

Souvenir Sheet

America Issue A269

No. 758 — Guatemala City architecture: a, Edificio Las Gemas. b, TIC Intecap Building.

| 2022, Sept. 17 | Litho. | Perf. 10½ |
|---|---|---|
| 758 A269 15q Sheet of 2, #a-b | | 7.75 7.75 |

## SEMI-POSTAL STAMPS

**Regular Issues of 1935-36 Surcharged in Blue or Red**

| 1937, Mar. 15 | Unwmk. | Perf. 12½ |
|---|---|---|
| B1 A102 1c + 1c brn & crim | | .75 1.00 |
| B2 A103 3c + 1c rose car & pck grn | | .75 1.00 |

**B3** A103 3c + 1c red org & pck grn .75 1.00
**B4** A106 5c +1c bl & dk brn (R) .75 1.00
Nos. B1-B4 (4) 3.00 4.00
1st Phil. Exhib. held in Guatemala, Mar. 15-20.

> **Catalogue values for unused stamps in this section, from this point to the end of the section, are for Never Hinged items.**

## Type of Regular Issue, 1956

Designs: 5c+15c, Nurse, Patient and Red Cross Flag. 15c+50c, Red Cross, telephone and "5110." 25c+50c, Globe and Red Cross.

**1956, June 19   Engr.   Perf. 13x12½**
**B5** A148 5c + 15c ultra & red 1.00 1.40
  *a.* Imperf., pair 75.00
**B6** A148 15c + 50c dk vio & red 2.25 2.75
**B7** A148 25c + 50c bluish blk & car 2.25 2.75
Nos. B5-B7 (3) 5.50 6.90
The surtax was for the Red Cross.

Jesus and Esquipulas Cathedral — SP1

**1957, Oct. 29   Perf. 13**
**B8** SP1 1½c + ½c blk & brn .85 .30
The surtax was for the Esquipulas highway. See Nos. CB12-CB14.

## Type of Air Post Semi-Postal Stamps and

Arms — SP2

3c+3c, Wounded man, Battle of Solferino.

**1960, Apr. 9   Photo.   Perf. 13½x14**
**Cross in Rose Red**
**B9** SP2 1c + 1c red brn & bl .65 .30
**B10** SP2AP2 3c + 3c lil, bl & pink .65 .30
**B11** SP2 4c + 4c blk & bl .65 .30
Nos. B9-B11 (3) 1.95 .90

Cent. (in 1959) of the Red Cross idea. The surtax went to the Red Cross. Exist imperf. See Nos. CB15-CB21.

---

# AIR POST STAMPS

No. 229 Surcharged in Red

**1929, May 20   Unwmk.   Perf. 12½**
**C1** A64 3c on 15p blk 1.10 1.40
**C2** A64 5c on 15p blk .55 .45
**C3** A64 15c on 15p blk 1.50 .45
  *a.* Double surcharge (G & R) 100.00
**C4** A64 20c on 15p blk 2.25 2.25
  *a.* Inverted surcharge 100.00
  *b.* Double surcharge 100.00

No. 216 Surcharged in Red

**1929, May 20   Perf. 14**
**C5** A64 5c on 15p black 3.25 2.25
Nos. C1-C5 (5) 8.65 6.80

---

No. 218 Surcharged in Black

**1929, Oct. 9**
**C6** A75 3c on 2.50p dk vio 1.00 1.00

Airplane and Mt. Agua — AP3

**1930, June 4   Litho.   Perf. 12½**
**C7** AP3 6c rose red 5.00 5.00
  *a.* Imperf., pair 25.00 25.00
  *b.* Imperf., pair 390.00
For overprint see No. C14.

Nos. 227, 229 Surcharged in Black or Red

**1930, Dec. 9   Perf. 12½**
**C8** A57 1c on 3p grn (Bk) .40 .40
  *a.* Double surcharge 100.00
**C9** A57 2c on 3p grn (Bk) 1.10 1.50
**C10** A57 3c on 3p grn (R) 1.10 1.50
**C11** A57 4c on 3p grn (R) 1.10 1.50
**C12** A64 10c on 15p blk (R) 5.00 5.00
  *a.* Double surcharge 125.00
Nos. C8-C12 (5) 8.70 9.90

No. 237 Overprinted

**1931, May 19   Perf. 14**
**C13** A81 4c orange .40 .30
  *a.* Double overprint 40.00 50.00

## No. C7 Overprinted

**Perf. 12½**
**C14** AP3 6c rose red 2.00 2.00
  *a.* On No. C7a 30.00 30.00
  *b.* Inverted overprint 12.50 12.50

Nos. 240, 242 Overprinted in Red

**1931, Oct. 21   Perf. 14**
**C15** A36 15c ultra 2.00 .25
  *a.* Double overprint 125.00 125.00
**C16** A76 30c green 3.00 .95
  *a.* Double overprint 75.00 75.00

Nos. 235-236 Overprinted in Red or Green

**1931, Dec. 5**
**C17** A79 2c dp bl (R) 2.50 3.00
**C18** A80 3c dk vio (G) 2.50 3.00

No. 240 Overprinted in Red

**C19** A36 15c ultra 10.00 3.00
Nos. C17-C19 were issued in connection with the 1st postal flight from Barrios to Miami.

---

No. 224 Surcharged in Red

**1932-33   Perf. 12½**
**C20** A74 2c on 1.50p dk bl 2.50 .55

Nos. 227, 229 Surcharged in Violet, Red or Blue

**C21** A57 3c on 3p grn (V) .85 .25
  *a.* Inverted surcharge 45.00 45.00
  *b.* Vert. pair, imperf. horiz. 900.00
**C22** A57 3c on 3p grn (R) .85 .25
**C23** A64 10c on 15p blk (R) 9.00 6.25
  *a.* First "I" of "Interior" missing 10.00 10.00
**C24** A64 15c on 15p blk (Bl) 10.75 8.50
  *a.* First "I" of "Interior" missing 15.00 15.00
Nos. C20-C24 (5) 23.95 15.80
Issued: No. C22, 1/1/33; others, 2/11/32.

No. 237 Overprinted in Green

**1933, Jan. 1   Perf. 14**
**C25** A81 4c orange 2.50 .35
  *a.* Double overprint 40.00 40.00

Nos. 235, 238 and 240 Overprinted in Red or Black

**1934, Aug. 7**
**C26** A82 5c dk car (Bk) 3.00 .30
**C27** A36 15c ultra (R) 3.00 .30

Overprinted in Red

**C28** A79 2c deep blue .55 .30

View of Port Barrios — AP7

Designs: 15c, Tomb of Barrios. 30c, Equestrian Statue of Barrios.

**1935, July 19   Photo.   Perf. 12½**
**C29** AP7 10c yel brn & pck grn 6.00 4.50
**C30** AP7 15c gray & brn 1.50 1.75
**C31** AP7 30c car rose & bl vio 1.50 1.25
Nos. C29-C31 (3) 9.00 7.50
Birth cent. of Gen. Justo Rufino Barrios.

Lake Amatitlán — AP10

Designs: Nos. C36, C37, C45, C46. Different views of Lake Amatitlan. 3c, Port Barrios. No. C34, C35, Ruins of Fort San Felipe. 10c, Port Livingston. No. C39, C40, Port San Jose. No. C41, C42, View of Atitlan. No. C43, C44, Aurora Airport.

## Overprinted with Quetzal in Green

**1935-37    Size: 37x17mm**
**C32** AP10 2c org brn .55 .55
**C33** AP10 3c blue .55 .55
**C34** AP10 4c black .55 .55
**C35** AP10 4c ultra ('37) .55 .55
**C36** AP10 6c yel grn .55 .55
**C37** AP10 6c blk vio ('37) 9.00 .55
**C38** AP10 10c claret 1.10 .55
**C39** AP10 15c red org 1.50 .90
**C40** AP10 15c yel grn ('37) 1.50 1.50
**C41** AP10 30c olive grn 13.50 15.00
**C42** AP10 30c ol bis ('37) 1.75 1.10
**C43** AP10 50c rose vio 40.00 35.00

---

**C44** AP10 50c Prus bl ('36) 9.00 7.00
**C45** AP10 1q scarlet 40.00 45.00
**C46** AP10 1q car ('36) 10.00 7.00
Nos. C32-C46 (15) 130.10 116.35
Issue dates follow No. C69.
For overprints and surcharges see Nos. C70-C79, CB1-CB2.

Central Park, Antigua — AP11

Designs: 1c, Guatemala City. 2c, Central Park, Guatemala City. 3c, Monastery. Nos. C50-C51, Mouth of Dulce River. Nos. C52-C53, Plaza Barrios. Nos. C54-C55, Los Proceres Monument. No. C56, Central Park, Antigua. No. C57, Dulce River. Nos. C58-C59, Quezaltenango. Nos. C60-C61, Ruins at Antigua. Nos. C62-C63, Dock at Port Barrios. Nos. C64-C65, Port San Jose. Nos. C66-C67, Aurora Airport. 2.50q, Island off Atlantic Coast. 5q, Atlantic Coast view.

## Overprinted with Quetzal in Green

**Size: 34x15mm**
**C47** AP11 1c yel brn .60 .45
**C48** AP11 2c vermilion .60 .45
**C49** AP11 3c magenta 1.25 .45
**C50** AP11 4c org yel ('36) 4.25 2.50
**C51** AP11 4c car lake ('37) 2.50 1.40
**C52** AP11 5c dl bl .60 .45
**C53** AP11 5c org ('37) .60 .45
**C54** AP11 10c red brn 1.25 .65
**C55** AP11 10c ol grn ('37) 1.25 .55
**C56** AP11 15c rose red .60 .45
**C57** AP11 15c ver ('37) .60 .45
**C58** AP11 20c ultra 6.25 5.25
**C59** AP11 20c dp cl ('37) 1.25 .45
**C60** AP11 25c gray blk 7.50 6.25
**C61** AP11 25c bl grn ('37) 1.10 .45
  *a.* Quetzal omitted 1,100.
**C62** AP11 30c yel grn 3.75 3.25
**C63** AP11 30c rose red ('37) 1.25 .45
**C64** AP11 50c car rose 17.50 14.50
**C65** AP11 50c pur ('36) 17.00 13.50
**C66** AP11 1q dk bl 55.00 45.00
**C67** AP11 1q dk grn ('36) 19.00 13.50
**Size: 46x20mm**
**C68** AP11 2.50q rose red & ol grn ('36) 12.50 5.25
**C69** AP11 5q org & ind ('36) 17.50 7.25
  *a.* Quetzal omitted 1,500. 1,250.
Nos. C47-C69 (23) 174.95 123.35

Issued: Nos. C32-C34, C36, C38-C39, C41, C43, C45, C47-C49, C52, C54, C56, C58, C60, C62, 11/1/35; Nos. C44, C50, C67-C69, 10/1/36; Nos. C35, C37, C40, C42, C51, C53, C55, C57, C59, C61, C63, 1/1/37.
Value for No. C61a is for a sound stamp.
For overprints and surcharges see Nos. C80-C91, CB3-CB4.

Progressive Colony, Lake Amatitlan — AP11a

2c, Quezaltenango. 3c, Lake Atitlan. 6c, Carmen Hill. 10c, Relief map. 15c, National University. 30c, Espana Plaza. 50c, Police Station, Aurora Airport. 75c, Amphitheater. 1q, Aurora Airport.

## Center in Brown Black

**1937, May 18**
**Overprinted with Airplane in Blue**
**Size: 34x15mm**
**C70** AP11a 2c carmine .80 .50
**C71** AP11a 3c blue 3.25 2.50
**C72** AP11a 4c citron .80 .80
**C73** AP11a 6c yel grn 1.10 .50
**C74** AP11a 10c red vio 6.50 4.50
**C75** AP11a 15c orange 5.00 2.00
**C76** AP11a 30c ol grn 12.50 6.00
**C77** AP11a 50c pck bl 16.50 8.50
**C78** AP11a 75c dk vio 32.50 22.50
**C79** AP11a 1q dp rose 35.00 24.00
Nos. C70-C79 (10) 113.95 71.80

7th Ave., Guatemala City — AP11b

2c, Los Proceres Monument. 3c, Natl. Printing Office. 5c, Natl. Museum. 10c, Central Park. 15c, Escuintla. 20c, Motorcycle Police. 25c, Slaughterhouse, Escuintla. 30c, Exhibition Hall. 50c, Barrios Plaza. 1q, Polytechnic School. 1.50q, Aurora Airport.

## Overprinted with Airplane in Black

## Size: 33x15mm

| | | | | |
|---|---|---|---|---|
| **C80** | AP11b | 1c yel brn & brt bl | .35 | .35 |
| **C81** | AP11b | 2c crim & dp vio | .35 | .35 |
| **C82** | AP11b | 3c red vio & red brn | .75 | .75 |
| **C83** | AP11b | 5c pck grn & cop red | 6.00 | 4.50 |
| **C84** | AP11b | 10c car & grn | 1.90 | 1.50 |
| **C85** | AP11b | 15c rose & dl ol grn | .75 | .35 |
| **C86** | AP11b | 20c ultra & blk | 4.50 | 2.60 |
| **C87** | AP11b | 25c dk gray & scar | 3.75 | 3.75 |
| **C88** | AP11b | 30c grn & dp vio | 1.90 | 1.90 |
| **C89** | AP11b | 50c mag & ultra | 15.00 | 18.00 |

### Size: 42x19mm

| | | | | |
|---|---|---|---|---|
| **C90** | AP11b | 1q ol grn & red vio | 15.00 | 18.00 |
| **C91** | AP11b | 1.50q scar & ol brn | 15.00 | 18.00 |
| | | Nos. C80-C91 (12) | 65.25 | 70.05 |

Second term of President Ubico.

### Souvenir Sheet

**1938, Jan. 10**     **Perf. 12½**

| | | | | |
|---|---|---|---|---|
| **C92** | AP12 | Sheet of 4 | 8.00 | 8.00 |
| *a.* | | 15c George Washington | 1.50 | 1.50 |
| *b.* | | 4c Franklin D. Roosevelt | 1.50 | 1.50 |
| *c.* | | 4c Map of the Americas | 1.50 | 1.50 |
| *d.* | | 15c Pan American Union Building, Washington, DC | .75 | .75 |

150th anniv. of US Constitution.

President Arosemena, Panama — AP13

Flags of Central American Countries — AP19

Designs: 2c, Pres. Cortés Castro, Costa Rica. 3c, Pres. Somoza, Nicaragua. 4c, Pres. Carias Andino, Honduras. 5c, Pres. Martínez, El Salvador. 10c, Pres. Ubico, Guatemala.

**1938, Nov. 20**     **Unwmk.**

| | | | | |
|---|---|---|---|---|
| **C93** | AP13 | 1c org & ol brn | .25 | .25 |
| **C94** | AP13 | 2c scar, pale pink & sl grn | .30 | .25 |
| **C95** | AP13 | 3c grn, buff & ol brn | .40 | .30 |
| **C96** | AP13 | 4c dk cl, pale lil & brn | .55 | .35 |
| **C97** | AP13 | 5c bis, pale grn & ol brn | .50 | .60 |
| **C98** | AP13 | 10c ultra, pale bl & brn | 1.00 | 1.25 |
| | | Nos. C93-C98 (6) | 3.00 | 3.00 |

### Souvenir Sheet

| | | | | |
|---|---|---|---|---|
| **C99** | AP19 | Sheet of 6 | 8.00 | 8.00 |
| *a.* | | 1c Guatemala | .80 | .80 |
| *b.* | | 2c El Salvador | .80 | .80 |
| *c.* | | 3c Honduras | 1.10 | 1.10 |
| *d.* | | 4c Nicaragua | 1.40 | 1.40 |
| *e.* | | 5c Costa Rica | 1.40 | 1.40 |
| *f.* | | 10c Panama | 2.40 | 2.40 |

1st Central American Phil. Exhib., Guatemala City, Nov. 20-27.
For overprints see Nos. CO1-CO7.

La Merced Church, Antigua — AP20

---

Designs: 2c, Ruins of Christ School, Antigua. 3c, Aurora Airport. 4c, Drill ground, Guatemala City. 5c, Cavalry barracks. 6c, Palace of Justice. 10c, Customhouse, San José. 15c, Communications Building, Retalhuleu. 30c, Municipal Theater, Quezaltenango. 50c, Customhouse, Retalhuleu. 1q, Departmental Building.

### Inscribed "Aéreo Interior"
### Overprinted with Quetzal in Green

**1939, Feb. 14**

| | | | | |
|---|---|---|---|---|
| **C100** | AP20 | 1c ol bis & chnt | .25 | .25 |
| **C101** | AP20 | 2c rose red & sl grn | .25 | .25 |
| **C102** | AP20 | 3c dl bl & bis | .25 | .25 |
| **C103** | AP20 | 4c rose pink & yel grn | .25 | .25 |
| **C104** | AP20 | 5c brn lake & brt ultra | .30 | .25 |
| **C105** | AP20 | 6c org & gray brn | .35 | .25 |
| **C106** | AP20 | 10c bis brn & gray blk | .50 | .25 |
| **C107** | AP20 | 15c dl vio & blk | .75 | .25 |
| **C108** | AP20 | 30c dp bl & dk car | 1.10 | .25 |
| **C109** | AP20 | 50c org & brt vio | 1.50 | .40 |
| *a.* | | Quetzal omitted | | 1,750. |
| **C110** | AP20 | 1q yel grn & brt ultra | 2.50 | 1.25 |
| | | Nos. C100-C110 (11) | 8.00 | 3.90 |

See Nos. C111-C122. For overprint and surcharge see No. C124, C132.

View of Antigua — AP20a

### Inscribed "Aéreo Internacional" or "Aérea Exterior"

Designs: 1c, Mayan Altar, Aurora Park. 2c, Sanitation Building. 3c, Lake Amatitlan. 4c, Lake Atitlan. 5c, Tamazulapa River bridge. 10c, Los proceres Monument. 15c, Palace of Captains General. 20c, Church on Carmen Hill. 25c, Barrios Park. 30c, Mayan Altar. 50c, Charles III fountain.

### Overprinted with Quetzal in Green

**1939, Feb. 14**

| | | | | |
|---|---|---|---|---|
| **C111** | AP20a | 1c ol grn & gldn brn | .35 | .30 |
| **C112** | AP20a | 2c lt grn & blk | .40 | .30 |
| **C113** | AP20a | 3c ultra & cob bl | .35 | .30 |
| **C114** | AP20a | 4c org brn & yel grn | .35 | .30 |
| **C115** | AP20a | 5c sage grn & red org | .50 | .30 |
| **C116** | AP20a | 10c lake & sl blk | 2.40 | .30 |
| **C117** | AP20a | 15c ultra & brt rose | 2.40 | .30 |
| **C118** | AP20a | 20c grn & ap grn | .80 | .30 |
| **C119** | AP20a | 25c dl vio & lt ol | .80 | .30 |
| **C120** | AP20a | 30c dl rose & blk | 1.10 | .30 |
| **C121** | AP20a | 50c scar & brt yel | 2.00 | .30 |
| **C122** | AP20a | 1q org & yel grn | 3.50 | .40 |
| | | Nos. C111-C122 (12) | 14.95 | 3.70 |

No. 240 Overprinted in Carmine

**1940, Apr. 14**     **Perf. 14**

| | | | | |
|---|---|---|---|---|
| **C123** | A36 | 15c ultra | .60 | .30 |

Pan American Union, 50th anniversary.

No. C112 Overprinted in Carmine

**1941, Dec. 2**     **Perf. 12½**

| | | | | |
|---|---|---|---|---|
| **C124** | AP20 | 2c lt grn & blk | .40 | .30 |

Second Pan American Health Day.

San Carlos University, Antigua — AP21

**1943, June 25**    **Engr.**    **Perf. 11**

| | | | | |
|---|---|---|---|---|
| **C125** | AP21 | 15c dk red brn | .55 | .30 |
| *a.* | | Imperf., pair | 100.00 | |

---

Don Pedro de Alvarado — AP22

Type I

Type II

Type I — Diagonal shading lines running from lower left to upper right at inner edges of commemorative tablet.

Type II — Additional diagonal shading lines running from upper left to lower right added throughout tablet, resulting in crosshatched lines at inner edges.

**1943, Mar. 10**    **Unwmk.**    **Perf. 11½**

| | | | | |
|---|---|---|---|---|
| **C126** | AP22 | 15c dp ultra (II) | .60 | .30 |
| *a.* | | Type I | 29.00 | 17.50 |

400th anniv. of the founding of Antigua.

National Police Building — AP23

**1943, Aug. 3**     **Perf. 11**

| | | | | |
|---|---|---|---|---|
| **C127** | AP23 | 10c dp rose vio | .35 | .30 |

### Allegory of Revolution Type

**1945, Apr. 27**     **Engr.**

| | | | | |
|---|---|---|---|---|
| **C128** | A129 | 5c dp rose | .55 | .30 |
| **C129** | A129 | 6c dk bl grn | .55 | .30 |
| *a.* | | Imperf., pair | 110.00 | |
| **C130** | A129 | 10c violet | .55 | .30 |
| **C131** | A129 | 15c aqua | .55 | .30 |
| | | Nos. C128-C131 (4) | 2.20 | 1.20 |

No. C113 Surcharged in Red

**1945, July 25**     **Perf. 12½**

| | | | | |
|---|---|---|---|---|
| **C132** | AP20 | 2½c on 3c | 5.00 | 5.00 |

The 1945 Book Fair.

### Type of 1947 Overprinted in Carmine

**1945, Aug.**    **Engr.**    **Perf. 11**

| | | | | |
|---|---|---|---|---|
| **C133** | A127 | 5c rose car | .35 | .30 |
| *a.* | | Triple ovpt., one inverted | 50.00 | 25.00 |
| *b.* | | Double ovpt., one inverted | 65.00 | |

See Nos. C137A-C139.

### José Milla y Vidaurre Type

**1945**

| | | | | |
|---|---|---|---|---|
| **C134** | A131 | 7½c sepia | 1.10 | 1.00 |
| **C134A** | A131 | 7½c dark blue | .60 | .30 |

Issued: No. C134, 9/28; No. C134A, 12/6.
For overprint see No. C230.

---

### Torch Type

**1945, Oct. 19**

| | | | | |
|---|---|---|---|---|
| **C135** | A130 | 5c brt red vio | .40 | .30 |

### Souvenir Sheet
### *Imperf*

| | | | | |
|---|---|---|---|---|
| **C136** | A130 | Sheet of 2 | 5.00 | 4.00 |
| *a.* | | 5c bright red violet | .40 | .40 |

1st anniv. of the Revolution of Oct. 20, 1944.
See Nos. C147-C150.

> Catalogue values for unused stamps in this section, from this point to the end of the section, are for Never Hinged items.

### Payo Enriquez de Rivera Type

**1946, Jan. 22**    **Unwmk.**    **Perf. 11**

| | | | | |
|---|---|---|---|---|
| **C137** | A132 | 5c rose pink | .80 | .30 |

See Nos. C269, C311-C315.

### Palace Type of 1944

**1946-47**

| | | | | |
|---|---|---|---|---|
| **C137A** | A127 | 5c rose car ('47) | .90 | .30 |
| **C138** | A127 | 10c deep lilac | .50 | .30 |
| *a.* | | Imperf., pair | 100.00 | |
| **C139** | A127 | 15c blue | .90 | .30 |
| *a.* | | Imperf., pair | 100.00 | |
| | | Nos. C137A-C139 (3) | 2.30 | .90 |

For overprint see No. C133.

Sir Rowland Hill AP30

Globes, Quetzal AP31

**1946, Aug. 5**    **Photo.**    **Perf. 14x13**

| | | | | |
|---|---|---|---|---|
| **C140** | AP30 | 5c slate & brn (blk ovpt.) | .75 | .30 |
| *a.* | | Without "AEREO" ovpt. | 400.00 | 400.00 |
| **C141** | AP31 | 15c car lake, ultra & emer | .95 | .30 |

Centenary of the first postage stamp.

José Batres y Montufar — AP32

**1946, Sept. 16**    **Engr.**    **Perf. 11**

| | | | | |
|---|---|---|---|---|
| **C142** | AP32 | 10c Prus grn | .80 | .30 |
| *a.* | | Perf. 12½ | 10.00 | 10.00 |

Signing the Declaration of Independence — AP33

**1946, Dec. 19**     **Perf. 11**

| | | | | |
|---|---|---|---|---|
| **C143** | AP33 | 5c rose car | .45 | .30 |
| **C144** | AP33 | 6c ol brn | .45 | .30 |
| **C145** | AP33 | 10c violet | .60 | .30 |
| **C146** | AP33 | 20c blue | .80 | .30 |
| | | Nos. C143-C146 (4) | 2.30 | 1.20 |

125th anniv. of the signing of the Declaration of Independence.

### Torch Type of 1945
Dated 1944-1946

**1947, Feb. 3**     **Engr.**

| | | | | |
|---|---|---|---|---|
| **C147** | A130 | 1c green | .75 | .30 |
| **C148** | A130 | 2c carmine | .75 | .30 |
| **C149** | A130 | 3c violet | .75 | .30 |
| **C150** | A130 | 5c dp bl | .75 | .30 |
| | | Nos. C147-C150 (4) | 3.00 | 1.20 |

Inscribed "II Aniversario de la Revolucion." "Aereo" in color on a white background.
2nd anniv. of the Revolution of 10/20/44.

Franklin D. Roosevelt — AP34

## 1947, June 6

| | | | | |
|---|---|---|---|---|
| C151 | AP34 | 5c rose car | .30 | .25 |
| C152 | AP34 | 6c blue | .30 | .25 |
| C153 | AP34 | 10c dp ultra | .40 | .25 |
| C154 | AP34 | 30c gray blk | 1.90 | .90 |
| C155 | AP34 | 50c lt violet | 2.90 | 2.25 |
| a. | | Imperf., pair | 125.00 | |
| C156 | AP34 | 1q gray grn | 5.00 | 3.75 |
| a. | | Imperf., pair | 125.00 | |
| | | Nos. C151-C156 (6) | 10.80 | 7.65 |

### No. 296 Overprinted in Carmine

**1948, May 14**    *Perf. 12½*

C157   A122   5c blue & red    .65   .30

Soccer Game — AP35

## 1948, Aug. 31    Engr.
### Center in Black

| | | | | |
|---|---|---|---|---|
| C158 | AP35 | 3c brt carmine | .85 | .30 |
| C159 | AP35 | 5c blue green | 1.00 | .40 |
| C160 | AP35 | 10c dk violet | 1.10 | .95 |
| C161 | AP35 | 30c dp blue | 2.50 | 3.50 |
| C162 | AP35 | 50c bister | 5.00 | 4.50 |
| | | Nos. C158-C162 (5) | 10.45 | 9.65 |

4th Central American and Caribbean Soccer Championship, Mar. 1948.

Seal, University of Guatemala — AP36

## 1949, Nov. 29    *Perf. 12½*
### Center in Blue

| | | | | |
|---|---|---|---|---|
| C163 | AP36 | 3c carmine | .75 | .40 |
| C164 | AP36 | 10c green | 1.20 | .75 |
| C165 | AP36 | 50c yellow | 4.25 | 3.25 |
| | | Nos. C163-C165 (3) | 6.20 | 4.40 |

1st Latin American Cong. of Universities.

Lake Atitlan AP37    Tecum Uman Monument AP38

Designs: 8c, San Cristobal Church. 13c, Weaver. 35c, Momostenango Cliffs.

## 1950, Feb. 17    Photo.    *Perf. 14*
### Multicolored Centers

| | | | | |
|---|---|---|---|---|
| C166 | AP37 | 3c car rose | .45 | .25 |
| C167 | AP38 | 5c red brn | .45 | .25 |
| C168 | AP37 | 8c dk sl grn | .50 | .25 |
| C169 | AP38 | 13c brown | .90 | .25 |
| C170 | AP37 | 35c purple | 3.25 | 3.00 |
| | | Nos. C166-C170 (5) | 5.55 | 4.00 |

See No. C181.

Soccer AP39    Pole Vault AP40

Designs: 3c, Foot race. 8c, Tennis. 35c, Diving. 65c, Stadium.

## 1950, Feb. 25    Engr.    *Perf. 12½*
### Center in Black

| | | | | |
|---|---|---|---|---|
| C171 | AP39 | 1c purple | .75 | .25 |
| C172 | AP39 | 3c carmine | .80 | .25 |
| C173 | AP40 | 4c orange brn | 1.10 | .30 |
| C174 | AP39 | 8c red violet | 1.25 | .40 |
| C175 | AP39 | 35c lt blue | 2.90 | 3.25 |

### Center in Green

| | | | | |
|---|---|---|---|---|
| C176 | AP40 | 65c dk slate grn | 5.50 | 5.50 |
| | | Nos. C171-C176 (6) | 12.30 | 9.95 |

6th Central American and Caribbean Games.

Nurse and Patient — AP41

Designs: 10c, School of Nurses. 50c, Zacapa Hospital. 1q, Roosevelt Hospital.

## 1950, Sept. 6    Litho.    *Perf. 12*
### Quetzal in Blue Green

| | | | | |
|---|---|---|---|---|
| C177 | AP41 | 5c rose vio & car | .30 | .30 |
| a. | | Double impression (frame) | 25.00 | |
| C178 | AP41 | 10c ol brn & emer | .75 | .40 |
| C179 | AP41 | 50c ver & red vio | 3.75 | 3.75 |
| C180 | AP41 | 1q org yel & sage grn | 5.50 | 5.50 |
| a. | | Souv. sheet, #C177-C180 | 14.00 | 14.00 |
| | | Nos. C177-C180 (4) | 10.30 | 9.95 |

National Hospital Fund.
Nos. C177-C180 exist with colors reversed, perf. and imperf. These are proofs.

No. C168 Perf. 12½ or 12 diagonally through center

**1951, Apr.**    *Perf. 14*

| | | | | |
|---|---|---|---|---|
| C181 | AP37 | (4c) multi | 27.50 | 25.00 |
| a. | | Unsevered pair | 60.00 | 50.00 |

Counterfeits of diagonal perforation exist.

Ceremonial Stone Ax — AP42

## 1953, Feb. 11    Photo.    *Perf. 14x13½*

| | | | | |
|---|---|---|---|---|
| C182 | AP42 | 3c dk bl & ol gray | .70 | .45 |
| C183 | AP42 | 5c dk gray & hn brn | .80 | .45 |
| C184 | AP42 | 10c dk pur & slate | 1.50 | .45 |
| | | Nos. C182-C184 (3) | 3.00 | 1.35 |

National Flag and Emblem — AP43

## 1953, Mar. 14    *Perf. 13½*
### Multicolored Center

| | | | | |
|---|---|---|---|---|
| C185 | AP43 | 1c maroon | .55 | .30 |
| C186 | AP43 | 2c slate green | .55 | .30 |
| C187 | AP43 | 4c dark brown | .60 | .30 |
| | | Nos. C185-C187 (3) | 1.70 | .90 |

Issued to mark the passing of the presidency from J. J. Arevalo to Col. Jacobo Arbenz Guzman.

Regional Dance AP44    Horse Racing AP45

Designs: 4c, White nun — national flower. 5c, Allegory of the fair. 20c, Zakuleu ruins. 30c, Symbols of Agriculture. 50c, Champion bull. 65c, Bicycle racing. 1q, Quetzal.

## 1953, Dec. 18    Engr.    *Perf. 12½*

| | | | | |
|---|---|---|---|---|
| C188 | AP44 | 1c dp ultra & car | .30 | .25 |
| C189 | AP44 | 4c org & grn | 1.30 | .30 |
| C190 | AP44 | 5c emer & choc | .85 | .40 |
| C191 | AP45 | 15c choc & dk pur | 1.20 | 1.00 |
| C192 | AP45 | 20c car & ultra | 1.00 | 1.00 |
| C193 | AP44 | 30c dp ultra & choc | 1.30 | 1.25 |
| C194 | AP45 | 50c pur & blk | 1.30 | 1.25 |
| C195 | AP45 | 65c lt bl & dk grn | 2.60 | 2.50 |
| C196 | AP44 | 1q dk bl grn & dk red | 26.00 | 15.00 |
| | | Nos. C188-C196 (9) | 35.85 | 22.95 |

National Fair, Oct. 20, 1953.

Indian — AP46

## 1954, Apr. 21    Unwmk.    *Perf. 12½*

| | | | | |
|---|---|---|---|---|
| C197 | AP46 | 1c carmine | .35 | .25 |
| C198 | AP46 | 2c dp blue | .35 | .25 |
| C199 | AP46 | 4c yellow grn | .35 | .25 |
| C200 | AP46 | 5c aqua | .70 | .25 |
| C201 | AP46 | 6c orange | .70 | .25 |
| C202 | AP46 | 10c violet | 1.40 | .30 |
| C203 | AP46 | 20c black brn | 4.00 | 3.25 |
| | | Nos. C197-C203 (7) | 7.85 | 4.80 |

Guatemala and ODECA Flags — AP47

## 1954, Oct. 13    Photo.    *Perf. 14x13½*

| | | | | |
|---|---|---|---|---|
| C204 | AP47 | 1c multicolored | .80 | .50 |
| C205 | AP47 | 2c multicolored | .80 | .50 |
| C206 | AP47 | 4c multicolored | .80 | .50 |
| | | Nos. C204-C206 (3) | 2.40 | 1.50 |

3rd anniv. of the formation of the Organization of Central American States.

Rotary Emblem, Map of Guatemala — AP48

## 1956, Sept. 8    Engr.

| | | | | |
|---|---|---|---|---|
| C207 | AP48 | 4c bl & dl yel | .40 | .25 |
| C208 | AP48 | 6c lt bl grn & dl yel | .40 | .25 |
| C209 | AP48 | 35c pur & dl yel | 2.00 | 1.75 |
| | | Nos. C207-C209 (3) | 2.80 | 2.25 |

50th anniv. of Rotary Intl. (in 1955).

Mayan Warrior Holding Dagger Cross of the Liberation — AP49

4c, Family looking into the sun. 5c, The dagger of the Liberation destroying communist symbols. 6c, Hands holding cogwheel & map of Guatemala. 20c, Monument to the victims of communism & flag. 30c, Champerico harbor. 65c, Radio tower, Mercury & map of Guatemala. 1q, Flags of the American nations. 5q, Pres. Carlos Castillo Armas.

## 1956, Oct. 10    Photo.    *Perf. 14x13½*

| | | | | |
|---|---|---|---|---|
| C210 | AP49 | 2c dp grn, red, bl & brn | .25 | .25 |
| C211 | AP49 | 4c dp car & gray blk | .25 | .25 |
| C212 | AP49 | 5c bl & red brn | .25 | .25 |
| C213 | AP49 | 6c dk brn & dp ultra | .30 | .25 |
| C214 | AP49 | 20c vio, brn & bl | 1.40 | 1.75 |
| C215 | AP49 | 30c dp bl & ol | 1.80 | 2.00 |
| C216 | AP49 | 65c chnt brn & grn | 2.60 | 3.00 |
| C217 | AP49 | 1q dk brn & multi | 3.50 | 4.00 |
| C218 | AP49 | 5q multi | 14.50 | 15.00 |
| | | Nos. C210-C218 (9) | 24.85 | 26.75 |

Liberation of 1954-55.

For overprints see Nos. C233, C243, C265-C266, C417.

Red Cross, Map and Quetzal — AP50

Designs: 2c, José Ruiz Angulo and woman with child, vert. 3c, Pedro de Bethancourt with sick man. 4c, Rafael Ayau.

### *Perf. 13½x14, 14x13½*
**1958, May 13**    Unwmk.

| | | | | |
|---|---|---|---|---|
| C219 | AP50 | 1c multicolored | 1.10 | .40 |
| C220 | AP50 | 2c multicolored | .65 | .25 |
| C221 | AP50 | 3c multicolored | .65 | .25 |
| C222 | AP50 | 4c multicolored | .65 | .25 |
| | | Nos. C219-C222 (4) | 3.05 | 1.15 |

Issued in honor of the Red Cross.
For overprints and surcharges see Nos. C235-C242, C251-C254, C283-C298, C390-C395.

Col. Carlos Castillo Armas — AP51

## 1959, Feb. 27    *Perf. 14x13½*
### Center in Dark Blue and Yellow

| | | | | |
|---|---|---|---|---|
| C223 | AP51 | 1c black | .40 | .25 |
| C224 | AP51 | 2c rose red | .40 | .25 |
| C225 | AP51 | 4c brown | .40 | .25 |
| C226 | AP51 | 6c dk bl grn | .40 | .25 |
| C227 | AP51 | 10c dk purple | .60 | .30 |
| C228 | AP51 | 20c blue grn | 1.75 | .75 |
| C229 | AP51 | 35c gray | 2.40 | 1.40 |
| | | Nos. C223-C229 (7) | 6.35 | 3.45 |

Pres. Carlos Castillo Armas (1914-1957).

No. C134A Overprinted in Carmine

**1959, Mar. 4**    Engr.    *Perf. 11*

C230   A131   7½c dk blue    1.50   1.25

Issued to honor the United Nations.

Galleon of 1532 and Freighter "Quezaltenango" AP52

**1959, May 15**    Litho.    *Perf. 11*

C231   AP52   6c ultra & rose red    1.25   .30

Issued to honor the formation of the Guatemala-Honduras merchant fleet.
For overprint see No. C467.

Type of 1950 Overprinted in Dark Blue

**1959, Oct. 9**    *Perf. 12*

| | | | | |
|---|---|---|---|---|
| C232 | A140 | 5c dk bl & lt brn | 1.00 | .30 |
| a. | | Inverted overprint | 200.00 | 35.00 |

Issued to state Guatemala's claim to British Honduras. Overprint reads: "Belize is ours." Map includes "BRITISH HONDURAS" and its borderline, and excludes bit extending above "A" of "GUATEMALA" on No. 337.
No. C232 is known without overprint in multiples.

No. C213 Overprinted in Red

**1959, Oct. 26 Photo. Perf. 14x13½**
C233 AP49 6c dk brn & dp ultra .90 .30
Centenary of coffee export.

Pres. and Mrs. Villeda of Honduras AP53

**1959, Nov. 3 Litho. Perf. 11**
C234 AP53 6c pale brown .95 .30
Visit of President Ramon Villeda Morales of Honduras, Oct. 12, 1958.
For overprint see No. C415.

**Nos. C219-C222 Overprinted in Green, Violet, Blue or Brown**

No. C235          No. C236

**Perf. 13½x14, 14x13½**
**1960, Apr. 23 Photo. Unwmk.**
C235 AP50 1c multi (G) 2.25 2.00
C236 AP50 2c multi (V) 1.00 .95
C237 AP50 3c multi (Bl) 1.00 .95
C238 AP50 4c multi (Br) 1.00 .95

**Nos. C219-C222 Overprinted**

C239 AP50 6c on 1c multi 5.50 5.00
C240 AP50 7c on 2c multi 2.75 2.50
C241 AP50 10c on 3c multi 4.50 4.00
C242 AP50 20c on 4c multi 5.00 4.50
     Nos. C235-C242 (8) 23.00 20.85

Nos. C235-C242 issued to publicize World Refugee Year, July 1, 1959-June 30, 1960.

No. C213 Overprinted in Red

**1960, Apr. 30 Perf. 14x13½**
C243 AP49 6c dk brn & dp ultra 1.60 1.25
Founding of the city of Melchor de Mencos.

UNESCO and Eiffel Tower, Paris — AP54

**1960, Nov. 4 Photo. Perf. 12½**
C244 AP54 5c dp mag & vio .35 .25
C245 AP54 6c ultra & vio brn .35 .25
C246 AP54 8c emer & magenta .55 .25
C247 AP54 20c org brn & dl bl 2.00 1.40
     Nos. C244-C247 (4) 3.25 2.15

Issued to honor UNESCO.
For overprints see Nos. C258, C267-C268.

---

Abraham Lincoln — AP55

**1960, Oct. 29 Engr. Perf. 11**
C248 AP55 5c violet blue .30 .25
C249 AP55 30c violet 1.20 1.40
C250 AP55 50c gray 6.00 6.50
     Nos. C248-C250 (3) 7.50 8.15

Sesquicentenary of the birth of Abraham Lincoln.
An 8c was also printed, but was not issued and all copies were destroyed.

Nos. C219-C222 Overprinted in Green, Blue or Brown

**Perf. 13½x14, 14x13½**
**1961, Apr. 20 Photo. Unwmk.**
C251 AP50 1c multi (G) .85 .45
C252 AP50 2c multi (Bl) .85 .45
C253 AP50 3c multi (Bl) .85 .45
C254 AP50 4c multi (Br) .85 .45
     Nos. C251-C254 (4) 3.40 1.80

Issued to honor the Red Cross.

Proclamation of Independence AP56

**1962 Engr. Perf. 11**
C255 AP56 4c sepia .35 .25
C256 AP56 5c violet blue .55 .25
C257 AP56 15c brt violet 1.90 .65
     Nos. C255-C257 (3) 2.80 1.15

140th anniv. of Independence (in 1961).
Issue dates: 4c, 5c, May 23; 15c, Aug. 10.

No. C245 Overprinted in Red

**1962, Oct. 4 Photo. Perf. 12½**
C258 AP54 6c ultra & vio brn 1.25 1.40
WHO drive to eradicate malaria.

Dr. José Luna — AP57

Guatemalan physicians: 4c, Rodolfo Robles. 5c, Narciso Esparragoza y Gallardo. 6c, Juan J. Ortega. 10c, Dario Gonzalez. 20c, José Felipe Flores.

**1962, Dec. 12 Photo. Perf. 14x13½**
C259 AP57 1c ol bis & dl pur 1.00 .25
C260 AP57 4c org yel & gray ol 1.00 .25
C261 AP57 5c pale bl & red brn 1.00 .25
C262 AP57 6c salmon & blk 1.00 .25
C263 AP57 10c pale grn & red brn 1.40 .25
C264 AP57 20c pale pink & bl 1.60 .80
     Nos. C259-C264 (6) 7.00 2.05

---

No. C213 Overprinted in Red

**1962, Dec. Photo. Perf. 14x13½**
C265 AP49 6c dk brn & dp ultra 1.50 .80
Pres. Ydigoras' tour of Central America, Dec. 14-20, 1962.

No. C213 Overprinted in Vermilion

**Perf. 14x13½**
**1963, Mar. 18 Unwmk.**
C266 AP49 6c dk brn & dp ultra 6.25 3.00

Meeting of Pres. John F. Kennedy with the Presidents of the Central American Republics, San Jose, Costa Rica, Mar. 18-21.

Nos. C245-C246 Overprinted in Magenta or Black

**1963, Mar. 14 Perf. 12½**
C267 AP54 6c ultra & vio brn (M) .80 .30
C268 AP54 8c emerald & mag .85 .30

Signing of the new charter of the Organization of Central American States (ODECA).

**Enriquez de Rivera Type of 1946**
**Perf. 11, 11½, 12½**
**1963, Mar. 26 Engr.**
C269 A132 5c olive bister .60 .30

Woman Carrying Fruit Basket — AP58

**1963, Mar. 14 Litho. Perf. 11, 12½**
C270 AP58 1c multicolored .60 .30
Spring Fair, 1960.

Reaper — AP59

**1963, July 25 Photo. Perf. 14**
C271 AP59 5c Prus green .50 .30
C272 AP59 10c dark blue 1.00 .30
FAO "Freedom from Hunger" campaign.

Ceiba Tree — AP60

**1963 Unwmk. Perf. 12**
C273 AP60 4c brown & green 1.60 .30

Patzun Palace — AP61

---

Buildings: 3c, Coban. 4c, Retalhuleu. 5c, San Marcos. 6c, Captains General of Antigua.

**1964, Jan. 15 Perf. 13½x14**
C274 AP61 1c rose red & brn .70 .30
C275 AP61 3c rose cl & Prus grn .70 .30
C276 AP61 4c vio bl & rose lake .70 .30
C277 AP61 5c brown & blue .95 .30
C278 AP61 6c green & slate .95 .30
     Nos. C274-C278 (5) 4.00 1.50

City Hall, Guatemala City — AP62

Design: 4c, Social Security Institute.

**1964, Jan. 15 Photo. Perf. 12x11½**
C279 AP62 3c brt bl & brn .65 .30
C280 AP62 4c brn & brt bl .85 .30

See Nos. C281-C282A. For overprints see Nos. C360-C361, C421.

**1964-65 Engr. Perf. 11½**
Designs: 3c, Social Security Institute. 4c, University administration building. No. C282, City Hall, Guatemala City. No. C282A, Engineering School.

**Different Frames**
C281 AP62 3c dull green .80 .30
C281A AP62 4c gray ('65) .80 .30
C282 AP62 7c blue .85 .30
C282A AP62 7c olive bis ('65) .85 .35
     Nos. C281-C282A (4) 3.30 1.25

Nos. C219-C222 Ovptd. in Green, Blue or Black

**1964 Photo. Perf. 13½x14, 14x13½**
C283 AP50 1c multi (G) 1.50 1.50
C284 AP50 2c multi (Bl) 1.50 1.50
C285 AP50 3c multi (G) 1.50 1.50
C286 AP50 4c multi (Bk) 1.50 1.50
     Nos. C283-C286 (4) 6.00 6.00

18th Olympic Games, Tokyo, 10/10-25/64.

Nos. C219-C222 Surcharged in Green, Blue or Black

**1964**
C287 AP50 7c on 1c multi (G) .40 .30
C288 AP50 9c on 2c multi (Bl) .55 .45
C289 AP50 13c on 3c multi (Bl) .75 .50
C290 AP50 21c on 4c multi (Bk) 1.50 1.00
     Nos. C287-C290 (4) 3.20 2.25

Nos. C219-C222 Ovptd. in Green, Blue or Black

**1964, June 25**
C291 AP50 1c multi (G) 1.05 .85
C292 AP50 2c multi (Bl) 1.05 .85
C293 AP50 3c multi (G) 1.05 .85
C294 AP50 4c multi (Bk) 1.05 .85
     Nos. C291-C294 (4) 4.20 3.40

New York World's Fair.

**Nos. C219-C222 Ovptd. in Green, Blue or Black**

## 1964

| | | |
|---|---|---|
| **C295** AP50 1c multi (G) | 1.80 | 1.60 |
| **C296** AP50 2c multi (Bl) | 1.80 | 1.60 |
| **C297** AP50 3c multi (G) | 1.80 | 1.60 |
| **C298** AP50 4c multi (Bk) | 2.90 | 2.50 |
| *Nos. C295-C298 (4)* | 8.30 | 7.30 |

Eighth Bicycle Race.

Pres. John F. Kennedy — AP63

**1964   Engr.   Perf. 11½**

| | | |
|---|---|---|
| **C299** AP63 1c violet | 1.80 | .70 |
| **C300** AP63 2c yellow grn | 1.80 | .70 |
| **C301** AP63 3c brown | 1.80 | .70 |
| **C302** AP63 7c deep blue | 1.80 | .70 |
| **C303** AP63 50c dk gray | 14.00 | 7.50 |
| *Nos. C299-C303 (5)* | 21.20 | 10.30 |

Minute letters "TEOK" are in lower right corner of 1c, 2c, 3c and 50c.
Issue dates: 7c, July 10; others, Aug. 21.

Centenary Emblem — AP64

**Perf. 11x12**
**1964, Sept. 9   Unwmk.   Photo.**

| | | |
|---|---|---|
| **C304** AP64 7c ultra, sil & red | 1.00 | .25 |
| **C305** AP64 9c org, sil & red | 1.00 | .40 |
| **C306** AP64 13c pur, sil & red | 1.50 | .55 |
| **C307** AP64 21c brt grn, sil & red | 1.20 | 1.00 |
| **C308** AP64 35c brn, sil & red | 2.25 | 1.40 |
| **C309** AP64 1q lem, sil & red | 4.00 | 3.00 |
| *Nos. C304-C309 (6)* | 10.95 | 6.60 |

Centenary (in 1963) of the Intl. Red Cross.
For overprints see Nos. C323-C327, C395-C400.

### Type of Regular Issue 1963
Souvenir Sheet

**1964   Engr.   Imperf.**

| | | |
|---|---|---|
| **C310** Sheet of 2 | 10.00 | 10.00 |
|   **a.** A151 10c violet blue | 4.00 | 4.00 |
|   **b.** A151 20c carmine | 4.00 | 4.00 |

15th UPU Congress, Vienna, May-June, 1964.

### Enriquez de Rivera Type of 1946

**1964, Dec. 18   Engr.   Perf. 11½**

| | | |
|---|---|---|
| **C311** A132 5c gray | .55 | .30 |
| **C312** A132 5c orange | .55 | .30 |
| **C313** A132 5c lt green | .55 | .30 |
| **C314** A132 5c lt ultra | .55 | .30 |
| **C315** A132 5c dull violet | .55 | .30 |
| *Nos. C311-C315 (5)* | 2.75 | 1.50 |

Bishop Francisco Marroquin — AP65

**1965, Jan. 21   Photo.   Unwmk.**

| | | |
|---|---|---|
| **C316** AP65 4c lilac & brn | .35 | .30 |
| **C317** AP65 7c gray & sepia | .90 | .30 |
| **C318** AP65 9c vio bl & blk | 1.00 | .30 |
| *Nos. C316-C318 (3)* | 2.25 | .90 |

Issued to honor Bishop Francisco Marroquin.

### Bethancourt Type of Regular Issue, 1964

**1965, Apr. 20   Engr.   Perf. 11½**

| | | |
|---|---|---|
| **C319** A152 2½c violet blue | .55 | .30 |
| **C320** A152 3c orange | .55 | .30 |
| **C321** A152 4c purple | .55 | .30 |
| **C322** A152 5c yellow grn | .65 | .30 |
| *Nos. C319-C322 (4)* | 2.30 | 1.20 |

For overprints see Nos. C381-C382.

Nos. C304-C308 Overprinted in Red

**1965, June 18   Photo.   Perf. 11x12**

| | | |
|---|---|---|
| **C323** AP64 7c ultra, sil & red | .60 | .45 |
| **C324** AP64 9c org, sil & red | .75 | .55 |
| **C325** AP64 13c pur, sil & red | .80 | .55 |
| **C326** AP64 21c brt grn, sil & red | 1.10 | .80 |
| **C327** AP64 35c brn, sil & red | 1.40 | 1.25 |
| *Nos. C323-C327 (5)* | 4.65 | 3.60 |

Guatemalan Boy Scout Emblem — AP66

Designs: 9c, Campfire and Scouts. 10c, Scout emblem and Scout carrying torch and flag. 15c, Scout emblem, flags and Scout giving Scout sign. 20c, Lord Baden-Powell.

**1966, Mar. 3   Photo.   Perf. 14x13½**

| | | |
|---|---|---|
| **C328** AP66 5c multicolored | .75 | .55 |
| **C329** AP66 9c multicolored | .90 | .70 |
| **C330** AP66 10c multicolored | 1.20 | .85 |
| **C331** AP66 15c multicolored | 1.50 | 1.10 |
| **C332** AP66 20c multicolored | 2.10 | 1.50 |
| *Nos. C328-C332 (5)* | 6.45 | 4.70 |

5th Interamerican Regional Training Conf., Guatemala City, Mar. 1-3.
For overprints see Nos. C376-C380.

### Central American Independence Issue

Flags of Central American States — AP67

**1966, Mar. 9   Perf. 12½x13½**

| | | |
|---|---|---|
| **C333** AP67 6c multicolored | .70 | .30 |

Queen Nefertari Temple, Abu Simbel — AP68

**1966, Oct. 3   Photo.   Perf. 12**

| | | |
|---|---|---|
| **C334** AP68 21c violet & ocher | 1.20 | .45 |

UNESCO world campaign to save historic monuments in Nubia.

Coat of Arms — AP69

**1966-70   Engr.   Perf. 13½**

| | | |
|---|---|---|
| **C335** AP69 5c orange | 1.10 | .30 |
| **C336** AP69 5c green | 1.10 | .30 |
|   **a.** 5c yel grn, perf. 11½ ('69) | 2.00 | .30 |
| **Perf. 11½** | | |
| **C337** AP69 5c blue ('67) | 1.10 | .30 |
|   **a.** 5c dk bl, perf. 12½ ('69) | .75 | .30 |
| **Perf. 12½** | | |
| **C338** AP69 5c gray ('67) | 1.10 | .30 |
| **C339** AP69 5c purple ('67) | 1.10 | .30 |
|   **a.** 5c bright violet ('69) | .75 | .30 |
| **Perf. 11½** | | |
| **C339B** AP69 5c dp mag ('70) | 1.80 | .30 |
| **C339C** AP69 5c grn, yel ('70) | 2.10 | .30 |
| *Nos. C335-C339C (7)* | 9.40 | 2.10 |

Issued: No. C335, 10/31; No. C336, 12/15/66; No. C337, 2/9/67; Nos. C338-C339, 4/28/67; No. C336a, 12/3/69; No. C339a, 12/11/69; No. C339B, 7/8/70; No. C339C, 10/16/70.

Msgr. Mariano Rossell y Arellano — AP70

**1966, Nov. 3   Engr.   Perf. 13½**

| | | |
|---|---|---|
| **C340** AP70 1c dp violet | .30 | .25 |
| **C341** AP70 2c green | .40 | .25 |
| **C342** AP70 3c brown | .40 | .25 |
| **C343** AP70 7c blue | .65 | .40 |
| **C344** AP70 50c gray | 2.25 | 2.00 |
| *Nos. C340-C344 (5)* | 4.00 | 3.15 |

Issued to honor Msgr. Mariano Rossell y Arellano, apostolic delegate.

Mario Mendez Montenegro — AP71

**1966-67   Perf. 13½**

| | | |
|---|---|---|
| **C345** AP71 2c rose red ('67) | .40 | .30 |
| **C346** AP71 3c orange ('67) | .45 | .30 |
| **C347** AP71 4c rose claret ('67) | .65 | .30 |
| **C348** AP71 5c gray | .85 | .30 |
| **C349** AP71 5c lt ultra ('67) | .85 | .30 |
| **C350** AP71 5c green ('67) | .85 | .30 |
| **C351** AP71 5c bluish blk ('67) | .85 | .30 |
| *Nos. C345-C351 (7)* | 4.90 | 2.10 |

Mario Mendez Montenegro (1910-65), founder of the Revolutionary Party.

Morning Glory and Map of Guatemala — AP72

Flowers: 8c, Bird of paradise, horiz. 10c, White nun orchid, national flower, horiz. 20c, Nymphs of Amatitlan.

**1967, Jan. 12   Photo.   Perf. 12**
**Flowers in Natural Colors**

| | | |
|---|---|---|
| **C352** AP72 4c orange | 1.60 | .60 |
| **C353** AP72 8c green | 1.60 | .60 |
| **C354** AP72 10c dk blue | 1.80 | 1.10 |
| **C355** AP72 20c dk red | 4.00 | 2.40 |
| *Nos. C352-C355 (4)* | 9.00 | 4.70 |

Pan-American Institute Emblem AP73

**1967, Apr. 13   Photo.   Perf. 13½**

| | | |
|---|---|---|
| **C356** AP73 4c lt brn, lil & blk | .50 | .25 |
| **C357** AP73 5c ol, bl & blk | 1.00 | .25 |
| **C358** AP73 7c org yel, bl & blk | 1.50 | .40 |
| *Nos. C356-C358 (3)* | 3.00 | .90 |

8th Gen. Assembly of the Pan-American Geographical and Historical Institute in 1965.

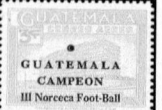

No. C281 Overprinted

**1967, Apr. 28   Engr.   Perf. 11½**

| | | |
|---|---|---|
| **C360** AP62 3c dull green | 1.90 | 1.10 |

Guatemala's victory in the 3rd Norceca Soccer Games (Caribbean, Central and North American).

No. C281A Overprinted in Red

**1967, June 28   Engr.   Perf. 11½**

| | | |
|---|---|---|
| **C361** AP62 4c gray | 1.40 | 1.10 |

Meeting of American Presidents, Punta del Este, Apr. 10-12.

Handshake AP74

**1967, June 28   Photo.   Perf. 12**

| | | |
|---|---|---|
| **C362** AP74 7c pink, brn & grn | .75 | .25 |
| **C363** AP74 21c lt bl, grn & brn | 1.10 | .55 |

"Peace and Progress through Cooperation."
For overprint see No. C416.

Church of Santo Domingo — AP75

1c, Yurrita Church, vert. 3c, Church of St. Francis. 4c, Antonio José de Irisarri, vert. 5c, Church of the Convent, vert. 7c, Mercy Church, Antigua. 10c, Metropolitan Cathedral.

**1967, Aug.   Perf. 11½x12, 12x11½**

| | | |
|---|---|---|
| **C364** AP75 1c grn, lt bl & dk brn | .60 | .30 |
| **C365** AP75 2c plum, sal pink & brn | .65 | .30 |
| **C366** AP75 3c brt rose, gray & blk | .65 | .30 |
| **C367** AP75 4c mar, sl grn & org | .65 | .30 |
| **C368** AP75 5c lil, pale grn & dk brn | .65 | .30 |
| **C369** AP75 7c ultra, lil rose & blk | .80 | .30 |
| **C370** AP75 10c pur, yel & blk | 1.40 | .30 |
| *Nos. C364-C370 (7)* | 5.40 | 2.10 |

Abraham Lincoln (1809-1865) — AP76

**1967   Engr.   Perf. 13½, 11½ (9c)**

| | | |
|---|---|---|
| **C371** AP76 7c gray & dp org | .70 | .25 |
| **C372** AP76 9c dk grn & grysh | .90 | .25 |
| **C373** AP76 11c brn org & slate | .70 | .30 |
| **C374** AP76 15c ultra & vio brn | 1.00 | .40 |
| **C375** AP76 30c magenta & grn | 2.40 | 1.50 |
| *Nos. C371-C375 (5)* | 5.70 | 2.70 |

Issued: 7c, 9c, Oct. 9; others, Dec. 12.
For surcharge see No. C554.

Nos. C328-C332 Overprinted

**1967, Dec. 1   Photo.   Perf. 14x13½**

| | | |
|---|---|---|
| **C376** AP66 5c multicolored | .60 | .40 |
| **C377** AP66 9c multicolored | 1.05 | .65 |
| **C378** AP66 10c multicolored | 1.40 | .85 |
| **C379** AP66 15c multicolored | 1.40 | .85 |
| **C380** AP66 20c multicolored | 1.75 | 1.00 |
| *Nos. C376-C380 (5)* | 6.20 | 3.75 |

Issued to commemorate the 8th Central American Boy Scout Camporee, Dec. 1-8.

Nos. C320-C321
Overprinted

"Premio Nobel de Literatura - 10 diciembre 1967 - Miguel Angel Asturias".

**1967, Dec. 11**    **Engr.**    **Perf. 11½**
| | | | |
|---|---|---|---|
| C381 | A152 | 3c orange | .80 .55 |
| C382 | A152 | 4c purple | .80 .55 |

Awarding of the Nobel Prize for Literature to Miguel Angel Asturias, Guatemalan writer.

Institute
Emblem — AP77

**1967, Dec. 12**    **Engr.**    **Perf. 11½**
| | | | |
|---|---|---|---|
| C383 | AP77 | 9c black & grn | 4.00 4.00 |
| C384 | AP77 | 25c car & brn | 5.00 5.00 |
| C385 | AP77 | 1q ultra & bl | 18.00 19.00 |
| | Nos. C383-C385 (3) | | 27.00 28.00 |

Inter-American Agriculture Institute, 25th anniv.

UNESCO
Emblem and
Children — AP78

**1967, Dec. 12**
| | | | |
|---|---|---|---|
| C386 | AP78 | 4c blue green | .40 .25 |
| C387 | AP78 | 5c blue | .50 .25 |
| C388 | AP78 | 7c gray | .70 .35 |
| C389 | AP78 | 21c brt rose lil | 1.60 1.10 |
| | Nos. C386-C389 (4) | | 3.20 1.95 |

20th anniv. (in 1966) of UNESCO.

Nos. C219-C221
and C304-C308
Ovptd. in Black or
Yellow Green

**Perf. 13½x14, 14x13½, 11x12**
**1968, Jan. 23**      **Photo.**
| | | | |
|---|---|---|---|
| C390 | AP50 | 1c multi | 1.00 .55 |
| C391 | AP50 | 1c multi (G) | 1.00 .80 |
| C392 | AP50 | 2c multi | 1.00 .80 |
| C393 | AP50 | 2c multi (G) | 1.00 .80 |
| C394 | AP50 | 3c multi | 1.00 .80 |
| C395 | AP50 | 3c multi (G) | 1.00 .80 |
| C396 | AP64 | 7c multi | 1.00 .80 |
| C397 | AP64 | 9c multi | 1.30 1.10 |
| C398 | AP64 | 13c multi | 2.00 1.10 |
| C399 | AP64 | 21c multi | 2.25 1.10 |
| C400 | AP64 | 35c multi | 2.25 1.90 |
| | Nos. C390-C400 (11) | | 14.80 10.55 |

3rd meeting of Central American Presidents, Nov. 15-18, 1967.

Our Lady of the
Coro — AP79

**1968-74**    **Engr.**    **Perf. 13½, 11½**
| | | | |
|---|---|---|---|
| C403 | AP79 | 4c ultra | .65 .25 |
| C404 | AP79 | 7c slate | .60 .25 |
| C405 | AP79 | 9c green | .60 .25 |
| C406 | AP79 | 9c lilac ('74) | .65 .25 |
| C407 | AP79 | 10c brick red | 1.10 .25 |
| C408 | AP79 | 10c gray | .70 .25 |
| C408A | AP79 | 10c vio bl ('74) | .50 .25 |
| C409 | AP79 | 1q vio brn | 4.75 3.50 |
| C410 | AP79 | 1q org yel | 4.75 3.50 |
| | Nos. C403-C410 (9) | | 14.30 8.75 |

Perf. 13½ applies to 4c and Nos. C407, C409-C410; perf. 11½ to 4c, 7c, 9c and Nos. C408, C408A.

Nos. 396-398
Overprinted

**1968, Mar. 25**    **Litho.**    **Perf. 14x13½**
| | | | |
|---|---|---|---|
| C411 | A153 | 4c multicolored | 1.10 .85 |
| C412 | A153 | 5c multicolored | 1.10 .85 |
| C413 | A153 | 6c multicolored | .95 .70 |
| | Nos. C411-C413 (3) | | 3.15 2.40 |

The 11th Bicycle Race.

Miguel Angel Asturias,
Flags of Guatemala
and Sweden — AP80

**1968, June 18**    **Engr.**    **Perf. 11½**
| | | | |
|---|---|---|---|
| C414 | AP80 | 20c ultra | 5.75 5.50 |

Awarding of the Nobel Prize for Literature to Miguel Angel Asturias.

## No. C234 Overprinted in Carmine

**1968, July 18**    **Litho.**    **Perf. 11**
| | | | |
|---|---|---|---|
| C415 | AP53 | 6c pale brown | 1.05 .40 |

International Human Rights Year.

No. C362
Overprinted

**1968, July 18**    **Photo.**    **Perf. 12**
| | | | |
|---|---|---|---|
| C416 | AP74 | 7c pink, brn & grn | .95 .40 |

Issued to publicize forest conservation.

No. C213 Overprinted
in Brown

**1968, Aug. 23**    **Photo.**    **Perf. 14x13½**
| | | | |
|---|---|---|---|
| C417 | AP49 | 6c dk brn & dp ultra | .95 .65 |

Nahakin scientific expedition along the route of the Mayas undertaken jointly with Peru.

Views, Quetzal and
White Nun
Orchid — AP81

**1968, Aug. 23**    **Engr.**    **Perf. 13½**
| | | | |
|---|---|---|---|
| C418 | AP81 | 10c dp cl & grn | 3.25 2.00 |
| C419 | AP81 | 20c dp org & blk | 4.25 3.00 |
| C420 | AP81 | 50c ultra & car | 5.25 5.00 |
| | Nos. C418-C420 (3) | | 12.75 10.00 |

Issued for tourist publicity.

No. C281A
Overprinted in
Carmine

**1968, Nov. 4**      **Perf. 11½**
| | | | |
|---|---|---|---|
| C421 | AP62 | 4c gray | .90 .55 |

20th anniv. of the Federation of Central American Universities.

Presidents
Gustavo Diaz
Ordaz and Julio
Cesar Mendez
Montenegro
AP82

**1968, Dec. 3**    **Litho.**    **Perf. 14x13½**
| | | | |
|---|---|---|---|
| C422 | AP82 | 5c multicolored | .35 .25 |
| C423 | AP82 | 10c multicolored | .60 .25 |
| C424 | AP82 | 25c multicolored | 1.40 .85 |
| | Nos. C422-C424 (3) | | 2.35 1.35 |

Mutual visits of the Presidents of Mexico and Guatemala.

ITU Emblem, Old
and New
Communication
Equipment
AP83

## Engraved and Photogravure
**1968-74**    **Perf. 11½, 12½ (21c)**
| | | | |
|---|---|---|---|
| C425 | AP83 | 7c violet blue | .30 .25 |
| C426 | AP83 | 15c gray & emer | .50 .25 |
| C426A | AP83 | 15c vio brn & org ('74) | .70 .25 |
| C427 | AP83 | 21c magenta | .80 .45 |
| C428 | AP83 | 35c rose red & emer | 1.10 .45 |
| C429 | AP83 | 75c green & red | 2.75 2.40 |
| C430 | AP83 | 3q brown & red | 10.50 7.75 |
| | Nos. C425-C430 (7) | | 16.65 11.80 |

Cent. (in 1965) of the ITU.
Nos. C425, C427 are engr. only; on others denominations are photo. No. C426A is on thin, toned paper.
Issued: No. C426A, 2/18/74; others 12/13/68.
For surcharges see Nos. C454, C516.

Nos. 399-403
Overprinted in Red,
Black or Gold

## Lithographed and Engraved
**1969**    **Perf. 11½, 13½ (1c)**
| | | | |
|---|---|---|---|
| C431 | A154 | 1c blk, lt grn & red (R) | .95 2.00 |
| C432 | A154 | 5c yel, lt grn & red | 1.30 2.00 |
| C433 | A154 | 8c org, lt grn & red | 1.50 4.00 |
| C434 | A154 | 15c bl, lt grn & red | 1.75 4.00 |
| C435 | A154 | 30c lt vio, lt grn & red (G) | 2.10 4.00 |
| | Nos. C431-C435 (5) | | 7.60 16.00 |

Dante
Alighieri — AP84

**1969, July 17**    **Engr.**    **Perf. 12½**
| | | | |
|---|---|---|---|
| C436 | AP84 | 7c rose vio & ultra | .50 .25 |
| C437 | AP84 | 10c dk blue | .55 .25 |
| C438 | AP84 | 20c green | .85 .25 |
| C439 | AP84 | 21c gray & brn | 1.40 .80 |
| C440 | AP84 | 35c pur & brt grn | 3.25 1.75 |
| | Nos. C436-C440 (5) | | 6.55 3.30 |

Dante Alighieri (1265-1321), Italian poet.

Map of Latin
America
AP85

Design: 9c, Seal of University.

**1969, Oct. 29**    **Typo.**    **Perf. 13**
**Size: 44x27mm**
| | | | |
|---|---|---|---|
| C441 | AP85 | 2c brt pink & blk | .40 .30 |

**Size: 35x27mm**
| | | | |
|---|---|---|---|
| C442 | AP85 | 9c gray & blk | .90 .30 |

**Souvenir Sheet**
**Imperf**
| | | | |
|---|---|---|---|
| C443 | AP85 | Sheet of 2 | 1.90 1.90 |
| a. | 2c light blue & black | | .60 .60 |
| b. | 9c orange & black | | .60 .60 |

20th anniv. of the Union of Latin American Universities.

### Moon Landing Issue

Moon Landing — AP86

**1969-70**    **Engr.**    **Perf. 11½**
| | | | |
|---|---|---|---|
| C444 | AP86 | 50c maroon & blk | 3.00 3.00 |
| C445 | AP86 | 1q ultra & blk | 5.00 5.00 |

**Souvenir Sheet**
**Imperf**
| | | | |
|---|---|---|---|
| C446 | AP86 | 1q yel grn & ultra | 6.75 6.75 |

See note after US No. C76. No. C446 contains one stamp with simulated perforations.
Issued: Nos. C445-C446, 12/19/69; No. C444, 1/6/70.

Giant Grebe
Family on Lake
Atitlan — AP87

Designs: 4c, Lake Atitlan. 20c, Grebe chick, eggs atop floating nest, vert.

**1970, Mar. 31**    **Litho.**    **Perf. 13½**
| | | | |
|---|---|---|---|
| C447 | AP87 | 4c red & multi | 1.10 .25 |
| C448 | AP87 | 9c red & multi | 1.80 .30 |
| a. | Souv. sheet of 2, #C447-C448 | | 18.00 18.00 |
| C449 | AP87 | 20c red & multi | 3.25 .85 |
| | Nos. C447-C449 (3) | | 6.15 1.40 |

Protection of zambullidor ducks.

Dr. Victor Manuel
Calderon — AP88

**1970**    **Litho. & Engr.**    **Perf. 13, 12½**
| | | | |
|---|---|---|---|
| C450 | AP88 | 1c lt bl & blk | .50 .30 |
| C451 | AP88 | 2c pale grn & blk | .50 .30 |

**Perf. 13**
| | | | |
|---|---|---|---|
| C452 | AP88 | 9c yellow & blk | 1.00 .30 |
| | Nos. C450-C452 (3) | | 2.00 .90 |

Dr. Victor Manuel Calderon (1889-1969), who described microfilaria, a blood parasite.

Hand Holding
Bible — AP89

**1970**    **Litho. & Typo.**    **Perf. 13x13½**
| | | | |
|---|---|---|---|
| C453 | AP89 | 5c red & multi | .60 .35 |

Fourth centenary of the Bible in Spanish.

No. C430 Surcharged

**1971, Mar. 11**    **Engr.**    **Perf. 11½**
C454 AP83 50c on 3q brn & red   2.25 2.00

Arms of Guatemala, Newspapers AP90

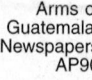

Official Decree of First Issue — AP91

**1971**    **Litho.**    **Perf. 11½, 12½**
C455 AP90 2c dk bl & red   .45 .30
C456 AP90 5c brn & red   .45 .30
C457 AP90 25c brt bl & red   1.40 .50
   Nos. C455-C457 (3)   2.30 1.10

### Souvenir Sheet
### Lithographed and Engraved
### Imperf
C458 AP91 Sheet of 5   2.25 2.25

Cent. of Guatemala's postage stamps.
Nos. C456-C457 have white value tablet.
No. C458 contains a litho. 4c black and engr. reproductions of Nos. 1-4 in colors similar to 1871 issue. Simulated perforations.
In 1974 No. C458 was overprinted "Conmemorativa / al Campeonato Mundial de Foot Ball / Munich 1974" and Munich Games emblem in black. Value $16. Overprint in gold or other colors was not authorized.
See Nos. C569-C570.

Mayas with CARE Package AP92

**1971**    **Typo.**    **Perf. 11½**
C459 AP92 5c multi   .70 .40
   a. Souv. sheet of 2   3.00 2.50

25th aniversary of CARE, a US-Canadian Cooperative for American Relief Everywhere.
No. C459a contains imperf. stamps similar to Nos. 416 and C459.

J. Rufino Barrios, M. Garcia Granados, Map of Guatemala, Quetzal AP93

**1971, June 30**    **Perf. 11½**
C460 AP93 2c multi, perf 13½   .80 .25
   a. Value in pink ('72)   .70 .25
C461 AP93 10c multi   1.50 .30
   a. Value in pink, perf. 12½ ('72)   1.50 .30
C462 AP93 50c multi   8.50 3.25
C463 AP93 1q multi   12.50 6.50
   Nos. C460-C463 (4)   23.30 10.30

Centenary of the liberal revolution of 1871.

Chavarry Arrué and León Bilak — AP94

**Perf. 11½, 11x12½, 12½**
**1971-72**    **Engr.**
C464 AP94 1c grn & blk ('72)   .45 .30
C465 AP94 2c lt brn & blk ('72)   .55 .30
C466 AP94 5c org & blk   .75 .30
   Nos. C464-C466 (3)   1.75 .90

Honoring J. Arnoldo Chavarry Arrué, stamp engraver; León Bilak, philatelist.

No. C231 Overprinted

**1971, Oct. 25**    **Litho.**    **Perf. 11½**
C467 AP52 6c ultra & rose red   5.25 3.00

INTERFER 71, Intl. Fair, Guatemala, Oct. 30-Nov. 21.

Flag and Map of Guatemala — AP95

**Perf. 13½ (1c), 12½ (3c, 9c), 11 (5c)**
**1971-75**    **Typo.**
C468 AP95 1c blk, bl & lil   .55 .30
   a. Lithographed ('75)   .55 .30
C469 AP95 3c brn, brt pink & bl   .55 .30
C470 AP95 5c brn, org & bl   .55 .30
   a. Lithographed, perf. 12½ ('74)   .55 .30
C471 AP95 9c blk, emer & bl   .55 .30
   Nos. C468-C471 (4)   2.20 1.20

Central American independence, sesqui.
Issued: Nos. C469-C471, 7/10/72.

UNICEF Emblem and Mayan Figure — AP96

**1971-75**    **Engr.**    **Perf. 11½**
C472 AP96 1c yel grn   .30 .25
C472A AP96 2c purple   .30 .25
C473 AP96 50c vio brn   2.25 1.90
C474 AP96 1q ultra   3.50 3.00
   Nos. C472-C474 (4)   6.35 5.40

25th anniv. UNICEF.
Issued: 2c, 2/24/75; others, 11/71.

Early Boeing Planes — AP97

Design: 10c, Bleriot's plane.

**1972**    **Typo.**    **Perf. 11½**
C475 AP97 5c lt brn & brt bl   1.00 .30
C476 AP97 10c dark blue   1.50 .30

Military aviation in Guatemala, 50th anniv.

Arches, Antigua AP98

Nos. C481, C487, C493, C501, Cathedral. Nos. C482, C490, C496, C498 Fountain, Central Park. Nos. C483, C491, C497, C499, Capuchin Monastery. Nos. C484, C488, C494,

C502, Fountain and Santa Clara. Nos. C485, C489, C495, C503, Portal of San Francisco.

**1972-73**    **Typo.**    **Perf. 11½**
**Dark Blue and Light Blue**
C480 AP98 1c multicolored   .55 .25
C481 AP98 1c multicolored   .55 .25
C482 AP98 1c multicolored   .55 .25
C483 AP98 1c multicolored   .55 .25
C484 AP98 1c multicolored   .55 .25
C485 AP98 1c multicolored   .55 .25
   a. Block of 6, #C480-C485   3.25 2.50

**Black, Lilac Rose, and Silver**
C486 AP98 2½c multicolored   .75 .25
C487 AP98 2½c multicolored   .75 .25
C488 AP98 2½c multicolored   .75 .25
C489 AP98 2½c multicolored   .75 .25
C490 AP98 2½c multicolored   .75 .25
C491 AP98 2½c multicolored   .75 .25
   a. Block of 6, #C3486-C491   4.75 4.75

**Blue, Orange and Black**
C492 AP98 5c shown   1.00 .50
C493 AP98 5c multicolored   1.00 .50
C494 AP98 5c multicolored   1.00 .50
C495 AP98 5c multicolored   1.00 .50
C496 AP98 5c multicolored   1.00 .50
C497 AP98 5c multicolored   1.00 .50
   a. Block of 6, #C492-C497   7.75 5.00

Nos. C492-C497 exist perf. 12½, same value.

**Perf. 12½**
**Red, Blue and Black**
C498 AP98 1q multicolored   4.75 2.50
C499 AP98 1q multicolored   4.75 2.50
C500 AP98 1q multicolored   4.75 2.50
C501 AP98 1q multicolored   4.75 2.50
C502 AP98 1q multicolored   4.75 2.50
C503 AP98 1q multicolored   4.75 2.50
   a. Block of 6, #C498-C503   27.50 15.00
   Nos. C480-C503 (24)   42.30 21.00

Earthquake ruins of Antigua. 1c printed se-tenant in sheets of 90 (10x9); 2½c, 5c se-tenant in sheets of 30 (5x6); 1q se-tenant in sheets of 6 (3x2).
On Nos. C498-C503 the inks were applied by a thermographic process giving a shiny raised effect.
Issued: Nos. C480-C485, 12/14; Nos. C486-C491, 1/22/73; Nos. C492-C497, 3/12/73; Nos. C498-C503, 8/22/73.
Nos. C480-C485 were overprinted "II Feria Internacional / INTERFER/73 / 31 Octubre — Noviembre 18 / 1973 / GUATEMALA" in black or lilac rose and issued 11/3/73. Value, each set $4.50.
See Nos. C528-C545, C770-C775F. For overprints see Nos. C517-C523.

Simon Bolivar and Map of Americas — AP99

**1973-74**    **Perf. 11½**
C504 AP99 3c brt lil rose & blk   .30 .25
C505 AP99 3c org & dk bl ('74)   5.75 2.00
C506 AP99 5c yel & multi   .30 .25
C507 AP99 5c brt grn & blk   .30 .25
   Nos. C504-C507 (4)   6.65 2.75

Indian with CARE Package, World Map AP100     CARE Package AP101

**1973, June 14**    **Typo.**    **Perf. 12½**
C508 AP100 2c blk & multi   .30 .25
C509 AP101 10c blk & multi   1.00 .40
   a. Souvenir sheet of 2   2.00 2.00

25th anniversary of CARE (in 1971), a US-sponsored relief organization and 10th anniversary of its work in Guatemala.
No. C509a contains 2 stamps similar to Nos. C508-C509 with simulated perforations.

Guatemala No. 1, Laurel — AP102

**1973-74**    **Engr.**    **Perf. 12½, 11½ (1q)**
C510 AP102 1c yel brn ('74)   .30 .25
C511 AP102 1q rose claret   3.50 2.50

Centenary (in 1971) of Guatemala postage stamps. See Nos. C574-C576A.

Oak Wreath and Star — AP103

**1973, Aug. 22**    **Typo.**    **Perf. 12½**
C512 AP103 5c brn, yel & bl   .80 .30

Centenary of Escuela Politecnica, Guatemala's military academy. See Nos. C552-C553.

Eleanor Roosevelt — AP104

**Perf. 11½, 12½**
**1973, Sept. 11**    **Engr.**
C513 AP104 7c blue   .70 .30

Eleanor Roosevelt (1884-1962), lecturer, writer, UN delegate.

Boys' School, Chiquimula AP105

**1973-74**    **Typo.**    **Perf. 12½**
C514 AP105 3c blk & bl   .75 .30
C515 AP105 5c blk & dp lil rose   .75 .30

Centenary of the Instituto Varones in Chiquimula.
Issued: 5c, 12/5/73; 3c, 6/13/74.

### No. C430 Surcharged in Red

**1974**    **Engr. & Photo.**    **Perf. 11½**
C516 AP83 50c on 3q brn & red   2.25 2.00

### Nos. C480-C485 and C509a Overprinted

**1974, June 13**    **Typo.**    **Perf. 11½**
C517 AP98 1c dk bl & lt bl   .65 .30
C518 AP98 1c dk bl & lt bl   .65 .30
C519 AP98 1c dk bl & lt bl   .65 .30
C520 AP98 1c dk bl & lt bl   .65 .30
C521 AP98 1c dk bl & lt bl   .65 .30
C522 AP98 1c dk bl & lt bl   .65 .30
   Nos. C517-C522 (6)   3.90 1.80

### Souvenir Sheet
C523 Sheet of 2   17.00 17.00

Centenary of Universal Postal Union.
No. C523 consists of an overprint on No. C509a, including "UNIVERSAL POSTAL UNION" instead of "UPU."
The overprint on No. C523 in red was not authorized by the Post Office. Value $65.

### Antigua Type of 1972-73

No. C528, Capuchin Monastery. No. C529, Arches. No. C530, Cathedral. No. C531,

Fountain and Santa Clara. No. C532, Portal of San Francisco. No. C533, Fountain.

**1974, Oct. 8    Typo.    Perf. 11½**

**Black and Light Brown**

| | | | | |
|---|---|---|---|---|
| C528 | AP98 | 2c multicolored | .55 | .30 |
| C529 | AP98 | 2c multicolored | .55 | .30 |
| C530 | AP98 | 2c multicolored | .55 | .30 |
| C531 | AP98 | 2c multicolored | .55 | .30 |
| C532 | AP98 | 2c multicolored | .55 | .30 |
| C533 | AP98 | 2c multicolored | .55 | .30 |
| | Nos. C528-C533 (6) | | 3.30 | 1.80 |

**Antigua Type of 1972-73**

No. C540, Capuchin Monastery. No. C541, Arches. No. C542, Cathedral. No. C543, Fountain and Santa Clara. No. C544, Portal of San Francisco. No. C545, Fountain.

**1974, Sept. 24    Black and Yellow**

| | | | | |
|---|---|---|---|---|
| C540 | AP98 | 20c multicolored | 1.20 | 1.20 |
| C541 | AP98 | 20c multicolored | 1.20 | 1.20 |
| C542 | AP98 | 20c multicolored | 1.20 | 1.20 |
| C543 | AP98 | 20c multicolored | .55 | 1.20 |
| C544 | AP98 | 20c multicolored | 1.20 | 1.20 |
| C545 | AP98 | 20c multicolored | 1.20 | 1.20 |
| | Nos. C540-C545 (6) | | 6.55 | 7.20 |

Earthquake ruins of Antigua. Each group of six printed se-tenant in sheets of 30 (5x6). Value $2.

Nos. C528-C533 were printed in 1975 in black and bister se-tenant in sheets of 24 (4x6) on whiter paper. Value $5.

Generals Justo Rufino Barrios and M. Garcia Granados AP106

Polytechnic School — AP107

**1974-75   Typo.   Perf. 12½, 11½ (25c)**

| | | | | |
|---|---|---|---|---|
| C552 | AP106 | 6c red, gray & bl | .55 | .30 |
| C553 | AP107 | 25c multi | .80 | .30 |

Centenary (in 1973) of Escuela Politecnica, Guatemala's military academy. Issued: 6c, 9/17; 25c, 1/1/75.

No. C373 Surcharged in Black and Green

**1974, Dec. 3    Engr.    Perf. 13½**

| | | | | |
|---|---|---|---|---|
| C554 | AP76 | 10c on 11c multi | 1.40 | .50 |

Nature protection. The quetzal, Guatemala's national bird.

Costume San Martin Sacatepequez — AP108

Costumes of Women: 2c, Solola. 9c, Coban. 20c, Chichicastenango.

**1974-75    Typo.    Perf. 12½**

| | | | | |
|---|---|---|---|---|
| C556 | AP108 | 2c car & multi | .60 | .30 |
| C557 | AP108 | 2½c bl, car & brn | .60 | .30 |
| C559 | AP108 | 9c bl & multi | .85 | .30 |
| a. | | Perf. 12½x13½ | .85 | |
| C561 | AP108 | 20c red & multi | 1.50 | .30 |
| | Nos. C556-C561 (4) | | 3.55 | 1.20 |

Issue dates: 2½c, Dec. 16, 1974; 20c, Jan. 14, 1975; 2c, 9c, May 19, 1975.

Quetzals and Maya Quekchi Woman Wearing Huipil AP109

**1975, June 25    Litho.    Perf. 13½**

| | | | | |
|---|---|---|---|---|
| C565 | AP109 | 8c bl & multi | 2.00 | .25 |
| C566 | AP109 | 20c red & multi | 3.50 | .40 |

International Women's Year 1975.

Rotary Emblem AP110

**1975-76    Typo.    Perf. 13½**

| | | | | |
|---|---|---|---|---|
| C567 | AP110 | 10c bl & multi | 2.50 | .30 |

**Perf. 11½**

| | | | | |
|---|---|---|---|---|
| C568 | AP110 | 15c bl & multi | 3.00 | .30 |

Guatemala City Rotary Club, 50th anniv. Issued: 10c, 10/1; 15c, 12/21/76.

**Gaceta Type of 1971 Redrawn**

**1975-76    Typo.    Perf. 12½**

| | | | | |
|---|---|---|---|---|
| C569 | AP90 | 5c brn & red | .40 | .25 |
| C570 | AP90 | 50c brt rose & brn | 1.75 | .55 |

The white background around numeral and on right of arms has been filled in. Issued: 5c, 12/12; 50c, 12/1/76.

IWY Emblem and White Nun Orchid — AP111

**1975-76    Perf. 12½x13½, 11½ (8c)**

| | | | | |
|---|---|---|---|---|
| C571 | AP111 | 1c multi | 1.00 | .30 |
| C572 | AP111 | 8c yel & multi | 1.40 | .30 |
| C573 | AP111 | 26c rose & multi | 3.25 | .30 |
| | Nos. C571-C573 (3) | | 5.65 | .90 |

International Women's Year 1975. Issued: 1c, 12/19; 8c, 12/12; 26c, 5/10/76.

**Stamp Centenary Type of 1973**

**1975-77    Engr.    Perf. 11½**

| | | | | |
|---|---|---|---|---|
| C574 | AP102 | 6c orange | .55 | .30 |
| C575 | AP102 | 6c green ('76) | .55 | .30 |
| C576 | AP102 | 6c gray ('77) | .55 | .30 |
| C576A | AP102 | 6c vio bl ('77) | .55 | .30 |
| | Nos. C574-C576A (4) | | 2.20 | 1.20 |

Issued: No. C574, 12/31; No. C575, 5/10; others, 8/10.

Destroyed Joyabaj Village AP112

Designs (Guatemala Flag and): 3c, Emergency food distribution. 5c, Jaguar Temple, Tikal. 10c, Destroyed bridge. 15c, Outdoors emergency hospital. 20c, Sugar cane harvest. 25c, Destroyed house. 30c, New building, Tecpan. 50c, Destroyed Cerro del Carmen church. 75c, Cleaning up debris. 1q, Military help. 2q, Lake Atitlan.

**1976, June 4    Litho.    Perf. 12½**

| | | | | |
|---|---|---|---|---|
| C577 | AP112 | 1c red & multi | .30 | .25 |
| C578 | AP112 | 3c multi | .30 | .25 |
| C579 | AP112 | 5c pink & multi | .30 | .25 |
| C580 | AP112 | 10c red & multi | .35 | .25 |
| C581 | AP112 | 15c multi | .55 | .45 |
| C582 | AP112 | 20c pink & multi | .55 | .35 |
| C583 | AP112 | 25c red & multi | .95 | .40 |
| C584 | AP112 | 30c multi | 1.10 | .60 |
| C585 | AP112 | 50c red & multi | 1.50 | 1.25 |
| C586 | AP112 | 75c multi | 2.40 | 2.00 |
| C587 | AP112 | 1q multi | 3.50 | 3.00 |
| C588 | AP112 | 2q multi | 7.00 | 5.25 |
| | Nos. C577-C588 (12) | | 18.80 | 14.80 |

Earthquake of Feb. 4, 1976, and gratitude for foreign help. Inscriptions in colored panels vary. 3 imperf. souvenir sheets exist (50c, 1q, 2q). Size: 112x83mm. Value, each $15.50.

Allegory of Independence — AP113

Designs: 2c, Boston Tea Party. 3c, Thomas Jefferson, vert. 4c, 20c, 35c, Allegory of Independence (each different; 4c, 35c, vert.). 5c, Warren's Death at Bunker Hill. 10c, Washington at Valley Forge. 15c, Washington at Monmouth. 25c, The Generals at Yorktown. 30c, Washington Crossing the Delaware. 40c, Declaration of Independence. 45c, Patrick Henry, vert. 50c, Congress Voting Independence. 1q, Washington, vert. 2q, Lincoln, vert. 3q, Franklin, vert. 5q, John F. Kennedy, vert. The historical designs and portraits are after paintings.

**1976, July 30    Litho.    Perf. 12½**

**Size: 46x27mm, 27x46mm**

| | | | | |
|---|---|---|---|---|
| C592 | AP113 | 1c multicolored | .35 | .30 |
| C593 | AP113 | 2c multicolored | .35 | .30 |
| C594 | AP113 | 3c multicolored | .35 | .30 |
| C595 | AP113 | 4c multicolored | .35 | .30 |
| C596 | AP113 | 5c multicolored | .35 | .30 |
| C597 | AP113 | 10c multicolored | .35 | .30 |
| C598 | AP113 | 15c multicolored | .35 | .30 |
| C599 | AP113 | 20c multicolored | .70 | .30 |
| C600 | AP113 | 25c multicolored | .70 | .60 |
| C601 | AP113 | 30c multicolored | 1.20 | 1.10 |
| C602 | AP113 | 35c multicolored | 1.20 | 1.10 |
| C603 | AP113 | 40c multicolored | 1.20 | 1.10 |
| C604 | AP113 | 45c multicolored | 1.50 | 1.30 |
| C605 | AP113 | 50c multicolored | 2.10 | 1.90 |
| C606 | AP113 | 1q multicolored | 3.50 | 3.00 |
| a. | | Souvenir sheet | 4.50 | 4.50 |
| C607 | AP113 | 2q multicolored | 6.50 | 5.50 |
| a. | | Souvenir sheet | 8.00 | 8.00 |
| C608 | AP113 | 3q multicolored | 8.25 | 7.25 |
| a. | | Souvenir sheet | 10.00 | 10.00 |

**Size: 35x55mm**

| | | | | |
|---|---|---|---|---|
| C609 | AP113 | 5q multicolored | 14.00 | 12.50 |
| a. | | Souvenir sheet | 19.00 | 19.00 |
| | Nos. C592-C609 (18) | | 43.30 | 37.75 |

American Bicentennial. Souvenir sheets contain one imperf. stamp each.

1974 Quetzal Coin — AP114

**Lithographed and Engraved**

**1976, Dec. 1    Perf. 11½**

| | | | | |
|---|---|---|---|---|
| C610 | AP114 | 8c org, blk & bl | .45 | .30 |

**Perf. 13½**

| | | | | |
|---|---|---|---|---|
| C611 | AP114 | 20c brt rose, bl & blk | 1.10 | .30 |

50th anniv. of introduction of Quetzal currency.

Engineers at Work — AP115

**1976, Dec. 21    Engr.    Perf. 11½**

| | | | | |
|---|---|---|---|---|
| C612 | AP115 | 9c ultra | .60 | .30 |
| C613 | AP115 | 10c green | .60 | .30 |

School of Engineering, Guatemala City, centenary.

**Holy Week Type of 1977**

Designs: Sculptures of Christ from various Guatemalan churches. 4c, 7c, 9c, 20c, vert.

**1977, Apr. 4    Litho.    Perf. 11**

| | | | | |
|---|---|---|---|---|
| C614 | A159 | 3c pur & multi | .55 | .35 |
| C615 | A159 | 4c pur & multi | .55 | .35 |
| C616 | A159 | 7c pur & multi | .55 | .35 |
| C617 | A159 | 9c pur & multi | .65 | .35 |
| C618 | A159 | 20c pur & multi | 1.30 | .70 |
| C619 | A159 | 26c pur & multi | 1.40 | .75 |
| | Nos. C614-C619 (6) | | 5.00 | 2.85 |

**Souvenir Sheet**

**Roulette 7½**

| | | | | |
|---|---|---|---|---|
| C620 | A159 | 30c pur & multi | 4.25 | 4.25 |

Holy Week 1977.

City Hall and Bank of Guatemala AP116

Designs: 6c, Deed to original site, vert. 8c, Church and farm house, site of first legislative session. 9c, Coat of arms of Pedro Cortes, first archbishop. 22c, Arms of Guatemala City, vert.

**Perf. 13½ (6c); 11½ (others)**

**1977, Aug. 10    Litho.**

| | | | | |
|---|---|---|---|---|
| C621 | AP116 | 6c multicolored | .60 | .25 |
| C622 | AP116 | 7c multicolored | .60 | .25 |
| C623 | AP116 | 8c multicolored | .60 | .25 |
| C624 | AP116 | 9c multicolored | .80 | .25 |
| a. | | Souvenir sheet | 1.25 | 1.00 |
| C625 | AP116 | 22c multicolored | 1.25 | .25 |
| a. | | Souvenir sheet | 1.30 | 1.30 |
| | Nos. C621-C625 (5) | | 3.85 | 1.25 |

Bicentenary of the founding of Nueva Guatemala de la Asuncion (Guatemala City). Nos. C624a-C625a contain one stamp each with simulated perforations.

Arms of Quetzaltenango AP117

City Hall and Torch AP118

**1977, Sept. 11    Litho.    Perf. 11½**

| | | | | |
|---|---|---|---|---|
| C626 | AP117 | 7c blk & sil | .45 | .30 |
| C627 | AP118 | 30c bl & yel | 1.20 | .30 |

Founding of Quetzaltenango, 150th anniv.

Mayan Bas-relief AP119

**1977, Nov. 7**

| | | | | |
|---|---|---|---|---|
| C628 | AP119 | 10c brt car & blk | 1.05 | .30 |

14th Intl. Cong. of Latin Notaries.

Children Bringing Gifts to Christ Child — AP120

Christmas: 1c, Mother and children, horiz. 4c, Guatemalan children's Nativity scene.

**1977, Dec. 16    Litho.    Perf. 11½**

| | | | | |
|---|---|---|---|---|
| C629 | AP120 | 1c multicolored | .85 | .30 |
| C630 | AP120 | 2c multicolored | .85 | .30 |
| C631 | AP120 | 4c multicolored | .85 | .30 |
| | Nos. C629-C631 (3) | | 2.55 | .90 |

Almolonga Costume, Cancer League Emblem — AP121

Regional Costumes after Paintings by Carlos Mérida and Cancer League Emblem: 2c, Nebaj woman. 5c, San Juan Cotzal couple. 6c, Todos Santos couple. 20c, Regidores men. 30c, San Cristobal woman.

**Perf. 14 (1c, 5c, No. C636); Perf. 12 (2c, 6c, No. C636a, 30c)**

**1978, Apr. 3    Litho.**

| | | | | |
|---|---|---|---|---|
| C632 | AP121 | 1c gold & multi | .55 | .30 |
| C633 | AP121 | 2c gold & multi | .55 | .30 |
| C634 | AP121 | 5c gold & multi | .55 | .30 |
| C635 | AP121 | 6c gold & multi | .60 | .30 |

| | | | |
|---|---|---|---|
| C636 | AP121 | 20c gold & multi | 2.10 .30 |
| a. | | Souv. sheet of 1 | 4.25 4.25 |
| C637 | AP121 | 30c gold & multi | 2.10 .40 |
| | | Nos. C632-C637 (6) | 6.45 1.90 |

Part of proceeds from sale of stamps went to National League to Fight Cancer.

Virgin of Sorrows, Antigua — AP122

Statues from Various Churches: 4c, Virgin of Mercy, Antigua. 5c, Virgin of Anguish, Yurrita. 6c, Virgin of the Rosary, Santo Domingo. 8c, Virgin of Sorrows, Santo Domingo. 9c, Virgin of the Rosary, Quetzaltenango. 10c, Virgin of the Immaculate Conception, Church of St. Francis. 20c, Virgin of the Immaculate Conception, Cathedral Church.

**1978**    **Litho.**    **Perf. 11½**

| | | | |
|---|---|---|---|
| C638 | AP122 | 2c multicolored | .65 .30 |
| C639 | AP122 | 4c multicolored | .65 .30 |
| C640 | AP122 | 5c multicolored | .65 .30 |
| C641 | AP122 | 6c multicolored | .65 .30 |
| C642 | AP122 | 8c multicolored | .65 .30 |
| C643 | AP122 | 9c multicolored | .65 .30 |
| C644 | AP122 | 10c multicolored | .65 .30 |
| C645 | AP122 | 20c multicolored | 1.80 .30 |
| | | Nos. C638-C645 (8) | 6.35 2.40 |

Holy Week 1978. A 30c imperf. souvenir sheet shows the Pietà from Calvary Church, Antigua. Size: 71x101mm. Value $4.75.
Issued: 6c, 10c, 20c, 9/28; others, 5/22.

Soccer Player, Argentina '78 Emblem — AP123

**1978, July 3**    **Litho.**    **Perf. 12**

| | | | |
|---|---|---|---|
| C646 | AP123 | 10c multicolored | .75 .30 |

11th World Cup Soccer Championship, Argentina, June 1-25.

Gymnastics — AP124

**1978, Sept. 4**      **Perf. 12**

| | | | |
|---|---|---|---|
| C647 | AP124 | 6c shown | 1.10 .30 |
| C648 | AP124 | 6c Volleyball | 1.10 .30 |
| C649 | AP124 | 6c Target shooting | 1.10 .30 |
| C650 | AP124 | 6c Weight lifting | 1.10 .30 |
| a. | | Block of 4, #C647-C650 | 5.50 5.50 |
| C651 | AP124 | 8c Track & field | 1.10 .30 |
| | | Nos. C647-C651 (5) | 5.50 1.50 |

13th Central American and Caribbean Games, Medellin, Colombia.

Cattleya Pachecoi — AP125

Orchids: No. C653, Sobralia. No. C654, Cypripedium. No. C655, Oncidium. No. C656, Cattleya bowrigiana. No. C657, Encyclia. No. C658, Epidendrum. No. C659, Barkeria. No. C660, Spiranthes. No. C661, Lycaste.

**1978, Dec. 7**    **Litho.**    **Perf. 12**

| | | | |
|---|---|---|---|
| C652 | AP125 | 1c shown | 3.00 3.00 |
| C653 | AP125 | 1c multi | 3.00 3.00 |
| C654 | AP125 | 1c multi | 3.00 3.00 |
| C655 | AP125 | 1c multi | 3.00 3.00 |
| a. | | Block of 4, #C652-C655 | 21.00 21.00 |
| C656 | AP125 | 3c multi | 3.50 3.50 |
| C657 | AP125 | 3c multi | 3.50 3.50 |
| C658 | AP125 | 3c multi | 3.50 3.50 |
| C659 | AP125 | 3c multi | 3.50 3.50 |
| a. | | Block of 4, #C656-C659 | 21.00 21.00 |

| | | | |
|---|---|---|---|
| C660 | AP125 | 8c multi | 17.50 8.00 |
| C661 | AP125 | 20c multi | 27.50 12.50 |
| | | Nos. C652-C661 (10) | 71.00 46.50 |

Seal of University AP126     Students of Different Departments AP127

Designs: 12c, Student in 17th cent. clothes. 14c, Student and molecular model.

**1978, Dec. 7**

| | | | |
|---|---|---|---|
| C662 | AP126 | 6c multicolored | .50 .30 |
| C663 | AP127 | 7c multicolored | .50 .30 |
| C664 | AP126 | 12c multicolored | .60 .30 |
| C665 | AP126 | 14c multicolored | .85 .30 |
| | | Nos. C662-C665 (4) | 2.45 1.20 |

San Carlos University of Guatemala, tercentenary.

Brown and White Children AP128     A Helping Hand AP129

Designs: 7c, Child at play. 14c, Hands sheltering Indian girl.

**1978, Dec. 7**

| | | | |
|---|---|---|---|
| C666 | AP128 | 6c multicolored | .50 .30 |
| C667 | AP128 | 7c multicolored | .50 .30 |
| C668 | AP129 | 12c multicolored | .60 .30 |
| C669 | AP129 | 14c multicolored | .85 .30 |
| | | Nos. C666-C669 (4) | 2.45 1.20 |

Year of the Children of Guatemala.

Tree Planting and FAO Emblem — AP130

Forest protection: 8c, Burnt forest. 9c, Watershed, river and trees. 10c, Sawmill. 26c, Forests, river and cultivated terraces.

**1979, Apr. 16**    **Litho.**    **Perf. 13½**

| | | | |
|---|---|---|---|
| C670 | AP130 | 6c multicolored | 1.00 .30 |
| C671 | AP130 | 8c multicolored | 1.00 .30 |
| C672 | AP130 | 9c multicolored | 1.00 .30 |
| C673 | AP130 | 10c multicolored | 1.00 .30 |
| C674 | AP130 | 26c multicolored | 2.00 .30 |
| a. | | Souv. sheet of 5, #C670-C674 | 10.75 10.75 |
| | | Nos. C670-C674 (5) | 6.00 1.50 |

Peten Wild Turkey — AP131

Wildlife conservation: 3c, White-tailed deer, horiz. 5c, King buzzard. 7c, Horned owl. 9c, Young wildcat. 30c, Quetzal.

**1979, June 14**    **Litho.**    **Perf. 13½**

| | | | |
|---|---|---|---|
| C675 | AP131 | 1c multicolored | 2.00 .70 |
| C676 | AP131 | 3c multicolored | 1.10 .70 |
| C677 | AP131 | 5c multicolored | 6.00 .70 |

| | | | |
|---|---|---|---|
| C678 | AP131 | 7c multicolored | 13.00 2.75 |
| C679 | AP131 | 9c multicolored | 2.90 .70 |
| | | Nos. C675-C679 (5) | 25.00 5.55 |

**Souvenir Sheet**

| | | | |
|---|---|---|---|
| C680 | AP131 | 30c multicolored | 16.50 16.50 |

Clay Jar, 50-100 A.D. — AP132

Archaeological Treasures from Tikal: 3c, Mayan woman, ceramic head, 900 A.D. 4c, Earring, 450 A.D. 5c, vase, 700 A.D. 6c, Boy, 200-50 B.C. 7c, Bone carving, 700 A.D. 8c, Striped vase, 700 A.D. 10c, Covered vase on tripod, 450 A.D.

**1979, Sept. 19**    **Litho.**    **Perf. 13**

| | | | |
|---|---|---|---|
| C681 | AP132 | 2c multi | .60 .25 |
| C682 | AP132 | 3c multi | .85 .40 |
| C683 | AP132 | 4c multi | 1.10 .55 |
| C684 | AP132 | 5c multi | 1.50 .55 |
| C685 | AP132 | 6c multi | 1.90 .80 |
| C686 | AP132 | 7c multi | 2.25 .95 |
| C687 | AP132 | 8c multi | 2.40 1.00 |
| C688 | AP132 | 10c multi | 2.60 1.25 |
| | | Nos. C681-C688 (8) | 13.20 5.75 |

Presidential Guard Patches — AP133

Presidential Guard, 30th anniv.: 10c, Guard Headquarters.

**1979, Dec. 6**    **Litho.**    **Perf. 11½**

| | | | |
|---|---|---|---|
| C689 | AP133 | 8c multi | .55 .30 |
| C690 | AP133 | 10c multi | .55 .30 |

National Coat of Arms — AP134

Arms of Guatemalan Municipalities: No. C692, Alta Verapaz. No. C693, Baja Verapaz. No. C694, Chimal Tenango. No. C695, Chiquimula. No. C696, Escuintla. No. C697, Flores. No. C698, Guatemala. No. C699, Huehuetenango. No. C700, Izabal. No. C701, Jalapa. No. C702, Jutiapa. No. C703, Mazatenango. No. C704, Progreso. No. C705, Quezaltenango. No. C706, Quiche. No. C707, Retalhuleu. No. C708, Sacatepequez. No. C709, San Marcos. No. C710, Santa Rosa. No. C711, Solola. No. C712, Totonicapan. No. C713, Zacapa.
No. C714, 1st & current national arms.

**1979, Dec. 27**    **Litho.**    **Perf. 13½**

| | | | |
|---|---|---|---|
| C691 | AP134 | 8c shown | .85 .25 |
| C692 | AP134 | 8c multi | .85 .25 |
| C693 | AP134 | 8c multi | .85 .25 |
| C694 | AP134 | 8c multi | .85 .25 |
| C695 | AP134 | 8c multi | .85 .25 |
| C696 | AP134 | 8c multi | .85 .25 |
| C697 | AP134 | 8c multi | .85 .25 |
| C698 | AP134 | 8c multi | .85 .25 |
| C699 | AP134 | 8c multi | .85 .25 |
| C700 | AP134 | 8c multi | .85 .25 |
| C701 | AP134 | 8c multi | .85 .25 |
| C702 | AP134 | 8c multi | .85 .25 |
| C703 | AP134 | 8c multi | .85 .25 |
| C704 | AP134 | 8c multi | .85 .25 |
| C705 | AP134 | 8c multi | .85 .25 |
| C706 | AP134 | 8c multi | .85 .25 |
| C707 | AP134 | 8c multi | .85 .25 |
| C708 | AP134 | 8c multi | .85 .25 |
| C709 | AP134 | 8c multi | .85 .25 |
| C710 | AP134 | 8c multi | .85 .25 |
| C711 | AP134 | 8c multi | .85 .25 |
| C712 | AP134 | 8c multi | .85 .25 |
| C713 | AP134 | 8c multi | .85 .25 |
| | | Nos. C691-C713 (23) | 19.55 5.75 |

**Miniature Sheet**

**Imperf**

| | | | |
|---|---|---|---|
| C714 | AP134 | 50c multi | 5.50 3.50 |

No. C714 is horizontal.

Scenes from Popul Vuh (Sacred Book of the Ancient Quiches of Guatemala) — AP135

Designs: No. C715, Creation of the World. No. C716, Origin of the Twin Semi-gods. No. C717, Populating the earth. No. C718, Balam Quitze. No. C719, Quiche monarch Cotuha. No. C720, Birth of the Stick Men. No. C721, Princess Xquic's punishment. No. C722, Caha Paluma. No. C723, Cotuha and Iztayul invincible. No. C724, Odyssey of Hun Ahpu and Xbalanque. No. C725, Balam Acab. No. C726, Chief of all Nations. No. C727, Destruction of the Stick Men. No. C728, The Test in Xibalba. No. C729, Chomiha. No. C730, Warrior with captive. No. C731, Creation of the Corn Men. No. C732, Multiplication of the Prodigies. No. C733, Mahucutah. No. C734, Undefeatable king. No. C735, Thanksgiving. No. C736, Deification of Hun Ahpu and Xbalanque. No. C737, Tzununiha. No. C738, Greatness of the Quiches (battle scene).

**1981**    **Litho.**    **Perf. 12**

**Background Color**

| | | | |
|---|---|---|---|
| C715 | AP135 | 1c lilac | .50 .75 |
| C716 | AP135 | 1c pink | .50 .75 |
| C717 | AP135 | 2c green | .50 .75 |
| C718 | AP135 | 2c brt lilac | .50 .75 |
| C719 | AP135 | 3c blue | .60 .75 |
| C720 | AP135 | 4c dk blue | 1.15 .75 |
| C721 | AP135 | 4c blue vio | 1.15 .75 |
| C722 | AP135 | 4c blue | 1.15 .75 |
| C723 | AP135 | 4c lilac | 1.15 .75 |
| C724 | AP135 | 6c brown | 1.15 .75 |
| C725 | AP135 | 6c pink | 1.00 .75 |
| C726 | AP135 | 6c org brn | .60 .50 |
| C727 | AP135 | 8c citron | 1.50 1.00 |
| C728 | AP135 | 8c green | 1.50 1.00 |
| C729 | AP135 | 8c yel grn | 1.50 1.00 |
| C730 | AP135 | 8c gray | 1.50 1.00 |
| C731 | AP135 | 10c orange | 1.50 1.00 |
| C732 | AP135 | 10c brt yellow | 1.50 1.00 |
| C733 | AP135 | 10c blue green | 1.50 1.00 |
| C734 | AP135 | 10c dull green | 1.50 1.00 |
| C735 | AP135 | 22c brown | 1.50 1.25 |
| C736 | AP135 | 26c dull bl grn | 1.57 1.25 |
| C737 | AP135 | 30c gray grn | 2.75 1.50 |
| C738 | AP135 | 50c red violet | 4.25 2.00 |
| | | Nos. C715-C738 (24) | 32.02 22.75 |

Issued: Nos. C715, C717, 3c, C727, C731, 22c, 1/29; Nos. C716, C718, C721-C722, C724-C725, C728-C729, C732-C733, 26c, 30c, 3/16; others, 1981.

Thomas Edison (Phonograph Centenary) — AP136

Talking Movies, 50th Anniv. AP137

Telephone Centenary (1976) AP138     Lindbergh's Atlantic Flight, 50th Anniv. (1977) AP139

12c, Jose Cecilio del Valle, patriot. 25c, Jesus Castillo (1877-1949), composer.

**Perf. 11½, 12½ (25c)**

**1981, June 1**      **Litho.**

| | | | |
|---|---|---|---|
| C739 | AP136 | 3c multi | .35 .25 |
| C740 | AP137 | 5c multi | .40 .25 |
| C741 | AP138 | 6c multi | .55 .25 |

C742 AP139 7c multi .65 .30
C743 AP139 12c multi 1.10 .45
C744 AP139 25c multi 2.10 1.00
Nos. C739-C744 (6) 5.15 2.50

First Police Chief
Roderico Toledo
and Present Chief
German Chupina
AP140

**1981, Sept. 12** **Litho.** **Perf. 11½**
C745 AP140 2c shown .70 .30
C746 AP140 4c Headquarters .70 .30

Mayan Rock of
the Sun Calendar
AP141

**1981, Oct. 9**
C747 AP141 1c multi .55 .30

Gen. Jose Gervasio
Artigas of
Uruguay — AP142

Liberators of the Americas: 2c, Bernardo
O'Higgins (Chile). 4c, Jose de San Martin
(Argentina). 10c, Miguel Garcia Granados. 2c,
4c, 10c, 31x47mm.

**1982, Apr. 2** **Litho.** **Perf. 11½**
C748 AP142 2c multi 1.40 1.00
C749 AP142 3c multi .35 .25
**Perf. 12½**
C750 AP142 4c multi 1.40 1.00
C751 AP142 10c tan & blk .35 .25
Nos. C748-C751 (4) 3.50 2.50

Occidents Bank
Centenary
(1981) — AP143

1c, Justo Rufino Barrios (1st pres.), Main
Office, Quezaltenango. 2c, Main Office, 3c,
Emblem, vert. 4c, Commemorative medals,
vert.

**1982, July 28** **Litho.** **Perf. 11½**
C752 AP143 1c multi .65 .30
C753 AP143 2c multi .65 .30
C754 AP143 3c multi .65 .30
C755 AP143 4c multi .65 .30
Nos. C752-C755 (4) 2.60 1.20

50th Anniv. of
Natl. Mortgage
Bank
(1980) — AP144

Various emblems. 5c vert.

**1982, Oct. 18** **Litho.** **Perf. 11½**
C756 AP144 1c multi .65 .30
C757 AP144 2c multi .65 .30
C758 AP144 5c multi .65 .30
C759 AP144 10c multi .65 .30
Nos. C756-C759 (4) 2.60 1.20

AP145

**1983, May 16** **Litho.** **Perf. 11½**
C760 AP145 1c Portrait .45 .30
C761 AP145 20c Aparition, horiz. 1.00 .40
20th Anniv. of Beatification of Pedro
Bethancourt (1626-1667).

AP146

**1983, July 25** **Litho.** **Perf. 11½**
C762 AP146 10c multi .75 .30
World Telecommunications and Health Day,
May 17, 1981.

Evangelical Church
Centenary
(1982) — AP147

3c, Hands holding bible. 5c, Church.

**1983, Aug. 9**
C763 AP147 3c multi .65 .30
C764 AP147 5c multi .85 .30

Natl. Railroad
Centenary
AP148

10c, 1st locomotive crossing Puenta de Las
Vacas. 25c, General Justo Rufino Barrios,
Railroad Yard. 30c, Spanish Diesel, Amatitlan
crossing.

**1983, Sept. 28** **Litho.** **Perf. 11½**
C765 AP148 10c multi 1.30 .80
C766 AP148 25c multi 3.00 1.75
C767 AP148 30c multi 4.00 2.00
Nos. C765-C767 (3) 8.30 4.55

World Food
Day — AP149

8c, Globe, wheat, vert.

**1983, Oct. 16** **Photo.** **Perf. 11½**
C768 AP149 8c multi 1.25 .75
C769 AP149 1q shown 8.50 4.00

**Architecture Type of 1972**
**1984, Feb. 20** **Typo.** **Perf. 12½**
**Black and Green**
C770 AP98 1c like #C480 .40 .30
C771 AP98 1c like #C481 .40 .30
C772 AP98 1c like #C482 .40 .30
C773 AP98 1c like #C483 .40 .30
C774 AP98 1c like #C484 .40 .30
C775 AP98 1c like #C485 .40 .30
g. Strip of 6, #C770-C775 2.60 2.60

**Black, Brown and Orange Brown**
C775A AP98 5c like #C484 1.00 .40
C775B AP98 5c like #C485 1.00 .40
C775C AP98 5c like #C482 1.00 .40
C775D AP98 5c like #C483 1.00 .40
C775E AP98 5c like #C480 1.00 .40
C775F AP98 5c like #C481 1.00 .40
h. Strip of 6, #C775A-C775F 6.50 6.50

Visit of Pope
John Paul II, Mar.
8-9,
1983 — AP150

4c, Pope, arms. 8c, Receiving Mayan
indian, vert.

**1984, Mar. 26** **Litho.** **Perf. 11½**
C776 AP150 4c multi 1.75 .35
C777 AP150 8c multi 2.25 .35

Rafael Landivar (1731-
93), Poet — AP151

2c, Portrait. 4c, Tomb, horiz.

**1984, Aug. 6** **Litho.** **Perf. 11½**
C778 AP151 2c multi .50 .30
C779 AP151 4c multi .65 .30

Cardinal Mario
Casariego y
Acevedo — AP152

10c, 16th archbishop of Guat. (1909-83).

**1984, Aug. 6**
C780 AP152 10c multicolored .75 .30

Central American
Bank for Economic
Integration, 20th
Anniv. — AP153

30c, Bank emblem, map.

**1984, Sept. 10** **Litho.** **Perf. 11½**
C781 AP153 30c multicolored 1.30 .60

Coffee
Production,
1870 — AP154

Modern Coffee
Production
AP155

Designs: 1c, Planting coffee. 2c, Harvesting. 3c, Drying beans. 4c, Loading beans on
steamer. 5c, Reyna plant grafting method.
10c, Picking beans, coffee cup. 12c, Drying
unripened beans. Gardiola Freeze-drying
machine. 25c, Cargo transports.

**1984, Dec. 19** **Perf. 11½**
C782 AP154 1c sep & pale brn .40 .25
C783 AP154 2c sep & pale org
brn .40 .25
C784 AP154 3c sep & beige .40 .25
C785 AP154 4c sep & pale yel
brn .40 .25
C786 AP155 5c multi .50 .25
C787 AP155 10c multi 1.00 .40
C788 AP155 12c multi 1.30 .45
C789 AP155 25c multi 2.50 1.00
Nos. C782-C789 (8) 6.90 3.10

Natl. coffee production and export. An
86x112mm 25c stamp of Type AP154 and a
105x85mm 30c stamp of Type AP155 exist,
value $100 and $135, respectively.

Natl. Scouting
Assoc. — AP156

Scouting emblems and: 5c, Beaver scout,
Pyramid of Tikal. 6c, Wolf scout, Palace of the
Captains-General and Ahua Volcano. 8c,
Scout, San Pedro Volcano and Marimba

player. 10c, Rover scout and conquest mask
dance. 20c, Lord Baden-Powell and Col. Carlos Cipriani, natl. founder.

**1985, July 1**
C792 AP156 5c multi .75 .25
C793 AP156 6c multi .90 .25
C794 AP156 8c multi 1.00 .30
C795 AP156 10c multi 1.25 .40
C796 AP156 20c multi 2.50 .85
Nos. C792-C796 (5) 6.40 2.05

Inter-American Family
Unity Year — AP157

**1985, Oct. 16**
C797 AP157 10c multi .75 .30

Central American
Aeronautics Admin.,
25th Anniv. — AP158

**1985, Nov. 11**
C798 AP158 10c multi 1.25 .30

Natl. Telegraph,
Cent. — AP159

Portraits: Samuel Morse, telegraph inventor, and Justo Rufino Barrios, communications
pioneer.

**1985, Nov. 20** **Perf. 12**
C799 AP159 4c brn & blk .75 .30

Intl. Olympic
Committee, 90th
Anniv. — AP160

Designs: 8c, Mayan bust of ancient sports-
man. 10c, Baron Pierre de Coubertin (1863-
1937), father of modern Games, 1st committee president.

**1986, Jan. 28** **Litho.** **Perf. 11½**
C800 AP160 8c multi .80 .30
C801 AP160 10c multi 1.00 .30

Volunteer Fire
Department — AP161

**1986, Feb. 6** **Litho.** **Perf. 11½**
C802 AP161 6c multi 2.75 .30

Temple of
Minerva
AP162

Quetzaltenango Coat of Arms, City
Hall — AP163

**1986, July 16 Litho. Perf. 12½, 11½**
C803 AP162 8c multi .45 .30
C804 AP163 10c multi .85 .30
Quetzaltenango Independence Fair, cent.

Volunteer Fire Department AP164

**1986, Oct. 10 Litho. Perf. 11½**
C805 AP164 8c Rescue 1.50 .45
C806 AP164 10c Ruins 2.00 .55

Assoc. of Telegraphers and Radio-Telegraph Operators, 25th Anniv. — AP165

**1986, Oct. 10 Perf. 12**
C807 AP165 6c multi .80 .30

San Carlos University School of Architecture, 25th Anniv. — AP166

**1987, Feb. 16 Litho. Perf. 11½**
C808 AP166 10c multi 1.00 .30

ICAO, 40th Anniv. (in 1984) — AP167

8c, Aviateca Airlines jet. 10c, Jet, vert.

**1987, Apr. 2 Litho. Perf. 11½**
C809 AP167 8c multicolored .60 .30
C810 AP167 10c multicolored .80 .30

Chixoy Hydroelectric Power Plant AP168

**1987, May 18 Litho. Perf. 11½**
C811 AP168 2c multi 1.00 .40
Nat'l. Electrification Institute inauguration (in 1985).

San Jose de los Infantes College, 200th Anniv. (in 1981) — AP169

8c, Portrait of Archbishop Cayetano Francos y Monroy, founder. 10c, College crest.

**1987, June 10**
C812 AP169 8c multi, vert. .40 .30
C813 AP169 10c multi .70 .30

Promotion of Literacy in Latin America and Caribbean AP170

**1987, Aug. 20 Litho. Perf. 11½**
C814 AP170 12c apple grn, blk & brt org .65 .30

---

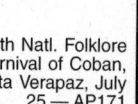

19th Natl. Folklore Carnival of Coban, Alta Verapaz, July 25 — AP171

1q, Three girls from Tamahu.

**1987, Oct. 12**
C815 AP171 1q multicolored 5.75 2.00

**1987, Dec. 8**
C816 AP171 50c Girl weaving 3.00 1.00
See No. C831.

9th Pan American Games, Caracas — AP172

**1987, Nov. 5 Perf. 12½**
C817 AP172 10c blk & sky blue 10.00 5.00

Writers and Historians — AP173

Designs: 1c, Flavio Herrera, poet, novelist. 2c, Rosendo Santa Cruz, novelist. 3c, Werner Ovalle Lopez, poet. 4c, Enrique A. Hidalgo, poet, humorist. 5c, Enrique Gomez Carrillo (1873-1927), novelist. 6c, Cesar Branas (1899-1976), journalist. 7c, Clemente Marroquin Rojas, historian. 8c, Rafael Arevalo Martinez (1884-1975), poet. 9c, Jose Milla y Vidaurre (1822-1882), historian. 10c, Miguel Angel Asturias, Nobel laureate for literature.

**1987-90 Perf. 11½**
C818 AP173 1c blk & lil .55 .30
C819 AP173 2c blk & dl org .55 .30
C820 AP173 3c blk & brt bl .55 .30
C821 AP173 4c blk & ver .55 .30
C822 AP173 5c blk & org brn .55 .30
C823 AP173 6c blk & org .55 .30
C824 AP173 7c blk & grn .55 .30
C825 AP173 8c blk & brt red .55 .30
C826 AP173 9c blk & brt rose lil .55 .30
C827 AP173 10c blk & yel .55 .30
Nos. C818-C827 (10) 5.50 3.00

Issued: 6c, 8c, 9c, 11/5/87; 4c, 5c, 1/13/88; 7c, 3/23/90; 1c, 2c, 3c, 10c, 4/9/90.

Esquipulas II — AP174

**1988, Jan. 15 Perf. 12½**
C828 AP174 10c dark olive grn .45 .25
C829 AP174 40c plum 1.75 1.00
C830 AP174 60c deep blue vio 2.90 1.50
Nos. C828-C830 (3) 5.10 2.75

2nd Meeting of the Central American Peace Plan. Nos. C828-C829 horiz.

**Folklore Festival Type of 1987 Souvenir Sheet**

**1988, Dec. 6 Litho. Imperf.**
C831 AP171 2q Music ensemble, horiz. 10.50 10.50

---

St. John Bosco (1815-1888), Educator — AP175

**1989, Feb. 1 Litho. Perf. 11½**
C832 AP175 40c gold & blk 1.90 .55

French Revolution, Bicent. — AP176

**1989, Oct. 18 Litho. Perf. 11½**
C833 AP176 1q dk red, blk & dp blue 5.25 2.00

America Issue — AP177

UPAE emblem and: 10c, Detail of the Madrid Codex. 20c, Temple of the Gran Jaguar of Tikal, Tikal Natl. Park.

**1990, Jan. 25 Litho. Perf. 11½**
C834 AP177 10c shown 1.50 1.50
C835 AP177 20c brown & multi 5.00 3.75

Institute of Nutrition of Central America and Panama, 40th Anniv. — AP178

**1990, May 18**
C837 AP178 20c multicolored 1.10 .30

Red Cross, Red Crescent Societies, 125th Anniv. — AP179

**1990, June 8**
C838 AP179 50c multicolored 1.90 .40

Defense Ministry General Staff, Cent. — AP180

**1991, May 8 Litho. Perf. 11½**
C839 AP180 20c multicolored 1.10 .30

America AP181

UPAE: 10c, Pacaya Volcano Erupting at Night. 60c, Lake Atitlan.

**1991, July 30 Litho. Perf. 11½**
C840 AP181 10c multicolored .30 .30
C841 AP181 60c multicolored 2.75 2.25

America Issue — AP182

Designs: 40c, Pinzon brothers, Nina. 60c, Columbus, Santa Maria, vert.

---

**1992, July 27 Litho. Perf. 11½**
C842 AP182 40c green & black 1.30 .80
C843 AP182 60c green & black 3.00 2.00

AP183

**1992, Oct. 6 Litho. Perf. 12½**
C844 AP183 10c multicolored 5.25 5.25
Interamerican Institute for Agricultural Cooperation, 50th anniv.

AP184

**1992, Dec. 1 Photo. Perf. 11½**
C845 AP184 1q multicolored 4.25 .80
World campaign against AIDS.

Orchids — AP185

AP185a

AP185c

AP185b

AP185d

20c, Phragmipedium caudatum. 50c, Encyclia cochleata. 1q, Encyclia vitellina. 1.50q, Odontoglossum laeve 2q, Odontoglossum uroskinneri.

**1994, Aug. 9 Litho. Perf. 11½**
C845A AP185 20c multi .65 .60
C846 AP185a 50c multi 1.20 .80
C847 AP185b 1q multi 2.60 .80
C847A AP185c 1.50q multi 5.25 4.75
C848 AP185d 2q multi 5.25 1.50
Nos. C845A-C848 (5) 14.95 8.45

Nos. C845A, C847A put on sale 8/16/96. Font sizes differ slightly on Nos. C845A-C848.

Tourism AP186

Designs: 20c, Rafting. 40c, Water sports. 60c, Boats on Lake Atitlan, volcanic mountain. 80c, Tourist boat on Lake Atitlan. 1q, Mt. Pacaya erupting. 2q, Guatemala City. 3q, Macaws, vert. 4q, Temple of the Gran Jaguar, vert. 5q, Holy Week procession from Antigua, carpet of colored saw dust, vert.

## 1995-96 Litho. Perf. 12½

| | | | |
|---|---|---|---|
| C849 | AP186 20c multicolored | .55 | .30 |
| C850 | AP186 40c multicolored | .90 | .30 |
| C851 | AP186 60c multicolored | .80 | .30 |
| C852 | AP186 80c multicolored | 1.90 | .40 |
| C853 | AP186 1q multicolored | .90 | .30 |
| C854 | AP186 2q multicolored | 1.90 | .60 |
| C855 | AP186 3q multicolored | 2.25 | .85 |
| C856 | AP186 4q multicolored | 3.25 | 1.25 |
| C857 | AP186 5q multicolored | 4.00 | 1.75 |
| | Nos. C849-C857 (9) | 16.45 | 6.05 |

Issued: No. C850, 7/5/96; No. C852, 7/9/96.
For surcharges see Nos. 568-570, 574.

Visit of Pope
John Paul
II — AP187

Papal arms, quotation, Pope John Paul II: 10c, With arms outstreached, dove, "That all the people join hands for peace." 1q, Kissing infant, "Let the children come unto me." 1.75q, Holding crucifix, "The house of the Lord is my house." 1.90q, Looking forward, "Blessed is he who comes in the name of the Lord." 2.90q, Waving hand, "Remember that all men are our brothers."

## 1996, Jan. 5 Litho. Perf. 12½

| | | | |
|---|---|---|---|
| C858 | AP187 10c multicolored | .45 | .25 |
| C859 | AP187 1q multicolored | 1.10 | .45 |
| C860 | AP187 1.75q multicolored | 1.90 | .85 |
| C861 | AP187 1.90q multicolored | 2.00 | .95 |
| C862 | AP187 2.90q multicolored | 3.25 | 1.50 |
| | Nos. C858-C862 (5) | 8.70 | 4.00 |

Distinguished
Guatemalans
AP188

Designs: 40c, Carlos Merida (Self-portrait). 50c, José Eulalio Samayoa. 60c, Manuel Montufar y Coronado.

## 1996, Oct. 21 Litho. Perf. 12½

| | | | |
|---|---|---|---|
| C863 | AP188 40c blue, black | .60 | .25 |
| C864 | AP188 50c red brn, blk, blue | .75 | .25 |
| C865 | AP188 60c brn, blue, blk | .85 | .30 |
| | Nos. C863-C865 (3) | 2.20 | .80 |

For surcharge see No. 572.

Mother
Breastfeeding
AP190

## 1997, Mar. 6 Perf. 11½

| | | | |
|---|---|---|---|
| C868 | AP190 1q multicolored | 1.25 | .60 |

Public
Finance
Projects
AP191

Designs: 20c, Education. 60c, Health care. 80c, Road construction. 1q, Family security.

## 1997, Oct. 6 Litho. Perf. 11½x12½

| | | | |
|---|---|---|---|
| C869 | AP191 20c multicolored | .50 | .25 |
| C870 | AP191 60c multicolored | .55 | .25 |
| C871 | AP191 80c multicolored | .80 | .40 |
| C872 | AP191 1q multicolored | .95 | .45 |
| | Nos. C869-C872 (4) | 2.80 | 1.35 |

For surcharges see Nos. 571, 575.

Jorge Rybar
and Machine
AP192

## 1998 Litho. Perf. 12½

| | | | |
|---|---|---|---|
| C873 | AP192 10c multi | 1.00 | .25 |

Plastics industry in Guatemala, 50th anniv.

Intl. Society
of Guatemala
Collectors,
50th Anniv.
AP193

## 1999, May 14 Litho. Perf. 11½x12½

| | | | |
|---|---|---|---|
| C874 | AP193 1q Quetzel note | 1.60 | .60 |

1993
Census — AP194

## 2001, Dec. 6 Litho. Perf. 11½

| | | | |
|---|---|---|---|
| C875 | AP194 10c multi | 100.00 | 90.00 |

No. C875 was withdrawn from sale 12/11/01.

---

## AIR POST SEMI-POSTAL STAMPS

Air Post Stamps of
1937 Surcharged in
Red or Blue

## 1937, Mar. 15 Unwmk. Perf. 12½

| | | | |
|---|---|---|---|
| CB1 | AP10 4c + 1c ultra (R) | .90 | 1.25 |
| CB2 | AP10 6c + 1c blk vio (R) | .90 | 1.25 |
| CB3 | AP11 10c + 1c ol grn (Bl) | .90 | 1.25 |
| CB4 | AP11 15c + 1c ver (Bl) | .90 | 1.25 |
| | Nos. CB1-CB4 (4) | 3.60 | 5.00 |

1st Phil. Exhib. held in Guatemala, Mar. 15-20.

> **Catalogue values for unused stamps in this section, from this point to the end of the section, are for Never Hinged items.**

### Type of Regular Issue, 1956

Designs: 35c+1q, Red Cross, Ambulance and Volcano. 50c+1q, Red Cross, Hospital and Nurse. 1q+1q, Nurse and Red Cross.

#### Perf. 13x12½

## 1956, June 19 Engr. Unwmk.

| | | | |
|---|---|---|---|
| CB5 | A148 35c + 1q red & ol grn | 5.75 | 5.75 |
| CB6 | A148 50c + 1q ultra & red | 5.75 | 5.75 |
| CB7 | A148 1q + 1q dk grn & dk red | 5.75 | 5.75 |
| | Nos. CB5-CB7 (3) | 17.25 | 17.25 |

The surtax was for the Red Cross.

Nos. B5-B7
Overprinted

## 1957, May 11

| | | | |
|---|---|---|---|
| CB8 | A148 5c + 15c | 7.00 | 8.00 |
| a. | Imperf., pair | 225.00 | |
| CB9 | A148 15c + 50c | 7.00 | 8.00 |
| a. | Overprint inverted | 275.00 | |
| CB10 | A148 25c + 50c | 7.00 | 8.00 |
| | Nos. CB8-CB10 (3) | 21.00 | 24.00 |

The surtax was for the Red Cross.

### Type of Semi-Postal Stamps, 1957 and

Esquipulas
Cathedral — SPAP1

15c+1q, Cathedral & crucifix. 20c+1q, Christ with crown of thorns and part of globe. 25c+1q, Archbishop Mariano Rossell y Arellano.

#### Perf. 13½x14½, 13

## 1957, Oct. 29 Engr. Unwmk.

| | | | |
|---|---|---|---|
| CB11 | SPAP1 10c + 1q choc & emer | 7.25 | 7.50 |
| CB12 | SP1 15c + 1q dl grn & sep | 7.25 | 7.50 |
| CB13 | SP1 20c + 1q bl gray & brn | 7.25 | 7.50 |
| CB14 | SP1 25c + 1q lt vio & car | 7.25 | 7.50 |
| | Nos. CB11-CB14 (4) | 29.00 | 30.00 |

The tax was for the Esquipulas highway.

Wounded Man,
Battle of
Solferino — SPAP2

Designs: 6c+6c, 20c+20c, Flood disaster. 10c+10c, 25c+25c, Earth, moon and stars. 15c+15c, 30c+30c, Red Cross headquarters.

## 1960, Apr. 9 Photo. Perf. 13½x14

| | | | |
|---|---|---|---|
| CB15 | SPAP2 5c + 5c multi | 2.75 | 3.00 |
| CB16 | SPAP2 6c + 6c multi | 2.75 | 3.00 |
| CB17 | SPAP2 10c + 10c multi | 2.75 | 3.00 |
| CB18 | SPAP2 15c + 15c multi | 2.75 | 3.00 |
| CB19 | SPAP2 20c + 20c multi | 2.75 | 3.00 |
| CB20 | SPAP2 25c + 25c multi | 2.75 | 3.00 |
| CB21 | SPAP2 30c + 30c multi | 2.75 | 3.00 |
| | Nos. CB15-CB21 (7) | 19.25 | 21.00 |

Cent. (in 1959) of the Red Cross idea. The surtax went to the Red Cross. Exist imperf.

---

## AIR POST OFFICIAL STAMPS

Nos. C93-C98
Overprinted in
Black

## 1939, Apr. 29 Unwmk. Perf. 12½

| | | | |
|---|---|---|---|
| CO1 | AP13 1c org & ol brn | 1.60 | 1.60 |
| CO2 | AP13 2c multi | 1.60 | 1.60 |
| CO3 | AP13 3c multi | 1.60 | 1.60 |
| CO4 | AP13 4c multi | 1.60 | 1.60 |
| CO5 | AP13 5c multi | 1.60 | 1.60 |
| CO6 | AP13 10c multi | 1.60 | 1.60 |
| | Nos. CO1-CO6 (6) | 9.60 | 9.60 |

## No. C99 Overprinted in Black

## 1939

| | | | |
|---|---|---|---|
| CO7 | AP19 Sheet of 6 | 5.00 | 5.00 |
| a. | 1c yel org, blue & blk | .75 | .75 |
| b. | 2c lake, org, blue & blk | .75 | .75 |
| c. | 3c olive, blue & orange | .75 | .75 |
| d. | 4c dk claret, bl, org & blk | .75 | .75 |
| e. | 5c grnsh bl, bl, red, org & blk | .75 | .75 |
| f. | 10c olive bister, red & org | .75 | .75 |

---

## SPECIAL DELIVERY STAMPS

No. 237 Overprinted in
Red

## 1940, June Unwmk. Perf. 14

| | | | |
|---|---|---|---|
| E1 | A81 4c orange | 1.50 | .35 |

No. E1 paid for express service by motorcycle messenger between Guatemala City and Coban.

> **Catalogue values for unused stamps in this section, from this point to the end of the section, are for Never Hinged items.**

Motorcycle
Messenger
SD1

### Black Surcharge

## 1948, Sept. 3 Photo. Perf. 14x12½

| | | | |
|---|---|---|---|
| E2 | SD1 10c on 4c bl grn & gray blk | 3.50 | 1.50 |

No. E2 without surcharge was issued for regular postage, not special delivery. See No. 337B.

---

## OFFICIAL STAMPS

O1

## 1902, Dec. 18 Typeset Perf. 12

| | | | |
|---|---|---|---|
| O1 | O1 1c green | 9.00 | 5.50 |
| O2 | O1 2c carmine | 9.00 | 5.50 |
| O3 | O1 5c ultra | 9.00 | 4.50 |
| O4 | O1 10c brown violet | 12.00 | 4.50 |
| O5 | O1 25c orange | 12.00 | 4.50 |
| a. | Horiz. pair, imperf. between | 125.00 | |
| | Nos. O1-O5 (5) | 51.00 | 24.50 |

Nos. O1-O5 printed on thin paper with sheet watermark "AMERICAN LINEN BOND." Nos. O1-O3 also printed on thick paper with sheet watermark "ROYAL BANK BOND." Values are for stamps that do not show the watermark. Counterfeits of Nos. O1-O5 exist. Counterfeits the corners are joined.

## PERFORATED OFFICIAL STAMPS

By a 1912 decree, all external mail sent from government offices in the capital was to be franked with regular stamps perforated "OFICIAL." Stamps so perforated were prepared as requisitioned from available stocks, so no formal dates of issue were available. Theoretically, any 1912-26 stamps could have been so treated, but the listing below contains those values that are known to exist.

The perforating device was damaged in the earthquakes of 1917-18, and it was sent to England for repair. An attempt to use regular stamps met with substantial pilferage, leading to the use of an OFICIAL handstamp pending the return of the repaired perforator in 1924.

The OFICIAL perforation exists reading normal, inverted, reverse and reverse inverted. The handstamped overprints were applied in violet, black, blue and red, most existing in a variety of colors. Inverted and double overprints exist for many values.

Counterfeits exist of all of the perforated and handstamped issues.

Type I - Top and bottom of "C" Flat — O6ovpt

**1912-17**

| O6 | A28 | 1c grn & claret (#114) | 1.50 | .75 |
|---|---|---|---|---|
| O7 | A29 | 2c lake & blk (#115) | 1.50 | .75 |
| O8 | A30 | 5c blue & blk (#116) | 1.50 | .75 |
| O9 | A31 | 6c bis & grn (#117) | 1.50 | .75 |
| O10 | A32 | 10c org & blue (#118) | 1.50 | .75 |
| O11 | A38 | 12½c blue & blk (#132) | 1.50 | .75 |
| O12 | A33 | 20c rose lil & blk (#119) | 1.50 | .75 |
| O13 | A40 | 25c blue & blk (#141) | 22.50 | 16.00 |
| O14 | A51 | 25c blue & brn (#158) | 10.00 | 9.00 |
| O15 | A34 | 50c red brn & blue (#120) | 3.00 | 1.00 |
| O16 | A35 | 75c gray lil & blk (#121) | 4.50 | 1.00 |
| O17 | A36 | 1p brn & blk (#122) | 4.50 | 1.00 |
| O18 | A37 | 3p ver & blk (#123) | 6.00 | 1.50 |
| O19 | A41 | 5p red & blk (#142) | 9.00 | 4.00 |
| | | Nos. O6-O19 (14) | 70.00 | 38.75 |

Stamps of 1902-24 Handstamped in Violet, Black, Blue or Red

**1924**

| O20 | A31 | 6c bis & grn (#117) | 25.00 | 25.00 |
|---|---|---|---|---|
| O21 | A31 | 6c bister (#210) | 5.00 | 2.25 |
| O22 | A32 | 10c org & blue (#118) | 5.00 | 2.25 |
| O23 | A69 | 12½c green (#202) | 5.00 | 2.25 |
| O24 | A70 | 25c brown (#203) | 5.00 | 2.25 |
| O25 | A70 | 25c brown (#211) | 5.00 | 2.25 |
| O26 | A71 | 50c rose (#204) | 5.00 | 2.25 |
| O27 | A34 | 50c red (#212) | 6.00 | 2.25 |
| O28 | A55 | 60c ol grn & blk (#163) | 25.00 | 25.00 |
| O29 | A35 | 75c gray lil & blk (#121) | 5.00 | 2.25 |
| O30 | A56 | 90c red brn & blk (#164) | 5.00 | 2.25 |
| O31 | A36 | 1p brn & blk (#122) | 5.00 | 3.00 |
| O32 | A72 | 1p dk grn (#205) | 5.00 | 3.00 |
| O33 | A62 | 1p on 1.50p bl & org (#172) | 5.00 | 1.50 |
| O34 | A35 | 1p org brn (#213) | 5.00 | 1.50 |
| O35 | A73 | 1p on 1.25p on 5p orange (#208) | 6.00 | 3.00 |
| O36 | A73 | 1.25p on 5p orange (#208) | 6.00 | 2.25 |
| O37 | A74 | 1.25p blue (#217) | 6.00 | 2.25 |
| O38 | A62 | 1.50p bl & red org (#172) | 6.00 | 2.25 |
| O39 | A37 | 2p ver & blk (#123) | 6.00 | 2.25 |
| O40 | A37 | 2p orange (#214) | 6.00 | 2.25 |
| O41 | A75 | 2.50p dk violet (#218) | 6.00 | 2.25 |
| O42 | A57 | 3p dk grn & blk (#165) | 27.50 | 25.00 |
| O43 | A57 | 3p dp grn (#215) | 15.00 | 9.00 |
| O44 | A73 | 5p orange (#206) | 15.00 | 9.00 |
| O45 | A64 | 15p black (#216) | 21.00 | 9.00 |
| | | Nos. O20-O45 (26) | 236.50 | 147.75 |

Type II - Top and Bottom of "C" Curved

**1924**

| O46 | A31 | 6c bister (#210) | 3.75 | 3.00 |
|---|---|---|---|---|
| O47 | A69 | 12½c green (#202) | 2.25 | 1.50 |
| O48 | A70 | 25c brown (#211) | 1.50 | .75 |
| O49 | A34 | 50c red (#212) | 2.25 | 1.50 |
| O50 | A36 | 1p org brn (#213) | 4.50 | 1.50 |
| O51 | A74 | 1.25p blue (#217) | 4.50 | 1.50 |
| O52 | A37 | 2p orange (#214) | 4.50 | 1.50 |
| O53 | A75 | 2.50p dk vio (#218) | 4.50 | 1.50 |

| O54 | A57 | 3p dp grn (#215) | 4.50 | 1.50 |
|---|---|---|---|---|
| O55 | A64 | 15p black (#216) | 14.00 | 9.00 |
| | | Nos. O46-O55 (10) | 46.25 | 23.25 |

Perforation is vertical on Nos. O51 and O53.

### Nos. 219-229 Perforated Type II
**1926**

| O56 | A31 | 6c bister | 1.50 | 1.50 |
|---|---|---|---|---|
| O57 | A76 | 12½c green | 1.50 | 1.50 |
| O58 | A70 | 25c brown | 1.50 | .75 |
| O59 | A77 | 50c red | 2.25 | 1.50 |
| O60 | A36 | 1p orange brn | 2.25 | 1.50 |
| O61 | A74 | 1.25p dk blue | 2.25 | 1.50 |
| O62 | A78 | 2p orange | 2.25 | .75 |
| O63 | A75 | 2.50p dk violet | 12.00 | 9.00 |
| O64 | A57 | 3p dk green | 4.50 | 1.50 |
| O65 | A63 | 5p brn violet | 4.50 | 1.50 |
| O66 | A64 | 15p black | 15.00 | 9.00 |
| | | Nos. O56-O66 (11) | 49.50 | 30.00 |

Perforation is vertical on Nos. O61 and O63.

### No. RA2 perforated Type II
**1927**

| O67 | PT2 | 1c olive green | 4.50 | 3.75 |
|---|---|---|---|---|

The perforated officials were replaced by Nos. O68-O74 in January 1929.

 National Emblem — O2

**1929, Jan.** — Engr. — Perf. 14

| O68 | O2 | 1c pale grnsh bl | .30 | .30 |
|---|---|---|---|---|
| O69 | O2 | 2c dark brown | .30 | .30 |
| O70 | O2 | 3c green | .30 | .30 |
| O71 | O2 | 4c deep violet | .40 | .35 |
| O72 | O2 | 5c brown car | .40 | .35 |
| O73 | O2 | 10c brown orange | .70 | .70 |
| O74 | O2 | 25c dark blue | 1.40 | 1.10 |
| | | Nos. O68-O74 (7) | 3.80 | 3.40 |

## POSTAL TAX STAMPS

National Emblem — PT1

**Perf. 13½, 14, 15**
**1919, May 3** — Engr. — Unwmk.

| RA1 | PT1 | 12½c carmine | .30 | .30 |
|---|---|---|---|---|

Tax for rebuilding post offices.

G. P. O. and Telegraph Building — PT2

**1927, Nov. 10** — Typo. — Perf. 14

| RA2 | PT2 | 1c olive green | .55 | .30 |
|---|---|---|---|---|

Tax to provide a fund for building a post office in Guatemala City.

No. RA2 Overprinted in Green

**1936, June 30**

| RA3 | PT2 | 1c olive green | 5.75 | 4.00 |
|---|---|---|---|---|

Liberal revolution, 65th anniversary.

No. RA2 Overprinted in Blue

**1936, Sept. 15**

| RA4 | PT2 | 1c olive green | .55 | .55 |
|---|---|---|---|---|

115th anniv. of the Independence of Guatemala.

No. RA2 Overprinted in Red Brown

**1936, Nov. 15**

| RA5 | PT2 | 1c olive green | .55 | .45 |
|---|---|---|---|---|

National Fair.

No. RA2 Overprinted in Red

**1937, Mar. 15**

| RA6 | PT2 | 1c olive green | .55 | .55 |
|---|---|---|---|---|

No. RA2 Overprinted in Blue

**1938, Jan. 10** — Perf. 14x14½

| RA7 | PT2 | 1c olive green | .30 | .30 |
|---|---|---|---|---|
| a. | | "1937-1939" omitted | 110.00 | |

150th anniv. of the US Constitution.

No. RA2 Overprinted in Blue or Red

**1938** — Perf. 14

| RA8 | PT2 | 1c olive green (Bl) | .40 | .30 |
|---|---|---|---|---|
| RA9 | PT2 | 1c olive green (R) | .40 | .30 |

No. RA2 Overprinted in Violet

**1938, Nov. 20**

| RA10 | PT2 | 1c olive green | .40 | .30 |
|---|---|---|---|---|

1st Central American Philatelic Exposition.

No. RA2 Overprinted in Green or Black

**1939**

| RA11 | PT2 | 1c olive green (G) | .40 | .30 |
|---|---|---|---|---|
| RA12 | PT2 | 1c olive green (Bk) | .40 | .30 |

No. RA2 Overprinted in Violet or Brown

**1940**

| RA13 | PT2 | 1c olive green (V) | 2.50 | .30 |
|---|---|---|---|---|
| RA14 | PT2 | 1c olive green (Br) | 2.50 | .30 |

No. RA2 Overprinted in Red

**1940, Apr. 14**

| RA15 | PT2 | 1c olive green | .40 | .30 |
|---|---|---|---|---|

Pan American Union, 50th anniversary.

No. RA2 Overprinted in Red

**1941**

| RA16 | PT2 | 1c olive green | .55 | .30 |
|---|---|---|---|---|

No. 235 Surcharged in Red

| RA17 | A79 | 1c on 2c deep blue | 1.50 | .30 |
|---|---|---|---|---|

No. 235 Surcharged in Carmine

**1942, Jan.**

| RA18 | A79 | 1c on 2c deep blue | 1.50 | .30 |
|---|---|---|---|---|

PT3

**With Imprint Below Design**
**1942, June 3** — Engr. — Perf. 11, 12x11

| RA19 | PT3 | 1c black brown | 21.00 | 8.00 |
|---|---|---|---|---|

**No imprint; Thin Paper**
**Perf. 11, 12x11, 11x12, 11x12x11x11**
**1942, July 18**

| RA20 | PT3 | 1c black brown | .65 | .30 |
|---|---|---|---|---|

Arch of Communications Building — PT4

**1943** — Perf. 11, 12x11, 12

| RA21 | PT4 | 1c orange | .65 | .30 |
|---|---|---|---|---|

PT5

**Perf. 11, 12½ and Compound**
**1945, Feb.** — Unwmk.

| RA22 | PT5 | 1c orange | .55 | .30 |
|---|---|---|---|---|

**1949** — Perf. 12½

| RA23 | PT5 | 1c deep ultra | .55 | .30 |
|---|---|---|---|---|

# GUINEA

'gi-nē

LOCATION — Coast of West Africa, between Guinea-Bissau and Sierra Leone
GOVT. — Republic
AREA — 94,926 sq. mi.
POP. — 7,538,953 (1999 est.)
CAPITAL — Conakry

This former French Overseas Territory of French West Africa proclaimed itself an independent republic on October 2, 1958.

100 Centimes = 1 Franc
100 Caury = 1 Syli (1973)
100 Centimes = 1 Guinean Franc (1986)

Catalogue values for all unused stamps in this country are for Never Hinged items.

Common Design Types pictured following the introduction.

French West Africa No. 79 Overprinted

**1959 Unwmk. Photo. Perf. 12x12½**
168 CD104 10fr multi 3.00 2.50

French West Africa No. 78 Surcharged in Red

**Engr.**
**Perf. 13**
169 A33 45fr on 20fr multi 3.50 2.25

Map, Dove and Pres. Sékou Touré — A12

**1959 Unwmk. Engr. Perf. 13**
170 A12 5fr rose car .30 .25
171 A12 10fr ultramarine .40 .25
172 A12 20fr orange .70 .30
173 A12 65fr slate green 2.10 .95
174 A12 100fr violet 3.50 2.10
Nos. 170-174 (5) 7.00 3.85

Proclamation of independence, Oct. 2, 1958.

Bananas — A13

**1959 Litho. Perf. 11½**
175 A13 10fr shown .25 .25
176 A13 15fr Grapefruit .40 .25
177 A13 20fr Lemons .70 .25
178 A13 25fr Avocados .80 .25
179 A13 50fr Pineapple 1.75 .25
Nos. 175-179 (5) 3.90 1.25

For overprints see Nos. 209-213.

Fishing Boats and Tamara Lighthouse — A14

5fr, Coco palms & sailboat, vert. 10fr, Launching fishing pirogue. 15fr, Elephant's

---

head. 20fr, Pres. Sékou Touré & torch, vert. 25fr, Elephant.

**1959 Engr. Perf. 13½**
180 A14 1fr rose .25 .25
181 A14 2fr green .25 .25
182 A14 3fr brown .25 .25
183 A14 5fr blue .40 .25
184 A14 10fr claret .40 .25
185 A14 15fr light brn 1.20 .30
186 A14 20fr claret 1.20 .35
187 A14 25fr red brown 2.25 .60
Nos. 180-187 (8) 6.20 2.50

Flag Raising, Labé — A15

**1959 Litho. Perf. 12**
188 A15 50fr multicolored 1.10 .25
189 A15 100fr multicolored 2.00 .50

For overprints see Nos. 201-202.

UN Headquarters, New York, and People of Guinea — A16

**1959 Perf. 12**
190 A16 1fr vio blue & org .25 .25
191 A16 2fr red lil & emer .25 .25
192 A16 3fr brn & crimson .25 .25
193 A16 5fr brn & grnsh bl .25 .25
Nos. 190-193,C22-C23 (6) 3.40 2.65

Guinea's admission to the UN, first anniv. For overprints see Nos. 205-208, C27-C28.

Uprooted Oak Emblem — A17

**1960 Photo. Perf. 11½**
**Granite Paper**
194 A17 25fr multicolored .80 .25
195 A17 50fr multicolored 1.10 .25

World Refugee Year, 7/1/59-6/30/60. For surcharges see Nos. B17-B18.

UPU Monument, Bern — A18

**1960 Granite Paper Unwmk.**
196 A18 10fr gray brn & blk .25 .25
197 A18 15fr lil & purple .45 .25
198 A18 20fr ultra & dk blue .65 .25
199 A18 25fr yel grn & sl grn .85 .25
200 A18 50fr red org & brown .90 .25
Nos. 196-200 (5) 3.10 1.25

Nos. 199-200 are vertical. Admission to the UPU, first anniv.

**Nos. 188-189 Overprinted in Black, Orange or Carmine: "Jeux Olympiques Rome 1960" and Olympic Rings**

**1960 Litho. Perf. 12**
201 A15 50fr multi (Blk) 8.00 6.00
202 A15 100fr multi (O or C) 12.50 9.00
Nos. 201-202,C24-C26 (5) 92.25 67.25

17th Olympic Games, Rome, 8/25-9/11. See note after No. C26.

Map and Flag of Guinea — A19

---

**1960 Photo. Perf. 11½**
203 A19 25fr multicolored .60 .30
204 A19 30fr multicolored .80 .30

Second anniversary of independence.

## Nos. 190-193 Overprinted

**1961 Litho. Perf. 12**
205 A16 1fr vio blue & org .25 .25
206 A16 2fr red lil & emer .25 .25
207 A16 3fr brn & crimson .25 .25
208 A16 5fr brn & grnsh bl .25 .25

Nos. 175-179 Overprinted in Black or Orange

**Perf. 11½**
**Fruits in Natural Colors**
209 A13 10fr red .25 .25
210 A13 15fr grn & pink .40 .25
211 A13 20fr red brn & bl .50 .25
212 A13 25fr bl & yel (O) .50 .25
213 A13 50fr dk vio blue 1.00 .40
Nos. 205-213,C27-C28 (11) 6.15 3.35

15th anniversary of United Nations.

Defassa Waterbuck — A20

**1961, Sept. 1 Photo. Perf. 11½**
**Multicolored Design; Granite Paper**
214 A20 5fr bright grn .25 .25
215 A20 10fr emerald .35 .25
216 A20 25fr lilac .40 .25
217 A20 40fr orange .60 .25
218 A20 50fr red orange 1.20 .30
219 A20 75fr ultramarine 2.25 .75
Nos. 214-219 (6) 5.05 2.05

For surcharges see Nos. B19-B24.

Exhibition Hall — A21

**1961, Oct. 2 Perf. 11½**
**Flag in Red, Yellow & Green**
**Granite Paper**
220 A21 5fr ultra & red .25 .25
221 A21 10fr brown & red .25 .25
222 A21 25fr gray grn & red .30 .25
Nos. 220-222 (3) .80 .75

First Three-Year Plan.

Gray-breasted Helmet Guinea Fowl — A22

**1961 Unwmk. Perf. 13x14**
223 A22 5fr rose lil, sepia & bl .25 .25
224 A22 10fr dp org, sepia & bl .30 .25
225 A22 25fr cerise, sepia & bl .35 .25
226 A22 40fr ocher, sepia & bl .70 .25
227 A22 50fr lemon, sepia & bl 1.00 .25
228 A22 75fr apple grn, sep & bl 1.40 .30
Nos. 223-228 (6) 4.00 1.55

For surcharges see Nos. B30-B35.

Patrice Lumumba and Map of Africa — A23

---

**1962, Feb. 13 Photo. Perf. 11½**
229 A23 10fr multicolored .25 .25
230 A23 25fr multicolored .55 .25
231 A23 50fr multicolored .75 .25
Nos. 229-231 (3) 1.55 .75

Death anniv. (on Feb. 12, 1961) of Patrice Lumumba, Premier of the Congo Republic.

King Mohammed V of Morocco and Map of Africa — A24

**1962, Mar. 15 Litho. Perf. 13**
232 A24 25fr multicolored .75 .25
233 A24 75fr multicolored 2.25 .60

First anniv. of the conference of African heads of state at Casablanca. For surcharges see Nos. B36-B37.

## African Postal Union Issue

Map of Africa and Post Horn — A25

**1962, Apr. 23 Photo. Perf. 13½x13**
234 A25 25fr org, blk & grn .60 .25
235 A25 100fr deep brn & org 1.90 .55

Establishment of African Postal Union.

Bolon Player — A26

Musical Instruments: 30c, 25fr, 50fr, Bote, vert. 1fr, 10fr, Flute, vert. 1.50fr, 3fr, Koni. 2fr, 20fr, Kora. 40fr, 75fr, Bolon.

**Perf. 13½x13, 13x13½**
**1962, June 15**
236 A26 30c bl, dk grn & red .25 .25
237 A26 50c sal, brn & brt grn .25 .25
238 A26 1fr yel grn, grn & lil .25 .25
239 A26 1.50fr yel, red & bl .25 .25
240 A26 2fr rose lil, red lil & grn .25 .25
241 A26 3fr brn grn, grn & lil .25 .25
242 A26 10fr org, brn & bl .25 .25
243 A26 20fr ol, dk ol & car .45 .25
244 A26 40fr ol, dk ol & lil .55 .25
245 A26 40fr bl, grn & red lil .80 .25
246 A26 50fr rose, dp rose & Prus bl 1.10 .25
247 A26 75fr dl yel, brn & Prus bl 1.50 .60
Nos. 236-247,C32-C34 (15) 16.10 9.10

Hippopotamus A27

25fr, 75fr, Lion. 30fr, 100fr, Leopard.

**1962, Aug. 25 Litho. Perf. 13x13½**
248 A27 10fr org, grn & brn .35 .25
249 A27 25fr emer, blk & brn .55 .25
250 A27 30fr yel grn, dk brn & grn .90 .25
251 A27 50fr vio bl, dk brn & grn 1.10 .30
252 A27 75fr lil, lt lil & red brn 1.75 .50
253 A27 100fr grnsh bl, dk brn & yel 2.40 .60
Nos. 248-253 (6) 7.05 2.15

See Nos. 340-345

Child at Blackboard — A28

Designs: 10fr, 20fr, Adult class.

**1962, Sept. 19   Photo.   Perf. 13½x13**
| | | | |
|---|---|---|---|
| 254 | A28 | 5fr yel, dk brn & org | .25 .25 |
| 255 | A28 | 10fr org & dk brn | .25 .25 |
| 256 | A28 | 15fr yel grn, dk brn & red | .30 .25 |
| 257 | A28 | 20fr bl & dk brn | .40 .25 |
| | | Nos. 254-257 (4) | 1.20 1.00 |

Campaign against illiteracy.

### Imperforates
From late 1962 onward, most Guinea stamps exist imperforate.

Alfa Yaya — A29

30fr, King Behanzin. 50fr, King Ba Bemba. 75fr, Almamy Samory. 100fr, Tierno Aliou.

**1962, Oct. 2   Perf. 13½**
**Gold Frame**
| | | | |
|---|---|---|---|
| 258 | A29 | 25fr brt bl & sepia | .25 .25 |
| 259 | A29 | 30fr yel & sepia | .40 .25 |
| 260 | A29 | 50fr brt pink & sepia | .65 .30 |
| 261 | A29 | 75fr yel grn & sepia | 1.25 .45 |
| 262 | A29 | 100fr org, red & sepia | 1.90 .70 |
| | | Nos. 258-262 (5) | 4.45 1.95 |

Heroes and martyrs of Africa.

Gray Parrot — A30

Birds: 30c, 3fr, 50fr, Crowned crane (vert). 1fr, 20fr, Abyssinian ground hornbill. 1.50fr, 25fr, White spoonbill. 2fr, 40fr, Bateleur eagle.

**1962, Dec.   Perf. 13½x13, 13x13½**
| | | | |
|---|---|---|---|
| 263 | A30 | 30c multicolored | .25 .25 |
| 264 | A30 | 50c multicolored | .25 .25 |
| 265 | A30 | 1fr multicolored | .25 .25 |
| 266 | A30 | 1.50fr multicolored | .25 .25 |
| 267 | A30 | 2fr multicolored | .25 .25 |
| 268 | A30 | 3fr multicolored | .65 .25 |
| 269 | A30 | 10fr multicolored | .80 .25 |
| 270 | A30 | 20fr multicolored | .90 .25 |
| 271 | A30 | 25fr multicolored | .95 .25 |
| 272 | A30 | 40fr multicolored | 1.10 .25 |
| 273 | A30 | 50fr multicolored | 1.60 .35 |
| 274 | A30 | 75fr multicolored | 2.10 .50 |
| | | Nos. 263-274,C41-C43 (15) | 27.10 11.60 |

Wheat Emblem and Globe — A31

**1963, Mar. 21   Photo.   Perf. 13x14**
| | | | |
|---|---|---|---|
| 275 | A31 | 5fr red & yellow | .25 .25 |
| 276 | A31 | 10fr emerald & yel | .25 .25 |
| 277 | A31 | 15fr brown & yel | .25 .25 |
| 278 | A31 | 25fr dark ol & yel | .25 .25 |
| | | Nos. 275-278 (4) | 1.00 1.00 |

FAO "Freedom from Hunger" campaign.

Basketball — A32

50c, 4fr, 30fr, Boxing. 1fr, 5fr, Running. 1.50fr, 10fr, Bicycling. 2fr, 20fr, Single sculls.

**1963, Mar. 16   Unwmk.   Perf. 14**
| | | | |
|---|---|---|---|
| 279 | A32 | 30c ver, dp claret & grn | .25 .25 |
| 280 | A32 | 50c lilac & blue | .25 .25 |
| 281 | A32 | 1fr dl org, sep & grn | .25 .25 |
| 282 | A32 | 1.50fr org, ultra & mag | .25 .25 |
| 283 | A32 | 2fr aqua, dk bl & mag | .25 .25 |
| 284 | A32 | 3fr ol, dp cl & grn | .25 .25 |
| 285 | A32 | 4fr car rose, pur & bl | .25 .25 |
| 286 | A32 | 5fr brt grn, ol & mag | .25 .25 |
| 287 | A32 | 10fr lil rose, ultra & mag | .25 .25 |
| 288 | A32 | 20fr red org, dk bl & crim | .25 .25 |
| 289 | A32 | 25fr emer, dp cl & dk grn | .35 .25 |
| 290 | A32 | 30fr gray, pur & bl | .35 .25 |
| | | Nos. 279-290,C44-C46 (15) | 15.20 7.60 |

For overprints and surcharges see Nos. 312-314, C58-C60.

A33

Various Butterflies.

**1963, May 10   Photo.   Perf. 12**
| | | | |
|---|---|---|---|
| 291 | A33 | 10c dp rose, blk & gray | .25 .25 |
| 292 | A33 | 30c rose, blk & yel | .25 .25 |
| 293 | A33 | 40c yel grn, brn & yel | .25 .25 |
| 294 | A33 | 50c pale vio, blk & grn | .25 .25 |
| 295 | A33 | 1fr yel, blk & emer | .40 .25 |
| 296 | A33 | 1.50fr bluish grn, blk & sep | .40 .25 |
| 297 | A33 | 2fr multi | .40 .25 |
| 298 | A33 | 3fr multi | 1.10 .25 |
| 299 | A33 | 10fr rose lil, blk & grn | 1.25 .25 |
| 300 | A33 | 20fr gray, blk & grn | 1.40 .25 |
| 301 | A33 | 25fr yel grn, blk & gray | 1.60 .25 |
| 302 | A33 | 40fr multi | 2.00 .45 |
| 303 | A33 | 50fr ultra, blk & yel | 2.50 .55 |
| 304 | A33 | 75fr yel, blk & grn | 3.25 .80 |
| | | Nos. 291-304,C47-C49 (17) | 30.40 11.80 |

Handshake, Map and Dove — A34

**1963, May 22   Perf. 13½x14**
| | | | |
|---|---|---|---|
| 305 | A34 | 5fr bluish grn & dk brn | .25 .25 |
| 306 | A34 | 10fr org yel & dk brn | .25 .25 |
| 307 | A34 | 15fr ol & dk brn | .25 .25 |
| 308 | A34 | 25fr bis brn & dk brn | .30 .25 |
| | | Nos. 305-308 (4) | 1.05 1.00 |

Conference of African heads of state for African Unity, Addis Ababa.

Globe Encircled by Satellite A35

**1963, July 25   Engr.   Perf. 10½**
| | | | |
|---|---|---|---|
| 309 | A35 | 5fr green & car | .25 .25 |
| 310 | A35 | 10fr vio bl & car | .40 .25 |
| 311 | A35 | 15fr yellow & car | .50 .25 |
| | | Nos. 309-311,C50 (4) | 1.90 1.00 |

Centenary of the International Red Cross.

### Nos. 279-281 Surcharged in Carmine, Yellow or Orange

**1963, Nov. 20   Photo.   Perf. 14**
| | | | |
|---|---|---|---|
| 312 | A32 | 40fr on 30c (C or Y) | 1.40 1.10 |
| 313 | A32 | 50fr on 50c (C or O) | 2.10 1.75 |
| 314 | A32 | 75fr on 1fr (C or O) | 3.50 2.50 |
| | | Nos. 312-314,C58-C60 (6) | 18.00 13.75 |

Meeting of the Olympic Games Preparatory Commission at Conakry. The overprint is in a circular line on #312, in 3 lines on each side on #313-314.

Jewelfish — A36

Fish: 40c, 30fr, Golden pheasant. 50c, 40fr, Blue gularis. 1fr, 75fr, Banded Jewelfish. 1.50fr, African lyretail. 2fr, Six-barred epiplatys. 5fr, Jewelfish.

**1964, Feb. 15   Litho.   Perf. 14x13½**
| | | | |
|---|---|---|---|
| 315 | A36 | 30c car rose & multi | .25 .25 |
| 316 | A36 | 40c pur & multi | .25 .25 |
| 317 | A36 | 50c car rose & multi | .25 .25 |
| 318 | A36 | 1fr blue & multi | .25 .25 |
| 319 | A36 | 1.50fr blue & multi | .25 .25 |
| 320 | A36 | 2fr pur & multi | .60 .25 |
| 321 | A36 | 5fr blue & multi | .65 .25 |
| 322 | A36 | 30fr grn & multi | .85 .25 |
| 323 | A36 | 40fr pur & multi | 1.75 .40 |
| 324 | A36 | 75fr multi | 2.50 .55 |
| | | Nos. 315-324,C54-C55 (12) | 17.60 4.90 |

John F. Kennedy — A37

**1964, Mar. 5   Engr.   Perf. 10½**
**Flag in Red and Blue**
| | | | |
|---|---|---|---|
| 325 | A37 | 5fr blk & pur | .25 .25 |
| 326 | A37 | 25fr grn & pur | .40 .25 |
| 327 | A37 | 50fr brn & pur | .70 .30 |
| | | Nos. 325-327,C56 (4) | 2.85 1.60 |

Issued in sheets of 20 with marginal quotations in English and French. Two sheets for each denomination. See No. C56.

Workers Welding Pipe — A38

5fr, Pipe line over mountains, vert. 10fr, Waterworks. 30fr, Transporting pipe. 50fr, Laying pipe.

**1964, May 1   Photo.   Perf. 11½**
| | | | |
|---|---|---|---|
| 328 | A38 | 5fr deep mag | .25 .25 |
| 329 | A38 | 10fr bright pur | .25 .25 |
| 330 | A38 | 20fr org red | .30 .25 |
| 331 | A38 | 30fr ultra | .50 .25 |
| 332 | A38 | 50fr yel grn | .70 .25 |
| | | Nos. 328-332 (5) | 2.00 1.25 |

Completion of the water-supply pipeline to Conakry, Mar. 1964.

Ice Hockey — A39

**1964, May 15   Perf. 13x12½**
| | | | |
|---|---|---|---|
| 333 | A39 | 10fr shown | .40 .25 |
| 334 | A39 | 25fr Ski jump | .60 .25 |
| 335 | A39 | 50fr Slalom | 1.10 .40 |
| | | Nos. 333-335,C57 (4) | 4.35 1.30 |

9th Winter Olympic Games, Innsbruck, Jan. 29-Feb. 9, 1964.

Eleanor Roosevelt Reading to Children — A40

**1964, June 1   Engr.   Perf. 10½**
| | | | |
|---|---|---|---|
| 336 | A40 | 5fr green | .25 .25 |
| 337 | A40 | 10fr red org | .25 .25 |
| 338 | A40 | 15fr bright bl | .25 .25 |
| 339 | A40 | 25fr car rose | .25 .25 |
| | | Nos. 336-339,C61 (5) | 1.75 1.25 |

Eleanor Roosevelt, 15th anniv. of the Universal Declaration of Human Rights (in 1963).

### Animal Type of 1962

Designs: 5fr, 30fr, Striped hyenas. 40fr, 300fr, Black buffaloes. 75fr, 100fr, Elephants.

**1964, Oct. 8   Litho.   Perf. 13x13½**
| | | | |
|---|---|---|---|
| 340 | A27 | 5fr yellow & blk | .25 .25 |
| 341 | A27 | 30fr light bl & blk | .45 .25 |
| 342 | A27 | 40fr lil rose & blk | 1.00 .25 |
| 343 | A27 | 75fr yel grn & blk | 2.25 .40 |
| 344 | A27 | 100fr bister & blk | 2.50 .75 |
| 345 | A27 | 300fr orange & blk | 6.50 2.75 |
| | | Nos. 340-345 (6) | 12.95 4.65 |

Guinea Exhibit, World's Fair — A41

**1964, Oct. 26   Engr.   Perf. 10½**
| | | | |
|---|---|---|---|
| 346 | A41 | 30fr vio & emerald | .35 .25 |
| 347 | A41 | 40fr red lil & emer | .50 .25 |
| 348 | A41 | 50fr sepia & emer | .65 .25 |
| 349 | A41 | 75fr rose red & dk bl | .95 .25 |
| | | Nos. 346-349 (4) | 2.45 1.00 |

New York World's Fair, 1964-65.
See Nos. 372-375, C62-C63, C69-C70.

Queen Nefertari Crowned by Isis and Hathor — A42

Designs: 25fr, Ramses II in battle. 50fr, Submerged sphinxes, sailboat, Wadies-Sebua. 100fr, Ramses II holding crook and flail, Abu Simbel. 200fr, Feet and legs of Ramses statues, Abu Simbel.

**1964, Nov. 19   Photo.   Perf. 12**
| | | | |
|---|---|---|---|
| 350 | A42 | 10fr dk bl, red brn & cit | .25 .25 |
| 351 | A42 | 25fr blk, dl red & brn | .30 .25 |
| 352 | A42 | 50fr dk brn, bl & vio | .55 .25 |
| 353 | A42 | 100fr dk brn, yel & pur | 1.10 .40 |
| 354 | A42 | 200fr pur, dl grn & buff | 2.00 .75 |
| | | Nos. 350-354,C64 (6) | 7.70 3.30 |

UNESCO campaign to preserve Nubian monuments.

For overprint see No. 415.

Weight Lifter and Caucasian, Japanese and Negro Children — A43

10fr, Runner carrying torch. 25fr, Pole vaulting and flags. 40fr, Runners. 50fr, Judo. 75fr, Japanese woman, flags and stadium.

**1965, Jan. 18   Photo.   Perf. 13x12½**
| 355 | A43 | 5fr gold, claret & blk | .25 | .25 |
| 356 | A43 | 10fr gold, blk, ver & bl | .40 | .25 |
| 357 | A43 | 25fr gold, blk, yel grn & red | .45 | .25 |
| 358 | A43 | 40fr gold, blk, brn & yel | .50 | .25 |
| 359 | A43 | 50fr gold, blk & grn | .70 | .30 |
| 360 | A43 | 75fr gold & multi | 1.50 | .40 |
| | | Nos. 355-360,C65 (7) | 5.55 | 2.05 |

18th Olympic Games, Tokyo, 10/10-25/64.
For overprints see Nos. 410-414.

Doudou Mask, Boké — A44

Designs: 40c, 1fr, 15fr, Various Niamou masks, N'Zérékoré region. 60c, "Yoki," wood-carved statuette of a girl, Boke. 80c, Masked woman dancer from Guekedou. 2fr, Masked dancer from Macenta. 20fr, Beater from Tam-tam. 60fr, Bird dancer from Macenta. 80fr, Bassari dancer from Koundara. 100fr, Sword dancer from Karana.

**1965, Feb. 15   Unwmk.   Perf. 14**
| 361 | A44 | 20c multicolored | .25 | .25 |
| 362 | A44 | 40c multicolored | .25 | .25 |
| 363 | A44 | 60c multicolored | .25 | .25 |
| 364 | A44 | 80c multicolored | .25 | .25 |
| 365 | A44 | 1fr multicolored | .25 | .25 |
| 366 | A44 | 2fr multicolored | .25 | .25 |
| 367 | A44 | 15fr multicolored | .30 | .25 |
| 368 | A44 | 20fr multicolored | .35 | .25 |
| 369 | A44 | 60fr multicolored | 1.10 | .40 |
| 370 | A44 | 80fr multicolored | 1.50 | .50 |
| 371 | A44 | 100fr multicolored | 1.75 | .50 |
| | | Nos. 361-371,C68 (12) | 11.75 | 6.15 |

**World's Fair Type of 1964 Inscribed "1965"**

**1965, Mar. 24   Engr.   Perf. 10½**
| 372 | A41 | 30fr grn & orange | .30 | .25 |
| 373 | A41 | 40fr car & brt grn | .45 | .25 |
| 374 | A41 | 50fr brt grn & vio | .60 | .25 |
| 375 | A41 | 75fr brown & vio | .90 | .35 |
| | | Nos. 372-375 (4) | 2.25 | 1.10 |

See Nos. C69-C70.

Blacksmith — A45

Handicrafts: 20fr, Potter. 60fr, Cloth dyers. 80fr, Basketmaker.

**1965, May 1   Photo.   Perf. 14**
| 376 | A45 | 15fr multicolored | .25 | .25 |
| 377 | A45 | 20fr multicolored | .50 | .25 |
| 378 | A45 | 60fr multicolored | .80 | .30 |
| 379 | A45 | 80fr multicolored | .95 | .40 |
| | | Nos. 376-379,C71-C72 (6) | 9.25 | 2.80 |

ITU Emblem, Old and New Communication Equipment — A46

**1965, May 17   Unwmk.**
| 380 | A46 | 25fr yel, gray, gold & blk | .45 | .25 |
| 381 | A46 | 50fr yel, grn, gold & blk | .45 | .25 |
| | | Nos. 380-381,C73-C74 (4) | 4.75 | 1.55 |

ITU centenary. Exist in tete-beche pairs.

Maj. Virgil I. Grissom A47

Moon from 258mi. A48

Sputnik Over Earth — A49

American Achievements in Space: 10fr, Lt. Com. John W. Young. 25fr, Moon from 115mi. 30fr, Moon from 58mi. 100fr, Grissom and Young in Gemini 3 spaceship.

**1965, July 19   Photo.   Perf. 13**
| | | **Size: 21x29mm** | | |
| 382 | A47 | 5fr dk red & multi | .25 | .25 |
| 383 | A47 | 10fr dk red & multi | .25 | .25 |
| 384 | A48 | 15fr gold, bl & dk bl | .25 | .25 |
| | | **Size: 39x28mm** | | |
| 385 | A48 | 25fr gold, bl & dk bl | .25 | .25 |
| | | **Size: 21x29mm** | | |
| 386 | A48 | 30fr gold, bl & dk bl | .25 | .25 |
| | | **Size: 39x28mm** | | |
| 387 | A47 | 100fr multi & dk red | .50 | .40 |
| a. | | Sheet of 15, #382-387 | 9.00 | |

Russian Achievements in Space: 5fr, Col. Pavel Belyayev. 10fr, Lt. Col. Alexei Leonov. 15fr, Vostoks 3 & 4 in space. 30fr, Vostoks 5 & 6 over Earth. 100fr, Leonov floating in space.

| | | **Size: 21x29mm** | | |
| 388 | A47 | 5fr bl & multi | .25 | .25 |
| 389 | A47 | 10fr bl & multi | .25 | .25 |
| 390 | A49 | 15fr bl & multi | .25 | .25 |
| | | **Size: 39x28mm** | | |
| 391 | A49 | 25fr bl & multi | .25 | .25 |
| | | **Size: 21x29mm** | | |
| 392 | A49 | 30fr bl & multi | .25 | .25 |
| | | **Size: 39x28mm** | | |
| 393 | A47 | 100fr blk, dk red & gold | .50 | .40 |
| a. | | Sheet of 15, #388-393 | 9.00 | |
| | | Nos. 382-393 (12) | 3.50 | 3.30 |

American and Russian achievements in space. Nos. 387a and 393a contain five triptychs each: four rows with 5fr, 100fr and 10fr, and a center row with 15fr, 25fr and 30fr stamps each.

ICY Emblem, UN Headquarters and Skyline, New York — A50

**1965, Sept. 8   Perf. 10½**
| 394 | A50 | 25fr yel grn & ver | .35 | .25 |
| 395 | A50 | 45fr vio & orange | .40 | .25 |
| 396 | A50 | 75fr red brn & org | .65 | .25 |
| | | Nos. 394-396,C75 (4) | 2.65 | 1.10 |

Intl. Cooperation Year, 1965.

Polytechnic Institute, Conakry A51

New Projects, Conakry: 30fr, Hotel Camayenne. 40fr, Gbessia Airport. 75fr, Stadium "28 September."

**1965, Oct. 2   Photo.   Perf. 13½**
| 397 | A51 | 25fr multicolored | .30 | .25 |
| 398 | A51 | 30fr multicolored | .35 | .25 |
| 399 | A51 | 40fr multicolored | .60 | .30 |
| 400 | A51 | 75fr multicolored | .75 | .40 |
| | | Nos. 397-400,C76-C77 (6) | 8.75 | 5.20 |

Seventh anniversary of independence.

Photographing Far Side of Moon — A52

10fr, Trajectories of Ranger VII on flight to moon. 25fr, Relay satellite. 45fr, Vostoks I & II & globe.

**1965, Nov. 15   Litho.   Perf. 14x13½**
| 401 | A52 | 5fr blk, pur & ocher | .25 | .25 |
| 402 | A52 | 10fr red brn, lt grn & yel | .25 | .25 |
| 403 | A52 | 25fr blk, bl & bis | .50 | .25 |
| 404 | A52 | 45fr blk, lt ultra & bis | 1.00 | .25 |
| | | Nos. 401-404,C78-C79 (6) | 5.50 | 2.50 |

For overprints and surcharges see Nos. 529-530, C112-C112B.

Sword Dance, Karana — A53

Designs: 30c, Dancing girls, Lower Guinea. 50c, Behore musicians of Tiekere playing "Eyoro," horiz. 5fr, Doundouba dance of Kouroussa. 40fr, Bird man's dance of Macenta.

**1966, Jan. 5   Photo.   Perf. 13½**
| | | **Size: 26x36mm** | | |
| 405 | A53 | 10c multicolored | .25 | .25 |
| 406 | A53 | 30c multicolored | .25 | .25 |
| | | **Size: 36x28½mm** | | |
| 407 | A53 | 50c multicolored | .45 | .25 |
| | | **Size: 26x36mm** | | |
| 408 | A53 | 5fr multicolored | .45 | .25 |
| 409 | A53 | 40fr multicolored | .75 | .25 |
| | | Nos. 405-409,C80 (6) | 3.40 | 1.75 |

Festival of African Art and Culture. See Nos. 436-441.

Engraved Overprint in Red or Orange on Nos. 355-356 and Nos. 358-360

**1966, Mar. 14   Perf. 13x12½**
| 410 | A43 | 5fr multi (R) | .40 | .25 |
| 411 | A43 | 10fr multi (R) | .50 | .25 |
| 412 | A43 | 40fr multi (O) | .85 | .25 |
| 413 | A43 | 50fr multi (R) | 1.10 | .40 |
| 414 | A43 | 75fr multi (R) | 2.00 | .65 |
| | | Nos. 410-414,C81 (6) | 6.10 | 2.25 |

4th Pan Arab Games, Cairo, Sept. 2-11, 1965. The same overprint was also applied to imperf. sheets of No. 357.

Engraved Red Orange Overprint on No. 352

**1966, Mar. 14   Perf. 12**
| 415 | A42 | 50fr dk brn, bl & vio | 1.00 | .50 |

1st Egyptian postage stamps, cent. See #C82.

Vonkou Rock, Telimélé — A54

Views: 25fr, Artificial lake, Coyah. 40fr, Kalé waterfalls. 50fr, Forécariah bridge. 75fr, Liana bridge.

**1966, Apr. 4   Photo.   Perf. 13½**
| 416 | A54 | 20fr multicolored | .25 | .25 |
| 417 | A54 | 25fr multicolored | .45 | .25 |
| 418 | A54 | 40fr multicolored | .50 | .25 |
| 419 | A54 | 50fr multicolored | .70 | .25 |
| 420 | A54 | 75fr multicolored | .90 | .30 |
| | | Nos. 416-420,C83 (6) | 4.20 | 1.90 |

See Nos. 475-478, C83, C90-C91. For overprints see Nos. 482-488, C93-C95.

UNESCO Emblem — A55

**1966, May 2   Photo.   Unwmk.**
| 421 | A55 | 25fr multicolored | .70 | .25 |

20th anniv. of UNESCO. See Nos. C84-C85.

Woman of Guinea and Morning Glory — A56

Designs: Women and Flowers of Guinea.

**1966, May 30   Photo.   Perf. 13½**
| | | **Size: 23x34mm** | | |
| 422 | A56 | 10c multicolored | .25 | .25 |
| 423 | A56 | 20c multicolored | .25 | .25 |
| 424 | A56 | 30c multicolored | .25 | .25 |
| 425 | A56 | 40c multicolored | .25 | .25 |
| 426 | A56 | 3fr multicolored | .25 | .25 |
| 427 | A56 | 4fr multicolored | .25 | .25 |
| 428 | A56 | 10fr multicolored | .25 | .25 |
| 429 | A56 | 25fr multicolored | .65 | .25 |
| | | **Size: 28x43mm** | | |
| 430 | A56 | 30fr multicolored | .80 | .25 |
| 431 | A56 | 50fr multicolored | 1.00 | .35 |
| 432 | A56 | 80fr multicolored | 1.50 | .45 |
| | | Nos. 422-432,C86-C87 (13) | 14.20 | 5.85 |

Symbolic Water Cycle and UNESCO Emblem — A57

**1966, Sept. 26   Engr.   Perf. 10½**
| 433 | A57 | 5fr bl & dp org | .25 | .25 |
| 434 | A57 | 25fr grn & dp org | .30 | .25 |
| 435 | A57 | 100fr brt rose lil & dp org | .85 | .35 |
| | | Nos. 433-435 (3) | 1.40 | .85 |

Hydrological Decade (UNESCO), 1965-74.

**Dance Type of 1966**

Various folk dances. 25fr, 75fr, horizontal.

**1966, Oct. 24   Photo.   Perf. 13½**
| | | **Sizes: 26x36mm, 36x28½mm** | | |
| 436 | A53 | 60c multicolored | .25 | .25 |
| 437 | A53 | 1fr multicolored | .25 | .25 |
| 438 | A53 | 1.50fr multicolored | .25 | .25 |
| 439 | A53 | 25fr multicolored | .75 | .25 |
| 440 | A53 | 50fr multicolored | .95 | .25 |
| 441 | A53 | 75fr multicolored | 1.40 | .50 |
| | | Nos. 436-441 (6) | 3.85 | 1.75 |

Guinean National Dancers.

Child's Drawing and UNICEF Emblem — A58

Children's Drawings: 2fr, Elephant. 3fr, Girl. 20fr, Village, horiz. 25fr, Boy playing soccer. 40fr, Still life. 50fr, Bird in a tree.

**1966, Dec. 12   Photo.   Perf. 13½**
| 442 | A58 | 2fr multicolored | .25 | .25 |
| 443 | A58 | 3fr multicolored | .25 | .25 |
| 444 | A58 | 10fr multicolored | .25 | .25 |
| 445 | A58 | 20fr multicolored | .25 | .25 |
| 446 | A58 | 25fr multicolored | .40 | .25 |
| 447 | A58 | 40fr multicolored | .45 | .25 |
| 448 | A58 | 50fr multicolored | .65 | .25 |
| | | Nos. 442-448 (7) | 2.50 | 1.75 |

20th anniv. of UNICEF. Printed in sheets of 10 stamps and 2 labels with ornamental borders and inscriptions.

Laboratory Technician A59

WHO Emblem and: 50fr, Physician examining infant. 75fr, Pre-natal care & instruction. 80fr, WHO Headquarters, Geneva.

**1967, Jan. 20    Photo.    Perf. 13½**

| | | | | |
|---|---|---|---|---|
| 449 | A59 | 30fr multicolored | .30 | .25 |
| 450 | A59 | 40fr multicolored | .40 | .25 |
| 451 | A59 | 75fr multicolored | .60 | .25 |
| 452 | A59 | 80fr multicolored | .70 | .35 |
| | | Nos. 449-452 (4) | 2.00 | 1.10 |

Inauguration (in 1966) of WHO Headquarters, Geneva.

Niamou Mask, N'Zerekore — A60

Designs: 10c, 1fr, 30fr, Small Banda mask, Kanfarade, Boké region. 1.50fr, 50fr, Like 30c. 50c, 5fr, 75fr, Bearded Niamou mask. 60c, 25fr, 100fr, Horned Yinadjinkele mask, Kankan region.

**1967, Mar. 25    Photo.    Perf. 14x13**

| | | | | |
|---|---|---|---|---|
| 453 | A60 | 10c org & multi | .25 | .25 |
| 454 | A60 | 30c cit & brn blk | .25 | .25 |
| 455 | A60 | 50c dp lil rose, blk & red | .25 | .25 |
| 456 | A60 | 60c dp org, blk & bis | .25 | .25 |
| 457 | A60 | 1fr yel grn & multi | .25 | .25 |
| 458 | A60 | 1.50fr sal pink & brn blk | .25 | .25 |
| 459 | A60 | 5fr ap grn, blk & red | .25 | .25 |
| 460 | A60 | 25fr red lil, blk & bis | .45 | .25 |
| 461 | A60 | 30fr bis & multi | .50 | .25 |
| 462 | A60 | 50fr grnsh bl & brn blk | .70 | .25 |
| 463 | A60 | 75fr yel, blk & red | 1.00 | .25 |
| 464 | A60 | 100fr lt ultra, blk & bis | 1.60 | .55 |
| | | Nos. 453-464 (12) | 6.00 | 3.40 |

Ball Python — A61

20c, Pastoria Research Institute. 50c, 75fr, Extraction of snake venom. 1fr, 50fr, Rock python. 2fr, Men holding rock python. 5fr, 30fr, Gaboon viper. 20fr, West African mamba.

**1967, May 15    Litho.    Perf. 13½**
**Size:  43½x20mm**

| | | | | |
|---|---|---|---|---|
| 465 | A61 | 20c multicolored | .25 | .25 |
| 466 | A61 | 30c multicolored | .25 | .25 |
| 467 | A61 | 50c multicolored | .25 | .25 |
| 468 | A61 | 1fr multicolored | .25 | .25 |
| 469 | A61 | 2fr multicolored | .25 | .25 |
| 470 | A61 | 5fr multicolored | .25 | .25 |

**Size:  56x26mm**

| | | | | |
|---|---|---|---|---|
| 471 | A61 | 20fr multicolored | .65 | .25 |
| 472 | A61 | 30fr multicolored | .90 | .25 |
| 473 | A61 | 50fr multicolored | 1.00 | .25 |
| 474 | A61 | 75fr multicolored | 1.60 | .25 |
| | | Nos. 465-474,C88-C89 (12) | 12.65 | 6.00 |

Research Institute for Applied Biology of Guinea (Pastoria). For souvenir sheet see No. C88a.

**Scenic Type of 1966**

Views: 5fr, Loos Island. 30fr, Tinkisso Waterfalls. 70fr, "The Elephant's Trunk" Hotel, Mt. Kakoulima. 80fr, Evening at the shore, Ratoma.

**1967, June 20    Photo.    Perf. 13½**

| | | | | |
|---|---|---|---|---|
| 475 | A54 | 5fr multicolored | .25 | .25 |
| 476 | A54 | 30fr multicolored | .25 | .25 |
| 477 | A54 | 70fr multicolored | .60 | .25 |
| 478 | A54 | 80fr multicolored | .85 | .25 |
| | | Nos. 475-478,C90-C91 (6) | 4.30 | 2.55 |

People's Palace, Conakry A62

Elephant — A63

**1967, Sept. 28    Photo.    Perf. 13½**

| | | | | |
|---|---|---|---|---|
| 479 | A62 | 5fr silver & multi | .25 | .25 |
| 480 | A63 | 30fr silver & multi | .30 | .25 |
| 481 | A62 | 55fr gold & multi | .50 | .25 |
| | | Nos. 479-481 (3) | 1.05 | .75 |

20th anniv. of the Democratic Party of Guinea and the opening of the People's Palace, Conakry. See No. C92.

Nos. 418-420 and 475-478 Overprinted

**1967, Nov. 6**

| | | | | |
|---|---|---|---|---|
| 482 | A54 | 5fr multicolored | .45 | .25 |
| 483 | A54 | 30fr multicolored | .90 | .25 |
| 484 | A54 | 40fr multicolored | .75 | .25 |
| 485 | A54 | 50fr multicolored | .80 | .25 |
| 486 | A54 | 70fr multicolored | 1.00 | .30 |
| 487 | A54 | 75fr multicolored | 1.45 | .50 |
| 488 | A54 | 80fr multicolored | 1.90 | .50 |
| | | Nos. 482-488,C93-C95 (10) | 12.90 | 5.60 |

50th anniversary of Lions International.

WHO Office for Africa — A64

**1967, Dec. 4    Photo.    Perf. 13½**

| | | | | |
|---|---|---|---|---|
| 489 | A64 | 30fr lt ol grn, bis & dk grn | .45 | .25 |
| 490 | A64 | 75fr red org, bis & dk bl | .80 | .30 |

Inauguration of the WHO Regional Office for Africa in Brazzaville, Congo.

Human Rights Flame — A65

**1968, Jan. 15    Photo.    Perf. 13½**

| | | | | |
|---|---|---|---|---|
| 491 | A65 | 30fr ocher, grn & dk car | .50 | .25 |
| 492 | A65 | 40fr vio, grn & car | .60 | .25 |

International Human Rights Year, 1968.

Coyah, Dubréka Region — A66

Homes and People: 30c, 30fr, Kankan Region. 40c, Kankan, East Guinea. 50c, 15fr, Woodlands Region. 60c, Fulahmori, Gaoual Region. 5fr, Cognagui, Kundara Region. 40fr, Fouta Djallon, West Guinea. 100fr, Labé, West Guinea.

**1968, Apr. 1    Photo.    Perf. 13½x14**
**Size:  36x27mm**

| | | | | |
|---|---|---|---|---|
| 493 | A66 | 20c gold & multi | .25 | .25 |
| 494 | A66 | 30c gold & multi | .25 | .25 |
| 495 | A66 | 40c gold & multi | .25 | .25 |
| 496 | A66 | 50c gold & multi | .25 | .25 |

**Perf.  14x13½**
**Size:  57x36mm**

| | | | | |
|---|---|---|---|---|
| 497 | A66 | 60c gold & multi | .25 | .25 |
| 498 | A66 | 5fr gold & multi | .25 | .25 |
| 499 | A66 | 15fr gold & multi | .25 | .25 |
| 500 | A66 | 30fr gold & multi | .35 | .25 |
| 501 | A66 | 30fr gold & multi | .40 | .25 |
| 502 | A66 | 40fr gold & multi | .55 | .25 |
| 503 | A66 | 100fr gold & multi | 1.50 | .30 |
| | | Nos. 493-503,C100 (12) | 9.05 | 4.05 |

The Storyteller A67

African Legends: 15fr, The Little Genie of Mt. Nimba. No. 506, The Legend of the Moons and the Stars. No. 507, Lan, the Child Buffalo, vert. 40fr, Nianablas and the Crocodiles. 50fr, Leuk the Hare Playing the Drum, vert. 75fr, Leuk the Hare Selling his Sister, vert. 80fr, The Hunter and the Antelopewoman. The designs are from paintings by students of the Academy of Fine Arts in Bellevue.

**1968    Photo.    Perf. 13½**

| | | | | |
|---|---|---|---|---|
| 504 | A67 | 15fr multicolored | .25 | .25 |
| 505 | A67 | 25fr multicolored | .25 | .25 |
| 506 | A67 | 30fr multicolored | .25 | .25 |
| 507 | A67 | 30fr multicolored | .25 | .25 |
| 508 | A67 | 40fr multicolored | .40 | .25 |
| 509 | A67 | 50fr multicolored | .65 | .25 |
| a. | | Souv. sheet of 4 | 5.50 | 5.50 |
| 510 | A67 | 75fr multicolored | .65 | .25 |
| 511 | A67 | 80fr multicolored | 1.10 | .25 |
| | | Nos. 504-511,C101-C104 (12) | 12.85 | 4.80 |

Issued in sheets of 10 plus 2 labels. No. 509a contains 4 imperf. stamps similar to Nos. 508-509, C101 and C104. "Poste Aerienne" omitted on the 70fr and 300fr of the souvenir sheet.
Issued: #505-506, 510-511, 5/16; #504, 507-509, 9/16.

Anubius Baboon A68

African Animals: 10fr, Leopards. 15fr, Hippopotami. 20fr, Nile crocodile. 30fr, Ethiopian wart hog. 50fr, Defassa waterbuck. 75fr, Cape buffaloes.

**1968, Nov. 25    Photo.    Perf. 13½**
**Size:  44x31mm**

| | | | | |
|---|---|---|---|---|
| 512 | A68 | 5fr gold & multi | .25 | .25 |
| 513 | A68 | 10fr gold & multi | .60 | .25 |
| 514 | A68 | 15fr gold & multi | .65 | .25 |
| a. | | Souv. sheet of 3, #512-514 | 1.50 | 1.50 |
| 515 | A68 | 20fr gold & multi | .75 | .25 |
| 516 | A68 | 30fr gold & multi | .75 | .25 |
| 517 | A68 | 50fr gold & multi | .90 | .25 |
| a. | | Souv. sheet of 3, #515-517 | 3.75 | 3.75 |
| 518 | A68 | 75fr gold & multi | 1.45 | .30 |
| a. | | Souv. sheet of 3 | 10.50 | 10.50 |
| | | Nos. 512-518,C105-C106 (9) | 10.60 | 4.45 |

No. 518a contains one No. 518 and one each similar to Nos. C105-C106 without "POSTE AERIENNE" inscription. The three souvenir sheets contain 3 stamps and one green and gold label inscribed "FAUNE AFRICAINE."

Senator Robert F. Kennedy — A69

Portraits: 75fr, Rev. Martin Luther King, Jr. 100fr, Pres. John F. Kennedy.

**1968, Dec. 16**

| | | | | |
|---|---|---|---|---|
| 519 | A69 | 30fr yel & multi | .55 | .25 |
| 520 | A69 | 75fr multicolored | 1.00 | .25 |
| 521 | A69 | 100fr multicolored | 1.40 | .30 |
| | | Nos. 519-521,C107-C109 (6) | 9.75 | 2.55 |

Robert F. Kennedy, John F. Kennedy and Martin Luther King, Jr., martyrs for freedom.
The stamps are printed in sheets of 15 (3x5) containing 10 stamps and five yellow-green and gold center labels. Sheets come either with English or French inscriptions on label.

Sculpture and Runner — A70

Sculpture and Soccer — A71

Designs (Sculpture and): 10fr, Boxing. 15fr, Javelin. 30fr, Steeplechase. 50fr, Hammer throw. 75fr, Bicycling.

**1969, Feb. 18    Photo.    Perf. 13½**

| | | | | |
|---|---|---|---|---|
| 522 | A70 | 5fr multicolored | .25 | .25 |
| 523 | A70 | 10fr multicolored | .25 | .25 |
| 524 | A70 | 15fr multicolored | .40 | .25 |
| 525 | A71 | 25fr multicolored | .40 | .25 |
| 526 | A70 | 30fr multicolored | .40 | .25 |
| 527 | A70 | 50fr multicolored | .50 | .25 |
| 528 | A70 | 75fr multicolored | .75 | .25 |
| | | Nos. 522-528,C110-C111A (10) | 11.45 | 4.05 |

19th Olympic Games, Mexico City, 10/12-27.

No. 404 Srchd. and Ovptd. in Red

**1969, Mar. 17    Litho.    Perf. 14x13½**

| | | | | |
|---|---|---|---|---|
| 529 | A52 | 30fr on 45fr multi | .60 | .35 |
| 530 | A52 | 45fr multicolored | .60 | .35 |
| | | Nos. 529-530,C112-C112B (5) | 4.60 | 2.60 |

US Apollo 8 mission, the first men in orbit around the moon, Dec. 21-27, 1968.
Nos. 529-530 also exist with surcharge and overprint in black. These sell for about 10% more.

Tarzan — A72

Designs: 30fr, Tarzan sitting in front of Pastoria Research Institute gate. 75fr, Tarzan and his family. 100fr, Tarzan sitting in a tree.

**1969, June 6    Photo.    Perf. 13½**

| | | | | |
|---|---|---|---|---|
| 531 | A72 | 25fr orange & multi | .45 | .25 |
| 532 | A72 | 30fr bl grn & multi | .60 | .25 |
| 533 | A72 | 75fr yel grn & multi | 1.25 | .25 |
| 534 | A72 | 100fr yellow & multi | 1.90 | .35 |
| | | Nos. 531-534 (4) | 4.20 | 1.10 |

Tarzan was a Guinean chimpanzee with superior intelligence and ability.

Campfire — A73

25fr, Boy Scout & tents. 30fr, Marching Boy Scouts. 40fr, Basketball. 45fr, Senior Scouts, thatched huts & mountain. 50fr, Guinean Boy Scout badge.

**1969, July 1**

| | | | | |
|---|---|---|---|---|
| 535 | A73 | 5fr gold & multi | .25 | .25 |
| 536 | A73 | 25fr gold & multi | .30 | .25 |
| 537 | A73 | 30fr gold & multi | .30 | .25 |
| 538 | A73 | 40fr gold & multi | .45 | .25 |
| 539 | A73 | 45fr gold & multi | .60 | .25 |
| 540 | A73 | 50fr gold & multi | .65 | .25 |
| a. | | Min. sheet of 6, #535-540 | 3.50 | 3.50 |
| | | Nos. 535-540 (6) | 2.55 | 1.50 |

Issued to honor the Boy Scouts of Guinea.

Launching Apollo 11 — A74

Designs: 30fr, Earth showing Africa as seen from moon. 50fr, Separation of lunar landing module and spaceship. 60fr, Astronauts and module on moon. 75fr, Module on moon and earth. 100fr, Module leaving moon. 200fr, Splashdown.

"a" stamps are inscribed in French. "b" stamps are inscribed in English.

**1969, Aug. 20    Photo.    Perf. 13½**
**Size: 34x55mm**

| | | | | |
|---|---|---|---|---|
| 541 | A74 | 25fr Pair, #541a, 541b | .40 | .25 |
| 542 | A74 | 30fr Pair, #542a, 542b | .50 | .25 |
| 543 | A74 | 50fr Pair, #543a, 543b | .75 | .25 |
| 544 | A74 | 60fr Pair, #544a, 544b | 1.25 | .35 |
| 545 | A74 | 75fr Pair, #545a, 545b | 1.50 | .40 |

**Size: 34x71mm**

| | | | | |
|---|---|---|---|---|
| 546 | A74 | 100fr Pair, #546a, 546b | 2.50 | .60 |

**Size: 34x55mm**

| | | | | |
|---|---|---|---|---|
| 547 | A74 | 200fr Pair, #547a, 547b | 5.00 | 1.50 |
| | | Nos. 541-547 (7) | 11.90 | 3.60 |

Man's 1st landing on the moon, 7/20/69.

Harvest and ILO Emblem — A75

ILO, 50th Anniv.: 25fr, Power lines and blast furnaces. 30fr, Women in broadcasting studio. 200fr, Potters.

**1969, Oct. 28    Photo.    Perf. 13½**

| | | | | |
|---|---|---|---|---|
| 548 | A75 | 25fr gold & multi | .25 | .25 |
| 549 | A75 | 30fr gold & multi | .30 | .25 |
| 550 | A75 | 75fr gold & multi | .65 | .25 |
| 551 | A75 | 200fr gold & multi | 1.90 | .60 |
| | | Nos. 548-551 (4) | 3.10 | 1.35 |

Mother and Sick Child — A76

25fr, Sick child. 40fr, Girl receiving vaccination. 50fr, Boy receiving vaccination. 60fr, Mother receiving vaccination. 200fr, Edward Jenner, M.D.

**1970, Jan. 15    Photo.    Perf. 13½**

| | | | | |
|---|---|---|---|---|
| 552 | A76 | 25fr multicolored | .25 | .25 |
| 553 | A76 | 30fr multicolored | .35 | .25 |
| 554 | A76 | 40fr multicolored | .40 | .25 |
| 555 | A76 | 50fr multicolored | .50 | .25 |
| 556 | A76 | 60fr multicolored | .60 | .25 |
| 557 | A76 | 200fr multicolored | 2.00 | 1.00 |
| | | Nos. 552-557 (6) | 4.10 | 2.25 |

Campaign against smallpox and measles.

Map of Africa — A77

**1970, Feb. 3    Litho.    Perf. 14½x14**

| | | | | |
|---|---|---|---|---|
| 558 | A77 | 30fr lt bl & multi | .25 | .25 |
| 559 | A77 | 200fr lt vio & multi | 1.75 | .75 |

Meeting of statesmen of countries bordering on Senegal River: Mali, Guinea, Senegal and Mauritania.

Open Book and Radar — A78

**1970, July 6    Litho.    Perf. 14**

| | | | | |
|---|---|---|---|---|
| 560 | A78 | 5fr lt bl & blk | .25 | .25 |
| 561 | A78 | 10fr rose & blk | .25 | .25 |
| 562 | A78 | 50fr yellow & blk | .60 | .25 |
| 563 | A78 | 200fr lilac & blk | 2.10 | .90 |
| | | Nos. 560-563 (4) | 3.20 | 1.65 |

International Telecommunications Day.

Lenin — A79

Designs: 20fr, Meeting with Lenin, by V. Serov. 30fr, Lenin Addressing Workers, by V. Serov. 40fr, Lenin with Red Guard Soldier and Sailor, by P. V. Vasiliev. 100fr, Lenin Speaking from Balcony, by P. V. Vasiliev. 200fr, Like 5fr.

**1970, Nov. 16    Photo.    Perf. 13**

| | | | | |
|---|---|---|---|---|
| 564 | A79 | 5fr gold & multi | .25 | .25 |
| 565 | A79 | 20fr gold & multi | .40 | .25 |
| 566 | A79 | 30fr gold & multi | .50 | .25 |
| 567 | A79 | 40fr gold & multi | .70 | .25 |
| 568 | A79 | 100fr gold & multi | 1.60 | .30 |
| 569 | A79 | 200fr gold & multi | 3.00 | .75 |
| | | Nos. 564-569 (6) | 6.45 | 2.05 |

Lenin (1870-1924), Russian communist leader.

Phenecogrammus Interruptus — A80

Designs: Various fish from Guinea.

**1971, Apr. 1    Photo.    Perf. 13**

| | | | | |
|---|---|---|---|---|
| 570 | A80 | 5fr gold & multi | .25 | .25 |
| 571 | A80 | 10fr gold & multi | .25 | .25 |
| 572 | A80 | 15fr gold & multi | .30 | .25 |
| 573 | A80 | 20fr gold & multi | .30 | .25 |
| 574 | A80 | 25fr gold & multi | .30 | .25 |
| 575 | A80 | 30fr gold & multi | .45 | .25 |
| 576 | A80 | 40fr gold & multi | .60 | .25 |
| 577 | A80 | 45fr gold & multi | .70 | .25 |
| 578 | A80 | 50fr gold & multi | 1.00 | .25 |
| 579 | A80 | 75fr gold & multi | 1.75 | .55 |
| 580 | A80 | 100fr gold & multi | 2.25 | .65 |
| 581 | A80 | 200fr gold & multi | 5.00 | 1.10 |
| | | Nos. 570-581 (12) | 13.15 | 4.55 |

Violet-crested Touraco — A81

Birds: 20fr, European golden oriole. 30fr, Blue-headed coucal. 40fr, Northern shrike. 75fr, Vulturine guinea fowl. 100fr, Southern ground hornbill.

**1971, June 18    Photo.    Perf. 13**
**Size: 34x34mm**

| | | | | |
|---|---|---|---|---|
| 582 | A81 | 5fr gold & multi | .25 | .25 |
| 583 | A81 | 20fr gold & multi | .35 | .25 |
| 584 | A81 | 30fr gold & multi | .55 | .25 |
| 585 | A81 | 40fr gold & multi | .65 | .25 |
| 586 | A81 | 75fr gold & multi | 2.00 | .55 |
| 587 | A81 | 100fr gold & multi | 2.50 | .80 |
| | | Nos. 582-587,C113-C113B (9) | 14.15 | 4.80 |

UNICEF Emblem, Map of Africa — A82

**1971, Dec. 24    Perf. 12x12½**

| | | | | |
|---|---|---|---|---|
| 588 | A82 | 25fr orange & blk | .25 | .25 |
| 589 | A82 | 30fr pink & black | .35 | .25 |
| 590 | A82 | 50fr gray grn & blk | .60 | .25 |
| 591 | A82 | 60fr gray bl & blk | .70 | .25 |
| 592 | A82 | 100fr lt rose & blk | 1.10 | .25 |
| | | Nos. 588-592 (5) | 3.00 | 1.25 |

UNICEF, 25th anniv.
For overprints see Nos. 625-629.

Imaginary Prehistoric Space Creature — A83

Various imaginary prehistoric space creatures.

**1972, Apr. 1    Perf. 13½x13**

| | | | | |
|---|---|---|---|---|
| 593 | A83 | 5fr multicolored | .25 | .25 |
| 594 | A83 | 20fr multicolored | .25 | .25 |
| 595 | A83 | 30fr multicolored | .25 | .25 |
| 596 | A83 | 40fr multicolored | .50 | .25 |
| 597 | A83 | 100fr multicolored | 1.00 | .35 |
| 598 | A83 | 200fr multicolored | 2.10 | .75 |
| | | Nos. 593-598 (6) | 4.35 | 2.10 |

Black Boy, Men of 4 Races, Emblem — A84

Designs: 20fr, Oriental boy. 30fr, Indian youth. 50fr, Caucasian girl. 100fr, Men of 4 races and Racial Equality emblem.

**1972, May 14    Perf. 13x13½**

| | | | | |
|---|---|---|---|---|
| 599 | A84 | 15fr gold & multi | .25 | .25 |
| 600 | A84 | 20fr gold & multi | .25 | .25 |
| 601 | A84 | 30fr gold & multi | .25 | .25 |
| 602 | A84 | 50fr gold & multi | .40 | .25 |
| 603 | A84 | 100fr gold & multi | .75 | .30 |
| | | Nos. 599-603,C119 (6) | 3.00 | 2.30 |

Intl. Year Against Racial Discrimination, 1971.

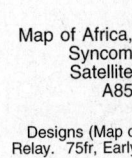

Map of Africa, Syncom Satellite A85

Designs (Map of Africa and Satellites): 30fr, Relay. 75fr, Early Bird. 80fr, Telstar.

**1972, May 17    Litho.    Perf. 13**

| | | | | |
|---|---|---|---|---|
| 604 | A85 | 15fr multicolored | .25 | .25 |
| 605 | A85 | 30fr red org & multi | .30 | .25 |
| 606 | A85 | 75fr grn & multi | .80 | .25 |
| 607 | A85 | 80fr multicolored | .90 | .45 |
| | | Nos. 604-607,C120-C121 (6) | 5.85 | 2.80 |

4th World Telecommunications Day.

Carrier Pigeon, UPAF Emblem — A86

**1972, July 10**

| | | | | |
|---|---|---|---|---|
| 608 | A86 | 15fr brt bl & multi | .25 | .25 |
| 609 | A86 | 30fr multicolored | .25 | .25 |
| 610 | A86 | 75fr lil & multi | .65 | .25 |
| 611 | A86 | 80fr multicolored | .80 | .45 |
| | | Nos. 608-611,C122-C123 (6) | 4.60 | 3.00 |

Book Year Emblem, Reading Child — A87

Designs (Book Year Emblem and): 15fr, Book as sailing ship. 40fr, Young woman with flower and book. 50fr, Book as key. 75fr, Man reading and globe. 200fr, Book and laurel.

**1972, Aug. 2    Photo.    Perf. 14x13½**

| | | | | |
|---|---|---|---|---|
| 612 | A87 | 5fr red & multi | .25 | .25 |
| 613 | A87 | 15fr multicolored | .25 | .25 |
| 614 | A87 | 40fr yel & multi | .45 | .25 |
| 615 | A87 | 50fr blue & multi | .65 | .25 |
| 616 | A87 | 75fr dk red & multi | .75 | .45 |
| 617 | A87 | 200fr org & multi | 1.50 | .90 |
| | | Nos. 612-617 (6) | 3.85 | 2.35 |

International Book Year 1972.

Javelin, Olympic Emblems, Arms of Guinea — A88

**1972, Aug. 26    Photo.    Perf. 13**

| | | | | |
|---|---|---|---|---|
| 618 | A88 | 5fr shown | .25 | .25 |
| 619 | A88 | 10fr Pole vault | .25 | .25 |
| 620 | A88 | 25fr Hurdles | .35 | .25 |
| 621 | A88 | 30fr Hammer throw | .50 | .25 |
| 622 | A88 | 40fr Boxing | .65 | .25 |
| 623 | A88 | 50fr Vaulting | .80 | .35 |
| 624 | A88 | 75fr Running | 1.20 | .45 |
| | | Nos. 618-624,C124-C125 (9) | 9.00 | 3.75 |

20th Olympic Games, Munich, 8/26-9/11.

Nos. 588-592 Overprinted

**1972, Sept. 28    Photo.    Perf. 12x12½**
**Map in Olive**

| | | | | |
|---|---|---|---|---|
| 625 | A82 | 25fr org & blk | .40 | .25 |
| 626 | A82 | 30fr pink & blk | .60 | .25 |
| 627 | A82 | 50fr gray grn & blk | .90 | .25 |
| 628 | A82 | 60fr gray bl & blk | 1.50 | .25 |
| 629 | A82 | 100fr lil rose & blk | 2.10 | .80 |
| | | Nos. 625-629 (5) | 5.50 | 1.80 |

UN Conference on Human Environment, Stockholm, June 5-16.

Dimitrov at Leipzig Trial — A89

25fr, In Moabit Prison, 1933. 40fr, Writing his memoirs. 100fr, Portrait.

**1972, Sept. 28    Perf. 13**
**Gold, Dark Green & Black**

| | | | | |
|---|---|---|---|---|
| 630 | A89 | 5fr shown | .25 | .25 |
| 631 | A89 | 25fr multicolored | .25 | .25 |
| 632 | A89 | 40fr multicolored | .50 | .25 |
| 633 | A89 | 100fr multicolored | 1.20 | .30 |
| | | Nos. 630-633 (4) | 2.20 | 1.05 |

George Dimitrov (1882-1949), Bulgarian Communist party leader and Premier.

Emperor Haile Selassie — A90

Design: 200fr, Emperor facing right.

**1972, Oct. 2**
| | | | |
|---|---|---|---|
| 634 | A90 | 40fr blk & multi | .50 .25 |
| 635 | A90 | 200fr multicolored | 2.50 .95 |

Syntomeida
Epilais — A91

Designs: Various insects.

**1973, Mar. 5  Photo.  Perf. 14x13½**
| | | | |
|---|---|---|---|
| 636 | A91 | 5fr shown | .25 .25 |
| 637 | A91 | 15fr Ladybugs | .35 .25 |
| 638 | A91 | 30fr Green locust | 1.00 .30 |
| 639 | A91 | 40fr Honey bee | 1.40 .40 |
| 640 | A91 | 50fr Photinus pyralis | 1.75 .60 |
| 641 | A91 | 200fr Ancyluris formosissima | 5.50 1.75 |
| | | Nos. 636-641 (6) | 10.25 3.55 |

Kwame
Nkrumah — A92

Various portraits of Kwame Nkrumah.

**1973, May 25  Photo.  Perf. 13½**
| | | | |
|---|---|---|---|
| 642 | A92 | 1.50s lt grn, gold & brn | .25 .25 |
| 643 | A92 | 2.50s lt grn, gold & brn | .35 .25 |
| 644 | A92 | 5s lt grn, gold & brn | .60 .25 |
| 645 | A92 | 10s gold & dark vio | 1.75 .45 |
| | | Nos. 642-645 (4) | 2.95 1.20 |

OAU, 10th anniversary.

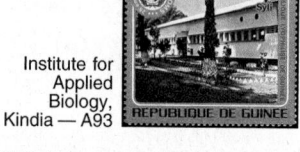

Institute for
Applied
Biology,
Kindia — A93

WHO Emblem and: 2.50s, Technicians inoculating egg. 3s, Filling vaccine into ampules. 4s, Sterilization of vaccine. 5s, Assembling of vaccine and vaccination gun. 10s, Inoculation of steer. 20s, Vaccination of woman.

**1973, Nov. 16  Photo.  Perf. 13½**
Size: 40x36mm
| | | | |
|---|---|---|---|
| 646 | A93 | 1s gold & multi | .25 .25 |
| 647 | A93 | 2.50s gold & multi | .35 .25 |
| 648 | A93 | 3s gold & multi | .35 .25 |
| 649 | A93 | 4s gold & multi | .50 .25 |

Size: 47½x31mm
| | | | |
|---|---|---|---|
| 650 | A93 | 5s gold & multi | .80 .25 |
| 651 | A93 | 10s gold & multi | 1.20 .40 |
| 652 | A93 | 20s gold & multi | 2.75 1.00 |
| | | Nos. 646-652 (7) | 6.20 2.65 |

WHO, 25th anniversary.

Copernicus, Heliocentric System,
Primeval Landscape — A94

Nicolaus
Copernicus
A95

Designs (Copernicus and): 2s, Sun rising over volcanic desert, and spacecraft. 4s, Earth, moon and spacecraft. 5s, Moon scape and spacecraft. 10s, Jupiter and spacecraft. 20s, Saturn and heliocentric system.

**1973, Dec. 17  Photo.  Perf. 13½**
| | | | |
|---|---|---|---|
| 653 | A94 | 50c gold & multi | .25 .25 |
| 654 | A94 | 2s gold & multi | .25 .25 |
| 655 | A94 | 4s gold & multi | .40 .25 |
| 656 | A94 | 5s gold & multi | .50 .25 |
| 657 | A94 | 10s gold & multi | 1.10 .40 |
| 658 | A94 | 20s gold & multi | 2.40 .90 |
| | | Nos. 653-658 (6) | 4.90 2.30 |

**Souvenir Sheet**
| | | | |
|---|---|---|---|
| 659 | | Sheet of 4 | 16.00 16.00 |
| a. | | A95 20s Single stamp | 3.00 3.00 |

Nicolaus Copernicus (1473-1543), Polish astronomer. No. 659 contains center label showing rocket and heliocentric system in gold margin.

Loading
Bauxite on
Freighter
A96

**1974, Mar. 1  Litho.  Perf. 13½**
| | | | |
|---|---|---|---|
| 660 | A96 | 4s shown | .60 .25 |
| 661 | A96 | 6s Freight train | 1.20 .25 |
| 662 | A96 | 10s Mining | 2.00 .65 |
| | | Nos. 660-662 (3) | 3.80 1.15 |

Bauxite mining, Boke.

Clappertonia
Ficifolia — A97

1s, Rothmannia longiflora. 2s, Oncoba spinosa. 3s, Venidium fastuosum. 4s, Bombax costatum. 5s, Clerodendrum splendens. 7.50s, Combretuni grandiflorum. 10s, Mussaendra erythrophylla. 12s, Argemone mexicana.

**1974, May 20  Photo.  Perf. 13**
Size: 25x36mm
| | | | |
|---|---|---|---|
| 663 | A97 | 50c shown | .25 .25 |
| 664 | A97 | 1s multicolored | .25 .25 |
| 665 | A97 | 2s multicolored | .25 .25 |
| 666 | A97 | 3s multicolored | .30 .25 |

Size: 31x42mm
| | | | |
|---|---|---|---|
| 667 | A97 | 4s multicolored | .40 .25 |
| 668 | A97 | 5s multicolored | .75 .25 |
| 669 | A97 | 7.50s multicolored | .85 .30 |
| 670 | A97 | 10s multicolored | 1.00 .35 |

Size: 38x38mm (Diamond)
| | | | |
|---|---|---|---|
| 671 | A97 | 12s multicolored | 1.25 .45 |
| | | Nos. 663-671,C127-C129 (12) | 18.80 7.40 |

Drummers,
Pigeon, UPAF
and UPU
Emblems — A98

Designs (Carrier Pigeon, African Postal Union and UPU Emblems): 6s, Runner with letter stick. 7.50s, Monorail and mail truck. No. 675, Jet and ocean liner.
No. 676, Balloon and dugout canoe. 20s, Satellites over earth.

**1974, Oct. 16  Photo.  Perf. 13½x14**
| | | | |
|---|---|---|---|
| 672 | A98 | 5s mag & multi | .60 .25 |
| 673 | A98 | 6s grn & multi | .80 .25 |
| 674 | A98 | 7.50s ver & multi | 1.25 .35 |
| 675 | A98 | 10s Prus bl & multi | 1.75 .60 |
| | | Nos. 672-675 (4) | 4.40 1.45 |

**Souvenir Sheets**
Perf. 13½
| | | | |
|---|---|---|---|
| 676 | A98 | 10s ocher & multi | 6.00 6.00 |
| 677 | | Sheet of 4, multi | 12.00 12.00 |
| a. | | A98 20s Single stamp | 1.60 1.60 |

Centenary of Universal Postal Union.
No. 676 contains one 70x60mm stamp.

Rope Bridge — A99

Designs (Pioneers): 2s, Field observation. 4s, Communication. 7.50s, Cooking in camp. 10s, Basketball.

**1974, Nov. 22  Photo.  Perf. 14x13½**
| | | | |
|---|---|---|---|
| 678 | A99 | 50c multicolored | .25 .25 |
| 679 | A99 | 2s multicolored | .35 .25 |
| 680 | A99 | 4s multicolored | .45 .25 |
| 681 | A99 | 5s multicolored | .75 .25 |
| 682 | A99 | 7.50s multicolored | 1.10 .25 |
| 683 | A99 | 10s multicolored | 1.90 .45 |
| a. | | Souv. sheet of 2, #682-683 | 4.00 4.00 |
| | | Nos. 678-683 (6) | 4.80 1.70 |

National Pioneer Movement.

**Souvenir Sheet**

Fruit — A100

**1974, Nov. 22  Photo.  Perf. 13x14**
| | | | |
|---|---|---|---|
| 684 | A100 | Sheet of 5 | 12.00 12.00 |
| a. | | 4s Limes | 1.00 .75 |
| b. | | 4s Oranges | 1.00 .85 |
| c. | | 5s Bananas | 1.50 1.25 |
| d. | | 5s Mangos | 1.50 1.25 |
| e. | | 12s Pineapple | 2.75 2.50 |

Chimpanzee
A101

2s, Impala. 3s, Wart hog. 4s, Kobus defassa. 5s, Leopard. 6s, Greater kudu. 6.50s, Zebra. 7.50s, Cape buffalo. 8s, Hippopotamus. 10s, Lion. 12s, Black rhinoceros. 15s, Elephant.

**1975, May 14  Photo.  Perf. 13½**
| | | | |
|---|---|---|---|
| 685 | A101 | 1s shown | .25 .25 |
| 686 | A101 | 2s multi | .35 .25 |
| 687 | A101 | 3s multi | .50 .25 |
| 688 | A101 | 4s multi | .65 .25 |
| a. | | Souv. sheet of 4, #685-688 | 7.00 7.00 |
| 689 | A101 | 5s multi | .80 .25 |
| 690 | A101 | 6s multi | 1.00 .25 |
| 691 | A101 | 6.50s multi | 1.10 .25 |
| 692 | A101 | 7.50s multi | 1.75 .25 |
| a. | | Souv. sheet of 4, #689-692 | 7.00 7.00 |
| 693 | A101 | 8s multi | 2.40 .85 |
| 694 | A101 | 10s multi | 2.75 .85 |
| 695 | A101 | 12s multi | 3.75 1.00 |
| 696 | A101 | 15s multi | 4.75 1.50 |
| a. | | Souv. sheet of 4, #693-696 | 17.50 17.50 |
| | | Nos. 685-696 (12) | 20.05 6.20 |

Sheets exist perf. and imperf.
Stamps in Nos. 692a, 696a are inscribed "Poste Aerienne."

Lions, Pipe Line
and ADB
Emblem — A102

Designs (African Development Bank Emblem, Pipe Line and): 7s, Elephants. 10s, Male lions. 20s, Elephant and calf.

**1975, June 16  Photo.  Perf. 13½**
| | | | |
|---|---|---|---|
| 697 | A102 | 5s gold & multi | .70 .25 |
| 698 | A102 | 7s gold & multi | .95 .25 |
| 699 | A102 | 10s gold & multi | 1.40 .35 |
| 700 | A102 | 20s gold & multi | 2.50 .70 |
| | | Nos. 697-700 (4) | 5.55 1.55 |

African Development Bank, 10th anniv.

Women Musicians,
IWY Emblem — A103

IWY Emblem and: 7s, Women banjo & guitar players. 9s, Woman railroad shunter & train. 15s, Woman physician examining infant. 20s, Male & female symbols.

**1976, Apr. 12  Photo.  Perf. 13½**
| | | | |
|---|---|---|---|
| 701 | A103 | 5s multicolored | .55 .25 |
| 702 | A103 | 7s multicolored | .90 .25 |
| 703 | A103 | 9s blue & multi | 1.25 .45 |
| 704 | A103 | 15s multicolored | 2.00 .75 |
| a. | | Souvenir sheet | 3.00 3.00 |
| 705 | A103 | 20s vio bl & multi | 2.50 1.00 |
| a. | | Souvenir sheet of 4 | 13.00 13.00 |
| | | Nos. 701-705 (5) | 7.20 2.70 |

International Women's Year 1975. No. 704a contains one stamp similar to No. 704 with gold frame. No. 705a contains 4 stamps similar to No. 705 with gold frame.

Woman
Gymnast — A104

Montreal Olympic Games Emblem and: 4s, Long jump. 5s, Hammer throw. 6s, Discus. 6.50s, Hurdles. 7s, Javelin. 8s, Running. 8.50s, Bicycling. 10s, High jump. 15s, Shot put. 20s, Pole vault. No. 717, Soccer. No. 718, Swimming.

**1976, May 17  Photo.  Perf. 13½**
Size: 38x38mm
| | | | |
|---|---|---|---|
| 706 | A104 | 3s multicolored | .35 .25 |
| 707 | A104 | 4s grn & multi | .45 .25 |
| 708 | A104 | 5s yel & multi | .55 .25 |
| 709 | A104 | 6s multicolored | .70 .25 |
| 710 | A104 | 6.50s plum & multi | .80 .25 |
| 711 | A104 | 7s blue & multi | .90 .30 |
| 712 | A104 | 8s ultra & multi | 1.10 .30 |
| 713 | A104 | 8.50s org & multi | 1.10 .30 |
| 714 | A104 | 10s multicolored | 1.25 .40 |
| 715 | A104 | 15s multicolored | 2.25 .75 |
| 716 | A104 | 20s multicolored | 2.75 .95 |
| 717 | A104 | 25s grn & multi | 3.50 1.00 |
| | | Nos. 706-717 (12) | 15.70 5.30 |

**Souvenir Sheet**
| | | | |
|---|---|---|---|
| 718 | A104 | 25s multicolored | 4.50 4.50 |

21st Olympic Games, Montreal, Canada, July 17-Aug. 1. No. 718 contains one 32x32mm stamp. See No. C130.

A. G. Bell,
Telephone,
1900 — A105

7s, Wall telephone, 1910. 12s, Syncom telecommunications satellite. No. 722, Telstar satellite.
No. 723, Telephone switchboard operator, 1914.

**1976, Nov. 15  Photo.  Perf. 13**
| | | | |
|---|---|---|---|
| 719 | A105 | 5s multicolored | .75 .25 |
| 720 | A105 | 7s multicolored | 1.00 .25 |
| 721 | A105 | 12s multicolored | 1.40 .45 |
| 722 | A105 | 15s multicolored | 1.75 .60 |
| a. | | Souvenir sheet of 4, #719-722 | 7.00 7.00 |
| | | Nos. 719-722 (4) | 4.90 1.55 |

**Souvenir Sheet**
| | | | |
|---|---|---|---|
| 723 | A105 | 15s multicolored | 6.25 6.25 |

Centenary of first telephone call by Alexander Graham Bell, Mar. 10, 1876.

Collybia Fusipes
A106

Mushrooms: 7s, Lycoperdon perlatum. 9s, Boletus edulis. 9.50s, Lactarius deliciosus. 11.50s, Agaricus campestris.

**1977, Feb. 6    Photo.    Perf. 13**

**Size: 48x26mm**

| | | | | |
|---|---|---|---|---|
| 724 | A106 | 5s multicolored | 1.75 | .25 |
| 725 | A106 | 7s multicolored | 2.25 | .25 |
| 726 | A106 | 9s multicolored | 3.25 | .55 |
| a. | | Souvenir sheet of 2, #724, 726 | 7.00 | 7.00 |
| 727 | A106 | 9.50s multicolored | 3.50 | .65 |

**Size: 48x31mm**

| | | | | |
|---|---|---|---|---|
| 728 | A106 | 11.50s multicolored | 4.50 | 1.10 |
| | | Nos. 724-728,C131-C133 (8) | 30.50 | 6.50 |

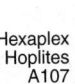

Hexaplex Hoplites
A107

Sea Shells: 2s, Perrona lineata. 4s, Marginella pseudofaba. 5s, Tympanotonos radula. 7s, Marginella strigata. 8s, Harpa doris. 10s, Demoulia pinguis. 20s, Bursa scrobiculator. 25s, Marginella adansoni.

**1977, Apr. 25    Photo.    Perf. 13**

**Size: 50x25mm**

| | | | | |
|---|---|---|---|---|
| 729 | A107 | 1s gold & multi | .25 | .25 |
| 730 | A107 | 2s gold & multi | .30 | .25 |
| 731 | A107 | 4s gold & multi | .75 | .30 |
| 732 | A107 | 5s gold & multi | 1.15 | .35 |
| 733 | A107 | 7s gold & multi | 1.60 | .40 |
| 734 | A107 | 8s gold & multi | 1.90 | .60 |

**Size: 50x30mm**

| | | | | |
|---|---|---|---|---|
| 735 | A107 | 10s gold & multi | 2.50 | .90 |
| 736 | A107 | 20s gold & multi | 5.00 | 1.25 |
| 737 | A107 | 25s gold & multi | 6.50 | 1.75 |
| | | Nos. 729-737 (9) | 19.95 | 6.05 |

Farmers and Ox Plow — A108

Designs: 5s, Pres. Touré addressing rally. 20s, Soldier driving farm tractor. 25s, Pres. Touré addressing UN General Assembly. 30s, 40s, Pres. Sékou Touré, vert.

**1977, May 14    Perf. 13½x13, 13x13½**

| | | | | |
|---|---|---|---|---|
| 738 | A108 | 5s gold & multi | .55 | .25 |
| 739 | A108 | 10s gold & multi | 1.00 | .40 |
| 740 | A108 | 20s gold & multi | 2.00 | .90 |
| 741 | A108 | 25s gold & multi | 2.40 | 1.25 |
| a. | | Souvenir sheet of 4, #738-741 | 7.00 | 7.00 |
| 742 | A108 | 30s gold & dk brn | 3.25 | 1.25 |
| 743 | A108 | 40s gold & sl grn | 5.25 | 1.50 |
| a. | | Souvenir sheet of 2, #742-743 | 10.00 | 10.00 |
| | | Nos. 738-743 (6) | 14.45 | 5.55 |

Democratic Party of Guinea, 30th anniv.

Nile Monitor
A109

Reptiles and Snakes: 4s, Frogs. 5s, Lizard (uromastix). 6s, Sand skink. 6.50s, Agama. 7s, Black-lipped spitting cobra. 8.50s, Ball python. 20s, Toads.

**1977, Oct. 10    Photo.    Perf. 13½**

**Size: 46x20mm**

| | | | | |
|---|---|---|---|---|
| 744 | A109 | 3s multi | .50 | .25 |
| 745 | A109 | 4s multi | .70 | .25 |
| 746 | A109 | 5s multi | .70 | .25 |

**Size: 46x30mm**

| | | | | |
|---|---|---|---|---|
| 747 | A109 | 6s multi | 1.15 | .25 |
| 748 | A109 | 6.50s multi | 1.45 | .25 |
| 749 | A109 | 7s multi | 1.90 | .55 |
| 750 | A109 | 8.50s multi | 2.10 | .65 |
| 751 | A109 | 20s multi | 5.00 | 1.40 |
| | | Nos. 744-751,C134-C136 (11) | 28.50 | 7.35 |

Eland
A110

Endangered Animals: 2s, Chimpanzee. 2.50s, Pygmy elephant. 3s, Lion. 4s, Palm squirrel. 5s, Hippopotamus. Each animal shown male, female and young.

**1977, Dec. 12    Photo.    Perf. 14x13½**

| | | | | |
|---|---|---|---|---|
| 752 | A110 | Strip of 3 | .95 | .95 |
| a.-c. | | 1s any single | | .25 |
| 753 | A110 | Strip of 3 | 1.50 | .25 |
| a.-c. | | 2s any single | | .35 |
| 754 | A110 | Strip of 3 | 1.90 | .30 |
| a.-c. | | 2.50s any single | | .50 |
| 755 | A110 | Strip of 3 | 2.50 | .40 |
| a.-c. | | 3s any single | | .60 |
| 756 | A110 | Strip of 3 | 3.00 | .55 |
| a.-c. | | 4s any single | | .95 |
| 757 | A110 | Strip of 3 | 4.00 | .65 |
| a.-c. | | 5s any single | | 1.25 |
| | | Nos. 752-757,C137-C142 (12) | 50.60 | 22.40 |

Russian October Revolution, 60th Anniv. — A111

Designs: 2.50s, First Lenin debate, Moscow. 5s, Lenin speaking, 1917. 7.50s, Lenin and people. 8s, Lenin in first parade on Red Square.

**1978, Feb. 27    Photo.    Perf. 14**

| | | | | |
|---|---|---|---|---|
| 758 | A111 | 2.50s gold & multi | .60 | .25 |
| 759 | A111 | 5s gold & multi | 1.00 | .25 |
| 760 | A111 | 7.50s gold & multi | 1.50 | .30 |
| 761 | A111 | 8s gold & multi | 1.60 | .35 |
| | | Nos. 758-761,C143-C144 (6) | 14.10 | 4.05 |

Pres. Giscard d'Estaing at Microphones
A112

Pres. Valery Giscard d'Estaing of France and Pres. Sekou Toure of Guinea: 5s, 10s, In conference. 6.50s, Signing agreement. 7s, Attending official meeting. 8.50s, With their wives. 20s, Drinking a toast.

**1979, Sept. 14    Photo.    Perf. 13**

| | | | | |
|---|---|---|---|---|
| 762 | A112 | 3s lt brn & brn | .80 | .25 |
| 763 | A112 | 5s green & brn | 1.40 | .25 |
| 764 | A112 | 6.50s red lil & brn | 1.75 | .25 |
| 765 | A112 | 7s ultra & brn | 1.90 | .30 |
| 766 | A112 | 8s dk red & brn | 2.25 | .55 |
| 767 | A112 | 10s vio & brown | 2.40 | .80 |
| 768 | A112 | 20s yel grn & brn | 4.00 | 1.10 |
| | | Nos. 762-768,C145 (8) | 18.50 | 5.50 |

Visit of Pres. Valery Giscard d'Estaing to Guinea.

Twenty Thousand Leagues Under the Sea — A113

Jules Verne Stories: 3s, Children of Capt. Grant. 5s, Mysterious Island. 7s, A Captain at Fifteen. 10s, The Borsac Mission.

**1979, Nov. 8    Litho.    Perf. 12x12½**

| | | | | |
|---|---|---|---|---|
| 769 | A113 | 1s multicolored | .25 | .25 |
| 770 | A113 | 3s multicolored | .35 | .25 |
| 771 | A113 | 5s multicolored | .65 | .25 |
| 772 | A113 | 7s multicolored | 1.10 | .30 |
| 773 | A113 | 10s multicolored | 1.60 | .40 |
| | | Nos. 769-773,C146-C147 (7) | 10.05 | 2.65 |

Jules Verne (1828-1905), French science fiction writer.

"Aerial Steam Carriage," 1842
A114

Aviation Retrospect: 5s, Wright's Flyer 1 1903. 6.50s, Caudron, 1934. 7s, Spirit of St. Louis, 1927. 8.50s, Bristol Beaufighter, 1940. 10s, Bleriot XI, 1909. No. 780, Concorde. No. 781, Boeing 727, 1963.

**1979, Nov. 22    Photo.    Perf. 14**

| | | | | |
|---|---|---|---|---|
| 774 | A114 | 3s multicolored | .45 | .25 |
| 775 | A114 | 5s multicolored | .70 | .25 |
| 776 | A114 | 6.50s multicolored | .85 | .25 |
| 777 | A114 | 7s multicolored | 1.00 | .25 |
| 778 | A114 | 8.50s multicolored | 1.10 | .30 |
| 779 | A114 | 10s multicolored | 1.75 | .30 |
| 780 | A114 | 20s multicolored | 3.00 | .65 |
| 781 | A114 | 20s multicolored | 3.00 | .65 |
| | | Nos. 774-781 (8) | 11.85 | 2.90 |

Hafia Soccer Team
A115

Designs: 2s, Players and Sekou Touré cup, vert. 5s, Pres. Touré presenting cup. 7s, Pres. Touré and player holding cup, vert. 8s, Sekou Touré cup, vert. 10s, Team captains and referees, vert. 20s, The winning goal.

**Perf. 12½x12, 12x12½**

**1979, Dec. 18    Litho.**

| | | | | |
|---|---|---|---|---|
| 782 | A115 | 1s multicolored | .25 | .25 |
| 783 | A115 | 2s multicolored | .25 | .25 |
| 784 | A115 | 5s multicolored | .65 | .25 |
| 785 | A115 | 7s multicolored | 1.00 | .35 |
| 786 | A115 | 8s multicolored | 1.25 | .40 |
| 787 | A115 | 10s multicolored | 1.50 | .45 |
| 788 | A115 | 20s multicolored | 3.00 | .75 |
| | | Nos. 782-788 (7) | 7.90 | 2.70 |

Hafia Soccer Team, African triple champions, 1977.

Train, IYC Emblem
A116

IYC Emblem and: 2s, Children dancing around tree, vert. 4s, "1979" and leaves, vert. 7s, Village. 10s, Boy climbing tree. 25s, Boys of different races, flowers, sun.

**1980, Jan. 14    Perf. 13x13½, 13½x13**

| | | | | |
|---|---|---|---|---|
| 789 | A116 | 2s multicolored | .25 | .25 |
| 790 | A116 | 4s multicolored | .50 | .25 |
| 791 | A116 | 5s multicolored | .70 | .25 |
| 792 | A116 | 7s multicolored | 1.00 | .30 |
| 793 | A116 | 10s multicolored | 1.40 | .40 |
| 794 | A116 | 25s multicolored | 4.00 | 1.10 |
| | | Nos. 789-794 (6) | 7.85 | 2.55 |

International Year of the Child (1979).

Butterflyfish
A117

2s, Porgy. 3s, Zeus conchifer, vert. 4s, Grouper. 5s, Sea horse, vert. 6s, Hatchet fish. 7s, Pisodonophis semicinctus. 8s, Flying gurnard, vert. 9s, Squirrelfish. 10s, Psettus sebae, vert. 12s, Abudefuf hoeffleri. 15s, Triggerfish.

**1980, Apr. 1    Perf. 12½x12, 12x12½**

| | | | | |
|---|---|---|---|---|
| 795 | A117 | 1s shown | .25 | .25 |
| 796 | A117 | 2s multicolored | .25 | .25 |
| 797 | A117 | 3s multicolored | .45 | .25 |
| 798 | A117 | 4s multicolored | .60 | .25 |
| 799 | A117 | 5s multicolored | .75 | .25 |
| 800 | A117 | 6s multicolored | 1.00 | .35 |
| 801 | A117 | 7s multicolored | 1.25 | .40 |
| 802 | A117 | 8s multicolored | 1.60 | .50 |
| 803 | A117 | 9s multicolored | 1.75 | .65 |
| 804 | A117 | 10s multicolored | 2.10 | .65 |
| 805 | A117 | 12s multicolored | 3.00 | .75 |
| 806 | A117 | 15s multicolored | 5.00 | 1.00 |
| | | Nos. 795-806 (12) | 18.00 | 5.55 |

Apollo 11 Take-Off — A118

2s, Earth from moon. 4s, Armstrong leaving module. 5s, Armstrong on moon. 7s, Collecting samples. 8s, Re-entry. 12s, Recovery. 20s, Crew.

**1980, July 20    Photo.    Perf. 14**

| | | | | |
|---|---|---|---|---|
| 807 | A118 | 1s shown | .25 | .25 |
| 808 | A118 | 2s multicolored | .25 | .25 |
| 809 | A118 | 4s multicolored | .45 | .25 |
| 810 | A118 | 5s multicolored | .70 | .25 |
| 811 | A118 | 7s multicolored | .85 | .35 |
| 812 | A118 | 8s multicolored | 1.25 | .45 |
| 813 | A118 | 12s multicolored | 2.10 | .45 |
| 814 | A118 | 20s multicolored | 3.75 | .75 |
| | | Nos. 807-814 (8) | 9.60 | 3.00 |

Apollo 11 moon landing, 10th anniv. (1979).

Intl. Palestinian Solidarity Day — A119

**1981, Nov. 21    Photo.    Perf. 13½**

| | | | | |
|---|---|---|---|---|
| 815 | A119 | 8s multicolored | 1.20 | .45 |
| 816 | A119 | 11s multicolored | 2.00 | .60 |

Soccer
A120

**1982    Litho.    Perf. 12½x12**

| | | | | |
|---|---|---|---|---|
| 817 | A120 | 1s shown | .25 | .25 |
| 818 | A120 | 2s Basketball | .45 | .25 |
| 819 | A120 | 3s Diving | .60 | .25 |
| 820 | A120 | 4s Gymnast | .75 | .25 |
| 821 | A120 | 5s Boxing | .90 | .25 |
| 822 | A120 | 6s Pole vault | 1.10 | .30 |
| 823 | A120 | 7s Running | 1.25 | .35 |
| 824 | A120 | 8s Long jump | 1.40 | .40 |
| | | Nos. 817-824,C148-C152 (13) | 17.55 | 5.00 |

22nd Summer Olympic Games, Moscow, July 19-Aug. 3, 1980.

5th Anniv. of West African Economic Community
A121

**1982, May 14    Perf. 13½**

| | | | | |
|---|---|---|---|---|
| 825 | A121 | 6s multicolored | 1.00 | .25 |
| 826 | A121 | 7s multicolored | 1.20 | .55 |
| 827 | A121 | 9s multicolored | 1.75 | .55 |
| | | Nos. 825-827 (3) | 3.95 | 1.15 |

Kemal Ataturk Birth Centenary — A122

Designs: 10s, Ataturk in formal attire. 25s, Equestrian statue, horiz.

**1982, July 19    Photo.    Perf. 13½**

| | | | | |
|---|---|---|---|---|
| 828 | A122 | 7s multi | 1.00 | .35 |
| 829 | A122 | 10s multi | 1.50 | .45 |
| 830 | A122 | 25s multi | 4.25 | .85 |
| | | Nos. 828-830,C153 (4) | 11.00 | 2.45 |

1982 World Cup — A123

Designs: Various soccer players.

**1982, Aug. 23**

| | | | | |
|---|---|---|---|---|
| 831 | A123 | 6s multicolored | .85 | .25 |
| 832 | A123 | 8s multicolored | 1.25 | .25 |
| 833 | A123 | 9s multicolored | 1.75 | .45 |
| 834 | A123 | 10s multicolored | 2.10 | .60 |
| | *Nos. 831-834,C154-C156 (7)* | | 18.80 | 4.90 |

**Nos. 831-834 Overprinted in Red and Green**

**1982, Aug. 23 — Photo. — Perf. 13½**

| | | | | |
|---|---|---|---|---|
| 835 | A123 | 6s multicolored | .85 | .25 |
| 836 | A123 | 8s multicolored | 1.25 | .25 |
| 837 | A123 | 9s multicolored | 1.75 | .45 |
| 838 | A123 | 10s multicolored | 2.10 | .60 |
| | *Nos. 835-838,C157-C159 (7)* | | 18.80 | 4.90 |

Italy's victory in 1982 World Cup.

23rd Olympic Games, Los Angeles, July 28-Aug. 12, 1984 — A124

**1983, July 1 — Litho. — Perf. 13½**

| | | | | |
|---|---|---|---|---|
| 839 | A124 | 5s Wrestling | 1.10 | .25 |
| 840 | A124 | 7s Weightlifting | 1.40 | .30 |
| 841 | A124 | 10s Gymnastics | 2.00 | .55 |
| 842 | A124 | 15s Discus | 3.25 | .95 |
| 843 | A124 | 20s Kayak | 4.50 | 1.40 |
| 844 | A124 | 25s Equestrian | 5.00 | 1.60 |
| | *Nos. 839-844 (6)* | | 17.25 | 5.05 |

**Litho. & Embossed**
**Size: 39x58mm**

| | | | | |
|---|---|---|---|---|
| 844A | A124 | 100s Running | 45.00 | 37.50 |

**Souvenir Sheets**
**Litho.**

| | | | | |
|---|---|---|---|---|
| 845 | A124 | 30s Running | 5.00 | 1.60 |

**Litho. & Embossed**

| | | | | |
|---|---|---|---|---|
| 845A | A124 | 100s Show jumping | 15.00 | 12.50 |

Nos. 844A, 845A are airmail. No. 845A contains one 58x39mm stamp.

First Manned Balloon Flight, 200th Anniv. — A125

Designs: 5s, Marquis D'Arlandes, Pilatre de Rozier. 7s, Marie Antoinette Balloon, Rozier. 10s, Dirigible, Dupuy De Lome, horiz. 15s, Dirigible, Major A. Perseval, horiz.

**1983, Aug. 1 — Litho. — Perf. 13½**

| | | | | |
|---|---|---|---|---|
| 846 | A125 | 5s multicolored | .65 | .25 |
| 847 | A125 | 7s multicolored | .95 | .25 |
| 848 | A125 | 10s multicolored | 1.40 | .45 |
| 849 | A125 | 15s multicolored | 2.10 | .75 |
| | *Nos. 846-849,C160-C161 (6)* | | 10.95 | 3.85 |

Intl. Year of the Handicapped A126

**1983, Aug. 24 — Litho.**

| | | | | |
|---|---|---|---|---|
| 850 | A126 | 10s multicolored | 2.75 | 1.00 |
| 851 | A126 | 20s multicolored | 5.50 | 1.50 |

Dr. Robert Koch (1843-1910), TB Bacillus — A127

Various phases of research.

**1983, Aug. 24 — Litho.**

| | | | | |
|---|---|---|---|---|
| 852 | A127 | 6s multicolored | 1.25 | .30 |
| 853 | A127 | 10s multicolored | 1.75 | .40 |
| 854 | A127 | 11s multicolored | 2.10 | .50 |
| 855 | A127 | 12s multicolored | 2.50 | .80 |
| 856 | A127 | 15s multicolored | 3.50 | .95 |
| 857 | A127 | 20s multicolored | 4.25 | 1.10 |
| 858 | A127 | 25s multicolored | 5.00 | 1.40 |
| | *Nos. 852-858 (7)* | | 20.35 | 5.45 |

Mosque, Conakry — A128

**1983, Oct. 2 — Litho. — Perf. 13½**

| | | | | |
|---|---|---|---|---|
| 859 | A128 | 1s grn & multi | .25 | .25 |
| 860 | A128 | 2s yel & multi | .35 | .25 |
| 861 | A128 | 5s org & multi | .75 | .25 |
| 862 | A128 | 10s pink & multi | 1.40 | .55 |
| | *Nos. 859-862 (4)* | | 2.75 | 1.30 |

**Souvenir Sheet**

| | | | | |
|---|---|---|---|---|
| 863 | A128 | 25s white & multi | 4.00 | 1.90 |

Natl. independence, 25th anniv. No. 863 airmail.

Mano River Union, 10th Anniv. — A129

2s, Development program graduates. 7s, Emblem. 8s, Pres. Toure of Guinea, Stevens of Sierra Leone, Doe of Liberia. 10s, 20s, Signing treaty.

**1983, Oct. 3**

| | | | | |
|---|---|---|---|---|
| 864 | A129 | 2s blue & multi | .30 | .25 |
| 865 | A129 | 7s org & multi | .70 | .30 |
| 866 | A129 | 8s yel & multi | .85 | .40 |
| 867 | A129 | 10s lt. org & multi | 1.00 | .40 |
| | *Nos. 864-867 (4)* | | 2.85 | 1.35 |

**Souvenir Sheet**

| | | | | |
|---|---|---|---|---|
| 868 | A129 | 20s lt. org & multi | 2.50 | 1.50 |

No. 868 airmail.

14th Winter Olympics, Sarajevo, Feb. 8-19, 1984 A130

5s, Biathlon. 7s, Bobsledding. 10s, No. 874A, 100s, Downhill skiing. 15s, Speed skating. 20s, Ski jumping. 25s, Figure skating. 30s, Hockey. No. 875A, 4-man bobsled.

**1983, Dec. 5 — Litho. — Perf. 13½**

| | | | | |
|---|---|---|---|---|
| 869 | A130 | 5s multicolored | .75 | .25 |
| 870 | A130 | 7s multicolored | .95 | .30 |
| 871 | A130 | 10s multicolored | 1.40 | .40 |
| 872 | A130 | 15s multicolored | 2.25 | .65 |
| 873 | A130 | 20s multicolored | 3.00 | .85 |
| 874 | A130 | 25s multicolored | 3.50 | 1.10 |
| | *Nos. 869-874 (6)* | | 11.85 | 3.55 |

**Litho. & Embossed**
**Size: 58x39mm**

| | | | | |
|---|---|---|---|---|
| 874A | A130 | 100s multicolored | 15.00 | 5.00 |

**Souvenir Sheets**
**Litho.**

| | | | | |
|---|---|---|---|---|
| 875 | A130 | 30s multicolored | 5.00 | 1.60 |

**Litho. & Embossed**

| | | | | |
|---|---|---|---|---|
| 875A | A130 | 100s multicolored | 15.00 | 12.50 |
| 875B | A130 | 100s as No. 874A | 40.00 | 32.50 |

Nos. 873-875A airmail. No. 875A contains one 58x39mm stamp.

Self-portrait and Virgin with Blue Diadem, by Raphael — A131

Designs: 7s, Self-portrait and Holy Family, by Rubens. 10s, Self-portrait and Portrait of Saskia, by Rembrandt. 15s, Portrait of Goethe and scene from Young Werther. 20s, Scouting Year. 25s, Paul Harris, Rotary emblem. 30s, J.F. Kennedy, Apollo XI. 100s, Paul Harris, 3 other men in Rotary meeting.

**1984, Jan 2 — Litho. — Perf. 13**

| | | | | |
|---|---|---|---|---|
| 876 | A131 | 5s multicolored | .50 | .30 |
| 877 | A131 | 7s multicolored | .80 | .35 |
| 878 | A131 | 10s multicolored | 1.25 | .45 |
| 879 | A131 | 15s multicolored | 1.75 | .60 |
| 880 | A131 | 20s multicolored | 2.40 | .75 |
| 881 | A131 | 25s multicolored | 3.25 | .90 |
| | *Nos. 876-881 (6)* | | 9.95 | 3.35 |

**Souvenir Sheets**

| | | | | |
|---|---|---|---|---|
| 882 | A131 | 30s multicolored | 4.50 | 1.50 |

**Litho. & Embossed**
**Perf. 13½**

| | | | | |
|---|---|---|---|---|
| 882A | A131 | 100s gold & multi | 9.00 | 9.00 |

Nos. 880-882A airmail. No. 882A contains one 51x42mm stamp.
For overprints see Nos. C164-C165.

Transportation A132

5s, Congo River steamer. 7s, Graf Zeppelin LZ 127. 10s, Daimler automobile, 1886. 15s, E. African RR Beyer-Garrat. 20s, Latecoere 28, 1929. 25s, Sial Marchetti S.M. 73, 1934. 30s, Series B locomotive.

**1984, May 7 — Litho. — Perf. 13½**

| | | | | |
|---|---|---|---|---|
| 883 | A132 | 5s multicolored | .65 | .25 |
| 884 | A132 | 7s multicolored | 1.00 | .25 |
| 885 | A132 | 10s multicolored | 1.50 | .30 |
| 886 | A132 | 15s multicolored | 2.10 | .65 |
| 887 | A132 | 20s multicolored | 2.50 | .65 |
| 888 | A132 | 25s multicolored | 2.75 | .85 |
| | *Nos. 883-888 (6)* | | 10.50 | 2.95 |

**Souvenir Sheet**

| | | | | |
|---|---|---|---|---|
| 889 | A132 | 30s multicolored | 4.50 | 2.00 |

Nos. 887-889 airmail.

Anniversaries and Events — A133

Famous men: 5s, Abraham Lincoln, log cabin, the White House. 7s, Jean-Henri Dunant, Red Cross at Battle of Solferino. 10s, Gottlieb Daimler, 1892 Motor Carriage. 15s, Louis Bleriot, monoplane. 20s, Paul Harris, Rotary Intl. 25s, Auguste Piccard, bathyscaphe Trieste. 100s, Paul Harris, Rotary Intl. emblem.

30s, Anatoly Karpov, world chess champion, chessboard and knight.

**1984, Aug. 20 — Litho. — Perf. 13½**

| | | | | |
|---|---|---|---|---|
| 890 | A133 | 5s multicolored | .50 | .25 |
| 891 | A133 | 7s multicolored | .95 | .25 |
| 892 | A133 | 10s multicolored | 1.40 | .35 |
| 893 | A133 | 15s multicolored | 2.10 | .50 |
| 894 | A133 | 20s multicolored | 2.75 | .65 |
| 895 | A133 | 25s multicolored | 3.50 | .80 |
| | *Nos. 890-895 (6)* | | 11.20 | 2.80 |

**Litho. & Embossed**
**Size: 60x30mm**

| | | | | |
|---|---|---|---|---|
| 895A | A133 | 100s gold & multi | 16.00 | — |
| b. | | Min. sheet of 1, 91x70mm | 60.00 | — |
| c. | | Min. sheet of 1, 121x70mm | 16.00 | 12.50 |

**Souvenir Sheet**

| | | | | |
|---|---|---|---|---|
| 896 | A133 | 30s multicolored | 5.00 | 1.50 |

Nos. 894-896 are airmail.
For overprints see Nos. C163, C166.

The Holy Family, by Durer — A134

Painting details: 5s, The Mystic Marriage of St. Catherine and St. Sebastian, by Correggio. 10s, The Veiled Woman, by Raphael. 15s, Portrait of a Young Man, by Durer. 20s, Portrait of Soutine, by Modigliani. 25s, Esterhazy Madonna, by Raphael. 30s, Impannata Madonna, by Raphael.

**1984, Aug. 23**

| | | | | |
|---|---|---|---|---|
| 897 | A134 | 5s multicolored | .55 | .25 |
| 898 | A134 | 7s multicolored | .90 | .30 |
| 899 | A134 | 10s multicolored | 1.60 | .35 |
| 900 | A134 | 15s multicolored | 2.25 | .75 |
| 901 | A134 | 20s multicolored | 2.75 | .85 |
| 902 | A134 | 25s multicolored | 3.25 | 1.00 |
| | *Nos. 897-902 (6)* | | 11.30 | 3.50 |

**Souvenir Sheet**

| | | | | |
|---|---|---|---|---|
| 903 | A134 | 30s multicolored | 4.75 | 1.50 |

Nos. 901-903 airmail.

1984 Winter Olympics, Sarajevo — A135

Gold medalists: 5s, East German two-man bobsled. 7s, Thomas Wassberg, Sweden, 50-kilometer cross-country. 10s, Gaetan Boucher, Canada, 1000 and 1500-meter speed skating. 15s, Katarina Witt, DDR, singles figure skating. 20s, Bill Johnson, US, men's downhill. 25s, Soviet Union, ice hockey. No. 909A, 100s, Phil Mahre, US, slalom skiing.

No. 910, 30s, Jens Weissflog, DDR, 70-meter ski jump. No. 910A, 100s, Jayne Torvill & Christopher Dean, Great Britain, ice dancing.

**1985, Sept. 23 — Litho. — Perf. 13½**

| | | | | |
|---|---|---|---|---|
| 904 | A135 | 5s multicolored | .60 | .25 |
| 905 | A135 | 7s multicolored | .75 | .25 |
| 906 | A135 | 10s multicolored | 1.20 | .35 |
| 907 | A135 | 15s multicolored | 1.75 | .45 |
| 908 | A135 | 20s multicolored | 2.25 | .60 |
| 909 | A135 | 25s multicolored | 3.00 | .75 |
| | *Nos. 904-909 (6)* | | 9.55 | 2.60 |

**Litho. & Embossed**
**Size: 51x36mm**

| | | | | |
|---|---|---|---|---|
| 909A | A135 | 100s gold & multi | 60.00 | 30.00 |

**Souvenir Sheets**
**Litho.**

| | | | | |
|---|---|---|---|---|
| 910 | A135 | 30s multicolored | 6.00 | 2.10 |

**Litho. & Embossed**

| | | | | |
|---|---|---|---|---|
| 910A | A135 | 100s gold & multi | 18.00 | 15.00 |

Nos. 908A-910A are airmail. No. 910A contains one 51x36mm stamp.

1984 Los Angeles Summer Olympics — A136

Medalists: 5s, T. Ruiz and C. Costie, US, synchronized swimming. 7s, West Germany, team dressage. 10s, US, yachting, flying Dutchman class. 15s, Mark Todd, New Zealand, individual 3-day equestrian event. 20s, Daley Thompson, G.B., decathlon. 25s, US, team jumping.

30s, Carl Lewis, US, long jump, 100 and 200-meter run, 4x100 relay.

**1985, Mar. 18 — Litho. — Perf. 13½**

| | | | | |
|---|---|---|---|---|
| 911 | A136 | 5s multicolored | .45 | .25 |
| 912 | A136 | 7s multicolored | .70 | .25 |
| 913 | A136 | 10s multicolored | .90 | .25 |
| 914 | A136 | 15s multicolored | 1.40 | .40 |

| | | | | |
|---|---|---|---|---|
| 915 | A136 | 20s multicolored | 1.60 | .45 |
| 916 | A136 | 25s multicolored | 2.40 | .60 |
| | | *Nos. 911-916 (6)* | 7.45 | 2.20 |

**Souvenir Sheet**

| | | | | |
|---|---|---|---|---|
| 917 | A136 | 30s multicolored | 6.00 | 2.10 |

Nos. 915-917 airmail.

Fungi — A137

5s, Rhodophyllus callidermus. 7s, Agaricus niger. 10s, Thermitomyces globulus. 15s, Amanita robusta. 20s, Lepiota subradicans. 25s, Cantharellus rhodophyllus. 30s, Phlebopus sylvaticus.

**1985, Mar. 21    Litho.    Perf. 13½**

| | | | | |
|---|---|---|---|---|
| 918 | A137 | 5s multicolored | 1.25 | .30 |
| 919 | A137 | 7s multicolored | 1.60 | .45 |
| 920 | A137 | 10s multicolored | 2.00 | .75 |
| 921 | A137 | 15s multicolored | 2.75 | 1.00 |
| 922 | A137 | 20s multicolored | 3.75 | 1.25 |
| 923 | A137 | 25s multicolored | 4.75 | 1.50 |
| | | *Nos. 918-923 (6)* | 16.10 | 5.25 |

**Souvenir Sheet**

| | | | | |
|---|---|---|---|---|
| 924 | A137 | 30s multicolored | 5.50 | 4.00 |

Nos. 922-924 airmail.
For surcharges see Nos. 962-968.

Scientist Herman J. Oberth, and Two-Stage Rocket — A138

Space achievements: 10s, Lunik 1, USSR, 1959. 15s, Lunik 2 on the Moon, 1959. 20s, Lunik 3 photographing the Moon, 1959. 30s, US astronauts Armstrong, Aldrin, Collins and Apollo 11, 1969. 35s, Sally Ride, 1st American woman in space, 1983. No. 930A, 200s, Guion S. Bluford, 1st black American astronaut.

50s, Recovering a Palapa B satellite, 1984. No. 931A, 200s, Viking probe on Mars.

**1985, May 26    Litho.    Perf. 13½**

| | | | | |
|---|---|---|---|---|
| 925 | A138 | 7s multicolored | .65 | .75 |
| 926 | A138 | 10s multicolored | 1.10 | .25 |
| 927 | A138 | 15s multicolored | 1.75 | .40 |
| 928 | A138 | 20s multicolored | 2.40 | .60 |
| 929 | A138 | 30s multicolored | 4.00 | 1.00 |
| 930 | A138 | 35s multicolored | 4.75 | 1.25 |
| | | *Nos. 925-930 (6)* | 14.65 | 3.75 |

**Litho. & Embossed
Size: 51x36mm**

| | | | | |
|---|---|---|---|---|
| 930A | A138 | 200s gold & multi | 37.50 | — |

**Souvenir Sheet
Litho.**

| | | | | |
|---|---|---|---|---|
| 931 | A138 | 50s multicolored | 6.50 | 3.25 |

**Litho. & Embossed**

| | | | | |
|---|---|---|---|---|
| 931A | A138 | 200s gold & multi | 27.50 | — |

Nos. 929-931A are airmail. No. 931A contains one 51x36mm stamp.

Maimonides (1135-1204), Jewish Scholar, Cordoba Jewish Quarter A139

Anniversaries and events: 10s, Christopher Columbus departing from Palos for New World, 1492. 15s, Frederic Auguste Bartholdi (1834-1904), sculptor, architect, and Statue of Liberty, cent. 20s, Queen Mother, 85th birthday. 30s, Ulf Merbold, German physicist, US space shuttle Columbia. 35s, Wedding of Prince Charles and Lady Diana, 1981. 100s, Queen Mother Elizabeth's 85th birthday.

50s, Charles, Diana, Princes Henry and William.

**1985, Sept. 23**

| | | | | |
|---|---|---|---|---|
| 932 | A139 | 7s multicolored | .80 | .25 |
| 933 | A139 | 10s multicolored | 1.10 | .25 |
| 934 | A139 | 15s multicolored | 1.75 | .40 |
| 935 | A139 | 20s multicolored | 2.25 | .55 |
| 936 | A139 | 30s multicolored | 3.25 | .80 |
| 937 | A139 | 35s multicolored | 4.00 | .90 |
| | | *Nos. 932-937 (6)* | 13.15 | 3.15 |

**Litho. & Embossed
Size: 42x51mm**

| | | | | |
|---|---|---|---|---|
| 937A | A139 | 100s gold & multi | 13.00 | 12.50 |

**Souvenir Sheet
Litho.**

| | | | | |
|---|---|---|---|---|
| 938 | A139 | 50s multicolored | 6.50 | 3.25 |

Nos. 936-938 airmail. No. 938 contains one 51x36mm stamp. Nos. 934 and 937A exist in souvenir sheets of one.

Audubon Birth Bicent. A140

Illustrations of bird species from Birds of America: 7s, Coccyzus erythrophtalmus. 10s, Conuropsis carolinensis. 15s, Anhinga anhinga. 20s, Buteo lineatus. 30s, Otus asio. 35s, Toxostoma rufum.

50s, Zenaidura macroura.

**1985, Sept. 23    Litho.    Perf. 13½**

| | | | | |
|---|---|---|---|---|
| 939 | A140 | 7s multicolored | .75 | .25 |
| 940 | A140 | 10s multicolored | 1.20 | .30 |
| 941 | A140 | 15s multicolored | 2.00 | .50 |
| 942 | A140 | 20s multicolored | 2.50 | .70 |
| 943 | A140 | 30s multicolored | 4.25 | 1.25 |
| 944 | A140 | 35s multicolored | 4.50 | 1.50 |
| | | *Nos. 939-944 (6)* | 15.20 | 4.50 |

**Souvenir Sheet**

| | | | | |
|---|---|---|---|---|
| 945 | A140 | 50s multicolored | 6.50 | 3.00 |

Nos. 941, 944 vert. Nos. 943-945 are airmail. No. 945 contains one 51x36mm stamp. Nos. 939-944 exist in souvenir sheets of one. Value, set $90.

1986 World Cup Soccer Championships, Mexico — A141

Famous soccer players: 7s, Bebeto, Brazil. 10s, Rinal Dassaev, USSR. 15s, Phil Neal, Great Britain. 20s, Jean Tigana, France. 30s, Fernando Chalana, Portugal. 35s, Michel Platini, France.

50s, Karl Heinz Rummenigge, West Germany.

**1985, Oct. 26**

| | | | | |
|---|---|---|---|---|
| 946 | A141 | 7s multicolored | .95 | .25 |
| 947 | A141 | 10s multicolored | 1.25 | .25 |
| 948 | A141 | 15s multicolored | 1.90 | .40 |
| 949 | A141 | 20s multicolored | 2.50 | .60 |
| 950 | A141 | 30s multicolored | 3.50 | .85 |
| 951 | A141 | 35s multicolored | 4.50 | .95 |
| | | *Nos. 946-951 (6)* | 14.60 | 3.30 |

**Souvenir Sheet**

| | | | | |
|---|---|---|---|---|
| 952 | A141 | 50s multicolored | 7.50 | 3.00 |

Nos. 950-952 airmail.

Cats and Dogs — A142

7s, Blue-point Siamese. 10s, Cocker spaniel. 15s, Poodles. 20s, Blue Persian. 25s, European red-and-white tabby. 30s, German shepherd. 35s, Abyssinians. 40s, Boxer.

50s, Pyrenean mountain dog, chartreux cat.

**1985, Oct. 26**

| | | | | |
|---|---|---|---|---|
| 953 | A142 | 7s multicolored | .80 | .25 |
| 954 | A142 | 10s multicolored | 1.25 | .25 |
| 955 | A142 | 15s multicolored | 2.00 | .40 |
| 956 | A142 | 20s multicolored | 2.75 | .60 |
| 957 | A142 | 25s multicolored | 3.75 | .70 |
| 958 | A142 | 30s multicolored | 4.00 | .85 |
| 959 | A142 | 35s multicolored | 4.50 | .95 |
| 960 | A142 | 40s multicolored | 4.75 | 1.25 |
| | | *Nos. 953-960 (8)* | 23.80 | 5.25 |

**Souvenir Sheet**

| | | | | |
|---|---|---|---|---|
| 961 | A142 | 50s multicolored | 6.50 | 2.50 |

Nos. 958-961 airmail. No. 961 contains one 51x30mm stamp.

Nos. 918-924 Surcharged

**1985, Nov. 15**

| | | | | |
|---|---|---|---|---|
| 962 | A137 | 1s on 5s multi | .80 | .25 |
| 963 | A137 | 2s on 7s multi | .85 | .25 |
| 964 | A137 | 8s on 10s multi | 1.75 | .40 |
| 965 | A137 | 30s on 15s multi | 6.50 | 1.60 |
| 966 | A137 | 35s on 20s multi | 7.50 | 2.25 |
| 967 | A137 | 40s on 25s multi | 9.00 | 2.75 |
| | | *Nos. 962-967 (6)* | 26.40 | 7.50 |

**Souvenir Sheet**

| | | | | |
|---|---|---|---|---|
| 968 | A137 | 50s on 30s multi | 9.50 | 4.00 |

Nos. 966-968 airmail.

Locomotives A143

Designs: 7s, 8F Class steam, Great Britain. 15s, Bobo 5500 Series III electric, German Fed. Railways. 25s, Pacific A Mazout No. 270, African Railways. 35s, Serie 420 electric train set, Suburban S-Bahn, Germany. 50s, ICE high-speed train, German Fed. Railways.

**1985, Dec. 18    Litho.    Perf. 13½**

| | | | | |
|---|---|---|---|---|
| 969 | A143 | 7s multicolored | .95 | .25 |
| 970 | A143 | 15s multicolored | 2.10 | .70 |
| 971 | A143 | 25s multicolored | 3.50 | .90 |
| 972 | A143 | 35s multicolored | 5.00 | 1.25 |
| | | *Nos. 969-972 (4)* | 11.55 | 3.10 |

**Souvenir Sheet**

| | | | | |
|---|---|---|---|---|
| 973 | A143 | 50s multicolored | 6.50 | 2.75 |

Nos. 972-973 airmail.
For surcharges see Nos. 991-995.

Columbus Discovering America, 1492 A144

10s, Pinta. 20s, Santa Maria. 30s, Nina. 40s, Santa Maria, sighting land. 50s, Columbus and Nina.

**1985, Dec. 18**

| | | | | |
|---|---|---|---|---|
| 974 | A144 | 10s multicolored | 1.25 | .25 |
| 975 | A144 | 20s multicolored | 2.50 | .65 |
| 976 | A144 | 30s multicolored | 4.00 | .95 |
| 977 | A144 | 40s multicolored | 5.75 | 1.25 |
| | | *Nos. 974-977 (4)* | 13.50 | 3.10 |

**Souvenir Sheet**

| | | | | |
|---|---|---|---|---|
| 978 | A144 | 50s multicolored | 6.50 | 3.00 |

Nos. 976-978 airmail.

Intl. Youth Year — A145

**1986, Jan. 21**

| | | | | |
|---|---|---|---|---|
| 979 | A145 | 10s Chopin | 1.20 | .40 |
| 980 | A145 | 20s Botticelli | 2.40 | .85 |
| 981 | A145 | 25s Picasso | 4.00 | 1.10 |
| 982 | A145 | 35s Rossini | 2.75 | 1.50 |
| | | *Nos. 979-982 (4)* | 10.35 | 3.85 |

**Souvenir Sheet**

| | | | | |
|---|---|---|---|---|
| 983 | A145 | 50s Michelangelo | 6.50 | 2.75 |

Nos. 981, 983 airmail.
For surcharges see Nos. 996-1000.

Halley's Comet A146

Sightings: 5fr, Bayeux Tapestry (detail), c. 1092, France. 30fr, Arab, astrolabe, 1400. 40fr, Montezuma II, Aztec deity. 50fr, Edmond Halley, trajectory diagram. 300fr, Halley, Sir Isaac Newton. 500fr, Halley, Giotto, Soviet and NASA space probes, comet. 600fr, Hally commemorative medal, Giotto probe.

**1986, July 1    Litho.    Perf. 13½
5fr-500fr Surcharged with New Currency in Silver or Black**

| | | | | |
|---|---|---|---|---|
| 984 | A146 | 5fr multi | .25 | .25 |
| 985 | A146 | 30fr multi | .25 | .25 |
| 986 | A146 | 40fr multi | .30 | .25 |
| 987 | A146 | 50fr multi | .40 | .25 |
| 988 | A146 | 300fr multi | 2.10 | .75 |
| 989 | A146 | 500fr multi | 4.00 | 1.25 |
| | | *Nos. 984-989 (6)* | 7.30 | 3.00 |

**Souvenir Sheet**

| | | | | |
|---|---|---|---|---|
| 990 | A146 | 600fr multi | 5.50 | 2.50 |

Nos. 988-990 are airmail. Nos. 984-989 not issued without surcharge.

**No. 969 Surcharged**

**Nos. 970-973 Surcharged**

**1986, Aug. 25    Litho.    Perf. 13½**

| | | | | |
|---|---|---|---|---|
| 991 | A143 | 2fr on 7s multi (B on S) | .30 | .25 |
| 992 | A143 | 25fr on 15s multi | .50 | .25 |
| 993 | A143 | 50fr on 25s multi | 1.00 | .25 |
| 994 | A143 | 90fr on 35s multi | 1.60 | .55 |
| | | *Nos. 991-994 (4)* | 3.40 | 1.30 |

**Souvenir Sheet**

| | | | | |
|---|---|---|---|---|
| 995 | A143 | 500fr on 50s multi | 5.00 | 2.10 |

**Nos. 979-983 Surcharged**

**1986, Aug. 25**

| | | | | |
|---|---|---|---|---|
| 996 | A145 | 5fr on 10s multi | .40 | .25 |
| 997 | A145 | 35fr on 20s multi | .50 | .25 |
| 998 | A145 | 50fr on 25s multi | 1.10 | .30 |
| 999 | A145 | 90fr on 35s multi | 1.25 | .40 |
| | | *Nos. 996-999 (4)* | 3.25 | 1.20 |

**Souvenir Sheet**

| | | | | |
|---|---|---|---|---|
| 1000 | A145 | 500fr on 50s multi | 6.00 | 2.10 |

Locomotives A147

Designs: 20fr, Dietrich 640 CV. 100fr, T.13 7906. 300fr, Vapeur 01220. 400fr, ABH Type 3 5020. 600fr, Renault ABH 3 (300 CV).

## 1986, Nov. 1

| | | | | |
|---|---|---|---|---|
| 1001 | A147 | 20fr multi | .35 | .25 |
| 1002 | A147 | 100fr multi | 1.00 | .35 |
| 1003 | A147 | 300fr multi | 3.00 | .95 |
| 1004 | A147 | 400fr multi | 4.25 | 1.25 |
| | *Nos. 1001-1004 (4)* | | 8.60 | 2.80 |

**Souvenir Sheet**

| | | | | |
|---|---|---|---|---|
| 1005 | A147 | 600fr multi | 7.00 | 2.50 |

Nos. 1004-1005 are airmail.

Discovery of
America,
500th Anniv.
(in 1992)
A148

Designs: 40fr, Columbus at Ft. Navidad construction, Santa Maria, 1492. 70fr, Landing at Hispaniola, 2nd voyage, 1494. 200fr, Aboard ship, 3rd voyage, 1498. 500fr, Trading with Indians. 600fr, At court of Ferdinand and Isabella, 1493.

## 1986, Nov. 1

| | | | | |
|---|---|---|---|---|
| 1006 | A148 | 40fr multi | .50 | .25 |
| 1007 | A148 | 70fr multi | .80 | .25 |
| 1008 | A148 | 200fr multi | 2.25 | .70 |
| 1009 | A148 | 500fr multi | 5.50 | 1.75 |
| | *Nos. 1006-1009 (4)* | | 9.05 | 2.95 |

**Souvenir Sheet**

| | | | | |
|---|---|---|---|---|
| 1010 | A148 | 600fr multi | 7.00 | 2.50 |

Nos. 1009-1010 are airmail.

Anniversaries &
Events — A149

30fr, Prince Charles and Diana, 5th wedding anniv. 40fr, Alain Prost, San Marino, 1985 Formula 1 Grand Prix world champion. 100fr, Wedding of Prince Andrew and Sarah Ferguson. 300fr, Elvis Presley. 500fr, Michael Jackson. 600fr, M. Dassault (1892-1986), aerospace engineer.

## 1986, Nov. 12

| | | | | |
|---|---|---|---|---|
| 1011 | A149 | 30fr multi | .35 | .25 |
| 1012 | A149 | 40fr multi | .45 | .25 |
| 1013 | A149 | 100fr multi | 1.10 | .40 |
| 1014 | A149 | 300fr multi | 3.00 | 1.25 |
| 1015 | A149 | 500fr multi | 5.00 | 2.40 |
| | *Nos. 1011-1015 (5)* | | 9.90 | 4.55 |

**Souvenir Sheet**

| | | | | |
|---|---|---|---|---|
| 1016 | A149 | 600fr multi | 6.50 | 2.75 |

Nos. 1015-1016 are airmail.

1986 World Cup Soccer
Championships — A150

Various players and final scores.

## 1986, Nov. 12

| | | | | |
|---|---|---|---|---|
| 1017 | A150 | 150fr Pfaff | 1.00 | .35 |
| 1018 | A150 | 300fr Platini | 3.00 | .95 |
| 1019 | A150 | 400fr Matthaus | 4.00 | 1.50 |
| 1020 | A150 | 500fr D. Maradona | 5.00 | 2.10 |
| | *Nos. 1017-1020 (4)* | | 13.00 | 4.90 |

**Souvenir Sheet**

| | | | | |
|---|---|---|---|---|
| 1021 | A150 | 600fr Maradona, trophy | 7.00 | 2.50 |

Nos. 1020-1021 are airmail. No. 1021 contains one 51x42mm stamp.
For surcharge see No. 1182A.

1988
Summer
Olympics,
Seoul
A151

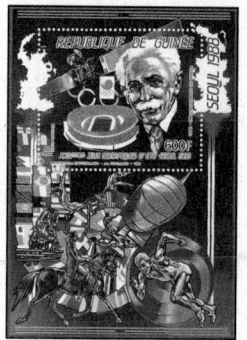

Pierre de Coubertin (1863-1937),
Seoul Stadium, Telecommunications
Satellite — A151a

20fr, Judo. 30fr, High jump. 40fr, Team handball. 100fr, Women's gymnastics. 300fr, Javelin. 500fr, Equestrian.

## 1987, Jan. 17    Litho.    *Perf. 13½*

| | | | | |
|---|---|---|---|---|
| 1022 | A151 | 20fr multicolored | .25 | .25 |
| 1023 | A151 | 30fr multicolored | .35 | .25 |
| 1024 | A151 | 40fr multicolored | .45 | .25 |
| 1025 | A151 | 100fr multicolored | 1.00 | .25 |
| 1026 | A151 | 300fr multicolored | 3.00 | .90 |
| 1027 | A151 | 500fr multicolored | 5.00 | 2.10 |
| | *Nos. 1022-1027 (6)* | | 10.05 | 4.00 |

**Souvenir Sheet**

| | | | | |
|---|---|---|---|---|
| 1028 | A151a | 600fr multi | 6.50 | 2.50 |

Dated 1986. Nos. 1026-1028 are airmail.

1988 Winter
Olympics,
Calgary
A152

50fr on 40fr, Biathlon. 100fr, Cross-country skiing. 400fr, Ski jumping. 500fr, Two-man bobsled.
600fr, Woman skater, satellite.

## 1987, Mar. 23    Litho.    *Perf. 13½*

| | | | | |
|---|---|---|---|---|
| 1029 | A152 | 50fr on 40fr multi | .50 | .25 |
| 1030 | A152 | 100fr multicolored | 1.00 | .35 |
| 1031 | A152 | 400fr multicolored | 4.00 | 2.50 |
| 1032 | A152 | 500fr multicolored | 5.00 | 2.10 |
| | *Nos. 1029-1032 (4)* | | 10.50 | 5.20 |

**Souvenir Sheet**

| | | | | |
|---|---|---|---|---|
| 1033 | A152 | 600fr multicolored | 6.50 | 2.50 |

No. 1029 not issued without overprint. Nos. 1031-1033 are airmail.

1988 Winter
Olympics,
Calgary — A153

Telecommunications satellite, athletes and emblem: 25fr, Women's slalom. 50fr, Hockey. 100fr, Men's figure skating. 150fr, Men's downhill skiing. 300fr, Speed skating. 500fr, Four-man bobsled.
600fr, Ski jumping.

## 1987, May 1

| | | | | |
|---|---|---|---|---|
| 1034 | A153 | 25fr multicolored | .25 | .25 |
| 1035 | A153 | 50fr multicolored | .40 | .25 |
| 1036 | A153 | 100fr multicolored | .80 | .30 |
| 1037 | A153 | 150fr multicolored | 1.20 | .45 |
| 1038 | A153 | 300fr multicolored | 2.25 | 1.25 |
| 1039 | A153 | 500fr multicolored | 4.00 | 2.10 |
| | *Nos. 1034-1039 (6)* | | 8.90 | 4.60 |

**Souvenir Sheet**

| | | | | |
|---|---|---|---|---|
| 1040 | A153 | 600fr multicolored | 5.50 | 2.00 |

Nos. 1038-1040 are airmail.

Famous
Men — A154

Intl. Cardiology Congresses in
Chicago, Washington and New
York — A155

Designs: 50fr, Lafayette, military leader during American and French revolutions. 100fr, Ettore Bugatti (1881-1947), Italian automobile manufacturer. 200fr, Garri Kasparov, Russian chess champion. 300fr, George Washington. 400fr, Boris Becker, 1987 Wimbledon tennis champion. 500fr, Sir Winston Churchill.

## 1987, Nov. 1    Litho.    *Perf. 13½*

| | | | | |
|---|---|---|---|---|
| 1041 | A154 | 50fr multi | .45 | .25 |
| 1042 | A154 | 100fr multi | 1.00 | .40 |
| 1043 | A154 | 200fr multi | 1.90 | .60 |
| 1044 | A154 | 300fr multi | 2.75 | 1.25 |
| 1045 | A154 | 400fr multi | 3.75 | 1.60 |
| 1046 | A154 | 500fr multi | 4.75 | 2.00 |
| | *Nos. 1041-1046 (6)* | | 14.60 | 6.30 |

**Souvenir Sheet**

| | | | | |
|---|---|---|---|---|
| 1047 | A155 | 1500fr multi | 16.00 | 12.50 |

Nos. 1045-1047 are airmail. Stamp in No. 1047 divided into three sections by simulated perforations.
For surcharge see No. 1182B.

Cave Bear — A156

Prehistoric Animals — A157

50fr, Dimetrodon. 100fr, Iguanodon. 200fr, Tylosaurus. 400fr, Saber-tooth tiger. 500fr, Stegosaurus.
600fr, Triceratops.

## 1987, Nov. 1

| | | | | |
|---|---|---|---|---|
| 1048 | A156 | 50fr multicolored | .90 | .25 |
| 1049 | A156 | 100fr multicolored | 1.75 | .50 |
| 1050 | A156 | 200fr multicolored | 3.50 | 1.00 |
| 1051 | A156 | 300fr shown | 5.25 | 1.50 |
| 1052 | A156 | 400fr multicolored | 3.75 | 2.10 |
| 1053 | A156 | 500fr multicolored | 4.75 | 2.50 |
| | *Nos. 1048-1053 (6)* | | 19.90 | 7.85 |

**Souvenir Sheet**

| | | | | |
|---|---|---|---|---|
| 1054 | A157 | 600fr multicolored | 7.00 | 2.00 |

Nos. 1052-1054 are airmail.
For surcharge see No. 1182C.

1988 Summer
Olympics,
Seoul — A158

Male and female tennis players in action.

## 1987, Nov. 28

| | | | | |
|---|---|---|---|---|
| 1055 | A158 | 50fr multi | .40 | .25 |
| 1056 | A158 | 100fr multi, diff. | .80 | .35 |
| 1057 | A158 | 150fr multi, diff. | 1.20 | .60 |
| 1058 | A158 | 200fr multi, diff. | 1.60 | .75 |
| 1059 | A158 | 300fr multi, diff. | 2.40 | 1.25 |
| 1060 | A158 | 500fr multi, diff. | 4.00 | 1.90 |
| | *Nos. 1055-1060 (6)* | | 10.40 | 5.10 |

**Souvenir Sheet**

| | | | | |
|---|---|---|---|---|
| 1061 | A158 | 600fr multi | 5.50 | 2.00 |

Reintroduction of tennis as an Olympic event. Nos. 1059-1061 are airmail.

1992 Summer
Olympics,
Barcelona
A159

Athletes participating in events, Barcelona highlights: 50fr, Discus, courtyard of St. Croix and St. Paul Hospital. 100fr, High jump, Pablo Casals playing cello. 150fr, Long jump, Labyrinth of Horta. 170fr, Javelin, lizard from Guell Park. 400fr, Gymnastics, Mercy Church. 500fr, Tennis, Picasso Museum.
600fr, Running, tapestry by Miro.

## 1987, Dec. 28    Litho.    *Perf. 13½*

| | | | | |
|---|---|---|---|---|
| 1062 | A159 | 50fr multi | .45 | .25 |
| 1063 | A159 | 100fr multi | .90 | .35 |
| 1064 | A159 | 150fr multi | 1.25 | .55 |
| 1065 | A159 | 170fr multi | 1.40 | .60 |
| 1066 | A159 | 400fr multi | 3.50 | 1.40 |
| 1067 | A159 | 500fr multi | 4.50 | 1.75 |
| | *Nos. 1062-1067 (6)* | | 12.00 | 4.90 |

**Souvenir Sheet**

| | | | | |
|---|---|---|---|---|
| 1068 | A159 | 600fr multi | 6.50 | 2.00 |

Nos. 1066-1068 are airmail.
For surcharges see Nos. 1182D-1182E.

Wildlife — A160

50fr, African wild dog pups. 70fr, Adult. 100fr, Adults circling gazelle. 170fr, Chasing gazelle. 400fr, Crown cranes. 500fr, Derby elands.
600fr, Vervet monkeys.

## 1987, Dec. 28

| | | | | |
|---|---|---|---|---|
| 1069 | A160 | 50fr multicolored | 1.75 | .75 |
| 1070 | A160 | 70fr multicolored | 2.25 | 1.00 |
| 1071 | A160 | 100fr multicolored | 2.75 | 1.25 |
| 1072 | A160 | 170fr multicolored | 3.25 | 1.50 |
| 1073 | A160 | 400fr multicolored | 4.00 | 1.40 |
| 1074 | A160 | 500fr multicolored | 5.00 | 2.50 |
| | *Nos. 1069-1074 (6)* | | 19.00 | 8.40 |

**Souvenir Sheet**

| | | | | |
|---|---|---|---|---|
| 1075 | A160 | 600fr multicolored | 7.00 | 5.50 |

Nos. 1069-1072 picture World Wildlife Fund emblem; Nos. 1073, 1075, picture Scouting trefoil and No. 1074 pictures Rotary Intl. emblem. Nos. 1073-1075 are airmail.
Nos. 1069-1072 exist in a souvenir sheet of 4. Value, $30.
For surcharges see Nos. 1182F-1182G.

Reconciliation
Summit
Conference, July
11-12,
1986 — A161

Heads of state and natl. flags: Dr. Samuel Kanyon Doe of Liberia, Colonel Lansana Conte of Guinea and Maj.-Gen. Joseph Saidu Momoh of Sierra Leone.

## 1987    Litho.    *Perf. 13½*

| | | | | |
|---|---|---|---|---|
| 1076 | A161 | 40fr multi | .65 | .25 |
| 1077 | A161 | 50fr multi | .80 | .45 |
| 1078 | A161 | 75fr multi | 1.10 | .60 |
| 1079 | A161 | 100fr multi | 1.60 | .75 |
| 1080 | A161 | 150fr multi | 2.40 | .85 |
| | *Nos. 1076-1080 (5)* | | 6.55 | 2.90 |

Space
Exploration
A162

50fr, Galaxie-Grasp. 150fr, Energia-Mir.
200fr, NASA Space Station. 300fr, Ariane 5-
E.S.A. 400fr, Mars-Rover. 450fr, Venus-Vega.
500fr, Mars-Phobos.

**1988, Apr. 16**
| | | | | |
|---|---|---|---|---|
| **1081** | A162 | 50fr multicolored | .45 | .25 |
| **1082** | A162 | 150fr multicolored | 1.25 | .50 |
| **1083** | A162 | 200fr multicolored | 1.75 | .35 |
| **1084** | A162 | 300fr multicolored | 2.50 | .60 |
| **1085** | A162 | 400fr multicolored | 3.50 | .75 |
| **1086** | A162 | 450fr multicolored | 4.00 | 1.00 |
| | | *Nos. 1081-1086 (6)* | 13.45 | 3.45 |

**Souvenir Sheet**
| | | | | |
|---|---|---|---|---|
| **1087** | A162 | 500fr multicolored | 5.00 | 2.00 |

Nos. 1085-1087 are airmail.

A163

Boy Scouts watching birds and butterflies:
50fr, Spermophaga ruficapilla. 100fr, Medon
nymphalidae. 150fr, Euplecte orix. 300fr,
Nectarinia pulchella. 400fr, Sophia
nymphalidae. 450fr, Rumia nymphalidae.
750fr, Opis nymphalidae, Psittacula krameri.

**1988, July 5    Litho.    Perf. 13½**
| | | | | |
|---|---|---|---|---|
| **1088** | A163 | 50fr multicolored | .50 | .25 |
| **1089** | A163 | 100fr multicolored | 1.05 | .35 |
| **1090** | A163 | 150fr multicolored | 1.45 | .60 |
| **1091** | A163 | 300fr multicolored | 3.00 | 1.25 |
| **1092** | A163 | 400fr multicolored | 3.75 | 1.50 |
| **1093** | A163 | 450fr multicolored | 4.50 | 1.75 |
| | | *Nos. 1088-1093 (6)* | 14.25 | 5.70 |

**Souvenir Sheet**
| | | | | |
|---|---|---|---|---|
| **1094** | A163 | 750fr multicolored | 7.50 | 6.50 |

Druya antimachus
— A163a

**1990, Aug. 3    Litho. & Embossed**
| | | | | |
|---|---|---|---|---|
| **1094A** | A163a | 1500fr multi | 20.00 | 12.50 |

Nos. 1092-1094A are airmail. No. 1094 contains one 35x50mm stamp.
#1094A exists in souvenir sheet of 1. Value
$45.
For surcharge and overprints see Nos.
1182H, 1240-1246.

A164

Famous People: 200fr, Queen Elizabeth II,
Prince Philip and crown jewels. 250fr, Fritz von
Opel (1899-1971), German automotive industrialist, and 1928 RAK 2 Opel. 300fr, Wolfgang
Amadeus Mozart, composer, and Masonic
emblem. 400fr, Steffi Graf, tennis champion.
450fr, Buzz Aldrin and Masonic emblem.
500fr, Paul Harris, Rotary Intl. founder, and
organization emblem.
750fr, Thomas Jefferson, horiz.

**1988, July 5**
| | | | | |
|---|---|---|---|---|
| **1095** | A164 | 200fr multi | 1.75 | .45 |
| **1096** | A164 | 250fr multi | 2.25 | .45 |
| **1097** | A164 | 300fr multi | 2.25 | .60 |
| **1098** | A164 | 400fr multi | 3.50 | .75 |

| | | | | |
|---|---|---|---|---|
| **1099** | A164 | 450fr multi | 4.00 | .90 |
| **1100** | A164 | 500fr multi | 4.75 | 1.00 |
| | | *Nos. 1095-1100 (6)* | 18.50 | 4.15 |

**Souvenir Sheet**
| | | | | |
|---|---|---|---|---|
| **1101** | A164 | 750fr multi | 7.00 | 2.00 |

40th wedding anniv. of Queen Elizabeth II
and Prince Philip (200fr).
Nos. 1099-1101 are airmail. No. 1101 contains one 42x36mm stamp.
For surcharges see Nos. 1182I, 1182Q.

1988 Winter Olympics
Gold Medalists  A165

Designs: 50fr, Vreni Schneider, Switzerland,
women's giant slalom and slalom. 100fr,
Frank-Peter Roetsch, East Germany, 10 and
20-kilometer biathlon. 150fr, Matti Nykaenen,
Finland, 70 and 90-meter ski jumping. 250fr,
Marina Kiehl, West Germany, women's downhill. 400fr, Frank Piccard, France, super giant
slalom. 450fr, Katarina Witt, East Germany,
women's figure skating.
750fr, Pirmin Zurbriggen, Switzerland,
men's downhill.

**1988, Oct. 2    Litho.    Perf. 13½**
| | | | | |
|---|---|---|---|---|
| **1102** | A165 | 50fr multi, vert. | .45 | .25 |
| **1103** | A165 | 100fr multi, vert. | 1.25 | .25 |
| **1104** | A165 | 150fr multi, vert. | 2.10 | .45 |
| **1105** | A165 | 250fr multi, vert. | 3.50 | .75 |
| **1106** | A165 | 400fr multi, vert. | .85 | .45 |
| **1107** | A165 | 450fr multi, vert. | 3.75 | 1.00 |
| | | *Nos. 1102-1107 (6)* | 11.90 | 3.15 |

**Souvenir Sheet**
| | | | | |
|---|---|---|---|---|
| **1108** | A165 | 750fr multi | 6.75 | 2.00 |

Nos. 1103, 1107-1108 are airmail.
For surcharge see No. 1182J.

African Postal
Union, 25th
Anniv. — A165a

**1988    Litho.    Perf. 13½**
| | | | | |
|---|---|---|---|---|
| **1108A** | A165a | 50fr multicolored | .45 | .25 |
| **1108B** | A165a | 75fr multicolored | .75 | .25 |
| **1108C** | A165a | 100fr multicolored | .85 | .25 |
| **1108D** | A165a | 150fr multicolored | 1.25 | .40 |
| | | *Nos. 1108A-1108D (4)* | 3.30 | 1.15 |

World Health
Day — A165b

50fr, Medical research. 150fr, Immunization.
500fr, Dentistry.

**1988, Oct. 2    Litho.    Perf. 13½**
| | | | | |
|---|---|---|---|---|
| **1108E** | A165b | 50fr multi | .45 | .25 |
| **1108F** | A165b | 150fr multi | 1.25 | .35 |
| **1108G** | A165b | 500fr multi | 4.25 | 1.00 |
| | | *Nos. 1108E-1108G (3)* | 5.95 | 1.60 |

For surcharge see No. 1182K.

Opening of MT 20 Intl.
Communications
Center — A165c

**1988, Dec. 8    Litho.    Perf. 13½**
| | | | | |
|---|---|---|---|---|
| **1108H** | A165c | 50fr multicolored | .45 | .25 |
| **1108I** | A165c | 100fr multicolored | .85 | .25 |
| **1108J** | A165c | 150fr multicolored | 1.25 | .45 |

Pierre de
Coubertin, Founder
of Intl. Olympic
Committee
A165d

**1988    Litho.    Perf. 13½y**
| | | | | |
|---|---|---|---|---|
| **1108K** | A165d | 50fr multi | .45 | .25 |
| **1108L** | A165d | 100fr multi | .85 | .25 |
| **1108M** | A165d | 150fr multi | 1.25 | .35 |
| **1108N** | A165d | 500fr multi | 4.25 | 1.10 |
| | | *Nos. 1108K-1108N (4)* | 6.80 | 1.95 |

For surcharge see No. 1182L.

1992
Summer
Olympics,
Barcelona
A166

50fr, Diving. 100fr, Running, vert. 150fr,
Shooting. 250fr, Tennis, vert. 400fr, Soccer.
500fr, Equestrian, vert.
750fr, Yachting, vert.

**1989, May 3    Litho.    Perf. 13½**
| | | | | |
|---|---|---|---|---|
| **1109** | A166 | 50fr multi | .45 | .25 |
| **1110** | A166 | 100fr multi | 1.00 | .55 |
| **1111** | A166 | 150fr multi | 1.75 | .95 |
| **1112** | A166 | 250fr multi | 2.75 | 1.50 |
| **1113** | A166 | 400fr multi | 4.25 | 2.40 |
| **1114** | A166 | 500fr multi | 5.25 | 3.00 |
| | | *Nos. 1109-1114 (6)* | 15.45 | 8.65 |

**Souvenir Sheet**
| | | | | |
|---|---|---|---|---|
| **1115** | A166 | 750fr multi | 7.50 | 2.50 |

Nos. 1113-1115 are airmail.
For surcharge see No. 1182M.

French Revolution, Bicent. — A167

Personalities of and scenes from the revolution: 250fr, Jean-Sylvain Bailly (1736-1793)
leading proceedings in Tennis Court, June 20,
1789. 300fr, Count Mirabeau (1749-1791) at
royal session, June 23, 1789. 400fr, Lafayette
(1757-1834), federation anniversary celebration, July 18, 1790. 450fr, Jerome Petion de
Villeneuve (1756-1794), king's arrest at Varen-
nes-en-Argonne, June 21, 1791.
750fr, Camille Desmoulins (1760-1794),
destruction of the Bastille, July 1789.

**1989, July 7    Litho.    Perf. 13½**
| | | | | |
|---|---|---|---|---|
| **1116** | A167 | 250fr multi | 2.40 | .60 |
| **1117** | A167 | 300fr multi | 2.90 | .75 |
| **1118** | A167 | 400fr multi | 4.00 | 1.10 |
| **1119** | A167 | 450fr multi | 4.75 | 1.20 |
| | | *Nos. 1116-1119 (4)* | 14.05 | 3.65 |

**Souvenir Sheet**
| | | | | |
|---|---|---|---|---|
| **1120** | A167 | 750fr multi | 8.00 | 2.50 |

Nos. 1119-1120 airmail.
Nos. 1116-1119 exist in souvenir sheets of
1. Sold for 100fr extra.
For surcharge and overprints see Nos.
1182N, 1216-1220.

Planting — A168

50fr, Irrigation. 75fr, Milking. 100fr, Fishing.
150fr, Farmers in corn field. 300fr, Public well.

**1989    Litho.    Perf. 13½**
| | | | | |
|---|---|---|---|---|
| **1121** | A168 | 25fr shown | .25 | .25 |
| **1122** | A168 | 50fr multi | .40 | .25 |
| **1123** | A168 | 75fr multi | .65 | .25 |
| **1124** | A168 | 100fr multi | .80 | .30 |
| **1125** | A168 | 150fr multi | 1.20 | .40 |
| **1126** | A168 | 300fr multi | 2.40 | .80 |
| | | *Nos. 1121-1126 (6)* | 5.70 | 2.25 |

Natl. Campaign for Self-sufficiency in Food
Production and 10th anniv. of the Intl. Fund for
Agricultural Development (in 1988). Dated
1988.

African
Development
Bank, 25th
Anniv. — A169

**1989, Nov. 4    Litho.    Perf. 13½**
| | | | | |
|---|---|---|---|---|
| **1127** | A169 | 300fr multicolored | 3.00 | 1.10 |

Mano River
Union, 15th
Anniv. — A170

Design: 300fr, Map of Guinea, Sierra Leone
and Liberia, leaders' portraits.

**1989, Nov. 4**
| | | | | |
|---|---|---|---|---|
| **1128** | A170 | 150fr multicolored | 1.50 | .65 |
| **1129** | A170 | 300fr multicolored | 3.00 | 1.25 |

World Cup Soccer,
Italy — A171

Various soccer plays and: 200fr, Spire of
San Domenico, Naples. 250fr, Piazza San
Carlo, Turin. 300fr, Church of San Cataldo.
450fr, Church of San Francesco, Utine.
750fr, Statue of Dante, Florence and World
Cup Soccer Trophy.

**1990, Aug. 3    Litho.    Perf. 13½**
| | | | | |
|---|---|---|---|---|
| **1130** | A171 | 200fr multicolored | 1.50 | .80 |
| **1131** | A171 | 250fr multicolored | 2.00 | 1.00 |
| **1132** | A171 | 300fr multicolored | 2.50 | 1.25 |
| **1133** | A171 | 450fr multicolored | 4.00 | 1.90 |
| | | *Nos. 1130-1133 (4)* | 10.00 | 4.95 |

**Souvenir Sheet**
| | | | | |
|---|---|---|---|---|
| **1134** | A171 | 750fr multicolored | 7.25 | 2.75 |

No. 1133-1134 airmail.
For overprints see Nos. 1221-1225.

Concorde,
TGV Atlantic
A172

**1990, Aug. 3**
| | | | | |
|---|---|---|---|---|
| **1135** | A172 | 400fr multicolored | 4.00 | 1.50 |

No. 1135 exists in a souvenir sheet of 1.
For surcharge see No. 1182O.

Pope John
Paul II, Pres.
Gorbachev
A173

**1990, Aug. 3**
| | | | | |
|---|---|---|---|---|
| **1136** | A173 | 300fr multicolored | 3.00 | .60 |

Summit Meeting, Dec. 2, 1989. No. 1136
exists in a souvenir sheet of 1. Value $10.

1992 Winter Olympics,
Albertville — A174

150fr, Downhill skiing. 250fr, Cross country
skiing. 400fr, Two-man bobsled. 500fr,
Speedskating.
750fr, Slalom skiing.

## 1990, Aug. 3

| | | | | |
|---|---|---|---|---|
| 1137 | A174 | 150fr multicolored | .80 | .25 |
| 1138 | A174 | 250fr multicolored | 2.10 | .45 |
| 1139 | A174 | 400fr multicolored | 3.50 | .75 |
| 1140 | A174 | 500fr multicolored | 4.50 | 1.00 |
| | | Nos. 1137-1140 (4) | 10.90 | 2.45 |

### Souvenir Sheet

| | | | | |
|---|---|---|---|---|
| 1141 | A174 | 750fr multicolored | 6.50 | 2.00 |

Nos. 1140-1141 airmail. Nos. 1137-1140 exist in souvenir sheets of 1. Value, set $16.
For overprints and surcharge see Nos. 1182P, 1225-1230.

Pres. Bush, Pres. Gorbachev A175

### 1990, Aug. 3 Litho. Perf. 13½

| | | | | |
|---|---|---|---|---|
| 1142 | A175 | 200fr multicolored | .40 | .75 |

Summit Meeting Dec. 3, 1989. No. 1142 exists in a souvenir sheet of 1.

De Gaulle's Call for French Resistance, 50th Anniv. A176

### 1990

| | | | | |
|---|---|---|---|---|
| 1143 | A176 | 250fr multi | .45 | 1.00 |

No. 1143 exists in a souvenir sheet of 1.

A177

World Cup Soccer Championships, Italy 1990 — A178

200fr, Rudi Voller. 250fr, Uwe Bein. 300fr, Pierre Littbarski. 400fr, Jurgen Klinsmann. 450fr, Lothar Matthaus. 500fr, Andreas Brehme.
750fr, Brehme, diff. No. 1152, Player, Chateau Saint-Ange.

### 1991, Apr. 1 Litho. Perf. 13½

| | | | | |
|---|---|---|---|---|
| 1144 | A177 | 200fr multi | 1.60 | .80 |
| 1145 | A177 | 250fr multi | 2.00 | 1.00 |
| 1146 | A177 | 300fr multi | 2.40 | 1.25 |
| 1147 | A177 | 400fr multi | 3.25 | 1.90 |
| 1148 | A177 | 450fr multi | 3.25 | 1.90 |
| 1149 | A177 | 500fr multi | 4.75 | 2.00 |
| | | Nos. 1144-1149 (6) | 17.25 | 8.85 |

### Litho. & Embossed

| | | | | |
|---|---|---|---|---|
| 1150 | A178 | 1500fr gold & multi | 24.00 | 18.00 |

### Souvenir Sheets
### Litho.

| | | | | |
|---|---|---|---|---|
| 1151 | A177 | 750fr multi | 6.50 | 2.00 |

### Litho. & Embossed

| | | | | |
|---|---|---|---|---|
| 1152 | A178 | 1500fr gold & multi | 16.00 | 12.50 |

Nos. 1148-1152 are airmail. Nos. 1144-1150 exist in souvenir sheets of 1.

Christmas — A179

Paintings by Raphael: 50fr, Della Tenda Madonna. 100fr, Cowper Madonna. 150fr, Tempi Madonna. 250fr, Niccolini Madonna.

300fr, Orleans Madonna. 500fr, Solly Madonna.
750fr, Madonna of the Fish.

### 1991, Apr. 1 Litho.

| | | | | |
|---|---|---|---|---|
| 1153 | A179 | 50fr multi | .40 | .25 |
| 1154 | A179 | 100fr multi | .80 | .45 |
| 1155 | A179 | 150fr multi | 1.20 | .65 |
| 1156 | A179 | 200fr multi | 2.00 | 1.00 |
| 1157 | A179 | 300fr multi | 2.40 | 1.25 |
| 1158 | A179 | 500fr multi | 4.00 | 2.00 |
| | | Nos. 1153-1158 (6) | 10.80 | 5.60 |

### Souvenir Sheet

| | | | | |
|---|---|---|---|---|
| 1159 | A179 | 750fr multi | 6.50 | 2.00 |

Nos. 1157-1159 are airmail. Nos. 1153-1158 exist in souvenir sheets of 1.

A180

World War II Battles A181

Designs: 100fr, Sinking of the Bismarck, May 27, 1941, Adm. Raeder and Adm. Tovey. 150fr, Battle of Midway, June 3, 1942, Adm. Yamamoto and Adm. Nimitz. 200fr, Guadalcanal, Oct. 7, 1942, Adm. Kondo and Adm. Halsey. 250fr, Battle of El Alamein, Oct. 23, 1942, Field Marshal Erwin Rommel, Field Marshal Montgomery. 300fr, Battle of the Bulge, Dec. 16, 1944, Gen. Guderian and Gen. Patton. 450fr, Sinking of the Yamato, Apr. 7, 1945, Adm. Kogo and Gen. MacArthur. No. 1166, 1500fr, Review of Free French Forces, July 14, 1940, Gen. Charles De Gaulle.
750fr, Boeing B-17G, Gen. Dwight Eisenhower. No. 1168, 1500fr, De Gaulle's Call for French Resistance, June 18, 1940.

### 1991, Apr. 8 Litho. Perf. 13½

| | | | | |
|---|---|---|---|---|
| 1160 | A180 | 100fr multicolored | .90 | .45 |
| 1161 | A180 | 150fr multicolored | 1.25 | .70 |
| 1162 | A180 | 200fr multicolored | 1.75 | .90 |
| 1163 | A180 | 250fr multicolored | 2.25 | 1.10 |
| 1164 | A180 | 300fr multicolored | 2.75 | 1.25 |
| 1165 | A180 | 450fr multicolored | 6.00 | 3.00 |
| a. | | Sheet of 6, #1160-1165 | 16.00 | 8.00 |

### Litho. & Embossed

| | | | | |
|---|---|---|---|---|
| 1166 | A181 | 1500fr gold & multi | 17.00 | 11.00 |

### Souvenir Sheets
### Litho.

| | | | | |
|---|---|---|---|---|
| 1167 | A180 | 750fr multicolored | 8.00 | 3.00 |

### Litho. & Embossed

| | | | | |
|---|---|---|---|---|
| 1168 | A181 | 1500fr gold & multi | 15.00 | 10.00 |

Nos. 1164-1168 are airmail. No. 1160-1166 exist in souvenir sheets of 1. Value, set $32.
For overprint see No. C177.

Doctors Without Borders — A182

### 1991, Feb. 22 Litho. Perf. 13½

| | | | | |
|---|---|---|---|---|
| 1169 | A182 | 300fr multicolored | 3.25 | 1.50 |

Telecom '91 — A183

### 1991, Jan. 15

| | | | | |
|---|---|---|---|---|
| 1170 | A183 | 150fr multi, vert. | 1.50 | 1.25 |
| 1171 | A183 | 300fr shown | 2.75 | 2.40 |

6th World Forum and Exposition on Telecommunications, Geneva, Switzerland.

American Entertainers and Films A184

Designs: 100fr, Nat King Cole Trio. 150fr, Yul Brynner, The Magnificent Seven. 250fr, Judy Garland, The Wizard of Oz. 300fr, Steve McQueen, Papillon. 500fr, Gary Cooper, Sergeant York. 600fr, Bing Crosby, High Society.
750fr, John Wayne, How the West Was Won.

### 1991, Oct. 2 Litho. Perf. 13½

| | | | | |
|---|---|---|---|---|
| 1172 | A184 | 100fr multicolored | .75 | .45 |
| 1173 | A184 | 150fr multicolored | 1.10 | .60 |
| 1174 | A184 | 250fr multicolored | 2.00 | 1.00 |
| 1175 | A184 | 300fr multicolored | 2.40 | 1.25 |
| 1176 | A184 | 500fr multicolored | 4.00 | 2.00 |
| 1177 | A184 | 600fr multicolored | 8.75 | 4.25 |
| | | Nos. 1172-1177 (6) | 19.00 | 9.55 |

### Souvenir Sheet

| | | | | |
|---|---|---|---|---|
| 1178 | A184 | 750fr multicolored | 8.00 | 3.00 |

Nos. 1176-1178 are airmail. No. 1172-1177 exist in souvenir sheets of 1.

Care Bears Promoting Environmental Protection A184a

Designs: 50fr, Care Bears circling earth, vert. 100fr, Save water, vert. 200fr, Recycle, vert. 300fr, Control noise, vert. 400fr, Elephant.
500fr, Care Bear emblem, end of rainbow. 600fr, Scout, tent, Lord Baden-Powell.

### 1991 Litho. Perf. 13½

| | | | | |
|---|---|---|---|---|
| 1178A | A184a | 50fr multi | .40 | .25 |
| 1178B | A184a | 100fr multi | .85 | .40 |
| 1178C | A184a | 200fr multi | 1.75 | .85 |
| 1178D | A184a | 300fr multi | 2.50 | 1.25 |
| 1178E | A184a | 400fr multi | 3.50 | 1.75 |
| | | Nos. 1178A-1178E (5) | 9.00 | 4.50 |

### Souvenir Sheets

| | | | | |
|---|---|---|---|---|
| 1178F | A184a | 500fr multi | 4.25 | 2.25 |
| 1178G | A184a | 600fr multi | 5.00 | 2.50 |

Nos. 1178F-1178G each contain one 39x27mm stamp. No. 1178G is airmail.

African Tourism Year — A185

100fr, Dancer, vert. 150fr, Baskets. 250fr, Drum. 300fr, Flute player, vert.

### 1991, Aug. 16 Litho. Perf. 13½

| | | | | |
|---|---|---|---|---|
| 1179 | A185 | 100fr multi | 1.25 | .60 |
| 1180 | A185 | 150fr multi | 2.00 | .90 |
| 1181 | A185 | 250fr multi | 3.25 | 1.25 |
| 1182 | A185 | 300fr multi | 3.50 | 1.60 |
| | | Nos. 1179-1182 (4) | 10.00 | 4.35 |

### Stamps of 1986-92 Surcharged in Black or Silver

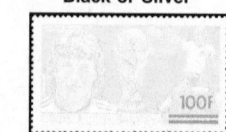

Nos. 1182A, 1182M, 1182P, 1182R Surcharged

Nos. 1182B, 1182D, 1182H, 1182I, 1182N Surcharged

Nos. 1182C, 1182E, 1182O Surcharged

Nos. 1182F, 1182J, 1182K, 1182L, 1182Q Surcharged

### 1991 Litho. Perfs. as Before

| | | | | |
|---|---|---|---|---|
| 1182A | A150 | 100fr on 400fr #1019 | .85 | .40 |
| 1182B | A154 | 100fr on 400fr #1045 | .85 | .40 |
| 1182C | A156 | 100fr on 400fr #1052 | .85 | .40 |
| 1182D | A159 | 100fr on 170fr #1065 | .85 | .40 |
| 1182E | A159 | 100fr on 400fr #1066 | .85 | .40 |
| 1182F | A160 | 100fr on 170fr #1072 | 125.00 | — |
| 1182G | A160 | 100fr on 400fr #1073 | 4.00 | 1.00 |
| 1182H | A163 | 100fr on 400fr #1092 | .85 | .40 |
| 1182I | A164 | 100fr on 400fr #1098 | .85 | .40 |
| 1182J | A165 | 100fr on 400fr #1106 | .85 | .40 |
| 1182K | A165b | 100fr on 500fr #1108G | .85 | .40 |
| 1182L | A165d | 100fr on 500fr #1108N | .85 | .40 |
| 1182M | A166 | 100fr on 400fr #1113 | .85 | .40 |
| 1182N | A167 | 100fr on 250fr #1116 | .85 | .40 |
| 1182O | A172 | 100fr on 400fr #1135 | .85 | .40 |
| 1182P | A174 | 100fr on 400fr #1139 | .85 | .40 |
| 1182Q | A164 | 300fr on 450fr #1099 | 2.50 | 1.25 |
| 1182R | AP14 | 300fr on 450fr #C170 | 2.50 | 1.25 |
| | | Nos. 1182A-1182R (18) | 145.90 | 9.10 |

Nos. 1182B-1182C, 1182E, 1182G, 1182M, 1182Q-1182R are airmail.

Visit by Pope John Paul II — A185a

### 1992, Feb. 24 Litho. Perf. 13½

| | | | | |
|---|---|---|---|---|
| 1182S | A185a | 150fr multicolored | 3.00 | 1.75 |

1994 World Cup
Soccer, US — A186

A186a

Player, World Cup Trophy and scenes of Atlanta: 100fr, Little Five Points. 300fr, Fulton County Stadium. 400fr, Inman Park. 500fr, High Museum of Art.
1000fr, Intelsat VI, Capitol. No. 1187A, Player in white shirt. No. 1187B, Player in red.

| 1992, Apr. 27 | | Litho. | Perf. 13½ | |
|---|---|---|---|---|
| 1183 | A186 | 100fr multi | 1.10 | .40 |
| 1184 | A186 | 300fr multi | 3.25 | 1.25 |
| 1185 | A186 | 400fr multi | 4.50 | 1.75 |
| 1186 | A186 | 500fr multi | 5.50 | 2.25 |
| | | Nos. 1183-1186 (4) | 14.35 | 5.65 |

**Souvenir Sheets**

| 1187 | A186 | 1000fr multi | 8.00 | 4.00 |
|---|---|---|---|---|

**Litho. & Embossed**

| 1187A | A186a | 1500fr gold & | | |
|---|---|---|---|---|
| | | multi | 12.00 | 12.00 |

**Souvenir Sheet**

| 1187B | A186a | 1500fr gold & | | |
|---|---|---|---|---|
| | | multi | 20.00 | 20.00 |

Nos. 1186-1187B are airmail. Nos. 1183-1187A exist in souvenir sheets of 1.

Lions Intl., 75th
Anniv. — A187

| 1992, May 22 | | Litho. | Perf. 13½ | |
|---|---|---|---|---|
| 1188 | A187 | 150fr blue & multi | 1.20 | .45 |
| 1188A | A187 | 400fr lilac rose & | | |
| | | multi | 3.25 | 1.50 |

Anniversaries and
Events — A188

Designs: 100fr, Satellite ERS-1 in orbit. 150fr, Vase with Fourteen Sunflowers, by Vincent van Gogh. 200fr, Napoleon Bonaparte. 250fr, Henri Dunant, Red Cross workers. 300fr, Brandenburg Gate. 400fr, Pope John Paul II. 450fr, Garry Kasparov, Anatoly Karpov, chess pieces. 500fr, African child, dove, emblems of Rotary and Lions Clubs.

| 1992, Nov. 10 | | Litho. | Perf. 13½ | |
|---|---|---|---|---|
| 1189 | A188 | 100fr multicolored | 1.00 | .45 |
| 1190 | A188 | 150fr multicolored | 1.50 | .75 |
| 1191 | A188 | 200fr multicolored | 2.25 | 1.00 |
| 1192 | A188 | 250fr multicolored | 2.50 | 1.25 |
| 1193 | A188 | 300fr multicolored | 3.25 | 1.50 |
| 1194 | A188 | 400fr multicolored | 4.25 | 2.10 |
| 1195 | A188 | 450fr multicolored | 4.75 | 2.25 |
| 1196 | A188 | 500fr multicolored | 5.50 | 2.50 |
| | | Nos. 1189-1196 (8) | 25.00 | 11.80 |

Intl. Space Year (#1189). Vincent van Gogh, cent. of death (in 1990) (#1190). Napolean Bonaparte, 170th anniv. of death (in 1991) (#1191). Founding of Red Cross (in 1864) (#1192). Brandenburg Gate, bicent. (#1193). Pope John Paul II's visit to Africa in 1989 (#1194). World Chess Championships (#1195). Lions Intl., 75th anniv. (#1196).
Nos. 1195-1196 are airmail. Nos. 1189-1196 exist in souvenir sheets of one.
For overprint see No. C178.

Anniversaries and Events — A189

Designs: 200fr, The Devil and Kate, Antonin Dvorak. 300fr, Antonio Vivaldi. 350fr, Graf Zeppelin, flying boat, Count Ferdinand von Zeppelin. 400fr, English Channel Euro-Tunnel Train. 450fr, Konrad Adenauer, Brandenburg Gate. 500fr, Japanese naval ensign, Emperor Hirohito.
750fr, Tunnel Train, diff.

| 1992, Nov. 10 | | | | |
|---|---|---|---|---|
| 1197 | A189 | 200fr multicolored | 2.00 | .40 |
| 1198 | A189 | 300fr multicolored | 2.75 | .40 |
| 1199 | A189 | 350fr multicolored | 3.25 | .45 |
| 1200 | A189 | 400fr multicolored | 3.50 | .65 |
| 1201 | A189 | 450fr multicolored | 4.00 | .75 |
| a. | | Souvenir sheet of 2, #1199, 1201 | 6.50 | 1.50 |
| 1202 | A189 | 750fr multicolored | 4.50 | 1.10 |
| | | Nos. 1197-1202 (6) | 20.00 | 3.75 |

**Souvenir Sheet**

| 1203 | A189 | 750fr multicolored | 6.50 | 1.50 |
|---|---|---|---|---|

Antonin Dvorak, 90th anniv. of death (in 1994) (#1197). Antonio Vivaldi, 250th anniv. of death (in 1991) (#1198). Count Ferdinand von Zeppelin, 75th anniv. of death (#1199). Opening of English Channel Tunnel (in 1994) (#1200, 1203). Konrad Adenauer, 25th anniv. of death, Brandenburg Gate, bicent. (#1201). Death of Emperor Hirohito (in 1989) (#1202).
Nos. 1201-1203 are airmail. Nos. 1197-1202 exist imperf. and in souvenir sheets of one. No. 1203 exists imperf. and contains one 60x42mm stamp.

Anniversaries and
Events — A190

Designs: 50fr, Modern Times, film by Charlie Chaplin. 100fr, Expo '92 Seville, Columbus. 150fr, St. Peter's Square, Rome. 200fr, Marlene Dietrich, roses. 250fr, Michael Schumacher, Benetton Ford B192. 300fr, Mercury rocket, John Glenn. 400fr, Bill Koch, America 3. 450fr, Mark Rypien, quarterback of Washington Redskins. 500fr, Rescue of Intelsat VI by shuttle Endeavour.

| 1992, Dec. 3 | | | | |
|---|---|---|---|---|
| 1204 | A190 | 50fr multicolored | .45 | .25 |
| 1205 | A190 | 100fr multicolored | .90 | .40 |
| 1206 | A190 | 150fr multicolored | 1.40 | .65 |
| 1207 | A190 | 200fr multicolored | 1.90 | .85 |
| 1208 | A190 | 250fr multicolored | 2.25 | 1.10 |
| 1209 | A190 | 300fr multicolored | 2.75 | 1.25 |
| 1210 | A190 | 400fr multicolored | 3.50 | 1.75 |
| 1211 | A190 | 450fr multicolored | 4.00 | 1.90 |
| 1212 | A190 | 500fr multicolored | 4.50 | 2.10 |
| | | Nos. 1204-1212 (9) | 21.65 | 10.25 |

Discovery of America, 500th anniv. (#1205). First US orbital space flight, 30th anniv. (#1209). Americas Cup yacht race (#1210). Super Bowl XXVI football game (#1211).
Nos. 1210-1212 are airmail. Nos. 1204-1212 exist in souvenir sheets of one.

Intl. Conference on
Nutrition,
Rome — A191

| 1992, Nov. 10 | | Litho. | Perf. 13½ | |
|---|---|---|---|---|
| 1213 | A191 | 150fr multi | 1.20 | .70 |
| 1214 | A191 | 400fr multi | 3.25 | 1.90 |
| 1215 | A191 | 500fr multi | 4.00 | 2.25 |
| | | Nos. 1213-1215 (3) | 8.45 | 4.85 |

**Nos. 1116-1120 Ovptd. in Silver**

| 1992, Feb. 24 | | Litho. | Perf. 13½ | |
|---|---|---|---|---|
| 1216 | A167 | 250fr multicolored | 2.50 | 1.10 |
| 1217 | A167 | 300fr multicolored | 3.00 | 1.40 |
| 1218 | A167 | 400fr multicolored | 4.00 | 1.75 |
| 1219 | A167 | 450fr multicolored | 4.75 | 2.00 |
| | | Nos. 1216-1219 (4) | 14.25 | 6.25 |

**Souvenir Sheet**

| 1220 | A167 | 750fr multicolored | 9.00 | 4.50 |
|---|---|---|---|---|

Nos. 1219-1220 are airmail. Nos. 1216-1219 exist in souvenir sheets of 1. Sold for 100fr extra.

Nos. 1130-1134
Ovptd. in Gold

| 1992, Feb. 24 | | Litho. | Perf. 13½ | |
|---|---|---|---|---|
| 1221 | A171 | 200fr multicolored | 2.00 | .80 |
| 1222 | A171 | 250fr multicolored | 2.50 | 1.00 |
| 1223 | A171 | 300fr multicolored | 3.00 | 1.25 |
| 1224 | A171 | 450fr multicolored | 5.00 | 2.00 |
| | | Nos. 1221-1224 (4) | 12.50 | 5.05 |

**Souvenir Sheet**

| 1225 | A171 | 750fr multicolored | 8.00 | 3.00 |
|---|---|---|---|---|

Nos. 1137
Ovptd. in Gold

Nos. 1138
Ovptd. in Gold

Nos. 1139
Ovptd. in Gold

Nos. 1141
Ovptd. in Gold

| 1992 | | Litho. | Perf. 13½ | |
|---|---|---|---|---|
| 1226 | A174 | 150fr multicolored | 1.45 | .70 |
| 1227 | A174 | 250fr multicolored | 2.00 | 1.10 |
| 1228 | A174 | 400fr multicolored | 3.25 | 1.75 |
| 1229 | A174 | 500fr multicolored | 4.25 | 2.10 |
| | | Nos. 1226-1229 (4) | 10.95 | 5.65 |

**Souvenir Sheet**

| 1230 | A174 | 750fr multicolored | 6.25 | 3.00 |
|---|---|---|---|---|

Overprints read: 150fr, 750fr, "SLALOM GEANT / Alberto Tomba, Italie." 250fr, "SKI NORDIQUE / Vegard Ulvang, Norvege." 400fr, "BOB A DEUX / G. Weder / D Acklin, Suisse." 500fr, "PATINAGE DE VITESSE / Olaf Zinke 1000m., Allemagne."

A192

1994 World Cup
Soccer
Championships,
US — A192a

Soccer player, city skyline: 100fr, San Francisco. 300fr, Washington, DC. 400fr, Detroit. 500fr, Dallas.
1000fr, New York.

| 1993, Sept. 24 | | Litho. | Perf. 13½ | |
|---|---|---|---|---|
| 1233 | A192 | 100fr multicolored | 1.20 | .45 |
| 1234 | A192 | 300fr multicolored | 2.00 | 1.50 |
| 1235 | A192 | 400fr multicolored | 3.25 | 1.90 |
| 1236 | A192 | 500fr multicolored | 4.00 | 2.40 |
| | | Nos. 1233-1236 (4) | 10.45 | 6.25 |

**Souvenir Sheet**

| 1237 | A192 | 1000fr multicolored | 8.00 | 5.50 |
|---|---|---|---|---|

**Litho. & Embossed**

| 1237A | A192a | 1500fr gold & | | |
|---|---|---|---|---|
| | | multi | 16.00 | 12.50 |

Nos. 1236-1237A are airmail. No. 1237A exists in a souvenir sheet of 1.

**Miniature Sheet**

Dinosaurs — A193

No. 1238: a, 50fr, Euparkeria. b, 50fr, Plateosaurus. c, 50fr, Anchisaurus. d, 50fr, Ornithosuchus. e, 100fr, Megalosaurus. f, 100fr, Scelidosaurus. g, 100fr, Camptosaurus. h, 100fr, Ceratosaurus. i, 250fr, Ouranosaurus. j, 250fr, Dicraeosaurus. k, 250fr, Tarbosaurus. l, 250fr, Gorgosaurus. m, 250fr, Polacanthus. n, 250fr, Deinonychus. o, 250fr, Corythosaurus. p, 250fr, Spinosaurus.
1000fr, Tyrannosaurus rex.

**1993, Oct. 27**

| 1238 | A193 | Sheet of 16, #a.-p. | 25.00 | 15.00 |
|---|---|---|---|---|

**Souvenir Sheet**

| 1239 | A193 | 1000fr multicolored | 10.00 | 4.50 |
|---|---|---|---|---|

No. 1239 is airmail and contains one 50x60mm stamp.

Nos. 1088-1094 Ovptd.
in Silver

| 1993, Feb. 24 | | Litho. | Perf. 13½ | |
|---|---|---|---|---|
| 1240 | A163 | 50fr multicolored | .45 | .25 |
| 1241 | A163 | 100fr multicolored | 1.10 | .50 |
| 1242 | A163 | 150fr multicolored | 1.75 | .65 |
| 1243 | A163 | 300fr multicolored | 3.25 | 1.40 |
| 1244 | A163 | 400fr multicolored | 3.75 | 1.90 |
| 1245 | A163 | 450fr multicolored | 4.75 | 2.00 |
| | | Nos. 1240-1245 (6) | 15.05 | 6.70 |

**Souvenir Sheet**

| 1246 | A163 | 750fr multicolored | 8.00 | 3.25 |
|---|---|---|---|---|

Nos. 1244-1246 are airmail.

A194

1994 Winter
Olympic Games,
Lillehammer
A195

Views of Lillehammer: 150fr, Ice hockey. 250fr, Bobsled. 400fr, Biathlon. 450fr, Ski jump.
1000fr, Slalom skiing. 1500fr, Ice skating.

| | | | | |
|---|---|---|---|---|
| **1993, July 16** | | **Litho.** | | **Perf. 13½** |
| 1247 | A194 | 150fr multicolored | 1.25 | .65 |
| 1248 | A194 | 250fr multicolored | 2.75 | 1.25 |
| 1249 | A194 | 400fr multicolored | 4.25 | 2.10 |
| 1250 | A194 | 450fr multicolored | 4.75 | 2.25 |
| | *Nos. 1247-1250 (4)* | | 13.00 | 6.25 |
| | **Souvenir Sheet** | | | |
| 1251 | A194 | 1000fr multicolored | 10.00 | 5.00 |
| | **Litho. & Embossed** | | | |
| 1252 | A195 | 1500fr gold & multi | 16.00 | 12.50 |

Nos. 1249-1252 are airmail.
For overprints see #1267A-1267E.

A196

1996
Summer
Olympic
Games,
Atlanta —
A197

Event, scenes of Atlanta: 150fr, Soccer, "Little White House." 250fr, Cycling, Georgia World Congress Center. 400fr, Basketball, underground Atlanta. 500fr, Baseball, new Georgia Railroad.
1000fr, Table tennis, Atlanta at night. 1500fr, Running, Georgia State Capitol, Olympic torch.

| | | | | |
|---|---|---|---|---|
| **1993, July 16** | | **Litho.** | | **Perf. 13½** |
| 1253 | A196 | 150fr multi | 1.50 | .65 |
| 1254 | A196 | 250fr multi | 2.75 | 1.25 |
| 1255 | A196 | 400fr multi | 4.75 | 2.10 |
| 1256 | A196 | 500fr multi | 6.00 | 2.50 |
| | *Nos. 1253-1256 (4)* | | 15.00 | 6.50 |
| | **Souvenir Sheet** | | | |
| 1257 | A196 | 1000fr multi | 10.00 | 5.00 |
| | **Litho. & Embossed** | | | |
| 1257A | A197 | 1500fr gold & multi | 16.00 | 12.50 |

Nos. 1256-1257A are airmail.
#1253-1256 exist in souvenir sheets of 1.

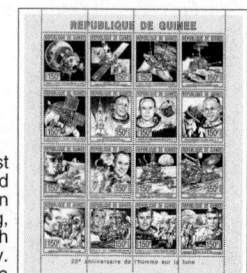

First
Manned
Moon
Landing,
25th
Anniv.
A197a

d, Luna 3, 1959. e, Ranger 7, 1964. f, Luna 9, 1966. g, Surveyor 1, 1966. h, Lunar Orbiter 1, 1966. i, Launch of Apollo 11, Neil Armstrong, 1969. j, Michael Collins, Apollo 11 command module. k, Apollo 11 landing on Moon, "Buzz" Aldrin. l, Apollo 12, 1969. m, Apollo 13, 1969. n, Luna 16, 1970. o, Luna 17,

1970. p, Apollo 14, 1971. q, Apollo 15, 1971. r, Apollo 16, 1972. s, Apollo 17, 1972.

| | | | | |
|---|---|---|---|---|
| **1993, July 27** | | **Litho.** | | **Perf. 13½** |
| | **Sheet of 16** | | | |
| 1257B | A197a | 150fr #d.-s. | 25.00 | 12.25 |

D-Day Landings, Normandy, 50th Anniv. — A198

Battle scenes and: No. 1258a, 150fr, Field Marshal Irwin Rommel (1891-1944), Germany. b, 600fr, Gen. Dwight D. Eisenhower (1890-1969), Allies. c, 150fr, Gen. George S. Patton, Jr. (1885-1945), Allies.
Battle of the Bulge, 1944: No. 1259a, 150fr, Lt. Gen. William H. Simpson. b, 600fr, Battle scene. c, 150fr, Gen. Heinz Guderian (1888-1954).
Austerlitz, Dec. 2, 1805: No. 1260a, 150fr, John I, Prince of Liechtenstein (1760-1836). b, 600fr, Napoleon I. c, 150fr, Marshal Joachim Murat (1767-1815).
Battle of Borodino, Sept. 7, 1812: No. 1261a, 150fr, Marshal Michael Ney (1769-1815). b, 600fr, Battle scene. c, 150fr, Prince Pyotr Ivanovich Bagration (1765-1812).

| | | | | |
|---|---|---|---|---|
| **1994, Jan. 26** | | **Litho.** | | **Perf. 13½** |
| 1258 | A198 | Strip of 3, #a.-c. | 11.00 | 4.75 |
| 1259 | A198 | Strip of 3, #a.-c. | 11.00 | 4.75 |
| 1260 | A198 | Strip of 3, #a.-c. | 11.00 | 4.75 |
| 1261 | A198 | Strip of 3, #a.-c. | 11.00 | 4.75 |
| | *Nos. 1258-1261 (4)* | | 44.00 | 19.00 |

No. 1258b, 1259b, 1260b, 1261b are 60x46mm. Nos. 1258-1261 are each a continuous design.

Astronomers and Spacecraft — A199

Designs: a, 300fr, Johannes Kepler, Pluto probe. b, 500fr, Copernicus, Galileo probe. c, 300fr, Sir Isaac Newton, Voyager.

| | | | | |
|---|---|---|---|---|
| **1994, Jan. 26** | | | | |
| 1262 | A199 | Strip of 3, #a.-c. | 15.00 | 6.75 |

No. 1262b is 60x46mm. No. 1262 has a continuous design.

Nos. 1233-1237
Ovptd. in Silver

| | | | | |
|---|---|---|---|---|
| **1994, Sept. 14** | | **Litho.** | | **Perf. 13½** |
| 1263 | A192 | 100fr multicolored | 1.00 | .50 |
| 1264 | A192 | 300fr multicolored | 3.00 | 1.75 |
| 1265 | A192 | 400fr multicolored | 4.00 | 2.25 |
| 1266 | A192 | 500fr multicolored | 4.75 | 2.50 |
| | *Nos. 1263-1266 (4)* | | 12.75 | 7.00 |
| | **Souvenir Sheet** | | | |
| 1267 | A192 | 1000fr multicolored | 10.00 | 5.00 |

Nos. 1266-1267 are airmail.

No. 1247 Overprinted
in Gold

No. 1248 Overprinted
in Gold

No. 1249 Overprinted
in Gold

No. 1250 Overprinted
in Gold

| | | | | |
|---|---|---|---|---|
| **1994, Sept. 14** | | **Litho.** | | **Perf. 13½** |
| 1267A | A194 | 150fr multi | 1.25 | .65 |
| 1267B | A194 | 250fr multi | 2.40 | 1.25 |
| 1267C | A194 | 400fr multi | 3.75 | 1.90 |
| 1267D | A194 | 450fr multi | 4.50 | 2.10 |
| | *Nos. 1267A-1267D (4)* | | 11.90 | 5.90 |
| | **Souvenir Sheet** | | | |
| 1267E | A194 | 1000fr multi | 10.00 | 5.00 |

Overprints read: 1000fr, T. MOE / U.S.A.
Nos. 1267C-1267E are airmail.

Birds — A200

150fr, Carduelis carduelis. 250fr, Luscinia megarhynchos. No. 1270, Serinus canaria. No. 1271, Fringilla coelebs. No. 1272, Carduelis chloris.
No. 1273, Erithacus rubecula.

| | | | | |
|---|---|---|---|---|
| **1995, Aug. 31** | | **Litho.** | | **Perf. 13** |
| 1268 | A200 | 150fr multicolored | .50 | .25 |
| 1269 | A200 | 250fr multicolored | .80 | .35 |
| 1270 | A200 | 500fr multicolored | 1.60 | .80 |
| 1271 | A200 | 500fr multicolored | 1.60 | .80 |
| 1272 | A200 | 500fr multicolored | 1.60 | .80 |
| | *Nos. 1268-1272 (5)* | | 6.10 | 3.00 |
| | **Souvenir Sheet** | | | |
| 1273 | A200 | 1000fr multicolored | 6.00 | 3.00 |

No. 1273 contains one 32x40mm stamp.

1996 Summer
Olympics,
Atlanta — A201

| | | | | |
|---|---|---|---|---|
| **1995, Aug. 5** | | | | |
| 1274 | A201 | 150fr Javelin | .50 | .25 |
| 1275 | A201 | 250fr Boxing | .80 | .40 |
| 1276 | A201 | 500fr Basketball | 1.60 | .80 |
| 1277 | A201 | 500fr Weight lifting | 1.60 | .80 |
| 1278 | A201 | 500fr Soccer | 1.60 | .80 |
| | *Nos. 1274-1278 (5)* | | 6.10 | 3.05 |
| | **Souvenir Sheet** | | | |
| 1279 | A201 | 1000fr Archery | 4.75 | 2.50 |

No. 1279 contains one 32x40mm stamp.

African Animals
A202

Designs: 150fr, Cercopithecus mona, vert. 250fr, Cercopithecus aethiops, vert. No. 1282, Galagoides demidovi, vert. No. 1283, Manis gigantea. No. 1284, Lepus crawshayi.
1000fr, Aonyx capensis, vert.

| | | | | |
|---|---|---|---|---|
| **1995, Sept. 25** | | | | |
| 1280 | A202 | 150fr multicolored | .50 | .25 |
| 1281 | A202 | 250fr multicolored | .80 | .35 |
| 1282 | A202 | 500fr multicolored | 1.60 | .80 |
| 1283 | A202 | 500fr multicolored | 1.60 | .80 |
| 1284 | A202 | 500fr multicolored | 1.60 | .80 |
| | *Nos. 1280-1284 (5)* | | 6.10 | 3.00 |
| | **Souvenir Sheet** | | | |
| 1285 | A202 | 1000fr multicolored | 6.00 | 3.00 |

1998 World Cup
Soccer
Championships,
France — A203

Opposing two players wearing: No. 1288, Yellow shirt & blue shorts, red shirt & white shorts. No. 1289, Red & white uniform, red shirt & white shorts. No. 1290, Striped shirt & blue shorts, red & yellow shirt & green shorts.
1000fr, Three players.

| | | | | |
|---|---|---|---|---|
| **1995, Oct. 30** | | **Litho.** | | **Perf. 13** |
| 1286 | A203 | 150fr multicolored | .50 | .25 |
| 1287 | A203 | 250fr multicolored | .80 | .35 |
| 1288 | A203 | 500fr multicolored | 1.60 | .80 |
| 1289 | A203 | 500fr multicolored | 1.60 | .80 |
| 1290 | A203 | 500fr multicolored | 1.60 | .80 |
| | *Nos. 1286-1290 (5)* | | 6.10 | 3.00 |
| | **Souvenir Sheet** | | | |
| 1291 | A203 | 1000fr multicolored | 6.00 | 3.00 |

No. 1291 contains one 32x40mm stamp.

Domestic
Cats — A204

150fr, Tortoiseshell. 250fr, Tabby and white. No. 1294, Tortoiseshell and white longhair. No. 1295, Red tabby. No. 1296, Smoke longhaired.
1000fr, Chinchilla.

| | | | | |
|---|---|---|---|---|
| **1995, July 25** | | | | |
| 1292 | A204 | 150fr multicolored | .65 | .40 |
| 1293 | A204 | 250fr multicolored | 1.10 | .55 |
| 1294 | A204 | 500fr multicolored | 2.10 | 1.25 |
| 1295 | A204 | 500fr multicolored | 2.10 | 1.25 |
| 1296 | A204 | 500fr multicolored | 2.10 | 1.25 |
| | *Nos. 1292-1296 (5)* | | 8.05 | 4.70 |
| | **Souvenir Sheet** | | | |
| | **Perf. 12½** | | | |
| 1297 | A204 | 1000fr multicolored | 4.50 | 2.50 |

No. 1297 contains one 40x32mm stamp.

Production of
Electrical
Power
A205

Designs: 100fr, Banéa Dam. 150fr, Water Chamber, Donkea. 200fr, Tinkisso Spillway, vert. 250fr, Cascades of Grand Falls. 500fr, Building, Kinkon.

| | | | | |
|---|---|---|---|---|
| **1995, July 18** | | | | **Perf. 12½** |
| 1298 | A205 | 100fr multicolored | .40 | .25 |
| 1299 | A205 | 150fr multicolored | .65 | .35 |
| 1300 | A205 | 200fr multicolored | .80 | .50 |
| 1301 | A205 | 250fr multicolored | 1.00 | .65 |
| 1302 | A205 | 500fr multicolored | 2.25 | 1.25 |
| | *Nos. 1298-1302 (5)* | | 5.10 | 3.00 |

FAO, 50th
Anniv. — A206

Designs: 200fr, Man, oxen, boy. 750fr, Instructing women, children on nutrition.

| | | | | |
|---|---|---|---|---|
| **1995, Oct. 16** | | | | **Perf. 13** |
| 1303 | A206 | 200fr multicolored | .80 | .40 |
| 1304 | A206 | 750fr multicolored | 3.25 | 1.10 |

Light Aircraft
A207

100fr, Pup-150, UK. 150fr, Gardan GY-80
Horizon, France. 250fr, Piper Cub J-3, US. No.
1308, Valmet L-90TP Redigo, Finland. No.
1309, Pilatus PC-6 Porter, Switzerland. No.
1310, Piper PA-28 Cherokee Arrow, US.
1000fr, Stol DO-27, Germany.

| | 1995, Oct. 1 | | Perf. 12½ | |
|---|---|---|---|---|
| 1305 | A207 | 100fr multicolored | .40 | .25 |
| 1306 | A207 | 150fr multicolored | .65 | .25 |
| 1307 | A207 | 250fr multicolored | 1.10 | .40 |
| 1308 | A207 | 500fr multicolored | 2.10 | .75 |
| 1309 | A207 | 500fr multicolored | 2.10 | .75 |
| 1310 | A207 | 500fr multicolored | 2.10 | .75 |
| | | Nos. 1305-1310 (6) | 8.45 | 3.15 |

**Souvenir Sheet**

| 1311 | A207 | 1000fr multicolored | 4.50 | 2.50 |
|---|---|---|---|---|

No. 1311 contains one 40x32mm stamp.

Flowers — A208

100fr, Sprekelia formosissima. 150fr, Rudbeckia purpurea. 250fr, Meconopsis
betonicifolia. No. 1315, Gail Borden rose. No.
1316, Lathyrus odoratus. No. 1317, Iris
starshine.
1000fr, Cypripedium alma gaevert.

| | 1995, Oct. 12 | | | |
|---|---|---|---|---|
| 1312 | A208 | 100fr multicolored | .40 | .25 |
| 1313 | A208 | 150fr multicolored | .65 | .25 |
| 1314 | A208 | 250fr multicolored | 1.10 | .40 |
| 1315 | A208 | 500fr multicolored | 2.10 | .75 |
| 1316 | A208 | 500fr multicolored | 2.10 | .75 |
| 1317 | A208 | 500fr multicolored | 2.10 | .75 |
| | | Nos. 1312-1317 (6) | 8.45 | 3.15 |

**Souvenir Sheet**

| 1318 | A208 | 1000fr multicolored | 4.50 | 2.50 |
|---|---|---|---|---|

No. 1318 contains one 32x40mm stamp.

Historic Buses
A209

250fr, 1832 Omnibus. 300fr, 1898 Daimler.
400fr, 1904 V.H. Bussing. 450fr, 1906 Autobus
M.A.N. 500fr, 1904 Autocar M.A.N.

| | 1995, Dec. 3 | Litho. | Perf. 12½ | |
|---|---|---|---|---|
| 1319 | A209 | 250fr multicolored | .65 | .35 |
| 1320 | A209 | 300fr multicolored | .75 | .45 |
| 1321 | A209 | 400fr multicolored | .80 | .60 |
| 1322 | A209 | 450fr multicolored | .90 | .60 |
| 1323 | A209 | 500fr multicolored | .95 | .75 |
| | | Nos. 1319-1323 (5) | 4.05 | 2.75 |

Arabian
Horses — A210

Various horses.

| | 1995 | **Background Colors** | | |
|---|---|---|---|---|
| 1324 | A210 | 100fr dk bl, vert. | .40 | .25 |
| 1325 | A210 | 150fr tan, vert. | .65 | .25 |
| 1326 | A210 | 250fr lt bl, vert. | .90 | .40 |
| 1327 | A210 | 500fr pink, vert. | 1.20 | .75 |
| 1328 | A210 | 500fr lilac, vert. | 1.20 | .75 |
| 1329 | A210 | 500fr sage | 1.20 | .75 |
| | | Nos. 1324-1329 (6) | 5.55 | 3.15 |

**Souvenir Sheet**

| 1330 | A210 | 1000fr white & gray | 4.75 | 3.00 |
|---|---|---|---|---|

No. 1330 contains one 32x40mm stamp.

Mushrooms — A211

150fr, Leccinum nigrescens. 250fr, Boletus
rhodoxanthus. No. 1333, Paxillus involutus.
No. 1334, Cantharellus lutescens. No. 1335,
Xerocomus rubellus.
1000fr, Gymnopilus junonius.

| | 1995 | Litho. | Perf. 12½ | |
|---|---|---|---|---|
| 1331 | A211 | 150fr multicolored | .40 | .25 |
| 1332 | A211 | 250fr multicolored | .75 | .40 |
| 1333 | A211 | 500fr multicolored | .95 | .75 |
| 1334 | A211 | 500fr multicolored | .95 | .75 |
| 1335 | A211 | 500fr multicolored | .95 | .75 |
| | | Nos. 1331-1335 (5) | 4.00 | 2.90 |

**Souvenir Sheet**

| 1336 | A211 | 1000fr multicolored | 5.00 | 3.00 |
|---|---|---|---|---|

No. 1336 contains one 32x40mm stamp.

Tourism — A212

200fr, Mountain cliff. 750fr, Young child.
1000fr, Women carrying wood.

| | 1996, Sept. 5 | Litho. | Perf. 12½ | |
|---|---|---|---|---|
| 1337 | A212 | 200fr multicolored | .80 | .40 |
| 1338 | A212 | 750fr multicolored | 3.50 | 1.20 |
| 1339 | A212 | 1000fr multicolored | 4.50 | 1.75 |
| | | Nos. 1337-1339 (3) | 8.80 | 3.35 |

Dogs — A213

200fr, Bull terrier. 250fr, Elkhound. 300fr,
Akita. 400fr, Collie. 450fr, Rottweiler. 500fr,
Boxer.
1000fr, German pointer.

| | 1996, Oct. 20 | | | |
|---|---|---|---|---|
| 1340 | A213 | 200fr multi | .80 | .30 |
| 1341 | A213 | 250fr multi | .95 | .35 |
| 1342 | A213 | 300fr multi | 1.20 | .45 |
| 1343 | A213 | 400fr multi | 1.40 | .60 |
| 1344 | A213 | 450fr multi | 1.60 | .65 |
| 1345 | A213 | 500fr multi | 2.10 | .75 |
| | | Nos. 1340-1345 (6) | 8.05 | 3.10 |

**Souvenir Sheet**
**Perf. 13**

| 1346 | A213 | 1000fr multi | 4.00 | 2.50 |
|---|---|---|---|---|

No. 1346 contains one 32x40mm stamp.

Mushrooms — A214

200fr, Chestnut. 250fr, Granular. 300fr,
Destroying angel. 400fr, Milky blue. 450fr, Violet cortinarius. 500fr, Rough-stemmed.
1000fr, Hygrophorus.

| | 1996, Dec. 20 | Litho. | Perf. 12½ | |
|---|---|---|---|---|
| 1347 | A214 | 200fr multicolored | .80 | .30 |
| 1348 | A214 | 250fr multicolored | .95 | .35 |
| 1349 | A214 | 300fr multicolored | 1.20 | .45 |
| 1350 | A214 | 400fr multicolored | 1.40 | .60 |
| 1351 | A214 | 450fr multicolored | 1.50 | .65 |
| 1352 | A214 | 500fr multicolored | 2.00 | .75 |
| | | Nos. 1347-1352 (6) | 7.85 | 3.10 |

**Souvenir Sheet**
**Perf. 13**

| 1353 | A214 | 1000fr multicolored | 4.00 | 2.50 |
|---|---|---|---|---|

No. 1353 contains one 32x40mm stamp.

Locomotives
A215

Designs: 200fr, Tom Thumb, 1829. 250fr,
Genf, 1858. 300fr, Dübs and Company, 1873.
400fr, W.G. Bagnall of Castle Engine Works,
1932. 450fr, Werner von Siemens, 1879.
500fr, North London Tramways Co., 1885-89.
1000fr, General, 1862.

| | 1996, Aug. 30 | | Perf. 12½ | |
|---|---|---|---|---|
| 1354 | A215 | 200fr multicolored | .80 | .30 |
| 1355 | A215 | 250fr multicolored | 1.00 | .40 |
| 1356 | A215 | 300fr multicolored | 1.25 | .45 |
| 1357 | A215 | 400fr multicolored | 1.40 | .60 |
| 1358 | A215 | 450fr multicolored | 1.75 | .65 |
| 1359 | A215 | 500fr multicolored | 2.25 | .75 |
| | | Nos. 1354-1359 (6) | 8.45 | 3.15 |

**Souvenir Sheet**

| 1360 | A215 | 1000fr multicolored | 4.50 | 2.50 |
|---|---|---|---|---|

Nos. 1355, 1358 are each 68x27mm. No.
1360 contains one 40x32mm stamp.

Cats — A216

200fr, Tortoiseshell short-hair. 250fr, Black
and white short-hair. 300fr, Japanese. 400fr,
Himalayan. 450fr, Brown long-hair. 500fr, Blue
Persian.
1000fr, Tortoiseshell long-hair.

| | 1996, Nov. 15 | | Perf. 12½ | |
|---|---|---|---|---|
| 1361 | A216 | 200fr multicolored | .80 | .30 |
| 1362 | A216 | 250fr multicolored | .95 | .40 |
| 1363 | A216 | 300fr multicolored | 1.20 | .45 |
| 1364 | A216 | 400fr multicolored | 1.40 | .60 |
| 1365 | A216 | 450fr multicolored | 1.60 | .65 |
| 1366 | A216 | 500fr multicolored | 2.10 | .75 |
| | | Nos. 1361-1366 (6) | 8.05 | 3.15 |

**Souvenir Sheet**

| 1367 | A216 | 1000fr multicolored | 4.00 | 2.50 |
|---|---|---|---|---|

No. 1367 contains one 32x40mm stamp.

Birds — A217

Designs: 200fr, Carduelis cucullata. 250fr,
Uraeginthus bengalus. 300fr, Lonchura cas-
taneothorax. 400fr, Amadina erythrocephala.
450fr, Chloebia gouldiae. 500fr, Euplectes
orix.
1000fr, Poephila guttata.

| | 1996, Sept. 28 | | Perf. 12½ | |
|---|---|---|---|---|
| 1368 | A217 | 200fr multicolored | .80 | .30 |
| 1369 | A217 | 250fr multicolored | .95 | .40 |
| 1370 | A217 | 300fr multicolored | 1.20 | .45 |
| 1371 | A217 | 400fr multicolored | 1.40 | .60 |
| 1372 | A217 | 450fr multicolored | 1.60 | .65 |
| 1373 | A217 | 500fr multicolored | 2.10 | .75 |
| | | Nos. 1368-1373 (6) | 8.05 | 3.15 |

**Souvenir Sheet**

| 1374 | A217 | 1000fr multicolored | 4.00 | 2.50 |
|---|---|---|---|---|

No. 1374 contains one 32x40mm stamp.

Orchids — A218

Designs: 200fr, Paphiopedilum millmoore.
250fr, Paphiopedilum ernest read. 300fr,
Paphiopedilum harrisianum. 400fr, Paphiopedilum gaudianum. 450fr, Paphiopedilum
papa röhl. 500fr, Paphiopedilum sea cliffl.
1000fr, Paphiopedilum gowenanum.

| | 1997, Mar. 3 | Litho. | Perf. 12½ | |
|---|---|---|---|---|
| 1375 | A218 | 200fr multicolored | .80 | .30 |
| 1376 | A218 | 250fr multicolored | .95 | .40 |
| 1377 | A218 | 300fr multicolored | 1.20 | .45 |
| 1378 | A218 | 400fr multicolored | 1.40 | .60 |
| 1379 | A218 | 450fr multicolored | 1.60 | .65 |
| 1380 | A218 | 500fr multicolored | 2.10 | .75 |
| | | Nos. 1375-1380 (6) | 8.05 | 3.15 |

**Souvenir Sheet**

| 1381 | A218 | 1000fr multicolored | 4.00 | 2.50 |
|---|---|---|---|---|

No. 1381 contains one 32x40mm stamp.

1998 World Cup
Soccer
Championships,
France — A219

Various soccer plays.

| | 1997, Jan. 15 | | | |
|---|---|---|---|---|
| 1382 | A219 | 200fr multi, vert. | .80 | .25 |
| 1383 | A219 | 250fr multi, vert. | .95 | .25 |
| 1384 | A219 | 300fr multi, vert. | 1.20 | .30 |
| 1385 | A219 | 400fr multicolored | 1.40 | .40 |
| 1386 | A219 | 450fr multicolored | 1.60 | .45 |
| 1387 | A219 | 500fr multicolored | 2.10 | .75 |
| | | Nos. 1382-1387 (6) | 8.05 | 2.40 |

**Souvenir Sheet**

| 1388 | A219 | 1000fr Goalie at net | 4.00 | 2.50 |
|---|---|---|---|---|

No. 1388 contains one 32x40mm stamp.

Wild Animals
A220

Designs: 200fr, Giraffa camelopardalis.
250fr, Cerotherium simun, vert. 300fr,
Phacochoerus aethiopicus. 400fr, Acinonyx
jubatus. 450fr, Loxodonta africana, vert. 500fr,
Choeropsis liberiensis.
1000fr, Okapia johnstoni.

| | 1997, Apr. 15 | Litho. | Perf. 12½ | |
|---|---|---|---|---|
| 1389 | A220 | 200fr multicolored | .80 | .25 |
| 1390 | A220 | 250fr multicolored | .95 | .30 |
| 1391 | A220 | 300fr multicolored | 1.20 | .35 |
| 1392 | A220 | 400fr multicolored | 1.40 | .60 |
| 1393 | A220 | 450fr multicolored | 1.60 | .50 |
| 1394 | A220 | 500fr multicolored | 2.10 | .75 |
| | | Nos. 1389-1394 (6) | 8.05 | 2.75 |

**Souvenir Sheet**

| 1395 | A220 | 1000fr multicolored | 4.00 | 2.00 |
|---|---|---|---|---|

19th Century
Warships
A221

Designs: 200fr, Captain, England, 1870.
250fr, Konig Wilhelm, Germany, 1869. 300fr,
Téméraire, England, 1877. 400fr, Mouillage,
Italy, 1866. 450fr, Inflexible, England, 1881.
500fr, Magenta, France, 1862.
1000fr, Redoutable, France, 1878.

| | 1997, May 20 | Litho. | Perf. 12½ | |
|---|---|---|---|---|
| 1396 | A221 | 200fr multicolored | .80 | .25 |
| 1397 | A221 | 250fr multicolored | .95 | .35 |
| 1398 | A221 | 300fr multicolored | 1.20 | .35 |
| 1399 | A221 | 400fr multicolored | 1.40 | .50 |
| 1400 | A221 | 450fr multicolored | 1.60 | .50 |
| 1401 | A221 | 500fr multicolored | 2.10 | .75 |
| | | Nos. 1396-1401 (6) | 8.05 | 2.70 |

**Souvenir Sheet**

| 1402 | A221 | 1000fr multicolored | 4.00 | 2.50 |
|---|---|---|---|---|

No. 1402 contains one 32x40mm stamp.

Fish — A222

Designs: 200fr, Siganus trispilos. 250fr, Scarus niger. 300fr, Choerodon fasciata. 400fr, Naso lituratus. 450fr, Hypoplectrus gemma. 500fr, Acanthurus achilles. 1000fr, Zebrasoma flavescens.

**1997, June 15    Litho.    Perf. 13**

| | | | | |
|---|---|---|---|---|
| 1403 | A222 | 200fr multicolored | .35 | .25 |
| 1404 | A222 | 250fr multicolored | .80 | .50 |
| 1405 | A222 | 300fr multicolored | 1.00 | .60 |
| 1406 | A222 | 400fr multicolored | 1.50 | .80 |
| 1407 | A222 | 450fr multicolored | 1.75 | .90 |
| 1408 | A222 | 500fr multicolored | 1.75 | .95 |
| | | Nos. 1403-1408 (6) | 7.15 | 4.00 |

**Souvenir Sheet**
**Perf. 12½**

| 1409 | A222 | 1000fr multicolored | 3.50 | 2.50 |
|---|---|---|---|---|

No. 1409 contains one 40x32mm stamp.

 Chess Pieces — A222a

200fr, Thailand, 14th cent. 250fr, China, 1930. 300fr, Portugal, 1920. 400fr, Germany. 450fr, Russia. 500fr, Pieces by Max Ernst. 1000fr, France, 18th cent.

**1997, Oct. 20    Litho.    Perf. 13**

| | | | | |
|---|---|---|---|---|
| 1409A | A222a | 200fr multi | .65 | .45 |
| 1409B | A222a | 250fr multi | .75 | .55 |
| 1409C | A222a | 300fr multi | 1.00 | .70 |
| 1409D | A222a | 400fr multi | 1.25 | .90 |
| 1409E | A222a | 450fr multi | 1.50 | 1.00 |
| 1409F | A222a | 500fr multi | 1.75 | 1.10 |
| | | Nos. 1409A-1409F (6) | 6.90 | 4.70 |

**Souvenir Sheet**
**Perf. 12½**

| 1409G | A222a | 1000fr multi | 3.50 | 2.75 |
|---|---|---|---|---|

No. 1409G contains one 32x40mm stamp.

 Dogs — A223

200fr, Siberian husky. 250fr, Dachshund. 300fr, Boston terrier. 400fr, Basset hound. 450fr, Dalmatian. 500fr, Rottweiler. 1000fr, Golden retriever.

**1997, Nov. 10    Litho.    Perf. 12½**
**Stamp + Label**

| | | | | |
|---|---|---|---|---|
| 1410 | A223 | 200fr multi | .50 | .35 |
| 1411 | A223 | 250fr multi | .65 | .45 |
| 1412 | A223 | 300fr multi | .80 | .50 |
| 1413 | A223 | 400fr multi | .95 | .70 |
| 1414 | A223 | 450fr multi | 1.10 | .75 |
| 1415 | A223 | 500fr multi | 1.25 | .85 |
| | | Nos. 1410-1415 (6) | 5.25 | 3.60 |

**Souvenir Sheet**

| 1416 | A223 | 1000fr multi | 4.50 | 2.75 |
|---|---|---|---|---|

Nos. 1410-1415 are each printed with se-tenant label.

 Prehistoric Animals A224

200fr, Dilophosaurus. 250fr, Psittacosaurus. 300fr, Dromiceiomimus. 400fr, Stenonychosaurus. 450fr, Opisthocoelicaudia. 500fr, Ornitholestes. 1000fr, Anchiceratops.

**1997    Litho.    Perf. 12½**

| | | | | |
|---|---|---|---|---|
| 1417 | A224 | 200fr multi | .50 | .40 |
| 1418 | A224 | 250fr multi, vert. | .65 | .50 |
| 1419 | A224 | 300fr multi | .85 | .55 |
| 1420 | A224 | 400fr multi, vert. | 1.00 | .75 |
| 1421 | A224 | 450fr multi | 1.20 | .80 |
| 1422 | A224 | 500fr multi | 1.40 | .90 |
| | | Nos. 1417-1422 (6) | 5.60 | 3.90 |

**Souvenir Sheet**

| 1423 | A224 | 1000fr multicolored | 3.00 | 2.00 |
|---|---|---|---|---|

No. 1423 contains one 40x32mm stamp.

 UNICEF — A224a

Design: 200fr, Children at school, horiz. 300fr, Baby receiving inoculation, horiz. 750fr, Mother nursing child. 1500fr, Women reading, horiz.

**1997    Litho.    Perf. 13¼**

| | | | | |
|---|---|---|---|---|
| 1423A | A224a | 200fr multi | — | — |
| 1423B | A224a | 300fr multi | — | — |
| 1423C | A224a | 750fr multi | — | — |
| 1423D | A224a | 1500fr multi | — | — |

 Butterflies A225

200fr, Eueides cleobaea. 250fr, Danaus cleophile. 300fr, Dryas julia. 400fr, Dismorphia cubana. 450fr, Pyrrhocalles antiga. 500fr, Phoebis orbis. 1000fr, Morpho adonis.

**1998**

| | | | | |
|---|---|---|---|---|
| 1424 | A225 | 200fr multicolored | .50 | .40 |
| 1425 | A225 | 250fr multicolored | .70 | .50 |
| 1426 | A225 | 300fr multicolored | .85 | .55 |
| 1427 | A225 | 400fr multicolored | 1.00 | .75 |
| 1428 | A225 | 450fr multicolored | 1.20 | .80 |
| 1429 | A225 | 500fr multicolored | 1.40 | .90 |
| | | Nos. 1424-1429 (6) | 5.65 | 3.90 |

**Souvenir Sheet**

| 1430 | A225 | 1000fr multicolored | 3.00 | 2.00 |
|---|---|---|---|---|

No. 1430 contains one 40x32mm stamp.

 Environmental Protection Week A225a

Mount Nimba and frame in: 200fr, Brown. 300fr, Blue. 750fr, Green.

**1998    Litho.    Perf. 13¼x13½**

| 1430A-1430C | A225a | Set of 3 | — | — |
|---|---|---|---|---|

 Domestic Cats — A226

200fr, English shorthair bicolor. 250fr, Scottish fold. 300fr, Birman. 400fr, American coarse hair. 450fr, Snowshoe. 500fr, Maine coon. 1000fr, Malaysian.

**1998    Litho.    Perf. 12½**

| | | | | |
|---|---|---|---|---|
| 1431 | A226 | 200fr multicolored | .65 | .30 |
| 1432 | A226 | 250fr multicolored | .70 | .45 |
| 1433 | A226 | 300fr multicolored | .85 | .60 |
| 1434 | A226 | 400fr multicolored | 1.20 | .75 |
| 1435 | A226 | 450fr multicolored | 1.40 | .90 |
| 1436 | A226 | 500fr multicolored | 1.50 | .90 |
| | | Nos. 1431-1436 (6) | 6.30 | 4.00 |

**Souvenir Sheet**
**Perf. 13**

| 1437 | A226 | 1000fr multicolored | 3.00 | 2.00 |
|---|---|---|---|---|

No. 1437 contains one 32x40mm stamp.

 Diana, Princess of Wales (1961-97) — A227

Various portraits.

**1998    Litho.    Perf. 13½**
**Sheets of 9**

| | | | | |
|---|---|---|---|---|
| 1438 | A227 | 200fr #a.-i. | 8.00 | 4.00 |
| 1439 | A227 | 300fr #a.-i. | 12.00 | 6.00 |
| 1440 | A227 | 750fr #a.-i. | 30.00 | 15.00 |

**Souvenir Sheets**

| 1441 | A227 | 1500fr multicolored | 10.00 | 5.00 |
|---|---|---|---|---|
| 1442 | A227 | 2000fr multicolored | 10.00 | 5.00 |

Dated 1997.

 1998 World Cup Soccer Championships, France — A228

Various soccer plays.

**1998    Litho.    Perf. 12½**

| | | | | |
|---|---|---|---|---|
| 1443 | A228 | 200fr multi, vert. | .55 | .40 |
| 1444 | A228 | 250fr multi, vert. | .70 | .50 |
| 1445 | A228 | 300fr multi, vert. | .95 | .55 |
| 1446 | A228 | 400fr multi, vert. | 1.20 | .75 |
| 1447 | A228 | 450fr multi | 1.40 | .80 |
| 1448 | A228 | 500fr multi | 1.50 | .90 |
| | | Nos. 1443-1448 (6) | 6.30 | 3.90 |

**Souvenir Sheet**
**Perf. 13**

| 1449 | A228 | 1000fr multi | 4.50 | 2.75 |
|---|---|---|---|---|

No. 1449 contains one 32x40mm stamp.

 Old Germanic Military Uniforms — A228a

Designs: 200fr, Officer, Von Witerfeldt's Regiment. 250fr, Non-commissioned officer, Von Kanitz's Regiment. 300fr, Private, Prince Franz von Anhalt-Dessau's Regiment. 400fr, Private, Von Kalnein's Regiment. 450fr, Grenadier, Duke Ferdinand of Brunswick's Regiment. 500fr, Musician, Rekow's Guards Battalion. 1000fr, Pioneer.

**1997, Aug. 17    Litho.    Perf. 12½**

| 1449A-1449F | A228a | Set of 6 | 8.00 | 5.00 |
|---|---|---|---|---|

**Souvenir Sheet**

| 1449G | A228a | 1000fr multi | 4.00 | 2.25 |
|---|---|---|---|---|

No. 1449G contains one 32x40mm stamp.

 Steam Locomotives A229

200fr, Baldwin Locomotive Works, 0-4-2. 250fr, American Locomotive Co., 0-6-0. 300fr, Vulcan Iron Works, 0-6-0. 400fr, Baldwin Locomotive Works, 0-6-0. 450fr, H.K. Porter Co., 0-6-0. 500fr, Vulcan Iron Works, 0-6-0, diff. 1000fr, Baldwin Locomotive Works, 0-6-0, diff.

**1997, Sept. 10    Litho.    Perf. 12½**

| 1450-1455 | A229 | Set of 6 | 6.00 | 3.50 |
|---|---|---|---|---|

**Souvenir Sheet**

| 1456 | A229 | 1000fr multicolored | 5.00 | 3.00 |
|---|---|---|---|---|

No. 1456 contains one 40x32mm stamp.

 Nectophrynoides Occidentalis A230

Color of border: 200fr, green. 300fr, blue. 750fr, pale rose.

**1998    Perf. 13½**

| 1457-1459 | A230 | Set of 3 | 5.50 | 2.75 |
|---|---|---|---|---|

 Intl. Year of the Ocean — A231

Marine life — No. 1460: a, Physeter macrocephalus, neophova cinerea. b, Melanogrammus aeglefinus. c, Delphinapterus leucas. d, Megaptera novaengliae. e, Notorhynchus cependianus. f, Manta birostris. g, Delphinaterusleucas, macrozoarces americanus. h, Physalia physalis, pollachius virens. i, Manta birostris. j, Odontapis taurus. k, Thalassoma ruppelli, octopus vulgaris. l, Sebestes marinus. 1500fr, Megaptera novaengliae, diff.

**1998**

| 1460 | A231 | 200fr Sheet of 12, #a.-l. | 11.00 | 11.00 |
|---|---|---|---|---|

**Souvenir Sheet**

| 1461 | A231 | 1500fr multicolored | 9.00 | 4.25 |
|---|---|---|---|---|

Antique Cars — A232

200fr, 1932 Chrysler, 8 cylinders, US. 300fr, 1907 Napier, 60HP, England. 450fr, 1903 Mercedes, 60HP, Germany. 750fr, 1925 Fiat 509, Italy.
No. 1466: a, 1929 Alfa Romeo 6C 1750 Zagato, Italy. b, 1932 Hispano-Suiza Type 68, Spain. c, 1931 Horsch V12, Germany. d, 1909 Rolland Pilain, 16hp, France. e, 1920 McLaughlin, Canada. f, 1930 Walter 6B, Czechoslovakia.
No. 1467: a, 1914 Fischer SS, Switzerland. b, 1922 Excelsior Adex C, Belgium. c, 1912 Pilain Torpedo, France. d, 1932 Franklin, 6 cylinders, US. e, 1912 Abadal 18/24hp, Spain. f, 1923 Alvis 12/50, England.
No. 1468, 1500fr, 1925 Rolls Royce Phantom 1, England. No. 1468A, 1500fr, 1932 Ford V8, US.

**1998, Aug. 21**

| 1462-1465 | A232 | Set of 4 | 8.50 | 4.25 |
|---|---|---|---|---|

**Sheets of 6**

| 1466 | A232 | 450fr #a.-f. | 13.00 | 6.50 |
|---|---|---|---|---|
| 1467 | A232 | 750fr #a.-f. | 24.00 | 11.50 |

**Souvenir Sheets**

| 1468-1468A | A232 | Set of 2 | 18.00 | 8.50 |
|---|---|---|---|---|

Nos. 1468-1468A each contain one 56x42mm stamp.

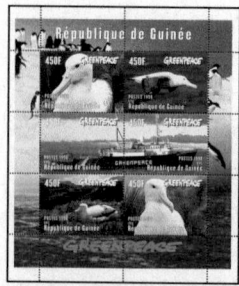 Greenpeace — A233

Designs: a, Albatross looking left. b, Albatross in flight. c, Stern of Greenpeace ship, helicopter. d, Bow of Greenpeace ship. e, Albatross nesting. f, Albatross looking right.

2000fr, Albatross with chick.

| 1998 | | Litho. | | Perf. 13½ |
|---|---|---|---|---|
| 1469 | A233 | 450fr Sheet of 6, | | |
| | | #a.-f. | 10.00 | 8.00 |

**Souvenir Sheet**

| 1470 | A233 | 2000fr multicolored | 9.50 | 4.75 |
|---|---|---|---|---|

No. 1470 contains one 40x46mm stamp.

Endangered Species — A234

Designs, vert: 200fr, Lynx pardellus. 300fr, Lepilemur mustelinus. 450fr, Canis rufus. 750fr, Bison bonasus.

No. 1475: a, Leopard. b, Civet (f). c, Bird (d). d, Hawk. e, Rhinoceros, impala. f, Okapi (e, h, i). g, Lion. h, Chimpanzee. i, Gorilla. j, Bird (long, curved beak). k, Hippopotamus (l). l, Antelope (h).

No. 1476: a, Falco pereginus. b, Acinonyx jubatus. c, Antilocapre americana. d, Mustela nigripes. e, Ursus maritimus. f, Rhinoceros unicornis.

No. 1477: a, Gymnobelideus leadbeater. b, Felis concolor. c, Felis pardalis. d, Panthera pardus. e, Bufo hemiophyrs. f, Mustela rutorius.

No. 1478, 1500fr, Muscardinus avellanarius. No. 1479, 1500fr, Aepyceros melampus, vert. No. 1480, 1500fr, Panthera uncia.

| 1998, Sept. 8 | | | | |
|---|---|---|---|---|
| 1471-1474 | A234 | Set of 4 | 9.00 | 4.50 |

**Sheets of 12 & 6**

| 1475 | A234 | 200fr #a.-l. | 10.00 | 5.00 |
|---|---|---|---|---|
| 1476 | A234 | 450fr #a.-f. | 12.00 | 5.75 |
| 1477 | A234 | 750fr #a.-f. | 18.00 | 9.00 |

**Souvenir Sheets**

| 1478-1480 | A234 | Set of 3 | 24.00 | 12.00 |
|---|---|---|---|---|

Locomotives of the World — A235

No. 1481: a, Sir Nigel Gresley, England. b, Switzerland. c, Canada. d, EMU 102-6 Tobu Railway Spacia, Japan. e, Krauss Maffei V200, Germany. f, IC 580 Portugal. g, Amtrak No. 5, US. h, TGV, France.

No. 1482: a, Nippon Pacific No. 82, Middle East. b, Russia. c, Freight train, Albania. d, Dart No. 8319, Ireland. e, No. 141-F-177, France. f, EMU No. 69625, Norway. g, Bo-Bo, New Zealand. h, Azusa, Japan.

No. 1483: a, Syrian Railways 2-8-0, Iraq. b, The Irish Mail, England. c, Four car EMU, Italy. d, Sprinter, England. e, Van Golu Express, Turkey. f, No. 11.2110, Norway. g, Two-car EMU, New Zealand. h, Grey Mouse, France.

No. 1484: a, The Flying Scotman, United Kingdom. b, National Railways, Japan. c, North Africa. d, F-40M Winnebago, US. e, Federal Railways Class 10, three cylinder 4-6-2, Germany. f, DX5500, New Zealand. g, CIE, Ireland. h, Intercity class 43, England.

No. 1485, 1500fr, D2157, New Zealand. No. 1486, 1500fr, 140.7410, German Railways. No. 1487, 1500fr, JR Shinkansen 221-204, Japan. No. 1488, Egyptian Railways, Bo-Bo.

**Sheets of 8**

| 1998, Oct. 30 | | | | |
|---|---|---|---|---|
| 1481 | A235 | 200fr #a.-h. | 8.00 | 3.75 |
| 1482 | A235 | 300fr #a.-h. | 12.00 | 5.75 |
| 1483 | A235 | 450fr #a.-h. | 16.00 | 7.75 |
| 1484 | A235 | 750fr #a.-h. | 24.00 | 12.00 |

**Souvenir Sheets**

| 1485-1488 | A235 | Set of 4 | 30.00 | 15.00 |
|---|---|---|---|---|

Aircraft — A236

Amphibians & flying boats — No. 1489: a, Boeing Model 1, 1916. b, Grumman G-21 Goose, 1937. c, Latecoere 631, 1942. d, Cessna Model 205. e, Sikorsky S-42, 1934. f, Boeing Model 314 Clipper. g, De Havilland Canada DHC-2 Beaver, 1947. h, Lake Buccaneer, 1979.

Balloons and Dirigibles — No. 1490: a, Henri Giffard, 1852. b, Santos-Dumont "Baladeuse," 1903. c, Zeppelin L37. d, R101,

1930. e, Santos-Dumont, 1898. f, Baldwin, 1908. g, Norge, 1926. h, Hindenburg, 1936.

Helicopters — No. 1491: a, Sikorsky VS-300, 1940. b, Sikorsky S-61, 1957. c, Bell Long Ranger, 1966. d, Dauphin SA 365, 1972. e, Bell 47, 1946. f, Boeing Vertol 243LR, 1958. g, Aerospatial SA 315 Blama. h, Bell Model 222, 1981.

Spacecraft — No. 1492: a, Mercury Capsule, 1961. b, Gemini 8, 1966. c, Apollo Lunar Module, 1968. d, Soviet Vostok, 1961. e, Apollo Command Module, 1968. f, Soviet Soyuz, 1975.

No. 1493, 1500fr, Cessna 208 Caravan, 1980. No. 1494, 1500fr, Goodyear Blimp. No. 1495, 1500fr, Miles Mi-26, 1983. No. 1496, 1500fr, Space Shuttle Columbia, 1981.

**Sheets of 8 & 6**

| 1998, Oct. 30 | | | | |
|---|---|---|---|---|
| 1489 | A236 | 200fr #a.-h. | 9.00 | 4.25 |
| 1490 | A236 | 300fr #a.-h. | 13.00 | 6.25 |
| 1491 | A236 | 450fr #a.-h. | 18.00 | 9.00 |
| 1492 | A236 | 750fr #a.-f. | 22.50 | 11.00 |

**Souvenir Sheets**

| 1493-1496 | A236 | Set of 4 | 20.00 | 10.00 |
|---|---|---|---|---|

No. 1489a incorrectly inscribed "1961."

Dinosaurs — A237

No. 1497: a, Dicraeosaurus. b, Parasaurolophus. c, Sauronithoides. d, Dilophosaurus. e, Titanosaurus, bagaceratops. f, Iguanodon. g, Tenontosaurus. h, Dryosaurus. i, Ceratosaurus.

1500fr, Yangchuanosaurus, brachiosaurus.

| 1998 | | Litho. | | Perf. 13½ |
|---|---|---|---|---|
| 1497 | A237 | 750fr Sheet of 9, | | |
| | | #a.-i. | 27.50 | 13.50 |

**Souvenir Sheet**

| 1498 | A237 | 1500fr multicolored | 6.00 | 3.00 |
|---|---|---|---|---|

Minerals A238

a, Calcite. b, Wolframite. c, Spodumene. No. 1500D: e, Psilomelane. f, Heterosite. g, Columbo-tantalite.

| 1998 | | Litho. | | Perf. 13½ |
|---|---|---|---|---|
| | | **Strip of 3** | | |
| 1499 | A238 | 750fr Green background, | | |
| | | #a.-c. | 10.50 | 5.25 |

**Souvenir Sheets of 3**

| 1500 | A238 | 750fr Gray blue background, | | |
|---|---|---|---|---|
| | | #a.-c. | 10.50 | 5.25 |
| 1500D | A238 | 1500fr #e-g | 21.00 | 21.00 |

Sailing Ships — A239

No. 1501, each 450fr: a, "Theseus." b, "Euphrates." c, Phoenician War Galley. d, Chinese Junk.

No. 1502, each 450fr: a, "Juan Sebastian." b, "Santa Maria." c, Frigate. d, Madurese Jukung rig.

No. 1503, vert, each 750fr: a, Windjammer, "Wavertree." b, British frigate, "Rose." c, Tromp's flagship, "Golden Leeuw." d, Danish Timber Barque.

No. 1504, vert, each 750fr: a, Kraeck. b, Clipper ship, "Golden State." c, English ship, "Resolution." d, "Eagle."

No. 1505, 1500fr, British barque, "Garthpool." No. 1506, 1500fr, HMS Victory.

| 1998, Nov. 10 | | | | Perf. 14 |
|---|---|---|---|---|
| 1501-1502 | A239 | Set of 2 | 16.00 | 7.75 |
| 1503-1504 | A239 | Set of 2 | 30.00 | 15.00 |

**Souvenir Sheets**

| 1505-1506 | A239 | Set of 2 | 15.00 | 15.00 |
|---|---|---|---|---|

Novotel Hotel, Conakry — A239a

| 1998 | | Litho. | | Perf. 13x13½ |
|---|---|---|---|---|
| 1506A | A239a | 200fr multi | — | — |
| 1506B | A239a | 300fr multi | — | — |
| 1506C | A239a | 750fr multi | — | — |

**Modern Guinean Arts**

A239b

A239c

A239d

A239e

A239f

A239g

A239h

A239i

| 1998, Dec. 8 | | Litho. | | Perf. 13¼x13 |
|---|---|---|---|---|
| 1506D | A239b | 750fr Dance | — | — |
| 1506E | A239c | 750fr Painting | — | — |
| 1506F | A239d | 750fr Ceramics | — | — |
| 1506G | A239e | 750fr Sculpture | — | — |
| 1506H | A239f | 750fr Sculpture | — | — |
| 1506I | A239g | 750fr Dance | — | — |
| 1506J | A239h | 750fr Painting | — | — |
| 1506K | A239i | 750fr Painting | — | — |

Horses — A240

Designs: 150fr, Trotteur Russe. 200fr, Brabant. 300fr, Camargue. No. 1510, 450fr, Unidentified breed. No. 1511, 450fr, Dales pony. No. 1512, 750fr, Fjord.

No. 1513, vert.: a, Kabardin. b, Shire. c, Arabian. d, Mustang. e, Quarter horse. f, Appaloosa.

No. 1514, vert.: a, Thoroughbred. b, Lipizzaner. c, Belgian. d, Palomino. e, Haflinger. f, Fjord, diff.

No. 1515, 1500fr, Mustang, diff. No. 1516, 1500fr, Thoroughbred colt.

| 1999, May 1 | | Litho. | | Perf. 14 |
|---|---|---|---|---|
| 1507-1512 | A240 | Set of 6 | 11.00 | 11.00 |

**Sheets of 6**

| 1513 | A240 | 450fr #a.-f. | 12.00 | 12.00 |
|---|---|---|---|---|
| 1514 | A240 | 750fr #a.-f. | 21.00 | 21.00 |

**Souvenir Sheets**

| 1515-1516 | A240 | Set of 2 | 17.00 | 17.00 |
|---|---|---|---|---|

Guinea — People's Republic of China Diplomatic Relations, 40th Anniv. — A240a

Designs: 200fr, Shown. 300fr, Building with flat roof, horiz. 750fr, Building with slanted roof, horiz.

| 1999 | | Litho. | | Perf. 13¼x13 |
|---|---|---|---|---|
| 1516A | A240a | 200fr multi | — | — |
| 1516B | A240a | 300fr multi | — | — |
| 1516C | A240a | 750fr multi | — | — |

Dogs — A241

Designs: 200fr, Newfoundland. No. 1518, 750fr, St. Bernard.

No. 1519, vert.: a, Bulldog. b, Miniature schnauzer. c, Dachshund. d, Beagle. e, Bloodhound. f, Miniature pinscher.

1500fr, Irish setter.

| 1999, May 1 | | | | |
|---|---|---|---|---|
| 1517-1518 | A241 | Set of 2 | 5.00 | 5.00 |

**Sheet of 6**

| 1519 | A241 | 750fr #a.-f. | 18.00 | 18.00 |
|---|---|---|---|---|

**Souvenir Sheet**

| 1520 | A241 | 1500fr multi | 8.00 | 8.00 |
|---|---|---|---|---|

Modern Guinean Sculptures — A241a

Various sculptures.

| 1999, Aug. 9 | | Litho. | | Perf. 13¼x13 |
|---|---|---|---|---|
| 1520A | A241a | 200fr multi | 2.40 | 2.40 |
| 1520B | A241a | 250fr multi | 2.40 | 2.40 |
| 1520C | A241a | 300fr multi | 2.40 | 2.40 |
| 1520D | A241a | 500fr shown | 2.40 | 2.40 |
| 1520E | A241a | 750fr multi | 2.40 | 2.40 |

PhilexFrance '99.

A242

Dinosaurs & Prehistoric Animals — A243

Designs: 300fr, Ouranosaurus. No. 1522, 450fr, Centrosaurus. No. 1523, 450fr, Dilophosaurus, vert.

No. 1524: a, Cymbospondylus. b, Kronosaurus. c, Ichthyosaurus. d, Eurhinosaurus. e, Stenopterygius. f, Ophthalmosaurus. g, Shonisaurus. h, Temnodontosaurus. i, Mixosaurus.

No. 1525, vert.: a, Eudimorphodon. b, Sordes. c, Dimorphodon. d, Albertosaurus. e, Triceratops. f, Alioramus. g, Mesosaurus. h, Labidosaurus. i, Struthiomimus.

No. 1526: a, Saltosaurus. b, Corythosaurus. c, Protoceratops. d, Baryonyx. e, Pachycephalosaurus. f, Maiasaurus. g, Spinosaurus. h, Lambeosaurus.

2500fr, Elasmosaurus, vert. No. 1528, Tyrannosaurus Rex. No. 1529, Utahraptor. No. 1530, Parasaurolophus, vert.

## 1999, Aug. 12

| 1521-1523 | A242 | Set of 3 | 5.00 | 5.00 |
|---|---|---|---|---|

**Sheets of 9**

| 1524 | A243 | 350fr #a.-i. | 15.00 | 15.00 |
|---|---|---|---|---|
| 1525 | A243 | 450fr #a.-i. | 18.00 | 18.00 |

**Sheet of 8**

| 1526 | A242 | 450fr #a.-h | 18.00 | 18.00 |
|---|---|---|---|---|

**Souvenir Sheets**

| 1527 | A243 | 2500fr multi | 13.00 | 13.00 |
|---|---|---|---|---|
| 1528 | A243 | 3000fr multi | 13.00 | 13.00 |
| 1529-1530 | A242 | 3000fr Set of 2 | 28.00 | 28.00 |

No. 1527 contains one 42x56mm stamp. No. 1528 contains one 56x42mm stamp.

Return of Macao to People's Republic of China, Dec. 20, 1999 — A244

No. 1531, each 650fr: a, Current view of Nam Van (tall buildings). b, Nam Van in 1850s (hilltop and bay). c, Current view of Largo de Senado. d, Largo de Senado in 1900s.
No. 1532, each 650fr: a, Current view of Nam Van (highway). b, Nam Van in 1850s (buildings at water's edge). c, Current view of Nam Van (boat). d, Nam Van in 1850s (ships).

## 1999, Aug. 20  Perf. 14¼x14½

**Sheets of 4, #a.-d.**

| 1531-1532 | A244 | Set of 2 | 24.00 | 24.00 |
|---|---|---|---|---|

China 1999 World Philatelic Exhibition.

Paintings of Zhang Daqian (1899-1983) A245

No. 1533: a, Ink Lotus. b, Ink Peony. c, Red Cliff Excursion at Night. d, Poetic Landscape. e, Landscape in the Evening. f, Spring Landscape. g, Chatting at Leisure in Mountains. h, Pine Nesting. i, Pine in Thunder. j, Blue and Green Landscape.
No. 1534: a, Landscape. b, Versing in the Landscape.

## 1999, Aug. 20  Litho.  Perf. 13¼

| 1533 | A245 | 330fr Sheet of 10, #a.-j. | 15.00 | 15.00 |
|---|---|---|---|---|

**Souvenir Sheet of 2**

**Perf. 13**

| 1534 | A245 | 1150fr #a.-b. | 4.50 | 4.50 |
|---|---|---|---|---|

No. 1534 contains two 51x39mm stamps. China 1999 World Philatelic Exhibition

First French Postage Stamp, 150th Anniv. — A245a

**Litho. with Hologram Applied**
## 1999, Sept. 10  Perf. 13

| 1534C | A245a | 750fr multi | 4.75 | 4.75 |
|---|---|---|---|---|

Trains — A246

100fr, Diesel TGV, East Germany. No. 1536, 200fr, 1900 horsepower Diesel-electric, Finland. No. 1537, 200fr, Type MLW 3000 horsepower Diesel-electric. No. 1538, 250fr, A-4, Britain. No. 1539, 250fr, Class R 4-6-4. No. 1540, 250fr, Class M, 4-6-2, Tasmania. No. 1541, 400fr, Class 68000 Diesel-electric, France. No. 1542, 450fr, 4-8-4 Daylight Express. No. 1543, 450fr, Electric TGV, Italy. No. 1544, 450fr, Western Class Hydraulic-Diesel.
No. 1545: a, Class 10 3-cylinder 4-6-2. b, SD18 Diesel-electric. c, Hikari Super Express Train, Japan. d, Diesel-electric No. 10000. e,

PA-1 Diesel-electric. f, 2500 horsepower experimental gas turbine locomotive.
No. 1546: a, YP Class, India. b, Class 47, Standard Type 4 Diesel-electric. c, DSI Class 2-8-2, Japan. d, Class D-341 Diesel-electric. e, S1 Class 2-6-4. f, 3600 horsepower electric, India.
No. 1547: a, 2000 horsepower GP-20 Diesel-electric. b, Class C-53 3-cylinder, Japan. c, Multiple-unit Diesel, Japan. d, Royal Scot Class 4-6-0. e, Deltic electric prototype. f, W.P. Standard 4-6-2.
No. 1548: 2500fr, Class 40 electric, England.
Each 3000fr: No. 1549, GP-40 Diesel-electric. No. 1550, 9780 horsepower DM-3, Sweden. No. 1551, 1750 horsepower Diesel-electric, Denmark.

## 1999, Oct. 25  Perf. 14

| 1535-1544 | A246 | Set of 10 | 13.00 | 13.00 |
|---|---|---|---|---|

**Sheets of 6**

| 1545 | A246 | 300fr #a.-f. | 8.50 | 8.50 |
|---|---|---|---|---|
| 1546 | A246 | 450fr #a.-f. | 12.00 | 12.00 |
| 1547 | A246 | 750fr #a.-f. | 21.00 | 21.00 |

**Souvenir Sheets**

| 1548 | A246 | 2500fr multi | 11.00 | 11.00 |
|---|---|---|---|---|
| 1549-1551 | A246 | Set of 3 | 40.00 | 40.00 |

Mushrooms and Insects — A247

Mushrooms and unidentified insects: No. 1552, 100fr, Lentinellus cochleatus. No. 1553, 100fr, Lactarius blennius. No. 1554, 150fr, Lactarius sanguifluus. No. 1555, 150fr, Leucocortinarius bulbiger. No. 1556, 300fr, Clitocybe phyllophila. No. 1557, 300fr, Calocybe ionides. No. 1558, 300fr, Lactarius porninsis. No. 1559, 300fr, Cystoderma amianthinum. No. 1560, 300fr, Limacella guttata. No. 1561, 450fr, Suillus placidus. No. 1562, 450fr, Suillus grevillei. No. 1563, 450fr, Suillus luteus. No. 1564, 450fr, Suillus granulatus. No. 1565, 450fr, Pleurotus cornuscopiae. No. 1566, 450fr, Calocybe carnea. No. 1567, 450fr, Panus tigrinus.
Mushrooms and insects — No. 1568: a, Hygrocybe nigreseens, Argynnis paphia. b, Hygrocybe subglobispora, Pterophoridae. c, Oudemansiella mucida, Tettigonia viridissima. d, Amanita rubescens, unidentified insect. e, Amanita muscaria, Oedipoda caerulescens. f, Suillus luteus, Happarchia fagi. g, Coprinus picaceus, Aphantopus hyperantus. h, Gymnopilus junonius, Ourapteryx sambucaria. i, Amanita muscaria, Catocala nupta.
No. 1569: a, Macrolepiota procera, Pieris brassicae. b, Lactarius britannicus, Pyrochroa cocci. c, Cortinarius sanguineus, Tabicina haematodes. d, Amanita muscaria, Sympetrum. e, Aerocomus badius, Issoria lathonia. f, Laccaria amethystea, Sympetrum. g, Paxillus atrotomentosus, Inachis io. h, Armillaria mellea, Chrystoxum cautum. i, Amanita echinocephala, Vanessa atalanta.
Each 2500fr: No. 1570, Lactarius brittanicus, Coccinella punctala. No. 1571, Amanita phalloides, Ochlodes venatus. No. 1572, Coprinus atramentarius, unidentified insect.
Each 3000fr: No. 1573, Amanita citrina, unidentified insect. No. 1574, Amanita pantherina, Aperia syringaria.

## 1999, Nov. 11

| 1552-1567 | A247 | Set of 16 | 24.00 | 24.00 |
|---|---|---|---|---|

**Sheets of 9**

| 1568 | A247 | 300fr #a.-i. | 12.00 | 12.00 |
|---|---|---|---|---|
| 1569 | A247 | 450fr #a.-i. | 18.00 | 18.00 |

**Souvenir Sheets**

| 1570-1572 | A247 | Set of 3 | 35.00 | 35.00 |
|---|---|---|---|---|
| 1573-1574 | A247 | Set of 2 | 24.00 | 24.00 |

A248

Birds A249

Designs: No. 1575, 200fr, Catamblyrhychus diadema. No. 1576, 200fr, Tichodrome. No. 1577, 300fr, Turtle dove. No. 1578, 300fr, Flamingo. No. 1579, 300fr, Duck. No. 1580, 300fr, Woodpecker. No. 1581, 450fr, Warbler. No. 1582, 450fr, Bullfinch.
No. 1583: a, Wild turkey. b, Ring-necked pheasant. c, Gray partridge. d, Woodcock. e, Capercaillie. f, Rock partridge.
No. 1584: a, Cuban hummingbird. b, Rufous-breated hermit. c, Green-throated hummingbird. d, Bee-eater. e, Puerto Rican hummingbird. f, Antillean hummingbird.
No. 1585: a, Gould's finch. b, Oriole. c, Psarismus dalhousiae. d, Woodchat shrike. e, Pitta guajana. f, Neodreponis coruscans.
No. 1586, horiz.: a, Purple-throated Carib. b, Bahamas hummingbird. c, Blue-bearded hummingbird. d, Green hummingbird. e, Jamaican hummingbird. f, Vervaine.
Each 2500fr: No. 1587, Spotted waxwing. No. 1588, Red-banded bee-eater.
Each 2500fr: No. 1589, Bahamas hummingbird, horiz. No. 1590, Antillean crested hummingbird.
No. 1591, 3000fr, Emerald hummingbird.

## 1999, Nov. 22

| 1575-1582 | A248 | Set of 8 | 10.00 | 10.00 |
|---|---|---|---|---|

**Sheets of 6**

| 1583 | A248 | 450fr #a.-f. | 12.00 | 12.00 |
|---|---|---|---|---|
| 1584 | A249 | 500fr #a.-f. | 15.00 | 15.00 |
| 1585 | A248 | 600fr #a.-f. | 16.00 | 16.00 |
| 1586 | A249 | 750fr #a.-f. | 20.00 | 20.00 |

**Souvenir Sheets**

| 1587-1588 | A248 | Set of 2 | 24.00 | 24.00 |
|---|---|---|---|---|
| 1589-1590 | A249 | Set of 2 | 24.00 | 24.00 |
| 1591 | A249 | 3000fr multi | 14.00 | 14.00 |

Butterflies A250

Designs: No. 1592, 300fr, Acraea acerata. No. 1593, 300fr, Charaxes protoclea. No. 1594, 300fr, Charaxes hadrianus. No. 1595, 300fr, Colotis halimede. No. 1596, 300fr, Colotis eucharis. No. 1597, 300fr, Papilio dardanus.
No. 1598, vert.: a, Papilio charopus. b, Papilio dardanus. c, Acraea zetes. d, Hypolimnas salmacis. e, Cymothoe beckeri. f, Papilio nobilis.
No. 1599, vert.: a, Iolaus Ialos. b, Graphium gudenusi. c, Hewitsonia boisduvali. d, Graphium ucalegon. e, Danaus chrysippus. f, Acraea satis.
Each 2500fr: No. 1600, Euxanthe tiberius. No. 1601, Colotis danae.

## 1999, Nov. 22

| 1592-1597 | A250 | Set of 6 | 7.50 | 7.50 |
|---|---|---|---|---|

**Sheets of 6**

| 1598 | A250 | 450fr #a.-f. | 12.00 | 12.00 |
|---|---|---|---|---|
| 1599 | A250 | 750fr #a.-f. | 20.00 | 20.00 |

**Souvenir Sheets**

| 1600-1601 | A250 | Set of 2 | 24.00 | 24.00 |
|---|---|---|---|---|

Wedding of Prince Edward and Sophie Rhys-Jones — A251

No. 1602: a, Edward in blue striped shirt. b, Sophie with scarf. c, Edward looking left. d, Sophie looking right. e, Edward with blue checked shirt. f, Sophie with black blouse.
3000fr, Couple.

## 1999, Dec. 6

| 1602 | A251 | 750fr Sheet of 6, #a.-f. | 21.00 | 21.00 |
|---|---|---|---|---|

**Souvenir Sheet**

| 1603 | A251 | 3000fr multi | 14.00 | 14.00 |
|---|---|---|---|---|

Hokusai Paintings — A252

No. 1604, each 750fr: a, Actor Ichikawa Ebizo. b, Drawings (man with fan). c, Actor Sakata Hangoro. d, Geisha and Madam. e, Drawings (man with sword). f, Kabuki Actor Hanshiro IV.
No. 1605, each 750fr: a, Kintaro and Wild Animals. b, Drawings (man with clasped hands). c, Lady Walking in the Snow. d, Lady and Maiden on an Outing. e, Drawings (man with incense burner). f, Girls at Their Toilette.
Each 3000fr: No. 1606, Sumo Wrestlers. No. 1607, Geisha House and Madam at Leisure with Child.

## 1999, Dec. 6  Perf. 12¼

**Sheets of 6, #a.-f.**

| 1604-1605 | A252 | Set of 2 | 35.00 | 35.00 |
|---|---|---|---|---|

**Souvenir Sheets**

| 1606-1607 | A252 | Set of 2 | 27.50 | 27.50 |
|---|---|---|---|---|

Johann Wolfgang von Goethe (1749-1832), German Poet — A253

No. 1608, each 1000fr: a, Mephistopheles tempts Faust with Margaret. b, Goethe and Friedrich von Schiller. c, The witches' kitchen, a potion brewed.
3000fr, Euphorion.

## 1999, Dec. 6  Perf. 14

| 1608 | A253 | Sheet of 3, #a.-c. | 14.00 | 14.00 |
|---|---|---|---|---|

**Souvenir Sheet**

| 1609 | A253 | 3000fr multi | 14.00 | 14.00 |
|---|---|---|---|---|

A254

A255

Space Exploration A256

Designs: No. 1610, 300fr, Pioneer 10. No. 1611, 300fr, Viking 1.
No. 1612: a, Takao Doi. b, Frank Borman. c, Alan B. Shepard, Jr. d, M. Scott Carpenter. e, Ulf Merbold. f, David R. Scott. g, Mamoru Mohri. h, Gherman Titov. i, Sally K. Ride. j, Walter M. Schirra. k, John L. Swigert, Jr. l, Yuri A. Gagarin.
No. 1613, each 500fr: a, Venus. b, Neptune. c, Jupiter. d, Uranus. e, Saturn. f, Mercury.
No. 1614, each 500fr: a, Mariner 4. b, HL-20. c, Mariner 2. d, Voyager 1. e, Venture Star. f, Phobos.
No. 1615, each 750fr: a, 1961 drawing of lunar ferry. b, 1960 drawing of lunar lander. c, 1959 drawing of lunar lander. d, 1962 drawing of lunar lander. e, 1962 drawing of lunar lander trainer. f, 1961 drawing of lunar lander.
No. 1616, vert, each 750fr: a, Apollo 5. b, Apollo 6, c, Apollo 7. d, Apollo escape test. e, Apollo "Little Joe." f, Apollo 4.
No. 1617, 1500fr, John Glenn.
No. 1618, 1500fr, Apollo 11 command module, vert. No. 1619, 1500fr, Collecting moon rocks.
No. 1620, 2000fr, Viking, diff. No. 1621, 2000fr, Mars Global Surveyor. No. 1622, 2000fr, Sojourner.

**1999, Dec. 9**

| | | | | |
|---|---|---|---|---|
| 1610-1611 | A254 | Set of 2 | 3.00 | 3.00 |

**Sheet of 12, #a.-l.**

| | | | | |
|---|---|---|---|---|
| 1612 | A255 | 450fr multi | 27.50 | 27.50 |

**Sheets of 6, #a.-f.**

| | | | | |
|---|---|---|---|---|
| 1613-1614 | A254 | Set of 2 | 24.00 | 24.00 |
| 1615-1616 | A256 | Set of 2 | 40.00 | 40.00 |

**Souvenir Sheets**

| | | | | |
|---|---|---|---|---|
| 1617 | A255 | 1500fr multi | 8.00 | 8.00 |
| 1618-1619 | A256 | Set of 2 | 15.00 | 15.00 |
| 1620-1622 | A254 | Set of 3 | 26.50 | 26.50 |

Nos. 1620-1622 each contain one 50x37mm stamp.

Queen Mother (b. 1900) — A257

No. 1623: a, In 1934. b, With tiara. c, Lady of the Garter. d, In 1997.
3000fr, With tiara, diff.

**1999, Dec. 6**      *Perf. 14*

| | | | | |
|---|---|---|---|---|
| 1623 | A257 | 1000fr Sheet of 4, #a.-d., + label | 19.00 | 19.00 |

**Souvenir Sheet**
*Perf. 13¾*

| | | | | |
|---|---|---|---|---|
| 1624 | A257 | 3000fr multi | 14.00 | 14.00 |

No. 1624 contains one 38x50mm stamp.

Cats — A257a

Designs: 300fr, Ragdoll. No. 1626, 400fr, Egyptian Mau.
No. 1627, vert.: a, Tonkinese. b, Korat. c, Siamese. d, British Shorthair. e, Bengal. f, Persian.
1500fr, Calico Shorthair, vert.

**1999**      *Perf. 14*

| | | | | |
|---|---|---|---|---|
| 1625-1626 | A257a | Set of 2 | 3.25 | 3.25 |

**Sheet of 6**

| | | | | |
|---|---|---|---|---|
| 1627 | A257a | 450fr #a.-f. | 12.00 | 12.00 |

**Souvenir Sheet**

| | | | | |
|---|---|---|---|---|
| 1628 | A257a | 1500fr multi | 8.00 | 8.00 |

Romance of the Three Kingdoms — A258

No. 1629, each 460fr: a, Archer and four men. b, Two men and tea pot. c, Spear carrier, man, woman. d, Horsemen jousting. e, Four men.
No. 1630, each 460fr: a, Swordsman on white horse. b, Spear carrier on black horse. c, Bed chamber. d, Man being speared. e, At sea.
2000fr, Three men with tea cups.

**1999**    **Sheets of 5, #a.-e.**    *Perf. 13¼*

| | | | | |
|---|---|---|---|---|
| 1629-1630 | A258 | Set of 2 | 20.00 | 20.00 |

**Souvenir Sheet**

| | | | | |
|---|---|---|---|---|
| 1631 | A258 | 2000fr multi | 9.00 | 9.00 |

No. 1631 contains one 48x58mm stamp.

Millennium — A354

No. 1823 — Marco Polo's Voyages: a, Young Marco Polo. b, Piazza San Marco. c, Polo's ship. d, Priest buying incense. e, Houses in Syria. f, Ruins of Saveh. g, Persian ventilator. h, Moncia costume. i, Ulan Bator Abbey. j, Buddha, 5th cent. k, Great Wall of China. l, Warrior of Kublai Khan's Army. m, Ship on the Yangtze. n, Japanese archer. o, Golden plate. p, Medallion of Marco Polo, horiz. (60x40mm). q, Kublai Khan.
No. 1824 — Expansion of Knowledge: a, Election of King Sigismund I of Hungary as Holy Roman Emperor, 1411. b, Filippo Brunelleschi wins architectural contest to build the dome of the Santa Maria di Fiore, 1420. c, Lorenzo Ghiberti sculpts human forms on doors of the Florence Baptistry, 1425. d, Death of Juliana of Norwich, c. 1443. e, Chinese Ming capital moves from Nanjing to Beijing, 1420. f, Europeans begin to use Chinese method of black printing, 1423. g, King Henry V of England defeats French at Battle of Agincourt, 1415. h, Tamerlane defeats Ottomans at Battle of Ankyra, 1402. i, Joan of Arc leads French forces at Siege of Orleans, 1429. j, Korea prospers under rule of King Sejong, 1419. k, Thomas à Kempis writes *The Imitation of Christ*, 1427. l, King Casimir IV of Poland unites Polish Kingdom with Grand Duchy of Lithuania, 1447. m, End of the Great Schism, 1417. n, John Hus burnt at the stake, 1415. o, Medici family dominates the government of Florence, 1434. p, Chaucer completes *Canterbury Tales*, 1400, horiz. (60x40mm). q, Shogun Yoshima Ashikaga begins rule in Japan, 1449.
No. 1825 — Across the Continents: a, Engraving, c. 1598. b, Caribbean warriors. c, Viking ship, 12th cent. d, Ship of Vasco da Gama. e, Detail from Italian engraving. f, Columbus's letter of 1493. g, Kokyrboom tree, h, Megalzina virens. i, Details from a map, Moon between Earth and Sun. j, Details from a map, Earth between Sun and Moon. k, Maori wood carving. l, Astrolabes. m, Frilled lizard (inscribed "Gila monster"). n, White ibises. o, Tahitian utensils. p, Ocean monsters, horiz. (60x40mm). q, Samoan boat.

*Perf. 12¾x12½*

**2000, Feb. 18**      *Litho.*
**Sheets of 17, #a-q, + Label**

| | | | | |
|---|---|---|---|---|
| 1823 | A354 | 200fr multi | 16.00 | 16.00 |
| 1824 | A354 | 250fr multi | 21.00 | 21.00 |
| 1825 | A354 | 300fr multi | 24.00 | 24.00 |
| | | Nos. 1823-1825 (3) | 61.00 | 61.00 |

New Year 2000 (Year of the Dragon) A355

No. 1826 — Dragon with background in: a, Red, claws near "Office." b, Green. c, Blue. d, Red, tail near "Office."
2000fr, Light blue.

**2000, Feb. 18**      *Perf. 13¾*

| | | | | |
|---|---|---|---|---|
| 1826 | A355 | 400fr Sheet of 4, #a-d | 7.50 | 7.50 |

**Souvenir Sheet**

| | | | | |
|---|---|---|---|---|
| 1827 | A355 | 2000fr multi | 9.50 | 9.50 |

No. 1826 contains four 48x32mm stamps.

Miniature Sheet

Vacation Photographs — A356

No. 1828: Various photographs making up a photomosaic of the Titanic.

**2000, Feb. 18**

| | | | | |
|---|---|---|---|---|
| 1828 | A356 | 750fr Sheet of 8, #a-h | 24.00 | 24.00 |

2000 Summer Olympics, Sydney — A357

No. 1829: a, Women's discus. b, Javelin. c, Men's discus. d, Shot put. e, Hammer throw.
No. 1830: a, Women's volleyball. b, Water polo. c, Women's beach volleyball. d, Handball. e, Women's soccer.
No. 1831: a, Women's judo. b, Wrestling. c, Men's judo. d, Boxing, pink background. e, Boxing, green background.
No. 1832: a, Women's diving. b, Synchronized swimming. c, Women's swimming. d, Women's sailing. e, Kayaking.
No. 1833: a, Badminton. b, Field hockey. c, Baseball. d, Fencing. e, Weight lifting.
No. 1834: a, Dressage. b, Archery. c, Show jumping. d, Rifle shooting. e, Pistol shooting.
No. 1835: a, Table tennis, two men. b, Table tennis, one man, blue and purple background. c, Table tennis, one man, green and yellow background. d, Women's table tennis. e, Table tennis, four players.
No. 1836: a, Women's tennis, blue background. b, Men's tennis, green background. c, Women's tennis, bister background. d, Men's tennis, gray background. e, Men's tennis, blue background.
No. 1837: a, Women's basketball. b, Men's basketball (Michael Jordan dunking basketball). c, Men's basketball, two players. d, Men's basketball (Jordan dribbling). e, Men's basketball, blue background.
No. 1838: a, Cycling Road Race (Route). b, Cycling Sprint Race (Vitesse). c, Cycling Team Pursuit. d, Cycling Points Race (Kilometre). e, Cycling Time Trial (Contre la montre).

**2000, Nov. 14**      *Perf. 13¼*
**Sheets of 5, #a-e, + Label**

| | | | | |
|---|---|---|---|---|
| 1829 | A357 | 150fr multi | 3.50 | 3.50 |
| 1830 | A357 | 150fr multi | 3.50 | 3.50 |
| 1831 | A357 | 200fr multi | 4.50 | 4.50 |
| 1832 | A357 | 200fr multi | 4.50 | 4.50 |
| 1833 | A357 | 300fr multi | 7.00 | 7.00 |
| 1834 | A357 | 300fr multi | 7.00 | 7.00 |
| 1835 | A357 | 600fr multi | 13.50 | 13.50 |
| 1836 | A357 | 600fr multi | 13.50 | 13.50 |
| 1837 | A357 | 750fr multi | 17.00 | 17.00 |
| 1838 | A357 | 750fr multi | 17.00 | 17.00 |
| | | Nos. 1829-1838 (10) | 91.00 | 91.00 |

Sports and Chess A358

No. 1839 — Golf: a, Golfer with purple cap. b, Golfer with white pants. c, Golfer with white cap. d, Golfer with green shirt.
No. 1840 — Soccer: a, Marcel Dessally. b, Zinedine Zidane. c, Youri Djorkaeff. d, Thierry Henry.
No. 1841 — Auto racing: a, Ayrton Senna. b, Mika Hakkinen. c, Alain Prost. d, Michael Schumacher.
No. 1842 — Chess: a, Player with hands on forehead. b, Player with blue jacket. c, Player with gray jacket. d, Female player.

**2000, Nov. 14**      **Sheets of 4, #a-d**

| | | | | |
|---|---|---|---|---|
| 1839 | A358 | 450fr multi | 8.00 | 8.00 |
| 1840 | A358 | 450fr multi | 8.00 | 8.00 |
| 1841 | A358 | 750fr multi | 14.00 | 14.00 |
| 1842 | A358 | 750fr multi | 14.00 | 14.00 |
| | | Nos. 1839-1842 (4) | 44.00 | 44.00 |

Locomotives — A359

No. 1843, horiz.: a, De Witt Clinton. b, American 220. c, Triplet Mallet. d, Philadelphia & Reading 422 Baldwin. e, Mason Bogie. f, Promontory Point 220 No. 119. g, Mogul. h, Best Friend of Charleston. i, John Bull.
No. 1844, horiz.: a, Union Pacific Bo-Bo-Bo-Bo. b, Bipolar No. 2. c, Burlington Northern-Series SD 40-2 No. 7044. d, Amtrak Metroliner No. 880. e, Rio Grande Western Series F. f, Union Pacific Series DD 40AX. g, Lake Superior & Ishpeming Co-Co 025C No. 2500. h, Chicago, Milwaukee, St. Paul & Pacific Bipolar 3000V No. 4. i, Southern Pacific Krauss-Maffei C-C No. 9006.
No. 1845, horiz.: a, Southern Pacific GM-EMD Series F No. 98. b, Union Pacific M-10001. c, Union Pacific Switcher No. 4466. d, Chesapeake & Ohio Series M No. 500. e, Amtrak Series P32 No. 513. f, Southern Pacific EMD SD 40-2 No. 9368. g, Great Northern Series W-1 No. 5018. h, Grand Canyon 140. i, Pennsylvania Railroad 6100.
No. 1846, horiz.: a, Burlington Northern Santa Fe No. 4326. b, Conrail Series GP EMD No. 8194. c, Kansas City Southern No. 6639. d, Southern Pacific No. 9800. e, Pennsylvania Railroad 661 No. 4835. f, Union Pacific No. 8182. g, Burlington Northern No. 2917. h, Gulf, Mobile & Ohio Railroad Series F. i, Santa Fe No. 627.
No. 1847, horiz.: a, Norfolk Southern No. 6627. b, Grand Trunk No. 6219. c, Soo Line No. 6401. d, Santa Fe BNSF No. 2512. e, Chessie System No. 6035. f, Utah Railway No. 9010. g, Chicago & Northwestern No. 6866. h, Norfolk Southern No. 3328. i, Canadian National No. 4634.
No. 1848, horiz.: a, Canadian Pacific Budd Autorail Diesel No. 9112. b, New York Central 2-Do-2 No. 113. c, British Columbia Railway Series C630 No. 703. d, Chesapeake & Ohio Series GP9 No. 6137. e, Amtrak 661 No. 902. f, Santa Fe GP9 No. 2293. g, Trainmaster Type Co-Co. h, Chicago, Burlington & Quincy Pioneer Zephyr. i, Denver & Rio Grande Western No. 5350.
No. 1849, 2000fr, Tom Thumb, 2-2-0. No. 1850, 2000fr, Norfolk & Western Class J. No. 1851, 2000fr, Royal Gorge CC No. 403. No. 1852, 2000fr, Hudson 4-6-4 No. 490.

**2000, Dec. 7**      **Sheets of 9, #a-i**

| | | | | |
|---|---|---|---|---|
| 1843 | A359 | 200fr multi | 5.25 | 5.25 |
| 1844 | A359 | 300fr multi | 8.00 | 8.00 |
| 1845 | A359 | 350fr multi | 10.00 | 10.00 |
| 1846 | A359 | 400fr multi | 11.00 | 11.00 |
| 1847 | A359 | 450fr multi | 12.00 | 12.00 |
| 1848 | A359 | 500fr multi | 14.00 | 14.00 |
| | | Nos. 1843-1848 (6) | 60.25 | 60.25 |

**Souvenir Sheets**

| | | | | |
|---|---|---|---|---|
| 1849-1852 | A359 | Set of 4 | 22.50 | 22.50 |

Nos. 1843-1848 each contain nine 51x36mm stamps.

A360

First Zeppelin flight, Cent. A361

No. 1853: a, Zeppelin LZ-11 Viktoria Luise. b, E. T. Willows. c, Hindenburg. d, Astra-Torres 1. e, Beta. f, Schutte-Lanz SL3.

No. 1854: a, Gross-Basenach M1. b, Schutte-Lanz SL1. c, Parseval PL25. d, Siemens-Schuckert. e, Delta. f, Parseval PL VIII.

No. 1855: a, LZ-9. b, LZ-10 Schwaben. c, LZ-11 Viktoria Luise, diff. d, LZ-127 Graf Zeppelin. e, LZ-129 Hindenburg. f, LZ-130.

No. 1856: a, LZ-1. b, LZ-2. c, LZ-3. d, LZ-4. e, LZ-5. f, LZ-6.

No. 1857, Graf Zeppelin and airplane. No. 1858, LZ-1, diff.

**2000, Dec. 11**      **Perf. 14**
**Sheets of 6, #a-f**

| | | | | |
|---|---|---|---|---|
| 1853 | A360 | 300fr multi | 8.50 | 8.50 |
| 1854 | A360 | 450fr multi | 12.00 | 12.00 |
| 1855 | A361 | 1000fr multi | 27.50 | 27.50 |
| 1856 | A361 | 1000fr multi | 27.50 | 27.50 |
| | Nos. 1853-1856 (4) | | 75.50 | 75.50 |

**Souvenir Sheets**

| | | | | |
|---|---|---|---|---|
| 1857 | A360 | 4000fr multi | 20.00 | 20.00 |
| 1858 | A361 | 4000fr multi | 20.00 | 20.00 |

**Miniature Sheet**

Flowers A362

No. 1859: Various photographs making up a photomosaic of Queen Mother Elizabeth.

**2000, Dec. 11**

| | | | | |
|---|---|---|---|---|
| 1859 | A362 | 750fr Sheet of 8, #a-h | 20.00 | 20.00 |

Prince William of Wales, 18th Birthday A363

No. 1860: a, Wearing red tie. b, Wearing black and white checked tie. c, With Prince Harry. d, Wearing blue sweater.

4000fr, Wearing scarf.

**2000, Dec. 11**      **Perf. 14**

| | | | | |
|---|---|---|---|---|
| 1860 | A363 | 1000fr Sheet of 4, #a-d | 18.00 | 18.00 |

**Souvenir Sheet**
**Perf. 13¾**

| | | | | |
|---|---|---|---|---|
| 1861 | A363 | 4000fr multi | 19.00 | 19.00 |

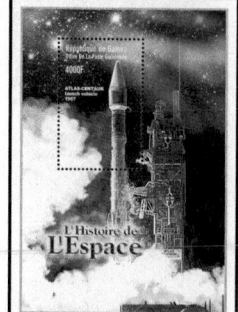

History of Space Exploration — A364

No. 1862, 200fr: a, Discovery of gunpowder. b, Fire arrows. c, Wan Hu's rocket glider. d, Konstantin Tsiolkovsky. e, Telescope of William Herschel. f, Galileo Galilei. g, Nicolaus Copernicus. h, Robert H. Goddard. i, Paper hot air balloons. j, Wernher von Braun. k, Launch of first rocket by Goddard. l, V-1 missile buzz-bomb.

No. 1863, 200fr: a, First American spacewalk by Ed White, Gemini 4. b, First man on the Moon, Apollo 11. c, Space Shuttle Atlantis. d, Voskhod 2. e, Sputnik 1. f, Apollo-Soyuz. g, John Glenn, first American to orbit Earth. h, Valentina Tereshkova, first woman in space. i, Yuri Gagarin, first man in space. j, Apollo 17. k, Robotic lunar explorer. l, Hubble Space Telescope.

No. 1864, 4000fr, Atlas-Centaur launch vehicle. No. 1865, International Space Station.

**2000, Dec. 11**      **Perf. 14**
**Sheets of 12, #a-l**

| | | | | |
|---|---|---|---|---|
| 1862-1863 | A364 | Set of 2 | 17.00 | 17.00 |

**Souvenir Sheets**

| | | | | |
|---|---|---|---|---|
| 1864-1865 | A364 | Set of 2 | 12.00 | 12.00 |

Apollo-Soyuz Mission, 25th Anniv. — A365

No. 1866, 1000fr: a, Saturn IB rocket. b, Apollo 18 command and service modules with docking adapter. c, Apollo 18 Commander Thomas P. Stafford. d, A-2 Soyuz rocket. e, Soyuz 19 spacecraft. f, Soyuz 19 Commander Alexei Leonov.

No. 1867, 1000fr, vert.: a, Lunar Module Eagle, upside-down. b, Lunar Module Eagle, with thrusters firing. c, Apollo 11 command module Columbia. d, Edwin E. Aldrin, Jr. on lunar module ladder. e, Apollo 11 Saturn V rocket. f, Re-entry of Apollo 11 capsule.

4000fr, Aldrin and lunar module on Moon.

**2000, Dec. 11**      **Sheets of 6, #a-f**

| | | | | |
|---|---|---|---|---|
| 1866-1867 | A365 | Set of 2 | 42.50 | 42.50 |

**Souvenir Sheet**

| | | | | |
|---|---|---|---|---|
| 1868 | A365 | 4000fr multi | 6.00 | 6.00 |

Marine Life — A367

Designs: No. 1873, 400fr, Coral grouper. No. 1874, 400fr, Candy cane sea star. 450fr, Hippocampus kuda.

No. 1876, 750fr: a, Chromis caerulea. b, Brittle star. c, Calloplesiops altivelis. d, Ewa blenny. e, Coral polyp. f, Butterflyfish.

No. 1877, 750fr: a, Chelonia mydas. b, Ptereleotris evides. c, Halichoeres iridis. d, Sea fan. e, Florometra serratissima. f, Gramma loreto.

No. 1878, 5000fr, Clownfish. No. 1879, 5000fr, Bigeye scad, horiz.

**Perf. 13½x13¼, 13¼x13½**
**2001, Feb. 28**

| | | | | |
|---|---|---|---|---|
| 1873-1875 | A367 | Set of 3 | 5.50 | 5.50 |

**Sheets of 6, #a-f**

| | | | | |
|---|---|---|---|---|
| 1876-1877 | A367 | Set of 2 | 40.00 | 40.00 |

**Souvenir Sheets**

| | | | | |
|---|---|---|---|---|
| 1878-1879 | A367 | Set of 2 | 42.50 | 42.50 |

Marine Life — A368

Designs: No. 1880, 400fr, Chaetodon semilarvatus. No. 1881, 400fr, Amphiprion ocellarus. No. 1882, 450fr, Gramma malecara. No. 1883, 450fr, Amphiprion bicinctuc.

No. 1884, 200fr: a, Diodon hystrix. b, Synchiropus splendidos. c, Lactoria cornuta. d, Canthigaster solandri. e, Gymnothorax tesselatus. f, Gramma loreto.

No. 1885, 200fr: a, Synchiropus picturatus. b, Pygoplytes diacanthus. c, Pomacanthus imperator. d, Holocanthus ciliaris. e, Phinecanthus aculeatus. f, Lienardella fasciatus.

No. 1886, 5000fr, Pterois antennata, vert. No. 1887, 5000fr, Hippocampus kuda, vert.

**Perf. 13¼x13½, 13½x13¼**
**2001, Feb. 28**

| | | | | |
|---|---|---|---|---|
| 1880-1883 | A368 | Set of 4 | 6.00 | 6.00 |

**Sheets of 6, #a-f**

| | | | | |
|---|---|---|---|---|
| 1884-1885 | A368 | Set of 2 | 9.00 | 9.00 |

**Souvenir Sheets**

| | | | | |
|---|---|---|---|---|
| 1886-1887 | A368 | Set of 2 | 35.00 | 35.00 |

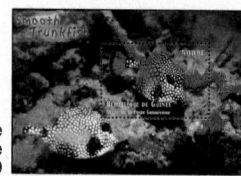

Marine Life A369

No. 1888, 1000fr: a, Jackknife fish. b, Requiem shark. c, Great white shark (Grand blanc). d, Holocanthus ciliaris. e, Brain coral. f, Bluehead wrasse.

No. 1889, 1000fr: a, Sergeant major. b, Bottlenose dolphin. c, Swordfish. d, Sea horse. e, Slate pencil urchin. f, Gold-spotted snake eel.

No. 1890, 1000fr: a, Great white shark (Grand requin blanc). b, Baird's beaked whale. c, Butterflyfish. d, Turtle. e, Solenostomus paradoxus. f, Australian pineapple fish.

No. 1891, 1000fr: a, Hawksbill turtle. b, Killer whale. c, Manta ray. d, Filefish. e, Graysby. f, Striped-eel catfish.

No. 1892, 5000fr, Smooth trunkfish. No. 1879, 5000fr, Dolphin.

**2001, Feb. 28**      **Perf. 13¼x13½**
**Sheets of 6, #a-f**

| | | | | |
|---|---|---|---|---|
| 1888-1891 | A369 | Set of 4 | 80.00 | 80.00 |

**Souvenir Sheets**

| | | | | |
|---|---|---|---|---|
| 1892-1893 | A369 | Set of 2 | 35.00 | 35.00 |

Flora and Fauna A370

No. 1894, 300fr — Bears: a, Spectacled bear. b, Giant panda. c, Silver bear. d, Cannelle (Pyreneean bear). e, Syrian bear. f, Grizzly bear.

No. 1895, 300fr — Primates: a, Howler monkey. b, Macaque. c, Drill. d, Yellow baboon. e, Anubis baboon. f, Gelada.

No. 1896, 300fr, vert. — Lemurs: a, Crowned lemur (couronné). b, Black lemur (macao). c, Albifrons lemur. d, Mongoz lemur. e, Sanfordi lemur. f, Fulvus lemur.

No. 1897, 300fr, vert. — Fish: a, Sebastes nigrocinctus. b, Lampris guttatus. c, Cyclopterus lumpus. d, Carnegiella strigata. e, Parosphromenus dreissneri. f, Syncniropus splendidus.

No. 1898, 300fr, vert. — Flowers: a, Peony (Pivoine des rocheuses). b, Hypericum richeri. c, Flamboyant. d, Bird of paradise (oiseau du paradis). e, Hesperantha petitiana. f, Moraea neopavonia.

No. 1899, 750fr — Lemurs: a, Lepilemur leucopus. b, Wooly avahi (avahi laineux). c, Black lemur (macao). d, Verreaux's sifaka (Propithecus verreauxi deckeni). e, Phaner. f, Verreaux's sifaka (Propithecus verrauxi majori).

No. 1900, 750fr — Flowers: a, Thunia alba. b, Eulophia guineensis. c, Polystacha bella. d, Oeceoclades maculata. e, Serapias cordigera. f, Angraecum distichum.

No. 1901, 750fr — Birds: a, Black cockatoo. b, Rosalbin cockatoo. c, Leadbetter's cockatoo. d, Goffin's cockatoo. e, Gray parrot. f, Senegal parrot.

No. 1902, 750fr, vert. — Owls: a, Hibou des marais. b, Hibou petit duc. c, Grand duc Americain. d, Chouette chevechette perlée. e, Hibou grand duc. f, Harphang des neiges.

No. 1903, 750fr, vert. — Insects: a, Giant Himalayan bee. b, Phyllium. c, Magicicada septemdecim. d, Petasida ephippigera. e, Graphosoma semipunctatum. f, Honeybee.

**2001, Mar. 28**    **Litho.**    **Perf. 13¼**
**Sheets of 6, #a-f**

| | | | | |
|---|---|---|---|---|
| 1894-1903 | A370 | Set of 10 | 125.00 | 125.00 |

Guinean Railways Locomotive — A371

Design: 200fr, Front view. 300fr, Side view, horiz. 750fr, Rear view.

**2001, May 16**

| | | | | |
|---|---|---|---|---|
| 1904-1906 | A371 | Set of 3 | 5.50 | 5.50 |

Nos. 1904-1906 each exist in souvenir sheets of 1, containing stamps lacking printer's inscription.

Locomotives A372

Designs: 300fr, Union Pacific Jupiter. 400fr, No. 7200 Philadelphia. 600fr, C-28 Type 2-8-0. 800fr, Wainwright P Type 0-6-0. 1300fr, Union Pacific Rogers 119. 1600fr, Northwestern 4-6-0 steam engine.

No. 1913, 950fr: a, Oliver Cromwell. b, Big Boy 4-8-8-4 No. 4019. c, 1858 Rogers. d, Gray Lady. e, Old No. 1. f, Jones Goods 2-4-0.

No. 1914, 950fr: a, Jubilee Type No. SS96. b, Iron Horse. c, 4-6-0. d, Type OS2 2-10-0. e, Single Driver 1887 Johnson. f, King George V 4-6-0.

No. 1915, 950fr: a, Hardwicke Western 2-4-0, No. 790. b, High-wheeled Pacific, Texas State Railroad. c, Longhorne. d, City of Truro 4-4-0 No. 3440. e, Leander Type Jubilee. f, The American.

No. 1916, 4000fr, Stanier Black 5-4-6-0. No. 1917, 4000fr, LMS 5305. No. 1918, 4000fr, Duchess of Hamilton.

**2001, June 8**      **Perf. 13¼x13½**

| | | | | |
|---|---|---|---|---|
| 1907-1912 | A372 | Set of 6 | 21.00 | 21.00 |

**Sheets of 6, #a-f**

| | | | | |
|---|---|---|---|---|
| 1913-1915 | A372 | Set of 3 | 70.00 | 70.00 |

**Souvenir Sheets**

| | | | | |
|---|---|---|---|---|
| 1916-1918 | A372 | Set of 3 | 55.00 | 55.00 |

Locomotives A373

Designs: 500fr, Ae 6/6 Co-Co electric. 750fr, Hikari Super Express. 1000fr, Krauss-Maffei V200 Diesel-electric. 1250fr, 46 Type electric.

No. 1923, 950fr: a, EW Type Bo-Bo-Bo electric. b, 68000 Type Diesel-electric. c, Type Ge 6/6 electric. d, 19,000 horsepower Diesel-electric. e, Express Co-Co electric. f, AL6 Bo-Bo electric.

No. 1924, 950fr: a, 1,750 horsepower Diesel-electric. b, 7000 Co-Co electric. c, Type E10 Bo-Bo electric. d, D341 Type Diesel-electric. e, Diesel-hydraulic express. f, 5E1 electric.

No. 1925, 4000fr, Santa Fe F9 Diesel-electric. No. 1926, 4000fr, Type SSI Co-Co electric. No. 1918, 4000fr, Union Pacific electric.

**2001, June 8**

| | | | | |
|---|---|---|---|---|
| 1919-1922 | A373 | Set of 4 | 15.00 | 15.00 |

**Sheets of 6, #a-f**
1923-1924 A373 Set of 2 45.00 45.00
**Souvenir Sheets**
1925-1927 A373 Set of 3 55.00 55.00
Belgica 2001 Intl. Stamp Exhibition, Brussels.

Locomotives
A374

Designs: 750fr, Type 18 4-6-2, Allemagne. 1000fr, ICE. 1250fr, Type G.
No. 1931, 950fr: a, Type WP 4-6-2. b, ETR 450. c, EU-07 Bo-Bo. d, Type 25 4-8-4. e, TGV. f, Type 345 Bo-Bo.
No. 1932, 950fr: a, Type SY 2-6-2. b, GM F7 War Bonnet. c, Type 4-4-0. d, Type A2/1 4-6-2. e, Type BB 22200. f, Type OL-49 4-6-2.
No. 1933, 4000fr, VT601. No. 1934, 4000fr, Type QJ 2-10-2.

**2001, June 8**
1928-1930 A374 Set of 3 13.00 13.00
**Sheets of 6, #a-f**
1931-1932 A374 Set of 2 45.00 45.00
**Souvenir Sheets**
1933-1934 A374 Set of 2 37.50 37.50
Belgica 2001 Intl. Egyptian Exhibition, Brussels.

Famous People
A375

No. 1935 — Explorers: a, Vasco da Gama. b, Sir Francis Drake. c, Ferdinand Magellan. d, Capt. James Cook. e, Jacques Cartier. f, Christopher Columbus.
No. 1936: a, Albert Einstein. b, Albert Schweitzer. c, Henri Dunant. d, Sir Alexander Fleming. e, Marie Curie. f, Louis Pasteur.
No. 1937 — Space pioneers: a, Yuri Gagarin. b, John Glenn. c, Edward White. d, Neil Armstrong. e, John Young. f, Thomas Stafford and Alexei Leonov.
No. 1938 — Pope John Paul II: a, As baby, with mother and dove. b, Wearing miter and holding crucifix. c, In garden. d, Kneeling. e, Holding crucifix, with dove. f, With arms raised.
No. 1939 — Lord Robert Baden-Powell, Scouts and: a, Psittacus enthacus. b, Charaxes eupale. c, Pluvianus aegyptius. d, Catacroptera cloanthe. e, Merops albicollis. f, Euphaedra eupalus.

**2001, June 14** Perf. 13¼
**Sheets of 6, #a-f**
1935 A375 350fr multi 10.00 10.00
1936 A375 450fr multi 12.00 12.00
1937 A375 475fr multi 13.00 13.00
1938 A375 600fr multi 16.00 16.00
1939 A375 750fr multi 21.00 21.00
Nos. 1935-1939 (5) 72.00 72.00
Nos. 1936a-1936f and 1939a-1939f each exist in souvenir sheets of one.

Birds — A377

Designs: 200fr, Guinea fowl (pintade vulturine). 250fr, African fish eagle (pygarve vocifer). 300fr, Striped hoopoe (huppe fasciée). 350fr, Jacana. 400fr, Secretary bird (serpentaire). 450fr, Wild Guinea fowl (pintade sauvage).
No. 1948, 950fr: a, Verreaux's eagle (aigle de verreaux). b, White pelican. c, Swallow (hirondelle de rivage). d, Egyptian geese (ouette d'Egypte). e, Crane (grue cendrée). f, Heron.
No. 1949, 950fr: a, Swallow (hirondelle de fenetre). b, Dwarf bee-eater (guepier nain). c, Blue rock thrush (merle solitaire rouge). d, Senegal jabiru. e, Ibis. f, Purple swamphen (talève sultane).

No. 1950, 950fr: a, Vulture (vautour chaugoun). b, Red and yellow barbet (barbican à tete rouge). c, Buzzard (buse rounoir). d, Tufted lark (cochevis). e, Gray wagtail (bergeronnette des ruisseaux). f, Red-heades shrike (pie grieche à tete rouge).
No. 1951, 4000fr, Flamingo (petit flamant). No. 1952, 4000fr, Anhinga. No. 1953, 4000fr, Marabout. No. 1954, 4000fr, Ostrich (autriche).

**2001, Aug. 27** Perf. 13½x13¼
1942-1947 A377 Set of 6 8.50 8.50
**Sheets of 6, #a-f**
1948-1950 A377 Set of 3 52.50 52.50
**Souvenir Sheets**
1951-1954 A377 Set of 4 16.50 16.50
Phila Nippon '01, Japan (#1948-1954).

Birds — A378

Designs: 200fr, Heron. 300fr, Ibis. 500fr, Stonechat (tarier patre). 550fr, Sparrow (hirondelle striée). 600fr, Egyptian courser (pluvian fluviatile). 650fr, Jacana.
No. 1961, 750fr: a, Variable sunbird (souimanga à ventre jaune). b, Long-tailed sunbird (souimanga à longue queue). c, Scarlet-chested sunbird (souimanga à poitrine rouge). d, Abyssinian roller (rollier d'Abyssinie). e, Blue-breasted roller (rollier à ventre bleu). f, Broad-billed roller (rolle violet).
No. 1962, 750fr: a, Black bee-eater (guepier noir). b, Blue-headed bee-eater (guepier à tete bleue). c, White-throated bee-eater (guepier à gorge blanche). d, Red-throated bee-eater (guepier à gorge rouge). e, Rosy bee-eater (guepier gris-rose). f, Carmine bee-eater (guepier supreme).
No. 1963, 750fr: a, Blue-breasted kingfisher (martin-chasseur à poitrine bleue). b, Gray-headed kingfisher (martin-chasseur à tete grise). c, Chocolate-backed kingfisher (martin-chasseur marron). d, Dwarf kingfisher (martin-pécheur à tete rousse). e, Malachite kingfisher (martin-pécheur huppé). f, Giant kingfisher (alcyon géant).
No. 1964, 4000fr, Touraco. No. 1965, 4000fr, White-faced whistling duck (dendrocygne veuf). No. 1966, 4000fr, Denham's bustard (outarde du Denham).

**2001, Aug. 27**
1955-1960 A378 Set of 6 11.00 11.00
**Sheets of 6, #a-f**
1961-1963 A378 Set of 3 55.00 55.00
**Souvenir Sheets**
1964-1966 A378 Set of 3 52.50 52.50
Phila Nippon '01, Japan (#1961-1966).

A379

Les Papillons D'Afrique

Butterflies — A380

Designs: 700fr, Icolotis zoe. 750fr, Catopsilia florella. 800fr, Kallimoides rumia. 850fr, Charaxes eupale. No. 1971, 950fr, Physcaeneura leda. 1000fr, Mylothris chloris.
No. 1973, 900fr: a, Papilio demodocus. b, Anaphaeis auroto. c, Charaxes superbus. d, Amauris echeria. e, Euxanthe wakefieldi. f, Papilio dardanus.
No. 1974, 900fr: a, Hypolimnas salmacis. b, Myrena silenus. c, Charaxes smagardus. d, Papilio zalmoxis. e, Salamis parnassus. f, Charaxes bohemani.

No. 1975, 900fr: a, Charaxes fournierae. b, Eurema floricola. c, Mimacraea marshalli. d, Charaxes candiope. e, Catacroptera cloanthe. f, Danaus chrysippus.
No. 1976, 950fr: a, Castalius isis. b, Axioceres amanga. c, Eurema brenda. d, Epamera stenogrammica. e, Pseudaletis agrippina. f, Alaena margaritalea.
No. 1977, 950fr: a, Papilio dardanus, diff. b, Charaxes eupale, diff. c, Acraea cerasa. d, Precis clelia. e, Colotis celimene. f, Pseudacraea poggei.
No. 1978, 4000fr, Papilio antimachus. No. 1979, 4000fr, Acraea zetes. No. 1980, 4000fr, Colotis danae.
No. 1981, 4000fr, Hypolimnas deceptor. No. 1982, 4000fr, Euphaedra perseis.

**2001, Aug. 27** Perf. 13¼x13½
1967-1972 A379 Set of 6 20.00 20.00
**Sheets of 6, #a-f**
1973-1975 A379 Set of 3 21.00 21.00
1976-1977 A380 Set of 2 35.00 35.00
**Souvenir Sheets**
1978-1980 A379 Set of 3 52.50 52.50
1981-1982 A380 Set of 2 35.00 35.00
Phila Nippon '01, Japan (#1973-1982). Rectangles replace the accented "e's" on all stamps of type A380.

Hummingbirds
A387

Designs: No. 2038, 900fr, Anthracothorax manga. No. 2039, 900fr, Eulampis holosericeus. No. 2040, 1000fr, Archilochus colubris. No. 2041, 1000fr, Chlorostilbon ricordii.
No. 2042, 1000fr: a, Selasphorus rufus. b, Mellisuga helenae. c, Eutoxeres aquila. d, Anthracothorax viridis. e, Allamanda cathartica. f, Orthorhynchus cristatus.
No. 2043, 1000fr: a, Archilochus alexandri. b, Calliphlox evelynae. c, Chlorostilbon maugaeus. d, Musta ornata. e, Phaethornis superciliosus. f, Eulampis jugularis.
No. 2044, 1000fr: a, Cyanophaia bicolor. b, Glaucis hirsuta. c, Chlorostilbon swainsonni. d, Heliconia. e, Heliconia bihai. f, Anthracothorax dominicus.
No. 2045, 4000fr, Amazilia violiceps. No. 2046, 4000fr, Trochilus scitulus. No. 2047, 4000fr, Trochilus polytmus, vert.

**Perf. 13¼x13½, 13½x13¼**
2001 Litho.
2038-2041 A387 Set of 4 14.00 14.00
**Sheets of 6, #a-f**
2042-2044 A387 Set of 3 65.00 65.00
**Souvenir Sheets**
2045-2047 A387 Set of 3 47.50 47.50

Trains of Africa — A390

Designs: No. 2050, 750fr, 0-6-4, Z.A.S.M. Transvaal, 1858. No. 2051, 750fr, 4-6-2, Central South Africa, 1858. No. 2052, 750fr, 4-4-0, Cape Province, 1903. No. 2053, 750fr, 4-8-2 Class 12, South Africa, 1920. No. 2054, 750fr, 4-6-2 Class 10 RB, South Africa, 1950. No. 2055, 750fr, 4-8-2, Benguela, 1951. No. 2056, 750fr, 4-6-4+4-6-4 Class 15A, South Africa, 1952. No. 2057, 750fr, 4-8-4 Class 25 NC, South Africa, 1953.
No. 2058, 200fr: a, Cape Province locomotive, 1895. b, 2-8-2, Central South Africa, 1920. c, 4-4-2, Cape Province, 1898. d, 4-8-2 Class 23, South Africa, 1930. e, Natal Province locomotive, 1901. f, 2-8-4 Class 24, South Africa, 1940.
No. 2059, 300fr: a, 4-6-2 Class 16E, South Africa, 1935. b, 4-8-4 Class 25, South Afirca, 1953. c, 2-D-1+1-D-2 Class 20, South Africa, 1954. d, 4-8-2+2-8-4 Class 59, East Africa, 1955. e, 1-Co-Co-1 Class 92, East Africa, 1971. f, 2-D-2 Class 26, South Africa, 1982.
No. 2060, 750fr: a, 4-8-2 Class 15F, South Africa, 1948. b, 4-8-2+2-8-4 GEA Beyer-Garret, South Africa, 1950. c, 4-8-2 Class 11, South Africa, 1951. d, 4-8-2+2-8-4 GEA Beyer-Garret, South Africa, 1954. e, 1-Co-Co-1 Class 4E, South Africa, 1954. f, Co-Co Class 9E, South Africa, 1978.
No. 2061, 4000fr, Umtali-Salisbury Class 4-4-0, 1897. No. 2062, 4000fr, Bo-Bo Class 5E, Blue Train, South Africa, 1969.

**2002, Feb. 8 Litho.** Perf. 13¼x13½
2050-2057 A390 Set of 8 21.00 21.00

**Sheets of 6, #a-f**
2058-2060 A390 Set of 3 26.50 26.50
**Souvenir Sheets**
2061-2062 A390 Set of 2 12.00 12.00

Watercraft — A391

Designs: No. 2063, 750fr, Three-masted schooner, 1866. No. 2064, 750fr, Two-masted schooner, 1932. No. 2065, 750fr, Bark, 1968. No. 2066, 750fr, Sailboard. No. 2067, 750fr, Galleass, 16th cent., horiz. No. 2068, 750fr, Sailboat, horiz.
No. 2069, 750fr: a, Galleon, 16th cent. b, 17th cent. ship. c, Corvette, 18th cent. d, Gaffrig yacht. e, Dinghy. f, Catamaran.
No. 2070, 4000fr, Full-rigged ship, 20th cent., horiz. No. 2071, 4000fr, Pinnace, 17th cent., horiz.

**Perf. 13½x13¼, 13¼x13½**
2002, Feb. 8
2063-2068 A391 Set of 6 16.00 16.00
2069 A391 750fr Sheet of 6, #a-f 17.00 17.00
**Souvenir Sheets**
2070-2071 A391 Set of 2 12.00 12.00
Nos. 2070-2071 each contain one 56x42mm stamp.

Airplanes and Ships A392

No. 2072, 750fr: a, Wright Brothers Flyer. b, Super Sabre F-100. c, Junkers J1. d, De Havilland Comet. e, Douglas DC-3. f, Boeing 747.
No. 2073, 750fr: a, Egyptian wooden boat. b, 18th cent. sailboat. c, Viking longboat. d, Great Eastern. e, Spanish galleon, 16th cent. f, Savannah.
No. 2074, 4000fr, Concorde. No. 2075, 4000fr, Ocean Princess.

**2002, Feb. 8** Perf. 13¼x13½
**Sheets of 6, #a-f**
2072-2073 A392 Set of 2 9.25 9.25
**Souvenir Sheets**
2074-2075 A392 Set of 2 8.25 8.25

First Zeppelin Flight, Cent. A393

No. 2076: a, LZ-3. b, LZ-5. c, USS Macon. d, Zeppelin NT.
No. 2077, 4000fr, LZ-4. No. 2078, 4000fr, LZ-129.

**2002, Feb. 8**
2076 A393 750fr Sheet of 4, #a-d 12.00 12.00
**Souvenir Sheets**
2077-2078 A393 Set of 2 12.00 12.00

Airplanes A394

No. 2079: a, Lockheed Streamliner. b, Dornier Do-X. c, Lockheed Vega. d, Boeing 707. e, Douglas DC-3. f, De Havilland Comet. 4000fr, Concorde.

**2002, Feb. 8**

| 2079 | A394 | 750fr | Sheet of 6, #a-f | 17.00 | 17.00 |
|---|---|---|---|---|---|

**Souvenir Sheet**

| 2080 | A394 | 4000fr multi | 6.00 | 6.00 |
|---|---|---|---|---|

Airplanes
A395

Designs: No. 2081, 750fr, Tupelov TU-144. No. 2082, 750fr, Tri-star L-1011. No. 2083, 750fr, Airbus A-300-B. No. 2084, 750fr, Boeing 777-200.

No. 2085, 750fr: a, Junkers G-24. b, Armstrong Whitworth XV Atalanta. c, Aerospatiale SE 210 Caravelle III. d, De Havilland D. H. 106 Comet 4B. e, Armstrong Whitworth 650 Argosy 100. f, Douglas DC-9.

No. 2086, 750fr: a, Wright Brothers Flyer. b, Vickers Vimy. c, Spirit of St. Louis. d, Junkers G-38. e, Douglas DC-3. f, Vickers-Armstrong Viscount 700.

No. 2087, 4000fr, Boeing 747. No. 2088, 4000fr, Airbus A-3XX.

**2002, Feb. 8**

| 2081-2084 | A395 | Set of 4 | 11.00 | 11.00 |
|---|---|---|---|---|

**Sheets of 6, #a-f**

| 2085-2086 | A395 | Set of 2 | 32.50 | 32.50 |
|---|---|---|---|---|

**Souvenir Sheets**

| 2087-2088 | A395 | Set of 2 | 12.00 | 12.00 |
|---|---|---|---|---|

Military
Aircraft — A396

Designs: No. 2089, 750fr, Sopwith Camel. No. 2090, 750fr, Fokker Dr-1. No. 2091, 750fr, Messerschmitt Bf-109 E. No. 2092, 750fr, Mitsubishi Zero. No. 2093, 750fr, Northrop F-20 Tigershark. No. 2094, 750fr, Dassault-Breguet Mirage 2000.

No. 2095, 750fr: a, S.E. 5A. b, Fokker D-VII. c, Thomas Morse S4C. d, De Havilland D.H. 2. e, Boeing PW-9D. f, Spad XIII.

No. 2096, 750fr: a, Mustang P-51. b, Junkers Ju-87R. c, Curtiss Hawk 75A. d, Hawker Hurricane. e, Nakajima Ki-43 Hayabusa. f, Macchi M.C. 200 Saetta.

No. 2097, 750fr: a, Panavia Tornado Gr. Mk1. b, Mikoyan-Gurevich MiG-15. c, Vought A-7D Corsair 11. d, BAe Sea Harrier FRS Mk1. e, General Dynamics F-111. f, Dassault/Breguet Dornier Alpha Jet.

No. 2098, 4000fr, Saab Draken J35. No. 2099, 4000fr, Supermarine Spitfire.

**2002, Feb. 8**

| 2089-2094 | A396 | Set of 6 | 16.00 | 16.00 |
|---|---|---|---|---|

**Sheets of 6, #a-f**

| 2095-2097 | A396 | Set of 3 | 52.50 | 52.50 |
|---|---|---|---|---|

**Souvenir Sheets**

| 2098-2099 | A396 | Set of 2 | 12.00 | 12.00 |
|---|---|---|---|---|

Antique Automobiles — A397

No. 2100, 1000fr: a, 1920 Rolls-Royce. b, 1896 Ford. c, 1930 Hispano-Suiza. d, 1924 Stoewer Allemagne D10 D12. e, 1924 Chrysler. f, 1912 Hudson.

No. 2101, 1000fr: a, 1930 Bugatti SIA. b, 1901 Mercedes. c, 1926 Jordan Playboy. d, 1936 Cadillac V-16. e, 1914 Stutz Bearcat. f, 1904 Daimler.

No. 2102, 4000fr, 1886 Daimler-Benz. No. 2103, 4000fr, 1903 Ford Model A.

**2002, Feb. 8**      *Perf. 13¼x13½*

**Sheets of 6, #a-f**

| 2100-2101 | A397 | Set of 2 | 42.50 | 42.50 |
|---|---|---|---|---|

**Souvenir Sheets**

| 2102-2103 | A397 | Set of 2 | 12.00 | 12.00 |
|---|---|---|---|---|

Race
Cars — A398

Designs: No. 2104, 750fr, Marmon Wasp, 1911 Indianapolis 500. No. 2105, 750fr, Ferrari Dino 246, 1958 French Grand Prix. No. 2106, 750fr, Lotus 49, 1967 German Grand Prix. No. 2107, Tyrell 003, 1971 American Grand Prix.

No. 2108, 750fr: a, Mercedes, 1914 French Grand Prix. b, Duesenberg, 1921 French Grand Prix. c, Bugatti, 1924 French Grand Prix. d, Alfa Romeo P3, 1934 French Grand Prix. e, Auto Union, 1937 Nürburgring Rally. f, Maserati 8C, 1939 German Grand Prix.

No. 2109, 750fr: a, Vanwall, 1957 British Grand Prix. b, Cooper T43, 1958 Argentine Grand Prix. c, Lotus 25, 1965 British Grand Prix. d, Brabham-Repro BT-19, 1966 French Grand Prix. e, Renault RS 01, 1977 British Grand Prix. f, Ferrari 640, 1989 Brazilian Grand Prix.

No. 2110, 4000fr, Coventry Daimler, 1899 Paris-Ostende Race. No. 2111, 4000fr, Penske PC-23, 1994 Portland Race.

**2002, Feb. 8**

| 2104-2107 | A398 | Set of 4 | 11.00 | 11.00 |
|---|---|---|---|---|

**Sheets of 6, #a-f**

| 2108-2109 | A398 | Set of 2 | 17.00 | 17.00 |
|---|---|---|---|---|

**Souvenir Sheets**

| 2110-2111 | A398 | Set of 2 | 12.00 | 12.00 |
|---|---|---|---|---|

Pres. John F. Kennedy (1917-63) — A400

No. 2113: a, With ship's wheel. b, With doves. c, With arch.
4000fr, At podium with flag and map.

**2002, Feb. 20**      *Perf. 13½x13¼*      **Litho.**

| 2113 | A400 | 750fr Horiz. strip of 3, #a-c | 8.00 | 8.00 |
|---|---|---|---|---|

**Souvenir Sheet**

| 2114 | A400 | 4000fr multi | 7.00 | 7.00 |
|---|---|---|---|---|

No. 2113 printed in sheets of 2 strips.

Pres. Ronald Reagan (1911-2004) — A401

No. 2115: a, With stars. b, With curtain. c, With US Capitol.
4000fr, With Statue of Liberty and Presidential seal.

**2002, Feb. 20**

| 2115 | A401 | 750fr Horiz. strip of 3, #a-c | 8.00 | 8.00 |
|---|---|---|---|---|

**Souvenir Sheet**

| 2116 | A401 | 4000fr multi | 7.00 | 7.00 |
|---|---|---|---|---|

No. 2115 printed in sheets of 2 strips.

Princess Diana (1961-97) — A402

No. 2117: a, Wearing tiara. b, Holding flowers. c, Wearing hat.
4000fr, Wearing black dress.

**2002, Feb. 20**

| 2117 | A402 | 750fr Horiz. strip of 3, #a-c | 8.00 | 8.00 |
|---|---|---|---|---|

**Souvenir Sheet**

| 2118 | A402 | 4000fr multi | 7.00 | 7.00 |
|---|---|---|---|---|

No. 2117 printed in sheets of 2 strips.

Prince William of Wales
A403

No. 2119, 750fr: a, Wearing brown checked shirt. b, Wearing jacket and bow tie. c, Wearing green sweater. d, Wearing lilac sweater. e, Wearing brown suit, white shirt and blue tie. f, Wearing brown suit, striped shirt and blue gray tie.

No. 2120, 750fr: a, Wearing blue shirt. b, Wearing blue suit, blue background. c, Wearing riding helmet. d, Wearing blue suit, white background. e, Wearing blue sweater. f, Wearing ski gear.

No. 2121, 4000fr, With Prince Harry. No. 2122, 4000fr, With Prince Charles, horiz.

*Perf. 13½x13¼, 13¼x13½*

**2002, Feb. 20**      **Sheets of 6, #a-f**

| 2119-2120 | A403 | Set of 2 | 32.50 | 32.50 |
|---|---|---|---|---|

**Souvenir Sheets**

| 2121-2122 | A403 | Set of 2 | 14.00 | 14.00 |
|---|---|---|---|---|

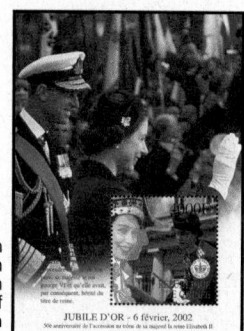

Queen Elizabeth II, 50th Anniv. of Reign
A404

No. 2123: a, Wearing blue coat and gloves. b, With Prince Philip. c, Wearing gray coat and hat. d, Wearing yellow suit and hat.
4000fr, Wearing red uniform.

**2002, Feb. 20**      *Perf. 14¼*

| 2123 | A404 | 1400fr Sheet of 4, #a-d | 12.00 | 12.00 |
|---|---|---|---|---|

**Souvenir Sheet**

| 2124 | A404 | 4000fr multi | 7.00 | 7.00 |
|---|---|---|---|---|

A405

A406

Elvis Presley (1935-77) — A407

No. 2125 — Background color: a, Blue. b, Yellow. c, Red. d, Pink. e, Lilac. f, Yellow green.

No. 2126: a, Red and white shirt. b, Blue shirt. c, Black and brown shirt. d, Purple shirt. e, Red jacket with neckerchief. f, Red shirt.

No. 2127: a, Wearing red and white shirt with scarf. b, Wearing black jacket and gray shirt. c, Holding guitar on shoulder. d, With hands resting on guitar. e, Singing. f, Wearing army uniform.

**2002, Feb. 20**      *Perf. 13½x13¼*

| 2125 | A405 | 750fr Sheet of 6, #a-f | 18.00 | 18.00 |
|---|---|---|---|---|
| 2126 | A406 | 750fr Sheet of 6, #a-f | 18.00 | 18.00 |
| 2127 | A407 | 750fr Sheet of 6, #a-f | 18.00 | 18.00 |

Nobel Prize Physics Laureates — A408

No. 2128, each 750fr: a, Hendrik Lorentz, 1902. b, Pieter Zeeman, 1902. c, Sir Joseph Thomson, 1906. d, Gabriel Lippman, 1908. e, Max von Laue, 1914. f, Jean B. Perrin, 1926.

No. 2129, each 750fr: a, Owen Richardson, 1928. b, Sir Chandrasekhara Venkata Raman, 1930. c, Victor F. Hess, 1936. d, Carl D. Anderson, 1936. e, Sir George Thompson, 1937. f, Clinton Davisson, 1937.

No. 2130, each 750fr: a, Enrico Fermi, 1938. b, Ernest Lawrence, 1939. c, Isidor I. Rabi, 1944. d, Patrick Blackett, 1948. e, Fritz Zernike, 1953. f, Donald A. Glaser, 1960.

No. 2131, each 750fr: a, Alfred Kastler, 1966. b, Luis W. Alvarez, 1968. c, Murray Gell-Mann, 1969. d, John Bardeen, 1972. e, Leon N. Cooper, 1972. f, John R, Schrieffer, 1972.

No. 2132: 4000fr, Wilhelm Röntgen, 1901. No. 2133, 4000fr, Marie Curie, 1903. No. 2134, 4000fr, Pierre Curie, 1903. No. 2135, 4000fr, Antoine Henri Becquerel, 1903.

**2002, Feb. 20**      **Litho.**

**Sheets of 6, #a-f**

| 2128-2131 | A408 | Set of 4 | 72.50 | 72.50 |
|---|---|---|---|---|

**Souvenir Sheets**

| 2132-2135 | A408 | Set of 4 | 27.50 | 27.50 |
|---|---|---|---|---|

Nobel Prizes, cent. (in 2001).

Albert Einstein (1879-1955), Physicist — A409

No. 2136: a, Smoking pipe. b, Wearing black jacket and tie, facing left. c, Wearing blue sweater. d, Wearing black jacket and tie, facing right. e, Wearing black sweater. f, Wearing brown jacket.
4000fr, With wife, Elsa.

**2002, Feb. 20**

| 2136 | A409 | 750fr Sheet of 6, #a-f | 17.00 | 17.00 |
|---|---|---|---|---|

**Souvenir Sheet**

| 2137 | A409 | 4000fr multi | 7.00 | 7.00 |
|---|---|---|---|---|

Pres. Theodore Roosevelt (1858-1919) — A410

No. 2138: a, As Assistant Navy Secretary. b, In Cuba, 1898. c, In Yellowstone Park, 1903. d, As President, 1901-09. e, Campaigning for war preparedness, 1916. f, In 1917.
4000fr, As colonel in Rough Riders.

**2002, Feb. 20**                          **Perf. 13¼**
2138 A410   950fr Sheet of 6,                      21.00 21.00
              #a-f
**Souvenir Sheet**
2139 A410   4000fr multi                            7.00  7.00

Jacqueline Kennedy Onassis (1929-94), First Lady — A411

Designs: No. 2140, 1000fr, Wearing white blouse, yellow background. 2000fr, With Pres. John F. Kennedy, horiz. No. 2142, 4000fr, Wearing Inaugural Ball gown.
No. 2143: a, Wearing necklace, shoulders showing, green background. b, Wearing hat. c, Facing left, green background. d, Wearing necklace, orange background. e, Wearing necklace, shoulders covered, green background. f, Wearing sunglasses.
No. 2144, 4000fr, As child.

**Perf. 13½x13¼, 13¼x13½**
**2002, Feb. 20**
2140-2142 A411   Set of 3              26.00 26.00
2143 A411   1000fr Sheet of 6,                      24.00 24.00
              #a-f
**Souvenir Sheet**
2144 A411   4000fr multi                            7.00  7.00

Famous People — A412

Designs: No. 2145, 750fr, Pres. John F. Kennedy (1917-63). No. 2146, 750fr, Pres. Ronald Reagan (1911-2004). No. 2147, 750fr, Chiune Sugihara, Japanese diplomat who saved Jews in World War II. No. 2148, 750fr, Queen Elizabeth II as younger woman, denomination at right. No. 2149, 750fr, Queen Elizabeth II wearing tiara, denomination at left. No. 2150, 750fr, Princess Diana (1961-97). No. 2151, 750fr, Queen Mother Elizabeth (1900-2002). No. 2152, 750fr, Prince William of Wales, denomination in red. No. 2153, 750fr, Prince William of Wales, denomination in yellow. No. 2154, 750fr, Prince William of Wales, denomination in violet. No. 2155, 750fr, Hereditary Prince Haakon and Princess Mette-Marie of Norway, horiz. No. 2156, 750fr, Prince Philippe and Princess Mathilde of Belgium, horiz.

**2002, Feb. 20**                          **Perf. 14**
2145-2156 A412   Set of 12             32.50 32.50

2002 Winter Olympic Games, Salt Lake City — A413

Designs: No. 2157, 750fr, Biathlon. No. 2158, 750fr, Luge. No. 2159, 750fr, Skiing. No. 2160, 750fr, Snowboarding, vert.

**Perf. 13¼x13½, 13½x13¼**
**2002, Feb. 20**
2157-2160 A413   Set of 4              11.00 11.00

Japanese Entertainment — A414

No. 2161, 750fr — Film stars: a, Miyoshi Umeki. b, Kimiko Ikegami. c, Masahiro Takashima. d, Sessue Hayakawa. e, Toshiro Mifune. f, Kaho Minami.
No. 2162, 750fr — Kabuki actors: a, Shinnosuke as Sukeroku. b, Kikugoro as Genkuro Kitsune. c, Ganjiro as Izaemon. d, Kikunosuke as Shiratama. e, Kikunosuke as Keisei. f, Shinnosuke as Matsuomaru.
No. 2163, 4000fr, Akira Kurosawa, film director. No. 2164, 4000fr, Danjuro as Kampei and Tamasaburo as Okaru, horiz.

**Perf. 13½x13¼, 13¼x13½**
**2002, Feb. 20**         **Sheets of 6, #a-f**
2161-2162 A414   Set of 2              32.50 32.50
**Souvenir Sheets**
2163-2164 A414   Set of 2              14.00 14.00

Scouts A422

No. 2208 — Scouts and shells: a, 200fr, Cypraea caurica. b, 300fr, Olivella nana. c, 5000fr, Marginella persicula.
No. 2209 — Scouts and sea mammals: a, 200fr, Balaena mysticetus. b, 300fr, Tursiops truncatus. c, 5000fr, Delphinus delphis.
No. 2210 — Scouts and dinosaurs: a, 200fr, Spinosaurus. b, 300fr, Ouranosaurus. c, 5000fr, Kentrosaurus.
No. 2211 — Scouts and dogs: a, 200fr, Bouvier Bernois. b, 750fr, Chihuahua. c, 5000fr, Irish wolfhound.
No. 2212 — Scouts and meteorites from: a, 200fr, Tatahouine. b, 750fr, Gao-Guenie. c, 5000fr, Great Sand Sea.
No. 2213 — Scouts and cats: a, 300fr, Japanese bobtail. b, 750fr, Egyptian Mau. c, 5000fr, Bombay.
No. 2214 — Scouts and minerals: a, 300fr, Anglesite. b, 750fr, Brucite. c, 5000fr, Beudantite.
No. 2215 — Scouts and mushrooms: a, 300fr, Aseroe rubra. b, 750fr, Boletus edulis. c, 5000fr, Hygrocybe punicea.
No. 2216 — Scouts and butterflies: a, 300fr, Anaphe panda. b, 750fr, Eurema brigitta. c, 5000fr, Acraea zetes.

**2002, Dec. 27   Litho.   Perf. 13¼**
**Sheets of 3, #a-c**
2208-2216 A422   Set of 9              62.50 62.50
Each stamp exists in souvenir sheet of 1.

Nicolaus August Otto (1832-91), Engineer — A423

Wright Brothers and Wright Flyer — A424

Astronaut Spacewalking A425

Pierre de Coubertin (1863-1937), Intl. Olympic Committee President A426

Winston Churchill, Franklin D. Roosevelt and Joseph Stalin A427

Newspaper Mastheads A428

Ferris Wheels on Film — A429

**2002**          **Perf. 13½x13¼, 13¼x13½**
2217 A423   200fr multi               1.60 1.60
2218 A424   300fr multi               1.60 1.60
2219 A425   750fr multi               1.60 1.60
2220 A426   1000fr multi              1.60 1.60
2221 A427   1250fr multi              1.60 1.60
2222 A428   1500fr multi              1.60 1.60
2223 A429   2000fr multi              1.60 1.60

Space — A430

Designs: No. 2224, 3000fr, Multi-scout Mars Lander. No. 2225, 3000fr, Stardust Probe. No. 2226, 3000fr, Mars Rover. No. 2227, 3000fr, Ceres-Vesta Probe. No. 2228, 3000fr, Deep Space Probe. No. 2229, 3000fr, NGST Space Telescope. No. 2230, 3000fr, Rosetta Probe. No. 2231, 3000fr, NEAR Probe.
No. 2232, 1500fr, horiz.: a, Newton Space Telescope. b, Darwin Space Telescope. c, Kepler Space Telescope. d, Herschel Space Telescope. e, Plank Space Telescope. f, Xeus Space Telescope. g, Mars Orbiter. h, Net Lander.
No. 2233, 1500fr, horiz.: a, Mission Specialist 4 Kalpana Chawla. b, Payload Commander Michael P. Anderson. c, Mission Specialist 1 David M. Brown. d, Pilot William C. McCool. e, Mission Specialist 4 Laurel B. Clark. f, Payload Specialist 4 Ilan Ramon. g, Commander Rick D. Husband. h, Columbia Space Shuttle.
No. 2234, 3000fr, Chawla, diff. No. 2235, 3000fr, Anderson, diff. No. 2236, 3000fr, Brown, diff. No. 2237, 3000fr, McCool, diff. No. 2238, 3000fr, Clark, diff. No. 2239, 3000fr, Ramon, diff. No. 2240, 3000fr, Husband, diff. No. 2241, 3000fr, Columbia Space Shuttle, diff. No. 2242, 6000fr, Corot Space Telescope, horiz. No. 2243, 6000fr, Crew of ill-fated Columbia Space Shuttle mission STS-107, horiz.

**2003, Mar. 3**                          **Perf. 13¼**
2224-2231 A430   Set of 8              25.00 25.00
**Sheets of 8, #a-h**
2232-2233 A430   Set of 2              30.00 30.00
**Souvenir Sheets**
2234-2243 A430   Set of 10             37.50 37.50
Nos. 2242 and 2243 each contain one 50x41mm stamp. Nos. 2224-2231 each exist in souvenir sheets of 1.

2004 Summer Olympics, Athens — A431

Designs: No. 2244, 750fr, No. 2252, 3000fr, Triathlon and Pentathlon. No. 2245, 750fr, No. 2253, 3000fr, Archery. No. 2246, 1500fr, No. 2254, 3000fr, Table tennis. No. 2247, 1500fr, No. 2255, 3000fr, Taekwondo and Judo. No. 2248, 1500fr, No. 2256, 3000fr, Equestrian. No. 2249, 1500fr, No. 2257, 3000fr, Women's tennis. No. 2250, 1500fr, No. 2258, 3000fr, Swimming. No. 2251, 1500fr, No. 2259, 3000fr, Track and field.
No. 2260, 6000fr, Soccer.

**2003, Nov. 12**                          **Perf. 13¼**
2244-2251 A431   Set of 8              15.00 15.00
**Souvenir Sheets**
2252-2260 A431   Set of 9              30.00 30.00
2259a       Souvenir sheet, #2252,              12.00 12.00
              2257-2259
No. 2260 contains one 36x51mm stamp.

Pope John Paul II (1920-2005) A433

Pope: 100fr, Hugging man. 150fr, In vestments, with open arms. 200fr, Face. 300fr, Praying at microphone. 350fr, Praying. 400fr, Holding crucifix. 450fr, Blessing bishop. 500fr, Kissing ground and with arms raised. 550fr, With Black Madonna of Czestochowa. 600fr, Wounded in assassination attempt. 650fr, With man. 1000fr, With children and Virgin Mary. 1500fr, Handshake. 2000fr, With Lech Walesa. 2500fr, With people tearing down Berlin Wall. 3000fr, Washing feet. 3500fr, Shaking hands of Fidel Castro. 4000fr, Meeting other religious leaders. 4500fr, Praying near town. 5000fr, With Mother Teresa. 5500fr, Holding crucifix, near church and statue. 6000fr, With crosses. 6500fr, With his coat of arms. 7000fr, With United Nations emblem. 7500fr, With crowd. 8000fr, Holding staff, in prayer. 8500fr, Holding crucifix and offering blessing.

**2004**          **Litho.**          **Perf. 13x13¼**
2263 A433   100fr multi        —   —
2264 A433   150fr multi        —   —
2265 A433   200fr multi        —   —
2266 A433   300fr multi        —   —
2267 A433   350fr multi        —   —
2268 A433   400fr multi        —   —
2269 A433   450fr multi        —   —
2270 A433   500fr multi        —   —
2271 A433   550fr multi        —   —
2272 A433   600fr multi        —   —
2273 A433   650fr multi        —   —
2274 A433   1000fr multi       —   —
2275 A433   1500fr multi       —   —
2276 A433   2000fr multi       —   —
2277 A433   2500fr multi       —   —
2278 A433   3000fr multi       —   —
2279 A433   3500fr multi       —   —
2280 A433   4000fr multi       —   —
2281 A433   4500fr multi       —   —
2282 A433   5000fr multi       —   —
2283 A433   5500fr multi       —   —
2284 A433   6000fr multi       —   —
2285 A433   6500fr multi       —   —
2286 A433   7000fr multi       —   —
2287 A433   7500fr multi       —   —
2288 A433   8000fr multi       —   —
2289 A433   8500fr multi       —   —

**SEMI-POSTAL STAMPS**

Eye Examination SP1

Microscopic Examination SP2

#B13, Medical laboratory. #B14, Insect control. #B16, Surgical operation.

## Engraved and Lithographed

| 1960 | Unwmk. | | Perf. 11½ | |
|---|---|---|---|---|
| B12 | SP1 | 20fr + 10fr ultra & car | .95 | .60 |
| B13 | SP1 | 30fr + 20fr brn org & violet | .95 | .60 |
| B14 | SP1 | 40fr + 20fr rose lil & blue | 1.25 | .80 |
| B15 | SP2 | 50fr + 50fr grn & brn | 1.90 | 1.25 |
| B16 | SP2 | 100fr + 100fr lil & grn | 2.25 | 1.50 |
| | Nos. B12-B16 (5) | | 7.30 | 4.75 |

Issued for national health propaganda. For overprints see Nos. B25-B29.

Nos. 194-195 Surcharged in Red or Orange

| 1961, June 6 | | Photo. | |
|---|---|---|---|
| B17 | A17 | 25fr + 10fr (R or O) | 5.50 | 3.50 |
| B18 | A17 | 50fr + 20fr (R or O) | 5.50 | 3.50 |

Nos. B17-B18 exist with orange surcharges transposed: "1961 + 10FRS." on 50fr and "1961 + 20FRS." on 25fr.

Nos. 214-219 Surcharged in Green, Lilac, Orange or Blue

## Photo., Surcharge Engr.

### 1961, Dec. 8
### Multicolored Design; Granite Paper

| B19 | A20 | 5fr + 5fr brt grn (G) | .70 | .25 |
|---|---|---|---|---|
| B20 | A20 | 10fr + 5fr emer (G) | .75 | .25 |
| B21 | A20 | 25fr + 5fr lilac (L) | 1.90 | .35 |
| B22 | A20 | 40fr + 5fr org (O) | 2.50 | .45 |
| B23 | A20 | 50fr + 5fr red org (O) | 3.50 | .65 |
| B24 | A20 | 75fr + 5fr ultra (B) | 4.75 | .90 |
| | Nos. B19-B24 (6) | | 14.10 | 2.85 |

The surtax was for animal protection.

Nos. B12-B16 Overprinted in Red or Orange

## Engr. & Litho.

| 1962, Feb. | | | Perf. 11½ | |
|---|---|---|---|---|
| B25 | SP1 | 20fr + 10fr (R or O) | .35 | .25 |
| B26 | SP1 | 30fr + 20fr (R or O) | .50 | .35 |
| B27 | SP1 | 40fr + 20fr (R or O) | .60 | .40 |
| B28 | SP2 | 50fr + 50fr (R or O) | 1.25 | .80 |
| B29 | SP2 | 100fr + 100fr (R or O) | 2.40 | 1.60 |
| | Nos. B25-B29 (5) | | 5.10 | 3.40 |

WHO drive to eradicate malaria. No. B25 also exists with black overprint.

Nos. 223-228 Srchd. in Red

## Photo., Surcharge Engr.

| 1962, May 14 | | | Perf. 13x14 | |
|---|---|---|---|---|
| B30 | A22 | 5fr + 5fr multi | .40 | .25 |
| B31 | A22 | 10fr + 5fr multi | .50 | .25 |
| B32 | A22 | 25fr + 5fr multi | .65 | .25 |
| B33 | A22 | 40fr + 5fr multi | .90 | .45 |
| B34 | A22 | 50fr + 5fr multi | 1.50 | .75 |
| B35 | A22 | 75fr + 5fr multi | 3.50 | 1.75 |
| | Nos. B30-B35 (6) | | 7.45 | 3.70 |

The surtax was for bird protection.

Nos. 232-233 Surcharged & Overprinted in Orange or Red

---

| 1962, Nov. 1 | Litho. | | Perf. 13 | |
|---|---|---|---|---|
| B36 | A24 | 25fr + 15fr multi | .60 | .45 |
| B37 | A24 | 75fr + 25fr multi | 1.40 | .90 |

Issued to help Algerian refugees.

Astronomers and Space Phenomena SP3

No. B38, Helical nebula. No. B39, Orion nebula. No. B40, Eagle nebula. No. B41, Trifide nebula. No. B42, Eta-carinae nebula. No. B43, NGC-2264 nebula. No. B44, Horse's Head nebula.

| 1989, Mar. 7 | Litho. | | Perf. 13½ | |
|---|---|---|---|---|
| B38 | SP3 | 100fr +25fr multi | 1.00 | .40 |
| B39 | SP3 | 150fr +25fr multi | 1.50 | .80 |
| B40 | SP3 | 200fr +25fr multi | 2.25 | 1.00 |
| B41 | SP3 | 250fr +25fr multi | 2.75 | 1.50 |
| B42 | SP3 | 300fr +25fr multi | 3.25 | 1.50 |
| B43 | SP3 | 500fr +25fr multi | 5.25 | 2.40 |
| | Nos. B38-B43 (6) | | 16.00 | 7.20 |

### Souvenir Sheet

| B44 | SP3 | 750fr +50fr multi | 7.25 | 3.00 |
|---|---|---|---|---|

Nos. B42-B44 are airmail.

---

# AIR POST STAMPS

Lockheed Constellation — AP1

Design: 500fr, Plane on ground.

## Lithographed and Engraved

### 1959, July 13    Unwmk.    Perf. 11½
### Size: 52½x24mm

| C14 | AP1 | 100fr dp car, ultra & emer | 2.10 | 1.00 |
|---|---|---|---|---|
| C15 | AP1 | 200fr emer, brn & lil | 2.75 | 2.00 |

### Size: 56½x26mm

| C16 | AP1 | 500fr multicolored | 7.25 | 3.50 |
|---|---|---|---|---|
| | Nos. C14-C16 (3) | | 12.10 | 6.50 |

For overprints see Nos. C24-C26, C52-C53.

Doves with Letter and Olive Twig — AP2

| 1959, Oct. 16 | Engr. | | Perf. 13½ | |
|---|---|---|---|---|
| C17 | AP2 | 40fr blue | .30 | .25 |
| C18 | AP2 | 50fr emerald | .60 | .40 |
| C19 | AP2 | 100fr dk car rose | 1.00 | 1.00 |
| C20 | AP2 | 200fr rose red | 1.90 | 1.75 |
| C21 | AP2 | 500fr red orange | 5.25 | 3.00 |
| | Nos. C17-C21 (5) | | 9.05 | 6.40 |

For overprints see Nos. C35-C38.

## Admission to UN Type of 1959
### Engr. & Litho.

### 1959, Dec. 12    Perf. 12
### Size: 44x26mm

| C22 | A16 | 50fr multicolored | 1.00 | .75 |
|---|---|---|---|---|
| C23 | A16 | 100fr multicolored | 1.40 | .90 |

For overprints see Nos. C27-C28.

## Nos. C14-C16 Overprinted in Carmine, Orange or Blue

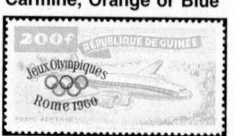

| 1960 | Litho. & Engr. | | Perf. 11½ | |
|---|---|---|---|---|
| | Size: 52½x24mm | | | |
| C24 | AP1 | 100fr multi (C or O) | 9.75 | 4.25 |
| C25 | AP1 | 200fr multi (Bl) | 17.00 | 8.00 |

---

### Size: 56½x26mm

| C26 | AP1 | 500fr multi (C or O) | 45.00 | 40.00 |
|---|---|---|---|---|
| | Nos. C24-C26 (3) | | 71.75 | 52.25 |

17th Olympic Games, Rome, 8/25-9/11. No. 201 overprinted in green and Nos. C24 and C26 overprinted in black were included in a souvenir gift booklet celebrating Guinea's 3rd anniversary of independence. The booklet was sold at the NY World's Fair, but the stamps were not valid for postage.

## Nos. C22-C23 Overprinted

## Engr. & Litho.

| 1961, Oct. 24 | | Perf. 12 | |
|---|---|---|---|
| C27 | A16 | 50fr multicolored | 1.00 | .40 |
| C28 | A16 | 100fr multicolored | 1.50 | .55 |

United Nations, 15th anniversary.

Mosquito and Malaria Eradication Emblem — AP3

| 1962, Apr. 7 | Engr. | | Perf. 10½ | |
|---|---|---|---|---|
| C29 | AP3 | 25fr orange & blk | .50 | .25 |
| C30 | AP3 | 50fr car rose & blk | .80 | .35 |
| C31 | AP3 | 100fr green & blk | 1.40 | .60 |
| | Nos. C29-C31 (3) | | 2.70 | 1.20 |

WHO drive to eradicate malaria. A souvenir sheet exists containing a 100fr green & sepia stamp, imperf. Sepia coat of arms in margin. Size: 102x76mm. Value $10.

## Musician Type of Regular Issue

Musical Instruments: 100fr, 200fr, Kora. 500fr, Balafon.

| 1962, June 15 | Photo. | | Perf. 13x13½ | |
|---|---|---|---|---|
| C32 | A26 | 100fr brt pink, dk car & Prus bl | 1.10 | .50 |
| C33 | A26 | 200fr lt & dk ultra & car rose | 2.10 | 1.25 |
| C34 | A26 | 500fr dl org, pur & Prus bl | 6.75 | 4.00 |
| | Nos. C32-C34 (3) | | 9.95 | 5.75 |

Nos. C17-C20 Ovptd. in Carmine, Orange or Black

| | | Perf. 13½ | | |
|---|---|---|---|---|
| 1962, Nov. 15 | Unwmk. | | Engr. | |
| C35 | AP2 | 40fr blue (C or O) | .60 | .25 |
| C36 | AP2 | 50fr emer (C or O) | .60 | .35 |
| C37 | AP2 | 100fr dk car rose (B) | 1.35 | .70 |
| C38 | AP2 | 200fr rose red (B) | 2.40 | 1.25 |
| | Nos. C35-C38 (4) | | 4.95 | 2.55 |

The conquest of space. Two types of overprint: Straight lines on 40fr and 50fr in carmine, 100fr (black). Curved lines on 40fr and 50fr in orange, 200fr (black).

## Bird Type of Regular Issue

Birds: 100fr, Hornbill. 200fr, White spoonbill. 500fr, Bateleur eagle.

| 1962, Dec. | Photo. | | Perf. 13x13½ | |
|---|---|---|---|---|
| C41 | A30 | 100fr multicolored | 2.50 | 1.10 |
| C42 | A30 | 200fr multicolored | 4.25 | 2.40 |
| C43 | A30 | 500fr multicolored | 11.00 | 4.75 |
| | Nos. C41-C43 (3) | | 17.75 | 8.25 |

## Sports Type of Regular Issue, 1963

Designs: 100fr, Running. 200fr, Bicycling. 500fr, Single sculls.

| 1963, Mar. 16 | | Perf. 14 | |
|---|---|---|---|
| C44 | A32 | 100fr dp rose, sep & grn | 1.50 | .60 |
| C45 | A32 | 200fr ol bis, ultra & mag | 3.00 | 1.00 |
| C46 | A32 | 500fr ocher, dk bl & red | 7.50 | 3.00 |
| | Nos. C44-C46 (3) | | 12.00 | 4.60 |

## Butterfly Type of Regular Issue

Various Butterflies.

---

| 1963, May 10 | Unwmk. | | Perf. 12 | |
|---|---|---|---|---|
| C47 | A33 | 100fr cit, dk brn & gray | 1.60 | .35 |
| C48 | A33 | 200fr sal pink, blk & green | 5.00 | 2.40 |
| C49 | A33 | 500fr multicolored | 8.50 | 4.50 |
| | Nos. C47-C49 (3) | | 15.10 | 7.25 |

## Red Cross Type of Regular Issue

| 1963, July 25 | Engr. | | Perf. 10½ | |
|---|---|---|---|---|
| C50 | A35 | 25fr black & car | .75 | .25 |

### Souvenir Sheet
### Imperf

| C51 | A35 | 100fr green & car | 4.00 | 3.00 |
|---|---|---|---|---|

## Nos. C14-C15 Overprinted

## Lithographed and Engraved

| 1963, Oct. 28 | | Perf. 11½ | |
|---|---|---|---|
| C52 | AP1 | 100fr dp car, ultra & emer | 1.60 | .70 |
| C53 | AP1 | 200fr emer, brn & lil | 3.75 | 1.25 |

1st Pan American air service from Conakry to New York, July 30, 1963.

## Fish Type of Regular Issue, 1964

100fr, African lyretail. 300fr, Six-barred epiplatys.

| 1964, Feb. 15 | Litho. | | Perf. 14x13½ | |
|---|---|---|---|---|
| C54 | A36 | 100fr grn & multi | 2.25 | .55 |
| C55 | A36 | 300fr brn & multi | 7.75 | 1.40 |

## Kennedy Type of Regular Issue, 1964

| 1964, Mar. 5 | Engr. | | Perf. 10½ | |
|---|---|---|---|---|
| C56 | A37 | 100fr multicolored | 1.50 | .80 |

See note after No. 327.

## Olympic Type of Regular Issue

Design: 100fr, Women's ice skating.

| 1964, May 15 | Photo. | | Perf. 13x12½ | |
|---|---|---|---|---|
| C57 | A39 | 100fr gold, brn org & ind | 2.25 | .40 |

## Nos. C44-C46 Overprinted in Carmine or Orange

| 1964, May 15 | Unwmk. | | Perf. 14 | |
|---|---|---|---|---|
| C58 | A32 | 100fr (C or O) | 1.75 | 1.40 |
| C59 | A32 | 200fr (C or O) | 2.75 | 2.00 |
| C60 | A32 | 500fr (C or O) | 6.50 | 5.00 |
| | Nos. C58-C60 (3) | | 11.00 | 8.40 |

18th Olympic Games, Tokyo, Oct. 10-25.

## Mrs. Roosevelt Type of Regular Issue

| 1964, June 1 | Engr. | | Perf. 10½ | |
|---|---|---|---|---|
| C61 | A40 | 50fr violet | .75 | .25 |

### Souvenir Sheets

Unisphere, "Rocket Thrower" and Guinea Pavilion — AP4

**1964, Oct. 26**     **Engr.**     *Imperf.*
C62   AP4   100fr dk blk & org    1.60   .80
C63   AP4   200fr rose red & emer    3.75   1.90
NY World's Fair, 1964-65. See Nos. C69-C70.

### Nubian Monuments Type of Regular Issue

300fr, Queen Nefertari, Abu Simbel.

**1964, Nov. 19**     **Photo.**     *Perf. 12*
C64   A42   300fr gold, dl red brn & sal    3.50   1.40

For overprint see No. C82.

Japanese Hostess, Plane and Map of Africa — AP5

**1965, Jan. 18**     *Perf. 12½x13*
C65   AP5   100fr gold, blk & red lil    1.75   .35
18th Olympic Games, Tokyo, Oct. 10-25, 1964. Two multicolored souvenir sheets (200fr vert. and 300fr horiz.) exist, showing different views of Mt. Fuji. Sizes: 86x119mm, 119x86mm. Value, both: $12.50 perf; $40 imperf.

For overprint see No. C81.

### Mask Type of Regular Issue

300fr, Niamou mask from N'Zérékoré.

**1965, Feb. 15**     **Photo.**     *Perf. 14*
C68   A44   300fr multicolored    5.25   2.75

### World's Fair Type of 1964
Souvenir Sheets

**1965, Mar. 24**     **Engr.**     *Imperf.*
C69   AP4   100fr green & brn    2.40   1.00
C70   AP4   200fr grn & car rose    4.75   2.50

### Handicraft Type of Regular Issue

100fr, Cabinetmaker. 300fr, Ivory carver.

**1965, May 1**     **Photo.**     *Perf. 14*
C71   A45   100fr multicolored    1.50   .35
C72   A45   300fr multicolored    5.25   1.25

### ITU Type of Regular Issue, 1965

**1965, May 17**     *Unwmk.*
C73   A46   100fr multicolored    1.10   .30
C74   A46   200fr multicolored    2.50   .75

Exist imperf.

### ICY Type of Regular Issue, 1965

**1965, Sept. 8**     **Engr.**     *Perf. 10½*
C75   A50   100fr bl & yel org    1.25   .35

West Facade, Polytechnic Institute — AP6

Design: 200fr, North facade.

**1965, Oct. 2**     **Photo.**     *Perf. 13½*
C76   AP6   200fr gold & multi    1.75   1.00
C77   AP6   500fr gold & multi    5.00   3.00

Seventh anniversary of independence. For overprints see Nos. C84-C85.

### Moon Type of 1965

100fr, Ranger VII approaching moon, vert. 200fr, Launching of Ranger VII, Cape Kennedy, vert.

**1965, Nov. 15**     **Litho.**     *Perf. 13½x14*
C78   A52   100fr rose red, yel & dk brown    1.00   .50
C79   A52   200fr multicolored    2.50   1.00

For overprints & surcharge see Nos. C112-C112B.

### Dancer Type of Regular Issue, 1966

100fr, Kandia Kouyate, national singer.

**1966, Jan. 5**     **Photo.**     *Perf. 13½*
       **Size: 36x28½mm**
C80   A53   100fr multi, horiz.    1.25   .50

---

Engraved Overprint on No. C65

**1966, Mar. 14**     **Photo.**     *Perf. 12½x13*
C81   AP5   100fr gold, blk & red lil    1.25   .45
Fourth Pan Arab Games, Cairo, Sept. 2-11, 1965. The same overprint was applied to two souvenir sheets noted after No. C65 (red ovpt. on 200fr, black ovpt. on 300fr).

Engraved Dark Blue Overprint on No. C64

**1966, Mar. 14**     *Perf. 12*
C82   A42   300fr gold, dl red brn & sal    2.75   1.50
Centenary of first Egyptian postage stamp.

### Scenic Type of Regular Issue

View: Boulbinet Lighthouse.

**1966, Apr. 4**     *Perf. 13½*
C83   A54   100fr multicolored    1.40   .60
See Nos. C90-C91. For overprints see Nos. C93-C95.

### Nos. C76-C77 Ovptd. in Blue or Yellow

**1966, May 2**     **Photo.**     *Perf. 13½*
C84   AP6   200fr multi (Bl)    2.25   1.10
C85   AP6   500fr multi (Y)    5.00   2.75

UNESCO, 20th anniv.

### Woman-Flower Type of Regular Issue

Designs: Women and flowers of Guinea.

**1966, May 30**     **Photo.**     *Perf. 13½*
       **Size: 28x34mm**
C86   A56   200fr multicolored    3.50   .70
C87   A56   300fr multicolored    5.00   2.10

### Snake Type of Regular Issue

Designs: 200fr, Pastoria Research Institute. 300fr, Men holding rock python.

**1967, May 15**     **Litho.**     *Perf. 13½*
       **Size: 56x20mm**
C88   A61   200fr multicolored    2.50   1.25
    *a.*   Souv. sheet of 3, #471, 474, C88   9.00   6.50
C89   A61   300fr multicolored    4.50   2.25

### Scenic Type of Regular Issue

Views: 100fr, House of explorer Olivier de Sanderval. 200fr, Conakry.

**1967, June 20**     **Photo.**     *Perf. 13½*
C90   A54   100fr multicolored    .75   .45
C91   A54   200fr multicolored    1.60   1.10

For overprints see Nos. C94-C95.

### Elephant Type of Regular Issue, 1967

**1967, Sept. 28**     **Photo.**     *Perf. 13½*
C92   A63   200fr gold & multi    1.60   .75

Nos. C83 and C90-C91 Overprinted

---

**1967, Nov. 6**
C93   A54   100fr multi (#C83)    1.45   .90
C94   A54   100fr multi (#C90)    1.45   .90
C95   A54   200fr multi (#C91)    2.75   1.50
    *Nos. C93-C95 (3)*    5.65   3.30
50th anniversary of Lions International.

Detail from Mural by José Vela Zanetti AP7

Family, Mural by Per Krohg — AP8

The designs of the 30fr, 50fr and 200fr show mankind's struggle for a lasting peace after the mural in the lobby of the UN Conference Building, NY. The designs of the 100fr and of Nos. C98a-C98b show mankind's hope for the future after a mural in the UN Security Council Chamber.

**1967, Nov. 11**
C96   AP7   30fr multicolored    .30   .25
C97   AP7   50fr multicolored    .40   .25
C98   AP8   100fr multicolored    .85   .35
    *a.*   Souv. sheet of 3, English inscription    2.25   2.25
    *b.*   As "a," French inscription    2.25   2.25
C99   AP7   200fr multi    1.90   .50
    *Nos. C96-C99 (4)*    3.45   1.35

Nos. C98a and C98b each contain a 100fr stamp similar to No. C98 and two 50fr stamps showing festival scenes. The 50fr stamps have not been issued individually.

### People and Dwellings Type of Regular Issue

Design: 300fr, People and village of Les Bassari, Kundara Region.

**1968, Apr. 1**     **Photo.**     *Perf. 14x13½*
       **Size: 57x36mm**
C100   A66   300fr gold & multi    4.50   1.25

### Legends Type of Regular Issue

70fr, The Girl and the Hippopotamus. 100fr, Old Faya's Inheritance, vert. 200fr, Soumangourou Kante Killed by Djegue (woman on horseback). 300fr, Little Gouné, Son of the Lion, vert.

**1968**     **Photo.**     *Perf. 13½*
C101   A67   70fr multicolored    .90   .25
C102   A67   100fr multicolored    1.40   .30
C103   A67   200fr multicolored    2.75   1.00
    *a.*   Souv. sheet of 4    7.00   7.00
C104   A67   300fr multicolored    4.00   1.25
    *Nos. C101-C104 (4)*    9.05   2.80

Issued in sheets of 10 plus 2 labels. No. C103a contains 4 imperf. stamps similar to Nos. 510-511 and C102-C103.;
For souvenir sheet see No. 509a.

Issued: Nos. C102-C103, 5/16; Nos. C101, C104, 9/16.

### African Animal Type of Regular Issue

**1968, Nov. 25**     **Photo.**     *Perf. 13½*
       **Size: 49x35mm**
C105   A68   100fr Lions    1.75   .55
C106   A68   200fr Elephant    3.50   2.10

For souvenir sheet see No. 518a.

### Robert F. Kennedy Type of Regular Issue, 1968

Portraits: 50fr, Senator Robert F. Kennedy. 100fr, Rev. Martin Luther King, Jr. 200fr, Pres. John F. Kennedy.

**1968, Dec. 16**
C107   A69   50fr yel & multi    .90   .25
C108   A69   100fr multicolored    1.90   .25
C109   A69   200fr multicolored    4.00   1.25
    *Nos. C107-C109 (3)*    6.80   1.75

The stamps are printed in sheets of 15 (3x5) containing 10 stamps and five green and gold center labels. Sheets come either with English or French inscriptions on label.

---

### Olympic Type of Regular Issue

Sculpture &: 100fr, Gymnast on pommel horse. 200fr, Gymnast on rings. 300fr, Pole vault.

**1969, Feb. 1**     **Photo.**     *Perf. 13½*
C110   A71   100fr multicolored    1.25   .30
C111   A71   200fr multicolored    2.75   .90
C111A   A71   300fr multicolored    4.50   1.10
    *Nos. C110-C111A (3)*    8.50   2.30

Nos. C78-C79 Surcharged and Overprinted in Red

**1969, Mar. 17**     **Litho.**     *Perf. 13½x14*
C112   A52   25fr on 200fr multi    .40   .25
C112A   A52   100fr multicolored    1.00   .65
C112B   A52   200fr multicolored    2.00   1.00
    *Nos. C112-C112B (3)*    3.40   1.90

See note after No. 530.
Nos. C112-C112B also exist with surcharge and overprint in orange (25fr, 200fr) or black (100fr). These sell for a small premium.

### Bird Type of Regular Issue

Birds: 50fr, Violet-crested touraco. 100fr, European golden oriole. 200fr, Vulturine guinea fowl.

**1971, June 18**     **Photo.**     *Perf. 13*
       **Size: 41x41mm**
C113   A81   50fr gold & multi    1.10   .40
C113A   A81   100fr gold & multi    2.25   .80
C113B   A81   200fr gold & multi    4.50   1.25
    *Nos. C113-C113B (3)*    7.85   2.45

John and Robert Kennedy, Martin Luther King, Jr. — AP9

### Embossed on Metallic Foil

**1972**     *Die Cut Perf. 10½*
C114   AP9   300fr silver    35.00   35.00

### Embossed & Typo.
C114A   AP9   1500fr gold, cream & green    55.00   55.00

Jules Verne, Moon Rocket AP10

### Embossed on Metallic Foil

**1972**     *Die Cut Perf. 10½*
C115   AP10   300fr silver    35.00   35.00
C115A   AP10   1200fr gold    85.00   85.00

Richard Nixon AP11

Nixon and Mao AP12

Nixon's Trip to People's Republic of China: a, Nixon. b, Chinese table tennis player. c,

American table tennis player, Capitol dome. d, Mao Tse-tung.

## Embossed on Metallic Foil

**1972**                **Die Cut Perf. 10½**

C116 AP11    90fr Block of 4,
             #a.-d., sil-
             ver                        27.50 27.50
C117 AP11   290fr Block of 4,
             #a.-d.,
             gold                        45.00 45.00

### Embossed & Typo.

C118 AP12  1200fr gold & red             70.00 70.00
Perforations within blocks of 4 are perf. 11.

## Racial Equality Year Type of Regular Issue

Design: 100fr, Men of 4 races and racial equality emblem (like No. 603).

**1972, May 14  Photo.    Perf. 13x13½**
C119 A84   100fr gold & multi             1.10 1.00

## Satellite Type of Regular Issue

Designs: 100fr, Map of Africa and Relay. 200fr, Map of Africa and Early Bird.

**1972, May 17   Litho.    Perf. 13**
C120 A85   100fr yel & multi              1.20 .70
C121 A85   200fr multicolored             2.40 .90

## African Postal Union Type of Regular Issue

Air mail envelope and UPAF emblem.

**1972, July 10**
C122 A86   100fr multicolored             .90 .55
C123 A86   200fr multicolored            1.75 1.25

## Olympic Type of Regular Issue

100fr, Gymnast on rings. 200fr, Bicycling. 300fr, Soccer.

**1972, Aug. 26   Photo.    Perf. 13**
C124 A88   100fr multi                   1.75 .60
C125 A88   200fr multi                   3.25 1.10

### Souvenir Sheet

C126 A88   300fr multi                   7.00 7.00

## Flower Type of 1974

20s, Thunbergia alata. 25s, Diascia barberae. 50s, Kigelia africana.

**1974, May 20   Photo.    Perf. 13**
**Size: 38x38mm (Diamond)**
C127 A97   20s multi                     2.75 .95
C128 A97   25s multi                     3.50 1.10
C129 A97   50s multi                     7.25 2.75
      Nos. C127-C129 (3)                13.50 4.80

## Olympic Games Type of 1976

Souvenir Sheet

**1976, May 17   Photo.    Perf. 13½**
C130       Sheet of 4                    16.00 12.50
   a.  A104 25s Soccer                    2.50  2.50
No. C130 contains 32x32mm stamps.

## Mushroom Type of 1977

Mushrooms: 10s, Morchella esculenta. 12s, Lepiota procera. 15s, Cantharellus cibarius.

**1977, Feb. 6   Photo.    Perf. 13**
**Size: 48x31mm**
C131 A106   10s multicolored             3.50 .70
C132 A106   12s multicolored             5.00 .90
C133 A106   15s multicolored             6.75 2.10
      Nos. C131-C133 (3)                15.25 3.70

## Reptile Type of 1977

Reptiles: 10s, Flap-necked chameleon. 15s, Nile crocodiles. 25s, Painted tortoise.

**1977, Oct. 10   Photo.    Perf. 13½**
**Size: 46x30mm**
C134 A109   10s multicolored             3.50 .80
C135 A109   15s multicolored             4.50 1.10
C136 A109   25s multicolored             7.00 1.60
      Nos. C134-C136 (3)                15.00 3.50

## Animal Type of 1977

Endangered Animals: 5s, Eland. 8s, Pygmy elephant. 9s, Hippopotamus. 10s, Chimpanzee. 12s, Palm squirrel. 13s, Lion. Male, female and young of each animal shown.

**1977, Dec. 12   Photo.    Perf. 14x13½**
C137 A110   Strip of 3                   3.50 1.75
   a.-c.  5s any single                        .95
C138 A110   Strip of 3                   5.50 2.75
   a.-c.  8s any single                       1.60
C139 A110   Strip of 3                   5.75 3.00
   a.-c.  9s any single                       1.75

---

C140 A110   Strip of 3                   6.00 3.50
   a.-c.  10s any single                      1.75
C141 A110   Strip of 3                   7.50 4.00
   a.-c.  12s any single                      2.25
C142 A110   Strip of 3                   8.50 5.00
   a.-c.  13s any single                      2.50
      Nos. C137-C142 (6)                36.75 20.00

## Russian Revolution Type, 1978

10s, Russian ballet. 30s, Pushkin Monument.

**1978, Feb. 27   Photo.    Perf. 14**
C143 A111   10s gold & multi            2.40 .80
C144 A111   30s gold & multi            7.00 2.10

## Giscard d'Estaing Type of 1979

Pres. Valery Giscard d'Estaing of France, vert.

**1979, Sept. 14   Photo.    Perf. 13**
C145 A112   25s multicolored            4.00 2.00

## Jules Verne Type of 1979

Designs: 20s, Five Weeks in a Balloon. 25s, Robur the Conqueror.

**1979, Nov. 8   Litho.    Perf. 12x12½**
C146 A113   20s multicolored            2.60 .45
C147 A113   25s multicolored            3.50 .75

## Olympic Type of 1982

**1982  Litho.   Perf. 12½x12, 12x12½**
C148 A120    9s Fencing                 1.40 .45
C149 A120   10s Soccer, vert.           1.60 .45
C150 A120   11s Basketball, vert.       1.75 .45
C151 A120   20s Diving, vert.           2.60 .60
C152 A120   25s Boxing, vert.           3.50 .75
      Nos. C148-C152 (5)               10.85 2.70

## Ataturk Type of 1982

**1982, July 19   Photo.    Perf. 13½**
C153 A122   25s like #830               4.25 .80

## World Cup Type of 1982

Designs: Various soccer players.

**1982, Aug. 23**
C154 A123   10s multicolored            2.60 .75
C155 A123   20s multicolored            4.25 1.10
C156 A123   25s multicolored            6.00 1.50
      Nos. C154-C156 (3)               12.85 3.35

### Nos. C154-C156 Overprinted

**1982, Aug. 23   Photo.    Perf. 13½**
C157 A123   10s multicolored            2.60 .75
C158 A123   20s multicolored            4.25 1.10
C159 A123   25s multicolored            6.00 1.50
      Nos. C157-C159 (3)               12.85 3.35

Location of flag in overprint varies.

### Balloon Type

Designs: 20s, Graf Zeppelin, Airship, horiz. 25s, Double Eagle II, L. Newman, B. Abruzzo, M. Anderson. 30s, Le Geant Hot Air Balloon, Nadar; Dirigible, Dumont.

**1983, Aug. 1   Litho.    Perf. 13½**
C160 A125   20s multicolored            2.60 .90
C161 A125   25s multicolored            3.25 1.25

### Souvenir Sheet

C162 A125   30s multicolored            4.50 1.75

### Nos. 894, 880-881 & 896 Overprinted

No. C163

No. C164

---

30s, "Kasparov / champion / du Monde".

**1985, Nov. 5   Litho.    Perf. 13½**
C163 A133   20s multi                   2.75 1.25
C164 A131   20s multi                   2.75 1.25
C165 A131   25s Ovpt. like
             #C163                       3.50 1.50
      Nos. C163-C165 (3)                9.00 4.00

### Souvenir Sheet

C166 A133   30s multi                  15.00 10.00

US Space Shuttle Challenger Explosion, Jan. 28, 1986 — AP13

Designs: 100fr, Lift-off, crew names. 170fr, Shuttle design, Christa McAuliffe holding shuttle model. 600fr, Lift-off, vert.

### 100fr, 170fr Surcharged in Silver and Black

**1986, July 1**
C167 AP13  100fr multicolored            1.10 .30
C168 AP13  170fr multicolored            1.60 .50

### Souvenir Sheet

C169 AP13  600fr multicolored            7.00 2.75
Nos. C167-C168 not issued without surcharge.
Souvenir sheets of one exist containing Nos. C167 and C168.

Robin Yount, Milwaukee Brewers Baseball Player — AP14

**1990, Aug. 3   Litho.    Perf. 13½**
C170 AP14  450fr multicolored            5.00 2.10
No. C170 exists in a souvenir sheet of 1.
For surcharge see No. 1182R.

Souvenir Sheet

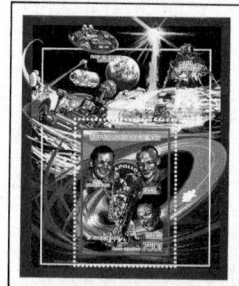

Armstrong, Aldrin, Collins and Apollo 11 Emblem — AP15

**1990, Aug. 3   Litho.    Perf. 13½**
C171 AP15  750fr multicolored            8.00 3.25

Galileo Spacecraft — AP16

**1990, Aug. 3**
C172 AP16  500fr multicolored            5.25 2.25
No. C172 exists as a souvenir sheet of 1.

Pope John Paul II, Visit to Africa — AP18

---

Portrait and: No. C174, Raising hand in benediction. No. C175, Child.

### Litho. & Embossed

**1992, Oct. 26               Perf. 13½**
C174 AP18  1500fr gold & multi          24.00 19.00

### Souvenir Sheet

C175 AP18  1500fr gold & multi          18.00 15.00
No. C175 exists imperf.

Elvis Presley, 15th Anniv. of Death — AP19

**1992, Nov. 10**
C176 AP19  1500fr gold & multi          24.00 20.00
No. C176 exists in miniature sheet of one.

### De Gaulle Type of 1991 Overprinted "6 JUNE 1944 / DEBARQUEMENT"

**1994  Litho. & Embossed   Perf. 13½**
C177 A181  1500fr like #1168            15.00 12.50

No. 1195 Overprinted in Silver

**1993, Feb. 24   Litho.    Perf. 13½**
C178 A188  450fr multicolored            4.50 2.25
No. C178 exists in souvenir sheet of 1.

---

## POSTAGE DUE STAMPS

D5

**1959   Unwmk.   Litho.   Perf. 11½**
J36 D5    1fr emerald                    .30 .25
J37 D5    2fr lilac rose                 .30 .25
J38 D5    3fr brown                      .55 .25
J39 D5    5fr blue                      1.40 .25
J40 D5   10fr orange                    2.10 .55
J41 D5   20fr rose lilac                4.25 .95
      Nos. J36-J41 (6)                  8.90 2.50

D6

**1960             Engr.     Perf. 13½**
J42 D6    1fr dark carmine               .25 .25
J43 D6    2fr brown orange               .25 .25
J44 D6    3fr dark car rose              .30 .25
J45 D6    5fr bright green               .70 .25
J46 D6   10fr dark brown                1.50 .55
J47 D6   20fr dull blue                 3.00 1.25
      Nos. J42-J47 (6)                  6.00 2.90

# GUINEA-BISSAU

'gi-nē-bi-'sau̯ⁿ

LOCATION — West coast of Africa between Senegal and Guinea
GOVT. — Republic
AREA — 13,948 sq. mi.
POP. — 1,234,555 (1999 est.)
CAPITAL — Bissau

Guinea-Bissau, the former Portuguese Guinea, attained independence September 10, 1974. The state includes the Bissagos Islands.

100 Centavos = 1 Escudo
100 Centavos = 1 Peso
100 Centimes = 1 Franc (1997)

> Catalogue values for all unused stamps in this country are for Never Hinged items.

Amilcar Cabral, Map of Africa and Flag — A27

Design: Flag of the PAIGC (African Party of Independence of Guinea-Bissau and Cape Verde) shows location of Guinea-Bissau on map of Africa.

### Perf. 11x10½
**1974, Sept. 10**    Litho.    Unwmk.
| | | | | |
|---|---|---|---|---|
| 345 | A27 | 1p brown & multi | 1.00 | .55 |
| 346 | A27 | 2.50p brown & multi | 1.40 | .80 |
| 347 | A27 | 5p brown & multi | 22.50 | 8.00 |
| 348 | A27 | 10p brown & multi | 3.75 | 6.00 |
| | | Nos. 345-348 (4) | 28.65 | 15.35 |

First anniv. of Proclamation of Independence, Sept. 24, 1973.

Portuguese Guinea No. 344 Overprinted in Black

**1975**    Litho.    Perf. 13
| | | | | |
|---|---|---|---|---|
| 349 | CD61 | 2c brown & multi | 2.00 | 1.25 |

No. 349 exists with overprint in brown. Value, $5.

Amilcar Cabral, Map of Africa, Flag — A29

**1975, Sept.**    Litho.    Perf. 11
| | | | | |
|---|---|---|---|---|
| 350 | A29 | 1p brown & multi | .75 | .75 |
| 351 | A29 | 2.50p brown & multi | 1.25 | 1.25 |
| 352 | A29 | 5p brown & multi | 8.00 | 7.00 |
| 353 | A29 | 10p brown & multi | 8.00 | 7.00 |
| | | Nos. 350-353 (4) | 18.00 | 16.00 |

Nos. 350-353 are dated Sept. 24, 1973, in the design. Also exist dated Sept. 21, 1973. Value of latter set, $20.

Flag and Arms of Guinea-Bissau and Amilcar Cabral — A30

Flag, Arms and: 2e, No. 358, Family. 3e, 5e, Pres. Luiz Cabral. No. 359, like 1e.

**1975, Sept.**    Perf. 14
| | | | | |
|---|---|---|---|---|
| 354 | A30 | 1e yel & multi | 1.75 | 1.15 |
| 355 | A30 | 2e multicolored | 1.75 | 1.50 |
| 356 | A30 | 3e red & multi | 2.60 | 1.75 |
| 357 | A30 | 5e yel & multi | 7.25 | 4.50 |
| 358 | A30 | 10e red & multi | 11.00 | 5.75 |
| 359 | A30 | 10e brt grn & multi | 11.00 | 5.75 |
| | | Nos. 354-359 (6) | 35.35 | 20.40 |

Amilcar Cabral's 51st birth anniv. (1e, No. 359); African Party of Independence of Guinea-Bissau and Cape Verde, 19th anniv. (2e, No. 358); Proclamation of Independence, 2nd anniv. (3e, 5e).

For surcharges see Nos. 367-367E.

Henry Knox, Cannons of Ticonderoga — A30a

Designs: 10e, Israel Putnam, Battle of Bunker Hill. 15e, Washington crossing the Delaware. 20e, Tadeusz Kosciuszko, Battle of Saratoga. 30e, Von Steuben, winter at Valley Forge. 40e, Lafayette, Washington rallying troops at Monmouth. 50e, Signing the Declaration of Independence.

**1976, May 5**    Litho.    Perf. 13½
| | | | | |
|---|---|---|---|---|
| 360 | A30a | 5e multicolored | .45 | .25 |
| 360A | A30a | 10e multicolored | .45 | .25 |
| 360B | A30a | 15e multicolored | .90 | .40 |
| 360C | A30a | 20e multicolored | 2.00 | .85 |
| 360D | A30a | 30e multicolored | 2.50 | 1.00 |
| 360E | A30a | 40e multicolored | 2.75 | 1.10 |
| | | Nos. 360-360E (6) | 9.05 | 3.85 |

#### Souvenir Sheet
| | | | | |
|---|---|---|---|---|
| 360F | A30a | 50e multicolored | | 13.50 |

American Revolution, bicentennial. Nos. 360D-360F are airmail.

Nos. 360-360E exist in miniature sheets of 1, perf. and imperf. Value, set of six perf or imperf sheets, $37.50. No. 360F contains one 75x45mm stamp and exists imperf. Value, $22.50.

See Nos. 371-371A.

Masked Dancer — A30b

3p, Dancer, drummer. 5p, Dancers on stilts. 10p, Dancer with spear, bow. 15p, Masked dancer, diff. 20p, Dancer with striped cloak.

**1976, May 10**    Perf. 11
#### Denomination in Black on Silver Block
| | | | | |
|---|---|---|---|---|
| 361 | A30b | 2p shown | .35 | .25 |
| 361A | A30b | 3p multicolored | .40 | .25 |
| 361B | A30b | 5p multicolored | .60 | .25 |
| 361C | A30b | 10p multicolored | .65 | .25 |
| 361D | A30b | 15p multicolored | 2.00 | .75 |
| 361E | A30b | 20p multicolored | 4.00 | 1.25 |
| | | Nos. 361-361E (6) | 8.00 | 3.00 |

#### Souvenir Sheet
| | | | | |
|---|---|---|---|---|
| 361F | A30b | 50p Like No. 361E | 7.00 | 7.00 |

Nos. 361C-361F are airmail. Silver block obliterates original denomination. Not issued without surcharge.

Nos. 361-361F Ovptd. in Black

**1976, June 8**    Perf. 11
| | | | | |
|---|---|---|---|---|
| 362 | A30b | 2p on No. 361 | .50 | .25 |
| 362A | A30b | 3p on No. 361A | .60 | .25 |
| 362B | A30b | 5p on No. 361B | .90 | .25 |
| 362C | A30b | 10p on No. 361C | 1.25 | .45 |
| 362D | A30b | 15p on No. 361D | 1.75 | .65 |
| 362E | A30b | 20p on No. 361E | 2.50 | .95 |
| | | Nos. 362-362E (6) | 7.50 | 2.80 |

#### Souvenir Sheet
| | | | | |
|---|---|---|---|---|
| 362F | A30b | 50p on No. 361F | 4.25 | 4.25 |

UPU cent. (in 1974). Nos. 362C-362F are airmail.

Nos. 362-362F exist imperf, and Nos. 362-362E in imperf miniature sheets of 1, all with black or red overprints.

Cabral, Guinean Mother and Children — A31

**1976, Sept. 3**    Litho.    Perf. 13½
| | | | | |
|---|---|---|---|---|
| 363 | A31 | 3p multicolored | .25 | .25 |
| 364 | A31 | 5p multicolored | .25 | .25 |
| 365 | A31 | 6p multicolored | .45 | .25 |
| 366 | A31 | 10p multicolored | .55 | .25 |
| | | Nos. 363-366 (4) | 1.50 | 1.00 |

Third anniv. of assassination of Amilcar Cabral (1924-1973), revolutionary leader.

Nos. 363-366 exist in souvenir sheets of one. Value, set of four sheets $25.

### Nos. 354-359 Surcharged in Black on Silver

**1976, Sept. 12**    Litho.    Perf. 14
| | | | | |
|---|---|---|---|---|
| 367 | A30 | 1p on 1e No. 354 | .40 | .25 |
| 367A | A30 | 2p on 2e No. 355 | .40 | .25 |
| 367B | A30 | 3p on 3e No. 356 | .40 | .25 |
| 367C | A30 | 5p on 5e No. 357 | 1.40 | .25 |
| 367D | A30 | 10p on 10e No. 358 | 1.45 | .25 |
| 367E | A30 | 10p on 10e No. 359 | 1.45 | .25 |
| | | Nos. 367-367E (6) | 5.50 | 1.50 |

1876 Bell Telephone and Laying First Trans-Atlantic Cable — A31a

Telephones of: 3p, France, 1890, and first telephone booth, 1893. 5p, Germany, 1903, and automatic telephone, 1898. 10p, England, 1910, and relay station, 1963. 15p, France, 1924, and communications satellite. 20p, Modern telephone, 1970, and Molniya satellite. 50p, Picture phone.

**1976, Oct. 18**    Perf. 13½
| | | | | |
|---|---|---|---|---|
| 368 | A31a | 2p multicolored | .25 | .25 |
| 368A | A31a | 3p multicolored | .25 | .25 |
| 368B | A31a | 5p multicolored | .25 | .25 |
| 368C | A31a | 10p multicolored | .75 | .45 |
| 368D | A31a | 15p multicolored | 1.25 | .70 |
| 368E | A31a | 20p multicolored | 1.75 | .85 |
| | | Nos. 368-368E (6) | 4.50 | 2.75 |

#### Souvenir Sheet
| | | | | |
|---|---|---|---|---|
| 368F | A31a | 50p multicolored | 4.50 | 4.50 |

Nos. 368C-368F are airmail. No. 368F contains one 68x42mm stamp. No. 368F exists imperf. Nos. 368-368E exist in souvenir sheets of one, perf. and imperf.

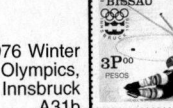

1976 Winter Olympics, Innsbruck A31b

1p, Women's figure skating. 3p, Ice hockey. 5p, Two-man bobsled. 10p, Pairs figure skating. 20p, Cross country skiing. 30p, Speed skating.

50p, Downhill skiing.

**1976, Nov. 3**    Perf. 14x13½
| | | | | |
|---|---|---|---|---|
| 369 | A31b | 1p multicolored | .25 | .25 |
| 369A | A31b | 3p multicolored | .25 | .25 |
| 369B | A31b | 5p multicolored | .40 | .25 |
| 369C | A31b | 10p multicolored | .90 | .25 |
| 369D | A31b | 20p multicolored | 1.45 | .65 |
| 369E | A31b | 30p multicolored | 1.75 | .85 |
| | | Nos. 369-369E (6) | 5.00 | 2.50 |

#### Souvenir Sheet
| | | | | |
|---|---|---|---|---|
| 369F | A31b | 50p multicolored | 4.50 | 4.50 |

Nos. 369C-369F are airmail. No. 369F exists imperf. Nos. 369-369E exist in souvenir sheets of one, perf. and imperf.

1976 Summer Olympics, Montreal — A31c

**1976, Nov. 24**    Perf. 13½
| | | | | |
|---|---|---|---|---|
| 370 | A31c | 1p Soccer | .25 | .25 |
| 370A | A31c | 3p Pole vault | .25 | .25 |
| 370B | A31c | 5p Women's hurdles | .40 | .25 |
| 370C | A31c | 10p Discus | .75 | .40 |
| 370D | A31c | 20p Sprinting | 1.40 | .60 |
| 370E | A31c | 30p Wrestling | 2.00 | .75 |
| | | Nos. 370-370E (6) | 5.05 | 2.50 |

#### Souvenir Sheet
| | | | | |
|---|---|---|---|---|
| 370F | A31c | 50p Cycling, horiz. | 5.25 | 5.25 |

Nos. 370E-370F are airmail. No. 370F contains one 47x38mm stamp. No. 370F exists imperf. Nos. 370-370E exist in souvenir sheets of one, perf. and imperf.

### American Revolution Type of 1976

Designs: 3.50p, Crispus Attucks, Boston Massacre. 5p, Martin Luther King, US Capitol.

**1977, Jan. 27**    Perf. 13½
#### Denomination in Black on Gold Block
| | | | | |
|---|---|---|---|---|
| 371 | A30a | 3.50p multicolored | .35 | .25 |
| 371A | A30a | 5p multicolored | .45 | .25 |
| | | Nos. 371-371A (2) | .80 | .50 |

Gold block obliterates original denomination. Not issued without surcharge. Exist in souvenir sheets of one, perf. and imperf.

Cabral Addressing UN General Assembly — A32

Design: 50c, Cabral and guerrilla fighters.

**1977, July**    Litho.    Perf. 13½
| | | | | |
|---|---|---|---|---|
| 372 | A32 | 50c multicolored | .25 | .25 |
| 373 | A32 | 3.50p multicolored | .45 | .25 |

For surcharges see Nos. C12-C13.

Henri Dunant, Nobel Peace Prize, 1901 — A32a

Nobel Prize Winners: 5p, Einstein, Physics, 1921. 6p, Irene and Frederic Joliot-Curie, Chemistry, 1935. 30p, Fleming, Medicine, 1945. 35p, Hemingway, Literature, 1954. 40p, J. Tinbergen, Economics, 1969. 50p, Nobel Prize Medal.

**1977, July 27**
| | | | | |
|---|---|---|---|---|
| 374 | A32a | 3.50p multicolored | .35 | .25 |
| 374A | A32a | 5p multicolored | .40 | .25 |
| 374B | A32a | 6p multicolored | .65 | .25 |
| 374C | A32a | 30p multicolored | 1.75 | 1.20 |
| 374D | A32a | 35p multicolored | 3.25 | 1.40 |
| 374E | A32a | 40p multicolored | 5.00 | 1.90 |
| | | Nos. 374-374E (6) | 11.40 | 5.25 |

#### Souvenir Sheet
| | | | | |
|---|---|---|---|---|
| 374F | A32a | 50p multicolored | 4.50 | 4.50 |

Nos. 374D-374F are airmail. No. 374F contains one 57x39mm stamp. No. 374F exists imperf. Nos. 374-374E exist in souvenir sheets of one, perf. and imperf.

Postal Runner, Telstar Satellite A32b

UPU Centenary (in 1974): 5p, Biplane, satellites encircle globe. 6p, Mail truck, satelite control room. 30p, Stagecoach, astronaut canceling letters on Moon. 35p, Steam locomotive, communications satellite. 40p, Space shuttle, Apollo-Soyuz link-up. 50p, Semaphore signalling system, satellite dish.

**1977, Sept. 30**

| | | | | |
|---|---|---|---|---|
| 375 | A32b | 3.50p multicolored | .25 | .25 |
| 375A | A32b | 5p multicolored | .25 | .25 |
| 375B | A32b | 6p multicolored | .35 | .25 |
| 375C | A32b | 30p multicolored | 2.25 | .75 |
| 375D | A32b | 35p multicolored | 2.40 | 1.25 |
| 375E | A32b | 40p multicolored | 3.00 | 1.50 |
| | *Nos. 375-375E (6)* | | 8.50 | 4.25 |

**Souvenir Sheet**

| | | | | |
|---|---|---|---|---|
| 375F | A32b | 50p multicolored | 4.00 | 4.00 |

Nos. 375D-375F are airmail. No. 375F exists imperf. Nos. 375-375E exist in souvenir sheets of one, perf. and imperf.

Torch and Party Emblem — A33

**1977, Sept.　　Litho.　　Perf. 14**

| | | | | |
|---|---|---|---|---|
| 376 | A33 | 3p yel & multi | .25 | .25 |
| 377 | A33 | 15p sal & multi | .95 | .60 |
| 378 | A33 | 50p lt grn & multi | 2.25 | 1.50 |
| | *Nos. 376-378 (3)* | | 3.45 | 2.35 |

African Party of Independence of Guinea-Bissau and Cape Verde, 20th anniversary.

Queen Elizabeth II, Silver Jubilee A33a

Designs: 5p, Coronation ceremony. 10p, Yeoman of the Guard, Crown Jewels. 20p, Trumpeter. 25p, Royal Horse Guard. 30p, Royal Family. 50p, Queen Elizabeth II.

**1977, Oct. 15**

| | | | | |
|---|---|---|---|---|
| 379 | A33a | 3.50p multicolored | .35 | .25 |
| 379A | A33a | 5p multicolored | .40 | .25 |
| 379B | A33a | 10p multicolored | .85 | .25 |
| 379C | A33a | 20p multicolored | 1.90 | .40 |
| 379D | A33a | 25p multicolored | 2.75 | .60 |
| 379E | A33a | 30p multicolored | 3.25 | 1.00 |
| | *Nos. 379-379E (6)* | | 9.50 | 2.75 |

**Souvenir Sheet**

| | | | | |
|---|---|---|---|---|
| 379F | A33a | 50p multicolored | 4.00 | 4.00 |

Nos. 379D-379F are airmail. No. 379F contains one 42x39mm stamp. No. 379F exists imperf. Nos. 379-379E exist in souvenir sheets of one, perf. and imperf.

Massacre of the Innocents by Rubens — A33b

Paintings by Peter Paul Rubens: 5p, Rape of the Daughters of Leukippos. 6p, Lamentation of Christ, horiz. 30p, Francisco IV Gonzaga, Prince of Mantua. 35p, The Four Continents. 40p, Marquise Brigida Spinola Doria. 50p, The Wounding of Christ.

**1977, Nov. 15**

| | | | | |
|---|---|---|---|---|
| 380 | A33b | 3.50p multicolored | .40 | .25 |
| 380A | A33b | 5p multicolored | .55 | .25 |
| 380B | A33b | 6p multicolored | .65 | .30 |
| 380C | A33b | 30p multicolored | 2.25 | 1.20 |
| 380D | A33b | 35p multicolored | 2.75 | 1.40 |
| 380E | A33b | 40p multicolored | 3.75 | 1.60 |
| | *Nos. 380-380E (6)* | | 10.35 | 5.00 |

**Souvenir Sheet**

| | | | | |
|---|---|---|---|---|
| 380F | A33b | 50p multicolored | 4.50 | 4.50 |

Nos. 380D-380F are airmail. Nos. 380-380F exist imperf. Nos. 380-380E exist in souvenir sheets of one, perf. and imperf.

Congress Emblem — A34

**1977, Nov. 15　　Litho.　　Perf. 14**

| | | | | |
|---|---|---|---|---|
| 381 | A34 | 3.50p multicolored | .30 | .25 |

3rd PAIGC Congress, Bissau, Nov. 15-20.

Santos-Dumont's Airship, 1901 — A34a

Airships: 5p, R-34 crossing the Atlantic, 1919. 10p, Norge over North Pole, 1926. 20p, Graf Zeppelin over Abu Simbel, 1931. 25p, Hindenburg over New York, 1937. 30p, Graf Zeppelin, Concorde, space shuttle. 50p, Ferdinand von Zeppelin, horiz.

**1978, Feb. 27**

| | | | | |
|---|---|---|---|---|
| 382 | A34a | 3.50p multicolored | .25 | .25 |
| 382A | A34a | 5p multicolored | .35 | .25 |
| 382B | A34a | 10p multicolored | .65 | .25 |
| 382C | A34a | 20p multicolored | 1.40 | .50 |
| 382D | A34a | 25p multicolored | 1.75 | 1.00 |
| 382E | A34a | 30p multicolored | 2.10 | 1.40 |
| | *Nos. 382-382E (6)* | | 6.50 | 3.65 |

**Souvenir Sheet**

| | | | | |
|---|---|---|---|---|
| 382F | A34a | 50p multicolored | 4.00 | 4.00 |

Nos. 382D-382F are airmail. No. 382F exists imperf. Nos. 382-382E exist in souvenir sheets of one, perf. and imperf.

World Cup Soccer Championships, Argentina — A34b

Soccer players and posters from previous World Cup Championships: 3.50p, 1930. 5p, 1938. 10p, 1950. 20p, 1962. 25p, 1970. 30p, 1974. 50p, Argentina '78 emblem.

**1978, Mar. 15**

| | | | | |
|---|---|---|---|---|
| 383 | A34b | 3.50p multicolored | .25 | .25 |
| 383A | A34b | 5p multicolored | .25 | .25 |
| 383B | A34b | 10p multicolored | .65 | .35 |
| 383C | A34b | 20p multicolored | 1.35 | .75 |
| 383D | A34b | 25p multicolored | 1.75 | 1.25 |
| 383E | A34b | 30p multicolored | 2.10 | 1.50 |
| | *Nos. 383-383E (6)* | | 6.35 | 4.35 |

**Souvenir Sheet**

| | | | | |
|---|---|---|---|---|
| 383F | A34b | 50p multicolored | 4.00 | 4.00 |

Nos. 383D-383F are airmail. Nos. 383-383F exist imperf. Nos. 383-383E exist in miniature sheets of one, perf. and imperf.
For surcharges see Nos. 393-393F.

Endangered Species — A34c

3.50p, Black antelope. 5p, Fennec. 6p, Secretary bird. 30p, Hippopotami. 35p, Cheetahs. 40p, Gorillas.
50p, Cercopithecus erythotis.

**1978, Apr. 17**

| | | | | |
|---|---|---|---|---|
| 384 | A34c | 3.50p multicolored | .25 | .25 |
| 384A | A34c | 5p multicolored | .40 | .25 |
| 384B | A34c | 6p multicolored | .60 | .30 |
| 384C | A34c | 30p multicolored | 3.00 | 1.45 |
| 384D | A34c | 35p multicolored | 3.25 | 1.75 |
| 384E | A34c | 40p multicolored | 3.50 | 2.00 |
| | *Nos. 384-384E (6)* | | 11.00 | 6.00 |

**Souvenir Sheet**

| | | | | |
|---|---|---|---|---|
| 384F | A34c | 50p multicolored | 6.00 | 6.00 |

Nos. 384D-384F are airmail. No. 384F contains one 39x42mm stamp. No. 384F exists imperf. Nos. 384-384E exist in souvenir sheets of one, perf. and imperf.

Antenna, ITU Emblem — A35

**1978, May 17　　Litho.　　Perf. 13½**

| | | | | |
|---|---|---|---|---|
| 385 | A35 | 3.50p silver & multi | .25 | .25 |
| 386 | A35 | 10p gold & multi | .65 | .45 |

10th World Telecommunications Day.

Boy — A36

3p, Infant and grandfather. 5p, Boys. 30p, Girls.

**1978　　　　　　　　Perf. 14**

| | | | | |
|---|---|---|---|---|
| 387 | A36 | 50c yel grn & dk bl | .25 | .25 |
| 388 | A36 | 3p claret & car rose | .25 | .25 |
| 389 | A36 | 5p ocher & brown | .30 | .25 |
| 390 | A36 | 30p car & ocher | 1.60 | 1.10 |
| | *Nos. 387-390 (4)* | | 2.40 | 1.85 |

Children's Day.

Queen Elizabeth II, Silver Jubilee — A36a

Elizabeth, Imperial State Crown — A36b

Designs: 5p, Queen, Prince Philip in Coronation Coach. 10p, Queen, Prince Philip. 20p, Mounted drummer. 25p, Imperial State Crown, St. Edward's Crown. 30p, Queen holding orb and scepter. 50p, Queen on Throne flanked by Archbishops. No. 391H, Coronation Coach.

**1978, June 15**

| | | | | |
|---|---|---|---|---|
| 391 | A36a | 3.50p multicolored | .25 | .25 |
| 391A | A36a | 5p multicolored | .25 | .25 |
| 391B | A36a | 10p multicolored | .55 | .40 |
| 391C | A36a | 20p multicolored | 1.30 | .80 |
| 391D | A36a | 25p multicolored | 1.60 | 1.00 |
| 391E | A36a | 30p multicolored | 1.75 | 1.10 |
| | *Nos. 391-391E (6)* | | 5.70 | 3.80 |

**Litho. & Embossed**

| | | | | |
|---|---|---|---|---|
| 391F | A36b | 100p gold & multi | 16.00 | — |

**Souvenir Sheets**

| | | | | |
|---|---|---|---|---|
| 391G | A36a | 50p multicolored | 4.00 | 4.00 |

**Litho. & Embossed**

| | | | | |
|---|---|---|---|---|
| 391H | A36b | 100p gold & multi | 11.00 | — |

Nos. 391D-391H are airmail. Nos. 391-391E exist in souvenir sheets of one, perf. and imperf. Nos. 391F-391H exist imperf.

History of Aviation A36c

3.50p, Wright Brothers. 10p, Santos-Dumont. 15p, Bleriot. 20p, Lindbergh, Spirit of St. Louis. 25p, Lunar module. 30p, Space shuttle.
50p, Concorde.

**1978, June 15　　Litho.　　Perf. 13½**

| | | | | |
|---|---|---|---|---|
| 392 | A36c | 3.50p multicolored | .25 | .25 |
| 392A | A36c | 10p multicolored | .70 | .25 |
| 392B | A36c | 15p multicolored | .95 | .45 |
| 392C | A36c | 20p multicolored | 1.35 | .60 |
| 392D | A36c | 25p multicolored | 1.60 | .70 |
| 392E | A36c | 30p multicolored | 2.00 | .95 |
| | *Nos. 392-392E (6)* | | 6.85 | 3.20 |

**Souvenir Sheet**

| | | | | |
|---|---|---|---|---|
| 392F | A36c | 50p multicolored | 4.50 | 4.50 |

Nos. 392D-392F are airmail. Nos. 392-392E exist in souvenir sheets of one, perf. and imperf. No. 392F exists imperf.

**Nos. 383-383F Ovptd. in Gold**

**1978, Oct. 2**

| | | | | |
|---|---|---|---|---|
| 393 | A34b | 3.50p on No. 383 | .25 | .25 |
| 393A | A34b | 5p on No. 383A | .25 | .25 |
| 393B | A34b | 10p on No. 383B | .65 | .45 |
| 393C | A34b | 20p on No. 383C | 1.45 | .60 |
| 393D | A34b | 25p on No. 383D | 1.90 | .70 |
| 393E | A34b | 30p on No. 383E | 2.50 | .95 |
| | *Nos. 393-393E (6)* | | 7.00 | 3.20 |

**Souvenir Sheet**

| | | | | |
|---|---|---|---|---|
| 393F | A34b | 50p on No. 383F | 4.00 | 4.00 |

Nos. 393D-393F are airmail. Nos. 393-393F exist imperf. Nos. 393-393E exist in miniature sheets of 1 perf. and imperf. No. 393F exists overprinted in silver.

Virgin and Child by Albrecht Durer — A36d

Different Paintings of the Virgin and Child (Virgin only on 30p) by Durer.

**1978, Nov. 14**

| | | | | |
|---|---|---|---|---|
| 394 | A36d | 3.50p multicolored | .25 | .25 |
| 394A | A36d | 5p multicolored | .35 | .25 |
| 394B | A36d | 6p multicolored | .40 | .25 |
| 394C | A36d | 30p multicolored | 2.10 | .75 |
| 394D | A36d | 35p multicolored | 2.40 | 1.10 |
| 394E | A36d | 40p multicolored | 2.75 | 1.40 |
| | *Nos. 394-394E (6)* | | 8.25 | 4.00 |

**Souvenir Sheet**

| | | | | |
|---|---|---|---|---|
| 394F | A36d | 50p multicolored | 4.50 | 4.50 |

Nos. 394D-394F are airmail. No. 394F contains one 51x56mm stamp. Nos. 394-394E exist in souvenir sheets of one, perf. and imperf. No. 394F exists imperf.

Sir Rowland Hill (1795-1879), Wurttemberg No. 53 — A36e

Hill and: 5p, Belgium #1. 6p, Monaco #10. 30p, Spain 2r stamp of 1851 in blue. 35p,

Switzerland #5. 40p, Two Sicilies #8. 50p, Portuguese Guinea #13 in brown.

## 1978, Dec. 15

| | | | | |
|---|---|---|---|---|
| 395 | A36e | 3.50p multicolored | .25 | .25 |
| 395A | A36e | 5p multicolored | .50 | .25 |
| 395B | A36e | 6p multicolored | .75 | .25 |
| 395C | A36e | 30p multicolored | 2.50 | .30 |
| 395D | A36e | 35p multicolored | 4.00 | .30 |
| 395E | A36e | 40p multicolored | 4.50 | .70 |
| | | Nos. 395-395E (6) | 12.50 | 2.00 |

### Souvenir Sheet

| | | | | |
|---|---|---|---|---|
| 395F | A36e | 50p multicolored | 5.00 | 5.00 |

Nos. 395D-395F are airmail. No. 395F contains one 51x42mm stamp. Nos. 395-395E exist in souvenir sheets of one, perf. and imperf. No. 395F exists imperf.

Intl. Day of the Child — A36f

10p, Children drinking. 15p, Child with book. 20p, Space plane. 25p, Skylab. 30p, Children playing chess.
50p, Children watching spaceship.

## 1979, Jan. 15          Perf. 14

| | | | | |
|---|---|---|---|---|
| 396 | A36f | 3.50p shown | .25 | .25 |
| 396A | A36f | 10p multicolored | .75 | .25 |
| 396B | A36f | 15p multicolored | 1.10 | .55 |
| 396C | A36f | 20p multicolored | 1.30 | .65 |
| 396D | A36f | 25p multicolored | 1.60 | .85 |
| 396E | A36f | 30p multicolored | 1.75 | .95 |
| | | Nos. 396-396E (6) | 6.75 | 3.50 |

### Souvenir Sheet

| | | | | |
|---|---|---|---|---|
| 396F | A36f | 50p multicolored | 5.00 | 5.00 |

Nos. 396C-396F are airmail. Nos. 396-396E exist in souvenir sheets of one, perf. and imperf. No. 396F exists imperf.

A36g

## 1979, Aug. 3          Litho.          Perf. 13

| | | | | |
|---|---|---|---|---|
| 397 | A36g | 4.50p multicolored | .45 | .25 |

Massacre of Pindjiguiti, 20th anniv.

A36h

## 1979, May 17          Litho.          Perf. 14

| | | | | |
|---|---|---|---|---|
| 397A | A36h | 50c shown | .25 | .25 |
| 397B | A36h | 4p People, rainbow, diff. | .30 | .25 |

World Telecommunications Day.

Family — A37

## 1979, April 16          Litho.          Perf. 12x11½

| | | | | |
|---|---|---|---|---|
| 398 | A37 | 50c multicolored | .25 | .25 |
| 399 | A37 | 2p multicolored | .45 | .25 |
| 400 | A37 | 4p multicolored | .90 | .25 |
| | | Nos. 398-400 (3) | 1.60 | .75 |

General population census, Apr. 16-30.

Cassaca Conference, 16th Anniv. — A37a

## 1980, Feb. 13          Litho.          Perf. 14x14¼

| | | | | |
|---|---|---|---|---|
| 400A | A37a | 3.50p multi | .25 | .25 |
| 400B | A37a | 6.50p multi | .30 | .25 |
| 400C | A37a | 10p multi | .65 | .30 |

Ernst Udet and Fokker D.VII — A38

5p, Charles Nungesser, Nieuport 17. 6p, von Richthofen, Fokker DR.1. 30p, Francesco Baracca, Spad XIII.

## 1979, Sept. 3          Litho.          Perf. 13½

| | | | | |
|---|---|---|---|---|
| 401 | A38 | 3.50p shown | .30 | .25 |
| 401A | A38 | 5p multicolored | .40 | .25 |
| 401B | A38 | 6p multicolored | .50 | .30 |
| 401C | A38 | 30p multicolored | 2.00 | 1.00 |
| | | Nos. 401-401C,C14-C14A (6) | 8.60 | 4.40 |

Lake Placid Emblem, Speed Skating — A39

## 1980, Dec. 10

| | | | | |
|---|---|---|---|---|
| 402 | A39 | 3.50p shown | .35 | .25 |
| 402A | A39 | 5p Downhill skiing | .55 | .25 |
| 402B | A39 | 6p Luge | .65 | .25 |
| 402C | A39 | 30p Cross-country skiing | 2.10 | .70 |
| | | Nos. 402-402C,C15-C16 (6) | 9.05 | 4.05 |

13th Winter Olympic Games, Lake Placid, NY, Feb. 12-24.

Shot-put — A40

5p, Athlete on rings. 6p, Running. 30p, Fencing.

## 1980, Jan. 21          Litho.          Perf. 13½

| | | | | |
|---|---|---|---|---|
| 403 | A40 | 3.50p shown | .30 | .25 |
| 403A | A40 | 5p multi | .60 | .25 |
| 403B | A40 | 6p multi | .80 | .25 |
| 403C | A40 | 30p multi | 3.00 | .70 |
| | | Nos. 403-403C,C18-C19 (6) | 12.45 | 4.05 |

22nd Summer Olympic Games, Moscow, July 19-Aug. 3.

Pres. Luis Cabral, Children and Workers — A41

5p, Pres. Cabral holding books.

## 1980, Feb. 4          Litho.          Perf. 13½

| | | | | |
|---|---|---|---|---|
| 404 | A41 | 3.50p multicolored | .35 | .25 |
| 405 | A41 | 5p multicolored | .50 | .25 |

Literacy campaign. See Nos. C21-C22.

Cooperation Among Developing Countries — A42

## 1980, Feb. 14

| | | | | |
|---|---|---|---|---|
| 406 | A42 | 3.50p multicolored | .50 | .25 |
| 407 | A42 | 6p multicolored | .55 | .25 |
| 408 | A42 | 30p multicolored | 1.50 | .25 |
| | | Nos. 406-408 (3) | 2.55 | .75 |

Baskets A43

3p, Bird, family wood statues, vert. 20p, Head, doll carvings.

## 1980, Feb. 26          Litho.          Perf. 13½

| | | | | |
|---|---|---|---|---|
| 409 | A43 | 3p multi | .25 | .25 |
| 410 | A43 | 6p shown | .30 | .25 |
| 411 | A43 | 20p multi | 1.10 | .45 |
| | | Nos. 409-411 (3) | 1.65 | .95 |

Infant and Toy Train, Locomotive, IYC Emblem — A44

6p, Classroom, horiz. 10p, Boy reading Jules Verne story. 35p, Archer, boy with bow. 50p, Students in lab.

## 1979, April 12

| | | | | |
|---|---|---|---|---|
| 412 | A44 | 6p multi | .40 | .30 |
| 412A | A44 | 10p multi | .65 | .55 |
| 412B | A44 | 25p shown | 1.50 | .80 |
| 412C | A44 | 35p multi | 2.40 | 1.25 |
| | | Nos. 412-412C (4) | 4.95 | 2.90 |

### Souvenir Sheet

| | | | | |
|---|---|---|---|---|
| 412D | A44 | 50p multi | 4.25 | 4.25 |

International Year of the Child (1979).

Columbia Space Shuttle and Crew — A45

Space Exploration: 3.50p, Galileo, satellites. 5p, Wernher von Braun. 6p, Jules Verne, rocket.

## 1981, Feb. 5          Litho.          Perf. 13½

| | | | | |
|---|---|---|---|---|
| 413 | A45 | 3.50p multicolored | .35 | .25 |
| 413A | A45 | 5p multicolored | .40 | .25 |
| 413B | A45 | 6p multicolored | .45 | .30 |
| 413C | A45 | 30p multicolored | 2.10 | 1.10 |
| | | Nos. 413-413C,C23-C24 (6) | 9.05 | 5.15 |

Soccer Players, World Cup, Argentina '78 and Espana '82 Emblems — A46

Soccer scenes and famous players: 3.50p, Platini, France. 5p, Bettega, Italy. 6p, Rensenbrink, Netherlands. 30p, Rivelino, Brazil.

## 1981, March 11

| | | | | |
|---|---|---|---|---|
| 414 | A46 | 3.50p multicolored | .35 | .25 |
| 414A | A46 | 5p multicolored | .40 | .25 |
| 414B | A46 | 6p multicolored | .45 | .30 |
| 414C | A46 | 30p multicolored | 2.10 | 1.10 |
| | | Nos. 414-414C,C26-C27 (6) | 9.05 | 5.15 |

Prince Charles and Lady Diana, St. Paul's Cathedral — A47

Royal Wedding (Couple and): 3.50p, Diana leading horse. 5p, Charles crowned Prince of Wales. 6p, Diana with kindergarten children.

## 1981, Aug. 5          Litho.          Perf. 13½

| | | | | |
|---|---|---|---|---|
| 415 | A47 | 3.50p multicolored | .40 | .25 |
| 415A | A47 | 5p multicolored | .40 | .25 |
| 415B | A47 | 6p multicolored | .50 | .30 |
| 415C | A47 | 30p multicolored | 2.10 | 1.25 |
| | | Nos. 415-415C,C29-C30 (6) | 10.65 | 5.30 |

Woman Before a Mirror, by Picasso (1881-1973) — A48

Picasso Birth Cent.: Various paintings.

## 1981, Sept. 22          Litho.          Perf. 13½

| | | | | |
|---|---|---|---|---|
| 416 | A48 | 3.50p multi | .30 | .25 |
| 417 | A48 | 5p multi | .45 | .25 |
| 418 | A48 | 6p multi | .65 | .30 |
| 419 | A48 | 30p multi | 3.00 | 1.25 |
| | | Nos. 416-419,C32-C33 (6) | 14.65 | 5.45 |

Henrique Vermelho and his Ship, Drakkar — A49

Navigators and their ships: 5p, Vasco de Gama, St. Gabriel. 6p, Ferdinand Magellan, Victoria. 30p, Jacques Cartier, Emerillon.

## 1981, Aug. 28          Litho.          Perf. 13½

| | | | | |
|---|---|---|---|---|
| 420 | A49 | 3.50p multicolored | .30 | .25 |
| 421 | A49 | 5p multicolored | .45 | .25 |
| 422 | A49 | 6p multicolored | .55 | .30 |
| 423 | A49 | 30p multicolored | 2.50 | 1.25 |
| | | Nos. 420-423,C35-C36 (6) | 11.30 | 5.65 |

Christmas — A50

Designs: Virgin and Child paintings.

## 1981, Nov. 19

| | | | | |
|---|---|---|---|---|
| 424 | A50 | 3.50p Mantegna | .30 | .25 |
| 425 | A50 | 5p Bellini | .45 | .25 |
| 426 | A50 | 6p Mantegna, diff. | .55 | .30 |
| 427 | A50 | 25p Correggio | 2.50 | 1.25 |
| | | Nos. 424-427,C38-C39 (6) | 11.05 | 5.65 |

Scouting Year — A51

## 1982, June 9          Litho.          Perf. 13½

| | | | | |
|---|---|---|---|---|
| 428 | A51 | 3.50p Archery | .30 | .25 |
| 429 | A51 | 5p First aid training | .35 | .25 |
| 430 | A51 | 6p Bugler | .45 | .30 |
| 431 | A51 | 30p Cub scouts | 2.25 | .85 |
| | | Nos. 428-431,C41-C42 (6) | 9.35 | 4.90 |

1982 World Cup A52

Various soccer players and cup.

**1982, June 13    Litho.    Perf. 13½**

| | | | | |
|---|---|---|---|---|
| 432 | A52 | 3.50p Keegan | .30 | .25 |
| 433 | A52 | 5p Rossi | .35 | .25 |
| 434 | A52 | 6p Zico | .45 | .30 |
| 435 | A52 | 30p Arconada | 2.25 | .85 |
| | | *Nos. 432-435,C44-C45 (6)* | 9.35 | 4.90 |

21st Birthday of Princess Diana A53

Portraits and scenes of Diana.

**1982, Oct. 21**

| | | | | |
|---|---|---|---|---|
| 436 | A53 | 3.50p multicolored | .35 | .25 |
| 437 | A53 | 5p multicolored | .35 | .25 |
| 438 | A53 | 6p multicolored | .45 | .25 |
| 439 | A53 | 30p multicolored | 2.50 | .65 |
| | | *Nos. 436-439,C47-C48 (6)* | 10.15 | 4.25 |

For overprints see Nos. 450-456.

Visit by Portuguese President Eanes — A54

4.50p, Portugal and Guinea-Bissau flags.

**1982, Dec. 2    Litho.    Perf. 13½**

| | | | | |
|---|---|---|---|---|
| 440 | A54 | 4.50p multicolored | .40 | .25 |
| 441 | A54 | 20p multicolored | 1.60 | 1.10 |

Manned Flight Bicentenary A55

Various hot air balloons.

**1983, Jan. 15    Litho.    Perf. 11**

| | | | | |
|---|---|---|---|---|
| 442 | A55 | 50c multicolored | .25 | .25 |
| 443 | A55 | 2.50p multicolored | .25 | .25 |
| 444 | A55 | 3.50p multicolored | .30 | .25 |
| 445 | A55 | 5p multicolored | .50 | .25 |
| 446 | A55 | 10p multicolored | .55 | .25 |
| 447 | A55 | 20p multicolored | 1.25 | .35 |
| 448 | A55 | 30p multicolored | 1.60 | .45 |
| | | *Nos. 442-448 (7)* | 4.70 | 2.05 |

**Souvenir Sheet**
**Perf. 12½**

| | | | | |
|---|---|---|---|---|
| 449 | A55 | 50p multicolored | 4.00 | 2.00 |

No. 449 contains one 47x47mm stamp.

**Nos. 436-439, C47-C49B Overprinted**

**1982, Dec. 28    Litho.    Perf. 13½**

| | | | | |
|---|---|---|---|---|
| 450 | A53 | 3.50p multicolored | .45 | .25 |
| 451 | A53 | 5p multicolored | .55 | .25 |
| 452 | A53 | 6p multicolored | .65 | .25 |
| 453 | A53 | 30p multicolored | 2.75 | .70 |
| 454 | A53 | 35p multicolored | 3.25 | .90 |
| 455 | A53 | 40p multicolored | 3.75 | 1.25 |
| | | *Nos. 450-455 (6)* | 11.40 | 3.60 |

**Souvenir Sheet**

| | | | | |
|---|---|---|---|---|
| 456 | A53 | 50p multicolored | 6.75 | 1.25 |

**Litho. & Embossed**

| | | | |
|---|---|---|---|
| 456A | A53a | 200p gold & multi | 14.50 |

**Souvenir Sheet**

| | | | |
|---|---|---|---|
| 456B | A53a | 200p gold & multi, vert. | 32.50 |

Nos. 454-456A are airmail.

African Apes and Monkeys — A56

1p, Comopithecus hamadryas. 1.50p, Gorilla gorilla. 3.50p, Theropithecus gelada. 5p, Mandrillus sphinx. 8p, Pan trogladytes. 20p, Colobus abyssinicus. 30p, Cercopithecus diana.

**1983, Mar. 15    Litho.    Perf. 13½**

| | | | | |
|---|---|---|---|---|
| 457 | A56 | 1p multicolored | .25 | .25 |
| 458 | A56 | 1.50p multicolored | .25 | .25 |
| 459 | A56 | 3.50p multicolored | .30 | .25 |
| 460 | A56 | 5p multicolored | .40 | .25 |
| 461 | A56 | 8p multicolored | .90 | .25 |
| 462 | A56 | 20p multicolored | 1.45 | .30 |
| 463 | A56 | 30p multicolored | 2.00 | .45 |
| | | *Nos. 457-463 (7)* | 5.55 | 2.00 |

**Souvenir Sheet**

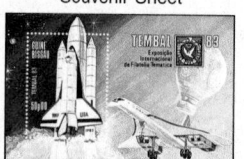

TEMBAL '83, Stamp Exhibition, Basel — A57

**1983, May 21**

| | | | | |
|---|---|---|---|---|
| 464 | A57 | 50p Space shuttle | 5.00 | 1.50 |

A58

Designs: Various telecommunications satellites and space shuttles.

**1983, May 25    Litho.    Perf. 13½**

| | | | | |
|---|---|---|---|---|
| 465 | A58 | 1p multicolored | .25 | .25 |
| 466 | A58 | 1.50p multicolored | .25 | .25 |
| 467 | A58 | 3.50p multicolored | .25 | .25 |
| 468 | A58 | 5p multicolored | .35 | .25 |
| 469 | A58 | 8p multicolored | .45 | .25 |
| 470 | A58 | 20p multicolored | 1.10 | .40 |
| 471 | A58 | 30p multicolored | 1.60 | .65 |
| | | *Nos. 465-471 (7)* | 4.25 | 2.30 |

**Souvenir Sheet**

| | | | | |
|---|---|---|---|---|
| 472 | A58 | 50p multicolored | 3.50 | 1.10 |

History of Chess — A59

Early Chess Game A60

Various chess pieces.

**1983, June 13    Litho.    Perf. 12**

| | | | | |
|---|---|---|---|---|
| 473 | A59 | 1p multicolored | .25 | .25 |
| 474 | A59 | 1.50p multicolored | .25 | .25 |
| 475 | A59 | 3.50p multicolored | .25 | .25 |
| 476 | A59 | 5p multicolored | .35 | .25 |
| 477 | A59 | 10p multicolored | .70 | .25 |
| 478 | A59 | 20p multicolored | 1.25 | .25 |
| 479 | A59 | 40p multicolored | 3.00 | .60 |
| | | *Nos. 473-479 (7)* | 6.05 | 2.10 |

**Souvenir Sheet**

| | | | | |
|---|---|---|---|---|
| 480 | A60 | 50p brown & blk | 4.00 | 1.25 |

Raphael, 500th Birth Anniv. — A61

Various paintings.

**1983, June 30    Litho.    Perf. 12½**

| | | | | |
|---|---|---|---|---|
| 481 | A61 | 1p gold & multi | .25 | .25 |
| 482 | A61 | 1.50p gold & multi | .25 | .25 |
| 483 | A61 | 3.50p gold & multi | .25 | .25 |
| 484 | A61 | 5p gold & multi | .30 | .25 |
| 485 | A61 | 8p gold & multi | .45 | .25 |
| 486 | A61 | 15p gold & multi | .75 | .25 |
| 487 | A61 | 30p gold & multi | 1.75 | .45 |
| | | *Nos. 481-487 (7)* | 4.00 | 1.95 |

**Souvenir Sheet**

| | | | | |
|---|---|---|---|---|
| 488 | A61 | 50p gold & multi | 3.25 | 1.25 |

1984 Summer Olympics, Los Angeles — A62

**1983, July 20    Litho.    Perf. 12½**

| | | | | |
|---|---|---|---|---|
| 489 | A62 | 1p Swimming | .25 | .25 |
| 490 | A62 | 1.50p Jumping | .25 | .25 |
| 491 | A62 | 3.50p Fencing | .35 | .25 |
| 492 | A62 | 5p Weightlifting | .35 | .25 |
| 493 | A62 | 10p Running | .45 | .25 |
| 494 | A62 | 20p Equestrian | 1.05 | .25 |
| 495 | A62 | 40p Bicycling | 2.10 | .70 |
| | | *Nos. 489-495 (7)* | 4.80 | 2.20 |

**Souvenir Sheet**

| | | | | |
|---|---|---|---|---|
| 496 | A62 | 50p Stadium | 4.00 | 1.25 |

**Souvenir Sheet**

BRASILIANA '83, Philatelic Exhibition — A63

**1983, July 29    Litho.    Perf. 13**

| | | | | |
|---|---|---|---|---|
| 497 | A63 | 50p multicolored | 7.50 | 7.50 |

Local Fish — A64

1p, Monodactylus sebae, vert. 1.50p, Botia macracanthus. 3.50p, Ctenopoma acutirostre. 5p, Roloffia bertholdi. 8p, Aphyosemion bualanum. 10p, Aphyosemion bivittatum. 30p, Aphyosemion australe.

**Perf. 12x11½, 11½x12**
**1983, Dec. 8        Litho.**

| | | | | |
|---|---|---|---|---|
| 498 | A64 | 1p multicolored | .25 | .25 |
| 499 | A64 | 1.50p multicolored | .25 | .25 |
| 500 | A64 | 3.50p multicolored | .30 | .25 |
| 501 | A64 | 5p multicolored | .35 | .25 |
| 502 | A64 | 8p multicolored | .50 | .25 |
| 503 | A64 | 10p multicolored | .75 | .25 |
| 504 | A64 | 30p multicolored | 2.25 | .95 |
| | | *Nos. 498-504 (7)* | 4.65 | 2.45 |

1984 Winter Olympics, Sarajevo — A65

**1983, Oct. 10    Litho.    Perf. 13**

| | | | | |
|---|---|---|---|---|
| 505 | A65 | 1p Speed skating | .25 | .25 |
| 506 | A65 | 1.50p Ski jumping | .25 | .25 |
| 507 | A65 | 3p Biathlon | .35 | .25 |
| 508 | A65 | 5p Bobsledding | .45 | .25 |
| 509 | A65 | 10p Hockey | .55 | .25 |
| 510 | A65 | 15p Figure skating | 1.00 | .25 |
| 511 | A65 | 20p Luge | 1.40 | .30 |
| | | *Nos. 505-511 (7)* | 4.25 | 1.80 |

**Souvenir Sheet**

| | | | | |
|---|---|---|---|---|
| 512 | A65 | 50p Downhill skiing | 4.50 | 4.50 |

No. 512 contains one 31x40mm stamp.

A66

**1983, Nov. 7        Perf. 12½**

| | | | | |
|---|---|---|---|---|
| 513 | A66 | 4.50p Emblem | .50 | .25 |
| 514 | A66 | 7.50p Woman, flag | .70 | .25 |
| 515 | A66 | 9p Sewing | .95 | .25 |
| 516 | A66 | 12p Farm workers | 1.25 | .25 |
| | | *Nos. 513-516 (4)* | 3.40 | 1.00 |

First anniv. of Women's Federation.

A67

Designs: Local flowers: 1p, Canna coccinea. 1.50p, Bouganville litoralis. 3.50p, Euphorbia milii. 5p, Delonix regia. 8p, Bauhinia variegata. 10p, Spathodea campanulata. 30p, Hibiscus rosa-sinensis.

**1983, Nov. 12    Litho.    Perf. 13**

| | | | | |
|---|---|---|---|---|
| 517 | A67 | 1p multicolored | .25 | .25 |
| 518 | A67 | 1.50p multicolored | .25 | .25 |
| 519 | A67 | 3.50p multicolored | .25 | .25 |
| 520 | A67 | 5p multicolored | .30 | .25 |
| 521 | A67 | 8p multicolored | .45 | .25 |
| 522 | A67 | 10p multicolored | .60 | .25 |
| 523 | A67 | 30p multicolored | 1.75 | .80 |
| | | *Nos. 517-523 (7)* | 3.85 | 2.30 |

JAAC Congress, Sept. 8-12 — A68

**1983, Sept. 1    Litho.    Perf. 13**

| | | | | |
|---|---|---|---|---|
| 524 | A68 | 4p shown | 1.00 | .25 |
| 524A | A68 | 5p Emblem | 1.00 | .25 |

World Food Day — A69

10p, Hoeing, vert.

**1983, Oct. 16    Litho.    Perf. 12½x12**
**Frame Color**

| | | | | |
|---|---|---|---|---|
| 525 | A69 | 1.50p green | .25 | .25 |
| 526 | A69 | 2p blue | .30 | .25 |
| 527 | A69 | 4p red | .40 | .25 |

**Imperf**
**Size: 61x62mm**

| | | | | |
|---|---|---|---|---|
| 528 | A69 | 10p lt. blue | 2.50 | 1.10 |
| | | *Nos. 525-528 (4)* | 3.45 | 1.85 |

1984 Winter Olympics, Sarajevo — A70

**1984, Jan. 8**      **Perf. 12**

| | | | | |
|---|---|---|---|---|
| 529 | A70 | 50c Ski jumping | .25 | .25 |
| 530 | A70 | 2.50p Speed skating | .30 | .25 |
| 531 | A70 | 3.50p Hockey | .40 | .25 |
| 532 | A70 | 5p Biathlon | .45 | .25 |
| 533 | A70 | 6p Downhill skiing | .50 | .25 |
| 534 | A70 | 20p Figure skating | 1.20 | .45 |
| 535 | A70 | 30p Bobsledding | 2.00 | .45 |
| | | Nos. 529-535 (7) | 5.10 | 2.10 |

**Souvenir Sheet**
**Perf. 11½**

| | | | | |
|---|---|---|---|---|
| 536 | A70 | 50p Skiing | 4.00 | 4.00 |

No. 536 contains one 32x43mm stamp.

World Communications Year — A71

50c, Rowland Hill. 2.50p, Samuel Morse. 3.50p, H.R. Hertz. 5p, Lord Kelvin. 10p, Alex. Graham Bell. 20p, G. Marconi. 30p, V. Zworykin.
50p, Satellites.

**1983, Aug. 30**   **Litho.**   **Perf. 12½**

| | | | | |
|---|---|---|---|---|
| 537 | A71 | 50c multicolored | .30 | .25 |
| 538 | A71 | 2.50p multicolored | .35 | .25 |
| 539 | A71 | 3.50p multicolored | .40 | .25 |
| 540 | A71 | 5p multicolored | .55 | .25 |
| 541 | A71 | 10p multicolored | 1.00 | .25 |
| 542 | A71 | 20p multicolored | 2.00 | .60 |
| 543 | A71 | 30p multicolored | 3.00 | .75 |
| | | Nos. 537-543 (7) | 7.60 | 2.60 |

**Souvenir Sheet**

| | | | | |
|---|---|---|---|---|
| 544 | A71 | 50p multicolored | 4.00 | 3.25 |

No. 544 contains one stamp 31x39mm.

Vintage Cars — A72

5p, Duesenberg, 1928. 8p, MG Midget, 1932. 15p, Mercedes, 1928. 20p, Bentley, 1928. 24p, Alfa Romeo, 1929. 30p, Datsun, 1932. 35p, Lincoln, 1932.
100p, Gottlieb Daimler.

**1984, Mar. 20**      **Perf. 12**

| | | | | |
|---|---|---|---|---|
| 545 | A72 | 5p multicolored | .25 | .25 |
| 546 | A72 | 8p multicolored | .40 | .25 |
| 547 | A72 | 15p multicolored | .55 | .25 |
| 548 | A72 | 20p multicolored | .65 | .30 |
| 549 | A72 | 24p multicolored | .75 | .35 |
| 550 | A72 | 30p multicolored | 1.10 | .50 |
| 551 | A72 | 35p multicolored | 1.25 | .55 |
| | | Nos. 545-551 (7) | 4.95 | 2.45 |

**Souvenir Sheet**

| | | | | |
|---|---|---|---|---|
| 552 | A72 | 100p multicolored | 6.00 | 4.25 |

No. 552 contains one stamp 50x42mm.

Madonna and Child, by Morales — A73

Paintings by Spanish Artists (Espana '84): 6p, Dona Tadea Arias de Enriquez, by Goya. 10p, Santa Cassilda, by Zurbaran. 12p, Saints Andrew and Francis, by El Greco. 15p, Infanta Isabel Clara Eugenia, by Coello. 35p, Queen Maria of Austria, by Velazquez. 40p, Holy Trinity, by El Greco. 100p, Clothed Maja, by Goya.

**1984, Apr. 20**

| | | | | |
|---|---|---|---|---|
| 553 | A73 | 3p multicolored | .25 | .25 |
| 554 | A73 | 6p multicolored | .25 | .25 |
| 555 | A73 | 10p multicolored | .25 | .25 |
| 556 | A73 | 12p multicolored | .45 | .25 |
| 557 | A73 | 15p multicolored | .60 | .25 |
| 558 | A73 | 35p multicolored | 1.45 | .60 |
| 559 | A73 | 40p multicolored | 1.75 | .65 |
| | | Nos. 553-559 (7) | 5.00 | 2.50 |

**Souvenir Sheet**

| | | | | |
|---|---|---|---|---|
| 560 | A73 | 100p multicolored | 5.00 | 4.75 |

No. 560 contains one stamp 29x50mm.

Carnivorous Animals — A74

**1984, June 28**

| | | | | |
|---|---|---|---|---|
| 561 | A74 | 3p Panthera tigris | .25 | .25 |
| 562 | A74 | 6p Panthera leo | .40 | .25 |
| 563 | A74 | 10p Neofelis nebulosa | .45 | .25 |
| 564 | A74 | 12p Acinonyx jubatus | .60 | .30 |
| 565 | A74 | 15p Lynx lynx | .65 | .30 |
| 566 | A74 | 35p Panthera pardus | 1.75 | .60 |
| 567 | A74 | 40p Uncia uncia | 1.90 | .70 |
| | | Nos. 561-567 (7) | 6.00 | 2.65 |

Intl. Civil Aviation Org., 40th Anniv. — A75

**1984, Apr. 4**   **Litho.**   **Perf. 12½**

| | | | | |
|---|---|---|---|---|
| 568 | A75 | 8p Caravelle | .40 | .25 |
| 569 | A75 | 22p DC-6B | .85 | .35 |
| 570 | A75 | 80p IL-76 | 3.00 | 1.25 |
| | | Nos. 568-570 (3) | 4.25 | 1.85 |

1984 Summer Olympics, Los Angeles — A76

6p, Soccer. 8p, Dressage. 15p, Yachting. 20p, Field hockey. 22p, Women's team handball. 30p, Canoeing. 40p, Boxing.
100p, Windsurfing.

**1984, May 24**      **Perf. 12**

| | | | | |
|---|---|---|---|---|
| 571 | A76 | 6p multicolored | .25 | .25 |
| 572 | A76 | 8p multicolored | .25 | .25 |
| 573 | A76 | 15p multicolored | .55 | .25 |
| 574 | A76 | 20p multicolored | .70 | .25 |
| 575 | A76 | 22p multicolored | .75 | .25 |
| 576 | A76 | 30p multicolored | 1.10 | .40 |
| 577 | A76 | 40p multicolored | 1.40 | .80 |
| | | Nos. 571-577 (7) | 5.00 | 2.45 |

**Souvenir Sheet**
**Perf. 11½**

| | | | | |
|---|---|---|---|---|
| 578 | A76 | 100p multicolored | 5.50 | 3.75 |

World Heritage — A77

Wood sculptures: 3p, Pearl throne, Cameroun and Central Africa. 6p, Antelope, South Sudan. 10p, Kneeling woman, East Africa. 12p, Mask, West African coast. 15p, Leopard, Guinea coast. 35p, Standing woman, Zaire. 40p, Funerary statues, Southeast Africa and Madagascar.

**1984, Aug. 15**      **Perf. 12½**

| | | | | |
|---|---|---|---|---|
| 579 | A77 | 3p multicolored | .35 | .25 |
| 580 | A77 | 6p multicolored | .40 | .25 |
| 581 | A77 | 10p multicolored | .45 | .25 |
| 582 | A77 | 12p multicolored | .75 | .25 |
| 583 | A77 | 15p multicolored | .95 | .30 |
| 584 | A77 | 35p multicolored | 1.90 | .65 |
| 585 | A77 | 40p multicolored | 2.10 | .70 |
| | | Nos. 579-585 (7) | 6.90 | 2.65 |

Amilcar Cabral, 60th Birth Anniv. — A78

5p, Public speaking. 12p, In combat fatigues. 20p, Memorial building, Bafata. 50p, Mausoleum, Bissau.

**1984, Sept. 12**      **Perf. 13**

| | | | | |
|---|---|---|---|---|
| 586 | A78 | 5p multicolored | .50 | .25 |
| 587 | A78 | 12p multicolored | .55 | .25 |
| 588 | A78 | 20p multicolored | 1.00 | .35 |
| 589 | A78 | 50p multicolored | 2.25 | .80 |
| | | Nos. 586-589 (4) | 4.30 | 1.65 |

Independence, 11th Anniv. — A79

3p, Mechanic. 6p, Student. 10p, Mason. 12p, Health care, vert. 15p, Seamstress, vert. 35p, Telecommunications. 40p, PAIGC building.

**1984, Sept. 24**

| | | | | |
|---|---|---|---|---|
| 590 | A79 | 3p multi | .30 | .25 |
| 591 | A79 | 6p multi | .35 | .25 |
| 592 | A79 | 10p multi | .45 | .25 |
| 593 | A79 | 12p multi | .60 | .30 |
| 594 | A79 | 15p multi | .75 | .30 |
| 595 | A79 | 35p multi | 1.50 | .70 |
| 596 | A79 | 40p multi | 1.75 | .75 |
| | | Nos. 590-596 (7) | 5.70 | 2.80 |

Whales — A80

5p, Eschrichtius gibbosus. 8p, Balaenoptera musculus. 15p, Tursiops truncatus. 20p, Physeter macrocephalus. 24p, Orcinus orca. 30p, Balaena mysticetus. 35p, Balaenoptera borealis.

**1984, Sept. 30**      **Perf. 12**

| | | | | |
|---|---|---|---|---|
| 597 | A80 | 5p multicolored | .45 | .25 |
| 598 | A80 | 8p multicolored | .60 | .25 |
| 599 | A80 | 15p multicolored | .90 | .35 |
| 600 | A80 | 20p multicolored | 1.75 | .35 |
| 601 | A80 | 24p multicolored | 2.75 | .45 |
| 602 | A80 | 30p multicolored | 2.75 | .55 |
| 603 | A80 | 35p multicolored | 2.75 | .60 |
| | | Nos. 597-603 (7) | 11.95 | 2.80 |

Butterflies — A81

3p, Hypolimnas dexithea. 6p, Papilio arcturus. 10p, Morpho menelaus terrestris. 12p, Apaturina erminea papuana. 15p, Prepona praeneste. 35p, Ornithoptera paradisea. 40p, Morpho hecuba obidona.

**1984, Oct. 6**      **Perf. 12½x13**

| | | | | |
|---|---|---|---|---|
| 604 | A81 | 3p multicolored | .35 | .25 |
| 605 | A81 | 6p multicolored | .45 | .25 |
| 606 | A81 | 10p multicolored | .50 | .25 |
| 607 | A81 | 12p multicolored | .65 | .25 |
| 608 | A81 | 15p multicolored | .85 | .35 |
| 609 | A81 | 35p multicolored | 1.20 | .65 |
| 610 | A81 | 40p multicolored | 1.75 | .75 |
| | | Nos. 604-610 (7) | 5.75 | 2.75 |

1984 Los Angeles Summer Olympic Winners — A82

National flag, medal and: 6p, Carl Lewis, 4x100 relay, US. 8p, Koji Gushiken, gymnastics, Japan. 15p, Reiner Klimke, equestrian, Federal Republic of Germany. 20p, Tracie Ruiz, synchronized swimming, US. 22p, Mary Lou Retton, gymnastics, US. 30p, Michael Gross, swimming, Federal Republic of Germany. 40p, Edwin Moses, hurdler, US. 100p, Daley Thompson, decathlon, Great Britain.

**1984, Nov. 27**      **Perf. 13**

| | | | | |
|---|---|---|---|---|
| 611 | A82 | 6p multicolored | .25 | .25 |
| 612 | A82 | 8p multicolored | .30 | .25 |
| 613 | A82 | 15p multicolored | .50 | .25 |
| 614 | A82 | 20p multicolored | .75 | .25 |
| 615 | A82 | 22p multicolored | .80 | .30 |
| 616 | A82 | 30p multicolored | 1.25 | .45 |
| 617 | A82 | 40p multicolored | 1.60 | .65 |
| | | Nos. 611-617 (7) | 5.45 | 2.40 |

**Souvenir Sheet**
**Perf. 12½**

| | | | | |
|---|---|---|---|---|
| 618 | A82 | 100p multicolored | 5.25 | 3.75 |

No. 618 contains one stamp 32x40mm.

Locomotives A83

5p, White Mountain Central No. 4. 8p, Kessler 2-6-OT, 1886. 15p, Langen tram, 1901. 20p, Gurjao No. 6. 24p, Achenseebahn. 30p, Vitznau-Rigi steam locomotive. 35p, Riggenbach rackrail, 1873.

**1984, Dec. 15**      **Perf. 13**

| | | | | |
|---|---|---|---|---|
| 619 | A83 | 5p multicolored | .30 | .25 |
| 620 | A83 | 8p multicolored | .40 | .25 |
| 621 | A83 | 15p multicolored | .50 | .30 |
| 622 | A83 | 20p multicolored | .65 | .35 |
| 623 | A83 | 24p multicolored | .85 | .40 |
| 624 | A83 | 30p multicolored | 1.05 | .55 |
| 625 | A83 | 35p multicolored | 1.25 | .85 |
| | | Nos. 619-625 (7) | 5.00 | 2.95 |

**Souvenir Sheet**
**Perf. 12½**

| | | | | |
|---|---|---|---|---|
| 625A | A83 | 100p like #621 | 5.75 | 3.50 |

No. 625A contains one stamp 40x32mm.

Native Crafts — A83a

LUBRAPEX '84: a, Numbe mask. b, Sono statue. c, Erande statue. d, Kokumba arms. e, Oma mask. f, Koni mask.

**1984, May 9**   **Litho.**   **Perf. 13½**

| | | | | |
|---|---|---|---|---|
| 626 | A83a | 7.50p Strip of 6, #a.-f. | 5.00 | 3.50 |

Motorcycle Cent. — A84

**1985, Feb. 20**      **Perf. 13x12½**

| | | | | |
|---|---|---|---|---|
| 627 | A84 | 5p Harley-Davidson | .30 | .25 |
| 628 | A84 | 8p Kawasaki | .45 | .25 |
| 629 | A84 | 15p Honda | .70 | .25 |
| 630 | A84 | 20p Yamaha | 1.10 | .35 |
| 631 | A84 | 25p Suzuki | 1.60 | .40 |
| 632 | A84 | 30p BMW | 1.90 | .55 |
| 633 | A84 | 35p Moto Guzzi | 2.75 | .60 |
| | | Nos. 627-633 (7) | 8.80 | 2.65 |

## Souvenir Sheet
### Perf. 12½
**634** A84 100p Daimler Motorized Bicycle, 1885, vert. 9.00 6.00

No. 634 contains one 32x40mm stamp.

### Miniature Sheet

Mushrooms — A85

**1985, May 15**     **Perf. 13**
**635** A85   Sheet of 6   6.50 2.10
  *a.*   7p Clitocybe gibba   .35 .25
  *b.*   9p Morchella elata   .40 .25
  *c.*   12p Lepista nuda   .55 .30
  *d.*   20p Lactarius deliciosus   .95 .35
  *e.*   30p Russula virescens   1.35 .45
  *f.*   35p Chroogomphus rutilus   1.50 .55

Henri Dunant (1828-1910), Red Cross Founder, Plane — A87

**1985, June 12**     **Perf. 12½**
**643** A87 20p shown   .60 .25
**644** A87 25p Ambulance   .70 .25
**645** A87 40p Helicopter   1.50 .45
**646** A87 80p Speed boat   3.00 .80
  *Nos. 643-646 (4)*   5.80 1.75

Cats — A88

**1985, July 5**     **Perf. 13**
**647** A88   7p multicolored   .25 .25
**648** A88 10p multicolored   .25 .25
**649** A88 12p multicolored   .35 .25
**650** A88 15p multicolored   .55 .25
**651** A88 20p multicolored   .80 .25
**652** A88 40p multicolored   1.15 .25
**653** A88 45p multicolored   1.75 .40
  *Nos. 647-653 (7)*   5.10 1.90

### Souvenir Sheet
**654** A88 100p multicolored   5.50 4.00

ARGENTINA '85. No. 654 contains one 40x32mm stamp.

Composers and Musical Instruments — A89

Designs: 4p, Vincenzo Bellini (1801-1835), harp, 1820, and descant viol, 16th cent. 5p, Schumann (1810-1856) and Viennese pyramid piano, 1829. 7p, Chopin (1810-1849) and piano-forte, 1817. 12p, Luigi Cherubini (1760-1842) and 18th cent. Baryton violin and Quinton viol. 20p, G. B. Pergolesi (1710-1736) and double-manual harpsichord, 1734. 30p, Handel (1685-1759), valve trumpet, 1825, and timpani drum, 18th cent. 50p, Heinrich Schutz (1585-1672), bass viol and two-stop oboe, 17th cent. 100s, Bach (1685-1750) and St. Thomas Church organ, Leipzig.

**1985, Aug. 5**     **Perf. 12**
**655** A89   4p multicolored   .25 .25
**656** A89   5p multicolored   .30 .25
**657** A89   7p multicolored   .45 .25
**658** A89 12p multicolored   .70 .25
**659** A89 20p multicolored   1.00 .25

**660** A89 30p multicolored   1.60 .30
**661** A89 50p multicolored   2.50 .60
  *Nos. 655-661 (7)*   6.80 2.15

### Souvenir Sheet
### Perf. 11½
**662** A89 100p multicolored   6.50 4.25

No. 662 contains one 30x50mm stamp.

Santa Maria, 15th Cent., Spain — A90

Ships: 15p, Carack, 16th cent., Netherlands. 20p, Mayflower, 17th cent., Great Britain. 30p, St. Louis, 17th cent., France. 35p, Royal Sovereign, 1635, Great Britain. 45p, Soleil Royal, 17th cent., France. 80p, English brig, 18th-19th cent.

**1985, Sept. 12**     **Perf. 13**
**663** A90   8p multicolored   .30 .25
**664** A90 15p multicolored   .45 .25
**665** A90 20p multicolored   .60 .25
**666** A90 30p multicolored   1.00 .30
**667** A90 35p multicolored   1.15 .30
**668** A90 45p multicolored   1.50 .45
**669** A90 80p multicolored   3.00 .75
  *Nos. 663-669 (7)*   8.00 2.55

UN, 40th Anniv. — A91

10p, Emblem, doves, vert. 20p, Emblem, 40.

**1985, Oct. 17**
**670** A91 10p multicolored   .60 .25
**671** A91 20p multicolored   1.40 .50

Venus and Mars, by Sandro Botticelli (1445-1510) — A92

Botticelli paintings (details): 7p, Virgin with Child and St. John. 12p, St. Augustine in the Work Hall. 15p, Awakening of Spring. 20p, Virgin and Child. 40p, Virgin with Child and St. John, diff. 45p, Birth of Venus. 100p, Virgin and Child with Two Angels.

**1985, Oct. 25**     **Perf. 12½x13**
**672** A92   7p multicolored   .35 .25
**673** A92 10p multicolored   .40 .25
**674** A92 12p multicolored   .50 .25
**675** A92 15p multicolored   .55 .25
**676** A92 20p multicolored   .75 .25
**677** A92 40p multicolored   1.50 .40
**678** A92 45p multicolored   1.90 .45

### Size: 73x106mm
### Imperf
**679** A92 100p multicolored   7.00 5.50
  *Nos. 672-679 (8)*   12.95 7.60

ITALIA '85.

Intl. Youth Year — A93

**1985, Nov. 29**   **Litho.**   **Perf. 12½**
**680** A93   7p Dance   .25 .25
**681** A93 13p Wind surfing   .30 .25
**682** A93 15p Rollerskating   .35 .25
**683** A93 25p Hang gliding   .65 .25
**684** A93 40p Surfing   1.00 .30
**685** A93 50p Skateboarding   1.25 .50
**686** A93 80p Parachuting   2.25 .70
  *Nos. 680-686 (7)*   6.05 2.50

### Souvenir Sheet
### Perf. 13
**687** A93 100p Self-defense   6.00 4.50

No. 687 contains one 40x32mm stamp.

Halley's Comet A94

1986 World Cup Soccer Championships, Mexico — A95

24th Summer Olympics, Seoul, 1988 — A96

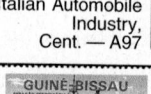

Italian Automobile Industry, Cent. — A97

German Railways, 150th Anniv. — A98

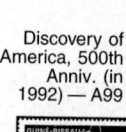

Discovery of America, 500th Anniv. (in 1992) — A99

First American Manned Space Flight, 25th Anniv. — A100

1986 Wimbledon Tennis Championships A101

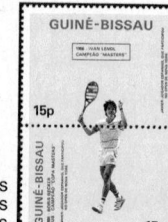

1986 Masters Tennis Championships A102

Giotto Space Probe A103

Designs: a, Comet tail. b, Comet. c, Trophy. d, Trophy base. e, Five-ring Olympic emblem. f, Alfa Tourer, Italy, c. 1905. g, Railway station, Frankfurt-on Main, c. 1914. h, Barcelona, site of Discovery of America exhibition and 1992 Olympics. i, Space station solar panels and tanks. j, Space station. k, Removing cargo from space shuttle. l, Docking facility, station panels. m, Boris Becker swinging tennis racket. n, Becker, diff. o, Ivan Lendl holding racket. p, Lendl, diff.

### Miniature Sheet
**1986, Dec. 30**   **Litho.**   **Perf. 13½**
**688**   Sheet of 16   100.00
  *a.-p.* A94-A102 15p any single   6.00 3.25

### Souvenir Sheet
**689** A103 100p multicolored   14.00 10.00

Nos. 688a-688b, 688c-688d, 688i-688l, 688m-688n, 688o-688p are se-tenant in continuous designs. Inscription on Nos. 688i-688l incorrect; should read "TRIPULADO MERCURY / 5-5-1961."

Discovery of America, 500th Anniv. (in 1992) — A104

Designs: No. 690, Christopher Columbus aboard caravelle. No. 691, Guadalquivir Port, Seville, c. 1490. No. 692, Pedro Alvars Cabral landing at Bahia, Brazil. No. 693, Bridge over the Guadalquivir River, Seville. No. 694, Port, Lisbon, 15th cent.

**1987, Feb. 27**
**690** A104 50p multicolored   3.50 1.20
**691** A104 50p multicolored   3.50 1.20
**692** A104 50p multicolored   3.50 1.20
**693** A104 50p multicolored   3.50 1.20
  *Nos. 690-693 (4)*   14.00 4.80

### Souvenir Sheet
**694** A104 150p multicolored   14.00 9.00

No. 694 exists with pink or yellow anniv. emblem pictured in vignette. Values are the same.

Portuguese Guinea Nos. 306-309, 313, 316-317, Ovptd., Guinea-Bissau No. 349 Srchd.

**1987, July**   **Litho.**   **Perf. 13½**
**696** A21 100p on 20c #306   1.75 .60
**697** A21 200p on 35c #307   3.25 1.25
**698** A21 300p on 70c #308   5.00 1.60
**699** A21 400p on 80c #309   5.50 2.00
**700** A21 500p on 3.50e #313   7.75 2.75
**701** A21 1000p on 15e #316   20.00 5.50
**702** A21 2000p on 20e #317   40.00 13.50
    **Perf. 13**
**703** CD61 2500p on 2e #349   50.00 14.50
  *Nos. 696-703 (8)*   133.25 41.70

Placement of "Bissau," new denomination and obliterating bar varies. No. 698 is known to have been sold in April 1986.

1988 Winter Olympics, Calgary — A106

5p, Pairs figure skating. 10p, Luge. 50p, Skiing. 200p, Slalom skiing. 300p, Skibobbing. 500p, Ski jumping, vert. 800p, Speed skating, vert.

900p, Two-man luge.

| 1988, Jan. 15 | | Litho. | Perf. 13 | |
|---|---|---|---|---|
| 704 | A106 | 5p multicolored | .30 | .25 |
| 705 | A106 | 10p multicolored | .50 | .25 |
| 706 | A106 | 50p multicolored | .60 | .25 |
| 707 | A106 | 200p multicolored | .75 | .35 |
| 708 | A106 | 300p multicolored | 1.35 | .50 |
| 709 | A106 | 500p multicolored | 2.00 | .65 |
| 710 | A106 | 800p multicolored | 3.50 | 2.25 |
| | | Nos. 704-710 (7) | 9.00 | 4.50 |

**Souvenir Sheet**

| 710A | A106 | 900p multicolored | 7.00 | 3.50 |
|---|---|---|---|---|

No. 710A contains one 40x32mm stamp.

Soccer — A107

Various soccer plays.

| 1988, Apr. 14 | | Litho. | Perf. 13 | |
|---|---|---|---|---|
| 711 | A107 | 5p multi | .25 | .25 |
| 712 | A107 | 10p multi, diff. | .25 | .25 |
| 713 | A107 | 50p multi, diff. | .55 | .25 |
| 714 | A107 | 200p multi, diff. | 1.10 | .40 |
| 715 | A107 | 300p multi, diff. | 1.75 | .50 |
| 716 | A107 | 500p multi, diff. | 2.00 | .65 |
| 717 | A107 | 800p multi, diff. | 4.00 | 1.75 |
| | | Nos. 711-717 (7) | 9.90 | 4.05 |

**Souvenir Sheet**

| 718 | A107 | 900p multi | 7.00 | 4.75 |
|---|---|---|---|---|

ESSEN '88 stamp exhibition. No. 718 contains one 32x40mm stamp.

1988 Summer Olympics, Seoul — A108

5p, Yachting, vert. 10p, Equestrian. 50p, High jump. 200p, Shooting. 300p, Long jump, vert. 500p, Tennis, vert. 800p, Women's archery, vert.

900p, Soccer.

| | Perf. 12½x12, 12x12½ | | | |
|---|---|---|---|---|
| 1988, Feb. 26 | | | | Litho. |
| 719 | A108 | 5p multi | .25 | .25 |
| 720 | A108 | 10p multi | .25 | .25 |
| 721 | A108 | 50p multi | .35 | .25 |
| 722 | A108 | 200p multi | 1.15 | .50 |
| 723 | A108 | 300p multi | 1.75 | .60 |
| 724 | A108 | 500p multi | 2.75 | .75 |
| 725 | A108 | 800p multi | 4.50 | 1.50 |
| | | Nos. 719-725 (7) | 11.00 | 4.10 |

**Souvenir Sheet**
*Perf. 12½*

| 726 | A108 | 900p multi | 5.00 | 2.25 |
|---|---|---|---|---|

No. 726 contains one 40x32mm stamp.

Ancient Ships A109

Designs: 5p, Egyptian, c. 3300 B.C. 10p, Pharaoh Sahure's ship, c. 2700 B.C. 50p, Queen Hatsepsowe's ship, c. 1500 B.C. 200p, Ramses III's ship, c. 1200 B.C. 300p, Greek trireme, 480 B.C. 500p, Etruscan bireme, 600 B.C. 800p, Venetian galley, 12th cent.

| 1988 | | Litho. | Perf. 13x12½ | |
|---|---|---|---|---|
| 727 | A109 | 5p multi | .25 | .25 |
| 728 | A109 | 10p multi | .25 | .25 |
| 729 | A109 | 50p multi | .45 | .25 |
| 730 | A109 | 200p multi | 1.10 | .35 |
| 731 | A109 | 300p multi | 1.50 | .40 |
| 732 | A109 | 500p multi | 2.50 | .60 |
| 733 | A109 | 800p multi | 4.00 | 1.00 |
| | | Nos. 727-733 (7) | 10.05 | 3.10 |

FINLANDIA '88 — A110

Chess champions, board and chessmen: 5p, Philidor. 10p, Staunton. 50p, Anderssen. 200p, Morphy. 300p, Steinitz. 500p, Lasker. 800p, Capablanca.

900p, Ruy Lopez.

| 1988 | | Litho. | Perf. 12x12½ | |
|---|---|---|---|---|
| 734 | A110 | 5p multi | .25 | .25 |
| 735 | A110 | 10p multi | .25 | .25 |
| 736 | A110 | 50p multi | .50 | .25 |
| 737 | A110 | 200p multi | 1.25 | .25 |
| 738 | A110 | 300p multi | 1.60 | .30 |
| 739 | A110 | 500p multi | 3.00 | .40 |
| 740 | A110 | 800p multi | 4.50 | .65 |
| | | Nos. 734-740 (7) | 11.35 | 2.35 |

**Souvenir Sheet**
*Perf. 13*

| 741 | A110 | 900p multi | 7.00 | 4.75 |
|---|---|---|---|---|

No. 741 contains one 40x32mm stamp.

Dogs — A111

5p, Basset hound. 10p, Great blue of Gascony. 50p, Sabujo of Italy. 200p, Yorkshire terrier. 300p, Small musterlander. 500p, Pointer. 800p, German setter.

900p, German shepherd.

| 1988, Sept. 29 | | | Perf. 13x12½ | |
|---|---|---|---|---|
| 742 | A111 | 5p multicolored | .25 | .25 |
| 743 | A111 | 10p multicolored | .35 | .25 |
| 744 | A111 | 50p multicolored | .35 | .25 |
| 745 | A111 | 200p multicolored | .85 | .40 |
| 746 | A111 | 300p multicolored | 1.40 | .70 |
| 747 | A111 | 500p multicolored | 2.25 | 1.25 |
| 748 | A111 | 800p multicolored | 3.50 | 1.75 |
| | | Nos. 742-748 (7) | 8.95 | 4.85 |

**Souvenir Sheet**
*Perf. 12½*

| 749 | A111 | 900p multicolored | 5.50 | 2.50 |
|---|---|---|---|---|

No. 749 contains one 40x32mm stamp.

Intl. Red Cross and Red Crescent Organizations, 125th Anniv. — A112

10p, Jean-Henri Dunant. 50p, Dr. T. Maunoir. 200p, Dr. Louis Appia. 800p, Gustave Moynier.

| 1988 | | | Perf. 13 | |
|---|---|---|---|---|
| 750 | A112 | 10p multicolored | .25 | .25 |
| 751 | A112 | 50p multicolored | .50 | .25 |
| 752 | A112 | 200p multicolored | .85 | .50 |
| 753 | A112 | 800p multicolored | 4.00 | .90 |
| | | Nos. 750-753 (4) | 5.60 | 1.90 |

Maps and Fauna A113

5p, Panthera leo. 10p, Glaucidium brasilianum. 50p, Upupa epops. 200p, Equus burchelli antiquorum. 300p, Loxodonta africana. 500p, Acryllium vulturinum. 800p, Diceros bicornis.

| 1988 | | | Perf. 12½x13, 13x12½ | |
|---|---|---|---|---|
| 754 | A113 | 5p multicolored | .25 | .25 |
| 755 | A113 | 10p multicolored | .25 | .25 |
| 756 | A113 | 50p multicolored | .50 | .25 |
| 757 | A113 | 200p multicolored | 1.10 | .25 |
| 758 | A113 | 300p multicolored | 1.60 | .30 |
| 759 | A113 | 500p multicolored | 2.50 | .75 |
| 760 | A113 | 800p multicolored | 4.25 | 1.75 |
| | | Nos. 754-760 (7) | 10.45 | 3.80 |

Nos. 754-755, 758-760 vert. The genus "Upupa" is misspelled on the 50p and "Loxodonta" is misspelled on the 300p.

Samora Machel (1933-1986), Pres. of Mozambique — A114

50p, Raising fist. 200p, With sentry. 300p, Wearing earphones at UN.

| 1988 | | | Perf. 13 | |
|---|---|---|---|---|
| 761 | A114 | 10p shown | .25 | .25 |
| 762 | A114 | 50p multicolored | .40 | .25 |
| 763 | A114 | 200p multicolored | 1.25 | .50 |
| 764 | A114 | 300p multicolored | 2.10 | .80 |
| | | Nos. 761-764 (4) | 4.00 | 1.80 |

Mushrooms A115

370p, Peziza aurantia. 470p, Morchella. 600p, Amanita caesarea. 780p, Amanita muscaria. 800p, Amanita phalloides. 900p, Agaricus bisporus. 945p, Cantharellus cibarius.

| 1988 | | Litho. | Perf. 13x12½ | |
|---|---|---|---|---|
| 765 | A115 | 370p multicolored | 1.40 | .35 |
| 766 | A115 | 470p multicolored | 1.75 | .40 |
| 767 | A115 | 600p multicolored | 2.75 | .60 |
| 768 | A115 | 780p multicolored | 4.00 | .70 |
| 769 | A115 | 800p multicolored | 4.00 | .70 |
| 770 | A115 | 900p multicolored | 4.75 | .90 |
| 771 | A115 | 945p multicolored | 4.25 | .95 |
| | | Nos. 765-771 (7) | 22.90 | 4.60 |

1992 Winter Olympics, Albertville A116

50p, Speed skating. 100p, Women's figure skating. 200p, Ski jumping. 350p, Skiing. 500p, Skiing, diff. 800p, Bobsled. 1000p, Ice hockey.

1500p, Ice hockey, diff.

| 1989, Oct. 12 | | Litho. | Perf. 12½x12 | |
|---|---|---|---|---|
| 772 | A116 | 50p multicolored | .40 | .25 |
| 773 | A116 | 100p multicolored | .55 | .25 |
| 774 | A116 | 200p multicolored | 1.10 | .25 |
| 775 | A116 | 350p multicolored | 1.25 | .40 |
| 776 | A116 | 500p multicolored | 2.10 | .55 |
| 777 | A116 | 800p multicolored | 3.25 | .95 |
| 778 | A116 | 1000p multicolored | 4.25 | 1.10 |
| | | Nos. 772-778 (7) | 12.90 | 3.75 |

**Souvenir Sheet**
*Perf. 12½*

| 779 | A116 | 1500p multicolored | 6.00 | 5.00 |
|---|---|---|---|---|

No. 779 contains one 32x40mm stamp.

World Cup Soccer Championships, Italy — A117

Various soccer players.

| 1989, Aug. 14 | | Litho. | Perf. 12½ | |
|---|---|---|---|---|
| 780 | A117 | 50p multicolored | .25 | .25 |
| 781 | A117 | 100p multicolored | .45 | .25 |
| 782 | A117 | 200p multicolored | .60 | .25 |
| 783 | A117 | 350p multicolored | 1.00 | .35 |
| 784 | A117 | 500p multicolored | 1.20 | .45 |
| 785 | A117 | 800p multicolored | 2.50 | .80 |
| 786 | A117 | 1000p multicolored | 3.00 | .90 |
| | | Nos. 780-786 (7) | 9.00 | 3.25 |

**Souvenir Sheet**
*Perf. 13*

| 786A | A117 | 1500p multicolored | 4.50 | 3.00 |
|---|---|---|---|---|

No. 786A contains one 40x32mm stamp.

Lilies (Lilium) — A118

50p, Limelight. 100p, Candidum. 200p, Pardalinum. 350p, Auratum. 500p, Canadense. 800p, Enchantment. 1000p, Black Dragon.

1500p, Lilium pyrenaicum.

| 1989, June 15 | | | Perf. 12½ | |
|---|---|---|---|---|
| 787 | A118 | 50p multi | .25 | .25 |
| 788 | A118 | 100p multi | .40 | .25 |
| 789 | A118 | 200p multi | .70 | .35 |
| 790 | A118 | 350p multi | 1.15 | .65 |
| 791 | A118 | 500p multi | 1.35 | .70 |
| 792 | A118 | 800p multi | 2.75 | 1.50 |
| 793 | A118 | 1000p multi | 3.50 | 1.90 |
| | | Nos. 787-793 (7) | 10.10 | 5.60 |

**Souvenir Sheet**

| 794 | A118 | 1500p multi | 5.25 | 3.00 |
|---|---|---|---|---|

No. 794 contains one 32x40mm stamp.

Trains — A119

Various railroad engines.

| 1989, May 24 | | Litho. | Perf. 13 | |
|---|---|---|---|---|
| 795 | A119 | 50p multicolored | .25 | .25 |
| 796 | A119 | 100p multicolored | .35 | .25 |
| 797 | A119 | 200p multicolored | .60 | .35 |
| 798 | A119 | 350p multicolored | 1.25 | .70 |
| 799 | A119 | 500p multicolored | 1.75 | .95 |
| 800 | A119 | 800p multicolored | 2.50 | 1.60 |

| | | Perf. 12½ | | |
|---|---|---|---|---|
| | | Size: 68x27mm | | |
| 801 | A119 | 1000p multicolored | 3.25 | .85 |
| | | Nos. 795-801 (7) | 9.95 | 4.95 |

**Souvenir Sheet**
*Perf. 12½*

| 802 | A119 | 1500p multicolored | 5.00 | 3.00 |
|---|---|---|---|---|

No. 802 contains one 32x40mm stamp.

La Marseillaise by Francois Rude — A120

Paintings: 100p, Armed mob. 200p, Storming the Bastille. 350p, Lafayette, Liberty, vert. 500p, Dancing around the Liberty tree. 800p, Rouget de Lisle singing La Marseillaise by Pils. 1000p, Storming the Bastille, diff. 1500p, Arms of the Republic of France.

| | Perf. 12½, 12x12½ (350p) | | | |
|---|---|---|---|---|
| 1989, July 5 | | | | |
| 803 | A120 | 50p shown | .25 | .25 |
| 804 | A120 | 100p multicolored | .25 | .25 |
| 805 | A120 | 200p multicolored | .55 | .40 |
| 806 | A120 | 350p multicolored, 27x44mm | 1.10 | .50 |
| 807 | A120 | 500p multicolored | 1.60 | .90 |
| 808 | A120 | 800p multicolored | 2.50 | 1.40 |
| 809 | A120 | 1000p multicolored | 3.00 | 1.75 |
| | | Nos. 803-809 (7) | 9.25 | 5.45 |

**Souvenir Sheet**
*Perf. 13*

| 810 | A120 | 1500p multicolored | 5.00 | 2.75 |
|---|---|---|---|---|

Birds — A121

Designs: 50p, Alectroenas pulcherrima. 100p, Streptopelia senegalensis. 200p, Oena capensis. 350p, Claravis mondetoura. 500p, Streptelia roseogrisea. 800p, Otidiphaps nobilis. 1000p, Chalcophaps indica. 1500p, Reinwardtoena Reinwardtsi.

**1989, Apr. 28**    **Litho.**    **Perf. 12½**
| | | | | |
|---|---|---|---|---|
| 811 | A121 | 50p multicolored | .25 | .25 |
| 812 | A121 | 100p multicolored | .30 | .25 |
| 813 | A121 | 200p multicolored | .60 | .40 |
| 814 | A121 | 350p multicolored | 1.10 | .50 |
| 815 | A121 | 500p multicolored | 1.60 | .90 |
| 816 | A121 | 800p multicolored | 2.50 | 1.50 |
| 817 | A121 | 1000p multicolored | 3.00 | 1.75 |
| | | Nos. 811-817 (7) | 9.35 | 5.55 |

**Souvenir Sheet**
| | | | | |
|---|---|---|---|---|
| 818 | A121 | 1500p multicolored | 6.50 | 3.00 |

Pioneers Organization A122

10p, Children presenting flag, vert. 50p, Children saluting, vert. 300p, Children playing ball.

**1989, Sept. 24**     **Perf. 13**
| | | | | |
|---|---|---|---|---|
| 819 | A122 | 10p multicolored | .25 | .25 |
| 820 | A122 | 50p multicolored | .55 | .25 |
| 821 | A122 | 200p shown | 2.25 | .75 |
| 822 | A122 | 300p multicolored | 3.00 | 1.10 |
| | | Nos. 819-822 (4) | 6.05 | 2.35 |

Town of Cacheu, 400th Anniv. — A123

**1989, Nov. 30**
| | | | | |
|---|---|---|---|---|
| 823 | A123 | 10p Monument, vert. | .25 | .25 |
| 824 | A123 | 50p shown | .25 | .25 |
| 825 | A123 | 200p Old building | .40 | .40 |
| 826 | A123 | 300p Church | 1.75 | .60 |
| | | Nos. 823-826 (4) | 2.65 | 1.50 |

Dated 1988.

A124

Prehistoric creatures: 50p, Trachodon. 100p, Edaphosaurus. 200p, Mesosaurus. 350p, Elephas primigenius. 500p, Tyrannosaurus. 800p, Stegosaurus. 1000p, Cervus megaceros.

**Perf. 13, 12½x12 (100p)**
**1989, Sept. 15**
| | | | | |
|---|---|---|---|---|
| 827 | A124 | 50p multicolored | .25 | .25 |
| 828 | A124 | 100p multi, | | |
| | | 68x27mm | .35 | .25 |
| 829 | A124 | 200p multicolored | .60 | .35 |
| 830 | A124 | 350p multicolored | 1.05 | .50 |
| 831 | A124 | 500p multicolored | 1.75 | .80 |
| 832 | A124 | 800p multicolored | 2.75 | 1.20 |
| 833 | A124 | 1000p multicolored | 3.25 | 1.50 |
| | | Nos. 827-833 (7) | 10.00 | 4.85 |

Nos. 828, 831-833 horiz.

A125

Designs: Musical instruments.

**1989, Apr. 10**    **Litho.**    **Perf. 13**
| | | | | |
|---|---|---|---|---|
| 834 | A125 | 50p Bombalon | .30 | .25 |
| 835 | A125 | 100p Flauta | .45 | .25 |
| 836 | A125 | 200p Tambor | .90 | .30 |
| 837 | A125 | 350p Dondon | 1.45 | .40 |
| 838 | A125 | 500p Balafon | 1.75 | .75 |
| 839 | A125 | 800p Kora | 2.25 | 1.10 |
| 840 | A125 | 1000p Nhanhero | 2.40 | 1.25 |
| | | Nos. 834-840 (7) | 9.50 | 4.30 |

A126

Indian artifacts — 50p, Teotihuacan. 100p, Mochica. 200p, Jaina. 350p, Nayarit. 500p, Inca. 800p, Hopewell. 1000p, Taina. 1500p, Indian statuette.

**1989, July 13**    **Perf. 12x12½**
| | | | | |
|---|---|---|---|---|
| 841 | A126 | 50p multicolored | .25 | .25 |
| 842 | A126 | 100p multicolored | .30 | .25 |
| 843 | A126 | 200p multicolored | .55 | .35 |
| 844 | A126 | 350p multicolored | 1.25 | .40 |
| 845 | A126 | 500p multicolored | 1.75 | .80 |
| 846 | A126 | 800p multicolored | 2.75 | 1.20 |
| 847 | A126 | 1000p multicolored | 3.25 | 1.40 |
| | | Nos. 841-847 (7) | 10.10 | 4.65 |

**Souvenir Sheet**
**Perf. 12½**
| | | | | |
|---|---|---|---|---|
| 848 | A126 | 1500p multicolored | 4.50 | 2.50 |

Brasiliana '89 Philatelic Exhibition. Nos. 841-847 printed se-tenant with multicolored label showing scenes of colonization. No. 848 contains one 32x40mm stamp.

1992 Summer Olympics, Barcelona A127

50p, Hurdles. 100p, Boxing. 200p, High jump. 350p, Sprinters in the blocks. 500p, Woman sprinter. 800p, Gymnastics. 1000p, Pole vault. 1500p, Soccer.

**1989, June 3**    **Perf. 12½x13**
| | | | | |
|---|---|---|---|---|
| 849 | A127 | 50p multicolored | .30 | .25 |
| 850 | A127 | 100p multicolored | .40 | .25 |
| 851 | A127 | 200p multicolored | .60 | .25 |
| 852 | A127 | 350p multicolored | .95 | .40 |
| 853 | A127 | 500p multicolored | 1.60 | .80 |
| 854 | A127 | 800p multicolored | 2.50 | 1.20 |
| 855 | A127 | 1000p multicolored | 3.25 | 1.40 |
| | | Nos. 849-855 (7) | 9.60 | 4.55 |

**Souvenir Sheet**
| | | | | |
|---|---|---|---|---|
| 856 | A127 | 1500p multicolored | 4.50 | 2.40 |

No. 856 contains one 32x40mm stamp.

Wild Animals — A128

50p, Syncerus caffer. 100p, Equus quagga. 200p, Diceros bicornis. 350p, Okapia johnstoni. 500p, Macaca mulatta. 800p, Hippopotamus amphibius. 1000p, Acinonyx jubatus. 1500p, Panthera leo.

**1989, Nov. 24**    **Perf. 12½**
| | | | | |
|---|---|---|---|---|
| 857 | A128 | 50p multicolored | .30 | .25 |
| 858 | A128 | 100p multicolored | .45 | .25 |
| 859 | A128 | 200p multicolored | .60 | .25 |
| 860 | A128 | 350p multicolored | 1.00 | .40 |
| 861 | A128 | 500p multicolored | 1.25 | .60 |
| 862 | A128 | 800p multicolored | 2.10 | 1.00 |
| 863 | A128 | 1000p multicolored | 2.40 | 1.25 |
| 864 | A128 | 1500p multicolored | 3.75 | 1.75 |
| | | Nos. 857-864 (8) | 11.85 | 5.75 |

Christmas — A129

Paintings of the Madonna and Child (50p) and the Adoration of the Magi: 50p, Fra Filippo Lippi. 100p, Pieter Brueghel. 200p, Mostaert. 350p, Durer. 500p, Rubens. 800p, Van der Weyden. 1000p, Francia, horiz.

**1989, Dec. 10**    **Perf. 13**
| | | | | |
|---|---|---|---|---|
| 865 | A129 | 50p multicolored | .35 | .25 |
| 866 | A129 | 100p multicolored | .45 | .25 |
| 867 | A129 | 200p multicolored | .60 | .25 |
| 868 | A129 | 350p multicolored | .95 | .35 |
| 869 | A129 | 500p multicolored | 1.60 | .60 |
| 870 | A129 | 800p multicolored | 2.75 | .90 |
| 871 | A129 | 1000p multicolored | 3.25 | 1.25 |
| | | Nos. 865-871 (7) | 9.95 | 3.85 |

Womens' Hairstyles — A130

Various hairstyles.

**1989, Mar. 8**    **Perf. 12½x13**
| | | | | |
|---|---|---|---|---|
| 872 | A130 | 50p multicolored | .25 | .25 |
| 873 | A130 | 100p multicolored | .40 | .25 |
| 874 | A130 | 200p multicolored | .65 | .35 |
| 875 | A130 | 350p multicolored | 1.15 | .40 |
| 875A | A130 | 500p multicolored | 1.50 | .80 |
| 876 | A130 | 800p multicolored | 2.75 | 1.20 |
| 877 | A130 | 1000p multicolored | 3.25 | 1.40 |
| | | Nos. 872-877 (7) | 9.95 | 4.65 |

Vegetables — A131

50p, Capisium annum. 100p, Solanium. 200p, Curcumis peco. 350p, Solanium licopersicum. 500p, Solanium itiopium. 800p, Hibiscus esculentus. 1000p, Oseille de guine.

**1989, May 20**    **Perf. 12½**
| | | | | |
|---|---|---|---|---|
| 878 | A131 | 50p blue | .25 | .25 |
| 879 | A131 | 100p purple | .25 | .25 |
| 880 | A131 | 200p blue grn | .70 | .25 |
| 881 | A131 | 350p org red | 1.30 | .40 |
| 882 | A131 | 500p brown | 1.75 | .60 |
| 883 | A131 | 800p org brn | 2.75 | .95 |
| 884 | A131 | 1000p olive grn | 3.50 | 1.25 |
| | | Nos. 878-884 (7) | 10.50 | 3.95 |

Visit of Pope John Paul II — A132

**1990, Jan. 27**    **Litho.**    **Perf. 13½**
| | | | | |
|---|---|---|---|---|
| 885 | A132 | 500p shown | 1.75 | 1.60 |
| 886 | A132 | 1000p multi, diff. | 3.25 | 3.25 |

**Souvenir Sheet**
| | | | | |
|---|---|---|---|---|
| 887 | A132 | 1500p multi, diff., vert. | 4.50 | 3.25 |

**Souvenir Sheet**

Belgica '90 — A133

**1990, June 1**     **Perf. 14½**
| | | | | |
|---|---|---|---|---|
| 888 | A133 | 3000p multicolored | 5.50 | 3.50 |

World Meteorology Day — A134

1000p, Radar weather map. 3000p, Heliograph.

**1990, Oct. 1**    **Litho.**    **Perf. 13**
| | | | | |
|---|---|---|---|---|
| 889 | A134 | 1000p multicolored | 1.75 | .70 |
| 890 | A134 | 3000p multicolored | 6.25 | 2.25 |

LUBRAPEX '90 — A135

**1990, Sept. 21**    **Perf. 14**
| | | | | |
|---|---|---|---|---|
| 891 | A135 | 500p Rooster, hen | .85 | .40 |
| 892 | A135 | 800p Turkey | 1.60 | .60 |
| 893 | A135 | 1000p Duck, ducklings | 2.00 | .80 |
| | | Nos. 891-893 (3) | 4.45 | 1.80 |

**Souvenir Sheet**
**Perf. 13½**
| | | | | |
|---|---|---|---|---|
| 894 | A135 | 1500p Rooster, turkey, ducks | 5.00 | 2.75 |

UN Development Program, 40th Anniv. — A136

**1990**    **Litho.**    **Perf. 14**
| | | | | |
|---|---|---|---|---|
| 895 | A136 | 1000p multicolored | 2.25 | .65 |

Fight against AIDS.

Textile Manufacturing — A137

No. 896: a, Gossypium hirsutum. b, Processing cotton. c, Spinning thread. d, Picking cotton. e, Moth, silkworms. f, Dyeing thread. g, Weaving. h, Animal design. i, Multicolored stripes design. j, Stripes, dots design.

**1990**
| | | | | |
|---|---|---|---|---|
| 896 | | Sheet of 10 | 2.00 | |
| | a.-j. | A137 150p any single | .25 | .25 |
| 897 | A137 | 400p like #896a | .30 | .25 |
| 898 | A137 | 500p like #896g | .40 | .25 |
| 899 | A137 | 600p like #896h | .50 | .35 |
| | | Nos. 896-899 (4) | 3.20 | .85 |

Carnival Masks — A138

## 1990 Litho. Perf. 14

| | | | | |
|---|---|---|---|---|
| 900 | A138 | 200p Mickey Mouse | .45 | .25 |
| 901 | A138 | 300p Hippopotamus | .55 | .25 |
| 902 | A138 | 600p Bull | 1.15 | .35 |
| 903 | A138 | 1200p Bull, diff. | 2.25 | .60 |
| | | Nos. 900-903 (4) | 4.40 | 1.45 |

Fish — A139

Designs: 300p, Pentanemus quinquarius. 400p, Psettias sabae. 500p, Chaetodipterus goreensis. 600p, Trachinotus goreensis.

## 1991, Mar. 10 Litho. Perf. 14

| | | | | |
|---|---|---|---|---|
| 904 | A139 | 300p multicolored | .65 | .35 |
| 905 | A139 | 400p multicolored | 1.00 | .45 |
| 906 | A139 | 500p multicolored | 1.10 | .55 |
| 907 | A139 | 600p multicolored | 1.25 | .70 |
| | | Nos. 904-907 (4) | 4.00 | 2.05 |

Fire Trucks — A140

## 1991, Aug. 19 Litho. Perf. 14

| | | | | |
|---|---|---|---|---|
| 908 | A140 | 200p shown | .40 | .25 |
| 909 | A140 | 500p Ladder truck | .85 | .45 |
| 910 | A140 | 800p Rescue vehicle | 1.25 | .70 |
| 911 | A140 | 1500p Ambulance | 2.50 | 1.25 |
| | | Nos. 908-911 (4) | 5.00 | 2.65 |

Birds — A141

Designs: 100p, Kaupifalco monogrammicus. 250p, Balearica pavonina. 350p, Bucorvus abyssinicus. 500p, Ephippiorhynchus senegalensis. 1500p, Kaupifalco monogrammicus, diff.

## 1991, Sept. 10

| | | | | |
|---|---|---|---|---|
| 912 | A141 | 100p multicolored | .75 | .25 |
| 913 | A141 | 250p multicolored | 1.10 | .25 |
| 914 | A141 | 350p multicolored | 1.75 | .55 |
| 915 | A141 | 500p multicolored | 2.40 | .75 |
| | | Nos. 912-915 (4) | 6.00 | 1.80 |

### Souvenir Sheet

#### Perf. 14½

| | | | | |
|---|---|---|---|---|
| 916 | A141 | 1500p multicolored | 5.00 | 5.00 |

No. 916 contains one 40x50mm stamp.

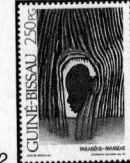

Messages — A142

## 1991, Oct. 28 Litho. Perf. 14

| | | | | |
|---|---|---|---|---|
| 917 | A142 | 250p Congratulations | .35 | .25 |
| 918 | A142 | 400p With love | .65 | .40 |
| 919 | A142 | 800p Happiness | 1.15 | .80 |
| 920 | A142 | 1000p Seasons Greetings | 1.40 | .95 |
| | | Nos. 917-920 (4) | 3.55 | 2.40 |

Fruits — A143

Designs: 500p, Landolfia owariensis. 1500p, Dialium guineensis. 2000p, Adansonia digitata. 3000p, Parkia biglobosa.

## 1992, Mar. 25 Litho. Perf. 14

| | | | | |
|---|---|---|---|---|
| 921 | A143 | 500p multicolored | .30 | .30 |
| 922 | A143 | 1500p multicolored | .75 | .75 |
| 923 | A143 | 2000p multicolored | 1.10 | 1.10 |
| 924 | A143 | 3000p multicolored | 1.75 | 1.75 |
| | | Nos. 921-924 (4) | 3.90 | 3.90 |

For surcharges, see Nos. 1022, 1027.

Healthy Hearts — A144

Designs: 1500p, Cigarette butts, healthy heart. 4000p, Heart running over junk food.

## 1992, Apr. 7

| | | | | |
|---|---|---|---|---|
| 925 | A144 | 1500p multicolored | 1.75 | .80 |
| 926 | A144 | 4000p multicolored | 3.75 | 2.10 |

Traditional Costumes — A145

Designs: a, 400p, Fula. b, 600p, Balanta. c, 1000p, Fula, diff. d, 1500p, Manjaco.

## 1992, Feb. 28 Litho. Perf. 14

| | | | | |
|---|---|---|---|---|
| 927 | A145 | Strip of 4, #a.-d. | 3.00 | 2.10 |

Canoes — A146

Designs: Nos. 928-931, Various types of canoes. No. 932, Alcedo cristata galerita.

## 1992, May 10

| | | | | |
|---|---|---|---|---|
| 928 | A146 | 750p multicolored | .40 | .40 |
| 929 | A146 | 800p multicolored | .55 | .55 |
| 930 | A146 | 1000p multicolored | .65 | .65 |
| 931 | A146 | 1300p multicolored | .80 | .80 |
| | | Nos. 928-931 (4) | 2.40 | 2.40 |

### Souvenir Sheet

#### Perf. 13½

| | | | | |
|---|---|---|---|---|
| 932 | A146 | 1500p multicolored | 5.75 | 5.75 |

For surcharges, see Nos. 1018, 1021.

Trees A147

a, 100p, Cassia alata. b, 400p, Perlebia purpurea. c, 1000p, Caesalpina pulcherrima. d, 1500p, Adenanthera pavonina. 3000p, Caesalpina pulcherrima, diff.

## 1992, May 8 Perf. 14

| | | | | |
|---|---|---|---|---|
| 933 | A147 | Block of 4, #a.-d. | 5.50 | 5.50 |

### Souvenir Sheet

#### Perf. 13½

| | | | | |
|---|---|---|---|---|
| 934 | A147 | 3000p multicolored | 5.00 | 5.00 |

1992 Summer Olympics, Barcelona A148

## 1992, July 28 Litho. Perf. 14

| | | | | |
|---|---|---|---|---|
| 935 | A148 | 600p Basketball | .25 | .25 |
| 936 | A148 | 1000p Volleyball | .55 | .30 |
| 937 | A148 | 1500p Team handball | .80 | .35 |
| 938 | A148 | 2000p Soccer | 1.10 | .65 |
| | | Nos. 935-938 (4) | 2.70 | 1.55 |

Trees — A149

Designs: 1000p, Afzelia africana Smith. 1500p, Kaya senegalenses. 2000p, Militia regia. 3000p, Pterocarpus erinaceus.

## 1992, Sept. 11 Perf. 12

| | | | | |
|---|---|---|---|---|
| 939 | A149 | 1000p multicolored | .45 | .45 |
| 940 | A149 | 1500p multicolored | .60 | .60 |
| 941 | A149 | 2000p multicolored | .85 | .80 |
| 942 | A149 | 3000p multicolored | 1.25 | 1.10 |
| | | Nos. 939-942 (4) | 3.15 | 2.95 |

For surcharge, see No. 1023.

### Souvenir Sheet

Discovery of America, 500th Anniv. — A150

## 1992, Sept. 18

| | | | | |
|---|---|---|---|---|
| 943 | A150 | 5000p multicolored | 3.75 | 3.75 |

Genoa '92.

Procolobus Badius Temminckii — A151

Designs: a, Pair in tree. b, Adult seated in vegetation c, Adult seated in tree fork. d, Female with young.

## 1992 Litho. Perf. 12x11½

| | | | | |
|---|---|---|---|---|
| 944 | A151 | 2000p Strip of 4, #a.-d. | 5.25 | 5.25 |

World Wildlife Fund.

Reptiles — A152

1500p, Bitis sp. 3000p, Osteolaemus tetraspis. 4000p, Varanus nitolicus. 5000p, Agama agama.

## 1993, May 18 Litho. Perf. 14

| | | | | |
|---|---|---|---|---|
| 945 | A152 | 1500p multicolored | .50 | .25 |
| 946 | A152 | 3000p multicolored | 1.10 | .55 |
| 947 | A152 | 4000p multicolored | 1.50 | .70 |
| 948 | A152 | 5000p multicolored | 1.90 | .85 |
| a. | | Souvenir sheet of 4, #945-948 | 5.50 | 5.50 |
| | | Nos. 945-948 (4) | 5.00 | 2.35 |

### Souvenir Sheet

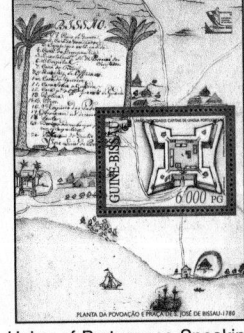

Union of Portuguese Speaking Capitals — A153

## 1993, July 30 Litho. Perf. 13½

| | | | | |
|---|---|---|---|---|
| 949 | A153 | 6000p Fort | 1.75 | 1.75 |

Brasiliana '93.

Tourism — A154

Designs: a, 1000p. b, 2000p. c, 4000p. d, 5000p.

## 1993, Nov. 15 Litho. Perf. 14

| | | | | |
|---|---|---|---|---|
| 950 | A154 | Block of 4, #a.-d. | 4.50 | 4.50 |

Traditional Jewelry — A155

## 1993, Nov. 30 Perf. 14½

| | | | | |
|---|---|---|---|---|
| 951 | A155 | 1500p Bracelet | .45 | .25 |
| 952 | A155 | 3000p Mask pendant | 1.10 | .50 |
| 953 | A155 | 4000p Circle pendant | 1.50 | .65 |
| 954 | A155 | 5000p Filigree pendant | 1.75 | .80 |
| | | Nos. 951-954 (4) | 4.80 | 2.20 |

## 1994, Nov. 30 Souvenir Sheet

| | | | | |
|---|---|---|---|---|
| 955 | A155 | 18,000p like #952 | 8.00 | 8.00 |

Hong Kong '94 (No. 955). No. 955 has continuous design.

1994 World Cup Soccer Championships, US — A156

Various stylized designs of player, ball, net.

## 1994, June 17 Litho. Perf. 14

| | | | | |
|---|---|---|---|---|
| 956 | A156 | 4000p multicolored | 1.00 | .85 |
| 957 | A156 | 5000p multicolored | 1.25 | 1.10 |
| 958 | A156 | 5500p multicolored | 1.60 | 1.25 |
| 959 | A156 | 6500p multicolored | 2.00 | 1.60 |
| | | Nos. 956-959 (4) | 5.85 | 4.80 |

Flowering Plants — A157

Designs: 2000p, Erythrina senegalensis. 3000p, Cassia occidentalis. 4000p, Gardenia ternifolia. 6000p, Cochlospermum tinctorium.

## 1994, May 30 Litho. Perf. 14

| | | | | |
|---|---|---|---|---|
| 960 | A157 | 2000p multicolored | .90 | .45 |
| 961 | A157 | 3000p multicolored | 1.25 | .70 |
| 962 | A157 | 4000p multicolored | 1.60 | .90 |
| 963 | A157 | 6000p multicolored | 2.75 | 1.50 |
| | | Nos. 960-963 (4) | 6.50 | 3.55 |

Snakes
A158

No. 964: a, Dasypeltis scabra. b, Philothamnus. c, Naja melanoleuca. d, Python sebae.
15,000p, Thelotornis kirtlandii.

**1994, Aug. 16    Litho.    Perf. 14**
964 A158   5000p Block of 4,
           #a.-d.                    8.00 8.00
**Souvenir Sheet**
**Perf. 13½**
965 A158   15,000p multicolored      6.50 6.50
PHILAKOREA '94, SINGPEX '94. No. 965 contains one 60x50mm stamp.

Palmeira
Dendem — A159

3000p, Climbing tree to pick fruit. 6500p, Hand processing palm fruit into baskets. 7500p, Mechanical processing. 8000p, Palm oil, uses.

**1995, Feb. 27    Litho.    Perf. 14**
966 A159   3000p multicolored    .75   .35
967 A159   6500p multicolored   1.50   .70
968 A159   7500p multicolored   1.75   .80
969 A159   8000p multicolored   2.00   .85
       Nos. 966-969 (4)          6.00  2.70

FAO, 50th
Anniv. — A160

3000p, Net fishing. 6500p, Disking field. 7500p, Hands holding fruit. 8000p, Vendors along road.

**1995    Litho.    Perf. 13½**
970 A160   3000p multicolored    .70   .45
971 A160   6500p multicolored   1.25   .85
972 A160   7500p multicolored   1.50  1.00
973 A160   8000p multicolored   1.75  1.10
   a.    Souvenir sheet of 2, #972-973   4.00  4.00
       Nos. 970-973 (4)          5.20  3.40

UN, 50th
Anniv. — A161

**1995, Oct. 24    Litho.    Perf. 13½**
974 A161   4000p shown        1.00   .55
975 A161   5500p UN flag      1.25   .75
976 A161   7500p Natl. flag   1.75  1.00
977 A161   8000p Hand on dove 2.00  1.10
       Nos. 974-977 (4)        6.00  3.40
**Souvenir Sheet**
978 A161   15,000p UN emblem   4.50  4.50

**100 Centimes = 1 Franc (1997)**

Endangered Animals — A166

No. 995: a, 5000p, Hippopotamus. b, 7500p, Crocodile. c, 10,000p, Chelonia mydas. d, 12,000p, Trichechus senegalensis.

**1997    Litho.    Perf. 12x11¾**
995 A166   Block of 4, #a-d      75.00   —
Despite change to franc currency on May 2, 1997, Nos. 995-997 have denominations in pesos.

Venomous Animals — A167

No. 996: a, 7500p, Pandinus imperator. b, 8000p, Naja nigricollis. c, 10,000p, Scolopendra morsitans. d, 11,000p, Lycosa tarentula.

**1997**
996 A167   Block of 4, #a-d      75.00   —

Economic
Community of
West African
States, 20th
Anniv. (in
1995) — A168

**1997, Dec. 26**
997 A168   25,000p multi        5.00 5.00

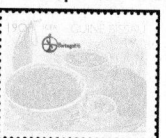

Native
Foods — A169

Designs: 100fr, Caldo branco. 120fr, Siga. 160fr, Caldo de amendoin. 190fr, Caldo de chabeu.

**1998, June 1**
998-1001 A169   Set of 4        5.00 5.00

**No. 1001 Overprinted in Brown**

**1998, Sept. 4    Litho.    Perf. 12x11¾**
1002 A169   190fr on No. 1001   2.00 2.00

Maritime
Discoveries
A170

**1998, Oct. 9           Perf. 12x11¾**
1003 A170   200fr multi         2.00 2.00
   a.    Souvenir sheet of 1, perf. 12½   5.00 5.00

Marine
Life — A171

Designs: 150fr, Cultellus tenuis. 170fr, Penaeus keraethurus. 200fr, Periophthalmus papilio. 250fr, Istiophorus albicans.

**1998, Dec. 28           Perf. 12x11¾**
1004-1007 A171   Set of 4       6.00 6.00
  1007a   Souvenir sheet, #1004-
          1007, perf. 12½       6.00 6.00

SOS Children's
Villages, 50th
Anniv. (in
1999) — A172

Designs: 130fr, Children, map of Guinea-Bissau. 160fr, Children in school, child in wheelchair, children at table. 170fr, Children playing in playground. 300fr, 50th anniv. emblem.

**Perf. 12¼x11¾**
**2000, June 15           Litho.**
1008 A172   130fr multi          —   4.00
1009 A172   160fr multi          —   4.00
1010 A172   170fr multi          —   4.00
1011 A172   300fr multi          —   4.00

Millennium — A173

Designs: 100fr, Dove, trees, dancers. 190fr, Circle of people around tree. 200fr, Drummer, dancers, and traditional house. 350fr, Head of dove, map of Guinea-Bissau.

**Perf. 11¾x12¼**
**2000, Sept. 24          Litho.**
1012 A173   100fr multi              2.50
1013 A173   190fr multi              2.50
1014 A173   200fr multi              3.00
1015 A173   350fr multi

**Souvenir Sheet**

España 2000 World Philatelic
Exhibition — A174

**2000    Litho.    Perf. 13x12¾**
1016 A174   1000fr multi            6.00

Nos. 922, 924, 931,
940 & 963 Srchd.

**Methods and Perfs As Before
2000 ?**
1017 A143   100fr on 500p
            #921               —
1018 A146   150fr on 1000p
            #930               —
1019 A146   200fr on 800p
            #929               —
1020 A149   1000fr on 1000p
            #939               —
1021 A146   250fr on 1300p
            #931               —
1022 A143   450fr on 1500p
            #922               —
1023 A149   450fr on 1500p
            #940               —
1024 A155   450fr on 1500p
            #951               —
1025 A143   500fr on 2000p
            #923               —
1026 A157   500fr on 2000p
            #960               —
1027 A143   1000fr on 3000p
            #924               —
1028 A155   1000fr on 3000p
            #952               —
1029 A157   1000fr on 3000p
            #961               —

1029A A157   1500fr on 4000p
             #962               —
1030  A157   2000fr on 6000p
             #963               —

**AIR POST STAMPS**

Liftoff of Soyuz
Spacecraft — AP1

Apollo-Soyuz mission: 10p, Launch of Apollo spacecraft. 15p, Leonov, Stafford and meeting in space. 20p, Eclipse of the sun. 30p, Infra-red photo of Earth. 40p, Return to Earth. 50p, Apollo and Soyuz docked, horiz.

**1976, Oct. 4           Perf. 13½**
C10  AP1   5p multicolored     .50   .30
C10A AP1   10p multicolored    .65   .40
C10B AP1   15p multicolored   1.30   .55
C10C AP1   20p multicolored   1.75   .80
C10D AP1   30p multicolored   2.25  1.20
C10E AP1   40p multicolored   3.25  1.50
       Nos. C10-C10E (6)      9.70  4.75
**Souvenir Sheet**
C10F AP1   50p multicolored   4.75  4.75

No. C10F contains one 60x42mm stamp. Nos. C10-C10E exist in souvenir sheets of one, perf. and imperf.

Viking Spacecraft
Orbiting
Mars — AP2

35p, Viking gathering Martian soil samples.

**1977, Jan. 27**
C11  AP2   25p multicolored   3.00  1.10
C11A AP2   35p multicolored   3.00  1.25

**Nos. 372-373 Surcharged in Black
on Silver Panels**

**1978    Litho.    Perf. 13½**
C12 A32   15p on 3.50p multi   .95   .40
C13 A32   30p on 50c multi    1.45   .60

**History of Aviation Type of 1980**

35p, Willy de Houthulst, Hanriot HD.1. 40p, Charles Guynemer, Spad S. VII. 50p, Comdr. de Rose, Nieuport.

**1980    Litho.    Perf. 13½**
C14  A38   35p multicolored   2.40  1.20
C14A A38   40p multicolored   3.00  1.40
**Souvenir Sheet**
C14B A38   50p multicolored   5.25  4.00

No. C14B contains one stamp 37x55mm.

**Winter Olympics Type of 1980**
**1980**
C15 A39   35p Slalom          2.40  1.20
C16 A39   40p Figure skating  3.00  1.40
**Souvenir Sheet**
C17 A39   50p Ice hockey, horiz.   5.50  4.00

**Summer Olympics Type of 1980**
**1980, Aug.    Litho.    Perf. 13½**
C18 A40   35p Somersault       3.50  1.20

| | | | |
|---|---|---|---|
| C19 | A40 | 40p Running | 4.25 1.40 |

**Souvenir Sheet**

| | | | |
|---|---|---|---|
| C20 | A40 | 50p Emblem | 5.50 4.25 |

**Literacy Type of 1980**

**1980, Aug.      Litho.      Perf. 13½**

| | | | |
|---|---|---|---|
| C21 | A41 | 15p like #404 | 1.60 .60 |
| C22 | A41 | 25p like #405 | 2.75 .80 |

**Space Type of 1981**

35p, Viking 1 & 2. 40p, Apollo-Soyuz craft & crew. 50p, Apollo 11 crew, craft & emblem.

**1981, May      Litho.      Perf. 13½**

| | | | |
|---|---|---|---|
| C23 | A45 | 35p multicolored | 2.75 1.50 |
| C24 | A45 | 40p multicolored | 3.00 1.75 |

**Souvenir Sheet**

| | | | |
|---|---|---|---|
| C25 | A45 | 50p multicolored | 7.00 4.75 |

No. C25 contains one stamp 60x42mm.

**Soccer Type of 1981**

Designs: 35p, Rummenigge, Germany. 40p, Kempes, Argentina. 50p, Juanito, Spain.

**1981, May**

| | | | |
|---|---|---|---|
| C26 | A46 | 35p multicolored | 2.75 1.50 |
| C27 | A46 | 40p multicolored | 3.00 1.75 |

**Souvenir Sheet**

| | | | |
|---|---|---|---|
| C28 | A46 | 50p multicolored | 8.75 6.00 |

No. C28 contains one stamp 56x40mm.

**Royal Wedding Type of 1981**

**1981      Litho.      Perf. 13½**

| | | | |
|---|---|---|---|
| C29 | A47 | 35p Palace | 3.25 1.50 |
| C30 | A47 | 40p Prince of Wales arms | 4.00 1.75 |

**Souvenir Sheet**

| | | | |
|---|---|---|---|
| C31 | A47 | 50p Couple | 7.25 4.75 |

**Picasso Type of 1981**

**1981, Dec.      Litho.      Perf. 13½**

| | | | |
|---|---|---|---|
| C32 | A48 | 35p multicolored | 4.50 1.50 |
| C33 | A48 | 40p multicolored | 5.75 1.90 |

**Souvenir Sheet**

| | | | |
|---|---|---|---|
| C34 | A48 | 50p multicolored | 7.25 4.75 |

No. C34 contains one stamp 41x50mm.

**Navigator Type of 1981**

35p, Francis Drake, Golden Hinde. 40p, James Cook, Endeavor. 50p, Columbus, Santa Maria.

**1981      Litho.      Perf. 13½**

| | | | |
|---|---|---|---|
| C35 | A49 | 35p multicolored | 3.50 1.60 |
| C36 | A49 | 40p multicolored | 4.00 2.00 |

**Souvenir Sheet**

| | | | |
|---|---|---|---|
| C37 | A49 | 50p multicolored | 10.00 7.25 |

**Christmas Type of 1981**

**1981**

| | | | |
|---|---|---|---|
| C38 | A50 | 30p Memling | 3.25 1.60 |
| C39 | A50 | 35p Bellini, diff. | 4.00 2.00 |

**Souvenir Sheet**

| | | | |
|---|---|---|---|
| C40 | A50 | 50p Fra Angelico | 7.25 4.75 |

No. C40 contains one 35x59mm stamp.

**Scout Type of 1982**

**1982, June 9      Litho.      Perf. 13½**

| | | | |
|---|---|---|---|
| C41 | A51 | 35p Canoeing | 2.75 1.50 |
| C42 | A51 | 40p Flying model planes | 3.25 1.75 |

**Souvenir Sheet**

| | | | |
|---|---|---|---|
| C43 | A51 | 50p Playing chess | 14.00 5.00 |

No. C43 contains one 48x38mm stamp.

**Soccer Type of 1982**

**1982, June 13      Litho.      Perf. 13½**

| | | | |
|---|---|---|---|
| C44 | A52 | 35p Kempes | 2.75 1.50 |
| C45 | A52 | 40p Kaltz | 3.25 1.75 |

**Souvenir Sheet**

| | | | |
|---|---|---|---|
| C46 | A52 | 50p Stadium | 7.25 4.75 |

**Diana Type of 1982 and**

Princess Diana, 21st Birthday AP3

**1982**

| | | | |
|---|---|---|---|
| C47 | A53 | 35p multicolored | 3.00 1.25 |
| C48 | A53 | 40p multicolored | 3.50 1.60 |

**Souvenir Sheet**

| | | | |
|---|---|---|---|
| C49 | A53 | 50p multi, vert. | 8.00 4.25 |

**1982, Oct. 1      Litho. & Embossed**

| | | | |
|---|---|---|---|
| C49A | AP3 | 200p gold & multi | 14.50 |

**Souvenir Sheet**

| | | | |
|---|---|---|---|
| C49B | AP3 | 200p gold & multi, vert. | 32.50 |

For overprints see Nos. 456A-456B.

**Audubon Birth Bicent. — AP4**

5p, Brown pelican. 10p, American white pelican. 20p, Great blue heron. 40p, American flamingo.

**1985, Apr. 16      Litho.      Perf. 12**

| | | | |
|---|---|---|---|
| C50 | AP4 | 5p multicolored | .60 .25 |
| C51 | AP4 | 10p multicolored | 1.00 .30 |
| C52 | AP4 | 20p multicolored | 1.25 .80 |
| C53 | AP4 | 40p multicolored | 2.50 1.00 |
| | | Nos. C50-C53 (4) | 5.35 2.35 |

**VALUE THE WORLD**

# 2024 Scott Postage Stamp Catalogues

- Two-book volumes 1-6 improve user experience
- Thousands of value changes keep pace with market fluctuations
- Hundreds of new stamp listings
- Editorial enhancements throughout include added stamp images, expanded footnotes and much more

| Item# | Description | Retail | AA | Release Dates |
|---|---|---|---|---|
| C241 | 2024 Scott Volumes 1A & 1B (U.S., U.N. and Countries A-B) | $149.99 | $114.99 | 4/1/23 |
| C242 | 2024 Scott Volumes 2A & 2B (Countries C-F) | $149.99 | $114.99 | 5/1/23 |
| C243 | 2024 Scott Volumes 3A & 3B (Countries G-I) | $149.99 | $114.99 | 6/1/23 |
| C244 | 2024 Scott Volumes 4A & 4B (Countries J-M) | $149.99 | $114.99 | 7/1/23 |
| C245 | 2024 Scott Volumes 5A & 5B (Countries N-SAM) | $149.99 | $114.99 | 8/1/23 |
| C246 | 2024 Scott Volumes 6A & 6B Countries SAN-Z) | $149.99 | $114.99 | 9/1/23 |
| C24SET | 2024 Scott Volume 1-6 Set | $846.64 | $624.94 | |
| C24S | 2024 Scott U.S. Specialized | $139.99 | $104.99 | 10/1/23 |
| C24C | 2024 Scott Classic Specialized | $179.99 | $159.99 | 11/1/23 |

# AmosAdvantage.com
## 1-800-572-6885

*AA prices apply to paid subscribers of Amos Media titles, or orders placed online.
Prices, terms and product availability subect to change.
Shipping and handling rates will apply.

# GUYANA

gī-'a-nə

LOCATION — Northeast coast of South America
GOVT. — Republic
AREA — 83,000 sq. mi.
POP. — 705,156 (1999 est.)
CAPITAL — Georgetown

The former Crown Colony of British Guiana became an independent member of the British Commonwealth May 26, 1966, taking the name Guyana. On February 23, 1970, Guyana became a republic, remaining a Commonwealth nation.

100 Cents = 1 Dollar

> **Catalogue values for all unused stamps in this country are for Never Hinged items.**

## Watermark

Wmk. 364 — Lotus Bud Multiple

British Guiana #254-256, 258-260, 267 Overprinted

### Perf. 12½x13, 13

| | | | | |
|---|---|---|---|---|
| **1966, May 26** | | **Wmk. 4** | | **Engr.** |
| 1 | A60 | 2c dark green | .55 | .45 |
| 1A | A60 | 3c red brn & ol | 2.50 | 6.00 |
| 2 | A61 | 4c violet | 3.00 | .90 |
| 3 | A60 | 6c yellow green | .55 | .25 |
| 4 | A60 | 8c ultra | 3.00 | 1.75 |
| 5 | A61 | 12c brn & blk | 4.00 | 1.25 |
| 6 | A61 | $5 blk & ultra | 27.50 | 57.50 |
| | | *Nos. 1-6 (7)* | 41.10 | 68.10 |

## Same Overprint on British Guiana Stamps and Types of 1954
### Engr.; Center Litho. on $1

| | | | | |
|---|---|---|---|---|
| **1966-67** | | **Wmk. 314 Upright** | | |
| 7 | A60 | 1c black ('67) | .25 | .40 |
| 8 | A60 | 3c red brn & ol (#279) | 1.40 | .25 |
| 9 | A61 | 4c violet ('67) | .35 | 1.25 |
| 10 | A60 | 5c blk & red (#280) | .50 | .25 |
| 10A | A60 | 6c yel green ('67) | .35 | .30 |
| 11 | A60 | 8c ultra ('67) | 3.00 | 1.90 |
| 12 | A61 | 12c brn & blk (#281) | .25 | .25 |
| 13 | A60 | 24c org & blk (#282) | 6.50 | 1.00 |
| 14 | A60 | 36c blk & rose (#283) | .40 | .40 |
| 15 | A61 | 48c red brn & ultra (#284) | 4.75 | 12.50 |
| 16 | A61 | 72c emer & rose (#285) | .90 | .90 |
| 17 | A60 | $1 blk & multi (#286) | 7.50 | .50 |
| 18 | A61 | $2 mag (#287) | 2.00 | 1.25 |
| 19 | A61 | $5 blk & ultra | 1.75 | 5.00 |
| | | *Nos. 7-19 (14)* | 29.90 | 26.15 |

For surcharges see Nos. 543, 544A, 625-626, 1446.

| | | | | |
|---|---|---|---|---|
| **1966-67** | | **Wmk. 314 Sideways** | | |
| 7a | A60 | 1c black | .25 | .25 |
| 9a | A61 | 4c violet | .25 | .25 |
| 11a | A60 | 8c ultramarine | .25 | .25 |
| 12a | A61 | 12c brown & black ('67) | .25 | .25 |
| 13a | A60 | 24c orange & black | 2.50 | .90 |
| 14a | A60 | 36c black & rose ('67) | .35 | 2.00 |
| 15a | A61 | 48c red brown & ultra | .35 | .35 |
| 16a | A61 | 72c emerald & rose ('67) | 3.25 | 7.00 |
| 17a | A60 | $1 black & multi ('67) | 9.00 | 6.00 |
| 18a | A60 | $2 magenta ('67) | 3.00 | 3.75 |
| 19a | A61 | $5 blk & ultra ('67) | 1.50 | 3.75 |
| | | *Nos. 7a-19a (11)* | 20.95 | 24.45 |

See Nos. 32-32T and note. For surcharges see Nos. 544, 627-628, 1447.

---

Flag and Map of Guyana — A1

Designs: 25c, $1, Arms of Guyana.

### Unwmk.

| | | | | |
|---|---|---|---|---|
| **1966, May 26** | | **Photo.** | | **Perf. 14** |
| 20 | A1 | 5c violet & multi | .25 | .25 |
| 21 | A1 | 15c dk red brown & multi | .30 | .25 |
| 22 | A1 | 25c brt blue & multi | .30 | .25 |
| 23 | A1 | $1 sepia & multi | .85 | .85 |
| | | *Nos. 20-23 (4)* | 1.70 | 1.60 |

Guyana's independence, May 26, 1966.

Bank of Guyana — A2

| | | | | |
|---|---|---|---|---|
| **1966, Oct. 11** | | | | **Perf. 13½x14** |
| 24 | A2 | 5c yel grn, blue, blk & gold | .25 | .25 |
| 25 | A2 | 25c blue, black & gold | .25 | .25 |

Establishment of the Bank of Guyana.

British Guiana No. 13 — A3

| | | | | |
|---|---|---|---|---|
| **1967, Feb. 23** | | **Litho.** | | **Perf. 12½** |
| 26 | A3 | 5c multicolored | .25 | .25 |
| a. | | Imperf., pair | | |
| 27 | A3 | 25c multicolored | .25 | .25 |

Issued to honor the unique British Guiana 1c black on magenta stamp of 1856.

### Canceled to Order

Remainders of Nos. 26-30, 33-38 and 54-67 were canceled and sold by the Post Office in 1969. Values are for these canceled to order stamps. Postally used examples do not command a significant premium.

Chateau Margot — A4

Designs: 15c, Independence Arch. 25c, Guyana Fort, Fort Island, horiz. $1, Parliament, National Assembly Hall, horiz.

| | | | | |
|---|---|---|---|---|
| | | | **Perf. 14, 14½x14, 14x14½** | |
| **1967, May 26** | | **Photo.** | | **Unwmk.** |
| 28 | A4 | 6c multicolored | .25 | .25 |
| 29 | A4 | 15c multicolored | .25 | .25 |
| 30 | A4 | 25c multicolored | .25 | .25 |
| 31 | A4 | $1 multicolored | .25 | .25 |
| | | *Nos. 28-31 (4)* | 1.00 | 1.00 |

First anniversary of independence.

British Guiana Stamps and Types of 1954 Locally Overprinted

| | | | | |
|---|---|---|---|---|
| **1967** | | | **Wmk. 4** | |
| 32 | A60 | 1c black | .25 | .25 |
| 32A | A60 | 2c dark green | .25 | .25 |
| 32B | A60 | 3c red brown & ol | .40 | .25 |
| 32C | A61 | 4c violet | .30 | .25 |
| 32D | A60 | 6c yellow green | .30 | .25 |
| 32E | A60 | 8c ultramarine | .30 | .25 |
| 32F | A61 | 12c brown & black | .30 | .25 |

---

| | | | | |
|---|---|---|---|---|
| 32G | A60 | $2 magenta | 1.75 | 3.00 |
| 32H | A61 | $5 black & ultra | 2.25 | 2.75 |
| | | *Nos. 32-32H (9)* | 6.10 | 7.50 |

The 24c with Wmk. 4 also exists with this overprint. Value: unused $450; used $110.

| | | | | |
|---|---|---|---|---|
| **1967-68** | | **Wmk. 314 Upright** | | |
| 32I | A60 | 1c black ('68) | .25 | 1.00 |
| 32J | A60 | 2c dk green ('68) | .80 | 2.00 |
| 32K | A60 | 3c red brown & ol | .35 | .25 |
| 32L | A61 | 4c violet ('68) | .25 | 1.25 |
| 32M | A60 | 5c black & red | 1.50 | 2.50 |
| 32N | A60 | 6c yel green ('68) | .40 | .90 |
| 32O | A60 | 24c orange & blk | 6.00 | .25 |
| 32P | A60 | 36c black & rose | 2.50 | .25 |
| 32Q | A61 | 48c red brn & ultra | 1.25 | 1.50 |
| 32R | A61 | 72c emer & rose | 2.50 | 1.10 |
| 32S | A60 | $1 black & multi | 4.00 | .60 |
| 32T | A60 | $2 magenta | 4.25 | 4.00 |
| | | *Nos. 32I-32T (12)* | 24.05 | 15.60 |

The 1c, 4c, 6c, 8c and $5 with Wmk. 314 were not issued without overprint.
For surcharges see Nos. 540, 542, 543A.

## Christmas Issues

"Millie," the Bilingual Macaw — A5

| | | | | |
|---|---|---|---|---|
| **1967, Nov. 6** | | | | **Perf. 14½x14** |
| 33 | A5 | 5c olive green & multi | .25 | .25 |
| 33A | A5 | 25c purple & multi | .25 | .25 |

| | | | | |
|---|---|---|---|---|
| **1968, Jan. 22** | | | | |
| 34 | A5 | 5c red & multi | .25 | .25 |
| 35 | A5 | 25c yel green & multi | .25 | .25 |

Wicketkeeper, Emblem of West Indies Cricket Team — A6

Designs: 6c, Batsman and emblem of Marylebone Cricket Club. 25c, Bowler and emblem of West Indies Cricket Team.

| | | | | |
|---|---|---|---|---|
| **1968, Jan. 8** | | **Photo.** | | **Perf. 14** |
| 36 | A6 | 5c multicolored | .25 | .25 |
| 37 | A6 | 6c multicolored | .25 | .25 |
| 38 | A6 | 25c multicolored | .35 | .25 |
| a. | | Strip of 3, #36-38 | 1.00 | 1.00 |

Visit of the Marylebone Cricket Club to the West Indies, Jan.-Feb. 1968. Printed in sheets of 9.

Sunfish (Pike Cichlid) — A7

Marudi (Marail Guan) — A8

Designs: 2c, Pirai (Piranha). 3c, Lukunani (Cichla ocellaris). 5c, Hassar (Armored catfish). 6c, Patua (Two-spotted cichlid). 15c, Harpy eagle. 20c, Canje pheasant (Hoatzin). 25c, Cock-of-the-rock. 40c, Kiskadee. 50c, Accouri (Agouti). 60c, Peccary. $1, Labba (Paca). $2, Armadillo. $5, Ocelot.

| | | | | |
|---|---|---|---|---|
| | | *Perf. 14x14½, 14½x14* | | |
| **1968, Mar. 4** | | **Photo.** | | **Unwmk.** |
| 39 | A7 | 1c chalky blue & multi | .25 | .25 |
| 40 | A7 | 2c gray & multi | .25 | .25 |
| 41 | A7 | 3c grnsh bl & multi | .25 | .25 |
| 42 | A7 | 5c ultra & multi | .25 | .25 |
| 43 | A7 | 6c brt olive & multi | .60 | .25 |
| 44 | A8 | 10c yel green & multi | .75 | .25 |
| 45 | A8 | 15c green & multi | 1.60 | .25 |
| 46 | A8 | 20c ap grn & multi | 1.00 | .25 |
| 47 | A8 | 25c brt green & multi | .75 | .25 |
| 48 | A8 | 40c pale brn & multi | 3.00 | .80 |
| 49 | A7 | 50c rose brn & multi | 1.50 | .75 |
| 50 | A7 | 60c lilac rose & multi | 1.50 | .25 |
| 51 | A7 | $1 dp orange & multi | 1.50 | .25 |

---

| | | | | |
|---|---|---|---|---|
| 52 | A7 | $2 ocher & multi | 1.75 | 3.50 |
| 53 | A7 | $5 red & multi | 2.50 | 4.25 |
| | | *Nos. 39-53 (15)* | 17.45 | 12.05 |

See Nos. 68-82.
For overprints & surcharges see Nos. 357, 410-413, 603, 752, 756, 761a, 1463, 1501, 1839, 2045.

Christ of St. John of the Cross, by Salvador Dali — A9

| | | | | |
|---|---|---|---|---|
| **1968, Mar. 25** | | | | **Perf. 14x14½** |
| 54 | A9 | 5c car rose & multi | .25 | .25 |
| 55 | A9 | 25c brt violet & multi | .25 | .25 |

Easter.

"Efficiency Year" — A10

Designs: 30c, 40c, "Savings bonds."

| | | | | |
|---|---|---|---|---|
| **1968, July 22** | | **Litho.** | | **Perf. 14** |
| 56 | A10 | 6c green & multi | .25 | .25 |
| 57 | A10 | 25c fawn & multi | .25 | .25 |
| 58 | A10 | 30c multicolored | .25 | .25 |
| 59 | A10 | 40c multicolored | .25 | .25 |
| | | *Nos. 56-59 (4)* | 1.00 | 1.00 |

Issued to promote the sale of savings bonds and to publicize Efficiency Year.

Open Koran — A11

| | | | | |
|---|---|---|---|---|
| | | **Perf. 14x13½** | | |
| **1968, Oct. 9** | | **Photo.** | | **Unwmk.** |
| 60 | A11 | 6c sal pink, gold & blk | .25 | .25 |
| 61 | A11 | 25c pale vio, gold & blk | .25 | .25 |
| 62 | A11 | 30c pale yel grn, gold & blk | .25 | .25 |
| 63 | A11 | 40c pale blue, gold & blk | .25 | .25 |
| | | *Nos. 60-63 (4)* | 1.00 | 1.00 |

Koran's 1400th anniversary.
For overprints & surcharges see Nos. 354, 355, 441, 445, 487-488, 575, 630, 1464-1465.

Dish Aerials, Thomas Lands, Guyana — A12

Designs: 30c, 40c, Map showing connection between Guyana and Trinidad. All stamps are inscribed: "Guyana Sends Christmas Greetings to the World."

| | | | | |
|---|---|---|---|---|
| | | **Wmk. 364** | | |
| **1968, Nov. 11** | | **Litho.** | | **Perf. 14** |
| 64 | A12 | 6c blue, gray, ocher & emer | .25 | .25 |
| 65 | A12 | 25c brt rose lil, brn & emer | .25 | .25 |
| 66 | A12 | 30c blue grn & dk blue grn | .25 | .25 |
| 67 | A12 | 40c blue grn & red | .25 | .25 |
| | | *Nos. 64-67 (4)* | 1.00 | 1.00 |

Christmas; communications link with Trinidad by the tropospheric scatter system.

## Types of 1968

Designs as before.

| | | | | |
|---|---|---|---|---|
| | | *Perf. 14x14½, 14½x14* | | |
| **1968** | | **Photo.** | | **Wmk. 364** |
| 68 | A7 | 1c chalky bl & multi | .25 | .25 |
| 69 | A7 | 2c gray & multi | .25 | .25 |
| 70 | A7 | 3c grnsh bl & multi | .25 | .25 |
| 71 | A7 | 5c ultra & multi | .25 | .25 |
| 72 | A7 | 6c brt olive & multi | .25 | .25 |
| 73 | A8 | 10c yel grn & multi | .35 | .25 |
| 74 | A8 | 15c green & multi | .50 | .25 |
| 75 | A8 | 20c apple grn & multi | .50 | .40 |

| | | | |
|---|---|---|---|
| 76 | A8 | 25c brt green & multi | .50 | .25 |
| 77 | A8 | 40c pale brn & multi | 1.00 | .65 |
| 78 | A7 | 50c rose brn & multi | .55 | .25 |
| 79 | A7 | 60c lilac rose & multi | .55 | .90 |
| 80 | A7 | $1 dp org & multi | 1.10 | 1.10 |
| 81 | A7 | $2 ocher & multi | 1.75 | 3.00 |
| 82 | A7 | $5 red & multi | 2.10 | 4.50 |
| | | Nos. 68-82 (15) | 10.15 | 12.80 |

For overprints & surcharges see Nos. 373, 376-377, 413D, 565-566, 633, 635, 704-705, 744, 749, 752a, 757-758, 761-762, 1862-1863, 1981, 4107, 4164, 4187, O2.

Celebrants Spraying Perfumed Powder — A13

Phagwah (Holi) Hindu Festival: 25c, 40c, Two celebrants spraying colored water.

**1969, Feb. 26    Litho.    Perf. 13½**

| 83 | A13 | 6c multicolored | .25 | .25 |
|---|---|---|---|---|
| 84 | A13 | 25c multicolored | .25 | .25 |
| 85 | A13 | 30c multicolored | .25 | .25 |
| 86 | A13 | 40c multicolored | .25 | .25 |
| | | Nos. 83-86 (4) | 1.00 | 1.00 |

The Last Supper, by Salvador Dali — A14

**1969, Mar. 10    Photo.    Perf. 13**

| 87 | A14 | 6c dp carmine & multi | .25 | .25 |
|---|---|---|---|---|
| 88 | A14 | 25c green & multi | .25 | .25 |
| 89 | A14 | 30c org brown & multi | .25 | .25 |
| 90 | A14 | 40c dp violet & multi | .25 | .25 |
| | | Nos. 87-90 (4) | 1.00 | 1.00 |

Easter. For overprints and surcharges see Nos. 393-394, 482-485, 572, 576, 634, 765, 772, 1407-1410, 1813, 1815-1817, 2050, 4108.

Map of Caribbean — A15

Design: 25c, "Strength in Unity," horiz.

**1969, Apr. 30    Litho.    Wmk. 364    Perf. 13½**

| 91 | A15 | 6c violet blue & multi | .25 | .25 |
|---|---|---|---|---|
| 92 | A15 | 25c brt rose, yel & brown | .25 | .25 |

1st anniv. of CARIFTA (Caribbean Free Trade Area).

Prow of Aluminum Ship — A16

50th Anniv. of the ILO: 40c, Bauxite processing plant, horiz.

**1969, Apr. 30    Perf. 12x11, 11x12**

| 93 | A16 | 30c black, blue & silver | .40 | .25 |
|---|---|---|---|---|
| 94 | A16 | 40c multicolored | .60 | .25 |

Flag Raising — A17

Designs: 8c, 30c, Campfire.

**1969, Aug. 13    Litho.    Perf. 13½x13**

| 95 | A17 | 6c pale green & multi | .25 | .25 |
|---|---|---|---|---|
| 96 | A17 | 8c orange & multi | .25 | .25 |
| 97 | A17 | 25c pale brown & multi | .25 | .25 |

| 98 | A17 | 30c multicolored | .25 | .25 |
|---|---|---|---|---|
| 99 | A17 | 50c rose & multi | .25 | .25 |
| | | Nos. 95-99 (5) | 1.25 | 1.00 |

60th anniv. of Scouting in Guyana; 3rd Caribbean Scout Jamboree, Georgetown, Aug. 13-22. For overprints and surcharges see Nos. 392, 395, 397, 402, 404-405, 453.

Gandhi and Spinning Wheel — A18

**1969, Oct. 1    Perf. 14½x14**

| 100 | A18 | 6c olive, blk & lt brn | .30 | .65 |
|---|---|---|---|---|
| 101 | A18 | 15c rose lilac, blk & lt brn | 1.00 | .65 |

Mohandas K. Gandhi (1868-1948), leader in India's fight for independence.

Mother Sally Troupe A19 — City Hall, Georgetown A20

**1969, Nov. 17    Perf. 14x13½**

| 102 | A19 | 5c multicolored | .25 | .25 |
|---|---|---|---|---|
| 103 | A20 | 6c blue & multi | .25 | .25 |
| 104 | A19 | 25c multicolored | .25 | .25 |
| 105 | A20 | 60c orange & multi | .25 | .25 |
| | | Nos. 102-105 (4) | 1.00 | 1.00 |

Christmas. The 5c, 6c, and 25c exist without the "Christmas 1969" overprint.

Prime Minister Forbes Burnham and Map — A21

6c, "Rural Self Help Project" (man & woman building house). 15c, University of Guyana, horiz. 25c, President's Residence, horiz.

**1970, Feb. 23    Litho.    Perf. 14**

| 106 | A21 | 5c blue, brn & ocher | .25 | .25 |
|---|---|---|---|---|
| 107 | A21 | 6c blue, blk ocher & brn | .25 | .25 |
| 108 | A21 | 15c apple grn & multi | .25 | .25 |
| 109 | A21 | 25c multicolored | .25 | .25 |
| | | Nos. 106-109 (4) | 1.00 | 1.00 |

Issued for Republic Day, Feb. 23, 1970.

Descent from the Cross, by Rubens — A22

Easter: 6c, 25c, Christ on the Cross, by Rubens.

**1970, Mar. 24    Perf. 14x14½**

| 110 | A22 | 5c blue & multi | .25 | .25 |
|---|---|---|---|---|
| 111 | A22 | 6c rose lilac & multi | .25 | .25 |
| 112 | A22 | 15c dark red & multi | .25 | .25 |
| 113 | A22 | 25c yellow & multi | .25 | .25 |
| | | Nos. 110-113 (4) | 1.00 | 1.00 |

"Peace" and UN Emblem — A23

UN 25th Anniv.: 6c, 25c, UN emblem, panning for gold and drilling for minerals.

**1970, Oct. 26    Perf. 14½x14**

| 114 | A23 | 5c red & multi | .25 | .25 |
|---|---|---|---|---|
| 115 | A23 | 6c blue & multi | .25 | .25 |
| 116 | A23 | 15c multicolored | .25 | .25 |
| 117 | A23 | 25c brown & multi | .25 | .25 |
| | | Nos. 114-117 (4) | 1.00 | 1.00 |

Mother and Child, by Philip Moore — A24

**1970, Dec. 8    Litho.    Perf. 13½**

| 118 | A24 | 5c violet & multi | .25 | .25 |
|---|---|---|---|---|
| 119 | A24 | 6c brown & multi | .25 | .25 |
| 120 | A24 | 15c dk green & multi | .25 | .25 |
| 121 | A24 | 25c maroon & multi | .25 | .25 |
| | | Nos. 118-121 (4) | 1.00 | 1.00 |

Christmas.

National Cooperative Bank — A25

**1971, Feb. 23    Wmk. 364    Perf. 14**

| 122 | A25 | 6c red & multi | .25 | .25 |
|---|---|---|---|---|
| 123 | A25 | 15c yellow & multi | .25 | .25 |
| 124 | A25 | 25c ultra & multi | .25 | .25 |
| | | Nos. 122-124 (3) | .75 | .75 |

Republic Day.

"Togetherness, Vision, Understanding" — A26

**1971, Mar. 22    Perf. 14½x14**

| 125 | A26 | 5c yel grn & multi | .25 | .25 |
|---|---|---|---|---|
| 126 | A26 | 6c lil rose & multi | .25 | .25 |
| 127 | A26 | 15c multicolored | .25 | .25 |
| 128 | A26 | 25c yellow & multi | .25 | .25 |
| | | Nos. 125-128 (4) | 1.00 | 1.00 |

Intl. year against racial discrimination.

Volunteer Felling Tree, by John Criswick — A27

**1971, July 19    Perf. 14**

| 129 | A27 | 5c blue & multi | .25 | .25 |
|---|---|---|---|---|
| 130 | A27 | 20c green & multi | .25 | .25 |
| 131 | A27 | 25c yellow & multi | .25 | .25 |
| 132 | A27 | 50c brown & multi | .40 | 1.25 |
| | | Nos. 129-132 (4) | 1.15 | 2.00 |

1st anniv. of the Natl. Self-help Road Project.

Yellow Allamanda — A28

Flora: 1c, Pitcher plant of Mt. Roraima. 3c, Heliconia collinsiana. 5c, Annatto tree. 6c, Cannonball tree. 10c, Cattleya violacea. 15c, Christmas orchid. 20c, Paphinia cristata. 25c, Gongora quinquinervis. 40c, Tiger beard. 50c, Guzmania lingulata. 60c, Soldier's cap. $1, Chelonanthus uliginoides. $2, Norantea guianensis. $5, Odontadenia grandiflora.

**1971-76    Litho.    Perf. 13x13½**

| 133 | A28 | 1c multi ('72) | .25 | .25 |
|---|---|---|---|---|
| 134 | A28 | 2c lilac & multi | .25 | .25 |
| 135 | A28 | 3c multicolored | .25 | .25 |
| 136 | A28 | 5c lt blue & multi | .25 | .25 |
| 137 | A28 | 6c dull rose & multi | .25 | .25 |

**Perf. 13½**

| 138 | A28 | 10c multi ('72) | 3.50 | .25 |
|---|---|---|---|---|
| a. | | Perf. 13 | 5.25 | .25 |
| 139 | A28 | 15c multi ('72) | 1.10 | .25 |
| a. | | Perf. 13 ('76) | 1.00 | .25 |
| 140 | A28 | 20c multi ('72) | 3.25 | .40 |
| | | Perf. 13 | 5.00 | .40 |
| 141 | A28 | 25c multi, 25c at center ('72) | 5.00 | 9.00 |
| 141A | A28 | 25c multi, 25c right of center ('73) | .45 | .55 |
| b. | | Perf. 13 ('76) | .45 | .30 |
| 142 | A28 | 40c multi ('72) | 3.50 | .25 |
| 143 | A28 | 50c multi ('73) | .50 | .80 |
| 144 | A28 | 60c multi ('73) | .40 | .65 |
| 145 | A28 | $1 multi ('73) | .40 | .40 |
| 146 | A28 | $2 multi ('73) | .60 | .60 |
| 147 | A28 | $5 multi ('73) | .75 | .75 |
| | | Nos. 133-147 (16) | 20.70 | 15.15 |

No. 141 has 2 blossoms at left, 3 at right; this is reversed on No. 141A.

The overprint "REVENUE / ONLY" between rules was applied to Nos. 134-136, 141A, 142-147 in 1975. Postal use was permitted in Nov.-Dec., 1975. Value, set $20.

See Nos. 433-434, 731-732, 4125-4126.

For overprints and surcharges see Nos. 192, 209, 234, 331-335, 351, 358-359, 367, 370, 372, 374-375A, 379-383, 385-390A, 401, 407, 422-425, 433-434, 438-440, 447, 450, 451, 457-458, 460-461, 464-466, 497-500, 545-546, 549b, 550, 563-564, 597, 602, 618, 631-632, 641-642, 666-667, 727, 747-748, 750-751, 753-754, 759-760, 803, 805, 807-808, 810-812, 847-848, 910-911, 995, 1361, 1382-1383, 1385-1386, 1391-1392, 1452, 1454, 1456-1460, 1466, 1499, 1778-1779, 1781-1784, 1837-1838, 1870-1872, 1898-1900, 2046-2049, 2225-2227, 4133, 4165, 4185, 4195, 4196, C2-C4, O1, O3-O5, O7, O13-O14, Q1-Q4, QO1.

The Lord's Prayer, by School Girl Veronica Bassoo A29

Guyana Masker, by School Boy Michael Austin — A30

**Perf. 13½x14, 14x13½**

**1971, Nov. 15    Litho.    Wmk. 364**

| 148 | A29 | 5c brt green & multi | .25 | .25 |
|---|---|---|---|---|
| 149 | A29 | 20c brt green & multi | .25 | .25 |
| 150 | A30 | 25c multicolored | .25 | .25 |
| 151 | A30 | 50c multicolored | .30 | .30 |
| | | Nos. 148-151 (4) | 1.05 | 1.05 |

Christmas.

Guyana Dollar — A31

**1972, Feb. 23    Litho.    Perf. 14½x14**

| 152 | A31 | 5c blk, dp org & silver | .25 | .25 |
|---|---|---|---|---|
| 153 | A31 | 20c blk, dp lil rose & sil | .25 | .25 |
| 154 | A31 | 25c black, ultra & silver | .25 | .25 |
| 155 | A31 | 50c black, emer & sil | .25 | .25 |
| | | Nos. 152-155 (4) | 1.00 | 1.00 |

Republic Day.

Handclasp and Mosque — A32

**1972, Apr. 3**      **Perf. 14**
| | | | | |
|---|---|---|---|---|
| 156 | A32 | 5c brown & multi | .25 | .25 |
| 157 | A32 | 25c blue & multi | .25 | .25 |
| 158 | A32 | 30c green & multi | .25 | .25 |
| 159 | A32 | 60c yellow brn & multi | .25 | .25 |
| | | *Nos. 156-159 (4)* | 1.00 | 1.00 |

Youman Nabi (Peaceful Prophet), Mohammedan festival.

Map of South America, Emblem of Non-aligned Countries — A33

**1972, July 20**
| | | | | |
|---|---|---|---|---|
| 160 | A33 | 8c violet & multi | .25 | .25 |
| 161 | A33 | 25c yellow grn & multi | .25 | .25 |
| 162 | A33 | 40c orange & multi | .25 | .25 |
| 163 | A33 | 50c red brown & multi | .25 | .25 |
| | | *Nos. 160-163 (4)* | 1.00 | 1.00 |

Conf. of Foreign Ministers of Nonaligned Countries, Georgetown, Aug. 7-12.
For overprints & surcharges see Nos. 573, 611, O17.

CARIFESTA '72 Emblem — A34

**1972, Aug. 25**
| | | | | |
|---|---|---|---|---|
| 164 | A34 | 8c orange & multi | .25 | .25 |
| 165 | A34 | 25c orange & multi | .25 | .25 |
| 166 | A34 | 40c orange & multi | .25 | .25 |
| 167 | A34 | 50c orange & multi | .25 | .35 |
| | | *Nos. 164-167 (4)* | 1.00 | 1.10 |

Caribbean Festival of Arts (CARIFESTA), Georgetown, Aug. 25-Sept. 15.

Holy Family — A35

**1972, Oct. 18**    **Litho.**    **Perf. 13x13½**
| | | | | |
|---|---|---|---|---|
| 168 | A35 | 8c blue & multi | .25 | .25 |
| 169 | A35 | 25c blue & multi | .25 | .25 |
| 170 | A35 | 40c blue & multi | .25 | .25 |
| 171 | A35 | 50c blue & multi | .25 | .30 |
| | | *Nos. 168-171 (4)* | 1.00 | 1.05 |

Christmas.

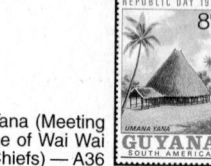

Umana Yana (Meeting Place of Wai Wai Chiefs) — A36

Designs: 25c, 40c, Bethel Chapel.

**1973, Feb. 23**    **Litho.**    **Perf. 14x14½**
| | | | | |
|---|---|---|---|---|
| 172 | A36 | 8c brt blue & multi | .25 | .25 |
| 173 | A36 | 25c rose red & multi | .25 | .25 |
| 174 | A36 | 40c emerald & multi | .25 | .25 |
| 175 | A36 | 50c black & multi | .35 | .25 |
| | | *Nos. 172-175 (4)* | 1.10 | 1.00 |

Republic Day.

Pomegranate, Fertility and Church Symbol — A37

---

Map of Guyana and People Looking to the Cross — A38

**1973, Apr. 19**    **Perf. 14x14½, 13½**
| | | | | |
|---|---|---|---|---|
| 176 | A37 | 8c pink & multi | .25 | .25 |
| 177 | A38 | 25c yellow & multi | .25 | .25 |
| 178 | A38 | 40c ultra & multi | .25 | .25 |
| 179 | A37 | 50c yellow & multi | .25 | .25 |
| | | *Nos. 176-179 (4)* | 1.00 | 1.00 |

Easter.

Symbolic of Blood Donation — A39

**Perf. 14x14½**

**1973, Oct. 1**      **Wmk. 364**
| | | | | |
|---|---|---|---|---|
| 180 | A39 | 8c red & black | .25 | .25 |
| 181 | A39 | 25c red & lilac | .25 | .25 |
| 182 | A39 | 40c red & vio blue | .40 | .50 |
| 183 | A39 | 50c red & brown | .65 | .90 |
| | | *Nos. 180-183 (4)* | 1.55 | 1.90 |

Guyana Red Cross, 25th anniversary.

Steel Band, Star, Pegasus Hotel — A40     Madonna and Child, St. Philip's Anglican Church, Georgetown — A41

**1973, Nov. 20**    **Litho.**    **Perf. 14x14½**
| | | | | |
|---|---|---|---|---|
| 184 | A40 | 8c lilac & multi | .25 | .25 |
| 185 | A40 | 25c lilac & multi | .25 | .25 |

**Perf. 13½x14**
| | | | | |
|---|---|---|---|---|
| 186 | A41 | 40c violet blue & multi | .40 | .70 |
| 187 | A41 | 50c violet blue & multi | .40 | .70 |
| | | *Nos. 184-187 (4)* | 1.30 | 1.90 |

Christmas.

"One People, One Nation, One Destiny" — A42

Designs: 25c, 50c, Wai Wai Indian.

**1974, Feb. 23**    **Litho.**    **Perf. 13½**
| | | | | |
|---|---|---|---|---|
| 188 | A42 | 8c multicolored | .25 | .25 |
| 189 | A42 | 25c multicolored | .25 | .25 |
| 190 | A42 | 40c multicolored | .25 | .30 |
| 191 | A42 | 50c multicolored | .25 | .40 |
| | | *Nos. 188-191 (4)* | 1.00 | 1.20 |

Republic Day.

**No. 137 Surcharged with New Value and 2 Bars**

**Perf. 13x13½**

**1974, Mar. 18**      **Wmk. 364**
| | | | | |
|---|---|---|---|---|
| 192 | A28 | 8c on 6c multi | .30 | .30 |

For overprints and surcharges see Nos. 424, 459, 1453, 1500, 1780.

---

Crucifix Superimposed on Eddy Bow Kite — A43     Crucifix in Pre-Columbian Timehri Style — A44

**1974, Apr. 8**      **Perf. 13½x14**
| | | | | |
|---|---|---|---|---|
| 193 | A43 | 8c green & multi | .25 | .25 |
| 194 | A44 | 25c black, green & gray | .25 | .25 |
| 195 | A44 | 40c black, gray & car | .25 | .25 |
| 196 | A43 | 50c gold & multi | .25 | .25 |
| | | *Nos. 193-196 (4)* | 1.00 | 1.00 |

Easter.

UPU Emblem and British Guiana Type of 1863 — A45

Mailman and UPU Emblem — A46

**1974, June 18**    **Litho.**    **Perf. 14, 14½**
| | | | | |
|---|---|---|---|---|
| 197 | A45 | 8c rose & multi | .30 | .25 |
| 198 | A46 | 25c yellow green & multi | .45 | .25 |
| 199 | A45 | 40c blue & multi | .45 | .30 |
| 200 | A46 | 50c yellow green & multi | .55 | .55 |
| | | *Nos. 197-200 (4)* | 1.75 | 1.35 |

Centenary of Universal Postal Union.

Girl Guides Holding Banner — A47

Designs: 25c, 40c, Guides in camp cooking and carrying water. 50c, Like 8c.

**1974, Aug. 1**      **Perf. 14½**
| | | | | |
|---|---|---|---|---|
| 201 | A47 | 8c multicolored | .25 | .25 |
| 202 | A47 | 25c multicolored | .35 | .25 |
| 203 | A47 | 40c multicolored | .50 | .40 |
| 204 | A47 | 50c multicolored | .50 | .50 |
| a. | | Souvenir sheet of 4, #201-204 | 2.00 | 2.00 |
| | | *Nos. 201-204 (4)* | 1.60 | 1.40 |

Girl Guides of Guyana, 50th anniv. For overprints see Nos. 574, 1352.

Buck Toyeau — A48

Christmas (Fruit): 35c, Carambola (starfruit) and awaras. 50c, Pawpaw and tangerine. $1, Pineapple and sapodillas.

**1974, Nov. 18**    **Litho.**    **Perf. 14x13½**
| | | | | |
|---|---|---|---|---|
| 205 | A48 | 8c multicolored | .25 | .25 |
| 206 | A48 | 35c multicolored | .25 | .25 |
| 207 | A48 | 50c multicolored | .25 | .25 |
| 208 | A48 | $1 multicolored | .40 | .75 |
| a. | | Souvenir sheet of 4, #205-208 | 1.00 | 3.00 |
| | | *Nos. 205-208 (4)* | 1.15 | 1.50 |

For overprints & surcharges see Nos. 551, 612, 716, 4173.

**No. 135 Surcharged with New Value and Two Bars**

**1975, Jan. 20**    **Litho.**    **Perf. 13x13½**
| | | | | |
|---|---|---|---|---|
| 209 | A28 | 8c on 3c multi | .25 | .25 |

For surcharge see No. 423.

---

Golden Arrow of Courage — A49

Republic Day: 35c, Cacique's Crown of Honour. 50c, Cacique's Crown of Valour. $1, Order of Excellence.

**1975, Feb. 23**      **Perf. 13x13½**
| | | | | |
|---|---|---|---|---|
| 210 | A49 | 10c brown & multi | .25 | .25 |
| 211 | A49 | 35c brown red & multi | .25 | .25 |
| 212 | A49 | 50c green & multi | .25 | .35 |
| 213 | A49 | $1 violet bl & multi | .50 | .65 |
| | | *Nos. 210-213 (4)* | 1.25 | 1.50 |

For overprints and surcharges see Nos. 360, 368, 398, 637, 1359.

Old Sluice Gate — A50     Modern Sluice Gate — A51

**1975, May 2**      **Perf. 14**
| | | | | |
|---|---|---|---|---|
| 214 | A50 | 10c bister & multi | .25 | .25 |
| 215 | A51 | 35c brown & multi | .25 | .25 |
| 216 | A50 | 50c bister & multi | .25 | .40 |
| 217 | A51 | $1 green & multi | .50 | .75 |
| a. | | Souvenir sheet of 4, #214-217 | 1.25 | 3.50 |
| | | *Nos. 214-217 (4)* | 1.25 | 1.65 |

Intl. Commission on Irrigation and Drainage, 25th anniv.
For overprints see Nos. 361, 592, 794-795, 1374-1375.

IWY Emblem, Symbolic Man and Woman — A52

Designs: IWY emblem and petroglyph designs of men and women.

**1975, July 1**    **Litho.**    **Wmk. 364**
| | | | | |
|---|---|---|---|---|
| 218 | A52 | 10c yellow & dull grn | .25 | .25 |
| 219 | A52 | 35c Prus blue & pur | .25 | .25 |
| 220 | A52 | 50c orange & dk blue | .25 | .25 |
| 221 | A52 | $1 ultra & brown | .40 | .50 |
| a. | | Souvenir sheet of 4, #218-221, perf. 14½ | 1.50 | 1.25 |
| | | *Nos. 218-221 (4)* | 1.15 | 1.25 |

Intl. Women's Year. For overprints and surcharges see Nos. 362, 399, 555.

Freedom Monument, Georgetown — A53

Designs: Various views of Freedom Monument, Georgetown.

**1975, Aug. 26**    **Litho.**    **Perf. 14**
| | | | | |
|---|---|---|---|---|
| 222 | A53 | 10c gray & multi | .25 | .25 |
| 223 | A53 | 35c yellow & multi | .25 | .25 |
| 224 | A53 | 50c lilac & multi | .30 | .30 |
| 225 | A53 | $1 olive & multi | .40 | .40 |
| | | *Nos. 222-225 (4)* | 1.20 | 1.20 |

Namibia Day (independence for South-West Africa).
For overprints and surcharges see Nos. 330, 582, 593, 619, 1360.

"GNS," Flower and
Clasped Hands — A54

"GNS" and Clasped hands: 35c, Wheel.
50c, Soccer ball. $1, Uniform cap.

**1975, Oct. 2      Wmk. 364      Perf. 14**
226 A54 10c violet, yel & grn      .25   .25
227 A54 35c brt bl, org & grn      .25   .25
228 A54 50c lt brn, brt bl & grn      .25   .25
229 A54 $1 grn, vio & brt grn      .40   .40
  a.  Souvenir sheet of 4, #226-229      1.25   3.00
    Nos. 226-229 (4)      1.15   1.15

Guyana National Service, 1st anniv. For
overprint & surcharges see Nos. 448, 636,
638.

Foresters'
Building and
Badge — A55

35c, Rock painting of hunter. 50c, Crossed
axes and hunting horn. $1, Bow and arrow.

**1975, Nov. 14      Litho.      Wmk. 364**
230 A55 10c red, black & gold      .25   .25
231 A55 35c red, black & gold      .25   .25
232 A55 50c gold & multi      .25   .25
233 A55 $1 gold & multi      .45   .45
  a.  Souvenir sheet of 4, #230-233      1.00   3.00
    Nos. 230-233 (4)      1.20   1.20

Ancient Order of Foresters, centenary.
For overprints and surcharges see Nos.
356, 363, 400, 422, 583, 4170.

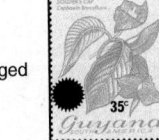

No. 144 Surcharged

**1976, Feb. 10      Perf. 13½**
234 A28 35c on 60c multi      .40   .40

For overprints see Nos. 703-703a, 852.

St. John Ambulance
Emblem — A56

**1976, Mar. 29      Litho.      Perf. 14**
235 A56 8c black, lil rose & sil      .25   .25
236 A56 15c black, orange & sil      .25   .25
237 A56 35c black, emer & silver      .25   .25
238 A56 40c black, blue & sil      .30   .30
    Nos. 235-238 (4)      1.05   1.05

Guyana St. John Ambulance, 50th anniv.
For surcharges see Nos. 715, 717, 1411.

Independence Arch,
1966 — A57

Stylized Designs: 15c, Victoria regia. 35c,
Letter "S" for socialism. 40c, Worker with
pitchfork.

**1976, May 25      Perf. 13½**
239 A57 8c silver & multi      .25   .25
240 A57 15c silver & multi      .25   .25
241 A57 35c silver & multi      .25   .25

242 A57 40c silver & multi      .25   .25
  a.  Souvenir sheet of 4, #239-242,
    perf. 14      1.00   1.50
    Nos. 239-242 (4)      1.00   1.00

10th anniv. of independence. For
surcharges see Nos. 567, 639, 1444.

Map of West Indies,
Bats, Wicket and
Ball — A57a

Prudential
Cup — A57b

**Unwmk.**
**1976, Aug. 3      Litho.      Perf. 14**
243 A57a 15c light blue & multi      1.25   1.75
244 A57b 15c lilac rose & black      1.25   1.75

World Cricket Cup, won by West Indies
Team, 1975.
For overprints & surcharges see Nos. 352-
353, 653-654.

Lamp — A58

Designs: 15c, Hand and flame. 35c, Flame.
40c, Lakshmi, Hindu goddess of wealth.

**1976, Oct. 21      Perf. 14**
245 A58 8c multicolored      .25   .25
246 A58 15c orange & multi      .25   .25
247 A58 35c purple & multi      .25   .25
248 A58 40c ultra & multi      .30   .30
  a.  Souvenir sheet of 4, #245-248      1.25   1.75
    Nos. 245-248 (4)      1.05   1.05

Deepavali, Hindu Festival of Lights.
For surcharges see Nos. 719-721.

Guitar-Sitar, Benin
Head — A59

**1977, Feb. 1      Litho.      Perf. 14½**
249 A59 10c gold & multi      .25   .25
250 A59 35c gold & multi      .25   .25
251 A59 50c gold & multi      .35   .35
252 A59 $1 gold & multi      .50   .50
  a.  Souvenir sheet of 4, #249-252      1.60   3.50
    Nos. 249-252 (4)      1.35   1.35

2nd World Black and African Festival,
Lagos, Nigeria, Jan. 15-Feb. 12. Nos. 249-
252a were not issued without black bar.
For overprints see Nos. 364, 369, 584.

1c and 5c
Coins — A60

Coins (Obverse): 15c, 10c and 25c. 35c,
50c and $1. 40c, $5 and $10. $1, $50 and
$100. $2, Reverse, Coat of arms.

**1977, May 26      Perf. 14**
253 A60 8c multicolored      .35   .35
254 A60 15c multicolored      .40   .40
255 A60 35c multicolored      .70   .70
256 A60 40c multicolored      .85   .85
257 A60 $1 multicolored      1.25   1.25
258 A60 $2 multicolored      2.00   2.00
    Nos. 253-258 (6)      5.55   5.55

New coinage. For overprints and surcharges
see Nos. 539, 541A, 568, 594, O18, O20, Q5.

Hand Pump,
c.
1850 — A61

National Fire Prevention Week: 15c, Steam
engine, c. 1860. 35c, Fire engine, c. 1930.
40c, Fire engine, 1977.

**Perf. 14x14½**
**1977, Nov. 15      Litho.      Wmk. 364**
259 A61 8c multicolored      1.25   .25
260 A61 15c multicolored      2.00   .25
261 A61 35c multicolored      2.25   1.10
262 A61 40c multicolored      2.50   1.25
    Nos. 259-262 (4)      8.00   2.85

For surcharges see Nos. 1370-1371.

Cuffy Monument — A62

8c, 35c, Cuffy statue from monument.

**1977, Dec. 7      Litho.      Perf. 14**
263 A62 8c multicolored      .25   .25
264 A62 15c multicolored      .25   .25
265 A62 35c multicolored      .25   .25
266 A62 40c multicolored      .25   .25
    Nos. 263-266 (4)      1.00   1.00

Cuffy, Guyana's national hero, led a slave
revolution in 1763. The monument was
unveiled in 1976. For overprints see Nos. 446,
569, 613.

Wildlife
Protection — A63

**1978, Feb. 15      Perf. 14**
267 A63 8c Manatee      1.00   .25
268 A63 15c Giant sea turtle      1.25   .40
269 A63 35c Harpy eagle      6.00   2.75
270 A63 40c Iguana      4.75   2.75
    Nos. 267-270 (4)      13.00   6.15

8c, 15c are horiz. For overprints and
surcharges see Nos. 443, 722-723, 1416.

Parliament
and Prime
Minister
Burnham
A64

Prime Minister and: 15c, Student and school
children. 35c, Bauxite mine. 40c, Cooperative
village.

**1978, Apr. 27      Litho.      Perf. 13½x14**
271 A64 8c violet & black      .25   .25
272 A64 15c gray, blk & bl      .25   .25
273 A64 35c multicolored      .25   .25
274 A64 40c gray, blk & org      .25   .25
  a.  Souvenir sheet of 4, #271-274      .90   1.75
    Nos. 271-274 (4)      1.00   1.00

Prime Minister Linden Forbes Burnham,
25th anniv. of his entry into parliament. For
surcharges see Nos. 648-649.

Dr. George Giglioli,
Anopheles
Mosquito — A65

30c, Institute of Applied Science & Technology, proposed for University of Guyana. 50c,
Map of Guyana & National Science Research
Council emblem. 60c, Commonwealth Science Council emblem.

**Perf. 13½x14, 14x13½**
**1978, Sept. 4      Litho.      Wmk. 364**
275 A65 10c multi      .25   .25
276 A65 30c multi, horiz.      .25   .25
277 A65 50c multi      .30   .30
278 A65 60c multi, horiz.      .30   .30
    Nos. 275-278 (4)      1.10   1.10

For overprints see Nos. 577, 585, 590.

Agrias Claudina — A66

5c, Prepona pheridamas. 10c, Archonias
bellona. 15c, Eryphanis polyxena. 20c,
Helicopis cupido. 25c, Nessaea batesli. 30c,
Nymphidium mantus. 35c, Siderone galanthis.
40c, Morpho rhetenor, male. 50c, Hamadryas
amphinone. 60c, Papilio androgeus. $1,
Agrias claudina, vert. $2, Morpho rhetenor,
female. $5, Morpho deidamia. $10, Elbella
patrobas.

**1978-80      Perf. 14x13½**
**Size: 22x16mm**
279 A66 5c multicolored      1.50   .25
280 A66 10c multicolored      1.50   .25
281 A66 15c multicolored      1.50   .25
282 A66 20c multicolored      1.75   .25
283 A66 25c multicolored      1.75   .25
283A A66 30c multi ('80)      1.25   3.25
284 A66 35c multicolored      1.75   .25
285 A66 40c multicolored      1.75   .25
286 A66 50c multicolored      1.75   .30
286A A66 60c multi ('80)      1.25   1.75

**Perf. 13½x13**
287 A66 $1 multicolored      3.75   .35
288 A66 $2 multicolored      5.50   .70
289 A66 $5 multicolored      6.50   1.50
289A A66 $10 multi, perf. 14
    ('80)      4.50   6.25
    Nos. 279-289A (14)      36.00   15.85

Issued: Nos. 279-283, 284-286, 287-289,
10/1/78. For overprints and surcharges see
Nos. 391, 406, 436-436A, 481, 486, 554, 668-
670, 733-743, 871, 936-939, 944, 969, 1373,
1418, 1455, 1786, 1812, 1814, 1832-1833,
1873, 1901, 1912-1913, 1984-1988, 2051,
2053, 2054C, 2055, 2057, 2057B-2057C,
2058-2059, 2081-2111, 4188, 4189, C5-C6,
O15-O16, O23-O29.

Indian Making Stone
Chip Grater — A67

UNESCO Emblem and: 30c, Arawak Cassiri
jar and decorated Amerindian jar. 50c, Gate to
old Dutch fort, Kykover-al. 60c, Fort Island,
Dutch ruins.

**1978, Dec. 27      Wmk. 364      Perf. 14**
290 A67 10c green & multi      .25   .25
291 A67 30c green & multi      .25   .25
292 A67 50c green & multi      .25   .25
293 A67 60c green & multi      .25   .25
    Nos. 290-293 (4)      1.00   1.00

National and International Heritage Year.
For surcharges see Nos. 604-606.

Earth Station at
Dawn,
Georgetown — A68

Designs: 30c, Earth Station in daylight,
Georgetown. 50c, Intelsat V. $3, Intelsat IVa.

**1979, Feb. 7      Litho.      Perf. 14x14½**
294 A68 10c multicolored      .25   .25
295 A68 30c multicolored      .25   .25
296 A68 50c multicolored      .40   .25
297 A68 $3 multicolored      1.00   .90
    Nos. 294-297 (4)      1.90   1.65

For surcharges see Nos. 384, 655, 714,
1376-1377, 1380, O9.

British Guyana
No. 5 — A69

Designs: 30c, British Guiana No. 13, vert. 50c, British Guiana No. 152. $3, Printing press used for 1c Magenta, vert.

**1979, June 11    Wmk. 364    Perf. 14**

| | | | | |
|---|---|---|---|---|
| 298 | A69 | 10c multicolored | .25 | .25 |
| 299 | A69 | 30c multicolored | .30 | .25 |
| 300 | A69 | 50c multicolored | .40 | .25 |
| 301 | A69 | $3 multicolored | .50 | .50 |
| | | Nos. 298-301 (4) | 1.45 | 1.25 |

Sir Rowland Hill (1795-1879), originator of penny postage.
For overprints & surcharges see Nos. 409, 426, 428, 449, 479, 480, 578, 586, 598, 614, O6.

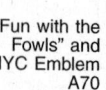

"Fun with the Fowls" and IYC Emblem A70

Children's Drawings and IYC Emblem: 10c, "Me and my sister," vert. 50c, "Two boys catching ducks." $3, "Mango season."

**1979, Aug. 20    Litho.    Perf. 13½**

| | | | | |
|---|---|---|---|---|
| 302 | A70 | 10c multicolored | .25 | .25 |
| 303 | A70 | 30c multicolored | .25 | .25 |
| 304 | A70 | 50c multicolored | .25 | .25 |
| 305 | A70 | $3 multicolored | .50 | 1.25 |
| | | Nos. 302-305 (4) | 1.25 | 2.00 |

Intl. Year of the Child. For overprints and surcharges see Nos. 435, 579, 587, 599, 615, 943.

H. N. Critchlow, Worker Hauling Sack — A71

Critchlow and: 30c, Baker, horiz. 50c, Flag and crowd. $3, Portrait only.

**1979, Sept. 27    Litho.    Perf. 14**

| | | | | |
|---|---|---|---|---|
| 306 | A71 | 10c multicolored | .25 | .25 |
| 307 | A71 | 30c multicolored | .25 | .25 |
| 308 | A71 | 50c multicolored | .25 | .25 |
| 309 | A71 | $3 multicolored | .60 | .90 |
| | | Nos. 306-309 (4) | 1.35 | 1.65 |

Guyana Labor Union, 60th anniversary. For surcharges see Nos. 403, 429, 718.

Cooperative Republic, 10th Anniv. — A72

35c, Demerara River Bridge. 60c, Kaieteur Falls. $3, Makanaima, American Indian.

**Wmk. 364**
**1980, Feb. 23    Litho.    Perf. 14**

| | | | | |
|---|---|---|---|---|
| 313 | A72 | 10c shown | .25 | .25 |
| 314 | A72 | 35c multicolored | .30 | .25 |
| 315 | A72 | 60c multicolored | .50 | .25 |
| 316 | A72 | $3 multicolored | .75 | .75 |
| | | Nos. 313-316 (4) | 1.80 | 1.50 |

For overprints and surcharges see Nos. 365, 371, 450A, 442, 591, 656.

**Miniature Sheet**

Snoek, London 1980 Emblem — A73

London 80 Emblem and Fish; a, Snoek. b, Haimara. c, Electric eel. d, Golden rivulus. e, Pencil fish. f, Four-eyed fish. g, Pirai. h, Smoking hassar. i, Devil ray. j, Flying patwa. k, Arapaima. l, Lukanani.

**1980, May 6    Wmk. 373    Perf. 14**

| | | | | |
|---|---|---|---|---|
| 317 | A73 | Sheet of 12 | 4.75 | 4.75 |
| a.-l. | | 35c any single | .35 | .35 |

London 1980 Intl. Stamp Exhib., May 6-14. For overprints & surcharges see Nos. 444, 725-726, 1414.

Children's Convalescent Home, Rotary Emblem — A74

Rotary International, 75th anniversary (Emblem and): 30c, Georgetown club emblem. 50c, District 404 emblem (hibiscus), vert. $3, Anniversary emblem, vert.

**Perf. 14x14½, 14½x14**
**1980, June 23    Litho.    Wmk. 364**

| | | | | |
|---|---|---|---|---|
| 318 | A74 | 10c multicolored | .25 | .25 |
| 319 | A74 | 30c multicolored | .25 | .25 |
| 320 | A74 | 50c multicolored | .35 | .35 |
| 321 | A74 | $3 multicolored | .75 | .75 |
| | | Nos. 318-321 (4) | 1.60 | 1.60 |

For overprints and surcharges see Nos. 552, 580, 601, C1.

Emblem and Caduceus — A75

60c, Scientist, beach scene. $3, Emblems over island.

**Wmk. 364**
**1980, Sept. 23    Litho.    Perf. 13½**

| | | | | |
|---|---|---|---|---|
| 322 | A75 | 10c shown | .25 | .25 |
| 323 | A75 | 60c multicolored | .40 | .25 |
| 324 | A75 | $3 multicolored | 1.25 | 1.00 |
| | | Nos. 322-324 (3) | 1.90 | 1.50 |

Commonwealth Caribbean Medical Research Council, 25th anniversary. For overprints and surcharges see Nos. 366, 427, 430, 494, 553.

Virola Surinamensis (Christmas 1980) — A76

**1980, Nov. 1    Wmk. 373    Perf. 14**

| | | | | |
|---|---|---|---|---|
| 325 | A76 | 10c shown | .25 | .25 |
| 326 | A76 | 30c Hymenaea courbaril | .30 | .25 |
| 327 | A76 | 50c Mora excelsa | .40 | .25 |
| 328 | A76 | $3 Peltogyne venosa | 1.00 | 1.60 |
| | | Nos. 325-328 (4) | 1.95 | 2.35 |

For overprints and surcharges see Nos. 431, 773, 790, 792-793, 4169, 4175.

**Miniature Sheet**

A77

Designs: a, Tree porcupine. b, Howler monkeys. c, Squirrel monkeys. d, Two-toed sloth. e, Tapir. f, Collared peccary. g, Six-banded armadillo. h, Anteater. i, Great anteaters. j, Mouse opossums. k, Four-eyed opossum. l, Orange-rumped agouti.

**1981, Mar. 2    Wmk. 364    Perf. 14**

| | | | | |
|---|---|---|---|---|
| 329 | A77 | Sheet of 12 | 8.00 | 8.00 |
| a.-l. | | 30c any single | .40 | .40 |
| m. | | As #329g, perf. 12 | 3.00 | 40 |

For overprints see Nos. 581, 819, 1399, 1503, 1844.

During 1981-91, there were numerous sources creating stamps for Guyana, with as many as 5-7 parties being active at any given time.

No. 222 Surcharged

**1981, May 4**

| | | | |
|---|---|---|---|
| 330 | A53 | $1.05 on 10c multi | .60 |

For surcharges see Nos. 396, 620.

**Nos. 135, 145-147 Surcharged**

 No. 331     No. 332

 No. 333     No. 334

$7·20 ROYAL WEDDING 1981
No. 335

**1981    Litho.    Wmk. 364    Perf. 13½**

| | | | | |
|---|---|---|---|---|
| 331 | A28 | 60c on 3c #135 | 3.00 | |
| 332 | A28 | 75c on $5 #147 | 3.00 | |
| 333 | A28 | $1.10 on $2 #146 | 3.00 | |
| a. | | Blue overprint | 4.00 | |
| 334 | A28 | $3.60 on $5 #147 (Blk) | 4.00 | |
| a. | | Black overprint | 4.00 | |
| 335 | A28 | $7.20 on $1 #145 (Bl) | 4.00 | |
| a. | | Black overprint | 6.00 | |

No. 333 is airmail. Issue dates: $3.60, $7.20, 5/6. Others 7/22. Diagonal overprint on No. 332. Vertical overprint on No. 333. Location of surcharge varies.
See Nos. 621, 666-667, Q4, QO5. For overprints and surcharges see Nos. 378, 489-496, 547, 549, 646, 818, 867-868, O11, Q3, QO3.

Map of Guyana — A78

**1981, May 11    Photo.    Perf. 13½**
**Color of Map**

| | | | |
|---|---|---|---|
| 336 | A78 | 10c on 3c dl brn | 1.20 |
| 337 | A78 | 30c on 2c gray | 1.20 |
| 338 | A78 | 50c on 2c gray | 1.20 |
| 339 | A78 | 60c on 2c gray | 1.20 |
| 340 | A78 | 75c on 3c dl brn | 1.20 |
| | | Nos. 336-340 (5) | 6.00 |

Revenue stamps surcharged for postal use. For surcharge, see No. 503. For similar revenue stamps surcharged, see Nos. 501-502, 504-538, 934a. For surcharge see No. 503.

**Nos. J5-J8 Surcharged in Red, Black, or Brown**

a

b

**Type "a"**

**1981, June 8    Typo.    Perf. 13½x14**

| | | |
|---|---|---|
| 341 | D1 | 10c on 2c #J6 |
| 342 | D1 | 15c on 12c #J8 (Blk) |
| 343 | D1 | 20c on 1c #J5 |
| 344 | D1 | 45c on 2c #J6 |
| 345 | D1 | 55c on 4c #J7 |
| 346 | D1 | 60c on 4c #J7 (Brn) |
| 347 | D1 | 65c on 2c #J6 |
| 348 | D1 | 70c on 4c #J7 |
| 349 | D1 | 80c on 4c #J7 |
| | | Nos. 341-349 (9)    11.00 |

**Type "b"**

| | | |
|---|---|---|
| 341a | D1 | 10c on 2c #J6 |
| 342a | D1 | 15c on 12c #J8 (Blk) |
| 343a | D1 | 20c on 1c #J5 |
| 344a | D1 | 45c on 2c #J6 |
| 345a | D1 | 55c on 4c #J7 |
| 347a | D1 | 65c on 2c #J6 |
| 348a | D1 | 70c on 4c #J7 |
| 349a | D1 | 80c on 4c #J7 |
| | | Nos. 341a-349a (8)    11.00 |

Pairs with types a and b exist for all values except the 60c.

Nos. 48, 61-62, 74, 139, 142-143, 145-147, 212-213, 216, 220, 231-232, 243-244, 251-252, 315-316, and 323 Overprinted in Black or Red

**1981    Perfs. as Before**
**Watermarks & Printing Methods as Before**

| | | | | |
|---|---|---|---|---|
| 350 | A8 | 15c on #74 (R) | 17.50 | |
| 351 | A28 | 15c on #139 | | |
| a. | | Red overprint | 7.00 | |
| b. | | On #139a, red overprint | 8.00 | |
| 352 | A57a | 15c on #243 | 8.50 | |
| 353 | A57b | 15c on #244 | 5.00 | |
| 354 | A11 | 25c on #61 (R) | .75 | |
| 355 | A11 | 30c on #62 (R) | .75 | |
| 356 | A55 | 35c on #231 (R) | 3.00 | |
| 357 | A8 | 40c on #48 | 12.00 | |
| 358 | A28 | 40c on #142 | | |
| 359 | A28 | 50c on #143 | 4.00 | |
| 360 | A49 | 50c on #212 | 3.25 | |
| 361 | A50 | 50c on #216 | 1.50 | |
| 362 | A52 | 50c on #220 | 26.00 | |
| 363 | A55 | 50c on #232 | 3.25 | |
| 364 | A59 | 50c on #251 | 15.00 | |
| 365 | A72 | 60c on #315 | .90 | |
| 366 | A75 | 60c on #323 | .90 | |
| 367 | A28 | $1 on #145 | 3.50 | |
| a. | | Red overprint | 2.00 | |
| 368 | A49 | $1 on #213 | 7.50 | |
| 369 | A59 | $1 on #252 | 6.50 | |
| 370 | A28 | $2 on #146 | 8.00 | |
| a. | | Red overprint | 2.00 | |
| b. | | Black ovpt. with serifs | 25.00 | |
| 371 | A72 | $3 on #316 | 3.00 | |
| 372 | A28 | $5 on #147 | 4.25 | |
| | | Nos. 350-372 (23) | 50.00 | |

Issued: Nos. 354-356, 367, 6/8; Nos. 350, 357, 370, 7/1; Nos. 351-353, 359-366, 368-369, 371-372, 7/7.
Location and size of overprint varies. Refer to second paragraph in footnote following No. 147 for Nos. 358-359.
For surcharges and overprints see Nos. 556, 607, 659, 745, 849-850, 1362, 4132.

Nos. 68, 135-136, 139, 145-147, 297, 333 Surcharged or Overprinted

**1981    Litho.    Perfs. as Before**
**Watermarks & Printing Methods as Before**

| | | | | |
|---|---|---|---|---|
| 373 | A7 | 15c on 1c #68 | 1.10 | |
| 374 | A28 | 50c on 5c #136 | 3.00 | |
| 375 | A28 | 75c on 5c #136 | 35.00 | |
| 375A | A28 | 80c on 15c #139 | | |
| 376 | A7 | 100c on 1c #68 | 1.00 | |
| 377 | A7 | 110c on 1c #68 | 1.00 | |
| a. | | Strip of 3, #373, 376-377 | 5.50 | 4.00 |
| 378 | A28 | $1.10 on #333 | 15.00 | |
| 379 | A28 | 120c on $1 #145 | 2.50 | |
| 380 | A28 | 140c on $1 #145 | 2.50 | |
| 381 | A28 | 150c on $2 #146 | 2.50 | |
| 382 | A28 | 210c on $5 #147 | 35.00 | |
| 383 | A28 | 220c on 5c #136 | 30.00 | |
| 384 | A68 | 220c on $3 #297 | 5.00 | |
| 385 | A28 | 250c on $5 #147 | 2.75 | |
| 386 | A28 | 280c on $5 #147 | 2.75 | |
| 387 | A28 | 360c on $2 #146 | 3.50 | |
| 388 | A28 | 375c on $5 #147 | 3.00 | |
| 389 | A28 | $7.20 on 3c #135 | 100.00 | |
| 390 | A28 | 720c on 60c #144 | 3.75 | |
| 390A | A28 | $20 on 5c #136 | | |

Location and size of surcharge and obliterator varies. Obliterator is an "X" on Nos. 381-388, 390, two solid boxes on Nos. 379-380, and five bars on No. 389. Numeral "7" is placed before 5 to make surcharge on No. 375. "Royal Wedding 1981" obliterated by three bars on No. 378. New denomination on No. 375A does not have cent sign. Obliterator on No. 390A is three horizontal bars.

Refer to second paragraph in footnote following No. 147 for Nos. 381, 387 and 390. Nos. 376-378 are airmail.

Issued: #375, 382, 6/8; #373-374, 376-388, 390, 7/1.

For overprint and surcharges see Nos. 408, 788, 859-860, 863-864, 1379, 1417.

### No. 281 Overprinted "ESSEQUIBO / IS OURS"

**1981, July**   **Litho.**   **Perf. 14x13½**
391 A66 15c on #281 ... 8.50
  a.   Ovpt. without serifs

### Nos. 87, 95-96, 142, 146, 210, 218, 230, 309, 330, O15 Surcharged

**1981**   **Perfs. as Before**
**Watermarks & Printing Methods as Before**
392 A17 55c on 6c #95 ... 4.50
393 A14 70c on 6c #87 ... 1.25
394 A14 100c on 6c #87 ... 1.50
395 A17 100c on 8c #96 ... 4.50
396 A53 100c on #330 (surcharge reading down) ... 40.00
  a.   Surcharge reading up ... 50.00
397 A17 110c on 6c #95 ... 3.00
398 A49 110c on 10c #210 ... 3.00
399 A52 110c on 10c #218 ... 7.00
400 A55 110c on 10c #230 ... 7.00
401 A28 125c on $2 #146 ... 15.00
402 A17 180c on 6c #95 ... 4.50
403 A71 240c on $3 #309 ... 12.00
404 A17 400c on 6c #95 ... 4.50
405 A17 $4.40 on 6c #95 ... 2.25
  a.   Fours same size ... 11.00
406 A66 550c on $10 #O15 ... 10.00
407 A28 625c on 40c #142 ... 17.50

Issued: Nos. 392, 394-395, 397-399, 405, 405a, 407, 7/7; Nos. 393, 402-404, 406, 9/15. Refer to 2nd paragraph in footnote after No. 147 for 407. For overprints and surcharges see Nos. 651-652, 996, 1858-1859, 1861, O8, O10, O12.

### No. 383 Ovptd. "Espana 82"
### No. 301 Surcharged "1831-1981 / Von Stephan"
**Perfs. as Before**

**1981, July 22**   **Litho.**   **Wmk. 364**
408 A28 220c on #383 ... 7.00
409 A69 330c on $3 #301 ... 10.00

For surcharges see Nos. 616, 622.

### Nos. 43, 72 Surcharged
**1981 Photo. Unwmk. Perf. 14x14½**
410 A7 12c on 12c on 6c #43
411 A7   Pair, #a.-b.
  a.   15c on 10c on 6c #43
  b.   15c on 30c on 6c #43
412 A7   Pair, #a.-b.
  a.   15c on 50c on 6c #43
  b.   15c on 60c on 6c #43
413 A7   Strip of 3, #a.-c.
  a.   12c On 6c #43
  b.   50c On 6c #43
  c.   $1 On 6c #43

**Wmk. 364**
413D A7   Strip of 3, #e.-g.
  e.   12c On 6c #72
  f.   50c On 6c #72
  g.   $1 On 6c #72

Issue dates: Nos. 410-412, Aug. 24. No. 413-413D, Nov. 10.

Nos. 410-412 were not issued without large numeral surcharges. Obliterator is black box on Nos. 410-412, "X" on Nos. 413a & 413De. Nos. 413b-413c, 413Df-g are airmail.

For overprints and surcharges see Nos. 728-728a, 914, 994, 994a, 1400-1401, 4174.

16th Anniv. of the Guyana Defense Force — A79

---

15c on 10c, Armed Ranger, 1772. 50c, Private, Foot Regiment, 1825. $1 on 30c, Marine Private, 1775. $1.10 on $3, Defense Force officers, 1966.

**1981, Oct. 1**   **Wmk. 364**   **Perf. 13½**
414 A79 15c on 10c multi ... .35 .35
415 A79 50c multicolored ... .90 .45
416 A79 $1 on 30c multi ... 1.75 1.75
417 A79 $1.10 on $3 multi ... 2.00 2.00
      Nos. 414-417 (4) ... 5.00 4.45

Nos. 414, 416-417 not issued without surcharge. For overprints see Nos. 570, 588, 595, 1368-1369.

Louis Braille and Boy Reading Braille — A80

Intl. Year of the Disabled: 50c, Helen Keller and Rajkumari Singh. $1, Beethoven and Sonny Thomas. $1.10, Renoir and painting.

**1981, Nov. 2**   **Perf. 13½x14**
418 A80 15c on 10c multi ... .25 .25
419 A80 50c multi ... .75 .75
420 A80 60c on 6c multi ... 1.25 1.25
421 A80 $1.10 on $3 multi ... 2.00 2.00
      Nos. 418-421 (4) ... 4.25 4.25

Nos. 418, 420-421 not issued without surcharge. For overprints and surcharge see Nos. 571, 589, 596, 1913A.

### Nos. 192, 209, 230, 298, 301, 309, 322, 324, 328, O1 Surcharged in Blue or Red
**Watermarks & Printing Methods as Before**

**1981, Nov. 14**   **Perfs. as Before**
422 A55 110c on 10c on #230 ... 6.00
423 A28 110c on #209 ... 5.00
424 A28 110c on #192 ... 5.00
425 A28 110c on #O1 ... 5.00
426 A69 110c on 10c on #298 (R) ... 3.00
427 A75 110c on 10c on #322 ... 15.00
428 A69 110c on $3 #301 (R) ... 3.50
429 A71 110c on $3 #309 ... 8.50
430 A75 110c on $3 #324 ... 6.00
  a.   Red surcharge ... 9.00
431 A76 110c on $3 #328 ... 9.00
  a.   Red surcharge ... 60.00
      Nos. 422-431 (10) ... 66.00

Nos. 423-424 were issued with two 110c surcharges of different sizes. Refer to second paragraph in footnote below No. 147 for No. 425. For overprints and surcharges see Nos. 791, 820, 855, 1000, 1364-1366.

### Flower Type of 1971-76 Surcharged
**1981, Nov. 24**   **Photo.**   **Perf. 15x14**
**Size: 20x23mm**
**Coil Stamps**
433 A28 15c on 2c like #134 ... .35
434 A28 15c on 8c Mazaruni Pride ... .35
  a.   Pair, #433-434 ... 1.10

Nos. 433-434 were not issued without surcharge. See Nos. 731-732.

### No. 305 Surcharged "U.N.I.C.E.F. / 1946-1981"
**Wmk. 364**
**1981, Nov. 14**   **Litho.**   **Perf. 13½**
435 A70 125c on $3 #305 ... 4.00

For surcharge see No. 942.

### No. 279 Surcharged "Nov. 81" (#436) or "Cancun 81" (#436A)
**1981, Nov. 14**   **Perf. 14x13½**
436 A66 50c on 5c #279
436A A66 50c on 5c #279 ... 6.50

Conversion to Metric System, Jan. 2 — A81

a, Tape measure. b, Juggler. c, Man, envelope. d, Baby on scale. e, Canje Bridge. f, Liter bucket.

---

**Perf. 14½x14**
**1982, Jan. 18**   **Wmk. 364**
437 A81 15c Sheet of 6, #a.-f. ... 3.25 3.25

For surcharge see No. 557.

### Nos. 61, 63, 139, 140, 141A, 143-144, 146-147, 228, 266, 269, 300, 314 and 316-317 Ovptd. "1982" Vertically or Horizontally in Blue or Violet
**Watermarks & Printing Methods as Before**

**1982-83**   **Perfs. as Before**
438 A28 15c on #139 ... 8.00
  a.   On #139a ... 65.00
439 A28 20c on #140 ... 4.00
440 A28 25c on #141A ... 7.50
441 A11 25c on #61 (V) ... 2.00
442 A72 35c on #314 ... 1.00
443 A63 35c on #269 ... 6.00
444 A73 35c on block of 6, #317-317f ... 20.00
445 A11 40c on #63 (V) ... 1.00
446 A62 40c on #266 ... 1.00
447 A28 50c on #143 ... 3.00
448 A54 50c on #228 ... 2.00
449 A69 50c on #300 ... 1.00
449A A28 60c on #144 ... 7.00
450 A28 $2 on #146 ... 1.50
450A A72 $3 on #316 ... 2.25
451 A28 $5 on #147 ... 1.50
      Nos. 438-451 (16) ... 68.75

Issued: Nos. 439-441, 2/8; Nos. 450-451, 4/23; Nos. 445-446, 4/27; No. 438, 6/17; Nos. 443-444, 8/16; No. 442, 9/15; Nos. 447-449, 10/11; No. 449A, 7/1/83; No. 450A, 11/3/83. For other stamps overprinted "1982" only, see Nos 482-483, 555.

For overprints and surcharges see Nos. 806, 809, 813-814, 851, 999, 1354, 1415, 4134, 4171.

### Nos. 97, O3, O4, O9-O10 Ovptd. "POSTAGE" in Blue
**Watermarks and Printing Methods as Before**

**1982**   **Perfs. as Before**
452 A28 15c on #O3 ... 10.00
453 A17 25c on #97 ... 6.00
454 A28 50c on #O4 ... 1.50
455 A68 100c on #O9 ... 2.50
456 A17 110c on #O10 ... 3.00

For surcharge see No. 853. For similar overprints see Nos. 729-730. Refer to second paragraph in footnote following No. 147 for No. 454.

### Nos. 133, 137, 142, and 192 Surcharged in Blue or Green

**Perfs. as Before**
**1982**   **Litho.**   **Wmk. 364**
457 A28 20c on 6c #137 ... 1.00
458 A28 20c on 6c #137 (G) ... 1.00
459 A28 125c on #192 ... 1.00
460 A28 180c on #142 ovpt. "1982" ... 6.00
461 A28 220c on 1c #133 ... 2.00
      Nos. 457-461 (5) ... 11.00

No. 458 has no obliterator, "20c" is 23mm long.

Issued: Nos. 457-459, 2/8; No. 460, 4/8; No. 461, 4/23.

Refer to 2nd paragraph in footnote following No. 147 for No. 460.

For overprints see Nos. 755, 856, 862.

Savings Campaign A81a

No. 462, Soldier & flag. No. 463, Two soldiers, flag.

**1982**   **Litho.**   **Perf. 14½**
462 A81a $1 multi ... 1.00
463 A81a $1.10 on $5 multi ... 7.50
  a.   Inverted comma before "OURS"

Size of obliterator differs on Nos. 463 and 463a. Nos. 462-463a are revenue stamps ovptd. for postal use.

Issued: No 462, 2/8; No. 463, 3/3; No. 463a, 7/13.

---

### Nos. 134, 136, & 192 Surcharged in Black or Green

Surcharges read: Nos. 464a, 465a, 466a: "BADEN-POWELL / 1857-1982" .
Nos. 464b, 465b, 466b: "Scout Movement / 1907-1982"
Nos. 464c, 465c, 466c: "1907-1982"
Nos. 464d, 465d, 466d: "1857-1982"
Nos. 464e, 465e, 466e: "1982"

**Perf. 13x13½**
**1982, Feb. 22**   **Litho.**   **Wmk. 364**
**Sheets of 25**
464   8 #a.-b., 4 #c.-d., 1 #e. ... 20.00
  a.-e.   A28 110c on 2c #134, any single ... .70
465   8 #a.-b., 4 #c.-d., 1 #e. ... 35.00
  a.-e.   A28 110c on 5c #136, any single ... 1.00
466   8 #a.-b., 4 #c.-d., 1 #e. ... 35.00
  a.-e.   A28 125c on #192, any single (G) ... 1.00

Lord Robert Baden-Powell, 125th anniv. of birth. Boy Scout Movement, 75th anniv.

For overprints and surcharges see Nos. 558, 778-784, 836-837, 1347.

### Nos. 289, 299, 301 Surcharged or Overprinted in Black or Blue

 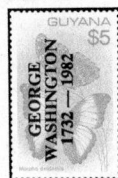

**Perfs. as Before**
**1982, Feb. 15**   **Litho.**   **Wmk. 364**
479 A69 100c on $3 #301 ... 2.00 1.00
480 A69 400c on 30c #299 ... 3.00 2.00
481 A66 $5 on #289 (Bl) ... 15.00 10.00
      Nos. 479-481 (3) ... 20.00 13.00

For surcharges see Nos. 617, 904-906, 937-939, O22-O29.

### Nos. 88-89 Ovptd. "1982" in Blue and Nos. 87, 90 Surcharged in Blue or Red

**1982, Mar. 15**   **Photo.**   **Perf. 13**
482 A14 25c on #88
483 A14 30c on #89
484 A14 45c on 6c #87
485 A14 75c on 40c #90 (R)
      Nos. 482-485 (4) ... 3.00

For overprints see Nos. 766-767.

### Nos. 60, 284, 324, and 331-333 Surcharged in Black or Blue

### Watermarks & Printing Methods as Before

**1982**   **Perfs. as Before**
486 A66 20c on 35c #284 ... 7.50
487 A11 80c on 6c #60 (Bl) ... 3.00
488 A11 85c on 6c #60 (Bl) ... 3.00
489 A28 85c on #331 ... 6.00
490 A28 130c on #331 ... 4.00
491 A28 160c on #333 (Bl) ... 3.00
  a.   Black surcharge ... 5.00
492 A28 170c on #333 ... 15.00
493 A28 210c on 30c #332 (Bl) ... 3.00
494 A75 210c on $3 #324 (Bl) ... 4.00
495 A28 235c on #332 ... 5.00
  a.   Blue surcharge ... 9.00
496 A28 330c on #333 ... 4.00
      Nos. 486-496 (11) ... 57.50

Nos. 491-491a, 492, & 496 are airmail. Obliterators differ.

Issue dates: No. 486, 3/15. Others, 4/27.

For surcharges see Nos. 647, 1367.

### Nos. 135, 137, 144 & 145 Overprinted or Surcharged in Blue or Black

Overprints read: Nos. 497-498, 500: "ESPANA / 1982". No. 499: "ESPANA / 1982" and "ITALY".

**1982 Litho. Wmk. 364 Perf. 13½**
497 A28 $1 on #145 (Blk) 1.50
498 A28 110c on 3c #135 1.50
499 A28 $2.35 on 180c on 60c #144 14.00
500 A28 250c on 6c #137 2.00

Refer to second paragraph in footnote below No. 147 for No. 499.
No. 499 not issued without $2.35 surcharge.
See No. 597 for stamp with one-line Espana 1982 overprint. For surcharges see Nos. 774-777.
Issued: Nos. 497-498, 500, 5/15; No. 499, 7/15.

Map Revenue Surcharged in Black, Blue, or Red

**1982-83 Photo. Wmk. 364 Perf. 13**
Color of Map
501 A78 15c on 2c gray (Bl)
502 A78 20c on 2c gray (Bl)
503 A78 20c on 10c #336 dl brn (Bl)
504 A78 25c on 2c gray
  a. Blue surcharge
  b. Red surcharge 1.00
505 A78 30c on 2c gray (Bl)
506 A78 40c on 2c gray (Bl)
  a. Blue surcharge
507 A78 45c on 2c gray (Bl)
508 A78 50c on 2c gray (Bl)
509 A78 60c on 2c gray (Bl)
510 A78 75c on 2c gray (Bl)
511 A78 80c on 2c gray (Bl)
512 A78 85c on 2c gray (Bl)
513 A78 $1.00 on 3c dl brn
514 A78 $1.10 on 3c dl brn
515 A78 $1.20 on 3c dl brn
516 A78 $1.25 on 3c dl brn
517 A78 $1.30 on 3c dl brn
518 A78 $1.50 on 3c dl brn
519 A78 $1.60 on 3c dl brn
520 A78 $1.70 on 3c dl brn
521 A78 $1.75 on 3c dl brn
522 A78 $1.80 on 3c dl brn
523 A78 $2.00 on 3c dl brn
524 A78 $2.10 on 3c dl brn
525 A78 $2.20 on 3c dl brn
526 A78 $2.35 on 3c dl brn
527 A78 $2.40 on 3c dl brn
528 A78 $2.50 on 3c dl brn
529 A78 $3.00 on 3c dl brn
530 A78 $3.30 on 3c dl brn
531 A78 $3.75 on 3c dl brn
532 A78 $4.00 on 3c dl brn
533 A78 $4.40 on 3c dl brn
534 A78 $5.00 on 3c dl brn
535 A78 $5.50 on 3c dl brn
536 A78 $6.25 on 3c dl brn
537 A78 $15 on 2c gray (R)
538 A78 $20 on 3c gray (R)
  Nos. 501-538 (38) 210.00

Revenue stamps surcharged for postal use. Issue dates: Nos. 501-502, 504-538, May 17, 1982; No. 503, Mar. 14, 1983.
For surcharges see Nos. 935, 4135, 4186, 4191, 4192, 4197.

British Guiana Nos. 254, 255, 279, Guyana 10A, 13, 13a, 32J, 32K, 32N Surcharged "H.R.H. / Prince William / 21st June 1982" in Blue

British Guiana stamps also have "GUYANA."

**1982, July 12 Perfs. as Before**
Watermarks & Printing Methods as Before
539 A60 50c on 2c #254 1.00 .45
540 A60 50c on 2c #32J 10.00 4.50
541 A66 $1.10 on 5c #279 3.00 .65
541A A60 $1.10 on 3c #255 2.00 .55
542 A60 $1.10 on 3c #32K 32.50 4.50
543 A60 $1.25 on 6c #10A
543A A60 $1.25 on 6c #32N .85 .85
544 A60 $2.20 on 24c #13a 4.00
544A A60 $2.20 on 24c #13 2.00 2.00

For surcharges see Nos. 797-800.

Nos. 133-134 Surcharged "C.A. & CARIB / Games / 1982"
Perf. 13x13½
**1982, Aug. 16 Litho. Wmk. 364**
545 A28 50c on 2c #134 2.25 .40
546 A28 60c on 1c #133 2.75 .25
  Nos. 545-546 (2) 5.00

Central American and Caribbean Games, Havana. For overprint see No. 816.

---

**Nos. 135, 331, C2 Surcharged**
**1982, Sept. 15**
547 A28 130c on #331 3.00
548 A28 170c on #C2 4.00
549 A28 440c on 60c on 3c #331 ovptd. "1982" 3.50
  a. Without "1982" 80.00
  b. As No. 549, but with Royal Wedding overprint like No. 332 — —
  Nos. 547-549 (3) 10.50

For surcharge see No. 802.

No. 137 Surcharged "Commonwealth / GAMES / AUSTRALIA / 1982" in Blue
**1982, Sept. 27**
550 A28 $1.25 on 6c #137 2.25 .50

For surcharge see No. 789.

Nos. 207, 221, 287, 320, 323, 332 Ovptd. in Blue, Dark Blue, Green or Blue Green

Overprints or Surcharges read: No. 551, "INT. / FOOD DAY / 1982"; No. 552, "INT. YEAR / OF THE / ELDERLY"; No. 553, "Dr. R. KOCH / CENTENARY / TBC BACILLUS / DISCOVERY"; No. 554, "F.D. ROOSEVELT / 1882-1982 "; No. 555, "1982"; No. 556, "GAC Inaug. Flight /Georgetown-/ Boa Vista, Brasil" in Blue and "1982" in Blue Green.

Watermarks & Printing Methods as Before
**1982, Oct. 15 Perfs. as Before**
551 A48 50c on #207 (DB) 21.00 1.00
552 A74 50c on #320 (DB) 9.00 1.00
553 A75 60c on #323 (DB) 6.00 .55
554 A66 $1 on #287 (G) 6.00 1.00
555 A52 $1 on #221 (Bl) 6.00 1.25
556 A28 200c on #332 (Bl, Bl G) 24.00 2.75
  Nos. 551-556 (6) 72.00 7.55

For surcharges see Nos. 895, 902, 936, 1363.

No. 437 Surcharged "CARICOM / Heads of Gov't / Conference / July 1982"
Perf. 14½x14
**1982, Jan. 18 Litho. Wmk. 364**
557 Sheet of 6 15.00 12.50
  a.-f. A81 50c on 15c, any single 2.25 1.00

Nos. 464 Ovptd. "CHRISTMAS / 1982" in Red
**1982, Dec. 1 Perf. 13x13½**
558 Sheet of 25, 8 #a.-b., 4 #c.-d., 1 #e. 32.50 32.50
  a.-b. A28 15c on #464a-464b, either single .90 .45
  c.-d. A28 15c on #464c-464d, either single 2.10 .45
  e. A28 15c on #464e 24.00 24.00

Nos. 134, 137 Surcharged

Perf. 13x13½
**1982-83 Litho. Wmk. 364**
563 A28 15c on 2c #134 (Bl) .75
  a. Red surcharge 2.00
  b. Black surcharge .75
564 A28 20c on 6c #137 (Bk) .75
  a. Green surcharge .75

Issued: Nos. 563, 12/15; No. 564, 1/5/83. Compare No. 564 with Nos. 631-632. For surcharges see Nos. 846, 846a, 846b.

No. 72 Surcharged
**1982, Dec. 15 Photo. Perf. 14x14½**
565 A7 50c on 6c #72 .75 .25
566 A7 $1.00 on 6c #72 1.25 .45
  Nos. 565-566 (2) 2.00 .70

---

**Nos. 62, 88-89, 144, 161, 202, 217, 224-225, 232, 240, 251, 254, 257, 264, 276-278, 299-301, 303-305, 315, 319, 321, 329m, 414-416, and 418-420 Ovptd. "1983" Vertically or Horizontally**
**1983 Perfs. as Before**
Watermarks & Printing Methods as Before
567 A57 15c on #240 6.00
568 A60 15c on #254 1.50
569 A62 15c on #264 1.00
570 A79 15c on 10c #414 1.00
571 A80 15c on 10c #418 .25
572 A14 25c on #88 .50
573 A33 25c on #161 14.00
574 A47 25c on #202 .50
575 A11 30c on #62 1.50
576 A14 30c on #89 .50
577 A65 30c on #276 12.50
578 A69 30c on #299 5.00
579 A70 30c on #303 10.00
580 A74 30c on #319 6.00
581 A77 30c on #329m 3.00
582 A53 50c on #224 2.00
583 A55 50c on #232 5.00
584 A59 50c on #251 7.00
585 A65 50c on #277 5.00
586 A69 50c on #300 2.00
587 A70 50c on #304 30.00
588 A79 50c on #415 1.00
589 A80 50c on #419 2.00
590 A65 60c on #278 5.50
591 A72 60c on #315 7.00
592 A51 $1 on #217 10.00
593 A53 $1 on #225 10.00
594 A60 $1 on #257 6.00
595 A79 $1 on 30c #416 2.75
596 A80 $1 on 60c #420 7.50
597 A28 180c on 60c #144 2.00
598 A69 $3 on #301 12.00
599 A70 $3 on #305 15.00
601 A74 $3 on #321 75.00
602 A28 360c on $2 #146 2.25

Issued: Nos. 567-571, 583, 585-586, 2/1; No. 596, 3/7; No. 573, 3/11; Nos. 572, 576, 3/17; Nos. 582, 584, 587, 588, 589, 592-595, 598-599, 601, 4/1; No. 574, 5/23; Nos. 575, 577-580, 590-591, 7/1; No. 602, 11/3; No. 581, 11/15; No. 597, 12/14.
Refer to the second paragraph in footnote under No. 147 for Nos. 597 & 602. No. 597 contains unissued overprint, "ESPANA 1982."
For overprints and surcharges see Nos. 724, 901, 940, 943A.

No. O2 Ovptd. "POSTAGE" in Red
Perf. 14½x14
**1983, Feb. 1 Photo. Wmk. 364**
603 A8 15c on #O2 16.00 .50

For surcharge see Nos. 746-746a.

Nos. 291-293, 356 Surcharged in Blue or Black
Wmk. 364
**1983, Feb. 8 Litho. Perf. 14**
604 A67 90c on 30c #291 (Blk) 2.00 1.00
605 A67 90c on 50c #292 1.25 .30
606 A67 90c on 60c #293 2.00 1.00
607 A55 90c on #356 4.75 .50
  Nos. 604-607 (4) 10.00 2.80

For overprints and surcharges see Nos. 763-764, 768-769, 770-771.

Flag — A82

Cooperative Youth Palace — A83

**1983, Feb. 19 Perf. 14½x14**
608 A82 Pair 1.00 1.00
  a. 25c Flag flying right .40 .40
  b. 25c Flag flying left .40 .40
Perf. 13½
609 A83 $1.30 shown 1.00 1.00
Size: 43x25mm
Perf. 14½
610 A83 $6 Map 3.75 3.75

60th birthday of Pres. Linden Forbes Burnham. No. 608a inscribed for birthday; No. 608b for Burnham's 30th anniv. of election to parliament.
See Nos. 660, 913. For overprints & surcharges see Nos. 826-835, 924-926, 1404-1406.

---

Nos. 160, 205, 222, 263, 298, 302, 330, 333, 408-409, 480, C4, O1 and Q3 Ovptd. in Blue or Red

Watermarks & Printing Methods as Before
**1983 Litho. Perfs. as Before**
611 A33 50c on 8c #160 (R) 25.00
612 A48 50c on 8c #205 2.25
613 A62 50c on 8c #263 8.00
614 A69 50c on 10c #298 (R) 1.50
615 A69 50c on 10c #302 4.00
616 A69 50c on 8c #409 4.50
617 A69 50c on #480 2.00
618 A28 50c on #O1 5.00
619 A53 $1 on #222 8.50
620 A53 $1 on #330 5.00
621 A28 $1 on #333 5.00
622 A28 $1 on #408 10.00
623 A28 $1 on #C4 1.50
624 A28 $1 on #Q3 25.00

No. 621 has Royal Wedding ovpt. similar to No. 331. No. 624 also ovptd. "1982." See Nos. 648-649 for similar surcharges. For overprint see Nos. 815, 941. Issued: Nos. 614, 617, 619-624, 3/7; No. 611, 3/11; others, 4/1.

Nos. 10A, 13a Surcharged "Commonwealth / Day / 14 March 1983" and Emblem in Blue or Black
Wmk. 314 Upright
**1983, Mar. 14 Engr. Perf. 12½x13**
625 A60 25c on 6c #10A
626 A60 $1.20 on 6c #10A (Bl)
Wmk. 314 Sideways
627 A60 $1.30 on 24c #13a
628 A60 $2.40 on 24c #13a (Bl)
  Nos. 625-628 (4) 5.00

For overprints see Nos. 1823-1825.

Intl. Maritime Organization, 25th Anniv. — A84

Red Overprint on British Guiana 1889 Revenue Stamp
Perf. 14
**1983, Mar. 17 Typo. Wmk. 3**
629 A84 $4.80 grn & blue 7.50

Nos. 60, 72, 87 & 137 Surcharged in Black or Blue
Watermarks & Printing Methods as Before
**1983 Perfs. as Before**
630 A11 15c on 6c #60 .75
  a. Blue surcharge 1.00
631 A28 20c on 6c #137, two obliterators 1.00
632 A28 20c on 6c #137 1.00
633 A7 50c on 6c #72 .75
634 A14 50c on 6c #87 1.00
  Nos. 630-634 (5) 4.50

Issued: Nos. 630, 632-633, 5/23; No. 630a, 631, 634, 5/2.
Surcharge on No. 632 has "c" after value. No. 564 does not.
For surcharge see No. 916.

No. 72 Surcharged in Black or Red
Perf. 14x14½
**1983 Photo. Wmk. 364**
635 A7 $1 on 6c #72 1.60
  a. Red overprint, 4mm high 1.60

Issued: No. 635, 5/2. No. 635a, 5/23.
For surcharge see No. 916A.

Nos. 142, 147, 211, 226-227, 239 & 249 Surcharged in Blue
**1983 Perfs. as Before**
Watermarks & Printing Methods as Before
636 A54 110c on 10c #226 3.00
637 A49 120c on 35c #211 4.50
638 A54 120c on 35c #227 4.50
639 A57 120c on 8c #239 4.50
640 A59 120c on 10c #249 4.50
641 A28 250c on 40c #142 12.00
642 A28 400c on $5 #147 9.00
  Nos. 636-642 (7) 42.00

Issued: Nos. 636, 641-642, 5/2. Others, 7/1.
For surcharge see No. 865.

## Nos. 332, 495a, C3 Surcharged in Red or Blue

Surcharges read: No. 643, "ITU / 1983"; No. 644, "WHO / 1983"; No. 645, "17 MAY '83 / ITU/WHO"; Nos. 646-647, "ITU/WHO / 17 MAY / 1983".

**1983, May 17**    Perfs. as Before
Watermarks & Printing Methods as Before

| | | | | |
|---|---|---|---|---|
| 643 | A28 | 25c on #C3 | 4.00 | .90 |
| 644 | A28 | 25c on #C3 | 4.00 | .90 |
| 645 | A28 | 25c on #C3 | 4.00 | .90 |
| a. | | Strip of 3, #643-645 | 22.50 | 10.00 |
| 646 | A28 | $4.50 on #332 (Bl) | 16.00 | 2.00 |
| 647 | A28 | $4.50 on #495a (Bl) | 16.00 | |

Nos. 643-645 issued in sheets of 25 with 8 each Nos. 643-644 and 9 No. 645.

## Nos. 272, 274 Surcharged in Dark Blue

### Perf. 13½x14

**1983, May 18**    Litho.    Wmk. 364

| | | | | |
|---|---|---|---|---|
| 648 | A64 | $1 on 15c #272 | 5.50 | 1.00 |
| 649 | A64 | $1 on 40c #274 | 9.00 | 1.00 |
| | | Nos. 648-649 (2) | 14.50 | 2.00 |

Surcharge on No. 648 also contains overprint "1983."

## Nos. 402, 404, O8 Surcharged or Overprinted "CANADA 1983"

### Perf. 13½x13

**1983, June 15**

| | | | | |
|---|---|---|---|---|
| 650 | A17 | $1.30 on #O8 | 4.50 | 3.00 |
| 651 | A17 | 180c on #402 | 4.50 | 4.50 |
| 652 | A17 | $3.90 on #404 | 10.00 | 10.00 |
| | | Nos. 650-652 (3) | 19.00 | 17.50 |

For surcharge see No. 1860.

## Nos. 243-244 Surcharged

**1983, June 22**    Unwmk.    Perf. 14

| | | | | |
|---|---|---|---|---|
| 653 | A57a | 60c on 15c #243 | 15.00 | 1.00 |
| 654 | A57b | $1.50 on 15c #244 | 22.50 | 2.50 |
| | | Nos. 653-654 (2) | 37.50 | 3.50 |

## Nos. 297, 313 Surcharged

### Perfs. as Before

**1983, July 1**    Wmk. 364

| | | | | |
|---|---|---|---|---|
| 655 | A68 | 120c on #297 | 7.50 | 1.25 |
| 656 | A72 | 120c on 10c #313 (R) | 7.50 | 1.25 |

No. 655 has unissued surcharge, "INTERNATIONAL / SCIENCE YEAR / 375."

## British Guiana No. J1 and Guyana No. J5 Surcharged "120 / GUYANA" in Dark Blue

**1983, July 1**    Wmk. 4    Perf. 13½x14

| | | | | |
|---|---|---|---|---|
| 657 | D1 | 120c on 1c #J1 | 6.00 | 1.25 |

**Wmk. 364**

| | | | | |
|---|---|---|---|---|
| 658 | D1 | 120c on 1c #J5 | 6.00 | 1.25 |

## No. 371 Surcharged in Red "CARICOM DAY 1983"

**1983, July 1**    Wmk. 364    Perf. 14

| | | | | |
|---|---|---|---|---|
| 659 | A72 | 60c on $3 #371 | 3.00 | |

## Type A82 Without Inscription

**1983, July 1**    Litho.    Perf. 14½x14

| | | | | |
|---|---|---|---|---|
| 660 | A82 | Pair | 1.00 | 1.00 |
| a. | | 25c, Flag flying right | .40 | .40 |
| b. | | 25c, Flag flying left | .40 | .40 |

River Steamers — A85

**1983, July 11**    Litho.    Perf. 14

| | | | | |
|---|---|---|---|---|
| 661 | A85 | 30c Kurupukari | .25 | .25 |
| a. | | Tete-beche pair | | |
| 662 | A85 | 60c Makouria | .50 | .50 |
| a. | | Tete-beche pair | | |
| 663 | A85 | 120c Powis | 1.00 | 1.00 |
| a. | | Tete-beche pair | | |
| 664 | A85 | 130c Pomeroon | 1.25 | 1.25 |
| a. | | Tete-beche pair | | |
| 665 | A85 | 150c Lukanani | 1.50 | 1.50 |
| a. | | Tete-beche pair | | |
| | | Nos. 661-665 (5) | 4.50 | 4.50 |

For surcharge, see No. 4020J.

## No. 146 Surcharged in Dark Blue

**1983, July 22**    Perf. 13½

| | | | |
|---|---|---|---|
| 666 | A28 | $2.30 on $1.10 on $2 | |
| 667 | A28 | $3.20 on $1.10 on $2 | |
| | | Nos. 666-667 (2) | 8.00 |

Nos. 666-667 have unissued surcharge of "$1.10 / Royal Wedding / 1981" similar to No. 331.

## Nos. 282-283 & 283A Overprinted as Shown or with Various Initials in Red or Blue

Overprints: No. 668a, BW. b, LM. c, GY 1963 / 1983. d, JW. e, CU. f. Mont Golfier / 1783-1983.

No. 669a, BGI. b, GEO. c, MIA. d, BVB. e, PBM. f, Mont Golfier / 1783-1983. g, POS. h, JFK.

No. 670a, AHL. b, BCG. c, BMJ. d, EKE. e, GEO. f, GFO. g, IBM. h, Mont Golfier / 1783-1983. i, KAI. j, KAR. k, KPG. l, KRG. m, KTO. n, LTM. o, MHA. p, MWI. q, MYM. r, NAI. s, ORJ. t, USI. u, VEG.

**1983, Sept. 5**    Perf. 14x13½
Sheets of 25

| | | | |
|---|---|---|---|
| 668 | A66 | 20c 4 each #a.-e., 5 #f | 30.00 |
| 669 | A66 | 25c 2 each #a., c.-e., g.-h., 8 #b., 5 #f. | 45.00 |
| 670 | A66 | 30c #a.-e., g.-u., 5 #f., (Bl) | 40.00 |

Manned flight, bicentennial and Guyana Airways, 20th anniv. For ovpts. see Nos. 871, 969.

## No. 234 Surcharged in Dark Blue

**1983, Sept. 14**    Perf. 13½

| | | | | |
|---|---|---|---|---|
| 703 | A28 | 240c on #234 | 3.00 | 1.25 |
| a. | | "4" with serif | 3.50 | 1.50 |

Nos. 703, 703a appear in same sheet.

## Nos. 68, 70 Surcharged "FAO 1983" in Red

### Perf. 14x14½

**1983, Sept. 15**    Photo.    Wmk. 364

| | | | | |
|---|---|---|---|---|
| 704 | A7 | 30c on 1c #68 | .50 | .25 |
| 705 | A7 | $2.60 on 3c #70 | 2.50 | 2.50 |
| | | Nos. 704-705 (2) | 3.00 | 2.75 |

For overprints see Nos. 1497-1498.

Great Britain, Postal Use In British Guiana, 150th Anniv. — A86

Stamps: a, #20. b, #26. c, #27. d, #28.

**1983, Oct. 1**    Litho.    Perf. 14
Inscribed in Black

| | | | | |
|---|---|---|---|---|
| 706 | A86 | 25c on #20 | .25 | .25 |
| 707 | A86 | 30c on #26 | .25 | .25 |
| 708 | A86 | 60c on #27 | .30 | .30 |
| 709 | A86 | 120c on #28 | 1.00 | 1.00 |

**Inscribed in Blue**

| | | | | |
|---|---|---|---|---|
| 710 | | Block of 4 | .80 | .80 |
| a.-d. | A86 | 25c any single | .25 | .25 |
| 711 | | Block of 4 | 1.00 | 1.00 |
| a.-d. | A86 | 30c any single | .25 | .25 |
| 712 | | Block of 4 | 1.00 | 1.00 |
| a.-d. | A86 | 45c any single | .25 | .25 |
| 713 | | Block of 4 | 3.50 | 3.50 |
| a. | A86 | 120c on #20 | .65 | .65 |
| b. | A86 | 130c on #26, Demerara | .75 | .75 |
| c. | A86 | 150c on #27, Berbice | .90 | .90 |
| d. | A86 | 200c on #28, Essequibo | 1.20 | 1.20 |
| | | Nos. 706-713 (8) | 8.10 | 8.10 |

Nos. 706-709 printed in sheets with bottom two rows inverted. Nos. 710-712 printed in sheets of 60. No. 713 printed in sheets with blue marginal text.

For overprints and surcharges see Nos. 796, 903, 912, 1448, 1982.

## Nos. 206, 235, 238, 297 & 309 Surcharged

Surcharges read: No. 714, "INT. / COMMUNICATIONS / YEAR"; No. 716, "Int. Food Day / 1983"; No. 718, "1918-1983 / I.L.O."

**1983, Oct. 15**    Perfs. as Before
Watermarks & Printing Methods as Before

| | | | |
|---|---|---|---|
| 714 | A68 | 50c on 375c on $3 #297 | 6.00 |
| 715 | A56 | 75c on 8c #235 | 7.50 |
| 716 | A48 | $1.20 on 35c #206 | 1.75 |
| 717 | A56 | $1.20 on 40c #238 | 7.50 |
| 718 | A71 | 240c on $3 #309 | 2.25 |
| | | Nos. 714-718 (5) | 25.00 |

No. 714 was not issued without 375c surcharge. For overprint see No. 821.

## Nos. 245, 247-248 Surcharged

### Unwmk.

**1983, Nov. 1**    Litho.    Perf. 14

| | | | | |
|---|---|---|---|---|
| 719 | A58 | 25c on 8c #245 | .35 | .25 |
| 720 | A58 | $1.50 on 35c #247 | 2.40 | 1.00 |
| 721 | A58 | $1.50 on 40c #248 | 1.25 | 1.00 |
| | | Nos. 719-721 (3) | 4.00 | 2.25 |

## Nos. 268 & 270 Surcharged

**1983, Nov. 15**    Wmk. 364

| | | | | |
|---|---|---|---|---|
| 722 | A63 | 60c on 15c #268 | 2.50 | .50 |
| 723 | A63 | $1.20 on 40c #270 | 2.50 | .90 |

## No. 601 Ovptd. "Human Rights / Day"

**1983, Dec. 1**    Perf. 14½x14

| | | | | |
|---|---|---|---|---|
| 724 | A74 | $3 on #601 | 3.50 | 1.75 |

For surcharge see footnote following No. 998.

## Nos. 317 and 726 Surcharged "LOS ANGELES / 1984"

**1983, Dec. 6**    Wmk. 373

| | | | |
|---|---|---|---|
| 725 | | Sheet of 12 | 80.00 |
| a.-l. | A73 | 55c on 125c on 35c #726a-726l, any single | — |
| 726 | | Sheet of 12 | 120.00 |
| a.-l. | A73 | 125c on 35c #317a-317l, any single | — |

For surcharge see No. 1897.

## No. 133 Surcharged "COMMONWEALTH / HEADS OF GOV'T / MEETING--INDIA / 1983"

### Perf. 13x13½

**1983, Dec. 14**    Litho.    Wmk. 364

| | | | | |
|---|---|---|---|---|
| 727 | A28 | 150c on 1c #133 | 4.00 | 1.00 |

## Nos. 413a, 413e Surcharged "CHRISTMAS / 1983"

**1983, Dec. 14**    Photo.    Perf. 14x14½
Watermarks as before

| | | | | |
|---|---|---|---|---|
| 728 | A7 | 20c on #413a | 1.50 | .25 |
| a. | | 20c on #413De | .50 | .25 |

## Nos. 146, O15 Ovptd. "POSTAGE" in Blue

**1984, Jan. 8**    Perfs. as before

| | | | | |
|---|---|---|---|---|
| 729 | A28 | $2 on #146 | 4.25 | 1.00 |
| 730 | A66 | 550c on $10 #O15 | 22.00 | 10.00 |

Refer to second paragraph in footnote following No. 147 for No. 729.

## Flower Type of 1971-76 Surcharged in Blue

### Perf. 15x14

**1984, Jan.**    Photo.    Unwmk.
Size: 20x23mm
Coil Stamps

| | | | | |
|---|---|---|---|---|
| 731 | A28 | 17c on 2c, like #134 | 2.00 | 1.50 |
| 732 | A28 | 17c on 8c, Mazaruni Pride | 2.00 | 1.50 |
| a. | | Pair, #731-732 | 4.00 | 4.00 |

Nos. 731-732 were intended for use on 8c envelopes to increase postage rate to 25c and were not issued without surcharge.

## Nos. 284, 286A Surcharged in Black or Overprinted in Dark Blue

Surcharges or Overprints Read: Nos. 733, 741, "ALL / OUR HERITAGE"; Nos. 734, 743, "1984" 7mm long; Nos. 735, 742, "REPUBLIC / DAY"; No. 737, "BERBICE"; No. 738, "DEMERARA"; No. 739, "ESSEQUIBO"; No. 740, "1984" 18mm long.

### Perf. 14x13½

**1984, Feb. 24**    Litho.    Wmk. 364

| | | | | |
|---|---|---|---|---|
| 733 | A66 | 25c on 35c | .75 | .25 |
| 734 | A66 | 25c on 35c | 1.25 | .50 |
| 735 | A66 | 25c on 35c | 1.25 | .50 |
| 736 | A66 | 25c on 35c #284 | 1.25 | .50 |
| 737 | A66 | 25c on 35c | 6.00 | 4.50 |
| 738 | A66 | 25c on 35c | 6.00 | 4.50 |
| 739 | A66 | 25c on 35c | 6.00 | 4.50 |
| 740 | A66 | 25c on 35c | 14.00 | 14.00 |
| 741 | A66 | 60c on #286A (DBl) | 3.50 | 1.00 |
| 742 | A66 | 60c on #286A (DBl) | 3.50 | 1.00 |
| 743 | A66 | 60c on #286A (DBl) | 3.50 | 1.00 |

Nos. 733-740 were issued in sheets of 25, 6 No. 733, 4 each Nos. 734-736, 2 each Nos. 737-739, 1 No.740. Nos. 741-743 were issued in sheets of 25, 8 each Nos. 741-742, 9 No. 743.

## Nos. 49-50, 52, 73-74, 77-80, 82, 139, 141A-143, 350, 603 Surcharged or Overprinted in Black and/or Blue "Protecting Our Heritage"

**1984, Mar. 5**    Perfs. as Before
Watermarks & Printing Methods as Before

| | | | | |
|---|---|---|---|---|
| 744 | A8 | 20c on 15c #74 | 8.00 | .50 |
| a. | | Blue surcharge (value and words) | 20.00 | |
| 745 | A8 | 20c on 15c #350 | 8.50 | .50 |
| 746 | A8 | 20c on 15c #603 (Bl) | 15.00 | 2.00 |
| a. | | "Protecting our Heritage" in black | 40.00 | |
| 747 | A28 | 25c on #141A | 12.50 | .50 |
| a. | | 25c on #141b | 65.00 | .60 |
| 748 | A28 | 30c on 15c #139 | 24.00 | .60 |
| 749 | A8 | 40c on #77 | 10.00 | .60 |
| 750 | A28 | 50c on #143 | 1.75 | |
| 751 | A28 | 50c on #143 (Revenue Ovpt.) | 1.75 | .60 |
| 752 | A7 | 60c on #50 | 12.00 | .60 |
| a. | | 60c on #79 | 90.00 | |
| 753 | A28 | 90c on 40c #142 | 17.50 | .90 |
| 754 | A28 | 90c on 40c #142 (Revenue ovpt.) | 125.00 | |
| 755 | A28 | 180c on #460 | 17.50 | 1.50 |
| 756 | A7 | $2 on #52 | 65.00 | 2.25 |
| 757 | A8 | 225c on 10c on #73 | 21.00 | 1.75 |
| 758 | A7 | 260c on $1 #80 | 15.00 | 1.50 |
| 759 | A28 | 320c on 40c #142 | 15.00 | 3.25 |
| 760 | A28 | 350c on 40c #142 | 25.00 | 4.25 |
| 761 | A7 | 390c on 50c #78 | 8.00 | 4.00 |
| a. | | 390c on #49 | 125.00 | |
| 762 | A7 | 450c on $5 #82 | 10.00 | 4.00 |
| | | Nos. 744-762 (19) | 412.50 | |

Nos. 748, 753-754, 759-760 use row of "X", 6mm high, as obliterator. Nos. 744-746, 757 have new value printed vertically over old value. Nos. 758, 761-762 have new value printed horizontally over old value. Refer to second paragraph in footnote under No. 147 for Nos. 751, 754-755.

## No. 87 Surcharged
## Nos. 89, 484-485, 606 Overprinted or Surcharged in Dark Blue

Overprint or Surcharges read: Nos. 765-767, 773, "1984"; Nos. 764a, 769a, 771a, "INT. / CHESS / FED. / 1924-1984".

**1984**    Perfs. as Before
Watermarks & Printing Methods as Before

| | | | | |
|---|---|---|---|---|
| 763 | A67 | 25c on #606 | 2.00 | |
| 764 | A67 | 25c on #606 | 4.00 | |
| a. | | Pair, #763-764 | 10.00 | |
| 765 | A14 | 30c on #89 | .75 | |
| 766 | A14 | 45c on 6c #484 | .75 | |
| 767 | A14 | 75c on 40c #485 | .75 | |
| 768 | A67 | 75c on #606 | 1.00 | |
| 769 | A67 | 75c on #606 | 3.00 | |
| a. | | Pair, #768-769 | 8.00 | |
| 770 | A67 | 90c on #606 | 1.00 | |
| 771 | A67 | 90c on #606 | 3.00 | |
| a. | | Pair, #770-771 | 9.00 | |
| 772 | A14 | 130c on 6c #87 | .50 | |
| 773 | A76 | $3 on #328 | 3.00 | |
| | | Nos. 763-773 (11) | 19.75 | |

Issued: Nos. 765-767, 772, 3/17; No. 773, 6/15; Nos. 763-764, 768-769, 770-771, 7/20. No. 767 exists with surcharge either above old value or in center of stamp.

## Nos. 497-500 Surcharged

**1984, Apr. 2**    Litho.    Perf. 13½

| | | | | |
|---|---|---|---|---|
| 774 | A28 | 75c on #497 | 11.00 | .55 |
| 775 | A28 | 75c on #498 | 13.00 | .55 |
| 776 | A28 | 225c on #500 | 3.50 | 1.75 |
| 777 | A28 | 230c on #499 | 4.00 | 1.25 |
| | | Nos. 774-777 (4) | 31.50 | 4.10 |

## Nos. 464e, 465a, 465b, 465e, 466a, 466b, 466e Surcharged Like No. 748

**1984, May 2**

| | | | | |
|---|---|---|---|---|
| 778 | A28 | 20c on #464e | 1.75 | .50 |
| 779 | A28 | 75c on #465e | 8.75 | 1.00 |
| 780 | A28 | 90c on #465a | 5.25 | 1.25 |
| 781 | A28 | 90c on #465b | 7.25 | 1.25 |
| 782 | A28 | 120c on #466a | 8.25 | 1.50 |
| 783 | A28 | 120c on #466e | 8.25 | 1.50 |
| 784 | A28 | 120c on #466b | 2.75 | 1.50 |

## Nos. C3, 386 Surcharged

Surcharges read: No. 785, "ITU DAY / 1984"; No. 786, "WHO DAY / 1984"; Nos. 787-788, "ITU/WHO / DAY / 1984".

## 1984, May 17

| | | | | |
|---|---|---|---|---|
| 785 | A28 | 25c on #C3 | 1.60 | 1.60 |
| 786 | A28 | 25c on #C3 | 1.60 | 1.60 |
| 787 | A28 | 25c on #C3 | 1.60 | 1.60 |
| 788 | A28 | $4.50 on #386 | 2.50 | 2.50 |
| | | *Nos. 785-788 (4)* | 7.30 | 7.30 |

The surcharge is vertical on Nos. 785-787, horizontal on No. 788.

## No. 550 Surcharged
## 1984, June 11

| | | | | |
|---|---|---|---|---|
| 789 | A28 | 120c on #550 | 8.75 | 1.00 |

## Nos. 325-327, 431 Surcharged in Blue or Black
## Wmk. 373
## 1984, June 15　　Litho.　　*Perf. 14*

| | | | | |
|---|---|---|---|---|
| 790 | A76 | 55c on 30c #326 (Blk) | 5.00 | .50 |
| 791 | A76 | 75c on #431 | 1.10 | .75 |
| 792 | A76 | 160c on #327 | 1.50 | 1.25 |
| 793 | A76 | 260c on 10c #325 | 2.50 | 1.75 |
| | | *Nos. 790-793 (4)* | 10.10 | 4.25 |

## No. 214 Surcharged
## 1984, June 18　　Litho.　　Wmk. 364

| | | | | |
|---|---|---|---|---|
| 794 | A50 | 55c on 110c on 10c | 1.25 | .50 |
| 795 | A50 | 90c on 110c on 10c | 1.50 | .75 |

No. 214 surcharged 110c only was never issued.

## No. 713 Ovptd. "UPU / Congress 1984 / Hamburg"
## 1984, June 19

| | | | | |
|---|---|---|---|---|
| 796 | | Block of 4 | 5.00 | 5.00 |
| a. | A86 | 120c on #713a | .75 | .75 |
| b. | A86 | 130c on #713b | .90 | .90 |
| c. | A86 | 150c on #713c | 1.00 | 1.00 |
| d. | A86 | 200c on #713d | 1.25 | 1.25 |

## Nos. 539, 541, 543-544 Surcharged in Black, Blue or Dark Green
## 1984, June 21　　*Perfs as Before*
## Watermarks & Printing Methods as Before

| | | | | |
|---|---|---|---|---|
| 797 | A60 | 45c on #539 | .50 | .50 |
| 798 | A66 | 60c on #541 (DkG) | 2.50 | .60 |
| a. | | 60c on British Guiana #255 (DkG) | | |
| 799 | A60 | 120c on #543 | .75 | .55 |
| 800 | A60 | 200c on #544 (Bl) | 6.75 | 1.50 |
| | | *Nos. 797-800 (4)* | 10.50 | 3.15 |

## Nos. 135, 548, C2-C3 Surcharged in Blue or Black
## No. C4 Overprinted "1984"
## *Perf. 13x13½*
## 1984, June 30　　Litho.　　Wmk. 364

| | | | | |
|---|---|---|---|---|
| 801 | A28 | 75c on #C2 (Blk) | 1.50 | .50 |
| 802 | A28 | 120c on #548 (Blk) | 1.90 | .75 |
| 803 | A28 | 150c on #135 | 1.60 | .80 |
| 804 | A28 | 200c on #C3 | 17.50 | 2.50 |
| 804A | A28 | 330c on #C4 | 3.00 | 3.00 |
| | | *Nos. 801-804A (5)* | 25.50 | 7.55 |

Surcharge on Nos. 801-802, 804 is like No. 748. Surcharge on No. 803 is like No. 457.

## Nos. 135, 450A Surcharged

Surcharges read: No. 805, "CARICOM / HEADS OF GOV'T / CONFERENCE / JULY 1984"; No. 806, "CARICOM DAY 1984".

## 1984, June 30　　*Perfs as Before*
## Watermarks & Printing Methods as Before

| | | | | |
|---|---|---|---|---|
| 805 | A28 | 60c on 3c #135 | .75 | .60 |
| 806 | A72 | 60c on #450A | .75 | .60 |

## Nos. 140-141, 141A, 329, 334, 427, 439a-440, 546, 611, 718, O13 Ovptd. "1984" in Black or Blue
## 1984　　　　　*Perfs as Before*
## Watermarks & Printing Methods as Before

| | | | | |
|---|---|---|---|---|
| 807 | A28 | 20c on #140 | 12.50 | |
| a. | | On #140a | 150.00 | |
| 808 | A28 | 20c on #140 | 55.00 | |
| a. | | On #140a | 150.00 | |
| 809 | A28 | 20c on #439, 1984 omitted | 60.00 | |
| 810 | A28 | 25c on #141 | 100.00 | |
| a. | | 1984 omitted | 100.00 | |
| 811 | A28 | 25c on #141 (Revenue Only) | 6.00 | |
| 812 | A28 | 25c on #141A | | |
| 813 | A28 | 25c on #141, 1982 ovpt., 1984 omitted | 40.00 | |
| 814 | A28 | 25c on #440, 1984 omitted | 40.00 | |
| 815 | A33 | 50c on #611 (Bl) | 10.00 | |
| 816 | A28 | 60c on #546 (Bl) | 1.00 | |
| 817 | A28 | $2 on #O13 (Bl) | 2.50 | |

| | | | | |
|---|---|---|---|---|
| 818 | A28 | $3.60 on #334 | 10.00 | |
| c. | | As #818, fleur-de-lis omitted | 5.00 | |
| d. | | On #334a (Bl) | 5.00 | |
| e. | | As "d," fleur-de-lis omitted | 5.00 | |
| 819 | | Sheet of 12 | 6.00 | |
| a.-l. | | A77 30c on #329a-329l, any single | | |
| 820 | A71 | 240c on #429 | | 4.75 |
| 821 | A71 | 240c on #718 | | 4.75 |

Overprint on Nos. 808-814, 818 contains fleur-de-lis. Refer to second paragraph in footnote below No. 147 for Nos. 811-812, 817.
Issued: No. 819, 9/15; Nos. 820-821, 10/15.

Teachers' Assoc. Centenary — A87

## 1984, July 16　　Wmk. 364　　*Perf. 14*

| | | | | |
|---|---|---|---|---|
| 822 | A87 | 25c Children dancing | .25 | .25 |
| 823 | A87 | 25c Torch, graduate | .25 | .25 |
| 824 | A87 | 25c Torch concentric circles | .25 | .25 |
| 825 | A87 | 25c Teachers, school | .25 | .25 |
| a. | | Block of 4 | 1.00 | 1.00 |

## No. 609 Surcharged in Blue:

Surcharges read: Nos. 826, 831, "CYCLING"; Nos. 827, 832, "TRACK / AND / FIELD"; Nos. 828, 833, "OLYMPIC / GAMES / 1984"; Nos. 829, 834, "BOXING"; Nos. 830, 835, "OLYMPIC / GAMES / 1984 / LOS ANGELES".

## *Perf. 14½x14*
## 1984, July 28　　Litho.　　Wmk. 364

| | | | | |
|---|---|---|---|---|
| 826 | A83 | 25c on $1.30 | 1.00 | .80 |
| 827 | A83 | 25c on $1.30 | 1.00 | .80 |
| 828 | A83 | 25c on $1.30 | 1.00 | .80 |
| 829 | A83 | 25c on $1.30 | 3.75 | 2.00 |
| 830 | A83 | 25c on $1.30 | 3.75 | 2.25 |
| 831 | A83 | $1.20 on $1.30 | 3.00 | 2.50 |
| 832 | A83 | $1.20 on $1.30 | 3.00 | 2.50 |
| 833 | A83 | $1.20 on $1.30 | 3.00 | 2.50 |
| 834 | A83 | $1.20 on $1.30 | 5.50 | 3.00 |
| 835 | A83 | $1.20 on $1.30 | 5.50 | 4.00 |

Nos. 826-828 and 831-833 exist in strips of 3. Nos. 827, 829-830 and 832, 834-835 exists in booklets.

## Nos. 465-466 Surcharged "GIRL / GUIDES / 1924-1984" in Blue
## 1984, Aug. 15　　*Perf. 13x13½*
## Sheets of 25

| | | | | |
|---|---|---|---|---|
| 836 | | 8 #a.-b., 4 #c.-d., 1 #e. | | |
| a.-e. | | A28 25c on #465a-465e, any single | | |
| 837 | | 8 #a.-b., 4 #c.-d., 1 #e. | | |
| a.-e. | | A28 25c on #466a-466e, any single | | |
| | | *Nos. 836-837 (2)* | 28.00 | |

## Nos. 138-139, 234, 335, 351, 378, 380, 388, 401, 423, 438, 452, 459, 461, 563, 642, O3, O11-O12, O14 Surcharged
## 1984　　　　*Perfs as Before*
## Watermarks & Printing Methods as Before

| | | | | |
|---|---|---|---|---|
| 846 | A28 | 20c on #563 | 1.00 | |
| a. | | 20c on #563a (Blk over R) | 1.00 | |
| b. | | 20c on #563b (Blk over Bl) | 1.00 | |
| 847 | A28 | 25c on #138 | 27.50 | |
| a. | | 25c on #138a | 55.00 | |
| 848 | A28 | 25c on #139 | 150.00 | |
| 849 | A28 | 25c on #351a | 20.00 | |
| a. | | 25c on #351 | 70.00 | |
| 850 | A28 | 25c on #351b | 8.50 | |
| 851 | A28 | 25c on #438 | 8.00 | |
| a. | | 25c on #438a | 150.00 | |
| 852 | A28 | 25c on #234 | 100.00 | |
| 853 | A28 | 25c on #452 | 8.00 | |
| 854 | A28 | 25c on #O3 | 8.00 | |
| 855 | A28 | 60c on #423, two obliterators, small 110 only | 45.00 | |
| a. | | Single obliterator, small 110 only | | |
| 856 | A28 | 120c on #459 | 5.00 | |
| 857 | A28 | 120c on #401 | 35.00 | |
| 858 | A28 | 120c on #O12 | 2.00 | |
| 859 | A28 | 120c on #380 | 6.00 | |
| 860 | A28 | 130c on #378 | 100.00 | |
| 861 | A28 | 130c on #O11 | 12.50 | |
| 862 | A28 | 200c on #461 | 5.00 | |
| 863 | A28 | 320c on #378 | 5.50 | |
| 864 | A28 | 350c on #388 | 5.00 | |
| 865 | A28 | 390c on #642 | 6.00 | |
| 866 | A28 | 450c on #O14 | 5.75 | |
| 867 | A28 | 600c on #335 | 15.00 | |
| a. | | 600c on #335a | 10.00 | |
| 868 | A28 | 600c on #335a | 17.50 | |
| a. | | 600c on #335 | 4.00 | |
| | | *Nos. 846-868 (23)* | 596.25 | |

Nos. 860-861 are airmail. Obliterator on Nos. 846, 856-859, 862-866 is row of "X", on Nos. 847, 850, 852 is single line, on Nos. 848-849, 851, 853-854 is fleur-de-lis, on No. 855 is a block of 6 lines, on No. 867 is 3 lines, on No. 868 is 3 lines and fleur-de-lis.

## Nos. 556, 670, C4 Overprinted in Blue or Surcharged in Blue and Black

Overprints — No. 871:a-f, ICAO on #670a-f. g, IMB/ICAO on #670g. h, KCV/ICAO on #670h. i, KAI/ICAO on #670i. j-k, ICAO on #670j-670k. l, 1984 on #670h. m, KPM/ICAO on #670h. n-p, ICAO on #670 l-670n. q, PMT/ICAO on #670h. r-x, ICAO on #670o-670u.

## *Perf. 14x13½*
## 1984, Sept. 6　　Litho.　　Wmk. 364

| | | | | |
|---|---|---|---|---|
| 871 | A66 | 30c Sheet of 25, #a.-k., m.-x., 2 #l | 65.00 | 65.00 |
| 895 | A28 | 200c ICAO on #556 | 5.50 | 2.25 |
| 896 | A28 | 200c ICAO on #C4 (Bl & Blk) | 3.00 | 2.00 |

No. 896 is airmail with unissued "GAC" overprint. For surcharge see No. 1470.

## Nos. J3-J4, J7-J8 Surcharged "120 / GUYANA" in Blue
## *Perf. 13½x14*
## 1984, Oct. 1　　Typo.　　Wmk. 314

| | | | | |
|---|---|---|---|---|
| 897 | D1 | 120c on 4c #J3 | 5.25 | .80 |
| 898 | D1 | 120c on 12c #J4 | 5.25 | .80 |

## Wmk. 364

| | | | | |
|---|---|---|---|---|
| 899 | D1 | 120c on 4c #J7 | 20.00 | .80 |
| 900 | D1 | 120c on 12c #J8 | 5.25 | 1.25 |
| | | *Nos. 897-900 (4)* | 35.75 | 3.65 |

## Nos. 551, 571 Surcharged in Black or Blue
## *Perfs. as Before*
## 1984, Oct. 15　　　　Wmk. 364

| | | | | |
|---|---|---|---|---|
| 901 | A80 | $1.50 on #571 (Bl) | 14.00 | 1.50 |
| 902 | A28 | 150c on 50c #551 | 3.00 | 1.00 |

Obliterator is "X" on No. 901. Surcharge on No. 902 places "1" before existing 50c value, obliterates "1982" and adds "1984."

## Nos. 712, 479-481 Surcharged
## 1984, Oct. 22　　　　*Perf. 14*

| | | | | |
|---|---|---|---|---|
| 903 | | Block of 4 | 1.25 | 1.25 |
| a.-d. | A86 | 25c on 45c on #712a-712d, any single | .25 | .25 |
| 904 | A69 | 120c on #479 | 9.50 | .75 |
| 905 | A69 | 120c on #480 | 1.25 | .75 |
| 906 | A66 | 320c on #481 | 20.00 | 2.75 |
| | | *Nos. 903-906 (4)* | 32.00 | 5.50 |

## Nos. 135-136 Surcharged "MAHA SABHA / 1934-1984" in Blue
## 1984, Nov. 1　　*Perf. 13x13½*

| | | | | |
|---|---|---|---|---|
| 910 | A28 | 25c on 5c #136 | .75 | .25 |
| 911 | A28 | $1.50 on 3c #135 | 4.25 | 1.50 |
| | | *Nos. 910-911 (2)* | 5.00 | 1.75 |

## No. 713 Ovptd. "Philatelic Exhibition / New York 1984" in Red
## 1984, Nov. 15　　　　*Perf. 14*

| | | | | |
|---|---|---|---|---|
| 912 | | Block of 4 | 5.00 | 5.00 |
| a. | A86 | 120c on No. 713a | 1.00 | .80 |
| b. | A86 | 130c on No. 713b | 1.10 | .90 |
| c. | A86 | 150c on No. 713c | 1.25 | 1.00 |
| d. | A86 | 200c on No. 713d | 1.50 | 1.25 |

## Type A83 Inscribed with Olympic Rings and "OLYMPIC GAMES 1984 / LOS ANGELES"
## 1984, Nov. 16　　　　*Perf. 13½*

| | | | | |
|---|---|---|---|---|
| 913 | A83 | $1.20 multicolored | 3.00 | 3.00 |

Copies with numbers stamped on back are coils.
For similar stamp overprinted see No. 923.
For surcharges see Nos. 1953-1957.

## Nos. 410, 413e, 633, 635a Surcharged
## 1984, Nov. 24　　Photo.　　*Perf. 14x14½*
## Watermarks as Before

| | | | | |
|---|---|---|---|---|
| 914 | A7 | 20c on #410 | 1.00 | .25 |
| 915 | A7 | 120c on #413De | 92.50 | 7.50 |
| 916 | A7 | 120c on #633 | .50 | .25 |
| 916A | A7 | 60c on #635a | 1.00 | .45 |

No. 914 has an "X" obliterating a "1" and no obliterating lines. No. 1400 has obliterating lines and small "20" in UR.

Elanoides Forficatus — A88

Designs: a, Pair in tree. b, Landing on branch. c, In flight, wings up. d, In flight, wings down. e, In flight, wings outstretched.

## 1984, Dec. 3　　Wmk. 364　　*Perf. 14½*

| | | | | |
|---|---|---|---|---|
| 917 | A88 | 60c Strip of 5, #a.-e. | 18.00 | 18.00 |

Inscribed "Christmas 1982."
For surcharges see Nos. 1502, 1840.

High Street Architecture A89

Designs: 25c, St. George's Cathedral, 1892, Colonial Life Insurance Co. 60c, No. 920a, Demerara Mutual Life Assurance Soc., Ltd. No. 920b, 200c, Town Hall, 1888, City Engineers Office. No. 920c, 300c, Victoria Law Courts, 1887.

## 1985, Feb. 8　　　　*Perf. 14*

| | | | | |
|---|---|---|---|---|
| 918 | A89 | 25c multi | .25 | .25 |
| 919 | A89 | 60c multi | .25 | .25 |
| 920 | | Triptych | 1.40 | 1.40 |
| a.-c. | | A89 120c, any single | .45 | .45 |
| d. | | Triptych, unwmkd. | 1.75 | 1.75 |
| e.-g. | | As "d," any single | .60 | .60 |
| 921 | A89 | 200c multi | .90 | .90 |
| 922 | A89 | 300c multi | 1.40 | 1.40 |
| | | *Nos. 918-922 (5)* | 4.20 | 4.20 |

For surcharge see No. 1850.

## Type A83 Ovptd. "INTERNATIONAL / YOUTH YEAR 1985"
## Wmk. 364
## 1985, Feb. 15　　Litho.　　*Perf. 14½*

| | | | | |
|---|---|---|---|---|
| 923 | A83 | $1.20 multi | 3.00 | .75 |

Bars obliterate Olympic Games inscription with second line spelled "LOS ANGELLES." No. 913 spells "Los Angeles" correctly.

## Nos. 608, 610 Ovptd. in Red

Overprint reads "Republic / Day / 1970-1985" or "1970 / 1985 / Republic / Day"

## 1985, Feb. 22　　*Perfs. as Before*

| | | | | |
|---|---|---|---|---|
| 924 | A82 | 25c on #608 | | |
| 925 | A83 | 120c on $6 #610 | | |
| 926 | A83 | 130c on $6 #610 | | |
| | | *Nos. 924-926 (3)* | 3.00 | 2.25 |

Ocelot Cub Xica — A90

Macaw Nena — A90a

## *Perf. 12½x13*
## 1985, Mar. 11　　　　Wmk. 364

| | | | | |
|---|---|---|---|---|
| 927 | A90 | 25c multi | 1.10 | .30 |
| 928 | A90 | 60c multi | .30 | .30 |
| 929 | | Triptych | 2.75 | 2.75 |
| a.-c. | | A90 120c, like #927-928, 930 | 1.10 | 1.10 |
| 930 | A90 | 130c multi | .70 | .70 |

## *Perf. 14½*

| | | | | |
|---|---|---|---|---|
| 931 | A90a | 320c shown | 4.25 | 2.00 |
| 932 | A90a | 330c Cub on hind legs | 2.00 | 2.00 |
| | | *Nos. 927-932 (6)* | 11.10 | 8.05 |

No. 929, perf. 14, inscribed "1986," were from the liquidation of stock held by the printer, value 75c.
For overprints see Nos. 1903-1905, 1983, 2032.

## Map Revenue Type A78 and Nos. 481, 501, 554, O6 Surcharged in Black or Blue
## 1985　　　　*Perfs as Before*
## Watermarks & Printing Methods as Before

| | | | | |
|---|---|---|---|---|
| 933 | A69 | 30c on 50c on #O6 (Bl) | 1.00 | .25 |
| 934 | A78 | 55c on 2c gray | 1.00 | .25 |
| a. | | "ESSEQUIBO IS OURS" omitted | 15.00 | |
| 935 | A78 | 55c on #501 | 1.00 | .40 |
| 936 | A66 | 90c on #554 (Bl) | 7.00 | .65 |
| 937 | A66 | 225c on #481 | 10.00 | 2.00 |

| | | | | |
|---|---|---|---|---|
| 938 | A66 | 230c on #481 (Bl) | 10.00 | 2.25 |
| 939 | A66 | 260c on #481 (Bl) | 10.00 | 2.50 |
| | | *Nos. 933-939 (7)* | 40.00 | 8.30 |

Issued: Nos. 933-936, 938-939, 3/11; No. 937, 4/11.

Obliterator on Nos. 934-935 is fleur-de-lis.

### Nos. 305, 435, 587, 599, & 615
**Ovptd. "INTERNATIONAL / YOUTH YEAR / 1985" in Blue**
Wmk. 364

| 1985, Apr. 15 | | Litho. | Perf. 13½ | |
|---|---|---|---|---|
| 940 | A70 | 50c on #587 | 2.00 | .30 |
| 941 | A70 | 50c on #615 | 7.00 | .30 |
| 942 | A70 | 120c on #435 | 2.25 | .55 |
| 943 | A70 | $3 on #305 | 35.00 | |
| 943A | A70 | $3 on #599 | 2.25 | 1.25 |
| | | *Nos. 940-943A (5)* | 48.50 | 2.40 |

### No. 280 Surcharged with Names of 1860 Post Offices or Postal Agencies in Blue

Overprints: a, Airy Hall. b, Belfield / Arab. Coast. c, Belfield / E.C. Dem. d, Belladrum. e, Beterver- / wagting. f, Blairmont / Ferry. g, Boeraserie. h, Brahn. i, Bushlot. j, De / Kinderen. k, Fort / Wellington. l, Georgetown. m, Hague. n, Leguan. o, Mahaica. p, Maha-icony. q, New / Amsterdam. r, Plaisance. s, No. 6 Police / Station. t, Queenstown. u, Verte-noegen. v, Vigilance. w, Vreed-en- / Hoop. x, Wakenaam. y, Windsor / Castle.

**Perf. 14x13½**

| 1985, May 2 | | Litho. | Wmk. 364 | |
|---|---|---|---|---|
| | | **Sheet of 25** | | |
| 944 | A66 | 25c on 10c #a.-y. | 27.50 | 27.50 |

Colonial Post Office, 125th anniv.

### Nos. 670 Ovptd. "1985" or with Letters in Red

Overprints: a-f, 1985 on #670a-670f. g, I on #670g. h, T on #670h. i, U on #670i. j-k, 1985 on #670j-670k. l, W on #670h. m, H on #670h. n, O on #670h. o-p, 1985 on #670 l-670m. q, D on #670n. r, A on #670h. s, Y on #670o. t-y, 1985 on #670p-#670u.

| 1985, May 17 | | | **Sheet of 25** | |
|---|---|---|---|---|
| 969 | A66 | 30c #a.-y. | 20.00 | 20.00 |

### Nos. 413a & 413e Surcharged

| 1985, May 21 | Photo. | Perf. 14x14½ | | |
|---|---|---|---|---|
| | | **Watermarks as Before** | | |
| 994 | A7 | 20c on #413a | 10.00 | .30 |
| a. | | 20c on #413De | 14.00 | 2.00 |

No. 994a has "20" at left and 11 obliterating lines. No. 1401 has "20" at right and 12 lines.

### No. 135 Surcharged "CARDI / 1975-1985"

**Perf. 13x13½**

| 1985, May 29 | | Litho. | Wmk. 364 | |
|---|---|---|---|---|
| 995 | A28 | 60c on 3c #135 | 1.75 | .40 |

Caribbean Agricultural Research Development Institute, 10th anniv.

### No. 407 Surcharged

| 1985, June 3 | | | | |
|---|---|---|---|---|
| 996 | A28 | 600c on #407 | 40.00 | 5.00 |

### Nos. 288, 724, C1 Surcharged "ROTARY / INTERNATIONAL / 1905-1985" in Red

| 1985, June 21 | | Perfs. as Before | | |
|---|---|---|---|---|
| | | **Watermarks & Printing Methods as Before** | | |
| 997 | A74 | 120c on #C1 | 14.50 | 1.00 |
| 998 | A66 | 300c on #288 | 10.00 | 3.50 |

No. 724 with a similar surcharge is usually found on first day covers.

### Nos. 426 and 450A Surcharged in Red

Surcharges read: No. 999, "CARICOM DAY / 1985"; No. 1000, "135th Anniversary / Cotton Reel / 1850-1985".

| 1985, June 28 | | Perfs. as Before | | |
|---|---|---|---|---|
| | | **Watermarks & Printing Methods as Before** | | |
| 999 | A72 | 60c on #450A | 1.00 | .50 |
| 1000 | A69 | 120c on #426 | 1.00 | .50 |

Orchids from Reichenbachia, by Sanders — A91

**Wmk. 364 (#1027, 1031, 1036, 1046, 1049, 1052, 1054, 1071, 1074, 1076, 1079, 1084, 1091, 1108), Unwmkd.**

| 1985-87 | | Series 1 | Perf. 14 | |
|---|---|---|---|---|
| 1021 | A91 | 120c Plate No. 1 | 1.75 | .80 |
| 1022 | A91 | 60c Plate No. 2 | 1.10 | .80 |
| 1023 | A91 | 130c Plate No. 3 | 1.75 | 1.00 |
| 1024 | A91 | 200c Plate No. 4 | 2.10 | 1.60 |
| 1025 | A91 | 60c Plate No. 5 | 1.25 | .90 |
| 1026 | A91 | 75c like #1025 | .80 | .60 |
| a. | | Wmk. 364 ('87) | 12.50 | 12.50 |
| 1027 | A91 | 100c Plate No. 6 | 1.25 | 1.00 |
| a. | | Wmk. 364 | — | — |
| 1028 | A91 | 130c like #1027 | 2.40 | 1.00 |
| a. | | Wmk. 364 ('86) | 1.25 | 1.25 |
| 1029 | A91 | 60c Plate No. 7 | 1.10 | .60 |
| 1030 | A91 | 25c Plate No. 8 | 1.25 | .60 |
| 1031 | A91 | 50c Plate No. 9 | .60 | .60 |
| a. | | Wmk. 364 | — | — |
| 1032 | A91 | 55c like #1031 | 1.00 | .75 |
| a. | | Wmk. 364 ('86) | .60 | .60 |
| 1033 | A91 | 60c Plate No. 10 | 1.10 | .60 |
| 1034 | A91 | 120c Plate No. 11 | 1.75 | .80 |
| 1035 | A91 | 25c Plate No. 12 | .80 | .60 |
| 1036 | A91 | 100c Plate No. 13 | 1.25 | 1.00 |
| a. | | Wmk. 364 | — | — |
| 1037 | A91 | 130c like #1036 | 1.75 | 1.00 |
| a. | | Wmk. 364 ('86) | 5.00 | 3.00 |
| 1038 | A91 | 200c Plate No. 14 | 1.75 | 1.00 |
| 1039 | A91 | 55c Plate No. 15 | .60 | .60 |
| 1040 | A91 | 180c like #1039 | 1.60 | 1.60 |
| a. | | Wmk. 364 ('87) | 11.00 | 11.00 |
| | | *Nos. 1021-1040 (20)* | 26.95 | 17.65 |

Issued: Nos. 1022-1024, 1028-1029, 1033, 1035, 1037, 7/9; No. 1032, 8/12; Nos. 1021, 1030, 1034, 1038, 9/16; No. 1026, 2/26/86; No. 1040, 7/24/86; No. 1025, 1027, 1031, 1036, 1039, 8/21/86.

Nos. 1021, 1034 horiz.

| 1041 | A91 | 130c Plate No. 16 | 1.50 | 1.10 |
|---|---|---|---|---|
| 1042 | A91 | 55c Plate No. 17 | .60 | .60 |
| a. | | Wmk. 364 ('87) | 7.50 | 7.50 |
| 1043 | A91 | 80c like #1042 | 2.25 | .70 |
| 1044 | A91 | 130c Plate No. 18 | 3.50 | 1.00 |
| 1045 | A91 | 60c Plate No. 19 | 1.10 | .60 |
| 1046 | A91 | 100c Plate No. 20 | 2.25 | 1.00 |
| a. | | Wmk. 364 | — | — |
| 1047 | A91 | 130c like #1046 | 1.25 | 1.00 |
| a. | | Wmk. 364 ('86) | 4.00 | 2.50 |
| 1048 | A91 | 200c Plate No. 21 | 1.75 | 1.00 |
| 1049 | A91 | 50c Plate No. 22 | .60 | .60 |
| a. | | Wmk. 364 | — | — |
| 1050 | A91 | 55c like #1049 | 1.00 | .75 |
| a. | | Wmk. 364 ('86) | .60 | .60 |
| 1051 | A91 | 25c Plate No. 23 | 1.25 | .60 |
| 1052 | A91 | 50c Plate No. 24 | 4.00 | 1.50 |
| a. | | Wmk. 364 | — | — |
| 1053 | A91 | 225c like #1052 | 2.00 | 1.60 |
| a. | | Wmk. 364 ('86) | 6.50 | 4.00 |
| 1054 | A91 | 100c Plate No. 25 | .90 | .90 |
| a. | | Wmk. 364 | — | — |
| 1055 | A91 | 130c like #1054 | 1.75 | 1.00 |
| a. | | Wmk. 364 ('86) | 6.50 | 4.00 |
| 1056 | A91 | 150c Plate No. 26 | 2.75 | .75 |
| 1057 | A91 | 120c Plate No. 27 | 1.75 | 1.00 |
| 1058 | A91 | 120c Plate No. 28 | 1.75 | .80 |
| 1059 | A91 | 130c Plate No. 29 | 2.60 | 1.00 |
| 1060 | A91 | 130c Plate No. 30 | 2.60 | 1.00 |
| | | *Nos. 1041-1060 (20)* | 37.15 | 18.50 |

Issued: Nos. 1044-1045, 1047, 1055, 1057, 1059-1060, 7/9; No. 1041, 1050, 8/12; Nos. 1048, 1051, 1058, 9/16; Nos. 1042, 1053, 1056, 7/10/86; No. 1046, 1049, 1052, 1054, 8/21/86; No. 1043, 11/25/86.

Nos. 1048, 1058 horiz.

| 1061 | A91 | 60c Plate No. 31 | 1.10 | .60 |
|---|---|---|---|---|
| 1062 | A91 | 150c Plate No. 32 | 1.50 | 1.10 |
| 1063 | A91 | 200c Plate No. 33 | 3.50 | 1.40 |
| 1064 | A91 | 150c Plate No. 34 | 1.50 | 1.10 |
| 1065 | A91 | 150c Plate No. 35 | 1.50 | 1.10 |
| 1066 | A91 | 120c Plate No. 36 | 1.50 | 1.10 |
| 1067 | A91 | 120c Plate No. 37 | 2.60 | .60 |
| 1068 | A91 | 130c Plate No. 38 | 1.50 | 1.10 |
| 1069 | A91 | 80c Plate No. 39 | .60 | .60 |
| 1070 | A91 | 260c like #1069 | 2.50 | 2.00 |
| a. | | Wmk. 364 ('87) | 6.50 | 5.50 |
| 1071 | A91 | 100c Plate No. 40 | .80 | .80 |
| 1072 | A91 | 150c like #1071 | 1.25 | 1.00 |
| a. | | Wmk. 364 ('86) | 6.50 | 3.50 |
| 1073 | A91 | 150c Plate No. 41 | 1.50 | 1.10 |
| 1074 | A91 | 100c Plate No. 42 | .90 | .90 |
| 1075 | A91 | 150c like #1074 | 1.25 | 1.00 |
| a. | | Wmk. 364 ('86) | 6.50 | 3.50 |
| 1076 | A91 | 100c Plate No. 43 | .80 | .80 |
| 1077 | A91 | 200c like #1076 | 1.75 | 1.25 |
| a. | | Wmk. 364 ('86) | 6.50 | 3.25 |
| 1078 | A91 | 60c Plate No. 44 | 1.00 | 1.00 |
| 1079 | A91 | 100c Plate No. 45 | .90 | .90 |
| 1080 | A91 | 150c like #1079 | 1.25 | 1.00 |
| a. | | Wmk. 364 ('86) | 6.50 | 3.50 |
| | | *Nos. 1061-1080 (20)* | 29.20 | 20.45 |

Issued: No. 1061, 7/9; Nos. 1062, 1064-1066, 1068, 1073, 1078, 8/12; Nos. 1072,
1075, 1077, 1080, 9/16; Nos. 1063, 1067, 1070, 7/10/86; Nos. 1069, 1071, 1074, 1076, 1079, 8/21/86.

Nos. 1063, 1071-1072, 1074-1077, 1079-1080 horiz.

| 1081 | A91 | 120c Plate No. 46 | 2.60 | .60 |
|---|---|---|---|---|
| 1082 | A91 | 60c Plate No. 47 | 1.00 | .75 |
| 1083 | A91 | 150c Plate No. 48 | 1.50 | 1.10 |
| 1084 | A91 | 50c Plate No. 49 | 1.50 | .75 |
| a. | | Wmk. 364 | — | — |
| 1085 | A91 | 55c like #1084 | 1.00 | .75 |
| a. | | Wmk. 364 ('86) | 4.00 | 4.00 |
| 1086 | A91 | 60c Plate No. 50 | 3.00 | 2.60 |
| 1087 | A91 | 320c like #1086 | 4.00 | 2.10 |
| a. | | Wmk. 364 ('87) | 10.00 | 9.50 |
| 1088 | A91 | 25c Plate No. 51 | 1.25 | .60 |
| 1089 | A91 | 25c Plate No. 52 | 1.00 | 1.00 |
| 1090 | A91 | 30c Plate No. 53 | 1.40 | .60 |
| a. | | Wmk. 364 ('86) | 3.25 | 3.25 |
| 1091 | A91 | 50c like #1090 | .60 | .60 |
| a. | | Wmk. 364 | — | — |
| 1092 | A91 | 45c Plate No. 54 | .75 | .60 |
| a. | | Wmk. 364 ('87) | 10.00 | 10.00 |
| 1093 | A91 | 60c like #1092 | .60 | .60 |
| 1094 | A91 | 50c Plate No. 55 | 2.60 | 1.10 |
| a. | | Wmk. 364 | — | — |
| 1095 | A91 | 55c like #1094 | 1.40 | 1.40 |
| 1096 | A91 | 75c like #1094 | .60 | .60 |
| a. | | Wmk. 364 | 3.25 | 3.25 |
| 1097 | A91 | 120c Plate No. 56 | 2.60 | .70 |
| 1098 | A91 | 60c Plate No. 57 | 1.60 | .60 |
| 1099 | A91 | 120c Plate No. 58 | 2.60 | .70 |
| 1100 | A91 | 25c Plate No. 59 | 1.25 | .50 |
| a. | | Dark red flowers ('86) | 4.00 | 4.00 |
| | | *Nos. 1081-1100 (20)* | 32.85 | 18.25 |

Issued: Nos. 1082-1083, 1085, 1089, 8/12; No. 1088, 9/16; No.1095, 10/7; Nos. 1087, 1092, 2/26/86; No. 1081, 1090, 1096-1100, 7/10/86; Nos. 1086, 1091, 1093, 8/21/86; No. 1084, 12/22/86; No. 1094, 1/16/87.

No. 1098 horiz.

| 1101 | A91 | 75c Plate No. 60 | .70 | .60 |
|---|---|---|---|---|
| 1102 | A91 | 225c like #1101 | 3.00 | 1.75 |
| a. | | Wmk. 364 ('87) | 13.00 | 13.00 |
| 1103 | A91 | 25c Plate No. 61 | 1.25 | .60 |
| 1104 | A91 | 150c Plate No. 62 | 1.50 | 1.10 |
| 1105 | A91 | 25c Plate No. 63 | 1.25 | .60 |
| 1106 | A91 | 50c Plate No. 64 | 1.50 | 1.25 |
| a. | | Wmk. 364 | — | — |
| 1107 | A91 | 55c like #1106 | 1.00 | .75 |
| a. | | Wmk. 364 ('86) | 4.25 | 4.25 |
| 1108 | A91 | 50c like #1065 | 2.60 | .60 |
| a. | | Wmk. 364 | — | — |
| 1109 | A91 | 100c like #1108 | .60 | .60 |
| a. | | Wmk. 364 | 4.00 | 4.00 |
| 1110 | A91 | 130c Plate No. 66 | 2.75 | .65 |
| 1111 | A91 | 120c Plate No. 67 | 2.60 | .60 |
| 1112 | A91 | 40c Plate No. 68 | 1.40 | 1.00 |
| 1113 | A91 | 60c like #1112 | .60 | .60 |
| a. | | Wmk. 364 ('86) | 6.50 | 6.50 |
| 1114 | A91 | 60c Plate No. 69 | .60 | .60 |
| 1115 | A91 | 120c like #1114 | 2.00 | 1.10 |
| a. | | Wmk. 364 ('87) | 14.00 | 14.00 |
| 1116 | A91 | 60c Plate No. 70 | 1.25 | .60 |
| 1117 | A91 | 25c like #1116 | .80 | .60 |
| a. | | Wmk. 364 ('87) | 15.00 | 15.00 |
| 1118 | A91 | 60c Plate No. 71 | .70 | .70 |
| 1119 | A91 | 25c Plate No. 72 | 1.25 | .60 |
| 1120 | A91 | 60c Plate No. 73 | 1.60 | .60 |
| | | *Nos. 1101-1120 (20)* | 28.95 | 15.60 |

Issued: Nos. 1104, 1107, 8/12; Nos. 1103, 1105, 1116, 1119, 9/16; Nos. 1102, 1115, 1117, 4/4/86; Nos. 1109-1111, 1113, 1120, 7/10/86; Nos. 1101, 1108, 1114, 1118, 8/21/86; No. 1112, 11/25/86.

No. 1114-1115, 1117-1118, 1120 horiz.

| 1121 | A91 | 80c Plate No. 74 | .70 | .70 |
|---|---|---|---|---|
| 1122 | A91 | 250c like #1121 | 2.25 | 2.00 |
| a. | | Wmk. 364 ('87) | 6.50 | 6.50 |
| 1123 | A91 | 60c Plate No. 75 | 1.60 | .60 |
| 1124 | A91 | 65c Plate No. 76 | .60 | .60 |
| 1125 | A91 | 150c like #1124 | 1.25 | 1.25 |
| a. | | Wmk. 364 ('87) | 14.00 | 14.00 |
| 1126 | A91 | 40c Plate No. 77 | .75 | .60 |
| a. | | Wmk. 364 ('87) | 12.00 | 12.00 |
| 1127 | A91 | 45c like #1126 | 1.00 | 1.00 |
| 1128 | A91 | 45c Plate No. 78 | 1.40 | 1.25 |
| 1129 | A91 | 150c like #1128 | 1.25 | .75 |
| a. | | Wmk. 364 ('87) | 14.00 | 14.00 |
| 1130 | A91 | 60c Plate No. 79 | .60 | .60 |
| 1131 | A91 | 200c like #1130 | 1.75 | 1.60 |
| a. | | Wmk. 364 ('87) | 14.00 | 14.00 |
| 1132 | A91 | 65c Plate No. 80 | .60 | .60 |
| 1133 | A91 | 330c like #1132 | 3.00 | 2.75 |
| a. | | Wmk. 364 ('87) | 15.00 | 15.00 |
| 1134 | A91 | 45c Plate No. 81 | .50 | .50 |
| a. | | Wmk. 364 | 15.00 | 15.00 |
| 1135 | A91 | 55c like #1134 | 1.00 | 1.00 |
| 1136 | A91 | 55c Plate No. 82 | .60 | .60 |
| 1137 | A91 | 320c like #1136 | 3.00 | 2.50 |
| a. | | Wmk. 364 ('87) | 15.00 | 15.00 |
| 1138 | A91 | 75c Plate No. 83 | .70 | .70 |
| 1139 | A91 | 300c like #1138 | 3.00 | 2.50 |
| a. | | Wmk. 364 ('87) | 15.00 | 15.00 |
| 1140 | A91 | 45c Plate No. 84 | 1.10 | .75 |
| 1141 | A91 | 90c like #1140 | .60 | .60 |
| a. | | Wmk. 364 ('87) | 14.00 | 14.00 |
| | | *Nos. 1121-1141 (21)* | 27.25 | 23.45 |

Issued: Nos. 1126, 1129, 1131, 1139, 1141, 2/26/86; Nos. 1122-1123, 7/10/86; Nos. 1125, 1133-1134, 1137, 7/24/86; Nos. 1121, 1124, 1127-1128, 1130, 1132, 1135-1136, 1138, 1140, 8/21/86.

No. 1123 horiz.

| 1142 | A91 | 45c Plate No. 85 | 1.00 | 1.00 |
|---|---|---|---|---|
| 1143 | A91 | 360c like #1142 | 3.50 | 3.00 |
| a. | | Wmk. 364 ('87) | 15.00 | 15.00 |
| 1144 | A91 | 30c Plate No. 86 | .60 | .60 |
| a. | | Wmk. 364 ('87) | 7.50 | 7.50 |

| 1145 | A91 | 40c like #1144 | 1.10 | 1.10 |
|---|---|---|---|---|
| 1146 | A91 | 60c Plate No. 87 | .60 | .60 |
| 1147 | A91 | 150c like #1146 | 2.50 | 1.25 |
| a. | | Wmk. 364 ('87) | 17.50 | 17.50 |
| 1148 | A91 | 65c Plate No. 88 | .60 | .60 |
| 1149 | A91 | 100c like #1148 | .65 | .65 |
| a. | | Wmk. 364 ('87) | 15.00 | 15.00 |
| 1150 | A91 | 55c Plate No. 89 | .75 | .75 |
| 1151 | A91 | 90c like #1150 | .60 | .60 |
| a. | | Wmk. 364 ('87) | 15.00 | 15.00 |
| 1152 | A91 | 40c Plate No. 90 | .60 | .60 |
| 1153 | A91 | 375c like #1152 | 3.00 | 3.00 |
| a. | | Wmk. 364 ('87) | 8.00 | 8.00 |
| 1154 | A91 | 40c Plate No. 91 | 3.50 | 2.50 |
| 1155 | A91 | 130c like #1154 | 1.25 | 1.00 |
| a. | | Wmk. 364 ('87) | 7.50 | 7.50 |
| 1156 | A91 | 50c Plate No. 92 | .75 | .60 |
| a. | | Wmk. 364 ('87) | 15.00 | 15.00 |
| 1157 | A91 | 75c Plate No. 93 | .70 | .70 |
| 1158 | A91 | 60c like #1156 | .60 | .60 |
| a. | | Wmk. 364 ('87) | 7.50 | 7.50 |
| 1159 | A91 | 80c like #1158 | .70 | .70 |
| 1160 | A91 | 50c Plate No. 94 | .60 | .60 |
| 1161 | A91 | 350c like #1160 | 4.00 | 3.00 |
| a. | | Wmk. 364 ('87) | 15.00 | 15.00 |
| 1162 | A91 | 60c Plate No. 95 | .80 | .75 |
| a. | | Wmk. 364 ('87) | 15.00 | 15.00 |
| 1163 | A91 | 75c like #1162 | .70 | .70 |
| a. | | Wmk. 364 ('87) | — | — |
| 1164 | A91 | 40c like #1156 | .60 | .60 |
| a. | | Wmk. 364 ('87) | 14.00 | 14.00 |
| 1165 | A91 | 65c like #1164 | .70 | .70 |
| | | *Nos. 1142-1165 (24)* | 30.40 | 26.15 |

See note below No. 1341. Issued: Nos. 1143, 1156, 1162, 2/26/86; Nos. 1147, 1161, 4/4/86; Nos. 1144, 1153, 1155, 1158, 7/10/86; Nos. 1149, 1151, 1164, 7/24/86; Nos. 1142, 1146, 1148, 1150, 1152, 1157, 1159-1160, 1163, 1165, 8/21/86; No. 1154, 9/26/86; No. 1145, 10/23/86.

Some stamps printed in sheets of 25, blocks of 4 each of different stamps separated by gutter containing 2 No. 1337 and strip of 5 No. 1339. Margin contains separation marks for Nos. 1337, 1339.

Nos. 1146-1147, 1160-1161 horiz.

Nos. 1025, 1027, 1031, 1036, 1039, 1046, 1049, 1052, 1054, 1069, 1071, 1074, 1076, 1079, 1086, 1091, 1093, 1101, 1108, 1114, 1118, 1121, 1124, 1127-1128, 1130, 1132, 1135-1136, 1138, 1140, 1142, 1146, 1148, 1150, 1152, 1157, 1159-1160, 1163, 1165 sold as singles in booklets only. Two booklets of 48 stamps each contain these numbers and previous values issued in the series. Value, each booklet, $80.

See No. 1372. For overprints and surcharges see Nos. 1342-1346, 1393, 1402-1403, 1412-1413, 1494, 1511-1670F, 1731-1740, 1742-1750, 1755-1759, 1761, 1764-1773, 1785, 1845-1849, 1906-1909, 1914-1933, 1939-1941, 1943-1947, 1958-1959, 1960-1979, 2000, 2619A-2619E, 4205-4210, C7, C9-C12, E2, E4.

| 1986-89 | | Litho. Unwmk. | Perf. 14 | |
|---|---|---|---|---|
| | | **Series 2** | | |
| 1166 | A91 | 175c Plate No. 1 | 1.50 | .65 |
| 1167 | A91 | 560c like #1166 | 4.50 | 1.60 |
| 1168 | A91 | 90c like #1166 | 1.25 | 1.25 |
| 1169 | A91 | 200c like #1168 | 2.75 | 1.25 |
| 1170 | A91 | 50c Plate No. 3 | .50 | .50 |
| 1171 | A91 | 90c like #1170 | .75 | .75 |
| 1172 | A91 | 90c Plate No. 4 | 1.25 | .60 |
| 1173 | A91 | 140c like #1172 | 1.25 | .50 |
| 1174 | A91 | 130c Plate No. 5 | 1.10 | .50 |
| 1175 | A91 | 160c like #1174 | 1.60 | .80 |
| 1176 | A91 | 50c Plate No. 6 | .50 | .50 |
| 1177 | A91 | 390c like #1176 | 3.75 | 2.00 |
| 1178 | A91 | 30c Plate No. 7 | .50 | .50 |
| 1179 | A91 | 40c like #1178 | .50 | .50 |
| 1180 | A91 | 70c Plate No. 8 | .50 | .50 |
| 1181 | A91 | 75c like #1180 | 1.00 | .60 |
| 1182 | A91 | 70c like #1180 | .50 | .50 |
| 1183 | A91 | 200c like #1182 | 2.00 | 1.00 |
| 1184 | A91 | 90c like #1166 | 3.25 | 1.40 |
| 1185 | A91 | 320c like #1184 | 3.00 | 1.75 |
| | | *Nos. 1166-1185 (20)* | 31.95 | 17.65 |

Issued: Nos. 1172, 1175, 1181, 1183, 9/23; No. 1184, 10/23; No. 1177, 1185, 10/31; No. 1169, 11/25; Nos. 1171, 1179, 12/27; No. 1168, 1/5/87; No. 1167, 4/24/87; Nos. 1166, 1170, 1173-1174, 1176, 1178, 1180, 1182, 8/23/88.

Nos. 1174-1175 horiz.

| 1186 | A91 | 200c Plate No. 11 | 1.75 | .75 |
|---|---|---|---|---|
| 1187 | A91 | 70c Plate No. 12 | .50 | .50 |
| 1188 | A91 | 320c like #1187 | 3.50 | 1.60 |
| 1189 | A91 | 50c Plate No. 13 | 1.50 | 1.50 |
| 1190 | A91 | 90c like #1189 | .60 | .60 |
| 1191 | A91 | 30c Plate No. 14 | .50 | .50 |
| 1192 | A91 | 120c like #1191 | 1.00 | 1.00 |
| 1193 | A91 | 50c Plate No. 15 | 4.25 | 4.25 |
| 1194 | A91 | 85c like #1193 | .60 | .60 |
| 1195 | A91 | 260c like #1193 | 2.25 | .75 |
| 1196 | A91 | 320c like #1195 | 3.25 | 1.40 |
| 1197 | A91 | 45c Plate No. 17 | .50 | .50 |
| 1198 | A91 | 70c like #1197 | .50 | .50 |
| 1199 | A91 | 85c Plate No. 18 | .60 | .60 |
| 1200 | A91 | 320c like #1199 | 3.00 | 3.00 |
| 1201 | A91 | 175c Plate No. 19 | 1.50 | .50 |
| 1202 | A91 | 450c like #1201 | 3.75 | 1.25 |
| 1203 | A91 | 25c Plate No. 20 | .50 | .50 |
| 1204 | A91 | 50c like #1203 | .50 | .50 |
| 1205 | A91 | 45c Plate No. 21 | 2.00 | 2.00 |
| | | *Nos. 1186-1205 (20)* | 32.65 | 23.05 |

Issued: Nos. 1188, 1205, 9/23; Nos. 1190, 1197, 10/31; No. 1189, 12/3; Nos. 1192, 1194,

1200, 1203, 12/27; Nos. 1193, 1199, 1/5/87; No. 1202, 4/24/87; No. 1196, 6/1/88. Nos. 1186-1187, 1191, 1198, 1201, 1204, 8/23/88; No. 1195, 7/7/89.

Nos. 1201-1202, 1205, horiz.

| 1206 | A91 | 30c Plate No. 22 | .50 | .50 |
|---|---|---|---|---|
| 1207 | A91 | 150c like #1206 | 1.25 | 1.25 |
| 1208 | A91 | 200c Plate No. 23 | 1.75 | .75 |
| 1209 | A91 | 85c Plate No. 24 | 2.25 | 1.60 |
| 1210 | A91 | 225c like #1209 | 4.75 | 4.75 |
| 1211 | A91 | 140c like #1206 | 1.25 | .55 |
| 1212 | A91 | 230c like #1211 | 2.25 | 1.10 |
| 1213 | A91 | 200c Plate No. 26 | 1.75 | .75 |
| 1214 | A91 | 60c Plate No. 27 | .80 | .50 |
| 1215 | A91 | 90c like #1214 | 2.25 | 1.10 |
| 1216 | A91 | 30c Plate No. 28 | .50 | .50 |
| 1217 | A91 | 330c like #1216 | 3.00 | 3.00 |
| 1218 | A91 | 130c Plate No. 29 | 1.00 | .50 |
| 1219 | A91 | 350c like #1218 | 3.75 | 1.75 |
| 1220 | A91 | 30c Plate No. 30 | 3.25 | 3.25 |
| 1221 | A91 | 875c Plate No. 31 | 6.00 | 3.50 |
| 1222 | A91 | 50c Plate No. 32 | .50 | .50 |
| 1223 | A91 | 130c like #1222 | 1.00 | 1.00 |
| 1224 | A91 | 50c Plate No. 33 | .50 | .50 |
| 1225 | A91 | 100c like #1224 | .90 | .90 |
| | | Nos. 1206-1225 (20) | 39.20 | 28.25 |

Issued: Nos. 1219, 1220, 9/23; Nos. 1214, 1224, 10/31; No. 1210, 11/25; Nos. 1209, 1215, 12/15; Nos. 1207, 1217, 1223, 12/27; No. 1212, 2/14/87; No. 1221, 6/15/88; Nos. 1206, 1208, 1211, 1213, 1216, 1218, 1222, 1225, 8/23/88.

Nos. 1218-1219 horiz.

| 1226 | A91 | 140c Plate No. 34 | 1.10 | .50 |
|---|---|---|---|---|
| 1227 | A91 | 360c like #1226 | 3.75 | 1.75 |
| 1228 | A91 | 380c Plate No. 35 | 3.25 | 1.40 |
| 1229 | A91 | 525c Plate No. 36 | 4.00 | 2.25 |
| 1230 | A91 | 175c Plate No. 37 | 1.25 | .65 |
| 1231 | A91 | 390c like #1230 | 3.00 | 1.25 |
| 1232 | A91 | 130c Plate No. 38 | 1.00 | .65 |
| 1233 | A91 | 140c like #1232 | 1.25 | .65 |
| 1234 | A91 | 175c Plate No. 39 | 1.50 | .65 |
| 1235 | A91 | 260c like #1234 | 2.00 | .75 |
| 1236 | A91 | 250c Plate No. 40 | 4.50 | 1.90 |
| 1237 | A91 | $10 like #1236 | 7.50 | 5.75 |
| 1238 | A91 | 140c Plate No. 41 | 1.10 | .50 |
| 1239 | A91 | 180c like #1238 | 1.75 | 1.00 |
| 1240 | A91 | 80c Plate No. 42 | .50 | .50 |
| 1241 | A91 | 130c like #1240 | 1.10 | .50 |
| 1242 | A91 | 200c Plate No. 43 | 3.50 | 1.00 |
| 1243 | A91 | 100c like #1243 | .80 | .80 |
| 1244 | A91 | 200c like #1243 | 2.00 | 1.00 |
| 1245 | A91 | 35c Plate No. 45 | .75 | .50 |
| 1246 | A91 | 85c like #1245 | 1.00 | .60 |
| | | Nos. 1226-1246 (21) | 47.10 | 24.40 |

Issued: Nos. 1227, 1232, 1240, 9/23; Nos. 1244, 1246, 10/31; No. 1245, 1/5/87; No. 1239, 2/14/87; No. 1231, 1235, 4/24/87; No. 1242, 9/29/87; No. 1237, 3/24/88; No. 1229, 6/1/88; Nos. 1226, 1228, 1230, 1233-1234, 1236, 1238, 1241, 1243, 8/23/88.

Nos. 1230-1231, 1240-1241 horiz.

| 1247 | A91 | 225c Plate No. 46 | 1.50 | .80 |
|---|---|---|---|---|
| 1248 | A91 | 175c Plate No. 47 | 1.25 | .65 |
| 1249 | A91 | 240c like #1248 | 1.75 | .70 |
| 1250 | A91 | 200c Plate No. 48 | 3.50 | 1.00 |
| 1251 | A91 | 200c Plate No. 49 | 1.40 | .55 |
| 1252 | A91 | 720c like #1251 | 6.50 | 6.00 |
| 1253 | A91 | 160c Plate No. 50 | 2.10 | 1.00 |
| 1254 | A91 | 300c like #1253 | 3.00 | 1.50 |
| 1255 | A91 | 175c Plate No. 51 | 2.25 | 1.25 |
| 1256 | A91 | 500c like #1255 | 3.00 | 1.50 |
| 1257 | A91 | 140c Plate No. 52 | 1.00 | .40 |
| 1258 | A91 | 590c like #1257 | 4.00 | 2.60 |
| 1259 | A91 | 200c Plate No. 53 | 1.25 | .55 |
| 1260 | A91 | 290c like #1259 | 3.25 | 2.00 |
| 1261 | A91 | 175c Plate No. 54 | 1.25 | .60 |
| 1261A | A91 | 460c like #1261 | 2.75 | 1.40 |
| 1262 | A91 | 120c Plate No. 55 | .90 | .35 |
| 1263 | A91 | 75c Plate No. 56 | 1.00 | .50 |
| 1264 | A91 | 100c like #1263 | .50 | .50 |
| 1265 | A91 | 225c Plate No. 57 | 1.25 | .60 |
| | | Nos. 1247-1265 (20) | 43.40 | 24.45 |

Issued: Nos. 1254, 1263, 10/31; No. 1258, 2/14/87; Nos. 1249, 1256, 1261A, 4/24/87; No. 1250, 9/29/87; Nos. 1252, 1260, 11/23/87; Nos. 1247-1248, 8/23/88; Nos. 1253, 1255, 11/3/88; Nos. 1251, 1257, 1259, 1261-1262, 1264-1265, 1/3/89.

Nos 1261, 1261A horiz.

| 1266 | A91 | 175c Plate No. 58 | 1.25 | .50 |
|---|---|---|---|---|
| 1267 | A91 | 275c like #1266 | 2.00 | .85 |
| 1268 | A91 | 775c Plate No. 59 | 4.00 | 3.25 |
| 1269 | A91 | 200c Plate No. 60 | 1.50 | .55 |
| 1270 | A91 | 575c like #1269 | 5.00 | 3.50 |
| 1271 | A91 | 255c Plate No. 61 | 3.25 | 1.75 |
| 1272 | A91 | 280c Plate No. 62 | 2.60 | 1.75 |
| 1273 | A91 | 700c like #1272 | 4.75 | 4.25 |
| 1274 | A91 | 285c Plate No. 63 | 3.25 | 1.75 |
| 1275 | A91 | 200c Plate No. 64 | 1.00 | .55 |
| 1276 | A91 | 680c like #1275 | 6.00 | 3.50 |
| 1277 | A91 | 140c Plate No. 65 | .70 | .40 |
| 1278 | A91 | 650c like #1277 | 5.00 | 3.50 |
| 1279 | A91 | 280c Plate No. 66 | 1.25 | .75 |
| 1280 | A91 | 750c like #1279 | 6.50 | 6.00 |
| 1281 | A91 | 280c Plate No. 67 | 1.25 | .75 |
| 1282 | A91 | $15 like #1281 | 8.50 | 7.50 |
| 1283 | A91 | 325c Plate No. 68 | 1.40 | 1.40 |
| 1284 | A91 | 530c Plate No. 69 | 3.00 | 2.75 |
| 1285 | A91 | 280c Plate No. 70 | 1.25 | .75 |
| | | Nos. 1266-1285 (20) | 68.55 | 49.00 |

Issued: No. 1278, 2/14/87; No. 1267, 4/24/87; Nos. 1270, 1283, 10/26/87; Nos. 1271, 1276, 1280, 11/23/87; Nos. 1282, 1284, 6/1/88; Nos. 1268, 1273, 6/15/88; No. 1285,

---

8/15/88; Nos. 1272, 1274, 11/3/88; Nos. 1266, 1269, 1275, 1277, 1279, 1281, 1/3/89.

Nos. 1266-1267, 1283, 1285 horiz.

| 1286 | A91 | 670c Plate No. 71 | 4.50 | 4.25 |
|---|---|---|---|---|
| 1287 | A91 | 300c Plate No. 72 | 1.50 | .80 |
| 1288 | A91 | $25 like #1287 | 12.00 | 12.00 |
| 1289 | A91 | 130c Plate No. 73 | .80 | .25 |
| 1290 | A91 | 475c like #1289 | 2.75 | 2.50 |
| 1291 | A91 | 350c Plate No. 74 | 2.25 | 2.00 |
| 1291A | A91 | 900c like #1291 | 6.50 | 6.00 |
| 1291B | A91 | 600c on 900c #1291A | | |
| 1292 | A91 | 200c Plate No. 75 | 2.25 | 1.25 |
| 1293 | A91 | 250c Plate No. 76 | 1.25 | .65 |
| 1294 | A91 | 850c like #1293 | 8.00 | 6.50 |
| 1295 | A91 | 300c Plate No. 77 | 1.50 | .80 |
| 1296 | A91 | 480c like #1295 | 2.75 | 1.75 |
| 1297 | A91 | 280c Plate No. 78 | 1.40 | .75 |
| 1298 | A91 | 950c like #1298 | 6.50 | 6.00 |
| 1299 | A91 | 250c Plate No. 79 | 2.60 | 1.60 |
| 1300 | A91 | 800c like #1299 | 7.50 | 6.50 |
| 1301 | A91 | 300c Plate No. 80 | 1.50 | .80 |
| 1302 | A91 | 400c like #1301 | 2.25 | 1.40 |
| 1303 | A91 | 305c Plate No. 81 | 1.50 | .80 |
| 1304 | A91 | 250c Plate No. 82 | 1.25 | .65 |
| 1305 | A91 | 330c like #1304 | 3.25 | 1.25 |
| | | Nos. 1286-1291A, 1292-1305 (21) | 73.80 | 58.50 |

Issued: No. 1305, 2/14/87; Nos. 1288, 1296, 1302, 7/22/87; Nos. 1291A-1291B, 10/9/87; Nos. 1294, 1300, 11/23/87; No. 1290, 6/1/88; No. 1298, 6/15/88; No. 1291, 6/22/88; No. 1286, 8/15/88; Nos. 1292, 1299, 11/3/88; Nos. 1287, 1293, 1295, 1297, 1301, 1303-1304, 1/3/89; No. 1289, 7/7/89.

No. 1286 horiz.

| 1306 | A91 | 350c Plate No. 83 | 1.75 | .95 |
|---|---|---|---|---|
| 1307 | A91 | $20 like #1306 | 10.00 | 10.00 |
| 1308 | A91 | 360c Plate No. 84 | 2.25 | 2.00 |
| 1309 | A91 | 250c Plate No. 85 | 1.25 | .65 |
| 1310 | A91 | 300c like #1309 | 3.00 | 1.10 |
| 1311 | A91 | 350c Plate No. 86 | 1.75 | .95 |
| 1312 | A91 | 500c like #1311 | 3.00 | 2.00 |
| 1313 | A91 | 250c Plate No. 87 | 1.25 | .65 |
| 1314 | A91 | 425c like #1313 | 3.75 | 1.50 |
| 1315 | A91 | 250c Plate No. 88 | 1.25 | .65 |
| 1316 | A91 | 440c like #1315 | 3.75 | 1.50 |
| 1317 | A91 | 350c Plate No. 89 | 1.75 | .95 |
| 1318 | A91 | 520c like #1317 | 3.00 | 2.00 |
| 1319 | A91 | 270c Plate No. 90 | 1.25 | .65 |
| 1320 | A91 | 300c Plate No. 91 | 1.10 | .65 |
| 1321 | A91 | $12 like #1320 | 7.50 | 7.00 |
| 1322 | A91 | 200c Plate No. 92 | 3.50 | 1.00 |
| 1323 | A91 | 200c Plate No. 93 | 2.25 | 1.25 |
| 1324 | A91 | 300c Plate No. 94 | 1.50 | .80 |
| 1325 | A91 | 600c like #1324 | 3.50 | 2.75 |
| 1326 | A91 | 420c Plate No. 95 | 4.25 | 2.00 |
| 1327 | A91 | 200c Plate No. 96 | 1.60 | .50 |
| 1328 | A91 | 375c like #1327 | 4.25 | 2.25 |
| | | Nos. 1306-1328 (23) | 68.45 | 44.35 |

Issued: Nos. 1310, 1314, 1316, 2/14/87; Nos. 1307, 1312, 1318, 6/2/87; No. 1326, 7/22/87; No. 1322, 9/29/87; No. 1328, 10/26/87; No. 1321, 11/23/87; No. 1323, 3/24/88; Nos. 1308, 1319, 8/15/88; No. 1325, 11/3/88; Nos. 1306, 1309, 1311, 1313, 1315, 1317, 1320, 1324, 1/3/89; No. 1327, 7/7/89.

Nos. 1306, horiz.

Nos. 1166, 1170, 1174, 1176, 1178, 1180, 1182, 1187, 1191, 1193, 1198, 1201, 1204, 1206, 1211, 1216, 1218, 1222, 1225-1226, 1230, 1233-1234, 1236, 1238, 1248, 1257, 1261, 1264, 1266, 1271, 1279, 1281, 1287, 1293, 1295, 1297, 1301, 1304, 1306, 1308-1309, 1311, 1313, 1315, 1317, 1320, 1324 sold as singles in booklets only. Two booklets of 48 stamps each contain these numbers and previous values issued in the series. Value, each booklet, $80.

### Miniature Sheets of 4

Designs: Nos. 1329a, 1330b, 1331b, like #1303. Nos. 1329b, 1330a, 1332a, like #1265. Nos. 1329c, 1330c, 1332b, like #1247. Nos. 1330d, 1331a, 1332c, like #1262.

| 1329 | #1262, 1329a-1329c | 4.50 | 4.50 |
|---|---|---|---|
| a.-c. | A91 120c any single | 1.00 | 1.00 |
| 1330 | #a.-d. | 4.50 | 4.50 |
| a.-d. | A91 150c any single | 1.00 | 1.00 |

---

| 1331 | | #1247, 1265, 1331a-1331b | 5.00 | 5.00 |
|---|---|---|---|---|
| a.-b. | A91 | 225c any single | .95 | .95 |
| 1332 | | #1303, 1332a-1332c | 5.00 | 5.00 |
| a.-c. | A91 | 305c any single | .95 | .95 |
| 1333 | | | 7.00 | 7.00 |
| a. | A91 | 320c like #1262 | 1.25 | 1.25 |
| b. | A91 | 330c like #1247 | 1.25 | 1.25 |
| c. | A91 | 350c like #1303 | 1.50 | 1.50 |
| d. | A91 | 500c like #1265 | 2.40 | 2.40 |
| 1334 | | | 7.00 | 7.00 |
| a. | A91 | 320c like #1247 | 1.25 | 1.25 |
| b. | A91 | 330c like #1265 | 1.25 | 1.25 |
| c. | A91 | 350c like #1262 | 1.50 | 1.50 |
| d. | A91 | 500c like #1303 | 2.40 | 2.40 |
| 1335 | | | 7.00 | 7.00 |
| a. | A91 | 320c like #1303 | 1.25 | 1.25 |
| b. | A91 | 330c like #1265 | 1.25 | 1.25 |
| c. | A91 | 350c like #1262 | 1.50 | 1.50 |
| d. | A91 | 500c like #1247 | 2.40 | 2.40 |
| 1336 | | | 7.00 | 7.00 |
| a. | A91 | 320c like #1265 | 1.25 | 1.25 |
| b. | A91 | 330c like #1303 | 1.25 | 1.25 |
| c. | A91 | 350c like #1247 | 1.50 | 1.50 |
| d. | A91 | 500c like #1262 | 2.40 | 2.40 |

Issued: Nos. 1329-1332, 7/7/89; others, 2/26/88.

For surcharges & overprints see Nos. 1671-1727, 1776-1777, 1834-1835, 1942, 1948-1952, 1998-1999, 2031, 2033-2044, 2064, 2619A-2619D, 2578A-2578C, 2907A-2907G, 2928A-2928D, E3, E5, O40-O56.

Natl. Arms — A92

| 1985-87 | | | Perf. 14 Vert. |
|---|---|---|---|
| 1337 | A92 | 25c multi | .50 .50 |
| 1338 | A92 | 25c multi ('87) | 1.25 .75 |
| | | | **Perf. 14 Horiz.** |
| 1339 | A92 | 25c multi | .25 .25 |
| 1340 | A92 | 25c multi ('87) | 1.25 .75 |
| | | Nos. 1337-1340 (4) | 3.25 2.25 |
| | | | **Perf. 14** |
| 1341 | A92 | 25c multi | |
| a. | | Wmk. 364 | — — |

Nos. 1337-1340 were cut from orchid sheet gutters. Stamps vary considerably in size.

Nos. 1338, 1340 are Nos. 1337 and 1339 redrawn to include black border.

Issue dates: Nos. 1337, 1339, 1341, July 1985. No. 1338, 1340 June 2, 1987.

See Nos. 1467-1468. For surcharges see Nos. 1777A-1777C, 4166-4168, 4190, 4193, 4194, 4199, 4203.

### Nos. 1024, 1044, 1047, 1059, 1060 Surcharged or Overprinted in Blue or Black "QUEEN MOTHER 1900-1985" on 1 or 2 Lines

Nos. 1345a, 1346a overprinted "LADY BOWES-LYON 1900-1923". Nos. 1345b, 1346b overprinted "DUCHESS OF YORK 1923-1937". Nos. 1345c, 1346c overprinted "QUEEN ELIZABETH 1937-1952". Surcharge on No. 1346 sans serif.

| 1985 | | | Perfs. as Before |
|---|---|---|---|
| 1342 | A91 | 130c on #1044 | |
| 1343 | A91 | 130c on #1059 | |
| 1344 | A91 | 130c on #1060 | |
| | | Nos. 1342-1344 (3) | 6.25 |

### Miniature sheets

| 1345 | | Sheet of 4 | 7.50 |
|---|---|---|---|
| a.-d. | A91 | 200c on #1024, any single | |
| 1346 | | Sheet of 4 | 12.00 |
| a.-d. | A91 | 200c on 130c #1047, any single (Bk) | |

Issued: Nos. 1342-1345, 7/9; No. 1346, 9/12.
For overprints see Nos. 1741, 1751-1754, 1774-1775.

### Nos. 465 Surcharged in Red "INTERNATIONAL / YOUTH YEAR / 1985"

| | | | Perf. 13x13½ |
|---|---|---|---|
| 1985, July 18 | Litho. | | Wmk. 364 |
| 1347 | | Sheet of 25, 8 #a.-b., 4 #c.-d., 1 #e. | 175.00 |
| a.-e. | A28 | 25c on #465a-465e, any single | |

### Nos. 203 and 443 Surcharged

---

1982

**1985, July 26 — Perfs. as Before**
**Watermarks & Printing Methods as Before**

| 1352 | A47 | 225c on #203 | 55.00 | 6.50 |
|---|---|---|---|---|
| 1354 | A63 | 240c on #443 | 55.00 | 8.00 |

Girl Guides, 75th anniv. (No. 1352), John J. Audubon, bicentennial of birth. No. 203 surcharged only with 350c, $2.25 or surcharged with both was not issued.

Abolition of Slavery, Sesquicent. A93

Designs: 25c, Revolution leaders, 1763. 60c, Damon's execution, 1834. 130c, Demerara Uprising, 1823. 150c Den Arendt slave ship.

| | | | Unwmk. |
|---|---|---|---|
| 1985, July 29 | Litho. | | Perf. 14 |
| 1355 | A93 | 25c gray & black | .40 .25 |
| 1356 | A93 | 60c pink & black | .25 .25 |
| 1357 | A93 | 130c blue grn & blk | .45 .45 |
| 1358 | A93 | 150c lilac & blk | .85 .60 |
| | | Nos. 1355-1358 (4) | 1.95 1.55 |

See Nos. 1994-1997 for changed colors.

### Nos. 135, 210 Surcharged; No. 223 Surcharged in Brown

Surcharges read: No. 1359, "Guyana/Libya / Friendship 1985"; No. 1361, "Mexico / 1986".

**1985, Aug. 16 — Perfs. as Before**
**Watermarks and Printing Methods as Before**

| 1359 | A49 | 150c on #210 | 10.00 | 3.00 |
|---|---|---|---|---|
| 1360 | A53 | 150c on #223 | 3.50 | .85 |
| 1361 | A28 | 275c on 3c #135 | 9.00 | 1.75 |
| | | Nos. 1359-1361 (3) | 22.50 | 5.60 |

Refer to 2nd paragraph under No. 147 for No. 1361. See No. 1452 for 225c Mexico 1986 surcharge.

### Nos. 366, 427, 430, 430a, 494, & 553 Ovptd. or Surcharged "1955-1985" Vertically or Horizontally
#### Wmk. 364

| 1985, Sept. 23 | Litho. | | Perf. 13½ |
|---|---|---|---|
| 1362 | A75 | 60c on #366 | .35 .35 |
| 1363 | A75 | 60c on #553 | .35 .35 |
| 1364 | A75 | 120c on #427 | .70 .70 |
| 1365 | A75 | 120c on #430 | .70 .70 |
| 1366 | A75 | 120c on #430a | .70 .70 |
| 1367 | A75 | 120c on #494 | .70 .70 |
| | | Nos. 1362-1367 (6) | 3.50 3.50 |

### No. 417 Surcharged "1965-1985" Vertically

| 1985, Sept. 30 | | | |
|---|---|---|---|
| 1368 | A79 | 25c on #417 | .80 .30 |
| 1369 | A79 | 225c on #417 | 2.75 1.50 |

### Nos. 260 & 262 Surcharged "1985"

| 1985, Oct. 5 | Litho. | | Perf. 14x14½ |
|---|---|---|---|
| 1370 | A61 | 25c on 40c #262 | 20.00 1.00 |
| 1371 | A61 | 320c on 15c #260 | 30.00 9.50 |

### Orchid Type of 1985 Surcharged in Red "CRISTOBAL COLON / 1492-1992"

| 1985, Oct. 12 | | | Perf. 14 |
|---|---|---|---|
| 1372 | A91 | 350c on 120c like #1108 | 13.00 6.00 |

No. 1372 not issued without surcharge. For overprint see No. E1. For surcharge see No. 1591A.

### No. 288 Overprinted "SIR WINSTON CHURCHILL / 1965-1985"

| 1985, Oct. 15 | | | Perf. 13½x13 |
|---|---|---|---|
| 1373 | A66 | $2 on #288 | 26.00 8.00 |

## No. 214 Surcharged "1950-1985"

**1985, Oct. 15**    **Perf. 14**
| | | | | |
|---|---|---|---|---|
| 1374 | A50 | 25c on 110c on 10c | .25 | .25 |
| 1375 | A50 | 200c on 110c on 10c | 1.00 | 1.00 |

No. 214 with 110c surcharge only was not issued.

## Nos. 295-297, 384, and O9 Overprinted or Surcharged "United / Nations / 1945-1985"

**1985, Oct. 28**    **Perf. 14x14½**
| | | | | |
|---|---|---|---|---|
| 1376 | A68 | 30c on #295 | 1.75 | .25 |
| 1377 | A68 | 50c on #296 | 1.75 | .30 |
| 1378 | A68 | 100c on #O9 | 1.75 | .50 |
| 1379 | A68 | 225c on #384 | 30.00 | 4.00 |
| 1380 | A68 | $3 on #297 | 4.00 | 4.00 |
| | | Nos. 1376-1380 (5) | 39.25 | 9.05 |

## Nos. 142-144, 289A, O4-O5, O7, O15, and QO1-QO2 Ovptd. "POSTAGE"

**1985, Oct. 29**    **Perfs. as Before**
**Watermarks and Printing Methods as Before**
| | | | | |
|---|---|---|---|---|
| 1381 | A28 | 30c on #O4 | 1.00 | .30 |
| 1382 | A28 | 40c on #142 | 60.00 | 1.50 |
| 1383 | A28 | 50c on #143 | 1.00 | .50 |
| 1384 | A28 | 50c on #O5 | 1.00 | .40 |
| 1385 | A28 | 60c on #144 | 4.25 | .50 |
| 1386 | A28 | 60c on #144 (Revenue Only) | 1.00 | .35 |
| 1387 | A28 | 60c on #O7 | 3.00 | .40 |
| 1388 | A66 | $10 on #O15 | 35.00 | 9.00 |
| 1389 | A28 | $15 on #QO1 | 17.50 | 12.00 |
| 1390 | A28 | $20 on #QO2 | 17.50 | 13.00 |
| | | Nos. 1381-1390 (10) | 141.25 | 37.95 |

Refer to 2nd paragraph in footnote following No. 147 for Nos. 1381, 1384, 1386-1387.

## Nos. 133-134 Surcharged "Deepavali / 1985"

**1985, Nov. 1**
| | | | | |
|---|---|---|---|---|
| 1391 | A28 | 25c on 2c #134 | 2.00 | .35 |
| 1392 | A28 | 150c on 1c #133 | 4.50 | 1.75 |

## No. 1050 Ovptd. in Red

Overprinted: a, "Christmas 1985." b, "Happy New Year." c, "Merry Christmas." d, "Happy Holidays."

**1985, Nov. 3**    **Unwmk.**    **Perf. 14**
| | | | | |
|---|---|---|---|---|
| 1393 | A91 | 55c Sheet of 4, #a.-d. | 12.00 | 7.00 |

For surcharge see No. 1670F.

Clive Lloyd, Cricketer A94

Lloyd Holding Intl. Cup — A95

No. 1394s: a, $2.25, Lloyd playing cricket. b, $1.30, Lloyd, bat and wicket. c, 60c, Gloves, wicket, bat, natl. flag.

**1985, Nov. 7**    **Perf. 14½x14**
| | | | | |
|---|---|---|---|---|
| 1394 | A94 | Triptych | 1.50 | 1.50 |
| a.-c. | | 25c any single | .45 | .45 |
| | | **Size: 30x38mm** | | |
| | | **Perf. 14x14½** | | |
| 1395 | A94 | 60c multi | .55 | .55 |
| 1396 | A94 | $1.30 multi | .90 | .90 |
| 1397 | A94 | $2.25 multi | 1.60 | 1.60 |
| 1398 | A95 | $3.50 multi | 2.60 | 2.60 |
| | | Nos. 1394-1398 (5) | 7.15 | 7.15 |

For surcharge see No. 1504.

## No. 329 Ovptd. "1985" in Red
### Wmk. 364

**1985, Nov. 15**    **Litho.**    **Perf. 14**
| | | | | |
|---|---|---|---|---|
| 1399 | A77 | 30c Sheet of 12, #a.-l. | 17.50 | 17.50 |

---

## Nos. 410 and 413e Surcharged

**1985, Dec. 23**   **Photo.**   **Perf. 14x14½**
**Watermarks as Before**
| | | | | |
|---|---|---|---|---|
| 1400 | A7 | 20c on #410 | 8.00 | .50 |
| 1401 | A7 | 20c on #413De | 8.00 | .50 |

Compare No. 1400 with No. 914 and 1401 with No. 994a.

## Nos. 1075, 1077 Ovptd. "REICHENBACHIA 1886-1986" in Purple

**1986, Jan. 13**    **Litho.**    **Perf. 14**
| | | | | |
|---|---|---|---|---|
| 1402 | A91 | 150c on #1075 | 9.00 | 1.00 |
| 1403 | A91 | 200c on #1077 | 9.00 | 1.10 |

For surcharge and overprints see Nos. 1553, 1760, 1762-1763.

## Nos. 608, 610 Surcharged "Republic Day / 1986"
### Perfs. as Before

**1986, Feb. 22**    **Wmk. 364**
| | | | |
|---|---|---|---|
| 1404 | A82 | 25c on #608 | |
| 1405 | A83 | 120c on $6 #610 | |
| 1406 | A83 | 225c on $6 #610 | |
| | | Nos. 1404-1406 (3) | 2.00 |

## No. 87 Surcharged "1986"

**1986, Mar. 24**    **Photo.**    **Perf. 13**
| | | | | |
|---|---|---|---|---|
| 1407 | A14 | 25c on 6c #87 | .30 | .25 |
| 1408 | A14 | 50c on 6c #87 | .50 | .45 |
| 1409 | A14 | 100c on 6c #87 | .90 | .85 |
| 1410 | A14 | 200c on 6c #87 | 1.75 | 1.50 |
| | | Nos. 1407-1410 (4) | 3.45 | 3.05 |

## No. 237 Surcharged "1926 / 1986"

**1986, Mar. 27**    **Litho.**    **Perf. 14**
| | | | | |
|---|---|---|---|---|
| 1411 | A56 | 150c on 35c #237 | 5.50 | 1.00 |

St. John Ambulance, 60th anniv.

## Nos. 1028, 1037 Surcharged "Queen Elizabeth / 1926 1986"

**1986, Apr. 21**    **Unwmk.**
| | | | | |
|---|---|---|---|---|
| 1412 | A91 | Sheet of 4 | 8.50 | 8.50 |
| a. | | 130c on 130c #1028 | 1.75 | 1.50 |
| b. | | 200c on 130c #1028 | 1.75 | 1.50 |
| c. | | 260c on 130c #1028 | 1.75 | 1.50 |
| d. | | 330c on 130c #1028 | 1.75 | 1.50 |
| 1413 | A91 | 130c on #1037 | 7.50 | 2.75 |

Location of overprint on No. 1413 differs from No. 1412.
For overprints & surcharges see Nos. 1670A, 1738B.

## Nos. 267, 317g-317 l, 444a-444f Surcharged "Protect the"
### Wmk. 373

**1986, May 3**    **Litho.**    **Perf. 14**
| | | | | |
|---|---|---|---|---|
| 1414 | A73 | 60c on 35c #317g-317l, block of 6, #a.-f. | 3.00 | 3.00 |
| 1415 | A73 | 60c on 35c #444, block of 6, #a.-f. | 65.00 | 25.00 |
| | | **Wmk. 364** | | |
| 1416 | A63 | $6 on 8c #267 | 5.00 | 4.00 |

## No. 390 Surcharged

**1986, May 5**    **Litho.**    **Perf. 13**
| | | | | |
|---|---|---|---|---|
| 1417 | A28 | 600c on #390 | 24.00 | 2.75 |

## No. 283A Surcharged

Overprints: a, Abary. b, Anna Regina. c, Aurora. d, Bartica Grove. e, Bel Air. f, Belle Plaine. g, Clonbrook. h, T.P.O. Dem. / Railway. i, Enmore. j, Fredericks / burg. k, Good Success. l, 1986. m, Mariabba. n, Massaruni. o, Nigg. p, No. 50. q, No. 63 / Benab. r, Philadelphia. s, Sisters. t, Skeldon. u, Suddie. v, Taymouth / Manor. w, Wales. x, Whim.

**Perf. 14x13½**
**1986, May 15**    **Litho.**    **Wmk. 364**
| | | | | |
|---|---|---|---|---|
| 1418 | | Sheet of 25, #a.-k., m.-x., 2 #l. | 32.50 | 32.50 |
| a.-x. | | A66 25c on 30c, any single | 1.00 | .75 |

## Nos. 10A, 13a, 241, 713a-713d, British Guiana No. 254 Surcharged

Surcharges read: Nos. 1443, 1445, "GUYANA / INDEPENDENCE 1966-1986"; Nos. 1446-1447, "1986"; Nos. 1448a-1448d, "INDEPENDENCE / 1966-1986".

**1986, May 26**    **Perfs. as Before**
**Watermarks and Printing Methods as Before**
| | | | | |
|---|---|---|---|---|
| 1443 | A60 | 25c on 2c British Guiana #254 | .25 | .25 |
| 1444 | A57 | 25c on 35c #241 | .25 | .25 |
| 1445 | A60 | 60c on 2c British Guiana #254 | .45 | .30 |
| 1446 | A60 | 120c on 6c #10A | .50 | .35 |

---

| | | | | |
|---|---|---|---|---|
| 1447 | A60 | 130c on 24c #13a | 9.00 | .75 |
| 1448 | | Block of 4 | 1.75 | 1.75 |
| a. | | A86 25c on 120c #713a | .35 | .25 |
| b. | | A86 25c on 130c #713b | .35 | .25 |
| c. | | A86 25c on 150c #713c | .35 | .25 |
| d. | | A86 225c on 130c #713d | .70 | .70 |
| | | Nos. 1443-1448 (6) | 12.20 | |

## No. 135 Surcharged "MEXICO / 1986" in Blue
### Perf. 13x13½

**1986, May 31**    **Litho.**    **Wmk. 364**
| | | | | |
|---|---|---|---|---|
| 1452 | A28 | 225c on 3c #135 | 20.00 | 3.75 |

World Cup Soccer Championships, Mexico City.

## Nos. 136, 192 and 266A Surcharged or Ovptd. in Blue

Surcharge and Overprint Read: Nos. 1453-1454, "CARICOM HEADS OF GOV'T / CONFERENCE / JULY 1986"; No. 1455, "CARICOM / DAY 1986".

**1986**    **Perfs. as Before**
**Watermarks and Printing Methods as Before**
| | | | | |
|---|---|---|---|---|
| 1453 | A28 | 25c on #192 | 2.75 | .75 |
| 1454 | A28 | 60c on 3c #135 | 3.50 | .30 |
| 1455 | A66 | 60c on #286A | 11.00 | .75 |
| | | Nos. 1453-1455 (3) | 17.25 | |

Issued: No. 1455, 6/28; Nos. 1453-1454, 7/1.

## Nos. 133 and 137 Surcharged "INT. YEAR / OF PEACE" in Black or Blue

**1986, July 14**    **Litho.**    **Perf. 13x13½**
| | | | | |
|---|---|---|---|---|
| 1456 | A28 | 25c on 1c #133 (Bl) | .75 | 1.75 |
| 1457 | A28 | 60c on 6c #137 | 1.75 | 1.75 |
| 1458 | A28 | 120c on 6c #137 | 1.75 | 1.75 |
| 1459 | A28 | 130c on 6c #137 | 1.75 | 1.75 |
| 1460 | A28 | 150c on 6c #137 | 1.75 | 1.75 |
| | | Nos. 1456-1460 (5) | 7.75 | |

Halley's Comet A96

Designs: a, Br. Guiana #172. b, Guyana #931.

**1986, July 19**    **Perf. 14**
| | | | | |
|---|---|---|---|---|
| 1461 | A96 | 320c Pair, #a.-b. | 3.00 | 3.00 |
| c. | | Imperf. | 7.50 | |

No. 1461 has continuous design. No. 1461 exists imperf. between. Most were overprinted. For overprints and surcharges see Nos. 1822, 1836, 2029, E5-E6, E11, E14.

## No. 43 Surcharged

**1986, July 28**    **Photo.**    **Perf. 14x14½**
| | | | | |
|---|---|---|---|---|
| 1463 | A7 | 20c on 6c #43 | 11.00 | .40 |

## Nos. 60-61 Surcharged "GUSIA / 1936-1986"
### Perf. 14x13½

**1986, Aug. 15**    **Photo.**    **Unwmk.**
| | | | | |
|---|---|---|---|---|
| 1464 | A11 | 25c on #61 | 6.00 | .50 |
| 1465 | A11 | $1.50 on 6c #60 | 11.00 | 4.50 |

## No. 136 Surcharged "REGIONAL / PHARMACY / CONFERENCE / 1986" in Blue
### Perf. 13x13½

**1986, Aug. 15**    **Litho.**    **Wmk. 364**
| | | | | |
|---|---|---|---|---|
| 1466 | A28 | 130c on 5c #136 | 12.00 | 1.75 |

## Nos. 1337, 1339, 1341 Inscribed "1966-1986"
### Perfs. as Before

**1986, Sept. 23**    **Unwmk.**
| | | | | |
|---|---|---|---|---|
| 1467 | A92 | 25c on #1337 | 2.50 | .30 |
| 1468 | A92 | 25c on #1339 | 2.50 | .30 |
| 1469 | A92 | 25c on #1341 | 2.50 | .30 |
| | | Nos. 1467-1469 (3) | 7.50 | .90 |

For surcharges, see Nos. 4200-4201.

## No. 871 Surcharged
### Perf. 14x13½

**1986, Oct. 1**    **Litho.**    **Wmk. 364**
### Sheet of 25
| | | | | |
|---|---|---|---|---|
| 1470 | | #a.-k., m.-x., 2 #l | 55.00 | 40.00 |
| a.-x. | | A66 120c any single | 2.00 | 1.25 |

---

## No. 1145 Surcharged "12th World Orchid Conference" / "TOKYO JAPAN MARCH 1987"
### Unwmk.

**1986, Oct. 6**    **Litho.**    **Perf. 14**
| | | | | |
|---|---|---|---|---|
| 1494 | A91 | 650c on 40c #1145 | 19.00 | 6.50 |

For overprint see No. 1851.

## Orchid Type like No. 1052 Surchd. in Black and Red or Red

Surcharge reads: "1492-1992" and "CHRISTOPHER COLUMBUS".

**1986, Oct.**
| | | | | |
|---|---|---|---|---|
| 1495 | A91 | 320c on 150c | 7.50 | 3.00 |
| 1496 | A91 | 320c on 150c (R) | 7.50 | 3.00 |

Issued: No. 1495, 10/10; No. 1496, 10/30. Nos. 1495-1496 not issued without surcharge.

## Nos. 704 and 705 Surcharged "1986"
### Perf. 14x14½

**1986, Oct. 15**    **Photo.**    **Wmk. 364**
| | | | | |
|---|---|---|---|---|
| 1497 | A7 | 50c on #704 | 6.50 | .60 |
| 1498 | A7 | 225c on #705 | 18.00 | 5.50 |

## Nos. 134, 192 Surcharged "Deepavali /1986"

**1986, Nov. 3**    **Litho.**    **Perf. 13x13½**
| | | | | |
|---|---|---|---|---|
| 1499 | A28 | 25c on 2c #134 | 3.00 | .50 |
| 1500 | A28 | 200c on #192 | 11.00 | 4.00 |

## No. 43 Surcharged "CHRISTMAS / 1986" in Red

**1986, Nov. 26**    **Perfs. as Before**
**Watermarks and Printing Methods as Before**
| | | | | |
|---|---|---|---|---|
| 1501 | A7 | 20c on 6c #43 | 5.00 | .30 |
| | | **Miniature Sheet** | | |
| | | **No. 917 Surcharged in Red** | | |
| 1502 | A88 | 120c on 60c on #a.-e. | 8.50 | 8.50 |

No. 1502 is surcharged on an unissued miniature sheet containing No. 917. No. 1501 exists on a 2013 cover with "cents" obliterated with a felt-tip marker.

## No. 329 Ovptd. "1986" in Blue
### Wmk. 364

**1986, Nov. 26**    **Litho.**    **Perf. 14**
| | | | | |
|---|---|---|---|---|
| 1503 | A77 | 30c Sheet of 12, #a.-l. | 27.50 | 27.50 |

## No. 1398 Surcharged in Red

**1986, Dec. 1**    **Litho.**    **Perf. 14x14½**
| | | | | |
|---|---|---|---|---|
| 1504 | A95 | $15 on $3.50 #1398 | 47.50 | 22.50 |

L.F.S. Burnham, President 1980-85 — A97

25c, Tomb. 120c, Flags, map. 130c, Government building. $6, Portrait, necklace, vert.

**1986, Dec. 13**    **Litho.**    **Perf. 12½x13**
| | | | | |
|---|---|---|---|---|
| 1505 | A97 | 25c multi | .25 | .25 |
| 1506 | A97 | 120c multi | .35 | .35 |
| 1507 | A97 | 130c multi | .45 | .45 |
| 1508 | A97 | $6 multi | 2.00 | 2.00 |
| | | Nos. 1505-1508 (4) | 3.05 | 3.05 |

## Orchid Type of 1985-87 Surcharged "GPOC / 1977 - 1987"

**1987, Jan. 19**    **Perf. 14**
| | | | | |
|---|---|---|---|---|
| 1509 | A91 | 225c on 25c like #1090 | 4.50 | 1.00 |
| 1510 | A91 | $10 on 50c like #1052 | 11.00 | 11.00 |

Nos. 1509-1510 not issued without surcharge. No. 1509 adds "2" to 25c value, No. 1510 uses flower as obliterator.

## Stamps of Type A91 Surcharged in Black or Red

a

b

c

d

e

f

g

h

i

j

k

l

**1987-89**      *Perfs. as Before*
**Design A91**
**Series 1**
**(Plate Number in Parentheses)**
**On Nos. 1022-1039**

| | | | |
|---|---|---|---|
| 1511 | (a) | 120c on 60c (2) | 2.75 |
| 1512 | (b) | 120c on 60c (2) | 1.10 |
| 1513 | (a) | 120c on 60c (5) | 2.10 |
| 1514 | (c) | 200c on 60c (5) | 1.10 |
| 1515 | (c) | 200c on 75c (5) | 1.10 |

Obliterator invtd. in surch. on Nos. 1514-1515.

| | | | |
|---|---|---|---|
| 1516 | (d) | 200c on 60c (7) | 1.10 |
| 1517 | (d) | 200c on 25c (8) | 1.60 |
| 1518 | (e) | 200c on 25c (8) | 1.10 |
| 1519 | (a) | 120c on 50c (9) | 1.10 |
| 1520 | (b) | 120c on 50c (9) | |
| 1521 | (f) | 120c on 50c (9) | 1.10 |
| 1522 | (g) | 120c on 50c (9) | |
| 1523 | (a) | 120c on 55c (9) | 2.25 |
| 1524 | (f) | 120c on 55c (9) | 1.60 |
| a. | | 120c on 55c on #1032a | 2.00 |
| 1525 | (g) | 120c on 55c (9) | 1.10 |
| 1526 | (a) | 120c on 60c (10) | 2.25 |
| 1527 | (d) | 200c on 60c (10) | 1.10 |
| 1528 | (h) | $2 on 25c (12) | 1.10 |

Surcharge on No. 1528 lacks obliterator.

| | | | |
|---|---|---|---|
| 1529 | (f) | 120c on 55c (15) | 1.40 |
| 1530 | (a) | 120c on 55c (15) | 5.50 |

Issued: Nos. 1518, 1528, 3/6; Nos. 1514-1515, 3/17; Nos. 1516-1517, 1522, 1525, 1527, 3/87; Nos. 1521, 1524, 1529, 7/87; No. 1511, 1513, 1519, 1523, 1526, 9/87; Nos. 1512, 1520, 7/88.

**On Nos. 1042-1061**

| | | | |
|---|---|---|---|
| 1531 | (b) | 120c on 55c (17) | |
| 1532 | (d) | 200c on 55c (17) | 1.60 |
| 1533 | (a) | 600c on 80c (17) | 3.25 |
| 1534 | (a) | 120c on 60c (19) | 2.25 |
| 1535 | (d) | 200c on 60c (19) | 1.10 |
| 1536 | (a) | 120c on 50c (22) | |
| 1537 | (b) | 120c on 50c (22) | 1.10 |
| 1538 | (f) | 120c on 50c (22) | 1.10 |
| 1539 | (c) | 200c on 50c (22) | 1.10 |
| 1540 | (i) | 225c on 50c (22) | 1.60 |
| 1541 | (a) | 120c on 55c #1050a (22) | 2.25 |
| 1542 | (f) | 120c on 55c #1050a (22) | 1.75 |
| 1543 | (c) | 200c on 55c #1050a (22) | 1.10 |
| 1544 | (h) | $2 on 25c (23) | 1.40 |
| 1545 | (a) | 120c on 50c (24) | 2.25 |
| 1546 | (a) | 200c on 50c (24) | |
| 1547 | (a) | 200c on 50c (24) | 1.10 |
| 1548 | (a) | 120c on 60c (31) | 2.25 |
| 1549 | (a) | 200c on 60c (31) | |

Issued: No. 1544, 3/6; Nos. 1539, 1543, 3/17; Nos. 1532, 1535, 1547, 1549, 3/87; No. 1540, 6/87; Nos. 1538, 1542, 7/87; Nos. 1533-1534, 1536, 1541, 1545-1546, 1548, 9/87; Nos. 1531, 1537, 7/88.

**On Nos. 1069-1091**

| | | | |
|---|---|---|---|
| 1550 | (b) | 120c on 80c (39) | |
| 1551 | (a) | 600c on 80c (39) | 3.25 |
| 1552 | (g) | $15 on 80c (39) | 4.50 |
| 1553 | (i) | 225c on #1402 (42) | 1.60 |
| 1554 | (d) | 200c on 60c (44) | 1.10 |
| 1555 | (a) | 200c on 60c (47) | 1.10 |
| 1556 | (a) | 120c on 50c (49) | |

| | | | |
|---|---|---|---|
| 1557 | (f) | 120c on 50c (49) | 1.50 |
| 1558 | (a) | 120c on 55c #1085a (49) | 2.25 |
| 1559 | (f) | 120c on 55c (49) | 1.40 |
| a. | | 120c on 55c on #1085a | 2.50 |
| 1560 | (d) | 200c on 55c (49) | 1.25 |
| a. | | 200c on 55c on #1085a | 4.50 |
| 1561 | (a) | 120c on 60c (50) | 2.25 |
| 1562 | (b) | 120c on 60c (50) | |
| 1563 | (e) | 200c on 25c (51) | 1.40 |
| 1564 | (d) | 200c on 25c (52) | 1.10 |
| 1565 | (b) | 120c on 30c (53) | |
| a. | | 120c on 30c on #1090a | |
| 1566 | (a) | 120c on 50c (53) | 2.25 |
| a. | | 120c on 50c #1091a | — |
| 1567 | (d) | 200c on 30c #1090a (53) | 1.10 |
| 1568 | (a) | 120c on 50c (53) | |
| 1569 | (d) | 200c on 50c (53) | 1.10 |
| 1570 | (g) | $10 on 25c (53) | 3.25 |
| 1571 | (g) | $25 on 25c (53) | 6.50 |

Surcharge on No. 1571 lacks obliterator and places a "$" in front of original denomination. Nos. 1570-1571 not issued without surcharge.
Issued: No. 1563, 3/6; Nos. 1552, 1554-1555, 1560, 1564, 1567, 1569-1571, 3/87; No. 1553, 6/87; Nos. 1557, 1559, 7/87; Nos. 1551, 1556, 1558, 1561, 1566, 1568, 9/87; Nos. 1550, 1562, 1565, 7/88.

**On Nos. 1092-1108, 1372**

| | | | |
|---|---|---|---|
| 1572 | (b) | 120c on 45c (54) | |
| 1573 | (a) | 120c on 60c (54) | 2.25 |
| 1574 | (b) | 120c on 60c (54) | 1.10 |
| 1575 | (a) | 200c on 60c (55) | |
| 1576 | (i) | 225c on 60c (55) | 1.60 |
| 1577 | (b) | 120c on 60c (57) | 1.10 |
| a. | | New value at bottom | |
| 1578 | (d) | 200c on 60c (57) | 1.10 |
| 1579 | (b) | 120c on 25c (59) | 1.10 |
| 1580 | (a) | 120c on 75c (60) | 2.25 |
| 1581 | (c) | 200c on 75c (60) | 2.75 |
| 1582 | (b) | 120c on 25c (61) | |
| 1583 | (a) | 120c on 25c (63) | 1.10 |
| 1584 | (a) | 120c on 50c (64) | |
| 1585 | (f) | 120c on 50c (64) | 1.60 |
| 1586 | (a) | 120c on 55c, wmkd. (64) | 2.25 |
| 1587 | (f) | 120c on 55c (64) | 1.10 |
| a. | | 120c on 55c on #1107a | 1.40 |
| 1588 | (g) | 120c on 55c (64) | 1.10 |
| a. | | 120c on 55c on #1107a | 1.25 |

Surcharge on Nos. 1522, 1525, 1588-1588a does not contain date.

| | | | |
|---|---|---|---|
| 1589 | (a) | 120c on 50c (65) | 2.25 |
| 1590 | (a) | 200c on 50c (65) | |
| 1591 | (d) | 200c on 50c (65) | 1.10 |
| 1591A | (i) | 225c on #1372 (65) | |

Issued: No. 1581, 3/17; Nos. 1578, 1588, 1591, 3/87; No. 1576, 6/87; Nos. 1585, 1587, 7/87; Nos. 1573, 1575, 1580, 1584, 1586, 1589-1590, 9/87; No. 1591A, 10/9/87; Nos. 1572, 1574, 1577, 1579, 1582-1583, 7/88.

**On Nos. 1112-1124**

| | | | |
|---|---|---|---|
| 1592 | (b) | 120c on 40c (68) | 1.10 |
| 1593 | (c) | 200c on 40c (68) | 1.10 |
| a. | | Obliterator inverted | 1.25 |
| 1594 | (a) | 225c on 40c (68) | 2.75 |
| 1595 | (a) | 120c on 60c (69) | |
| 1596 | (b) | 120c on 60c (69) | 1.10 |
| 1597 | (b) | 120c on 25c (70) | |
| 1598 | (b) | 120c on 25c (71) | |
| 1599 | (b) | 120c on 60c (71) | 2.25 |
| 1600 | (d) | 200c on 25c (71) | 1.10 |
| 1601 | (d) | 200c on 60c (71) | 1.10 |
| 1602 | (j) | 120c on 25c (72) | |
| 1603 | (d) | 200c on 25c (72) | 1.10 |
| 1604 | (b) | 120c on 60c (73) | |
| 1605 | (b) | 200c on 60c (73) | .80 |
| 1606 | (b) | 120c on 80c (74) | |
| 1607 | (a) | 600c on 80c (74) | 3.25 |
| 1608 | (g) | $12 on 80c (74) | 3.75 |
| 1609 | (d) | 200c on 50c (75) | |
| a. | | New value at bottom | |
| 1610 | (d) | 200c on 50c (75) | 1.10 |
| 1611 | (a) | 225c on 65c (76) | 2.75 |

Issued: No. 1593, 3/17; Nos. 1600-1601, 1603, 1605, 1608, 1610, 3/87; Nos. 1594-1595, 1599, 1611, 9/87; Nos. 1592, 1596-1598, 1604, 1606-1607, 1609, 7/88; No. 1602, 9/88.

**On Nos. 1126-1142**

| | | | |
|---|---|---|---|
| 1612 | (b) | 120c on 40c (77) | |
| a. | | New value at UL | |
| 1613 | (d) | 200c on 40c (77) | 1.10 |
| 1614 | (a) | 200c on 45c (77) | 3.25 |
| 1615 | (a) | 200c on 45c (77) | 1.10 |
| 1616 | (a) | 200c on 45c (78) | 3.25 |
| 1617 | (a) | 200c on 45c (78) | 1.10 |
| 1618 | (a) | 120c on 60c (79) | 3.25 |
| 1619 | (b) | 120c on 60c (79) | |
| 1620 | (a) | 225c on 65c (80) | 3.25 |
| 1621 | (b) | 120c on 45c (81) | |
| 1622 | (f) | 120c on 55c (81) | 1.40 |
| 1623 | (d) | 200c on 45c (81) | 1.10 |
| 1624 | (a) | 200c on 55c (81) | 4.50 |
| 1625 | (f) | 120c on 55c (82) | 1.75 |
| 1626 | (a) | 200c on 55c (82) | 11.50 |
| 1627 | (a) | 120c on 75c (83) | 3.25 |
| 1628 | (b) | 120c on 90c (84) | |
| 1629 | (a) | 200c on 45c (84) | 3.25 |
| 1630 | (a) | 200c on 45c (85) | |
| 1631 | (a) | 200c on 45c (85) | 1.10 |

Issued: Nos. 1613, 1615, 1617, 1623, 1631, 3/87; Nos. 1622, 1625, 7/87; Nos. 1614, 1616, 1618, 1620, 1624, 1626-1627, 1629-1630, 9/87; Nos. 1612, 1619, 1621, 1628, 7/88.

**On Nos. 1144-1153**

| | | | |
|---|---|---|---|
| 1632 | (b) | 120c on 30c (86) | |
| 1633 | (b) | 120c on 40c (86) | 1.10 |
| 1634 | (d) | 200c on 30c (86) | 1.10 |
| 1635 | (d) | 200c on 40c (86) | |
| 1636 | (a) | 225c on 40c (86) | 3.25 |
| a. | | Inscribed "ONTOGLOS-SUM" | 2.75 |
| 1637 | (a) | 120c on 60c (87) | 2.25 |
| a. | | Surcharge reading up | |
| 1638 | (d) | 200c on 60c (87) | 1.10 |
| 1639 | (a) | 225c on 65c (88) | 2.75 |
| 1640 | (f) | 120c on 55c (89) | 1.40 |
| 1641 | (b) | 120c on 90c (89) | |
| 1642 | (a) | 200c on 55c (89) | 5.25 |
| 1643 | (a) | 225c on 90c (89) | 1.10 |
| 1644 | (a) | 120c on 40c (90) | 2.25 |
| 1645 | (a) | 120c on 40c (90) | 1.10 |
| 1646 | (c) | 200c on 40c (90) | 1.10 |
| 1647 | (d) | 200c on 40c (R) (90) | 1.40 |
| 1648 | (c) | 200c on 375c (90) | 1.10 |
| a. | | 200c on 375c #1153a | 4.50 |
| 1649 | (a) | 225c on 40c (90) | 2.75 |
| 1650 | (i) | 225c on 40c (90) | 1.75 |
| 1651 | (k) | 260c on 375c (90) | 1.10 |

Issued: No. 1647, 2/9/87; Nos. 1646, 1648, 3/17/87; Nos. 1634-1635, 1638, 1643, 3/87; No. 1650, 6/87; No. 1640, 7/87; Nos. 1636-1637, 1639, 1642, 1644, 1649, 9/87; Nos. 1632-1633, 1641, 1645, 7/88; No. 1651, 10/88.

Surcharge on No. 1651 is placed over original value and has no obliterator.

**On Nos. 1154-1165**

| | | | |
|---|---|---|---|
| 1652 | (i) | 120c on 40c (91) | 2.25 |
| 1653 | (b) | 120c on 40c (91) | 1.10 |
| a. | | New value at LR | |
| 1654 | (a) | 225c on 40c (91) | 3.25 |
| 1655 | (i) | 225c on 40c (91) | 1.60 |
| 1656 | (b) | 120c on 50c (92) | |
| 1657 | (a) | 120c on 75c (92) | 2.75 |
| 1658 | (c) | 200c on 50c (92) | |
| 1659 | (c) | 200c on 75c (92) | 1.10 |
| 1660 | (b) | 120c on 60c (93) | |
| 1661 | (b) | 120c on 80c (93) | |
| 1662 | (i) | 225c on 60c (93) | 1.75 |
| 1663 | (i) | 225c on 80c (93) | 1.75 |
| 1664 | (b) | 600c on 80c (93) | |
| 1665 | (a) | 120c on 60c (94) | |
| 1666 | (b) | 120c on 60c (94) | |
| 1667 | (b) | 120c on 60c (95) | 1.10 |
| 1668 | (a) | 120c on 75c (95) | 3.50 |
| 1669 | (b) | 120c on 40c (96) | |
| 1670 | (a) | 225c on 65c (96) | 2.75 |

**Miniature Sheets**

| | | | |
|---|---|---|---|
| 1670A | | Sheet of 4 | 27.50 |
| b. | (a) | 600c on 130c #1412a (6) | |
| c. | (a) | 600c on 200c #1412b (6) | |
| d. | (a) | 600c on 260c #1412c (6) | |
| e. | (a) | 600c on 330c #1412d (6) | |
| 1670F | | Sheet of 4 | 15.00 |
| g. | (i) | 225c on #1393a (22) | |
| h. | (i) | 225c on #1393b (22) | |
| i. | (i) | 225c on #1393c (22) | |
| j. | (i) | 225c on #1393d (22) | |

Issued: Nos. 1658-1659, 3/17/87; Nos. 1655, 1662-1663, 6/87; Nos. 1652, 1654, 1657, 1664-1665, 1668, 1670, 9/87; No. 1670F, 11/9/87; No. 1670A, 11/20/87; Nos. 1653, 1656, 1660-1661, 1666-1667, 1669, 7/88.

For overprints see Nos. 1975, 1979.

**Series 2**
**On Nos. 1168-1204**

| | | | |
|---|---|---|---|
| 1671 | (b) | 120c on 90c (2) | 1.10 |
| 1672 | (b) | 120c on 50c (3) | 1.10 |
| 1673 | (b) | 120c on 50c (3) | 1.10 |
| 1674 | (b) | 200c on 90c (4) | |
| 1675 | (b) | 120c on 50c (6) | 1.10 |
| 1676 | (f) | 120c on 50c (6) | 1.10 |
| 1677 | (b) | 120c on 30c (7) | 1.10 |
| 1678 | (b) | 120c on 70c (8) | 1.10 |
| 1679 | (b) | 120c on 70c (9) | 1.10 |
| a. | | New value at LR | |
| 1680 | (b) | 120c on 90c (10) | 1.10 |
| 1681 | (b) | 120c on 70c (12) | 1.10 |
| a. | | New value at LL | |
| 1682 | (b) | 120c on 50c (13) | 1.10 |
| 1683 | (b) | 120c on 90c (13) | |
| 1684 | (b) | 120c on 30c (14) | |
| a. | | New value at UR | |
| 1685 | (b) | 120c on 50c (15) | 1.10 |
| 1686 | (b) | 120c on 85c (15) | |
| 1687 | (b) | 120c on 70c (17) | 13.50 |
| 1688 | (b) | 120c on 85c (18) | 1.10 |
| 1689 | (c) | 200c on 85c (18) | |
| 1690 | (b) | 120c on 50c (20) | 1.10 |
| 1691 | (f) | 120c on 50c (20) | 1.75 |

Issued: No. 1689, 3/17/87; Nos. 1673, 1676, 1691, 7/87; Nos. 1671-1672, 1674-1675, 1677-1688, 1690, 7/88.

**On Nos. 1205-1240**

| | | | |
|---|---|---|---|
| 1692 | (b) | 120c on 45c (21) | 1.10 |
| 1693 | (b) | 120c on 30c (22) | 1.10 |
| 1694 | (l) | 350c on 330c #O52 (23) | 1.10 |
| 1695 | (b) | 120c on 85c (24) | 1.10 |

| | | | | |
|---|---|---|---|---|
| 1696 | (j) | 120c on 140c (R) (25) | | 1.10 |
| 1697 | (l) | 250c on 225c #O46 (26) | | 1.10 |
| a. | | New value at UL | | |
| 1698 | (b) | 120c on 60c (27) | | 2.25 |
| 1699 | (b) | 120c on 90c (27) | | 1.10 |
| 1700 | (b) | 120c on 30c (28) | | 1.10 |
| a. | | New value at UL | | 2.25 |
| 1701 | (b) | 120c on 30c (30) | | 1.10 |
| 1702 | (k) | 240c on 140c (30) | | 1.10 |

No. 1702 not issued without surcharge.

| | | | | |
|---|---|---|---|---|
| 1703 | (l) | 150c on 175c #O44 (31) | | 1.10 |
| 1704 | (b) | 120c on 50c (32) | | 1.10 |
| 1705 | (f) | 120c on 50c (32) | | 1.10 |
| 1706 | (k) | 240c on 140c (34) | | 1.10 |
| 1707 | (l) | 125c on 175c #O42 (36) | | 1.10 |
| 1708 | (k) | 120c on 140c (38) | | 1.10 |
| 1709 | (k) | 120c on 140c (41) | | 1.10 |
| 1710 | (b) | 200c on 80c (42) | | 1.10 |
| 1711 | (l) | 150c on 140c (43) | | 1.10 |

Issued: No. 1705, 7/87; Nos. 1692-1693, 1695, 1698-1701, 1704, 1710, 7/88; Nos. 1702, 1706, 10/88; Nos. 1696, 1708, 1709, 2/22/89; Nos. 1694, 1697, 1703, 1711, 3/89.

### On Nos. 1245-1314

| | | | | |
|---|---|---|---|---|
| 1712 | (b) | 120c on 35c (45) | | 1.10 |
| 1713 | (b) | 120c on 85c (45) | | 1.10 |
| 1714 | (j) | 120c on 140c (R) (52) | | 1.10 |
| 1715 | (k) | 300c on 290c (53) | | 1.10 |
| 1716 | (j) | 120c on 175c (54) | | 1.10 |
| 1717 | (k) | 170c on 175c (58) | | 1.10 |
| 1718 | (l) | 250c on #048 (59) | | 1.10 |
| 1719 | (j) | 120c on 140c (R) (65) | | 1.10 |
| 1720 | (k) | 250c on 280c (66) | | 1.10 |
| 1721 | (k) | 250c on 280c (67) | | 1.10 |
| 1722 | (l) | 250c on 230c #O47 (68) | | 1.10 |
| 1723 | (l) | 250c on 260c #O49 (69) | | 1.10 |
| a. | | New value at UR | | 1.10 |
| 1724 | (l) | 600c on #O54 (70) | | 1.10 |
| 1725 | (l) | $12 on #O55 (71) | | 1.10 |
| 1726 | (l) | $15 on #O56 (84) | | 1.10 |
| 1727 | (k) | 240c on 425c (87) | | 1.10 |
| 1728 | (l) | 300c on 275c #O50 (90) | | 1.10 |
| 1729 | (l) | 125c on 130c #O41 (92) | | 1.10 |
| 1730 | (l) | 350c on #O53 (95) | | 1.10 |

On No. 1730 "Postage" reads up or down.

Issued: Nos. 1712-1713, 7/88; No. 1727, 10/88; Nos. 1714, 1716, 1719, 2/22/89; Nos. 1715, 1717-1718, 1720-1726, 1728-1730, 3/89.

Obliterator on Nos. 1708-1709, 1715, 1717, 1720-1721 has two thick bars.

### Stamps of Type A91 Overprinted

m    n

o    p

**1987**        *Perfs. as Before*

### Series 1

| | | | | |
|---|---|---|---|---|
| 1731 | (m) | 120c on #1021 (1) | | 5.25 |
| 1732 | (n) | 130c on #1023 (3) | | 2.50 |
| 1733 | (m) | 130c on #1028a (6) | | 5.00 |
| 1734 | (n) | 130c on #1028 (6) | | 2.50 |
| a. | | 130c on #1028a | | 2.50 |
| 1735 | (m) | 130c on #1034 (11) | | 5.00 |
| 1736 | (m) | 130c on #1037a (13) | | 3.25 |
| 1737 | (n) | 130c on #1413 (13) | | 5.00 |
| 1738 | (o) | 130c on #1037 (13) | | 5.00 |
| a. | | 130c on #1037a | | 1.10 |
| 1738B | (p) | 130c on #1413 (13) | | |
| 1739 | (n) | 200c on #1038 (14) | | 3.50 |
| 1740 | (n) | 130c on #1041 (16) | | 1.10 |
| 1741 | (n) | 130c on #1342 (18) | | 1.10 |
| 1742 | (o) | 130c on #1342 (18) | | 1.10 |
| 1743 | (m) | 130c on #1047a (20) | | 2.25 |

---

| | | | | |
|---|---|---|---|---|
| 1744 | (n) | 130c on #1047a (20) | | 2.50 |
| | | 130c on #1047 | | 4.00 |
| 1745 | (m) | 200c on #1048 (21) | | 2.25 |
| 1746 | (m) | 200c on #1048 (21) | | 2.25 |
| 1747 | (m) | 130c on #1055a (25) | | 4.50 |
| 1748 | (o) | 130c on #1055 (25) | | 1.10 |
| | | 130c on #1055a | | 1.10 |
| 1749 | (p) | 150c on #1056 (26) | | 1.10 |
| 1750 | (m) | 120c on #1058 (28) | | 5.00 |
| 1751 | (m) | 130c on #1343 (29) | | 1.10 |
| 1752 | (p) | 130c on #1343 (29) | | 1.10 |

Issued: Nos. 1732, 1734, 1737-1741, 1744, 1746, 1748, 1751, Mar; Nos. 1731, 1733, 1735-1736, 1743, 1745, 1747, 1750, July; No. 1738B, 11/20; Nos. 1742, 1749, 1752, Dec.

| | | | | |
|---|---|---|---|---|
| 1753 | (m) | 130c on #1344 (30) | | 1.10 |
| 1754 | (p) | 130c on #1344 (30) | | 1.10 |
| 1755 | (m) | 200c on #1063 (33) | | 1.10 |
| 1756 | (m) | 120c on #1067 (37) | | 1.60 |
| 1757 | (m) | 260c on #1070 (39) | | 2.25 |
| 1758 | (m) | 150c on #1072a, ovpt. reading up (40) | | 2.00 |
| a. | | 150c on #1072 | | 3.25 |
| 1759 | (m) | 150c on #1075a (42) | | 3.50 |
| 1760 | (m) | 150c on #1402 (42) | | 5.50 |
| 1761 | (m) | 200c on #1077a (43) | | 5.50 |
| 1762 | (m) | 150c on #1403 (43) | | 5.50 |
| 1763 | (m) | 200c on #1403 (43) | | 3.50 |
| 1764 | (m) | 150c on #1080 reading down (45) | | 2.25 |
| a. | | 150c on #1080a reading up | | 3.25 |
| 1765 | (m) | 120c on #1081 (46) | | 8.50 |
| 1766 | (m) | 120c on #1097 (56) | | 3.25 |
| 1767 | (m) | 130c on #1099 (58) | | 3.25 |
| 1768 | (n) | 130c on #1110 (66) | | 3.25 |
| 1769 | (p) | 130c on #1110 (66) | | 1.10 |
| 1770 | (p) | 120c on #1111 (67) | | 1.10 |
| 1771 | (m) | 250c on #1122 (74) | | 1.40 |
| 1772 | (n) | 200c on #1131 (79) | | 1.10 |
| 1773 | (o) | 130c on #1155 (91) | | 1.60 |

### Miniature Sheets of 4

| | | | | |
|---|---|---|---|---|
| 1774 | (n) | 200c on #1345 (4) | | 4.00 |
| 1775 | (n) | 200c on 130c #1346 (20) | | 5.50 |

### Series 2

| | | | | |
|---|---|---|---|---|
| 1776 | (n) | 200c on #1169 (5) | | 7.00 |
| 1777 | (n) | 200c on #1183 (9) | | 1.75 |

Issued: Nos. 1753, 1755, 1757, 1763, 1768, 1771-1777, Mar.; Nos. 1756, 1758, 1759-1762, 1764-1767, July. Nos. 1754, 1769-1770, Dec.

Overprint reads up on Nos. 1759, 1761. Overprint reads down on Nos. 1731, 1735, 1745, 1750, 1755, 1758a, 1760, 1762, 1763. See Nos. 1813-1814, 1844 for other stamps overprinted "1987" only.

### Nos. 1337, 1339, 1341 Surcharged

**1987, Mar. 6**      *Perfs. as Before*

| | | | | |
|---|---|---|---|---|
| 1777A | A92 | 200c on #1337 | 6.00 | 2.00 |
| 1777B | A92 | 200c on #1339 | 6.00 | 2.00 |
| 1777C | A92 | 200c on #1341 | 6.00 | 2.00 |
| | | Nos. 1777A-1777C (3) | 18.00 | 6.00 |

See note following No. 1341.

### Nos. 134, 136, 139a, and 192 Surcharged "Post Office / Corp. / 1977-1987" in Blue

*Perfs. as Before*

**1987, Feb. 17**    Litho.    **Wmk. 364**

| | | | | |
|---|---|---|---|---|
| 1778 | A28 | 25c on 2c #134 | .25 | .25 |
| 1779 | A28 | 25c on 5c #136 | .25 | .25 |
| 1780 | A28 | 25c on #192 | .25 | .25 |
| 1781 | A28 | 25c on 15c #139a | 5.50 | .50 |
| 1782 | A28 | 60c on 15c #139a | 12.00 | .40 |
| 1783 | A28 | $1.20 on 2c #134 | .85 | .85 |
| 1784 | A28 | $1.30 on 15c #139a | 13.00 | 3.75 |
| | | Nos. 1778-1784 (7) | 32.10 | 6.25 |

### Nos. 1032, 1032a Surcharged "12th World Orchid Conference" and "TOKYO JAPAN"

**1987, Mar. 12**    Unwmk.    *Perf. 14*

| | | | | |
|---|---|---|---|---|
| 1785 | A91 | 650c on 55c #1032 | 11.00 | 6.50 |
| a. | | 650c on 55c #1032a | 12.00 | 7.00 |

### No. 280 Surcharged with Names of Post Offices Operating in 1885

Overprints: a, AGRICOLA. b, BAGOTVILLE. c, BOURDA. d, BUXTON. e, CABACABURI. f, CAR- / MICHAEL STREET. g, COTTON / TREE. h, DUNOON. i, FELLOW- / SHIP. j, GROVE. k, HACKNEY. l, LEONORA. m, 1987. n, MALLALI. o, PROVI- / DENCE. p, RELIANCE. q, SPARTA. r, STEWART- / VILLE. s, TARLOGY. t, T.P.O. / BERBICE RIV. u, T.P.O. / DEM. RIV. v, T.P.O. / ESSEQ. RIV. w, T.P.O. / MASSARUNI / RIV. x, TUSCHEN / (De / VRIENDEN). y, ZORG.

*Perf. 14x13½*

**1987, Mar. 17**      **Wmk. 364**

| | | | | |
|---|---|---|---|---|
| 1786 | | Sheet of 25, #a.-y. | 42.50 | 35.00 |
| a.-y. | | A66 25c on 10c, any single | 1.50 | 1.25 |

British Guiana Post Office, 125th Anniv.

---

Columbus' Discovery of America, 500th Anniv. (in 1992) — A98

Paintings: 120c, Discovery of America, by Dali. 225c, Preparations Before the Journey, by unknown artist. 360c, Catholic Kings from Prado Museum. $6, Columbus' Fleet, by R. Monleon.

**1987, Mar. 30**    Litho.    *Perf. 13½*

| | | | | |
|---|---|---|---|---|
| 1787 | A98 | 120c multicolored | 1.75 | 1.00 |
| 1788 | A98 | 225c multicolored | 4.00 | 3.00 |
| 1789 | A98 | 360c multicolored | 6.25 | 3.00 |
| a. | | Strip of 3, #1787-1789 | 13.50 | 13.50 |

**Souvenir Sheet**

| | | | | |
|---|---|---|---|---|
| 1790 | A98 | $6 gold & multi | 15.00 | 15.00 |

No. 1790 exists with silver border.

### No. 289A Ovptd. "28 MARCH 1927 / PAA / GEO-POS"

**1987, Mar. 28**      *Perf. 13½x13*

| | | | | |
|---|---|---|---|---|
| 1811 | A66 | $10 on #289A | 24.00 | 13.00 |

First Georgetown to Port-of-Spain Flight, 50th Anniv.

### No. 285 Surcharged

**1987, Apr. 6**      *Perf. 14x13½*

| | | | | |
|---|---|---|---|---|
| 1812 | A66 | 25c on 40c #285 | 16.00 | .50 |

### Nos. 87-88, 90, 287 Surcharged or Overprinted "1987"

**1987, Apr.**      *Perfs. as Before*
**Watermarks and Printing Methods as Before**

| | | | | |
|---|---|---|---|---|
| 1813 | A14 | 25c on #88 | .75 | .10 |
| 1814 | A66 | $1 on #287 | 17.00 | 1.00 |
| 1815 | A14 | 120c on 6c #87 | .90 | .25 |
| 1816 | A14 | 320c on 6c #87 | 1.50 | .75 |
| 1817 | A14 | 500c on 40c #90 | 2.00 | 2.00 |
| | | Nos. 1813-1817 (5) | 22.15 | 4.10 |

Issued: Nos. 1813, 1815-1817, 4/21; No. 1814, Apr.

### No. 1461 Ovptd. "CAPEX '87"

**1987, June 10**    Litho.    *Perf. 14*

| | | | | |
|---|---|---|---|---|
| 1822 | A96 | 320c Pair, #a.-b. | 5.50 | 5.50 |
| c. | | on #1461, imperf. between | | 11.00 |

For surcharges see Nos. 2030, E15.

### Nos. 626-628 Ovptd. "1987"

**Wmk. 314 Upright**

**1987, July 15**    Engr.    *Perf. 12½x13*

| | | | | |
|---|---|---|---|---|
| 1823 | A60 | $1.20 on #626 | 1.00 | .25 |

**Wmk. 314 Sideways**

| | | | | |
|---|---|---|---|---|
| 1824 | A60 | $1.30 on #627 | 12.00 | 1.00 |
| 1825 | A60 | $2.40 on #628 | 15.00 | 5.00 |
| | | Nos. 1823-1825 (3) | 28.00 | 6.25 |

A99

A100

Locomotives — A101

Nos. 1826a, 1827a, Alexandra 4. Nos. 1826b, 1827b, Diesel locomotive facing right. Nos. 1826c, 1827c, Steam locomotive facing right. Nos. 1826d, 1827d, Diesel locomotive No. 21 facing left.

---

Nos. 1829a, 1830b, Alexandra 4. Nos. 1829b, 1830a, Diesel locomotive. Nos. 1829c, 1830d, Steam locomotive facing right. Nos. 1829d, 1830c, Diesel locomotive No. 21. No. 1830e, Photograph of trains in Georgetown Station. No. 1831, Steam locomotive pulling cattle cars, map of routes from Parika to Vreedenhoop and from Georgetown to Rosignol.

**1987, Aug. 3**      *Perf. 15*

| | | | | |
|---|---|---|---|---|
| 1826 | | Block of 4 | 2.00 | 2.00 |
| a.-d. | | A99 $1.20 green, any single | .40 | .40 |
| 1827 | | Block of 5 | 5.00 | 5.00 |
| a.-d. | | A99 $3.20 blue, any single | .85 | .85 |
| e. | | A100 $3.20 blue | .85 | .85 |
| 1828 | A101 | $12 shown | 4.00 | 4.00 |
| | | Nos. 1826-1828 (3) | 11.00 | 11.00 |

**1987, Dec. 4**

| | | | | |
|---|---|---|---|---|
| 1829 | | Block of 4 | 2.40 | 2.40 |
| a.-d. | | A99 $1.20 rose lake, any single | .50 | .50 |
| 1830 | | Block of 5 | 6.25 | 6.25 |
| a.-d. | | A99 $3.30 blk, any single | 1.10 | 1.10 |
| e. | | A100 $3.30 black | 1.10 | 1.10 |
| 1831 | A101 | $10 multi | 4.50 | 4.50 |
| | | Nos. 1829-1831 (3) | 13.15 | 13.15 |

Sizes: Nos. 1827e, 1830e, 84x57mm. Nos. 1828, 1831, 90x40mm.

For surcharges see Nos. E12-E13. For overprints see Nos. 1910-1911, 1935-1938, 2024-2028F, 2054, 2056.

### No. 287 Overprinted

Overprints read: No. 1832, "FAIREY NICHOLL / 15 AUG 1927 / GEO-MAB"; No. 1833, "FAIREY NICHOLL / 8 AUG 1927 / GEO-MAZ".

**1987, Aug. 7**    Litho.    *Perf. 13½x13*

| | | | | |
|---|---|---|---|---|
| 1832 | A66 | $1 "MAB" on #287 | 16.00 | 11.00 |
| 1833 | A66 | $1 "MAZ" on #287 | 16.00 | 11.00 |
| a. | | Pair, #1832-1833 | 32.50 | 27.50 |

### Nos. 1291A and 1461c Surcharged

Surcharges Read: No. 1834, "CRISTOVAO COLOMBO / 1492 — 1992"; No. 1835, "CHRISTOPHE COLOMB / 1492 — 1992"; No. 1836, "THE PASSING OF HALLEY'S COMET: / PROPHESY OF THE ARRIVAL OF / HERNAN CORTES 1519. / V CENTENARY OF THE LANDING OF / CHRISTOPHER COLUMBUS / IN THE AMERICAS".

**Unwmk.**

**1987, Oct. 9**    Litho.    *Perf. 14*

| | | | | |
|---|---|---|---|---|
| 1834 | A91 | 950c on 900c #1291A | 3.00 | 3.50 |
| 1835 | A91 | 950c on 900c #1291A | 3.00 | 3.50 |
| a. | | Pair, #1834-1835 | 7.50 | 7.50 |

**Imperf**

| | | | | |
|---|---|---|---|---|
| 1836 | A96 | $20 on 320c #1461c | 8.50 | 8.50 |

### Nos. 135-136 Surcharged "DEEPAVALI / 1987"

**1987, Nov. 2**    Litho.    *Perf. 13x13½*

| | | | | |
|---|---|---|---|---|
| 1837 | A28 | 25c on 3c #135 | 3.00 | .40 |
| 1838 | A28 | $3 on 5c #136 | 9.00 | 5.00 |

### No. 43 Surcharged "CHRISTMAS / 1987" in Red

**Watermarks and Printing Methods as Before**

**1987, Nov. 9**      *Perfs. as Before*

| | | | | |
|---|---|---|---|---|
| 1839 | A7 | 20c on 6c #43 | 5.00 | .50 |

### No. 1502 Surcharged "1987" in Blue Miniature Sheet

| | | | | |
|---|---|---|---|---|
| 1840 | A88 | 120c on 60c #1502 | 1.75 | 1.75 |

### No. 920 surcharged in Red Nos. 329, 1037, 1040, 1056, 1110-1111, 1494 Overprinted or Surcharged

Overprint or Surcharges read: No. 1844, "1987"; Nos. 1845-1849, 1851, "PROTECT OUR HERITAGE '87"; No. 1850, "Protect Our Heritage '87".

**1987, Dec. 9**      *Perfs. as Before*
**Watermarks and Printing Methods as Before**

| | | | | |
|---|---|---|---|---|
| 1844 | A77 | 30c Sheet of 12, #a.-l., on #329 | 7.00 | 7.00 |
| 1845 | A91 | 120c on #1111 | 1.50 | 1.50 |
| 1846 | A91 | 130c on #1110 | 1.75 | 1.75 |
| 1847 | A91 | 150c on #1056 | 2.25 | 2.25 |
| 1848 | A91 | 180c on #1040 | 2.50 | 2.50 |
| 1849 | A91 | 320c on #1137 | 3.00 | 3.00 |
| 1850 | A89 | 320c Triptych, #a.-c. on 120c #920 | 9.00 | 9.00 |
| 1851 | A91 | 650c on #1494 | 5.00 | 5.00 |
| | | Nos. 1844-1851 (8) | 32.00 | 32.00 |

1988 Summer Olympics, Seoul — A102

**1987, Dec. 30    Litho.    Perf. 13½x14**
| | | | |
|---|---|---|---|---|
| 1852 | A102 | $2 Jumping | 2.50 | 2.25 |
| 1853 | A102 | $3 Discus | 3.75 | 3.25 |
| 1854 | A102 | $5 Vase | 6.50 | 5.50 |
| a. | | Strip of 3, #1852-1854 | 13.50 | 13.50 |

**Souvenir Sheet**
**Perf. 14**
| | | | |
|---|---|---|---|
| 1855 | A102 | $3.50 Olympic Rings, horiz. | 10.00 | 10.00 |

**Christmas 1987 — A103**

Paintings — No. 1856: a, The Virgin of the Rocks, by Da Vinci. b, Virgin with Grapes, by Mignard. c, Sacred Family, by Raphael. d, Virgin Mary, by Lucas Cranach. No. 1857, Adoration of Three Kings, by Rubens.

**1988, Jan. 7    Litho.    Perf. 14**
| | | | |
|---|---|---|---|
| 1856 | A103 | $2 Strip of 4, #a.-d. | 7.50 | 7.50 |

**Souvenir Sheet**
| | | | |
|---|---|---|---|
| 1857 | A103 | $10 Sheet of 1 | 13.50 | 13.50 |

Dated 1987.

**Nos. 397, 405 and 651 Ovptd. or Surcharged "'AUSTRALIA' / 1987 JAMBOREE 1988" in Red**

**1988, Jan. 7    Perf. 13½x13**
| | | | |
|---|---|---|---|
| 1858 | A17 | $4.40 on #405 | |
| 1859 | A17 | $10 on #397 | |
| 1860 | A17 | $10 on #651 | |
| 1861 | A17 | $10 on #405 | |
| a. | | $10 on #405a | |
| | | Nos. 1858-1861 (4) | 10.00 |

Obliterator on Nos. 1859-1861 is red fleur-de-lis. Size and location of overprint varies.

**Nos. 68 and 70 Surcharged "IFAD / For a World / Without Hunger"**
**Perf. 14x14½**

**1988, Jan. 26    Photo.    Wmk. 364**
| | | | |
|---|---|---|---|
| 1862 | A7 | 25c on 1c #68 | 2.00 | .30 |
| 1863 | A7 | $5 on 3c #70 | 7.00 | 3.00 |
| | | Nos. 1862-1863 (2) | 9.00 | 3.30 |

No. 1862 uses new denomination as obliterator and No. 1863 uses "X."

Flora and Fauna A104

Mushrooms — No. 1864: a, Corprinus comatus. b, Amanita muscaria. c, Pholiota aurivella. d, Laccaria amethstina.
Birds — No. 1865: a, Starling. b, Reed warbler. c, Kingfisher. d, Goldcrest.
Cats — No. 1866: a, Himalayan. b, American shorthaired. c, Maine coon. d, Abyssinian.
Cactus flowers — No. 1866: e, Sulcorebutia densiseta. f, Subutia hyalacantha. g, Echinopsis. h, Lobivia polycephala.
Nos. 1866a-1866h horiz.

**1988, Jan. 28    Perf. 14**
| | | | |
|---|---|---|---|
| 1864 | A104 | $2 Strip of 4, #a.-d. | 10.50 | 10.50 |
| 1865 | A104 | $2 Strip of 4, #a.-d. | 9.50 | 9.50 |

**Miniature Sheet**
**Perf. 14x13½**
| | | | |
|---|---|---|---|
| 1866 | A104 | $2 Sheet of 8, #a.-h. | 13.00 | 13.00 |

Dated 1987.

---

Santa Maria A105

Ships: a, Santa Maria. b, Grande Francoise. No. 1869, San Martin, horiz.

**1988, Feb. 10    Litho.    Perf. 13½x14**
| | | | |
|---|---|---|---|
| 1867 | A105 | $7 Pair, #a.-b., pale yel & multi | 6.00 | 6.00 |
| 1868 | A105 | $7 Pair, #a.-b., bl & multi | 6.00 | 6.00 |

**Souvenir Sheet**
**Perf. 14**
| | | | |
|---|---|---|---|
| 1869 | A105 | $7 silver & multi | 12.00 | 12.00 |

Discovery of America, 500th anniv. (in 1992). Nos. 1867-1868 printed checkerwise with se-tenant labels describing ship dimensions. No. 1869 exists with gold border.

**Nos. 136, 139a, and 146 Surcharged "Republic / Day / 1988" in Blue**
**Perfs. as Before**

**1988, Feb. 23    Litho.    Wmk. 364**
| | | | |
|---|---|---|---|
| 1870 | A28 | 25c on 5c #136 | .25 | .25 |
| 1871 | A28 | 120c on 15c #139a | 4.50 | .75 |
| 1872 | A28 | $10 on $2 #146 | 2.00 | 2.00 |
| | | Nos. 1870-1872 (3) | 6.75 | 3.00 |

**No. 283A Surcharged with Names of Post Offices Operating in 1900**

Overprints: a, Albouystown. b, Anns Grove. c, Amacura. d, Arakaka. e, Baramanni. f, Cuyuni. g, Hope Placer. h, HMPS. i, Kitty. j, M'M'Zorg. k, Maccasema. l, 1988. m, Morawhanna. n, Naamryck. o, Purini. p, Potaro / Landing. q, Rockstone. r, Rosignol. s, Stanleytown. t, Santa Rosa. u, Tumatumari. v, Weldaad. w, Wismar. x, TPO Berbice / Railway.

**1988, Apr. 5    Perf. 14x13½**
| | | | |
|---|---|---|---|
| 1873 | A66 | 25c Sheet of 25, #a.-k., m.-x., 2 #l. | 40.00 | 32.50 |

British Guiana Post Office, 125th Anniv.

**No. 725 Surcharged "Olympic / Games / 1988"**
**Perf. 14½x14**

**1988, May 3    Litho.    Wmk. 373**
| | | | |
|---|---|---|---|
| 1897 | A73 | 120c Sheet of 12, #a.-l. | 18.00 | 18.00 |

**Nos. 136-137 and 146 Surcharged "Caricom Day / 1988"**
**Perf. 13x13½**

**1988, June 15    Litho.    Wmk. 364**
| | | | |
|---|---|---|---|
| 1898 | A28 | 25c on 5c #136 | .90 | .25 |
| 1899 | A28 | $1.20 on #137 | .90 | .25 |
| 1900 | A28 | $10 on $2 #146 | 4.50 | 6.00 |
| | | Nos. 1898-1900 (3) | 6.30 | 6.50 |

**No. 286A Overprinted**

Overprints: a, 1988. b, WHO / 1948-1988.

**1988, June 17    Litho.    Perf. 14x13½**
| | | | |
|---|---|---|---|
| 1901 | | Sheet of 25, 24 #a., 1 #b. | 27.50 | 25.00 |
| a. | | A28 60c any single | .40 | .40 |
| b. | | A28 60c | 17.50 | 17.50 |

World Health Day, 40th anniv.

**Nos. 929, 1053a, 1063, 1131 and 1161 Overprinted**

Overprints: No. 1903, "CONSERVE TREES" on ocher stamp, "CONSERVE ELECTRICITY on green stamp, "CONSERVE WATER on brown stamp. No. 1904, "CONSERVE ELECTRICITY" on ocher stamp, "CONSERVE WATER on green stamp, "CONSERVE TREES on brown stamp. No. 1905, "CONSERVE WATER" on ocher stamp, "CONSERVE TREES on green stamp, "CONSERVE ELECTRICITY on brown stamp. Nos. 1906-1909, "CONSERVE / WATER".

**Perfs. as Before**

**1988, July 15    Litho.**
**Watermarks as Before**
| | | | |
|---|---|---|---|
| 1903 | | Triptych | 3.50 | 3.50 |
| a.-c. | | A90 120c any single | .90 | .60 |
| 1904 | | Triptych | 3.50 | 3.50 |
| a.-c. | | A90 120c any single | .90 | .60 |
| 1905 | | Triptych | 3.50 | 3.50 |
| a.-c. | | A90 120c any single | .90 | .90 |
| 1906 | A91 | 200c on #1063 | 1.10 | 1.10 |
| 1907 | A91 | 200c on #1131 | | |

---

| | | | | |
|---|---|---|---|---|
| 1908 | A91 | 225c on #1053a | 1.10 | 1.10 |
| 1909 | A91 | 350c on #1161 | 1.10 | 1.10 |
| | | Nos. 1903-1909 (7) | 14.90 | 14.90 |

Location and size of overprint varies.

**Nos. 1826 and 1829 Overprinted**

Overprints read: Nos. 1910a, 1911a, "BEWARE / OF ANIMALS"; Nos. 1910b, 1911b, "BEWARE / OF CHILDREN"; Nos. 1910c, 1911c, "DRIVE SAFELY"; Nos. 1910d, 1911d, "DO NOT / DRINK AND DRIVE".

**Unwmk.**

**1988, July 15    Litho.    Perf. 15**
**Block of 4, #a.-d.**
| | | | |
|---|---|---|---|
| 1910 | A99 | $1.20 on #1826 | 7.50 | 7.50 |
| 1911 | A99 | $1.20 on #1829 | 7.50 | 7.50 |
| | | Nos. 1910-1911 (2) | 15.00 | 15.00 |

**No. 287 Ovptd. or Surcharged**
**Perf. 13½x13**

**1988, July    Wmk. 364**
| | | | |
|---|---|---|---|
| 1912 | A66 | $1 "1988" on #287 | 13.00 | 1.50 |
| 1913 | A66 | 120c on $1 #287 | 13.00 | 1.50 |

**No. 421 Surcharged with New Value and "1988"**

**1988?    Litho.    Perf. 13½x14**
| | | | |
|---|---|---|---|
| 1913A | A80 | $1.20 on $1.10 on $3 #421 | | |

**Nos. 1037a, 1047a, 1056-1057, 1066-1068, 1097, 1099, 1109-1109a, 1110-1111, 1113, 1115, 1122, 1125, 1129, 1147, 1149, and 1155 Ovptd. "CONSERVE / OUR RESOURCES"**

**1988, July    Perf. 14**
**Watermarks as Before**
**Series 1**
**Plate Numbers in Parentheses**
| | | | |
|---|---|---|---|
| 1914 | | 130c on #1037a (13) | 1.25 | .75 |
| a. | | Overprint inverted | | 2.00 |

No. 1914a probably is as common as No. 1914.

| | | | | |
|---|---|---|---|---|
| 1915 | A91 | 130c on #1047a (20) | 1.25 | .75 |
| 1916 | A91 | 150c on #1056 (26) | 1.25 | .75 |
| 1917 | A91 | 120c on #1057 (27) | 1.25 | .75 |
| 1918 | A91 | 120c on #1066 (36) | 1.25 | .75 |
| 1919 | A91 | 120c on #1067 (37) | 1.25 | .75 |
| 1920 | A91 | 130c on #1068 (38) | 1.25 | .75 |
| 1921 | A91 | 120c on #1097 (56) | 1.25 | .75 |
| 1922 | A91 | 120c on #1099 (58) | 1.25 | .75 |
| 1923 | A91 | 100c on #1109 (65) | 1.25 | .75 |
| a. | | 100c on #1109a | | |
| 1924 | A91 | 130c on #1110 (66) | 1.25 | .75 |
| 1925 | A91 | 130c on #1111 (67) | 1.25 | .75 |
| 1926 | A91 | 100c on #1113 (68) | 1.25 | .75 |
| 1927 | A91 | 130c on #1115 (69) | 1.25 | .75 |
| 1928 | A91 | 250c on #1122 (74) | 1.25 | .75 |
| 1929 | A91 | 150c on #1125 (76) | 1.25 | .75 |
| 1930 | A91 | 150c on #1129 (78) | 1.25 | .75 |
| 1931 | A91 | 150c on #1147 (87) | 1.25 | .75 |
| 1932 | A91 | 100c on #1149 (88) | 1.25 | .75 |
| 1933 | A91 | 130c on #1155 (91) | 1.25 | .75 |

**Nos. 1827a-1827d and 1830a-1830d Ovptd. with Red Cross**

**1988, Aug. 3    Litho.    Perf. 15**
| | | | |
|---|---|---|---|
| 1935 | A99 | $3.20 Pair, #a.-b., on #1827a, 1827c | 3.50 | 3.50 |
| 1936 | A99 | $3.20 Pair, #a.-b., on #1827b, 1827d | 3.50 | 3.50 |
| 1937 | A99 | $3.30 Pair, #a.-b., on #1830a, 1830c | 3.50 | 3.50 |
| 1938 | A99 | $3.30 Pair, #a.-b., on #1830b, 1830d | 3.50 | 3.50 |
| | | Nos. 1935-1938 (4) | 14.00 | 14.00 |

**Nos. 1038, 1131 Ovptd. and Nos. 1147, 1175 Surcharged "1928-1988 / CRICKET / JUBILEE"**

**1988, Sept. 5    Litho.    Perf. 14**
**Watermarks as Before**
**Plate Numbers in Parentheses**
| | | | |
|---|---|---|---|
| 1939 | A91 | 200c on #1038 (14) | 25.00 | 30.00 |
| 1940 | A91 | 200c on #1131 (79) | 1.25 | .50 |
| 1941 | A91 | 800c on 150c #1147 (87) | 10.00 | 14.00 |
| 1942 | A91 | 800c on 160c #1175 (5) | 3.75 | 3.75 |
| | | Nos. 1939-1942 (4) | 40.00 | 48.25 |

---

**Series 1**
**Plate Numbers in Parentheses**
**Nos. 1063, 1081, 1139, 1147, 1161, 1185, 1219, 1232, and 1305 Ovptd. and No. 1227 Surcharged "OLYMPIC GAMES / 1988"**

**1988, Sept. 16    Unwmk.**
| | | | |
|---|---|---|---|
| 1943 | A91 | 200c on #1063 (33) | .70 | .70 |
| 1944 | A91 | 120c on #1081 (46) | .70 | .70 |
| 1945 | A91 | 300c on #1139 (83) | .70 | .70 |
| 1946 | A91 | 150c on #1147 (87) | .70 | .70 |
| 1947 | A91 | 350c on #1161 (94) | .90 | .90 |

**Series 2**
| | | | |
|---|---|---|---|
| 1948 | A91 | 320c on #1185 (10) | .90 | .90 |
| 1949 | A91 | 350c on #1219 (29) | .90 | .90 |
| 1950 | A91 | 300c on 360c #1227 (34) | .90 | .90 |
| 1951 | A91 | 130c on #1232 (38) | .90 | .90 |
| 1952 | A91 | 330c on #1305 (82) | .90 | .90 |

Overprint reads up on No. 1947.

**Type A83 Ovptd. or Surcharged "OLYMPICS 1988" (a.) or "KOREA 1988" (b.)**

**1988    Litho.    Wmk. 364    Perf. 13½**
| | | | |
|---|---|---|---|
| 1953 | A83 | $1.20 Pair, #a.-b. | 1.25 | 1.25 |
| 1954 | A83 | 130c on $1.20, pair, #a.-b. | 1.25 | 1.25 |
| 1955 | A83 | 150c on $1.20, pair, #a.-b. | 1.25 | 1.25 |
| 1956 | A83 | 200c on $1.20, pair, #a.-b. | 1.50 | 1.50 |
| 1957 | A83 | 350c on $1.20, pair, #a.-b. | 1.75 | 1.75 |
| c. | | Strip of 5, #1953a-1957a | 7.00 | 7.00 |
| d. | | Strip of 5, #1953b-1957b | 7.00 | 7.00 |

Overprint obliterates inscription spelled "LOS ANGELLES."

**No. 1087 Overprinted, No. 1143 Surcharged**

Overprint or Surcharge reads: "V CENTENARY OF / THE LANDING OF / CHRISTOPHER COLUMBUS / IN THE AMERICAS".

**Unwmk.**

**1988, Oct. 12    Litho.    Perf. 14**
| | | | |
|---|---|---|---|
| 1958 | A91 | 320c on #1087 | 2.50 | .75 |
| 1959 | A91 | $15 on 360c #1143 | 5.00 | 5.00 |
| | | Nos. 1958-1959 (2) | 7.50 | 5.75 |

**Nos. 1027, 1036, 1040, 1046, 1054, 1062, 1070, 1071, 1074, 1076, 1079, 1102, 1104, 1133, 1137 and 1143 Surcharged in Blue or Black; Nos. 1053, 1053a, 1102, 1591A and 1670F Ovptd. or Surcharged in Blue**

Overprints read: Nos. 1960-1963, 1965-1974, 1976-1978, "SEASON's / GREETINGS"; Others, "SEASON'S / GREETINGS / 1988".

**1988, Nov. 10    Perfs. as Before**
**Watermarks and Printing Methods as Before**
**Plate Numbers in Parentheses**
| | | | |
|---|---|---|---|
| 1960 | A91 | 120c on 100c #1027 (6) | 2.00 | |
| 1961 | A91 | 120c on 100c #1036 (13) | 2.00 | |
| 1962 | A91 | 240c on 180c #1040 (15) (Bk) | 1.00 | |
| 1963 | A91 | 120c on 100c #1046 (20) | 2.00 | |
| 1964 | A91 | 225c on #1053 (24) | 1.00 | |
| a. | | 225c on #1053a | 2.50 | |
| 1965 | A91 | 120c on 100c #1054 (25) | 2.00 | |
| 1966 | A91 | 150c on 100c #1062 (32) (Bk) | 1.00 | |
| 1967 | A91 | 260c on 100c #1070 (39) (Bk) | 1.00 | |
| 1968 | A91 | 120c on 100c #1071 (40) | 2.00 | |
| 1969 | A91 | 120c on 100c #1074 (42) (Bk) | 2.00 | |
| 1970 | A91 | 120c on 100c #1076 (43) | 2.00 | |
| 1971 | A91 | 120c on 100c #1079 (45) | 2.00 | |
| 1972 | A91 | 225c on #1102 (60) (Bk) | 1.00 | |
| 1973 | A91 | 225c on #1102 (60) | 1.00 | |
| 1974 | A91 | 150c on #1104 (62) (Bk) | 1.00 | |
| 1975 | A91 | 225c on #1591A (65) | 1.50 | |
| 1976 | A91 | 330c on #1133 (80) (Bk) | 1.00 | |
| 1977 | A91 | 120c on #1137 (82) (Bk) | 1.00 | |
| 1978 | A91 | 360c on #1143 (85) (Bk) | 1.00 | |
| | | Nos. 1960-1978 (19) | 27.50 | |

**Miniature Sheet**
| | | | |
|---|---|---|---|
| 1979 | A91 | 225c on #1670F (22) | 4.75 | 4.75 |

Size and location of overprint varies.

## Nos. 72, 713 and 932 Surcharged or Ovptd. "CHRISTMAS / 1988" in Red or Black

**1988, Nov. 16**     *Perfs. as Before*
**Watermarks and Printing Methods as Before**

| | | | | |
|---|---|---|---|---|
| **1981** | A7 | 20c on 6c #72 | .35 | .25 |
| **1982** | A86 | Block of 4 (Bk) | 4.00 | 6.00 |
| a. | | 120c on #713a | 1.00 | 1.50 |
| b. | | 120c on 130c #713b | 1.00 | 1.50 |
| c. | | 120c on 150c #713c | 1.00 | 1.50 |
| d. | | 120c on 200c #713d | 1.00 | 1.50 |
| **1983** | A90a | 500c on 330c #932 | 2.50 | 3.00 |
| | | *Nos. 1981-1983 (3)* | 6.85 | 9.25 |

Overprint reads up on No. 1983.

## Nos. 288, 289, and 289A Surcharged or Ovptd. for Prevention of AIDS

Beginnning of overprint reads: Nos. 1984a, 1985e, "Get information..." Nos. 1984b, 1985a, "Get the facts..." Nos. 1984c, 1985b, "Say no to drugs..." Nos. 1984d, 1985c, $2, $5, $10, "Protect yourself..." Nos. 1984e, 1985d, "Be compassionate..."

*Perf. 13½x13*
**1988, Dec. 1**    Litho.    **Wmk. 364**

| | | | | |
|---|---|---|---|---|
| **1984** | A66 | 120c Strip of 5, #a.-e., on #289 | 18.50 | 18.50 |
| **1985** | A66 | 120c Strip of 5, #a.-e., on #289A | 18.50 | 18.50 |
| **1986** | A66 | $2 on #288 | 12.00 | 3.00 |
| **1987** | A66 | $5 on #289 | 14.00 | 7.50 |
| **1988** | A66 | $10 on #289A | 16.00 | 12.00 |
| | | *Nos. 1984-1988 (5)* | 79.00 | 59.50 |

For surcharge, see No. 4176.

1988 Winter Olympics, Calgary — A106

Design: $3.50, Olympic rings.

**1988, Dec. 1**      *Perf. 14*

| | | | | |
|---|---|---|---|---|
| **1989** | A106 | $7 Downhill skiing | 11.00 | 11.00 |

**Souvenir Sheet**

| | | | | |
|---|---|---|---|---|
| **1990** | A106 | $3.50 Sheet of 1 | 6.00 | 6.00 |

No. 1989 exists in souvenir sheet of 1. Value $40.

Christmas A107

Paintings: No. 1991a, Virgin and Child Between St. George and St. Catherine, by Titian. b. Adoration of the Magi, by Titian. No. 1992a, Holy Family, by Rubens. b, Adoration of the Shepherds, by Rubens. $8, The Madonna, by Titian.

*Perf. 14x13½, 13½x14*
**1988, Dec. 15**      Litho.

| | | | | |
|---|---|---|---|---|
| **1991** | A107 | $2 Pair, #a.-b. | 7.00 | 7.00 |
| **1992** | A107 | $2 Pair, #a.-b. | 7.00 | 7.00 |

**Souvenir Sheet**
*Perf. 13½x14*

| | | | | |
|---|---|---|---|---|
| **1993** | A107 | $8 multicolored | 17.00 | 17.00 |

Nos. 1991a-1991b, 1992a-1992b exist in souvenir sheets of 1.

## Abolition of Slavery Type of 1985

**1988, Dec. 16**    Litho.    *Perf. 14*
**Designs as Before**

| | | | | |
|---|---|---|---|---|
| **1994** | A93 | 25c brown & black | .25 | .25 |
| **1995** | A93 | 60c magenta & black | .50 | .50 |
| **1996** | A93 | 130c green & black | 1.00 | 1.00 |
| **1997** | A93 | 150c blue & black | 1.25 | 1.25 |
| | | *Nos. 1994-1997 (4)* | 3.00 | 3.00 |

## Nos. 1087, 1167, and 1200 Surcharged "SALUTING WINNERS / OLYMPIC GAMES / 1988"

**Unwmk.**
**1989, Jan. 3**    Litho.    *Perf. 14*

| | | | | |
|---|---|---|---|---|
| **1998** | A91 | $5.50 on 560c #1167 | 1.75 | 1.25 |
| **1999** | A91 | $9 on 320c #1200 | 2.25 | 2.25 |
| **2000** | A91 | $10.50 on 320c #1087 | 3.00 | 3.00 |
| | | *Nos. 1998-2000 (3)* | 7.00 | 6.50 |

**Miniature Sheets**

Red Cross, 125th Anniv. — A108

Designs: No. 2001, Henri Dunant, vert. No. 2002, First maritime ambulance. No. 2003, Red Cross hospital ship in African War. No. 2004, Red Cross air ambulance. No. 2005, Red Cross train.

Nos. 2001-2004 printed with red cross in center of sheet. Each stamp contains part of the red cross at the: a, LR. b, LL. c, UR. d, UL.

*Perf. 13½x14, 14x13½*
**1989, Jan. 5**       Litho.

| | | | | |
|---|---|---|---|---|
| **2001** | A108 | $2 Sheet of 4, #a.-d. | 10.00 | 10.00 |
| **2002** | A108 | $2 Sheet of 4, #a.-d. | 10.00 | 10.00 |
| **2003** | A108 | $2 Sheet of 4, #a.-d. | 10.00 | 10.00 |
| **2004** | A108 | $2 Sheet of 4, #a.-d. | 10.00 | 10.00 |
| | | *Nos. 2001-2004 (4)* | 40.00 | 40.00 |

**Souvenir Sheet**
*Perf. 14x13½*

| | | | | |
|---|---|---|---|---|
| **2005** | A108 | $7 Sheet of 1 | 11.00 | 11.00 |

Dated 1988.

Trains — A109

Designs: a, Hernalser sleeping carriage. b, 5 Forney locomotive. c, Austrian sleeping carriage. d, Pacific 231 locomotive. $10, First Japanese imperial train.

**1989, Jan. 5**    Litho.    *Perf. 14*

| | | | | |
|---|---|---|---|---|
| **2006** | A109 | $2 Sheet of 4, #a.-d. | 18.00 | 18.00 |

**Souvenir Sheet**

| | | | | |
|---|---|---|---|---|
| **2007** | A109 | $10 multicolored | 12.00 | 12.00 |

Nos. 2006a-2006d exist in souvenir sheets of 1. Value, each $3.75. Dated 1988.

Naval Airship LZ 92, 1916 — A110

No. 2008: a, Astronaut on moon. b, Graf Zeppelin over San Francisco Bay, 1929. c, Testu-Brissy on horseback ascending in balloon, 1798. No. 2009, Graf Zeppelin LZ 127.

**1989, Jan. 26**      *Perf. 14*

| | | | | |
|---|---|---|---|---|
| **2007A** | A110 | $2 black | 3.00 | 3.00 |
| **2008** | A110 | $2 Strip of 3, #a.-c. | 8.00 | 8.00 |

**Souvenir Sheet**

| | | | | |
|---|---|---|---|---|
| **2009** | A110 | $2 Sheet of 1 | 10.00 | 6.00 |

Nos. 2007A, 2008b, 2009, Ferdinand von Zeppelin, 150th birth anniv. in 1988. No. 2008a, 1st moon landing, 20th anniv. in 1989. The inscriptions on Nos. 2007A and 2009 are in error. Dated 1988.

Mushrooms — A111

No. 2010: a, Cortinarius bolaris. b, Cortinarius laniger. c, Tricholoma sulphureum. d, Lepiota cristata.
No. 2011, Sarcoscypha coccinea, vert.

**1989, Feb. 1**      *Perf. 14x13½*

| | | | | |
|---|---|---|---|---|
| **2010** | A111 | $2 Block of 4, #a.-d. | 15.00 | 15.00 |

**Souvenir Sheet**
*Perf. 13½x14*

| | | | | |
|---|---|---|---|---|
| **2011** | A111 | $5 Sheet of 1 | 11.00 | 11.00 |

Dated 1988.

Boy Scout Jamboree, Australia A112

Design: $8, Scouts of different races.

**1989, Feb. 10**

| | | | | |
|---|---|---|---|---|
| **2012** | A112 | $10 grn, black & yel | 15.00 | 15.00 |

**Souvenir Sheet**

| | | | | |
|---|---|---|---|---|
| **2013** | A112 | $8 Sheet of 1 | 15.00 | 15.00 |

Dated 1988. No. 2012 exists in souvenir sheet of 1.

1988 Summer Olympics, Seoul — A113     Emblem of South American Soccer Federation — A113a

1992 Winter Olympics, Albertville — A113b

Designs: No. 2014, Florence Griffith-Joyner. No. 2015, Carl Lewis. No. 2016, Equestrian. No. 2017, Runners, horiz. No. 2018, City skyline, Olympic Rings, horiz. No. 2019, 1988 & 1992 Olympic mascots, horiz. No. 2022, Griffith-Joyner, Lewis, horiz. No. 2023, Cosmic Athlete by Dali, horiz.

**1989, Feb. 15**    Litho.    *Perf. 14*

| | | | | |
|---|---|---|---|---|
| **2014** | A113 | $2 multicolored | 3.50 | 3.50 |
| **2015** | A113 | $2 multicolored | 3.50 | 3.50 |
| **2016** | A113 | $2 multicolored | 3.50 | 3.50 |
| **2017** | A113 | $2 multicolored | 3.50 | 3.50 |
| **2018** | A113 | $2 multicolored | 3.50 | 3.50 |
| **2019** | A113 | $2 multicolored | 3.50 | 3.50 |
| **2020** | A113a | $2 multicolored | 3.50 | 3.50 |
| **2021** | A113b | $2 multicolored | — | |

**Souvenir Sheets**

| | | | | |
|---|---|---|---|---|
| **2022** | A113 | $3.50 multicolored | 15.00 | 15.00 |
| **2023** | A113 | $3.50 multicolored | 15.00 | 15.00 |

No. 2023 exists with gold border and inscriptions. Nos. 2014-2020 inscribed 1988.

## Nos. 1826, 1829 and 1831 Ovptd. "REPUBLIC DAY 1989" in Red

**1989, Feb. 22**    Litho.    *Perf. 15*

| | | | | |
|---|---|---|---|---|
| **2024** | A99 | $1.20 Block of 4, #a.-d., on #1826 | 4.50 | 4.50 |
| **2025** | A99 | $1.20 Block of 4, #a.-d., on #1829 | 4.50 | 4.50 |
| **2026** | A101 | $10 on #1831 | 7.50 | 7.50 |
| | | *Nos. 2024-2026 (3)* | 16.50 | 16.50 |

## Nos. 1827a-1827d and 1830a-1830d Surcharged in Red

**1989, Feb. 22**

| | | | | |
|---|---|---|---|---|
| **2027** | A99 | $5 Pair, #a.-b., on $3.20 #a., c. | 7.50 | 7.50 |
| **2028** | A99 | $5 Pair, #a.-b., on $3.20 #b., d. | 7.50 | 7.50 |
| **2028C** | A99 | $5 Pair, #d.-e., on $3.30 #a., c. | 7.50 | 7.50 |
| **2028F** | A99 | $5 Pair, #g.-h., on $3.30 #b., d. | 7.50 | 7.50 |

## Nos. 1461, 1822 Surcharged in Red

**1989, Feb. 22**    Litho.    *Perf. 14*

| | | | | |
|---|---|---|---|---|
| **2029** | A96 | $10 #a.-b. on #1461 | 10.00 | 10.00 |
| **2030** | A96 | $10 #a.-b. on #1822 | 10.00 | 10.00 |

## No. 1188 Surcharged "EASTER"

**1989, Mar. 22**      *Perf. 14*

| | | | | |
|---|---|---|---|---|
| **2031** | A91 | Sheet of 4 on #1188 | 5.00 | 5.00 |
| a. | | 125c on 320c #1188 | .50 | .50 |
| b. | | 250c on 320c #1188 | 1.00 | 1.00 |
| c. | | 300c on 320c #1188 | 1.25 | 1.25 |
| d. | | 350c on 320c #1188 | 1.50 | 1.50 |

## No. 927 Surcharged

**1989, Mar.**    Wmk. 364    *Perf. 14*

| | | | | |
|---|---|---|---|---|
| **2032** | A90 | 250c on 25c #927 | 6.00 | 1.25 |

Inscribed "1986."

## No. 1197 Surcharged "RED CROSS / 1948 / 1988"

**1989, Apr.**    Unwmk.    *Perf. 14*

| | | | | |
|---|---|---|---|---|
| **2033** | A91 | 375c on 45c #1197 | 5.50 | 5.50 |
| **2034** | A91 | 425c on 45c #1197 | 5.50 | 5.50 |

Guyana Red Cross, 40th anniv.

## Nos. 1263 & 1252 Surcharged in Pairs

Surcharges read: a, "ALL FOR / HEALTH"; b, "HEALTH / FOR ALL".

**1989, Apr. 3**

| | | | | |
|---|---|---|---|---|
| **2035** | A91 | 250c on 75c #1263 (56), pair | 8.00 | 8.00 |
| **2036** | A91 | 675c on 720c #1252 (49), pair | 10.00 | 10.00 |

For surcharge see No. 2052.

## Nos. 1224-1225, 1254, 1272-1273 Overprinted or Surcharged

Overprint or Surcharges read: Nos. 2037a-2039a, "BOY SCOUTS / 1909  1989"; Nos. 2037b-2039b, "GIRL GUIDES / 1924  1989"; Nos. 2040-2041, "LADY BADEN POWELL / 1889-1989".

**1989, Apr. 11**

| | | | | |
|---|---|---|---|---|
| **2037** | A91 | 250c on 100c, pair, #a.-b. | 5.00 | 5.00 |
| **2038** | A91 | $2.50 on 50c, pair, #a.-b. | 5.00 | 5.00 |
| **2039** | A91 | 300c Pair, #a.-b. | 5.00 | 5.00 |
| c. | | Pair, #d.-e., Prussian bl ovpt. | | |
| **2040** | A91 | $25 on 280c #1272 | 7.00 | 7.00 |
| a. | | Prussian blue overprint | | |
| **2041** | A91 | $25 on 700c #1273 | 7.00 | 7.00 |
| a. | | Prussian blue overprint | | |
| | | *Nos. 2037-2041 (5)* | 29.00 | 29.00 |

Nos. 2037-2039, Boy Scouts in Guyana, 80th anniversary and Girl Guides, 65th anniversary. Nos. 2040-2041, Lady Baden Powell, birth centenary.

## No. 1177 Surcharged "PHOTOGRAPHY / 1839-1989"

**1989, Apr. 15**

| | | | | |
|---|---|---|---|---|
| **2042** | A91 | 550c on 390c | 7.00 | 7.00 |
| **2043** | A91 | 650c on 390c, 2 bar obliterator | 7.00 | 7.00 |
| a. | | 6 bar obliterator | 7.00 | 7.00 |
| | | *Nos. 2042-2043, 2043a (3)* | 21.00 | 21.00 |

Nos. 2042-2043 printed in sheets of 4 with alternating overprints.

## No. 1263 Surcharged "I.L.O. / 1919-1989"

**1989, May 2**

| | | | | |
|---|---|---|---|---|
| **2044** | A91 | 300c on 75c #1263 | 12.00 | 3.00 |

Intl. Labor Organization, 70th anniversary.

Nos. 43, 87, 134-137, 279-280, 284-285, and 286A 288, 1827, 1830, and 2035-2036 Surcharged in Black or Blue

q

s          r

t          u

**1989-92          Perfs. as Before**
**Watermarks and Printing Methods**
**as Before**

| | | | | |
|---|---|---|---|---|
| 2045 | A7(q) | 80c on 6c #43 | .60 | .35 |
| a. | A7(u) 80c on 6c #43 | | .60 | .35 |
| 2045B | A28(r) | 80c on 2c #134 | | — |
| 2045C | A28(r) | 80c on 3c #135 | | — |
| 2046 | A28(q) | $1 on 2c #134 | .60 | .35 |
| a. | A28(r) $1 on 2c #134 | | .60 | .35 |
| 2047 | A28(q) | $2.05 on 3c #135 | .60 | .35 |
| 2048 | A28(q) | $2.55 on 5c #136 | .60 | .35 |
| a. | A28(r) $2.55 on 5c #136 | | .60 | .35 |
| 2049 | A28(q) | $3.25 on 6c #137 | .60 | .40 |
| a. | A28(r) $3.25 on 6c #137 | | .60 | .40 |
| 2050 | A14(q) | $5 on 6c #87 | .60 | .35 |
| a. | A14(s) $5 on 6c #87 | | .60 | — |
| b. | A14(r) $5 on 6c #87 | | | — |
| 2051 | A66(q) | $6 on 5c #279 | | |
| 2052 | A91 | 640c Pair, #2036 | 5.00 | 5.00 |
| 2053 | A66(q) | $6.40 on 10c #280 | 9.00 | 1.00 |
| a. | A66(u) $6.40 on 10c #280 | | 6.00 | .90 |
| b. | A66(r) $6.40 on 10c #280 | | 6.00 | .90 |
| 2054 | Block of 5, #a.-e. on #1830 | | 42.50 | 42.50 |
| a.-d. | A99(t) $6.40 on $3.30 #a.-d. | | 5.00 | 2.00 |
| e. | A100(t) $190 on $3.30 #e. | | 22.50 | 20.00 |
| 2054F | A66(r) | $7.65 on 35c #284 | 9.00 | 1.50 |
| g. | on 35c #284 | | | |
| 2055 | A66(u) | $7.65 on 40c #285 | 8.25 | 1.50 |
| 2056 | Block of 5, #a.-e. on #1827 | | 42.50 | 42.50 |
| a.-d. | A99(t) $7.65 on $3.20 #a.-d. | | 5.00 | 2.00 |
| e. | A100(t) $225 on $3.20 #e. | | 22.50 | 20.00 |
| 2057 | A66(q) | $8.90 on 60c #286A | 11.00 | 1.50 |
| a. | A66(q) $8.90 on 60c #286A | | 1.00 | .60 |
| 2057B | A66(q) | $30 on 10c #280 | 1.00 | .60 |
| 2057C | A66(q) | $35 on 35c #284 | 1.00 | .60 |
| 2058 | A66(r) | $50 on $2 #288 (Bl) | 22.00 | 11.00 |
| 2059 | A66(r) | $100 on $2 #288 | 32.00 | 24.00 |

Issued: Nos. 2045a, 2053-2053a, 2054F, 2055, 5/18; No. 2057, 5/26; Nos. 2058-2059, 6/5; Nos. 2045, 2049, 2046a, 2048a, 2049a, 6/15; Nos. 2050-2050a, 2051, 2052, 2054, 2056, 8/16; No. 2050b, 1992.
Nos. 2045a, 2053a, 2055, 2057a have no obliterator. New denominations are larger on Nos. 2045a, 2053a and 2057a. No. 2045a has no cent sign. Denomination on No. 2050b is above "X" obliterator. Sizes of obliterator bars on No. 2057C, and perhaps other stamps, varies.
Nos. 2054e, 2056b additionally overprinted "SPECIAL DELIVERY."

### No. 1244 Surcharged "CARICOM / DAY"
**Unwmk.**

**1989, June 26     Litho.     Perf. 14**

| | | | | |
|---|---|---|---|---|
| 2064 | A91 | 125c on 200c #1244, 2 bar obliterator | 8.00 | 1.50 |
| a. | 6 bar obliterator | | 10.00 | 1.75 |

### No. 280 Overprinted in Silver for 40th Birthday of Prince Charles

No. 2081 — Overprints read: a, "1948- / 1988." b, "H.R.H. / Prince / of Wales." c, "H.R.H / Prince / Charles." d, "40th / Birthday." e, "1948."

**Perf. 14x13½**
**1989, Apr.     Litho.     Wmk. 364**

| | | | |
|---|---|---|---|
| 2081 | Sheet of 25, 4 #2081a, 8 #2081b, 6 #2081c, 5 #2081d, 2 #2081e | | |
| a.-e. | A66 10c on #280, any single | — | — |

### No. 280 Ovptd. in Gold or Silver for Gold Medalists at 1988 Summer Olympics

Overprints read: Nos. 2082a, 2083a, "SEOUL / OLYMPICS." Nos. 2082b, 2083b, "Men's 800M / Ereng / Kenya." Nos. 2082c, 2083c, "KOREA." Nos. 2082d, 2083d, "Men's / Gymnastics / Artemov / USSR." Nos. 2082e, 2083e, "Men's / Swimming / Louganis / USA." Nos. 2082f, 2083f, "Woman's / Swimming / Otto / DDR." Nos. 2082g, 2083g, "Men's Fencing / Lamour / France." Nos. 2082h, 2083h, "Men's / Gymnastics / Lou / China." Nos. 2082i, 2083i, "Women's / Cycling / Knol / Holland." Nos. 2082j, 2083j, "Men's / Swimming / Szabo / Hungary." Nos. 2082k, 2083k, "1988." Nos. 2082l, 2083l, "Men's / Swimming / Nesty / Suriname." Nos. 2082m, 2083m, "Men's Boxing / Lewis / Canada." Nos. 2082n, 2083n, "Men's Javelin / Korjus / Finland." Nos. 2082o, 2083o, "Basketball / USA." Nos. 2082p, 2083p, "Men's / Equestrian / Klimke / W. Germany." Nos. 2082q, 2083q, "Men's Boxing / Park / Korea." Nos. 2082r, 2083r, "Women's / Marathon / Mota / Portugal." Nos. 2082s, 2083s, "Men's / Swimming / Suzuki / Japan." Nos. 2084a, 2085a, "Men's 100M / Lewis / USA." Nos. 2084b, 2085b, "Men's / Pole Vault / Bubka / USSR." Nos. 2084c, 2085c, "Women's / 100-200m / Joyner / USA." Nos. 2084d, 2085d, "Men's Pentathlon / Martinek / Hungary." Nos. 2084e, 2085e, "Men's Wrestling / Sako / Japan." Nos. 2084f, 2085f, "Men's Judo / Saito / Japan." Nos. 2084g, 2085g, "Women's 800M / Wodars / DDR." Nos. 2084h, 2085h, "Men's Boxing / Gross / W. Germany." Nos. 2084i, 2085i, "Men's Boxing / Maske / DDR." Nos. 2084j, 2085j, "Men's Boxing / Kim / Korea." Nos. 2084k, 2085k, "Woman's / Swimming / Evans / USA." Nos. 2084l, 2085l, "Soccer / USSR." Nos. 2084m, 2085m, "Woman's / Gymnastics / Silivas / Romania." Nos. 2084n, 2085n, "Men's Boxing / Mercer / USA." Nos. 2084o, 2085o, "Men's Marathon / Bordin / Italy." Nos. 2084p, 2085p, "Women's Tennis / Graf / W. Germany."

**Perf. 14x13½**
**1989, Apr.     Litho.     Wmk. 364**
**Sheets of 25**

| | | | | |
|---|---|---|---|---|
| 2082 | 5 #a., 3 #c., #b., d.-s. | | 12.50 | 12.50 |
| a.-s. | A66 10c on #280, any single | | .45 | .45 |
| 2083 | 5 #a., 3 #c., #b., d.-s. (S) | | 12.50 | 12.50 |
| a.-s. | A66 10c on #280, any single | | .45 | .45 |
| 2084 | #a.-p., 5 #2082a, 3 #2082c, #2082k | | 12.50 | 12.50 |
| a.-p. | A66 10c on #280, any single | | .45 | .45 |
| 2085 | #a.-p., 5 #2083a, 3 #2083c, #2083k (S) | | 12.50 | 12.50 |
| a.-p. | A66 10c on #280, any single | | .45 | .45 |

### Nos. 280 Ovptd. in Gold or Silver for Gold Medalists at 1988 Winter Olympics

Overprints read: Nos. 2086a, 2087a, "Gold Medal / Winners." Nos. 2086b, 2087b, "Ice Hockey / USSR." Nos. 2086c, 2087c, "CALGARY / OLYMPICS." Nos. 2086d, 2087d, "Bobsled / Kipours-Kozlov / USSR." Nos. 2086e, 2087e, "Women's Skating / 1500-3000-5000M / Gennip / Netherlands." Nos. 2086f, 2087f, "Men's / Speed / Skating / 5000-10000M / Gustafson / Sweden." Nos. 2086g, 2087g, "Men's Figure / Skating / Boitano / USA." Nos. 2086h, 2087h, "Women's / 500M Skating / Blair / USA." Nos. 2086i, 2087i, "Women's / Figure Skating / Witt / DDR." Nos. 2086j, 2087j, "Men's Giant / Slalom / Tomba / Italy." Nos. 2086k, 2087k, "CANADA." Nos. 2086l, 2087l, "Men's Super / Giant Slalom / Picard / France." Nos. 2086m, 2087m, "Women's / Downhill Skiing / Kiehl / W. Germany." Nos. 2086n, 2087n, "Men's 50km Skiing Svan / Sweden." Nos. 2086o, 2087o, "Men's Nordic / Combined Skiing / Mueller-Pohl / Schwarz / W. Germany." Nos. 2086p,

2087p, "Women's / Giant Slalom / Schneider / Switzerland." Nos. 2086q, 2087q, "Women's / 5-km Skiing / Matikainen / Finland." Nos. 2086r, 2087r, "Men's Downhill / Alpine Skiing / Zurbriggen / Switzerland." Nos. 2086s, 2087s, "Men's Ski / Jumping / Nykanen / Finland."

**1989, Apr.**

| | | | | |
|---|---|---|---|---|
| 2086 | 4 #a., 3 #c., #b., d.-s., #2082k | | 12.50 | 12.50 |
| a.-s. | A66 10c on #280, any single | | .45 | .45 |
| 2087 | 4 #a., 3 #c., #b., d.-s., #2083k (S) | | 12.50 | 12.50 |
| a.-s. | A66 10c on #280, any single | | .45 | .45 |

### No. 281 Ovptd. in Gold or Silver in Memory of Hirohito, Emperor of Japan

Overprints read: Nos. 2088a, 2089a, "Emperor / Hirohito." Nos. 2088b, 2089b, "Showa / Era." Nos. 2088c, 2089c, "Chrysanthemum / Dynasty." Nos. 2088d, 2089d, "Emperor / of Japan." Nos. 2088e, 2089e, "1901." Nos. 2088f, 2089f, "1989." Nos. 2088g, 2089g, "Emperor / Hirohito / 1901-1989."

**1989, Apr.**

| | | | | |
|---|---|---|---|---|
| 2088 | 5 #a., 4 #c.-d., 9 #b., #e.-g. | | 12.50 | 12.50 |
| a.-g. | A66 15c on #281, any single | | .45 | .45 |
| 2089 | 5 #a., 4 #c.-d., 9 #b., #e.-g. (S) | | 12.50 | 12.50 |
| a.-g. | A66 15c on #281, any single | | .45 | .45 |

### No. 280 Ovptd. in Gold or Silver for Enthronment of Akihito, Emperor of Japan

Overprints reads: Nos. 2090a, 2091a, "Honoring / His / Majesty." Nos. 2090b, 2091b, "Emperor / of Japan." Nos. 2090c, 2091c, "1989." Nos. 2090d, 2091d, "HEISI / ERA."

**1989, Apr.**

| | | | | |
|---|---|---|---|---|
| 2090 | 12 #a, 8 #b., 4 #c., #d. | | 12.50 | 12.50 |
| a.-d. | A66 10c on #280, any single | | .45 | .45 |
| 2091 | 12 #a., 8 #b., 4 #c., #d. (S) | | 12.50 | 12.50 |
| a.-d. | A66 10c on #280, any single | | .45 | .45 |

Overprint is 10mm long on Nos. 2090c, 2091c.

### Nos. 280-281 and 283 Ovptd. with Emblems of Scouts, Rotary Intl., and Lions Intl. in Gold, Silver, Metallic Red, Metallic Green and Black

Overprints: Nos. 2092a, 2093a, 2094a, 2095a, 2096b, 2097b, 2098b, 2099b, 2100c, 2101c, 2102c, 2103c, Scouting emblem. Nos. 2092b, 2093b, 2094b, 2095b, 2096a, 2097a, 2098a, 2099a, 2100b, 2101b, 2102b, 2103b, Rotary emblem. Nos. 2092c, 2093c, 2094c, 2095c, 2096c, 2097c, 2098c, 2099c, 2100a, 2101a, 2102a, 2103a, Lions emblem. Nos. 2092d, 2093d, 2094d, 2095d, 2096d, 2097d, 2098d, 2099d, 2100d, 2101d, 2102d, 2103d, "1989." Nos. 2092e, 2093e, 2094e, 2095e, Large scouting emblem. Nos. 2096e, 2097e, 2098e, 2099e, Large Rotary emblem. Nos. 2100e, 2101e, 2102e, 2103e, Large Lions emblem.

**1989, Apr.**

| | | | | |
|---|---|---|---|---|
| 2092 | 8 #a.-b., 6 #c., 2 #d., #e. | | 12.50 | 12.50 |
| a.-e. | A66 10c on #280, any single | | .45 | .45 |
| 2093 | 8 #a.-b., 6 #c., 2 #d., #e. (S) | | 12.50 | 12.50 |
| a.-e. | A66 10c on #280, any single | | .45 | .45 |
| 2094 | 8 #a.-b., 6 #c., 2 #d., #e. (R) | | 12.50 | 12.50 |
| a.-e. | A66 10c on #280, any single | | .45 | .45 |
| 2095 | 8 #a.-b., 6 #c., 2 #d., #e. (Bk) | | 12.50 | 12.50 |
| a.-e. | A66 10c on #280, any single | | .45 | .45 |
| 2096 | 8 #a.-b., 6 #c., 2 #d., #e. | | 12.50 | 12.50 |
| a.-e. | A66 15c on #281, any single | | .45 | .45 |
| 2097 | 8 #a.-b., 6 #c., 2 #d., #e. (S) | | 12.50 | 12.50 |
| a.-e. | A66 15c on #281, any single | | .45 | .45 |
| 2098 | 8 #a.-b., 6 #c., 2 #d., #e. (R) | | 12.50 | 12.50 |
| a.-e. | A66 15c on #281, any single | | .45 | .45 |
| 2099 | 8 #a.-b., 6 #c., 2 #d., #e. (Gr) | | 12.50 | 12.50 |
| a.-e. | A66 15c on #281, any single | | .45 | .45 |
| 2100 | 8 #a.-b., 6 #c., 2 #d., #e. | | 12.50 | 12.50 |
| a.-e. | A66 25c on #283, any single | | .45 | .45 |
| 2101 | 8 #a.-b., 6 #c., 2 #d., #e. (S) | | 12.50 | 12.50 |
| a.-e. | A66 25c on #283, any single | | .45 | .45 |
| 2102 | 8 #a.-b., 6 #c., 2 #d., #e. (R) | | 12.50 | 12.50 |
| a.-e. | A66 25c on #283, any single | | .45 | .45 |
| 2103 | 8 #a.-b., 6 #c., 2 #d., #e. (Gr) | | 12.50 | 12.50 |
| a.-e. | A66 25c on #283, any single | | .45 | .45 |

"1989" overprints are 7½mm long.

### No. 280 Ovptd. in Gold or Silver for Halley's Comet

Overprints read: Nos. 2104a, 2105a, "Halley's / Comet." Nos. 2104b, 2105b, "Famous / Space Event." Nos. 2104c, 2105c, "Edmund / Halley / 1656-1742." Nos. 2104d, 2105d, "1910." Nos. 2104e, 2105e, "1986."

**1989, Apr.**

| | | | | |
|---|---|---|---|---|
| 2104 | 11 #a., 6 #b., 4 #c., 2 #d.-e. | | 12.50 | 12.50 |
| a.-e. | A66 10c on #280, any single | | .45 | .45 |
| 2105 | 11 #a., 6 #b., 4 #c., 2 #d.-e. (S) | | 12.50 | 12.50 |
| a.-e. | A66 10c on #280, any single | | .45 | .45 |

### No. 280 Ovptd. in Gold or Silver for Space Achievements

Overprints read: Nos. 2106a, 2107a, "Sputnik I / Oct. 4, 1957." Nos. 2106b, 2107b, "Explorer I / Jan. 31, 1958." Nos. 2106c, 2107c, "Sputnik II / Laika / Spacedog / Nov. 3, 1957." Nos. 2106d, 2107d, "Alan Shepard, Jr. / Mercury III / May 5, 1961." Nos. 2106e, 2107e, "Yuri Gagarin / Vostok I / April 12, 1961." Nos. 2106f, 2107f, "John Glenn / Mercury VI / Feb. 20, 1962." Nos. 2106g, 2107g, "Vostok III / Vostok IV / Aug. 12, 1962." Nos. 2106h, 2107h, "Grissom-Young / Gemini III / March 23, 1965." Nos. 2106i, 2107i, "Luna III / Oct. 4, 1959." Nos. 2106j, 2107j, "Edward H. White II / Gemini IV / June 3, 1965." Nos. 2106k, 2107k, "V. Tereshkova / First Woman / in Space / June 16-19, 1963." Nos. 2106 l, 2107 l, "Surveyor I / June 2, 1966." Nos. 2106m, 2107m, "Space / Achievements." Nos. 2106n, 2107n, "Voskod I / First 3 Man Crew / Oct. 12-13, 1964." Nos. 2106o, 2107o, "Apollo I / Jan. 27, 1967." Nos. 2106p, 2107p, "Alexei A. Leonov / First Walk in Space / March 18-19, 1965." Nos. 2106q, 2107q, "Apollo VIII / Dec. 21-27, 1968." Nos. 2106r, 2107r, "V. Komarov / Soyuz I / April 24, 1967." Nos. 2106s, 2107s, "Apollo XI / First Man on Moon / July 20, 1969." Nos. 2106t, 2107t, "Lunokhod I / Dec. 10, 1970." Nos. 2106u, 2107u, "Apollo XIII / April 11-17, / 1970." Nos. 2106v, 2107v, "Soyuz XI / June 30, 1971." Nos. 2106w, 2107w, "Viking I / July 20, 1976." Nos. 2106x, 2107x, "Vega I / March 6, 1986." Nos. 2106y, 2107y, "Columbia Sts-1 / April 12-14, / 1981."

**1989, Apr.**

| | | | | |
|---|---|---|---|---|
| 2106 | #a.-y. | | 12.50 | 12.50 |
| a.-y. | A66 10c on #280, any single | | .45 | .45 |
| 2107 | #a.-y. (S) | | 12.50 | 12.50 |
| a.-y. | A66 10c on #280, any single | | .45 | .45 |

### No. 280 Ovptd. in Gold or Silver

Overprints read: Nos. 2108a, 2109a, "1969-/ 1989." Nos. 2108b, 2109b, "Apollo XI." Nos. 2108c, 2109c, "First Man on Moon." Nos. 2108d, 2109d, "USA." Nos. 2108e, 2109e, "Neil A. / Armstrong." Nos. 2108f, 2109f, "Col. Edwin E. / Aldrin, Jr." Nos. 2108g, 2109g, "Lt. Col. / Michael / Collins."

**1989, Apr.**

| | | | | |
|---|---|---|---|---|
| 2108 | 5 #a, 7 b, 4 c, 6 d, e-g | | 12.50 | 12.50 |
| a.-g. | A66 10c on #280, any single | | .45 | .45 |
| 2109 | 5 #a, 7 b, 4 c, 6 d, e-g (S) | | 12.50 | 12.50 |
| a.-g. | A66 10c on #280, any single | | .45 | .45 |

Moon Landing, 20th anniv.

### No. 281 Ovptd. in Gold or Silver for Space Shuttle Program

Overprints read: Nos. 2110a, 2111a, "Enterprise / Aug. 12, 1977." Nos. 2110b, 2111b, "Columbia / April 12, 1981." Nos. 2110c, 2111c, "Space / Shuttles." Nos. 2110d, 2111d, "Discovery / Aug. 30, 1984." Nos. 2110e, 2111e, "Atlantis / Oct. 3, 1985." Nos. 2110f, 2111f, "Challenger / Heroes." Nos. 2110g, 2111g, "Resnik / McAuliffe / Jarvis." Nos. 2110h, 2111h, "In Memoriam / Challenger / Jan. 28, 1986." Nos. 2110i, 2111i, "Onizuka / Smith / McNair / Scobee."

**1989, Apr.**

| | | | | |
|---|---|---|---|---|
| 2110 | 4 #a.-e., 2 #f., #g.-i. | | 12.50 | 12.50 |
| a.-i. | A66 15c on #281, any single | | .45 | .45 |
| 2111 | 4 #a.-e., 2 #f., #g.-i. (S) | | 12.50 | 12.50 |
| a.-i. | A66 15c on #281, any single | | .45 | .45 |

Butterflies — A115

80c, Stalachtis calliope. $2.25, Morpho rhetenor. $5, Agrias claudia. $6.40, Marpesia marcella. $7.65, Papilio zagreus. $8.90, Chorinea faunus. $25, Cepheuptychia cephus. $100, Nessaea regina.

**1989, Sept. 7 — Litho. — Perf. 14**

| | | | | |
|---|---|---|---|---|
| 2208 | A115 | 80c multicolored | .50 | .25 |
| 2209 | A115 | $2.25 multicolored | .60 | .25 |
| 2210 | A115 | $5 multicolored | .75 | .40 |
| 2211 | A115 | $6.40 multicolored | .85 | .70 |
| 2212 | A115 | $7.65 multicolored | 1.00 | .90 |
| 2213 | A115 | $8.90 multicolored | 1.25 | 1.10 |
| 2214 | A115 | $25 multicolored | 4.00 | 3.00 |
| 2215 | A115 | $100 multicolored | 13.50 | 12.50 |
| | | *Nos. 2208-2215 (8)* | 22.45 | 19.10 |

See Nos. E16-E17. For overprints see Nos. 2251-2254, 2256-2257, 2260-2261, 2283-2290, E19-E22, E24, E26-E27, E31.

A116

Women in Space, 25th Anniv. (in 1988): $6.40, Kathryn Sullivan, 1st US woman to walk in space. $12.80, Svetlana Savitskaya, 1st Soviet woman to walk in space. $15.30, Judy Resnik & Christa McAuliffe, astronauts killed in Challenger explosion. $100, Sally Ride, 1st US woman astronaut.

**1989, Nov. 8**

| | | | | |
|---|---|---|---|---|
| 2216 | A116 | $6.40 multicolored | 1.00 | .25 |
| 2217 | A116 | $12.80 multicolored | 1.75 | 1.25 |
| 2218 | A116 | $15.30 multicolored | 2.00 | 1.50 |
| 2219 | A116 | $100 multicolored | 11.50 | 11.50 |
| | | *Nos. 2216-2219 (4)* | 16.25 | 14.50 |

See No. E18. For overprints see Nos. 2255, 2258-2259, 2262, E23, E25, E28, E32.

1990 World Cup Soccer Championships, Italy — A117

Various soccer players: No. 2221, Yellow shirt, vert. No. 2222, Goalie. No. 2223, Green shirt, vert.

No. 2224, Championships emblem, vert.

**Perf. 14x13½, 13½x14**

**1989, Nov. 20**

| | | | | |
|---|---|---|---|---|
| 2220 | A117 | $2.55 shown | 5.00 | 5.00 |
| 2221 | A117 | $2.55 multi | 5.00 | 5.00 |
| 2222 | A117 | $2.55 multi | 5.00 | 5.00 |
| 2223 | A117 | $2.55 multi | 5.00 | 5.00 |
| | | *Nos. 2220-2223 (4)* | 20.00 | 20.00 |

**Souvenir Sheet**

| | | | | |
|---|---|---|---|---|
| 2224 | A117 | $20 multi | 17.50 | 17.50 |

Nos. 2220-2223 exist in souvenir sheets of 1. For surcharges see Nos. 2263-2267.

**No. 134-136 Surcharged "AHMADIYYA / CENTENARY / 1889-1989"**

**Perf. 13x13½**

**1989, Nov. 22 — Litho. — Wmk. 364**

| | | | | |
|---|---|---|---|---|
| 2225 | A28 | 80c on 2c #134 | 4.50 | .60 |
| 2226 | A28 | $6.40 on 3c #135 | 13.50 | 5.50 |
| 2227 | A28 | $8.90 on 5c #136 | 15.00 | 8.00 |
| | | *Nos. 2225-2227 (3)* | 33.00 | 14.10 |

1992 Summer Olympics, Barcelona — A118

No. 2229, Boxing, horiz. No. 2230, Chariot racing, horiz. No. 2231, Javelin, horiz. No. 2232, Running, horiz. No. 2233, Wrestling. No. 2234, Running, vert., diff. No. 2235, Columbus Walk by Picasso.

**1989, Dec. 5 — Perf. 13½x14, 14x13½**

| | | | | |
|---|---|---|---|---|
| 2228 | A118 | $2.55 shown | 4.50 | 4.50 |
| 2229 | A118 | $2.55 multicolored | 4.50 | 4.50 |
| 2230 | A118 | $2.55 multicolored | 4.50 | 4.50 |
| 2231 | A118 | $2.55 multicolored | 4.50 | 4.50 |
| 2232 | A118 | $2.55 multicolored | 4.50 | 4.50 |
| 2233 | A118 | $2.55 multicolored | 4.50 | 4.50 |

| | | | | |
|---|---|---|---|---|
| | | *Nos. 2228-2233 (6)* | 24.00 | 24.00 |

**Souvenir Sheets**

| | | | | |
|---|---|---|---|---|
| 2234 | A118 | $10 multicolored | 15.00 | 15.00 |
| 2235 | A118 | $10 multicolored | 15.00 | 15.00 |
| | | *Nos. 2234-2235 (2)* | 30.00 | 30.00 |

Nos. 2228-2233 exist in souvenir sheets of 1.

Christmas A119

Paintings: No. 2236, Child Declaring in Favor of His Mother, by Titian. No. 2237, The Sacred Family, by Rubens. No. 2238, Saint Anne, the Virgin and Child, by Durer. No. 2239, Madonna Enthroned, Surrounded by Saints, by Rubens. $20, Saint Ildefonso, by Rubens.

**1989, Dec. 26 — Perf. 14x13½, 13½x14**

| | | | | |
|---|---|---|---|---|
| 2236 | A119 | $2.55 multi | 4.50 | 4.50 |
| 2237 | A119 | $2.55 multi, vert. | 4.50 | 4.50 |
| 2238 | A119 | $2.55 multi, vert. | 4.50 | 4.50 |
| 2239 | A119 | $2.55 multi, vert. | 4.50 | 4.50 |
| | | *Nos. 2236-2239 (4)* | 16.00 | 16.00 |

**Souvenir Sheet**

| | | | | |
|---|---|---|---|---|
| 2240 | A119 | $20 multi, vert. | 20.00 | 20.00 |

Nos. 2236-2239 exist in souvenir sheets of 1.

Harpy Eagle A120 — Channel-billed Toucan A121

$2.25, Eagle's head. $5, Eagle with prey. $8.90, Eagle facing right. $25, Blue & yellow macaw. $30, Eagle facing left. $50, Wattled jacana, horiz. $60, Hoatzin, horiz.

No. 2249, Great kiskadee, horiz. No. 2250, Amazon kingfisher, horiz.

**1990, Jan. 23 — Litho. — Perf. 14**

| | | | | |
|---|---|---|---|---|
| 2241 | A120 | $2.25 multicolored | 1.00 | .50 |
| 2242 | A120 | $5 multicolored | 1.25 | .75 |
| 2243 | A120 | $8.90 multicolored | 1.50 | 1.00 |
| 2244 | A121 | $15 shown | 1.00 | .90 |
| 2245 | A120 | $25 multicolored | 1.50 | 1.00 |
| 2246 | A120 | $30 multicolored | 3.75 | 3.50 |
| 2247 | A121 | $50 multicolored | 2.50 | 2.25 |
| 2248 | A121 | $60 multicolored | 3.00 | 2.75 |
| | | *Nos. 2241-2248 (8)* | 15.50 | 12.65 |

**Souvenir Sheets**

| | | | | |
|---|---|---|---|---|
| 2249 | A121 | $100 multicolored | 5.25 | 5.25 |
| 2250 | A121 | $100 multicolored | 5.25 | 5.25 |

Nos. 2241-2243, 2246, World Wildlife Fund.

**Nos. 2208-2184 Ovptd. in Silver**

Overprint includes Rotary Emblem and "ROTARY INTERNATIONAL 1905-1990" on 2 or 3 Lines.

**1990, Mar. 15**

| | | | | |
|---|---|---|---|---|
| 2251 | A115 | 80c on #2208 | | |
| 2252 | A115 | $2.25 on #2209 | | |
| 2253 | A115 | $5 on #2210 | | |
| 2254 | A115 | $6.40 on #2211 | | |
| 2255 | A116 | $6.40 on #2216 | | |
| 2256 | A115 | $7.65 on #2212 | | |
| 2257 | A115 | $8.90 on #2213 | | |
| 2258 | A116 | $12.80 on #2217 | | |
| 2259 | A116 | $15.30 on #2218 | | |
| 2260 | A115 | $25 on #2214 | | |
| 2261 | A115 | $100 on #2215 | | |
| 2262 | A116 | $100 on #2219 | | |
| | | *Nos. 2251-2262 (12)* | | 37.50 |

**Nos. 2220-2224 Surcharged**

Surcharges read: Nos. 2263-2265, 2267, "GERMANY / CHAMPION"; No. 2266, "GERMANY / CHAMPION / ARGENTINA / SUBCHAMPION"

| **1990** | | | **Perfs. as Before** | |
|---|---|---|---|---|
| 2263 | A117 | $75 on #2220 | | |
| 2264 | A117 | $75 on #2221 | | |
| 2265 | A117 | $75 on #2222 | | |
| 2266 | A117 | $75 on #2223 | | |
| | | *Nos. 2263-2266 (4)* | | 10.00 |

**Souvenir Sheet**

| | | | | |
|---|---|---|---|---|
| 2267 | A117 | $225 on #2224 | | 8.00 |

Nos. 2263-2266 exist in souvenir sheets of 1.

**Miniature Sheets**

Penny Black, 150th Anniv., 500th Anniv. of Thurn & Taxis Postal Service — A122

No. 2268: a, Banghy Post runner, 1832. b, Penny Black, Sir Rowland Hill. c, Dutch mail ship. d, Paddle steamer Monarch, 1830. e, Paddle steamer Hindostan, 1842. f, Mail steamer Chusan. g, Sailing ship Madagascar, 1853. h, Paddle steamer Orinoco, 1855. i, Packet Orpheus, 1835.

No. 2269: a, Imperial postal messenger. b, Swiss messenger, 1499. c, River messenger, 15th century. d, Russian courier, Middle Ages. e, Oldenburg postilions, 1820. f, Indian mail coach, 1829. g, Baden mail coach postilions, 1820. h, Pony Express, 1860. i, Camel rider.

No. 2270: a, Mail coach, 1840. b, Danish Ball Post, 1815. c, Australian Bush mailman, 1838. d, Japanese postmen, 1870. e, Mail cart, 1857. f, Russian mail troika. g, Wells, Fargo Overland Express. h, Phantoms of the Night, 1853. i, Cobb & Co. coach, Australia.

No. 2271: a, Postilions, 1850. b, Mounted postilion, Holland. c, Paddle steamer Arctic, 1850. d, Peruvian swimming couriers. e, First London post box, 1855. f, Indian mail cart, 1870. g, Balloon post, 1870. h, Bath Mail Coach. i, Postrider, 1837.

No. 2272: a, Northeastern Railway post office. b, Traveling post office, 1838. c, American Express. d, Graf Zeppelin. e, Columbia Post airplane, 1925. f, Calcutta flying boat. g, Junkers JU-52/3M mail plane. h, Douglas M2 mail plane. i, US air mail service, DH-4.

No. 2273: a, First Atlantic Airways. b, Morris post office van, 1931. c, Swiss post-passenger bus. d, Westland-Sikorsky S51 helicopter mail flight. e, Union Pacific Railway. f, Boeing Model 314 flying boat, Yankee Clipper. g, Boeing 747. h, Concorde. i, Apollo 11, US #C76.

No. 2274, Mounted postilion. No. 2275, Thurn & Taxis #7. No. 2276, Thurn & Taxis #45.

**1990, May 3**

| | | | | |
|---|---|---|---|---|
| 2268 | A122 | $15.30 Sheet of 9, #a.-i. | 9.00 | 9.00 |
| 2269 | A122 | $15.30 Sheet of 9, #a.-i. | 9.00 | 9.00 |
| 2270 | A122 | $15.30 Sheet of 9, #a.-i. | 9.00 | 9.00 |
| 2271 | A122 | $17.80 Sheet of 9, #a.-i. | 10.00 | 10.00 |
| 2272 | A122 | $20 Sheet of 9, #a.-i. | 11.00 | 11.00 |
| 2273 | A122 | $20 Sheet of 9, #a.-i. | 11.00 | 11.00 |
| | | *Nos. 2268-2273 (6)* | 59.00 | 59.00 |

**Souvenir Sheets**

| | | | | |
|---|---|---|---|---|
| 2274 | A122 | $150 multi | 7.00 | 7.00 |
| 2275 | A122 | $150 multi | 7.00 | 7.00 |
| 2276 | A122 | $150 multi | 7.00 | 7.00 |

For overprint see No. 2551.

**Nos. 1028, 1032, 1055, 1085, 1107 Surcharged**

Surcharge reads "ROTARY / DISTRICT 405 / 9th CONFERENCE / MAY 1990 / GEORGETOWN".

**Unwmk.**

**1990, May 8 — Litho. — Perf. 14**

**Design A91**

**Plate Numbers in Parentheses**

| | | | | |
|---|---|---|---|---|
| 2277 | | 80c on 55c #1032 (9) | | |
| 2278 | | 80c on 55c #1085 (49) | | |
| 2279 | | 80c on 55c #1107 (64) | | |
| 2280 | | $6.40 on 130c #1028 (6) | | |
| 2281 | | $6.40 on 130c #1055 (25) | | |
| 2282 | | $7.65 on 130c #1055 (25) | | |
| | | *Nos. 2277-2282 (6)* | | 10.00 |

Nos. 2208-2215 Overprinted

**1990, June 8 — Litho. — Perf. 14**

| | | | | |
|---|---|---|---|---|
| 2283 | A115 | 80c on #2208 | 2.00 | .50 |
| 2284 | A115 | $2.25 on #2209 | 2.25 | .60 |
| 2285 | A115 | $5 on #2210 | 2.75 | .70 |

| | | | | |
|---|---|---|---|---|
| 2286 | A115 | $6.40 on #2211 | 3.00 | .75 |
| 2287 | A115 | $7.65 on #2212 | 3.25 | .90 |
| 2288 | A115 | $8.90 on #2213 | 3.25 | 1.00 |
| 2289 | A115 | $25 on #2214 | 9.00 | 6.50 |
| 2290 | A115 | $100 on #2215 | 20.00 | 20.00 |
| | | *Nos. 2283-2290 (8)* | 45.50 | 30.95 |

See Nos. E26-E27.

Locomotives A123

No. 2291, Class 3F. No. 2292, Class A4. No. 2293, Liner Class A34. No. 2294, Pacific Class. No. 2295, Grange Class. No. 2296, Castle Class, vert. No. 2297, Southern Railway.

**1990, July 15 — Perf. 14x13½**

| | | | | |
|---|---|---|---|---|
| 2291 | A123 | $2.55 multi | 3.00 | 3.00 |
| 2292 | A123 | $2.55 multi | 3.00 | 3.00 |
| 2293 | A123 | $2.55 multi | 3.00 | 3.00 |
| 2294 | A123 | $2.55 multi | 3.00 | 3.00 |
| 2295 | A123 | $2.55 multi | 3.00 | 3.00 |
| | | *Nos. 2291-2295 (5)* | 13.50 | |

**Souvenir Sheets**

**Perf. 13½x14, 14x13½**

| | | | | |
|---|---|---|---|---|
| 2296 | A123 | $20 multi | 12.50 | 12.50 |
| 2297 | A123 | $20 multi | 12.50 | 12.50 |
| | | *Nos. 2296-2297 (2)* | 22.50 | |

Still Life with Guitar, by Picasso A124

Paintings: No. 2299, Horseman, by Velazquez. No. 2300, Sunflowers, by Van Gogh, vert. No. 2301, Man Wearing Striped Shirt, by Miro, vert. No. 2302, Franz von Taxis, by Durer, vert. No. 2303, Virgin and Child, by Titian, vert. No. 2304, Presentation of Marie de Medici, by Rubens, vert.

**Perf. 14x13½, 13½x14**

**1990, Aug. 1 — Litho.**

| | | | | |
|---|---|---|---|---|
| 2298 | A124 | $2.55 multicolored | 3.00 | 3.00 |
| 2299 | A124 | $2.55 multicolored | 3.00 | 3.00 |
| 2300 | A124 | $2.55 multicolored | 3.00 | 3.00 |
| 2301 | A124 | $2.55 multicolored | 3.00 | 3.00 |
| 2302 | A124 | $2.55 multicolored | 3.00 | 3.00 |
| | | *Nos. 2298-2302 (5)* | 11.50 | |

**Souvenir Sheets**

| | | | | |
|---|---|---|---|---|
| 2303 | A124 | $20 multi | 12.50 | 12.50 |
| 2304 | A124 | $20 multi | 12.50 | 12.50 |
| | | *Nos. 2303-2304 (2)* | 18.00 | |

Postal System of Thurn and Taxis, 500th anniv. (No. 2302). Titian, 500th birth anniv. (No. 2303). Rubens, 350th death anniv. (No. 2304).

Birds — A125

Designs: 80c, Guiana partridge, horiz. $2.55, Collared trogon. $3.25, Derby aracari. $5, Black-necked aracari. $5.10, Green aracari. $5.80, Ivory-billed aracari. $6.40, Guiana toucanet. $6.50, Sulphur-breasted toucan. $7.55, Red-billed toucan. $7.65, Toco toucan. $8.25, Natterers toucanet. $8.90, Welcome trogon. $9.75, Doubtful trogon. $11.40, Banded aracari. $12.65, Golden-headed train bearer. $12.80, Rufus-breasted hermit. $13.90, Band-tail barbthroat. $15.30, White-tipped sickle bill. $17.80, Black jacobin. $19.20, Fiery topaz. $22.95, Tufted coquette. $26.70, Ecuadorian pied-tail. $30, Quetzal. $50, Green-crowned brilliant. $100, Emerald-chinned hummingbird. $190, Lazuline sabrewing. $225, Berylline hummingbird.

**1990, Sept. 12 — Litho. — Perf. 14**

| | | | | |
|---|---|---|---|---|
| 2305 | A125 | 80c multi | .25 | .25 |
| 2306 | A125 | $2.55 multi | .25 | .25 |
| 2307 | A125 | $3.25 multi | .25 | .25 |
| 2308 | A125 | $5 multi | .25 | .25 |
| 2309 | A125 | $5.10 multi | .25 | .25 |
| 2310 | A125 | $5.80 multi | .25 | .25 |

| | | | | | |
|---|---|---|---|---|---|
| 2311 | A125 | $6.40 multi | | .25 | .25 |
| 2312 | A125 | $6.50 multi | | .25 | .25 |
| 2313 | A125 | $7.55 multi | | .35 | .35 |
| 2314 | A125 | $7.65 multi | | .45 | .45 |
| 2315 | A125 | $8.25 multi | | .55 | .55 |
| 2316 | A125 | $8.90 multi | | .65 | .65 |
| 2317 | A125 | $9.75 multi | | .65 | .65 |
| 2318 | A125 | $11.40 multi | | .70 | .70 |
| 2319 | A125 | $12.65 multi | | .75 | .75 |
| 2320 | A125 | $12.80 multi | | .80 | .80 |
| 2321 | A125 | $13.90 multi | | .90 | .90 |
| 2322 | A125 | $15.30 multi | | 1.10 | 1.10 |
| 2323 | A125 | $17.80 multi | | 1.25 | 1.25 |
| 2324 | A125 | $19.20 multi | | 1.40 | 1.40 |
| 2325 | A125 | $22.95 multi | | 1.60 | 1.60 |
| 2326 | A125 | $26.70 multi | | 1.90 | 1.90 |
| 2327 | A125 | $30 multi | | 2.00 | 2.00 |
| 2328 | A125 | $50 multi | | 3.25 | 3.25 |
| 2329 | A125 | $100 multi | | 6.00 | 6.00 |
| 2330 | A125 | $190 multi | | 11.50 | 11.50 |
| 2331 | A125 | $225 multi | | 14.00 | 14.00 |
| | | *Nos. 2305-2331 (27)* | | 51.80 | 51.80 |

For surcharge, see No. 4020M.

Butterflies — A126

Designs: 80c, Melinaea idae. $2.55, Rhetus dysonii. $5, Actinote anteas. $6.40, Heliconius tales. $7.65, Thecla telemus. $8.90, Theope eudocia. $50, Heliconius vicini. $100, Amarynthis meneria.

No. 2340, vert.: a, Thecla falerina. b, Pheles heliconides. c, Echenais leucocyana. d, Heliconius xanthocles. e, Mesopthalma idotea. f, Parides aeneas. g, Heliconius numata. h, Thecla critola. i, Themone pais. j, Nymula agle. k, Adelpha cocala. l, Anaea eribotes. m, Prepona demophon. n, Selenophanes cassiope. o, Consul hippona. p, Antirrhaea avernus.

No. 2341, vert.: a, Thecla telemus. b, Thyridia confusa. c, Heliconius burneyi. d, Parides lysander. e, Eunica orphise. f, Adelpha melona. g, Morpho menelaus. h, Nymula phylleus. i, Stalachtis phlegia. j, Theope barea. k, Morpho perseus. l, Lycorea ceres. m, Archonias bellona. n, Caerois chorinaeus. o, Vila azeca. p, Nessaea batesii.

No. 2342: a, Heliconius silvana. b, Eunica alcmena. c, Mechanitis polymnia. d, Mesosemia ephyne. e, Thecla erema. f, Callizona acesta. g, Stalachtis phaedusa. h, Battus belus. i, Nymula phliasus. j, Parides childrenae. k, Stalachtis euterpe. l, Dysmathia portia. m, Tithorea hermias. n, Prepona pheridamas. o, Dismorphia fortunata. p, Hamadryas amphinome.

No. 2343: a, Heliconius vetustus. b, Mesosemia eumene. c, Parides phosphorus. d, Polystichtis emylius. e, Xanthocleis aedesia. f, Doxocopa agathina. g, Adelpha plesaure. h, Heliconius wallacei. i, Notheme eumeus. j, Melinaea mediatrix. k, Theritas coronata. l, Dismorphia orise. m, Phyciodes ianthe. n, Morpho aega. o, Zaretis isidora. p, Pierella lena.

No. 2344, Heliconius aoede. No. 2345, Phyciodes clio, horiz. No. 2346, Nymphidium caricae. No. 2347, Thecla hemon.

**1990, Sept. 26   Litho.   Perf. 14**

| | | | | |
|---|---|---|---|---|
| 2332 | A126 | 80c multicolored | .85 | .85 |
| 2333 | A126 | $2.55 multicolored | .85 | .85 |
| 2334 | A126 | $5 multicolored | .85 | .85 |
| 2335 | A126 | $6.40 multicolored | .85 | .85 |
| 2336 | A126 | $7.65 multicolored | .85 | .85 |
| 2337 | A126 | $8.90 multicolored | 1.10 | 1.10 |
| 2338 | A126 | $50 multicolored | 4.50 | 4.50 |
| 2339 | A126 | $100 multicolored | 9.50 | 9.50 |
| | | *Nos. 2332-2339 (8)* | 19.35 | 19.35 |

**Miniature Sheets**

| | | | | |
|---|---|---|---|---|
| 2340 | A126 | $10 Sheet of 16, | | |
| | | #a.-p. | 16.00 | 16.00 |
| 2341 | A126 | $10 Sheet of 16, | | |
| | | #a.-p. | 16.00 | 16.00 |
| 2342 | A126 | $10 Sheet of 16, | | |
| | | #a.-p. | 16.00 | 16.00 |
| 2343 | A126 | $10 Sheet of 16, | | |
| | | #a.-p. | 16.00 | 16.00 |

**Souvenir Sheets**

| | | | | |
|---|---|---|---|---|
| 2344 | A126 | $150 multicolored | 10.00 | 10.00 |
| 2345 | A126 | $150 multicolored | 10.00 | 10.00 |
| 2346 | A126 | $190 multicolored | 15.00 | 15.00 |
| 2347 | A126 | $190 multicolored | 15.00 | 15.00 |

For surcharges see Nos. 2415-2425, 2596-2606.

Mushrooms — A127

Designs: No. 2348, Oudemanseilla mucida. No. 2349, Pholiota squarosa. No. 2350, Coprinus comatus. No. 2351, Anellaria semiovaja. $20, Phallus impudicus.

**1990, Oct. 12**

| | | | |
|---|---|---|---|
| 2348 | A127 | $2.55 multicolored | |
| 2349 | A127 | $2.55 multicolored | |
| 2350 | A127 | $2.55 multicolored | |
| 2351 | A127 | $2.55 multicolored | |
| | | *Nos. 2348-2351 (4)* | 14.00 |

**Souvenir Sheet**

| | | | |
|---|---|---|---|
| 2352 | A127 | $20 multicolored | 14.00 |

Sailing Ships — A128

No. 2353, Brig century. No. 2354, Dutch marine ship. No. 2355, Galleon, 1588. No. 2356, Warship, 16th cent. No. 2357, Hulk, 17th cent.

No. 2358, Dutch ships, 16th-17th cent.

**1990, Oct. 12**

| | | | |
|---|---|---|---|
| 2353 | A128 | $2.55 multicolored | |
| 2354 | A128 | $2.55 multicolored | |
| 2355 | A128 | $2.55 multicolored | |
| 2356 | A128 | $2.55 multicolored | |
| 2357 | A128 | $2.55 multicolored | |
| | | *Nos. 2353-2357 (5)* | 13.00 |

**Souvenir Sheet**

| | | | |
|---|---|---|---|
| 2358 | A128 | $20 multicolored | 13.00 |

No. 2358 printed in continuous design. Discovery of America, 500th anniv. (in 1992).

Flora — A129

Orchids: $7.65, Vanilla inodora. $8.90, Epidendrum ibaguense. No. 858, Maxillaria parkeri. $15.30, Epidendrum nocturnum. $17.80, Catasetum discolor. $20, Scuticaria hadwenii. $25, Epidendrum fragrans. $100, Epistephium parviflorum.

No. 2367: a, Dichea muricata. b, Octomeria erosilabia. c, Spiranthes orchiodes. d, Brassavola nodosa. e, Epidendrum rigidum. f, Brassia caudata. g, Pleurothallis diffusa. h, Aspasia variegata. i, Stenia pallida. j, Cyrtopodium punctatum. k, Cattleya deckeri. l, Cryptarrhena lunata. m, Cattleya violacea. n, Caularthron bicornutum. o, Oncidium carthagenense. p, Galeandra devoniana.

No. 2368: a, Bifrenaria aurantiaca. b, Epidendrum ciliare. c, Dichaea picta. d, Scaphyglottis violacea. e, Cattleya percivaliana. f, Map of Guyana (no flower). g, Epidendrum difforme. h, Eulophia maculata. i, Spiranthes tenuis. j, Peristeria guttata. k, Pleurothallis pruinosa. l, Cleistes rosea. m, Maxillaria variabilis. n, Brassavola cucullata. o, Epidendrum moyobambae. p, Oncidium orthostates.

No. 2369: a, Brassavola martiana. b, Paphinia cristata. c, Aganisia pulchella. d, Oncidium lanceanum. e, Lockhartia imbricata. f, Caularthron bilamellatum. g, Oncidium nanum. h, Pleurothallis ovalifolia. i, Galeandra dives. j, Cycnoches loddigesii. k, Ada aurantiaca. l, Catasetum barbatum. m, Palmorchis pubescens. n, Epidendrum anceps. o, Huntleya meleagris. p, Sobralia sessilis.

No. 2370: a, Maxillaria camaridii. b, Vanilla pompona. c, Stanhopea grandiflora. d, Oncidium pusillum. e, Polycycnis vittata. f, Cattleya lawrenceana. g, Menadenium labiosum. h, Rodriguezia secunda. i, Mormodes buccinator. j, Otostylis brachystalix. k, Maxillaria discolor. l, Liparis elata. m, Gongora maculata. n,

Koellensteinia graminea. o, Rudolfiella aurantiaca. p, Scuticaria steelei.

Flowering Trees: No. 2371: a, Cochlospermum vitifolium. b, Eugenia malaccensis. c, Plumiera rubra. d, Erythrina glauca. e, Spathodea campanulata. f, Jacaranda filicifolia. g, Samanea saman. h, Cassia fistula. i, Abutilon integerrimum. j, Lagerstroemia speciosa. k, Tabebuia serratifolia. l, Guaiacum officinale. m, Solanum macranthum. n, Peltophorum roxburghii. o, Bauhinia variegata. p, Plumiera alba.

Flowering Vines: No. 2372: a, Gloriosa rothschildiana. b, Pseudocalymma alliaceum. c, Callichlamys latifolia. d, Disticts riversii. e, Maurandya barclaiana. f, Beaumontia fragrans. g, Phaseolus caracalla. h, Mandevilla splendens. i, Solandra longiflora. j, Passiflora coccinea. k, Allamanda cathartica. l, Bauhinia galpini. m, Verbena maritima. n, Mandevilla suaveolens. o, Phryganocydia corymbosa. p, Jasminum sambac.

No. 2373, Galeandra devoniana. No. 2374, Delonix regia. No. 2375, Hexisea bidentata. No. 2376, Lecythis ollaria. No. 2377, Ionopsis utricularioides.

**1990, Oct. 16   Litho.   Perf. 14**

| | | | | |
|---|---|---|---|---|
| 2359 | A129 | $7.65 multicolored | .40 | .40 |
| 2360 | A129 | $8.90 multicolored | .55 | .55 |
| 2361 | A129 | $12.80 multicolored | .85 | .85 |
| 2362 | A129 | $15.30 multicolored | .90 | .90 |
| 2363 | A129 | $17.80 multicolored | 1.00 | 1.00 |
| 2364 | A129 | $20 multicolored | 1.25 | 1.25 |
| 2365 | A129 | $25 multicolored | 1.50 | 1.50 |
| 2366 | A129 | $190 multicolored | 6.50 | 6.50 |
| | | *Nos. 2359-2366 (8)* | 12.95 | 12.95 |

**Miniature Sheets**

| | | | | |
|---|---|---|---|---|
| 2367 | A129 | $10 Sheet of 16, | | |
| | | #a.-p. | 8.00 | 8.00 |
| 2368 | A129 | $10 Sheet of 16, | | |
| | | #a.-p. | 8.00 | 8.00 |
| 2369 | A129 | $12.80 Sheet of 16, | | |
| | | #a.-p. | 12.00 | 12.00 |
| 2370 | A129 | $12.80 Sheet of 16, | | |
| | | #a.-p. | 12.00 | 12.00 |
| 2371 | A129 | $12.80 Sheet of 16, | | |
| | | #a.-p. | 12.00 | 12.00 |
| 2372 | A129 | $12.80 Sheet of 16, | | |
| | | #a.-p. | 12.00 | 12.00 |
| | | *Nos. 2367-2372 (6)* | 64.00 | 64.00 |

**Souvenir Sheets**

| | | | | |
|---|---|---|---|---|
| 2373 | A129 | $150 multicolored | 9.00 | 9.00 |
| 2374 | A129 | $150 multicolored | 9.00 | 9.00 |
| 2375 | A129 | $150 multicolored | 9.00 | 9.00 |
| 2376 | A129 | $150 multicolored | 9.00 | 9.00 |
| 2377 | A129 | $190 multicolored | 11.00 | 11.00 |
| | | *Nos. 2373-2377 (5)* | 47.00 | 47.00 |

Nos. 2370-2375 are horiz. For surcharges see Nos. 2487A-2487B, 2593-2595, 4020N, 4119, 4120, 4121, 4178, 4179, 4181, 4181Q, 4202.

**Souvenir Sheet**

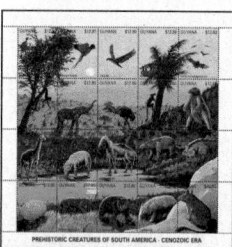

Cenozoic Era Wildlife — A130

Designs: a, Palaelodus. b, Archaeotrogon. c, Vulture. d, Bradyrus tridactylus. e, Natalus stramineus bat. f, Cebidae. g, Cuvieronius. h, Phororhacos. i, Smilodectes. j, Megatherium. k, Titanotylopus. l, Teleoceras. m, Macrauchenia. n, Mylodon. o, Smilodon. p, Glyptodon. q, Protohydrocherus. r, Archaeohyrax. s, Pyrotherium. t, Platypittamys.

**1990, Nov. 6**

| | | | | |
|---|---|---|---|---|
| 2378 | A130 | $12.80 Sheet of 20, | | |
| | | #a.-t. | 15.00 | 15.00 |

**Miniature Sheets**

Endangered Wildlife — A131

No. 2379: a, Ivory-billed woodpecker. b, Cauca guan. c, Sun conure. d, Quetzal. e, Long-wattled umbrellabird. f, Banded cotinga. g, Blue-chested parakeet. h, Rufous-bellied chachalaca. i, Yellow-faced amazon. j, Toucan barbet. k, Red siskin. l, Cock-of-the-rock. m, Hyacinth macaw. n, Yellow cardinal. o, Bare-necked umbrellabird. p, Saffron toucanette. q, Red-billed curassow. r, Spectacled parrotlet. s, Lovely cotinga. t, Black-breasted gnateater.

No. 2380: a, Swallow-tailed kite. b, Hoatzin. c, Ruby topaz hummingbird. d, Black vulture. e, Rufous-tailed jacamar. f, Scarlet macaw. g, Rose-breasted thrush tanager. h, Toco toucan. i, Bearded bellbird. j, Blue-crowned motmot. k, Green oropendola. l, Pompadour cotinga. m, Vermilion flycatcher. n, Blue and yellow macaw. o, White-barred piculet. p, Great razor-billed curassow. q, Ruddy quail-dove. r, Paradise tanager. s, Anhinga. t, Greater flamingo.

No. 2381: a, Harpy eagle. b, Andean condor. c, Amazonian umbrellabird. d, Spider monkeys. e, Hyacinth macaw, diff. f, Red siskin, diff. g, Toucan barbet, diff. h, Three-toed sloth. i, Guanaco. j, Spectacled bear. k, White-lipped peccary. l, Maned wolf. m, Jaguar. n, Spectacled caiman. o, Giant armadillo. p, Giant anteater. q, South American river otter. r, Yapok. s, Central American river turtle. t, Cauca guan, diff.

**Perf. 14x13½, 13½x14**

**1990, Nov. 6   Litho.**

| | | | | |
|---|---|---|---|---|
| 2379 | A131 | $12.80 Sheet of 20, | | |
| | | #a.-t. | 17.00 | 17.00 |
| 2380 | A131 | $12.80 Sheet of 20, | | |
| | | #a.-t. | 17.00 | 17.00 |
| 2381 | A131 | $12.80 Sheet of 20, | | |
| | | #a.-t. | 17.00 | 17.00 |

Nos. 2381a-2381t are horiz. No. 2380s incorrectly inscribed Anhigna. See Nos. E29-E30.

Numbers have been reserved for additional values in this set.

Independence, 25th Anniv. — A132

**1991, June 25   Litho.   Imperf.**

| | | | | |
|---|---|---|---|---|
| 2389 | A132 | $225 multicolored | 9.00 | 9.00 |

**Miniature Sheets**

Olympic Gold Medal Winners — A133

No. 2390: a, Ramon Fonst. b, Lucien Gaudin. c, Ole A. Lilloe-Olsen. d, Morris Fisher. e, Ray C. Ewry. f, Hubert Van Innes. g, Alvin Kraenzlein. h, Johnny Weissmuller. i, Hans Winkler.

No. 2391: a, Viktor Chukarin. b, Agnes Keleti. c, Barbel Wochel. d, Eric Heiden. e, Alvodar Gerevich. f, Giuseppe Delfino. g, Alexander Tikhonov. h, C.F. Pahud de Mortanges. i, Patricia McCormick.

No. 2392: a, Nelli Kim. b, Viktor Krovopuskov. c, Viktor Sidiak. d, Nikolai Andrianov. e, Nadia Comaneci. f, Mitsuo Tsukahara. g, Yelena Novikova-Belova. h, John Naber. i, Kornelia Ender.

No. 2393: a, Olga Korbut. b, Lyudmila Turischeva. c, Lasse Viren. d, George Miez. e, Roland Matthes. f, Pal Kovaks. g, Jesse Owens. h, Mark Spitz. i, Eduardo Mangiarotti.

No. 2394: a, Sawao Kato. b, Rudolf Karpati. c, Jeno Fuchs. d, Emil Zatopek. e, Fanny Blankers-Koen. f, Melvin Sheppard. g, Gert Fredriksson. h, Paul Elvstrom. i, Harrison W. Dillard.

No. 2395: a, Lydia Skoblikova. b, Ivar Ballangrud. c, Clas Thunberg. d, Anton Heida. e, Akinori Nakayama. f, Sixten Jernberg. g, Yevgeniy Grischin. h, Paul Radmilovic. i, Charles Daniels.

No. 2396: a, Betty Cuthbert. b, Vera Caslavska. c, Galina Kulakova. d, Yukio Endo. e, Vladimir Morozov. f, Boris Shaklin. g, Don Schollander. h, Gyozo Kulscar. i, Christian D'Oriola.

No. 2397: a, Al Oerter. b, Polina Astakhova. c, Takashi Ono. d, Valentin Muratov. e, Henri St. Cyr. f, Iain Murray Rose. g, Larissa Latynina. h, Carlo Pavesi. i, Dawn Fraser.

No. 2398, Paavo Nurmi, vert. No. 2399, Johannes Kolehmainen, vert. $190. Nedo Nadi, vert.

**1991, Aug. 12   Litho.   Perf. 14x13½**

| 2390 | A133 | $15.30 | Sheet of 9, | | |
| | | | #a.-i. | 5.00 | 5.00 |
| 2391 | A133 | $17.80 | Sheet of 9, | | |
| | | | #a.-i. | 5.50 | 5.50 |
| 2392 | A133 | $20 | Sheet of 9, | | |
| | | | #a.-i. | 6.00 | 6.00 |
| 2393 | A133 | $20 | Sheet of 9, | | |
| | | | #a.-i. | 6.00 | 6.00 |
| 2394 | A133 | $25 | Sheet of 9, | | |
| | | | #a.-i. | 6.50 | 6.50 |
| 2395 | A133 | $25 | Sheet of 9, | | |
| | | | #a.-i. | 6.50 | 6.50 |
| 2396 | A133 | $30 | Sheet of 9, | | |
| | | | #a.-i. | 7.50 | 7.50 |
| 2397 | A133 | $30 | Sheet of 9, | | |
| | | | #a.-i. | 7.50 | 7.50 |
| | | Nos. 2390-2397 (8) | | 50.50 | 50.50 |

**Souvenir Sheets**
**Perf. 13x13½**

| 2398 | A133 | $150 multicolored | 4.50 | 4.50 |
| 2399 | A133 | $150 multicolored | 4.50 | 4.50 |
| 2400 | A133 | $190 multicolored | 7.00 | 7.00 |

For overprints see Nos. 2552-2557.

Discovery of America, 500th Anniv. (in 1992) — A134

Birds: $6.40, Phoenicopterus ruber. $7.65, Ostinops decumanus. $50, Falco peregrinus. $100, Nymphicus hollandicus. $190, Vultur feriphus. $260, Merganetta armata, horiz.

**1991, Sept. 15   Litho.   Perf. 13½x14**

| 2401 | A134 | $6.40 multicolored | | |
| 2402 | A134 | $7.65 multicolored | | |
| 2403 | A134 | $50 multicolored | | |
| 2404 | A134 | $100 multicolored | | |
| 2405 | A134 | $190 multicolored | | |
| | | Nos. 2401-2405 (5) | 16.50 | |

**Souvenir Sheet**
**Perf. 14x13½**

| 2406 | A134 | $360 multicolored | 15.00 | |

A135

Various orchids: No. 2411, Odontoglossum. No. 2413, Cycnoches ventricosum. No. 2414, Miltonia hibrida, horiz.

**Perf. 13½x14, 14x13½**
**1991, Sept. 30**

| 2407 | A135 | $6.40 multicolored | | |
| 2408 | A135 | $7.65 multi, horiz. | | |
| 2409 | A135 | $50 multicolored | | |
| 2410 | A135 | $100 multicolored | | |
| 2411 | A135 | $190 multicolored | | |
| | | Nos. 2407-2411 (5) | 8.00 | |

**Souvenir Sheets**

| 2412 | A135 | $360 multicolored | | |
| 2413 | A135 | $360 multicolored | | |
| 2414 | A135 | $360 multicolored | | |
| | | Nos. 2412-2414 (3) | 22.50 | |

**Nos. 2332-2339, 2343-2345 Ovptd. or Surcharged**

Overprints: 80c, $2.55, Nos. 2421-2422, 2423a, 2423p, Rotary emblem and "1905-1990." $5.00, $6.40, Nos. 2420, 2423d, 2423m, Rotary emblem and "Paul Percy Harris Founder 1868-1947" on 2 or 3 lines. Nos. 2423b, 2423l, 2423n, Boy Scout emblem and "1907-1992." Nos. 2423c, 2423i, 2423k, Lions Intl. emblem and "1917-1992." Nos. 2423e, 2423h, Red Cross emblem and "125 Years / Red Cross." Nos. 2423f-2423g, 2423j-2423k have parts of larger Rotary emblem. Nos. 2424-2425 ovptd. with service emblems in sheet margins.

**1991, Oct. 29   Perfs. as Before**

| 2415 | A126 | 80c on #2332 | .25 | .25 |
| 2416 | A126 | $2.55 on #2333 | .25 | .25 |
| 2417 | A126 | $5 on #2334 | .25 | .25 |

| 2418 | A126 | $6.40 on #2335 | .25 | .25 |
| 2419 | A126 | $7.65 on #2336 | .25 | .25 |
| 2420 | A126 | $100 on $8.90 | | |
| | | #2337 | 1.75 | 1.75 |
| 2421 | A126 | $190 on $50 | | |
| | | #2338 | 2.75 | 2.75 |
| 2422 | A126 | $225 on $100 | | |
| | | #2339 | 3.00 | 3.00 |
| | | Nos. 2415-2422 (8) | 8.75 | 8.75 |

**Miniature Sheet**

| 2423 | A126 | Sheet of 16 | 8.00 | 8.00 |
| a.-l. | | $10 any single | .25 | .25 |
| m. | | $50 on $10 #2343m | .90 | .90 |
| n. | | $75 on $10 #2343n | 1.00 | 1.00 |
| o. | | $100 on $10 #2343o | 1.50 | 1.50 |
| p. | | $190 on $10 #2343p | 3.25 | 3.25 |

**Souvenir Sheets**

| 2424 | A126 | $400 on $150 | | |
| | | #2344 | 12.00 | 12.00 |
| 2425 | A126 | $500 on $150 | | |
| | | #2345 | 13.00 | 13.00 |

Swiss Confederation, 700th Anniv. — A136

Designs: $6.40, Painting by Diego Giacometti. $7.65, Swiss puppets. $50, Man in top hat by Goya. $100, Stained glass window of Mary & Joseph. $190, Stained glass window of Jesus healing the sick.
No. 2431, Ship's cross-section, by Le Corbusier. No. 2432, Portrait of Giovanna Tornabuoni.

**1991, Oct. 30   Perf. 13½x14**

| 2426 | A136 | $6.40 multicolored | | |
| 2427 | A136 | $7.65 multicolored | | |
| 2428 | A136 | $50 multicolored | | |
| 2429 | A136 | $100 multicolored | | |
| 2430 | A136 | $190 multicolored | | |
| a. | | Sheet of 5 + label, #2426-2430 | 9.00 | |

**Souvenir Sheets**

| 2431 | A136 | $360 multicolored | | |
| 2432 | A136 | $360 multicolored | | |
| | | Nos. 2431-2432 (2) | 16.00 | |

Phila Nippon '91 — A137

Trains: $6.40, Class 581 12-car. $7.65, Class EF-81. $50, Class 381 9-car. $100, Kodama 8-car. $190, Shin-Kansen 16-car. No. 2438, Shin-Kansen 16-car, diff. No. 2439, Japanese locomotives in Calcutta.

**1991, Nov. 16   Perf. 14x13½**

| 2433 | A137 | $6.40 multicolored | | |
| 2434 | A137 | $7.65 multicolored | | |
| 2435 | A137 | $50 multicolored | | |
| 2436 | A137 | $100 multicolored | | |
| 2437 | A137 | $190 multicolored | | |
| | | Nos. 2433-2437 (5) | 15.00 | |

**Souvenir Sheets**

| 2438 | A137 | $360 multicolored | | |
| 2439 | A137 | $360 multicolored | | |
| | | Nos. 2438-2439 (2) | 30.00 | |

Swiss Confederation, 700th anniv., No. 2439.

Common Design Types pictured following the introduction.

**Royal Family Birthday, Anniversary**
**Common Design Type**

| 1991, Nov. | | Litho. | | Perf. 14 |
| 2440 | CD347 | $8.90 multi | .30 | .25 |
| 2441 | CD347 | $12.80 multi | .30 | .30 |
| 2442 | CD347 | $15.30 multi | .30 | .30 |
| 2443 | CD347 | $50 multi | 1.00 | .80 |
| 2444 | CD347 | $75 multi | 1.25 | 1.25 |
| 2445 | CD347 | $100 multi | 1.25 | 1.25 |
| 2446 | CD347 | $130 multi | 1.50 | 1.50 |
| 2447 | CD347 | $150 multi | 2.50 | 2.50 |
| 2448 | CD347 | $190 multi | 3.00 | 3.00 |
| 2449 | CD347 | $200 multi | 2.50 | 2.50 |
| | | Nos. 2440-2449 (10) | 13.90 | 13.65 |

**Souvenir Sheets**

| 2450 | CD347 | $225 Elizabeth | 3.50 | 3.50 |
| 2451 | CD347 | $225 Charles, Diana, sons | 4.00 | 4.00 |

$8.90, $50, $75, $190, No. 2451, Charles and Diana, 10th wedding anniversary. $130, $150, Prince Philip, 70th birthday. Others, Queen Elizabeth II, 65th birthday.

**Miniature Sheet**

Japanese Attack on Pearl Harbor, 50th Anniv. — A138

No. 2452: a, Akagi launches attack planes. b, Sakamaki's midget submarine beached. c, Mistubishi ASM Zero fighter. d, USS Arizona under attack. e, Aichi D3A1 Val dive bomber. f, USS California. g, P40 defends Pearl Harbor. h, USS Cassin and Downes hit at dry dock. i, B17 crash lands at Bellows Field. j, USS Nevada burns at Hospital Point.

**1991, Dec. 7   Perf. 14½x15**

| 2452 | A138 | $50 Sheet of 10, | | |
| | | #a.-j. | 10.00 | 10.00 |

1992 Winter Olympics, Albertville A139

Walt Disney characters at the Olympics: $6.40, Gus Gander playing ice hockey. $7.65, Mickey, Minnie in bobsled. $8.90, Huey, Dewey, Louie pretending to luge. $12.80, Goofy freestyle skiing. $50, Goofy ski jumping. $100, Donald, Daisy Duck speed skating. $130, Pluto cross-country skiing. $190, Mickey, Minnie ice dancing. No. 2461, Scrooge McDuck slalom skiing. No. 2462, Huey curling.

**1991, Dec. 12   Perf. 13½x13**

| 2453 | A139 | $6.40 multi | .35 | .35 |
| 2454 | A143 | $7.65 multi | .40 | .40 |
| 2455 | A139 | $8.90 multi | .45 | .45 |
| 2456 | A143 | $12.80 multi | .65 | .65 |
| 2457 | A143 | $50 multi | 1.40 | 1.40 |
| 2458 | A139 | $100 multi | 2.25 | 2.25 |
| 2459 | A143 | $130 multi | 2.75 | 2.75 |
| 2460 | A143 | $190 multi | 4.00 | 4.00 |
| | | Nos. 2453-2460 (8) | 12.25 | 12.25 |

**Souvenir Sheets**

| 2461 | A139 | $225 multi | 6.50 | 6.50 |
| 2462 | A143 | $225 multi | 6.50 | 6.50 |

Mushrooms A140

Designs: $6.40, Boletus satanoides. $7.65, Russula nigricans. $50, Cortinarius glaucopus. $100, Lactarius camphoratus. $190, Cortinarius callisteus. No. 2468, Russula integra. No. 2469, Coprinus micaceus, vert.

**1991, Dec. 16   Litho.   Perf. 14x13½**

| 2463 | A140 | $6.40 multicolored | | |
| 2464 | A140 | $7.65 multicolored | | |
| 2465 | A140 | $50 multicolored | | |
| 2466 | A140 | $100 multicolored | | |
| 2467 | A140 | $190 multicolored | | |
| | | Nos. 2463-2467 (5) | 15.00 | |

**Souvenir Sheets**
**Perf. 14x13½, 13½x14**

| 2468 | A140 | $360 multicolored | | |
| 2469 | A140 | $360 multicolored | | |
| | | Nos. 2468-2469 (2) | 28.00 | 28.00 |

Walt Disney Christmas Cards A141

Designs and year of issue: 80c, Mickey, friends singing carols, 1989. $2.55, Mickey, friends riding trolley car, 1962. $5, Donald, Pluto wrapping package, 1971. $6.40, Mickey holding candle, 1948. $7.65, Mickey with Santa mask, 1947. $8.90, Pinocchio's shadow, 1939. $50, Three Little Pigs, dancing on wolf's back, 1933. $200, Mickey, mice singing carols, 1949.
No. 2478: a, Conductor, Donald. b, Elephant with book. c, Goofy, centaurs. d, Snow White, dwarfs. e, Pluto, dinosaur.
No. 2479: a, Mickey in sleigh. b, Three little pigs, Winnie-the-Pooh, Bambi. c, Dalmatian, bear, monkey, Lady and the Tramp. d, Alice, Goofy, Mad Hatter. e, Pinocchio, Tinker Bell, Peter Pan, Seven Dwarfs, Donald Duck. f, Pluto, 1974.
No. 2480, Mickey and friends riding in coach, 1932. No. 2481, Mickey, Pluto greeting friends, 1935. No. 2482, Donald, Jose Carioca, 1944. No. 2483, Couple dancing, baseball batter, 1945. No. 2484, Mickey, Donald, Goofy, 1946. No. 2485, Santa in chimney, 1969. No. 2486, Portrait of Winnie-the-Pooh hanging on wall, 1969. No. 2487, Mickey, 1978.

**1991, Dec. 17   Perf. 14x13½**

| 2470 | A141 | 80c multi | .25 | .25 |
| 2471 | A141 | $2.55 multi | .25 | .25 |
| 2472 | A141 | $5 multi | .25 | .25 |
| 2473 | A141 | $6.40 multi | .35 | .25 |
| 2474 | A141 | $7.65 multi | .35 | .25 |
| 2475 | A141 | $8.90 multi | .35 | .25 |
| 2476 | A141 | $50 multi | 1.40 | 1.40 |
| 2477 | A141 | $200 multi | 5.25 | 5.25 |
| 2478 | A141 | $50 Strip of 5, | | |
| | | #a.-e. | 7.00 | 7.00 |
| 2479 | A141 | $50 Strip of 6, | | |
| | | #a.-f. | 8.50 | 8.50 |
| | | Nos. 2470-2479 (10) | 23.95 | 23.65 |

**Souvenir Sheets**

| 2480 | A141 | $260 multi | 6.00 | 6.00 |
| 2481 | A141 | $260 multi | 6.00 | 6.00 |
| 2482 | A141 | $260 multi | 6.00 | 6.00 |
| 2483 | A141 | $260 multi | 6.00 | 6.00 |
| 2484 | A141 | $260 multi | 6.00 | 6.00 |
| 2485 | A141 | $260 multi | 6.00 | 6.00 |
| 2486 | A141 | $260 multi | 6.00 | 6.00 |
| 2487 | A141 | $260 multi | 6.00 | 6.00 |
| | | Nos. 2480-2487 (8) | 48.00 | 48.00 |

Nos. 2478a-2478e, 2479a-2479f, 2480-2481, 2485 and 2487 are vert.

**No. 2373 Surcharged**
**1991, Dec. 19   Litho.   Perf. 14**

| 2487A | A129 | $600 on $150 #2373 | — | — |

**No. 2377 Surcharged**

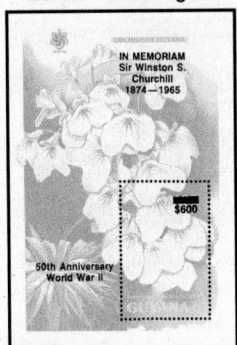

**1991, Dec. 19   Litho.   Perf. 14**

| 2487B | A129 | $600 on $190 #2377 | — | — |

Christmas — A142

Paintings: $6.40, Madonna and Child with Angels, by Titian, horiz. $7.65, Madonna and Child with Angels, by Rubens. $50, Madonna and Child, by Raphael. $100, Madonna and Child, by Durer. $190, Madonna, by Durer. No. 2493, Madonna and Child, by Rubens, horiz. No. 2494, Madonna, by Durer, diff.

**1991, Dec. 30**    **Perf. 14x13½, 13½x14**

| | | | |
|---|---|---|---|
| 2488 | A142 | $6.40 multicolored | |
| 2489 | A142 | $7.65 multicolored | |
| 2490 | A142 | $50 multicolored | |
| 2491 | A142 | $100 multicolored | |
| 2492 | A142 | $190 multicolored | |
| | | Nos. 2488-2 92(5) | 15.00 |

### Souvenir Sheets

| | | | |
|---|---|---|---|
| 2493 | A142 | $360 multicolored | |
| 2494 | A142 | $360 multicolored | |
| | | Nos. 2493-2494 (2) | 35.00 |

Brandenburg Gate, Bicent. — A143

Designs: $10, Map of Berlin. $25, US Pres. George Bush, Polish Pres. Lech Walesa. $100, German Chancellor Helmut Kohl, Foreign Minister Hans-Dietrich Genscher. $190, Armored helmet.

**1991, Dec.**    **Perf. 14**

| | | | | |
|---|---|---|---|---|
| 2495 | A143 | $10 multicolored | .30 | .30 |
| 2496 | A143 | $25 multicolored | .75 | .75 |
| 2497 | A143 | $100 multicolored | 2.50 | 2.50 |
| | | Nos. 2495-2497 (3) | 3.55 | 3.55 |

### Souvenir Sheet

| | | | | |
|---|---|---|---|---|
| 2498 | A143 | $190 multicolored | 4.00 | 4.00 |

Wolfgang Amadeus Mozart, Death Bicent. — A144

Portrait of Mozart and: $75, Laxenburg. $80, Death of Leopold II. $100, Mozart's birthplace, Salzburg.

**1991, Dec.**

| | | | | |
|---|---|---|---|---|
| 2499 | A144 | $75 multicolored | 2.00 | 2.00 |
| 2500 | A144 | $80 multicolored | 2.25 | 2.25 |
| 2501 | A144 | $100 multicolored | 2.50 | 2.50 |
| | | Nos. 2499-2501 (3) | 6.75 | 6.75 |

### Souvenir Sheet

| | | | | |
|---|---|---|---|---|
| 2502 | A144 | $190 Bust of Mozart, vert. | 4.00 | 4.00 |

17th World Scout Jamboree, Korea — A145

Designs: $30, Scouts hiking. $40, Emblems, flag. $100, Lord Baden-Powell, vert. $190, Rocket cover with US No. 1145.

**1991, Dec.**

| | | | | |
|---|---|---|---|---|
| 2503 | A145 | $25 multicolored | .80 | .80 |
| 2504 | A145 | $30 multicolored | 1.00 | 1.00 |
| 2505 | A145 | $40 multicolored | 1.10 | 1.10 |
| 2506 | A145 | $100 multicolored | 2.50 | 2.50 |
| | | Nos. 2503-2506 (4) | 5.40 | 5.40 |

### Souvenir Sheet

| | | | | |
|---|---|---|---|---|
| 2507 | A145 | $190 multicolored | 4.00 | 4.00 |

Charles de Gaulle — A146

De Gaulle: $60, In Venice, 1944. $75, With Khrushchev, 1960. $80, In Algiers, 1958. $100, With Pope John VI, 1967.

**1991, Dec.**

| | | | | |
|---|---|---|---|---|
| 2508 | A146 | $60 multicolored | 2.00 | 2.00 |
| 2509 | A146 | $75 multicolored | 2.50 | 2.50 |
| 2510 | A146 | $80 multicolored | 2.75 | 2.75 |
| 2511 | A146 | $100 multicolored | 3.25 | 3.25 |
| | | Nos. 2508-2511 (4) | 10.50 | 10.50 |

### Souvenir Sheets

| | | | | |
|---|---|---|---|---|
| 2512 | A146 | $150 Portrait, vert. | 7.50 | 7.50 |
| 2513 | A146 | $190 Portrait, diff, vert. | 9.75 | 9.75 |

No. 2511 inscribed incorrectly as "Pope John VI", should be "Pope Paul VI."

Anniversaries and Events — A147

Designs: No. 2515, Caroline Herschel, astronomer, Old Town Hall, Hanover. No. 2516, Map of Switzerland, woman in traditional dress. $80, Otto Lilienthal's glider No. 3. $100, Locomotive. $190, Arms of Bern and Solothurn.

**1991, Dec.**

| | | | | |
|---|---|---|---|---|
| 2515 | A147 | $75 multicolored | 2.00 | 2.00 |
| 2516 | A147 | $75 multicolored | 2.00 | 2.00 |
| 2517 | A147 | $80 multicolored | 2.25 | 2.25 |
| 2518 | A147 | $100 multicolored | 2.50 | 2.50 |
| | | Nos. 2515-2518 (4) | 8.75 | 8.75 |

### Souvenir Sheet

| | | | | |
|---|---|---|---|---|
| 2519 | A147 | $190 multicolored | 4.00 | 4.00 |

Hanover, 750th anniv. (No. 2515), Swiss Confederation, 700th anniv. (Nos. 2516, 2519), first glider flight, cent. (No. 2517), Trans-Siberian Railway, cent. (No. 2518).

Discovery of America, 500th Anniv. — A148

Designs: $6.40, Columbus lands on Trinidad. $7.65, Columbus, globe. $8.90, Ships blown off course by hurricane. $12.80, Map, hands in chains. $15.30, Land sighted. $50, Nina, Pinta. $75, Santa Maria. $100, Columbus trading with natives. $125, Superstitions & sea monsters. $130, Map, Columbus ashore. $140, Priest & natives. $150, Columbus kneeling before King Ferdinand and Queen Isabella. No. 2532, Map of New World. No. 2533, One of Columbus' ships, vert. No. 2534, Columbus.

**1992, Jan. 2**    **Perf. 14**

| | | | | |
|---|---|---|---|---|
| 2520 | A148 | $6.40 multi | .40 | .35 |
| 2521 | A148 | $7.65 multi | .45 | .40 |
| 2522 | A148 | $8.90 multi | .50 | .45 |
| 2523 | A148 | $12.80 multi | .55 | .50 |
| 2524 | A148 | $15.30 multi | .60 | .55 |
| 2525 | A148 | $50 multi | 1.75 | 1.75 |
| 2526 | A148 | $75 multi | 2.25 | 2.25 |
| 2527 | A148 | $100 multi | 3.00 | 3.00 |
| 2528 | A148 | $125 multi | 3.75 | 3.75 |
| 2529 | A148 | $130 multi | 4.00 | 4.00 |
| 2530 | A148 | $140 multi | 4.25 | 4.25 |
| 2531 | A148 | $150 multi | 4.50 | 4.50 |
| | | Nos. 2520-2531 (12) | 26.00 | 25.75 |

### Souvenir Sheets

| | | | | |
|---|---|---|---|---|
| 2532 | A148 | $280 multi | 8.50 | 8.50 |
| 2533 | A148 | $280 multi | 8.50 | 8.50 |
| 2534 | A148 | $280 multi | 8.50 | 8.50 |

Movie Posters — A149

Designs: $8.90, The Great K & A Train Robbery. $12.80, Cimarron. $15.30, Buzzin' Around. $25, Adventures of Captain Marvel. $30, The Mummy. $50, A Sainted Devil. $75, A Tale of Two Cities. $100, A Tugboat Romeo. $130, Thief of Bagdad. $150, Bacon Grabbers. $190, A Night at the Opera. $200, Citizen Kane. No. 2547, She Done Him Wrong. No. 2548, The Circus. No. 2549, Babe Comes Home. No. 2550, Zeppelin, horiz.

**1992, Mar. 11**    **Litho.**    **Perf. 14**

| | | | | |
|---|---|---|---|---|
| 2535 | A149 | $8.90 multi | .60 | .50 |
| 2536 | A149 | $12.80 multi | .65 | .55 |
| 2537 | A149 | $15.30 multi | .70 | .65 |
| 2538 | A149 | $25 multi | .80 | .75 |
| 2539 | A149 | $30 multi | .90 | .85 |
| 2540 | A149 | $50 multi | 1.50 | 1.40 |
| 2541 | A149 | $75 multi | 2.25 | 2.00 |
| 2542 | A149 | $100 multi | 3.00 | 2.75 |
| 2543 | A149 | $130 multi | 3.75 | 3.50 |
| 2544 | A149 | $150 multi | 4.50 | 4.25 |

| | | | | |
|---|---|---|---|---|
| 2545 | A149 | $190 multi | 5.75 | 5.50 |
| 2546 | A149 | $200 multi | 6.00 | 5.75 |
| | | Nos. 2535-2546 (12) | 30.40 | 28.45 |

#### Size: 70x100mm, 100x70mm

#### *Imperf*

| | | | | |
|---|---|---|---|---|
| 2547 | A149 | $225 multi | 6.75 | 6.75 |
| 2548 | A149 | $225 multi | 6.75 | 6.75 |
| 2549 | A149 | $225 multi | 6.75 | 6.75 |
| 2550 | A149 | $225 multi | 6.75 | 6.75 |

#### No. 2273 Overprinted or Surcharged with Olympic Rings and "ALBERTVILLE '92" or "XVIth Olympic Winter / Games in Albertville" (No. 2551e)

**1992**    **Perfs. as Before**

| | | | |
|---|---|---|---|
| 2551 | A122 | Sheet of 9 | |
| a.-f. | | $20 on #2273a-2273f | |
| g. | | $70 on $20 #2273g | |
| h. | | $100 on $20 #2273h | |
| i. | | $190 on $20 #2273i | |

#### Nos. 2391g, 2395c, 2396c, 2398, 2400 Ovptd. "ALBERTVILLE '92"
#### No. 2399 Ovptd. "Barcelona '92" and emblems in Sheet Margin

**1992**    **Perfs. as Before**

| | | | | |
|---|---|---|---|---|
| 2552 | A133 | $17.80 on #2391g | 12.00 | 12.00 |
| 2553 | A133 | $25 on #2395c | 12.00 | 12.00 |
| 2554 | A133 | $30 on #2396c | 12.00 | 12.00 |

### Souvenir Sheets

| | | | | |
|---|---|---|---|---|
| 2555 | A133 | $150 on #2398 | 7.00 | 7.00 |
| 2556 | A133 | $150 on #2399 | 7.00 | 7.00 |
| 2557 | A133 | $190 on #2400 | 7.00 | 7.00 |

Nos. 2552-2554 printed in sheets of 9, overprint applied to only one stamp per sheet. Overprint on Nos. 2555, 2557 applied to sheet margin.

Easter — A150

Various details from paintings by Durer: $6.40, $12.80, $50, $130, No. 2567, The Martyrdom of Ten Thousand. $7.65, $15.30, $100, $190, No. 2566, Adoration of the Trinity.

**1992**    **Litho.**    **Perf. 13½x14**

| | | | | |
|---|---|---|---|---|
| 2558 | A150 | $6.40 multi | .30 | .25 |
| 2559 | A150 | $7.65 multi | .30 | .25 |
| 2560 | A150 | $12.80 multi | .45 | .25 |
| 2561 | A150 | $15.30 multi | .55 | .45 |
| 2562 | A150 | $50 multi | 1.50 | 1.25 |
| 2563 | A150 | $100 multi | 2.75 | 2.75 |
| 2564 | A150 | $130 multi | 3.75 | 3.75 |
| 2565 | A150 | $190 multi | 5.75 | 5.75 |
| | | Nos. 2558-2565 (8) | 15.35 | 14.70 |

### Souvenir Sheets

| | | | | |
|---|---|---|---|---|
| 2566 | A150 | $225 multi | 6.50 | 6.50 |
| 2567 | A150 | $225 multi | 6.50 | 6.50 |

A151

Queen Elizabeth II: $8.90, With Prince Philip. $12.80, In uniform. $100, At coronation. $130, Wearing black cape and hat. No. 2572, Coronation portrait. No. 2573, Fortieth anniv. portrait.

**1992**    **Litho.**    **Perf. 14**

| | | | | |
|---|---|---|---|---|
| 2568 | A151 | $8.90 multicolored | 1.00 | .50 |
| 2569 | A151 | $12.80 multicolored | 1.25 | .60 |
| 2570 | A151 | $100 multicolored | 5.00 | 4.00 |
| 2571 | A151 | $130 multicolored | 6.00 | 5.00 |
| | | Nos. 2568-2571 (4) | 13.25 | 10.10 |

### Souvenir Sheets

| | | | | |
|---|---|---|---|---|
| 2572 | A151 | $225 multi | 6.50 | 6.50 |
| 2573 | A151 | $225 multi | 6.50 | 6.50 |

Queen Elizabeth II's Accession to the Throne, 40th Anniv.

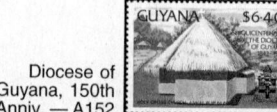

Diocese of Guyana, 150th Anniv. — A152

Designs: $6.40, Holy Cross Church, Annai Bupununi. $50, St. Peter's Church. $100, St. George's Cathedral, interior, vert. $190, Map, vert. $225, Religious symbols.

**1992**    **Litho.**    **Perf. 14**

| | | | | |
|---|---|---|---|---|
| 2574 | A152 | $6.40 multicolored | .35 | .30 |
| 2575 | A152 | $50 multicolored | 1.00 | 1.00 |
| 2576 | A152 | $100 multicolored | 2.40 | 2.40 |
| 2577 | A152 | $190 multicolored | 3.75 | 3.75 |
| | | Nos. 2574-2577 (4) | 7.50 | 7.45 |

### Souvenir Sheet

| | | | | |
|---|---|---|---|---|
| 2578 | A152 | $225 multicolored | 6.50 | 6.50 |

Nos. 1033, 1045 and 1061 Surcharged

#### Method, Perfs, and Watermarks As Before

**1992, May 29**

| | | | | |
|---|---|---|---|---|
| 2578A | A91 | $6.40 on 60c #1033 | — | — |
| 2578B | A91 | $7.65 on 60c #1061 | — | — |
| 2578C | A91 | $8.90 on 60c #1045 | — | — |

An additional stamp was issued in this set. The editors would like to examine any example of it.

#### Miniature Sheet

Horses A153

No. 2579: a, Palomino. b, Appaloosa. c, Clydesdale. d, Arab. e, Morgan. f, Friesian. g, Pinto. h, Thoroughbred. No. 2580, Lipizzaner.

**1992, Aug. 10**

| | | | | |
|---|---|---|---|---|
| 2579 | A153 | $190 Sheet of 8, #a.-h. | 30.00 | 30.00 |

### Souvenir Sheet

| | | | | |
|---|---|---|---|---|
| 2580 | A153 | $190 multicolored | 7.50 | 7.50 |

No. 2580 contains one 58x29mm stamp.

Cats — A154

$5, Burmese. $6.40, Turkish van. $12.80, American shorthair. $15.30, Egyptian. $50, Egyptian mau. $100, Japanese bobtail. $130, Abyssinian. $225, Oriental shorthair. No. 2588A: b, Russian blue. c, Havana brown. d, Himalayan. e, Manx. f, Cornish rex. g, Black Persian. h, Scottish fold. i, Siamese. No. 2589, Chartreuse, vert. No. 2590, Turkish angora. No. 2591, Maine coon. No. 2592, Chinchilla.

**1992, Aug. 10**    **Perf. 14½x14**

| | | | | |
|---|---|---|---|---|
| 2581 | A154 | $5 multi | .30 | .25 |
| 2582 | A154 | $6.40 multi | .30 | .25 |
| 2583 | A154 | $12.80 multi | .40 | .25 |
| 2584 | A154 | $15.30 multi | .55 | .50 |
| 2585 | A154 | $50 multi | 1.75 | 1.50 |
| 2586 | A154 | $100 multi | 3.25 | 3.25 |
| 2587 | A154 | $130 multi | 4.00 | 4.00 |
| 2588 | A154 | $225 multi | 7.50 | 7.50 |
| | | Nos. 2581-2588 (8) | 18.05 | 17.60 |

#### Miniature Sheet
#### Perf. 14x13½

| | | | | |
|---|---|---|---|---|
| 2588A | A154 | $50 Sheet of 8, #b.-i. | 12.00 | 12.00 |

## Souvenir Sheets
### Perf. 14x14½

| | | | | | |
|---|---|---|---|---|---|
| 2589 | A152 | $250 multi | | 7.25 | 7.25 |
| 2590 | A154 | $250 multi | | 7.25 | 7.25 |
| 2591 | A154 | $250 multi | | 7.25 | 7.25 |
| 2592 | A154 | $250 multi | | 7.25 | 7.25 |

No. 2589 has continuous design. Nos. 2590-2592 are vert. and have continous design.

**Nos. 2368-2369 Surcharged on 4 stamps and Overprinted in Red**

Surcharge and overprint reads: "PHILA NIPPON '91 / WORLD STAMP EXHIBITION NIPPON '91" and Show Emblem in Sheet Margin

| 1992 | | | Perfs. as Before | |
|---|---|---|---|---|
| 2593 | A129 | Sheet of 12, #a.-d., #2368a-2368l | | 19.00 |
| a. | | $25 on $10 #2368m | | |
| b. | | $50 on $10 #2368n | | |
| c. | | $75 on $10 #2368o | | |
| d. | | $130 on $10 #2368p | | |
| 2594 | A129 | Sheet of 16, #a.-d., 2369a-2369l | | 19.00 |
| a. | | $25 on $12.80 #2369m | | |
| b. | | $50 on $12.80 #2369n | | |
| c. | | $75 on $12.80 #2369o | | |
| d. | | $130 on $12.80 #2369p | | |

**No. 2376 Surcharged in Red Souvenir Sheet**

| 2595 | A129 | $250 on $150 #2376 | | |
|---|---|---|---|---|

**Nos. 2332-2340, 2346-2347 Overprinted or Surcharged**

Overprints: 80c, $2.55, Nos. 2602-2603, Lions emblem and "Lions International / 1917-1992." $5, $6.40, $7.65, Nos. 2601, 2604d, 2604m, Lions emblem and "Melvin Jones Founder 1880-1961" on 2 or 3 lines. Nos. 2604a, 2604p, Lions emblem and "1917-1992." Nos. 2604b, 2604i, 2604o, Rotary emblem and "1905-1990." Nos. 2604c, 2604l, 2604n, Boy Scout emblem and "1907-1992." Nos. 2604e, 2604h, Red Cross emblem and "125 Years Red Cross." Nos. 2604f-2604g, 2604j-2604k have parts of larger Lions emblem. Nos. 2605-2606 have service organization emblems in sheet margins.

| 1992 | | | Perfs. as Before | |
|---|---|---|---|---|
| 2596 | A126 | 80c on #2332 | | |
| 2597 | A126 | $2.55 on #2333 | | |
| 2598 | A126 | $5 on #2334 | | |
| 2599 | A126 | $6.40 on #2335 | | |
| 2600 | A126 | $7.65 on #2336 | | |
| 2601 | A126 | $100 on $8.90 #2337 | | |
| 2602 | A126 | $190 on $50 #2338 | | |
| 2603 | A126 | $225 on $100 #2339 | | |

**Miniature Sheet**

| 2604 | | Sheet of 16 | 45.00 |
|---|---|---|---|
| a.-l. | A126 | $10 any single | |
| m. | A126 | $50 on $10 #2340m | |
| n. | A126 | $75 on $10 #2340n | |
| o. | A126 | $100 on $10 #2340o | |
| p. | A126 | $190 on $10 #2340p | |

**Souvenir Sheets**

| 2605 | A126 | $400 on $190 #2346 | |
|---|---|---|---|
| 2606 | A126 | $500 on $190 #2347 | |

Elephants — A155

No. 2607: a, Mammoth, Oligocene Epoch. b, Stegodon, mid- Miocene Epoch. c, Mammoth, Pliocene Epoch. d, Hannibal's army crossing Alps. e, Royal elephant of the Maharaja of Mysore, India. f, Elephant pulling tree trunks, Burma. g, Tiger hunt, India. h, Elephant towing raft on River Kwai, Thailand. $225, African elephants, Kenya.

| 1992, Aug. 10 | | Litho. | Perf. 14 | |
|---|---|---|---|---|
| 2607 | A155 | $50 Sheet of 8, #a.-h. | 16.00 | 16.00 |

**Souvenir Sheet**

| 2608 | A155 | $225 multicolored | 11.00 | 11.00 |
|---|---|---|---|---|

No. 2607 has continuous design.

---

Animals of Guyana — A156

$8.90, Red howler monkey. $12.80, Ringtailed coati. $15.30, Jaguar. $25, Two-toed sloth. $50, Giant armadillo. $75, Giant anteater. $100, Capybara. $130, Ocelot. No. 2617, Wooly opossum, vert. No. 2618, Three-striped night monkey.

| 1992, Aug. 10 | | | | |
|---|---|---|---|---|
| 2609 | A156 | $8.90 multicolored | .25 | .25 |
| 2610 | A156 | $12.80 multicolored | .30 | .25 |
| 2611 | A156 | $15.30 multicolored | .40 | .35 |
| 2612 | A156 | $25 multicolored | .65 | .60 |
| 2613 | A156 | $50 multicolored | 1.40 | 1.25 |
| 2614 | A156 | $75 multicolored | 2.00 | 2.00 |
| 2615 | A156 | $100 multicolored | 2.75 | 2.75 |
| 2616 | A156 | $130 multicolored | 3.50 | 3.50 |
| | | Nos. 2609-2616 (8) | 11.25 | 10.95 |

**Souvenir Sheets**

| 2617 | A156 | $225 multicolored | 7.00 | 7.00 |
|---|---|---|---|---|
| 2618 | A156 | $225 multicolored | 7.00 | 7.00 |

### Souvenir Sheet

Statue of Liberty, New York A157

| 1992, Oct. 28 | | | | |
|---|---|---|---|---|
| 2619 | A157 | $325 multicolored | 11.00 | 11.00 |

Postage Stamp Mega Event '92, New York City.

**Nos. 1072a, 1075a, 1077a and 1080a Surcharged**

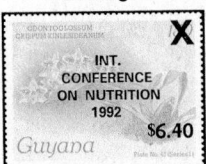

**Methods, Perfs, and Watermarks As Before**

| 1992, Nov. 2 | | | | |
|---|---|---|---|---|
| 2619A | A91 | $6.40 on 150c #1080a | — | — |
| 2619B | A91 | $7.65 on 150c #1075a | — | — |
| 2619C | A91 | $8.90 on 150c #1072a | — | — |
| 2619D | A91 | $10 on 200c #1077a | — | — |
| 2619E | A91 | $50 on 60c #1022 | — | — |

### Miniature Sheets

Model Trains — A158

Marklin toy locomotives: No. 2620a, 2-4-4-2 Crocodile locomotive, 1 gauge, 1933. b, French prototype streetcar, 1 gauge, 1933. c, British prototype Flatiron 2-4-4 tank engine, O gauge, 1913. d, German National Railways 0-6-0 switching engine, Z gauge, 1970. e, Smoking/non-smoking third class car, 1 gauge, 1909. f, American style 0-4-0 locomotive, O gauge, 1904. g, Zurich, Switzerland prototype streetcar, O gauge, 1928. h, Central London Railway Bo-Bo, 1 gauge, 1904. i, "The Great Bear" Pacific, 1 gauge, 1909.

No. 2621: a, 0-4-4 American style locomotive, 2 gauge, 1904. b, German first and second class passenger car, 1 gauge, 1908. c, British Great Eastern Railway 4-4-0, 1 gauge, 1908. d, English prototype steeplecab, O gauge, 1904. e, Santa Fe Railroad diesel, 1962. f, British Great Northern 4-4-0, 3 gauge, live steam model, 1903. g, Caledonian Railway "Cardean" of Scotland, 1 gauge, 1904. h, British LNWR passenger car, 1 gauge, 1903. i,

---

Swiss Gotthard Rwy. 0-4-0 locomotive, O gauge, 1920.

No. 2622: a, British LB & SCR tank engine, O gauge, 1920. b, Central London Railway, tunnel locomotive, 1 gauge, 1904. c, "Borsig" 4-6-4 streamliner, O gauge, 1935. d, French PLM first class car, 1 gauge, 1929. e, American style 0-4-0 locomotive #1021, 1 gauge, 1904. f, "Paris-Orsay" long-nose steeplecab, 1 gauge, 1920. g, British "Cock O' The North," 1 gauge, 1936. h, Prussian State Railways P8 4-6-0 live steam model, 1 gauge, 1975. i, 1937 German "Schnell Treibwagen," O gauge, 1937.

No. 2623: a, Marklin North British Railway "Atlantic," 1 gauge, 1913. b, Bing British London & Western Railway 4-4-2 "Precursor," O gauge, clockwork model, 1916. c, Marklin British Great Western "King George V," O gauge, 1937. d, Marklin passenger car, "Kaiser Train," 1 gauge, 1901. e, Bing 4-4-0 side tank engine, 1 gauge, live steam model, 1904. f, Marklin short-nose steeplecab, 1 gauge, 1912. g, Marklin "Der Adler," 1 gauge, 1935. h, Bing British Great Western Railway "County of Northampton," 1 gauge, live steam model, 1909. i, Bing British Midland Railway "Black Prince," 3 gauge, live steam model, 1906.

Bing toy locomotives: No. 2624: a, Midland Railway "Deeley Type" 4-4-0, 1 gauge clockwork model, 1909. b, No. 2631, British Midland Railway 0-4-0, 3 gauge clockwork model, 1903. c, German 4-6-2 Pacific, O gauge, 1926. e, British Great Western Railway, third class coach, O gauge, 1926. e, British London & Southwestern "M7" 0-4-4, 1 gauge clockwork model, 1909. f, "Pilot" 4-4-0 side tank engine, 3 gauge live steam model, 1901. g, British London & Northwestern Railway Webb "Cauliflower," O gauge clockwork model, 1912. h, No. 112, 4-4-0 side tank locomotive, 1 gauge live steam model, 1910. i, British Great Northern Railway, "Stirling Single," 2 gauge live steam model, 1904.

Carette toy locomotives: No. 2625: a, Lithographed tin "Penny Bazaar" train, 1904. b, Winteringham 0-4-0 locomotive, O gauge, 1917. c, British Northeastern Railway, Smith Compound, 3 gauge, 1905. d, SE & CR 2-2-4 steam railcar, 1 gauge, live steam model, 1908. e, No. 776 British Great Northern Railway Stirling "Single," 3 gauge, live steam model, 1903. f, British Midland Railway 4-4-0, O gauge, clockwork model, 1911. g, London Metropolitan Railway "Westinghouse," 1 gauge, 1908. h, Clestory coach, 1 gauge, 1907. i, Steam railcar No. 1, O gauge, live steam model, 1906.

Marklin toy locomotives: No. 2626: a, LMS "Precursor" 4-4-2 tank engine, O gauge clockwork model, 1923. b, American "Congressional Limited" passenger car, 1 gauge, 1908. c, Swiss prototype "Ae 3/6" locomotive, O gauge, 1934. d, German National Railways class 80, 0-6-0, 1 gauge, 1975. e, British Southern Railway third class coach, O gauge, 1926. f, "Bowen-Cooke" 4-6-2 tank engine, O gauge, 1913. g, First electric prototype model, "Two Penny Tube," London, 1 gauge clockwork model, 1901. h, "Paris-Orsay" steeplecab, 1 gauge, 1902. i, 0-2-2 Passenger engine, O gauge clockwork model, 1895.

Bing toy locomotives: No. 2627: a, 2-2-0 engine and tender, 2 gauge live steam model, 1895. b, British Midland Railway "single," O gauge clockwork model, 1913. c, #524/510 reversible express passenger locomotive, 1 gauge, 1916. d, "Kaiser Train" passenger car with Gothic windows, 1 gauge, 1902. e, Tinplate model, British rural station, 1 gauge, 1915. f, British LSMR "M7" side tank locomotive, O gauge clockwork model, 1909. g, 4-4-4 "Windcutter," 1 gauge live steam model, 1912. h, British Great Central Railway "Sir Sam Fay," 1 gauge clockwork model, 1914. i, "Dunalastair" locomotive Caledonian Railway, 1 gauge clockwork model, 1910.

No. 2628, German National Railroad class 0-1 Pacific, O gauge, 1937. No. 2629, Bing 0-4-0 Contractor's locomotive, 4 gauge, 1904. No. 2630, Rack Railway "Steeplecab" locomotive, 2 gauge, 1908. No. 2631, Bing Pabst Blue Ribbon Beer refrigerator car, O gauge, 1925. No. 2632, Marklin "Commodore Vanderbilt," O gauge, 1937. No. 2633, Bing British Great Western Railway "County of Northampton," 1 gauge, live steam model, 1909. No. 2634, Marklin French Prototype PLM Pacific, 1 gauge, live steam model, 1912. No. 2635, Marklin "Mountain Etat" second series, O gauge, 1933.

| 1992, Nov. 19 | | | Perf. 14 | |
|---|---|---|---|---|
| 2620 | A158 | $45 Sheet of 9, #a.-i. | 8.00 | 8.00 |
| 2621 | A158 | $45 Sheet of 9, #a.-i. | 8.00 | 8.00 |
| 2622 | A158 | $45 Sheet of 9, #a.-i. | 8.00 | 8.00 |
| 2623 | A158 | $45 Sheet of 9, #a.-i. | 8.00 | 8.00 |
| 2624 | A158 | $45 Sheet of 9, #a.-i. | 8.00 | 8.00 |
| 2625 | A158 | $45 Sheet of 9, #a.-i. | 8.00 | 8.00 |
| 2626 | A158 | $45 Sheet of 9, #a.-i. | 8.00 | 8.00 |
| 2627 | A158 | $45 Sheet of 9, #a.-i. | 8.00 | 8.00 |

---

## Souvenir Sheets

| 2628 | A158 | $350 multicolored | 7.00 | 7.00 |
|---|---|---|---|---|
| 2629 | A158 | $350 multicolored | 7.00 | 7.00 |

### Perf. 14x13½

| 2630 | A158 | $350 multicolored | 7.00 | 7.00 |
|---|---|---|---|---|

### Perf. 13x13½, 13½x13

| 2631 | A158 | $350 multicolored | 7.00 | 7.00 |
|---|---|---|---|---|
| 2632 | A158 | $350 multicolored | 7.00 | 7.00 |
| 2633 | A158 | $350 multicolored | 7.00 | 7.00 |
| 2634 | A158 | $350 multicolored | 7.00 | 7.00 |
| 2635 | A158 | $350 multicolored | 7.00 | 7.00 |

Genoa '92. Nos. 2628-2635 each contain one 50x39mm stamp.

While Nos. 2622-2623 & 2631 have the issue date as Nos. 2620-2621 & 2628-2630, the face value of Nos. 2622-2623 & 2631 was lower when they were released.

Anniversaries and Events — A159

Designs: $12.80, Zeppelin over Lake Constance, 1909. No. 2638, Voyager 1, Jupiter. No. 2639, Konrad Adenauer, John F. Kennedy. No. 2640, Aeromedical airlift. No. 2641, Amazon dolphins. No. 2642, Lift-off of Voyager 1, 1977. No. 2643, Baby gorilla. No. 2644, America's Cup yacht Stars and Stripes. No. 2644A, Eye screening van, doctor with patient. $190, Adenauer, Charles de Gaulle. $225, Zeppelin preparing for takeoff. No. 2647, Count Zeppelin, vert. No. 2648 View of Earth from space, vert. No. 2649, Konrad Adenauer, vert. No. 2650, Tree frog, vert.

| 1993, Jan. | | Litho. | Perf. 14 | |
|---|---|---|---|---|
| 2637 | A159 | $12.80 multi | .75 | .75 |
| 2638 | A159 | $50 multi | 1.75 | 1.75 |
| 2639 | A159 | $50 multi | 2.00 | 2.00 |
| 2640 | A159 | $100 multi | 4.50 | 4.50 |
| 2641 | A159 | $100 multi | 3.00 | 3.00 |
| 2642 | A159 | $130 multi | 4.25 | 4.25 |
| 2643 | A159 | $130 multi | 3.75 | 3.75 |
| 2644 | A159 | $130 multi | 4.75 | 4.75 |
| 2644A | A159 | $130 multi | 4.75 | 4.75 |
| 2645 | A159 | $190 multi | 6.00 | 6.00 |
| 2646 | A159 | $225 multi | 6.50 | 6.50 |
| | | Nos. 2637-2646 (11) | 42.00 | 42.00 |

**Souvenir Sheets**

| 2647 | A159 | $225 multi | 7.50 | 7.50 |
|---|---|---|---|---|
| 2648 | A159 | $225 multi | 7.00 | 7.00 |
| 2649 | A159 | $225 multi | 7.00 | 7.00 |
| 2650 | A159 | $225 multi | 7.00 | 7.00 |

Count Zeppelin, 75th anniv. of death (Nos. 2637, 2646-2647). Intl. Space Year (Nos. 2638, 2642, 2648). Konrad Adenauer, 25th anniv. of death (Nos. 2639, 2645, 2649). World Health Organization (No. 2640). Earth Summit, Rio (Nos. 2641, 2643, 2650). America's Cup Yacht Race (No. 2644). Lions Intl., 75th anniv. (No. 2644A).

### Miniature Sheet

Biblical Story of David and Goliath — A160

No. 2651: a, City of Jerusalem, two birds in flight. b, City, bird in flight at right. c, City, sun above. d, City, bird in flight at left. e, City with clouds above. f, Philistine army (i-k, q-r). g, Goliath. h, Goliath's arm, spear shaft (b, i, n). l, Goliath's leg (m, q-s), shield. n, David (r-t, w) with slingshot. o, Jewish soldiers with spears or swords (p-y).

| 1992, Dec. 29 | | Litho. | Perf. 14 | |
|---|---|---|---|---|
| 2651 | A160 | $25 Sheet of 25, #a.-y. | 18.00 | 18.00 |

No. 2651 has a continuous design.

Parrots — A161

80c, Hyacinth macaw. $6.40, Scarlet macaw. $7.65, Green macaw, vert. $15.30, Tovi parakeet. $50, Blue & yellow macaw. $100, Military macaw, vert. $130, Red & green macaw, vert. $190, Severa macaw.
No. 2660, Scarlet macaw, diff. No. 2661, Green parakeet, vert.

**1993, Mar. 10**

| | | | | |
|---|---|---|---|---|
| 2652 | A161 | 80c multicolored | .35 | .25 |
| 2653 | A161 | $6.40 multicolored | .60 | .30 |
| 2654 | A161 | $7.65 multicolored | .60 | .30 |
| 2655 | A161 | $15.30 multicolored | .80 | .60 |
| 2656 | A161 | $50 multicolored | 1.25 | .95 |
| 2657 | A161 | $100 multicolored | 2.50 | 2.40 |
| 2658 | A161 | $130 multicolored | 3.25 | 3.25 |
| 2659 | A161 | $190 multicolored | 3.75 | 3.75 |
| | | Nos. 2652-2659 (8) | 13.10 | 11.80 |

**Souvenir Sheet**

| | | | | |
|---|---|---|---|---|
| 2660 | A161 | $225 multicolored | 6.00 | 6.00 |
| 2661 | A161 | $225 multicolored | 6.00 | 6.00 |

While Nos. 2654-2656, 2659, 2661 have the same issue date as Nos. 2652-2653, 2657-2658, 2660, the value of Nos. 2654-2656, 2659, 2661 was lower when released.
For surcharge, see No. 4172.

**Miniature Sheets**

Dinosaurs — A162

No. 2662: a, Archaeopteryx. b, Pteranodon. c, Quetzalcoatlus. d, Protoavis. e, Dicraeosaurus. f, Moschops. g, Lystrosaurus. h, Dimetrodron. i, Staurikosaurus. j, Cacops. k, Diarthrognathus. l, Estemmenosuchus.
No. 2663: a, Pteranodon. b, Cearadactylus. c, Eudimorphodon. d, Pterodactylus. e, Stauirkosaurus. f, Euoplocephalus. g, Tuojiangosaurus. h, Oviraptor. i, Protoceratops. j, Panaoplosaurus. k, Psittacosaurus. l, Corythosaurus.
No. 2664: a, Sordes. b, Quetzalcoatlus. c, Archaeopteryx. d, Rhamphorynchus. e, Spinosaurus. f, Anchisaurus. g, Stegosaurus. h, Leaellynosaurus. i, Minmi. j, Heterdontosaurus. k, Lesothosaurus. l, Deninonychus.

**1993, Mar. 10   Litho.   Perf. 14**

| | | | | |
|---|---|---|---|---|
| 2662 | A162 | $30 Sheet of 12, #a.-l. | 7.00 | 7.00 |
| 2663 | A162 | $30 Sheet of 12, #a.-l. | 7.00 | 7.00 |
| 2664 | A162 | $30 Sheet of 12, #a.-l. | 7.00 | 7.00 |

For surcharge, see No. 4117.

**Miniature Sheet**

Signs of the Zodiac — A163

No. 2665: a, Aquarius. b, Pisces. c, Aries. d, Taurus. e, Gemini. f, Cancer. g, Leo. h, Virgo. i, Libra. j, Scorpio. k, Sagittarius. l, Capricorn.

**1992, Dec. 29   Litho.   Perf. 14x13½**
**Sheet of 12**

| | | | | |
|---|---|---|---|---|
| 2665 | A163 | $30 Sheet of 12, #a.-l. | 17.00 | 17.00 |

Caribbean Manatee — A164

Designs: $6.40, Adult sticking head out of water. $7.65, Adult, eating, with young. $8.90,

Adult swimming underwater. $50, Adult swimming with young.

**1993, Mar. 10   Litho.   Perf. 15x14½**

| | | | | |
|---|---|---|---|---|
| 2666 | A164 | $6.40 multicolored | 1.10 | 1.00 |
| 2667 | A164 | $7.65 multicolored | 1.10 | 1.00 |
| 2668 | A164 | $8.90 multicolored | 1.10 | 1.00 |
| 2669 | A164 | $50 multicolored | 4.25 | 4.25 |
| | | Nos. 2666-2669 (4) | 7.55 | 7.25 |

World Wildlife Federation. Exists imperf. Value, set $36.

Fauna A165

No. 2670: a, Southern tamandua. b, Three-toed sloth. c, Red howler monkey. d, Four-eyed opossum. e, Black spider monkey. f, Giant otter. g, Red brocket. h, Tree porcupine. i, Tayra. j, Tapir. k, Ocelot. l, Giant armadillo.
No. 2671: a, Crimson topaz hummingbird. b, Bearded bellbird (f). c, Amazonian umbrellabird. d, Paradise jacamar (h). e, Paradise tanager. f, White-tailed trogon (i-j). g, Scarlet macaw (k). h, Red fan parrot. i, Red-billed toucan. j, White plumed antbird. k, Crimson-hooded manakin. l, Guyanan cock-of-the-rock.
No. 2672, Paca. No. 2673, Tufted coquettes, horiz.

**1993, Mar. 10   Perf. 14**

| | | | | |
|---|---|---|---|---|
| 2670 | A165 | $50 Sheet of 12, #a.-l. | 10.00 | 10.00 |
| 2671 | A165 | $50 Sheet of 12, #a.-l. | 10.00 | 10.00 |

**Souvenir Sheets**

| | | | | |
|---|---|---|---|---|
| 2672 | A165 | $325 multicolored | 6.00 | 6.00 |
| 2673 | A165 | $325 multicolored | 6.00 | 6.00 |

Coronation of Queen Elizabeth II, 40th Anniv. — A166

No. 2674: a, $25, Official coronation photograph. b, $50, Gems from royal collection. c, $75, Queen, Duke of Edinburgh. d, $130, Queen opening Parliament.
$325, State Portrait, by Sir James Gunn, 1954-56.

**1993, June 2   Litho.   Perf. 13½x14**

| | | | | |
|---|---|---|---|---|
| 2674 | A166 | Sheet, 2 each #a.-d. | 14.00 | 14.00 |

**Souvenir Sheet**
**Perf. 14**

| | | | | |
|---|---|---|---|---|
| 2675 | A166 | $325 multicolored | 9.00 | 9.00 |

No. 2675 contains one 28x42mm stamp. For overprints see Nos. 2793-2795.

Jurassic Period Animals — A166a

No. 2675A — Animals from Jurassic period similar in appearance to animals from recent periods: b, Bird in flight. c, Ostriches. d, Mammoth. e, Reptile on shore, foliage and tree in

background. f, Koala. g, Ape. h, Aquatic reptile, head at right. i, Reptile standing in water, head at left. j, Crocodile.
No. 2675K, Allosaurus, horiz. No. 2675L, Diplodocus, horiz. No. 2675M, Plateosaurus, horiz. No. 2675N, Stegosaurus, horiz. No. 2675O, Styracosaurus, horiz. No. 2675P, Tyrannosaurus rex, horiz.

**1993, July 21   Litho.   Perf. 14**

| | | | | |
|---|---|---|---|---|
| 2675A | A166a | $25 Block of 9, #b-j | 7.50 | 7.50 |

**Souvenir Sheets**

| | | | | |
|---|---|---|---|---|
| 2675K | A166a | $250 multi | — |
| 2675L | A166a | $250 multi | — |
| 2675M | A166a | $250 multi | — |
| 2675N | A166a | $250 multi | — |
| 2675O | A166a | $250 multi | — |
| 2675P | A166a | $250 multi | — |

A167

Famous People — A168

Athletes: No. 2676: a, O. J. Simpson, football. b, Rohan B. Kanhai, cricket. c, Gabriela Sabatini, tennis. d, Severiano Ballesteros, golf. e, Peace dove, blue background. f, Franz Beckenbauer, soccer. g, Pele, soccer. h, Wilt Chamberlain, basketball. i, Nadia Comaneci, gymnastics.
Scientists: No. 2677: a, Louis Leakey, archaeology. b, Jonas Salk, polio vaccine. c, Hideyo Noguchi, yellow fever. d, Karl Landsteiner, blood transfusions. e, Peace dove, blue green background. f, Sigmund Freud, psychoanalysis. g, Louis Pasteur. h, Madame Curie, radium tubes. i, Jean Baptiste Perrin, physics.
Artists, entertainers: No. 2678: a, Gabriel Marquez, writer. b, Pablo Picasso, artist. c, Cecil DeMille, film director. d, Martha Graham, dance. e, Peace dove, purple background. f, Charles Chaplin, actor. g, Paul Robeson, singer. h, Rudolph Dunbar, musician. i, Louis Armstrong, musician.
Politicians: No. 2679: a, Jawaharlal Nehru. b, Dr. Eric Williams, first prime minister of Trinidad and Tobago. c, John F. Kennedy. d, Hugh Desmond Hoyte, president of Guyana. e, Peace dove over map. f, Friedrich Ebert. g, Franklin D. Roosevelt. h, Mikhail Gorbachev. i, Winston Churchill.
Humanitarians: No. 2680: a, Gandhi. b, Dalai Lama. c, Michael Manley, prime minister of Jamaica. d, Javier Perez de Cuellar, former UN Secretary General. e, Peace dove, globe. f, Mother Teresa. g, Martin Luther King, Jr. h, Nelson Mandela. i, Raoul Wallenberg.
Transportation, communication: No. 2681: a, DC-3 cargo plane. b, Space shuttle. c, Concorde. d, Ferdinand von Zeppelin. e, Peace dove. f, Guglielmo Marconi. g, Adrian Thompson, mountaineer. h, Bullet train, Japan. i, John von Neumann, mathematician.
No. 2682, UN Flag, natl. flags. No. 2683, Jackie Robinson. No. 2684, Einstein's formula. No. 2685, Elvis Presley. No. 2686, Nobel Peace Prize certificate. No. 2687, Apollo Moon Landing.

**1993, July 26   Litho.   Perf. 14**

| | | | | |
|---|---|---|---|---|
| 2676 | A167 | $50 Sheet of 9, #a.-i. | 12.00 | 12.00 |
| 2677 | A167 | $50 Sheet of 9, #a.-i. | 12.00 | 12.00 |
| 2678 | A167 | $50 Sheet of 9, #a.-i. | 12.00 | 12.00 |
| 2679 | A168 | $100 Sheet of 9, #a.-i. | 12.00 | 12.00 |
| 2680 | A168 | $100 Sheet of 9, #a.-i. | 12.00 | 12.00 |
| 2681 | A168 | $100 Sheet of 9, #a.-i. | 12.00 | 12.00 |

**Souvenir Sheets**

| | | | | |
|---|---|---|---|---|
| 2682 | A168 | $250 multi, vert. | 7.00 | 7.00 |
| 2683 | A167 | $250 multi, vert. | 7.00 | 7.00 |
| 2684 | A167 | $250 multi, vert. | 7.00 | 7.00 |
| 2685 | A167 | $250 multi, vert. | 7.00 | 7.00 |
| 2686 | A168 | $250 multi, vert. | 7.00 | 7.00 |
| 2687 | A168 | $250 multi | 7.00 | 7.00 |

Mushrooms — A168a

Designs: $7.65, Amanita phalloides. $8.90, Boletus satanas. $50, Suillus granulatus. $100, Gymnopilus spectabilis. $250, Pluteus leonirus.
No. 2687F, Coprinus plicatilis. No. 2687G, Hypholoma fasciculare. No. 2687H, Hygrocybe chlorophana. No. 2687I, Omphalotus illudens. No. 2687J, Kuehnevomyces mutabilis, vert.

**1993, July 28   Litho.   Perf. 14x13½**

| | | | | |
|---|---|---|---|---|
| 2687A | A168a | $7.65 multi | .25 | .25 |
| 2687B | A168a | $8.90 multi | .25 | .25 |
| 2687C | A168a | $50 multi | 1.00 | 1.00 |
| 2687D | A168a | $100 multi | 2.00 | 2.00 |
| 2687E | A168a | $250 multi | 5.00 | 5.00 |
| | | Nos. 2687A-2687E (5) | 8.50 | 8.50 |

**Souvenir Sheet**
**Perf. 14**

| | | | | |
|---|---|---|---|---|
| 2687F | A168a | $500 multi | 2.50 | 2.50 |
| 2687G | A168a | $500 multi | 2.50 | 2.50 |
| 2687H | A168a | $500 multi | 2.50 | 2.50 |
| 2687I | A168a | $500 multi | 2.50 | 2.50 |
| 2687J | A168a | $500 multi | 2.50 | 2.50 |
| | | Nos. 2687F-2687J (5) | 12.50 | 12.50 |

Nos. 2687A-2687E exist perf. 10.

Willy Brandt (1913-1992), German Chancellor A169

Designs: $25, Brandt, Golda Meir, 1969. $190, Brandt at steel mill, 1969. $325, Brandt.

**1993, Aug. 16   Litho.   Perf. 14**

| | | | | |
|---|---|---|---|---|
| 2688 | A169 | $25 multicolored | 1.00 | 1.00 |
| 2689 | A169 | $190 multicolored | 5.00 | 5.00 |

**Souvenir Sheet**

| | | | | |
|---|---|---|---|---|
| 2690 | A169 | $325 multicolored | 7.50 | 7.50 |

Armillary Sphere — A170

Copernicus (1473-1543): $190, Satellite antenna. $300, Copernicus.

**1993, Aug. 16**

| | | | | |
|---|---|---|---|---|
| 2691 | A170 | $50 multicolored | 1.50 | 1.50 |
| 2692 | A170 | $190 multicolored | 5.50 | 5.50 |

**Souvenir Sheet**

| | | | | |
|---|---|---|---|---|
| 2693 | A170 | $300 multicolored | 7.00 | 7.00 |

Georg Hackl, Luge Gold Medalist, 1992 — A171

1994 Winter Olympics, Lillehammer, Norway: $130, Karen Magnussen, figure skater, 1972. $325, German bobsled team, 1992.

**1993, Aug. 16**

| | | | | |
|---|---|---|---|---|
| 2694 | A171 | $50 multicolored | 1.00 | 1.00 |
| 2695 | A171 | $130 multicolored | 3.00 | 3.00 |

**Souvenir Sheet**

| | | | | |
|---|---|---|---|---|
| 2696 | A171 | $325 multicolored | 7.50 | 7.50 |

A172

World War II — A173

Designs: $6.40, Audie Murphy. $7.65, British, US forces link up in France, June 8, 1944. $8.90, Monte Cassino falls to Allies, May 18, 1944. $12.80, Battleship Yamato attacked by US in Battle of East China Sea, Apr. 7, 1945. $15.30, St. Basil's Cathedral, Moscow, Foreign Ministers Conf., Oct. 19, 1943. $50, US forces cross Rhine River, Mar. 7, 1945. $100, B-29s begin bombing raids on Japan from China, June 15, 1944. $130, Gen. George S. Patton, Jr., Battle of Sicily ends, Aug. 17, 1943. $190, Battleship Tirpitz sunk, Nov. 12, 1944. $200, US Sherman tank, US forces enter Brittany after taking Normandy, Aug. 1, 1944. $225, End of fighting in Italy, May 2, 1945.

No. 2708 — War at Sea, 1943: a, Adm. Yamamoto launches air offensive, Apr. 7. b, PT-109 in Blackett Strait, Aug. 1. c, USS Enterprise. d, Allied ships attack Rabaul, Oct. 12. e, US troops land at Cape Gloucester, Dec. 26. f, USS Bogue enters service, Feb. g, Wildcat fighters sink U-118. h, Battle of Atlantic reaches peak, U-boats sink 108 ships. i, Italian fleet surrenders at Malta, Sept. 10. j, Battleship Duke of York sinks Scharnhorst, Dec. 26.

No. 2709 — War in the Air, 1943: a, Royal Australian Air Force Beaufighter, Battle of Bismark Sea, Mar. 2-4. b, P-38 Lightening shoots down Adm. Yamamoto's plane over Bougainville, Apr. 7. c, B-24 Liberators bomb Tarawa prior to landings, Sept. 17-19. d, B-25 Mitchell of Fifth Air Force bombs Rabaul, Oct. 12. e, US Navy aircraft attack Makin, Nov. 19. f, US Army Air Force's first daylight raid over Germany, Jan. 27. g, Royal Air Force Mosquito bombers make first daylight raid on Berlin, Jan. 30. h, Allies devastate Hamburg with first firestorm, July 24-30. i, B-24 bombers raid Ploesti oil refineries in Romania, Aug. 1. j, Battle of Berlin begins, Nov. 18.

No. 2710, $325, US, Russian infantry meeting at Elbe River, Apr. 25, 1945.

| 1993, Oct. 18 | Litho. | | Perf. 14 | |
|---|---|---|---|---|
| 2697 | A172 | $6.40 multicolored | .30 | .30 |
| 2698 | A172 | $7.65 multicolored | .30 | .30 |
| 2699 | A172 | $8.90 multicolored | .30 | .30 |
| 2700 | A172 | $12.80 multicolored | .30 | .30 |
| 2701 | A172 | $15.30 multicolored | .30 | .30 |
| 2702 | A172 | $50 multicolored | 1.25 | 1.25 |
| 2703 | A172 | $100 multicolored | 2.50 | 2.50 |
| 2704 | A172 | $130 multicolored | 3.00 | 3.00 |
| 2705 | A172 | $190 multicolored | 4.00 | 4.00 |
| 2706 | A172 | $200 multicolored | 4.50 | 4.50 |
| 2707 | A172 | $225 multicolored | 5.25 | 5.25 |
| | Nos. 2697-2707 (11) | | 22.00 | 22.00 |

**Miniature Sheets**
**Perf. 15**

| 2708 | A173 | $50 Sheet of 10, #a.-j. | 12.00 | 12.00 |
|---|---|---|---|---|
| 2709 | A172 | $50 Sheet of 10, #a.-j. | 12.00 | 12.00 |

Nos. 2709a-2709j are 35½x22mm.

**Souvenir Sheet**
**Perf. 14**

| 2710 | A172 | $325 multicolored | 8.00 | 8.00 |
|---|---|---|---|---|

1994 World Cup Soccer Championships, U.S. — A174

Player, country: $5, Stuart Pearce, England. $6.40, Ronald Koeman, Holland. $7.65, Gianluca Vialli, Italy. $12.80, McStay, Scotland, Alemao, Brazil. $15.30, Ceulemans, Belgium, Butcher, England. $50, Dragan Stojkovic, Yugoslavia. $100, Ruud Gullit, Holland. $130, Miloslav Kadlec, Czechoslovakia. $150, Ramos, Uruguay, Berthold, Germany. $190, Baggio, Italy; Wright, England. $200, Yarentchuck, Russia, Renquin, Belgium. $225, Timofte, Romania; Aleinikov, Russia. No. 2724, Rene Higuita, Colombia. No. 2723, Salvatore Schillaci, Italy, horiz.

| 1993, Oct. 18 | Litho. | | Perf. 14 | |
|---|---|---|---|---|
| 2711 | A174 | $5 multicolored | .25 | .25 |
| 2712 | A174 | $6.40 multicolored | .25 | .25 |
| 2713 | A174 | $7.65 multicolored | .25 | .25 |
| 2714 | A174 | $12.80 multicolored | .25 | .25 |
| 2715 | A174 | $15.30 multicolored | .25 | .25 |
| 2716 | A174 | $50 multicolored | .90 | .90 |
| 2717 | A174 | $100 multicolored | 2.00 | 2.00 |
| 2718 | A174 | $130 multicolored | 2.50 | 2.50 |
| 2719 | A174 | $150 multicolored | 2.75 | 2.75 |
| 2720 | A174 | $190 multicolored | 3.50 | 3.50 |
| 2721 | A174 | $200 multicolored | 3.75 | 3.75 |
| 2722 | A174 | $225 multicolored | 4.25 | 4.25 |
| | Nos. 2711-2722 (12) | | 20.90 | 20.90 |

**Souvenir Sheets**

| 2723 | A174 | $325 multicolored | 7.00 | 7.00 |
|---|---|---|---|---|
| 2724 | A174 | $325 multicolored | 7.00 | 7.00 |

Order of the Caribbean Community — A175

No. 2725, William Demas. No. 2726, Derek Walcott. No. 2727, Sir Shridath Ramphal.

| 1993, Sept. 27 | Litho. | | Perf. 14 | |
|---|---|---|---|---|
| 2725 | A175 | $7.65 multi | 1.00 | .75 |
| 2726 | A175 | $7.65 multi | 1.00 | .75 |
| 2727 | A175 | $7.65 multi | 2.00 | 1.00 |
| | Nos. 2725-2727 (3) | | 4.00 | 2.50 |

Christmas — A176

Details from Holy Family Under the Apple Tree, by Rubens: No. 2728, $6.40, No. 2730, $12.80, No. 2733, $130, No. 2734, $190.
Details from The Virgin in Glory, by Durer: No. 2729, $7.65, No. 2731, $15.30, No. 2732, $50, No. 2735, $250.
No. 2736, Holy Family Under the Apple Tree (entire). No. 2737, The Virgin in Glory (entire).

| 1993, Dec. 1 | | Perf. 13½x14 | |
|---|---|---|---|
| 2728-2735 | A176 Set of 8 | 10.00 | 10.00 |

**Souvenir Sheets**

| 2736 | A176 | $325 multicolored | 6.00 | 6.00 |
|---|---|---|---|---|
| 2737 | A176 | $325 multicolored | 6.00 | 6.00 |

For surcharge, see No. 4177.

Louvre Museum, Bicent. — A177

Details or entire paintings: No. 2738, Mona Lisa, by Da Vinci.
No. 2739, $50: a, La Femme à la Puce, by Crespi. b, La Femme Hydropique, by Dou. c, Portrait d'un Couple, by Ittenbach. d, Cléopâtre Assise, Demi Face, sur un Trône Elevé, by Moreau. e, La Richesse, by Vouet. f, Vieillard et Jeune Garçon, by Ghirlandaio. g, Louis XIV, by Rigaud. h, La Buveuse, by Pieter De Hooch.
No. 2740, $50: a, Autoportrait aux Besicles, by Chardin. b, L'Infante Marie-Thérèse, by Velasquez. c, Le Printemps, by Arcimboldo. d, La Vierge de Douleur, by Bouts. e, L'Etude, by Fragonard. f, François 1er, by Clouet. g, Le Condottière, by Antonello Da Messina. h, La Bohémienne, by Hals.
No. 2741, $50: a, La Femme à la Puce, entire, by Crespi. b, Autoportrait au Chevalet, by Rembrandt. c, Femmes d'Alger dans Leur Appartement, by Delacroix. d, Tête de Jeune Homme, by Raphael. e, Vénus et les Grâces, by Botticelli. f, Nature Morte à l'Echiquier, by Lubin Baugin. g, Lady MacBeth Somnambule, by Fussli. h, La Tabagie, by Chardin.
Nos. 2742, $50: a-c, L'Accordée de Village (left, center, right), by Greuze. d, Autoportrait, by Melendez. e, Le Chevalier, La Jeune Fille et La Mont, by Baldung-Grien. f, Le Jeune Mendiant, by Murillo. g-h, Les Pèlerins d'Emmaus (left, right), by Mathieu Le Nain.
No. 2743, $50: a-b, Le Vierge au Lapin (diff. details), by Titian. c, La Belle Jardinière, by Raphael. d, La Dentellière, by Vermeer. e, Jeanne d'Aragon, by Raphael. f, L'Astronome, by Vermeer. g, Le Pont du Rialto, by Canaletto. h, Sigismond Malatesta, by Piero Della Francesca.
No. 2744, $325, Cour de Ferme, by Jan Brueghel, the Younger. No. 2745, $325, Le Pont du Rialto, by Canaletto. No. 2746, $325,

Le Sacre de Napoléon 1er, by David. No. 2747, $325, Details and painting of Mona Lisa. No. 2748, $325, La Diseuse de Bonne Aventure, by Caravaggio. No. 2749, $325, Les Noces de Cana, by Veronese.

| 1993, Dec. 6 | Litho. | | Perf. 13½x14 | |
|---|---|---|---|---|
| 2738 | A177 | $50 multicolored | .75 | .75 |
| a. | Sheet of 8 + label | | 6.00 | 6.00 |

**Sheets of 8, #a-h, + Label**

| 2739-2743 | A177 | Set of 5 | 35.00 | 35.00 |
|---|---|---|---|---|

**Souvenir Sheets**
**Perf. 12**

| 2744-2749 | A177 | Set of 6 | 30.00 | 30.00 |
|---|---|---|---|---|

Nos. 2744-2746 each contain one 80x47mm stamp. Nos. 2747-2749 one 80x53mm stamp.

Christmas — A177a

Entire paintings or details: $7.65, St. Anne with Mary and the Child Jesus, by Dürer. $8.90, Mary Being Crowned by Two Angels, by Dürer. $50, Pentecost, by Dürer. $100, Samson and Delilah, by Rubens. $250, Origin of the Milky Way, by Rubens.
No. 2749F, $500, The Descent from the Cross, by Rubens, horiz. No. 2749G, $500, The Descent from the Cross, by Dürer, horiz.

| 1993 | Litho. | Perf. 13½x14, 14x13½ |
|---|---|---|
| 2749A-2749E | A177a | Set of 5 12.00 12.00 |

**Souvenir Sheets**

| 2749F-2749G | A177a | Set of 2 13.00 13.00 |
|---|---|---|

Polska '93 (Paintings) A178

Designs: $50, $130, Pantaloons, by Tadeusz Brzozowski, 1966. $75, Photo of fortress in Miedzyrecz. $325, Children in the Garden, by Wladyslaw Podkowinski, 1892, horiz.

| 1993 | | Perf. 14 | |
|---|---|---|---|
| 2750 | | $50 multicolored | 1.25 | 1.25 |
| 2751 | A178 | $75 multicolored | 1.75 | 1.75 |
| 2752 | | $130 multicolored | 4.00 | 4.00 |
| a. | A178 Pair, #2750, #2752 | | 6.00 | 6.00 |
| | Nos. 2750-2752 (3) | | 7.00 | 7.00 |

**Souvenir Sheet**

| 2753 | A178 | $325 multicolored | 7.00 | 7.00 |
|---|---|---|---|---|

Picasso (Paintings) — A179

Designs: $15.30, Bather, Paris, 1909. $100, Two Nudes, 1906. $190, Nude Seated on a Rock, 1921. $325, The Rescue, 1922.

| 1993, Nov. | Litho. | | Perf. 14 | |
|---|---|---|---|---|
| 2754 | A179 | $15.30 multi | .40 | .40 |
| 2755 | A179 | $100 multi | 2.40 | 2.40 |
| 2756 | A179 | $190 multi | 4.50 | 4.50 |
| | Nos. 2754-2756 (3) | | 7.30 | 7.30 |

**Souvenir Sheet**

| 2756A | A179 | $325 multi | 7.00 | 7.00 |
|---|---|---|---|---|

Rebirth of Democracy, 1st Anniv. — A180

Designs: $6.40, Dr. Cheddie B. Jagan, Guyana Pres. $325, Sunburst, "REBIRTH OF DEMOCRACY," horiz.

| 1993, Dec. 17 | Litho. | Perf. 13½x14 |
|---|---|---|
| 2757 | A180 | $6.40 multicolored .70 .70 |

**Souvenir Sheet**
**Perf. 13**

| 2757A | A180 | $325 multicolored | 6.50 | 6.50 |
|---|---|---|---|---|

Aladdin A181

Nos. 2758: a-h, Various characters from Disney animated film, vert.
Nos. 2759: a-i, Various film scenes.
Nos. 2760: a-i, Various scenes from Disney animated film.
No. 2761, Genie, Jasmine, and Aladdin. No. 2762, Aladdin, the Genie, Abu, Magic Carpet. No. 2763, Aladdin as Prince Ali Ababwa. No. 2764, Aladdin, Abu, Jasmine.

| 1993, Dec. 20 | Litho. | | Perf. 14x13½ | |
|---|---|---|---|---|
| 2758 | A181 | $7.65 Sheet of 8, #a.-h. | 2.00 | 2.00 |
| 2759 | A181 | $50 Sheet of 9, #a.-i. | 8.00 | 7.00 |
| 2760 | A181 | $65 Sheet of 9, #a.-i. | 11.00 | 8.00 |
| | Nos. 2758-2760 (3) | | 21.00 | 17.00 |

**Souvenir Sheets**

| 2761 | A181 | $325 multicolored | 6.50 | 6.50 |
|---|---|---|---|---|
| 2762 | A181 | $325 multicolored | 6.50 | 6.50 |
| 2763 | A181 | $325 multicolored | 6.50 | 6.50 |
| 2764 | A181 | $325 multicolored | 6.50 | 6.50 |

A182

Hong Kong '94 A183

Stamps, photograph of Happy Valley Horse Race Course: No. 2765, Hong Kong #437, scoreboard. No. 2766, Track, horses, #2545.
No. 2767 — Snuff boxes, Qing Dynasty: a, Painted enamel in shape of bamboo. b, Painted enamel with human figure. c, Amber with lions playing ball. d, Agate in shape of two gourds. e, Glass overlay with dog. f, Glass, foliage design.
No. 2768 — Porcelain, Ch'ing Dynasty: a, Covered jar with dragon. b, Rotating brush holder. c, Covered jar with horses. d, Amphora vase with bats & peaches. e, Tea caddy with Fo dogs. f, Vase with wild camellia & peaches.

| 1994, Feb. 18 | | Perf. 14 | |
|---|---|---|---|
| 2765 | A182 | $50 multicolored | .80 | .80 |
| 2766 | A182 | $50 multicolored | .80 | .80 |
| a. | Pair, #2765-2766 | | 1.75 | 1.75 |

**Miniature Sheets**

| 2767 | A183 | $20 Sheet of 6, #a.-f. | 5.00 | 5.00 |
|---|---|---|---|---|
| 2768 | A183 | $20 Sheet of 6, #a.-f. | 5.00 | 5.00 |

Nos. 2765-2766 issued in sheets of 5 pairs. No. 2766a is continuous design.
New Year 1994 (Year of the Dog) (Nos. 2767e, #2768e).

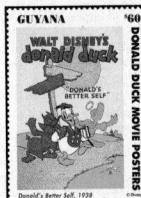

Vintage Donald Duck — A184

No. 2769, $60 — Movie posters: a, Donald's Better Self, 1938. b, Donald's Golf Game, 1938. c, Sea Scouts, 1939. d, Donald's Penguin, 1939. e, A Good Time for a Dime, 1941. f, Truant Officer Donald. g, Orphan's Benefit, 1941. h, Chef Donald, 1941.

No. 2770, $60: a, The Village Smithy, 1942. b, Donald's Snow Fight, 1942. c, Donald's Garden, 1942. d, Donald's Gold Mine, 1942. e, The Vanishing Private, 1942. f, Sky Trooper, 1942. g, Bellboy Donald, 1942. h, The New Spirit, 1942.

No. 2771, $60: a, Saludos Amigos, 1943. b, The Eyes Have It, 1945. c, Donald's Crime, 1945. d, Straight Shooters, 1947. e, Donald's Dilemma, 1947. f, Bootle Beetle, 1947. g, Daddy Duck, 1948. h, Soup's On, 1948.

No. 2772 — Story boards from Pirate Gold, horiz.: a, Pirate ship. b, Carrying treasure chest. c, Donald Duck with map. d, Donald, souvenir shop. e, Donald following Aracuan bird. f, Angry Donald.

No. 2773, $80 — Movie posters: a, Donald's Happy Birthday, 1949. b, Sea Salts, 1949. c, Honey Harvester, 1949. d, All in a Nutshell, 1949. e, The Greener Yard, 1949. f, Slide, Donald, Slide, 1949. g, Lion Around, 1950. h, Trailer Horn, 1950.

No. 2774, $80: a, Bee at the Beach, 1950. b, Out on a Limb, 1950. c, Corn Chips, 1951. d, Test Pilot Donald, 1951. e, Lucky Number, 1951. f, Out of Scale, 1951. g, Bee on Guard, 1951. h, Let's Stick Together, 1952.

No. 2775, $80: a, Trick or Treat, 1952. b, Don's Fountain of Youth, 1953. c, Rugged Bear, 1953. d, Canvas Back Duck, 1953. e, Dragon Around, 1954. f, Grin and Bear It, 1954. g, The Flying Squirrel, 1954. h, Up a Tree, 1955.

No. 2776, Studio Fan Card, Melody Time, 1948.

No. 2777, $500, Scene from picture book of first movie, The Wise Little Hen, 1944, horiz. No. 2778, $500, Sketch for closing scene of Timber, 1941. No. 2779, $500, Donald Duck, horiz. No. 2780, $500, Studio fan card, The Three Caballeros, 1945, horiz.

Movie posters contained in No. 2780A are listed as designs for Nos. 2769-2771, 2774-2775, 2777, 2780.

### Perf. 14x13½, 13½x14

**1993, Dec. 6**　　　　　　　　**Litho.**
**Sheets of 8, #a-h**

| | | | |
|---|---|---|---|
| 2769-2771 | A184 | Set of 3 | 25.00 25.00 |
| 2772 | A184 | $80　Sheet of 6, #a.-f. | 8.00 8.00 |

**Sheets of 8, #a-h**

| | | | |
|---|---|---|---|
| 2773-2775 | A184 | Set of 3 | 27.50 27.50 |

**Size: 130x104mm**
**Imperf**

| | | | |
|---|---|---|---|
| 2776 | A184 | $500　multi | 10.00 10.00 |

**Souvenir Sheets**
### Perf. 14x13½, 13½x14

| | | | |
|---|---|---|---|
| 2777-2780 | A184 | Set of 4 | 40.00 40.00 |

**Imperf**
**Self-Adhesive**
**Size: 64x89mm**

| | | | |
|---|---|---|---|
| 2780A | A184 | $60　Set of 50 | 70.00 |

No. 2780A exists with backing labels printed in English or French. Value is for either set. No. 2780A was printed on thin card and sold in sealed cellophane packages containing 10 stamps. To affix stamps, backing containing film information must be removed.

Nos. 2769-2771, 2773-2775 exist in sheets of 7 $5 stamps + label. The label replaces Nos. 2769f, 2770b, 2771h, 2773a, 2774d, 2775e. These sheets became available Nov. 20, 1996.

Tropical Flowers — A185

Designs: $6.40, Cestrum parqui. $7.65, Brunfelsia calycina. $12.80, Datura rosei. $15.30, Ruellia macrantha. No. 2785, $50, Portlandia albiflora. $130, Pachystachys coccinea. $190, Beloperone guttata. $250, Ferdinandusa speciosa.

No. 2789, $50: a, Clusia grandiflora. b, Begonia haageana. c, Fuchsia simplicicaulis. d, Guaiacum officinale (a). e, Pithecoctenium cynanchoides. f, Sphaeralcea umbellata. g, Erythrina poeppigiana. h, Steriphoma paradoxa. i, Allemanda violacea (f). j, Centropogon cornutus (g). k, Passiflora quadrangularis. l, Victoria amazonica.

No. 2790, $50: a, Cobaea scandens. b, Pyrostegia venusta (c). c, Petrea kohautiana (b). d, Hippobroma longiflora (a). e, Cleome hassleriana (b, d, f, h, i). f, Verbena peruviana (c). g, Tropaeolum peregrinum. h, Plumeria rubra (g, i). i, Selenicereus grandiflorus. j,

Mandevilla splendens (g). k, Pereskia aculeata. l, Ipomoea learii.
No. 2791, $325, Columnea fendleri. No. 2792, $325, Lophospermum erubescens.

**1994, Feb. 10**　　**Litho.**　**Perf. 13½**

| | | | |
|---|---|---|---|
| 2781-2788 | A185 | | 10.00 10.00 |

**Sheets of 12, #a-l**
**Perf. 14**

| | | | |
|---|---|---|---|
| 2789-2790 | A185 | Set of 2 | 20.00 20.00 |

**Souvenir Sheets**
**Perf. 13**

| | | | |
|---|---|---|---|
| 2791-2792 | A185 | Set of 2 | 10.00 10.00 |

For surcharges, see Nos. 4110, 4111, 4113, 4114.

### Nos. 2674-2675 Ovptd. "ROYAL VISIT FEB 19-22, 1994" in One or Two Lines

**1994**　　　　　**Litho.**　　**Perf. 13½x14**

| | | | |
|---|---|---|---|
| 2793 | A166 | Sheet, 2 each #a.- b. | 14.00 14.00 |

**Souvenir Sheet**
**Perf. 14**

| | | | |
|---|---|---|---|
| 2794 | A166 | $325　multicolored | 7.50 7.50 |

Hummel Figurines — A186

Designs: No. 2795, $20, No. 2803a, $30, Girl holding basket and heart. No. 2796, $25, Boy holding heart. No. 2797, $35, No. 2804a, $20, Chef holding dessert. No. 2798, $50, No. 2804b, $130, Girl holding planter of mushrooms. No. 2799, $60, Girl holding plant, horn. No. 2800, $130, No. 2803b, $6, Four girls. No. 2801, $190, Two girls, boy and puppy. No. 2802, $250, No. 2804c, $35, Boy holding covered dish, puppy.

**1994, May 5**　　**Litho.**　　**Perf. 14**

| | | | |
|---|---|---|---|
| 2795-2802 | A186 | Set of 8 | 12.00 12.00 |

**Souvenir Sheets**

| | | | |
|---|---|---|---|
| 2803 | A186 | Sheet of 4, #a.-b., #2796, 2801 | 4.00 4.00 |
| 2804 | A186 | Sheet of 4, #a.-c., #2799 | 4.00 4.00 |

Sierra Club, Cent. — A187

No. 2805 — Various animals or scenic places: a-b, American alligator. c-d, Italian Alps. e-f, Mono Lake.
No. 2806: a, Red kangaroo. b-d, Whooping crane. e-f, Alaskan brown bear. g, Bald eagle. h, Giant panda.
No. 2807, vert.: a-b, Red kangaroo. c, American alligator. d, Alaskan brown bear. e-f, Bald eagle. g-h, Giant panda.
No. 2808, vert.: a-c, Sea lion. d, Mono Lake. e, Sierra Club centennial emblem. f, Italian Alps. g-i, Matterhorn.

**1994, May 20**　**Litho.**　　**Perf. 14**

| | | | |
|---|---|---|---|
| 2805 | A187 | $70　Sheet of 6, #a.-f. | 7.50 7.50 |
| 2806 | A187 | $70　Sheet of 8, #a.-h. | 10.00 10.00 |
| 2807 | A187 | $70　Sheet of 8, #a.-h. | 10.00 10.00 |
| 2808 | A187 | $70　Sheet of 9, #a.-i. | 11.00 11.00 |
| | | Nos. 2805-2808 (4) | 38.50 38.50 |

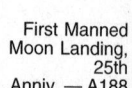

First Manned Moon Landing, 25th Anniv. — A188

No. 2809, $60: a, Robert R. Gilruth, Apollo 16. b, Ernst Stuhlinger, Apollo 17. c, Christopher C. Kraft, X-30 National Aero-Space Plane. d, Rudolf Opitz, Me-163, July 24, 1943. e, Clyde W. Tombaugh, "Face on Mars." f, Hermann Oberth, Scene from "The Girl in the Moon."
No. 2810, $60: a, Wernher von Braun, Apollo 11. b, Rocco A. Petrone, Apollo 11. c, Eberhard Rees, Apollo 12. d, Charles A.

Berry, Apollo 13. e, Thomas O. Paine, Apollo 14. f, A.F. Staats, Apollo 15.
No. 2811, $60: a, Walter Dornberger, 1st A-4 launch. b, Rudolph Nebel, Surveyor 1. c, Robert H. Goddard, Apollo 7. d, Kurt Debus, Apollo 8. e, James T. Webb, Apollo 9. f, George E. Mueller, Apollo 10.
No. 2812, Frank J. Everest, Jr.

**1994, July 20**　**Litho.**　　**Perf. 14**
**Sheets of 6, #a-f**

| | | | |
|---|---|---|---|
| 2809-2811 | A188 | Set of 3 | 20.00 20.00 |

**Souvenir Sheet**

| | | | |
|---|---|---|---|
| 2812 | A188 | $325　multicolored | 7.00 7.00 |

A189

World War II — A190

Designs: $6, Photo reconnaissance Spitfire. $35, 226 Squadron B-25. $190, 76 Squadron P-47 Thunderbolts.
No. 2816 — Europe and North Africa, 1944: a, Allied landings, Anzio, Jan. 22. b, RAF bombs Amiens prison, Feb. 18. c, Sevastopol falls to Red Army, May 9. d, Allies breach Gustav Line, May 19. e, D-Day, June 6. f, V-1 attacks on London begin, June 13. g, Cease fire declared for Paris, Aug. 19. h, Germany launches V-2 rockets, Sept. 8. i, German battleship Tirpitz sunk, Nov. 12. j, Siege of Bastogne lifted, Dec. 29.
No. 2817 — D-Day: a, Paratroops drop behind enemy lines. b, Glider-born commandos land behind enemy lines. c, USS Arkansas shells Omaha beach defenses. d, Allied aircraft attack enemy movements. e, Allied landing craft hit the beach. f, Allied troops pinned down by enemy fire. g, Commandos exit landing craft. h, Specialized Allied tanks destroy enemy mines. i, Allies break through beach defenses. j, Consolidation of position.
No. 2818, RAF Lancaster bomber.

**1994, June 20**　　　　　　**Perf. 14**

| | | | | |
|---|---|---|---|---|
| 2813 | A189 | $6 | multicolored | .30 .25 |
| 2814 | A189 | $35 | multicolored | .85 .50 |
| 2815 | A189 | $190 | multicolored | 3.75 3.25 |
| | | Nos. 2813-2815 (3) | | 4.90 4.00 |

**Perf. 13**

| | | | |
|---|---|---|---|
| 2816 | A190 | $60　Sheet of 10, #a.-j. | 12.00 10.00 |
| 2817 | A190 | $60　Sheet of 10, #a.-j. | 12.00 10.00 |

**Souvenir Sheet**
**Perf. 14**

| | | | |
|---|---|---|---|
| 2818 | A189 | $325　multicolored | 7.00 7.00 |

A191

Butterflies A192

Designs: $6, Heliconius melpomene. $20, Helicopius cupido. $25, Agrias claudina. $30, Parides coelus. $50, Heliconius hecale. $60, Morpho diana. $190, Dismorphia orise. $250, Morpho deidamia.
No. 2827: a, Anaea marthesia. b, Brassolis astyra. c, Heliconius melpomene. d, Haetera piera. e, Morpho diana dixey. f, Parides coelus. g, Catagramma pitheas. h, Nessaea obrinus. i, Automeris janus. j, Papilio torquatus. k, Eunica sophonisba. l, Ceratinia nise. m, Panacea procilla. n, Pyrrhogyra neaerea. o, Morpho deidamia. p, Dismorphia orise.
No. 2829, $325, Eunica sophonisba. No. 2830, $325, Anaea eribotes.
No. 2831, $325, Hamadryas velutina. No. 2832, $325, Agrias claudina.

**1994, July 5**　　**Litho.**　　**Perf. 14**

| | | | |
|---|---|---|---|
| 2819-2826 | A191 | Set of 8 | 13.00 13.00 |
| 2827 | A192 | $50　Sheet of 16, #a.-p. | 12.00 12.00 |

**Souvenir Sheets**

| | | | |
|---|---|---|---|
| 2829-2830 | A191 | Set of 2 | 10.00 10.00 |
| 2831-2832 | A192 | Set of 2 | 10.00 10.00 |

Nos. 2829-2830 each contain one 43x28mm stamp.

Bible Stories — A193

No. 2833 — Story of Ruth and Naomi: a-f, Ruth & Naomi preparing to leave Moab & return to Israel. g-l, Ruth harvesting grain in fields of Boaz. m-r, Boaz receives a man's sandal, finalizing sale of Naomi's field. s-x, Naomi, Boaz, Ruth and Obed, who was David's grandfather.
No. 2834 — Story of Joseph: a-d, Jacob made Joseph a coat of many colors. e-h, Joseph's brothers take his coat and cast him into pit. i-l, Joseph is sold to the Ishmaelites. m-p, Joseph is accused by Potiphar's wife and thrown into prison. q-t, Joseph interprets Pharoah's dreams. u-x, Joseph is reunited with his brothers.
No. 2835 — Parting of the Red Sea: a-x, Moses leading Israelites through sea, Pharoah's army drowning.
No. 2836 — Daniel and the Lions: a-x, Daniel in lion's den surrounded by various animals, angel.

**1994, Aug. 4**　　　**Litho.**　　**Perf. 14**
**Sheets of 24, #a-x**

| | | | |
|---|---|---|---|
| 2833-2836 | A193 | $20　Set of 4 | 40.00 40.00 |

Nos. 2835-2836 have continuous design.

A194　　　　　　A195

Philakorea '94: $6, Statues of socialist ideals, Pyongyang. $25, Statue of Adm. Yi Sun-sin. $120, Sokkat'ap Pagoda, Pulguksa. $130, Village guardian, Chejudo Island.
No. 2841, $60 — Ten-fold screens: a, Shown. b-e, Cranes. h-i, Deer. j, Deer, mushrooms, waterfall.
No. 2842, $60: b-d, Cranes. f-h, Deer. c, h, Waterfalls. i-j, Mushrooms.
No. 2843, $325, Falled Rock, horiz. No. 2844, $325, Westerners at Korean Court, horiz.

**1994, June 20**　**Litho.**　　**Perf. 14**

| | | | |
|---|---|---|---|
| 2837-2840 | A194 | Set of 4 | 5.00 5.00 |

**Sheets of 10, #a-j**
**Perf. 13**

| | | | |
|---|---|---|---|
| 2841-2842 | A195 | Set of 2 | 20.00 20.00 |

**Souvenir Sheets**
**Perf. 14**

| | | | |
|---|---|---|---|
| 2843-2844 | A194 | Set of 2 | 10.00 10.00 |

Nos. 2841-2842 have continuous design.

Entertainers of Takarazuka Revue, Japan — A196

No. 2845: a, $60, Mira Anju. b, $60, Yuki Amami. c, $60, Maki Ichiro. d, $60, Yu Shion. e, $20, Miki Maya. f, $20, Fubuki Takane. g, $20, Seika Juze. h, $20, Saki Asaji.

**1994**　　　　　　　　　**Perf. 14½**

| | | | |
|---|---|---|---|
| 2845 | A196 | Sheet of 8, #a.-h. + 4 labels | 8.00 8.00 |

Nos. 2845a-2845d are 34x47mm.

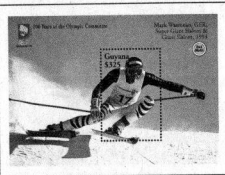

Intl. Olympic Committee,
Cent. — A198

Designs: $20, Nancy Kerrigan, US, figure skating, 1994. $35, Sawao Kato, Japan, gymnastics, 1976. $130, Florence Griffith-Joyner, US, 100-, 200-meters, 1988.
$325, Mark Wasmeier, Germany, super giant & giant slalom, 1994.

**1994, June 20**
| | | | | |
|---|---|---|---|---|
| 2846-2848 | A197 | Set of 3 | 4.00 | 4.00 |

**Souvenir Sheet**
| | | | | |
|---|---|---|---|---|
| 2849 | A198 | $325 multicolored | 7.00 | 7.00 |

1994 World Cup
Soccer Championships,
U.S. — A199

Player, country: $6, Paulo Futre, Portugal. $35, Lyndon Hooper, Canada. $60, Enzo Francescoli, Uruguay. $190, Freddy Rincon, Colombia.
No. 2854, $60: a, Paolo Maldini, Italy. b, Guyana player. c, Bwalya Kalusha, Zambia. d, Diego Maradona, Argentina. e, Andreas Brehme, Germany. f, Eric Wynalda, US.
No. 2855, $60: a, John Doyle, US. b, Eric Wynalda, US, diff. c, Thomas Dooley, US. d, Ernie Stewart, US. f, Marcelo Balboa, US. g, Coach Bora Milutinovic, US.
No. 2856, $325, 1994 World Cup program cover. No. 2857, $325,Oiler Watson.

**1994, Aug. 8**
| | | | | |
|---|---|---|---|---|
| 2850-2853 | A199 | Set of 4 | 5.00 | 5.00 |

**Sheets of 6, #a-f**
| | | | | |
|---|---|---|---|---|
| 2854-2855 | A199 | Set of 2 | 15.00 | 15.00 |

**Souvenir Sheets**
| | | | | |
|---|---|---|---|---|
| 2856-2857 | A199 | Set of 2 | 14.00 | 14.00 |

Birds — A200

No. 2858, $35: a, Goshawk. b, Lapwing. c, Ornate umbrellabird. d, Slatey-headed parakeet. e, Regent bowerbird. f, Egytian goose. g, White-winged crossbill. h, Waxwing. i, Ruff. j, Hoopoe. k, Superb starling. l, Great jacamar.
No. 2859, $35: a, Peregrine falcon. b, Great spotted woodpecker. c, White-throated kingfisher. d, Peruvian cock-of-the-rock. e, Yellow-headed Amazon. f, Victoria crowned pigeon. g, Little owl. h, Pheasant. i, Goldfinch. j, Jay. k, Sulphur-brasted toucan. l, Japanese blue flycatcher.
No. 2860, $325, Gould's violet-ear. No. 2861, $325, Bald eagle.

**1994, Sept. 15      Sheets of 12, #a.-l.**
| | | | | |
|---|---|---|---|---|
| 2858-2859 | A200 | Set of 2 | 17.00 | 17.00 |

**Souvenir Sheets**
| | | | | |
|---|---|---|---|---|
| 2860-2861 | A200 | Set of 2 | 16.00 | 16.00 |

PHILAKOREA '94. For surcharges, see Nos. 4118, 4184.

1996 Summer
Olympics,
Atlanta — A201

German athletes: $6, Anja Fichtel, fencing, 1988, horiz. $25, Annegret Richter, 100-meter dash, 1976. $30, Heike Henkel, high jump, 1982. $35, Armin Hary, 100-meter dash, 1960. $50, Heide Rosendahl, long jump, 1972. $60, Josef Neckermann, equestrian grand prix, 1968. $130, Heike Drechsler, long jump, 1988. $190, Ulrike Mayfarth, high jump, 1984. $250, Michael Gross, swimming, 1984, horiz.
No. 2870A: b, $135, Markus Wasmeier, skiing, 1994. c, $190, Katja Seizinger, skiing, 1994.
No. 2871, $325, Franziska van Almsick, swimming, 1992. No. 2872, $325, Steffi Graf, tennis, 1992.

**1994, Sept. 28**
| | | | | |
|---|---|---|---|---|
| 2862-2870 | A201 | Set of 9 | 13.00 | 13.00 |

**Souvenir Sheets**
| | | | | |
|---|---|---|---|---|
| 2870A | A201 | Sheet of 2, #b.-c. | 5.50 | 5.50 |
| 2871-2872 | A201 | Set of 2 | 11.00 | 11.00 |

Space Missions,
First Manned
Moon Landing,
25th
Anniv. — A202

No. 2873, $60: a, Laika, first dog in space. b, Yuri Gagarin, first man in space. c, John Glenn, first American to orbit earth. d, Edward White, first American to walk in space. e, Neil Armstrong, first to step foot onto moon. f, Luna 16. g, Luna 17. h, Skylab 1. i, 1975 Apollo-Soyuz.
No. 2874, $60 — Unmanned probes: a, Mars 3, Mars. b, Mariner 10, Mercury. c, Voyager, planetary grand tour. d, Pioneer, Venus. e, Giotto, Halley's Comet. f, Megellan, Venus. g, Galileo, Jupiter. h, Ulysses, Sun. i, Cassini, Titan.
No. 2875, $325, "Buzz" Aldrin, Neil Armstrong, Michael Collins. No. 2876, $325, Pioneer 1, 2.

**1994, Nov. 10      Litho.      Perf. 13½**
**Sheets of 9, #a-i**
| | | | | |
|---|---|---|---|---|
| 2873-2874 | A202 | Set of 2 | 18.00 | 18.00 |

**Souvenir Sheets**
| | | | | |
|---|---|---|---|---|
| 2875-2876 | A202 | Set of 2 | 11.00 | 11.00 |

Steam
Locomotives
A203

Designs: No. 2877, $25, South Eastern Railway #285, 1882. No. 2878, $25, West Point Foundry, 1830. No. 2879, $300, Mt. Washington Cog Railway, 1886. No. 2880, $300, Stroudley-Brighton, 1872.
No. 2881, $30: a, "John Bull," 1831. b, Stephenson, 1837. c, "Atlantic," 1832. d, Stourbridge Lion, 1829. e, Polonceau, 1854. f, Rogers, 1856. g, "Vulcan," 1858. h, "Namur," 1846.
No. 2882, $30: a, West Point Foundry, 1832. b, Sequin, 1830. c, Stephenson's Planet, 1830. d, Norris 4-2-0, 1840. e, Union Iron Works on San Francisco, 1867. f, Andrew Jackson, 1832. g, Herald, 1831. h, Cumberland, 1845.
No. 2883, $30: a, Pennsylvania's Class K, 1880. b, Cooke, 1885. c, John B. Turner, 1867. d, Baldwin, 1871. e, Richard Trevithick, 1804. f, John Stephens, 1825. g, John Blenkinsop, 1814. h, Pennsylvania, 1803.
$250, Est Railway, 1878. $300, "Claud Hamilton," 1840.

**1994, Nov. 15      Perf. 14**
| | | | | |
|---|---|---|---|---|
| 2877-2880 | A203 | Set of 4 | 10.00 | 10.00 |

**Sheets of 8, #a-h, + Label**
| | | | | |
|---|---|---|---|---|
| 2881-2883 | A203 | Set of 3 | 14.00 | 14.00 |

**Souvenir Sheets**
| | | | | |
|---|---|---|---|---|
| 2884 | A203 | $250 multicolored | 5.00 | 5.00 |
| 2885 | A203 | $300 multicolored | 6.00 | 6.00 |

For surcharge, see No. 4116.

English Touring
Cricket,
Cent. — A204

Designs: $20, C.H. Lloyd, Guyana/West Indies, vert. $35, C.W. Hooper, Guyana/West Indies, Wisden Trophy. $60, G.A. Hick, England, Wisden Trophy.
$200, First English Team, 1895.

**1994, June 20      Litho.      Perf. 14**
| | | | | |
|---|---|---|---|---|
| 2886-2888 | A204 | Set of 3 | 2.00 | 2.00 |

**Souvenir Sheet**
| | | | | |
|---|---|---|---|---|
| 2889 | A204 | $200 multicolored | 3.25 | 3.25 |

Christmas — A205

Paintings: $6, Joseph with the Christ Child, by Guido Reni. $20, Adoration of the Christ Child, by Girolamo Romanino. $25, Adoration of the Christ Child with St. Barbara and St. Martin, by Raffaello Botticini. $30, Holy Family, by Pompeo Girolam Batoni. $35, Flight into Egypt, by Bartolommeo Carducci. $60, Holy Family and the Baptist, by Andrea del Sarto. $120, Sacred Conversation, by Cesare de Sesto. $190, Madonna and Child with Sts. Joseph & John the Baptist, by Pontormo.
No. 2898, $325, Holy Family and St. Elizabeth and St. John the Baptist, by Francisco Primaticcio. No. 2899, $325, Presentation of Christ in the Temple, by Fra Bartolommeo.

**1994, Dec. 5      Perf. 13½x14**
| | | | | |
|---|---|---|---|---|
| 2890-2897 | A205 | Set of 8 | 12.00 | 6.00 |

**Souvenir Sheets**
| | | | | |
|---|---|---|---|---|
| 2898-2899 | A205 | Set of 2 | 10.00 | 10.00 |

Order of the
Caribbean
Community
A206

First award recipients: No. 2900, $60, Sir Shridath Ramphal, statesman, Guyana. No. 2901, $60, William Demas, economist, Trinidad & Tobago. No. 2902, $60, Derek Walcott, writer, St. Lucia.

**1994      Perf. 14**
| | | | | |
|---|---|---|---|---|
| 2900-2902 | A206 | Set of 3 | 4.00 | 4.00 |

Motion Picture,
Star Trek
Generations
A207

A207a

No. 2903, "Boldly Go," Starship Enterprise. No. 2904, $100: a, Capt. Picard. b, Cmdr. Riker. c, Capt. Kirk. d, Villain with phaser. e, Kirk, Picard on horseback. f, Klingons L'rsa and B'tor. g, Kirk, Picard, diff. h, Counselor Troi. i, Picard, Lt. Cmdr. Data.
No. 2905, $100: a, Troi, Riker. b, Worf. c, Picard, diff. d, Worf, Lt. Cmdr. LaForge. e, Sailing ship, Enterprise. f, Picard, Riker. g. Data. h, Worf. i, Dr. Crusher.
No. 2906, Like No. 2903, horiz. $1000, Kirk and Picard.
No. 2906D: e, Capt. Picard. f, Capt. Kirk.

**1994      Litho.      Perf. 13½x14**
| | | | | |
|---|---|---|---|---|
| 2903 | A207 | $100 multicolored | 1.50 | 1.50 |

**Sheets of 9, #a-i**
| | | | | |
|---|---|---|---|---|
| 2904-2905 | A207 | Set of 2 | 40.00 | 40.00 |

**Souvenir Sheet**
**Perf. 14x13½**
| | | | | |
|---|---|---|---|---|
| 2906 | A207 | $500 multicolored | 8.00 | 8.00 |

**Litho. & Embossed**
**Die Cut Perf. 9**
| | | | | |
|---|---|---|---|---|
| 2906C | A207a | $1000 gold & multi | 25.00 | 25.00 |

**Souvenir Sheet**
**Die Cut Perf. 9 on Outside**
| | | | | |
|---|---|---|---|---|
| 2906D | A207a | $500 Sheet of 2, #e.-f. | 25.00 | 25.00 |

Issued: No. 2906C, 11/18, others 12/7. No. 2903 was issued in sheets of 9. Nos. 2906e-2906f are imperf.

Sisters of Mercy of
Guyana, Cent. — A208

**1994, Dec. 12      Perf. 14**
| | | | | |
|---|---|---|---|---|
| 2907 | A208 | $60 multicolored | 1.90 | 1.90 |

**Nos. 1037a, 1097, 1099 Surcharged**

Surcharge reads: "ILO / 75th Anniversary / 1919-1994".

**Perfs & Printing Methods as Before**
**1994**
| | | | |
|---|---|---|---|
| 2907A | A91 | $6 on 130c #1037a | |
| 2907B | A91 | $30 on 120c #1099 | |
| 2907C | A91 | $35 on 120c #1097 | |

**Nos. 1063, 1098, 1120, 1123**
**Surcharged in Blue**

Surcharge reads: "CENTENARY / Sign For The / MAHDI / 1894-1994".

**Perfs. & Printing Methods as Before**
**1994**
| | | | |
|---|---|---|---|
| 2907D | A91 | $6 on 60c #1120 | |
| 2907E | A91 | $20 on 200c #1063 | |
| 2907F | A91 | $30 on 60c #1098 | |
| 2907G | A91 | $35 on 60c #1123 | |

Cricket — A209

Designs: $20, Sobers congratulates Lara. $30, Brian Lara setting world record, vert. $375, Lara, Chanderpaul.
$300, Brian Lara walking under "avenue of bats," vert.

**1995, Feb. 3      Litho.      Perf. 14**
| | | | | |
|---|---|---|---|---|
| 2908-2910 | A209 | Set of 3 | 7.00 | 7.00 |

**Souvenir Sheet**
| | | | | |
|---|---|---|---|---|
| 2911 | A209 | $300 multicolored | 5.50 | 5.50 |

A210          A211

Babe Ruth (1895-1948) — A212

Type A211 various portraits like #2914.
$2000, Portrait, Ruth holding bat, vert.

**1995, Feb. 6      Litho.      Perf. 14**
| | | | | |
|---|---|---|---|---|
| 2912 | A210 | $65 multi | 1.40 | 1.40 |

## Self-Adhesive (#2913)
### Size: 64x89mm (#2913)

| | | | | |
|---|---|---|---|---|
| 2913 | A211 | $350 Set of 12 | 50.00 | 50.00 |

### Litho. & Embossed
### Perf. 12

| | | | |
|---|---|---|---|
| 2914 | A212 | $1000 gold & sep | 25.00 |

### Embossed

| | | | |
|---|---|---|---|
| 2914A | A212 | $2000 gold | 29.00 |

### Litho.
### Perf. 14

| | | | | |
|---|---|---|---|---|
| 2915 | A211 | $65 Sheet of 12, #a.-l. | 12.00 | 12.00 |

### Souvenir Sheet

| | | | | |
|---|---|---|---|---|
| 2916 | A211 | $500 like #2912a, horiz. | 10.00 | 10.00 |

No. 2912 issued in sheets of 9. Portraits of Babe Ruth in No. 2913 are same as in No. 2915, but surrounded by gold frame, gold autograph, baseballs, and simulated perfs. No. 2913 was sold in sealed celophane package. To affix stamps, backing containing biographical information must be removed.

Disney Characters at Work A213

No. 2917, $30 — Animal workers: a, Veterinarian. b, Animal trainer. c, Animal psychiatrist. d, Ornithologist. e, Dog groomer. f, Herpetologist. g, Pet shop keeper. h, Park ranger. i, Aquarist.

No. 2918, $30 — Arts & crafts: a, Mickey the animator, Pluto. b, Goofy the tailor, Mickey. c, Pete the glass blower, Morty. d, Clarabelle modeling for Minnie the artist. e, Daisy sculpts Donald. f, Donald, nephews working with clay. g, Watchmakers, Chip & Dale. h, Locksmith Donald, nephews. i, Grandma Duck makes a quilt.

No. 2919, $30 — Medical group: a, Family doctor. b, Optometrist. c, Nurse. d, Psychiatrist. e, Physical therapist. f, Dentist. g, Radiologist. h, Pharmacist. i, Chiropractor.

No. 2920, $35 — Hard hat & company, vert.: a, Mickey, Pluto in truck. b, Mickey at work. c, Goofy jackhammer. d, Minnie at work. e, Forklifters. f, Construction contractor. g, Carpenter. h, Bulldozer.

No. 2921, $35 — Home services, vert.: a, Mickey, plumber. b, Mickey, paperboy. c, Huey, Dewey, Louie, moving service. d, Pete, handyman. e, Donald, newphews' house painting service. f, Goofy, washer repairman. g, Minnie, babysitter. h, Daisy cares for Grandma Duck.

No. 2922, $35 — Public service workers, vert.: a, Policeman. b, Fireman. c, Ambulance driver. d, Crossing guard. e, Museum docent. f, Census taker. g, Street maintenance workers. h, Sanitation worker.

No. 2923, $200, Goofy, zoo keeper. No. 2924, $200, Camera, Pluto, vert. No. 2925, $200, Goofy, surgeon. No. 2926, $200, Minnie, pups, tool chest. No. 2927, $200, Minnie, maid. No. 2928, $200, Horace, politician.

### 1995, Feb. 23   Litho.   Perf. 13½x14
### Sheets of 9, #a-i

| | | | | |
|---|---|---|---|---|
| 2917-2919 | A213 | Set of 3 | 15.00 | 15.00 |

### Sheets of 8, #a-h
### Perf. 14x13½

| | | | | |
|---|---|---|---|---|
| 2920-2922 | A213 | Set of 3 | 15.00 | 15.00 |

### Souvenir Sheets

| | | | | |
|---|---|---|---|---|
| 2923-2928 | A213 | Set of 6 | 32.50 | 32.50 |

Nos. 2917-2922 exist in sheets of 7 or 8 $5 stamps + label. The label replaces Nos. 2917e, 2918e, 2919g, 2920h, 2921h, 2922e. These sheets became available Nov. 20, 1996.

For surcharges, see Nos. 4122, 4123, 4124.

### Nos. 1022, 1033, 1045, 1061
### Surcharged in Red

Surcharge reads: "SALVATION / ARMY / 1895-1995"

### 1995, Apr. 24   Litho.   Perf. 14

| | | | |
|---|---|---|---|
| 2928A | A91 | $6 on 60c #1033 | |
| 2928B | A91 | $20 on 60c #1045 | |
| 2928C | A91 | $30 on 60c #1022 | |
| 2928D | A91 | $35 on 60c #1061 | |

New Year 1995 (Year of the Boar) A214

No. 2929 — Stylized boars: a, $20. b, $30. c, $50, Facing forward. denomination LR. d, $100. f, $50, "Abundant Year of the Pig." g, $50, "Fortunate Year of the Pig." h, $50, Facing forward, denomination LL. $150, Face, Chinese inscriptions.

### 1995, May 4   Litho.   Perf. 14½

| | | | | |
|---|---|---|---|---|
| 2929 | | Block of 4, #a.-d. | 5.00 | 5.00 |
| e. | A214 | Souvenir sheet of 4, #c, f.-h. | 6.00 | 6.00 |

### Souvenir Sheet

| | | | | |
|---|---|---|---|---|
| 2930 | A214 | $150 multicolored | 5.00 | 5.00 |

No. 2929 was issued in miniature sheets of 4.

A215

Birds: $5, Goshawk. $6, Lapwing. $8, Ornate umbrellabird. $15, Slatey-headed parakeet. $19, Regent bowerbird. $20, Egyptian goose. $25, White-winged crossbill. $30, Waxwing. $35, Ruff. $60, Hoopoe. $100, Superb starling. $500, Great jacamar.

### 1995, May 8   Litho.   Perf. 14½x13½

| | | | | |
|---|---|---|---|---|
| 2931 | A215 | $5 multicolored | .25 | .25 |
| 2932 | A215 | $6 multicolored | .25 | .25 |
| 2933 | A215 | $8 multicolored | .25 | .25 |
| 2934 | A215 | $15 multicolored | .25 | .25 |
| 2935 | A215 | $19 multicolored | .30 | .30 |
| 2936 | A215 | $20 multicolored | .30 | .30 |
| 2937 | A215 | $25 multicolored | .30 | .30 |
| 2938 | A215 | $30 multicolored | .40 | .40 |
| 2939 | A215 | $35 multicolored | .50 | .50 |
| 2940 | A215 | $60 multicolored | .80 | .80 |
| 2941 | A215 | $100 multicolored | 1.60 | 1.60 |
| 2942 | A215 | $500 multicolored | 7.00 | 7.00 |
| | | Nos. 2931-2942 (12) | 12.20 | 12.20 |

For surcharges, see Nos. 4020K, 4020O, 4112, 4136, 4204.

Lapwing — A215a

### 1995 ?   Litho.   Perf. 13¼

| | | | |
|---|---|---|---|
| 2942A | A215a | $6 multi | |

For surcharges see Nos. 4020L, 4020P.

Nolan Ryan, Baseball Player A216

No. 2943: a, Looking left, Mets. b, With bat, Mets. c, Pitching, Mets. d, Looking toward home plate, Angels. e, Pitching, Angels. f, Without hat, Angels. g, In red cap, Astros. h, Pitching, Astros. i, In black cap, Astros. j, Pitching, Rangers. k, Getting ready to pitch, Rangers. l, Up close, Rangers.

### 1995   Litho.   Imperf.
### Self-Adhesive
### Size: 64x89mm

| | | | | |
|---|---|---|---|---|
| 2943 | A216 | $350 Set of 12, #a.-l. | 60.00 | 60.00 |

Nos. 2943a-2943l are printed on thin cards, distributed in boxed sets containing certificate of aunthenticity and sealed in celophane packages. To affix stamps, backing containing biographical information must be removed.

### Miniature Sheets

Singapore '95 — A217

No. 2944, $35 — Dogs: a, Gordon setter. b, Long-haired chihuahua. c, Dalmation. d, Afghan. e, English bulldog. f, Miniature schnauzer. g, Clumber spaniel. h, Pekingese. i, St. Bernard. j, English cocker spaniel. k, Alaskan malamute. l, Rottweiler.

No. 2945, $35 — Cats: a, Norwegian forest cat. b, Scottish fold. c, Red burmese. d, British blue-hair. e, Abyssinian. f, Siamese. g, Exotic shorthair. h, Turkish van cat. i, Black Persian. j, Black-tipped burmilla. k, Singapura. l, Calico shorthair.

No. 2946, $35 — Horses: a, Chestnut thoroughbred colt. b, Liver chestnut quarter horse. c, Black Freisian. d, Chestnut Belgian. e, Appaloosa. f, Lipizzanas. g, Chestnut hunter. h, British shire. i, Palomino. j, Seal brown point. k, Arab. l, Afghanistan Kabardin.

No. 2947, $300, Golden retriever. No. 2948, $300, Maine coon. No. 2949, $300, American Anglo-Arab.

### 1995, June 1   Perf. 14
### Sheets of 12, #a-l

| | | | | |
|---|---|---|---|---|
| 2944-2946 | A217 | Set of 3 | 20.00 | 20.00 |

### Souvenir Sheets

| | | | | |
|---|---|---|---|---|
| 2947-2949 | A217 | Set of 3 | 12.00 | 12.00 |

Pocahontas A218

No. 2950 — Characters from Disney animated film: a, Pocahontas, Meeko. b, John Smith. c, Chief Powhatan. d, Kocoum. e, Ratcliffe. f, Wiggins. g, Nakoma. h, Thomas. No. 2951, Meeko, horiz.

### 1995, June 23   Litho.   Perf. 13½x14

| | | | | |
|---|---|---|---|---|
| 2950 | A218 | $50 Sheet of 8, #a.-h. | 7.00 | 7.00 |

### Souvenir Sheet
### Perf. 14x13½

| | | | | |
|---|---|---|---|---|
| 2951 | A218 | $300 multicolored | 5.00 | 5.00 |

See Nos. 2985-2990.

UN, 50th Anniv. — A219

No. 2952 — Map of: a, $35, North, South America. b, $60, Europe, Africa. c, $200, Asia, Australia. $300, Secretary General Boutros-Ghali.

### 1995   Litho.   Perf. 14

| | | | | |
|---|---|---|---|---|
| 2952 | A219 | Strip of 3, #a.-c. | 4.50 | 4.50 |

### Souvenir Sheet

| | | | | |
|---|---|---|---|---|
| 2953 | A219 | $300 multicolored | 4.00 | 4.00 |

No. 2953 was printed with incorrect (1945-1955) dates, and correct dates (1945-1995).

End of World War II, 50th Anniv. — A220

No. 2954: a, P61 Black Widow. b, PT boat. c, B26 Marauder. d, Cruiser USS San Juan. e, US Gato class submarine. f, US destroyer.

No. 2955: a, Jan. 1945, Battle of Bulge is over. b, Sigfried Line is breached. c, Liberation of concentration camps. d, Operation "Manna," Allies drop food to starving Dutch. e, GIs looking for snipers at end of Italian campaign. f, Newspaper headline announces Hitler's suicide. g, Soviet tanks pour into Berlin. h, U-858, first German warship to surrender in US waters.

No. 2956, $300, Battleship, aircraft carrier. No. 2957, $300, Top of Brandenburg Gate.

### 1995, July 6

| | | | | |
|---|---|---|---|---|
| 2954 | A220 | $60 Sheet of 6, #a.-f. + label | 6.00 | 6.00 |
| 2955 | A220 | $60 Sheet of 8, #a.-h. + label | 8.00 | 8.00 |

### Souvenir Sheets

| | | | | |
|---|---|---|---|---|
| 2956-2957 | A220 | Set of 2 | 8.00 | 8.00 |

No. 2957 contains one 57x42mm stamp.

FAO, 50th Anniv. — A221

No. 2958: a, $35, Girl carrying sack on head. b, $60, Man carrying sack, woman sorting sacks. c, $300, Woman lifting sack. $300, Pouring from ladle into bowl.

### 1995, July 6   Litho.   Perf. 14

| | | | | |
|---|---|---|---|---|
| 2958 | A221 | Strip of 3, #a.-c. | 4.50 | 4.50 |

### Souvenir Sheet

| | | | | |
|---|---|---|---|---|
| 2959 | A221 | $300 multicolored | 4.00 | 4.00 |

No. 2958 is a continuous design.

Rotary Intl., 90th Anniv. — A222

Designs: $200, Paul Harris, Rotary emblem. $300, Old, new Rotary emblems.

### 1995, July 6

| | | | | |
|---|---|---|---|---|
| 2960 | A222 | $200 multicolored | 3.50 | 3.50 |

### Souvenir Sheet

| | | | | |
|---|---|---|---|---|
| 2961 | A222 | $300 multicolored | 4.50 | 4.50 |

1995 Boy Scout Jamboree, Netherlands A223

Slogan, emblem, and: $20, Campfire. $25, Scout, beach. $30, Hiking. $35, Snorkeling. $60, Natl. flag, scout salute. $200, Fishing from boat.
No. 2968, $300, Canoeing. No. 2969, $300, Camping.

### 1995, July 6

| | | | | |
|---|---|---|---|---|
| 2962-2967 | A223 | Set of 6 | 6.00 | 6.00 |

### Souvenir Sheets

| | | | | |
|---|---|---|---|---|
| 2968-2969 | A223 | Set of 2 | 8.50 | 8.50 |

Queen Mother, 95th Birthday — A224

No. 2970: a, Drawing. b, Violet hat. c, Formal portrait. d, Green blue hat.
$325, As younger woman.

**1995, July 6**          **Perf. 13½x14**
2970 A224 $100 Strip or block of
4, #a.-d.                    7.00 7.00
**Souvenir Sheet**
2971 A224 $325 multicolored        6.00 6.00

No. 2970 issued in sheets of 2.
Sheets of Nos. 2970 and 2971 exist with black border in margin with text "In Memoriam/1900-2002."

Holidays of the World — A225

No. 2972: a, Thanksgiving, US. b, Christmas, Germany. c, Hanukkah, Israel. d, Easter, Spain. e, Carnivale, brazil. f, Bastill Day, France. g, Independence Day, India. h, St. Patrick's Day, Ireland.
$300, Chinese New Year, China.

**1995, Aug. 8       Litho.      Perf. 14**
2972 A225 $60 Sheet of 8, #a.-
h.                          8.00 8.00
**Souvenir Sheet**
2973 A225 $300 multicolored        4.00 4.00

Marine Life — A226

No. 2974, vert: a, Cocoa damselfish. b, Sergeant major. c, Beau gregory. d, Yellowtail damselfish.
No. 2975: a, $30, Butterflyfish. b, $35, Bluehead. c, $60, Yellow damselfish. d, $200, Clown wrasse.
No. 2976: a, $30, Lemon shark. b, $35, Green turtle. c, $60 Sawfish. d, $200, Stingray.
No. 2977, $60: a, Tiger shark. b, Needlefish. c, Horse-eye jack. d, Princess parrotfish. e, Yellowtail snapper. f, Spotted snake eel. g, Trunkfish. h, Cherubfish. i, French angelfish.
No. 2978, $60: a, Sei whale. b, Barracuda. c, Mutton snapper. d, Hawksbill turtle. e, Spanish hogfish. f, Queen angelfish. g, Porkfish. h, Trumpetfish. i, Electric ray.
No. 2979, $300, Carcharodon carcharias. No. 2980, $300, Dermochelys coriacea.

**1995, Sept. 5       Litho.      Perf. 14**
2974 A226 $80 Strip of 4, #a.-
d.                          4.50 4.50
**Sheets of 4, #a-d**
2975-2976 A226 Set of 2        14.00 14.00
**Sheets of 9, #a-i**
2977-2978 A226 Set of 2        20.00 20.00
**Souvenir Sheets**
2979-2980 A226 Set of 2        8.00 8.00

No. 2974 was issued in sheets of 4.

### Miniature Sheets

1996 Summer Olympics, Atlanta — A227

No. 2981 $60: a, Shot put. b, Relay. c, Balance beam. d, Cycling. e, Synchronized swimming. f, Hurdles. g, Pommel horse. h, Discus thrower, head down.
No. 2982, $60: a, Pole vault. b, Long jump. c, Track. d, Wrestling. e, Discus thrower, head up. f, Basketball. g, Boxing. h, Weight lifting.
No. 2983, $300, Long jump. No. 2984, $300, Runners.

**1995, Oct. 2       Litho.      Perf. 14**
**Sheets of 8, #a-h**
2981-2982 A227 Set of 2        14.00 14.00
**Souvenir Sheets**
2983-2984 A227 Set of 2        8.00 8.00

### Pocahontas Type of 1995
**Miniature Sheets**

Nos. 2985-2987: Various scenes from Disney animated film, horiz.
No. 2988, $325, Pocahontas behind tree branch, horiz. No. 2989, Pocahontas, Powhatan, horiz. No. 2990, $325, Pocahontas kneeling.

**Perf. 14x13½, 13½x14 (#2990)**
**1995, Oct. 9                    Litho.**
2985 A218 $8 Sheet of 9,
#a.-i.                      3.50 3.50
2986 A218 $30 Sheet of 9,
#a.-i.                      11.50 11.50
2987 A218 $35 Sheet of 9,
#a.-i.                      15.00 15.00
**Souvenir Sheets**
2988-2990 A218 Set of 3        32.50 32.50

Fauna — A228

No. 2991: a, $35, House martin. b, $60. Hobby. c, $20, Sand martin (a). d, $200, Long-tailed skua (b).
No. 2992: a, Olive colobus. b, Violet-backed starling. c, Diana monkey. d, African palm civet. e, Giraffe, zebras. f, African linsang. g, Royal antelope (fawn). h, Royal antelope (adult, fawn) (g, i). i, Palm squirrel.
No. 2993, $300, Brush pig. No. 2994, $300, Chimpanzee.

**1995, Oct. 18       Litho.      Perf. 14**
2991 A228 Block of 4, #a.-d.        4.50 4.50
2992 A228 $60 Sheet of 9,
#a.-i.                      7.50 7.50
**Souvenir Sheets**
2993-2994 A228 Set of 2        10.00 10.00

No. 2991 was issued in sheets of 16 stamps.

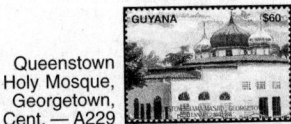

Queenstown Holy Mosque, Georgetown, Cent. — A229

**1995, Dec. 1       Litho.      Perf. 14**
2995 A229 $60 multicolored        1.00 1.00

Christmas — A230

Details or entire paintings, by Carracci: $25, The Angel of Annunciation. $30, Annunciation of the Virgin. $35, Assumption of the Virgin. $60, Baptism of Christ. $100, Madonna and Child. $300, Birth by the Virgin.
No. 3002, $325, Madonna and Ten Saints, by Fiorentino. No. 3003, $325, Mystical Marriage of St. Catherine, by Carracci.

**1995, Dec. 4                    Perf. 13½x14**
2996-3001 A230 Set of 6        7.00 7.00
**Souvenir Sheets**
3002-3003 A230 Set of 2        9.00 9.00

Guyana Defense Force, 30th Anniv. — A231

**1995, Dec. 7                    Perf. 14**
3004 A231 $6 Woman with gun        .25 .25
3005 A231 $60 Man with gun        .75 .75

For surcharge, see No. 4109.

John Lennon (1940-80) — A232

**1995**
3006 A232 $35 multicolored        .75 .75

No. 3006 was issued in sheets of 16.

Nobel Prize Fund Established, Cent. — A233

No. 3007, $35: a, Henri Becquerel, physics, 1903. b, Igor Tamm, physics, 1958. c, Georges Köhler, medicine, 1984. d, Gerhard Domagk, medicine, 1939. e, Yasunari Kawabata, literature, 1968. f, Maurice Allais, economics, 1988. g, Aristide Briand, peace, 1926. h, Pavel Cherenkov, physics, 1958. i, Feodor Lynen, medicine, 1964.
No. 3008 $35: a, Adolf von Baeyer, chemistry, 1905. b, Hideki Yukawa, physics, 1949. c, George W. Beadle, medicine, 1958. d, Edwin M. McMillian, chemistry, 1951. e, Samuel C.C. Ting, physics, 1976. f, Saint-John Perse, literature, 1960. g, John F. Enders, medicine, 1954. h, Felix Bloch, physics, 1952. i, P.B. Medawar, medicine, 1960.
No. 3009, $35: a, Albrecht Kossel, medicine, 1910. b, Arthur H. Compton, physics, 1927. c, N.M. Butler, peace, 1931. d, Charles Laveran, medicine, 1907. e, George R. Minot, medicine, 1934. f, Henry H. Dale, medicine, 1936. g, Jacques Monod, medicine, 1965. h, Alfred Hershey, medicine, 1969. i, Pär Lagerkvist, literature, 1951.
No. 3010, $35: a, Francis Crick, medicine, 1962. b, Manne Siegbahn, physics, 1924. c, Eisaku Sato, peace, 1974. d, Robert Koch, medicine, 1905. e, Edgar D. Adrian, medicine, 1932. f, Erwin Neher, medicine, 1991. g, Henry Taube, chemistry, 1983. h, Norman Angell, peace, 1933. i, Robert Robinson, chemistry, 1947.
No. 3011 $35: a, Nikolai Basov, physics, 1964. b, Klas Arnoldson, peace, 1908. c, René Sully-Prudhomme, literature, 1901. d, Robert W. Wilson, physics, 1978. e, Hugo Theorell, medicine, 1955. f, Nelly Sachs, literature, 1966. g, Hans von Euler-Chelpin, chemistry, 1929. h, Mairead Corrigan, peace, 1976. i, Willis E. Lamb, Jr, physics, 1955.
No. 3012 $35: a, Norman F. Ramsey, physics, 1989. b, Chen Ning Yang, physics, 1957. c, Earl W. Sutherland, Jr., medicine, 1971. d, Paul Karrer, chemistry, 1937. e, Harmut Michel, chemistry, 1988. f, Richard Kuhn, chemistry, 1938. g, P.A.M. Dirac, physics, 1933. h, Victor Grignard, chemistry, 1912. i, Richard Willstätter, chemistry, 1915.
No. 3013, $300, Le Duc Tho, peace, 1973. No. 3014, $300, Yasunari Kawabata, literature, 1968. No. 3015, $300, Heinrich Böll, literature, 1972. No. 3016, $300, Henry Kissinger, peace, 1973. No. 3017, $300, Kenichi Fukui, chemistry, 1981. No. 3018, $300, Lech Walesa, peace, 1983.

**1995, Dec. 20       Litho.      Perf. 14**
**Sheets of 9, #a-i**
3007-3012 A233 Set of 6        50.00 50.00
**Souvenir Sheets**
3013-3018 A233 Set of 6        30.00 30.00

Caribbean Development Bank, 25th Anniv. — A234

**1995, Dec. 29       Litho.      Perf. 14**
3019 A234 $60 multicolored        .75 .75

Marilyn Monroe (1926-62) — A235

No. 3020, Various portraits. No. 3021, Portrait, horiz.

**1995, Dec. 29                    Perf. 13½x14**
3020 A235 $60 Sheet of 9, #a.-
i.                          7.50 7.50
**Souvenir Sheet**
**Perf. 14x13½**
3021 A235 $300 multicolored        4.00 4.00

David Copperfield, Magician — A236

Nos. 3022-3023, Various portraits, magic acts.

**1995, Dec. 29                    Perf. 13½x14**
3022 A236 $60 Sheet of 9,
#a.-i.                      8.00 8.00
**Souvenir Sheet**
3023 A236 $300 multicolored        4.00 4.00

New Year 1996 (Year of the Rat) — A237

No. 3024 — Stylized rats: a, $20. b, $30. c, $50, light brown & multi. d, $100.
No. 3025: a, Like #3024a, b, Like #3024b. c, Like #3024c, darker brown & multi. d, Like #3024d.
No. 3026, Rat facing forward.

**1996, Jan. 2                    Perf. 14½**
3024 A237 Block of 4, #a.-d.        3.00 3.00
**Miniature Sheet**
3025 A237 $50 Sheet of 4, #a.-
d.                          2.50 2.50
**Souvenir Sheet**
3026 A237 $150 multicolored        2.50 2.50

No. 3024 was issued in sheets of 16 stamps.

UNICEF, 50th Anniv. — A238

No. 3027: a, Children, building in background. b, Man, boy, tree in background. c, Children behind tree. d, Man, children.

**1996, Jan. 2                    Perf. 14**
3027 A238 $1100 Sheet of 4,
#a.-d.                      30.00 30.00

No. 3027 is a continuous design. Extreme speculation might have occurred with this issue.

Paintings by Peter Paul Rubens — A239

Details or entire paintings: $6, The Garden of Love. $10, Two Sleeping Children. $20, All

Saints Day. $25, Sacrifice of Abraham. $30, The Last Supper. $35, The Birth of Henry of Navarre. $40, Standing Female Saint Study. $50, $60, The Garden of Love, each diff. No. 3037, $200, The Martyrdom of St. Livinus. No. 3038, $200, Der Heilige Franz Von Paula. $300, The Union of Maria de Medici and Henry IV.

No. 3039, $325, The Three Crosses. No. 3040, $325, Decius Mus Addressing the Legions, horiz. No. 3041, $325, Triumph of Henry IV, horiz.

**1996, Jan. 29    Litho.    Perf. 14**
3028-3038A   A239   Set of 11      15.00 15.00
**Souvenir Sheets**
3039-3041   A239   Set of 3          15.00 15.00

Nos. 3039-3041 each contain one 57x85mm or 85x57mm stamp.

### Miniature Sheets

A240

Prehistoric Animals — A241

No. 3042: a, Tarbosaurus. b, Hadrosaurus. c, Polacanthus. d, Psittacosaurus. e, Ornitholestes. f, Yangchuanosaurus. g, Scelidosaurus. h, Kentrosaurus. i, Coelophysis. j, Lesothosaurus. k, Plateosaurus. l, Staurikosaurus.

No. 3043, $35: a, Eudimorphodon. b, Criorynchus. c, Elasmosaurus. d, Rhomaleosaurus. e, Ceresiosaurus. f, Mesosaurus. g, Grendelius. h, Nothosaurus. i, Mixosaurus. j, Placodus. k, Coelacanth. l, Mosasaurus.

No. 3044, $35: a, Ornithomimus. b, Pteranodon. c, Rhamphorynchus. d, Ornitholestes. e, Brachiosaurus. f, Parasaurolophus. g, Ceratosaurus. h, Camarasaurus. i, Euoplocephalus. j, Scutellosaurus. k, Compsognathus. l, Stegoceras.

No. 3045, $35: a, Apatosaurus. b, Archaeopteryx. c, Dimorphodon. d, Deinonychus. e, Coelophysis. f, Tyrannosaurus. g, Triceratops. h, Anatosaurus. i, Saltasaurus. j, Allosaurus. k, Oviraptor. l, Stegosaurus.

No. 3046, $60: a, Heterodontosaurus (b). b, Compsognathus (c). c, Ornithomimus (b).

No. 3047, $60: a, Saurolophus. b, Muttaburrasaurus (a). c, Dicraeosaurus (b).

No. 3048, $300, Apatosaurus, allosaurus, horiz. No. 3049, $300, Tyrannosaurus rex.

No. 3050, $300, Quetzalcoatlus. No. 3051, $300, Lagosuchus. No. 3052, $300Struthiomimus.

**1996, Feb. 12**
3042   A240   $35 Sheet of 12,
                        #a.-l.              6.00   6.00
**Sheets of 12, #a-l**
3043-3045   A241   Set of 3        20.00 20.00
**Sheets of 3, #a-c**
3046-3047   A240   Set of 2          6.00   6.00
**Souvenir Sheets**
3048-3049   A240   Set of 2        10.00 10.00
3050-3052   A241   Set of 3        15.00 15.00

Pandas — A242

No. 3053 — In tree: a, Lying on back, looking right. b, Arms, legs around branch. c, Paws holding onto tree. d, Sitting, looking left.

No. 3054 — On rocks by stream: a, Standing. b, Sitting, holding bamboo stick. c, Holding bamboo to mouth. d, Lying on stomach.

**1996, Apr. 12    Litho.    Perf. 14**
3053   A242   $60 Sheet of 4, #a.-d.   4.00 4.00
3054   A242   $60 Sheet of 4, #a.-d.   4.00 4.00

China '96, 9th Asian Intl. Philatelic Exhibtion.

Mushrooms, Insects and Coral — A243

Designs: $20, Yellow morce, leaf beetle. $25, Green spored mushroom. $30, Leaf beetle, common mushroom. $35, Monarch caterpillars, pine cone mushroom.

No. 3059, $60: a, Green-beaded jelly club. b, Aspic puffball. c, Stalkless paxillus. d, Stout-stalked amanita.

No. 3060, $60: a, Fly agaric. b, Graying yellow russula, click beetle. c, Netted stinkhorn, housefly. d, Butterfly hunter, stropharia.

No. 3061, $60: a, Cockle-shell lentinus. b, Parasitic volvariella. c, Deadly lepiota. d, Shaggy-stalked boleta.

No. 3062: a, Armillauella mellea. b, Sealy vase chanterelle. c, Bitter pholiota. d, Flute white helvella. e, Fading scarlet waxy cap. f, Jask's lantern. g, Hygzocybe acutoconica. h, Mycena viscosa.

No. 3063, $300, Orange mycena. No. 3064, $300, Violet-branched coral, Red raspberry slime, yellow-tipped coral, horiz.

**1996, May 3    Litho.    Perf. 14**
3055-3058   A243   Set of 4           3.50   3.50
**Strips of 4, #a-d**
3059-3061   A243   Set of 3         13.50 13.50
3062   A243   $60 Sheet of 8,
                        #a.-h.              9.00   9.00
**Souvenir Sheets**
3063-3064   A243   Set of 2           9.00   9.00

Nos. 3059-3061 were issued in sheets of 8 stamps.

Deng Xiaoping, Chinese Communist Leader A244

No. 3065: a, Painting inscription. b, With dignitaries, waving. c, Signing autograph. d, Waving.

$300, Wearing white shirt, vert.

**1996**                              **Perf. 13**
3065   A244   $30 Strip or block of
                        4, #a.-d.           1.50   1.50
**Souvenir Sheet**
3066   A244   $300 multicolored    4.00   4.00

No. 3065 issued in sheets of 16 stamps.

Queen Elizabeth II, 70th Birthday — A245

No. 3067: a, Portrait wearing blue dress. b, Wearing blue green dress, hat. c, On throne, opening Parliament.

$325, In ceremonial attire.

**1996, May 3    Litho.    Perf. 13½x14**
3067   A245   $100 Strip of 3, #a.-c.   4.00 4.00
**Souvenir Sheet**
3068   A245   $325 multicolored    4.25   4.25

No. 3067 was issued in sheets of 9 stamps, with each strip having a different order.

Jerusalem, 3000th Anniv. — A246

No. 3069: a, $30. The Hulda Gates. b, $35, Old City, View from Mt. of Olives. c, $200, Absalom's Memorial, Kidron Valley. c, $300, Children's Memorial.

**1996          Litho.    Perf. 14**
3069   A246   Sheet of 3, #a.-c.      4.00 4.00
**Souvenir Sheet**
3070   A246   $300 multicolored    4.00 4.00

Birds — A247

No. 3071: a, Blue & yellow macaw. b, Andean condor. c, Crested eagle. d, White-tailed trogon. e, Toco toucan. f, Great horned owl. g, Andean cock-of-the-rock. h, Great curassow.

No. 3071I — Hummingbirds: j, Long-billed starthroat. k, Velvet-purple coronet. l, Racket-tailed coquette. m, Violet-tailed sylph. n, Broad-tailed hummingbird. o, Blue-tufted starthroat. p, White-necked jacobin. q, Ruby-throated hummingbird.

No. 3072, Ornate hawk eagle, horiz. No. 3073, Gould's violet-ear.

**1996, July 10**
3071   A247   $60 Sheet of 8,
                        #a.-h.              6.00   6.00
3071I   A247   $60 Sheet of 8, #j.-
                        q.                  6.00   6.00
**Souvenir Sheets**
3072   A247   $300 multicolored    4.50 4.50
3073   A247   $300 multicolored    4.50 4.50

Radio, Cent. — A248

Entertainers: $20, Frank Sinatra. $35, Gene Autry. $60, Groucho Marx. $200, Red Skelton. $300, Burl Ives.

**1996, July 25**
3074-3077   A248   Set of 4           4.00 4.00
**Souvenir Sheet**
3078   A248   $300 multicolored    4.00 4.00

1996 Summer Olympic Games, Atlanta — A249

Designs: $20, Pancratium. $30, Olympic Stadium, 1956. $60, Leonid Spirin, 20k walk, 1956, vert. $200, Lars Hall, modern pentathlon, 1952, 1956, vert.

No. 3083, vert.: a, Florence Griffith-Joyner. b, Ines Geissler. c, Nadia Comaneci. d, Tatiana Gutsu. e, Olga Korbut. f, Barbara Krause. g, Olga Bryzgina. h, Fanny Blankers-Koen. i, Irena Szewinska.

No. 3084, $50, vert.: a, Gerd Wessig. b, Jim Thorpe. c, Norman Read. d, Lasse Viren. e, Milt Campbell. f, Abebe Bikila. g, Jesse Owens. h, Viktor Saneev. i, Waldemer Cierpinski.

No. 3085, $50, vert.: a, Dietmar Schmidt. b, Pam Shriver. c, Zina Garrison. d, Hyun Jung-Hwa. e, Steffi Graf. f, Michael Jordan. g, Karch Kiraly. h, "Magic" Johnson. i, Ingolf Wiegert.

No. 3086, $50: a, Volleyball. b, Basketball. c, Tennis. d, Table tennis. e, Baseball. f, Handball. g, Field hockey. h, Water polo. i, Soccer.

No. 3087, $50, vert.: a, Cycling. b, Hurdles. c, High jump. d, Diving. e, Weight lifting. f,

Canoeing. g, Wrestling. h, Gymnastics. i, Running.

No. 3088, $300, Carl Lewis, track and field gold medalist. No. 3089, $300, US defeats Korea for gold medal in baseball, 1988.

**1996, July 25**
3079-3082   A249   Set of 4           4.00 4.00
**Sheets of 9, #a-i**
3083-3087   A249   Set of 5         27.50 27.50
**Souvenir Sheets**
3088-3089   A249   Set of 2           8.00 8.00

Olymphilex '96 (No. 3088).

Disney Cartoons — A250

No. 3090 — Mickey outdoors: a, Mickey's Bait Shop. b, Ol' Mickey, The Lumbercamp Legend and Pluto the Yellow Dog. c, For All Men Are Equal Before Fish.

No. 3091, vert. — Super sports: a, BMX Championships. b, Goofy, Hockey Superstar. c, Malibu Surf City.

No. 3092, vert. — Nautical Mickey: a, The Path to Adventure is Shown in the Stars. b, Captain Mickey's Steamship School. c, Ahoy, Follow the Wind on Waves of Fortune.

No. 3093, $250, M. Mouse, ESQ, Lawman, vert.: No. 3094, $250, All Aboard, Ride the Great American Transcontinental Railroad. No. 3095, $250, Mouse and Pinkerton, Wild West Detective Agency, vert.

$300, Donald's Rock & Ice Mountaineers. $325, Guided by The Great Spirit, vert.

**1996, July 26    Perf. 14x13½, 13½x14**
3090   A250   $60 Strip of 3,
                        #a.-c.              3.50   3.50
3091   A250   $80 Strip of 3,
                        #a.-c.              5.00   5.00
3092   A250   $100 Strip of 3,
                        #a.-c.              7.50   7.50
**Souvenir Sheets**
3093-3095   A250   Set of 3         20.00 20.00
3096   A250   $300 multi             6.50   6.50
3097   A250   $325 multi             7.00   7.00

Nos. 3090-3092 were issued in sheets of 9 stamps.

Disney Antique Toys — A251

No. 3098: a, Two-Gun Mickey. b, Wood-jointed Mickey doll. c, Donald Jack-in-the-Box. d, Rocking Minnie. e, Fireman Donald Duck. f, Long-billed Donald Duck. g, Painted wood Mickey doll. h, Wind-up Jiminy Cricket.

No. 3099, $300, Mickey doll. No. 3100, $300, Carousel train.

**1996, July 26          Perf. 13½x14**
3098   A251   $6 Sheet of 8, #a.-
                        h.                  6.00   6.00
**Souvenir Sheets**
3099-3100   A251   Set of 2         14.00 14.00

Elvis Presley's First "Hit" Year, 40th Anniv. — A252

Various portraits.

**1996, Sept. 8    Litho.    Perf. 13½x14**
3101   A252   $100 Sheet of 6,
                        #a.-f.              9.00   9.00

Domestic Cats — A253

No. 3102, $60: a, Birman. b, American curl. c, Turkish Angora. d, European shorthair. e, Persian. f, Scottish fold. g, Sphynx. h, Malayan. i, Cornish rex.

No. 3103, $60, vert: a, Norwegian forest. b, Russian shorthair. c, European shorthair. d, Birman. e, Ragdoll. f, Egyptian mau. g, Persian. h, Angora. i, Siamese.

No. 3104, $300, Maine coon, vert. No. 3105, $300, Himalayan.

**1996, Sept. 18**      *Perf. 14*
**Sheets of 9, #a-i**
3102-3103 A253 Set of 2   15.00 15.00
**Souvenir Sheets**
3104-3105 A253 Set of 2   9.00 9.00

**Souvenir Sheet**

Mars Meteorite ALH84001 — A253a

**1996, Oct. 7 Litho.**   *Perf. 14½x14¼*
3105A A253a $50 multi    —   —

Deep Ocean Exploration A254

No. 3106: a, Goblin shark, coelacanth. b, Remote operated vehicle, JASON. c, Deep water invertebrates. d, Submarine NR1 (e). e, Giant squid (b, c, f, g, h, j, m). f, Sperm whale (b, c). g, Volcanic vents, submersible ALVIN. h, Air-recycling pressure suit, shipwreck. i, Bacteria survey, submersible SHINKAI 6500. j, Giant tube worms. k, Anglerfish. l, Six-gill shark (k). m. Autonomous underwater vehicle ABE. n, Viperfish. o, Swallower, hatchetfish. $300, Sea anemone.

**1996, Dec. 2 Litho.**   *Perf. 14*
3106 A254 $30 Sheet of 15,   6.50 6.50
#a.-o.
**Souvenir Sheet**
3107 A254 $300 multicolored   4.00 4.00

Characters from Disney's Snow White in Christmas Scenes — A255

Designs: $6, Snow White. $20, Doc. $25, Dopey, Sneezy. $30, Sleepy, Happy, Bashful. $35, Dopey, Santa. $60, Dopey, fireplace. $100, Dopey, Grumpy. $200, Dopey as Santa.
No. 3116, $300, Snow White looking at squirrel in box. No. 3117, $300, Dopey placing star on tree.

**1996, Dec. 16**     *Perf. 13½x14*
3108-3115 A255 Set of 8   14.00 14.00
**Souvenir Sheets**
3116-3117 A255 Set of 2   18.00 18.00

Marine Life — A256

No. 3118: a, Red gorgonians. b, Plexaura homomalla, butterflyfish (a, c). c, Dendronephtbya. d, Common clownfish, anemone, mushroom coral (a). e, Anemone, horse-eyed jack (d, g-h). f, Slender snappers (c), splendid coral trout. g, Anemones. h, Brain coral, Indo-Pacific hard coral. i, Cup coral (f, h).

**1996, Dec. 2 Litho.**   *Perf. 14*
3118 A256 $60 Sheet of 9,   9.00 9.00
#a.-i.

New Year 1997 (Year of the Ox) — A257

No. 3119 — Denomination at: a, $20, LR. b, $30, LL. c, $35, UR. d, $50, UL.
No. 3120: a, Like #3119a. b, Like #3119b. c, Like #3119c.
$150, Ox, facing.

**1997, Jan. 2 Litho.**   *Perf. 14½*
3119 A257 Block of 4, #a.-d.   3.00 3.00
3120 A257 $50 Sheet of 4, #a.-   4.00 4.00
c. + #3119d
**Souvenir Sheet**
3121 A257 $150 multicolored   3.00 3.00
No. 3119 was issued in sheets of 16 stamps.

Mickey and Friends Celebrate Chinese Lunar New Year — A258

No. 3122: a, $6, Mickey. b, $20, Home visit. c, $25, Fortune lantern. d, $30, Silhouette. e, $35, Flower market. f, $60, Harmonious man, woman.
No. 3123: a, Red-pocket money. b, Lion dance. c, Calligraphy. d, Surplus every year. e, Fireworks. f, Ox.
$150, Mickey marching, vert. $200, Mickey, ox.

**1997, Jan. 2**     *Perf. 14x13½*
3122 A258 Sheet of 6, #a.-f.   4.00 4.00
3123 A258 $30 Sheet of 6, #a.-   4.50 4.50
f.
**Souvenir Sheets**
*Perf. 13½x14, 14x13½*
3124 A258 $150 multicolored   4.00 4.00
3125 A258 $200 multicolored   4.50 4.50

Marine Life — A259

No. 3126, $6, Angelfish. No. 3127, $6, Hyed snapper. $20, Box fish. $25, Golden damselfish. $35, Clown triggerfish. $200, Harlequin tuskfish.
$300, Caribbean flower coral.

**1996**      **Litho.**   *Perf. 14*
3126-3131 A259 Set of 6   6.00 6.00
**Souvenir Sheet**
3132 A259 $300 multicolored   5.00 5.00

Hotel Tower, 50th Anniv. A260

**1996, Dec. 28**
3133 A260 $30 multicolored   .50 .50
For surcharge, see No. 4180.

Souvenir Sheet

The Summer Palace, Beijing — A261

**1996, Apr. 12 Litho.**   *Perf. 13*
3134 A261 $60 multicolored   2.00 2.00
China '96. No. 3134 was not available until March 1997.

Transfer of Hong Kong A262

No. 3135, $80: a, Tortoise. b, Dragon. c, Unicorn. d, Phoenix.
No. 3136, $80, vert.: a, Swallow & willow. b, Kingfisher & chrysanthemum. c, Crane & pine. d, Peacock & peony.
No. 3137, $80, vert.: a-d, Various kites.
No. 3138, vert.: a-b, Paintings of mountains and lakes.

**1997, Feb. 12**     *Perf. 14*
**Sheets of 4 , #a-d**
3135-3137 A262 Set of 3   15.00 15.00
3138 A262 $200 Sheet of 2,   6.00 6.00
#a.-b.
Hong Kong '97. No. 3138 contains two 70x44mm stamps.

Motion Pictures, Cent. — A263

No. 3139 — Movie star, World War II films: a, Burgess Meredith, "The Story of GI Joe." b, M.E. Clifton-James, "I Was Monty's Double." c, Audie Murphy, "To Hell and Back." d, Gary Cooper, "The Story of Dr. Wassell." e, James Mason, "The Desert Fox." f, Manart Kippen, "Mission to Moscow." g, Robert Taylor, "Above and Beyond." h, James Cagney, "The Gallant Hours." i, John Garfield, "Pride of the Marines."
$300, George C. Scott, "Patton," horiz.

**1997, Feb. 21**     *Perf. 13½x14*
3139 A263 $50 Sheet of 9,   10.00 10.00
#a.-i.
**Souvenir Sheet**
*Perf. 14x13½*
3140 A263 $300 multicolored   5.00 5.00

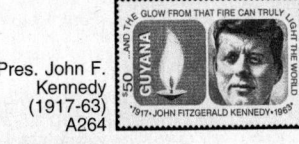

Pres. John F. Kennedy (1917-63) A264

**1997, Mar. 14 Litho.**   *Perf. 14*
3141 A264 $50 blue   1.00 1.00

George Washington A265

Designs from works of art: No. 3142: a, Washington in battle. b, Washington taking oath. c, Washington Seated in Armchair, from engraving after Chappel. d, Col. Washington of Virginia Militia, by Charles W. Peale. e,

George Washington, by Rembrandt Peale. f, Washington Addressing Constitutional Convention, by Junius Brutus Stearns. g, Washington on His Way to the Continental Congress. h, Washington on a White Charger, by John Faed. i, Washington as a Surveyor, from an engraving by G.R. Hall after Darley's drawing. j, Bas-relief of Washington Praying at Valley Forge. k, Death of Gen. Mercer at Battle of Princeton, by John Trumbull. l, Washington Taking Command of the Continental Army at Cambridge. m, George Washington, by Gilbert Stuart.

No. 3143: a, Washington Before the Battle of Trenton, by John Trumbull. b, Washington, His Family at Mt. Vernon, by Alonzo Chappel. c, Inauguration of Washington in New York City, by Chappel. d, Washington, by Adolph Ulrich Wertmuller. e, Washington Accepts His Commission as Commander-in-Chief, June 1775, Currier & Ives lithograph. f, Washington from a mezzotint by Sartain. g, On the Lawn at Mt. Vernon after the War. h, Washington Conversing with a Farmhand During the Baling Season with Nelly and Washington Custus Playing Nearby, from anonymous print after Junius Brutus Stearns. i, Nellie Custis' Wedding on Washington's Last Birthday, by Ogden. j, Washington Crossing the Delaware, by Leutze. k, Washington Receives Orders from Mortally Wounded Gen. Braddock at 1755 Battle of Monongahela. l, Washington Birthplace (supposed) on the Potomac, Currier & Ives lithograph. m, Washington at Yorktown, by James Peale.

**1997, Mar. 14 Litho.**   *Perf. 14*
3142    Sheet of 13   12.50 12.50
  a.-l. A265 $60 any single    .75 .75
  m. A265 $300 imperf.   3.00 3.00
3143    Sheet of 13   12.50 12.50
  a.-l. A265 $60 any single    .75 .75
  m. A265 $300 imperf.   3.00 3.00
Nos. 3142m, 3143m are each 66x91mm and have simulated perforations.
No. 3142m exists perf. 14½.

Mushrooms — A266

Designs: $6, Morchella hortensis. $20, Boletus chyrsenteron. $25, Hygrophorus agathosmus. $30, Cortinarius violaceus. $35, Acanthocystis geogenius. $60, Mycena polygramma. $200, Hebeloma radicosum. $300, Coprinus comatus.
No. 3152, $80: a, Coprinus picaceus. b, Stropharia umbonatescens. c, Paxillus involutus. d, Amanita inaurata. e, Lepiota rhacodes. f, Russula amoena.
No. 3153, $80: a, Volvaria volvacea. b, Psalliota augusta. c, Tricholoma aurantium. d, Pholiota spectabilis. e, Cortinarius armillatus. f, Agrocybe dura.
No. 3154, $300, Pholiota mutabilis. No. 3155, $300, Amanita muscaria.

**1997, Apr. 2 Litho.**   *Perf. 14*
3144-3151 A266 Set of 8   10.50 10.50
**Sheets of 6, #a-f**
3152-3153 A266 Set of 2   16.00 16.00
**Souvenir Sheets**
3154-3155 A266 Set of 2   10.00 10.00

Flowers — A267

Designs: No. 3156, $6, Pineapple lily. No. 3157, $6, Blue columbine. $20, Petunia. $25, Lily of the Nile. $30, Bird of Paradise. $35, African daisy. $60, Cape daisy. $80, Gazania. $100, Cape water lily. $200, Insigne lady's slipper.
No. 3166: a, Monarch supperwart. b, Passion flower. c, Butterfly iris. d, Red-hot poker. e, Dir. G.T. Moore water lily. f, Superbissima painted tongue. g, Orchid. h, Annual chrysanthemum.
No. 3167: a, Tulips. b, Liatris. c, Roses. d, Gerber daisies. e, Sunflowers. f, Chrysanthemums.
No. 3168, Petunia.

**1997, Apr. 2**

| | | | | |
|---|---|---|---|---|
| 3156-3165 | A267 | Set of 10 | 12.00 | 12.00 |
| 3166 | A267 | $60 Sheet of 8, #a.-h. | 8.50 | 8.50 |
| 3167 | A267 | $80 Sheet of 6, #a.-f. | 8.50 | 8.50 |

**Souvenir Sheet**

| | | | | |
|---|---|---|---|---|
| 3168 | A267 | $300 multicolored | 5.00 | 5.00 |

Deng Xiaoping (1904-97) — A268

**1997, May 1**

| | | | | |
|---|---|---|---|---|
| 3169 | A268 | $100 shown | 1.75 | 1.75 |

**Souvenir Sheet**

| | | | | |
|---|---|---|---|---|
| 3170 | A268 | $150 Portrait, diff. | 2.75 | 2.75 |

No. 3169 was issued in sheets of 3.

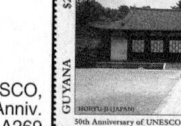

UNESCO, 50th Anniv. A269

Designs: $20, Horyu-Ji, Japan. $25, Scandola Nature Reserve, France. $30, Great Wall Defenses, China. $35, Wurzburg, Germany. $60, Monastery of Batalha, Portugal. $200, Dubrovnik, Croatia.

No. 3177, $60, vert. — Sites in Germany: a, Cathedral of Aquisgran, Aachen. b, Cathedral at Trier. c, Column of Augusta Treveror, Trier. d, f, Residences, Wurzburg. e, Church interior, Wurzburg. g, House of the River at Inselstadt, Bamberg. h, Cathedral interior, Speyer.

No. 3178, $60, Sites in Greece, vert: No. 3178: a, Monastery of Thessaloniki. b, d, e, Monastery at Mystras. c, Church of Santa Sofia, Thessaloniki. f, City, Thessaloniki. g, Painting, Mystras. h, Museum of Byzantine Art, Thessaloniki.

No. 3179, $60, vert.: a, Monastery of Poblet Catalonia, Spain. b, Old City of Salamanca, Spain. c, Toledo, Spain. d, Cathedral of Florence, Italy. e, Tower of Pisa, Italy. f, g, h, Convent of Christ, Tomar, Portugal.

No. 3180, $80 — Sites in Japan: a, d, e, Horyu-Ji. b, c, Kyoto.

No. 3181, $80 — Sites in the Americas: a, Cuzco, Peru. b, Potosi, Bolivia. c, Fortress, San Lorenzo, Panama. d, Sangay Natl. Park, Ecuador. e, Los Glaciares Natl. Park, Argentina.

No. 3182, $80 — Sites in US: a, Monticello. b, Yosemite Natl. Park. c, Yellowstone Natl. Park. d, Olympic Natl. Park. e, Everglades.

No. 3183, $300, Mount Taishan Shrine, China. No. 3184, $300, Monastery of Batalha, Portugal. No. 3185, $300, Bamberg Cathedral (detail), Germany. No. 3186, $300, Monastery, Mount Athos, Greece.

**1997, May 20**

| | | | | |
|---|---|---|---|---|
| 3171-3176 | A269 | Set of 6 | 9.00 | 9.00 |

**Sheets of 8, #a-h + Label**

| | | | | |
|---|---|---|---|---|
| 3177-3179 | A269 | Set of 3 | 22.50 | 22.50 |

**Sheets of 5**

| | | | | |
|---|---|---|---|---|
| 3180-3182 | A269 | Set of 3 | 17.50 | 17.50 |

**Souvenir Sheets**

| | | | | |
|---|---|---|---|---|
| 3183-3186 | A269 | Set of 4 | 18.50 | 18.50 |

Queen Elizabeth II, Prince Philip, 50th Wedding Anniv. — A270

No. 3187: a, Queen. b, Royal Arms. c, Wedding portrait. d, Queen, Prince. e, Broadlands House. f, Prince Philip. $300, Queen Elizabeth II.

**1997, May 20    Litho.    Perf. 14**

| | | | | |
|---|---|---|---|---|
| 3187 | A270 | $60 Sheet of 6, #a.-f. | 7.00 | 7.00 |

**Souvenir Sheet**

| | | | | |
|---|---|---|---|---|
| 3188 | A270 | $300 multicolored | 5.50 | 5.50 |

---

Paintings, by Hiroshige (1797-1858) A271

No. 3189: a, Oumayagashi. b, Ryogoku Ekoin & Moto-Yanagibashi Bridge. c, Pine of Success and Oumayagashi Asakusa River. d, Fireworks at Ryogoku. e, Dyers' Quarter, Kanda. f, Cotton-goods Lane, Odenma-cho. No. 3190, $300, Suruga-cho. No. 3191, $300, Yatsukoji, inside Sujikai Gate.

**1997, May 20    Perf. 13½x14**

| | | | | |
|---|---|---|---|---|
| 3189 | A271 | $80 Sheet of 6, #a.-f. | 6.75 | 6.75 |

**Souvenir Sheets**

| | | | | |
|---|---|---|---|---|
| 3190-3191 | A271 | Set of 2 | 10.00 | 10.00 |

Heinrich von Stephan (1831-97), Founder of UPU — A272

No. 3192: a, Frieze of Roman post service. b, UPU emblem. c, Cable car, Boston, 1907. $300, Von Stephan, Egyptian messenger.

**1997, May 20    Litho.    Perf. 14**

| | | | | |
|---|---|---|---|---|
| 3192 | A272 | $100 Sheet of 3, #a.-c. | 8.00 | 8.00 |

**Souvenir Sheet**

| | | | | |
|---|---|---|---|---|
| 3193 | A272 | $300 multicolored | 9.00 | 9.00 |

PACIFIC 97.

Paul P. Harris (1868-1947), Founder of Rotary, Intl. — A273

Designs: $200, Health, hunger and humanity, portrait of Harris. $300, Mutual respect among all faiths, races and cultures.

**1997, May 20**

| | | | | |
|---|---|---|---|---|
| 3194 | A273 | $200 multicolored | 2.75 | 2.75 |

**Souvenir Sheet**

| | | | | |
|---|---|---|---|---|
| 3195 | A273 | $300 multicolored | 4.25 | 4.25 |

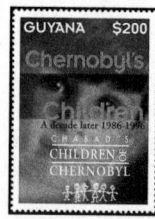

Chernobyl Disaster, 10th Anniv. — A274

Designs: No. 3196, Chabad's Children of Chernobyl. No. 3197, UNESCO.

**1997, May 20    Perf. 13½x14**

| | | | | |
|---|---|---|---|---|
| 3196 | A274 | $200 multicolored | 3.00 | 3.00 |
| 3197 | A274 | $200 multicolored | 3.00 | 3.00 |

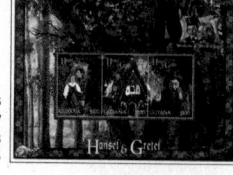

Grimm's Fairy Tales A275

---

Mother Goose A276

Scenes from "Hansel & Gretel:" No. 3198: a, Hansel & Gretel in forest. b, Gingerbread house. c, Wicked witch. $500, Witch trying to capture Gretel, horiz.
$300, Rooster from "Cock-A-Doodle-Doo."

**1997, May 20    Perf. 13½x14**

| | | | | |
|---|---|---|---|---|
| 3198 | A275 | $100 Sheet of 3, #a.-c. | 5.50 | 5.50 |

**Souvenir Sheets**

**Perf. 14, 14x13½**

| | | | | |
|---|---|---|---|---|
| 3199 | A276 | $300 multicolored | 5.00 | 5.00 |
| 3200 | A275 | $500 multicolored | 8.25 | 8.25 |

US Pres. Bill Clinton's Visit to Caribbean, May 1997 — A277

Designs: $30, Guyana Pres. Cheddi Jagan, Pres. Clinton, map of Caribbean, vert. $100, Clinton, Jagan, flags of US, Guyana, palm trees, beach.

**Perf. 13½x14, 14x13½**

**1997, June 23**

| | | | | |
|---|---|---|---|---|
| 3201 | A277 | $30 multicolored | .50 | .50 |
| 3202 | A277 | $100 multicolored | 1.50 | 1.50 |

Nos. 3201-3202 each issued in sheets of 9. See Nos. 3237-3238.

A278

1998 Winter Olympic Games, Nagano — A279

Medalists: $30, Georg Thoma. $35, Katja Seizinger. $60, Georg Hackl. $200, Katarina Witt.

No. 3207, $60: a, Gunda Niemann, 3000- & 5000-m speed skating, 1992. b, Tony Nash, Robin Dixon, 2-man bobsled, 1964. c, Switzerland 4-man bobsled, 1988. d, Piet Kleine, speed skating, 1976.

No. 3208, $60: a, Oksana Baiul, figure skating, 1994. b, Cathy Turner, 500-m short track speed skating, 1994. c, Brian Boitano, figure skating, 1988. d, Nancy Kerrigan, figure skating, 1994.

No. 3209: a, Markus Wasmeier. b, Jens Weissflog. c, Erhard Keller. d, Rosi Mittermaier. e, Gunda Niemann. f, Peter Angerer.

No. 3210, Swiss 4-Man bobsled team.
No. 3211, $300, Jean-Claude Killy, slalom, 1968. No. 3212, $300, Chen Lu, figure skating, 1992.

**1997, July 1    Perf. 14**

| | | | | |
|---|---|---|---|---|
| 3203-3206 | A278 | Set of 4 | 4.75 | 4.75 |

**Strips or Blocks of 4, #a-d**

| | | | | |
|---|---|---|---|---|
| 3207-3208 | A279 | Set of 2 | 12.00 | 12.00 |
| 3209 | A278 | $30 Sheet of 6, #a.-f. | 3.00 | 3.00 |

**Souvenir Sheets**

| | | | | |
|---|---|---|---|---|
| 3210 | A278 | $300 multicolored | 6.00 | 6.00 |
| 3211-3212 | A279 | Set of 2 | 12.00 | 12.00 |

Nos. 3207-3208 issued in sheets of 8 stamps.

---

Return of Hong Kong to China — A280

**Litho. & Embossed**

**1997, July 1    Perf. 14**

| | | | | |
|---|---|---|---|---|
| 3213 | A280 | $500 gold & multi | 7.50 | 7.50 |

Domestic Cats — A281

Designs, vert.: $30, Norwegian forest cat. $35, Oriental spotted tabby. $200, Asian smoke.

No. 3217: a, Abyssinian. b, Chocolate colorpoint shorthair. c, Silver tabby. d, Persian. e, Maine coon cat & kitten. f, Brown shaded Burmese. g, Persian kitten. h, Siamese. i, British shorthair.
$300, Manx, vert.

**1997, July 29**

| | | | | |
|---|---|---|---|---|
| 3214-3216 | A281 | Set of 3 | 4.25 | 4.25 |
| 3217 | A281 | $60 Sheet of 9, #a.-i. | 8.50 | 8.50 |

**Souvenir Sheet**

| | | | | |
|---|---|---|---|---|
| 3218 | A281 | $300 multi | 5.50 | 5.50 |

Birds — A282

Designs: $25, Verdin. $30, Wood thrush, vert. $60, Rofous-sided towhee. $200, Pygmy nuthatch, vert.

No. 3223, $80: a, Groove-billed ani. b, Green honeycreeper. c, Toucanet. d, Wire-tailed manakin. f, Hoatzin. f, Tiger heron.

No. 3224, $80 — Hummingbirds: a, Magenta-throated woodstar. b, Long-tailed hermit. c, Red-footed plumeleteer. d, Anna's. e, White-tipped sicklebill. f, Fiery-throated.

No. 3225, $300, Pinnated bittern. No. 3226, $300, Keel-billed toucan.

**1997, Aug. 12    Litho.    Perf. 14**

| | | | | |
|---|---|---|---|---|
| 3219-3222 | A282 | Set of 4 | 6.00 | 6.00 |

**Sheets of 6, #a-f**

| | | | | |
|---|---|---|---|---|
| 3223-3224 | A282 | Set of 2 | 16.00 | 16.00 |

**Souvenir Sheets**

| | | | | |
|---|---|---|---|---|
| 3225-3226 | A282 | Set of 2 | 12.00 | 12.00 |

Dogs — A283

Designs: $20, Chihuahua. $25, Norfolk terrier. $60, Welsh terrier.

No. 3230: a, Shar-pei. b, Chihuahua. c, Chow chow. d, Sealyham terrier. e, Collie. f, German shorthair pointer. g, Bulldog. h, German shepherd. i, Old English sheepdog.
$300, Tibetan spaniel.

**1997, July 29    Litho.    Perf. 14**

| | | | | |
|---|---|---|---|---|
| 3227-3229 | A283 | Set of 3 | 3.75 | 3.75 |
| 3230 | A283 | $60 Sheet of 9, #a.-i. | 8.50 | 8.50 |

**Souvenir Sheet**

| | | | | |
|---|---|---|---|---|
| 3231 | A283 | $300 multicolored | 5.50 | 5.50 |

Pres. Cheddi Jagan's 1st Election to Parliament, 50th Anniv. — A284

## 1997, Oct. 6 — Litho. — Perf. 14
| | | | | |
|---|---|---|---|---|
| 3232 | A284 | $6 green & multi | .25 | .25 |
| 3233 | A284 | $30 pale yellow & multi | 4.25 | 4.25 |

Nos. 3232-3233 each issued in sheets of 9.

Diana, Princess of Wales (1961-97) — A285

No. 3234: a-f, Various portraits.
No. 3235, $300, Wearing red dress. No. 3236, $300, With longer hair.

## 1997, Oct. 15
| | | | | |
|---|---|---|---|---|
| 3234 | A285 | $80 Sheet of 6, #a.-f. | 8.25 | 8.25 |

### Souvenir Sheets
#### Perf. 14½
| | | | | |
|---|---|---|---|---|
| 3235-3236 | A285 | Set of 2 | 10.00 | 10.00 |

Nos. 3235-3236 each contain one 34x52mm stamp.

### US Pres. Bill Clinton's Visit Type of 1997

Designs: $6, Like #3201. No. 3238, Clinton, Jagan, flags, sun on horizon.

#### Perf. 13½x14, 14x13½
## 1997, Nov. 10
| | | | | |
|---|---|---|---|---|
| 3237 | A277 | $6 multi | .25 | .25 |
| 3238 | A277 | $30 multi | .50 | .50 |

Nos. 3237-3238 each issued in sheets of 9. For surcharge, see No. 4115.

### Souvenir Sheets

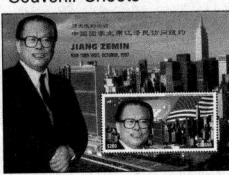

Chinese Pres. Jiang Zemin's Visit to New York A286

Pres. Zemin, New York skyline, and: $200, Flags of China, UN, US. $300, Flags of China, US.

## 1997, Nov. 10 — Perf. 14
| | | | | |
|---|---|---|---|---|
| 3239 | A286 | $200 multicolored | 3.00 | 3.00 |
| 3240 | A286 | $300 multicolored | 4.50 | 4.50 |

Buildings in Guyana A287

## 1997, Dec. 8 — Litho. — Perf. 14
| | | | | |
|---|---|---|---|---|
| 3241 | A287 | $6 W. Fogarty #1 | .25 | .25 |
| 3242 | A287 | $30 Public building | .60 | .60 |

Christmas — A288

Entire paintings, details, or sculptures: $25, $30, Diff. angels from The Triumph of Galatea, by Raphael. $35, Primavera, by Botticelli. $60, Angel Musicians, by Agostino di Duccio, (bas relief). $100, From cover of Life Magazine, #1212, 1906. $200, Madonna and Saints, by Rosso Fiorentino.
No. 3249, $300, The Gardens of Love, by Rubens. No. 3250, $300, Cherubs, by Philippe de Champaigne.

## 1997, Dec. 8
| | | | | |
|---|---|---|---|---|
| 3243-3248 | A288 | Set of 6 | 7.50 | 7.50 |

### Souvenir Sheets
| | | | | |
|---|---|---|---|---|
| 3249-3250 | A288 | Set of 2 | 12.00 | 12.00 |

Historical Events — A289

Designs: No. 3251, $60, Explorers discover tomb of Tutankhamun, 1922. No. 3252, $60, Lincoln Memorial dedicated, Washington, DC, 1922. No. 3253, $60, Alexander Graham Bell dies, 1922. No. 3254, $60, Calvin Coolidge becomes President, 1923. No. 3255, $60, John L. Baird develops 1st experimental television, 1923. No. 3256, $60, Warren G. Harding dies, 1923. No. 3257, $60, First Winter Olympic Games, Chamonix, France, 1924. No. 3258, $60, Tennessee bans teaching of evolution in schools, 1925. No. 3259, $60, Chinese leader Sun Yat-Sen dies, 1925. No. 3260, $60, Robert Goddard launches 1st liquid fuel rocket, 1926. No. 3261, $60, Richard E. Byrd is 1st to fly over North Pole, 1926. No. 3262, $60, Sesquicentennial Exposition, Philadelphia, 1926.

## 1997, Dec. 8
| | | | | |
|---|---|---|---|---|
| 3251-3262 | A289 | Set of 12 | 12.50 | 12.50 |

New Year 1998 (Year of the Tiger) — A290

No. 3263 — Various stylized tigers with denomination in: a, LR. b, LL. c, UR. d, UL. $150, Tiger, red background.

## 1998, Jan. 5 — Litho. — Perf. 14½
| | | | | |
|---|---|---|---|---|
| 3263 | A290 | $50 Sheet of 4, #a.-d. | 5.00 | 5.00 |

### Souvenir Sheet
| | | | | |
|---|---|---|---|---|
| 3264 | A290 | $150 multicolored | 4.25 | 4.25 |

Prehistoric Wildlife — A291

Designs: $25, Kentrosaurus. $30, Lesothosaurus. $35, Stegoceras. $60, Lagosuchus. $100, Herrerasaurus. $200, Iguanodon.
No. 3271, $55: a, Quetzalcoatlus (d). b, Pteranodon (a, c). c, Peteinosaurus. d, Criorhychus (g). e, Pterodaustro. f, Eudimorphodon. g, Archeopteryx. h, Dimorphodon. i, Sharovipteryx.
No. 3272, $55: a, Ceresiosaurus. b, Nothosaurus. c, Rhomaleosaurus. d, Grendelius. e, Mixosaurus. f, Mesosaurus. g, Placodus. h, Stethacanthus. i, Coelacanth.
No. 3273, $300, Styracosaurus, vert. No. 3274, $300, Yangchuanosaurus, vert.

## 1998, Feb. 23 — Litho. — Perf. 14
| | | | | |
|---|---|---|---|---|
| 3265-3270 | A291 | Set of 6 | 7.00 | 7.00 |

### Sheets of 9, #a-i
| | | | | |
|---|---|---|---|---|
| 3271-3272 | A291 | Set of 2 | 16.00 | 16.00 |

### Souvenir Sheets
| | | | | |
|---|---|---|---|---|
| 3273-3274 | A291 | Set of 2 | 8.50 | 8.50 |

1998 World Cup Soccer Championships, France — A292

Group A: No. 3275, $30, Brazil. No. 3276, $30, Morocco. No. 3277, $30, Norway. No. 3278, $30, Scotland.
Group B: No. 3279, $30, Austria. No. 3280, $30, Cameroun. No. 3281, $30, Chile. No. 3282, $30, Italy.

Group C: No. 3283, $30, Denmark. No. 3284, $30, France. No. 3285, $30, Saudi Arabia. No. 3286, $30, South Africa.
Group D: No. 3287, $30, Bulgaria. No. 3288, $30, Nigeria. No. 3289, $30, Paraguay. No. 3290, $30, Spain.
Group E: No. 3291, $30, Belgium. No. 3292, $30, Holland. No. 3293, $30, S. Korea. No. 3294, $30, Mexico.
Group F: No. 3295, $30, Germany. No. 3296, $30, Iran. No. 3297, $30, US. No. 3298, $30, Yugoslavia.
Group G: No. 3299, $30, Colombia. No. 3300, $30, England. No. 3301, $30, Romania. No. 3302, $30, Tunisia.
Group H: No. 3303, $30, Argentina. No. 3304, $30, Croatia. No. 3305, $30, Jamaica. No. 3306, $30, Japan.
Japanese players, vert.: No. 3306A, $300, Okada. No. 3306B, $300, Nakata.

## 1998, Apr. 8 — Litho. — Perf. 14x13½
| | | | | |
|---|---|---|---|---|
| 3275-3306 | A292 | Set of 32 | 14.00 | 14.00 |

#### Perf. 13½x14
### Souvenir Sheets
| | | | | |
|---|---|---|---|---|
| 3306A-3306B | A292 | Set of 2 | 8.50 | 8.50 |

Nos. 3275-3306 were each issued in sheets of 8 + 1 label.
For overprints see Nos. 3317-3324.

The Titanic — A293

No. 3307: a, J. Bruce Ismay, managing director, White Star Line. b, Jack Phillips, radio operator. c, Margaret "Unsinkable Molly" Brown, passenger. d, Capt. Edward J. Smith. e, Frederick Fleet, lookout. f, Thomas Andrews, managing director of Harland and Wolff.
$300, Titanic sinking.

## 1998, June 17 — Litho. — Perf. 14
| | | | | |
|---|---|---|---|---|
| 3307 | A293 | $80 Sheet of 6, #a.-f. | 6.75 | 6.75 |

### Souvenir Sheet
| | | | | |
|---|---|---|---|---|
| 3308 | A293 | $300 multicolored | 4.25 | 4.25 |

Sailing Ships — A294

No. 3309, $80: a, Viking double-ended ship, 14th cent. b, Portuguese caravel. c, "Nina." d, Fannie, 1896. e, "Victoria," 1519. f, Arab sambook.
No. 3310, $80: a, "Dutch Fluyt." b, "Alastor." c, "Falcon." d, "Red Rover." e, "British Anglesey." f, "Archibald Russel."
No. 3311, $300, Oseberg ship. No. 3312, $300, "Half Moon," 1609.

## 1998, June 17 — Litho. — Perf. 14
### Sheets of 6, #a-f
| | | | | |
|---|---|---|---|---|
| 3309-3310 | A294 | Set of 2 | 13.50 | 13.50 |

### Souvenir Sheets
| | | | | |
|---|---|---|---|---|
| 3311-3312 | A294 | Set of 2 | 8.50 | 8.50 |

Diana, Princess of Wales (1961-97) — A295

Designs: No. 3313, $1500, Diana in black and brown fur trimmed hat and coat. No. 3314, $1500, Diana wearing suit and hat.

### Litho. & Embossed
## 1998, Aug. 3 — Die Cut 7½
| | | | | |
|---|---|---|---|---|
| 3313-3314 | A295 | $1500 Set of 2 | 150.00 | |

Queen Mother — A296

## 1998, Aug. 4 — Perf. 13½
| | | | | |
|---|---|---|---|---|
| 3315 | A296 | $90 multicolored | 1.40 | 1.40 |

CARICOM, 25th Anniv. — A297

## 1998, July 4 — Litho. — Perf. 13½
| | | | | |
|---|---|---|---|---|
| 3316 | A297 | $20 multicolored | .40 | .40 |

### Nos. 3275, 3282-3286, 3289, 3304 Ovptd. "FRANCE WINNERS" in Gold

## 1998, Aug. 20 — Litho. — Perf. 14x13½
| | | | | |
|---|---|---|---|---|
| 3317 | A292 | $30 on #3275 | .45 | .45 |
| 3318 | A292 | $30 on #3282 | .45 | .45 |
| 3319 | A292 | $30 on #3283 | .45 | .45 |
| 3320 | A292 | $30 on #3284 | .45 | .45 |
| 3321 | A292 | $30 on #3285 | .45 | .45 |
| 3322 | A292 | $30 on #3286 | .45 | .45 |
| 3323 | A292 | $30 on #3289 | .45 | .45 |
| 3324 | A292 | $30 on #3304 | .45 | .45 |
| | | Nos. 3317-3324 (8) | 3.60 | 3.60 |

Nos. 3317-3324 were each issued in sheets of 8+label. Each sheet contains additional overprints in sheet margins.

National Hockey League Players — A298

No. 3325: a, Bryan Berard. b, Ray Bourque. c, Martin Brodeur. d, Pavel Bure. e, Chris Chelios. f, Sergei Fedorov. g, Peter Forsberg. h, Wayne Gretzky. i, Dominik Hasek. j, Brett Hull. k, Jarome Iginla. l, Jaromir Jagr. m, Paul Kariya. n, Saku Koivu. o, John LeClair. p, Brian Leetch. q, Eric Lindros. r, Patrick Marleau. s, Mark Messier. t, Mike Modano. u, Chris Osgood. v, Zigmund Palffy. w, Felix Potvin. x, Jeremy Roenick. y, Patrick Roy. z, Joe Sakic. aa, Sergei Samsonov. ab, Teemu Selanne. ac, Brendan Shanahan. ad, Ryan Smyth. ae, Jocelyn Thibault. af, Joe Thornton. ag, Keith Tkachuk. ah, John Vanbiesbrouck. ai, Steve Yzerman. aj, Dainius Zubrus.

## 1998, Apr. 1 — Litho. — Perf. 13½
| | | | | |
|---|---|---|---|---|
| 3325 | A298 | $35 Sheet of 36, #a.-aj. | 18.00 | 18.00 |

Aircraft — A299

No. 3326, $80 — Military aircraft: a, A7K Corsair II. b, A6E Intruder. c, U2 Spy plane. d, Blackhawk. e, F-16. f, Phantom II.
No. 3327, $80 — Pioneers of aviation: a, Wright Brothers, 1903. b, Bleriot, 1911. c, Curtiss Jenny, 1919. d, Airship Schwaben, 1911. e, W-8B, 1923. f, DH-66, 1926.
No. 3328, $300, A-10 Warthog. No. 3329, $300HH-65A Dolphin.

## 1998, Sept. 28 — Perf. 14
### Sheets of 6, #a-f
| | | | | |
|---|---|---|---|---|
| 3326-3327 | A299 | Set of 2 | 13.50 | 13.50 |

### Souvenir Sheets
| | | | | |
|---|---|---|---|---|
| 3328-3329 | A299 | Set of 2 | 8.50 | 8.50 |

Endangered Species — A300

Nos. 3330, $80, 3332, $300, Various pictures of the giant panda.
Nos. 3331, $80, 3333, $300, Various pictures of the mountain gorilla.

| **1998, Oct. 8** | | **Sheets of 6, a-f** | |
| 3330-3331 | A300 | Set of 2 | 17.00 17.00 |
| **Souvenir Sheets** | | | |
| 3332-3333 | A300 | Set of 2 | 18.00 18.00 |

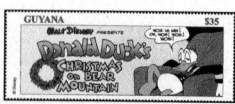

Donald Duck Adventures, Christmas on Bear Mountain — A301

No. 3334 — Cartoon panels: a, 1-8. b, 9-16. c, 17-24. d, 25-32. e, 33-40. f, 41-48. g, 49-56. h, 57-64. i, 65-72. j, 73-80. k, Pane of 2, Carl Barks, vert., bears and duck.

| **1998, Oct. 15** | **Perf. 14x13½, 13½x14** | | |
| 3334 | Complete booklet | | 45.00 45.00 |
| a.-j. | A301 $35 Any pane of 4 | | 2.75 2.75 |
| k. | A301 $300 Pane of 2 | | 10.00 10.00 |

Disney's Uncle Scrooge, by Carl Barks, 50th anniv.

Organization of American States, 50th Anniv. — A302

| **1998, Oct. 29** | | **Perf. 14** | |
| 3335 | A302 $40 multicolored | | .55 .55 |

Ferrari Automobiles — A302a

No. 3335A: c, 212 Export. d, 410 Superamerica chassis. e, 125 S. $300, 512 S Racer.

| **1998, Oct. 29** | **Litho.** | **Perf. 14** | |
| 3335A | A302a $100 Sheet of 3, #c-e | | 5.00 5.00 |
| **Souvenir Sheet** | | | |
| 3335B | A302a $300 multi | | 5.00 5.00 |

No. 3335A contains three 39x25mm stamps.

Diana, Princess of Wales (1961-97) — A303

No. 3336: a, Inscription panel at left. b, Panel at right.

| **1998, Oct. 29** | | | |
| 3336 | A303 $60 Horiz. pair, #a-b | | 2.00 2.00 |

---

**Self-Adhesive**
*Serpentine Die Cut Perf. 11½*
**Sheet of 1**
**Size: 53x65mm**

| 3336A | A303 $300 Diana, buildings, bridge | 65.00 |

No. 3336 was issued in sheets of 3 pairs. Soaking in water may affect the multi-layer image of No. 3336A.
Issued: $60, 10/29; $300, 11/5/98.

Grand Prix Champion Racing Cars and Drivers — A304

No. 3337, $80: a, 1914 Grand Prix Mercedes, Christian Lautenschlager. b, 1930 Bugati Type 35B, P. Etancelin. c, 1934 Alfa Romeo P3, Louis Chiron. d, 1938 Mercedes Benz W154, Richard Seaman. e, 1938 Auto Union D Type, Tazio Nuvolari. f, 1951 Alfa Romeo 158, Juan Manuel Fangio.
No. 3338, $80: a, 1955 Mercedes Benz W196, Stirling Moss. b, 1960 Ferrari Dino 246, Phil Hill. c, 1966 Brabham-Repco BT19, Jack Brabham. d, 1970 Lotus Ford 72, John Miles. e, 1983 Renault RE40, Alain Prost. f, 1998 McLaren Mercedes MP4/13, David Coulthard.
No. 3339, $300, 1906 Grand Prix Renault, Ferenc Szisz. No. 3340, $300, 1956 Maserati 250F, Stirling Moss.

| **1998, Oct. 29** | | **Sheets of 6, #a-f** | |
| 3337-3338 | A304 | Set of 2 | 13.50 13.50 |
| **Souvenir Sheets** | | | |
| 3339-3340 | A304 | Set of 2 | 8.50 8.50 |

Nos. 3339-3340 contain one 57x42mm stamp.

Tigger's Happy New Year A304a

No. 3340A, vert. — Tigger: d, Giving gift to Winnie the Pooh. e, With fireworks. f, Giving flowers to Kanga. g, With Piglet. h, At door. i, With Eeyore.
No. 3340B, $300, Tigger beating drum. No. 3340C, $300, Tigger carrying staff for dragon.

| **1998, Oct. 29** | **Litho.** | **Perf. 13¼** | |
| 3340A | A304a $60 Sheet of 6, #d-i | | 5.75 5.75 |
| **Souvenir Sheets** | | | |
| 3340B-3340C | A304a | Set of 2 | 8.50 8.50 |

Gandhi — A305

No. 3341: a, Age 37, 1906. b, Age 77, 1946. c, Age 78, 1948. d, Age 77, 1947. $300, Age 76, 1946, horiz.

| **1998, Oct. 29** | | | |
| 3341 | A305 $100 Sheet of 4, #a-d | | 5.50 5.50 |
| **Souvenir Sheet** | | | |
| 3342 | A305 $300 multicolored | | 4.25 4.25 |

No. 3341b-3341c are each 53x38mm.

Pablo Picasso — A306

Paintings, details: $25, Sleeping Peasants, 1919. $60, Large Nude in Red Armchair, 1929, vert. $200, Sculpture, "Female Head," 1931, vert.
$300, Man and Woman, 1971, vert.

---

| **1998, Oct. 29** | | **Perf. 14½** | |
| 3343-3345 | A306 | Set of 3 | 4.00 4.00 |
| **Souvenir Sheet** | | | |
| 3346 | A306 $300 multicolored | | 4.50 4.50 |

Royal Air Force, 80th Anniv. — A307

No. 3347, $100: a, Avro Lancaster B2. b, PBY-5A Catalina Amphibian. c, BAe Hawk TIA trainers (Red Arrows). d, Avro Lancaster, DeHavilland Mosquito.
No. 3348, $100: a, BAe Hawk TIA. b, C130 Hercules. c, Panavia Tornado GRI. d, BAe Hawk 200.
No. 3349 $150: a, BAe Nimrod RIP. b, Panavia Tornado F3 ADV. c, CH-47 Chinook helicopter. d, Panavia Tornado GRIA.
No. 3350, $200, Biplane, hawks in flight. No. 3351, $200, Eurofighter, Spitfire. No. 3352, $300, Eurofighters. No. 3353, $300, Head of hawk, hawk spreading wings, biplane. No. 3354, $300, Tiger Moth, Eurofighter. No. 3355, $300, Hawk spreading wings, biplane.

| **1998, Oct. 29** | | **Perf. 14** | |
| **Sheets of 4, #a.-d.** | | | |
| 3347-3349 | A307 | Set of 3 | 20.00 20.00 |
| **Souvenir Sheets** | | | |
| 3350-3355 | A307 | Set of 6 | 22.50 22.50 |

1998 World Scout Jamboree, Chile — A308

No. 3356: a, James E. West, 1st scout executive with early Eagle Scouts. b, Pres. Kennedy greets Explorers, 51st Scouts anniv., 1961. c, Astronaut Walter Schirra receives a special merit badge, 1962.

| **1998, Oct. 29** | **Litho.** | **Perf. 14** | |
| 3356 | A308 $160 Sheet of 3, #a.-c. | | 7.00 7.00 |

Paintings by Eugene Delacroix (1798-1863) — A309

No. 3357, $60: a, The Sultan of Morocco Receives the Count de Mornay. b, Armed Indian with a Gurkha Scimitar. c, Portrait presumed to be of the Singer Baroihet in Turkish Dress. d, Moroccan Notebook: Studies of Jewish Women. e, Arab Horseman Giving a Signal. f, Arab Cavalry Practicing a Charge. g, A Seated Moor. h, Jewish Woman in Traditional Dress.
No. 3358, $60: a, Corner of the Studio; the Stove. b, Room in the Apartment the Count de Mornay. c, Hamlet and Horatio in the Graveyard. d, George Sand. e, The Bride of Abydos. f, Elysian Fields. g, A Lioness Standing by a Tree. h, Monsieur Alfred Bruyas.
No. 3359, $300, Moroccan Jewish Wedding, horiz. No. 3360, $300, Death of Sardanapulus, horiz.

| **1998, Oct. 29** | | **Sheets of 8, #a.-h.** | |
| 3357-3358 | A309 | Set of 2 | 13.50 13.50 |
| **Souvenir Sheets** | | | |
| 3359-3360 | A309 | Set of 2 | 8.50 8.50 |

Ferry and Flag of Guyana — A309a

| **1998, Oct. 31** | **Litho.** | **Perf. 13¼x13¾** | |
| **Color of Ferry** | | | |
| 3360A | A309a $20 blue | | — — |
| 3360B | A309a $30 sepia | | — — |

See Surinam Nos. 1148-1149.
For surcharge, see No. 4127.

---

St. Andrew's Church, Georgetown, 180th Anniv. — A310

Various views of front of church: $6, $30, $60.

| **1998** | **Litho.** | **Perf. 14** | |
| 3361-3363 | A310 | Set of 3 | 1.25 1.25 |

New Year 1999 (Year of the Rabbit) — A311

No. 3364 — Various stylized rabbits with denomination at: a, LR. b, LL. c, UR. d, UL. $150, Red background, Chinese inscription.

| **1999, Jan. 4** | **Litho.** | **Perf. 14½** | |
| 3364 | A311 $50 Sheet of 4, #a.-d. | | 3.00 3.00 |
| **Souvenir Sheet** | | | |
| 3365 | A311 $150 multicolored | | 2.25 2.25 |

Disney Characters in Sporting Activities — A312

No. 3366, $80 — Skateboarding: a, Huey. b, Mickey. c, Dewey. d, Louie. e, Goofy. f, Donald.
No. 3367, $80 — Rollerblading: a, Minnie. b, Goofy. c, Daisy. d, Baby Duck. e, Donald. f, Mickey.
No. 3368, $80 — Skateboarding, rollerblading, red, white & blue background: a, Baby Duck. b, Daisy. c, Mickey. d, Goofy. e, Dewey. f, Donald.
No. 3369, $300, Dewey. No. 3370, $300, Daisy. No. 3371, $300, Goofy, horiz.

| **Perf. 13½x14, 14X13½** | | | |
| **1999, Mar. 1** | | **Litho.** | |
| **Sheets of 6, #a-f** | | | |
| 3366-3368 | A312 | Set of 3 | 25.00 25.00 |
| **Souvenir Sheets** | | | |
| 3369-3371 | A312 | Set of 3 | 18.50 18.50 |

Mickey Mouse, 70th anniv.

Disney Characters in Trains — A313

No. 3372, $100 — 101 Dalmatians Express: a, Locomotive. b, Flatcar. c, Car with pillars. d, "Basket" car. e, Caboose.
No. 3373, $100 — Robin Hood Train: a, Engine. b, Marian, Robin Hood. c, Royal coach. d, Flatcar. e, Caboose.
No. 3374, $100 — Snow White, Diamond Mine Railroad: a, Engine. b, Flatcar. c, Snow White, Prince Charming. d, Passenger car. e, Pump car.
No. 3375, $100 — Little Mermaid Railroad: a, Engine. b, Fish holding pearls. c, Little Mermaid. d, Various marine life in car. e, "Bah Hum Bug!"
No. 3376, a, Dwarf from Diamond Mine Railroad driving locomotive. b, Dwarf on pump car. No. 3377, $300, Bandits, Cruela De Vil. No. 3378, $300, Robin Hood, Bear. No. 3379, $300, Little Mermaid kissing Prince under mistletoe. No. 3380, $300, Little Mermaid holding starfish.

| **1999, Mar. 1** | | **Perf. 13½x14** | |
| **Sheets of 5, #a-e** | | | |
| 3372-3375 | A313 | Set of 4 | 36.00 36.00 |

**3376** A313 $200 Sheet of 2,
#a.-b.     9.00   9.00

**Souvenir Sheets**

**3377-3380** A313 Set of 4   22.00 22.00

Caribbean Butterflies — A314

No. 3381, $80: a, Scarce Bamboo Page. b, Spicebush swallowtail. c, Isabella. d, The mosaic. e, Gulf fritillary. f, Figure-of-eight.

No. 3382, $80: a, Hewitson's blue hair-streak. b, Polydamas swallowtail. c, Common morpho. d, Blue-green reflector. e, Malachite. f, Grecian shoemaker.

No. 3383, $300, Giant swallowtail, vert. No. 3384, $300, Pipevine swallowtail, vert.

**1999, Mar. 15**     *Perf. 14*

**Sheets of 6, #a-f**

**3381-3382** A314 Set of 2   14.50 14.50

**Souvenir Sheets**

**3383-3384** A314 Set of 2   9.00 9.00

Flowers — A315

No. 3385, $60: a, Geranium. b, Oncidium macranthum. c, Bepi orchidglades. d, Sun-flowers (2). e, Cattleya walkeriana. f, Cattleya frasquita. g, Helianthus maximilani (one). h, Paphiopedilum insigne sanderae, lily. i, Lily (2).

No. 3386, $60: a, Dendrobium nobile. b, Phalaenopsis schilleriana. c, Cymbidium alex-ette. d, Rhododendron. e, Phragmipedium besseae, laelia cinnabarina. f, Masdevallia veitchiana. g, Calochortus nuttallii. h, Brasso-laeliocattleya pure gold. i, Laelia cinnabarina.

No. 3387: a, Leptotes bicolor, masdevallia ignea. b, Sophrolaeliocattleya, anguloa clowesii. c, Laelia pumila. d, Masdevallia ignea. e, Dendrobium phalaenopsis. f, Anguloa clowesii.

No. 3388, $300, Asocentrum miniatum, vert. No. 3389, $300, Iris pseudacorus.

**1999, Mar. 15**   **Litho.**   *Perf. 14*

**Sheets of 9, #a-i**

**3385-3386** A315 Set of 2   16.00 16.00
**3387** A315 $90 Sheet of 6,
#a.-i.     7.50 7.50

**Souvenir Sheet**

**3388-3389** A315 Set of 2   8.50 8.50

Akira Kurosawa (1910-98), Film Director — A316

No. 3390 — Films, vert.: a, "The Dream." b, "Rashomon." c, "Kagemusha." d, "Red Beard." e, "Seven Samurai." f, "Yojimbo."

No. 3391 — Portraits: a, Pointing. b, Hand on face. c, Standing. d, With camerman. $300, Scene from "Dreams."

**1999, Mar. 22**

**3390** A316 $80 Sheet of 6, #a.-
f.     6.75 6.75
**3391** A316 $130 Sheet of 4, #a.-
d.     7.25 7.25

**Souvenir Sheet**

**3392** A316 $300 multicolored   4.25 4.25

Mushrooms — A317

Designs: $25, Coprinus atramentarius. $35, Hebeloma crustuliniforme. $100, Russula nigricans. $200, Tricholoma aurantium.

No. 3397, $60: a, Boletus aereus. b, Coprinus comatus. c, Inocybe godeyi. d, Morchella crassipes. e, Lepiota acutes-quamosa. f, Amanita phalloides. g, Boletus spadiceus. h, Cortinarius collinitus. i, Lepiota procera.

No. 3398, $60: a, Russula ochroleuca. b, Hygrophorus hypotheius. c, Amanita rubescens. d, Boletus satanas. e, Amanita echinocephala. f, Amanita muscaria. g, Bole-tus badius. h, Hebeloma radicosum. i, Mycena polygramma.

No. 3399, $300, Lepiota acutequamoso. No. 3400, $300, Pluteus cervinus.

**1999, May 6**   **Litho.**   *Perf. 14*

**3393-3396** A317 Set of 4   4.25 4.25

**Sheets of 9, #a-i**

*Perf. 14½*

**3397-3398** A317 Set of 2   16.50 16.50

**Souvenir Sheet**

**3399-3400** A317 Set of 2   9.00 9.00

Nos. 3397-3398 each contain nine 32x41mm stamps. Nos. 3399-3400 each con-tain one 32x41mm stamp.

Trains A318

No. 3401, $80: a, Burlington Northern GP 39-2, 1974. b, CSX GP40-2, 1967. c, Erie Lackawana Railroad GP 9, 1956. d, Amtrak P 42 Genesis, 1993. e, Erie Railroad S-2, 1948. f, Pennsylvania Railroad S-1, 1947.

No. 3402, $80: a, Northern and Western #610, c. 1933. b, Pennsylvania Railroad M1B Mountain, 1930. c, Reading Railroad FP7A, 1951. d, New York Central 2-8-4, c. 1940. e, Union Pacific Challenger Big Boy, 1963. f, GP 15-15-1, 1956.

No. 3403, $80: a, Shinkansen Bullet 100 series, 1984, Japan. b, Ukranian Diesel ZMGR, 1983, Russia. c, Rhatische Bahn GE 6/6 II, Germany. d, Eurostar TGV, 1986, France. e, Atlantique TGV, 1989, France. f, Class 86-6, UK.

No. 3404, $80: a, Joseph Clark 0-4-0, 1868. b, Diamond Stack Bethel 4-4-0, 1863. c, New York Central #999, 1890. d, Boston & Maine Ballardville 0-4-0, 1876. e, Atlantic 4-4-0 Port-land Rochester Railroad, 1863. f, America 4-4-0 Baltimore & Ohio Railroad, 1881.

Railroad pioneers: No. 3405, $300, George Stephen, vert. No. 3406, $300, Alfred de Glehn, vert. No. 3407, $300, George Nagelmackers, vert. No. 3408, $300, R.F. Trevithick, vert.

**1999, May 10**     *Perf. 14*

**Sheets of 6, #a.-f.**

**3401-3404** A318 Set of 4   29.00 29.00

**Souvenir Sheets**

**3405-3408** A318 Set of 4   17.00 17.00

Australia '99 World Stamp Expo.

Wedding of Prince Edward and Sophie Rhys-Jones — A319

Various portraits: No. 3409, $150, deep magenta sheet margin. No. 3411, $300, mauve sheet margin. Nos. 3410, $150, 3412, $300, yellow brown sheet margin.

**1999, June 19**   **Litho.**   *Perf. 14¼*

**Sheets of 4, #a.-d.**

**3409-3410** A319 Set of 2   17.00 17.00

**Souvenir Sheets**

**3411-3412** A319 Set of 2   8.50 8.50

Nos. 3411-3412 are horiz.

Johann Wolfgang von Goethe (1749-1832), Poet — A320

No. 3413: a, Lynceus sings from the watch-tower. b, Portaits of Von Goethe and Friedrich von Schiller (1759-1805), poet. c, The fallen Icarus.

$300, Mephistopheles appears as salaman-der, vert.

**1999, June 22**   **Litho.**   *Perf. 14*

**3413** A320 $150 Sheet of 3, #a.-
c.     6.25 6.25

**Souvenir Sheet**

**3414** A320 $300 multicolored   4.25 4.25

IBRA '99, World Philatelic Exhibition, Nuremberg — A321

Designs: $60, Class E10 Bo-bo electric locomotive, BMW offices, Munich, 1952, vert. $200, Class 01, 4-6-2 steam express train, 1926.

**1999, June 22**

**3415** A321 $60 multicolored     .90 .90
**3416** A321 $200 multicolored   2.75 2.75

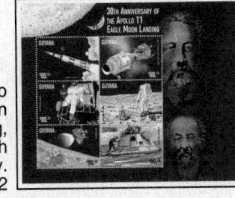

Apollo 11 Moon Landing, 30th Anniv. A322

No. 3417, $80: a, Blast off. b, Command Module docked with Lunar Lander. c, First man on moon. d, Seismic experiments pack-age. e, Back to the orbiter. f, Astronauts being picked up.

No. 3418, $80, vert: a, Sputnik, 1959, Kon-stantin Tsiolkovsky. b, Apollo 11 liftoff. c, On the moon. d, Collecting samples of lunar rocks. e, Apollo 11 Lunar Module. f, Splashdown.

No. 3419, $300, Salute to the flag. No. 3420, $300, Michael Collins.

**1999, June 22**     **Sheets of 6, #a-f**

**3417-3418** A322 Set of 2   13.00 13.00

**Souvenir Sheet**

**3419-3420** A322 Set of 2   8.50 8.50

PhilexFrance '99, World Philatelic Exhibition — A323

Designs: No. 3421, $300, Co-Co 7000 Class High Speed 1949-55. No. 3422, $300, 241-P Class 4-8-2 Express 1947-49.

**1999, June 22**

**3421-3422** A323 Set of 2   9.00 9.00

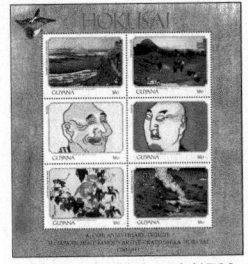

Paintings by Hokusai (1760-1849) — A324

No. 3423, $80: a, Travelers Climbing a Mountain Path. b, Washing in a River. c, The Blind (eyes & mouth open). d, The Blind (eyes & mouth shut). e, Convolvulus and Tree-Frog. f, Fishermen Hauling a Net.

No. 3424, $80: a, Hibiscus and Sparrow. b, Hydrangea and Swallow. c, The Blind (eyes shut, mouth open). d, The Blind (eyes open, mouth shut). e, Irises. f, Lilies.

No. 3425, $300, Flowering Cherries at Mount Yoshino, vert. No. 3426, $300, A View of a Stone Causeway, vert.

**1999, June 22**   **Litho.**   *Perf. 14x13¾*

**Sheets of 6, #a-f**

**3423-3424** A324 Set of 2   13.50 13.50

**Souvenir Sheets**

*Perf. 13¾x14*

**3425-3426** A324 Set of 2   8.50 8.50

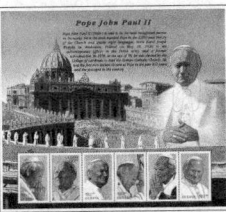

Pope John Paul II A325

**1999, June 22**     *Perf. 14*

**3427** A325 $80 Sheet of 6, #a.-f. 7.50 7.50

John Glenn's Return to Space — A326

No. 3428: a, In space suit, 1962. b, After landing, 1962. c, As Senator. d, With helmet, 1998. e, Without helmet, 1998.

**1999, June 22**     *Perf. 14½x14¼*

**3428** A326 $100 Sheet of 5, #a.-
e.     7.00 7.00

Parrots and Parakeets — A327

No. 3429, $60: a, Hyacinth macaw. b, Blue and gold macaw. c, Blue-fronted Amazon parrot. d, Amazon parrot. e, Sun Conure. f, Tivi parakeet. g, Bavaria's conure. h, Fairy lorikeet.

No. 3430, $60: a, Marron macaw. b, Thick-billed parrot. c, Golden-crowned canure. d, Yellow-naped macaw. e, Double yellow-headed parrot. f, Golden-fronted parakeet. g, Maroon-billed conure. h, Nandaya conure.

No. 3431, $300, Jendaya conure, horiz. No. 3432, $300, Gray-cheeked parakeet.

**1999, Aug. 3**      **Perf. 14**
**Sheets of 8, #a.-h.**
3429-3430 A327 Set of 2    14.00 14.00
**Souvenir Sheets**
3431-3432 A327 Set of 2    8.50 8.50

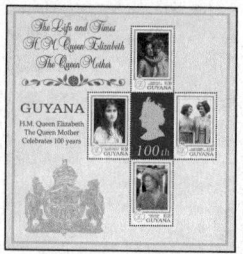

Queen Mother, 100th Birthday (in 2000) A328

No. 3433: a, Duchess of York, Princess Elizabeth, 1928. b, Lady Elizabeth Bowles-Lyon, 1914. c, Queen Elizabeth, Princess Elizabeth, 1940. d, Queen Mother, Venice, 1984. $400, Queen Mother, Canada, 1988.

**1999, Aug. 4**      **Gold Frames**
3433 A328 $130 Sheet of 4, #a.-
   d. + label    8.00 8.00
**Souvenir Sheet**
**Perf. 13¾**
3434 A328 $400 multicolored    5.50 5.50
No. 3434 contains one 38x50mm stamp. Margins of sheets are embossed. See Nos. 3689-3690.

China Soccer League Superstars — A329

Nos. 3435a-3435g, 3436a-3436g, Various players. Nos. 3435h, 3436h, League emblem.

**1999, Aug. 16**      **Perf. 14½x14¼**
3435 A329 $50 Sheet of 8, #a.-h. 5.25 5.25
3436 A329 $60 Sheet of 8, #a.-h. 6.25 6.25

Rights of the Child — A330

No. 3437: a, Denomination at LL, flag at UR. b, Denomination at UL, flag at LL. c, Denomination at UL, flag at UR. $300, Prince Talal.

**1999, June 22**    **Litho.**    **Perf. 14**
3437 A330 $150 Sheet of 3, #a.-
   c.    5.50 5.50
**Souvenir Sheet**
3438 A330 $300 multicolored    4.00 4.00

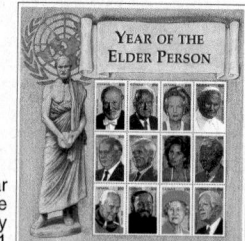

Intl. Year of the Elderly A331

No. 3439: a, Kurt Masur. b, Rupert Murdoch. c, Margaret Thatcher. d, Pope John Paul II. e, Mikhail Gorbachev. f, Ted Turner. g, Sophia Loren. h, Nelson Mandela. i, John Glenn. j, Luciano Pavarotti. k, Queen Mother. l, Jimmy Carter.

No. 3440 — Ronald Reagan: a, As young man. b, In uniform. c, Feeding chimp. d, With campaign poster. e, With cowboy hat. f, With wine glass.

$300, Reagan in star.

**1999, June 22**    **Litho.**    **Perf. 14**
3439 A331 $50 Sheet of 12,
   #a.-l.    8.50 8.50
3440 A331 $100 Sheet of 6, #a.-
   f.    7.00 7.00
**Souvenir Sheet**
3441 A331 $300 multicolored    3.50 3.50
**Souvenir Sheet**

Mei Lan Fang, Chinese Actor A332

**1999, Aug. 16**    **Litho.**    **Perf. 13¾**
3442 A332 $400 multicolored    4.50 4.50

First Balloon Flight Around the World — A333

No. 3443: a, Orbiter 3. b, Emblem. c, Bertrand Piccard. d, Brian Jones. $300, Orbiter 3, flight path.

**1999, Aug. 16**    **Litho.**    **Perf. 14**
3443 A333 $150 Sheet of 4, #a.-
   d.    7.25 7.25
**Souvenir Sheet**
3444 A333 $300 multicolored    4.00 4.00

The Kennedy Family — A334

No. 3445: a, Jacqueline and John, Jr. b, John and John, Jr. c, John and Jacqueline. d, Jacqueline. e, John, Jr. and Caroline. f, John. No. 3445G: h, John, Jr. as adult and child. i, John, Jr. and Jacqueline. j, John Jr.

**1999, Oct. 4**    **Litho.**    **Perf. 13¾**
3445 A334 $80 Sheet of 6,
   #a.-f.    6.25 6.25
3445G A334 $160 Sheet of 3,
   #h.-j.    5.75 5.75

 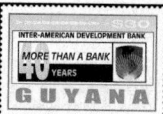

Inter-American Development Bank, 40th Anniv. — A335

**1999, Nov. 15**    **Litho.**    **Perf. 14**
3446 A335 $30 multicolored    .40 .40

Ferrari Automobiles A336

Designs: $30, 312 T2. $35, 553 F.1. $60, D 50. $200, 246 F.1. $300, 126/C2. $400, 312/B2.

**1999**    **Litho.**    **Perf. 14**
3447-3452 A336 Set of 6    11.50 11.50

Sidney Sheldon, Novelist — A337

**1999**    **Litho.**    **Perf. 14**
3453 A337 $80 multicolored    1.00 1.00
   Issued in sheets of 4.

A338

No. 3454: a, During World War II. b, Wedding photo. c, As child. d, At coronation of George VI. e, In 1971. f, In 1991. g, in 1914. h, In 1988. i, At Royal Agricultural show. j, On 60th birthday.
$1,000, Portrait.

**1999**    **Litho.**    **Perf. 12**
3454 A338 $60 Sheet of 10,
   #a.-j.    8.75 8.75
**Imperf**
**Size: 51x76mm**
3455 A338 $1000 multicolored 12.00 12.00
Sheets of No. 3454 exist with black border in margin with text "In Memoriam/1900-2002."

Queen Mother (b. 1900) — A339

**Litho. & Embossed**
**1999, Aug. 4**    **Die Cut Perf. 8¾**
3456 A339 $1500 gold & multi    35.00

Millennium — A340

No. 3457, Founding of first university, 1088.
No. 3458 — Highlights of the 11th Century: a, Anasazi trade center. b, "Black Virgin." c, Seljuk warrior. d, Appearance of Halley's Comet. e, Battle of Hastings. f, William of Normandy crowned King of England. g, Power of the Fujiwara is checked. h, Holy Roman Emperor Henry IV. i, Muslims build Timbuktu. j, Like No. 3457. k, Gondolas come into use in Venice. l, El Cid. m, First crusade. n, Crusaders capture Jerusalem. o, Chinese statue of Guanyin. p, Rubaiyat of Omar Khayyam (60x40mm). q, Syrian storage jar.

No. 3459 — Highlights of the 1910s: a, Manet and Post-impressionists show, Grafton Gallery, London. b, Standard Oil loses Supreme Court antitrust suit. c, Harriet Quimby, 1st female pilot in US d, US enters World War I. e, Titanic sinks. f, Pu Yi resigns as Chinese Emperor. g, Grand Central Station built in NYC. h, Assassination of Archduke Francis Ferdinand. i, Panama Canal opens. j, Lawrence of Arabia. k, Easter Uprising, Ireland. l, 1917 Russian Revolution. m, Execution of the Romanovs. n, Treaty of Versailles ends World War I. o, Influenza epidemic. p, Leo Tolstoy & Mark Twain die (60x40mm). q, Bauhaus opens, Weimar, Germany.

**1999, Dec. 20**    **Litho.**    **Perf. 13¼x13**
3457 A340 $35 multi    .50 .50
**Perf. 12¾x12½**
3458 A340 $35 Sheet of 17,
   #a.-q.    7.50 7.50
3459 A340 $35 Sheet of 17,
   #a.-q., + label    7.50 7.50

Flowers A341

No. 3460: Various flowers making up a photomosaic of Princess Diana.
No. 3461: Various details of paper money of the world making up a photomosaic of George Washington's portrait on $1 bill.

## 1999-2000 Litho. Perf. 13¾

3460 A341 $80 Sheet of 8,
    #a.-h.     12.00 12.00
3461 A341 $80 Sheet of 8,
    #a.-h.     10.00 10.00

Issued: No. 3460, 12/31; No. 3461, 3/27/00.
See Nos. 3568-3569.

New
Year
2000
(Year of
the
Dragon)
A342

No. 3462 — Dragons with denomination in:
a, LR. b, LL. c, UR, d, UL.
$300, LR.

## 2000, Feb. 5 Perf. 14¾

3462 A342 $100 Sheet of 4,
    #a.-d.     5.00 5.00

### Souvenir Sheet

3463 A342 $300 multi     3.50 3.50

Automobiles — A344

No. 3464, $100: a, Nicholas Cugnot's
steam-powered Fardier, 1769. b, Siegfried
Marcus's motor carriage, 1875. c, Karl Benz's
Velo, 1894. d, Virgilio Bordino's steam carriage, 1854. e, 1886 Benz. f, 1908 Ford Model
T.
No. 3465, $100: a,1926 Duesenberg Model
A Phaeton. b, 1927 Mercedes-Benz Model K.
c, 1928, Rolls-Royce Phantom I limousine. d,
1935 Auburn 851 Speedster. e, 1936 Merce-
des-Benz 540K Cabriolet B. f, 1949, Volkswagen Cabriolet Beetle.
No. 3466, $100: a, 1957 Ford Thunderbird.
b, 1957 Jaguar XK150. c, 1968 Chevrolet Cor-
vette Stingray. d, 1973 BMW 2002 Turbo. e,
1975 Porsche 911 Turbo. f, 1999 Volkswagen
Beetle.
No. 3467, $100: a, 1886 Daimler motor car.
b, 1898 Opel Luzman. c, 1899 Benz Landaulet
coupe. d, 1892 Peugeot Vis-a-vis. e, 1886
Benz. f, 1894 Benz Velo, diff.
No. 3468, $100: a, 1896 Ford. b, 1903 De
Dion-Bouton Populare. c, 1900 Adler. d, 1904
Vauxhall. e, 1908 Rolls-Royce Silver Ghost. f,
1908 Ford Model T, diff.
No. 3469, $400, 1904 Mercedes-Benz
60/70. No. 3470, $400, 1939 Mercedes-Benz
Type 320 Cabriolet. No. 3471, $400, 1954
Mercedes-Benz 300SL Gullwing.
No. 3472, $400, 1904 Turner-Miesse. No.
3473, $400, 1910 Runabout.

## 2000, Mar. 13 Litho. Perf. 13½

### Sheets of 6, #a.-f.

3464-3466 A343   Set of 3    22.00 22.00

### Perf. 14

3467-3468 A344   Set of 2    14.00 14.00

### Souvenir Sheets
#### Perf. 14½

3469-3471 A343   Set of 3    13.50 13.50

#### Perf. 14¼

3472-3473 A344   Set of 2     9.00 9.00

Size of stamps from Nos. 3463-3466,
41x25mm; from Nos. 3467-3468, 42x28mm.

---

No. 1341
Surcharged in Red

## 2000 ? Litho. Unwmk. Perf. 14

3473A A92 $6 on 25c #1341    —

Marine
Life — A345

Designs: $30, Lachnolaimus maximus. $35,
Cyphoma gibbosum. $60, Trachinotus fal-
catus. $100, Bodianus pulchellus. $200,
Anisotremus virginicus. $300, Etheostoma
spectabile.
No. 3480, $80: a, Hypoplectrus indigo. b,
Chlamys hastata. c, Sebastes rubrivinctus. d,
Selene vomer. e, Marginella carnea. f, Phoca
vitulina. g, Coryphaena hippurus. h, Epinephe-
lus fulvus.
No. 3481, $80: a, Sphyraena barracuda. b,
Saccopharynx sp. c, Chromodoris amoena. d,
Makaira nigricans. e, Orcinus orca. f, Hippo-
campus reidi. g, Chelonia mydas. h,
Emblemaria pandionis.
No. 3482, $80, vert.: a, Pterois volitans. b,
Tursiops truncatus. c, Diplulmaris antarctica.
d, Pomacanthus arcuatus. e, Aetobatus
narinari. f, Carcharhinus amblyrhynchos. g,
Sacura margaritacea. h, Octopus dolfeini.
No. 3483, $400, Asteroschema tenue, vert.
No. 3484, $400, Apodichthys flavidus, vert.
No. 3485, $400, Periclimenes pedersoni.

## 2000, May 15 Perf. 14

3474-3479 A345   Set of 6    8.50 8.50

### Sheets of 8, #a.-h.

3480-3482 A345   Set of 3    25.00 25.00

### Souvenir Sheets

3483-3485 A345   Set of 3    14.00 14.00

No. 3485 contains one 57x42mm stamp.

### Souvenir Sheet

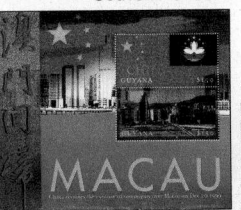

1999
Return of
Macao to
People's
Republic
of China
A346

No. 3486: a, Flag. b, Skyline.

## 2000, May 15

3486 A346 $150 Sheet of 2, #a.-
    b.     3.75 3.75

100th Test Match at
Lord's Ground — A347

Designs: $100, Rohan Kanhai. $300, Clive
Lloyd.
$400, Lord's Ground, horiz.

## 2000, May 15 Litho. Perf. 14

3487-3488 A347   Set of 2    5.00 5.00

### Souvenir Sheet

3489 A347 $400 multi     5.25 5.25

---

HRH Prince William · 18th Birthday, 21st June 2000

Prince
William,
18th
Birthday
A348

No. 3490: a, With Prince Harry. b, Wearing
sweater. c, In profile. d, In suit.
$400, In ski wear.

## 2000, May 15 Perf. 14

3490 A348 $100 Sheet of 4, #a-d   5.50 5.50

### Souvenir Sheet
#### Perf. 13¾

3491 A348 $400 multi     5.25 5.25

No. 3490 contains four 28x42mm stamps. It
exists imperf.

First
Zeppelin
Flight,
Cent.
A349

No. 3492 — Ferdinand von Zeppelin and: a,
LZ-1. b, LZ-2. c, LZ-9.
$400, LZ-127.

## 2000, May 15 Perf. 14

3492 A349 $200 Sheet of 3, #a-c 7.25 7.25

### Souvenir Sheet

3493 A349 $400 multi     4.75 4.75

No. 3492 contains three 40x24mm stamps.

Berlin
Film
Festival,
50th
Anniv.
A350

No. 3494: a, Das Boot Ist Voll. b, David. c,
Hong Gao Liang (Red Sorghum). d, Die Ehe
der Maria Braun. e, Edith Evans. f, Michel
Simon.
$400, Love Streams.

## 2000, May 15

3494 A350 $100 Sheet of 6, #a-f 7.00 7.00

### Souvenir Sheet

3495 A350 $400 multi     4.50 4.50

Apollo-Soyuz Mission, 25th
Anniv. — A351

---

No. 3496: a, Vance D. Brand, Thomas P.
Stafford. b, Apollo 18, docking adapter. c, Stafford, Valeri Kubasov.
$400, Stafford, Donald K. Slayton.

## 2000, May 15

3496 A351 $200 Sheet of 3, #a-c 7.25 7.25

### Souvenir Sheet

3497 A351 $400 multi     4.50 4.50

### Souvenir Sheets

2000 Summer Olympics,
Sydney — A352

No. 3498: a, Henry Robert Pearce. b, Volleyball. c, Olympic Park, Montreal, and Canadian flag. d, Ancient Greek runners.

## 2000, May 15

3498 A352 $160 Sheet of 4, #a-d 7.50 7.50

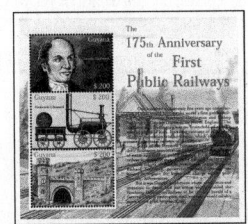

Public Railways, 175th Anniv. — A353

No. 3499: a, Timothy Hackworth. b, Sans
Pareil. c, Branhope Tunnel.

## 2000, May 15

3499 A353 $200 Sheet of 3, #a-c 7.00 7.00

Johann Sebastian Bach (1685-
1750) — A354

## 2000, May 15

3500 A354 $400 multi     4.75 4.75

### Souvenir Sheet

Albert Einstein (1879-1955) — A355

## 2000, May 15 Litho. Perf. 14¼

3501 A355 $400 multi     5.00 5.00

Space
A356

No. 3502, $100: a, Amsat IIIc. b, SRET. c, Inspector. d, Stardust. e, Temisat. f, Arsene.
No. 3503, $100, horiz.: a, Sun and Echo satellite (inscribed Apollo 11). b, Saturn, and Pioneer. c, Moon and Apollo 11 (inscribed Echo satellite). d, Mars and Mars Explorer. e, Space Shuttle, Intl. Space Station. f, Halley's Comet and Giotto.
No. 3504, $100, horiz.: a, Cesar, Argentine, Spanish flags. b, Sirio 2, Italian flag. c, Taos S.80, French flag. d, Viking, Swedish flag. e, SCD 1, Brazilian flag. f, Offeq 1, Israeli flag.
No. 3505, $400, Clementine. No. 3506, $400, Solar Max, horiz.

**2000, May 15    Litho.    Perf. 14**
**Sheets of 6, #a-f**
3502-3504  A356  Set of 3    22.00 22.00
**Souvenir Sheets**
3505-3506  A356  Set of 2    9.25 9.25
World Stamp Expo 2000, Anaheim.

The Three Stooges
A357

No. 3507: a, Shemp, Moe, Larry, man with glasses. b, Skeleton, Larry, Moe. c, Shemp. d, Stooges with fingers in mouths. e, Stooges reading book. f, Stooges attacking man. g, Stooges with candle. h, Stooges, man, fire bucket. i, Moe, Shemp, man in window.
No. 3508, $400, Moe in doorway. No. 3509, $400, Larry, skeleton.

**2000, July 27    Perf. 13¾**
3507  A357  $80 Sheet of 9, #a-i    8.75 8.75
**Souvenir Sheets**
3508-3509  A357  Set of 2    9.00 9.00
See Nos. 3542-3544.

Betty Boop
A358

No. 3510: a, In striped blouse. b, With shopping bags. c, On cushion. d, As belly dancer. e, In red lingerie. f, In cutoff shorts. g, With musical notes. h, In flowered pants. i, In black dress.
No. 3511, $400, In fur coat. No. 3512, $400, In polka dot bathing suit, with flamingos.

**2000, July 27    Perf. 13¾**
3510  A358  $80 Sheet of 9, #a-i    9.00 9.00
**Souvenir Sheets**
3511-3512  A358  Set of 2    9.00 9.00
See Nos. 3545-3552.

Third Annual Caribbean Media Conference — A359

**2000, Aug. 14    Perf. 14**
3513  A359  $100 multi    1.25 1.25

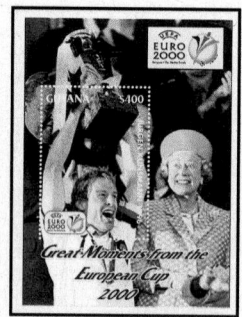

European Soccer Championships — A360

No. 3514, $80, horiz.: a, Denmark. b, Germany. c, Italy. d, Netherlands. e, Portugal. f, Romania. g, Czech Republic. h, Norway.
No. 3515, $80, horiz.: a, Turkey. b, Slovenia. c, Yugoslavia. d, Sweden. e, Belgium. f, Spain. g, France. h, England.
No. 3516, $400, Jurgen Klinsmann. No. 3517, $400, Stefan Kuntz.

**2000, Aug. 21    Perf. 13¾**
**Sheets of 8, #a-h, + label**
3514-3515  A360  Set of 2    16.00 16.00
**Souvenir Sheets**
3516-3517  A360  Set of 2    9.50 9.50

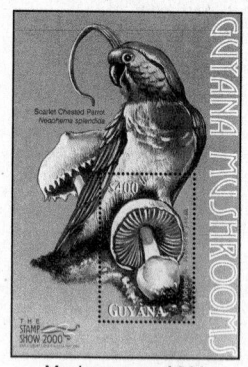

Mushrooms — A361

No. 3518, $100, horiz.: a, Sealy vase chanterelle. b, Caesar's mushroom. c, Greenheaded jelly club. d, Salmon unicorn entoloma. e, White oysterette. f, Variable cort.
No. 3519, $100, horiz.: a, Coccora. b, Winter polypore. c, Turpentine waxy cap. d, Aeryginosa. e, Fly agaric. f, Honey mushroom.
No. 3520, $100, horiz: a, Salmon waxy cap. b, Shellfish-scented russula. c, Scarlet waxy cap. d, Stuntz's blue legs. e, Netted rhodotus. f, Indigo milky.
No. 3521, $400, Tiny volvariella. No. 3522, $400, Turkey tail, horiz. No. 3523, $400, Pinwheel marasmius, horiz.

**2000, Oct. 4    Perf. 14**
**Sheets of 6, #a-f**
3518-3520  A361  Set of 3    22.50 22.50
**Souvenir Sheets**
3521-3523  A361  Set of 3    14.00 14.00
The Stamp Show 2000, London.

A362

Flowers — A363

Designs: No. 3524, $35, Bougainvillea spectabilis. No. 3525, $60, Euphorbia milii. No. 3526, $200, Catharanthus roseus. No. 3527, $300, Ipomoea carnea.
No. 3528, $35, Russelia equisetiformis. No. 3529, $60, Sprekelia formosissima. No. 3530, $200, Passiflora quadrangularis. No. 3531, $300, Mirabilis jalapa.
No. 3532, $100: a, Lantana camara. b, Jatropha integerrima. c, Plumeria alba. d, Strelitzia reginae. e, Clerodendrum splendens. f, Thunbergia grandiflora.
No. 3533, $100, vert.: a, Cordia sebestena. b, Heliconia wagneriana. c, Dendrobium phalaenopsis. d, Passiflora caerulea. e, Oncidium nubigenum. f, Hibiscus rosasinensis.
No. 3534, $100: a, Ipomoea tricolor. b, Lantana camara (inscribed canara). c, Cantua buxifolia. d, Fuchsia. e, Eichornia crassipes. f, Cosmos sulphureus.
No. 3535, $100: a, Bignonia capreolata. b, Calceolaria herbeo-hybrida. c, Canna generalis. d, Bauhinia grandiflora. e, Amaranthus caudatus. f, Abutilon megapotamicum.
No. 3536, $400, Guzmania lingulata. No. 3537, $400, Cattleya granulosa, vert.
No. 3538, $400, Tacsonia van-volxemii. No. 3539, $400, Oeceoclades maculata.

**2000, Oct. 30    Perf. 14**
3524-3527  A362  Set of 4    6.75 6.75
3528-3531  A363  Set of 4    6.75 6.75
**Sheets of 6, #a-f**
3532-3533  A362  Set of 2    14.00 14.00
3534-3535  A363  Set of 2    14.00 14.00
**Souvenir Sheets**
3536-3537  A362  Set of 2    9.50 9.50
3538-3539  A363  Set of 2    9.50 9.50

A364

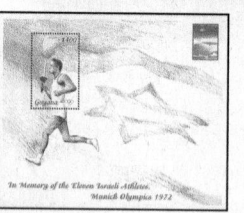

Munich Olympics Massacre — A364a

No. 3540: a, Yaakov Springer. b, Andrei Schpitzer. c, Amitsur Shapira. d, David Berger. e, Ze'ev Friedman. f, Joseph Gottfreund. g, Moshe Weinberg. h, Kahat Shor. i, Mark Slavin. j, Eliezer Halfin. k, Joseph Romano. l, Poster of Munich Olympics.

**2000, Oct. 30**
3540  A364  $40 Sheet of 12, #a-l    7.00 7.00
**Souvenir Sheet**
3541  A364a  $400 Torch bearer    5.50 5.50

**Three Stooges Type of 2000**
No. 3542: a, Moe with seltzer bottle, Shemp, Larry. b, As cave men trying to break rock. c, Moe with cow. d, Two women, Shemp, Moe. e, As cave men, seated. f, As cave men, Shemp holding large rock. g, Stooges wearing pith helmets. h, Stooges, picture frames. i, Stooges with fake beards.
No. 3543, $400, Larry, woman, vert. No. 3544, $400, Moe in plaid shirt, vert.

**2000, July 27    Litho.    Perf. 13¾**
3542  A357  $80 Sheet of 9, #a-i    8.75 8.75
**Souvenir Sheets**
3543-3544  A357  Set of 2    9.00 9.00

**Betty Boop Type of 2000**
**Souvenir Sheets**
No. 3545, At football field. No. 3546, With tennis racquet. No. 3547, With ankh earrings, winking. No. 3548, With red swimsuit. No. 3549, As portrait of queen. No. 3550, As Can-can girl. No. 3551, Standing on shell. No. 3552, As Mona Lisa, horiz.

**2000, July 27**
3545-3552  A358  $400 Set of 8    40.00 40.00

I Love Lucy
A365

No. 3553: a, Lucy reading book. b, Ricky, Lucy with book. c, Ricky kissing Lucy. d, Lucy near window. e, Lucy grabbing Ethel. f, Ricky holding scarf, Lucy in bed. g, Ethel, Lucy, frying pan. h, Ricky with frying pan. i, Lucy, Ethel, coffee table.
No. 3554, $400, Lucy in pink robe. No. 3555, $400, Lucy with garbage can lid.

**2000, July 27**
3553  A365  $60 Sheet of 9, #a-i    6.75 6.75
**Souvenir Sheets**
3554-3555  A365  Set of 2    9.00 9.00

FIN. K. L
A366

No. 3556: a, Lee Hyo-Ri. b, Ok Ju-Hyun. c, Lee Jin. d, Lee Jin. e, Group. f, Sung Yu-Ri. g, Lee Hyo-Ri. h, Sung Yu-Ri. i, Ok Ju-Hyun. Nos. a, d, f, i, full color, others, sepia tone.

**2000, Sept. 7    Perf. 13½**
3556  A366  $80 Sheet of 9, #a-i    9.00 9.00

Queen Mother, 100th Birthday — A367

**2000, Dec. 1    Perf. 14**
3557  A367  $100 multi    1.40 1.40
Printed in sheets of 6.

Christmas — A368

$60, No. 3562b, Heads of 2 angels, org background. $90, No. 3562a, 2 full angels, bl background. $120, No. 3562c, Heads of 2 angels, bl background. No. 3561, $400, No. 3562d, 2 full angels, org background.
No. 3563, Baby Jesus, horiz.

**2000, Dec. 18**
3558-3561  A368  Set of 4    8.50 8.50
3562  A368  $180 Sheet of 4, #a-d    8.25 8.25
**Souvenir Sheet**
3563  A368  $400 multi    4.75 4.75

New Year 2001 (Year of the Snake) A369

No. 3564: a, Green snake head. b, Red snake head. c, Blue snake head. d, Yellow snake head.
$250, Purple snake head, vert.

**2001, Jan. 2     Litho.     Perf. 13½x13**
3564 A369  $80 Sheet of 4, #a-d  4.25 4.25

**Souvenir Sheet**
**Perf. 13x13½**
3565 A369  $250 multi          3.00 3.00

Tourist Attractions A370

Designs: No. 3566, $90, Prime Minister's residence. No. 3567, $90, Kaiteur Falls, vert.

**2001, Jan. 30          Perf. 13¼**
3566-3567 A370  Set of 2      2.25 2.25

**Flower Photomosaic Type of 1999**

No. 3568, $80: Various photographs of flowers making up a photomosaic of the Queen Mother.
No. 3569, $100: Various photographs of religious sites making up a photomosaic of Pope John Paul II.

**2001, Feb. 13          Perf. 13¾**
**Sheets of 8, #a-h**
3568-3569 A341  Set of 2      19.00 19.00

**Souvenir Sheet**

Chow Yun-Fat, Actor A371

Background color: a, Blue green. b, Dark red. c, Olive brown. d, Red violet. e, Dark blue. f, Purple.

**2001, Feb. 13          Perf. 13¾x13¼**
3570 A371  $60 Sheet of 6, #a-f  4.25 4.25

Pokémon A372

No. 3571: a, Staryu. b, Seaking. c, Tentacool. d, Magikarp. e, Seadra. f, Goldeen.

**2001, Feb. 13          Perf. 13¾**
3571 A372  $100 Sheet of 6, #a-f  7.50 7.50

**Souvenir Sheet**
3572 A372  $400 Horsea          4.50 4.50

**Betty Boop Type of 2000**

Designs: No. 3573, $400, In pink hat. No. 3574, $400, As singer on stage. No. 3575,

$400, With red top and necklace, on beach. No. 3576, $400, In orange and black hat, horiz.

**2001 ?     Litho.     Perf. 13¾**
3573-3576 A358  Set of 4      18.00 18.00

**I Love Lucy Type of 2000**

Designs: No. 3577, $400, Dressed like Carmen Miranda. No. 3578, $400, With blue hat and gloves. No. 3579, $400, As knife thrower's target. No. 3580, $400, At table, wearing blue hat. No. 3581, $400, Wearing glasses with thick black frames.

**2001 ?**
3577-3581 A365  Set of 5      22.50 22.50

A373

A374

Cats and Dogs A375

Designs: No. 3582, $35, Boxer. No. 3583, $60, Cinnamon ocicat. No. 3584, $100, Smooth dachshund. $300, White Manx.
No. 3586, $35, Chihuahua. No. 3587, $60, Persian tabby. No. 3588, $100, Colorpoint shorthair. $200, Cocker spaniel.
No. 3590 — Names of dogs (border color and location of denomination): $100: a, Pup (pink, bottom). b, Yogi (orange, bottom). c, Hooch (yellow, bottom) d, Huxley Blu (orange, top) e, Snowflake (yellow, top). f, Red (pink, top).
No. 3591 — Names of cats (border color and location of denomination): $100: a, Tom (orange, bottom). b, Puff (yellow, bottom). c, Jag (pink, bottom). d, Fritz (yellow, top). e, Smokey (pink, top). f, Thor, (orange, top).
No. 3592, $60: a, Devon rex. b, Egyptian mau. c, Turkish angora. d, Sphynx. e, Persian. f, American wirehair. g, Exotic shorthair. h, American curl.
No. 3593, $80: a, Airedale terrier. b, Greyhound. c, Afghan hound. d, Samoyed. e, Field spaniel. f, Scottish terrier. g, Brittany spaniel. h, Boston terrier.
No. 3594, $80: a, American shorthair. b, Somali. c, Singapura. d, Balinese. e, Egyptian mau. f, Scottish fold. g, Sphynx. h, Korat.
No. 3595, $80: a, Rottweiler. b, German shepherd. c, Bernese mountain dog. d, Sharpei. e, Dachshund. f, Jack Russell terrier. g, Boston terrier. h, Welsh corgi.
No. 3596, $400, Dalmatian. No. 3597, $400, Birman. No. 3598, $400, Abyssinian. No. 3599, $400, Beagle. No. 3600, $400, German shepeherd named Baron of Fillmore. No. 3601, $400, Cat named Spike.

**2001, Mar. 1                 Perf. 14**
3582-3585 A373  Set of 4      6.25 6.25
3586-3589 A374  Set of 4      5.25 5.25

**Sheets of 6, #a-f**
3590-3591 A375  Set of 2      16.00 16.00

**Sheets of 8, #a-h**
3592-3593 A373  Set of 2      15.00 15.00
3594-3595 A374  Set of 2      16.50 16.50

**Souvenir Sheets**
3596-3597 A373  Set of 2      9.50 9.50
3598-3599 A374  Set of 2      9.50 9.50
3600-3601 A375  Set of 2      9.50 9.50

Hong Kong 2001 Stamp Exhibition (Nos. 3592-3593, 3596-3597).

**Souvenir Sheets**

Hello Kitty A376

Western children's stories with Hello Kitty characters: No. 3602, $400, Cinderella. No. 3603, $400, The Wizard of Oz. No. 3604, $400, Little Red Riding Hood. No. 3605, $400, Peter Pan. No. 3606, $400, Heidi. No. 3607, $400, Alice in Wonderland.
Asian children's stories with Hello Kitty characters: No. 3608, $400, The Fishermen. No. 3609, $400, In the Snow. No. 3610, $400, Bamboo Princess. No. 3611, $400, Three in a Boat. No. 3612, $400, Up a Tree. No. 3613, $400, On a Bear.

**2001, Mar. 28     Litho.     Perf. 13¾**
3602-3613 A376  Set of 12     55.00 55.00

GUYANA $25     Phila Nippon '01, Japan — A377

Designs: No. 3614, $25, Hanaogi with Maidservant, by Eisho Chokosai. No. 3615, $25, Girl at a Hot Spring Resort, by Goyo Hashiguchi. No. 3616, $25, Morokoshi of the Echizenya, by Eiri Rekisentei. No. 3617, $30, Courtesan Receiving Letter of Invitation, by Harunobu Suzuki. No. 3618, $35, Two Girls on Their Way to or from the Bathhouse, by Suzuki. No. 3619, $35, Mother and Daughter on an Outing, by Hokusai. No. 3620, $60, Matron in Love, by Utamaro. No. 3621, $60, Girl and Frog, by Suzuki. No. 3622, $100, The Courtesan Midorigi, by Eisho Chokosai. No. 3623, $100, Three Beauties of High Fame, by Utamaro. No. 3624, $200, Maiko, by Bakusen Tsuchida. No. 3625, $200, Girl Breaking Off the Branch of a Flowering Tree, by Suzuki.
No. 3626 — Paintings by Jakuchu Ito (28x84mm): a, Insects, Reptiles and Amphibians at a Pond. b, Rose Mallows and Fowl. c, Rooster, Sunflower and Morning Glories. d, A Group of Roosters. e, Black Rooster and Nandina. f, Birds and Autumn Maples. g, Wagtail and Roses. h, Cockatoos in a Pine.
No. 3627 — Predominate features of sections of Procession to the Shugakuin Imperial Villa, by Sesshin Kakimoto (28x84mm): a, Bridge. b, High mountain, road and bridge. c, Large tree in foreground. d, Small island in foreground. e, Building at bottom. f, Building and large tree at bottom.
No. 3628 — Paintings of Women (28x84mm): a, Girls After the Bath, by Utamaro. b, Summer Evening on the Riverbank at Hama-cho, by Kiyonaga Torii. c, A Beauty in the Wind, by Ando Kaigetsudo. d, Sisters by Shoen Uemura. e, Kasamori Osen, by Suzuki.
No. 3629 — Details from Backstage at a Kabuki Theater, by Moronobu Hishikawa (30x38mm): a, Top of screen. b, Man with red kimono. c, Man with stringed instrument. e, Man on chair.
No. 3630, $400, Portrait of Senseki Takami, by Kazan Watanabe. No. 3631, $400, Fish and Octopus From the Colorful Realm of Living Beings, by Ito. No. 3632, $400, Woman Holding a Flower, by Hisako Kajiwara, horiz. No. 3633, $400, Palace of Immortals in an Autumn Valley, by Yako Okochi, horiz. No. 3634, $400, Wintry Sky, by Hosen Higashibara, horiz.

**2001, June 18                 Perf. 14**
3614-3625 A377  Set of 12     11.00 11.00
3626 A377  $80 Sheet of 8, #a-h  8.25 8.25
3627 A377  $100 Sheet of 6, #a-f  7.50 7.50
3628 A377  $120 Sheet of 5, #a-e  6.75 6.75
3629 A377  $160 Sheet of 4, #a-d  7.50 7.50

**Sizes: 90x120mm, 120x90mm**
**Imperf**
3630-3634 A377  Set of 5      22.50 22.50

Giuseppe Verdi (1813-1901), Opera Composer — A378

No. 3635: a, Verdi, score at LR. b, Actor, score from Rigoletto. c, Actor, score from Ernani. d, Verdi, scores at left.
$400, Verdi and scores.

**2001, June 18          Perf. 14**
3635 A378  $160 Sheet of 4, #a-d  8.25 8.25

**Souvenir Sheet**
3636 A378  $400 multi          5.50 5.50

Toulouse-Lautrec Paintings — A379

No. 3637, horiz.: a, Maurice Joyant in the Baie de Somme. b, Monsieur Boileau. c, Monsieur, Madame and the Dog.
$300, Man from Monsieur, Madame and the Dog.

**2001, June 18          Perf. 13¾**
3637 A379  $160 Sheet of 3, #a-c  5.50 5.50

**Souvenir Sheet**
3638 A379  $300 multi          5.25 5.25

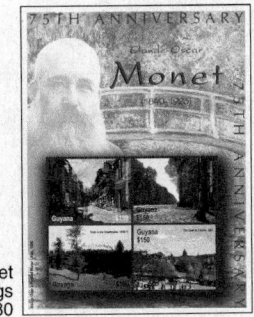

Monet Paintings A380

No. 3639, horiz.: a, Village Street in Normandy, Near Honfleur. b, The Road to Chailly. c, Train in the Countryside. d, The Quai du Louvre.
$400, Flowering Garden.

**2001, June 18**
3639 A380  $150 Sheet of 4, #a-d  7.50 7.50

**Souvenir Sheet**
3640 A380  $400 multi          5.25 5.25

Queen Victoria (1819-1901) — A381

Pictures of Victoria from — No. 3641, $200: a, 1829. b, 1837. c, 1840. d, 1897 (with crown).
No. 3642, $200: a, 1850. b, 1843. c, 1859. d, 1897 (with hat).
No. 3643, $400, 1885 (with crown). No. 3644, $400, Undated.

**2001, June 18**      **Perf. 14**
**Sheets of 4, #a-d**
3641-3642 A381 Set of 2    19.00 19.00
**Souvenir Sheets**
3643-3644 A381 Set of 2    9.50 9.50

Queen Elizabeth II, 75th Birthday A382

No. 3645: a, Pink hat. b, Red hat. c, White hat. d, Tiara.

**2001, June 18**      **Perf. 14**
3645 A382 $150 Sheet of 4, #a-d   7.50 7.50
**Souvenir Sheet**
**Perf. 13¾**
3646 A382 $400 shown    5.25 5.25
No. 3645 contains four 28x42mm stamps.

Photomosaic of Queen Elizabeth II — A383

**2001, June 18**      **Perf. 14**
3647 A383 $80 multi    .90 .90
Printed in sheets of 8, with and without inscription reading "In Celebration of the 50th Anniversary of H.M. Queen Elizabeth II's Accession to the Throne."

**Flower Photomosaic Type of 1999-2000**

No. 3648: Various pictures of American scenes making up a photomosaic of Pres. John F. Kennedy.

**2001, June 18**
3648 A341 $80 Sheet of 8, #a-h   7.50 7.50

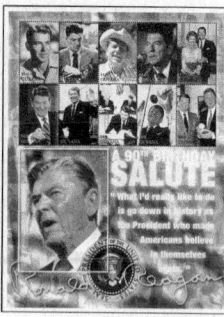

Pres. Ronald Reagan A384

Reagan: a, In checked shirt. b, With Bonzo. c, With cowboy hat. d, With dark tie. e, With wife, Nancy. f, With striped tie. g, Waving. h, Signing treaty with Mikhail Gorbachev. i, With hammer and chisel. j, With Pres. Clinton.

**2001, June 18**
3649 A384 $60 Sheet of 10, #a-j   8.25 8.25

**Betty Boop Type of 2000**

Designs: $400, With swimsuit and sunglasses. No. 3651, $400, With lilac headdress. No. 3652, $400, With purple top and pirate's hat. No. 3653, $400, Dancing on radio, horiz.
No. 3654, $400, In orange and yellow polka dot swimsuit, holding gift. No. 3655, $400, Holding on to anchor. No. 3556, $400, In red bikini, surfing. No. 3557, $400, Wearing birthday hat, horiz.

**2001**      **Perf. 13¾**
3650-3653 A358 Set of 4   18.00 18.00
3654-3657 A358 Set of 4   18.00 18.00

**Historical Events Type of 1997**

No. 3658: a, Securities and Exchange Commission formed, 1934. b, Herbert Hoover is elected president, 1928. c, The Jazz Singer is first talking movie, 1927. d, J. Edgar Hoover becomes director of FBI, 1924. e, Alexander Fleming discovers penicillin, 1928. f, FCC established to regulate broadcasting, 1934. g, Lindbergh becomes first to fly solo across Atlantic, 1927. h, Albert Einstein is awarded Nobel Prize for Physics, 1921. i, Hindenburg dies and Hitler becomes German Führer, 1934. j, Social Security Act provides safety for Americans, 1935. k, Earhart is first to fly solo from Hawaii to California, 1935. l, Marcus Garvey's prison sentence is commuted, 1927.

**2001, Mar. 28**      **Perf. 14¼x14¾**
3658 A289 $60 Sheet of 12, #a-l   9.50 9.50

Prehistoric Animals — A385

Designs: $20, Allosaurus. $30, Spinosaurus. $35, Pteranodon. $60, Cetiosaurus. $200, Archaeopteryx. $300, Parasaurolophus.
No. 3665, $100, horiz.: a, Alamosaurus. b, Archaeopteryx, diff. c, Pachycephalosaurus. d, Parasaurolophus, diff. e, Edmontosaurus. f, Triceratops.
No. 3666, $100, horiz.: a, Brachiosaurus and two palm trees. b, Dimorphodon. c, Coelophysis. d, Velociraptor. e, Antrodemus. f, Euparkeria.
No. 3667, $100, horiz.: a, Ichthyostega. b, Eryops. c, Ichthyosaur. d, Pliosaur. e, Dunklosteus. f, Eogyrinus.
No. 3668, $100, horiz.: a, Brachiosaurus and palm tree. b, Pteranodon, diff. c, Compsognathus. d, Corythosaurus. e, Allosaurus, diff. f, Torosaurus.
No. 3669, $400, Brachiosaurus, diff. No. 3670, $400, Torosaurus, diff., horiz. No. 3671, $400, Ichthyosaur, diff., horiz. No. 3672, $400, Pteranodon, diff., horiz.

**2001, Oct. 15**      **Perf. 14**
3659-3664 A385 Set of 6   7.25 7.25
**Sheets of 6, #a-f**
3665-3668 A385 Set of 4   27.50 27.50
**Souvenir Sheets**
3669-3672 A385 Set of 4   18.00 18.00
Vegaspex (Nos. 3665-3672).

Animals of Tropical Rainforests A386

Designs: $35, Mandrill, vert. $100, Leaf cutting ants.
No. 3675, $80: a, Elephant. b, Impala. c, Leopard. d, Gray parrot. e, Hippopotamus. f, Pygmy chimp. g, African green python. h, Mountain gorilla.
No. 3676, $80: a, Three-toed sloth. b, Lion tamarin. c, Ringtail lemur. d, Sugar glider. e, Toucan. f, Trogons. g, Pygmy marmoset. h, Poison arrow frog.
No. 3677, $400, Tapir, vert. No. 3678, $400, Sable antelope, vert.

**2001, Oct. 15**
3673-3674 A386 Set of 2   1.50 1.50
**Sheets of 8, #a-h**
3675-3676 A386 Set of 2   14.50 14.50
**Souvenir Sheets**
3677-3678 A386 Set of 2   9.00 9.00

Tropical Birds A387

No. 3679, $100, horiz.: a, Rainbow lorikeet. b, King bird of paradise. c, Yellow-chevroned parakeet. d, Masked lovebird. e, Scarlet ibis. f, Toco toucan.
No. 3680, $100, horiz.: a, Hyacinth macaw. b, Wire-tailed manakin. c, Scarlet macaw. d, Sun parakeet. e, Roseate spoonbill. f, Red-billed toucan.
No. 3681, $400, Eclectus parrot. No. 3682, $400, Sulfur-crested cockatoo.

**2001, Oct. 15**      **Litho.**
**Sheets of 6, #a-f**
3679-3680 A387 Set of 2   15.00 15.00
**Souvenir Sheets**
3681-3682 A387 Set of 2   11.00 11.00

New Year 2002 (Year of the Horse) A388

No. 3683 — Evolution of Chinese character for "horse": a, Two characters outside, one character inside parentheses at UR. b, Three characters outside, one character inside parentheses at UR. c, Four characters outside, one character inside parentheses at UR. d, Three characters outside, two characters inside parentheses at UR.
No. 3684 — Figure on horse: a, Denomination at UL. b, Denomination at UR.

**2001, Oct. 15**      **Perf. 13**
3683 A388 $100 Sheet of 4, #a-d   6.50 6.50
**Perf. 13¼**
3684 A388 $150 Sheet of 2, #a-b   5.50 5.50
No. 3684 contains two 38x50mm stamps.

2002 World Cup Soccer Championships, Japan and Korea — A389

No. 3685, $100 — Posters from: a, 1950, and player. b, 1954, and Jules Rimet. c, 1958, Pelé and teammates. d, 1962, and Zito scoring goal. e, 1966, and English players celebrating. f, 1970, and Jairzinho.
No. 3686, $100 — Posters from: a, 1978, and Daniel Passarella. b, 1982, and Paolo Rossi. c, 1986, and Diego Maradona. d, 1990, and German players celebrating. e, 1994, and Brazilian players celebrating. f, 1998, and Zinedine Zidane.
No. 3687, $400, 1930 poster, head from Jules Rimet Trophy. No. 3688, $400, Head and globe from World Cup trophy.

**2001, Dec. 26**      **Perf. 13¾x14¼**
**Sheets of 6, #a-f**
3685-3686 A389 Set of 2   14.00 14.00
**Souvenir Sheets**
**Perf. 14¼**
3687-3688 A389 Set of 2   9.00 9.00

**Queen Mother Type of 1999 Redrawn**

No. 3689: a, With Princess Elizabeth, 1928. b, Lady Elizabeth-Bowles Lyon, 1914. c, With Princess Elizabeth, 1950. d, In Venice, 1984. $400, In Canada, 1988.

**2001, Dec.**      **Perf. 14**
**Yellow Orange Frames**
3689 A328 $130 Sheet of 4, #a-d, + label   5.75 5.75
**Souvenir Sheet**
**Perf. 13¾**
3690 A328 $400 multi   4.50 4.50
Queen Mother's 101st birthday. No. 3690 contains one 38x50mm stamp with a bluer cast than that found on No. 3434. Sheet margins of Nos. 3689-3690 lack embossing and gold arms and frames found on Nos. 3433-3434.

**I Love Lucy Type of 2000**
**Souvenir Sheets**

Designs: No. 3691, $400, Lucy wearing leis, with hands up. No. 3692, $400, Lucy with checked shirt and apron, with mouth open.

**2001 ?**      **Perf. 13¾**
3691-3692 A365 Set of 2   9.00 9.00

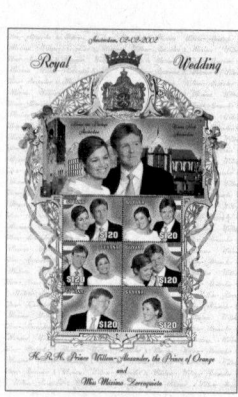

Wedding of Netherlands Prince Willem-Alexander and Máxima Zorreguieta — A390

No. 3693: a, Couple (Máxima at left), flag colors at left. b, Couple (heads apart), flag colors at right. c, Couple (Máxima at right), flag colors at left. d, Couple (heads together), flag colors at right. e, Willem-Alexander. f, Máxima.

**2002, Jan. 7**    **Litho.**    **Perf. 14¾x14¼**
3693 A390 $120 Sheet of 6, #a-f   8.00 8.00

United We Stand — A391

**2002, Feb. 6** — **Perf. 13½x13¼**
3694 A391 $200 multi 2.25 2.25
Printed in sheets of four.

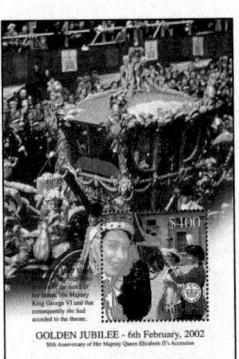

Reign of Queen Elizabeth II, 50th Anniv. A392

No. 3695: a, Blue hat. b, Feathered hat. c, Waving. d, With horse at right. $400, With horse at left.

**2002, Feb. 6** — **Perf. 14½**
3695 A392 $150 Sheet of 4, #a-d 6.75 6.75
**Souvenir Sheet**
3696 A392 $400 multi 4.50 4.50

**Flower Photomosaic Type of 1999-2000**

No. 3697: Various science photographs making up a photomosaic of Albert Einstein.

**2002, Feb. 25** — **Perf. 13¾**
3697 A341 $80 Sheet of 8, #a-h 7.25 7.25

Nobel Prizes, Cent. (in 2001) A393

No. 3698, $100 — Chemistry laureates: a, Harold C. Urey, 1934. b, Willard F. Libby, 1960. c, Frederick Sanger, 1958 and 1980. d, Theodor Svedberg, 1926. e, Cyril N. Hinshelwood, 1956. f, Nikolai Semenov, 1956.
No. 3699, $100: a, Alexander Todd, Chemistry, 1957. b, John Steinbeck, Literature, 1962. c, Edward C. Kendall, Physiology or Medicine, 1950. d, Frederick G. Banting, Physiology or Medicine, 1923. e, Charles Nicolle, Physiology or Medicine, 1928. f, Charles Richet, Physiology or Medicine, 1913.
No. 3700, $400, International Red Cross, Peace, 1917. No. 3701, $400, John J. R. MacLeod, Physiology or Medicine, 1923. No. 3702, $400, Derek H. R. Barton, Chemistry, 1969.

**2002, Feb. 25** — **Perf. 14**
**Sheets of 6, #a-f**
3698-3699 A393 Set of 2 13.50 13.50
**Souvenir Sheets**
3700-3702 A393 Set of 3 13.50 13.50

2002 Winter Olympics, Salt Lake City — A394

Designs: No. 3703, $200, Skier. No. 3704, $200, Figure skater.

**2002, July 1 Litho. Perf. 13¼x13½**
3703-3704 A394 Set of 2 4.50 4.50
a. Souvenir sheet, #3703-3704 4.50 4.50

Guyana — People's Republic of China Diplomatic Relations, 30th Anniv. — A395

Designs: No. 3705, $100, Chinese flag, Kaieteur Falls, Guyana. No. 3706, $100, Guyanese flag, Great Wall of China.

**2002, July 1** — **Perf. 14**
3705-3706 A395 Set of 2 2.25 2.25

Intl. Volunteers Year (in 2001) — A396

Emblem, Guyanese flag and: $35, Person on ladder touching Guyana on map. $60, Map of Guyana and IVY emblem. $300, People.

**2002, July 1**
3707-3709 A396 Set of 3 4.50 4.50

Intl. Year of Ecotourism — A397

No. 3710: a, Owl. b, Waterfall and tourists. c, Baboon. d, Butterfly. e, Flower. f, Otter. $400, Leopard.

**2002, July 1** — **Perf. 13¼x13**
3710 A397 $100 Sheet of 6, #a-f 6.75 6.75
**Souvenir Sheet**
3711 A397 $400 multi 4.50 4.50

Intl. Year of Mountains — A398

No. 3712: a, Devil's Tower, US. b, Schreckhorn, Switzerland. c, Mt. Rainier, US. d, Mt. Everest, Nepal and Tibet. No. 3713: Mt. McKinley. U.S.

**2002, July 1** — **Perf. 13½x13¼**
3712 A398 $200 Sheet of 4, #a-d 14.00 14.00
**Souvenir Sheet**
3713 A398 $400 multi 7.00 7.00
See Nos. 3848-3851.

20th World Scout Jamboree, Thailand — A399

No. 3714: a, Environmental Science merit badge. b, Citizenship in the World merit badge. c, Life Saving merit badge. $400, Mascot, Scout emblem.

**2002, July 1**
3714 A399 $200 Sheet of 3, #a-c 6.75 6.75
**Souvenir Sheet**
3715 A399 $400 multi 4.50 4.50

Flora and Fauna A400

No. 3716, $100 — Butterflies: a, Sweet oil. b, Swallowtail. c, Southern white admiral. d, Prepona pheridamas. e, Plain tiger. f, Common eggfly.
No. 3717, $100 — Moths: a, Burgena varia. b, Lime hawkmoth. c, Spurge hawkmoth. d, Eligma laetipicta. e, Io moth. f, Pine hawkmoth.
No. 3718, $100 — Birds: a, Flycatcher. b, Barbary shrike. c, Red-faced mousebird. d, Red-footed booby. e, White-fronted goose. f, Great crested grebe.
No. 3719, $100 — Whales: a, Sperm. b, Pygmy sperm. c, Blue. d, Bottlenose. e, Killer. f, True's beaked.
No. 3720, $100, vert. — Orchids: a, Masdevallia tovarensis. b, Encyclia vitellina. c, Dendrobium nobile. d, Masdevallia falcata. e, Calanthe vestita. f, Brassolaeliacattleya Rising Sun.
No. 3721, $400, Zebra butterfly. No. 3722, $400, Callimorpha quadripuntaria. No. 3723, $400, Whiskered tern. No. 3724, $400, Beluga whale. No. 3725, $400, Brassavola nodosa.

**2002, Aug. 7** — **Perf. 14**
**Sheets of 6, #a-f**
3716-3720 A400 Set of 5 47.50 47.50
**Souvenir Sheets**
3721-3725 A400 Set of 5 35.00 35.00

Elvis Presley (1935-77) — A401

Designs: No. 3726, $60, In army uniform. No. 3727, $60, Singing.

**2002, Aug. 16** — **Perf. 13¾**
3726-3727 A401 Set of 2 2.25 2.25
Each stamp was printed in a sheet of nine.

Popeye A402

No. 3728: a, Popeye. b, Olive Oyl. c, Wimpy. d, Jeep. e, Swee'Pea and Olive Oyl. f, Swee'Pea. $400, Popeye, diff.

**2002, Oct. 7** — **Perf. 14**
3728 A402 $100 Sheet of 6, #a-f 8.50 8.50
**Souvenir Sheet**
3729 A402 $400 multi 6.50 6.50

New Year 2003 (Year of the Ram) A403

Rams and background color of: a, Red. b, Orange. c, Bright pink. d, Yellow green.

**2003, Jan. 27 Litho. Perf. 14¼x14½**
3730 A403 $100 Sheet of 4, #a-d 6.50 6.50

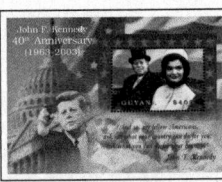

Pres. John F. Kennedy (1917-63) — A404

No. 3731, vert.: a, Pres. Kennedy, Presidential seal. b, Pres. Kennedy, Dr. Martin Luther King, Jr. c, Pres. Kennedy, space capsule. d, Pres. Kennedy, US flag, White House. e, Pres. Kennedy, map of Cuba, missile. f, Jacqueline and John F. Kennedy, Jr., US flag.
$400, Pres. Kennedy and wife, Jacqueline.

**2003, Jan. 27** — **Perf. 14**
3731 A404 $100 Sheet of 6, #a-f 8.00 8.00
**Souvenir Sheet**
3732 A404 $400 multi 6.50 6.50

Pres. Ronald Reagan A405

No. 3733, vert. — Pres. Reagan: a, And eagle. b, As actor. c, And Mt. Rushmore. d, And wife Nancy. e, And White House. f, Riding horse.
$400, With Mikhail Gorbachev.

**2003, Jan. 27** — 
3733 A405 $100 Sheet of 6, #a-f 8.00 8.00
**Souvenir Sheet**
3734 A405 $400 multi 7.00 7.00

Princess Diana (1961-97) — A406

No. 3735: a-f, Various depictions of Princess wearing tiaras or bridal veils. $400, Wearing pink and yellow dress.

**2003, Jan. 27** — 
3735 A406 $100 Sheet of 6, #a-f 7.00 7.00
**Souvenir Sheet**
3736 A406 $400 multi 5.00 5.00

Paintings of Lucas Cranach the Elder (1472-1553) A407

Designs: $35, Portrait of a Man. $60, Portrait of a Woman. $100, Duchess Catherine of Mecklenburg. $200, Portrait of Duke Henry of Saxony.
No. 3741: a, The Virgin, c. 1518. b, The Virgin and Child Under the Apple Tree. c, The Virgin, c, 1535. d, The Virgin, c. 1525.
$400, The Virgin and Child Holding a Piece of Bread.

**2003, June 17 Litho. Perf. 14¼**
3737-3740 A407 Set of 4 4.50 4.50
3741 A407 $150 Sheet of 4, #a-d 6.75 6.75
**Souvenir Sheet**
3742 A407 $400 multi 4.50 4.50

Art by Kunichika
Toyohara (1835-
1900)
A408

Designs: $60, The Actor Shikan Nakamura
IV. $80, The Actor Danjuro Ichikawa IX as
Sukeroku, 1883. $100, The Actor Tatsunosuke
Onoe. $300, The Actor Sadanji Ichikawa I as
Kyusuke.
No. 3747: a, The Actor Sansho Kawarazaki
as Watonai. b, The Actor Danjuro Ichikawa IX
as Gongoru Kagemasa Kamakura. c, The
Actor Sadanji Ichikawa I as Sadakuro. d, The
Actor Danjuro Ichikawa IX as Sukeroku, 1898.
$400, The Actor Danjuro Ichikawa IX as
Shukeigashira Kiyomasa Kato, horiz.

**2003, June 17**
3743-3746 A408  Set of 4  6.00 6.00
3747 A408 $150 Sheet of 4, #a-d 6.75 6.75
**Souvenir Sheet**
3748 A408 $400 multi  4.50 4.50

Paintings by
Wassily Kandinsky
(1866-1944)
A409

Designs: $25, Tension in Red. $30, Black
Accompaniment. $35, Calm Tension. $60,
Hard and Soft. $100, Yellow Point, horiz. $300,
Composition VIII, horiz.
No. 3755: a, Red Oval. b, On the White II. c,
Mutual Agreement. d, Inclination.
No. 3756, $400, White Center, horiz. No.
3757, $400, Black Weft, horiz.

**2003, June 17**
3749-3754 A409  Set of 6  6.25 6.25
3755 A409 $150 Sheet of 4, #a-d 6.75 6.75
**Size: 104x84mm**
*Imperf*
3756-3757 A409  Set of 2  9.00 9.00

Caribbean
Community, 30th
Anniv. — A410

Anniversary emblem and: $20, Map of
Guyana, vert. $60, Bank of Guyana Building.
$100, Hands with torch, vert. $160, Stethoscope and AIDS ribbon, vert.

**2003, July 7**  *Perf. 14*
3758-3761 A410  Set of 4  3.75 3.75

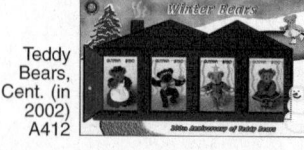

Teddy
Bears,
Cent. (in
2002)
A412

No. 3762 — Background color: a, Lilac. b,
Dull greenish blue. c, Light blue. d, Dull yellow
green. e, Dull blue green. f, Dull gray green. h,
Gray. i, Dull green. j, Gray blue.
No. 3763 — Bear with: a, Red dress. b,
Menorah. c, Christmas lights. d, Blue dress.

**2003, Aug. 25**
3762 A411 $80 Sheet of 9, #a-i 8.50 8.50
3763 A412 $150 Sheet of 4, #a-d 7.00 7.00

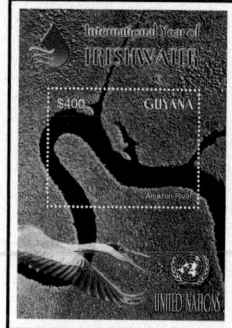

Intl. Year
of Fresh
Water
A413

No. 3764 — Kaieteur Falls: a, Top. b, Middle. c, Base.
$400, Amazon River.

**2003, Aug. 25**  *Perf. 13¾*
3764 A413 $200 Sheet of 3, #a-c 8.25 8.25
**Souvenir Sheet**
3765 A413 $400 multi  6.00 6.00

Tour de
France
Bicycle
Race,
Cent.
A414

No. 3766: a, Jacques Anquetil, 1964. b,
Felice Gimondi, 1965. c, Lucien Aimar, 1966.
d, Roger Pingeon, 1967.
$400, Jan Janssen, 1968.

**2003, Aug. 25**  *Perf. 13½x13*
3766 A414 $150 Sheet of 4, #a-d 7.25 7.25
**Souvenir Sheet**
3767 A414 $400 multi  5.00 5.00

Coronation of Queen Elizabeth II, 50th
Anniv. — A415

No. 3768: a, Wearing tiara. b, Wearing dark
blue dress. c, Wearing lilac dress.
$400, Wearing crown.

**2003, Aug. 25**  *Perf. 14*
3768 A415 $200 Sheet of 3, #a-c 6.75 6.75
**Souvenir Sheet**
3769 A415 $400 multi  4.50 4.50

Prince
William,
21st
Birthday
A416

No. 3770: a, As toddler. b, As adult. c, As
infant.
$400, As young boy.

**2003, Aug. 25**
3770 A416 $200 Sheet of 3, #a-c 7.00 7.00
**Souvenir Sheet**
3771 A416 $400 multi  5.50 5.50

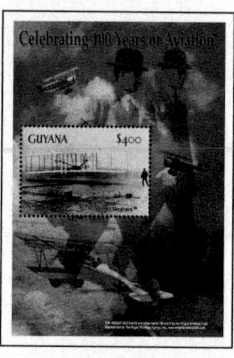

Powered
Flight,
Cent.
A417

Designs: $100, Airplane of Sir Alliot Verdon
Roe. $160, Airplane of Samuel Franklin Cody.
No. 3772, $150: a, Wright Flyer. b, Spad 13.
c, Sopwith F-1. d, Albatros D.II.
No. 3773, $150: a, Nieuport 17. b, S. E. 5a.
c, D. H. 4. d, German biplane.
No. 3774, $400, Wright Flyer making first
flight. No. 3775, $400, Fokker D.VIIs.

**2003, Aug. 25**
3771A A417 $100 multi  1.10 1.10
3771B A417 $160 multi  1.75 1.75
**Sheets of 4, #a-d**
3772-3773 A417  Set of 2  13.50 13.50
**Souvenir Sheets**
3774-3775 A417  Set of 2  10.00 10.00

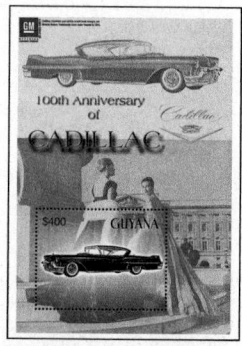

General Motors Automobiles — A418

No. 3776, $150 — Cadillacs: a, 1948 Sixty
Special. b, 1966 Fleetwood Sixty Special. c,
1967 Eldorado. d, 1976 Eldorado convertible.
No. 3777, $150 — Corvettes: a, 1964 Sting-
ray. b, 1963 Stingray. c, 1966 Stingray. 4. d,
1969.
No. 3778, $400, Undescribed Cadillac
(1957 Coupe de Ville). No. 3779, $400, 1971
Corvette.

**2003, Aug. 25**  **Sheets of 4, #a-d**
3776-3777 A418  Set of 2  14.50 14.50
**Souvenir Sheets**
3778-3779 A418  Set of 2  9.50 9.50

Butterflies — A419

Designs: $20, Grecian shoemaker. $55,
Clorinde. $80, Orange-barred sulphur. $100,
Atala. $160, White peacock. $200, Polydamus
swallowtail. $300, Giant swallowtail. $400,
Banded king shoemaker. $500, Blue night.
$1000, Orange theope. $2000, Small lacewing. $3000, Common morpho.

**2003, Nov. 4**  **Litho.**  *Perf. 13¼*
3780 A419 $20 multi  .30 .30
3781 A419 $55 multi  .85 .85
3782 A419 $80 multi  1.25 1.25
3783 A419 $100 multi  1.50 1.50
3784 A419 $160 multi  2.25 2.25
3785 A419 $200 multi  3.00 3.00
3786 A419 $300 multi  4.25 4.25
3787 A419 $400 multi  5.75 5.75
3788 A419 $500 multi  7.25 7.25
3789 A419 $1000 multi  13.50 13.50
3790 A419 $2000 multi  27.50 27.50
3791 A419 $3000 multi  40.00 40.00
Nos. 3780-3791 (12)  107.40 107.40

Worldwide Fund
for Nature
(WWF) — A420

No. 3792: a, Head of channel-billed toucan.
b, Two toco toucans on branch. c, Channel-
billed toucan on branch. d, Toco toucan and
chick.

**2003, Dec. 1**  *Perf. 14*
3792  Horiz. strip of 4, #a-d  5.00 5.00
a.-d. A420 $100 Any single  1.20 1.20
e. Souvenir sheet, 2 each
#3792a-3792d  10.50 10.50

Mushrooms
A421

Designs: No. 3793, $20, Clitocybe gibba.
No. 3794, $20, Clitocybe clavipes. $30, Calocybe carnea. $300, Marasmius.
No. 3797: a, Amanita spissa. b, Boletus
aestivalis. c, Boletus rubellus. d, Clathrus
archeri.
$400, Volvariella bombycina.

**2003, Dec. 1**
3793-3796 A421  Set of 4  4.50 4.50
3797 A421 $150 Sheet of 4, #a-d 7.25 7.25
**Souvenir Sheet**
3798 A421 $400 multi  5.75 5.75

Mammals
A422

Designs: $25, Common tenrec. $60, Humboldt's woolly monkey, vert. $100, Gundi.
$200, Harbor seal.
No. 3803: a, Prevost's squirrel. b, Mountain
tapir. c, Sea otter. d, Indus dolphin.
$400, Peter's disk-winged bat, vert.

**2003, Dec. 1**
3799-3802 A422  Set of 4  4.25 4.25
3803 A422 $150 Sheet of 4, #a-d 6.75 6.75
**Souvenir Sheet**
3804 A422 $400 multi  4.50 4.50

Flowers — A423

Designs: $20, Begonia sedeni. $30, Dahlia.
$35, Eschecholzia californica. $300, Lupinus
perennis.
No. 3809: a, Agapanthus africanus. b, Hyacinth cultivars. c, Protea linearis. d, Hippes-
trum aulicum.
$400, Crocus sativus, horiz.

**2003, Dec. 1**
3805-3808 A423  Set of 4  4.25 4.25
3809 A423 $150 Sheet of 4, #a-d 6.75 6.75
**Souvenir Sheet**
3810 A423 $400 multi  5.00 5.00

Fish — A424

Designs: $25, Regal tang. $60, Pajama
tang. $100, Coral beauty. $200, Emperor
angelfish.
No. 3815: a, High hat. b, Regal angelfish. c,
Fire clown. d, Domino damselfish.
$400, Tomato clown.

**2003, Dec. 1**
3811-3814 A424  Set of 4  4.75 4.75

3815 A424 $150 Sheet of 4, #a-d 9.00 9.00
**Souvenir Sheet**
3816 A424 $400 multi 5.50 5.50

Guyana — Brazil Diplomatic Relations, 35th Anniv. — A425

**2003, Dec. 18**
3817 A425 $20 multi .25 .25

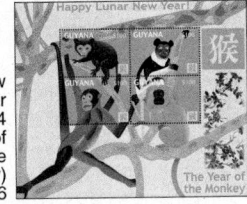

New Year 2004 (Year of the Monkey) A426

No. 3818: a, Dark brown monkey with orange face. b, Dark brown and white monkey with brown face. c, Brown monkey. d, Orange monkey with black face.

**2004, Jan. 5**
3818 A426 $100 Sheet of 4, #a-d 4.75 4.75

Paintings by Tang Yin (1470-1524) — A427

No. 3819, vert.: a, Concubines of Emperor Chu. b, Lady. c, Untitled painting depicting woman. d, Untitled painting depicting landscape.
$400, Mountain Scene.

**2004, Jan. 21    Litho.    Perf. 13¼**
3819 A427 $150 Sheet of 4, #a-d 6.75 6.75
**Souvenir Sheet**
3820 A427 $400 multi 4.50 4.50

Birth of Princess Catherina Amalia of the Netherlands — A428

No. 3821: a, Princess, one hand shown. b, Princess and father, Prince Willem-Alexander. c, Princess, two hands shown.

**2004, Feb. 15    Perf. 14¼**
3821 A428 $200 Sheet of 3, #a-c 7.00 7.00

FIFA (Fédération Internationale de Football Association), Cent. A429

World Cup championship teams: No. 3822, $80, Uruguay, 1930. No. 3823, $80, Italy, 1934. No. 3824, $80, Italy, 1938. No. 3825, $80, Uruguay, 1950. No. 3826, $80, Germany, 1954. No. 3827, $80, Brazil, 1958. No. 3828, $80, Brazil, 1962. No. 3829, $80, England, 1966. No. 3830, $80, Brazil, 1970.

**2004, Feb. 16    Perf. 13¼**
3822-3830 A429 Set of 9 8.25 8.25

Paintings by Norman Rockwell (1894-1978) — A430

No. 3831, vert.: a, Doctor and Doll. b, Babysitter with Screaming Infant. c, Girl with Black Eye. d, Checkup.
$400, Girl Running with Wet Canvas (Wet Paint).

**2004, Feb. 16    Perf. 14¼**
3831 A430 $150 Sheet of 4, #a-d 6.75 6.75
**Souvenir Sheet**
3832 A430 $400 multi 4.50 4.50

Paintings by Pablo Picasso (1881-1973) — A431

No. 3833: a, Woman in Yellow Hat. b, Seated Woman, 1962. c, Head of a Woman, d, Large Profile.
$400, Seated Woman, 1971.

**2004, Feb. 16    Perf. 14¼**
3833 A431 $150 Sheet of 4, #a-d 6.75 6.75
**Imperf**
3834 A431 $400 multi 4.50 4.50
No. 3833 contains four 38x50mm stamps.

Rembrandt Paintings — A432

Designs: $35, A Woman Bathing. $60, Flora. $100, The Poet, Jan Hermansz Krul. $200, Portrait of a Young Man.
No. 3839: a, The Apostle James. b, The Apostle Bartholemew. c, The Evangelist Matthew Inspired by an Angel. d, The Apostle Peter Standing.
$400, Balaam and the Ass.

**2004, Feb. 16    Perf. 14¼**
3835-3838 A432 Set of 4 4.50 4.50
3839 A432 $150 Sheet of 4, #a-d 6.75 6.75
**Souvenir Sheet**
3840 A432 $400 multi 4.75 4.75

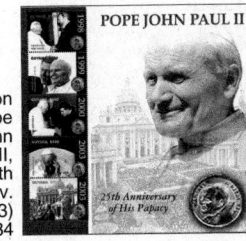

Paintings in the Hermitage, St. Petersburg, Russia A433

Designs: $35, Mercury Giving Bacchus to Nymphs to Raise, by Laurent de La Hyre. $60, Satyr and Bacchante, by Nicolas Poussin, vert. $100, Parting of Abelard and Eloisa, by Angelica Kauffman. $200, Pastoral Scene, by François Boucher.

No. 3845, vert.: a, The Union of Earth and Water, by Peter Paul Rubens. b, Hercules Between Love and Wisdom, by Pompeo Girolano Batoni. c, Innocence Choosing Love Over Wealth, by Pierre-Paul Prud'hon. d, Mars and Venus, by Joseph Marie Vien.
No. 3846, Allegory of Virtuous Life, by Hendrik Van Balen. No. 3847, Statue of Ceres, by Rubens, vert.

**2004, Feb. 16    Perf. 14¼**
3841-3844 A433 Set of 4 4.50 4.50
3845 A433 $150 Sheet of 4, #a-d 7.00 7.00
**Imperf**
**Size: 77x55mm**
3846 A433 $400 multi 5.50 5.50
**Size: 56x77mm**
3847 A433 $400 multi 5.50 5.50

**Intl. Year of Mountains Type of 2002**
Designs: $80, Mt. Kosciuszko, Australia. $100, Mt. Elbrus, Russia. $150, Mt. Vinson, Antarctica. $400, Mt. Everest, Nepal.

**2004    Perf. 14**
3848-3850 A398 Set of 3 3.75 3.75
**Souvenir Sheet**
3851 A398 $400 multi 4.50 4.50

**Miniature Sheet**

Election of Pope John Paul II, 25th Anniv. (in 2003) A434

No. 3852: a, With Fidel Castro, 1998. b, With Pres. Bill Clinton, 1999. c, With bishop and man, 2000. d, With hands on head, 2003. e, In Popemobile, 2003.

**2004, Sept. 27    Litho.    Perf. 14**
3852 A434 $100 Sheet of 5, #a-e 5.75 5.75

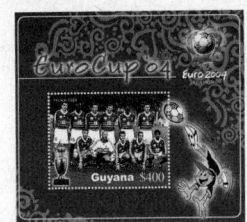

2004 Summer Olympics, Athens — A435

Designs: $60, Poster for 1912 Stockholm Olympics. $80, High jump, 1932 Los Angeles Olympics, horiz. $100, Commemorative medal for 1932 Olympics. $200, Ancient Greek runners, horiz.

**2004, Sept. 27    Perf. 14¼**
3853-3856 A435 Set of 4 6.75 6.75

European Soccer Championships, Portugal — A436

No. 3857, vert.: a, Michel Platini. b, Luis Arconada. c, Bruno Bellone. d, Parc des Princes, Paris.
$400, 1984 France team.

**2004, Sept. 27    Litho.**
3857 A436 $150 Sheet of 4, #a-d 8.00 8.00
**Souvenir Sheet**
3858 A436 $400 multi 5.00 5.00
No. 3857 contains four 28x47mm stamps.

FIFA (Fédération Internationale de Football Association), Cent. — A437

No. 3859: a, Alf Ramsey. b, Pele. c, Lothar Matthaus. d, Dennis Bergkamp.
$400, Fabien Barthez.

**2004, Sept. 27    Perf. 12¾x12½**
3859 A437 $150 Sheet of 4, #a-d 7.00 7.00
**Souvenir Sheet**
3860 A437 $400 multi 5.00 5.00

A438

D-Day, 60th Anniv. A439

No. 3861, $150: a, Operation Overlord begins. b, Troops in landing craft storm the beaches of Normandy. c, Troops deep behind enemy lines. d, Churchill announces landings a success.
No. 3862, $150: a, Royal Scots Fusiliers. b, 2nd Company, 101st Heavy Tank Battalion. c, Anti-tank gun of 7th Green Howards. d, 229th Engineer Combat Battalion.
No. 3863, $150, vert.: a, Michael Wittmann. b, Lt. Robert Edlin. c, CSM Stanley Hollis. d, Kurt Meyer.
No. 3864, vert.: a, Rear Admiral John L. Hall. b, Rear Admiral Carlton F. Bryant. c, General Dwight D. Eisenhower. d, General Hap Arnold.
No. 3865, $400, Tank battle, Cotentin Peninsula. No. 3866, $400, Seaforth Highlanders of Canada. No. 3867, $400, Sgt. Clifton Barker. No. 3868, Major General Maxwell D. Taylor.

**2004, Sept. 27    Perf. 13½**
**Sheets of 4, #a-d**
3861-3863 A438 Set of 3 21.00 21.00
3864 A439 $150 Sheet of 4, #a-d 7.00 7.00
**Souvenir Sheets**
3865-3867 A438 Set of 3 15.00 15.00
3868 A439 $400 multi 5.00 5.00

A440

A441

A442

Locomotives — A443

No. 3869: a, Santa Fe Depot. b, LD Porta. c,
D9000 Royal Scots Gray. d, TGV.
No. 3870, $150: a, Hercules 4-4-0. b, Ster-
ling 8 ft Single Class 4-2-2. c, Class YP 4-6-2.
d, Class 01.10 4-6-2.
No. 3871, $150: a, GWR King Class 4-6-0.
b, 4500 Class 4-6-2. c, Class F 4-6-2. d, Class
231C 4-6-2.
No. 3872, $150: a, Western Railway,
France, 1856. b, Dutch State Railway, 1880. c,
Southern Railway, England, 1890. d, Madras
and Southern Mahratta Railway, India, 1891.
No. 3873, $150: a, Baltimore and Ohio Rail-
road, US, 1856. b, Utica and Schenectady
Railway, US, 1837. c, Great Southern Rail-
way, Spain, 1913. d, Victorian Government
Railway, Australia, 1906.
No. 3874, $150: a, Shantung Railway,
China, 1919. b, Great Indian Peninsula Rail-
way, 1898. c, Cumberland Valley Railroad,
US, 1851. d, Central Pacific Railroad, US,
1863.
No. 3875, $150: a, Great Northern Railway,
Ireland, 1876. b, London and Northwestern
Railways, 1873. c, Shanghai-Nanking Railway,
China, 1910. d, London, Brighton and South
Coast Railway, 1846.
No. 3876, $400, No. 999, 4-4-0. No. 3877,
$400, Northumbrian 0-2-2, vert.
No. 3878, $400, Netherlands State Railway,
1888. No. 3879, $400, Austrian State Railway,
1868. No. 3880, $400, London, Midland and
Scottish Railway, 1923. No. 3881, $400, Penn-
sylvania Railroad, 1848.
No. 3882, TGV Atlantique.

**2004, Sept. 27**                 *Perf. 13½*
3869  A440 $150 Sheet of 4,
                     #a-d           7.00  7.00
         **Sheets of 4, #a-d**
3870-3871  A441  Set of 2    14.00 14.00
3872-3875  A442  Set of 4    30.00 30.00
         **Souvenir Sheets**
3876-3877  A441  Set of 2    10.00 10.00
3878-3881  A442  Set of 4    20.00 20.00
3882  A443 $400 multi          5.00  5.00

Souvenir Sheet

Deng Xiaoping (1904-97), Chinese
Leader — A444

**2004**                            *Perf. 14*
3883  A444 $400 multi          4.75  4.75

South American Reptiles, Fish, Bats
and Flowers — A445

No. 3884, $160 — Reptiles: a, Red-foot tor-
toise. b, Emerald tree boa. c, Green iguana. d,
Cuvier's dwarf caiman.
No. 3885, $160 — Fish: a, Velvet cichlid. b,
Freshwater sting ray. c, Splash tetra. d, Red
piranha.
No. 3886, $160 — Bats: a, Mexican funnel-
eared bat. b, Greater bulldog bat. c, Vampire
bat. d, Doffroy's tailless bat.
No. 3887, $160, vert. — Flowers: a, Blue
passion flower. b, Scarlet passion flower. c,
Passion vine. d, Bromeliad flower.
No. 3888, $400, Eyelash viper. No. 3889,
$400, Tambaqui, vert. No. 3890, $400, Short-
tailed fruit bat, vert. No. 3891, $400, Epiphytic
blueberry, vert.

*Perf. 13¼x13½, 13½x13¼*
**2005, Jan. 10**                   Litho.
         **Sheets of 4, #a-d**
3884-3887  A445  Set of 4   36.00 36.00
         **Souvenir Sheets**
3888-3891  A445  Set of 4   19.50 19.50

New Year 2005 (Year of the Rooster)
A446

No. 3892: a, Rooster with dark feathers. b,
Rooster with white feathers.

**2005, Jan. 24**                  *Perf. 12¾*
3892  A446 $50 Pair, #a-b      1.40  1.40
Printed in sheets containing two pairs.

Prehistoric Animals — A447

No. 3893, $150: a, Eustreptospondylus. b,
Rhamphorhynchus. c, Utahraptor. d,
Entelodonts.
No. 3894, $150: a, Moeritherium. b, Dei-
nonychus. c, Ophthalmosaurus. d, Grendelius.
No. 3895, $150: a, Spinosaurus. b,
Tarbosaurus. c, Coelophysis. d,
Sinosauropteryx prima.
No. 3896, $400, Velociraptor babies. No.
3897, $400, Ophthalmosaurus baby. No.
3898, $400, Iguanodon bernissartensis, vert.

**2005, Jan. 24**   Litho.   *Perf. 12¾*
         **Sheets of 4, #a-d**
3893-3895  A447  Set of 3   20.00 20.00
         **Souvenir Sheets**
3896-3898  A447  Set of 3   15.00 15.00

Eddy Grant,
Musician — A448

Designs: $20, Grant at UR. $80, Grant at
UL.
No. 3901 — Portrait in: a, Blue. b, Yellow
green. c, Blue violet. d, Red violet.

$400, Grant with guitar.

**2005, Feb. 17**                  *Perf. 12¾*
3899-3900  A448  Set of 2    1.25  1.25
3901  A448 $190 Sheet of 4, #a-d  9.75  9.75
         **Souvenir Sheet**
3902  A448 $400 multi          4.75  4.75

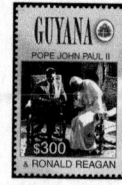

Pope John Paul II
(1920-2005) and Pres.
Ronald Reagan (1911-
2004) — A449

**2005, Aug. 12**   Litho.   *Perf. 13½*
3903  A449 $300 multi          3.25  3.25

Battle of Trafalgar,
Bicent. — A450

Designs: $25, Vice-admiral Cuthbert Col-
lingwood. $35, Admiral Horatio Nelson injured
at Battle of Santa Cruz. $60, Nelson's funeral
car arriving at St. Paul's Cathedral, horiz. $80,
Nelson and Flag Captain Thomas M. Hardy.
$100, First shots of Battle of Trafalgar, horiz.
$300, British ship hoists signals to begin pin-
cer movement.
$400, Nelson.

**2005, Aug. 12**                  *Perf. 13¼*
3904-3909  A450  Set of 6    6.50  6.50
         **Souvenir Sheet**
             *Perf. 12*
3910  A450 $400 multi          5.00  5.00

V-E Day,
60th
Anniv.
A451

No. 3911, horiz.: a, Neville Chamberlain
makes peace with Adolf Hitler, 1938. b, The
Royal Air Force hits back. c, Victory, 1945.
$400, Netherlands #277.

**2005, Aug. 12**                  *Perf. 12¾*
3911  A451 $200 Sheet of 3, #a-c  7.25  7.25
         **Souvenir Sheet**
3912  A451 $400 multi          5.00  5.00

V-J Day,
60th
Anniv.
A452

No. 3913: a, Japan attacks Pearl Harbor,
1941. b, Iwo Jima War Memorial, Harlington,
Texas. c, Newspaper announcing Japanese
surrender, 1945.
$400, Seebees celebrate Japanese
surrender.

**2005, Aug. 12**
3913  A452 $200 Sheet of 3, #a-c  7.25  7.25
         **Souvenir Sheet**
3914  A452 $400 multi          5.00  5.00

Rotary International, Cent. — A453

No. 3915: a, Dentist examining patient's
mouth. b, 2005 Rotary President-elect Carl-
Wilhelm Stenhammar. c, Rotary District of
Guyana first couple.
$400, Homer Wood, founder of second
Rotary Club.

**2005, Aug. 12**
3915  A453 $150 Sheet of 3, #a-c  6.25  6.25
         **Souvenir Sheet**
3916  A453 $400 multi          4.75  4.75

Friedrich von Schiller (1759-1805),
Writer — A454

Designs: $400, Schiller and Ludwig van
Beethoven.
No. 3918: a, Schiller. b, Schiller and his
house. c, Beethoven.

**2005, Aug. 12**
3917  A454 $400 multi          4.75  4.75
         **Souvenir Sheet**
3918  A454 $200 Sheet of 3, #a-c  7.00  7.10
No. 3918 contains three 42x28mm stamps.

Hans Christian Andersen (1805-75),
Author — A455

No. 3919: a, The Traveling Companion. b,
The Shadow. c, The Drop of Water.
$400, The Emperor's New Suit.

**2005, Aug. 12**                  *Perf. 12¾*
3919  A455 $200 Sheet of 3, #a-c  7.00  7.00
         **Souvenir Sheet**
             *Perf. 12*
3920  A455 $400 multi          4.75  4.75
No. 3919 contains three 42x28mm stamps.

Jules Verne (1828-1905),
Writer — A456

No. 3921, vert.: a, Verne. b, Book illustration. c, Space capsule as imagined by Verne.
d, Space capsule.
$400, Man on the Moon.

**2005, Aug. 12**                  *Perf. 12¾*
3921  A456 $150 Sheet of 4, #a-d  6.50  6.50
         **Souvenir Sheet**
3922  A456 $400 multi          5.00  5.00

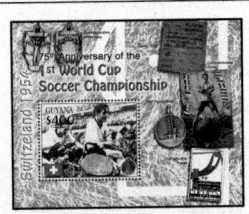

World Cup Soccer Championships, 75th Anniv. — A457

No. 3923: a, 1954 Germany team. b, Final goal in 1954 German victory over Hungary. c, Wankdorf Stadium. d, Helmut Rahn. $400, German players celebrating victory.

**2005, Aug. 12**     **Perf. 12**
3923 A457 $150 Sheet of 4, #a-d   8.00 8.00
**Souvenir Sheet**
3924 A457 $400 multi     4.75 4.75

Space A458

No. 3925: a, Luna 9 in space. b, Luna 9 capsule. c, Oceanus Procellarum region of Moon. d, Sergei Korolev. e, First images of the Moon. f, Launch of Molniya 8K78M rocket.
No. 3926, $200: a, Space Shuttle Discovery docked with International Space Station Destiny Laboratory. b, Astronaut Stephen K. Robinson attached to Canadarm 2. c, View of Discovery during docking operation. d, Discovery and stairway truck.
No. 3927, $200, vert.: a, First launch of Space Shuttle Columbia. b, Astronaut Robert C. Crippen. c, Astronaut John W. Young. d, Mission control.
No. 3928, $200, vert.: a, Launch vehicle MV-5 rocket. b, Hayabusa satellite. c, Composite color image of Itokawa asteroid. d, Projected return to Earth of satellite.
No. 3929, $400, Venus Express. No. 3930, $400, Lunar Reconnaissance Orbiter. No. 3931, $400, Calipso satellite. No. 3932, $400, Hayabusa satellite over Itokawa asteroid.

**2006**     **Litho.**     **Perf. 14**
3925 A458 $160 Sheet of 6, #a-f   12.50 12.50
**Sheets of 4, #a-d**
3926-3928 A458 Set of 3   28.00 28.00
**Souvenir Sheets**
3929-3932 A458 Set of 4   17.00 17.00
Issued: Nos. 3925, 3926, 3930, 7/10, Nos. 3928, 3932, 7/27.

Souvenir Sheet

"Penny Magenta" Stamp, 150th Anniv. — A459

**2006, July 27**     **Perf. 12x11½**
3933 A459 $400 multi     4.50 4.50

Souvenir Sheet

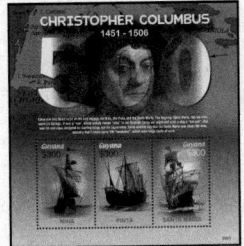

Christopher Columbus (1451-1506), Explorer — A460

No. 3934: a, Nina. b, Pinta. c, Santa Maria.

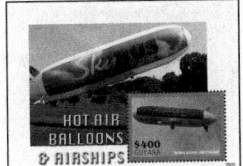

Airships A461

No. 3935: a, De Beers Zeppelin NT. b, Lockheed Martin LTA 2004. c, Strattelite concept airship.
$400, Skybus Airship.

**2006, July 27**     **Perf. 13¼**
3935 A461 $200 Sheet of 3, #a-c   7.25 7.25
**Souvenir Sheet**
3936 A461 $400 multi     4.50 4.50

Rembrandt (1606-69), Painter — A462

No. 3937 — Details from The Music Makers: a, Man with viola. b, Woman with shawl. c, Man with harp. d, Woman with tiara.
$400, Old Man with a Jewelled Cross.

**2006, July 27**     **Perf. 13¼**
3937 A462 $160 Sheet of 4, #a-d   8.25 8.25
**Imperf**
3938 A462 $400 shown     4.50 4.50
No. 3937 contains four 37x50mm stamps.

Queen Elizabeth II, 80th Birthday A463

No. 3939: a, Queen and Guyana Parliament Building. b, Queen wearing black and white hat.
$400, Queen and flags of Guyana and Great Britain.

**2006, July 27**     **Perf. 13¼**
3939 A463 $200 Pair, #a-b   4.50 4.50
**Souvenir Sheet**
3940 A463 $400 multi     5.25 5.25
No. 3939 printed in sheets containing two pairs.

Souvenir Sheet

2006 World Cup Soccer Championships, Germany — A464

**2006, July 27**     **Perf. 13¼**
3934 A460 $300 Sheet of 3, #a-c   11.00 11.00

No. 3941 — 2006 World Cup emblem, World Cup and: a, $80, Man in Japanese clothing. b, $100, Kemari players. c, $160, Tsu chu players. d, $300, People's Republic of China #2073.

**2006, Sept. 14**    **Litho.**    **Perf. 13¼**
3941 A464   Sheet of 4, #a-d   7.00 7.00

Betty Boop A465

No. 3942, vert.: a, With top hat and cane. b, Holding mirror. c, Holding flower bouquet. d, In city. e, At microphone. f, Lifting dress.
No. 3943: a, Sitting with legs crossed. b, In car.

**2006, Dec. 14**    **Litho.**    **Perf. 14**
3942 A465 $100 Sheet of 6, #a-f   6.50 6.50
**Souvenir Sheet**
3943 A465 $200 Sheet of 2, #a-b   4.25 4.25

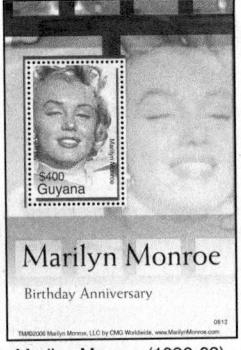

Marilyn Monroe (1926-62), Actress — A466

No. 3944: a, Wearing beret. b, Wearing red dress, horizontal post at both sides of neck. c, Wearing red dress, horizontal post at left of neck. d, With eyes closed.
$400, With eyes partially closed.

**2007, Feb. 15**     **Perf. 13¼**
3944 A466 $200 Sheet of 4, #a-d   8.00 8.00
**Souvenir Sheet**
3945 A466 $400 multi     4.00 4.00

Dogs A467

No. 3946: a, Papillon. b, Dogue de Bordeaux. c, Cavalier King Charles spaniel. d, Neapolitan mastiff.
$400, Basset hound.

**2007, Feb. 15**     **Perf. 14**
3946 A467 $160 Sheet of 4, #a-d   6.50 6.50
**Souvenir Sheet**
3947 A467 $400 multi     4.00 4.00

Cats — A468

Designs: $25, Chartreux. $35, Seal snowshoe. $60, Maine coon cat. $300, Turkish Angora.
$400, Blue Burmese, vert.

**2007, Feb. 15**
3948-3951 A468   Set of 4   4.25 4.25
**Souvenir Sheet**
3952 A468 $400 multi     4.00 4.00

Birds — A469

Designs: $25, Summer tanager. $35, Graycheeked thrush. $60, Blackpoll warbler. $300, Thick-billed parrot.
No. 3957, vert.: a, Golden-tailed warbler. b, Blue-crowned parakeet. c, White-winged parakeet. d, Yellow-green vireo.
No. 3958, $400, Pacific golden plover, vert. No. 3959, $400, Bobolink, vert.

**2007, Feb. 15**
3953-3956 A469   Set of 4   4.25 4.25
3957 A469 $160 Sheet of 4, #a-d   6.50 6.50
**Souvenir Sheets**
3958-3959 A469   Set of 2   8.00 8.00
For overprint, see No. 4025.

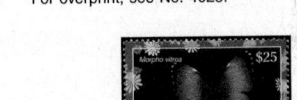

Butterflies A470

Designs: $25, Morpho vitrea. $35, Rothschildia hesperus. $60, Anaea nessus. $300, Dryas iulia.
No. 3964: a, Callithea sapphira. b, Prepona buckleyana. c, Lycorea pasinutia. d, Danaus eresimus.
No. 3965, $400, Cithaerias aurorina. No. 3966, $400, Eurytides protesilaus.

**2007, Feb. 15**
3960-3963 A470   Set of 4   4.25 4.25
3964 A470 $160 Sheet of 4, #a-d   6.50 6.50
**Souvenir Sheets**
3965-3966 A470   Set of 2   8.00 8.00

Orchids — A471

Designs: $25, Bletia florida. $35, Basiphyllaea corallicola. $60, Calopogon multiflorus. $300, Bletia purpurea.
No. 3971: a, Cypripedium acaule. b, Calopogon tuberosus. c, Calopogon pallidus. d, Bletia patula.
$400, Cypripedium reginae.

**2007, Feb. 15**
3967-3970 A471   Set of 4   4.25 4.25
3971 A471 $160 Sheet of 4, #a-d   6.50 6.50
**Souvenir Sheet**
3972 A471 $400 multi     4.00 4.00

Souvenir Sheet

New Year 2007 (Year of the Pig) A472

No. 3973 — Pig at: a, $55, Right. b, $80, Left. c, $100, Right. d, $160, Left.

**2007, Mar. 21**     **Perf. 13¼**
3973 A472 Sheet of 4, #a-d    4.00 4.00

**Souvenir Sheet**

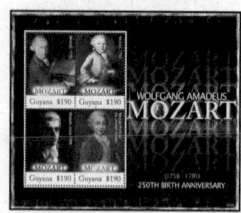

Wolfgang Amadeus Mozart (1756-91), Composer — A473

No. 3974 — Mozart: a, In 1770. b, In 1762. c, Circa 1789. d, Portrait by Joseph Grassi.

**2007, Mar. 21**
3974 A473 $190 Sheet of 4, #a-d 7.50 7.50

Scouting, Cent. A474

No. 3975, horiz.: a, Lord Robert Baden-Powell and dove. b, Scouts on raft. c, Scouts pulling tug-of-war rope.
$400, Dove and hand of Baden-Powell.

**2007, Mar. 21**
3975 A474 $180 Sheet of 3, #a-c 5.50 5.50

**Souvenir Sheet**
3976 A474 $400 multi     4.00 4.00

**Souvenir Sheets**

Pres. John F. Kennedy (1917-63) — A475

No. 3977: a, $80, Taking oath of office. b, $100, Giving inaugural speech. c, $160, Portrait. d, $190, With wife at inaugural ball.
No. 3978: a, $80, Peace Corps. b, $100, Space program. c, $160, Civil rights. d, $190, Portrait, diff.

**2007, Mar. 21**     **Perf. 13¼**
**Sheets of 4, #a-d**
3977-3978 A475 Set of 2    10.50 10.50

Elvis Presley (1935-77) A476

No. 3979, $160: a, Wearing glasses, blue panel at top. b, Without glasses, red background.
No. 3980, $160: a, Without glasses, orange panel at bottom. b, With glasses, red background.

**2007, Mar. 21**     **Perf. 14**
**Pairs, #a-b**
3979-3980 A476 Set of 2    6.50 6.50
Nos. 3979-3980 each were printed in sheets containing two pairs.

---

2007 Cricket World Cup, West Indies — A477

Designs: $100, Cricket World Cup emblem, map and flag of Guyana. $200, Guyana cricket team, horiz.
$500, Cricket World Cup emblem.

**2007, Mar. 28**     **Perf. 13¼**
3981-3982 A477 Set of 2    3.00 3.00
**Souvenir Sheet**
3983 A477 $500 multi    5.00 5.00

A478

Pope Benedict XVI A479

**2007, Apr. 17**   **Litho.**   **Perf. 13¼**
3984 A478 $80 multi     .80 .80
**Litho. & Embossed**
***Serpentine Die Cut***
**Without Gum**
3985 A479 $1500 multi    15.00 15.00
No. 3984 was printed in sheets of 8.

Concorde A480

No. 3986, $100: a, Concorde Prototype 002 and towing vehicle. b, Concorde Prototype 002 and stairway.
No. 3987, $100: a, Concorde and Royal Air Force Red Arrows. b, Concorde, Red Arrows and Queen Elizabeth 2.

**2007, Apr. 17**   **Litho.**   **Perf. 13¼**
**Pairs, #a-b**
3986-3987 A480 Set of 2    4.00 4.00
Nos. 3986-3987 were each printed in sheets containing 3 pairs.

**Miniature Sheet**

2008 Summer Olympics, Beijing — A481

No. 3988: a, Field hockey. b, Basketball. c, Judo. d, Shooting.

**2008, Apr. 22**   **Litho.**   **Perf. 13¼x13**
3988 A481 $100 Sheet of 4, #a-d 4.00 4.00

---

10th Caribbean Festival of Arts — A482

Map in: $20, Yellow and white, frame in red. $55, White, frame in green. $80, Yellow and white, frame in blue green. $160, Green, frame in white and yellow.

**2008, Aug. 19**     **Perf. 14¼**
3989-3992 A482 Set of 4    3.25 3.25

Jesuits in Guyana, 150th Anniv. — A483

Designs: $80, St. Stanislaus College. $100, Sacred Heart Church. $160, Father Cuthbert Cary-Elwes, missionary, and indigenous people.

**2008, Aug. 25**   **Litho.**   **Perf. 13x13¼**
3993-3995 A483 Set of 3    3.50 3.50

**Souvenir Sheet**

Sir James Douglas (1803-77), First Governor of British Columbia — A484

**2008, Aug. 25**     **Perf. 13¼**
3996 A484 $160 multi    1.60 1.60

Peony — A485

**2009, Apr. 10**     **Litho.**
3997 A485 $80 multi     .80 .80
Printed in sheets of 8.

**Miniature Sheet**

Elvis Presley (1935-77) — A486

No. 3998 — Presley with: a, Red and blue jacket, bright yellow face, holding microphone. b, Brown jacket, holding microphone. c, White

---

jacket and red shirt. d, Tan and white shirt. e, Gray face, holding microphone. f, With hand open.

**2009, July 7**     **Perf. 12**
3998 A486 $160 Sheet of 6, #a-f 9.50 9.50

**Miniature Sheet**

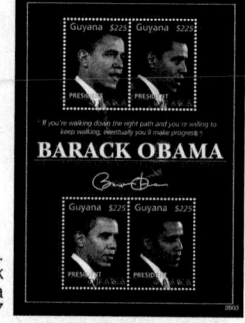

US Pres. Barack Obama A487

No. 3999 — Pres. Obama with: a, Gray tie, with "O" on jacket and shirt collar and "B" on shirt collar and tie. b, Gray tie, with "O" on jacket and shirt collar and "B" on tie and jacket. c, Red tie. d, Gray tie, with "O" on jacket and "B" on tie and shirt collar.

**2009, July 7**     **Perf. 12**
3999 A487 $225 Sheet of 4, #a-d 9.00 9.00

**Miniature Sheet**

China 2009 World Stamp Exhibition, Luoyang — A488

No. 4000 — Unnamed works of art by Wang Hui (1632-1717): a, Flowers. b, Mountain at right. c, Mountain at left in clouds, part of show emblem at LR. d, Mountain in center, part of show emblem at LL.

**2009, Apr. 10**   **Litho.**   **Perf. 12**
4000 A488 $100 Sheet of 4, #a-d 4.00 4.00

**Miniature Sheet**

Georgetown Rotary Club, 50th Anniv. — A489

No. 4001 — Map of Guyana, Rotary International emblem and: a, $80, 50th anniversary commemorative magazine. b, $80, Santa Claus visiting the elderly. c, $160, Poster showing people in wheelchairs. d, $160, Man and boy in front of canopy.

**2009, July 22**     **Perf. 11½**
4001 A489   Sheet of 4, #a-d   4.75 4.75

**Miniature Sheet**

Ferrari Race Cars A490

No. 4002: a, 1952 500 F2. b, 1953, 500 F2. c, 1958, 246 F1. d, 1976 312 T2.

**2009, July 22**     **Perf. 14¼**
4002 A490 $200 Sheet of 4, #a-d 8.00 8.00

## Souvenir Sheet

Takutu Bridge A491

**2009, Sept. 14**      *Perf. 13¼*
4003 A491 $400 multi     4.00 4.00

Scouting — A492

Designs: No. 4004, $55, Parade for Guyana Scouting centenary. No. 4005, $55, Scout shooting arrow at 14th Caribbean Jamboree, vert. No. 4006, $80, Scout leader, Scout and tent. No. 4007, $80, Scouts lashing logs together. No. 4008, $160, Guyana Scouting Centenary emblem. No. 4009, $160, Emblem of 14th Caribbean Jamboree.

     *Perf. 14¾x14, 14x14¾*
**2009, Sept. 29**
4004-4009 A492    Set of 6     5.75 5.75

### Miniature Sheets

A493

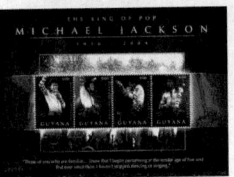

Michael Jackson (1958-2009), Singer — A494

No. 4010: a, Wearing jacket with red collar. b, Wearing hat. c, Wearing black jacket, with microphone at mouth. d, Wearing red and black shirt, with microphone at mouth.

No. 4011: a, Facing forward, with microphone at mouth. b, Facing right, with microphone at waist. c, Facing left, with microphone at mouth. d, Facing forward with arms at side, with microphone at waist.

**2009, Oct. 9**      *Perf. 11½x11¼*
4010 A493 $180 Sheet of 4, #a-d   7.25 7.25
     *Perf. 11¼x11½*
4011 A494 $180 Sheet of 4, #a-d   7.25 7.25

### Miniature Sheets

Teams in 2009 National Basketball Association Finals — A495

No. 4012, $90 — Los Angeles Lakers: a, Trevor Ariza. b, Shannon Brown. c, Jordan Farmar. d, Andrew Bynum. e, Kobe Bryant. f, Derek Fisher. g, Pau Gasol. h, Lamar Odom. i, Luke Walton.

---

No. 4013, $90 — Orlando Magic: a. Rafer Alston. b, Marcin Gortat. c, Rashard Lewis. d, Courtney Lee. e, Dwight Howard. f, Jameer Nelson. g, Mickael Pietrus. h, J. J. Redick. i, Hedo Türkoglu.

**2009, Oct. 9**      *Perf. 14¼*
     **Sheets of 9, #a-i**
4012-4013 A495   Set of 2    16.00 16.00

British Commonwealth, 60th Anniv. — A496

**2009, Nov. 25**   Litho.   *Perf. 12x11½*
4014 A496 $60 multi      .60 .60
    Printed in sheets of 6.

### Miniature Sheet

National Library, Cent. A497

No. 4015: a, Building exterior, black and white photograph. b, Building exterior, color photograph. c, Interior, color photograph. d, Interior, black and white photograph.

**2009, Dec. 15**      *Perf. 11½x12*
4015 A497 $100 Sheet of 4, #a-d   4.00 4.00

Chinese Aviation, Cent. A498

No. 4016: a, J-8II. b, J-11. c, J-10 with landing gear visible. d, J-10 with landing gear retracted.
$100, J-10, diff.

**2009, Dec. 15**      *Perf. 14*
4016 A498 $150 Sheet of 4, #a-d   6.00 6.00
     **Souvenir Sheet**
     *Perf. 14¼*
4017 A498 $100 multi      1.00 1.00
  Aeropex 2009, Beijing. No. 4016 contains four 42x28mm stamps.

Pope Benedict XVI and Pope John Paul II A499

No. 4018 — Pope Benedict XVI (while Cardinal) and Pope John Paul II with: a, Part of dome of St. Peter's Basilica at LL. b, Upper section of Basilica entablature at bottom. c, Columns of Basilica at bottom, with dark grayish yellow area next to denomination. d, As "c," with smaller light grayish yellow area next to denomination.

No. 4019: a, Pope Benedict XVI (while Cardinal). b, Pope John Paul II.

**2009, Dec. 15**      *Perf. 11½*
4018 A499 $200 Sheet of 4, #a-d   8.00 8.00
     **Souvenir Sheet**
     *Perf. 11½x12*
4019 A499 $400 Sheet of 2, #a-b   8.00 8.00

---

### Miniature Sheet

Chinese Zodiac Animals A500

No. 4020: a, Rat. b, Ox. c, Tiger. d, Rabbit. e, Dragon. f, Snake. g, Horse. h, Ram. i, Monkey. j, Cock. k, Dog. l, Pig.

**2010, Jan. 4**      *Perf. 12*
4020 A500 $45 Sheet of 12, #a-l   5.25 5.25

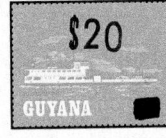

No. 661 Srchd.

### Method, Perf and Watermark As Before

**2010**
4020J A85 $20 on 30c #661     —
  Obliterator is a marker line over old denomination.

Nos. 2316, 2363, 2932, 2935 and 2942A Handstamped Surcharged in Violet and Black

### Methods, Perfs and Watermarks As Before

**2010**
| | | | |
|---|---|---|---|
| 4020K | A215 | $20 on $6 #2932 | 40.00 40.00 |
| 4020L | A215a | $20 on $6 #2942A | 40.00 40.00 |
| 4020M | A125 | $20 on $8.90 #2316 | — |
| 4020N | A129 | $20 on $17.80 #2363 | 90.00 90.00 |
| 4020O | A215 | $20 on $19 #2935 | 40.00 40.00 |

  Obliterators are marker lines over old denominations.

No. 2942A Surcharged

**2010**    **Method and Perf As Before**
4020P A215a $20 on $6 #2942A   150.00 150.00
  Obliterator is a printed rectangle, which was augmented with a marker line when the rectangle missed the old denomination.

### Miniature Sheet

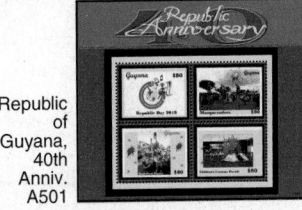

Republic of Guyana, 40th Anniv. A501

No. 4021: a, 2010 Republic Day emblem. b, Masqueraders. c, Mash float parade. d, Children's costume parade.

**2010, Mar. 17**      *Perf. 11½x12*
4021 A501 $80 Sheet of 4, #a-d   3.25 3.25

---

Personalizable Stamp — A502

**2010, Apr. 26**   Litho.   *Perf. 14¾x14*
4022 A502 $160 gray & black   1.60 1.60
  The image shown is generic. No. 4022 was available in sheets of 12 without any image ("Guyana $160" only), and vignette portions could be personalized.

Pope Benedict XVI A503

### Litho. & Embossed
**2010, Apr. 26**   *Die Cut Perf. 8½*
     **Without Gum**
4023 A503 $2000 multi   20.00 20.00

### Souvenir Sheet

Presidents of the United States and People's Republic of China — A504

No. 4024: a, Pres. Barack Obama. b, Pres. Hu Jintao.

**2010, Apr. 26**   Litho.   *Perf. 11½*
4024 A504 $300 Sheet of 2, #a-b   6.00 6.00

### No. 3957 Overprinted
     Miniature Sheet

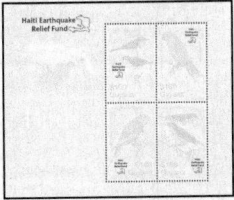

### Methods and Perfs As Before
**2010, Apr. 26**
4025 A469 $160 Sheet of 4, #a-d   6.25 6.25

### Miniature Sheets

Princess Diana (1961-97) — A505

No. 4026, $225 — Diana wearing: a, Tiara. b, Red and black hat. c, Blouse with red collar and cuffs. d, Sailor's hat.
No. 4027, $225 — Diana wearing: a, Black hat. b, Beige hat. c, White dress. d, Blue hat.

**2010, Apr. 26**   Litho.   *Perf. 12*
     **Sheets of 4, #a-d**
4026-4027 A505   Set of 2   18.00 18.00

## Souvenir Sheets

A506

A507

A508

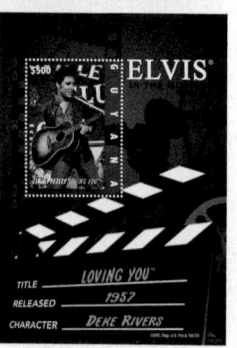

A509

Elvis Presley (1935-77) — A509

| 2010, Apr. 26 | | | | Perf. 13¼ | |
|---|---|---|---|---|---|
| 4028 | A506 | $500 | multi | 5.00 | 5.00 |
| 4029 | A507 | $500 | multi | 5.00 | 5.00 |
| 4030 | A508 | $500 | multi | 5.00 | 5.00 |
| 4031 | A509 | $500 | multi | 5.00 | 5.00 |
| | Nos. 4028-4031 (4) | | | 20.00 | 20.00 |

### Souvenir Sheet

New Year 2010 (Year of the Tiger) A510

No. 4032 — Tiger with denomination in: a, Green. b, White.

| 2010, Jan. 4 | Litho. | | Perf. 12 | |
|---|---|---|---|---|
| 4032 | A510 | $450 Sheet of 2, #a-b | 9.00 | 9.00 |

---

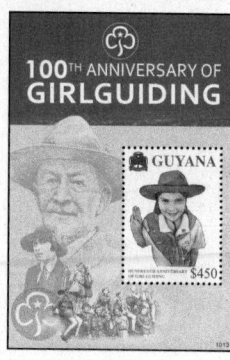

Girl Guides, Cent. A511

No. 4033, horiz.: a, Three Girl Guides wearing rabbit ears. b, Two Girl Guides. c, Three Girl Guides wearing blue uniforms. d, Four Girl Guides holding rope.
$450, Girl Guide saluting.

| 2010, July 14 | | Perf. 11½x12 | |
|---|---|---|---|
| 4033 | A511 $275 Sheet of 4, #a-d | 11.00 | 11.00 |

**Souvenir Sheet**
**Perf. 11¼x11½**

| 4034 | A511 $450 multi | 4.50 | 4.50 |
|---|---|---|---|

### Miniature Sheet

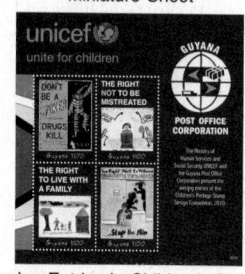

Winning Entries In Children's Postage Stamp Design Contest — A512

No. 4035 — Slogan: a, Don't Be a Joker - Drugs Kill. b, The Right Not to be Mistreated. c, The Right to Live With a Family. d, Your Right Not to Witness Domestic Violence.

| 2010, Sept. 2 | | Perf. 12 | |
|---|---|---|---|
| 4035 | A512 $100 Sheet of 4, #a-d | 4.00 | 4.00 |

### Miniature Sheet

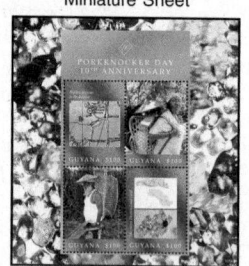

Porkknocker Day, 10th Anniv. — A513

No. 4036: a, Map of area near Bartica. b, Cyrilda de Jesus, female porkknocker (miner). c, Dick Manning, male porkknocker. d, Mazaruni diamonds and gold nuggets.

**2010, Oct. 14**

| 4036 | A513 $100 Sheet of 4, #a-d | 4.00 | 4.00 |
|---|---|---|---|

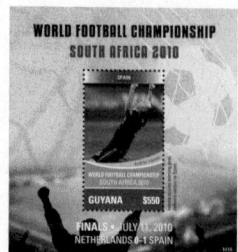

2010 World Cup Soccer Championships, South Africa — A514

No. 4037, $120: a, Joan Capdevila. b, Arjen Robben. c, Pedro. d, Gregory Van Der Wiel. e, Xabi Alonso. f, Wesley Sneijder.

---

No. 4038, $120: a, Dennis Aogo. b, Diego Forlan. c, Bastian Schweinsteiger. d, Martin Caceres. e, Stefan Kiessling. f, Maximiliano Pereira.
No. 4039, $550, Andres Iniesta. No. 4040, $550, Thomas Mueller.

| 2011, Feb. 21 | | Litho. | Perf. 12 | |
|---|---|---|---|---|
| **Sheets of 6, #a-f** | | | | |
| 4037-4038 | A514 | Set of 2 | 14.00 | 14.00 |
| **Souvenir Sheets** | | | | |
| 4039-4040 | A514 | Set of 2 | 11.00 | 11.00 |

### Miniature Sheets

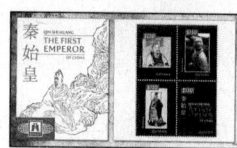

Qin Shi Huang (259 B.C-210 B.C), First Emperor of China A515

Deng Xiaoping (1904-97), Paramount Leader of People's Republic of China — A516

Jiang Zemin, President of People's Republic of China, 1993-2003 — A517

No. 4041: a, 21x22mm painting of Qin Shi Huang. b, Sculpture. c, 16x28 painting of Qin Shi Huang. d, Text.
No. 4042: Various photographs of Deng Xiaoping, as shown.
No. 4043: Various photographs of Jiang Zemin, as shown.

**2011, Feb. 21**

| 4041 | A515 | $150 Sheet of 4, #a-d | 6.00 | 6.00 |
|---|---|---|---|---|
| 4042 | A516 | $150 Sheet of 4, #a-d | 6.00 | 6.00 |
| 4043 | A517 | $150 Sheet of 4, #a-d | 6.00 | 6.00 |
| | Nos. 4041-4043 (3) | | 18.00 | 18.00 |

Beijing 2010 Intl. Stamp Exhibition.

### Souvenir Sheet

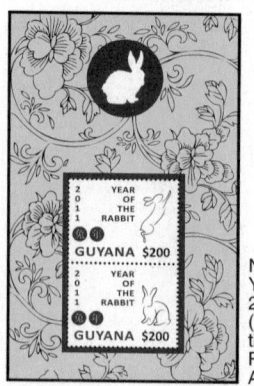

New Year 2011 (Year of the Rabbit) A518

No. 4044 — Rabbit: a, Leaping. b, Sitting.

| 2011, Feb. 21 | Litho. | | Perf. 12 | |
|---|---|---|---|---|
| 4044 | A518 | $200 Sheet of 2, #a-b | 4.00 | 4.00 |

Christmas 2010 — A519

---

Paintings: $80, The Adoration of the Magi, by Hieronymus Bosch. $100, The Adoration of the Magi, by Peter Paul Rubens. $225, Madonna and Child, by Carlo Crivelli. $500, The Flight into Egypt, by Lucas Cranach the Elder.

| 2011, Mar. 9 | Litho. | | Perf. 12¾x12½ | |
|---|---|---|---|---|
| 4045-4048 | A519 | Set of 4 | 9.00 | 9.00 |

### Miniature Sheets

A520

Pope John Paul II (1920-2005) — A521

No. 4049: With "G" of "Guyana" on Papal Arms: a, Orange denomination, wearing vestments without clerical collar. b, Wearing white vestments and zucchetto. c, Wearing miter. d, Orange denomination, wearing vestments with clerical collar.
No. 4050: With "G" of Guyana to right of Papal Arms: a, Black denomination, praying. b, Wearing white vestments. c, Holding crucifix. d, White denomination, praying.

| 2011, Mar. 9 | | | Perf. 13x13¼ | |
|---|---|---|---|---|
| 4049 | A520 | $225 Sheet of 4, #a-d | 9.00 | 9.00 |
| 4050 | A521 | $225 Sheet of 4, #a-d | 9.00 | 9.00 |

Text on Nos. 4049a-4049d is incorrectly placed on stamps.

A522

Pope Benedict XVI A523

No. 4052: a, Blue sky at UL. b, Blue sky at UR. c, Part of bird above "XVI." d, Birds above "N" and last "A" in "Guyana."

| 2011, Mar. 9 | | | Perf. 13x13¼ | |
|---|---|---|---|---|
| 4051 | A522 | $225 multi | 2.25 | 2.25 |
| **Perf. 12** | | | | |
| 4052 | A523 | $225 Sheet of 4, #a-d | 9.00 | 9.00 |

### Souvenir Sheets

Popes and Their Coats of Arms A524

No. 4053, $725: a, Pope Benedict XV (1854-1922). b, Arms of Pope Benedict XV.
No. 4054, $725: a, Pope Pius XI (1857-1939). b, Arms of Pope Pius XI.

| 2011, Mar. 9 | Litho. | | Imperf. | |
|---|---|---|---|---|
| **Sheets of 2, #a-b** | | | | |
| **Without Gum** | | | | |
| 4053-4054 | A524 | Set of 2 | 29.00 | 29.00 |

## Miniature Sheets

Intl. Year of Astronomy (in 2009) — A525

No. 4055, $225: a, UNITEC-1. b, IKAROS. c, KSAT Negai. d, Waseda-sat 2.
No. 4056, $255: a, Phobos-Grunt arrival. b, Phobos-Grunt landing. c, Mars Reconnaissance Orbiter. d, Phobos-Grunt liftoff.

**2011, Mar. 9    Litho.    Perf. 13x13¼**
**Sheets of 4, #a-d**
4055-4056  A525  Set of 2    19.00 19.00

A526

U.S. Pres. Abraham Lincoln (1809-65) — A527

No. 4057 — Lincoln: a, With beard. b, Without beard.
No. 4058 — Background color above shoulder at right: a, Gray. b, Pink. c, Greenish gray. d, Lilac.

**2011, Mar. 9    Litho.    Perf. 13¼x13**
4057  A526  $225 Pair, #a-b    4.50 4.50
          **Perf. 12½**
4058  A527  $225 Sheet of 4, #a-d  9.00 9.00
No. 4057 was printed in sheets containing two pairs.

### Miniature Sheets

United States Civil War, 150th Anniv. A528

No. 4059, $225 — Eagle, shield, Union and Confederate flags, Lieutenant Colonel John Pegram and Brigadier General William S. Rosecrans of Battle of Rich Mountain, July 11, 1861, and: a, Engagement at Rich Mountain. b, Battle of Rich Mountain (purple vignette). c, Battle of Rich Mountain (red brown vignette). d, Confederate prisoners.
No. 4060, $225 — Eagle, shield, Union and Confederate flags, Brigadier General James Longstreet and General Daniel Tyler of Battle of Blackburn's Ford, July 18, 1861, and: a, Blackburn's Ford. b, Members of Longstreet's brigade. c, Fairfax County Courthouse. d, Battle of Blackburn's Ford.
No. 4061, $225 — Eagle, shield, Union and Confederate flags, Brigadier General Joseph E. Johnston and Brigadier General Irvin McDowell of First Battle of Bull Run, July 21, 1861, and: a, First Battle of Bull Run. b, Confederate fortifications, Manassas. c, Union charge at Bull Run. d, Henry House in ruins.

**2011, Apr. 4    Perf. 13 Syncopated**
**Sheets of 4, #a-d**
4059-4061  A528  Set of 3    27.00 27.00

Engagement of Prince William and Catherine Middleton — A529

Designs: No. 4062, Couple (black-and-white photo).
No. 4063 — Color photographs: a, Couple holding hands. b, Couple, Middleton wearing hat. c, Middleton. d, Prince William.
No. 4064 — Black-and-white photographs: a, Prince William. b, Middleton.
$450, Couple, Middleton at left.

**2011, Apr. 4    Perf. 12**
4062  A529  $200 multi    2.00 2.00
4063  A529  $200 Sheet of 4, #a-d  8.00 8.00
**Souvenir Sheets**
**Perf. 13 Syncopated**
4064  A529  $225 Sheet of 2, #a-b  4.50 4.50
4065  A529  $450 multi    4.50 4.50
No. 4062 was printed in sheets of 4.

Mother Teresa (1910-97), Humanitarian — A530

**2011, Apr. 4    Perf. 12**
4066  A530  $225 multi    2.25 2.25
Printed in sheets of 4.

Indipex 2011 Intl. Philatelic Exhibition, New Delhi — A531

No. 4067, $225 — Taj Mahal, Agra: a, Interior hallway. b, Large and small domes. c, Mausoleum, minarets and reflecting pool. d, Exterior wall and arches.
No. 4068, $225: a, Temple of Shiva, Varanasi. b, Ramnagar Fort. c, Kangra Valley. d, Khajuraho Temple.
$450, Statue of Lord Shiva.

**Perf. 13 Syncopated**
**2011, Apr. 4    Litho.**
**Sheets of 4, #a-d**
4067-4068  A531  Set of 2    17.50 17.50
**Souvenir Sheet**
**Perf. 12¾**
4069  A531  $450 multi    4.50 4.50
No. 4069 contains one 38x51mm stamp.

Worldwide Fund for Nature (WWF) — A532

No. 4070 — Bush dogs: a, Three at water hole. b, Four at water hole. c, Three in den. d, Head of adult.

**2011, June 6    Litho.    Perf. 13¼**
4070        Block of 4    6.00 6.00
  a.-d.    A532 $150 Any single  1.50 1.50
  e.    Souvenir sheet of 8, 2 each  12.00 12.00
        #4070a-4070d

Tenth World Cricket Cup Championships, India, Sri Lanka and Bangladesh A533

Designs: $100, Shivnarine Chanderpaul. $150, Sardar Patel Stadium, Ahmedabad, India, horiz.
$300, Cricket World Cup.

**2011, June 20    Perf. 12¾**
4071-4072  A533  Set of 2    2.50 2.50
**Souvenir Sheet**
**Perf. 13 Syncopated**
4073  A533  $300 multi    3.00 3.00

U.S. Pres. Barack Obama A534

No. 4074, $225: a, Black background. b, Blue background.
No. 4075, $225: a, Bister background. b, Red background.

**2011, June 20    Perf. 13 Syncopated**
**Pairs, #a-b**
4074-4075  A534  Set of 2    8.75 8.75
Nos. 4074-4075 each were printed in sheets containing two pairs.

A535

U.S. Pres. John F. Kennedy (1917-63) — A536

No. 4076: a, Head of Kennedy. b, Kennedy at lectern in stadium. c, Kennedy at lectern (black-and-white photo).
No. 4077: a, Kennedy and wife, Jacqueline (black-and-white photo). b, Kennedy presidential campaign button. c, Kennedy talking to person. d, Kennedy and wife (color photo).

**2011, June 20    Perf. 13 Syncopated**
4076  A535  $175 Horiz. strip of 3,    5.25 5.25
          #a-c
4077  A536  $225 Sheet of 4, #a-d  8.75 8.75
No. 4076 was printed in sheet containing two strips.

Wedding of Prince William and Catherine Middleton — A537

No. 4078, $250 — Black-and-white photos of: a, Prince William. b, Couple. c, Procession in streets. d, Middleton.
No. 4079, $275, vert. — Color photos of: a, Couple holding hands (30x40mm. b, Couple in coach. c, Couple (60x40mm, with perforations in middle of stamp).
$500, Couple kissing, vert.

**2011, Sept. 19    Perf. 12½x12**
4078  A537  $250 Sheet of 4,    10.00 10.00
          #a-d
          **Perf. 12x12½**
4079  A537  $275 Sheet of 3,    8.25 8.25
          #a-c
          **Souvenir Sheet**
          **Perf. 13¼**
4080  A537  $500 multi    5.00 5.00
No. 4080 contains one 38x51mm stamp.

### Souvenir Sheet

Visit to Germany of Pope Benedict XVI A538

**Litho. & Embossed**
**2011, Sept. 19    Microrouletted**
**Without Gum**
4081  A538  $3000 multi    30.00 30.00

Princess Diana (1961-97) — A539

No. 4082 — Princess Diana wearing: a, Pink hat and dress. b, White dress and veil. c, Striped sweater.
$450, Princess Diana wearing black hat, horiz.

**2011, Oct. 12    Litho.    Perf. 12x12½**
4082  A539  $275 Sheet of 3, #a-c  8.25 8.25
          **Souvenir Sheet**
          **Perf. 13¼**
4083  A539  $450 multi    4.50 4.50
No. 4083 contains one 51x38mm stamp.

### Miniature Sheets

A540

A541

Elvis Presley (1935-77) — A542

No. 4084 — Presley: a, Outdoors wearing leis. b, Holding microphone with hand even with his neck. c, Holding microphone with hand below his neck. d, Waving.
No. 4085 — Presley: a, With hand touching head. b, Playing guitar, figures in background out of focus. c, Playing guitar, figures in background in focus. d, Dancing, with jail bars in background.

No. 4086 — Presley albums: a, Viva Las Vegas. b, Elvis (curved lettering). c, Elvis (block letters in lights). d, I Got Stung.

No. 4087 — Presley albums: a, Blue Hawaii. b, Elvis' Gold Records. c, Elvis Presley. d, Moody Blue.

| | | | | |
|---|---|---|---|---|
| **2011, Oct. 12** | | | **Perf. 12x12½** | |
| 4084 | A540 | $225 Sheet of 4, #a-d | 9.00 | 9.00 |
| 4085 | A541 | $225 Sheet of 4, #a-d | 9.00 | 9.00 |
| | | **Perf. 12½x12** | | |
| 4086 | A542 | $225 Sheet of 4, #a-d | 9.00 | 9.00 |
| 4087 | A542 | $225 Sheet of 4, #a-d | 9.00 | 9.00 |
| | Nos. 4084-4087 (4) | | 36.00 | 36.00 |

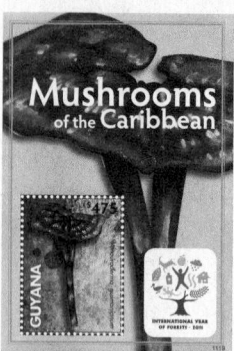

Mushrooms — A543

No. 4088: a, Pseudotulostoma volvata. b, Inocybe ayangannae. c, Amanita perphaea. d, Entoloma olivaceacoloratum. e, Panaeolus cyanescens. f, Tylopilus vinaceipallidus.

No. 4089: a, Boletellus dicymbophilus. b, Inocybe epidendron. c, Tylopilus pakaraimensis. d, Amanita aurantiobrunnea.

No. 4090, $475, Amauroderma gusmanianum. No. 4091, $475, Craterellus excelsus.

| | | | | |
|---|---|---|---|---|
| **2011, Oct. 12** | | | **Perf. 11½** | |
| 4088 | A543 | $150 Sheet of 6, #a-f | 9.00 | 9.00 |
| 4089 | A543 | $225 Sheet of 4, #a-d | 9.00 | 9.00 |
| | **Souvenir Sheets** | | | |
| 4090-4091 | A543 | Set of 2 | 9.50 | 9.50 |

Intl. Year of Forests.

**Miniature Sheet**

Chinese Zodiac Animals A544

No. 4092: a, Rat. b, Ox. c, Tiger. d, Rabbit. e, Dragon. f, Snake. g, Horse. h, Sheep. i, Monkey. j, Rooster. k, Dog. l, Boar.

**Litho. With Foil Application**

| | | | | |
|---|---|---|---|---|
| **2012, Jan. 9** | | | **Perf. 13 Syncopated** | |
| 4092 | A544 | $50 Sheet of 12, #a-l | 6.00 | 6.00 |

King Edward VIII (1894-1972) — A545

King Edward VIII wearing: $300, Top hat. $700, Uniform, horiz.

| | | | | |
|---|---|---|---|---|
| **2012, May 30** | **Litho.** | | **Perf. 12** | |
| 4093 | A545 | $300 multi | 3.00 | 3.00 |
| a. | Inscribed "King Edward VIII" | | 3.00 | 3.00 |
| | **Souvenir Sheet** | | | |
| 4094 | A545 | $700 multi | 7.00 | 7.00 |
| a. | Inscribed "King Edward VIII" | | 7.00 | 7.00 |

No. 4094 contains one 50x30mm stamp. Nos. 4093-4094 are incorrectly inscribed "King Edward XIII."

A546

Birds A547

No. 4095, $160: a, Anhinga. b, Least grebe. c, Scarlet ibis. d, Neotropic cormorant.

No. 4096, $1.60: a, Northern caracara. b, Cocoi heron. c, Tricolored heron. d, Jabiru.

No. 4097, $400, Glossy ibis. No. 4098, $400, White-tailed kite, vert.

| | | | | |
|---|---|---|---|---|
| **2012, May 30** | | | **Perf. 14** | |
| | **Sheets of 4, #a-d** | | | |
| 4095-4096 | A546 | Set of 2 | 13.00 | 13.00 |
| | **Souvenir Sheets** | | | |
| | **Perf. 12** | | | |
| 4097-4098 | A547 | Set of 2 | 8.00 | 8.00 |

Butterflies — A548

No. 4099, $250, horiz.: a, Iphiclus sister. b, Gaudy altinote. c, Gulf fritillary. d, Tiger crescent.

No. 4100, $250, horiz.: a, Orange-banded gem. b, Red-barred amarynthis. c, Thesprotia sister. d, Orange-barred sister.

No. 4101, $500, White-barred sister. No. 4102, $500, Blue duskywing.

| | | | | |
|---|---|---|---|---|
| **2012, May 30** | | | **Perf. 14** | |
| | **Sheets of 4, #a-d** | | | |
| 4099-4100 | A548 | Set of 2 | 20.00 | 20.00 |
| | **Souvenir Sheets** | | | |
| | **Perf. 12½** | | | |
| 4101-4102 | A548 | Set of 2 | 10.00 | 10.00 |

Nos. 4099-4100 each contain four 40x30mm stamps.

A549

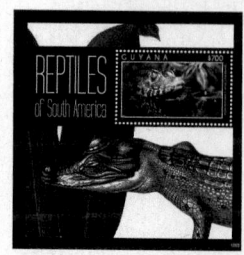

Reptiles A550

No. 4103, $250: a, Giant tortoise. b, Caiman lizard. c, Marine iguana. d, Milk snake.

No. 4104, $250: a, Rainbow whiptail. b, Emerald tree boa. c, Green vine snake. d, Green iguana.

No. 4105, $700, Spectacled caiman. No. 4106, $700, Boa constrictor, vert.

| | | | | |
|---|---|---|---|---|
| **2012, May 30** | | | **Perf. 14** | |
| | **Sheets of 4, #a-d** | | | |
| 4103-4104 | A549 | Set of 2 | 20.00 | 20.00 |
| | **Souvenir Sheets** | | | |
| | **Perf. 12** | | | |
| 4105-4106 | A550 | Set of 2 | 14.00 | 14.00 |

No. 4106 contains one 30x80mm stamp.

**Nos. 70, 89, 2367, 2368, 2370, 2662, 2781, 2782, 2783, 2784, 2859, 2883, 2933, 3004, and 3238 Handstamp Surcharged in Violet, Blue and/or Black**

No. 4107

No. 4108

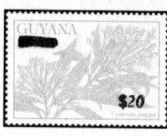

No. 4110

**Methods, Perfs and Watermarks As Before**

| | | | | |
|---|---|---|---|---|
| **2012** | | | | |
| 4107 | A7 | $20 on 3c #70 | 35.00 | 35.00 |
| 4108 | A14 | $20 on 30c #89 | 75.00 | 75.00 |
| 4109 | A231 | $20 on $6 #3004 | 45.00 | 45.00 |
| 4110 | A185 | $20 on $6.40 #2781 | 25.00 | 25.00 |
| 4111 | A185 | $20 on $7.65 #2782 | 25.00 | 25.00 |
| 4112 | A215 | $20 on $8 #2933 | | — |
| 4113 | A185 | $20 on $12.80 #2783 | 25.00 | 25.00 |
| 4114 | A185 | $20 on $15.30 #2784 | 25.00 | 25.00 |
| 4115 | A277 | $20 on $30 #3238 | 75.00 | 75.00 |
| | **Miniature Sheet of 8, #a-h** | | | |
| 4116 | A203 | $20 on $30 #2883 | | — |
| | **Miniature Sheets of 12, #a-l** | | | |
| 4117 | A162 | $20 on $30 #2662 | | — |
| 4118 | A200 | $20 on $35 #2859 | | — |
| | **Miniature Sheets of 16, #a-p** | | | |
| 4119 | A129 | $20 on $10 #2367 | | — |
| 4120 | A129 | $20 on $10 #2368 | | — |
| 4121 | A129 | $20 on $12.80 #2370 | | — |

**Footnoted Disney Types of 1995 Surcharged in Violet, Blue and Black**

No. 4122

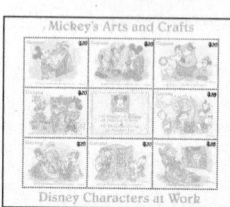

No. 4123

**Methods and Perfs As Before**

| | | | | |
|---|---|---|---|---|
| **2012** | | | | |
| | **Miniature Sheets of 8, #a-h, + Label** | | | |
| 4122 | A217 | $20 on $5 #2917 footnote | | — |
| 4123 | A213 | $20 on $5 #2918 footnote | | — |

**Miniature Sheet of 7, #a-g, + Label**

| | | | | |
|---|---|---|---|---|
| 4124 | A213 | $20 on $5 #2920 footnote | | — |

Flower Type of 1971-76 Surcharged in Violet and Blue

| | | | | |
|---|---|---|---|---|
| 4125 | A28 | $20 on 2c Yellow allamanda | 75.00 | 75.00 |
| 4126 | A28 | $20 on 8c Mazaruni Pride | 75.00 | 75.00 |
| a. | Pair, #4125-4126 | | | |

Nos. 4125-4126 were not issued without surcharge.

**No. 3360B Surcharged**

| | | | | |
|---|---|---|---|---|
| **2012** | **Litho.** | | **Perf. 13¼x13¾** | |
| 4127 | A309a | $20 on $30 #3360B | 35.00 | 35.00 |

**Souvenir Sheet**

Diplomatic Relations Between Guyana and People's Republic of China, 40th Anniv. — A552

No. 4128: a, Tiananmen, Beijing, China. b, Guyana International Conference Center.

| | | | | |
|---|---|---|---|---|
| **2012, June 27** | **Litho.** | | **Perf. 12½x12** | |
| 4128 | A552 | $350 Sheet of 2, #a-b | 7.00 | 7.00 |

2012 Summer Olympics, London — A553

No. 4129 — Mascots: a, Wenlock (with torch). b, Mandeville (without torch).

| | | | | |
|---|---|---|---|---|
| **2012, June 27** | | | **Perf. 14** | |
| 4129 | A553 | $125 Horiz. pair, #a-b | 2.50 | 2.50 |

No. 4129 was printed in sheets containing four pairs.

Orchids — A554

No. 4130: a, Ada aurantiaca. b, Cattleya labiata. c, Masdevallia haryana. d, Masdevallia davisii.

$700, Zygopetalum clayi.

| | | | | |
|---|---|---|---|---|
| **2012, Aug. 28** | | | **Perf. 13¾** | |
| 4130 | A554 | $250 Sheet of 4, #a-d | 10.00 | 10.00 |
| | **Souvenir Sheet** | | | |
| 4131 | A554 | $700 multi | 7.00 | 7.00 |

No. 357 Handstamp
Surcharged

**Method and Perf. As Before**

**2012 ?**

| | | | | |
|---|---|---|---|---|
| 4132 | A8 | $20 on 40c #357 | 50.00 | 50.00 |

Nos. 142 With
"Revenue Only"
Overprint, 445 and
506 Handstamp
Surcharged in Black

**2012 ?**                        **Litho.**

| | | | | |
|---|---|---|---|---|
| 4133 | A28 | $20 on 40c #142 with "Revenue Only" Overprint | 40.00 | 40.00 |
| 4134 | A11 | $20 on 40c on #445 | 65.00 | 65.00 |
| 4135 | A78 | $20 on 40c on 2c #506 | 65.00 | 65.00 |

No. 2937 Surcharged

**Method and Perf. As Before**

**2012 ?**

| | | | | |
|---|---|---|---|---|
| 4136 | A215 | $55 on $25 #2937 | | — |

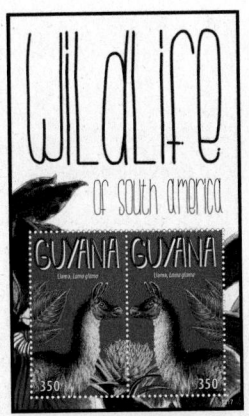

South American Wildlife — A555

No. 4137: a, Jaguar. b, Toucan. c, Chinchilla.
No. 4138: a, Llama facing right. b, Llama facing left.

**2012, Oct. 23    Litho.    Perf. 12**

| | | | | |
|---|---|---|---|---|
| 4137 | A555 | $300 Sheet of 3, #a-c | 9.00 | 9.00 |

**Souvenir Sheet**

| | | | | |
|---|---|---|---|---|
| 4138 | A555 | $350 Sheet of 2, #a-b | 7.00 | 7.00 |

A556

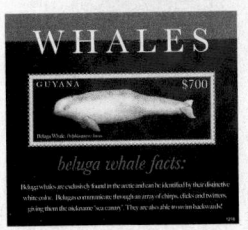

Whales
A557

No. 4139: a, Killer whale. b, Humpback whale. c, Blue whale.
$700, Beluga whale.

**2012, Oct. 23**

| | | | | |
|---|---|---|---|---|
| 4139 | A556 | $300 Sheet of 3, #a-c | 9.00 | 9.00 |

**Souvenir Sheet**

| | | | | |
|---|---|---|---|---|
| 4140 | A557 | $700 multi | 7.00 | 7.00 |

Dolphins
A558

No. 4141, $300: a, Spinner dolphin. b, Atlantic spotted dolphin. c, Amazon River dolphin.
No. 4142, $300: a, Clymene dolphin. b, Dusky dolphin. c, White-sided dolphin.
No. 4143, $700, Common dolphin. No. 4144, $700, Bottlenose dolphin, vert.

**Sheets of 3, #a-c**

**2012, Oct. 23    Perf. 14, 12 (#4144)**

| | | | | |
|---|---|---|---|---|
| 4141-4142 | A558 | Set of 2 | 18.00 | 18.00 |

**Souvenir Sheets**

| | | | | |
|---|---|---|---|---|
| 4143-4144 | A558 | Set of 2 | 14.00 | 14.00 |

Shells
A559

No. 4145: a, Melampus coffeus coffeus. b, Nerita fulgurans. c, Nerita peloronta. d, Littorina nebulosa. e, Tectarius muricatus. f, Hyalina avena.
No. 4146: a, Cassis flammea. b, Liguus virgineus. c, Trigonostoma rugosum. d, Neritina virginea.
No. 4147: a, Cassis raderi. No. 4148, $500, Cassis madagascariensis.

**2012, Oct. 23    Perf. 13 Syncopated**

| | | | | |
|---|---|---|---|---|
| 4145 | A559 | $175 Sheet of 6, #a-f | 10.50 | 10.50 |
| 4146 | A559 | $225 Sheet of 4, #a-d | 9.00 | 9.00 |

**Souvenir Sheets**

| | | | | |
|---|---|---|---|---|
| 4147-4148 | A559 | Set of 2 | 10.00 | 10.00 |

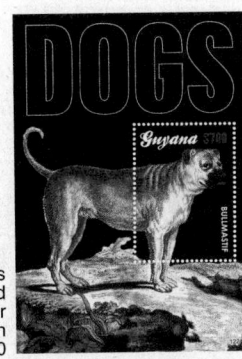

Dogs and Their Evolution
A560

No. 4149, horiz.: a, Gray wolf. b, Canaan dog. c, Maltese. d, Greyhound. e, Golden retriever.
No. 4150, horiz.: a, Coyote. b, Alaskan husky. c, Red fox. d, Yorkshire terrier.
No. 4151, $700, Bull mastiff. No. 4152, $700, Dalmatian.

**2012, Oct. 23    Perf. 12**

| | | | | |
|---|---|---|---|---|
| 4149 | A560 | $225 Sheet of 5, #a-e | 11.00 | 11.00 |
| 4150 | A560 | $250 Sheet of 4, #a-d | 10.00 | 10.00 |

**Souvenir Sheets**

**Perf. 14**

| | | | | |
|---|---|---|---|---|
| 4151-4152 | A560 | Set of 2 | 14.00 | 14.00 |

Completion of Painting of the Sistine Chapel Ceiling by Michelangelo, 500th Anniv. — A561

No. 4153, horiz. — Painting details: a, Joel. b, Daniel. c, The Libyan Sibyl.
No. 4154: a, Michelangelo. b, Detail of Ancestors of Christ.

**2012, Oct. 29    Perf. 12**

| | | | | |
|---|---|---|---|---|
| 4153 | A561 | $225 Sheet of 3, #a-c | 6.75 | 6.75 |

**Souvenir Sheet**

| | | | | |
|---|---|---|---|---|
| 4154 | A561 | $350 Sheet of 2, #a-b | 7.00 | 7.00 |

No. 4153 contains three 40x30mm stamps.

**Miniature Sheets**

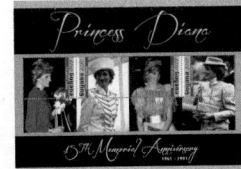

Princess Diana (1961-97) — A562

No. 4155, $250 — Stamps with blue panels with Princess Diana: a, Holding flowers. b, Wearing white hat. c, Wearing tiara. b, Wearing beige hat with ribbon.
No. 4156, $250 — Stamps with yellow green panels with Princess Diana wearing: a, Red jacket and lei. b, Patterned dress and necklace. c, Jacket and tie. d, White jacket and leis.

**Sheets of 4, #a-d**

**2012, Oct. 29    Perf. 14, 12 (#4156)**

| | | | | |
|---|---|---|---|---|
| 4155-4156 | A562 | Set of 2 | 20.00 | 20.00 |

**Souvenir Sheets**

Elvis Presley (1935-77) — A563

Designs: No. 4157, $700, Color photograph of Presley, red frame with country name outlined in black. No. 4158, $700, Black-and-white photograph of Presley, red frame with country name outlined in white. No. 4159, $700, Color photograph of Presley, black frame. No. 4160, $700, Color photograph of Presley, gray frame. No. 4161, $700, Black-and-white photograph of Presley, purple frame.

**2012, Oct. 29    Perf. 12¾**

| | | | | |
|---|---|---|---|---|
| 4157-4161 | A563 | Set of 5 | 35.00 | 35.00 |

Chinese Zodiac Animals — A564

Designs: No. 4162, $50, Rabbits. No. 4163, $50, Tiger.

**2012, Dec. 5    Perf. 13¼x13**

| | | | | |
|---|---|---|---|---|
| 4162-4163 | A564 | Set of 2 | 1.00 | 1.00 |

Nos. 68, 136, 208, 231, 326, 328, 413Dg, 442, 1337-1339, 1987, 2360, 2361, 2652, 2728, 3133 Surcharged in Violet and Black

No. 4164

No. 4176

No. 4179

**Methods, Perfs and Watermarks As Before**

**2012**

| | | | | |
|---|---|---|---|---|
| 4164 | A7 | $20 on 1c #68 | 35.00 | 35.00 |
| 4165 | A28 | $20 on 5c #136 | 50.00 | 50.00 |
| 4166 | A92 | $20 on 25c #1337 | | |
| 4167 | A92 | $20 on 25c #1338 | | 150.00 |
| 4168 | A92 | $20 on 25c #1339 | | |
| 4169 | A76 | $20 on 30c #326 | 85.00 | 85.00 |
| 4170 | A55 | $20 on 35c #231 | — | — |
| 4171 | A72 | $20 on 35c #442 | — | — |
| 4172 | A161 | $20 on 80c #2652 | — | — |
| 4173 | A48 | $20 on $1 #208 | — | — |
| 4174 | A7 | $20 on $1 on 6c #413Dg | 25.00 | 25.00 |
| 4175 | A76 | $20 on $3 #328 | — | — |
| 4176 | A66 | $20 on $5 #1987 | — | — |
| 4177 | A176 | $20 on $6.40 #2728 | — | — |
| 4178 | A129 | $20 on $8.90 #2360 | — | — |
| 4179 | A129 | $20 on $12.80 #2361 | — | — |
| 4180 | A260 | $20 on $30 #3133 | — | — |

Nos. 2369, 2372, 2858 Handstamp Surcharged Like No. 4020K

**Methods and Perfs. As Before**

**2012    Sheet of 16, #a-p**

| | | | | |
|---|---|---|---|---|
| 4181 | A129 | $20 on $12.80 #2369 | — | — |

**Sheet of 16, #r-ag**

| | | | | |
|---|---|---|---|---|
| 4181Q | A129 | $20 on $12.80 #2372 | — | — |

**Sheet of 12, #a-l**

| | | | | |
|---|---|---|---|---|
| 4184 | A200 | $20 on $35 #2858 | — | — |

**No. 144 With "Revenue Only" Overprint and No. 520 Handstamp Surcharged Like No. 4133**

**Methods, Perfs and Watermarks As Before**

**2012-13 ?**

| | | | | |
|---|---|---|---|---|
| 4185 | A28 | $20 on 60c #144 with "Revenue Only" Overprint | | |
| 4186 | A78 | $20 on $1.70 on 3c #520 | | |

Nos. 72, 280, 283, 512 and 1340 Handstamp Surcharged

No. 4188

## Methods, Perfs and Watermarks as Before

**2012-13 ?**

| | | | |
|---|---|---|---|
| 4187 | A7 | $20 on 6c #72 | 25.00 |
| 4188 | A66 | $20 on 10c #280 | — |
| 4189 | A66 | $20 on 25c #283 | — |
| 4190 | A92 | $20 on 25c #1340 | — |
| 4191 | A78 | $20 on 85c on 2c #512 | — |

### Nos. 143 and 144 With "Revenue Only" Overprint, and Nos. 501, 526, 1337 and 1338 Handstamp Surcharged

No. 4192

## Methods, Perfs and Watermarks As Before

**2012-13 ?**

| | | | |
|---|---|---|---|
| 4192 | A78 | $20 on 15c on 2c #501 | — |
| 4193 | A92 | $20 on 25c #1337 | — |
| 4194 | A92 | $20 on 25c #1338 | — |
| 4195 | A28 | $20 on 50c #143, "Revenue Only" Overprint | — |
| 4196 | A28 | $20 on 60c #144, "Revenue Only" Overprint | — |
| 4197 | A78 | $20 on $2.35 on 3c #526 | — |

### Nos. 1341, 1467, 1468, 2362, 2934 Surcharged and No. 1337 Surcharged Like No. 4020J

No. 4200     No. 4203

## Methods, Perfs and Watermarks As Before

**2012-13**

| | | | |
|---|---|---|---|
| 4199 | A92 | $20 on 25c #1341 | — |
| 4200 | A92 | $20 on 25c #1467 | 150.00 |
| 4201 | A92 | $20 on 25c #1468 | — |
| 4202 | A129 | $20 on $15.30 #2362 | — |
| 4203 | A92 | $20 on 25c #1337 | — |
| 4204 | A215 | $20 on $15 #2934 | — |

Issued: No. 4201, 4204, 2012; Nos. 4199, 4200, 4202, 4203, 2013.

### Nos. 1026, 1096, 1101, 1138, 1157 and 1163 Surcharged in Violet and Black

## Methods and Perfs. As Before

**2012 ?**     Unwmk.

| | | | |
|---|---|---|---|
| 4205 | A91 | $20 on 75c #1026 (Series 1, Plate No. 5) | — — |
| 4206 | A91 | $20 on 75c #1096 (Series 1, Plate No. 55) | — — |
| 4207 | A91 | $20 on 75c #1101 (Series 1, Plate No. 60) | — — |
| 4208 | A91 | $20 on 75c #1138 (Series 1, Plate No. 83) | — — |
| 4209 | A91 | $20 on 75c #1157 (Series 1, Plate No. 92) | — — |
| 4210 | A91 | $20 on 75c #1163 (Series 1, Plate No. 95) | — — |

---

**Miniature Sheet**

Intl. Horticultural Exposition, Qingdao, People's Republic of China — A565

No. 4211 — Mascot: a, Waving, hand raised at right. b, Waving, hand raised at left. c, Watering smaller mascot. d, With smaller mascot in automobile. e, Surfing. f, Snorkeling.

**2013, Jan. 1**   Litho.   **Perf. 13¾**
4211 A565 $140 Sheet of 6, #a-f, + central label   8.25   8.25

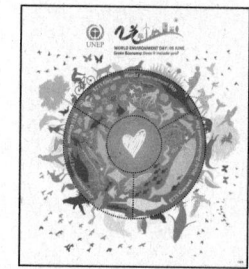

World Environment Day — A566

No. 4212 — Various fish and marine life and parts of map depicting: a, North America and Eastern Asia. b, Oceania, Australia, and Antarctica. c, Antarctica, South America and Central America.
$710, Heart.

**2013, Apr. 3**   Litho.   **Perf. 13**
4212 A566 $275 Sheet of 3, #a-c, + central label   7.75   7.75

**Souvenir Sheet**
**Perf.**
4213 A566 $710 multi   6.75   6.75
No. 4213 contains one 38mm diameter stamp.

Sharks A567

No. 4214: a, Great white shark. b, Mako shark. c, Great hammerhead shark. d, Blue shark. e, Blacktip reef shark. f, Nurse shark.
$710, Whale shark.

**2013, Apr. 3**   Litho.   **Perf. 12**
4214 A567 $225 Sheet of 6, #a-f   13.00   13.00

**Souvenir Sheet**
4215 A567 $710 multi   6.75   6.75
No. 4215 contains one 80x30mm stamp.

---

Flowers A568

No. 4216, $225: a, Asclepias curassavica. b, Passiflora tarminiana. c, Heliconia bihai. d, Aphelandra squarrosa.
No. 4217, $225: a, Bunchosia argentea. b, Strelitzia reginae. c, Aechmea chantinii. d, Acanthocereus tetragonus.
No. 4218, $710, Iris germanica, vert. No. 4219, $710, Fuchsia magellanica, vert.

**2013, Apr. 3**   Litho.   **Perf. 13¾**
**Sheets of 4, #a-d**
4216-4217 A568   Set of 2   17.00   17.00
**Souvenir Sheets**
**Perf. 12¾**
4218-4219 A568   Set of 2   13.50   13.50
Nos. 4218 and 4219 each contain one 38x51mm stamp.

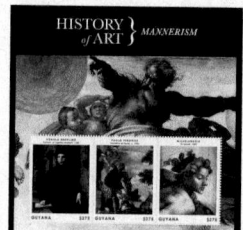

History of Art A569

No. 4220, $275 — Mannerist paintings: a, Portrait of Ugolino Martelli, by Agnolo Bronzino. b, Sacrifice of Isaac, by Paolo Veronese. c, Ignudi, by Michelangelo.
No. 4221, $275 — Renaissance paintings of the Madonna: a, Madonna and Child, by Andrea del Verrocchio. b, Madonna, by Carlo Crivelli. c, Madonna, by Mathias Gothart Grünewald.
$710, Penitent Magdalene, by Tintoretto, horiz.

**2013, Apr. 4**   Litho.   **Perf. 12¾**
**Sheets of 3, #a-c**
4220-4221 A569   Set of 2   15.50   15.50
**Souvenir Sheet**
4222 A569 $710 multi   6.75   6.75

A570

A571

A572

A573

A574

New Year 2013 (Year of the Snake) — A575

---

**Perf. 13 Syncopated**
**2013, Apr. 29**   Litho.
4223 A570 $225 multi   2.25   2.25
**Miniature Sheet**
**Perf. 13¼**
4224   Sheet of 20, #4224a-4224d, 16 #4224e   16.00   16.00

| | | | | |
|---|---|---|---|---|
| a. | A571 | $80 multi | .80 | .80 |
| b. | A572 | $80 multi | .80 | .80 |
| c. | A573 | $80 multi | .80 | .80 |
| d. | A574 | $80 multi | .80 | .80 |
| e. | A575 | $80 multi | .80 | .80 |

No. 4223 was printed in sheets of 4.

**Miniature Sheet**

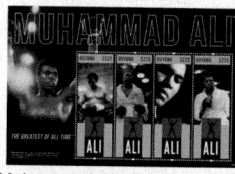

Muhammad Ali, Boxer — A576

No. 4225 — Ali: a, With wrists taped. b, Wearing robe, both hands in boxing gloves. c, Close-up of face. d, Wearing robe, one hand in boxing glove visible.

**Perf. 13 Syncopated**
**2013, Apr. 29**   Litho.
4225 A576 $225 Sheet of 4, #a-d   9.00   9.00

Sinking of the Titanic, Cent. (in 2012) A577

No. 4226 — Members of the Titanic's orchestra: a, W. Hartley. b, G. Krins. c, J. L. Hume. d, J. W. Woodward. e, P. C. Taylor. f, W. T. Brailey.
$700, Titanic, horiz.

**2013, Apr. 29**   Litho.   **Perf. 12**
4226 A577 $200 Sheet of 6, #a-f   12.00   12.00
**Souvenir Sheet**
4227 A577 $700 multi   7.00   7.00
No. 4227 contains one 80x30mm stamp.

Pres. John F. Kennedy (1917-63) — A578

No. 4228 — Pres. Kennedy: a, With wife and children. b, Meeting Soviet Premier Nikita Khrushchev. c, Meeting with Dr. Martin Luther King, Jr., and others. d, Looking at recovered space capsule.
No. 4229, vert. — Campaign poster picturing: a, Kennedy. b, Lyndon B. Johnson.

**2013, Apr. 29**   Litho.   **Perf. 12½**
4228 A578 $225 Sheet of 4, #a-d   9.00   9.00
**Souvenir Sheet**
**Perf. 14**
4229 A578 $355 Sheet of 2, #a-b   7.00   7.00
No. 4229 contains two 30x40mm stamps.

Birds — A579

No. 4230: a, Black-backed tanager. b, Golden-hooded tanager. c, Turquoise tanager. d, Burnished-buff tanager.
$710, Goldent tanager, vert.

**2013, Apr. 29**    **Litho.**    **Perf. 13¾**
4230 A579 $225 Sheet of 4, #a-d   9.00   9.00
**Souvenir Sheet**
**Perf. 12½**
4231 A579 $710 multi      7.00   7.00
No. 4231 contains one 38x51mm stamp.

Miniature Sheets

Butterflies — A580

No. 4232, $150: a, Danaus gilippus berenice. b, Lycorea halia cleobaea. c, Hypothyris lycaste. d, Danaus gilippus thersippus. e, Danaus plexippus. f, Libytheana fulvescens.
No. 4233, $200: a, Battus philenor orsua. b, Dismorphia eunoe desine. c, Dismorphia spio. d, Lieinix viridifascia. e, Lyropteryx lyra cleadas. f, Neophasia terlooii.

**2013, Apr. 29**    **Litho.**    **Perf. 13¾**
**Sheets of 6, #a-f**
4232-4233 A580   Set of 2    21.00   21.00

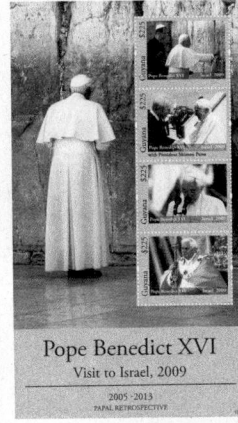

2009 Visit of Pope Benedict XVI to Israel A581

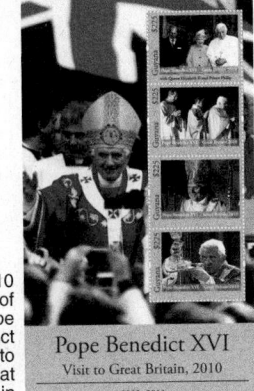

2010 Visit of Pope Benedict XVI to Great Britain A582

No. 4234 — Pope Benedict XVI: a, Touching Western Wall. b, Meeting Israeli President Shimon Peres. c, Behind microphones. d, Holding crucifix.
No. 4235 — Pope Benedict XVI: a, With Queen Elizabeth II and Prince Philip. b, Holding censer. c, Wearing miter. d, Holding chalice.
No. 4236, Pope Benedict XVI praying at Western Wall. No. 4237, Pope Benedict XVI and clergymen, British flag.

**Perf. 13 Syncopated**
**2013, Apr. 29**     **Litho.**
4234 A581 $225 Sheet of 4, #a-d   9.00   9.00
4235 A582 $225 Sheet of 4, #a-d   9.00   9.00
**Souvenir Sheets**
4236 A581 $710 multi      7.00   7.00
4237 A582 $710 multi      7.00   7.00

Aircraft Carriers A583

No. 4238: a, Liaoning, People's Republic of China (previously Varyag, Russia). b, Foch, France. c, USS Yorktown, U.S. d, Giuseppe Garibaldi, Italy.
$700, Admiral Flota Sovetskogo Soyuza Kuznetsov, Russia, horiz.

**2013, Apr. 29**    **Litho.**    **Perf. 13¾**
4238 A583 $250 Sheet of 4, #a-d   9.75   9.75
**Souvenir Sheet**
**Perf. 12½**
4239 A583 $700 multi      7.00   7.00
No. 4239 contains one 51x38mm stamp.

Miniature Sheets

A584

Exploration of Mars — A585

No. 4240: a, Mars Rover. b, Mars Spirit. c, Curiosity. d, Mars Reconnaissance Orbiter.
No. 4241: a, Mariner 4. b, Mariner 9. c, Phoenix. d, Odyssey.

**Perf. 13 Syncopated**
**2013, Apr. 29**       **Litho.**
4240 A584 $225 Sheet of 4, #a-d   9.00   9.00
4241 A585 $225 Sheet of 4, #a-d   9.00   9.00

**Souvenir Sheet**

Jigong Mountains, People's Republic of China — A586

**2013, May 1**    **Litho.**    **Perf. 12**
4242 A586 $1000 multi     9.75   9.75

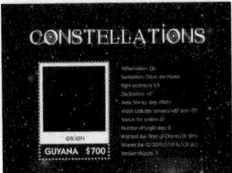

Constellations — A587

No. 4243, $250: a, Aries. b, Gemini. c, Leo. d, Scorpius.
No. 4244, $250: a, Cancer. b, Taurus. c, Capricornus. d, Pisces.
No. 4245, $700, Orion. No. 4246, $700, Pegasus.

**2013, July 30**    **Litho.**    **Perf. 14**
**Sheets of 4, #a-d**
4243-4244 A587   Set of 2   20.00   20.00
**Souvenir Sheets**
4245-4246 A587   Set of 2   14.00   14.00

Caves of Thailand A588

No. 4247: a, Temple at Phraya Nakhon Cave. b, Boat outside of entrance to cave at Phang Nga Bay. c, Phayanakorn Cave.
$710, Suwan Kuha Temple statue of Buddha in cave.

**2013, Aug. 26**    **Litho.**    **Perf. 12½**
4247 A588 $275 Sheet of 3, #a-c   8.00   8.00
**Souvenir Sheet**
4248 A588 $710 multi      7.00   7.00
2013 Thailand World Stamp Exhibition, Bangkok.

Birth of Prince George of Cambridge — A589

No. 4249: a, Duchess of Cambridge holding Prince George. b, Duke of Cambridge holding Prince George. c, Duke and Duchess of Cambridge, Prince George.
$710, Duchess of Cambridge holding Prince George.

**2013, Sept. 10**    **Litho.**    **Perf. 14**
4249 A589 $225 Sheet of 4,
    #4249a,
    4249b, 2
    #4249c      8.75   8.75
**Souvenir Sheet**
**Perf. 12½**
4250 A589 $710 multi      7.00   7.00
No. 4250 contains one 38x51mm stamp.

New Year 2014 (Year of the Horse) A590

No. 4251 — Various horses with background color of: a, Light blue. b, Yellow. c, Pink. d, Pale orange. e, Lilac. f, Light green.
$710, Horse with yellow background.

**2013, Oct. 10**    **Litho.**    **Perf. 14**
4251 A590 $200 Sheet of 6,
    #a-f      12.00   12.00
**Souvenir Sheet**
**Perf. 12**
4252 A590 $710 multi      7.00   7.00

Tourist Attractions in Brazil — A591

No. 4253: a, Mask from Le Roi Soleil Carnival. b, Old Colonial building. c, Ipanema Beach. d, Favela buildings. e, Tiled steps, Lapa, Rio de Janeiro. f, Toucan.
$710, Christ the Redeemer Statue, Rio de Janeiro, vert.

**2013, Nov. 11**    **Litho.**    **Perf. 13¾**
4253 A591 $200 Sheet of 6,
    #a-f      12.00   12.00
**Souvenir Sheet**
**Perf. 12½**
4254 A591 $710 multi      7.00   7.00
Brasiliana 2013 Intl. Stamp Exhibition, Rio de Janeiro. No. 4254 contains one 38x51mm stamp.

Evangelical Lutheran Church in Guyana, 270th Anniv. — A592

Emblem and background color of: $20, Gray. $80, Light brown.

**2013, Oct. 6**    **Litho.**    **Perf. 14**
4255-4256 A592   Set of 2    1.00   1.00

A593

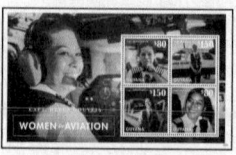

Women in Aviation A594

Designs: No. 4257, $20, Cheryl Moore, first female pilot in Guyana Defense Force. No. 4258, $20, Beverley Drake, first Guayanese commercial pilot. No. 4259, $80, Drake and Moore.

No. 4260 — Capt. Debra Gouveia, first female captain for a local airline: a, $80, Holding intercom. b, $80, Smiling. c, $150, Standing in front of airplane. d, $150, Leaning on airplane.

| 2013, Oct. 9 | Litho. | Perf. 13¾ | |
|---|---|---|---|
| 4257-4259 | A593 | Set of 3 | 1.25 1.25 |
| 4260 | A594 | Sheet of 4, #a-d | 4.50 4.50 |

Miniature Sheet

Elvis Presley (1935-77) — A595

No. 4261: a, Album cover with Presley playing guitar. b, Presley holding microphone at Ottawa concert, 1957. c, Presely wearing jacket. d, "Essential Elvis Presley" album cover.

| 2013, Dec. 2 | Litho. | Perf. 13¾ | |
|---|---|---|---|
| 4261 | A595 | Sheet of 4, #a-d | 8.75 8.75 |

Christmas — A596

Paintings: $20, Madonna, by Fra Angelico. $80, Madonna and Child, by Fra Filippo Lippi. $225, Merode Altarpiece, by Robert Campin. $550, Madonna, by Vitale da Bologna. $710, Rest During the Flight to Egypt, by Joachim Patinir.

| 2013, Dec. 2 | Litho. | Perf. 12½ | |
|---|---|---|---|
| 4262-4265 | A596 | | 8.50 8.50 |
| | | Souvenir Sheet | |
| 4266 | A596 | $710 multi | 7.00 7.00 |

Pres. Barack Obama — A597

Designs: No. 4268, $710, Pres. Obama with Israeli Prime Minister Benjamin Netanyahu, Israeli Pres. Shimon Peres and other men at Yad Vashem Holocaust Memorial, Jerusalem, horiz. No. 4269, $710, Pres. Obama on telephone in Oval Office.

| 2013, Dec. 9 | Litho. | Perf. 14 | |
|---|---|---|---|
| 4267 | A597 | $225 multi | 2.25 2.25 |
| | | Souvenir Sheets | |
| | | Perf. 12 | |
| 4268-4269 | A597 | Set of 2 | 14.00 14.00 |

No. 4267 was printed in sheets of 4. No. 4269 contains one 30x50mm stamp.

A598 A599

Nelson Mandela (1918-2013), President of South Africa — A600

No. 4270 — Mandela: a, In suit and tie. b, Seated next to trophy. c, Seated.

No. 4271 — Mandela: a, In suit and tie. b, With Olympic torch. c, Wearng patterned shirt.

$710, Mandela, diff. $1000, Mandela, diff.

| 2013, Dec. 15 | Litho. | Perf. 13¾ | |
|---|---|---|---|
| 4270 | A598 | $200 Vert. strip of 3, #a-c | 6.00 6.00 |
| 4271 | A599 | $200 Vert. strip of 3, #a-c | 6.00 6.00 |
| | | Souvenir Sheets | |
| 4272 | A599 | $710 multi | 7.00 7.00 |
| | | Imperf | |
| 4273 | A600 | $1000 multi | 9.75 9.75 |

Nos. 4270 and 4271 each were printed in sheets containing two strips.

Cats A601

No. 4274 — Cat breeds: a, Chartreaux. b, Bobtail. c, Siamese. d, Abyssinian. $710, Ocicat.

| 2013, Dec. 23 | Litho. | Perf. 14 | |
|---|---|---|---|
| 4274 | A601 | $225 Sheet of 4, #a-d | 8.75 8.75 |
| | | Souvenir Sheet | |
| 4275 | A601 | $710 multi | 7.00 7.00 |

A603

New Year 2014 (Year of the Horse) — A604

| 2014, Jan. 2 | Litho. | Perf. 13¾ | |
|---|---|---|---|
| 4278 | A603 | $180 multi | 1.75 1.75 |
| 4279 | A604 | $180 multi | 1.75 1.75 |

Nos. 4278 and 4279 were printed together in sheets of 8, containing 4 of each stamp, + a central label.

Miniature Sheets

A605

Mao Zedong (1893-1976), Chinese Communist Leader — A606

No. 4280 — Painting of Mao Zedong: a, Standing near chair. b, Wearing black coat, walking in snow. c, Wearing gray overcoat, holding cigarette. d, Wearign tan overcoat.

No. 4281: a, Mao Zedong with arm raised. b, Mao Zedong and table. c, Mao Zedong and Chinese flag. d, Mao Zedong at lectern with three microphones. e, Mao Zedong behind microphones holding picture of Chinese national emblem. f, Great Wall of China.

| 2014, Jan. 20 | Litho. | Perf. 12 | |
|---|---|---|---|
| 4280 | A605 | $50 Sheet of 4, #a-d | 2.00 2.00 |
| | | Perf. 14 | |
| 4281 | A606 | $50 Sheet of 6, #a-f | 3.00 3.00 |

Souvenir Sheet

Elvis Presley (1935-77) — A607

| 2014, Jan. 20 | Litho. | Imperf. | |
|---|---|---|---|
| 4282 | A607 | $2000 multi | 19.50 19.50 |

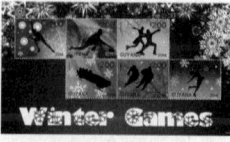

Sports of the Winter Olympics A608

No. 4283: a, Speed skating. b, Curling. c, Ice dancing. d, Bobsledding. e, Ice hockey. f, Figure skating.

No. 4284, vert.: a, Biathlon. b, Snowboarding. c, Freestyle skiing. c, Alpine skiing.

| 2014, Feb. 26 | Litho. | Perf. 14 | |
|---|---|---|---|
| 4283 | A608 | $200 Sheet of 6, #a-f | 12.00 12.00 |
| | | Perf. 12¾ | |
| 4284 | A608 | $250 Sheet of 4, #a-d | 9.75 9.75 |

No. 4284 contains four 38x51mm stamps. Inscription on No. 4284d is incorrect as stamp shows slalom skier.

Guinea Pigs A609

No. 4285, $350: a, American (brown and white fur), denomination in brown. b, Skinny, denomination in green. c, Abyssinian (long brown and black fur, feet not visible), denomination in dark green. d, Teddy, denomination in yellow green.

No. 4286, $350: a, Teddy, denomination in brown. b, American, denomination in green. c, Skinny, denomination in dark green. d, Abyssinian, denomination in yellow green.

No. 4287, $350: a, American (gray animal), denomination in brown. b, Abyssinian (short brown and black fur, feet visible), denomination in green.

No. 4288, $500: a, Silkie. b, Teddy, diff.

| 2014, Feb. 26 | Litho. | Perf. 13¾ | |
|---|---|---|---|
| | | Sheets of 4, #a-d | |
| 4285-4286 | A609 | Set of 2 | 27.50 27.50 |
| | | Souvenir Sheets | |
| 4287 | A609 | $350 Sheet of 2, #a-b | 7.00 7.00 |
| 4288 | A609 | $500 Sheet of 2, #a-b | 9.75 9.75 |

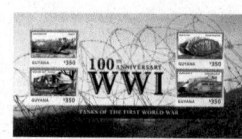

World War I, Cent. A610

No. 4289, $350: a, Saint-Chomond tank, France. b, Mark IX tank, United Kingdom. c, Schneider CA1 tank, France. d, Medium Mark C tank, United Kingdom.

No. 4290, $350, vert.: a, Emperor Nicholas II of Russia. b, King Victor Emmanuel III of Italy. c, King Albert I of Belgium. d, U.S. Pres. Woodrow Wilson.

No. 4291, $350, vert.: a, Renault FT tank, France. b, A7V tank, Germany.

No. 4292, vert.: a, French Prime Minister Aristide Briand. b, United Kingdom Prime Minister David Lloyd George.

| 2014, Feb. 26 | Litho. | Perf. 14 | |
|---|---|---|---|
| | | Sheets of 4, #a-d | |
| 4289-4290 | A610 | Set of 2 | 27.50 27.50 |
| | | Souvenir Sheets | |
| | | Perf. 12 | |
| 4291 | A610 | $700 Sheet of 2, #a-b | 13.50 13.50 |
| 4292 | A610 | $700 Sheet of 2, #a-b | 13.50 13.50 |

Pope Francis A611

No. 4293, $350 — Pope Francis: a, With Italian Prime Minister Enrico Letta. b, In front of black background. c, With hand raised. d, Wearing green vestments.

No. 4294, $350 — Pope Francis: a, At lectern. b, With Croatian President Ivo Josipovic. c, With Panamanian President Ricardo Alberto Martinelli Berrocal. d, Waving to crowd.

No. 4295, $700 — Pope Francis: a, With man in background. b, With arm raised.

No. 4296, $700 — Pope Francis: a, Holding crucifix. c, With Brazilian President Dilma Rousseff.

Reptiles A602

No. 4276: a, Saban anole. b, Whiptail lizard. c, Barbados leaf-toed gecko. d, Anegada ground iguana.

$710, Dominican ground lizard.

| 2013, Dec. 23 | Litho. | Perf. 13¾ | |
|---|---|---|---|
| 4276 | A602 | $225 Sheet of 4, #a-d | 8.75 8.75 |
| | | Souvenir Sheet | |
| 4277 | A602 | $710 multi | 7.00 7.00 |

**2014, Feb. 26** Litho. *Perf. 14*
**Sheets of 4, #a-d**
4293-4294 A611 Set of 2 27.50 27.50
**Souvenir Sheets of 2, #a-b**
*Perf. 12½*
4295-4296 A611 Set of 2 27.50 27.50
Nos. 4295 and 4296 each contain two 38x51mm stamps.

Chinese Space Program
A612

No. 4297: a, Shenzhou crew members, stars and satellite in background. b, Shenzhou crew members, Earth and Chinese flag in background. c, Shenzhou 5 mission patch.
No. 4298: a, View of China from space. b, Astronaut Jing Haipeng. c, Astronaut Liu Yang. d, Shenzhou 7 and Chinese flag.
No. 4299, $700, horiz.: a, Shenzhou 7 docking in space. b, Crew of Shenzhou 7 in space.
No. 4300, $700, horiz.: a, Astronaut Liu Wang. b, Earth and sunrise from space.

**2014, Feb. 26** Litho. *Perf. 14*
4297 A612 $350 Sheet of 4,
#4297a,
4297b, 2
#4297c 13.50 13.50
4298 A612 $350 Sheet of 4,
#a-d 13.50 13.50
**Souvenir Sheets of 2, #a-b**
4299-4300 A612 Set of 2 27.50 27.50
Nos. 4299 and 4300 each contain two 51x38mm stamps.

Trains and Flags
A613

No. 4301 — Train and flag from: a, Brazil. b, Israel. c, Australia. d, Hungary.
$710, Train and flag from Mexico.

**2014, Mar. 5** Litho. *Perf. 12½*
4301 A613 $200 Sheet of 4, #a-d 7.75 7.75
**Souvenir Sheet**
4302 A613 $710 multi 7.00 7.00

Pink Flamingos — A614

No. 4303: a, Flamingo, no legs visible. b, Flamingo preening. c, Flamingo from front. d, Flamingo facing right.
No. 4304: a, Head of flamingo facing right. b, Head of flamingo facing left.

*Perf. 13 Syncopated*
**2014, Mar. 10** Litho.
4303 A614 $200 Sheet of 4, #a-d 7.75 7.75
**Souvenir Sheet**
4304 A614 $400 Sheet of 2, #a-b 7.75 7.75
No. 4304 contains two 30x40mm stamps.

Characters From *Downton Abbey* Television Series — A615

---

No. 4305: a, Lady Edith Crawley. b, Tom Branson. c, Lady Rose MacClare. d, Lavinia Swire.
$800, Matthew Crawley and Lady Mary Crawley, horiz.

**2014, Mar. 19** Litho. *Perf. 14*
4305 A615 $225 Sheet of 4, #a-d 8.75 8.75
**Souvenir Sheet**
4306 A615 $800 multi 7.75 7.75

Paintings by Henri de Toulouse-Lautrec (1864-1901) — A616

No. 4307, $200: a, Ambassadeurs — Aristide Bruant. b, Divan Japonais. c, Jane Avril. d, La Revue Blanche.
No. 4308, $200, horiz.: a, The Spanish Dancer. b, Vincent van Gogh. c, The Grand Tier. d, The Laundress.
No. 4309, $400: a, Moulin Rouge: La Goulue poster. b, The German Babylon.
No. 4310, $400: a, Moulin Rouge: La Goulue painting. b, Ball at the Moulin de la Galette.

**2014, Mar. 24** Litho. *Perf. 12*
**Sheets of 4 #a-d**
4307-4308 A616 Set of 2 15.50 15.50
**Souvenir Sheets of 2, #a-b**
4309-4310 A616 Set of 2 15.50 15.50

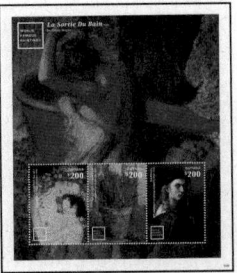

Paintings A617

No. 4311, $200: a, Mother and Child, by Gustav Klimt. b, Flowerpot with Chives, by Vincent van Gogh. c, Portrait of Bindo Altoviti, by Raphael.
No. 4312, $200: a, Dancer in Her Dressing Room, by Edgar Degas. b, The Garden of Earthly Delights, by Hieronymus Bosch. c, The Complain of the Watch, by Jean-Baptiste Greuze.
No. 4313, $800, The Music Lesson, by Johannes Vermeer. No. 4314, $800, Portrait of a Young Man, by Vincenzo Catena.

**2014, Mar. 24** Litho. *Perf. 12½*
**Sheets of 3, #a-c**
4311-4312 A617 Set of 2 12.00 12.00
**Size: 100x100mm**
*Imperf*
4313-4314 A617 Set of 2 15.50 15.50

Worldwide Fund for Nature (WWF) — A618

Nos. 4315 and 4316 — Guiana spider monkey: a, Sitting on branch. b, With young. c, Climbing tree. d, Eating.

**2014, Apr. 2** Litho. *Perf. 14*
4315 A618 $180 Block or vert.
strip of 4, #a-d 7.00 7.00
4316 A618 $200 Block or vert.
strip of 4, #a-d 7.75 7.75

---

Panama Canal, Cent. A619

No. 4317: a, Construction, 1907. b, Gatun Lake. c, Construction, 1913. d, Map of Panama Canal.
No. 4318, horiz.: a, SS Ancon in Panama Canal, 1914. b, Centennial Bridge.

**2014, May 12** Litho. *Perf. 12*
4317 A619 $200 Sheet of 4, #a-d 7.75 7.75
**Souvenir Sheet**
4318 A619 $400 Sheet of 2, #a-b 7.75 7.75

A620

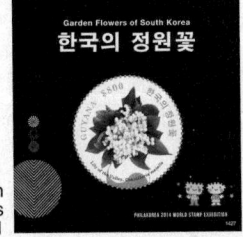

Korean Flowers A621

No. 4319: a, Rhododendron. b, Tawny daylily. c, Hydrangea. d, Camellia. e, Magnolia. f, Daylily hybrid.
$800, Lily of the valley.

**2014, May 12** Litho. *Perf. 13¾*
4319 A620 $200 Sheet of 6, #a-f 12.00 12.00
**Souvenir Sheet**
4320 A621 $800 multi 7.75 7.75
Philakorea 2014 World Stamp Exhibition, Seoul.

Wildlife — A622

Designs: No. 4321, South American tapir. No. 4322, Squirrel monkey. No. 4323, Two-toed sloth. No. 4324, Giant anteater. No. 4325, Giant otter. No. 4326, Jaguar. No. 4327, Black caiman. No. 4328, Leatherback turtle. No. 4329, Red-billed toucan. No. 4330, Yellow-crowned Amazon. No. 4331, Purple honeycreeper. No. 4332, Scarlet macaw. No. 4333, Guianan cock-of-the-rock. No. 4334, Scarlet ibis. No. 4335, Black curassow. No. 4336, Harpy eagle. $130, Purple honeycreeper. $150, Red-billed toucan. $160, Scarlet ibis. $200, Black curassow.

**2014, July 1** Litho. *Perf. 13¾*
4321 A622 $80 multi .80 .80
4322 A622 $80 multi .80 .80
4323 A622 $80 multi .80 .80
4324 A622 $80 multi .80 .80
4325 A622 $80 multi .80 .80
4326 A622 $80 multi .80 .80
4327 A622 $80 multi .80 .80
4328 A622 $80 multi .80 .80
4329 A622 $80 multi .80 .80
4330 A622 $80 multi .80 .80
4331 A622 $80 multi .80 .80
4332 A622 $80 multi .80 .80
4333 A622 $80 multi .80 .80
4334 A622 $80 multi .80 .80
4335 A622 $80 multi .80 .80
4336 A622 $80 multi .80 .80
4337 A622 $130 multi 1.25 1.25
4338 A622 $150 multi 1.50 1.50
4339 A622 $160 multi 1.60 1.60
4340 A622 $200 multi 2.00 2.00
Nos. 4321-4340 (20) 19.15 19.15

---

A623

A624

Monarch Butterflies — A625

No. 4341, $200 — Monarch butterfly with: a, Green foliage. b, Yellow flowers. c, Red flowers. d, Purple flower.
No. 4342, $200, vert.: a, Monarch butterfly caterpillar. b, Monarch butterfly chrysalis. c, Monarch butterfly exiting chrysalis. d, Monarch butterfly on purple flower.
No. 4343 — Monarch butterfly on: a, White and purple flower. b, Orange red flower.
No. 4344: a, Monarch butterflies. b, Monarch butterflies, diff.

*Perf. 12½x12, 12x12½*
**2014, July 1** Litho.
**Sheets of 4, #a-d**
4341-4342 A623 Set of 2 15.50 15.50
**Souvenir Sheets**
4343 A624 $400 Sheet of 2, #a-b 7.75 7.75
4344 A625 $400 Sheet of 2, #a-b 7.75 7.75

South American Animals — A626

No. 4345: a, Powis (black curassow). b, Gray-winged trumpeter. c, Poison arrow frog. d, Anole.
No. 4346, $750, Yellow-crowned Amazon. No. 4347, $750, Toco toucan.

**2014, July 1** Litho. *Perf. 14*
4345 A626 $300 Sheet of 4, #a-d 12.00 12.00
**Souvenir Sheets**
*Perf. 12½*
4346-4347 A626 Set of 2 14.50 14.50
Nos. 4346 and 4347 each contain one 38x51mm stamp.

## Souvenir Sheet

Full Gospel Fellowship of Churches, 50th Anniv. — A627

No. 4348: a, $80, 50th anniversary emblem. b, $160, Apostle Philip Mohabir.

**2014, July 6      Litho.      Perf. 13¼**
4348 A627   Sheet of 2, #a-b      2.40 2.40

British Guiana No. 13, Map of Guyana — A628

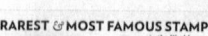

British Guiana No. 13 A630

British Guiana No. 13, Map of South America A631

**2014, Aug. 27      Litho.      Perf. 14**
4349 A628   $80 multi            .80   .80
### Souvenir Sheets
**Perf. 13½x12½**
4351 A630   $800 multi          7.75 7.75
**Perf. 13¼**
4352 A631   $800 multi          7.75 7.75
No. 4349 was printed in sheets of 12.

### Miniature Sheet

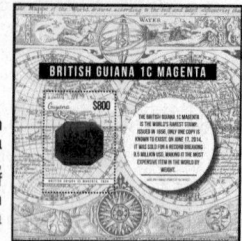

British Guiana No. 13, World Map A629

No. 4350 — Map depicting: a, North and Central America. b, Atlantic Ocean. c, Africa and Europe. d, Asia.

**Perf. 13¼x12½**
**2014, Aug. 27      Litho.**
4350 A629   $200 Sheet of 4, #a-d 7.75 7.75

### Miniature Sheet

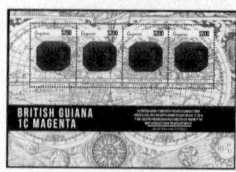

2014 World Cup Soccer Championships, Brazil — A632

No. 4353, $80 — Team from: a, Chile. b, Greece. c, Japan. d, Argentina. e, Belgium. f,

Bosnia & Herzegovina. g, Brazil. h, Ivory Coast.
No. 4354, $80 — Team from: a, Costa Rica. b, Croatia. c, England. d, Algeria. e, Colombia. f, France. g, Germany. h, Ghana.
No. 4355, $80 — Team from: a, Honduras. b, Iran. c, Netherlands. d, Mexico. e, Nigeria. f, Cameroun. g, Portugal. h, South Korea.
No. 4356, $80 — Team from: a, Ecuador. b, Italy. c, Switzerland. d, Uruguay. e, Russia. f, United States. g, Australia. h, Spain.

**2014, Sept. 4      Litho.      Perf. 12½**
**Sheets of 8, #a-h, + Label**
4353-4356 A632   Set of 4   25.00 25.00

Mei Lanfang (1894-1961), Chinese Opera Performer — A633

No. 4357 — Paintings of: a, Birds and flowers. b, Tree branch with buds and flowers. c, Mei Lanfang in costume. c, Pink flowers in vase. c, Fish and tree. d, Blue leaves and white flowers on branch in vase.
$800, Mei Lanfang in costume, diff.

**2014, Sept. 4      Litho.      Perf. 12**
4357 A633   $200 Sheet of 6, #a-f            12.00 12.00
### Souvenir Sheet
**Perf. 12½**
4358 A633   $800 multi          8.00 8.00
No. 4358 contains one 38x51mm stamp.

Chinese Art A634

No. 4359 — Paintings by Zhang Daqian (1899-1983): a, Untitled abstract painting (60x40mm). b, Flower (Chinese text at UL, 30x40mm). c, Flower (Chinese text at UR, 30x40mm). d, Bird's Eye View of Mount Hehuan, diff. (60x40mm).
No. 4360, vert.: a, Wine container, Eastern Zhou Dynasty. b, Bottle with Immortal Zhongli Quan, Ming Dynasty. c, Stele with Buddha Dipankara, Northern Wei Dyansty. d, Buddha Vairocana, Tang Dynasty. e, Mirror back, Tang Dynasty. f, Tray, Yuan Dynasty.
No. 4361, $800, Painting of mountains by Wang Ximeng. No. 4262, $800, Painting of horse, by Xu Beihong, vert.

**2014, Sept. 15      Litho.      Perf. 14**
4359 A634   $200 Sheet of 4, #a-d      8.00 8.00
4360 A634   $200 Sheet of 6, #a-f      12.00 12.00
### Souvenir Sheets
**Perf. 12**
4361-4362 A634   Set of 2   16.00 16.00
Painting on No. 4359d is reversed and upside-down.

## Miniature Sheet

University of Guyana, 50th Anniv. — A635

No. 4363: a, $80, Graduates facing left. b, $80, Two female graduates. c, $150, University building and pond. d, $150, University gate.

**2014, Oct. 3      Litho.      Perf. 14**
4363 A635   Sheet of 4, #a-d      4.50 4.50

British Guiana Stamps A636

No. 4364: a, British Guiana #2, map of Iberian Peninsula. b, British Guiana #4, map of Mediterranean Sea. c, British Guiana #5, map of Central Asia.
$800, British Guiana #1, map of Eastern Europe.

**2014, Nov. 3      Litho.      Perf. 14**
4364 A636   $300 Sheet of 3, #a-c   8.75 8.75
### Souvenir Sheet
**Perf. 12**
4365 A636   $800 multi          7.75 7.75

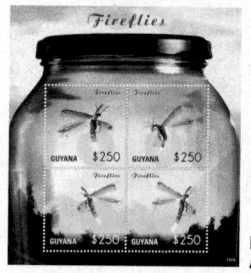

Fireflies A637

No. 4366: a, Firefly facing right, denomination in black. b, Firefly facing left, denomination in black. c, Firefly facing left, denomination in white. d, Firefly facing right, denomination in white.
$800, Firefly, vert.

**2014, Nov. 3      Litho.      Perf. 13¾**
4366 A637   $250 Sheet of 4, #a-d 9.75 9.75
### Souvenir Sheet
**Perf. 12½**
4367 A637   $800 multi          7.75 7.75
No. 4367 contains one 38x51mm stamp.

Christmas — A638

Paintings by Peter Paul Rubens: $160, The Circumcision of Christ. $200, The Ildefonso Altarpiece. $300, The Resurrection of Christ. $400, Madonna in a Garland of Flowers.

**2014, Nov. 24      Litho.      Perf. 12½**
4368-4371 A638   Set of 4   10.50 10.50
Painting on No. 4371 is misidentified on stamp.

## Souvenir Sheet

Guyana Defense Force, 50th Anniv. A639

No. 4372 — Emblem and: a, $80, Helicopter. b, $80, Soldiers. c, $150, Headquarters.

**2014, Nov. 11      Litho.      Perf. 12**
4372 A639   Sheet of 3, #a-c      3.00 3.00

A640

A641

New Year 2015 (Year of the Ram) A642

No. 4373: a, $80, Chinese character, butterfly, flowers, fish. b, $80, Chinese character, cranes, peaches, flowers. c, $80, Ram. d, $150, Chinese character, crane and flowers. e, $80, Chinese character, birds on branch, flowers. f, $150, Ram.
No. 4374: a, Black ram standing. b, Red ram looking left. c, Black ram leaping. d, Red ram looking right.
No. 4375: a, Three rams. b, Man on ram facing right.

**2014, Nov. 24      Litho.      Perf. 13¾**
4373 A640   Sheet of 20, #4373a, 4373b, 4373d, 4373e, 8 each #4373c, 4373f            22.50 22.50
4374 A641   $200 Sheet of 4, #a-d      7.75 7.75
### Souvenir Sheet
**Perf. 12**
4375 A642   $400 Sheet of 2, #a-b      7.75 7.75

## Miniature Sheet

Women in Aviation A643

No. 4376 — Map and: a, $80, Jet and Paula McAdam. b, $80, Airplane and Sandra Persaud. c, $150, McAdam, Persaud, and propeller. d, $150, Persaud, McAdam and airport control tower.

**2014, Dec. 7    Litho.    Perf. 12x12½**
4376  A643  Sheet of 4, #a-d       4.50  4.50

Prince George of Cambridge, 1st Birthday — A644

No. 4377, $250 — Denomination at UL: a, Duke and Duchess of Cambridge, Prince George. b, Duke of Cambridge holding Prince George, Prince George looking right. c, Duke of Cambridge holding Prince George, Prince George looking left. d, Prince George

No. 4378, $250 — Denomination at UR: a, Duchess of Cambridge holding Prince George. b, Duke and Duchess of Cambridge, Prince George, diff. c, Duke of Cambridge holding Prince George. d, Prince George, diff.

No. 4379, $800, Prince George, diff. No. 4380, $800, Duke and Duchess of Cambridge, Prince George, horiz.

**Perf. 12x12½, 12½x12 (#4380)**
**2014, Dec. 16                      Litho.**
4377-4378  A644  Set of 2    19.50  19.50
**Souvenir Sheets**
4379-4380  A644  Set of 2    15.50  15.50

Pope Emeritus Benedict XVI A645

No. 4381 — Pope Benedict XVI: a, With both arms waving, crowd in background. b, Waving, building and statue in background. c, Wearing red vestments. d, Waving, dome of St. Peter's Basilica in background.
$800, Pope Benedict XVI, vert.

**2014, Dec. 31  Litho.    Perf. 12½x12**
4381  A645  $250 Sheet of 4, #a-d    9.75  9.75
**Souvenir Sheet**
**Perf. 12x12½**
4382  A645  $800 multi           7.75  7.75

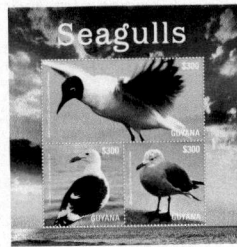

Seagulls A646

No. 4383, $300: a, Black-headed gull (70x35mm). b, California gull (35x35mm). c, Heermann's gull (35x35mm).

No. 4384, $300: a, Franklin's gull (35x70mm). b, Black-legged kittiwake (35x35mm). c, Glaucous-winged gull (35x35mm).

No. 4385, $800, Western gull, horiz. No. 4386, $800, Laughing gull, vert.

**2015, Jan. 5    Litho.    Perf. 13¾**
**Sheets of 3, #a-c**
4383-4384  A646  Set of 2    17.50  17.50
**Souvenir Sheets**
**Perf. 12**
4385-4386  A646  Set of 2    15.50  15.50
No. 4385 contains one 50x30mm stamp.
No. 4386 contains one 30x50mm stamp.

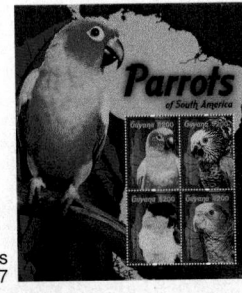

Parrots A647

No. 4387, $200: a, Sun conure. b, Redtailed Amazon. c, Black-headed caique. d, Yellow-crowned Amazon.

No. 4388, $200: a, Scarlet macaw. b, Lilacine Amazon. c, Jandaya parakeet. d, Blue-headed pionus.

No. 4389, $800, Blue-crowned parakeet. No. 4390, $800, Brown-hooded parrot, horiz.

**Perf. 13 Syncopated**
**2015, Jan. 5                      Litho.**
**Sheets of 4, #a-d**
4387-4388  A647  Set of 2    15.50  15.50
**Souvenir Sheets**
4389-4390  A647  Set of 2    15.50  15.50

Personalizable Stamp — A647a

**2015, Feb. 16    Litho.    Perf. 13¼**
4390A  A647a  $80 multi            —    —
No. 4390A could be personalized. The stamp shown has a handstamped personalization.

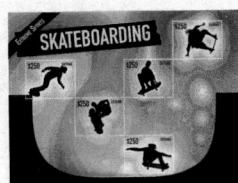

Skateboarding — A648

No. 4391 — Skateboarder: a, In air with hand near country name. b, On lip of vert ramp. c, In air touching skateboard. d, In air with hand on hip. e, In air with arms extended to sides.
$800, Skateboarder in air with right arm extended up next to denomination.

**2015, Mar. 2    Litho.    Perf. 14**
4391  A648  $250 Sheet of 5,
#a-e                 12.50  12.50
**Souvenir Sheet**
**Perf. 12**
4392  A648  $800 multi           7.75  7.75

International Year of Light — A649

**2015, Mar. 24    Litho.    Perf. 13¼**
4393  A649  $250 multi           2.40  2.40
**Souvenir Sheet**
4394  A649  $800 Earth, Sun at
side                 7.75  7.75

UNESCO World Heritage Sites in the Americas — A650

No. 4395: a, Ischigualasto Provincial Park, Argentina. b, Belize Barrier Reef Reserve System, Belize. c, Chichen Itza, Mexico. d, Yellowstone National Park, United States. e, San Agustín Archaeological Park, Colombia. f, Pitons Management Area, St. Lucia.
$800, Machu Picchu, Peru.

**Perf. 12½x13¼**
**2015, Mar. 24                      Litho.**
4395  A650  $250 Sheet of 6,
#a-f                 14.50  14.50
**Souvenir Sheet**
4396  A650  $800 multi           7.75  7.75

Duke of Cambridge in People's Republic of China — A651

No. 4397: a, Duke of Cambridge seated. b, Chinese President Xi Jinping seated.

No. 4398, $800, Duke of Cambridge with Zhang Yaoguang in Forbidden City. No. 4399, $800, Duke of Cambridge with staff members of British Embassy in China. No. 4400, $800, Duke of Cambridge shaking hands with Pres. Xi Jinping, horiz.

**2015, May 4    Litho.    Perf. 12**
4397  A651  $450 Sheet of 2,
#a-b                  8.75  8.75
**Souvenir Sheets**
4398-4400  A651  Set of 3    23.00  23.00

Royal Navy Ships of World War I — A652

No. 4401, $80: a, HMS Albion. b, HMS Anemone. c, HMS Azalea. d, HMS Barham. e, HMS Caesar. f, HMS Carlisle. g, HMS Coventry. h, HMS Eclipse. i, HMS Foyle. j, HMS Gibraltar. k, HMS Inconstant. l, HMS India. m, HMS Juno. n, HMS Odin. o, HMS Pelorus. p, HMS Proserpine.

No. 4402, $80: a, HMAS Sydney. b, HMS Achilles. c, HMS Africa. d, HMS Albemarle. e, HMS Bee. f, SS Empress. g, HMS Cumberland. h, HMS Bramble. i, HMS Argonaut. j, HMS Delhi. k, HMS Attentive. l, SS Ambrose. m, SS Lepanto. n, SS Knight Templar. o, HMS Suffolk. p, HMS Canopus.

**2015, May 4    Litho.    Perf. 14**
**Sheets of 16, #a-p, + Label**
4401-4402  A652  Set of 2    25.00  25.00

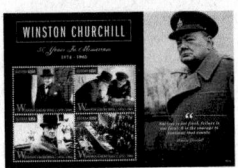

Sir Winston Churchill (1874-1965) — A653

No. 4403 — Churchill: a, Standing near fence. b, With military officer. c, In automobile. d, At lectern.
$800, Churchill in automobile hoisting his hat in air on walking stick.

**2015, June 20    Litho.    Perf. 14**
4403  A653  $250 Sheet of 4, #a-d  9.75  9.75
**Souvenir Sheet**
**Perf. 12**
4404  A653  $800 multi           7.75  7.75

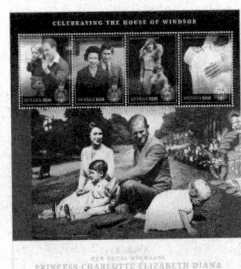

Birth of Princess Charlotte of Cambridge — A654

No. 4405: a, Duke of Cambridge holding Prince George. b, Queen Elizabeth II and Prince Charles. c, Queen Mother with Princess Elizabeth. d, Duchess of Cambridge holding Princess Charlotte.
$800, Duchess of Cambridge holding Princess Charlotte, diff.

**2015, July 13    Litho.    Perf. 14**
4405  A654  $250 Sheet of 4, #a-d  9.75  9.75
**Souvenir Sheet**
**Perf. 12**
4406  A654  $800 multi           7.75  7.75

**Miniature Sheets**

Stamps of United Nations Countries — A655

No. 4407, $250: a, Burma (Myanmar) #1. b, Namibia #659. c, Nauru #1. d, Nepal #51. e, Netherlands #1. f, New Zealand #1.

No. 4408, $250: a, Nicaragua #1. b, Niger #1. c, Nigeria #1. d, Norway #1. e, Oman #1. f, Pakistan #1.

No. 4409, $250: a, Palau #1. b, Panama #1. c, Papua New Guinea #11. d, Paraguay #1. e, Peru #3. f, Philippines #6.

No. 4410, $250: a, Poland #1. b, Portugal #1. c, Qatar #1. d, Romania #22. e, Russia #1. f, Rwanda #1.

No. 4411, $250: a, Samoa #1a. b, San Marino #1. c, St. Thomas and Prince Islands (Sao Tome and Principe) #1. d, Saudi Arabia #138. e, Senegal #1. f, Serbia #1.

No. 4412, $250: a, Seychelles #1. b, Sierra Leone #1. c, Singapore #1. d, Slovakia #1. e, Slovenia #100. f, Solomon Islands #1.

No. 4413, $250: a, Somalia #1. b, South Africa #1. c, South Sudan #1. d, Spain #1. e, Ceylon (Sri Lanka) #1. f, St. Lucia #1.

No. 4414, $250: a, St. Vincent Grenadines #1. b, St. Kitts-Nevis # 1. c, Sudan #6. d, Surinam #3. e, Swaziland #1. f, Sweden #1.

**2015, July 13    Litho.    Perf. 12½**
**Sheets of 6, #a-f**
4407-4414  A655    Set of 8    120.00 120.00

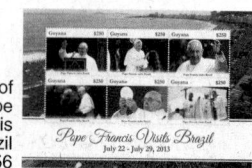

Visit of Pope Francis to Brazil A656

No. 4415 — Pope Francis: a, At lectern, waving. b, Blessing girl. c, Waving. d, With priests. e, Holding eucharist. f, Holding cross.
$800, Pope Francis holding statue of Madonna of Aparecida, vert.

**2015, Sept. 2    Litho.    Perf. 14**
4415  A656  $250  Sheet of 6,
                    #a-f                 15.00 15.00
**Souvenir Sheet**
**Perf. 12**
4416  A656  $800 multi              8.00 8.00
No. 4416 contains one 30x50mm stamp.

**Miniature Sheet**

Hand-in-Hand Insurance Company, 150th Anniv. — A657

No. 4417 — Building and: a, $80, Three people in street near lamp post, sepia-toned. b, $80, People lined up on sidewalk. c, $150, Other buildings, mauve & maroon photograph. d, Building in background, color photograph.

**2015, Oct. 1    Litho.    Perf. 12½x12**
4417  A657    Sheet of 4, #a-d    4.50 4.50

Bank of Guyana, 50th Anniv. — A658

Obverse and reverse of 2015 $5000 coin with background colors of: $80, Blue. $150, Green.

**2015, Oct. 15    Litho.    Perf. 14**
4418-4419  A658    Set of 2    2.25 2.25

Christmas — A659

Paintings by Fra Filippo Lippi: No. 4420, $80, Adoration of the Magi. No. 4421, $80, Madonna Enthroned with Saints. No. 4422, $150, Annunciation with Two Kneeling Donors. No. 4423, $150, Madonna with the Child and Two Angels.

**2015, Nov. 2    Litho.    Perf. 12¾**
4420-4423  A659    Set of 4    4.50 4.50

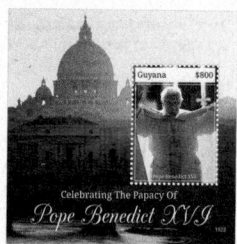

Pope Benedict XVI A660

No. 4424 — Pope Benedict XVI and candle with panel color of: a, $80, White. b, $140, Orange. c, $150, Dark blue.
$800, Pope Benedict with arms extended.

**2015, Nov. 20    Litho.    Perf. 14**
4424  A660  Horiz. strip of 3, #a-c 3.75 3.75
**Souvenir Sheet**
**Perf. 12**
4425  A660  $800 multi              7.75 7.75
No. 4424 was printed in sheets containing two strips.

Pres. Abraham Lincoln (1809-65) — A661

No. 4426 — Lincoln as seen on: a, U.S. one-cent piece. b, Mount Rushmore. c, Lincoln Memorial statue. d, U.S. five-dollar bill.
$800, Lincoln Memorial statue.

**2015, Dec. 21    Litho.    Perf. 14**
4426  A661  $250  Sheet of 4, #a-d 9.75 9.75
**Souvenir Sheet**
**Perf. 12½**
4427  A661  $800 multi              7.75 7.75
No. 4427 contains one 51x38mm stamp.

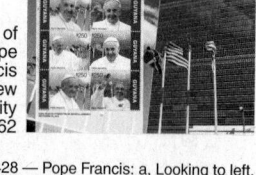

Visit of Pope Francis to New York City A662

No. 4428 — Pope Francis: a, Looking to left, flags and sky in background. b, Waving, United Nations in background. c, As "a," waving. d, As "b," not waving. e, As "a," facing right. f, As "b," waving, mouth open.
$800, Pope Francis and flags, diff.

**2015, Dec. 21    Litho.    Perf. 14**
4428  A662  $250  Sheet of 6,
                    #a-f              14.50 14.50
**Souvenir Sheet**
**Perf. 12**
4429  A662  $800 multi              7.75 7.75

A664

New Year 2016 (Year of the Monkey) A665

No. 4430 — Background color: a, Beige. b, White.
No. 4431: a, Two monkeys. b, Monkey with fruit.
No. 4432: a, Like #4431a. b, Like #4431b.

**2015, Dec. 21    Litho.    Perf. 13¾**
4430  A663  $80  Horiz. pair, #a-b 1.60 1.60
4431  A664  $100  Vert. pair, #a-b 2.00 2.00
**Souvenir Sheet**
4432  A665  $200  Sheet of 2, #a-b 4.00 4.00

Fruit Trees A666

No. 4433: a, Acerolas. b, Cacao. c, Pomelos. d, Pomegranates.
No. 4434: a, Camu camus. b, Starfruit. c, Genipapos. d, Green lemons. e, Papayas. f, Common guavas.
$800, Bananas.

**2015, Dec. 30    Litho.    Perf. 12**
4433  A666  $250  Sheet of 4,
                    #a-d              9.75 9.75
4434  A666  $250  Sheet of 6,
                    #a-f             14.50 14.50
**Souvenir Sheet**
**Perf. 12½**
4435  A666  $800 multi              7.75 7.75
No. 4435 contains one 38x51mm stamp.

Independence, 50th Anniv. (in 2016) — A667

Jaguar and "50" with denomination color of: $80, Bister. $130, Red brown. $150, Black. $200, Bister.

**2015, Dec. 31    Litho.    Perf. 14**
4436-4439  A667    Set of 4    5.50 5.50

Queen Elizabeth II, Longest-Reigning British Monarch — A668

No. 4440 — Queen Elizabeth II wearing: a, Diamond diadem, panel at right. b, Diamond diadem, panel at left. c, Imperial state crown, panel at right. d, Imperial state crown, panel at left.
$800, Queen Elizabeth II in carriage.

**2015, Dec. 31    Litho.    Perf. 14**
4440  A668  $250  Sheet of 4, #a-d 9.75 9.75
**Souvenir Sheet**
**Perf. 12**
4441  A668  $800 multi              7.75 7.75

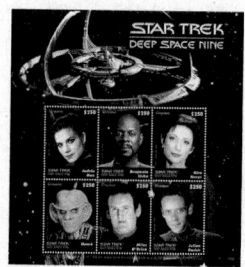

Characters From *Star Trek: Deep Space Nine* Television Series — A669

No. 4442: a, Jadzia Dax. b, Benjamin Sisko. c, Kira Nerys. d, Quark. e, Miles O'Brien. f, Julian Bashir.
$800, Dax and Sisko, horiz.

**2015, Dec. 31    Litho.    Perf. 14**
4442  A669  $250  Sheet of 6,
                    #a-f             14.50 14.50
**Souvenir Sheet**
4443  A669  $800 multi              7.75 7.75
No. 4443 contains one 80x30mm stamp.

**Souvenir Sheets**

Elvis Presley (1935-77) — A670

Designs: No. 4444, $800, Unique dance style. No. 4445, $800, A long train ride home. No. 4446, $800, Presley performing at Cynthia Milk Benefit Concert. No. 4447, $800, Family moves to Memphis, horiz. No. 4448, $1000, Presley reports to local draft board, horiz. No. 4449, $1000, Marquee on Memphian Theater, rented by Presley. No. 4450, $1000, Presley displaying honorary sherrif's badge. No. 4451, $1000, Presley meets Tom Jones in Las Vegas.

***Perf. 12, 14 (#4446), 13x13¼ (#4448),***
***13¼x13 (#4449-4451)***
**2016                            Litho.**
4444-4451  A670    Set of 8    70.00 70.00
Issued: Nos. 4444-4447, 1/31; Nos. 4448-4451, 6/30.

Capybaras — A671

No. 4452: a, Bird on capybara. b, Capybara on grass, facing right. c, Capybara in water, facing right. d, Capybara in water, facing forward. e, Capybara in tall grass, facing left. f, Capybara standing on hillside.
$800, Five capybaras.

| 2016, Feb. 20 | Litho. | Perf. 14 |
| --- | --- | --- |
| 4452 A671 $250 Sheet of 6, | | |
| #a-f | 14.50 | 14.50 |

**Souvenir Sheet**
**Perf. 12**

| 4453 A671 $800 multi | 7.75 | 7.75 |
| --- | --- | --- |

**Miniature Sheets**

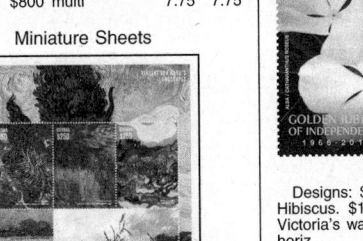

Paintings by Vincent van Gogh (1853-90) — A672

No. 4454, $250 — Landscapes: a, Doctor Gachet's Garden in Auvers, 1890 (51x38mm). b, Edge of a Wheatfield with Poppies, 1887 (38x51mm). c, The Olive Trees, 1889 (38x51mm). d, View of Arles with Irises, 1888 (38x51mm). e, Green Ears of Wheat, 1888 (76x51mm).
No. 4455, $250 — Self-portraits from: a, 1888 (38x51mm). b, 1889 (38x51mm). c, 1888 (with hat and pipe) (38x51mm). d, 1888 (with hat) (38x51mm). e, 1887 (76x51mm).

| 2016, Feb. 20 | Litho. | Perf. 12½ |
| --- | --- | --- |
| Sheets of 5, #a-e | | |
| 4454-4455 A672 Set of 2 | 24.00 | 24.00 |

Muhammad Ali (1942-2016), Boxer — A673

No. 4456 — Various photographs of Ali in boxing ring, as shown.
$800, Ali throwing punch, horiz.

| 2016, Feb. 20 | Litho. | Perf. 13¾ |
| --- | --- | --- |
| 4456 A673 $250 Sheet of 6, | | |
| #a-f | 14.50 | 14.50 |

**Souvenir Sheet**
**Perf. 14**

| 4457 A673 $800 multi | 7.75 | 7.75 |
| --- | --- | --- |

No. 4457 contains one 80x30mm stamp.

Plants and Flowers A674

No. 4458: a, Yerba mate. b, Torch ginger. c, Zebra plant. d, Queen Victoria's water lily.
No. 4459: a, Bravo blue vein petunia. b, Cannonball tree. c, False bird-of-paradise. d, Pride of India. e, Pink banana flower. f, Red-flowering currant.
$800, Red pineapple flower.

| 2016, Feb. 20 | Litho. | Perf. 14 |
| --- | --- | --- |
| 4458 A674 $250 Sheet of 4, | | |
| #a-d | 9.75 | 9.75 |
| 4459 A674 $250 Sheet of 6, | | |
| #a-f | 14.50 | 14.50 |

**Souvenir Sheet**
**Perf. 12**

| 4460 A674 $800 multi | 7.75 | 7.75 |
| --- | --- | --- |

Flowers — A675

Designs: $80, Catharanthus roseus. $130, Hibiscus. $150, Bougainvillea. $160, Queen Victoria's water lily. $200, Cannonball flower, horiz.

| 2016, Apr. 7 | Litho. | Perf. 12 |
| --- | --- | --- |
| 4461-4465 A675 Set of 5 | 7.00 | 7.00 |

Independence, 50th anniv.

Independence, 50th Anniv. — A676

Designs: $80, Crowd. $130, Independence ceremony, May 26, 1966. $150, Fort Kyk-Over-Al, vert. $160, St. George's Cathedral, Georgetown, vert. $200, Flag of Guyana.

| 2016, Apr. 7 | Litho. | Perf. 12½ |
| --- | --- | --- |
| 4466-4470 A676 Set of 5 | 7.00 | 7.00 |

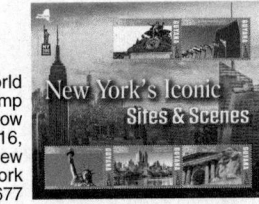

World Stamp Show 2016, New York A677

No. 4471 — World Stamp Show emblem and New York City landmarks: a, Grand Central Terminal. b, United Nations Headquarters. c, Statue of Liberty. d, Jacqueline Kennedy Onassis Reservoir. e, New York Public Library. $1000, Empire State Building and other buildings, vert.

| 2016, May 2 | Litho. | Perf. 12 |
| --- | --- | --- |
| 4471 A677 $250 Sheet of 5, | | |
| #a-e | 12.50 | 12.50 |

**Souvenir Sheet**

| 4472 A677 $1000 multi | 9.75 | 9.75 |
| --- | --- | --- |

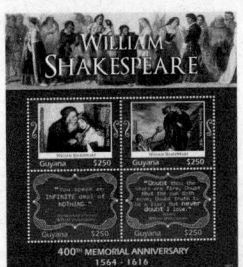

William Shakespeare (1564-1616), Writer — A678

No. 4473: a, Shylock and Jessica (characters from The Merchant of Venice), by Maurycy Gottlieb. b, Hamlet and Horation in the Graveyard (characters in Hamlet), by Eugène Delacroix. c, Line from The Merchant of Venice. d, Line from Hamlet.
No. 4474: a, The Wrestling Scene from As You Like It, by Francis Hayman. b, Scene from Shakespeare's The Tempest, by William Hogarth. c, The Revelation of Olivia's Betrothal from Act V, Scene I of Twelfth Night,

by William Hamilton. d, Line from As You Like It. e, Line from The Tempest. f, Line from Twelfth Night.
$1000, The Reconciliation of the Montagues and the Capulets over the Dead Bodies of Romeo and Juliet, by Frederic Leighton.

| 2016, May 30 | Litho. | Perf. 14 |
| --- | --- | --- |
| 4473 A678 $250 Sheet of 4, | | |
| #a-d | 9.75 | 9.75 |

**Perf. 12**

| 4474 A678 $250 Sheet of 6, | | |
| --- | --- | --- |
| #a-f | 14.50 | 14.50 |

**Souvenir Sheet**

| 4475 A678 $1000 multi | 9.75 | 9.75 |
| --- | --- | --- |

No. 4475 contains one 50x30mm stamp.

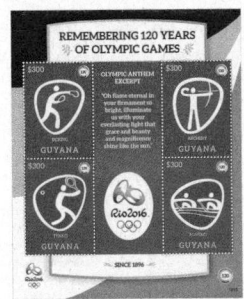

2016 Summer Olympics, Rio de Janeiro — A679

No. 4476: a, Boxing. b, Archery. c, Tennis. d, Rowing.
No. 4477: a, Handball. b, Weight lifting. c, Diving. d, Soccer.
No. 4478: a, Artistic gymnastics. b, Takashi Ono, Olympic gymnast.

| 2016, July 7 | Litho. | Perf. 14 |
| --- | --- | --- |
| Sheets of 4, #a-d | | |
| 4476-4477 A679 Set of 2 | 23.50 | 23.50 |

**Souvenir Sheet**
**Perf. 12½**

| 4478 A679 $500 Sheet of 2, | | |
| --- | --- | --- |
| #a-b | 9.75 | 9.75 |

No. 4478 contains two 38x51mm stamps.

A680

Queen Elizabeth II, 90th Birthday A681

Various photographs of Queen Elizabeth II, as shown.

| 2016, July 25 | Litho. | Perf. 14 |
| --- | --- | --- |
| 4479 A680 $250 Sheet of 6, | | |
| #a-f | 14.50 | 14.50 |

**Souvenir Sheet**
**Perf.**

| 4480 A681 $500 Sheet of 2, | | |
| --- | --- | --- |
| #a-b | 9.75 | 9.75 |

Characters From Star Trek: The Next Generation Television Series — A682

No. 4481: a, Worf. b, William Riker. c, Data. d, Beverly Crusher. e, Geordi La Forge. f, Deanna Troi.
$1000, Captain Jean-Luc Picard.

| 2016, Aug. 29 | Litho. | Perf. 12 |
| --- | --- | --- |
| 4481 A682 $250 Sheet of 6, | | |
| #a-f | 14.50 | 14.50 |

**Souvenir Sheet**
**Perf. 12½**

| 4482 A682 $1000 multi | 9.75 | 9.75 |
| --- | --- | --- |

No. 4482 contains one 38x51mm stamp.

ExoMars Mission to Mars A683

No. 4483: a, ExoMars rover on Mars. b, NASA Deep Space Station 35. c, ExoMars trace gas orbiter, denomination at UR. d, ExoMars trace gas orbiter, denomination at LR.
$1000, Proton rocket over Earth, vert.

| 2016, Sept. 9 | Litho. | Perf. 14 |
| --- | --- | --- |
| 4483 A683 $250 Sheet of 4, #a-d | 9.75 | 9.75 |

**Souvenir Sheet**
**Perf. 12**

| 4484 A683 $1000 multi | 9.75 | 9.75 |
| --- | --- | --- |

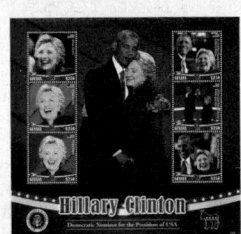

Hillary Clinton, 2016 Democratic Presidential Candidate — A684

No. 4485 — Various photographs of Secretary Clinton (#4485a, 4485c, 4485e) or Secretary Clinton and Pres. Barack Obama (#4485b, 4485d, 4485f), as shown.
$1000, Clinton and Obama, vert.

| 2016, Sept. 30 | Litho. | Perf. 13¾ |
| --- | --- | --- |
| 4485 A684 $250 Sheet of 6, | | |
| #a-f | 15.00 | 15.00 |

**Souvenir Sheet**
**Perf. 12½**

| 4486 A684 $1000 multi | 9.75 | 9.75 |
| --- | --- | --- |

No. 4486 contains one 38x51mm stamp.

**Miniature Sheet**

Bauxite Mining in Guyana, Cent. A685

No. 4487: a, $80, Kiln panorama. b, $140, Bauxite centennial emblem. c, $150, Mining of bauxite. d, $160, 1300 Dragline.

| 2016, Oct. 27 | Litho. | Perf. 12½x12 |
| --- | --- | --- |
| 4487 A685 Sheet of 4, #a-d | 5.25 | 5.25 |

National Day of Villages — A686

Scenes depicting Exodus from Plantation Northbrook, 1839, with frame color of: $80, Bright green. $150, Orange vermilion.

**2016, Nov. 7    Litho.    Perf. 12½x13¼**
4488-4489 A686    Set of 2          2.25  2.25

Worldwide Fund for Nature (WWF) — A687

No. 4490 — Giant armadillo: a, On ground, facing left. b, Facing forward. c, Climbing. d, Facing right.

**2016, Nov. 17    Litho.    Perf. 14**
4490 A687 $400 Block of 4,
          #a-d                        15.50 15.50
  e.  Miniature sheet of 8, 2 each
      #4490a-4490d                    31.00 31.00

A688

**2016, Dec. 5    Litho.    Perf. 13¾**
4491 A688 $250 Pair, #a-b            5.00  5.00
    **Souvenir Sheets**
          **Perf. 12**
4492 A689 $600 Sheet of 2,
          #a-b                       12.00 12.00
          **Perf.**
4493 A690 $800 multi                 8.00  8.00

A689

New Year 2017 (Year of the Rooster) A690

No. 4491 — Rooster with background color of: a, Pale green. b, Light blue.
No. 4492: a, Rooster and Chinese character for "rooster." b, Rooster, fish and flowers.

---

Golden Rocket Frog A691

No. 4494: Various depictions of frog, as shown.
No. 4495: a, Two frogs. b, Tadpole.

**2016, Dec. 30    Litho.    Perf.**
4494 A691 $400 Sheet of 4,
          #a-d                       16.00 16.00
    **Souvenir Sheet**
          **Perf. 12**
4495 A691 $600 Sheet of 2,
          #a-b                       12.00 12.00
No. 4495 contains two 64x32mm triangular stamps.

New Year 2017 (Year of the Rooster) — A692

Various roosters with number in LR corner of: No. 4496, $88, (3-1). No. 4497, $88, (3-2). No. 4498, $88, (3-3).

**2017, Jan. 8    Litho.    Perf. 13¼x13**
4496-4498 A692    Set of 3           2.60  2.60

Pres. John F. Kennedy (1917-63) — A693

No. 4499 — Various photographs of Pres. Kennedy, as shown.
No. 4500 — Pres. Kennedy sitting: a, In rocking chair. b, In chair near window. c, On steps.

**2017, Apr. 5    Litho.    Perf. 14**
4499 A693 $250 Sheet of 6,
          #a-f                       14.50 14.50
    **Souvenir Sheet**
4500 A693 $400 Sheet of 3,
          #a-c                       11.50 11.50
    **Miniature Sheet**

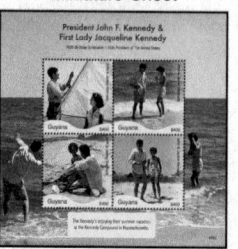

Pres. John F. Kennedy (1917-63), and Wife, Jacqueline (1929-94) — A694

No. 4501 — Pres. and Mrs. Kennedy: a, In sailboat. b, Standing in water. c, Sitting on beach. d, Standing on beach.

**2017, Apr. 5    Litho.    Perf. 13¾**
4501 A694 $400 Sheet of 4,
          #a-d                       15.50 15.50

---

Return of Hong Kong to China, 20th Anniv. — A695

Designs: No. 4502, $80, Deng Xiaoping, flag of People's Republic of China, doves and Hong Kong buildings (10-1). No. 4503, $80, Dove, Hong Kong buildings (10-2). No. 4504, $80, Flag of People's Republic of China, doves over Gate of Heavenly Peace, Beijing (10-3). No. 4505, $80, Buildings with decorations and signs (10-4). No. 4506, $80, Flag of Hong Kong and doves over buildings (10-5). No. 4507, $80, Flag of People's Republic of China and doves over Golden Bauhinia Statue (10-6). No. 4508, $80, Giant pandas, bamboo and Hong Kong Convention and Exhibition Center (10-7). No. 4509, $80, Doves and aerial view of Hong Kong (10-8). No. 4510, $80, Sleeping Beauty Castle, Hong Kong Disneyland, Hong Kong Film Awards Statue (10-9). No. 4511, $80, Ship and Hong Kong skyline (10-10).

**2017, May 5    Litho.    Perf. 14**
4502-4511 A695    Set of 10          7.75  7.75

    **Miniature Sheet**

Princess Diana (1961-97) — A696

No. 4512 — Princess Diana: a, $180, Wearing tiara (64x32mm). b, $200, Wearing white hat (64x32mm). c, $200, Wearing tiara, diff. (64x32mm). d, $200, Wearing beret with badge (64x32mm). e, $200, Without hat, black-and-white photograph (64x32mm). f, $200, Wearing sailor's cap (64x32mm). g, $200, As young woman (64x32mm). h, $200, Wearing wedding gown (64x32mm). i, $200, As young girl, black-and-white photograph (64x32mm). j, $200, As toddler, black-and-white photograph (64x32mm). k, $400, Wearing tiara, black-and-white phtotograph (64x64mm).

**2017, June 7    Litho.    Perf. 12**
4512 A696    Sheet of 11, #a-k   23.00 23.00

Animals A697

No. 4513: a, Moon jellyfish. b, Poison dart frog. c, Three-banded armadillo. d, Red bird-of-paradise.
$800, Reticulated giraffe, vert.

**2017, Apr. 14    Litho.    Perf. 12¾**
4513 A697 $500 Sheet of 4,
          #a-d                       19.50 19.50
    **Souvenir Sheet**
4514 A697 $800 multi                 7.75  7.75

Toucans A698

No. 4515: a, Yellow-throated toucan. b, Toco toucan. c, Keel-billed toucan. d, White-throated toucan.
No. 4516, vert.: a, Keel-billed toucan, denomination in black, diff. b, Keel-billed toucan, denomination in white, diff.

---

**2017, Aug. 7    Litho.    Perf. 12**
4515 A698 $400 Sheet of 4,
          #a-d                       15.50 15.50
    **Souvenir Sheet**
4516 A698 $600 Sheet of 2,
          #a-b                       12.00 12.00

New Year 2018 (Year of the Dog) A699

No. 4517: $400: a, Shih tzu. b, Chow chow.
No. 4518, $400: a, Pekingese. b, Chinese crested dog.

**2017, Aug. 8    Litho.    Perf. 14**
    **Horiz. pairs, #a-b**
4517-4518 A699    Set of 2           15.50 15.50
Nos. 4517-4518 were each printed in sheets containing two pairs.

Lions Clubs International, Cent. — A700

No. 4519: a, Yellow frame. b, Blue violet frame.
No. 4520, horiz.: a, Royal blue frame. b, Yellow frame.

**2017, Sept. 11    Litho.    Perf. 12½**
4519 A700 $400 Pair, #a-b            7.75  7.75
    **Souvenir Sheet**
          **Perf. 13¼**
4520 A700 $600 Sheet of 2,
          #a-b                       12.00 12.00
No. 4519 was printed in sheets containing two pairs. No. 4520 contains two 51x38mm stamps.

Sloths A701

No. 4521: a, Hoffman's two-toed sloth, hanging with legs together. b, Brown-throated sloth. c, Adult and juvenile Brown-throated sloths. d, Hoffman's two-toed sloth, hanging with legs separated.
No. 4522, horiz. — Brown-throated sloth: a, With one paw visible and extended. b, Climbing tree. c, With front paw below head.

**2017, Sept. 11    Litho.    Perf. 14**
4521 A701 $400 Sheet of 4,
          #a-d                       15.50 15.50
    **Souvenir Sheet**
4522 A701 $400 Sheet of 3,
          #a-c                       12.00 12.00

Amazon Rainforest — A702

No. 4523: a, House on stilts. b, Fishing boats. c, Bend in river. d, Rainbow. e, Canoe and banks of tributary. d, Houses near river.
No. 4524: a, River and its banks. b, Water lilies. c, Tree in water.

**2017, Nov. 22    Litho.    Perf. 14**
4523 A702 $250 Sheet of 6,
          #a-f                       14.50 14.50

**Souvenir Sheet**
4524 A702 $400 Sheet of 3, #a-c  11.50 11.50

**Miniature Sheet**

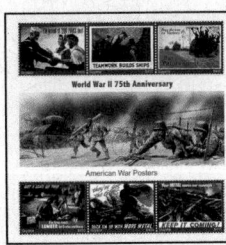

World War II, 75th Anniv. A703

No. 4525 — Posters inscribed: a, "I'm proud of you folks, too!" b, "Teamwork builds ships." c, "Buy Victory Bonds." d, "The Army needs lumber for crates and boxes." e, "Back 'em up with more metal." f, "Keep it coming!"

**2017, Dec. 4   Litho.   Perf. 12½x13¼**
4525 A703 $400 Sheet of 6, #a-f  23.50 23.50

Jaguars A704

No. 4526: a, Jaguar on tree branch. b, Head of jaguar facing forward. c, Jaguar with open mouth. d, Jaguar with torso at right.
$800, Jaguar, vert.

**2017, Dec. 7   Litho.   Perf. 14**
4526 A704 $400 Sheet of 4, #a-d  15.50 15.50

**Souvenir Sheet**
**Perf. 12¾**
4527 A704 $800 multi  7.75 7.75
No. 4527 contains one 38x51mm stamp.

Wildlife of the Galapagos Islands — A705

No. 4528: a, Galapagos penguin. b, Magnificent frigatebird. c, Marine iguana. d, Blue-footed booby. e, Small ground finch. f, Galapagos sea lion.
$800, Giant tortoise.

**2017, Dec. 26   Litho.   Perf. 14**
4528 A705 $250 Sheet of 6, #a-f  14.50 14.50

**Souvenir Sheet**
**Perf. 12½**
4529 A705 $800 multi  7.75 7.75
No. 4529 contains one 51x38mm stamp.

A706

A707

Elvis Presley (1935-77) — A708

No. 4530 — Presley: a, With guitar slung over shoulder. b, Playing guitar. c, Holding microphone stand and pointing.
No. 4531 — Presley: a, Wearing turtleneck sweater. b, Wearing plaid shirt, playing guitar. c, With arms crossed. d, Sitting, playing guitar.
Inscriptions: No. 4532, $800, Elvis' only international concerts. No. 4533, $800, Record donation in support of acting colleagues. No. 4534, $800, Elvis' final movie - Change of Habit. No. 4535, $800, G.I. Blues - Elvis' most successful album.

**2017, Dec. 26   Litho.   Perf. 14**
4530 A706 $400 Sheet of 3, #a-c  12.00 12.00
4531 A707 $400 Sheet of 4, #a-d  15.50 15.50
**Souvenir Sheets**
**Perf. 12½**
4532-4535 A708 Set of 4  31.00 31.00

Jaguarundis — A709

No. 4536 — Various photographs of jaguarundis with text at right in: a, $300, White. b, $300, Black. c, $500, White. d, $500, Black.
No. 4537, horiz. — Various photographs of jaguarundis: a, $550. b, $650.

**2018, Jan. 24   Litho.   Perf. 14**
4536 A709 Sheet of 4, #a-d  15.50 15.50
**Souvenir Sheet**
**Perf. 12½**
4537 A709 Sheet of 2, #a-b  11.50 11.50
No. 4537 contains two 51x38mm stamps.

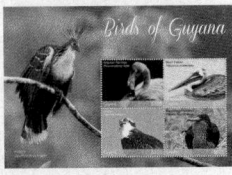

Birds A710

No. 4538: a, $125, American flamingo. b, $225, Brown pelican. c, $325, Osprey. d, $525, Magnificent frigatebird.
No. 4539: a, $350, Scarlet ibis. b, $450, White-faced whistling duck. c, $550, Maguari stork.

**2018, Jan. 24   Litho.   Perf. 14**
4538 A710 Sheet of 4, #a-d  11.50 11.50
**Souvenir Sheet**
**Perf. 12**
4539 A710 Sheet of 3, #a-c  13.00 13.00

**Souvenir Sheet**

Engagement of Prince Harry and Meghan Markle — A711

No. 4540 — Couple, with Prince Harry: a, Wearing scarf. b, Without scarf.

**2018, Jan. 31   Litho.   Perf. 14**
4540 A711 $800 Sheet of 2, #a-b  11.50 11.50

Coronation Anniversary Medals — A712

1953 Coronation Medal — A713

No. 4541, $400 — Dull pink bottom panel and side of 1977 Silver Jubilee medal showing: a, Head of Queen Elizabeth II. b, Crown, wreath and text.
No. 4542, $400 — Blue violet bottom panel and side of 2002 Golden Jubilee medal showing: a, Head of Queen Elizabeth II. b, Arms and dates.
No. 4543, $400 — Carmine red bottom panel and side of 2012 Diamond Jubilee medal showing: a, Head of Queen Elizabeth II. b, Crown, royal cypher and dates.

**2018, Feb. 8   Litho.   Perf. 12**
**Sheets of 2, #a-b**
4541-4543 A712 Set of 3  23.00 23.00
**Souvenir Sheet**
**Perf. 14**
4544 A713 $800 multi  7.75 7.75

**Souvenir Sheet**

Kaieteur Falls A714

No. 4545 — Various photographs: a, $300 (40x30mm). b, $400 (40x30mm). c, $500 (40x60mm).

**2018, Mar. 14   Litho.   Perf. 14**
4545 A714 Sheet of 3, #a-c  12.00 12.00

**Souvenir Sheet**

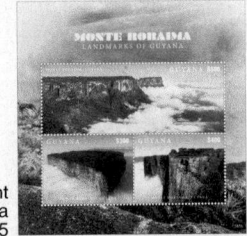

Mount Roraima A715

No. 4546 — Various photographs: a, $300 (40x30mm). b, $400 (40x30mm). c, $500 (80x30mm).

**2018, Mar. 14   Litho.   Perf. 14**
4546 A715 Sheet of 3, #a-c  12.00 12.00

Frogs A716

No. 4547: a, $150, Three-striped poison frog. b, $200, Amazon milk frog. c, $250, Tiger-legged monkey frog. d, $300, Map tree frog. e, $350, Bumble bee poison dart frog. f, $400, Amazonian horned frog.
$800, Golden rocket frog.

**2018, Mar. 14   Litho.   Perf. 14**
4547 A716 Sheet of 6, #a-f  16.00 16.00
**Souvenir Sheet**
**Perf. 12½**
4548 A716 $800 multi  8.00 8.00
No. 4548 contains one 51x38mm stamp.

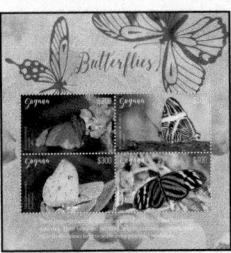

Butterflies — A717

No. 4549: a, $200, Julia butterfly. b, $300, Cloudless sulphur butterfly. c, $400, Isabella tiger longwing butterfly. d, $500, Zebra mosaic butterfly.
No. 4550: a, $250, Red postman butterfly. b, $350, Lemon butterfly. c, $450, Doris longwing butterfly. d, $550, Malachite butterfly.
No. 4551, $400 — Emperor butterflies: a, On flower with wings closed. b, On rock with wings open.

**2018, Mar. 14   Litho.   Perf. 12**
**Sheets of 4, #a-d**
4549-4550 A717 Set of 2  29.00 29.00
**Souvenir Sheet**
4551 A717 $400 Sheet of 2, #a-b  7.75 7.75

**Miniature Sheet**

Pres. Cheddi Jagan (1918-97) — A718

No. 4552 — Various photogrpahs of Jagan in: a, $50, Black-and-white, looking left. b, $80, Color, flag in background. c, $100, Black-and-white, looking right. d, $100, Color, at podium.

**2018, Mar. 16   Litho.   Perf. 12**
4552 A718 Sheet of 4, #a-d  3.25 3.25

Mao Zedong (1893-1976), Chairman of the Communist Party of China — A719

No. 4553 — Various photographs of Mao Zedong: a, $200. b, $300. c, $500.
$800, Mao Zedong at desk.

**2018, Mar. 27    Litho.    Perf. 12**
4553 A719  Sheet of 3, #a-c    9.75 9.75
**Souvenir Sheet**
4554 A719  $800 multi    7.75 7.75

**Souvenir Sheet**

Fu Hao Owl-shaped Vessel From Yin Ruins, People's Republic of China — A720

**2018, May 3    Litho.    Perf. 12**
4555 A720  $500 multi    4.75 4.75

Wildlife — A721

Designs: $25, Scarlet macaw. $80, Jaguar. $100, Black caiman. $140, Black curassow. $150, Red-billed toucan.

**2018, June 7    Litho.    Perf. 12½**
4556-4560 A721  Set of 5    4.75 4.75

**Miniature Sheet**

Visit of Pres. Donald Trump to Saudi Arabia A722

No. 4561: a, Pres. Trump and wife, Melania, red panel at bottom. b, Pres. Trump and wife, blue panel at bottom. c, Ivanka Trump, Jared Kushner and King Salman. d, Pres. Trump and King Salman.

**2018, July 13    Litho.    Perf. 12**
4561 A722  $400 Sheet of 4, #a-d    15.50 15.50

Hoatzins A723

No. 4562 — Various photographs of hoatzins: a, $200 (40x30mm). b, $300 (40x30mm). c, $400 (40x60mm). d, $500 (40x60mm).
$850, Hoatzin, diff.

**2018, July 13    Litho.    Perf. 14**
4562 A723  Sheet of 4, #a-d    13.50 13.50
**Souvenir Sheet**
**Perf. 12**
4563 A723  $850 multi    8.25 8.25
No. 4563 contains one 30x50mm stamp.

**Miniature Sheets**

A724

A725

Wedding of Prince Harry and Meghan Markle A726

No. 4564: a, $400, Prince Harry. b, $400, Meghan Markle in wedding dress. c, $450, Couple in coach. d, $450, Couple in formal wear holding hands.
No. 4565: a, $400, Couple holding hands. b, $400, Prince Charles and bride's mother, Doria Ragland. c, $450, Prince Harry moving bride's veil. d, $450, Couple on wedding day.
No. 4566 — Royal brides in their wedding gowns: a, $400, Duchess of Cambridge. b, $400, Princess Diana of Wales. c, $450, Duchess of Sussex. d, $450, Queen Elizabeth II.

**2018, July 13    Litho.    Perf. 12**
4564 A724  Sheet of 4, #a-d    16.50 16.50
4565 A725  Sheet of 4, #a-d    16.50 16.50
4566 A726  Sheet of 4, #a-d    16.50 16.50
  Nos. 4564-4566 (3)    49.50 49.50

Elvis Presley (1935-77) — A727

**2018, July 26    Litho.    Perf. 12**
4567 A727  $450 multi    4.50 4.50
No. 4567 was printed in sheets of 3.

**Miniature Sheets**

Nebulae A728

No. 4568: a, $200, Dumbbell Nebula (30x40mm). b, $200, Butterfly Nebula (30x40mm). c, $200, Ring Nebula (30x40mm). d, $300, Dumbbell Nebula, diff. (30x50mm). e, $300, Butterfly Nebula, diff. (30x50mm). f, $300, Ring Nebula, diff. (30x50mm).
No. 4569: a, $200, Abell 31 (30x40mm). b, $200, Helix Nebula (30x40mm). c, $200, Little Ghost Nebula (30x40mm). d, $300, Abell 31, diff. (30x50mm). e, $300, Helix Nebula, diff.

(30x50mm). f, $300, Little Ghost Nebula, diff. (30x50mm).

**Perf. 14 ($200 stamps), 12x12x14x12 ($300 stamps)**
**2018, July 26    Litho.**
**Sheets of 6, #a-f**
4568-4569 A728  Set of 2    29.00 29.00

**Souvenir Sheet**

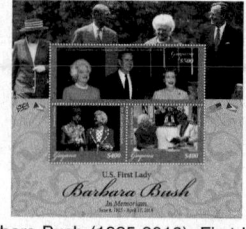

Barbara Bush (1925-2018), First Lady of the United States — A729

No. 4570 — Mrs. Bush and: a, $400, Princess Diana (both standing, 40x30mm). b, $400, Princess Diana (both seated, 40x30mm). c, $500, Husband, Pres. George H. W. Bush, and Queen Elizabeth II (80x30mm).

**2018, Aug. 5    Litho.    Perf. 14**
4570 A729  Sheet of 3, #a-c    12.50 12.50

Fish A730

No. 4571: a, $250, Atlantic sailfish. b, $350, Blackfin tuna. c, $450, Atlantic bluefin tuna. d, $550, Dolphinfish.
$850, Atlantic blue marlin.

**2018, Aug. 5    Litho.    Perf. 12**
4571 A730  Sheet of 4, #a-d    15.50 15.50
**Souvenir Sheet**
4572 A730  $850 multi    8.25 8.25

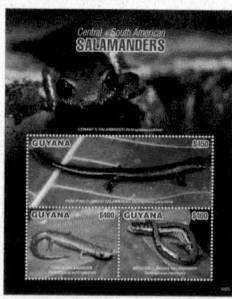

Salamanders — A731

No. 4573: a, $400, Cocle salamander (40x30mm). b, $400, Mexican climbing salamander (40x30mm). c, $450, Peruvian climbing salamander (80x30mm).
$820, Axolotl.

**2018, Aug. 5    Litho.    Perf. 14**
4573 A731  Sheet of 3, #a-c    12.00 12.00
**Souvenir Sheet**
4574 A731  $820 multi    8.00 8.00
No. 4574 contains one 80x30mm stamp.

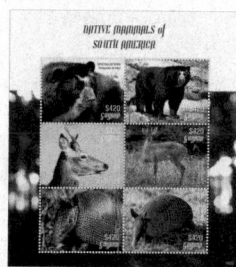

Mammals — A732

No. 4575: a, Head of Spectacled bear. b, Entire Spectacled bear. c, Head of Red brocket deer. d, Entire Red brocket deer. e, Head of Nine-banded armadillo. f, Entire Nine-banded armadillo.
$830, Spectacled bear, vert.

**2018, Aug. 8    Litho.    Perf. 14**
4575 A732  $420 Sheet of 6, #a-f    24.00 24.00
**Souvenir Sheet**
**Perf. 12**
4576 A732  $830 multi    8.00 8.00
No. 4576 contains one 40x60mm stamp.

**Miniature Sheets**

Wild Cats A733

No. 4577: a, $380, Oncilla. b, $400, Margay. c, $420, Ocelot. d, $440, Puma.
No. 4578, vert.: a, $380, Oncilla. b, $400, Margay. c, $420, Ocelot. d, $440, Puma.

**2018, Aug. 8    Litho.    Perf. 12**
**Sheets of 4, #a-d**
4577-4578 A733  Set of 2    32.00 32.00

**Miniature Sheet**

New Year 2019 (Year of the Boar) A734

No. 4579: a, Pink pig standing. b, Brown pig lying down. c, Pink pig lying down. d, Brown pig standing.

**2018, Aug. 8    Litho.    Perf. 14**
4579 A734  $400 Sheet of 4, #a-d    15.50 15.50

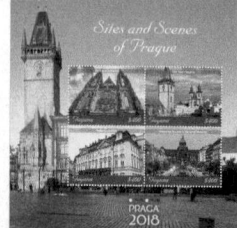

Prague Tourist Attractions — A735

No. 4580: a, St. Vitus Cathedral. b, Old Town Square. c, National Gallery. d, Wenceslas Square and National Museum.
$800, Charles Bridge.

**2018, Aug. 15** Litho. *Perf. 14*
4580 A735 $400 Sheet of 4,
#a-d            15.50 15.50
**Souvenir Sheet**
4581 A735 $800 multi      7.75 7.75
Praga 2018 World Stamp Exhibition, Prague. No. 4581 contains one 80x30mm stamp.

**Souvenir Sheet**

New Year 2019 (Year of the Boar) A736

**2018, Sept. 8** Litho. *Perf. 13¾*
4582 A736 $800 multi      7.75 7.75

Relations Between Guyana and Brazil, 50th Anniv. — A737

No. 4583 — Flags of Guyana and Brazil: a, $80. b, $200.

**2018, Oct. 19** Litho. *Perf. 12½x12*
4583 A737     Vert. pair, #a-b      2.75 2.75
No. 4583 was printed in sheets containing 2 pairs.

**Souvenir Sheet**

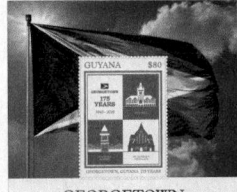

Georgetown, 175th Anniv. — A738

**2018, Oct. 29** Litho. *Perf. 13¼*
4584 A738 $80 multi      .80 .80

A739

Atta Cephalotes — A740

Designs: $530, Queen leafcutter ant.
No. 4596: a, $200, Leafcutter ants carrying leafs (50x30mm). b, $400, Leafcutter ant carrying leaf on tree trunk (40x30mm). c, $400, Leafcutter ants and leaf (40x30mm). d, $400, Leafcutter ant and leaf (40x30mm).

**2018, Nov. 20** Litho. *Perf. 14*
4585 A739 $530 multi      5.00 5.00
**Miniature Sheet**
*Perf. 12*
4586 A740     Sheet of 4, #a-d      13.50 13.50
No. 4585 was printed in sheets of 2.

Tanagers A741

No. 4587: a, Silver-throated tanager. b, Silver-beaked tanager. c, Bay-headed tanager. d, Scarlet tanager. e, Golden-hooded tanager. f, Guira tanager.
No. 4588: a, $500, Speckled tanager facing right. b, $550, Speckled tanager facing left.

**2018, Nov. 20** Litho. *Perf. 14*
4587 A741 $200 Sheet of 6,
#a-f            11.50 11.50
**Souvenir Sheet**
4588 A741     Sheet of 2, #a-b      10.00 10.00

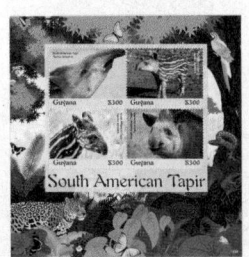

South American Tapirs — A742

No. 4589: a, Tapir's head facing right, no stripes visible. b, Tapir facing left. c, Head and striped neck of tapir facing right. d, Tapir facing forward.
No. 4590: a, $500, Tapir facing right. b, $550, Tapir facing right, diff.

**2018, Nov. 20** Litho. *Perf. 14*
4589 A742 $300 Sheet of 4,
#a-d            11.50 11.50
**Souvenir Sheet**
4590 A742     Sheet of 2, #a-b      10.00 10.00

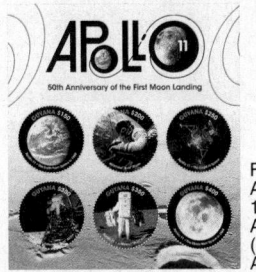

Flight of Apollo 11, 50th Anniv. (in 2019) A743

No. 4591: a, $150, Picture of Earth from space. b, $200, Astronaut Edwin A. "Buzz" Aldrin. c, $250, Lunar Module. d, $300, Aldrin on ladder of Lunar Module. e, $350, Aldrin carrying equipment on Moon. f, $400, Picture of Moon from space.
No. 4592: a, Plaque on Lunar Module. b, Eagle from mission patch.

**2018, Nov. 20** Litho. *Perf.*
4591 A743     Sheet of 6, #a-f      16.00 16.00
**Souvenir Sheet**
*Perf. 13¾*
4592 A743 $600 Sheet of 2,
#a-b            11.50 11.50
No. 4592 contains two 35x35mm stamps.

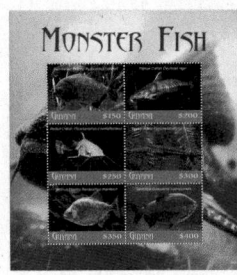

Fish A744

No. 4593: a, $150, Red-bellied piranha. b, $200, Ripsaw catfish. c, $250, Redtail catfish. d, $300, Tiger sorubim. e, $350, Redeye piranha. f, $400, Tambaqui. $850, Arapaima.

**2018, Dec. 18** Litho. *Perf. 14*
4593 A744     Sheet of 6, #a-f      16.00 16.00
**Souvenir Sheet**
4594 A744 $850 multi      8.25 8.25
No. 4594 contains one 80x30mm stamp.

**Souvenir Sheet**

Fenshan Rose A745

**2019, Apr. 15** Litho. *Perf. 14x13½*
4595 A745 $800 multi      7.75 7.75
2019 World Federation of Rose Societies Convention, Nanyang, People's Republic of China.

**Miniature Sheets**

South American Wildlife — A746

No. 4596: a, $200, Parrot and vulture. b, $200, Peccary, rhea, deer, and vicuña. c, $200, Frog, snake, and armadillo. d, $400, Bat's wing, monkey, and birds. e, $400, Toucan and birds. f, $400, Jaguar. No. 4597, vert. — Various Red howler monkeys: a, $200. b, $300. c, $400. d, $500.

**2019, May 1** Litho. *Perf. 12*
4596 A746     Sheet of 6, #a-f      17.50 17.50
*Perf. 14*
4597 A746     Sheet of 4, #a-d      13.50 13.50

**Miniature Sheet**

Valerie Rodway (1919-70), Composer — A747

No. 4598: a, $100, Bird and song title "O Beautiful Guyana." b, $100, Rodway facing right. c, $150, Rodway wearing dress with lace collar. d, $150, Rodway wearing patterned blouse.

**2019, May 16** Litho. *Perf. 14*
4598 A747     Sheet of 4, #a-d      5.00 5.00

Inca Terns A748

No. 4599 — Various photographs of Inca tern: a, $100. b, $300. c, $500. d, $700. $800, Inca tern, horiz.

**2019, May 16** Litho. *Perf. 14*
4599 A748     Sheet of 4, #a-d      15.50 15.50
**Souvenir Sheet**
4600 A748 $800 multi      7.75 7.75

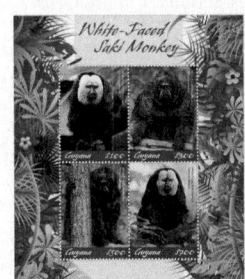

White-faced Saki Monkey — A749

No. 4601 — Various depictions of monkey: a, $100. b, $300. c, $500. d, $700. $800, White-faced saki monkey, diff.

**2019, May 28** Litho. *Perf. 14*
4601 A749     Sheet of 4, #a-d      15.50 15.50
**Souvenir Sheet**
4602 A749 $800 multi      7.75 7.75

China 2019 World Stamp Exhibition, Wuhan, People's Republic of China — A750

No. 4603 — Various photographs of Wuhan: a, $100, Intercontinental Hotel. b, $300, Roof of Chinese building. c, $500, Building and statue. d, $700, Bridge and city skyline. $800, Yellow Crane Tower, vert.

**2019, June 10** Litho. *Perf. 14*
4603 A750     Sheet of 4, #a-d      15.50 15.50
**Souvenir Sheet**
*Perf. 12½*
4604 A750 $800 multi      7.75 7.75
No. 4604 contains one 38x51mm stamp.

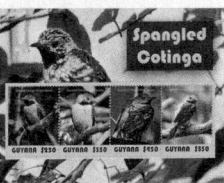

Spangled Cotingas — A751

No. 4605 — Various photographs of Spangled cotingas: a, $250. b, $350. c, $450. d, $550. $800, Spangled cotinga, diff.

**2019, June 17 Litho. Perf. 12**
4605 A751 Sheet of 4, #a-d 15.50 15.50
**Souvenir Sheet**
**Perf. 12½**
4606 A751 $800 multi 7.75 7.75
No. 4606 contains one 38x51mm stamp.

Victoria Amazonica — A752

No. 4607 — Various photographs of Victoria amazonica: a, $100. b, $300. c, $500. d, $700. $800, Victoria amazonica, diff.

**2019, June 17 Litho. Perf. 14**
4607 A752 Sheet of 4, #a-d 15.50 15.50
**Souvenir Sheet**
4608 A752 $800 multi 7.75 7.75

Miniature Sheet

Birth of Archie Mountbatten-Windsor — A753

No. 4609: a, $300, Duke and Duchess of Sussex standing. b, $300, Duke and Duchess of Sussex walking. c, $500, Duke and Duchess of Sussex with infant son. d, $500, As "c," with pillar and busts in background.

**2019, Aug. 21 Litho. Perf. 14**
4609 A753 Sheet of 4, #a-d 15.50 15.50

National Insurance Plan, 50th Anniv. — A754

**2019, Sept. 24 Litho. Perf. 14**
4610 A754 $50 multi .50 .50
No. 4610 was printed in sheets of 2.

Dorje Chang Buddha III, Buddhist Religious Leader — A755

**Perf. 13½x12½**
**2019, Sept. 27 Litho.**
4611 A755 $400 multi 4.00 4.00
No. 4611 was printed in sheets of 4.

Miniature Sheet

Mohandas K. Gandhi (1869-1948), Indian Nationalist Leader — A756

No. 4612 — Statue of Gandhi in: a, $80, Chennai, India. b, $200, Parliament Square, London. c, $450, Puducherry, India. d, $550, Ahmedabad, India.

**2019, Oct. 1 Litho. Perf. 14**
4612 A756 Sheet of 4, #a-d 12.50 12.50

Moths A757

No. 4613: a, $300, Comet moth. b, $400, Cecropia moth. c, $500, Polythemus moth. $800, Hyataphora cecropia, vert.

**2019, Nov. 6 Litho. Perf. 13¾**
4613 A757 Sheet of 3, #a-c 11.50 11.50
**Souvenir Sheet**
**Perf. 12**
4614 A757 $800 multi 7.75 7.75
No. 4614 contains one 30x40mm stamp.

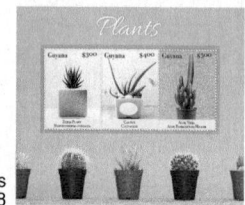

Plants A758

No. 4615: a, $300, Zebra plant. b, $400, Cactus. c, $500, Aloe vera. $800, Cacti, diff.

**2019, Dec. 25 Litho. Perf. 14**
4615 A758 Sheet of 3, #a-c 11.50 11.50
**Souvenir Sheet**
**Perf. 12**
4616 A758 $800 multi 7.75 7.75
No. 4616 contains one 30x50mm stamp.

Miniature Sheet

Republic of Guyana, 50th Anniv. (in 2020) A759

No. 4617: a, $80, 50th anniversary emblem. b, $80, Dancers celebrating Republic Day. c, $150, Mace in use from 1957-70 and current mace. d, $150, Offshore support vessel Liza Destiny.

**2019, Dec. 30 Litho. Perf. 14**
4617 A759 Sheet of 4, #a-d 4.50 4.50

New Year 2020 (Year of the Rat) A760

No. 4618 — Various depictions of rats with denominations of: a, $100. b, $300. c, $500. d, $700. $800, Rat, diff.

**2020, Mar. 24 Litho. Perf. 12½**
4618 A760 Sheet of 4, #a-d 15.50 15.50
**Souvenir Sheet**
**Perf. 12**
4619 A760 $800 multi 7.75 7.75
No. 4619 contains one 30x40mm stamp.

Woodpeckers — A761

No. 4620: a, Lewis's woodpecker on side of tree. b, Pileated woodpecker on side of tree. c, Red-bellied woodpecker on side of tree. d, Great spotted woodpecker on side of tree. e, Lewis's woodpecker on stump. f, Pileated woodpecker and chicks. g, Red-bellied woodpecker at bird bath. h, Great spotted woodpecker on stump.
$800, Great spotted woodpecker on branch.

**2020, Mar. 24 Litho. Perf. 14**
4620 A761 $250 Sheet of 8, #a-h 19.00 19.00
**Souvenir Sheet**
**Perf. 12½**
4621 A761 $800 multi 7.75 7.75
No. 4621 contains one 38x51mm stamp.

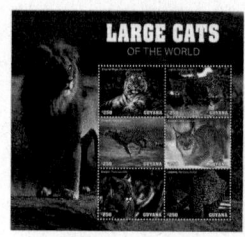

Large Cats A762

No. 4622: a, Siberian tiger. b, Jaguar. c, Cheetah. d, Eurasian lynx. e, Cougar. f, Leopard.
$1000, African lion, vert.

**2020, June 26 Litho. Perf. 11½x12**
4622 A762 $250 Sheet of 6, #a-f 14.50 14.50
**Souvenir Sheet**
**Perf. 13¼x12½**
4623 A762 $1000 multi 9.75 9.75

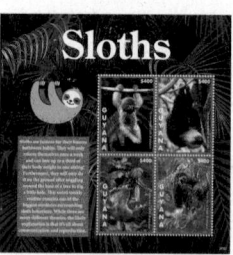

Three-toed Sloths — A763

No. 4624 — Various photographs of Three-toed sloths, as shown.
$800, Head of Three-toed sloth.

**2020, Aug. 11 Litho. Perf. 14**
4624 A763 $400 Sheet of 4, #a-d 15.50 15.50
**Souvenir Sheet**
**Perf.**
4625 A763 $800 multi 7.75 7.75
No. 4625 contains one 38mm diameter stamp.

Miniature Sheet

COVID-19 Pandemic — A764

No. 4626: a, Directional signs. b, Rubber gloves and protective face mask. c, Person wearing protective face mask. d, Crowd of people wearing protective face masks.

**2020, Aug. 31 Litho. Perf. 14**
4626 A764 $400 Sheet of 4, #a-d 15.50 15.50

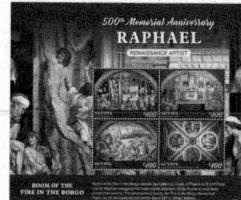

Frescoes in Vatican's Room of the Fire in the Borgo Painted by Raphael (1483-1520) — A765

No. 4627: a, Fire in the Borgo. b, Oath of Leo III. c, Battle of Ostia. d, Ceiling.
$800, The Coronation of Charlemagne.

**2020, Aug. 31 Litho. Perf. 14**
4627 A765 $400 Sheet of 4, #a-d 15.50 15.50
**Souvenir Sheet**
4628 A765 $800 multi 7.75 7.75

Miniature Sheet

Victory in Europe (V-E Day) in World War II, 75th Anniv. A766

No. 4629: a, British Field Marshal Bernard Montgomery (1887-1976). b, German Field Marshal Wilhelm Keitel (1882-1946). c, U.S. Pres. Franklin D. Roosevelt (1882-1945). d, French General Charles de Gaulle (1890-1970).

**2020, Sept. 30 Litho. Perf. 14**
4629 A766 $400 Sheet of 4, #a-d 15.50 15.50

Battle of Hué, Tet Offensive of the Vietnam War A767

No. 4630: a, Marine machine gun team. b, Soldier advancing under fire. c, Tanks rolling into Hué. d, Grenadier targeting sniper.
$800, Marines clearing buildings, horiz.

**2020, Sept. 30 Litho. Perf. 12½**
4630 A767 $400 Sheet of 4, #a-d 15.50 15.50
**Souvenir Sheet**
4631 A767 $800 multi 7.75 7.75

A768

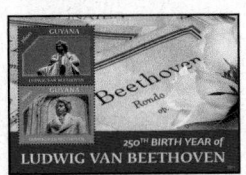

Ludwig van Beethoven (1770-1827),
Composer — A769

No. 4632 — Various drawings of Beethoven
with background color of: a, Yellow green. b,
Green. c, Tan. d, White. e, Orange yellow.
No. 4633 — Various statues depicting Beethoven: a, With sky in background. b, In niche.

**2020, Sept. 30**    **Litho.**    *Perf. 14*
4632 A768 $300 Sheet of 5,
     #a-e        14.50 14.50
     **Souvenir Sheet**
4633 A769 $600 Sheet of 2,
     #a-b        11.50 11.50

A770

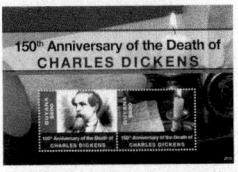

Charles Dickens (1812-70),
Writer — A771

No. 4634 — Various depictions of Dickens:
a, Wearing hat and holding pipe. b, Seated
(black and white image). c, Looking left. d,
Holding papers. e, As young man, with long
hair.
No. 4635: a, Drawing of Dickens. b, Candle
and handwritten letter.

**2020, Sept. 30**    **Litho.**    *Perf. 14*
4634 A770 $300 Sheet of 5,
     #a-e        14.50 14.50
     **Souvenir Sheet**
4635 A771 $600 Sheet of 2,
     #a-b        11.50 11.50

A772

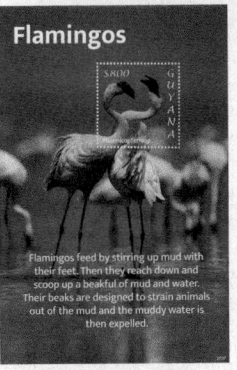

Flamingos — A773

No. 4636: a, Two flamingos (30x80mm). b,
One flamingo (30x40mm). c, Tthree flamingos
(30x40mm).
$800, Flamingos, diff.

**2020, Sept. 30**    **Litho.**    *Perf. 14*
4636 A772 $450 Sheet of 3,
     #a-c        13.00 13.00

     **Souvenir Sheet**
     *Perf. 13¾*
4637 A773 $800 multi      7.75 7.75

Owls
A774

Owls
A775

No. 4638: a, Horned owl. b, Burrowing owl.
c, Short-eared owl. d, Pygmy owl.
No. 4639: a, Common barn owl. b, Screech
owl.

**2020, Sept. 30**    **Litho.**    *Perf. 14*
4638 A774 $400 Sheet of 4,
     #a-d        15.50 15.50
     **Souvenir Sheet**
4639 A775 $600 Sheet of 2,
     #a-b        11.50 11.50

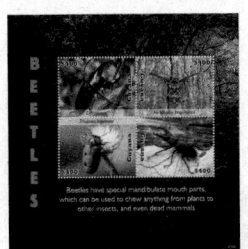

BEETLES
A776

No. 4640: a, Dynastinae. b, Aerochinus
longimanus. c, Tituboea biguttata. d,
Lucaridae.
$800, Coccinellidae.

**2020, Sept. 30**    **Litho.**    *Perf. 14*
4640 A776 $400 Sheet of 4,
     #a-d        15.50 15.50
     **Souvenir Sheet**
     *Perf. 13¾*
4641 A777 $800 multi      7.75 7.75

Beetles
A777

Caiman
Lizards
A778

Caiman
Lizards
A779

No. 4642 — Various photographs of Northern caiman lizard with denomination at: a, LL.
b, LR. c, UL. d, UR.
$800, Caiman lizard, diff.

**2020, Sept. 30**    **Litho.**    *Perf. 12*
4642 A778 $400 Sheet of 4,
     #a-d        15.50 15.50
     **Souvenir Sheet**
4643 A779 $800 multi      7.75 7.75

     **Miniature Sheet**

Janet Jagan (1920-2009), Sixth
President of Guyana — A780

No. 4644 — Various photographs of Pres.
Jagan: a, $80. b, $130. c, $150. d, $160.

**2020, Oct. 20**    **Litho.**    *Perf. 12*
4644 A780    Sheet of 4, #a-d    5.00 5.00

A781

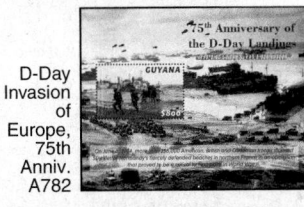

D-Day
Invasion
of
Europe,
75th
Anniv.
A782

No. 4645: a, U.S. Army First Division troops
disembarking from USS Samuel Chase. b,
HMS Holmes dropping depth charge on a sus-
pected U-boat. c, Bofors gun crew ready to
fire. d, HMS Warspite shelling German gun
batteries. e, British troops walking up gangway
of SS Empire Lance.
$800, Commando troops coming ashore.

**2020, Nov. 20**    **Litho.**    *Perf. 13¾*
4645 A781 $300 Sheet of 5,
     #a-e        14.50 14.50
     **Souvenir Sheet**
     *Perf. 12*
4646 A782 $800 multi      7.75 7.75

A783

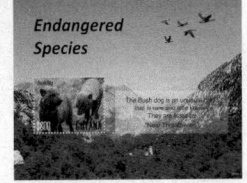

Endangered Animals — A784

No. 4647: a, West Indian manatee. b,
White-lipped peccary. c, Giant otter. d, Jaguar.
e, Margay. f, Giant anteater.
$800, Bush dogs.

**2020, Nov. 20**    **Litho.**    *Perf. 14*
4647 A783 $300 Sheet of 6,
     #a-f        17.50 17.50
     **Souvenir Sheet**
     *Perf. 12*
4648 A784 $800 multi      7.75 7.75

     **Miniature Sheet**

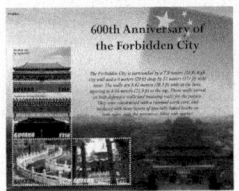

New
Year
2021
(Year of
the Ox)
A785

No. 4649 — Ox: a, Head at right, facing
right. b, Head at left, facing right. c, Facing
forward. d, Head at left, facing left.

**2021, Jan. 14**    **Litho.**    *Perf. 13¼*
4649 A785 $400 Sheet of 4,
     #a-d        15.50 15.50

     **Miniature Sheet**

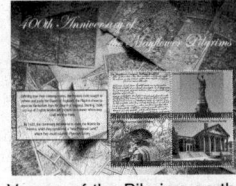

Forbidden City, Beijing, 600th Anniv.
(in 2020) — A786

No. 4650: a, Meridian Gate. b, Patterns on
Imperial Palace. c, Golden Water River. d,
Imperial Garden.

**2021, Apr. 5**    **Litho.**    *Perf. 14*
4650 A786 $350 Sheet of 4,
     #a-d        13.50 13.50

     **Miniature Sheet**

Voyage of the Pilgrims on the
Mayflower, 400th Anniv. (in
2020) — A787

No. 4651: a, Mayflower Compact. b,
National Monument to the Forefathers, Plym-
outh, Massachusetts. c, The Puritan, sculpture
by Augustus Saint-Gaudens (1848-1907),
Springfield, Massachusetts. d, Pilgrim Hall
Museum, Plymouth, Massachusetts.

**2021, Apr. 5**    **Litho.**    *Perf. 14*
4651 A787 $400 Sheet of 4,
     #a-d        15.50 15.50

     **Miniature Sheet**

Metropolitan Museum of Art, 150th
Anniv. (in 2020) — A788

No. 4652: a, Museum entrance. b, Washington Crossing the Delaware, painting by Emanuel Leutze (1816-68). c, Amathus sarcophagus. d, Memantra, sculpture by Frank Stella.

**2021, Apr. 5**    **Litho.**    *Perf. 14*
4652 A788 $400 Sheet of 4,
     #a-d        15.50 15.50

## Miniature Sheet

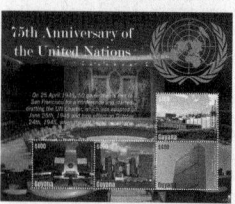

United Nations, 75th Anniv. (in 2020) A789

No. 4653: a, Flagpoles with flags of member nations. b, General Assembly chamber. c, Riverside view of United Nations Headquarters. d, United Nations Secretariat Building.

**2021, Apr. 5      Litho.      Perf. 14**
4653 A789 $400 Sheet of 4,
    #a-d                      15.50 15.50

## Miniature Sheet

Dropping of Atomic Bombs on Hiroshima and Nagasaki, 75th Anniv. (in 2020) — A790

No. 4654: a, Mushroom cloud over Hiroshima. b, Letter authorizing the dropping of the first atomic bomb. c, Leaflet dropped on Hiroshima and Nagasaki urging surrender. d, Mushroom cloud over Nagasaki.

**2021, Apr. 5      Litho.      Perf. 14**
4654 A790 $400 Sheet of 4,
    #a-d                      15.50 15.50

Joseph R. Biden, Jr., 46th President of the United States — A791

No. 4655 — President Biden: a, Behind microphones. b, Wearing striped tie. c, Wearing protective face mask. d, With Christmas wreath in background.
$800, Pres. Biden and his wife, Jill.

**2021, Apr. 5      Litho.      Perf. 14**
4655 A791 $460 Sheet of 4,
    #a-d                      17.50 17.50
**Souvenir Sheet**
**Perf. 12½**
4656 A791 $800 multi              7.75  7.75
No. 4656 contains one 51x38mm stamp.

A792

Range Rovers, 50th Anniv. (in 2020) A793

No. 4657: a, 2016 Range Rover Sport. b, 2014 Land Range Rover Evoque. c, 2007

Land Range Rover. d, 2013 Land Range Rover.
$800, 2014 Land Range Rover Evoque, diff.

**2021, Apr. 5      Litho.      Perf. 12**
4657 A792 $350 Sheet of 4,
    #a-d                      13.50 13.50
**Souvenir Sheet**
4658 A793 $800 multi              7.75  7.75

A794

95th Birthday of Queen Elizabeth II (1926-2022) — A795

No. 4659 — Queen Elizabeth II wearing: a, White and blue hat with flower. b, White hat. c, Lilac jacket and hat. d, Tiara. e, Crown.
$800, Princess Elizabeth holding Prince Charles as infant.

**2021, Apr. 5      Litho.      Perf. 14**
4659 A794 $300 Sheet of 5,
    #a-e                      14.50 14.50
**Souvenir Sheet**
**Perf. 12½**
4660 A795 $800 multi              7.75  7.75
Nos. 4659a-4659e state that the date the photograph of Queen Elizabeth was taken is 2011, which is incorrect for at least two of the stamps.

Third Wedding Anniversary of the Duke and Duchess of Sussex — A796

No. 4661 — Prince Harry and wife, Meghan: a, Waving in car. b, Holding hands. c, In cathedral, looking at each other. d, Lifting of bridal veil. e, Outdoors, looking at each other. f, On cathedral steps, holding hands.
$800, Prince Harry and wife kissing.

**2021, Apr. 30      Litho.      Perf. 14**
4661 A796 $300 Sheet of 6,
    #a-f                      17.50 17.50
**Souvenir Sheet**
**Perf. 12½**
4662 A796 $800 multi              7.75  7.75
No. 4656 contains one 51x38mm stamp.

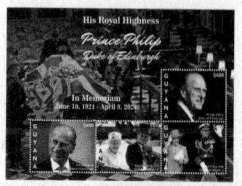

Prince Philip (1921-2021) — A797

No. 4663 — Prince Philip: a, Wearing striped tie. b, Wearing blue patterned tie. c, In

coach with his wife, Queen Elizabeth II. d, With Queen Elizabeth II, waving.
$800, Prince Philip holding young Prince Charles and being touched by Princess Anne, vert.

**2021, June 7      Litho.      Perf. 14**
4663 A797 $400 Sheet of 4,
    #a-d                      15.50 15.50
**Souvenir Sheet**
4664 A797 $800 multi              7.75  7.75

Mammals — A798

No. 4665: a, Capybaras. b, Sloth. c, Capuchin monkey. d, Jaguar. e, Hare. f, Anteater.
$800, Puma.

**2021, June 21      Litho.      Perf. 14**
4665 A798 $300 Sheet of 6,
    #a-f                      17.50 17.50
**Souvenir Sheet**
**Perf. 13¾**
4666 A798 $800 multi              7.75  7.75
No. 4666 contains one 35x35mm stamp.

Jaguars A799

No. 4667 — Panthera onca: a, $250, Head facing right, with foliage in background. b, $250, With log in background. c, $300, Head at right, looking left, dark background. d, $300, On ground, foliage in background. e, $350, Standing. f, $350, On rock.
$800, Panthera onca on log.

**2021, June 21      Litho.      Perf. 14**
4667 A799    Sheet of 6, #a-f    17.50 17.50
**Souvenir Sheet**
4668 A799 $800 multi              7.75  7.75

Hummingbirds — A800

No. 4669 — Various images of Trochilidae hummingbirds, as shown.
$800, Trochilidae, vert.

**2021, June 21      Litho.      Perf. 14**
4669 A800 $300 Sheet of 6,
    #a-f                      17.50 17.50
**Souvenir Sheet**
4670 A800 $800 multi              7.75  7.75

Ducks A801

No. 4671: a, Blue-winged teal. b, Brazilian teal. c, Northern pintail. d, Muscovy duck.
$800, Fulvous whistling duck.

**2021, June 21      Litho.      Perf. 14**
4671 A801 $400 Sheet of 4,
    #a-d                      15.50 15.50
**Souvenir Sheet**
**Perf. 12½**
4672 A801 $800 multi              7.75  7.75
No. 4672 contains one 51x38mm stamp.

Butterflies — A802

No. 4673: a, Blue morpho butterfly. b, Monarch butterfly. c, Red admiral butterfly. d, Old World swallowtail butterfly.
$800, Cabbage white butterfly.

**2021, June 21      Litho.      Perf. 14**
4673 A802 $400 Sheet of 4,
    #a-d                      15.50 15.50
**Souvenir Sheet**
4674 A802 $800 multi              7.75  7.75

## Miniature Sheet

2020 Summer Olympics, Tokyo — A803

No. 4675: a, $200, Beach volleyball. b, $300, Judo. c, $400, Badminton. d, $500, Fencing.

**2021, Aug. 2      Litho.      Perf. 14**
4675 A803    Sheet of 4, #a-d    13.50 13.50
The 2020 Summer Olympics were postponed until 2021 because of the COVID-19 pandemic.

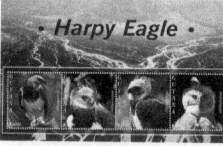

Harpy Eagles A804

No. 4676 — Various photographs of Harpia harpyja: a, $200. b, $300. $400. d, $500.
$800, Harpia harpyja, diff.

**2021, Sept. 1      Litho.      Perf. 13¾**
4676 A804    Sheet of 4, #a-d    13.50 13.50
**Souvenir Sheet**
4677 A804 $800 multi              7.75  7.75

Praying Mantises A805

No. 4678 — Mantodea: a, $150. b, $250, With multiple blades of grass. c, $250, With single blade of grass. d, $350, With denomination in black. e, $350, With denomination in white. f, $450.

No. 4679 — Hymenopus coronatus with denomination at: a, UR. b, LR.

**2021, Sept. 1**    Litho.    *Perf. 14*
4678 A805   Sheet of 6, #a-f   17.50 17.50
**Souvenir Sheet**
4679 A805 $600 Sheet of 2, #a-b    11.50 11.50

Turtles — A806

No. 4680: a, $250, Green sea turtle. b, $350, Yellow-spotted river turtle. c, $450, Leatherback sea turtle. d, $550, Hawksbill sea turtle.
$800, Olive ridley sea turtle.

**2021, Sept. 1**    Litho.    *Perf. 14*
4680 A806   Sheet of 4, #a-d   15.50 15.50
**Souvenir Sheet**
*Perf. 13¾*
4681 A806 $800 multi    7.75 7.75
No. 4681 contains one 35x35mm stamp.

Crocodiles — A807

No. 4682: a, Head of crocodile, country name at UL. b, Four crocodiles. c, Crocodile with open mouth. d, Head of crocodile, country name at LR.
$800, Crocodile's eye above water, horiz.

**2021, Sept. 1**    Litho.    *Perf. 13¾*
4682 A807 $400 Sheet of 4, #a-d    15.50 15.50
**Souvenir Sheet**
*Perf. 14*
4683 A807 $800 multi    7.75 7.75
No. 4683 contains one 40x30mm stamp.

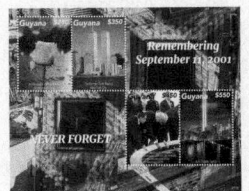

September 11, 2001 Terrorist Attacks, 20th Anniv. — A808

No. 4684: a, $250, White rose at September 11 Memorial. b, $350, Twin Towers of the World Trade Center. c, $450, Governor of New York State David Paterson, Vice President Joseph R. Biden, Jr. and his wife, Jill, laying roses at September 11 Memorial, 2010. d, $550, Tribute in light.
$800, One World Trade Center.

**2021, Sept. 11**    Litho.    *Perf. 14*
4684 A808   Sheet of 4, #a-d   15.50 15.50
**Souvenir Sheet**
*Perf. 12*
4685 A808 $800 multi    7.75 7.75
No. 4685 contains one 30x50mm stamp.

Nocturnal Animals — A809

No. 4686: a, $100, Big brown bat. b, $200, Gray wolf. c, $300, Mountin lion. d, $400, Red fox. e, $400, North American raccoon. f, $500, Nine-banded armadillo.
$800, Barn owl, vert.

**2021, Sept. 13**    Litho.    *Perf. 14*
4686 A809   Sheet of 6, #a-f   18.00 18.00
**Souvenir Sheet**
*Perf. 12½*
4687 A809 $800 multi    7.75 7.75
No. 4687 contains one 38x51mm stamp.

A810

A811

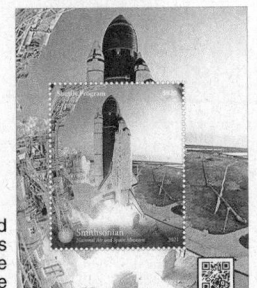

United States Space Shuttle Program A813

No. 4688: a, Space Shuttle Atlantis with cargo bay doors open. b, Two astronauts at work in space.
No. 4689: a, Space Shuttle on launch pad. b, Launch of Space Shuttle, nose of Shuttle

above top of launch pad. c, Galileo probe in space. d, Front of Space Shuttle and U.S. flag. e, Untethered astronaut in space. f, Launch of Space Shuttle, nose of Shuttle below top of launchpad.
No. 4690, Launch of Space Shuttle, diff. No. 4691, Launch of Space Shuttle, ground near launch pad in background.

**2021, Oct. 1**    Litho.    *Perf. 13*
4688 A810 $680 Pair, #a-b   13.00 13.00
**Miniature Sheet**
4689 A811 $370 Sheet of 6, #a-f    21.50 21.50
**Souvenir Sheets**
*Perf. 13¼x13*
4690 A812 $820 multi    8.00 8.00
*Perf. 13x13¼*
4691 A813 $820 multi    8.00 8.00
No. 4688 was printed in sheets containing two pairs.

Independence of India, 75th Anniv. (in 2022) — A814

Color of panel and denomination: $80, Orange brown. $150, Blue.

**2021, Oct. 2**    Litho.    *Perf. 12½*
4692-4693 A814   Set of 2    2.25 2.25

Elvis Presley (1935-77) — A815

No. 4694 — Presley: a, Playing white guitar. b, Holding microphone. c, Playing red guitar. d, Holding heart-shaped pillow. e, Saluting, wearing Army uniform. f, Against white background.

**2021, Nov. 22**    Litho.    *Perf. 14*
4694 A815 $300 Sheet of 6, #a-f    17.50 17.50

Flight of Apollo 15, 50th Anniv. A816

No. 4695: a, Crew of Apollo 15 in London after spaceflight. b, Apollo 15 Command Module at National Museum of the United States Air Force. c, Apollo 15 Command Module splashing down in Pacific Ocean. d, Apollo 15 emblem and crew members David R. Scott, Alfred M. Worden, and James B. Irwin. e, Apollo 15 Command and Service Modules in space.
$800, Apollo 15 on launch pad, vert.

**2021, Nov. 22**    Litho.    *Perf. 14*
4695 A816 $200 Sheet of 5, #a-e 9.50 9.50
**Souvenir Sheet**
*Perf. 12*
4696 A816 $800 multi    7.75 7.75
No. 4696 contains one 30x80mm stamp.

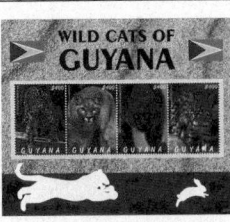

Wild Cats A817

No. 4697: a, Jaguar. b, Cougar. c, Jaguarundi. d, Oncilla.
No. 4698: a, Margay. b, Ocelot.

**2021, Nov. 22**    Litho.    *Perf. 14*
4697 A817 $400 Sheet of 4, #a-d    15.50 15.50
**Souvenir Sheet**
4698 A817 $600 Sheet of 2, #a-b    11.50 11.50

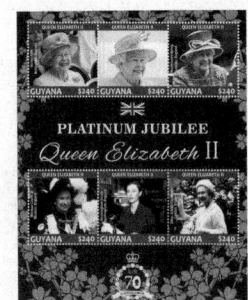

New Year 2022 (Year of the Tiger) A818

No. 4699 — Various drawings of tiger heads, as shown.

**2022, Feb. 1**    Litho.    *Perf. 12½*
4699 A818 $300 Sheet of 6, #a-f    17.50 17.50

Reign of Queen Elizabeth II (1926-2022), 70th Anniv. — A819

No. 4700 — Queen Elizabeth II at: a, Vernon Park, Nottingham. b, Ocean Cruise Terminal, Southampton. c, Westminster Abbey, London. d, Windsor Castle, Windsor. d, Sandringham Estate, Sandringham. e, Silver Jubilee ceremony, London.
$770, Queen Elizabeth II, vert.

**2022, Feb. 6**    Litho.    *Perf. 13¾*
4700 A819 $240 Sheet of 6, #a-f    14.00 14.00
**Souvenir Sheet**
*Perf. 14*
4701 A819 $770 multi    7.50 7.50
No. 4701 contains one 30x40mm stamp.

**Souvenir Sheet**

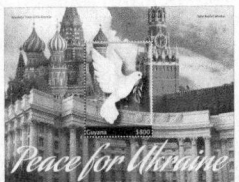

Peace Dove, Ukrainian Parliament Building, Kyiv, and Kremlin, Moscow — A820

**2022, May 30**    Litho.    *Perf. 12½*
4702 A820 $800 multi    7.75 7.75

## Souvenir Sheet

Diplomatic Relations Between Guyana and People's Republic of China, 50th Anniv. — A821

**2022, June 29    Litho.    Perf. 12½**

| | | | |
|---|---|---|---|
| 4703 | A821 | $500 multi | 4.75 4.75 |

---

## AIR POST STAMPS

### No. 321 Surcharged in Blue "HUMAN RIGHTS / DAY / 1981 / 110 AIR"

**1981, Nov. 14    Perfs. as Before**

| | | | |
|---|---|---|---|
| C1 | A74 | 110c on $3 No. 321 | 3.00 |

For surcharge see No. 997.

### Nos. 133, 136 and 146 Surcharged in Red, Black or Blue "AIR / Princess / of Wales / 1961-1982"

**1982, June 25    Perfs. as Before**
**Printing Methods as Before**

| | | | | |
|---|---|---|---|---|
| C2 | A28 | 110c on 5c No. 136 (R) | 3.00 | 1.00 |
| C3 | A28 | 220c on 1c No. 133 | 4.00 | 1.40 |
| C4 | A28 | 330c on $2 No. 146 (Bl) | 4.00 | 1.60 |
| | | Nos. C2-C4 (3) | 11.00 | 4.00 |

For surcharges see Nos. 623, 643-645, 785-787, 801, 804-804A, O19, O21, O30-O39.

### No. 287 Surcharged in Dark Blue

Surcharges read: No. C5, "UNICEF / 1946-1986 / AIR"; No. C6, "UNESCO / 1946-1986 / AIR".

**Perfs. as Before**

**1986, Oct. 24    Litho.**

| | | | | |
|---|---|---|---|---|
| C5 | A66 | 120c on $1 UNICEF | 15.00 | 12.00 |
| C6 | A66 | 120c on $1 UNESCO | 15.00 | 12.00 |
| a. | | Pair, #C5-C6 | 30.00 | 24.00 |

Nos. 1026, 1095, 1096, 1096a, 1100, 1138, 1163 Surcharged

**1987-88    Litho.    Perf. 14**
**Design A91**
**Plate Numbers in Parentheses**

| | | | | |
|---|---|---|---|---|
| C7 | 75c on 25c No. 1100 (59) | | 13.50 | 1.50 |
| C8 | 60c on 95c No. 1095 (55) | | 11.00 | 10.00 |
| C9 | 75c on No. 1026 (5) | | 1.25 | .65 |
| C10 | 75c on No. 1096 (55) | | 1.25 | .65 |
| a. | 75c on No. 1096a | | | |
| C11 | 75c on No. 1138 (83) | | 1.25 | .65 |
| C12 | 75c on No. 1163 (95) | | 1.25 | .65 |

Issued: No. C7, 11/87; No. C8, 12/87; Nos. C9-C12, 8/88.

---

## SPECIAL DELIVERY STAMPS

### Orchid Type of 1985 Overprinted or Surcharged "EXPRESS"

**1986-87    Litho.    Perf. 14**
**Plate Numbers in Parentheses**

| | | | | |
|---|---|---|---|---|
| E1 | A91 | $12 on #1372 (65) | 11.00 | 11.00 |
| E2 | A91 | $15 on 40c #1145 (86) | 11.00 | 11.00 |
| E3 | A91(p) | $15 on #E2 (86) | 10.00 | 10.00 |
| E4 | A91 | $25 on 25c like #1090 (53) | 13.00 | 13.00 |
| | | Nos. E1-E4 (4) | 45.00 | |

Issued: $12, $25, No. E2, 11/10. No. E3, 12/1987. No. E4 not issued without surcharge.

---

### No. 1461c Surcharged "EXPRESS"

**1986-87    Litho.    Imperf.**

| | | | | |
|---|---|---|---|---|
| E5 | A96 | $20 on 320c #1461c | 10.00 | 10.00 |

### No. E5 Ovptd. with Maltese Cross

**1987, Mar. 3**

| | | | | |
|---|---|---|---|---|
| E6 | A96 | $20 on No. E5 | 10.00 | 10.00 |

### Orchid Type of 1985 Inscribed "Express"

**1987-88    Litho.    Perf. 14**
**Series 2**
**Plate Numbers in Parentheses**

| | | | | |
|---|---|---|---|---|
| E7 | A91 | $15 like #1186 (11) | 4.00 | 4.00 |
| E8 | A91 | $20 like #1323 (93) | 7.50 | 7.50 |
| E9 | A91 | $25 like #1274 (63) | 6.50 | 6.50 |
| E10 | A91 | $45 like #1228 (35) | 12.00 | 12.00 |
| | | Nos. E7-E10 (4) | 30.00 | 30.00 |

Issued: $45, 9/1; $15, 9/29; $25, 10/26; $20, 5/17/88.

### No. "1461" Surcharged "EXPRESS / FORTY DOLLARS"

**1987, Nov.    Perf. 14**

| | | | | |
|---|---|---|---|---|
| E11 | A96 | $40 on 320c No. 1461, imperf. btwn. | 15.00 | 15.00 |

A five-pointed star appears between the lines of the surcharge on No. E11. See No. E14.

### Nos. 1827e, 1830e Surcharged in Red "SPECIAL DELIVERY"

**1988, Aug. 10    Perf. 15**

| | | | | |
|---|---|---|---|---|
| E12 | A100 | $40 on $3.20 #1827e | 12.00 | 12.00 |
| E13 | A100 | $45 on $3.30 #1830e | 12.00 | 12.00 |

See Nos. 2054b, 2056b.

### Nos. "1461," 1822c Surcharged in Red "EXPRESS / FORTY DOLLARS"

**1989, Mar.    Perf. 14**

| | | | | |
|---|---|---|---|---|
| E14 | A96 | $40 on 320c #1461, imperf. btwn. | 7.00 | 7.00 |
| E15 | A96 | $40 on 320c #1822c, imperf. btwn. | 7.00 | 7.00 |

### Butterflies Type of 1989 Inscribed "EXPRESS"

**Souvenir Sheets**

**1989, Sept. 7    Litho.    Perf. 14**

| | | | | |
|---|---|---|---|---|
| E16 | A115 | $130 Phareas coeleste | 7.75 | 7.75 |
| E17 | A115 | $190 Papilio torquatus | 12.50 | 12.50 |

For overprints see Nos. E19-E22, E24, E26-E27, E31.

### Women in Space Type of 1989 Inscribed "EXPRESS"

**Souvenir Sheets**

**1989, Nov. 8**

| | | | | |
|---|---|---|---|---|
| E18 | A116 | $190 Valentina Tereshkova | 5.00 | 5.00 |

For overprints see No. E23, E25, E28, E32.

### Nos. E16-E17 Ovptd. with World Stamp Expo '89 Emblem

**1989, Nov. 17**

| | | | | |
|---|---|---|---|---|
| E19 | A115 | $130 on No. E16 | 7.00 | 7.00 |
| E20 | A115 | $190 on No. E17 | 7.00 | 7.00 |

### Nos. E16-E18 Ovptd. in Sheet Margin "Stamp World London 90" and Show Emblem

**1990, May 3**

| | | | | |
|---|---|---|---|---|
| E21 | A115 | $130 on No. E16 | | |
| E22 | A115 | $190 on No. E17 | | |
| E23 | A116 | $190 on No. E18 | | |
| | | Nos. E21-E23 (3) | 20.00 | |

### Nos. E17-E18 Ovptd. in Sheet Margin with Rotary Emblem and "ROTARY / INTERNATIONAL / 1905-1990"

**1990, Mar.**

| | | | | |
|---|---|---|---|---|
| E24 | A115 | $190 on No. E17 | | |
| E25 | A116 | $190 on No. E18 | | |
| | | Nos. E24-E25 (2) | 22.50 | |

---

### Nos. E16-E18 Ovptd. in Sheet Margin "90th BIRTHDAY / H.M. THE / QUEEN MOTHER"

**1990, June 8    Litho.    Perf. 14**

| | | | | |
|---|---|---|---|---|
| E26 | A115 | $130 on No. E16 | 7.75 | 7.75 |
| E27 | A115 | $190 on No. E17 | 12.50 | 12.50 |
| E28 | A116 | $190 on No. E18 | 12.50 | 12.50 |
| | | Nos. E26-E28 (3) | 32.75 | 32.75 |

### Endangered Wildlife Type
**Souvenir Sheets**

**1990, Nov. 6    Litho.    Perf. 14**

| | | | | |
|---|---|---|---|---|
| E29 | A131 | $130 Harpy eagle | 7.00 | 7.00 |
| E30 | A131 | $150 Ocelot | 7.50 | 7.50 |

Nos. E29-E30 each contain one 43x57mm stamp.

### Nos. E16, E18 Ovptd. in Sheet Margin with "BELGICA PHILATELIC / EXPOSITION 1990" and Scout, Lions, Rotary and Show Emblems

**1990, June 2**

| | | | | |
|---|---|---|---|---|
| E31 | A115 | $130 on No. E16 | 7.50 | 7.50 |
| E32 | A116 | $190 on No. E18 | 7.50 | 7.50 |

No. E31 has Scout and Lions emblems. No. E32 has Scout and Rotary emblems.

---

## POSTAGE DUE STAMPS

### Type of British Guiana Inscribed "Guyana"

**Perf. 13½x14**

**1967-68    Wmk. 314    Typo.**

| | | | | |
|---|---|---|---|---|
| J2 | D1 | 2c black ('68) | 1.00 | 1.00 |
| J3 | D1 | 4c ultramarine | .50 | .50 |
| J4 | D1 | 12c carmine | .75 | .75 |
| | | Nos. J2-J4 (3) | 2.25 | 2.25 |

For surcharges see Nos. 897-898.

**1973    Wmk. 364**

| | | | | |
|---|---|---|---|---|
| J5 | D1 | 1c green | .35 | 2.00 |
| J6 | D1 | 2c black | .35 | 2.00 |
| J7 | D1 | 4c ultramarine | .35 | 2.00 |
| J8 | D1 | 12c carmine | .40 | 2.00 |
| | | Nos. J5-J8 (4) | 1.45 | 8.00 |

For surcharges see Nos. 341-349, 658, 899-900.

---

## OFFICIAL STAMPS

Nos. 74, 139, 141, 143-144, 146-147, 289A, 297, 300, 333, 395, 397, 401 Srchd. in Black, Red, or Black and Red

**1981-82    Perfs. as Before**
**Printing Methods as Before**

| | | | | |
|---|---|---|---|---|
| O1 | A28 | 10c on 25c #141 (Bk & R) | 4.00 | 2.25 |
| O2 | A8 | 15c on #74 | 10.00 | 2.00 |
| O3 | A28 | 15c on #139 | 13.50 | 1.00 |
| O4 | A28 | 30c on $2 #146 (Bk & R) | 1.00 | .50 |
| O5 | A28 | 50c on #143 (R) | 2.00 | .75 |
| O6 | A69 | 50c on #300 | 1.50 | .40 |
| O7 | A28 | 60c on #144 (R) | 1.50 | .25 |
| O8 | A17 | 100c on #395 | 2.00 | 2.00 |
| O9 | A68 | 100c on $3 #297 (Bk & R) | 5.00 | .75 |
| O10 | A17 | 110c on #397 | 4.00 | 2.00 |
| O11 | A28 | $1.10 on #333 (R) | | |
| O12 | A28 | 125c on #401 (R) | 4.50 | .80 |
| O13 | A28 | $2 on #146 (R) | 12.50 | |
| O14 | A28 | $5 on #147 (R) | 6.00 | 6.00 |
| O15 | A66 | $5 on #289A | 7.00 | |

Issued: Nos. O1, O5, O7, O15, 6/8; Nos. O2, O4, O9, O11-O12, 7/1; No. O13, 7/12/82; others, 7/7.

Surcharge on Nos. O3, O6, O8, O10, O13-O14 have no obliterator. No. O11 is airmail.

Refer to 2nd paragraph in footnote following No. 147 for Nos. O1, O4-O5, O7 and O13.

For overprints and surcharges see Nos. 406, 425, 452, 454-456, 603, 618, 650, 817, 854, 861, 866, 933, 1378, 1381, 1384, 1387-1388.

Nos. 162, 256, 258, 282, 480, C2-C3 Srchd. in Blue or Black

---

**1982    Perfs. as Before**
**Printing Methods as Before**

| | | | | |
|---|---|---|---|---|
| O16 | A66 | 20c on #282 | 10.00 | 1.25 |
| O17 | A33 | 40c on #162 | 3.00 | 1.50 |
| O18 | A60 | 40c on #256 | 2.00 | 1.00 |
| O19 | A28 | 110c on #C2 (Bk) | 6.00 | 2.00 |
| O20 | A60 | $2 on #258 | 18.00 | 3.50 |
| O21 | A28 | 220c on #C3 | 4.00 | 1.00 |
| O22 | A69 | 250c on #480 | 2.00 | 1.00 |
| | | Nos. O16-O22 (7) | 45.00 | |

Issued: 110c, 9/15; others, 5/17. Nos. O19, O21 are airmail.

### No. 481 Surcharged "OPS" Reading Up in Blue Violet or Blue Violet and Black

**1984, Apr. 2    Perfs. as Before**

| | | | | |
|---|---|---|---|---|
| O23 | A66 | 150c on $5 | 6.00 | 3.00 |
| O24 | A66 | 200c on $5 | 6.50 | 3.25 |
| O25 | A66 | 225c on $5 (BV & Bk) | 6.50 | 3.25 |
| O25A | A66 | 230c on $5 | 6.75 | 3.50 |
| O26 | A66 | 260c on $5 | 7.00 | 3.75 |
| O27 | A66 | 320c on $5 | 7.00 | 3.75 |
| O28 | A66 | 350c on $5 | 7.50 | 3.75 |
| O29 | A66 | 600c on $5 | 8.00 | 4.25 |
| | | Nos. O23-O29 (8) | 10.00 | 6.00 |

### Nos. C2-C3 Surcharged "OPS" in Black and Blue, Black or Blue

**1984, June 25    Perfs. as Before**

| | | | | |
|---|---|---|---|---|
| O30 | A28 | 25c on No. C2 (Bk) | | |
| O31 | A28 | 30c on No. C2 | 1.00 | .50 |
| O32 | A28 | 45c on No. C3 | 1.00 | .50 |
| O33 | A28 | 55c on No. C2 (Bk) | 1.25 | .60 |
| O34 | A28 | 75c on No. C3 | 1.50 | .60 |
| O35 | A28 | 75c on No. C3 | 2.00 | .70 |
| O36 | A28 | 90c on No. C3 (Bl) | 2.00 | .70 |
| O37 | A28 | 120c on No. C3 | 2.25 | .90 |
| O38 | A28 | 130c on No. C3 (Bl) | 2.25 | 1.25 |
| O39 | A28 | 330c on No. C3 (Bl) | 4.00 | 1.25 |
| | | Nos. O30-O39 (10) | 17.25 | |

Overprint reads up on No. O39.

### Orchid Type of 1985 Series 2
**Plate Numbers in Parentheses**

**1987-88    Litho.    Unwmk.    Perf. 14**

| | | | | |
|---|---|---|---|---|
| O40 | A91 | 120c like #1250 (48) | 1.50 | .40 |
| O41 | A91 | 130c like #1322 (92) | 1.50 | .40 |
| O42 | A91 | 140c like #1229 (36) | 1.00 | .40 |
| O43 | A91 | 150c like #1242 (43) | 1.50 | .50 |
| O44 | A91 | 175c like #1221 (31) | 1.00 | .50 |
| O45 | A91 | 200c like #1271 (61) | 1.50 | .60 |
| O46 | A91 | 225c like #1213 (26) | 1.50 | .60 |
| O47 | A91 | 230c like #1283 (68) | .75 | .60 |
| O48 | A91 | 250c like #1268 (59) | .75 | .60 |
| O49 | A91 | 260c like #1284 (69) | .75 | .60 |
| O50 | A91 | 275c like #1319 (90) | 1.75 | .75 |
| O51 | A91 | 320c like #1292 (75) | 1.75 | .85 |
| O52 | A91 | 330c like #1208 (23) | 2.00 | 1.00 |
| O53 | A91 | 350c like #1326 (95) | 1.00 | 1.00 |
| O54 | A91 | 600c like #1285 (70) | 1.50 | 1.50 |
| O55 | A91 | $12 like #1286 (71) | 2.50 | 2.50 |
| O56 | A91 | $15 like #1308 (84) | 3.00 | 3.00 |
| | | Nos. O40-O56 (17) | 25.25 | 15.80 |

Nos. O47, O53-O56 horiz.
Issued: Nos. O42, O44, O48, O49, 10/5/88; others, 10/5/87.

For overprints & surcharges see Nos. 1694, 1697, 1703, 1707, 1722-1726, 1728-1730.

---

## PARCEL POST STAMPS

### No. 145 Surcharged "PARCEL POST"

**1981, June 8    Litho.    Perf. 13½**

| | | | | |
|---|---|---|---|---|
| Q1 | A28 | $15 on $1 No. 145 | 15.00 | 7.00 |
| Q2 | A28 | $20 on $1 No. 145 | 10.00 | 10.00 |
| | | Nos. Q1-Q2 (2) | 38.00 | |

For overprints see Nos. QO1-QO2.

### No. 333 Surcharged "PARCEL POST" in Blue

**1983, Jan. 15**

| | | | | |
|---|---|---|---|---|
| Q3 | A28 | $12 on No. 333 | 13.00 | 2.00 |

For surcharge see No. 624.

### No. 146 Surcharged "Parcel Post"

**1983, Sept. 14**

| | | | | |
|---|---|---|---|---|
| Q4 | A28 | $12 on $1.10 on $2 | 3.00 | 3.00 |

No. Q4 has a horizontal Royal Wedding / 1981 surcharge similar to No. 331. For overprint see No. QO5.

## No. 255 Surcharged in Red

Surcharge reads: "TWENTY FIVE DOLLARS / PARCEL POST 25.00".

**1985, Apr. 25**        *Perf. 14*
Q5 A60 $25 on 35c No. 255    33.00 27.50

---

### PARCEL POST OFFICIAL STAMPS

#### Nos. Q1-Q2 Overprinted "OPS" in Red

**1981, June 8**
QO1   A28 $15 on No. Q1    12.00 5.50
QO2   A28 $20 on No. Q2    13.00 8.50

For surcharges see Nos. 1389-1390.

#### No. 333 Surcharged in Blue

Surcharge reads: "OPS / 1982 / Parcel Post / $12.00".

**1983, Jan. 15**
QO3   A28 $12 on No. 333    115.00 20.00

#### No. QO3 Overprinted "OPS" in Black

**1983, Aug. 22**
QO4   A28 $12 on No. QO3    42.50 4.00

#### No. Q4 Overprinted "OPS" in Blue

**1983, Nov. 3**
QO5   A28 $12 on No. Q4    15.00 4.00

# Storage Solutions

## SCOTT ADVANTAGE STOCK PAGES

Scott Advantage Stock sheets provide the protection and durability of crystal acetate pockets. Designed with the collector in mind, the Advantage Stocksheets fit directly in your 3-ring or 2-post binder and match Scott National or Specialty pages in every respect. Perfect for storing new issues, minor varieties and collateral material.
Size: 10" x 11 1/2". Sold in Packs of 10

| Item# | | | Retail | AA |
|---|---|---|---|---|
| AD11 | 1 Pocket 242mm | National | $22.99 | $20.69 |
| AD21 | 1 Pocket 242mm | Specialty | $22.99 | $20.69 |
| AD12 | 2 Pocket 119mm | National | $22.99 | $20.69 |
| AD22 | 2 Pocket 119mm | Specialty | $22.99 | $20.69 |
| AD13 | 3 Pocket 79mm | National | $22.99 | $20.69 |
| AD23 | 3 Pocket 79mm | Specialty | $22.99 | $20.69 |
| AD14 | 4 Pocket 58mm | National | $22.99 | $20.69 |
| AD24 | 4 Pocket 58mm | Specialty | $22.99 | $20.69 |
| AD15 | 5 Pocket 45mm | National | $22.99 | $20.69 |
| AD25 | 5 Pocket 45mm | Specialty | $22.99 | $20.69 |
| AD16 | 6 Pocket 37mm | National | $22.99 | $20.69 |
| AD26 | 6 Pocket 37mm | Specialty | $22.99 | $20.69 |
| AD17 | 7 Pocket 34mm | National | $22.99 | $20.69 |
| AD27 | 7 Pocket 34mm | Specialty | $22.99 | $20.69 |
| AD18 | 8 Pocket 31mm | National | $22.99 | $20.69 |
| AD28 | 8 Pocket 31mm | Specialty | $22.99 | $20.69 |

## PRINZ STOCK PAGES

Prinz stock pages offer convenience and flexibility. Pages are produced on thick, archival-quality paper with acetate pockets glued from the bottom of each pocket. Size: 8 1/2" x 11". Sold in Packs of 5

| Item# | | | Retail | AA |
|---|---|---|---|---|
| S1 | 1 Pocket 242 mm | Black (Single-Sided) | $11.99 | $8.75 |
| S1D | 1 Pocket 242 mm | Black (Double-Sided) | $17.99 | $13.13 |
| S2 | 2 Pockets 119mm | Black (Single-Sided) | $11.99 | $8.75 |
| S2D | 2 Pockets 119mm | Black (Double-Sided) | $17.99 | $13.13 |
| S3 | 3 Pockets 79mm | Black (Single-Sided) | $11.99 | $8.75 |
| S3D | 3 Pockets 79mm | Black (Double-Sided) | $17.99 | $13.13 |
| S4 | 4 Pockets 58mm | Black (Single-Sided) | $11.99 | $8.75 |
| S4D | 4 Pockets 58mm | Black (Double-Sided) | $17.99 | $13.13 |
| S5 | 5 Pockets 45mm | Black (Single-Sided) | $11.99 | $8.75 |
| S5D | 5 Pockets 45mm | Black (Double-Sided) | $17.99 | $13.13 |
| S6 | 6 Pockets 37mm | Black (Single-Sided) | $11.99 | $8.75 |
| S6D | 6 Pockets 37mm | Black (Double-Sided) | $17.99 | $13.13 |
| S7 | 7 Pockets 31mm | Black (Single-Sided) | $11.99 | $8.75 |
| S7D | 7 Pockets 31mm | Black (Double-Sided) | $17.99 | $13.13 |
| S8 | 8 Pockets 27mm | Black (Single-Sided) | $11.99 | $8.75 |
| S8D | 8 Pockets 27mm | Black (Double-Sided) | $17.99 | $13.13 |
| S9 | 3 Pockets 36mm/67mm/139mm | Black (Single-Sided) | $11.99 | $8.75 |
| S9D | 3 Pockets 36mm/67mm/139mm | Black (Double-Sided) | $17.99 | $13.13 |

Prices are subject to change. See **AmosAdvantage.com** for current pricing.

# AmosAdvantage.com

## 1-800-572-6885

**ORDERING INFORMATION:** *AA prices apply to paid subscribers of Amos Media titles, or for orders placed online. Prices, terms and product availability subject to change. **SHIPPING & HANDLING:** U.S.: Orders total $0-$10.00 charged $4.99 shipping. U.S. Order total $10.01-$74.99 charged $9.99 shipping. Orders totaling $75+ will ship FREE! Taxes will apply in CA, OH, & IL. Canada: 20% of order total. Minimum charge $19.99 Maximum charge $200.00. Foreign orders are shipped via FedEx Intl. or USPS and billed actual freight.

# INDEX AND IDENTIFIER

All page numbers shown are those in this Volume 3A.

Postage stamps that do not have English words on them are shown in the Scott *Stamp Illustrated Identifier*. To purchase it visit AmosAdvantage.com or call Amos Media at 800-572-6885.

# Vols. 3A-3B number additions, deletions and changes

| Number in 2023 Catalogue | Number in 2024 Catalogue |
|---|---|
| **Great Britain – Offices Abroad** | |
| **Offices in Turkish Empire** | |
| new | 8a |
| new | 13a |
| | |
| **Hong Kong** | |
| new | 162b |
| | |
| **India – Feudatory States** | |
| **Alwar** | |
| 4c | 5 |
| | |
| **Bamra** | |
| 14 | 7D |
| 15 | 7F |
| new | 8D |
| new | 9C |
| 16 | 10B |
| 11 | 11B |
| new | 11 |
| 17 | 11D |
| 18 | 12D |
| new | 12F |
| 19 | 13E |
| | |
| **Barawani** | |
| new | 10a |
| new | 10b |
| new | 11b |
| new | 11c |
| new | 11D |
| new | 12a |
| new | 12b |
| new | 13a |
| new | 14a |
| new | 14b |
| new | 14c |
| new | 14d |
| new | 14e |
| new | 14f |
| new | 15a |
| new | 16a |
| 17 | 17C |
| new | 17Ca |
| new | 17 |
| new | 17A |
| new | 17B |
| new | 17Ba |
| new | 17D |
| 22a | deleted |
| new | 22a |
| new | 22b |
| new | 22c |
| new | 23a |
| new | 23b |
| new | 26A |
| new | 27A |
| new | 28A |
| 29a | deleted |
| 29b | deleted |
| new | 29A |
| new | 30A |
| 33a | 33Ab |
| new | 36A |
| | |
| **Bhopal** | |
| 6b | 6a |
| 6c | 6b |
| 6d | 6c |
| new | 11c |
| new | 12c |

| Number in 2023 Catalogue | Number in 2024 Catalogue |
|---|---|
| **Bhopal** | |
| 19d | 19e |
| new | 19d |
| new | 23d |
| new | 23e |
| new | 29c |
| new | 29d |
| new | 29e |
| new | 30c |
| 66 | deleted |
| 67 | deleted |
| new | 75a |
| new | 75c |
| new | 75h |
| new | 83b |
| new | 99b |
| new | O1d |
| new | O1e |
| new | O1f |
| new | O2b |
| new | O3a |
| new | O8b |
| new | O8c |
| new | O8d |
| new | O13d |
| new | O13e |
| new | O15a |
| new | O19a |
| new | O19b |
| new | O19c |
| new | O19d |
| new | O19e |
| new | O19f |
| new | O19g |
| new | O19h |
| new | O19i |
| new | O19j |
| new | O19k |
| new | O20b |
| new | O21b |
| new | O21c |
| new | O21d |
| new | O21e |
| new | O21g |
| new | O21h |
| new | O21i |
| new | O24a |
| new | O24b |
| new | O24c |
| new | O25a |
| new | O25b |
| new | O25c |
| new | O25d |
| new | O25e |
| new | O25f |
| new | O28a |
| new | O28b |
| new | O28c |
| new | O28d |
| new | O28e |
| new | O29b |
| new | O35d |
| new | O35e |
| new | O35f |
| new | O35g |
| new | O38a |
| new | O38b |
| new | O38c |
| new | O38d |
| new | O38e |
| O40a | O40g |

| Number in 2023 Catalogue | Number in 2024 Catalogue |
|---|---|
| **Bhopal** | |
| new | O40a |
| O40e | O40h |
| new | O40e |
| new | O40f |
| O41b | O41e |
| new | O41b |
| new | O46a |
| new | O46b |
| new | O46c |
| new | O47a |
| new | O47b |
| new | O47c |
| new | O49a |
| new | O50a |
| new | O50b |
| new | O52b |
| new | O52c |
| new | O53a |
| new | O53b |
| new | O53c |
| new | O54b |
| new | O54c |
| O57a | deleted |
| O58c | O58a |
| | |
| **Bhor** | |
| new | 1a |
| new | 1b |
| new | 2a |
| | |
| **Bijawar** | |
| 1b | 1d |
| new | 1b |
| new | 1c |
| new | 1e |
| 2a | 2e |
| new | 2a |
| new | 2b |
| new | 2c |
| new | 2d |
| 3a | 3e |
| new | 3a |
| new | 3b |
| new | 3c |
| new | 3d |
| 4a | 4f |
| new | 4a |
| new | 4b |
| new | 4c |
| new | 4d |
| new | 4e |
| 5a | 5e |
| new | 5a |
| new | 5b |
| new | 5c |
| new | 5d |
| new | 6a |
| new | 6b |
| new | 7a |
| new | 7b |
| new | 8a |
| new | 9a |
| | |
| **Bundi** | |
| new | 1f |
| new | 1Ad |
| new | 1Ae |
| new | 2a |
| new | 14a |
| new | 16a |

| Number in 2023 Catalogue | Number in 2024 Catalogue |
|---|---|
| **Bundi** | |
| new | 21a |
| 32 | 41 |
| new | 32 |
| new | 32a |
| 33 | 42 |
| new | 33 |
| new | 43 |
| new | 34 |
| new | 34a |
| 35 | 44 |
| new | 35 |
| 36 | 47 |
| new | 36 |
| 37 | 48 |
| new | 37 |
| 38 | 49 |
| new | 38 |
| 39 | 50 |
| new | 39 |
| 40 | 51 |
| new | 40 |
| 41 | 52 |
| 42 | 53 |
| new | 45 |
| new | 46 |
| 43 | 54 |
| 44 | 55 |
| 45 | 56 |
| 46 | 57 |
| 47 | 58 |
| 48 | 59 |
| 49 | 60 |
| new | O1a |
| new | O1b |
| new | O2a |
| new | O2b |
| new | O2c |
| new | O5a |
| new | O6a |
| new | O6b |
| new | O7a |
| new | O8a |
| new | O9a |
| new | O10a |
| new | O11a |
| new | O12a |
| new | O13a |
| new | O13b |
| new | O14a |
| new | O17a |
| new | O17b |
| new | O18a |
| new | O18b |
| new | O18c |
| new | O20a |
| new | O21a |
| new | O22a |
| new | O23a |
| new | O24a |
| new | O25a |
| new | O26a |
| new | O28a |
| new | O29a |
| new | O33a |
| new | O34a |
| new | O36A |
| new | O36B |
| new | O36Be |
| new | O38a |
| new | O39 |

# Vols. 3A-3B number additions, deletions and changes

| Number in 2023 Catalogue | Number in 2024 Catalogue |
|---|---|
| **Bundi** | |
| new | O41a |
| new | O41b |
| new | O41c |
| new | O42a |
| O44 | deleted |
| new | O44 |
| new | O44a |
| new | O44B |
| new | O44C |
| new | O44Ce |
| new | O45a |
| new | O46a |
| new | O49 |
| new | O49a |
| new | O50 |
| new | O51 |
| new | O51a |
| new | O51b |
| new | O51c |
| new | O52 |
| new | O52a |
| new | O53 |
| new | O53a |
| new | O54 |
| new | O55 |
| new | O56 |
| new | O57 |
| new | O58 |
| new | O59 |
| new | O60 |
| new | O60a |
| new | O61 |
| new | O61a |
| new | O62 |
| new | O63 |
| new | O64 |
| new | O64a |
| new | O65 |
| new | O66 |
| new | O67 |
| new | O68 |
| new | O69 |
| new | O69a |
| new | O70 |
| new | O71 |
| new | O71a |
| new | O72 |
| new | O72a |
| new | O73 |
| new | O74 |
| new | O74a |
| new | O75 |
| O47 | O76 |
| O48 | O77 |
| O49 | O78 |
| O50 | O79 |
| O51 | O80 |
| O52 | O81 |
| O53 | O82 |
| **Bussahir** | |
| new | 1a |
| new | 2a |
| new | 4a |
| new | 4b |
| new | 5a |
| new | 5b |
| new | 6b |
| new | 6c |
| new | 7a |

| Number in 2023 Catalogue | Number in 2024 Catalogue |
|---|---|
| **Bussahir** | |
| new | 7b |
| new | 8a |
| new | 8b |
| new | 9a |
| new | 9b |
| new | 10a |
| 11a | 11D |
| new | 11a |
| new | 12D |
| new | 12De |
| 12a | 12Df |
| new | 12a |
| new | 12b |
| new | 12c |
| new | 12Dg |
| 13a | 13D |
| new | 13a |
| new | 13b |
| new | 13c |
| new | 14a |
| new | 14b |
| new | 14c |
| new | 13De |
| new | 13Df |
| 15a | 16D |
| 16a | 15D |
| new | 19a |
| new | 19b |
| new | 20a |
| new | 20b |
| new | 21a |
| new | 21b |
| new | 21c |
| new | 22a |
| new | 23a |
| new | 23b |
| 24a | deleted |
| new | 24a |
| new | 24b |
| 25 | deleted |
| new | 26a |
| new | 26b |
| new | 26c |
| new | 27a |
| new | 27b |
| new | 28a |
| new | 29a |
| new | 29b |
| new | 29c |
| new | 30 |
| new | 30a |
| new | 31a |
| 32 | deleted |
| 33 | 32 |
| new | 33 |
| 34 | 33b |
| new | 33a |
| 34a | 34 |
| new | 34a |
| new | 34B |
| new | 34Bc |
| new | 34Bd |
| new | 35a |
| new | 35b |
| **Charkhari** | |
| 1 | 3 |
| new | 1 |
| 2 | 3B |
| 3 | 3C |

| Number in 2023 Catalogue | Number in 2024 Catalogue |
|---|---|
| **Charkhari** | |
| new | 2 |
| new | 3a |
| 3A | 3D |
| new | 3Df |
| new | 3E |
| new | 4a |
| new | 10a |
| new | 21e |
| new | 21f |
| new | 21g |
| 21Ab | 21Ac |
| new | 21Ab |
| new | 22a |
| new | 22b |
| new | 22c |
| 23A | 23a |
| new | 23b |
| new | 23C |
| new | 25c |
| new | 25Ab |
| new | 28a |
| new | 28b |
| new | 28c |
| new | 29a |
| new | 29b |
| new | 29c |
| new | 29d |
| new | 30a |
| new | 30b |
| new | 30c |
| new | 30d |
| new | 30e |
| new | 31a |
| new | 32a |
| new | 32b |
| new | 32c |
| new | 33a |
| new | 33b |
| new | 33c |
| new | 33d |
| new | 34a |
| new | 35a |
| new | 35b |
| new | 35c |
| new | 36a |
| new | 36b |
| new | 36c |
| new | 41a |
| new | 41b |
| new | 43a |
| new | 43b |
| new | 43c |
| **Cochin** | |
| new | 10d |
| new | 10e |
| new | 11c |
| new | 12m |
| new | 12Bk |
| new | 12Bo |
| new | 12Bp |
| new | 13d |
| new | 34h |
| new | 34i |
| new | 34j |
| new | 34k |
| new | 34m |
| new | 34n |
| 63a | 63A |
| 63b | 63B |

| Number in 2023 Catalogue | Number in 2024 Catalogue |
|---|---|
| **Cochin** | |
| 64a | 64A |
| 67 | 67b |
| 67a | 67A |
| 67b | 67 |
| 68 | 68a |
| 68a | 68 |
| 69a | 69A |
| new | 69B |
| 70a | 70A |
| 72 | 72A |
| 72a | 72 |
| 73A | deleted |
| 73b | 73A |
| new | 73Ab |
| new | 74B |
| new | 74C |
| new | 74D |
| 76a | 76A |
| new | 85b |
| new | 86B |
| new | 90c |
| new | 93a |
| new | 96a |
| new | O14a |
| **Dhar** | |
| new | 1d |
| new | 1e |
| new | 1f |
| new | 1g |
| new | 1h |
| new | 3a |
| new | 3b |
| new | 4a |
| new | 4b |
| new | 9a |
| **Dungarpur** | |
| 2 | 2A |
| 3a | deleted |
| new | 3a |
| new | 3b |
| new | 9B |
| 14 | deleted |
| 15 | deleted |
| 16 | deleted |
| 19b | deleted |

# INDEX TO ADVERTISERS
## 2024 VOLUME 3A

# 2024
# VOLUME 3A
# DEALER DIRECTORY
# YELLOW PAGE LISTINGS

**This section of your Scott Catalogue contains advertisements to help you conveniently find what you need, when you need it...!**

## Appraisals

**DR. ROBERT FRIEDMAN &
SONS STAMP & COIN
BUYING CENTER**
2029 W. 75th St.
Woodridge, IL 60517
PH: 800-588-8100
FAX: 630-985-1588
stampcollections@drbobstamps.com
www.drbobfriedmanstamps.com

## Auctions

**DUTCH COUNTRY AUCTIONS**
The Stamp Center
4115 Concord Pike
Wilmington, DE 19803
PH: 302-478-8740
FAX: 302-478-8779
auctions@dutchcountryauctions.com
www.dutchcountryauctions.com

## British Commonwealth

**ARON R. HALBERSTAM
PHILATELISTS, LTD.**
PO Box 150168
Van Brunt Station
Brooklyn, NY 11215-0168
PH: 718-788-3978
arh@arhstamps.com
www.arhstamps.com

**ROY'S STAMPS**
PO Box 28001
600 Ontario Street
St. Catharines, ON
CANADA L2N 7P8
Phone: 905-934-8377
Email: roystamp@cogeco.ca
www.roysstamps.com

**THE STAMP ACT**
PO Box 1136
Belmont, CA 94002
PH: 650-703-2342
thestampact@sbcglobal.net

## Buying

**DR. ROBERT FRIEDMAN &
SONS STAMP & COIN
BUYING CENTER**
2029 W. 75th St.
Woodridge, IL 60517
PH: 800-588-8100
FAX: 630-985-1588
stampcollections@drbobstamps.com
www.drbobfriedmanstamps.com

## Canada

**CANADA STAMP FINDER LLC**
2800 N 6th Street, Unit 1-708
St. Augustine, FL 32084
PH: 904-217-2166
Canadian Address:
PO Box 92591
Brampton, ON L6W 4R1
PH: 514-238-5751
Toll Free in North America:
877-412-3106
FAX: 323-315-2635
canadastampfinder@gmail.com
www.canadastampfinder.com

**ROY'S STAMPS**
PO Box 28001
600 Ontario Street
St. Catharines, ON
CANADA L2N 7P8
Phone: 905-934-8377
Email: roystamp@cogeco.ca
www.roysstamps.com

## China

**THE STAMP ACT**
PO Box 1136
Belmont, CA 94002
PH: 650-703-2342
thestampact@sbcglobal.net

## Collections

**DR. ROBERT FRIEDMAN &
SONS STAMP & COIN
BUYING CENTER**
2029 W. 75th St.
Woodridge, IL 60517
PH: 800-588-8100
FAX: 630-985-1588
stampcollections@drbobstamps.com
www.drbobfriedmanstamps.com

## Ducks

**MICHAEL JAFFE**
PO Box 61484
Vancouver, WA 98666
PH: 360-695-6161
PH: 800-782-6770
FAX: 360-695-1616
mjaffe@brookmanstamps.com
www.brookmanstamps.com

## Hong Kong

**THE STAMP ACT**
PO Box 1136
Belmont, CA 94002
PH: 650-703-2342
thestampact@sbcglobal.net

## Israel

**HENRY GITNER
PHILATELISTS, INC.**
PO Box 3077-S
Middletown, NY 10940
PH: 845-343-5151
PH: 800-947-8267
FAX: 845-343-0068
hgitner@hgitner.com
www.hgitner.com

## Italy

**HENRY GITNER
PHILATELISTS, INC.**
PO Box 3077-S
Middletown, NY 10940
PH: 845-343-5151
PH: 800-947-8267
FAX: 845-343-0068
hgitner@hgitner.com
www.hgitner.com

## Korea

**THE STAMP ACT**
PO Box 1136
Belmont, CA 94002
PH: 650-703-2342
thestampact@sbcglobal.net

## New Issues

**DAVIDSON'S STAMP SERVICE**
Personalized Service since 1970
PO Box 36355
Indianapolis, IN 46236-0355
PH: 317-826-2620
ed-davidson@earthlink.net
www.newstampissues.com

## Stamp Stores

### Delaware

**DUTCH COUNTRY AUCTIONS**
The Stamp Center
4115 Concord Pike
Wilmington, DE 19803
PH: 302-478-8740
FAX: 302-478-8779
auctions@dutchcountryauctions.com
www.dutchcountryauctions.com

### Florida

**DR. ROBERT FRIEDMAN &
SONS STAMP & COIN
BUYING CENTER**
PH: 800-588-8100
FAX: 630-985-1588
stampcollections@drbobstamps.com
www.drbobfriedmanstamps.com

### Illinois

**DR. ROBERT FRIEDMAN &
SONS STAMP & COIN
BUYING CENTER**
2029 W. 75th St.
Woodridge, IL 60517
PH: 800-588-8100
FAX: 630-985-1588
stampcollections@drbobstamps.com
www.drbobfriedmanstamps.com

## Stamp Stores

### Indiana

**KNIGHT STAMP & COIN CO.**
237 Main St.
Hobart, IN 46342
PH: 219-942-4341
PH: 800-634-2646
knight@knightcoin.com
www.knightcoin.com

### New Jersey

**BERGEN STAMPS &
COLLECTIBLES**
306 Queen Anne Rd.
Teaneck, NJ 07666
PH: 201-836-8987
bergenstamps@gmail.com

**TRENTON STAMP & COIN**
Thomas DeLuca
Store: Forest Glen Plaza
1800 Highway #33, Suite 103
Hamilton Square, NJ 08690
Mail: PO Box 8574
Trenton, NJ 08650
PH: 609-584-8100
FAX: 609-587-8664
TOMD4TSC@aol.com
www.trentonstampandcoin.com

## British Commonwealth

**British Empire 1840 - 1935**

Aden to Zululand Mint & Used
Most complete stock in North America

44(10)

For over 40 years, we have built some of the world's finest collections. Our expert *Want List Services* can do the same for you. Over 50 volumes filled with singles, sets and rare stamps, we are sure we have what you need. We welcome your Want Lists in Scott or Stanley Gibbons numbers.

Put our expertise to work for you today!
You'll be glad you did!

*Colonial Stamp Company*
"Rarity and quality are remembered
...long after price is forgotten."
5757 Wilshire Blvd., Penthouse 8
Los Angeles, CA 90036 USA
Tel: +1 (323) 933-9435 Fax: +1 (323) 939-9930
Email: Info@ColonialStamps.com
www.ColonialStamps.com

Ask for your free
Public Auction
Catalogue today!

## Stamp Stores

### New York

**CHAMPION STAMP CO., INC.**
432 West 54th St.
New York, NY 10019
PH: 212-489-8130
FAX: 212-581-8130
championstamp@aol.com
www.championstamp.com

### Ohio

**HILLTOP STAMP SERVICE**
Richard A. Peterson
PO Box 626
Wooster, OH 44691
PH: 330-262-8907 (0)
PH: 330-201-1377 (H)
hilltop@bright.net
hilltopstamps@sssnet.com
www.hilltopstamps.com

### Supplies

**BROOKLYN GALLERY COIN & STAMP, INC.**
8725 4th Ave.
Brooklyn, NY 11209
PH: 718-745-5701
FAX: 718-745-2775
info@brooklyngallery.com
www.brooklyngallery.com

### Topicals

**E. JOSEPH MCCONNELL, INC.**
PO Box 683
Monroe, NY 10949
PH: 845-783-9791
ejstamps@gmail.com
www.EJMcConnell.com

### Topicals - Columbus

**MR. COLUMBUS**
PO Box 1492
Fennville, MI 49408
PH: 269-543-4755
David@MrColumbus1492.com
www.MrColumbus1492.com

### United States

**ACS STAMP COMPANY**
2914 W 135th Ave
Broomfield, Colorado 80020
303-841-8666
www.ACSStamp.com

**BROOKMAN STAMP CO.**
PO Box 90
Vancouver, WA 98666
PH: 360-695-1391
PH: 800-545-4871
FAX: 360-695-1616
info@brookmanstamps.com
www.brookmanstamps.com

### U.S. Classics/Moderns

**BARDO STAMPS**
PO Box 7437
Buffalo Grove, IL 60089
PH: 847-634-2676
jfb7437@aol.com
www.bardostamps.com

## U.S.-Collections Wanted

**DUTCH COUNTRY AUCTIONS**
The Stamp Center
4115 Concord Pike
Wilmington, DE 19803
PH: 302-478-8740
FAX: 302-478-8779
auctions@dutchcountryauctions.com
www.dutchcountryauctions.com

**DR. ROBERT FRIEDMAN & SONS STAMP & COIN BUYING CENTER**
2029 W. 75th St.
Woodridge, IL 60517
PH: 800-588-8100
FAX: 630-985-1588
stampcollections@drbobstamps.com
www.drbobfriedmanstamps.com

### Wanted - Worldwide Collections

**DUTCH COUNTRY AUCTIONS**
The Stamp Center
4115 Concord Pike
Wilmington, DE 19803
PH: 302-478-8740
FAX: 302-478-8779
auctions@dutchcountryauctions.com
www.dutchcountryauctions.com

### Websites

**ACS STAMP COMPANY**
2914 W 135th Ave
Broomfield, Colorado 80020
303-841-8666
www.ACSStamp.com

### Worldwide

**GUILLERMO JALIL**
Maipu 466, local 4
1006 Buenos Aires
Argentina
guillermo@jalilstamps.com
philatino@philatino.com
www.philatino.com (worldwide stamp auctions)
www.jalilstamps.com (direct sale, worldwide stamps)

### Worldwide-Collections

**DR. ROBERT FRIEDMAN & SONS STAMP & COIN BUYING CENTER**
2029 W. 75th St.
Woodridge, IL 60517
PH: 800-588-8100
FAX: 630-985-1588
stampcollections@drbobstamps.com
www.drbobfriedmanstamps.com

# New Edition is Now Available!

**SCOTT**
IDENTIFICATION GUIDE TO U.S. STAMPS
REGULAR ISSUES 1847-1934
7th EDITION

BY CHARLES N. MICARELLI

## SCOTT IDENTIFICATION GUIDE OF US REGULAR ISSUE STAMPS 1847-1934, 7TH ED.

**Item #: Z807**
**Retail $49.95**

# AA $39.95

This 7th edition has been thoroughly updated from the previous 6th edition that was published in 2013. Get your copy today!

# AmosAdvantage.com
# 1-800-572-6885

**ORDERING INFORMATION:** *AA prices apply to paid subscribers of Amos Media titles, or for orders placed online. Prices, terms and product availability subject to change. **SHIPPING & HANDLING:** U.S.: Orders total $0-$10.00 charged $4.99 shipping. U.S. Order total $10.01-$74.99 charged $9.99 shipping. Orders totaling $75+ will ship FREE! Taxes will apply in CA, OH, & IL. Canada: 20% of order total. Minimum charge $19.99 Maximum charge $200.00. Foreign orders are shipped via FedEx Intl. or USPS and billed actual freight.

# SCOTT *DIGITAL*

**With the Scott Digital Catalogue subscriptions, always have the latest values & listings, whenever you need them.**

"No more damaged paper pages.
Needed this 15 years ago!"
-*Jim S.*

## TRY IT FOR FREE
amosadvantage.com/sdcs

The Scott Catalogue

**SINCE 1868**

Published by:

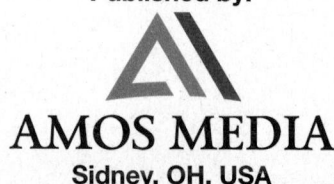

**AMOS MEDIA**
Sidney, OH, USA